NeuroRestorative™ Pediatric Programs

Serving Children and Adolescents with Post Acute Brain Injury Rehabilitation, Educational, and Behavioral Needs

NeuroRestorative™ is a provider of the country's most comprehensive rehabilitation services delivered in concert with specialized educational programs for children and adolescents, between the ages of 4 and 18, who are experiencing behavioral, physical, communication, and educational difficulties following acquired brain injuries. Our unique, home-like treatment centers offer dedicated pediatric and adolescent settings promoting peer interactions in our on-site school and residential environments.

Key Program Components

• Restorative Therapies (PT, OT, SLP) within an Educational Setting

• Psycho-Social Services and Post-Acute Health Management

• Integrated Behavioral Approach

• Family Education and Support

Neuro Restorative™
Rebuilding Lives After Brain Injury

NeuroRestorative™ Timber Ridge
Benton, Arkansas
Licensed by the State of Arkansas
Accredited by JCAHO and CARF

NeuroRestorative™ Carbondale
Carbondale, Illinois
Licensed by the State of Illinois
Accredited by CARF

Referral line: (800) 743-6802
NeuroRestorative.com

2012

The National Directory of Children, Youth & Family Services

To the best of the Publisher's knowledge, the information contained herein is accurate.
Please accept an apology, however, for any circumstances beyond control that may render
any part of it incorrect or obsolete.

Dorland Health, a division of Access Intelligence, Publisher
4 Choke Cherry Road 2nd Floor
Rockville, MD 20850
1-301-354-2000

Printed and bound in the United States of America
First Printing, 1979; Twenty-Eighth Printing, 2011
Library of Congress International Standard Serial Number ISSN 1072-902X
Federal Identification Number 52-2270063
ISBN 978-1-885461-46-9

Thank you for purchasing *The National Directory of Children, Youth & Families Services.* We hope you'll continue to rely on its unmatched accuracy, simplicity, and usefulness. Dorland Health provides information critical to the success of health and human service professionals throughout North America. For 50 years, our directories and other products have been utilized to improve lives, solve problems, and serve people.

We're confident you'll find *The National Directory of Children, Youth & Families Services.* to be a valuable asset to your organization. If for some reason you're not satisfied with your purchase, call a customer service representative at 888-707-5814.

DORLAND HEALTH
a division of **Access Intelligence**

The National Directory of

Children, Youth & Families Services

THE PROFESSIONALS' REFERENCE 2012

Cal Farley's

Boys Ranch® • Girlstown, U.S.A.®
& Family Resource Centers

Strengthening Children and Families Since 1939

TRAIN WITH THE BEST!

Cal Farley's offers countless resources for professionals with a wide array of evidence-based trainings in Leadership, Management, Clinical Skills, Consultation, Strengths-based Childcare, Trauma-informed Care, and much more. Most sessions are eligible for Texas professional social work CEU credits.

National/International Training & Consultation
Visit our beautiful Boys Ranch Campus or we can come to you.

Topics include:
Life Space Crisis Intervention (LSCI)
Response Ability Pathways (RAP)
Satori Alternatives to Managing Aggression (SAMA)
Child and Adolescent Functional Assessment Scale (CAFAS)

Strengths-based childcare sessions include: Professional Ethics for Social Work • Cultural Diversity • Brain Development • Neurobiological and Psychological Effects of Trauma • Impact of Drug Abuse on the Developing Brain • Infant Brain Development • Containment Prevention Tools • Child Abuse/Neglect • Working with Emotional Intelligence • Connecting With the Inside Child • Suicide Awareness • and much more.

For more information, contact Jim Taylor or Suzanne Wright at (800) 687-3722 or visit www.calfarley.org.

Cal Farley's ...

provides professional programs and services in a Christ-centered atmosphere to strengthen families and support the overall development of children.

Cal Farley's is one of America's largest privately-funded child and family service providers specializing in both residential and community-based services at no cost to the families of children in our care.

Cal Farley's provides excellent benefits for staff including medical, dental, vision, life and disability insurance, paid vacation and sick leave, along with a 401K retirement plan. Certain 24-hr on-campus positions (i.e. house parents) have additional benefits such as paid utilities and housing.

Cal Farley's offers a wide array of employment opportunities.

Check **www.calfarley.org/jobs** for current job openings.

(800) 687-3722 • www.calfarley.org • P.O. Box 1890 • Amarillo, Texas 79174-0001

Licensed, State of Texas. Accredited, Council on Accreditation. Tax exempt [501(c)(3)] for charitable gift purposes. Inter-denominational.

Table of Contents

PART I

Guide to State, County and Major City Agencies and Services

Alphabetical list of states. The listing begins with state-level information identifying how each state's Social/Human Services, Health Services, Juvenile Justice Agencies and Education Departments function throughout the respective state.

Each state is divided by counties or major cities. Categories are: Social Services, Health and Mental Health Services, Juvenile Justice Agencies, Education Services and Private Sector Agencies.

PART II

This section lists Federal Government programs responsible for policies serving children, youth and families.

Alphabetical list of organizations offering services and information nationwide. Informative descriptions are included.

Advertisers Index

Abbreviations

DIRECTORY ABBREVIATIONS

CASA	Court Appointed Special Advocates
CHDP	Child Health and Disability Prevention Program
CHINS	Child in Need of Supervision
CHIP	Children's Health Insurance Program
CMHC	Community Mental Health Center
CPS	Child Protective Services
CWS	Child Welfare Services
CYF	Children, Youth & Family
DD	Developmental Disability
EPSDT	Early Periodic Screening, Diagnosis & Treatment
GAL	Guardian Ad Litem
ICAMA	Interstate Compact on Adoption / Medical Assistance
ICJ	Interstate Compact on Juveniles
ICMH	Interstate Compact on Mental Health
ICPC	Interstate Compact on the Placement of Children
LTC	Long-Term Care
MCH	Maternal & Child Health
M/F	Males & Females
MH	Mental Health
MR	Mental Retardation
RADAR	Alcohol & Drug Information Clearinghouse
RTC	Residential Treatment Center
TANF	Temporary Assistance for Needy Families
WIC	Women, Infants & Children

TITLE ABBREVIATIONS

Act.	Acting
Adm.	Administrator
Assoc.	Associate
Asst.	Assistant
CEO	Chief Executive Officer
CHO	Chief Health Officer
CJPO	Chief Juvenile Probation Officer
Comm.	Commissioner
Coor.	Coordinator
CPO	Chief Probation Officer
CPPO	Chief Probation / Parole Officer
DA	District Attorney
Dep.	Deputy Dir. Director
Esq.	Esquire
Gen.	General
LCSW	Licensed Clinical Social Worker
LISW	Licensed Social Worker
LSSW	Licensed Social Services Worker
MD	Medical Director
Mgr.	Manager
MSW	Master Social Worker
NASMHPD	National Association of State Mental Health Program
PHN	Public Health Nurse
RN	Registered Nurse
Supt.	Superintendent

Getting the Most Out of Your Directory

PART I – GUIDE TO SERVICES BY STATE

This section is broken down in alphabetical order by state. Within each state you'll find State Government Agencies, County/City Government Agencies and Special Service Agencies. Each state includes the following:

State Government Agencies – provides information about the state level offices:

■ **Social Services**
- Department of Social Services
- Interstate Compact on the Placement of Children
- Office of Child Support Enforcement
- State Child Care Licensing Office

■ **Health Services**
- Children with Special Health Needs
- Department of Health
- Health Insurance Assistance Programs
- Maternal & Child Health
- Medicaid Agency
- WIC

■ **Mental Health Services**
- Department of Mental Health
- Division of Developmental Disabilities
- Division Of Rehabilitation Services
- Interstate Compact on Mental Health

■ **Justice Agencies**
- Attorney General's Office
- Department of Juvenile Corrections
- Department of Public Safety
- Department of Victim's Assistance

■ **Courts**
- Administrative Office of the Courts

■ **Police & Sheriff**
- Police Association
- Sheriff's Association

■ **Education Services**
- Department of Education
- Head Start Association
- Homeless Education
- State School for Blind & Visually Impaired
- State School for Deaf & Hard of Hearing
- Special Education Department

County Government Agencies – provides information about each county's local offices, including:

- Department of Social Services
- Department of Health Services
- Department of Mental Health Services
- CASA/GAL Agencies

- Juvenile Hall/Parole/Probation
- County/Juvenile/Circuit/District/Teen Courts
- Police & Sheriff Departments
- Special Education

Special Service Agencies – provides information about public and private agencies within the state providing various types of services which include:

- Adoption Agencies
- Advocacy Resources
- Behavioral Health Treatment
- Counseling Services
- Crisis & Shelter Care
- Foster Care Agencies

- Home Medical Equipment Providers - NEW
- Pediatric Home Care - NEW
- Social Services
- Special Needs – NEW
- Substance Abuse Treatment

PART II – WHO'S WHO IN FEDERAL AND NATIONAL PROGRAMS SERVING SENIORS

Federal Agencies – a listing of federal administrators and policymakers of programs that assist children, youth and families.

National Organizations – alphabetical listing of national organizations and programs that serve children, youth and families.

NEW FOR 2012

Inclusion of CARF (Commission for Accreditation of Rehabilitation Facilities), COA (Council on Accreditation) and Joint Commission accredited programs. Listings accredited by any of these organization are noted as such. These listings can be found within the Special Service Agencies within each state.

JOINT COMMISSION ACCREDITATION:
A MARK OF DISTINCTION

The Joint Commission

Health Resources & Hotline Numbers

Child Abuse
  Childhelp USA..800.422.4453
  Girls & Boys Town National Hotline..800.448.3000

Child Sexual Abuse
  Stop It Now...888.773.8367
  Rape & Incest National Network...800.656.4673x1

Crime Victims
  National Center for Victims of Crime..800.394.2255

Family Violence
  National Domestic Violence Hotline..800.799.7233

Missing/Abducted Children
  Child Find of America...800.426.5678
  National Center for Missing & Exploited Children..............................800.843.5678
  Parental Abduction & Dispute Resolution Hotline...............................800.292.9688

Substance Abuse
  Alcoholics Anonymous..212.870.3400
  Mothers Against Drunk Drivers..877.6233.4357
  National Clearinghouse for Alcohol & Drug Information......................800.729.6686
  National Drug & Alcohol Treatment Referral.......................................800.252.6465

Youth in Trouble/Runaways
  Covenant House Nineline..800.999.9999
  National Runaway Switchboard...800.786.2929

State Child Protective Services Hotlines

State	Number	State	Number
Alabama	334-242-9500	Montana	866-820-5437
Alaska	800-784-4444	Nebraska	402-595-1324
Arizona	888-767-2445	Nevada	775-684-4400
Arkansas	800-482-5964	New Hampshire	603-271-6563
California	916-445-2771	New Jersey	800-792-8610
Colorado	303-727-3000	New Mexico	800-797-3260
Connecticut	800-842-2288	New York	518-474-8740
Delaware	800-292-9582	North Carolina	800-662-7030
District of Columbia	877-671-7233	North Dakota	701-328-2316
Florida	800-962-2873	Ohio	614-466-0995
Georgia	404-657-3408	Oklahoma	800-522-3511
Hawaii	808-832-5300	Oregon	800-854-3508
Idaho	208-334-0808	Pennsylvania	717-783-8744
Illinois	217-785-4010	Rhode Island	800-742-4453
Indiana	800-562-2407	South Carolina	803-898-7318
Iowa	800-362-2178	South Dakota	605-773-3227
Kansas	785-296-0044	Tennessee	877-237-0004
Kentucky	502-595-4550	Texas	800-252-5400
Louisiana	225-342-8632	Utah	800-678-9399
Maine	800-452-1999	Vermont	802-241-2131
Maryland	800-332-6347	Virginia	804-786-8536
Massachusetts	617-566-0858	Washington	800-562-5624
Michigan	800-942-4357	West Virginia	800-352-6513
Minnesota	651-431-4661	Wisconsin	608-266-3036
Mississippi	601-359-4991	Wyoming	307-777-7922
Missouri	573-751-3448		

Corrections Requested

As the directory user, you are the front-line source for new information. If you encounter a listing that is incorrect and/or has become obsolete, or if you know of a new program or agency that should be listed, please use the form below to inform Contexo Media of the change(s). Submitted corrections and additions will be included in the 2013 Edition of *The National Directory of Children, Youth & Families Services*. If the form has already been used, send any corrections in a letter or visit kluna@accessintel.com. Thank you for your assistance.

The National Directory of Children, Youth & Families Services 2013

❏ Correction   ❏ Addition

❏ Government Agency   ❏ Private Agency

Name of Program or Agency_____

Address (Mailing)_____

Address (Facility)_____

City, State, Zip Code_____

Telephone_____ Fax_____

E-mail_____ Website_____

Contact Name and Title_____

(Use separate sheet for more corrections or additions)

Mail to:

Attn: Corrections
Dorland Health
4 Choke Cherry Road 2nd Floor
Rockville, MD 20850

Or email kluna@accessintel.com with your corrections/updates

THE NATIONAL DIRECTORY OF CHILDREN, YOUTH & FAMILIES SERVICES

The Most Comprehensive Children, Youth & Families Services Directory Available Today

The 1,000+ page *National Directory* is used by social workers, health and mental health professionals, justice personnel, library reference shelves, sales and marketing professionals, search firms, and information and referral agencies throughout the United States.

OUR MARKET

An invaluable time-saver. With the *National Directories* low price and satisfaction guarantee, it's easy to justify having comprehensive, current information at your fingertips. That's why the following professionals buy the *National Directory* each year:

- Social Workers
- Law Enforcement
- Mental Health Centers
- Reference Librarians
- Military Family Support Centers
- Army Community Services
- Justice Professionals

- Department of Children & Families
- Case Managers
- Nurse Practitioners
- Pediatricians
- Medical Directors
- Physician Assistants

DISTRIBUTION

The *National Directory of Children, Youth & Families Services* is used by more than 87,000 social service professionals annually.

CONTACT US

Kim Luna
Product Manager
720.870.2440
kluna@accessintel.com

DORLAND HEALTH
a division of Access Intelligence

19307

Dorland Health Children, Youth & Families Services Database

Proven, Targeted Mailing Lists

Try the mailing lists that will live up to your expectations! Others claim to have current/clean lists, ours really are! We use these lists for our own success!

Reach over 41,000 **Professional Providers** of services for at-risk children and adolescents who are waiting to hear from you!

There are **21,000 email addresses available.**

We take pride in offering a reliable link to the decision makers at the nation's federal, state, county, city governments and private agencies.

Your success depends on a targeted mailing list. Money spent on a great promotional piece will not go to waste, you can reach every segment of the field.

2012
The National Directory of
CHILDREN, YOUTH & FAMILIES SERVICES
The Professionals' Reference

⬡ DORLAND HEALTH
Access Intelligence

⬡ **DORLAND HEALTH**
a division of Ⓐ **Access Intelligence**

- Focus On Qualified Buyers
- Treatment Center Services
- Recruit Large Conference Audiences/ Training Workshops
- Publications & Books
- Research & Academic Grants
- Continuing Education Programs
- Introduce New Products

Please call for your consultation.
You'll be glad you did!
Call: 720-870-2440
E-mail: kluna@accessintel.com
www.dorlandhealth.com
Contact: Kim Luna, Product Manager

19307

The National Directory of

Children, Youth & Families Services

THE PROFESSIONALS' REFERENCE 2012

PART I

GUIDE TO STATES, COUNTIES AND MAJOR CITIES

Social Services

Health Services

Mental Health Services

Juvenile Justice Agencies

Education Services

Special Service Agencies

Alabama

Robert Bentley, Governor
State Capitol, 600 Dexter Avenue
Montgomery, AL 36130
334.242.7100
334.353.0004 (Fax)
www.governor.state.al.us

Kathleen Rasmussen, Juvenile Justice Specialist
ADECA-LETS Division
PO Box 5690 401 Adams Avenue, Room 466
Montgomery, AL 36103-5690
334.242.5813
334.242.0712 (Fax)
kathleen.rasmussen@adeca.alabama.gov

Gerald Love, SAG Chair
PO Box 1381
Dothan, AL 36302-1381
334.983.8377
334.983.1289 (Fax)
lovegeraldh@yahoo.com

CRISIS NUMBERS

Child Abuse Reporting . . .334.242.9500   Criminal Info Center 334.353.1172

STATE SERVICES

SOCIAL SERVICES

Child Care Srvs Div AL **334.242.1425**
Fax 334.352.1491
50 Ripley St, Montgomery, AL 36130
Dianne Wright, Director

Dept of Human Resources **334.242.1310**
Fax 334.353.1115
50 N Ripley St, Montgomery, AL 36130

GENERAL HEALTH SERVICES

Alabama Medicaid Agency **334.242.0566**
Fax 334.242.5097
Web . . . . .www.medicaid.state.al.us
E-mail . . . . .carol.herrmann.steckel@medicaid.alabama.gov
501 Dexter Ave, Montgomery, AL 36104-3744
Carol Herrmann-Steckel, Commissioner

Bureau of Fam Health Svcs AL **334.206.5675**
Fax 334.206.2950
E-mail . . . . .acowden@adph.state
1100 W 49th St, Montgomery, AL 36130
A Cowden, Director

Children with Special Health Needs AL **334.293.7500**
Fax 334.613.3553
E-mail . . . . .crs@rehab.alabama.gov
602 S Lawrence St, Montgomery, AL 36104
Dr. Cary Boswell, Commissioner

State Laboratory **334.260.3400**
E-mail . . . . .sharon.nightingale@adph.state.al.us
814 Aurm Dr, Montgomery, AL 36124
Dr. Sharon Nightingale, Director

MENTAL HEALTH SERVICES

Interstate Compact on Mental Health **334.242.3038**
Fax 334.242.0924
Web . . . . .www.mh.alabama.gov
100 North Un Rm 536, Montgomery, AL 36130
Courtney Tarver, Director Of Legal Division

JUSTICE AGENCY

Alabama Dept of Corrections **334.353.3883**
Fax 334.353.3967
Web . . . . .www.doc.alabama.gov
E-mail . . . . .pio@doc.state.al.us
301 S Ripley St, Montgomery, AL 36130-1501
James Deloach, Deputy Commissioner

Attorney General's Ofc **334.242.7300**
Fax 334.242.7458
501 Washington Ave, Montgomery, AL 36130
Luther Strange, Attorney General

Correctional Education Division AL **334.285.5177**
Fax 334.285.2521
E-mail . . . . .dchambers@ingram.cc.al.us
JF Ingram State Technical Col, JF Ingram State
Technical Col, Deatsville, AL 36022
D Chambers, Director

Dept of Youth Svcs **334.215.3800**
Fax 334.215.1453
Web . . . . .www.dys.alabama.gov
E-mail . . . . .walter.wood@dys.alabama.gov
1000 Industrial School Rd, Mount Meigs, AL 36057
J. Walter Wood, Jr., Executive Director

COURTS

Administrative Ofc Of The Courts **866.954.9411**
Fax 334.954.5000
Web . . . . .www.alacourt.gov
E-mail . . . . .callie.dietz@alacourt.gov
300 Dexter Ave, Montgomery, AL 36104-3741
Callie T. Dietz, Director

District Judge Circuit **256.354.7633**
Fax 256.354.3429
E-mail . . . . .alatham@usa.net
2nd Flr. Clay County Courthouse, Ashland,
AL 36251-0880
Annie M. Latham, Senior Judicial Assistant

POLICE AND SHERIFF

Alabama Sheriffs Association **334.264.7827**
Fax 334.269.5588
Web . . . . .www.alabamasheriffs.com
E-mail . . . . .alsheriffs@aol.com
514 Washington Ave, Montgomery, AL 36104-4346
Robert D. "bobby" Timmons, Executive Director

EDUCATION SERVICES

Alabama Department of Education **334.242.9700**
Fax 334.242.9708
50 N Ripley St, Montgomery, AL 36104
Dr. Joseph Morton, State Superintendent

Edu for Homeless Children and Youth AL **334.242.8199**
Fax 334.242.0496
E-mail . . . . .bthompson@alsde.edu
50 N Rippley St, Gordon Persons Bldg Rm 5348,
Montgomery, AL 36130
B Thompson, Director

Special Education Services AL **334.242.8114**
Fax 334.242.9192
E-mail . . . . .speced@alsde.edu
50 N Ripley St, Montgomery, AL 36104
Mabrey Whetstone, Director

LABOR & WORKFORCE EDUCATION

Ofc of Workforce Development **334.353.1490**
Fax 334.353.2005
E-mail . . . . .tim.alford@adeca.state.al.us
401 Adams Avenue , Suite 590, Montgomery,
AL 36104
Tim Alford, Director

COUNTY SERVICES

Autauga County

SOCIAL SERVICES

Dept Of Human Resources **334.358.5000**
Fax 334.365.3274
Web . . . . .www.dhr.state.al.us
203 N Court St, Prattville, AL 36067-3003
Onya Johnson, Director

GENERAL HEALTH SERVICES

Health Dept **334.361.3743**
Fax 334.361.3718
Web . . . . .www.adch.org
219 N Court St, Prattville, AL 36067-3003
Bobby H. Bryan, Executive Director

COURTS

District Court **334.358.6801**
Fax 334.361.3810
134 N Court St Ste 110, Prattville, AL 36067-3049
Honorable Joy P Booth, Presiding Judge

Teen Court..334.358.4900
Fax...334.358.4909
E-mail......................................teencrt@bellsouth.net
   1849 Glenwood Dr, Prattville, AL 36066
   Steve Whitehead, Director

Baldwin County

GENERAL HEALTH SERVICES

Health Dept..................................251.947.1910
Fax...251.947.5703
Web..www.adph.org
   23280 Gilbert Dr, Robertsdale, AL 36567
   Ricky Elliott, Administrator

JUSTICE AGENCY

Family Court..................................251.937.0235
E-mail...........................ccarmen.bosch@alacourt.gov
   312 Courthouse Sq Suite 23, Bay Minette, AL 36507
   Carmen Bosch, Judge

Juvenile Detention Ctr.....................251.580.2540
Fax...251.580.2541
Web................................www.alacourt.state.al.us
   43405 Nicholsville Road, Bay Minette, AL 36507
   Camen Bosch, Judge

COURTS

District Court/Judge Carmen Bosch's
Ofc...251.937.0235
Fax...251.937.0315
Web...www.alacourt.gov
E-mail..............................carmen.bosch@alacourt.gov
   312 Courthouse Sq, Ste 23, Bay Minette, AL 36507
   Honorable Carmen Bosch, Circuit Judge

EDUCATION SERVICES

Special Education.........................251.972.6860
Fax...251.972.6861
Web...www.bcbe.org
   1091 B Ave, Loxley, AL 36551
   Carol Palumbo, Special Education Coordinator

Barbour County

SOCIAL SERVICES

Dept Of Human Resources.................334.775.2000
Fax...334.775.2050
E-mail.........................deana.stinson@dhr.alabama.gov
   276 Highway 239, Clayton, AL 36016-4640
   Deana Stinson, Director

GENERAL HEALTH SERVICES

Health Dept..................................334.687.4808
Fax...334.687.6470
E-mail.............................ckirkland@adph.state.al.us
   634 School St, Eufaula, AL 36027
   Corey Kirkland, Administrator

JUSTICE AGENCY

Juvenile Probation Ofc.....................334.687.1566
Fax...334.687.1599
   303 E Broad St Ste 103, Eufaula, AL 36027
   Robert Condrey, Chief Performance Officer

COURTS

Clerks Ofc/District Court.....................334.687.1515
Fax...334.687.1599
   303 E Broad St Ste 201, Eufaula, AL 36027-1654
   David Nix, Clerk

POLICE AND SHERIFF

Sheriff's Ofc....................................334.775.3434
Fax...334.775.1118
E-mail..............................leroyupshaw@yahoo.com
   24 Robertson Airport Rd, Clayton, AL 36016
   Leroy Upshaw, Sheriff

Bibb County

SOCIAL SERVICES

Dept Of Human Resources..................205.926.2900
Fax...205.926.5641
   84 Library St, Centreville, AL 35042
   Karen Smith, Director

GENERAL HEALTH SERVICES

Health Dept..................................205.926.9702
Fax...205.926.6536
   281 Alexander Ave, Centreville, AL 35042-2953
   Tammy Yager, Executive Director

COURTS

Juvenile Court................................205.926.3101
Fax...205.926.3127
   35 Court Sq E Ste 104, Centreville, AL 35042-2274
   Keith Stringfellow, Chief JPO

POLICE AND SHERIFF

Sheriff's Ofc....................................205.926.4683
Fax...205.926.3110
E-mail.................................hannahk@dot.state.al.us
   183 SW Davidson Dr Ste A, Centreville,
   AL 35042-2298
   Keith Hannah, Sheriff

Blount County

SOCIAL SERVICES

Dept Of Human Resources..................205.274.5200
Fax...205.625.4296
Web....................................www.dhr.state.al.us
E-mail.............................mparker@dhr.state.al.us
   415 5th Ave E Ste A, Oneonta, AL 35121-1400
   Marcia Parker, Director

MENTAL HEALTH SERVICES

Mental Health Clinic........................205.625.3882
Fax...205.625.4201
   1002A 2nd Ave E, Oneonta, AL 35121
   John Atchison, Director

JUSTICE AGENCY

Children's Ctr, Inc............................205.274.7226
Fax...205.274.9226
   106 1st Ave W, Oneonta, AL 35121
   Jim Ed Clayton, Director

COURTS

District Court.................................205.625.4153
E-mail............................jdobson@dca.state.al.us
   220 2nd Ave E, Ste 208, Oneonta, AL 35121
   Honorable John J. Dobson, Director

Butler County

SOCIAL SERVICES

Dept Of Human Resources..................334.382.4400
Fax...334.382.4460
Web....................................www.dhr.state.al.us
   109 Caldwell St, Greenville, AL 36037-2507
   Lisa Syler, Director

GENERAL HEALTH SERVICES

Health Dept..................................334.382.3154
Fax...334.382.3530
   350 Old Searcy Rd, Greenville, AL 36037
   Ziba M. Anderson, Executive Director

JUSTICE AGENCY

Juvenile Probation Ofc.....................334.382.5443
Fax...334.382.3506
Web....................................www.juv.alacourt.gov
E-mail...........................terry.lewis@alacourt.gov
   201 S Conecuh St, Greenville, AL 36037
   Terry Lewis, CPO

COURTS

District Court.................................334.382.6125
Fax...334.382.5263
Web...www.dca.state.al.us
E-mail.................................mack@mackrussel.com
   700 E Commerce st, Ste 18, Greenville,
   AL 36037-2393
   Honorable J. Macdonald Russell, Jr, District Judge

POLICE AND SHERIFF

Sheriff's Ofc....................................334.382.6521
Fax...334.382.7491
   700 Court Sq Ste 1, Greenville, AL 36037-2334
   Kenny Hardeen, Sheriff

Calhoun County

SOCIAL SERVICES

Dept of Human Resources..................256.231.7500
E-mail............................Doug.heath@dhr.alabama.gov
   801 Noble Street, Anniston, AL 36201
   Doug Heath, Director

GENERAL HEALTH SERVICES

Health Dept..................................256.237.7523
Fax...256.237.7974
   3400 McClellan Blvd, Anniston, AL 36201-2128
   Lori Bell, Nursing Director

MENTAL HEALTH SERVICES

Calhoun Cleburne Community Mental Health Clinic
(CMHC)..256.236.3403
Fax...256.238.6263
Web...www.ccmhc.net
   331 E 8th St, Anniston, AL 36207-5731
   Mickey Turner, Executive Director

JUSTICE AGENCY

Regional Detention Ctr.....................256.237.2881
Fax...256.237.3088
Web.................................www.juv.alacourt.gov
E-mail...........................mike.rollins@alacourt.gov
   4625 Mcclellan Blvd, Anniston, AL 36206-1858
   Mike Rollins, Executive Director

COURTS

Juvenile Court/Probation Ofc..............256.231.1731
Fax...256.231.1702
E-mail..........................randy.reaves@alacourt.gov
   25 W 11th St Ste 120, Anniston, AL 36201
   Randy Reaves, Chief Probation Officer

POLICE AND SHERIFF

Anniston Police Dept.......................256.238.1800
Fax...256.231.7676
   1200 Gurnee Ave, Anniston, AL 36201
   Chief Layton Mcgrady, Chief

Sheriff's Dept...............................256.236.6600
Fax...256.237.6321
   400 W 8th St, Anniston, AL 36201
   Larry Amerson, Sheriff

Chambers County

SOCIAL SERVICES

Alabama Dept of Human
Resources......................................334.864.4000
Fax...334.864.7917
   410 9th Ave SW, PO Box 409, Lafayette, AL 36862

POLICE AND SHERIFF

Sheriff's Dept...............................334.864.4333
Fax...334.864.4309
E-mail.....................chiefdeputy@chamberscounty.com
   2 Lafayette St, Lafayette, AL 36862
   Sid Lockhart, Sheriff

Cherokee County

SOCIAL SERVICES

Dept Of Human Resources 256.927.1440
Fax 256.927.2798
　　202 Deanbuttram Ave, Centre, AL 35960
　　Teresa Sauls, Director

GENERAL HEALTH SERVICES

Health Dept 256.927.3132
Fax 256.927.2809
Web .... www.jacksonvilleprogress.com
E-mail .... jburt@jacksonvilleprogress.com
　　833 Cedar Bluff Road, Centre, AL 35960
　　Mary Gomillioen, Executive Director

EDUCATION SERVICES

Cedar Bluff Head Start 256.779.6846
　　3358 Reese St, Cedar Bluff, AL 35959
　　Billy Marshall, Director

Chilton County

SOCIAL SERVICES

Dept of Human Resources 205.755.3250
Fax 205.755.8188
　　1515 W Bypass, Andalusia, AL 36420
　　Winifred Adams, Director

GENERAL HEALTH SERVICES

Health Dept 205.755.1287
Fax 205.755.2027
Web .... www.adph.org
　　301 Health Center Dr, Clanton, AL 35045-2349
　　James Martin, Executive Director

MENTAL HEALTH SERVICES

Chilton-Shelby Mental Health Ctr 205.755.8800
Fax 205.755.7060
Web .... www.chiltonshelby.org
E-mail .... kcrouthers@chiltonshelby.org
　　110 Medical Center Dr, Clanton, AL 35045
　　Kathryn T. Crouthers, Lcsw, Clinical Director

POLICE AND SHERIFF

Sheriff's Dept 205.755.4698
Fax 205.280.7245
Web .... www.chiltoncountyso.org
　　500 2nd Ave N, Clanton, AL 35045-3421
　　Kevin Davis, Sheriff

Choctaw County

SOCIAL SERVICES

Dept Of Human Resources 205.459.9701
Fax 205.459.2452
　　1003 S Mulberry Ave, Butler, AL 36904
　　Rosa Mikles, Director

GENERAL HEALTH SERVICES

Health Dept 205.459.4026
Fax 205.459.4027
Web .... www.adph.org/choctaw
E-mail .... jackie.holliday@adph.state.al.us
　　1001 S Mulberry Ave, Butler, AL 36904
　　Jackie Holliday, Administartor

COURTS

District Court/Judge Scurlock III,
Ofc 205.459.3828
Fax 205.459.4795
　　117 S Mulberry Ave Ste 15, Butler, AL 36904
　　Karen Enstrom, Clerk

EDUCATION SERVICES

Choctaw Head Start Ctr 251.843.4635
Web .... www.acf.hhs.gov
　　1558 Shady Grove Rd, Silas, AL 36919-6342
　　Lillie Chess, Director

Clarke County

SOCIAL SERVICES

Dept Of Human Resources 251.275.7001
Fax 251.275.2069
E-mail .... lboykin@dhr.state.al.us
　　22609 Highway 84 E, Grove Hill, AL 36451
　　Lou Boykin, Director

JUSTICE AGENCY

Juvenile Probation Ofc 251.275.3534
Fax 251.275.3652
　　114 Court St, Grove Hill, AL 36451
　　Jackie Thompson, Chief Performance Officer

COURTS

District Court/Judge William Kimbrough's
Ofc 251.275.8296
　　117 Court St, Grove Hill, AL 36451
　　James Morgan, District Judge

POLICE AND SHERIFF

Fulton Police Dept 334.636.9527
　　141 main st, Fulton, AL 36446-0067
　　David Fredrickson, Police Chief

Clay County

SOCIAL SERVICES

Dept Of Human Resources 256.396.6800
Fax 256.396.6341
　　86930 Highway 9, Lineville, AL 36266
　　Kay Robertson, Director

GENERAL HEALTH SERVICES

Health Dept 256.396.6421
Fax 256.396.9172
　　86892 Highway 9, Lineville, AL 36266
　　Ramona Warren, Officer Manager

Home Health 256.396.9307
Fax 256.396.9236
　　86892 Highway 9, Lineville, AL 36266
　　Ramona Warrenn, Office Manager

JUSTICE AGENCY

Juvenile Probation Ofc 256.354.3411
Fax 256.354.2249
　　25 Ct Square, Ashland, AL 36251
　　Julie Lett, CPO

Cleburne County

SOCIAL SERVICES

Dept Of Human Resources 256.463.1700
Fax 256.463.5445
　　732 Oxford St, Heflin, AL 36264-1175
　　Marsha Busby, Director

GENERAL HEALTH SERVICES

Health Dept 256.463.2296
Fax 256.463.2772
　　90 Brockford Rd, Heflin, AL 36264
　　Judy Dean, Executive Director

COURTS

Juvenile Court/Judge Sarrell's Ofc 256.463.5955
Fax 256.463.2257
E-mail .... warren.sarrell@alacourt.gov
　　120 Vickery St, Heflin, AL 36264
　　Honorable Warren. G. Sarrell, Jr., District Judge

Coffee County

SOCIAL SERVICES

Dept Of Human Resources 334.348.2000
Fax 334.393.1551
Web .... www.dhr.state.al.us
　　3881 Salem Rd, Enterprise, AL 36330
　　Brandon Hardin, Director

GENERAL HEALTH SERVICES

Health Dept 334.347.9574
Fax 334.347.7104
Web .... www.enterprisealabama.com
　　2841 Neal Metcalf Rd, Enterprise, AL 36330
　　Peggy Blakeney, Administrator

JUSTICE AGENCY

Juvenile Probation Ofc 334.393.2618
Fax 334.393.5789
E-mail .... gary.watson@alacourt.gov
　　99 S Edwards St, Enterprise, AL 36330
　　Gary Watson, Chief Performance Officer

COURTS

District Court 334.393.2949
Fax 334.393.6675
Web .... www.dca.state.al.us
E-mail .... paul.sherling@alacourt.gov
　　99 S Edwards St Ste 8, Enterprise, AL 36330-2561
　　Honorable Paul Sherling, District Judge

POLICE AND SHERIFF

Sheriff's Dept 334.894.5535
Fax 334.894.6472
E-mail .... dsutton@coffeecounty.net
　　4 County Complex, New Brockton, AL 36351-9791
　　Dave Sutton, Sheriff

Colbert County

SOCIAL SERVICES

Dept Of Human Resources Child
Support 256.314.4900
Fax 256.383.5215
E-mail .... ltaylor@dhr.state.al.us
　　3105 George Wallace Blvd, Muscle Shoals,
　　AL 35661-3203
　　Lewise Taylor, Director

JUSTICE AGENCY

Juvenile Probation Ofc 256.386.8574
Fax 256.386.8575
　　1098 Joe Wheeler Dr, Tuscumbia, AL 35674
　　Dennis O. Box, Chief Performance Officer

TN Valley Youth Detention Ctr 256.381.3520
Fax 256.381.3504
E-mail .... trobertson@tuscumbia.k12.al.us
　　2216 Missouri St, Tuscumbia, AL 35674
　　T.l. Robertson, Administrator

COURTS

District Court 256.386.8542
Fax 256.389.8614
　　201 N Main St, Tuscumbia, AL 35674-2042
　　Chad Coker, District Judge

POLICE AND SHERIFF

Sheriff's Ofc 256.383.0741
Fax 256.386.8599
E-mail .... ccsd@colbertcounty.org
　　201 N Main St, Tuscumbia, AL 35674
　　Ronnie May, Sheriff

Conecuh County

SOCIAL SERVICES

Human Resources 251.578.3900
　　856 Liberty Hill Dr, Evergreen, AL 36401

GENERAL HEALTH SERVICES

Conecuh Health Dept **251.578.1952**
Fax 251.578.5566
   102 Wild Ave, Evergreen, AL 36401
   Marita Wiley, Office Mgr

JUSTICE AGENCY

Juvenile Probation Ofc **251.578.7035**
Fax 251.578.7042
E-mail ....jerry.harrelson@alacourt.gov
   Highway 31 S, Evergreen, AL 36401
   Jerry W. Harrelson, Chief Performance Officer

COURTS

District Court/Ofc Of Judge Brock **251.578.2421**
Fax 251.578.7042
Web ....www.alacourt.gov
E-mail ....jeff.brock@alacourt.gov
   111 Court Street, Evergreen, AL 36401
   Honorable Jeffrey Brock, District Judge

Coosa County

SOCIAL SERVICES

Dept Of Human Resources **256.377.2000**
Fax 256.377.2593
   300 S Jackson St, Rockford, AL 35136
   Angela Pidtrzak, Director

GENERAL HEALTH SERVICES

Health Dept **256.377.4364**
Fax 256.377.4354
Web ....www.adph.state.al.us
   1 Main st, Rockford, AL 35136
   Marie Gomillion, Area Administrator

POLICE AND SHERIFF

Sheriff's Dept **256.377.4922**
Fax 256.377.2690
E-mail ....alsheriffs@aol.com
   1 School St, Rockford, AL 35136
   Terri Wilson, Sheriff

Covington County

SOCIAL SERVICES

Dept Of Human Resources **334.427.7900**
Fax 334.222.3608
Web ....www.dhr.state.al.us
E-mail ....cleverington@dhr.state.al.us
   1515 Martin Luther King Jr. Expressway, Andalusia, AL 36420
   Cathy A Leverington, Director

GENERAL HEALTH SERVICES

Health Dept **334.222.1175**
Fax 334.222.1570
   23989 Al Highway 55, Andalusia, AL 36420
   Lisa Weeks, Home Health Supervisor

MENTAL HEALTH SERVICES

**South Central Alabama Mental Health
Board** **334.222.2525**
Fax 334.222.4660
E-mail ....scamhb@alaweb.com
   19815 Bay Branch Rd, Andalusia, AL 36420
   Cynthia Hataway, Executive Director

COURTS

District Court **334.428.2570**
Fax 334.428.2547
E-mail ....david.pearce@alacourt.gov
   1 K N Court Square, Andalusia, AL 36420
   David Ray Pearce, Youth Services Director

POLICE AND SHERIFF

Sheriff's Dept **334.428.2643**
Fax 334.428.2665
Web ....www.co.madison.al.us
E-mail ....dmates@co.madison.al.us
   290 Hillcrest Dr, Andalusia, AL 36420-2589
   Dennis Mates, Sheriff

EDUCATION SERVICES

Florala Head Start **334.858.3060**
   22583 8th Ave, Florala, AL 36442
   Lynda Christian, Director

Crenshaw County

SOCIAL SERVICES

Dept Of Human Resources **334.335.7000**
Fax 334.335.7050
Web ....www.dhr.state.al.us
   25 Hospital Dr, Luverne, AL 36049
   Kristi Maddox, Interim Director

GENERAL HEALTH SERVICES

Health Dept **334.335.2471**
Fax 334.335.3795
   100 E 4th St, Luverne, AL 36049-2110
   Allen Jp Luverne, Director

POLICE AND SHERIFF

Dozier Police Dept **334.496.3742**
   7874 S Main St, Dozier, AL 36028

Sheriff's Dept **334.335.6568**
Fax 334.335.5805
   100 E 4th St, Luverne, AL 36049
   Charles West, Sheriff

Cullman County

SOCIAL SERVICES

**Dept Of Human Resources Children's
Svcs** **256.737.5300**
Fax 256.739.9353
Web ....www.dhr.state.al.us
E-mail ....cdenard@dhr.state.al.us
   1225 Joseph St NW, Cullman, AL 35055-4102
   Catherine Denard, Director

GENERAL HEALTH SERVICES

Health Dept **256.734.1030**
Fax 256.737.9646
Web ....www.cullman.com
   600 Logan Ave SW, Cullman, AL 35055-4503
   Judy Smith, Supervisor

MENTAL HEALTH SERVICES

Mental Health Authority **256.734.4688**
Fax 256.255.0026
E-mail ....chrisv@camha.com
   1909 Commerce Ave, Cullman, AL 35055
   Chris Van Dyke, Executive Director

JUSTICE AGENCY

Juvenile Probation Svcs **256.775.4772**
Fax 256.739.3042
   1908 Beech Ave SE, Cullman, AL 35055
   Susan Martin, Juvenile Judicial Volunteer Coordinator

EDUCATION SERVICES

Cold Springs Head Start Program **256.287.0670**
   9010 County Road 109, Bremen, AL 35033
   Janice Sweatman, Director

Dale County

SOCIAL SERVICES

Dept Of Human Resources **334.445.4900**
Fax 334.774.1590
   513 Carroll Ave, Ozark, AL 36360
   Judy M. Jochen, Director

JUSTICE AGENCY

Autauga Campus **334.361.9161**
Fax 334.361.4147
   1601 County Road 57, Prattville, AL 36068
   Keith Duck, Superintendent

Dallas County

SOCIAL SERVICES

Dept Of Human Resources **334.874.1400**
Phone 334.875.2450
Fax 334.874.6250
Web ....www.selmaalabama.com
E-mail ....jware@dhr.state.al.us
   200 Samuel O. Mosley Dr, Selma, AL 36702-1210
   Wanda Goodwin, Director

COURTS

**District Court/Judge Armstrong's
Ofc** **334.874.2529**
Fax 334.877.0633
   105 Lauderdale Street, Selma, AL 36701
   Honorable Robert Armstrong, Iii, District Judge

POLICE AND SHERIFF

Sheriff's Dept **334.874.2530**
Fax 334.874.2563
Web ....www.geocities.com
E-mail ....dallascountyso@bellsouth.net
   102 Church St Ste 102, Selma, AL 36701-4600
   Harris Huffman, Jr., Sheriff

De Kalb County

SOCIAL SERVICES

**Alabama Dept of Human
Resources** **256.844.2700**
Fax 256.844.2771
   PO Box 680049, Fort Payne, AL 35968

GENERAL HEALTH SERVICES

Dept Of Human Resources **256.844.2700**
Fax 256.844.2770
Web ....www.dhr.georgia.gov
E-mail ....draines@dhr.state.al.us
   2301 Briarwood Ave SW, Fort Payne, AL 35968-8484
   Denise Raines, Director

Health Dept **256.845.1931**
Fax 256.845.2967
   2401 Calvin Dr SW, Fort Payne, AL 35967
   Jamie Woods, RN, Home Health Nursing Supervisor

JUSTICE AGENCY

Juvenile Probation Ofc **256.845.8573**
Fax 256.845.8580
Web ....www.juv.alacourt.gov
E-mail ....jimmy.wilbanks@alacourt.gov
   300 Grand Ave SW, Ste 101, Fort Payne, AL 35967-1879
   Jimmy Wilbanks, CPO

COURTS

**District Court/Judge Whitmire's
Ofc** **256.845.8574**
Fax 256.845.8580
   300 Grand Ave SW Ste 101, Fort Payne, AL 35967
   Honorable Steven Whitmire, District Judge

POLICE AND SHERIFF

Sheriff's Dept......................256.845.8561
Fax......................256.845.8564
Web......................www.dekalbcountysheriff.org
E-mail......................dcso@dekalbcountysheriff.org
　2801 Jordan Rd SW, Fort Payne, AL 35968-3672
　Jimmy Harris, Sheriff

Elmore County

SOCIAL SERVICES

Dept Of Human Resources..................334.514.3200
Fax......................334.514.0609
Web......................www.dhr.state.al.us
E-mail......................lindabuchanan@dhr.state.al.us
　73932 Tallassee Hwy, Wetumpka, AL 36092-9702
　Linda Buchanan, Director

GENERAL HEALTH SERVICES

Elmorehealth Dept......................334.567.1171
Fax......................334.567.1186
Web......................www.adph.org
E-mail......................carol.wilson@adph.state.al.us
　6501 US Highway 231, Wetumpka, AL 36092-2837
　Carol Wilson, Nursing Supervisor

COURTS

District Court/Child Support
Juvenile......................334.567.1128
Fax......................334.567.5957
　8935 US Highway 231, Wetumpka, AL 36092
　Honorable Maura E. Culberson, Family Court Judge

POLICE AND SHERIFF

Sheriff's Dept......................334.567.5546
Fax......................334.514.5849
Web......................www.usacops.com
E-mail......................bfranklin@usacops.com
　8955 US Highway 231, Wetumpka, AL 36092-8256
　Bill Franklin, Sheriff

Escambia County

SOCIAL SERVICES

Dept of Human Resources..................251.809.2000
Fax......................251.809.1910
Web......................www.myescambia.com
E-mail......................rpowell@co.escambia.al.us
　326 Evergreen Avenue, Brewton, AL 36426
　Rod Powell, HR Director

Poarch Creek Native Social Svcs......................251.368.9136
Fax......................251.368.0832
Web......................www.poarchcreekindians.org
E-mail......................cwhite@poarchcreekindians-nsn.gov
　5811 Jack Springs Rd, Atmore, AL 36502-5025
　Carolyn White, Director

GENERAL HEALTH SERVICES

Health Dept......................251.867.5765
Fax......................251.867.5179
E-mail......................hbyrd@adph.state.al.us
　1115 Azalea Pl Ste A, Brewton, AL 36426
　Avis Whitworth, Nursing Supervisor

JUSTICE AGENCY

Juvenile Probation Ofc......................251.867.0259
Fax......................251.867.5719
　318 Belleville Ave, Brewton, AL 36426
　Frederick Lancaster, JPO

Etowah County

SOCIAL SERVICES

Dept of Human Resources..................256.549.4100
Fax......................256.549.4135
　210 Hoke St, Gadsden, AL 35903
　Jon M. Costa, Director

GENERAL HEALTH SERVICES

Health Dept......................256.547.6311
Fax......................256.549.1579
Web......................www.adph.org
E-mail......................katie.robinson@adph.state.al.us
　709 E Broad St, Gadsden, AL 35903
　Katie Robinson, Nursing Director

JUSTICE AGENCY

Juvenile Probation Ofc......................256.549.5473
Fax......................256.549.2170
E-mail......................barbara.roberts@alacourt.gov
　800 Forest Avenue E, Ste 221, Gadsden, AL 35901
　Barbara Roberts, Chief Performance Officer

COURTS

District Court/Judge Owen's Ofc......................256.549.5321
Fax......................256.549.2197
E-mail......................wayne.owen@alacourt.gov
　801 Forrest Ave Ste 201, Gadsden, AL 35901
　Honorable Bill Russell, District Judge

Fayette County

SOCIAL SERVICES

Dept Of Human Resources..................205.932.1665
Fax......................205.932.7459
　410 16th St NE, Fayette, AL 35555-1356
　Jason Cowart, Director

GENERAL HEALTH SERVICES

Health Dept......................205.932.5260
Fax......................205.932.3532
Web......................www.adaph.org
　215 1St Ave Nw, Fayette, AL 35555
　Tammy Yager, Director

JUSTICE AGENCY

Juvenile Probation Ofc......................205.932.3417
Fax......................205.932.4523
Web......................www.juv.alacourt.gov
E-mail......................martha.mitchell@alacourt.gov
　PO Box 616, Fayette, AL 35555-0616
　Debbie Sarris, Chief Performance Officer

COURTS

District Court......................205.932.4613
Fax......................205.932.4523
E-mail......................jclary@dca.state.al.us
　113 Temple Ave N, Fayette, AL 35555
　Honorable Jerry L. Clary, District Judge

EDUCATION SERVICES

Head Start......................205.932.3560
Fax......................205.932.3561
　2020 Academy Dr NW, Fayette, AL 35555-1206
　Anglia White, Director

Franklin County

SOCIAL SERVICES

Dept Of Human Resources..................256.331.5900
Fax......................256.332.9261
Web......................www.dhr.state.al.us
E-mail......................jgroce@dhr.state.al.us
　737 Highway 48, Russellville, AL 35654-8368
　Jerry W. Groce, Director

GENERAL HEALTH SERVICES

Health Dept......................256.332.2700
Fax......................256.332.1563
　801 Highway 48, Russellville, AL 35653
　Karen Landers, Area Health Officer

COURTS

District Court......................256.332.8886
Fax......................256.332.8421
E-mail......................sscott@dca.state.al.us
　410 Jackson Ave N, Ste 18, Russellville, AL 35653
　Sylvester Scott Jr., Chief Performance Officer

POLICE AND SHERIFF

Sheriff's Dept......................256.332.8811
Fax......................256.332.8816
Web......................www.usacops.com
　748 Walnut Gate Rd, Russellville, AL 35654
　Shannon Oliver, Sheriff

Geneva County

SOCIAL SERVICES

Dept Of Human Resources..................334.684.5800
Fax......................334.684.7114
E-mail......................ghayes@dhr.state.al.us
　617 S Commerce St, Geneva, AL 36340-2410
　Glenda Sue Hayes, Director

GENERAL HEALTH SERVICES

Health Dept......................334.684.2257
Fax......................334.684.3970
Web......................www.medicaid.state.al.us
E-mail......................kball@medicaid.state.al.us
　606 S Academy St, Geneva, AL 36340-2527
　Kenneth Ball, Executive Director

Public Health Dept......................256.383.1231
Fax......................256.383.8843
　1000 S Jackson Hwy, Sheffield, AL 35660
　Adelia Reynolds, Hiv/aids Service Coordinator

JUSTICE AGENCY

Juvenile Probation Ofc......................334.684.5680
Fax......................334.684.5634
　200 N Commerce St, Geneva, AL 36340
　Toby Seay, Chief Performance Officer

COURTS

District Court......................334.684.5620
Fax......................334.684.5634
Web......................www.dca.state.al.us
E-mail......................charles.fleming@alacourt.gov
　200 N Commerce St, Geneva, AL 36340
　Stephen Smith, District Judge

POLICE AND SHERIFF

Sheriff's Dept......................334.684.5660
Fax......................334.684.5666
　200 N Commerce Street, Geneva, AL 36340
　Greg Ward, Sheriff

Greene County

SOCIAL SERVICES

Dept Of Human Resources..................205.372.4334
After hours......................205.372.4334
Phone......................205.372.5000
Fax......................205.372.0125
E-mail......................wmorgan@dhr.state.al.us
　Highway 43 South, Eutaw, AL 35462
　Wilson Morgan, Director

GENERAL HEALTH SERVICES

Health Dept......................205.372.9361
Fax......................206.372.9283
　412 Morrow Ave, Eutaw, AL 35462
　J. Fred Grady, Director

COURTS

District Court......................205.372.3143
Fax......................205.372.1508
　400 Morrow Ave., Eutaw, AL 35462
　Moses D. Finch, Chief JPO

POLICE AND SHERIFF

Sheriff's Dept................................**205.372.3242**
Fax..205.372.4600
E-mail.............................gcsheriff@greene-county.us
  400 Morrow Avenue, Eutaw, AL 35462
  Johnathan Benison, Sheriff

Hale County

SOCIAL SERVICES

Dept Of Human Resources................**334.624.5820**
Fax..334.624.4122
  906 Whelan St, Hale County Act. Bldg., Greensboro,
  AL 36744
  Sharon V. Jay, Director

GENERAL HEALTH SERVICES

Health Dept...................................**334.624.3018**
Fax..334.624.4721
E-mail...........................ashvin.parikh@adph.state.al.us
  670 Hall St, Greensboro, AL 36744
  Ashvin Parikh, Director

JUSTICE AGENCY

Juvenile Probation Ofc.....................**334.624.2023**
Fax..334.624.8841
Web...www.usdoj.gov
E-mail..............................sharon.snyder@usdoj.gov
  1001 Main St, Rm 8AA, Greensboro, AL 36744
  Brandon Croom, Chief Performance Officer

COURTS

District Court...............................**334.624.8561**
Fax..334.624.8841
Web...www.alacourt.state.al.us
E-mail..............................william.ryan@alacourt.gov
  1001 Main St, Greensboro, AL 36744
  Honorable William A. Ryan, District Judge

POLICE AND SHERIFF

Sheriff's Dept................................**334.624.3081**
Fax..334.624.0218
E-mail...alsheriffs@aol.com
  1001 Main St, Greensboro, AL 36744
  Kenneth W. Ellis, Sheriff

Henry County

SOCIAL SERVICES

Dept Of Human Resources................**334.585.4100**
Fax..334.585.6792
E-mail..........................smcknight@dhr.state.al.us
  507 Kirkland St, Abbeville, AL 36310
  Stephanie Mcknight, Director

COURTS

District Court...............................**334.585.2753**
Fax..334.585.5006
  101 Court Sq Ste J, Abbeville, AL 36310
  Shirlene Vickers, Clerk Of Court

Houston County

SOCIAL SERVICES

**Alambama Dept of Human
Resources**.....................................**334.677.0400**
Fax..334.678.0559
  PO Box 2027, Dothan, AL 36302

GENERAL HEALTH SERVICES

Dept Of Human Resources................**334.677.0400**
Fax..334.671.0389
E-mail..............................mpaulk@dhr.state.al.us
  1605 Ross Clark Cir, Dothan, AL 36301-5438
  Mary L. Paulk, Director

Health Dept...................................**334.678.2800**
Fax..334.678.2802
Web...www.adph.state.al.us
E-mail.............................clawford@adph.state.al.us
  1781 E Cottonwood Rd, Dothan, AL 36301-5309
  Cyndy Lawford, Home Health Director

JUSTICE AGENCY

Juvenile Probation Svcs....................**334.793.4429**
Fax..334.712.7784
Web...www.juv.alacourt.gov
E-mail..................angela.underwood@alacourt.gov
  179 N Foster St, Dothan, AL 36303-4539
  Angela Underwood, Probation Officer

Southeast Alabama Diversion Ctr............**334.983.5031**
Fax..334.983.1835
E-mail...saysdothan.com
  2850 Horace Shepard Dr, Dothan, AL 36303
  Joe Easley, Manager

COURTS

Circuit Court.................................**334.677.4848**
  143 N Oates St, Dothan, AL 36302
  Dutch Binford, Circuit Judge

POLICE AND SHERIFF

Sheriff's Dept................................**334.677.4888**
Fax..334.671.8775
Web...www.houstoncounty.org
  144 North Oates St, Dothan, AL 36303
  Andy Hughes, Sheriff

EDUCATION SERVICES

**Dothan City Preschool & Head
Start**...**334.794.1447**
Fax..334.712.9379
  900 W Powell St, Dothan, AL 36303
  Jerryneta Evans, Director

Early Head Start 3 Year Program.............**334.794.4929**
E-mail..............................lynnl@adeca.state.al.us
  545 W Main St Ste 404, Dothan, AL 36301
  Linda O'Connell, Project Director

Jackson County

SOCIAL SERVICES

Dept Of Human Resources................**256.574.0300**
Fax..256.259.2049
  205 Liberty Ln, Scottsboro, AL 35769
  Sheenia B. Little, Director

GENERAL HEALTH SERVICES

Health Dept...................................**256.259.4161**
Fax..256.259.1330
  204 Liberty Lane, Scottsboro, AL 35769
  Judy Smith, Director

JUSTICE AGENCY

Juvenile Probation Ofc.....................**256.574.9365**
Fax..256.574.9235
Web...www.alacourt.gov
E-mail.............................melissa@alacourt.gov
  110 E Appletree St, Scottsboro, AL 35768-1836
  Melissa King, Chief Performance Officer

COURTS

District Court...............................**256.574.9355**
Fax..256.259.9981
  102 E Laurel St Ste 315, Scottsboro, AL 35768
  Honorable Ralph H. Grider, District Court Judge

Jefferson County

SOCIAL SERVICES

**Alabama Dept of Human
Resources**.....................................**205.918.5100**
Fax..205.918.2408
  1321 5th Ave S, PO Box 11926, Birmingham,
  AL 35202

GENERAL HEALTH SERVICES

Dept of Health...............................**205.933.9110**
Web...www.jcdh.org
E-mail.............................michael.fleenor@jcdh.org
  1400 6th Ave S, Birmingham, AL 35202
  Dr. Michael Fleenor, Chief Health Officer

JUSTICE AGENCY

CASA..**205.325.5019**
Fax..205.325.4825
  120 2nd Ct N, Birmingham, AL 35204-4718
  Rennae Williams, Program Director

Regional Detention Ctr.....................**205.325.5498**
Fax..205.325.5966
  140 2nd Ct N, Birmingham, AL 35204-4718
  Tommy Rouse, Director

Vacca Campus...............................**205.833.2361**
Fax..205.836.9993
  8950 Roebuck Blvd, Birmingham, AL 35206-1524
  James Thomas, Director

COURTS

Circuit House................................**205.325.5355**
Fax..205.325.4882
E-mail.....................williamsonk@jcc.co.jefferson.al.us
  716 Richard Arrington Jr Blvd N Rm 530,
  Birmingham, AL 35203
  Kerri Williamson, Coordinator

Family Court Bessemer District Ofc...........**205.744.3555**
Fax..205.744.3552
  1801 3rd Ave N Ste 511, Bessemer, AL 35020
  Honorable Jill Ganus, Judge

POLICE AND SHERIFF

**Birmingham Police Dept East
District**.......................................**205.254.2684**
Fax..205.833.6171
  600 Red Lane Rd, Birmingham, AL 35215
  Alan Hatcher, Captain

**Birmingham Police Dept North
Precinct**.......................................**205.254.2860**
Fax..205.254.6469
Web...www.bhampolice.com
  2600 31st Ave N, Birmingham, AL 35207-4507
  Henry Roby, Manager

**Birmingham Police Dept West
Precinct**.......................................**205.254.2683**
Fax..205.870.1914
Web...www.bhampolice.com
  616 19th St Ensley, Birmingham, AL 35218-1656
  Dr. Camptain Walice, Camptain

Sheriff's Dept................................**205.325.5700**
Fax..205.325.5364
E-mail.............................sheriff@jeffcosheriff.org
  2200 8th Ave N, Birmingham, AL 35203
  Mike Hale, Sheriff

EDUCATION SERVICES

Special Education............................**205.379.2033**
Fax..205.379.2305
Web...www.jefcoed.com
E-mail...swirt@jefcoed.com
  2100 RICHARD ARRINGTON JR BLVD S, Birmingham,
  AL 35209
  Susan Wirt, Director

Lamar County

SOCIAL SERVICES

Dept Of Human Resources **205.695.5000**
Fax 205.695.7665
E-mail .... martha.trentham@dhr.alabama.gov
250 Springfield Rd, Vernon, AL 35592
Martha K. Trentham, Director

GENERAL HEALTH SERVICES

Health Dept **205.695.9195**
Fax 205.695.9214
Web .... www.adph.state.al.us
E-mail .... wdenton@adph.state.al.us
300 Sprintfield Rd, Vernon, AL 35592
William W. Denton, Director

COURTS

District Court **205.695.9427**
Fax 205.695.7427
Web .... www.dca.state.al.us
330 1st Street NE, Vernon, AL 35592
Alex Brown, District Judge

POLICE AND SHERIFF

Sheriff's Dept **205.695.7470**
Fax 205.695.1871
E-mail .... tperkins@sos.al.gov
330 1st St SE, Vernon, AL 35592
Terry Perkins, Sheriff

Lauderdale County

SOCIAL SERVICES

Dept Of Human Resources **256.765.4000**
Fax 256.718.1656
Web .... www.dhr.state.al.us
E-mail .... cynthiabratcher@dhr.state.al.gov
424 Veterans Dr, Florence, AL 35630-5744
Cynthia L. Bratcher, Director

JUSTICE AGENCY

CASA **256.765.0041**
Fax 256.764.0088
E-mail .... director@lauderdalecasa.org
300 Industry St, Florence, AL 35631
Andrea Holt, Ex Director

Juvenile Probation Ofc **256.760.5850**
Fax 256.768.0706
200 S Court St Ste 220, Florence, AL 35630-5659
Vicki Perry, Probation Officer

COURTS

Circuit Court **256.760.5825**
Fax 256.760.5824
200 S Court St Ste 317, Florence, AL 35630
Billy Jackson, Circuit Court Judge

POLICE AND SHERIFF

Sheriff's Dept **256.760.5757**
Fax 256.760.5765
Web .... www.florencepd.org
200 S Court St, Florence, AL 35630
Ronnie Willis, Sheriff

EDUCATION SERVICES

Even Start Family Literacy
Program **256.768.3400**
955 Beale St, Florence, AL 35630
Cindy Jackson, Director

Lawrence County

SOCIAL SERVICES

Dept Of Human Resources **256.905.3100**
Fax 256.974.5945
Web .... www.dhr.state.al.us
E-mail .... tnewton@dhr.state.al.us
13280 Al Highway 157, Moulton, AL 35650
Tyron Newton, Director

GENERAL HEALTH SERVICES

Health Dept **256.974.1141**
Fax 256.974.5587
13299 Alabama Hwy 157, Moultan, AL 35650
Donald Williamson, State Health Officer

COURTS

District Court **256.974.2450**
Fax 256.974.2518
14330 Court St, Ste 307, Moulton, AL 35650-1139
Honorable Angela Terry, District Judge

Lee County

SOCIAL SERVICES

Dept Of Human Resources Children's
Svcs **334.737.1100**
Fax 334.737.1250
Web .... www.dhr.state.al.us
E-mail .... cwburke@dhr.state.al.us
1715 Corporate Dr, Opelika, AL 36801
Cynthia W. Burke, Director

MENTAL HEALTH SERVICES

East Alabama Mental Health Mental Retardation
Board **800.815.0630**
Fax 334.742.2707
Web .... www.eastalabamamhc.org
E-mail .... anne.penney@eastalabamamhc.org
2506 Lambert Dr, Opelika, AL 36801-7237
Anne Penney, Director

JUSTICE AGENCY

Youth Development Ctr **334.749.2996**
Fax 334.749.3102
E-mail .... lcydcall@aol.com
1109 Spring Dr, Opelika, AL 36801
Laura Cooper, Executive Director

COURTS

Juvenile Court **334.737.7141**
Fax 334.749.2949
2311 Gateway Dr Ste 119, Opelika, AL 36801
Pam Seidler, CPO

POLICE AND SHERIFF

Sheriff's Dept **334.749.5651**
Fax 334.749.4835
Web .... www.leecountysheriff.org
E-mail .... jayjones@leecountysheriff.org
1900 Frederick Road, Opelika, AL 36801
Jay Jones, Sheriff

EDUCATION SERVICES

ACHR Child Development Ctr **334.821.8336**
Fax 334.826.6397
Web .... www.achr.com
E-mail .... faye.crandall@achr.com
319 West Glenn, Auburn, AL 36831-0409
Janet Burns, Coordinator

Limestone County

SOCIAL SERVICES

Dept of Human Resources **256.216.6380**
Fax 256.233.6475
Web .... www.dhr.state.al.us
1007 W Market St, Athens, AL 35612-2465
Caroline Page, Director

GENERAL HEALTH SERVICES

Health Dept **256.232.3200**
Fax 256.232.6632
Web .... www.adph.org
E-mail .... judy.smith@adph.ao.us
20371 Clyde Mabry Dr, Athens, AL 35611
Judy Smith, Director

COURTS

District Court **256.233.6406**
E-mail .... janderson@dca.state.al.us
200 W Washington St, Athens, AL 35611
Honorable Jeanna W. Anderson, Judge

Juvenile Court **256.233.6425**
Fax 256.233.6499
1109 W Market St Ste E, Athens, AL 35611
Robert Valls, CPO

POLICE AND SHERIFF

Sheriff's Dept **256.232.0111**
Fax 256.233.6473
E-mail .... sheriff@limestonesheriff.com
101 W Elm St, Athens, AL 35611
Randy King, Chief Deputy

Lowndes County

SOCIAL SERVICES

Dept Of Human Resources **334.548.3800**
Fax 334.548.2807
E-mail .... rachelwaters@dhr.alabama.gov
382 Commerce St, Hayneville, AL 36040
Rachel A. Waters, Director

GENERAL HEALTH SERVICES

Health Dept **334.548.2564**
Fax 334.548.2566
507 E Tuskeena St, Hayneville, AL 36040
Ziba M. Anderson, Director

Macon County

SOCIAL SERVICES

Dept of Human Resources **334.725.2100**
Fax 334.725.2200
404 N Main St, Tuskegee, AL 36083
Courtney Hall, Director

GENERAL HEALTH SERVICES

Health Dept **334.727.1800**
Fax 334.727.7100
Web .... www.adph.org
812 Hospital Rd, Tuskegee, AL 36083-1541
James Martin, Director

JUSTICE AGENCY

Juvenile Probation Ofc **334.724.2609**
Fax 334.724.2534
101 E Rosa Parks Ave Ste 108, Tuskegee, AL 36083
Oneal Hardmon, Sr., Chief Performance Officer

COURTS

Court House **334.724.2614**
Fax 334.727.6483
Web .... www.sos.alabama.gov
101 E Rosa Parks Ave Ste 300, Tuskegee,
AL 36083-1735
Honorable Aubrey Ford Jr., Judge

Madison County

SOCIAL SERVICES

Dept Of Human Resources 256.535.4500
Fax 256.535.4516
2206 Oakwood Ave NW, Huntsville, AL 35810-4499
Jennifer Demarcus, Assistant Director

GENERAL HEALTH SERVICES

Health Dept 256.539.3711
Fax 256.536.2084
Web .... www.adph.state.al.us
E-mail .... lrobey@adph.state.al.us
301 Eustis Ave SE, Huntsville, AL 35811-3118
Lawrence L. Robey, Director

JUSTICE AGENCY

Juvenile Probation 256.532.0300
Fax 256.532.0326
817 Cook Ave NW, Huntsville, AL 35801
John Riise, Detention Supervisor

COURTS

CAJA 256.532.6988
Fax 256.532.1583
Web www.caja4kids.org
E-mail .... cajadir@co.madison.al.us
100 Northside Sq, Huntsville, AL 35801-4800
Shirley Ingram, CEO

POLICE AND SHERIFF

Huntsville Police Dept 256.427.7001
Fax 256.564.8015
Web .... www.ci.huntsville.al.us/police
815 Wheeler Ave, Huntsville, AL 35801
Mark Hudson, Chief Of Police

Sheriff's Office 256.532.3412
Fax 256.532.6976
E-mail .... sheriff@co.madison.al.us
100 Northside Sq, Huntsville, AL 35801
Blake L. Dorning, Sheriff

EDUCATION SERVICES

Special Education 256.852.7073
Fax 256.852.1086
Web www.madison.k12.al.us
E-mail .... mboone@madison.k12.al.us
146 Shields Rd Ste A, Huntsville, AL 35811-8936
Lorraine Boone, Special Education Director

Marengo County

SOCIAL SERVICES

Human Resources 334.295.2000
Web .... www.dhr.state.al.us
701 S Shiloh St, Linden, AL 36748-2014
Ellen Wallace, Director

GENERAL HEALTH SERVICES

Health Dept 334.295.4205
Fax 334.295.0124
303 Industrial Dr, Linden, AL 36748
Jackie Holliday, Administrator

COURTS

District Court 334.295.8774
Fax 334.295.9889
Web .... www.dca.state.al.us
E-mail .... darren.glass@alacourt.gov
101 E Coats Ave, Linden, AL 36748
Darren Glass, Chief JPO

POLICE AND SHERIFF

Sheriff's Dept 334.295.4208
Fax 334.295.2226
101 Dunn St, Linden, AL 36748
Richard Bates, Sheriff

Marion County

SOCIAL SERVICES

**Dept Of Human Resources Children's
Svcs** 205.921.6000
Fax 205.921.6050
E-mail .... briley@dhr.state.al.us
760 Industrial Dr, Hamilton, AL 35570
Bonnie S. Riley, Director

JUSTICE AGENCY

Juvenile Probation Ofc 205.921.4562
Fax 205.921.4563
E-mail .... jennifer.nix@alacourt.gov
132 Military St S, Hamilton, AL 35570
Jennifer Nix, Chief Performance Officer

COURTS

Court House 205.921.7451
Fax 205.952.9851
E-mail .... james@sonet.net
132 Military St S, Hamilton, AL 35570
Honorable James C. Cashion, District Judge

Marshall County

SOCIAL SERVICES

Dept Of Human Resources 888.658.5132
Fax 256.582.7160
E-mail .... jsellers@dhr.state.al.us
1925 Gunter Ave, Guntersville, AL 35976-2111
James Wayne Sellers, Director

GENERAL HEALTH SERVICES

Health Dept 256.582.3174
Fax 256.582.3548
E-mail .... cathy.hughes@adph.state.al.us
4200 B Highway 79 S, Guntersville, AL 35976
Cathy Hughes, Nursing Supervisor

EDUCATION SERVICES

Big Springs Lake Head Start 256.878.5807
257 Country Club Rd, Albertville, AL 35951
Donna Dobbs, Director

Mobile County

SOCIAL SERVICES

Child Welfare 251.450.9100
Fax 251.476.1753
E-mail .... hjordan@dhr.alabama.gov
3103 Airport Blvd, Mobile, AL 36606
Hank Jordan, Assistant Director

GENERAL HEALTH SERVICES

Children's Rehabilitation Svcs 251.432.4560
Fax 251.432.9013
Web .... www.rehab.state.al.us
E-mail .... btrammell@rehab.state.al.us
1610 Center St, Ste A, Mobile, AL 36604-1512
Bobbi Jo Trammell, Supervisor

Health Dept 251.690.8158
Fax 334.432.7443
Web .... www.mobilecountyhealth.org
251 N Bayou St, Mobile, AL 36603
Bernard H. Eichold, Health Officer

COURTS

**Juvenile Court/James T. Strickland Youth
Ctr** 251.574.1450
Fax 251.574.5319
2315 Costarides St, Mobile, AL 26617
Edmond Naman, Judge

POLICE AND SHERIFF

Mobile City Police Dept 251.208.7211
Fax 251.208.1001
2460 Government St, Mobile, AL 36606
Michael Williams, Chief

Sheriff's Office 251.574.7827
Fax 251.574.8631
510 South Royal Street, Mobile, AL 36603
Sam Cochran, Sheriff

EDUCATION SERVICES

E A Palmer Head Start Ctr 251.457.9612
628 A-S Martin L King Dr, Prichard, AL 36610
Doris Jones, Director

Special Education 251.221.4220
Fax 251.221.4232
E-mail .... smartin@mcpss.com
1 Magnum Pass, Mobile, AL 36618
Dr. Shelia Martin, Special Education Director

Monroe County

SOCIAL SERVICES

Dept Of Human Resources 251.743.5900
Fax 251.575.4667
25 Legion Dr, Monroeville, AL 36460
Voncile Jackson, Interim Director

MENTAL HEALTH SERVICES

**Southwest Alabama Mental Health
Board** 251.575.4203
Fax 251.575.9459
Web .... www.swamh.com
E-mail .... candace@swamh.com
328 W Claiborne St, Monroeville, AL 36460-1738
Candace Goodson, Director

COURTS

Court House 251.743.4107
Fax 251.575.5933
Web .... www.sos.al.gov
E-mail .... gelbercht@sos.al.gov
Courthouse Square, Monroeville, AL 36461
Honorable George K. Elbercht, Judge

POLICE AND SHERIFF

Sheriff's Dept 251.575.2963
Fax 251.575.7661
65 N Alabama Ave Ste 136, Monroeville,
AL 36460-1800
Tom Tate, Sheriff

Montgomery County

SOCIAL SERVICES

Child Support Enforcement Div 334.242.9300
Fax 334.242.0606
Web .... www.dhr.state.al.us
E-mail .... dmccampbell@dhr.state.al.us
50 N Ripley St, Montgomery, AL 36130-1001
Diane McCambell, Director

Dept Of Human Resources 334.293.3100
Fax 334.293.3453
Web .... www.dhr.state.al.us
E-mail .... tbenton@dhr.state.al.us
3030 Mobile Hwy, Montgomery, AL 36108-4027
Terry Benton, Director

GENERAL HEALTH SERVICES

Children's Rehabilitation Svc 334.293.7500
Fax 334.293.7371
Web .... www.rehab.alabama.gov
E-mail .... cary.boswell@rehab.alabama.gov
602 S Lawrence St, Montgomery, AL 36104
Cary Boswell, Commissioner

Health Dept 334.293.6400
Fax 334.293.6410
　3060 Mobile Hwy, Montgomery, AL 36108
　James Martin, Area Administrator

COURTS

Court House 334.832.4950
Fax 334.261.4132
　100 S Lawrence St, Montgomery, AL 36104
　Michael Provitt, Detention Center Director

POLICE AND SHERIFF

Montgomery Police Dept Juvenile
Div 334.241.2866
Fax 334.241.2877
E-mail .... jgraboys@montgomeryal.gov
　320 N Ripley St, Montgomery, AL 36101
　Major J N Graboys, Division Commander

EDUCATION SERVICES

Special Education 334.269.3808
Fax 334.269.3799
Web www.mps.k12.al.us
　1153 S Lawrence St, Montgomery, AL 36104
　Yolanda Gracie, Director Of Special Education

Morgan County

SOCIAL SERVICES

Dept Of Human Resources 256.340.5840
Fax 256.340.5907
Web .... www.dhr.state.al.us
E-mail .... tphipps@dhr.state.al.us
　507 14th St SE, Decatur, AL 35601-5907
　Tonita Phipps, Director

GENERAL HEALTH SERVICES

Health Dept 256.353.7021
Fax 256.350.9823
　510 Cherry St NE, Decatur, AL 35601-1970
　Leland Screws, Director

COURTS

District Court 256.351.4715
Fax 256.351.4688
Web .... www.jpo.morgan.alacourt.gov
　302 Lee Street Northeast, Decatur, AL 35601
　Honorable Shelly Waters, Director

POLICE AND SHERIFF

Sheriff's Dept 256.351.4800
Fax 256.351.4822
　119 Lee St NE, Decatur, AL 35601
　Ana Franklin, Sheriff

EDUCATION SERVICES

Bear Creek Head Start 205.486.8815
　1909 Central Pkwy SW, Decatur, AL 35601
　Shirley Cochran, Director

Special Education 256.309.2117
Fax 256.309.2180
Web www.morgank12.org
　1325 Point Mallard Pkwy, Decatur, AL 35601-6542
　Lana Tew, Special Education Coordinator

Perry County

SOCIAL SERVICES

Dept of Human Resources 334.683.5500
Fax 334.683.9799
　1609 Highway, Marion, AL 36756
　Alvin J. Reed, Director

GENERAL HEALTH SERVICES

Health Dept 334.683.6153
Fax 334.683.4509
　Highway 45 S, Marion, AL 36756
　Ashvin Parikh, Director

COURTS

District Court 334.683.2215
Fax 334.683.6078
　300 Washington St, Marion, AL 36756
　Honorable Don Mcmillin, District Judge

POLICE AND SHERIFF

Sheriff's Dept 334.683.6534
Fax 334.683.9354
E-mail .... pcjhood@yahoo.com
　202 Pickens St, Marion, AL 36756
　James Hood, Sheriff

Pickens County

SOCIAL SERVICES

Dept Of Human Resources 205.367.1500
Fax 205.367.1517
E-mail .... shea.cobb-england@dhr.alabama.gov
　401 Tuscaloosa Ave, Carrollton, AL 35447
　Shea Cobb-england, Director

GENERAL HEALTH SERVICES

Health Dept 205.367.8157
Fax 205.367.8376
Web .... www.adph.state.al.us
E-mail .... fredgrady@adph.state.al.us
　80 William E Hill Dr, Carrollton, AL 35447-3231
　J. Fred Grady, Director

COURTS

District Court 205.367.2076
Fax 205.367.8417
　20 Phoenix Ave, Carrollton, AL 35447
　James Fields, CPO

Pike County

SOCIAL SERVICES

Alabama Dept of Human
Resources 334.807.6120
Fax 334.807.6171
　717 S 3 Notch St, PO Box 966, Troy, AL 36081

JUSTICE AGENCY

Juvenile Probation Ofc 334.566.5548
Fax 334.566.8944
　1301 Elba Hwy, Troy, AL 36079
　Patricia Smith, Chief Performance Officer

POLICE AND SHERIFF

Sheriff's Dept 334.566.4347
Fax 334.807.0555
　120 W Church St Rm 40, Troy, AL 36081
　Russell Thomas, Sheriff

EDUCATION SERVICES

YMCA 334.347.4513
Fax 334.347.3372
E-mail .... victor.cipkin@ymca.net
　904 Ozark Hwy, Enterprise, AL 36330
　Victor Cipkin, Director

Randolph County

SOCIAL SERVICES

Dept of Human Resources 256.357.3000
Fax 256.357.2070
　865 Hill Crest Ave, Wedowee, AL 36278
　Sharonda Pettaway, Director

GENERAL HEALTH SERVICES

Health Dept 334.863.8981
Fax 334.863.8975
　329 St, Roanoke, AL 36274-2132
　Mary Gomillian, Director

COURTS

District Court 256.357.4921
Fax 256.357.4315
　1 Main St S, Wedowee, AL 36278
　Honorable W. Patrick Whaley, District Judge

Russell County

SOCIAL SERVICES

Dept Of Human Resources 334.214.5780
Fax 334.297.0604
E-mail .... phuffman@dhr.state.al.us
　1003 25th St, Phenix City, AL 36867
　Wanda S. Martin, Director

GENERAL HEALTH SERVICES

Health Dept 334.298.5581
Fax 334.298.0498
Web .... www.adph.state.al.us
E-mail .... lanithompson@adph.state.al.us
　1850 Crawford Rd, Phenix City, AL 36867-4222
　Lani Thompson, HIV/AIDS Service Coordinator

JUSTICE AGENCY

Juvenile Probation Ofc 334.297.5369
Fax 334.298.6919
Web .... www.juv.alacourt.gov
E-mail .... michael.suber@alacourt.gov
　501 14th St, Phoenix City, AL 36867-5142
　Michael Suber, Chief Performance Officer

COURTS

District Court 334.297.1347
Fax 334.214.9802
E-mail .... efunderburk@dca.state.al.us
　501 14th Street, Phenix City, AL 36867
　Honorable Eric B. Funderburk, District Judge

Shelby County

SOCIAL SERVICES

Alabama Dept of Human
Resources 205.669.3000
Fax 205.669.3096
　987 Hwy 70, PO Box 1096, Columbiana, AL 35051

GENERAL HEALTH SERVICES

Dept Of Human Resources 205.669.3000
Fax 205.669.3096
　987 Highway 70, Columbiana, AL 35051
　Kim Mashego, Director

Health Dept 205.664.2470
Fax 205.664.4148
E-mail .... mgomillion@adph.state.al.us
　2000 County Services Dr, Pelham, AL 35124
　Mary Gomillion, Aria Administrator

MENTAL HEALTH SERVICES

Chilton-Shelby Mental Health Ctr 205.663.1252
Fax 205.663.3175
Web .... www.chiltonshelby.org
E-mail .... mcrawford@chiltonshelby.org
　2100 County Services Dr, Pelham, AL 35040
　Melodie D. Crawford, Executive Director

JUSTICE AGENCY

Juvenile Detention Facility 205.669.3990
Fax 205.669.8580
Web .... www.shelbycountyalabama.com
　222 McDow Rd, Columbiana, AL 35051
　Debra Roulaine, Manager

Juvenile Probation Ofc 205.669.3831
Fax 205.669.3704
Web .... www.alacourt.gov
E-mail .... gregory.lancaster@inl.gov
　112 N Main St, #136, Columbiana, AL 35051
　Greg Lancaster, Probation Officer

Alabama

COURTS

District Court 205.669.3730
Fax 205.669.8554
E-mail ....jkramer@dca.state.al.us
   112 N Main Street, Columbiana, AL 35051
   Honorable James R. Kramer, Director

EDUCATION SERVICES

Special Education 205.682.5850
Fax 205.682.5855
Web www.shelbyed.k12.al.us
E-mail ....maldrich@shelbyed.k12.al.us
   2284 Hwy 35, Telham, AL 35124-8002
   Dr. Marla Aldrich, Special Education Coordinator

St. Clair County

SOCIAL SERVICES

Dept of Human Resources 205.812.2100
Fax 205.812.2160
Web ....www.dhr.state.al.us
   1310 Comar Ave, Pell City, AL 35125-1494
   Cherri Pilkington, Director

GENERAL HEALTH SERVICES

Health Dept 205.338.3357
Fax 205.338.4863
Web ....www.adph.org
E-mail ....mgomillion@adph.state.al.us
   1175 23rd St N, Pell City, AL 35125-9310
   Mary Gomillion, Director

JUSTICE AGENCY

Juvenile Probation Ofc 205.884.1253
Fax 205.814.1509
   1815 Cogswell Ave Ste 104, Pell City, AL 35125
   Mitzi Draxler, Probation Officer

Juvenile Probation Ofc 205.594.2179
Fax 205.594.2177
   100 6th Avenue, Ashville, AL 35953-3215
   Scott Kearley, Probation Officer

COURTS

District Court 205.338.3869
Fax 205.884.0115
E-mail ....phil.seay@alacourt.gov
   1815 Cogswell Ave Ste 308, Pell City, AL 35125
   Honorable Phil Seay, District Court Judge

POLICE AND SHERIFF

Sheriff's Dept 205.594.2140
Fax 205.594.2146
Web ....www.stclairco.com
E-mail ....sheriff@stclairco.com
   48 6th St Ste 300, Ashville, AL 35953-3844
   Terry Surles, Sheriff

Sumter County

SOCIAL SERVICES

Dept Of Human Resources 205.652.5000
Fax 205.652.4407
   108 W Main St, Livingston, AL 35470
   Vanessa Patton, Director

GENERAL HEALTH SERVICES

Health Dept 205.652.7972
Fax 205.652.4331
E-mail ....ashvin.parikh@adph.state.al.us
   1121 N Washington St, Livingston, AL 35470
   Ashvin Parikh, Director

MENTAL HEALTH SERVICES

West Alabama Mental Health Ctr 205.652.6731
Fax 205.652.6732
   1121 N Washington St, Livingston, AL 35470
   Lashaundra Cistrunk, County Coordinator

POLICE AND SHERIFF

Sheriff's Dept 205.652.7984
Fax 205.652.7981
Web ....www.co.livingston.ny.us
E-mail ....Sheriffsoffice@aol.com
   118 Hospital Dr, Livingston, AL 35470-5741
   Tyrone Clark Sr., Sheriff

Talladega County

SOCIAL SERVICES

Coosa Valley Resources Women 256.208.8888
Fax 256.208.8804
   1259 Talladega Hwy, Sylacauga, AL 35150-1604

Dept of Human Resources 256.761.6600
Fax 256.761.6798
Web ....www.dhr.state.al.us
   1010 Ashland Hwy, Talladega, AL 35160-2805
   Mary Ashcraft, Director

GENERAL HEALTH SERVICES

Health Dept 256.362.2593
Fax 256.362.0529
Web ....www.adph.state.al.us
   1004 South St East, Talladega, AL 35160-2448
   Mary Gomillion, Director

COURTS

Court House 256.249.1005
Fax 256.249.1006
Web ....www.sos.alabama.gov
E-mail ....tommy.dobson@sos.alabama.gov
   Court House Square, Talladega, AL 35160
   Honorable Tommy Dobson, Presiding Juvenile Judge

District Court 256.761.2113
   148 East St, Talladega, AL 35160
   Jeb S. Fannin, Juvenile District Court Judge

Juvenile Court 256.249.1003
Fax 256.249.3801
   400 N Norton Ave, Sylacauga, AL 35150-2010
   Bill Monck, Probation Officer

Juvenile Probation Court 256.761.2111
Fax 256.761.2143
E-mail ....mitzi.ford@alacourt.gov
   148 East St N, Talladega, AL 35160-2066
   Mitzi Ford, Chief Performance Officer

POLICE AND SHERIFF

Sheriff's Dept 256.362.2748
Fax 256.761.2140
E-mail ....jerry.studdard@talladegacountyal.org
   148 East St N, Talladega, AL 35160
   Jerry Studdard, Sheriff

EDUCATION SERVICES

Alabama Institute For Deaf And
Blind 256.761.3200
Fax 256.761.3344
Web ....www.aidb.org
E-mail ....graham.terry@aidb.state.al.us
   205 South St E, Talladega, AL 35160-2411
   Terry Graham, Ph.d, President

Child Resiliency Interactive
Bonding 256.245.4343
Fax 256.245.3675
Web ....www.safesylacauga.com
E-mail ....harrisk@safesylacauga.com
   78 Betsy Ross Lane, Sylacauga, AL 35150
   Karen Harris, Even Start Director

Tallapoosa County

SOCIAL SERVICES

Dept Of Human Resources 256.825.2755
Fax 256.825.7412
E-mail ....mhanks@dhr.state.al.us
   353 N Broadnax Street, Dadeville, AL 36853
   Marsha J Hanks, Director

GENERAL HEALTH SERVICES

Health Dept 256.825.9203
Fax 256.825.6546
E-mail ....dthompson@medicaid.state.al.us
   220 W Lafayette St, Dadeville, AL 36853
   Debbie Thompson, RN, Nursing Supervisor

COURTS

Court House 256.825.1098
Fax 256.825.1371
E-mail ....kenneth.taylor@alacourt.gov
   125 N Broadnax St Rm 131, Dadeville,
   AL 36853-1300
   Honorable Clayton Kim Taylor, District Judge

Tuscaloosa County

SOCIAL SERVICES

Dept Of Human Resources 205.554.1100
Fax 205.554.3322
Web ....www.dhr.state.al.us
E-mail ....jgyoung@dhr.state.al.us
   3716 12th Ave E, Tuscaloosa, AL 35405-2500
   Judy Young, Director

GENERAL HEALTH SERVICES

Public Health Area 3 ....205.554.4500
Fax 205.556.2701
Web ....www.adph.org
E-mail ....shakina.wheeler@adph.state.al.us
   1200 37th St E, Tuscaloosa, AL 03507
   Shakina Wheeler, Hiv/aids Service Coordinator

JUSTICE AGENCY

Regional Detention Ctr 205.349.3131
Fax 205.349.3196
Web ....www.djj.state.fl.us
E-mail ....john.faile@djj.state.fl.us
   6941 12 Ave E, Tuscaloosa, AL 35405-5163
   John Faile, Director

COURTS

6th Circuit Court 205.349.3870
Fax 205.758.0247
Web ....www.tuscco.com
E-mail ....fbrazeal@tuscco.com
   714 Greensboro Avenue, # 241, Tuscaloosa,
   AL 35401
   Honorable Frances Brazeal, Judge

POLICE AND SHERIFF

Police Dept 205.349.2121
Fax 205.349.0174
Web ....www.cityoftuscaloosa.us.org
E-mail ....asmith@ci.tuscaloosa.al.us
   3801 Millcreek Ave, Tuscaloosa, AL 35401
   Lt Antony Smith, Director Juvenile Division

Sheriff's Office 205.752.0616
Fax 205.752.6985
E-mail ....tsexton@tusco.com
   714 1/2 Greensboro Ave, Tuscaloosa, AL 35401
   Ted Sexton, Sheriff

EDUCATION SERVICES

Special Education 205.342.2756
Fax 205.342.2729
Web ....www.tcss.net
E-mail ....ppowell@tuscumbia.k12.al.us
1324 Rice Mine Rd, Northport, AL 35476-5011
Patricia Powell, Secondary Special Education Coordinator

Walker County

SOCIAL SERVICES

Dept Of Human Resources 205.387.5400
Fax 205.387.5494
1901 Hwy 78 E, Jasper, AL 35501
Randal C. Redmill, Director

GENERAL HEALTH SERVICES

Health Dept 205.221.9775
Fax 205.221.8810
705 20th Ave E, Jasper, AL 35501
Don cardwell, Director

JUSTICE AGENCY

Juvenile Probation Ofc 205.384.7243
Fax 205.384.7001
Walker County Ct House Annex, Jasper, AL 35501
Mark Jarvis, Chief Performance Officer

COURTS

14th Circuit Court 205.384.7234
Fax 205.384.7002
Web ....www.walkercounty.com
E-mail ....doug.farris@alacourt.gov
Court House Annex, Jasper, AL 35501
Honorable Doug Farris, Circuit Court Judge/Family/Juvenile

POLICE AND SHERIFF

Sheriff's Dept 205.302.6464
Fax 205.302.6100
Web ....www.sonet.net
E-mail ....sheriff@sonet.net
2001 2nd Ave S, Jasper, AL 35501-5805
John Mark Tirey, Sheriff

Washington County

SOCIAL SERVICES

Dept Of Human Resources 251.847.6100
Fax 251.847.3554
14921 Saint Stephens Ave, Chatom, AL 36518
Brenda T. Taylor, Director

GENERAL HEALTH SERVICES

Health Dept 334.847.2245
Fax 334.847.3480
Web ....www.adph.state.al.us
E-mail ....runderwood@adph.state.al.us
Court St & Granada Ave, Chatom, AL 36518
Ruth Underwood, Director

COURTS

District Court 251.847.2164
Fax 251.847.6633
45 Court St, #220, Chatom, AL 36518
Judge Turner, District Judge

Wilcox County

SOCIAL SERVICES

Dept Of Human Resources 334.682.1200
Fax 334.682.9021
231 Depot St, Camden, AL 36726
Lathesia Saulsberry, Director

GENERAL HEALTH SERVICES

Health Dept 334.682.4515
Fax 334.682.4796
Web ....www.wilcoxcountyalabama.com
107 Union St, Camden, AL 36726-1728
Ziba M. Anderson, Director

COURTS

District Court 334.682.4619
Fax 334.682.4025
Web ....www.dca.state.al.us
12 Water Street, Suite 302, Camden, AL 36726
Christopher Browder, Jpo

POLICE AND SHERIFF

Sheriff's Dept 334.682.4715
Fax 334.682.9425
E-mail ....sheriffevans@frontier.com
12 Water St, Camden, AL 36726
Earnest Evans, Sheriff

Winston County

SOCIAL SERVICES

Dept Of Human Resources Children's
Svcs 205.489.1500
Fax 205.489.2157
E-mail ....dhendrix@dhr.state.al.us
Hwy 33 N, Double Springs, AL 35553
Dale F. Hendrix, Jr., Director

SPECIAL SERVICES AGENCIES

ADOPTION AGENCIES

A Angel Adoptions 205.621.0316
Fax 205.621.0379
911 Creek Site Ct, Ste A, Helena, AL 35080

Adoption Attorneys 256.534.4571
Fax 256.534.4578
Web ....www.brodowski.com
E-mail ....brodowski@brodowski.com
415 Church St NW Ste 200, Huntsville,
AL 35801-5594
Mike Brovowski, Director

Adoption Home Study Svc 251.626.9011
Fax 251.626.9011
1203 US Highway 98 Ste 3G, Daphne, AL 36526
Bill Board, Director

Agape 334.393.1990
Fax 334.393.0224
Web ....www.agapeforchildren.org
E-mail ....agapelynn@msn.com
211 W College St, Enterprise, AL 36330-2903
Lynn Elllis, Director

Alabama Mentor 251.478.5243
Fax 251.478.5254
601 Bel Air Blvd Ste 200, Mobile, AL 36606
Bobbie Slowsam, Administrative Assistant

Alabama Post Adoption Connect 251.460.2727
Fax 251.460.2729
Web ....www.casapac.org
E-mail ....dfinnley@casapac.org
857 Downtowner Blvd Ste B, Mobile, AL 36609-5420
Deb Finnley, Director

Alabama Pre and Post Adoption
Connection 334.409.9477
E-mail ....info@childrensa.org
401 Interstate Park Dr Ste 425, Montgomery,
AL 36109
Jill Sexton, Coordinator

Blake Payne Law Ofcs 205.221.4660
Fax 205.221.4652
Web ....www.bpaynelaw.com
1816 3rd Ave S Ste 101, Jasper, AL 35501-5395
Blake Payne, Administrator

Bryant A. Whitmire, Jr. 205.324.6631
Fax 205.324.6632
Web ....www.alafamlaw.org
215 Richard Arrington Jr Blvd N Ste 501, Birmingham,
AL 35203-3722
Bryant A. Whitmire, Jr., Attorney

Catholic Ctr Of Concern 256.536.0041
Fax 256.534.3141
1010 Church St NW, Huntsville, AL 35801-5912
Laura Dimwhitty, Director

Children Of The World 251.990.3550
Fax 251.990.3494
Web ....www.childrenoftheworld.com
E-mail ....adoption@childrenoftheworld.com
82 Plantation Pt # 292, Fairhope, AL 36532-2014
Bill Harrison, Director

Family Adoption Svcs 205.414.6003
Fax 205.414.3097
Web ....www.familyadoptionservices.com
2010 Lancaster Rd, Birmingham, AL 35209
Rick Wyatt, Director

Gateway Therapeutic Foster Care 205.510.2720
Fax 205.510.2750
Web ....www.gway.org
E-mail ....dkilmer@gway.org
1401 20th St S, Birmingham, AL 35205
David Kilmer, Director

Harris Home For Children 256.837.0332
Fax 256.837.2837
Web ....www.harrishomeforchildren.org
1210 Church St NW, Huntsville, AL 35801
Antonio McGinnis, Administrator

Outward Bound Discovery - Five Rivers 251.990.0323
Fax 251.990.0326
Web ....www.outwardbound.org
265 Young Street, Fairhope, AL 36532
COA accredited organization.

Rena Advantage 256.237.4990
Fax 256.237.9205
Web ....www.southernsocialworks.com
E-mail ....sosocwrks@aol.com
7 E 13th St, Ste 227, Anniston, AL 36201
Jim-Ellis Fisher, Executive Director

Womens Care Medical Center 251.947.2111
18555 Carolina St, Robertsdale, AL 36567
Sue Levans, Director

ADVOCACY RESOURCES

Brook's Place CAC Of Cullman, Inc. 256.739.2243
Fax 256.739.2428
Web ....www.cullmancac.com
E-mail ....kbevis@cullmancac.com
1003 4th Ave NE, Cullman, AL 35055
Kim Bevis, Executive Director

C.A.R.E. House 251.580.2546
Fax 251.580.1665
Web ....www.bccarehouse.org
E-mail ....carehouse@bellsouth.net
108 Blackburn Ave, Bay Minette, AL 36507
Jerry Haase, Executive Director

Calhoun/Cleburne Children's Ctr 256.238.0902
Fax 256.238.0910
E-mail ....ccccnabors@bellsouth.net
2100 Leighton Ave, Anniston, AL 36207
Joe Nabors, Director

Child Advocacy Ctr 256.582.8492
Fax 256.582.3902
E-mail ....cac@marshallcac.org
825 Gunter Ave, Guntersville, AL 35976
Leslie Wright, Executive Director

Child Advocacy Ctr 334.297.4962
Fax 334.297.4794
E-mail ....rccac@bellsouth.net
67 Downing Dr, Phenix City, AL 36869
Lynn Hart, Executive Director

Child Advocacy Ctr Of East Alabama, Inc. 334.705.0770
Fax 334.705.0741
E-mail ....caccea@earthlink.net
1810 Corporate Dr, Opelika, AL 36801
Emilyn Gipson, Executive Director

Child Protect, Inc. 334.262.1220
Fax 334.262.2252
Web ....www.childprotect.org
E-mail ....bailey@childprotect.org
935 S Perry St, Montgomery, AL 36104
Jannah Bailey, Executive Director

Children's Advocacy Ctr 205.338.8847
Fax 205.338.1979
E-mail ....sccac@coosahs.net
18200 Al Hwy 174, Pell City, AL 35125
Pam Kelley, Executive Director

Children's Advocacy Ctr 256.997.9700
Fax 256.997.9111
Web ....www.dekalbcac.org
E-mail ....director@dekalbcac.org
104 Alabama Ave NW, Fort Payne, AL 35967-2052
Elizabeth Rusk-wheatley, Director

Children's Advocacy Ctr, Inc. 334.382.8584
Fax 334.383.9485
107 Caldwell St, Greenville, AL 36037
Kathy Smyth, Executive Director

Northwest Alabama Children's Advocacy
Ctr 256.760.1140
Fax 256.764.3164
Web ....www.cramerchildrenscenter.com
E-mail ....lmase@cramerchildrenscenter.com
404 W Tennessee St, Florence, AL 35630
Leigh Mase, Director

Owens House Advocacy Ctr, Inc. 205.669.3333
Fax 205.669.0364
E-mail ....shelbycountycac@bellsouth.net
22747 Hwy 25, Columbiana, AL 35051
Cindy Greer, Director

Partnership for a Drug Free Community 256.539.7339
Fax 256.539.7386
Web ....www.hiwaay.net
E-mail ....partner@hiwaay.net
312 Randolph Ave, Huntsville, AL 35801
Deborah Soule, Executive Director

Prescott House 205.930.3622
Fax 205.930.3625
Web ....www.prescotthouse.org
E-mail ....mary@prescotthouse.org
1730 14th Ave S, Birmingham, AL 35205-5539
Mary Murphy, Director

Southeast Alabama Advocacy Ctr 334.671.1779
Fax 334.677.1767
Web ....www.southeastcac.org
E-mail ....sdpwalker@comcast.net
110 Harmony Ln, Dothan, AL 36303
Sherryl Walker, Executive Director

The Child Advocacy Ctr, Inc. 251.432.1101
Fax 251.432.0330
E-mail ....pguyton@cacmobile.org
1351 Spring Hill Ave, Mobile, AL 36604-3210
Patrick F. Guyton, Executive Director

The Clayhouse 205.481.4155
Fax 205.481.4254
E-mail ....bcacenter@bellsouth.net
1830 Dartmouth Ave, Bessemer, AL 35020
Debbi Land, Director

Tuscaloosa Children's Ctr 205.752.7711
Fax 205.345.7297
Web ....www.tuscaloosachildrenscenter.org
E-mail ....tuscaloosacc@bellsouth.net
520 Martin Luther King Jr. Blvd, Tuscaloosa,
AL 35401
Patricia Steele, Director

BEHAVIORAL HEALTH TREATMENT

A Center for Eating Disorders 205.933.0041
Web ....www.acenterforeatingdisorders.com
E-mail ....wilsons08@aol.com
2401 Arlington Ave S, Birmingham, AL 35205
Ms. Shirley Wilson, Accreditation Manager
Joint Commission accredited organization.

Alabama Baptist Children's Homes And Family
Ministries 251.639.1022
Fax 251.639.1160
Web ....www.abchome.org
6512 Grelot Rd, Mobile, AL 36695-2657

Alabama Clinical Schools, Inc 205.836.9923
E-mail ....pam.smith@uhsinc.com
1221 Alton Drive, Birmingham, AL 35210
Mrs. Pam Smith, Accreditation Manager
Joint Commission accredited organization.

Alabama Sheriffs' Youth Ranches, Inc. 334.213.2071
Fax 334.213.1195
Web ....www.sheriffsranch.org
E-mail ....asyr@sheriffsranch.org
2680 Bell Road, Montgomery, AL 36117
Nicholas Rauccio, CEO

AltaPointe Health Systems, Inc. 251.450.5901
Web ....www.altapointe.org
E-mail ....salexander@altapointe.org
5750-A Southland Drive, Mobile, AL 36693
Ms. Sherill Alexander, Accreditation Manager
Joint Commission accredited organization.

Attention Home 256.767.0972
Fax 256.767.1086
E-mail ....info@attentionhomes.net
300 Industry St, Florence, AL 35630
Teresa Robertson, Executive Director

Bayview Professional Associates Ctr 251.450.2250
Fax 251.342.2414
501 N Bishop Ln, Mobile, AL 36608
John Conrad, Lcsw, Supervisor

Behavioral Medicine 334.877.3322
E-mail ....behavioralealth2009@hotmail.com
1306 Old Orrville Rd, Selma, AL 36701-6931
Richard Reynolds, Psychiatrist

Birmingham Health Care 205.212.5600
Web ....www.birminghamhealthcare.org
E-mail ....rbolle@bhc-al.org
1600 20th Street South, Birmingham, AL 35205
Mrs. Raeanna Bolle, Accreditation Manager
Joint Commission accredited organization.

Bradford Health Services - Huntsville
Lodge 256.461.7272
Web ....www.bradfordhealth.com
E-mail ....mhays@bradfordhealth.net
1600 Browns Ferry Road, Madison, AL 35758
Ms. Margo Hays, Accreditation Manager
Joint Commission accredited organization.

Bradford Health Services - Warrior Lodge 205.647.1945
Web ....www.bradfordhealth.com
E-mail ....rramsey@bradfordhealth.net
1189 Allbritton Road, Birmingham, AL 35205
Mr. Roy Ramsey, Accreditation Manager
Joint Commission accredited organization.

Bradford Health Svcs 256.895.3848
Fax 256.895.3213
Web ....www.bradfordhealth.net
E-mail ....cjohnson@bradfordhealth.net
555 Sparkman Dr NW Ste 208, Huntsville,
AL 35816-3400
Charlotte Johnson, Director

Claybon Clinic 205.933.6151
1716 14th Ave S, Birmingham, AL 35205-5539
Earnest Claybon MD, Director

Ctr For Counseling / Development 334.774.7704
191 Katherine Ave, Ozark, AL 36360-1976

Eastside Mental Health Ctr 205.836.7283
Fax 205.836.7824
Web ....www.accmhb.org
E-mail ....accmhb@aol.com
129 E Park Cir, Birmingham, AL 35235-3000
Beverly Francis, Executive Director

Family Counseling Center of Mobile, Inc. 251.602.0909
Fax 251.660.2831
Web ....www.lifelinesmobile.org
P.O. Box 91068, Mobile, AL 36691
COA accredited organization.

Family Counseling Svcs 205.752.2504
Fax 205.345.4842
Web ....www.counselingservice.org
E-mail ....deavers@counselingservice.org
2020 Paul W Bryant Dr, Tuscaloosa, AL 35401-2312
Lary Deavers, Director

Fitzpatrick Medical Practice 205.871.2001
3100 Independence Dr Ste 209, Birmingham,
AL 35209-4103
Karen Fitzpatrick, Psychiatrist

Glenwood, Inc. 205.969.2880
Web ....www.glenwood.org
E-mail ....bmurbach@glenwood.org
150 Glenwood Lane, Birmingham, AL 35242
Ms. Barbara Murbach, Accreditation Manager
Joint Commission accredited organization.

Grandview Behavioral Health 334.409.9242
Fax 334.409.9186
E-mail ....v_barlow@bellsouth.net
315 Saint Lukes Dr, Montgomery, AL 36117-7109
Venessa Barlow, Clinic Director

Hill Crest Behavioral Health Services 205.833.9000
Web ....www.hillcrestbhs.com
E-mail ....carrie.sanders@psysolutions.com
6869 Fifth Avenue South, Birmingham, AL 35212
Mrs. Carrie Sanders, Accreditation Manager
Joint Commission accredited organization.

Laurel Oaks Behavioral Health Center 334.794.7373
Web ....www.psysolutions.com
E-mail ....amanda.mcdaniel@uhsinc.com
700 East Cottonwood Road, Dothan, AL 36301
Ms. Amanda McDaniel, Accreditation Manager
Joint Commission accredited organization.

Mobile Group Home 251.478.3339
Fax 251.478.1929
563 Stanton Rd, Mobile, AL 36617
Charmaine Griffin, Group Home Director

Mountain View Hospital **256.546.9265**
Web ....www.mtnviewhospital.com
E-mail ....djensen@mtnviewhospital.com
　3001 Scenic Highway, Gadsden, AL 35902
　Mr. David Jensen, Accreditation Manager
Joint Commission accredited organization.

Pathway, Inc. **334.894.5591**
E-mail ....medcphq@yahoo.com
　Private Road 1201, Building 39, New Brockton,
　AL 36351
　Ms. Barbara Morrison, Accreditation Manager
Joint Commission accredited organization.

Presbyterian Home For Children **256.362.2114**
Fax 256.362.0120
Web ....www.phfc.org
E-mail ....bwills@phfc.org
　905 Ashland Hwy, Talladega, AL 35160-2586
　Bill Wills, President

The King's Ranch **205.678.8331**
Fax 205.678.7273
Web ....www.kingshome.org
E-mail ....lmasters@kingsranch.org
　221 kingshome dr, Chelsea, AL 35043
　Lisa Masters, Social Services Coordinator

Three Springs New Beginnings **256.725.7170**
Fax 256.725.7169
Web ....www.threesprings.com
E-mail ....angie.knight@threesprings.com
　318 Hamer Road, Owens Crossroads, AL 35763
　Angie Knight, Director-Human Resources
CARF accredited programs available.

**Three Springs Outdoor Treatment Program For
Boys** **256.776.2503**
Fax 256.776.2561
Web ....threesprings.com
E-mail ....erin.braley@threesprings.com
　3890 County Road 20, Trenton, AL 35774-7423
　Dana Hampson, Administrator

**Three Springs Outdoor Treatment Program For
Girls** **256.776.3078**
Fax 256.776.3012
E-mail ....kathy.demellier@threesprings.com
　3850 County Road 20, Trenton, AL 35774-7423
　Kathy Demellier, Administrator/Director Of Admissions

United Methodist Children's Home **334.875.7283**
Fax 334.875.5161
Web ....www.umch.net
E-mail ....umchalwf@bellsouth.net
　1712 Broad St, Selma, AL 36701-4102
　Rev. Joe Lisenby, President & CEO

CHILDREN'S HOSPITAL

Baptist Medical Center South **334.288.2100**
　2105 East South Blvd, Montgomery, AL 36116
　Robin Barca, Chief Executive Officer

Childrens Hospital of Alabama **205.939.9100**
E-mail ....mike.warren@chsys.org
　1600 Seventh Ave S, Birmingham, AL 35233
　Mike Warren, Chief Executive Officer

Citizens Baptist Medical Center **256.362.8111**
　604 Stone Ave, Talladega, AL 35160
　Joel Taylor, Administrator

Community Hospital **251.847.2223**
　14600 St Stephens Ave, Chatom, AL 36518
　Douglas Canner, Chief Executive Officer

Cullman Regional Medical Center **256.737.2000**
　1912 Alabama Highway 157, Cullman, AL 35055
　Jim Weidner, Director

D W McMillan Memorial Hospital **251.867.8061**
　1301 Belleville Ave, Brewton, AL 36426
　Chris Griifin, Chief Executive Officer

Dale Medical Center **334.774.2601**
E-mail ....vljohnson@dalemedical.org
　126 Hospital Ave, Ozark, AL 36360
　Vernon Johnson, Director

DCH Regional Medical Center **205.759.7111**
　809 University Boulevard East, Tuscaloosa, AL 35401
　Kamala Boyle, Director

Decatur General Hospital **256.341.2000**
E-mail ....dean.graffin.s@decatur.general.org
　1201 Seventh Street SE, Decatur, AL 35601
　Dean Graffin, Chief Executive Officer

DeKalb Regional Medical Center **256.845.3150**
　200 Medical Center Dr, Fort Payne, AL 35968
　Debbie Clifton, Administrative Assistant

East Alabama Medical Center **334.749.3411**
　2000 Pepperell Pkwy, Opelika, AL 36802
　Terry Andrus, President

Eliza Coffee Memorial Hospital **256.768.9191**
　205 Marengo St, Florence, AL 35630

Flowers Hospital **334.793.5000**
　4370 West Main St, Dothan, AL 36305
　Suzanne Wood, Chief Executive Officer

Grove Hill Memorial Hospital **251.275.3191**
　295 South Jackson St, Grove Hill, AL 36451
　Elaine Averette, Chief Executive Officer

Helen Keller Hospital **256.386.4196**
　1300 S Montgomery Ave, Sheffield, AL 35660
　Sam Strickland, Chief Executive Officer

Highlands Medical Center **256.259.4444**
　380 Woods Cove Rd, Scottsboro, AL 35768

Huntsville Hospital **256.265.1000**
Web ....www.huntsville.org
　101 Sivley Rd, Huntsville, AL 35801
　David Stillers, Chief Executive Officer

Jackson Hospital and Clinic **334.293.8000**
E-mail ....hendersond@jackson.org
　1725 Pine St, Montgomery, AL 36106
　Donald Henderson, Chief Executive Officer

Jackson Medical Center **251.246.9021**
　220 Hospital Dr, Jackson, AL 36545
　Amy Gibson, Chief Executive Officer

Lake Martin Community Hospital **256.825.7821**
　201 Mariarden Rd, Dadeville, AL 36853
　Mike Bruce, Chief Executive Officer

Medical Center Enterprise **334.347.0584**
　400 North Edwards St, Enterprise, AL 36330
　Jeffrey Brennon, Chief Executive Officer

Mobile Infirmary Medical Center **251.435.2400**
　5 Mobile Infirmary Drive North, Mobile, AL 36607
　Suzanne Byrd, Nursing Director

Northeast Alabama Regional Medical Ctr **256.235.5121**
Web ....www.rmccares.org
　400 East Tenth St, Anniston, AL 36207
　Elaine Davis, Vice President, Nursing Services.

Providence Hospital **251.633.1000**
　6801 Airport blvd, Mobile, AL 36608
　Susan Breslin, Chief Nursing Officer

Russell Medical Center **256.329.7100**
　3316 Highway 280, Alexander City, AL 35010
　Jim Pace, Chief Executive Officer

South Baldwin Regional Medical Center **251.949.3400**
　1613 North McKenzie St, Foley, AL 36535
　Rich McAuliffe, Chief Executive Officer

Southeast Alabama Medical Center **334.793.8111**
E-mail ....kaykid@samc.org
　1108 Ross Clark Circle, Dothan, AL 36301
　Ron Owen, Executive Director

Springhill Memorial Hospital **251.344.9630**
　3719 Dauphin St, Mobile, AL 36608
　Cesar Roca, Executive Director

Thomas Hospital **251.928.2375**
　750 Morphy Ave, Fairhope, AL 36532
　William Mclaughlin, Chief Executive Officer

Univ of South Alabama WC Hospital **251.415.1000**
　1700 Center St, Mobile, AL 36604
　Bob Lowry, Sr. Director Of Public Relation

Vaughan Regional Medical Center **334.418.4100**
　1015 Medical Center Pkwy, Selma, AL 36701
　Barry Keel, Chief Executive Officer

Veterans Affairs Medical Center **205.933.8101**
　700 South 19th St, Birmingham, AL 35233
　Rica Lewis, Director

COUNSELING SERVICES

Agape **334.272.9466**
Fax 334.272.0378
Web ....www.agapeforchildren.org
E-mail ....jdobbsagape@gmail.com
　3800 Vaughn Rd, Montgomery, AL 36106
　Jimmy Dobbs, Director

**Alabama Baptist Children's Homes And Family
Ministries** **334.677.7856**
Fax 334.678.2642
Web ....www.albamachilds.org
E-mail ....kmcgainey@abchome.org
　1302 Ross Clark Cir, Dothan, AL 36301-4117
　Kim McGainey, Director

**American Counseling Assoc Alabama (Southern
Region)** **205.652.1712**
Fax 205.652.1576
Web ....www.alabamacounseling.org
E-mail ....alca@alabamacounseling.org
　217 Daryle St, Livingston, AL 35470-5641
　Ervin Wood, Director

Catholic Social Svcs **251.434.1550**
Fax 251.434.1549
Web ....www.cssmobile.org
E-mail ....mdking@cssmobile.org
　400 Government St, Mobile, AL 36602-2394
　Marilyn Davis King, Director

Catholic Social Svcs **334.288.8890**
Fax 334.288.9322
E-mail ....smeehan@cssalabama.org
　4455 Narrow Lane Rd, Montgomery, AL 36116-2953
　Barry Cavan, Director

Lifeline Children's Svcs **205.967.0811**
Fax 205.969.2137
Web ....www.lifelineadoption.org
E-mail ....lifeline@lifelineadoption.org
　2908 Pump House Rd, Birmingham, AL 35216-1857
　Herbie Newell, Director

CRISIS & SHELTER CARE

13th Place **256.547.8971**
Fax 256.547.6814
E-mail ....13thplac@bellsouth.net
　405 S 12th St, Gadsden, AL 35901-3529
　Kimberly Payne, Executive Director

2nd Chance, Inc. Domestic Violence **256.236.7381**
Fax 256.236.1614
E-mail ....ssshipman@cableone.net
　304 S. Wilmer Ave, Anniston, AL 36201
　Susan Shipman, Director

**Alabama Baptist Children's Homes And Family
Ministries** **256.355.6893**
Fax 256.355.6955
Web ....www.abchome.org
E-mail ....brian@abchdecatur.org
　1404 16th Ave SE, Decatur, AL 35601-4329
　Michael Smith, Director

Alabama

Brewer-Porch Children's Ctr **205.348.7236**
Fax 205.348.9368
   2501 Woodland Road, Tuscaloosa, AL 35404
   Dr. James W. Thompson, Executive Director

Children's Svcs, Inc **256.236.3434**
Fax 256.237.0461
E-mail ....childserve@aol.com
   501 Quintard Ave Ste 14, Anniston, AL 36201
   Kay Tolbert, Director

Cope **334.834.2673**
Fax 334.264.9143
   2158 Madison Ave, Montgomery, AL 36107-1948
   Lori Mollin, Director

Crisis Ctr **334.297.4484**
Fax 334.297.4445
Web ....www.acadv.org
E-mail ....viodiocor@ccosoc.org
   PO Box 2835, Phenix City, AL 36868-2835
   Valerie Mclain, Director

Family Connection, Inc. **205.663.6301**
Fax 205.663.6371
Web ....www.familyconnection-inc.org
E-mail ....shelbyyouth@charterinternet.com
   26 East, Alabaster, AL 35007
   Susan Johnston, Director

Pathway, Inc. **334.894.5591**
Fax 334.894.5264
Web ....www.pathway-inc.com
E-mail ....duncan_mcdougall@pathway-inc.com
   39 Private Road 1201, New Brockton, AL 36351
   Duncan Mcdougall, CEO

Penelope House Domestic Violence **251.342.3144**
Fax 251.414.3581
E-mail ....penelopehouse@penelopehouse.org
   PO Box 9127, Mobile, AL 36691-0127
   Toniann Torrans, Director

Salvation Army Women Shelter **256.236.5644**
Fax 256.236.4280
Web ....www.usn.salvationarmy.org
E-mail ....linda_smith@usn.salvationarmy.org
   420 Noble St, Anniston, AL 36201-5655
   Phyllis Frisaby, Director

Specialized Alternatives For Youth **334.270.3181**
Fax 334.270.5805
Web ....www.safy.org
E-mail ....parnelld@safy.org
   4520 Executive Park Dr, Ste B100, Montgomery,
   AL 36116
   Demetria Parnell, Director

St. Mary's Home **251.344.7733**
Fax 251.344.9753
   4350 Moffett Rd, Mobile, AL 36618
   Andy Wynne, Administrator

Tennessee Valley Family Svcs **256.582.0377**
Fax 256.582.4315
Web ....www.tvfsahome.net
E-mail ....ahome@hiwaay.net
   1372 Gunter Ave, Guntersville, AL 35976
   Alice Henderson, Director

The House Of Ruth, Inc. **334.793.5214**
Fax 334.671.1023
Web ....www.houseofruthdothan.org
E-mail ....Exedirector@Houseofruthdothan.Org
   PO Box 968, Dothan, AL 36302-0968
   Beverly Yuouse, Director

EDUCATION

**Alabama Baptist Children's Homes And Family
Ministries** **205.982.1112**
Fax 205.982.9992
Web ....www.alabamachild.org
E-mail ....alabapt@aol.com
   2681 Rocky Ridge Ln, Birmingham, AL 35216-4809
   Dr. Louise Green, Director Of Special Programs

Alabama Youth Svcs Chalkville Campus **205.681.8841**
Fax 205.680.8543
   5849 Old Springville Rd, Pinson, AL 35126-3711
   Angie Tony, Superintendent

Child Development Ctr **256.372.8158**
Fax 256.372.5433
E-mail ....shelia.foster@aamu.edu
   116 Carver Complex Hobson Wing, Normal,
   AL 35762
   Sheila Foster, Director

The Arc **256.539.2266**
Fax 256.533.2836
Web ....www.thearcofmadisoncounty.com
E-mail ....sklingel@thearcofmadisoncounty.com
   1100 Washington St NW, Huntsville, AL 35801-4678
   Susan Klingel, Program Coordinator

The Exchange Club Family Ctr Of Mobile **251.479.5700**
Fax 251.479.5055
Web ....www.familycentermobile.org
E-mail ....kids101@comcast.net
   601 Bel Air Blvd Ste 100, Mobile, AL 36606-3504
   Lydia Pettijohn, Director

FOSTER CARE AGENCIES

Alabama Foster & Adoptive Parent Assoc **888.545.2372**
   1901 County Road 1659, Cullman, AL 35058
   William Hooper, Director

Alabama Foster & Adoptive Parent Assoc **256.796.7351**
Fax 775.667.8282
E-mail ....Frogmh@aol.com
   1091 County Rd 1659, Cullman, AL 35058

Children's Aid Society (CAS) **205.251.7148**
E-mail ....cas@childrensaid.org
   181 W Valley Ave, Ste 300, Homewood, AL 35209
   Gayle Watts, Director

HOME MEDICAL EQUIPMENT PROVIDERS

Medical Accessories and Supply **850.682.9777**
Fax 850.682.2996
E-mail ....mashchresview@belsouth.net
   PO Box 384, Alabaster, AL 35007
   Dot Agro, Manager

National Seating & Mobility **334.273.1112**
Fax 334.273.1148
E-mail ....nsm15@nsm-seating.com
   646 Oliver Rd, Montgomery, AL 36117
   Randy Holcomd, Owner

PEDIATRIC HOME CARE

**Bureau of Home and Community Services, Alabama
Department of Public Health** **800.225.9770**
Fax 334.206.5712
Web ....http://www.adph.org/homehealth/
E-mail ....carolyn.obryan@adph.state.al.us
   201 Monroe St., Suite 1200, Montgomery, AL 36067
   Carolyn O'Bryan-Miller, Home Health Social Work Consultant

SOCIAL SERVICES

Brewer-Porch Children's Center **205.348.9340**
Fax 205.348.9368
   PO Box 870156, Tuscaloosa, AL 35487-0156
   COA accredited organization.

Catholic Family Svcs **256.768.1550**
E-mail ....cfsrivard@bellsouth.net
   1111 E. College Street, Florence, AL 35630
   Michele Rivard, Director

Catholic Family Svcs **205.324.6561**
Fax 205.323.0475
Web ....www.cfsbhm.org
E-mail ....tcook@cfsbhm.org
   1515 12th Ave S, Birmingham, AL 35205-2825
   Tom Cook, Director

Catholic Social Svcs **205.838.8322**
Fax 205.836.1910
Web ....www.bhmdiocese.org
E-mail ....amanzella@bhmdiocese.org
   2121 3rd Avenue North, Birmingham, AL 35202
   Albert Manzella, Director

Child Abuse Prevention Svcs **205.758.1159**
Fax 205.758.1182
E-mail ....capstuscaloosa@bellsouth.net
   618 14th St, Tuscaloosa, AL 35401-3453
   Nancy Angelo, Director

Child Care Central **256.362.1390**
Fax 256.761.0252
   925 North St E, Talladega, AL 35160
   Kay Jenningson, Executive Director

**Child Care Management Agency of North Central
Alabama** **256.534.5110**
Fax 256.534.0548
E-mail ....mary.carlton@dhr.alabama.gov
   709 Ward Ave NE, Huntsville, AL 35801
   Mary Lynn Carlton, Executive Director

Child Care Resource Network **256.845.8238**
Fax 256.845.6731
Web ....www.cma.dhr.state.al.us
E-mail ....judydavidson.crn@hotmail.com
   659 Wallace Avenue NE, # A, Fort Payne, AL 35967
   Judy Davidson, Provider Specialist

Child Development Resources **205.348.2650**
Fax 205.348.0660
Web ....www.ches.ua.edu
E-mail ....sedwards@ches.ua.edu
   651 5th Ave E, Tuscaloosa, AL 35404
   Sally Edwards, Director

Children's Aid Society **205.251.7148**
Fax 205.252.3828
Web ....www.childrensaid.org
E-mail ....cas@childrensaid.org
   181 W Valley Ave Ste 300, Birmingham,
   AL 35209-3698
   Gayle Watts, ACSW, LCSW, Executive Director
   COA accredited organization.

Children's Trust Fund **334.242.5710**
Fax 334.242.5711
Web ....www.ctf.alabama.gov
E-mail ....ctfstaff@ctf.alabama.gov
   100 N Union St Ste 350, Montgomery,
   AL 36104-3748
   Kelley Parris-Barnes, Director

Collat Jewish Family Services **205.879.3438**
Fax 205.871.5939
E-mail ....jfs@cjfsbham.org
   3940 Montclair Rd # 205, Birmingham, AL 35213
   Lauren Perlman, Director

Drug Education Council, Inc **251.478.7855**
Fax 251.478.7865
Web ....www.drugeducation.org
E-mail ....vguy@drugeducation.org
   3000 Television Ave, Mobile, AL 36606-2915
   Virginia Guy, Executive Director

**Early Childhood Svcs Ctrs For The Developmentally
Disabled** **256.350.1458**
Fax 256.350.1485
   1602 Church St SE, Decatur, AL 35601-3402
   Missy Cooper, Human Resources Director

Family Guidance Ctr Of Alabama **334.712.7777**
Fax 334.712.7788
Web ....www.familyguidancecenter.org
E-mail ....jsellers@cma.dhr.state.al.us
   2431 W Main St Ste 1102, Dothan, AL 36301
   Joann Carpentor, Director

Family Sunshine Ctr 334.206.2100
Fax 334.206.2111
Web ....www.familysunshine.org
E-mail ....ksellers@familysunshine.org
  PO Box 5160, Montgomery, AL 36103-5160
  Karen B. Sellers, Executive Director

Family Svcs Ctr **256.231.2240**
Fax 256.231.2275
E-mail ....dwalton@cableone.net
  13 E 11th St, Anniston, AL 36201-4671
  Don Walton, Director

Gateway **205.510.2600**
Fax 205.510.2621
Web ....www.gway.org
E-mail ....marketing@gway.org
  1401 20th St S, Birmingham, AL 35205-4913
  Jim Loop, Chief Executive Officer
  COA accredited organization.

GRCMA Early Childhood Directions **251.473.1060**
Fax 251.450.3856
Web ....www.grcma.org
E-mail ....wmcearchern@grcma.org
  97 W I-65 Services Rd N, Mobile, AL 36616
  Dee Wendy, Director

Sequel Youth & Family Services **256.637.2199**
Fax 256.637.8911
Web ....www.sequeltsi.com
E-mail ....rwiggins@sequeltsi.com
  349 Madison St, Courtland, AL 35618
  Rose Wiggins, Admissions

Seraaj Family Homes, Inc. **334.271.2402**
Fax 334.271.2405
Web ....www.seraajfh.com
  400 Cotton Gin Road, Montgomery, AL 36117
  COA accredited organization.

Specialized Alternatives For Youth **205.945.7483**
Fax 205.945.7083
Web ....www.safy.org
E-mail ....dancyl@safy.org
  601 Beacon Pkwy W Ste 204, Birmingham,
  AL 35209-3123
  Larry Dancy, Director

United Methodist Children's Home **334.413.6263**
Fax 334.386.5358
Web ....www.umch.net
  3140 Zelda Court, Montgomery, AL 36106
  COA accredited organization.

Youth Development Center **334.749.2996**
Fax 334.321.0264
Web ....www.lcydc.org
  1109 Spring Drive, Opelika, AL 36801
  COA accredited organization.

SPECIAL NEEDS

Alabama Disability Action Coalition **251.414.5364**
E-mail ....jridgeway11@bellsouth.net
  3801 Cabana Club Blvd # 108, Mobile, AL 36609

Alabama Parent Education Center **334.567.2252**
Toll-free 866.532.7660
Fax 334.567.9938
E-mail ....jwinter@alabamaparentcenter.com
  10520 US Hwy 231, Wetumpka, AL 36092
  Jeana Winter, Director

Alabama PTA **800.328.1897**
E-mail ....alabamapta@yahoo.com
  470 S Union St, Montgomery, AL 36104
  Larry Hoof, President

Autism Society of Alabama **205.951.1364**
  4217 Dolly Ridge Rd, Birmingham, AL 35243

Childrens Hospital of Alabama **205.996.7633**
  1600 7th Ave S, Birmingham, AL 35233
  Jayne Ness, Md Phd Center Director

Easter Seals Alabama **800.388.7325**
E-mail ....info@al.easterseals.com
  5960 E Shirley Ln, Montgomery, AL 36117

Epilepsy Foundation of Alabama **251.341.0170**
E-mail ....mgarrett@efala.org
  273 Azalea Rd Ste 310, Mobile, AL 36609

J. L. Bedsole/Rotary Rehabilitation
Hospital **251.435.3400**
Fax 251.435.3404
Web ....www.MobileInfirmary.org
  Five Mobile Infirmary Circle, Mobile, AL 36607
  CARF accredited programs available.

Lakeshore Foundation **888.868.2303**
  4000 Ridgeway Dr, Birmingham, AL 35209

Laurel Oaks Behavioral Health Ctr **334.794.7373**
Fax 334.702.2883
E-mail ....nelson.handel@psysolutions.com
  700 E Cottonwood Rd, Dothan, AL 36301-3644
  Dr. Rob Turner, CEO

Learning Disabilities Assn of Alabama **334.277.9151**
  PO Box 11588, Montgomery, AL 36111

Lindamood-Bell Learning Processes **251.473.6808**
Fax 251.473.6807
  2864 Dauphin St, Ste D, Mobile, AL 36606

NAMI Alabama **334.396.4797**
E-mail ....wlaird@namialabama.org
  4122 Wall St, Montgomery, AL 36106
  Wanda Laird, Executive Director

National Multiple Sclerosis Society **205.879.8881**
Fax 205.879.8869
E-mail ....ALC@NMSS.ORG
  3840 Ridgeway Dr, Birmingham, AL 35209
  Jan Bell, Chapter President

Partners in Policymaking of Alabama **800.846.3735**
E-mail ....jchase1040@aol.com
  PO Box 301410, Montgomery, AL 36130

Special Education Action Committee **334.478.1208**
Fax 334.473.7877
E-mail ....seacofmobile@zebra.net
  600 Bel Air Blvd Ste 210, Mobile, AL 36606

Speech & Hearing Association of Alabama **256.325.8885**
E-mail ....info@alabamashaa.org
  PO Box 357, Normal, AL 35762

Spina Bifida Association of Alabama **256.325.8600**
E-mail ....al_spina_bifida_support@hotmail.com
  140 Lansdowne Dr, Madison, AL 35758

The Arc of Alabama Inc **866.243.9557**
E-mail ....info@thearcofalabama.com
  557 S Lawrence St, Montgomery, AL 36104-4611
  Thomas Holmes, Director

The Horizons School **205.322.6606**
Fax 205.322.6605
Web ....www.horizonsschool.org
  2018 15th Ave S, Birmingham, AL 35205
  Jade Carter, Director

United Cerebral Palsy of Birmingham **800.654.4483**
E-mail ....gedwards@ucpbham.com
  120 Oslo Cir, Birmingham, AL 35211
  Gary Edwards, Executive Director

United Cerebral Palsy of Mobile Inc **888.630.7102**
  3058 Dauphin Square Connector, Mobile, AL 36607
  Glen Harger, President

Alaska

Sean Parnell, Governor
PO Box 110001
Juneau, AK 99811-0001
907.465.3500
907.465.3532 (Fax)
governor@gov.state.ak.us
www.gov.state.ak.us

Barbara Murray, Juvenile Justice Specialist
PO Box 110635
Juneau, AK 99811-0635
907.465.2116
907.465.2333 (Fax)
barbara.murray@alaska.gov

Carol Brenckle, SAG Chair
502 Hemlock Ave
Kenai, AK 99611
907.283.4343
907.283.4464 (Fax)
cbrenckle@alaska.net

CRISIS NUMBERS

Child Abuse Reporting . . . 907.465.3191

STATE SERVICES

SOCIAL SERVICES

Alaska Dept Of Health & Social Svcs **907.465.3030**
Fax 907.465.3068
Web . . . . http://www.hss.state.ak.us/
350 Main Street, Rm 404, Juneau, AK 99811
William Streur, Commissioner

GENERAL HEALTH SERVICES

Alaska DHSS Div Of Health Care Svcs **907.334.2400**
Fax 907.561.1684
Web . . . . www.alaska.gov
E-mail . . . . william.streur@alaska.gov
4501 Business Park Blvd, Ste 24, Anchorage,
AK 99503-0660
Bill Streur, Director

Alaska DHSS Div of Public Health (DPH) **907.465.3090**
Fax 907.465.4632
E-mail . . . . veverly_wooley@health.state.ak.us
Alaska Office Building, Suite 503, Juneau, AK 99811
Veverly K. Wooley, Director

Dept of Health and Social Svcs **907.269.4500**
Fax 907.269.1064
Web . . . . www.health.state.ak.us
E-mail . . . . ccpo@health.state.ak.us
619 E Ship Creek Ave Ste 230, Anchorage,
AK 99501-1677

WIC **907.465.3100**
Fax 907.465.3416
Web . . . . www.hss.state.ak.us
E-mail . . . . kathleen_wayne@health.state.ak.us
130 Seward St Ste 508, Room 508, Juneau, AK 99801
Kathleen Wayne, Director

Womens Child & Family Health AK **907.269.3400**
Fax 907.269.3465
E-mail . . . . stephanie.wrightsman-birch@alaska.gov
3601 C St Ste 322, Anchorage, AK 99503
Stephanie Wrightsman Birch, Director

Womens Childrens and Family Health AK **907.334.2424**
Fax 907.269.3465
E-mail . . . . stephanie_birch@health.state.ak.us
4701 Bus Prk Blvd Ste 20, Div of Public Hlth Bldg J,
Anchorage, AK 99503
Stephanie Birch, Director

MENTAL HEALTH SERVICES

Alaska Psychiatric Institute **907.269.7100**
Fax 907.269.7251
Web . . . . www.hss.state.ak.us/dbh/api
2800 Providence Dr, Anchorage, AK 99508
Ron Adler, CEO

Division of Voc Rehab AK **907.465.2814**
Fax 907.465.2856
E-mail . . . . dawn.duval@alaska.gov
801 W 10th St Ste A, Juneau, AK 99801
Dawn Duval, Director

Tobacco Youth Education and Enforcement
Program **907.269.3600**
Fax 907.264.0786
E-mail . . . . joe.darnell@alaska.gov
303 K St, Suite 878, Anchorage, AK 99501
Joe Darnell, Investigator

JUSTICE AGENCY

Dept of Corrections **907.269.7397**
Fax 907.269.7390
Web . . . . www.correct.state.ak.gov
E-mail . . . . candace.strandberg@alaska.gov
550 W 7th Ave Ste 601, Anchorage, AK 99501
Candace Strandberg, Executive Secretary

Inmate Programs AK **907.269.7434**
Fax 907.269.7420
E-mail . . . . annaherzberger@alaska.gov
550 W 7th Ave Ste 601, Anchorage, AK 99501
Anna Herzberger, Director

Interstate Compact **907.465.2116**
Fax 907.465.2333
E-mail . . . . barbara_murray@health.state.ak.us
240 Main St Ste 701, Juneau, AK 99801-2107
Barbara Murray, Administrator

Superior Court-2nd District **907.852.4800**
Fax 907.852.4804
Web . . . . www.state.ak.us/courts
E-mail . . . . mjeffery@courts.state.ak.us
1250 Agvik St, Barrow, AK 99723
Honorable Michael I. Jeffery, Director

POLICE AND SHERIFF

Alaska State Troopers **907.269.5511**
Fax 907.337.2059
Web . . . . www.state.ak.us
E-mail . . . . keith.mallard@alaska.gov
5700 E Tudor Rd, Anchorage, AK 99507
Keith Mallard, Carnal

EDUCATION SERVICES

Alaska Ctr For The Blind And Visually
Impaired **907.248.7770**
Fax 907.248.7517
Web . . . . www.alaskabvi.org
E-mail . . . . info@alaskabvi.org
3903 Taft Dr, Anchorage, AK 99517-3069
Karla Jutzi, Executive Director

Alaska State School For Deaf And Hard Of
Hearing **907.742.4243**
Fax 907.742.6075
Web . . . . . http://www.asd.k12.ak.us/schooldetails.asp?id=345
5530 E Northern Lights Blvd, Anchorage,
AK 99504-3135
Tracy Pifer, Director

Dept Bilingual/Multicultural Education **907.465.2888**
Fax 907.465.2989
Web . . . . www.eed.state.ak.us
E-mail . . . . pattie.adkisson@alaska.gov
801 W 10th St, Ste 200, Juneau, AK 99811
Patricia Adkisson, Director

Dept of Education **907.465.2800**
Fax 907.465.3452
Web . . . . www.eed.state.ak.us
801 West 10th Street, Suite 200, Juneau, AK 99801
Art Arnold, Director of Special Ed

Edu for Homeless Children and Youth AK **907.465.3826**
Fax 907.465.2989
E-mail . . . . katherine.holmes@alaska.gov
801 West 10th St, Ste 200, Juneau, AK 99811
Katherine Holmes, Director

Governor's Council on Disabilities and Special
Education **907.269.8990**
Fax 907.269.8995
E-mail . . . . sheryl.cobb@alaska.gov
3601 C St, Suite 740, Anchorage, AK 99503
Millie Ryan, Executive Director

Special Education Office Alaska **907.465.8693**
Fax 907.465.2806
E-mail . . . . Andrew.Koval@alaska.gov
801 W 10th St Ste 200, PO Box 110500, Juneau,
AK 99811
Andrew Koval, Director

COUNTY SERVICES

Aleutians West County

POLICE AND SHERIFF

State Trooper Post.........................**907.581.1432**
Fax...907.581.1407
Web................................www.dps.state.ak.us
E-mail..........................robin.morrisett@alaska.gov
   2315 Airport Beach Road, 101, Dutch Harbor, AK 99692
Robin Morrisett, Sargent

Anchorage County

SOCIAL SERVICES

Anchorage Public Assistance Ofc..............**907.269.6599**
Fax...907.269.6520
Web.............................www.health.state.ak.us
   400 Gambell St, Anchorage, AK 99501-2721
Suzi Pulzcinski, Regional Manager

Children's Svcs-Anchorage Regional Ofc.......................................**907.269.4000**
Fax...907.269.3901
   323 E 4th Ave, Anchorage, AK 99501
Sara Childress, Childrens Services Manager

GENERAL HEALTH SERVICES

Alaska Native Medical Ctr....................**907.729.1994**
Fax...907.729.1984
Web....................................www.anlc.org
E-mail............................djessop@anthc.org
   4315 Diplomacy Dr, Anchorage, AK 99508-5926
Danielle Jessop, Interim Administrator

Alaska Native Tribal Health Consortium..................................**907.729.1900**
Fax...907.729.1901
Web...................................www.anthc.org
   4000 Ambassador Dr, Administration Office, Anchorage, AK 99508-5909
Paul Sherry, CEO

Municipality Of Anchorage Health & Human Svcs..**907.343.4799**
Fax...907.343.4832
Web....................................hhs.muni.org
E-mail.............................walterswc@muni.org
   825 L St, Anchorage, AK 99501
Wendy Walters, Supervisor Of Disease Prevention And Control

Municipality Of Anchorage Reproductive Health Clinic...................................**907.343.4623**
Fax...907.343.7992
   825 L St, Ste 102, Anchorage, AK 99501
Rebecca Schmitz, STD Program Manager

Southwest Regional Nursing.................**907.334.2260**
Fax...907.334.2270
Web...................................www.alaska.gov
E-mail........................annette.james@alaska.gov
   3601 C St, Ste 760, Anchorage, AK 99503
Annette James, Southwest Regional Nurse Manager

JUSTICE AGENCY

Alaska CASA................................**907.269.3500**
Fax...907.269.3535
Web.................................www.alaskacasa.org
E-mail..........................otammany@alaska.gov
   900 W 5th Ave Ste 525, Anchorage, AK 99501-2048
Tammany Waterman, Assistant Manager

COURTS

Superior Court-3rd District...................**907.274.8611**
Fax...907.264.0610
   825 W 4th Ave, Anchorage, AK 99501
Honorable Sharon Gleason, Presiding Judge

Youth Court...............................**907.274.5986**
Fax...907.272.0491
Web.....................................www.ayc.ak.org
E-mail..................info@anchorageyouthcourt.org
   838 W 4th Ave, Anchorage, AK 99501
Ashley Lutes, Executive Director

POLICE AND SHERIFF

C Detachment Headquarters State Troopers...................................**907.248.1410**
Fax...907.248.9834
E-mail..................steve_arlow@dps.state.ak.us
   4500 W 50th Ave, Anchorage, AK 99502-1046
Capt. Steve Arlow, Detachment Commander

State Trooper Post.........................**907.783.0972**
Fax...907.783.2026
Web...................................www.alaska.gov
E-mail.......................michael.zweifel@alaska.gov
   Mile 93 Seward Hwy Tesoro Mall, Ste 8, Girdwood, AK 99587
Mike Zweifel, Sgt.

EDUCATION SERVICES

Communities In Schools Alaska, Inc....**907.333.4003**
Fax...907.333.4008
Web.................................www.cisalaska.org
E-mail...............cisakstatedirector@alaska.net
   1569 Bragaw St, Anchorage, AK 99508-3109
Tom Morgan, State Director

Special Education Svc Agency (SESA)......................................**907.334.1300**
Fax...907.562.0545
E-mail................................sesa@sesa.org
   3501 Denali St Ste 101, Anchorage, AK 99503
Patrick Pillai, Executive Director

Tugatch Head Start - Southcentral Foundation.................................**907.729.6100**
Fax...907.729.6160
Web.......................................www.scfcc
E-mail.............kbergay@southcentralfoundation.org
   6901 E Tudor Rd, Anchorage, AK 99507-1241
Kim Bergay, Program Manager

Bethel County

SOCIAL SERVICES

Office of Children's Services..................**907.543.3141**
Fax...907.543.4143
Web...................................www.alaska.gov
   313 Willow St., Bethel, AK 99559
Diane Moehring, Admin Officer

GENERAL HEALTH SERVICES

Kuskokwim Native Assoc...................**907.675.4384**
Fax...907.675.4387
Web...................................www.kuskokwim.org
E-mail.............................csimeon@kuskokwim.org
   127 Airport Road, Aniak, AK 99557
Cynthia Navarrette, Director

Public Health Nursing......................**907.543.2110**
Fax...907.543.0435
Web...................................www.alaska.gov
   1490 State Highway, Bethal, AK 99559
Penny Pieper, Director

MENTAL HEALTH SERVICES

Yukon-Kuskokwim Health Corporation-Developmental Disabilities Dept........................**907.543.2762**
Fax...907.543.3152
Web...................................www.ykhc.org
E-mail........................kathy_turner@ykhc.org
   1795 Chief Eddie Hoffman Hwy, Bethel, AK 99559
Kathy Turner, Director

JUSTICE AGENCY

Bethel Youth Facility.......................**907.543.5200**
Fax...907.543.2710
   950 State Hwy, Bethel, AK 99559
Patricia Zulkoskoy, Youth Facility Superintendent

POLICE AND SHERIFF

State Trooper Post.........................**907.675.4398**
Fax...907.675.4498
Web................................www.dps.state.ak.us
   1 Trooper Ln, Aniak, AK 99557
Nicholas Zito, Sergeant

Bristol Bay County

POLICE AND SHERIFF

State Trooper Post.........................**907.246.3464**
Fax...907.246.6259
Web................................www.dps.state.ak.us
E-mail........................john_holm@dps.state.ak.us
   PO Box 187, King Salmon, AK 99613-0187
John Holm, State Trooper

City and Borough of Juneau County

SOCIAL SERVICES

Juneau Public Assistance Ofc.................**907.465.3537**
Fax...907.465.4657
Web.............................http://www.state.ak.us
   10002 Glacier Hwy Ste 200, Juneau, AK 99801
Ellie Fitzjrrald, Director

Ofc of Children's Svcs......................**907.465.3191**
Fax...907.465.3397
Web...........................www.hss.state.ak.us/ocs
E-mail..................tammy.sandoval@alaska.gov
   130 Seward St., Juneau, AK 99811
Tammy Sandoval, Deputy Commissioner

Office of Children's Services.................**907.465.1650**
Fax...907.465.1668
Web..............................www.hss.state.ak.us
   3025 Clinton Dr, Ste 100, Juneau, AK 99801-7154
Christy Lawson, Director

GENERAL HEALTH SERVICES

Public Health.............................**907.465.3150**
Fax...907.465.3913
Web....................www.hss.state.ak.us/dth/nursing
E-mail......................rhonda.richtsmeier@alaska.gov
   410 Willoughby Ave, # 103, Juneau, AK 99811
Rhonda Richtsmeier, Chief Of Nursing

Southeastern Regional Public Health Svcs..**907.465.3353**
Fax...907.465.3389
Web...................................www.alaska.gov
   3412 Glacier Hwy, Juneau, AK 99801-9501
Katy Slotnick, Regional Nurse Manager

JUSTICE AGENCY

Div of Juvenile Justice......................**907.465.2212**
Fax...907.465.2333
Web.............................www.hss.state.ak.us/djj/
E-mail..........................djj@health.state.ak.us
   240 Main St Ste 700, Juneau, AK 99801-2107
Barbara Henjum, Director

Alaska

Alaska

Johnson Youth Ctr 907.586.9433
Fax 907.463.4933
   3252 Hospital Dr, Juneau, AK 99801
Dennis Weston, Superintendant

Office of Public Advocacy 907.465.4173
Fax 907.463.4980
Web .... www.admin.state.ak.us
E-mail .... joshua_fink@admin.state.ak.us
   211 4th St, Suite 103, Juneau, AK 99801
Joshua Fink, Director

COURTS

Superior Court-1st District 907.463.4742
Fax 907.463.3788
   PO Box 114100, Juneau, AK 99811-4100
Jeanne Whiteman, Court Administrator

POLICE AND SHERIFF

Alaska State Troopers 907.465.4000
Fax 907.465.3333
   2760 Sherwood Ln, Juneau, AK 99811
Timothy Birt, Post Supervisor

City and Borough of Ketchikan County

SOCIAL SERVICES

Ofc Of Children's Svcs 907.225.6611
Fax 907.247.6611
Web .... www.hss.state.ak.us
   415 Main St Ste 201, Ketchikan, AK 99901-6352
Christy Lawton, Director

GENERAL HEALTH SERVICES

Ketchikan Public Health Ctr 907.225.4350
Fax 907.247.0978
   3054 5th Ave, Ketchikan, AK 99901
Sue Bergmann, Nurse Manager

JUSTICE AGENCY

Ketchikan Regional Youth Facility 907.225.8900
Fax 907.247.8900
Web .... www.hss.state.ak.us/djj
   3058 5th Ave, Ketchikan, AK 99901-5773
Rob Austin, Unit Surpervisor

COURTS

Superior Court-First District 907.225.3195
Fax 907.225.7849
   415 Main St Ste 400, Ketchikan, AK 99901-6377
Honorable Trevor N. Stephens, Superior

City and Borough of Petersburg Wrangell County

GENERAL HEALTH SERVICES

Petersburg Public Health Ctr 907.772.4611
Fax 907.772.4617
E-mail .... ann.haifler@alaska.gov
   103 Fram St., Petersburg, AK 99833
Ann Haifler, Public Health Nurse

Wrangell Public Health Ctr 907.874.3615
Fax 907.874.2991
Web .... www.seapac.net
E-mail .... phnwphc@seapac.net
   215 Front St., Wrangell, AK 99929
Janet Strom, Supervisor

COURTS

Petersburg Trial Court 907.772.3824
Fax 907.772.3018
Web .... www.courts.alaska.gov
   17 Nordic D, Petersburg, AK 99833
Magistrate Darlene A. Whitethorn, Judge

Wrangell Trial Court 907.874.2311
Fax 907.874.3509
   431 Zimovia Highway, Wrangell, AK 99929-0869
Magistrate Chris Ellis, Director

Youth Court 907.874.3304
Fax 907.874.2173
Web .... www.aptalaska.net
E-mail .... youthcourt@aptalaska.net
   431 Zimovia Highway, Wrangell, AK 99929
Dorthea Rooney, Coordinator

City and Borough of Sitka County

GENERAL HEALTH SERVICES

Sitka Public Health Ctr 907.747.3255
Fax 907.747.4899
Web .... www.alaska.gov
E-mail .... penny.lehmann@alaska.gov
   210 Moller Ave, Sitka, AK 99835-7100
Penny Lehmann, Public Health Nurse

JUSTICE AGENCY

Juvenile Justice Div 907.747.8608
Fax 907.747.5141
Web .... www.hss.state.ak.us
   210 Moller Ave Ste A, Sitka, AK 99835-7100
Diane Climio, SSA

Public Safety Academy 907.747.6611
Fax 907.747.5606
Web .... www.dps.state.ak.us
E-mail .... larry_nicholson@dps.state.ak.us
   877 Sawmill Creek Rd, Sitka, AK 99835-7460
Sgt. Larry Nicholson, Commander

EDUCATION SERVICES

Mt. Edgecumbe High School 907.966.3200
Fax 907.966.2442
Web .... www.mehs.us
E-mail .... randyh@mehs.us
   1330 Seward Ave, Sitka, AK 99835-9418
Randy Hawk, Director

Cordova County

GENERAL HEALTH SERVICES

Public Health Ctr 907.424.4547
Fax 907.424.4548
Web .... www.health.state.ak.us
E-mail .... timothy.struna@alaska.gov
   110 Nicholoff Way, Cordova, AK 99574
Timothy Struna, Regional Nurse Manager

POLICE AND SHERIFF

State Trooper Post 907.424.3184
Fax 907.424.5454
Web .... www.dps.state.ak.us
E-mail .... marc.cloward@alaska.gov
   711 First St, Cordova, AK 99574
Marc Cloward, Sergeant

Denali County

POLICE AND SHERIFF

State Trooper Post 907.768.2202
Fax 907.768.2203
Web .... www.dps.state.ak.us
   Nenana Ave, Cantwell, AK 99729
Mark Piftoya, Supervisor

Dillingham County

SOCIAL SERVICES

Office of Children's Services 907.842.2341
Fax 907.842.5924
   104 Main St., Dillingham, AK 99576
Mary Gray, Supervisor

JUSTICE AGENCY

Division Juvenile Justice 907.842.2341
Fax 907.842.5924
   104 Main Street, Dillingham, AK 99576
Blinn Dull, Supervisor

COURTS

Trial Court 907.842.5215
Fax 907.842.5746
Web .... www.alaska.gov
   715 Seward St, Dillingham, AK 99576
Fred Torrisi, Superior Court Judge

POLICE AND SHERIFF

State Trooper Post 907.842.5641
Fax 907.842.5795
Web .... www.dps.state.ak.us
E-mail .... tim_stuckwood@dps.state.ak.us
   536 Kenny Wren Rd, Dillingham, AK 99576
Tim Stuckwood, Sergeant

Fairbanks North Star County

SOCIAL SERVICES

Children's Svcs-Northern Regional Ofc 907.451.2650
Fax 907.451.2616
Web .... www.alaska.gov
   751 Old Richardson Hwy Ste 300, Fairbanks, AK 99701-7805
Coleen Turner, Children's Services Manager

Dept Of Health & Social Svcs Div Of Public Assistance ... 907.451.2850
Fax 907.451.2923
E-mail .... mike_thibodeau@health.state.ak.us
   675 7th Ave Ste D, Fairbanks, AK 99701-4531
Mike Thibodeau, Manager

JUSTICE AGENCY

Fairbanks Youth Facility 907.451.2150
Fax 907.451.2038
   1502 Wilbur St, Fairbanks, AK 99701
Walter Evans, Jpo

Ofc Of Public Advocacy CASA Program 907.451.2812
Fax 907.451.2868
Web .... www.admin.state.ak.us
E-mail .... casa-fairbanks@admin.state.ak.us
   100 Cushman St Ste 502, Fairbanks, AK 99701-4659
Jane Atkinson, Program Coordinator

POLICE AND SHERIFF

Alaska State Troopers 907.451.5100
Fax 907.451.5165
Web .... www.dps.state.ak.us
   1979 Peger Rd, Fairbanks, AK 99709-5298
Captain Burke Barrick, Detachment Commander

EDUCATION SERVICES

Head Start - Fairbanks Native Assoc 907.456.4989
Fax 907.456.5311
Web .... fairbanksnative.org
E-mail .... eekada@fairbanksnative.org
   320 2nd Ave, Ste 200, Fairbanks, AK 99701
Evelyn Ekada, Director

Head Start - Play & Learn 907.452.4267
Fax 907.452.4203
Web .... www.pnlchs.net
E-mail .... amattacchione@pnlchs.net
   1949 Gillam Way Ste A, Fairbanks, AK 99701-6089
Anne Marie Mattcchione, Director

Haines County

POLICE AND SHERIFF

State Trooper Post 907.766.2552
Fax 907.766.3265
Web .... www.dps.state.ak.us
E-mail .... josh_bentz@dps.state.ak.us
   259 Main St, # 16, Haines, AK 99827
Officer Josh Bentz, Director

Kenai Borough

SOCIAL SERVICES

Ofc Of Children's Svcs **907.283.3136**
Fax 907.283.9093
145 Main Street Loop Ste 100, Kenai, AK 99611
William Galic, Intake Supervisor

Kenai Peninsula County

SOCIAL SERVICES

**Ofc Of Children's Svcs & Juvenile
Probation** **907.235.7114**
Fax 907.235.2484
Web .... www.hss.state.ak.us/ocs
3670 Lake St Ste 100, Homer, AK 99603
Margit Garry, Ocs Supervisor

GENERAL HEALTH SERVICES

Homer Public Health Ctr **907.235.8857**
Fax 907.235.7090
Web .... www.hss.state.ak.us
195 E Bunnell Ave Ste C, Homer, AK 99603-7815
Leslie Callaway, Public Health Nurse

Seward Public Health Ctr **907.224.5567**
Fax 907.224.2385
E-mail .... lois.daubney@alaska.gov
201 3rd Ave, Seward, AK 99664
Lois Daubney, Phn, Manager

MENTAL HEALTH SERVICES

Community Mental Health **907.235.7701**
Fax 907.235.2290
Web .... spbhs.org
E-mail .... nallen@spbhs.org
3948 Ben Walters Ln, Homer, AK 99603
Nina Allen, Executive Director

JUSTICE AGENCY

**Kenai Peninsula Youth Facility
(KPYF)** **907.335.3100**
Fax 907.335.3134
405 Marathon Rd, Kenai, AK 99611-7857
Steve Kiefer, Probation Supervisor

COURTS

District Court-Third District **907.235.8171**
Fax 907.235.4257
E-mail .... mlmurphy@courts.state.ak.us
3670 Lake St Bldg A, Homer, AK 99603
Honorable Margaret L. Murphy, Director

Kenai Peninsula Youth Court **907.235.4985**
Fax 907.283.2634
Web .... www.kpoalaska.org
E-mail .... youthct@xyz.net
355 W Pioneer Ave, Ste 103, Homer, AK 99603
Ginny Espenshade, Director

Trial Court **907.224.3075**
Fax 907.224.7192
Web .... www.courts.state.ak.us
E-mail .... gpeck@courts.state.ak.us
410 Adams St, Seward, AK 99664
Magistrate George Peck, Director

POLICE AND SHERIFF

Alaska State Troopers **907.262.4453**
Fax 907.262.4046
Web .... www.dps.state.ak.us
E-mail .... peter.mlymarik@alaska.gov
46333 Kalifornsky Beach Rd, Soldotna,
AK 99669-9799
Pete Mlymarick, Director

Seward Police Dept **907.224.3338**
Fax 907.224.8480
E-mail .... spdchief@cityofseward.net
410 Adams, Seward, AK 99664
Thomas Clemons, Chief Of Police

Kodiak Island

SOCIAL SERVICES

Ofc Of Children's Svcs **907.486.6174**
Fax 907.486.4107
316 Mission Rd Ste 215, Kodiak, AK 99615
Mary Gray, Supervisor

GENERAL HEALTH SERVICES

Kodiak Health Ctr **907.486.3319**
Fax 907.486.8149
E-mail .... ruth-anne_ogorman@health.state.ak.us
316 Mission Rd Ste 207, Kodiak, AK 99615-7327
Ruth-Anne O'gorman, PHN, Manager

COURTS

Superior Court-3rd District **907.486.1600**
Fax 907.486.1660
Web .... www.state.ak.us/courts
E-mail .... jbolger@courts.state.ak.us
204 Mission Rd Rm 124, Kodiak, AK 99615-7312
Honorable Joel H. Bolger, Director

POLICE AND SHERIFF

State Trooper Post **907.486.4121**
Fax 907.486.5810
2921 Mill Bay Rd # A, Kodiak, AK 99615-7809
Christopher Hill, Sargent

Matanuska-Susitna County

SOCIAL SERVICES

**Children's Svcs-South Central Regional
Ofc** **907.357.9780**
Fax 907.357.9763
Web .... www.hss.state.ak.us
695 E Parks Hwy Ste 3, Wasilla, AK 99654-8170
Tim Bolt, Children Services Manager

GENERAL HEALTH SERVICES

Glennallen Health Ctr **907.352.6600**
Fax 907.376.3096
Web .... www.hss.state.ak.us
E-mail .... jd.pross@alaska.gov
3223 E Palmer Wasilla Hwy Ste 3, Wasilla,
AK 99654-7277
J.D. Pross, Public Health Nurse

COURTS

Superior Court-Third District **907.746.8181**
Fax 907.746.4151
Web .... www.courts.alaska.gov
435 S Denali St, Palmer, AK 99645-6437
Teresa Shaw, Clerk Of Court

POLICE AND SHERIFF

Alaska State Troopers **907.745.2131**
Fax 907.269.5465
Web .... www.alaskastatetroopers.gov
E-mail .... hans.brinke@alaska.gov
453 S Valley Way, Palmer, AK 99645-6494
Captain Hans Brinke, Detachment Commander

State Trooper Post **907.733.2256**
Fax 907.733.1225
Web .... www.dps.state.ak.us
E-mail .... troy.shuey@alaska.gov
3 Talkeetna Spur Road, Talkeetna, AK 99676
Troy Shuey, Sargent

EDUCATION SERVICES

CCS - Palmer Ctr **907.746.4483**
Fax 907.745.4060
Web .... www.ccsalaska.org
E-mail .... mlackey@ccsalaska.org
403 S Alaska St, Palmer, AK 99645-6339
Mark Lackey, Director

Nome County

SOCIAL SERVICES

Ofc Of Children's Svcs **907.443.5247**
Fax 907.443.2100
Web .... www.health.state.ak.us
E-mail .... mark_klavons@health.state.ak.us
103 E. French Street, Nome, AK 99762
Mark Klavons, Supervisor

JUSTICE AGENCY

Youth Corrections/Probations **907.443.2674**
Fax 907.443.3128
E-mail .... christina.agloinga@alaska.gov
804 E 4th Ave, Nome, AK 99762
Christina Agloinga, Supervisor

COURTS

Superior Court-Second District **907.443.5216**
Fax 907.443.2192
113 E Front St, Federal Building 2nd Floor, Nome,
AK 99762-9800
Magistrate Bradley Gater, Director

POLICE AND SHERIFF

State Trooper Post **907.443.2835**
Fax 907.443.5840
Web .... www.stape.alaska.gov
E-mail .... andrew.merrill@alaska.gov
214 E Front St, 2, Nome, AK 99762
Andrew Merrill, Sgt.

EDUCATION SERVICES

Communties In Schools **907.443.2231**
Fax 907.443.5144
Web .... www.nomeschools.com
E-mail .... apotter@nomeschools.com
Mile 4 Nome Teller Hwy, Nome, AK 99762
Arty Potter, Behaviral Specialist

North Slope County

SOCIAL SERVICES

Family & Youth Svcs **907.852.3397**
Fax 907.852.3392
Web .... www.alaska.gov
1250 Agvik St, ste#269, Barrow, AK 99723
Michele Davis, Supervisor

Social Svcs **907.852.4411**
Fax 907.852.4413
E-mail .... msolomon@nvbarrow.net
6090 Ahmaogak Boxer St, Barrow, AK 99723
Marjorie Solomon, Director

JUSTICE AGENCY

Barrow Juvenile Probation **907.852.5437**
Fax 907.852.8477
1250 Agvik St, 255, Barrow, AK 99723
Dwight Anderson, Jpo Iii

EDUCATION SERVICES

Communities In Schools **907.852.9778**
Fax 907.852.4334
Web .... www.nsbsd.org
E-mail .... becky.crabtree@nsbsd.org
5245 Karluck St, Barrow, AK 99723
Becky Crabtree, Director

Alaska

Prince of Wales-Outer Ketchikan County

SOCIAL SERVICES

Metlakatla Social Svcs 907.886.6911
Fax 907.886.6913
   55 Milton St, Metlakatla, AK 99926
   Sharon Coe, Director

Skagway-Hoonah-Angoon County

COURTS

Hoonah District Court 907.945.3668
Fax 907.945.3637
   300 Front St, Hoonah, AK 99829
   Maureen Desrosiers, Judge

Southeast Fairbanks County

GENERAL HEALTH SERVICES

Public Health Ctr 907.895.4292
Fax 907.895.4264
Web .... www.alaska.gov
E-mail .... rachelle.hill@alaska.gov
   2857 Alaska Hwy, Jarvis Office Center, Delta Junction, AK 99737
   Rachelle Hill, Public Health Nurse

COURTS

Tok Trial Court 907.883.5171
Fax 907.883.4367
   Mile Post 1313.5 Alaska Hwy, Tok, AK 99780
   David Roghair, Magistrate

Valdez County

SOCIAL SERVICES

Office of Children's Services 907.835.4789
Fax 907.835.2651
   213 Meals Street, # 5, Valdez, AK 99686
   Julie Linnell, Juvenile Probation

GENERAL HEALTH SERVICES

Valdez Health Ctr 907.835.4612
Fax 907.835.2419
Web .... www.health.state.ak.us
E-mail .... pam_shirrell@health.state.ak.us
   1001 Meals Ave, Valdez, AK 99686
   Pam Shirrell, PHN LII

COURTS

Third District Court 907.835.2266
Fax 907.835.3764
Web .... www.state.ak.us
E-mail .... dschally@courts.state.ak.us
   213 Meals St., Valdez, AK 99686
   Honorable Daniel Schally, Director

POLICE AND SHERIFF

State Trooper Post of Game

Warren 907.835.4307
Fax 907.835.5607
E-mail .... tony_beck@dps.state.ak.us
   Meals Avenue, Valdez, AK 99686
   Tony Beck, Trooper

Wade Hampton County

COURTS

St. Marys Trial Court 907.438.2912
Fax 907.438.2819
Web .... www.courts.state.ak.us
   Dickson Cir, Saint Marys, AK 99658
   Magistrate Nancy Phillips, Judge

Yakutat County

JUSTICE AGENCY

Yakutat Dept of Public Safety-Police
Dept 907.784.3206
Fax 907.784.3523
   609 Forest Hwy 10, Yakutat, AK 99689
   John Nichols, Police Chief

Yukon-Koyukuk County

GENERAL HEALTH SERVICES

Galena Itinerant Health Ctr 907.656.1200
Fax 907.656.1525
   PO Box 64, Galena, AK 99741-0064
   Margaret Huntingon, Chief Executive Officer

Public Health Nursing Ctr 907.662.2889
Fax 907.465.3913
Web .... www.hss.state.ak.us
   1 Spruce St, Fort Yukon, AK 99740
   Paula Ciniero, Public Health Nurse

Yukon Health Ctr 907.662.2460
Fax 907.662.2709
   1 Spruce St, Fort Yukon, AK 99740
   Paula Ciniero-bowen, Public Health Nurse

SPECIAL SERVICES AGENCIES

ADOPTION AGENCIES

Alaska International Adoption Agency 907.677.2888
Fax 907.274.5941
Web .... www.akadoptions.com
E-mail .... info@akadoptions.com
   3705 Arctic Blvd, Ste 1336, Anchorage, AK 99503
   Alex Bortnick, Executive Director

Denali Family Services 907.274.8281
Fax 907.274.4055
Web .... www.denalifs.org
   1251 Muldoon Road, Suite 116, Anchorage, AK 99504
   COA accredited organization.

Fairbanks Counseling And Adoption 907.456.4729
Fax 907.456.4623
Web .... www.fcaalaska.org
E-mail .... fca@fcaalaska.org
   912 Barnette St, Fairbanks, AK 99701-4510
   Camille Connelly-Terhune, Director

ADVOCACY RESOURCES

Cook Inlet Tribal Coucil Inc 907.793.3600
Fax 907.793.3602
Web .... www.citci.org
   3600 Jeromimo Drive, Anchorage, AK 99508
   Katie Lee, Behavioral Health Officer

Law Office of Kirsten Swanson 907.586.8200
E-mail .... k_swanson2000@yahoo.com
   417 Harris St, Juneau, AK 99801
   Kirsten Swanson, Lawyer

Office of Public Advocacy 907.746.4162
E-mail .... janine.reep@alaska.gov
   PO Box 110225, Juneau, AK 99811
   Janine Reep

BEHAVIORAL HEALTH TREATMENT

Advisory Board on Alcoholism and Drug
Abuse 907.465.8920
Fax 907.465.4410
E-mail .... kate.burkhart@alaska.gov
   431 N Franklin St Ste 203, Juneau, AK 99801-1186
   Kate Burkhart, Director

Akeela, Inc. 907.565.1200
Fax 907.258.6052
Web .... www.akeela.org
   4111 Minnesota Drive, Anchorage, AK 99503
   CARF accredited programs available.

Alaska Children's Services Inc. 907.346.2101
Web .... www.akchild.org
E-mail .... awilson@akchild.org
   4600 Abbott Road, Anchorage, AK 99507-4314
   Ms. Arlene Wilson, Accreditation Manager
   Joint Commission accredited organization.

Anchorage Community Mental Health Svcs -
Outpatient 907.762.2800
Fax 907.561.7093
Web .... www.acmhs.com
E-mail .... dfoster@acmhs.com
   4045 Lake Otis Pkwy Ste 101, Anchorage, AK 99508-5227
   Dee Foster, Director Of Child And Family Services

Boys and Girls Home of Alaska, Inc. 907.459.4700
Web .... www.boysandgirlshome.com
E-mail .... johnsonc@bghome.net
   3101 Lathrop Street, Fairbanks, AK 99701
   Ms. Cyndy Johnson, Accreditation Manager
   Joint Commission accredited organization.

Bristol Bay Area Health Corporation 907.842.5201
E-mail .... bmettin@bbahc.org
   6000 Kanakanak Road, Dillingham, AK 99576
   Mr. Bruce Mettin, Accreditation Manager
   Joint Commission accredited organization.

Bristol Bay Counseling Ctr 907.842.1230
Fax 907.842.5174
Web .... www.bbahc.org
E-mail .... rloera@bbahc.org
   6000 Kanakanak Road, Dillingham, AK 99576
   Rose Loera, Director

Chugach Valley Counseling 907.696.4041
   11723 Old Glenn Hwy, Eagle River, AK 99577-7733
   Janet Runyan, Director

Fairbanks Native Association, Inc. 907.452.1648
Fax 907.456.4148
Web .... www.fairbanksnative.org
   605 Hughes Avenue, Suite 100, Fairbanks, AK 99701
   CARF accredited programs available.

Hansen House 907.747.3682
Fax 907.747.8099
E-mail .... cdembinskyyas@yahoo.com
   216 Lance Dr, Sitka, AK 99835-9749
   David Voluck, Executive Director

Maniilaq Association: Behavioral Health
Services 907.442.7640
Fax 907.442.7822
Web .... www.maniilaq.org
   733 Second Avenue, Frank R. Ferguson Building, Kotzebue, AK 99752
   CARF accredited programs available.

Matt Sue Health Svcs 907.376.2411
Fax 907.352.3373
Web .... www.mattsuehealthservices.org
E-mail .... vknapp@bhs-mat-su.com
   1363 W Spruce Ave, Wasilla, AK 99654
   Victoria Knapp, Coordinator Of Case Managers

Mclaughlin Youth Ctr Sexual Offender

Program **907.261.4399**
Fax 907.261.4308
Web ....www.health.hss.state.ak.us\djj\
2600 Providence Dr, Anchorage, AK 99508-4678
D Williams, Superintendent

Nakenu Family Ctr **907.283.6693**
Fax 907.283.7088
E-mail ....jshowalter@kenaitze.org
110 N Willow St, Kenai, AK 99611-7701
Jennifer Showalter, Director

North Star Behavioral Health **907.258.7575**
Web ....www.northstarbehavioral.com
E-mail ....laura.mckenzie@uhsinc.com
2530 DeBarr Road, Anchorage, AK 99508-2948
Ms. Laura McKenzie, Accreditation Manager
Joint Commission accredited organization.

Polaris House **907.780.6775**
Fax 907.780.6774
Web ....www.polarishouse.net
E-mail ....polarishouse@alaska.net
434 W Willoughby Ave, Juneau, AK 99801
Dorothy Green, Director

Providence Adolescent Residential Treatment

Program **907.272.2148**
E-mail ....rraffert@provak.org
3400 East 20th, Anchorage, AK 99508
Ms. Renee Rafferty, Accreditation Manager
Joint Commission accredited organization.

Railbelt Mental Health and Addictions **907.832.5557**
Fax 907.832.5564
Web ....www.railbelt.com
E-mail ....rmha@mtaonline.net
302 East 2nd Street, Nenana, AK 99760
Traci Wiggins, Director

Railbelt Mental Health And Addictions **907.683.2743**
Fax 907.683.2598
Web ....www.railbelt.com
E-mail ....rmha@mtaonline.net
Coal Street Dry Creek, Healy, AK 99743
Mary Allen, Administrative Director

Sitka Counseling And Prevention Svcs **907.747.8994**
Fax 907.747.5316
E-mail ....gblue@scpsak.org
701 Indian River Rd, Sitka, AK 99835-7480
Gordon Blue, Executive Director

Southcentral Foundation **907.729.4955**
Fax 907.729.4924
Web ....www.scf.cc
4501 Diplomacy Drive, Anchorage, AK 99508
CARF accredited programs available.

SouthEast Alaska Regional Health

Consortium **907.966.2411**
Fax 907.966.8494
Web ....www.searhc.org
222 Tongass Drive, Sitka, AK 99835
CARF accredited programs available.

The Salvation Army Booth Memorial and Cares for Kids

Services **907.279.0522**
Fax 907.279.0525
Web ....www.salvationarmy.org/alaska
3600 East 20th Avenue, Anchorage, AK 99508
CARF accredited programs available.

Volunteers of America of Alaska, Inc. **907.279.9634**
Fax 907.276.5489
Web ....www.voaak.org
1675 C Street, Suite 201, Anchorage, AK 99501
CARF accredited programs available.

Yukon Kuskokwim Delta Regional

Hospital **907.543.6300**
Web ....www.ykhc.org
E-mail ....jeffrey_murchison@ykhc.org
700 Chief Eddie Hoffman Highway, Bethel, AK 99559
Mr. Jeffrey Murchison, Accreditation Manager
Joint Commission accredited organization.

CHILDREN'S HOSPITAL

Alaska Native Medical Center **907.563.2662**
4315 Diplomacy Dr, Anchorage, AK 99508
Gary Shaw, Administrator

Alaska Regional Hospital **907.264.1754**
2801 Debarr Rd, Anchorage, AK 99508

Fairbanks Memorial Hospital **907.452.8181**
1650 Cowles St, Fairbanks, AK 99701
Mike Powers, Chief Executive Officer

Petersburg Medical Center **907.772.4291**
103 Fram St, Petersburg, AK 99833
Liv Woodyard, Chief Executive Officer

Providence Alaska Medical Center **907.562.2211**
3200 Providence Dr, Anchorage, AK 99508

Providence Kodiak Island Medical Center **907.486.3281**
1915 East Rezanof Dr, Kodiak, AK 99615
Donald Rush, Director

Providence Valdez Medical Center **907.835.2249**
911 Meals Ave, Valdez, AK 99686
Lori Sailors, Administrative Assistant

South Peninsula Hospital **907.235.8101**
4300 Bartlett St, Homer, AK 99603
Robert Letson, Chief Executive Officer

COUNSELING SERVICES

Anchorage Multi-Svcs Counseling Ctr **907.561.2805**
Fax 907.561.2982
Web ....www.anchoragemultiservices.org
E-mail ....drbrown@anchoragemultisvs.org
4325 Laurel St, Ste 101A, Anchorage, AK 99508
Dr. Washington Brown, Director

Eastern Aleutian Tribes, Inc. **907.532.2000**
Fax 907.532.2001
Web ....www.easternaleutiantribes.com
65 Airport Rd, Cold Bay, AK 99571

Eastern Aleutians Tribes, Inc. **907.277.1440**
Fax 907.277.1446
E-mail ....eat_anchorage@eatribes.net
3380 C St Ste 100, Anchorage, AK 99503
Michael Christensen, Executive Director

Lynn Canal Counseling Svcs **907.766.2177**
Fax 907.766.2977
E-mail ....info@lccsak.org
215 Willard Street, Haines, AK 99827
Becky Chapin, Director

Maniilaq Counseling Svcs **907.442.7400**
Fax 907.442.7306
Web ....www.maniilaq.org
436 5th & Ted Stevens Way, Kotzebue, AK 99752
Margene Andrews, Counseling Services Supervisor

Rainforest Recovery Ctr **907.586.9508**
Fax 907.586.5605
Web ....www.bartletthospital.org
3250 Hospital Dr, Juneau, AK 99801-7808
Sandi Kohtz, Director

CRISIS & SHELTER CARE

Advocates for Victims of Violence, Inc. **907.835.2999**
Fax 907.835.2981
Web ....www.avvalaska.org
E-mail ....executive@avvalaska.org
551 Woodside St, Valdez, AK 99686
Rowena Palomar, Executive Director

Aiding Women In Abuse-Rape & Domestic

Violence **907.586.6623**
Fax 907.586.2479
E-mail ....stabachnick@aware.alaska.com
1547 Old Glacier Hwy, Juneau, AK 99802
Saralyn Tabachnick, Director

Alaska Family Svcs -Domestic Violence **907.746.4080**
Fax 907.746.1177
E-mail ....donn@akafs.org
1825 S Chugach St, Palmer, AK 99645
Donn Bennice, Director

Cordova Family Resource Ctr-Domestic

Violence **907.424.5674**
Fax 907.424.5673
E-mail ....cfrc@ctcak.net
705 2nd St, Cordova, AK 99574
Nicole Songer, Executive Director

Kodiak Womens Resource-Crisis Ctr **907.486.6171**
Fax 907.486.4264
Web ....www.kodiak.org
E-mail ....rebecca@kodiak.org
422 Hillside Drive, Kodiak, AK 99615
Rebecca Shields, Director

Presbyterian Hospitality House **907.456.6445**
Fax 907.456.6402
E-mail ....drendatingner@aol.com
209 Forty Mile Ave, Ste 100, Fairbanks, AK 99701
Drenda Tigner, Director

Providence Adolescent Residential

Treatment **907.272.2148**
Fax 907.272.2169
E-mail ....r.raffer@prov.aska.org
3400 E 20th Ave, Anchorage, AK 99508-3412
Renee Rafferty, Director

Residential Youth Care, Inc. **907.225.4664**
Fax 907.247.4664
E-mail ....jduckworth@residentialyouthcare.org
2514 1st Ave, Ketchikan, AK 99901-5804
Jack Duckworth, Executive Director

Sitkans Against Family Violence **907.747.3370**
Fax 907.747.3450
207 Seward St, Sitka, AK 99835
Christine Bauman, Director

South Peninsula Haven House-Domestic

Violence **907.235.8943**
Fax 907.235.2733
Web ....www.havenhousealaska.org
E-mail ....coleman.peg@gmail.com
3776 Lake St Ste 100, Homer, AK 99603-7647
Peg Coleman, Director

Unalaskan-Sexual-Family Violence

Program **907.581.1500**
Fax 907.581.4568
PO Box 36, Unalaska, AK 99685-0036
Lynn Crane, Director

EDUCATION

Alaska Assoc of Secondary School

Principals **907.746.9300**
Fax 907.746.9301
Web ....www.alaskaprincipal.org
E-mail ....aassp@alaskaprincipal.org
326 4th St, Juneau, AK 99801
Carol Kane, Executive Director

Big Brothers And Big Sisters/Sitka Ofc **907.747.3500**
Fax 907.747.3003
Web ....www.bbbs.org
408 Oja Way Ste C, Sitka, AK 99835-7663
James Diffin, Program Manager

Booth Memorial Youth And Family Svcs 907.279.0522
Fax 907.279.0525
Web ....www.salvationarmy.org/alaska
3600 E 20th Ave, Anchorage, AK 99508-3416
Kimberly Stephens, Executive Director

Hydaburg Clinic 907.285.3465
Fax 907.285.3802
8th St Ext, Hydaburg, AK 99922
Gary Morrison, Counselor

Kids Corps, Inc. Head Start 907.272.0133
Fax 907.272.0312
Web ....www.kcialaska.org
3710 E 20th Ave Ste 2, Anchorage, AK 99508-3418
Dirk Shumaker, Executive Director

Nea Alaska 907.274.0536
Fax 907.274.0551
Web ....www.neaalaska.org
4100 Spenard Rd, Anchorage, AK 99517-2901
Barb Angiak, President

FOSTER CARE AGENCIES

Alaska Attachment & Bonding Assoc
(AABA) 907.376.0366
E-mail ....eleanor@akattachment.org
619 S Knik-Goose-Bay Rd Ste J, PO Box 872188,
Wasilla, AK 99687
Eleanor Oakley, Chief Executive Officer

Alaska Ctr for Resource Families (ACRF) 907.479.7307
E-mail ....adoptionsupport@nwresource.org
815 2nd Ave, Ste 101, Fairbanks, AK 99701

North American Council on Adoptable 907.452.5397
1018 26th Ave, Fairbanks, AK 99701
Sue White, Representative

HOME MEDICAL EQUIPMENT PROVIDERS

Alaska Stairlift & Elevator, LLC 907.245.5438
Fax 907.245.5439
Web ....www.alaskastairlift.com
230 East Potter Drive, Suite 5, Anchorage, AK 99518
CARF accredited programs available.

SOCIAL SERVICES

AEYC SEA 907.789.1235
Fax 907.789.1238
Web ....www.aeyc-sea.org
E-mail ....info@aeyc-sea.org
3100 Channel Drive, Suite 215, Juneau, AK 99801

Akeela, Inc 907.565.1200
Fax 907.258.6052
Web ....www.akeela.org
E-mail ....rnadeau@akeela.org
360 W Benson Blvd Ste 300, Anchorage, AK 99503
Rosalie Nadeau, Executive Director

Alaska Cares 907.561.8301
Fax 907.561.8170
Web ....www.provak.org
E-mail ....cbryant@provak.org
3925 Tudor Centre Dr Ste 100, Anchorage,
AK 99508-5931
Cory Bryant, Center Manager

Alaska Family Services, Inc. 907.746.4080
Fax 907.746.1177
Web ....www.akafs.org
1825 South Chugach Street, Palmer, AK 99645
COA accredited organization.

Alaska Youth & Parent Foundation 907.929.2633
Fax 907.243.9504
Web ....www.aypfalaska.org
E-mail ....aypf@aypfalaska.org
700 W 6th Ave, Anchorage, AK 99501
Heather Harris, Executive Director

Armed Svcs YMCA Anchorage 907.552.9622
Fax 907.552.4651
Web ....www.asymcaofalaska.org
E-mail ....welcome.cente@akasymca.org
7135 Dolittle St, JBER, AK 99506
Marijo Imig, Executive Director

Assets, Inc. 907.279.6617
Fax 907.274.0636
Web ....www.assetsinc.org
E-mail ....matt_jones@assetsinc.org
2330 Nichols St, Anchorage, AK 99508-3458
Matthew Jones, Executive Director

Catholic Diocese Of Fairbanks 907.374.9500
Fax 907.374.9580
Web ....www.cbna.info
E-mail ....receptionist@cbna.org
1316 Peger Rd, Fairbanks, AK 99709-5199
Don Kettler, Bishop

Catholic Social Svcs 907.222.7300
Fax 907.258.1091
Web ....www.cssalaska.org
E-mail ....catholicsocialservices@css-ak.org
3710 E 20th Ave, Anchorage, AK 99508
Susan Bomalaski, Executive Director
COA accredited organization.

Community Family Svc 907.755.4919
Fax 907.755.2993
Web ....www.searhc.org
E-mail ....pryan@searhc.org
PO Box 69, Klawock, AK 99925-0069
Dennis Pilgrim, Clinical Psychologist

Cook Inlet Tribal Council 907.793.3600
Fax 907.793.3602
Web ....www.citci.com
3600 San Jeronimo Ct, Anchorage, AK 99508-2869
Gloria ONeill, CEO

Covenant House Alaska 907.272.1255
Fax 907.272.1466
Web ....www.covenanthouseak.org
E-mail ....dphayer@covhouse.alaska.com
609 F St, Anchorage, AK 99501-3596
Deirdre Cronin, Executive Director

Denali Family Svcs. 907.274.8281
Fax 907.274.4055
Web ....www.denalifs.org
E-mail ....info@denalifs.org
1251 Muldoon Rd Ste 116, Anchorage, AK 99504
Yvonne Chase, Executive Director

Fairbanks Alaska Chapter NCPCA 907.456.2866
Fax 907.451.8125
Web ....www.rcpcfairbanks.org
E-mail ....cturner@rcpcfairbanks.org
1726 26th Ave, Fairbanks, AK 99701
Coleen Turner, Executive Director

Fairbanks Native Assoc New Life Program 907.452.1274
Fax 907.452.1282
Web ....www.fairbanksnative.org
E-mail ....rellington@fairbanksnative.org
3100 S Cushman St, Fairbanks, AK 99701-7516
Rita Ellington, Director Of Youth Services

Hope Community Resources, Inc. 907.561.5335
Fax 907.564.7492
Web ....www.hopealaska.org
540 W Intl Airport Rd, Anchorage, AK 99518
Steve Lesko, Director

Ketchikan Indian Community 907.228.4941
Fax 907.228.5224
E-mail ....dpatton@kictribe.org
2960 Tongass Ave, Ketchikan, AK 99901
Debbie Patton, General Manager

R.I.T.E., Inc. 907.562.7483
Fax 907.561.3274
Web ....www.gci.net
E-mail ....maryellen.wright@gci.net
307 E Northern Lights Blvd, Ste 201, Anchorage,
AK 99503-2701
Jim Morgan, Program Manager

Thread 907.265.3100
Fax 907.265.3191
Web ....www.threadalaska.org
E-mail ....info@threadalaska.org
3350 Commercial Dr Ste 203, Anchorage,
AK 99501-3023
Stephanie Berglund, Chief Executive Officer

SPECIAL NEEDS

Alaska Congress of Parents & Teachers 907.279.9345
E-mail ....akpta@alaska.net
555 W Northern Pike, Anchorage, AK 99520
Al Tamingi Jr, President

Alaska Speech-Language-Hearing Assn 907.212.0211
E-mail ....kelly.brewer@providence.org
3211 Starboard Ln, Anchorage, AK 99516
Kelly Brewer, Rehab Manager

Asthma & Allergy Foundation 907.696.4810
Web ....www.aafaalaska.com
E-mail ....aafaalaska@gci.net
PO Box 201927, Anchorage, AK 99520
Dale Knutson, Executive Director

Easter Seals Alaska 907.277.7325
E-mail ....vgosborne@gci.net
670 W Firewood Ln Ste 105, Anchorage, AK 99503
V Gosborne, Chief Executive Officer

Golden Heart Autism Society 907.374.4421
E-mail ....ak-goldenheart@autismsocietyofamerica.org
607 Old Steese Ste B, Fairbanks, AK 99701

LINKS Mat-Su Parent Resource Center 907.373.3632
E-mail ....linksdf@gci.net
6177 E Mountain Heather Way, Ste 3, Palmer,
AK 99645

Stone Soup Group 907.561.3702
Fax 907.561.3702
E-mail ....pams@stonesoupgroup.org
307 E Northern Lights Blvd, Suite 100, Anchorage,
AK 99503

Stone Soup Group 907.561.3701
E-mail ....ssg@stonesoupgroup.org
3350 Commercial Dr Ste 100, Anchorage, AK 99501

Stone Soup Group 907.561.3701
Fax 907.561.3702
E-mail ....ssg@stonesoupgroup.org
307 E Northern Lights Blvd, Suite 100, Anchorage,
AK 99503
Kelly Donnelly, Executive Director

Arizona

Jan Brewer, Governor
State Capitol
1700 W. Washington
Phoenix, AZ 85007
602.542.4331
602.542.1381 (Fax)
azgov@az.gov
www.azgovernor.gov

Christy Alonzo-Silvestri, Juvenile Justice Specialist
AZ Juvenile Justice Commissions
1700 W Washington, Ste. 101
Phoenix, AZ 85007
602.542.3404
602.542.4644 (Fax)
calonzo@az.gov

Judge Cecil B. Patterson, Jr., SAG Chair
1849 E Guadalupe Rd Ste C-101
PMB 125
Tempe, AZ 85283
480.650.6119
480.730.8864 (Fax)
cpatterson3@cox.net

CRISIS NUMBERS

Child Abuse Reporting . . .888.767.2445

STATE SERVICES

SOCIAL SERVICES

Arizona Div of Emergency Management
Agency.....................602.244.0504
Fax..........................602.231.6271
Web.......................www.azdema.gov
E-mail.............judy.kioski@azdema.gov
5636 E Mcdowell Rd, Phoenix, AZ 85008
Judy Kioski, Public Information Officer

Child Care Licensing Office Arizona..........602.364.2539
Fax..........................602.364.4768
150 North 18th Ave, Fourth Flr, Phoenix, AZ 85007

Dept of Economic Security...............602.542.4791
Fax..........................602.542.5339
Web.......................www.de.state.az.us
E-mail.............twareing@azdes.gov
1717 W Jefferson St, Phoenix, AZ 85007
Liz Barker, Director Of Public Info

Interstate Compact on The Placement of
Children.............................602.235.9134
Fax..........................602.532.5553
E-mail.............j.odonell@azdes.gov
4000 N Central Ave Ste 2200, Phoenix, AZ 85012
Jim Odonell, Deputy Compact Administrator

GENERAL HEALTH SERVICES

Bureau of Womens & Children Health.........602.364.1400
Fax..........................602.364.1494
E-mail.............shiela.sjolander@azdhs.gov
150 N 18th Ave Ste 320, Phoenix, AZ 85007
Shiela Sjolander, Bureau Officer

Children with Special Health Care Needs AZ....602.542.1860
Fax..........................602.542.2589
E-mail.............ocean@azdhs.gov
150 N 18th Ave, Ste 320, Phoenix, AZ 85007
Marta Urbina, Chief

Ofc of Medicaid............................602.417.4111
Fax..........................602.252.6536
Web.......................www.azvets.com
E-mail.............tom.beclach@azahcccs.gov
801 E Jefferson St, Phoenix, AZ 85034-2217
Thomas Beclach, Director

MENTAL HEALTH SERVICES

DHS Div of Behavioral Health Svcs...........602.364.4558
Fax..........................602.364.4570
Web.......................www.hs.state.az.us
E-mail.............lnelson@hs.state.az.us
150 N 18th Ave Fl 2, Phoenix, AZ 85007-3203
Dr Laura Nelson, Deputy Director

Div of Developmental Disabilities............602.542.0419
Fax..........................602.542.6870
Web.......................www.azds.gov
1789 W Jefferson St, Phoenix, AZ 85007-3202
Barbara Brent, Assistant Director

Rehab Svcs Administration AZ...............602.542.3332
Fax..........................602.542.3778
E-mail.............klevandowsky@azdes.gov
1789 W Jefferson 2 NW, 2nd Flr Site Code 930A,
Phoenix, AZ 85007
Kathy Levandowsky, Director

JUSTICE AGENCY

Arizona Dept Of Corrections.................602.542.5886
Fax..........................602.542.2859
Web.......................www.azcorrections.gov
E-mail.............directorsoffice@azcorrections.gov
1601 W Jefferson St, Phoenix, AZ 85007-3056
Charles Ryan, Director

Arizona Dept Of Juvenile Corrections.........602.542.4302
Fax..........................602.542.5156
Web.......................www.azdjc.gov
E-mail.............mbranham@dj.state.az.us
1624 W Adams St, Phoenix, AZ 85007
Michael Branham, Director

Arizona Dept Of Public Safety...............602.223.2000
Fax..........................602.223.2949
2102 W Encanto Blvd, Phoenix, AZ 85009
Robert Halliday, Director

Community Legal Svcs.....................602.258.3434
Fax..........................602.254.9059
Web.......................www.clsaz.org
E-mail.............kstuart@clsaz.org
305 S 2nd Ave, Phoenix, AZ 85003-2402
Karen Stuart, Hiv Project Director

Correctional Education Bureau AZ...........602.542.5620
Fax..........................602.364.0550
E-mail.............bganz@azcorrections.gov
1601 W Jefferson 3rd Flr, Phoenix, AZ 85007
Barbara Ganz, Director

Criminal Justice Commission................602.364.1146
Fax..........................602.364.1175
Web.......................www.azcjc.gov
E-mail.............jrblackburn@azcjc.gov
1110 W Washington St Ste 230, Phoenix,
AZ 85007-2958
John Blackburn Jr., Executive Director

Dept of Public Safety (Victim Assistance)......602.223.2000
Fax..........................602.223.2943
E-mail.............halliday@azdts.gov
2102 W Encanto Blvd, #1320, Phoenix, AZ 85009
Robert Halliday, Director

Governor's Div for Substance Abuse
Prevention...............................602.364.2232
Fax..........................602.542.3643
1700 W Washington St, Ste 101, Phoenix,
AZ 85007-2831
Rob Evans, Director

State Attorney General's Ofc...............602.542.5025
Fax..........................602.542.4085
E-mail.............thomas.horne@ag.state.az.us
1275 W Washington St, Phoenix, AZ 85007
Thomas Horne, Attorney General

EDUCATION SERVICES

Arizona State Schools for the Deaf & Blind....520.770.3700
Fax..........................520.770.3711
Web.......................www.asdb.state.az.us
E-mail.............robert.h@asdb.az.gov
1200 W Speedway Blvd, Tucson, AZ 85745
Robert Hill, Superintendent

AZ Department of Education.................602.542.4361
Fax..........................602.542.5440
E-mail.............adeinbox@azed.gov
1535 W Jefferson St, Phoenix, AZ 85007
John Huppenthal, Superintendent Of Public Instruction

Exceptional Student Svcs...................602.542.4013
Fax..........................602.542.5404
Web.......................www.ade.state.az.us
1535 W Jefferson St, Phoenix, AZ 85007-3209
Joan Macdonald, Interim Director

Homeless Education........................602.542.4963
Fax..........................602.542.5175
1535 W Jefferson St, Bin #14, Phoenix, AZ 85007
Frank Migali, Education Program Specialist

Pilot Parents of Southern Arizona...........520.324.3150
Fax..........................520.324.3152
E-mail.............ppsa@pilotparents.org
2600 N Wyatt Dr, Tucson, AZ 85712
Lynn Kallis, Executive Director

RAISING Special Kids AZ...................602.242.4366
Fax..........................602.242.4306
E-mail.............info@raisingspecialkids.org
5025 E Washington St ste 204, Phoenix, AZ 85034
Joyce Millard Hoie, Director

COUNTY SERVICES

Apache County

SOCIAL SERVICES

DES District III 928.337.4359
Fax...928.337.2364
Web...www.azdes.gov
E-mail.................................arussell@azdes.gov
  395 South Washington, Saint Johns, AZ 85936
  Ann Russell, Unit Supervisor

Navajo Children & Family Svcs
Program.....................................928.871.6806
Fax...928.871.7667
  Bia Bldg 50 Window Rock Blvd, Window Rock,
  AZ 86515
  Regina Yazzie, Program Director

GENERAL HEALTH SERVICES

Navajo Area Indian Svc.....................928.871.5811
Fax...928.871.5872
Web...www.ihs.gov
E-mail............................john.hubbard@ihs.hhs.gov
  Highway 264 & Saint Michaels, Window Rock,
  AZ 86511
  John Hubbard, Jr, Area Director

JUSTICE AGENCY

Juvenile Court Svcs.........................928.337.7549
Fax...928.337.2525
E-mail.....................ygreer@courts.sp.state.az.us
  50 W Cleveland, St Johns, AZ 85936
  Chuck Moter, Director

COURTS

Navajo Nation District & Family Court Chinle Judicial
District.......................................928.674.2084
Fax...928.674.2089
  1 Mile E of US 191 Route 7, Chinle, AZ 86503
  Cynthia Thompson, Judge

POLICE AND SHERIFF

Sheriff's Ofc................................928.337.4321
Fax...928.337.2709
Web...www.usa.com
E-mail.................................apacheone@usa.com
  370 S Washington, Saint Johns, AZ 85936
  Joseph Dedman, Sheriff

EDUCATION SERVICES

Springerville Head Start.....................928.333.4888
Fax...928.333.4769
  119 Silva Ln, Springerville, AZ 85938
  Ms Margie Tapia, Director

Cochise County

SOCIAL SERVICES

Child Protective Svcs........................520.432.5337
Fax...520.432.5645
Web..www.cfcare.org
E-mail.................................mscott@azdes.gov
  207 Bisbee Rd, Bisbee, AZ 85603-1122
  Mary Scott, CPS Supervisor

DES District VI..............................520.432.5703
Fax...520.432.7301
  209 Bisbee Rd, Bisbee, AZ 85603-1122
  Roseann Earnest, Secretary

DES Family Assistance Admin...............520.432.5415
Fax...520.432.5644
  207 Bisbee Rd, Bisbee, AZ 85603
  Lupe Saucedo, Acting Supervisor

DES Multi Svc Ctr 520.364.4446
Fax...520.364.4278
Web...www.azdes.gov
E-mail.................................dsalazar@azdes.gov
  1140 F Ave, Douglas, AZ 85607-1919
  Diane Salazar, CPS Supervisor

GENERAL HEALTH SERVICES

Health Dept 520.803.3900
Fax...520.459.8195
Web.................................www.cochisecounty.com
  4115 E Foothills Dr, Sierra Vista, AZ 85635
  Jane Wical, District Nurse

Health Dept 520.805.5600
Fax...520.364.5453
Web.................................www.cochisecounty.com
  515 E 7th St, Douglas, AZ 85607
  Irene Cornejo, Lpn, District Nurse

Health Dept 520.432.9400
Fax...520.432.9480
Web.............................www.co.cochise.az.gov
  1415 W Melody Ln, Bldg A, Bisbee, AZ 85603
  Carol Wentland, Nursing Director

Health Dept Willcox Satellite Ofc.............520.384.7100
Fax...520.384.0309
Web.............................www.cochisecounty.az.gov
E-mail.........................mgonzales@co.cochise.az.gov
  450 S Haskell Ave Ste E, Willcox, AZ 85643-2790
  Maryann Gonzales, Lpn, Health Nurse

JUSTICE AGENCY

CASA Program..............................520.432.7521
Fax...520.432.7247
E-mail.........................jhansen@courts.az.gov
  915 Tovreaville Rd, Bisbee, AZ 85603
  Joan Hansen, Coordinator

Juvenile Court Svcs.........................520.432.7523
Fax...520.432.0393
Web.............................www.co.cochise.az.us
  915 Tovreaville Rd, Bisbee, AZ 85603
  Delcy Scull, Probation Director

Victim/Witness Program.....................520.432.8700
Fax...520.432.8777
  150 Quality hill, Bisbee, AZ 85603
  Edward G. Rheinheimer, County Attorney

COURTS

Superior Court..............................520.432.8570
Fax...520.432.4850
Web.............................www.co.cochise.az.us
  100 Quality Hill, Bisbee, AZ 85603
  Denise Lundin, Clerk

POLICE AND SHERIFF

City Of Bisbee Police........................520.432.2261
Fax...520.432.6058
E-mail.........................cobpolice@cityofbisbee.com
  1 W Highway 92, Bisbee, AZ 85603
  Jim Elkins, Police Chief

EDUCATION SERVICES

La Escuelita Head Start Ctr..................520.882.0100
Fax...520.622.1927
Web.............................www.childparentcenters.org
E-mail.........................afrisby@childparentcenters.org
  650 F Ave, Douglas, AZ 85607
  Ms Angelica Frisby, Director

Coconino County

SOCIAL SERVICES

Child Protective Svcs........................928.779.3681
Fax...928.214.9567
Web...www.state.az.us
  397 S Malpais Ln Ste 11, Flagstaff, AZ 86001-6254
  Martin Rothman, Unit Supervisor

GENERAL HEALTH SERVICES

Health Dept Clinical Svcs....................928.679.7222
Fax...928.679.7351
Web.............................www.co.coconino.az.us
  2625 N King St, Flagstaff, AZ 86004-1884
  Barbara L. Worgess, Mph, Director

JUSTICE AGENCY

Coconino CASA Program....................928.226.5423
Fax...928.226.5455
E-mail.........................kmeadows@courts.az.gov
  1001 E Sawmill Rd, Flagstaff, AZ 86001
  Kathy Meadows, Program Coordinator

Juvenile Court Svcs.........................928.226.5400
Fax...928.226.5454
Web.............................www.courts.sp.state.az.us
  1001 E Sawmill Rd, Flagstaff, AZ 86001-5833
  Bryon Mesutda, Director Of Juvenile

COURTS

Superior Court..............................928.679.7600
  200 N San Francisco St, Flagstaff, AZ 86001
  Honorable Mark Moran, Presiding Judge

POLICE AND SHERIFF

Sheriff's Dept...............................928.226.5012
Fax...928.226.5095
E-mail.........................bpribil@coconino.az.gov
  911 E Sawmill Rd, Flagstaff, AZ 86001
  Bill Pribil, Sheriff

EDUCATION SERVICES

Cogdill Head Start..........................928.774.5552
Fax...928.774.4961
E-mail.........................cogdill@macog.org
  301 S Paseo Del Flag, Flagstaff, AZ 86001
  Carolyn Spann, Coordinator

Flagstaff Early Head Start...................928.214.8461
Fax...928.773.0621
E-mail.........................veronica@nacog.org
  3401 N 4th St, Flagstaff, AZ 86004-1710
  Veronica Guiterrez, Director

Gila County

SOCIAL SERVICES

DES District V...............................928.425.3101
Fax...928.425.7950
  605 S Seventh St, Globe, AZ 85501-1405
  Stella Hutchinson, CYF Supervisor

San Carlos Apache Tribe Social Svc...........928.475.2313
Fax...928.475.2342
Web...www.scatcom.net
E-mail...tss@scatcom.net
  7 San Carlos Ave, San Carlos, AZ 85550
  Terry Ross, Director

GENERAL HEALTH SERVICES

Health Dept.................................928.425.3189
E-mail.........................ldalrymple@co.gila.az.us
  5515 S Apache Ave, Globe, AZ 85501
  Lorraine Dalrymple, Rn, Nursing Director

Health Dept **928.474.1210**
Fax 928.474.7069
Web ....www.co.gila.az.us
107 W Frontier St Ste A, Payson, AZ 85541
Melinda Williams, Hiv Coordinator

JUSTICE AGENCY

CASA Program **928.425.7987**
Fax 928.425.9638
Web ....www.azcasa.org
E-mail ....cgonzal2@courts.az.us
1100 E Monroe St Ste 200, Globe, AZ 85501-1487
Cecelia M. Gonzales, Case/Foster Care Director

Probation Dept **928.425.7971**
Fax 928.425.9638
Web ....www.courts.az.gov
1100 E Monroe St Ste 200, Globe, AZ 85501-1341
Robert Maccarone, State Director

COURTS

Probation **928.474.2242**
Fax 928.474.1752
E-mail ....cmasters-webb@courts.sp.state.az.us
714 S Beeline Hwy Ste 104, Payson, AZ 85541
Cecille Masters-webb, Director

Superior Court **928.425.3231**
Fax 928.425.7802
1400 E Ash St, Globe, AZ 85501-1483
Honorable Anita Escobedo, Clerk Of Court

POLICE AND SHERIFF

Sheriff's Ofc **928.425.4449**
Fax 928.425.0819
E-mail ....jarmer@co.gila.az.us
1100 South St, Globe, AZ 85501
John R. Armer, Sheriff

Graham County

JUSTICE AGENCY

Victim/Witness Program **928.428.4787**
Fax 928.428.7200
E-mail ....mperu@graham.az.gov
800 W Main St, Safford, AZ 85546
Marie Peru, Director

POLICE AND SHERIFF

Sheriff's Dept **928.428.3141**
Fax 928.428.2487
Web ....www.graham.az.gov
E-mail ....pallred@graham.az.gov
523 S 10th Ave, Safford, AZ 85546-3120
Preston Allred, Sheriff

Greenlee County

JUSTICE AGENCY

CASA Program **928.865.2072**
Fax 928.865.4417
253 5th St, Clifton, AZ 85533
Stacy Armstrong, Case Program Coordinator

COURTS

Superior Court **928.865.3872**
Fax 928.865.5358
Web ....www.courts.sp.state.az.us
223 Fifth St, Clifton, AZ 85533
Honorable Monica L. Stauffer, Director

POLICE AND SHERIFF

Sheriff's Ofc **928.865.4149**
Fax 928.865.4161
Web ....www.co.greenlee.az.us
E-mail ....stucker@co.greenlee.az.us
824 S Coronado Blvd, Clifton, AZ 85533
Steve Tucker, Sheriff

La Paz County

SOCIAL SERVICES

Dept of Economic Security District
V **928.669.9293**
Fax 928.669.8627
E-mail ....jsuchaire@azdes.gov
1032 S Hopi Ave, Parker, AZ 85344
Janice Suchaire, Child Protective Svcs Unit Supervisor

GENERAL HEALTH SERVICES

Health Dept **928.669.1100**
Fax 928.669.6703
Web ....www.co.la-paz.az.us
E-mail ....mshontz@co.la-paz.az.us
1112 S Joshua Ave Ste 206, Parker, AZ 85344-5756
Marion Shontz, Director

JUSTICE AGENCY

Juvenile Court Svcs **928.669.6188**
Fax 928.669.9770
Web ....www.courts.sp.state.az.us
E-mail ....jdyess@courts.sp.state.az.us
1312 S Kofa Ave Ste 501, Parker, AZ 85344-5762
John Dyess, Deputy CPO

COURTS

Superior Court **928.669.6131**
Fax 928.669.2186
E-mail ....snewman@courts.az.gov
1316 S Kofa Ave Ste 607, Parker, AZ 85344
Sheri Newman, Clerk

POLICE AND SHERIFF

Arizona Sheriff's Assoc **928.669.6141**
Fax 928.669.2008
Web ....www.lapazsherrif.org
1109 W Arizona Ave, Parker, AZ 85344-5743
Dawn Lowery, Sheriff

EDUCATION SERVICES

Wacog Ehrenberg-Head Start **928.923.9866**
Fax 928.923.7016
E-mail ....maria@wacog.com
49241 Ehrenberg Poston Hwy, Ehrenberg, AZ 85334
Cecilia Gartia, Manager

Maricopa County

SOCIAL SERVICES

Bureau Of Indian Affairs **602.379.6785**
Fax 602.379.3010
Web ....www.bia.gov
E-mail ....marjorie.eagleman@bia.gov
2600 N Central Ave, Phoenix, AZ 85004
Marjorie Eagleman, Regional Social Worker

Child Protective Svcs **888.767.2445**
Fax 602.530.1832
E-mail ....davidgraham@azdes.gov
PO Box 44240, Phoenix, AZ 85064-4240
David Graham, Program Manager

Child Protective Svcs **602.863.0799**
Fax 602.866.0078
E-mail ....teveritt@azbes.gov
13450 N Black Canyon Hwy Ste 170, Phoenix, AZ 85029
Tracey Everitt, Program Manager

DES District I **602.264.1360**
Fax 602.241.9162
Web ....www.de.state.az.us
E-mail ....gene.burns@mail.de.state.az.us
3221 N 16th St Ste 400, Phoenix, AZ 85016-7153
Gene Burns, ACYF Program Manager

Div Of Child Support Enforcement **602.771.8000**
Fax 602.274.8250
Web ....www.azdes.gov/dcse
E-mail ....vragland@azdes.gov
3443 N Central Ave, Ste 419, Phoenix, AZ 85012
Veronica Ragland, Assistant Director

Div Of Children, Youth And
Families **602.542.3981**
Fax 602.542.3330
Web ....www.azdes.gov
1789 W Jefferson St, # 750A, Phoenix, AZ 85007
Jakki Kolzow, Deputy Director

Div Of Human Svcs **602.506.5911**
Fax 602.506.8789
Web ....www.maricopa.gov/humanservices
234 N Central Ave Ste 3201, Phoenix,
AZ 85004-2256
Trish Georgeff, Director

GENERAL HEALTH SERVICES

Banner Behavioral Health Hospital **480.941.7500**
Fax 480.941.7548
Web ....www.bannerhealth.com
7575 E Earll Dr, Scottsdale, AZ 85251-6998
Patricia Little-upah, CEO

Community Health Nursing **602.506.6767**
Fax 602.506.8444
Web ....www.maricopa.gov
4041 N Central Ave Ste 600, Phoenix,
AZ 85012-3337
Machrina Leach, Director

Dept Of Public Health **602.506.6900**
Fax 602.506.6885
Web ....www.maricopa.gov
14th Floor 4041 N Central Ave, Phoenix, AZ 85012
Bob England, Director

MENTAL HEALTH SERVICES

Arizona State Hospital **602.244.1331**
Fax 602.220.6234
Web ....www.azdhs.gov
2500 E Van Buren St, Phoenix, AZ 85008
C.nelson, CEO

Div Of Behavioral Health Svcs **602.364.2536**
Fax 602.364.4570
150 N 18th Ave Ste 410, Phoenix, AZ 85007
Mary Wiley, Deputy Director

Div Of Developmental Disabilities **602.542.6853**
Fax 602.364.1422
Web ....www.de.state.az.des.gov
1789 W Jefferson St, Fl 4, Phoenix, AZ 85007
Barbara Brett, Assistant Director

JUSTICE AGENCY

CASA Program **602.506.4083**
Fax 602.506.5512
Web ....www.maricopacasa.org
E-mail ....justine@maricopacasa.org
3131 W Durango St, Phoenix, AZ 85009-6217
Justine Grabowsky, Community Outreach Specialist

Juvenile Probation **602.506.4210**
Fax 602.506.8901
Web ....www.juvenile.maricopa.gov
E-mail ....carboo@juvenile.maricopa.gov
3125 W Durango, Mesa, AZ 85210-6235
Carol Boone, Chief JPO

Victim/Witness Program **928.718.4967**
Fax 928.718.4966
325 Pine St, Kingman, AZ 86401
Lisa Samftag, Manager

Arizona

Victim/Witness Program 602.506.8522
Fax 602.506.3942
301 W Jefferson St Fl 9, Phoenix, AZ 85003-2152
Jennifer Heisid, Director

COURTS

Juvenile Court Ctr Durango Facility 602.506.4533
Fax 602.506.1372
Web .... www.superiorcourt.maricopa.gov
3131 W Durango St, Phoenix, AZ 85325
Michael Jeanes, Community Services Director

Juvenile Court Ctr Southeast
Facility 602.506.2544
Fax 602.506.6467
Web .... www.superiorcourt.maricopa.gov
1810 S Lewis, Mesa, AZ 85210-6236
Honorable Eileen Keppel, Director

POLICE AND SHERIFF

Phoenix Police Dept 602.262.7626
Fax 602.495.5620
Web .... www.pheonixpolice.com
E-mail .... jack.harris@phoenix.gov
620 W Washington St, Phoenix, AZ 85003-2186
Jack Harris, Chief

Sheriff's Ofc 602.876.1800
Fax 602.251.3877
Web .... www.mcso.org
E-mail .... h_gonzales@mcso.maricopa.gov
100 W Washington St Ste 1900, Phoenix,
AZ 85003-0615
Joseph M. Arpaio, Sheriff

EDUCATION SERVICES

A.E.S.D #68-Alhambra Opportunity
Klub-Sev 602.242.0281
Fax 602.242.2791
Web www.alhambra.k12.az.us
E-mail .... dstatick@alhambra.k12.az.us
3801 W Missouri Ave, Phoenix, AZ 85019-2133
Debbie Statick, USD Director

Alhambra Head Start Office 602.246.5155
Fax 623.849.1944
Web www.alhambra.k12.az.us
4530 W Campbell Ave, Phoenix, AZ 85031
Geri Martinez, Director

B.T. Washington Child Development Head
Start 602.252.4743
Fax 602.252.4894
E-mail .... kpollins@btwchild.org
1519 E Adams St, Phoenix, AZ 85034
Kim Pollins, Director

City Of Phoenix Head Start 602.262.4040
Fax 602.495.5690
Web .... www.phoenix.gov
E-mail .... patricia.nightangale@phoenix.gov
200 W Washington St, Fl 19, Phoenix, AZ 85003
Patricia Nightangale, Director

Exceptional Students 602.452.4700
Fax 602.452.4720
Web .... www.mcrsd.org
E-mail .... steve.zimmerman@mcrsd.org
358 N 5th Ave, Phoenix, AZ 85003-1508
Steve Zimmerman, Superintendent

Head Start Of Village Meadows 602.467.6400
Fax 602.467.6380
2020 W Morningside Dr, Phoenix, AZ 85023-2360

Phoenix Day School For The Deaf 602.336.6800
Fax 602.336.6944
E-mail .... bknudson@asdb.state.az.us
1935 W Hayward Ave, Phoenix, AZ 85021
Bradley Knudson, Principal

Stevensen Head Start-East Mesa 480.380.1951
638 S 96th St, Rm H-6, Mesa, AZ 85208
Quennie Lucas, Supervisor

Western Valley Elementary-Head Start
Program 623.474.7260
Web .... www.wves.fesd.org
6250 W Durango St, Phoenix, AZ 85043-6580
Vince Madina, Director

Mohave County

SOCIAL SERVICES

Bureau Of Indian Affairs 928.769.2286
Fax 928.769.2444
Web .... www.bia.gov
13067 E Hwy 66, Truxton Canyon Agency, Valentine,
AZ 86437-1127
James Williams, Superintendent

DES District III 928.753.5056
Fax 928.753.5036
Web .... www.azdes.gov
519 E Beale St, Ste 150, Kingman, AZ 86401
Heather Buchanan, Intake Supervisor

DES District IV 928.704.7776
Fax 928.704.7080
Web .... www.azdes.gov
2601 Highway 95, Bullhead City, AZ 86442-7747

COURTS

Superior Court 928.753.0713
Fax 928.753.0781
Web .... www.mohavecourts.com
E-mail .... richard.weiss@co.mohave.az.us
401 E Spring St, Kingman, AZ 86401-5800
Richard Weiss, Presiding Judge

POLICE AND SHERIFF

Sheriff's Ofc 928.753.0753
Fax 928.753.0765
E-mail .... debbie.fransen@co.mohave.az.us
600 W Beale St, Kingman, AZ 86402
Thomas M. Sheahan, Sheriff

Navajo County

SOCIAL SERVICES

DES District III 928.289.3312
Fax 928.289.4446
319 E Third St, Winslow, AZ 86047
Mary Jane Barret, CYF Supervisor

GENERAL HEALTH SERVICES

Health Dept 928.524.4750
Fax 928.524.4754
Web .... www.navahocounty.az.gov
E-mail .... mary.tyler@co.navajo.az.us
117 E Buffalo St, Holbrook, AZ 86025-2605
Mary Tyler, Assistant Health Director

JUSTICE AGENCY

CASA Program 928.524.4135
Fax 928.524.4325
Web .... www.azcasa.org
E-mail .... kgrugel@courts.az.gov
PO Box 668, Holbrook, AZ 86025-0668
Kirk Grugel, Coordinator

Probation Dept 928.524.4197
Fax 928.524.4238
100 East Carter Dr, Holbrook, AZ 86025

Victim/Witness Program 928.524.4332
Fax 928.524.4244
E-mail .... evelyn.marez@navajocountyaz.gov
100 East Carter Road, P O Box 668, Holbrook,
AZ 86025
Evelyn G. Marez, Director Of Victim Services

COURTS

Superior Court 928.524.4188
Fax 928.524.4261
Web .... www.co.navajo.az.us
E-mail .... mrandell@courts.az.gov
100 E Code Tarters Dr, Holbrook, AZ 86025
Marla Randell, Administrator

POLICE AND SHERIFF

Sheriff's Ofc 928.524.4300
Fax 928.524.4773
Web .... www.navajocountyaz.gov
E-mail .... gary.butler@navajocountyaz.gov
137 W Arizona St, Holbrook, AZ 86025-2823
Gary H. Butler, Sheriff

EDUCATION SERVICES

St. John's Head Start 928.337.4211
Fax 928.337.2591
E-mail .... stjohns@nacog.org
245 W 1st St, Snowflake, AZ 85937
Becky Towle, Director

Pima County

SOCIAL SERVICES

Child Protective Svcs Broadway
Ofc 520.884.4755
Fax 520.884.1551
E-mail .... lemon@aol.com
1700 E Broadway Blvd, Tucson, AZ 85719
Sandy Lemon, CPS Supervisor

Child Protective Svcs Eastside Ofc 520.721.3097
Fax 520.721.9446
6840 E Broadway Blvd, Tucson, AZ 85710
Lori Clark, CPS Supervisor

Child Protective Svcs Northside
Ofc 520.887.7577
Fax 520.887.8057
Web .... www.azdes.gov
E-mail .... fjulien@azdes.gov
1075 E Fort Lowell Rd Ste A, Tucson, AZ 85719-2159
Franzie Julien-chinn, CPS Supervisor

Dept Of Economic Security District
II 520.628.6810
Fax 520.628.6862
Web .... www.azdes.gov
E-mail .... lilliandowning@azdes.gov
400 W Congress St Ste 420, Tucson, AZ 85701-1363
Lillian Downing, Cps, Program Manager

GENERAL HEALTH SERVICES

Health Dept 520.740.8261
Fax 520.623.1432
Web .... www.pimahealth.org
E-mail .... ddouglas@mail.healtha.co.pima.az.us
3950 S Country Club Rd Ste 400, Tucson,
AZ 85714-2230
Dennis W. Douglas, Director

Kino Teen Ctr 520.740.4600
Fax 520.740.4621
E-mail .... ssmith@csd.pima.gov
2801 E Ajo Way, Tucson, AZ 85713-6217
Stephanie Smith, Program Coord.

JUSTICE AGENCY

CASA Program 520.740.2060
Fax 520.243.2211
Web .... www.azcasa.org
E-mail .... vanessa.ponce-maez@pcjcc.pima.gov
2225 E Ajo Way, Tucson, AZ 85713-6201
Vanessa Maez, Program Coordinator

Superior Court 925.202.5441
E-mail ....rmstahl@gmail.com
   255 N Granada Ave Apt 12103, Tucson, AZ 85701
Rebecca Stahl

Victim/Witness Program 520.740.5525
Fax 520.628.7306
   32 N Stone Ave, Fl 14, Tucson, AZ 85701
Kent Burbank, Director

COURTS

Juvenile Court Ctr 520.740.2000
Fax 520.243.2222
Web ....www.pcjcc.co.pima.az.us
   2225 E Ajo Way, Tucson, AZ 85713-6295
Rick Schmidt, Director Of Juvenile Court Services

Superior Court 520.740.4217
Fax 520.622.0269
   110 W Congress St, Pima County Superior Court,
   Tucson, AZ 85701
David Sanders, Chief Adult Provision Officer

POLICE AND SHERIFF

Sheriff's Ofc 520.351.4600
Fax 520.351.4789
   1750 E Benson Hwy, Tucson, AZ 85714
Clarence W. Dupnik, Sheriff

Tucson Police Dept 520.791.4444
Fax 520.791.5421
Web ....www.tucsonaz.gov/police
E-mail ....roberto.villasenor@tucsonaz.gov
   270 S Stone Ave, Tucson, AZ 85701-1923
Roberto Villasenor, Chief

EDUCATION SERVICES

Exceptional Students 520.383.6750
Fax 520.383.5970
Web ....www.bia.gov
E-mail ....joefrazier@bia.gov
   PO Box 248, Sells, AZ 85634-0248
Joe Frazier, Superintendent

Pinal County

SOCIAL SERVICES

DES District V 520.836.2351
Fax 520.426.9023
Web ....www.azdes.gov
E-mail ....bwhite@azdes.gov
   2510 N Trekell Rd, Casa Grande, AZ 85122
Beverly White, Assistant

GENERAL HEALTH SERVICES

Div Of Public Health District 520.866.7301
Fax 520.866.7358
Web ....www.co.pinal.az.us
E-mail ....tom.schryer@co.pinal.az.us
   500 So Central, Florence, AZ 85232
Tom Schryer, Director Of Nursing

Health Dept 520.866.7357
Fax 520.866.7322
Web ....www.co.pinal.az.us
E-mail ....denise.keller@co.pinal.az.us
   188 S Main St, Coolidge, AZ 85228-4410
Denise, Director Of Nursing

JUSTICE AGENCY

CASA Program 520.866.7710
Fax 520.866.7081
Web ....www.azcasa.org.
E-mail ....pburke@courts.az.gov
   PO Box 906, Florence, AZ 85232-0906
Pamela Burke, Casa Coordinator

Juvenile Court Svcs 520.866.7065
Fax 520.866.7090
   574 So Central, Florence, AZ 85132
Diane Mcginnis, Director

COURTS

Superior Court 520.866.5300
Fax 520.866.5320
Web ....www.co.pinal.az.us/clerksc
E-mail ....dmcginni@courts.az.gov
   971 Jason Lopes Cir Building A, Florence, AZ 85232
Dianne Mcginnis, Juvenile Services Director

POLICE AND SHERIFF

Sheriff's Office 520.866.6800
Fax 520.866.5195
Web ....www.co.pinal.az.us/sheriff/
   971 N Jason Lopez Circle, Ste C, Florence, AZ 85131
Paul Babeu, Sheriff

EDUCATION SERVICES

CHS Mini Bears Club 520.723.2366
Fax 520.723.2326
Web www.cusd.k12.az.us
E-mail ....kdavis@cusd.k12.az.us
   800 W Northern Ave, Rm 308, Coolidge, AZ 85228
Kevin Davis, Principal

Exceptional Students 520.866.6565
Fax 520.866.6973
E-mail ....oroberts@pinalcso.org
   75 N Bailey St, Florence, AZ 85132
Orlenda Roberts, Superintendent

Santa Cruz County

JUSTICE AGENCY

CASA Program 520.375.7740
Fax 520.375.7741
E-mail ....mfish@courts.sp.state.az.us
   2150 N Congress Dr, Nogales, AZ 85621
Margie Fish, Program Coordinator

Victim Witness Program Court
House 520.375.7800
Fax 520.375.7793
Web ....www.co.santa-cruz.az.us
E-mail ....aarriola@co.santa-cruz.az.us
   2150 N Congress Dr, Ste 201, Nogales, AZ 85621
Augustine Arriola, Director

COURTS

Superior Court 520.375.7700
Fax 520.375.7703
Web ....www.sccazcourts.org
   2150 N Congress Dr, Ste 215, Nogales,
   AZ 85621-1090
Yamin Zeinun-Ostler, Chief Deputy Clerk

POLICE AND SHERIFF

Sheriff's Dept 520.761.7869
Fax 520.375.8118
Web ....www.co.santa-cruz.az.us
E-mail ....sheriff@co.santa-cruz.az.us
   2170 N Hohokam Dr, Nogales, AZ 85621
Tony Estrada, Sheriff

Yavapai County

SOCIAL SERVICES

DES District III 928.649.6800
Fax 928.649.6852
E-mail ....ctrembley@azdes.gov
   1500 E Cherry St Ste B, Cottonwood, AZ 86326
Cindy Trembley, CPS Unit Supervisor

DES District III/CPS 928.277.2825
Fax 928.277.2779
   1519 W Gurley St, Ste 2, Prescott, AZ 86305
Dawn Kimsey, CYF Supervisor

GENERAL HEALTH SERVICES

Health Dept 928.583.1000
Fax 928.771.3369
   1090 Commerce Dr, Prescott, AZ 86305
Sandra Halldorson, RN, Director Of Public Health Services

JUSTICE AGENCY

CASA Program 928.771.3165
Fax 928.771.3387
Web ....www.azcasa.org
E-mail ....tsauer@courts.az.gov
   Courthouse, Room 402, Prescott, AZ 86303
Tracy Sauer, Coordinator

Juvenile Court Svcs 928.771.3156
Fax 928.771.3445
Web ....www.court.sp.state.az.us
E-mail ....smabery@court.sp.state.az.us
   960 Division St, Prescott, AZ 86301-1604
Scott Mabery, Director Of Juvenile Court Services

Victim Svcs 928.771.3485
Fax 928.771.3414
   255 E Gurley St, Prescott, AZ 86301-3803
Pam Moraton, Director

COURTS

Superior Court 928.771.3312
Fax 928.771.3111
   120 S Cortez St, Prescott, AZ 86303
Sandra Markham, Clerk Of Court

Superior Court - Verde Valley Judicial District
Branch 928.567.7741
Fax 928.567.7720
E-mail ....ralph.hess@co.yavapai.az.us
   2840 N CommonWealth Dr, Camp Verde, AZ 86322
Sandra Markham, Clerk Of Court

POLICE AND SHERIFF

Prescott Police Dept 928.777.1988
Fax 928.778.3739
   222 S Marina St, Prescott, AZ 86303
Mike Kabbel, Chief Of Police

Sheriff's Dept 928.771.3291
Fax 928.771.3294
E-mail ....cathy.porteouse@co.yavapai.az.us
   255 E Gurley St, Prescott, AZ 86301
Steve Waugh, Sheriff

EDUCATION SERVICES

Exceptional Students 928.634.7531
Fax 928.639.4236
Web ....www.mingusunion.com
   1801 E Fir St, Cottonwood, AZ 86326-4556
Pamara Addis, Principal

Prescott Unified School 928.445.5400
Fax 928.776.0243
Web ....www.prescottschools.com
E-mail ....dave.smucker@prescottschools.com
   146 S Granite St, Prescott, AZ 86303-4710
Dave Smucker, Superintendent

School District 928.634.2288
Fax 928.634.2309
Web www.cocsd.k12.az.us
E-mail ....patosborne@cocsd.k12.az.us
   1 N Willard St, Cottonwood, AZ 86326
Pat Osborne, Sped Director

Yuma County

GENERAL HEALTH SERVICES

Fort Yuma Indian Hospital 760.572.4100
Fax 760.572.4183
   PO Box 1368, Yuma, AZ 85366-1368
Rhonda Jackson, Nursing Director

Health Dept 928.317.4540
Fax 928.317.4620
  2200 W 28th St, Ste 256, Yuma, AZ 85364
  Martha Rodrieguez, Hiv Case Manager

JUSTICE AGENCY

Court Appointed Special Advocate (CASA)

Program 928.314.1830
Fax 928.317.4598
Web ....www.accasa.org
E-mail ....ppray@co.yuma.az.us
  2440 W 28th St, Yuma, AZ 85364-6955
  Perry Pray, Program Coordinator

COURTS

Juvenile Court Ctr 928.314.1900
Fax 928.726.4720
E-mail ....thardy@courts.az.gov
  2440 W 28th St, Yuma, AZ 85364-7798
  Tim Hardy, Director Of Juvenile Court Services

Superior Court 928.817.4210
Fax 928.817.4211
Web ....www.courts.sp.state.az.us
E-mail ....dgaumon@courts.sp.state.az.us
  250 W 2nd St Ste B, Yuma, AZ 85364-2226
  Honorable Denise Gaumon, Director

POLICE AND SHERIFF

Sheriff's Dept 928.783.4427
Fax 928.329.0309
  141 S 3rd Ave, Yuma, AZ 85364
  Ralph E. Ogden, Sheriff

Yuma Police Dept 928.783.4421
Fax 928.376.6229
Web ....www.yumaaz.gov
E-mail ....jerry.geier@yumaaz.gov
  1500 S 1st Ave, Yuma, AZ 85364
  Jerry Geier, Chief

EDUCATION SERVICES

Exceptional Students 928.502.4300
Fax 928.502.4442
Web ....www.yuma.org
E-mail ....ktams@yumaed.org
  450 W 6th St, Yuma, AZ 85364-2973
  Kitsi Tams, Sped Director

Exceptional Students 928.373.3400
Fax 928.782.6831
E-mail ....srodriguez@craneschools.org
  4250 W 16th St, Yuma, AZ 85364-4031
  Dr. Salvador Rodriguez, Sped Director

SPECIAL SERVICES AGENCIES

ADOPTION AGENCIES

Adoption Specialists Of Arizona 602.248.8248
Fax 602.264.8967
E-mail ....adoptionarizona@aol.com
  1118 E Missouri Ave Ste A1, Phoenix, AZ 85014-2710
  Arghur Rojas, Executive Director

Casey Family Program 520.323.0886
Fax 520.323.6819
Web ....www.casey.org
E-mail ....crodriguez@casey.org
  310 S Williams Blvd Ste 106, Tucson, AZ 85711-4446
  Cat Rodriguez, Supervisor

Casey Family Programs 602.252.9449
Fax 602.252.9665
Web ....www.casey.org
  378 E Palm Ln, Phoenix, AZ 85004
  Susan Hallett, Director

Christian Family Care Agency 602.234.1935
Fax 602.234.0022
Web ....www.cfcare.org
  3603 N. 7th Avenue, Phoenix, AZ 85013-3638
  COA accredited organization.

Dillon Southwest 480.945.2221
Fax 480.945.3956
Web ....www.dillonsouthwest.org
E-mail ....info@dillonsouthwest.org
  3014 N Hayden Rd Ste 101, Scottsdale, AZ 85251-6531
  Marsha Usdane, Director

McCarthy Weston 928.779.4252
Fax 928.779.0243
Web ....www.mccarthyweston.com
  508 N Humphreys St, Flagstaff, AZ 86001-3056
  Janette Smith, Office Manager

Oasis Adoption Svcs, Inc. 520.579.5578
Fax 520.579.5578
Web ....www.oasisadoption.com
E-mail ....cb@oasisadoption.com
  11795 N Via De La Verbenita, Tucson, AZ 85737-7294
  Catherine Braman, Director

ADVOCACY RESOURCES

Brain Injury Association of Arizona 602.508.8024
Fax 602.508.8285
Web ....www.biaaz.org
E-mail ....info@biaaz.org
  5025 E Washington St #108, Phoenix, AZ 85034
  Mattie Cummins, Lmsw, Executive Director

BEHAVIORAL HEALTH TREATMENT

A New Leaf, Inc. 480.969.4024
Web ....www.turnanewleaf.org
E-mail ....dmurillo@turnanewleaf.org
  868 East University Drive, Mesa, AZ 85203
  Mr. Daniel Murillo, Accreditation Manager
  Joint Commission accredited organization.

A New Life-East Valley Community Behavioral Health

Svcs 480.833.9200
Fax 480.969.0039
  1655 E University Dr Ste 100, Mesa, AZ 85203-8170

Achieve Human Svcs 928.341.0335
Fax 928.341.0990
Web ....www.excelgroup.org
E-mail ....ccarr@achievehs.org
  3250 A E 40th St, Yuma, AZ 85365-7748
  Carol Carr, CEO

Advanced Medical Labs 928.344.8525
Fax 928.726.3434
  2435 S Avenue A, Yuma, AZ 85364
  Noman Waked, Director

Advances In Applied Psychology 480.391.1184
Fax 480.391.9717
  9375 E Shea Blvd, Ste 100, Scottsdale, AZ 85260
  Mamiko Odegard, Director

Amy B. Bjorkman LLC 480.688.4987
E-mail ....amybjorkman@cox.net
  10229 N 92nd St, Scottsdale, AZ 85258
  Amy Bjorkman, Director

ANASAZI Foundation 480.892.7403
Web ....www.anasazi.org
E-mail ....julie.jones@anasazi.org
  1424 S. Stapley Dr., Mesa, AZ 85204
  Mrs. Julie Jones, Accreditation Manager
  Joint Commission accredited organization.

Andersen Junior High 480.883.5300
Fax 480.883.5320
E-mail ....laffel.joyce@chandler.k12.az.us
  1255 N Dobson Rd, Chandler, AZ 85224-8541
  Joyce Laffel, Counselor

Area Agency on Aging, Region One 602.264.2255
Fax 602.230.9132
Web ....www.aaaphx.org
  1366 East Thomas Road, Suite 108, Phoenix, AZ 85014
  COA accredited organization.

Arizona's Children Assoc 520.327.7122
Fax 520.327.8231
Web ....www.arizonaschildren.org
E-mail ....jfuhriman@arizonaschildren.org
  3618 E Pima St, Tucson, AZ 85716-3321
  Janet Fuhriman, Director Of Operations

Arizona's Children Assoc 928.443.1991
Fax 928.771.2351
  440 N Washington Ave, Prescott, AZ 86301
  Virginia Health, Regional Director

Arizona's Children Assoc 520.423.8434
Fax 520.423.0323
Web ....www.aca.org
E-mail ....fchaffey@arizonaschildren.org
  360 S Ocotillo Ave, Benson, AZ 85602-6401
  Fred Chaffey, Director

Arizona's Children Assoc 480.503.8530
Fax 480.503.8531
Web ....www.arizonaschildren.org
E-mail ....vyrun@arizonaschildren.org
  2066 W Apache Trl Ste 111, Apache Junction, AZ 85220-3733
  Virginia Yrun, Director Of Organizational Leadership

Arizona's Children Assoc 520.377.0843
Fax 520.761.1272
Web ....www.aca.org
E-mail ....fchaffey@arizonaschildren.org
  156 W Mariposa Rd, Ste 8, Nogales, AZ 85621
  Fred Chaffey, Director

Arizona's Children Association 520.622.7611
Fax 520.624.7042
Web ....www.arizonaschildren.org
  2700 South Eighth Avenue, Tucson, AZ 85713
  COA accredited organization.

Aurora Behavioral Health System 623.344.4400
E-mail ....carolyn.valentine@aurorabehavioral.com
  6015 W Peoria Ave, Glendale, AZ 85302
  Ms. Carolyn Valentine, Accreditation Manager
  Joint Commission accredited organization.

Az Dept Of Corrections 520.574.0024
Fax 520.574.7300
  10000 S Wilmot Rd, Tucson, AZ 85756-8699
  Randall Garland, Director

Behavioral Awareness Center, Inc. 520.629.9126
Fax 520.629.9282
Web ....www.bacmethadone.com
  2002 West Anklam Road, Tucson, AZ 85745
  COA accredited organization.

Blue Ridge High School **928.368.6328**
Fax 928.368.9572
E-mail ....eharmen@brusd.k12.az.us
   1200 W White Mountain Blvd, Lakeside,
   AZ 85929-6532
Eric Harmen, Principal

Blum Medical Practice **520.750.8868**
Fax 520.584.9220
Web ....www.bennettblummd.com
E-mail ....bennettblum@aol.com
   5425 E Broadway Blvd, Tucson, AZ 85711-3704
Bennett Blum, MD, Psychiatrist

Burr Medical Practice **520.325.8485**
   2928 N Orlando Ave, Tucson, AZ 85712-1247
John Burr, MD, Psychiatrist

Camus Clinic For Psychiatry **928.204.1661**
   41 Arrow Dr, Sedona, AZ 86336-6517
Thelma Camus, Md, Psychiatrist

Canyon State Academy **480.987.9700**
Fax 480.987.9701
E-mail ....bheath@riteofpassage.com
   20061 S Rittenhouse Rd, Queen Creek,
   AZ 85242-9715
Brian Heath, Program Director

Carol Collins **928.773.1782**
E-mail ....collins_carol@lacoe.edu
   1133 W Coy Dr, Flagstaff, AZ 86001-8512
Carol Collins, Psychiatrist

Casa de los Niños **520.624.5600**
Fax 520.623.2443
Web ....www.casadelosninos.org
   1101 N. 4th Avenue, Tucson, AZ 85705
COA accredited organization.

Casas Adobes Baptist Church **520.297.7238**
Web ....www.casaschurch.org
E-mail ....chetw@casaschurch.net
   10801 N La Cholla Blvd, Tucson, AZ 85742-8688
Chet Weld, Director

Chicanos Por La Causa **602.257.0700**
Fax 602.256.2740
E-mail ....edmundohildado@cplc.com
   1112 E Buckeye Rd, Phoenix, AZ 85034
Edmundo Hildado, Vice President

Chicanos Por La Causa, Inc **928.425.9244**
Fax 928.425.9249
Web ....www.cplc.org
E-mail ....mayani.jinel@cplc.org
   4443 E Broadway, Claypool, AZ 85532
Mayani Jinel, Director

Chrysalis **602.955.9059**
Web ....www.chrysalis-shelter.org
E-mail ....admin@noabuse.org
   1010 E McDowell Rd Ste 301, Phoenix,
   AZ 85006-2609
Patricia Klahr, Director

Ci Inc **602.495.1432**
E-mail ....ci.inc@att.net
   1117 N 3rd St, Phoenix, AZ 85004-1811
Melissa Jenkins, Director

Cienega High School **520.879.2800**
Fax 520.879.2801
Web www.vail.k12.az.us
   12775 E Mary Ann Cleveland Way, Vail,
   AZ 85641-8600
Tricia Peña, Principal

Cleary Medical Practice **480.946.7917**
   PO BOX 276, Scottsdale, AZ 85252-0276
Michael Cleary, Psychiatrist

CODAC Behavioral Health Services, Inc. **520.327.4505**
Fax 520.202.1889
Web ....www.codac.org
   127 South Fifth Avenue, Tucson, AZ 85701-2044
CARF accredited programs available.

Cohen Medical Practice **602.996.7920**
E-mail ....mariam.cohen@asu.edu
   4810 E Andora Dr, Scottsdale, AZ 85254-3514
Mariam Cohen, MD, Psychiatrist

Collins Medical Practice **602.264.5029**
   300 W Clarendon Ave, Phoenix, AZ 85013
Tracy Collins, Psychiatrist

Community Bridges, Inc. **480.831.7566**
Fax 480.831.7563
Web ....www.communitybridgesaz.org
   1811 South Alma School Road, Suite 160, Mesa,
   AZ 85210
CARF accredited programs available.

Community Counseling Centers, Inc. **928.524.6701**
E-mail ....bhead@ccc-az.org
   105 North Fifth Avenue, Holbrook, AZ 86025
Mr. Brad Head, Accreditation Manager
Joint Commission accredited organization.

Community Counseling Ctr **928.537.2951**
Fax 928.537.4841
Web ....www.ccc-inc.org
   2500 E Show Low Lake Rd, Show Low,
   AZ 85901-7929
Kirsten Hendershot, Program Director

Community Intervention Associates **928.376.0026**
Fax 928.782.2298
Web ....www.ciayuma.com
E-mail ....dlewis@ciayuma.com
   2851 S Ave B Bldg 4, Yuma, AZ 85364-4107
Dureen Lewis, CEO

Concepcion Medical Practice **602.944.9810**
Fax 602.944.1547
   8836 N 23Rd Ave, Phoenix, AZ 85021-4185
Nancy Concepcion, MD, Psychiatrist

Corrections Corp Of America **520.868.3668**
Fax 520.868.3667
Web ....www.correctionscorp.com
   1155 N Pinal Pkwy, Florence, AZ 85132-8867
Marie Rolfsneier, Executive Assistant

Cottonwood De Tucson **520.743.0411**
Fax 520.743.7991
Web ....www.cottonwooddetucson.com
E-mail ....general.information@cottonwooddetucson.com
   4110 W Sweetwater Dr, Tucson, AZ 85745-9348
Fran Moore, MD, Medical Director
CARF accredited programs available.

CRS Psychology **602.406.4000**
   124 W Thomas Rd, Phoenix, AZ 85013-4430
Cynthia Monheim, Psychologist

Daniell Medical Practice **480.324.2400**
   3450 N Higley Rd, Mesa, AZ 85215-9702
Laura Daniell, Md, Psychiatrist

Desert View Counseling **623.487.7763**
Web ....www.desertviewcounseling.com
   13460 N 94th Dr, Ste J 2, Peoria, AZ 85381
George Franco, Counsellor

Desert Visions Youth Wellness Center **520.562.4205**
Web
.........www.ihs.gov/FacilitiesServices/areaOffices/Phoenix.cfm
E-mail ....holly.elliott@ihs.gov
   198 South Skill Center Road, Sacaton, AZ 85247
Ms. Holly Elliott, Accreditation Manager
Joint Commission accredited organization.

Devereux/Arizona - Richard L. Raskin Treatment
Network **480.998.2920**
Web ....www.devereux.org
E-mail ....beicher@devereux.org
   11000 N Scottsdale Rd, Ste 260, Scottsdale,
   AZ 85254
Ms. Brandi Eicher, Accreditation Manager
Joint Commission accredited organization.

Diezdepinos Medical Practice **520.741.2351**
   1210 E Pennsylvania St, Tucson, AZ 85714-1675
Steven Diezdepinos Md, Psychiatrist

Dy Medical Practices SW Network **480.838.5550**
Fax 480.756.8201
   1440 S Country Club Dr Ste 12, Mesa, AZ 85210
Ryan Paulson, Director

EMPACT-SPC **480.784.1514**
Fax 480.967.3528
Web ....www.empact-spc.com
E-mail ....lhartline@empact-spc.com
   1232 East Broadway Road, Suite 120, Tempe,
   AZ 85282
Lynn Hartline, Director of Operations
CARF accredited programs available.

Erie Elementary School **480.812.6300**
Fax 480.812.6320
E-mail ....attaway.jennifer@chandler.k12.az.us
   1150 W Erie St, Chandler, AZ 85224-4387
Jennifer Attaway, Student Service Coordinator

Esteves Medical Practice **602.251.0650**
   1300 N Central Ave, Phoenix, AZ 85004-1722
Joao Esteves, MD, Psychiatrist

Family Svcs Of Conciliation Ct **520.723.3077**
Web ....www.co.pinal.az.us
E-mail ....sue.morris@co.pinal.az.us
   119 W Central Ave, Coolidge, AZ 85228-4405
Sue Morris, Director

Finston Medical Practice **928.771.2190**
Fax 928.445.8210
E-mail ....pfin99@yahoo.com
   101 E Gurley St, Prescott, AZ 86301
Peggy Finston, MD, Psychiatrist

Florence Crittenton Svcs Of Arizona **602.274.7318**
Fax 602.274.7549
Web ....www.florencecrittentonofaz.org
E-mail ....lvolhein@flocrit.org
   715 W Mariposa St Ste A, Phoenix, AZ 85013-2449
Linda Volhein, Executive Director

Free Arts Of AZ **602.258.8100**
Fax 602.258.1881
E-mail ....info@freeartsaz.org
   103 W Highland Ave Ste 200, Phoenix, AZ 85013
Barbara Fenster, Executive Director

Friedland Medical Practice **480.391.1821**
   10250 N 92nd St, Scottsdale, AZ 85258
Steven Friedland, MD, Psychiatrist

Guidance Ctr **928.635.4272**
Fax 928.635.9143
Web ....www.tgcaz.org
   220 W Grant, Williams, AZ 86046-2324
Marilyn Mcnabb, Director

Healthcare Southwest **520.458.8767**
Fax 520.458.8767
   1827 Paseo San Luis, Sierra Vista, AZ 85635
David Ruben, MD, Psychiatrist

Helping Associates, Inc. **520.836.1029**
Web ....www.helpingassociates.com
E-mail ....jmcgillicuddy@helpingassociates.com
   1901 North Trekell Road, Ste A, Casa Grande,
   AZ 85122
Dr. Joan McGillicuddy, Accreditation Manager
Joint Commission accredited organization.

Horizon Human Services, Inc. **520.836.1688**
Web ....www.horizonhumanservices.org
E-mail ....dpfohl@horizonhumanservices.org
   210 East Cottonwood Lane, Casa Grande, AZ 85122
Mr. David Pfohl, Accreditation Manager
Joint Commission accredited organization.

Horizon Human Svcs **520.723.9800**
Fax 520.723.3345
E-mail ....nmudd@horizonhumanservices.org
   5497 W McCartney Rd, Coolidge, AZ 85128
Norman Mudd, Director

Horizon Human Svcs **520.836.1688**
Fax 520.421.2708
210 E Cottonwood Ln, Casa Grande, AZ 85122
Norman Mudd, Director

Horizon Human Svcs **928.402.9099**
Fax 928.402.8032
Web ....www.horizonhumanservices.org
E-mail ....tmurray@horizonhumanservices.org
1100 N Broad St Ste A, Globe, AZ 85501-2700
Tim Murray, Information Systems Director

Horizon Human Svcs- Peart Iv **520.876.1796**
Fax 520.836.1675
Web ....www.horizonhumanservices.org
E-mail ....mhutchison@horizonhumanservices.org
2271 S Peart Rd, Casa Grande, AZ 85222-8545
Mike Hutchison, Rehabilitation Director

**Horizon Human Svcs-Hagen Hill Out-Patient
Clinic** **928.402.9297**
Fax 928.402.9414
Web ....www.horizonhumanservices.org
E-mail ....bholiday@horizonhumanservices.org
415 W Easeline Spur, Globe, AZ 85502
Billy Holiday, Assistant Director

Horizon Human Svcs-Peart Iv **520.836.1688**
Fax 520.836.4046
E-mail ....rrusiecki@horizonhumanservices.org
2271 S Peart Rd, Casa Grande, AZ 85122
Ronda Rusiecki, Program Supervisor

Jewish Family And Children's Svcs **602.279.7655**
Fax 602.253.7065
Web ....www.jfcsaz.org
E-mail ....michael.venz@jfcsaz.org
4747 N 7th St Ste 100, Phoenix, AZ 85014
Michael Venz, Director

La Frontera Center, Inc. **520.838.5600**
Fax 520.792.0654
Web ....www.lafrontera.org
E-mail ....bmagnotto@lafrontera.org
504 West 29th Street, Tucson, AZ 85713
Bill Magnotto, Director of Housing
CARF accredited programs available.

La Frontera Ctr **520.884.9920**
Fax 520.792.0654
Web ....www.lafrontera.org
E-mail ....dranieri@lafrontera.org
502 W 29th St, Tucson, AZ 85713-3394
Dan Ranieri, Director

La Frontera Ctr, Inc **520.838.3804**
Fax 520.792.0654
Web ....www.lafrontera.org
E-mail ....kpeterson@lafrontera.org
2222 N Craycroft Rd, Ste 120, Tucson,
AZ 85712-2830
Kayla Peterson, Director

Little Colorado Behavioral Health Centers **928.337.4301**
Web ....www.lcbhc.org
E-mail ....mdowns@lcbhc.org
470 W. Cleveland, Saint Johns, AZ 85936
Mr. Michael Downs, Accreditation Manager
Joint Commission accredited organization.

**Mingus Mountain Estate Residential Center,
Inc.** **602.335.2000**
Web ....www.mmaaz.com
E-mail ....rst.romain@mmaaz.com
15801 E. Don Carlos Drive, Prescott Valley, AZ 86315
Mr. Reggie St. Romain, Accreditation Manager
Joint Commission accredited organization.

Mirasol, Inc. **520.546.3200**
Fax 520.546.3205
Web ....www.mirasol.net
10490 E Escalante Rd, Tucson, AZ 85730
Dawn Bantel, Medical Director
CARF accredited programs available.

Mohave Mental Health **928.718.4800**
Fax 928.718.5666
Web ....www.mmhc-inc.org
E-mail ....rengel@mmhc-inc.org
2002 Stockton Hill Rd Ste 104, Kingman, AZ 86401
Rene Engel, Facility Manager

Mohave Mental Health **928.855.3432**
Fax 928.855.0103
Web ....www.mmhc-inc.org
E-mail ....jeff@mmhc-inc.org
2187 Swanson Ave, Lake Havasu City,
AZ 86403-6838
Jeff Oeake, Facility Manager

Mohave Mental Health Clinic, Inc. **928.757.8111**
Web ....mmhc-inc.org
E-mail ....bedelblu@mmhc-inc.org
1743 Sycamore Avenue, Kingman, AZ 86409
Mrs. Bonnie Edelblute, Accreditation Manager
Joint Commission accredited organization.

**Northern Arizona Regional Behavioral Health Ofc Of Client
Svcs** **928.774.7128**
Fax 928.774.5665
Web ....www.narbha.org
E-mail ....mick.pattinson@narbha.org
1300 S Yale St, Flagstaff, AZ 86001-6328
Mick Pattinson, Executive Director

Pantano Behavioral Health Svcs **520.623.9833**
Fax 520.623.9083
Web ....www.pantanobh.org
E-mail ....sguthery@pantanobh.org
5055 E Broadway Blvd Ste C104, Tucson,
AZ 85711-3641
Steve Guthery, Director Human Resources

Parc Place **480.917.9301**
Web ....www.parc-place.com
E-mail ....cynthia.tyler@yfcs.com
2190 North Grace Boulevard, Chandler, AZ 85225
Ms. Cynthia Tyler, Accreditation Manager
Joint Commission accredited organization.

**Park Place Outreach and Counseling Centers,
Inc.** **520.466.8850**
Fax 520.466.8851
9373 West Battaglia Road, Arizona City, AZ 85223
CARF accredited programs available.

**Pascua Yaqui Tribe New Beginnings Opioid Treatment
Program** **520.879.6060**
Fax 520.879.6099
Web http://notescl.pascuayaqui-nsn.gov:8008/
7490 South Camino de Oeste, Centered Spirit,
Tucson, AZ 85746
Stephen Hall, Director
CARF accredited programs available.

Pinal Hispanic Council **520.466.7765**
Web ....www.pinalhispaniccouncil.org
E-mail ....eflores@pinalhispaniccouncil.org
712 North Main Street, Eloy, AZ 85231
Ms. Elizabeth Flores, Accreditation Manager
Joint Commission accredited organization.

Pinal Hispanic Council **520.723.7405**
Fax 520.723.7410
Web ....www.pinalhispaniccouncil.org
E-mail ....jdozoretz@pinalhispaniccouncil.org
556 S Arizona Blvd, Coolidge, AZ 85228-5106
John Telles, Director

Providence Svc Corp. **520.744.4376**
Fax 520.579.1138
Web ....www.provcorp.com
3295 W Ina Rd Ste150, Tucson, AZ 85741
Sherry Barughton, Supervisor

Providence Svc Corp. **602.455.4626**
Fax 602.455.4624
Web ....www.provcorp.com
E-mail ....cjones@provcorp.com
3602 W Thomas Rd, Phoenix, AZ 85019
Carmen Jones, Administrator

Recovery Innovations, Inc. **602.650.1212**
Web ....www.recoveryinnovations.org
E-mail ....andrew.terech@recoveryinnovations.org
2701 N. 16th Street, Suite 316, Phoenix, AZ 85006
Mr. Andrew Terech, Accreditation Manager
Joint Commission accredited organization.

Remuda Ranch **928.684.3913**
Web ....www.remudaranch.com
E-mail ....nancy.stokes@havenbehavioral.com
One East Apache Street, Wickenburg, AZ 85390
Ms. Nancy Stokes, Accreditation Manager
Joint Commission accredited organization.

**Remuda Ranch Programs For Eating and Anxiety
Disorders** **800.445.1900**
Fax 928.684.4507
Web ....www.remudaranch.com
E-mail ....info@remudaranch.com
1 E Apache St, Wickenburg, AZ 85390
Dr. David Wall, Director Psychology Services

Rosewood Ranch L.P. **928.684.9594**
Web ....www.rosewoodranch.com
E-mail ....lsalmons@aurorabehavioral.com
36075 South Rincon Road, Wickenburg, AZ 85390
Ms. Lori Salmons, Accreditation Manager
Joint Commission accredited organization.

SEABHS-Psychiatric Health Facility **520.586.7737**
Fax 520.586.7939
Web ....www.seabhs.org
E-mail ....ramona_smith@seabhssolutions.org
470 S Ocotillo Ave, Benson, AZ 85602
Ramona Smith, Administrator

Sideman Medical Practices **602.216.3104**
E-mail ....lsideman@argosy.edu
10269 N Central Ave, Phoenix, AZ 85020-1051
Lawrence Sideman, Director

**SouthEastern Arizona Behavioral Health Services,
Inc.** **520.586.0800**
Fax 520.586.0116
Web ....www.seabhs.org
611 West Union Street, Benson, AZ 85602
CARF accredited programs available.

**Southeastern Arizona Behavioral Health Svcs (SEABHS)
Outpatient** **928.428.4550**
Fax 928.428.4588
Web ....www.seabhs.org
1615 S 1st Ave, Safford, AZ 85546
Jim Rubio, Director

**Southeastern Arizona Behavioral Health Svcs (SEABHS) Youth
And Family Ctr** **520.458.3932**
Fax 520.458.2021
Web ....www.seabhs.org
4755 Campus Dr, Sierra Vista, AZ 85635
Dr. Gary Oberg, Director

**Southeastern Arizona Behavioral Health Svcs (SEABHS) Youth
And Family Ctr** **520.459.2290**
Fax 520.459.5372
Web ....www.seabhs.org
4755 Campus Dr, Sierra Vista, AZ 85635-2528
Gary Oberg, Director

**Southern Arizona Mental Health
Corporation** **520.617.0043**
Web ....www.samhc.com
E-mail ....grover.glenn@samhc-crisis.org
2502 North Dodge Boulevard, Suite 190, Tucson,
AZ 85716
Mr. Grover Glenn, Accreditation Manager
Joint Commission accredited organization.

Southwest Behavioral Health Services 602.257.9339
Fax 602.265.8574
Web ....www.sbhservices.org
E-mail ....christinem@sbhservices.org
  3450 North Third Street, Phoenix, AZ 85012-2331
  Christine Montague, Director Community & Youth Development Prevention Program
  CARF accredited programs available.

Spring Ridge Academy 928.632.4602
Fax 928.632.7661
Web ....www.springridgeacademy.com
E-mail ....info@springridgeacademy.com
  13690 S Burton Rd, Mayer, AZ 86333-4245
  Joseph Gubbins, Academic Director

St Luke's Behavior Health Ctr 602.251.8535
Fax 602.251.8707
Web ....www.stlukesmedcenter.com
E-mail ....gjahn@stlukesmedcenter.com
  1800 E Van Buren St, Phoenix, AZ 85006-3702
  Greg Jahn, CMO

St. Luke's Behavioral Hospital, LP 602.251.8808
Web ....www.stlukesbehavioralhealth.com
E-mail ....dbrandt@iasishealthcare.com
  1800 East Van Buren, Phoenix, AZ 85006
  Ms. Deborah Brandt, Accreditation Manager
  Joint Commission accredited organization.

Stephen Stewart Psychiatry 928.978.4490
  1006 N Whitehouse Dr, Payson, AZ 85541-3451
  Stephen Stewart, Psychiatrist

TERROS, Inc. 602.685.6000
Fax 602.265.6973
Web ....www.terros.org
  3003 North Central Avenue, Suite 200, Phoenix, AZ 85012
  CARF accredited programs available.

The Arizona Council Of Human Svc
Providers 602.252.9363
Fax 602.252.8664
Web ....www.azcouncil.com
E-mail ....info@azcouncil.com
  2100 N Central Ave Ste 225, Phoenix, AZ 85004
  David F. Miller, CEO

The Guidance Center, Inc. 928.527.1899
Web ....www.tgcaz.org
E-mail ....rhays@tgcaz.org
  2187 North Vickey Street, Flagstaff, AZ 86004
  Ms. Rebekah Hays, Accreditation Manager
  Joint Commission accredited organization.

The New Foundation 480.945.3302
Web ....thenewfoundation.org
E-mail ....jkiesel@thenewfoundation.org
  1200 North 77th Street, Scottsdale, AZ 85257
  Mr. Jim Kiesel, Accreditation Manager
  Joint Commission accredited organization.

Touchstone Behavioral Health 623.930.8705
Web ....www.touchstonebh.org
E-mail ....susan.pullen@touchstonebh.org
  15648 N. 35th Ave, Phoenix, AZ 85053
  Ms. Susan Pullen, Accreditation Manager
  Joint Commission accredited organization.

UBH of Phoenix LLC 940.320.8994
Web ....www.ascendhealth.net
E-mail ....nstarr@ascendhealth.net
  3550 East Pinchot, Phoenix, AZ 85018
  Ms. Nikki Starr, Accreditation Manager
  Joint Commission accredited organization.

Valle del Sol, Inc. 602.258.6797
Fax 602.248.8113
Web ....www.valledelsol.com
  3807 North Seventh Street, Phoenix, AZ 85014
  CARF accredited programs available.

Verde Valley Guidance Clinic, Inc. 928.634.2236
Web ....www.verdevalleyguidanceclinic.com
E-mail ....laurar@vvgclinic.org
  8 East Cottonwood Street, Cottonwood, AZ 86326
  Mrs. Laura Robinson, Accreditation Manager
  Joint Commission accredited organization.

Via Linda Senior Ctr 480.312.5810
E-mail ....kaetymyers@gov
  10440 E Via Linda, Scottsdale, AZ 85258-6088
  Kaety Myers, Manager

Vistacare 520.378.6466
Fax 520.378.6553
Web ....www.vistacare.com
E-mail ....kheindel@sierrasummitacademy.com
  4120 E Ramsey Rd, Hereford, AZ 85615-8917
  Kris Heindel, Executive Director

West Yavapai Guidance Clinic 928.445.5211
Web ....www.wygc.org
E-mail ....p.pierce@wygc.org
  505 South Cortez Street, Prescott, AZ 86303
  Ms. Pamela Pierce, Accreditation Manager
  Joint Commission accredited organization.

Wright Medical Practice 928.213.5600
Fax 928.774.2801
  1515 N San Francisco St, Flagstaff, AZ 86001
  B Cody Wright, MD, Psychiatrist

Yavapai Family Advocacy Ctr 928.775.0669
Fax 928.759.0474
Web ....www.yfac.org
  8485 E Yavapai, PrescottValley, AZ 86312
  Katharyn Chapman, Director

Youth Development Institute 602.256.5300
Web ....www.ydi.org
E-mail ....trish.cocoros@ydi.org
  1830 East Roosevelt Street, Phoenix, AZ 85006
  Ms. Trish Cocoros, Accreditation Manager
  Joint Commission accredited organization.

CHILDREN'S HOSPITAL

Banner Del E Webb Medical Center 623.214.4000
  14502 West Meeker Blvd, Sun City West, AZ 85375
  John Harrington, Chief Executive Officer

Banner Thunderbird Medical Center 602.865.5555
E-mail ....tom.dickson@bannerhealth.com
  5555 West Thunderbird Rd, Glendale, AZ 85306
  Tom Dickson, Chief Executive Officer

Carondelet Holy Cross Hospital 520.285.3000
  1171 West Target Range Rd, Nogales, AZ 85621

Casa Grande Regional Medical Center 520.381.6300
  1800 East Florence Blvd, Casa Grande, AZ 85222
  Rebina Becky, Chief Executive Officer

Flagstaff Medical Center 928.779.3366
  1200 North Beaver St, Flagstaff, AZ 86001
  Joanne Parkes, Director

John C Lincoln Deer Valley Hospital 623.879.6100
  19829 N 27th Ave, Phoenix, AZ 85027
  Bruce Pearson, Chief Executive Officer

Kingman Regional Medical Center 928.757.2101
  3269 Stockton Hill Rd, Kingman, AZ 86409
  Brian Turney, Chief Executive Officer

Lttle Colorado Medical Center 928.289.4691
  1501 Williamson Ave, Winslow, AZ 86047
  Jeff Hamblen, Chief Executive Officer

Maricopa Medical Center 602.344.5011
  2601 East Roosevelt St, Phoenix, AZ 85008
  Betsey Bayless, President/CEO

Payson Regional Medical Center 928.474.3222
  807 South Ponderosa St, Payson, AZ 85541
  Chris Wolfe, Chief Executive Officer

Phoenix Childrens Hospital 602.546.1000
  1919 East Thomas Rd, Phoenix, AZ 85016

Phoenix Veterans Affairs Health CareSys 602.277.5551
  650 E Indian School Rd, Phoenix, AZ 85012

Scottsdale Healthcare Shea Medical Ctr 480.323.3000
  9003 East Shea Blvd, Scottsdale, AZ 85260
  Tom Sadvary, Chief Executive Officer

Sierra Vista Regional Health Center 520.458.4641
  300 El Camino Real, Sierra Vista, AZ 85635
  Margaret Hetburn, Chief Executive Officer

St Josephs Hospital and Medical Center 602.406.3000
  350 West Thomas Rd, Phoenix, AZ 85013
  Linda Hunt, Chief Executive Officer

Tuba City Regional Hospital 928.283.2501
E-mail ....joseph.angleken@tchealth.org
  167 Main St, Tuba City, AZ 86045
  Joseph Angleken, Chief Executive Officer

Tucson Medical Center 520.327.5461
  5301 East Grant Rd, Tucson, AZ 85712

University Medical Center 520.694.0111
  1501 N Campbell Ave, Tucson, AZ 85724
  Karen Mlazsky, Chief Executive Officer

US Public Health Srv Indian Hospital 928.338.4911
  200 West Hospital Dr, Whiteriver, AZ 85941
  Michelle Martinez, Chief Executive Officer

Verde Valley Medical Center 928.639.6000
  269 South Candy Ln, Cottonwood, AZ 86326
  James Bleicher, President

Yuma Regional Medical Center 928.344.2000
  2400 South Avenue A, Yuma, AZ 85364
  Pat Walz, Chief Executive Officer

COUNSELING SERVICES

ABCS Eastern Regional Ctr 928.536.4760
Fax 928.536.4769
E-mail ....abcs@cableone.net
  1016 S Main St, Snowflake, AZ 85937
  Elaine Gaston, Director

ABCS Southwestern Regional Ctr 928.726.5568
Fax 928.726.5583
E-mail ....svanhorn@abcsyuma.org
  2855 S 4th Ave Ste 122, Yuma, AZ 85364-8189
  Sheryl Vanhorn, Administrator

Arizona Baptist Children's Svcs 520.795.7541
Fax 520.795.7581
E-mail ....hanna@abcs.org
  1779 N Alvernon Way, Tucson, AZ 85712-3301
  Steve Hanna, Director

Arizona Children's Assoc 928.344.8800
Fax 928.344.8837
Web ....www.arizonaschildren.org
  3780 S 4th Ave Ste K, Yuma, AZ 85365-4539
  Sheryl Derby, Director

Arizona Children's Assoc. 602.234.3733
Fax 602.234.1252
Web ....www.arizonaschildren.org
E-mail ....metcheverry@arizonaschildren.org
  2833 N 3rd St, Phoenix, AZ 85004-1003
  Marilyn Etcheverry, Grant Writer

Child & Family Resources 520.325.5778
Fax 520.325.8780
Web ....www.azchildcare.org
E-mail ....cfr@cfraz.org
  2800 E Broadway Blvd, Tucson, AZ 85716-5310
  Eric Schindler, Executive Director

Christian Family Care Agency 602.234.1935
Fax 602.234.0022
Web ....www.cfcare.org
E-mail ....info@cfcare.org
  3603 N 7th Ave, Phoenix, AZ 85013-3638
  Mark Upton, President

Devereux Arizona **480.998.2920**
Fax 480.443.5587
Web ....www.devereuxarizona.org
  11000 N Scottsdale Rd Ste 260, Scottsdale,
  AZ 85254-6200
  Lane Barker, Executive Director

Family Svc Agency **602.264.9891**
Fax 602.234.2639
Web ....www.fsaphoenix.org
E-mail ....sorrel@fsaphoenix.org
  2400 N Central Ave, Ste 400, Phoenix,
  AZ 85004-1315
  Sorrel Bowman-rogers, President/CEO

LDS Family Svcs Of Mesa **480.968.2995**
Fax 480.967.4103
E-mail ....fam-ga@ldschurch.org
  235 S El Dorado Cir, Mesa, AZ 85202-1044
  Michelle Hooper, Director

Omega Counseling Svcs **602.495.9306**
Fax 602.495.9931
Web ....www.omegacounseling.net
  5800 N 19th Ave #117, Phoenix, AZ 85004-2051
  Elizabeth Sedano, Director

CRISIS & SHELTER CARE

A New Leaf **480.969.4024**
Fax 480.969.0039
Web ....www.turnanewleaf.org
E-mail ....mhughes@prehab.org
  868 E University Dr, Mesa, AZ 85203-8033
  Michael Hughes, CEO

**ABCS Little Canyon Residential Treatment
Ctr** **602.346.2300**
Fax 601.346.2399
Web ....www.abcs.org
E-mail ....jelder@abcs.org
  1717 W Northern Ave, Phoenix, AZ 85021-5469
  John Elder, President

Against Abuse Inc. **520.836.1239**
Fax 520.836.7757
Web ....www.against-abuse.org
E-mail ....aai@against-abuse.org
  119 N Florence St, Casa Grande, AZ 85122
  Patricia Griffen, Executive Director

**Ama Doo Alchini Bighan- Domestic
Violence** **928.674.8314**
Fax 928.674.8218
E-mail ....adabi87@yahoo.com
  Hwy 191, Chinle, AZ 86503
  Lorena Halwoac, Director

Amberly's Place **928.373.0849**
Fax 928.373.0852
E-mail ....dianedumphress@AmberlysPlace.Com
  1350 W Colorado St, Frnt, Yuma, AZ 85364
  Diane Umphress, Director

**Autumn House- Domestic Violence
Program** **480.835.5555**
Fax 480.844.1183
E-mail ....dmartinez@turnanewleas.org
  868 E University Dr, Mesa, AZ 85203-8033
  Dana Martinez, Director

Casa De Los Ninos, Inc. **520.624.5600**
Fax 520.623.2443
Web ....www.casadelosninos.org
E-mail ....info@casadelosninos.org
  1101 N 4th Ave, Tucson, AZ 85705-7467
  Susie Huhne, Executive Director

**Centro De Amistad-Domestic Violence
Program** **480.839.2926**
Fax 480.839.9985
  8202 S Avenida Del Yaqui, Guadalupe, AZ 85283
  Rita Marie Monroy, President and CEO

Child & Family Svcs Of Yuma **928.329.9005**
Fax 928.783.0633
Web ....www.cfsyuma.com
E-mail ....info@cfsyuma.com
  257 S 3rd Ave, Yuma, AZ 85364-2359
  Judy Smith, Director

Child Crisis Ctr **480.969.2308**
Fax 480.969.9277
Web ....www.childcrisis.org
E-mail ....kidsfirst@childcrisis.org
  604 W 9th St, Mesa, AZ 85201
  Christine Scarpati, Executive Director

Chrysalis Shelter-Domestic Violence **602.944.4999**
Fax 602.944.9619
Web ....www.noabuse.org
E-mail ....chrysalis@noabuse.org
  303 E Vogel Ave, Phoenix, AZ 85020-2048
  Angela Stewart, Director

**Chrysalis Shelter-Domestic Violence
Program** **602.944.4999**
Fax 602.944.9619
Web ....www.noabuse.org
E-mail ....Chrysalis@noabuse.org
  8201 E Osborn Rd, Scottsdale, AZ 85251
  Angie Swart, Director

Colorado River Reg Dom Crisis Shelter **928.669.0107**
Fax 928.669.5377
E-mail ....dperez@crrcs.com
  1301 Joshua st ste C, Parker, AZ 85344-1643
  Denise Perez, Director

Crisis Nursery Inc **602.273.7363**
Fax 602.244.1316
Web ....www.crisisnurseryphx.org
E-mail ....mporter@crisisnurseryphx.org
  2334 E Polk St, Phoenix, AZ 85006-3916
  Marsha Porter, Executive Director

Emerge Centre Against Domestic Abuse **520.795.8001**
Fax 520.795.1559
Web ....www.emergecenter.org
E-mail ....info@Emergecenter.Org
  2545 E Adams St, Tucson, AZ 85716
  Sarah Jones, CEO

Family Advocacy Ctr-Domestic Violence **602.534.2120**
Fax 602.534.2122
Web ....www.phoenix.gov
E-mail ....joann.del-colle@phoenix.gov
  2120 N Central Ave Ste 250, Phoenix,
  AZ 85004-1453
  JoAnn Del-Colle, Director

Hopi Domestic Violence Program **928.738.1115**
Fax 928.738.1119
Web ....www.hopicourts.com
  PO Box 1226, Keams Canyon, AZ 86034-0306
  Crystal Russell, Director

Hopi Guidance Ctr **928.737.2665**
Fax 928.737.2697
  86043 Hopi Guidance Ctr, Second Mesa, AZ 86043
  Lorence Sekayomptewa, Director

**House Of Hope- Domestic Violence
Program** **520.364.2465**
Fax 520.364.4061
E-mail ....house.hope@hotmail.com
  PO Box 1218, Douglas, AZ 85608-1218
  Charles Fisher, Coordinator

Indian Health Svcs Domestic Violence Prg **520.295.2400**
Fax 520.295.2593
  7900 S J Stock Rd, Tucson, AZ 85746-7012
  George Bearpaw, Director

Kingman Aid To Abused People **928.753.6222**
Fax 928.753.2590
E-mail ....kaap@citlink.net
  2701 E Andy Divine Ste 103 A, Kingman, AZ 86401
  Suzanne Clarke, Director

**Mount Graham, Safe House- Domestic
Violence** **928.348.9104**
Fax 928.424.4438
E-mail ....Mgshinc@vtc.net
  1601S 20th Ave, Safford, AZ 85546-4009
  Jeanette Aston, Executive Director

New Life Ctr-Domestic Violence **623.932.4404**
Fax 623.536.1147
E-mail ....pdenial@newlifectr.org
  PO Box 5005, Goodyear, AZ 85338-0608
  Paul Denial, Executive Director

Northland Family Help Ctr **928.527.1900**
Fax 928.774.5809
Web ....www.northlandfamily.org
  2724 N Steves Blvd, # 5274288, Flagstaff, AZ 86004
  Sonja Burkhalter, Executive Director

Open-Inn **520.670.9040**
Fax 520.670.9101
E-mail ....npanico@openinn.org
  630 E 9th St, Tucson, AZ 85705
  Nancy Panico, Executive Director

Page Regional Domestic Violence Svcs **928.645.5300**
Fax 928.645.3414
E-mail ....anotherway@cableone.net
  835 Newborn Rd, Page, AZ 86040
  Katherine Reusing, Director

**Prehab Of Arizona La Mesita Family
Shelter** **480.834.8723**
Fax 480.834.8784
Web ....www.prehab.org
E-mail ....cjohnson@prehab.org
  2254 W Main St, Mesa, AZ 85201-6806
  Candace Johnson, Vice President Of Emergency And Shelter Services

Safe Home **928.402.0648**
Fax 928.402.9020
Web ....www.horizonhumanservices.org
E-mail ....domesticviol@Horizonhumanservices.Org
  415 W Baseline Spur, Globe, AZ 85502
  Dr. Fred Karst, Director

Safe House Of Bullhead City **928.763.7233**
Fax 928.763.7015
Web ....www.westcare.com
E-mail ....tstevens@westcare.com
  1610 Riverview Dr Ste 12, Bullhead City,
  AZ 86442-7556
  Tracy Stevens, Director

Safe House Of Yuma- Domestic Violence **928.782.0077**
Fax 928.819.0112
Web ....www.ccs-westaz.org
  690 E 32nd St, Yuma, AZ 85365-3437
  Sis. Betty Adams, Director

**Sarah's House-Child & Family Advocacy
Ctr** **928.757.8103**
Fax 928.757.8135
Web ....www.co.mohave.az.us
E-mail ....Sarahshousebnb@Yahoo.Com
  1770 Airway Ave, Kingman, AZ 86409-3621
  Gene Jackson, Office Manager

**Save The Family- Domestic Violence
Program** **480.898.0228**
Fax 480.898.9007
Web ....www.savethefamily.org
E-mail ....janicep@savethefamily.org
  450 W 4th Pl, Mesa, AZ 85201
  John Lamkin, Chief Operations Officer

Sojourner Ctr-Domestic Violence Program **602.244.0997**
Fax 602.244.8006
  357 N 4th Ave, Phoenix, AZ 85036
  Connie Phillips, Director

Time Out Inc, Domestic Violence Shelter 928.472.8007
Fax.................................928.472.8747
Web ....www.cybertrails.com
E-mail ....toshelt@npgcable.com
PO Box 306, Payson, AZ 85547-0306
Gerry Bailey, Director

Tohdenasshai Shelter Home-Domestic
Violence 928.697.3635
Fax.................................928.697.8592
Web ....www.npgcable.com
E-mail ....Toshelt@Npgcable.Com
PO Box 1510, Kayenta, AZ 86033-1510
Geraldine Laughter, Director

Verde Valley Sanctuary Domestic Violence 928.634.2511
Fax.................................928.634.3690
E-mail ....jhausner@sedona.net
PO Box 595, Sedona, AZ 86339-0595
Jane Hausner, Director

White Mountain Safe House-Domestic
Violence 928.367.6017
Fax.................................928.367.0223
Web ....www.safehouse.org
E-mail ....sasafehouse@frontier.com
1450 E. White Mountain Road, Pinetop, AZ 85935
Hugh Kealer, Director

Youth Development Institute 602.254.0884
Fax.................................602.258.4033
E-mail ....david.cocoros@ydi.org
1830 E Roosevelt St, Phoenix, AZ 85306
David Cocoros, CEO

Youth Evaluation & Treatment Ctrs 602.285.5550
Fax.................................602.285.5551
Web ....www.youthetc.org
E-mail ....joleson@youthetc.org
4414 N 19th Ave, Phoenix, AZ 85015
Jim Oleson, Executive Director

EDUCATION

Accel School..............................602.995.7366
Fax.................................602.995.0867
Web ....www.accel.org
E-mail ....claird@accel.org
10251 N 35th Ave, Phoenix, AZ 85051-1305
Connie Laird, Director

Arizona Project/Challenge 480.988.4100
Fax.................................480.988.4121
Web ....www.azpc.org
20395 S Rittenhouse Rd, Queen Creek,
AZ 85242-7080

Ctr For Education Equity & Language
Diversity 480.965.7134
Fax.................................480.965.5164
Web ....www.asu.edu/educ/sceed
E-mail ....josue@asu.edu
PO Box 871511, Tempe, AZ 85287-1511
Josue Gonzales, Executive Director

Desert Dove Farm, Inc......................520.296.0320
Web ....www.desertdovefarm.net
E-mail ....gandolfi@theriver.com
9640 E Elm Tree Circle, Tucson, AZ 85749
Faye Gandolfi, Director

Parenting Arizona 602.248.0428
Fax.................................602.248.0496
Web ....www.parentingaz.org
E-mail ....andrea.martinez@parentingaz.org
6741 N 7th St, Phoenix, AZ 85014-1004
Andrea Martinez, Executive Director

Visionquest National, Ltd. Corporate
Headquarters 520.881.3950
Fax.................................520.881.3269
600 N Swan Rd, Tucson, AZ 85711-2102
Pete Renalli, CEO

FOSTER CARE AGENCIES

Aid to Adoption of Special Kids 602.254.2275
Fax.................................602.212.2564
E-mail ....info@aask-az.org
2320 N 20th St, Phoenix, AZ 85006

APlace to Call Home (APCH) 480.456.0549
Fax.................................480.456.0553
1830 S Alma School Rd, Ste 122, Mesa, AZ 85210

Arizona Adoptive Families Support Group 480.451.9831
10926 N 128th Pl, Scottsdale, AZ 85259

Arizona Assoc for Foster & Adoptive
Parent 602.488.2374
Fax.................................602.485.1810
E-mail ....kris@azafap.org
2320 N 20th St, Phoenix, AZ 85006
Kris Jacober, President

Arizona Families for Children 520.327.3324
Fax.................................520.881.0768
1011 N Craycroft, Ste 470, Tucson, AZ 85711

Arizona's Children 928.680.4458
Fax.................................928.680.9724
Web ....www.arizonaschildren.org
E-mail ....jgreen@arizonaschildren.org
296 London Bridge Rd Ste A, Lake Havasu City,
AZ 86403-4669
Jeniffer Green, Family Development Manager

Arizonans For Children 480.895.0189
Fax.................................480.491.0197
E-mail ....kaye.mccarthy@fosterangelsaz.org
1020 N Horne, Mesa, AZ 85203
Kaye Mccarthy, President

Children With AIDS Project of America 480.774.9718
Fax.................................480.921.0449
2409 S Rural Rd, Ste B-1, Tempe, AZ 85282

Christian Family Care Agency (CFCA) 520.296.8255
Fax.................................520.296.8773
E-mail ....susan@cfcare.org
6063 E Grant Rd, Tucson, AZ 85712

Christian Family Care Agency Inc (CFCA) 602.234.1935
E-mail ....info@cfcare.org
3603 N 7th Ave, Phoenix, AZ 85013
Mark Upton, President

Foster Care Info Line 520.795.1858
Fax.................................520.795.4948
1011 N Craycroft Rd Ste 404, Tucson, AZ 85711
Judy Taylor, Secretary

Foster Parents Legal Solutions 928.427.0088
Fax.................................928.427.0421
E-mail ....fplegalsolutions@gmail.com
608 Ghost Town Rd, Congress, AZ 85332
Marilyn Harrison, Administrator

Hand in Hand International Adoptions 520.745.1322
Fax.................................520.745.1343
E-mail ....arizona@hihiadopt.org
2910 W Bayleaf Dr, Ste 108, Tucson, AZ 85741

LDS Family Services of Snowflake 928.536.4117
E-mail ....fam-az-snowflake@ldschurch.org
641 S Main, Snowflake, AZ 85937

Southwest Adoption Services (SWAS) 480.380.6248
Fax.................................480.986.2618
E-mail ....mrubin@swadoption.com
7254 E Southern Ave, Ste 123, Mesa, AZ 85209
Mariann Rubin, Executive Director

HOME MEDICAL EQUIPMENT PROVIDERS

Ability Center 623.879.0800
Fax.................................623.879.0822
23606 N 19th Ave, Phoenix, AZ 85085
Mark Dean, Site Manager

American Southwest CPM & Medical Supply,
Inc..............................602.957.4700
Fax.................................602.264.9015
21617 North Third Avenue, Suite A, Phoenix,
AZ 85027
CARF accredited programs available.

OxiMedical Respiratory 866.696.9558
E-mail ....angela@oximedical.com
3102 W Thomas Rd Ste 901, Phoenix, AZ 85017
Larry Pellerato, Manager

Redman Power Chair 800.727.6684
1674 S Research Loop # 402, Tucson, AZ 85710

Western Spinal Center, PLLC 623.334.9689
Fax.................................623.334.9687
8751 North 51st Avenue, Suite 124, Glendale,
AZ 85302
CARF accredited programs available.

PEDIATRIC HOME CARE

Bayada Nurses 520.885.5100
Fax.................................520.546.5786
Web ....www.bayada.com
6367 East Tanqueverde Road, Suite 140, Tucson,
AZ 85715

Bayada Nurses 602.870.6364
Fax.................................602.997.8893
Web ....www.bayada.com
706 East Bell Road, Suite 101, Phoenix, AZ 85022
Mary Hayth, Director

Bayada Nurses 520.721.0056
Fax.................................520.721.9111
Web ....www.bayada.com
6367 East Tanque Verde Road, Suite 130, Tucson,
AZ 85715
Pam Sensky, Director

Bayada Nurses 480.820.1700
Fax.................................480.831.8067
Web ....www.bayada.com
40 West Baseline Rd, Suite 216, Tempe, AZ 85283
Jeff Stone, Director

Bayada Nurses 520.531.0020
Fax.................................520.531.8400
Web ....www.bayada.com
7070 North Oracle Rd, Ste 110, Tucson, AZ 85704
Cindy Sheller, Director

Bayada Nurses 520.721.8800
Fax.................................520.721.5007
Web ....www.bayada.com
6367 East Tanque Verde Road, Suite 150, Tucson,
AZ 85715
Marlene Deakins, Director

Bayada Nurses 520.648.7170
Fax.................................520.531.8400
Web ....www.bayada.com
7070 North Oracle Road, Suite 110, Tucson,
AZ 85704
Cindy Sheller, Chief Executive Officer

Interim Healthcare 520.747.1800
Fax.................................520.747.0138
5055 E Broadway Ste D104, Tucson, AZ 85711
Daren York, Business Manager

Interim Healthcare 602.443.0111
Fax.................................602.443.0110
8125 N 23rd Ave Ste 221, Phoenix, AZ 85021
Greg Korpita, Owner

SOCIAL SERVICES

Arizona Children's Assoc 623.583.2523
Fax.................................623.583.2671
Web ....www.arizonaschildren.org
E-mail ....lgavin@arizonaschildren.org
11327 W Bell Rd Ste 300, Surprise, AZ 85378
Latricia Gavin, Program Supervisor

Arizona Children's Assoc 520.458.2131
Fax 520.459.2959
Web ....www.arizonaschildren.org
E-mail ....jschmitt@arizonaschildren.org
400 W Fry Blvd Ste 11, Sierra Vista, AZ 85635-1760
Judith Schmitt, Program Coordinator

Arizona Children's Assoc 928.402.8046
Fax 928.402.8025
Web ....www.arizonaschildren.org
E-mail ....malonzo@arizonaschildren.org
2123 Sunset Point, Ste A-B, Globe, AZ 85502
Melanie Alonzo, Director

Arizona Children's Assoc 480.814.7789
Fax 480.963.3294
Web ....www.arizonaschildren.org
E-mail ....jmason@arizonaschildren.org
2775 N Arizona Ave Ste 4, Chandler, AZ 85225-7700
Jill Mason, Director

Arizona Right To Life 602.285.0063
Fax 602.285.0082
Web ....www.azrtl.org
E-mail ....azrtl@azrtl.org
3333 N 44th St Ste 4, Phoenix, AZ 85016-6532
Virginia Perron, President

Assoc For Supportive Child Care 602.244.2678
Fax 480.820.7288
Web ....www.arizonachildcare.org
E-mail ....mjohnson@asccaz.org
3910 S Rural Rd Ste E, Tempe, AZ 85282-5567
Melody Johnson, Marketing Director

Catholic Charities 928.778.2531
Fax 928.776.8568
Web ....www.catholiccharitiesaz.org
434 W Gurley St, Prescott, AZ 86301
Cathy Peterson, Director

Catholic Charities Community Services 602.650.4836
Fax 602.285.0311
Web ....www.catholiccharitiesaz.com
4747 N. 7th Avenue, Phoenix, AZ 85013-2401
COA accredited organization.

Catholic Community Svcs Of Southern Arizona 520.623.0344
Fax 520.770.8578
Web ....www.ccs-soaz.org/css.htm
140 W Speedway Blvd Ste 130, Tucson, AZ 85705-7687
Ronald A. Dankowski, Director

Catholic Social Svcs 602.285.1999
Fax 602.285.9470
Web ....www.catholicsocialserviceaz.org
E-mail ....bbrown@diocesephoenix.org
4747 N 7th Ave, Phoenix, AZ 85013-2401
Bob Brown, CEO

Catholic Social Svcs Of Central And Northern Arizona 602.997.6105
Fax 602.285.0311
Web ....www.cc.az.org
E-mail ....css_communications@diocesephoenix.org
1825 W Northern Ave, Phoenix, AZ 85021-5260
Carrie Mascaro, Regional Director

Child & Family Resources, Inc. 520.881.8940
Fax 520.325.8780
Web ....www.childfamilyresources.org
2800 East Broadway Boulevard, Tucson, AZ 85716
COA accredited organization.

Childhelp Children's Ctr Of Arizona 602.271.4500
Fax 602.282.0102
Web ....www.childhelpusa.org
E-mail ....mdomogala@childhelpusa.org
2346 N Central Ave, Phoenix, AZ 85004
Marinne Domogala, Director

Childhelp USA National Child Abuse Hotline 480.922.8212
Fax 480.922.7061
Web ....www.childhelpusa.org
E-mail ....lhenderson@childhelp.org
15757 N 78th St Ste C, Scottsdale, AZ 85260-1680
John Reid, Executive Director

Ctr Against Family Violence 480.644.4075
Fax 480.644.4084
Web ....www.cityofmesa.org
130 N Robson, Mesa, AZ 85201-6609
Lt. Patrick Foster, Director

Dillon Southwest 480.945.2221
Fax 480.945.3956
3014 North Hayden Road, #101, Scottsdale, AZ 85251
COA accredited organization.

Empowerment Systems, Inc. 480.367.6937
Fax 480.982.7320
Web ....www.pgbha.org
E-mail ....jbeveridge@emsysonline.com
2066 W Apache Trl Ste 116, Apache Junction, AZ 85120
Ellen Summo, Director, Greater Valley Area Health Education Center

Family Support Resources 623.931.9300
Fax 623.931.9822
Web ....www.fsrfamily.com
E-mail ....mgreen@fsrfamily.com
5800 W Glenn Dr Ste 200, Glendale, AZ 85301-2481
Alta Douglas, Executive Director

Florence Crittenton Services of Arizona 602.274.7318
Fax 602.274.7549
Web ....www.florencecrittentonofaz.org
715 West Mariposa Street, Phoenix, AZ 85013
COA accredited organization.

Fresh Start Womens Resource Ctr 602.252.8494
Fax 602.257.9692
E-mail ....chansonhebert@fswf.org
1130 E Mcdowell Rd, Phoenix, AZ 85006-2611
Barbara Ralston, Interim CEO

ICAN: Improving Chandler Area Neighborhoods 480.821.4207
Fax 480.821.6742
Web ....www.icanaz.org
201 South Washington Street, Chandler, AZ 85225
COA accredited organization.

Jewish Family & Children's Service, Inc. 602.279.7655
Fax 602.241.5756
Web ....www.jfcsaz.org
4747 N. 7th Street, Suite 100, Phoenix, AZ 85014
COA accredited organization.

Jewish Family & Childrens Services of S Ariz 520.795.0300
Fax 520.795.8206
E-mail ....jfcsinfo@jfcstucson.org
4301 E 5th St, Tucson, AZ 85711
Shira Ledman, Director

Jewish Family And Children's Svcs 602.279.7655
Fax 602.253.7065
Web ....www.jfcsaz.org
4747 N 7 St #100, Phoenix, AZ 85014
Michael Zent, Director

Jewish Family and Childrens Service 602.452.4627
Fax 602.452.4679
E-mail ....kathy.rood@jfcsarizona.com
4747 North 7th St Ste 100, Phoenix, AZ 85014
Kathy Rood

JFCS Catalina Behaviroal Health Site 602.343.0703
Fax 602.353.0715
3306 W Catalina Dr, Phoenix, AZ 85017

JFCS Center for Life Enrichment 602.923.1694
Fax 602.923.1913
4545 East Shea Blvd Ste 174, Phoenix, AZ 85028

JFCS Glendale Behaviroal Health Site 623.486.8202
Fax 623.486.2739
5701 W Talavi Blvd, Glendale, AZ 85306
Alicia Woodbury, Operations Coordinator

JFCS Homebased Program 602.257.9314
Fax 602.254.8824
2033 North 7th St, Phoenix, AZ 85006
Thomas Bigelow, Director

JFCS Mesa Behavioral Health Site 480.820.0825
Fax 480.820.7863
1930 S Alma School Rd Ste A104, Mesa, AZ 85210

JFCS Real World Development 602.279.0084
Fax 602.274.3452
5625 North 7th St, Phoenix, AZ 85014

JFCS Senior Center 602.943.2198
Fax 602.943.2241
1118 West Glendale Ave, Phoenix, AZ 85021

Our Family Services, Inc. 520.323.1708
Fax 520.323.9077
Web ....www.ourfamilyservices.org
3830 East Bellevue Street, Tucson, AZ 85716
COA accredited organization.

Parent Support Ctr 602.506.6339
Fax 602.506.6444
E-mail ....geraldineboone@mail.maricopa.gov
1645 E Roosevelt St, Phoenix, AZ 85006-3638
Geraldine Boone, Director

Parenting Arizona 928.773.9133
Fax 928.773.0075
Web ....www.parentingaz.org
E-mail ....kathy.vandenberg@parentingaz.org
201 E Birch Ave Ste 1, Flagstaff, AZ 86001
Cathy Vandenberg, Regional Manager

Phoenix Job Corps Ctr 602.322.2886
Fax 602.322.7087
518 S 3rd St, Phoenix, AZ 85004-2599
Alvin Fort, Center Director

Steele Memorial Children's Research Ctr 520.626.5170
Fax 520.626.7176
Web ....www.peds.arizona.edu
E-mail ....fghishan@peds.arizona.edu
1501 N Campbell Ave, Tucson, AZ 85724-5073
Fayez Ghishan, MD, Dept. Head

The Irving Greenfield Tucson Loan Chest 520.624.3367
Fax 520.624.5228
E-mail ....tboiling@jfcstucson.org
3919 E Pima St, Tucson, AZ 85712
Tim Boiling, Director

Tumbleweed Center for Youth Development 602.271.9904
Fax 602.271.0240
Web ....www.tumbleweed.org
E-mail ....rgeasland@tumbleweed.org
1419 N 3rd St Ste 102, Phoenix, AZ 85004-1639
Richard Geasland, Director

UMOM New Day Centers 602.275.7852
Fax 602.275.6548
Web ....www.umom.org
3333 E. Van Buren Street, Phoenix, AZ 85008
COA accredited organization.

Youth Evaluation & Treatment Centers (YETC) 602.285.5550
Fax 602.285.5551
Web ....www.youthetc.org
4414 North 19th Avenue, Phoenix, AZ 85015
COA accredited organization.

SPECIAL NEEDS

Academic Behavioral Alternatives &
Cenpa **520.885.9567**
Fax 866.925.3009
Web ....www.abaschools.com
　7400 N Oracle Rd Ste 143, Tempe, AZ 85283
　Erik Ryan, Director

Arizona Alliance for the Mentally Ill **602.244.8166**
E-mail ....namiaz@namiaz.org
　5025 E Washington St, Phoenix, AZ 85034
　Susan Junck, Director

Arizona Congress of Parents & Teachers **602.279.1811**
E-mail ....azpta@andiamo-tel.com
　2721 N 7th Ave, Phoenix, AZ 85007

Arizona Spina Bifida Association Inc **602.274.3323**
E-mail ....office@azspinabifida.org
　1001 E Fairmont Ave, Phoenix, AZ 85014

ARSHA **602.354.8062**
E-mail ....office@arsha.org
　PO Box 12334, Tempe, AZ 85284

Autism Society of Greater Phoenix **480.940.1093**
E-mail ....info@phxautism.org
　PO Box 10543, Phoenix, AZ 85064

Brain Injury Association of Arizona **602.508.8024**
E-mail ....info@biaaz.org
　5025 E Washington st ,ste 108, Phoenix, AZ 85034
　Mattie Cummins, Director

Down Syndrome Network Inc **480.759.9150**
Fax 480.759.9180
E-mail ....info@dsnetworkaz.org
　4025 E Chandler Blvd # 70-C3, Phoenix, AZ 85048
　Michele Fiorenza, President

Easter Seals Arizona **800.626.6061**
E-mail ....frontdesk@azseals.org
　2075 S cottonwood Dr, Tempe, AZ 85282

Epilepsy Foundation of Arizona **888.768.2690**
E-mail ....efaz@chw.edu
　240 Thomas Rd 2nd Fl, Phoenix, AZ 85013
　Mark Valentino, Chief Executive Officer

Foundation for Blind Children **602.331.1470**
E-mail ....info@seeitourway.org
　1235 E Harmont Dr, Phoenix, AZ 85020
　Mark Ashton, Chief Executive Officer

LearningRx Learning Center **480.855.9099**
E-mail ....chandler.az@learningrx.ne t
　565 W Chandler Blvd Ste 116, Chandler, AZ 85225

Life Development Institute **623.773.2774**
Fax 623.773.2788
E-mail ....info@life-development-inst.org
　18001 N 79th Ave E-71, Glendale, AZ 85308
　Rob Crawford, Director

Lindamood-Bell Learning Processes **480.922.5675**
Fax 480.922.5785
　10617 N Hayden Rd Bldg B, Ste 101, Scottsdale,
　AZ 85260
　Jennifer Freenan, Office Manager

Mental Health Association of Arizona **480.994.4407**
E-mail ....andya@mikid.org
　6411 E Thomas Rd, Scottsdale, AZ 85251
　Andy Arnowitz, Coordinator

National Multiple Sclerosis Society **480.968.2489**
Fax 480.966.4049
E-mail ....Info@Aza.NMSS.org
　5025 E Washington St Ste 102, Phoenix, AZ 85034
　Jim Elsline, President

Parent Information Network **877.230.7467**
E-mail ....becky.raabe@azed.gov
　2384 N Steves Blvd, Flagstaff, AZ 86004
　Becky Raabe, Director

Pilot Parents of Southern Arizona **877.365.7220**
E-mail ....lynn@pilotparents.org
　2600 N Wyatt Dr, Tucson, AZ 85712
　Lynn Kallis, Executive Director

PIMA Prevention Partnership **520.791.2711**
Fax 520.791.2202
　3130 E Broadway Blvd, Ste 180, Tucson, AZ 85716

Raising Special Kids **800.237.3007**
E-mail ....info@raisingspecialkids.org
　5025 E Washington St Ste 204, Phoenix, AZ 85034
　Joyce Millard Hoie, Director

Rehab Without Walls - A Gentiva
Company **602.943.1012**
Fax 602.943.2075
Web ....www.rehabwithoutwalls.com
　7227 North 16th Street, Suite 107, Phoenix,
　AZ 85020
　CARF accredited programs available.

Save the Family Foundation of Arizona **480.898.0228**
Fax 480.898.9007
Web ....www.savethefamily.org
　450 W. 4th Place, Mesa, AZ 85201
　COA accredited organization.

Sharing Down Syndrome **480.926.6500**
Web ....www.sharingds.com
E-mail ....info@sharingds.org
　745 N Gilbert Rd # 124, Gilbert, AZ 85234
　Gina Johnson, Director

Sierra Academy Of Scottsdale **480.767.8659**
Fax 480.767.9776
E-mail ....dspotleson@sierra-school.com
　17800 N Perimeter Dr, Ste 110, Scottsdale, AZ 85255
　Debbie Spotleson, Administrative Assistant

Southwest Autism Research & Resource
Ctr **602.340.8717**
E-mail ....sarrc@autismcenter.org
　300 N 18th St, Phoenix, AZ 85006

St Josephs Hospital and Medical Center **602.406.6000**
Fax 602.406.4608
E-mail ....shafeeq.ladha@chw.edu
　500 W Thomas Rd Ste 710, Phoenix, AZ 85013
　Shafeeq Ladha Md, Director

St. Joseph's Hospital and Medical Center/Barrow Neurological
Institute **602.406.6715**
Fax 602.406.4969
Web ....www.ichosestjoes.com
　350 West Thomas Road, Phoenix, AZ 85013-4409
　CARF accredited programs available.

The Arc of Arizona **866.501.2721**
E-mail ....thearcaz@gmail.com
　3839 N 3rd St Ste 105, Phoenix, AZ 85012

United Cerebral Palsy of Central Arizona **602.943.5472**
E-mail ....info@ucpofaz.org
　1802 W Parkside Ln, Phoenix, AZ 85027
　Armando Contreras, Executive Officer

University Physicians Healthcare **520.874.2747**
Fax 520.874.2742
E-mail ....kscherer @uph.org
　2800 E Ajo Way, Tucson, AZ 85713
　Katalin Scherer MD

VSA Arts of Arizona **520.795.6502**
E-mail ....vsaaz@vsaaz.org
　3321 N Chapel Ave, Tucson, AZ 85716

SUBSTANCE ABUSE TREATMENT

Anasazi Foundation **480.892.7403**
Fax 480.892.6701
Web ....www.anasazi.org
E-mail ....mike@anasazi.org
　1424 S Stapley Dr, Mesa, AZ 85204
　Virginia Robinson, Admissions Director

Desert Visions Youth Wellness Ctr/Rtc (Indian Health
Svc) **520.562.8801**
Fax 520.562.3415
Web ....www.ihs.gov
E-mail ....holly.elliot@ihs.gov
　198 S. Skill Rd., Sacaton, AZ 85147
　Holly Elliott, CEO

In Balance Ranch Academy **520.722.9631**
Fax 520.722.9676
Web ....www.inbalranch.com
E-mail ....sdexter@inbalranch.com
　6107 E Grant Rd, Tucson, AZ 85712-5828
　Shannon Dexter, Director

The San Carlos Apache Tribe - Wellness
Center **928.475.4875**
Fax 928.475.4880
　5 San Carlos Blvd, San Carlos, AZ 85550
　Dr. Gail Sims, Executive Director
　CARF accredited programs available.

Arizona

Arkansas

Mike Beebe, Governor
State Capitol, Room 250
Little Rock, AR 72201
501.682.2345
501.682.1382 (Fax)
www.governor.arkansas.gov

Gwendolyn Trigleth-Jackson, Juvenile Justice Specialist
700 Main St
Box 1437, S503
Little Rock, AR 72203-1437
501.683.2191
gwen.trigleth-jackson@arkansas.gov

Jerry Walsh, SAG Chair
124 S Jackson, Ste 308
Magnolia, AR 71753
870.234.6550
jkwalsh@sbcglobal.net

CRISIS NUMBERS

Child Abuse Reporting . . .800.482.5964   Domestic Violence 800.269.4668

STATE SERVICES

SOCIAL SERVICES

Arkansas Dept of Human Svcs (ADHS) 501.682.1001
Fax 501.682.6836
Web . . . . .www.arkansas.gov/dhs
South Slot S201, Little Rock, AR 72203
John Selig, Director

Arkansas Emergency Management Agency . . .501.683.6700
Fax 501.683.7890
Web . . . . .www.adem.arkansas.gov
E-mail .david.maxwell@adem.arkansas.gov
9501 Building Camp Joseph T Robinson, North Little Rock, AR 72199-9600
David Maxwell, Director

Child Support Enforcement 501.682.8398
Fax 501.682.6002
Web . . . . .www.childsupport.arkansas.gov
400 E Capitol Ave, Little Rock, AR 72203
Dan Mcdonald, Administrator

Dept Of Human Svcs 870.598.2282
Fax 870.598.5764
E-mail .duane.dutka@arkansas.gov
187 N 2nd Ave, Piggott, AR 72454-2022
Duane Dutka, DHS County Administrator

Div of C C and Early Childhood Edu AR 501.682.8590
Fax 501.682.2317
Slot S 140, Slot S 140, Little Rock, AR 72203
Tanya Rusell, Director

Div of Children and Family Svcs 501.682.8008
Fax 501.682.6968
Web . . . .http://www.state.ar.us/dhs/chilnfam/ind ex.htm
E-mail .cecilia.blucker@arkansas.gov
700 Main St, Little Rock, AR 72201-4608
Cecilia Blucker, Director

GENERAL HEALTH SERVICES

Children with Special Health Needs 501.682.2277
Fax 501.682.8247
E-mail .nancy.holder@arkansas.gov
700 Main St Slot S380, PO Box 1437, Little Rock, AR 72203
Nancy Holder, Director

Marternal and Child Health AR 501.661.2480
Fax 501.661.2464
E-mail .bradley.planey@arkansas.gov
4815 W Markham St, Slot H 16, Little Rock, AR 72205
Bradley Planey, Director

MENTAL HEALTH SERVICES

Div of Svcs for the Blind AR 501.682.5463
Fax 501.682.0366
E-mail .donna.walker@arkansas.gov
700 Main St, Little Rock, Little Rock, AR 72201
Donna Walker, Director

JUSTICE AGENCY

Arkansas Correctional School 870.267.6725
Fax 870.267.6731
E-mail .dubs.byers@arkansas.gov
8000 Correction Circle, Pine Bluff, AR 71603
Dubs Byers, Director

Arkansas Dept Of Corrections 870.267.6999
Fax 870.267.6258
Web . . . . .www.state.ar.us/doc
E-mail .ray.hobbs@arkansas.gov
6814 Princeton Pike, Pine Bluff, AR 71602
Ray Hobbs, Director

Crime Victims Reparations Board 501.682.2007
Fax 501.682.5313
Web . . . . .www.ag.state.ar.us
E-mail .oag@arkansas.gov
323 Center St Ste 200, Little Rock, AR 72201-2619
Honorable Dustin Mcdaniel, Attorney General

Dept of Human Svcs Div of Youth Svcs 501.682.8654
Web . . . . .www.arkansas.gov
700 Main St, Little Rock, AR 72201

POLICE AND SHERIFF

Arkansas Sheriff's Assoc 501.758.0020
Fax 501.791.0326
Web . . . . .www.arkansassheriffsassociation.com
E-mail .clange123@aol.com
1 Sheriffs Ln, North Little Rock, AR 72114
Chuck Lange, Executive Director

EDUCATION SERVICES

AR Department of Education 501.682.4204
Fax 501.682.1079
Four State Capitol Mall, Rm 304A, Little Rock, AR 72201
Dr. Tom Kimbrell, Director

Arkansas Dept Of Education 501.682.4786
Fax 501.682.1079
Web . . . . .www.arkansased.org
E-mail .tom.kimbrell@arkansas.gov
4 Capitol Mall, Little Rock, AR 72201-1019
Dr. Tom Kimbrell, Commissioner

Arkansas Disability Coalition 501.614.7020
Fax 501.614.9082
E-mail .adcoalition@earthlink.net
1123 S University Ave Ste 225, Little Rock, AR 72204
Wanda Stovall, Executive Director

Arkansas School For The Blind 501.296.1810
Fax 501.296.1831
Web . . . . .www.arkansasschoolfortheblind.org
2600 W Markham St, Little Rock, AR 70023
Jim Hill, Superintendent

Arkansas School for the Deaf 501.324.9506
Fax 501.324.9553
Web . . . . .www.arkansas.gov/asd
E-mail .mikep@asd.k12.ar.us
2400 W Markham St, Little Rock, AR 72205-6199
Mike Phillips, Superintendent

Even Start/Homeless Programs 501.682.4847
Fax 501.682.5136
Web www.arkedu.k12.ar.us
E-mail .chogue@arkedu.k12.ar.us
4 Capitol Mall, Little Rock, AR 72201-1013
Cindy Hogue, Program Advisor

Head Start Assoc 501.371.0740
Fax 501.370.9109
Web . . . . .www.arheadstart.org
E-mail .deanah@arheadstart.org
1400 W Markham St Ste 406, Little Rock, AR 72201-1844
Deana Howell, Service Manager

Special Education 501.682.4225
Fax 501.682.4313
Web www.arksted.k12.ar.us
E-mail .marie.dukes@arkansas.gov
1401 W Capitol Ave Ste 450, Little Rock, AR 11906
Sandra Reifeiss, Director Of Early Childhood

Special Education unit AR 501.682.4221
Fax 501.682.5159
E-mail .marie.dukes@arkansas.gov
1401 W Capitol Ave, Victory Bldg Ste 450, Little Rock, AR 72201
Marie Dukes, Director

LABOR & WORKFORCE EDUCATION

Arkansas Workforce Investment Board 501.371.1022
Fax 501.371.1030
E-mail .sandra.winston@arkansas.gov
PO Box 2981, Little Rock, AR 72203-2981
Colette Honorable, Executive Director

COUNTY SERVICES

Arkansas County

SOCIAL SERVICES

Dept Of Human Svcs 870.946.4519
Fax 870.946.4510
Web ....www.arkansas.gov
E-mail ....jessica.evans@arkansas.gov
   100 Court Sq, De Witt, AR 72042-2049
Jessica Evans, Administrator

Dept Of Human Svcs 870.673.3597
Fax 870.673.6591
Web ....www.arkansas.gov
E-mail ....deborah.hteverson@arkansas.gov
   203 S Leslie St, Stuttgart, AR 72160-4340
Deborah Halvorson, Children & Family Services Supervisor

GENERAL HEALTH SERVICES

Health Dept 870.946.2934
Fax 870.946.4463
   1616 S Madison St, De Witt, AR 72042
Chastiti Letine, Hiv Coordinator

POLICE AND SHERIFF

Sheriff's Ofc 870.946.3161
Fax 870.946.1715
Web ....www.centurytel.net
E-mail ....acarcosheriff@centurytel.net
   1000 Rice Belt Ave, De Witt, AR 72042-3486
Allen Cheek, Sheriff

Ashley County

SOCIAL SERVICES

Dept Of Human Svcs 870.853.9816
Fax 870.853.9819
   201 W Lincoln St, Hamburg, AR 71646-2905
Doris Smith, Administrator

GENERAL HEALTH SERVICES

Arkansas Health Dept 870.364.2115
Fax 870.364.3505
   1300 W 5th Ave, Crossett, AR 71635-2500
Eddra Young, Rn, Hiv/aids Coordinator

Health Dept 870.853.5525
Fax 870.853.4433
   401 N Cherry St, Hamburg, AR 71646
Tammy Cook, Administrator

POLICE AND SHERIFF

Sheriff's Ofc 870.853.2040
Fax 870.853.0017
   842 Ashley Road 12 W, Hamburg, AR 71646
Marilyn Smith, Chief Deputy

EDUCATION SERVICES

Crossett Head Start 870.364.8640
E-mail ....chs8640@windstream.net
   708 Main St, Crossett, AR 71635
Mary Jones, Director

Baxter County

SOCIAL SERVICES

Dept Of Human Svcs 870.425.6011
Fax 870.424.5186
Web ....www.arkansas.gov
E-mail ....marcia.anglani@mail.state.ar.us
   204 Bucher Dr, Mountain Home, AR 72653-3400
Marcia Anglani, Supervisor

GENERAL HEALTH SERVICES

Health Unit 870.425.3072
Fax 870.424.6646
Web ....www.healthyarkansas.net
   206 Bucher Dr, Mountain Home, AR 72653
Judy Martin, Administrator

COURTS

14th Judicial Circuit Court 870.425.8625
Fax 870.425.8630
E-mail ....judgeisbell@ozarkmountains.com
   301 E 6th St Ste 154, Mountain Home,
   AR 72653-3903
Honorable Gary Isbell, Court Judge

POLICE AND SHERIFF

Sheriff's Ofc 870.425.7000
Fax 870.424.4048
E-mail ....sheriff@baxtercountysheriff.com
   904 Highway 62 W, Mountain Home, AR 72653
John Montgomery, Sheriff

EDUCATION SERVICES

Cotter Head Start Ctr 870.435.5040
   210 Lucille St, Cotter, AR 72626
Susanna Hardman, Director

Benton County

SOCIAL SERVICES

Dept Of Human Svcs 479.273.9011
Fax 479.273.9055
   900 SE 13th Ct, Bentonville, AR 72712
Preston Haley, Administrator

JUSTICE AGENCY

Juvenile Probation 479.271.1047
Fax 479.271.5700
Web ....www.co.benton.ar.us
   203 E Central Ave, Bentonville, AR 72712-5304
Petie Cobb, Probation Officer

COURTS

19th Judicial Circuit Court 479.271.1020
Fax 479.271.5752
E-mail ....bridley@co.benton.ar.us
   203 E Central Ave, Bentonville, AR 72712
Honorable Jay Finch, Judge

POLICE AND SHERIFF

Sheriff's Ofc 479.271.1008
Fax 479.273.0036
Web ....www.co.benton.ar.us
E-mail ....kferguson@co.benton.ar.us
   1300 SW 14th St, Bentonville, AR 72712-3632
Keith Ferguson, Sheriff

EDUCATION SERVICES

Bentonville Head Start 479.273.2496
Fax 479.273.2496
Web ....www.nwaheadstart.org
E-mail ....kdunfee@nwaheadstart.org
   802 NW A St, Bentonville, AR 72712-4733
Kathy Dunfee, Director

Decatur Head Start 479.752.3704
Fax 479.752.3704
   363 E Jo Ave, Decatur, AR 72722-9432
Maria Upshaw, Director

Boone County

SOCIAL SERVICES

Dept Of Human Svcs 870.741.6107
Fax 870.741.6198
   2126 Capps Rd, Harrison, AR 72601-3944
Jerry Jones, Administrator

GENERAL HEALTH SERVICES

Health Dept 870.743.5244
Fax 870.743.6003
   1622 Campus Ave, Harrison, AR 72601
Debbie Johnson, Administrator

JUSTICE AGENCY

CASA 14th Judicial District 870.743.2212
Fax 870.365.3837
E-mail ....casa@casa14.com
   200 E Rush Ave, Harrison, AR 72601
Jana Cowgill, President

POLICE AND SHERIFF

Sheriff's Ofc 870.741.8404
Fax 870.741.6038
E-mail ....boonecosheriff@alltel.net
   5800 Law Dr, Harrison, AR 72601-3722
Danny Hickman, Sheriff

EDUCATION SERVICES

Flippin Head Start Ctr 870.453.7112
   209 Alford St, Flippin, AR 72602
Diane Miller, Teacher

Bradley County

SOCIAL SERVICES

Dept Of Human Svcs 870.226.5879
Fax 870.226.5631
Web ....www.state.ar.us
E-mail ....dorothy.henderson@mail.state.ar.us
   902 Halligan St, Warren, AR 71671-8600
Dorothy Henderson, Administrator

GENERAL HEALTH SERVICES

Health Dept 870.226.8440
Fax 870.226.6291
   208 Bragg St, Warren, AR 71671
Diane Fowler, Administrator

POLICE AND SHERIFF

Sheriff's Dept 870.226.3491
Fax 870.226.8408
E-mail ....bradleycountyso@hotmail.com
   101 E Cedar Ste B, Warren, AR 71671
Rick Anders, Sheriff

Calhoun County

SOCIAL SERVICES

Dept Of Human Svcs 870.798.4201
Fax 870.798.4202
E-mail ....glen.brown@arkansas.gov
   136 Archer St, Hampton, AR 71744
Glen Brown, Administrator

GENERAL HEALTH SERVICES

Health Dept 870.798.2808
Fax 870.798.2897
Web ....www.arkansas.gov
   1119 Prestress Dr, Hampton, AR 71744-8811
Glenda Gopcher, Chief Executive Officer

JUSTICE AGENCY

Juvenile Ofc 870.352.3813
   3rd & Oak St, Fordyce, AR 71742
Becky Cathey, Chief Probation Officer

Arkansas

POLICE AND SHERIFF

Sheriff's Dept .870.798.2323
Fax 870.798.4944
Web . . . . .www.cji.net
E-mail . . . . .calhouncoar@cji.net
 449 9th Street, Hampton, AR 71744
Robert Dunn, Sheriff

Carroll County

SOCIAL SERVICES

Dept Of Human Svcs 870.423.3351
Fax 870.423.3521
 304 Hailey Rd, Berryville, AR 72616-5076
Amanda Bunch, County Administrator

GENERAL HEALTH SERVICES

Health Dept 870.423.2923
Fax 870.423.5315
Web .www.healthyarkansas.gov
 402 Hailey Rd, Berryville, AR 72616
Sherri Plumlee, Rn, Nursing Supervisor

JUSTICE AGENCY

Juvenile Ofc 870.423.6822
Fax 870.423.7023
 210 W Church Ave, Berryville, AR 72616-4222
Steven Johnson, Probation Officer

POLICE AND SHERIFF

Sheriff's Dept 870.423.2901
Fax 870.423.5898
E-mail . . . . .ccsoadmin@weindstream.net
 205 Hailey Rd, Berryville, AR 72616-5147
Robert Grudek, Sheriff

Chicot County

SOCIAL SERVICES

Dept Of Human Svcs 870.265.3821
Fax 870.265.2503
Web . . . . .www.state.ar.us
E-mail . . . . .mary.warfield@mail.state.ar.us
 1736 S Highway 65 82, Lake Village, AR 71653-1560
Mary Warfield, Supervisor

GENERAL HEALTH SERVICES

Health Unit 870.265.2236
Fax 870.265.8001
E-mail . . . . .yolanda.porter@arkansas.gov
 1742 Hwy 65 & 82 S, Lake Village, AR 71653
Yolanda Porter, Administator

POLICE AND SHERIFF

Sheriff's Ofc 870.265.8020
Fax 870.265.5102
 513 Main St, Lake Village, AR 71653
Ronald Nichols, Sheriff

EDUCATION SERVICES

Dermott Head Start 870.538.5866
Fax 870.538.5866
Web . . . . .www.arheadstart.org
E-mail . . . . .lou@arheadstart.org
 524 E Beet Way, Dermott, AR 71638
Lou Johnson, Director

Clark County

SOCIAL SERVICES

Dept Of Human Svcs 870.246.9886
Fax 870.246.4603
 602 S 10th St, Arkadelphia, AR 71923
Jack Farr, Administrator

GENERAL HEALTH SERVICES

Health Dept 870.246.4471
Fax 870.246.9619
 605 S 10th St, Arkadelphia, AR 71923
Cindy Humphries, Administrator

JUSTICE AGENCY

Juvenile Ofc 870.246.7071
Fax 870.246.1424
 414 Court St, Arkadelphia, AR 71923
Darrell Middleton, Intake Officer

POLICE AND SHERIFF

Sheriff's Ofc 870.246.2222
Fax 870.246.3443
E-mail . . . . .ccso@cji.net
 406 S 5th St, Arkadelphia, AR 71923
Jason Watson, Sheriff

EDUCATION SERVICES

Amity Head Start Ctr 870.342.5358
Fax 870.342.5120
 213 N Clark St, Amity, AR 71921
Carla Merkel, Director

Arkadelphia Head Start 870.246.8931
Fax 870.246.5359
Web . . . . .www.cadc.com
E-mail . . . . .cmerkel@cadc.com
 301 N 23rd St, Arkadelphia, AR 71923-4369
Carla Merkel, Director

Clay County

GENERAL HEALTH SERVICES

Clay Health Unit 870.857.6281
Fax 870.857.3330
Web . . . . .www.healthy.arkansas.gov
 301 N Missouri Ave Ste 18, Corning, AR 72422-1603
Kim Donner, Administrator

JUSTICE AGENCY

Juvenile Ofc 870.857.5031
Fax 870.857.5378
 437 SW 2nd St, Corning, AR 72422
Betty S. Thomas, Intake Officer

POLICE AND SHERIFF

Sheriff's Ofc 870.598.2270
Fax 870.598.3146
 268 S 2nd Ave, Piggott, AR 72454-2601
Gerald Mcclung, Sheriff

Cleburne County

SOCIAL SERVICES

Dept Of Human Svcs 501.362.3298
Fax 501.362.2406
E-mail . . . . .etta.turner@arkansas.gov
 1521 W Main St, Heber Springs, AR 72543
Etta Turner, Administrator

GENERAL HEALTH SERVICES

Health Dept 501.362.7581
Fax 501.362.4684
 2319 HWY 110 W, Heber Springs, AR 72543-4201
Hazel Thompson, Administrator

JUSTICE AGENCY

CASA - Court Appointed Special Advocates For
Children 501.362.4609
Fax 501.362.5908
Web . . . . .www.arkansascasa.org
E-mail . . . . .casa16th2@hotmail.com
 301 W Main St, Cleburne County Courthouse, Heber
 Springs, AR 72543-3015
Rebekah Burnham, Executive Director

POLICE AND SHERIFF

Sheriff's Dept 501.362.8143
Fax 501.362.7386
E-mail . . . . .dclemon@internet.cox.com
 914 S 9th St, Heber Springs, AR 72543
Marty Moth, Sheriff

Cleveland County

GENERAL HEALTH SERVICES

Health Dept 870.325.6311
Fax 870.325.6159
Web .www.healthyarkansas.com
E-mail . . . . .vferry@healthyarkansas.com
 409 East Magnolia, Rison, AR 71665
Gwen Paul, Administrator

POLICE AND SHERIFF

Sheriff's Dept 870.325.6222
Fax 870.325.7866
E-mail . . . . .ccso1@tds.net
 20 Magnolia Street, Rison, AR 71665
Judy King, Sheriff

Columbia County

SOCIAL SERVICES

Dept Of Human Svcs 870.234.4190
Fax 870.234.4199
Web . . . . .www.state.ar.us
E-mail . . . . .summers@mail.state.ar.us
 601 E University St, Magnolia, AR 71753-2155
Charles Ellro, Administrator

GENERAL HEALTH SERVICES

Health Unit -- Home Health 870.235.3798
Fax 870.235.3755
 207 S Jefferson, Magnolia, AR 71753-3506
Melinda Harrell, Administrator

JUSTICE AGENCY

Juvenile Ofc 870.234.9029
Fax 870.234.7740
 231 A St, Magnolia, AR 71753
Jerry Walsh, Executive Director

POLICE AND SHERIFF

Sheriff's Office 870.235.3747
Fax 870.235.3715
E-mail . . . . .mloe52@sbcglobal.net
 82 Columbia 300, Magnolia, AR 71754
Mikeloe, Sheriff

Conway County

SOCIAL SERVICES

Dept Of Human Svcs 501.354.2418
Fax 501.354.2427
Web . . . . .www.state.ar.us
E-mail . . . . .linda.smith@arkansas.gov
 2 Bruce St, Morrilton, AR 72110-9600
Linda Smith, Administrator

GENERAL HEALTH SERVICES

Health Dept 501.354.4652
Fax 501.354.3537
 100 Hospital Dr, Morrilton, AR 72110
Tamara Ketchum, Administrator

POLICE AND SHERIFF

Sheriff's Dept 501.354.2411
Fax 501.354.9647
E-mail . . . . .conwaycountyso2@tcworks.net
 1823 Highway 113, Morrilton, AR 72110
Mike Smith, Sheriff

Craighead County

SOCIAL SERVICES

Dept Of Human Svcs 870.972.1732
Fax 870.972.5506
Web ....www.arkansas.gov
E-mail ....hubert.gray@arkansas.gov
   2920 Mcclellan Dr, Jonesboro, AR 72401
Janice Grissin, Administrator

GENERAL HEALTH SERVICES

Health Dept 870.933.4585
Fax 870.933.6416
   611 E Washington Ave Ste B, Jonesboro, AR 72401
Amy Howell, Administrator

JUSTICE AGENCY

Juvenile Detention Ctr 870.933.4578
Fax 870.933.4524
   901 Willett Rd, Jonesboro, AR 72401
Ty Koonas, Director

Juvenile Probation Ofc 870.933.4545
Fax 870.933.4597
Web ....www.craigheadcounty.org
E-mail ....ashley@craigheadcounty.org
   511 Union St Ste 310, Jonesboro, AR 72401-2863
Ashley Boles, Superintendent

Public Defender 870.932.6226
E-mail ....tgjones_atty@yahoo.com
   511 S Union St, Ste 207, Jonesboro, AR 72401
Terry Goodwin-jones, Manager

POLICE AND SHERIFF

Sheriff's Dept 870.933.4551
Fax 870.933.4595
Web ....www.craigheadso.org
   901 Willett Rd, Jonesboro, AR 72401-8950
Jack Mccann, Sheriff

Crawford County

SOCIAL SERVICES

Dept Of Human Svcs 479.474.7595
Fax 479.474.3150
   704 Cloverleaf Cir, Van Buren, AR 72956
Joyce Alexander, Supervisor

GENERAL HEALTH SERVICES

Health Dept 479.474.6391
Web ....www.telsiear.org
   2040 Chestnut St, Van Buren, AR 72956
Teddie Emmrich, Hiv Coordinator

JUSTICE AGENCY

Juvenile Ofc 479.474.5049
Fax 479.471.3238
Web ....www.crawford-county.org
E-mail ....emata@crawford-county.org
   220 S 4th Ste A, Van Buren, AR 72956
Erin Mata, Intake Officer

POLICE AND SHERIFF

Sheriff's Ofc 479.474.2261
Fax 479.471.3232
Web ....www.crawfordcountysheriff.org
   317 Main St, Van Buren, AR 72956-5768
Ron Brown, Sheriff

Crittenden County

SOCIAL SERVICES

Dept of Human Svcs 870.732.5170
Fax 870.732.4491
Web ....www.arkansas.gov
E-mail ....carole.marcellini@arkansas.gov
   401 S College Blvd, West Memphis, AR 72301-3891
Carole Marcellini, Administrator

GENERAL HEALTH SERVICES

Health Dept 870.735.4334
Fax 870.735.1398
   901 N 7th St, West Memphis, AR 72301
Susan Burlington, Administrator

Health Unit 870.792.7393
Web ....www.arkansas.gov
E-mail ....susanbrewinton@arkansas.gov
   841 Ruth St, Earle, AR 72331-1337
Susan Brewinton, Acting Administrator

JUSTICE AGENCY

Juvenile Dept 870.739.4401
Fax 870.739.2342
   116 Center St, Marion, AR 72364
D Barnes, Chief Officer

POLICE AND SHERIFF

Sheriff's Ofc 870.702.2010
Fax 870.702.2096
   350 Afco Rd, West Memphis, AR 72301
Mike Allen, Sheriff

EDUCATION SERVICES

Earle Head Start 870.792.8137
   1124 Throgmartin St, Earle, AR 72331
Jacqueline Lathon, Director

Cross County

SOCIAL SERVICES

Dept Of Human Svcs 870.238.8553
Fax 870.238.7522
Web ....www.arkansas.gov
E-mail ....pat.roberts@arkansas.gov
   803 Highway 64 E, Wynne, AR 72396-7414
Pat Roberts, Administrator

GENERAL HEALTH SERVICES

Health Unit 870.238.2101
Fax 870.238.4569
Web ....www.healthyarkansas.com
   704 Canal Ave E, Wynne, AR 72396-3042
Jitty Bingham, Administrator

POLICE AND SHERIFF

Sheriff's Ofc 870.238.5700
Fax 870.238.5704
   705 Union Ave E Ste 11, Wynne, AR 72396
J.R. Smith, Sheriff

Dallas County

SOCIAL SERVICES

Dept Of Human Svcs 870.352.5115
Fax 870.352.3823
E-mail ....rosborne@arkansas.gov
   1202 W 3rd St, Fordyce, AR 71742-3016
Ramona Osborne, Administrator

GENERAL HEALTH SERVICES

Health Dept 870.352.7197
Fax 870.352.7198
Web ....www.healthyarkansas.com
E-mail ....dserguson@healthyarkansas.com
   201 N Spring St, Fordyce, AR 71742-3315
Donna Serguson, Administrator

POLICE AND SHERIFF

Sheriff's Dept 870.352.2002
Fax 870.352.3700
E-mail ....dallascoso@cji.net
   106 S. Charlotte, Fordyce, AR 71742
Donny Ford, Sheriff

Desha County

SOCIAL SERVICES

Dept Of Human Svcs 870.222.4144
Fax 870.222.4171
E-mail ....lerone.thomas@arkansas.gov
   200 N First St, McGehee, AR 71654
Lerone Thomas, Administrator

POLICE AND SHERIFF

Sheriff's Dept 870.877.2327
Fax 870.877.3406
E-mail ....deshaso@creark.net
   604 President St, Arkansas City, AR 71630
Jim Snyder, Sheriff

EDUCATION SERVICES

Dumas Head Start Ctr 870.382.0462
E-mail ....bobbiebrooks1970@centurylink.net
   244 S Main St, Dumas, AR 71639
Bobbie Brooks, Director

Dumas Migrant Head Start 870.382.1450
Fax 870.382.1450
E-mail ....dumas@centurytel.net
   HC 66 Industrial Rd, Dumas, AR 71639
Romona Weatherford, Director

Drew County

SOCIAL SERVICES

Dept Of Human Svcs 870.367.6835
Fax 870.367.6944
E-mail ....jacqeline.bryant@arkansas.gov
   444 Highway 425 N, Monticello, AR 71655-4016
Jacqeline Bryant, Administrator

GENERAL HEALTH SERVICES

Health Dept 870.367.6234
Fax 870.460.6210
Web ....www.healthy.arkansas.gov
   940 Scogin Dr, Monticello, AR 71655-5732
Karen Brown, Administrator

POLICE AND SHERIFF

Sheriff's Ofc 870.367.6211
Fax 870.460.6217
E-mail ....h.markgober@yahoo.com
   210 S Main St, Monticello, AR 71655-4730
Mark Gober, Sheriff

EDUCATION SERVICES

Special Education 870.367.3544
Fax 870.367.4208
Web ....www.drewcentral.org
E-mail ....cjohnston@drewcentral.org
   250 University Dr, Monticello, AR 71655-9765
Sharlena Johnston, Director Of Special Education

Faulkner County

SOCIAL SERVICES

Dept Of Human Svcs 501.730.9900
Fax 501.730.9910
E-mail ....lela.alexander@arkansas.gov
   1000 E. Siebenmorgan Rd., Conway, AR 72033
Lela Alexander, Administrator

GENERAL HEALTH SERVICES

Conway Health Dept 501.450.4941
Fax 501.329.2607
   811 N Creek Dr, Conway, AR 72033
Elese Brown, Administrator

COURTS

20th Judicial Circuit Court **501.450.4924**
Fax 501.450.4957
Web www.faulkercircuitcourt5.com
E-mail .... rwood@faulknercc.org
1423 Caldwell St, Conway, AR 72034-5318
Honourable Rhonda Wood, 4th Division Judge

POLICE AND SHERIFF

Sheriff's Office **501.450.4914**
Fax 501.450.4916
801 Locust St, Conway, AR 72034
Karl Byrd, Sheriff

EDUCATION SERVICES

Conway's Promise For New Beginning Even
Start **501.450.6693**
Fax 501.450.6693
E-mail .... masonb@conwayschools.net
615 E Robins St, Conway, AR 72032
Brenda Mason, Even Start Director

Migrant Head Start/Community Action Program for Central
Arkansas **501.329.0977**
Fax 501.329.9247
Web .... www.capcainc.org
E-mail .... archie.musselman@capcainc.org
707 Robins St Ste 118, Conway, AR 72034-6517
Archie Musselman, Director

Franklin County

SOCIAL SERVICES

Dept Of Human Svcs **479.667.2379**
Fax 479.667.5044
Web .... www.arkansas.gov
E-mail .... yvonnecase@arkansas.gov
800 W Commercial St, Ozark, AR 72949-3010
Yvonne Case, Administrator

GENERAL HEALTH SERVICES

Health Unit **479.667.2555**
Fax 479.667.4274
799 W River St, Ozark, AR 72949
Rebecca Wright, Administrator

JUSTICE AGENCY

Juvenile Ofc **479.667.4731**
Fax 479.667.0207
320 N 2nd St Ste 200, Ozark, AR 72949
Fred Nichols, Intake Officer

POLICE AND SHERIFF

Sheriff's Dept **479.667.4127**
Fax 479.667.1857
Web .... www.fcsdark.com
E-mail .... rhaynes@fcsdark.com
101 W Main St, Ozark, AR 72949
Reed Haynes, Sheriff

Fulton County

GENERAL HEALTH SERVICES

Health Dept **870.895.3300**
Fax 870.895.4340
Web .... www.healthyarkansas.com
E-mail .... wanda.koelling@arkansas.gov
510 S Main St, Salem, AR 72576-9422
Wanda Koelling, Administrator

JUSTICE AGENCY

CASA **870.895.3764**
Fax 870.895.3765
Web .... www.arkansascasa.org
E-mail .... casa16th3@hotmail.com
140 N Pickren Street, Salem, AR 72576
Rebecca Burnham, Program Director

POLICE AND SHERIFF

Sheriff's Dept **870.895.2601**
Fax 870.895.4114
E-mail .... fultoncoso@centurytel.net
114 S. Locust, Salem, AR 72576
Kenneth Foley, Sheriff

Garland County

SOCIAL SERVICES

Change Point **501.624.2273**
Fax 501.624.2269
E-mail .... changepointcentre@gmail.com
115 Liberty St, Hot Springs, AR 71913
Joanne Carter, Director

Dept Of Human Svcs **501.321.2583**
Fax 501.623.2645
Web .... www.arkansas.gov
E-mail .... richard.sutton@arkansas.gov
115 Stover St, Hot Springs, AR 71913-4711
Richard Sutton, County Administrator

GENERAL HEALTH SERVICES

Health Dept **501.624.3394**
Fax 501.624.2706
E-mail .... lgrinnis@healthyarkansas.com
1425 Malvern Ave, Hot Springs, AR 71901-6316
Linda Grinnis, Administrator

JUSTICE AGENCY

CASA **501.321.9269**
Fax 501.321.9021
E-mail .... gccasa@hotsprings.net
600 W Grand Ave Ste 104, Hot Springs, AR 71901
Sandra Forde, Executive Director

Juvenile Detention Ctr **501.622.3643**
Fax 501.622.3646
Web .... www.garlandcounty.org
222 Woodbine St, Hot Springs, AR 71901-5121
Lt. Belinda Cosgrove, Administrator

COURTS

18th Judicial Circuit Court **501.622.3770**
Fax 501.321.0067
607 Ouachita Ave Rm 120, Hot Springs, AR 71901
Sharon Smith, Intake Officer

POLICE AND SHERIFF

Sheriff's Dept **501.622.3660**
Fax 501.321.4212
Web .... www.garlandcounty.org
525 Ouachita Ave, Hot Springs, AR 71901-5185
Larry Sanders, Sheriff

EDUCATION SERVICES

Arkansas Human Dev Corp Early Head
Start **501.620.4323**
Fax 501.760.3522
E-mail .... jblees@arkansasbabies.com
102 College Dr, Hot Springs, AR 71913
Jouana Blees, Director

Grant County

SOCIAL SERVICES

Dept Of Human Svcs **870.942.5151**
Fax 870.942.5153
16 Opportunity Dr, Sheridan, AR 72150
Angela Newcomb, Children & Family Services Supervisor

JUSTICE AGENCY

Juvenile Ofc **870.942.8924**
Fax 870.942.7460
Center St, Courthouse Room 112, Sheridan,
AR 72150
Scarlete Lancaster, Probation Officer

POLICE AND SHERIFF

Sheriff's Dept **870.942.5039**
Fax 870.942.2442
Web .... www.grantcountysheriff-collector.com
E-mail .... grantso@yahoo.com
101 Center St, Room 110, Sheridan, AR 72150
Lance Huey, Sheriff

Greene County

SOCIAL SERVICES

Dept Of Human Svcs **870.236.8723**
Fax 870.239.6340
809 Goldsmith Rd, Paragould, AR 72450-9509

GENERAL HEALTH SERVICES

Health Dept **870.236.7782**
Fax 870.239.6329
E-mail .... linda.hutchinson@ocse.state.ar.us
801 Goldsmith Rd, Paragould, AR 72450-9509
Linda Hutchison, Administrator

POLICE AND SHERIFF

Sheriff's Ofc **870.236.7612**
Fax 870.239.6344
E-mail .... gc1@grnco.net
1809 N Rockingchair Rd, Paragould, AR 72450
Dan Langston, Sheriff

Hempstead County

SOCIAL SERVICES

Dept Of Human Svcs **870.777.8656**
Fax 870.777.4025
116 N Laurel St, Hope, AR 71801
Ellen Haywood, Administrator

GENERAL HEALTH SERVICES

Health Dept **870.777.2191**
Fax 870.777.6607
Web .... www.healthy.arkansas.gov
E-mail .... jeannine.wilson@arkansas.gov
808 W 5th St, Hope, AR 71801-5020
Jeannine Wilson, Administrator

JUSTICE AGENCY

Juvenile Ofc **870.777.9822**
Fax 870.777.3494
Web .... www.arkleg.state.ar.us
402 S Washington St, Hope, AR 71801
David Powers, Juvenile Intake Officer

POLICE AND SHERIFF

Sheriff's Ofc **870.777.6727**
Fax 870.777.1903
312 S Washington St, Hope, AR 71802
James Singleton, Sheriff

EDUCATION SERVICES

Blevins Head Start **870.874.3302**
Fax 870.874.3302
308 College St, Blevins, AR 71825
Nora Marquez, Director

Hot Springs County

SOCIAL SERVICES

Dept Of Human Svcs **501.332.2718**
Fax 501.332.3368
Web .... www.arkleg.state.ar.us
E-mail .... maryfranklin@arkleg.state.ar.us
2505 Pine Bluff St, Malvern, AR 72104-4822
Mary Franklin, Administrator

© 2011 Dorland Health

GENERAL HEALTH SERVICES

Health Dept.....................................501.332.6972
Fax..501.332.6889
Web..www.healthyarkansas.com
E-mail..........................suellen.simpson@arkansas.gov
2204 E Sullenberger Ave, Malvern, AR 72104
Suellen Simpson, Administrator

JUSTICE AGENCY

Juvenile Court...............................501.337.4328
Fax..501.337.5670
E-mail.............................rbrown@hotsprings.org
210 Locust St Ste 2, Malvern, AR 72104
Robert Brown, Intake Officer

POLICE AND SHERIFF

Sheriff's Dept................................501.332.3671
Fax..501.337.0435
215 E Highland Ave Ste 119, Malvern, AR 72104
Chad Ledbetter, Sheriff

EDUCATION SERVICES

Bismarck Head Start.....................501.865.1882
Fax..501.865.1883
2078 Arlie Moore Rd, Bismarck, AR 71929
Beverly Jackson, Director

Howard County

SOCIAL SERVICES

Dept Of Human Svcs.....................870.845.4334
Fax..870.845.4339
Web...www.state.ar.us
E-mail................debbie.hopkins@mail.state.ar.us
534 N Main St, Nashville, AR 71852-3921
Debbie Hopkins, Administrator

GENERAL HEALTH SERVICES

Nashville Health Dept...................870.845.2208
Fax..870.845.7545
Web...www.arkansas.gov
201 E Hempstead St Ste 2, Nashville, AR 71852-2518
Donna Webb, Administrator

POLICE AND SHERIFF

Sheriff's Dept................................870.845.2626
Fax..870.845.7542
E-mail.............................howardco1@sbcglobal.net
101 Isaac Perkins Blvd, Nashville, AR 71852
Randall Morris, Sheriff

Independence County

SOCIAL SERVICES

Dept Of Human Svcs.....................870.698.1876
Fax..870.698.2938
Web...www.arkansas.gov
100 Weaver Ave, Batesville, AR 72501-7314

GENERAL HEALTH SERVICES

Health Dept..................................870.793.8848
Fax..870.793.8887
120 Weaver Ave, Batesville, AR 72501
Sonia Nix, Administrator

POLICE AND SHERIFF

Sheriff's Dept................................870.793.8838
Fax..870.612.6849
1750 Myers St, Batesville, AR 72501
Alan Cockrill, Chief Deputy

EDUCATION SERVICES

Batesville Head Start.....................870.698.9127
922 Elm St, Batesville, AR 72501-3433
Wyvonia Neal, Director

East Batesville Head Start................870.698.0014
625 S 18th St, Batesville, AR 72501
Linda Cooper, Director

Izard County

SOCIAL SERVICES

Dept Of Human Svcs.....................870.368.4318
Fax..870.368.4737
Web..www.arkansas.gov
E-mail..........................donna.mccurley@arkansas.gov
278 E Main St, Melbourne, AR 72556
Donna Mccurley, Lsw, Children & Family Services Supervisor

GENERAL HEALTH SERVICES

Health Dept..................................870.368.7790
Fax..870.368.7060
Web..www.healthyarkansas.com
E-mail.......................tengelhardt@healthyarkansas.gov
149 Haley St, Melbourne, AR 72556
Treva Engelhardt, Administrator

JUSTICE AGENCY

Juvenile Probation Ofc..................870.793.8809
Fax..870.612.6806
368 E Main St, Batesville, AR 72501-5605
Carol King, Case Coordinator

POLICE AND SHERIFF

Sheriff's Ofc.................................870.368.4203
Fax..870.368.5226
Web.........................www.izardcountysheriff.org
300 Circle Dr, Melbourne, AR 72556
Tate Lawrence, Sheriff

EDUCATION SERVICES

Brockwell Head Start.....................870.368.5228
Fax..501.370.9109
Web..www.arheadstart.org
E-mail................................lindac@arheadstart.org
77,Box 40 Chaple Hill Rd., Brockwell, AR 72517
Linda Cooper, Director

Calico Rock Head Start..................870.297.8853
Web...www.calicorock.us
E-mail..........................calicorock@centurytel.net
301 Maple St, Calico Rock, AR 72519
Teresa Sanders, Director

Jackson County

SOCIAL SERVICES

Dept of Human Svcs.....................870.523.9820
Fax..870.523.6107
E-mail...........................leroy.mansko@arkansas.gov
3rd & Hazel St, Newport, AR 72112
Leroy Mansko, Administrator

JUSTICE AGENCY

Juvenile Justice Ctr.......................870.523.7460
Fax..870.523.7465
E-mail.............................jacksonintake@yahoo.com
208 Main St, Newport, AR 72112-3234
Tommie Schulz, Intake Officer

POLICE AND SHERIFF

Sheriff's Ofc.................................870.523.5842
Fax..870.523.7418
Web.........................www.jacksoncountysheriff.org
2nd & Elm St, Newport, AR 72112
David Lucas, Sheriff

EDUCATION SERVICES

Carlew Templeton Head Start...............870.523.5438
Web..www.neaheadstart.com
3119 N Highway 367, Newport, AR 72112-2136
Patricia Reed, Director

Jefferson County

SOCIAL SERVICES

Dept of Human Svcs.....................870.534.4200
Fax..870.534.3421
E-mail.................................lee.turner@arkansas.gov
1222 W 6th Ave, Pine Bluff, AR 71601
Lee Turner, Administrator

GENERAL HEALTH SERVICES

Health Dept..................................870.535.2142
Fax..870.536.3006
2306 Rike Dr, Pine Bluff, AR 71611
Terri Jackson, Administrator

MENTAL HEALTH SERVICES

Southeast Arkansas Behavioral Health Care System,
Inc...870.534.1834
Fax..870.534.5798
Web...www.sabhs.org
E-mail..................................kathy@sabhs.org
2500 Rike Dr, Pine Bluff, AR 71603-3937
Kathy Harris, Executive Director

JUSTICE AGENCY

Juvenile Ofc.................................870.541.5455
Fax..870.541.8504
301 E 2nd Ave, Pine Bluff, AR 71601-4463
Juawana Jackson, Deputy Chief

POLICE AND SHERIFF

Sheriff's Ofc.................................870.541.5351
Fax..870.541.5348
Web.........................www.jeffersoncountysheriff.org
E-mail.................jeffco.webmaster@jeffcoso.com
101 E Barraque St, Ste 112, Pine Bluff, AR 71601
Gerald Robinson, Sheriff

EDUCATION SERVICES

Arkansas River Education Svc
Cooperative(Aresc)........................870.534.6129
Fax..870.534.7162
E-mail..........................mccoyc@aresc.k12.ar.us
912 W 6th Ave, Pine Bluff, AR 71601
Carolynn Mccoy, Director

Johnson County

SOCIAL SERVICES

Dept of Human Svcs.....................479.754.2355
Fax..479.754.6202
Web...www.arkansas.gov
900 S Rogers St, Clarksville, AR 72830-4331
Kenneth Mcdearman, Administrator

Lafayette County

SOCIAL SERVICES

Dept Of Human Svcs.....................870.921.4283
Fax..870.921.4285
2612 Spruce St, Lewisville, AR 71845-8638
Judy Betty, Administrator

GENERAL HEALTH SERVICES

Health Dept..................................870.921.5744
Fax..870.921.5733
1113 Chestnut Street, Lewisville, AR 71845
Tonya Clark, Administrator

POLICE AND SHERIFF

Sheriff's Ofc.................................870.921.4252
Fax..870.921.4256
Web..www.whti.net
5 Courthouse Sq, Lewisville, AR 71845-8801
Victor Rose, Sheriff

Arkansas

Lawrence County

SOCIAL SERVICES

Dept of Human Svcs 870.886.2408
Fax 870.886.7716
Web ....www.arkansas.gov
E-mail ....judy.videll@arkansas.gov
   400 NW 4th St, Walnut Ridge, AR 72476-1501
   Brenda Poienbexter, Administrator

GENERAL HEALTH SERVICES

Health Dept 870.886.3201
Fax 870.886.1722
Web ....www.healthyarkansas.com
E-mail ....bobby.bridges@arkansas.gov
   1050 W Free St, Walnut Ridge, AR 72476-1752
   Bobby Bridges, Administrator

COURTS

3rd Judicial Circuit Court 870.886.1112
Fax 870.886.1128
E-mail ....lawcocircuit@yahoo.com
   315 W Main St, Rm 7, Walnut Ridge, AR 72476-0581
   Honorable Harold Irwin, Director

Lee County

SOCIAL SERVICES

Dept Of Human Svcs 870.295.2597
Fax 870.295.6337
   772 W Chestnut St, Marianna, AR 72360
   Barbara Metcalf, Economic Services Supervisor

GENERAL HEALTH SERVICES

Health Dept 870.295.2400
Fax 870.295.2803
E-mail ....veronica.sellers@arkansas.gov
   141 N Hicky St, Marianna, AR 72360
   Veronica Sellers Rn, Administrator

POLICE AND SHERIFF

Sheriff's Ofc 870.295.7777
Fax 870.295.7735
E-mail ....oxnerj@cablelynx.com
   15 E Chestnut St Ste 6, Marianna, AR 72360
   Jack Oxner, Sheriff

Lincoln County

SOCIAL SERVICES

Dept of Human Svcs 870.628.4105
Fax 870.628.4101
Web ....www.dhs.arkansas.com
E-mail ....mhawkins@healthyarkansas.com
   101 W Wiley Ave, Star City, AR 71667-5109
   Marsha Hawkins, Administrator

GENERAL HEALTH SERVICES

Health Dept 870.628.5121
Fax 870.628.1272
Web ....www.arkansas.gov
E-mail ....deborah.riley@arkansas.gov
   101 W Wiley Ave, Star City, AR 71667-5109
   Deborah J Riley, Rn, Administrator

MENTAL HEALTH SERVICES

**Southeast Arkansas Behavioral Health
Systems** 870.628.4181
Fax 870.628.5369
Web ....www.mhca.org
   612 E Arkansas St, Star City, AR 71667-4842
   Kathy Harris, Administrator

POLICE AND SHERIFF

Sheriff's Office 870.628.4271
Fax 870.628.4251
Web ....www.cji.net
E-mail ....lincolncoar@cji.net
   300 S Drew St Rm B103, Star City, AR 71667-5144
   Larry Mcgee, Sheriff

Little River County

SOCIAL SERVICES

Dept Of Human Svcs 870.898.5155
Fax 870.898.4596
   90 Waddell St, Ashdown, AR 71822
   Mark Muenzmaier, Administrator

JUSTICE AGENCY

**Juvenile Intake Ofc Of Circuit
Court** 870.898.7259
Fax 870.898.8660
   351 N 2nd St, Ashdown, AR 71822
   Elaine Ashley, Intake Officer

COURTS

9th Judicial Circuit Court 870.898.7228
Fax 870.898.7262
   PO Box 214, Ashdown, AR 71822-0546
   Carolyn Pullen, Case Coordinator

POLICE AND SHERIFF

Sheriff's Dept 870.898.5115
Fax 870.898.7260
   351 N 2nd St Ste 2, Ashdown, AR 71822
   Danny R. Russel, Sheriff

EDUCATION SERVICES

Ashdown Headstart 870.772.0089
Fax 870.774.0162
   1320 Foster Dr, Ashdown, AR 71822-3216
   Marilyn Griffin, Director

Logan County

SOCIAL SERVICES

Dept Of Human Svcs 479.675.3091
Fax 479.675.2654
Web ....www.arkansas.gov
   398 E 2nd St, Booneville, AR 72927
   Donna Samples, County Administrator

Dept of Human Svcs 479.963.2783
Fax 479.963.3975
Web ....www.arkansas.gov
E-mail ....ronald.ford@arkansas.gov
   17 W McKeen St, Paris, AR 72855-4935
   Ronald Ford, Administrator

GENERAL HEALTH SERVICES

Health Unit 479.675.2593
Fax 479.675.5852
   721 W 1st St, Booneville, AR 72927
   Judy Huston, Administrator

Health Unit 479.963.6126
Fax 479.963.6674
   150 S Lowder St, Paris, AR 72855
   Judy Houston, Administrator

MENTAL HEALTH SERVICES

**Western Arkansas Counseling & Guidance
Ctr** 479.675.3909
Fax 479.675.3914
Web ....www.wacgc.org
E-mail ....gina_misner@wacgc.org
   174 N Welsh Ave, Booneville, AR 72927-4130
   Gina Misner, Director

JUSTICE AGENCY

Juvenile Ofc 479.963.2219
Fax 479.963.2224
   25 W Walnut St, Paris, AR 72855-3845
   James Richardson, Intake Officer

POLICE AND SHERIFF

Sheriff's Dept 479.963.3271
Fax 479.963.2215
Web ....www.magtel.com
E-mail ....logan1@magtel.com
   508 W Grober St, Paris, AR 72855
   Steve Smith, Sheriff

Lonoke County

SOCIAL SERVICES

Dept Of Human Svcs 501.676.3113
Fax 501.676.3115
Web ....www.arkansas.gov
   100 Park Street, Lonoke, AR 72086
   Doug Jones, County Administrator

GENERAL HEALTH SERVICES

Health Unit 501.843.7561
Fax 501.843.9371
E-mail ....mgarris@healthyarkansas.com
   118 N 1st St, Cabot, AR 72023-2656
   Milton Garris, Administrator

Health Unit 501.676.2268
Fax 501.676.0578
Web ....www.healthyarkansas.gov
E-mail ....mgarris@healthyarkansas.gov
   306 N Center St, Lonoke, AR 72086-2849
   Milton Garris, Administrator

JUSTICE AGENCY

Juvenile Ofc 501.676.3035
Fax 501.676.3004
Web ....www.lcjd.org
E-mail ....ldollinger@lcjd.org
   311 Court St, Lonoke, AR 72086-2858
   Lori Dollinger, Probation Officer

POLICE AND SHERIFF

Sheriff's Dept 501.676.6494
Fax 501.676.6609
   301 Court St, Lonoke, AR 72086-2858
   Jim Roberson, Sheriff

Madison County

SOCIAL SERVICES

Dept Of Human Svcs 479.738.2161
Fax 479.738.2095
E-mail ....donna.samples1@arkansas.gov
   1013 N College, Huntsville, AR 72740
   Donna Samples, Administrator

POLICE AND SHERIFF

Sheriff's Ofc 479.738.2320
Fax 479.738.1525
Web ....www.madisoncounty.net
E-mail ....mcso501@madisoncounty.net
   1 Main St, Huntsville, AR 72740-0476
   Phillip Morgan, Sheriff

Marion County

SOCIAL SERVICES

Dept Of Human Svcs 870.449.4058
Fax 870.449.6720
   114 E Old Main St, Yellville, AR 72687
   Kay Query, Administrator

GENERAL HEALTH SERVICES

Health Dept..............................870.449.4259
Fax..870.449.5922
707 Highway 202 W, Yellville, AR 72687

POLICE AND SHERIFF

Sheriff's Dept............................870.449.4236
Fax..870.449.4869
E-mail...............................marioncountyso@yahoo.com
491 Highway 62 West, Yellville, AR 72687
Roger Vickers, Sheriff

Miller County

SOCIAL SERVICES

Dept Of Human Svcs.......................870.773.0563
Fax..870.772.0630
E-mail...............................mason.steve@epa.gov
3809 Airport Plaza Dr, Texarkana, AR 71854-1500
Steve Mason, Administrator

GENERAL HEALTH SERVICES

Health Unit -- Home & Health................870.773.2108
Fax..870.773.3292
Web...............................www.healthy.arkansas.gov
503 Walnut St, Texarkana, AR 71854-5286
Jerry B. Stringfellow, MD, Health Officer

JUSTICE AGENCY

Juvenile Detention Ctr.....................870.773.3776
Fax..870.772.4438
2200 Bankes Rd, Texarkana, AR 71854
Tyna Studebaker, Administrator

Youth Svcs Ofc.............................870.774.9396
Fax..870.774.4216
601 Hazel St, Texarkana, AR 71854
David Beardon, Case Manager

COURTS

8th Judicial Circuit Court..................870.772.9618
Fax..870.773.3354
E-mail...............................kwebb@cableone.net
400 Laurel St Ste 202, Texarkana, AR 71854
Brent Haltom, Judge

POLICE AND SHERIFF

Sheriff's Dept.............................870.774.3001
Fax..870.779.7834
2300 East St, Texarkana, AR 71854-8023
Ron Stovall, Sheriff

Mississippi County

SOCIAL SERVICES

Dept of Human Svcs.........................870.563.5234
Fax..870.563.3081
E-mail...............................joe.guy@arkansas.gov
437 S Country Club Rd, Osceola, AR 72370
Joe A Guy, Administrator

Dept Of Human Svcs.........................870.763.7093
Fax..870.763.2243
Web...............................www.arkleg.state.ar.us
1104 Byrum Rd, Blytheville, AR 72315-8030
Joe A Guy, Administrator

GENERAL HEALTH SERVICES

Health Dept...............................870.763.7064
Fax..870.763.9104
E-mail...............................walter.holloway@arkansas.gov
1299 N 10th St, Blytheville, AR 72315-1614
Walter Holloway, Administrator

Health Unit...............................870.563.2521
Fax..870.563.2741
E-mail...............................bakert@arkleg.state.ar.us
720 W Lee Ave, Osceola, AR 72370-3004
Tonia Baker, Administrator

POLICE AND SHERIFF

Sheriff's Dept.............................870.658.2242
Fax..870.658.2510
E-mail...............................misscoso@bscn.com
685 N County Road 599, Luxora, AR 72358-4808
Sheriff James W. Sanders, Sheriff

Monroe County

SOCIAL SERVICES

Dept of Human Svcs.........................870.734.1445
Fax..870.734.2313
E-mail...............................floyd.williams@arkansas.gov
301 1/2 N New Orleans Ave, Brinkley, AR 72021
Floyd Williams, Administrator

Dept Of Human Svcs.........................870.747.3329
Fax..870.747.5416
302 North, Clarendon, AR 72029
Floyd Williams, County Administrator

GENERAL HEALTH SERVICES

Monroe Health Dept........................870.734.1461
Fax..870.734.1466
Web...............................www.healthyarkansas.com
E-mail...............................betty.rodgers@arkansas.gov
306 W King Dr, Brinkley, AR 72021
Betty Rodgers, Administrator

JUSTICE AGENCY

Juvenile Ofc..............................870.747.5449
Fax..870.747.5910
Web...............................www.courts.mo.gov
E-mail...............................bpearson@courts.mo.gov
123 Madison St, Clarendon, AR 72029-2704
Brenda Pearson, Intake Officer

POLICE AND SHERIFF

Sheriff's Dept.............................870.747.3811
Fax..870.747.3674
Web...............................www.futura.net
E-mail...............................gfhenard@aol.com
200 S Main St, Clarendon, AR 72029-2722
Gary Henard, Sheriff

EDUCATION SERVICES

Brinkley-Fargo Head Start..................870.734.3526
551 Floyd Brown Rd, Brinkley, AR 72021
Linda King, Director

Clarendon Pre-K...........................870.747.3351
Fax..870.747.5963
E-mail...............................GRAYM@LIONS.GRSC.K12.AR.US
199 N 9, Clarendon, AR 72029
Monica Gray, Director

Montgomery County

SOCIAL SERVICES

Dept Of Human Svcs.........................870.867.3184
Fax..870.867.3185
Web...............................www.arkansas.gov
E-mail...............................celeste.sorrells@arkansas.gov
232 Graham St, Mount Ida, AR 71957
Celeste Sorrells, Economic Services Supervisor

GENERAL HEALTH SERVICES

Health Dept...............................870.867.2331
Fax..870.867.3656
Web...............................www.healthyarkansas.com
E-mail...............................kimberly.adams@arkansas.gov
346 Luzerne St, Mount Ida, AR 71957
Kim Adams, RN, Administrator

Nevada County

SOCIAL SERVICES

Dept Of Human Svcs.........................870.887.6626
Fax..870.887.6628
Web...............................www.arkansas.gov
E-mail...............................elaine.halliday@arkansas.gov
355 W 1st St N, Prescott, AR 71857-3617
Elaine Halliday, Administrator

GENERAL HEALTH SERVICES

Health Dept...............................870.887.2004
Fax..870.887.6407
Web...............................www.healthyarkansas.com
1501 W 1st St N, Prescott, AR 71857
Debbie Henderson, Administrator

POLICE AND SHERIFF

Sheriff's Dept............................870.887.2616
Fax..870.887.5131
215 E 2nd St S, Prescott, AR 71857
Danny Mortan, Sheriff

Newton County

SOCIAL SERVICES

Dept of Human Svcs.........................870.446.2237
Fax..870.446.2249
Web...............................www.state.ar.us
E-mail...............................mary.emmett@mail.atate.ar.us
100 Spring St, Jasper, AR 72641
Mary Lynn Emmett, Administrator

GENERAL HEALTH SERVICES

Health Unit - Home & Health................870.446.2216
Fax..870.446.2280
Web...............................www.healthyarkansas.com
506 W Court St, Jasper, AR 72641
Kathy Taylor, Director Of Nurses/Administrator

POLICE AND SHERIFF

Sheriff's Ofc.............................870.446.5124
Fax..870.446.2106
401 N Sping St, Jasper, AR 72641
Keith Slape, Sheriff

Ouachita County

SOCIAL SERVICES

Dept Of Human Svcs.........................870.836.8166
Fax..870.836.7441
Web...............................www.state.ar.us
E-mail...............................erma.brown@arkansas.gov
222 Van Buren St NW, Camden, AR 71701-3931
Kaithreen Bouston, Administrator

GENERAL HEALTH SERVICES

Health Dept...............................870.836.5033
Fax..870.837.1488
Web...............................www.healthyarkansas.com
E-mail...............................rwright@healthyarkansas.com
740 California Ave SW, Camden, AR 71701-4606
Rebecca Wright, Administrator

JUSTICE AGENCY

CASA-13th Judicial District................870.836.4700
Fax..870.836.4701
E-mail...............................casaouachita@sbcglobal.net
530 Jefferson St SW, Camden, AR 71701
Sandy Jilliam, Executive Director

Juvenile Ofc..............................870.837.2275
Fax..870.837.2276
E-mail...............................glendahanna@hotmail.com
141 Jackson St SW, Camden, AR 71701-3939
Glenda Hanna, Intake Officer

© 2011 Dorland Health

COURTS

13th Judicial Circuit Court **870.837.2270**
Fax 870.837.2273
  145 Jefferson St SW Ste 8, Camden, AR 71701
Honorable Edwin A. Keaton, Director

POLICE AND SHERIFF

Sheriff's Ofc **870.231.5300**
Fax 870.231.4329
  109 Good Game St, Camden, AR 71701-3921
Paul Lucas, Sheriff

Perry County

SOCIAL SERVICES

Dept of Human Svcs **501.889.5105**
Fax 501.889.5107
  213 Houston Ave, Perryville, AR 72126
Greg Spinks, Administrator

GENERAL HEALTH SERVICES

Health Dept **501.889.5156**
Fax 501.889.5484
  1039 N Fourche Ave, Perryville, AR 72126
Michele Barlow, Administrator

JUSTICE AGENCY

Juvenile Ofc **501.889.5126**
Fax 501.889.5759
Web ....www.arbbs.net
  310 Main St, Perryville, AR 72126
Peggy Caines, Intake Officer

POLICE AND SHERIFF

Sheriff's Ofc **501.889.2333**
Fax 501.889.5711
  106 N Oak St, Perryville, AR 72126
Scott Mcgomery, Sheriff

Phillips County

SOCIAL SERVICES

Dept Of Human Svcs **870.816.3200**
Fax 870.338.9358
Web ....www.state.ar.us
E-mail ....china.graham@arkansas.gov
  104 Danna Place, Helena, AR 72342
China Graham, Administrator

GENERAL HEALTH SERVICES

Health Dept **870.572.9028**
Fax 870.572.6256
Web ....www.arkansas.gov
E-mail ....robyn.i.clark@arkansas.gov
  110 Shirley Hicks Dr, West Helena, AR 72390
Robyn Clark, Administrator

POLICE AND SHERIFF

Sheriff's Ofc **870.338.5555**
Fax 870.338.5557
  626 Cherry St, Helena, AR 72342
Ronnie White, Sheriff

Pike County

SOCIAL SERVICES

Dept Of Human Svcs **870.285.3111**
Fax 870.285.3360
Web ....www.arkansas.gov
  331 E 13th St, Murfreesboro, AR 71958
Celeste Sorrells, Administrator

GENERAL HEALTH SERVICES

Health Dept **870.285.3154**
Fax 870.285.2156
  15 Caddo Dr, Murfreesboro, AR 71958
Christy Cox, Clinic Coordinator

POLICE AND SHERIFF

Sheriff's Ofc **870.285.3315**
Fax 870.285.2626
E-mail ....pcsoglenn@yahoo.com
  305 Industrial Park Dr, Murfreesboro, AR 71958
Preston Glenn, Sheriff

EDUCATION SERVICES

Delight Head Start **870.379.2270**
Fax 870.379.2327
E-mail ....bbaxter@cadc.com
  611 Webb St, Delight, AR 71940
Barbie Baxter, Director

Poinsett County

SOCIAL SERVICES

Dept of Human Svcs **870.578.5491**
Fax 870.578.5417
Web ....www.arkansas.gov
E-mail ....Diane.straling@arkansas.gov
  406 N Illinois St, Harrisburg, AR 72432-1112
Diane Straling, Administrator

GENERAL HEALTH SERVICES

Health Dept **870.578.4480**
Fax 870.578.9270
E-mail ....janicemitchusson@healthyarkansas.com
  119 N Main St, Harrisburg, AR 72432
Janice Mitchusson, Administrator

COURTS

Juvenile Court **870.578.4450**
Fax 870.578.4451
  110 East St, Harrisburg, AR 72432-1910
Cindy Smith, Probation Officer

POLICE AND SHERIFF

Sheriff's Ofc **870.578.5411**
Fax 870.578.4417
E-mail ....sheriffmills@hotmail.com
  1500 Justice Dr, Harrisburg, AR 72432-9336
Larry K. Mills, Sheriff

EDUCATION SERVICES

Special Education **870.578.5426**
Fax 870.578.5896
  1606 Pine Grove Ln, Harrisburg, AR 72432
John Manning, Director

Polk County

SOCIAL SERVICES

Dept Of Human Svcs **479.394.3100**
Fax 479.394.3632
Web ....www.arkansasstate.gov
  606 Pine Ave Ste 7, Mena, AR 71953
Carolyn Strickland, Supervisor

GENERAL HEALTH SERVICES

Health Unit **479.394.2707**
Fax 479.394.6610
  702 Hornbeck Ave, Mena, AR 71953
Brenda Huff, Administrator

COURTS

18th Judicial Circuit Court **479.394.8107**
Fax 479.394.8109
E-mail ....mboehler@cswnet.com
  507 Church Ave, Mena, AR 71953
J W Looney, Judge

POLICE AND SHERIFF

Sheriff's Dept **479.394.2511**
Fax 479.394.1975
Web ....www.cji.net
E-mail ....polkso@cji.net
  507 Church Ave, Mena, AR 71953-3257
Mike Godfrey, Sheriff

EDUCATION SERVICES

Education Station **479.394.3424**
  1314 Amsterdam St, Mena, AR 71953
Linda Willard, Director

Pope County

SOCIAL SERVICES

Dept of Human Svcs **479.968.5596**
Fax 479.968.2102
Web ....www.arkansas.gov
E-mail ....elayne.coffman@arkansas.gov
  701 N Denver Ave, Russellville, AR 72801-3403
Elayne Coffman, Administrator

JUSTICE AGENCY

Juvenile Ofc **479.967.1520**
Fax 479.858.7025
  100 W Main St, Russellville, AR 72801
Harold Taylor, Probation Officer

COURTS

5th Judicial Circuit Court **479.968.3869**
Fax 479.880.1810
  100 W Main St, Russellville, AR 72801-3723
Honorable Ken D. Coker Jr., Judge

POLICE AND SHERIFF

Sheriff's Dept **479.968.2558**
Fax 479.968.6145
  3 Emergency Ln, Russellville, AR 72802-9426
Aaron Duvall, Sheriff

Prairie County

SOCIAL SERVICES

Dept Of Human Svcs **870.998.2581**
Fax 870.998.2582
E-mail ....kelly.chapman@arkansas.gov
  663 Market St, DeValls Bluff, AR 72041
Kelly Chapman, Administrator

GENERAL HEALTH SERVICES

Health - Home Care **870.256.3065**
Fax 870.256.3783
E-mail ....donna.speight@arkansas.gov
  204 Main St, Des Arc, AR 72040
Donna Speight, Rn, Administrator

JUSTICE AGENCY

Juvenile Ofc **870.256.4990**
Fax 870.256.4434
E-mail ....pracojuvcourt@hotmail.com
  204 Courthouse Square, Ste 203, Des Arc, AR 72040
Janie Paosen, Intake Officer

POLICE AND SHERIFF

Sheriff's Dept **870.256.4137**
Fax 870.256.3367
E-mail ....prariecoso@pbsolven.net
  200 Court House Sq, Des Arc, AR 72040
Gary Burnett, Sheriff

EDUCATION SERVICES

Des Arc Head Start **870.256.4491**
Fax 870.256.4491
Web ....www.arheadstart.org
E-mail ....jackie@arheadstart.org
  111 S 3rd St, DesArc, AR 72040
Jackie Pate, Director

Pulaski County

SOCIAL SERVICES

Dept of Human Svcs **501.371.1200**
Fax 501.371.1201
E-mail ....vicki.weems@arkansas.gov
  2636 W Main St, Jacksonville, AR 72076
Vicki Weems, Acting Administrator

Dept Of Human Svcs South 501.682.9200
Fax 501.682.9382
E-mail ....vicki.weems@arkansas.gov
   1105 Martin Luther King Dr, Little Rock, AR 72203
   Vicki Weems, Administrator

Dept Of Human Svcs SW 501.371.1100
Fax 501.371.1101
   6801 Baseline Rd, Little Rock, AR 72209-7400
   Tony Eckline, Administrator

GENERAL HEALTH SERVICES

Central Health Unit **501.280.3100**
Fax 501.280.3180
   3915 W 8th St, Little Rock, AR 72204-2028
   Veronica McDaniel, Administrator

College Station Health Unit **501.490.1602**
Fax 501.490.0156
Web ....www.healthyarkansas.com
E-mail ....ldavis@healthyarkansas.com
   4206 Frazier Pike, College Station, AR 72053
   Larnell Davis, Executive Director

Health Dept **501.982.7477**
   3000 N 1st St, Jacksonville, AR 72076
   Patricia Henderson, Administrator

North Little Rock Health Dept **501.791.8551**
Fax 501.791.8615
Web ....www.arkansas.gov
   2800 N Willow St, North Little Rock, AR 72114-2230
   Carey Wood, Administrator

Southwest Health Unit **501.565.9311**
Fax 501.565.7960
Web ....www.arkansas.gov
E-mail ....vickie.jones@arkansas.gov
   6800 Baseline Rd, Little Rock, AR 72209-5268
   Vickie Jones, Administrator

JUSTICE AGENCY

Youth Svcs **501.340.8250**
Fax 501.340.8259
   201 Broadway St Ste 220, Little Rock, AR 72201
   Charles Mobley, Director

COURTS

**6th Judicial Circuit Court Juvenile Court
Ctr** **501.340.6700**
Fax 501.340.7012
   3001 W Roosevelt Rd, Little Rock, AR 72204
   Honorable Wiley Branton Jr., Judge

POLICE AND SHERIFF

Sheriff's Dept **501.340.6600**
Fax 501.340.7880
   2900 S Woodrow St, Little Rock, AR 72204
   Doc Holladay, Sheriff

EDUCATION SERVICES

**College Station Elementary Head
Start** **501.490.5750**
Fax 501.490.5756
   4710 Frazier Peak, College Station, AR 72053
   Darlene Crosby, Director

**For Incarcerated Parents-Even
Start** **501.660.6833**
Fax 501.666.5997
E-mail ....retajohnson@aristotle.net
   5905 Forest Pl Ste 205, Little Rock, AR 72207
   Reta Johnson, Even Start Director

Randolph County

SOCIAL SERVICES

Dept Of Human Svcs **870.892.4475**
Fax 870.892.9805
   1408 Pace Rd, Pocahontas, AR 72455-4307
   Brenda Pointdexter, Acting Administrator

POLICE AND SHERIFF

Sheriff's Dept **870.892.8888**
Fax 870.892.8681
   1510 Pace Rd, Pocahontas, AR 72455
   Gary Tribble, Sheriff

Saline County

SOCIAL SERVICES

Dept Of Human Svcs **501.315.1600**
Fax 501.778.1260
Web ....www.arkansasstate.gov
E-mail ....albert.marlar@mail.state.ar.us
   1603 Edison Ave, Benton, AR 72015-4629
   Albert Marlar, Administrator

GENERAL HEALTH SERVICES

Health Dept **501.303.5650**
Fax 501.303.5602
E-mail ....karen.mays@arkansa.gov
   1612 Edison Ave, Benton, AR 72015-4630
   Karen Mays, Administrator

JUSTICE AGENCY

Juvenile Ofc **501.303.5730**
Fax 501.303.5665
Web ....www.countyofsaline.org
   102 S Main St, Benton, AR 72015-4330
   Carol Childs, Intake Officer

COURTS

22nd Judicial Circuit Court **501.303.5664**
Fax 501.303.5695
   200 N Main St, Benton, AR 72015-3767
   Honorable Gary M. Arnold, Judge

POLICE AND SHERIFF

Sheriff's Ofc **501.303.5609**
Fax 501.315.5747
   735 S Neeley, Benton, AR 72015
   Bruce Pennington, Sheriff

Scott County

SOCIAL SERVICES

Dept of Human Svcs **479.637.4141**
Fax 479.637.4143
   143 Parker Plz, Waldron, AR 72958
   Linda Tallmadge, Administrator

GENERAL HEALTH SERVICES

Health Dept **479.637.2165**
Fax 479.637.5660
Web ....www.healthy.arkansas.gov
E-mail ....darla.mortimore@arkansas.gov
   316 Featherston St, Waldron, AR 72958
   Darla Mortimore, Administrator

JUSTICE AGENCY

Juvenile Ofc **479.637.4715**
Fax 479.637.5615
E-mail ....scott783@centuryl.net
   190 W 1st St Ste 9, Waldron, AR 72958
   Rodney Hitchcock, Intake Officer

POLICE AND SHERIFF

Sheriff's Ofc **479.637.4156**
Fax 479.637.2610
   100 W 1st St, Waldron, AR 72958
   Cody Carpenter, Sheriff

Searcy County

SOCIAL SERVICES

Dept Of Human Svcs **870.448.3153**
Fax 870.448.5716
Web ....www.adeq.state.ar.us
E-mail ....thomas.sheppard@arkansas.gov
   106 School St, Marshall, AR 72650-8806
   Thomas Sheppard, County Administator

POLICE AND SHERIFF

Sheriff's Dept **870.448.2340**
Fax 870.448.2106
E-mail ....searcycoso2003@yahoo.com
   208 Factory Rd, Marshall, AR 72650
   Kenny Cassell, Sheriff

Sebastian County

SOCIAL SERVICES

Dept Of Health & Human Svcs **479.782.4555**
Fax 479.782.4995
Web ....www.arkansas.gov
E-mail ....gwen.lovelace@arkansas.gov
   616 Garrison Ave Ste 231, Fort Smith,
   AR 72901-2521
   Gwen Lovelace, Administrator

JUSTICE AGENCY

Comprehensive Juvenile Svcs **479.785.4031**
Fax 479.785.5354
   1606 S J St, Fort Smith, AR 72901
   Jon Fernes, Executive Director

Juvenile Detention Ctr **479.783.3532**
Fax 479.784.1532
   801 S A St, Fort Smith, AR 72901-3725
   Fran Hall, Administrator

Juvenile Ofc **479.996.4681**
Fax 479.784.1535
E-mail ....khammond@co.sebastian.ar.us
   301 E. Center St, Rm 202, Greenwood, AR 72936
   Kelly Hammond, Probation Officer

POLICE AND SHERIFF

Fort Smith Police **479.709.5100**
Fax 479.709.5179
   100 S 10th St, Fort Smith, AR 72901
   Kevin Lindsey, Chief

Sheriff's Ofc **479.783.1051**
Fax 479.784.1595
   800 South A St, Fort Smith, AR 72903
   Bill Hollenbeck, Sheriff

EDUCATION SERVICES

Briarwood Head Start **479.648.1908**
   3400 Duke Ave, Fort Smith, AR 72908
   Charlene Carson, Director

Fort Smith Even Start **479.784.8182**
Fax 479.709.6001
Web www.parker.fssc.k12.ar.us
E-mail ....kobrien@fortsmithschools.org
   811 N T St, Fort Smith, AR 72904-5367
   Kathryn O'brien, Even Start Director

Sevier County

SOCIAL SERVICES

Dept of Health & Human Svcs **870.642.2623**
Fax 870.642.2082
Web ....www.arkansas.gov
E-mail ....julia.dyer-moore@arkansas.gov
   304 W Collin Raye Dr Ste 108A, De Queen,
   AR 71832-2000
   Julia Dyer-moore, Administrator

GENERAL HEALTH SERVICES

Health Dept **870.642.2535**
Fax 870.642.5229
Web ....www.Arkansas.gov
   304 N 4th St, De Queen, AR 71832-2829
Teresa Morris, Administrator

COURTS

9th Judicial Circuit Court West **870.584.3592**
Fax 870.584.3599
   183 Hwy. 399 Office 129, Cossatot Community
   College, De Queen, AR 71832

POLICE AND SHERIFF

Sheriff's Ofc **870.642.2125**
Fax 870.642.3916
E-mail ....seviersheriff@windstream.net
   137 W Robinson Rd, De Queen, AR 71832
Monte Stringfellow, Sheriff

EDUCATION SERVICES

De Queen Head Start **870.642.7435**
Fax 870.642.7435
   915 E Heynecker Ave, De Queen, AR 71832
Rose Winer, Director

**Dequeen/Mena Educational
Cooperative** **870.386.2251**
Fax 870.386.7731
Web www.dmec1.dmsc.k12.ar.us
E-mail ....dhicks@dmecl.dmsc.k12.ar.us
   305 South Hornberg Avenue, Gillham, AR 71841
Dianna Hicks, Pre-school Director

Sharp County

GENERAL HEALTH SERVICES

Health Dept **870.994.7364**
Fax 870.994.7117
Web ....www.arkansas.gov
   724 Ash Flat Dr, Ash Flat, AR 72513-9103
Mary Scott, Public Health Nurse

POLICE AND SHERIFF

Sheriff's Ofc **870.994.7355**
Fax 870.994.2212
Web ....www.centurytel.net
E-mail ....sharpcoso@centurytel.net
   30 A Cot Dr, Ash Flat, AR 72513
Mark Counts, Sheriff

EDUCATION SERVICES

Evening Shade Head Start **870.266.3460**
E-mail ....eveningshadeheadstart@yahoo.com
   200 School Dr, Evening Shade, AR 72532
Gina Miller, Director

St. Francis County

SOCIAL SERVICES

Dept of Human Svcs **870.633.1242**
Fax 870.633.5683
Web ....www.state.ar.us
E-mail ....charles.fleming@state.ar.us
   1200 E Broadway St, Forrest City, AR 72335-3919
Charles E. Fleming, Administrator

GENERAL HEALTH SERVICES

Health Dept **870.633.1340**
Fax 870.633.6988
Web ....www.arkansas.gov
   413 N Division St, Forrest City, AR 72335-3231
Bonnie Datson, Administrator

COURTS

1st Judicial Circuit Court **870.633.5995**
Fax 870.630.1203
   313 S Izard Street # 31, Forrest, AR 72335
Ann B Hudson, Judge

POLICE AND SHERIFF

Sheriff's Dept **870.633.2611**
Fax 870.261.1784
Web ....www.cji.net
E-mail ....stfranciscoso@cji.net
   313 S Izard St, Forrest City, AR 72335-3852
Bobby May, Sheriff

EDUCATION SERVICES

Forrest City HS 1 CRDC **870.633.2821**
   954 Rice St, Forrest City, AR 72335-3030
Dorothy Fertha, Director

Stone County

SOCIAL SERVICES

Dept Of Human Svcs **870.269.4321**
Fax 870.269.4324
Web ....www.state.ar.us/dhs
E-mail ....jane.shipman@arkansas.gov
   1821 E Main St, Mountain View, AR 72560
Jane Shipman, Administrator

COURTS

Juvenile Court **870.269.5576**
Fax 870.269.2303
   107 W Main St Ste B, Mountain View,
   AR 72560-9610
Jackie Heck, Probation Officer

POLICE AND SHERIFF

Sheriff's Ofc **870.269.3825**
Fax 870.269.2299
E-mail ....sherifflancebonds@hotmail.com
   1009 Sheriffs Drive, Mountain View, AR 72560
Lance Bonds, Sheriff

Union County

SOCIAL SERVICES

Dept Of Health & Human Svcs **870.862.6631**
Fax 870.862.3907
E-mail ....james.scott@arkansas.gov
   123 W 18th St, El Dorado, AR 71730-3363
James Scott, Administrator

GENERAL HEALTH SERVICES

Health Dept **870.863.5101**
Fax 870.863.0905
Web ....www.healthyarkansas.com
E-mail ....susan.blake@arkansas.gov
   301 American Rd, El Dorado, AR 71730-6554
Susan Blake, Administrator

JUSTICE AGENCY

CASA-13th Judicial District **870.862.2272**
Fax 870.862.2276
E-mail ....13thcasa@sbcglobal.net
   100 West Rd Ste 304, El Dorado, AR 71730-5644
Donnah Martin, Executive Director

Juvenile Ofc **870.863.5153**
Fax 870.863.5154
   300 Thompson Ave, El Dorado, AR 71730-7376
Chris Gilliam, Probation Officer

POLICE AND SHERIFF

Calion Police Dept **870.748.2293**
Fax 870.748.2356
Web ....www.cityofcamden.net
E-mail ....info@arpublicsafety.net
   125 East Main, Calion, AR 71724
Mark Thomas, Police Chief

Sheriff's Dept **870.864.1970**
Fax 870.864.1992
   250 American Rd, El Dorado, AR 71730
Mike Mcdough, Sheriff

Van Buren County

SOCIAL SERVICES

Dept Of Health & Human Svcs **501.745.4192**
Fax 501.745.6400
   449 Ingram St, Clinton, AR 72031-6604
Stephen Geise, Administrator

GENERAL HEALTH SERVICES

Health Dept **501.745.2485**
Fax 501.745.2435
Web ....www.healthy.arkansas.gov
E-mail ....donna.branscum@arkansas.gov
   526 Quality Dr, Clinton, AR 72031
Donna Branscum, Administrator

POLICE AND SHERIFF

Sheriff's Ofc **501.745.3838**
Fax 501.745.4898
E-mail ....sheriffbradley@vbcso.com
   184 Detention Drive, Clinton, AR 72031
Scott Bradley, Sheriff

Washington County

SOCIAL SERVICES

**Washington Dept Of Health & Human
Svcs** **479.521.1270**
Fax 479.521.2311
Web ....www.arkansas.gov
E-mail ....sandra.allen@arkansas.gov
   4044 N Frontage Rd, Fayetteville, AR 72703-5134
Sandra Allen, Administrator

GENERAL HEALTH SERVICES

Health Dept **479.521.8181**
Fax 479.973.8482
   3270 N Wimberly Dr, Fayetteville, AR 72703-4032
Nancy Taylor, Administrator

HIV Clinic **479.973.8450**
Fax 479.973.8452
   3270 N Wimberly Dr, Fayetteville, AR 72703
Dr. Linda Mcghee, Medical Director

MENTAL HEALTH SERVICES

Community Mental Health Svcs **479.750.2020**
Fax 479.750.1739
Web ....www.ozarkguidance.org
E-mail ....rob.gershon@ozarkguidance.org
   2400 S 48th St, Springdale, AR 72762-6683
Rob Gershon, Director

Vista Health Serv **479.521.5731**
Fax 479.521.7683
   4253 N Crossover Rd, Fayetteville, AR 72703
Connie Borengasser, CEO

JUSTICE AGENCY

CASA Of NW Arkansas **479.725.2213**
Fax 479.927.3640
Web ....www.nwacasa.org
E-mail ....crystal@nwacasa.org
   614 E Emma Ave Ste 203, Springdale, AR 72764
Crystal Vickmark, Executive Director

Juvenile Detention Ctr **479.444.1670**
Fax 479.444.1675
   885 W Clydesdale Dr, Fayetteville, AR 72701
Jean E. Mack, Director

COURTS

4th Judicial Circuit Court **479.444.1739**
Fax 479.444.1749
   885 W Clydesdale Dr, Washington County Juvenile
   Court, Fayetteville, AR 72701-8209
Jennifer Bryant, Criminal Intake Officer

Teen Court 479.444.1631
Fax 479.444.1749
E-mail ....lsgage129@cs.com
PO Box 3425, Fayetteville, AR 72702-3425
Scott Gage, Teen Court Coordination

POLICE AND SHERIFF

Fayetteville Police Dept 479.587.3555
Fax 479.587.3563
E-mail ....gtabor@ci.fayetteville.ar.us
100 W Rock St, Ste A, Fayetteville, AR 72701
Greg Tabor, Police Chief

EDUCATION SERVICES

Old Farmington Road Head Start 479.582.5260
Fax 479.521.7809
2350 W Old Farmington Rd, Fayetteville,
AR 72701-6278
Ellen Smith, Director

White County

SOCIAL SERVICES

Dept Of Human Svcs 501.268.8696
Fax 501.268.4803
E-mail ....loyal.crawford@arkansas.gov
608 Rodgers Dr, Searcy, AR 72143
Loyal Crawford, Administrator

JUSTICE AGENCY

Juvenile Ofc 501.279.6234
Fax 501.279.6228
E-mail ....amylynn77@sbcglobal.net
417 N Spruce St, Searcy, AR 72143-4222
Amy Light, Intake Officer

POLICE AND SHERIFF

Sheriff's Dept 501.279.6279
Fax 501.279.6287
Web ....www.wcso.cc
E-mail ....rshourd@sbcglobal.net
1600 E Booth Rd Ste 100, Searcy, AR 72143-8488
Rickey Shourd, Sheriff

EDUCATION SERVICES

Bald Knob Head Start 501.724.3918
Fax 501.724.3918
Web ....www.arheadstart.org
E-mail ....baldknob@capcainc.org
103 W Park Ave, Bald Knob, AR 72010-3162
Donna Edom, Director

Beebe Head Start Ctr 501.882.3803
Fax 501.882.3803
E-mail ....bambig@capcainc.org
1201 W Center St, Beebe, AR 72012-3103
Bambi George, Director

Woodruff County

SOCIAL SERVICES

Woodruff Dept Of Human Svcs 870.347.2537
Fax 870.347.2539
Web ....www.arkansas.gov/dhs
1200 Highway 33 N, Augusta, AR 72006
Elma M Brown, Administrator

GENERAL HEALTH SERVICES

Health Dept 870.347.5915
Fax 870.347.2153
Web ....www.healthy.arkansas.gov
623 N 9th St, Augusta, AR 72006-2129
Debra Neal, Administrator

POLICE AND SHERIFF

Sheriff's Dept 870.347.5152
Fax 870.347.2915
E-mail ....woodruffcoso@cji.net
500 N 3rd St, Augusta, AR 72006
Bruce Golden, Sheriff

Yell County

SOCIAL SERVICES

Dept Of Human Svcs 479.495.2723
Fax 479.495.3051
Web ....www.arkansas.gov
E-mail ....deloris.beasley@arkansas.gov
904 M St, Danville, AR 72833
Deloris Beasley, Administrator

GENERAL HEALTH SERVICES

Health Dept 479.229.3509
Fax 479.229.2386
719 N 5th St, Dardanelle, AR 72834
J M Graves, Administrator

COURTS

15th Judicial Circuit Court 479.495.7975
Fax 479.495.2607
105 E 4th St, Danville, AR 72833-0400
Honorable Terry Sullivan, Circuit Judge

POLICE AND SHERIFF

Sheriff's Ofc 479.495.2811
Fax 479.495.4892
Web ....www.arkwest.com
E-mail ....blgilkey@arkwest.com
4th & Main St, Danville, AR 72833
Bill Gilkey, Sheriff

SPECIAL SERVICES AGENCIES

ADOPTION AGENCIES

Abba Adoption LLC 501.776.2566
Fax 501.776.2564
E-mail ....kandi@abbaadoption.com
422 West Sevier St., Benton, AR 72015
Katie Cox, Director

American Adoptions 479.631.8223
Fax 479.631.8069
Web ....www.americanadoptions.com
217 W Chestnut St, Rogers, AR 72756
Laura Sundusky, Director

American Adoptions 501.370.9191
Fax 479.631.8069
Web ....www.americanadoptions.com
103 S 3rd St, Rogers, AR 72756-6654
Laura Sundusky, Director

Amy Blackwood Law 501.375.5711
Fax 501.481.0003
Web ....www.jahlawfirm.com
E-mail ....aablackwood@sbcglobal.net
1304 W 2nd St, Little Rock, AR 72201-1914
Amy Blackwood, Attorney At Law

Bethany Christian Svcs 501.664.5729
Fax 501.664.5740
Web ....www.bethany.org/arkansas
E-mail ....bcslittlerock@bethany.org
1100 N University Ave Ste 66, Little Rock,
AR 72207-6300
Beth James, Administrative Assistant

**Children's House Crisis Child Care
Program** 479.443.5239
Fax 479.443.9009
2190 S Razorback Rd, Fayetteville, AR 72701
Perri Peters, Education Coordinator

Dana Dean Watson Law Ofc 479.750.2990
Fax 479.750.3343
E-mail ....dwatsonlaw@sbcglobal.net
1748 W Sunset Ave Ste A, Springdale,
AR 72762-5135
Dana Watson, Attorney

Families Are Special 501.758.9184
Fax 501.758.4704
E-mail ....familiesarespecial@comcast.net
2200 Main St N, Little Rock, AR 72114
William Barling, Director

**Treatment Homes, Inc Treatment Foster
Care** 501.372.5039
Fax 501.372.5529
Web ....www.treatmenthomes.org
E-mail ....cajames@treatmenthomes.org
700 W 4th St, Little Rock, AR 72201-2204
James Consevella, Executive Director

Treatment Homes, Inc. 501.372.5039
Fax 501.372.5529
Web ....www.treatmenthomes.org
P.O. Box 1400, Little Rock, AR 72203-1400
COA accredited organization.

United Methodist Children's Home 501.661.0720
Fax 501.296.1714
Web ....www.methodistfamily.org
E-mail ....aaltom@methodistfamily.org
2002 S Fillmore St, Little Rock, AR 72204-4909
Andy Altom, Director

ADVOCACY RESOURCES

Administrative Office of the Courts 501.682.9400
E-mail ....aoc@arkansas.gov
625 Marshall, Little Rock, AR 72201
Jd Gingerich, Director

**AR Dept of Human Services Office of Chief
Counsel** 501.682.8593
E-mail ....misty.boweneubanks@arkansas.gov
PO Box 1437 Slot S260, Little Rock, AR 72225
Misty Eubanks

Attorney ad Litem 501.340.5336
E-mail ....tbyrd29@hotmail.com
1920 N Main St Ste 216, North Little Rock, AR 72114
Tjuana Byrd, attorney

Attorney ad Litem 501.617.1693
E-mail ....dayncourt@cablelynx.com
181 Seashore Point, Hot Springs, AR 71913
Jonnie Dolan

Attorney ad Litem 501.658.3699
E-mail ....kendall.sample@comcast.net
PO Box 7174, North Little Rock, AR 72124
Kendall Sample, attorney

Attorney ad Litem 870.774.7525
E-mail ....amyfreedman@cableone.net
610 Laurel St, Texarkana, AR 71854
Amy Freedman

Children's Advocacy Ctr 479.621.0385
Fax 479.621.0467
E-mail ....cac@nwark.net
2113 Little Flock Dr, Rogers, AR 72756
Beverly Engle, Director

**Disability Rights Ctr-Protection and Advocacy
System** 501.296.1775
Fax 501.296.1779
Web ....www.arkdisabilityrights.org
E-mail ....nanelleneast@arkdisabilityrights.org
1100 N University Ave, Ste 201, Little Rock,
AR 72207-6359
Nan Ellen East, Executive Director

Arkansas

The Children's Advocacy Ctr Of Pine Bluff 870.850.7105
Fax 870.850.7658
E-mail ....cacdirector@pbreynoldscenter.org
211 W 3rd Ave Ste 130, Pine Bluff, AR 71601
Vickie Hooker, Director

BEHAVIORAL HEALTH TREATMENT

Aavalon 501.660.6644
2801 Lee Ave, Little Rock, AR 72205-4327
Les Smith, Psychiatrist

Amicare of Arkansas 479.587.1408
E-mail ....jbice@amicarebehavioral.com
4253 Crossover Road, Fayetteville, AR 72703
Mr. Jack Bice, Accreditation Manager
Joint Commission accredited organization.

Arkansas Baptist Home For Children 870.367.5358
Fax 870.367.5856
Web ....www.abchomes.org
E-mail ....rluper@abchomes.org
222 W Pope St, Monticello, AR 71655
Randy Luper, Director

Arkansas Counseling and Psychodiagnostics,
Inc...870.230.8217
Fax 870.230.8201
E-mail ....ron.snead@arkansas.gov
2506 Country Club Road, Arkadelphia, AR 71923
Ron Snead, Deputy Director
CARF accredited programs available.

Arkansas State Hospital 501.686.9000
E-mail ....linda.wofford@arkansas.gov
305 South Palm Street, Little Rock, AR 72205
Ms. Margie Wofford, Accreditation Manager
Joint Commission accredited organization.

Ascent Children's Health Svcs 870.819.0200
Fax 870.819.0215
Web ....www.ascentchs.com
3012 Turman Dr, Jonesboro, AR 72404
David Guy, Health Officer
CARF accredited programs available.

Baptist Health Medical Center - Little Rock 501.202.2000
Web ....www.baptist-health.org
E-mail ....mkperkin@baptist-health.org
9601 Interstate 630, Exit 7, Little Rock,
AR 72205-7299
Mr. Mike Perkins, Accreditation Manager
Joint Commission accredited organization.

Baxter Regional Medical Center/Center for Individual and
Family Development 870.435.5511
Fax 870.435.5513
Web ....www.baxterregional.org
7345 Highway 62 West, Gassville, AR 72635
CARF accredited programs available.

BHC Pinnacle Pointe Hospital, Inc.............501.223.3322
Web ....www.pinnaclepointehospital.com
E-mail ....michael.beck@psysolutions.com
11501 Financial Centre Parkway, Little Rock,
AR 72211
Mr. Michael Beck, Accreditation Manager
Joint Commission accredited organization.

Billingsley Medical Practice 479.442.2161
230 W Center St, Fayetteville, AR 72701-5934
Robert Billingsley, Psychiatrist

Bost, Inc...479.478.5554
Fax 479.478.5552
Web ....www.bost.org
7701 South Zero Street, Fort Smith, AR 72903
CARF accredited programs available.

Cedar Haven of Mena Regional Health
System 479.243.2380
Fax 479.243.2386
Web ....www.menaregional.com
311 North Morrow, Mena, AR 71953
CARF accredited programs available.

Child Study Ctr...................................501.364.5150
Fax 501.364.1592
Web ....www.childstudycenter.uams.edu
E-mail ....kubacakbrianm@uams.edu
1120 Marshall St, Fl 5, Little Rock, AR 72202
Brianm Kubacak, MD, Medical Director

Children's Homes, Inc...........................870.239.4031
Fax 870.236.1236
Web ....www.childrenshomes.org
E-mail ....micah@childrenshomes.org
5515 Walcott Rd, Paragould, AR 72450-3398
Micah Brinkley, Director Child And Family Services

Community Counseling Services, Inc..........501.624.7111
Web ....www.communitycounselingservices.org
E-mail ....kathy@hsccs.org
125 Dons Way, Hot Springs National Park, AR 71913
Ms. Kathy White, Accreditation Manager
Joint Commission accredited organization.

Community Service, Inc.........................501.354.4589
Fax 501.354.5410
Web ....www.communityserviceinc.com
P.O. Box 679, Morrilton, AR 72110
COA accredited organization.

Conway Human Development Center 501.329.6851
Fax 501.327.2266
Web ....www.CHDConline.com
150 East Siebenmorgen Road, Conway,
AR 72032-4000
CARF accredited programs available.

Cornerstone Community Counseling
Corp...870.869.1500
E-mail ....amwroberts@yahoo.com
106 East Third Street, Imboden, AR 72434
Mrs. Angela Roberts, Accreditation Manager
Joint Commission accredited organization.

Counseling and Education Center, Inc........870.338.8447
E-mail ....ggonner0614@yahoo.com
406 Pecan Street, Helena, AR 72342
Ms. Gracie Giles-Gonner, Accreditation Manager
Joint Commission accredited organization.

Counseling Associates Inc 479.968.1298
Fax 479.968.6053
Web ....www.caiinc.org
E-mail ....bhefley@caiinc.org
110 Skyline Dr, Russellville, AR 72801
Dianne Skaggs, Program Director

Counseling Associates, Inc....................501.327.4889
Fax 501.327.4492
Web ....www.caiinc.org
350 Salem Road, Suite 1, Conway, AR 72034
CARF accredited programs available.

Counseling Consultants, Inc...................870.739.5852
Fax 870.739.1265
Web ....www.ccihelp.com
2860 I-55 Service Road, Marion, AR 72364
CARF accredited programs available.

Counseling Svcs Of Eastern Arkansas 870.338.3900
Fax 870.338.7798
Web ....www.csoea.org
801 Newman Dr, Helena, AR 72342-8950
Terry Anderson, Clinic Coordinator

DaySpring Services of Arkansas, LLC 479.872.5580
Fax 479.872.5581
Web ....www.dayspringbhs.com
E-mail ....mmeggers@dayspringbhs.com
5537 Bleaux Ave, Springdale, AR 72762
Michele Meggers, Business Office Manager
CARF accredited programs available.

Delta Counseling Assoc 870.222.4301
Fax 870.222.6741
Web ....www.deltacounseling.org
2410 Highway 65 N, Mc Gehee, AR 71654-9437
Heather Wagner, Director

Delta Counseling Assoc 870.382.4001
Fax 870.382.6094
Web ....www.deltacounseling.org
E-mail ....p.dottley@deltacounseling.org
741 Highway 65 S, Dumas, AR 71639-3003
Paul Dottley, Director

Delta Counseling Associates, Inc..............870.367.9732
Web ....www.deltacounseling.org
E-mail ....s.davis@deltacounseling.org
790 Roberts Drive, Monticello, AR 71655
Ms. Stacey Davis, Accreditation Manager
Joint Commission accredited organization.

Delta Family Health and Fitness Center for Children,
Inc...870.853.4224
Web ....www.deltafamilycenter.com
E-mail ....deandfc@yahoo.com
815 East St. Louis Street, Hamburg, AR 71646
Mr. Dea Hill, Accreditation Manager
Joint Commission accredited organization.

DHHS Southeast AR HDC 870.226.6774
Fax 870.226.5968
Web ....www.arkansas.gov
E-mail ....judy.adams@arkansas.gov
1 Center Cir, Warren, AR 71671-3033
Judy Adams, Director

Families, Inc. of Arkansas 870.933.6886
Web ....www.familiesinc.net
E-mail ....agatlin@familiesinc.net
1815 Pleasant Grove Road, Jonesboro, AR 72401
Ms. Anna Gatlin, Accreditation Manager
Joint Commission accredited organization.

Family Service Agency, Inc....................501.372.4242
Fax 501.372.6565
Web ....www.helpingfamiliesfirst.org
628 West Broadway, North Little Rock, AR 72114
COA accredited organization.

Florence Crittenton Svc, Inc 501.663.3129
Fax 501.666.8897
E-mail ....djs_fcs@yahoo.com
3600 W 11th St, Little Rock, AR 72204-2121
Debbie Stripling, Operations Manager

Habilitation Centers, Inc........................870.352.8203
E-mail ....matt.wiltshire@millcreekcenters.com
1810 Industrial Drive, Fordyce, AR 71742
Mr. Matt Wiltshire, Accreditation Manager
Joint Commission accredited organization.

Health Resources of Arkansas 870.793.8900
Fax 870.793.4258
Web ....www.healthresourcesofarkansas.com
25 Gap Road, Batesville, AR 72501
CARF accredited programs available.

Hometown Behavorial Health Services of Arkansas,
Inc...870.886.1333
Web ....www.hometownbhs.com
E-mail ....lprondzinski@hometownbhs.com
503 SE Lindsey St., Hoxie, AR 72433
Mrs. Laura Prondzinski, Accreditation Manager
Joint Commission accredited organization.

Hope Behavioral Health Care 870.257.3336
Web ....www.hopebehavioralhealthcare.net
E-mail ....drbokker@yahoo.com
4 Cherokee Village Mall, Cherokee Village,
AR 72529
Dr. Paul Bokker, Accreditation Manager
Joint Commission accredited organization.

Horizon 479.478.6664
Fax 479.478.6793
E-mail ....rob_covington@wacgc.org
3113 S 70th St, Fort Smith, AR 72903-5017
Dr. Rob Covington, Substance Abuse Program Director

KIDS FIRST/UAMS Department of
Pediatrics **501.364.3610**
Fax 501.364.3994
Web ....www.arpediatrics.org/kidsfirst
   1919 West 12th Street, West Suite, Little Rock,
   AR 72202
   CARF accredited programs available.

Kids For the Future, Inc. **870.633.1737**
Fax 870.739.6819
   3998 Highway One North, Forrest City, AR 72335
   CARF accredited programs available.

Life Strategies Counseling, Inc. **870.972.1268**
Web ....www.lscihelp.com
E-mail ....nellie.caldwell@lscihelp.com
   1217 Stone Street, Jonesboro, AR 72401
   Ms. Nellie Caldwell, Accreditation Manager
   Joint Commission accredited organization.

Life Strategies of Arkansas, LLC **870.732.1878**
Web ....www.lifestrategiesar.com
E-mail ....shella.pounds@lifestrategiesar.com
   703 Calvin Avery, West Memphis, AR 72301
   Ms. Shella Pounds, Accreditation Manager
   Joint Commission accredited organization.

Living Hope Southeast, LLC **501.663.5473**
Web ....www.lhsoutheast.com
E-mail ....mikeg@lhsoutheast.com
   100 South University, Suite 401, Little Rock,
   AR 72205
   Mr. Michael Grundy, Accreditation Manager
   Joint Commission accredited organization.

Maxus, Inc. **870.647.1400**
E-mail ....kannkirk@yahoo.com
   1033 Old Burr Road, Warm Springs, AR 72478
   Mrs. Kristi Kirk, Accreditation Manager
   Joint Commission accredited organization.

NeuroRestorative Timber Ridge **800.743.6802**
Fax 501.758.8778
Web ....www.neurorestorative.com
E-mail ....neuroinfo@thementornetwork.com
   PO Box 208, Benton, AR 72018
   Steve Wilkinson, Pediatric Program Director
   Established in 1984, NeuroRestorative Timber Ridge is one of the largest pediatric
   brain injury facilities in the country and has helped hundreds of children and
   adolescents receive the specialized supports, therapies and education they need
   in a setting that promotes growth and independence. Rehabilitative services are
   provided by an interdisciplinary team of clinicians within a specialized Arkansas
   Education Department approved school setting. Family education and training
   is provided to assist families in the child's return to home and community schools.
   NeuroRestorative Timber Ridge is accredited by the Joint Commission on
   Accreditation of Healthcare Organizations (JCAHO) and the Commission on
   Accreditation of Rehabilitation Facilities (CARF).

New Beginnings Behavioral Health Services,
LLC **501.330.1225**
Fax 501.663.1839
Web ....www.nbbhs.org
   20700 Highway 113S, Bigelow, AR 72016
   COA accredited organization.

Northeast Arkansas Community Mental Health Center, Inc.
dba Mid-South Health Systems, Inc. **870.972.4000**
Fax 870.972.4968
   2707 Browns Lane, Jonesboro, AR 72401
   CARF accredited programs available.

Ozark Guidance Center, Inc. **479.750.2020**
Web ....www.ozarkguidance.org
E-mail ....louise.mashburn@ozarkguidance.org
   2400 South 48th Street, Springdale, AR 72762
   Mrs. Louise Mashburn, Accreditation Manager
   Joint Commission accredited organization.

Ozark Guidance Ctr **870.423.2758**
Fax 870.423.3199
Web ....www.ozarkguidance.org
E-mail ....deborah.dawes@ozarkguidance.org
   208 Highway 62 W, Berryville, AR 72616
   Deborah Dawes, Director

Ozark Guidance Ctr **479.738.2878**
Fax 479.738.1132
Web ....www.ozarkguidance.org
E-mail ....cheri.carden@ozarkguidance.org
   1104 N College St, Huntsville, AR 72740
   Cheri Carden, Director

Pathfinder, Inc. **501.982.0528**
Fax 501.985.1462
Web ....www.pathfinderinc.org
   2520 West Main, Jacksonville, AR 72076
   Colleen Black, Director
   CARF accredited programs available.

People Advocating Transition, Inc. **501.812.5545**
Fax 501.812.5546
   4702 West Commerical Drive, Suite C, North Little
   Rock, AR 72116
   CARF accredited programs available.

Perspectives Behavioral Health Management,
LLC **479.452.5040**
Fax 479.452.5047
   P.O. Box 23070, Barling, AR 72923
   COA accredited organization.

Pioneer Ridge Ctr **479.587.1408**
   4253 N Crossover Rd, Fayetteville, AR 72703-4593
   Jennifer Kelly, Assistant Administrator

Professional Counseling Associates **501.221.1843**
Fax 501.221.2376
Web ....www.pca-ar.org
E-mail ....lesley.nalley@pca-ar.org
   3601 Richards Road, North Little Rock, AR 72117
   Lesley Nalley, Executive Director
   CARF accredited programs available.

Rivendell Behavioral Health Services of
Arkansas **501.316.1255**
Web ....www.rivendellofarkansas.com
E-mail ....laura.davis@uhsinc.com
   100 Rivendell Drive, Benton, AR 72019
   Ms. Laura Davis, Accreditation Manager
   Joint Commission accredited organization.

Simple Truths Counseling **479.461.3281**
Web ....simple_truths@gmail.com
E-mail ....simple_truths@cox-internet.com
   3023 Moss Rd, Van Buren, AR 72956-6889
   Kathleen Marks-Henderson, Director

South Arkansas Regional Health Center **870.862.7921**
Fax 870.864.2490
Web ....www.sarhc.org
   715 North College, El Dorado, AR 71730
   CARF accredited programs available.

South Arkansas Youth Services, Inc. **870.234.6550**
Fax 870.234.3822
Web ....www.saysyouth.org
E-mail ....jkwalsh@sbcglobal.net
   124 South Jackson, Ste 308, Magnolia, AR 71753
   Jerry Walsh, Director
   CARF accredited programs available.

Southeast Arkansas Behavioral Healthcare System,
Inc. **870.534.1834**
Fax 870.534.5798
Web ....www.sabhs.org
   2500 Rike Drive, Pine Bluff, AR 71603
   Bessie Lancelin, Director of Clinical Services
   CARF accredited programs available.

Southwest Arkansas Counseling and Mental Health Center,
Inc. **870.773.4655**
Fax 870.772.4650
Web ....www.swacmhc.com
E-mail ....thickerson@swacmhc.com
   2904 Arkansas Boulevard, Texarkana, AR 71854
   Tim Hickerson, Program Director
   CARF accredited programs available.

Texarkana Behavioral Associates, L.C. **479.494.5700**
Web ....vistahealthservices.com
E-mail ....sharons@vistahealthservices.com
   10301 Mayo Drive, Barling, AR 72923
   Mrs. Sharon Shultz, Accreditation Manager
   Joint Commission accredited organization.

Texarkana Behavioral Associates, L.C. **479.521.5731**
Web ....vistahealthservices.com
E-mail ....rosew@vistahealthservices.com
   4253 Crossover Road, Fayetteville, AR 72703
   Mrs. Rose Marie Woods, Accreditation Manager
   Joint Commission accredited organization.

The BridgeWay, Inc. **501.771.1500**
Web ....www.thebridgeway.com
E-mail ....barry.pipkin@uhsinc.com
   21 BridgeWay Road, North Little Rock, AR 72113
   Mr. Barry Pipkin, Accreditation Manager
   Joint Commission accredited organization.

The Centers for Youth and Families **501.666.8686**
Web ....www.youthandfamilies.org
E-mail ....mdawson@cfyf.org
   5800 W. 10th Street, Ste. 101, Little Rock, AR 72204
   Ms. Melissa Dawson, Accreditation Manager
   Joint Commission accredited organization.

The Logan Centers, Inc. **870.494.4600**
Web ....logancenters.com
E-mail ....jeannie.boeckmann@logancenters.com
   1800 Lindauer Rd., Forrest City, AR 72335
   Ms. Jeannie Boeckmann, Accreditation Manager
   Joint Commission accredited organization.

Trinity Behavioral Health Care System,
Inc. **870.647.1400**
E-mail ....kannkirk@yahoo.com
   1033 Old Burr Road, Warm Springs, AR 72478
   Mrs. Kristi Kirk, Accreditation Manager
   Joint Commission accredited organization.

United Methodist Behavioral Hospital **501.803.3388**
Web ....www.methodistfamily.org
E-mail ....aaltom@methodistfamily.org
   1601 Murphy Drive, Maumelle, AR 72113
   Mr. Andy Altom, Accreditation Manager
   Joint Commission accredited organization.

United Methodist Children's Home, Inc. **501.661.0720**
Web ....www.methodistfamily.org
E-mail ....cgammon@methodistfamily.org
   2002 South Fillmore Street, Little Rock, AR 72204
   Mr. Craig Gammon, Accreditation Manager
   Joint Commission accredited organization.

University of Arkansas for Medical
Sciences **501.526.8100**
Web ....www.psych.uams.edu
E-mail ....tpetty@uams.edu
   4224 Shuffield Drive, Little Rock, AR 72205
   Mrs. Tracy Petty, Accreditation Manager
   Joint Commission accredited organization.

Arkansas

Watersprings Ranch 870.772.7187
Fax 870.772.3782
Web ....www.watersprings.com
E-mail ....davidw@watersprings.com
7707 Sanderson Ln, Texarkana, AR 71854
Aaron Allen, Director Of Social Services

**Western Arkansas Counseling and Guidance
Center** 479.452.6650
Fax 479.785.9495
Web ....www.wacgc.org
E-mail ....jim_west@wacgc.org
3111 S 70th St, Fort Smith, AR 72903
Jim West, Director
CARF accredited programs available.

Youth Bridge, Inc. 479.575.9471
Fax 479.575.9149
Web ....www.youthbridge.com
2153 Joyce, Suite 201, Fayetteville, AR 72703
COA accredited organization.

Youth Home, Inc. 501.821.5500
Web ....www.youthhome.org
E-mail ....beverly.foti@youthhome.org
20400 Colonel Glenn Road, Little Rock,
AR 72210-5323
Ms. Beverly Foti, Accreditation Manager
Joint Commission accredited organization.

CHILDREN'S HOSPITAL

Arkansas Methodist Medical Center 870.239.7000
900 West Kingshighway, Paragould, AR 72450
Brad Bloemer, Administration

Baptist Health Medical Center 501.202.2000
9601 Interstate 630 Exit 7, Little Rock, AR 72205
Doug Weeks, Director

**Baptist Health Medical Center - North Little
Rock** 501.202.3000
E-mail ....harrison.dean@baptist-health.org
3333 Springhill Dr, North Little Rock, AR 72117
Harrison Dean, Vice President

Conway Regional Medical Center 501.329.3831
2302 College Ave, Conway, AR 72034
James Lambert, Chief Executive Officer

De Queen Medical Center 870.584.4111
1306 Collin Raye Dr, De Queen, AR 71832
Angie House, Director

Delta Memorial Hospital 870.382.4303
811 South Highway 65, Dumas, AR 71639
Cris Bolin, Manager

Drew Memorial Hospital 870.367.2411
E-mail ....m.leyfield@drewmemorial.org
778 Scogin Dr, Monticello, AR 71655
Michael Leyfield, Chief Executive Officer

Eureka Springs Hospital 479.253.7400
24 Norris St, Eureka Springs, AR 72632
Jodi Smith, Director

Forrest City Medical Center 870.261.0000
1601 Newcastle Rd, Forrest City, AR 72335
Brett Kinman, Chief Executive Officer

Great River Medical Center 870.838.7300
1520 N Division St, Blytheville, AR 72315

Harris Hospital 870.523.8911
1205 McLain St, Newport, AR 72112
Misty Gates, Chief Financial Officer

Jefferson Regional Medical Center 870.541.7100
1600 West 40th Ave, Pine Bluff, AR 71603
Walter Johnson, Administrator

Magnolia Hospital 870.235.3000
101 Hospital Dr, Magnolia, AR 71753
Margaret West, Chief Executive Officer

Mercy Medical Center 479.338.8000
2710 Rife Medical Ln, Rogers, AR 72758

National Park Medical Center 501.321.1000
1910 Malvern Ave, Hot Springs, AR 71901
Mandy Golleher, Public Relations Director

Northwest Medical Center Bentonville 479.553.1000
3000 Medical Center Pkwy, Bentonville, AR 72712
Tripp Smith, Chief Executive Officer

Northwest Medical Center Springdale 479.751.5711
609 West Maple Ave, Springdale, AR 72764

Ouachita Medical Center 870.836.1000
638 California St, Camden, AR 71701
David Cicero, Chief Executive Officer

River Valley Medical Center 479.229.4677
200 North Third St, Dardanelle, AR 72834
Joe Mitchell, Chief Executive Officer

Saint Marys Regional Medical Center 479.968.2841
1808 West Main St, Russellville, AR 72801
Mike Mccor, Chief Executive Officer

Saline Memorial Hospital 501.776.6000
1 Medical Park Dr, Benton, AR 72015

Sparks Regional Medical Center 479.441.4000
1001 Towson Ave, Fort Smith, AR 72901
Robert Freeman, Director Of Human Resources

St Bernards Medical Center 870.972.4100
225 East Jackson Ave, Jonesboro, AR 72401
Chris Barber, President/CEO

St Edward Mercy Medical Center 479.314.6000
7301 Rogers Ave, Fort Smith, AR 72903
Jeff Johnston, Director

St Josephs Mercy Health Center 501.622.1000
300 Werner St, Hot Springs, AR 71913
Tim Johnson, Chief Executive Officer

COUNSELING SERVICES

**Southwest Arkansas Counseling And Mental Health
Ctr** 870.845.3110
Fax 870.845.5617
E-mail ....mcluts@swacmhc.com
508 N 2nd St, Nashville, AR 71852-0576
Mike Cluts, Director

Southwest Arkansas Counseling Ctr 870.921.5482
Fax 870.921.5482
27 Courthouse Sq, Lewisville, AR 71845
Angie Brown, Case Manager

St Bernard's Counseling 870.930.9090
Fax 870.931.4581
615 E Matthews Ave Ste A, Jonesboro, AR 72401
Dr. Laneel Lovelace, Office Manager

CRISIS & SHELTER CARE

Abuse Prevention Program 870.269.9941
Fax 870.269.9942
205 Blanchard Ave, Mountain View, AR 72560
Judd Farar, Director

Angels Of Grace-Domestic Violence Svcs 870.338.8447
Fax 870.338.8048
E-mail ....ggonner0614@yahoo.com
406 Pecan, Helena, AR 72342-3212
Gracie Gonner, Director

Consolidated Youth Svcs 870.239.8865
205 S 3 1/2 St, Paragould, AR 72450
Tom Underwood, Counselor And Non-Residential Case Worker

Consolidated Youth Svcs 870.972.1110
Fax 870.972.5433
4220 Stadium Blvd, Jonesboro, AR 72404
Bonnie Smith, Director

Courage House-Domestic Violence Ctr 870.246.3122
Fax 870.246.6912
E-mail ....Awac1@Sbcglobal.Net
1419 Hunter St, Arkadelphia, AR 71923
Cheryl Allen, Director

Crisis Ctr For Women 479.782.1821
Fax 479.782.9035
Web ....www.crisisinterventioncenter.org
E-mail ....nbabb@crisisinterventioncenter.org
5603 S 14th St, Fort Smith, AR 72901-4641
Nicki Babb, Director

Ctrs For Youth And Families 501.666.6833
Fax 501.666.5997
Web ....www.centersforyouthandfamilies.org
5905 Forest Pl Ste 205, Little Rock, AR 72207
Heather Bennett, Marketing Director

Domestic Violence Prevention Hotline 501.278.4673
Fax 501.278.5829
E-mail ....wcdvp@sbcglobal.net
307 W Woodruff, Searcy, AR 72145
Kaye Candlish, Director

Dove House Inc-Domestic Violence 501.745.5657
Fax 501.745.7406
Web ....www.clintoncable.net
E-mail ....Dove@Clintoncable.Net
PO Box 806, Clinton, AR 72031-0806
Christina Stone, Director

East AR Youth Svcs 870.739.4219
Fax 870.739.4479
E-mail ....madelyn.keith@eays.org
104 Cypress Ave, Marion, AR 72364-1819
Madelyn P. Keith, Director

Families In Transition-Domestic Violence 870.732.4077
Fax 870.732.1061
E-mail ....fitfamilies@comcast.net
PO Box 15, West Memphis, AR 72303-0015
Marla Peden, Director

Family Resource Center 870.942.7373
Fax 870.942.5808
1685 Highway 270 East, Sheridan, AR 72150
Sandra Wallace, Director

Family Violence Prevention 870.793.4011
Fax 870.793.2788
E-mail ....fvp2943@sbcglobal.net
PO Box 2943, Batesville, AR 72503-2943
Rebecca Riley, Director

Human Development Ctr Jonesboro 870.932.4043
Fax 870.935.3463
E-mail ....forrest.steele@arkansas.gov
4701 Colony Dr, Jonesboro, AR 72404
Forrest Steele, Superintendent

Margies Haven House Inc 501.362.6757
Fax 501.362.7370
E-mail ....rsanford@arlegalservices.org
PO Box 954, Heber Springs, AR 72543-0954
Rita Sanford, Director

Millcreek Of Arkansas 870.352.8203
Fax 870.352.5311
Web ....www.yfcs.com/millcreek_ar.html
E-mail ....info.mc-ar@yfcs.com
Hwy 79 N, Fordyce, AR 71742
Lindsey Walley, Medical Director

Options Inc-Domestic Violence Program 870.460.0684
Fax 870.460.0784
E-mail ....watchman59@yahoo.com
110 N Main St, Monticello, AR 71655
Brenda Noble, Director

Ouachita Children's Ctr 501.623.5591
Fax 501.623.4226
E-mail ....wharris@occnet.org
339 Charteroak St, Hot Springs, AR 71901
Linda Ragsdale, Director

**Peace At Home Family Shelter-Domestic
Violence** 479.442.9811
Fax 479.587.1817
Web ....www.nwark.com
E-mail ....tmills@nwark.com
1200 N Garland Ave, Fayetteville, AR 72703
Terasa Mills, Director

Rape Crisis Ctr 501.801.2700
Fax 501.801.2702
   628 W Broadway St Ste 300, North Little Rock,
   AR 72206
   Kathy Findley, Director

Restoration Of Hope-Domestic Violence 870.672.4341
Fax 870.672.4777
E-mail ....restofhope@cpomail.net
   111 W. 6th Street, Stuttgart, AR 72160
   Charlotte Carrol, Director

Safe Haven-Crisis Line 501.315.7233
Fax 501.315.3991
E-mail ....s.c.safehaven@sbcglobal.net
   PO Box 1100, Benton, AR 72018-1100
   Cinthia Gattin, Director

Serenity House-Domestic Violence
Program 870.424.7576
Fax 870.424.7498
E-mail ....serenity@mtnhome.com
   213 E 5th St, Mountain Home, AR 72653
   Lori Adkins, Director

Southern Christian Home 501.354.2428
Fax 501.354.2429
Web ....www.schome.org
E-mail ....sch@schome.org
   100 W Harding St, Morrilton, AR 72110-2018
   Wayne Bartley, Director

Support Of Women's Svcs 870.435.6200
Fax 870.435.2063
Web ....www.suddenlinkmail.com
E-mail ....drlprinc@netscape.net
   116 Snow Ball Drive, Gassville, AR 72635
   Darleen Prine, Executive Director

The Dorcas House-Domestic Violence 501.374.4022
Fax 501.370.0804
   823 S Park St, Little Rock, AR 72202
   Dorcas Vangilst, Director

The Haven-Northeast Arkansas-Domestic
Violence 870.532.6669
Fax 870.532.6660
E-mail ....thehavennea@att.net
   PO Box 1062, Blytheville, AR 72316-1062
   Angelia Cooper, Director

The Lord's Ranch 870.647.2541
Fax 870.647.2337
   1033 Old Burr Rd, Warm Springs, AR 72478-9077
   Ted Suhl, Executive Director

The Safe Place-Domestic Violence 501.354.1884
Fax 501.354.4668
E-mail ....Thesafeplace@Suddenlinkmail.Com
   PO Box 364, Morrilton, AR 72110-0364
   Jo Warren, Director

Vera Lloyd Presbyterian Home & Family
Svcs 501.666.8195
Fax 501.666.8197
Web ....www.veralloyd.org
E-mail ....lynwhaley@veralloyd.org
   1501 N University Ave Ste 345, Little Rock, AR 72207
   Lyn Whaley, CEO

Vera Lloyd Presbyterian Home & Family
Svcs 870.367.9035
Fax 870.367.9038
Web ....www.seark.net
   745 Old Warren Rd, Monticello, AR 71655-9713
   Raymon Parson, Campus Director

Women's Shelter-Domestic Violence 479.246.9999
Fax 479.246.7074
E-mail ....aalbright@nwaws.org
   PO Box 1059, Rogers, AR 72757
   Angie Albright, Director

Womens Crisis Ctr Of South Arkansas 870.836.0375
Fax 870.836.0394
E-mail ....acadv6@yahoo.com
   1116 W Washington St, Camden, AR 71711
   Tesha Sandero, Director

EDUCATION

Cass Job Corp 479.667.3686
Fax 479.667.3989
   21424 N Highway 23, Ozark, AR 72949
   Jesse James III, Center Director

Neuro Restorative™
Rebuilding Lives After Brain Injury

NeuroRestorative Timber Ridge 800.743.6802
Fax 501.758.8778
Web ....www.neurorestorative.com
E-mail ....neuroinfo@thementornetwork.com
   PO Box 208, Benton, AR 72018
   Steve Wilkinson, Pediatric Program Director

Established in 1984, NeuroRestorative Timber Ridge is one of the largest pediatric brain injury facilities in the country and has helped hundreds of children and adolescents receive the specialized supports, therapies and education they need in a setting that promotes growth and independence. Rehabilitative services are provided by an interdisciplinary team of clinicians within a specialized Arkansas Education Department approved school setting. Family education and training is provided to assist families in the child's return to home and community schools. NeuroRestorative Timber Ridge is accredited by the Joint Commission on Accreditation of Healthcare Organizations (JCAHO) and the Commission on Accreditation of Rehabilitation Facilities (CARF).

FOSTER CARE AGENCIES

Fmailies Are Special Inc (FASI) 501.785.9184
Fax 501.758.4704
   2200 Main St, North Little Rock, AR 72119

Gladney Center for Adoption 501.791.3126
E-mail ....info@gladney.org
   PO Box 1306, Fayetteville, AR 72701

SOCIAL SERVICES

Arkansas Children's Hospital 501.364.1100
Fax 501.364.3938
   1 Childrens Way, Little Rock, AR 15698
   Dr Jonathan Bates, CEO

Arkansas Resource And Referral System 501.682.9699
Fax 501.682.4897
Web ....www.arkansas.gov/childcare
   700 Main St, Little Rock, AR 72203
   Kathy Stegall, Administrator

Arkansas Sheriff's Youth Ranch 870.793.6841
Fax 870.793.9012
Web ....www.youthranches.com
E-mail ....mike@youthranches.com
   100 Saint Vincent Pl, Batesville, AR 72501-7902
   Thomas M. Comnock, CEO

CASA 479.880.1195
Fax 479.880.0163
E-mail ....arcasa5gb@centurytel.net
   100 West Main Street, Russellville, AR 72811
   Genney Baker, Program Director

Children Of North Central Arkansas 870.793.5233
Fax 870.793.4035
Web ....www.wrpdd.org
   1652 White Dr, Batesville, AR 72503
   Debbie Webb, Director

Children's Safety Ctr 479.872.6183
Fax 479.750.2190
   614 E Emma Ave Ste 200, Springdale, AR 72764
   Elizabeth Shackelford, Director

Crowley's Ridge Development Council, Inc.....870.931.6331
Fax 870.935.1330
Web ....www.daycarefoodprog.org
E-mail ....jennifer@crdcnea.com
   213 N Fisher Street, Jonesboro, AR 72401
   Jenifer Carlisle, Director

Easter Seals Arkansas 501.227.3600
Fax 501.227.3658
Web ....www.ar.easterseals.com
   3920 Woodland Heights Road, Little Rock, AR 72212
   CARF accredited programs available.

Friends For Life 501.305.4500
E-mail ....kim.moss@friendsforlifecorp.org
   914 E Race Ave, Searcy, AR 72143-4617
   Kim Moss, Director Of Grants Management

Methodist Counceling Clinic 479.582.5565
Fax 479.582.5574
   2592 N Gregg Ave, Fayetteville, AR 72703
   Cindy Coleman, Director Of Outpatient Services

North West Arkansas Child Care Resource And Referral Ctr,
Inc..479.751.3463
Fax 479.751.1110
Web ....www.nwachildcare.org
E-mail ....cthornto@jtlshop.jonesnet.org
   614 E Emma Ave Ste 135, Springdale,
   AR 72764-4400
   Carleen Thornton, Director

Ouachita Children's Center 501.623.5591
Fax 501.623.4226
   P.O. Box 1180, Hot Springs, AR 71902-1180
   COA accredited organization.

United Family Services, Inc..................870.534.3386
Fax 870.534.0350
Web ....www.ufamservices.com
   616 S. Linden Street, Pine Bluff, AR 71601
   COA accredited organization.

SPECIAL NEEDS

Arkansas Children's Hospital Progressive Rehabilitation
Program 501.364.1390
Fax 501.364.1139
Web ....www.archildrens.org
   800 Marshall Street, Little Rock, AR 72202-3591
   CARF accredited programs available.

Arkansas Congress of Parents & Teachers 501.753.5247
E-mail ....arpta_office@yahoo.com
   PO Box 1015, North Little Rock, AR 72115

Arkansas Project Children w/Deaf-Blind 501.682.4222
   1401 W Capitol Ste 450, Little Rock, AR 72201
   Martha Asti, Director

BAPTIST HEALTH Rehabilitation Institute 501.202.7008
Fax 501.202.7693
Web ....www.baptist-health.org
   9601 Interstate 630, Exit 7, Little Rock, AR 72205
   CARF accredited programs available.

Brain Injury Association of Arkansas 800.235.2443
E-mail ....info@brainassociation.org
   PO Box 26236, Little Rock, AR 72221

DDS Children's Services 501.682.1461
E-mail ....refarley@juno.com
   PO Box 1437, Little Rock, AR 72203

Easter Seals Arkansas 501.227.3600
E-mail ....info@eastersealsar.com
   3920 Woodland Heights Rd, Little Rock, AR 72212
   Sharon Moone-Jochums, Chief Executive Officer

Learning Disabilities Association 501.666.8777
E-mail ....ldaa@sbcglobal.net
   7509 Cantrell Rd Ste 103C, Little Rock, AR 72207

Arkansas

LearningRx Learning Center **501.223.9500**
E-mail ....jcaldwell@learninggateways.com
   11825 Hinson Rd, Ste 102, Little Rock, AR 72212
   Jenny Caldwell, Director

Mental Health America in NW Arkansas **479.571.3024**
E-mail ....marymartin7@gmail.com
   PO Box 4714, Fayetteville, AR 72702

NAMI Arkansas **800.844.0381**
E-mail ....nami-ar@nami.org
   712 W 3rd St Ste 200, Little Rock, AR 72201
   Kim Arnold, Executive Director

National Multiple Sclerosis Society **501.663.8104**
Fax 501.666.4355
E-mail ....ARR@NMSS.ORG
   1100 N University Ste 255, Little Rock, AR 72207

Neuro Restorative™
Rebuilding Lives After Brain Injury

NeuroRestorative Timber Ridge **800.743.6802**
Fax 501.758.8778
Web ....www.neurorestorative.com
E-mail ....neuroinfo@thementornetwork.com
   PO Box 208, Benton, AR 72018
   Steve Wilkinson, Pediatric Program Director

Established in 1984, NeuroRestorative Timber Ridge is one of the largest pediatric brain injury facilities in the country and has helped hundreds of children and adolescents receive the specialized supports, therapies and education they need in a setting that promotes growth and independence. Rehabilitative services are provided by an interdisciplinary team of clinicians within a specialized Arkansas Education Department approved school setting. Family education and training is provided to assist families in the child's return to home and community schools. NeuroRestorative Timber Ridge is accredited by the Joint Commission on Accreditation of Healthcare Organizations (JCAHO) and the Commission on Accreditation of Rehabilitation Facilities (CARF).

Northwest Arkansas Community Parent Ctr **800.748.9768**
E-mail ....ldonald@supports.org
   6836 Isaacs Orchard Rd, Springdale, AR 72762
   Keith Vire, Chief Executive Officer

PEACE **501.852.8448**
E-mail ....tinaalexander@peaceinark.com
   PO Box 224, Vilonia, AR 72173

The Arc of Arkansas **501.375.7770**
E-mail ....shitt@arcark.org
   2004 S Main St, Little Rock, AR 72206
   Steven Hitt, Executive Director

UCP of Arkansas **800.228.6174**
E-mail ....info@ucpcark.org
   9720 N Rodney Parham Rd, Little Rock, AR 72227

Univ of Arkansas for Medical Sciences **501.686.5135**
Fax 501.686.8689
   4301 W Markham # 500, Little Rock, AR 72205
   John Greenfield Phd, Chairman

SUBSTANCE ABUSE TREATMENT

Counseling Clinic, Inc. **501.315.4224**
Fax 501.776.0411
Web ....www.cc-inc.org
   307 East Sevier Street, Benton, AR 72015
   Michelle Johnson, director
   CARF accredited programs available.

Prevention Resource Ctr **501.372.4242**
Fax 501.372.6565
Web ....www.helpingfamiiles.org
E-mail ....hmiller@fsainc.org
   628 W Broadway St Ste 300, North Little Rock, AR 72114-5547
   Hayse Miller, Program Director

California

Edmund Brown, Governor
State Capital Building
Sacramento, CA 95814
916.445.2841
916.558.3160 (Fax)
www.govmail.ca.gov
www.gov.ca.gov

Shalinee Hunter, Juvenile Justice Specialist
Correction Standard Authority
600 Bercut Drive
Sacramento, CA 95811
916.322.8081
916.445.5796 (Fax)
shalinee.hunter@cdcr.ca.gov

Sandra McBrayer, SAG Chair
San Diego Children's Initiative
4438 Inghram St
San Diego, CA 92109
858.581.5880
cislm@san.rr.com

CRISIS NUMBERS

Child Abuse Reporting . . .916.445.2771   Missing Child Reporting . .800.587.4357

STATE SERVICES

SOCIAL SERVICES

California Dept of Social Svcs 916.657.2598
Fax 916.651.6569
E-mail . . . . .will.lightbourne@dss.ca.gov
  744 P St, Sacramento, CA 95814
  Will Lightbourne, Director

California Health and Human Svcs Agency 916.654.3454
Fax 916.654.3343
Web . . . . .www.chhs.ca.gov
  1600 9th St Ste 460, Sacramento, CA 95814-6439
  Diana Dooley, Secretary

GENERAL HEALTH SERVICES

California Dept of Health Care Svcs (DHS) 916.440.7400
Fax 916.440.7404
Web . . . . .www.dhs.ca.gov
E-mail . . . . .toby.douglas@dhcs.ca.gov
  1501 Capitol Ave, Sacramento, CA 95814-5005
  Toby Douglas, Director

California Dept of Rehabilitation 916.324.1313
Fax 916.558.5806
Web . . . . .www.dor.ca.gov
  721 Capitol Mall, Sacramento, CA 95814-4702
  Anthony P Sour, Director

Children with Special Health Needs CA 916.327.1400
Fax 916.327.1106
  PO Box 997413, Sacramento, CA 95899
  Robert Dimand, Director

Maternal, Child & Adolescent Health CA 916.650.0300
Fax 916.650.0305
E-mail . . . . .KCamacho@cdph.ca.gov
  1615 Capitol Ave MS 8300, Sacramento, CA 95814
  Katherine Camacho, Director

MENTAL HEALTH SERVICES

California Dept of Rehabilitation 916.558.5874
Fax 916.321.1313
E-mail . . . . .publicaffairs@dor.ca.gov
  721 Capitol Mall, Sacramento, CA 95814

Dept Of Alcohol And Drug Programs 916.445.1943
Fax 916.324.7338
Web . . . . .www.adp.ca.gov
E-mail . . . . .rzito@adp.ca.gov
  1700 K St, Sacramento, CA 95811
  Michael Cunningham, Director

JUSTICE AGENCY

California Dept of Corrections 916.323.6001
Fax 916.322.2877
Web . . . . .www.cdcr.ca.gov
E-mail . . . . .john.dovey@cdcr.ca.gov
  1515 S Street, Suite 502, Sacramento, CA 95814
  John Dovey, Director

California Dept of Corrections and Rehabilitation Div of
Juvenile Justice 510.563.5348
Fax 510.563.5359
  338 Pendleton Way, Ste 338, Oakland, CA 94621
  Mark Sirdlund, Supervisor

Correctional Educ Division CA 916.445.8035
Fax 916.324.1416
E-mail . . . . .doug.mckeever@cdcr.ca.gov
  PO Box 942883, Sacramento, CA 94283
  Doug Mckeever, Director

Dept of Juvenile Justice .916.262.1480
Fax 916.442.2637
Web . . . . .www.cya.ca.gov/
E-mail . . . . .bernard.warner@cdcr.ca.gov
  1515 S St, Suite 502, Sacramento, CA 95814
  Bernard Warner, Chief Deputy Director

District Attorney Administration 213.974.3512
Fax 213.687.8525
E-mail . . . . .scooley@da.lacounty.gov
  210 W Temple St Fl 18, Los Angeles, CA 90012
  Steve Cooley, District Attorney

Victim/Witness Program 209.385.7385
Fax 209.725.3668
E-mail . . . . .ldesantis@co.merced.ca.us
  720 W 20th St, Merced, CA 95340-3702
  Lisa Desantis, Program Coordinator

Victims Compensation Program 800.777.9229
Fax 916.323.4626
  630 K St, Sacramento, CA 95814
  Richard Anderson, Chief Deputy Executive Officer

COURTS

Administrative Ofc Of The Courts 415.865.4200
Fax 415.865.4228
  455 Golden Gate Ave, San Francisco, CA 94102

POLICE AND SHERIFF

Highway Patrol 916.843.3000
  PO Box 942898, Sacramento, CA 94298-0001

EDUCATION SERVICES

California Dept of Education 916.319.0800
Fax 916.319.0100
Web . . . . .www.cde.ca.gov
  1430 N St, Suite 5602, Sacramento, CA 95814
  Tom Porlakson, State Superintendent Of Public Instruction

California School For The Blind 510.794.3800
Fax 510.794.3813
Web . . . . .www.csb-cde.ca.gov
E-mail . . . . .swittenstein@csb-cde.ca.gov
  500 Walnut Ave, Fremont, CA 94536-4365
  Stuart Wittenstein, Superintendent

California School For The Deaf 510.794.3666
Fax 510.794.2409
E-mail . . . . .hklopping@csdfe-cde.ca.gov
  39350 Gallaudet Dr, Fremont, CA 94538
  Henry Klopping, Superintendent

Exceptional Parents Unlimited 559.229.2000
Fax 559.229.2956
E-mail . . . . .info@exceptionalparents.org
  4440 N First St, Fresno, CA 93726
  Narion Karian, Executive Director

Homeless Education California 916.319.0383
Fax 916.319.0972
E-mail . . . . .lwheeler@cde.ca.gov
  1430 N St Ste 4401, Sacramento, CA 95814
  Leanne Wheeler, Director

Special Education Divison California 916.445.4613
Fax 916.327.3706
E-mail . . . . .fbalcon@cde.ca.gov
  1430 North St Ste 2401, Sacramento, CA 95814
  Fred Balcon, Director

LABOR & WORKFORCE EDUCATION

Labor and Workforce Development Agency 916.327.9064
Fax 916.327.9158
Web . . . . .www.labor.ca.gov
  801 K St Ste 2101, Sacramento, CA 95814-3521
  Marty Morgenstern, Secretary

California

COUNTY SERVICES

Alameda County

SOCIAL SERVICES

Children & Family Svcs **510.670.9765**
Fax 510.780.8620
E-mail .... eshore@acgov.org
24100 Amador Street, 5th Floor, Hayward, CA 94577
Erika Shore, Division Director (Concurrent Planning)

Family Svcs Section III/Adoptions **510.268.2444**
Fax 510.268.7022
401 Broadway, Oakland, CA 94607-3806
Sally Lee, Program Manager

Human Resource Svcs **510.272.6425**
Fax 510.272.6424
Web .... www.acgov.org
E-mail .... denise.eaton-may@acgov.org
1405 Lakeside Dr, Oakland, CA 94612-4306
Denise Eaton-may, Director

Public Health **510.267.8000**
Fax 510.267.3212
Web .... www.acphd.org
1000 Broadway Ste 500, Oakland, CA 94607-4033
Anita Siego, Director

GENERAL HEALTH SERVICES

Public Health **510.267.8000**
Fax 510.267.3212
Web .... www.acphd.org
1000 Broadway Ste 500, Oakland, CA 94607-4033
Anita Siego, Director

MENTAL HEALTH SERVICES

Alameda Community Support Ctr **510.522.4668**
Fax 510.521.6729
E-mail .... callendar@bhcs.mail.co.alameda.ca.us
1429 Oak St, Alameda, CA 94501
Damon Eazes, Childrenæs Services Supervisor

Mental Health **530.822.7200**
Fax 530.822.7108
1965 Live Oak Blvd, Yuba City, CA 95992
Brad Lund, Director Of Mental Health

Mental Health **510.567.8100**
Fax 510.567.8130
Web .... www.acbhcs.org
E-mail .... mthomas@acbhcs.org
2000 Embarcadero Ct Ste 400, Oakland,
CA 94606-5300
Marye L. Thomas, Director

Mental Health Children's Specialized
Svcs **510.383.5100**
Fax 510.383.5117
Web .... www.acbhcs.org
E-mail .... euno@acbhcs.org
7200 Bancroft Ave, Eastmount Towne Center,
Oakland, CA 94605
Elizabeth Uno, Chief Of Services

Second Chance Newark Crisis Ctr
Hotline **510.792.4357**
Fax 510.745.1693
Web .... www.secondchanceinc.com
E-mail .... pobox643@aol.com
6330 Thornton Ave, Newark, CA 94560-3734
Mark Mcconville, Director

JUSTICE AGENCY

CASA **510.618.1950**
Fax 510.618.1966
E-mail .... info@casaofalamedacounty.org
1000 San Leandro Blvd Ste 300, San Leandro,
CA 94577
Ginni Ring, Director

CASA **510.663.8440**
Fax 510.663.8441
Web .... www.californiacasa.org
E-mail .... rallen@californiacasa.org
660 13th St Ste 300, Oakland, CA 94612-1078
Robin Allen, State Director

Juvenile Hall (East) **510.667.4999**
Fax 510.667.3972
E-mail .... hrobinso@acgov.org
2500 Fairmont Dr, San Leandro, CA 94578
Herb Robinson, Superintendent

Probation **510.667.4488**
Fax 510.667.3612
Web .... www.acglv.org
E-mail .... eroquemore@acglv.org
2500 Fairmont Dr, San Leandro, CA 94578-1003
Haleh Soltani, Supervisor

Probation Dept **510.268.7252**
Fax 510.832.1469
400 Broadway, Oakland, CA 94607
Patricia Fair, Information Center Director

Victim/Witness Program **510.272.6180**
Fax 510.208.9565
Web .... www.vcgcb.ca.gov
E-mail .... lfoster@co.alameda.ca.us
1401 Lakeside Dr Ste 802, Oakland, CA 94612
Harolz Boscovich, Acting Director

COURTS

Juvenile Court **510.618.1100**
Fax 510.268.7960
Web .... www.alameda.courts.ca.gov
E-mail .... nlonsdale@alameda.courts.ca.gov
400 Broadway, Oakland, CA 94607-3807
Commissioner Nancy Lonsdale, Director

Youth Court **510.832.5858**
Fax 510.834.4421
Web .... www.youthcourt.org
E-mail .... rachel@youthcourt.org
285 17th St, Oakland, CA 94612
Sean Duren, Executive Director

POLICE AND SHERIFF

Berkeley Police Dept **510.981.5900**
Web .... www.ci.berkeley.ca.us
E-mail .... jlewis@cityofberkeley.info
2100 Martin Luther King Jr Way, Berkeley,
CA 94704-1109
Jennifer Lewis, Youth Services Director

Oakland Police Dept **510.777.3333**
Fax 510.238.6411
Web .... www.oaklandnet.com
E-mail .... ssection@oaklandnet.com
455 7th St, Oakland, CA 94607-3985
Special Victims Section, Director

San Leandro Police Dept **510.577.2740**
Fax 510.577.3296
Web .... www.sanleandro.org
901 E 14th St, San Leandro, CA 94577-3729
Ian Willis, Police Chief

Sheriff's Ofc **510.272.6878**
Fax 510.272.3796
Web .... www.acgov.org
E-mail .... gahern@acgov.org
1401 Lakeside Dr, Fl 12, Oakland, CA 94612
Gregory J. Ahern, Sheriff

EDUCATION SERVICES

Berkeley YMCA Head Start - Ocean
View **510.559.2090**
Web .... www.baymca.org
E-mail .... cwright@baymca.org
1422 San Pablo Ave, Berkeley, CA 94702-1024
Carman Wright, Director

Berkeley YMCA Head
Start/Sacramento **510.547.6683**
3155 Sacramento St, Berkeley, CA 94702
Pamm Shaw, Director

Cape - Head Start - Hill N Dale
Preschool **925.426.8341**
Fax 925.426.4714
E-mail .... rvasquez@capeheadstart.org
4150 Doreman Rd, Livermore, CA 94550
Rebecca Vasquez, Director

Alpine County

SOCIAL SERVICES

Health & Human Svcs Dept **530.694.2146**
Fax 530.694.2770
Web .... www.alpinecountyca.gov
E-mail .... solson@alpinecountyca.gov
75 Diamond Valley Rd Unit A, Markleeville,
CA 96120-9579
Stacey Olson, Social Services Director

Social Svcs **530.694.2235**
Fax 530.694.2252
Web .... www.hhs.alpinecountyca.com
E-mail .... solfon@hhsalpinecountyca.com
75 Diamond Valley Rd Unit A, Markleeville,
CA 96120-9579
Stacy Olfon, Director

JUSTICE AGENCY

Probation Dept **530.694.2192**
Fax 530.694.2213
E-mail .... drublaitus@alpineso.com
14777 State Rte 89, Markleeville, CA 96120
Doug Rublaitus, Chief Performance Officer

COURTS

Superior Court **530.694.2113**
Fax 530.694.2119
14777 State Rte 89, Markleeville, CA 96120
Honorable David L. Devore, Judge

POLICE AND SHERIFF

Sheriff's Ofc **530.694.2231**
Fax 530.694.2956
14777 State Route 89, Markleeville, CA 96120
John M. Crawford, Sheriff

Amador County

SOCIAL SERVICES

Dept Of Social Svcs **209.223.6550**
Web .... www.co.amador.ca.us
10877 Conductor Blvd, Suttercreeck, CA 95685
John Meiswilson, Director

GENERAL HEALTH SERVICES

Public Health **209.223.6407**
Fax 209.223.1562
E-mail ....ljagoda@amadorgov.org
10877 Conductor Blvd Ste 400, Sutter Creek,
CA 95685
Lori Jagoda, Aids Coordinator

MENTAL HEALTH SERVICES

Mental Health **209.223.6412**
Fax 209.223.0920
Web ....www.co.amador.ca.us/pub/depts
10877 Conductor Blvd, Ste 300, Suttercreek,
CA 95685
Kristen Bengyel, Director

JUSTICE AGENCY

**Pine Grove Youth Conservation
Camp** **209.296.7581**
Fax 209.296.7855
Web ....www.cdcr.ca.gov
E-mail ....mike.roots@cdcr.ca.gov
13630 Aqueduct-Volcano Rd, Pine Grove, CA 95665
Mike Roots, Superintendent

Preston Youth Correctional Facility **209.274.8000**
Fax 209.274.4235
Web ....www.pycf.cya.ca.gov
201 Waterman Rd, Ione, CA 95640-9701
Kim Mahoney, Superintendent

Probation Dept **209.223.6387**
Fax 209.223.6403
675 New York Ranch Rd Ste 1, Jackson, CA 95642
Mark Bonini, Chief CPO

Victim/Witness Program **209.223.6474**
Fax 209.223.6480
708 Court St, Ste 101, Jackson, CA 95642-2329
Harla Ward, Coordinator

POLICE AND SHERIFF

Sheriff's Ofc **209.223.6500**
Fax 209.223.1609
700 Court St, Jackson, CA 95642-2130
Martin A. Ryan, Sheriff

Butte County

GENERAL HEALTH SERVICES

Public Health **530.891.2731**
Fax 530.891.8743
Web ....www.buttecounty.net
E-mail ....tstorm@buttecounty.net
695 Oleander Ave, Chico, CA 95926
Trulie Storm, Clinic Manager

Public Health Clinic **530.538.7342**
Fax 530.538.5294
Web ....www.buttecountypublichealth.org
78 Cable Mountain Blvd, Oroville, CA 95965
Alice Kienzle, Clinic Manager

Public Health Department **530.538.7581**
Fax 530.538.2165
Web ....www.buttecounty.net/publichealth
202 Mira Loma Dr, Oroville, CA 95965

JUSTICE AGENCY

**Chico Sub-Ofc Of Sacramento Juvenile
Parole** **530.343.5121**
Fax 530.343.5129
Web ....www.cya.ca.gov
E-mail ....tweber@cya.ca.gov
2210 Robailey Dr, Chico, CA 95928
Ted Weber, Supervising Parole Agent

Juvenile Hall **530.538.7311**
Fax 530.538.6695
Web ....www.buttecounty.net
E-mail ....banderson@buttecounty.net
41 County Center Dr, Oroville, CA 95965-3334
Brian Anderson, Superintendent

Probation Dept **530.538.7661**
Fax 530.538.6826
42 County Center Dr, Oroville, CA 95965
John Wardell, Chief Performance Officer

Victim/Witness Program **530.538.7340**
Fax 530.534.8301
Web ....www.buttecounty.net
42 County Center Dr, Oroville, CA 95965-3335
Aaron Smith, Coordinator

COURTS

Superior Court-Juvenile Div **530.532.7010**
Fax 530.538.9361
1 Court St, Oroville, CA 95965
Tamara Mosbarger, Presiding Judge

POLICE AND SHERIFF

Oroville Police Deptartment **530.538.2451**
Fax 530.538.2409
Web ....www.cityoforoville.org
E-mail ....brownmj@cityoforoville.org
2055 Lincoln St, Oroville, CA 95966-5385
Bill Lagrone, Chief Of Police

Sheriff's Ofc **530.538.7321**
Fax 530.538.2099
Web ....www.buttecounty.net/sheriff
E-mail ....infosheriff@buttecounty.net
33 County Center Dr, Oroville, CA 95965
Jerry Smith, Sheriff

EDUCATION SERVICES

**Chico USD Chapman Elementary
School** **530.891.3100**
E-mail ....jfrancis@chicousd.org
1071 E 16th St, Chico, CA 95928
Jennifer Francis, Director

Special Education **530.532.5650**
Fax 530.532.5794
Web ....www.bcoe.org/selpa
E-mail ....rapplega@bcoe.org
1859 Bird St, Oroville, CA 95965-4854
Roy L. Applegate, Education Edd

Calaveras County

SOCIAL SERVICES

Senior Svcs **209.754.3967**
Fax 209.754.3508
E-mail ....calaverasseniorinc@att.net
956 Mt. Ranch, San Andreas, CA 85249
Heidi Harding, Director

GENERAL HEALTH SERVICES

Public Health Dept **209.754.6460**
Fax 209.754.1709
Web ....www.calaverascounty.com
891 Mountain Ranch Rd, San Andreas, CA 95249
Jane Loeffler, Aids Coordinator

MENTAL HEALTH SERVICES

Behavioral Svcs **209.754.6525**
Fax 209.754.6534
Web ....www.co.calaveras.ca.us/dept.s/mhealth
891 Mountain Ranch Rd, Dept. 127, Government
Center, San Andreas, CA 95249
Rita Downs, Medical Director

JUSTICE AGENCY

Probation Dept **209.754.6466**
Fax 209.754.4913
E-mail ....thall@co.calaveras.ca.us
891 Mountain Ranch Rd, San Andreas, CA 95249
Teri Hall, Chief Executive Officer

Victim/Witness Program **209.754.6565**
Fax 209.754.6645
Web ....www.co.calaveras.ca.us
E-mail ....belben@co.calaveras.ca.us
891 Mountain Ranch Rd, San Andreas, CA 95249
Barbara Elben, Coordinator

POLICE AND SHERIFF

Police Dept **209.736.2567**
Fax 209.736.0517
E-mail ....acpd@angelscamp.gov
200 Monte Verda, Angels Camp, CA 95222
Todd Fordahl, Sergeant

EDUCATION SERVICES

Calavaras Head Start **209.722.3980**
Fax 209.754.4014
Web ....www.theresourceconnection.net
42 S Hwy 26, Valley Springs, CA 95252-9485
Sheila Neal, Director

Calaveras State Head Start **209.772.3980**
598 W Saint Charles St, San Andreas, CA 95249
Nancy Tiffany, Director

Colusa County

SOCIAL SERVICES

Health & Human Svcs **530.458.0380**
Fax 530.458.4136
Web ....www.colusadhhs.org
251 E Webster St, Colusa, CA 95932-2951
Elizabeth Kelly, Social Services Director

COURTS

Superior Court **530.458.5149**
Fax 530.458.2230
Web ....www.colusa.courts.ca.gov
E-mail ....info@colusa.courts.ca.gov
532 Oak St Ofc B, Colusa, CA 95932-2570
Honorable John H. Tierman, Director

POLICE AND SHERIFF

Police Dept **530.458.7777**
Fax 530.458.2391
Web ....www.colusacounty.com
260 6th St, Colusa, CA 95932
Ross Stark, Chief Of Police

Sheriff's Ofc **530.458.0200**
Fax 530.458.4697
929 Bridge St, Colusa, CA 95932
Scott Marshall, Sheriff

EDUCATION SERVICES

Colusa B/Childcare Head Start **530.458.0340**
Web www.colusa-coe.k12.ca.us
345 5th St Ste A, Colusa, CA 95932-2445
Kathleen Davidson, Director

Contra Costa County

SOCIAL SERVICES

California Children's Svcs **925.313.6100**
Fax 925.313.6115
Web ....www.dhs.ca.gov/pcfh/cms/ccs
E-mail ....bsheehy@hsd.cccounty.us
597 Center Ave Ste 110, Martinez, CA 94553-4669
Barbara Sheehy, Administrator

Employment & Human Svcs Dept 925.313.1500
Fax 925.313.1575
   40 Douglas Dr, Martinez, CA 94553
   Joe Valentine, Director

GENERAL HEALTH SERVICES

Health Dept 925.957.5400
Fax 925.957.5401
   50 Douglas Dr, # 310, Martinez, CA 94553
   Jackie Peterson, Admin Secetatry

Public Health Concord Health Ctr 925.646.5275
Fax 925.646.5498
   2355 Stanwell Cir, Concord, CA 94520-4868
   Phil Harrison, Coordinator

WIC Program 925.646.5370
Fax 925.646.5029
Web ....www.fns.usda.gov
   2355 Stanwell Cir, Concord, CA 94520-4806
   Beverly Clark, Director

MENTAL HEALTH SERVICES

Child and Adolescent Mental Health
Svcs 925.427.8664
Fax 925.427.8645
   3501 Lone Tree Way Ste 200, Antioch, CA 94509
   Eileen Brooks, Program Manager

Community Mental Health Ctr 925.646.5468
Fax 925.646.5102
Web ....www.cmhcinc.org
E-mail ....gwyborny@hsd.co.contra-costa.ca.us
   1026 Oak Grove Rd Ste 11, Concord,
   CA 94518-3253
   Grant Wyborny, Program Supervisor

Mental Health Admin 925.957.5150
Fax 925.957.5156
Web ....www.hsd.co.contra-costa.ca.us
   1340 Arnold Dr Ste 200, Martinez, CA 94553-4189
   Susanne Tavano, Director

JUSTICE AGENCY

CASA 925.256.7284
Fax 925.256.7286
E-mail ....casa@cccocasa.org
   2020 N Broadway Ste 204, Walnut Creek, CA 94596
   Keith Archuleta, Director

Juvenile Hall 925.957.2700
Fax 925.957.2742
E-mail ....bpelle@prob.cccounty.us
   202 Glacier Dr, Martinez, CA 94553
   Bruce Pelle, Superintentent

Probation Dept 925.313.4180
Fax 925.313.4191
   50 Douglas Dr, # 201, Martinez, CA 94553
   Philip Kader, Deputy CPO

POLICE AND SHERIFF

Concord Police Dept 925.671.3220
Fax 925.671.6691
Web ....www.cityofconcord.org
   1350 Galindo St, Concord, CA 94520
   Guy Swanger, Chief Of Police

Martinez Police Dept 925.372.3440
Fax 925.228.3753
E-mail ....gpeterson@cityofmartinez.org
   525 Henrietta St, Martinez, CA 94553
   Gary Peterson, Chief Of Police

Sheriff's Ofc 925.335.1500
Fax 925.335.1508
Web ....www.prob.cccounty.us
   651 Pine St Fl 7, Martinez, CA 94553-1294
   David Livingston, Sheriff

EDUCATION SERVICES

Childstart Ambro 925.427.8463
   3103 Willow Pass Rd, Baypoint, CA 94565
   Elsie Witt, Director

Contra Costa Coe College Even
Start 510.235.7800
Fax 510.236.6768
E-mail ....groberts@contracosta.edu
   2600 Mission Bell Dr, San Pablo, CA 94806
   Glenda P Roberts, Even Start Director

Mt. Diablo Special Education 925.682.8000
Fax 925.674.0514
E-mail ....lawrences@mgusd.k12.ca.us
   1936 Carlotta Dr, Concord, CA 94519
   Steven Lawrence, Superintendent

Special Education 510.741.2801
Fax 510.724.8829
Web ....www.wccusd.net
E-mail ....scollins@wccusd.net
   2465 Dolan Way, San Pablo, CA 94806-1668
   Steve Collins, Selpa Director

Del Norte County

SOCIAL SERVICES

Social Svcs 707.464.3191
Fax 707.465.1783
Web ....www.dnco.org
E-mail ....gblatnick@co.del-norte.ca.us
   880 Northcrest Dr, Crescent City, CA 95531-2313
   Gary Blatnick, Social Services Director

JUSTICE AGENCY

CASA 707.464.3320
Fax 707.464.5561
Web ....www.casadn.org
E-mail ....sminx@casadn.org
   579 US Hwy 101, Crescent City, CA 95531-4335
   Susan Minx, Executive Director

Juvenile Hall 707.464.7243
Fax 707.465.0389
E-mail ....tcrowell@co.del-norte.ca.us
   1115 Williams Dr, Crescent City, CA 95531
   Tom Crowell, Deputy CPO

Victim/Witness Program 707.464.7273
Fax 707.464.2975
E-mail ....abaxter@co.del-norte.ca.us
   458 H St Rm 182, Crescent City, CA 95531
   Alison Baxter, Project Coordinator

COURTS

Superior Court 707.464.8115
Fax 707.465.4005
   450 H St Rm 209, Crescent City, CA 95531
   Honorable William H. Follett, Presiding Judge

POLICE AND SHERIFF

Sheriff's Dept 707.464.4191
Fax 707.465.5742
Web ....www.co.del-norte.ca.us
   650 5th St, Crescent City, CA 95531-3918
   Dean Wilson, Sheriff

El Dorado County

SOCIAL SERVICES

Social Svcs 530.642.7300
Fax 530.626.7427
   3057 Briw Rd Ste A, Placerville, CA 95667
   Daniel Nielson, Director

Tahoe Youth & Family Svcs 530.541.2445
Fax 530.541.0517
Web ....www.tahoeyouth.org
E-mail ....alissa@tahoeyouth.org
   1021 Fremont Ave, South Lake Tahoe,
   CA 96150-8136
   Alissa Nourse, Director

MENTAL HEALTH SERVICES

Health Dept South Lake Tahoe Ctr 530.573.3155
Fax 530.541.8409
Web ....www.co.el-dorado.ca.us/publichealth
   1360 Johnson Blvd Ste 103, South Lake Tahoe,
   CA 56150
   Josefina Solino, Supervisor

JUSTICE AGENCY

District Attorney's Ofc 530.621.6472
Fax 530.621.1280
Web ....www.co.el-dorado.ca.us
E-mail ....cwarchol@edcgov.us
   515 Main St, Placerville, CA 95667-5609
   Cheryl A. Warchol, Mdic Coordinator

Juvenile Hall 530.621.5585
Fax 530.295.2519
   299 Fair Ln, Placerville, CA 95667
   Vince Janette, Suprintendent

Juvenile Justice Commission 530.621.5644
Fax 530.621.2430
Web ....www.co.el-dorado.ca.us
E-mail ....ohopkins@co.el-dorado.ca.us
   471 Pierroz Rd, Placerville, CA 95667-4043
   Olga Hopkins, Chairperson

Probation Dept 530.621.5625
Fax 530.621.2430
Web ....www.co.el-dorado.ca.us
   3974 Durck Rd Ste 205, Shingle Strings, CA 95682
   Gregory Sly, Chief Performance Officer

Victim/Witness Program 530.573.3337
Fax 530.544.6413
Web ....www.co.el-dorado.ca.us
E-mail ....smeyer@co.el-dorado.ca.us
   1360 Johnson Blvd Ste 105, South Lake Tahoe,
   CA 96150-8201
   Susan Meyer, Coordinator

COURTS

Superior Court 530.621.6451
Fax 530.622.9774
E-mail ....cambria@eldoradocourt.org
   495 Main St, Placerville, CA 95667
   Honorable Suzanne Kingsbury, Presiding Judge

POLICE AND SHERIFF

Police Dept 530.642.5210
Fax 530.642.5258
Web ....www.cityofplacerville.org
   730 Main St, Placerville, CA 95667-5783
   George Nielson, Chief Of Police

Sheriff's Ofc 530.621.5655
Fax 530.626.8091
Web ....www.edso.org
E-mail ....sheriff@edso.org
   300 Fair Ln, Placerville, CA 95667-4102
   John D Egostini, Sheriff

EDUCATION SERVICES

Charlie Brown State Pre-School 916.621.1832
   6520 Oak Dell Rd, Placerville, CA 95667
   Lynn Lucas, Director

El Dorado SELPA-Special
Education **530.295.2228**
Fax 530.621.9137
E-mail ....twatson@edcoe.org
  6767 Green Valley Rd, Placerville, CA 95667
  Tammy Watson, Director

Special Education- Tahoe Schools 530.541.2850
Fax 530.541.5930
Web ....www.ltusd.org
  1021 Al Tahoe Blvd, South Lake Tahoe, CA 96150
  Marie Meagher, Special Services Director

Fresno County

SOCIAL SERVICES
**Economic Opportunities
Commission** **559.263.1000**
Fax 559.263.1286
Web ....www.fresnoeoc.org
  1920 Mariposa Mall, Ste 300, Fresno, CA 93721
  Brian Angus, Executive Director

Social Svcs- Children & Family Svcs **559.600.6400**
Fax 559.600.2365
  1404 L St, Fresno, CA 93721-1203
  Kathryn Martindale, Program Manager

GENERAL HEALTH SERVICES
Dept Of Community Health **559.445.3249**
Fax 559.445.3370
Web ....www.fcdth.org
  1221 Fulton Mall, Fresno, CA 93775
  Roberta Bynum, Sr. Staff Analyst

MENTAL HEALTH SERVICES
Children's Mental Health Svc **559.453.8918**
Fax 559.453.6700
  3133 N Millbrook Ave, Fresno, CA 93703
  Donna Taylor, Director

Dept Of Behavioral Health **559.253.9180**
Fax 559.253.9144
E-mail ....dtaylor@co.fresno.ca.us
  4441 E Kings Canyon Rd, Fresno, CA 93702
  Donna Taylor, Mental Health Director

JUSTICE AGENCY
California Youth Authority **559.243.4039**
Fax 559.243.4063
Web ....www.cdcr.ca.gov
  3040 N Fresno St Ste 105, Fresno, CA 93703-1188
  James Mora, Supervising Parole Agent

CASA **559.244.6485**
Fax 559.243.0791
Web ....www.casafresno.org
E-mail ....nathanlee@casafresno.org
  1252 Fulton Mall, Fresno, CA 93721-3608
  Nathan Lee, Director

Crime Victim Assistance Ctr **559.600.2822**
Fax 559.600.1680
  2233 Kern St, Fresno, CA 93721
  Lori Willits, Coordinator

Family Court Svcs **559.488.3241**
Fax 559.262.4362
  2220 Tulare St ste 1111, Fresno, CA 93721
  Fran Collin, Director

Juvenile Hall **559.495.3602**
Fax 559.495.3636
Web ....www.co.fresno.ca.us
E-mail ....odimeryratliff@co.fresno.ca.us
  3333 E American Ave, Fresno, CA 93725-9235
  Ollie Dimery-Ratliff, Director

Juvenile Svcs/Probation **559.455.5310**
Fax 559.455.5182
Web ....www.co.fresno.ca.us
E-mail ....lpenner@co.fresno.ca.us
  808 S 10th St, Fresno, CA 93702-3506
  Linda Penner, Director

COURTS
**Superior Court- Juvenile
Delinquency** **559.455.5195**
Fax 559.455.5349
  742 S 10th St, Fresno, CA 93702-3505
  Honorable Martin Suits, Director

POLICE AND SHERIFF
Sheriff's Ofc **559.488.3939**
Fax 559.488.1899
Web ....www.fresnosheriff.org
E-mail ....sheriff@fresnosheriff.org
  2200 Fresno St, Fresno, CA 93721-1703
  Margaret Mims, Sheriff

EDUCATION SERVICES
FCEOC Cantua Creek Head Start **559.829.3373**
E-mail ....rosie.rosas@fresnoeoc.org
  1920 Mariposa Mall, Cantua Creek, CA 93608
  Rosie Rosas, Director

**FCEOC Cedarwood Head Start
Preschool** **559.237.5254**
Web ....www.fresnoeoc.org
E-mail ....deborah.rix@fresnoeoc.org
  2055 S Cedar Ave, Fresno, CA 93702-4505
  Deborah Rix, Director

FCEOC Citrus Head Start **559.626.0542**
E-mail ....tamala.olsby@fresnoeoc.org
  112 N 4th St, Orange Coast, CA 93702
  Tamala Olsby, Director

**FCEOC College Community Head
Start** **559.348.1734**
Web ....www.fresnoeoc.org
E-mail ....rose.redondo@fresnoeoc.org
  2529 Willow Ave, Clovis, CA 93612
  Rose Marie Redondo, Director

FCEOC Jefferson Head Start **559.637.0025**
E-mail ....adriana.gomez@fresnoeoc.org
  1240 E Washington Ave, Reedley, CA 93654
  Adriana Gomez, Director

FCEOC Maple Vista Head Start **559.252.9506**
E-mail ....rachel.martinez@fresnoeoc.org
  4609 E Illinois Ave, Fresno, CA 93702
  Rachel Martinez, Director

FCEOC Roosevelt Head Start **559.263.1200**
Fax 559.263.1287
E-mail ....beatrice.rodriguez@fresnoeoc.org
  1701 Alton St Ste A, Selma, CA 93662
  Beatrice Rodriguez, Teacher/director

FCEOC Wilson Head Start **559.896.0142**
  1325 Stillman St, Selma, CA 93662
  Angelita Rodriguez, Director

**Firebaugh - Las-Deltas USD Even
Start** **559.659.1476**
E-mail ....info@fldufz.k12.ca.us
  1976 Morris Kyle Dr, Firebaugh, CA 93622
  Alecia Allard, Program Director

Franklin Head Start Ctr **559.233.0882**
  1189 Martin St, Fresno, CA 93706
  Tamala Olsby, Director

Special Education **559.265.3000**
Fax 559.265.3076
Web www.scoe.k12.ca.us
  1111 Van Ness Ave, Fresno, CA 93721
  Lisa Chaney, Administrator

Glenn County

GENERAL HEALTH SERVICES
Health Svcs **530.934.6588**
Fax 530.934.6463
Web ....www.countyofglenn.net
E-mail ....gnorton@glenncountyhealth.net
  240 N Villa Ave, Willows, CA 95988
  Dr. James Corona, Md, Health Officer

Northern Valley Indian Health **530.934.9293**
Fax 530.934.4081
Web ....www.nvih.org
  207 N Butte St, Willows, CA 95988-2803
  Inder Wadwha, Director

MENTAL HEALTH SERVICES
Mental Health **530.934.6582**
Fax 530.934.6592
Web ....www.glenncountyhealth.net
E-mail ....sgruendl@glenncountyhealth.net
  242 N Villa Ave, Willows, CA 95988-2693
  Scott Gruendl, Director

JUSTICE AGENCY
Juvenile Hall **530.934.6682**
Fax 530.934.6335
Web ....www.countyofglenn.net
  306 N Villa Ave, Willows, CA 95988-2641
  Rick Beatty, Manager

Probation Dept **530.934.6416**
Fax 530.934.6468
Web ....www.hra.co.glenn.ca.us
  541 W Oak St, Willows, CA 95988-2939
  Brandon Thompson, Chief Probation Officer

COURTS
Superior Court **530.934.6415**
Fax 530.934.6449
Web ....www.glenncourt.ca.gov
  526 W Sycamore St Ste B, Willows, CA 95988-2746
  Donlad Cole Byrd, Director

POLICE AND SHERIFF
Police Dept **530.865.1616**
Fax 530.865.1626
Web ....www.cityoforland.com
  817 4th St, Orland, CA 95963-1714
  Paula Carr, Chief Of Police

Sheriff's Dept **530.934.6441**
Fax 530.934.6473
Web ....www.countyofglenn.net
E-mail ....mbstanbery@countyofglenn.net
  543 W Oak St, Willows, CA 95988-2939
  Larry Jones, Sheriff

EDUCATION SERVICES
Butte Street Head Start **530.934.6596**
E-mail ....bhutchins@glenncoe.org
  649 12 S Butte, Willows, CA 95988
  Betty Hutchins, Director

Humboldt County

SOCIAL SERVICES
Dept of Social Svcs **707.476.4700**
Fax 707.441.2096
Web ....www.co.humboldt.ca.us/hhs/socialservices
  929 Koster St, Eureka, CA 95501-0106
  Katherine Young, Branch Director

Social Svcs **707.445.6103**
Fax 707.441.5600
E-mail ....blewis@co.humboldt.ca.us
  929 Koster St, Eureka, CA 95501-0106
  Catherine Young, Director

California

GENERAL HEALTH SERVICES

Health Dept **707.445.6200**
Fax 707.445.6097
Web ....www.co.humboldt.ca.us
E-mail ....sbuckley@co.humboldt.ca.us
   529 I St, Eureka, CA 95501-1180
   Susan Buckley, Director Of Health Education

Health Dept Garberville **707.923.2779**
Fax 707.923.7207
Web ....www.co.humboldt.ca.us
   727 Cedar St, Garberville, CA 95542-3201
   Shirley Hillman, Public Health Nurse

MENTAL HEALTH SERVICES

Children and Family Svcs **707.268.2800**
Fax 707.445.7270
E-mail ....dwheeler@co.humboldt.ca.us
   1711 3rd St, Eureka, CA 95501
   Donna Wheeler, Executive Director

Mental Health Svcs **707.268.2990**
Fax 707.476.4049
   720 Wood St, Eureka, CA 95501-4413
   Shelly Nelson, Deputy Director

JUSTICE AGENCY

CASA **707.443.3197**
Fax 707.443.3243
Web ....www.humboldtcasa.org
E-mail ....info@humboldtcasa.org
   2356 Myrtle Ave, Eureka, CA 95501
   Steve Volow, Executive Director

Probation Dept **707.445.7401**
Fax 707.443.7139
Web ....www.co.humboldt.ca.us
   2002 Harrison Ave, Eureka, CA 95501-3212
   Ray Watson, Juvenile Hall Director Of Institutions

**Victim/Witness Program HRA-Community Action
Div** **530.934.6510**
Fax 530.934.6521
   420 E Laurel St, Willows, CA 95988
   Scott Grundel, Director

COURTS

Superior Court **707.269.1200**
Fax 707.445.7041
   825 5th St, Eureka, CA 95501
   W Bruce Watson, Judge

Superior Court Juvenile Div **559.713.3157**
Fax 559.713.3175
Web ....www.courtinfo.ca.gov
   11200 Avenue 368, Visalia, CA 93291-8940
   Juliet Boccone, Judge

POLICE AND SHERIFF

Eureka Police Dept **707.441.4060**
Fax 707.441.4334
E-mail ....gnielson@eurekapd.org
   604 C St, Eureka, CA 95501
   Garr Nielson, Chief Of Police

Sheriff's Ofc **707.445.7251**
Fax 707.445.7298
E-mail ....hso@co.humboldt.ca.us
   826 4th St, Eureka, CA 95501
   Michael Downey, Sheriff

EDUCATION SERVICES

Arcata Head Start Daycare **707.822.2131**
   75 Frank Martin Ct, Arcata, CA 95521
   Shannon Lindholm, Supervisor

Cresent City Head Start **707.464.1224**
Fax 707.465.4226
E-mail ....cpatterson@northcoast.com
   475 7th St, Crescent City, CA 95531
   Cindy Patterson, Director

**Special Education Student
Programs** **707.445.7043**
Fax 707.445.7143
E-mail ....tcirce@humboldt.k12.ca.us
   901 Myrtle Ave, Eureka, CA 95501
   Mindy Sattig, Selpa Director

Imperial County

SOCIAL SERVICES

Social Svcs **760.337.6800**
Fax 760.337.5716
E-mail ....jamessemmes@imperialcounty.net
   2995 S 4th St Ste 105, El Centro, CA 92243-6008
   James Semmes, Director

GENERAL HEALTH SERVICES

Health Dept **760.482.4438**
Fax 760.352.9933
   935 Broadway St, El Centro, CA 92243
   Robin Hodgkin, Director Of Public Health

Health Dept **760.482.4438**
Fax 760.352.9933
Web
   935 Broadway St, El Centro, CA 92243
   Robin Hodgkin, Director Of Public Health

MENTAL HEALTH SERVICES

Mental Health **760.482.4000**
Fax 760.482.4182
Web ....www.imperialcounty.net
E-mail ....michaelhorn@co.imperial.ca.us
   202 N 8th St, El Centro, CA 92243-2302
   Michael Horn, Director

JUSTICE AGENCY

CASA **760.353.7456**
Fax 760.353.4465
Web ....www.casaimperialcounty.org
E-mail ....casa@imperialcounty.org
   690 Broadway St Ste 6, El Centro, CA 92243-5103
   Alex Cardnas, Executive Director

Probation And Corrections **760.339.6288**
Fax 760.352.8933
   324 Applestille Rd, El Centro, CA 92243
   Martin J Krizay, Chief Performance Officer

Probation Dept **760.339.6229**
Fax 760.352.8933
   324 Applestille Rd, El Centro, CA 92243
   Gloria Munoz, Juvenile Hall Division Manager

COURTS

Superior Court **760.482.4374**
Fax 760.337.7742
   939 W Main St Ste 101, El Centro, CA 92243-2847
   Honorable Jeffery B. Jones, Superior Court Judge

POLICE AND SHERIFF

El Centro Police Dept **760.352.2111**
Fax 760.353.7301
Web ....www.ecpd.org
E-mail ....jmcginley@ecpd.org
   150 N 11th St, El Centro, CA 92243-2898
   Jim Mcginley, Chief Of Police

Sheriff's Dept **760.339.6301**
Fax 760.339.0170
Web ....www.imperialcounty.net
E-mail ....haroldcarter@imperialcounty.net
   328 Applestille Rd, El Centro, CA 92243-9661
   Raymond Loera, Sheriff

EDUCATION SERVICES

Campsinos Unidos Head Start **760.353.9419**
   1042 Heber Ave, Heber, CA 92249
   Rachel Richard, Director

Campsinos Unidos IX Head Start **760.355.2194**
Fax 760.355.4120
   303 S D St, Imperial, CA 92251-1433
   Sara Palacios, Director

**CUI Kathryn M Moore Memorial Head
Start** **760.353.9413**
Fax 760.353.2229
   223 S 1St St, El Centro, CA 92243-2701
   Alexandra Seaman, Director

Special Education SELPA **760.312.6419**
Fax 760.312.6522
Web ....www.icoe.org/icoe
E-mail ....kleptich@icoe.org
   1398 Sperber Rd, El Centro, CA 92243-9621
   Kurt Leptich, Administrator

Inyo County

SOCIAL SERVICES

Health & Human Svcs **760.878.0237**
Fax 760.878.0266
   155 E Market, Independence, CA 93526
   Sue Stoutenburg, Rn, Hiv Specialist

Health & Human Svcs **760.878.0247**
Fax 760.878.0266
   162 Grove St Ste J, Bishop, CA 93514-2652
   Jean Dickenson, Phd, Health & Human Services Director

Social Svcs **760.876.5545**
Fax 760.876.5127
   380 N Mount Whitney Dr, Lone Pine, CA 93545
   Jean Turner, Director

GENERAL HEALTH SERVICES

Health Dept **760.873.7868**
Fax 760.873.7800
   207 A W South St, Bishop, CA 93514
   Tamara Cohn, Administrator

JUSTICE AGENCY

District Court **760.878.0282**
Fax 760.878.2383
   168 N. Edwards St, Independence, CA 93526
   Arthur J. Maillet, District Attorney

Juvenile Institutions **760.878.0350**
Fax 760.878.0414
E-mail ....info@canyon.us
   201 Mazourka Canyon Rd., Independence, CA 93526
   Mark Thomson, Director

Probation Dept **760.878.0274**
Fax 760.878.0436
   168 N. Edwards St, Independence, CA 93526
   Jeffrey Thompson, Chief Performance Officer

POLICE AND SHERIFF

Police Dept **760.873.5866**
Fax 760.872.3485
E-mail ....ccarter@bishoppd.org
   207 W Line St, Bishop, CA 93514
   Chris Carter, Chief Of Police

Sheriff's Ofc **760.878.0326**
Fax 760.878.0389
E-mail ....blutze@inyocounty.us
   550 So. Clay St, Independence, CA 93526
   William Lutze, Sheriff

Kern County

SOCIAL SERVICES

Human Svcs **661.631.6000**
Fax 661.631.6631
Web ....www.co.kern.ca.us
E-mail ....johnsonbev@co.kern.ca.us
   100 E California Ave, Bakersfield, CA 93302-1031
   Beverly Beasley-johnson, Director

MENTAL HEALTH SERVICES

Mental Health Dept......................**661.868.6600**
Fax...................................661.868.6666
Web........................www.co.kern.ca.us/kcmh/
E-mail..........................koditekd@co.kern.ca.us
3300 Truxtun Ave Ste 290, Bakersfield,
CA 93301-3145
Diane Koditek, MFT, Director

JUSTICE AGENCY

CASA...............................**661.631.2272**
Fax...................................661.328.9787
Web.................................www.kerncasa.org
E-mail..................cmcgauley@kerncasa.org
2000 24th St, Ste 130, Bakersfield CA 93301
Colleen A. Mcgauley, Executive Director

James G. Bowles Juvenile Hall...........**661.868.4300**
Fax...................................661.868.4434
1831 Ridge Rd, Bakersfield, CA 93385
Matt Sondiane, Director

Juvenile Justice Commission

Probation.........................**661.868.4102**
Fax...................................661.868.4186
E-mail..........................gomezl@co.kern.ca.us
2005 Ridge Rd, Bakersfield, CA 93305
Lupe Gomez, Office Services Technician

Probation Dept....................**661.868.4100**
Fax...................................661.868.4199
Web..............................www.co.kern.ca.us
2005 Ridge Rd, Bakersfield, CA 93305-4123
David Kuge, CEO

Victim/Witness Program...............**661.868.4535**
Fax...................................661.868.4586
E-mail..........................perezg@co.kern.ca.us
1415 Truxtun Ave, 6th Floor, Bakersfield, CA 93301
Lupe Perez, Project Coordinator

COURTS

Juvenile Court....................**661.868.4270**
Fax...................................661.868.4414
Web..............................www.kerngov.net
E-mail..................jon.stuebbe@kern.courts.ca.gov
2100 College Ave, Juvenile Justice Center, Bakersfield, CA 93305-4172
Honorable Jon Stuebbe, Presiding Judge

POLICE AND SHERIFF

Bakersfield Police Dept...............**661.326.3800**
Fax...................................661.852.2158
Web..............................www.bakersfieldcity.us
E-mail..................wrector@ci.bakersfield.ca.us
PO Box 59, Bakersfield, CA 93302-0059
William Rector, Chief Of Police

Sheriff's Dept....................**661.391.7771**
Fax...................................661.391.7515
Web..............................www.kernsheriff.us
E-mail..................sheriff@kernsheriff.com
1350 Norris Rd, Bakersfield, CA 93308-2231
Donny Youngbroot, Sheriff

EDUCATION SERVICES

Botton Willow Child Development Ctr...........**661.764.6812**
400 McKitrick Hwy 58, Bakersfield, CA 93301
Toni Santillan, Director

Buena Vista Migrant Head Start...........**661.845.7726**
Fax...................................661.845.7741
8325 Buena Vista Blvd, Lamont, CA 93241
Giovanni Aragon, Director

California City Child Develpment Ctr...........**760.373.7605**
E-mail..................ifigueroa-villegas@gmu.edu
9124 Catalpa Ave, California City, CA 93501
Inez Figueroa-villegas, Site Supervisor

Casa Loma Child Develpoment Ctr...........**661.835.5430**
Fax...................................661.833.8415
525 E Casa Loma Dr, Bakersfield, CA 79303
Simitrio Garza, Supervisor

Delano Child Development Ctr...........**661.725.8952**
Fax...................................661.725.8654
1835 Cecil Ave, Delano, CA 93215
Irene Lopez, Supervisor

Fairview Child Development Ctr...........**661.835.5440**
425 E Fairview Rd, Bakersfield, CA 93304
Esther Garza, Director

SELPA...............................**661.636.4801**
Fax...................................661.636.4810
E-mail..........................grrhoten@kern.org
1300 17th St, Bakersfield, CA 93301
Greg Rhoten, Director

Special Education....................**661.827.3105**
Fax...................................661.827.3303
5801 Sundale Ave, Bakersfield, CA 93309
John Ferguson, Manager

Special Education....................**661.631.4600**
Fax...................................661.631.3101
Web..............................www.bcsd.com
E-mail..........................steelej@bcsd.com
714 Williams St, Bakersfield, CA 93305-5440
Dr. Julia Steele, Director

Kings County

GENERAL HEALTH SERVICES

Health Dept......................**559.584.1401**
Fax...................................559.582.7618
Web..............................www.countyofkings.com
330 Campus Dr, Hanford, CA 93630
Keith Winkler, Health Director

MENTAL HEALTH SERVICES

Dept of Mental Health...............**559.582.4481**
Fax...................................559.582.6547
1393 Bailey dr, Hanford, CA 93230
Brenda Johnson Hill, Executive Director

JUSTICE AGENCY

Victim/Witness Assistance Program...........**559.582.3211**
Fax...................................559.585.0346
1400 W Lacey Blvd, Hanford, CA 93230
Margie Wilhelm, CPO

COURTS

Superior Court....................**559.582.1010**
Fax...................................559.585.3267
E-mail..................gorndoff@kings.courts.ca.gov
1426 South Dr, Hanford, CA 93230
Honorable George Orndoff, Director

POLICE AND SHERIFF

Police Dept......................**559.585.2535**
Fax...................................559.585.4792
Web..............................www.ci.hanford.ca.us
E-mail..................cmestas@ci.hanford.ca.us
425 N Irwin St, Hanford, CA 93230-4425
Carlos Mestas, Chief Of Police

Sheriff's Dept....................**559.584.9276**
Fax...................................559.584.4738
Web..............................www.co.kings.ca.us
E-mail..................amcclain@co.kings.ca.us
1444 W Lacey Blvd, Hanford, CA 93230-5905
David Robinson, Sheriff

EDUCATION SERVICES

Avenal Head Start Ctr...............**559.386.0196**
Fax...................................559.386.0176
945 Skyline Blvd, Hanford, CA 93230
Carla Enriquez, Director

Ofc Of Education....................**559.584.1441**
Fax...................................559.589.7000
Web..............................www.kingscoe.org
E-mail..........................bzaino@kingscoe.org
1144 W Lacey Blvd, Hanford, CA 93230-5956
Barbara Zaino, Director

Lake County

SOCIAL SERVICES

Child Protective Svcs...............**707.262.0235**
Fax...................................707.262.0299
E-mail..................carol@dss.co.lake.ca.us
926 S Forbes St, Lakeport, CA 95453
Carol Huchingson, Director

Social Svcs......................**707.995.4200**
Fax...................................707.995.4204
Web..............................http://dss.co.lake.ca.us
15975 Anderson Ranch Pkwy, Lower Lake, CA 95457
Carol Hutchinson, Director

GENERAL HEALTH SERVICES

Health Dept......................**707.263.1090**
Fax...................................707.262.4280
E-mail..................karent@co.lake.ca.us
922 Bevins Ct, Lakeport, CA 95453-9739
Dr. Karen Tait, Health Service Director

JUSTICE AGENCY

Probation Dept....................**707.262.4285**
Fax...................................707.262.4292
Web..............................www.co.lake.ca.us
E-mail..................dhurst@co.lake.ca.us
201 S Smith St, Lakeport, CA 95453-4921
Dan Hurst, CPO

Victim/Witness Program...............**707.262.4282**
Fax...................................707.262.5851
Web..............................www.co.lake.ca.us
420 2nd St, Lakeport, CA 95453
Deborah Walace, Program Administrator

COURTS

Superior Court....................**707.263.2374**
Fax...................................707.262.1327
255 N Forbes St, Lakeport, CA 95453
Mary Smith, Director

POLICE AND SHERIFF

Police Dept......................**707.263.5491**
Fax...................................707.263.3846
E-mail..................brasmussen@lakeportpolice.org
916 N Forbes St, Lakeport, CA 95453
Brad Rasmussen, Chief Of Police

Sheriff's Ofc....................**707.262.4200**
Fax...................................707.262.4220
Web..............................www.co.lake.ca.us
1220 Martin St, Lakeport, CA 95453-9708
Francisco Rivero, Sheriff

Lassen County

SOCIAL SERVICES

Child Protective Svcs...............**530.251.8277**
Fax...................................530.251.2661
E-mail..................awilhelmi@co.lassen.ca.us
1445 Bunyan Rd, Susanville, CA 96130
Anita Wilhelmi, Supervisor

GENERAL HEALTH SERVICES

Public Health Dept...............**530.251.8183**
Fax...................................530.251.2668
Web..............www.co.lassen.ca.us/public_mission.html
E-mail..................jzimmermann@co.lassen.ca.us
1445 Paul Bunyan Rd, Susanville, CA 96130
Joanna Zimmermann, Phn, Ii, Director

California

MENTAL HEALTH SERVICES

Mental Health **530.251.8108**
Fax 530.251.8394
   555 Hospital Ln Ste A, Susanville, CA 96130
Ken Crandall, Mental Health Director

JUSTICE AGENCY

CASA **530.257.4599**
Fax 530.257.4205
Web .... www.lassencrisis.frontiernet.net
E-mail .... ddwinell@frontiernet.net
   1306 Riverside Drive, Susanville, CA 96130
Darla Dwinell, Executive Director

Juvenile Hall **530.251.8324**
Fax 530.251.1891
E-mail .... rroadifer@co.lassen.ca.us
   1415 Chestnut St, Susanville, CA 96130
Robert Roadifer, Juvenile Hall Superintendent

Probation Dept **530.251.8212**
Fax 530.257.9160
E-mail .... lmartin@co.lassen.ca.us
   107 S Roop St, Susanville, CA 96130-4337
Letha Martin, Chief Probation Officer

Victim Witness Assistance
Program **530.251.8281**
Fax 530.251.2695
E-mail .... dstelzer@co.lassen.ca.us
   220 S Lassen St, Ste 8, Susanville, CA 96130
Denise Stelzer, Program Coordinator

COURTS

Superior Court **530.251.8189**
Fax 530.251.8257
Web .... www.lassencourts.ca.gov
   220 S Lassen St Ste 2, Susanville, CA 96130-4357
Dawn Tornell, Juvenile Justice Commission Director

POLICE AND SHERIFF

Police Dept **530.257.5603**
Fax 530.257.7366
E-mail .... police@cityofsusanville.org
   1801 Main St, Susanville, CA 96130-4518
Jeff Attkinson, Chief

Sheriff's Ofc **530.257.6121**
Fax 530.257.9363
Web .... www.co.lassen.ca.us
   1415 Sheriff Cady Ln, Susanville, CA 96130-3782
Dean Growdon, Sheriff

Los Angeles County

SOCIAL SERVICES

Department of Children & Family
Service **213.351.5507**
Fax 213.487.4431
E-mail .... ricesh@dcfs.lacounty.gov
   425 Shatto Pl, Fl 6, Los Angeles, CA 90020
Sheila Rice, Ombudsman

Dept Of Children & Family Svcs **213.386.3116**
Fax 213.386.6334
Web .... www.dcfs.lacounty.gov
E-mail .... shanna@dcfs.lacounty.gov
   425 Shatto Pl Ste 304, Los Angeles, CA 90020-1759
Anita Shannon, Executive Assistant To The Director

Dept Of Public Social Svcs
Headquarters **562.908.8400**
Fax 562.908.0459
E-mail .... philipbrowning@dpss.lacounty.gov
   12860 Crossroads Pkwy S, City of Industries,
   CA 91746
Philip Browning, Director

GENERAL HEALTH SERVICES

Long Beach City Health Ofc **562.570.4000**
Fax 562.570.4049
Web .... www.longbeach.gov/health
   2525 Grand Ave, Long Beach, CA 90815-1765
Helene Calvet, Health Officer

Pasadena Health Dept **626.744.6000**
Fax 626.744.6113
Web .... www.cityofpasadena.net
   1845 N Fair Oaks Ave, Pasadena, CA 91103-1620
Angelica Palmeros, Program Manager

MENTAL HEALTH SERVICES

Children's System Of Care **213.738.2147**
Fax 213.386.5282
E-mail .... b.mershon@dmh.lacounty.com
   550 S Vermont Ave, #1204E, Los Angeles, CA 90020
Bryan Mershon, Deputy Director

Long Beach Health And Human
Svcs **562.570.4000**
Fax 562.570.4049
Web .... www.longbeach.gov/health
E-mail .... ron_arias@longbeach.gov
   2525 Grand Ave, Long Beach, CA 90815
Ron Arias, Director

San Antonio Mental Health **562.903.5085**
Fax 562.944.2316
Web .... www.co.la.ca.us
   10355 Slusher Dr, Santa Fe Springs, CA 90670
Phyllis Noriega, Acting Director

JUSTICE AGENCY

Barry J. Nidorf Juvenile Hall **818.364.2011**
Fax 818.362.7260
   16350 Filbert St, Sylmar, CA 91342
Sean Porter, Superintendent

California Dept Of Corrections & Rehabilitation- Juvenile
Div **626.967.4351**
Fax 626.332.9955
   907 N Grand Ave, Covina, CA 91724
Kathryn Johnson, Deputy Director

California Dept. Of Corrections & Rehabilitation- Juvenile
Div **323.277.4530**
Fax 323.277.4534
Web .... www.cdcr.ca.gov
E-mail .... brenda.hall2@cdcr.ca.gov
   9110 S Central Ave, Los Angeles, CA 90002-1743
Carol Barker, Supervising Parole Agent

Camp Clinton B. Afflerbaugh **909.593.4937**
Fax 909.596.6392
   6631 Stephens Ranch Rd, La Verne, CA 91750-1197
Trenier Woodland, Director

Camp David Gonzales **818.222.1192**
Fax 818.222.1164
   1301 Las Virgenes Rd, Calabasas, CA 91302-1999
Larry Vangor, Director

Camp Fred Miller **818.889.0260**
Fax 818.707.0364
Web .... www.scgdemo.com
   433 Encinal Canyon Rd, Malibu, CA 90265-2404
Matt Moore, Director

Camp Glenn Rockey **909.599.2391**
Fax 909.592.3559
Web .... www.scgdemo.com
   1900 Sycamore Canyon Rd, San Dimas,
   CA 91773-1220
Mark Garcia, Director

Camp John Munz **661.724.1211**
Fax 661.724.1088
Web .... www.scgdemo.com
   42220 Lake Hughes Rd, Lake Hughes,
   CA 93532-1012
Dan Marino, Director

Camp Joseph Paige **909.593.4921**
Fax 909.596.6870
Web .... www.probation.org
   6601 Stephens Ranch Rd, La Verne, CA 91750-1199
Eduardo Silva, Director

Camp Joseph Scott **661.296.8500**
Fax 661.296.7946
   28700 Bouquet Canyon Rd, Santa Clarita, CA 91390
Cheryl Jackson, Director

Camp Vernon Kilpatrick **818.889.1353**
Fax 818.707.9352
Web .... www.labaptist.org
E-mail .... jtippet@labaptist.org
   427 Encinal Canyon Rd, Malibu, CA 90265-2404
Dan Mereno, Director

Camp William Mendelhall **661.724.1213**
Fax 661.724.1032
   42230 Lake Hughes Rd, Lake Hughes, CA 93532
Norberto Zaragoza, Manager

CASA **310.325.8208**
Fax 310.325.8217
Web .... www.casadelosangelitos.org
E-mail .... info@sbcglobal.net
   954 Koleeta Dr, Harbor City, CA 90710-1818
Agnes Palacios, Administrator

CASA **323.526.6666**
Fax 323.264.5020
Web .... www.lasuperiorcourt.org
E-mail .... tlune@casala.org
   201 Centre Plaza Dr Rm 1100, Monterey Park,
   CA 91754-2142
Teresa Lune, Director

Central Juvenile Hall **323.226.8611**
Fax 323.221.4879
   1605 Eastlake Ave, Los Angeles, CA 90033-1093
Daniel Aceveces, Superintendent

Challenger Memorial Youth Ctr **661.940.4011**
Fax 661.940.4021
Web .... http://www.probation.co.la.ca.gov
   5300 W Avenue I, Lancaster, CA 93536
Michael Edwards, Regional Manager

Community Detention Program **323.226.8579**
Fax 323.227.1466
Web .... www.da.co.la.ca.us
   1601 Eastlake Ave, Los Angeles, CA 90033-1009
Paula Heath, Director

David V. Kenyon Juvenile Justice
Ctr **323.586.6098**
Fax 323.582.5264
E-mail .... dgroman@lasuperior.org
   7625 S Central Ave, Los Angeles, CA 90001
Honorable, Donna Groman, Judge

Dorothy Kirby Ctr **323.981.4301**
Fax 323.266.0155
   1500 S McDonnell Ave, Commerce, CA 90040
Jennifer Owen, Director

East San Fernando Valley
Probation **818.374.2000**
Fax 818.781.7044
   14414 Delano St, Van Nuys, CA 91401-2703
Lynn Duke, Director

Eastlake Juvenile Court **323.226.8926**
Fax 323.221.2223
   1601 Eastlake Ave, Rm J, Los Angeles, CA 90033
Rosalia Rousssel, Manager

Intake & Detention Ctr 323.226.8511
Fax 323.342.9540
1601 E lake Ave, Los Angeles, CA 90033
Paula Heath, Director

Los Angeles Probation And Northeast Juvenile Justice
Ctr 323.226.8765
Fax 323.226.8231
Web .... www.saccourt.com
E-mail .... gyd3@sbcglobal.net
1601 Eastlake Ave #4, Los Angeles, CA 90033
Ronalld Lelefore, Director

Los Padrinos Juvenile Hall 562.940.8681
Fax 562.803.4779
Web .... www.scgdemo.com
7285 Quill Dr, Downey, CA 90242-2098
Cheryl Cooke, Superintendent

Operation Safe Streets Bureau
(Anti-Gangs) 310.603.3100
Fax 310.639.2650
E-mail .... rmrifkin@lasd.org
3010 E Victoria St, Compton, CA 90221-5617
Robert M Rifkin, Director

Southern Youth Correctional Reception
Ctr 562.868.9979
Fax 562.929.2666
13200 Bloomfield Ave, Norwalk, CA 90650
Cassandra Stansberry, Superintendent

Special Victims Bureau 562.946.8531
Fax 326.415.1638
Web .... www.lasd.org
11515 Colima Rd, Whittier, CA 90604
Richard Ruiz, Oes Save Team

Star Unit (Success Through Awareness &
Resistance) 562.946.7263
Fax 562.941.8673
Web .... www.lasd.org
E-mail .... ltlevario@lasd.org
11515 Colima Rd, Bldg D-111, Whittier, CA 90604
Sdp. Allan Lamonte, Manager

Victim/Wittness Program 213.974.7499
Fax 213.625.8104
210 W Temple St Ste 12-514, Los Angeles,
CA 90012-3058
Donna Wills, Program Director

COURTS

Compton Juvenile Court 310.603.5046
Fax 310.764.0928
200 W Compton Blvd, Ste 403, Compton, CA 90220
Honorable Charles Scarlett, Judge

Inglewood Juvenile Court 310.419.5267
Fax 310.672.9351
110 E Regent St, Inglewood, CA 90301
Honorable Irma Brown, Judge

Los Angeles Juvenile Court 323.526.6377
Fax 323.881.3794
201 Centre Plaza Dr Ste 3, Monterey Park, CA 91754
Honorable Margaret Henry, Judge

San Fernando Valley Juvenile
Court 818.364.2111
Fax 818.367.5587
E-mail .... mrochman@lasuperiorcourt.org
16350 Filbert St, Sylmar, CA 91342-1002
Honorable Morton Rochman, Judge

Teen Court 818.880.6461
Fax 818.880.6457
Web .... www.cityofcalabasas.com
E-mail .... jrubin@ci.calabasas.ca.us
3701 Lost Hills Rd, Agoura Hills, CA 91301-5399
Jeff Ruebin, Director

Teen Court 661.723.6257
Fax 661.723.5913
Web .... www.cityoflancasterca.org
E-mail .... jcampbell@cityoflancasterca.org
44933 Fern Ave, Lancaster, CA 93534-2461
Gerald Wesley, Supervisor

POLICE AND SHERIFF

77th St. Community Police Station 213.485.4185
Fax 323.753.2178
7600 S Broadway, Los Angeles, CA 90003-2040
Robert Green, Director

Alhambra Police Dept 626.570.5151
Fax 626.576.4803
211 S 1st St, Alhambra, CA 91801
Jim Hudsen, Police Chief

Covina Police Dept 626.384.5595
Fax 626.384.5659
Web .... www.ci.covina.ca.us
E-mail .... kraney@ci.covina.ca.us
444 N Citrus Ave, Covina, CA 91723-2065
Kim Raney, Chief

Foothill Community Police Station 818.756.8861
Fax 818.756.7775
Web .... www.lapdonline.org
E-mail .... contact@lapdonline.org
12760 Osborne St, Pacoima, CA 91331-3331
Charlie Beck, Chief Police

Glendale Police Dept 818.548.4840
Fax 818.243.9212
E-mail .... radams@gardenapd.org
131 N Isabel St, Glendale, CA 91206-4382
Ron Depompa, Chief

Hawthorne Police Dept 310.349.2700
Fax 310.978.9355
Web .... www.cityofhawthorne.org
E-mail .... rfager@cityofhawthorne.org
12501 Hawthorne Blvd, Hawthorne, CA 90250-4404
Robert Fager, Chief

Hollywood Community Police
Station 213.485.4302
Fax 323.957.6489
Web .... www.lapd.lacity.org
E-mail .... captainm@lapd.lacity.org
1358 Wilcox Ave, Los Angeles, CA 90028-8195
Captain Michael Moriarty, Chief

Inglewood Unified School District Police
Dept 310.680.5250
Fax 310.330.4485
401 S Inglewood Ave, Inglewood, CA 90301
William T Carter, Chief

Long Beach Police Dept 562.570.7301
Fax 562.570.7111
Web .... www.longbeach.gov
E-mail .... valerie.davis@longbeach.gov
400 W Broadway, Long Beach, CA 90802-4497
Jim Mcdonnell, Chief

Los Angeles School District Police
Dept 213.625.6631
Fax 213.742.0221
1330 W Pico Blvd, Los Angeles, CA 14358
Steven Zipperman, Chief

Newton Community Police Station 323.846.6547
Fax 323.846.6539
Web .... www.lapdonline.org
3400 S Central Ave, Los Angeles, CA 90011-2520
Captain Mark Olvera, Commanding Officer

North Hollywood Community Police
Station 818.623.4016
Fax 818.623.4117
Web .... www.lapd.lacity.org
11640 Burbank Blvd, North Hollywood,
CA 91601-2316
Justin Eisenberg, Director

Northeast Community Police
Station 213.485.2563
Fax 213.847.0669
3353 N San Fernando Rd, Los Angeles, CA 90065
Captain Perez, Captain

Pacific Community Police Station 310.482.6334
Fax 310.482.6342
12312 Culver Blvd, Los Angeles, CA 90066
Charlie Beck, Chief Of Police

San Rafael Police Dept 415.485.3000
Fax 415.485.3043
Web .... www.srpd.org
E-mail .... roy.leon@srpd.org
1400 Fifth Avenue, San Rafael, CA 94901
Roy Leon, Officer Juvenile Dept.

Sheriff's Dept 323.267.4800
Fax 323.267.6690
Web .... www.lasd.org
E-mail .... ldbaca@lasd.org
4700 W Ramona Blvd Unit 1, Monterey Park,
CA 91754-2156
Lee D. Baca, Sheriff

Southeast Community Police
Station 213.972.7828
Fax 213.972.1000
145 W 108th St, Los Angeles, CA 90061-2001
Captain Tingirides, Director

West Los Angeles Community Police
Station 310.444.0702
Fax 310.444.0775
1663 Butler Ave, Los Angeles, CA 90025
Nathan Evanglyen, Chief

Whittier Police Dept 562.945.8250
Fax 562.945.8246
7315 Painter Ave, Whittier, CA 90602
David Singer, Chief

EDUCATION SERVICES

Aeolian Head Start 562.692.4213
11600 1/2 Aeolian St, Whittier, CA 90606
Calvin Moore, Director

Azusa Ctr 626.969.2400
Fax 626.969.2171
328 N Orange Pl, Pico Rivera, CA 90660
Delia Castaneda, Director

Bassett Head Start Don Julian 626.931.3000
E-mail .... srodriguez@bassett.k12.ca.us
13855 Don Julian Rd, La Puente, CA 91746-2518
Sal Rodriguez, Director

Carver Head Start 562.865.1257
Fax 562.402.8678
Web .... www.ci.cerritos.ca.us
E-mail .... carolyn_astella@ci.cerritos.ca.us
16700 Norwalk Blvd, Cerritos, CA 90703-1838
Carolyn Astella, Director

CCRC Woodman Headstart 818.989.2379
5944/5939/Woodman/Bu Ave, Van Nuys, CA 91406

Child Development - Azteca
Headstart 323.780.3770
Fax 818.980.7634
522 N Dangler Ave, Los Angeles, CA 90022
Felix Cruz, Director

Communities In Schools Of Greater Los
Angeles **818.891.9399**
Fax 818.891.2510
Web ....www.cis.gla.org
E-mail ....rarias@cisgla.org
    8743 Burnet Ave, North Hills, CA 91343
    Robert Arias, President

Delta Sigma Thetalos Amigos Ctr **310.450.1792**
    1905 20th St, Santa Monica, CA 90404
    Jaqueline Kirkwood, CEO

Delta Sigma Thetawoods Ctr Head
Start **310.399.3371**
    682 Broadway St, Venice, CA 90291-3404
    C. Buchanan, Director

Downey Road Head Start **323.263.6642**
Web ....www.voa.org
    475 S Downey Rd, Los Angeles, CA 90063
    Selix Cruz, Director

Duarte USD Head Startstate
Preschool-BEA **626.599.5120**
Fax 626.599.5174
Web www.duarte.k12.ca.us
E-mail ....kekstrand@duarte.k12.ca.us
    1433 Crestville Dr, Duarte, CA 91010-3322
    Kaye Ekstrand, Director

East Los Angeles Occupational Ctr
HEA **323.223.1283**
Fax 323.223.6365
    2100 Marengo St, El Monte, CA 90033
    Liz Lozano, Office Manager

Echo Park Head Start **323.666.5227**
Fax 323.572.5102
    1962 Echo Park Ave, El Monte, CA 91731
    Irma Hernandez, Director

Edgewood Academy- Head Start State
Preschool **626.931.7801**
Web www.bassett.k12.ca.us
E-mail ....kbasulto@bassett.k12.ca.us
    14135 Fairgrove Ave, La Puente, CA 91746-1708
    Kathy Basulto, Director

El Campito Head Start **909.628.2298**
    951 E Philadelphia St, El Monte, CA 91731
    Kathy Morales, Director

El Monte City School District **818.575.2393**
    11121 Bryant Rd, El Monte, CA 91731-2053
    Suzanne Seymour, Director

Special Education **818.241.3111**
Fax 818.548.9041
E-mail ....dsheehan@gusd.net
    223 N Jackson St, Glendale, CA 91206
    Richard Sheehan, Superintendent

Special Education **213.241.6701**
Fax 213.241.8915
Web ....www.lausd.net
    333 S Beaudry Ave, Flr 17, Los Angeles, CA 90017
    Dr. Daisy, Superintendent

Special Education (SELPA) **626.966.1679**
Fax 626.339.0027
    1400 N Ranger Dr, East San Gabriel Valley Selpa,
    Covina, CA 91722
    Kathleen Calbert, Director

Special Education (SELPA) **562.866.9011**
Fax 562.866.3287
    16703 Clark Ave, Bellflower, CA 90706
    Raymond Guilleaume, Selpa Director

Volunteer of America **818.837.0097**
    454 S Kalisher St, San Fernando, CA 91340
    John Mcgowan, Director

Madera County

SOCIAL SERVICES

Welfare Dept **559.675.7841**
Fax 559.675.7603
Web ....www.co.madera.ca.us
E-mail ....kwoodard@mcdoss.net
    700 E Yosemite Ave, Madera, CA 93638-3359
    Kelly Woodard, Director

GENERAL HEALTH SERVICES

Madera Health Dept **559.675.7893**
Fax 559.674.7262
Web ....www.madera-county.com
    14215 Road 28, Madera, CA 93638
    Cheryl Edgar, Nursing Director

MENTAL HEALTH SERVICES

Mental Health **559.673.3508**
Fax 559.661.2818
Web ....www.madera-county.com
    14277 Road 28, Madera, CA 93638-5795
    Janice Melton, Lcsw, Director

JUSTICE AGENCY

Juvenile Hall **559.675.7899**
Fax 559.675.7620
    28219 Ave 14, Madera, CA 93638
    Doug White, Superintendent

Victim/Witness Program **559.661.1000**
Fax 559.661.8389
Web ....www.maderacap.org
E-mail ....tfigueroa@maderacap.org
    1225 Gill Ave, Madera, CA 93637-5234
    Tina Figueroa, Program Manager

COURTS

Juvenile Court **559.675.7786**
Fax 559.673.0542
Web ....www.madera.courts.ca.gov
E-mail ....nancy.staggs@madera.courts.ca.gov
    209 W Yosemite Ave, Madera, CA 93637-3534
    Honorable Nancy Staggs, Director

POLICE AND SHERIFF

Police Dept **559.675.4200**
Fax 559.675.6654
    330 S P Street, Madera, CA 93638
    Michael Kime, Chief Of Police

Sheriff's Ofc **559.675.7770**
Fax 559.675.8413
Web ....www.madera-county.com
E-mail ....janderson@madera-county.com
    14143 Road 28, Madera, CA 93638-5714
    John Anderson, Sheriff

EDUCATION SERVICES

East Side Head Start Ctr **559.674.1268**
Fax 559.664.4318
    1112 S A St, Madera, CA 93638-3908
    Martha Navia, Director

Marin County

SOCIAL SERVICES

DHHS- Div Of Social Svcs **415.499.7118**
Fax 415.499.7162
Web ....www.co.marin.ca.us
E-mail ....lmeredith@co.marin.ca.us
    3250 Kerner Blvd, San Rafael, CA 94901
    Larry Merideth, Director

Health And Human Svcs Dept **415.499.3696**
Fax 415.499.3791
    20 N San Pedro Rd, # 102, San Rafael, CA 94903
    Larry Meredith, Phd, Director Of Human Services

Health And Human Svcs Health Svcs
Div **415.499.6841**
Fax 415.499.6855
Web ....www.co.marin.ca.us
E-mail ....lmeredith@co.marin.ca.us
    920 Grand Ave, San Rafael, CA 94901-3595
    Larry Meredith, Health Director

GENERAL HEALTH SERVICES

Marin Community Clinic **415.448.1500**
Fax 415.461.7334
Web ....www.marinclinic.org
    250 Bon Air Rd, Greenbrae, CA 94904
    Georgeanna Farren, MD, Medical Director

Public Health Nursing **415.473.6007**
Fax 415.473.6881
E-mail ....dbeetham@co.marin.ca.us
    899 Northgate Dr Ste 100, San Rafael, CA 94903
    Diane Beetham, Nursing Director/Chief Of Clinical Services

WIC Program **415.499.6889**
E-mail ....afarrer@co.marin.ca.us
    361 3rd St Ste C, San Rafael, CA 94901
    Anna Farrer, Coordinator

Women's Health Svcs **415.507.4030**
Fax 415.507.4018
Web ....www.co.marin.ca.us
E-mail ....mjacobs@co.marin.ca.us
    3260 Kerner Blvd, San Rafael, CA 94901-3580
    Mark Jacobs, Md, Medical Director

MENTAL HEALTH SERVICES

Mental Health Dept **415.499.6769**
Fax 415.499.3791
Web ....www.co.marin.ca.us
E-mail ....bgurganus@co.marin.ca.us
    20 N San Pedro Rd Ste 2028, San Rafael,
    CA 94903-4158
    Scott Smolar, Medical Director

JUSTICE AGENCY

CASA **415.507.9016**
Fax 415.507.9265
Web ....www.marinadvocates.org
    30 N San Pedro Rd, Ste 275, San Rafael, CA 94903
    Cyndy Doherty, Case Program Director

Juvenile Svcs Ctr **415.499.6659**
Fax 415.499.6978
E-mail ....nkuhn@co.marin.ca.us
    4 Jeannette Prandi Way, San Rafael, CA 94903
    Nicki Kuhn, Director

Probation/Juvenile Hall **415.499.6705**
Fax 415.499.6703
    16 Jeannette Prandi Way, San Rafael, CA 94903
    Steve Blair, Superintendent

Victim/Witness Program **415.499.6450**
Fax 415.499.3719
    3501 Civic Center Dr Rm 130, San Rafael, CA 94903
    Rob Guidi, Supervisor

COURTS

Superior Court Juvenile Court **415.473.6244**
Fax 415.473.7897
Web ....www.co.marin.ca.us
E-mail ....lduryee@co.marin.ca.us
    Hall Of Justice, Civic Center, San Rafael, CA 94913
    Honorable Lynn Duryee, Director

POLICE AND SHERIFF

Sheriff's Ofc **415.499.7250**
Fax 415.507.4126
Web ....www.co.marin.ca.us
E-mail ....seakke@co.marin.ca.us
    3501 Civic Center Dr Rm 145, San Rafael,
    CA 94903-4189
    Robert T. Doyle, Sheriff

EDUCATION SERVICES

Special Education/SELPA **415.499.5850**
Fax 415.499.5813
   1111 Las Gallinas Ave, San Rafael, CA 94903
   Penny Valentine, Director Of Selpa

Mariposa County

SOCIAL SERVICES

Human Svcs **209.966.2000**
Fax 209.966.8251
Web .... www.mariposacounty.org
E-mail .... jrydings@kingsview.org
   5263 Lemee Ln, Mariposa, CA 95338
   James Rydingsword, Director

Social Svcs **209.966.2000**
Fax 209.742.5854
   5085 Bollion St, Mariposa, CA 95338
   Nancy Bell, Executive Director

GENERAL HEALTH SERVICES

Health Dept **209.966.3689**
Fax 209.966.4929
Web .... www.mariposacounty.org
E-mail .... mch@mariposacounty.org
   4988 11th St, Mariposa, CA 95338
   Ruth Mckinney, Nursing Director

JUSTICE AGENCY

Probation Dept **209.966.3612**
Fax 209.742.5961
Web .... www.mariposacounty.org
E-mail .... pjudy@mariposacounty.org
   5091 Bullion St, Mariposa, CA 95338
   Pege Judy, Chief Performance Officer

Victim/Witness Program **209.742.7441**
Fax 209.742.5780
E-mail .... vicwit@mariposacounty.org
   4975 9th St, Mariposa, CA 95338
   Megan Kehoe, Advocate

COURTS

Superior Court **209.966.2005**
Fax 209.742.6860
Web .... www.mariposacourts.org
E-mail .... parrishw@mariposacourts.org
   5088 Bullion St, Mariposa, CA 95338
   Honorable Wayne R. Parrish, Assistant Presiding Officer

POLICE AND SHERIFF

Sheriff's Dept **209.966.3615**
Fax 209.742.5090
E-mail .... sheriff@mariposacounty.org
   5099 Old Hwy. North, Mariposa, CA 95338
   Brian Muller, Sheriff

Mendocino County

SOCIAL SERVICES

Social Svcs **707.463.7700**
Fax 707.463.7960
Web .... www.mcdss.org
   737 S State St, Ukiah, CA 95482-5815
   Becky Wilson, Social Services Director

GENERAL HEALTH SERVICES

Health Dept **707.472.2600**
Fax 707.472.2735
Web .... www.co.mendocino.ca.us/ph
   1120 S Dora St, Ukiah, CA 95482-6340
   Gloria Gutfeld, Nursing Director

MENTAL HEALTH SERVICES

Mental Health **707.463.4303**
Fax 707.463.6395
Web .... www.co.mendocino.ca.us
E-mail .... rogerst@co.mendocino.ca.us
   860 N Bush St, Ukiah, CA 95482-3919
   Tom Pinizotto, Interim Director

JUSTICE AGENCY

CASA **707.463.6503**
Fax 707.463.4624
Web .... www.mendocinocasa.org
E-mail .... casamc@pacific.net
   327 N State St Ste 204, Ukiah, CA 95482
   Sheryn Hildebrand, Director

Juvenile Justice Commission **707.467.8257**
Web .... www.co.mendocino.ca.us
E-mail .... brownjim@co.mendocino.ca.us
   585 Low Gap Rd, Ukiah, CA 95482-3734
   Jim Brown, Juvenile Hall Superintendent

Probation Dept **707.463.5750**
Fax 707.463.5749
   589 Low Gap Rd # B, Ukiah, CA 95482
   Jean Goentzer, Juvenile Unit Director

Victim/Witness Program **707.463.4218**
Fax 707.468.3371
E-mail .... tostea@co.mendocino.ca.us
   100 N. State St Room 501, Ukiah, CA 95482
   Anita Toste, Coordinator

COURTS

Superior Court **707.463.4481**
Fax 707.468.3459
Web .... www.mendocino.courts.ca.gov
E-mail .... ciryjema@mendocino.courts.ca.gov
   100 N State St, Ukiah, CA 95482-4416
   Honorable Cindee Mayfield, Family Law

POLICE AND SHERIFF

Police Dept **707.463.6262**
Fax 707.462.6068
Web .... www.cityofukiah.com
E-mail .... cdewey@cityofukiah.com
   300 Seminary Ave, Ukiah, CA 95482-5400
   Chris Dewey, Chief Of Police

Sheriff's Ofc **707.463.4411**
Fax 707.468.3404
E-mail .... sheriff@co.mendocino.ca.us
   951 Low Gap Rd, Ukiah, CA 95482
   Thomas Allman, Sheriff

Merced County

GENERAL HEALTH SERVICES

Golden Valley Health Ctr **209.383.7441**
Fax 209.383.0136
E-mail .... sdiego@gvhc.org
   737 W Childs Ave, Merced, CA 95341
   Sylvia Diego, Chief Medical Officer

Health Dept **209.381.1010**
Fax 209.381.1034
Web .... www.co.merced.ca.us
   260 E 15th St, Merced, CA 95340
   Timothy Livermore, California Childrenæs Services Director

MENTAL HEALTH SERVICES

Mental Health **209.381.6813**
Fax 209.725.3676
Web .... www.co.merced.ca.us
E-mail .... manuel.jimenez@co.merced.ca.us
   480 E 13th St, Merced, CA 95341-6214
   Manuel Jimenez, Director

JUSTICE AGENCY

Iris Garrett Juvenile Justice Correctional
Complex **209.381.1400**
Fax 209.725.3505
Web .... www.co.merced.ca.us
   2840 W Sandy Mush Rd, Merced, CA 95341-8009
   Lisa Naples, Program Manager

Juvenile Justice Delinquency Prevention
Commission **209.385.7494**
Fax 209.725.3999
Web .... www.co.modoc.ca.us
   2150 M St, Merced, CA 95340-3709
   Lamar Henderson, Chairperson

Probation Department **209.385.7495**
Fax 209.725.3999
   2150 M Street, Merced, CA 95340-3709
   Scott M Ball, Chief Probation Officer

Probation Dept **209.385.7494**
Fax 209.725.3999
   2150 M St, Fl 2, Merced, CA 95340
   Scott Ball, Chief Performance Officer

COURTS

Superior Court Juvenile Div **209.725.4119**
Fax 209.726.6585
   627 W 21st St, Merced, CA 95340-3744
   Thomas Burr, Commissioner, Delinquency

POLICE AND SHERIFF

Police Dept **209.385.6912**
Fax 209.385.8800
Web .... www.cityofmerced.org
   611 W 22nd St, Merced, CA 95340-3737
   Norman Andrade, Chief Of Police

Modoc County

SOCIAL SERVICES

Social Svcs **530.233.6501**
Fax 530.233.2136
   120 N Main St, Alturas, CA 96101
   Pauline Cravens, Director

GENERAL HEALTH SERVICES

Health Dept **530.233.6311**
Fax 530.233.5754
Web .... www.modocohealthservices.com
   441 N Main St Ste 1, Alturas, CA 96101-3490
   Kelly Crosby, Phn, Nursing Director

JUSTICE AGENCY

CASA **530.233.3111**
Fax 530.233.4744
E-mail .... ccallaghan@teachinc.org
   112 E 2nd St, Alturas, CA 96101-4008
   Carol Callaghan, Director

Probation Dept **530.233.6324**
Fax 530.233.6363
E-mail .... leofernandez@leo.mo.ca.us
   326 S Main St Ste A, Alturas, CA 96101-4086
   Elias Fernandez Jr., Chief Performance Officer

Victim/Witness Assistance **530.233.3311**
Fax 530.233.4917
   204 S Court St, Rm 108, Alturas, CA 96101
   Christopher Brooke, District Attorney

COURTS

Superior Court **530.233.6222**
Fax 530.233.6500
   205 S East St, Alturas, CA 96101-4079
   Francis Barclay, Presiding Judge

California

POLICE AND SHERIFF

Police Dept......................**530.233.2011**
Fax....................................530.233.4105
200 W North St, Alturas, CA 96101
Ken Barnes, Chief Of Police

Mono County

SOCIAL SERVICES

Social Svcs......................**760.932.5600**
Fax....................................760.932.5287
Web...................................www.mono.ca.gov
E-mail...........................jtiede@mono.ca.gov
85 Emigrant St, Bridgeport, CA 93517
Julie Tiede, Director

GENERAL HEALTH SERVICES

Health Dept.....................**760.932.5580**
Fax....................................760.932.5284
221 Twin Lakes Road, Bridgeport, CA 93517
Lynda Salcido, Rn, Public Health Director

Health Dept.....................**760.924.1830**
Fax....................................760.924.1831
Web...................................www.monohealth.com
E-mail..........................apearce@mono.ca.gov
437 Old Mammoth Rd, Mammoth Lakes, CA 93546
Andrea Pearce, Aids Coordinator

JUSTICE AGENCY

**Juvenile Justice Commission/Juvenile
Hall**.................................**760.932.5570**
Fax....................................760.932.5571
Web...................................www.mono.ca.gov
E-mail..........................bbryant@mono.ca.gov
57 Bryant St, Bridgeport, CA 93517
Beverlee Bryant, Chief Performance Officer

Victim/Witness Program......**760.924.1710**
Fax....................................760.924.1711
Sierra Center Mall, 3rd Fl, Mammoth Lakes, CA 93546
Tamara Donnelly, Coordinator

COURTS

Superior Court..................**760.932.5239**
Fax....................................760.932.7520
Web...................................www.monocourt.org
E-mail...........................info@monocourt.org
Highway 395 & School St, Bridgeport, CA 93517
Hector Gonzalez, Director

POLICE AND SHERIFF

Sheriff's Ofc....................**760.932.5279**
Fax....................................760.932.7435
E-mail.......................rscholl@monosheriff.org
100 Bryant St, Bridgeport, CA 93517
Richard C. Scholl, Sheriff

Monterey County

GENERAL HEALTH SERVICES

Health Dept.....................**831.755.4500**
Fax....................................831.755.4797
Web...................................www.co.monterey.ca.us/health
E-mail.........................fosterl@co.monterey.ca.us
1270 Natividad Rd, Salinas, CA 93906-3122
Len Foster, Director Of Health

JUSTICE AGENCY

CASA..............................**831.455.6800**
Fax....................................831.455.6802
Web...................................www.casamonterey.org
E-mail.......................sarah@casamonterey.org
945 S Main St Ste 107, Salinas, CA 93901
Siobhan Greene, Director

Probation Dept..................**831.755.3913**
Fax....................................831.759.7246
E-mail.......................realm@co.monterey.ca.us
1422 Natividad Rd, Salinas, CA 93906
Manuel Real, Chief Probation Officer

Probation Dept..................**831.647.7739**
Fax....................................831.647.7881
Web...................................www.co.monterey.ca.us
E-mail.......................realm@co.monterey.ca.us
1200 Aguajito Rd, Ste 008, Monterey, CA 93940
Manuel Real, Chief Performance Officer

Probation Dept..................**831.755.3900**
Fax....................................831.755.3990
Web...................................www.co.monterey.ca.us
E-mail.......................realm@co.monterey.ca.us
1422 Natividad Rd, Salinas, CA 93906-3102
Manuel Real, CPO

Youth Ctr........................**831.759.6700**
Fax....................................831.784.0254
Web...................................www.co.monterey.ca.us
970 Circle Dr, Salinas, CA 93905-2150
Richard Gray, Director

COURTS

Superior Court..................**831.775.5400**
Web...................................www.monterey.courts.ca.gov
240 Church St Ste 320, Salinas, CA 93901-2683
Connie Mazzei, Chief Executive Officer

POLICE AND SHERIFF

Salinas Police Dept.............**831.758.7090**
Fax....................................831.758.7982
222 Lincoln Ave, Salinas, CA 93901
Louis Fetherolf, Chief Of Police

Sheriff's Ofc....................**831.755.3700**
Fax....................................831.755.3810
E-mail.................kanalakism@co.monterey.ca.us
1414 Natividad Rd, Salinas, CA 93906
Mike Kanalakis, Sheriff

EDUCATION SERVICES

Special Education................**831.755.0340**
Fax....................................831.769.0732
E-mail.................sholiton@monterey.k12.ca.us
901 Blanco Cir, Salinas, CA 93901
Martina Sholiton, Assistant Superintendent

Napa County

SOCIAL SERVICES

Children's Welfare Svcs.........**707.253.4261**
Fax....................................707.259.8310
E-mail...............randy.snowden@countynapa.org
2344 Old Sonoma Rd, Napa, CA 94559
Randy Snowden, Director

Health & Human Svcs Agency....**707.253.4279**
Fax....................................707.253.6172
Web...................................www.countyofnapa.org
2344 Old Sonoma Rd, Napa, CA 94559
Randolph F Snowden, Director

GENERAL HEALTH SERVICES

Health Dept.....................**707.253.4461**
Fax....................................707.253.4880
2344 Old Sonoma Rd, Bldg G, Napa, CA 94559
Karen Smith, Md, Health Officer

JUSTICE AGENCY

CASA A Voice For Children.......**707.257.2272**
Fax....................................707.257.2278
E-mail.........................jdiverde@napacasa.org
1804 Soscol Ave 203, Napa, CA 94559
Julie Diverde, Executive Director

**Juvenile Justice
Commission/Probation**..........**707.253.4361**
Fax....................................707.253.6098
Web...................................www.co.napa.ca.us
212 Walnut St, Napa, CA 94559-3703
Amanda Gibbs, Interim

Victim/Witness Program.........**707.252.6222**
Fax....................................707.226.5179
Web...................................www.volunteernapa.org
E-mail...................gokelley@volunteernapa.org
1820 Jefferson St, Napa, CA 94559-1618
Gayle OÆKelley, Program Coordinator

POLICE AND SHERIFF

Police Dept.....................**707.257.9573**
Fax....................................707.257.9281
Web...................................www.cityofnapa.org
E-mail...................rmelton@cityofnapa.org
1539 1st St, Napa, CA 94559-2883
Richard Melton, Chief Of Police

Sheriff's Ofc....................**707.253.4440**
Fax....................................707.253.4193
E-mail...................douglask@co.napa.ca.us
1535 Airport Blvd, Napa, CA 94558
Douglas Koford, Sheriff

EDUCATION SERVICES

**Napa Valley Unified School District Special Education
Svcs**...............................**707.253.6865**
Fax....................................707.259.8552
Web...................................www.nvusd.k12.ca.us
E-mail...................pdillon@nvusd.k12.ca.us
2425 Jefferson St, Napa, CA 94558-4931
Adam Stein, Edd, Director

Nevada County

SOCIAL SERVICES

Human Svcs......................**530.265.1340**
Fax....................................530.265.9860
Web...................................www.mynevadacounty.com
950 Maidu Ave, Nevada City, CA 95959
Jeff Brown, Director

GENERAL HEALTH SERVICES

Health Dept.....................**530.265.1450**
Web...................................www.mynevadacounty.com
500 Crown Point Circle, Ste 110, Grass Valley, CA 95945
Rona Martin, Administrative Assistant

Public Defender's Ofc...........**707.565.4400**
Fax....................................707.565.4411
Web...................................www.sonoma-county.org
E-mail...................mmaddux@sonoma-county.org
224 Main St, Nevada City, CA 95959-2509
Don E Lown, Public Defender

JUSTICE AGENCY

Carl S. Bryant Juvenile Hall.....**530.470.2600**
Fax....................................530.478.7976
E-mail...................carol.frazier@co.nevada.ca.us
15434 State Hwy 49, Nevada City, CA 95945
Daniel Prince, Superintendent

Juvenile Justice Commission.....**530.265.1300**
Fax....................................530.265.6280
Web...................................www.mynevadacounty.com
109 1/2 N Pine St, Nevada City, CA 95959-2511
Pat Riley, Chairperson

Probation Dept..................**530.265.1200**
Fax....................................530.265.6280
E-mail...................mike.dent@co.nevada.ca.us
109 1/2 N Pine St, Nevada City, CA 95959-2511
Mike Dent, Program Manager Juvenile Unit

Public Defender's Ofc 530.265.1400
Fax 530.478.5626
Web ....www.co.nevada.ca.us
   224 Main St, Nevada City, CA 95959-2509
Don E Lown, Public Defender

Victim/Witness Program 530.265.1246
Fax 530.265.6304
Web ....www.co.nevada.ca.us
E-mail ....loletta.hadel@co.nevada.ca.us
   109 1/2 N Pine St, Nevada City, CA 95959-2511
Loletta Hadel, Victim Advocate

POLICE AND SHERIFF

Nevada City Police Dept 530.265.2626
Fax 530.265.9259
Web ....www.cityofnevadacity.com
   317 Broad St, Nevada City, CA 95959-2496
Louis Trovato, Chief Of Police

Sheriff's Ofc 530.265.1471
Fax 530.470.0439
   950 Maidu Ave, Nevada City, CA 95959
Keith Royal, Sheriff

Orange County

SOCIAL SERVICES

Social Svcs Agency 714.541.7700
Fax 714.541.7781
Web ....www.ssa.ocgov.com
E-mail ....michael.riley@ssa.ocgov.com
   888 N Main St Ste 1000, Santa Ana, CA 92701
Michael Riley, Director

GENERAL HEALTH SERVICES

Health Care Agency-General Info 714.834.4722
Fax 714.834.5506
   1725 W 17th St, Santa Ana, CA 92706-2316
Alan Albright, Children & Youth Services Division Manager

MENTAL HEALTH SERVICES

Mental Health 714.834.6032
Fax 714.834.5506
Web ....www.ochealthinfo.com
E-mail ....mrefowitz@ochca.com
   405 W 5th St, Rm 726, Santa Ana, CA 92701
Mark Refowitz, Director

JUSTICE AGENCY

CASA 714.619.5155
Fax 714.619.5152
Web ....www.casaoc.org
E-mail ....ghoward@casaoc.org
   1615 E 17th St, # 100, Santa Ana, CA 92705
Gene Howard, Executive Director

Joplin Youth Ctr 949.635.2600
Fax 949.589.7927
E-mail ....jeff.corp@prob.ocgov.com
   19480 Rose Canyon Road, Trabuco Canyon,
   CA 92678
Jeff Corp, Probation Division Director

Juvenile Hall 714.935.6660
Fax 714.935.7581
   331 The City Dr S, Orange, CA 92868
Dave Burnham, Director

Probation Dept 714.569.2000
Fax 714.569.2178
   909 N Main St Ste 1, Santa Ana, CA 92701
Steven Sentman, Chief Performance Officer

Probation Dept 714.935.6611
Fax 714.935.6358
   301 The City Dr S, Orange, CA 92868
Steven J. Sentman, Chief

Victim/Witness Assistance
Program 949.975.0244
Fax 949.975.0250
E-mail ....info@cspinc.org
   1821 E Dyer Rd Ste 200, Santa Ana, CA 92705
Ronnetta Johnson, Director

Youth Guidance Ctr 714.836.2700
Fax 714.836.2727
Web ....www.oc.ca.gov
   3030 N Hesperian St, Santa Ana, CA 92711
Doug Sanger, Director

POLICE AND SHERIFF

Anaheim Police Dept 714.765.1900
Fax 714.765.1549
E-mail ....jsharkey@anaheim.net
   425 S Harbor Blvd, Anaheim, CA 92805
Sgt. Jack Sharkey, Juvenile & Sex Crimes

Anaheim Police Dept East District 714.765.3800
   8201 E Santa Ana Canyon Rd Ste A, Anaheim,
   CA 92808
John Welter, Police Chief

Orange Police Dept 714.744.7444
Fax 714.744.7320
Web ....www.cityoforange.org
E-mail ....bgustafson@cityoforange.org
   1107 N Batavia St, Orange, CA 92867-4615
Robert Gustafson, Chief Of Police

Santa Ana Police Dept 714.834.4211
Fax 714.245.8606
E-mail ....pwalters@ci.santa-ana.ca.us
   60 Civic Center Plz, Santa Ana, CA 91701
Paul Walters, Chief Of Police

Sheriff's Dept 714.647.1800
Fax 714.953.3092
Web ....www.ocsd.org
E-mail ....shutchens@ocsd.org
   550 N Flower St, Santa Ana, CA 92703-2361
Sandra Hutchens, Sheriff

EDUCATION SERVICES

Brea Head Start 714.990.4391
Fax 714.990.2045
   2501 S pulman St, Ste100, santa ana, CA 92705
Collen Versteed, Director

Buena Park Head Start 714.521.1909
Fax 714.521.1917
Web ....www.ochsinc.org
E-mail ....alma.lopez@ophisd.org
   6725 Dale St, Buena Park, CA 90621-3687
Alma Lopez, Director

Capistrano USD Even Start P.A.T. 949.234.5991
Fax 949.496.4238
Web ....www.capousd.org
E-mail ....vgvelarde@capousd.org
   2 Via Positiva, San Juan Capistrano, CA 92675-4318
Valerie Velarde, Even Start Director

Capo Valley Head Start 949.661.6978
Fax 949.661.2375
   31485 El Camino Real, Santa Ana, CA 92704
Susy Collings, Director

Centralia Head Start 714.228.9004
Fax 714.228.9040
   6627 La Cienaga Dr, Buena Park, CA 90620
Angelica Alaniz, Director

Council Of Affiliated Negro
Organization 714.835.4110
Fax 714.835.0626
   1735 N Grand Ave, Santa Ana, CA 92705-7017
Alta Manning, Director

Special Education 714.628.4153
Fax 714.628.4166
   1401 N Handy St, Orange, CA 92867
Karen Hanson, Administrator

Special Education 949.936.5000
Fax 949.936.5239
Web ....www.iusd.org
E-mail ....mbervernick@iusd.org
   5050 Barranca Pkwy, Irvine, CA 92604-4652
Mary Bevernick, Director

Special Education 714.730.7301
Fax 714.832.9087
Web www.tustin.k12.ca.us
   300 S C St, Tustin Unified School District, Tustin,
   CA 92780-3633
Lori Stillings, Assistant Superintendent

Special Education (SELPA) 714.828.1766
Fax 714.828.6763
   5967 Ball Rd, Cypress, CA 90630
Frank Donavan, Administrator

Special Education (SELPA) 949.580.3411
Fax 949.580.3414
Web ....www.svusd.org
E-mail ....lappid@svusd.org
   25631 Peter A Hartman Way, Mission Viejo,
   CA 92691-3142
Diane Lappi, Director

Placer County

SOCIAL SERVICES

Health & Human Svcs 530.889.7141
Fax 530.889.7198
Web ....www.placer.ca.gov
   11484 B ave, Auburn, CA 95603
Richard J Burton, Director & Ph Officer

Health & Human Svcs 530.889.7610
Fax 530.889.7608
Web ....www.placer.ca.gov
E-mail ....rburton@placer.ca.gov
   11552 B Ave, Auburn, CA 95603-2604
Richard J. Burton, Md, Director

GENERAL HEALTH SERVICES

Chape-De Indian Health 530.887.2800
Fax 530.887.2849
   11670 Atwood Rd, Auburn, CA 95603
Susan Navarro, Director

Community Health 530.889.7141
Fax 530.889.7198
Web ....www.placer.ca.gov
   11484 B Ave, Auburn, CA 95603
Mary Jo Sweeney, Director Of Nursing

MENTAL HEALTH SERVICES

Mental Health 530.886.5401
Fax 530.265.9376
E-mail ....bbautista@placer.ca.gov
   101 Cirby Hills Dr, Roseville, CA 95678
Richard Hill, Director Of Adult System Of Care

JUSTICE AGENCY

Fouts Springs Youth Facility 530.963.3101
Fax 530.963.3486
Web ....www.solanocounty.com
E-mail ....rkrygier@solanocounty.com
   1333 Fouts Springs Rd., Stonyford, CA 95979
Richard Krygier, Probation Services Manager

Juvenile Hall/Detention Ctr 530.889.7900
Fax 530.886.4874
Web ....www.placer.ca.gov
E-mail ....jcann@placer.ca.gov
   11260 B Ave, Auburn, CA 95603-2607
Jeff Cann, Superintendent

Juvenile Justice Commission 530.889.7900
Fax 530.889.7950
Web ....www.placer.ca.gov
   2929 Richardson Dr, Ste B, Auburn, CA 95603
   Marshall Hopper, Chief

COURTS

Peer Court 916.663.9227
Fax 916.663.2965
Web ....www.peercourt.com
E-mail ....placerpeercourt@aol.com
   671 Newcastle Rd Ste 7, Newcastle, CA 95658
   Karen Green, Coordinator

POLICE AND SHERIFF

Auburn Police Dept (Business Ofc) 530.823.4237
Fax 530.823.4224
E-mail ....jruffcorn@auburn.ca.gov
   1215 Lincoln Way, Auburn, CA 95603
   John Ruffcorn, Chief Of Police

Sheriff's Dept 530.889.7800
Fax 530.889.6883
Web ....www.placer.ca.gov
   2929 Richardson Dr, Auburn, CA 95604
   Edward N. Bonner, Sheriff

EDUCATION SERVICES

**Early Head Start-Baby Steps Child
Development** 916.652.3284
Fax 916.652.3285
   5400 Barton Rd, Auburn, CA 95603
   Vanessa Huff, Interim Director

Special Education 530.745.1310
Fax 530.745.1405
Web www.placercoe.k12.ca.us
E-mail ....rsarrell@placercoe.k12.ca.us
   11700 Enterprise Dr, Auburn, CA 95603-3731
   Philip Wiliams, Administrator

Plumas County

SOCIAL SERVICES

Dept Of Social Svcs 530.283.6350
Fax 530.283.6368
Web ....www.countyofplumas.com
E-mail ....elliottsmart@countyofplumas.com
   270 County Hospital Rd Ste 207, Quincy,
   CA 95971-9174
   Elliott Smart, Director

GENERAL HEALTH SERVICES

Health Dept 530.283.6330
Fax 530.283.6110
   270 County Hospital Rd Ste 111, Quincy, CA 95971
   Tina Venable, Nursing Director

MENTAL HEALTH SERVICES

Mental Health 530.283.6307
Fax 530.283.6045
Web ....www.kingsview.org
E-mail ....jsebold@kingsview.org
   270 County Hospital Rd Ste 109, Quincy,
   CA 95971-9173
   John Sebold, Lcsw, Director

JUSTICE AGENCY

Probation Dept 530.283.6200
Fax 530.283.6165
Web ....www.coutyofplumas.com
   1446 E Main St, Quincy, CA 95971-9402
   Sharon Reineert, Chief Performance Officer

Victim/Witness Program 530.283.6285
Fax 530.283.6226
Web ....www.countyofplumas.com
E-mail ....victimwitness@countyofplumas.com
   520 Main St, Rm 408, Quincy, CA 95971-9116
   Kori Langrehr, Director

COURTS

Superior Court 530.283.6297
Fax 530.283.6144
   520 Main St Rm 304, Quincy, CA 95971
   Honorable Janet Hilde, Judge

POLICE AND SHERIFF

Fairfield Police 707.428.7300
Fax 707.428.7733
   1000 Webster St, Fairfield, CA 94533-4836
   Jeff Osgood, Gang Suppression

Sheriff's Dept 530.283.6375
Fax 530.283.6344
   1400 E Main St, Quincy, CA 95971
   Greg Hagwood, Sheriff

Riverside County

SOCIAL SERVICES

Child Protective Serv 760.773.6700
Fax 760.773.6793
   68625 Perez Rd Ste 2, Cathedral City, CA 92234
   Carol Ritos, Regional Supervisor

Children's Protective Svcs 760.863.7210
Fax 760.863.7225
   48113 Jackson St, Indio, CA 92201-7496
   Nancy Satterwhite, Director

Children's Protective Svcs 951.600.6600
Fax 951.600.6640
   27464 Commerce Center Dr Ste E, Temecula,
   CA 92590-2546
   Dean Wilson, Manager

Children's Protective Svcs - West 951.358.3700
Fax 951.358.3677
   11070 Magniolia St, Riverside, CA 92505
   Susan Mahoney, Regional Manager

Perris Dept Of Social Svcs 951.940.6600
Fax 951.940.6610
   2055 N Perris Blvd Ste B, Perris, CA 92571
   Virgina Irvin, Regional Manager

Social Svcs 951.358.3000
Fax 951.358.3036
   4060 County Circle Dr, Riverside, CA 92503
   Susan Loew, Director Of Social Svcs

Social Svcs 760.921.5800
Fax 760.921.5802
   1267 W Hobsonway, Blythe, CA 92225
   Irene Osaigande, CPS Supervisor

Social Svcs 951.922.7550
Fax 951.922.7595
   901 E Ramsey, Banning, CA 92220
   Mary Ellen Johnston, Regional Manager

GENERAL HEALTH SERVICES

Health Dept 951.358.5000
Fax 951.358.4529
E-mail ....info@healthandnutritionservices.org
   4065 County Circle Dr, Riverside, CA 92503
   Gayle Hoxter, Program Director Of Nutrition Services

Indio Family Health Ctr 760.863.8283
Fax 760.863.8366
Web ....www.rivco-familycarecenters.org
   47923 Oasis St Ste A, Indio, CA 92201-9788
   Gloria Robinson, Manager

Lake Elsinore Family Health Ctr 951.471.4200
Fax 951.471.4205
Web ....www.rivcoph.org
   2499 E Lakeshore Dr, Lake Elsinore, CA 92530-4446
   Lily Murvine, Clinic Manager

MENTAL HEALTH SERVICES

Mental Health Svcs 951.358.4500
Fax 951.358.4513
Web ....www.rcdmh.org
E-mail ....wengerd@rcmhd.org
   4095 County Circle Dr, Riverside, CA 92503-3410
   Jerry Wengerd, Director

JUSTICE AGENCY

**California Dept Of Corrections & Rehab Inland Parole Juvenile
Div** 951.782.3214
Fax 951.782.4918
Web ....www.cdcr.ca.gov
   5700 Division St, Fl 2, Riverside, CA 92506
   Sandra Abacherli, Supervising Parole Agent

CASA 760.863.7424
Fax 760.863.7431
E-mail ....info@casalaboursitecounty.org
   44199 Monroe St, Indio, CA 92201
   Deborah Sutton, Executive Director

Corona Probation Ofc 951.272.5671
Fax 951.272.5687
   505 S Buena Vista Ave Ste 102, Corona, CA 92882
   Gina Rubio, Office Assistant

Indio Juvenile Hall 760.863.7600
Fax 760.863.7615
Web ....www.riversidecounty.us.ca
E-mail ....romiller@rcprob.us
   47665 Oasis St, Indio, CA 92201-6999
   Ron Miller, Probation Division Director

Juvenile Hall 951.358.4200
Fax 951.358.4213
   3933 Harrison St, Riverside, CA 92503-3523
   Loretta Malone, Probation Division Director

Probation Dept - Juvenile Div 951.358.4310
Fax 951.358.4253
   9889 County Farm Rd, Riverside, CA 92503
   Bryce Hulstrom, Probation Division Director

Van Horn Youth Ctr 951.358.4400
Fax 951.358.4420
   10000 County Farm Rd, Riverside, CA 92503
   Chris Wright, Probation/division Director

Victim/Witness Program 951.955.5450
Fax 951.955.5640
Web ....www.co.riverside.ca.us
   3960 Orange St, Riverside, CA 92501
   Gabrielle Beaudoin, Secretary

Youth Accountability Board 951.275.8783
Fax 951.275.8784
Web ....www.probation.co.riverside.ca.us
E-mail ....ldjones@rcprob.us
   4168 12th St, Riverside, CA 92501-3409
   Lynette Jones-Martin, Coordinator

COURTS

Superior Court Juvenile Div 951.358.4137
   9991 County Farm Rd Ste 108, Riverside,
   CA 92503-3551
   Honorable Charles Koosed, Presiding Judge

POLICE AND SHERIFF

Riverside City Police Dept 951.826.5700
Fax 951.826.5405
Web ....www.riversideca.gov
E-mail ....sdiaz@riversideca.gov
   4102 Orange St, Riverside, CA 92501-3671
   Sergil Diaz, Chief

Sheriff's Ofc 951.955.2400
Fax 951.955.2428
E-mail ....ssniff@riversidesheriff.org
   4095 Lemon St Fl 1st, Riverside, CA 92502
   Stanley Sniff, Sheriff

© 2011 Dorland Health

EDUCATION SERVICES

Desert Hightlands Head Start Ctr 760.416.8090
Fax...760.416.8413
Web.................................www.psusd.k12.ca.us
E-mail.......................................lgoff@psusd.k12.ca.us
  1000 Tahquitz Canyon Way, Palm Springs, CA 92262
  Ms Linda Goff, Director

Sacramento County

SOCIAL SERVICES

California Children's Svcs 916.875.9900
Fax...916.369.0639
Web...www.saccounty.com
E-mail...............................snesbitt@dhs.ca.gov
  9616 Micron Ave, Ste 970, Sacramento,
  CA 95827-2627
  Sue Nesbitt, Administrator

Children & Family Svcs Div 916.657.2614
Fax...916.657.2049
Web.....................................www.childsworld.ca.gov
E-mail.................................greg.rose@dss.ca.gov
  744 P St, Mail Station - 17-18, Sacramento,
  CA 95814
  Greg Rose, Deputy Director

Dept Of Health & Human Svcs 916.875.6091
Fax...916.875.8213
Web...www.sacdhhs.com
  7001 East Pkwy # A, Sacramento, CA 95823-2501
  Ann Edwards, Director

Public Affairs Ofc 916.657.2268
Fax...916.657.2281
  744 P St, # MS17-09, Sacramento, CA 95814
  Michael Weston, Deputy Director

GENERAL HEALTH SERVICES

**Child Health Disabilty Prevention
Program** 916.875.7151
Fax...916.854.9232
Web.................................www.dhs.ca.gov/chdp
  9333 Tech Center Dr Ste 800, Sacramento,
  CA 95826
  Pat Dorais, Program Coordinator

MENTAL HEALTH SERVICES

Behavioral Health Svcs 916.875.7070
Fax...916.875.9775
Web...www.sacdhhs.com
  7001A East Pkwy, Ste 400, Sacramento, CA 95823
  Ann Edwards-buckley, Director

JUSTICE AGENCY

California Youth Authority 916.445.5993
Fax...916.322.4181
Web...www.cya.ca.gov
E-mail..................................fmijares@cya.ca.gov
  1608 T St, Sacramento, CA 95811-7290
  Cerolina Garcia, Parole Agent

**Corrections Standards Authority/ Corrections Planning And
Programs Div/ Juvenile Justice Grants
Program** 916.445.5073
Fax...916.327.3317
Web...www.cdcr.ca.gov
E-mail...........................marlon.yarber@cdcr.ca.gov
  600 Bercut Dr, Sacramento, CA 95811-0131
  Marlon Yarber, Deputy Director, Corrections, Planning And Programs

Div of Juvenile Justice 916.262.1500
Fax...916.262.1510
Web...www.cdcr.ca.gov
  4241 Williamsbourgh Dr, Sacramento, CA 95823
  David Murphy, Deputy Superintendent

Probation Dept 916.875.0300
Fax...916.875.0203
  3201 Florin Perkins Rd, Sacramento, CA 95826
  Don L Meyer, Chief

Victim/Witness Program 916.874.5701
Fax...916.874.5271
Web...www.saccounty.net
E-mail...................................martink@sacda.net
  901 G St, Sacramento, CA 95814-1801
  Kerry Martin, Program Coordinator

**William Ridgeway Family Relations
Courthouse** 916.875.3400
Fax...916.875.3480
Web...www.saccourt.com
E-mail...................................setzerj@saccourt.com
  3341 Power Inn Rd, Sacramento, CA 95826
  Julie Setzer, Court Manager

COURTS

Superior Court Juvenile Div 916.876.7753
Fax...916.876.9016
E-mail..saccourt.ca.gov
  9605 Kieser Blvd, Sacramento, CA 95827-3831
  Honorable Jane Yre, Judge

POLICE AND SHERIFF

**Elk Grove Unified School District Police
Dept** 916.686.7786
Fax...916.689.3804
E-mail..................................tjenkins@egusd.net
  8431 Gerber Rd, Sacramento, CA 95829
  Tom Jenkins, Chief

Police Chiefs Assoc 916.481.8000
Fax...916.481.8008
E-mail..................lmcgill@californiapolicechiefs.org
  1127 11th St Ste 830, Sacramento, CA 95814-3811
  Leslie Mcgill, Executive Director

Police Dept 916.264.5471
Fax...916.264.7770
Web...www.sacpd.org
  5770 Freeport Blvd Ste 100, Sacramento,
  CA 95822-3516
  Rick Braziel, Chief Of Police

Sheriff's Ofc 916.874.7146
Fax...916.874.5332
  711 G St, Sacramento, CA 95814
  Scott Jones, Sheriff

EDUCATION SERVICES

Dyer Kelly Head Start 916.566.2151
Fax...916.566.2150
  2236 Edison Ave, Carmichael, CA 95608

Special Education 916.228.2446
Fax...916.228.2445
Web.......................................www.sac-co.k12.ca.us
E-mail............................jholsing@sac-co.k12.ca.us
  10474 Mather Blvd, Sacramento, CA 95826
  Judy Holsinger, Executive Director

San Benito County

SOCIAL SERVICES

Human Svcs 831.636.4180
Fax...831.637.9754
Web...................................www.sanbenitohhsa.org
E-mail.............................kflores@sanbenitohhsa.org
  1111 San Felipe Rd Ste 206, Hollister,
  CA 95023-2814
  Kathy Flores, Director

GENERAL HEALTH SERVICES

Health Dept 831.637.5367
Fax...831.637.9073
Web...www.sanbenitoco.org
  439 4th St, Hollister, CA 95023-3801
  Jeanne Melius, Public Health Nurse

JUSTICE AGENCY

Juvenile Hall 831.636.4050
Fax...831.636.4055
Web...www.sbcprob.org
E-mail..............................kevin.nitzel@sbcprob.org
  708 Flynn Rd, Hollister, CA 95023-9308
  Kevin Nitzel, Superintendent

**Probation & Delinquency Prevention
Commission** 831.636.4070
Fax...831.636.5682
  400 Monterey St, Hollister, CA 95023-3854
  Prent Cardall, Chief Probation Officer

Victim/Witness Assistance 831.634.1397
Fax...831.634.1398
Web...www.cosb.us
E-mail...jroybal@cosb.us
  419 4th St, Hollister, CA 95023-3801
  Julie Roybal, Program Coordinator

COURTS

Superior Court 831.636.4057
Fax...831.636.2046
Web.............................www.sanbenito.courts.ca.gov
E-mail.....................harry.tobias@sanbenito.courts.ca.gov
  440 5th St Rm 205, Hollister, CA 95023-3843
  Honorable Harry J. Tobias, Director

POLICE AND SHERIFF

Hollister Police Dept 831.636.4330
Fax...831.636.4339
Web.................................www.police.hollister.ca.us
  395 Apollo Way, Hollister, CA 95023-2557
  Jeff Miller, Chief Of Police

Sheriff's Dept 831.636.4080
Fax...831.636.1416
Web...www.sbcsheriff.org
E-mail..............................ngutierrez@sbcsheriff.org
  451 4th St, Hollister, CA 95023-3840
  Darren Thompson, Sheriff

San Bernardino County

SOCIAL SERVICES

California Children Svcs 909.387.8400
Fax...909.387.8401
  150 Carousel Mall, San Bernardino, CA 92415
  Ken Adams, Program Manager

Children's CSOC 909.421.9300
Fax...909.421.9411
  850 E Foothill Blvd, Rialto, CA 92376-5230
  Rosa Gomez, Interim Deputy Director

Dept Of Children Social Svcs 909.386.1100
Fax...909.386.1913
  1504 S Gifford Ave, San Bernardino, CA 92415
  Mae Harris-oglesby, Regional Director

**Rancho Cucamonga Child Protective
Svcs** 909.945.3762
Fax...909.945.4605
  9638 7th St, Rancho Cucamonga, CA 91730
  Helen Parrot, Deputy Director

GENERAL HEALTH SERVICES

Dept of Public Health 909.387.6219
Fax...909.387.6228
Web..................................www.sbcounty.gov/pubhlth
E-mail..............................vlong@dph.sbcounty.gov
  799 E Rialto Ave, San Bernardino, CA 92415-1005
  Vanessa Long, Disease Control Manager

California

STD Clinic **909.383.3266**
Fax 909.383.3058
Web ....www.co.san-bernardino.ca.us
  799 E Rialto Ave, San Bernardino, CA 92415-1005
  Wilfred Shiu, Hiv Specialist

JUSTICE AGENCY

Juvenile Hall **909.383.1769**
Fax 909.387.7577
Web ....www.prob.sbcounty.gov
  900 E Gilbert St, San Bernardino, CA 92415-1004
  Luciano Perez, Superintendent

Juvenile Probation Svcs **909.383.2700**
Fax 909.383.2705
Web ....www.prob.sbcounty.gov
  150 W 5th St, San Bernardino, CA 92415-1026
  Michelle Scray, Chief Performance Officer

Probation Dept **909.387.5874**
Fax 909.387.5600
Web ....www.co.sbcounty.gov/probation
  175 W 5th St, San Bernardino, CA 92415
  Michelle Scray, Chief Performance Officer

Victim/Witness Program **909.387.6540**
Fax 909.387.6362
Web ....www.da.co.san-bernardino.ca.us
E-mail ....da@da.co.san-bernardino.ca.us
  316 N Mountain View Ave, San Bernardino,
  CA 92415-1016
  Michael Ramos, District Attorney

COURTS

**Superior Court Juvenile Div
(Delinquency)** **909.387.7538**
Fax 909.387.7625
Web ....www.co.san-bernardino.ca.us
E-mail ....jsheer@co.san-bernardino.ca.us
  900 E Gilbert St, San Bernardino, CA 92415-1004
  Jannette Sheer, Information Desk

POLICE AND SHERIFF

Police Dept **909.384.5742**
Fax 909.388.4841
  710 N D St, San Bernardino, CA 92401
  Keith Kilmer, Chief Of Police

Sheriff's Ofc **909.884.0156**
Fax 909.387.3688
E-mail ....lguerra@sbcsd.org
  655 E 3rd St, San Bernardino, CA 92402
  Rod Hoops, Sheriff

EDUCATION SERVICES

Baker Head Start **760.733.4160**
  72100 Schoolhouse Ln, Baker, CA 92309
  Keith Thomes, Superintendent

**Colton Jusd Head Start
Bloomington** **909.876.6342**
Fax 909.423.0622
  18829 Orange St, Colton, CA 92324
  Mr Dan Rocha, Principal

**San Bernadino City Unified School District Special
Education** **909.880.6863**
Fax 909.880.1584
Web www.sbcusd.k12.ca.us
E-mail ....patty.imbiorski@sbcusd.k12.ca.us
  1535 W Highland Ave, San Bernardino, CA 92411
  Patricia Imbiorski, Phd, Interim Director

San Diego County

SOCIAL SERVICES

California Children's Svcs **619.528.4000**
Fax 619.528.4087
  6160 Mission Gorge Rd Ste 400, San Diego,
  CA 92120
  Maureen Brewer, Director

Children's Svcs Bureau **858.694.5141**
Fax 858.694.5144
  6950 Levant St, San Diego, CA 92111
  Deborah Zanderwilois, Director

Children's Svcs East **619.401.3800**
Fax 619.401.3745
  151 Van Houten Ave, El Cajon, CA 92020
  Nicole Del Toro, Administrative Assistant

**San Diego Health And Human Svcs-
Rosecrans** **619.515.6770**
Fax 619.692.8543
Web www2.sdcounty.ca.gov/hhsa
E-mail ....robert.gilcheck@sdcounty.ca.gov
  3851 Rosecrans St, Health Services Complex, San
  Diego, CA 92110
  Robert Gilcheck, Director

GENERAL HEALTH SERVICES

Health Svcs **760.736.6700**
Fax 760.736.8643
Web ....www.nchs-health.org
  150 Valpreda Rd Frnt, San Marcos, CA 92069
  Mary Langlois, Hiv Projects Manager

Maternal Health **619.692.8808**
Fax 619.692.8827
Web ....www.dph.sf.ca.us
E-mail ....amethyst.cureg@sdcounty.ca.gov
  3851 Rosecrans St, San Diego, CA 92110
  Ameythist Curet, Md, CHDP Program Medical Director

Public Health Ctr - Central Region **619.229.5400**
Fax 619.229.5439
Web www2.sdcounty.ca.gov/hhsa
  5202 University Ave, San Diego, CA 92105
  Bonnie Copeland, Clinic Manager

Public Health Ctr East **619.441.6500**
Fax 619.441.6532
Web www2.sdcounty.ca.gov/hhsa
E-mail ....martha.bartzen@sdcounty.ca.gov
  460 N Macnolia St Ste 110, El Cajon, CA 92020-3819
  Martha Bartzen, Clinic Manager

Public Health Ctr North Coastal **760.967.4401**
Fax 760.967.4644
Web ....www.sdcounty.ca.gov/hhsa
  104 S Barnes St, Oceanside, CA 92054-3492
  Audrey Lopez, Clinic Manager

Public Health Ctr South Region **619.409.3110**
Fax 619.409.3113
Web www2.sdcounty.ca.gov/hhsa
E-mail ....paulina.bobenreth@sdcounty.ca.gov
  690 Oxford St Ste E, Chula Vista, CA 91911-7116
  Paulina Bobenreth, Clinic Manager

MENTAL HEALTH SERVICES

Children's Mental Health Svcs **619.758.6227**
Fax 619.758.6255
  3320 Kemper St Ste 206, San Diego, CA 92110
  Frances Edwards, Chief

Mental Health **619.563.2700**
Fax 619.563.2775
Web ....www.sdcounty.ca.gov
  3255 Camino Del Rio S., San Diego, CA 92108
  Alfredo Aguirre, Mental Health Director

JUSTICE AGENCY

Camp Barrett **619.401.4900**
Fax 619.401.4921
Web ....www.sdcounty.ca.gov
E-mail ....jim.seal@sdcounty.ca.gov
  21077 Lyons Valley Rd, Alpine, CA 91901-3400
  Jim Seal, CEO

Girls Rehabilitation Facility **858.694.4510**
Fax 858.514.8488
E-mail ....leanncowalski@sdcounty.ca.gov
  2861 Meadow Lark Dr, San Diego, CA 92123
  Leann Cowalski, Supervising Probation Officer

Juvenile Hall **858.694.4500**
Fax 858.694.4333
  2801 Meadow Lark Dr, San Diego, CA 92123-2793
  Yevepte Klepin, Superintendent

Probation Dept **858.514.3200**
Fax 858.514.3121
E-mail ....john.hensley@sdcounty.ca.gov
  9444 Balboa Ave Ste 500, San Diego,
  CA 92123-4393
  John Hansley, Chief Performance Officer

Voices For Children/CASA **858.569.2019**
Fax 858.569.7151
E-mail ....sharonl@voices4children.com
  2851 Meadow Lark Dr, San Diego, CA 92123
  Sharon Lawrence, Executive Director

POLICE AND SHERIFF

Oceanside Police Dept **760.435.4900**
Fax 760.966.3154
E-mail ....fmccoy@ci.oceanside.ca.us
  3855 Mission Ave, Oceanside, CA 92058
  Frank Mccoy, Chief Of Police

San Diego City Schools Police Dept **619.725.7000**
Fax 619.291.7169
Web ....www.sandi.net/policeservices
E-mail ....pdrecords@sandi.net
  4100 Normal St, San Diego, CA 92103
  Don Braun, Chief Of Police

San Diego Police Dept **619.531.2000**
Fax 619.531.2708
Web ....www.sandiegoda.com
  1401 Broadway, San Diego, CA 92101-5729
  Kathy Ammon, Administrator

**San Diego Police/ Domestic
Violence** **619.533.3500**
Fax 619.533.3502
E-mail ....bcolon@pd.sandiego.gov
  1122 Broadway Ste 200, San Diego, CA 92101
  Bernie Colon, Supervisor

Sheriff's Dept **858.974.2104**
Fax 858.974.2059
Web ....www.sdsheriff.net
E-mail ....bill.Gore@sdsheriff.org
  9621 Ridgehaven Ct, San Diego, CA 92123-1636
  Bill Gore, Sheriff

EDUCATION SERVICES

AKA Grand Avenue Head Start **619.444.0503**
  638 W Madison Ave, El Cajon, CA 92020
  Gloria Sanchez, Director

Aka Head Start - Casa De Oro **619.660.9772**
Fax 619.660.9811
Web ....www.akaheadstart.org
E-mail ....shimp@akaheadstart.org
  10235A Ramona Dr, El Cajon, CA 92020
  Adonica Shimp, Director

Aka Head Start - Marilla **619.443.9266**
Fax 619.561.4967
E-mail ....ashimp@akaheadstart.org
  9745 Marilla Dr, El Cajon, CA 92020
  Adonica Goettsch, Director

Ecs - Nestor Head Start **619.423.4986**
Fax 619.423.2361
E-mail ....lb@ecscalifornia.org
  2399 Grove Ave, San Diego, CA 92154
  Laura B, Director

Ecs Harrison Head Start 619.475.1765
Fax 619.475.2509
Web .... www.ecscalifornia.org
   1540 S Harbison Ave, National City, CA 91950-3936
   Carmen Carrillo, Supervisor

Special Education 619.590.3920
Fax 619.588.2495
   924 E Main St, El Cajon, CA 92021
   Tim Glover, Senior Director

San Francisco County

SOCIAL SERVICES

Social Svcs Dept 415.557.5000
Fax 415.431.9270
E-mail .... trent.rhorer@sfgov.org
   170 Otis St, San Francisco, CA 94103-1221
   Trent Rhorer, Executive Director

GENERAL HEALTH SERVICES

Chinatown Public Health Ctr 415.364.7600
Fax 415.986.1130
Web .... www.dph.sf.ca.us
E-mail .... albert.yu@sfdph.org
   1490 Mason St, San Francisco, CA 94133-4222
   Albert Yu, Center Director

Maxine Hall Heatlh Ctr 415.292.1300
Fax 415.928.6487
Web .... www.dph.sf.ca.us/chn/hlthctrs
E-mail .... cjames@sfusd.k12.ca.us
   1301 Pierce St, San Francisco, CA 94115
   Catharine James, MD, Medical Director

Public Health Dept 415.554.2600
Fax 415.554.2710
Web .... www.sfdph.org
   101 Grove St Ste 308, San Francisco, CA 94102
   Barbara Garcia, Director

San Francisco Department of Public
Health 415.206.3073
Fax 415.206.6900
E-mail .... pierre_marie-rose@dph.sf.ca.us
   San Francisco General Hospital, Dept. of Pediatrics,
   1001 Potrero Ave., San Francisco, CA 94110
   *Pierre-Joseph Marie-Rose, Medical Director, Second Chance Tattoo
   Removal Program*

San Francisco Public Health Dept 415.554.2500
Fax 415.575.5790
Web .... www.dph.sf.ca.us
   101 Grove St, San Francisco, CA 94102
   Ellen Wolfe, CMS, Director

MENTAL HEALTH SERVICES

Div Of Mental Health 415.255.3400
Fax 415.255.3567
Web .... www.dph.sf.ca.us
E-mail .... info@dph.sf.ca.us
   1380 Howard St, Fl 5, San Francisco, CA 94103-2652
   Dr. Irene Sung, Medical Director

JUSTICE AGENCY

CASA Program 415.398.8001
Fax 415.398.8068
Web .... www.sfcasa.org
E-mail .... info@sfcasa.org
   100 Bush St Ste 650, San Francisco, CA 94104-3932
   Sally Coates, Executive Director

Commissioner Of Delinquency 415.753.7800
Fax 415.753.7888
E-mail .... shannon.martin@sfgov.org
   375 Woodside Ave, San Francisco, CA 94127-1221
   Tony Gevaro, Supervisor

Juvenile Hall 415.753.7500
Fax 415.753.4429
Web .... www.ilrc.org
   375 Woodside Ave, San Francisco, CA 94127-1221
   Dennis Doyle, Director

Juvenile Probation Dept 415.753.7800
Fax 415.753.7715
E-mail .... liz.jackson-simpson@sfgov.org
   375 Woodside Ave, San Francisco, CA 94127
   William Siffermann, Probation Officer

Victim/Witness Program District
Ofc 415.553.9044
Fax 415.553.1034
   850 Bryant St Ste 320, San Francisco, CA 94103
   Jacqueline Ortiz, Deputy Chief Of Victim Services

POLICE AND SHERIFF

San Francisco Police Dept 415.553.1551
Fax 415.553.1554
Web .... www.sfgov.org
E-mail .... chiefsuhr@sfgov.org
   850 Bryant St Fl 5 Rm 525, San Francisco,
   CA 94103-4666
   Gregory Suhr, Chief Of Police

Sheriff's Dept 415.554.7225
Fax 415.554.7050
E-mail .... sheriff@sfgov.org
   1 Doctor Carlton B. Goodlepp Place, Room 456, San
   Francisco, CA 94102
   Michael Hennessey, Sheriff

EDUCATION SERVICES

Economic Opportunity Council 415.749.5600
Fax 415.749.3956
   1426 Fillmore St Ste 204, San Francisco, CA 94115
   Dennis Yee, Director

San Joaquin County

SOCIAL SERVICES

Human Svcs Agency 209.468.1000
Fax 209.468.1985
Web .... www.sjgov.org
E-mail .... jchelli@sjgov.org
   333 E Washington St, Stockton, CA 95202-3200
   Joseph Chelli, Director

GENERAL HEALTH SERVICES

Health Dept 209.468.3412
Fax 209.468.3823
Web .... www.sjgov.org/phs/
E-mail .... kfurst@phs.hs.co.san-joaquin.ca.us
   1601 E Hazelton Ave, Stockton, CA 95205
   William Mitchell, Mph, Director

MENTAL HEALTH SERVICES

Children's Mental Health 209.468.2385
Fax 209.468.8024
E-mail .... mrowland@sjcbhs.org
   1212 N California St, Fl 2, Stockton, CA 95202
   Michelle Rowland-bird, Deputy Director

Mental Health Svcs 209.468.8700
Fax 209.468.2399
Web .... www.sjcbhs.org
E-mail .... vsingh@sjcbhs.org
   1212 N California St, Stockton, CA 95202-1594
   Victor Singh, Director

JUSTICE AGENCY

California Youth Authority 209.948.7669
Fax 209.467.4954
E-mail .... abeasley@cya.ca.gov
   31 E Channel St Ste 112, Stockton, CA 95202-2314
   Anthony Beasley, Supervising Parole Agent

Juvenile Hall 209.468.4200
Fax 209.468.5240
Web .... www.co.san-joaquin.ca.us
   535 W Mathews Rd, French Camp, CA 95231-9758
   Carla Contente, Deputy CPO

Juvenile Justice Delinquency Prevention
Commission 209.468.4789
Fax 209.468.5041
E-mail .... melliot@sjgov.org
   535 W Mathews Rd, French Camp, CA 95231
   Mark Elliott, Assistant Deputy Chief Probation Officer

O.H. Close Youth Correctional
Facility 209.944.6301
Fax 209.944.5612
E-mail .... patricia.hartt@cvcar.gov
   7650 So Newcastle Road, Stockton, CA 95215
   Patti Hart, Office Technician

Probation Dept 209.468.4000
Fax 209.468.4040
Web .... www.co.san-joaquin.ca.us
E-mail .... chope@co.san-joaquin.ca.us
   575 W Mathews Rd, French Camp, CA 95231-9798
   Chris Hope, CPO

Regional CYA Headquarters 209.944.1301
Fax 209.948.0932
Web .... www.cya.ca.gov
E-mail .... zkhalfani@cya.ca.gov
   Northern Parole Region, Stockton, CA 95213
   Zakiya Zkhalfani, Regional Administrator

Victim/Witness Program District Attorney's
Ofc 209.468.2500
Fax 209.468.2521
   222 E Weber Ave, Rm 229, Stockton, CA 95202
   Gabriela Jaurequie, Project Coordinator

POLICE AND SHERIFF

Police Dept 209.937.8377
Fax 209.937.8601
Web .... www.ci.santa-clara.ca.us
E-mail .... whose@ci.santa-clara.ca.us
   22 E Market St, Stockton, CA 95202-2876
   Bleir Ulring, Chief Of Police

Sheriff's Ofc 209.468.4400
Fax 209.468.4780
   7000 Michael Canlis Blvd, French Camp, CA 95231
   Steve Moore, Sheriff

EDUCATION SERVICES

Special Education 209.933.7120
Fax 209.943.7716
E-mail .... kBextraze@stockton.k12.ca.us
   1800 S Sutter St, Stockton, CA 95206
   Kelly Bextraze, Director

Special Education 209.468.4925
Fax 209.468.4979
Web .... www.sjcoe.org
E-mail .... kskeels@sjcoe.org
   2707 Transworld Dr, Stockton, CA 95213
   Kathline Skeels, Selpa Director

San Luis Obispo County

SOCIAL SERVICES

Social Svcs Dept 805.781.1600
Fax 805.781.1686
Web .... www.co.slo.ca.us
E-mail .... lcollins@co.slo.ca.us
   3433 S Higuera St, San Luis Obispo, CA 93401-7301
   Lee Collins, Director

GENERAL HEALTH SERVICES

Public Health Dept **805.781.5500**
Fax 805.781.5543
Web ....www.slocounty.ca.gov/publichealth
2191 Johnson Ave, San Luis Obispo, CA 93406
Penny Borenstein, Health Officer/director

MENTAL HEALTH SERVICES

Mental Health Svcs **805.781.4700**
Fax 805.781.1232
2178 Johnson Ave, San Luis Obispo, CA 93401
Dr. Karen Baylor, Director

JUSTICE AGENCY

CASA For Children **805.541.6542**
Fax 805.541.5637
Web ....www.slocasa.org
E-mail ....ttardiff@slocasa.org
75 Highderra, San Luis Obispo, CA 93401
Teresa Tardiff, Executive Director

Juvenile Court Svcs **805.781.5352**
Fax 805.781.1231
Web ....www.co.slo.ca.us
E-mail ....mdutra@co.slo.ca.us
1065 Kansas Ave, San Luis Obispo, CA 93408-0001
Mike Dutra, Juvenile Division Supervising Manager

Victim/Witness Program District Attorney's
Ofc **805.781.5821**
Fax 805.781.5828
Web ....www.co.slo.ca.us
E-mail ....cabsey@co.slo.ca.us
County Government Ctr Rm 384, San Luis Obispo, CA 93408-0001
Cindy Marie Absey, Victim/Witness Director

COURTS

Superior Court - Juvenile **805.781.5164**
Fax 805.781.1121
Web ....www.co.marin.ca.us
1065 Kansas Ave, San Luis Obispo, CA 93408-0001
Ginger Garrett, Judge

POLICE AND SHERIFF

San Luis Obispo Police **805.781.7317**
Fax 805.543.8108
Web ....www.slocity.org
1042 Walnut St, San Luis Obispo, CA 93401-2781
Adam Stahnke, Juvenile Detective

Sheriff's Ofc **805.781.4540**
Fax 805.781.1075
Web ....www.slosheriff.org
E-mail ....slosheriff@fix.net
1585 Kansas Ave, San Luis Obispo, CA 93405-7604
Patrick Hedges, Sheriff

EDUCATION SERVICES

Special Education **805.543.7732**
Fax 805.541.2605
E-mail ....jcrocker@slocoe.org
3350 Education Dr, San Luis Obispo, CA 93405
Julian Crocker, Superintendent

San Mateo County

SOCIAL SERVICES

Human Svcs Agency **650.802.7500**
Fax 650.802.7516
Web ....www.co.sanmateo.ca.us
E-mail ....mlane@co.sanmateo.ca.us
400 Harbor Blvd Bldg B, Belmont, CA 94002-4047
Mark Lane, Children & Family Services Director

GENERAL HEALTH SERVICES

Health Ctr **650.301.8600**
Fax 650.301.8626
Web ....www.co.sanmateo.ca.us
E-mail ....klehmkuhl@co.sanmateo.ca.us
380 90th St, Daly City, CA 94015-1807
Kathy Lehmkuhl, Supervisor

Public Health **650.573.2757**
Fax 650.573.2116
Web ....www.smhealth.org
E-mail ....smorrow@co.sanmateo.ca.us
225 37th Ave, San Mateo, CA 94403-4324
Scott Morrow, Health Officer

MENTAL HEALTH SERVICES

Behavioral Health and Recovery
Svcs **650.573.2541**
Fax 650.573.2841
E-mail ....skaplan@co.sanmateo.ca.us
225 37th Ave, Fl 3, San Mateo, CA 94403
Steve Kaplan, Director

Behaviour & Health Recovery
Services **650.312.5322**
Fax 650.312.5305
222 Paul Scannell Dr, San Mateo, CA 94402
Scott Peyton, Mft, Unit Supervisor

JUSTICE AGENCY

Camp Glenwood **650.363.4373**
Fax 650.747.0160
E-mail ....johnson@sanmateo.ca.us
400 Log Cabin Ranch Road, La Honda, CA 94020
Bill Johnson, Facility Manager

Probation Dept/Juvenile **650.312.8816**
Fax 650.312.5354
E-mail ....rhori@co.sanmateo.ca.us
222 Paul Scannell Dr, San Mateo, CA 94402
Richard Hori, Juvenile Hall Director

Victim/Witness Program **650.599.7479**
Fax 650.839.1734
Web ....www.co.sanmateo.ca.us
400 County Ctr, Fl 3, Redwood City, CA 94063
Grace Nelson, Project Director/coordinator

COURTS

Superior Court Juvenile Div **650.312.5395**
Fax 650.312.8881
222 Paul Scannell Dr, San Mateo, CA 94402
Honorable Elizabeth Lee, Judge

POLICE AND SHERIFF

Redwood City Police Dept **650.780.7100**
Fax 650.780.7112
1301 Maple St, Redwood City, CA 94063

Sheriff's Ofc **650.599.1664**
Fax 650.599.1327
Web ....www.smcsheriff.com
E-mail ....gmunks@co.sanmateo.ca.us
400 County Ctr, Redwood City, CA 94063-1662
Greg Munks, Sheriff

Santa Barbara County

GENERAL HEALTH SERVICES

Health Care Clinic **805.346.7230**
Fax 805.346.7306
Web ....www.santabarbaracounty.gov
2115 Centerpointe Pkwy Fl 1, Santa Maria, CA 93455-1335
Linda Penny, Clinic Manager

Public Health Dept (Admin) **805.681.5220**
Fax 805.681.5191
Web ....www.sbcphd.org
E-mail ....anne.eecrik@sbcphd.org
300 N San Antonio Rd, Bldg3, Santa Barbara, CA 93110
Anne Eecrik, Health Officer/director

MENTAL HEALTH SERVICES

Mental Health **805.681.5233**
Fax 805.681.5262
Web ....www.co.santa-barbara.ca.us
E-mail ....mcarste@co.santa-barbara.ca.us
300 N San Antonio Rd, Bldg 3, Santa Barbara, CA 93110
Ann Detrick, Director

Mental Health Svcs For Children **805.884.1600**
Fax 805.884.1602
429 N San Antonio Rd, Santa Barbara, CA 93110
Tom Verica, Marriage And Family Therapist

JUSTICE AGENCY

Juvenile Svcs **805.692.4840**
Fax 805.692.4841
Web ....www.countyofsb.org
E-mail ....mbrickley@countyofsb.org
4500 Hollister Ave, Santa Barbara, CA 93110-1710
Mark Brickley, Supervising Probation Officer

Lompoc Probation **805.737.7800**
Fax 805.737.7811
E-mail ....heitman@co.santa-barbara.ca.us
115 Civic Center Plz, Lompoc, CA 93436-6916
Tanja Heightman, Juvenile Supervisor/ Probation Manager

Los Prietos Boys' Camp **805.692.1750**
Fax 805.692.1772
E-mail ....dfarrah@co.santa-barbara.ca.us
3900 Paradise Rd, Santa Barbara, CA 93105
Dean Farrah, Camp Director

Victim/Witness Program **805.346.7529**
Fax 805.346.7585
312 E Cook St, Ste D, Santa Maria, CA 93454
Ann Bramsen, Assistant District Attorney

Victim/Witness Program Santa Barbara District
Attorney **805.568.2350**
Fax 805.568.2453
Web ....www.co.santa-barbara.ca.us
1112 Santa Barbara St, Santa Barbara, CA 93101-2008
Megan Riker, Director

COURTS

Santa Barbara Teen Court **805.963.1433**
Fax 805.963.4099
E-mail ....ecue@cadasb.org
1111 Garden St, Santa Barbara, CA 93101
Edwardo Cue, Director

POLICE AND SHERIFF

Police Dept **805.897.2300**
Fax 805.897.2434
Web ....www.sbpd.com
215 E Figueroa St, Santa Barbara, CA 93101-2120
Camerino Sanchez, Chief Of Police/Detective Division

Santa Clara County

SOCIAL SERVICES

Family & Children's Svcs **408.292.9353**
Fax 408.287.3104
950 W Julian St, San Jose, CA 95126
Diane Nieman, Director

California

GENERAL HEALTH SERVICES

Health Dept **408.792.5040**
Fax 408.792.5031
Web ....www.sccphd.com
E-mail ......marty.fenstersheib@hhs.co.scl.ca.us
　976 Lenzen Ave, San Jose, CA 95126-2737
　Kevin Hutchcroft, Aids Program Manager

Park Alameda Health Facility **408.792.5055**
Fax 408.947.8751
　976 Lenzen Ave, Rm 1700, San Jose, CA 95126
　Alma Burrell, Maternal & Child Health Director

MENTAL HEALTH SERVICES

Downtown Mental Health Ctr **408.299.6175**
Fax 408.298.0192
Web ....www.hhs.sccgov.org
E-mail ....deborah.styner@hhs.sccgov.org
　1075 E Santa Clara St, San Jose, CA 95116-2244
　Deborah Styner, Program Manager

Mental Health Ctr **408.852.2400**
Fax 408.852.2256
　7475 Camino Arroyo, Gilroy, CA 95020
　Dinh Chu, Supervisor

Mental Health Dept **408.885.5770**
Fax 408.885.5789
　828 S Bascom Ave Ste 200, San Jose, CA 95128
　Tiffany Ho, Md, Medical Director

JUSTICE AGENCY

Child Advocates **408.416.0400**
Fax 408.416.0406
Web ....www.cadvocates.org
E-mail ....gisela@cadvocates.org
　509 Valley Way, Milpitas, CA 95035-4105
　Gisela B. Bushey, Executive Director

Juvenile Probation **408.278.5800**
Fax 408.277.0784
Web ....www.pro.sccgov.org
　840 Guadalupe Pkwy, San Jose, CA 95110-1714
　Shiela Mitchell, Chief Probation Officer

San Jose Youth Authority **408.277.1221**
Fax 408.277.1413
　118 W Taylor St, San Jose, CA 95110
　Zakiya Khalfani, Supervisor Parole Agent

Victim/Witness Program **408.295.2656**
Fax 408.289.5430
Web ....www.victim.org
　777 N 1st St Ste 220, San Jose, CA 95112-6352
　Pat Mitchell, Director

COURTS

Courts Security **408.808.7400**
Fax 408.808.7490
　190 W Hedding St, San Jose, CA 95110
　Frank Damiano, Captain

Family Court Svcs **408.534.5600**
Fax 408.534.5704
Web ....www.sccsuperiorcourt.org
　170 Park Center Plz, San Jose, CA 95113-2207
　Honorable Vincent J Chiarello, Director

**Lincoln Glen Manor For Senior
Citizens** **408.265.3222**
Fax 408.265.2839
Web ....www.lgmanor.org
　2671 Plummer Ave, San Jose, CA 95125
　Loren Kroeker, Executive Director

**Superior Court Criminal Juvenile Delinquency
Div** **408.808.6200**
Fax 408.808.6290
Web ....www.scselfservice.org
　840 Guadalupe Pkwy, Rm 221, San Jose, CA 95110
　Honorable Katherine Lucero, Director

POLICE AND SHERIFF

San Jose Police Dept **408.277.4728**
Fax 408.277.3880
Web ....www.sjpd.org
E-mail ......christopher.moore@sanjoseca.gov
　201 W Mission St, San Jose, CA 95110-1780
　Christopher Moore, Chief

Sheriff's Dept **408.808.4900**
Fax 408.283.0562
　55 W Younger Ave, San Jose, CA 95110
　Laurie Smith, Sheriff

EDUCATION SERVICES

Dept of Special Education **408.453.6542**
Fax 408.453.6656
Web ....www.sccoe.org
E-mail ....mary-anne_bosward@sccoe.org
　1290 Ridder Park Dr, MC-273, San Jose,
　CA 95131-2304
　Maryanne Bosward, Director Of Special Education

SELPA (NW) **408.453.6725**
Fax 408.453.4337
Web ....
E-mail ....michele_syth@sccoe.org
　1290 Ridder Park Dr, MC-227, San Jose,
　CA 95131-2304
　Michele Syth, Director Of Selpa (nw)

SELPA (SE) **408.223.3771**
Fax 408.532.9311
E-mail ....jrussell@mountpleasant.k12.ca.us
　3434 Marten Ave, San Jose, CA 95148
　Jim Russell, Director Of Selpa (SE)

Santa Cruz County

SOCIAL SERVICES

Special Investigations Unit **831.454.4108**
Fax 831.454.4869
Web ....www.hra.co.santa-cruz.ca.us
E-mail ....park.cuseo@hra.co.santa-cruz.ca.us
　1020 Emeline Ave, Santa Cruz, CA 95060-1913
　Park Cuseo, Chief Investigator

GENERAL HEALTH SERVICES

Health Dept **831.454.4000**
Fax 831.454.4770
　1080 Emeline Ave, Santa Cruz, CA 95060
　Bob Kennedy, Nursing Services Public Health Chief

**Santa Cruz Health Ctr - Community Health And Outreach
Svcs** **831.454.4100**
Fax 831.454.4296
Web ....www.santacruzhealth.org
E-mail ....socorro.gutierrez@health.co.santa-cruz.ca.us
　1070 Emeline Ave, Santa Cruz, CA 95061-0962
　Socorro Gutierrez, Sr Health Educator

JUSTICE AGENCY

CASA Program **831.761.2956**
Fax 831.761.2913
Web ....www.casaofsantacruz.org
E-mail ....nancys@casaofsantacruz.org
　813 Freedom Blvd, Watsonville, CA 95076-1381
　Ken Gold Stein, Executive Director

Juvenile Justice Commission **831.457.8208**
Fax 831.457.0389
Web ....www.barriosunidos.net
E-mail ....general@barriosunidos.net
　1817 Soquel Ave, Santa Cruz, CA 95062-1307
　Carmen Perez, Chairperson

Juvenile Probation Ofc **831.763.8070**
Fax 831.763.8233
E-mail ....judy.cox@co.santa-cruz.ca.us
　1430 Freedom Blvd Ste 14, Watsonville, CA 95706
　Judith Cox, CPO

Probation Dept **831.454.3800**
Fax 831.454.3827
　3650 Graham Hill Road, Felton, CA 95061
　Laura Garnette, Juvenile Division Director

EDUCATION SERVICES

Bradley Head Start Ctr **831.728.6366**
Fax 831.728.6946
Web ....www.bradley.pvusd.net
E-mail ....kathy_arola@pvusd.net
　321 Corralitos Rd, Watsonville, CA 95076-0522
　Kathy Arola, Director

Shasta County

SOCIAL SERVICES

Children's Svcs **530.225.5650**
Fax 530.225.5190
Web ....www.cws.state.ca.us
E-mail ....bolenn@cws.state.ca.us
　1313 Yuba St, Redding, CA 96001-1012
　Nancy Bolen, Program Manager

**Health & Human Svcs Agency-Children's Svcs
Branch** **530.225.5650**
Fax 530.225.5190
Web ....www.co.shasta.ca.us
E-mail ....dssweb@co.shasta.ca.us
　1313 Yuba St, Redding, CA 96001
　Maxine Wayda, Director

GENERAL HEALTH SERVICES

Child Health (CHDP) **530.225.5122**
Fax 530.225.5017
Web ....www.co.shasta.ca.us
　2650 Breslauer Way, Redding, CA 96001
　Linda Reynolds, Deputy Director

Shasta Public Health **530.225.5591**
Fax 530.225.5074
Web ....www.shastapublichealth.net
　2650 Breslauer Way, Redding, CA 96001-4246
　Heidi Vert, Hiv Coordinator

MENTAL HEALTH SERVICES

Mental Health **530.225.5200**
Fax 530.225.5977
Web ....www.co.shasta.ca.us
E-mail ....mmontgomery@co.shasta.ca.us
　2640 Breslauer Way, Redding, CA 96001-4246
　Mark Montgomery Psy.d., Director Of Mental Health

JUSTICE AGENCY

Juvenile Hall **530.225.5838**
Fax 530.225.5841
Web ....www.co.shasta.ca.us
E-mail ....emiller@co.shasta.ca.us
　2680 Radio Ln, Redding, CA 96001-4232
　Edward Miller, Division Director

Juvenile Justice Commission **530.245.6216**
Fax 530.245.6241
　1525 Court St Fl 1, Redding, CA 96001
　Steve MacFarland, Chairperson

Juvenile Justice Ctr **530.225.5230**
Fax 530.225.5448
Web ....www.co.shasta.ca.us
　2680 Radio Ln, Redding, CA 96001-4232
　Ann Stow, Division Director

Victim/Witness Program **530.225.5220**
Fax 530.225.5484
E-mail ....afitzgerald@co.shasta.ca.us
　1355 W St, Redding, CA 96001
　Angela Fitzgerald, Program Coordinator

COURTS

Superior Court **530.225.5631**
Fax 530.229.8170
Web .... www.ci.redding.ca.us
E-mail .... aanderson@ci.redding.ca.us
   1500 Court St Ste 319, Redding, CA 96001-1629
Honorable Anthony Anderson, Director

Youth/Peer Court **530.244.7194**
Fax 530.244.4150
Web .... www.yvpc.org
E-mail .... yvpc2@sbcglobal.net
   1700 Pine St Ste 250, Redding, CA 96001-1939
Charles Menorah, Executive Director

POLICE AND SHERIFF

Police Dept **530.225.4200**
Fax 530.225.4553
Web .... www.reddingpolice.org
E-mail .... lmoty@reddingpolice.org
   1313 California St, Redding, CA 96001-0698
Leonard Moty, Chief Of Police

Sheriff's Dept **530.245.6025**
Fax 530.245.6054
Web .... www.co.shasta.ca.us
E-mail .... sheriff@co.shasta.ca.us
   1525 Court St Fl 2, Redding, CA 96001-1679
Tom Bosenko, Sheriff-coroner

EDUCATION SERVICES

Anderson Head Start **530.241.1036**
Fax 530.241.2703
Web .... www.shastaheadstart.org
E-mail .... cellaj@shastaheadstart.org
   375 Lake Blvd # 100, Redding, CA 96003-2504
Cella Jacoby, Director

Enterprise SD Lassen View Even
Start **530.224.4150**
Fax 530.224.4151
Web www.enterprise.k12.ca.us
E-mail .... kkinoshita@enterprise.k12.ca.us
   705 Loma Vista Dr, Redding, CA 96002-3199
Kimi Kinoshita, Even Start Director

Special Education, SELPA **530.225.0100**
Fax 530.225.0105
Web .... www.shastacoe.org
   1644 Magnolia Ave, Redding, CA 96001
Conde Kungman, Selpa Director

Sierra County

SOCIAL SERVICES

Social Svcs **530.993.6720**
Fax 530.993.6767
E-mail .... croberts@sierracounty.ws
   202 Front St, Loyalton, CA 96118
Carol Roberts, Director

GENERAL HEALTH SERVICES

Health Dept **530.993.6700**
Fax 530.993.6790
Web .... www.sierracounty.ws
E-mail .... pholland@sierracounty.ws
   202 Front St, Loyalton, CA 96118
Penny Holland, RN, Nursing Director

MENTAL HEALTH SERVICES

Mental Health **530.993.6746**
Fax 530.993.6759
Web .... www.sierracounty.ws
E-mail .... croberts@sierracounty.ws
   704 Mill St, Loyalton, CA 96118
Carol Roberts, Deputy Director

JUSTICE AGENCY

Probation Dept **530.289.3277**
Fax 530.289.2821
E-mail .... jniccoli@sierracounty.ws
   100 Courthouse Square, 2nd Fl, Downieville,
   CA 95936
Jeff Bosworth, Chief Performance Officer

Victim/Witness Program **530.993.4617**
Fax 530.993.1667
E-mail .... sierravw@digitalpath.net
   513 Main St, Loyalton, CA 96118
Sara Wright, Coordinator

COURTS

Superior Court **530.289.3698**
Fax 530.289.0205
E-mail .... superiorcourt@sierracourt.org
   100 Courthouse Square, Downieville, CA 95936
Lee Kirby, Court Executive Officer

POLICE AND SHERIFF

Sheriff's Ofc **530.289.3700**
Fax 530.289.3318
E-mail .... hangman@sierracounty.ws
   100 Courthouse Square, Downieville, CA 95936
John Evans, Sheriff

Siskiyou County

SOCIAL SERVICES

Social Svcs **530.841.2700**
Fax 530.841.2723
Web .... www.co.siskiyou.ca.us
   818 S Main St, Yreka, CA 96097-3321
Michael Noda, Director

GENERAL HEALTH SERVICES

Karuk Tribal Health **530.493.5305**
Fax 530.493.5322
Web .... www.karuk.us
E-mail .... mschrock@karuk.us
   64236 2nd Ave, Happy Camp, CA 96039
Martha Schrock, Health Director

Siskiyou Public Health Dept **530.841.2100**
Fax 530.841.4076
Web .... www.co.siskiyou.ca.us/phs
   806 S Main St, Yreka, CA 96097
Blaire Loftus, AIDS Coordinator

JUSTICE AGENCY

Juvenile Justice Commission And
Probation **530.841.4180**
Fax 530.841.4188
Web .... www.co.siskiyou.ca.us
   805 Juvenile Ln, Yreka, CA 96097-3001
Todd Heie, Chief Performance Officer

COURTS

Superior Court **530.842.8330**
Fax 530.842.8339
Web .... www.siskiyou.courts.ca.gov
E-mail .... jpeery@siskiyou.courts.ca.gov
   311 4th St, Yreka, CA 96097-2912
Jan Peery, Admin Service Officer

POLICE AND SHERIFF

Sheriff's Ofc **530.841.2900**
Fax 530.842.8356
Web .... www.co.siskiyou.ca.us
E-mail .... jon.lopey@co.siskiyou.ca.us
   305 Butte St, Yreka, CA 96097
Jon Lopey, Sheriff

Solano County

SOCIAL SERVICES

Child Protective Svcs **707.784.8280**
Fax 707.421.7709
   275 Beck Ave, Fairfield, CA 94533-6804
Linda Orrante, Deputy Director

Health & Social Svcs **707.784.8600**
Fax 707.421.6618
Web .... www.co.solano.ca.us
E-mail .... poduterte@solanocounty.com
   275 Beck Ave, # 5-240, Fairfield, CA 94533
Patrick O Duterte, Director

GENERAL HEALTH SERVICES

Family Health Svcs Clinic **707.784.2010**
Fax 707.784.1494
Web .... www.solano.ca.us
   2201 Courage Dr, Fairfield, CA 94533-6717
Michael Stacey, Director

MENTAL HEALTH SERVICES

Mental Health Dept Children Svcs **707.399.4900**
Fax 707.399.4957
Web .... www.co.solano.ca.us/hss
   1745 Enterprise Dr, Bldg 2, Fairfield, CA 94533
Patrick Duterte, Director

JUSTICE AGENCY

Crime Victim Assistance Program **707.784.6844**
Fax 707.784.7986
Web .... www.solanocounty.com
E-mail .... sperthes@solanocounty.com
   675 Texas St Ste 4500, Fairfield, CA 94533-6340
Susanne Perthes, Victim/Witness Coordinator

Juvenile Hall **707.784.6570**
Fax 707.784.2428
Web .... www.solanocounty.com
   740 Beck Ave, Fairfield, CA 94533-4440
Richard Watson, Superintendent

Probation Dept **707.784.7600**
Fax 707.784.7605
Web .... www.solanocounty.com
E-mail .... ivoit@solanocounty.com
   475 Union Ave, Fairfield, CA 94533-6319
Isabelle Voit, Chief

Vallejo Probation **707.553.5531**
Fax 707.553.5021
Web .... www.solanocounty.com
E-mail .... lwilson@solanocounty.com
   355 Tuolumne St, Fl 3, Vallejo, CA 94590
Isabelle Voit, Probation Officer

EDUCATION SERVICES

Special Education **707.399.4460**
Fax 707.863.4176
Web .... www.solanocoe.net
   5100 Business Center Dr, Fairfield, CA 94534
Sam Neustadt, Assistant Superintendent

Sonoma County

SOCIAL SERVICES

CHDP **707.565.4460**
Fax 707.565.4473
Web .... www.dhs.ca.gov/pcfh/cms
E-mail .... mgonzales@mail.co.stanislaus.ca.us
   625 5th St, Santa Rosa, CA 95404-4428
Nepheiba, Director

Human Svcs Dept **707.565.2715**
Fax 707.565.2929
   2550 Paulin Drive, Santa Rosa, CA 95402
Jo Weber, Director

MENTAL HEALTH SERVICES

Mental Health - Youth & Family
Services **707.565.4810**
Fax 707.565.4907
E-mail ....lfarmer@sonoma-county.org
   3322 Chanate Rd, Santa Rosa, CA 95404-1707
John Kolhoven, Ed.d, Section Manager

Mental Health Svcs **707.565.4850**
Fax 707.565.4892
Web ....www.sonoma-county.org
   3322 Chanate Rd, Santa Rosa, CA 95404-1708
Arthur Eurt, Director

JUSTICE AGENCY

Court Appointed Special
Advocates **707.565.6375**
Fax 707.565.6379
Web ....www.sonomacasa.org
E-mail ....info@sonomacasa.org
   365 Casa Manana Rd, Bldng K Room L, Santa Rosa,
   CA 95409
Millie Gilson, Director

Juvenile Div Probation Dept **707.565.6229**
Fax 707.565.6329
E-mail ....jirizary@sonoma-county.org
   7425 Rancho Los Guilicos Rd Dept B, Santa Rosa,
   CA 95409
Jesse Irizary, Director

Victim Assistance Ctr-District Attorney's
Ofc **707.565.8250**
Fax 707.565.8262
   600 Administration Dr Rm 212J, Santa Rosa,
   CA 95403
Gloris Erotis, Coordinator

COURTS

Superior Court Juvenile Div **707.565.6305**
Fax 707.521.6760
   7425 Rancho Los Guilicos Rd., Santa Rosa, CA 95409
Honorable Mark Tansil, Director

POLICE AND SHERIFF

Santa Rosa Police **707.543.3600**
Fax 707.543.3615
   965 Sonoma Ave, Santa Rosa, CA 95404
Cpt. Tom Schwedhelm, Police Chief

Sheriff's Dept **707.565.2511**
Fax 707.526.0403
Web ....www.sonoma-county.org
E-mail ....sfreitas@sonoma-county.org
   2796 Ventura Ave, Santa Rosa, CA 95403-2875
Steve Freitas, Sheriff

EDUCATION SERVICES

Special Education **707.524.2750**
Fax 707.524.2754
Web ....www.sonomaselpa.com
   5340 Skylane Blvd, Santa Rosa, CA 95403-1082
Cathereen Conrado, Director

Stanislaus County

GENERAL HEALTH SERVICES

Public Health **209.558.7700**
Fax 209.558.7286
Web ....www.hsahealth.org
   820 Scenic Dr, Modesto, CA 95350
John Walker, Health Officer

Stanislaus Community Health Svcs **209.558.7400**
Fax 209.558.8315
Web ....www.schsa.org
   830 Scenic Dr, Bldg 3, Modesto, CA 95350
Cleopathia Moore, Director Of Community Health Services

WIC **209.558.7377**
Fax 209.558.1244
Web ....www.wicworks.ca.gov
   251 E Hackett Rd, Modesto, CA 95358
Elaine Emery, Director

JUSTICE AGENCY

Juvenile Hall **209.525.4580**
Fax 209.525.5469
   2215 Blue Gum Ave, Modesto, CA 95358-1052
Pete Judy, Chief Deputy Probation Officer

Juvenile Justice Commission **209.525.4598**
Fax 209.525.5486
E-mail ....kattel.g@stancounty.com
   2215 Blue Gum Ave, Modesto, CA 95358
Jerry Powers, Chief Of Probation Officers

Probation Dept **209.525.5400**
Fax 209.525.4588
Web ....www.stancounty.com
E-mail ....powersj@stancounty.com
   2215 Blue Gum Ave, Modesto, CA 95358-1052
Jerry Powers, CPO

Victim Witness Program-District Attorneys
Ofc **209.525.5550**
Fax 209.558.4027
   832 12th St, Modesto, CA 95354
Gay Mçdaniel, Program Coordinator For Victim Services

COURTS

Superior Court Juvenile Div **209.558.6000**
Fax 209.525.5456
Web ....www.stanct.org
E-mail ....traffic.request@stance.org
   2215 Blue Gum Ave, Modesto, CA 95358-1052
Judge Donald Shaver, Commissioner

POLICE AND SHERIFF

Modesto Police Dept **209.572.9500**
Fax 209.523.4082
Web ....www.modestopolice.com
E-mail ....hardenm@modestopd.com
   600 10th St, Modesto, CA 95354
Michael Harden, Chief Of Police

Sheriff's Ofc **209.525.7116**
Fax 209.525.7111
Web ....www.stanislaussheriff.com
   250 E Hackett Rd, Modesto, CA 95358-9415
Adam Christensen, Sheriff

EDUCATION SERVICES

Bret Harte Head Start **209.576.4673**
Fax 209.576.4288
Web www.monet.k12.ca.us
   909 Glenn Ave, Modesto, CA 95358
Ruth Flores, Administrator

Capistrano Head Start **209.527.9865**
Fax 209.527.9857
E-mail ....summerrain_411@yahoo.com
   400 Capistrano Dr, Modesto, CA 95354-3243
Marsha Bennett, Director

Cunningham Head Start Turlock Joint
Elem **209.668.7594**
   324 W Linwood Ave, Turlock, CA 95380-6220
Tim Norton, Principal

El Vista Head Start **209.576.4665**
Fax 209.576.4567
   450 El Vista Ave, Modesto, CA 95354-1802
Maria Gutierrez, Administrator

Empire Head Start/Hughes **209.527.9884**
Fax 209.526.6421
E-mail ....lelam@empire.k12.ca.us
   116 N Mcclure Rd, Modesto, CA 95357-1329
Linda Elam, Director

Sutter County

SOCIAL SERVICES

Human-Social-Welfare-Svcs **530.822.7230**
Fax 530.822.7212
Web ....www.co.sutter.ca.us
E-mail ....lharrah@co.sutter.ca.us
   190 Garden Hwy, Yuba City, CA 95991-5554
Lori Harrah, Assistant Director

GENERAL HEALTH SERVICES

Health Dept **530.822.7215**
Fax 530.822.7223
Web ....www.suttercounty.org
E-mail ....healthofficer@co.sutter.ca.com
   1445 Veterans Memorial Cir, Yuba City,
   CA 95993-3011
Amerjit Bhattal, Health Director

JUSTICE AGENCY

Probation Dept **530.822.7320**
Fax 530.822.7470
E-mail ....codom@co.sutter.ca.us
   595 Boyd St, Yuba City, CA 95991-5028
Christine D. Odom, Chief Probation Officer

POLICE AND SHERIFF

Sheriff's Dept **530.822.7307**
Fax 530.822.7318
E-mail ....sheriff@co.sutter.ca.us
   1077 Civic Center Blvd, Yuba City, CA 95993
Paul Parker, Sheriff

Yuba City Police Dept **530.822.4661**
Fax 530.822.4799
Web ....www.ycpd.org
   1545 Poole Blvd, Yuba City, CA 95993-2615
Robert Landon, Chief

Tehama County

SOCIAL SERVICES

Social Svcs **530.527.1911**
Fax 530.527.5410
Web ....www.tcdss.org
E-mail ....capplegate@tcdss.org
   310 S Main St, Red Bluff, CA 96080-4314
Christine Applegate, Director

GENERAL HEALTH SERVICES

Health Dept **530.527.6824**
   1860 Walnut St, Red Bluff, CA 96080
Sydney Wilby, Deputy Director

MENTAL HEALTH SERVICES

Mental Health (Crisis) **530.527.8491**
Fax 530.527.0232
Web ....www.tcha.net
E-mail ....lucerov@tcha.net
   3300 S Fairway St, Visalia, CA 93277-8109
Valerie Lucero, Director

JUSTICE AGENCY

Juvenile Justice Ctr **530.527.5380**
Fax 530.527.2717
   1790 Walnut Street, Red Bluff, CA 96080
Richard Muench, Chief Executive Officer

Probation Dept **530.527.4052**
Fax 530.527.1579
Web ....www.tcprobation.org
   1840 Walnut St, Red Bluff, CA 96080-3611
Richard Muench, Chief Of Probation

Victim/Witness Program **530.527.4296**
Fax 530.527.4735
E-mail ....tcvic1@tehamada.org
   444 Oak St, Red Bluff, CA 96080
Jean Moran, Victim/witness Coordinator

California

POLICE AND SHERIFF

Red Bluff Police Dept **530.527.3131**
Fax 530.529.4768
Web ....www.rbpd.org
E-mail ....pnanfito@rbpd.org
　555 Washington St Ste B, Red Bluff, CA 96080
　Paul Nanfito, Chief

Sheriff's Ofc **530.529.7900**
Fax 530.529.7933
Web ....www.tehamaso.org
E-mail ....cparker@tehamaso.org
　502 Oak St, Red Bluff, CA 96080
　Clay Parker, Sheriff

Trinity County

SOCIAL SERVICES

Dept Of Human Svcs **530.623.1265**
Fax 530.623.1250
Web ....www.trinitycounty.org
　51 Industrial Pkwy, Weaverville, CA 96093
　Linda Wright, Director

GENERAL HEALTH SERVICES

Health Dept **530.623.1358**
Fax 530.623.1297
Web ....www.trinitycounty.com
　51 Industrial Pkwy, Weaverville, CA 96093
　Elise Osvold-doppelhaur, Hiv Educator

MENTAL HEALTH SERVICES

Behavioral Health **530.623.1362**
Fax 530.623.1447
E-mail ....ngorham@kingsview.com
　1450 Main St, Weaverville, CA 96093
　Nancy Gorham, Administrative Asst

JUSTICE AGENCY

District Attorney's Ofc **530.623.1304**
Fax 530.623.8346
E-mail ....mharper@trinitycounty.org
　11 Court St Ste 220, Weaverville, CA 96093
　Mike Harper, District Attorney

COURTS

Superior Court (Juvenile Div) **530.623.1208**
Fax 530.623.3762
E-mail ....lwills@trinityconty.org
　11 Court St, Weaverville, CA 96093
　Laurie Wills, Administrative Assistant

Victim/Witness Program **530.623.1204**
Fax 530.623.1237
E-mail ....asaxon@trinitycounty.org
　333 Tom Bell Rd, Weaverville, CA 96093
　Andrea Saxon, Coordinator

POLICE AND SHERIFF

Sheriff's Ofc **530.623.8108**
Fax 530.623.3926
Web ....www.trinitycounty.org
E-mail ....bhaney@trinitycounty.org
　101 Memorial Dr., Weaverville, CA 96093
　Bruce Haney, Sheriff

Tulare County

JUSTICE AGENCY

CASA **559.625.4007**
Fax 559.625.3165
Web ....www.casatulareco.org
E-mail ....beth@casatulareco.org
　1146 N Chinowth St, Visalia, CA 93291-4113
　Marilyn Barr, Executive Director

CSET **559.732.4194**
Fax 559.732.0739
　312 NW 3RD AVE, Visalia, CA 93291
　Carolyn Rose, Director

Juvenile Hall **559.735.1600**
Fax 559.713.3046
Web ....www.co.tulare.ca.us
　11200 Avenue 368, Visalia, CA 93291-8940
　Mary Raborn, Superintendent

**Victim/Witness Assistance Bureau-District
Attorney** **559.733.6754**
Fax 559.730.2931
Web ....www.da-tulareco.org
　221 S Mooney Blvd Rm 264, Visalia, CA 93291-4547
　Gayle Cain, Program Coordinator

POLICE AND SHERIFF

Sheriff's Ofc **559.733.6218**
Fax 559.730.2756
E-mail ....bill@annearundelhomes.com
　2404 W Burrel Ave, Visalia, CA 93291
　Bill Whitman, Sheriff

EDUCATION SERVICES

Burton Ctr Head Start **559.784.4852**
Fax 559.788.2583
　7000 W Doe Ave Ste C, Visalia, CA 93291-8623
　Ernestine Hernandez, Director

Office of Education **559.651.3022**
Fax 559.651.3802
Web ....www.cc.tcoe.org
E-mail ....rchavez@cc.tcoe.org
　7000 W Doe Ave Ste C, Visalia, CA 93291-8623
　Ray Chavez, Director

Tuolumne County

SOCIAL SERVICES

Social Svcs **209.533.5711**
Fax 209.533.5714
E-mail ....aconnolly@co.tuolumne.ca.us
　20075 Cedar Rd N, Sonora, CA 95370-5900
　Ann Connolly, Director

JUSTICE AGENCY

Probation Dept **209.533.7500**
Fax 209.533.7564
E-mail ....sjuhl@co.tuolumne.ca.us
　465 S Washington St, Sonora, CA 95370-5118
　Shirlee Juhl, CPO

Victim/Witness Program **209.588.5440**
Fax 209.588.5455
Web ....www.co.tuolumne.ca.us
　423 N Washington St, Sonora, CA 95370-5525
　Ginger Martin, Victim/witness Coordinator

COURTS

Superior Court **209.533.5650**
Fax 209.533.5618
Web ....www.tuolumne.courts.ca.gov
E-mail ....eric@tuolumne.courts.ca.gov
　41 Yaney Ave, Sonora, CA 95370-4611
　Honorable Eric L. Dutemple, Court Judge

POLICE AND SHERIFF

Sheriff's Dept **209.533.5855**
Fax 209.533.5831
Web ....www.tuolomnecounty.ca.gov
E-mail ....sheriff@tuolomnecounty.ca.gov
　28 Lower Sunset Dr, Sonora, CA 95370-4942
　James W. Meele, Sheriff

Sonora Police Dept **209.532.8141**
Fax 209.532.4845
Web ....www.sonorapd.com
E-mail ....mstinson@sonorapd.com
　100 S Green St, Sonora, CA 95370-4643
　Mark Stinson, Chief

EDUCATION SERVICES

Amador Head Start-Soulsbyville **209.533.0361**
Fax 209.533.0470
Web ....www.atcaa.org
E-mail ....mwilliam@atcaa.org
　427 Highway 49 Ste 202, Sonora, CA 95370-5666
　Marcia William, Director

Ventura County

SOCIAL SERVICES

Children & Family Svcs **805.654.3409**
Fax 805.654.3454
E-mail ....elaine.martinez@ventura.org
　4245 Market St Ste 204, Ventura, CA 93003-8009
　Elaine Martinez, Central Program Manager

**Children & Family Svcs - Oxnard
Region** **805.240.2700**
Fax 805.240.2710
　1400 Vanguard Dr, Oxnard, CA 93033
　David Weinreich, Program Manager

**Children & Family Svcs - Ventura
Region** **805.654.3444**
Fax 805.654.5514
Web ....www.countyofventura.org
E-mail ....tim.myers@ventura.org
　4245 Market St Ste 204, Ventura, CA 93003-8009
　Tim Myers, Program Manager

CPS **805.955.2290**
Fax 805.581.7821
　970 Enchanted Way, Simi Valley, CA 93065
　Tim Myers, Program Manager

**Human Svcs Agency - Children & Family Admin
Svcs** **805.477.5312**
Fax 805.477.5345
　855 Partridge Dr, Ventura, CA 93003
　Judy Webber, CFS Deputy Director

GENERAL HEALTH SERVICES

Oxnard Public Health Clinic **805.385.8652**
Fax 805.385.9134
E-mail ....rigoberto.vargas@ventura.org
　2500 S C St Ste D, Oxnard, CA 93033
　Rigo Vargas, Director

Public Health-Admin **805.981.5101**
Fax 805.981.5110
Web ....www.ventura.org
　2240 E Gonzales Rd Ste 210, Oxnard, CA 93036
　Barry Fisher, Director Of Public Health

MENTAL HEALTH SERVICES

Children's Mental Health Svcs **805.777.3505**
Fax 805.777.3574
Web ....www.countyofventura.org
　72 Moody Ct, Thousand Oaks, CA 91360
　Ophra Ashur, Supervisor

**Mental Health Ctr-Behavioral Health Admin
Ofc** **805.981.6830**
Fax 805.981.6838
E-mail ....denise.castillo@ventura.org
　1911 Williams Dr Ste 200, Oxnard, CA 93036
　Meloney Roy, Director

JUSTICE AGENCY

**Ventura Youth Correctional
Facility** **805.485.7951**
Fax 805.988.1861
E-mail ....david.finley@cdcr.ca.gov
　3100 Wright Rd, Camarillo, CA 93010
　David Finley, Superintendent

Victim/Witness Program 805.654.3622
Fax 805.662.6523
Web .... www.ventura.org/vcda
E-mail .... catherine.duggan@ventura.org
   800 S Victoria Ave Rm 311, Ventura, CA 93009
Catherine Duggan, Director

COURTS

Superior Court Juvenile Div 805.981.5988
Fax 805.981.5965
Web .... www.ventura.courts.ca.gov
E-mail .... doncoleman@ventura.courts.ca.gov
   4353 E Vineyard Ave Rm 122, Oxnard,
   CA 93036-0832
Honorable Donald D Coleman, Supervising Juvenile Judge

POLICE AND SHERIFF

Sheriff's Ofc 805.654.2315
Fax 805.645.1391
   800 S Victoria Ave, Ventura, CA 93009
Geof Dean, Sheriff

Ventura Police Dept 805.339.4400
Fax 805.644.0361
   1425 Dowell Dr, Ventura, CA 93003-7361
Ken Corney, Police Chief

EDUCATION SERVICES

Colonia Head Start 805.486.0850
Fax 805.486.3888
   1500 Camino Del Sol, Oxnard, CA 93030-3725
Mona Thompson, Director

White Pine County

GENERAL HEALTH SERVICES

Public Health Nursing Right to Life 775.289.2107
Fax 559.229.1040
Web .... www.rtlcc.org
E-mail .... jonathan@rtlcc.org
   1742 E Griffith Way, Fresno, CA 93726
John Keller, Executive Director

Yolo County

SOCIAL SERVICES

Employment & Social Svcs Dept 530.661.2750
Fax 530.661.2658
Web .... www.yolocounty.org
E-mail .... pam.miller@yolocounty.org
   25 N Cottonwood St, Woodland, CA 95695-6609
Pam Miller, Dess Director

GENERAL HEALTH SERVICES

Health Dept 530.666.8645
Fax 530.666.7337
Web .... www.yolocounty.org
E-mail .... d.gillian@yolocounty.org
   137 N Cottonwood St Ste 2500, Woodland,
   CA 95695
Dede Gillian, Nursing Services Director

JUSTICE AGENCY

CASA 530.661.4200
Fax 530.662.0970
Web .... www.yolocasa.org
E-mail .... volunteer@yolocasa.org
   724 Main St Ste 101, Woodland, CA 95695
Tracy Fauver, Executive Director

Juvenile Hall 530.406.5300
Fax 530.669.5802
Web .... www.yolocounty.org
E-mail .... ray.simmons@yolocounty.org
   2880 E Gibson Rd, Woodland, CA 95776-5160
Ray Simmons, Juvenile Hall Superintendent

Probation 530.406.5320
Fax 530.661.1211
Web .... www.yolocounty.org
   2780 E Gibson Rd, Woodland, CA 95776-5147
Marjorie Risk, Chief Probation Officer

Victim/Witness Program-District Attorney's
Ofc 530.666.8187
Fax 530.666.8185
Web .... www.yolocounty.org
   301 2nd St, Woodland, CA 95695-3415

COURTS

Superior Court 530.406.6700
Fax 530.406.6734
Web .... www.yolo.courts.ca.gov
   725 Court St, Woodland, CA 95695

POLICE AND SHERIFF

California State Sheriff's Assoc 916.375.8000
Fax 916.375.8017
Web .... www.calsheriffs.org
   1231 I St Ste 200, Sacramento, CA 95814
Carmen Green, Executive Director

Police Dept 530.661.7800
Fax 530.662.5356
Web .... www.cityofwoodland.org
E-mail .... dan.bellini@cityofwoodland.org
   1000 Lincoln Ave, Woodland, CA 95695-4100
Dan Bellini, Chief Of Police

Sheriff's Dept 530.668.5280
Fax 530.668.5238
E-mail .... carol.gonzales@yolocounty.org
   2500 E Gibson Rd, Woodland, CA 95776-5158
E.g. Prieto, Sheriff

EDUCATION SERVICES

Early Head Start 530.668.5177
Fax 530.668.6949
Web www.yolo.k12.ca.us
   1230 Half Lemen Ave, Woodland, CA 95776
Connie Luna, Director

Yuba County

SOCIAL SERVICES

Social Svcs 530.749.6311
Fax 530.749.6281
E-mail .... snobles@co.yuba.ca.us
   5730 Packard Ave Ste 100, Marysville, CA 95901
Susanne Nobles, Director

JUSTICE AGENCY

Juvenile Hall 530.741.6371
Fax 530.741.6304
Web .... www.co.yuba.ca.us
E-mail .... jsorgea@co.yuba.ca.us
   1023 14th St, Camp Singer, Marysville,
   CA 95901-4115
Frank Sorgea, Superintendent

Probation Dept 530.749.7550
Fax 530.749.7364
Web .... www.co.yuba.ca.us
E-mail .... jarnold@co.yuba.ca.us
   215 5th St Ste 154, Marysville, CA 95901-5737
Jim Arnold, Probation Program Manager

Youth Facility 559.735.1400
Fax 559.740.4489
E-mail .... dlopez@co.tulare.ca.us
   11150 Ave 368, Visalia, CA 93291
David Lopez, Probation Division Manager

COURTS

Superior Court 530.749.7600
Fax 530.749.7351
Web .... www.yubacourts.org
   215 5th St Ste 200, Marysville, CA 95901-5737
Stephen Konishi, Court Executive Officer

POLICE AND SHERIFF

Marysville Police Dept 530.749.3900
Fax 530.749.3990
   316 6th St, Marysville, CA 95901
Wallace Fullerton, Police Chief

Sheriff's Dept 530.749.7777
Fax 530.741.6445
   215 5th St Ste 150, Marysville, CA 95901-5737
Steve Duffer, Sheriff

SPECIAL SERVICES AGENCIES

ADOPTION AGENCIES

A Balanced Approach-Mediation 925.274.0900
Fax 925.274.0364
Web .... www.fjansenlaw.com
   540 Lennon Ln, Ste 290, Walnut Creek, CA 94598
Faith Jansen, Attorney

A Rainbow's End Adoption Svcs 714.839.3283
Fax 714.593.2399
E-mail .... adoptnca@yahoo.com
   9550 Warner Ave, 250-16, Fountain Valley, CA 92708
Irene Riley, Director

A Unique Adoption 951.600.2575
Fax 951.677.9098
Web .... www.uniqueadoptions.com
   23425 Applegate Ct, Murrieta, CA 92562-5025
Patrice Hill, Owner

A. Mariam Jamisson Ctr 661.334.3500
Fax 661.366.6591
Web .... www.kccfc.org
   1010 Shalimar Dr, Bakersfield, CA 93306-5633
Carl Guilford, Program Director

ABC Foster Family Agency 714.545.2046
Fax 714.545.4064
Web .... www.abcfoster.com
E-mail .... sjakana@abcfoster.com
   1520 Brookhollow Dr Ste 35, Santa Ana,
   CA 92705-5427
Sam Jakana, Director

About A Child 650.596.2816
   556 Keelson Cir, Redwood City, CA 94065
Victoria Case, Director

California

Adopt Help 818.789.3477
Fax 818.783.3176
Web ....www.adopthelp.com
E-mail ....inquiries@adopthelp.com
  15450 Ventura Blvd Ste 202, Sherman Oaks,
  CA 91403-3063
  Mark Gouldman, President/director

Adopt International 415.934.0300
Fax 415.934.0700
Web ....www.adoptinter.org
E-mail ....adopt@adoptinter.org
  1000 Brannan St, Ste 301, San Francisco,
  CA 94103-4888
  Lynne Jacobs, Director

Adoption Associates 323.664.5600
Fax 323.664.4551
E-mail ....felice@felicewebster.com
  4525 Wilshire Blvd Ste 201, Los Angeles,
  CA 90010-3846
  Felice A. Webster, Attorney

Adoption Attorney Janie Beach 805.527.9392
Fax 805.527.0798
Web ....www.adoptinbeach.com
E-mail ....adoptacherub@aol.com
  1464 Madera Rd Ste N183, Simi Valley,
  CA 93065-3063
  Janie Beach, Attorney

Adoption Choices 530.891.0302
Fax 530.893.9347
E-mail ....adoptionchoices@cawhs.org
  1469 Humboldt Rd Ste 200, Chico, CA 95928
  Mary Katherine, Director

Adoption Connection Jewish Family & Children Svcs 415.359.2494
Fax 415.359.2490
Web ....www.adoptionconnection.org
E-mail ....families@adoptionconnection.org
  2150 Post St, San Francisco, CA 94115
  Lynn Fingerman, Co-Director

Adoption Ctr 858.535.3033
Fax 858.535.3032
  6046 Cornerstone Ct W Ste 135, San Diego,
  CA 92121
  Sarah Jensen, Director

Adoption Ctr 530.888.1311
Fax 530.888.7529
Web ....www.adoption-center.com
E-mail ....adopt@adoption-center.com
  1253 High St, Auburn, CA 95603-5016
  Nanci Worchester, Director

Adoption Insight 760.356.5565
Fax 760.356.5545
E-mail ....la@adoptioninsight.com
  439 W Sid St, Holtville, CA 92250
  Lori Arvon, Director

Adoption Network Law Ctr 949.499.8400
Fax 949.855.5110
  23161 Lake Center Dr Ste 210, Lake Forest,
  CA 92630
  Rebecca, Director

Adoption Options, Inc. 619.294.7772
Fax 619.294.7771
Web ....www.adoption-options.org
E-mail ....info@adoption-options.org
  411 Camino Del Rio S Ste 200, San Diego, CA 92108
  Brent Yoder, Executive Director

Agape Villages 925.866.3020
Fax 925.866.0305
Web ....www.agapevillages.org
E-mail ....jkleyn@agapevillages.org
  3160 Crow Canyon Rd Ste 120, San Ramon,
  CA 94583-1382
  Janet Kleyn, CEO

Agape Villages 916.485.9181
Fax 916.485.0981
Web ....www.agapevillages.com
E-mail ....agapesac@sbcglobal.net
  2220 Watt Ave Ste C180, Sacramento,
  CA 95825-0513
  Rochelle Bard, Program Director

Alternative Family Svcs Adoption Agency 415.656.0116
Fax 415.656.0117
Web ....www.alternativefamilyservices.org
E-mail ....jberlin@afs4kids.org
  250 Executive Park Blvd Ste 4900, San Francisco,
  CA 94134-3335
  Jay Berlin, Executive Director

Attorney Assisted California 714.937.5291
Fax 714.937.5652
E-mail ....chernandez@attyassisted.com
  1740 W Katelra Ave Ste Q, Orange, CA 92867
  Christina Hernandez, Administrator

Bal Jagat Children's World 562.597.5029
Fax 562.597.7696
Web ....www.baljagat.org
E-mail ....baljagat@verizon.net
  5199 E Pacific Coast Hwy Ste 204, Long Beach,
  CA 90804-3387
  Hemlata Momaya, Director

Barbara A Rohan 415.459.1438
Fax 415.459.3668
Web ....www.barbararohan.com
  1534 5th Ave Ste 4, San Rafael, CA 94901-1818

Bay Area Adoption Svcs 650.964.3800
Fax 650.964.6467
Web ....www.baas.org
E-mail ....baas@baas.org
  465 Fairchild Dr Ste 215, Mountain View,
  CA 94043-2251
  Andrea Stawitcke, Director

Bethany Christian Svcs 559.432.9696
Fax 559.432.9697
Web ....www.bethany.org
E-mail ....bcsfresno@bethany.org
  726 W Barstow Ave Ste 116, Fresno, CA 93704
  Sandi Hiatt, South Valley Director

Bethany Christian Svcs- North Region 209.522.5121
Fax 209.522.4045
Web ....www.bethany.org/modesto
E-mail ....bcsmodesto@bethany.org
  3048 Hahn Dr, Modesto, CA 95350-6503
  Lynette Stime, Director

Better Life 916.641.0661
Fax 916.641.0664
Web ....www.better-life.org
E-mail ....betterlife@better-life.org
  1337 Howe Ave Ste 107, Sacramento,
  CA 95825-3305
  Winifred Mcneil, Director

Black Adoption Placement & Research Ctr 510.430.3600
Fax 510.430.3615
Web ....www.baprc.org
E-mail ....family@baprc.org
  10440 International Blvd, Oakland, CA 94603
  Gloria King, Executive Director

Casey Family Programs 619.543.0774
Fax 619.543.0743
Web ....www.casey.org
E-mail ....jcabrera@casey.org
  3878 Old Town Ave Ste 100, San Diego, CA 92110
  Jorge Cabrera, Director

Catholic Charities Adoption Agency 619.231.2828
Fax 619.232.3807
Web ....www.ccdsd.org
E-mail ....ppetterson@ccdsd.org
  349 Cedar St, San Diego, CA 92101-3112
  Raymonda Duvall, Executive Director

Children's Hope Foster Family 530.846.4955
Fax 530.846.4954
Web ....www.childrenshopeffa.org
E-mail ....bpayne@childrenshopeffa.org
  567 Virginia St, Gridley, CA 95948
  Ben Payne, Administrator

Children's Way 310.645.5227
Fax 310.645.9840
Web ....www.cihssinc.org
  8929 S Sepulveda Blvd, Ste 200, Los Angeles,
  CA 90045-3643
  William Marshall, President

Christian Credit Counselors, Inc. 760.804.8515
Fax 760.448.8095
Web ....www.ibudget.org
  5838 Edison Place, Suite 200, Carlsbad, CA 92008
  COA accredited organization.

David H Baum Law Ofc 818.501.8355
Fax 818.501.8465
  16255 Ventura Blvd Ste 704, Encino, CA 91436
  David H Baum, Director

Denise Wagner 707.321.3405
  PO Box 817, Cotati, CA 94931-0817

Desert Behavioral Health 760.946.2070
Fax 760.946.1511
E-mail ....desertbehavioralhlth@msn.com
  16195 Siskiyou Rd Ste 120A, Apple Valley,
  CA 92307-1346
  Judy Davis, Director

Diane Michelsen Law Ofcs 925.945.1880
Fax 925.933.6807
E-mail ....info@familyformation.com
  3190 Old Tunnel Rd Ste A, Lafayette, CA 94549-4151
  Shannon Matteson, Attorney

Dillon International Inc 714.734.8600
Fax 714.734.8688
Web ....www.dillonadopt.com
E-mail ....info@dillonadopt.com
  18001 Irvine Blvd Ste 101, Tustin, CA 92780-3343
  Deniese Dillon, Executive Director

Eggleston Family Svcs 323.954.1464
Fax 323.954.9515
  3701 Stocker St Ste 200, Los Angeles, CA 90008
  Kenneth Cook, Director

EMQ Families First 916.641.9595
Fax 916.641.9599
Web ....www.emqff.org
  2330 Glendale Ln Ste 100, Sacramento, CA 95825
  Carlos Figueroa, Office Manager

Extraordinary Conceptions 760.798.2265
Fax 760.798.4255
E-mail ....mario@extraconceptions.com
  1225 Fan Eligo Rd, San Marcos, CA 92078-5300
  Mario Caballero, Executive Director

Families First 209.523.3710
Fax 209.523.3725
Web ....www.emq.org
E-mail ....modestopfc@familiesfirstinc.org
  1620 N Carpenter Rd Ste C23, Modesto,
  CA 95351-1157
  Agnes Perez, Placement Supervisor

Families First 408.369.2220
Fax 408.369.2221
Web ....www.familiesfirstinc.org
E-mail ....dcharron@familiesfirstinc.org
  1475 S Bascom Ave Ste 112, Campbell,
  CA 95008-0628
  Dawn Charron, Director

Families For Children 707.435.0166
Fax 707.435.0172
E-mail ....ffc@families4children.com
  370 Chadbourne Rd, Ste C, Fairfield, CA 94534
  Ursala Devere, CEO

Families For Children 510.663.5250
Fax 510.663.5255
Web www.families4children.com
E-mail ....udevere@families4children.com
   2201 Broadway Ste 508, Oakland, CA 94612-3063
Ursula Devere, Director

Families For Children 209.956.1211
Fax 209.956.1215
E-mail ....udevere@families4children.com
   7488 Shoreline Drive, Suite A-1, Stockton,
   CA 95219-5435
Urshula Devere, Executive Director

Family Builders By Adoption 510.272.0204
Fax 510.272.0277
Web ....www.familybuilders.org
E-mail ....kids@familybuilders.org
   401 Grand Ave Ste 400, Oakland, CA 94610
Jill Jacobs, Executive Director

Family Connection Adoptions Southern Ca
Ofc 760.966.0531
Fax 760.966.0473
Web ....www.fcadoptions.org
E-mail ....alisonfoster@fcadoptions.org
   2191 S El Camino Real Ste 202, Oceanside,
   CA 92054-6226
Alison Foster, Executive Director

Family Connections Adoptions 805.477.7400
Fax 805.477.7404
   2421 Portola Rd Ste A, Ventura, CA 93003
Gwen Addison, Branch Manager

Family Connections Christian Adoption 209.524.8844
Fax 209.578.9823
Web ....www.fcadoptions.org
E-mail ....waynemott@fcadoptions.org
   1120 Tully Rd, Modesto, CA 95350-4932
Wayne Mott, Ffa Administrator

Family Connections Christian Adoptions Central Valley
Ofc 559.325.9388
Fax 559.325.9373
Web ....www.fcadoptions.org
   7257 N Maple Ave Ste 101, Fresno, CA 93720
Diane Wagers, Branch Director

Foster Family Agency 714.516.9484
Fax 714.516.9485
   322 W Katella Ave, # 5B, Orange, CA 92867
Marcello Cavrera, Administrator

Foster Family Svc 916.487.2111
Fax 916.487.2173
Web ....www.fosterfamilyservice.org
E-mail ....johnj@fosterfamilyservice.org
   2775 Cottage Way Ste 11, Sacramento, CA 95825
John Johnson, Director

Foster Family Svcs 530.544.2111
   2580 Lake Tahoe Blvd Ste D, South Lake Tahoe,
   CA 96150
Megan Ciampa, Social Worker

God's Families International Adoption
Svcs 949.858.7621
Fax 949.858.5431
Web ....www.godsfamilies.org
E-mail ....director@godsfamilies.org
   19389 Live Oak Canyon Road, Trabuco Canyon,
   CA 92679
James Molter, Executive Director

Hannah's Children's Home 909.483.2552
Fax 909.483.2532
   9269 Utica Ave Ste 120, Rancho Cucamonga,
   CA 91730
Melinda Williams, Supervisor

Heartsent Adoptions, Inc. 925.254.8883
Fax 925.254.8866
Web ....www.heartsent.org
   15 Altarinda Rd Ste 100, Orinda, CA 94563-2607
Val Free, Director

Holt International 916.487.4658
Fax 916.487.7068
Web ....www.holtintl.org
E-mail ....cynthias@holtintl.org
   1555 River Park Dr, Ste 100, Sacramento, CA 95815
Cynthia Shockensy, Branch Director

Holy Family Svcs 213.202.3900
Fax 213.202.3942
Web ....www.holyfamilyservices.org
E-mail ....hfsadopt@aol.com
   840 Echo Park Ave, Pasadena, CA 90026
Debra Richardson, Director

Holy Family Svcs 714.528.6300
Fax 714.528.6305
Web ....www.holyfamilyservices.org
E-mail ....hfsadopt@aol.com
   701 W Kimberly Ave, Ste 115, Placentia, CA 92870
Debra Richardson, Director

Independent Adoption Ctr 310.215.3180
Fax 310.215.3252
Web ....www.adoptionhelp.org
E-mail ....jbliss@adoptionhelp.org
   5777 W Century Blvd Ste 1450, Los Angeles,
   CA 90045-5681
Jennifer Bliss, Co-Director

Independent Adoption Ctr 800.877.6736
Fax 925.603.0820
Web ....www.adoptionhelp.org
E-mail ....awrixon@adoptionhelp.org
   391 Taylor Blvd Ste 100, Pleasant Hill,
   CA 94523-2294
Ann Wrixon, Director

Indian Child & Family Svcs 951.676.8832
Fax 951.676.3950
Web ....www.infantofprague.org
E-mail ....lmadrigal@infantofprague.org
   29377 Rancho California Rd Ste 200, Temecula,
   CA 92591-5206
Louis Madrigal, Director

Infant Of Prague 559.447.3333
Fax 559.447.3322
Web ....www.infantofprague.org
E-mail ....info@infantofprague.org
   6059 N Palm Ave, Fresno, CA 93704-1623
Stephanie Grant, Executive Director

Inner Circle Foster Care And Adoption
Svcs 818.988.6300
Fax 818.988.7087
Web ....www.fosterfamily.org
   7120 Hayvenhurst Ave Ste 205, Van Nuys, CA 91406
Pam Jordan, Director

Int'l Christian Adoptions 951.695.3336
Fax 951.308.1753
Web www.4achild.org
E-mail ....info@4achild.org
   41745 Rider Way # 2, Temecula, CA 92590-4826
Laura Duke, Executive Director

Kinship Ctr 831.455.9965
Fax 831.455.4777
Web ....www.kinshipcenter.org
E-mail ....info@kinshipcenter.org
   124 River Rd, Salinas, CA 93908
Carol Biddle, President

Kinship Ctr 714.979.2365
Fax 714.979.8135
Web ....www.kinshipcenter.org
E-mail ....mdodson@kinshipcenter.org
   18302 Irvine Blvd Ste 300, Tustin, CA 92780
Melissa Dodson, Director

Koinonia Foster Home 559.635.8926
Fax 559.635.0718
Web ....www.kfh.org
E-mail ....dsweeney@kfh.org
   1640 W Mineral King Ave Ste 202, Visalia,
   CA 93291-4440
Trudence Morris, Social Worker

Lilliput Children's Svcs 530.896.1920
Fax 530.896.1885
Web ....www.lilliput.org
   8 Williamsburg Ln, Chico, CA 95926
Miko Wilson, Social Worker

Little's Foster Home 559.733.7477
   1636 W Laura Ave, Visalia, CA 93277-6309
Derrick Little, Director

Olive Crest 714.543.5437
Fax 714.543.5463
Web ....www.olivecrest.org
E-mail ....donald-verleur@olivecrest.org
   2130 E 4th St Ste 200, Santa Ana, CA 92705-3818
Donald Verleur, Executive Chief Of Operations

Olive Crest Foster Family Agency 818.866.8956
Fax 562.461.2893
Web ....www.olivecrest.org
   17800 Woodruff Ave, Bellflower, CA 90706
John Anderson, CEO

Open Line Foster Family 530.241.5178
Fax 530.246.1030
   4625 Mountain Lakes Blvd, Redding, CA 96003
Georgia Wolske, Administrator

Parter for Adoption 925.934.1090
Fax 925.934.1013
Web ....www.russianadoption.com
E-mail ....info@russianadoption.com
   800 S Broadway, Walnut Creek, CA 94596
Diana Revutsky, Director

Redwood Children's Svcs 707.263.0372
Fax 707.263.0374
   320 1st St, Lakeport, CA 95453
Jillian Barrna, Program Supervisor

Rosemary Children's Services 626.844.3033
Fax 626.844.3034
Web ....www.rosemarychildren.org
   36 S. Kinneloa Avenue, Suite 200, Pasadena,
   CA 91107
COA accredited organization.

Sierra Forever Family Svcs 916.368.5114
Fax 916.368.5157
Web ....www.sierraff.org
E-mail ....sassac@sierraff.org
   8928 Volunteer Ln Ste 100, Sacramento,
   CA 95826-3238
Bob Herne, Executive Director

Southern California FFA- Adoption 213.365.2900
Fax 213.365.0228
   155 N Occidental Blvd, Los Angeles, CA 90026
Sylvia Fogleman, CEO

Springboard Non-Profit Consumer Credit Management,
Inc. 951.781.0114
Fax 951.328.7724
Web ....www.credit.org
   4351 Latham Street, Riverside, CA 92501
COA accredited organization.

Triad Family Svcs 209.340.2800
Fax 209.340.2815
E-mail ....info@traidfs.org
   2445 Albatross Way Ste 105, sacrmento, CA 95815
Mark Dandeneau, Chief Executive Officer

Trinity Foster Care 760.245.4676
Fax 760.245.7714
Web ....www.trinitycfs.org
E-mail ....victorvilledirector@trinitycfs.org
   15500 W Sand St Ste 7, Victorville, CA 92392
Shaun-kathryn Robles, Director

California

Trinity Foster Care **909.980.4755**
Fax 909.980.2396
Web ....www.trinityys.org
E-mail ....coffenstein@trinityys.org
9600 Center Ave, Ste 100, Rancho Cucamonga,
CA 91730
Christine Offenstein, Director

Walden Family Svcs **619.584.5777**
Fax 619.584.5760
Web ....www.waldenfamily.org
E-mail ....info@waldenfamily.org
6150 Mission Gorge Rd Ste 210, San Diego,
CA 92120-4098
Sue Evans, Program And Clinical Director

Walden Family Svcs **951.788.5905**
Fax 951.788.5903
Web ....www.waldenfamily.org
E-mail ....sevans@waldenfamily.org
3576 Arlington Ave Ste 106, Riverside,
CA 92506-3907
Sue Evans, Program Director

ADVOCACY RESOURCES

24 Hour Angels **714.694.5936**
Fax 714.464.5317
Web www.24hourangels.com
E-mail ....customercare@24hourangels.com
18032 Lemon Dr. Unit C-140, Yorba Linda,
CA 92886
Deanna Blair, Owner

California Bar Assn **530.284.1644**
E-mail ....maryshelters@gmail.com
4008 Arlington Rd, PO Box 2, Taylorsville, CA 95983
Mary Shelters

California Children's Hospital Assoc **916.552.7111**
Fax 916.552.7119
E-mail ....ddooley@ccha.org
1215 K St Ste 1930, Sacramento, CA 95814-3911
Cindy Ehnes, CEO

CDF-California Headquarters **510.663.1783**
Fax 510.663.1783
2201 Broadway Ste 705, Oakland, CA 94612

Child Advocacy Ctr **209.468.6185**
Fax 209.468.6852
Web ....www.dss.ca.gov
E-mail ....wrueb@sjgov.org
6861 Mary Graham Ln, French Camp, CA 95231
Wanda Rueb, Clinical Coordinator

Children's Law Center **323.980.5761**
E-mail ....villafanl@clcla.org
201 Centre Plaza Dr # 9, Monterey Park, CA 91754
Lucrecia Villafan, Director

Children's Law Center **323.980.7700**
E-mail ....arnerichd@clcla.org
201 Centre Plaza Dr Ste 7, Monterey Park, CA 91754
Danielle Arnerich Combs, Attorney

Children's Law Center of Los Angeles **323.980.1595**
E-mail ....kittlerc@clcla.org
201 Centre Plaza Dr Ste 9, Monterey Park, CA 91754
Carol Gasa Kittler

Children's Law Center of Los Angeles **323.980.1544**
E-mail ....jervikk@clcla.org
201 Centre Plaza Dr, Ste 205, Monterey Park,
CA 91754
Kevin Jervik, Attorney

Childrens Defense Fund - Los Angeles **213.355.8787**
Fax 213.355.8795
E-mail ....cdsca@childernsdefense.org
3333 Wilshire Blvd Ste 550, Los Angeles, CA 90010
Kim Brett-Schneider, Director

CLCLA **323.980.1524**
E-mail ....iglesiasd@clcla.org
201 Centre Plaza Dr, Monterey Park, CA 91754
Diana Iglesias, Manager

CLCLA **323.980.7757**
E-mail ....cheungj@clcla.org
201 Centre Plaza Dr # 7, Monterey Park, CA 91754
Jenny Cheung, Manager

CLCLA **323.980.1525**
E-mail ....aspaturiann@clcla.org
201 Centre Plaza Dr Ste 7, Monterey Park, CA 91754
David Estep, Director

Counsel **323.526.6191**
E-mail ....rramirez@counsel.lacounty.gov
201 Centre Plaza Dr Ste 1, Monterey Park, CA 91754
Olivia Ramirez

**Court Appointed Special Advocates (CASA) -
Sacramento** **916.875.6460**
Fax 916.875.6879
E-mail ....carol@sacramentocasa.org
301 Bicentennial Circle, Suite 220, Sacramento,
CA 95826
Carol Noreen, Executive Director

Dennis S Reid Attorney at Law **510.438.6882**
E-mail ....dsrlawyer@yahoo.com
249 Estudillo Ave, San Leandro, CA 94577
Dennis Reid, Attorney

Futuro Infantil Hispano FFA **626.339.1824**
E-mail ....mailfuturoinfantil.org
2227 E Garvey Ave N, West Covina, CA 91791
Lily Olan, Administrator

Goodman & Bhutani **412.206.0882**
E-mail ....bhtani@goodman-bhutani.com
102 A Valencia St, San Francisco, CA 94111
Nina Bhutani

Iglesias Law Firm **323.262.2353**
E-mail ....reeda@ladlinc.org
1000 Corporate Center Dr, Ste 400, Monterey Park,
CA 91754
Adam Reed, Supervisor

Innovative Healthcare Consultants, Inc. **760.731.1334**
Fax 760.731.1490
Web ....www.innovativehc.com
E-mail ....colleenvanhorn@sbcglobal.net
557 E. Alvarado St., Fallbrook, CA 92028
Colleen Van Horn, CEO, Rn, Bsn, Phn, Ccm

Law Office of Felipe C Castillo **510.452.0203**
E-mail ....lousygus@yahoo.com
160 Franklin St, Ste 208, Oakland, CA 94607
Felipe C Castillo, Judge

Law Office of Gary Gonzalez **415.931.0335**
E-mail ....gary_gonzalez@comcast.net
419 Central Ave, San Francisco, CA 94117
Gary Gonzalez

Law Offices of Bonnie L Miller **650.595.0444**
E-mail ....blmesq@aol.com
1313 Laurel St Ste 114, San Carlos, CA 94070
Bonnie Miller, Director

Law Offices of Jill M Klein **760.918.5585**
E-mail ....jmk_legal@yahoo.com
1902 Wright Pl Ste 200, Carlsbad, CA 92008
Jill Klein, Judge

Law Offices of John Cahill **818.565.0440**
E-mail ....constantandcahill@prodigy.net
2550 Hollywood Way Ste 202, Burbank, CA 91505
John Cahill, Attorney

Legal Advocates for Children **408.350.7253**
E-mail ....jezette.luster@lawfoundation.org
111 W Saint John St Ste 315, San Jose, CA 95113
Jezette Luster, Manager

Legal Advocates for Children **408.350.7258**
E-mail ....jeanine.mckelvey@lawfoundation.org
111 W Saint John St Ste 315, San Jose, CA 95113
Jeanine McKelvey

Legal Advocates for Children **408.350.7259**
E-mail ....heidi.koh@lawfoundation.org
111 W Saint John St Ste 315, San Jose, CA 95113
Heidi Koh

Legal Advocates for Children **408.280.2440**
152 merced st fl 3, San Jose, CA 95112
Jeniffer Talleher, Director

Legal Advocates for Children **408.350.7255**
E-mail ....amy.guy@lawfoundation.org
152 N 3rd St 3rd Flr, San Jose, CA 95112
Amy Guy, Attorney

Legal Advocates for Children & **408.350.7254**
E-mail ....bene@lawfoundation.org
152 N 3rd St, San Jose, CA 95112
Ben Ebert, Staff Attorney

Legal Advocates for Children & Youth **408.280.2483**
E-mail ....molly.dunn@lawfoundation.org
111 W St John St Ste 315, San Jose, CA 95113
Molly Dunn

Legal Advocates for Children And Youth **408.350.7265**
E-mail ....rachel.fightmaster@lawfoundation.org
111 W St John St ,Ste 315, San Jose, CA 95113
Rachael Fightmaster

Legal Advocates for Children and Youth **408.350.7268**
E-mail ....amanda.kennedy@lawfoundation.org
111 W St John St Ste 315, San Jose, CA 95113
Amanda Kennedy, Attorney

Legal Advocates for Children and Youth **408.350.7256**
E-mail ....maighna.jain@lawfoundation.org
111 W St John St Ste 315, San Jose, CA 95113
Maighna Jain

Legal Services for Children In **415.863.3762**
1254 Market St 3rd Fl, San Francisco, CA 94102
Shannan Wiber, Director

Legal Services for Children Inc **415.863.3762**
E-mail ....shannan@lsc-sf.org
1254 Market St 3rd Fl, San Francisco, CA 94102
Shannan Wilber, Director

Legal Services for Children Inc **415.863.3762**
E-mail ....shannon@lsc-sf.org
1254 Market St 3rd Fl, San Francisco, CA 94102
Shannon Wilber, Executive Director

Legal Svcs for Children Inc **415.863.3762**
E-mail ....swilber@lsc-sf.org
1254 Market St 3rd Fl, San Francisco, CA 94102
Shannon Wilber, Director

Legal Svcs for Children Inc **415.863.3762**
1254 Market St 3rd Fl, San Francisco, CA 94102
Shannan Wilber, Executive Director

Los Angeles Dependency Lawyers **323.545.7792**
E-mail ....wayne.morrow@gmail.com
1000 Corporate Center Dr, Ste 430, Monterey Park,
CA 91754
Wayne Morrow

Los Angeles Dependency Lawyers **323.859.3507**
E-mail ....attenboroughlj@aol.com
1000 Corporate Center Dr #410, Monterey Park,
CA 91754
Lynda Attenborough

Los Angeles Dependency Lawyers **310.572.9212**
E-mail ....furthm@ladlinc.org
12214 Charnock Rd, Los Angeles, CA 90066
Marlene Furth

Los Angels Dependency Lawyers **323.859.4527**
E-mail ....bacak@ladlinc.org
1000 Corporate Center Dr, Suite 430, Monterey Park,
CA 91754
Katie Baca

Los Angels Dependency Lawyers **328.859.4505**
E-mail ....bacone@ladlinc.org
1000 Corporate Center Dr, Monterey Park, CA 91754
Ellen Bacon

National Center for Youth Law **501.853.8098**
E-mail .... billgrimm@youthlaw.org
405 14th St 15th Fl, Oakland, CA 94612
Bill Grimm, Director

National Ctr for Youth Law **510.835.8098**
E-mail .... tschroth@youthlaw.org
405 14th St 15th Fl, Oakland, CA 94612
Tracy Schroth

**Parents And Teachers Against Violence In Education
(PTAVE)** **925.831.1661**
Web .... www.nospank.net
E-mail .... riak@nospank.net
PO Box 1033, Alamo, CA 94507
Jordan Riak, Executive Director

Sacramento Child Advocates Inc **916.364.2350**
E-mail .... naweber@sacchildadv.org
8745 Folsom Blvd Ste 150, Sacramento, CA 95826
Nicole Weber

Soter & Park **415.355.1940**
E-mail .... parklaw@mindspring.com
459 Fulton St Ste 300, San Francisco, CA 94102
Alicia Park

Stand Against Domestic Violence **925.676.2845**
Fax 925.676.0532
Web .... www.standffov.org
1410 Danzig Plz, Fl 2, Concord, CA 94520
Gloria Sandoval, Director

Victim/Witness Program **760.336.3930**
Fax 760.353.3292
E-mail .... pamlittrell@imperialcounty.net
217 S 10th St, Bldg A, El Centro, CA 92243
Monica Chavez, Advocate Specialist

BEHAVIORAL HEALTH TREATMENT

A Ctr For Cognitive Therapy **805.687.8021**
E-mail .... dr_richard@compuserve.com
22 W Mission St Ste B, Santa Barbara,
CA 93101-2450
Richard Kelliher Md, Psychiatrist

A Professional Corp **707.857.3319**
PO Box 1084, Geyserville, CA 95441-1084
Seymour Boorstein, Psychiatrist

A Professional Corp **310.275.6642**
433 N Camden Dr, Beverly Hills, CA 90210-4430
Peter Gruenberg, Psychiatrist

A Woman's Care **650.327.8326**
200 Middlefield Rd Ste 100, Menlo Park,
CA 94025-4003
Carol Achtman Md, Psychiatrist

Abouesh Medical Practice **530.899.3150**
Fax 530.899.3160
Web .... www.therapeuticsolutionspc.com
3255 Espoanade St, Chico, CA 95973
Ahmed Abouesh, Md, Psychiatrist

Abrams Medical Practice **323.655.4233**
8383 Wilshire Blvd Ste 112, Beverly Hills,
CA 90211-2430
Mathis Abrams, Psychiatrist

Achamallah Nagui General **925.681.2645**
Fax 925.687.4032
2700 Grant St, Concord, CA 94520
Achamallah Nagui, MD, Psychiatrist

Ackerman Medical Practice **805.682.3601**
E-mail .... ruthackerman@earthville.net
2417 Castillo St, Santa Barbara, CA 93105-4301
Ruth Ackerman, Psychiatrist

Action Family Counseling, Inc. **661.297.6644**
Web .... actionfamily.org
E-mail .... action_corporate@yahoo.com
23502 Lyons Ave #301, Santa Clarita, CA 91350
Ms. Mari Lane, Accreditation Manager
Joint Commission accredited organization.

Adolescent Growth, Inc. **323.948.9998**
Web .... www.adolescentgrowth.com
E-mail .... joilynlewis@adolescentgrowth.com
6323 Zindell Avenue, Commerce, CA 90040
Dr. Joilyn Holmes, Accreditation Manager
Joint Commission accredited organization.

Adult Adolescent & Child Pshyc **858.485.6622**
Web .... www.sheldonzablowmd.com
15525 Pomerado Rd Ste B1, Poway, CA 92064-2425
Sheldon Zablow, Psychiatrist

Agape Villages Foster Family Agency **925.829.7211**
Fax 925.829.7212
11875 Dublin Blvd Ste A105, Dublin, CA 94568
Dave Roach, Administrator

Ahart Medical Practice **707.522.8641**
509 7th St Ste 201B, Santa Rosa, CA 95401-5265
Susan Ahart, MD, Psychiatrist

Alameda Psychiatric Medical **510.521.4323**
512 Westline Dr Ste 203, Alameda, CA 94501-7605
H Theodore Freeland, MD, Psychiatrist

Alexander Medical Practice **310.530.1050**
23545 Crenshaw Blvd, Torrance, CA 90505
Phillip Alexander, Psychiatrist

Alfred Goldberg Inc **310.472.6669**
801 Broom Way, Los Angeles, CA 90049-1921
Alfred Goldberg, Psychiatrist

Allied Psychiatric Med Group **650.854.9366**
1050 University Dr, Menlo Park, CA 94025
Eric Rothenberg Md, Psychiatrist

Alta Bates Medical Ctr **510.526.7203**
Fax 510.526.7203
1035 San Pablo Ave Ste 8, Albany, CA 94706-2277
David Golub, Psychiatrist

**Alternative Options Intensive Outpatient Treatment
Program** **562.921.5701**
Fax 562.921.5703
Web .... www.altoptions.com
17326 Edwards Road, Suite A115, Cerritos, CA 90703
CARF accredited programs available.

Alternatives In Psychiatry **925.945.8440**
Fax 925.945.8448
2255 Ygnacio Valley Rd, Walnut Creek,
CA 94598-3343
Robert Picker, Psychiatrist

American Academy-Nutritional **530.222.8118**
Fax 530.222.6495
3874 Bechelli Ln, Redding, CA 96002-2426
William Weathers, Psychiatrist

Ampudia Medical Practice **310.539.1952**
3250 Lomita Blvd Ste 103, Torrance, CA 90505-5005
Peter Ampudia, Psychiatrist

Anderson Medical Practice **707.763.9122**
Fax 707.782.9074
Web .... www.davidjohnandersonmd.com
E-mail .... djamd@davidjohnandersonmd.com
30 5th St, Petaluma, CA 94952-3042
David Anderson, Psychiatrist

Ann Martin Ctr **510.655.7880**
Fax 510.655.3379
Web .... www.annmartin.org
E-mail .... davidtheis@annmartin.org
1250 Grand Ave, Oakland, CA 94610-1070
Robert Schreiber, MD, Medical Director

Anshin Medical Practice **323.653.2220**
Fax 404.685.9420
116 N Robertson Blvd Ste 811, Los Angeles,
CA 90048-3111
Roman Anshin, Psychiatrist

Armbrust Medical Practice **650.329.1861**
Fax 479.271.6518
250 Middlefield Rd, Palo Alto, CA 94301-1342
Jill Armbrust Md, Psychiatrist

Aron Medical Practice **831.728.0255**
Fax 831.604.9989
E-mail .... stearon@msn.com
240 Westgate Dr Ste 235, Watsonville,
CA 95076-2453
Stephen Aron, MD, Psychiatrist

Arthur J Ourieff Inc **310.474.7100**
Fax 310.476.9789
320 N Cliffwood Ave, Los Angeles, CA 90049-2618
Arthur Ourieff, Psychiatrist

Ashley Medical Practice **818.881.7595**
Fax 818.773.9302
9029 Reseda Blvd Ste 209, Northridge,
CA 91324-3932
Patricia Ashley, Psychiatrist

Associates in Counseling & Mediation **714.978.1090**
Web .... associatesincounseling.com
E-mail .... associatesincounseling@yahoo.com
265 S. Anita Drive - Suite 117, Orange, CA 92868
Ms. Marianne Abulone, Accreditation Manager
Joint Commission accredited organization.

Associates In Neuropsychiatry **650.212.4900**
E-mail .... firestone@forensicneuropsychiatry.com
520 S El Camino Real, San Mateo, CA 94402-1716
Marvin Firestone Md, Psychiatrist

Auerbach Medical Practice **415.387.3731**
Fax 563.852.5072
3663 Sacramento St, San Francisco, CA 94118-1709
Nina Auerbach, Psychiatrist

Auerbach Medical Practice **818.990.3876**
15760 Ventura Blvd Ste 2021, Encino,
CA 91436-3002
Daniel Auerbach, Psychiatrist

Aurora Behavioral Health Care/ San Diego **858.487.3200**
Web .... www.aurorabehavioral.com
E-mail .... michael.elmore@aurorabehavioral.com
11878 Avenue of Industry, San Diego, CA 92128
Mr. Michael Elmore, Accreditation Manager
Joint Commission accredited organization.

Aurora Charter Oak - Los Angeles, L.L.C. **626.966.1632**
Web .... aurorabehavioral.com
E-mail .... gwebb@aurorabehavioral.com
1161 East Covina Boulevard, Covina, CA 91724
Ms. Gail Webb, Accreditation Manager
Joint Commission accredited organization.

Aurora Vista Del Mar Hospital **805.653.6434**
Fax 805.652.2065
E-mail .... mkrebsbach@aurorabehavioral.com
801 Seneca St, Ventura, CA 93001-1411
Mayla Krebsbach, CEO/Administrator

Axis Community Health, Inc. **925.462.5544**
Fax 925.485.1273
Web .... www.axishealth.org
4361 Railroad Avenue, Pleasanton, CA 94566
CARF accredited programs available.

Babus Medical Practice **805.682.6867**
Fax 805.967.1293
504 W Pueblo St Ste 304, Santa Barbara,
CA 93105-6211
Howard Babus, Psychiatrist

Bae Medical Practice **415.440.8998**
2224 Fillmore St, San Francisco, CA 94115-2222
James Bae, Psychiatrist

Baig Medical Practice **909.425.7657**
PO Box 237, Patton, CA 92369-0237
Sanobar Baig Md, Psychiatrist

Ballinger Medical Practice **650.321.7675**
Fax 303.355.7784
1187 University Dr, Menlo Park, CA 94025-4423
Barbara Ballinger Md, Psychiatrist

California

Barbara Sinatra Children's Ctr At Eisenhower Medical Ctr 760.340.2336
Fax 760.340.1851
39000 Bob Hope Dr, Rancho Mirage, CA 92270
Susan Reynolds, Executive Vice-president

Barron Medical Practice 858.550.0979
3252 Holiday Ct, La Jolla, CA 92037
R William Barron Md, Psychiatrist

Barshack Medical Practice 415.927.6690
Fax 415.927.6688
2 Fifer Ave, Corte Madera, CA 94925
Scott Barshack, Psychiatrist

Barton Medical Practice 310.434.9222
530 Wilshire Blvd Ste 209, Santa Monica, CA 90401-1423
Brooke Barton, Md, Psychiatrist

Bass Medical Practice 323.876.1500
Fax 323.876.1515
7801 W Sunset Blvd, Los Angeles, CA 90046
Tsilya Bass, Md, Psychiatrist

Bauman Medical Practice 707.544.6022
Fax 707.537.1277
2455 Bennett Valley Rd, Ste B30, Santa Rosa, CA 95404-5663
Martin Bauman, Psychiatrist

Baumbacher Medical Practice 415.924.3840
Fax 415.925.1701
300 Tamal Plz, Corte Madera, CA 94925
Gordon Baumbacher, Psychiatrist

Beaumont Medical Practice 650.349.6121
Fax 650.349.7077
4100 S El Camino Real, San Mateo, CA 94403-5131
Graham Beaumont Md, Psychiatrist

Beebee Medical Practice 626.577.1305
Fax 626.795.3527
97 W Bellevue Dr, Pasadena, CA 91105-2501
Alexander Beebee, Psychiatrist

Behavior Therapy & Family 818.706.9913
Fax 805.491.8272
E-mail ....barry@behaveanalysis.com
32123 Lindero Canyon Rd, Westlake Village, CA 91361-5424
Barry Barmann, MD, Psychiatrist

Behavioral Medicine Group 661.323.7792
Fax 661.392.7770
3805 Union Ave, Bakersfield, CA 93305-2400
Marjorie Ta Voularis, MD, Psychiatrist

Bellman Medical Practice 949.706.0068
400 Newport Center Dr Ste 100, Newport Beach, CA 92660-7652
Jonathan Bellman Md, Psychiatrist

Benchmark Young Adult School 800.474.4848
Fax 909.748.6424
Web ....www.benchmarkyoungadultschool.com
E-mail ....jselby@benchmarkyas.com
20291 Mansard Ln, Huntington Beach, CA 92646-5135
Jamie Selby-Longnecker, Executive Director

Bender Medical Practice 310.208.7218
10921 Wilshire Blvd Ste 602, Los Angeles, CA 90024-4003
David Bender, Psychiatrist

Benson Medical Practice 323.938.6463
6214 Drexel Ave, Los Angeles, CA 90048-4702
Christina Benson, Psychiatrist

Berg Medical Practice 415.346.5633
Fax 415.567.3297
3022 Fillmore St, San Francisco, CA 94123-4010
Ulrich Berg Md, Psychiatrist

Berger Medical Practice 415.567.5778
2001 Union St Ste 300, San Francisco, CA 94123-4108
Charles Berger Md, Psychiatrist

Berglund Medical Practice 818.784.4706
4419 Van Nuys Blvd Ste 204, Sherman Oaks, CA 91403-5711
Robin Berglund, Psychiatrist

Berkeley Psychotherapy Medical 510.841.5949
2739 Parker St, Berkeley, CA 94704-3122
David Tower, Psychiatrist

Bernstein Medical Practice 415.474.7567
3529 Sacramento St, San Francisco, CA 94118
Mark Bernstein Md, Psychiatrist

Bert S Lebenson 415.386.6242
351 Buena Vista Ave E, San Francisco, CA 94117
Fredric Phillips, Psychiatrist

Bhakta Medical Practice 925.227.1967
5674 Stoneridge Dr Ste 217, Pleasanton, CA 94588-8532
Dipti Bhakta, Md, Psychiatrist

BHC Alhambra Hospital 626.286.1191
Web ....psysolutions.com
E-mail ....robert.vandesteeg@uhsinc.com
4619 North Rosemead Boulevard, Rosemead, CA 91770
Dr. Robert Vande Steeg, Accreditation Manager
Joint Commission accredited organization.

BHC Fremont Hospital 510.796.1100
Web ....www.fremonthospital.com
E-mail ....frances.fentzke@uhsinc.com
39001 Sundale Drive, Fremont, CA 94538
Ms. Frances Fentzke, Accreditation Manager
Joint Commission accredited organization.

BHC Heritage Oaks Hospital 916.489.3336
E-mail ....courtney.cook@uhsinc.com
4250 Auburn Boulevard, Sacramento, CA 95841
Ms. Courtney Cook, Accreditation Manager
Joint Commission accredited organization.

BHC Sierra Vista Hospital 916.288.0300
Web ....www.sierravistahospital.com
E-mail ....sterling.alexander@uhsinc.com
8001 Bruceville Road, Sacramento, CA 95823
Dr. Sterling Alexander, Accreditation Manager
Joint Commission accredited organization.

Bhushan Medical Practice 650.562.3635
Web ....www.workforcemed.com
1121 Jefferson Ave, Redwood City, CA 94063-1814
Bharat Bhushan, Psychiatrist

Biofeedback Svcs-Ofcs 650.342.2126
1777 Borel Pl, San Mateo, CA 94402
Sam Naifeh Md, Psychiatrist

Blanc Medical Practice 310.657.8393
Fax 310.454.4310
E-mail ....alan.blanc@verizon.net
116 N Robertson Blvd, Ste 801, Los Angeles, CA 90048-3111
Alan Blanc, Psychiatrist

Blanco Medical Practice 916.452.5909
2015 21St St, Sacramento, CA 95818-1752
Robert Blanco Md, Psychiatrist

Blasband Medical Practice 415.331.2536
E-mail ....rablasband@sbcglobal.net
2 Lincoln Dr, Sausalito, CA 94965-1610
Richard Blasband, Md, Psychiatrist

Blaustein Medical Practice 415.928.6100
Fax 415.913.6102
E-mail ....melblausteinmd@yahoo.com
1199 Bush St Ste 600, San Francisco, CA 94109-5977
Mel Blaustein Md, Psychiatrist

Blinder Medical Practice 415.453.8920
Web ....www.martinblindermd.com
130 Melville Ave, San Anselmo, CA 94960-2719
Martin Blinder, Md, Psychiatrist

Bloch Medical Practice 310.208.6800
924 Westwood Blvd Ste 625, Los Angeles, CA 90024-2927
Sheldon Bloch, MD, Psychiatrist

Blue Medical Practice 909.307.9663
Fax 909.307.8813
312 Brookside Ave, Redlands, CA 92373-4608
Kelly Blue Md, Psychiatrist

Blumenfeld Medical Practice 510.849.3932
Fax 510.849.3932
2110 6th St, Berkeley, CA 94710
Neal Blumenfeld, Psychiatrist

Boerlin Medical Practice 949.753.1143
Fax 800.471.4858
15615 Alton Pkwy Ste 220, Irvine, CA 92618-7305
Harold Boerlin, Psychiatrist

Bolter Medical Practice 619.440.4270
338 W Lexington Ave Ste 107, El Cajon, CA 92020-4443
Sidney Bolter Md, Psychiatrist

Booth Medical Practice 916.456.4662
Fax 916.457.7685
3015 O St, Sacramento, CA 95816-6516
John Booth Md, Psychiatrist

Borenstein Medical Practice 310.472.7386
151 N Canyon View Dr, Los Angeles, CA 90049-2721
Daniel Borenstein, Md, Psychiatrist

Borodkin Medical Practice 310.541.2542
927 Deep Valley Dr Ste 190, Palos Verdes Peninsula, CA 90274-3809
Robert Borodkin, Psychiatrist

Boswell Medical Practice 925.947.6640
Web ....www.medhyp.com
E-mail ....medhyp@earthlink.net
26 Fraser Dr, Walnut Creek, CA 94596-5426
Louis Boswell, MD, Psychiatrist

Boyle Medical Practice 916.564.0377
835 University Ave, Sacramento, CA 95825-6724
John Boyle, Psychiatrist

Boys Republic 909.628.1217
Fax 909.627.9222
Web ....www.boysrepublic.org
E-mail ....mscott@boysrepublic.org
3493 Grand Ave, Chino Hills, CA 91709-1481
Max Scott, Executive Director

Boys Republic Silverlake Residence 323.661.6905
Fax 323.661.3935
Web ....www.boysrepublic.org
E-mail ....dhosey@boysrepublic.org
1815 Redcliff St, Los Angeles, CA 90026-1133
Devon Hosey, Director

Bresnick Medical Practice 415.391.1144
250 Montgomery St Ste 920, San Francisco, CA 94104-3421
William Bresnick, Psychiatrist

Brewer Medical Practice 415.567.2082
2919 Sacramento St, # 2, San Francisco, CA 94115-2116
Emily Brewer Md, Psychiatrist

Brickman Medical Practice 310.471.1425
E-mail ....bbrickman@ucla.edu
9400 Brighton Way Ste 401, Beverly Hills, CA 90210-4711
Bernard Brickman, Psychiatrist

Brown Medical Practice 707.964.1820
Fax 707.961.2698
347 Cypress St, Fort Bragg, CA 95437
Michael Brown, Psychiatrist

Brown Medical Practice 818.990.2527
15760 Ventura Blvd Ste 1929, Encino, CA 91436-3032
Murray Brown, Psychiatrist

Bruns Medical Practice **858.535.0091**
9255 Towne Centre Dr Ste 370, San Diego,
CA 92121-3036
Bryan Bruns, Psychiatrist

Brust Medical Practice **310.832.7943**
Fax 310.514.8017
2403 S Moray Ave, San Pedro, CA 90732
James Brust, Psychiatrist

Burdi Medical Practice **949.219.0700**
Fax 909.478.9563
1303 Avocado Ave Ste 180, Newport Beach,
CA 92660-7803
Gianfranco Burdi, Psychiatrist

Caine Medical Practice **310.326.5102**
Fax 310.303.7906
3250 Lomita Blvd Ste 205, Torrance, CA 90505-5007
Edwin Caine, Psychiatrist

**CALM (Child Abuse Listening And
Mediation)** **805.965.2376**
Fax 805.963.6707
Web www.calm4kids.org
E-mail .... akokotovic@calm4kids.org
1236 Chapala St, Santa Barbara, CA 93101-3116
Cecilia Rodriguez, Executive Director

Canan Medical Practice **707.939.2771**
E-mail .... jancanan@vom.com
772 Ernest Dr, Sonoma, CA 95476-4614
Janine Canan, Psychiatrist

Canyon Professional Assoc **925.743.7887**
Fax 925.743.1937
E-mail .... questcamps@aol.com
2333 San Ramon Valley Blvd Ste 125, San Ramon,
CA 94583-1613
Brad Gould, Psychiatrist

Carder Medicial Practice **626.395.7677**
259 S Euclid Ave, Pasadena, CA 91101-2717
Scott Carder, Pyschiatrist

Carlin Medical Practice **714.835.0879**
616 Island View Dr, Seal Beach, CA 90740-5737
Jean Carlin, MD, Psychiatrist

Carol J Spar Inc **310.824.2957**
941 Westwood Blvd Ste 211, Los Angeles,
CA 90024-2940
Carol Spar, Psychiatrist

Carolyn Doty-Jonson **530.251.5889**
E-mail .... flying.horseshoe@frontiernet.net
702-310 Richmond Rd E, Susanville, CA 96130-5031
Carolyn Doty-Johnson, Director

Carroll Medical Practice **310.475.2990**
Fax 310.454.6063
E-mail .... robertcarroll@att.net
1314 Westwood Blvd, Ste 210, Los Angeles,
CA 90024
Robert Carroll, Psychiatrist

Carter Medical Practice **714.532.6699**
Fax 714.532.3999
741 E Chapman Ave, Orange, CA 92866-1620
Jennifer Carter, Accupunturist

Ceasar Medicial Practice **310.373.7989**
3655 Lomita Blvd Ste 412, Torrance, CA 90505-1931
Harold Ceasar, Psychiatrist

Century City Medical Plaza **310.553.1617**
Fax 310.472.9951
2080 Century Park E Ste 507, Los Angeles,
CA 90067-2008
Robert Elstad, MD, Psychiatrist

Cermak Medical Practice **415.381.4009**
E-mail .... tcermak@aol.com
239 Miller Ave Ste 1, Mill Valley, CA 94941-2866
Timmen Cermak, Psychiatrist

Chaffee Medical Practice **562.433.3220**
2280 University Dr, Newport Beach, CA 92660-3319
Jon Chaffee, Psychiatrist

Chan Medical Practice **415.982.1008**
4600 Fairfax Ave, Oakland, CA 94601-4808
Joe Chan, Psychiatrist

Chang Medical Practice **650.692.2520**
1838 El Camino Real Ste 205, Burlingame,
CA 94010-3110
Jacquelyn Chang, Psychiatrist

Chapman House, Inc. **866.288.9779**
Fax 714.288.6130
Web .... www.chapmanhouseinc.com
1412 East Chapman Avenue, Orange, CA 92866
CARF accredited programs available.

Chappell Medical Practice **510.451.6959**
400 29th St Ste 512, Oakland, CA 94609-3550
Ann Chappell, Psychiatrist

Charis Youth Ctr **530.477.9800**
Fax 530.477.9803
Web .... www.charisyouthcenter.org
E-mail .... office@charisyouthcenter.org
714 W Main St, Grass Valley, CA 95945-6410
Carol Fuller Powell, Executive Director

Charles Medical Practice **714.871.5411**
Fax 714.871.2401
1501 N Harbor Blvd, Ste 203, Fullerton,
CA 92835-3803
Marc Charles, Md, Psychiatrist

Charles P Sternberg Medical Practice **530.265.8264**
411 Coyote St, Nevada City, CA 95959-2230
Charles Sternberg, Psychiatrist

Chase Medical Practice **310.394.7020**
E-mail .... gary@doctorchase.com
11611 San Vicent Blvd, Los Angeles, CA 90049
Gary Chase, Psychiatrist

Childhelp USA **323.465.4016**
Fax 323.466.4432
Web .... www.childhelp.org
1345 N El Centro Ave, Los Angeles, CA 90028-8216
Sara Oæmeara, CEO

Children's Bureau Of Southern California **661.272.9996**
Fax 661.272.0438
E-mail .... jwhitaker@all4kids.org
1529 E Palmdale Blvd Ste 210, Palmdale,
CA 93550-2029
John Whittaker, Director

Children's Guidance Clinic **510.667.3000**
Fax 510.667.3005
Web .... www.acbhcs.org
E-mail .... mnelson@acbhcs.org
2500 Fairmont Dr, San Leandro, CA 94578
Madeline Nelson, Chief Of Services

Children's Home **209.466.0853**
Fax 209.466.1770
430 N Pilgrim Street, Stockton, CA 95205
Elizabeth Bridges, Interim Director

Chinen Medical Practice **415.564.3337**
Web .... www.ucsf.edu
E-mail .... allan.chinen@ucsf.edu
525 Irving St, San Francisco, CA 94122-2599
Allan Chinen, Psychiatrist

Cho Medical Practice **323.733.1111**
3130 W Olympic Blvd, Ste 370, Los Angeles,
CA 90006-2657
Man Chul Cho, Psychiatrist

Chung Medical Practice **949.548.3115**
Fax 949.495.2137
833 Dover Dr, Newport Beach, CA 92663
Bill White, Psychiatrist

Cipriano Medical Practice **818.707.9440**
5743 Corsa Ave Ste 117, Thousand Oaks,
CA 91362-6459
William Cipriano, Md, Psychiatrist

Clegg Medical Practice **831.689.5881**
9057B Soquel Dr, Aptos, CA 95003-4098
Denis Clegg, Psychiatrist

Clinic At Sierra Vista Behaviour Health **661.725.2788**
Fax 661.725.1957
Web .... www.clinicasierravista.org
828 High St, Ste C, Delano, CA 93215-2960
Gary Farber, Md, Psychiatrist

Clinica Sierra Vista **661.635.3050**
Web .... www.clinicasierravista.org
E-mail .... asches@clinicasierravista.org
1430 Truxtun Avenue Suite 400, Bakersfield,
CA 93302-1559
Ms. Susan Asche, Accreditation Manager
Joint Commission accredited organization.

College Hospital **562.924.9581**
Web .... collegehospitals.com
E-mail .... caraj@mail.collegehospitals.com
10802 College Place, Cerritos, CA 90703
Ms. Cara Jenson, Accreditation Manager
Joint Commission accredited organization.

College Hospital Costa Mesa **949.642.2734**
Web .... www.collegehospitals.com
E-mail .... cindyh@mail.collegehospitals.com
301 Victoria Street, Costa Mesa, CA 92627
Mrs. Cynthia Harlowe, Accreditation Manager
Joint Commission accredited organization.

Colman Medical Practice **415.332.5627**
Web .... www.arthurcolman.com
E-mail .... colman@drybridge.com
2003 Bridgeway, Sausalito, CA 94965-1736
Arthur Colman, Md, Psychiatrist

**Community Counseling for Individuals and Families, Inc. dba
Eating Disorder Center of California** **310.457.9958**
Fax 310.457.8442
Web .... www.edcca.com
520 South Sepulveda, Suite 208, Brentwood,
CA 90049
CARF accredited programs available.

Community Psychiatry & Assoc **510.657.9700**
Fax 510.657.7335
Web .... www.communitypsychiatry.com
E-mail .... aliyabakr@communitypsychiatry.com
39899 Balentine Dr Ste 210, Newark,
CA 94560-5361
Aliya Bakr, Psychiatrist

Community Recovery Resources **530.273.9541**
Fax 530.273.7740
Web .... www.corr.us
440 Henderson Street, Suite C, Grass Valley,
CA 95945
CARF accredited programs available.

**Community Svc Programs, Inc. Gang Prevention Intervention
Program** **949.250.0488**
Fax 949.251.1659
Web .... www.cspinc.org
E-mail .... gangprevention@cspinc.org
1821 E Dyer Rd Ste 200, Santa Ana, CA 92705-5700
Margo Carlson, Executive Director

Community Youth Ctr **415.775.2636**
Fax 415.775.1345
Web .... www.cycsf.org
E-mail .... sarahw@cycsf.org
1038 Post St, San Francisco, CA 94109
Sarah Wang, Executive Director

Concept 7 .... **909.483.2077**
Fax 909.483.2081
2990 Inland Empire Blvd Ste 100, Ontario,
CA 91764-4899
Melanya Harris, Supervisor

Constance M Taylor Phd **909.557.7755**
Fax 909.798.5188
222 E Olive Ave, Redlands, CA 92373-5268
Constance Taylor, Director

California

Cotlove Medical Practice 310.312.2500
Fax 310.966.1947
11600 Wilshire Blvd Ste 500, Los Angeles,
CA 90025-1788
Candace Cotlove, MD, Psychiatrist

Cotsen Medical Practice 310.659.8640
116 N Robertson Blvd Ste 908, Los Angeles,
CA 90048-3112
T Adam Cotsen, Psychiatrist

Cox Medical Practice 707.763.2801
111 Liberty St Ste 1, Petaluma, CA 94952-2946
Brent Cox, MD, Psychiatrist

Cox Medical Practice 858.531.5310
E-mail ....info@drcoxconsulting.com
3928 Georgia St, San Diego, CA 92103-5419
Barbara Cox, Md, Psycologist

CPC Fremont Hospital 510.796.1100
Fax 510.574.4888
E-mail ....bill.lightfoot@psysolutions.com
39001 Sundale Dr, Fremont, CA 94538-2005
Bill Lightfoot, Clinical Director

Creastwood Manor 510.651.1244
Fax 510.651.1543
Web ....www.thecrestwoodmanor.com
3400 Stevenson Blvd, Fremont, CA 94538
Lee Labrie, Administrator

Creative Alternatives 209.723.6030
Fax 209.723.6032
Web ....www.creative-alternatives.org
E-mail ....jbiddle@creative-alternatives.org
3195 M St Ste D, Merced, CA 95348-2406
Joy Biddle, Program Director, Residential Care Homes

Creative Alternatives, Inc 209.668.9361
Fax 209.668.0539
Web ....www.creative-alternatives.org
E-mail ....jbiddle@creative-alternatives.org
2855 Geer Rd Ste A, Turlock, CA 95382-1133
Joy Biddle, Executive Director

Crisis Resolution Ctr 916.652.2749
Fax 916.652.2748
E-mail ....bryland@kfh.org
3751 Magnolia St, Loomis, CA 95650
Bill Ryland, Director

Crisis Stabilization Unit 925.646.2800
Fax 925.370.5770
Web ....www.crisis-center.org
2500 Alhambra Ave, Unit 3-C, Martinez, CA 94553
Charles Saldanha, Director

**Crittenton Services for Children and
Families** 714.680.9000
Fax 714.680.8207
Web ....www.crittentonsocal.org
P.O. Box 9, Fullerton, CA 92836-0009
COA accredited organization.

Ctr For Human Svcs 209.550.4850
1025 15th St, Modesto, CA 95354-1101
Raphael Palma, Director

Ctr Point, Inc 415.492.4444
Fax 415.492.8844
E-mail ....cpinc@cpinc.org
135 Paul Dr, San Rafael, CA 94903-2023
Sushma Taylor, Chief Executive Director

Curtis Medical Practice 818.780.4409
Web ....www.tacurtismd.com
14531 Hamlin St Ste 100, Van Nuys, CA 91411-4195
Thomas Curtis, Psychiatrist

Danan Edmee Medical Practice 707.823.6074
120 Pleasant Hill Ave N, Sebastopol, CA 95472-3164
Marguerite Danan Edmee, Psychiatrist

Daniels Medical Practice 415.922.3991
2294 Geary Blvd, San Francisco, CA 94115-3416
Owen Daniels Md, Psychiatrist

David Medical Practice 415.776.3172
399 Laurel St, San Francisco, CA 94118-1907
George David Md, Psychiatrist

Davidson Medical Practice 310.274.9600
566 S San Vicente Blvd, Los Angeles, CA 90048-4650
P Waverly Davidson, Psychiatrist

De Francisco Medical Practice 949.752.1671
Web ....www.defrancisco.com
E-mail ....ddefran911@aol.com
1601 Dove St, Newport Beach, CA 92660
Don De Francisco, Psychiatrist

Deikman Medical Practice 415.381.0236
E-mail ....deikman@sbcglobal.net
10 Millwood St, Mill Valley, CA 94941
Arthur Deikman, Psychiatrist

Del Amo Hospital 310.530.1151
Web ....www.delamohospital.com
E-mail ....lisa.montes@uhsinc.com
23700 Camino Del Sol, Torrance, CA 90505
Ms. Lisa Montes, Accreditation Manager
Joint Commission accredited organization.

Denis Clegg Practice 800.590.7565
39560 Stevenson Pl, Fremont, CA 94539
Denis Clegg, Psychiatrist

Desert Mountain SELPA Children's Center 760.242.6336
Fax 760.946.0819
Web http://dmselpa.sbcss.k12.ca.us
E-mail ....jenae_tucker@sbcss.k12.ca.us
17800 Us Highway 18, Apple Valley, CA 92307-1221
Ronald Powell, Administrator

Di Bella Medical Practice 714.520.9759
2555 E Chapman Ave, Fullerton, CA 92831
Geoffrey Di Bella, MD, Psychiatrist

Di Di Hirsch Community Mental Health 310.855.0031
Fax 310.855.0138
Web ....www.didihirsch.org
E-mail ....jclegg@didihirsch.org
1233 S La Cienega Blvd, Los Angeles,
CA 90035-2520
Jocelyn Clegg, Director

Diamreyan Medical Practice 760.947.0070
Fax 760.947.3494
16279 Walnut St, Hesperia, CA 92345-3622
Rick, Administrative Assistant

Didi Hirsch Community Mental Health Ctr 310.677.7808
Fax 310.846.2139
Web ....www.didihirsch.org
111 N La Brea Ave Ste 700, Inglewood,
CA 90301-4651
Wayne Alexander, Coordinator

DIDI Hirsch Community Mental Health Ctr 310.390.6612
Fax 310.398.5690
Web ....www.didihirsch.org
E-mail ....kcurry@didihirsch.org
4760 Sepulveda Blvd, Culver City, CA 90230-4888
Kita Curry, Executive Director

Dillon Medical Practice 510.548.3404
Fax 510.525.5506
E-mail ....mdillonmd@yahoo.com
2702 Dana St, Berkeley, CA 94705-1136
Marcia Dillon, Psychiatrist

Dimon Medical Practice 415.346.1309
2116 Sutter St Ste 2, San Francisco, CA 94115-3191
Jim Dimon Md, Psychiatrist

Dinaburg Medical Practice 925.820.8224
913 San Ramon Valley Blvd, Danville, CA 94526
Daniel Dinaburg, MD, Psychiatrist

Discovery Practice Management, Inc 714.981.0700
Web ....www.centerfordiscovery.com
E-mail ....greg.corbin@centerfordiscovery.com
4281 Katella Ave, Suite 111, Los Alamitos, CA 90720
Mr. Gregory Corbin, Accreditation Manager
Joint Commission accredited organization.

Donoghue Medical Practice 831.464.1425
6233 Soquel Dr Ste A, Aptos, CA 95003-3184
Doris Donoghue, Psychiatrist

Dorman Medical Practice 310.276.1474
450 N Bedford Dr Ste 306, Beverly Hills,
CA 90210-4307
Daniel Dorman, Psychiatrist

Douglas Medical Practice 310.370.5055
4305 Torrance Blvd Ste 205, Torrance,
CA 90503-4416
Florence Douglas, Psychiatrist

Dr Rosas Clinic Inc 951.506.9112
Fax 951.506.9113
Web ....www.mcrbh.com
32605 Temecula Pkwy Ste 219, Temecula,
CA 92592-6840
Dr. Marylou Rosas, Psychiatrist

Durphy Medical Practice 415.459.3366
412 Red Hill Ave Ste 5, San Anselmo, CA 94960-2468
Michael Durphy, Psychiatrist

Earl P Petrus Inc 310.820.7197
Fax 818.882.6404
12304 Santa Monica Blvd, Los Angeles, CA 90025
Earl Petrus, Psychiatrist

Eduardo Escobar & Assoc 626.440.1911
595 E Colorado Blvd, Pasadena, CA 91101-2039
Rogelio Whyte, MD, Psychiatrist

Egerman Medical Practice 310.276.3943
610 N Oakhurst Dr, Beverly Hills, CA 90210-3531
Lynn Egerman, Psychiatrist

Eggen Medical Practice 209.523.7297
112 E Fairmont Ave, Modesto, CA 95354-0221
Gib Eggen, Psychiatrist

Ehrlich Medical Practice 707.829.1118
171 N High St, Sebastopol, CA 95472-3704
Neil Ehrlich, MD, Psychiatrist

El Nido Family Ctrs 818.830.3646
Fax 818.891.6547
Web ....www.elnidofamilycenters.org
E-mail ....herrera@elnidofamilycenters.org
10200 Sepulveda Blvd Ste 350, Mission Hills,
CA 91345-3318
Liz Herrera, Executive Director

Eldorado Community Service Center 661.254.6630
Fax 661.254.6644
Web ....www.eldoradocsc.org
26460 Summit Circle, Santa Clarita, CA 91350
COA accredited organization.

Elliott L Markoff Inc 310.550.1515
1345 Tower Grove Dr, Beverly Hills, CA 90210-2137
Elliott Markoff, Psychiatrist

Elliott Medical Practice 310.829.5540
3017 Santa Monica Blvd, Santa Monica,
CA 90404-2534
Edward Elliott, Psychiatrist

EMQ FamiliesFirst 408.379.3790
Fax 408.364.4013
Web ....http://www.emqff.org/
251 Llewellyn Avenue, Campbell, CA 95008
COA accredited organization.

Engel Medical Practice 650.327.7559
825 Oak Grove Ave, Menlo Park, CA 94025
Nancy Engel Md, Psychiatrist

Equine Connection 619.368.1306
Web ....www.cts.com
E-mail ....dsherman@cts.com
1145 Alpine Heights Rd, Alpine, CA 91901-2815
Diane Sherman, Director

Eroshevich Medical Practice 818.784.2011
16133 Ventura Blvd Ste 1220, Encino,
CA 91436-2416
Christine Eroshevich, Psychiatrist

Eroshevich Medical Practice 323.931.6623
    6010 Wilshire Blvd, Ste 305, Los Angeles,
    CA 90036-3625
    Christine Eroshevich, Psychiatrist

Ettari Medical Practice 858.552.8928
    Fax 858.552.8926
    9834 Genesee Ave Ste 427, La Jolla, CA 92037-1264
    Charles Ettari Md, Psychiatrist

Ettie Lee Youth & Family Svcs 626.960.4861
    Fax 626.337.2621
    Web ....www.ettielee.org
    E-mail ....info@ettielee.org
    5146 Maine Ave, Baldwin Park, CA 91706-1658
    Clayton L. Downey, Ma, President/CEO

Excell Youth Programs 209.667.0327
    Fax 209.634.6975
    2513 Youngstown Rd, Turlock, CA 95380-9749
    Rekell Barker, Administrator

Families First 559.248.8550
    Fax 559.248.8555
    Web ....www.familiesfirstinc.org
    E-mail ....ghernandez@familiesfirstinc.org
    7080 N Marks Ave Ste 104, Fresno, CA 93711-0288
    Gina Hernandez, Service Manager

Families First 707.399.4520
    Fax 707.423.2020
    Web ....www.emqff.org
    2420 Martin Rd Ste 200, Fairfield, CA 94534
    Nan Thibodeaux, Program Manager

Family Connections 530.626.5164
    Fax 530.626.0670
    Web ....www.familyconnected.org
    E-mail ....info@familyconnected.org
    2860 Smith Flat School Rd, Placerville,
    CA 95667-3973
    Wendy Wood, Director

Family Counseling Svcs Of West San Gabriel
Valley 626.308.1414
    Fax 626.308.1818
    121 S Santa Anita Ave, San Gabriel, CA 91776-1148
    Jennifer Foote, Director

Family Services 650.403.4300
    Fax 650.403.4303
    E-mail ....lwishard@fssm.org
    24 2nd Ave, San Mateo, CA 94401-3828
    Laurie Wishard, President

Fast Medical Practice 310.246.1040
    462 N Linden Dr Ste 345, Beverly Hills,
    CA 90212-4900
    Daniel Fast, Md, Psychiatrist

Feinstein Medical Practice 310.454.7212
    11601 Wilshire Blvd Ste 2490, Los Angeles,
    CA 90025-0407
    Beverly Feinstein, Psychiatrist

Feldman Medical Practice 510.848.2195
    1942 University Ave, Berkeley, CA 94704
    Jay Feldman, Psychiatrist

Feldman Medical Practice 530.756.7212
    231 C St, Davis, CA 95616-4521
    Jay Feldman, MD, Psychiatrist

Fernandez Medical Practice 661.845.5100
    Fax 661.845.5106
    E-mail ....fernandezd@clinicasierravista.org
    PO Box 1559, Bakersfield, CA 93302-1559
    Danilo Fernandez, Md, Psychiatrist

Ferrer Medical Practice 650.952.4364
    Fax 609.695.2779
    1475 Huntington Ave, South San Francisco,
    CA 94080
    Adelardo Ferrer Md, Psychiatrist

Ficarra Medical Practice 650.348.3989
    1035 Parrott Dr, Burlingame, CA 94010-7416
    Joseph Ficarra, Psychiatrist

Fisher Medical Practice 510.527.8824
    E-mail ....charlep@aol.com
    1491 Hopkins St, Berkeley, CA 94702-1244
    Charles Fisher, Psychiatrist

Fitzgerald Medical Practice 858.481.1900
    740 Lomas Santa Fe Dr Ste 210, Solana Beach,
    CA 92075-1441
    Michael Fitzgerald, Psychiatrist

Fleckles Medical Practice 415.927.1444
    Fax 415.927.1646
    240 Tamal Vista Blvd, Corte Madera, CA 94925
    Charles Fleckles, Psychiatrist

Flicker Medical Practice 310.278.4363
    450 N Bedford Dr, Beverly Hills, CA 90210-4324
    Marvin Flicker, Psychiatrist

Flynn Medical Practice 805.388.3663
    Fax 805.388.3663
    340 Rosewood Ave, Camarillo, CA 93010
    Daniel Flynn, Md, Psychiatrist

Fogelson Medical Practice 310.828.5015
    Fax 310.829.3877
    E-mail ....psychsecretary@earthlink.net
    2730 Wilshire Blvd Ste 325, Santa Monica,
    CA 90403-4747
    David Fogelson, Md, Psychiatrist

Foothill Family Svc 626.564.1613
    Fax 626.795.7080
    Web ....www.foothillfamily.org
    E-mail ....hwolf@foothillfamily.org
    118 S Oak Knoll Ave, Pasadena, CA 91101-2667
    Helen Morran-wolf, Executive Director

For The Child 562.427.7671
    Fax 562.595.4704
    E-mail ....info@forthechild.org
    4001 Long Beach Blvd, Long Beach, CA 90807-2616
    Michelle Winterstein, Executive Director

For The Child Cedar House, Inc 562.422.8472
    Fax 562.422.1102
    E-mail ....info@forthechild.org
    4565 California Ave, Long Beach, CA 90807-1507
    Michelle Winterstein, Executive Director

Ford Medical Practice 650.321.1225
    E-mail ....kathrynford@comcast.net
    1220 University Dr Ste 201, Menlo Park,
    CA 94025-4259
    Kathryn Ford, MD, Psychiatrist

Franklin Medical Practice 310.276.0809
    Fax 716.264.6057
    E-mail ....drfranklin@jeromefranklinmd.com
    416 N Bedford Dr Ste 403, Beverly Hills,
    CA 90210-4318
    Jerome Franklin, Psychiatrist

Frazier-Grubbs Medical Practice 916.609.4200
    Fax 916.609.4250
    1150 Eastern Ave, Sacramento, CA 95864-5308
    Demitrous Frazier, Psychiatrist

Fred Finch Youth Center 510.482.2244
    Fax 510.488.1960
    Web ....www.fredfinch.org
    3800 Coolidge Avenue, Oakland, CA 94602
    Barbara Bautista, Administrative Assistant to the CEO
    CARF accredited programs available.

Freeland Medical Practice 415.387.4843
    2166 Hayes St Ste 203, San Francisco,
    CA 94117-1033
    H Theodore Freeland Md, Psychiatrist

Freeman Medical Practice 415.378.6678
    Fax 415.888.3149
    E-mail ....michael.freeman@marincounty.net
    1036 Sir Francis Drake Blvd Ste 1, Greenbrae,
    CA 94904-1445
    Michael Freeman, Psychiatrist

Freinhar Medical Practice 310.373.5717
    24445 Hawthorne Blvd, Torrance, CA 90505-6562
    Jack Freinhar, Psychiatrist

Fremont Psychiatrist Practice 510.797.5800
    1999 Mowry Ave, Fremont, CA 94536
    George David Md, Psychiatrist

Friar Medical Practice 818.905.1566
    18034 Ventura Blvd, Encino, CA 91316-3516
    Christina Friar, Psychiatrist

Friedman Medical Practice 310.207.6268
    1990 S Bundy Dr Ste 345, Los Angeles,
    CA 90025-5254
    Raymond Friedman, Psychiatrist

Fujii Medical Practice 310.824.3512
    941 Westwood Blvd Ste 210, Los Angeles,
    CA 90024-2940
    June Fujii, Psychiatrist

Fukushima Medical Practice 310.826.9550
    11980 San Vicente Blvd, Los Angeles, CA 90049
    Susan Fukushima, Psychiatrist

Fuller Psychological And Family Svcs 626.584.5555
    Fax 626.584.5558
    E-mail ....rwilliamson@fuller.edu
    180 N Oakland Ave, Pasadena, CA 91101-1714
    Rick Williamson, Clinical Director

Gateways Hospital & Mental Health Ctr 323.644.2000
    Fax 323.666.1417
    Web ....www.gatewayshospital.org
    1891 Effie St, Los Angeles, CA 90026-1793
    Jeff Emery, Chief Finance Officer

Girls Pathways Counseling 510.357.5515
    Fax 510.357.5112
    Web ....www.girlsinc-alameda.org
    E-mail ....info@girlsinc-alameda.org
    13666 E 14th St, San Leandro, CA 94578-2538
    Linda Boessenecker, Executive Director

Girls Republic 626.357.0957
    Fax 626.357.4387
    E-mail ....girlsrepublic@verizon.net
    184 N Ivy Ave, Monrovia, CA 91016-2220
    Sheila Maxon, Director

Glendale Adventist Medical Center 818.409.8000
    Web ....www.glendaleadventist.com
    E-mail ....emeryvj@ah.org
    1509 Wilson Terrace, Glendale, CA 91206
    Ms. Valena Emery, Accreditation Manager
    Joint Commission accredited organization.

Good Samaritan Hospital 661.215.7500
    E-mail ....mlong@goodsamhospital.com
    901 Olive Drive, Bakersfield, CA 93308
    Mr. Maurice Long, Accreditation Manager
    Joint Commission accredited organization.

Good Samaritan Hospital 661.398.1800
    Fax 661.241.5587
    E-mail ....gstarr@lighthouseexpress.org
    5201 White Ln, Bakersfield, CA 93309-6200
    Gerald Starr, Administrator

Good Samaritan Hospital, LP 408.559.2011
    Web ....www.goodsamsanjose.com
    E-mail ....dana.stevens@hcahealthcare.com
    2425 Samaritan Drive, San Jose, CA 95124
    Mrs. Dana Stevens, Accreditation Manager
    Joint Commission accredited organization.

Grace Ctr 626.355.4545
    Fax 626.798.9043
    Web www.5acres.org
    E-mail ....grace/center@5acres.org
    PO Box 40250, Pasadena, CA 91114-7250
    Leticia Lepe, Program Director

California

Grizzly Youth Academy/ Challenge **805.782.6880**
Fax 805.782.6885
Web .... www.ngycp.org/ca
PO Box 3209, San Luis Obispo, CA 93403-3209
Nancy L. Baird, LC Director

Hathaway Sycamore's Children & Family Svcs **818.896.8366**
Fax 818.896.8392
12450 Van Nuys Blvd, Pacoima, CA 91331
Jana Shrock, Program Director

Hathaway-Sycamores Child and Family Services **626.395.7100**
Web .... hathaway-sycamores.org
E-mail .... davehickel@hathaway-sycamores.org
210 S DeLacey Ave, Ste 110, Pasadena, CA 91105
Dr. David Hickel, Accreditation Manager
Joint Commission accredited organization.

Hillsides Home For Children **323.254.2274**
Fax 323.257.1742
940 Avenue 64, Pasadena, CA 91105-2711
Joseph M Costa, Executive Director

Huckleberry Teen Health Program **415.258.4944**
Fax 415.258.4943
Web .... www.huckleberryyouth.org
E-mail .... jstevenson@huckleberryyouth.org
361 3rd St Ste G, San Rafael, CA 94901-3580
Jasmine Stevenson, Program Manager

Huckleberry Youth Programs Administrative Ofcs **415.668.2622**
Fax 415.668.0631
E-mail .... gkawamoto@huckleberryyouth.org
3310 Geary Blvd, San Francisco, CA 94118-3324
Bruce Fisher, Executive Director

Interagency Svcs For Families **951.358.4850**
Fax 951.358.4852
Web .... www.mentalhealth.co.riverside.ca.us
E-mail .... emccoy@co.riverside.ca.us
3840 Myers St 2nd Fl, Riverside, CA 92503-3505
Esther Mccoy, Supervisor

Irlen International Institute For Perceptual & Learning Development **562.496.2550**
Fax 562.429.8699
Web .... www.irlen.com
E-mail .... irleninstitute@irlen.com
5380 E Village Rd, Long Beach, CA 90808-1634
Helen L. Irlen, Ma, Director

John Muir Behavioral Health **925.674.4100**
Web .... www.johnmuirhealth.com
E-mail .... lora.dungo@johnmuirhealth.com
2740 Grant Street, Concord, CA 94520
Ms. Lora Dungo, Accreditation Manager
Joint Commission accredited organization.

Kids First Foundation **760.631.7550**
Fax 760.630.5248
Web .... www.kidsfirstfoundation.net
1025 Service Place, Suite 103, Vista, CA 92084
CARF accredited programs available.

La Cheim Schools **925.777.9550**
Fax 925.777.1090
E-mail .... sue@lacheim.org
1413 F St, Antioch, CA 94509-2220
Sue Herrera, Director

Langley Porter Psychiatric Hospital and Clinics - UCSF **415.476.7000**
Web .... www.ucsf.edu
E-mail .... andread@lppi.ucsf.edu
401 Parnassus Avenue, HOS 0984, San Francisco, CA 94143-0984
Ms. Andrea DeRochi, Accreditation Manager
Joint Commission accredited organization.

Lincoln Child Ctr **510.531.3111**
Fax 510.530.8083
Web .... www.lincolnchildcenter.org
E-mail .... ronitt@lincolnchildcenter.org
4368 Lincoln Ave, Oakland, CA 94602-2596
Ronit Tulloch, Executive Assistant

Loma Linda University Behavioral Medicine Center **909.558.9204**
Web .... www.llu.edu
E-mail .... dalberts@llu.edu
1710 Barton Road, Redlands, CA 92373
Ms. Diana Albertson, Accreditation Manager
Joint Commission accredited organization.

Long Beach Child/Adolescent Mental Health **562.599.9274**
Fax 562.218.4076
240 E 20th St, Long Beach, CA 90806-5412
Heather Jenson, Director

Los Angeles Job Corps Ctr **213.748.0133**
Fax 213.746.9211
E-mail .... brown.ruby@jobcorps.org
1106 S Broadway, Los Angeles, CA 90015-2206
Ruby Brown, Center Director

Mandometer, Inc. **888.306.2636**
Fax 858.451.0808
Web .... www.mandometer.com
11777 Bernardo Plaza Court, Suite 206, San Diego, CA 92128
CARF accredited programs available.

Margarita Mendez Children's Mental Health Ctr **323.832.9795**
Fax 323.832.9796
1000 Goodrich Blvd, Los Angeles, CA 90022-5103

Maryvale **626.280.6510**
Fax 626.288.8903
7600 Graves Ave, Rosemead, CA 91770-3453
Stede Guncher, Executive Director

Matrix Institute on Addictions **310.478.6006**
Fax 310.478.6117
Web .... www.matrixinstitute.org
1849 Sawtelle Boulevard, Suite 470, West Los Angeles, CA 90025
CARF accredited programs available.

McKinley Children's Center **909.599.1227**
Fax 909.592.3841
Web .... www.mckinleycc.org
762 West Cypress Street, San Dimas, CA 91773
COA accredited organization.

Medical Ctr-Fairmont Hospital **510.895.4200**
Web .... www.acmedctr.org
15400 Foothill Blvd, San Leandro, CA 94578
Andrea Bro, Public Information Officer

Mendocino Community Health Clinic, Inc. **707.468.1010**
Web .... www.mchcinc.org
E-mail .... jniemer@mchcinc.org
333 Laws Avenue, Ukiah, CA 95482
Dr. Jaisingh Niemer, Accreditation Manager
Joint Commission accredited organization.

MHS Btsr **760.758.1092**
550 W Vista Way Ste 407, Vista, CA 92083-5714
Michael Essex Md, Psychiatrist

Mission Hospital Regional Medical Center **949.365.2248**
Web www.mission4health.com
E-mail .... jan.brewer@stjoe.org
27700 Medical Center Road, Mission Viejo, CA 92691
Dr. Jan Brewer, Accreditation Manager
Joint Commission accredited organization.

Monte Nido Residential Center, Inc. **310.457.9958**
Web .... www.montenido.com
E-mail .... jeff@montenido.com
514 Live Oak Circle, Calabasas, CA 91302
Mr. Jeff Radant, Accreditation Manager
Joint Commission accredited organization.

Montecatini **760.436.2657**
Fax 760.436.2022
Web .... www.crchealth.com
E-mail .... dlullo@crchealth.com
2524 La Costa Ave, Carlsbad, CA 92009
Danielle Lullo, Director
CARF accredited programs available.

Muriel Wright Residential Ctr **408.227.8022**
Fax 408.972.4824
Web .... www.pro.sccgov.org
298 Bernal Rd, San Jose, CA 95119-1809
Rita Loncarich, Manager

Narcotic Addiction Treatment Agency, Inc. **818.768.5525**
Fax 818.768.5530
Web .... www.nataclinic.com
8741 Laurel Canyon Boulevard, Sun Valley, CA 91352
COA accredited organization.

Nawa Academy **530.359.2215**
Fax 530.359.2229
Web .... www.nawa-academy.com
E-mail .... info@nawa-academy.com
17351 Trinity Mountain Rd, French Gulch, CA 96033-9709
David Hull, Executive Director

New Connections **925.363.5000**
Fax 925.363.5075
Web .... www.newconnections.org
3024 Willow Pass Road, Concord, CA 94519-2588
CARF accredited programs available.

New Dawn Recovery Centers and New Dawn Eating Disorders Recovery Center **916.723.1319**
Fax 916.723.7015
Web .... www.newdawnrecovery.com
7447 Antelope Road, Suite 103, Citrus Heights, CA 95621
CARF accredited programs available.

North Valley School **707.523.2334**
Fax 707.523.0133
3164 Condo Ct, Santa Rosa, CA 95403-2557
Lorna Kenney, Principal

Northridge Hospital Medical Center **818.885.5321**
Web .... www.northridgehospital.com
E-mail .... holly.hessel-altman@chw.edu
18300 Roscoe Boulevard, Northridge, CA 91328
Mrs. Holly Hessel-Altman, Accreditation Manager
Joint Commission accredited organization.

Oak Grove Center for Education Treatment & the Arts **951.677.5599**
Web .... www.oakgrovecenter.org
E-mail .... tammyw@oakgrovecenter.org
24275 Jefferson Avenue, Murrieta, CA 92562
Mrs. Tamara Wilson, Accreditation Manager
Joint Commission accredited organization.

Optimist Boy's Home & Ranch, Inc. dba Optimist Youth Homes & Family Services **323.443.3175**
Fax 323.443.3221
Web .... www.oyhfs.org
P.O. Box 41-1076, Los Angeles, CA 90041-1076
COA accredited organization.

Optimist Youth Homes And Family Svcs **323.341.7810**
Fax 323.443.3264
Web .... www.oyhfs.org
E-mail .... silorlando@oyhfs.org
6957 N Figueroa St, Los Angeles, CA 90042-1245
Sylvio J. Orlando, Director

Orrin Allen Youth Rehab Facility **925.427.8660**
Fax 925.427.8663
E-mail .... bpelle@prob.cccounty.us
4491 Vixler Road, Byron, CA 94514
Bruce Pelle, Manager

Our Common Ground, Inc.....................**650.364.7988**
Fax..650.364.7987
Web..www.ocgworks.org
  631 Woodside Road, Redwood City, CA 94061
  CARF accredited programs available.

Pacifica Recovery Services..................**909.447.5081**
Web..www.pacificarecovery.com
E-mail..............................pacificarecovery@aol.com
  415 W. Foothill Blvd., Suite 210, Claremont,
  CA 91711
  Mr. James Rhoads, Accreditation Manager
  Joint Commission accredited organization.

Para Los Niños.................................**213.250.4800**
Fax..213.250.4900
Web..www.paralosninos.org
  500 Lucas Avenue, Los Angeles, CA 90017-2002
  COA accredited organization.

Penny Lane Ctrs..............................**818.892.3423**
Fax..818.892.3574
E-mail..............................imarkovits@pennylane.org
  15317 Rayen St, North Hills, CA 91343-5198
  Ive Markovits, Director

Phoenix Academy............................**818.686.3000**
Fax..818.899.6501
  11600 Eldridge Ave, Sylmar, CA 91342-6506
  Elizabeth Stanley Salazar, Director

Phoenix Houses of California..................**818.686.3015**
Fax..818.896.4859
Web..www.phoenixhouse.org
  11600 Eldridge Avenue, Lake View Terrace, CA 91342
  CARF accredited programs available.

Progress Ranch, Inc..........................**530.753.2566**
Fax..530.753.0284
Web..www.progressranch.org
E-mail..............................rkusama@sbcglobal.net
  2725 Loyola Dr, Davis, CA 95617
  Russell Kusama, Director

Quality Foster Care..........................**559.255.8519**
Fax..559.252.1121
  4928 E Clinton Way Ste 108, Fresno, CA 93727-1526
  May Johnson, Director

R House, Inc...................................**707.571.2215**
Web..www.rhouseinc.org
E-mail..............................carley.rhouse@gmail.com
  429 Speers Road, Santa Rosa, CA 95405
  Ms. Carley Moore, Accreditation Manager
  Joint Commission accredited organization.

Rader Programs...............................**800.841.1515**
Fax..818.880.3750
Web..www.raderprograms.com
E-mail..............................rader@raderprograms.com
  2130 N Ventura Rd, Oxnard, CA 93036
  Daniel Rozdial, Clinical Director

Rainbow Valley Foster Care, Inc...............**209.722.0202**
Fax..209.385.9921
  2841 G St, Merced, CA 95340-2133
  Mabel Patten, Executive Director

Rebekah Childrens Svcs.....................**408.846.2100**
Fax..408.846.4847
Web..www.rcskids.org
  290 I O O F Ave, Gilroy, CA 95020
  Lisa Apodata, Executive Director

Redlands Community Hospital...............**909.335.5500**
Web..www.redlandshospital.org
E-mail..............................cb5@redlandshospital.org
  350 Terracina Boulevard, Redlands, CA 92373
  Ms. Cathi Bell, Accreditation Manager
  Joint Commission accredited organization.

Reins Of Hope.................................**805.797.5539**
E-mail..............................jgiove@thacher.org
  260 Maple Ct, Ventura, CA 93003
  Julie Giove, Director

Reiss-Davis Child Study Ctr..................**310.836.1223**
Fax..310.839.4958
E-mail..............................incorvaiaj@harborfieldscsd.org
  3200 Motor Ave, Los Angeles, CA 90034-3710
  James Incorvaia, Director

Remi Vista.....................................**530.224.7160**
Fax..530.224.7168
Web..www.remivistainc.org
E-mail..............................jbeldon@remivistainc.org
  3191 Churn Creek Rd, Redding, CA 96002-2123
  Jared Beldon, Director

Remi Vista.....................................**530.245.5805**
Fax..530.245.0340
Web..www.remivista.com
E-mail..............................jtillery@remivistainc.org
  393 Park Marina Cir, Redding, CA 96001-0965
  John Tillery, Executive Director

Remi Vista.....................................**707.464.4349**
Fax..707.464.4572
Web..www.remivista.net
E-mail..............................dpittman@remivistainc.org
  370 9th St, Crescent City, CA 95531
  Doug Pittman, Director

Remi Vista.....................................**530.893.4784**
Fax..530.893.6144
Web..www.remivista.com
E-mail..............................mfasol@remivistainc.org
  2550 Floral Ave # 30, Chico, CA 95973-9143
  Beckey Winton, Director

River Oak Center for Children................**916.609.5100**
Web..www.riveroak.org
E-mail..............................lclothier@riveroak.org
  5030 El Camino Avenue, Carmichael, CA 95608
  Ms. Laurie Clothier, Accreditation Manager
  Joint Commission accredited organization.

Sacramento Children's Home................**916.452.3981**
Fax..916.454.5031
Web..www.kidshome.org
E-mail..............................roy.alexander@kidshome.org
  2750 Sutterville Rd, Sacramento, CA 95820-1093
  Roy Alexander, CEO

Salvation Army Door Of Hope Haven
Program...**858.279.1100**
Fax..858.279.1755
Web..www.sandiego.salvationarmy.org
E-mail..............................susan_rothman@usn.salvationarmy.org
  2799 Health Center Dr, San Diego, CA 92123
  Susan Rothman, Administrator

San Diego Ctr For Children..................**858.277.9550**
Fax..858.279.2763
Web..www.centerforchildren.org
  3002 Armstrong St, San Diego, CA 92111-5798
  Nancy Macnamara, Principal

San Gabriel/Pomona Regional Ctr...........**909.620.7722**
Fax..909.622.5123
Web..www.sgprc.org
E-mail..............................ecruz@sgprc.org
  761 Corporate Center Dr Ste A, Pomona,
  CA 91768-2648
  Ernie Cruz, Supervisor Of Community Resources

Seneca Family of Agencies..................**510.317.1444**
Web..www.senecacenter.org
E-mail..............................jennifer_cardenas@senecacenter.org
  2275 Arlington Drive, San Leandro, CA 94578
  Ms. Jennifer Cardenas, Accreditation Manager
  Joint Commission accredited organization.

Sharp Mesa Vista Hospital..................**858.278.4110**
Web..www.Sharp.com
E-mail..............................joan.eng@sharp.com
  7850 Vista Hill Avenue, San Diego, CA 92123
  Ms. Joan Eng, Accreditation Manager
  Joint Commission accredited organization.

Shoreline Treatment Center, Inc.............**562.434.6007**
Fax..562.856.2370
Web..www.shoreline-eatingdisorders.com
  191 Argonne, Suite 3, Long Beach, CA 90803
  CARF accredited programs available.

Sierra Vista Child And Family Svcs...........**209.523.4573**
Fax..209.550.5866
Web..www.svcfs.org
E-mail..............................jkindle@svcfs.org
  100 Poplar Ave, Modesto, CA 95354-1018
  Judy Kindle, Director

Sovereign Health of California...............**949.369.1300**
Web..www.sovcal.com
E-mail..............................r.lewis@sovhealth.com
  209 Avenida Fabricante, San Clemente, CA 92672
  Ms. Ruth Lewis, Accreditation Manager
  Joint Commission accredited organization.

Spectrum Ctr For Education And Behavioral
Development....................................**510.741.5440**
Fax..510.741.2775
Web..www.spectrumschools.com
E-mail..............................hr@esa-education.com
  16360 San Pablo Ave, San Pablo, CA 94806-1242
  Chris Holmes, Executive Director

St. Anne's......................................**213.381.2931**
Fax..213.381.7804
Web..www.stannes.org
E-mail..............................twalker@stannes.org
  155 N Occidental Blvd, Los Angeles, CA 90026-4641
  Tony Walker, CEO

St. Helena Hospital Center for Behavioral
Health...**707.648.2200**
Web..www.sthelenahospital.org
E-mail..............................bergermb@ah.org
  525 Oregon Street, Vallejo, CA 94590
  Ms. Mary Bergerson, Accreditation Manager
  Joint Commission accredited organization.

St. Mary's Medical Center...................**415.668.1000**
Web..www.stmarysmedicalcenter.org
E-mail..............................heather.otanez@chw.edu
  450 Stanyan Street, San Francisco, CA 94117
  Ms. Heather Otanez, Accreditation Manager
  Joint Commission accredited organization.

Star View Adolescent Ctr....................**310.373.4556**
Fax..310.373.2826
  4025 W 226th St, Torrance, CA 90505-2340
  Natalie Spiteri, Administrator

Star View Community Svcs..................**562.427.6818**
Fax..562.427.3367
Web..www.starsinc.com
  100 E Wardlow Rd, Long Beach, CA 90807
  Christine Graham, Administrator

Star View Community Svcs..................**310.787.1500**
Fax..310.787.9713
E-mail..............................shoogerberuge@starsinc.com
  370 Crenshaw Blvd Ste E100, Torrance,
  CA 90503-1728
  Steve Hoogerbeugge, Administrator

Star View Community Svcs..................**323.999.2404**
Fax..323.999.2414
Web..www.starsinc.com
E-mail..............................smusetti@starsinc.com
  5420 N Figueroa St, Los Angeles, CA 90042-4118
  Susan Musetti, Director

Starlight Community Services...............**408.284.9000**
Fax..408.284.9048
  455 Silicon Valley Blvd, San Jose, CA 95138-1858
  Michelle Mcdonald, Director

California

Stars Behavioral Health 510.635.9705
Fax 510.635.9715
Web .... www.starsgroup.org
E-mail .... info@starsgroup.org
   7700 Edgewater Dr Ste 658, Oakland,
   CA 94621-3022
   Mary Jane Gross, President

Stars Behavioral Health 510.352.6200
Fax 510.352.3120
Web .... www.starsinc.com
E-mail .... sansimmons@starsinc.com
   545 Estudillo Ave, San Leandro, CA 94577-4611
   Sandy Simmons, Administrator

Stars Behavioral Health Group 310.221.6336
Fax 310.221.6350
E-mail .... kmillet@starsinc.com
   1501 Hughes Way Ste 150, Long Beach,
   CA 90810-1878
   Kathy Millet, Director

**Stewart & Lynda Resnick Neuropsychiatric Hospital at
UCLA** 310.267.9092
Web .... www.uclahealth.org
E-mail .... cdavidson@mednet.ucla.edu
   150 Medical Plaza 4230C , MC 746330, Los Angeles,
   CA 90095
   Ms. Colleen Davidson, Accreditation Manager
   Joint Commission accredited organization.

Strategies for Change 916.473.5764
Fax 916.473.5766
Web www.strategies4change.org
   4441 Auburn Boulevard, Suite E, Sacramento,
   CA 95841
   CARF accredited programs available.

**SunBridge Harbor View Rehabilitation
Center** 562.591.8701
Fax 562.591.0235
Web .... www.hvgrouphomeinc.org
   490 West 14th Street, Long Beach, CA 90813
   Natalie Spiteri, Director
   CARF accredited programs available.

Sunny Hills Children's Garden Svcs 415.457.3200
Fax 415.456.4679
Web .... www.sunnyhillsservices.org
E-mail .... jcosta@shcg.org
   300 Sunnyhills Dr, San Anselmo, CA 94960-1995
   Mary Denzon, CEO

Sunset Mental Health Svcs 415.753.7255
Fax 415.753.0164
Web .... www.sfdph.org
E-mail .... signey.lam@sfdph.org
   1990 41St Ave, San Francisco, CA 94116-1101
   Signey Lam, Program Director

Sutter East Bay Hospitals 510.204.2606
Web .... www.altabatessummit.org
E-mail .... tungd@sutterhealth.org
   2450 Ashby Avenue, Berkeley, CA 94705
   Ms. Debbie Tung, Accreditation Manager
   Joint Commission accredited organization.

Sutter Medical Center, Sacramento 916.454.2222
Web .... www.suttermedicalcenter.org
E-mail .... frainj@sutterhealth.org
   2801 L Street, Sacramento, CA 95816
   Ms. Janet Frain, Accreditation Manager
   Joint Commission accredited organization.

Sweeney Youth Homes 805.563.0266
Fax 805.563.0507
E-mail .... syhomes3@yahoo.com
   100 N Hope Ave, Ste 14, Santa Barbara,
   CA 93110-2630
   Sharon Sweeney, President

Tarzana Treatment Centers, Inc. 818.654.3815
Web .... www.tarzanatc.org
E-mail .... kbachrach@tarzanatc.org
   18646 Oxnard Street, Tarzana, CA 91356
   Dr. Ken Bachrach, Accreditation Manager
   Joint Commission accredited organization.

Teen Triumph 209.477.9177
Fax 209.477.4667
E-mail .... martistk@aol.com
   5361 N Pershing Ave Ste H, Stockton,
   CA 95207-3839
   Marti Fredricks, Director

**TESSIE CLEVELAND COMMUNITY SERVICES
CORP.** 323.586.7333
Web .... WWW.TCCSC.ORG
E-mail .... sylviar@tccsc.org
   8019 S COMPTON AVENUE, Los Angeles, CA 90001
   Ms. Sylvia Ramirez, Accreditation Manager
   Joint Commission accredited organization.

**Tessie Cleveland Community Services
Corporation** 323.586.7333
Fax 323.588.5622
Web .... www.tccsc.org
   8019 South Compton Avenue, Los Angeles,
   CA 90001
   COA accredited organization.

The Almansor Ctr 323.257.3006
Fax 323.341.5642
Web .... www.redesignlearning.org
E-mail .... ahernandez@almansor.org
   1955 Fremont Ave, South Pasadena, CA 91030-4596
   Albert Hernandez, Director

**The Bella Vita, A Beautiful Life Psychology Group,
Inc.** 323.255.0400
Fax 323.255.0177
Web .... www.thebellavita.com
E-mail .... drpitts@thebellavita.com
   766 Colorado Boulevard, Los Angeles, CA 90041
   Patricia Pitts, Clinical Director
   CARF accredited programs available.

The Help Group 818.781.0360
Fax 818.779.5191
Web .... www.thehelpgroup.org
   13130 Burbank Boulevard, Sherman Oaks, CA 91401
   CARF accredited programs available.

**Thunder Road Chemical Dependency Recovery Hospital and
Group Home** 510.653.5040
Fax 510.653.6475
Web .... www.thunderroadtreatment.org
   390 40th Street, Oakland, CA 94609
   CARF accredited programs available.

**Touchstones: A Program Of Social Model Recovery
Systems** 714.639.5542
Fax 714.639.5037
Web .... www.socialmodel.com
E-mail .... mikes@socialmodel.com
   525 N Parker St, Orange, CA 92868-1323
   Patti Ochoa, Program Director

Transitions Mental Health 805.540.6500
Fax 805.540.6501
Web .... www.t-mha.org
E-mail .... info@t-mha.org
   784 High St, San Luis Obispo, CA 93401-5039
   Jill Bolster-white, Director

Tri-City Child Outpatient 510.795.2434
Fax 510.793.3972
   39155 Liberty St, Ste G710, Fremont, CA 94538
   Beth Armstrong, Clinical Supervisor

Trinity Children And Family Svcs 619.585.1508
Fax 619.585.1591
Web .... www.trinityys.org
E-mail .... sddirector@trinityys.org
   835 3rd Ave Ste E, Chula Vista, CA 91911
   Grace Montgomery, Director

Trinity Youth Svcs 909.825.5588
Fax 909.824.2586
Web .... www.trinityys.org
E-mail .... teresav@trinityys.org
   1470 E Cooley Dr, Colton, CA 92324-3933
   Gilbert Quinbar, Executive Director Of Residential Services

Twin Town Corp. 562.594.8844
Web .... www.twintowntreatmentcenters.com
E-mail .... dlisonbee@twintowntreatmentcenters.com
   4388 E. Katella Ave, Los Alamitos, CA 90720
   Mr. David Lisonbee, Accreditation Manager
   Joint Commission accredited organization.

UCLA Neuropsychiatric Hospital 310.825.0511
Fax 310.825.0323
E-mail .... pwhybrow@mednet.ucla.edu
   10833 Le Conte Ave, Los Angeles, CA 90095-1759
   Peter Whybrow, Md, Professor/executive Chairman

**UCSD, Child And Adolescent Psychiatry
Svc** 619.229.3700
Fax 619.583.7383
Web .... www.ucsd.edu
   6535 Alvarado Rd, San Diego, CA 92120
   Saul Levine, Md, Executive Director

Valley Star Children And Family Svcs 909.388.2222
Fax 909.388.2220
Web .... www.starsgroup.org
E-mail .... steventhorpe@starsinc.com
   1585 S D St Ste 101, San Bernardino,
   CA 92408-3235
   Steven Thorpe, Administrator

Valley Teen Ranch 559.437.1144
Fax 559.438.5004
Web .... www.valleyteenranch.org
E-mail .... connie.clendenan@valleyteenranch.org
   2610 W Shaw Ln Ste 105, Fresno, CA 93711-2775
   Connie Clendenan, CEO

**VIA Rehabilitation Svcs / First Step Early Intervention
Program** 408.243.7861
Fax 408.243.0452
Web .... www.viaservices.org
E-mail .... info@viaservices.org
   2851 Park Ave, Santa Clara, CA 95050-6006
   Jacqui Chapmen, Director

Victor Family Of Programs 760.243.5417
Fax 760.245.5896
Web .... www.victor.org
   14360 Saint Andrews Dr Ste 11, Victorville, CA 92395
   Debbie Reno-smith, Director

Victor Family Of Programs 530.893.0758
Fax 530.893.0502
Web .... www.victor.org
   2561 California Park Drive, Chico, CA 95928
   Dr. Douglas Scott, Chief Executive Officer

**Victor Family Of Programs- Family Intervention And
Community Support** 530.671.3427
Fax 530.671.3877
Web .... www.victor.org
   103 D St, Ste A, Marysville, CA 95901
   Doug Scott, CEO

Victor Treatment Centers, Inc. 530.893.0758
Fax 530.230.1286
Web .... www.victor.org
   P.O. Box 5361, Chico, CA 95927
   COA accredited organization.

Vista Del Mar Child and Family Services 310.836.1223
Web .... www.vistadelmar.org
E-mail .... dlocken@vistadelmar.org
   3200 Motor Avenue, Los Angeles, CA 90034
   Mr. David Locken, Accreditation Manager
   Joint Commission accredited organization.

West Oakland Health Council 510.835.9610
Web ....www.wohc.org
E-mail ....robertc@wohc.org
700 Adeline Street, Oakland, CA 94607
Dr. Robert Cooper, Accreditation Manager
Joint Commission accredited organization.

WestCare California, Inc. 559.251.4800
Fax 559.453.6969
Web ....westcare.com/slcalifornia.jsp
4944 East Clinton Way, Suite 101, Fresno, CA 93727
CARF accredited programs available.

Western Medical Center Anaheim 714.533.6220
Web ....www.westernmedanaheim.com
E-mail ....shela.kaneshiro@ihhioc.com
1025 S. Anaheim Boulevard, Anaheim,
CA 92805-0880
Mrs. Shela Kaneshiro, Accreditation Manager
Joint Commission accredited organization.

Western Pacific Med Corp 818.956.3737
Fax 818.543.6767
Web ....www.westpacmed.com
4632 San Fernando Road, Glendale, CA 91204
COA accredited organization.

Western Youth Svcs 714.871.5646
Fax 714.817.7368
E-mail ....lorry.leigh@westernyouthservices.org
505 N Euclid St Ste 300, Anaheim, CA 92801-5514
Lorry Leigh, Executive Director

Westside Community Mental Health Ctr 415.431.9000
Fax 415.431.1813
Web ....www.westside-health.org
E-mail ....aboles@westside-health.org
1153 Oak St, San Francisco, CA 94117-2216
Mary Ann Jones, Executive Director

William F. James Boys Ranch 408.201.7600
Fax 408.779.4393
E-mail ....nick.brichard@pro.sccgov.org
19050 Malaguerra Ave, Morgan Hill, CA 95037
Nick Brichard, Probation Manager

CHILDREN'S HOSPITAL

Anaheim General Hospital 714.947.5800
3350 West Ball Rd, Anaheim, CA 92804
Michael Choo, Chief Executive Officer

Antelope Valley Hospital 661.949.5000
Web ....www.avhospital.org
1600 West Avenue J, Lancaster, CA 93534
Edward Mirzabegian, Chief Executive Officer

Bakersfield Memorial Hospital 661.327.1792
420 34th St, Bakersfield, CA 93301
Terri Church, Nursing Director

Barton Memorial Hospital 530.541.3420
2170 South Ave, South Lake Tahoe, CA 96150
John Williams, Chief Executive Officer

Bellflower Medical Center 562.925.8355
9542 East Artesia Blvd, Bellflower, CA 90706
Michael Choo, Chief Executive Officer

Beverly Hospital 323.726.1222
309 West Beverly Blvd, Montebello, CA 90640
Gary Kiff, Chief Executive Officer

California Pacific Medical Center 415.600.6000
2333 Buchanan St, San Francisco, CA 94115
Warren Browner, Chief Executive Officer

Cedars Sinai Medical Center 310.423.5000
8700 Beverly Blvd, Los Angeles, CA 90048
Thomas Priselac, Chief Executive Officer

Childrens Hospital 714.997.3000
455 South Main St, Orange, CA 92868
Kimberly Cripe, Chief Executive Officer

Childrens Hospital and Research Center 510.428.3000
747 52nd St, Oakland, CA 94609
Bertram Lubin, Chief Executive Officer

Childrens Hospital Central California 559.353.3000
9300 Valley Childrens Place, Madera, CA 93636
Golden Alexander, Chief Executive Officer

Childrens Hospital Los Angeles 323.660.2450
4650 Sunset Blvd, Los Angeles, CA 90027
Richard Cordova, Chief Executive Officer

City of Hope 626.256.4673
1500 East Duarte Rd, Duarte, CA 91010
Michael Friedman, Chief Executive Officer

Coastal Communities Hospital 714.754.5454
2701 South Bristol St, Santa Ana, CA 92704
Crait Meyer, Chief Executive Officer

Community Hospital Monterey Peninsula 831.624.5311
E-mail ....mary.parker@charles.org
23625 Holman Hwy, Monterey, CA 93940
Mary Parker, Director

Community Hospital of San Bernardino 909.887.6333
1805 Medical Center Dr, San Bernardino, CA 92411
Diane Nitta, Nursing Director

Community Memorial Hospital 805.652.5011
147 North Brent St, Ventura, CA 93003
Gary Wilde, Chief Executive Officer

Community Regional Medical Center 559.459.6000
2823 Fresno St, Fresno, CA 93721

Contra Costa Regional Medical Center 925.370.5000
2500 Alhambra Ave, Martinez, CA 94553
Larry Parson, Director

Corona Regional Medical Center 951.737.4343
800 South Main St, Corona, CA 92882
Kevin Metcalfe, Chief Executive Officer

Dameron Hospital 209.944.5550
525 West Acacia St, Stockton, CA 95203
Dr. Christopher Arismendi, Chief Executive Officer

Delano Regional Medical Center 661.725.4800
1401 Garces Highway, Delano, CA 93215
Kathy Wright, Administrator

Desert Regional Medical Center 760.323.6511
1150 North Indian Canyon Dr, Palm Springs,
CA 92262
Henry Hudson, Director

Doctors Medical Center 209.578.1211
1441 Florida Ave, Modesto, CA 95350
Dennis Litos, Chief Executive Officer

Dominican Hospital 831.462.7700
1555 Soquel Dr, Santa Cruz, CA 95065
Juana Castillo, Director of Nursing

East Los Angeles Doctors Hospital 323.268.5514
4060 East Whittier Blvd, Los Angeles, CA 90023
Araceli Lonergan, Chief Executive Officer

Eisenhower Medical Center 760.340.3911
39000 Bob Hope Dr, Rancho Mirage, CA 92270
Aubrey Serfling, President

El Camino Hospital 650.940.7000
2500 Grant Rd, Mountain View, CA 94040

El Centro Regional Medical Center 760.339.7100
1415 Ross Ave, El Centro, CA 92243
David Green, Chief Executive Officer

Emanuel Medical Center 209.667.4200
825 Delbon Ave, Turlock, CA 95382
John Sigsbury, Chief Executive Officer

Enloe Medical Center 530.332.7300
1531 Esplanade, Chico, CA 95926
Michael Wilterhod, Chief Executive Officer

Fairchild Medical Center 530.842.4121
444 Bruce St, Yreka, CA 96097
Peggy Amaral, Manager

Foothill Presbyterian Hospital 626.963.8411
250 South Grand Ave, Glendora, CA 91741
Diana Cenner, Nursing Officer

Fountain Valley Regional Hospital 714.966.7200
17100 Euclid St, Fountain Valley, CA 92708
Debbie Walsh, Chief Executive Officer

French Hospital Medical Center 805.543.5353
Web ....www.frenchemedicalcenter.org
1911 Johnson Ave, San Luis Obispo, CA 93401
Alan Iftiniuk, Chief Executive Officer

Good Samaritan Hospital 408.559.2011
2425 Samaritan Dr, San Jose, CA 95124

Greater El Monte Community Hospital 626.579.7777
1701 Santa Anita Ave, South El Monte, CA 91733
Dale Gascho, Chief Executive Officer

Henry Mayo Newhall Memorial Hospital 661.253.8000
23845 McBean Pkwy, Valencia, CA 91355
Roger Seaver, Chief Executive Officer

Hi Desert Medical Center 760.366.3711
6601 White Feather Rd, Joshua Tree, CA 92252
Chad Wick, Chief Executive Officer

Hoag Memorial Hospital Presbyterian 949.764.4624
One Hoag Dr, Newport Beach, CA 92663
Richard Asable, Director

Hollywood Presbyterian Medical Center 323.913.4800
1300 North Vermont Ave, Los Angeles, CA 90027
Michael Bernstein, Chief Executive Officer

Huntington Memorial Hospital 626.397.5000
E-mail ....stephen.ralph@huntingtonhospital.com
100 West California Blvd, Pasadena, CA 91105
Stephen Ralph, Chief Executive Officer

John F Kennedy Memorial Hospital 760.347.6191
47111 Monroe St, Indio, CA 92201
Dan Bowers, Chief Executive Officer

John Muir Medical Center 925.939.3000
1601 Ygnacio Valley Rd, Walnut Creek, CA 94598
Elizabeth Stallings, Director

Kaiser Foundation Hospital 909.427.5000
9961 Sierra Ave, Fontana, CA 92335

Kaiser Foundation Hospital 650.299.2000
1150 Veterans Blvd, Redwood City, CA 94063

Kaiser Foundation Hospital 714.279.4000
441 North Lakeview Ave, Anaheim, CA 92807
Julie Miller-Phipps, Chief Executive Officer

Kaiser Foundation Hospital 818.719.2000
5601 DeSoto Ave, Woodland Hills, CA 91365

Kaiser Foundation Hospital 951.353.2000
10800 Magnolia Ave, Riverside, CA 92505
Vita Willett, Director

Kaiser Foundation Hospital 562.657.9000
9333 Imperial Hwy, Downey, CA 90242
Jim Branchick, Nursing Director

Kaiser Foundation Hospital 408.236.6400
700 Lawrence Expressway, Santa Clara, CA 95051

Kaiser Foundation Hospital Sunset 323.783.4011
4867 Sunset Blvd, Los Angeles, CA 90027
Mark Costa, Chief Executive Officer

**Kaiser Permanente Sacramento Med
Center** 916.973.5000
2025 Morse Ave, Sacramento, CA 95825
Charlene Taylor, Chief Nursing Officer

Kaiser Permanente San Diego Med Center 619.528.5000
4647 Zion Ave, San Diego, CA 92120
George Harrison, Chief Executive Officer

Kaiser Permanente San Francisco 415.833.2000
2200 O Farrell St, San Francisco, CA 94115

Kaiser Permanente West Los Angeles 323.857.2201
6041 Cadillac Ave, Los Angeles, CA 90034
Norair Jemian, Chief Executive Officer

Kaweah Delta Medical Center 559.624.2000
400 West Mineral King Ave, Visalia, CA 93291
Lindsay Mann, Chief Executive Officer

Loma Linda University Medical Center 909.558.4000
11234 Anderson St, Loma Linda, CA 92354
Fike Ruthita, Chief Executive Officer

Los Robles Hospital & Medical Center 805.497.2727
215 W Janss Rd, Thousand Oaks, CA 91360
Greg Ingle, President

Lucile Packard Childrens Hospital 650.497.8000
725 Welch Rd, Palo Alto, CA 94304

Mammoth Hospital 760.934.3311
85 Sierra Park Rd, Mammoth Lakes, CA 93546

Marian Medical Center 805.739.3000
1400 East Church St, Santa Maria, CA 93454
Charles Cova, Administrator

Medical Center 805.652.6000
3291 Loma Vista Rd, Ventura, CA 93003

Medical Center 909.580.1000
400 North Pepper Ave, Colton, CA 92324
Patrick Petre, Chief Executive Officer

Memorial Medical Center 209.526.4500
1700 Coffee Rd, Modesto, CA 95355
James Conforti, Chief Executive Officer

Mercy San Juan Medical Center 916.537.5000
6501 Coyle Ave, Carmichael, CA 95608
Brian Ivie, President

Methodist Hospital of Southern CA 626.898.8000
300 West Huntington Dr, Arcadia, CA 91007

Miller Childrens Hospital 562.933.5437
2801 Atlantic Ave, Long Beach, CA 90806
barry

Mills Peninsula Health Services 650.696.5400
1501 Trousdale Dr, Burlingame, CA 94010
Robert Mullen, Chief Executive Officer

Monterey Park Hospital 626.570.9000
900 South Atlantic Blvd, Monterey Park, CA 91754
Phillip Cohen, Chief Executive Officer

Natividad Medical Center 831.755.4111
1441 Constitution Blvd, Salinas, CA 93906
Harry Werf, Chief Executive Officer

Naval Medical Centers San Diego 619.532.6400
34800 Bob Wilson Dr, San Diego, CA 92134
Admiral Faison, Chief Officer

Northern Inyo Hospital 760.873.5811
150 Pioneer Ln, Bishop, CA 93514
John Halsen, Administrator

O Connor Hospital 408.947.2500
2105 Forest Ave, San Jose, CA 95128
Jim Dover, Chief Executive Officer

Oak Valley Hospital District 209.847.3011
350 South Oak St, Oakdale, CA 95361
John Friel, Chief Executive Officer

Pacifica Hospital of the Valley 818.767.3310
9449 San Fernando Rd, Sun Valley, CA 91352
A Moussa, Chief Executive Officer

Palomar Medical Center 760.739.3000
555 East Valley Pkwy, Escondido, CA 92025
Michael Covert, President

Paradise Valley Hospital 619.470.4321
2400 East Fourth St, National City, CA 91950
Louis Leon, Chief Executive Officer

Parkview Community Hospital Medical Ctr 951.688.2211
3865 Jackson St, Riverside, CA 92503
Doug Drumwoight, Chief Executive Officer

Pomona Valley Hospital Medical Center 909.865.9500
1798 North Garey Ave, Pomona, CA 91767
Richard Yochum, Chief Executive Officer

Presbyterian Intercommunity Hospital 562.698.0811
12401 Washington Blvd, Whittier, CA 90602
James West, Chief Executive Officer

Providence Little Company of Mary 310.540.7676
4101 Torrance Blvd, Torrance, CA 90503
Elizabeth Dunn, Chief Executive Officer

Providence Little Company of Mary 310.832.3311
1300 West Seventh St, San Pedro, CA 90732
Nancy Carlson, Chief Executive Officer

Providence Tarzana Medical Center 818.881.0800
18321 Clark St, Tarzana, CA 91356
Dale Surowitz, President

Rady Childrens Hospital 858.488.2120
3020 Childrens Way, San Diego, CA 92123

Regional Medical Center of San Jose 408.259.5000
225 North Jackson Ave, San Jose, CA 95116
Mike Johnson, Chief Executive Officer

Regional Medical Ctr 951.486.4000
26520 Cactus Ave, Moreno, CA 92555

Ridgecrest Regional Hospital 760.446.3551
E-mail ....jim.suever@rrh.org
1081 North China Lake Blvd, Ridgecrest, CA 93555
Jim Suever, Chief Executive Officer

Riverside Community Hospital 951.788.3000
4445 Magnolia Ave, Riverside, CA 92501
Patrick Brilliant, Chief Executive Officer

Ronald Reagan UCLA Medical Center 310.825.9111
757 Westwood Plz, Los Angeles, CA 90095
David Feinberg, Chief Executive Officer

Salinas Valley Memorial Hospital 831.757.4333
450 East Romie Ln, Salinas, CA 93901
Lwell Johnson, Chief Executive Officer

San Antonio Community Hospital 909.985.2811
999 San Bernardino Rd, Upland, CA 91786
Harris Koenig, Chief Executive Officer

San Francisco General Hospital 415.206.8000
1001 Potrero Ave, San Francisco, CA 94110

San Joanquin General Hospital 209.468.6000
500 West Hospital Rd, French Camp, CA 95231
Kem Cohen, Chief Executive Officer

San Joaquin Community Hospital 661.395.3000
2615 Chester Ave, Bakersfield, CA 93301
Jona Williams, Secretary

San Mateo Medical Center 650.573.2222
222 West 39th Ave, San Mateo, CA 94403
Susan Ehrlich, Chief Executive Officer

Santa Barbara Cottage Hospital 805.682.7111
Pueblo at Bath Streets, Santa Barbara, CA 93105
Ron Werft, Chief Executive Officer

Santa Clara Valley Medical Center 408.885.5000
751 South Bascom Ave, San Jose, CA 95128

Santa Monica UCLA Medical Center 310.319.4000
1250 16th St, Santa Monica, CA 90404

Santa Rosa Medical Center 707.393.4000
401 Bicentennial Way, Santa Rosa, CA 95403
Dr. Kirk Pattas, Physician In Chief

Santa Rosa Memorial Hospital 707.546.3210
1165 Montgomery Dr, Santa Rosa, CA 95405
Kevin Klockenga, Chief Executive Officer

Seton Medical Center 650.992.4000
1900 Sullivan Ave, Daly City, CA 94015
Lorraine Auerbach, Chief Executive Officer

Sharp Grossmont Hospital 619.740.6000
E-mail ....www.sharp.com
5555 Grossmont Center Dr, La Mesa, CA 91942
Michele Tarbet, Chief Executive Officer

Shasta Regional Medical Center 530.244.5400
1100 Butte St, Redding, CA 96001
Randall Hempling, Chief Executive Officer

Shriners Hospital for Children N Clfnia 916.453.2000
2425 Stockton Blvd, Sacramento, CA 95817
Debbie Rubenn, Human Resource Director

Shriners Hospitals for Children at LA 213.388.3151
3160 Geneva St, Los Angeles, CA 90020
Terrance Cunningham, Administrator

Sierra View District Hospital 559.784.1110
465 West Putnam Ave, Porterville, CA 93257
Dennis Coleman, Chief Executive Officer

Sierra Vista Regional Medical Center 805.546.7600
1010 Murray St, San Luis Obispo, CA 93405
Candice Markwith, Chief Executive Officer

St Bernardine Medical Center 909.883.8711
2101 North Waterman Ave, San Bernardino,
CA 92404
Steve Barron, Chief Executive Officer

St Elizabeth Community Hospital 530.529.8000
2550 Sister Mary Columba Dr, Red Bluff, CA 96080
Lisa Lebanco, Chief Executive Officer

St Francis Medical Center 310.900.8900
3630 East Imperial Hwy, Lynwood, CA 90262

St Joseph Hospital 707.445.8121
2700 Dolbeer St, Eureka, CA 95501

St Josephs Medical Center 209.943.2000
1800 North California St, Stockton, CA 95204

St Mary Medical Center 760.242.2311
18300 Highway 18, Apple Valley, CA 92307
Alan Garrett, Chief Executive Officer

St Mary Medical Center 562.491.9000
1050 Linden Ave, Long Beach, CA 90813
Christopher Dicicco, Chief Executive Officer

Surprise Valley Healthcare District 530.279.6111
741 North Main St, Cedarville, CA 96104

Sutter Auburn Faith Hospital 530.888.4500
11815 Education St, Auburn, CA 95602
Mitchell Hanna, Chief Executive Officer

Sutter Delta Medical Center 925.779.7200
3901 Lone Tree Way, Antioch, CA 94509
Gary Rapaport, Chief Executive Officer

Sutter Lakeside Hospital 707.262.5000
5176 Hill Road East, Lakeport, CA 95453

Sutter Medical Center 916.454.3333
5151 F St, Sacramento, CA 95819
Tom Gagan, Chief Executive Officer

Sutter Solano Medical Center 707.554.4444
300 Hospital Dr, Vallejo, CA 94589

Sutter Tracy Community Hospital 209.835.1500
1420 North Tracy Blvd, Tracy, CA 95376
Dave Thompson, Chief Executive Officer

Torrance Memorial Medical Center 310.325.9110
3330 Lomita Blvd, Torrance, CA 90505
Craig Leach, Chief Executive Officer

Tri City Medical Center 760.724.8411
4002 Vista Way, Oceanside, CA 92056
Larry Anderson, Chief Executive Officer

Tulare Regional Medical Center 559.688.0821
869 North Cherry St, Tulare, CA 93274

UCLA Med Ctr 310.222.2345
1000 West Carson St, Torrance, CA 90502
Kim McKenzie, Chief Executive Officer

Univ of CA San Francisco Medical Center 415.476.1000
E-mail ....Mark.laret@ucsfctr.org
500 Parnassus Ave, San Francisco, CA 94143
Mark Laret, Chief Executive Officer

Univ of California Davis Medical Center 916.734.2011
E-mail ....Ann.rice@ucdmc.ucdavis.edu
2315 Stockton Blvd, Sacramento, CA 95817
Ann Rice, Chief Executive Officer

Univ of California Irvine Medical Ctr 714.456.6011
101 The City Dr, Orange, CA 92868
Terry Belmonte, Chief Executive Officer

USC Medical Center 323.226.2622
2051 morengo St, Los Angeles, CA 90033
Pete Delgado, Chief Executive Officer

Valley Presbyterian Hospital 818.782.6600
15107 Vanowen St, Van Nuys, CA 91405
Gus Valdespino, Chief Executive Officer

ValleyCare Medical Center 925.847.3000
5555 West Las Positas Blvd, Pleasanton, CA 94588
Mercy Feit, Chief Executive Officer

Washington Health Care District 510.797.1111
2000 Mowry Ave, Fremont, CA 94538
Nancy Farber, Chief Executive Officer

Western Medical Center Santa Ana 714.835.3555
1001 North Tustin Ave, Santa Ana, CA 92705
Daniel Brochman, Chief Executive Officer

White Memorial Medical Center 323.268.5000
1720 Cesar E Chavez Ave, Los Angeles, CA 90033
Beth Zachary, President

COUNSELING SERVICES

A Better Way 510.601.0203
Fax 510.601.4002
Web ....www.abetterwayinc.net
E-mail ....mail@abetterwayinc.net
3200 Adeline St, Berkeley, CA 94703-2407
Shahnaz Mazandarani, Director

Bethany Christian Svcs 714.994.0500
Fax 714.994.0515
Web ....www.bethany.org
E-mail ....info@lamirada-bethany.org
16700 Valley View Ave Ste 210, La Mirada,
CA 90638-5832
Jess Carlson, Director

Birth Choice Of Temecula 951.699.9808
Fax 951.699.7268
E-mail ....birthchoice@timvalley.com
27488 W Enterprise Cir, Ste 4, Temecula, CA 92590
Jennifer Cartell, Director

Bridge Us 530.363.0761
Fax 530.642.2420
E-mail ....mickeyd@eagala.org
PO Box 1234, El Dorado, CA 95623-1234
Mickey, Director

Cascade Counseling 805.544.1412
Fax 805.544.1412
Web ....www.cascadecounselinginc.com
600 Redondo Ct, Grover Beach, CA 93433-2931
Jolie Lucas-Holt, Counselor

Central CA Amputee Education and Support
Group 559.432.6035
E-mail ....lzemke@sbcglobal.net
233 E. Portland Ave., Fresno, CA 93720
Liz Zemke, Amputee Liaison

Children's Bureau Of Southern California 323.953.7350
Fax 323.661.7306
Web www.all4kids.org
E-mail ....amorales@all4kids.org
3910 Oakwood Ave, Los Angeles, CA 90004-3464
Alex Morales, President & CEO

Conejo Valley Women's Resource Ctr 805.373.1222
Fax 805.371.5331
Web ....www.wrcoptions.org
E-mail ....info@womens-resource.com
80 E Hillcrest Dr Ste 130, Thousand Oaks,
CA 91360-4280
Michele Reithmayr, Executive Director

Crittenton Svcs (Corporate Ofc) 714.680.8200
Fax 714.680.8207
Web ....www.kidsmatter.org
E-mail ....jcappelle@kidsmatter.org
801 E Chapman Ave Ste 230, Fullerton,
CA 92831-3847
Joyce Cappelle, Director

Families First 925.602.1750
Fax 925.602.1754
Web ....www.healthkids.org
3350 Clayton Rd, Ste 100, Concord, CA 94519
Antonette Harris, Services Manager

Family Guidance Ctr 562.924.5526
Fax 562.924.1040
E-mail ....cfgcmurase@aol.com
10929 South St Ste 208B, Cerritos, CA 90703
Richard Murase, Executive Director

Family Svc Agency Of San Francisco 415.474.7310
Fax 415.931.3773
Web ....www.fsasf.org
E-mail ....bbennett@fsasf.org
1010 Gough St, San Francisco, CA 94109-7697
Bob Bennett, Executive Director

Kara 650.321.5272
Fax 650.473.1828
Web ....www.kara-grief.org
E-mail ....info@kara-grief.org
457 Kingsley Ave, Palo Alto, CA 94301
Susan Christensen, Office Manager

LDS Family Services 909.824.0480
Fax 909.824.0487
Web ....www.itsaboutlove.org
E-mail ....fam-ca-colton@ldschurch.org
791 N Pepper Ave, Colton, CA 92324-1800
Sarah Bonilla, Unwed Mother Counselor

LDS Family Svcs 559.255.1446
Fax 559.255.4876
Web ....www.ldsfamilyservices.org
E-mail ....andersonb@ldschurch.org
1425 N Rabe Ave Ste 101, Fresno, CA 93727-2117
Brian Anderson, Clinical Manager

LDS Family Svcs 916.483.2154
Fax 916.483.2850
E-mail ....stewartk@ldschurch.org
3000 Auburn Blvd Ste A, Sacramento,
CA 95821-1831
Kenneth Stewart, Director

LDS Family Svcs 714.444.3463
Fax 714.444.1768
E-mail ....fam-ca-ftnvalley@ldschurch.org
17350 Mount Herrmann St Ste A, Fountain Valley,
CA 92708-4114
Jackie Peters, Office Manager

LDS Family Svcs 925.685.2941
Fax 925.685.2958
Web ....www.itsaboutlove.org
E-mail ....stewartk@ldschurch.org
1063 Detroit Ave, Ste A, Concord, CA 94518
Kenneth Stewart, Director

LDS Family Svcs California San Diego
Agency 858.467.9170
Fax 858.467.9183
Web ....www.itsaboutlove.com
E-mail ....huiskent@ldschurch.org
5675 Ruffin Rd Ste 325, San Diego, CA 92123-1391
Todd H. Huisken, Director

New Hope Teenline 714.971.4294
Fax 714.971.4327
Web ....www.myspace.com/newhopeteenline
E-mail ....luannep@crystalcathedral.org
12141 Lewis St, Garden Grove, CA 92840-4627
Bill Gaultiere, Executive Director

Remi Vista 707.268.8722
Fax 707.268.0218
E-mail ....sholmes@remivistainc.com
3960 Walnut Dr Ste B, Eureka, CA 95503-8939
Stephanie Holmes, Director

Remi Vista 530.926.1436
Fax 530.926.2305
Web ....www.remivista.com
1107 Ream Ave, Mount Shasta, CA 96067-2764
John Tillery, Regional Director

CRISIS & SHELTER CARE

1736 Family Crisis Ctr-Domestic Violence 323.737.3900
Fax 323.737.3993
Web www.1736fcc.org
E-mail ....jmontano@1736fcc.org
2116 Arlington Ave, Ste 200, Los Angeles,
CA 90018-1353
Jeanette Montano, Director

Alliance Against Family Violence 661.322.0931
Fax 661.322.2916
1921 19th St, Bakersfield, CA 93303
Lewis Gill, Director

Alpha House Womens Shelter 661.763.4357
Fax 661.763.4370
E-mail ....aalphahouse@bak.rr.com
207 7th St, Taft, CA 93268
Sondra Ryan, Manager

Alternatives To Violence 530.528.0226
Fax 530.528.9339
E-mail ....atvredbluff@sbcglobal.net
717 Pine St, Red Bluff, CA 96080
Geni Spurr, Executive Director

Angel's Flight 213.413.2311
Fax 213.413.5690
E-mail ....aferendeli@sbcglobal.net
357 S Westlake Ave, Los Angeles, CA 90057
Arlene Ferandeli, Director

Asian Pacific Womens Ctr-Domestic
Violence 213.250.2977
Fax 213.250.2949
Web ....www.apwcla.org
E-mail ....pckimofca@yahoo.com
1145 Wilshire Blvd, 1st Floor, Ste 102, Los Angeles,
CA 90017-1900
P C Kim, Director

Asian Womens Shelter-Domestic Vlnce 415.751.7110
Fax 415.751.0806
E-mail ....aiko@sfaws.org
3543 18th St Ste 19, San Francisco, CA 94110-1600
Orchid Pusey, Interim Director

Break The Cycle, Inc.-Domestic Violence 310.286.3383
Fax 310.286.3386
E-mail ....development@breakthecycle.org
5777 W Century Blvd Ste 1150, Los Angeles,
CA 90045
Marjorie Gilbert, Director

Building Futures With Women And
Children 866.292.9688
Fax 510.357.0688
Web ....www.bfwc.org
E-mail ....edecoligny@bfwc.org
1395 Bancroft Ave, San Leandro, CA 94577-5103
Elaine Decoligny, Director

California Alliance Of Child And Family
Svcs 916.449.2273
Fax 916.449.2294
Web ....www.cacfs.org
E-mail ....caalliance@cacfs.org
2201 K St, Sacramento, CA 95816
Carroll Schroeder, Executive Director

Casa De Esperanza-Domestic Violence 530.674.5400
Fax 530.674.3035
E-mail ....cdeinfo@casadeesperanzasite.com
820 Cooper Ave, Yuba City, CA 95991
Marsha Krause-taylor, Director

Casa Youth Shelter 562.594.6825
Fax 562.594.9185
Web ....www.casayouthshelter.org
E-mail ....luciannmaulhardt@casayouthshelter.org
10911 Reagan St, Los Alamitos, CA 90720-2434
Luciann Maulhardt, Director

California

Catalyst Domestic Violence Shelter 530.343.7711
Fax 530.343.3960
E-mail .... catalyst@catalystdvservices.org
330 Wall St Ste 50, Chico, CA 95928
Anastacia Snyder, Director

Center for a Non-Voilance Community 209.588.9305
Fax 209.588.9272
Web .... www.nonviolentcommunity.org
E-mail .... Liz@nonviolentcommunity.org
19900 Cedar Rd N, Sonora, CA 95370
Liz Sewell, Director

Center For Digital Story Telling 510.548.2065
Fax 510.548.1345
E-mail .... amylenita@storycenter.org
1803 Martin Luther King Jr Way, Berkeley, CA 94709
Ms. Amy Hill, Director

Center for Voilence free Relationship 530.626.1450
Fax 530.626.6895
Web .... www.thecenternow.org
34450 Dr Ste 11, Placerville, CA 95667-5844
Matt Huckabay, Director

Central California Family Crisis Ctr 559.781.7462
Fax 559.781.6240
E-mail .... ccfcc@ocsnet.net
770 N Main St, Porterville, CA 93257
Anna Green, Director

Chamberlain's Children Ctr, Inc. 831.636.2121
Fax 831.636.5296
1850 San Benito St, Hollister, CA 95023
Robert Freiri, Acting CEO

Child Abuse Registry 714.940.1000
Fax 714.938.0289
Web .... www.ssa.ocgov.com
800 N Eckhoff St, Orange, CA 92868-1008

Child Crisis Svc 415.970.3800
Fax 415.970.3855
Web .... www.mha-sf.org
3801 3rd St Ste 400, San Francisco, CA 94124
Shierly Chu, Director

Children's Receiving Home 916.482.2370
Fax 916.482.1539
E-mail .... dballard@crhkids.org
3555 Auburn Blvd, Sacramento, CA 95821
David Ballard, Director

Coalition To End Family Violence 805.983.6014
Fax 805.983.6240
E-mail .... Help@Thecoalition.Org
1030 N Ventura Rd, Oxnard, CA 93030
Cherie Duval, Director

Community Human Svcs 831.658.3811
Fax 831.658.3815
Web .... www.chservices.org
E-mail .... info@chservices.org
2560 Garden Rd, Monterey, CA 93940
Robin Mccrae, Executive Director

Community Overcoming Relationship Abuse
(CORA) 650.652.0800
Fax 650.652.0808
Web .... www.corasupport.org
E-mail .... melissal@corasupport.org
PO Box 4245, Burlingane, CA 94011
Melissa Lukin, Executive Director

Community Resource Domestic Violence 760.753.1156
Fax 760.753.0252
E-mail .... lpause@crcncc.org
650 Second St, Encinitas, CA 92024
Laurin Bose, Director

Community Solutions Domestic Violence 408.842.7138
Fax 408.842.0757
Web .... www.communitysolutions.org
E-mail .... erino@communitysolutions.org
6980 Chestnut St, Gilroy, CA 95020-6635
Erin Obrien, Director

Community Violence Solutions 510.237.0113
Fax 510.237.0177
Web .... www.cvsolutions.org
E-mail .... rjames@cvsolutions.org
2101 Van Ness St, San Pablo, CA 94806-3622
Rhonda James, Executive Director

Control For Community Svc-Domestic
Violence 858.272.5777
Fax 858.272.5361
E-mail .... vtabor@ccssd.org
4508 Mission Bay Dr, San Diego, CA 92109
Verna Griffin, Director

Crisis Intervention & Suicide Prevention
Ctr 650.579.0359
Fax 650.342.6727
Web .... www.crisiscenter.org
E-mail .... michelle.joyce@yfes.org
610 Elm St, San Carlos, CA 94070
Michelle Joyce, Program Director

Crisis Shelter Home Your House South 650.367.9687
Fax 650.367.6828
394 Sequoia Ave, Redwood City, CA 94061-3444
Julie Macecezic, Program Manager

Ctr For Family Solutions-Domestic
Violence 760.353.6922
Fax 760.353.8530
E-mail .... bshaver@womanhaven.org
741 W Main St, El Centro, CA 92243-2921
Barbara Shaver, Executive Director

Ctr For Human Svcs 209.526.1476
Fax 209.526.0908
Web .... www.centerforhumanservices.org
1700 McHenry Village Way, Ste 11, Modesto,
CA 95350
Cindy Duenas, Executive Director

Ctr For Pacific-Asian Family-Domestic
Violence 323.653.4045
Fax 323.653.7913
Web .... www.Cpaf.Info
E-mail .... Debras@Cpaf.Info
543 N Fairfax Ave, Ste 108, Los Angeles, CA 90036
Debra Sue, Director

Defensa De Mujeres 831.722.4532
Fax 831.722.4990
Web .... www.wcs-ddm.org
E-mail .... postmaster@wcs-ddm.org
220 E Lake Ave, Watsonville, CA 95076-4718
Laura Gallardo, Director

Desert Sanctuary Domestic Violence
Program 760.256.3733
Fax 760.256.3793
E-mail .... Haleyhouse@Verizon.Net
703 E Main St, Barstow, CA 92312
Peggi Fries, Director

Domestic Violence Ctr-Santa Clarita Valley 661.259.8175
Fax 661.259.1194
E-mail .... Dvcenter@Gmail.Com
23630 San Fernando Rd C, Newhall, CA 91321
Shanon Fors, Director

Domestic Violence Recovery Program 619.544.1453
Fax 619.544.1454
Web .... www.dhs.ca.gov
E-mail .... lgriffin@dhs.ca.gov
964 5th Ave, Ste 328, San Diego, CA 92101
Linda Griffin, Director

Domestic Violence Sexual Assualt
Coalition 530.272.2046
Fax 530.273.3780
E-mail .... info@dvsac.org
960 McCourtny Rd Ste E, Grass Valley, CA 95949
Miko Johnson, Director

Domestic Violence Solutions 805.735.1834
Fax 805.735.9230
E-mail .... kimb@dvsolutions.org
PO Box 1366, Lompoc, CA 93438-1366
Kim Barnett, Director

Domestic Violence Solutions 805.963.4458
Fax 805.963.1169
PO Box 1536, Santa Barbara, CA 93102-1536
Richard Kravitz, Executive Director

Domestic Violence Solutions 805.928.8701
Fax 805.925.5660
Web .... www.dvsolutions.org
E-mail .... kimb@dvsolutions.org
PO Box 314, Santa Maria, CA 93456-0314
Kim Barnett, Director

Donaldina Cameron House-Domestic
Violence 415.781.0401
Fax 415.781.0605
Web .... www.cameronhouse.org
E-mail .... monica@cameronhouse.org
920 Sacramento St, San Francisco, CA 94108-2015
Monica Walter, Executive Director

Doves-Big Bear Valley-Domestic Violence 909.866.1546
Fax 909.866.8580
41943 Big Bear Blvd, BigBearLake, CA 92315
Janett Trot, Director

Emergency Shelter Program 510.581.5626
Fax 510.581.5628
Web .... www.espca.org
E-mail .... ralph@espca.org
1180 B St, Hatward, CA 94541-4230
Ralph Johnson, Director

Families First 510.636.2000
Fax 510.639.4136
Web .... www.familiesfirstinc.org
E-mail .... oaklandpfc@familiesfirstinc.org
7801 Edgewater Dr Ste 1000, Oakland,
CA 94621-2000
Evelyn Trowell, Program Manager

Family and Youth Services 209.929.6700
Fax 209.929.6704
Web .... www.cppainc.org
E-mail .... ljmascarenas@cppainc.org
729 N California St, Stockton, CA 95202
Linda J. Mascarenas, Executive Director

Family Justice Ctr 510.267.8800
Fax 510.267.8809
E-mail .... cherri.allison@acgov.org
470 27th St, Oakland, CA 94612
Cherri Allison, Director

Family Violence Law Ctr 510.208.0220
Fax 510.208.3557
E-mail .... intake@fvlc.org
470 Franklin 27th St, Oakland, CA 94612
Cherri Allison, Director

Family Violence Project-Jewish Family
Svcs 818.789.1293
Fax 818.789.7581
E-mail .... krosenthal@jfsla.org
13949 Ventura Blvd Ste 320, Sherman Oaks,
CA 91423
Karen Rosenthal, Director

Florence Crittenton Svcs 714.680.9000
Fax 714.680.9007
E-mail .... jcapelle@kidsmatter.org
100 E Valley View Dr, Fullerton, CA 92832-1321
Joyce Capelle, Executive Director

Foothill Family Svc-Domestic Violence 626.338.9200
Fax 626.856.1560
E-mail .... huangsu@foothillfamily.org
1215 W West Covina Pkwy, Ste 200, West Covina,
CA 91790-2815
Victoria Huangsu, Director

California

Free Spirit-Bilingual Shelters-Domestic Violence 213.629.5800
Fax..213.430.0657
Web.........................www.worksourcecalifornia.com
E-mail...................Areyez@Worksourcecalifornia.Com
315 W 9th St X, Los Angeles, CA 90015
Alicia Reyez, Director

Gay & Lesbian Community Svcs Ctr 323.993.7400
Fax..323.308.4482
Web.................................www.lagaycenter.org
E-mail...............................ljean@lagaycenter.org
1625 Schrader Blvd, Los Angeles, CA 90028-6213
Lorri Jean, CEO

Girls And Boys Town Of Southern California 714.532.2399
Fax..714.532.6692
2740 N Grant Ave, Santa Anna, CA 92705
Sarah Terry, Program Director Residential Family Services

Good Shepherd Shelter-Domestic Violence 323.737.6111
Fax..323.737.6113
E-mail......................llengel@goodshepherdshelter.org
2561 Venice Blvd, Los Angeles, CA 90019
Lois Lengel, Director

Haven Hills Domestic Violence Program 818.887.7481
Fax..818.887.4796
Web..................................www.havenhills.org
E-mail..............................sberdine@havenhills.org
PO Box 260, Canoga Park, CA 91305-0260
Sara Berdine, Executive Director

Haven Of Peace Inc-Domestic Violence 209.982.0396
Fax..209.234.1010
Web.............................www.havenofpeaceinc.org
E-mail...................bcastellanos@havenofpeaceinc.org
7070 S Harlan Rd, French Camp, CA 95231-9629
Brenda Castellanos, Director

Haven Womens Ctr Stanislaus Co-Domestic Violence 209.524.4331
Fax..209.524.2045
618 13th St, Ste 1, Modesto, CA 95354
Belinda Rolicheck, Director

Helpline 951.329.4738
Fax..951.686.7417
Web..................................www.vcrivco.org
E-mail...............................gcuevas@vcrivco.org
2060 University Ave, Riverside, CA 92507
Gina Gutierrez, Crisis Intervention Director

High Deseret Domestic Violence Program 760.843.0701
Fax..760.843.9551
E-mail...................................hddvp@verizon.net
15075 7th St, 1700 bear valley rd, Victorville, CA 92392
Darryl Evey, Director

House Of Ruth-Domestic Violence Program 909.623.4364
Fax..909.621.3755
E-mail........................saebischer@houseofruthinc.org
599 N Main St, Pomona, CA 91768-3108
Sue Aebischer, Director

Huckleberry House 415.621.2929
Fax..415.621.4758
Web............................www.huckleberryyouth.org
E-mail......................fshearer@huckleberryyouth.org
1292 Page St, San Francisco, CA 94117
Franklin Shearer, Program Manager

Humboldt Domestic Violence Svcs 707.444.9255
Fax..707.444.3190
Web.....................................www.hdvs.org
E-mail..............................Sharyneharper@Hdvs.Org
PO Box 969, Eureka, CA 95502-0969
Sharyne Harper, Director

Humboldt Family Svc Ctr-Domestic Violence 707.443.7358
Fax..707.443.1092
1802 California St, Eureka, CA 95501
Paula Nedelcoff, Executive Director

Interface Children And Family Svcs 805.485.6114
Fax..805.983.0789
Web...www.icfs.org
E-mail...................................esternad@icfs.org
1305 Del Norte Rd Ste 130, Camarillo, CA 93010-8366
Erik Sternad, Executive Director

Interval House 562.594.9492
Fax..562.596.3370
E-mail...............................carol@intervalhouse.org
6615 E Pacific Coast Hwy Ste 170, Long Beach, CA 90803-4221
Carol Williams, Executive Director

Jenesse Ctr, Inc.-Domestic Violence 323.299.9496
Fax..323.299.0699
E-mail.....................................kearl10341@aol.com
3761 Stocker St Ste 100, Los Angeles, CA 90008-5129
Karen Earl, Director

Jewish Family Svc of Los Angeles 323.761.8800
Fax..323.761.8801
E-mail......................................pscastro@jfsla.org
3580 Wilshire Blvd, Ste 700, Los Angeles, CA 90010
Paul Castro, Executive Director

Julian Youth Academy 800.494.2200
Fax..909.590.7040
Web.................................www.teenrescue.com
E-mail...........................connect@teenrescue.com
PO Box 2167, Chino, CA 91708-2167
Phil Ludwig, Director

Korean American Family Svc Ctr-Domestic Violence 213.389.6755
Fax..213.389.5172
Web......................................www.kafscla.org
E-mail...................................admin@kafscla.org
3727 W 6th St, Ste 320, Los Angeles, CA 90020-5108
Connie Chung Joe, Director

La Commisssion On Assaults Against Women 213.955.9090
Fax..213.955.9093
E-mail..........................info@pteaveovervoilet.org
1015 Wilshre Blvd Ste 200, Los Angeles, CA 90017-1445
Patricia Giggans, Director

Lauras House Domestic Violence Program 949.361.3775
Fax..949.361.3548
Web................................www.laurashouse.org
E-mail.................................info@laurashouse.org
999 Corporate Dr, Ste 225, Ladera Ranch, CA 92694-2156
Margaret Bayston, Director

Leroy Haynes Ctr For Children 909.593.2581
Fax..909.596.3567
Web................................www.leroyhaynes.org
233 Base Line Rd, La Verne, CA 91750-2353
Dan Maydeck, CEO

Maitri-Domestic Violence Program 408.436.8393
Fax..408.436.8381
Web......................................www.maitri.org
E-mail..........................program_director@maitri.org
234 E Gish Rd Ste 200, San Jose, CA 95112-4724
Sarah Khan, Director

Marin Abused Womens Svcs 415.457.2464
Fax..415.457.6457
E-mail....................................contact@maws.org
734 A St, San Rafael, CA 94901
Donna Garske, Directror

Mariposa Domestic Womens Ctr 714.547.6494
Fax..714.547.9990
E-mail.........................de.wright@mariposacenter.org
812 W Town And Country Rd, Orange, CA 92868-4712
Diane Wright, Director

Marjaree Mason Ctr Domestic Violence 559.237.4706
Fax..559.237.0420
E-mail................................pam@mmcenter.org
1600 M St, Fresno, CA 93721
Pam Kallsen, Director

Modoc Crisis Center 530.233.4575
Fax..530.233.4744
E-mail...........................Ccallaghan@Teachinc.Org
112 E 2nd St, Alturas, CA 96101-4008
Carol Callaghan, Director

Morongo Basin Unity Home Domestic Violence 760.366.9663
Fax..760.366.2643
61607 Twenty-Nine Palms Hwy, Joshua Tree, CA 92252
Marietta Cowan, Executive Director

Mountian Crisis Svcs-Domestic Violence 209.742.5865
Fax..209.742.4246
E-mail......................................Mcs4You@Sti.Net
5079 Highway 140, Mariposa, CA 95338
Chevon Kothari, Director

Napa Emergency Women-Domestic Violence 707.252.3687
Fax..707.224.1560
1141 Pear Tree Ln Ste 220, Napa, CA 94558
Tracy Lamb, Director

New Life Advocacy-Domestic Violence Program 310.316.4035
Fax..310.370.2922
E-mail....................................Nladv@Verizon.Net
21213 Hawthorne Blvd, Torrance, CA 90503-5501
Karol Sikie, Director

New Morning Youth & Family Svcs 530.622.5551
Fax..530.622.5800
Web............................www.newmorningyfs.org
E-mail..........................david@newmorningyfs.org
6765 Green Valley Rd, Placerville, CA 95667
David Ashby, Executive Director

Northern California Family Ctr 925.370.1990
Fax..925.370.1993
Web...www.ncfc.us
E-mail......................................tfulton@ncfc.us
2244 Pacheco Blvd, Martinez, CA 94553-1968
Thomas Fulton, Director

Oak Grove Institute Jack Weaver School 951.677.5599
Fax..951.698.0461
Web...............................www.oakgrovecentre.org
E-mail............................tammyw@oak-grove.org
24275 Jefferson Ave, Murrieta, CA 92562-7285
Tammy Wilson, Chief Executive Officer

Operation Safehouse, Inc. 951.351.4418
Fax..951.351.4265
Web.......................www.operationsafehouse.org
E-mail......................jmoot@operationsafehouse.org
9685 Hayes St, Riverside, CA 92503-3660
Kathy Mcadara, Executive Director

Option House, Inc. Domestic Violence 909.383.1602
Fax..909.889.7312
Web...............................www.optionhouse.org
E-mail...............................info@optionhouse.org
813 N D St. Ste.3, San Bernardino, CA 92401
Velda Griffin, Director

Pacific Lodge Boys' Home 818.347.1577
Fax..818.883.5452
Web...www.plys.org
E-mail...............................sarah.pineda@plys.org
4900 Serrania Ave, Woodland Hills, CA 91364-3300
Princess Johns, Admissions Coordinator

Partnership For Safe Families 805.677.5403
Fax 805.289.0130
E-mail .... lori@mossbeachhomes.com
PO Box 7306, Ventura, CA 93006-7306
Lori Steinhauer, Director

Peace & Joy Care Ctr-Domestic Violence 310.763.7730
Fax 310.898.3118
E-mail .... wwi6221114@aol.com
1693 E Del Amo Blvd, Carson, CA 90746-2937
Wilma Wilson, Executive Director

Peace For Families 530.823.6224
Fax 530.889.8497
Web .... www.peaceforfamilies.org
E-mail .... michellecoleman@peaceforfamilies.org
PO Box 5462, Auburn, CA 95604-5462
Michelle Coleman, Director

Plumas Rural Svcs-Domestic Violence 530.283.5675
Fax 530.283.3647
Web .... www.plumasruralservices.org
586 Jackson St, Quincy, CA 95971-9747
Michelle Piller, Director

Project Peacemakers Inc-Domestic Violence Prevention 323.291.2525
Fax 323.291.0140
E-mail .... projpeacemakers@aol.com
1826 W 54th St, Los Angeles, CA 90062
Bernita R Walker, Director

Project Sanctuary, Inc.-Domestic Violence 707.462.9196
Fax 707.462.5869
Web .... www.projectsanctuary.org
E-mail .... dina@projectsanctuary.org
564 S Dora St Ste A, Ukiah, CA 95482
Dina Polkinhone, Director

Rainbow Svcs LTD-Domestic Violence 310.548.5450
Fax 310.548.0611
E-mail .... rainbowservices@rainbowservicesdv.org
453 W 7th St, San Pedro, CA 90731
Ben Schirmer, Director

Resource Connection 209.754.1300
Fax 209.754.1473
Web .... www.resourceconnection.net
E-mail .... kfraguero@resourceconnection.net
1404 Gold Hunter Rd, San Andreas, CA 95249
Kelli Fraguero, Director

Riley Ctr-Domestic Violence Svcs 415.552.2943
Fax 415.552.0337
E-mail .... director@rileycenter.org
3543 18th St Ste 4, San Francisco, CA 94110
Mari Alaniz, Director

Rural Human Svcs-Domestic Violence 707.465.3013
Fax 707.465.6464
286 M St Ste A, Crescent City, CA 95531-4115
Teri Mccurnrostra, Director

Safe Alternative To Violent Environments 510.574.2250
Fax 510.574.2252
Web .... www.save-dv.org
E-mail .... executivedirector@save-dv.org
1900 Mowly Ave, Fremont, CA 94538-1513
Rodney Clark, Director

Safequest Solano Inc-Domestic Violence 707.422.7345
Fax 707.422.7276
Web .... www.safequest.us
E-mail .... violet@safequest.us
1745 Enterprise Dr, Ste 2D, Fairfield, CA 94533-5867
Violet Barton, Director

Saint Claires Home Inc-Domestic Violence 760.741.0122
Fax 760.741.1241
Web .... www.stclareshome.org
E-mail .... sisterclaire@stclareshome.org
2201E Valley Pkwy Ste 1E, Escondido, CA 92027-2743
Marcella Prado, Director

San Diego Youth And Svcs 619.221.8600
Fax 619.221.8611
Web .... www.sdys.org
E-mail .... wphilips@sdys.org
3255 Wing St, San Diego, CA 92110
Walter Phillips, Executive Director

San Francisco Dept Public Hlth-Dom Vlnce 415.581.2400
Fax 415.581.2490
Web .... www.sfdph.org
E-mail .... virginia.smyly@sfdph.org
30 Van Ness Ave Ste 2300, San Francisco, CA 94102-6081
Patricia Erwin, Director

San Leandro Community Counseling-Domestic Vilonce 510.347.4620
Fax 510.483.4486
Web .... www.davisstreet.org
E-mail .... rjohnson@davisstreet.org
3081 Teagarden St, San Leandro, CA 94577-5720
Rose Padilla-johnson, Director

Santa Cruz Community Counseling Ctr 831.469.1700
Fax 831.425.1905
Web .... www.scccc.org
E-mail .... carolyn.coleman@scccc.org
195 Harvey West Blvd, Santa Cruz, CA 95060
Carolyn Coleman, Executive Director

Sexual Assault-Domestic Violence Ctr 530.661.6336
Fax 530.661.3021
Web .... www.sadvc.org
E-mail .... info@sadvc.org
933 Court St, Woodland, CA 95695-3518
Lynnette Irlmeier, Executive Director

Shalom Bayit-Domestic Violence Program 510.451.8874
Fax 510.451.8875
Web .... www.shalom-bayit.org
E-mail .... naomi@shalom-bayit.org
PO Box 10102, Oakland, CA 94610-0102
Naomi Tucker, Director

Shelter From The Storm-Domestic Violence 760.674.0400
Fax 760.674.0440
Web .... www.shelterfromthestorm.com
E-mail .... info@shelterfromthestorm.com
73555 Alessandro Dr Ste D, Palm Desert, CA 92260-3635
Lynn Mariarity, Director

Shelter Outreach Plus-Domestic Violence 831.384.3388
Fax 831.384.1308
E-mail .... info@sopinc.org
3087 Wittenmeyer Ct, Marina, CA 93933
Tom Melville, Director

Sheperds Gate-Domestic Violence Prog 925.443.4283
Fax 925.449.3114
E-mail .... shepgate@shepherdsgate.org
1660 Portola Ave, Livermore, CA 94551-1632
Steve Mcree, Director

Siskiyou Domestic Violence-Crisis Ctr 530.842.6629
Fax 530.842.9724
E-mail .... Sdvcc@Snowcrest.Net
118 Ranch Ln, Yreka, CA 96097
Linda Miles, Director

Southy Lake Tahoe Womens Ctr-Domestic Violence 530.544.2118
Fax 530.542.7624
Web .... www.sltwc.org
E-mail .... sltec@global.net
2941 Lake Tahoe Blvd, South Lake Tahoe, CA 96150-7804
Leann Wagoner, Director

St. Johns Shelter For Women And Children 916.453.1482
Fax 916.443.1425
Web .... www.stjohnsshelter.org
E-mail .... msteeb@stjohnsshelter.org
4410 Power Inn Rd, Sacramento, CA 95826-4352
Michelle Steeb, Director

Su Casa Family Crisis And Support Ctr 562.421.8106
Fax 562.421.8117
Web .... www.sucasadv.org
E-mail .... info@sucasadv.org
3840 Woodruff Ave, Ste 104, Long Beach, CA 90808-2149
Vicki Doolittle, Executive Director

Support Network For Battered Women 800.572.2782
Fax 408.541.1333
Web .... www.snbw.org
E-mail .... calfaro@snbw.org
1257 Tasman Dr Ste C, Sunnyvale, CA 94089-2251
Chata Alfaro, Executive Director

Tahoe Turning Point 530.541.4594
Fax 530.542.1200
E-mail .... rbarna@edcoe.k12.ca.us
2494 Lake Tahoe Blvd., Ste B5, South Lake Tahoe, CA 96150-7719
Rich Barna, Executive Director

Tahoe Womens Svcs-Domestic Violence 530.546.7804
Fax 530.546.1486
8520 Brook Ave, Kings Beach, CA 96143
Karen Edwards, Director

The Healing Artist 818.785.5290
Fax 818.785.0948
E-mail .... thehealingartist@mac.com
PO Box 55563, Sherman Oaks, CA 91413-0563
Janet Bernson, Director

The Salvation Army- The Way In 323.469.2946
Fax 323.468.8678
5939 Hollywood Blvd, Los Angeles, CA 90028
Tony Gonzalez, Executive Director

Tri-Valley Haven Domestic Violence Prog 925.449.5845
Fax 925.449.2684
Web .... www.trivalleyhaven.org
E-mail .... ann@trivalleyhaven.org
3663 Pacific Ave, Livermore, CA 94550-7062
Ms Ann King, Director

Trinity Children And Family Svcs 661.729.9540
Fax 661.942.3460
Web .... www.trinitycfs.org
E-mail .... tcfs070c3@aol.com
42225 W 10th St Ste D, Lancaster, CA 93534-7080
Sue Hernandez, Director

Trinity Children And Family Svcs 909.980.4755
Fax 909.980.2396
Web .... www.trinityys.org
E-mail .... chriso@trinityys.org
9600 Center Ave Ste 100, Rancho Cucamonga, CA 91730-5838
Christine Offenstein, Director

Trinity Youth Svcs 626.966.0500
Fax 626.814.3956
Web .... www.trinitycfs.org
E-mail .... intakedir@trinitycfs.org
1520 W Cameron Ave Ste 151, West Covina, CA 91790-2747
Laura Abujudeh, Intake Director

Valley Crisis Center 209.725.7900
Fax 209.725.7908
E-mail .... info@mcs4you.org
1960 W, P street, Merced, CA 95341
Genevieve Bartini, Director

Victor Valley Domestic Violence Program 760.955.8010
Fax 760.955.8248
Web .... www.abetterwaydomesticviolence.org
E-mail .... Vvdv@Verizon.Net
14114 Hesperia Rd, Victorville, CA 92395
Margaret Diaz, Director

Village Counseling Ctr-Domestic Violence 805.546.2656
Fax 805.473.4734
Web .... www.villagecounseling.net
E-mail .... clay@villagecounseling.net
101 W Branch St, Arroyo Grande, CA 93420
Mr Clay Watkins, Director

Volunteers Of America 213.389.1500
Fax 213.385.7599
Web ....www.voala.org
E-mail ....bpratt@voala.org
　　3600 Wilshire Blvd Ste 1500, Los Angeles,
　　CA 90010-2619
　　Robert Pratt, President

Walnut Avenue Womens Ctr 831.426.3062
Fax 831.426.3070
E-mail ....jobrainrojo@wawc.org
　　303 Walnut Ave, Santa Cruz, CA 95060
　　Jennifer O'Brian Rojo, Director

Weave, Inc. Domestic Violence 916.448.2321
Fax 916.443.7183
Web ....www.weaveinc.org
E-mail ....weave@weaveinc.org
　　1900 K St, Ste 200, Sacramento, CA 95811-4187
　　Beth Hassett, Director

Wild Iris Domestic Violence Program 760.873.6601
Fax 760.873.8104
E-mail ....wildiris@wild-iris.org
　　386 W Line St, Bishop, CA 93514-3413
　　Lisa Reel, Director

Wind Youth Ctr 916.561.2424
Fax 916.641.5571
Web ....www.windyouth.org
E-mail ....ellyb@windyouth.org
　　3148 WIND Youth Services, Sacramento, CA 95853
　　Ellyne Bell, Director

Wise Place-Domestic Violence Program 714.542.3577
Fax 714.542.3653
Web ....www.wiseplace.org
E-mail ....kbowmen@wiseplace.org
　　1411 N Broadway, Santa Ana, CA 92706-3904
　　Kathleen Davis Bowmen, Director

Woman Inc-Domestic Violence Program 415.864.4777
Fax 415.864.1082
E-mail ....director@womaninc.org
　　333 Valencia St, Ste 450, San Francisco, CA 94103
　　Roberta Toomer, Director

Women Helping Women-Employment Success
Program 949.631.2333
Fax 949.631.8439
E-mail ....reception@whw.org
　　711 W 17th St Ste A-10, Costa Mesa, CA 92627
　　Jeanne Flint, Director

Women Shelter Of Long Beach-Domestic
Violence 562.437.7233
Fax 562.436.4943
Web ....www.womenshelterlb.org
E-mail ....tsmylie@womenshelterlb.org
　　930 Pacific Ave, Long Beach, CA 90813
　　Tulynn Smylie, Executive Director

Women's Refuge 530.244.0118
Fax 530.244.2653
Web ....www.scwr.org
E-mail ....mjohn@scwr.org
　　2280 Benton Dr Ste A, Redding, CA 96003-5362
　　Margaret John, Director

Women's Resource Ctr Crisis Hotline 760.757.3500
Fax 760.757.0680
Web ....www.roadrunner.com
E-mail ....phenline@roadrunner.com
　　1963 Apple St, Oceanside, CA 92054-4426
　　Marva Bledsoe, Executive Director

Womens Shelter-Resource Ctr 805.461.1338
Fax 805.461.8115
E-mail ....jadams@ncwomensshelter.org
　　1030 pine st ca st, pasorobles, CA 93446
　　Jennifer Adams, Director

YWCA San Gabriel Valley 626.960.2995
Fax 626.338.5419
E-mail ....lisabrabo@ywcasgv.org
　　943 N Grand Ave, West Covina, CA 917724
　　Lisa Brabo, Director

EDUCATION

A Better Chance School 510.758.0433
Fax 510.758.1040
Web ....www.calautism.org
E-mail ....info@calautism.org
　　4075 Lakeside Dr, San Pablo, CA 94806-1937
　　Leslie Werosh, Director

Advanced Education Svcs 909.825.5797
Fax 909.825.5340
Web ....www.aes-schools.org
E-mail ....aes90h@aol.com
　　1460 Colton Ave, Colton, CA 92324
　　John Niber, Chief Executive Officer

Alchemy Academy 408.934.1811
Fax 408.351.9998
Web ....www.alchemyacademy.com
E-mail ....marta@alchemyacademy.com
　　3418 Sagewood Ln, San Jose, CA 95132
　　Marta D. Peterson, Founder/CEO

Aldar Academy 916.485.9685
Fax 916.485.1569
Web ....www.aldaracademy.org
E-mail ....aldar@aldaracademy.org
　　4436 Engle Rd, Sacramento, CA 95821-3306
　　Edward Noskowski, Director

All Peoples Christian Ctr 213.747.6357
Fax 213.747.0541
Web ....www.allpeoplescc.org
E-mail ....sbryant@allpeoplescc.org
　　822 E 20th St, Los Angeles, CA 90011-1104
　　Sandra Bryant, Director

Aseltine School 619.296.2135
Fax 619.296.3013
Web ....www.aseltine.org
E-mail ....hthomas@aseltine.org
　　4027 Normal St, San Diego, CA 92103-2694
　　Hayden Thomas, Phd, Director

Aspen Education Group 562.467.5500
Fax 562.402.7036
Web ....www.aspeneducation.com
E-mail ....aspenadmissions@educationcare.net
　　17777 Center Court Dr N Ste 300, Cerritos,
　　CA 90703-9328
　　Dana Stein, Director Of Admissions

Assistance League Of Southern California 323.469.5893
Fax 323.469.5896
Web ....www.assistanceleague.net
E-mail ....dzavala@assistanceleague.net
　　1360 N St Andrews Pl, Los Angeles, CA 90028-8529
　　Damien Zavala, Executive Director

Atkinson Youth Svcs School 916.977.3790
Fax 916.977.3793
Web ....www.atkinsonyouthservices.com
　　3600 Fair Oaks Blvd, Sacramento, CA 95864-7204
　　Johann Rubi-miller, Principal

Balboa City School 619.298.2990
Fax 619.295.8886
Web ....www.balboaschool.com
E-mail ....sparker@balboaschool.com
　　525 Hawthorn St, San Diego, CA 92101-2320
　　Stephen Parker, Phd, Director

Beacon School 408.265.8611
Fax 408.265.7324
Web ....www.beaconschool.com
　　5670 Camden Ave Ste 102, San Jose, CA 95124-6428
　　Teresa Malekzadeh, Director

Boys Republic Monrovia Day Program 626.358.4581
Fax 626.358.2510
Web ....www.boysrepublic.org
E-mail ....jruize@boysrepublic.org
　　128 E Palm Ave, Monrovia, CA 91016
　　Jessica Ruize, Director

Bridge School 650.696.7295
Fax 650.342.7598
Web ....www.bridgeschool.org
E-mail ....vcasella@bridgeschool.org
　　545 Eucalyptus Ave, Hillsborough, CA 94010-6404
　　Vicki Casella, Phd, Executive Director

Charles Armstrong School 650.592.7570
Fax 650.591.3114
Web ....www.charlesarmstrong.org
E-mail ....main@charlesarmstrong.org
　　1405 Solana Dr, Belmont, CA 94002-3699
　　Cludia Koochek, Director Of Admissions

Child Abuse Prevention Council 209.464.4524
Fax 209.464.2272
Web ....www.nochildabuse.org
E-mail ....info@nochildabuse.org
　　540 N California St, Stockton, CA 95202-2117
　　Lindy Turner, Executive Director

Crossroads School 818.782.2470
Fax 818.994.8742
　　6843 Lennox Ave, Van Nuys, CA 91405
　　Mike Madhin, Director

Desert Valley Hope Academy - Hemet 951.766.6020
Fax 951.658.2480
Web ....www.uhsinc.com
　　145 N Tahquitz Ave, Hemet, CA 92543
　　George Whitmore, Principal

Drew Child Development Corporation 323.249.2950
Fax 323.249.2970
Web ....www.drewcdc.org
E-mail ....mjackson@drewcdc.org
　　1770 E 118th St, Los Angeles, CA 90059-2518
　　Mike Jackson, Phd, President/CEO

Grand Terrace (Keystone) 909.783.8420
Fax 909.783.8469
Web ....www.keystoneyouth.com
　　11980 Mount Vernon Ave, Grand Terrace, CA 92313
　　Alfredo Alvarez, Director

Guiding Hands School 916.939.0553
Fax 916.939.0563
Web ....www.ghandsschool.com
E-mail ....ckeller@ghandsschool.com
　　4900 Windplay Dr, El Dorado Hills, CA 95762-9653
　　Cindy Keller, Executive Director

Hathaway School 805.488.2217
Fax 805.488.1304
E-mail ....hcosgrove@huensd.k12.ca.us
　　405 E Dollie St, Oxnard, CA 93033-7621
　　Feicas Terez, Principal

Hergl School 415.474.0191
Fax 415.673.9597
E-mail ....hergl@comcast.net
　　1570 Greenwich St, San Francisco, CA 94123
　　Sandra Carroll, Director

Institute For Health Policy Studies 415.476.4921
Fax 415.476.0705
　　3333 California St Ste 265, San Francisco, CA 94143
　　Claire Brindis, Executive Director

Joan Macy School 909.596.5921
Fax 909.596.8492
Web ....www.dmhome.org
E-mail ....richc@dmhome.org
　　1350 3rd St, La Verne, CA 91750-5201
　　Charles Rich, Director

Keystone: Victorville Campus 760.241.8386
Fax 760.241.3935
Web ....www.keystoneyouth.com
　　12199 Industrial Blvd, Victorville, CA 92395
　　Jeff Le Comte, Principal

California

Lattice Educational Svcs 707.571.1234
Fax 707.571.1230
3273 Airway Dr Ste A, Santa Rosa, CA 95403
Nancy Alcott Lucas, Director

Laureate Learning Ctr 916.483.2815
Fax 916.483.7245
E-mail ....principalparks@sbcglobal.net
5325 Engle Rd, Ste 200, Carmichael, CA 95608
Brad Parks, Principal

Log Cabin Ranch School 650.747.0257
Fax 650.747.0631
Web ....www.sfgov.org
E-mail ....allen.nance@sfgov.org
500 Log Cabin Rd, La Honda, CA 94020
Allen Nance, Interim Director

Matrix Parent Network and Resource Ctr 415.884.3535
Fax 415.884.3555
E-mail ....info@matrixparent.org
94 Galli Dr Ste C, Novato, CA 94949
Nora Thompson, Director

Millhous Ctr School 530.265.9057
Fax 530.292.3803
Web ....www.milhous.org
9451 Pond Ln, Wilton, CA 95693
Dick Millhous, Director

Missionville Academey 951.785.0504
Fax 951.785.0106
Web ....www.missionvilleacademy.com
9994 County Farm Rd, Riverside, CA 92053
Dr. Greg Alexander, Director

Morning Sky Residential School 951.659.4044
Fax 951.659.9797
Web ....www.sldc.net
E-mail ....tapplegarth@sldc.net
29375 Highway 243, Mountain Center, CA 92561
Tony Applegarth, Director

New Haven Youth And Family Svcs 760.630.4035
Fax 760.630.4030
Web ....www.newhavenyfs.org
E-mail ....dquinn@newhavenyfs.org
216 W Los Angeles Dr, Vista, CA 92083
Doreen Quinn, Executive Director

New Vista School 949.455.1270
Fax 949.455.1271
Web ....www.newvistaschool.org
23092 Mill Creek Dr, Laguna Hills, CA 92653
Nancy Donnelly, Director

New Vistas Christian School 925.370.7767
Web ....www.newvistaschristian.org
68 Morello Ave, Martinez, CA 94553
Maria Zablah, Principal & Administrator

North Hills Prep School 818.894.8388
Fax 818.894.2850
Web ....www.northhillsprep.com
E-mail ....e.bradley@northhillsprep.com
9433 Sepulveda Blvd, North Hills, CA 91343-3398
Elin Bradley, Director

North Valley School 530.378.1855
Fax 530.378.0857
Web ....www.victor.org
E-mail ....rbowman@victor.org
855 Canyon Rd, Redding, CA 96001-5544
Robin Bowman, Director

Northern Valley Catholic Social Svc 530.241.0552
Fax 530.241.6457
Web ....www.nvcss.org
E-mail ....dchapman@nvcss.org
2400 Washington Ave, Redding, CA 96001-2827
Don Chapman, Interm Executive Director

Northpoint Day Treatment 818.993.9311
Fax 818.993.8206
Web ....www.childguidance.org
E-mail ....rmarshall@childguidance.org
9650 Zelzah Ave, Northridge, CA 91325-2003
Roy Marshall, Executive Director

Oralingua School For The Hearing Impaired, Inc. 562.945.8391
Fax 562.945.0361
Web ....www.oralingua.org
E-mail ....elisa.rothe@oralingua.org
7056 Washington Ave, Whittier, CA 90602-1415
Elisa Rothe, Program Director

Orion Academy 925.377.0789
Fax 925.377.2028
Web ....www.orionacademy.org
E-mail ....office@orionacademy.org
350 Rheem Blvd, Moraga, CA 94556-1516
Kathreen Stewart, Director

Park Hill School 818.883.3500
Fax 818.883.1519
Web ....www.parkhillschool.com
E-mail ....secretary@parkhillschool.com
7401 Shoup Ave, West Hills, CA 91307-1750
Lindsay Leinbach, Principal

People Who Care Youth Ctr 323.778.8905
Fax 323.778.9060
Web ....www.pwcyc.org
E-mail ....cwatson@pwcyc.org
1500 W Slauson Ave, Los Angeles, CA 90047-1230
Connie Watson, Executive Director

Pheonix NPS 408.846.2113
Fax 408.846.2114
Web ....www.rcskids.org
E-mail ....jhummer@rcskids.org
290 I O O F Ave, Gilroy, CA 95020-5204
Joy Hummer, Director Of Educational Services

Pyramid Autism Ctr 714.637.1292
Fax 714.637.1294
E-mail ....skochanowski@pyramidautismcenter.com
2830 N Glassell St, Orange, CA 92865
Stacey Kochanowski, Director

Rancho Academy Of Learning 909.944.3765
Fax 909.944.3707
Web ....www.ranchoacademy.com
E-mail ....marilyn.summers@uhsinc.com
8968 Archibald Ave, Rancho Cucamonga, CA 91730
Marilyn Summers, Director

Richstone Family Ctr 310.970.1921
Fax 310.970.1330
Web ....www.richstonecenterfamily.org
E-mail ....rramirez@richstonefamily.org
13634 Cordary Ave, Hawthorne, CA 90250-7409
Rolando Ramirez, Executive Director

Rosemary Children's Svcs 626.844.3033
Fax 626.844.3034
3244 E Green St, Pasadena, CA 91107
Greg Wessels, Director

Russell Bede School 650.579.4400
Fax 650.579.4402
Web ....www.russellbedeschool.com
E-mail ....bonnieyamanerbs@gmail.com
446 Turner Ter, San Mateo, CA 94401-2414
Bonnie Yamane, Principal

Saint Francis Children's Ctr 310.900.8490
Fax 310.900.8889
E-mail ....tidwellderrell@dochs.org
3630 E Imperial Hwy, Lynwood, CA 90262
Derrell Tidwell, Director

Saint John's Child And Family Development Ctr 310.829.8921
Fax 310.829.8455
Web ....www.stjohns.org
E-mail ....rebecca.refuerzo@stjohns.org
1339 20th St, Santa Monica, CA 90404-2033
Rebecca Refuerzo, Lcsw, Executive Director

Sam & Rose Stein Education Ctr 619.281.5511
Fax 619.281.0453
Web ....www.vistahill.org
E-mail ....jrichards@vistahill.org
6145 Decena Dr, San Diego, CA 92120
Joan Richards, Director

Sam & Rose Stein Education Ctr 619.284.5511
Fax 619.284.0453
Web ....www.vistahill.org
E-mail ....jrichards@vistahill.org
6150 Christina Dr, San Diego, CA 92120-3434
Joan Richards, Executive Director

San Francisco 49ers Academy 650.614.4300
Fax 650.614.4310
Web www.49ers-academy.org
E-mail ....info@49ers-academy.org
2695 Fordham St, East Palo Alto, CA 94303
Michelle Sharkey, Director

San Francisco Hearing & Speech Of Northern California 415.921.7658
Fax 415.921.2243
Web ....www.hearingspeech.org
E-mail ....dkennedy@hearingspeech.org
1234 Divisadero St, San Francisco, CA 94115-3911
Dara Kennedy, Director

South Bay Ctr For Counseling 310.414.2090
Fax 310.414.2096
Web ....www.sbaycenter.com
E-mail ....sbaycenter@sbaycenter.com
360 N Sepulveda Blvd Ste 2075, El Segundo, CA 90245-4414
Colleen Mooney, Executive Director

Spectrum Ctr 510.724.4494
Fax 510.724.4430
Web ....www.spectrumcenter.org
16330 San Pablo Ave, San Pablo, CA 94806
Kathleen Bohrer, Director

Spectrum Ctr 707.864.0438
Fax 707.864.8659
Web ....www.spectrumschools.com
E-mail ....dyoung@spectrumschools.com
720 Link Rd, Fairfield, CA 94534-1642
Dale Young, Program Director

Spectrum Ctr 925.439.6929
Fax 925.439.6925
Web ....www.spectrumcenter.com
E-mail ....mcelis@spectrumcenter.com
135 E Leland Rd, Pittsburg, CA 94565-4948
Margaret Celis, Director

Spectrum Ctr 925.685.9703
Fax 925.685.5950
Web ....www.spectrumschools.com
E-mail ....lindsay@thelisteningcenter.net
1026 Oak Grove Rd, Ste A, Concord, CA 94518
Catherine Lindsey, Director

Springall Academy 619.460.5090
Fax 619.460.5091
Web ....www.springall.org
E-mail ....baker@springall.org
6460 Boulder Lake Ave, San Diego, CA 92119-3142
Arlene Baker, Edd, Director

Stars High School 510.352.9200
Fax 510.352.3120
Web ....www.starsinc.com
545 Estudillo Ave, San Leandro, CA 94577-4611
Karly Wiley, Assistant Administrator

Steele Canyon Campus 619.447.6776
Fax..619.447.3053
Web...............................www.ranchosdacademy.com
2815 Steele Canyon Rd, El Cajon, CA 92019-4619
Audrey Young, Principal

Sunset Neighborhood Beacon Ctr 415.759.3690
Fax..415.759.0883
Web...www.snbc.org
E-mail...info@snbc.org
3925 Noriega St, San Francisco, CA 94122
Michael Funk, Director

Team of Advocates for Special Kids CA 714.533.8275
Fax..714.533.2533
E-mail.......................................taskca@yahoo.com
100 W Cerritos Ave, Anaheim, CA 92805
Brenda Smith, Deputy Director

The Carolyn E. Wylie Ctr For Children, Youth &
Families 951.683.5193
Fax..951.300.1030
Web...www.wyliecenter.org
4164 Brockton Ave, Riverside, CA 92501
Melody Amaral, CEO

Therapeutic Education Ctr 714.998.6571
Fax..714.998.6573
Web...www.taftavenue.org
E-mail...info@olivecrest.org
2190 N Canal St, Orange, CA 92865-3601
Keely Hanley, Director

Timothy Murphy School 415.499.7616
Fax..415.499.0252
1 Saint Vincents Dr, San Rafael, CA 94903
Debra Countouriotis, Principal

Tobinworld.................................818.247.7474
Fax..818.247.6516
Web...www.tobinworld.org
920 E Broadway St, Glendale, CA 91205-1204
Judith Weber, Director

Tobinworld II...............................925.516.4245
Fax..925.516.8956
Web...www.tobinworld.org
2330 Coutry Hill Dr, Antioch, CA 94509
Richard Couch, Phd, Director

True To Life Children's Svcs 707.823.7300
Fax..707.823.3410
Web...www.tlc4kids.org
E-mail.....................................information@tlc4kids.org
1800 Gravenstein Hwy N, Sebastopol,
CA 95472-2607
Jim Galstener, Executive Director

UHS Schools Carmichael 916.482.9634
Fax..916.482.3921
Web...www.creeksideacademy.com
E-mail...shiela.mccarthy@uhsinc.com
2641 Kent Dr, Sacramento, CA 95821
Shiela Mccarthy, Principal

Valley Of The Moon Boys & Girls Club 707.938.8544
Fax..707.938.8556
Web...www.bgcvom.org
E-mail...dpier@bgcvom.org
100 Verano Ave, El Verano, CA 95433
David Pier, Director

Victor Family Of Programs 209.340.7900
Fax..209.340.7950
E-mail...dbaker@victor.org
9150 E Hwy 12, Victor, CA 95253
David Baker, Director

Village Glen School 818.779.5262
Fax..818.779.5295
Web...www.villageglen.org
E-mail...tkomp@thehelpgroup.org
4160 Grand View Blvd, Campus Locations:, Los
Angeles, CA 90066-5214
Tom Komp, Vice President/Admissions Director

Westmark School 818.986.5045
Fax..818.986.2605
Web...www.westmarkschool.org
E-mail...lbarnaby@westmarkschool.org
5461 Louise Ave, Encino, CA 91316-2540
Lesley Barnaby, Director

Wide Horizons Ranch 530.472.3223
Fax..530.472.3233
E-mail...admin@widehorizonsranch.com
27442 Oak Run To Fern Rd, Oak Run, CA 96069
Dennis Carver, Director/administrator

Winston School 858.259.8155
Fax..858.259.8356
Web...www.thewinstonschool.com
E-mail...mikep@thewinstonschool.com
215 9th St, Del Mar, CA 92014-2716
Mike Peterson, Director

FOSTER CARE AGENCIES

A New Beginning FFA Learning 760.244.8188
15885 Main St Ste 220, Hesperia, CA 92345
Mr. Mohammed, Director

Abrazo Foster Family Agency 559.228.9800
Fax..559.228.9802
Web...www.abrazoffa.net
E-mail...info@abrazoffa.net
1610 E Gettysburg Ave, Fresno, CA 93710-7708
John Lott, Director

Across the World Adoptions (ATWA) 925.356.6260
399 Taylor Blvd, Ste 102, Pleasant Hill, CA 94523
Lesley Siegel, Director

Adoption Horizons (AH) 707.444.9909
Fax..707.442.6672
E-mail...adoption@sbcglobal.net
10 W 7th St, Ste F, Eureka, CA 95501
. Cynthia Savage, Director

Adoption Information Center (AIC) 424.757.5170
Fax..424.757.5181
E-mail...la_adoptions@yahoo.com
1327 Post Ave, Ste K, Torrance, CA 90501
Susanne Rose, Executive Director

Adoption Parent Assc 760.635.7920
E-mail...rferr@sdcoe.k12.ca.us
1667 Clearwater Pl, Encinitas, CA 92024
Kerry Ferreirae, President

Adoption Paths 831.476.7252
E-mail...sara@adoptionpaths.com
PO Box 1174, Soquel, CA 95073

Adoption Support Group of Santa Monica 310.829.1438
E-mail...marlourussell@hotmail.com
1452 26th St, ste 103, Santa Monica, CA 90404

Adoptive Families Support Group 661.722.4220

Adoptive Fmly Therapeutic & Educational 408.554.2550
Fax..408.554.4219
South Bay Tower, 3031 Tisch Rd Ste 306, San Jose,
CA 95128

AFTER Adoptive Parent Education # 4 ....831.649.3033
Fax..831.649.4843
E-mail...carolyn@kinshipcenter.org
124 River Rd, Salinas, CA 93908

Alliance Human Svcs Inc.....................661.325.6937
Fax..661.325.6938
5300 Lennox Ave, Ste 103, Bakersfield, CA 93309
Eileen Wright, Director

Alternative Family Svcs Adoption Agency 415.656.0116
Fax..415.656.0117
250 Executive Park Blvd, Ste 4900, San Francisco,
CA 94134
Jay Berlin, Owner

Approachable Foster Family 209.723.2093
E-mail
....franklynvinvent@approachablefosterfamilyagency.com
710 W 18th St, Merced, CA 95340
Franklyn Vincent, Director

Aspiranet Adoption Program 559.222.4969
E-mail...nborn@aspiranet.org
1320 E Shaw st, Ste 140, Fresno, CA 93710
Diane Waren, Administrater

Bienvenidos Foster Family 818.772.5333
Fax..818.772.5454
255 N Sangabriel Blvd, Pasatena, CA 91107
Brian Fernandez, Director

Bridge Of Faith 562.789.8009
Web...www.bridgeoffaith.org
E-mail...bridgeoffaith@att.net
7702 Greenleaf Ave, Whittier, CA 90602-2105
Carol Reza, Executive Director & Founder

Bright Horizon Foster Family 909.514.0670
Fax..909.514.1156
1003 E Cooley Dr, Colton, CA 92324

CA State Foster Parent Assoc Inc (CSFPA) 805.239.8958
E-mail...leekay@hughes.net
12419 Oaks Ave, Chino, CA 90710
Lee Storey, Treasurer

California Foster Families, Inc................209.543.3991
Fax..209.543.3992
4300 Sisk Rd, Modesto, CA 95356
Tracy Tousley, Executive Director

California State Care Providers
Association 323.846.0007
1040 W 46th St, Los Angeles, CA 90037
Audrey Manuel, President

Children First Foster Family 530.528.2938
Fax..530.528.8034
E-mail...mlogan@childrenfirstffa.com
2995 Churn Creek Rd, Redding, CA 96002-1120
Mike Logan, Director

Children's Hope Foster Family 530.846.4955
Fax..530.846.4954
1585 Butte House Rd Ste E, Yuba City,
CA 95993-2200
Steve Hepworth, Program Director

Childrens Bureau Of California 310.523.9500
Fax..310.225.2725
460 E Carson Plaza Dr Ste 122, Carson, CA 90746
Lou Graham, Director

Chrysalis House Inc (CHI) 559.229.9862
Fax..559.229.9863
E-mail...peggy@chrysalishouse.com
7395 N Palm Bluffs, Ste 106, Fresno, CA 93711
Peggy Schulve, Adoption Services Manager

Clover House 707.275.9260
570 Clover Dr, Upper Lake, CA 95485-9217
Patty Chandler, Program Director

Compton City Wide Foster Parent Assoc 310.637.2706
140 W Harcourt St, Long Beach, CA 90805
Betsy Arbing, Chief Executive Officer

Concept 7 Foster Family Agency 714.966.9734
Fax..714.966.9743
Web...www.concept7.org
E-mail...gdunn@concept7.org
625 S Main St, Orange, CA 92868-6810
Giselle Dunn, Director

Covenant Foster Care 661.326.8304
Fax..661.326.8364
1616 29th St, Bakersfield, CA 93301-1906
Randy Martin, Chief Executive Officer

El Cajon Office 619.336.5740
Fax..619.336.3878
1000 W 24th St, National City, CA 91950

California

El Cajon Office **760.754.3456**
Fax 760.754.3530
  1320 Union Plaza Ct, Oceanside, CA 92054

EMQ Children & Family Services (EMQ) **408.874.7151**
Fax 408.874.4150
  251 Llewellyn Ave, Campbell, CA 95008

Environmental Alternatives **209.223.3888**
Fax 209.223.3883
  500 South Ave, Jackson, CA 95642
  Tim Wilkinson, Director

Environmental Alternatives **707.443.7370**
Fax 707.443.1569
E-mail ....eureka@ea.org
  2928 E St, Eureka, CA 95501
  Jim Harding, Director

Environmental Alternatives **530.283.3330**
E-mail ....yreka@ea.org
  326 W Miner St, Yreka, CA 96097
  Kelly Atchley, Office Manager

Environmental Alternatives **209.369.1939**
Fax 209.369.6597
Web ....www.ea.org
E-mail ....timw@ea.org
  525 W Kettleman Ln, Lodi, CA 95240-6005
  Tim Wilkinson, Director

Families First Inc **209.523.3710**
  1620 N Carpenter Rd, Ste C-23, Modesto, CA 95351
  Agnes Perez, Programme Director

Families for Attachment Resources **619.690.2840**
  9400 Riffin Court, San Diego, CA 92123

Families for Children (FFC) **916.789.8688**
Fax 916.789.7008
E-mail ....Admin@families4children.com
  2990 Lava Ridge Court, Ste 170, Roseville, CA 95661
  Chris Debere, Human Resource Manager

Family Builders Foster Care **559.248.0395**
Fax 559.685.9742
Web ....www.fbcares.org
E-mail ....ramona@fbcares.org
  2499 W Shaw Ave Ste 103, Fresno, CA 93711-3329
  Ramona Chadwell, Director

Family Connections Christian Adoptions **209.524.8844**
  1120 Tully Rd, Modesto, CA 95350
  Wayn Mott, Administrator

FARE Association **760.949.0830**
  15012 Orange St, Hesperia, CA 92345

Five Acres The Boys & Girls Aid Society **626.966.5110**
Fax 909.447.8730
E-mail ....mguilfoyle@5acres.org
  760 W Mountain View St, Pasadena, CA 91101

Foster Care & Adoptive Community (FC&AC) **818.998.4462**
E-mail ....Barbara@fosterparents.com
  9909 Topanga Canyon Blvd, Ste 278, Chatsworth, CA 91311
  Barbara Leiner, President

Foster Family Network **559.435.9987**
Fax 559.435.9988
  5588 N Palm Ave, Fresno, CA 93704
  Linda Chambers, Director

Foster Family Network **661.633.1700**
Fax 661.663.1785
  4540 California Ave Ste 340, Bakersfield, CA 93309
  Glenda Love, Director

Foster Family Network A DIV **562.494.7492**
Fax 562.494.1281
  4223 E Anaheim St, Long Beach, CA 90804

Foster Parent Assoc **209.541.3819**
  3900 Morgan Rd Ste B, Ceres, CA 95307

Foster Parent Assoc **510.357.6410**
  PO Box 4281, San Leandro, CA 94579

Foster Parent Assoc **916.689.5059**
  PO Box 1015, Rancho Cordova, CA 95741

Foster Parents Assoc **619.579.4900**
  1089 El Cajon Blvd Ste D, El Cajon, CA 92020

Future Families Inc **408.298.8789**
Fax 408.298.8870
  1671 The Alameda, Ste 201, San Jose, CA 95126

Hand in Hand-An Adoptive Family Support **916.806.2240**
E-mail ....pstewart@surewest.net
  4707 Tenbury Ln, Rocklin, CA 95677

Hannah's Children's Homes (HCH) **714.516.1077**
Fax 714.516.1080
E-mail ....hannahsadoption@yahoo.com
  1045 W Katella Ave, Ste 330, Orange, CA 92867
  Kimberly Berry, Director

Help One Child **650.917.1210**
E-mail ....info@helponechild.org
  858 University Ave, Los Altos, CA 94024
  Susan Hernan, Director

Independent Adoption Center (IAC) **925.827.2229**
Fax 925.603.0820
E-mail ....staff@adoptionhelp.org
  391 Taylor Blvd, Ste 100, Pleasant Hill, CA 94523
  Ann Wisen, Director

Inland Valley Foster Parent **909.242.2204**
  PO Box 8632, Moreno Valley, CA 92552

Institute for Black Parenting (IBP) **310.807.3350**
Fax 310.348.9154
E-mail ....cwillard@blackparenting.org
  11222 S La Cienega Blvd, Ste 233, Inglewood, CA 90304
  Cynthia Willard, Assistant Executive Director

Jewish Family Service **949.435.3460**
E-mail ....info@jfsoc.org
  1 Federation Way, Ste 220, Irvine, CA 92603
  Shalom Elcott, Director

Kern Bridges Youth Homes Adoption Agency **661.396.2301**
Fax 661.396.2349
E-mail ....MPyles@kernbridges.com
  1321 Stine Rd, Bakersfield, CA 93309
  Jim Vander Vawan, Director

Kinship Adoptive & Foster Parents **408.975.5309**
  373 W Julian St, San Jose, CA 95110
  Denise Marchu, Executive Director

Latino Family Institute **626.472.0123**
Fax 626.337.8752
E-mail ....mquintanilla@lfiservices.org
  1501 W Cameron Ave, Ste 240, West Covina, CA 91790
  Maria Quintanilla, Director

Lilliput Children's Services **916.941.8799**
Fax 916.941.8796
  1190 Suncast Ln Ste 2, El Dorado Hills, CA 95762

Lilliput Children's Svcs **916.923.5444**
Fax 916.923.2365
Web ....www.lilliput.org
E-mail ....director@lilliput.org
  1651 Response Rd Ste 300, Sacramento, CA 95815-5254
  Karen Alvord, Executive Director

Making a Difference Rancho Mediterrania **909.350.4895**
  700 E Washington St, Colton, CA 92324

McKinley Children's Center (MCC) **909.305.9412**
Fax 626.639.0243
E-mail ....masona@mckinleycc.org
  762 W Cypress St, San Dimas, CA 91773
  Al Mason, Director

Metro Plex Whilshire Bldg **800.735.4984**
  3530 Wilshire Blvd, Los Angeles, CA 90010

Mountain Circle Family Svcs Inc a Foster **530.284.7007**
E-mail ....srossington@mountaincircle.org
  312 Crescent St, Greenville, CA 95947
  Shauna Rossington, Executive Director

New Directions of Humboldt **707.777.3532**
  PO Box 1283, Eureka, CA 95502

Nightlight Christian Adoptions (NCA) **714.693.5437**
Fax 714.693.5438
E-mail ....info@nightlight.org
  4430 E Miraloma Ave, Ste B, Anaheim, CA 92807
  Ciara Collins, Office Manager

Nuevo Amanecer Latino Children's Services **323.720.9951**
Fax 323.720.9953
Web ....www.nalffa.org
  5400 Pomona Boulevard, Los Angeles, CA 90022
  COA accredited organization.

Olive Crest Adoption Services **714.543.5437**
Fax 714.543.5463
E-mail ....info@olivecrest.org
  2130 E 4th St, Ste 200, Santa Ana, CA 92705
  Donald Verleur, Chief Executive Officer

Optimist Foster Family & Adoption Agency **323.341.5561**
E-mail ....silorlando@oyhfs.org
  7003 N Figueroa St, Los Angeles, CA 90041
  Silvio Orlando, Chief Executive Officer

Post Adoption Services Project (PASP) **707.476.9210**
Fax 707.422.6672
E-mail ....cinsav@aol.com
  10 W 7th St, Ste H, Eureka, CA 95501

Rauline Atkins **323.935.4276**
Fax 323.965.1015
E-mail ....rauline@fosterparents.com
  2248 S Cloverdale Ave, Los Angeles, CA 90020
  Rauline Atkins, Director

Rebekah Children's Services Family **408.842.8815**
E-mail ....contactlinkage@rcskids.org
  290 IOOF Ave, Gilroy, CA 95020

Room for One More c/o Ward A.M.E Church **626.359.3680**
  1177 W 25th St, Los Angeles, CA 90007

Share Homes Adoption & Foster Care **209.334.6376**
Fax 209.334.4408
E-mail ....info@sharehomes.org
  210 N School St, Lodi, CA 95240

Stanford Home for Children's Foster Care **916.344.0199**
E-mail ....info@stanfordhome.org
  8912 Volunteer Ln, Sacramento, CA 95826
  Christina Cagle, Recruitment Specialist

Stars of David International Inc **949.262.3447**
E-mail ....starsdavid@aol.com
  7 Admiral, Irvine, CA 92714

Stars of David International Inc **408.832.1825**
E-mail ....dorothyheller@hotmail.com
  959 Astoria Dr, Sunnyvale, CA 94087

Stars of David International Inc **925.932.3078**
E-mail ....MikeREllen@aol.com
  107 Mandala Ct, Walnut Creek, CA 94596

The Family Network Inc (TFN) **831.462.8954**
Fax 831.462.8958
E-mail ....domestic@adopt-familynetwork.com
  2959 Park Ave, Ste D, Soquel, CA 95073
  Luke Leonard, Director

Tri Valley Foster Parent Association **909.623.8844**
Fax 909.865.5990
  1547 Via Amistad, Pomona, CA 91768

Yuba-Sutter Foster Adoptive Parent Assoc **530.743.8437**
Fax 530.634.7686
E-mail ....leneix@yccd.edu
  2785 Plute Rd, Marysville, CA 95901
  Leah Roberts, Director

HOME MEDICAL EQUIPMENT PROVIDERS

A 1 Rehab 818.842.1000
Fax 866.208.6513
E-mail ....info@bmedical.com
11030 Arrow Route 103, Rancho Cucamonga, CA 91730

Abbey Medical Plaza 559.431.1000
Fax 559.432.8036
6616 N Blackstone Ave, Fresno, CA 93710

Ability Center 714.890.8262
Fax 714.901.1492
E-mail ....kmiller@AbilityCenter.com
11600 Western Ave, Stanton, CA 90680
Dan Monaha, Manager

Ability Center 858.541.0552
Fax 858.541.1941
E-mail ....kmiller@AbilityCenter.com
4797 Ruffner St, San Diego, CA 92111
Terry Barton, General Manager

Abrams & Clark Pharmacy & Hlth Care Ctr 562.427.7901
Fax 562.427.9638
3841 Atlantic Ave, Long Beach, CA 90807
Fkyora, Director

Access Options Inc 831.722.6804
Fax 831.722.0236
109 Lee Road Ste D, Watsonville, CA 95076
Mark Sagal, Director

Accessible Design & Consulting Inc 310.215.3332
Fax 310.417.4096
E-mail ....Adam@accessibleconstruction.com
420 S Hindry Ave B, Hinglewood, CA 90301
Adam Fine, Chief Executive Officer

Accredited Medical Equipment 800.974.1234
Fax 818.808.0629
21142 Ventura Blvd, Encino, CA 913164
Jeanette Garrett, Manager

Ace Pharmacy Equipment & Supplies 415.731.3535
Fax 415.731.8650
E-mail ....gschan_sf@hotmail.com
2505 Noriega St, San Francisco, CA 94122
Michael Chin, Director

Achievable Foundation 310.258.4256
Fax 310.258.4191
E-mail ....info@achievable.org
5901 Green Valley Circle, Ste 320, Culver City, CA 90230

Achieve Comfort Med Equipment & Supply 323.852.6900
Fax 323.852.6904
E-mail ....negotiator33001@yahoo.com
359 S Fairfax Ave, Los Angeles, CA 90036

Acme Home Elevator Inc 707.748.4490
Fax 707.748.0249
E-mail ....info@acmehe.com
4740 E 2nd St Ste 20, Benicia, CA 94510

Acology Home Healthcare 310.451.6016
Fax 310.394.2955
E-mail ....acology1@yahoo.com
1414 Wilshire Blvd, Santa Monica, CA 90403
Tina Phan, Manager

Action VW Enterprises 562.694.8600
Fax 562.694.8655
E-mail ....don@actionvw.com
621 Lake Forest Dr, Brea, CA 92821
Don Gossett, Co-owner

Adaptive Equipment Systems San Francisco 800.611.4237
Fax 800.511.4237
6724 A Preston Ave, Livermore, CA 94551

AdvantaCare Medical Equipment 831.886.5987
E-mail ....info@advantacaremedical.com
5 Manderville Court, Monterey, CA 93940

Alamo Medical 818.787.6100
Fax 818.787.9266
7101 Valjean Ave, Van Nuys, CA 91406

Alans Wheelchairs & Medical Products 714.870.9840
E-mail ....alanswheelchairs@gmail.com
PO Box 685, tustin, CA 92781
Doug Ensor, Manager

All Is Well Corporation dba El Rapha Medical Supplies 661.424.9984
Fax 661.424.0275
27125 Sierra Highway, Suite 326, Santa Clarita, CA 91351
CARF accredited programs available.

Alliance Rehab Services 562.921.0353
Fax 562.921.1404
E-mail ....apo_LL@earthlink.net
14535 Valley View Ave, Santa Fe Springs, CA 90670

Alpine Home Medical 562.493.3910
Fax 562.799.0160
E-mail ....ralpine1@aol.com
13908 Seal Beach Blvd, Seal Beach, CA 90740
James Noriega, Owner

American Mobility Center, Inc. 760.722.9802
Fax 760.722.2637
3753 Mission Avenue, Suite 114, Oceanside, CA 92054
CARF accredited programs available.

Antelope Valley Sickroom Supply 661.942.0455
Fax 661.723.1016
44814 N Date Ave, Lancaster, CA 93534

Antioch Medical Supply 925.757.4099
Fax 925.757.4788
306 G St, Antioch, CA 94509

Apria Healthcare Chico 530.891.5226
Fax 800.277.4288
E-mail ....contact_us@apria.com
3028 Esplanade Ste G, Richardson Springs, CA 95973

Apria Healthcare Concord 925.827.8800
Fax 925.680.0799
E-mail ....contact_us@apria.com
4095 Pike Lane, Concord, CA 94520
Delores Barton, Branch Manager

Apria Healthcare Fresno 559.221.2251
E-mail ....contact_us@apria.com
3524 W Holland Ave, Fresno, CA 93722
Phil Chavez, Branch Manager

Apria Healthcare Lancaster 661.949.3447
Fax 661.949.0247
43301 Division St Ste 312, Lancaster, CA 93535
Terry Scott, Branch Manager

Apria Healthcare Merced 209.384.7100
E-mail ....contact_us@apria.com
2260 Cooper Ave Unit E, Merced, CA 95348
Wade, Clerk

Apria Healthcare Modesto 209.548.4400
E-mail ....contact_us@apria.com
4400 Sisk Rd, Modesto, CA 95356
Wade Frick, Branch Director

Apria Healthcare Monterey 831.655.4080
E-mail ....contact_us@apria.com
1 Lower Ragsdale Dr Bldg 3, Ste 600, Monterey, CA 93940
Joseph Ware, Manager

Apria Healthcare National 310.297.6986
E-mail ....contact_us@apria.com
26220 Enterprise Court, Lake Forest, CA 92630
Richards Hoertz, Branch Manager

Apria Healthcare Sacramento 916.921.1162
1450 Expo Parkway, Sacramento, CA 95815
Jim Hay, Director

Apria Healthcare San Fernando 818.838.4777
Fax 818.838.7700
E-mail ....contact_us@apria.com
555 1st St, San Fernando, CA 91340

Apria Healthcare San Jose 408.383.4400
E-mail ....contact_us@apria.com
2040 Corporate Ct, San Jose, CA 95131
Joseph Ware, Branch Manager

Apria Healthcare San Leandro Branch 510.346.4000
2476 Verma Ct, San Leandro, CA 94577

Apria Healthcare Santa Rosa 707.543.0979
E-mail ....contact_us@apria.com
3636 N Laughlin Rd Ste 190, Santa Rosa, CA 95403
Ban, Branch Manager

Apria Healthcare South San Francisco 650.588.9744
E-mail ....contact_us@apria.com
480 Carlton St, South San Francisco, CA 94080
Randy, Supervisor

Apria Healthcare Stockton 209.475.6860
E-mail ....contact_us@apria.com
7514 Murray Dr, Stockton, CA 95210
Robert Haire, Chief Executive Officer

Apria Healthcare Yuba City 530.673.5513
E-mail ....contact_us@apria.com
990 Klamath Lane Ste 11, Yuba City, CA 95993
Shari Dempsey, Branch Manager

Apria Menlo Park 650.330.2420
Fax 650.330.0731
3905 Bohannon CG, Menlo Park, CA 94025
Magen Griffin, Manager

Arbor Vitae Medical Sales 310.641.5296
Fax 310.641.5298
6208 W 87th St, Los Angeles, CA 90045

Arcadia Health Care Marin 415.472.2273
Fax 415.472.2290
4340 Redwood Hwy Ste F 123, San Rafael, CA 94903
Carol P, Director

Assisted Home Hospice 818.830.5003
Fax 818.894.8707
E-mail ....hometorest@aol.com
3550 Baloo Blvd # 282 NW, Granada Hills, CA 19325
Judy Turner, Manager

ATG Rehab 916.489.3651
Fax 916.489.5949
E-mail ....hrowe@atgrehab.com
1650 Tribute Road, Sacramento, CA 95815
Steve Graham, Regional Vice President

AV Pulmonary Care 888.382.9152
Fax 661.949.1904
E-mail ....avpc@avpulmonary.com
340 W Milling St, Lancaster, CA 93534

B& B Pharmacy 714.777.2737
Fax 714.777.6888
18525 Yorba Linda Blvd, Yorba Linda, CA 92886
Jim Negrege, Director

B& R Medical Equipment Inc 714.850.9326
Fax 714.850.9816
2520 S Fairview St Ste A1, Santa Ana, CA 92704

Benton Medical 650.625.1000
Fax 650.625.1133
E-mail ....Info@BentonMedical.com
3910 Middlefield Rd, Palo Alto, CA 94303

Bischoffs Medical Mart Burlingame 650.347.6606
Fax 650.347.1460
E-mail ....bischoffbg@hotmail.com
1465 A Chapmin Ave, Burlingame, CA 94010
Mark Abaya, Owner

Bischoffs Medical Mart San Jose 408.286.6651
E-mail ....bischoffsj@hotmail.com
225 N Bascom Ave, San Jose, CA 95128
Rusty Bischoff, Director

BJ Enterprise 530.534.3390
70 Stuart Court, Oroville, CA 95965

Bowermans Pharmacy 415.566.7734
Fax..415.566.2978
E-mail..........................lhegglir@byramhealthcare.com
595 Buckingham Way, San Francisco, CA 94132

Braun Corporation 714.891.4305
Fax..714.893.3061
15731 Graham St, Huntington Beach, CA 92649

Building Blocks Ped Home Hlth Srvs 949.448.5770
Fax..949.448.5775
E-mail..........................info@buildingblockspeds.com
Corporate Offices, 6 Journey Ste 135, Aliso Viejo,
CA 92656
Ron Mills, Owner

Burger Pediatric Therapy Center 916.353.5295
Fax..916.353.5297
101 E natoma St at Fargo, Folsom, CA 95630
Karen Netherton, Owner

Bus West 562.404.8700
Fax..310.984.3996
E-mail..........................sales@buswest.com
21101 S Chico St, Carson, CA 90745
Jim Bernacchi, President

California Medical Pharmacy 213.483.3736
Fax..213.413.2341
E-mail..........................info@calimed.com
2201 W Temple St, Los Angeles, CA 90026
Thomas Latude, Chief Executive Officer

California Rehabilitation Equipment 408.739.5750
Fax..408.739.6408
295 E Washington Ave, Sunnyvale, CA 94086

Casa Colina Wheelchair Sports 909.596.7733
Fax..909.593.0153
E-mail..........................cerehab@lightside.com
255 E Bonita, Pomona, CA 91769
Felice Loverso, Chief Executive Officer

Cedars Sinai Hospital Pharmacy 310.657.1524
Fax..310.659.1766
8631 West 3rd St Ste 315, Los Angeles, CA 90048
Nicole, Customer Service

Cirtec Medical Systems 408.395.0443
101 B Cooper Ct, Los Gatos, CA 95032

Citrus Medical Supply Company 818.997.8574
Fax..818.997.6770
E-mail..........................service@citrusmedical.com
KCK Industries Citrus Med Sup, 14941 Calvert St,
Van Nuys, CA 91411

Columbia Medical 310.454.6612
Fax..310.305.1718
E-mail..........................info@columbiamedical.com
13368 Beach Ave, Marina Del Rey, CA 90292
Gary Washman, Chief Executive Officer

Complete Access 310.474.8800
Fax..310.475.6303
E-mail..........................david@complete-access.com
Complete Access, 10468 Eastborne Ave, Los Angeles,
CA 90024
David Griffin, Director

**Continuum Health Inc. dba Valley Convalescent
Center** 760.352.8471
Fax..760.352.5573
1700 South Imperial Avenue, El Centro, CA 92243
CARF accredited programs available.

Convaid Inc 310.618.0111
Fax..310.618.8811
E-mail..........................custservice@convaid.com
PO Box 4209, Palos Verdes Pnsla, CA 90274

Convalescent Aid Society 626.793.1696
Fax..626.793.9706
E-mail..........................info@convalescentaidsociety.org
3255 E Foothill Blvd, Pasadena, CA 91107
J Avila, Administrator

Craft Wheelchair Repair 323.931.6164
Fax..323.931.2907
5515 San Vincente Blvd, Los Angeles, CA 90019
Shay M, Director

CTAP Access Service Center Sacramento 800.806.1191
Fax..800.889.3974
2033 Howe Ave Ste 150, Sacramento, CA 95825
Silke Brendel-Evans, Project Coordinator

Designing Mobility 562.921.0258
Fax..562.921.3730
12627 Hidden Creek Way, Cerritos, CA 90703
Troy Kubinski, General Manager

DexCom, Inc. 858.200.0233
Fax..858.200.0201
Web..dexcom.com
6340 Sequence Drive, San Diego, CA 92121
CARF accredited programs available.

DIESTCO Manufacturing Corporation 800.795.2392
Fax..530.893.2635
E-mail..........................info@diestco.com
PO Box 6504, Chico, CA 95927
Dan Diestco, Chief Executive Officer

Disabled Resources Center Inc 562.427.1000
Fax..562.427.2027
E-mail..........................info@drcinc.org
2750 E Spring St Ste 100, Long Beach, CA 90806
Dolores Nason, Executive Director

Durable Medical Equipment 800.400.4210
E-mail..........................info@durablemedical.com
1135 Eugenia Place Ste B, Carpinteria, CA 93013
Brian Himovitz, Director

Eagle Medical Supplies 818.559.6390
Fax..818.559.2355
922 1/2 S San Fernando Blvd, Burbank, CA 91502

Easter Seal Society Napa 707.584.1443
Fax..707.584.3438
5440 State Farm Dr, Rohnert Park, CA 94928
Craig King, President

Easter Seals 805.543.4122
Fax..805.543.8951
E-mail..........................info@ca-tr.easter-seals.org
4251 S Higuera St, Ste 101, San Luis Obispo,
CA 93401

Easter Seals 805.899.4557
Fax..805.899.4549
E-mail..........................info@ca-tr.easterseals.org
532 Santa Barbara St, Santa Barbara, CA 93101

Easter Seals 805.647.1141
Fax..805.647.1148
E-mail..........................info@ca-tr.easter-seals.org
10730 Henderson Road, Ventura, CA 93004

Easter Seals Central California 831.242.2110
Fax..831.242.2111
381 High St, Monterey, CA 93942

Easter Seals Central California 831.684.2166
Fax..831.684.1018
Administrative Offices, 9010 Soquel Dr, Aptos,
CA 95003

Easter Seals Northern CA San Rafael 415.382.7450
Fax..415.382.6052
E-mail..........................info@easter-seals.org
20 Pimenten Court Ste A 1, Novato, CA 94949
Mary Obrian, Human Resource Director

Electropedic Electric Medical Equipment 800.727.1954
Fax..818.953.7421
907 Hollywood Way, Burbank, CA 91505
Lloyd Araus, Director

Galaxy Medical Online 818.986.9833
Fax..818.986.9834
16756 Ventura Blvd, Encino, CA 91436
Brad, Manager

Golden Years Medical 415.333.0746
Fax..415.469.8908
1415 Ocean Ave, San Francisco, CA 94112

Grag Supply Co 831.757.8736
607 Brunken Ave, Salinas, CA 93901

Hanger Prosthetics and Orthotics 916.452.5724
Fax..916.452.2715
E-mail..........................091700@hanger.com
1248 32nd St, Sacramento, CA 95816
Bryan Hayes, Branch Manager

Health and Mobility Inc 951.600.1635
Fax..951.600.1409
40414 California Oaks Road, Suite I, Murrieta,
CA 92562
CARF accredited programs available.

Hi Med Medical Supplies Glendale 818.246.8444
Fax..818.246.0669
744 1/2 N Glendale Ave, Glendale, CA 91206
Aaion, Manager

Home Health Depot 310.891.1954
Fax..310.891.3713
E-mail..........................orderdesk@hhd1.com
2059 Pacific Coast Hwy, Lomita, CA 90717
James Leedom, Chief Executive Officer

Horsnyder Medical & Orthopedics 831.724.2453
Fax..831.724.2009
1433 Freedom Blvd, Watsonville, CA 95076

Horsnyder Medical & Orthopedics 831.458.1400
Fax..831.458.1401
1226 Soquel Ave, Santa Cruz, CA 95062

Horton & Converse Pharmacy 323.466.7606
Fax..323.966.5542
325 N Larchmont Blvd, Los Angeles, CA 90004

Hospice of the Valley 408.947.1233
Fax..408.288.4172
E-mail..........................request@hospicevalley.org
4850 Union Ave, San Jose, CA 95124
Sally Adelus, Chief Executive Officer

Hot Shot Products 310.533.5911
Fax..310.533.1971
E-mail..........................b1hotshot@aol.com
1920 Del Amo Blvd Ste A, Torrance, CA 90501

House Ear Institute and Clinic 213.483.4431
2100 W Third St, Los Angeles, CA 90057

Huskins Medical Supplies 323.254.6665
Fax..323.254.0549
3957 Eagle Rock Blvd, Los Angeles, CA 90065

Johnston Medical Equipment Recycling 510.843.2488
2801 Shattuck, Berkeley, CA 94705
Stewert Johnston, Owner

Kids Korner Medical Supply 408.971.1034
Fax..408.971.6665
165 Lewis Road Ste 10, San Jose, CA 95111

Life Care Home Health & Med 310.479.0094
Fax..310.477.0999
E-mail..........................lifecarem@aol.com
11843 Wilshire Blvd, Los Angeles, CA 90025
Sean Naim, Chief Executive Officer

Lincare Culver City 310.670.5282
Fax..310.670.5181
5767 A Uplander Way, Culver City, CA 90230

Lincare Fresno 559.435.6379
6687 N Blackstone Ave Ste 101, Fresno, CA 93710
Robert, Central Manager

Lincare Modesto 209.522.4985
Fax..209.522.4987
4600 North Star Way, Modesto, CA 95356
Meleisa Griswood, Manager

Lincare Salinas 831.758.4612
Fax 831.758.4723
    365 Victor St Ste I, Salinas, CA 93907
Stella Hughes, Manager

Lincare Watsonville 831.724.1211
Fax 831.724.2551
    444 Airport Blvd Ste 105, Watsonville, CA 95076
Elise Carroll, General Manager

Lincare Yuba City 530.755.0200
Fax 530.755.3637
    990 Klamath Lane Ste 25, Yuba City, CA 95993

Macs Lift Gate Inc 562.634.5962
Fax 562.634.4291
E-mail ....MacsLift@aol.com
    2715 Seaboard Lane, Long Beach, CA 90805

MAX Ability Inc Tech for a Barrier Free 707.575.5558
Fax 707.575.3856
E-mail ....lk@max-ability.com
    1275 Fourth St Ste 304, Santa Rosa, CA 95404
Lee Kaufman, Chief Executive Officer

Medical Home Care 818.503.1424
Fax 818.764.6008
    11860 Vose St, North Hollywood, CA 91605

MedicAlert 209.668.3333
Fax 209.669.2495
E-mail ....customer_service@medicalert.org
    2323 Colorado Ave, Turlock, CA 95382
Andrew Wigglesworth, Executive Director

Metro Med Inc Home Resp Specialists 818.840.9090
Fax 818.840.2730
E-mail ....mloos@metromed.com
    1701 N San Fernando Blvd, Burbank, CA 91504
Vaughan Gonzalez, Branch Manager

Michaels Pharmacy 626.793.7131
Fax 626.793.8602
E-mail ....michaelzafiert@mezrx.com
    960 E Green St, Pasadena, CA 91106
Michael Zafiert, Owner

Midway Drugs 626.448.7659
Fax 626.443.8253
    10410 Lower Azusa Rd, El Monte, CA 91731
Young Cho, Director

MJ Medical Supplies 619.644.2695
Fax 619.644.2698
    8893 La Mesa Blvd Ste E, La Mesa, CA 91942
Anja Mullins, Owner

Mobility Systems Inc 510.540.0295
Fax 510.540.0299
E-mail ....mobility@pacbell.net
    1715 64th St, Emeryville, CA 94608
Bill, Chief Executive Officer

Muscular Dystrophy Assoc & MDA Clinic 916.921.9518
Fax 916.921.1767
    3010 Lava Ridge Ct, Ste 160, Roseville, CA 95661
Andrew Sheehy, Executive Director

Muscular Dystrophy Assoc Long Beach 562.498.4923
Fax 562.498.4933
E-mail ....longbeach@mdausa.org
    Circle Business Center, 4510 E Pacific Coast Hwy Ste
    120, Long Beach, CA 90804
Jessica Bourdeau, Executive Director

Muscular Dystrophy Assoc Pleasanton 925.803.1100
Fax 925.803.2954
    7567 Amador Valley Blvd, Ste 101, Dublin, CA 94568

Muscular Dystrophy Assoc San Jose 408.423.9345
Fax 408.261.2658
E-mail ....sanjosedistrict@mdausa.or@gmail.com
    4300 Stevens Creek, Ste 117, San Jose, CA 95129

Muscular Dystrophy Association San Fran 415.673.7500
Fax 416.673.7501
E-mail ....835.office@mdausa.org
    1388 Sutter Ste 3505, San Francisco, CA 94109
Tina Faulkner, Executive Director

National Seating & Mobility Chatsworth 818.718.1771
Fax 818.718.1662
E-mail ....nsm08@nsm-seating.com
    21807 Plummer St, Chatsworth, CA 91311

National Seating & Mobility Stockton 866.389.4501
Fax 209.546.1797
E-mail ....Stockton@nsm-seating.com
    2474 Wigwam Dr Ste E, Stockton, CA 95205

National Seating and Mobility Anaheim 714.939.9322
Fax 714.939.9323
    1125 East Stanford Court, Anaheim, CA 92805
Tish Wordan, Director

Natural Access 310.392.9864
E-mail ....natural@superlink.net
    PO Box 5729, Santa Monica, CA 90409

Nestor Machine Company 818.707.1678
Fax 818.707.1611
E-mail ....standmaster@yahoo.com
    31143 Via Colinas 404, Thousand Oaks, CA 91362

North American Home Health Supply Inc 800.577.3579
Fax 818.782.3706
    16129 Cohasset St, Van Nuys, CA 91406
Michael Groman, Pharmacist

Olympic Medical Supply and Home Care 323.726.9230
    5740 E Olympic Blvd, Los Angeles, CA 90022

Oxia Respiratory & Home Med Equipment 310.995.0999
Fax 818.786.8056
E-mail ....oxiamedical@gmail.com
    7324 N Sepulveda Blvd, Van Nuys, CA 91405
Dyanne Chae, Director

Perpetual Home Medical Equipment and Supplies,
Inc. 213.388.9560
Fax 213.388.9561
    3018 Beverly Boulevard, Unit C, Los Angeles,
    CA 90057-1027
CARF accredited programs available.

Pico Med Products Sales & Rentals 323.936.4104
Fax 323.936.3454
E-mail ....order@shoppicomedical.com
    6035 W Pico Blvd, Los Angeles, CA 90035
Kimberly Edwards, Director

Piners Med Equip & Oxygen Supply 707.224.7921
E-mail ....pingary@aol.com
    1820 Pueblo Ave, Napa, CA 94558
Christine S, Office Manager

Playa Medical Services Los Angeles 800.647.7978
    5250 W Century Blvd, Los Angeles, CA 90045

Prime Medical Supply Inc 909.278.9111
Fax 909.278.9909
    12102 Severn Way, Riverside, CA 92503

Rancho Los Amigos Ntl Rehab Ctr Downey 562.401.7111
    7601 E Imperial Highway, Downey, CA 90242

Redwood Empire Med Supply Rohnert
Park 707.585.6800
Fax 707.585.6886
E-mail ....Sales@remsca.com
    6620 Redwood Dr Ste 1, Rohnert Park, CA 94928
Valerie F, Co-owner

Rehab Medical Inc 562.944.3495
Fax 562.944.3506
E-mail ....rehabmed@msn.com
    12015 Mora Dr Ste 2, Santa Fe Springs, CA 90670

Rehab Specialists Inc Campbell 408.376.2050
Fax 408.376.2780
E-mail ....mikem@rehabspecialists.co@msn.com
    256 East Hamilton Ave Ste C, Campbell, CA 95008

Rehab Specialists Inc Watsonville 831.724.5544
Fax 831.724.3334
E-mail ....lettied@rehabspecialists.com
    446 Westridge Dr, Watsonville, CA 95076

Rehab Specialists Mountain View 650.965.8282
Fax 650.966.8108
E-mail ....mikem@rehabspecialists.co@msn.com
    2557 Wyandotte St, Mountain View, CA 94043

Rhodora Fiore General Partnership dba R & F Home Medical
Equipment & Supplies 707.426.1770
Fax 707.426.1772
    1076 Horizon Drive, Unit 4, Fairfield, CA 94533
CARF accredited programs available.

Royal Medical Supply Inc Berkeley 510.540.0494
    2929 Telegraph Ave, Berkeley, CA 94705

Sacramento Ear Nose & Throat Surg &
Med 916.736.3399
Fax 916.736.3350
    1111 Exposition Blvd, Bldg 700, Sacramento,
    CA 95815
Jeff Dudley, Chief Executive Officer

San Jose Med Supply 408.453.1333
Fax 408.453.9114
    283 E Brokaw Rd, San Jose, CA 95112

Sarah Medical Equipment 310.396.5258
    2632 Lincoln Blvd, Santa Monica, CA 90405
Mike Chad, Chief Executive Officer

Sherman Oaks Medical Supply 818.981.9906
Fax 818.981.6698
E-mail ....Info@shermanoaksmedical.com
    4840 Van Nuys Blvd, Sherman Oaks, CA 91403
Jack Kell, Chief Executive Officer

Sierra Pediatric Therapy Clinic 916.791.2747
Fax 916.791.2189
    700 Sunrise Ave, Ste O, Granite Bay, CA 95661
Kristine Korns, Director

Social Vocational Srvs Inc 310.944.3303
Fax 310.944.3304
E-mail ....Haney@svsinc.org
    3555 Torrance Blvd, Torrance, CA 90503
Patricia Langley, Business Manager

South Bay Home Health Care 310.618.9555
Fax 310.618.0614
E-mail ....info@myhealthcenter.com
    1349 El Prado Ave, Torrance, CA 90501
Marian Tenne, Owner

Southern California Mobility 714.898.7838
Fax 714.898.9134
E-mail ....info@socalmobility.com
    11560 Seaboard Circle, Stanton, CA 90680

Spectra Concepts 888.744.4803
Fax 916.983.2549
E-mail ....srdeubel@covad.net
    182 Black Powder Circle, Folsom, CA 95630

Spina Bifida Association of Greater LA 562.929.6806
E-mail ....paula_sba@hotmail.com
    2400 S Flower St, Los Angeles, CA 90007
Paula Herman, Chairman

Supercare Medical Supply 626.854.2200
Fax 626.723.8270
E-mail ....info@supercaremed.com
    16017 Valley Blvd, La Puente, CA 91744
Katherine Golden, Human Resource Assistant

Superior Mobility 310.533.4840
Fax 310.212.3120
E-mail ....tlindsey@superiormobility.com
    Corporate Office & Retail Store, 360 Maple Ave,
    Torrance, CA 90503
Tracy Lindsey, Supervisor

Taylor Marketing Services 916.721.7518
Fax 916.721.4529
    6380 Tupelo Drive, Suite 4, Citrus Heights, CA 95621
CARF accredited programs available.

California

Terrapin Technologies T2000 ....310.212.3067
E-mail ....terrapinorthos@sbcglobal.net
1508 Cabrillo Ave, Torrance, CA 90501
Matthew Alegria, Manager

The Bone Store 559.226.7500
343 East Shaw, Fresno, CA 93710
Craig Clarke, Manager

THI Medical Equipment 909.672.2829
Fax 909.672.6773
E-mail ....sales@thimedical.com
27188 Sun City Blvd, Sun City, CA 92586

Titus Home Healthcare Center 626.284.3221
Fax 626.284.4993
160 S Garfield Ave, Alhambra, CA 91801

TL Shield & Associates Inc 818.509.8228
Fax 818.509.8596
E-mail ....info@tlshield.com
11800 Sheldon St Unit A, Sun Valley, CA 91352

Trinity Kids Care 310.530.3800
Fax 310.534.5095
E-mail ....julie.lutat@providence.org
2601 Airport Dr Ste 230, Torrance, CA 90505
Julie Lutat, Director

Unified Healthcare 562.404.8052
Fax 562.407.2834
E-mail ....nchacon@unifiedhealthcare.com
9234 Norwalk Blvd, Santa Fe Springs, CA 90670
Nancy Chacon, General Manager

United Wheelchairs 916.688.8890
Fax 916.688.8991
E-mail ....info@unitedwheelchairs.co@msn.com
PO Box 293704

Valley Oxygen Medical Equipment Napa 707.257.7785
Fax 707.257.7834
907 Trancas, Napa, CA 94558

Valley Patient Care 831.757.3268
401 Victor Way 2, Salinas, CA 93907

Western Drug Medical Supply 818.956.6691
Fax 818.956.6695
3604 San Fernando Rd, Glendale, CA 91204
Haig, Manager

Westside Home Medical Equipment 310.204.2375
Fax 310.204.2549
E-mail ....westsidehme@yahoo.com
2743 S Robertson Blvd, Los Angeles, CA 90034
Mike Kalifa, Manager

Wheelchair City, Inc. 951.677.5568
Fax 951.677.5724
Web ....www.wheelchaircity.com
41610 Date Street, Suite 105, Murrieta, CA 92562
CARF accredited programs available.

Wheelchairs of San Mateo & Wheelchair 925.427.3773
E-mail ....wcsmshop@mac.com
Wheelchairs of San Mateo, 1251 California Ave Ste
500, Pittsburg, CA 94565
Antonio Guttirez, Chief Executive Officer

Wishing Well Bay Area Medical 310.829.1777
Fax 310.829.2799
2314 Santa Monica Blvd, Santa Monica, CA 90404

Words Plus Inc. 800.869.8521
Fax 661.723.2114
Web ....www.words-plus.com
42505 Tenth Street West, Lancaster, CA 93534
CARF accredited programs available.

PEDIATRIC HOME CARE

Interim Healthcare 408.292.5680
Fax 408.292.5685
1762 Technology Dr Ste 211, San Jose, CA 95110
Robert Seawright, Chief Executive Officer

Interim Healthcare 916.486.8181
Fax 916.486.8136
2941 B Fulton Ave, Sacramento, CA 95821
Sherry Elia, Director

Interim Healthcare 925.944.5779
Fax 925.944.7011
1717 N California Blvd Ste 3A, Walnut Creek,
CA 94596
Joe Bettencourt, Director

Interim Healthcare 530.673.0300
Fax 530.673.2349
E-mail ....mgraham@interimhc.com
1557 Starr Dr Ste D, Yuba City, CA 95993
Marisa Graham, Manager

Interim Healthcare 310.338.1289
Fax 310.338.9154
8939 S Sepulveda Blvd Ste 261, Los Angeles,
CA 90045

Interim Healthcare 209.472.6040
Fax 209.952.5211
E-mail ....rmurphy@interimhealthcare.org
1110 Tully Ste C, Stockton, CA 95350
Ron Murphy, Director

Interim Healthcare 858.576.9501
Fax 858.576.1581
5625 Ruffin Rd Ste 225, San Diego, CA 92123
Jan Dutro, Office Manager

Interim Healthcare 760.432.9811
Fax 760.739.1366
425 W 5th Ave, Escondido, CA 92025
Wendy Olayvar, Administrator

Interim Healthcare 559.224.0560
Fax 559.224.9464
1320 E Shaw Ave, Ste 110, Fresno, CA 93710
Sarah Ahmed, Director

Interim Healthcare 714.937.2900
Fax 714.937.1201
23691 Birtcher Dr, Lake Forest, CA 92630

Interim Healthcare 951.684.6111
Fax 951.781.9947
7000 Indiana Ave Ste 107, Riverside, CA 92506

Interim Healthcare 661.395.1700
Fax 661.395.1800
4801 Truxtun Ave, Bakersfield, CA 93309

Interim Healthcare 562.207.6970
Fax 562.207.6981
16429 Berwyn Rd, Cerritos, CA 90703
John Shang, Chief Executive Officer

Interim Healthcare 530.722.1530
Fax 530.528.7791
2120 Main St Ste C, Red Bluff, CA 96080
Rhonda Robertson, Office Manager

Interim Healthcare 530.221.1212
Fax 530.221.7836
E-mail ....cindy@interimhc.com
970 Executive Way, Redding, CA 96002
Cindy Seawright, Owner

Interim Healthcare (Chico Home Style) 530.899.9777
Fax 530.566.0397
2060 Talbert Ave Ste 140, Chico, CA 95928

Interim Healthcare (Chico Staffing) 530.892.8200
Fax 530.566.0397
2060 Talbert Ave, Chico, CA 95928

Interim Healthcare (Grass Valley HomeSt 530.272.0300
Fax 530.272.1572
E-mail ....gemp@interimhc.com
406 E Main St Ste AB, Grass Valley, CA 95945
Robert Seawright, Director

Interim Healthcare (Modesto Home Style) 209.577.4625
Fax 209.544.8895
1110 Tully Rd Ste B, Modesto, CA 95350
John Murphy, Chief Executive Officer

Interim Healthcare (Redding Home Style) 530.422.4600
Fax 530.221.0389
2608 Victor Ave Ste A, Redding, CA 96002
Rhonda Robertson, Manager

Interim Healthcare (Sacramento Staffing 916.921.2121
Fax 916.921.6355
3100 Fite Cir Ste 102, Sacramento, CA 95827

Interim Healthcare (San Jose Home Style 408.286.6888
1762 Technology Dr Ste 203, San Jose, CA 95110
Lisa Northup, Manager

Interim Healthcare (San Jose Staffing) 408.298.7823
Web ....www.interimHealthcare.com
1762 Technology Dr Ste 203, San Jose, CA 95110
Lisa Northup, Manager

Sacramento PDN 916.929.3286
1401 El Camino Ave Ste 520, Sacramento, CA 95815
Debby Scott, Director Of Nursing

SOCIAL SERVICES

4C's 408.487.0747
Fax 408.943.8423
Web www.4c.org
E-mail ....maryellenh@4c.org
2515 N First St, San Jose, CA 95131-4702
Mary Ellen Haley, Director Community Child Care

Action Alliance For Children 510.444.7136
Fax 510.444.7138
Web www.4children.org
E-mail ....aac@4children.org
1201 Martin Luther King Jr Way Ste A, Oakland,
CA 94612
Lisaruth Shulman, Executive Director

Adoption Info Ctr 424.757.5170
Fax 424.757.5181
Web ....adoptioninformationcenter.net
E-mail ....la_adoptions@yahoo.com
1327 post ave ste k, Point, CA 90501
Susanne Rose, Executive Director

Alameda Foster Parent Assoc 510.430.1299
Fax 510.553.1565
2494 Truman Ave, Oakland, CA 94605-4839
Tina Hughes, President

Alpha Of San Diego, Inc 619.285.9999
Fax 619.285.1938
Web ....www.alphabhs.org
E-mail ....scotts@alphaofsandiego.org
4069 30th St, San Diego, CA 92104-2601
Olivier Sue, Operations Manager

American Health Services 661.254.6630
Fax 661.254.6644
Web ....www.ahsadm.com
26460 Summit Circle, Santa Clarita, CA 91350
COA accredited organization.

American Indian Child Resource Ctr 510.208.1870
Fax 510.208.1886
Web ....www.aicrc.org
E-mail ....mary@aicrc.org
522 Grand Ave, Oakland, CA 94610-3515
Mary Trimble Norris, Executive Director

Angels Way Maternity Home 818.346.2229
Fax 818.594.5746
Web ....www.angelswayhome.net
22212 Welby Way, Canoga Park, CA 91303-2463

Asian Pacific Family Ctr 626.287.2988
Fax 626.287.1937
Web ....www.pacificclinic.org
E-mail ....tgock@pacificclinics.org
9353 Valley Blvd, Rosemead, CA 91770
Terry Gock, Director

Aspira Foster And Family Svcs **925.753.2156**
Fax 925.753.2157
Web .... www.aspiranet.org
E-mail .... ocaton@aspiranet.org
3727 Sunset Ln, Antioch, CA 94509-4410
Odessa Caton, Director

Aviva Family and Children's Services dba Hamburger Home **323.876.0550**
Fax 323.436.7042
Web .... www.avivacenter.org
7120 Franklin Avenue, Los Angeles, CA 90046
COA accredited organization.

Bananas, Inc **510.658.0381**
Fax 510.658.8354
Web .... www.bananasinc.org
E-mail .... bananas@bananasin.org
5232 Claremont Ave, Oakland, CA 94618
Arlyce Currie, Director

Big Brothers & Big Sisters **805.484.2282**
Fax 805.484.3859
Web .... www.bbsvc.org
E-mail .... lwest@bbsvc.org
445 Rosewood Ave Ste Q, Camarillo, CA 93010-5931
Lynne West, CEO

Birth Choice Health Ctr **714.836.5447**
Fax 714.836.1855
E-mail .... stana@birthchoiceclinic.org
415 N Sycamore St Ste 200, Santa Ana, CA 92701
Krystal Lopez, Director

Blind Children's Ctr **323.664.2153**
Fax 323.665.3828
Web .... www.blindchildrencenter.org
E-mail .... info@blindchildrenscenter.org
4120 Marathon St, Los Angeles, CA 10029
Midge Horton, Executive Director

Calico Ctr **510.895.0702**
Fax 510.895.0706
Web .... www.calicocenter.org
E-mail .... calicomainr@yahoo.com
524 Estudillo Ave, San Leandro, CA 94577
Vicki Gwaisda, Executive Director

California Child Care Resource And Referral Network **415.882.0234**
Fax 415.882.6233
Web .... www.rrnetwork.org
E-mail .... info@rrnetwork.org
111 New Montgomery St, Fl 7, San Francisco, CA 94105
Patricia Siegal, CEO

California Wellness Foundation **818.702.1900**
Fax 818.702.1999
Web .... www.tcwf.org
E-mail .... gyates@tcwf.org
6320 Canoga Ave Ste 1700, Woodland Hills, CA 91367-2565
Gary Yates, President

Casa Pacifica **805.445.7800**
Fax 805.987.7237
Web .... www.casapacifica.org
1722 South Lewis Road, Camarillo, CA 93012
COA accredited organization.

Catholic Charities **805.643.4694**
Fax 805.643.4781
E-mail .... mperry@ccharitiesvc.org
303 N Ventura Ave, Ste A, Ventura, CA 93001
Michael Perry, Executive Director

Catholic Charities **909.388.1239**
Fax 909.384.1130
1450 N D St, San Bernardino, CA 92405
Kenneth Sawa, Director

Catholic Charities **707.224.4403**
Fax 707.224.2889
Web .... www.srcharities.org
1248 Haye St, Napa, CA 94559-2439
Brian O Callaghan, Regional Director

Catholic Charities **805.965.7045**
Fax 805.963.2978
Web .... www.catholiccharitiesla.org
E-mail .... frank.bognar@ccsbca.org
609 E Haley St, Santa Barbara, CA 93103-3160
Frank Bogner, Regional Director

Catholic Charities of Los Angeles, Inc. **213.251.3400**
Fax 213.380.4603
Web .... www.catholiccharitiesla.org
P.O. Box 15095, Los Angeles, CA 90015-0095
COA accredited organization.

Central Valley Children's Svcs Network **559.456.1100**
Fax 559.456.8381
Web .... www.cvcsn.org
E-mail .... info@cvsn.org
1911 N Helm Ave, Fresno, CA 93727-1614
Gayle Duffy, Director

Child Abuse Prevention Council **510.780.8989**
Fax 510.780.8710
E-mail .... bormaj@acgov.org
24100 Amador St Suite 537, Hayward, CA 94544-1225
Janette Bormann, Director

Child Abuse Prevention Council **760.353.8300**
Fax 760.353.8380
E-mail .... iccapc@sbcglobal.net
563 W Main St, El Centro, CA 92243-2906
Yvette Garcia, Director

Child Abuse Svcs Team Ctr **707.476.1240**
Fax 707.445.7538
E-mail .... humcocast@co.humboldt.ca.us
333 K St, Eureka, CA 95501-0528
Kelly Neel, Director

Child Care Resource And Referral **831.757.0775**
Fax 831.757.7549
Web .... www.maof.org
E-mail .... sviramontes@maof.org
3 Trail Run Cir, Salinas, CA 93907
Soledad Viramontes, Director

Child Development Resource **805.485.7878**
Fax 805.278.0775
Web .... www.cdrv.org
221 E Ventura Blvd, Oxnard, CA 92036
Tanya McMahan, Program Manager

Child Quest International, Inc. **408.287.4673**
Fax 408.287.4676
Web .... www.childquest.org
E-mail .... info@childquest.org
1060 N 4th St Ste 200, San Jose, CA 95112-4941
Marcia Slacke, Executive Director

Childnet Youth And Family Svcs **562.498.5500**
Fax 562.498.5501
Web .... www.childnet.net
E-mail .... tbender@childnet.net
5150 E Pacific Coast Hwy Ste 365, P.O. Box 4550, Long Beach, CA 90804-3323
Nabil Tafakji, Vp Foster Care & Adoption Services

Children's Bureau of Southern California **213.342.0100**
Fax 213.342.0200
Web www.all4kids.org
1910 Magnolia Avenue, Los Angeles, CA 90007-1220
COA accredited organization.

Children's Ctr Of The Antelope Valley **661.949.1206**
Fax 661.940.5452
Web .... www.childrenscenter.av.org
E-mail .... chldctr@qnet.com
45111 Fern Ave, Lancaster, CA 93534-2301
Jay Egan, Director

Children's Defense Fund **510.663.3224**
Fax 510.663.1783
Web .... www.cdfca.org
E-mail .... jlima@cdfca.org
2201 Broadway Ste 705, Oakland, CA 94612-3024
Julene Lima, Administrator

Children's Home Society **530.673.7503**
Fax 530.673.9215
E-mail .... gaileenb@chs-ca.org
990 Klamath Ln Ste 18, Yuba City, CA 95993
Gaileen Bumgarner, Administrator

Children's Home Society **858.715.5515**
Fax 858.715.5525
Web .... www.chs-ca.org
E-mail .... betty@chs-ca.org
8765 Aero Dr Ste 300, San Diego, CA 92123-1767
Betty Mroz, Director/president/CEO

Children's Home Society Of California **213.240.5900**
Fax 213.240.5945
Web .... www.chs-ca.org
1300 W 4th St, Los Angeles, CA 90017-1475
James T. Spradley Jr., President

Children's Institute International Burton E Green Ctr **310.783.4677**
Fax 310.783.4676
Web .... www.childrensinstitute.org
E-mail .... memmons@childrensinstitute.org
21810 Normandie Ave, Torrance, CA 90502-2047
Mary M. Emmons, Executive Director

Children's Interview Ctr **408.277.5688**
Fax 408.289.9649
777 N 1st St Ste 320, San Jose, CA 95112
Trish Martinez, Center Coordinator

Children's Shelter **408.558.5400**
Fax 408.558.5599
4525 Union Ave, San Jose, CA 95124
Doug Southard, Director

Children's Svcs Colusa Co. Ofc Of Education **530.458.0300**
Fax 530.458.0301
Web www.colusa-coe.k12.ca.us
E-mail .... rperyam@ccoe.net
345 5th St, Ste ABC, Colusa, CA 95932
Richard Peryam, Assistant Superintendent

Choices **530.926.6726**
Web .... www.snowcrest.net
E-mail .... choices@snowcrest.net
215 W Alma St, Mount Shasta, CA 96067-2205
Donna Mathwig, Director

Choices For Children **530.694.2129**
Fax 530.694.1889
Web www.choices4children.org
E-mail .... cfcalpine@gbis.com
100 Foothill Rd, Markleeville, CA 96120
Rachel Brothers, Director

CO OP Town Park Villas Branch **858.453.0182**
Fax 858.453.1601
6314 Gullstrand St, San Diego, CA 92122
Craig Lambert, Sr. Director

Coleman Advocates For Children & Youth **415.239.0161**
Fax 415.239.0584
Web .... www.colemanadvocates.org
E-mail .... info@colemanadvocates.org
459 Vienna St, San Francisco, CA 94112-2831
N Tanya Lee, Director

College Avenue Senior Center Branch **619.583.3300**
Fax 619.583.3303
4855 College Ave, San Diego, CA 92115
Sherry Fusco, Director

Community Action Partnership **805.541.2272**
Fax 805.541.0141
Web .... www.capslo.org
805 Fiero Ln Ste A, San Luis Obispo, CA 93401-8911
Shana Paulson, Resource And Referal Manager

Community Child Care Council 707.544.3077
Fax...707.544.2625
Web www.sonoma4cs.org
E-mail ....mdoan@sonoma4cs.org
  396 Tesconi Ct, Santa Rosa, CA 95401-4653
  Mary Anne Doan, Executive Director

Community Connection For Child Care 661.861.5200
Fax...661.861.5261
Web ....www.kcsos.kern.org/cccc
E-mail ....licuncanpurcell@kern.org
  2000 24th St, Ste 100, Bakersfield, CA 93301
  Lisa Purcell, Program Manager

Community Connection For Children 760.934.3343
Fax...760.934.2075
  625 Old Mammth Rd, Mammoth Lakes, CA 93546
  Robyn S, Director

Community Of Caring 209.465.5433
Fax...209.463.5937
E-mail ....respectlife@stocktondiocese.org
  1125 N Lincoln St, Stockton, CA 95203
  Nancy Bonnet, Director

Community Services Agency 209.558.2500
Fax...209.558.2558
Web ....www.stanworks.com
  P.O. Box 42, Modesto, CA 95353-0042
  COA accredited organization.

Community Svc Programs, Inc. Youth
Shelter 949.494.4311
Fax...949.497.4861
E-mail ....youthshelter@cspinc.org
  1821 E Dyer Rd Ste 200, Santa Ana, CA 92705-5700
  Carol Carlson, Program Director

Contra Costa Child Care Council 925.676.5442
Fax...925.825.2732
Web ....www.cocokids.org
E-mail ....central@cocokids.org
  1035 Detroit Ave, Ste 200, Concord, CA 94518
  Kate Ertzbergbr, Director

Contra Costa Crisis (Ofc) 925.939.1916
Fax...925.939.1933
Web ....www.crisis-center.org
E-mail ....johnb@crisis-center.org
  PO Box 3364, Walnut Creek, CA 94598-0364
  John Bateson, Executive Director

Contra Costa Office Branch 925.927.2000
Fax...925.927.3131
E-mail ....information@jfcs-eastbay.org
  1855 Olympic Blvd Ste 200, Walnut Creek, CA 94596
  Barbara Nelson, Chief Executive Officer

Covenant House California Hollywood 323.461.3131
Fax...323.461.6491
Web ....www.covca.org
E-mail ....glozano@covca.org
  1325 N Western Ave, Los Angeles, CA 90027-5615
  George Lozano, Executive Director

Crystal Stairs, Inc. 323.421.1029
Fax...323.421.2489
Web ....www.crystalstairs.org
E-mail ....jmajors@crystalstairs.org
  5110 W Goldleaf Cir Ste 150, Los Angeles, CA 90056
  Jackie Majors, Director

Ctr For The Violence Intervention
Program 323.226.2095
Fax...323.226.4588
  1721 Griffin Ave, Los Angeles, CA 90031
  Astrid H. Heger, Executive Director

Culture Of Life Family Care 619.692.4401
Fax...619.692.8147
E-mail ....margie@colfs.org
  550 Washington St Ste 801, San Diego,
  CA 92103-2232
  Margie Pierson, Director

Desert Area Resources and Training 760.375.9787
Fax...760.375.1288
Web ....www.dartontarget.org
  201 East Ridgecrest Boulevard, Ridgecrest, CA 93555
  CARF accredited programs available.

Diogenes Youth Svcs 916.369.5447
Fax...916.369.5389
  9719 Lincoln Village Dr Ste 110, Sacramento,
  CA 95827-3328
  Reyes Bonilla, Executive Director

Dubnoff Ctr For Child Development & Educational
Therapy 818.755.4950
Fax...818.752.0783
Web ....www.dubnoffcenter.org
E-mail ....sandrab@dubnoffcenter.org
  10526 Dubnoff Way, North Hollywood,
  CA 91606-3921
  Sandra Babcock, Executive Director

Early Childhood Svcs 530.529.3131
Fax...530.529.6631
Web ....www.ecsthama.com
  645 Antelope Blvd, Ste 34, Red Bluff, CA 96080
  Stacy Bergus, Manager

Edgewood Center for Children and
Families 415.681.3211
Fax...415.681.1065
Web ....www.edgewood.org
  1801 Vicente Street, San Francisco, CA 94116-2923
  COA accredited organization.

Edgewood Center for Children and
Families 415.376.7593
E-mail ....judym@edgewood.org
  957 Industrial Rd., San Carlos, CA 94070
  Judy Maller, Community Health Nurse

Emigre Services 415.449.2900
Fax...415.449.2901
E-mail ....ludmilaf@jfcs.org
  2534 Judah St, San Francisco, CA 94122
  Ludmila Fomina, Director

Families First 209.954.3000
Fax...209.957.8876
Web ....www.emqff.org
E-mail ....stocktonpfc@familiesfirstinc.org
  2291 W March Ln Ste C101, Stockton,
  CA 95207-6669
  Agnes Perez, Regional Manager

Family Ctr (CIFHS) 626.967.5103
Fax...626.967.1339
E-mail ....bnye@cifhs.org
  560 S San Jose Ave, Covina, CA 91723-3144
  Bill Nye, Director

Family Service Association 951.686.1096
Fax...951.686.5382
Web ....www.fsaca.org
  21250 Box Springs Road, Suite 212, Moreno Valley,
  CA 92557
  COA accredited organization.

Find The Children 310.314.3213
Fax...310.314.3169
  2656 29th St Ste 203, Santa Monica, CA 90405
  Karen Strickland, Executive Director

Five Acres Boys' And Girls' Aid Society 626.798.6793
Fax...626.797.7722
Web www.5acres.org
E-mail ....rketch@5acres.org
  760 W Mountain View St, Altadena, CA 91001-4996
  Robert Ketch, Chief Executive Officer

Fleet Family Support Svcs 831.656.3060
Fax...831.656.7423
  1280 Leahy Rd, Monterey, CA 93940-4842
  Jodi Pallet, Director

Foothill Family Service 626.564.1613
Fax...626.564.1651
  2500 E. Foothill Boulevard, Suite, Pasadena,
  CA 91107
  COA accredited organization.

Foster Family Svcs 530.676.6226
Fax...530.676.6026
Web ....www.fosterfamilyservice.org
E-mail ....johnj@fosterfamilyservice.org
  2514 Cameo Dr Ste B, Shingle Springs,
  CA 95682-9695
  John Johnson, Executive Director

Freda Mohr Multipupose Center for
Senior 323.937.5900
Fax...323.857.1872
  330 N Fairfax Ave, Los Angeles, CA 90036
  Susan Belgrade, Director

Fresno Madera Right To Life 559.229.2229
Fax...559.229.1040
Web ....www.rtl.org
E-mail ....ed@rtlcc.org
  1742 E Griffith Way, Fresno, CA 93726-4818
  Ed Hurlbutt, Director

Gain Div 562.908.8404
Fax...562.699.5385
Web ....www.ladpss.org
  12860 Crossroads Prkwy South, City Of Industry,
  CA 91746
  Luther Evans, Chief Of Police

George Mark Children's House 510.346.4624
Fax...510.346.4620
Web ....www.georgemark.org
  2121 George Mark Ln, San Leandro, CA 94578-1017
  John D Golenski, Edd, Executive Director

Grandparents As Parents, Inc. 818.264.0880
Fax...818.264.0882
Web ....www.grandparentsasparents.org
E-mail ....madelyn@grandparentsasparents.org
  22048 Sherman Way, #217, Canoga Park, CA 91303
  Madelyn Gordon, Executive Director

Harbor Regional Ctr 310.540.1711
Fax...310.540.9538
Web ....www.harborrc.org
E-mail ....pat.delmonaco@harborrc.org
  21231 Hawthorne Blvd, Torrance, CA 90503-5591
  Pat Delmonaco, Director

Hirsh Family Kosher Kitchen Branch 323.937.6560
Fax...323.934.0540
E-mail ....hperez@jfsla.org
  338 N Fairfax, Los Angeles, CA 90033
  Hugo Perez, Manager

Human Resource Council Child Care
Resources 209.754.1075
Fax...209.754.4244
Web ....www.hrcccr.org
E-mail ....ccb@hrcccr.org
  501F Gold Strike Rd., San Andreas, CA 95249
  Kelly Grachsch, Program Director

Human Response Network 530.623.2024
Fax...530.623.6343
Web ....www.humanresponsenetwork.org
E-mail ....dcrummey@tcoek12.org
  111 Mountain View St, Weaverville, CA 96093-2370
  David Crummey, Director Of Child Care

Human Svcs Assoc 562.806.5400
Fax...562.806.5394
Web ....www.hsala.org
E-mail ....leticia.chacon@hsala.org
  6800 Florence Ave, Bell, CA 90201-4958
  Leticia Chacon, Director

Infant Child Enrichment Svcs 209.533.0377
Fax 209.533.4017
Web ....www.icesagency.org
E-mail ....info@icesagency.org
   20993 Niagara River Dr, Sonora, CA 95370-9102
Evelyn Thompson, Director

Jewish Family & Childrens Service 562.427.7916
Fax 562.427.7910
E-mail ....jfcs@jfcslongbeach.org
   3801 E Willow St, Long Beach, CA 90815
Wendy Puzarne, CEO

Jewish Family & Childrens Services 415.449.3700
Fax 415.449.3742
E-mail ....sah@jfcs.org
   2150 Post St, San Francisco, CA 94115
Mark Spriggs, Administrator

Jewish Family & Childrens Services East
Bay 510.704.7475
Fax 510.704.7494
E-mail ....information@jfcs-eastbay.org
   2484 Shattuck Ave Ste 210, Berkeley, CA 94704
Awi Rose, Director

Jewish Family Service 805.641.6565
Fax 805.641.6560
E-mail ....jfsventura@sbcglobal.net
   857 E Main St, Ventura, CA 93001
Any Balchum, Director

Jewish Family Service of Los Angeles 626.564.8880
Fax 626.564.9348
E-mail ....tstead@jfsla.org
   PO Box 50007, Pasadena, CA 91115-0007
Tracy Stead, Director

Jewish Family Service of San Diego 858.637.3000
Fax 858.637.3001
E-mail ....jfs@jfssd.org
   Turk Family Center 8804 Balboa, San Diego, CA 92123
Jill Borg, Director

Jewish Family Service of Silicon Valley 408.556.0600
Fax 408.551.0091
E-mail ....jfs@jfssv.org
   14855 Oka Rd Ste 202, Los Gatos, CA 95032
Avital Agam, Director

Jewish Family Service of the Desert 760.325.4088
Fax 760.778.3781
E-mail ....info@jfsdesert.org
   801 E Tahquitz Canyon Way #202, Palm Springs, CA 92262
Michelle Anstadt, Executive Director

Jewish Family Services of Fresno CA 559.432.0529
Fax 559.432.0425
E-mail ....jfccjfs@sbcglobal.net
   406 West Shields Ave, Fresno, CA 93705
Mary Schilling

Jewish Family Services of Greater Santa
Barb 805.957.1116
Fax 805.957.9230
E-mail ....info@sbjf.org
   524 Chapala St, Santa Barbara, CA 93101
Barbara Kuhn, Director

Jewish Family Services of Silicon Valley 408.556.0600
Fax 408.551.0625
E-mail ....jfs@jfssv.org
   14855 Oka Rd Ste 202, Los Gatos, CA 95032
Mindy Berkowitz, Manager

Julia Ann Singer Ctr 310.202.0669
Fax 310.839.4158
   3200 Motor Ave, Los Angeles, CA 90034-3710
Diane Colvin, Director

Kids & Families Together 805.643.1446
Fax 805.643.0271
Web ....www.kidsandfamilies.org
E-mail ....david@kidsandfamilies.org
   856 E Thompson Blvd, Ventura, CA 93001-2918
David & Faith Friedlander, Directors

Korean Town Youth And Community Ctr 213.365.7400
Fax 213.383.1280
Web ....www.kyccla.org
E-mail ....johngsong@kyccla.org
   680 S Wilton Pl, Los Angeles, CA 90005-3200
Johng Ho Song, Executive Director

La Familia Counseling 510.881.5921
Fax 510.881.5925
Web ....www.lafamiliacounselingservices.com
E-mail ....finance_lfcs@sbcglobal.net
   26081 Mocine Ave, Hayward, CA 94544-2923
Hector Mendez, Director

La Familia Counseling Ctr, Inc 916.452.3601
Fax 916.452.7628
Web ....www.lafcc.com
E-mail ....anitab@lafcc.com
   5523 34th St, Sacramento, CA 95820-4725
Anita Barnes, Executive Director

Life Adoption Svcs 714.838.5433
Fax 714.838.1160
Web ....www.lifeadoption.org
E-mail ....info@lifeadoption.org
   440 W Main St, Tustin, CA 92780-4324
Joan Lejeune, Director

Lilliput Children's Svcs 530.722.9092
Fax 530.722.9153
Web ....www.lilliput.org
   2580 Victor Ave, Ste C, Redding, CA 96002
Karen Albord, Director

Lincoln Child Center 510.531.3111
Fax 510.530.8083
Web ....www.lincolnchildcenter.org
   4368 Lincoln Avenue, Oakland, CA 94602
COA accredited organization.

Marin Office Branch 415.491.7960
Fax 415.491.7958
E-mail ....marin@jfcs.org
   600 5th Ave, San Rafael, CA 94901

Mary Graham Children's Shelter 209.468.6966
Fax 209.468.7282
Web ....www.sjgov.org
   6861 W. Mary Graham Lane, French Camp, CA 95231
Brian Woods, Director

Mckinley Children's Ctr 909.599.1227
Fax 909.592.3841
Web ....www.mckinleycc.org
E-mail ....support@mckinleycc.org
   762 Cypress St, San Dimas, CA 91773
Al Mason, CEO

Medical Ctr Fairmont Hospital 510.895.4353
Fax 510.895.4359
Web ....www.acmedctr.org/hivfairmont.htm
   15400 Foothill Blvd, Fl 2, San Leandro, CA 94578-1009
Itta Aswad, Hiv Coordinator

Metro Region Office 310.858.8863
Fax 310.858.8582
   8846 W Pico Blvd, Los Angeles, CA 90035

National Ctr For Missing & Exploited
Children 714.508.0150
Fax 714.508.0154
Web ....www.missingkids.com
E-mail ....californiabranch@ncmec.org
   18111 Irvine Blvd, Tustin, CA 92780
Tom Hart, Sr. Case Manager

Noah's Anchorage YMCA Youth Shelter 805.963.8775
Fax 805.963.9675
E-mail ....mark.watson@ciymca.org
   301 W Figueroa St, Santa Barbara, CA 93101-3632
Mark Watson, Shelter Manager

North Coast Rape Crisis Team 707.443.2737
Fax 707.443.2755
   1833 H St, Eureka, CA 95501
Ruthanne Demirjyn, Fiscal Coordinator

Ofc of Education Children and Family Svcs 951.826.6626
Fax 908.826.4478
Web www.rcoe.k12.ca.us
E-mail ....phafner@rcoe.k12.ca.us
   4101 Almov St, Riverside, CA 92501
Saaron Bankett, Director

Olive Crest 714.543.5437
Fax 714.543.5463
Web ....www.olivecrest.org
   2130 E. Fourth Street, Suite 200, Santa Ana, CA 92705
COA accredited organization.

Parents Place Koret Family Resource Ctr 415.359.2454
Fax 415.359.2464
E-mail ....ParentsPlaceSF@jfcs.org
   1710 Scott St, San Francisco, CA 94115
Kenny Altman, Director Of Operations

Pathways 213.427.2700
Fax 213.427.2701
Web ....www.pathwaysla.org
E-mail ....ddennis@pathwaysla.org
   3550 W 6th St Ste 500, Los Angeles, CA 90020-2829
Duane Dennis, Director

Peninsula Office Branch 650.688.3030
Fax 650.330.0866
E-mail ....spen@jfcs.org
   200 Channing Ave, Palo Alto, CA 94301
Gayle Zahler, Director

Polly Klaas Foundation 707.769.1334
Fax 707.769.4019
Web ....www.pollyklaas.org
E-mail ....info@pollyklaas.org
   312 Western Ave, Petaluma, CA 94952-2919
Robert De Leo, Executive Director
Operates a nationwide 24-hour toll-free missing child hotline, disseminates child safety information, supports legislation benefiting children and helps build safer communities.

Raise Foundation 949.757.3635
Fax 949.757.4206
Web ....www.theraisefoundation.org
E-mail ....info@theraisefoundation.org
   1920 E. Warner Avenue, Ste A, Santa Ana, CA 92705
Russell Brammer, Executive Director

Rebekah Children's Services 408.846.2100
Fax 408.846.2430
Web ....www.rcskids.org
   290 I.O.O.F. Avenue, Gilroy, CA 95020
COA accredited organization.

Redwood Children's Ctr 707.565.6360
Fax 707.535.6352
Web ....www.schsd.org
   112 Childerns Cr, Santa Rosa, CA 95409-6540
Suni Levi, Coordinator

Remi Vista 916.941.8812
Fax 916.941.8815
E-mail ....sgivens@remivistainc.org
   4993 Golden Foothill Pkwy #5, El Dorado Hills, CA 95762
Shanda Givens, Mfti, Regional Director

San Fernando Valley Regional Off Branch 818.587.3333
Fax 818.703.1473
   22622 Vanowen St, West Hills, CA 91307

California

Santa Barbara Family Ctr Child Care Resource And Referral 805.963.6631
Fax 805.963.8292
Web ....www.sbfcc.org
E-mail ....referral@sbfcc.org
1124 Castillo St, Santa Barbara, CA 93101-3614

Siskiyou Child Care Council, Inc. 530.938.2748
Fax 530.938.2741
E-mail ....sisqchildcare2@snowcrest.net
170 Boles St, Weed, CA 96094-2518
Dennis Ball, Executive Director

Social Svcs 408.491.6800
Fax 408.975.4526
333 W Julian St 5th Floor, San Jose, CA 95110-2314
Gina Sessions, Interim Director

Social Svcs Dept 530.661.2750
Fax 530.661.2658
E-mail ....pam.miller@yolocounty.org
25 N Cottonwood St, Woodland, CA 95695-6609
Pam Miller, Director

Southern California Indian Ctr 213.387.5772
Fax 213.387.9061
Web ....www.indiancenter.org
E-mail ....pstarr@indiancenter.org
3440 Wilshire Blvd, Ste 904, Los Angeles, CA 90010-2123
Paula Starr, Executive Director

The Resource Connection- Child & Family 209.223.1624
Fax 209.223.5852
Web ....www.theresourceconnection.net
10877 Conducter Blvd, Suttercreek, CA 95685
Bed Stewart, Human Resource Director

Tirad Family Svcs 916.631.0771
Fax 916.631.0498
2445 Albatross Way Ste 101, Sacramento, CA 95815
Mark Dandeneau, Executive Director

Triad Family Svcs 510.351.3665
Fax 510.351.3906
E-mail ....info@triadfs.org
14433 Catalina St, San Leandro, CA 94577-5515
Nancy Reigh, Administrator

University City Senior Center Branch 858.550.5998
Fax 858.550.5997
9001 Towne Center Dr, San Diego, CA 92122
Aviva Saad, Program Coordinator

Valley Storefront for Seniors 818.984.1380
Fax 818.766.3926
12821 Victory Blvd, North Hollywood, CA 91606
Karen Leaf, Director

West Hollywood Senior Center 323.851.8202
Fax 323.876.6140
7377 Santa Monica Blvd, West Hollywood, CA 90046
Marina Berkman, Director

West Los Angeles Counseling Ctr Branch 310.820.4111
Fax 310.820.7787
2050 South Bundy Dr Ste 270, Los Angeles, CA 90025

Westside Children's Ctr 310.390.0551
Fax 310.397.2213
Web ....www.westsidechildrens.org
E-mail ....richardc@westsidechildrens.org
12120 Wagner St, Culver City, CA 90230-5844
Richard Cohen, Executive Director

SPECIAL NEEDS

1736 Family Crisis Center Los Angeles 213.737.3900
Fax 323.737.3993
E-mail ....fcc1736@cs.com
2116 Arlington Ave Ste 200, Los Angeles, CA 90018

1736 Family Crisis Center Redondo Beach 310.543.9900
Fax 310.543.9910
601 S Pacific Coast Hwy, Redondo Beach, CA 90277

4C Council 408.487.0747
Fax 408.943.8423
E-mail ....info@4c.org
2515 N 1st St, San Jose, CA 95112
Alfredo Villanor, Director

4Cs Com Child Care Coord Council of Alam 510.713.2557
39155 Liberty St Ste D410, Fremont Office, Fremont, CA 94538

4Cs Com Child Care Coord Council of Alam 510.272.0669
Fax 510.272.0363
Oakland Office, 756 21st St, Oakland, CA 94612
Dary Hanson, Executive Director

4Cs Com Child Care Coord Council of Alm 510.582.2182
E-mail ....sharynm@4c-alameda.org
22351 City Center Dr Ste 200, Hayward, CA 94541

5P Minus Society 562.804.4506
Fax 562.920.5240
E-mail ....laura5p@aol.com
PO Box 268, Lakewood, CA 90714
Laura Castillo, Executive Director

A Brighter Today 510.986.1811
E-mail ....info@abrightertoday.org
685 14th St, Piedmont, CA 94611

A Para Transit Corporation Inc 510.732.6304
Fax 510.732.5764
E-mail ....aparatransit@aol.com
A Para Transit Corporation, 22990 Clawiter Road, Hayward, CA 94545
Reena Kumar, Manager

A Special Nanny Ded to Fam of Child w Spe 408.395.5046
Fax 408.354.9053
E-mail ....info@specialnanny.com
A Special Nanny, 18290 Montevina Road, Los Gatos, CA 95030

A2Z Educational Advocates 310.573.1430
Fax 310.573.1425
E-mail ....officeadmin@a2zedad.com
16712 Marquez Ave, Pacific Palisades, CA 90272
Jane Dubovy, Owner

AAA Evans Paralegal Services 831.460.1940
289 Water St, Santa Cruz, CA 95060

AAFA Asthma Camp So CA Chapter 323.937.7859
Fax 323.937.7815
E-mail ....info@aafasocal.com
5900 Wilshire Blvd 2330, Los Angeles, CA 90036
Trina Celise, Director Of Operations

AArea Board 10 CA State Coun on Dev Disa 818.543.4631
E-mail ....ab10@pacbell.net
411 North Central Ave Ste 620, Glendale, CA 91203

ABA Physical Therapy Associates 650.558.0247
Fax 650.558.1735
E-mail ....abapt@aol.com
136 N San Mateo Dr Ste 201, San Mateo, CA 94401

ABC Pediatrics 562.594.8853
Fax 562.594.0305
E-mail ....DrRick@abcpediatrics.com
3772 West Katella Ste 101, Los Alamitos, CA 90720
Dr. Rick Blumenthal, Director

Abilities United 650.494.0550
Fax 650.855.9710
E-mail ....info@abilitiesunited.org
525 East Charleston Rd, Palo Alto, CA 94306
Linda Steele, Executive Director

Ability First Anaheim Center 714.821.7448
E-mail ....mjo@abilityfirst.org
2660 W Broadway, Anaheim, CA 92804
Lori, Manager

Ability First Camp Paivika 909.338.1102
Fax 909.338.2502
E-mail ....bstarkins@abilityfirst.o rg
6000 Playground Dr, Crestline, CA 92325

Ability First Claremont Center 909.621.4727
Fax 909.624.8388
E-mail ....jmartin@abilityfirst.org
480 S Indian Hill Blvd, Claremont, CA 91711
Julie Martin, Director

Ability First East Los Angeles Center 323.268.8178
Fax 323.268.2359
E-mail ....malcantar@abilityfirst.org
154 N Gage Ave, Los Angeles, CA 90063
Monica Alcantar, Director

Ability First Harry A Mier Center 323.753.3101
Fax 323.753.5472
E-mail ....rcrosby@abilityfirst.org
8090 Crenshaw Blvd, Inglewood, CA 90305
Monique Watts, Executive Director

Ability First Long Beach Center 562.426.6161
Fax 562.426.6148
E-mail ....bschlosser@abilityfirst.org
3770 East Willow St, Long Beach, CA 90815
Barbara Schlosser, Director

Ability First Prog for Indiv w/ Spec Need 626.396.1010
Fax 626.396.1021
E-mail ....contactus@abilityfirst.org
AbilityFirst, 1300 E Green St, Pasadena, CA 91106

Ability Resource Center Walnut Creek 510.595.5548
Fax 925.932.3912
E-mail ....glenn@abilityrc.com
1415 Oakland Blvd Ste 100, Walnut Creek, CA 94596

Ableriders Therapeutic Horse Riding 530.751.9526
Fax 530.751.1925
E-mail ....ableriders@scpn.org
1506 Starr Dr, Yuba City, CA 95993
Brenda Oeonhardt, Head Of Ableriders

Academic Guidance Services 310.435.1129
E-mail ....davidhung8@gmail.com
6399 Wilshire Blvd # 509, Los Angeles, CA 90048
David Hung, Director

Access and Authorization Program 415.255.3737
Fax 415.255.3629
1380 Howard St 1st Flr, San Francisco, CA 94103
Steve Benoit, Coordinator

Access for Infants and Mothers AIM 800.433.2611
Fax 888.889.9238
625 Cooledge Dr Ste 100, Sacramento, CA 95630

ACCESS Program 800.491.9099
Fax 510.346.1083
2035 Fairmont Dr, San Leandro, CA 94578

Access Services 800.827.0829
Fax 213.270.6057
633 W 5th St 9th Flr, Los Angeles, CA 90071

Access to Recreation 800.634.4351
Fax 805.498.8186
E-mail ....dkrebs@accesstr.com
8 Sandra Court, Newbury Park, CA 91320
Donna Krebs, President

Accredited Nursing Services 818.986.1234
Fax 818.986.2624
5955 Desoto Ave Ste 160, Woonwoodland, CA 91367

Achieve Palo Alto 650.494.1200
Fax 650.494.1243
E-mail ....intake@achievekids.org
3860 Middlefield Road, Palo Alto, CA 94303
Michael Gennette, Director

AchieveKids 408.928.5777
Fax 408.928.1758
E-mail ....intake@achievekids.org
1212 McGinness Ave, San Jose, CA 95127
Skye Cary, Director

Acorn Media **949.495.5563**
Fax 949.495.5308
E-mail ....acommedia@cox.net
  25132 Adelanto Dr, Laguna Niguel, CA 92677

Act for the Mental Health **408.287.2640**
E-mail ....actnow@actmentalhealth.org
  441 Park Ave, San Jose, CA 95110
  Vander Alexander, Chief Executive Officer

Action Home Health Care **323.653.5374**
Fax 323.653.7908
  6300 Wilshire Blvd Ste 1490, Los Angeles, CA 90048
  Renee Steel, Director

Active Care Physical Therapy Sports Med **415.387.6564**
Fax 415.387.2013
E-mail ....trainer@activecare.net
  3019 Geary Blvd, San Francisco, CA 94118
  Lisa Giannone, Director

Active Reading Clinic **925.944.5559**
E-mail ....activereading1023@sbcglobal.net
  1543 Sunnyvale Ave Ste 101, Walnut Creek, CA 94597
  Cyntaia Lemyre, Director

Activities for Retarded Children **818.762.4365**
Fax 818.762.1048
E-mail ....arcadults2003@yahoo.com
  6456 Whitsett Ave, North Hollywood, CA 91606
  Jane Sarture, Chief Executive Officer

Acute Rehabilitation Unit, Palomar Medical Center **760.739.3221**
Fax 760.739.3996
Web ....www.pph.org
  555 East Valley Parkway, Escondido, CA 92027
  CARF accredited programs available.

Adapted Computer Technologies **949.459.5241**
Fax 949.459.9581
E-mail ....ddutton@compuaccess.com
  16 Gingham, Trabuco Canyon, CA 92679

Addicott School **559.253.6517**
Fax 559.255.4184
E-mail ....kmdocke@fresno.k12.ca.us
  4784 E Dayton, Fresno, CA 93726
  Karen M Docke, Administrator

Addus HealthCare **847.303.5300**
Fax 847.303.5376
  401 29th St Ste 203, Oakland, CA 94609

Addus HealthCare Modesto **209.578.3231**
  817 Coffee Rd Bldg B, Modesto, CA 95355
  Barbara H, Interim Coordinator

Advanced Home Health Inc **916.978.0744**
Fax 916.978.0745
E-mail ....aallen@ahhsac.com
  4370 Auburn Blvd, Sacramento, CA 95841
  Angela Sehr, Administrator

Advanced Mobility Mobility Works **818.780.1788**
Fax 818.780.1240
E-mail ....info@advanced-mobility.com
  7720 N Sepulveda Blvd, Van Nuys, CA 91405
  Steve Cardenas, General Manager

Advanced Physical Therapy Associate **323.295.5836**
Fax 323.295.5960
  3717 S La Brea Ave, Los Angeles, CA 90016

Adventist Health Home Care **707.967.5770**
Fax 707.963.6295
  27 Woodland Road, Deer Park, CA 94574
  Patti Rutherford, Clinical Manager

Adventist Health Home Care Services **818.409.8379**
Fax 818.546.8964
  281 Harvey Dr, Glendale, CA 91206
  Wendy Brookshire, Director

Adventist Health Redbud Community Hospital **707.994.6486**
Fax 916.781.4772
  15630 18th Ave, Clearlake, CA 95422
  David Santos, Vice President

Affordable Hearing Aid Center **916.863.1404**
E-mail ....sales@affordablehearing.com
  5060 Sunrise Blvd Ste A 1, Fair Oaks, CA 95628

Ahead with Horses Inc Project AHEAD **818.767.6373**
Fax 818.767.6231
  9311 Del Arroyo Dr, Sun Valley, CA 91352

Aid for AIDS **323.656.1107**
Fax 323.650.4323
E-mail ....mmorrow@aidforaids.net
  8235 Santa Monica Blvd Ste 200, Los Angeles, CA 90046
  Terry Goddard, Administrator

AIDS Assistance Program **760.325.8481**
E-mail ....chriscambell@aidsassistance.org
  216 E Arenas Road, Palm Springs, CA 92262
  Chris Cambell, Administrator

AIDS Education Project **530.538.6109**
Fax 530.538.6221
E-mail ....nbiehler@buttecounty.net
  202 Mira Loma Dr, Oroville, CA 95965

AIDS Emergency Fund **415.558.6999**
Fax 415.558.6990
E-mail ....mikesmith@aef-sf.org
  12 Grace St, San Francisco, CA 94103
  Mike Smith, Executive Director

AIDS Healthcare Foundation **323.860.5200**
Fax 323.962.8513
E-mail ....webmaster@aidshealth.org
  6255 W Sunset Blvd 2100, Hollywood, CA 90028

AIDS Project Los Angeles David Geffen Ct **213.201.1600**
Fax 213.201.1392
E-mail ....gthompson@apla.org
  611 S Kingsley Dr, Los Angeles, CA 90005
  Greg Thompson, Director

AIDS Project of the East Bay **510.663.7979**
E-mail ....info@apeb.org
  1320 webt st, Oakland, CA 94612
  Alvin Quamina, Director

AIDS Service Center **626.441.8495**
Fax 626.799.6253
  909 S Fair Oaks Ave, Pasadena, CA 91105
  Trip Oldfield, Executive Director

AIDS Srvs Foundation **949.809.5700**
Fax 949.809.5779
E-mail ....asf@ocasf.org
  17982 Sky Park Circle Ste J, Irvine, CA 92614
  Phil Yaegei, Executive Director

Airport Marina Counseling Service **310.670.1410**
Fax 310.670.0919
E-mail ....info@airportmarina.org
  7891 La Tijera Blvd, Los Angeles, CA 90045
  Kathleen Lefferman, Director

AKSH Rehab **408.254.9900**
Fax 408.258.2175
  2664 Berryessa Rd, Ste 118, San Jose, CA 95132

Ala Costa Center for Developmentally Dis **510.527.2550**
Fax 510.527.4543
E-mail ....ackids@pacbell.net
  1300 Rose St, Berkeley, CA 94702

Alameda Alliance for Health **510.895.4500**
Fax 510.747.4502
  1240 South Loop Road, Alameda, CA 94502

American Cancer Society **559.673.9425**
Fax 559.673.9432
E-mail ....peggy.morris@cancer.org
  425 N Gateway Ste C, Madera, CA 93638

American Cancer Society **530.222.1058**
Fax 530.222.1409
  3290 Bechelli Ln, Redding, CA 96002

American Cancer Society **559.734.1391**
  300 N Willis, Visalia, CA 93291

American Cancer Society Central Contra **925.934.7640**
Fax 925.934.5372
  1885 Oak Park Blvd, Pleasant Hill, CA 94523

American Cancer Society Merced Mariopos **209.722.3341**
  Unit 301 W 18th St 101, Merced, CA 95340

American Cancer Society Mountain Valley **530.342.4567**
  754 Mangrove Ave, Chico, CA 95926
  Matthew Foor, Community Services Director

American Cancer Society Napa Unit **707.255.5911**
Fax 707.255.3823
  1031 Jefferson st, Napa, CA 94559
  Sandy Sparks, Director

American Cancer Society Northern CA **510.797.0600**
Fax 510.797.0698
  39277 Liberty St, Ste D 14, Fremont, CA 94538
  May Sung, Vice President

American Cancer Society Salinas Valley **831.442.2992**
  1184 Monroe St Ste 1, Salinas, CA 93906

American Cancer Society San Francisco **415.394.7100**
Fax 415.495.1877
  201 Mission St, Ste 720, San Francisco, CA 94105

American Cancer Society Stanislaus Unit **209.524.7242**
Fax 209.524.7454
  1604 Ford Ave 8, Modesto, CA 95350
  Cheryl Brunk, Director

American Cancer Society Tri Valley Unit **925.934.7640**
Fax 925.927.5016
  101 Ygnacio Valley Rd, Ste 110, Walnut Creek, CA 94596
  David Veneziano, Director

American Cancer Society Upper Napa Vall **800.227.2345**
  1031 Jefferson St, Napa, CA 94559

American Cancer Society Yuba Sutter Col **530.741.1366**
Fax 530.741.1383
  618 5th St, Marysville, CA 95901

AT Kratter & Company Inc **714.799.3000**
Fax 714.799.3100
E-mail ....info@atkratter.com
  12062 Valley View St Ste 109, Garden Grove, CA 92845
  At Kratter, Chief Executive Officer

Autism Society of California **800.869.7069**
E-mail ....ca-california@autismsocietyofamerica.org
  PO Box 1355, Glendora, CA 91740

Burdick Psychological Services **650.380.2011**
Fax 831.603.3018
E-mail ....info@drburdick.com
  415 Cambridge Ave, Palo Alto, CA 94306

California Assn of School Psychologists **916.444.1595**
E-mail ....memberservices@casponline.org
  1020 12th St Ste 200, Sacramento, CA 95814
  Suzane Fisher, Executive Director

California Pacific Medical Center **415.600.3604**
Fax 415.923.6567
  2324 Sacramento St, Ste 150, San Francisco, CA 94115
  Robert G Miller Md, Co-Director

California State PTA **916.440.1985**
E-mail ....info@capta.org
  2327 L St, Sacramento, CA 95816

Casa Colina Centers for Rehabilitation, Casa Colina Hospital, Children's Services Center **909.569.7733**
Fax 909.596.3548
Web .... www.casacolina.org
255 E Bonita Ave, PO Box 6001, Pomona, CA 91769-6001
Cindy Sendor, Director of Childrens Services

Casa Colina Centers for Rehabilitation, Transitional Living Center **909.596.7733**
Fax 909.593.7541
Web .... www.casacolina.org
255 East Bonita Avenue, Pomona, CA 91767
CARF accredited programs available.

Casa Pacifica **805.445.7872**
Fax 805.445.7834
Web .... www.casapacifica.org
1722 S Lewis Rd, Camarillo, CA 93012
Scott Mastroianni, Director

Cedars-Sinai Medical Center - Department of Rehabilitation **310.423.6271**
Fax 310.423.0153
Web www.cedars-sinai.edu/3934.html
E-mail .... beth.karlan@cshs.org
8700 Beverly Boulevard, Room 7215, Los Angeles, CA 90048
Beth Karlan, Director
CARF accredited programs available.

Center for Child Obesity **415.453.8886**
Fax 415.453.8888
Web .... www.childobesity.com
E-mail .... info@childobesity.com
1323 San Anselmo Ave, San Anselmo, CA 94960
Bob Mellin, Chief Executive Officer

Centre for Neuro Skills - Bakersfield **661.872.3408**
Fax 661.872.5150
Web .... www.neuroskills.com
2658 Mount Vernon Avenue, Bakersfield, CA 93306
CARF accredited programs available.

Centre for Neuro Skills - Los Angeles **818.783.3800**
Fax 818.783.8412
Web .... www.neuroskills.com
16542 Ventura Boulevard, Suite 500, Encino, CA 91436
CARF accredited programs available.

Child Testing & Treatment Specialists **800.585.6683**
Fax 305.768.5763
E-mail .... drmouton@yahoo.com
11601 Wilshire St ste 3000, Newport Beach, CA 92660

Child, Teen & Family Specialist Therapy **626.568.5651**
Fax 626.604.0332
E-mail .... sibrawer1@earthlink.net
766 E Colorado Blvd, Ste 203, Pasadena, CA 91101
Steven Brawer Phd, Clinical Psychologist

Children's Hospital Central California/Medical Rehabilitation Center **559.353.5725**
Fax 559.353.8650
Web .... www.childrenscentralcal.org
9300 Valley Children's Place, Mailstop GE18, Madera, CA 93636-8762
CARF accredited programs available.

Children's Hospital Central California/Medical Rehabilitation Center **559.353.6425**
Fax 559.353.6441
Web .... www.childrenscentralcal.org
9300 Valley Children's Place, Mailstop GE18, Madera, CA 93638-8762
Bryan Hainline, Clinic Director
CARF accredited programs available.

Childrens Liver Assoc for Support Serv **661.263.9099**
Fax 661.263.9099
E-mail .... info@classkids.org
25379 Wayne Mills Pl Ste 143, Valencia, CA 91355

Childrens Neurobiological Solutions Foundation **805.898.4442**
Fax 805.963.6633
E-mail .... info@cnsfoundation.org
909 E 1st St, Long Beach, CA 90802
Pamela Hope, Director

Chinese Parents Association **626.307.3837**
E-mail .... chen_rachel@hotmail.com
PO Box 2884, San Gabriel, CA 91778
Chen Rachel, Director

Cottage Rehabilitation Hospital of Santa Barbara Cottage Hospital **805.569.8999**
Fax 805.687.3707
Web .... www.risb.org
E-mail .... sallen@cottagehealthsystem.org
2415 De La Vina Street, Santa Barbara, CA 93105
Scott Allen, Director
CARF accredited programs available.

CSHA **916.921.1568**
E-mail .... csha@csha.org
825 University Ave, Sacramento, CA 95825

Ctr For Autism And Related Disorders (CARD) **818.345.2345**
Fax 818.758.8015
Web .... www.centerforautism.com
E-mail .... info@centerforautism.com
19019 Ventura Blvd, Fl 3, Tarzana, CA 91356-3253
Doreen Granteesheh, Director

Davis Dyslexia Association International **888.999.3324**
Fax 650.692.7075
E-mail .... ddai@dyslexia.com
1601 Bayshore Hwy ste # 260, Burlingame, CA 94010

DREDF **510.644.2555**
Fax 510.841.8645
E-mail .... info@dredf.org
3075 Adeline St Ste 210, Berkeley, CA 94703
Susane Henderson, Chief Executive Officer

Dyslexia Sltns of Northern California **415.479.1700**
E-mail .... davidcrosen@sbcglobal.net
950 Northgate Dr Ste 107, San Rafael, CA 94903

Easter Seals Bay Area **510.835.2131**
E-mail .... mpelfini@esba.org
180 Grand Ave Ste 300, Oakland, CA 94612

Epilepsy Foundation **800.564.0445**
E-mail .... pietsch@epilepsy-socalif.org
5777 W Century Blvd Ste 820, Los Angeles, CA 90045
Susan Estuetx, Executive Director

Epilepsy Foundation **619.296.0161**
E-mail .... info@epilepsysandiego.org
2055 El Cajon Blvd, San Diego, CA 92104
Susan Upchurch, Director Of Client Services

Etta Israel Center **818.985.3882**
Fax 818.487.9740
E-mail .... etta613@aol.com
12722 Riverside Dr, Ste 105, Valley Village, CA 91607

Exceptional Parents Unlimited **559.229.2000**
E-mail .... info@exceptionalparents.org
4440 N 1st St, Fresno, CA 93726
Marion Karian, Executive Director

Family Resource Network **800.847.3030**
E-mail .... frnfamilies@aol.com
5250 Claremont Ave Ste 239, Stockton, CA 95207

Fiesta Educativa Inc **323.221.6696**
Fax 323.221.6699
E-mail .... info@fiestaeducativa.org
161 S 24th Ave, Los Angeles, CA 90031

Foster Youth Resources for Education **800.348.4232**
E-mail .... shenderson@dredf.org
2212 6th St, Berkeley, CA 94710

Fuerza Inc **800.200.4323**
E-mail .... fuerz@fuerzainc.org
1340 E McWood St, West Covina, CA 91790

Gentiva Rehab Without Walls - Sacramento **916.567.1244**
Fax 916.929.2388
Web .... www.gentivarehabwithoutwalls.com
1485 Response Road, Suite 220, Sacramento, CA 95815
Brenda Collins, Director
CARF accredited programs available.

Girltalk-Puberty Seminars **510.595.3814**
Fax 510.595.1963
Web .... www.girltalk-puberty.com
E-mail .... girltalkgurls@sbcglobal.net
P.O. Box 20226, Piedmont, CA 94620
Mary Arnold ARNP- Women's Health, Nurse Practitioner

Greenhorn Creek Ranch **530.283.0930**
Fax 530.283.4401
E-mail .... lisa@greenhornranch.com
2116 Greenhorn Ranch Rd, Quincy, CA 95971
Sara Patrick, Manager

Hanna Boys Ctr **707.996.6767**
Fax 707.996.4742
E-mail .... rrussell@hannacenter.org
17000 Arnold Dr, Sonoma, CA 95476-3290
Richard Russell, Intake Director

Hawthorne Academy **310.644.8841**
Fax 310.644.8910
Web .... www.valleyhs.net
E-mail .... ray.richard@valleyhs.com
12500 Ramona Ave, Hawthorne, CA 90250-4330
Ray Richard, Executive Director

Health Clinic **510.795.2414**
Fax 510.494.7240
6066 Civic Terrace Ave, Newark, CA 94560

Herman & Associates **323.344.0123**
Fax 323.344.0132
E-mail .... herman@docherman.com
1137 Huntington Dr, Ste A-2, South Pasadena, CA 91030
Patricia A Sullivan, Director

Independence Center **310.202.7102**
Fax 310.202.7180
E-mail .... judym@independencecenter.com
3640 S Sepulveda Blvd, Ste 102, Los Angeles, CA 90034
Judy Maizlish, Executive Director

Innovative Speech & Language Pathology **310.486.1717**
E-mail .... odilia@innovativeslp.com
9171 Wilshire Blvd, Ste # PH12, Beverly Hills, CA 90210

Jean Weingarten Peninsula Oral School For The Deaf **650.365.7500**
Fax 650.365.7557
Web .... oraldeafed.org/schools/jwposd
E-mail .... jwposd@jwposd.org
3518 Jefferson Ave, Redwood City, CA 94062-3136
Kathleen Daniel Sussman, Ma, Principal

Kaiser Foundation Rehabilitation Center **707.651.2414**
Fax 707.651.4160
Web .... www.kaiserpermanente.org
975 Sereno Drive, Vallejo, CA 94589
CARF accredited programs available.

Lakeside Learning **877.763.7323**
E-mail .... info@lakeside-learning.com
3171 Los Feliz Blvd, Ste 303, Los Angeles, CA 90039
Scott Rickert, Director

Learning Disabilities Association **949.673.3612**
E-mail .... ca-lba@sbcglobal.net
808 W Balboa Blvd, Balboa, CA 92661
Louise Fundenberg, President

LearningRx Learning Center 559.275.3276
E-mail .... fresno.ca@learningrx.net
9495 N Fort Washington Rd, Fresno, CA 93720
Renee Bautista, Owner

LeRoy Haynes Education Center 909.593.2581
Fax 909.593.6224
Web .... www.leroyhaynes.org
233 W Baseline Rd, La Verne, CA 91750
Daniel S Maydeck, Direcor

Lindamood-Bell Learning Processes 858.259.3206
Fax 858.259.3208
445 Marine View Ave, Ste 290, Del Mar, CA 92014
Sarah Daub, Director

Lindamood-Bell Learning Processes 310.541.2977
Fax 310.541.2988
The Ave of the Peninsula, 550 Deep Valley Dr Ste 291, Rolling Hill Estates, CA 90274
Anita A, Office Manager

Lindamood-Bell Learning Processes 916.929.8183
Fax 916.929.8185
1610 Arden Way Ste 277, Sacramento, CA 95815
Terri Mehl, Director

Lindamood-Bell Learning Processes 831.372.5753
Fax 831.372.5773
262 El Dorado St Ste 200, Monterey, CA 93940
Heather Muran, Manager Of Marketing

Lindamood-Bell Learning Processes 626.396.0865
Fax 626.396.0864
959 E Walnut Ste 110, Pasadena, CA 91106
Anne Perry, Center Director

Lindamood-Bell Learning Processes 805.541.3836
Fax 805.543.0264
406 Higuera St, Ste 120, San Luis Obispo, CA 93401
Steve Rossi, Director

Lindamood-Bell Learning Processes 510.649.7618
Fax 510.649.7929
1625 Shattuck Ave, Ste 250, Berkeley, CA 94709
Ashley Thompson, Director

Lindamood-Bell Learning Processes 415.346.6056
Fax 415.346.6073
1600 Union St, 1st Fl, San Francisco, CA 94123
Samantha Eddy, Office Manager

Lindamood-Bell Learning Processes 408.867.1390
Fax 408.867.1916
E-mail .... saratoga.center@lindamoodbell.com
14320 Saratoga-Sunnyvale Rd, Saratoga, CA 95070
Cheri Garcia, Director

Lindamood-Bell Learning Processes 805.564.1854
Fax 805.564.1890
925 De La Vina St, Santa Barbara, CA 93101

Lindamood-Bell Learning Processes 650.321.1191
Fax 650.321.1163
801 El Camino Real, Menlo Park, CA 94025
Lindsey Bridgman, Director

Lindamood-Bell Learning Processes 415.721.0781
Fax 415.721.0784
1099 D St Penthouse B, San Rafael, CA 94901

Lindamood-Bell Learning Processes 949.252.9275
Fax 949.252.9276
4100 Campus Dr, Ste 100, Newport Beach, CA 92660
Heather Dugan, Director

Lindamood-Bell Learning Processes 310.481.2293
Fax 310.481.2294
E-mail .... jessica.corinne@lindamoodbell.com
1554 S Sepulveda Blvd, Ste 214, Los Angeles, CA 90025
Jessica Corinne, Director

Lindamood-Bell Learning Processes 925.943.1609
Fax 925.943.7445
1600 S Main St, Walnut Creek, CA 94596
Jennifer Robertson, President

Loma Linda University Medical Center/Rehabilitation Institute 909.558.6166
Fax 909.558.6669
Web .... www.lomalindahealth.org
25333 Barton Road, Loma Linda, CA 92354
CARF accredited programs available.

Loving Your Disabled Child 323.373.0323
Fax 323.230.7177
PO Box 90633, Los Angeles, CA 90009
Sherilyn Miles-Rosette, Director

Marina Psychological Services, Inc 310.822.0109
Fax 310.822.1240
E-mail .... marinapsych@hotmail.com
4640 Admiralty Way, Ste 318, Marina Del Rey, CA 90292

MATRIX Parent Network 800.578.2592
E-mail .... info@matrixparents.org
94 Galli Dr Ste C, Novato, CA 94949

MDA/ALS Center at UCI 714.456.2332
Fax 714.456.5997
E-mail .... mozaffar @uci.edu
200 S Manchester Ave Ste 110, Orange, CA 92868
Tahseen Mozaffar MD, Director

MDA/ALS Center at UCLA 310.825.7266
Fax 310.825.3995
E-mail .... mcgraves @mednet.ucla.edu
300 UCLA Medical Plz Ste B200, Los Angeles, CA 90095
Michael C Graves MD, Director

Med Center Fairmont 510.577.5604
6955 Foothill Blvd, Ste 200, Oakland, CA 94605

Medical Ctr Highland Hosp 510.437.4800
1411 East 31st St, Oakland, CA 94602
Christa Yoshino, Administrator

Mission Hospital Regional Medical Center - Acute Rehabilitation Unit 949.364.1400
Fax 949.364.4822
Web www.mission4health.com
E-mail .... soodabeh.abravesh@stjoe.org
27700 Medical Center Road, Mission Viejo, CA 92691
Soodabeh Abravesh, Medical Director
CARF accredited programs available.

Murphy & Associates 925.283.4002
E-mail .... info@spedtech.com
3280 Woodview Dr, Lafayette, CA 94549

NAMI California 916.567.0163
E-mail .... support@namicalifornia.org
1010 Hurley Way, Ste 195, Sacramento, CA 95825
Jessica Cruz, Director

National Federation of the Blind 510.248.0100
E-mail .... nfbcal@sbcglobal.net
39481 Gallaudet Dr Apt 127, Fremont, CA 94538
Mary Willows, Chief Executive Officer

National Multiple Sclerosis Society 760.448.8400
Fax 760.804.9266
E-mail .... msinfo@mspacific.org
5950 La Place Ct Ste 200, Carlsbad, CA 92008

National Multiple Sclerosis Society 310.479.4456
Fax 310.479.4436
E-mail .... MS@CAL.NMSS.ORG
2440 S Sepulveda Blvd Ste 115, Los Angeles, CA 90064
Leon Lebuffe, President

National Multiple Sclerosis Society 800.344.4867
E-mail .... info@msconnection.org
1700 Owens St Ste 190, San Francisco, CA 94158
Janelle Delcarlo, President

Northridge Hospital Medical Center, Center for Rehabilitation Medicine 818.885.8500
Fax 818.700.5695
Web .... www.northridgehospital.org
18300 Roscoe Boulevard, Northridge, CA 91328
CARF accredited programs available.

Of One Mind 310.479.9065
Fax 310.268.1200
E-mail .... robert@ofonemind.net
2001 S Barrington Ave, Ste 300, Los Angeles, CA 90025

Parents Helping Parents 408.727.5775
Fax 408.286.1116
E-mail .... info@php.com
1400 Parkmoor Ave Ste 100, San Jose, CA 95126
Mary Ellen Peterson, Chief Executive Officer

Parents of Watts (CPRC) 323.566.7556
Fax 323.569.3982
E-mail .... pow90059@yahoo.com
10828 Lou Dillon Ave, Los Angeles, CA 90059
Alice Harris, Chief Executive Officer

ParentsCAN CPRC 707.253.7444
E-mail .... Parents@parentscan.org
1909 Jefferson St, Napa, CA 94559
Joan Lockhart, Executive Director

Park Century School 310.840.0500
Fax 310.840.0591
Web .... www.parkcenturyschool.org
3939 Landmark St, Culver City, CA 90232
Genny Shain, Principal

PRIDE Learning Center 949.891.0125
E-mail .... info@pridelearningcenter.com
4030 Birch St Ste 102, Newport Beach, CA 92660

PRIDE Learning Center 310.322.2800
E-mail .... es@pridelearningcenter.com
130 E Grand Ave, Unit H, El Segundo, CA 90245
Karina Richland, Director

Providence Holy Cross Medical Center/Acute Rehabilitation Unit 818.898.4504
Fax 818.898.4472
Web .... www.providence.org
15031 Rinaldi Street, Mission Hills, CA 91345
Steven Weiss, Director - Marketing
CARF accredited programs available.

Rancho Los Amigos National Rehabilitation Center 562.401.7022
Fax 562.803.5876
Web .... www.rancho.org
7601 East Imperial Highway, HB 105, Downey, CA 90242
CARF accredited programs available.

Raskob Learning Institute & Day School 510.436.1275
Fax 510.436.1106
E-mail .... raskobinstitute@hnu.edu
3520 Mountain Blvd, Oakland, CA 94619

Rehab Without Walls - Bay Area 408.556.0420
4020 Moorpark Avenue, Suite 220, San Jose, CA 95117
CARF accredited programs available.

Rehab Without Walls - Sacramento 916.567.1244
1485 Response Road, Suite 220, Sacramento, CA 95815
CARF accredited programs available.

Rehab Without Walls- Southern CA 626.338.4884
1501 West Cameron Avenue, Suite 210, West Covina, CA 91790
CARF accredited programs available.

Robert H. Ballard Rehabilitation Hospital 909.473.1275
Fax 909.473.1276
Web .... www.ballardrehab.com
1760 West 16th Street, San Bernardino, CA 92411
CARF accredited programs available.

Rowell Family Empowerment Northern CA.....530.226.5129
Fax.....530.226.5141
E-mail.....sklowrance@aol.com
962 Maraglia St, Redding, CA 96002
Kat Lowrance, Director

Santa Clara Valley Medical Center.....408.885.5000
Fax.....408.885.5822
Web.....www.scvmed.org
751 South Bascom Avenue, San Jose, CA 95128
CARF accredited programs available.

Schwab Foundation for Learning.....650.655.2410
Fax.....650.655.2411
1650 S Amphlett Blvd Ste 300, San Mateo, CA 94402

Scripps Memorial Hospital, Encinitas - The Rehabilitation Center.....760.633.6518
Fax.....760.633.7348
Web.....www.scripps.org
E-mail.....biter.robert@scrippshealth.org
354 Santa Fe Drive, Encinitas, CA 92024
Robert Biter, Medical Director
CARF accredited programs available.

SELPA.....951.490.0375
Fax.....951.490.0376
E-mail.....sbalt@valverde.edu
975 Morgan St Bldg G, Perris, CA 92571-3103
Dr. Sue Balt, Executive Director

Seneca Center.....501.317.1444
Fax.....510.317.1426
Web.....www.senecacenter.org
2275 Arlington Dr, San Leandro, CA 94578
Ken Berrick

Senior Planning Services.....805.966.3312
Fax.....805.963.7146
Web.....www.seniorplanningservices.com
E-mail.....info@seniorplanningservices.com
1811 State Street, Santa Barbara, CA 93101
Cassi Noel, Community Liaison

Sharp Memorial Hospital Rehabilitation Services.....858.939.3085
Fax.....858.939.3117
Web.....www.sharp.com/rehab
2999 Health Center Dr, San Diego, CA 92123
David Brown, Director Of Rehab Program
CARF accredited programs available.

sherancares.....818.286.3070
Fax.....818.446.4744
Web.....sherancares.webs.com
E-mail.....sherancares@aol.com
9818 Balboa Blvd NW California, north Oridge, CA 91328
Sheran Cohen, Director

Sierra Madre Learning Center.....626.355.5160
Fax.....626.355.5173
E-mail.....seansurfas@totalprograms.org
370 W Sierra Madre Blvd, # B, Sierra Madre, CA 91024
Sean Surfas, Director

Special Education- SELPA.....925.827.0949
Fax.....925.825.1124
Web.....www.cccoe.k12.ca.us/selpa/ccselpa.htm
E-mail.....lambrosini@ccselpa.org
2520 Stanwell Dr Ste 270, Concord, CA 94520-4858
Laura Van Duyn, Administrator

Spina Bifida Association of San Diego.....619.491.9018
E-mail.....sbaofgsd@hotmail.com
PO Box 232272, San Diego, CA 92193

St. Jude Medical Center.....714.992.3000
Fax.....714.773.9278
Web.....www.stjudemedicalcenter.org
101 East Valencia Mesa Drive, Fullerton, CA 92835
CARF accredited programs available.

Stockdale Learning Ctr.....661.326.8084
Fax.....661.327.4752
Web.....www.stockdale-learning-center.com
E-mail.....slc@igalaxy.net
1701 Westwind Dr Ste 104, Bakersfield, CA 93301-3045
Andrew J. Barling, M.a., Prse, Et/p, Founder/director-educational Therapist/ Diagnostician Specialist In Specific Leanring Disabilities, Dyslexia, And Adhd

Support Families of Children w/Disabilit.....415.920.5040
E-mail.....jduenas@supportforfamilies.org
1663 Mission St 7Th Fl, San Francisco, CA 94103
Juno Duenas, Director

Support For Families of Children W/Disb.....415.282.7494
Fax.....415.282.1226
E-mail.....info@supportforfamilies.org
1663 Mission St # 606, San Francisco, CA 94110
Cathleen Schlier, Chief Executive Officer

Switzer Ctr School And Clinical Svcs.....310.328.3611
Fax.....310.328.5648
Web.....www.switzercenter.org
E-mail.....clinical@switzercenter.org
2201 Amapola Ct, Torrance, CA 90501-2299
Owen Fudim, Clinical Director

TASK.....866.828.8275
E-mail.....taskca@yahoo.com
100 W Cerritos Ave, Anaheim, CA 92805
Martha Amchoando, Executive Director

The Agape Center.....805.495.3937
Fax.....805.373.9843
E-mail.....AgapeOptom@aol.com
100 N Rancho Rd, Ste # 1, Thousand Oaks, CA 91362

The Arc of California.....916.552.6619
E-mail.....tonyanderson@arccalifornia.org
1225 8th St Ste 350, Sacramento, CA 95814
Tony Anderson, Executive Director

The Reading Clinic Palo Alto.....800.790.5302
E-mail.....info@thereadingclinic.com
445 Sherman Ave Ste N, Palo Alto, CA 94306

Therapeutic Education Centers.....714.543.5437
Fax.....714.543.5463
Web.....www.olivecrest.org
2130 E 4th St Ste 200, Santa Ana, CA 92705
Donald Verleur

UCSF Regional Pediatric MS Center.....415.353.3939
350 Parnassus Ave Ste 908, San Francisco, CA 94117
Emmanuelle Waubant, Md Phd Project Director

United Advocates for Children & Families.....866.643.1530
E-mail.....information@uacc4families.org
2035 Hurley Way Ste 290, Sacramento, CA 95825
Oscar Wright, Chief Executive Officer

United Cerebral Palsy of Sacramento.....916.565.7700
E-mail.....ucp@ucpsacto.org
191 Lathrop Way Ste N, Sacramento, CA 95815

Vietnamese Parents of Disabled Children.....949.724.2359
E-mail.....vpdcahung@yahoo.com
7526 Syracuse Ave, Stanton, CA 90680

Vista Del Mar Child & Family Services.....310.836.1223
Fax.....310.204.1405
Web.....www.vistadelmar.org
E-mail.....info@vistadelmar.com
3200 Motor Ave, Los Angeles, CA 90034
Elias Lefferman, CEO

Wellness Works Therapy.....818.763.0136
Fax.....818.763.3838
Web.....www.wellnessworkstherapy.com
E-mail.....info@wellnessworkstherapy.com
6400 Laurel Canyon Blvd, Ste 560, North Hollywood, CA 91606
Brandon Seigel, Director Of Intake Svcs

SUBSTANCE ABUSE TREATMENT

A Better Tomorrow.....800.517.4849
Fax.....800.401.8464
Web.....www.abettertomorrow.com
E-mail.....tami@abttc.com
41640 Corning Place, Murietta, CA 92562
Tami Scarcella, Director of Intake
CARF accredited programs available.

Adolescent Counseling Svcs.....650.424.0852
Fax.....650.424.9853
E-mail.....info@acs-teens.org
445 Sherman Ave Ste J, Palo Alto, CA 94306-1829
Connie Mayer, Director

Adolescent Counseling Svcs.....650.424.0852
Fax.....650.424.9853
E-mail.....philippe@acs-teens.org
1717 Emdarcatero Rd, Palo Alto, CA 94303-4761
Philippe Rey, Director

Alcohol And Drug Abuse Council Of Contra Costa, Inc.....925.932.8100
Fax.....925.932.8392
2020 N Broadway, Walnut Creek, CA 94596
Dee Folsum, Director

Alcohol And Drug Svcs.....707.565.7450
Fax.....707.565.7487
Web.....www.sonoma-county.org
E-mail.....mdonaghu@sonoma-county.org
1430 Neotomas Ave, Santa Rosa, CA 95405-7575
Gino Giannavola, Health Program Manager

Behavioral Health Services Inc.....310.679.9126
Fax.....310.679.2920
Web.....www.bhs-inc.org
E-mail.....candy@bhs-inc.org
15519 Crenshaw Blvd, 2nd Floor, Gardena, CA 90249-4525
Candy Cargill-fuller, Director
CARF accredited programs available.

Camp Recovery Ctr.....831.438.1868
Fax.....831.438.2789
Web.....www.camprecovery.com
3192 Glen Canyon Road, Scotts Valley, CA 95066
James Bailey, ex director
CARF accredited programs available.

Child Welfare Svcs.....209.533.5717
Fax.....209.533.5742
20111 Cedar Rd N, Sonora, CA 95370-5939
Bonnie Tule, Supervisor

Children's Svcs/Human & Social Svcs.....530.822.7227
Fax.....530.822.7384
1965 Live Oak Blvd, Yuba City, CA 95991-8828
Lisa Soto, Program Manager

Clare Foundation.....310.314.6200
Fax.....310.396.6974
Web.....www.clarefoundation.org
E-mail.....nvrataric@clarefoundation.org
1871 9th St, Santa Monica, CA 90404-4501
Nicolas Vrataric, Director

Grace Homes.....559.625.1329
Fax.....559.738.9871
Web.....www.gracehomes.org
E-mail.....glenda@gracehomes.org
1100 Sumter Ct, Visalia, CA 93292
Glenda Kuns, Program Director

Koinonia Foster Homes.....916.652.0171
Fax.....916.652.3979
Web.....www.kfh.org
E-mail.....bryland@kfh.org
5980 Webb St, Loomis, CA 95650-7625
Bill Ryland, Director

California

Matrix Institute on Addictions **310.478.8305**
Fax 310.478.8639
Web ....www.matrixinstitute.org
  1849 Sawtelle Boulevard, Suite 100, West Los
  Angeles, CA 90025
  Michael McCann, Director of Research
  CARF accredited programs available.

MFI Recovery Center **951.683.6596**
Fax 951.683.4239
Web ....www.mfirecovery.com
E-mail ....craiglambdin@mfirecovery.com
  5870 Arlington Avenue, Riverside, CA 92504
  Craig Lambdin, Executive Director
  CARF accredited programs available.

New Directions For Youth **818.503.6331**
Fax 818.982.6339
E-mail ....maustin@mail.ndfy.org
  7315 Lakersin Blvd, N Hollywood, CA 91605-1972
  Monica Austin-jackson, President

Pathway Society, Inc **408.244.1834**
Fax 408.244.5123
E-mail ....mpritchard@pathwayinc.com
  1659 Scott Blvd Ste 30, Santa Clara, CA 95050-4186
  Michael Pritchard, Director

Phoenix House **714.953.9373**
Fax 714.953.9155
Web ....www.phoenixhouse.org
E-mail ....jhenderson@phoenixhouse.org
  1207 E Fruit St, Santa Ana, CA 92701-4206
  Jeff Henderson, Director

Pine Ridge Treatment Centers, Inc. **760.248.9199**
Fax 760.248.6479
Web ....www.pineridgetreatmentcenters.com
  2727 Highland Drive, Running Springs, CA 92382
  CARF accredited programs available.

Pomona Community Crisis Ctr **909.623.1588**
Fax 909.629.2470
E-mail ....pomonacrisis@aol.com
  240 E Monterey Ave, Pomona, CA 91767-5427
  Michelle Vaughn, Director

Social Model Recovery Systems, Inc. **626.332.3145**
Fax 626.974.4164
Web ....www.socialmodel.com
  250 East Rowland Street, Covina, CA 91723
  CARF accredited programs available.

Social Svcs/Child Protective Svc **530.841.4200**
Fax 530.842.6277
  490 S Broadway St, Yreka, CA 96097-3019
  Kate O'shea, Director/Program Manager

Colorado

www.colorado.gov

John Hickenlooper, Governor
136 State Capitol
Denver, CO 80203-1792
303.866.2471
303.866.2003 (Fax)

Meg Williams, Juvenile Justice Specialist
Division of Criminal Justice
700 Kipling Street, Ste 1000
Denver, CO 80215
303.239.5717
303.239.4491 (Fax)
meg.williams@cdps.state.co.us

Dianne Van Voorhees, SAG Chair
1905 Sherman St, Ste 400
Denver, CO 80203
303.830.8210
720.264.3306 (Fax)
diannev@denbar.org

CRISIS NUMBERS

Child Abuse Reporting . . .303.866.5932

STATE SERVICES

SOCIAL SERVICES

Child Care Licensing Colorado 303.866.5958
Fax 303.866.4453
   1575 Sherman St, Denver, CO 80203
   Rosemarie Allen, Division Director

Colorado Dept of Human Svcs 303.866.5700
Fax 303.866.4214
Web ....www.cdhs.state.co.us
   1575 Sherman St, 8th floor, Denver, CO 80203-1702
   Reggie Bicha, Executive Director

GENERAL HEALTH SERVICES

Health Care for Child with Spec Needs CO 303.692.2418
Fax 303.782.5576
E-mail ....kathy.watters@state.co.us
   4300 Cherry Creek Dr S, Bldg A 4, Denver, CO 80246
   Kathy Watters, Director

Ofc of Medicaid Assistance 303.866.2993
Fax 303.866.2573
E-mail ....suzanne.brennan@state.co.us
   1570 Grant St, Denver, CO 80203-1818
   Suzanne Brennan, Medicaid Director

Rocky Mountain Ctr for Health Promotion &
Education 303.239.6494
Fax 303.239.8428
Web ....www.rmc.org
   7525 W 10th Ave, Denver, CO 80214-4493
   Sharon Murray, President

MENTAL HEALTH SERVICES

Div of Vocational Rehabilitation CO 303.866.4150
Fax 303.866.4905
E-mail ....Voc.Rehab@state.co.us
   1575 Sherman St 4th Flr, Denver, CO 80203
   Nancy Smith, Director

JUSTICE AGENCY

Attorney General's Ofc 303.866.4500
Fax 303.866.5691
   1525 Sherman St, Denver, CO 80203
   John Suthers, Attorney General

Colorado Bureau Of Investigation 303.239.4300
Fax 303.235.0568
Web ....www.cdps.state.co.us
E-mail ....cbi.denver@cdps.state.co.us
   690 Kipling St Ste 3000, Denver, CO 80215-5844
   Ronald Sloan, Administrator

Colorado CASA 303.623.5380
Fax 303.623.5382
Web ....www.coloradocasa.org
E-mail ....coloradocasa@cocasa.org
   1490 Lafayette St Ste 207, Denver, CO 80218-2392
   Lori Burkey, Executive Director

Colorado Dept of Public Safety 303.239.4400
Fax 303.239.4566
E-mail ....jim.davis@cdps.state.co.us
   700 Kipling St Ste 1000, Denver, CO 80215-5897
   Jim Davis, Executive Director

Correctional Education Division CO 719.226.4417
Fax 719.226.4424
E-mail ....ross.kimbrel@doc.state.co.us
   2862 S Circle Dr, Colorado Springs, CO 80906
   Ross Kimbrel, Director

Dept of Human Svcs Div of Youth Corrections .303.866.7345
Fax 303.866.7344
Web ....www.cdhs.state.co.us
E-mail ....john.gomez@state.co.us
   4255 S Knox Ct, Denver, CO 80236-3104
   John Gomez, Associate Director

POLICE AND SHERIFF

Sheriff's Dept 720.344.2762
Fax 720.344.6500
Web ....www.csoc.org
   9008 US Highway 85 N, Littleton, CO 80125
   Donald Christensen, Executive Director

EDUCATION SERVICES

Colorado Dept of Education 303.866.6600
Fax 303.830.0793
Web ....www.cde.state.co.us
E-mail ....gotlieb_d@cde.state.co.us
   201 E Colfax Ave Ste X, Denver, CO 80203
   Herminia Vigil, Director, Nutrition

Colorado School for the Deaf & Blind 719.578.2100
Fax 719.578.2239
Web ....www.csdb.org
E-mail ....csdbsupt@csdb.org
   33 N Institute St, Colorado Springs, CO 80903
   Carol Hilty, Superintendent

Edu for Homeless Children & Youth CO 303.866.6930
Fax 303.866.6785
E-mail ....scott_d@cde.state.co.us
   201 East Colfax Ave, Ste 306 E, Denver, CO 80203
   Dana Scott, Director

Exceptional Student Leadership Unit CO 303.866.6694
Fax 303.866.6767
E-mail ....hubbard_k@cde.state.co.us
   1560 Broadway Ste 1175, Denver, CO 80202
   K Hubbard, Director

Head Start Ofc 303.866.3390
Fax 303.866.5469
E-mail ....ami.wilson@state.co.us
   130 State Capitol, Denver, CO 80203
   Ami Wilson, Licencing Specialist

PEAK Parent Center Inc CO 719.531.9400
Fax 719.531.9452
E-mail ....info@peakparent.org
   611 N Weber Ste 200, Colorado Springs, CO 80903
   Barbara Buswell, Director

COUNTY SERVICES

Adams County

SOCIAL SERVICES

Children & Family Ctr 303.412.8121
Fax 303.412.5335
   7401 Broadway, Denver, CO 80221
   Darwin Cox, Division Director

Dept of Social Svcs 303.287.8831
Fax 303.227.2157
Web ....www.co.adams.co.us
   7190 Colorado Blvd, Commerce City,
   CO 80022-1812
   Donald Cassata, MD, Director

GENERAL HEALTH SERVICES

Health Dept 303.452.9547
Fax 303.452.9712
Web ....www.tchd.org
   10190 Bannock St Ste 100, Denver, CO 80260-6051
   Sandra Lopez, Program Director

JUSTICE AGENCY

CASA **303.654.3378**
Fax...303.654.3379
E-mail...........................casa17th@casa17th.com
   1100 Judicial Center Dr, Brighton, CO 80601
Simone Jones, Executive Director

Probation Dept.........................**303.451.5555**
Fax...303.452.7995
   12200 Pecos St, Westminster, CO 80234
Mike Garcia, Chief Performance Officer

POLICE AND SHERIFF

Aurora Police Dept District 1 ....**303.739.6000**
Fax...303.739.6055
Web...www.auroragov.org
E-mail.................................doates@auroragov.org
   150N 19th St, Brightton, CO 80014-7206
Daniel Oates, Chief

Sheriff's Ofc **303.655.3211**
Fax...303.655.3296
Web....................................www.adamscountysheriff.org
E-mail.................................sheriff@co.adams.co.us
   332 N 19th Ave, Brighton, CO 80601
Doug Darr, Sheriff

EDUCATION SERVICES

Special Education.........................**303.853.1000**
Fax...303.853.1194
   591 E 80th Ave, Denver, CO 80229
Diane Blumenschim, Executive Director Of Student Services

Special Education.........................**720.972.4770**
Fax...720.972.4799
Web...www.adams12.org
   1500 E 128th Ave, Denver, CO 80241-2601
Tami Cassel, Assistant Director

Alamosa County

SOCIAL SERVICES

Social Svcs..............................**719.589.2581**
Fax...719.589.9794
Web...www.alamosacounty.org
E-mail...lhenders@fone.net
   8900 Indepenence Way, Alamosa, CO 81101-2652
Larry Henderson, Director

GENERAL HEALTH SERVICES

Public Health Dept.........................**719.589.6639**
Fax...719.589.1103
Web...www.alamosacounty.org
E-mail.................................jgeiser@alamosacounty.org
   8900 Independence Way, Alamosa, CO 81101-9412
Julie Geiser, Nursing Director

JUSTICE AGENCY

District Attorney's Ofc....................**719.589.3691**
Fax...719.589.2734
   426 San Juan Ave, Alamosa, CO 81101
David Mahonne, District Attorney

POLICE AND SHERIFF

Sheriff's Ofc..............................**719.589.6608**
Fax...719.589.6134
Web...www.alamosacounty.org
E-mail.................................dstong@alamosacounty.org
   1315 17th St, Alamosa, CO 81101
David D. Stong, Sheriff

Arapahoe County

SOCIAL SERVICES

Dept Of Human Svcs.........................**303.636.1130**
Fax...303.636.1906
E-mail.................................bfield@co.arapahoe.co.us
   14980 E Alameda Dr, Ste 7, Aurora, CO 80012
Brian Field, Director

GENERAL HEALTH SERVICES

Health Dept..............................**303.761.1340**
Fax...303.761.1528
E-mail...rbeam@tchd.org
   4857 S Broadway, Englewood, CO 80113
Rita Beam, Rn, Nurse Manager

Health Dept..............................**303.341.9370**
Fax...303.367.2597
Web...www.pchd.org
   15400 E 14th Pl Ste 309, Aurora, CO 80011-5828
Christie Hage, Office Director

MENTAL HEALTH SERVICES

Arapahoe & Douglas Mental Health Ctr......**303.797.9346**
Fax...303.797.9348
Web...www.admhn.org
E-mail.................................scottthoempke@aumhc.org
   5500 S Sycamore St Ste 301, Littleton, CO 80120-8204
Scott Thoempke, Msn, Executive Director/CEO

JUSTICE AGENCY

Probation Dept..........................**303.708.8793**
Fax...303.662.5900
Web...www.judicial.state.co.us
E-mail.................................nancy.eagle@judicial.state.co.us
   7305 S Potomac St Ste 201, Englewood, CO 80112-4041
Nancy Eagle, Juvenile Probation Supervisor

POLICE AND SHERIFF

Littleton Police Dept.....................**303.794.1551**
Fax...303.795.3918
Web...www.littletongov.org
E-mail.................................lpdgm@littletongov.org
   2255 W Berry Ave, Littleton, CO 80120
Heather Coogan, Chief

Sheriff's Ofc **720.874.3600**
Fax...720.874.4158
Web...www.co.arapahoe.co.us
E-mail.................................grobinson@co.arapahoe.co.us
   13101 Broncos Pkwy, Englewood, CO 80112-4558
J. Grayson Robinson, Sheriff

EDUCATION SERVICES

Special Education.........................**303.347.3471**
Fax...303.347.3310
Web...www.littletonpublicschools.net
E-mail.................................mrcooper@lps.k12.co.us
   5776 S Crocker St, Littleton, CO 80120
Melissa Cooper, Director

Special Education.........................**303.806.2086**
Fax...303.806.2064
Web...www.englewood.k12.co.us
E-mail.................................callan_clark@englewood.k12.co.us
   4101 S Bannock St, Englewood, CO 80110-4605
Callan Clark, Executive Director Of Student Services

Special Education.........................**303.340.0510**
Fax...303.326.1285
Web...www.aps.k12.co.us
E-mail.................................ssburdelik@aps.k12.co.us
   15751 E 1st Ave, Aurora, CO 80011-9023
Sandra Burdelik, Director

Archuleta County

SOCIAL SERVICES

Dept Of Human Svcs.........................**970.264.2182**
Fax...970.264.2186
Web...www.archuletacounty.org
   551 Hot Springs, Pagosa Springs, CO 81147
Erlinda Gonzales, Director

COURTS

Court..............................**970.264.2400**
Fax...970.264.2407
   449 San Juan St, Pagosa Springs, CO 81147
Debbie Tully, Clerk Of Court

Baca County

SOCIAL SERVICES

Social Svcs..............................**719.523.4131**
Fax...719.523.4820
Web...www.state.co.us
E-mail.................................ruth.wallace@state.co.us
   772 Colorado St Ste 1, Springfield, CO 81073-1456
Ruth Porter, Director

GENERAL HEALTH SERVICES

Nursing Svcs..............................**719.523.6621**
Fax...719.523.6537
Web...www.bacadem.com/publichealth.htm
E-mail.................................rtrujillo@bacacounty.net
   741 Main St Ste 4, Springfield, CO 81073-1425
Robin Trujillo, Director

COURTS

Court..............................**719.523.4555**
Fax...719.523.4552
Web...www.courts.state.co.us
   741 Main St Ste 5, Springfield, CO 81073-1548
Debra M Gunkel, County Judge

POLICE AND SHERIFF

Sheriff's Ofc..............................**719.523.4511**
Fax...719.523.4587
Web...www.bacacounty.net
   265 E 2nd Ave, Springfield, CO 81073-1102
Dave Campbell, Sheriff

Bent County

SOCIAL SERVICES

Social Svcs..............................**719.456.2620**
Fax...719.456.2945
E-mail.................................william.schultz@bentcounty.net
   215 2nd St, Las Animas, CO 81054-1109
William Schultz, Director

MENTAL HEALTH SERVICES

Southeast Mental Health Svcs- Las Animas Ofc......**719.456.0069**
Fax...719.384.5672
Web...www.semhs.org
E-mail.................................bwhaley@semhs.org
   711 Barn Lajunta, Las Animas, CO 81054-1733
Robert Whaley, Executive Director

COURTS

Court..............................**719.456.1353**
Fax...719.456.0040
Web...www.judicial.state.co.us
   725 Bent Ave Ste 1, Las Animas, CO 81054-1757
Mark A. Macdonnell, Judge

POLICE AND SHERIFF

Sheriff's Ofc..............................**719.456.0796**
Fax...719.456.0476
E-mail.................................dencinias@bentcounty.net
   11100 County Road, GG5, Las Animas, CO 81054
David Encinias, Sheriff

Boulder County

SOCIAL SERVICES

Housing And Human Services **303.441.1000**
Fax 303.441.1289
Web ....www.bouldercounty.org
E-mail ....hofrontdesk@bouldercounty.org
   3400 Broadway St, Boulder, CO 80304
Frank Alexander, Director

GENERAL HEALTH SERVICES

Public Health **303.441.1100**
Fax 303.441.1452
Web ....www.bouldercounty.org
   3450 Broadway St, Boulder, CO 80304
Jeff Zayach, Director

MENTAL HEALTH SERVICES

The Mental Health Ctr Serving Boulder and Broomfield
Counties **720.406.3608**
Fax 303.449.6029
Web ....www.mhcbbc.org
E-mail ....aalvarez@mhcbbc.org
   1333 Iris Avenue, Boulder, CO 80304-2296
Amalia Alvarez, Office Manager

JUSTICE AGENCY

District Attorneys Ofc **303.441.3700**
Fax 303.441.4703
Web ....www.bouldercounty.org/da/index.htm
E-mail ....colguin@bouldercounty.org
   1777 6th Street, Boulder, CO 80302
Cathrine Olguin, Administrator

Probation Dept **303.441.4730**
Fax 303.441.4716
   1777 6th St, Fl 1, Boulder, CO 80302
Greg Brown, Jpo

Voices For Children CASA **303.440.7059**
Fax 303.440.9960
Web ....www.vfccasa.org
E-mail ....info@vfccasa.org
   2305 Canyon Blvd Ste 101, Boulder, CO 80302-5651
Marsha Caplan, Executive Director

COURTS

20th District Court **303.441.3750**
Fax 303.441.4750
Web ....www.courts.state.co.us
   1777 6th St, Boulder, CO 80306
Honorable T.J. Cole, Judge

POLICE AND SHERIFF

Boulder City Police Dept **303.441.3315**
Fax 303.441.1941
Web ....www.bouldercolorado.gov
E-mail ....becknerm@bouldercolorado.gov
   1805 33rd St, Boulder, CO 80301-2576
Mark Beckner, Police Chief

Sheriff's Ofc **303.441.3600**
Fax 303.441.4739
Web ....www.bouldersheriff.org
   6600 Slatiron Pkwy, Boulder, CO 80301-5814
Joe Pelle, Sheriff

EDUCATION SERVICES

Special Education **303.772.7700**
Fax 303.651.3066
   395 S Pratt Pkwy, Longmont, CO 80501
Jackie Woodington, Executive Director

Broomfield County

SOCIAL SERVICES

Child And Family Svcs **720.887.2201**
Fax 720.887.2268
Web ....www.broomfield.org
   6 Garden Ctr, Broomfield, CO 80020
Debbi Oldenettel, Director

Health And Human Svcs **720.887.2200**
Fax 303.469.2110
Web ....www.ci.broomfield.co.us/hhs
   6 Garden Ctr, Broomfield, CO 80020
Debbie Oldenettel, Human Services Director

GENERAL HEALTH SERVICES

Broomfield Self-Sufficiency &
Employment **720.887.2261**
Fax 303.469.2110
Web ....www.ci.broomfield.co.us
E-mail ....fschoengarth@ci.broomfield.co.us
   6 Garden Ctr, Broomfield, CO 80020-1730
Frank Shoengarth, Manager

MENTAL HEALTH SERVICES

Mental Health Ctr for the Boulder & Broomfield
Counties **303.466.3007**
Fax 303.464.1413
Web ....www.mhcbbc.org
E-mail ....esimpson@mhcbbc.org
   899 Hwy 287, Ste 300, Broomfield, CO 80020
Elizabeth Simpson, Team Leader

Chaffee County

POLICE AND SHERIFF

Sheriff's Dept **719.539.2814**
Fax 719.539.1077
E-mail ....records@chaffeecounty.org
   132 Crestone Ave, Salida, CO 81201
Timothy Walker, Sheriff

Cheyenne County

SOCIAL SERVICES

Social Svcs **719.767.5629**
Fax 719.767.5101
Web ....www.state.co.us
   51 S 1st, Cheyenne Wells, CO 80810
Kindra Mulch, Director

GENERAL HEALTH SERVICES

Public Health **719.767.5616**
Fax 719.767.8747
E-mail ....phn@co.cheyenne.co.us
   560 W 6th N, Cheyenne Wells, CO 80810
Linda Roth, Rn, Public Health Nurse

COURTS

Court **719.767.5649**
Fax 719.767.5671
E-mail ....stanley.brinkley@judicial.state.co.us
   51 S 1st St, Cheyenne Wells, CO 80810
Honorable Stanley Brinkley, District Judge

POLICE AND SHERIFF

Sheriff's Dept **719.767.5633**
Fax 719.767.5023
   91 E 1st, Cheyenne Wells, CO 80810
Virgil Drescher, Sheriff

Clear Creek County

SOCIAL SERVICES

Social Svcs **303.679.2365**
Fax 303.679.2443
Web ....www.state.co.us
E-mail ....cindy.dicken@state.co.us
   405 Argentine St, Courthouse, Georgetown,
   CO 80444
Cindy Dicken, Director

POLICE AND SHERIFF

Sheriff's Dept **303.679.2376**
Fax 303.679.2447
E-mail ....webadmin@clearcreeksheriff.us
   405 Argentine Street, Georgetown, CO 80444
Don Krueger, Sheriff

Conejos County

SOCIAL SERVICES

Dept Of Social Svcs **719.376.5455**
Fax 719.376.2389
E-mail ....maria.garcia2@state.co.us
   12989 County Rd, Ste G6, Conejos, CO 81129
Maria Garcia, Director

GENERAL HEALTH SERVICES

Public Health Nursing **719.274.4307**
Fax 719.274.4309
E-mail ....connie@co.conejos.co.us
   19023 US Highway 285, La Jara, CO 81140
Connie Edgar, Administrator

Costilla County

SOCIAL SERVICES

Social Svcs **719.672.4131**
Fax 719.672.4141
E-mail ....ramona.archuleta@state.co.us
   123 Gasper St, San Louis, CO 81152
Ramone Archuleta, Director

GENERAL HEALTH SERVICES

Public Health Nursing **719.672.3332**
Fax 719.672.3856
E-mail ....vgallegos@costillacounty-co.gov
   233 Main St, San Luis, CO 81152
Vivian Gallegos, Director Of Nursing/health Officer

Crowley County

SOCIAL SERVICES

Social Svcs **719.267.3546**
Fax 719.267.5296
   631 Main St, Ste 100, Ordway, CO 81063
Tonia Burnett, Director

COURTS

Court **719.267.4468**
Fax 719.267.3753
Web ....www.judicial.state.co.us
   110 E 6th St, Rm 303, Ordway, CO 81063
Honorable Susan A. Grant, Judge

Custer County

SOCIAL SERVICES

Social Svcs **719.783.2371**
Fax 719.783.0163
   205 S 6th St, Westcliffe, CO 81252
Laura Lockhart, Director

GENERAL HEALTH SERVICES

Medical Center **719.783.2380**
Fax 719.783.2377
Web ....www.custercountymedical.com
   704 Edwards St, Westcliffe, CO 81252
Terry Nimnicht, Administrator

Delta County

SOCIAL SERVICES

Social Svcs **970.874.2030**
Fax 970.874.2068
E-mail ....lemoine@deltacounty.com
   560 Dodge St, Courthouse Annex, Delta, CO 81416
William C Lemoine, Director

GENERAL HEALTH SERVICES

Health Dept **970.874.2165**
Fax 970.874.2175
Web ....www.deltacounty.com
   255 W 6th St, Delta, CO 81416
Pat Sullivan, Rn, Hiv Coordinator

JUSTICE AGENCY

Probation dept. **970.874.6271**
Fax 970.874.6272
   501 Palmer St,, ste 355, Delta, CO 81416
Joe Quintana, Probation Officer

COURTS

7th District Court **970.874.6280**
Fax 970.874.4306
   501 Palmer St Ste 338, Delta, CO 81416
Honorable Charles R. Greenacre, Judge

POLICE AND SHERIFF

Sheriff's Ofc **970.874.2000**
Fax 970.874.2027
E-mail ....fmckee@deltacounty.com
   555 Palmer St, Delta, CO 81416
Fred Mckee, Sheriff

Denver County

SOCIAL SERVICES

Human Resources **303.866.7100**
Fax 303.866.7127
Web ....www.state.co.us
E-mail ....brad.mallon@state.co.us
   3550 W Oxford Ave, Denver, CO 80236-3108
Brad Mallon, Director

GENERAL HEALTH SERVICES

Denver Health Medical Ctr **303.436.6000**
Fax 303.436.5131
Web ....www.denverhealth.org
   777 Bannock St, Denver, CO 80204
John Peterson, Adolescent Psychiatric Services Director

Westside Neighborhood Health
District **303.436.4200**
Fax 303.436.4405
Web ....www.denverhealth.org
E-mail ....mary.oconner@dhha.org
   1100 Federal Blvd, Denver, CO 80204-3295
Mary OÆConner, MD, Pediatric Clinical Director

MENTAL HEALTH SERVICES

Colorado Mental Health Fort
Logan **303.866.7080**
Fax 303.866.7066
Web ....www.state.co.us
E-mail ....keith.lagrenade@state.co.us
   3520 W Oxford Ave, Denver, CO 80236-3197
Keith Lagrenade, MD, Director

JUSTICE AGENCY

Child Advocates-Denver CASA **303.832.4592**
Fax 303.832.4712
Web ....www.denvercasa.org
   225 E 16th Ave Ste 1020, Denver, CO 80203
Lisa Odell-davis, Executive Director

District Attorney's Ofc **720.913.9000**
Fax 720.913.9035
   201 W Colfax Ave, Dept 801, Denver, CO 80202
Benita Martin, Juvenile Diversion Director

Div Of Youth Corrections, Central
Region **303.866.7850**
Fax 303.866.7818
Web ....www.colorado.gov
   4120 S Julian Way, Denver, CO 80236-3102
Maurice Williams, Director

Juvenile Probation Dept **720.913.4200**
Fax 720.913.4219
E-mail ....shawn.cohn@judicial.state.co.us
   303 W Colfax Ave, Dept 1401, Denver, CO 80204
Shawn Cohn, Chief JPO

COURTS

Denver Probate Court **720.865.8310**
Fax 720.865.8576
Web ....www.denverprobatecourt.org
   1437 Bannock St Rm 230, Denver, CO 80202
Honorable C. Jean Stewart, Judge

POLICE AND SHERIFF

Denver Police Dept **720.913.6010**
Fax 720.913.6790
E-mail ....megan.dodge@denvergov.org
   1331 Cherokee St, Denver, CO 80204
Megan Dodge, Juvenile Supervisor

Sheriff's Dept **720.337.0200**
Fax 720.337.0206
Web ....www.ci.denver.co.us
E-mail ....sheltons@ci.denver.co.us
   490 W Colfax Ave, Denver, CO 80204
Gary Wilson, Director Of Corrections

Dolores County

SOCIAL SERVICES

Dept Of Social Svcs **970.677.2250**
Fax 970.677.2859
Web ....www.state.co.us
E-mail ....dennis.story@state.co.us
   409 N Main, Dove Creek, CO 81324
Dennis Story, Director

GENERAL HEALTH SERVICES

Public Health **970.677.2387**
Fax 970.677.2948
Web ....www.sjbhd.org
E-mail ....maryrandolph@centurytel.net
   497 W 4th St, Dove Creek, CO 81324
Mary Randolph, Public Health Nurse

COURTS

Court **970.677.2258**
Fax 970.677.4156
Web ....www.judicial.state.co.us
E-mail ....dale.boyd@judicial.state.co.us
   409 N. Main, Dove Creek, CO 81324
Honorable E Dale Boyd, County Judge

Douglas County

SOCIAL SERVICES

Human Svcs **303.688.4825**
Fax 303.688.0292
   4400 castleton ct, Castle Rock, CO 80109
Barbara Drake, Director

GENERAL HEALTH SERVICES

Health Dept **303.663.7650**
Fax 303.688.8870
E-mail ....pallderdice@tchd.org
   4400 Castleton Cart, Castle Rock, CO 80109
Paula Allderdice, Rn, Nursing Manager

POLICE AND SHERIFF

Sheriff's Dept **303.660.7505**
Fax 303.814.8790
Web ....www.dcsheriff.net
E-mail ....dcso@douglas.co.us
   4000 Justice Way, Castle Rock, CO 80109-7543
David A. Weaver, Sheriff

Eagle County

SOCIAL SERVICES

Health & Human Svcs **970.328.8840**
Fax 970.328.8829
Web ....www.eaglecounty.us
   551 Broadway St, Eagle, CO 81631
Rachel Oys, Human Services Director

GENERAL HEALTH SERVICES

Public Health Nursing **970.704.2760**
Fax 970.704.2783
Web ....www.eaglecounty.us
   20 Eagle County Rd Unit E, Carbondale,
   CO 81623-9125
Teresa Carey, Public Health Nurse

Public Health Nursing **970.949.7026**
Fax 855.848.8829
Web ....www.eaglecounty.us
E-mail ....alison.christopher@eaglecounty.us
   100 W Beaver Creek, Ste 107, Avon, CO 81620
Alison Christopher, Public Health Nurse

MENTAL HEALTH SERVICES

Colorado West Regional Mental Health
Ctr **970.328.6969**
Fax 970.328.6329
Web ....www.cwrmhc.org
E-mail ....kmcclint@cwrmhc.org
   137 Howard, Eagle, CO 81631
Krista Mcclinton, Director

JUSTICE AGENCY

CASA Of The Continental Divide **970.513.9390**
Fax 970.513.9690
   330 Fiedler Avenue, Ste 207, Dillon, CO 80435
Kathy Reed, Executive Director

Probation Dept **970.704.2747**
Fax 970.704.2782
E-mail ....laurel.lamont@judicial.state.co.us
   20 Eagle County Rd Unit C, Carbondale, CO 81623
Laurel Lamont, CPO

POLICE AND SHERIFF

Sheriff's Dept **970.328.8500**
Fax 970.328.1448
Web ....www.eaglecounty.us
E-mail ....info@sheriff.eagle.co.us
   0885 E Chambers Ave, Eagle, CO 81631
Joseph D. Hoy, Sheriff

El Paso County

GENERAL HEALTH SERVICES

Health Dept **719.578.3199**
Fax 719.578.3192
   301 S Union Blvd, Colorado Springs, CO 80910
Mercedes Harden, Disease Prevention Director/ Medical Director

MENTAL HEALTH SERVICES

Aspen Pointe **719.572.6100**
Fax 719.572.6199
Web ....www.aspenpointe.org
E-mail ....morris.roth@aspenpointe.org
   525 N0 Cascade, Colorado Springs, CO 80903
Morris Roth, Msw, Lcsw, President & CEO

Colorado

Outpatient Svcs/ Child And Family 719.572.6300
Fax 719.572.6399
179 Parkside Dr, Colorado Springs, CO 80910
Jason DeaBueno, Division Director

JUSTICE AGENCY

4th District Probation Dept 719.448.7750
Fax 719.329.7085
270 S Tejon St, Ste W200, Colorado Springs,
CO 80903
Art Osier Ellen Walker, Chief Probation Officer

Attorney's Office 719.520.7020
E-mail ....carolwersich@elpasoco.com
105 E Vermijo Ste 415, Colorado Springs, CO 80903
Carol Wersich, Attorney

Attorney's Office 719.520.7021
E-mail ....donnaolalde@elpasoco.com
105 E Vermijo Ste 415, Colorado Springs, CO 80903
Donna Olalde

District Attorney's Ofc 719.520.6000
Fax 719.520.6185
Web www.elpasoteller911.org
105 E Vermijo Ave Ste 500, Colorado Springs,
CO 80903-2015
Jerry Ohare, Juvenile Diversion Director

State Dept Of Institutions Div Of Youth
Svcs 719.538.0204
Fax 719.538.0210
E-mail ....anne.freeman@state.co.us
321 S Tejon St, Colorado Springs, CO 80906-3542
Anne Freeman, Director Of Southern Region

COURTS

5th District Court 970.328.6373
Fax 970.328.6328
Web ....www.judicial.state.co.us
885 E Chambers Road, Eagle, CO 81631
Honorable Thomas Moorhead, Chief Judge

Teen Court 719.475.7815
Fax 719.385.6202
E-mail ....csteenct@uswest.net
108 E Kiowa Street, Colorado Springs, CO 80903
Patricia Ezell, Executive Director

POLICE AND SHERIFF

Sheriff's Ofc 719.520.7100
Fax 719.520.7171
Web ....www.elpasoco.com\sheriff
E-mail ....terrymaketa@elpasoco.com
210 S Tejon St, Colorado Springs, CO 80903-2203
Terry Maketa, Sheriff

EDUCATION SERVICES

Special Education 719.520.2148
Fax 719.520.2198
Web www.cssd11.k12.co.us
E-mail ....daybs@d11.org
1115 N El Paso St, Colorado Springs, CO 80903
Dr. Barbara Day, Executive Director

Special Education 719.391.3050
Fax 719.391.9142
930 Leta Dr, Colorado Springs, CO 80911
Lisa Humberd, Director

Special Education 719.494.1682
Fax 719.494.1688
Web www.d49.org
E-mail ....chardin@d49.org
7545 Mohawk Rd, Colorado Springs,
CO 80908-5005
Cindy Hardin, Director of Transportation

Special Education 719.382.1300
Fax 719.382.7338
Web www.ffc8.org
10665 Jimmy Camp Rd, Fountain, CO 80817-4175
Cheryl Serrano, Superintendent

Elbert County

MENTAL HEALTH SERVICES

Centennial Mental Health Ctr 303.646.4519
Fax 303.646.4451
Web ....www.centennialmhc.org
E-mail ....bonniea@centennialmhc.org
650 E Walnut, Elizabeth, CO 80107
Bonnie Adams, County Program Director

Fremont County

GENERAL HEALTH SERVICES

Fremont Nursing Svcs 719.275.1626
Fax 719.275.4328
Web ....www.fremontco.com
E-mail ....fcns@fremontco.com
172 Justice Center Rd, Canon City, CO 81212-9354
Becki Vettese, Administrator

MENTAL HEALTH SERVICES

Colorado Territorial Correctional
Facility 719.269.4002
Fax 719.269.4115
Web ....coloradoinjustice.org
275 West Highway 50, Caon City, CO 81215-1010
Joe Stommel, MA, Doc, Drug And Alcohol Services Director

COURTS

Teen Court 719.269.0170
Fax 719.269.0180
Web ....www.state.co.us
E-mail ....john.evans.senate@state.co.us
136 Justice Center Rd Rm 203, Canon City,
CO 81212-9322
John Evans, Coordinator

POLICE AND SHERIFF

Sheriff's Dept 719.276.5555
Fax 719.276.5593
100 Justice Center Rd, Canon City, CO 81212
James L. Beicker, Sheriff

Garfield County

GENERAL HEALTH SERVICES

Nursing Svcs 970.625.5200
Fax 970.625.4804
E-mail ....lgoodwin@garfield-county.com
195 W. 14th St., Rifle, CO 81650-2729
Laura Goodwin, Public Health Nurse

Public Health Nursing 970.945.6614
Fax 970.947.0155
Web ....www.garfieldcounty.com
E-mail ....mmeisner@garfield-county.com
2014 Blake Ave, Glenwood Springs, CO 81601-4229
Mary Meisner, RN, Health Officer

MENTAL HEALTH SERVICES

Colorado West Regional Mental Health
Ctr 970.945.2241
Fax 970.945.5523
Web ....www.cwrmhc.org
E-mail ....sraggio@cwrmhc.org
6916 Hwy 82 Ste A, Glenwood Springs,
CO 81601-9436
Sharon Raggio, Executive Director

Dept Of Human Svcs 970.625.5282
Fax 970.625.0927
E-mail ....mbaydarian@garfield-county.com
195 W 14th, Rifle, CO 81650
Mary Baydarian, Director

JUSTICE AGENCY

9th Judicial Probation Dept 970.945.6700
Fax 970.928.8539
Web ....www.judicial.state.co.us
109 8th St Ste 400, Glenwood Springs,
CO 81601-3363
Shawnee Barnes, Chief Probation Officer

COURTS

9th District Court 970.945.5075
Fax 970.945.8756
109 8th St Ste 104, Glenwood Springs, CO 81601
Honorable Paul Metzger, Judge

POLICE AND SHERIFF

Sheriff's Dept 970.945.0453
Fax 970.945.6430
Web ....www.garcosheriff.com
E-mail ....lvallario@garcosheriff.com
107 8th St, Glenwood Springs, CO 81601-3303
Lou Vallario, Sheriff

Gilpin County

SOCIAL SERVICES

Dept Of Human Svcs 303.582.5444
Fax 303.582.5798
E-mail ....bdonovan@co.gilpin.co.us
2960 Dory Hill Rd Unit 100, Black Hawk, CO 80422
Betty Donovan, Director

Grand County

SOCIAL SERVICES

Social Svcs 970.725.3331
Fax 970.725.3696
E-mail ....glen.chambers@state.co.us
620 Hemlock St, Hot Sulphur Springs, CO 80451
Glen Chambers, Director

GENERAL HEALTH SERVICES

Public Health Nursing Svc 970.725.3288
Fax 970.725.3438
Web ....www.co.grand.co.us
E-mail ....bbelew-ladue@co.grand.co.us
150 Moffat Avenue, Hot Sulphur Springs, CO 80451
Brenne Belew-ladue, Rn, Public Health Director

MENTAL HEALTH SERVICES

Colorado West Mental Health- Alpine
Ctr 970.887.2179
Fax 970.887.9311
1023 County Road 610, Granby, CO 80446
Cynthia Rose, Program Director

COURTS

14th District Court 970.725.3357
Web ....www.judicial.state.co.us
307 Moffat Ave, Hot Sulphur Springs, CO 80451
Honorable Mary Hoak, Judge

POLICE AND SHERIFF

Sheriff's Dept 970.725.3343
Fax 970.725.3227
E-mail ....rjohnson@co.grand.co.us
670 Spring St, Hot Sulphur Springs, CO 80451
Rodney D. Johnson, Sheriff

Gunnison County

GENERAL HEALTH SERVICES

Public Health......................**970.641.0209**
Fax...970.641.8346
E-mail ....cworrall@gunnisoncounty.org
225 N Pine St Ste E, Gunnison, CO 81230-2648
Carol Worrall, Rn, Public Health Nurse

JUSTICE AGENCY

Juvenile Diversion/ Courthouse...........**970.641.4710**
Fax...970.641.9079
Web..............................www.co.gunnison.co.us
E-mail ....jreinman@co.gunnison.co.us
225 N Pine St Ste C, Gunnison, CO 81230-2648
Janet Reinman, Director

Probation...............................**970.641.0695**
Fax...970.641.6876
Web..............................www.judicial.state.co.us
E-mail ....carol.warrener@judicial.state.co.us
200 E Virginia Ave, Gunnison, CO 81230-2248
Carol Warrener, CPO

POLICE AND SHERIFF

Sheriff's Dept...........................**970.641.1113**
Fax...970.641.7649
200 N Iowa St, Gunnison, CO 81230
Richard Becker, Sheriff

Hinsdale County

POLICE AND SHERIFF

Sheriff's Dept...........................**970.944.2291**
Fax...970.944.2744
E-mail ....sheriff@hinsdale-sheriff.com
311 N Henson St, Lake City, CO 81235
Ronald Bruce, Sheriff

Huerfano County

SOCIAL SERVICES

Social Svcs..............................**719.738.2810**
Fax...719.738.2549
121 W 6th St, Walsenburg, CO 81089
Sheila Hudson, Director

MENTAL HEALTH SERVICES

Spanish Peaks Mental Health Ctr.............**719.738.2386**
Fax...719.738.2021
Web...www.spmhc.org
E-mail ....walsenberg@spmhc.org
926 Russell Ave, Walsenburg, CO 81089-2134
Daniel Kolekowski, Program Director

COURTS

3rd District Court.......................**719.738.1040**
401 Main St Ste 304, Walsenburg, CO 81089
Honorable Claude W. Appel, Judge

POLICE AND SHERIFF

Sheriff's Dept...........................**719.738.1600**
Fax...719.738.3676
E-mail ....huerfanoso@aol.com
500 S Albert Ave, Walsenburg, CO 81089
Bruce Newman, Sheriff

Jackson County

SOCIAL SERVICES

Social Services..........................**970.723.4750**
Fax...970.723.4619
E-mail ....glen.chambers@state.co.us
350 McKinley St, Walden, CO 80480
Glen Chambers, Director

GENERAL HEALTH SERVICES

Public Health Nursing..................**970.723.8572**
Fax...970.723.8447
E-mail ....jcnsvc@aol.com
350 McKinley St, Walden, CO 80480
Missy White, Office Manager

Jefferson County

SOCIAL SERVICES

Social Svcs..............................**303.271.1388**
Fax...303.271.4444
900 Jefferson County Pkwy, Golden, CO 80401
Lynn Johnson, Director

GENERAL HEALTH SERVICES

Dept Of Health & Environment Lakewood
Clinic..................................**303.239.7078**
Fax...303.239.7088
Web..............................www.co.jefferson.co.us
E-mail ....ntubman@co.jefferson.co.us
260 S Kipling St, Denver, CO 80226-1099
Norma Tubman, Director

Health Dept.............................**303.271.5700**
Fax...303.271.5702
Web..............................www.co.jefferson.co.us
E-mail ....mjohnson@co.jefferson.co.us
1801 19th St, Golden, CO 80401-1709
Mark Johnson, Md, Medical Director

JUSTICE AGENCY

CASA Of Jefferson & Gilpin
Counties................................**303.271.6535**
Fax...303.279.9494
E-mail ....info@casajeffcogilpin.com
100 Jefferson County Pkwy, Ste 2040, Golden, CO 80401
Leah Varnell, Executive Director

Probation Dept..........................**303.271.6364**
Fax...303.271.6368
Web..............................www.judicialstate.co.us
E-mail ....cheryl.lammers@judicialstate.co.us
100 Jefferson County Pkwy, # 2070, Golden, CO 80401
Cheryl Lammers, Chief Performance Officer

COURTS

1st Judicial District....................**303.271.6215**
Fax...303.271.6188
Web..............................www.coures.state.co.us
E-mail ....bob.evans@judicial.state.co.us
100 Jefferson County Pkwy, Golden, CO 80401-6000
Robert C. Evans, Judicial District Administrator

Teen Court..............................**303.987.7440**
Fax...303.987.7470
E-mail ....jendun@lakewoodco.org
445 S Allison Pkwy, lakewood, CO 80226
Jennifer Dunn, Coordinator

Teen Court..............................**720.898.7171**
Fax...720.898.7164
Web...www.arvada.org
E-mail ....teencourt@arvada.org
8101 Ralston Rd, Arvada, CO 80002-2439
Tami Rice, Coordinator

POLICE AND SHERIFF

Sheriff's Ofc............................**303.271.5305**
Fax...303.271.5307
Web..............................www.jeffcosheriff.com
E-mail ....tmink@co.jefferson.co.us
200 Jefferson County Pkwy, Golden, CO 80401-6008
Ted Mink, Sheriff

EDUCATION SERVICES

Empire Head Start......................**303.271.4680**
5150 allison st, Arvada, CO 80002
Gayle Perriman, Director

Kiowa County

SOCIAL SERVICES

Social Svcs..............................**719.438.5541**
Fax...719.438.5370
1307 Main St, Eads, CO 81036
Dennis Pearson, Director

GENERAL HEALTH SERVICES

Public Health...........................**719.438.5782**
Fax...719.438.2208
E-mail ....kcnf@plans.net
1206 Luther, Eads, CO 81036
Renay Crane, Rn, Public Health Nurse

COURTS

Court...................................**719.438.5531**
Fax...719.438.5300
1305 Goff St, Eads, CO 81036
Gary W. Davis, Judge

Kit Carson County

COURTS

Court...................................**719.346.5524**
Fax...719.346.7805
E-mail ....henry.goddard@kitcarsoncounty.org
251 16th St, Ste 301, Burlington, CO 80807-1674
Henry Goddard, Director

POLICE AND SHERIFF

Sheriff's Dept...........................**719.346.8934**
Fax...719.346.7282
E-mail ....sheriff@kitcarsoncounty.org
251 16th St Ste 103, Burlington, CO 80807-1674
Ed Rapps, Sheriff

La Plata County

SOCIAL SERVICES

Human Svcs.............................**970.382.6150**
Fax...970.247.2208
Web..............................www.co.laplata.co.us
1060 E 2nd Ave, Courthouse, Durango, CO 81301-5113
Leslie Mayer, Director

Southern Ute Tribal Social Svcs.............**970.563.0100**
Fax...970.563.0334
Web..............................www.southern-ute.nsn.us
356 Ouray Dr, Leonard C Birch Bldg, Ignacio, CO 81137
Dale White, Director for Social Services

JUSTICE AGENCY

Probation Dept..........................**970.247.0982**
Fax...970.385.5804
1060 E 2nd Ave, Ste 107, Durango, CO 81301
Vic Blasi, CPO

POLICE AND SHERIFF

Sheriff's Dept...........................**970.247.1157**
Fax...970.247.1618
Web...www.lpcso.org
742 Turner Dr, Durango, CO 81303
Duke Schirard, Sheriff

EDUCATION SERVICES

Florida Mesa Head Start.................**970.382.7681**
Web..............................www.acf.hhs.gov
216 Highway 172, Durango, CO 81303-8295
Tammy Huntsman, Director

Lake County

POLICE AND SHERIFF

Sheriff's Dept **719.486.1249**
Fax 719.486.0139
  505 Harrison Avenue, Leadville, CO 80461
  Edward J. Holte, Sheriff

Larimer County

SOCIAL SERVICES

Social Svcs **970.498.6300**
Fax 970.498.7987
  1501 Blue Spruce Dr, Fort Collins, CO 80524
  Ginny Riley, Director

Social Svcs **970.498.6990**
Fax 970.498.6966
  2555 Midpoint Dr Ste F, Fort Collins,
  CO 80525-4425
  Angela Mead, Ongoing Deputy Division Manager

GENERAL HEALTH SERVICES

Health & Environment Dept **970.577.2050**
Fax 970.577.2060
Web ....www.larimer.org
E-mail ....alebailly@larimer.org
  1601 Brodie Ave, Estes Park, CO 80517-7486
  Adrienne Lebailly, Md, Medical Director

Health Dept **970.498.6700**
Fax 970.498.6772
Web ....www.larimer.org
  1525 Blue Spruce Dr, Fort Collins, CO 80524
  Nattie Underwood, Rn, Hiv Coordinator

MENTAL HEALTH SERVICES

Larimer Center for Mental Health **970.494.4200**
Fax 970.494.4240
Web ....www.larimercenter.org
E-mail ....randy.ratliff@larimercenter.org
  2001 S Shields St Bldg K, Fort Collins, CO 80526
  Randy Ratliff, Director

Larimer Ctr For Mental Health **970.494.9870**
Fax 970.613.4475
Web ....www.larimercenter.org
E-mail ....randy.ratliff@larimercenter.org
  1250 N Wilson Ave, Loveland, CO 80537-4461
  Randy Ratliss, Director

POLICE AND SHERIFF

Fort Collins Police Dept **970.221.6540**
Fax 970.221.6639
  2221 S Timberline Rd, Fort Collins, CO 80525
  David Wilson, School Resource Officer

Sheriff's Dept **970.498.5100**
Fax 970.482.8745
Web ....www.larimersheriff.org
  2501 Midpoint Dr, Fort Collins, CO 80525-4417
  Justin Smith, Sheriff

EDUCATION SERVICES

Special Education **970.490.3233**
Fax 970.490.3611
Web ....www.psdschools.org
E-mail ....sabelleau@psdschools.org
  2407 Laporte Ave, Fort Collins, CO 80521-2211
  Sarah Belleau, Special Education Director

Las Animas County

SOCIAL SERVICES

Dept Of Human Services **719.846.2276**
Fax 719.846.4269
E-mail ....catherine.salazar@state.co.us
  204 S Chestnut St, Trinidad, CO 81082-3035
  Robert Bertolino, Deputy Director

GENERAL HEALTH SERVICES

**Las Animas-Huerfano District Health
Dept** **719.846.2213**
Fax 719.846.4472
Web ....www.la-h-health.org
E-mail ....CMONTERA@la-h-health.org
  412 Benedicta Ave, Trinidad, CO 81082
  Cathy Montera, Rn, Public Health Nurse

POLICE AND SHERIFF

Sheriff's Dept **719.846.2211**
Fax 719.846.0171
E-mail ....casias@lasosheriff.org
  2309 E Main St, Trinidad, CO 81082
  James Casias, Sheriff

Lincoln County

GENERAL HEALTH SERVICES

Public Health Dept **719.743.2526**
Fax 719.743.2482
Web ....www.lincolncountyco.us
  326 8th St, Hugo, CO 80821
  Marti Wooton, Public Health Nurse

Logan County

GENERAL HEALTH SERVICES

Northeast Colorado Health Dept **970.522.3741**
Fax 970.522.1412
E-mail ....johnc@nchd.org
  700 Columbine St, Sterling, CO 80751
  John Crosthwait, Director

COURTS

13th District Court **970.522.6565**
Fax 970.522.6566
Web ....www.courts.state.co.us
E-mail ....michael.singer@judicial.state.co.us
  110 N Riverview Rd Rm 205, Sterling,
  CO 80751-8505
  Honorable Michael Singer, Judge

Court **970.522.1572**
Fax 970.526.5359
Web ....www.courts.state.co.us
  110 Riverview Rd Rm 210, Sterling, CO 80751-8505
  Honorable Robert B. Smith, Director

POLICE AND SHERIFF

Sheriff's Dept **970.522.2578**
Fax 970.522.7574
Web ....www.logancosheriff.com
E-mail ....bpowell@logancosheriff.com
  110 Riverview Rd Rm 116, Sterling, CO 80751-8503
  Brett Powell, Sheriff

Mesa County

SOCIAL SERVICES

Human Svcs **970.241.8480**
Fax 970.248.2849
E-mail ....tracey.garchar@mesacounty.us
  51029 1/2 Rd, Grand Junction, CO 81502
  Tracey Garchar, Director

GENERAL HEALTH SERVICES

Health Dept Family Planning **970.248.6900**
Fax 970.248.6913
E-mail ....valerie.pulsither@mesacounty.us
  510 29 1/2 Rd, Grand Junction, CO 81504
  Valerie Pulsither, Director

MENTAL HEALTH SERVICES

Colorado West Mental Health Ctr **970.241.6023**
Fax 970.242.8330
Web ....www.cwrmhc.org
E-mail ....msimpson@cwrmhc.org
  515 28 3/4 Rd, Grand Junction, CO 81501-5016
  Mark Simpson Phd, Assistant Executive Director

JUSTICE AGENCY

21st Judicial District Attorney's Ofc **970.244.1730**
Fax 970.244.1729
  125 N Spruce St, Grand Junction, CO 81501
  Pete Hautzinger, Chief Deputy District Attorney

**21st Judicial District Probation
Dept** **970.257.3600**
Fax 970.257.3690
E-mail ....susan.gilbert@judicial.state.co.us
  125 N Spruce St, Grand Junction, CO 81501
  Susan Gilbert, CPO

**Div Of Youth Corrections, Western
Region** **970.241.4886**
Fax 970.241.1922
Web ....www.state.co.us
E-mail ....dave.lee@state.co.us
  801 Grand Ave, Grand Junction, CO 81501-3424
  David Lee, Regional Director

Partners **970.245.5555**
Fax 970.245.7411
Web ....www.mesapartners.org
  1169 Colorado Ave, Grand Junction, CO 81501
  Joe Higgins, Director

POLICE AND SHERIFF

Sheriff's Dept **970.244.3500**
Fax 970.244.3503
Web ....www.sheriffmesacounty.us
E-mail ....shilkey@co.mesa.co.us
  215 Rice St, Grand Junction, CO 81501-5818
  Stan Hilkey, Sheriff

EDUCATION SERVICES

Special Education **970.257.7099**
Fax 970.257.7117
Web www.mesa.k12.co.us
E-mail ....jthornbu@mesa.k12.co.us
  930 Ute Ave, Grand Junction, CO 81501
  Judy Thornburg, Special Education Director

Mineral County

GENERAL HEALTH SERVICES

Public Health **719.658.2416**
Fax 719.658.3001
E-mail ....minco@centurytel.net
  802 Rio Grande Ave, Creede, CO 81130
  Joni Adelman, Public Health Nurse

POLICE AND SHERIFF

Sheriff's Dept **719.658.2600**
Fax 719.658.2764
Web ....www.centurytel.net
E-mail ....mincosheriff@centurytel.net
  1201 North Main, Creede, CO 81130
  Fred Hosselkuss, Sheriff

Moffat County

SOCIAL SERVICES

Social Svcs **970.824.8282**
Fax 970.824.9552
E-mail ....marie.peer@state.co.us
  595 Breeze St, Craig, CO 81625
  Marie Peer, Director

COURTS

14th District Court **970.824.8254**
Fax 970.824.8923
E-mail .... michael.ohara@judicial.state.co.us
   221 W Victory Way Ste 300, Craig, CO 81625
Michael Ohara, Chief Judge

POLICE AND SHERIFF

Sheriff's Dept **970.824.4495**
Fax 970.824.9780
   800 W 1st St Ste 100, Craig, CO 81625
Tim Jantz, Sheriff

Montezuma County

SOCIAL SERVICES

Indian Social Svcs **970.564.5307**
Fax 970.564.5300
E-mail .... csnow@utemountain.org
   400 Sunset Blvd, Towaoc, CO 81334
Carla Snow, Director

Social Svcs **970.565.3769**
Fax 970.565.8526
   109 W Main St Ste 203, Cortez, CO 81321-3128
Dennis Story, Director

GENERAL HEALTH SERVICES

Health Dept **970.565.3056**
Fax 970.565.0647
Web .... www.co.montezuma.co.us
E-mail .... lcooper@co.montezuma.co.us
   106 W North St, Cortez, CO 81321-3119
Lori Cooper, Nursing Director

JUSTICE AGENCY

District Courts **970.565.1111**
Fax 970.565.8516
   109 W Main St Ste 210, Cortez, CO 81321
Eric Hogue, District Adminstrator

COURTS

Court **970.565.7580**
Fax 970.565.8798
   601 N Mildred Rd Ste 1, Cortez, CO 81321
Jennilynn Lauren, County Judge

POLICE AND SHERIFF

Sheriff's Dept **970.565.8452**
Fax 970.565.3731
Web .... www.co.montezuma.co.us
E-mail .... dennis.spruell@montezumasheriff.org
   730 E Driscoll St, Cortez, CO 81321-2402
Dennis Spruell, Sheriff

Montrose County

SOCIAL SERVICES

Health & Human Svcs **970.252.5000**
Fax 970.252.5060
Web .... www.co.montrose.co.us
   1845 S Townsend Ave, Montrose, CO 81401-5448
Peg Mewes, Director

GENERAL HEALTH SERVICES

Public Health Nursing **970.864.7319**
Fax 970.864.7310
Web .... www.co.montrose.co.us
E-mail .... chartt@montrose.net
   851 Main St, Nucla, CO 81424
Cathy Hartt, Rn, Public Health Nurse

JUSTICE AGENCY

Attorney Office **970.252.4260**
Fax 970.252.4270
   1200 N Grand Ave Ste D, Montrose, CO 81401
Dan Hotsenpiller, District Attorney

Probation **970.252.4305**
Fax 970.252.4345
Web .... www.judicial.state.co.us
E-mail .... carrol.warner@judicial.state.co.us
   1200 N Grand Ave Ste B, Montrose, CO 81401-3164
Carol Warner, Chief Performance Officer

COURTS

7th District Court **970.252.4300**
Fax 970.252.4309
Web .... www.courts.state.co.us
   1200 N Grand Ave Ste A, Montrose, CO 81401-3164
Honorable Jeff Herron, Judge

Morgan County

SOCIAL SERVICES

Dept Of Social Svcs **970.542.3530**
Fax 970.542.3415
E-mail .... steve.romero@state.co.us
   800 E Beaver Ave, Fort Morgan, CO 80701
Steve Romero, Director

GENERAL HEALTH SERVICES

Northeast Colorado Health Dept **970.867.4918**
Web .... www.nchd.org
   228 W Railroad Ave, Fort Morgan, CO 80701-2324
Trish Mclane, Program Director

MENTAL HEALTH SERVICES

Centennial Mental Health Ctr **970.867.4924**
Fax 970.867.2695
Web .... www.centennialmhc.org
   910 E Railroad Ave, Fort Morgan, CO 80701-3399
Carl Cline, County Program Director

JUSTICE AGENCY

District Attorney's Ofc **970.542.3420**
Fax 970.542.3421
Web www.13thdistrictattorney.com
E-mail .... rwatson@13thdistrictattorney.com
   400 Warner St, Fort Morgan, CO 80701-3614
Robert E. Watson, District Attorney

Justice Ctr **970.542.3414**
Fax 970.542.3416
Web .... www.courts.state.co.us
   400 Warner St, Fort Morgan, CO 80701-3614
Honorable Michael Shingle, Judge

COURTS

13th District Court **970.542.3435**
Fax 970.542.3436
   400 Warner St, Fort Morgan, CO 80701
Honorable Douglas Vannoy, Judge

POLICE AND SHERIFF

Sheriff's Ofc **970.542.3445**
Fax 970.542.3453
E-mail .... senfante@co.morgan.co.us
   801 E Beaver Ave, Fort Morgan, CO 80701-3611
James E. Crone, Sheriff

Otero County

GENERAL HEALTH SERVICES

Health Dept **719.383.3040**
Fax 719.383.3060
Web .... www.oterogov.com
E-mail .... rritter@oterogov.org
   13 W 3rd St Ste 111, La Junta, CO 81050
Rick Ritter, Executive Director

COURTS

16th District Court **719.384.4951**
Fax 719.384.4991
Web .... www.judicial.state.co.us
E-mail .... tobin.wright@judicial.state.co.us
   13 W 3rd St Ste 207, La Junta, CO 81050-1566
Tobin Wright, Chief Performance Officer

POLICE AND SHERIFF

Sheriff's Dept **719.384.5941**
Fax 719.384.2272
E-mail .... cjohnson@oterogov.org
   222 E 2nd St, La Junta, CO 81050
Chris S. Johnson, Sheriff

Ouray County

SOCIAL SERVICES

Dept Of Social Svcs **970.325.4437**
Fax 970.325.4438
E-mail .... allen.gerstle@state.co.us
   541 4th St, Ouray, CO 81427
Allan Gerstle, Director

GENERAL HEALTH SERVICES

Public Health **970.325.4670**
Fax 970.325.7314
Web .... www.ouraycountyco.gov
E-mail .... croberts@ouraycountyco.gov
   302 2nd St, Ouray, CO 81427
Cheryl Roberts, Public Health Nurse

Park County

SOCIAL SERVICES

Dept Of Human Svcs **303.816.5939**
Fax 303.816.5942
E-mail .... joseph.homlar@state.co.us
   59865 US Hwy 285, Bailey, CO 80421
Joe Homlar, Director

GENERAL HEALTH SERVICES

Public Health **719.836.4161**
Fax 719.836.3433
   899 Steinfelt Pkwy, Fairplay, CO 80440
Robin Phillips, Director

Phillips County

COURTS

Court **970.854.3279**
Fax 970.854.3179
E-mail .... david.colver@judicial.state.co.us
   221 S Interocean Ave, Holyoke, CO 80734
David O. Colver, Judge

Pitkin County

GENERAL HEALTH SERVICES

Community Health Svcs **970.920.5420**
Fax 970.920.5419
E-mail .... liz.stark@co.pitkin.co.us
   405 Castle Creek Rd, Ste 6, Aspen, CO 81611
Liz Stark, Director

COURTS

9th District Court **970.925.7635**
Fax 970.925.6349
Web .... www.judicial.state.co.us
   506 Main St, Ste 300, Aspen, CO 81611
Honorable Erin Fernandez-Ely, County Court Judge

POLICE AND SHERIFF

Sheriff's Dept **970.920.5300**
Fax 970.920.5307
Web .... www.aspenpitkin.com
   506 E Main St Ste 101, Aspen, CO 81611
Joe Bi Salvo, Sheriff

Prowers County

GENERAL HEALTH SERVICES

Public Health **719.336.8721**
Fax 719.336.9763
Web ....www.prowerscounty.net
E-mail ....jbrown@prowerscounty.net
   1001 S Main St, Lamar, CO 81052-3838
Jackie Brown, Rn, Director

MENTAL HEALTH SERVICES

Southeast Mental Health Svcs- Lamar Branch
Ofc **719.336.7501**
Fax 719.336.7453
Web ....www.semhs.org
E-mail ....bwhaley@semhs.org
   3500 1st St S, Lamar, CO 81052
Robert Whaley, Executive Director

JUSTICE AGENCY

Probation Dept **719.336.2765**
Fax 719.336.7107
   301 S Main St Ste 110, Lamar, CO 81052
Byron Hall, Chief Performance Officer

POLICE AND SHERIFF

Sheriff's Dept **719.336.8050**
Fax 719.336.7900
Web ....www.prowerscounty.net
   103 E Oak St, Lamar, CO 81052-3270
James F. Faull, Sheriff

Pueblo County

JUSTICE AGENCY

CASA Pueblo **719.583.6326**
Fax 719.583.6327
Web ....www.casaofpueblo.org
E-mail ....casaofpueblo@aol.com
   130 W Abriendo Ave, Pueblo, CO 81004-4224
Zane Grant, Executive Director

District Attorney's Ofc **719.583.6030**
Fax 719.583.6666
Web ....www.co.pueblo.co.us
E-mail ....bill.thievaut@co.pueblo.co.us
   701 Court St, Pueblo, CO 81003
Bill Thievaut, District Attorney

Probation Dept **719.253.5600**
Fax 719.253.5631
E-mail ....david.simental@judicial.state.co.us
   1120 Court St, Pueblo, CO 81003
David Simental, Chief Performance Officer

Public Advocacy Program **719.583.6332**
Fax 719.583.4545
E-mail ....acooney@pueblocac.com
   301 W 13th St, Pueblo, CO 81003
Allen Cooney, Director

POLICE AND SHERIFF

Sheriff's Dept **719.583.6125**
Fax 719.583.6418
E-mail ....sheriff@co.pueblo.co.us
   909 Court St, Pueblo, CO 81003
Kirk M. Taylor, Sheriff

EDUCATION SERVICES

Exceptional Student Svcs Dept **719.253.6025**
Fax 719.549.7130
Web www.pueblo60.k12.co.us
   315 W 11th St, Pueblo, CO 81003-2804
Chris Cockrill, Director

Special Education **719.542.0220**
Fax 719.542.0225
Web www.district70.org
E-mail ....gkeasling@district70.org
   24951 E US Highway 50, Pueblo, CO 81006-2027
Greg Keasling, Director Of Special Education

Rio Blanco County

MENTAL HEALTH SERVICES

Colorado West Mental Health Clinic- Rio Blanco
Ctr **970.878.5112**
Fax 970.878.4315
E-mail ....mrobb@cwrmhc.org
   267 6th St, Meeker, CO 81641
Margot Robb, Program Director

Rio Grande County

SOCIAL SERVICES

Social Svcs **719.657.3381**
Fax 719.657.4013
E-mail ....jody.kern@state.co.us
   1015 6th St, Del Norte, CO 81132
Jody Kern, Director

GENERAL HEALTH SERVICES

Public Health Nursing **719.657.3352**
Fax 719.657.2286
E-mail ....health@rgcph.org
   925 6th St Ste 101, Del Norte, CO 81132
Patricia Perry, Public Health Director

Routt County

SOCIAL SERVICES

Social Svcs **970.879.1540**
Fax 970.870.5260
Web ....www.co.routt.co.us
E-mail ....rwhite@co.routt.co.us
   135 6th St, Steamboat Springs, CO 80477
Robert White, Director

Saguache County

SOCIAL SERVICES

Social Svcs **719.655.2537**
Fax 719.655.0206
E-mail ....genie.morris@state.co.us
   605 Christy Ave, Saguache, CO 81149
Genie Morris, Director

GENERAL HEALTH SERVICES

Nursing Svc **719.655.2533**
Fax 719.655.0105
Web ....www.saguachecounty.net
E-mail ....dvieira@saguachecounty-co.gov
   505 3Rd St, Saguache, CO 81149
Della Vieira, Public Health Nurse, Director

Public Health Nursing **719.754.2773**
Fax 719.754.2392
Web ....www.saguachecounty.gov
   220 Worth St, Center, CO 81125
Della Veira, Medical Director

POLICE AND SHERIFF

Sheriff's Dept **719.655.2544**
Fax 719.655.2240
E-mail ....mnorris@saguachecounty-co.gov
   530 5th St, Saguache, CO 81149
Mike Norris, Sheriff

San Juan County

SOCIAL SERVICES

Social Svcs **970.387.5631**
Fax 970.387.5326
   1557 Greene St, Silverton, CO 81433
Leslie Mayer, Director

COURTS

Court **970.387.5790**
Fax 970.387.0295
E-mail ....todd.risberg@judicial.state.co.us
   1557 Greene St, Silverton, CO 81433
Lyndon K. Skinner, Judge

POLICE AND SHERIFF

Sheriff's Dept **970.387.5531**
Fax 970.387.0251
E-mail ....sjcsheriff@frontier.net
   1557 Greene St, Silverton, CO 81433
Susan R. Kirtz, Sheriff

San Miguel County

GENERAL HEALTH SERVICES

Nursing Svcs **970.728.4289**
Fax 970.728.9276
Web ....www.sanmiguelcounty.org
E-mail ....junen@sanmiguelcounty.org
   333 W Colorado Ave, Ste 315, Telluride, CO 81435
June Nepsky, Nursing Director

JUSTICE AGENCY

Probation **970.369.4477**
Fax 970.728.6216
Web ....www.state.co.us
E-mail ....pam.stewart-naddox@state.co.us
   305 W Colorado Ave, Telluride, CO 81435
Pam Stewart-naddox, Director

POLICE AND SHERIFF

Sheriff's Dept **970.728.4442**
Fax 970.728.9206
Web ....www.sanmiguelcounty.org
E-mail ....billm@sanmiguelcounty.org
   684 CR 63L Rd, Telluride, CO 81435-9449
William S. Masters, Sheriff

Sedgwick County

GENERAL HEALTH SERVICES

Northeast Colorado Health Dept **970.474.2619**
Fax 970.474.2716
Web ....www.nchd.org
E-mail ....betsym@nchd.org
   118 W 3rd St, Julesburg, CO 80737-1542
Betsy Marquardt, Public Health Nurse

MENTAL HEALTH SERVICES

Centennial Mental Health Ctr **970.474.3769**
Fax 970.474.2099
Web ....www.centennialmhc.org
   118 W 3rd St, Julesburg, CO 80737-1542
Spencer Green, Deputy Director

COURTS

Court **970.474.3627**
Fax 970.474.2026
E-mail ....max.carlson@judicial.state.co.us
   Third And Pine, Julesburg, CO 80737
Max E. Carlson, County Court Judge

Summit County

SOCIAL SERVICES

Dept Of Social Svcs **970.668.9160**
Fax 970.668.4115
   360 Peak 1 Dr, Frisco, CO 80443
Deb Crook, Director

GENERAL HEALTH SERVICES

Public Health **970.668.5230**
Fax 970.668.4115
Web ....www.co.summit.co.us
E-mail ....debbiec@co.summit.co.us
  37 County Rd 1005, Frisco, CO 80443
  Debby Crook, RN, Public Health Director

COURTS

5th District Court **970.453.2241**
Fax 970.453.1134
Web ....www.judicial.state.co.us
  501 N Park, Breckenridge, CO 80424
  Honorable Karen Romeo, Judge

POLICE AND SHERIFF

Sheriff's Dept **970.453.2232**
Fax 970.453.7329
Web ....www.co.summit.co.us
E-mail ....johnm@co.summit.co.us
  501 N. Park Ave, Breckenridge, CO 80424
  John Minor, Sheriff

Teller County

GENERAL HEALTH SERVICES

Public Health **719.687.6416**
Fax 719.687.6501
Web ....www.tellercountypublichealth.org
E-mail ....rubinc@co.teller.co.us
  11115 W Hwy 24 Unit 2C, Divide, CO 80814-9212
  Christina Rubin, Rn, Nursing Director

Weld County

GENERAL HEALTH SERVICES

Health Dept **970.304.6410**
Fax 970.304.6416
Web ....www.co.weld.co.us
  1555 N 17th Ave, Greeley, CO 80631
  Linda Henry, Rn, Nursing Director

JUSTICE AGENCY

District Attorney's Ofc **970.356.4010**
Fax 970.352.8023
Web ....www.co.weld.co.us
E-mail ....kbuck@co.weld.co.us
  915 Tenth Street, Greeley, CO 80632
  Kennith R. Buck, District Attorney

Probation Dept **970.392.4589**
Fax 970.351.8695
E-mail ....kevin.nelan@judicial.state.co.us
  934 9th Ave, Greeley, CO 80631
  Kevin Nelan, Chief Performance Officer

COURTS

19th District Court **970.351.7300**
Fax 970.336.7245
Web ....www.courts.state.co.us
  915 10th St, Greeley, CO 80631-1117
  Karen Salas, Court Administrator

POLICE AND SHERIFF

Sheriff's Dept **970.356.4015**
Fax 970.304.6461
Web ....www.co.weld.state.co.us
E-mail ....jcooke@co.weld.co.us
  1950 O St, Greeley, CO 80631
  John B. Cooke, Sheriff

EDUCATION SERVICES

Dos Rios Head Start **970.330.3220**
  2201 34th St, Evans, CO 80631
  Claudia Story, Director

Migrant Head Start **970.353.3800**
Fax 970.304.6453
Web ....www.eswc.org
E-mail ....jflaugher@co.weld.co.us
  1551 N 17th Ave, Greeley, CO 80631-9117
  Janet Flaugher, Director

Special Education **970.686.8000**
Fax 970.686.8001
Web www.weldre4.k12.co.us
  1020 Main St, Windsor, CO 80550
  Jon Paul, Special Education Director

Special Education **970.348.6000**
Fax 970.348.6232
Web ....www.greeleyschools.org
  1025 9th Ave, Greeley, CO 80631
  Victoria Hubbard, Director

Yuma County

SOCIAL SERVICES

Social Svcs **970.332.4877**
Fax 970.332.4978
Web ....www.state.co.us
E-mail ....david.henson@state.co.us
  340 Birch St, Wray, CO 80758
  David Henson, Director

POLICE AND SHERIFF

Sheriff's Dept **970.332.4805**
Fax 970.332.5820
  310 Ash St Ste G, Wray, CO 80758
  Chad Day, Sheriff

SPECIAL SERVICES AGENCIES

ADOPTION AGENCIES

A Step Ahead Adoption Svc **719.532.0236**
Fax 719.532.0266
Web ....www.astepaheadadoption.com
E-mail ....info@astepaheadadoption.com
  7455 Hickorywood Dr, Colorado Springs,
  CO 80920-6649
  Diane Hogan, Director

Adoption Advocacy & Alternatives **970.356.3428**
Web ....www.adoptionna.org
E-mail ....jgallagher25@comcast.net
  1115 7th St, Greeley, CO 80631-3207
  Joanne Gallagher LCSW, Director

Adoption Advocacy And Alternatives **970.493.5868**
Fax 970.472.0352
E-mail ....jfgallagher25@comcast.net
  2500 S College Ave, Fort Collins, CO 80525
  Joanne Gallagher, Director

Adoption Alliance **303.584.9900**
Fax 303.584.9007
Web ....www.adoptall.org
E-mail ....info@adoptall.org
  2121 S Oneida St Ste 420, Denver, CO 80224
  Tracy Blustien, Executive Director

Adoption Choices of CO **303.670.4401**
Fax 877.451.7728
E-mail ....ginny@adoptionchoices.org
  35715 Highway 40 Ste D105, Evergreen,
  CO 80439-9657
  Brenda Hudson Retrum, Executive Director

Adoption Dreams Come True **970.493.2557**
Fax 970.493.4479
E-mail ....adoptdreams@yahoo.com
  316 W Mulberry St, Fort Collins, CO 80521
  Cindy Sarai, Director

Adoption Options **303.695.1601**
Fax 303.695.1626
Web ....www.adoption-options.com
E-mail ....info@adoption-options.com
  13900 E Harvard Ave, Ste 200, Aurora, CO 80014
  Carol Lawson, Executive Director

Adoption Options **970.245.9791**
Web ....www.adoption-options.com
E-mail ....clawson@adoption-options.com
  1425 N 5th St, Grand Junction, CO 81501-7526
  Carol Lawson, Executive Director

Angeldance International Adoption **303.433.6655**
Fax 303.433.6671
E-mail ....info@angeldance.org
  2237 W 30th Ave, Denver, CO 80211-3808
  Linda Baldwin, Director

Beltz & West **719.473.4444**
Fax 719.444.0186
E-mail ....wtbeltz@bestlawllp.com
  729 S Cascade Ave, Colorado Springs, CO 80903
  W. Thomas Beltz, President

Bethany Christian Svcs **719.591.7595**
Fax 719.598.3204
Web ....www.bethany.org/colorado
E-mail ....bcscoloradospr@bethany.org
  4820 Rusina Rd Ste C, Colorado Springs,
  CO 80907-8127
  Maddi Noleen, Director

Bethany Christian Svcs **303.221.0734**
Fax 303.221.0960
Web ....www.bethany.org
E-mail ....bcsdenver@bethany.org
  9185 E Kenyon Ave Ste 190, Denver,
  CO 80237-1856
  Maddi Noleen, Director

Chinese Children Adoption International **303.850.9998**
Fax 303.850.9997
Web ....www.chinesechildren.org
E-mail ....mail@chinesechildren.org
  6920 S Holly Cir, Englewood, CO 80112-1018
  Teresa Krier, Office Manager

Colorado Adoption Ctr **970.493.8816**
Fax 970.224.3866
  7791 Highland Meadows Pkwy Ste C, Fort Collins,
  CO 80528
  Julie Haralson, Associate Director

Community Credit Counseling Services **303.233.2773**
Fax 303.233.2797
Web ....www.community-credit.org
  2009 Wadsworth Boulevard, Suite 200, Lakewood,
  CO 80214
  COA accredited organization.

Creative Adoptions **303.730.7791**
Fax 303.730.8985
Web ....www.creativeadoptions.com
E-mail ....info@creativeadoptions.com
  4251 Kipping St Ste 560, Wheat Ridge, CO 80033
  Stephenie Robert, Executive Director

Colorado

Hope's Promise 303.660.0277
Fax 303.660.0297
Web ....www.hopespromise.com
E-mail ....hopes@henge.com
309 Jerry St Ste 202, Castle Rock, CO 80104
Paula Freeman, Director

Kids Crossing 719.632.4771
Fax 719.632.6573
1440 E Fountain Blvd, Colorado Springs,
CO 80910-3502
Lee Oesterle, Executive Director

Lutheran Family Svcs 719.227.7571
Fax 719.227.7583
Web ....www.lfsco.org
E-mail ....info@lfsco.org
108 E Saint Vrain St Ste 21, Colorado Springs,
CO 80903-1161
Gwen White, Director

Tennyson Center for Children at Colorado Christian
Home 303.433.2541
Fax 303.433.9701
2950 Tennyson Street, Denver, CO 80212-3029
COA accredited organization.

The Adoption Exchange 303.755.4756
Fax 303.755.1339
Web ....www.adoptex.org
E-mail ....dixie@adoptex.org
14232 E Evans Ave, Aurora, CO 80014-1432
Jacki Propernick, Vp Of Development

ADVOCACY RESOURCES

A Kid's Place 970.353.5970
Fax 970.353.9577
Web ....www.kidsplace.org
2540 11th Ave, Greeley, CO 80631
Gwen Schooley, Executive Director

Blue Sky Bridge 303.444.1388
Fax 303.444.2045
Web ....www.blueskybridge.org
E-mail ....info@blueskybridge.org
2617 Iris Hollow Pl, Boulder, CO 80304
Judy Poran Cousin, Executive Director

CASA Of The Pikes Peak Region 719.447.9898
Fax 719.667.1818
Web ....www.casappr.org
E-mail ....info@casappr.org
701 S Cascade Ave Ste A, Colorado Springs,
CO 80903-3943
Trudy A. Strewler, Director

Child Advocacy Ctr 970.407.9739
Fax 970.407.9743
Web ....www.larimercac.org
E-mail ....laura@larimercac.org
5529 S Timberline Rd, Fort Collins, CO 80528-9553
Laura Hunt, Executive Director

Children's Advocacy Ctr For Pike's Peak
Region 719.636.2460
Fax 719.636.1912
E-mail ....thuizar@safepassagecac.org
423 S Cascade Ave, Colorado Springs,
CO 80903-3840
Teresa Huizar-Humes, Executive Director

Denver Children's Advocacy Ctr 303.825.3850
Fax 303.825.6087
Web ....www.denvercac.org
E-mail ....info@denvercac.org
2149 Federal Blvd, Denver, CO 80211-4639
Gizane Indart, Director

Law Office of Kirk Garner 903.342.1110
E-mail ....garnerlawfirm@hotmail.com
422 E Verijo Ste 312, Colorado Springs, CO 80903
Kirk Garner, Director

NAMI Colorado 303.321.3104
Fax 303.321.0912
Web ....www.namicolorado.org
E-mail ....info@namicolorado.org
1100 Fillmore St, Ste 201, Denver, CO 80206
Lacey Berumen, Executive Director

National Association of Counsel for
Children 303.864.5322
E-mail ....Farrell-Stevenson.Maureen@tchden.org
13123 E 16th Ave B390, Aurora, CO 80045
Maureen Farrell-stevenson, Director

National Association of Counsel for
Children 303.864.5327
E-mail ....fox.elizabeth@tchden.org
13123 E 16th Ave B390, Aurora, CO 80045
Elizabeth Fox

Rocky Mountain Children's Law Center 303.692.1165
E-mail ....teirich@law.du.edu
1325 S Colorado Blvd, Ste 308, Denver, CO 80222
Tim Eirich

Stephanie A Ritland PC 303.819.0548
E-mail ....sritland03@law.du.edu
PO Box 3651, Englewood, CO 80155
Stephanie A Ritland

BEHAVIORAL HEALTH TREATMENT

ABC Mental Health Assessment And Svcs
Admin 303.751.9030
Fax 720.744.5130
Web ....www.coaccess.com
E-mail ....mike.mckitterick@coaccess.com
10065 E Harvard Ave Ste 600, Denver,
CO 80231-5963
Mike Mckitterick, RN, Director Of Clinical Support Services

Addictions Recovery Ctr 303.441.1275
Fax 303.441.1286
3470 Broadway St, Boulder, CO 80304
Ann Noonan, Program Manager

Adolescent and Family Institute of Colorado,
Inc. 303.238.1231
Web ....www.aficonline.com
E-mail ....mkpanio@gmail.com
10001 West 32nd Avenue, Wheat Ridge, CO 80033
Ms. Mary Panio, Accreditation Manager
Joint Commission accredited organization.

Alpine Counseling LLC 719.544.3343
Fax 719.542.1634
2502 Court St, Pueblo, CO 81003-2868
Gary Nichols, Co-owner

Anderson Medical Practice 720.488.5580
Fax 303.694.1274
3545 S Tamarac Dr Ste 370, Denver, CO 80237-1432
Kirk Anderson, MD, Psychiatrist

Anderson Medical Practice 303.300.0220
Web ....www.andersonlauramddenver.usdirectory.com
E-mail
......landerson@andersonlauramddenver.usdirectory.com
4900 Cherry Creek South Dr, Denver, CO 80246
Laura Anderson, Psychiatrist

Arapahoe-Douglas Mental Health
Network 303.688.6276
Fax 303.688.5327
Web ....www.admhn.org
E-mail ....lelliott@admhn.org
1189 S Perry St Ste 150, Castle Rock, CO 80104
Laurie Elliott, Lcsw, Clinical Director

Arapahoe-Douglas Mental Health
Network 303.805.4312
Fax 303.841.5140
Web ....www.admhn.org
19751 E Main St, Ste 247, Parker, CO 80138
Scott Thoemke, Director

AspenPointe Behavioral Health Services 719.572.6100
Web ....www.aspenpointe.org
E-mail ....kelly.phillips-henry@aspenpointe.org
525 N. Cascade Avenue, Suite 100, Colorado Springs,
CO 80903
Mrs. Kelly Phillips-Henry, Accreditation Manager
Joint Commission accredited organization.

Aurora Hills Middle Schools 303.341.7450
Fax 303.326.1250
E-mail ....dcstumpp@aps.k12.co.us
1009 S Uvalda St, Aurora, CO 80012-3407
Darla Stumpp, Principal

Aurora Mental Health 303.617.2300
Web ....www.aumhc.org
E-mail ....laneburleigh@aumhc.org
10782 E Alameda Ave, Aurora, CO 80014-1017
Lane Burleigh, Director

Aurora Mental Health Ctr 303.617.2560
Fax 303.617.2562
Web ....www.aumhc.org
E-mail ....sarahavrin@aumhc.org
1290 Chambers Rd, Aurora, CO 80011-7117
Sarah Avrin, Director

Barkhorn Medical Practice 303.443.8530
1542 High St, Boulder, CO 80304-4222
Rebecca Barkhorn, Psychiatrist

Berson Medical Practice 719.475.9363
1424 N Hancock Ave Ste 3W, Colorado Springs,
CO 80903-2671
Deane Bernson, Md, Psychiatrist

Beverly A Brauer Psyd Inc 303.754.7086
Fax 303.367.8607
E-mail ....bbrauerpsyd@hotmail.com
12101 E 2nd Ave Ste 110, Aurora, CO 80011-8328
Beverly Brauer, Director

Bograd Medical Practice 303.320.1968
3300 E 1st Ave, Denver, CO 80206
Susan Bograd, Psychiatrist

Braud Medical Practice 303.721.2901
Fax 303.721.2905
E-mail ....mbraud@earthlink.net
7940 S University Blvd, Centennial, CO 80122
Mary Braud, Psychiatrist

Broomfield High School 303.447.5375
Fax 303.447.5390
Web ....www.bvsd.org
E-mail ....ginger.ramsey@bvsd.org
1 Eagle Way, Broomfield, CO 80020-3532
Ginger Ramsey, Principal

Buzan Medical Practice 303.377.4956
Fax 303.377.4965
155 S Madison St Ste 222, Denver, CO 80209-3013
Randall Buzan, MD, Psychiatrist

Caiati Medical Practice 303.860.8640
1370 Pennsylvania St, Denver, CO 80203
Mary Ellen Caiati, MD, Psychiatrist

Capitol Hill ILT/CTT 303.504.1600
Fax 303.831.4604
1555 Humble St., Denver, CO 80218
Eric Smith, Program Manager

Carter Medical Practice 303.747.2926
PO Box 458, Allenspark, CO 80510-0458
Dorothy Carter, Psychiatrist

Castlehaven Retreat Ctr 303.680.6690
Fax 303.627.2907
E-mail ....shrynker.1@aol.com
5547 S Pitkin St, Aurora, CO 80015-2554
Linda S.Gunther M.A.P.C, Director

Catholic Charities 303.742.0823
Fax 303.455.3176
Web ....www.ccdenver.org
E-mail ....sdooley@ccdenver.org
    10531 E Maplewood Dr, Englewood,
    CO 80111-5768
Susan Dooley, Director

CBR YouthConnect 719.384.5981
Toll-free 800.790.4993
Fax 719.384.0470
Web ....www.cbryouthconnect.org
E-mail ....admissions@cbryouthconnect.org
    28071 State Highway 109
    La Junta, CO 81050-9675
Charles M. Thompson, President
CBR YouthConnect is an independent, non-profit psychiatric residential treatment program offering troubled boys ages 10-21 individualized mental health care, accredited education and vocational training. JCAHO accredited, TriCare approved.

Cedar Springs Hospital 719.633.4114
Fax 719.578.0857
Web ....www.cedarspringsbhs.com
    2135 Southgate Rd, Colorado Springs,
    CO 80906-2693
Dan Zarecky, Business Development Director

Cedar Springs Hospital, Inc. 719.633.4114
Web ....www.cedarspringsbhs.com
E-mail ....cristina.kolln@psysolutions.com
    2135 Southgate Road, Colorado Springs, CO 80906
Ms. Cristina Kolln, Accreditation Manager
Joint Commission accredited organization.

Centennial Peaks 303.673.9990
Web ....centennialpeaks.com
E-mail ....mary.engelmann@uhsinc.com
    2255 South 88th Street, Louisville, CO 80027
Ms. Mary Engelmann, Accreditation Manager
Joint Commission accredited organization.

Centennial Peaks Hospital 303.673.9990
Fax 303.673.9703
Web ....www.centennialpeaks.com
    2255 S 88th St, Louisville, CO 80027
Bill Sexton, CEO

Children's Ark At Green Mountain Falls 719.684.8001
Fax 719.684.9519
    10930 Hondo Ave, Green Mountain Falls, CO 80819
Tim Banton, CEO

Children's Ark, Inc. 719.684.9511
Fax 719.684.9498
Web ....www.childrensark.org
E-mail ....robert.horvath@childrensark.org
    10460 West Hwy 24, Green Mountain Falls,
    CO 80819
Robert Horvath, Director of Admissions
CARF accredited programs available.

Children's Hospital Colorado 720.777.1234
Web ....www.childrenscolorado.org
E-mail ....hyman.daniel@tchden.org
    13123 East 16th Avenue, Aurora, CO 80045
Dr. Daniel Hyman, Accreditation Manager
Joint Commission accredited organization.

Clark Medical Practice 303.797.2839
Fax 303.770.8588
E-mail ....rbarkleyclarkmd@mem.po.com
    7720 S Broadway Ste 390, Littleton, CO 80122-2624
R Barkley Clark, Psychiatrist

Co Neuropsychological & Behavioral Ctr 303.744.8355
    1001 S Monaco Pkwy, Denver, CO 80224
Bradley Mcmillan, Director

Cogan Medical Practice 303.221.2602
Fax 303.221.2603
E-mail ....cogan@pcisys.net
    4643 S Ulster St Ste 1220, Denver, CO 80237-2868
Dana Cogan, MD, Psychiatrist

Cohen Medical Practice 303.831.4447
    2005 FRANKLIN ST STE 502, Denver,
    CO 80205-5431
Jonathan Cohen, MD, Psychiatrist

Colarado West Psychatric Hospital 970.263.4918
Fax 970.683.7278
Web ....www.cwrmhc.org
E-mail ....rbrenda@cwrmhc.org
    515 28 3/4 Rd, Bldg D, Grand Junction,
    CO 81501-5016
Kim Boe, Hospital Administrator

Colorado Boys Ranch Foundation 719.384.5981
Web ....www.cbryouthconnect.org
E-mail ....mmasar@cbryouthconnect.org
    28071 Highway 109, La Junta, CO 81050
Mr. Martin Masar, Accreditation Manager
Joint Commission accredited organization.

Colorado Health Networks 719.538.1430
Fax 719.538.1433
Web ....www.chnpartnerships.com
E-mail ....steve.holsenbeck@valueoptions.com
    7150 Campus Dr Ste 300, Colorado Springs,
    CO 80920-6553
Steve Holsenbeck, Executive Director & Medical Director

Colorado Mood & Memory Clinic 303.682.9197
Fax 303.682.9306
Web ....coloradomoodandmemoryclinic.com
E-mail ....halehnekoorad@hotmail.com
    1308 Vivian St, Longmont, CO 80501-3217
Haleh Nekoorad-long, Md, Psychiatrist

Colorado West Mental Health - Steamboat Mental Health Ctr 970.879.2141
Fax 970.879.7912
E-mail ....tgangel@cwrmhc.org
    407 South Lincoln Ave, Steamboat Springs,
    CO 80477
Tom Gangle, Division Director

Comitis Crisis Ctr, Inc 303.341.9160
Fax 303.343.3907
Web ....www.comitis.org
    2178 Victor St, Aurora, CO 80045
Bob Dorshimer, Executive Director

Community Reach Ctr 303.853.3500
Fax 303.637.0514
Web ....www.communityreachcenter.org
E-mail ....m.shirley@communityreachcenter.org
    1850 Ebgert St Ste 200, Brighton, CO 80601
Matthew Shirley, Supervisor

Connect Care 719.572.6133
Fax 719.572.6089
Web ....www.ppbhg.org
E-mail ....annettef@ppbhg.org
    2864 S Circle Dr Ste 1000, Colorado Springs,
    CO 80906-4163
Annette Fryman, Senior Vice President

Coyle Medical Practice 303.393.0823
    50 S Steele St Ste 840, Denver, CO 80209-2841
Deborah Coyle, MD, Psychiatrist

Cucich Medical Practice 303.318.9725
Fax 303.813.4359
    658 Grant St, Denver, CO 80203-3507
Timothy Cucich, MD, Pychiatrist

David M Hurst Practice 303.832.5024
    601 Emerson St Ste 2, Denver, CO 80218-3258
David Hurst, Psychiatrist

Davila-Toro Medical Practice 303.504.1900
    75 Meade St, Denver, CO 80219-1351
Doctor Wagner, Psychiatrist

De Simone Medical Practice 303.431.8775
    6990 W 38th Ave, Wheat Ridge, CO 80033
Donna De Simone, Psychiatrist

Denver Children's Home 303.399.4890
Fax 303.399.9846
Web ....www.denverchildrenshome.org
    1501 Albion St, Denver, CO 80220-1028
Rebecca Hea, Executive Director
COA accredited organization.

Denver Mental Health Group 303.321.0738
    165 Cook St, Denver, CO 80206
David Muller, MD, Psychiatrist

Devereux Cleo Wallace 303.466.7391
Web ....www.devereux.org
E-mail ....pmay@devereux.org
    8405 Church Ranch Blvd, Westminster, CO 80021
Mr. Perry May, Accreditation Manager
Joint Commission accredited organization.

Devereux Cleo Wallace Westminster 303.466.7391
Fax 303.466.0904
Web ....www.cleowallace.org
E-mail ....bsmith2@devereux.org
    8405 Church Ranch Blvd, Broomfield, CO 80021
Bentley Smith, Executive Director

Dr Pie Frey 303.444.6500
    100 Arapahoe Ave, Boulder, CO 80302
Pie Frey, Psychiatrist

Dutmers Medical Practice 303.721.0905
    7600 E Orchard Rd Ste 120S, Englewood,
    CO 80111-2577
Barbara Dutmers, Psychiatrist

Dworetsky Medical Practice 303.721.8821
Fax 303.721.8820
    7600 E Orchard Rd Ste 120S, Englewood,
    CO 80111-2577
Steven Dworetsky, Psychiatrist

Eating Disorders Ctr-Colo 303.333.3163
E-mail ....jonathan.ritvo@dhha.org
    501 S Cherry St Ste 650, Denver, CO 80246-1397
Jonathan Ritivo, Psychiatrist

Eating Recovery Center, LLC 303.825.8584
Web ....www.eatingrecoverycenter.com
E-mail ....abraun@eatingrecoverycenter.com
    1830 Franklin Street Suite 500, Denver, CO 80218
Mr. Andrew Braun, Accreditation Manager
Joint Commission accredited organization.

El Pueblo Boys' & Girls' Ranch, Inc. 719.544.7496
Web ....www.elpueblokids.org
E-mail ....sherri.baca@elpueblokids.net
    One El Pueblo Ranch Way, Pueblo, CO 81006
Ms. Sherri Baca, Accreditation Manager
Joint Commission accredited organization.

Excelsior Youth Center, Inc. 303.693.1550
Fax 303.693.8309
Web ....www.excelsioryc.org
    15001 East Oxford Avenue, Aurora, CO 80014
COA accredited organization.

Falcon School Dist #49 ....719.495.1100
E-mail ....saxford@d49.org
    10850 E Woodmen Rd, Falcon, CO 80831-8127
Steve Axford, Director

Family Therapy Ctr Of Boulder 303.440.4062
Fax 303.440.6244
    1634 Walnut St Ste 201, Boulder, CO 80302-5400
Jed Shapiro, MD, Psychiatrist

Faris Medical Practice 303.641.6319
    5277 Manhattan Cir, Boulder, CO 80303
Dorothy Faris, MD, Psychiatrist

Fine Medical Practice 303.360.9448
730 Potomac St Ste 322, Aurora, CO 80011-6707
Alan Fine, Md, Psychiatrist

Fine Medical Practice 303.694.9122
7400 E Arapahoe Rd Ste 304, Englewood,
CO 80112-1281
Louis Fine, Psychiatrist

First Judicial Dist 303.271.4552
1200 Johnson Rd, Golden, CO 80401-2601
George Mumma, Director

Forest Heights Lodge 303.674.6681
Web ....www.forestheightslodge.org
E-mail ....jimorsund@forestheightslodge.org
4761 South Forest Hill Road, Evergreen, CO 80439
Mr. Jim Orsund, Accreditation Manager
Joint Commission accredited organization.

Forest Heights Lodge 303.674.6681
Fax 303.674.6805
Web ....www.forestheightslodge.org
4761 Forest Hill Rd, Evergreen, CO 80439
Linda Clefisch, Executive Director

Fort Collins Psychotherapy Group 970.495.4685
Fax 970.670.3309
2362 E Prospect Rd, Fort Collins, CO 80525
Kenneth Ash, MD, Psychiatrist

Griffith Centers for Children, Inc. 303.237.6865
Fax 303.237.6873
Web ....www.griffithcenters.org
8461 Turnpike Drive, Suite 100, Westminster,
CO 80031
COA accredited organization.

Griffith Ctr, Inc. 303.237.6865
Fax 303.237.6873
Web ....www.griffithcenters.org
E-mail ....howard.shiffman@griffithcenters.org
14142 Denver West Pkwy Ste 225, Golden,
CO 80401-3127
Howard Shiffman, CEO

Hands Up Homes For Youth 970.255.8000
Fax 970.255.9199
801 Coffman Rd, Whitewater, CO 81527
Meri Miyasaki, Program Director

Heaven Sent Horses 303.481.4257
Fax 303.481.4478
Web ....www.michaeldawsoncounseling.com
E-mail ....michael@michaeldawsoncounseling.com
13791 E Rice Pl, Aurora, CO 80015-1057
Michael Dawson, Owner

Hope House Of Colorado 303.429.1012
Fax 303.439.2136
Web ....www.hopehouseofcolorado.org
6475 Benton St, Arvada, CO 80006
Lisa Steven, Executive Director

Human Svcs 719.444.5764
Fax 719.444.5598
E-mail ....tingchan-burford@elpasoco.com
105 N Spruce St, Colorado Springs, CO 80905-1409
Ting Chan-Burford, Director

Jefferson Hills 303.989.4357
Fax 303.988.2017
Web ....www.jcmh.org
E-mail ....kareny@jcmh.org
421 Zang St, Denver, CO 80228-1052
Karen Yarberry, Executive Director

Kidz Ark, Inc. 970.522.5775
Fax 970.522.5983
Web ....www.kidzark.org
E-mail ....jwelsh@kidzark.org
17282 County Road 32, Sterling, CO 80751
Jana Welsh, Executive Director
CARF accredited programs available.

Lost And Found, Inc. 303.420.8080
Fax 303.420.9299
Web ....www.lostandfoundinc.org
E-mail ....harlhargett@lnfinc.org
6700 W 44th Ave, Wheat Ridge, CO 80033-4732
Harl Hargett, Executive Director

Medicine Horse Program 720.406.7630
Fax 720.406.7630
Web ....www.medicinehorse.org
E-mail ....kathy@medicinehorse.org
8778 Arapahoe Rd, Boulder, CO 80303
Kathy Johnson, Executive Director

Mental Health Assoc Of Colorado 720.208.2220
Fax 720.208.2250
Web ....www.mhacolorado.org
E-mail ....mentalhealth@mhacolorado.org
1385 S Colorado Blvd Ste 610, Denver, CO 80222
June Smigel, Vice President

Mental Health Corporation Of Denver 303.504.6670
Fax 303.757.8281
Web ....www.mhcd.org
4141 E Dickenson Pl, Denver, CO 80222
Dr. Carl Clark, CEO

Mental Health Institute 719.546.4000
Fax 719.546.4484
Web ....www.cdhs.state.co.us
E-mail ....john.dequardo@state.co.us
1600 W 24th St, Pueblo, CO 81003-1411
John Dequardo, Superintendent

Miller (SLT) 303.321.2482
Fax 303.321.2671
Web ....www.mhcd.org
E-mail ....ann.selling@mhcd.org
1920 E 13th Ave, Denver, CO 80206-2002
Ann Selling, Program Manager

Mount Saint Vincent Home, Inc. 303.458.7220
Fax 303.477.7559
Web ....www.msvhome.org
4159 Lowell Boulevard, Denver, CO 80211
COA accredited organization.

**Mountain Crest Regional Behavioral
Healthcare** 970.207.4802
Fax 970.207.4805
Web ....www.pvhs.org
4601 Corbett Dr, Fort Collins, CO 80528-9579
Monica Smith, Administrator

Mountain Star (At Cmhi-Fl) 303.866.7777
Fax 303.866.7776
3520 W Oxford Ave, Denver, CO 80236-3108
Laura Chauncey, Director

Mt. St. Vincent Home 303.458.7220
Fax 303.477.7559
Web ....www.msvhome.org
E-mail ....sawillcott@msvhome.org
4159 Lowell Blvd, Denver, CO 80211-1658
Sister Amy Willcott, Executive Director

Namaqua Ctr 970.669.7550
Fax 970.663.2907
Web ....www.namaqua.com
E-mail ....cyndi@namaqua.com
404 E 7th St, Loveland, CO 80537-4804
Cyndi Dodds, Executive Director

North Colorado Medical Center 970.352.4121
Web ....bannerhealth.com
E-mail ....tammy.coiner@bannerhealth.com
1801 16th Street, Greeley, CO 80631
Mrs. Tammy Coiner, Accreditation Manager
Joint Commission accredited organization.

North Range Behavioral Health 970.347.2120
Fax 970.346.9800
E-mail ....larry.pottroff@northrange.org
1300 N 17th Ave, Greeley, CO 80631
Larry Pottroff, Executive Director

Peak Parent Ctr, Inc 719.531.9400
Fax 719.531.9452
Web ....www.peakparent.org
E-mail ....info@peakparent.org
611 N Weber St Ste 200, Colorado Springs,
CO 80903
Barbara Buswell, Director

**Penrose-St. Francis Ctr For Behavioral
Health** 719.776.8482
Fax 719.776.2313
2222 N Nevada, Colorado Springs, CO 80907
Charlene Cossen, Manager

Porter Adventist Hospital 303.778.1955
Web ....www.porterhospital.org
E-mail ....kathybilys@centura.org
2525 South Downing Street, Denver, CO 80210
Ms. Kathy Bilys, Accreditation Manager
Joint Commission accredited organization.

Poudre Valley Hospital 970.495.7000
Web ....www.pvhs.org
E-mail ....red@pvhs.org
1024 South Lemay Avenue, Fort Collins,
CO 80524-3998
Mr. Ric Detlefsen, Accreditation Manager
Joint Commission accredited organization.

Remington House 970.484.7447
Fax 970.484.7471
1516 Remington St, Fort Collins, CO 80524-4140
Joel D. Painter, Director

Robert E Denier Youth Svcs Ctr 970.375.2781
Fax 970.375.2775
Web ....www.ridgeviewacademy.com
E-mail ....jay.koedan@.com
720 Turner Dr, Durango, CO 81303-7914
Jay Koedan, Program Director

Savio House 303.225.4100
Fax 303.225.4101
Web ....www.saviohouse.org
325 King Street, Denver, CO 80219-1326
COA accredited organization.

Shiloh Home, Inc. 303.932.9599
Fax 303.973.1269
Web ....www.shilohhouse.org
6400 W. Coal Mine Avenue, Littleton, CO 80123
COA accredited organization.

**Southern Peaks Regional Treatment
Center** 719.276.7511
E-mail ....lbillington@cornellcompanies.com
700 Four Mile Parkway, Canon City, CO 81212
Ms. Laurie Billington, Accreditation Manager
Joint Commission accredited organization.

Spanish Peaks Mental Health Ctr 719.545.2746
Fax 719.584.0110
Web ....www.spmhc.org
E-mail ....curtt@spmhc.org
1304 Chinook Ln, Pueblo, CO 81001-1869
Curt Tuffin Ma,lpc, Director Children Services

Teen-Heartbeat, Founding Chapter 719.596.2575
Fax 719.574.2930
Web ....www.heartbeatsurvivorsaftersuicide.org
E-mail ....archlj@msn.com
2015 Devon St, Colorado Springs, CO 80909-1617
Larita Archibald, Executive Director

The Conflict Ctr 303.433.4983
Fax 303.433.6166
Web ....www.conflictcenter.org
E-mail ....ron.ludwag@conflictcenter.org
4140 Tejon St, Denver, CO 80211-1813
Ron Ludwag, Executive Director

Third Way Ctr, Inc. 303.780.9191
Fax 303.780.9192
Web ....www.thirdwaycenter.org
E-mail ....deisner@thirdwaycenter.org
PO Box 61385, Denver, CO 80206-8385
David F. Eisner, Executive Director

Turning Point Center for Youth and Family Development, Inc. 970.221.0999
Fax 970.221.2727
Web ....www.turningpnt.org
1644 South College Avenue, Fort Collins, CO 80525
CARF accredited programs available.

University of Colorado Hospital Authority 720.848.7800
Web ....www.uch.edu
E-mail ....kristin.stocker@uch.edu
12401 E. 17th Avenue, F417, Aurora, CO 80045
Mrs. Kristin Stocker, Accreditation Manager
Joint Commission accredited organization.

CHILDREN'S HOSPITAL

Arkansas Valley Regional Medical Center 719.383.6000
1100 Carson Ave, La Junta, CO 81050

Avista Adventist Hospital 303.673.1000
100 Health Park Dr, Louisville, CO 80027
John S, Director

Boulder Community Hospital 303.440.2273
1100 Balsam Ave, Boulder, CO 80304
Ceciley, Administrator

Childrens Hospital Denver 720.777.1234
13123 E 16th Ave, Aurora, CO 80045
James Shmerling, Chief Executive Officer

Evans US Army Community Hospital 719.526.7200
1650 Cochrane Cir Bldg 7500, Fort Carson, CO 80913

Exempla Good Samaritan Medical Center 303.689.4000
200 Exempla Cir, Lafayette, CO 80026
Dave Hamm, Chief Executive Officer

Exempla Lutheran Medical Center 303.425.4500
8300 West 38th Ave, Wheat Ridge, CO 80033
Grant Wicklund, Chief Executive Officer

HealthOne Rose Medical Center 303.320.2121
4567 East Ninth Ave, Denver, CO 80220
Kenneth Sieler, Chief Executive Officer

Heart of the Rockies Regional Med Ctr 719.530.2200
E-mail ....john.ellis@hrrmc.net
1000 Rush Dr, Salida, CO 81201
John Ellis, Director

Keefe Memorial Hospital 719.767.5661
602 N 6th St West, Cheyenne Wells, CO 80810
Charlene Korrell, Chief Executive Officer

Littleton Adventist Hospital 303.730.8900
7700 South Broadway St, Littleton, CO 80122
Ken Bacon, Chief Executive Officer

Longmont United Hospital 303.651.5111
E-mail ....wlaughlin@luhcares.org
1950 West Mountain View Ave, Longmont, CO 80501
Warren Laughlin, Human Resource Director

Medical Center of Aurora 303.695.2600
1501 South Potomac St, Aurora, CO 80012
John Hill, Chief Executive Officer

Melissa Memorial Hospital 970.854.2241
1001 East Johnson St, Holyoke, CO 80734
John Ayoub, Chief Executive Officer

Mercy Regional Medical Center 970.247.4311
1010 3rd Springs Blvd, Durango, CO 81301
Kirk Dignum, Chief Executive Officer

Montrose Memorial Hospital 970.249.2211
800 South Third St, Montrose, CO 81401
David Hample, Chief Executive Officer

National Jewish Health 303.388.4461
1400 Jackson St, Denver, CO 80206

North Colorado Medical Center 970.352.4121
1801 16th St, Greeley, CO 80631
Rick Sutton, Chief Executive Officer

North Suburban Medical Center 303.451.7800
9191 Grant St, Thornton, CO 80229

Parkview Medical Center 719.584.4000
400 West 16th St, Pueblo, CO 81003
Mike Baxter, Chief Executive Officer

Penrose St Francis Health Services 719.571.1000
2222 North Nevada Ave, Colorado Springs, CO 80907
Margaret Bin, Chief Executive Officer

Platte Valley Medical Center 303.498.1600
1600 Prairie Center Pkwy, Brighton, CO 80601
John Hicks, Chief Executive Officer

Poudre Valley Hospital 970.495.7000
1024 South Lemay Ave, Fort Collins, CO 80524
Kevin Unger, President/CEO

Sky Ridge Medical Center 720.225.1000
10101 Ridge Gate Pkwy, Lonetree, CO 80124
Maureen Tarrant, Chief Executive Officer

St Mary Corwin Medical Center 719.557.4000
1008 Minnequa Ave, Pueblo, CO 81004
Rob Ryder, Chief Executive Officer

St Marys Hospital & Medical Center 970.244.2273
2635 North 7th St, Grand Junction, CO 81501
Michael Mcbride, Chief Executive Officer

St Vincent General Hospital District 719.486.0230
822 W 4th St, Leadville, CO 80461
Roger Oberg, Chief Executive Officer

Swedish Medical Center HealthOne 303.788.5000
501 East Hampden Ave, Englewood, CO 80113
Mary White, Chief Executive Officer

Yampa Valley Medical Center 970.879.1322
1024 Central Park Dr, Steamboat Springs, CO 80487

COUNSELING SERVICES

Family Tree, Karlis Family Ctr 303.462.1060
Fax 303.462.1315
Web ....www.thefamilytree.org
E-mail ....spt@thefamilytree.org
1777 Kipling St, Denver, CO 80215
Jody Bittrik, Director

Friends Of Children Of Various Nations 303.837.9446
Fax 303.837.9848
E-mail ....fcvnadoption@aol.com
1562 Pearl St, Denver, CO 80203
Cheryl Marks, Executive Director

LDS Family Svcs 303.371.1000
Fax 303.371.1002
E-mail ....jacobsj@ldschurch.org
3263 Fraser St Ste 3, Aurora, CO 80011-1245
Jim Jacobs, Director

North Huron Counseling 303.853.3500
Fax 303.853.3656
Web ....www.communityreachcenter.org
E-mail ....l.palmer@communityreachcenter.org
8931 Huron St, Denver, CO 80260
Libbi Palmer, Director

CRISIS & SHELTER CARE

A Womans Place-Domestic Violence Shelter 970.356.4226
Fax 970.351.6686
E-mail ....director@awpdv.org
PO Box 71, Greeley, CO 80631
Ellen Szabo, Director

Advocate Safehouse Project-Domestic Violence 970.945.2632
Fax 970.928.9026
PO Box 2036, Glenwood Springs, CO 81602-2036
Julie Olson, Director

Advocates Against Battering And Abuse 970.879.2034
Fax 970.879.4339
E-mail ....diane@advocatesaba.org
1250 South Lincoln Avenue, Steamboat Springs, CO 80477
Ms Diane Moore, Director

Advocates-Crisis Support Svcs 970.824.9709
Fax 970.824.5848
E-mail ....acss@qwetoffice.net
PO Box 1050, Craig, CO 81626-1050
Karen Aragon, Director

Advocates-Domestic Violence 303.679.2426
Fax 303.569.1105
Web ....www.clearcreekadvocates.us
PO Box 21, Georgetown, CO 80444-0021
Joni Hargitt, Director

Alliance Against Domestic Abuse 719.539.7347
Fax 719.539.2005
E-mail ....salidaalliance@qwestoffice.net
PO Box 173, Salida, CO 81201-0173
Mandy Trollip, Director

Alternative Horizons-Domestic Violence 970.247.4374
Fax 970.247.8408
E-mail ....director@alternativehorizons.org
701 Camino Del Rio Ste 318, Durango, CO 81302
Kim Zook, Director

Alternatives To Family Violence 303.428.9611
Fax 303.657.4754
Web ....www.atfv-adamsco.org
E-mail ....yolanadag@atfv-adamsco.org
7290 Samuel Drive, Denver, CO 80221
Yolanda Gotier, Director

Alternatives To Violence, Inc. 970.669.5150
Fax 970.669.5136
E-mail ....info@alternativestoviolence.org
313 E 4th St, Loveland, CO 80537
Linda Nielson, Director

Arkansas Valley Resource Ctr-Domestic Violence 719.384.7764
Fax 719.384.1938
Web ....www.bresnan.net
415 Colorado Ave, La Junta, CO 81050-2335
Sandra Leonard, Director

Attention Homes - Youth Shelter 303.447.1207
Fax 303.447.0623
Web ....www.attentionhomes.org
3080 Broadway St, Boulder, CO 80304
Jim Rianoshek, Executive Director

Brandon Ctr-Domestic Violence Program 303.620.9190
Fax 303.620.0917
E-mail ....Brandon2@Voacolorado.Org
1555 st., Denver, CO 80214
Natasha Raabe, Director

Children's Ark At Pueblo 719.543.7410
Fax 719.543.7425
Web ....www.childrensark.org
E-mail ....valita.speedie@state.co.us
400 E Routt Ave, Pueblo, CO 81004-2351
Valita Speedie, Eds, Executive Director

Christian Family Svcs 303.337.6747
Fax 303.368.4661
E-mail ....pam.cfs@pcisys.net
1399 S Havana St Ste 204, Aurora, CO 80012-4041
Pamela Fincher, Director

Community Care 303.777.0303
Fax 303.733.4565
Web ....www.cdhs.state.co.us
    800 Englewood Pkwy Ste B202, Englewood,
    CO 80110
    Louis Bruno, Md, Executive Director

Crossroads Safehouse-Domestic Violence 970.482.3535
Fax 970.482.3208
E-mail ....vlutz@crossroadssafehouse.org
    528 South College Ave, Fort Collins, CO 80524
    Vicki Lutz, Director

Denver Ctr For Crime Victims 303.860.0660
Fax 303.831.7282
E-mail ....admin@denvervictims.org
    1751 Gilpin St, Denver, CO 80218
    Cathy Phelps, Director

Domestic Safety Resource Ctr 719.336.4357
Fax 719.336.2909
    1001 South Main Street, Lamar, CO 81052
    Doris Hughes, Director

Domestic Violence Initiative For Women 303.839.5510
Fax 303.839.1181
E-mail ....Dvidenver@Aol.Com
    PO Box 300535, Denver, CO 80203-0535
    Sharon Hickman, Director

El Pueblo... An Adolescent Treatment
Community 719.544.7496
Fax 719.544.7705
Web ....www.elpueblokids.net
    1 El Pueblo Ranch Way, Pueblo, CO 81006-2103
    Sherri Baca, CEO

Families First 303.745.0327
Fax 303.309.3931
Web ....www.familiesfirstcolorado.org
E-mail ....mary@familiesfirstcolorado.org
    2163 S Yosemite St, Denver, CO 80231
    Mary Hencmann, Executive Director

Family Crisis Svcs, Inc.-Domestic Violence 719.275.2429
Fax 719.275.5967
    3228 Independence Road, Canon City, CO 81212
    Andrea Hammond, Director

Family Tree House Of Hope 303.762.9525
Fax 303.762.9552
Web ....www.thefamilytree.org
E-mail ....houseofhopeft@earthlink.net
    3301 S Grant St Unit A, Englewood, CO 80113
    Keith Singer, Supervisor

Family Tree-Women In Crisis Domestic
Violence 303.420.0412
Fax 303.420.0516
Web ....www.thefamilytree.org
E-mail ....jpemperton@thefamilytree.org
    3805 Marshall St. #100, Wheat Ridge, CO 80033
    Jane Pemberton, Director

Health Dept 970.304.6410
Fax 970.304.6416
Web ....www.co.weld.co.us
E-mail ....
    1555 N 17th Ave, Greeley, CO 80631
    Linda Henry, Rn, Nursing Director

Help For Abused Partners-Domestic
Violence 970.522.2307
Fax 970.522.1163
Web ....www.state.co.us
E-mail ....nicki.johnson@state.co.us
    500 Right of Way Rd, Sterling, CO 80751-8452
    Nicki Johnson, Director

Jubilee House 970.641.2712
Fax 970.641.5437
E-mail ....jubilee@gunnison.com
    304 W Tomichi Ave, Ste 22, Gunnison,
    CO 81230-2745
    Nancy Dolezal, Director

Kathleen Painter Littler Ctr 970.352.2201
Fax 970.352.0810
Web ....www.kinkadedds.com
    2350 W 3rd St Rd, Greeley, CO 80631-1548
    Joanna Martins, Program Director

Lutheran Family Svcs 970.266.1788
Fax 970.266.1799
Web ....www.lfsco.org
E-mail ....julie.witkowski@lfsco.org
    2032 Lowe St, Ste 200, Fort Collins, CO 80525
    Julie Witkowski, Director

Midway Youth Svcs 970.484.8427
Fax 970.482.8713
E-mail ....joel@jacobcenter.org
    729 Remington St, Fort Collins, CO 80524
    Joel D. Painter, Program/clinical Director

Project Safeguard-Domestic Violence 303.863.7416
Fax 303.837.1808
Web ....www.Psghelps.Org
E-mail ....Paula@Psghelps.Org
    815 E 22nd Ave, Denver, CO 80205-5104
    Paula Hammond, Director

Renew, Inc.-Domestic Violence Program 970.565.4886
Fax 970.564.0988
Web ....www.fone.net
E-mail ....director@renew-inc.org
    PO Box 169, Cortez, CO 81321-0169
    Cheryl Beene, Director

Resource Ctr-Domestic Violence 970.249.8345
Fax 970.240.4066
Web ....www.cbi.state.co.us
    540 S 1st St, Montrose, CO 81401-3911
    Becky Ela, Director

Response : Help For Survivors of Domestic Violence and Sexual
Assault 970.920.5357
Fax 970.920.9523
E-mail ....mcgavock@rof.net
    PO Box 1340, Aspen, CO 81612-1340
    Margaret Mcgavock, Executive Director

Safe Shelter Of St. Vrain Valley 303.772.0432
Fax 303.772.1576
E-mail ....jackie@safeshelterofstvrain.org
    82 21st Ave, Longmont, CO 80501
    Jackie List-warrilow, Executive Director

Safehouse Of Denver-Domestic Violence 303.318.9959
Fax 303.318.9979
Web ....www.safehouse-denver.org
E-mail ....estein@safehouse-denver.org
    1649 Downing St, Denver, CO 80218-1528
    Ellen Stein-Wallace, Director

Safehouse Progressive Alliance For
Nonviolence 303.449.8623
Fax 303.449.0169
Web ....www.safehousealliance.org
E-mail ....anne@safehousealliance.org
    835 North St, Boulder, CO 80304-3223
    Anne Tapp, Executive Director

San Miquel Resource Ctr-Domestic
Violence 970.728.5660
Fax 970.728.4894
E-mail ....director@sanmiguelresourcecenter.org
    300 S Pine St Ste 102, Telluride, CO 81435
    Melanie Montoya, Director

Servicios De La Raza 303.458.5851
Fax 303.459.5950
Web ....www.serviciosdelaraza.org
E-mail ....delaraza@aol.com
    4055 Tejon St, Denver, CO 80211-2214
    Rudy Gonzalez, Executive Director

Share, Inc.-Domestic Violence Program 970.867.4444
Fax 970.867.9055
Web ....www.safeshelterofstvrain.org
E-mail ....liz@safeshelterofstvrain.org
    220 Prospect St, Fort Morgan, CO 80701-3127
    Jacque Morse, Director

Tessa-Domestic Violence Ctr 719.633.1462
Fax 719.632.2342
Web ....www.tessacs.org
E-mail ....mvaldez@tessacs.org
    320 S El Paso St, Colorado Springs, CO 80903-3737
    Michelle Valdez, Director

The Advocates Victim Assistance Team 970.725.3442
Fax 970.725.3983
Web ....www.gcadvocates.org
E-mail ....info@gcadvocates.org
    PO Box 155, Hot Sulphur Springs, CO 80451-0155
    Deb Bittner, Director

Tu Casa, Inc-Domestic Violence 719.589.2465
Fax 719.589.1465
    202 Carson Ave, Alamosa, CO 81101
    Ashley Lopes, Director

Urban Peak 303.777.9198
Fax 303.777.9438
Web ....www.urbanpeak.org
E-mail ....kendall.rames@urbanpeak.org
    1630 S Acoma St, Denver, CO 80223-3602
    Kendall Rames, Clinical/Site Manager

Victim Assistance Program 970.264.9075
Fax 970.264.2186
    449 San Juan Dr, PagosaSprings, CO 81147
    Carmen Hubbs, Director

Volunteers Of America-SW Safehouse 970.259.5443
Fax 970.259.5245
E-mail ....fwfh@forentier.net
    1055 Aveniva, Durango, CO 81301
    Sarada Leavenworth, Director

Women's Crisis and Family Outreach
Center 303.688.1094
Fax 303.660.8889
E-mail ....jwalker@twcfoc.org
    PO Box 367, Castle Rock, CO 80104-0367
    Jennifer Walker, Executive Director

EDUCATION

Bridgeway 303.969.0515
Fax 303.988.0547
E-mail ....bridgeway@bridgewayhomes.org
    85 S Union Blvd Ste 204, Denver, CO 80228
    Carole Haas, Director

Collbran Civilian Job Corps 970.487.3576
Fax 970.487.3823
Web ....www.jobcorps.uc.usbr.gov\cjc
E-mail ....aker.gove@jobcorps.org
    57608 Highway 330, Collbran, CO 81624-9500
    Gove Aker, Center Director

Colorado Talking Book Library 303.727.9277
Fax 303.727.9281
Web ....www.cde.state.colorado.us/ctbl
E-mail ....ctbl.info@cde.state.co.us
    180 Sheridan Blvd, Denver, CO 80226-8101
    Debbie Macleod, Director

Denver St. School 303.860.1702
Fax 303.860.1402
Web ....www.denverstreetschool.com
    1380 Ammons St, Lakewood, CO 80214
    Thomas A. Tillapaugh, Director

Hurricane Island Outward Bound School 800.477.2627
Fax 720.497.2401
Web ....www.outwardbound.org
E-mail ....info@outwardbound.org
    910 Jackson St, Golden, CO 80401-1977
    Amy Saxton, Director Of Education Programs

Mi Casa Resource Ctr 303.573.1302
Fax 303.595.0422
Web ....www.micasaresourcecenter.org
E-mail ....info@micasaresourcecenter.org
  360 Acoma St Ste 11, Denver, CO 80223
  Karen Fox, Director Of Youth Development

Open Door Youth Gang Alternatives 303.893.4264
Fax 303.893.4208
Web ....www.therev.org
E-mail ....therev1953@aol.com
  1615 California St Ste 712, Denver, CO 80202-3727
  Leon Kelly, Director

Project Pave 303.322.2382
Fax 303.322.0032
Web ....www.projectpave.org
E-mail ....mjohnson@projectpave.org
  2051 York St, Denver, CO 80205-5713
  Mike Johnson, Director

Pueblo Youth Svc Bureau 719.542.5161
Fax 719.542.1335
E-mail ....pueblovouth@aol.com
  1920 Valley Dr, Pueblo, CO 81008-1764
  Sharon Johnson, Assistant To CEO

FOSTER CARE AGENCIES

AAC Adoption & Family Network Inc (AAC) 970.532.3576
Fax 970.532.9879
E-mail ....info@aacadoption.com
  735 E Hwy 56, Berthoud, CO 80513
  Marissa Bebo, Director

Adoption Alliance 303.584.9900
Fax 303.584.9007
Web ....www.adoptall.com
  2121 S. Oneida Street, Suite 420, Denver, CO 80122
  COA accredited organization.

Adoptive Family Resources-Family Circle 303.881.7630
E-mail ....jantomski@msn.com
  8734 W 14th Ave, Ste 100, Lakewood, CO 80215

Catholic Charities of Colorado Springs 719.866.6535
E-mail ....Info@ccharitiescs.org
  228 N Cascade Ave, Colorado Springs, CO 80903

Colorado Coalition of Adoptive Families 303.562.9864
Fax 303.562.9865
E-mail ....cocafcave@yahoo.com
  PO Box 270398, Louisville, CO 80027

Colorado State Foster Parent Assoc 303.463.7990
  2497 Fenton St, Lakewood, CO 80214
  Sherry Owens

Colorado State Foster Parent Association 303.463.7989
Fax 303.463.7990
E-mail ....office@csfpa.org
  2497 Fenton St, Edgewater, CO 80214

Denver Adoptive Mothers Club 303.935.3847
  1881 S Meade St, Denver, CO 80219
  Harlodine Frecka, Director

Foster & Adoptive Families of Larimer 970.481.7993
E-mail ....info@saflc.org
  246 S Cleveland Ave, Loveland, CO 80537
  Katie Montoya, Director

Fremont Ctny Dept of Social Services 719.275.2318
Fax 719.275.5206
  172 Justice Center Rd, Canon City, CO 81212
  Steve Clifton, Director

Jewish Children's Adoption Network
(JCAN) 303.573.8113
E-mail ....jcan@qwestoffice.net
  PO Box 147016, Denver, CO 80214

Kid's Crossing Inc 719.632.4569
Fax 719.632.6573
E-mail ....aharder@kidscrossing.com
  1440 E Fountain Blvd, Colorado Springs, CO 80910
  Amy Harder, Director

Littlest Angels International 970.856.6177
E-mail ....angels@kaycee.net
  21939 2225 Rd, Cedaredge, CO 81413

Lost and Found Inc.
  6700 West 44th Avenue, Wheat Ridge, CO 80033
  COA accredited organization.

The Institute for Attachment & Child 303.674.1910
Fax 303.670.3983
E-mail ....info@InstituteForAttachment.org
  5911 Middlefield 103, Littleton, CO 80123
  Forrest Lin, Director

HOME MEDICAL EQUIPMENT PROVIDERS

Air Lift 800.776.6771
E-mail ....info@airlift.com
  1212 Kerr Gulch Rd, Evergreen, CO 80439

PEDIATRIC HOME CARE

Aurora PDN (Denver) 719.548.5052
  14231 E 4th Ave, Bldg 1 Ste 200, Aurora, CO 80111
  Felicia Foster, Director

Bayada Nurses 303.333.2900
Fax 303.329.3215
Web ....www.bayada.com
  4155 East Jewell Avenue, Suite 716, Denver,
  CO 80222
  Diane Ream, Director

Bayada Nurses 303.650.1700
Fax 303.650.1706
Web ....www.bayada.com
E-mail ....CWRIGHT@BAYADA.COM
  8670 Wolff Court, Building 8, Suite 115, Westminster,
  CO 80031
  Channie Wright, Director

Bayada Nurses 719.598.9100
Fax 719.598.9199
Web ....www.bayada.com
  6190 Lehman Drive, Suite 100, Colorado Springs,
  CO 80918
  Patty Vandyke, Finance Service Manager

Bayada Nurses 303.782.0900
Fax 303.782.0901
Web ....www.bayada.com
  1385 S Colorado Blvd, Bldg A, Suite 222, Denver,
  CO 80222
  Linda Gaepani, Director

Bayada Nurses 303.782.0900
Fax 303.782.0901
Web ....www.bayada.com
  3333 South Wadsworth Boulevard, Suite 321,
  Lakewood, CO 80227
  Carol Bartoy, Manager

Interim Healthcare 970.472.4180
Fax 970.472.4183
E-mail ....mblomberg@interimhealthcare.com
  2000 Vermont Dr Ste 100, Fort Collins, CO 80525
  Margie Blomberg, Administrator

Interim Healthcare 719.632.9900
Fax 719.389.1485
E-mail ....dringling@interimhealthcare.org
  1901 N Union Ste 202, Colorado Springs, CO 80909
  Devin Ringling, Chief Executive Officer

Interim Healthcare 303.339.9219
Fax 303.339.9218
  325 S Boulder Rd, Louisville, CO 80027

Interim Healthcare 970.241.3166
Fax 970.241.2757
  2764 Compass Dr Ste 225, Compass Pk Office Bldg,
  Grand Junction, CO 81506
  Katherine Kylen, Owner

Interim Healthcare (Denver Home Care) 303.789.4686
Fax 303.789.1644
  333 W Hampden Ave Ste 705, Englewood,
  CO 80110
  Larry Martin, Owner

Interim Healthcare (Denver HomeStyle) 720.407.6309
Fax 303.339.9217
  333 W Hampden Ave Ste 705, Englewood,
  CO 80110
  Larry Martin, Director

Interim Healthcare (Denver Staffing) 303.789.3332
Fax 303.789.1644
  333 W Hampden Ave Ste 705, Englewood,
  CO 80110
  Tara, Staffing Coordinator

Interim Healthcare (Ft Collins Staffing 970.221.0714
Fax 970.472.4183
  2000 Vermont Dr Ste 100, Fort Collins, CO 80525

Interim Healthcare (Pueblo Staffing) 719.545.1184
Fax 719.545.1746
E-mail ....dyoung@interimhealthcare.com
  720 N Main St Ste 400, Pueblo, CO 81003
  Don Young, Administrator

Interim HealthCare of Pueblo 719.545.1184
Fax 719.545.1746
Web ....www.interimhealthcare.com/pueblo
  720 N. Main St. #400, Pueblo, CO 81003
  Donald Young, Rn, Msn, Administrator

Interim Hlthcare (Colorado Springs Staff) 719.632.9900
Fax 719.389.1485
E-mail ....dringling@interimhealthcare.com
  1901 N Union Ste 202, Colorado Springs, CO 80909
  Devin Ringling, Chief Executive Officer

Nurse-Family Partnerships 303.327.4240
Fax 303.327.4260
Web ....www.nursefamilypartnership.org
  1900 Grant St, Ste 400, Denver, CO 80203
  Karen Alexander, Office Manager

Pediatric Home Care 303.759.1342
Fax 720.493.4632
Web ....www.pediatrichomecare.com
  8000 E Prentice Ave, B11, Greenwood VIllage,
  CO 80111
  Anne Carrier, Director

SOCIAL SERVICES

Armed Svcs YMCA Colorado Springs 719.622.9622
Fax 719.622.3555
Web ....www.ppymca.org
E-mail ....aking@ppymca.org
  2190 Jet Wing Dr, Colorado Springs, CO 80916-2426
  Anette King, Executive Director

Asian Pacific Development Ctr 303.393.0304
Fax 303.388.1172
Web ....www.apdc.org
  1825 York St, Denver, CO 80206-1213
  Christine Wanifuchi, Director

Barbara Davis Ctr For Childhood Diabetes 303.724.2323
Fax 303.724.6779
Web ....www.barbaradaviscenter.org
E-mail ....george.eisenbarth@uchsc.edu
  PO Box 6511, Aurora, CO 80045-0511
  George S. Eisenbarth, Md, Ph.d, Executive Director

Boys & Girls Clubs of Metro Denver 303.892.9200
Fax 303.892.9210
Web ....www.bgcmd.org
E-mail ....tinam@bgcmd.org
  2017 W 9th Ave, Denver, CO 80204-3845
  Tina J. Martinez, Program Director

Boys And Girls Club 970.223.1709
Fax 970.206.9531
Web .... www.larimerboysandgirlsclubs.com
E-mail .... kwright@bgclarimer.org
103 Smokey St, Fort Collins, CO 80525-3801
Kathi Wright, Executive Director

Breckenridge Outdoor Education Ctr 970.453.6422
Fax 970.453.4676
Web .... www.boec.org
E-mail .... boec@boec.org
524 Wellington Rd, Breckenridge, CO 80424
Bruce Fitch, Executive Director

Casey Family Programs 303.871.8201
Fax 720.479.2948
Web .... www.casey.org
1999 Broadway St, Denver, CO 80202
Tiffany Washington, Administrative Assistant

**Catholic Charities and Community Services of the Archdiocese
of Denver, Inc.** 303.742.0828
Fax 303.742.0774
Web .... www.ccdenver.org
4045 Pecos Street, Denver, CO 80211
COA accredited organization.

Child Abuse Prevention 303.692.2942
Fax 303.691.7852
Web .... www.state.co.us
E-mail .... scott.bates@state.co.us
4300 Cherry Creek South Dr, Denver,
CO 80246-1523
Scott Bates, Director

Child Care Connections 719.638.2057
Fax 719.638.2059
Web .... www.childcareconnections.net
125 N Parkside Dr Ste 202, Colorado Springs,
CO 80909
Mary Sullivan, Director

Child Development 719.635.1536
Fax 719.634.8086
Web .... www.cpcdheadstart.org
E-mail .... nlandistyson@cpcd.org
2330 Robinson St, Colorado Springs, CO 80904
Noreen Landis-tyson, Director

**Children's Advocacy & Family Resources,
Inc.** 303.368.1065
Fax 303.368.1089
Web .... www.sungatekids.org
E-mail .... sungate@sungatekids.org
2400 South Wabash St, Denver, CO 80231
Diana Goldberg, Executive Director

**City Of Boulder Children Youth And
Families** 303.441.3544
Fax 303.441.4348
Web .... www.ci.boulder.co.us
E-mail .... fryj@ci.boulder.co.us
2160 Spruce St, Boulder, CO 80302-4508
Judy Fry, Director

Colorado Children's Campaign 303.839.1580
Fax 303.839.1354
Web .... www.coloradokids.org
E-mail .... info@coloradokids.org
1580 Lincoln St Ste 420, Denver, CO 80203-1506
Chris Watney, President

Colorado Christian Svcs 303.761.7236
Fax 303.761.7237
Web .... www.christianservices.org
E-mail .... elizabeth@christianservices.org
3959 E Arapahoe Rd Ste 200, Centennial, CO 80122
Elizabeth Bolz, Director

Colorado Right To Life 303.753.9394
Fax 303.753.9341
E-mail .... office@coloradorighttolife.org
1535 Grant St, Denver, CO 80203
Donna Vallentine, Office Manager

**Community Partnership Family Resource
Ctr** 719.686.0705
Fax 719.686.9129
Web .... www.cptconline.org
E-mail .... cpfrc@qwest.net
11115 W Hwy 242C, Divide, CO 80814
Sam Gould, Executive Director

Community Reach Ctr 303.853.3400
Web .... www.communityreachcenter.org
11285 Highline Dr, Denver, CO 80233
Vicki Esposito, Chief Executive Officer

Creative Options Ctr For Early Education 303.691.9668
Fax 303.691.0846
Web .... www.cpco.org
E-mail .... info@cpco.org
801 Yosemite St, Denver, CO 80230-6087
Wendy Edwards, Education Director

Ctr For Adolescent Self-Esteem 303.410.8167
E-mail .... stephanie@relationshiptoolkit.com
13575 Decatur Ct, Broomfield, CO 80020-5148
Stephanie Roth, The Relationship Maven

Ctr For Hearing, Speech & Language 303.322.1871
Fax 303.399.3411
Web .... www.chsl.org
E-mail .... chsl@chsl.org
4280 Hale Pkwy, Denver, CO 80220-3724
Jill Wayne, Executive Director

**Ctr For The Study & Prevention Of
Violence** 303.492.1032
Fax 303.443.3297
Web .... www.colorado.edu/cspv
E-mail .... cspv@colorado.edu
1440 15th St, Boulder, CO 80302
Delbert S. Elliot, Director

Denver Indian Ctr, Inc. 303.936.2688
Fax 303.936.2699
Web .... www.denverindiancenter.org
E-mail .... jaygrimm@denverindiancenter.org
4407 Morrison Rd, Denver, CO 80219
Jay Grimm, Executive Director

Denver Indian Health & Family Svcs, Inc. 303.781.4050
Fax 303.781.4333
E-mail .... dihfs@dihfs.org
1633 Silmar St, Denver, CO 80206
Delbert Nutter, Executive Director

Eastern Plans Womens Resource 303.822.9368
Fax 303.822.5368
E-mail .... epwrs@aol.com
228 W Front St, Byers, CO 80103-9730
Shelly Gambrell, Director

Excelsior Youth Ctr 303.693.1550
Fax 303.680.2430
Web .... www.excelsioryc.org
E-mail .... jimu@excelsioryc.org
15001 E Oxford Ave, Aurora, CO 80014-4186
Jim Uhernik, Admissions Director

**Family Advocacy Care, Education &
Support** 720.570.9333
Fax 720.570.9339
Web .... www.facesonline.org
1325 S Colorado Blvd Ste B 509, Denver,
CO 80222-2543
Debora Judish, Executive Director

Family Ctr 970.867.9606
Fax 970.867.9693
Web .... www.morganfamilycenter.org
E-mail .... childcare@aginformation.com
800 W Platte Ave Ste 1, Fort Morgan,
CO 80701-2961
Mary Gross, Executive Director

Family Tree, Inc. 303.422.2133
Fax 303.422.5707
Web .... www.thefamilytree.org
3805 Marshall St Ste 100, Wheat Ridge, CO 80033
Scott Shields, CEO

Family Violence Program 303.403.8525
Fax 303.403.8497
E-mail .... familyviolenceprogram@hotmail.com
4243 Harlan St, Wheat Ridge, CO 80033-5119
Greg Stieger, Executive Director

Family Visitor Program 970.945.1234
Fax 970.928.8328
Web .... www.familyvisitor.org
E-mail .... swan@rof.net
401 23rd St Ste 204, Glenwood Springs, CO 81601
Saundra Swanson, Rn, Executive Director

Girls Incorporated Of Metro Denver 303.893.4363
Fax 303.893.4352
Web .... www.girlsincdenver.org
E-mail .... cbowar@girlsincdenver.org
1499 Julian St, Denver, CO 80204-1641
Carol Bowar, President/CEO

**Halcyon School: Adolescent Treatment
Program** 303.499.1121
Fax 303.499.9332
3100 Bucknell Ct, Boulder, CO 80305-3465
Kate Parker, Director

Inn-Between 303.684.0810
Fax 303.651.7273
Web .... www.theinnbetween.org
E-mail .... theinn@theinnbetween.org
250 Kimbark St, Longmont, CO 80501
Donna Lovato, Executive Director

Jewish Family Service of Colorado 303.597.5000
Fax 303.597.7700
E-mail .... jfs@jewishfamilyservice.org
3201 S Tamarac Dr, Denver, CO 80231
Yana Vishnitsky, CEO

**Judi's House For Grieving Children &
Families** 720.941.0331
Fax 720.941.0728
Web .... www.judishouse.org
E-mail .... judy@judishouse.org
1741 Gaylord St, Denver, CO 80206-1208
Judy Becerra, Program Director

Kids First 970.928.7111
Fax 970.928.7333
Web .... www.corra.org
E-mail .... kidsfirst@sopris.net
401 23rd St Ste 207, Glenwood Springs, CO 81601
Shirley Ritter, CEO

Lifebound, LLC 303.327.5688
Fax 303.327.5684
Web .... www.lifebound.com
E-mail .... contact@lifebound.com
1530 High St, Denver, CO 80218-1705
Renee Brown, Office Manager

Longmont Youth Ctr 303.651.8580
Fax 303.651.8839
Web .... www.ci.longmont.co.us
E-mail .... christina.pacheco@ci.longmont.co.us
1050 Lashley St, Longmont, CO 80504
Christina Pacheco, Supervisor Of Youth Services

Lutheran Family Svcs of Colorado 303.922.3433
Fax 303.922.7335
Web .... www.lfsco.org
E-mail .... newhomesc@lfsco.org
363 S Harlan St Ste 200, Denver, CO 80226
Luci Draayer, Care Manager

Moriah Mounts 970.493.0022
Web .... www.frii.com
E-mail .... moriahmounts@frii.com
3312 Buckskin Trl, Laporte, CO 80535-9313
Condy Wright-Jones, Director

Northeast Colorado Child Care Resource And Referral.................................**970.848.3867**
Fax...970.848.3869
Web...www.ncccrr.org
E-mail..............................sanzlovar@ncccrr.org
204 S Main St, Yuma, CO 80759
Sheila Anzlorvar, Director

Pikes Peak Family Connections **719.520.1019**
Fax...719.471.3197
Web.........................www.familyconnections.org
E-mail.......................................ppfc@fetcf.org
2220 E Bijou St Ste 2E, Colorado Springs,
CO 80909-8001
Judy Slason, Executive Director

Pikes Peak United Way **719.632.1543**
Fax...719.632.8139
E-mail.............................jd@ppunitedway.org
518 N Nevada Ave, Colorado Springs, CO 80903
J.d. Dallager, President/CEO

Planet Youth (New Creations Church) **303.776.4225**
Fax...303.772.7214
Web.............................www.newcreations.net
737 Bross St, Longmont, CO 80501-4419
Maria Latini, Head Pastor

Rape Assistance & Awareness Program **303.329.9922**
Fax...303.329.9964
Web......................................www.raap.org
E-mail.......................................raap@raap.org
PO Box 18951, Denver, CO 80218
Carmen Carter, Executive Director

Red Ribbon Project **970.827.5900**
Fax...970.827.4176
E-mail..................redribbonprojectus@yahoo.com
37347 US Hwy 6, Avon, CO 81620
Karen Koenemann, Director

Rocky Mountain Youth Corps **970.879.2135**
Fax...970.879.1285
Web.......................www.rockymountainyouthcorps.org
E-mail...............gretchen@rockymountainyouthcorps.com
1705 13th st, Steamboat Springs, CO 80487
Gretchen Van De Carr, Executive Director

Social Svcs...**970.878.9640**
Fax...970.878.4893
E-mail...................bonnie.ruckman@state.co.us
345 Market St, Meeker, CO 81641
Kathleen Maybury, Casework Supervisor

Southwest Colorado Office Of Child Care Resource And Referral.....................................**970.247.5960**
Fax...970.247.5979
Web......................................www.tchs4c.org
E-mail..........................shannonb@tchs4c.org
1315 Main Ave STE 121, Durango, CO 81301
Charlotte Pirnat, Director

Sunrise Youth Shelter...........................**970.565.9634**
Fax...970.565.2619
E-mail.....................constance.lehi@state.co.us
322 Dry Creek Road, Towaoc, CO 81334
Constance Lehi, Director

The Black Canyon Boys And Girls Club **970.249.5168**
Fax...970.249.4173
Web......................................www.bcbgc.org
E-mail....................................info@bcbgc.org
635 E Main St Ste. 200, Montrose, CO 81401
Justin Kiehl, Chief Performance Officer

The Early Childhood Council **970.377.3388**
Fax...970.377.2866
Web......................................www.ecclc.org
E-mail....................................info@ecclc.org
1730 S College Ave #200, Fort Collins,
CO 80525-2558
Bev Thurber, Director

Third Way Center, Inc..........................**303.780.9191**
Fax...303.780.9192
Web...........................www.thirdwaycenter.org
P.O. Box 61385, Denver, CO 80206-8385
COA accredited organization.

United Way 211 ....**970.407.7066**
Fax...970.407.7011
Web..................................www.firstcall211.org
E-mail...............................info@firstcall-vc.org
424 Pine St Ste 102, Fort Collins, CO 80524-2421
Tracy Hayes, Director

Western Slope Ctr For Children **970.245.3788**
Fax...970.245.7550
E-mail........................office@wscchildren.org
259 Grand Ave, Grand Junction, CO 81501-7816
Shari Zen, Execuitve Director

Whinnian's Youth Development And Equine Therapy **303.750.9120**
Fax...303.750.0491
3138 S parker Rd, Aurora, CO 80014
Pamela Lindal-hansum, Director

SPECIAL NEEDS

Ability First Newport Mesa **303.840.0770**
Fax...303.840.0770
E-mail...........................jthomas@abilityfirst.org
15931 Parkside Dr, Parker, CO 80134

Adaptive Adventures National **877.679.2770**
Fax...303.670.8290
E-mail.....................info@adaptiveadventures.org
Colorado Office, 27888 Meadow Dr, Evergreen,
CO 80439

Autism Education Action Group **719.955.3767**
Fax...719.955.3768
Web......................www.alpineautismcenter.org
E-mail....................................info@aeag.org
2760 Fieldstone Rd, Colorado Springs,
CO 80919-3819
Tanna Rice, Clinical Director

Autism Society of Colorado **720.214.0794**
E-mail.............co-colorado@autismsocietyofamerica.org
550 S Wadsworth Blvd ,Ste 100, Lakewood,
CO 80226

Brain Injury Association of Colorado **303.355.9969**
4200 W Conejos Pl Ste 524, Denver, CO 80204
Gretchen Pate, Director

Colorado PTA **303.420.7820**
E-mail...................................office@copta.org
7859 W 38th Ave, Wheat Ridge, CO 80033

Colorado Speech-Language-Hearing Assn **720.733.9097**
E-mail...................................cshassoc@aol.com
PO Box 345, Sedalia, CO 80135

Colorado Spina Bifida Association **303.797.7870**
PO Box 22994, Denver, CO 80222

Denver Metro Community Parent Resource **303.365.2772**
E-mail...........................info@denvermetrocprc.org
14501 E Alameda Ave, Ste 205, Aurora, CO 80012
Yvette Plummer, Director

Easter Seals Colorado **303.233.1666**
E-mail...............lrobinson@eastersealscolorado.org
5755 W Alameda Ave, Lakewood, CO 80226

Eleanor Capron Inpatient Rehabilitation, Penrose St. Francis **719.776.5754**
Fax...719.776.2534
Web...........................www.penrosestfrancis.org
2222 North Nevada Avenue, Eighth Floor, W Tower,
Colorado Springs, CO 80907
CARF accredited programs available.

EMPOWER Colorado **866.213.4631**
E-mail.......................................jham@cpco.org
801 Yosemite St, Denver, CO 80230

Epilepsy Foundation of Colorado Inc **303.377.9774**
E-mail.....................gail@epilepsycolorado.org
234 Columbine St Ste 333, Denver, CO 80206
Gail Punesack, Executive Director

LearningRx Learning Center **719.527.0033**
E-mail..............cospringssouth.com@learningrx.com
1130 Wake Pl Dr, Colorado Springs, CO 80906
Napalie Speakman, Center Director

LearningRx Learning Center **303.284.6105**
E-mail...........................denver-cc.co@learningrx.net
88 Steele St, Ste 50, Denver, CO 80206
Michael Sebilla, Director

LearningRx Learning Center **970.672.2020**
E-mail...........................fortcollins.co@learningrx.net
1100 Haxton Dr, Ste 105, Fort Collins, CO 80525
Michael Wincell, Program Director

LearningRx Learning Center **719.550.8263**
E-mail..................cospringsnorth.co@learningrx.net
7075 Campus Dr, Ste 202, Colorado Springs,
CO 80920
Natalie Speakman, Director

Lindamood-Bell Learning Processes **720.528.8404**
Fax...720.528.8445
6 Inverness Ct E, Ste 250, Englewood, CO 80112

Mapleton Inpatient Rehabilitation Unit at Boulder Community Hospital **303.440.2250**
Fax...303.440.2291
Web......................................www.bch.org
E-mail.......................................mvince@bch.org
1100 Balsam Avenue, Inpatient Rehabilitaion Unit 4,
Boulder, CO 80301
Melissa Vince, Director PCU
CARF accredited programs available.

Mile High Down Syndrome Association Inc **303.797.1699**
E-mail.......................................darylk@mhdsa.org
31515 S Tamarak Dr Ste 320, Denver, CO 80224
Mac Macsobits, Executive Director

National Multiple Sclerosis Society **303.698.7400**
Fax...303.698.7421
E-mail.........................cocreceptionist@nmss.org
900 S Broadway 2nd Fl, Denver, CO 80209

Parent to Parent of Colorado **877.472.7201**
E-mail.......................................mail@p2p-co.org
801 Yosemite St, Denver, CO 80230

PEAK Parent Center Inc **719.531.9400**
Fax...719.531.9452
E-mail...........................info@peakparent.org
611 N Weber Ste 200, Colorado Springs, CO 80903

PEAK Parent Center, Inc......................**719.531.9400**
Fax...719.531.9452
E-mail...........................info@peakparent.org
611 North Rubber St Ste 200, Colorado Springs,
CO 80903
Patricia Maycott, Executive Director

PST Professional Training & Consultation **303.471.4142**
Fax...303.471.4149
E-mail.....................................pstedcon@aol.com
10642 S Baneberry St, Highlands Ranch, CO 80126

Rocky Mountain Stroke Association **303.730.8800**
E-mail.........................info@strokecolorado.org
5666 S Bannock St, Littleton, CO 80120
Esther Fretz, Director

Spalding Rehabilitation Hospital **303.367.1166**
Fax...303.360.8208
Web...........................www.spaldingrehab.com
900 Potomac Street, Aurora, CO 80011
CARF accredited programs available.

Summit Reading Center **303.221.1861**
Fax...720.974.0309
7200 E Dry Creek Rd, Ste G-103, Englewood,
CO 80112

Summit Reading Center **303.499.9729**
E-mail ....info@summitrc.com
  4730 Table Mesa Dr Ste A-100, Boulder, CO 80305
Nicolas Clausen, Director

Tetra Academy **303.730.7691**
Fax 720.974.0309
E-mail ....tetra.academy@comcast.net
  2081 Youngfield St, Golden, CO 80401

The Arc of Colorado **303.864.9334**
  8000 E Prentice Ave Ste D-1, Englewood, CO 80111

Tourette Syndrome Association Inc **720.212.7535**
E-mail ....tsarmr@att.net
  837 S Kuner Rd, Brighton, CO 80601

VSA Arts Colorado **303.777.0797**
E-mail ....vsaco@earthlink.net
  909 Santa Fe Dr, Denver, CO 80204

SUBSTANCE ABUSE TREATMENT

Adult/Youth Counseling Svcs **719.442.1779**
Fax 719.442.0538
  223 N Wahsatch Ave Ste 101, Colorado Springs, CO 80903
Roy Mcclendon, Director

Cornerstone **720.895.1000**
Fax 720.895.8000
Web ....www.cornerstoneprograms.com
  9085 E Mineral Circle Ste 235, Centenniao, CO 80112-3420
Joe Newman, Director

Gateway Youth And Family Svcs **970.874.7749**
Fax 970.874.5433
E-mail ....gtwyrccf@aol.com
  679 1675 Rd, Delta, CO 81416-3462
Marni Lyons, Program Director

Connecticut

Dannel Malloy, Governor
210 Capitol Ave
Hartford, CT 06106
800.406.1527
860.524.7396 (Fax)
governor.rell@po.state.ct.us

Valerie LaMotte, Juvenile Justice Specialist
450 Capitol Ave
MS# 52CJP
Hartford, CT 06106-1379
860.418.6316
860.418.6496 (Fax)
valerie.lamotte@ct.gov

Anthony Salius, SAG Chair
34 Silano Dr.
Harwinton, CT 06791
860.485.0339
ajsalius@snet.net

CRISIS NUMBERS

Child Abuse Reporting . . .800.842.2288

STATE SERVICES

SOCIAL SERVICES

Child Day Care Licensing Program CT 860.509.8045
Fax 860.509.7541
E-mail . . . . .debra.johnson@ct.gov
410 Capitol Ave MS 12 DAC, PO Box 340308,
Hartford, CT 06134
Debra Johnson, Director

Child Support Enforcement Div 860.569.6233
Fax 860.569.6557
Web . . . . .www.jud.ct.gov
287 Main St Fl 3, East Hartford, CT 06118-1887
Charisse Hutton, Director

Dept of Children and Families 860.550.6300
Fax 860.560.7086
Web . . . . .www.ct.gov/dcf
E-mail . . . . .tom.dematteo@ct.gov
505 Hudson St, Hartford, CT 06106
Thomas Dematteo, Administrative Law & Policy/licensing Director

GENERAL HEALTH SERVICES

Children & Youth with Special Health Care Needs CT
DPH 860.509.8057
Fax 860.509.7720
E-mail . . . . .mark.keenan@ct.gov
410 Capital Ave, PO Box 340308, MS 11MAT,
Hartford, CT 06134
Mark Keenan, Director

Connecticut Dept of Public Health 860.509.8000
Fax 860.509.7111
Web . . . . .www.dph.state.ct.us/dph
410 Capitol Ave, Hartford, CT 06134
Lisa Davis, Director

Maternal and Child Health CT 860.509.8074
Fax 860.509.7720
E-mail . . . . .lisa.davis@ct.gov
410 Capitol Ave MS 11 MAT, Hartford,
CT 06134-0308
Lisa Davis, Director

Medicaid Care Admin 860.424.5116
Fax 860.424.5114
E-mail . . . . .david.parrella@ct.gov
25 Sigourney St, Hartford, CT 06106
David Parrella, Director

MENTAL HEALTH SERVICES

Bureau of Rehab Svcs CT 860.424.4844
Fax 860.424.4850
E-mail . . . . .amy.porter@ct.gov
25 Sigourney St 11th Flr, Hartford, CT 06106
Amy Porter, Director

Dept of Mental Health and Addiction Svcs 860.418.7000
Fax 860.418.6691
Web . . . . .www.ct.gov
410 Capitol Ave, MS 14 Comm, Hartford,
CT 06106-1373
Patricia Rehmer, Commissioner

Dept. of Developmental Services 860.418.6000
Fax 860.418.6001
Web . . . . .www.ct.gov/dds
E-mail . . . . .terr.macy@ct.gov
460 Capitol Ave, Hartford, CT 06106-1380
Terrence Macy, Commissioner

Radar Network Agency 860.793.3500
Fax 860.793.3520
Web . . . . .www.ctclearinghouse.org
E-mail . . . . .jstonger@wheelerclinic.org
91 NW Dr, Connecticut Clearinghouse, Plainville,
CT 06062-1321
Judy Stonger, Associate Director

Voc Rehabilitation Division CT 860.602.4008
Fax 860.602.4030
E-mail . . . . .brian.sigman@ct.gov
184 Windsor Ave, Windsor, CT 06095
Brian Sigman, Director

JUSTICE AGENCY

Connecticut Dept of Corrections 860.692.7780
Fax 860.692.7783
Web . . . . .www.ct.gov/doc
E-mail . . . . .doc.pio@po.state.ct.us
24 Wolcott Hill Rd, Wethersfield, CT 06109-1176
Brian Garnett, Director Of External Affairs

Correctional Educ Division CT 860.692.7805
Fax 860.692.7538
E-mail . . . . .angela.jalbert@po.state.ct.us
24 Wolcott Hill Rd, Wethersfield, CT 06109
Angela Jalbert, Director

Ofc of Victim Svcs 860.263.2760
Fax 860.263.2777
Web . . . . .www.jud.state.ct.us
E-mail . . . . .linda.cimino@jud.ct.gov
225 Spring St, Wethersfield, CT 06109-3418
Linda J. Cimino, Director

COURTS

Court Support Svcs Div 860.721.2199
Fax 860.258.8976
Web . . . . .www.jud.ct.gov
936 Silas Deane Hwy Fl 3, Wethersfield,
CT 06109-4219
William H. Carbone, Executive Director

POLICE AND SHERIFF

Connecticut Police Chiefs Assoc 860.586.7506
Fax 860.586.7550
Web . . . . .www.cpcanet.org
E-mail . . . . .info@cpcanet.org
342 N Main St Ste 301, West Hartford, CT 06117
Pamela Hayes, Executive Director

Public Safety/Div of State Police 860.685.8441
Fax 860.685.8354
Web . . . . .www.po.state.ct.us
1111 Country Club Rd, Middletown, CT 06457-2390
James Thomas, Commisioner

EDUCATION SERVICES

American School For The Deaf 860.570.2300
Fax 860.570.2301
Web www.asd-1817.org
E-mail . . . . .ed.peltier@asd-1817.org
139 N Main St, West Hartford, CT 06107-1269
Dr. Edward F. Peltir, Director

Board of Education & Svcs for the Blind 860.602.4000
Fax 860.602.4030
Web . . . . .www.besb.state.ct.us/
E-mail . . . . .brian.sigman@ct.gov
184 Windsor Ave, Windsor, CT 06095-4536
Brian Sigman, Executive Director

Bureau of Health & Nutrition Family Services and Adult
Education 860.807.2050
Fax 860.807.2127
Web . . . . .www.state.ct.us/sde
E-mail . . . . .paul.flinter@ct.gov
25 Industrial Park Rd, Middletown, CT 06457
Paul Flinmter, Director

Bureau of Special Education CT 860.713.6912
Fax 860.713.7014
E-mail . . . . .lisa.spooner@ct.gov
165 Capitol Ave Rm 360, Hartford, CT 06145
Lisa Spooner, Administrator

Connecticut Dept of Education 860.713.6543
Fax 860.713.7005
Web . . . . .www.sde.ct.gov
165 Capitol Ave, Hartford, CT 06106
George Coleman, Acting Comissioner

Connecticut Institute for the Blind 860.242.2274
Fax 860.242.3103
Web . . . . .www.ciboakhill.org
E-mail . . . . .info@ciboakhill.org
120 Holcomb St, Hartford, CT 06112-1589
Patrick Johnson, President

Conneticut Head Start 860.424.5066
Fax 860.424.4960
E-mail ....grace.whitney@ct.gov
　25 Sigourney St, Hartford, CT 06106
　Grace Whitney, Director

CT Parent Advocacy Center Inc 860.739.3089
Fax 860.739.7460
E-mail ....cpac@cpacinc.org
　338 Main St, Niantic, CT 06357
　Nancy Prescott, Executive Director

Educ for Homeless Children and Youth CT 860.807.2058
Fax 860.807.2127
E-mail ....louis.tallarita@ct.gov
　25 Industrial Park Rd, Middletown, CT 06457
　Louis Tallarita, Director

Gifted and Talented 860.713.6745
Fax 860.713.7018
Web ....www.ct.gov
E-mail ....jeanne.purcell@ct.gov
　165 Capitol Ave Rm 215, Hartford, CT 06106-1626
　Jeanne Purcell, Education Consultant

LABOR & WORKFORCE EDUCATION

Ofc for Workforce Competitiveness 860.258.4304
Fax 860.258.4312
E-mail ....mary.ann.hanley@ct.gov
　100 Great Meadow Rd Ste 401, Wethersfield,
　CT 06109-2355
　Mary Ann Hanley, Executive Director

COUNTY SERVICES

Fairfield County

SOCIAL SERVICES

Bridgeport Dept Of Social Svcs 203.551.2700
Fax 203.579.6790
Web ....www.das.state.ct.us
E-mail ....frances.freer@po.state.ct.us
　925 Housatonic Ave, Bridgeport, CT 06606-5700
　Frances Freer, Administrator

Community Svcs 203.385.4095
Fax 203.381.2064
Web ....www.townofstratford.com
E-mail ....llobinco@townofstratford.com
　468 Birdseye St Ste 1, Stratford, CT 06615-6976
　Lisa Lobinco, Director

Connecticut Dept Of Social Svcs 203.251.9300
Fax 203.251.9310
Web ....www.po.state.ct.us
E-mail ....evelyn.balamaci@ct.gov
　1642 Bedford St, Stamford, CT 06905
　Evelyn Balamaci, Operations Manager

Danbury Dept Of Social Svcs 203.207.8900
Fax 203.207.8970
Web ....www.ct.gov/dss
E-mail ....patrick.hearn@ct.gov
　342 Main St, Danbury, CT 06810
　Patrick Hearn, Operations Manager

Dept Of Children & Families 203.207.5100
Fax 203.207.5170
Web ....www.ct.gov
　131 West St, Danbury, CT 06810
　Robert Allensworth, Area Director

Dept Of Children & Families 203.384.5300
Fax 203.384.5305
　100 Fairfield Ave Fl 3, Bridgeport, CT 06604
　Janice Currier, Program Director

Dept Of Children & Families 203.348.5865
Fax 203.964.9501
Web ....www.dcf.state.ct.us
　401 Shippan Ave, Stamford, CT 06902
　Judith Kallen, Director

Dept Of Children & Families 203.899.1400
Fax 203.853.3821
Web ....www.dcf.state.ct.us
　149 Water St Apt 2, Norwalk, CT 06854-3757
　Ingrid Aarons, Manager

Dept Of Social Svcs 203.622.3800
Fax 203.622.7762
Web ....www.greenwichct.org
　101 Field Point Rd, Greenwich, CT 06830-6463
　Dr Alan Barry, Commissioner

Youth Svc Bureau 203.854.7785
Fax 203.854.7991
E-mail ....youthservice@norwalk.org
　125 East Ave, Norwalk, CT 06856
　Linda Wilock, Director

Youth Svcs Bureau 203.924.7614
Fax 203.924.1072
Web ....www.cityofshelton.org
E-mail ....j.penry@cityofshelton.org
　120 Meadow St, Shelton, CT 06484-2276
　Julie Penry, Youth Services Bureau Director

Youth Svcs, Inc 203.748.2936
Fax 203.797.8568
Web ....www.danburyyouthservices.org
E-mail ....central.dys@snet.net
　91 West St, Danbury, CT 06810-6529
　Julie Schmitter, Executive Director

GENERAL HEALTH SERVICES

Bridgeport Public Health Dept 203.576.7464
Fax 203.332.5507
Web ....www.bridgeport.ct.us
　752 E Main St, Bridgeport, CT 06608-2335
　Michelle Mede, AIDS Director

Brookfield Health District 203.775.7315
Fax 203.740.7677
Web ....www.brookfield.org
E-mail ....mcarroll@brookfieldctcp.gov
　100 Pocono Rd, Brookfield, CT 06804-3322
　Raymond Sullivan, Director Of Health

Greenwich Health Dept 203.622.6488
Fax 203.622.7770
Web ....www.greenwichct.org
E-mail ....tmahoney@greenwichct.org
　101 Field Point Rd, Town Hall, Greenwich,
　CT 06830-6463
　Tom Mahoney, Special Clinical Services Director

Health Dept 203.268.6291
Fax 203.268.4928
Web ....www.eastonct.org
　225 Center Rd, Easton, CT 06612
　Pauley Edwards, Health Director

Health Dept 203.794.8539
Fax 203.794.8145
E-mail ....kelleyn@betheltownhall.org
　1 School St, Clifford J. Hurgin Municipal Ctr, Bethel,
　CT 06801
　Laura Vasile, Mph, Rs, Director

Health Dept 203.797.4625
Fax 203.796.1596
E-mail ....s.leroy@ci.danbury.ct.us
　155 Deer Hill Ave, Danbury City Hall, Danbury,
　CT 06810-7726
　Scott Lerroy, Director

Health Dept 203.256.3020
Fax 203.256.3080
Web ....www.fairfieldct.org
　725 Old Post Rd, Sullivan Independent Hall, Fairfield,
　CT 06824
　Sands Cleary, Director

Health Dept 203.594.3018
Fax 203.594.3125
Web ....www.newcanaan.info
E-mail ....briggs.geddis@ci.new-canaan.ct.us
　77 Main St, Town Hall, New Canaan, CT 06840-4710
　David Reed, Md, Director

Health Dept 203.563.0174
Fax 203.563.0148
Web ....www.wiltonct.org
E-mail ....steven.schole@wiltonct.org
　238 Danbury Rd, Wilton, CT 06897-4008
　Steven Schole, Mph, Rs, Director

Health Dept 203.576.7680
Fax 203.576.8311
Web ....www.ci.bridgeport.ct.us
E-mail ....kristin.dubay-horton@bridgeportct.gov
　752 E Main St, Bridgeport, CT 06608-2335
　Kristin Dubay, Health Director

Norwalk Health Dept 203.854.7776
Fax 203.854.7926
Web ....www.norwalkhealth.org
　137 East Ave, Norwalk, CT 06851-5702
　Lynette Gibson, Aids Coordinator

Stratford Health Dept 203.385.4090
Fax 203.381.2048
Web ....www.townofstratford.com
　468 Birdseye St Ste 3, Stratford, CT 06615
　Andrea Boissevain, Director

The Town Of Darien Health Dept 203.656.7320
Fax 203.656.7486
Web ....www.darienct.gov
E-mail ....dknauf@darienct.gov
　2 Renshaw Rd, Darien, CT 06820
　David Knauf, Director Of Health

Trumbull Health District 203.452.5195
Fax 203.452.5304
Web ....www.trumbull-ct.org
E-mail ....health@trumbull-ct.org
　2 Corporate Dr Ste 116, Trumbull, CT 06611-2466
　Patrice Sulik, Director

JUSTICE AGENCY

Juvenile Detention Ctr 203.579.6548
Fax 203.382.8422
E-mail ....geralddennison@jud.ct.gov
　60 Housatonic Ave, Bridgeport, CT 06604
　Jack Fitzgerald, Interim Supervisor

COURTS

Superior Court 203.965.5208
Fax 203.965.5355
Web ....www.jud.ct.gov
E-mail ....helen.kalmanides@jud.ct.gov
　123 Hoyt St GA1, Stamford, CT 06905-5703
　Helen Kalmanides, Deputy Chief Clerk

Superior Court - Juvenile

Probation **203.579.6588**
Fax 203.579.6804
Web ....www.jud.ct.gov
E-mail ....oliver.macklin@jud.ct.gov
60 Housatoniz Ave, Bridgeport, CT 06604-3822
Oliver Macklin, Supervisor

Superior Courtù Juvenile Matters **203.579.6544**
Fax 203.382.8430
60 Housatonic Ave, Bridgeport, CT 06604
Honorable Carol Wolven, Director

Superior Courtù Juvenile Matters **203.797.4407**
Fax 203.731.2813
Web ....www.jud.ct.gov
E-mail ....kevin.pate@jud.ct.gov
71 Main St, Danbury, CT 06810-7802
Kevin Pate, Probation Supervisor

POLICE AND SHERIFF

Police Dept **203.581.5100**
Fax 203.332.5617
300 Congress St, Bridgeport, CT 06604
Joseph Gaudett, Chief Of Police

Stamford Police Dept **203.977.4444**
Fax 203.977.5582
Web ....www.cityofstamford.org
805 Bedford St, Stamford, CT 06901-1194
Robert Nizakoff, Police Chief

EDUCATION SERVICES

ABCD Inner City Children's Daycare

Ctr **203.366.8241**
Fax 203.394.6175
Web ....www.abcd.org
E-mail ....mister.tisdell@abcd.org
1070 Park Ave, Bridgeport, CT 06604-3400
Mister Tisdell, Director

Hartford County

SOCIAL SERVICES

Bureau Of Human Resources **860.713.6690**
Fax 860.713.7011
Web ....www.po.state.ct.us
E-mail ....karen.shaw@po.state.ct.us
165 Capitol Ave, Hartford, CT 06106
Karen Shaw, Bureau Chief

Connecticut Dept Of Social Svcs North Central

Region **860.723.1000**
Fax 860.566.7144
Web ....www.ct.gov
E-mail ....silvana.flattery@ct.gov
3580 Main St, Hartford, CT 06120-1121
Silvana Flattery, Regional Administrator

Dept Of Children And Families Area

Ofc **860.418.8000**
Fax 860.418.8327
Web ....www.po.state.ct.us
250 Hamilton St, Hartford, CT 06106-2910
Michael Williams, Area Director

Human Svcs **860.665.8590**
Fax 860.665.8599
E-mail ....kfreidenberg@newington.ct.gov
131 Cedar St, Newington, CT 06111
Kenneth J. Freidenberg, Director

Protection and Advocacy System **860.297.4300**
Fax 860.566.8714
Web ....www.ct.gov/opapd
E-mail ....opa-information@ct.gov
60-B Weston St, Hartford, CT 06120
James Mcgaughey, Director

Social Svcs Dept **860.409.4346**
Fax 860.677.2847
E-mail ....arosenberg@town.avon.ct.us
60 W Main St, Avon, CT 06001
Alan E. Rosenberg, Social Services Director

Social Svcs Dept **860.658.3283**
Fax 860.408.7046
Web ....www.simsbury-ct.gov
E-mail ....mlecours-beck@simsbury-ct.gov
754 Hopmeadow St, Town Hall, Simsbury, CT 06070-2212
Michiline Lecours-beck, Director

Youth & Family Svcs **860.652.7661**
Fax 860.652.7659
321 Hubbard St, Glastonbury, CT 06033
Ann Grabowski, Director

Youth & Family Svcs **860.648.6361**
Fax 860.644.3951
Web ....www.southwindsor.org
150 Nevers Rd, South Windsor, CT 06074
Dennis Sheridan, Director Of Human Services

Youth Svc Bureau **860.314.4690**
Fax 860.314.4689
51 High St, Bristol, CT 06010
Eileen Mcnulty, Director

Youth Svc Bureau **860.253.6380**
Fax 860.253.5145
Web ....www.enfield-ct.gov
E-mail ....jhaughey@enfield-ct.org
19 N Main St, Enfield, CT 06082-3339
Jean Haughey, Director Of Youth

Youth Svc Bureau **860.721.2977**
Fax 860.721.2935
Web ....www.wethersfieldct.com
E-mail ....nancy.stilwell@wethersfieldct.com
505 Silas Deane Hwy, Wethersfield, CT 06109-2216
Nancy Stilwell, Phd, Director

Youth Svc Bureau **860.647.5213**
Fax 860.647.5253
Web ....www.ci.manchester.ct.us/ysb
E-mail ....ebromley@ci.manchester.ct.us
63 Linden Street, Manchester, CT 06040
Erica Bromley, Director

Youth Svcs **860.675.2390**
Fax 860.675.7140
E-mail ....marshb@farmington-ct.org
1 Montieth Dr, Farmington, CT 06032-1082
Nancy Parent, Director Of Community And Recreational Services

Youth Svcs **860.258.2718**
Fax 860.258.2796
Web ....www.ci.rocky-hill.ct.us
E-mail ....lstanczyc@ci.rocky-hill.ct.us
699 Old Main St, Rocky Hill, CT 06001
Lori Stanczyc, Coordinator Of Youth Services

Youth Svcs Bureau **860.793.0221**
Fax 860.747.9376
Web ....www.plainville-ct.gov
E-mail ....brown@plainville-ct.gov
50 Whiting St, Plainville, CT 06062-2221
Roberta L. Brown, Coordinator Of Youth Services

GENERAL HEALTH SERVICES

Central Connecticut Health District **860.721.2822**
Fax 860.721.2823
Web ....www.ccthd.org
E-mail ....paul.h@Wethersfieldct.com
505 Silas Deane Hwy, Wethersfield, CT 06109
Paul Hutcheon, Mph, Rs, Director

Central Connecticut Health District **860.828.7017**
Fax 860.828.9248
Web ....www.ccthd.org
E-mail ....nbrault@town.berlin.ct.us
240 Kensington Rd, Berlin, CT 06037
Nancy Brault, Chief of Enviornmental Health Services

Farmington Valley Health District **860.676.1953**
Fax 860.676.2131
E-mail ....rmatheny@fvhd.org
50 Avon Meadow Ln, Farmington Valley Health District, Avon, CT 06001
Richard Matheny, Jr., Mph, Mfs, Rs, Director Of Health

Health Care Systems Branch **860.509.7400**
Fax 860.509.7538
Web ....www.dph.state.ct.us
E-mail ....wendy.furniss@ct.gov
410 Capitol Ave, # 12Hcs, Hartford, CT 06106
Wendy Furniss, Bureau Chief

Health Dept **860.276.6275**
Fax 860.276.6277
93 Main St, Southington, CT 06489
Charles I. Motes, Jr., Ms, Mph, Rs, Director

Health Dept **860.652.7534**
Fax 860.652.7533
Web ....www.glastonbury.ct.gov
E-mail ....david.boone@glastonbury.ct.gov
2155 Main St, Glastonbury, CT 06033
David Boone, Mph, Rs, Director

Health Dept **860.757.4730**
Fax 860.722.6851
131 Coventry St, Hartford, CT 06112
Carlos Rivera, Director

Health Dept **860.291.7324**
Fax 860.291.7326
Web ....www.ci.east-hartford.ct.us
E-mail ....jcordier@ci.east-hartford.ct.us
740 Main St, East Hartford, CT 06108-3140
Jim Cordier, Director Of Health And Social Services

Health Dept **860.644.2511**
Fax 860.644.3781
Web ....www.southwindsor.org
E-mail ....robert.detula@southwindsor.org
1540 Sullivan Ave, South Windsor, CT 06074
Robert Detula, Director

Health Dept **860.647.3173**
Fax 860.647.3188
Web ....www.ci.manchester.ct.us
E-mail ....marya41@ci.manchester.ct.us
479 Main St, Manchester, CT 06040-4101
Maryann Lexius, Director

New Britain Health Dept **860.612.2771**
Fax 860.826.3475
E-mail ....eciccone@newbritainct.gov
56 Hawkins St, New Britain, CT 56051
Eugene Ciccone, Director

Town Of Windsor Health Dept **860.285.1823**
Fax 860.285.1809
Web ....www.townofwindsorct.com
E-mail ....health@townofwindsorct.com
275 Broad St, Windsor, CT 06095
Charles Petrillo, Jr., Mph, Ph, Msph, Director Of Health

COURTS

Superior Court- Juvenile Matters **860.515.5165**
Fax 860.515.5176
Web ....www.jud.ct.gov
20 Franklin Sq, Fl 3, New Britain, CT 06051
Debra Nayano, Probation Supervisor

POLICE AND SHERIFF

Hartford Police Dept **860.757.4000**
Fax 860.722.6134
E-mail ....policechief@hartford.gov
50 Jennings Rd, Hartford, CT 06120
Daryl Roberts, Police Chief

EDUCATION SERVICES

Bco Bristol Head Start-Lake Ave **860.584.9307**
Fax 860.585.1105
Web ....www.bco.org
E-mail ....vgiarratama@bcoct.org
254 Lake Ave, Bristol, CT 06010-7323
Valerie Giarratama, Coordinator

**Bureau Of Curriculum And
Instruction** **860.713.6740**
Fax 860.713.7018
Web ....www.sde.ct.gov
165 Capitol Ave Rm 215, Hartford, CT 06106-1626
Harriet Seldlauser, Bureau Chief

Crt Windsor Head Start Ctr **860.285.1441**
Fax 860.687.0827
114 Palisado Ave, Windsor, CT 06095-2531

**Douglas Street Early Care And
Education** **860.560.5460**
Fax 860.722.6036
Web ....www.hartford.gov
E-mail ....cfrancine@hartford.gov
170 Douglas St, Hartford, CT 06114-2424
Cathy Francine, Director

Litchfield County

SOCIAL SERVICES

Canaan Social Svcs **860.824.9855**
Fax 860.824.4506
Web ....www.canaanfallsvillage.org
E-mail ....canaan021sefectmen@comcasi.net
101 Main St, Falls Village, CT 06031
Bj Christinat, Director

Dept Of Children & Families **860.496.5700**
Fax 860.496.5740
Web ....www.po.state.ct.us
62 Commercial Blvd, Torrington, CT 06790-7213
Joette Katz, Commissioner

Social Svcs **860.824.3133**
Fax 860.824.3139
E-mail ....karen.stevens@snet.net
100 Pease St, Canaan, CT 06018
Karen Stevens, Director Of Social Services

Torrington Dept Of Social Svcs **860.496.6900**
Fax 860.496.6977
Web ....www.ct.gov/dss
62 Commercial Blvd, Ste 1, Torrington, CT 06790
John Soucheuns, Operations Manager

GENERAL HEALTH SERVICES

Health Dept **860.355.2985**
Fax 860.354.4028
E-mail ....donna.culbert@newtown-ct.gov
29 Main St, Town Of Roxbury, Roxbury, CT 06783
Donna Culbert Mph, Pe, Rs, Director Of Health

Health Dept **860.355.6035**
Fax 860.210.2664
Web ....www.newmilford.org
E-mail ....mcrespan@newmilford.org
10 Main St, New Milford, CT 06776
Michael A. Crespan, Mph, Rs, Director Of Health

Health Dept **860.364.0456**
Fax 860.364.5163
Web ....www.cthan.org
E-mail ....dohsharon@cthan.org
29 Hospital Hill Rd Ste 1200, Sharon, CT 06069
David Kurish, Md, Director

COURTS

Superior Court Juvenile Matters **860.489.0202**
Fax 860.489.6892
410 Winsted Rd, Torrington, CT 06790
Honorable Thomas Upson, Judge

Middlesex County

SOCIAL SERVICES

Tricon Youth Svc Bureau **860.526.3600**
Fax 860.526.3600
E-mail ....ttysd@aol.com
56 High Street, Deep River, CT 06417
Gail M. Onofrio, Director

Youth & Family Svcs **860.267.9982**
Fax 860.267.6453
20 E High St, East Hampton, CT 06424
Wendy Regan, Director

Youth & Family Svcs **860.395.3190**
Fax 860.395.3189
E-mail ....yfs@town.old-saybrook.ct.us
322 Main St, Old Saybrook, CT 06475
Heather Mcneil, Director

GENERAL HEALTH SERVICES

Chatham Health District **860.345.8531**
Fax 860.345.5169
Web ....www.chathamhealth.org
E-mail ....thad.king@chathamhealth.org
30 Field Park Dr, Haddam, CT 06438-1140
Thad King, Acting Health Director

**Clinton Youth And Family Svcs
Bureau** **860.669.1103**
Fax 860.664.4384
Web ....www.clintonyouthandfamily.org
E-mail ....ysbureau@snet.net
112 Glenwood Rd, Clinton, CT 06413-1423
Barbara Small, Director Of Youth And Family

Connecticut Valley Hospital **860.262.5000**
Fax 860.262.5989
Web ....www.po.state.ct.us
E-mail ....raeann.paperello@po.state.ct.us
Silver Street, Middletown, CT 06547
Raeann Paperello, Rn, Infection Control Coordinator

Health Dept **860.632.3426**
Fax 860.632.3477
Web ....www.cromwellct.com
E-mail ....wbell@cromwellct.com
41 West St, Fl 2, Cromwell, CT 06416
Wess Bell, Health Director

Health Dept **860.399.3047**
Fax 860.399.2084
E-mail ....nbishop@westbrookct.com
866 Boston Post Rd, Westbrook, CT 06498
Noel Bishop, CEO

Health Dept **860.342.6718**
Fax 860.342.6787
E-mail ....don.mitchell@chathamhealth.org
33 E Main St, Portland, CT 06480
Don Mitchell, Director Of Enviromental Health

Health Dept **860.344.3474**
Fax 860.344.3588
Web ....www.cityofmiddletown.com
E-mail ....joseph.havlicek@cityofmiddletown.com
245 Dekoven Dr, Municipal Building, Middletown,
CT 06457-3460
Dr. Joseph Havlicek, Director

Health Dept **860.395.2482**
Fax 860.395.6603
Web ....www.oldsaybrookct.org
E-mail ....smartinson@town.old-saybrook.ct.us
302 Main St, Old Saybrook, CT 06475-2384
William Irving, Director

Health Dept **860.767.4340**
Fax 860.767.8509
Web ....http://www.essexct.gov/departments/heal th.html
29 West Ave, Essex, CT 06426-1140
Lisa Sasulo, Director Of Health

Town In Middlefield Health Dept **860.349.7123**
Fax 860.349.8537
405 Main St Ste 1, Middlefield, CT 06455
Matthew Huddleston, Md, Health Director

COURTS

CT Problem Gambling Svcs **860.344.2244**
Fax 860.344.2360
Russell Hall, CVH, Middletown, CT 06457
Mary Lou Costanzo, Clinical Director

Superior Courtù Juvenile Matters **860.344.2986**
Fax 860.344.2089
Web ....www.jud.state.ct.us
230 Main Street Ext, Middletown, CT 06457-4406
Michael Angelo Palmieri, Court Support Service Division Supervisor

POLICE AND SHERIFF

Middletown Police Dept **860.344.3200**
Fax 860.343.8022
Web ....www.cityofmiddletownpolice.com
E-mail ....pmcmachon@middletownctpolice.com
222 Main St, Middletown, CT 06457-3439
Patrick Mcmachon, Chief Of Police

EDUCATION SERVICES

CRT Clinton Head Start **860.669.9497**
Fax 860.669.9497
E-mail ....lisa@cres-va.com
82 W Main St, Clinton, CT 06413-1623
Lisa Ellis, Director

New Haven County

SOCIAL SERVICES

Dept Of Children & Families **203.238.8400**
Fax 203.238.6425
1 W Main St, Meriden, CT 06451
Dakibu Muley, Program Manager

Dept Of Children And Families **203.786.0500**
Fax 203.786.0568
Web ....www.po.state.ct.us
E-mail ....kelly.mcvey@po.state.ct.us
1 Long Wharf Dr Ste 414, New Haven,
CT 06511-5940
Kelly McVey, Regional Director

Deptt Of Children & Families **203.759.7000**
Fax 203.759.7296
Web ....www.po.state.ct.us
395 W Main St, Waterbury, CT 06702-1125
Patricia Zucarelli, Regional Administrator

Health Dept And Human Svcs **203.630.4226**
Fax 203.639.0039
Web ....www.ci.meriden.ct.us
E-mail ....bvumbaco@ci.meriden.ct.us
165 Miller St, Meriden, CT 06450-4256
Beth Vumbaco, Rm, Ms, Director Of Health And Human Services

Human Resources Dept **203.783.3253**
Fax 203.783.3238
Web ....www.ci.milford.ct.us
150 Golf St, Thomas Parsons Complex, Milford,
CT 06460
Lisa E. Diamond-graham, Director

Human Serv 203.271.6690
Fax 203.271.6626
Web ....www.cheshirect.org
   84 S Main St, Cheshire, CT 06410
Michelle Piccerillo, Director

Southbury Midlebury Youth And Family
Svcs 203.758.1441
Fax 203.758.1658
Web ....www.southburymidlebury-yfs.org
   1287 Strongtown Rd, Southbury, CT 06488-1948
Deirdre Dicara, Executive Director

Waterbury Dept Of Social Svcs 203.597.4000
Fax 203.597.4048
   249 Thomaston Ave, Waterbury, CT 06702-1031
Marva Perrins, Operations Manager

Youth Social Svcs 203.294.2175
Fax 203.294.2703
   6 Fairfield Blvd, Wallingford, CT 06492
Craig Turner, Director

Youth Svc Bureau 203.777.2610
Fax 203.562.3498
E-mail ....srubino@hamden.com
   11 Pine St, Hamden, CT 06514-4924
Susan Rubino, Coordinator

Youth Svc Bureau 203.937.3633
Fax 203.937.3524
Web ....www.cityofwesthaven.com
E-mail ....bobmorton@aol.com
   355 Main St, West Haven, CT 06516-4310
Robert S. Morton, Director Of Youth Services

Youth Svc Bureau 203.720.5673
Fax 203.720.7200
Web ....www.naugatuck-ct.gov
E-mail ....naugys@netscape.net
   13 Scott St, Naugatuck, CT 06770-4307
Jane M. Lobdell, Mft, Director

GENERAL HEALTH SERVICES

Chesprocott Health District 203.272.2761
Fax 203.250.9412
Web ....www.chesprocott.org
E-mail ....chesprocott@snet.net
   1247 Highland Ave Ste 102, Cheshire,
   CT 06410-1657
Thomas Wegrzyn, Mph, Rs, Health Director

East Shore District Health Dept 203.481.4233
Fax 203.483.6894
Web ....www.esdhd.org
E-mail ....info@esdhd.org
   14 Business Park Dr, Branford, CT 06405-2909
Michael Pascucilla, Director

Health Dept 203.783.3285
Fax 203.783.3286
Web ....www.ci.milford.ct.us
E-mail ....health@ci.milford.ct.us
   82 New Haven Ave, Milford, CT 06460
A. Dennis Mcbride, MD, MPH, Director

Health Dept 203.245.5681
Fax 203.245.5613
E-mail ....bowersjn@madisonct.org
   8 Campus Dr, Madison, CT 06443
John Bowers, Ms, Rs, Director

Health Dept 203.453.8118
Fax 203.453.8034
E-mail ....johnsond@ci.guilford.ct.us
   50 Boston St, Guilford, CT 06437
Dennis Johnson, Health Director

Health Dept 203.937.3660
Fax 203.937.3676
Web ....www.whhd.org
E-mail ....hjohnson@westhaven-ct.gov
   355 Main St, Fl 2, West Haven, CT 06516
Helyn Johnson, Rn, Supervisor

Health Dept 203.393.2100
Fax 203.393.0821
Web ....www.bethany-ct.com
   40 Peck Rd, Bethany, CT 06524-3322
Derry Lyngorski, Director

Middlebury Health Dept 203.577.4011
Fax 203.598.7640
Web ....www.middlebury-ct.org
E-mail ....healthdept@middlebury-ct.org
   1212 Whittemore Rd, Middlebury, CT 06762-2425
Raymond Sullivan Md, Director

New Haven Health Dept AIDS Div 203.946.8351
Fax 203.946.7234
Web ....www.newhavenct.net
E-mail ....mlopez@newhavenct.net
   54 Meadow St, Gateway Center, New Haven,
   CT 06519
Matthew Lopez, Director

Pomperaug Health District 203.264.9616
Fax 203.262.1960
Web ....www.pomperaughealthdistrict.org
   800 Main St S Ste 124, Southbury, CT 06488-4212
Neal Lustig, Mph, Rs, Director

Quinnipiack Valley Health District 203.248.4528
Fax 203.248.6671
Web ....www.qvhd.org
E-mail ....lbalch@qvhd.org
   1151 Hartford Tpke, North Haven, CT 06473-3041
Leslie Balch, Mph, Rn, Director

Shoreline Medical Ctr 203.245.4933
Fax 203.245.4399
   1353 Boston Post Rd, Madison, CT 06443
Jennifer Swenson, Md, Director

Wallingford Health Dept 203.294.2065
Fax 203.294.2064
Web ....www.town.wallingford.ct.us
E-mail ....wlfdhealth@sbcglobal.net
   45 S Main St, Rm 215, Wallingford, CT 06492
Eloise E. Hazelwood, Director Of Health

Waterbury Health Dept 203.574.6780
Fax 203.597.3481
Web ....www.waterburyct.org
E-mail ....rwright@waterburyct.org
   1 Jefferson Sq, Waterbury, CT 06706-1103
Roseann Wright, Director

JUSTICE AGENCY

Dept Of Community Svcs 203.239.5321
Fax 203.234.2130
   18 Church St, North Haven, CT 06473-2503
Edward J Swinkoski, Director

Juvenile Detention Ctr 203.786.0343
Fax 203.786.0366
Web ....www.jud.ct.gov
E-mail ....brian.chamberlain@jud.ct.gov
   239 Whalley Ave, New Haven, CT 06511-3207
Brian Chamberlain, Assistant Supervisor

COURTS

Superior Courtù Juvenile Matters 203.786.0300
Fax 203.786.0379
   239 Whalley Ave, New Haven, CT 06511
Karen Eaddy, Probation Supervisor

POLICE AND SHERIFF

Police Dept 203.946.7273
Fax 203.946.8703
Web ....www.newhavenpolice.org
E-mail ....jsmith@newhavenct.net
   1 Union Ave, New Haven, CT 06519-1721
Lt. Jd Smith, Coordinator

Waterbury Police Dept 203.574.6911
Fax 203.574.6940
Web ....www.wtbypd.org
   255 E Main St, Waterbury, CT 06702-2389
Michael Gugili, Chief

EDUCATION SERVICES

New Opportunities For Family Preservation/Reunification
Program 203.575.9799
Fax 203.755.8254
Web ....www.newopportunitiesinc.org
E-mail ....jameshgatling@newopportunitiesinc.org
   232 N Elm St, Waterbury, CT 06702
James Gatling, Director

New London County

SOCIAL SERVICES

Dept Of Children & Families 860.886.2641
Fax 860.885.1300
Web ....www.state.ct.us
E-mail ....kyle.parkinson@ct.gov
   2 Courthouse Sq Ste 1, Norwich, CT 06360
Kyle Parkinson, Area Director

Human Svcs 860.535.5015
Fax 860.599.8290
Web ....www.stonington-ct.gov
E-mail ....bstewart@stonington-ct.gov
   166 S Broad St, Pawcatuck, CT 06379-1925
Bethany Stewart, Director

Montville Youth Svc Bureau 860.848.7724
Fax 860.848.4058
Web ....www.montvilleyouth.org
E-mail ....barbara@montvilleyouth.org
   289 Norwich New London Tpke, Uncasville,
   CT 06382-2515
Barbara Lockhart, Director

Norwich Dept Of Social Svcs 860.823.5000
Fax 860.823.5199
E-mail ....randy.mckenney@ct.gov
   401 W Thames St Unit 102, Norwich,
   CT 06360-7175
Randy Mckenney, Operations Manager

United Community & Family Svc, Inc. Youth Svc
Bureau 860.442.4319
Fax 860.437.2334
Web ....www.ucfs.org
   400 Bayonet St, Ste 103, New London,
   CT 06320-2600
Giulia Jaramillo, Supervisor

Youth & Family Svc 860.823.3782
Fax 860.892.6031
Web ....www.cityofnorwich.org
E-mail ....nyss@cityofnorwich.org
   80 Broadway, Norwich, CT 06360
Kathryn Eyberse, Coordinator

Youth Svc Bureau 860.464.8466
Fax 860.464.9148
   741 Colonel Ledyard Hwy, Ledyard, CT 06339-1511
Kate Sikorski, Youth Service Coordinator

Youth Svc Bureau 860.441.6760
Fax 860.441.6766
Web ....www.town.groton.ct.us
E-mail ....humanser@town.groton.ct.us
   2 Fort Hill Rd, Groton, CT 06340-4723
Marge Fondulas, Director

Connecticut

Youth Svc Bureau......................**860.537.7255**
Fax......................................860.537.0547
Web.............................www.colchesterct.gov
E-mail.......................vgeato@colchesterct.gov
   127 Norwich Ave, Colchester, CT 06415-1230
Valerie Geato, Director

Youth Svc Bureau......................**860.434.7208**
Fax......................................860.434.1580
Web..........................www.lymeyouthservices.org
E-mail.............lymesyouthbureau@sbcglobal.net
   59 Lyme St, Old Lyme, CT 06371
Mary Seidner, Director

GENERAL HEALTH SERVICES

Dept Of Health Enviroment.............**860.535.5010**
Fax......................................860.535.1023
Web..........................www.townofstonington.com
   152 Elm St, Stonington, CT 06378-1166
Receptionist, Director

G P Family Care........................**860.437.0333**
Fax......................................860.439.1330
   157 Montauk Ave, New London, CT 06320
Peter J. Gates, Md, Director

Health Dept...........................**860.642.7352**
Fax......................................860.822.6198
E-mail.......................dohfranklin@cthan.org
   7 Meeting House Hill Rd, North Franklin, CT 06254
Robert W. Powitz, PhD, Director Of Health

Health Dept...........................**860.537.7214**
Fax......................................860.537.7287
E-mail...............healthdirector@colchesterct.gov
   127 Norwich Ave, Colchester Town Hall, Colchester, CT 06415
Wendy Mis, Director Of Health Certified Health Education Specialist

Health Dept...........................**860.376.7060**
Fax......................................860.376.7109
Web.............................www.griswold-ct.org
E-mail.....................agosselin@griswold-ct.org
   28 Main St, Jewett City, CT 06351-2204
Albert Gosselin, Director

Ledge Light Health District...............**860.448.4882**
Fax......................................860.448.4885
Web.............................www.ledgelighthd.org
E-mail.........................boh@ledgelighthd.org
   216 Broad St, New London, CT 06320
Baker Salsbury, Director

Salem Health Dept......................**860.859.3873**
Fax......................................860.859.1184
E-mail...........................rtowitz@salemct.gov
   270 Hartford Rd, Town Hall, Salem, CT 06420
Robert Towitz, Director

The Town Of North Stonington...............**860.535.2877**
Fax......................................860.535.4554
Web.........................www.northstoningtonct.gov
E-mail...................selectmen@northstoningtonct.gov
   40 Main St, North Stonington, CT 06359-1612
Frank Greene, Health Director

Uncas Health District....................**860.823.1189**
Fax......................................860.887.7898
E-mail...........................doh@uncashd.org
   401 W Thanes St Ste 106, Norwich, CT 06360
Patrick Mccormick, Mph, Director Of Health

COURTS

Superior Court-Juvenile Matters.............**860.440.5890**
Fax......................................860.440.5865
Web................................www.jud.ct.gov
E-mail.........................mark.irons@jud.ct.gov
   978 Hartford Tpke, Waterford, CT 06385-4037
Honorable John Driscoll, Judge

POLICE AND SHERIFF

New London Police Dept...................**860.447.5261**
Fax......................................860.447.5277
E-mail.................mackley@ci.new-london.ct.us
   5 Governor Winthrop Blvd, New London, CT 06320
Margaret Ackley, Police Chief

Ridgefield County

GENERAL HEALTH SERVICES

Health Dept...........................**203.431.2745**
Fax......................................203.431.2737
Web..............................www.ridgefieldct.org
E-mail......................eb.health@ridgefieldct.org
   66 Prospect St, Ridgefield, CT 06877
Edward L. Briggs, Mph, Director Of Health

Tolland County

SOCIAL SERVICES

Family Svcs...........................**860.684.4239**
Fax......................................860.684.0511
E-mail.................familyservices@staffordct.org
   21 Hyde Park Rd, Stafford Springs, CT 06076
Ramona Singleton, Executive Director

Human Svcs...........................**860.742.5324**
Fax......................................860.742.3505
Web.............................www.coventryct.org
E-mail.......................cmorawitz@coventryct.org
   1712 Main St, Coventry, CT 06238-3615
Crystal Morawitz, Youth Services Coordinator

Youth Svc Bureau......................**860.228.9488**
Fax......................................860.228.1213
Web..............................www.ahmyouth.org
   25 Pendleton Dr, Hebron, CT 06248
Joel Rosenberg, Executive Director

Youth Svcs Bureau......................**860.870.3555**
Fax......................................860.870.3556
E-mail................aslobodien-ys@sbcglobal.net
   9 Elm St, Vernon, CT 06066
Alan Slobodien, Director

GENERAL HEALTH SERVICES

Health Dept...........................**860.487.0002**
Fax......................................860.429.1663
E-mail..........................rwinakor@wcmh.org
   34 Professional Park Rd, Storrs Mansfield, CT 06268
Ross Winakor, Doctor

Health Dept...........................**860.642.6028**
Fax......................................860.642.2022
Web.........................www.lebanontownhall.org
E-mail...................healthdept@lebanontownhall.org
   579 Exeter Rd, Lebanon, CT 06249
Robert Powitz, Md, Director Of Health

Health Dept...........................**860.763.8216**
Fax......................................860.763.8223
Web...............................www.somerct.gov
E-mail.........................wpca@somerct.gov
   600 Main St, Somers, CT 06071-2119
Richard A. Segoul, Director

Health Dept...........................**860.742.4064**
Fax......................................860.742.8911
Web.............................www.coventryct.org
E-mail.........................dgrady@coventryct.org
   1712 Main St, Coventry, CT 06238-3615
Dorothy Grady, Human Services Administrator

North Central District Health.............**860.684.5609**
Fax......................................860.684.1768
Web..................................www.ncdhd.org
E-mail...........................wblitz@ncdhd.org
   1 Main St, Town Hall, Stafford Springs, CT 06076-1412
William Blitz, Director

North Central District Health Dept.............**860.745.0383**
Fax......................................860.745.3188
Web..................................www.ncdhd.org
   31 N Main St, Enfield, CT 06082
William Blitz, Mph, Health Officer

Windham County

SOCIAL SERVICES

Dept Of Children & Families.................**860.450.2000**
Fax......................................860.450.1051
   322 Main St, Windham Mills, Willimantic, CT 06226
Diane Breton, CPS Director

Dept Of Social Svcs......................**860.465.3500**
E-mail.........................linda.roache@ct.gov
   676 Main St, Willimantic, CT 06226
Linda Roache, Director

GENERAL HEALTH SERVICES

Chaplin Health District....................**860.429.3325**
Fax......................................860.455.0027
Web...............................www.chaplinct.org
E-mail..........................jpolhemus@ehhd.org
   495 Phoenixville Rd, Chaplin, CT 06235-2420
Jeff Polhemus, Sanitarian

Northeast District Dept of Health.............**860.774.7350**
Fax......................................860.774.1308
Web..................................www.nddh.org
E-mail.........................sstarkey@nddh.org
   69 S Main St Unit 4, Brooklyn, CT 06234
Susan Starkey, Director

COURTS

Superior Court- Juvenile Matters.............**860.456.5700**
Fax......................................860.456.5702
Web............................www.jud.state.ct.us
   81 Columbia Ave Ste 1, Willimantic, CT 06226-1956
Edward Graziani, Judge

EDUCATION SERVICES

Access Head Start-Putnam.................**860.928.0004**
Fax......................................860.963.5357
E-mail...................easchenbrenner@eastconn.org
   33 Wicker St, Putnam, CT 06260
Elizabeth A Aschenbrenner, Director

East Connecticut Killingly Early Head Start......................**860.779.3770**
Fax......................................860.779.3384
Web..............................www.eastconn.org
   111 Connecticut Mills Ave, Danielson, CT 06239-1600
Paula Colen, Executive Director

East Connecticut Killingly Early Head Start......................**860.779.0410**
Fax......................................860.779.1377
E-mail......................dmcquade@eastconn.org
   1620 Upper Maple St, Dayville, CT 06241-1514
Dawn Mcquade, Site Director

Eastconn Head Start......................**860.564.7199**
Fax......................................860.564.2630
   10 Gorman St, Moosup, CT 06354-1341
Alison Morello, Project Specialist

SPECIAL SERVICES AGENCIES

ADOPTION AGENCIES

Adoption From The Heart 860.657.2626
Fax 860.659.1625
Web .... www.afth.org
E-mail .... pennyr@afth.org
　　2389 Main St, Glastonbury, CT 06033-4325
　　Penny Rearick, District Supervisor

Casey Family Svcs 203.401.6900
Fax 203.401.6901
Web .... www.caseyfamilyservices.org
　　127 Church St, New Haven, CT 06510
　　Raymond Torres, Executive Director

Casey Family Svcs 860.727.1030
Fax 860.727.9355
Web .... www.caseyfamilyservices.org
　　43 Woodland St, Ste 400, Hartford, CT 06105
　　Ed Reynolds, Interim Director

Casey Family Svcs 203.372.3722
Fax 203.372.3558
Web .... www.caseyfamilyservices.org
E-mail .... lgoldenberg@caseyfamilyservices.org
　　789 Reservoir Ave, Bridgeport, CT 06606-3956
　　Linda Goldenberg, Division Director

Catholic Charities, Diocese of Norwich, Inc. 860.889.8346
Fax 860.889.2658
Web .... www.ccfsn.org
　　331 Main Street, Norwich, CT 06360
　　COA accredited organization.

Ceil S. Gersten 860.769.7393
Fax 860.769.7394
　　33 Jerome Ave, Ste 204, Bloomfield, CT 06002
　　Ceil S Gersten, Attorney

Community Residences, Inc. 860.621.7600
Fax 860.621.2228
E-mail .... pam@criinc.org
　　732 West St, Ste 12, Southington, CT 06489
　　Pamela Paisey, Director

Connecticut Assoc Of Foster And Adoptive Parents, Inc 860.258.3400
Fax 860.258.3410
Web .... www.cafap.com
E-mail .... cafap@snet.net
　　2189 Silas Deane Hwy Ste 2, Rocky Hill, CT 06067-2324
　　Gene Fiorito, Executive Director

Covenant To Care For Children 860.243.1806
Fax 860.243.0100
　　120 Mountain Ave Ste 212, Bloomfield, CT 06002
　　Carol Halbert, Executive Director

Dare Family Svcs, Inc. 860.291.8688
Fax 860.291.8689
E-mail .... jsmith@darefamily.org
　　1184 Burnside Ave Ste E, East Hartford, CT 06108-1598
　　Jeremy Smith, Director

Jewish Family Service of New Haven, Inc. 203.389.5599
Fax 203.389.5904
Web .... www.jfsnh.org
　　1440 Whalley Avenue, New Haven, CT 06515
　　COA accredited organization.

North American Family Institute 860.645.7300
Fax 860.529.1802
Web .... www.nafi.com
E-mail .... loriwilkerson@nafi.com
　　415 Silas Deane Hwy Ste 402, Wethersfield, CT 06109-2119
　　Laura Wilkerson, Program Director

ADVOCACY RESOURCES

Connecticut Superior Court 203.965.5315
　　J.D. & G.A. 1 Courthouse, 123 Hoyt St, Stamford, CT 06905
　　Honorable Marie Sommer, Judge

Law Ofc of Nancy Owens McMahon 860.283.4802
E-mail .... attynomcmahon@sbcglobal.net
　　PO Box 494, Thomaston, CT 06787
　　Nancy McMahon

Lucia Lanzaro Goodwin 203.323.8329
E-mail .... goodwinl@optonline.net
　　60 Long Ridge Rd Ste 200, Stamford, CT 06902
　　Lucia Goodwin

Madison Youth Svcs Child Violence Intervention Project 203.245.5645
Fax 203.245.5648
Web .... www.madisonct.org/mys
E-mail .... melillod@madisonct.org
　　10 School St, Madison, CT 06443-3033
　　David Melillo, Director

BEHAVIORAL HEALTH TREATMENT

Abc Counseling Svc 860.886.7067
　　62 Broadway, Norwich, CT 06360-5702
　　Bujji Surapaneni, MD, Psychiatrist

Action Psychiatry 203.329.2005
E-mail .... drfreire@drfreire.com
　　148 Webbs Hill Rd, Stamford, CT 06903-4420
　　Joseph Freire, MD, Psychiatrist

Advanced Solutions Therapy Ctr. LLC 203.755.0707
Fax 203.755.9275
E-mail .... nanmonocchi@sbcglobal.net
　　1138 W Main St, Waterbury, CT 06708-2730
　　Nan Monocchi, Director

Alloy Medical Practice 860.231.9373
Fax 860.647.6825
　　660 Prospect Ave Ste 8, Hartford, CT 06105-4245
　　Stephen Alloy, Psychiatrist

Ansonia Board Of Education 203.736.5070
Fax 203.736.1044
Web .... www.ansonia.org
　　115 Howard Ave, Ansonia, CT 06401-2220
　　Lynn Bennett-Wallick, Principal

Arcuni Medical Practice 203.938.9033
　　4 Bartram Dr, Redding, CT 06896-1508
　　Orestes Arcuni, Md, Psychiatrist

Associated Psychological Svc 860.529.7006
　　1800 Silas Deane Hwy Ste 166, Rocky Hill, CT 06067-1317
　　Jack Esterson, Psychiatrist

Atlantic Health Svc 203.799.6100
　　378 Boston Post Rd, Orange, CT 06477
　　Jeffry Klugman, Psychiatrist

Attention Deficit Disorders 203.291.4043
　　60 Casmir Dr, Fairfield, CT 06825-1226
　　Renata Weissberg, Psychiatrist

Austen Medical Practice 203.397.2181
Fax 203.389.9896
　　30 Barberry Ln, Woodbridge, CT 06525-1326
　　Burton Austen, Psychiatrist

Ayre Medical Practice 860.233.1141
　　682 Prospect Ave Rear 12, Hartford, CT 06105-4244
　　Mary Ayre, Psychiatrist

Bailey Middle School 203.937.4380
Fax 203.937.4385
Web .... www.whschools.org
　　106 Morgan Ln, West Haven, CT 06506
　　Anthony Cordone, Director

Beech Medical Practice 203.974.7550
　　34 Park St, New Haven, CT 06519-1109
　　Robert Beech, MD, Psychiatrist

Bendor Medical Practice 860.442.8033
Web .... www.danielbendormd.com
　　567 Vauxhall Street Ext Ste 326, Waterford, CT 06385-4358
　　Daniel Bendor, Psychiatrist

Berv Medical Practice 203.972.1288
　　PO Box 5, New Canaan, CT 06840-0005
　　Kenneth Berv, MD, Psychiatrist

Bialos Medical Practice 203.245.9439
　　PO Box 6, Madison, CT 06443-0006
　　Saundra Bialos, MD, Psychiatrist

Birmingham Group Health Services, Inc. 203.736.2601
Fax 203.736.2641
Web .... www.bghealth.org
　　435 East Main Street, Ansonia, CT 06401
　　CARF accredited programs available.

Blatt Medical Practice 860.233.7866
Fax 313.882.8641
E-mail .... k.blatt@comcast.net
　　836 Farmington Ave Ste 112, West Hartford, CT 06119-1544
　　Kenneth Blatt, MD, Psychiatrist

Brafman Medical Practice 203.966.7719
　　95 Bennington Pl, New Canaan, CT 06840-3402
　　Carole Brafman, MD, Psychiatrist

Bridgeport Board Of Educations 203.576.8070
Web .... www.bridgeportedu.net
E-mail .... sstarkie@bridgeportedu.net
　　1 Lincoln Blvd, Bridgeport, CT 06606-5502
　　Susan Starkie, Director

Bridgeport Hospital 203.384.3000
Web .... www.bridgeporthospital.org
E-mail .... pmivy@bpthosp.org
　　267 Grant Street, Bridgeport, CT 06610
　　Dr. Michael Ivy, Accreditation Manager
　　Joint Commission accredited organization.

Bridges... A Community Support System, Inc. 203.878.6365
Fax 203.877.3088
Web .... www.bridgesmilford.org
　　949 Bridgeport Avenue, Milford, CT 06460
　　CARF accredited programs available.

Bristol Medical Practice 203.744.4092
　　152 Deer Hill Ave Ste 110, Danbury, CT 06810-7766
　　Josephine Bristol, Md, Psychiatrist

Brown Medical Practice 203.226.6670
Fax 203.221.0554
Web .... www.brownmed.com
　　23 White Birch Rd, Weston, CT 06883-3013
　　Harry Brown, MD, Psychiatrist

Capitol Region Education Council 860.748.8001
Web .... www.crec.org
E-mail .... jgiaccone@crec.org
　　10 Salerno Dr, Enfield, CT 06082-5350
　　Julie Giaccone, Director

Caraccio Medical Practice 203.622.7428
　　23 Mianus View Ter, Cos Cob, CT 06807-2219
　　Babette Caraccio, Psychiatrist

Connecticut

Cheshire Public Schools 203.272.3249
Fax 203.250.7614
Web www.cheshire.k12.ct.us
100 Park Pl, Cheshire, CT 06410-2145
Jeffrey Solan, Principal

Child Guidance Clinic For Central Connecticut,
Inc 203.235.5767
Fax 203.238.2010
Web .... www.cgccentralct.org
E-mail .... eelmeridencgc@sbcglobal.net
384 Pratt St, Meriden, CT 06450
Tom Czarkosky, Executive Director

Child Guidance Ctr Of Southern CT-Lower Fairfield Child Abuse
Task Force 203.324.6127
Fax 203.348.9378
Web .... www.childguidancect.org
103 W Broad St, Stamford, CT 06902
Sherry Perlstein, Executive Director

Ciancimino Medical Practice 203.372.5695
4697 Main St Ste 201, Bridgeport, CT 06606-1803
David Ciancimino, Psychiatrist

Clinical Associates Of Ct 203.458.0661
24 Water St, Guilford, CT 06437-2801
Richard Rubin, Md, Psychiatrist

Coffey Medical Practice 203.389.5696
1 Bradley Rd Ste 503, Woodbridge, CT 06525-2292
Margaret Coffey, Psychiatrist

Collaborative Counseling Svc 860.659.9177
155 Sycamore St Ste B, Glastonbury, CT 06033-4548
Steve Zimbel, Psychiatrist

Community Child Guidance Clinic 860.643.2101
Fax 860.645.1470
Web .... www.ccgcinc.org
E-mail .... clinic@ccgcinc.org
317 S Main St, Manchester, CT 06040-7004
Clifford Johnson, Executive Director

Community Health Resources, Inc 860.731.5522
Web .... www.chrhealth.org
E-mail .... hsovronsky@chrhealth.org
995 Day Hill Road, Windsor, CT 06095
Mr. Howard Sovronsky, Accreditation Manager
Joint Commission accredited organization.

Community Mental Health Affiliates (CMHA) Child Guidance
Clinic 860.223.2778
Fax 860.223.3297
Web .... www.cmhacc.org
E-mail .... mchaplin@cmhacc.org
26 Russell St, New Britain, CT 06052-1313
Margaret Chaplin, Medical Director

Community Mental Health Affiliates, Inc 860.826.1358
Web .... www.cmhacc.org
E-mail .... mmormile@cmhacc.org
270 John Downey Drive, New Britain, CT 06051
Ms. Marie Mehler, Accreditation Manager
Joint Commission accredited organization.

Community Prevention and Addiction Services,
Inc. 860.456.3215
Fax 860.450.7078
Web .... www.cpas-inc.org
1491 West Main Street, Willimantic, CT 06226
CARF accredited programs available.

Community Renewal Team 860.560.5784
Web .... www.crtct.org
E-mail .... nicholsont@crtct.org
555 Windsor Street, Hartford, CT 06120
Ms. Theresa Nicholson, Accreditation Manager
Joint Commission accredited organization.

Community Solutions, Inc. 860.683.7100
Fax 860.683.7199
Web .... www.csi-online.org
Four Griffin Road North, Windsor, CT 06095
CARF accredited programs available.

Connecticut Childrens Place 860.292.4000
Fax 860.292.4030
36 Gardner St, East Windsor, CT 06088
Diane Haggis, Principal

Connecticut Junior Republic 860.567.9423
Fax 860.567.9792
Web .... www.ctjuniorrepublic.org
E-mail .... info@ctjuniorrepublic.org
550 Goshen Rd, Litchfield, CT 06759-2405
John Boyd, Executive Director

Connecticut Mental Health Center 203.974.7300
E-mail .... pamela.dalton@po.state.ct.us
34 Park Street, New Haven, CT 06519
Ms. Pamela Dalton, Accreditation Manager
Joint Commission accredited organization.

Connecticut Renaissance, Inc. 203.336.5225
Fax 203.336.2851
Web .... www.ctrenaissance.com
350 Fairfield Avenue, Suite 701, Bridgeport,
CT 06604
CARF accredited programs available.

Cook Medical Practice 203.348.9091
373 Strawberry Hill Ave, Stamford, CT 06902-2512
Colin Cook, Md, Psychiatrist

Cornell Scott-Hill Health Corporation 203.503.3000
Web .... www.hillhealthcenter.com
E-mail .... mtaylor@hillhealthcenter.com
400 Columbus Avenue, New Haven, CT 06519
Mr. Michael Taylor, Accreditation Manager
Joint Commission accredited organization.

Cowan Medical Practice 203.454.1520
Fax 203.454.5810
27 Walker Ln, Weston, CT 06883-1939
Kay Cowan, MD, Psychiatrist

Ctr For Psycho Therapy 203.453.3456
105 Church St, Guilford, CT 06437
Steward Fisher, Psychiatrist

Da Costa Medical Practice 860.232.9209
836 Farmington Ave, West Hartford, CT 06119
Maria Da Costa, Psychiatrist

De Figueiredo Medical Practice 203.272.9628
E-mail .... johndefig@sbcglobal.net
1973 Highland Ave, Cheshire, CT 06410-1219
John De Figueiredo, Psychiatrist

Devereux Glenholme School 860.868.7377
Fax 860.868.0269
Web .... www.theglenholmeschool.org
81 Sabbaday Lane, Washington, CT 06793
COA accredited organization.

Dressler Medical Practice 203.263.5099
51 Sherman Hill Rd, Woodbury, CT 06798
David Dressler, MD, Psychiatrist

Duboczy Medical Practice 860.249.6885
100 Retreat Ave Ste 901, Hartford, CT 06106-2553
John Duboczy, MD, Psychiatrist

Eap Inc 203.234.8085
Web .... www.eaphelp.com
127 Washington Ave Ste 9D, North Haven,
CT 06473-1738
Nancy Sharp, Director

East Shore Assoc 203.245.3929
17 Woodland Rd, Madison, CT 06443-2342
John Corwin, Psychiatrist

Epstein Medical Practice 203.348.8579
91 Strawberry Hill Ave, Stamford, CT 06902
Simon Epstein, MD, Psychiatrist

Fairfield College Preparatory School 203.254.4200
Fax 203.254.4024
Web .... www.fairfieldprep.org
E-mail .... rdonahue@fairfieldprep.org
1073 N Benson Rd, Fairfield, CT 06824-5157
Robert Donahue, Director Of Development

Family Intervention Ctr 203.753.2153
Fax 203.756.6032
Web .... www.familyintervention.org
E-mail .... jfutschik.fic@sbcglobal.net
22 Chase River Rd, Waterbury, CT 06704-1034
Joseph E. Futschik, Lcsw, President

Family Services of Greater Waterbury, Inc. 203.756.8317
Fax 203.756.8310
Web .... www.familyservicesgw.org
34 Murray Street, Waterbury, CT 06710
COA accredited organization.

Fons Medical Practice 860.231.1233
Fax 860.231.1234
45 S Main St Ste 211, West Hartford, CT 06107-2402
Anthony Fons, Md, Psychiatrist

Foothills Couseling Assoc 203.426.4070
115 Mount Pleasant Rd, Newtown, CT 06470
Martin Olanoff, MD, Psychiatrist

Foster Medical Practice 203.629.5532
109 Dingletown Rd, Greenwich, CT 06830-3517
Patricia Foster, MD, Psychiatrist

Genesis Ctr 860.646.3888
Fax 860.645.4132
Web .... www.chrhearth.org
587 Middle Tpke E, Manchester, CT 06040-3731
John Santopietro, Clinical Services Director

Greater Bridgeport Community Mental Health
Ctr 203.551.7400
Fax 203.551.7446
Web .... www.dmhas.state.ct.us
1635 Central Ave, Bridgeport, CT 06610
Alan Barry, Associate Director

Grove School 203.245.2778
Fax 203.245.6098
Web .... www.groveschool.org
E-mail .... peter@groveschool.org
175 Copse Rd, Madison, CT 06443-2323
Peter Chorney, Executive Director

Hartford Community Mental Health Center,
Inc. 860.727.8703
Web hbh1.org
E-mail .... jvazquez@hbh1.org
One Main Street, Hartford, CT 06106
Ms. Josie Robles, Accreditation Manager
Joint Commission accredited organization.

Hartford Hospital 860.545.2100
Web .... www.harthosp.org
E-mail .... gnelson@harthosp.org
80 Seymour Street, Hartford, CT 06102-5037
Ms. Gail Nelson, Accreditation Manager
Joint Commission accredited organization.

High Meadows 203.281.8305
Fax 203.281.8391
E-mail .... gary.zera@po.state.ct.us
825 Hartford Tpke, Hamden, CT 06517-1624
Gary Zera, Superintendent

Hill Health Ctr 203.503.3000
Fax 203.503.3183
Web .... www.hillhealthcenter.com
E-mail .... kmichels@hillhealthcenter.com
428 Columbus Ave, New Haven, CT 06519
Karin Michels, Md, Medical Director

Hospital of Saint Raphael 203.789.3000
Web .... www.srhs.org
E-mail .... ahorne@srhs.org
1450 Chapel Street, New Haven, CT 06511
Ms. Anna Horne, Accreditation Manager
Joint Commission accredited organization.

InterCommunity, Inc **860.569.5900**
Web .... www.intercommunityct.org
E-mail .... mgaines@icmhg.org
281 Main Street, East Hartford, CT 06118
Mr. Marshall Gaines, Accreditation Manager
Joint Commission accredited organization.

Joshua Ctr **860.779.2101**
Fax 860.779.3807
E-mail .... amorelli@natchaug.org
934 N St, danielson, CT 06239
Anthony Morrelli, Director

Joshua Ctr **860.848.3098**
Fax 860.848.1152
Web .... www.natchaug.org
E-mail .... pderosa@natchaug.org
20 Maple Ave, Uncasville, CT 06382
Peter Derosa, Director

Klingberg Family Centers, Inc. **860.224.9113**
Web .... www.klingberg.com
E-mail .... steveg@klingberg.com
370 Linwood Street, New Britain, CT 06052
Dr. Steven Girelli, Accreditation Manager
Joint Commission accredited organization.

Lawrence & Memorial Hospital **860.442.0711**
Web .... www.lmhospital.org
E-mail .... sstrammiello@lmhosp.org
365 Montauk Avenue, New London, CT 06320
Ms. Sherry Strammiello, Accreditation Manager
Joint Commission accredited organization.

Liberation Programs, Inc. **203.851.2077**
Fax 203.323.1047
Web .... www.liberationprograms.org
Four Elmcrest Terrace, Norwalk, CT 06850
CARF accredited programs available.

Manchester Memorial Hospital **860.533.3432**
Web .... www.echn.org
E-mail .... lcrosskey@echn.org
71 Haynes Street, Manchester, CT 06040
Ms. Leona Crosskey, Accreditation Manager
Joint Commission accredited organization.

Mid-Fairfield Child Guidance Ctr, Inc **203.299.1315**
Fax 203.299.0015
E-mail .... sgreenbaum@mfcgc.org
100 East Ave, Norwalk, CT 06851-5010
Stuart Greenbaum, Executive Director

Middlesex Hospital **860.358.6000**
Web .... www.midhosp.org
E-mail .... jeffrey_lemkin@midhosp.org
28 Crescent Street, Middletown, CT 06457
Mr. Jeffrey Lemkin, Accreditation Manager
Joint Commission accredited organization.

Midwestern CT Council on Alcoholism, Inc. **203.792.4515**
Fax 203.748.2604
Web .... www.mccaonline.com
38 Old Ridgebury Road, Danbury, CT 06810
CARF accredited programs available.

Mount St. John **860.343.1300**
Fax 860.526.3846
Web .... www.mtstjohn.org
135 Kirtland St, Deep River, CT 06417-1816
Doug Decerdo, Executive Director
COA accredited organization.

Natchaug Hospital, Inc. **860.456.1311**
Web .... www.natchaug.org
E-mail .... scrawfo@natchaug.org
189 Storrs Road, Mansfield Center, CT 06250
Mr. Scott Crawford, Accreditation Manager
Joint Commission accredited organization.

New Hope Manor, Inc **860.645.4902**
Fax 860.645.4999
E-mail .... cheryl@newhopemanor.net
60 Hilliard St, Manchester, CT 06042-5921
Cheryl Sasano, President

Northwest Ctr For Family Svcs And Mental Health **860.435.2529**
Fax 860.435.8084
315 Main St, Lakeville, CT 06039-0153
Ray Garman, CEO

Perception Programs, Inc. **860.450.7122**
Web .... www.perceptionprograms.org
E-mail .... linda.mastrianni@perceptionprograms.org
54 North Street, Willimantic, CT 06226
Ms. Linda Mastrianni, Accreditation Manager
Joint Commission accredited organization.

Psycho Therapy Ofcs **860.523.9420**
Fax 860.667.3369
674 Prospect Ave, Hartford, CT 06105
Kim Cohen, Psychiatrist

Rushford Center, Inc. **203.235.1792**
Web .... rushford.org
E-mail .... odutka@rushford.org
883 Paddock Avenue, Meriden, CT 06450
Ms. Olga Dutka, Accreditation Manager
Joint Commission accredited organization.

Silver Hill Hospital **203.801.2297**
Web .... www.silverhillhospital.org
E-mail .... lbenton@silverhillhospital.org
208 Valley Road, New Canaan, CT 06840
Ms. Lisa Benton, Accreditation Manager
Joint Commission accredited organization.

Southwest Community Health Center, Inc. **203.332.3506**
Web .... www.swchc.org
E-mail .... skhalil@swchc.org
968 Fairfield Avenue, Bridgeport, CT 06605
Ms. Susan Khalil, Accreditation Manager
Joint Commission accredited organization.

St. Vincent's Medical Center **203.576.5473**
Web .... www.stvincents.org
E-mail .... keaton@stvincents.org
2800 Main Street, Bridgeport, CT 06606
Ms. Kerry Eaton, Accreditation Manager
Joint Commission accredited organization.

Stonington Behavioral Health, Inc. **860.535.1010**
Web .... www.stoningtoninstitute.com
E-mail .... william.aniskovich@uhsinc.com
75 Swantown Hill Road, North Stonington, CT 06359
Mr. William Aniskovich, Accreditation Manager
Joint Commission accredited organization.

Stonington Institute **860.535.1010**
Fax 860.535.9076
Web .... www.stoningtoninstitute.com
75 Swantown Hill Rd, North Stonington, CT 06359-1022
Dr. Jerome Smith, Clinical Director

The Charlotte Hungerford Hospital **860.496.6666**
Web .... www.charlottehungerford.org
E-mail .... jcapobianco@hungerford.org
540 Litchfield Street, Torrington, CT 06790
Mr. John Capobianco, Accreditation Manager
Joint Commission accredited organization.

The Children's Center of Hamden, Inc. **203.248.2116**
Web .... www.childrenscenterhamden.org
E-mail .... slockery@childrenscenterhamden.org
1400 Whitney Avenue, Hamden, CT 06517
Ms. Sarah Lockery, Accreditation Manager
Joint Commission accredited organization.

The Children's Home of Cromwell, CT Inc. **860.635.6010**
Fax 860.635.3425
Web .... www.childhome.org
60 Hicksville Road, Cromwell, CT 06416
COA accredited organization.

The Connection, Inc. **860.343.5500**
Fax 860.343.5517
Web .... www.theconnectioninc.org
955 South Main Street, Middletown, CT 06457
COA accredited organization.

The Danbury Hospital **203.739.7000**
Web .... www.danhosp.org
E-mail .... dawn.myles@danhosp.org
24 Hospital Avenue, Danbury, CT 06810
Ms. Dawn Myles, Accreditation Manager
Joint Commission accredited organization.

The Grace S. Webb School **860.545.7238**
Fax 860.545.7037
Web .... www.instituteofliving.org
E-mail .... klevingardner@harthosp.org
200 Retreat Ave, Hartford, CT 06106
Kikke Levin Gerdner, Director

The Waterbury Hospital **203.573.6000**
Web .... www.waterburyhospital.org
E-mail .... dkiraly@wtbyhosp.org
64 Robbins Street, Waterbury, CT 06721
Ms. Diana Kiraly, Accreditation Manager
Joint Commission accredited organization.

The Wellspring Foundation, Inc. **860.266.8000**
Web .... www.wellspring.org
E-mail .... janet.sorrell@wellspring.org
21 Arch Bridge Road, Bethlehem, CT 06751
Ms. Janet Samela-Sorrell, Accreditation Manager
Joint Commission accredited organization.

The Wheeler Clinic **860.793.3500**
Web .... www.wheelerclinic.org
E-mail .... scohen@wheelerclinic.org
91 Northwest Drive, Plainville, CT 06062
Ms. Sandra Cohen, Accreditation Manager
Joint Commission accredited organization.

United Community & Family Svcs **860.892.7042**
Fax 860.892.2320
Web .... www.ucfs.org
E-mail .... cmolina@ucfs.org
47 Town St Ste 6, Norwich, CT 06360-2330
Chuck Seman, Executive Director

United Services, Inc. **860.774.2020**
Web .... www.unitedservicesct.org
E-mail .... dvsllong@usmhs.org
1007 North Main Street, Dayville, CT 06241
Ms. Sandra Long, Accreditation Manager
Joint Commission accredited organization.

Wellpath Behavioral Health for Children & Families **203.574.9000**
Fax 203.574.9006
Web .... www.wellpathct.org
70 Pine Street, Waterbury, CT 06710
COA accredited organization.

Wellspring **203.266.8000**
Fax 203.266.8030
Web .... www.wellspring.org
E-mail .... nancyt@wellspring.org
21 Arch Bridge Rd, Bethlehem, CT 06751-1612
Nancy Thurston, Intake Coordinator

Yale - New Haven Hospital **203.688.4242**
Web .... www.ynhh.com
E-mail .... victoria.dahlvickers@ynhh.org
20 York Street, New Haven, CT 06510-3203
Mrs. Victoria Vickers, Accreditation Manager
Joint Commission accredited organization.

Yale New Haven Psychiatric Hospital **203.688.9216**
Fax 203.688.9709
Web .... www.ynhh.org
E-mail .... thomas.mcglashan@ynhh.org
184 Liberty St, New Haven, CT 06519
Thomas H. Mcglashan, MD, Executive Director

CHILDREN'S HOSPITAL

Bridgeport Hospital **203.384.3000**
267 Grant St, Bridgeport, CT 06610
William Jennings, President

Danbury Hospital 203.739.7000
24 Hospital Ave, Danbury, CT 06810
Dr. John Mercy, Chief Executive Officer

Day Kimball Hospital 860.928.6541
320 Pomfret St, Putnam, CT 06260
Amy Franklin, Administrative Assistant

Greenwich Hospital 203.863.3000
5 Perryridge Rd, Greenwich, CT 06830
Frank Corvino, Chief Executive Officer

Hospitl of St Raphael 203.789.3000
1450 Chapel St, New Haven, CT 06511

Johnson Memorial Hospital 860.684.4251
201 Chestnut Hill Rd, Stafford Springs, CT 06076
David Morgan, Interim CEO

Lawrence and Memorial Hospital 860.442.0711
E-mail ....bcumming@lmhosp.org
365 Montauk Ave, New London, CT 06320
Bruce Cumming, Chief Executive Officer

Manchester Memorial Hospital 860.646.1222
71 Haynes St, Manchester, CT 06040
Peter Karl, President/CEO

Middlesex Hospital 860.358.6000
28 Crescent St, Middletown, CT 06457
Vincent Capece, Chief Executive Officer

New Milford Hospital 860.355.2611
E-mail ....weymouth.d@wcthealthnetwork.org
21 Elm St, New Milford, CT 06776
Deborah Weymouth, Director

Rockville General Hospital 860.872.0501
31 Union St, Vernon-Rockville, CT 06066
Peter Karl, Chief Executive Officer

St Marys Hospital 203.709.6000
56 Franklin St, Waterbury, CT 06706
Chad Wable, Chief Executive Officer

Stamford Hospital 203.276.1000
30 Shelburne Rd, Stamford, CT 06902
Brian Grissler, Chief Executive Officer

The Charlotte Hungerford Hospital 860.496.6666
E-mail ....dmcintyre@hungerford.org
540 Litchfield St, Torrington, CT 06790
Daniel McIntyre, Director

Waterbury Hospital 203.573.6000
64 Robbins St, Waterbury, CT 06721
Sue Manzolino, Head Of The Nurses

William W Backus Hospital 860.889.8331
326 Washington St, Norwich, CT 06360

Windham Community Memorial Hospital 860.456.9116
112 Mansfield Ave, Willimantic, CT 06226

Yale New Haven Hospital 203.688.4242
20 York St, New Haven, CT 06510
Robert Hutchison, Marketing Director

COUNSELING SERVICES

Branford Counseling Ctr 203.481.4248
Fax 203.483.7727
E-mail ....pandriole@branford-ct.gov
342 Harbor St, Branford, CT 06405
Patricia Andriole, Director

Catholic Charities 203.750.9711
Fax 203.750.9651
Web ....www.ccfc-ct.org
E-mail ....mtintrup@ccfc-ct.org
1 Park St Ste 3, Norwalk, CT 06851
Melissa Glaser, Director

Family And Children's Agency 203.855.8765
Fax 203.838.3325
Web ....www.familyandchildrensagency.org
E-mail ....rcashel@fcagency.org
9 Mott Ave Ste 410, Norwalk, CT 06850-3337
Rob Cashel, President

Family Ctrs, Inc. 203.324.3167
Fax 203.358.2327
Web ....www.familycenters.org
E-mail ....barnold@familycenters.org
60 Palmers Hill Rd, Stamford, CT 06902-2113
Bob Arnold, President/CEO

Worth 203.596.9724
Fax 203.759.0566
Web ....www.cmhacc.org
E-mail ....sderosa@cmhacc.org
965 S Main St, Waterbury, CT 06706-1434
Suzanne Derosa, Program Coordinator

CRISIS & SHELTER CARE

Clifford W. Beers Clinic 203.772.1270
Fax 203.772.0051
E-mail ....info@cliffordbeers.org
93 Edwards St, New Haven, CT 06511-3986
Pieter Joost Vanwattum, Medical Director

Domestic Violence Crisis Ctr 203.588.9100
Fax 203.588.9101
777 Sommer st, Stamford, CT 06901
Rachelle Kuchera Mehra, Executive Director

Domestic Violence Crisis Ctr 203.853.0418
Fax 203.852.6729
Web ....www.ddccct.org
5 Eversley Ave Ste 303, Norwalk, CT 06851
Rachelle Kucera Mehra, Executive Director

Domestic Violence Svcs 203.789.8104
Fax 203.562.9450
Web ....www.dvsgnh.org
E-mail ....skoorejian@bghealth.org
291 Whitney Ave, Ste 401, New Haven, CT 06511
Sandra Koorejian, Director

Eagle Hill School 203.622.9240
Fax 203.622.0914
E-mail ....m.castro@eaglehill.org
45 Glenville Rd, Greenwich, CT 06831
Marjorie Castro, Headmaster

Hartford Interval House, Inc.-Domestic
Violence 860.246.9149
Fax 860.247.2042
E-mail ....cecile.enrico@intervalhousect.org
PO Box 340207, Hartford, CT 06134-0207
Cicil Enrico, Executive Director

Kids In Crisis 203.622.6556
Fax 203.622.8332
Web ....www.kidsincrisis.org
E-mail ....dqualey@kidsincrisis.org
1 Salem St, Cos Cob, CT 06807-2618
Denise Qualey, Program Director

Meriden-Wallingford Chrysalis-Domestic
Violence 203.630.1638
Fax 203.237.1097
5 Colony St, Ste 302, Meriden, CT 06451-3272
Jack Brooks, Director

Network Against Domestic Abuse 860.763.7430
Fax 860.763.7436
E-mail ....aosborne@nadact.org
139 Hazard Ave, Ste 3-9, Enfield, CT 06082
Kathy Barron, Director

Prudence Crandall Ctr-Women 860.225.5187
Fax 860.826.4994
Web ....www.prudencecrandall.org
594 Burritt St, New Britain, CT 06053
Barbara Damon, Executive Director

United Svcs Domestic Violence Program 860.774.7243
Fax 860.779.1694
139 Hazard Ave, Enfield, CT 06082
Ed Koistinen, Director

Women And Families Ctr 860.344.1474
Fax 860.346.5705
E-mail ....kgonzales@womenfamily.org
100 Riverview Ctr Ste 274, Middletown, CT 06457
Kristen Granatek, Director

Women's Emergency Shelter, Inc. Sexual Assault Crisis Svc
Safe Haven Crisis Hotline 203.753.3613
Fax 203.574.3306
Web ....www.safehavengw.org
E-mail ....mmalagutti@safehavenofgw.org
29 Central Ave, Waterbury, CT 06721
Melissa Malagutti, Program Director

Womens Ctr Of Southeastern Connecticut 860.447.0366
Fax 860.440.3327
E-mail ....czeiner@womenscenterofsect.org
16 Jay St, New London, CT 06320
Cathy Zeiner, Director

Womens Support Svc-Domestic Violence 860.364.1080
Fax 860.364.5767
Web ....www.wssdv.org
E-mail ....info@wssdv.org
158 Gay Street, Sharon, CT 06069
Lori Rivenburgh, Director

Youth Continuum 203.562.3396
Fax 203.867.5888
Web ....www.youthcontinuum.org
E-mail ....cschomo@youthcontinuum.org
24 River St, New Haven, CT 06513
Carol Schomo, Chief Executive Officer

YWCA-Greenwich 203.869.6501
Fax 203.628.8187
Web ....www.ywcagreenwich.org
E-mail ....s.adam@ywcagreenwich.org
259 E Putnam Ave, Greenwich, CT 06830-4873
Suzanne Adam, Director Of Domestic Abuse

EDUCATION

Cedarhurst School 203.764.9314
Fax 203.764.9321
E-mail ....betsy.donovan@yale.edu
871 Prospect St, Hamden, CT 06517-4026
Betsy Donovan, Director

Connecticut Job Corps Ctr 203.397.3775
Fax 203.907.4374
Web ....www.jobcorps.dol.gov
E-mail ....oa.newhaven@jobcorps.gov
455 Wintergreen Ave, New Haven, CT 06515-1012
Barbara Sandstrom, Center Director

Devereux Connecticut Glenholme School 860.868.7377
Fax 860.868.7413
Web ....www.theglenholmeschool.org
E-mail ....admissions@theglenholmeschool.org
81 Sabbaday Ln, Washington, CT 06793-1318
Maryann Campbell, Executive Director

Gengras Ctr 860.232.5616
Fax 860.231.6795
E-mail ....blindauer@sjc.edu
1678 Asylum Ave, West Hartford, CT 06117
Bernard Lindauer, Edd, Bs, Ms, Director

Hyde School 860.963.9096
Fax 860.963.0164
Web ....www.hyde.edu
150 Route 169, Woodstock, CT 06281-3318
Jason Mornick, Director Of Admissions

Kidsafe Connecticut 860.872.1918
Fax 860.872.8066
E-mail ....aatwater@kidsafect.com
19 Elm St, Vernon Rockville, CT 06066-3207
Angela Atwater, Executive Director

University Of Connecticut Institute Of Violence
Reduction **860.570.9260**
Fax 860.570.9139
Web ....www.uconn.edu
E-mail ....eleanor.lyon@uconn.edu
1798 Asylum Ave, West Hartford, CT 06117-2673
Eleanor Lyon, PhD, Director

Woodhouse Academy **203.877.9121**
Fax 203.877.4453
Web ....www.woodhouseacademy.com
E-mail ....woodhouseacademy@sbcglobal.net
4 Oxford Rd # F4, Milford, CT 06460
Bob Lepper, Director

Zigler Center **203.432.9935**
Fax 203.432.7147
Web ....www.ziglercenter.yale.edu
E-mail ....sandra.bishop@yale.edu
310 Prospect St, New Haven, CT 06511
Matia Finn-stevenson, Associate Director

FOSTER CARE AGENCIES

Catholic Charities Archdiocese of **860.728.2575**
839-841 Asylum Ave, Hartford, CT 06105
Lois Nesci, Chief Executive Officer

Catholic Charities Diocese of Norwich **860.889.8346**
Fax 860.889.2658
E-mail ....susansedensky@ccfsn.org
331 Main St, Norwich, CT 06360
Susan Sedensky, Director Of Adoption Services

CO Dept of Children & Families CPS **860.832.5200**
Fax 860.832.5318
1 Grove St 4th Fl, New Britain, CT 06053
Janet White, Area Director

CO Dept of Children & Families CPS **860.638.2100**
Fax 860.346.2585
2081 S Main St, Middletown, CT 06457
Dorieth Cooper, Manager

Connecticut Adoption & Family Services **860.444.0553**
E-mail ....director@ccadoption.org
2 Union Plz, Ste 300, New London, CT 06320
Sandra Coullard, Director

Downey Side **860.289.0708**
Fax 860.289.0710
E-mail ....admin@downeyside.org
34 Connecticut Blvd, Ste 7, East Hartford, CT 06108
Father Paul Engel, Executive Director

Faith Weavers Adoption Support Systems **203.634.4098**
E-mail ....MeredithJeffers@att.net
67 Dexter Ave, Meriden, CT 06450
Meredith Jeffers, Director

Institute of Professional Practice Inc **203.389.6356**
Fax 203.392.2113
E-mail ....mglaser@ippi.org
1764 Litchfield Tpke, Woodbridge, CT 06525

Jewish Family Svcs of Greenwich **203.622.1881**
Fax 203.622.1885
E-mail ....sbaranowski@jfsgreenwich.org
1 Holly Hill Ln, Greenwich, CT 06830
Steve Branowski, Director

Klingberg Family Centers Inc (KFC) **860.224.9113**
E-mail ....lindas@klingberg.org
370 Linwood St, New Britain, CT 06052
Stephen Girelli, Chief Executive Officer

Lutheran Social Services of New England **860.257.9899**
Fax 860.257.0340
E-mail ....adoption@lssne.org
2139 Silas Deane Hwy, Ste 201, Rocky Hill, CT 06067
Lynn Gabbard, Director Of Adoption Services

Stars of David Int Inc (Jewish Fmly Svc) **203.366.5438**
Fax 203.366.1580
2370 Park Ave, Bridgeport, CT 06604
Harbey Paris, Director

Thursday's Child Inc **860.242.5941**
Fax 860.243.9898
227 Tunxis Ave, Bloomfield, CT 06002

Village for Families & Children Inc **760.297.0582**
Fax 860.297.1033
E-mail ....RWassermann@villageforchildren.org
331 Wethersfield Ave, 1680 Albany Ave, Hartford,
CT 06114

Wheeler Clinic Inc **888.793.3500**
E-mail ....mlevine@wheelerclinic.org
91 NW Dr, Plainville, CT 06062
Susan Walkama, President

PEDIATRIC HOME CARE

Bayada Nurses **203.854.5100**
Fax 203.855.1889
Web ....www.bayada.com
200 Connecticut Avenue, Suite 5F, Norwalk,
CT 06854

Interim Healthcare **860.889.3388**
Fax 860.889.2084
12 Case St Ste 215, Norwich, CT 06360
Shierley Langord, Director

Interim Healthcare **860.677.0005**
Fax 860.677.2727
231 Farmington Ave, Farmington, CT 06032
John Kene, Chief Executive Officer

Interim Healthcare **860.434.9003**
Fax 860.434.1042
1081 Halls Rd, Old Lyme, CT 06371
Shirley Lungford, Owner

Interim Healthcare **203.574.3339**
Fax 203.597.1751
E-mail ....jhathaway@Interimhealthcare.com
541 Wolcott St, Waterbury, CT 06705
J Hathaway, Director

Interim Healthcare **203.230.4785**
Fax 203.230.4791
PO Box 280, North Haven, CT 06473
Ben Peterson, President

Interim Healthcare **860.456.3500**
Fax 860.423.4539
15 Wilson, Willimantic, CT 06226
Kathryn Rogers, Director Of Homecare Services

Plainville PDN **860.747.3306**
146 New Britain Ave, Plainville, CT 06062
Jeanne Silverwatch, Director

SOCIAL SERVICES

Boys & Girls Village, Inc. **203.877.0300**
Fax 203.876.0076
Web ....www.bgvillage.org
528 Wheelers Farms Road, Milford, CT 06461
COA accredited organization.

Boys & Girls Village, Inc. **203.877.0300**
Fax 203.876.0076
Web ....www.bgvillage.org
E-mail ....bgvillage.org
528 Wheelers Farms Rd, Milford, CT 06461-1874
John Cocciolone, Chief Executive Officer

BRANCH **203.454.4992**
Fax 203.921.4161
431 Post Road East, Ste 11, Westport, CT 06880

Brownstein JFS **203.267.3177**
Fax 203.267.3392
E-mail ....dhorowitz@jfed.net
444 Main Street N, Southbury, CT 06488
Debby Horowitz, Program Director

Casey Family Services **203.401.6900**
Fax 203.401.6901
Web ....www.caseyfamilyservices.org
127 Church Street, New Haven, CT 06510
COA accredited organization.

Catholic Charities **203.787.2207**
Fax 203.773.3626
Web ....www.ccaoh.org
501 Lombard st, New Haven, CT 06513
James Osborne, Director

Catholic Charities **203.743.4412**
Fax 203.744.3500
E-mail ....emalgieri@ccfc-ct.org
30 Main St Ste 503, Danbury, CT 06810
Elaine Malgieri, Executive Director

Catholic Charities **203.416.1305**
Fax 203.372.4555
Web ....www.diobpt.org
238 Jewett Avenue, Bridgeport, CT 06606
COA accredited organization.

Catholic Charities And Family Svcs **860.889.8346**
Fax 860.889.2658
Web ....www.ccfsn.org
E-mail ....marekkukulak@ccfsn.org
331 Main St, Norwich, CT 06360-5836
Marek Kukulak, Executive Director

Catholic Charities, Inc.-Archdiocese of
Hartford **860.493.1841**
Fax 860.548.9343
Web ....www.ccaoh.org
839-841 Asylum Avenue, Hartford, CT 06105
COA accredited organization.

Chapel Haven, Inc. **203.397.1714**
Fax 203.392.3698
Web ....www.chapelhaven.org
1040 Whalley Ave, New Haven, CT 06515
Michael Storz, President

Community Answers **203.622.7979**
Fax 203.622.7984
Web ....www.communityanswers.org
E-mail ....communityanswers@greenwichlibrary.org
101 W Putnam Ave, Greenwich CT Fairfield 06830,
Greenwich, CT 06830
Chitra Shambogue, Executive Director

Connecticut Junior Republic Association,
Inc. **860.567.9423**
Fax 860.567.3479
Web ....www.ctjuniorrepublic.org
P.O. Box 161, Litchfield, CT 06759
COA accredited organization.

Connecticut Right To Life **203.757.5213**
Fax 203.754.5862
55 Cole St, Waterbury, CT 06706-1215

Coordinating Council For Children In Crisis,
Inc. **203.624.2600**
Fax 203.562.6232
Web ....www.ccccnh.org
E-mail ....cburack@ccccnh.org
131 Dwight St, New Haven, CT 06511
Cheryl Burack, Executive Director

Family & Children's Agency, Inc. **203.855.8765**
Fax 203.838.3325
Web ....www.familyandchildrensagency.org
9 Mott Avenue, 4th Floor, Norwalk, CT 06850
COA accredited organization.

Family Centers Inc. **203.869.4848**
Fax 203.869.7764
Web ....www.familycenters.org
P.O. Box 7550, Greenwich, CT 06836-7550
COA accredited organization.

Foundation School **203.795.6075**
Fax 203.799.4797
Web ....www.foundationschool.org
E-mail ....jbell@foundationschool.org
   719 Derby-Milford Rd, Orange, CT 06477
   Walter J. Bell, Director

Franciscan Life Ctr, Inc. **203.237.8084**
Fax 203.639.1333
Web ....www.flcenter.org
E-mail ....flc@flcenter.org
   271 Finch Ave, Meriden, CT 06451-2715
   Sister Barbara Johnson, Executive Director

FSW, Inc. CT **203.368.4291**
Fax 203.332.7637
Web ....www.fswinc.org
   475 Clinton Avenue, Bridgeport, CT 06605
   COA accredited organization.

High Road Student Learning Ctr **203.284.0441**
Fax 203.265.6335
E-mail ....studentlearn.ctr@snet.net
   29 Village Ln, Wallingford, CT 06492
   Dr. Michael Kaufman, Executive Director

Human Services Counsel **203.849.1111**
Fax 203.849.1151
Web ....www.communityplanning.org
E-mail ....hsc@snet.net
   1 Park St, Norwalk, CT 06851
   Neal Esposito, Executive Director

Jewish Family Service **203.921.4161**
Fax 203.921.4169
   733 Summer St Ste 602, Stamford, CT 06901
   Matt Greenberg, CEO

Jewish Family Service of Stamford, Inc. **203.921.4161**
Fax 203.921.4169
Web ....www.ctjfs.org
   733 Summer Street 6th Floor, Stamford, CT 06901
   COA accredited organization.

Jewish Family Service, Inc. **203.366.5438**
Fax 203.366.1580
Web ....www.jfsct.org
   2370 Park Avenue, Bridgeport, CT 06604-1699
   COA accredited organization.

Jewish Family Services **203.794.1818**
Fax 203.748.5099
E-mail ....jfs@sbcglobal.net
   69 Kenosia Ave, Danbury, CT 06810
   Rosalind Kofstein

NAFI Connecticut, Inc. **860.284.1177**
Fax 860.284.1125
Web ....www.nafi.com
   20 Batterson Park Road, Suite 301, Farmington,
   CT 06032
   COA accredited organization.

New Britain Youth & Family Services **860.826.3366**
Fax 860.826.3367
E-mail ....cmontes@newbritainct.gov
   27 W Main St; # 301, New Britain, CT 06051
   Christopher L. Montes, Administrator

Newtown Youth and Family Services, Inc. **203.426.8103**
Fax 203.270.4338
Web ....www.newtownyouthandfamilyservices.org
   17 Church Hill Road, Newtown, CT 06470
   COA accredited organization.

St. Francis Behavioral Health Group **860.714.2750**
Fax 860.714.8591
   675 Tower Ave Ste 301, Hartford, CT 06112
   Richard Moed, CEO/Executive Director

The Bridge Family Ctr **860.521.8035**
Fax 860.521.8036
Web ....www.bridgefamilycenter.org
E-mail ....info@bridgefamilycenter.org
   1022 Farmington Ave, West Hartford, CT 06107
   Margaret A. Hann, Executive Director

**The Children's Community Programs of
Connecticut** **203.786.6403**
Fax 203.786.6407
Web ....www.childrenscommunityprograms.org
   446A Blake St, New Haven, CT 06515
   Brian Lynch, CEO
   COA accredited organization.

**The Exchange Club Ctr For The Prevention Of Child
Abuse** **203.327.9419**
Fax 203.359.8677
   141 Franklin St, Ste 207, Stamford, CT 06901
   Donna Miller, Executive Director

The Village for Families & Children, Inc. **860.236.4511**
Fax 860.233.6454
Web ....www.villageforchildren.org
   1680 Albany Avenue, Hartford, CT 06105
   COA accredited organization.

United Svcs **860.228.4480**
Fax 860.228.6921
Web ....www.unitedservicesct.org
   233 Route 6, Columbia, CT 06237-1125
   Michael Patota, Division Director

Waterbury Youth Svcs **203.573.0264**
Fax 203.755.4835
E-mail ....kcronin@waterburyyouthservices.org
   95 N Main St Fl 2, Waterbury, CT 06702-1411
   Kelly Cronin, Director

Waterford Country School, Inc. **860.442.9454**
Fax 860.442.2228
Web ....www.waterfordcountryschool.org
   P.O. Box 408, Quaker Hill, CT 06375
   COA accredited organization.

Youth Agency **860.354.0047**
Fax 860.210.2016
Web ....www.youthagency.org
E-mail ....mark@youthagency.org
   50 East St, New Milford, CT 06776-3030
   G. Mark Mankin, Director

Youth Svc Bureau **860.379.0708**
Fax 860.379.1328
   480 Main St, Winsted, CT 06098
   Susan H. Peck, Clinical Director

YWCA Time Out For Parents Nursery **860.525.1163**
Web ....www.ywcahartford.org
E-mail ....slane@ywca.com
   40 Pitkin St, Manchester, CT 06040-4408
   Sara Lane, Case Manager/Supervisor

SPECIAL NEEDS

Access Rehab Centers **203.419.0381**
Fax 203.419.0389
Web ....www.accessrehabcenters.com
   22 Tompkins Street, Waterbury, CT 06708
   CARF accredited programs available.

Assn of Centers Independent Living **860.656.0430**
E-mail ....gwaterhouse@cacil.net
   151 New Park Ave, Hartford, CT 06106

Autism Society of Connecticut **888.453.4975**
E-mail ....ct-connecticut@autismsocietyofamerica.org
   PO Box 1404, Guilford, CT 06437

Brain Injury Association **800.278.8242**
E-mail ....general@biact.org
   200 Day Hill Rd Ste 250, windsor, CT 06095
   Julie Peters, Executive Director

Connecticut Lifespan Respite Coalition **860.513.0172**
Fax 860.563.3961
E-mail ....ctrespite@cox.net
   2138 Silas Deane Highway, Suite 103, Rocky Hill,
   CT 06067
   Joy C Liebeskind, Statewide Coordinator

Connecticut Parent-Teachers Association **203.281.6617**
E-mail ....connecticut.pta@snet.net
   60 Connolly Pkwy Ste 12, Wilbur Cross Commons
   Bldg, Hamden, CT 06514
   Sally Boske, Executive Director

Disabilities Network of Eastern CT **860.823.1898**
   238 W Town St, Norwich, CT 06360
   Cathy Ferry, Executive Director

**Easter Seal Rehabilitation Center of Greater Waterbury,
Inc.** **203.754.5141**
Fax 203.757.1198
Web ....www.easterealswaterburyct.org
   22 Tompkins Street, Waterbury, CT 06708
   CARF accredited programs available.

Easter Seals Connecticut **800.874.7687**
E-mail ....dshugrue@easterealsct.org
   PO Box 100, Hebron, CT 06248

Eastern Rehabilitation Network, LLC **860.667.5480**
Fax 860.667.8416
Web ....www.easternrehab.net
   181 Patricia M. Genova Drive, Newington, CT 06111
   CARF accredited programs available.

Epilepsy Foundation of Connecticut Inc **800.899.3745**
E-mail ....efct@sbcglobal.net
   386 Main St, Middletown, CT 06457

**Gaylord Hospital, Inc. - Rehabilitation
Division** **203.284.2800**
Fax 203.294.8708
Web ....www.gaylord.org
   Gaylord Farm Road, Wallingford, CT 06492
   CARF accredited programs available.

**Hartford-New Haven Community Parent
Res** **860.297.4358**
E-mail ....afcamp@sbcglobal.net
   60 Weston St Ste B, Hartford, CT 06120
   Merva Jackson, Director

Hospital for Special Care **860.223.2761**
Fax 860.827.4849
Web ....www.hfsc.org
   2150 Corbin Avenue, New Britain, CT 06053
   CARF accredited programs available.

LDA-CT **860.560.1711**
E-mail ....ldact@ldact.org
   999 Asylum Ave Ste 504, Hartford, CT 06105
   Fran Ficocelli, Program Coordinator

Learning Clinic **860.774.5619**
Fax 860.774.1037
Web ....www.thelearningclinic.org
   PO Box 324, Brooklyn, CT 06234
   Raymond W Ducharme, Executive Director

Lindamood-Bell Learning Processes **203.656.0771**
Fax 203.656.0735
E-mail ....tom.mariani@lindamoodbell.org
   1574 Post Rd, Darien, CT 06820
   Tom Mariani, Director

Little Hearts Inc **860.635.0006**
Fax 860.635.0006
E-mail ....info@littlehearts.org
   110 Court St Ste 3A PO Box 171, Cromwell,
   CT 06416

MDA/ALS Center at Yale University **203.785.4867**
Fax 203.785.5694
E-mail ....jonathan.goldstein @yale.edu
   PO Box 208018, New Haven, CT 06520
   Jonathan M Goldstein MD, Director

Mental Health Association **860.529.1970**
E-mail ....pwyzik@mhact.org
   20-30 Beaver Rd Ste 108, Wethersfield, CT 06109
   Philip Wyzik, Executive Director

Montowese Health and Rehabilitation Center, Inc. **203.624.3303**
Fax 203.789.4433
Web ....www.montowesehealth.com
163 Quinnipiac Avenue, North Haven, CT 06473
CARF accredited programs available.

NAMI Connecticut **800.215.3021**
241 Main St, 5th Fl, Hartford, CT 06106
Jake Mattias, Executive Assistant

National Multiple Sclerosis Society **860.913.2550**
Fax 860.761.2466
E-mail ....info@ctfightsMS.org
659 Tower Ave 1st Fl, Hartford, CT 06112
Lisa Gerrol, President

PATH Parent to Parent **800.399.7284**
E-mail ....pathp2pct@pathct.org
PO Box 117, Northford, CT 06472
Carmina Cirioli, Co-Director

Raymond Hill School of Klingberg Family **860.225.9113**
Fax 860.826.8221
Web ....www.klingberg.org
370 Linwood St, New Britain, CT 06052
Steven Girelli, Executive Director

Saint Vincents Special Needs Svcs **203.375.6400**
95 Merritt Blvd, Trumbull Corporate Park, Trumbull, CT 06611
Ray Baldwin, Director

Spina Bifida Association **800.574.6274**
E-mail ....sbac@sbac.org
PO Box 2545, Hartford, CT 06146

The Acute Rehabilitation Unit at Norwalk Hospital **203.852.2964**
Fax 203.852.3393
Web ....www.norwalkhospital.org
24 Stevens Street, Norwalk, CT 06856
CARF accredited programs available.

The Arc of Connecticut **860.246.6400**
E-mail ....arcct@aol.com
43 Woodland St Ste 260, Hartford, CT 06105

The Special Kids Support Center **877.743.5516**
282 Washington St, Hartford, CT 06106
Susan Roman, Director

The Webb Schools **860.545.7238**
Fax 860.545.7037
Web ....www.instituteofliving.org/programs
200 rich St ave, Hartford, CT 06106
Dr. Kikke Levin Gerner, Director

UCP of Eastern Connecticut **860.443.3800**
E-mail ....mmorrison@ucpect.org
42 Norwich Rd, Quaker Hill, CT 06375

USA Reading Clinic **888.834.7323**
E-mail ....info@usareadingclinic.com
41 Crossroads Pl ste 273, West Hartford, CT 06117

Vista Vocational & Life Skills Center **860.399.8080**
Fax 860.399.3103
Web ....www.vistavocational.org
1356 Old Clinton Rd, Westbrook, CT 06498
Helen Bosch, Director

WeCAHR **203.792.3540**
211 Main St, Danbury, CT 06810
Shirley Ricart, Director

Youth Continuum, Inc. **203.562.3396**
Fax 203.867.5888
Web ....http://www.youthcontinuum.org/
24 River Street, New Haven, CT 06513
COA accredited organization.

SUBSTANCE ABUSE TREATMENT

ABC Women's Ctr, Inc. **860.344.9292**
Web ....www.abcwomenscenter.org
E-mail ....donnita@abcwomenscenter.org
180 E Main St, Middletown, CT 06457-4401
Donnita Young, Executive Director

Hispanic Health Council **860.527.0856**
Fax 860.724.0437
Web ....www.hispanichealth.com
E-mail ....virginiar@hispanichealth.com
175 Main St, Hartford, CT 06106
Virginia Ruiz, Associate Director

Institute Of Living **860.545.7000**
Fax 860.545.7049
E-mail ....hschwartz@harthosp.org
200 Retreat Ave, Hartford, CT 06106-3310
Harold Schwartz, Md, Medical Director

Regional Network of Programs, Inc./Regional Counseling Services **203.929.1954**
Fax 203.929.1279
Web ....www.regionalnetwork.org
Two Trap Falls Road, Suite 405, Shelton, CT 06484
Allison K., Accounting Supervisor
CARF accredited programs available.

The APT Foundation **203.781.4600**
Fax 203.781.4624
Web ....www.aptfoundation.org
E-mail ....naddenl@aptfoundation.org
One Long Wharf Drive, Suite 321A, New Haven, CT 06511
Lynn Nadden, Administrative Assistance
CARF accredited programs available.

The Children's Ctr Of Hamden **203.248.2116**
Fax 203.248.9339
Web ....www.childrenscenterhamden.org
1400 Whitney Ave, Hamden, CT 06517-2499
Eugene Roddy, Phd, Director Of Education

Connecticut

Delaware

Jack Markell, Governor
Tatnall Building
William Penn Street
Dover, DE 19901
302.739.4101
302.739.2775 (Fax)
lorilee.harrison@state.de.us

Valerie Smythe, Juvenile Justice Specialist
820 N. French Street, 10th Floor
Wilmington, DE 19801
302.577.8811
valerie/smythe@state.de.us

Michael W. Arrington, SAG Chair
Parkowski, Guerke & Swayze P.A.
800 King Street, Suite 203
Wilmington, DE 19801
302.594.3333
302.654.3033 (Fax)
marrington@pgslegal.com

CRISIS NUMBERS

Child Abuse Reporting . . .800.292.9582

STATE SERVICES

SOCIAL SERVICES

DE Youth & Family Svcs Admin 302.633.2650
Fax 302.633.2652
Web . . . . .www.state.de.us/kids
   1825 Faulkland Rd, Wilmington, DE 19805
   Laura Miles, Family Services Director

Delaware Emergency Management Agency 302.659.3362
Fax 302.659.6855
Web . . . . .www.state.de.us
E-mail . . . . .jamie.turner@state.de.us
   165 Brick Store Landing Rd, Smyrna, DE 19977-9628
   James E Turner, Iii, Director

Office of Child Care Licensing Delaware 302.892.5800
Fax 302.633.5112
   1825 Faulkland Road, Wilmington, DE 19805
   Patricia Queen, Administrator

GENERAL HEALTH SERVICES

Children with Spec Health Needs DE 302.744.4551
Fax 302.739.3313
E-mail . . . . .petti.cox@state.de.us
   417 Federal St, Dover, DE 19901
   Petti Cox, Administrative Specialist

Delaware Dept of Health & Social Svcs 302.255.9500
Fax 302.255.4454
E-mail . . . . .arachangelo@state.de.us
   1901 N Dupont Hwy Fl 1, DELAWARE HEALTH AND
   SOCIAL SERVICES CAMPUS, New Castle, DE 19720
   Elaine Archangelo, Director

Div of Developmental Disabilities Svcs 302.744.9600
Fax 302.744.9632
Web .http://dhssdelaware.gov/dhss/ddds
   1056 S Governors Ave, Woodbrook Professional
   Center, Dover, DE 19904
   Roy Lasontaine, Director

DPH Community Health Care Access Section . . .302.744.4700
Fax 302.739.6659
Web . . . . .www.state.de.us
   417 Federal St, Jesse S Cooper Building, Dover,
   DE 19901-3635
   Karyl Rattay, Director

Maternal and Child Health Program DE 302.744.4551
Fax 302.739.6653
E-mail . . . . .alisa.olshefsky@state.de.us
   417 Federal St, Dover, DE 19901
   Alisa Olshefsky, Director

MENTAL HEALTH SERVICES

Div of Voc Rehab DE 302.255.9800
Fax 302.255.9964
E-mail . . . . .rober.tdoyle@state.de.us
   1901 N DuPont Highway, DHSS Campus Biggs Bldg,
   New Castle, DE 19720
   Robert Doyle, Director

Div of Vocational Rehab DE 302.761.8275
Fax 302.761.6611
E-mail . . . . .edwin.tos@state.de.us
   4425 N Market St, PO Box 9969, Wilmington,
   DE 19809
   Edwin Tos, Deputy Director

JUSTICE AGENCY

Attorney General's Ofc 302.577.8500
Fax 302.577.2496
Web . . . . .www.biden.com
   820 N French St, Carvel State Office Building,
   Wilmington, DE 19801
   Joseph R. Biden, Attorney General

Correctional Education Division DE 302.857.5276
Fax 302.739.7215
E-mail . . . . .johnj.ryan@state.de.us
   245 McKee Rd, Dover, DE 19904
   John Ryan, Director

Delaware Dept of Corrections 302.857.5298
Fax 302.739.6740
Web . . . . .www.state.de.us
E-mail . . . . .carl.danberg@state.de.us
   245 Mckee Rd, Dover, DE 19904-2232
   Carl Danberg, Commissioner

Div of Youth Rehabilitative Svcs 302.633.2620
Fax 302.633.2636
Web . . . . .www.state.de.us/kids
E-mail . . . . .cgiddins@state.de.us
   1825 Faulkland Rd, Wilmington, DE 19805-1121
   Carlyse Giddins, Director

COURTS

Administrative Ofc of the Courts 302.255.0090
Fax 302.255.2218
Web . . . . .http://www.courts.state.de.us
   500 N King St Ste 11600, Wilmington, DE 19801
   Pat Griffin, State Court Administrator

POLICE AND SHERIFF

State Police 302.739.5901
   1441 N DuPont Hwy, PO Box 430, Dover,
   DE 19903-0430

EDUCATION SERVICES

Communities In Schools .302.678.4929
Fax 302.678.4737
Web . . . . .www.cisdelaware.org
E-mail . . . . .jpurcell@cisdelaware.org
   101 W Loockernan St Ste 2A, Dover, DE 19904-1383
   Jim Purcell, Director

Delaware Dept of Education 302.735.4000
Fax 302.739.4654
Web www.doe.k12.de.us
E-mail . . . . .akepner@doe.k12.de.us
   401 Federal St Ste 2, Dover, DE 19901
   Lillian Lowery, Secretary

Educ for Homeless Children and Youth DE 302.735.4273
Fax 302.739.4483
E-mail . . . . .drozumalski@doe.k12.de.us
   401 Federal St, Ste 2, Dover, DE 19901
   D Rozumalski, Director

Exceptional Child & Early Child Ed DE 302.735.4210
Fax 302.739.2388
E-mail . . . . .mtoomey@doe.k12.de.us
   401 Federal St Ste 2, Dover, DE 19901
   M Toomey, Director

Margaret S. Sterck Delaware School for the
  Deaf 302.454.2301
Fax 302.454.3493
Web . . . . .www.dsdhawks.org
E-mail . . . . .ridienhousem@christina.k12.de.us
   620 E Chestnut Hill Rd, Newark, DE 19713-1814
   Mindy Ridienhouse, Acting Senior Administrator

LABOR & WORKFORCE EDUCATION

Div of Employment and Training 302.761.8129
Fax 302.761.6617
Web . . . . .www.state.de.us
   4425 N Market St, Wilmington, DE 19802-1307
   Tom Smith, Director

Delaware

COUNTY SERVICES

Kent County

SOCIAL SERVICES

Delaware Health And Social Svcs Div Of Public
Health **302.744.4700**
Fax 302.739.6659
Web ....www.state.de.us
417 Federal St, JESSE S COOPER BUILDING, Dover, DE 19901-3635
Karyl Rattay, Director

Div Of Social Svcs Assistance Ofc **302.739.4437**
Fax 302.739.2124
E-mail ....carol.parnell@state.de.us
1114 S Dupont Hwy Ste 102, Dover, DE 19901
Carol Parnell, Social Services Administrator

Family Svcs **302.739.4800**
Fax 302.739.6236
Web ....www.state.de.us
E-mail ....ione.truesdale@state.de.us
821 Silver Lake Blvd Ste 200, Dover, DE 19904-2458
Ione Truesdale, Regional Administrator

JUSTICE AGENCY

Div Of Youth Rehab Svcs **302.739.5381**
Fax 302.739.6559
821 Silver Lake Blvd Ste 101, Dover, DE 19904-2458
Jehu Banks, Supervisor Juvenile Probation

Ofc Of Child Advocate **302.856.5720**
Fax 302.856.5722
Web ....www.courts.delaware.gov/childadvocate
6 W Market St Ste 1, Georgetown, DE 19947-1484
Leah Dickerson, Family Crisis Therapy For Kent & Suffolk Counties

COURTS

Family Court **302.672.1000**
Fax 302.739.6530
Web ....www.courts.delaware.gov/family
E-mail ....william.nicholas@state.de.us
400 Court St, Dover, DE 19901-3730
Honorable William N. Nicholas, Director

POLICE AND SHERIFF

Dover Police Dept **302.736.7111**
Fax 302.736.7142
Web ....www.doverpolice.org
400 S Queen St, Dover, DE 19904-3594
Keith Hester, Juvenile Division

Smyrna Police Dept **302.653.9217**
Fax 302.653.3491
325 W Glenwood Ave, Smyrna, DE 19977
Wilbert Bordley, Chief

New Castle County

SOCIAL SERVICES

Northeast State Svc Ctr Dept Of Social
Svcs **302.552.3530**
Fax 302.577.3805
Web ....www.dhss.delaware.gov
1624 N Jessup St, Wilmington, DE 19802-4210
Elexis Titlebaum, Operations Administrator

Social Svcs **302.255.9668**
Fax 302.255.4433
E-mail ....arachangelo@state.de.us
1901 N Dupont Hwy Fl 1, LEWIS BLDG, New Castle, DE 19720
Elaine Archangelo, Director

Social Svcs **302.255.9660**
Fax 302.255.4454
E-mail ....elaine.archamzelo@state.de.us
84 Churchman Rd Ste B, New Castle, DE 19720
Elaine Archamzelo, Director

Social Svcs **302.378.5771**
Fax 302.378.5784
122 Silver Lake Rd, Middletown, DE 19709
Lisa Scoon, Social Worker Case Manager

Social Svcs **302.577.3504**
Fax 302.577.2062
Web ....www.state.de.us
E-mail ....william.stoddard@state.de.us
509 W 8th St, Wilmington, DE 19801-1407
William Stoddard, Director

Social Svcs **302.798.4093**
Fax 302.798.4360
3301 Green St, Claymont, DE 19703-2052

Social Svcs **302.453.2800**
Fax 302.453.2854
Web ....www.state.de.us
501 Ogletown Rd, Newark, DE 19711-5403
Marietta Wharton, Administrator

Social Svcs **302.577.3814**
Fax 302.577.5548
500 Rogers Rd, New Castle, DE 19720-1324
Izy Jones, Building Manager

GENERAL HEALTH SERVICES

Hudson Dept Of Pubic Health **302.283.7587**
Fax 302.283.7556
E-mail ....skeegan@dshaweb.org
501 Ogletown Rd, Newark, DE 19711
Susan Keegan, Clinic Manager

Ofc Of Chief Medical Examiner **302.577.3420**
Fax 302.577.3416
200 S Adams St, Wilmington, DE 19801
Richard T. Callery, Md, Chief Medical Examiner

Westside Health Svc **302.655.5822**
Fax 302.655.3541
Web ....www.westsidehealth.org
E-mail ....wanda.bourgois@westsidehealth.org
1802 W 4th St, Wilmington, DE 19805-3420
Wanda Bourgois, Clinic Supervisor

MENTAL HEALTH SERVICES

Div of Substance Abuse & Mental
Health **302.255.9399**
Fax 302.205.4428
Web ....www.state.de.us
1901 N Dupont Hwy Fl 1, HERMAN HOLLOWAY CAMPUS ADMINISTRATION BLDG, New Castle, DE 19720-1160
Kevin Huckshors, Director

JUSTICE AGENCY

Board of Parole **302.577.5233**
Fax 302.577.3501
Web ....www.state.de.us
820 N French St Fl 5, Wilmington, DE 19801
Dewight Holden, Director

CASA **302.255.0461**
Fax 302.255.2613
Web ....www.casa.courts.delaware.gov
E-mail ....christina.harrison@state.de.us
500 N King St, Ste 901, Wilmington, DE 19801
Christina Harrison, Program Coordinator

Community Svcs/ Probation
Wilmington **302.577.6011**
Fax 302.577.1122
E-mail ....elaine.Stomer@state.de.us
119 Lower Beech St, Wilmington, DE 19805
Elaine Stomer, Operations Manager

DE Youth Rehabilitation Svcs **302.633.2665**
Fax 302.633.2652
1825 Faulkland Rd, Wilmington, DE 19805-1121
Nancy Pearsall, Director

Ofc Of The Public Defender **302.577.5200**
Fax 302.577.3995
E-mail ....brendan.oneill@state.de.us
Carvel State Office Bldg 3rd Fl, 820 N French St, Wilmington, DE 19801
J. Brendan O'Neill, Esq, Public Defender

POLICE AND SHERIFF

Newark Police Dept **302.366.7111**
Fax 302.366.7115
220 Elkton Rd, Newark, DE 19711
Paul Teirnan, Chief Of Police

Sheriff's Dept **302.395.8450**
Fax 302.395.8460
E-mail ....tlopz@nccbe.org
800 N French St Fl 5, Wilmington, DE 19801
Trinida Navarro, Sheriff

Wilmington Police Dept **302.654.5151**
Fax 302.571.4446
300 N Walnut St, Wilmington, DE 19801
Michael Zserba, Chief

Sussex County

SOCIAL SERVICES

Family Svcs/CPS **302.856.5450**
Fax 302.856.5062
Web ....www.state.de.us
E-mail ....susan.taylor-walls@state.de.us
546 S Bedford St, Georgetown, DE 19947-1852
Susan Taylor-walls, Regional Administrator

Social Svcs **302.424.7250**
Fax 302.424.2792
E-mail ....wendy.mayle@state.de.us
13 SW Front St Ste 105, Milford, DE 19963
Wendy Mayle, Office Manager

Social Svcs **302.628.2011**
Fax 302.628.2027
E-mail ....dthomas@state.de.us
350 Virginia Ave, Seaford, DE 19973
Diane Thomas, Director

Social Svcs **302.732.9501**
Fax 302.732.5486
34314 Pyle Center Rd, Unit 1, Frankford, DE 19945
Trenee Parker, Supervisor

Social Svcs **302.875.6943**
Fax 302.875.4960
Web ....www.state.de.us
E-mail ....candace.jones@state.de.us
31039 N Poplar St, Laurel, DE 19956-1027
Candace Jones, Director

Social Svcs **302.337.8261**
Fax 302.337.3204
Web ....www.state.de.us
E-mail ....regina.marvel@state.de.us
400 Mill St, Bridgeville, DE 19933-1100
Regina Marvel, Director

Delaware

GENERAL HEALTH SERVICES

Children & Families First 302.856.2388
Fax 302.856.2196
Web .... www.cffde.org
     410 S Bedford St, Georgetown, DE 19947
     Leslie Newman, Director

HIV Clinic 302.933.3420
Fax 302.933.3421
Web .... www.state.de.us
     26351 Patriots Way, Georgetown, DE 19947-2575
     Susan Wilson, Hiv Coordinator

JUSTICE AGENCY

CASA 302.855.7410
Fax 302.856.5090
Web .... www.courts.state.de.us/family
     22 The Cir, Georgetown, DE 19947-1500
     Crystal Baynard, Program Coordinator

DE Youth Rehabilitation Svcs 302.424.8100
Fax 302.422.1535
Web .... www.state.de.us
     750 N Dupont Blvd, Milford, DE 19963-1004
     John Stevenson, Superintendent

COURTS

Family Court 302.855.7400
Fax 302.856.5090
Web .... www.courts.delaware.gov/family
     22 The Cir, Georgetown, DE 19947-1505
     Honorable Kenneth Millman, Judge

POLICE AND SHERIFF

Georgetown Police Dept 302.856.6613
Fax 302.856.7374
Web .... www.georgetowndel.com
     335 N Race St, Georgetown, DE 19947
     William S. Topping, Chief Of Police

Milford Police Dept 302.422.8081
Fax 302.424.2330
Web .... www.cityofmilford.com
     400 NE Front St, Milford, DE 19963
     Keith Hudson, Chief Of Police

Rehoboth Beach Police 302.227.2577
Fax 302.227.6054
Web .... www.rehobothpolice.org
E-mail .... keith.banks@cj.state.de.us
     229 Rehoboth Ave, Rehoboth Beach, DE 19971-2137
     Keith Banks, Chief Of Police

Sheriff's Dept 302.855.7830
Fax 302.855.7832
Web .... www.sussexcountyde.gov
E-mail .... eswanson@sussexcountyde.gov
     22215 Dupont Blvd, PO Box 948, Georgetown,
     DE 19947
     Eric Swanson Jeff Christopher, Sheriff

SPECIAL SERVICES AGENCIES

ADOPTION AGENCIES

Adoptions From The Heart 302.658.8883
Fax 302.658.8873
Web .... www.adoptionsfromtheheart.org
E-mail .... adoptions@adoptionsfromtheheart.org
     18A Trolley Sq, Wilmington, DE 19806
     Jeanne Mcgee, Supervisor

Child & Home Study Assoc 302.475.5433
Web .... www.chsadoptions.org
E-mail .... info@chsadoptions.org
     242 N James St Ste 202, Wilmington, DE 19804
     Karen Burrill, Director

Children and Families First Delaware, Inc. 302.658.5177
Fax 302.658.5170
Web .... www.cffde.org
     2005 Baynard Boulevard, Wilmington, DE 19802
     COA accredited organization.

Children's Choice Of DE 302.678.0404
Fax 302.678.9080
Web .... www.childrenschoice.org
E-mail .... ceverwein@childrenschoice.org
     707 Walker Rd Ofc 1, Dover, DE 19904-2768
     Carolyn Everwein, Executive Director

ADVOCACY RESOURCES

Children's Advocacy Ctr Of Delaware, Inc. 302.854.0323
Fax 302.854.0335
Web .... www.cacofde.org
E-mail .... randall.williams@cacofde.org
     410 S Bedford St, Georgetown, DE 19947
     Randall Williams, Executive Director

Family Court of Delaware 302.255.0300
E-mail .... barbara.crowell@state.de.us
     New Castle County Courthouse, 500 King St Ste
     9400, Wilmington, DE 19808
     Barbara Crowell, Judge

BEHAVIORAL HEALTH TREATMENT

Aquila of Delaware 302.999.1106
Fax 302.999.1753
     1812 Newport Gap Pike, Wilmington, DE 19808
     CARF accredited programs available.

Behavioral Health Assoc Inc 302.421.9330
Fax 302.421.9333
     2509 Foulk Woods Rd, Wilmington, DE 19810-3636
     Alex Dever, MD, Psychiatrist

Brandywine Counseling & Community
Services 302.472.0381
Web .... www.brandywinecounseling.org
E-mail .... elombino@brandywinecounseling.org
     2500 West Fourth Street, Wilmington, DE 19805
     Adm. Elizabeth Lombino, Accreditation Manager
     Joint Commission accredited organization.

Brandywine Ctr For Wellness 302.655.1437
     515 W 18th St, Wilmington, DE 19802-4705
     Sal Muleh, Psychiatrist

Brandywine Program 302.995.2002
Fax 302.995.2121
Web .... www.diakon.org
     240 North James Street, Suite 200, Newport,
     DE 19804
     CARF accredited programs available.

Capiro Medical Practice 302.644.3777
Fax 302.644.3535
     16529 Coastal Hwy, Lewes, DE 19958-3605
     R Jose Capiro, Psychiatrist

Christiana Care -Christiana Hospital 302.733.1274
Web .... www.Christianacare.org
E-mail .... micampbell@christianacare.org
     4755 Ogletown-Stanton Road, Newark, DE 19718
     Ms. Michele Campbell, Accreditation Manager
     Joint Commission accredited organization.

Cohn Medical Practice 302.426.1118
     2300 Pennsylvania Ave Ste 3B, Wilmington,
     DE 19806-1333
     Robert Cohn, MD, Psychiatrist

DE Guidance Svcs 302.455.9333
Fax 302.455.9544
Web .... www.delawareguidance.org
E-mail .... tcannon@delawareguidance.org
     Polly Drummond Office Park, Ste 1208, Newark,
     DE 19711
     Terry Cannon, Site Coordinator

Delaware Guidance For Children And Youth/Out Patient
Clinic 302.645.5338
Fax 302.644.4976
Web .... www.delawareguidance.org
E-mail .... bkelsey@delawareguidance.org
     31168 Learning Ln, Lewes, DE 19958-3685
     Bruce Kelsey, Executive Director

Delaware Guidance Services for Children and Youth,
Inc. 302.652.3948
Web .... www.delawareguidance.org
E-mail .... hsims@delawareguidance.org
     1213 Delaware Avenue, Wilmington, DE 19806
     Mr. Howard Sims, Accreditation Manager
     Joint Commission accredited organization.

Delaware Guidance Svcs 302.652.3948
Fax 302.652.8297
Web .... www.delawareguidance.org
     1213 Delaware Ave, Wilmington, DE 19806
     Bruce Kelsey, Executive Director

Delaware Guidance Svcs For Children And Youth,
Inc. 302.678.3020
Fax 302.678.2458
Web .... www.delawareguidance.org
E-mail .... bkelsey@delawareguidance.org
     103 Mont Blanc Blvd, Dover, DE 19904-7615
     Bruce Kelsey, Executive Director

Division of Child Mental Health Services - State of
Delaware 302.633.2600
Fax 302.633.5118
Web .... www.state.de.us/kids
     1825 Faulkland Road, Wilmington, DE 19805
     Bob Arnold, Executive Director
     CARF accredited programs available.

Dover Behavioral Health System 302.747.1198
Web .... DoverBehavioral.com
E-mail .... william.weaver@uhsinc.com
     725 Horsepond Road, Dover, DE 19901
     Mr. William Weaver, Accreditation Manager
     Joint Commission accredited organization.

Fellowship Health Resources, Inc. 302.422.1530
Fax 302.422.6542
Web .... www.fellowshiphr.org
     12649 Dupont Hwy, Ellendale, DE 19941
     Pamela Daisey, Regional Director

Jewish Family Services of Delaware, Inc. 302.478.9411
Fax 302.479.9883
Web .... www.jfsdelaware.org
     99 Passmore Road, Wilmington, DE 19803
     COA accredited organization.

Mental Health Assoc In Delaware 302.654.6833
Fax 302.654.6838
Web .... www.mhainde.org
E-mail .... information@mhainde.org
     100 W 10th St, Ste 600, Wilmington, DE 19801-6604
     James Lafferty, Executive Director

Psychotherapeutic Services, Inc. 336.538.6990
Fax 336.538.6991
Web .... www.psychotherapeuticservices.com
     942 Walker Road, Suite B, Dover, DE 19904
     CARF accredited programs available.

Rockford Center 302.996.5480
Web .... www.rockfordcenter.com
E-mail .... mark.lawson@uhsinc.com
     100 Rockford Drive, Newark, DE 19713
     Mr. Mark Lawson, Accreditation Manager
     Joint Commission accredited organization.

Delaware

SODAT - Delaware, Inc........................302.656.4044
E-mail ....kblanchard@sodatdelaware.com
  625 N. Orange Street, Wilmington, DE 19801
  Ms. Kristen Blanchard, Accreditation Manager
  Joint Commission accredited organization.

CHILDREN'S HOSPITAL

Alfred I DuPont Hospital for Children 302.651.4000
  1600 Rockland Rd, Wilmington, DE 19803

Bayhealth Medical Center 302.674.4700
  640 S State St, Dover, DE 19901
  Terry Murphy, Chief Executive Officer

Christiana Care Hospital 302.733.1000
  4755 Ogletown Stanton Rd, Newark, DE 19718
  Robert Laskowski, Chief Executive Officer

Nanticoke Memorial Hospital 302.629.6611
  801 Middleford Rd, Seaford, DE 19973

CRISIS & SHELTER CARE

Child, Inc................................302.762.8989
Fax......................................302.762.8983
Web...................................www.childinc.com
E-mail ....tbrandau@childinc.com
  507 Philadelphia Pike, Wilmington, DE 19809-2177
  Tim Brandau, Executive Director

Delaware Volunteer Legal Svcs 302.478.8680
Fax......................................302.477.2227
E-mail ....jhoward@dvls.org
  4601 Concord Pike, Wilmington, DE 19803
  Janine Howard, Director

Domestic Violence 302.856.5843
Fax......................................302.856.5539
Web...................................www.childinc.com
E-mail ....Cfrench@Childinc.Com
  22 The Cir, Georgetown, DE 19947-1500
  Cindy French, Program Coordinator

EDUCATION

Centreville School 302.571.0230
Fax......................................302.571.0270
Web..............................www.centrevilleschool.org
E-mail ....centreville@centrevilleschool.org
  6201 Kennett Pike, Wilmington, DE 19807
  Denise Orenstin, Headmaster

Delaware Education Research & Development
Ctr 302.831.4433
Fax......................................302.831.4438
Web..................................www.rdc.udel.edu
E-mail ....ajnoble@udel.edu
  125 Academy St, University Of Delaware Rm 104,
  Newark, DE 19716-4399
  Audrey J. Noble, Title Ii Eisenhower Program

Educational Svc, Inc.........................302.655.6283
Fax......................................302.655.6284
Web.........................www.educationalservice.org
E-mail ....edserv@aol.com
  1701 Augustine Cut Off Ste 11, Wilmington,
  DE 19803-4494
  Tina Maida Masington, Director

FOSTER CARE AGENCIES

Adoptive Families With Information 302.571.8784
E-mail ....delawareafis@comcast.net
  112 School Rd, Wilmington, DE 19803

Bethany Christian Services Inc 302.369.3470
E-mail ....rcarwell@bethany.org
  Ste 201G Commonwealth Bldg, 260 Chapman Rd,
  Newark, DE 19702
  Raina Carwell, Social Worker

Childrens Choice of Delaware Inc 302.731.9512
Fax......................................303.731.9569
E-mail ....vjohnosn@childrenschoice.org
  25 S Old Baltimore Pike, Lafayette Bldg Ste 101,
  Newark, DE 19702
  Vivian Johnson, Program Coordinator

Delaware Dept of Serv for Children Youth 302.633.2655
E-mail ....adoption.dscyf@state.de.us
  1825 Faulkland Rd, Wilmington, DE 19805

Upper Bay Adoption & Counseling
Services 302.764.1890
Fax......................................302.764.1893
  700-A River Rd, Wilmington, DE 19809
  Leah Strelvick, Office Manager

PEDIATRIC HOME CARE

Bayada Nurses 302.836.1000
Fax......................................302.836.7320
Web...................................www.bayada.com
  1400 Peoples Plaza, Suite 111, Newark, DE 19702
  Carla Cauger, Director

Bayada Nurses 302.424.8200
Fax......................................302.424.0654
Web...................................www.bayada.com
  600 N.E. Front Street Extension, Milford, DE 19963
  Alice Knott, Director

Bayada Nurses 302.322.2300
Fax......................................302.322.6300
Web...................................www.bayada.com
  32 Reads Way, New Castle, DE 19720
  Patricia Watson, Director

Bayada Nurses 302.655.1333
Fax......................................302.656.2779
Web...................................www.bayada.com
E-mail ....rbuck@bayada.com
  750 Shipyard Drive, Suite 101, Wilmington,
  DE 19801
  Rick Buck, Communications Officer

Interim Healthcare 302.322.2743
Fax......................................302.328.5086
  New Castle Corporate Commons, 2 Read's Way Ste
  123, New Castle, DE 19720

SOCIAL SERVICES

Catholic Charities, Inc......................302.655.9624
Fax......................................302.655.9721
Web...................................www.ccwilm.org
  2601 West Fourth Street, Wilmington, DE 19805
  COA accredited organization.

Children's Advocacy Ctrs Of Delaware 302.651.4566
Fax......................................302.651.4569
Web..................................www.cacofde.org
E-mail ....randall.williams@cacofde.org
  1600 Rockland Rd, I Dupont Childrens Delaware,
  Wilmington, DE 19803-3607
  Randy Williams, Executive Director

Delaware Help Line 302.577.3000
Fax......................................302.577.5740
  900 N King St Ste 330, Wilmington, DE 19801
  Anna Maloney, Director

Relationship Center BRANCH 302.478.9411
Fax......................................302.479.9883
  288 East Main St, Newark, DE 19711
  Mark Casgrande, Clinical Director

SPECIAL NEEDS

ADDA 800.939.1019
E-mail ....info@add.org
  PO Box 7557, Wilmington, DE 19803

Alfred DuPont Hospital for Children 302.651.4000
E-mail ....infodupont@nemours.org
  1600 Rockland Rd, Wilmington, DE 19803
  Kevin Churchwell, Administrator

Autism Delaware 302.224.6020
E-mail ....delautism@delautism.org
  924 Old Harmony Rd Ste 201, Newark, DE 19713
  Theda Ellis, Director

Brain Injury Association of Delaware 800.411.0505
E-mail ....director@biade.org
  840 Walker Rd Ste A, Dover, DE 19903
  Esther Curtis, Executive Director

Delaware Congress of PTA 302.838.8770
E-mail ....de_office@pta.org
  925 Bear-Corbitt Rd Ste 101, Bear, DE 19701

Delawareans with Special Needs 302.697.1976
E-mail ....bethappenzeller@aol.com
  35 W Fairfield Dr, Dover, DE 19901

Easter Seals 800.677.3800
E-mail ....lscarpitti@esdel.org
  61 Corporate Cir, New Castle, DE 19720

Epilepsy Foundation of Delaware 800.422.3653
E-mail ....efd@efde.org
  240 N James St Ste 208, Wilmington, DE 19804
  Barbara Blair, Director

Interagency Council Birth to Three 302.255.9135
E-mail ....woodson@email.chop.edu
  1901 N DuPont Hwy, New Castle, DE 19720

Leukemia & Lymphoma Society 800.220.1617
E-mail ....michelle.sobczyk@lls.org
  100 W 10th St Ste 209, Wilmington, DE 19801
  Michelle Sobczyk, Director

National Multiple Sclerosis Society 302.655.5610
Fax......................................302.655.0993
E-mail ....kate.cowperthwait@msdelaware.org
  2 Mill Rd Ste 106, Wilmington, DE 19806
  Kate Cowperthwait, President

Nemours/Alfred I. duPont Hospital for
Children 302.651.5610
Fax......................................302.651.5628
Web...................................www.nemours.org
  1600 Rockland Road, Wilmington, DE 19803
  CARF accredited programs available.

Parent Info Center of Delaware 302.999.7394
Fax......................................302.999.7637
E-mail ....maghaz@picofdel.org
  5570 Kirkwood Hwy, Wilmington, DE 19808
  Marianne Aghazadian, Executive Director

Partners in Policymaking 302.739.7192
  410 Federal St Ste 2, Margaret O'Neill Bldg 2nd Fl,
  Dover, DE 19901

Pilot School 302.478.1740
Fax......................................302.478.1746
Web...................................www.pilotschool.org
  100 Garden of Eden Rd, Wilmington, DE 19803
  Kathleen B Craven, Director

The Arc of Delaware 302.996.9400
  2 south aujustine st, Wilmington, DE 19804
  Pam Scott, Interem Executive Director

United Cerebral Palsy of Delaware 302.764.2400
E-mail ....wmccool@ucpde.org
  700A River Rd, Wilmington, DE 19809
  Lindsay Pawlikowsky, Administrative Assistant

United Derebral Palsy of Delaware 302.764.2400
E-mail ....ccarpenter@ucpde.org
  3249 Midstate Rd, Felton, DE 19943
  Caima Carpenter, Manager

VSA Arts of Delaware 302.857.6699
E-mail ....jgunther@dsc.edu
  1200 N Dupont Hwy, Dover, DE 19901
  Jennifer Gunthar, Chief Executive Officer

Delaware

District of Columbia

www.dc.gov

Vincent Gray, Mayor
1350 Pennsylvania Ave NW
Washington, DC 20004
202.727.1681
202.727.2357 (Fax)
mayor@dc.gov

Molly Knopf, Juvenile Justice Specialist
1350 Pennsylvania Ave NW, Ste 407
Washington, DC 20004
202.727.6239
202.727.6332 (Fax)
molly.knopf@dc.gov

Chelsey Rodgers, Esq., SAG Chair
6101 16th St NW
Washington, DC 20011
chelsey.rodgers@gmail.com

CRISIS NUMBERS

Child Abuse Reporting 202.671.SAFE

STATE SERVICES

SOCIAL SERVICES

Child Care Licensing Office Dist of Colu 202.442.5888
Fax 202.442.9430
899 North Capitol St NE, Washington, DC 20002
Dr. Atkinson, Director

Child Support Enforcement 202.442.9900
Fax 202.724.3710
Web . . . . .http://cssd.dc.gov
E-mail . . . . .cssd.oag@dc.gov
441 4th St NW, Room 550-N, Washington, DC 20001
Benidia Rice, Director

District of Columbia - Dept of Human Svcs 202.671.4200
Fax 202.671.4326
Web . . . . .www.dhs.dc.gov
E-mail . . . . .david.berns@dc.gov
64 New York Ave NE, Washington, DC 20002
David Berns, Director

District of Columbia Emergency Management Agency 202.727.6161
Fax 202.673.2290
E-mail . . . . .millincent.west@dc.gov
2720 Martin Luther King Ave SE, Washington, DC 20032
Millicent West, Director

Family Svcs Admin 202.541.3915
Fax 202.541.3964
Web . . . . .www.dc.gov
E-mail . . . . .fred.swan@dc.gov
2146 24th Pl NE, Washington, DC 20018-1402
Fred Swan, Administrator

Ofc of Child Care Svcs .202.727.0284
Fax 202.727.9709
Web . . . . .dc.gov
E-mail . . . . .barbara.kamara@dc.gov
4001 14th St SW Ste 700, Washington, DC 20032-3213
Barbara Ferguson Kamara, Director

Protection and Advocacy Program 202.547.0198
Fax 202.547.2662
220 I St NE Ste 130, Washington, DC 20002
Sandy Brunsby, Director

GENERAL HEALTH SERVICES

Child w Spec Health Care Needs Bureau DC 202.442.5925
Fax 202.442.4947
E-mail . . . . .Karen.Watts@dc.gov
899 N capital St NE, Washington, DC 20002
Karen Watts, Director

Dept of Health DC 202.724.7481
Fax 202.442.4947
E-mail . . . . .holiday.johnson@dc.gov
825 N Capitol St NE, 4th Flr Ste 4400, Washington, DC 20002
Holiday Johnson, Director

District of Columbia Dept of Health 202.442.5955
Fax 202.442.4795
Web . . . . .www.doh.dc.gov
E-mail . . . . .doh@dc.gov
899 N Capitol St NE 5th Fl, Washington, DC 20002
Mohammad N Akhter, Medical Director

MENTAL HEALTH SERVICES

Dept of Health- Addiction Prevention & Recovery Admin (APRA) 202.727.8857
Fax 202.727.0092
Web . . . . .www.doh.gov
1300 1st St NE, 3rd Floor, Washington, DC 20002
Dr. Kimberly Leonard, Sr. Deputy Director Of Medical Affairs

Dept of Mental Health .202.673.7440
Fax 202.673.3433
64 New York Ave NE Fl 4, Washington, DC 20002
Stephen Baron, Director

Development On Disabilities Ser 202.730.1700
Fax 202.730.1843
Web . . . . .www.dds.dc.gov
1125 15th St NW Fl 4, Washington, DC 20005-2726
Laura Nuss, Director

Rehabilitation Svcs Admin 202.442.8663
Fax 202.442.8742
1125 15th St NW, Washington, DC 20005
Roy Albert, Deputy Director

JUSTICE AGENCY

Crime Victim Compensation Program 202.879.4216
Fax 202.879.4230
E-mail . . . . .reedlb@dcsc.gov
515 5th St NW, Suite 109, Washington, DC 20001
Laura Banks Reed, Director

District of Columbia - Dept of Corrections 202.673.7316
Fax 202.332.1470
Web . . . . .doc.dc.gov/main.shtm
E-mail . . . . .thomas.hoyer@dc.gov
1923 Vermont Ave NW, Room 207N, Washington, DC 20001
Thomas Hoyer, Director

Ofc of the Attorney General 202.727.3400
Fax 202.347.8922
Web . . . . .www.oag.dc.gov
1350 Pennsylvania Ave NW, Washington, DC 20004-3003
Irvin Nathan, Attorney General

COURTS

DC Superior Court Family Div Juvenile Branch . .202.879.1319
Fax 202.879.0099
Web . . . . .www.dcsc.gov
E-mail . . . . .dianneking@aol.com
500 Indiana Ave NW, Room 4310, Washington, DC 20001
Dianne King, Director Family Court

DC Time Dollar Youth Court 202.508.1612
Fax 202.508.1608
Web . . . . .www.tdyc.org
E-mail . . . . .info@tdyc.org
510 E St NW, Bldg. B, Washington, DC 20001
Carolyn Dallas, Director

POLICE AND SHERIFF

DC Police Dept Youth & Preventive Svcs Div 202.576.6768
Fax 202.576.6561
1700 Rhode Island Ave NE, Washington, DC 20018
Charnette Robinson, Commander

EDUCATION SERVICES

Advocates for Justice and Education Inc 202.678.8060
Fax 202.678.8062
E-mail . . . . .information@age-dc.org
1012 Pennsylvania Ave SE, Washington, DC 20003
Kim Jones, Director

Ofc of Early Childhood Development 202.727.1839
Fax 202.741.5304
E-mail . . . . .dakarai.thompson@dc.gov
810 1St NE 4 Florr, Washington, DC 20002
Dakarai Thompson, Interim Director

Office of Spec Educ for DC Public School 202.442.4800
E-mail . . . . .matthew.bachand@dc.gov
1200 First St NE, 9th Fl, Washington, DC 20002
Matthew Bachand, Director

Office of the State Super of Educ DC 202.727.6436
Fax 202.727.2019
810 St NE, Washington, DC 20002
Hosanna Mahaley, Director

Public School 202.442.5885
Fax 202.442.5026
E-mail . . . . .richard.nyankori@k12.dc.us
1200 1st St NE, Washington, DC 20002
Richard Nyankori, Chief Of Special Education Reform

LABOR & WORKFORCE EDUCATION

DC Dept of Employment Svcs 202.673.6976
Fax..202.673.6976

Web ....www.dc.gov
E-mail ....gregory.irish@dc.gov
64 New York Ave NE, Room 3000, Washington,
DC 20002
Summer Spencer, Director

SPECIAL SERVICES AGENCIES

ADOPTION AGENCIES

Adoption Ctr of Washington 202.452.8278
Fax..703.549.7778
Web ....www.adoptioncenter.com
E-mail ....linda@adoptioncenter.com
1726 M St NW Ste 600, Washington,
DC 20036-4528
Linda Brownlee, Director

Childrens Home Society Family Services 202.726.7193
Fax..301.587.3869
Web ....www.chsfs.org
E-mail ....inquire@chsfs.org
1003 K S NW Ste 207, Washington, DC 20001
Jennifer Hannett, Administrator

Datz Foundation 202.686.3400
Fax..703.242.8804
Web ....www.datzfoundation.org
E-mail ....datz@patriot.net
4545 42nd St NW Ste 302, Washington, DC 20016
Vivian Datoff, Director

International Families, Inc................202.667.5779
Fax..202.667.5922
Web ....http://ifiadopt.org
E-mail ....info@isiadopt.org
5 Thomas Cir NW Ste 9, Washington,
DC 20005-4167
Mrudula Rao, Executive Director

KidsPeace Foster Care & Family Svcs 202.544.9015
Fax..202.544.9018
Web ....www.fostercare.com
E-mail ....ray.culp@kidspeace.org
401 C St NE 2nd Fl, Washington, DC 20002-4307
Ray Culp, National Director Foster Care & Family Services

Law Ofc 202.783.2794
Fax..202.898.1995
800 7th St NW Ste 201, Washington,
DC 20001-3851
Marian Chou, Attorney

Nation's Capital Child & Family
Development 202.388.7560
Fax..202.388.7561
Web ....www.nccfdchildren.org
2229 M Street, NE, Suite 1, Washington,
DC 20002-2060
COA accredited organization.

ADVOCACY RESOURCES

ABA Center on Children and the Law 202.662.1782
E-mail ....kendallj@staff.abanet.org
740 NW 15th St, Washington, DC 20005
Jessica Kendall, Director

America Bar Assn 202.662.1731
E-mail ....rennej@staff.abanet.org
740 NW 15th St, Washington, DC 20005
Jennifer Renne, Director

Childrens Defense Fund Natl Headquarter 800.233.1200
E-mail ....cdfinfo@childrensdefense.org
25 E Street NW, Washington, DC 20001
Narian Wright Edelman, Director

National Alliance End Homeless 202.942.8257
E-mail ....awade@naeh.org
1518 K St NW Ste 410, Washington, DC 20005
Andre Wade, Policy & Program Anaylst

Office of the Attorney General for DC CP 202.727.7159
E-mail ....jennifer.hancock@dc.gov
400 6th St SW 5th Fl, Washington, DC 20024
Jennifer Hancock

Public Defender Svc of DC 202.824.2809
E-mail ....aacree@pdsdc.org
633 Indiana Ave NW, Washington, DC 20004
Angela Acree

The Childrens Law Ctr 202.467.4900
E-mail ....gsmith@childrenslawcenter.org
616 H St NW Ste 300, Washington, DC 20001
Genette Smith, Director

Thomas C Devlin PC 202.408.8814
E-mail ....tdevlin5@msn.com
800 7th St NW Ste 201, Washington, DC 20001
Thomas Devlin

BEHAVIORAL HEALTH TREATMENT

Advani Medical Practice 202.466.6729
Fax..202.466.6798
2440 Virginia Ave NW, Washington, DC 20037
Mohan Advani, Md, Psychiatrist

Aledort Medical Practice 202.965.8938
Fax..202.965.1688
E-mail ....saledort@gmail.com
1070 Thomas Jefferson St NW Ste 201, Washington,
DC 20007-3809
Stewart Aledort, Psychiatrist

Allen Medical Practice 202.362.5100
5225 Connecticut Ave NW, Washington,
DC 20015-1813
Laurence Allen, Psychiatrist

Anchor Mental Health 202.635.5978
Fax..202.635.5915
Web ....www.chatholiccharitiesdc.org
1001 Lawrence St NE, Washington, DC 20017-3513
Karen Ostlie, CSA Director

Band Medical Practice 202.362.0377
4545 42nd St NW Ste 310, Washington,
DC 20016-4623
Raymond Band, Psychiatrist

Barney Neighborhood House 202.939.9000
Fax..202.939.9049
Web ....www.barneyneighborhoodhouses.org
5656A 3rd St NE, Washington, DC 20011-2532
Ron Mclean, Executive Director

Barris Medical Practice 202.463.1215
908 New Hampshire Ave NW Ste 603, Washington,
DC 20037-2348
Madeleine Barris, MD, Psychiatrist

Benoit Medical Practice 202.607.3032
E-mail ....bartolom@aol.com
1015 33rd St NW, Washington, DC 20007
Marilyn Benoit, Md, Psychiatrist

Bergman Medical Practice 202.296.2399
1616 18th St NW, Washington, DC 20009
Eric Bergman, Md, Psychiatrist

Bristol Medical Practice 202.466.8690
Fax..202.466.8691
1325 18th St NW Ste 101, Washington,
DC 20036-6511
R Curtis Bristol, MD, Psychiatrist

Brown Medical Practice 202.234.0474
3000 Connecticut Ave NW Ste 238, Washington,
DC 20008-2531
Jessica Brown, MD, Psychiatrist

Burbach Medical Practice 202.483.2800
Fax..301.951.1830
2029 Q St NW, Washington, DC 20009
Rodney Burbach, Psychiatrist

Catholic Charities Archdiocese of Washington
DC 202.772.4300
Fax..202.772.4420
Web ....www.catholiccharitiesdc.org
E-mail ....edward.orzechowski@catholiccharitiesdc.org
924 G St NW, Washington, DC 20001-4532
Edward Orzechowski, CEO
COA accredited organization.

Chalick Medical Practice 202.659.4543
2450 Virginia Ave NW Ste E101, Washington,
DC 20037-2650
Morris Chalick, Psychiatrist

Chused Medical Practice 202.726.9273
E-mail ....jchused@chused.com
1805 Randolph St NW, Washington, DC 20011-5339
Judith Chused, Md, Psychiatrist

Costell Medical Practice 202.232.2121
Fax..312.988.9215
2501 NW Calvert St, Ste 101, Washington,
DC 20008-2604
Ronald Costell, Psychiatrist

Cox Medical Practice 202.223.8530
Fax..202.223.8531
E-mail ....toddscoxmd@aol.com
1133 Connecticut Ave NW, Washington, DC 20036
Todd Cox, Psychiatrist

Ctr for Student Supportive Svcs.............202.628.8848
Fax..202.628.8849
Web ....www.studentsupportcenter.org
E-mail ....cgardner@studentsupportcenter.org
1003 K St NW, Washington, DC 20001
Carolyn Gardner, Director

Dluhy Medical Practice 202.363.9400
Fax..202.362.4509
3709 Ingomar St NW, Washington, DC 20015-1819
John Dluhy, MD, Psychiatrist

Emma Medical Practice 202.337.0740
1015 33rd St NW, Washington, DC 20007
Robert Emma, Do, Psychiatrist

Episcopal Ctr for Children 202.363.1333
Fax..202.537.5044
E-mail ....akorz@eccofdc.org
5901 Utah Ave NW, Washington, DC 20015-1616
Alan C. Korz, Executive Director

Extended Health 202.636.4585
Fax..202.636.4587
1017 Brentwood Rd NE, Washington, DC 20018
Darrell Brown, Director

Frieman Medical Practice 202.452.0600
3 Washington Cir NW, Washington, DC 20037
Robert Frieman, MD, Psychiatrist

Girls and Boys Town of Washington DC 202.832.7343
Fax..202.832.9807
Web ....www.boystown.org
E-mail ....jeff.peterson@boystown.org
4801 Sargent Rd NE, Washington, DC 20017-2841
Jeff Peterson, Site Director/program Operations Manager

integrative psychiatry 202.537.6837
Fax 202.747.6530
E-mail ....jgordon@cmbm.org
    2934 Macomb St NW, Washington, DC 20008-3315
James Gordon, MD, Psychiatrist

Potomac Job Corps Ctr 202.574.5000
Fax 202.373.3181
Web ....www.jobcorps.org
E-mail ....belk.steven@jobcrops.org
    1 DC Village Ln SW, Washington, DC 20032-5229
Steven Belk, Center Director

Psychiatric Institute of Washington 202.885.5600
Fax 202.885.5614
Web ....www.psychinstitute.com
E-mail ....hoffman@piw-dc.com
    4228 Wisconsin Ave NW, Washington,
    DC 20016-2138
Howard Hoffman, Md, Medical Director

The Episcopal Center for Children 202.363.1333
Web ....www.eccofdc.com
E-mail ....davekjean@gmail.com
    5901 Utah Avenue, NW, Washington,
    DC 20015-1616
Mr. Dave Jean, Accreditation Manager
Joint Commission accredited organization.

CHILDREN'S HOSPITAL

Georgetown University Hospital 202.444.2000
    3800 Reservoir Rd NW, Washington, DC 20007
Dr. Richard Goldberg, President

Howard University Hospital 202.865.6100
    2041 Georgia Ave NW, Washington, DC 20006
Larry Warren, Director

COUNSELING SERVICES

Child & Adolescent Protection Ctr 202.476.4100
Fax 202.476.6997
Web ....www.dcchildrens.com
E-mail ....tgrisham@cnmc.org
    111 Michigan Ave NW, Childrens Hospital National
    Medical Center, Washington, DC 20010-2916
Tawanna Grisham, Office Manager

Sasha Bruce Youthwork, Inc. 202.675.9340
Fax 202.675.9358
Web ....www.sashabruce.org
E-mail ....dshore@sashabruce.org
    741 8th St SE, Washington, DC 20003-2802
Deborah Shore, Executive Director

CRISIS & SHELTER CARE

**Asian Pacific Islander-Domestic Violence Resources
Project** 202.464.4477
Fax 202.986.9332
Web ....www.dvrp.org
E-mail ....info@dvrp.org
    PO Box 14268, Washington, DC 20044-4268
Jessica Li, Program Director

**Covenant House Washington Administrative Ofcs &
Community Svc Ctr** 202.610.9600
Fax 202.610.9640
Web ....www.convenanthousedc.org
    2001 Mississippi Ave SE, Washington,
    DC 20020-6116
Daniel Brannen, Executive Director

DC Rape Crisis Ctr 202.333.7273
Fax 202.387.3812
Web ....www.dcrcc.org
E-mail ....dcrcc@dcrcc.org
    PO Box 34125, Washington, DC 20043-4125
Denise Snyder, Director

House of Ruth 202.667.7001
Fax 202.667.7047
Web ....www.houseofruth.org
E-mail ....cnichols@houseofruth.org
    5 Thomas Cir NW Fl 4, Washington, DC 20005-4153
Christel Nichols, President

**House of Ruth-Domestic Violence Support
Ctr** 202.667.7001
Fax 202.347.0506
Web ....www.houseofruth.org
E-mail ....houseofruth@houseofruth.org
    5 Thomas Cir NW Fl 4, Washington, DC 20005-4153
Fatu Sangowa, Director

Legal Aide Society 202.628.1161
Fax 202.727.2132
Web ....www.legalaiddc.org
    1331 8th St Nw, Ste 350, Washington,
    DC 20005-4526
Eric Angel, Director

Legal Momentum 202.326.0040
Fax 202.589.0511
E-mail ....lorloff@nowldef.org
    1522 K St Nw, Ste 550, Washington, DC 20005
Leslye Orloff, Director

Luther Place Shelter 202.387.5464
Fax 202.319.1508
    1226 Vermont Ave NW, Washington, DC 20005
Kristyn Carrillo, Director

**Lutheran Social Svcs of the National Capital
Area** 202.723.3000
Fax 202.723.3303
Web ....www.lssnca.org
E-mail ....rravesm@lssnca.org
    4406 Georgia Ave NW, Washington, DC 20011-7124
Melissa Graves, Executive Director

Mount Carma House 202.289.6315
Fax 202.289.1710
Web ....www.catholiccharitiesdc.org
E-mail ....mary.klikenbergh@catholiccharitiesdc.org
    471 G Pl NW, Washington, DC 20001-2665
Mary Bridget Klikenbergh, Director

My Sisters Place 202.529.5261
Fax 202.529.5984
Web ....www.mysistersplacedc.org
E-mail ....lvaughan@mysistersplacedc.org
    1513A Franklin St NE, Washington, DC 20018
Lauren Vaughan, Shelter Case Manager

Women Impowered Against Violence 202.452.9550
Fax 202.452.8255
E-mail ....info@weaveincorp.org
    1422 K St NW, Washington, DC 20005
Carol Losturthun, Director

EDUCATION

Academy for Educational Development 202.884.8000
Fax 202.884.8400
Web ....www.aed.org
E-mail ....mgalley@aed.org
    1825 Connecticut Ave NW, Washington, DC 20009
Michelle Galley, Senior Vp/director

For Love of Children 202.462.8686
Fax 202.462.9280
Web ....www.floc.org
E-mail ....tpayne@floc.org
    1763 NW Columbia Rd Ste 1, Washington,
    DC 20009-2834
Tim Payne, Executive Director

The Lab School of Washington 202.965.6600
Fax 202.454.2270
Web ....www.labschool.org
E-mail ....diana.meltzer@labschool.org
    4759 Reservoir Rd NW, Washington, DC 20007
Katherine Schanpz, Director

United Planning Organization 202.238.4600
Fax 202.588.0270
Web ....www.upo.org
E-mail ....info@upo.org
    301 Rhode Island Ave NW, Washington,
    DC 20001-1826
Dana Jones, Executive Director

SOCIAL SERVICES

Bureau of Indian Affairs 202.513.7642
Fax 202.208.2648
Web ....www.bia.gov
E-mail ....sue.settles@bia.gov
    1849 C St NW, Washington, DC 20240-0001
Sue Settles, Division Chief Of Human Services

DC Action For Children 202.234.9404
Fax 202.234.9108
Web ....www.dckids.org
E-mail ....info@dckids.org
    1432 K St Ste 1050, Washington, DC 20005
Tulli Dobler, Operations Manager

DC Child and Family Svcs Agency 202.442.6100
Fax 202.727.6505
Web ....www.cfsa.dc.gov
E-mail ....cfsa@dc.gov
    400 6th St SW, 5th Floor, Washington, DC 20024
Debra Porchia-Usher, Interim Director

Family Matters of Greater Washington 202.289.1510
Fax 202.518.8929
Web ....www.familymattersdc.org
    1509 16th Street, NW, Washington, DC 20036
COA accredited organization.

Inter Faith Conference 202.234.6300
Fax 202.234.6303
Web ....www.ifcmw.org
E-mail ....ifc@ifcmw.org
    100 Allison Sty NW, Washington, DC 20011-3330
Rev. Clark Lobenstine, Executive Director

Progressive Life Center, Inc. 202.842.4570
Fax 202.842.1035
Web ....www.plcntu.org
    1704 17th St. NE, Washington, DC 20002-1810
COA accredited organization.

The Fishing School 202.399.3618
Fax 202.386.1014
Web ....www.fishingschool.org
E-mail ....lgivs@fishingschool.org
    4737 Meade St NE, Washington, DC 20009
Leo Givs, Executive Director

**The Girl Scout Council of The Nation's
Capital** 202.237.1670
Fax 202.274.2161
Web ....www.gscnc.org
    4301 Connecticut Ave NW Ste M2, Washington,
    DC 20008-2388
Lidia Tesoto, Executive Director

Voices for America's Children 202.289.0777
Fax 202.289.0776
Web ....www.voices.org
E-mail ....voices@voices.org
    1000 Vermont Ave NW Ste 700, Washington,
    DC 20005
Jolie Johnson, Director Of Operations

Whitman-Walker Clinic 202.797.3500
Fax 202.797.4455
Web ....www.wwc.org
E-mail ....dblanchon@wwc.org
    1407 S St NW, Washington, DC 20009-3840
Don Blanchon, Executive Director

SPECIAL NEEDS

Advocates for Justice & Education Inc **888.327.8060**
E-mail .... kim.jones@aje-dc.org
   1012 Pensilvanie Ave SE, Washington, DC 20020
   Kim Jones, Judge

Advocates for Justice & Education Inc **202.265.1432**
E-mail .... caru.echenique@aje-dc.org
   4201 Georgia Ave NW, Washington, DC 20011
   Bush, Office Manager

Advocates for Justice And Education **202.678.8060**
Fax 202.678.8062
   1012 Pennsylvania SE, Washington, DC 20003
   S Bush, Manager

Anacostia Satellite Office **202.889.5802**
   2443 Good Hope Rd SE, Washington, DC 20020
   Richard Simms, Executive Director

Autism Society District of Columbia **202.561.5300**
E-mail .... dc-washington@autismsocietyofamerica.org
   5167 NE 7th St, Washington, DC 20011

Creating Opprtnts for Parent
Empowerment **202.543.6482**
Fax 202.543.6682
E-mail .... cope@erols.com
   300 I St Ste 112, Washington, DC 20002

DC Congress of PTA **202.543.0333**
E-mail .... dc_pres@pta.org
   1401 NE Brentwood Pkwy, Washington, DC 20002

Global Enrichment Solutions, LLC **202.882.2533**
Fax 202.882.0533
E-mail .... globalenrichment@aol.com
   5425 14th St NW, Washington, DC 20000

Joseph P Kennedy Institute **202.529.7600**
E-mail .... daphne.pallozzi@ccs-dc.or@gmail.com
   801 Buchanan St NE, Washington, DC 20017

Lindamood-Bell Learning Processes **202.237.7695**
Fax 202.237.6529
   3201 New Mexico Ave NW, Ste 320, Washington,
   DC 20016
   William Ramsten, Manager

Maria Zimmitti PhD & Associates **202.333.6251**
Fax 202.333.6255
E-mail .... mzimmitti@drzimmitti.com
   Hamilton Ct 1230 31 St NW, 2nd Fl, Washington,
   DC 20007
   Maria Zimmitti PhD

NAMI DC **202.546.0646**
E-mail .... namidc@juno.com
   422 8th St SE, Washington, DC 20003
   Janiene Ausbrooks, Office Manager

National Council on Independent Living **202.207.0334**
E-mail .... ncil@ncil.org
   1710 Rhode Island Ave NW, Washington, DC 20036
   Kelly Buckland, Executive Director

National Multiple Sclerosis Society **202.296.5363**
Fax 202.296.3425
E-mail .... Information@MSandYOU.org
   1800 M St NW Ste 750 S, Washington, DC 20036
   Christopher Broullire, President

Speech-Language-Hearing Association **202.877.1000**
   102 Irving St NW, Washington, DC 20010
   Don Rockwood, President

Spina Bifida Association **800.621.3141**
   4590 NW MacArthur Blvd, Ste 250, Washington,
   DC 20007
   Cindy Brownstein, Director

The Arc **202.636.2950**
E-mail .... mlmeccariello@arcdc.net
   817 Varnum St NE Ste 229, Washington, DC 20017

The Equal Rights Center **202.234.3062**
E-mail .... info@equalrightscenter.org
   11 Dupont Cir NW Ste 450, Washington, DC 20036
   Don Kahl, Executive Director

The HSC Pediatric Center **202.832.4400**
Fax 202.635.5751
Web .... www.hscpediatriccenter.org
   1731 Bunker Hill Road NE, Washington, DC 20017
   CARF accredited programs available.

The Quality Trust for Disabilities **202.448.1450**
   5335 Wisconsin Ave NW Ste 825, Washington,
   DC 20015
   Tina Campanella, Executive Director

Florida

Rick Scott, Governor
The State Capital
400 S Monroe Street
Tallahassee, FL 32399-0001
850.488.4441
850.487.0801 (Fax)

Steven Solomon, Juvenile Justice Specialist
Department of Juvenile Justice
2737 Centerview Drive
Tallahassee, FL 32399
850.921.6572
850.922.6189 (Fax)
steven.solomon@djj.state.fl.us

James Clark SAG Chair
4203 Southpoint Blvd
Jacksonville, FL 32216
904.296.1055 x1025
jclark@danielskids.org

CRISIS NUMBERS

Child Abuse Reporting . . .800.962.2873

STATE SERVICES

SOCIAL SERVICES

Agency For Persons With Disabilities 850.482.9109
Fax 850.482.9575
E-mail . . . . .bonnie_williams@apd.state.fl.us
4409 Constitution Ln, Marianna, FL 32448-4472
Bonnie Williams, Senior Human Services Program Specialist

Child Care Program Florida 850.488.4900
Fax 850.488.9584
1317 Winewood Blvd, Building Six Room 389,
Tallahassee, FL 32399
Debby Russo, Director

Child Support Enforcement 800.622.5437
Fax 904.488.4401
Web . . . . .dor.myflorida.com/dor/childsupport/
100 S Biscayne Blvd Ste 3100, Miami, FL 33131

Florida Department Of Children And Families . .850.487.1111
Fax 850.922.2993
1317 Winewood Blvd, Bldg 1 Rm 202, Tallahassee,
FL 32399

GENERAL HEALTH SERVICES

Agency For Healthcare Administrator 850.412.4000
Fax 850.488.2520
Web . . . . .www.ahcaweb
2727 Mahan Dr, Tallahassee, FL 32308
Liz Dudek, Secretary Of Agency

Childrens Medical Srvs FL 850.245.4200
Fax 850.488.3813
E-mail . . . . .childrensmedicalservices@doh.state.fl.us
4025 Esplanade Way, Bin A 06, Tallahassee, FL 32399
Dr. Phyllis Sloyer, Director

Div of Disability Determination 850.488.4222
Fax 850.617.4930
Web . . . . .www.ssa.gov
1321 Executive Center Dr, Ashley Bldg, Tallahassee,
FL 32399-6512
Rhonda Wilson, Director

Div of Family Health 850.245.4100
Fax 850.414.6091
E-mail . . . . .annette_phelps@doh.state.fl.us
4052 Bald Cypress Way, Tallahassee, FL 32311
Annette Phelps, Director

Health Dept 850.245.4444
Fax 850.410.1448
Web . . . . .www.doh.state.fl.us
E-mail . . . . .bonita_sorensen@doh.state.fl.us
4052 Bald Cypressway, Tallahassee, FL 32399-3645
Bonita Sorensen, Md, Director

Infant Mat & Reproductive Health FL 850.245.4465
Fax 850.245.4047
E-mail . . . . .kris-tena_albers@doh.state.fl.us
4052 Bald Cypress Way, HSFFM Bin A 13, Tallahassee,
FL 32399
Kristena Albers, Director

MENTAL HEALTH SERVICES

Div of Voc Rehab FL 850.245.3399
Fax 850.245.3316
2002 Old St Augustine Rd, Bldg A, Tallahassee,
FL 32301
Lila Swartz, Clerk

Div of Vocational Rehab FL 850.245.0300
Fax 850.245.0363
E-mail . . . . .stephanie.wilson@dbs.fldoe.org
325 W Gaines St, Turlington Bldg Ste 1114,
Tallahassee, FL 32399
Ellen Mccarron, Deputy Director

Substance Abuse and Mental Health 850.414.9063
Fax 850.922.4996
Web . . . . .www.myflorida.com
E-mail . . . . .david_sofferin@bcf.state.fl.us
1317 Winewood Blvd Ste 1, Tallahassee,
FL 32399-6570
David Sofferin, Assistant Secretary

JUSTICE AGENCY

Dept Of Juvenile Justice 407.445.5354
Fax 407.521.2608
Web . . . . .www.djj.state.fl.us
E-mail . . . . .virginia.snider@djj.state.fl.us
8500 Laurel Hill Dr, Orlando, FL 32818-4792
Virginia Snider, Deputy Chief Probation Officer

Dept Of Juvenile Justice 305.637.2911
Fax 305.637.2918
E-mail . . . . .terria.flakes@djj.state.fl.us
3300 NW 27th Ave, Ste 1116, Miami, FL 33142-5881
Terria Flakes, Chief Probation Officer

Dept of Juvenile Justice 850.921.8805
Fax 850.922.2992
Web . . . . .http://myflorida.com
E-mail . . . . .djj@state.fl.us
2737 Centerview Dr, Tallahassee, FL 32399-0998
Fred Schuknecht, Director Of Administration

**Div Of Victim Svcs And Criminal Justice
Programs 850.414.3360**
Fax 850.413.0633
Web . . . . .www.myfloridalegal.com
187 W Gaines St, Tallahassee, FL 32301
Emery Gainey, Director

Florida Dept of Corrections 850.488.5021
Fax 850.488.4534
Web . . . . .www.dc.state.fl.us
E-mail . . . . .crosby.james@mail.dc.state.fl.us
2601 Blairstone Rd, Tallahassee, FL 32399-6563
James Crosby, Secretary

Florida Div of Emergency Management 850.413.9969
Fax 850.488.1016
Web . . . . .www.floridadisaster.org
2555 Shumard Oak Blvd, Tallahassee, FL 32399
Bryan Koon, Director

Juvenile Detention Ctr .561.881.5020
Fax 561.881.5019
E-mail . . . . .anthony.flowers@djj.state.fl.us
1100 45th St Ste A, West Palm Beach, FL 33407-2397
Patricia Hammond, Assistant Superintendent

Office of Educatin and Initiatives FL 850.922.3621
Fax 850.922.2121
E-mail . . . . .overstreet.allen@mail.dc.state.fl.us
2601 Blair Stone Rd, Bldg B Rm 300, Tallahassee,
FL 32399
Crockett Mckinley, Director

Residential & Correctional Facilities 850.921.4188
Fax 850.414.2264
E-mail . . . . .laura.moneyham@bjj.state.fl.us
2737 Centerview Dr, Tallahassee, FL 32399
Laura Moneyham, Assistant Secratary

COURTS

States Courts Admin 850.922.5081
Fax 850.488.0156
Web . . . . .www.flcourts.org
E-mail . . . . .osca@flcourts.org
500 S Duval St, Tallahassee, FL 32399-6556
Elisabeth H. Goodner, Administrator

POLICE AND SHERIFF

Florida Police Chiefs' Assoc 850.219.3631
Fax 850.219.3640
Web . . . . .www.fpca.com
E-mail . . . . .amercer@fpca.com
924 N Gadsden St, Tallahassee, FL 32303
Amy Mercer, Executive Director

Florida Sheriffs' Assoc .850.877.2165
Fax 850.878.8665
Web . . . . .www.flsheriffs.org
2617 Mahan Dr, Tallahassee, FL 32308-5405
Steve Casey, Executive Director

EDUCATION SERVICES

Clearinghouse Information Center FL **850.245.0477**
Fax 850.245.0987
E-mail ....Myra.Rogers@fldoe.org
   325 W Gaines St, Tallahassee, FL 32399
Myra Rogers, Director

Florida Dept of Education **850.245.0505**
Fax 850.245.9667
Web ....www.fldoe.org
E-mail ....anna.moore@fldoe.org
   325 W Gaines St, Tallahassee, FL 32399
Anna Moore, Title 1 Programs Director

Florida School for the Deaf & Blind **904.827.2200**
Fax 904.827.2217
Web www.fsdb.k12.fl.us
   207 San Marco Ave, Saint Augustine, FL 32084
Danny Hutto, President

Parent to Parent of Miami Inc Florida **305.271.9797**
Fax 305.271.6628
E-mail ....jgarcia@ptopmiami.org
   7990 SW 117th Ave Ste 200, Miami, FL 33183
J Garcia, Director

LABOR & WORKFORCE EDUCATION

Agency For Workforce Innovation **850.245.7105**
Fax 805.921.3223
Web ....www.floridajobs.org
E-mail ....cynthia.lorenzo@awi.state.fl.us
   107 E Madison St # 100, Tallahassee, FL 32399
Cynthia Lorenzo, Director

COUNTY SERVICES

Alachua County

SOCIAL SERVICES

Child Protection Team **352.334.1300**
Fax 352.334.1521
   1701 SW 16th Ave, Bldg A, Gainesville, FL 32608
Debra Esernio-jenssen, Medical Director

GENERAL HEALTH SERVICES

Children's Medical Svcs **352.334.1400**
Fax 352.334.1476
Web ....http://www.cms-kids.com/
E-mail ....rick_bucciarelie@doh.state.fl.us
   1701 SW 16th Ave, Bldg B, Gainesville, FL 32608
Rick Bucciarelie, Md, CMS Nursing Director

Health Dept **352.334.7900**
Fax 352.334.8837
Web ....www.alachuacountyhealth.com
   224 SE 24th St, Gainesville, FL 32641-7516
John Colon, Medical Executive Director

JUSTICE AGENCY

Dept Of Juvenile Justice **386.418.5257**
Fax 386.418.5277
Web ....www.myflorida.com
E-mail ....jill.bessette@djj.state.fl.us
   14107 US Highway 441 N Bldg Ste 200, Alachua,
   FL 32615-6391
Jill Bessette, Chief Performance Officer

Guardian Ad Litem Program **352.374.3656**
Fax 352.491.4598
E-mail ....info@8thcircuit.gal.fl.gov
   14 S main st ste A, Gainesville, FL 32601
Chuck Orchowsky, Interim Circuit Director

Juvenile Detention Ctr **352.955.2105**
Fax 352.955.2092
Web ....www.djj.state.fl.us
   3440 NE 39th Ave, Gainesville, FL 32609
Forest Hallam, Assistant Supervisor

COURTS

8th Circuit Court Family Court **352.374.3694**
Fax 352.491.4667
Web www.circuit8.org
E-mail ....mcfetridge@circuit8.org
   201 E University Ave, Gainesville, FL 32601
Ted McFetridge, Court Administrator

POLICE AND SHERIFF

Sheriff's Ofc **352.367.4000**
Fax 352.374.1804
Web ....www.alachuasheriff.org
E-mail ....acso@alachuasheriff.org
   2621 SE Hawthorne Rd, Gainesville, FL 32641-7546
Craig Pelham, Teen Court Coordinator

EDUCATION SERVICES

Exceptional Student Education **352.955.7676**
Fax 352.955.7129
Web ....www.sbac.edu
E-mail ....blackkv@gm.sbac.edu
   1817 E university Ave, Gainesville, FL 32601-5448
Kathy Black, Executive Director

Baker County

GENERAL HEALTH SERVICES

Dept Of Health **904.259.6291**
Fax 904.259.1950
   480 W Lowder St, Macclenny, FL 32063
Vivian Crews, Hiv Coordinator

POLICE AND SHERIFF

Sheriff's Ofc **904.259.2231**
Fax 904.259.4254
E-mail ....jdobson@sheriffsoffice.co.baker.fl.us
   56 N 2nd St, Macclenny, FL 32063
Joey B. Dobson, Sheriff

Bay County

SOCIAL SERVICES

Florida Dept Of Children &
Families **850.872.7648**
Fax 850.872.4690
Web ....www.myflordia.com
E-mail ....dcfmail@dcf.state.fl.us
   500 W 11th St, Panama City, FL 32401
Courtney Peel, Operation Program Administrator

GENERAL HEALTH SERVICES

Children's Medical Svcs **850.872.4700**
Fax 850.872.4817
Web ....www.doh.state.fl.us
E-mail ....glenda_thomas@doh.state.fl.us
   230 N Kindall Pkwy, Panama City, FL 32404
Glenda Thomas, Rn, CMS Nursing Director

Dept of Health **850.872.4455**
Fax 850.747.5475
   597 W 11th St, Panama City, FL 32401
Laura Mccenny, Aids Coordinator

MENTAL HEALTH SERVICES

Behavioral Hospital **850.763.0017**
Fax 850.785.0580
Web ....www.psisolution.org
   1940 Harrison Ave, Panama City, FL 32405
Rick Smith, Vice President

JUSTICE AGENCY

Dept Of Juvenile Justice **850.872.7630**
Fax 850.747.5438
E-mail ....mike.nihill@djj.state.fl.us
   505 E 11th St, Panama City, FL 32401-3410
Michael Nihill, Circuit Manager

Guardian Ad Litem Program **850.747.5180**
Fax 850.747.5463
Web www.jud14.flcourts.org
   14th Judicial Circuit, Panama City, FL 32402
Fred Hadner, Circuit Director

COURTS

14th Circuit Court (Juvenile Div) **850.747.5119**
Fax 850.747.5781
   533 E 11th St, Juvenile Division, Panama City,
   FL 32401
Honorable Elijah Smiley, Judge

Teen Court **850.747.5191**
Fax 850.747.5443
Web www.jud14.flcourts.org
   456 E 11th St, Panama City, FL 32401
Suzanne Cox, Director

POLICE AND SHERIFF

Sheriff's Ofc **850.747.4700**
Fax 850.784.0949
E-mail ....fmckeithen@bayso.org
   3421 Highway 77, Panama City, FL 32405
Frank Mckeithen, Sheriff

EDUCATION SERVICES

Bayou George Head Start **850.722.0200**
   8332 Hudson Rd, Panama City, FL 32404-5640
Stephney Johnson, Director

Bradford County

GENERAL HEALTH SERVICES

Dept Of Children & Families **904.964.1500**
Fax 904.964.1577
Web ....www.dcf.state.fl.us
E-mail ....dawn_harper@dcf.state.fl.us
   1250 Andrews Cir, Starke, FL 32091-2132
Dawn Harper, Economic Services Supervisor

Dept Of Health **904.964.7732**
Fax 904.964.3024
E-mail ....amie_johns@doh.state.fl.us
   1801 N Temple Ave, Starke, FL 32091
Amie Johns, Rn, Nursing Director

JUSTICE AGENCY

Child Svcs/Dept Of Juvenile Justice **904.964.1515**
Fax 904.964.1531
   1250 Andrews Cir, Starke, FL 32091
Donna Bergum, Secretary

Guardian Ad Litem Program **904.966.6237**
Fax 904.966.6329
   945 N Temple Ave, Starke, FL 32091
Arthur Wright, Case Coordinator

POLICE AND SHERIFF

Sheriff's Ofc **904.966.6380**
Fax 904.966.6160
   945 N Temple Ave # B, Starke, FL 32091
Gordon Smith, Sheriff

Florida

EDUCATION SERVICES

Communities In Schools **904.964.7776**
Fax 904.964.7637
Web .... www.cisbradford.org
E-mail .... cisbrad@yahoo.com
  707 McMahon St, Starke, FL 32091-2519
  James Biggs, Director

Brevard County

SOCIAL SERVICES

Brevard C.A.R.E.S. **321.632.2737**
Web .... www.brevardcares.org
  4085 S US 1, Rockledge, FL 32955
  Valerie Holmes, Manager

Brevard Family Partnership **321.752.4650**
Web .... www.brevardfp.org
  2301 W Eaugalley blvd #4, Melbourne, FL 32935
  Patricia Nellios, Chief Executive Officer

Florida Dept Of Children &
Families **321.984.4745**
Fax 321.409.2132
  6100 Minton Road, Suite 201, Palm Bay, FL 32907
  Bobby Shea, Administrator

Florida Dept Of Children &
Families **321.634.3600**
Fax 321.634.3609
Web .... www.dcf.state.fl.us
E-mail .... maria_nistri@dcf.state.fl.us
  375 Commerce Pkwy Ste 102, Rockledge,
  FL 32955-4201
  Maria Nistri, Administrator

GENERAL HEALTH SERVICES

Health Dept **321.454.7151**
Fax 321.454.7129
Web .... www.doh.state.fl.us
E-mail .... heidar_hesmati@doh.state.fl.us
  2575 N Courtenay Pkwy, Merritt Island,
  FL 32953-4126
  Heidar Hesmati, Personal Health Services Director

JUSTICE AGENCY

Guardian Ad Litem Moore Justice
Ctr **321.690.6823**
Fax 321.690.6897
  2825 Judge Fran Jamieson Way, Melbourne,
  FL 32940
  Kimberly Delgaudio, Program Director

Juvenile Detention Ctr **321.690.3400**
Fax 321.690.3412
E-mail .... dick.hoffman@djj.state.fl.us
  5225 Dewitt Ave, Cocoa, FL 32927-4302
  Richard Hoffman, Superintendent

COURTS

Clerk Of Circuit **321.637.5413**
Fax 321.617.7245
  400 South St Ste 6A, 2ND FLOOR, WESTSIDE,
  Titusville, FL 32780-7698
  Honorable Lisa Davidson, Director

Teen Court **321.617.7294**
Fax 321.617.7511
Web www.sa18.state.fl.us
E-mail .... dadams@sa18.state.fl.us
  2725 Judge Fran Jamieson Way Bldg D, Viera,
  FL 32940-6605
  Darrin Adams, Coordinator

POLICE AND SHERIFF

Sheriff's Ofc **321.264.5201**
Fax 321.264.5360
Web .... www.brevardsheriff.com
E-mail .... admin@bcso.us
  700 S Park Ave, Bldg A, Titusville, FL 32780
  Jack Parker, Sheriff

EDUCATION SERVICES

Brevard Even Start Family Literacy **321.264.3099**
Fax 321.264.3149
  800 Lane Ave, Titusville, FL 32780
  Sally Shinn, Even Start Director

Exceptional Student Education **321.633.1000**
Fax 321.631.3589
Web www.brevard.k12.fl.us
  2700 Judge Fran Jamieson Way, Melbourne,
  FL 32940-6601
  Pam Tredwell, Director Of ESE Program Support

Broward County

SOCIAL SERVICES

Seminole Tribe Of Florida Family Svcs
Program **954.964.6338**
Fax 954.967.5182
Web .... www.seminoletribe.org
E-mail .... hmarchel@dhs.state.or.us
  3006 Josie Billie Ave, Hollywood, FL 33024-2918
  Helene Buster, Director

GENERAL HEALTH SERVICES

Children's Medical Svcs **954.713.3100**
Fax 954.713.3180
Web .... www.cms-kids.com
  1625 SE 3rd Ave, Ste 415, Ft Lauderdale, FL 33316
  Mary Hooshmand, Regional Executive Nursing Director

Health Dept **954.467.4700**
Fax 954.760.7798
  780 SW 24th St, Ft Lauderdale, FL 33315
  Dr Paula Thaqi, Acting Medical Executive Director

Seminole Tribe Of Florida Health
Admin **954.962.2009**
Fax 954.985.8456
E-mail .... conniew@semtribe.com
  3006 Josie Billie Ave, Hollywood, FL 33024
  Connie Whidden, Health Director

MENTAL HEALTH SERVICES

Fort Lauderdale Hospital **954.463.4321**
Fax 954.453.5497
Web .... www.ftlauderdalehospital.org
E-mail .... sbieniek@ftlauderdalehospital.org
  1601 E Las Olas Blvd, Fort Lauderdale,
  FL 33301-2393
  Sherry Bieniek, Md, Medical Director

Henderson Mental Health Ctr (Crisis
Ctr) **954.463.0911**
Fax 954.463.4778
Web .... www.hendersonmhc.org
E-mail .... dsasser@hendersonmhc.org
  4720 N State Rd 7, Bldg B, Ft Lauderdale, FL 33319
  Diane Sasser, Director

JUSTICE AGENCY

Guardian Ad Litem **954.831.6214**
Fax 954.831.7192
  524 S Andrews Ave Ste 300E, Ft Lauderdale,
  FL 33301
  Patty Walker, Circuit Director

Juvenile Detention Ctr **954.467.4563**
Fax 954.327.6361
E-mail .... darrel.wolf@djj.state.fl.us
  222 NW 22nd Ave, Ft Lauderdale, FL 33311
  Darrel Wolf, Superintendent

South Region Juvenile Justice **954.467.4381**
Fax 954.467.5996
  201 W Broward Blvd, # 208, Fort Lauderdale,
  FL 33301
  Lori Mannelli, Operations Manager

COURTS

17th Circuit Court **954.831.6565**
Fax 954.831.7047
Web www.clerk-17th-flcourts.org
E-mail .... dross@17th-flcourts.org
  201 SE 6th St Ste 444, Ft Lauderdale, FL 33301-3329
  Honorable Dale Ross, Director

POLICE AND SHERIFF

Sheriff's Dept **954.831.8901**
Fax 954.797.0936
Web .... www.sheriff.org
E-mail .... allenbirdy@sheriff.org
  2601 W Broward Blvd, Ft Lauderdale, FL 33312-1308
  Al Len Birdy, Sheriff

EDUCATION SERVICES

Exceptional Student Education **754.321.2200**
Fax 754.321.2715
Web .... www.browardschools.com
  600 SE 3rd Ave, Fl 9, Ft Lauderdale, FL 33301
  Denise Rusnak, Director

Calhoun County

GENERAL HEALTH SERVICES

Health Dept **850.674.5645**
Fax 850.674.5420
Web .... www.doh.state.fl.us
E-mail .... lisag_taylor@doh.state.fl.us
  19611 State Road 20 W, Blountstown,
  FL 32424-3917
  Lisa Taylor, Nursing Director

JUSTICE AGENCY

Guardian Ad Litem **850.674.2799**
Fax 850.674.2799
  20859 Central Ave E Ste 212, Blountstown, FL 32424
  Jane Powell, Case Coordinator

COURTS

14th Circuit Court **850.674.4545**
Fax 850.674.5553
  20859 Central Ave E Ste 130, Blountstown, FL 32424
  Gene Morris, Teen Court Director

POLICE AND SHERIFF

Sheriff's Dept **850.674.5049**
Fax 850.674.5586
Web .... www.calhounsheriff.com
E-mail .... sheriff@calhounsheriff.com
  20776 Central Ave E Ste 2, Blountstown,
  FL 32424-2282
  David Tatum, Sheriff

Charlotte County

SOCIAL SERVICES

Florida Dept Of Children &
Families **941.613.2000**
Fax 941.613.0989
Web .... www.myflorida.com
E-mail .... karen_laneuville@dcf.state.fl.us
  19500 Cochran Blvd Ste 100, Port Charlotte,
  FL 33948-2088
  Karen Laneuville, Child Protective Investigation Supervisor

JUSTICE AGENCY

Guardian Ad Litem **941.627.0643**
Fax 941.627.1490
Web .... www.gal.fl.gov
E-mail .... holly.rodriguez@gal.fl.gov
    21450 Gibralter Dr Ste 5, Port Charlotte,
    FL 33952-5417
Holly Rodrigiuez, Case Coordinator

COURTS

20th Circuit Court **941.637.2279**
Fax 941.637.2116
Web .... www.co.charlotte.fl.us
    350 E Marion, Punta Gorda, FL 33950
Barbara T. Scott, Clerk Of Court

Teen Court **941.637.2281**
Fax 941.637.2283
    350 E Marion Ave, Punta Gorda, FL 32950
Andrea Williams, Program Specialist Ii

POLICE AND SHERIFF

Sheriff's Ofc **941.639.0013**
Fax 941.205.5627
E-mail .... sheriff@ccso.org
    7474 Utilities Rd, Punta Gorda, FL 33982
Bill Cameron, Sheriff

EDUCATION SERVICES

Exceptional Student Education **941.255.0808**
Fax 941.255.7585
Web www.ccps.k12.fl.us
    1445 Education Way, Port Charlotte, FL 33948-1052
Dougles Whittaker, Superintendent

Citrus County

GENERAL HEALTH SERVICES

Dept Of Health **352.527.0068**
Fax 352.527.0629
Web .... www.citruscountyhealth.org
    3700 W Sovereign Path, Lecanto, FL 34461-8071
Michael Wallace, Aids Director

JUSTICE AGENCY

Dept Of Juvenile Justice **352.860.5105**
Fax 352.860.5104
Web .... www.djj.state.fl.us
E-mail .... brenda.frazier@djj.state.fl.us
    103 N Apopka Ave, Inverness, FL 34450-4237
Brenda Frazier, Supervisor

Guardian Ad Litem Program **352.344.1147**
Fax 352.344.1454
    110 N Apopka Ave, Inverness, FL 34450
Tracy Hoffman, Office Manager

COURTS

5th Circuit Court **352.341.6400**
Fax 352.341.6413
Web .... www.clerkcitrusfl.us
    110 N Apopka Ave Rm 101, Inverness, FL 34450
Betty Strifler, Clerk Of Court

EDUCATION SERVICES

Crystal River Head Start **352.795.0077**
Fax 352.795.1646
    628 NE 1st St, Crystal River, FL 34429
Cozette White, Director

Clay County

SOCIAL SERVICES

Florida Dept Of Children &
Families **904.541.3687**
Fax 904.541.3697
Web .... www.myflorida.com
E-mail .... linda_mccann@dcf.state.fl.us
    1845 Town Center Blvd Ste 2, Fleming Island,
    FL 32003-3359
Linda Mccann, P.i. Supervisor

JUSTICE AGENCY

Dept Of Juvenile Justice **904.529.2330**
Fax 904.529.2343
Web .... www.djj.state.fl.us
E-mail .... joy.curtis@djj.state.fl.us
    1417-2 S Orange Ave, Green Cove Springs,
    FL 32043-4342
Joy Curtis, Juvenile Probation Supervisor

Guardian Ad Litem Program **904.269.6312**
Fax 904.278.4756
Web .... www.clayclerk.com
E-mail .... waltonm@clayclerk.com
    PO Box 698, Green Cove Springs, FL 32043-0698
Mary Walton, County Coordinator

COURTS

4th Circuit Court (Teen Court) **904.269.6302**
Fax 904.284.2805
E-mail .... muellerd@clerk.co.clay.fl.us
    825 N Orange Ave, Green Cove Springs,
    FL 32043-2525
Deborah Mueller, Teen Court Coordinator

POLICE AND SHERIFF

Sheriff's Dept **904.284.7575**
Fax 904.284.0710
Web .... www.claysheriff.com
E-mail .... ccox@claysheriff.com
    901 N Orange Ave, Green Cove Springs,
    FL 32043-2527
Rick Beseler, Sheriff

Collier County

GENERAL HEALTH SERVICES

Children's Medical Svcs **239.552.7435**
Fax 239.552.7434
Web .... www.childrenmedicalservices.com
    1665 Medico Blvd, Naples, FL 34110
Erica Alessandri, Nursing Director

POLICE AND SHERIFF

Sheriff's Ofc **239.774.4434**
Fax 239.793.9333
Web .... www.colliersheriff.org
E-mail .... sheriff@colliersheriff.org
    3319 Tamiami Trl E Bldg J, Naples, FL 34112-4987
Kevin Rambosk, Sheriff

EDUCATION SERVICES

Even Start **239.377.1195**
Fax 239.377.9901
Web www.collier.k12.fl.us
E-mail .... sherrosu@collier.k12.fl.us
    614 S 5th St, Immokalee, FL 34142-4350
Susan Sherrod, Even Start Director

Exceptional Student Education **239.377.0131**
Fax 239.377.0158
Web www.collier.k12.fl.us
    5775 Osceola Trl, Naples, FL 34109
Victoria Sartorio, Md, Director

Columbia County

SOCIAL SERVICES

Dept Of Children & Families **386.758.1445**
Fax 386.758.1495
Web .... www.dcf.state.fl.us
E-mail .... lori_walker@dcf.state.fl.us
    1389 W US Highway 90 Ste 100, Lake City,
    FL 32055-6130
Lori Walker, Program Administrator

GENERAL HEALTH SERVICES

Dept Of Health **386.758.1068**
Fax 386.758.2180
E-mail .... hugh_giebieg@boh.state.fl.us
    217 NE Franklin St, Lake City, FL 32055
Hugh Giebeig, Administrator

JUSTICE AGENCY

Dept Of Juvenile Justice **386.758.1448**
Fax 386.758.1532
Web .... www.djj.state.fl.us
    690 E Duval St, Lake City, FL 32055-3485
Curtis Jenkins, Teen Court Executive Director

Guardian Ad Litem **386.758.1170**
Fax 386.758.1014
E-mail .... linda.dedge@gal.fl.gov
    885 SW Sisters Welcome Rd, Lake City, FL 32025
Linda Dedge, Program Director

COURTS

3rd Circuit Court **386.758.1342**
Fax 386.719.7401
    173 NE Hernando Ave, Lake City, FL 32056-2069
P Dewitt Cason, Clerk

POLICE AND SHERIFF

Sheriff's Ofc **386.752.9212**
Web .... www.columbiasheriff.com
E-mail .... sheriffmarkhunter@columbiasheriff.com
    4917 E US Highway 90, Lake City, FL 32055
Mark Hunter, Sheriff

DeSoto County

SOCIAL SERVICES

Florida Dept of Children & Families **863.993.4500**
Fax 863.993.4544
E-mail .... lynne_johnston@dcf.state.fl.us
    805 N Mills Ave, Arcadia, FL 34266-8716
Lynn Johnston, Program Administrator

GENERAL HEALTH SERVICES

Dept of Health **863.993.4601**
Fax 863.993.4606
Web .... www.doh.state.fl.us
E-mail .... cheryl_adams@doh.state.fl.us
    34 S Baldwin Ave, Arcadia, FL 34266-3387
Cheryl Adams, AIDS Services Coordinator

POLICE AND SHERIFF

Sheriff's Ofc **863.993.4700**
Fax 863.993.4712
Web .... www.desotosheriff.com
E-mail .... desotosheriff@earthlink.net
    208 E Cypress St, Arcadia, FL 34266-4410
William Wise, Sheriff

Dixie County

GENERAL HEALTH SERVICES

Dept Of Health **352.498.1360**
Fax 352.498.1363
    149 NE 241 St, Cross City, FL 32628-3305
Linda Hatch, Rn, Nursing Director

Florida

JUSTICE AGENCY

Guardian Ad Litem **863.993.4638**
Fax 863.993.4814
E-mail ....sandee.woods@gal.fl.gov
　223 E Oak St Ste 2, Arcadia, FL 34266
Amy Clark, Attorney

COURTS

3rd Circuit Court **352.498.1200**
Fax 352.498.1201
E-mail ....djohnson@dicksyclerk.com
　214 NE 351 HWY, Cross City, FL 32628
Dana Johnson, Head Clerk

Teen Court **352.498.6457**
Fax 352.498.1404
Web www.dixie.k12.fl.us
E-mail ....christykeen@dixie.k12.fl.us
　PO Box 1180, Cross City, FL 32628-1180
Christy Keen, Director

POLICE AND SHERIFF

Sheriff's Ofc **352.498.1220**
Fax 352.498.1226
　351 Highway, Suite L, Cross City, FL 32628
Dewey H. Hatcher, Sr., Sheriff

Duval County

GENERAL HEALTH SERVICES

Children's Medical Svcs **904.360.7070**
Fax 904.798.4568
Web ....www.cmsjaxweb.doh.state.fl.us
E-mail ....thomaschiu@jax.usl.edu
　910 N Jefferson St, Jacksonville, FL 32209-6810
Thomas Chiu, Md, Medical Director

**Florida Dept Of Children & Families - District
4** **904.723.2000**
Fax 904.348.2603
Web ....www.dcf.state.fl.us
E-mail ....nancy_dreicer@dcf.state.fl.us
　2747 Art Museum Dr, Jacksonville, FL 32207-5008
Nancy Dreicer, District Administrator

MENTAL HEALTH SERVICES

River Point Behavioral Health **904.724.9202**
Fax 904.727.9838
Web ....www.riverpointbehavioral.com
　6300 Beach Blvd, Jacksonville, FL 32216
Pat Grunwald, Director Of Nursing

JUSTICE AGENCY

Guardian Ad Litem **904.630.1200**
Fax 904.630.0757
Web ....www.guardianadlitem.gov
　220 E Bay St Fl 2, Jacksonville, FL 32202-3439
Hilary Creary, Circuit Director

Juvenile Detention Ctr **904.798.4820**
Fax 904.798.4825
Web ....www.djj.state.fl.us
E-mail ....steve.duram@djj.state.fl.us
　1241 E 8th St, Jacksonville, FL 32206-4061
Mr. Stephanie Duram, Superintendent

COURTS

4th Circuit Court-Juvenile Div **904.630.2072**
Fax 904.630.7675
Web ....www.duvalclerk.com
　330 E Bay St Ste 108, Jacksonville, FL 32202
Jim Fuller, Clerk of Court

POLICE AND SHERIFF

Sheriff's Dept **904.630.2120**
Fax 904.630.2107
E-mail ....6740ljm@jaxsheriff.com
　501 E Bay St, Jacksonville, FL 32202
John H. Rutherford, Sheriff

EDUCATION SERVICES

**Communities In Schools Of Jacksonville,
Inc.** **904.354.5918**
Fax 904.355.9009
Web ....www.cisjax.org
E-mail ....info@cisjax.org
　3100 University Blvd S Ste 300, Jacksonville, FL 32216
Jon Heymann, CEO

Exceptional Student Education **904.390.2071**
Fax 904.390.2435
E-mail ....suttonk@duvalschools.com
　1701 Prudential Dr, Fl 4, Jacksonville, FL 32207
Kenneth Sutton, General Director

Escambia County

GENERAL HEALTH SERVICES

Health Dept **850.595.6500**
Fax 850.595.6505
　1295 W Fairfield Dr, Pensacola, FL 32501
John Lanza, Md, CHD/Medical Director

JUSTICE AGENCY

Escambia Juvenile Detention Ctr **850.595.8820**
Fax 850.595.8676
　1800 Saint Mary Ave Ste 4, Pensacola, FL 32501
Paul Nabler, Superintendent

Guardian Ad Litem Program **850.595.3725**
Fax 850.595.0453
E-mail ....maureen.mcgill@gal.fl.gov
　1800 Saint Mary Ave Ste 3, Pensacola, FL 32501
Rosemary Ash, Circuit Director

COURTS

1st Circuit Court **850.595.3710**
Fax 850.595.3711
Web ....www.co.escambia.fl.us
E-mail ....edward.nickinson@flcourt1.gov
　2251 N Palafox St, Juvenile Justice Center, Pensacola,
　FL 32501-1722
Honorable Edward P. Nickinson, III, Inger Hill Teen Court Coordinator

POLICE AND SHERIFF

Sheriff's Ofc **850.436.9630**
Web ....www.escambiaso.com
　1700 W Leonard St, Pensacola, FL 32501
David Morgan, Sheriff

EDUCATION SERVICES

**Cap Head Start-Bratt Elementary
School** **850.327.6137**
Fax 850.327.4879
　5721 Highway 99, Century, FL 32535-3125
Jeanine Hall, Principal

Cap Head Start-Plesant Grove **850.492.7888**
　3000 Owen Bell Ln, Pensacola, FL 32507-9204
Vanessa Brooks, Director

Exceptional Student Education **850.469.5518**
Fax 850.429.2954
Web www.escambia.k12.fl.us
E-mail ....tszafran@escambia.k12.fl.us
　30 E Texar Dr, Pensacola, FL 32503
Teri Szafran, Director

Flagler County

GENERAL HEALTH SERVICES

Dept Of Health **386.437.7350**
Fax 386.437.7353
E-mail ....bonnie_welter@doh.state.fl.us
　301 S Dr Carter Blvd, Bunnell, FL 32110-6212
Bonnie Welter, Rn, Nursing Director/hiv Coord

JUSTICE AGENCY

Guardian Ad Litem Program **386.437.7398**
Fax 907.771.8381
E-mail ....richard.smith@gal.fl.gov
　2405 E Moody Blvd, #101, Bunnell, FL 32110
Richard P. Smith, Program Coordinator

COURTS

7th Circuit Court **386.437.8266**
Fax 386.586.5186
Web www.circuit7.org
E-mail ....rzambrano@circuit7.org
　1769 E Moody Blvd Bldg 1, Bunnell, FL 32110-5991
Honorable Raul Zambrano, Judge

POLICE AND SHERIFF

Sheriff's Dept **386.437.4116**
Fax 386.586.4811
Web ....www.myfcso.us
E-mail ....dfleming@myfcso.us
　1001 Justice Ln, Bunnell, FL 32110
Donald Fleming, Sheriff

Franklin County

GENERAL HEALTH SERVICES

Health Dept **850.653.2111**
Fax 850.653.9896
Web ....www.doh.state.fl.us
　139 12th St, Apalachicola, FL 32320-2100
Sharon Willis, Nursing Director

COURTS

2nd District Court **850.653.8861**
Fax 850.653.2261
Web ....www.franklinclerk.com
E-mail ....mmjohnson@franklinclerk.com
　33 Market St Rm 203, Apalachicola, FL 32320-2310
Honorable Marcia Johnson, Clerk Of Court

Gadsden County

GENERAL HEALTH SERVICES

Dept Of Health **850.875.7200**
Fax 850.875.7210
E-mail ....cannella_jefferies@doh.state.fl.us
　278 Lasalle Lefall Dr, Quincy, FL 32353
Cannella Jefferies, Nursing Director

JUSTICE AGENCY

Dept Of Juvenile Justice **850.875.9531**
Fax 850.627.4172
Web ....www.djj.state.fl.us
E-mail ....maresha.alexander@djj.state.fl.us
　305 W Crawford St, Quincy, FL 32351
Maresha Alexander, Supervisor

Guardian Ad Litem **850.627.4180**
Fax 850.627.2336
　221 N Madison St, Quincy, FL 32351
Deborah Moore, Circuit Director

COURTS

2nd Circuit Court **850.875.8601**
Fax 850.875.8612
E-mail ....nthomas@clerk.co.gadsden.fl.us
　24 N Adams St, Quincy, FL 32351-2402
Nicholas Thomas, Clerk Of Court

POLICE AND SHERIFF

Sheriff's Dept **850.627.9233**
Fax 850.627.5309
Web ....www.gadsdensheriff.org
E-mail ....gadsdensheriff@tds.net
　339 E Jefferson St, Quincy, FL 32353
Morris A. Young, Sheriff

Gilchrist County

GENERAL HEALTH SERVICES

Health Dept................................352.463.3120
Fax..352.463.3124
Web.....................................www.doh.state.fl.us
E-mail.................karina_quinn@doh.state.fl.us
119 NE 1st St, Trenton, FL 32693-3428
Karina Quinn, Nursing Director

JUSTICE AGENCY

Dept Of Juvenile Justice.................352.463.4150
Fax..352.463.4163
Web...www.djj.state.fl.us
E-mail.................Rebecca.Rogers@djj.state.fl.us
204 N Main St, Trenton, FL 32693
Rebecca Rogers, Supervisor

COURTS

8th Circuit Court.............................352.463.3170
Fax..352.463.3166
Web.............................www.mygilchristcounty.com
112 S Main St Ste 120, Trenton, FL 32693
Honorable Edward Philman, Judge

POLICE AND SHERIFF

Sheriff's Dept..............................352.463.3410
Fax..352.463.3183
Web...www.co.gilchrist.fl.us
9239 S US Hwy 129, Trenton, FL 32693-3253
Daniel Flaughter, Sheriff

Glades County

COURTS

20th Circuit Court..........................863.946.6010
Fax..863.946.0560
Web...www.myfloridacounty.com
500 Avenue J SW, Moore Haven, FL 33471
Honorable Jack Lundy, Director

Gulf County

SOCIAL SERVICES

**Florida Dept Of Children &
Families**..866.762.2237
Fax..866.873.0473
201 Monument Ave, Port St Joe, FL
Sheri Taylor, Economic Self-Sufficiency Supervisor

COURTS

14th Circuit Court..........................850.229.6113
Fax..850.229.6174
Web...www.gulfclerk.com
1000 Cecil G Costin Sr Blvd Rm 212, Port St Joe,
FL 32456-1647
Rebecca Norris, Clerk

POLICE AND SHERIFF

Sheriff's Dept..............................850.227.1115
Fax..850.227.2097
Web...www.gulfsheriff.com
1000 Cecil G. Costin Blvd, Port St Joe, FL 32456
Joe Nugent, Sheriff

Hamilton County

GENERAL HEALTH SERVICES

Dept Of Health.............................386.792.1414
Fax..386.792.2352
E-mail.........................nancy_sult@doh.state.fl.us
209 Central Ave SE, Jasper, FL 32052
Nancy Sult, Nursing Director

POLICE AND SHERIFF

Sheriff's Dept..............................386.792.2004
Fax..386.792.3133
Web...www.flcjn.net
E-mail.......................................reidh@flcjn.net
207 1st St NE Rm 114, Jasper, FL 32052-6669
Harrell Reid, Sheriff

Hardee County

GENERAL HEALTH SERVICES

Health Dept...............................863.773.4161
Fax..863.773.5056
Web...www.doh.state.fl.us
E-mail.................stevengordon@doh.state.fl.us
115 K D Revell Rd, Wauchula, FL 33873-2051
Steven Gordon, Medical Director

JUSTICE AGENCY

Guardian Ad Litem Program...............863.773.2505
Fax..863.773.4619
Web...www.gal.fl.gov
E-mail.................cookie.rousos@gal.fl.gov
417 W Main St Ste 109, Wauchula, FL 33873-2816
Cookie Rousos, Circuit Director

POLICE AND SHERIFF

Sheriff's Dept..............................863.773.0304
Fax..863.773.4593
900 E Summit St, Wauchula, FL 33873
Arnold Lanier, Sheriff

EDUCATION SERVICES

East Coast Migrant Head Start............863.773.2815
Fax..863.773.3903
Web...www.ecmhsp.org
E-mail.................leticia@ecmhsp.org
604 Martin Luther King Jr Ave, Wauchula,
FL 33873-3608
Leticia Enriquez, Director

Hendry County

SOCIAL SERVICES

**Florida Dept Of Children &
Families**..239.867.3300
Fax..239.867.3380
Web.........................www.myflorida.com/acessflorida
485 E Cowboy Way, Labelle, FL 33935-4402
Susan Wright, Director

GENERAL HEALTH SERVICES

Dept Of Health.............................863.674.4041
Fax..863.674.4604
1140 Pratt Blvd, Labelle, FL 33975
Patricia Dobbins, Rn, Administrator

JUSTICE AGENCY

Dept Of Juvenile Justice.................863.674.4181
Fax..863.674.4185
Web...www.djj.state.fl.us
E-mail.................lut.satrado@djj.state.fl.us
485 E Cowboy Way, Labelle, FL 33935-4402
Lut Satrado, Supervisor

COURTS

20th Circuit Court..........................863.675.5201
Fax..863.675.5238
25 E Hickpochee Ave, Labelle, FL 33935-5015
Honorable James D. Sloan, Judge

POLICE AND SHERIFF

Sheriff's Dept..............................863.674.5600
Fax..863.674.4626
Web.................www.hendrycountysheriffsoffice.org
101 S Bridge St, Labelle, FL 33975-4686
Steve Whitten, Sheriff

Hernando County

SOCIAL SERVICES

**Florida Dept Of Children &
Families**..352.754.6640
Fax..352.544.5171
661 S Broad St, Brooksville, FL 34601
Donna Stucchio, Child Protection Investigative Supervisor

JUSTICE AGENCY

Dept Of Juvenile Justice.................352.754.6684
Fax..352.544.5196
E-mail.........................harry.hill@djj.state.fl.us
16244 springhill dr, Brooksville, FL 34604
Harry Hill, Supervisor

Guardian Ad Litem.........................352.754.4226
Fax..352.754.4228
Web...www.gal.fl.gov
E-mail.................teresa.ashcraft@gal.fl.gov
20 N Main St, Ste 220, Brooksville, FL 34601
Teresa Ashcraft, Lead Coordinator

COURTS

5th Judicial Circuit Court.................352.754.4221
Fax..352.754.4245
Web.........................www.clerk.co.hernando.fl.us
E-mail.................dhagert@circuit5.org
20 N Main St, Rm 432, Brooksville, FL 34601
Diane Hagert, Judicial Assistant

POLICE AND SHERIFF

Sheriff's Dept..............................352.754.6830
Fax..352.796.0493
Web...www.hernandosheriff.org
18900 Cortez Blvd, Brooksville, FL 34601-3027
Al Nienhuis, Sheriff

EDUCATION SERVICES

Exceptional Student Education............352.797.7022
Fax..352.797.7122
900 Emerson Rd, Brooksville, FL 34601
Cathy Doska, Director

Highlands County

GENERAL HEALTH SERVICES

Dept Of Health.............................863.386.6040
Fax..863.386.6048
Web...www.doh.state.fl.us
7205 S George Blvd, Sebring, FL 33875-5847
Barbara Moore, Nursing Director

MENTAL HEALTH SERVICES

Human Svcs................................863.452.3858
Fax..863.452.3863
Web...www.tchsonline.com
100 W College Dr, Avon Park, FL 33825-9348

JUSTICE AGENCY

Dept Of Juvenile Justice.................863.471.5300
Fax..863.471.5320
Web...www.djj.state.fl.us
E-mail.................andrea.conner@djj.state.fl.us
4511 Sun N Lake Blvd Ste 111, Sebring,
FL 33872-2169
Andrea Conner, Supervisor

POLICE AND SHERIFF

Sheriff's Dept..............................863.402.7200
Fax..863.402.7296
Web...www.highlandssheriff.org
E-mail.................sbenton@highlandssheriff.org
434 N Fernleaf Ave, Sebring, FL 33870
Susan Benton, Sheriff

Hillsborough County

SOCIAL SERVICES

Florida Dept Of Children &
Families **813.558.5900**
Fax 813.558.5870
   9393 N Florida Ave, Tampa, FL 33612
   Mike Carroll, Regional Director

GENERAL HEALTH SERVICES

Florida Dept Of Children & Families - Sun Coast
Region **813.558.5500**
Fax 813.558.5538
Web .... www.dcf.state.fl.us
E-mail .... nick_cox@dcf.state.fl.us
   9393 N Florida Ave, Tampa, FL 33612-7907
   Nick Cox, District Administrator

Health & Social Svcs Dept/ Ryan White
Prog **813.272.6935**
Fax 813.276.8593
E-mail .... arnolda@hillsboroughcounty.org
   601 E Kennedy Blvd Fl 25, Tampa, FL 33602
   Aubrey Arnold, Program Manager

Health Dept **813.307.8000**
Fax 813.272.6984
   1105 E Kennedy Blvd, Tampa, FL 33602-3511
   Faye Coe, Nursing Director

JUSTICE AGENCY

Children's Justice Ctr **813.272.7179**
Fax 813.276.2404
Web www.fljud13.com
E-mail .... watermpl@fljud13.org
   700 E Twiggs St Ste 102, Tampa, FL 33602-4020
   Patricia Waterman, Director

Dept Of Juvenile Justice **813.744.8902**
Fax 813.744.8908
Web .... www.djj.state.fl.us
E-mail .... steven.mullis@djj.state.fl.us
   4524 Oak Fair Blvd Ste 100, Tampa, FL 33610
   Steven Mullis, Regional Director

Guardian Ad Litem **813.272.5110**
Fax 813.272.6821
   700 E Twiggs St Rm 750, Tampa, FL 33602
   Suzanne Parker, Director

Juvenile Detention Ctr **813.871.7650**
Fax 813.873.4764
Web .... www.djj.state.fl.us
E-mail .... shannon.burch@djj.state.fl.us
   3948 W Dr Martin Luther King Jr Blvd, Tampa,
   FL 33614-8404
   Shannon Burch, Assistant Superintendent

COURTS

13th Circuit Court **813.276.8100**
Fax 813.272.5146
   800 E Twiggs St Ste 102, GEORGE E EDGECOMB
   COURTHOUSE, Tampa, FL 33602
   Honorable Katherine G. Essrig, Juvenile Judge

Shock Education Program **813.272.6779**
Fax 813.301.3837
Web .... www.fljud.org
E-mail .... pinesmb@fljud13.org
   700 E Twiggs St Ste 810, Tampa, FL 33602-4020
   Maggie Pines, Shock Education Coordinator

POLICE AND SHERIFF

Sheriff's Dept **813.247.8000**
Fax 813.247.0980
Web .... www.hcso.tampa.fl.us
   2008 E 8th Ave, Tampa, FL 33605
   David Gee, Sheriff

EDUCATION SERVICES

Brandon Head Start **813.272.5140**
Fax 813.975.2161
   3639 W Waters Ave, Tampa, FL 33614
   Louis Finney Jr., Director

Deloris Mccloud Headstart **813.273.3688**
Fax 813.276.2169
   2103 N Rome Ave, Tampa, FL 33607-3509
   Sorbenia Menendez, Center Coordinator

Holmes County

SOCIAL SERVICES

Florida Dept Of Children &
Families **850.547.8530**
Fax 850.547.8682
Web .... www.myflorida.com
   117 S Waukesha St, Bonifay, FL 32425
   Beau Whitfield, Program Administrator

COURTS

14th Circuit Court **850.547.1101**
Fax 850.547.6630
Web .... www.holmesclerk.com
   201 N Oklahoma St Ste 201, Bonifay, FL 32425-2243
   Cody Taylor, Court Clerk

POLICE AND SHERIFF

Sheriff's Dept **850.547.3681**
Fax 850.547.2290
Web .... www.flcjn.net
   211 N Oklahoma St, Bonifay, FL 32425-2221
   Jena Prescott, Teen Court Coordinator

Indian River County

SOCIAL SERVICES

Florida Dept Of Children &
Families **772.770.6701**
Fax 772.778.7280
Web .... www.dcf.state.fl.us
E-mail .... info@doh.state.fl.us
   1145 18th Pl, Vero Beach, FL 32960-3798
   Tim Slaven, Supervisor

GENERAL HEALTH SERVICES

Health Dept **772.794.7400**
Fax 772.794.7453
Web .... www.myirchd.com
   1900 27th St, Vero Beach, FL 32960
   Joni Gathmann, Nutrition/wic Director

POLICE AND SHERIFF

Sheriff's Dept **772.569.6700**
Fax 772.569.8344
Web .... www.ircsheriff.org
E-mail .... ircsheriff@ircsheriff.org
   4055 41st Ave, Vero Beach, FL 32960-1802
   Deryl Loar, Sheriff

Jackson County

SOCIAL SERVICES

Anchorage Children's Home
Society **850.482.9568**
Fax 850.482.3183
E-mail .... pphillips@bigbendcbc.org
   4452 Clinton St, Marianna, FL 32446
   Patricia Phillips, Program Manager

GENERAL HEALTH SERVICES

Health Dept **850.526.2412**
Fax 850.482.9978
Web .... www.doh.state.fl.us
E-mail .... julie_mckinney@doh.state.fl.us
   3045 4th St, Marianna, FL 32446-2126
   Julie Mckinney, Nursing Director

JUSTICE AGENCY

Guardian Ad Litem Program **850.482.9127**
Fax 850.482.9108
Web .... www.gal.fl.gov
   2870 Madison St, Marianna, FL 32448-4610
   June Lashbrook, Director

COURTS

14th Circuit Court **850.482.9552**
Fax 850.482.7849
Web .... www.jacksonclerk.com
E-mail .... clerkjack@digitalexe.com
   4445 Lafayette St, Marianna, FL 32446
   Honorable William L. Wright, Judge

Teen Court **850.526.4496**
Fax 850.526.3221
E-mail .... jcteencourt@yahoo.com
   4440 Lafayette St Ste E, Marianna, FL 32446-3411
   Sylvia S. Henry, Director

POLICE AND SHERIFF

Sheriff's Dept **850.482.9624**
Fax 850.482.9017
Web .... www.jcsheriff.com
   4012 Lafayette St, Marianna, FL 32446-8927
   Lois Roberts, Sheriff

Jefferson County

COURTS

2nd Circuit Court **850.342.0218**
Fax 850.342.0222
Web .... www.jeffersoncountyclerk.com
   Jefferson County Courthouse, 1 Courthouse Cir,
   Monticello, FL 32344
   Honorable L. Ralph Smith, Judge

POLICE AND SHERIFF

Sheriff's Dept **850.997.2523**
Fax 850.997.5861
E-mail .... hobbsdc@flcjn.net
   171 Industrial Park, Monticello, FL 32344
   David C. Hobbs, Sheriff

EDUCATION SERVICES

Communities In Schools **850.342.0100**
Fax 850.342.0108
E-mail .... norton_k@firn.edu
   575 S Water St, Monticello, FL 32344
   Kevin Norton, Assistant Superintendent

Lafayette County

COURTS

3rd Circuit Court **386.294.1600**
Fax 386.294.4231
Web .... www.lafayetteclerk.com
E-mail .... rnlclerk@yahoo.com
   120 W Main St, Mayo, FL 32066
   Ricky Lyons, Court Clerk

POLICE AND SHERIFF

Sheriff's Dept **386.294.1222**
Fax 386.294.1190
E-mail .... blamb@lafayettecountysheriffsoffice.com
   178 NW Crawford, St.Mayo, FL 32066
   Brian Lamb, Sheriff

Lake County

GENERAL HEALTH SERVICES

Dept Of Health **352.589.6424**
Fax 352.589.6492
Web .... www.lakechd.com
E-mail .... donna_gregory@doh.state.fl.us
   16140 US Highway 441, Eustis, FL 32726-6508
   Donna Gregory, Administrator

COURTS

5th Circuit Court..........................**352.742.4121**
Fax..........................352.742.4166
550 W Main St, Tavares, FL 32778-3126
Honorable G. Richard Singletary, Judge

POLICE AND SHERIFF

Sheriff's Dept..........................**352.343.2101**
Fax..........................352.343.9505
Web..........................www.lcso.org
E-mail..........................sheriff@lcso.org
360 W Ruby St, Tavares, FL 32778-3826
Gary Borders, Sheriff

EDUCATION SERVICES

**Clermont Head Start And Early Head
Start**..........................**352.394.4289**
Fax..........................352.394.6657
690 E Desoto St, Clermont, FL 34711
Barbara Mcconnell, Director

**Eustis Head Start Child Development
Ctr**..........................**352.483.3976**
Fax..........................352.483.2360
Web..........................www.communityactionpartnership.com
550 E Mcdonald Ave, Eustis, FL 32726-3644
Patricia Miller, Director

Lee County

GENERAL HEALTH SERVICES

Children's Medical Svcs..........................**239.433.6723**
Fax..........................239.433.6739
Web..........................www.doh.state.fl.us
9800 S Healthpark Dr Ste 405, Fort Myers,
FL 33908-3630
John Ritrosky, MD, Cms Medical Director

Health Dept..........................**239.332.9501**
Fax..........................239.656.2514
Web..........................www.leechd.com
E-mail..........................judith_hartnermd@doh.state.fl.us
3920 Michigan Ave, Fort Myers, FL 33916-2205
Judith A. Hartner, Md, Mph, Chd Director

JUSTICE AGENCY

Dept Of Juvenile Justice..........................**239.338.2493**
Fax..........................239.338.2663
Web..........................www.djj.state.fl.us
E-mail..........................margaret.lamarca@djj.state.fl.us
2295 Victoria Ave Ste 195, Fort Myers,
FL 33901-3866
Margaret Lamarca, Chief Performance Officer

Guardian Ad Litem Program..........................**239.533.5437**
Fax..........................239.337.1380
Web..........................www.gal.fl.gov
E-mail..........................frank.prado@gal.fl.gov
2075 W 1st St Ste 300, Fort Myers, FL 33901
Frank Prado, Executive Director

Juvenile Detention Ctr..........................**239.332.6927**
Fax..........................239.332.6931
E-mail..........................vincent.verro@djj.state.fl.us
2525 Ortiz Ave, Fort Myers, FL 33905
Vincent Verro, Director

Juvenile Justice Ofc..........................**239.433.6710**
Fax..........................239.433.6720
6296 Corporate Ct Ste A101, Fort Myers, FL 33919
Lut Sagrado, Supervisor

POLICE AND SHERIFF

Sheriff's Dept..........................**239.477.1000**
Fax..........................239.477.1030
E-mail..........................mscott@sheriffleefl.org
14750 Ben C Pratt, 6 Mile Cypress Pkwy, Fort Myers,
FL 33912
Mike Scott, Sheriff

EDUCATION SERVICES

Exceptional Student Education..........................**239.337.8280**
Fax..........................239.337.8653
2855 Colonial Blvd, Fort Myers, FL 33966
Mike Bursztyn, Assistant Director

Leon County

SOCIAL SERVICES

**Florida Dept Of Children &
Families**..........................**850.488.9800**
Fax..........................850.922.4015
E-mail..........................necia_little@dcf.state.fl.us
1317 Winewood Blvd # 202, Tallahassee, FL 32399
Necia Little, Program Administrator

**Florida Dept Of Children & Family Safety Program
Ofc**..........................**850.488.8762**
Fax..........................850.487.0688
1317 Winewood Blvd Rm 157, Tallahassee, FL 32399
Alan Abramowitz, Director

GENERAL HEALTH SERVICES

Children's Medical Svcs..........................**850.487.2604**
Fax..........................850.922.2123
Web..........................www.cms-kids.com
2390 Phillips Rd, Tallahassee, FL 32308-5326
Mary Seay, CMS Nursing Director

MENTAL HEALTH SERVICES

Eastwood Medical Ctr..........................**850.513.0067**
Fax..........................850.561.6670
Web..........................www.eastwoodmedicalnutritioncenter.com
E-mail..........................jgibbson@eastwoodmedicalnutritioncenter.com
1626 N Plaza Dr, Tallahassee, FL 32308-5323
Janet Gibbson, Do, Medical Director

JUSTICE AGENCY

Dept Of Juvenile Justice..........................**850.487.4251**
Fax..........................850.922.0132
E-mail..........................rick.bedson@djj.state.fl.us
2737 Centerview Dr, Tallahassee, FL 32399
Richard Bedson, Regional Director

Juvenile Detention Ctr..........................**850.488.7672**
Fax..........................850.414.8780
Web..........................www.djj.state.fl.us
E-mail..........................cody.wood@djj.state.fl.us
2303 Ronellis Dr, Tallahassee, FL 32310-5927
Cody Wood, Superintendent

**Probation And Parole Field Svcs Program
Ofc**..........................**850.922.3623**
Fax..........................850.488.4790
Web..........................www.dc.state.fl.us
E-mail..........................tallahassee.cir@mail.dc.state.fl.us
1250 Blountstown Hwy Ste H, Tallahassee,
FL 32304-2762
John Walkup, Circuit Administrator

COURTS

2nd Circuit Court (Juvenile Div)..........................**850.577.4120**
Fax..........................850.577.8015
301 s monroe st, STE 100, Tallahassee, FL 32301
Karen Gievers, Judge

Teen Court..........................**850.577.4401**
Fax..........................850.487.7947
Web..........................www.leoncountyfl.gov/teencourt
E-mail..........................shawd@leoncountyfl.gov
301 S Monroe St, Rm 225, Tallahassee, FL 32301
Deborah Shaw, Director

POLICE AND SHERIFF

Sheriff's Office..........................**850.922.3300**
Fax..........................850.922.3337
2825 Municipal Way, Tallahassee, FL 32304
Larry Campbell, Sheriff

EDUCATION SERVICES

Bond Head Start..........................**850.222.9235**
Fax..........................850.201.2057
1805 Keith St, Tallahassee, FL 32310-5316
Annetenette Brown, Director

Exceptional Student Education..........................**850.487.7158**
Fax..........................850.487.7823
Web..........................www.leon.k12.fl.us
2757 W Pensacola St, Tallahassee, FL 32304-2907
Bev Owens, Executive Director

Levy County

GENERAL HEALTH SERVICES

Dept Of Health..........................**352.486.5300**
Fax..........................352.486.5307
Web..........................www.doh.state.fl.us
66 W Main St, Bronson, FL 32621-6338
Barbara Locke, Rn, Administrator

POLICE AND SHERIFF

Sheriff's Dept..........................**352.486.5111**
Fax..........................352.486.5116
E-mail..........................info@levyso.com
9150 NE 80th Ave, Bronson, FL 32621
Johnny Smith, Sheriff

Liberty County

GENERAL HEALTH SERVICES

Dept Of Health..........................**850.643.2415**
Fax..........................850.643.5689
E-mail..........................lisa_taylor@doh.state.fl.us
12832 NW Central Ave, Bristol, FL 32321
Lisa Taylor, Rn, Nursing Director

COURTS

2nd Circuit Court..........................**850.643.2215**
Fax..........................850.643.2866
Web..........................www.libertyclerk.com
10818 NW State Road 20, Bristol, FL 32321-6400
John C Cooper, Judge

POLICE AND SHERIFF

Sheriff's Dept..........................**850.643.2235**
Fax..........................850.643.1191
12499 NW Pogo St, Bristol, FL 32321
Donnie Conyers, Sheriff

Madison County

GENERAL HEALTH SERVICES

Dept Of Health..........................**850.973.5000**
Fax..........................850.973.5006
E-mail..........................bonnie_webb@doh.state.fl.us
218 SW Third Ave, Madison, FL 32340
Bonnie Webb, Rn, Nursing Director

JUSTICE AGENCY

Dept Of Juvenile Justice..........................**850.973.5212**
Fax..........................850.973.5214
1719 S Jefferson St, Perry, FL 32348-5612
Alen Hall, Supervisor

POLICE AND SHERIFF

Sheriff's Dept..........................**850.973.4151**
Fax..........................850.973.8508
E-mail..........................sheriff@mcso-fl.org
239 SW Pinckney St, Madison, FL 32340
Ben Stewart, Sheriff

Florida

Manatee County

SOCIAL SERVICES

Manatee Children's Svcs Child Protection
Team **941.345.1200**
Fax 941.345.1212
Web ....www.manateechildrensservices.com
E-mail ....info@mcsfl.com
465 Cortez Rd W, Bradenton, FL 34207-1544
Melinda Thompson, Executive Director

GENERAL HEALTH SERVICES

Dept Of Health **941.748.0747**
Fax 941.714.7207
Web ....www.doh.state.fl.us
E-mail ....robert_merlosi@doh.state.fl.us
410 6th Ave E, Bradenton, FL 34208-1986
Dr. Jennifer Bencie, Director

JUSTICE AGENCY

Dept Of Juvenile Justice **941.727.6300**
Fax 941.727.6241
Web ....www.djj.state.fl.us
E-mail ....virginia.donovan@djj.state.fl.us
701 Cortez Rd W, Bradenton, FL 34207-1557
Virginia Donovan, Chief Of Probation

Guardian Ad Litem **941.744.9473**
Fax 941.708.5723
Web www.12gal.org
1201 6th Ave W Ste 510, Bradenton, FL 34205-7420
Pam Hindman, Director

Juvenile Detention Ctr **941.741.3023**
Fax 941.741.3061
E-mail ....frank.gargett@djj.state.fl.us
1803 5th St W, Bradenton, FL 34205-8309
Frank Gargett, Superintendent

COURTS

Teen Court **941.741.4027**
Fax 941.749.7108
Web ....www.manateeclerk.com
1115 25th Ave W, Bradenton, FL 34205-7420
Sue Lockliear, Supervisor

POLICE AND SHERIFF

Sheriff's Ofc **941.747.3011**
Fax 941.749.5401
Web ....www.manateesheriff.com
600 301 Blvd W, Bradenton, FL 34205-7723
Brad Stube, Sheriff

EDUCATION SERVICES

Exceptional Student Ed. **941.708.8770**
Fax 941.708.8655
Web www.manatee.k12.fl.us
E-mail ....bealn@manateeschools.net
215 Manatee Ave W, Bradenton, FL 34205-8840
Nancy Beal, Executive Director, District Planning, Policy & Program Evaluation

Marion County

GENERAL HEALTH SERVICES

Dept Of Health **352.629.0137**
Fax 352.694.4824
Web ....www.doh.state.fl.us
1801 SE 32nd Ave, Ocala, FL 34478
Barbara Rahem, Aids Supervisor

JUSTICE AGENCY

Dept of Juvenile Justice **352.732.1727**
Fax 352.732.1343
1515 E Silver Springs Blvd Ste 117, Ocala, FL 34470
Jim Donnan, Supervisor

Dept Of Juvenile Justice **352.620.7405**
Fax 352.620.7804
Web ....www.djj.state.fl.us
E-mail ....rick.betson@djj.state.fl.us
3040 NW 10th St, Ocala, FL 34475-4553
Rick Betson, Chief Of Detention NE

Fifth Judicial Circuit Guardian Ad Litem
Program **352.369.2525**
Fax 352.620.3828
E-mail ....gina.johns@gal.fl.gov
223 SW Broadway St, Ocala, FL 34471
Marcia Hilty, Circuit Director

Juvenile Detention Ctr **352.732.1450**
Fax 352.732.1457
E-mail ....dixie.fosler@djj.state.fl.us
3040 NW 10th St, Ocala, FL 34475
Dixie Fosler, Superintendent

POLICE AND SHERIFF

Sheriff's Ofc **352.732.8181**
Fax 352.620.7209
Web ....www.sheriff.marioncountyfl.org
E-mail ....sheriff@marionso.com
692 NW 30th Ave, Ocala, FL 34475-5608
Ed Dean, Sheriff

EDUCATION SERVICES

Exceptional Student Education **352.671.6832**
Fax 352.671.6833
Web www.marion.k12.fl.us
E-mail ....wylane.cayasso@marion.k12.fl.us
1517 SE 30th Ave, Ste 2, Ocala, FL 34471-4932
Wylane Cayasso, Director Of Student Services

Martin County

GENERAL HEALTH SERVICES

Health Dept **772.221.4037**
Fax 772.221.4041
Web ....www.myflorida.com
E-mail ....maureen.ryan@myflorida.com
3441 SE Willoughby Blvd, Stuart, FL 34994-5060
Maureen Ryan, RN, BHS, Nursing Director

JUSTICE AGENCY

Dept Of Juvenile Justice **772.221.4921**
Fax 772.221.4940
1111 SE Federal Hwy Ste 210, Stuart, FL 34994-3834
Tara Tracy, Supervisor

POLICE AND SHERIFF

Sheriff's Ofc **772.220.7000**
Fax 772.220.7043
Web ....www.sheriff.martin.fl.us
E-mail ....rcrowder@sheriff.martin.fl.us
800 SE Monterey Rd, Stuart, FL 34994-4507
Robert L. Crowder, Sheriff

EDUCATION SERVICES

Exceptional Student Education **772.219.1200**
Fax 772.219.1228
Web ....www.sbmc.org
E-mail ....tedescc@martin.k12.fl.us
500 SE Ocean Blvd, Bldg 19, Stuart, FL 34994
Catherine Tedesco, Director Of Title 1

Miami-Dade County

SOCIAL SERVICES

Florida Dept Of Children &
Families **305.377.5055**
Fax 305.377.5770
Web ....www.state.fl.us/cf_web/
401 NW 2nd Ave Ste N1007, N TOWER, ROOM 1007, Miami, FL 33128
Gilda Ferradaz, Circuit Administrator

GENERAL HEALTH SERVICES

Children's Medical Svcs North **305.349.1330**
Fax 305.349.1332
Web ....www.cms-kids.com
155 S Miami Ave, Fl 10, Miami, FL 33130
Alma Vega, CMS Nursing Director

Ofc of Strategic Business
Management **305.375.5143**
Fax 305.375.5168
Web ....www.miamidade.gov
E-mail ....webmaster@miamidade.gov
111 NW 1st St, Fl 22, Miami, FL 33128
Jennifer Glazer-moon, Project Director

University Of Miami Child Protection
Team **305.243.7550**
Fax 305.243.7548
Web ....www.doh.state.fl.us
E-mail ....wlambert@med.miami.edu
1150 NW 14th St Ste 212, Miami, FL 33136-2113
Walter Lambert, Md, Medical Director

JUSTICE AGENCY

Delinquency Prevention Svcs **305.755.6283**
Fax 305.753.6301
275 NW 2nd St Fl 2, Miami, FL 33128-1760

Guardian Ad Litem **305.638.6861**
Fax 305.638.6017
Web www.voices4.org
3302 NW 27th Ave Unit N, Miami, FL 33142-5884
Sonia Ferrer, Executive Director

Juvenile Detention Ctr **305.637.4500**
Fax 305.637.2812
Web ....www.djj.state.fl.us
3300 NW 27th Ave, Miami, FL 33142
Dale Dobler, Superintendent

POLICE AND SHERIFF

Miami-Dade Police Dept **305.418.7200**
Fax 305.418.7221
E-mail ....dcbinfo@mdpd.com
1701 Nw 87th Ave, Ste 100, Doral, FL 33172
James K Loftus, Director

EDUCATION SERVICES

Biscayne Elementary Head Start **305.868.7727**
Fax 305.864.5543
E-mail ....biscayne@dadeschools.net
800 77th St, Miami Beach, FL 33141
Maria Costa, Principal

Carol City Elementary YMCA After School
Program **305.621.0509**
Fax 305.620.5638
4375 NW 173rd Dr, Opa Locka, FL 33055
Patricia Blood, Principal

Carrie P Meek Headstart &
Childcare **305.694.2769**
Web ....www.communityactionpartnership.com
E-mail ....jatru@miamidade.gov
1900 NW 75th St, Miami, FL 33147-6139
Janet Trujillo, Director

Colonial Drive Elementary Head
Start **305.238.2392**
Fax 305.232.9405
Web ....www.dadeschools.net
10755 SW 160th St, Miami, FL 33157-2999
Maria Chappotin, Principal

Communities In Schools Of Miami,
Inc. **305.252.5444**
Fax 305.252.4664
Web ....www.cismiami.org
11965 SW 142nd Ter Ste 102, Miami, FL 33186
Elizabeth Mejia, Executive Director

Douglas Elementary Head Start 305.371.4687
Fax 305.350.7590
Web .... www.frederickdouglass.dadeschools.net
　　314 NW 12th St, Miami, FL 33136-2597
　　Sanders White, Principal

Dr. Edward L. Whigham
Elementary 305.234.4840
Fax 305.234.4837
　　21545 SW 87th Ave, Miami, FL 33189-7322
　　Susan Lyle, Principal

Dupuis Elementary Head Start 305.558.1536
Fax 305.820.8553
E-mail .... jane_robinson@doh.state.fl.us
　　1150 W 59th Pl, Hialeah, FL 33012
　　Jane Robinson, Director

Florida Diagnostic And Learning Resource System
South 305.274.3501
Fax 305.598.7752
Web .... www.fdlrs-south.dadeschools.net
E-mail .... dyancoskie@dadeschools.net
　　5555 SW 93rd Ave, Miami, FL 33165-6548
　　Delsey Yancoskie, Instructional Supervisor

Ofc Of Special Education And Phsycological
Svcs 305.995.1721
Fax 305.995.2053
Web .... www.ese.dayschools.net
E-mail .... wgordillo@dadeschools.net
　　1500 Biscayne Blvd Ste 407, Miami, FL 33132-1435
　　William Gordillo, Administrative Director

Monroe County

SOCIAL SERVICES

Dept Of Children & Families 305.292.6745
Fax 305.292.6809
Web .... www.myflorida.com/access
E-mail .... elena_george@dcf.state.fl.us
　　1111 12th St Ste 304, Key West, FL 33040-3001
　　Elena George, Economic Services Supervisor

GENERAL HEALTH SERVICES

Children's Medical Svcs 800.342.1898
Fax 305.289.2781
　　10015 Overseas Hwy, Marathon, FL 33050
　　Dr. Alma Vega, Nursing Director

JUSTICE AGENCY

Dept Of Juvenile Justice 305.292.6737
Fax 305.293.6345
　　5503 College Rd Ste 209, Key West, FL 33040
　　Lawanna Tynes, Superintendent

Guardian Ad Litem 305.292.3485
Fax 305.295.3659
E-mail .... aclgal@aol.com
　　5503 College Rd, Ste 206, Key West, FL 33040
　　Alexsandra Leto, Circuit Director

COURTS

16th Circuit Court 305.292.3423
Fax 305.295.3611
E-mail .... dkolhage@keysso.net
　　302 Fleming St, Key West, FL 33040
　　Danny Kolhage, Clerk Of Court

POLICE AND SHERIFF

Sheriff's Dept 305.296.2424
Fax 305.292.7070
　　5525 College Rd, Key West, FL 33040
　　Robert Peryam, Sheriff

Nassau County

COURTS

4th Circuit Court 904.548.4600
Fax 904.548.4508
Web .... www.nassauclerk.com
E-mail .... gburgess@nassauclerk.com
　　76347 Veterans Way Ste 456, Yulee, FL 32097-5404
　　Honorable Granville Burgess, Judge

POLICE AND SHERIFF

Sheriff's Dept 904.225.0331
Fax 904.225.0443
E-mail .... sheriff@nassaucountysheriff.com
　　76001 Bobby Moore Cir, Yulee, FL 32097
　　Tommy Seagraves, Sheriff

Okaloosa County

SOCIAL SERVICES

Child Protection 850.833.9237
Fax 850.833.9238
Web .... www.eccac.org
　　401 McEwen Dr, Niceville, FL 32578-2741
　　Julie Hurst, Program Director

Florida Dept Of Children &
Families 850.689.7777
Fax 850.689.7772
Web .... www.dcf.state.fl.us
E-mail .... david_stout@dcf.state.fl.us
　　330 W Jameslee Blvd, Crestview, FL 32536-3799
　　David Stout, CPI Supervisor

GENERAL HEALTH SERVICES

Health Dept 850.833.9240
Fax 850.833.9252
Web .... www.doh.state.fl.us
　　221 Hospital Dr NE, Fort Walton Beach,
　　FL 32548-5066
　　Karen Chapman, Md, Mph, Director

JUSTICE AGENCY

Dept Of Juvenile Justice 850.833.3906
Fax 850.833.3794
　　111 Racetrack Rd NW Ste D, Fort Walton Beach,
　　FL 32547
　　Reba Chavis, Supervisor

Guardian Ad Litem Program 850.609.5467
Fax 850.609.5469
　　101 E James Lee Blvd, CRESTFEILD, FL 32536
　　Rosemary Ash, Circuit Director

Guardian Ad Litem Program 850.689.5060
Fax 850.689.5517
　　302 N Wilson St Ste 201, Crestview, FL 32536
　　Lecia Reeder, Case Coordinator

COURTS

Teen Court 850.609.1133
Fax 850.664.0187
E-mail .... sreed@lsfnet.org
　　51-B Yacht Club Drive, Ft. Walton Beach, FL 32548
　　Sean Reed, Project Coordinator

Teen Court-Hope House 850.682.2374
Fax 850.682.8495
Web .... www.lsfnet.org
　　5127 Eastland St, Crestview, FL 32539-7326
　　Sean Reed, Coordinator

POLICE AND SHERIFF

Fort Walton Beach Police
Department 850.833.9547
Fax 850.833.9563
E-mail .... tlitschauer@fwb.org
　　7 Hollywood Blvd NE, Fort Walton Beach, FL 32548
　　Ted Litschauer, Chief

EDUCATION SERVICES

Crestview Head Start 850.682.5931
Fax 850.683.3694
Web .... www.okaloosaheadstart.com
E-mail .... j.clark@okaloosaheadstart.com
　　227 Lakeview Dr, Crestview, FL 32536-2476
　　Janet Clark, Director

Exceptional Student Education 850.833.3164
Fax 850.833.3488
Web www.okaloosa.k12.fl.us
E-mail .... handzol@mail.okaloosa.k12.fl.us
　　120 Lowery Pl SE, Fort Walton Beach, FL 32548
　　Lois Handzo, Director

Ford Walton Head Start 850.244.2606
Fax 850.244.0426
Web .... www.hsi-headstart.org
E-mail .... jclark@hsi-headstart.org
　　22 McGriff St NE, Ft Walton Bch, FL 32548-4976
　　Janet Clark, Director

Okeechobee County

GENERAL HEALTH SERVICES

Dept Of Health 863.462.5819
Fax 863.462.5219
Web .... www.doh.state.fl.us
E-mail .... vicki_elkins@doh.state.fl.us
　　1728 NW 9th Ave, Okeechobee, FL 34972-4340
　　Vicki Elkins, Aids Coordinator

COURTS

19th Circuit Court 863.763.1240
Fax 863.763.1242
Web www.circuit19.org
E-mail .... mcmanuss@circuit19.org
　　312 NW 3rd St, Fl 348, Okeechobee, FL 34972
　　Honorable F. Shields Mcmanus, Judge

POLICE AND SHERIFF

Sheriff's Ofc 863.763.3117
Fax 863.763.7157
Web .... www.sheriff.co.okeechobee.fl.us
E-mail .... sheriff@sheriff.co.okeechobee.fl.us
　　504 NW 4th St, Okeechobee, FL 34972-2592
　　Paul C. May, Sheriff

EDUCATION SERVICES

Communities In Schools 863.462.5863
Fax 863.462.5067
E-mail .... cispaljr@live.com
　　575 SW 28th St, New Endeavour School Building,
　　Okeechobee, FL 34973
　　Jill Rogers, Director

Orange County

GENERAL HEALTH SERVICES

Children's Medical Svcs Network
Clinic 407.856.6519
Fax 407.856.6558
　　7000 Lake Ellenor Dr, Orlando, FL 32809
　　Joseph Chiaro, MD, CMS Medical Director

Eastside Health Ctr 407.249.6232
Fax 407.249.4456
Web .... www.myflorida.com
　　12050 E Colonial Dr, Orlando, FL 32826-4799
　　Wick, Clerk

Winter Park Family Health Ctr 407.679.9222
Fax 407.679.9061
　　2950 Aloma Ave Ste 100, Winter Park,
　　FL 32792-3694
　　Rahn Shaw, Physician

Florida

JUSTICE AGENCY

Juvenile Detention Ctr **407.897.2800**
Fax 407.897.2856
Web ....www.djj.state.fl.us
E-mail ....jeffrey.lomton@djj.state.fl.us
  2800 S Bumby Ave, Orlando, FL 32806-5698
  Jeffery Lomton, Director

COURTS

9th Circuit Court **407.836.7590**
Fax 407.836.7599
Web www.9circuit.org
E-mail ....ctadlb1@ocnjcc.org
  2000 E Michigan St, Juvenile Justice Center, Orlando,
  FL 32806-4941
  Laura Brimmer, Court Operations Manager

POLICE AND SHERIFF

Sheriff's Ofc **407.254.7000**
Fax 407.254.7255
  2500 W Colonial Dr, Orlando, FL 32802
  Jerry Demings, Sheriff

St. Cloud Police Dept **407.891.6700**
Fax 407.892.4569
Web ....www.stcloud.org
  4700 Neptune Rd, Saint Cloud, FL 34769-3308
  Peter Gauntlett, Chief

EDUCATION SERVICES

Bithlo Community Head Start **407.568.4025**
Fax 407.568.3620
  18501 Washington Ave, Orlando, FL 32820-2556
  Jarnac Williams, Director

ESE **407.317.3229**
Fax 407.317.3310
Web ....www.ocps.net
  445 W Amelia St, Fl 6, Orlando, FL 32801
  Anna D. Diaz, Associate Superintendent

Osceola County

GENERAL HEALTH SERVICES

Dept Of Health **407.343.2000**
Fax 407.343.2002
Web ....www.osceolahealth.org
E-mail ....rose_vince@doh.state.fl.us
  1875 Boggy Creek Rd, Kissimmee, FL 34744-4428
  Rose Vince, Nursing Director/aids Coordinator

POLICE AND SHERIFF

Kissimmee Police Dept **407.846.3333**
Fax 407.847.0460
  8 N Stewart Ave, Kissimmee, FL 34741
  Fran Iwanski, Chief Police

Sheriff's Ofc **407.348.1100**
Fax 407.348.3395
Web ....www.osceolasheriff.com
  2601 E Irlo Bronson Memorial Hwy, Kissimmee,
  FL 34744-4912
  Bob Hansell, Sheriff

Palm Beach County

SOCIAL SERVICES

**Florida Dept Of Children &
Families** **561.837.5078**
Fax 561.837.5696
Web ....www.dcf.state.fl.us
E-mail ....steve_faroni@dcf.state.fl.us
  111 S Sapodilla Ave Fl 3, West Palm Beach,
  FL 33401-5212
  Steve Faroni, Family Safety Program Administrator

MENTAL HEALTH SERVICES

Lifeskills Of Boca Raton **800.749.7149**
Fax 561.392.4341
Web ....www.lifeskillsofboca.com
E-mail ....info@lifeskillsofboca.com
  770 W Camino Real, Ste 100, Boca Raton, FL 33486

JUSTICE AGENCY

Guardian Ad Litem **561.355.2773**
Fax 561.355.2717
E-mail ....cicely.roberts@gal.fl.gov
  205 N Dixie Hwy, Ste 51130, West Palm Beach,
  FL 33401
  Cicely Roberts, Circuit Director

Guardian Ad Litem **561.992.1108**
Fax 561.996.4854
Web ....www.gal.fl.gov
E-mail ....maria.montesinos@gal.fl.gov
  2976 St Rd 15, Belle Glade, FL 33430-5300
  Maria Montesinos, Case Coordinator

COURTS

15th Circuit Juvenile Court **561.355.6227**
Fax 561.355.6701
  205 N Dixie Hwy, West Palm Beach, FL 33401-4522
  Stephen Mcgraw, Psychology Section Director

Youth Court **561.682.0032**
Fax 561.682.0037
Web www.palmbeach.k12.fl.us
E-mail ....cummings@palmbeach.k12.fl.us
  3400 Belvedere Rd, West Palm Beach, FL 33406-1525
  James Cummings, Center Manager

EDUCATION SERVICES

Communities In Schools **561.471.9681**
Fax 561.471.9682
Web ....www.cispbc.org
E-mail ....info@cispbc.org
  1660 Southern Blvd Ste N, West Palm Beach,
  FL 33406-3219
  Margaret Bagley, Executive Director

Exceptional Student Education **561.434.8626**
Fax 561.434.8384
Web www.palmbeach.k12.fl.us
  3378 Forest Hill Blvd, Ste A-203, West Palm Beach,
  FL 33406
  Laura Pincus, Director

Pasco County

SOCIAL SERVICES

**Florida Dept Of Children &
Families** **727.834.3900**
Fax 727.834.3903
Web ....www.myflorida.com/accessflorida
E-mail ....patty_wisman@dcf.state.fl.us
  7601 Little Rd, Fl 2, New Port Richey, FL 34654
  Patty Wisman, Program Administrator

GENERAL HEALTH SERVICES

Dept Of Health **727.861.5250**
Fax 727.861.4873
E-mail ....carol_cummins@doh.state.fl.us
  10841 Little Rd, New Port Richey, FL 34654-2513
  Carol Cummins, Nursing Director- AIDS Coord

JUSTICE AGENCY

Dept Of Juvenile Justice **727.841.4151**
Fax 727.841.4358
  7619 Little Rd, Ste C-200, New Port Richey, FL 34654
  Mike Schumaker, Supervisor

Dept Of Juvenile Justice

Dept Of Juvenile Justice **352.521.1320**
Fax 352.523.5079
Web ....www.djj.state.fl.us
E-mail ....harold.garvis@djj.state.fl.us
  14437 7th St, Dade City, FL 33523-3126
  Harold Garvis, Juvenile Justice Manager

Guardian Ad Litem **727.834.3493**
Fax 727.834.3470
E-mail ....mflanner@co.pinellas.fl.us
  7530 Little Rd, New Port Richey, FL 34654
  Donna Rasmussen, Circuit Director

Guardian Ad Litem Program **352.521.5178**
Fax 352.521.5156
Web www.guardianadlitem6.org
E-mail ....kelly.rossi@gal.fl.gov
  13920 17th St, Dade City, FL 33525-4602
  Kelly Rossi, Assistant Director-pasco

COURTS

**6th Circuit Court Clerk's Ofc (East
Side)** **352.521.4497**
  38053 Live Oak Ave, Dade City, FL 33523
  Paula O'Neil, Controller & Clerk

**6th Circuit Court Clerk's Ofc (West
Side)** **727.847.8178**
Web ....www.pascoclerk.com
E-mail ....ied.pittman@pascoclerk.com
  7530 Little Road New, Port Richey, FL 34654
  Paula O'Neil, Clerk Of Clerk

EDUCATION SERVICES

Exceptional Student Education **813.794.2600**
Fax 813.794.2117
Web www.pasco.k12.fl.us
E-mail ....mverra@pasco.k12.fl.us
  7227 Land OÆ Lakes Blvd, Land OÆ Lakes, FL 34638
  Dr. Monica Verra Tirado, Director

Pinellas County

SOCIAL SERVICES

**Florida Dept Of Children &
Families** **813.558.5900**
Fax 813.558.5853
Web ....www.myflorida.com
  9393 N Florida Ave, Tampa, FL 33612-7907
  Mike Carroll, Regional Director

JUSTICE AGENCY

Juvenile Detention Ctr **727.538.7101**
Fax 727.538.7318
Web ....www.djj.state.fl.us
E-mail ....janes.uliasz@djj.state.fl.us
  5255 140th Ave N, Clearwater, FL 33760-3742
  Monica Grey, Superintendent

**Sixth Judicial Circuit Guardian Ad Litem
Program** **727.464.6528**
Fax 727.464.7674
Web www.guardianadlitem6.org
E-mail ....donna.rasmussen@gal.fl.gov
  14250 49th St N, Criminal Justice Center, Clearwater,
  FL 33762-2800
  Donna Rasmussen, Director

POLICE AND SHERIFF

Clearwater Police Dept District 3 ....**727.562.4343**
E-mail ....police@clearwater.com
  645 Pierce St, Clearwater, FL 33756
  Anthony Halloway, Chief Of Police

Clearwater Police Dept District II **727.562.4120**
Fax 727.462.4309
E-mail ....anthony.holloway@myclearwater.com
  645 Pierce St, Clearwater, FL 33756-5400
  Anthony Holloway, Chief

Sheriff's Dept 727.582.6200
Fax 727.582.6459
Web ....www.pcsoweb.com
E-mail ....jcoats@pcsonet.com
 10750 Ulmerton Rd, Largo, FL 33779
 Jim Coats, Sheriff

St. Petersburg Police Dept 727.893.7780
Fax 727.892.5099
E-mail ....sppd@stpete.org
 1300 1st Ave N, Saint Petersburg, FL 33705
 Charles Harmond, Chief Of Police

EDUCATION SERVICES

Exceptional Student Education 727.588.6042
Fax 727.588.6441
E-mail ....moorep@tcsd.org
 301 4th St SW, Largo, FL 33770-3536
 Pam Moore, Assistant Superintendent

French Villa Head Start 727.546.3680
 6835 54th Ave N, Saint Petersburg, FL 33709
 Juanita Poinsette, Office Manager

Polk County

SOCIAL SERVICES

**Florida Dept Of Children &
Families** 863.534.7100
Fax 863.519.3891
Web ....www.myflorida.com
 1055 US Hwy 17 N, Bartow, FL 33830
 Julia Hermalbracht, Director

GENERAL HEALTH SERVICES

Health Dept 863.519.7900
Web ....www.mypolkchd.org
 1290 Golfview Ave, Fl 4, Bartow, FL 33830
 Susan Kistler, Nutrition/wic Director

JUSTICE AGENCY

Guardian Ad Litem 863.534.4605
Fax 863.534.2552
E-mail ....cookie.rousos@gal.fl.gov
 255 N Broadway Ave, Bartow, FL 33830
 Cookie Rousos, Circuit Director

Juvenile Detention Ctr 863.534.7090
Fax 863.534.7024
Web ....www.djj.state.fl.us
 2155 Bob Phillips Rd, Bartow, FL 33830-6700
 Elma Adame, Superintendent

EDUCATION SERVICES

Exceptional Student Education 863.534.0930
Fax 863.534.0031
Web ....www.polk-fl.net
 270 Bartow Municipal Airbase, Bartow, FL 33830
 Diane Callaway, Director

Putnam County

JUSTICE AGENCY

Dept Of Juvenile Justice 386.329.3566
Fax 386.329.2526
E-mail ....diane.weller@djj.state.fl.us
 400 N State Rd 19 Ste 42, Palatka, FL 32177
 Diane Weller, Supervisor

POLICE AND SHERIFF

Sheriff's Ofc 386.329.0800
Fax 386.329.0893
Web ....www.putnamsheriff.org
E-mail ....mail@putnamsheriff.org
 130 Orie Griffin Blvd, Palatka, FL 32177
 Jeff Hardy, Sheriff

EDUCATION SERVICES

Communities In Schools 386.328.8875
Fax 386.328.9939
Web ....www.cisnef.org
E-mail ....cisputnam@aol.com
 142 Ferry Rd E, Palatka, FL 32131
 Sandra Hartley, Director

Santa Rosa County

SOCIAL SERVICES

**Florida Dept Of Children &
Families** 850.936.6160
Fax 850.936.6166
 8748 Ortega Park Dr, Navarre, FL 32566

GENERAL HEALTH SERVICES

Dept Of Health 850.983.5200
Fax 850.983.5215
Web ....www.doh.state.fl.us
 5527 Stewart St, Milton, FL 32570-4375
 Jan Whitney, Rn, Nursing Director

JUSTICE AGENCY

Dept Of Juvenile Justice 850.626.3041
Fax 850.983.5519
Web ....www.djj.state.fl.us
E-mail ....martina.leverett@djj.state.fl.us
 6746 Caroline St, Milton, FL 32570-4850
 Martina Leverett, Act. Supervisor

COURTS

1st Circuit Court 850.981.5569
Fax 850.626.5705
 6865 Caroline St, Milton, FL 32570
 Mary M. Johnson, Clerk Of Court

Teen Court 850.626.4730
Fax 850.626.4620
Web ....www.lsfnet.org
E-mail ....jmilstid@lsfnet.org
 5139 Elmira St, Milton, FL 32570-2214
 Jessica Milstid, Project Coordinator

EDUCATION SERVICES

Communities In Schools 850.983.5650
Fax 850.983.5655
Web www.santarosa.k12.fl.us
E-mail ....snellgrovea@santarosa.k12.fl.us
 6658 Park Ave, Milton, FL 32570
 Patrick Mclelland, Director

Sarasota County

SOCIAL SERVICES

**Florida Dept Of Children &
Families** 941.316.6015
Fax 941.316.8099
Web ....www.dcf.state.fl.us
 1864 17th St, Sarasota, FL 34234-7501
 Lynne Johnston, Program Administrator

GENERAL HEALTH SERVICES

Children's Medical Svcs 941.361.6250
Fax 941.361.6272
 6055 Rand Blvd, Sarasota, FL 34238
 Robert Shamsey, Md, CMS Nursing Director

Dept Of Health 941.861.2900
Fax 941.861.2828
Web ....www.sarasotahealth.org
E-mail ....christine_griffith@doh.state.fl.us
 2200 Ringling Blvd, Sarasota, FL 34237-6199
 Christine Griffith, Hiv - Std Director

JUSTICE AGENCY

Dept Of Juvenile Justice 941.358.4215
Fax 941.358.4231
E-mail ....buddy.hall@djj.state.fl.us
 3135 N Washington Blvd, Sarasota, FL 34234
 Buddy Hall, Committment Manager

Guardian Ad Litem 941.861.4875
Fax 941.861.4840
Web www.12gal.org
E-mail ....galvolunteer12@gal.fl.gov
 2071 Ringling Blvd, Ste 625, Sarasota, FL 34237
 Pam Hindman, Program Director

POLICE AND SHERIFF

Sheriff's Ofc 941.861.5800
Fax 941.861.4039
 2071 Ringling Blvd, Sarasota, FL 34237
 Thomas Knight, Sheriff

EDUCATION SERVICES

Exceptional Student Education 941.927.9000
Fax 941.927.4014
 1960 Landings Blvd, Sarasota, FL 34231
 Lori White, Superintendent

Loveland Ctr 941.493.0016
Fax 941.497.6179
Web ....www.lovelandcenter.com
E-mail ....cpenxa@lovelandcenter.com
 157 S Havana Rd, Venice, FL 34292-3104
 Carl Penxa Jr, Executive Director

Seminole County

GENERAL HEALTH SERVICES

Health Dept 407.665.3000
Fax 407.665.3213
Web ....www.seminolecohealth.com
 400 W Airport Blvd, Sanford, FL 32773
 Mehdi Nabipour, Medical Director

JUSTICE AGENCY

Dept Of Juvenile Justice 407.330.6968
Fax 407.330.6997
 532 W Lake Mary Blvd, Sanford, FL 32773
 Denise Devlin, Chief JPO

Guardian Ad Litem 407.665.5370
Fax 407.665.5375
Web ....www.galseminolecounty.org
E-mail ....nadine.miller@gal.fl.gov
 190 Bush Blvd, Sanford, FL 32773-6706
 Nadine Miller, Circuit Director

COURTS

18th Circuit Court 407.665.5350
Fax 407.665.5349
 190 Bush Blvd, Sanford, FL 32773-6706
 Honorable Nancy F Alley, Judge

POLICE AND SHERIFF

Altamonte Springs Police Dept 407.339.2441
 175 Newburyport Ave, Altamonte Springs, FL 32701
 Robert C Merchant, Jr., Police Chief

Sheriff's Dept 407.665.6635
Fax 407.665.6587
Web ....www.seminolesheriff.org
E-mail ....deslinger@seminolesheriff.org
 100 Bush Blvd, Sanford, FL 32773-6706
 Donald Eslinger, Sheriff

EDUCATION SERVICES

Exceptional Student Education 407.320.0203
Fax 407.320.0294
Web www.scps.k12.fl.us
E-mail ....britt_smith@scps.k12.fl.us
 400 E Lake Mary Blvd, Sanford, FL 32773
 Britt Smith, Executive Director

Florida

St. John County

GENERAL HEALTH SERVICES

Dept of Health **904.825.5055**
Fax 904.823.2580
Web ....www.stjohnscountyhealthdepartment.org
E-mail ....dawn_allicock@doh.state.fl.us
   1955 US Highway 1 S Ste 100, Saint Augustine,
   FL 32086-5788
   Dawn Allicock, Director

COURTS

7th Circuit Court **904.819.3600**
Fax 904.819.3662
   4010 Lewis Speedway, Saint Augustine, FL 32084
   Honorable John M. Alexander, Judge

POLICE AND SHERIFF

Sheriff's Dept **904.824.8304**
Fax 904.810.6779
E-mail ....dshoar@co.st-johns.fl.us
   4015 Lewis Speedway, Saint Augustine,
   FL 32084-8611
   David Shoar, Sheriff

EDUCATION SERVICES

Communities In Schools **904.819.6351**
Fax 904.824.2383
Web ....www.stjohnspromise.org
E-mail ....cis2@fdn.com
   74 Riberia St, St Augustine, FL 32084-3562
   Cathy Drake, Director

St. Lucie County

JUSTICE AGENCY

Dept of Juvenile Justice **772.467.3166**
Fax 772.467.3190
   337 N US Highway 1, Suite 305, Fort Pierce,
   FL 34950
   Steve Brown, Chief Executive Officer

Guardian Ad Litem **772.785.5804**
Fax 772.785.5869
   584 NW University Blvd Ste 600, Port St Lucie,
   FL 34986
   Elizabeth Mackenzie, Circuit Director

Juvenile Detention Ctr **772.468.3940**
Fax 772.468.4005
Web ....www.djj.state.fl.us
   1301 Bell Ave, Fort Pierce, FL 34982-6544
   Kevin Housel, Superintendent

Juvenile Restorative Justice
Program **772.871.5294**
Fax 772.344.4298
Web ....www.cityofpsl.com
E-mail ....mmcmurtry@cityofpsl.com
   121 SW Port St Lucie Blvd, Port Saint Lucie,
   FL 34984-5042
   Roger Orr, Legal Advisor

COURTS

19th Circuit Court **772.462.6800**
Fax 772.462.6807
E-mail ....frye@stlucice.org
   435 N 7th St, Fort Pierce, FL 34950-2971
   Edwin M. Fry Jr., Clerk Of Court

POLICE AND SHERIFF

Sheriff's Ofc **772.462.7300**
Fax 772.489.5851
Web ....www.stluciesheriff.com
E-mail ....kmascara@stluciesheriff.com
   4700 W Midway Rd, Fort Pierce, FL 34981-4825
   Ken Mascara, Sheriff

EDUCATION SERVICES

Alpi Morningside Head Start **772.398.8203**
Fax 772.398.0757
E-mail ....cdames@alpi.org
   1420 SE Westmoorland Blvd, Port Saint Lucie,
   FL 34952
   Crystal Dames, Director

Exceptional Student Education **772.429.4570**
Fax 772.429.4589
Web ....www.stlucieschools.org
   4204 Okeechobee Rd, Fort Pierce, FL 34947-5414
   Bill Tomlinson, Assistant Superintendent Of Ese

Sumter County

GENERAL HEALTH SERVICES

Health Dept **352.793.6979**
Fax 352.793.1506
   415 Noble E Virginia Ave, Bushnell, FL 33513
   Keith Hunter, Assistant Health Director

Suwannee County

SOCIAL SERVICES

Florida Dept Of Children & Families
(Investigations) **386.362.2179**
Fax 386.364.1097
Web ....www.dcf.state.fl.us
E-mail ....julie_johnson@dcf.state.fl.us
   501 Demorest St SE, Live Oak, FL 32064-3320
   Julie Johnson, Supervisor

GENERAL HEALTH SERVICES

Dept Of Children & Families **386.362.1483**
Fax 386.364.1612
   501 Demorest St SE, Live Oak, FL 32064-3320
   Norman Crawford, Supervisor

Dept Of Health **386.362.2708**
Fax 386.362.6301
Web ....www.myflorida.com/accessflorida
   915 Nobles Ferry Rd, Live Oak, FL 32064
   Wanda Crowe, Rn, Nursing Director

JUSTICE AGENCY

Guardian Ad Litem **386.364.7720**
Fax 386.364.5419
   213 Howard St E, Live Oak, FL 32064
   Linda Dedge, Director

COURTS

3rd Circuit Court **386.362.0500**
Fax 386.362.0577
   200 Ohio Ave S Ste 102, Live Oak, FL 32064
   David W. Fina, Circuit Judge

POLICE AND SHERIFF

Sheriff's Ofc **386.362.2222**
Fax 386.364.1953
E-mail ....sheriff@suwanneesheriff.com
   200 Ohio Ave S Ste 105, Live Oak, FL 32064
   Tony Cameron, Sheriff

Taylor County

GENERAL HEALTH SERVICES

Dept Of Health **850.584.5087**
Fax 850.584.7335
Web ....www.doh.state.fl.us
E-mail ....joanie_cruce@doh.state.fl.us
   1215 N Peacock Ave, Perry, FL 32347-2117
   Joanie Cruce, Nursing Director

JUSTICE AGENCY

Dept Of Juvenile Justice **850.838.3660**
Fax 850.838.3670
Web ....www.djj.state.fl.us
E-mail ....alan.hall@djj.state.fl.us
   1719 S Jefferson St, Perry, FL 32348-5612
   Alan C. Hall, Supervisor

COURTS

3rd Circuit Court **850.838.3506**
Fax 850.838.3549
Web ....www.taylorclerk.com
E-mail ....smurphy@taylorclerk.com
   108 N Jefferson St, Perry, FL 32347
   Honorable Stephan Murphy, Director

POLICE AND SHERIFF

Sheriff's Dept **850.584.4225**
Fax 850.584.7016
E-mail ....dwelch@taylorcountysherifffl.org
   108 N Jefferson St Ste 103, Perry, FL 32347-3252
   Lawrence E Williams, Sheriff

Union County

SOCIAL SERVICES

Dept Of Children & Families **386.496.2417**
Fax 386.496.1577
   155 SE 6th Pl, Lake Butler, FL 32054-2213
   Dawn Harper, Economic Services Supervisor

GENERAL HEALTH SERVICES

Dept Of Health **386.496.3211**
Fax 386.496.1599
   495 E Main St, Lake Butler, FL 32054
   Amy Johns, Nursing Director

COURTS

8th Circuit Court **386.496.4244**
Fax 386.496.1718
   55 W Main St Rm 103, Lake Butler, FL 32054-1654
   Dianne Waters, Juvenile Deputy Clerk

POLICE AND SHERIFF

Sheriff's Ofc **386.496.2501**
Fax 386.496.3600
E-mail ....unionso@flcjn.net
   55 W Main St, Rm 102, Lake Butler, FL 32054
   Jerry Whitehead, Sheriff

Volusia County

SOCIAL SERVICES

Florida Dept Of Children & Families Child Abuse
Investigations **386.822.6392**
Fax 386.822.4459
Web ....www.dcf.state.fl.us
E-mail ....linda_mandizha@dcf.state.fl.us
   1344 S Woodland Blvd, Deland, FL 32720-7741
   Linda Mandizha, Program Management Director

Health And Human Svcs Circuit 7 ....**386.238.4691**
Web ....www.dcf.state.fl.us
   210 N Palmetto Ave, Ste 210, Daytona Beach,
   FL 32114
   Rediald William, Program Operations Administrator

GENERAL HEALTH SERVICES

Children's Medical Svcs Network **386.238.4980**
Fax 386.254.3937
Web ....www.doh.state.fl.us
   421 S Ceech St, Daytona Beach, FL 32114
   Judith Ryan, Rn, CMS Nursing Director

Dept Of Health **386.274.0500**
Fax 386.274.0812
   1845 Holsonback Dr, Daytona Beach, FL 32120
   William Lyons, AIDS Coordinator

© 2011 Dorland Health

Dept Of Health Deland Clinic 386.822.6215
Fax 386.822.6234
 1061 Medical Center Dr Ste 100, Orange City,
 FL 32763-8225
 Walter Sessions, Clerical Supervisor

JUSTICE AGENCY

Dept Of Juvenile Justice 386.736.5000
Fax 386.736.5013
E-mail ....kristine.mcmullen@djj.state.fl.us
 342 E New York Ave, Deland, FL 32724
 Kristine Mcmullen, Secretary

Dept Of Juvenile Justice 386.238.4615
Fax 386.238.4605
Web ....www.djj.state.fl.us
 210 N Palmetto Ave, Daytona Beach, FL 32114-4358
 David Kerr, Juvenile Justice Manager

Guardian Ad Litem 386.736.5958
Fax 386.943.7080
Web ....www.gal.fl.gov
E-mail ....jo.toubman@gal.fl.gov
 101 N Alabama Ave, Ste B253, Deland, FL 32724
 Jo Toubman, Deputy Circuit Director

COURTS

Clerk Of Court Ofc 386.822.5002
Fax 386.822.5041
Web ....www.clerk.org
 101 N Alabama Ave, Deland, FL 32724-4316
 Diane Matousek, Clerk Of Court

Court Office Juvenile 386.257.6001
Fax 386.248.8165
 125 E Orange Ave Ste 101, Daytona Beach, FL 32114
 Stephanie Reinhart, Superintendent

POLICE AND SHERIFF

Sheriff's Ofc 386.736.5962
Fax 386.822.5074
 123 W Indiana Ave Ste A, Deland, FL 32721
 Ben Johnson, Sheriff

EDUCATION SERVICES

Exceptional Student Education 386.255.6475
Fax 386.626.0042
Web www.volusia.k12.fl.us
E-mail ....blbush@volusia.k12.fl.us
 200 N Clara Ave, Deland, FL 32720
 Dr. Barbara Bush, Director Of Ese/student Services

Wakulla County

COURTS

2nd Circuit Court 850.926.0905
Fax 850.926.0938
 3056 Crawfordville Hwy, Crawfordville, FL 32327
 Honorable N. Sanders Sauls, Judge

POLICE AND SHERIFF

Sheriff's Dept 850.745.7100
Fax 850.926.0896
 15 Oak St, Crawfordville, FL 32327
 David F. Harvey, Sheriff

Walton County

SOCIAL SERVICES

Florida Dept Of Children &
Families 850.892.8647
Fax 850.892.8660
 79 N Davis Ln, Defuniak Springs, FL 32433-3108
 Carolyn Henderson, Child Investigation Protection Supervisor

COURTS

1st Circuit Court 850.892.8115
Fax 850.892.7551
 571 US Hwy 90 E Room 208, De Funiak Springs,
 FL 32433
 Honorable David Green, Delinquency/Judge

POLICE AND SHERIFF

Sheriff's Dept 850.892.8186
Fax 850.892.8422
Web ....www.waltonfl.org
E-mail ....sheriff@waltonso.org
 752 Triple G Rd, DeFuniak Springs, FL 32433
 Michael Adkinson, Sheriff

EDUCATION SERVICES

Chautauqua Head Start Ctr 850.892.6144
Fax 850.892.6310
 908 US Highway 90 W Ste B, Defuniak Springs,
 FL 32433-1436
 Michelle Howard, Director

Washington County

GENERAL HEALTH SERVICES

Dept Of Health 850.638.6240
Fax 850.638.6244
E-mail ....rick_davis@doh.state.fl.us
 1338 South Blvd, Chipley, FL 32428
 Richard Davis, Nursing Administrator

JUSTICE AGENCY

Guardian Ad Litem 850.638.6043
Fax 850.638.6097
Web ....www.gal.fl.gov
E-mail ....amy.griffn@gal.fl.gov
 1352 South Blvd, Chipley, FL 32428
 Amy Griffin, Case Coordinator

COURTS

14th Circuit Court 850.638.6285
Fax 850.638.6297
Web ....www.washingtonclerk.com
E-mail ....clerk@washingtonclerk.com
 1293 Jackson Ave Ste 100, Chipley, FL 32428-1833
 Christopher Patterson, Director

POLICE AND SHERIFF

Sheriff's Dept 850.638.6111
Fax 850.638.6184
E-mail ....sheriff@wcso.us
 1293 Jackson Ave Bldg 400, Chipley, FL 32428-1833
 Robert C. ""bobby"" Haddock, Sheriff

SPECIAL SERVICES AGENCIES

ADOPTION AGENCIES

A Adoption Advisor 850.577.3077
Fax 850.577.3079
 1566 Village Square Blvd Ste 2, Tallahassee,
 FL 32309-2765

A Chosen Child Inc 386.252.1307
Fax 407.895.0675
E-mail ....linda@achosenchild.com
 1516 E Colonial Dr, Orlando, FL 32803
 Linda Ratcliff, Director

A Christian Alternative 352.351.9994
Fax 352.378.6205
Web ....www.christianfamilyservices.com
E-mail ....info@cfsfl.org
 2720 SW 2nd Ave, Gainesville, FL 32607
 Jerry Callens, Director

Adoption Advocates, Inc. 727.391.8096
Fax 727.399.0026
Web ....www.adoptionadvocatesinc.com
E-mail ....adoptme@verizon.net
 11407 Seminole Blvd, Largo, FL 33778-3238
 Cathy Hayes, Director

Adoption By Shepherd Care 407.265.9599
Fax 407.265.9549
Web ....www.adoptionshepherdcare.com
E-mail ....orlando@adoptionshepherdcare.com
 2911 Lakeview Dr, Fern Erk, FL 32730
 Joseph Sica, Executive Director

Adoption Ctr 850.651.5225
Fax 850.651.3210
Web ....www.adoptioncenter.org
E-mail ....r.harrell@adoptionattorneys.org
 3 Clifford Dr, Shalimar, FL 32579-1250
 Robinson R. Harrell, Director

Adoption Home Studies-Angels 407.702.4718
Fax 407.366.7153
E-mail ....mbuzan@cfl.rr.com
 1001 Butler Creek Ct, Oviedo, FL 32765
 Margaret S. Buzan, Dcsw, Executive Director

Adotion & Family Support Ctr 386.760.5804
Fax 386.322.3349
E-mail ....angelaquick@hotmail.com
 709 Hills Blvd, Port Orange, FL 32127
 Angela Quick, Owner

Advocates for Children & Families 305.653.2474
Fax 305.775.8340
Web ....www.adoptionflorida.org
 16831 NE 6th Avenue, North Miami Beach, FL 33162
 Lori Slaven, Director
 COA accredited organization.

Alternate Family Care 561.746.4154
Fax 561.746.3067
E-mail ....kcarlson@altfam.com
 6650 W Indiantown Rd Ste 210, Jupiter,
 FL 33458-4629
 Kelly Carlson, Director

Alternate Family Care 954.746.5200
Fax 954.746.5216
Web ....www.altfam.com
E-mail ....dferguson@altfam.com
 10001 W Oakland Park Blvd Ste 301, Fort Lauderdale,
 FL 33351-6925
 David Ferguson, President

American Adoptions 727.497.0192
Fax 727.497.0256
Web ....www.americanadoptions.com
E-mail ....maryw@americanadoptions.com
 425 22nd Ave N Ste D, St Petersburg, FL 33704-4322
 Mary Wheatley, Director

Anthony B Marchese 813.877.6643
 4010 W Boy Scout Blvd Ste 590, Tampa, FL 33607
 Anthony B Marchese, Owner

Bay Area Behavioral Services 813.689.8828
Fax 813.689.8802
 135 N. Moon Avenue, Brandon, FL 33510
 COA accredited organization.

Florida

Bethany Christian Services **407.877.4006**
Fax 407.877.4061
Web ....www.bethany.org
E-mail ....bcsmaitland@bethany.org
29 West Smith Street, Winter Garden, FL 34787-3582
Michelle Barratt, Director

Big Bend Community Based Care **850.410.1020**
Fax 850.410.1076
Web ....www.bigbendcbc.org
525 N. Martin Luther King, Jr. Boulevard, Tallahassee,
FL 32301
COA accredited organization.

Bogin Munns & Munns **407.870.1919**
Fax 407.870.2419
E-mail ....dsinger@boginmunns.com
1524 N John Young Pkwy, Kissimmee, FL 34741
Denise Singler, Director

Bogin Munns & Munns **386.860.5200**
Fax 386.860.0701
Web ....www.boginmunns.com
E-mail ....bmm@boginmunns.com
770 Deltona Blvd Ste C, Deltona, FL 32725-7168
Denise Singler, Director

Brandon Family Law Ctr LLC **813.653.1744**
Fax 813.654.6830
Web ....www.brandonfamilylaw.com
E-mail ....mary@brandonfamilylaw.com
619 E Lumsden Rd, Brandon, FL 33511-6523
Mary Greenwood, Executive Director & Founder

Capital City Youth Services, Inc. **850.576.6000**
Fax 850.576.2580
Web ....www.ccys.org
2407 Roberts Avenue, Tallahassee, FL 32310
COA accredited organization.

Catholic Charities **850.244.2825**
Fax 850.664.9146
Web ....www.catholiccharitiesnwfl.com
E-mail ....ketchelc@cc.ptdiocese.org
11 1st St SE, Fort Walton Beach, FL 32548-5839
Carolyn Ketchel, Regional Director

Catholic Charities Bureau **904.829.6300**
Fax 904.829.0494
E-mail ....beckystringer@ccbstaug.org
225 W King St, Saint Augustine, FL 32085
Becky Stringer, Director

Catholic Charities of Central Florida **407.658.1818**
Web ....www.cflcc.org
1771 N. Semoran Boulevard, Orlando, FL 32807
COA accredited organization.

Celebrate Children Int'l **407.977.2810**
Fax 407.977.2811
1757 W Broadway St Ste 5, Oviedo, FL 32765
Sue Hedberg, Director

Cheryl Eisen Law Ofcs **561.330.9901**
Fax 561.330.2446
202 N Swinton Ave, Delray Beach, FL 33432
Kathleen, Director

Childnet **954.414.6000**
Fax 954.414.6019
Web ....www.childnet.us
E-mail ....lrein@childnet.us
313 N State Road 7, Fort Lauderdale, FL 33317-2809
Larry Rein, Interim CEO

Children Of Promise **863.699.1685**
Fax 863.699.2601
Web ....www.strato.net
140 Dunty Rd, Lake Placid, FL 33852-7221
Sandra Lopes, Director

Children's Home Society-FL **239.277.0096**
Fax 239.334.0244
Web ....www.chsfl.org
E-mail ....jamie.adcock@chsfl.org
1495 Maple Dr, Fort Myers, FL 33907-2347
Sherry Wenzel, Director

Christopher R Johnson, LLC **850.433.8529**
Fax 850.433.3795
E-mail ....crj@crjohnsonlaw.com
7 N Coyle St, Pensacola, FL 32502
Christopher R. Johnson, Director

**Clay and Baker Kids Net, Inc. dba Kids First of Florida,
Inc.** **904.278.5644**
Fax 904.278.5654
Web ....www.cbkn.org
1726 Kingsley Avenue, Suite 2, Orange Park,
FL 32073
COA accredited organization.

**Community Based Care of Brevard, Inc. dba Brevard Family
Partnership** **321.752.3183**
Fax 321.752.3188
Web ....www.cbcbrevard.org
760 North Drive, Suite E, Melbourne, FL 32934
COA accredited organization.

**Community Based Care of Central Florida,
Inc.** **407.688.9650**
Fax 407.333.8269
Web ....www.cbcseminole.org
4001 Pelee Street, Suite 200, Orlando, FL 32817
COA accredited organization.

ECKERD
EYA
YOUTH ALTERNATIVES

Eckerd **800.914.3937**
Fax 727.442.5911
Web ....www.eckerd.org
E-mail ....admissions@eckerd.org
100 Starcrest Dr, Clearwater, FL 33758-7450
David Dennis, President & CEO; Francene Hazel, Director of Admissions
A full continuum of behavioral health and child welfare programs throughout
Florida for children and youth from birth through age 23. Behavioral health
services range from early intervention & prevention to private residential
treatment centers schools, outdoor therapeutic programs, day treatment,
residential programs for adjudicated youth, in-home and community-based
counseling and aftercare services. Child welfare services include case management
services and child welfare system administration (Eckerd serves as the lead agency
for community-based child welfare in Pinellas and Pasco counties). For most
programs, youth are referred through contracts with public agencies. However,
parents and professionals can refer troubled youth ages 10 – 17 directly to our
Eckerd Academy at Brooksville program.

European Adoption Consultants **954.566.6624**
Fax 954.566.6272
E-mail ....margaret@eaci.com
4040 Galt Ocean Dr# 4, Fort Lauderdale, FL 33308
Margaret Cole, Executive Director

Family Services of Metro Orlando, Inc. **407.398.7975**
Fax 407.578.0074
Web ....www.fsmetroorlando.org
2600 Technology Drive, Suite 250, Orlando,
FL 32804
COA accredited organization.

Florida Baptist Children's Homes **863.687.8811**
Fax 863.682.3157
Web ....www.fbchomes.org
P.O. Box 8190, Lakeland, FL 33802
COA accredited organization.

Florida Home Studies And Adoption, Inc. **941.342.8189**
Fax 941.371.3125
Web ....www.flhomestudies.com
E-mail ....info@flhomestudies.com
5930 Palmer Blvd, Sarasota, FL 34232-2842

Fortson Consultant Svcs **407.246.1321**
Fax 407.246.1379
Web ....www.socialworkconsult.com
4565 Cassius St, Orlando, FL 32811-4815

Gift Of Life, Inc. **727.549.1416**
Fax 727.548.8174
Web ....www.giftoflifeadoptions.com
4437 Park Blvd, Pinellas Park, FL 33781-3540
Lee Scharrer, Director

Heartland for Children **863.519.8900**
Fax 863.519.8913
Web ....www.heartlandforchildren.org
P.O. Box 1017, Bartow, FL 33831
COA accredited organization.

Hillsborough Kids, Inc. **813.225.1105**
Fax 813.226.0661
Web ....www.hillsboroughkids.org
9309 N. Florida Avenue, Suite 107, Tampa,
FL 33612-7237
COA accredited organization.

InCharge Debt Solutions **407.291.3659**
Fax 407.291.8355
Web ....www.incharge.org
5750 Major Boulevard, Suite 175, Orlando, FL 32819
COA accredited organization.

Intervention Services, Inc. **407.215.0095**
Fax 407.261.0523
Web ....www.interventionservices.com
668 N. Orlando Avenue, Suite 210, Maitland,
FL 32751
COA accredited organization.

Law Offices Of Ellen Kaplan, PA **954.341.1309**
Fax 954.510.2292
Web ....www.ellenkaplanadoptions.com
E-mail ....ellen@ellenkaplanadoptions.com
9900 W Sample Rd, Fl 3, Coral Springs, FL 33065
Ellen M Kaplan, Pa, Attorney

Life For Kids **407.629.5437**
Fax 407.629.5812
E-mail ....lifeforkids@yahoo.com
315 N Wymore Rd, Winter Park, FL 32789-2822
Megan White, Interim Director

One Hope United - Florida Region
Web ....www.onehopeunited.org
5405 Diplomat Circle, Suite 200, Orlando, FL 32810
COA accredited organization.

Sarasota Family YMCA, Inc **941.366.3881**
Fax 941.366.5658
Web ....www.sarasota-ymca.org
E-mail ....clweinrich@sarasota-ymca.org
1 S School Ave Ste 301, Sarasota, FL 34237-6052
Lee Johnson, Executive Vice-President

**Shepherd Care Ministries, dba Adoption by Shepherd
Care** **954.981.2060**
Fax 954.981.2117
Web ....www.adoptionshepherdcare.com
5935 Taft Street, Hollywood, FL 33021
COA accredited organization.

Success 4 Kids & Families, Inc. **813.490.5490**
Fax 813.490.5495
Web www.s4kf.org
1311 N. West Shore Boulevard, Suite 302, Tampa,
FL 33607
COA accredited organization.

The Children's Home, Inc. 813.855.4435
Fax 813.855.8640
Web ....www.childrenshome.org
   10909 Memorial Highway, Tampa, FL 33615
   COA accredited organization.

Women in Distress 954.760.9800
Fax 954.687.0733
Web ....www.womenindistress.org
   P.O. Box 676, Ft. Lauderdale, FL 33302
   COA accredited organization.

ADVOCACY RESOURCES

Barbara M. Gold - RN, CCM, LNC 407.339.1239
E-mail ....nursegold2@cfl.rr.com
   Barbara M. Gold, Medical Consultant

C Michael Kelly PA 941.744.5291
E-mail ....MichaelK2010@Hotmail.com
   353 6th Ave W, Ste 207, Bradenton, FL 34205
   Charles Kelly, Attorney

Child Advocacy Ctr 352.376.9161
Fax 352.376.9165
Web ....www.childadvocacycentergainesville.org
E-mail ....admin@childadvocacycenter.org
   PO Box 1128, Gainesville, FL 32602-1128
   Sherry Kitchens, Director

Child Protection Team 321.637.7652
Fax 321.637.7661
Web ....www.doh.state.fl.us
   1133 Seminole Dr, Rockledge, FL 32955
   Charles Biehl, Director

Children's Advocacy Ctr 863.402.6845
Fax 863.402.6869
E-mail ....jroth@bcc.co.highlands.fl.us
   1000 S Highlands Ave, Sebring, FL 33870
   Jeffrey Roth, Executive Director

Children's Advocacy Ctr 407.317.7430
Fax 407.648.8213
Web ....www.orlandohelp.com/hpc
   601 W Michigan St, Orlando, FL 32805
   Marie Martinez, Director

Children's Advocacy Ctr 239.263.8383
Fax 239.263.7931
Web ....www.caccollier.org
   1036 6th Ave N, Naples, FL 34102-5603
   Jacqueline Griffith Stephens, Executive Director

**Children's Advocacy Ctr Children's Home Society Of
Florida** 863.519.3900
Fax 863.519.3913
Web ....www.chsfl.org
E-mail ....dhodgson@chsfl.org
   1260 Golfview Ave, Bartow, FL 33830
   Linda Kurtzweil, Director

Children's Home Society Of Florida 850.747.5411
Fax 850.747.5226
Web ....www.chsfl.org
E-mail ....william.coleman@chsfl.org
   914 Harrison Ave, Panama City, FL 32401
   William Buster-coleman, Executive Director

Community Legal Svcs Mid-Florida Inc 407.841.7777
E-mail ....sarahk@clsmf.org
   122 E Colonial Dr Ste 200, Orlando, FL 32801
   Sarah Koren

First Coast Child Protection Team 904.633.0300
Fax 904.633.0301
Web ....www.jax.ufl.edu
E-mail ....valerie.stanley@jax.ufl.edu
   4539 Beach Blvd, Bldg 4100, Jacksonville, FL 32207
   Valerie Stanley, Associate Director

**Florida Network Of Children's Advocacy
Ctrs** 850.833.9237
Fax 850.833.9238
Web ....www.ecc.acgcoxmail.com
E-mail ....julie@eccac.org
   401 Mcewen Dr 0, Niceville, FL 32578-2741
   Julie Hurst, Executive Director

Gulf Coast Children's Advocacy Ctr, Inc. 850.872.7760
Fax 850.872.7780
Web ....www.doh.state.fl.us
E-mail ....lemar_hobbs@doh.state.fl.us
   700 W 23rd St, Ste 40 Bldg E, Panama City, FL 32405
   Lemar Hobbs, Executive Director

Institute For Famliy Violence Studies 850.644.6303
Fax 850.644.8331
Web ....www.familyvio.ssw.fsu.edu
E-mail ....familyviolencestudies@fsu.edu
   Florida State University, C2309 University Ctr,
   Tallahassee, FL 32306-0001
   Karen Oehme, J.d., Director

**Kristi House, Inc./Orlowitz-Lee Children's Advocacy
Ctr** 305.547.6800
Fax 305.547.6837
Web ....www.kristihouse.org
   1265 NW 12th Ave, Miami, FL 33136-2140
   Trudy Novicki, Executive Director

Legal Services of N Florida 850.385.9007
E-mail ....steph@lsnf.org
   2119 Delta Blvd, Tallahassee, FL 32303
   Stephanie Johnson, Attorney

Putnam Behavioral Healthcare 386.329.3780
Fax 386.385.1269
Web ....www.pbh.com
E-mail ....
   330 Kay Larkin Drive, Palatka, FL 32177
   CARF accredited programs available.

BEHAVIORAL HEALTH TREATMENT

**561 The Treatment Center of the Palm Beaches,
LLC** 561.253.6790
Web ....www.thetreatmentcenter.com
E-mail ....lpotere@aol.com
   4905 Lantana Road, Lake Worth, FL 33463
   Ms. Linda Potere, Accreditation Manager
   Joint Commission accredited organization.

A & M Psychiatric Svcs 727.726.7442
Fax 727.288.1111
Web ....www.ampsychiatric.com
E-mail ....info@ampsychiatric.com
   1938 Soule Rd, Clearwater, FL 33759-1507
   Dr. Joseph I Adan, Md, Psychiatrist

Abraham Medical Practice 239.334.1478
   150 NW 70th Ave, Plantation, FL 33317
   Gerald Abraham, Psychiatrist

Abraham Medical Practice 239.261.2332
   501 Goodlette Rd N, Naples, FL 34102
   Gerald Abraham MD, Psychiatrist

Adoption Related Services of Pinellas, Inc. 727.423.7811
Fax 727.865.5178
Web ....http://arsponline.org
   8800 49th Street N., Suite 212, Pinellas Park,
   FL 33782
   COA accredited organization.

Advanced Mental Health Care 561.333.8884
Fax 561.333.2122
Web ....www.advancedmentalhealth.com
E-mail ....advancedmentalhealth@gmail.com
   11903 Southern Blvd Ste 104, West Palm Beach,
   FL 33411-7644
   Laura De Luca, Md, Psychiatrist

Aguinaga Medical Practice 305.923.9030
Fax 305.745.9875
   300 Southard St, Key West, FL 33040
   Jorge Aguinaga, MD, Psychiatrist

Alexander Medical Practice 813.908.5080
E-mail ....psa95md@verizon.net
   14043 N Dale Mabry Hwy, Tampa, FL 33618-2401
   Lycia Alexander, Psychiatrist

ALPHA Community Mental Health Center 305.264.3225
E-mail ....mssi29@aol.com
   7811 SW 24th Street # 137, Miami, FL 33155
   Ms. Maria Mussini, Accreditation Manager
   Joint Commission accredited organization.

Alpha House of Tampa, Inc. 813.875.2024
Fax 813.876.0657
Web ....www.alphahouseoftampa.org
   201 S. Tampania Avenue, Tampa, FL 33609
   COA accredited organization.

Alternate Family Care, Inc. 954.746.5200
Web ....www.altfam.com
E-mail ....dfergusafc@aol.com
   10001 W Oakland Park Blvd, Suite 200, Sunrise,
   FL 33351
   Dr. David Ferguson, Accreditation Manager
   Joint Commission accredited organization.

Amiel Medical Practice 352.377.1903
Fax 352.377.2510
   4131 NW 13th St Ste 225, Gainesville,
   FL 32609-1872
   Michael Amiel, Psychiatrist

Apalachee Center, Inc. 850.523.3333
Web ....apalacheecenter.org
E-mail ....suec@apalacheecenter.org
   2634-J Capital Circle NE, Tallahassee, FL 32308
   Mrs. Sue Conger, Accreditation Manager
   Joint Commission accredited organization.

Apalachee Centre 850.997.3958
Fax 850.997.0983
Web ....www.apalacheecenter.org
   1996 S Jefferson, Monticello, FL 32344
   Jessica Parker, Director

Apalachee Ctr 850.926.5900
Fax 850.926.2932
   85 High Dr, Crawfordville, FL 32327
   Billy Solberger, Supervisor

Apalachee Perry Ofc 850.584.5613
Fax 850.584.5687
Web ....www.apalacheecenter.org
   1421 Old Dixie Hwy, Perry, FL 32348
   Jessica Parker, Supervisor

Archways, Inc. 954.763.2030
Fax 954.763.9847
Web ....www.archways.org
   919 Northeast 13th Street, Fort Lauderdale, FL 33304
   Andrea Katz, CEO
   CARF accredited programs available.

Arnette House, Inc. 352.622.6135
Fax 352.622.2830
Web ....www.arnettehouse.org
   2310 NE 24th Street, Ocala, FL 34470
   COA accredited organization.

Arora Medical Practice 904.737.4606
Fax 904.737.4366
   8130 Baymeadows Cir W Ste 109, Jacksonville,
   FL 32256-1837
   Pradeep Arora, Md, Psychiatrist

Avanti Wellness Center 904.824.7597
Web ....www.avantiwellnesscenter.net
E-mail ....randi.brazer_avanti@earthlink.net
   3574 US 1 South Suite 113, Saint Augustine,
   FL 32086-6467
   Mrs. Randi Brazer, Accreditation Manager
   Joint Commission accredited organization.

Badiola Medical Practice 863.646.7733
Fax 863.646.7733
   204 Lake Harris Dr, Lakeland, FL 33813-2632
   Evaristo Badiola, Md, Psychiatrist

Barnett Medical Practice 305.538.9007
Fax 305.538.9227
   333 W 41st St Ste 702, Miami Beach, FL 33140-3608
   Mark Barnett, MD, Psychiatrist

BayCare Life Management 727.816.9851
Fax 727.372.5246
Web .... www.baycare.org/behavioralhealth
   6636 Rowan Road, New Port Richey, FL 34653
   Susan Wright, Director
   CARF accredited programs available.

Bayside Center for Behavioral Health 941.917.1779
Fax 941.917.2128
Web .... www.smh.com
E-mail .... miriam-lacher@smh.com
   1650 So. Osprey Ave., Sarasota, FL 34239
   Miriam Lacher, Manager

Bayside Ctr For Behavioral Health 941.917.7760
Fax 941.917.8849
Web .... www.smh.com
   1650 S Osprey Ave, Sarasota, FL 34239
   Ken Alexander, Executive Director

Behavioral Support Services, Inc. 407.831.6412
Web .... www.bssorlando.com
E-mail .... dorisduan@bssorlando.com
   315 N. Lakemont Avenue, Suite B, Winter Park,
   FL 32792
   Mrs. Doris Duan, Accreditation Manager
   Joint Commission accredited organization.

BGI of Pensacola dba Twelve Oaks 850.939.1200
Fax 850.939.1257
Web .... www.twelveoaksrecovery.com
   2068 Healthcare Avenue, Navarre, FL 32566
   CARF accredited programs available.

Brookwood Florida Central 727.822.4789
Fax 727.896.4475
Web .... www.brookwoodflorida.org
E-mail .... pjmesmer@brookwoodflorida.org
   901 7th Ave S, Saint Petersburg, FL 33705-1998
   Pamela Mesmer, Executive Director

Capiola Medical Practice 239.649.7494
   773 4th Ave N Ste A, Naples, FL 34102-5778
   Richard Capiola, MD, Psychiatrist

Care 4 America, Inc. 352.489.7444
Fax 866.531.1415
Web www.care4america.com
   P.O. Box 3373, Dunnellon, FL 34430
   COA accredited organization.

Carlaton Palms Educational Ctr 352.735.0588
Fax 352.735.4095
E-mail .... sheat@advoserv.com
   28308 Churchill Smith Ln, Mount Dora, FL 32757
   Tom Shea, Director

Carlton Manor, Inc. 727.343.3662
Fax 727.347.1649
Web .... www.carltonmanor.org
   45 Westwood Terrace N., St. Petersburg, FL 33710
   COA accredited organization.

Chacko Medical Practice 407.894.2664
Fax 407.894.2450
Web .... www.chackoforensicpsychiatry.com
E-mail .... devchackomd@cfl.rr.com
   2718 N Orange Ave Ste C, Orlando, FL 32804-7611
   Chowallur Chacko, Md, Psychiatrist

CHANGES Youth and Family Services, Inc. 321.610.7949
Fax 321.610.7647
Web .... http://changesyouthandfamilyservices.com
   3270 Suntree Boulevard, Suite 101, Melbourne,
   FL 32940
   CARF accredited programs available.

Charlotte Behavioral Health Care 941.639.8300
Fax 941.639.6831
Web .... www.cbhcfl.org
   1700 Education Avenue, Building A, Punta Gorda,
   FL 33950
   CARF accredited programs available.

Chemical Addictions Recovery Effort, Inc. 850.872.7676
Fax 850.872.9206
Web www.CARE4000.com
   4000 East Third Street, Panama City, FL 32404
   CARF accredited programs available.

Child Guidance Center, Inc. 904.448.4700
Fax 904.448.4717
Web .... www.childguidancecenter.org
   5776 Saint Augustine Road, Jacksonville, FL 32207
   Theresa Rulien, CEO
   CARF accredited programs available.

Choday Medical Practice 561.488.8874
Fax 561.488.8744
   8177 Glades Rd Ste 201, Boca Raton, FL 33434-4022
   Uma Choday, Psychiatrist

Circles Of Care 321.890.1580
Fax 321.634.6260
Web .... www.circlesofcare.org
   1770 Cedar St, Rockledge, FL 32955
   James Whitaker, President

Citrus Health Network, Inc 305.424.3100
Web .... www.citrushealth.org
E-mail .... carmenc@citrushealth.com
   4175 West 20th Avenue, Hialeah, FL 33012
   Mrs. Carmen Cantero, Accreditation Manager
   Joint Commission accredited organization.

Clay Behavioral Health Center, Inc. 904.291.5561
Fax 904.291.5575
Web .... www.ccbhc.org
E-mail .... james.larson@ccbhc.org
   3292 County Road 220, Middleburg, FL 32068
   James Larson, Director
   CARF accredited programs available.

Coastal Behavioral Health Care Inc 941.927.8900
Fax 941.927.6315
E-mail .... jthompson@coastalbh.org
   1565 State St, Sarasota, FL 34236
   Jerry Thompson Psyd, President/CEO

Coastal Behavioral Healthcare, Inc. 941.927.8900
E-mail .... jthompson@coastalbh.org
   1565 State Street, Sarasota, FL 34236
   Dr. Jerry Thompson, Accreditation Manager
   Joint Commission accredited organization.

Coastal Mental Health Services, Inc. 321.460.2039
E-mail .... domani@cfl.rr.com
   1745 Travertine Terrace, Sanford, FL 32771
   Mr. Mike Scaletta, Accreditation Manager
   Joint Commission accredited organization.

Columbia Hospital 561.863.3104
Web .... www.columbiahospital.com
E-mail .... isabel.finelli@hcahealthcare.com
   2201 45th Street, West Palm Beach, FL 33407
   Ms. Isabel Finelli, Accreditation Manager
   Joint Commission accredited organization.

**Community Counseling Center of Central Florida,
LLC** 407.291.8009
Fax 407.291.9620
Web .... www.ccccf.org
   499 North State Road 434, Suite 2007, Altamonte
   Springs, FL 32714
   CARF accredited programs available.

Community Health of South Florida, Inc. 305.252.4853
Web .... www.chisouthfl.org
E-mail .... aamofah@hcnetwork.org
   10300 S.W. 216 Street, Miami, FL 33190
   Dr. St. Anthony Amofah, Accreditation Manager
   Joint Commission accredited organization.

Community Ties of America, Inc. 615.661.4544
Web .... www.comties.com
E-mail .... t.lloyd@comties.com
   1802 North Alafaya Trail, Suite 158, Orlando,
   FL 32826
   Mr. Tim Lloyd, Accreditation Manager
   Joint Commission accredited organization.

Crosswinds Youth Services, Inc. 321.452.0800
Fax 321.394.0385
Web .... www.crosswindsyouthservices.org
   1407 Dixon Boulevard, Cocoa, FL 32922
   COA accredited organization.

Ctr For Emotional Wellness 727.669.3911
Fax 727.669.3813
   2329 Sunset Point Rd, Ste 203, Clearwater, FL 33765
   Joseph Shanklin, Psychiatrist

Ctr For Personal Growth 561.417.0004
   1499 W Palmetto Park Rd Ste 172, Boca Raton,
   FL 33486-3320
   Shawn Gersman, MD, Psychiatrist

**DACCO - Drug Abuse Comprehensive Coordinating Office,
Inc.** 813.635.0606
Fax 813.613.9373
Web .... www.dacco.org
E-mail .... marylynnu@dacco.org
   3107 N 50th St, Hillsborough, FL 33619
   Susan Casper, CFO

**DACCO - Drug Abuse Comprehensive Coordinating Office,
Inc.** 813.413.1065
Fax 813.571.9697
Web .... www.dacco.org
E-mail .... greerp@dacco.org
   915 S Parsons Ave, Brandon, FL 33511
   Mary Lynn Ulrey, CEO

**DACCO - Drug Abuse Comprehensive Coordinating Office,
Inc.** 813.621.8781
Web .... www.dacco.org
E-mail .... marylynnu@dacco.org
   3630 N 50th St, Tampa, FL 33619
   Mary Lynn Ulrey, CEO

**DACCO - Drug Abuse Comprehensive Corrdinating Office,
Inc.** 813.984.1818
Fax 813.987.2899
Web .... www.dacco.org
E-mail .... marylynnu@dacco.org
   4422 E Columbus Dr, Tampa, FL 33605
   Mary Lynn Ulrey, CEO

**Dade Family Counseling Community Mental Health
Center** 305.774.9570
Web .... www.dadefamily.com
E-mail .... lourdesrodriguez@dadefamily.com
   4343 West Flagler Street Suite 100, Miami, FL 33134
   Ms. Lourdes Rodriguez, Accreditation Manager
   Joint Commission accredited organization.

David Lawrence Center 239.455.8500
Web .... www.davidlawrencecenter.org
E-mail .... melbaa@dlcmhc.com
   6075 Bathey Lane, Naples, FL 34116
   Ms. Melba Arthur, Accreditation Manager
   Joint Commission accredited organization.

Del Campo Medical Practice 904.744.5543
E-mail .... onofre1965@yahoo.com
   6665 Banbury Rd, Jacksonville, FL 32211-5416
   Onofre Del Campo, Psychiatrist

Devabhaktuni Medical Practice 727.869.3227
   13908 Lakeshore Blvd Ste 210, Hudson,
   FL 34667-1492
   Raghu Devabhaktuni, Md, Psychiatrist

Devereux Florida 321.242.9100
Fax 321.242.1573
Web .... www.devereuxfl.org
E-mail .... referral@devereux.org
  8000 Devereux Dr, Melbourne, FL 32940-7907
  Steve Murphy, Executive Director

Diaz-Silveira Medical Practice 305.854.0841
  1330 coral way ste 408, Miami, FL 33145-4214
  Carlos Diaz-silveira, Md, Psychiatrist

Dippy Medical Practice 772.283.5721
  509 SE Riverside Dr Ste 204, Stuart, FL 34994-2579
  Walter Dippy, Md, Psychiatrist

Directions for Mental Health, Inc. 727.524.4464
Fax 727.524.4474
Web .... www.directionsmh.org
  1437 South Belcher Road, Clearwater, FL 33764
  CARF accredited programs available.

Doral Academy Charter High School 305.597.9950
Fax 305.477.6762
Web .... www.doralacademyprep.org
E-mail .... drodriguez@dadeschools.net
  11100 NW 27th St, Miami, FL 33172-5001
  Douglas Rodriguez, Principal

Dorfman Medical Practice 305.861.3717
Fax 305.866.4988
  260 95th St Ste 203, Miami Beach, FL 33154-2807
  Vernon Dorfman, MD, Psychiatrist

Draeger Medical Practice 727.584.0221
  10225 Ulmerton Rd, Ste 8B, Largo, FL 33771-3522
  J H Draeger, Md, Psychiatrist

Drug Abuse Comprehensive Coordinating Office,
Inc. 813.231.1340
Fax 813.623.3730
Web .... www.dacco.org
  4422 East Columbus Drive, Tampa, FL 33605-3233
  CARF accredited programs available.

Eckerd 800.914.3937
Fax 727.442.5911
Web .... www.eckerd.org
E-mail .... admissions@eckerd.org
  100 Starcrest Dr, Clearwater, FL 33758-7450
  David Dennis, President & CEO; Francene Hazel, Director of Admissions
  A full continuum of behavioral health and child welfare programs throughout Florida for children and youth from birth through age 23. Behavioral health services range from early intervention & prevention to private residential treatment centers schools, outdoor therapeutic programs, day treatment, residential programs for adjudicated youth, in-home and community-based counseling and aftercare services. Child welfare services include case management services and child welfare system administration (Eckerd serves as the lead agency for community-based child welfare in Pinellas and Pasco counties). For most programs, youth are referred through contracts with public agencies. However, parents and professionals can refer troubled youth ages 10 – 17 directly to our Eckerd Academy at Brooksville program.

Edgar Medical Practice 813.872.6061
E-mail .... edgar1@tampabay.rr.com
  508 S Habana Ave Ste 310, Tampa, FL 33609-4144
  James Edgar, Psychiatrist

Edgewood Children's Ranch, Inc. 407.295.2464
Fax 407.298.9125
Web .... www.edgewoodranch.com
E-mail .... stuart@edgewoodranch.com
  1451 Edgewood Ranch Rd, Orlando, FL 32835-5199
  Stuart Eldridge, Executive Director

Eisenberg Medical Practice 954.964.9242
  3990 Sheridan St Ste 204, Hollywood,
  FL 33021-3656
  Gail Eisenberg, MD, Psychiatrist

Endeavor Family Services 407.521.6141
Fax 407.521.6651
  2917 North Pine Hills Road, Orlando, FL 32808
  CARF accredited programs available.

Eric M Kaplan & Assoc. 813.948.8541
  146 Whitaker Rd Ste B, Lutz, FL 33549-5788
  Eric Kaplan, Md, Psychiatrist

Espejo R Perez Pa 407.897.6997
  2501 N Orange Ave Ste 307, Orlando,
  FL 32804-4642
  Espejo Perez, Md, Psychiatrist

Espinosa Medical Practice 305.935.3344
E-mail .... drjbe@bellsouth.net
  20820 W Dixie Hwy, Miami, FL 33180-1147
  Juan Espinosa, Md, Psychiatrist

Esquibel Medical Practice 352.637.4749
  801 Gospel Island Rd, Inverness, FL 34450-3592
  Edward Esquibel, Md, Psychiatrist

Estevez Medical Practice 727.821.2500
E-mail .... adamestevez@gmail.com
  1101 9th Ave N Ste 1, Saint Petersburg,
  FL 33705-1271
  Adam Estevez, MD, Psychiatrist

Fairwinds Treatment Center 727.449.0300
Web .... www.fairwindstreatment.com
E-mail .... don@fairwindstreatment.com
  1569 S Fort Harrison Avenue, Clearwater, FL 33756
  Ms. Debra Coon, Accreditation Manager
  Joint Commission accredited organization.

Fairwinds Treatment Ctr 727.449.0300
Fax 727.446.1022
Web .... www.fairwindstreatment.com
E-mail .... fairwinds@fairwindstreatment.com
  1569 S Fort Harrison Ave, Clearwater, FL 33756-2004
  Jay Leiva, Admissions Coordinator

Family Counseling Center of Brevard, Inc. 321.632.5792
Fax 321.632.5796
Web .... www.fccbrevard.com
  840 Brevard Avenue, Rockledge, FL 32955
  COA accredited organization.

Family Network On Disabilities Of Florida,
Inc. 727.523.1130
Fax 727.523.8687
Web .... www.fndusa.org
E-mail .... fnd@fndusa.org
  2196 main st ste K, GUNETIN, FL 34698
  Richard Labelle, Executive Director

Family Resource Center of South Florida,
Inc. 305.374.6006
Web .... www.frcflorida.org
E-mail .... deenaweiss@aol.com
  155 South Miami Ave. 4th Fl, Miami, FL 33130-1617
  Ms. deena weiss, Accreditation Manager
  Joint Commission accredited organization.

Finder Medical Practice 561.743.9233
Fax 561.743.2268
  10001 N US 1, Ste 409, Jupiter, FL 33477
  Jason Finder, Md, Psychiatrist

Florida Baptist Children's Home 863.688.4981
Fax 863.284.5684
Web .... www.fbchomes.org
E-mail .... jhaag@stch.org
  1015 Sikes Blvd, Lakeland, FL 33815-4499
  Steve Johnston, President

Florida Baptist Children's Home 305.271.4121
Fax 305.271.8891
  7748 SW 95th Ter, Miami, FL 33156-7599
  Stephen Robert, Administrator

Florida Institute for Neurologic Rehabilitation,
Inc. 863.773.2857
Web .... www.finr.org
E-mail .... b3800@strato.net
  1962 Vandolah Road, Wauchula, FL 33873
  Dr. Bridget Shore, Accreditation Manager
  Joint Commission accredited organization.

Florida MENTOR 954.423.1919
Fax 954.423.9959
Web .... www.thementornetwork.com
  600 North Pine Island Road, Suite 230, Plantation,
  FL 33324
  CARF accredited programs available.

Florida Sheriff's Youth Ranches, Inc. 386.842.5501
Fax 386.842.2429
Web .... www.youthranches.org
  2486 Cecil Webb Place, Live Oak, FL 32060-8337
  COA accredited organization.

Florida Therapy Services, Inc. 850.769.6001
Fax 850.769.6003
  648 Florida Avenue, Panama City, FL 32401
  CARF accredited programs available.

Focus Healthcare of Florida 954.680.2700
Web .... www.psysolutions.com
E-mail .... kathy.mcbrien@psysolutions.com
  5960 Southwest 106th Avenue, Cooper City,
  FL 33328
  Ms. Kathy McBrien, Accreditation Manager
  Joint Commission accredited organization.

Fort Lauderdale Hospital Management,
LLC 954.463.4321
Web .... www.uhsinc.com
E-mail .... kathy.mcbrien@psysolutions.com
  1601 East Las Olas Boulevard, Fort Lauderdale,
  FL 33301
  Ms. Kathy McBrien, Accreditation Manager
  Joint Commission accredited organization.

Fox Medical Practice 813.253.3797
  609 W Azeele St, Tampa, FL 33606-2205
  R. Michael Fox, MD, Psychiatrist

Fox-Fliesser Medical Practice 904.819.1888
  24 Cathedral Pl Ste 312, Saint Augustine,
  FL 32084-4465
  Judith Fox-Fliesser, MD, Psychiatrist

Frank Medical Practice 305.792.0855
E-mail .... sfrankmd@bellsouth.net
  1450 Madruga Ave Ste 201, Miami, FL 33146-3163
  Sheldon Frank, MD, Psychiatrist

Frett Medical Practice 561.483.9599
Fax 561.483.9274
  8177 Glades Rd Ste 204, Boca Raton, FL 33434-4022
  Cauvin Frett, Md, Psychiatrist

Friends of Children, Youth and Families,
Inc. 954.578.8399
Fax 954.572.8231
Web .... www.FriendsofChildren.net
  3500 N. State Road Seven, Suite 211-212, Lauderdale
  Lakes, FL 33319
  COA accredited organization.

Florida

Fusaro Medical Practice 305.442.4022
Fax 305.442.4022
E-mail ....saljasp@aol.com
    4040 Poinciana Ave, Miami, FL 33133-6329
    Sal Fusaro, Psychiatrist

Future Care Solution, Inc. 305.740.6960
E-mail ....futurecaresolution@hotmail.com
    3911 SW 67 Ave, Miami, FL 33155
    Ms. Christine Pena, Accreditation Manager
    Joint Commission accredited organization.

G4S Youth Services, LLC 904.692.2920
Fax 904.692.3611
    765 East Saint Johns Avenue, Hastings, FL 32145
    CARF accredited programs available.

Gainesville Job Corps Ctr 352.377.2555
Fax 352.374.8257
E-mail ....carld.rosoborough@jobcorps.org
    5301 NE 40th Ter, Gainesville, FL 32609-1599
    Carld Rosoborough, Center Director

Green Cross Health Systems, Inc. 305.443.9990
Web ....www.gchealth.com
E-mail ....anunez@gchealth.com
    2645 Douglas Road, Suite 601, Miami, FL 33133
    Adm. April Nunez, Accreditation Manager
    Joint Commission accredited organization.

Guidance/Care Center, Inc. 305.434.9000
Fax 305.434.9040
Web ....www.gcmk.org
    3000 41st Street, Ocean, Marathon, FL 33050
    CARF accredited programs available.

Gulf Coast Jewish Family Services, Inc. 727.479.1800
Fax 727.535.4774
Web ....www.gcjfs.org
E-mail ....nkelly@gcjfs.org
    14041 Icot Blvd, Clearwater, FL 33760
    Niki Kelly, Director of Refugee Youth Programs
    CARF accredited programs available.

Gulf Coast Treatment Center 850.863.4160
Web ....www.gulfcoasttreatment.com
E-mail ....bonnie.layne@psysolutions.com
    1015 Mar Walt Drive, Fort Walton Beach, FL 32547
    Ms. Bonnie Layne, Accreditation Manager
    Joint Commission accredited organization.

Halifax Behavioral Svcs 386.274.5333
Fax 386.274.4140
Web ....www.halifax.org
    841 Jimmy Ann Dr, Daytona Beach, FL 32117-4599
    Dr. Fariya Afridi, Md, Medical Director

Halifax Health 386.254.4060
Web ....www.halifaxhealth.org
E-mail ....cynthia.voigt@halifax.org
    303 N Clyde Morris Boulevard, Daytona Beach,
    FL 32114
    Ms. Cindy Voigt, Accreditation Manager
    Joint Commission accredited organization.

Hanley Center 561.841.1000
Web ....www.hanleycenter.org
E-mail ....ibeck@hanleycenter.org
    5200 East Avenue, West Palm Beach, FL 33407-2374
    Mrs. Ida Beck, Accreditation Manager
    Joint Commission accredited organization.

Helping People Succeed, Inc. 772.320.0770
Fax 772.320.0875
Web ....www.hpsfl.org
    1100 Southeast Federal Highway, Stuart, FL 34994
    CARF accredited programs available.

Henderson Mental Health Center, Inc. 954.486.4005
Fax 954.735.6717
Web ....www.hendersonmhc.org
    4740 North State Road 7, Suite 201, Fort Lauderdale,
    FL 33319
    CARF accredited programs available.

Hendry Glades Mental Health Clinic, Inc. 863.983.1423
E-mail ....wmeddock@comcast.net
    601 West Alverdez Avenue, Clewiston, FL 33440
    Mr. WAYNE MEDDOCK, Accreditation Manager
    Joint Commission accredited organization.

Here's Help, Inc. 305.685.8201
Fax 305.685.0158
Web ....www.hereshelpinc.com
    15100 Northwest 27th Avenue, Opa Locka, FL 33054
    CARF accredited programs available.

Hibiscus Children's Center, Inc. 772.334.9311
Fax 772.334.1991
Web ....www.hibiscuschildrenscenter.org
    2400 N.E. Dixie Highway, Jensen Beach, FL 34957
    COA accredited organization.

HMI/Canopy Cove 850.893.8800
Fax 850.893.6994
Web ....www.canopycove.com
    13305 Mahan Drive, Tallahassee, FL 32309
    CARF accredited programs available.

Homestead Behavioral Health Clinic 305.248.3488
E-mail ....deenaweiss@aol.com
    654 NE 9th Place, Homestead, FL 33030
    Mrs. Deena Weiss, Accreditation Manager
    Joint Commission accredited organization.

Horse Power, Inc. 352.373.4267
Fax 352.237.4381
E-mail ....msokolof@aol.com
    114 SE 1st St Ste 4, Gainesville, FL 32601-6879
    Marilyn Sokolof, Director

House of Hope, Inc. 954.524.8989
Fax 954.523.4673
Web ....www.houseofhopeonline.org
E-mail ....frank@houseofhopeonline.org
    908 Southwest First Street, Fort Lauderdale, FL 33312
    Frank Berardi, Program Director
    CARF accredited programs available.

Human Services Associates, Inc. 407.422.0880
Web ....www.hsainc.org
    1801 Lee Road, Suite 170, Winter Park, FL 32789
    CARF accredited programs available.

Jackson Memorial Hospital 305.585.1111
Web ....www.jhsmiami.org
E-mail ....klerett@jhsmiami.org
    1611 Northwest 12th Avenue, Miami,
    FL 33136-1094
    Ms. Kathryn Lerett, Accreditation Manager
    Joint Commission accredited organization.

**Jackson North Community Mental Health
Center** 786.466.2700
Web ....www.um-jmh.org
E-mail ....klerett@jhsmiami.org
    20201 NW 37th Ave, Opa Locka, FL 33056
    Ms. Kathryn Lerett, Accreditation Manager
    Joint Commission accredited organization.

Jackson South Community Hospital 305.251.2500
Fax 305.256.5101
Web ....www.jhsmiami.org
E-mail ....patricia.deegan@jhsmiami.org
    9333 SW 152nd St, Miami, FL 33157-1778
    Patricia Deegan, RN, Director Of Psychiatric Services

Jacksonville Job Corps Ctr 904.360.8200
Fax 904.632.5498
E-mail ....hill.kenderson@jobcorps.org
    4811 Payne Stewart Dr, Jacksonville, FL 32209-9208
    Kenderson Hill, Center Director

Jacksonville Psychiatric Svcs 904.399.5966
    4521 Atlantic Blvd ste D, Jacksonville, FL 32207
    David Cheshire, Md, Psychiatrist

**Jessie Trice Community Health Center,
Inc.** 305.805.1700
Web ....jtchc.org
E-mail ....rduval@hcnetwork.org
    700 S. Royal Poinciana Blvd, Suite 300, Miami,
    FL 33166
    Ms. Ruth Duval, Accreditation Manager
    Joint Commission accredited organization.

Jewish Adoption and Foster Care Options 954.749.7230
Fax 954.749.7231
Web ....https://www.jafco.org
    4200 North University Drive, Sunrise, FL 33351
    CARF accredited programs available.

Jewish Community Services of South Florida, Inc.
    735 NE 125th Street, North Miami, FL 33161
    COA accredited organization.

**Jewish Family & Children's Service of Sarasota-Manatee,
Inc.** 941.366.2224
Fax 941.366.2982
Web ....www.jfcs-cares.org
    2688 Fruitville Road, Sarasota, FL 34237
    COA accredited organization.

Kids Central Incorporated 352.873.6332
Fax 352.291.8658
Web ....www.kidscentralinc.org
    2117 SW Highway 484, Ocala, FL 34473
    COA accredited organization.

Kin-ship Services, Inc. 941.321.1027
Fax 941.792.9880
    3639 Cortez Road West, Suite 224, Bradenton,
    FL 34210
    CARF accredited programs available.

Kristi House, Inc. 305.547.6834
Fax 305.547.6814
Web ....www.kristihouse.org
    1265 N.W. 12th Avenue, Miami, FL 33136
    COA accredited organization.

**La Amistad Behavioral Health & Sea Harbor
Center** 407.647.0660
Fax 407.637.3068
Web ....www.lamistad.com
E-mail ....janice.seay@uhsinc.com
    1600 Dodd Rd, Winter Park, FL 32792-9408
    Jan Ellison-seay, Director Of Contracting

La Amistad Behavioral Health Services 407.647.0660
Web ....www.lamistad.com
E-mail ....irene.prezioso@uhsinc.com
    1650 Park Avenue North, Maitland, FL 32751
    Ms. Irene Prezioso, Accreditation Manager
    Joint Commission accredited organization.

**La Amistad Residential Treatment Center,
LLC** 407.370.0111
E-mail ....gayle.leonard@uhsinc.com
    6601 Central Florida Parkway, Orlando, FL 32821
    Ms. Gayle Leonard, Accreditation Manager
    Joint Commission accredited organization.

Lakeside Alternatives 407.875.3700
Fax 407.875.2717
Web ....www.lakesidecare.org
    434 Kennedy Blvd Ste A, Orlando, FL 32810-6429
    Vickie Garner, Vice President

Lakeside Behavioral Healthcare, Inc. 407.875.3700
Web ....www.lakesidecares.org
E-mail ....dj@lakesidecares.org
    434 West Kennedy Blvd, Orlando, FL 32810
    Ms. Diana Lee Jackson, Accreditation Manager
    Joint Commission accredited organization.

Lakeview Center, Inc. 850.469.3700
Fax 850.437.8994
Web ....www.elakeviewcenter.org
    1221 West Lakeview Avenue, Pensacola,
    FL 32501-1922
    CARF accredited programs available.

Lakeview Ctr Ofcs **850.432.1222**
Fax 850.469.3661
Web ....www.ebaptisthealthcare.org
E-mail ....mack.moore@bhcpns.org
1221 W Lakeview Ave, Pensacola, FL 32501-1836
Mack Moore, Assistant Director

Lee Memorial Health System Behavioral Health
Services **239.936.1114**
Web ....www.leememorial.org
E-mail ....chcrawford@leememorial.org
12550 New Brittany Blvd, Ste 200, 201, Fort Myers,
FL 33907
Ms. Christine Crawford, Accreditation Manager
Joint Commission accredited organization.

Lee Mental Health Center, Inc. **239.275.3222**
Fax 239.275.6037
Web ....www.leementalhealth.org
2789 Ortiz Avenue, Fort Myers, FL 33905
CARF accredited programs available.

Legacy Behavioral Health Center, Inc. **772.597.0411**
Fax 772.597.0412
Web ....www.legacybhc.com
15818 Southwest Warfield Boulevard, Indiantown,
FL 34956
CARF accredited programs available.

Legacy Behavioral Health Center, Inc. **561.616.8411**
Fax 561.616.8412
Web ....www.legacybhc.com
1551 Forum Place, Building 400 D&E, West Palm
Beach, FL 33401
CARF accredited programs available.

Life Management Center of Northwest Florida,
Inc. **850.522.4485**
Fax 850.522.4484
Web ....www.lifemanagementcenter.org
525 East 15th Street, Panama City, FL 32405
CARF accredited programs available.

Life Point Counseling Ctr **954.385.0353**
Fax 954.389.0886
E-mail ....lifepointct@aol.com
1625 N Commerce Pkwy, Ste 200, Weston, FL 33326
Janolyn Gregg, Psychologist

LifeStream Behavioral Center **352.315.7500**
Fax 352.360.6595
Web ....www.LSBC.net
515 West Main Street, Leesburg, FL 34748
CARF accredited programs available.

Lifestream Behavioral Ctr Crossroads II **352.315.7400**
Fax 352.360.1051
Web ....www.lsbc.net
E-mail ....krogers@lsbc.net
2018 Tally Rd, Leesburg, FL 34748
Karen Rogers, Director

Lifestream Crossroads II/Behavoiral Ctr **352.357.1550**
Fax 352.357.1103
Web ....www.lsbc.net
E-mail ....kfischer@lsbc.net
201 E Magnolia Ave, Eustis, FL 32726
Kyleen Fisher, Program Director

Manatee Glens **941.782.4299**
Web ....www.manateeglens.org
E-mail ....linda.transue@manateeglens.org
391 6th Avenue West, Bradenton, FL 34205
Ms. Linda Transue, Accreditation Manager
Joint Commission accredited organization.

Manatee Palms Group Homes **941.782.1765**
Web ....www.mpgh.com
E-mail ....lisa.zimmer@psysolutions.com
1324 37th Street East, Bradenton, FL 34208
Ms. Lisa Zimmer Raver, Accreditation Manager
Joint Commission accredited organization.

Manatee Palms Youth Services **941.792.2222**
Web ....www.manateepalmsyouthservices.com
E-mail ....cheryl.pearson@psysolutions.com
4480 51st Street West, Bradenton, FL 34210
Ms. Cheryl Pearson, Accreditation Manager
Joint Commission accredited organization.

Manatee Palms Youth Svcs **941.792.2222**
Fax 941.795.4359
Web ....www.ushinc.com
E-mail ....george.shopland@ushinc.com
4480 51st St W, Bradenton, FL 34210-2857
George Shopland, CEO

Mental Health Care, Inc. **813.272.2244**
Web ....www.mhcinc.org
E-mail ....mallen@mhcinc.org
5707 North 22nd Street, Tampa, FL 33610
Ms. Mona Allen, Accreditation Manager
Joint Commission accredited organization.

Mental Health Care, Inc. Main Ctr/Fasst 2/ MD/Family
Resource **813.272.2878**
Fax 813.272.3766
Web ....www.mhcinc.org
E-mail ....jrice@mhcinc.org
5707 N 22nd St, Tampa, FL 33610-4350
Julian Rice, CEO

Mental Health Care, Inc/ The Panos Ctr **813.707.7044**
Fax 813.707.7083
Web ....www.mhcinc.org
1403 W Reynolds St, Plant City, FL 33563
Susan Phillips, Supervisor

Mental Health Center, Inc. **561.637.1000**
Web ....www.scmhcinc.org
E-mail ....greenk@scmhcinc.org
16158 South Military Trail, Delray Beach, FL 33484
Ms. Karyn Green, Accreditation Manager
Joint Commission accredited organization.

Meridian Behavioral Healthcare, Inc. **352.487.0064**
Fax 352.487.0069
Web ....www.mbhci.org
E-mail ....maggie_labarta@mbhci.org
728 NE 7th St, Trenton, FL 32693-3637
Margarita Labarta, Director

Meridian Behavioral Healthcare, Inc. **352.374.5600**
Fax 352.371.9841
Web ....www.mbhci.org
4300 Southwest 13th Street, Gainesville, FL 32608
CARF accredited programs available.

Miami Behavioral Health Center, Inc. **305.757.0602**
Fax 305.757.2387
Web ....www.mbhc.org
11031 Northeast Sixth Avenue, Miami, FL 33161
CARF accredited programs available.

Multicultural Community Mental Health
Center **561.653.6292**
Web ....multiculturalcmhcinc.com
E-mail ....lpotere@aol.com
2721 Poinsettia Ave., West Palm Beach, FL 33407
Ms. Linda Potere, Accreditation Manager
Joint Commission accredited organization.

Multilingual Psychotherapy Centers, Inc. **561.712.8821**
Fax 561.721.8070
Web ....www.multilingualpsychotherapycenters.com
E-mail ....lconley@mpcipbc.com
1639 Forum Place, Suite 7, West Palm Beach,
FL 33401
Lilly Conley, Admissions Director
CARF accredited programs available.

National Deaf Academy, LLC **352.735.9500**
Web ....www.nationaldeafacademy.com
E-mail ....lynda.scaletta@uhsinc.com
19650 US Highway 441, Mount Dora, FL 32757
Ms. Lynda Scaletta, Accreditation Manager
Joint Commission accredited organization.

New Horizons Community Mental Health Center,
Inc. **305.637.7258**
Web ....www.nhcmhc.org
E-mail ....sfigel@nhcmhc.org
1469 NW 36th Street 2nd Floor, Miami, FL 33142
Mrs. Sherree Figel, Accreditation Manager
Joint Commission accredited organization.

New Horizons of the Treasure Coast, Inc. **772.468.5600**
Fax 772.468.5606
Web ....www.nhtcinc.org
4500 West Midway Road, Fort Pierce, FL 34981
CARF accredited programs available.

Northside Mental Health Center **813.977.8700**
Web ....www.northsidemhc.org
E-mail ....elaine.churton@northsidemh.org
12512 Bruce B. Downs Boulevard, Tampa,
FL 33612-9209
Ms. Elaine Churton, Accreditation Manager
Joint Commission accredited organization.

Northside Mental Health Center **813.977.8700**
Fax 813.971.2029
Web ....www.northsidemh.org
12512 Bruce B Downs Blvd, Tampa, FL 33612
Marsha Lewis Brown, LCSW, Executive Director/CEO

Northwest Behavioral Health Services,
Inc. **904.781.7797**
Fax 904.781.8685
Web ....www.nwbh.org
2392 Edgewood Avenue North, Jacksonville,
FL 32254
CARF accredited programs available.

Northwest Florida Comprehensive Services for Children dba
Families Count **850.474.3696**
Fax 850.474.4170
Web ....www.familiescount.net
4400 Bayou Boulevard, Suite 46, Pensacola, FL 32503
CARF accredited programs available.

Nurturing Ctr & Associates **850.434.6774**
Fax 850.434.6784
E-mail ....cjmckim@consultant.com
3301 N Pace Blvd Ste 310, Pensacola, FL 32505-5196
Candace Mckim, Office Manager

Oliver-Pyatt Centers, Inc. **305.663.1738**
Web ....www.olverpyattcenters.com
E-mail ....lpotere@aol.com
6150 SW 76 Street, Miami, FL 33143
Ms. Linda Potere, Accreditation Manager
Joint Commission accredited organization.

Operation PAR, Inc. **727.545.7564**
Fax 727.545.7584
Web ....www.operationpar.org
6655 66th Street North, Pinellas Park, FL 33781
CARF accredited programs available.

Our Children Our Future, Inc. **954.929.7515**
Fax 954.929.7510
1909 Tyler Street, Suite 504, Hollywood, FL 33020
CARF accredited programs available.

Parent's Info And Resource Ctr **954.785.8285**
Fax 954.928.0040
Web ....www.pricinc.com
E-mail ....gwilliams@pircinc.com
817 N Dixie Hwy, Pompano Beach, FL 33060-5621
Gretta Williams, Director

Parent's Information and Resource Center,
Inc. **954.785.8285**
Web ....www.pircinc.com
E-mail ....jwilson@pircinc.com
817 N. Dixie Highway, Pompano Beach, FL 33060
Ms. Jennifer Wilson, Accreditation Manager
Joint Commission accredited organization.

Park Place Behavioral Health Care, Inc. **407.846.0023**
Fax 407.933.4909
Web ....www.ppbh.org
206 Park Place Boulevard, Kissimmee, FL 34742
CARF accredited programs available.

PB Institute Partners Limited Partnership **800.433.5098**
Web ....www.pbinstitute.com
E-mail ....lsalmons@aurorabehavioral.com
1017 N. Olive Avenue, West Palm Beach, FL 33401
Ms. Lori Salmons, Accreditation Manager
Joint Commission accredited organization.

Peace River Center for Personal Development,
Inc. **863.519.0575**
Web ....www.peace-river.com
E-mail ....ballred@peacerivercenter.org
1239 East Main Street, Bartow, FL 33830
Mr. Bennie Allred, Accreditation Manager
Joint Commission accredited organization.

Personal Enrichment through Mental Health Services,
Inc. **727.545.6477**
Web ....www.pemhs.org
E-mail ....twedekind@pemhs.org
11254 58th Street North, Pinellas Park, FL 33782
Mr. Thomas Wedekind, Accreditation Manager
Joint Commission accredited organization.

PSI Family Services of Florida, Inc. **904.723.6049**
Fax 904.924.1832
Web ....www.psifamilyservices.com
3890 Dunn Avenue West, Suite 1104, Jacksonville,
FL 32218
RICKEY WALLACE, CEO
CARF accredited programs available.

Psychiatric Interventions **407.330.7393**
Fax 407.330.7356
115 Timberlachen Cir, Lake Mary, FL 32746
Alan Berns, Psychiatrist

PsychSolutions, Inc. **305.668.9000**
Fax 305.662.1788
Web ....www.psychsolutionsinc.com
701 SW 27 Avenue, Suite 500, Miami, FL 33135
COA accredited organization.

Putnam Behavioral Healthcare **386.329.3780**
Fax 386.385.1269
Web ....www.pbh.com
330 Kay Larkin Drive, Palatka, FL 32177
CARF accredited programs available.

RBHS & MHRC & MHCJ **904.743.1883**
E-mail ....lguthrie@rbhsinc.com
10550 Deerwood Park Blvd., Suite 600, Jacksonville,
FL 32256
Mrs. Leah Guthrie, Accreditation Manager
Joint Commission accredited organization.

Recapturing the Vision International, Inc. **305.232.6003**
Web ....www.recapturingthevision.org
E-mail ....judyjones247@yahoo.com
9780 E Indigo Street Suite 302, Palmetto Bay,
FL 33157
Ms. Judy Jones, Accreditation Manager
Joint Commission accredited organization.

Regis House, Inc. **305.642.7600**
Fax 305.642.6898
Web ....www.regishouse.org
2010 Northwest Seventh Street, Miami, FL 33125
CARF accredited programs available.

Renaissance Behavioral Health Systems,
Inc. **904.743.1883**
Fax 904.743.5109
10550 Deerwood Park Boulevard, Suite 600,
Jacksonville, FL 32256
CARF accredited programs available.

River Point Behavioral Health **904.724.9202**
Web ....www.riverpointbehavioral.com
E-mail ....natalie.pierce@uhsinc.com
6300 Beach Boulevard, Jacksonville, FL 32216
Ms. Natalie Pierce, Accreditation Manager
Joint Commission accredited organization.

River Region Human Services, Inc. **904.899.6300**
Fax 904.899.6380
Web ....www.rrhs.org
2055 Reyko Road, Jacksonville, FL 32207
CARF accredited programs available.

Sandy Pines Hospital **561.744.0211**
Fax 561.575.1445
Web ....www.psysolutions.com
11301 SE Tequesta Ter, Jupiter, FL 33469
John Mccarthy, CEO

Seminole Community Mental Health Center, Inc. dba Seminole
Behavioral Healthcare **407.831.2411**
Fax 407.831.0195
Web ....www.seminolecares.org
237 Fernwood Boulevard, Fern Park, FL 32730
CARF accredited programs available.

SequelCare of Florida **727.451.1600**
Fax 727.547.6752
3491 Gandy Boulevard, Suite 201, Pinellas Park,
FL 33781
CARF accredited programs available.

Serenity Center for Therapeutic Services,
Inc. **305.716.8603**
Fax 305.716.8693
8200 Northwest 27th Street, Miami, FL 33122
CARF accredited programs available.

SMA Behavioral Health Services, Inc. **386.236.3200**
Fax 386.236.3140
Web ....www.smabehavioral.org
1220 Willis Avenue, Daytona Beach, FL 32114
CARF accredited programs available.

SOS Children's Villages - Florida, Inc. **954.420.5030**
Fax 954.420.5034
Web ....www.sosflorida.com
3681 NW 59th Place, Coconut Creek, FL 33073
COA accredited organization.

South Florida Jail Ministries dba Agape **305.235.2616**
Fax 305.235.6178
Web ....www.theagapenetwork.org
22790 SW 112th Avenue, Miami, FL 33170
CARF accredited programs available.

Southwest Florida Addiction Services, Inc. **239.332.6937**
Fax 239.332.0287
Web ....www.swfas.org
3763 Evans Avenue, Fort Myers, FL 33901
Kevin Lewis, Executive Director
CARF accredited programs available.

SP Behavioral, LLC **561.744.0211**
Web ....www.psysolutions.com
E-mail ....john.mccarthy@uhsinc.com
11301 SE Tequesta Terrace, Tequesta, FL 33469
Mr. John McCarthy, Accreditation Manager
Joint Commission accredited organization.

Spectrum Programs, Adolescent Residential,
Inc. **954.941.9828**
Fax 954.941.9808
Web ....www.spectrumprograms.org
220 SW 2nd St, Pompano Beach, FL 33060-4611
Robert Salazar, Director

Spectrum Programs, Inc. **305.757.0602**
Fax 305.757.2387
Web ....http://www.mbhc.org
11031 Northeast Sixth Avenue, Miami, FL 33161
CARF accredited programs available.

St. Augustine Youth Services, Inc. **904.829.1770**
Fax 904.825.0604
Web ....www.staugustineyouthservices.com
50 Saragossa Street, Saint Augustine, FL 32084
Schuyler Skieler, Director
CARF accredited programs available.

Suncoast Center, Inc. **727.327.7656**
Fax 727.327.0350
Web ....www.suncoastcenter.org
4024 Central Avenue, Saint Petersburg, FL 33711
Amanda Smith, Director
CARF accredited programs available.

Suncoast Mental Health Center, Inc. **772.489.4726**
Web ....www.suncoastmentalhealthcenter.com
E-mail ....dstoddard@smhcinc.com
2814 S. US Hwy 1 Suite D - 4, Fort Pierce, FL 34982
Ms. Daun Stoddard, Accreditation Manager
Joint Commission accredited organization.

Susan B. Anthony Center, Inc. **954.733.6068**
Fax 954.733.0766
Web ....www.susanbanthonycenter.org
1633 Poinciana Drive, Pembroke Pines, FL 33025
CARF accredited programs available.

Sutton Place Behavioral Health Inc **904.225.8280**
Fax 904.225.8232
Web ....www.spbh.org
E-mail ....lpagel@spbh.org
463142 State Route 200, Yulee, FL 32097
Laureen Pagel, CEO
CARF accredited programs available.

The Bertha Abess Children's Center, Inc. **305.756.7116**
Web ....www.baccinc.org
5801 Biscayne Boulevard, Miami, FL 33137
COA accredited organization.

The Center For Drug-Free Living, Inc. **407.245.0045**
Fax 407.245.0049
Web ....www.cfdfl.com
3670 Maguire Boulevard, Suite 200, Orlando,
FL 32803-8350
CARF accredited programs available.

The Centers **352.291.5456**
Web ....www.thecenters.us
E-mail ....pnapier@thecenters.us
5664 SW 60th Ave, Ocala, FL 34474
Miss Penny Napier, Accreditation Manager
Joint Commission accredited organization.

The Centers, Inc. **352.628.5020**
Fax 352.628.5459
Web ....www.thecenters.us
E-mail ....mcubbiso@thecenters.us
3238 S Lecanto Hwy, Lecanto, FL 34461-9025
Mary Lee Cubbison, Director

The Centre for Women, Inc. **813.251.8437**
Web ....www.thecentre.org
E-mail ....sjohns@cfwtampa.org
305 South Hyde Park Avenue, Tampa, FL 33606
Mrs. Stephanie Johns, Accreditation Manager
Joint Commission accredited organization.

The Children's Place at Home Safe, Inc. **561.383.9800**
Fax 561.383.9857
Web ....www.helphomesafe.org
2840 Sixth Avenue, South, Lake Worth, FL 33461
COA accredited organization.

The Chrysalis Center, Inc. **954.587.1008**
Fax 954.587.0080
Web ....www.chrysaliscenter.org
3800 West Broward Boulevard, Suite 100, Ft.
Lauderdale, FL 33312
COA accredited organization.

The Ctrs **352.873.6500**
Fax 352.291.5580
Web ....www.thecenters.us
5664 SW 60th Ave, Ocala, FL 34474-5677
Wendy Fletcher, Hr Director

The Devereux Foundation, Inc. **407.362.9210**
Web .... www.devereux.org
E-mail .... dott@devereux.org
　5850 T. G. Lee Blvd, Suite 400, Orlando, FL 32822
　Dr. David Ott, Accreditation Manager
　Joint Commission accredited organization.

The Drug Abuse Treatment Association,
Inc. **561.743.1034**
Fax 561.743.1037
Web .... www.drugabusetreatment.org
　1016 Clemons Street, Suite 200, Jupiter, FL 33477
　CARF accredited programs available.

The Haven, Inc. **561.483.0962**
Fax 561.487.8007
Web www.haven4kids.org
　21441 Boca Rio Road, Boca Raton, FL 33433
　COA accredited organization.

The Jerome Golden Center for Behavioral Health,
Inc. **561.383.8000**
Web .... www.oakwoodcenter.org
E-mail .... srajpara@oakwoodcenter.org
　1041 45th Street, West Palm Beach, FL 33407
　Dr. Suresh Rajpara, Accreditation Manager
　Joint Commission accredited organization.

The Renrew Center of Florida **215.482.5353**
Web .... www.renfrewcenter.com
E-mail .... hrussock@renfrewcenter.com
　7700 Renfrew Lane, Coconut Creek, FL 33073
　Mr. Hayes Russock, Accreditation Manager
　Joint Commission accredited organization.

The Starting Place, Inc. **954.327.4060**
Fax 954.792.9122
Web .... www.startingplace.org
　351 North State Road 7, Suite 200, Plantation,
　FL 33317
　CARF accredited programs available.

The Village South, Inc. **305.573.3784**
Web .... www.villagesouth.com
E-mail .... fbundle@aol.com
　3050 Biscayne Boulevard, Miami, FL 33137
　Dr. Frank Scafidi, Accreditation Manager
　Joint Commission accredited organization.

The Vines Hospital **352.671.3130**
Web .... thevineshospital.com
E-mail .... vala.wagie@psysolutions.com
　3130 SW 27th Avenue, Ocala, FL 34471
　Ms. Vala Wagie, Accreditation Manager
　Joint Commission accredited organization.

Turn About, Inc. of Tallahassee **850.671.1920**
Fax 850.671.1922
Web .... www.turnabout.org
E-mail .... bgilbertson@turnabout.org
　2771 Miccosukee Road, Tallahassee, FL 32308-5413
　Barbara Gilbertson, Executive Director
　CARF accredited programs available.

Twin Oaks Juvenile Development, Inc. **850.643.1090**
Fax 850.643.1091
Web .... www.twinoaksfl.org
　11939 Northwest State Route 20, Bristol, FL 32321
　CARF accredited programs available.

Tykes & Teens **772.220.3439**
Web .... www.tykesandteens.org
E-mail .... joni@tykesandteens.org
　3577 SW Corporate Parkway, Palm City, FL 34990
　Ms. Joni Thieling, Accreditation Manager
　Joint Commission accredited organization.

United for Families **772.398.2920**
Fax 772.398.2925
Web .... www.uff.us
　10570 S. Federal Highway, Suite 300, Port St. Lucie,
　FL 34952
　COA accredited organization.

University Behavioral, LLC **407.281.7000**
Web .... www.psysolutions.com
E-mail .... david.beardsley@uhsinc.com
　2500 Discovery Drive, Orlando, FL 32826
　Mr. David Beardsley, Accreditation Manager
　Joint Commission accredited organization.

University Of Miami Jackson Memorial Hospital Mental
Health **305.355.7553**
Fax 305.355.7450
Web .... www.jhsmiami.org
E-mail .... dcastell@med.miami.edu
　1611 NW 12th Ave, Miami, FL 33136-1096
　Daniel Castellanos, Director Of Child And Adolescent Psychiatry

Vanguard School **863.676.6091**
Fax 863.676.8297
Web .... www.vanguardschool.org
E-mail .... vanadmin@vanguardschool.org
　22000 Hwy 27, Lake Wales, FL 33859-6858
　Melanie Anderson, Director Of Admissions

CHILDREN'S HOSPITAL

All Childrens Hospital **727.898.7451**
　801 Sixth Street S, Saint Petersburg, FL 33701
　Gary Carnes, Chief Executive Officer

Baptist Hospital of Miami **786.596.1960**
　8900 North Kendall Dr, Miami, FL 33176
　Becky Montesimo, Director

Baptist Medical Center **904.202.2000**
　800 Prudential Dr, Jacksonville, FL 32207
　Michael Mayo, President

Bay Medical Center **850.769.1511**
　615 North Bonita ave, Panama City, FL 32401
　Steve Johnson, Chief Executive Officer

Bethesda Memorial Hospital **561.737.7733**
　2815 South Seacrest Blvd, Boynton Beach, FL 33435
　Robert Hill, Chief Executive Officer

Brandon Regional Hospital **813.681.5551**
　119 Oakfield Dr, Brandon, FL 33511
　Mike Fencel, Chief Executive Officer

Broward General Medical Center **954.355.4400**
　1600 South Andrews Ave, Fort Lauderdale, FL 33316
　James Thaw, Chief Executive Officer

Broward Health Coral Springs Medical Ctr **954.344.3000**
　3000 Coral Hills Dr, Coral Springs, FL 33065
　Drew Grossman, Administrator

Citrus Memorial Hospital **352.726.1551**
　502 West Highland Blvd, Inverness, FL 34452
　Ryan Veaty, Chief Executive Officer

Doctors Memorial Hospital **850.584.0800**
　333 North Byron Butler Pkwy, Perry, FL 32347
　Michael Windham, Nursing Director

Flagler Hospital **904.819.5155**
　400 Health Park Blvd, Saint Augustine, FL 32086
　James Smith, Manager

Florida Hospital **407.303.6611**
　601 East Rollins St, Orlando, FL 32803
　Lars Houmann, Chief Executive Officer

Florida Hospital De Land **386.943.4522**
　701 West Plymouth Ave, DeLand, FL 32720
　Daryl Pol, Chief Executive Officer

Florida Hospital Heartland **863.314.4466**
　4200 Sun n Lake Blvd, Sebring, FL 33872
　Tim Cook, Chief Executive Officer

Fort Walton Beach Medical Center **850.862.1111**
　1000 Mar Walt Dr, Fort Walton Beach, FL 32547

Glades General Hospital **561.996.6571**
　1201 South Main St, Belle Glade, FL 33430
　Bob Philips, Chief Executive Officer

Halifax Health **386.254.4000**
　303 North Clyde Morris Blvd, Daytona Beach,
　FL 32114
　John Feasel, Chief Executive Officer

Health Central **407.296.1000**
　10000 West Colonial Dr, Ocoee, FL 34761
　Richard Irwin, Chief Executive Officer

Holmes Regional Medical Center **321.434.7000**
　1350 South Hickory St, Melbourne, FL 32901
　Jerry Senne, President

Homestead Hospital **786.243.8000**
　975 Baptist Way, Homestead, FL 33033
　Bill Duquette, Chief Executive Officer

Indian River Medical Center **772.567.4311**
　1000 36th st, Vero Beach, FL 32960
　Jeff Susi, Chief Executive Officer

Lake Wales Medical Center **863.676.1433**
　410 South 11th St, Lake Wales, FL 33853
　Scott Smith, Chief Executive Officer

Lakeland Regional Medical Center **863.687.1100**
　1324 Lakeland Hills Blvd, Lakeland, FL 33805
　Elaine Thompson, Chief Executive Officer

Lawnwood Regional Medical Center **772.461.4000**
　1700 South 23rd St, Fort Pierce, FL 34950
　Rodney Smith, Chief Executive Officer

Lee Memorial Hospital **239.243.2000**
　2776 Cleveland Ave, Fort Myers, FL 33901

Leesburg Regional Medical Center **352.323.5762**
　600 East Dixie Ave, Leesburg, FL 34748
　Phillis Baum, Chief Executive Officer

Martin Memorial Hospitals **772.287.5200**
　200 SE Hospital Ave, Stuart, FL 34994
　Mark Cocorullo, Chief Executive Officer

Memorial Hospital West **954.436.5000**
　703 North Flamingo Rd, Pembroke Pines, FL 33028
　Ken Hetlage, Chief Executive Officer

Memorial Regional Hospital **954.965.2000**
　3501 Johnson St, Hollywood, FL 33021
　Zeff Ross, Chief Executive Officer

Miami Childrens Hospital **305.666.6511**
　3100 SW 62nd Ave, Miami, FL 33155
　Narentra Kini, Chief Executive Officer

Morton Plant Hospital **727.462.7000**
　300 Pinellas St, Clearwater, FL 33756

Mount Sinai Medical Center **305.674.2121**
E-mail .... msm@msn.com
　4300 Alton Rd, Miami Beach, FL 33140
　Amy Perry, Chief Executive Officer

Munroe Regional Medical Center **352.351.7200**
　1500 SW 1st Ave, Ocala, FL 34471
　Steve Purves, President

Naples Community Hospital **239.436.5000**
　350 Seventh St N, Naples, FL 34102
　Allen Wiess, Chief Executive Officer

Nature Coast Regional Hospital **352.528.2801**
E-mail .... jgillman@troycountyhos.com
　125 SW Seventh St, Williston, FL 32696
　Jerry Gillman, Owner

Northwest Medical Center **954.974.0400**
　2801 North State Road 7, Margate, FL 33063
　Diane Goldenberg, Chief Executive Officer

Oak Hill Hospital **352.596.6632**
　11375 Cortez Blvd, Brooksville, FL 34613
　Mickey Smith, Chief Executive Officer

Orlando Regional Medical Center **407.841.5111**
　1414 Kuhl Ave, Orlando, FL 32806
　Shannon Elswick, President

Osceola Regional Medical Center **407.846.2266**
　700 West Oak St, Kissimmee, FL 34741
　Sylvia Lollis, Clerk

Florida

Palmetto General Hospital 305.823.5000
2001 West 68th St, Hialeah, FL 33016
Ana Mederos, Chief Executive Officer

Palms West Hospital .561.798.3300
13001 Southern Blvd, Loxahatchee, FL 33470
Bland Eng, Chief Executive Officer

Parrish Medical Center 321.268.6111
951 North Washington Ave, Titusville, FL 32796

Pasco Regional Medical Center 352.521.1100
13100 Fort King Rd, Dade City, FL 33525
Phil Minden, Chief Executive Officer

Peace River Regional Medical Center 941.766.4122
2500 Harbor Blvd, Port Charlotte, FL 33952
Minerva Gonzalez, Administrator

Plantation General Hospital 954.587.5010
401 NW 42nd Ave, Plantation, FL 33317
Barbara Simmons, Chief Executive Officer

Raulerson Hospital 863.763.2151
1796 Highway 441 North, Okeechobee, FL 34972
Robert Lee, Chief Executive Officer

Sacred Heart Hospital of Pensacola 850.416.7000
E-mail . . . . .snida@shhpens.org
5151 North 9th Ave, Pensacola, FL 32504
Laura Kaiser, Chief Executive Officer

Sarasota Memorial Hospital 941.917.9000
1700 S Tamiami Trl, Sarasota, FL 34239
Gwen Mackenzie, Chief Executive Officer

Shands at the University of Florida 352.265.0111
1600 SW Archer Rd, Gainesville, FL 32610
Tim Goldfarb, Chief Executive Officer

Shands Jacksonville Medical Center 904.244.0411
655 West Eighth St, Jacksonville, FL 32209

Shriners Hospitals for Children Tampa 813.972.2250
12502 USF Pine Dr, Tampa, FL 33612
Alice Lanford, Administrator

South Lake Hospital 352.394.4071
1900 Don Wickham Dr, Clermont, FL 34711
Leslie Longacre, Chief Executive Officer

St Lucie Medical Center 772.335.4000
1800 SE Tiffany Ave, Port Saint Lucie, FL 34952
Gary Cantrell, Chief Executive Officer

St Marys Medical Center 561.844.6300
901 45th St, West Palm Beach, FL 33407

Tallahassee Memorial Hospital 850.431.1155
1300 Miccosukee Rd, Tallahassee, FL 32308
Michael O Bryant, Chief Executive Officer

Tampa General Hospital 813.844.7000
1 Tampa General Circle, Tampa, FL 33606
Ron Hytoff, Chief Executive Officer

Univ of Miami Jackson Memorial Hospital 305.585.1111
1611 NW 12th Ave, Miami, FL 33136

University Community Hospital 813.971.6000
3100 East Fletcher Ave, Tampa, FL 33613
John Harding, Chief Executive Officer

Veterans Affairs Medical Center 727.398.6661
10000 Bay Pines Blvd, Bay Pines, FL 33744
Chris Brown, Director

West Boca Medical Center 561.488.8000
21644 State Road 7, Boca Raton, FL 33428
Mitch Feldman, Chief Executive Officer

Wuesthoff Medical Center 321.636.2211
110 Longwood Ave, Rockledge, FL 32955
Steve Patonai, Chief Executive Officer

Wuesthoff Medical Center 321.752.1200
E-mail . . . . .susantakacs@hma.com
250 North Wickham Rd, Melbourne, FL 32935
Susan Takacs, Administrator

COUNSELING SERVICES

Alpert Jewish Family And Children's Svc 561.684.1991
Fax 561.684.5366
Web . . . . .www.jfcsonline.com
E-mail . . . . .nnewstein@jfcsonline.com
5841 Corporate Way Ste 200, West Palm Beach,
FL 33407
Neil Newstein, Lcsw, Executive Director

Catholic Charities 561.842.2406
Fax 561.863.5379
Web . . . . .www.diocesepb.org
E-mail . . . . .gslcsw@bellsouth.net
900 54th St, West Palm Beach, FL 33407-2436
Gloria Stevenson, Supervisor

Catholic Charities Bureau 904.354.4846
Fax 904.354.4718
Web . . . . .www.ccbjax.org
E-mail . . . . .lhickey@ccbjax.org
134 E Church St, Jacksonville, FL 32202-3130
Laura Hickey, Executive Director

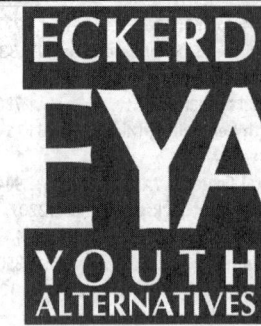

Eckerd 800.914.3937
Fax 727.442.5911
Web . . . . .www.eckerd.org
E-mail . . . . .admissions@eckerd.org
100 Starcrest Dr, Clearwater, FL 33758-7450
David Dennis, President & CEO; Francene Hazel, Director of Admissions
A full continuum of behavioral health and child welfare programs throughout Florida for children and youth from birth through age 23. Behavioral health services range from early intervention & prevention to private residential treatment centers schools, outdoor therapeutic programs, day treatment, residential programs for adjudicated youth, in-home and community-based counseling and aftercare services. Child welfare services include case management services and child welfare system administration (Eckerd serves as the lead agency for community-based child welfare in Pinellas and Pasco counties). For most programs, youth are referred through contracts with public agencies. However, parents and professionals can refer troubled youth ages 10 – 17 directly to our Eckerd Academy at Brooksville program.

Family Creations Inc. .941.727.9630
Fax 941.747.9233
Web . . . . .www.familycreationsinc.com
E-mail . . . . .familycreationsadoption@msn.com
5008 Manatee Ave W, Ste 1B, Bradenton, FL 34209
Kirk Zeppi, Chief Executive Officer

Jewish Family Svc of Broward 954.370.2140
Fax 954.916.1252
Web . . . . .www.jfsbroward.org
E-mail . . . . .kmoskowitz@jfsbroward.org
100 S Pine Island Rd Ste 230, Plantation, FL 33324
Ken Moskowitz, Executive Director

No Abuse Inc 407.228.9503
Fax 407.228.7865
E-mail . . . . .noabuse1@bellsouth.net
813 N Ferncreek Ave, Orlando, FL 32803
Paula Basil, Director

PX Equine Enterprises, Inc. 904.529.7999
Fax 904.529.7850
E-mail . . . . .pxequine@aol.com
6132 S County Road ste 209, Green Cove Springs,
FL 32043-8117
Starrlee Heady, Director

CRISIS & SHELTER CARE

Abuse Counseling And Treatment (ACT) 239.939.2553
Fax 239.939.4741
Web . . . . .www.actabuse.com
E-mail . . . . .jbenton@actabuse.com
2265 First Street, Fort Myers, FL 33901
Jennifer Benton, Director

Aid to Victims of Domestic Abuse 561.265.3797
Fax 561.265.2102
E-mail . . . . .pobrien@avda-fl.com
2905 S Federal Hwy, Delray Beach, FL 33483
Pamela Obrien, Director

Another Way 386.719.2700
Fax 386.719.2758
E-mail .donnafaganaw@msn.com
PO Box 1028, Lake City, FL 32056-1028
Donna Fagan, Director

Betty Griffin House 904.808.8544
Fax 904.808.8338
Web . . . . .www.bettygriffinhouse.org
1375 Arapaho Ave, Saint Augustine, FL 32084
Joyce Mahr, Director

Boys Town Central Florida 407.588.2170
Fax 407.588.2171
Web . . . . .www.boystown.org/central/florida
E-mail . . . . .gregory.zbylut@boystown.org
975 Oklahoma St, Oviedo, FL 32765-6233
Greg Zbylut, Executive Director

Boys Town Of North Florida 850.575.6422
Fax 850.575.7225
Web . . . . .www.boystownnorthflorida.org
E-mail . . . . .cindy.berta@boystown.org
3555 Common Wealth Blvd, Tallahassee,
FL 32303-1143
Kenneth Bender, Executive Director

Capital City Youth Svcs 850.576.6000
Fax 850.576.2580
Web . . . . .www.ccys.org
E-mail . . . . .information@ccys.org
2407 Roberts Ave, Tallahassee, FL 32310-8136
Kevin Winship, Program Services Director

CASA 352.344.8111
Fax 352.344.0548
1100 E Turner Camp Rd, Inverness, FL 34453
Diane Mcintosh, Director

Catholic Charities 407.658.1818
Fax 407.282.2891
Web . . . . .www.ccorlando.org
E-mail . . . . .arettig@ccorlando.org
1771 N Semoran Blvd, Orlando, FL 32807-3598
Alan Rettig, Director

Children's Crisis Svcs .813.272.2882
Fax 813.239.8046
Web . . . . .www.mhcinc.org
2212 E Henry Ave, Tampa, FL 33610-4433
Vimbai M, Program Manager

Crisis Ctr of Tampa Bay, Inc. 813.964.1964
Fax 813.964.1564
Web . . . . .www.crisiscenter.org
E-mail . . . . .dmross@crisiscenter.com
1 Crisis Center Plaza, Tampa, FL 33613
Dennis Ross, President & CEO

Ctr For Abuse And Rape Emergencies 941.639.5499
Fax 941.639.7079
PO Box 510234, Punta Gorda, FL 33951-0234
Kay Tvaroch, Director

Deveiux 407.522.2288
Fax 407.522.2291
E-mail .christine.connell@chsfl.org
5616 Clarcona Ocoee Rd, Orlando, FL 32810
Christine Connell, Director

Florida

Domestic Abuse Council, Inc. 386.257.2297
Fax 386.248.1985
Web ....www.domesticabusecouncil.com
E-mail ....cheryl@domesticabusecouncil.com
   1031 S Beach St, Daytona Beach, FL 32114
Cheryl Fuller, Director Of Operations

Domestic Abuse Shelter 305.743.5452
Fax 305.289.1589
E-mail ....vrgarvin@aol.com
   PO Box 522696, Marathon Shores, FL 33052-2696
Venita Garvin Valdez, Director

Domestic Violence Hotline 321.631.2764
Fax 321.631.7914
Web ....www.uss.salvationarmy.org
E-mail ....cindy_mitchell@uss.salvationarmy.org
   PO Box 940, Cocoa, FL 32923-0940
Cindy Mitchell, Director

Family Life Ctr 386.437.7610
Fax 386.437.1243
E-mail ....familycenter@flcsafehouse.org
   PO Box 2058, Bunnell, FL 32110-2058
Trish Giaccone, Executive Director

Family Resources, Inc. 727.521.5200
Fax 727.521.5210
Web ....www.family-resources.org
   5180 62nd Ave, Pinellas Park, FL 33781-5600
Jane Harper, President/CEO

First Call For Help Of Broward, Inc 954.537.0211
Fax 954.390.0499
Web www.211-broward.org
E-mail ....211-broward@211-broward.org
   3217 NW 10th Ter Ste 308, Ft Lauderdale,
   FL 33309-5939
Shiela Smith, President/CEO

Florida Keys Children's Shelter, Inc. 305.852.4246
Fax 305.852.6902
Web ....www.fkcs.org
E-mail ....ktuell@fkcs.org
   73 High Point Road, Tavernier, FL 33070
Angie Kemmer, LCSW, Counseling Services Coordinator; Ben Kemmer, Chief Learning and Evaluation Officer; Bill Mann, Chief Operating Officer; Dave Bley, Chief Financial Officer; Glen Deer, Lead House Parent; Jai Somers, Street Outreach Coordinator; Janey Wawerna, Chief Development Officer; Kathy Tuell, President & CEO; Loriann Collepardi, Residential Services Coordinator

Florida Sheriff's Youth Ranches 386.842.5501
Fax 386.842.2429
Web ....www.youthranches.org
   2486 Cecil Webb Pl, Live Oak, FL 32064
Roger Bouchard, President

Harbor House-Ctr Against Domestic
Violence 407.886.2244
Fax 407.886.0006
E-mail ....cwick@harborhousefl.com
   PO Box 680748, Orlando, FL 32868-0748
Carol Wick, CEO

Help Now, Inc 407.847.8562
Fax 407.847.7286
E-mail ....helpnowhsd@earthlink.net
   806 Verona St, Kissimmee, FL 34741
Tammy Douglas, Director

Hibiscus Children's Ctr 772.334.9311
Fax 772.334.1991
Web ....www.hibiscuschildren.org
   2400 NE Dixie Hwy, Jensen Beach, FL 34957-5949
Thomas B Maher, CEO

High Ridge Family Ctr 561.625.2540
Fax 561.840.4545
E-mail ....aspaniol@pbcgov.com
   4200 N Australian Ave, West Palm Beach,
   FL 33407-3622
Anthony Spaniol, Psy.d., Director

Hope Ctr For Teens, Inc. 850.434.1340
Fax 850.434.1345
Web www.hopecenter4teens.org
E-mail ....jyoung@hopecenter4teens.org
   891 N 10th Ave, Pensacola, FL 32501-3347
Jennifer Young, Director

Hope Family Serivces 941.747.8499
Fax 941.749.1796
Web ....www.hopefamilyservice.org
E-mail ....hopefamilyservic@aol.com
   PO Box 1624, Bradenton, FL 34206-1624
Laurel Lynch, Director

House Of Hope 407.843.8686
Fax 407.422.3816
Web ....www.houseofhopeorlando.org
   2036 36th St, Orlando, FL 32839-8810
Sara Trollinger, President

Interface-East 386.385.0405
Fax 386.385.0410
E-mail ....cindy_starling@cdsfl.org
   2919 Kennedy St, Palatka, FL 32177-4165
Pam Purnell, Residential Supervisor Runaway, Truant And Ungovernable Shelter

Jewish Community Svcs 305.672.8080
Fax 305.672.0030
Web ....www.jewishcommunityservices.org
E-mail ....mdrail@jcsfl.org
   300 W 41st St Ste 216, Miami Beach, FL 33140-3627
Melissa Drail, Director

Lippman Youth Shelter 954.568.2801
Fax 954.568.2729
Web ....www.lsfnet.org
E-mail ....abrowne@lsfnet.org
   221 NW 43rd Ct, Fort Lauderdale, FL 33309-4729
Alexander Browne, Shelter Manager

Lutheran Svcs Florida, Inc. 813.875.1408
Fax 813.875.1302
Web ....www.lsfnet.org
E-mail ....pleonard@lsfnet.org
   3627A W Waters Ave, Tampa, FL 33614-2783
Patricia Leonard, Regional Director

Martha's House Inc-Domestic Violence 863.763.0202
Fax 863.763.6712
Web ....www.marthashouse.org
E-mail ....talexandra@marthashouse.org
   4134 Hwy 441, Okeechobee, FL 34972
Teresa Alexandra, Director

Miami Bridge-Homestead/ South Dade 305.246.8956
Fax 305.242.8222
Web ....www.miamibridge.org
E-mail ....msmith@miamibridge.org
   326 NW 3rd Ave, Homestead, FL 33030-5805
Marc Smith, Shelter Services Coordinator

Ocala Domestic Violence/Sexual Assault
Ctr 352.622.8495
Fax 352.351.9455
E-mail ....csiokala@csl.rr.com
   2022 S Pine Ave, Ocala, FL 34471
Judy Wilson, Phd, CEO

Palm Beach Institute 561.833.7553
Fax 561.655.5327
Web ....www.pbinstitute.com
E-mail ....pbinst@aol.com
   1017 N Olive Ave, West Palm Beach, FL 33401-3511
Jeff Rocco, Director Of Admissions

Pasadena Villa 407.246.5250
Fax 407.246.5271
Web ....www.pasadenavilla.com
   119 Pasadena Pl, Orlando, FL 32803-3825
David Nissen, Executive Director

Peace River Ctr-Domestic Violence Shelter 863.413.2708
Fax 863.413.3079
E-mail ....kathy.platt@peace-river.com
   1860 S Crystal Lake Dr, Lakeland, FL 33801-6529
Kathy Platt, Director Of Victim Services

Peaceful Paths 352.377.5690
Fax 352.378.9033
E-mail ....theresah@peacefulpaths.org
   2100 NW 53rd Ave, Gainesville, FL 32653
Theresa B Harrison, Director

Quigley House, Inc. 904.284.0340
Fax 904.284.5407
E-mail ....executivedir@quigleyhouse.org
   PO Box 142, Orange Park, FL 32067-0142
Sharon Youngerman, Executive Director

Safe Place-Rape Crisis Ctr-Domestic
Violence 941.365.0208
Fax 941.365.4919
Web ....www.sparcc.net
E-mail ....sparcc@gte.net
   2139 Main St, Sarasota, FL 34237-6023
Olivia Thomas, Director

Safespace Crisis Hotline 305.758.2546
Fax 305.756.1347
   7831 NE Miami Ct, Miami, FL 33138
Oscie Fryer, Director

Salvation Army-Domestic Violence & Rape
Crisis 850.769.7989
Fax 850.769.5346
E-mail ....kimberly_swanson@uss.salvationarmy.org
   1824 W 15th ST, Ste C, Panama City, FL 32401-2251
Kimberly Swanson, Director

Saver House Of Northwest Florida 850.434.1177
Fax 850.434.9987
Web ....www.favorhouse.gccoxmail.com
   2001 W Blount St, Pensacola, FL 32501-2270
Sue Hand, Director

Serene Harbor 321.726.8282
Fax 321.726.8588
E-mail ....mrkbd2@msn.com
   PO Box 100039, Palm Bay, FL 32910-0039
Melody Keeth, Executive Director

Shelter For Abused Women & Children 239.775.3862
Fax 239.775.3061
E-mail ....info@naplesshelter.org
   PO Box 10102, Naples, FL 34101-0102
Nancy Whiteman, Admin Asst

Shelter House Inc-Domestic Violence 850.243.1201
Fax 850.243.6756
E-mail ....info@shelterhousenwsl.org
   102A Buck Dr NE, Fort Walton Beach, FL 32548
Michelle Sperzel, Director

The Haven 352.787.5889
Fax 352.787.4125
Web ....www.havenlakesumter.org
E-mail ....havenlscnty@aol.com
   2600 South St, Leesburg, FL 34748
Kelly Smallridge, Director

The Haven Of RCS-Domestic Violence Ctr 727.442.4128
Fax 727.461.5057
   PO Box 10594, Clearwater, FL 33757-8594
Besna Nedic, Director

The Renfrew Ctr 800.736.3739
Fax 954.698.9007
Web ....www.renfrewcenter.com
E-mail ....bsicard@renfrewcenter.com
   7700 NW 48th Ave, Pompano Beach, FL 33073-3508
Beth Sicard, Director

EDUCATION

Associated Marine Institutes 813.887.3300
Fax 813.889.8092
Web ....www.amikids.org
E-mail ....sdt@amikids.org
   5915 Benjamin Center Dr, Tampa, FL 33634-5239
Ob Stander, CEO

Florida

Children's Home Society 305.755.6500
Fax 305.326.7430
Web .... www.chsfl.org
E-mail .... jackie.gerstein@chsfl.org
800 NW 15th St, Miami, FL 33136-1495
Jacqueline Gerstin, Director

Killian Oaks Academy 305.274.2221
Fax 305.279.5460
Web .... www.killianoaksacademy.com
E-mail .... info@killianoaksacademy.com
10545 SW 97th Ave, Miami, FL 33176-2806
Dr. Mercedes Ricon, Director

North Florida Educational Development Corp. 850.856.5025
Fax 850.856.9268
Web .... www.nfedc.org
E-mail .... bossnfedc@netquincy.com
100 Beech Ave, Gretna, FL 32332
Carolyn Ford, Executive Director

Pace Brantley Hall School 407.869.8882
Fax 407.869.8717
Web .... mypbhs.org
E-mail .... doneal@mypbhs.org
3221 Sand Lake Rd, Longwood, FL 32779-5898
Donna A O'Neal, Executive Assistant

PACE Ctr For Girls 904.421.8585
Fax 904.421.8599
Web .... www.pacecenter.org
E-mail .... mary.marx@pacecenter.org
1 W Adams St Ste 301, Jacksonville, FL 32202-3644
Mary Marx, President & CEO

The Depaul School Of NE Florida 904.223.3391
Fax 904.223.8722
Web .... www.depaulschool.com
E-mail .... conniek@depaulschool.com
3044 San Pablo Rd S, Jacksonville, FL 32224
Connie Korte, President

FOSTER CARE AGENCIES

A Bond of Love Adoption Agency Inc (ABL) 941.957.0064
Fax 941.954.5134
E-mail .... abladopt@aol.com
4017 Swift Rd, Sarasota, FL 34231

Adoption 4KIDS 954.315.7553
Fax 954.556.4584
E-mail .... ava@adoption4kidsofsfl.org
2401 W Cypress Creek Rd, Fort Lauderdale, FL 33309

Adoption Affl of S Fl Adoption Spt Svcs 305.667.0387
E-mail .... adopt@adoptionaffiliates.net
7210 SW 57th Ave, Ste 202-D, Miami, FL 33143

Adoption STAR Inc 954.566.6055
Fax 716.639.3700
E-mail .... info@adoptionstar.com
1040 Bayview Dr Ste 318, Fort Lauderdale, FL 33304
Michelle Fried, Chief Executive Officer

Adoption Support & Consultation Services 813.425.2367
Fax 813.425.4365
E-mail .... info@ascsadopt.org
PO Box 6845, Brandon, FL 33508
Stacia

Adoptnet 352.377.6455
130 NW 28th St, Gainesville, FL 32607
Susan Weinstein, Coordinator

Camelot Community Care 813.635.9765
Fax 813.635.9725
Web .... www.camelotcommunitycare.org
E-mail .... kleffers@camelotcommunitycare.org
1412 Tech Blvd, Tampa, FL 33619
Katrina Leffers, Office Manager

Caring Heart Adoption Services Inc CHASI 561.333.9306
E-mail .... caringheartas@aol.com
13409 La Mirada Cir, West Palm Beach, FL 33414

Children In Crisis Inc 850.864.4242
Fax 850.226.7875
E-mail .... kenhair@childrenincrisisfl.org
1000 Lukes Way, Fort walton beach, FL 32547
Ken Hair, Executive Director

Children's Network of Southwest Florida 239.226.1524
E-mail .... info@childnetswfl.org
2232 Altamont Ave, Fort Myers, FL 33901
Nadereh Salim, Chief Executive Officer

Circle of Hope FL TRIAD Post Adoption 561.967.7079
Fax 561.967.7079
E-mail .... circle92@juno.com
3530 Pine Tree Ct A-1, Greenacres City, FL 33463

Cldrns Home Society of FL (CHS Florida) 850.921.0772
Fax 850.921.0726
E-mail .... Helen.Ervin@chsfl.org
1801 Miccosukee Commons Dr, Tallahassee, FL 32308
Joanna Waldron, Administrative Supervisor

Community Partnership for Children 386.238.4900
160 N Beach St, Daytona Beach, FL 32114
Mark Jone, Chief Executive Officer

Cornerstone Adoption Services Inc 850.524.5437
E-mail .... director@hiskidstoo.org
219 Delta Ct B, Tallahassee, FL 32303
Teresa Fillmon, Director

ECKERD EYA YOUTH ALTERNATIVES

Eckerd 800.914.3937
Fax 727.442.5911
Web .... www.eckerd.org
E-mail .... admissions@eckerd.org
100 Starcrest Dr, Clearwater, FL 33758-7450
David Dennis, President & CEO; Francene Hazel, Director of Admissions
A full continuum of behavioral health and child welfare programs throughout Florida for children and youth from birth through age 23. Behavioral health services range from early intervention & prevention to private residential treatment centers schools, outdoor therapeutic programs, day treatment, residential programs for adjudicated youth, in-home and community-based counseling and aftercare services. Child welfare services include case management services and child welfare system administration (Eckerd serves as the lead agency for community-based child welfare in Pinellas and Pasco counties). For most programs, youth are referred through contracts with public agencies. However, parents and professionals can refer troubled youth ages 10 – 17 directly to our Eckerd Academy at Brooksville program.

Everyday Blessings (EB) 813.982.9226
E-mail .... Everydayblessings@everybless.org
13129 Saint Francis Ln, Thonotosassa, FL 33592
Pat Burdett, Business Director

Family Creations Adoptions 941.747.9225
Fax 941.747.9233
E-mail .... familycreationsadoption@msn.com
5008 Manatee Ave W, Ste 1B, Bradenton, FL 34209
Kirk Zeppi, Executive Director

Family's First Of Florida 813.290.8560
Fax 813.354.2416
Web .... www.familiesfirstfl.com
E-mail .... pdebone@familiesfirstfl.com
4902 Eisenhower Blvd Ste 315, Tampa, FL 33634-6344
Agnus Turner, Office Adminstrator

Florida Adoption Information Center 904.353.0679
Fax 904.353.3472
E-mail .... adoptflorida@danielkids.org
4203 Southpoint Blvd, Jacksonville, FL 32216
Bob Rooks, Chief Executive Officer

Florida Mentor 863.607.4183
Fax 863.646.5843
Web .... www.thementornetwork.com
E-mail .... marsha.pope@thementornetwork.com
5304 S Florida Ave, ste 406, Lakeland, FL 33813
Marsha Pope, Program Supervisor

Foster & Adoptive Parents Assoc of PB 561.352.2540
4100 Okeechobee Blvd, West Palm Beach, FL 33409
Maria Bond, Director

Foster Parent Assoc N Branch Inc 305.622.3540
2475 NW 82nd St, Miami, FL 33147

Greater Jacksonville Foster Adoptive 904.343.4026
E-mail .... deewil4@yahoo.com
3618 Cedarcrest Dr, Jacksonville, FL 32210
Dee Wilson, President

Heart Attach 407.696.6383
Fax 407.659.5812
E-mail .... billorttfamily@yahoo.com
427 Centerpoint Cir, Ste 1878, Altamonte Springs, FL 32701

Heart of Adoptions Inc 813.258.6505
Fax 813.254.9058
418 W Platt St, Ste A, Tampa, FL 33606
Tammi Driver, Executive Director

Home at Last Adoption Agency (HAL) 321.868.2229
Fax 321.868.7810
E-mail .... info@homeatlastadoption.com
1727 N Atlantic Ave, Cocoa Beach, FL 32931
Rachael Fornes, Owner

Jewish Family & Community Services Inc 904.394.5763
Fax 904.448.0349
E-mail .... crodriguez@jfcsjax.org
6261 Dupont Station Ct E, Jacksonville, FL 32217
Colleen Rodriguez, Interim Executive Director

Kids Central Inc 352.735.0446
Fax 352.742.1590
E-mail .... info@kidscentralinc.org
1300 S Duncan Dr, Tavares, FL 32778

Northeast FL Foster/Adoptive Parent Asso 904.502.7932
E-mail .... blackshearqueenb@aol.com
11776 Tumbleweed Way, Jacksonville, FL 32218
Lillie Blackshear, President

Parents Adoption Lifeline 561.837.5054
319 Cordova St, West Palm Beach, FL 33401

Pinellas Council on Adoptable Children 727.776.1084
E-mail .... cbruningc@yahoo.com
4651 21st Ave S, Saint Petersburg, FL 33711
Christa Bruning, Director

Safe Children Coalition 941.721.7670
Fax 941.721.8950
E-mail .... dpammieri@sarasota-ymca.org
5729 Manatee Ave W, Bradenton, FL 34209

Stars of David International Inc 561.852.3380
Fax 561.852.3332
E-mail .... starsdavid@aol.com
21300 Ruth & Baron Coleman Blvd, Boca Raton, FL 33428
Danielle Hartman, Director

The Children's Home Inc 813.855.4432
E-mail .... lcooper@childrenshome.org
10909 Memorial Hwy, Tampa, FL 33615
Jim Hart, Chief Executive Officer

Universal Aid for Children Inc 954.785.0033
Fax 954.785.7003
E-mail .... uacadopt@aol.com
167 SW 6th St, Pompano Beach, FL 33060

Florida

HOME MEDICAL EQUIPMENT PROVIDERS

Access Ability 954.942.1882
Fax 954.781.1282
610 East Sample Road, Pompano Beach, FL 33064

Access Medical South 239.693.0035
Fax 239.693.0145
E-mail .... linda.bessen@baycare.org
5619 2 Corporate Circle, Fort Myers, FL 33905
Linda Bessen, Manager

Accessibility Services Inc 352.503.2012
Fax 888.410.8958
E-mail .... asi@asi-florida.com
6360 S Suncoast Blvd, Homosassa, FL 34446
Maggie Townsend, President

Accessibility Solutions 850.383.1100
Fax 850.383.1102
E-mail .... access.asi@comcast.net
2066 Thomasville Road, Tallahassee, FL 32308
Reta Hodges, Office Manager

Advanced Motion Control Inc 305.661.4776
4705 Southwest 72nd Ave, Miami, FL 33155
Hermi Silva, Director

Advanced Prosthetics of America 800.330.8881
Fax 800.261.9537
E-mail .... chauserman@hanger.com
123 S Industrial Dr Ste 104, Orange City, FL 32763
Travis Andersen, Supervisor

Advantage Vans of Central Florida 407.281.8369
Fax 407.281.0235
E-mail .... info502@wheelchairgetaways.com
1230 Almond Tree Court, Orlando, FL 32835

Advocate Medical Services 813.622.6459
Fax 813.630.1645
E-mail .... info@advocatemed.com
1202 Tech Blvd Ste 105, Tampa, FL 33619
Amy Holway, Office Manager

Affordable Medical Supply 954.484.7599
4255 West Commercial Blvd, Lauderdale Lakes, FL 33319
John McCarthy, Owner

Agency For Persons With Disabilities 239.338.1370
Fax 239.338.1359
E-mail .... Elaine_Gage@apd.state.fl.us
2295 Victoria Ave, Fort Myers, FL 33901
Elaine Gage, Human Services Program Analyst

All State Medical Equipment Inc 305.754.0713
Fax 305.754.0262
911 NE 79th St, Miami Shores, FL 33138
Maria Evera, President

Alpha Home Care 941.351.4727
Fax 941.351.4695
E-mail .... amobilit@verizon.net
1275 Tallevast Road, Sarasota, FL 34243
Wally Wallace, Sales Manager

American Cancer Society Gift Closet 904.244.1994
1910 Jefferson St Pavillon Bld, Jacksonville, FL 32209

American Cancer Society Gift Closet 904.249.0022
1430 Purdential Dr, Jacksonville Beach, FL 32207
Rachel Mcclure, Area Administrative Assistant

American Cancer Society Gift Closet 904.284.2661
E-mail .... jaclyn.rodriguez@cancer.org
7175 Us Hwy 17 Ste 3, Fleming Island, FL 32003
Jaclyn Rodriguez, Administrative Assistant

American Cancer Society Gift Closet 904.308.7348
1800 Barrs St, Jacksonville, FL 32204

American Mobility 941.358.8482
Fax 941.358.9277
E-mail .... info@scottersandlifts.com
4201 N Washington Blvd, Sarasota, FL 34234
William Shehwen, President

Apria Healthcare 850.433.7434
E-mail .... contact_us@apria.com
3636 D North L St, Pensacola, FL 32505

Apria Healthcare Sarasota 941.377.5458
327 Interstate Blvd, Sarasota, FL 34240

Blue Ribbon Health Services Inc 850.874.8280
Fax 850.874.1414
E-mail .... blribbon@gmail.com
6909 East Highway 22, Panama City, FL 32404
David Ferry, General Manager

BookHolder.com 800.928.2322
E-mail .... dave@bookholder.com
1934 Heritage Lakes Blvd, Lakeland, FL 33803
Dave Simon, Director

Bradenton Prosthetics & Orthotics 941.747.5407
Fax 941.747.4914
E-mail .... info@BradentonProsthetics.com
525 8th St W, Bradenton, FL 34205

Bremer Brace Southside 904.346.0086
Fax 904.396.2754
E-mail .... info@bremerbrace.com
3627 University Blvd Ste 425, Jacksonville, FL 32216
Jill, Secretary

Byram Healthcare Products & Srvs 800.234.1779
Fax 866.811.4500
E-mail .... clinical@byramhealthcare.com
Customer Service Center, 11400 47th St Ste A, Clearwater, FL 33762
Nick K, Director

CARE Medical Equipment 407.856.2273
E-mail .... info@caremedicalequipment.com
102 Drennen Rd B 1, Orlando, FL 32806
Jay Naab, Manager

Caring & Sharing Center for Independent 727.539.7550
Fax 727.539.7588
E-mail .... cascil@cascil.org
12552 Belcher Rd S, Largo, FL 33773
Jesse Broecker, Infomation Facilitator

Center for Independent Living of SW FL 239.277.1447
2321 Bruner Lane, Fort Myers, FL 33912
Marti Graf, Office Manager

Certified Medical Systems Ocala 352.237.4146
6122 SW Highway 200, Ocala, FL 34476

Certified Medical Systems Orange Park 904.272.3022
2141 Loch Rane Blvd, Ste 116, Orange Park, FL 32073
Mike Dillman, Chief Executive Officer

Certified Medical Systems St Augustine 904.810.9747
296 State Road 312, Saint Augustine, FL 32086
Mike Dillman, Owner

ChildrenFirst Home Hlth Care System 407.513.3000
E-mail .... reception@childrenfirsthomecare.com
4448 Edgewater Dr, Orlando, FL 32804
Mary Schiazi, Chief Executive Officer

Childrens Home Society of Florida 561.868.4300
Fax 561.868.4497
E-mail .... south.coastal@chsfl.org
3333 Forest Hill Blvd, West Palm Beach, FL 33406
Stephen Bardy, Executive Director

Christ Fellowship 561.799.7600
Fax 561.622.8445
E-mail .... gailb@cftoday.org
5343 Northlake Blvd, Palm Beach Gardens, FL 33418
Todd Mullins, Lead Pastor

Coastal Care Hearing Center Inc 904.565.1555
10909 Atlantic Blvd, Jacksonville, FL 32225

Deaf and Hard of Hearing Srvs of FL 727.853.1010
E-mail .... info@deafhhsfla.org
8610 Galen Wilson Blvd Bld B Ste 100, Port Richey, FL 34668
Jass Thomas, Director

Deaf and Hard of Hearing Srvs of NW FL 850.433.7128
Fax 850.438.0299
E-mail .... info@dhhsnwfl.org
945 W Michigan Ave Ste 4B, Pensacola, FL 32505

Deaf Srv Ctr of Southwest Florida 239.461.0334
Fax 239.461.0434
E-mail .... info@dsc.us
1860 Boy Scout Dr B208, Fort Myers, FL 33907
Lori Timson, Director

Deming Designs Inc 850.478.5765
Fax 850.476.3361
E-mail .... kmdeming@aol.com
1090 Cobblestone Dr, Pensacola, FL 32514
Km Deming, Director

Discount Medical Supply Sarasota 941.954.9066
2045 12th St, Sarasota, FL 34237
Gem, Manager

Don Smith Rehabilitation Engineering 407.695.9244
Fax 407.695.1148
E-mail .... dexsmith@juno.com
120 E Tradewinds Road, Winter Springs, FL 32708

First Coast Orthotics and Prosthetics 904.396.4400
Fax 904.396.4092
E-mail .... email@firstcoastandp.com
3728 Philips Highway Ste 2, Jacksonville, FL 32207

FISH of Sanibel 239.472.0404
The Village Shopps, 2340 Periwinkle Way Unit I, Sanibel, FL 33957

Fitting Designs Inc 850.484.9111
E-mail .... fittingd@bellsouth.net
8800 University Pkwy Ste B1, Pensacola, FL 32514

FL Agency for Persons with Disabilities 561.837.5584
E-mail .... dcf-osc@dcf.state.fl.us
111 S Sapodilla Ave, West Palm Beach, FL 33401

FL Dept of Health Brain and Spinal Cord 850.245.4045
E-mail .... tom_delilla@doh.state.fl.us
4025 Esplanade Way, Talla, FL 32399
Tom Delilla, Director

FL Dept of Health Brain and Spinal Cord 954.677.5639
E-mail .... rick_schwarz@doh.state.fl.us
2550 West Oakland Park Blvd, Fort Lauderdale, FL 33311

FL Dept of Health Brain and Spinal Cord 561.840.6013
901 45th St, West Palm Beach, FL 33407
Robert Borrego, Medical Director

FL Hospital Rehab & Sports Medicine 407.303.6733
7975 Lake Underhill Rd Ste 300, Orlando, FL 32822
Rod Olson, Office Manager

FL Hospital Respiratory & Equipment 407.830.1938
Fax 407.830.0936
556 Florida Central Parkway, Ste 1060, Longwood, FL 32750
Pedro Figueroa, Branch Manager

FL Medical Supply Fletchers Med Supply 904.387.4481
Fax 904.389.6965
E-mail .... wfletc2328@gmail.com
1080 Edgewood Ave, Jacksonville, FL 32205

FL Mobility & Medical Products 407.363.3535
Fax 407.363.4475
E-mail .... info@floridamobilityproducts.com
8451 S John Young Parkway, Orlando, FL 32819
Jim W, Director

Florida Prosthetics & Orthotics 305.553.1217
Fax 305.553.1237
E-mail .... info@flaprosthetics.com
11760 Bird Rd Ste 506, Miami, FL 33175
Maida Porres, Office Manager

Florida Surgical Supply 941.366.2345
E-mail .... floridasurgical@aol.com
4500 S Tamiami Trail, Sarasota, FL 34231

Florida

Gillette Wheelchair **850.438.7300**
Fax 850.438.7355
E-mail ....rgillette@earthlink.net
3936 N Davis Hwy, Pensacola, FL 32503
R Gillette, Director

Healthtech Medical Equipment Srvs **352.243.3478**
Fax 352.241.0371
E-mail ....info@healthtechmedical.co@msn.com
905 Jan Mar Court Ste E, Clermont, FL 34711

Hear 4 Kidz Inc Homestead **305.247.8227**
Fax 305.247.8228
E-mail ....info@hear4kidz.com
45 Northwest 8th St Ste 108, 45 55 Professional Bldg,
Homestead, FL 33030
Michelle Couture, Owner

HMP Medical Equipment & Supplies **941.794.2447**
5650 Cortez Rd W, Bradenton, FL 34210
Terry Seagers, Owner

Hollywood Medical Supply **954.923.4693**
Fax 954.923.4699
E-mail ....info@hollywoodmedical.com
2131 Hollywood Blvd, Ste 104, Hollywood, FL 33020

Hoveround Corporation **800.542.7236**
Fax 941.782.1475
2151 Whitfield Ind Way, Sarasota, FL 34243

Huber Health Mart Drugs **561.276.6477**
Fax 561.276.6385
331 E Atlantic Ave, Delray Beach, FL 33483

Jacksonville Hearing and Balance Inst **904.399.0350**
Fax 904.399.5914
10475 Centurion Pkwy N, Ste 303, Jacksonville,
FL 32256
Monica Babcock, Office Manager

Jupiter Drugs and Medical Supplies **561.746.7499**
Fax 561.746.9645
E-mail ....info@jupiterdrugs.com
1025 Military Trail, Jupiter, FL 33458
Barry Sternberg, Director

Kids medical Club Ped Srvs of America **904.731.0030**
Fax 904.731.9391
4051 Phillips Hughway Ste 2, Jacksonville, FL 32207

League for the Hard of Hearing FL **954.601.1930**
E-mail ....receptionfl@chchearing.org
2900 W Cypress Creek Rd, Ste 3, Fort Lauderdale,
FL 33309
Kim Schur, Executive Director

Lions Club Eye Clinic **850.438.8989**
3103 N H St, Pensacola, FL 32501

Medical Accessories and Supply Headquar **850.892.5773**
Fax 850.892.6318
E-mail ....mashcorporate@covad.net
579 E Nelson Ave, Greenwood, FL 32443

Medical Accessories and Supply Headquar **850.863.4515**
Fax 850.863.1319
242 NE Racetrack Road, Fort Walton Beach, FL 32547
Terry Pool, Manager

Medical Accessories and Supply
Headquarter **850.969.0220**
Fax 850.969.0412
5800 North W St, Ste 5, Pensacola, FL 32505
Tia Smith, Manager

Medical Care Products Inc **904.733.8500**
4836 Victor St, Jacksonville, FL 32207
Patricia Lang, President

Medical Decisions **954.772.1631**
Fax 954.772.1566
E-mail ....hecjr@medicaldecisions.net
2890 Marina Mile Blvd, Ste 102, Fort Lauderdale,
FL 33312
Juan Izquierdo, Manager

Medical Department Store Venice **941.497.2273**
1180 Jacaranda Blvd, Venice, FL 34292
Jerrika, Director

Medical Store **561.242.6200**
Fax 561.242.6240
E-mail ....info@tmsdme.com
300 N Point Pkwy Ste 301, Riviera Beach, FL 33404
David Zodnik, Director

Multiple Sclerosis Center of SW FL **239.435.1901**
Fax 239.435.1993
971 N 3rd Ave, Naples, FL 34102
Paul Pentz, Chairman Of The Board

Muscular Dystrophy Assoc Broward **954.971.0123**
Fax 954.971.0492
E-mail ....ftlauderdaledistrict@mdausa.org
1280 SW 36th Ave ste 303, Pompano Beach,
FL 33064
Joanne Bowsman, Director

Muscular Dystrophy Assoc St Petersburg **727.577.1700**
Fax 727.578.0930
Monroe Building Ste 110, 9720 Executive Center Dr
North, Saint Petersburg, FL 33702
Erin Authier, Director

National Multiple Sclerosis Society **800.344.0867**
E-mail ....Doris.Lill@nmss.org
4919 Memorial Hwy, Ste 160, Tampa, FL 33634

National Seating and Mobility Florida **305.262.3399**
Fax 305.262.3811
E-mail ....Miami@nsm-seating.com
4612 SW 74th Ave, Miami, FL 33155
Louis Gonzalez, Director

Ntl Multiple Sclerosis Society **954.731.4224**
Fax 954.739.1398
E-mail ....fls@nmss.org
3201 W Commercial Blvd, Ste 127, Fort Lauderdale,
FL 33309
Jaine Valtivia, Coordinator

Ocular Prosthetics Lab Inc **407.246.5451**
Fax 407.246.0222
E-mail ....MYEYE@OPLeye.com
36 W Illiana St, Orlando, FL 32806
Cindy, Manager

Option Care Crestview **850.683.0800**
Fax 850.683.1688
E-mail ....kathir@barneshc.com
2205 South Ferdon Blvd, Crestview, FL 32536

Orange Park Lions Club **904.264.5866**
Fax 904.851.4096
423 McIntosh Ave, Orange Park, FL 32073
Joe Cafrelli, President

ORO Physical Rehab Oxygen and Products **941.365.1499**
2187 Siesta Dr, Sarasota, FL 34239

Pearlman Family Campus **954.792.6700**
E-mail ....www.sorfjcc.org
6501 W Sunrise Blvd, Fort Lauderdale, FL 33313
Donald Graw, Executive Director

Pediatric Health Choice Clearwater Med Ct **727.723.1100**
Fax 866.646.0221
2364 Drew St, Clearwater, FL 33765

Pediatric Health Choice Lakeland **863.680.1444**
Fax 863.603.0128
E-mail ....randerson@pediatrichc.com
3131 Lakeland Hills Blvd, Lakeland, FL 33805
Robert Anderson, Customer Service

Pediatric Health Choice Tampa **800.783.9858**
Fax 866.646.0221
Tampa Clinical Offices, 4602 C North Armenia Ave,
Tampa, FL 33603

Pediatric Hlth Choice St Petersburg Med **727.343.0010**
Fax 727.347.8119
E-mail ....mfischer@pediatrichealthchoice.com
3110 75th St N, Perrine, FL 33170
Dawn Bielawski, Regional Administrator

Pediatric Services of America Inc **386.304.0702**
E-mail ....info@psakids.com
1110 Pelican Bay Dr, Daytona Beach, FL 32119
Brooke Walls, Chief Executive Officer

Pediatric Services of America Inc **850.444.4365**
Fax 850.432.5806
E-mail ....slewis@psakids.com
1300 North Palafox St Ste 106, Pensacola, FL 32501
Jodi Kendrick, Director

Pediatric Srvs of America Inc **561.683.4411**
Fax 561.683.4498
E-mail ....info@psakids.com
1920 Palm Beach Lakes Blvd, Ste 118, West Palm
Beach, FL 33409

Pedicraft Inc **800.223.7649**
Web ....www.pedicraft.com
E-mail ....dmaynard@pedicraft.com
4134 St Augustine Rd, Jacksonville, FL 32207
Doug Maynard, President

Professional Medical Equipment **877.665.9236**
Fax 305.665.5401
E-mail ....customerservice@promed1.net
6813 SW 81 St Ste B, Miami, FL 33143

Prosthetic Eye Institute **800.972.1354**
E-mail ....administration@prostheticeye.com
Banco Popular Bldg, 1118 S Organe Ave 204,
Orlando, FL 32806
Nichole Garonzik, Chief Executive Officer

Rehab Foundation of Northwest Florida **850.478.0297**
2929 Langley Ave Ste 202, Pensacola, FL 32504

Self Reliance Inc Ctr for Indep Living **813.375.3965**
Fax 813.375.3970
8901 North Armenia Ave, Tampa, FL 33604
Brenda Ruehl, Chief Executive Officer

South Florida Community Services **305.245.6150**
Fax 305.598.8240
E-mail ....Mhenry@sunrisegroup.org
22300 SW 162nd Ave, Perrine, FL 33170

South Florida Medical Equipment Co **305.261.8242**
Fax 305.261.6842
5735 NW 7th St, Miami, FL 33126
Rudy Hernandez, Chief Executive Officer

St Augustine Medical Equipment **904.829.1799**
105 Southpark Blvd, Saint Augustine, FL 32086

Suncoast Brace & Limb **941.798.3558**
Fax 941.798.3626
1878 59th St West, Bradenton, FL 34209
Tracy Decker, Office Manager

Suncoast Medicare Supply **941.758.7768**
Fax 941.758.9881
1145 53rd Ave W, Bradenton, FL 33420
Jeff Baldwin, Branch Manager

Sunrise Community **239.643.5338**
E-mail ....evandermeuse@sunrisegroup.org
3984 Arnold Ave, Naples, FL 34104
Ellie Vandermeuse, Director

SunShine Medical **239.262.6592**
Fax 239.280.9999
E-mail ....sunshine.hme.referrals@gmail.com
411 Ninth St N, Naples, FL 34102
Mike Eastman, Manager

Tub King Ing **904.732.9906**
6593 Powers Ave # 1, Jacksonville, FL 32217
Alan Knight, Office Manager

United Cerebral Palsy of Northwest FL **850.432.1596**
Fax 850.432.1930
E-mail ....info@ucpnwfl.org
2912 North E St, Pensacola, FL 32501
Trudy Obrien, Chief Executive Officer

Wheelchair Getaways of FL Palm Beach 561.748.8414
Fax...561.748.8677
E-mail ....gyear@aol.com
8 Bay Harbour Dr, Tequesta, FL 33469

Wheels for Kids 561.752.0799
E-mail ....info@wheelsforkids.org
PO Box 57, West Palm Beach, FL 33402

Wrightway Consulting Inc 727.577.7544
Fax...727.520.8130
2909 47th Ave North, Saint Petersburg, FL 33714
William Wright, Chief Executive Officer

PEDIATRIC HOME CARE

Bayada Nurses 727.530.1201
Fax...727.531.2582
Web ....www.bayada.com
13773 Icot Blvd, Suite 517, Clearwater, FL 33760
Kelly, Business Manager

Bayada Nurses 813.289.6900
Fax...813.286.9691
Web ....www.bayada.com
4100 West Kennedy Boulevard, Suite 128, Tampa,
FL 33609
Madeline Spannell, Director

Bayada Nurses 813.633.6834
Fax...813.633.6801
Web ....www.bayada.com
129 South Pebble Beach Blvd., Suite 102, Sun City
Center, FL 33573
Madeline Scannell, Director

Bayada Nurses 727.815.3400
Fax...727.815.3800
Web ....www.bayada.com
7421 Ridge Road, Suite 105, Port Richey, FL 34668
Catherine Adham, Associate Director

Ft Lauderdale PDN 954.567.9112
3115 NW 10th Ter Ste 103, Fort Lauderdale,
FL 33309
Robyn Gurien, Admin.

Ft Myers PDN 239.939.3159
1705 Colonial Blvd Unit C-4, Fort Myers, FL 33907
Erin Rounsifer, Administrator

Interim Healthcare 850.243.1152
Fax...850.862.8548
339 Racetrack Rd ste 16, Fort Walton Beach,
FL 32547
Lisa Anthony, Chief Executive Officer

Interim Healthcare 407.740.5284
Fax...407.539.1463
1890 State Rd 436 Ste 355, Winter Park, FL 32792
Greg Schltz, Administrator

Interim Healthcare 850.747.0080
Fax...850.747.0920
E-mail ....amelvin@interimhealthcare.com
2679 Jenks Ave, Panama City, FL 32405
Alicia Melvin, Director

Interim Healthcare 727.849.2828
Fax...727.849.9634
7305 Little Rd, New Port Richey, FL 34654
Jessica Mortenson, Clinical Services Manager

Interim Healthcare 386.322.0044
Fax...386.788.2906
Web ....www.interimhealthcare.com
2362 S Nova Rd, Daytona Beach, FL 32119
Frances Oneill, Nursing Director

Interim Healthcare 352.365.1521
Fax...352.430.0011
9 LaGrande Blvd, Lady Lake, FL 32159
Maureen Masters, Chief Executive Officer

Interim Healthcare 352.378.0333
Fax...352.375.5890
3760 NW 83rd St Ste 2, Gainesville, FL 32606

Interim Healthcare 904.448.1133
Fax...904.448.9130
7999 Phillips Hwy Ste 304, Jacksonville, FL 32256
Glen Reeves, President

Interim Healthcare 863.619.8822
Fax...863.619.8323
1547 Lakeland Hills Blvd, Lakeland, FL 33805
Greg Schltz, Director

Interim Healthcare 727.441.9585
Fax...727.461.4535
1940 Drew St Ste A, Clearwater, FL 33765
Marie, Office Manager

Interim Healthcare 352.637.3111
Fax...352.637.1176
581 E Gulf to Lake Hwy, Lecanto, FL 34461
Connie McNeilly, Director of Nursing

Interim Healthcare 904.824.6123
Fax...904.829.0999
3440 US 1 S Bldg 400 Ste 404, Saint Augustine,
FL 32086
Diana Twombley, Executive Director

Interim Healthcare 850.422.2044
Fax...850.386.6985
1962B Village Green Way, Tallahassee, FL 32308
Mary Roney, Director

Interim Healthcare 850.482.2770
Fax...850.482.4941
4306 5th Ave, Marianna, FL 32446
Lisa Carmichael, Director

Interim Healthcare 352.351.5040
Fax...352.351.5140
2143 SE Ft King St Ste 101, Old Oaks Professional,
Ocala, FL 34471
Lisa Anthony, Director

Interim Healthcare 352.326.0400
Fax...352.326.4441
32644 Blossom Ln, Leesburg, FL 34788
Moreen Master, Director

Interim Healthcare 813.877.9444
Fax...813.872.8150
4726 N Habana Ste 203, Tampa, FL 33614
Lewis Thomasina, Director

Interim Healthcare 850.474.0767
Fax...850.474.0763
1331 Creighton Rd Ste B, Pensacola, FL 32504
Liza Anthony, Administrative Assistant

Interim Healthcare 386.445.6079
Fax...386.445.4624
Nine Pine Cone Dr Ste 107, Palm Coast, FL 32137
Tara Dozier, Director

Interim Healthcare 954.978.1499
Fax...954.978.6996
2900 NW 62nd St, Ste # 6, Fort Lauderdale,
FL 33309

Interim Healthcare 561.616.9500
Fax...561.616.9909
2 Harvard Cir Ste 950, West Palm Beach, FL 33409
Jan Wahby, Administrator

Interim Healthcare (Ocala Staffing) 352.387.0274
Fax...352.351.5140
2110 NE 14th St Ste 100, Old Oaks Professional,
Ocala, FL 34470
Krystin, Director

Interim Healthcare W Palm Beach

HomeStyle 561.616.1980
Fax...561.616.9909
2 Harvard Cir Ste 950, West Palm Beach, FL 33409
Jan Wahby, Director

Jacksonville PDN 904.730.2200
8659 Baypine Rd, ste 102 Bldg 3, Jacksonville,
FL 32256
Jeanne Muse, Director

Pensacola Medi Weight Loss Clinic 850.444.4997
910 Royce St, Pensacola, FL 32503
Patricia Maxwell, Director

Tampa PDN 813.282.4920
205 S Hoover Blvd Ste 203, Tampa, FL 33609
Jennifer Isikseo, Interim Director

West Palm Beach PDN 561.684.5613
2753 Vista Pkwy, Unit J-12 Second Fl, West Palm
Beach, FL 33411
Robyn Gurien, Director

West Palm Beach PPEC 561.683.5758
2005 Vista Pkwy Ste 110A, West Palm Beach,
FL 33411
Alexandra Delgado, Director

West Palm Beach Rehab 561.683.6543
2005 Vista Pkwy Ste 110A, West Palm Beach,
FL 33411
Alexandra Delgado

SOCIAL SERVICES

A Women's Resource Ctr 386.328.9394
E-mail ....thinkyrpregnant@yahoo.com
3403 Saint Johns Ave, Palatka, FL 32177
Linda Faw, Director

Alpha Ctr, Inc. 850.479.4391
Fax...850.479.3618
6004 Pernella Rd, Pensacola, FL 32504-7653
Valarie Schumm, Director

Beachhouse 386.236.3111
Fax...386.236.3155
1004 Old Big Tree Rd, Daytona Beach,
FL 32119-2467
Heather Prince, Manager

Boys Town Of South Florida 954.590.2503
Fax...954.590.2504
Web ....www.boystown.org/southflorida
2301 W Sample Rd, Bldg 2, Pompano Beach,
FL 33073
Lourdes Zapata, Family Preservation Coordinator

Boys Town Of South Florida 561.366.9400
Fax...561.366.1133
Web ....www.boystown.org
E-mail ....amy.simpson@boystown.org
3111 S Dixie Hwy Ste 200, West Palm Beach,
FL 33405-1548
Amy Simpson, Site Director

Boys' Home Association, Inc. 904.743.3611
Fax...904.744.8131
Web ....www.jaxboyshome.org
2354 University Boulevard North, Jacksonville,
FL 32211
COA accredited organization.

Camelot Community Care, Inc. 727.593.0003
Fax...727.593.0735
Web ....www.camelotcommunitycare.org
4910-D Creekside Drive, Clearwater, FL 33760
COA accredited organization.

Catholic Charities of Northwest Florida,
Inc. 850.435.3500
Fax...850.436.6419
Web ....www.catholiccharitiesnwfl.org
1000 West Garden Street, Pensacola, FL 32501
COA accredited organization.

Catholic Charities of the Archdiocese of Miami,
Inc. 305.762.3002
Fax...305.754.6649
Web ....www.ccadm.org
1505 NE 26th Street, Wilton Manors, FL 33305
COA accredited organization.

Catholic Charities of the Diocese of Palm Beach,
Inc....**561.775.9560**
Fax...561.625.5906
Web..www.diocesepb.org
  PO Box 109650, Palm Beach Gardens,
  FL 33410-9650
  COA accredited organization.

Catholic Charities, Diocese of St. Petersburg,
Inc....**727.893.1314**
Fax...727.893.1307
Web..www.ccdosp.org
  1213 16th Street North, St. Petersburg, FL 33705
  COA accredited organization.

CDS Family & Behavioral Health Services,
Inc....**352.244.0618**
Fax...352.244.0699
Web...http://www.cdsfl.org
  3615 Southwest 13th Street, Suite 4, Gainesville,
  FL 32608
  CARF accredited programs available.

Center for Family and Child Enrichment,
Inc....**305.624.7450**
Fax...305.623.7893
Web..www.cfceinc.org
  1825 NW 167th Street, Miami Gardens, FL 33056
  COA accredited organization.

CHARLEE...**305.779.9701**
Fax...305.779.9733
Web..www.charleeprogram.org
  155 South Miami Avenue, #800, Miami, FL 33130
  COA accredited organization.

Child Abuse Prevention Project.............**352.334.1330**
Fax...352.334.1543
E-mail...capp@peds.ufl.edu
  1701 SW 16th Ave, Bldg A, Gainesville, FL 32608
  Annie Mcpherson, Director

Child Care Connection Of Sarasota..........**941.556.1600**
Fax...941.556.1606
E-mail...................lmason@childcareconnectionsarasota.org
  2886 Ringling Blvd # D, Sarasota, FL 34237
  Linda Mason, Director

Child Care Resource & Referral...............**904.208.2044**
Fax...904.208.2049
Web...www.jaxkids.org/
E-mail..smain@elcofduval.org
  8301 Cypress Plaza Dr, Ste 201, Jacksonville,
  FL 32256
  Susan Main, Executive Director

Childhood Development Svcs...................**727.569.1004**
Fax...727.569.1080
  6740 Commerce Ave, Port Richey, FL 34668-6814

Childhood Development Svcs...................**352.795.2667**
Fax...352.795.4041
Web..www.childhooddevelopment.org
E-mail...............................info@childhooddevelopment.org
  5641 W Gulf To Lake Hwy, Crystal River,
  FL 34429-7562

Childhood Development Svcs, Inc............**352.629.0055**
Fax...352.629.7766
Web..www.discovercds.org
  1601 NE 25th Ave Ste 900, Ocala, FL 34470
  Carrol Eurton, Chief Executive Director
  COA accredited organization.

ChildNet, Inc.......................................**954.414.6000**
Fax...954.414.6010
Web...www.childnet.us
  313 N. State Road 7, Plantation, FL 33317
  COA accredited organization.

Children's Advocacy Ctr Of Southwest
Florida..**239.939.2808**
Fax...239.939.4794
Web..www.cac-swfl.org
E-mail....................................jturner@cac-swfl.org
  3830 Evans Ave, Fort Myers, FL 33901
  Jill Turner, CEO

Children's Forum..................................**850.681.7002**
Fax...850.681.9816
Web...www.fcforum.org
  2807 Remington Green Cir, Tallahassee, FL 32308
  Tamella Nelloms, Human Resource

Children's Harbor, Inc..........................**954.252.3072**
Web..www.childrensharbor.org
  19425 SW 58 Manor, Pembroke Pines, FL 33332
  COA accredited organization.

Children's Home Society........................**321.752.3170**
Fax...321.752.3179
Web..www.chsfl.org
E-mail.....................................teresa.miles@chsfl.org
  326 Croton Rd, Melbourne, FL 32935
  Teresa Miles, Director

Children's Home Society........................**239.334.0222**
Fax...239.334.0244
Web..www.chsfl.org
E-mail...................................rebecca.mcguire@chsfl.org
  1940 Maravilla Ave, Fort Myers, FL 33901
  Rebecca Mcguire, Executive Director

Children's Home Society........................**352.334.0955**
Fax...352.334.0957
Web..www.chsfl.org
E-mail...................................jennifer.anchors@chsfl.org
  605 NE 1st St Ste c, Gainesville, FL 32601
  Jennifer Anchors, Executive Director

Children's Home Society........................**407.846.5220**
Fax...407.846.5225
Web..www.chsfl.org
E-mail...info@chsfl.org
  2647 Michigan Ave, Kissimmee, FL 34744-1936
  Tara Hormell, Director

Children's Home Society of Florida..........**321.397.3000**
Fax...321.397.3020
Web..www.chsfl.org
  1485 S. Semoran Boulevard, #1448, Winter Park,
  FL 32792-5508
  COA accredited organization.

Children's Home Society- Safe Harbor........**561.868.4444**
Fax...561.965.1169
Web..www.chsfl.org
  3335 Forest Hill Blvd, West Palm Beach,
  FL 33406-5812
  Rosby L. Glover, Director Of Program Operations

Collier Child Care Resourses..................**239.643.3908**
Fax...239.643.4906
Web..www.collierchildcare.org
E-mail................................NicoleH@Collierchildcare.org
  2400 Tamiami Trail N Ste 303, Naples, FL 34103
  Nicole Howard, Director

Communities In Schools........................**904.321.2000**
Fax...904.321.2531
Web..www.cisnassau.org
E-mail...susan@cisnassau.org
  516 S 10th Street, #205, Fernandina Beach,
  FL 32034-3511
  Susan Milana, Executive Director

Communities In Schools of Florida, Inc.........**850.201.9750**
Fax...850.201.9757
Web..www.cisfl.org
E-mail..graceyl@cisfl.org
  444 Appleyard Dr, Bldg 11, Rm 298, Tallahassee,
  FL 32304
  Lois Gracey, State Director

Community Coordinated Care for Children,
Inc....**407.522.2252**
Web...www.4cflorida.org
  3500 West Colonial Drive, Orlando, FL 32808
  COA accredited organization.

Coordinated Child Care Of Pinellas...........**727.547.5700**
Fax...727.547.5797
Web...www.childcarepinellas.org
E-mail..................................rr@childcarepinellas.org
  6500 102nd Ave, Pinellas Park, FL 33782
  Gail Gendrau, Office Manager

Covenant House Florida..........................**954.561.5559**
Fax...954.565.6551
Web..www.covenanthousefl.org
E-mail...............................jgress@covenanthousefl.org
  733 Breakers Ave, Ft Lauderdale, FL 33304-4100
  James Gress, Executive Director

Covenant House Florida..........................**407.482.0404**
Fax...407.482.0657
Web..www.covenanthousefl.org
E-mail.............................mission@covenanthousefl.org
  5931 E Colonial Dr, Orlando, FL 32807
  James Gress, Executive Director

Crosswinds Youth Svcs, Inc....................**321.394.0345**
Fax...321.394.0385
Web..www.crosswindsyouthservices.org
E-mail.........................janlokay@crosswindsyouthservices.org
  1407 Dixon Blvd, Cocoa, FL 32922-6411
  Jan Lokay, President/CEO

Daniel Memorial, Inc............................**904.296.1055**
Fax...904.296.1953
Web..www.danielkids.org
  4203 Southpoint Boulevard, Jacksonville, FL 32216
  COA accredited organization.

Dept Of Human Svcs.............................**305.514.6000**
Fax...305.514.6160
Web..www.miamidade.gov
E-mail.......................................laj@miamidade.gov
  2525 NW 62nd St, Fl 4, Miami, FL 33147
  Ana M Faraci, Phd, Director Of Psychological Services Division &
  Psychology Training Prog

Early Education And Care, Inc..................**850.872.7550**
Fax...850.769.1066
Web..www.ecskids.org
  450 Jenks Ave, Panama City, FL 32401-2626
  Pam Fleege, Director

Early Learning Coalition........................**386.323.2400**
Fax...386.323.2424
Web...www.elcfv.org
E-mail..debbies@elcfv.org
  230 N Beach St, Fl 2, Daytona Beach, FL 32114
  Lara Glaser, Deputy Director

Early Learning Coalition........................**352.754.5068**
Fax...352.799.8159
E-mail...sjones@cdsi.org
  26 S Brooksfield Ave, Brooksville, FL 34601-3832
  Shatasha Jones, Training Director

Early Learning Coalition of Floida
Heartland...**863.494.5233**
Fax...863.494.5291
Web...www.elcfh.org
E-mail...opolvera@elcfh.org
  4 W Oak St Ste H, Arcadia, FL 34266-3971
  Anne Bouhebent, Executive Director

Early Learning Coalition Of Florida's Gateway,
Inc....**386.752.9770**
Fax...386.752.9786
Web..www.elc-fg.org
E-mail..lsurrency@elc-fg.org
  1104 SW Main Blvd, Lake City, FL 32025-1589
  Lachon Surrency, Deputy Director

Episcopal Children's Svcs **904.726.1500**
Fax 904.726.1520
Web www.ecs4kids.org
E-mail .... bhenderson@ecs4kids.org
8443 Bay Meadows Rd Ste 1, Jacksonville, FL 32256
Connie Stophel, CEO

Exchange Club Center for the Prevention of Child Abuse of the Treasure Coast, Inc. dba CASTLE **772.465.6011**
Fax 772.465.6013
Web .... www.castletc.org
PO Box 12908, Ft. Pierce, FL 34979
COA accredited organization.

Face Life **561.641.0065**
E-mail .... yourfriend@facelife.org
3910 Canal 9 Rd, West Palm Beach, FL 33406
Susan Pine, Director

Family Central **561.514.3300**
Fax 561.514.3308
Web .... www.familycentral.org
E-mail .... dsimmons@familycentral.org
3111 S Dixie Hwy Ste 222, West Palm Beach, FL 33405-1548
Sally Laws, Director

Family Central, Inc. **954.720.1000**
Fax 954.724.3900
Web .... www.familycentral.org
840 SW 81st Avenue, North Lauderdale, FL 33068-2001
COA accredited organization.

Family Counseling Services of Greater Miami, Inc. **305.740.8998**
Fax 305.740.0259
Web .... www.familycounseling.org
7412 Sunset Drive, Miami, FL 33143
COA accredited organization.

Family Foundations of Northeast Florida, Inc. dba Family Foundations **904.396.4846**
Fax 904.398.6649
Web .... www.familyfoundationsjax.org
1639 Atlantic Boulevard, Jacksonville, FL 32207
COA accredited organization.

Family Preservation Services of Florida, Inc. **772.595.3773**
Fax 772.293.0076
Web .... www.fpscorp.com
121 North 2nd Street, Suite 301, Fort Pierce, FL 34950
COA accredited organization.

Family Resources, Inc. **727.521.5200**
Fax 727.521.5202
Web .... www.family-resources.org
5180 62nd Avenue North, Pinellas Park, FL 33781
COA accredited organization.

Family Resources- North Shelter **727.298.1606**
Fax 727.298.1695
Web .... www.family-resources.org
1615 Union St, Clearwater, FL 33755-1363
Kelly Reiss, Residential Supervisor

Family Resources- South Shelter **727.893.1893**
Fax 727.893.5544
Web .... www.family-resources.org
E-mail .... terrickmoyer@family-resources.org
3821 5th Ave N, Saint Petersburg, FL 33713-7547
Terrick Moyer, Supervisor

Family Support Services of North Florida, Inc. **904.421.5800**
Fax 904.421.5801
Web .... www.fssjax.org
4057 Carmichael Avenue, Building 3000, Suite 101, Jacksonville, FL 32207
COA accredited organization.

First Care Family Resources **561.744.2644**
Fax 561.427.6534
Web .... www.first-care.org
E-mail .... sarah@first-care.org
2023 N Australian Ave, West Palm Beach, FL 33407
Megan Rardin, Director

First Coast Women's Svc **904.246.7378**
224 N 3rd St., Jacksonville Beach, FL 32250
Melanie Steigletz, Director

Florida Certification Board **850.222.6314**
Fax 850.222.6247
Web .... www.slcertificationboard.org
E-mail .... namcgarry@flcertificationboard.org
1715 S Gadsden St, Tallahassee, FL 32301-5505
Neil Mcgarry, Director

Florida Keys Children's Shelter **305.852.4246**
Fax 305.852.6902
Web .... www.fkcs.org
73 High Point Road, Tavernier, FL 33070
COA accredited organization.

Florida Network Of Youth & Family Svcs **850.922.4324**
Fax 850.921.1778
Web .... www.floridanetwork.org
E-mail .... info@floridanetwork.org
2850 Pablo Ave, Tallahassee, FL 32308-4211
Stacy Gromatski, President/CEO

Florida United Methodist Children's Home, Inc. **386.668.4774**
Fax 386.668.4486
Web .... www.allchildrenfirst.org
51 Children's Way, Enterprise, FL 32725
COA accredited organization.

Girls And Boys Town Of South Florida **786.293.9680**
Fax 786.573.3468
Web .... www.girlsandboystown.org/southflorida
E-mail .... jarrettm@boystown.org
9722 SW 184th St, Miami, FL 33157-6987
Megan Jarrett, Family Preservation Coordinator

Haven W. Poe Runaway Ctr **813.272.6606**
Fax 813.272.7160
13505 N Lincoln St, Tampa, FL 33618
Daniel Husband, Program Manager

Hide House **850.784.1020**
Fax 850.784.4890
Web .... www.anchoragechildrenshome.org
E-mail .... jbooth@anchoragechildrenshome.org
2121 Lisenby Ave, Panama City, FL 32405-2910
Joel Booth, Shelter Director

Hillsborough Info Line **813.272.5900**
Fax 813.276.2621
Web .... www.hillsboroughcounty.org
E-mail .... info@hillsboroughcounty.org
900 N Asley dr, Tampa, FL 33602
Andrew Breidenbaugh, Manager

Hillsbourough Kids, Inc **813.225.1105**
Fax 813.226.0661
Web .... www.hillsboroughkids.org
E-mail .... jeff.rainey@hillsboroughkids.org
9309 N Florida Ave, Ste 107, Tampa, FL 33612
Jeff Rainey, Executive Director

His House Children's Home **305.430.0085**
Fax 305.430.8533
Web .... www.hhch.org
20000 NW 47th Avenue, Bldg 2, Opa Locka, FL 33055
COA accredited organization.

Institute for Child and Family Health, Inc. **305.685.6301**
Fax 305.685.2913
Web .... www.icfhinc.org
15490 NW 7th Avenue, Suite 200, Miami, FL 33169
COA accredited organization.

Jacksonville Children's Commission **904.630.3647**
Fax 904.630.3655
Web .... www.jaxkids.net
E-mail .... llanier@coj.net
1095 A Phillip Randolph Blvd, Jacksonville, FL 32206
Linda Lanier, Executive Director/CEO

JCS Aventura Office **305.933.9820**
Fax 305.933.9843
18999 Biscayne Blvd Ste 200, Aventura, FL 33180
Judith Liebre, Vice President

JCS Dadeland Office **305.670.1911**
Fax 305.670.2049
E-mail .... jangueira@jcsfl.org
9700 S Dixie Highway # 650, Miami, FL 33156
Janet Angueira, Office Manager

Jewish Community Ctr **407.387.5330**
Fax 407.387.5372
11184 South Apopka Vineland Rd, Orlando, FL 32836

Jewish Community Service of South FloridaInc **305.899.1587**
Fax 305.899.6367
E-mail .... info@jcsfl.org
735 NE 125th St, North Miami, FL 33161
Fred Stock, CEO

Jewish Family & Commuity Services Inc **904.394.5723**
Fax 904.448.0349
E-mail .... bshorstein@jfcsjax.org
6261 Dupont Station Court E, Jacksonville, FL 32217
Beth Shorstein, Manager

Jewish Family & Community Services, Inc. **904.448.1933**
Fax 904.448.0349
Web .... www.jfcsjax.org
6261 Dupont Station Court, E., Jacksonville, FL 32217
COA accredited organization.

Jewish Family And Community Svcs **904.448.1933**
Fax 904.448.0349
Web .... www.jfcsjax.org
E-mail .... crodriguez@jfcsjax.org
6261 Dupont Station Ct E, Jacksonville, FL 32217-2567
Colleen Rodriguez, Director

Jewish Family Services **239.325.4444**
Fax 239.263.3813
E-mail .... jfs@jewishnaples.org
2500 Vanderbilt Beach Rd #2201, Naples, FL 34109
David Willens

Jewish Family Services of Greater OrlandoInc **407.644.7593**
Fax 407.628.0773
E-mail .... info@jfsorlando.org
2100 Lee Rd, Winter Park, FL 32789
Barry Kudlowitz, Director

Juvenile Welfare Board **727.547.5600**
Fax 727.530.7416
Web .... www.jwbpinellas.org
E-mail .... glancaster@jwbpinellas.org
14155 58th St N, Clearwater, FL 33760
D. Gay Lancaster, Executive Director

Kids In Distress, Inc. **954.390.7654**
Fax 954.567.5636
Web .... www.kidsindistress.org
819 NE 26th Street, Wilton Manors, FL 33305
COA accredited organization.

Kids, Inc. Of The Big Bend **850.414.9800**
Fax 850.414.9810
Web .... www.kidsincorporated.org
E-mail .... info@kidsincorporated.org
1170 Capital Cir NE, Tallahassee, FL 32301-3519
Immogene Sanders, Director

LDS Family Svcs 407.850.9141
Fax 407.850.9687
Web .... www.ldschurch.org
E-mail .... fam-fl@ldschurch.org
    10502 Satellite Blvd Ste D, Orlando, FL 32837-8479
    Adam Barns, Director

Lifeline Of Central Florida 407.425.2624
Fax 407.425.5592
Web .... www.lifelinecentralflorida.org
E-mail .... llcf@lifelinecentralflorida.org
    1007 Pathfinder way, Ste 120, Orlando, FL 32803
    Wendy Perdue, Executive Director

Lutheran Services Florida, Inc. 813.875.1408
Fax 813.875.1302
Web .... www.lsfnet.org
    3627A West Waters Avenue, Tampa, FL 33614
    COA accredited organization.

Lutheran Svcs Florida/ Southeast 954.486.4222
Fax 954.486.9942
Web .... www.lsfnet.org
E-mail .... jshawdavis@lsfnet.org
    4675 N State Road 7, Fort Lauderdale,
    FL 33319-5857
    Joan Shaw-Davis, Regional Director

Lutheran Svcs Florida/Northwest 850.453.2772
Fax 850.453.2866
Web .... www.lsfnet.org
E-mail .... bdeck@lsfnet.org
    4610 W Fairfield Dr, Youth And Family Services,
    Pensacola, FL 32506-4106
    Beth Deck, Regional Director

Manatee Children's Services, Inc. 941.345.1200
Fax 941.345.1212
Web .... www.manateechildrensservices.com
    465 Cortez Road West, Bradenton, FL 34207
    COA accredited organization.

Miami Bridge Youth & Family Services,
Inc. 305.635.8953
Fax 305.636.3521
Web .... www.miamibridge.org
    2810 NW South River Drive, Miami, FL 33125
    COA accredited organization.

Neighbor To Family, Inc. 386.523.1440
Fax 386.523.1459
Web .... www.neighbortofamily.org
    220 S. Ridgewood Avenue, Suite 260, Daytona Beach,
    FL 32114
    COA accredited organization.

Parent-Child Center, Inc. 561.841.3500
Fax 561.841.3555
Web .... www.gocpg.org
    2001 W. Blue Heron Boulevard, Riviera Beach,
    FL 33404
    COA accredited organization.

Partnership for Strong Families 352.244.1500
Fax 352.244.1647
Web .... www.pfsf.org
    5950 NW 1st Place, Suite A, Gainesville, FL 32607
    COA accredited organization.

Partnership For Strong Families 386.758.5757
Fax 386.758.0485
Web .... www.pfsf.org
    1389 W US Highway 90 Ste 100, Lake City,
    FL 32055-6130

Peace River Ctr 863.519.3747
Fax 863.519.3715
Web .... www.peace-river.com
E-mail .... eweed@peace-river.com
    1255 Golfview Ave, Bartow, FL 33830-6736
    Edward G. Weed, Chairman

Phillip Roy, Inc. 800.255.9085
Fax 877.595.2685
Web .... www.philliproy.com
E-mail .... info@philliproy.com
    13064 Indian Rocks Rd, Largo, FL 33774-2001
    Phil Padol, Consultant

Respect Life 954.963.2229
Fax 954.963.2620
    5600 Hollywood Blvd, Hollywood, FL 33021
    Maureen Freeman, Director

Runaway Alternatives Project (RAP)
House 727.835.1777
Fax 727.835.1773
    7522 Plathe Rd, New Port Richey, FL 34653-4520
    Heather Numbers, Program Manager

Ruth Rales Jewish Family Service 561.852.3333
Fax 561.852.3332
Web .... www.ruthralesjfs.org
    21300 Ruth & Baron Coleman Boulevard, Boca Raton,
    FL 33428
    Danielle Hartman, Executive Director
    COA accredited organization.

Sarasota Family YMCA, Inc. 941.951.2916
Fax 941.955.0896
Web .... www.sarasota-ymca.org
    One South School Avenue, #301, Sarasota, FL 34237
    COA accredited organization.

Sarasota YMCA Youth Shelter/District 8A 941.955.5596
Fax 941.955.7195
E-mail .... mfitts@sarasota-ymca.org
    1106 S Briggs Ave, Sarasota, FL 34237-8140
    Marlin Fitts, Program Director

Shriners International Headquarters 813.281.0300
Web .... www.shrinershq.org
    2900 N Rocky Point Dr, Tampa, FL 33607
    Alice Lanford, Administrator

Southeastern Network Of Youth & Family
Svc 239.949.4414
Fax 239.949.4911
Web .... www.senetwork.org
E-mail .... tamyhopper@senetwork.org
    28331 S Tamiami Trl Ste 3, Bonita Springs, FL 33134
    Tamy Hopper, Executive Director

Speech & Hearing Ctr 904.355.3403
Fax 904.355.4149
Web .... www.shcjax.org
    1128 N Laura St, Jacksonville, FL 32206-4912
    Wiliam Mcquilkin, CEO

Suncoft Force 941.486.2682
Fax 941.480.3098
    897 E Venice Ave, Venice, FL 34285-7038
    Allie Evans, Site Manager

Tampa Jewish Family Services 813.960.1848
Fax 813.265.8239
E-mail .... tjfs@tjfs.org
    13009 Community Campus Dr, Tampa, FL 33625
    Michael Barnett, CEO

Tampa Jewish Family Services, Inc.
Web .... www.tjfs.org
    13009 Community Campus Drive, Tampa, FL 33625
    COA accredited organization.

The Center for Family Services 561.616.1222
Fax 561.616.1230
Web .... www.ctrfam.org
    4101 Parker Avenue, West Palm Beach, FL 33405
    COA accredited organization.

The Child Protection Ctr Inc. 941.365.1277
Fax 941.953.7181
Web .... www.cpcsarasota.org
    720 S Orange Ave, Sarasota, FL 34236
    Hal Hedley, Executive Director

The Children's Advocacy Center of Volusia and Flagler
Counties, Inc. 386.238.3830
Fax 386.238.3831
Web .... www.childrensadvocacy.org
    1011 W. International Speedway Boulevard, Daytona
    Beach, FL 32114
    COA accredited organization.

The Florida Center for Early Childhood,
Inc. 941.371.8820
Fax 941.377.3194
Web .... www.thefloridacenter.org
    4620 17th Street, Sarasota, FL 34235
    COA accredited organization.

The Henry and Rilla White Youth Foundation,
Inc. 850.922.8375
Fax 850.922.7856
Web .... www.hrwhite.org
    2833 Remington Green Circle, Tallahassee, FL 32308
    Ashley Nevels, Chief Financial Official
    CARF accredited programs available.

The House Next Door, Inc. 386.734.7571
Fax 386.734.0252
Web .... www.thehnd.com
    804 N. Woodland Boulevard, Deland, FL 32720
    COA accredited organization.

The Salvation Army/St. Petersburg Area
Command 727.550.8080
Fax 727.550.8077
Web .... www.uss.salvationarmy.org/uss/www_uss_st
    340 14th Avenue South, Saint Petersburg, FL 33701
    CARF accredited programs available.

The Toby Center for Family Transitions 561.509.6112
Fax 561.509.6114
Web .... www.thetobycenter.org
E-mail .... tobycenter@aol.com
    1100 S Federal Hwy, Ste 3, Boynton Beach, FL 33435
    Mark Roseman, PhD, Executive Director; Paloma Duran, Director of Marketing

The Toby Center provides a unique package of services – all sliding scale – to "preserve family ties when parents choose to separate."™ The Center offers couples, single, separated, divorced and never-married parents the resources to create positive relationships through multiple services including mediation, supervised visitation, support groups, parenting education and professional trainings. The Center is a uniquely holistic model addressing the individual's emotional, physiological, spiritual and physical needs to maximize personal growth. Research demonstrates that only in this way can child and parent outcomes be most positive and healthy. An onsite parent lounge and resource library completes the Center. Bring the Toby Center to your community!

United Way 2-1-1 For North Central
Florida 352.332.4636
Fax 352.331.2111
Web .... www.unitedwayncfl.org
E-mail .... info@unitedwayncfl.org
    6031 NW 1st Pl, Gainesville, FL 32607-2025
    Jan Zak, Director

United Way First Call For Help **386.253.0563**
Fax 386.253.9517
Web www.211live.org
3747 W International Speedway Blvd, Daytona Beach,
FL 32114
Tim Sylvia, Director

Wesley House Family Services, Inc. **305.809.5000**
Fax 305.809.5010
Web ....www.wesleyhouse.org
1304 Truman Avenue, Key West, FL 33040
COA accredited organization.

**World Good News, Inc. dba Jacksonville Youth
Sanctuary** **904.389.5231**
Fax 904.389.7067
Web ....www.jaxyouth.org
4570 St. Johns Avenue, Suite 3, Jacksonville,
FL 32210
COA accredited organization.

Youth and Family Alternatives, Inc. **727.835.4166**
Fax 727.835.3942
Web ....www.yfainc.org
7524 Plathe Road, New Port Richey, FL 34653-4520
COA accredited organization.

Youth Haven, Inc. **239.774.2904**
5867 Whitaker Road, Naples, FL 34112
COA accredited organization.

Youth Shelter **407.836.7626**
Fax 407.836.7469
E-mail ....tracy.salem@ocfl.net
1800 E Michigan St, Orlando, FL 32806-4900
Tracy Salem, Program Manager

SPECIAL NEEDS

211 Tampa Bay Cares **727.210.4233**
Fax 727.210.4234
E-mail ....ccr@211tampabay.org
50 S Belcher Rd Ste 116, Clearwater, FL 33765
Micki Thompson, Executive Director

4H & Youth Development **813.744.5519**
Fax 813.744.5776
E-mail ....hillsborough@ifas.ufl.edu
5339 CR 579, Seffner, FL 33584
Deborah Joe Kinella, Director

**5000 Role Models of Execel Miami Dade
Pu** **305.995.2451**
Fax 305.995.1488
E-mail ....rolemodels@dadeschools.net
1450 NE Second Ave, Miami, FL 33132

A. Bel Audiology Associates **954.435.9779**
E-mail ....abelaudio@aol.com
1861 NW 123 Ave, Pembroke Pines, FL 33026
Dr. Paula Liebeskind, Owner

ABC Learning Center **850.994.0054**
Fax 850.994.3355
3655 Highway 90, Pace, FL 32571

ABC Learning Center & Preschool **407.898.1699**
Fax 407.826.0104
2310 E Concord St, Orlando, FL 32803
Suzzanna Bodine, Director

Abrienddo Puertas **305.649.6449**
Fax 305.649.1459
E-mail ....jcdelatorre@abrienddopuertasfl.org
1401 SW 1st St, Miami, FL 33135
Jc Delatorre, Chief Executive Officer

Academic Achievement Center **813.654.4198**
Fax 813.654.4198
E-mail ....ALSofAAC@aol.com
313 Pruett Rd, Seffner, FL 33584
Arnold Stark, Educational Director

Academic High School for the Arts **561.929.0333**
E-mail ....academichs@aol.com
23114 Sandalfoot Plaza Dr, Boca Raton, FL 33428
Sheldon Klasfeld, Director

Achieve Tampa Bay United Cerebral Palsy ...**352.796.4469**
Fax 352.796.0680
215 Howell Ave, Brooksville, FL 34601

Achieve Tampa Bay United Cerebral Palsy **813.633.5768**
Fax 813.633.6879
E-mail ....bshort@ucptempa.org
1517 Sun City Center Plaza, Unit D&E, Sun City
Center, FL 33573
Britiny Short, Speech Therepist

Achieve Tampa Bay United Cerebral Palsy **813.239.1179**
Fax 813.237.3091
2215 E Henry Ave, Tampa, FL 33610
Patty Hanson, Chief Executive Officer

Acorn Early Learning Center **954.341.3554**
11550 Wiles Rd, Pompano Beach, FL 33076
Mara Juloski, Director

Action Community Center Transportation **305.545.9298**
Fax 305.545.0203
E-mail ....actioncm@bellsouth.net
970 SW First St Rm 304, Miami, FL 33130
Maria Alvo, Executive Director

ADD Warehouse **800.233.9273**
Fax 954.792.8545
Web ....www.addwarehouse.com
E-mail ....sales@addwarehouse.com
300 NW 70th Ave Ste 102, Fort Lauderdale,
FL 33317-2360
Parker, President

Adolph and Rose Levis Jewish Com Ctr **561.852.3200**
E-mail ....elinor@levisjcc.org
9801 Donna Klein Blvd, Boca Raton, FL 33428
E Linor, Director

Adopt A Family of the Palm Beaches Inc **561.253.1361**
E-mail ....JKieffer@adoptafamilypbc.org
1712 Second Ave North, Lake Worth, FL 33460
John Kieffer, Director

Advanced Air Ambulance **800.633.3590**
Fax 305.232.7734
E-mail ....info@flyambu.com
12360 S W 132nd Court, Ste 208, Miami, FL 33186
Richard Abbera, Director

Advanced Phys Therapy of Bradenton Inc **941.752.9719**
Fax 941.752.9739
5221 33rd St E, Bradenton, FL 34203
Dr. Kathleen Deveine, Doctor Of Physical Therapy

Advocacy Ctr for Persons with Disabiliti **800.342.0823**
Fax 850.488.8640
E-mail ....info@advocacycenter.org
2901 Sterling Road Ste 206, Fort Lauderdale,
FL 33312

Advocacy Ctr for Persons with Disabilities **850.488.9071**
Fax 850.488.8640
E-mail ....info@advocacycenter.org
2728 Centerview Dr, Ste 102, Tallahassee, FL 32301
Robert Whitney, Executive Director

**ADVOServe Advoc for and Srv People W
Dis** **352.838.3685**
Fax 352.735.0407
E-mail ....Markhams@advoserv.com
28308 Churchill Smith Lane, Mount Dora, FL 32757

After Hours Pediatrics **407.363.5753**
Fax 407.351.2141
E-mail ....info@afterhourspediatrics.com
Clinic and Administrative Office, 5018 Dr Phillips
Blvd, Orlando, FL 32819
Phyllis Shauffer, Director Of Operations

Agape Emergency Food Pantry **863.686.7153**
Fax 863.683.5515
625 McCue Rd, Lakeland, FL 33801

Agape House **904.282.5289**
2645 Blanding Blvd, Middleburg, FL 32068

Agency for Health Care Administration **727.552.1191**
Fax 727.552.1216
E-mail ....MedResource5@ahca.myflorida.com
525 Mirror Lake Dr North, Ste 510, Saint Petersburg,
FL 33701

Agency for Healthcare Administration **813.871.7600**
Fax 813.673.4592
E-mail ....help.dsa@ahca.myflorida.com
6800 N Dale Mabry Hwy Ste 220, Tampa, FL 33614
Sue Mcphee, Supervisor

Agency for Healthcare Administration **352.732.1349**
Fax 352.620.3076
E-mail ....schlottm@ahca.myflorida.com
2441 W Silver Springs Blvd, Ocala, FL 34475

**Agency for Hlth Care Admin Medicaid
Area** **904.798.4200**
Fax 904.265.2164
E-mail ....area4@ahca.myflorida.com
921 N Davis St, Bldg A Ste 160, Jacksonville,
FL 32209
Debbie Stokes, Supervisor

**Agency for Hlth Care Admin Medicaid
Area** **407.317.7851**
Fax 407.245.0847
E-mail ....Area7MedicaidHelp@ahca.myflorida.com
Hurston South Tower, 400 S West Robinson St Ste
309, Orlando, FL 32801

Agency for Persons with Disabilities **813.233.4300**
E-mail ....geriwilliams@apd.state.fl.us
1313 N Tampa St, Ste 515, Tampa, FL 33602
Geri Williams, Program Administrator

Akerman Senterfitt Attorney at Law **904.798.3700**
Fax 904.798.3730
50 North Laura St Ste 3100, Jacksonville, FL 32202
John Macdonald, Managing Shareholder

Alafaya Woods Kindercare **407.366.8923**
E-mail ....c1277@mail.kindercare.com
300 Alafaya Woods Blvd, Oviedo, FL 32765
Diane Basham, Director

**Alpert Jewish Family and Children's Service/Levine Jewish
Residential and Family Service** **561.684.1991**
Fax 561.684.5366
Web ....www.jfcsonline.com
P.O. Box 220627, West Palm Beach, FL 33422
COA accredited organization.

ARC Broward **954.577.4122**
Web ....www.arcbroward.com
E-mail ....jmaia@aol.com
10250 NW 53rd St, Sunrise, FL 33351
Dennis Haas, Chief Executive Officer

ARC/Florida **800.226.1155**
E-mail ....arcofflorida@gmail.com
2898 Mahan Dr Ste 1, Tallahassee, FL 32308
John Finch, Chief Operating Officer

Assn of Rehabilitation Facilities Inc **850.877.4816**
E-mail ....info@floridaarf.org
2475 Apalachee Pkwy Ste 205, Tallahassee, FL 32301
Suzanne Sewell, President

Autism Early Intervention Clinics **727.576.7600**
Fax 727.388.6879
Web ....www.autismclinics.com
E-mail ....info@autismclinics.com
8950 Dr Martin Luther King Jr St N Ste 170, Saint
Petersburg, FL 33702-3001
Frans Van Haaren, Director

Autism Society of Florida **954.349.2820**
Fax 954.571.2136
Web ....www.autismfl.com
E-mail ....rt66ellen@hotmail.com
PO Box 970646, Pompano Beach, FL 33097-0646

Florida

Autism Speaks South Florida Ofc **800.610.6227**
Fax 954.421.1054
Web ....www.autismspeaks.org
E-mail ....naarsouthfl@naar.org
   1166 W Newport Dr, Deerfield Beach,
   FL 33442-1100
   Jacklyn Merens, Director

AWARE Project **888.612.9273**
E-mail ....cfpc@cflparents.org
   1021 Delaware Ave, Palm Harbor, FL 34683

**Bayfront Medical Center Rehabilitation
Services** **727.893.6864**
Fax 727.893.6779
Web ....www.bayfront.org
   701 Sixth Street South, Saint Petersburg, FL 33701
   CARF accredited programs available.

**Biscayne Institutes of Health and Living,
Inc.** **305.932.8994**
Fax 305.932.9362
Web ....www.biscayneinstitutes.org
   2785 Northeast 183rd Street, Suite 100, Miami,
   FL 33160
   CARF accredited programs available.

Brain Injury Association **800.992.3442**
E-mail ....biafhelp@biaf.org
   1637 Metropolitan Blvd Ste B, Talahasee, FL 32308
   Valerie Breen, President

Brooks Rehabilitation Hospital **904.858.7600**
Fax 904.858.7610
Web ....www.brookshealth.org
   3599 University Boulevard South, Jacksonville,
   FL 32216
   CARF accredited programs available.

Catholic Charities, Diocese of Venice, Inc. **941.488.5581**
Fax 941.486.4758
Web ....www.catholiccharitiesdov.org
   1000 Pinebrook Road, Venice, FL 34285
   COA accredited organization.

Central Florida Parent Center **727.798.2400**
Fax 727.789.2454
E-mail ....cfpc@cflparents.org
   Assistance w/ Achieving Result, 1021 Delaware Ave,
   Palm Harbor, FL 34683
   Eileen Gilley

Central Florida Parent Center **727.789.2400**
Fax 727.789.2454
E-mail ....cpfc@cflparents.org
   1201 Delaware Ave, Palm Harbor, FL 34683
   Eileen Gilley, Director

Child Care Network **850.932.1637**
Fax 850.922.8888
   1269 Oriole Beach Road, Gulf Breeze, FL 32563
   Dianna Albridge, Director

**Children's Comprehensive Care Center/Pediatric Skilled
Nursing Facility** **954.943.7638**
Fax 954.943.5950
Web ....www.bcckids.org
E-mail ....mariel@bcckids.org
   200 SE 19th Ave, Pompano Beach, FL 33060
   Marie Luly, Director of Nursing
   CARF accredited programs available.

Cora Health Services, Inc. **904.573.0046**
Fax 904.573.0772
Web ....www.corahealth.com
   6248 103rd Street, Jacksonville, FL 32244
   mike ligmanowski, clinic manager
   CARF accredited programs available.

Ctr for Autism & Related Disabilities **800.754.5891**
E-mail ....card_info@ufl.edu
   PO Box 100234, Gainesville, FL 32610
   Leannis Maxwell, Program Assistant

**Ctr For Autism And Related Disabilities
(CARD)** **888.558.1908**
Fax 407.737.2571
Web ....www.ucf-card.org
E-mail ....ucfcard@mail.ucf.edu
   12001 Science Dr Ste 145, Orlando, FL 32826-2924
   Teresa Daly, Director

**Davis Center for Rehabilitation - Baptist
Hospital** **786.596.7120**
Fax 786.596.3640
Web ....www.baptisthealth.net
   8900 North Kendall Drive, Miami, FL 33183
   CARF accredited programs available.

Easter Seals Florida **407.629.7881**
E-mail ....info@fl.easterseals.com
   2010 Mizell Ave, Winter Park, FL 32792
   Susan Ventura, Chief Executive Officer

**Easter Seals of Volusia and Flagler Counties,
Florida** **386.255.4568**
Fax 386.258.7677
Web ....www.easterseals-volusiaflagler.org
   1219 Dunn Ave, Daytona Beach, FL 32114
   Lynn Sinnott, Director
   CARF accredited programs available.

Eden Florida/Eimerman Center **239.384.5620**
Fax 239.992.5622
Web ....www.edenservices.org
   2801 County Barn Rd, Naples, FL 34112
   Staci Thompson

Epilepsy Services Program **850.245.4330**
E-mail ....nikita_wiggins@doh.state.fl.us
   4052 Bald Cypress Way Bin A-18, Tallahassee,
   FL 32399
   Nikita Wiggins, Contract Manager

FLASHA **800.243.3574**
E-mail ....tkautter@kmgnet.com
   222 S Westmonte Dr # 101, Altamonte Springs,
   FL 32714
   Tina Kautter, Director

Florida Congress of PTA **407.855.7604**
E-mail ....tricia@floridapta.org
   1747 Orlando Central Pkwy, Orlando, FL 32809
   Tricia Sheldon, Executive Director

**Florida Institute for Neurologic Rehabilitation,
Inc.** **800.697.5390**
Fax 863.773.2041
Web ....http://www.finr.net
   1962 Vandolah Road, Wauchula, FL 33873
   CARF accredited programs available.

**HealthSouth Rehabilitation Hospital of
Sarasota** **941.921.8600**
Fax 941.922.6228
Web ....www.healthsouth.com
   6400 Edgelake Drive, Sarasota, FL 34240
   CARF accredited programs available.

**HEALTHSOUTH Sunrise Rehabilitation
Hospital** **954.749.0300**
Fax 954.746.1378
Web ....www.healthsouth.com
   4399 Nob Hill Road, Sunrise, FL 33351
   CARF accredited programs available.

Home Less **954.779.3990**
   920 NE 7th Ave, Fort Lauderdale, FL 33311
   Frances Esposido, Director

**Jackson Memorial Hospital Rehabilitation Center at Jackson
Health System** **305.585.7112**
Fax 305.355.4018
Web ....www.jhsmiami.org
   1611 Northwest 12th Avenue, Rehabilitation
   Building, Suite 310, Miami, FL 33136
   CARF accredited programs available.

Kessenich Family MDA ALS Center **305.243.7400**
Fax 305.243.1249
E-mail ....averma@med.miami.edu
   1150 NW 14th St Ste 701, Miami, FL 33136
   Ashok Verma Md, Dm Director

LearningRx Learning Center **561.488.6188**
E-mail ....bocaraton.fl@learningrx.net
   21073 Powerline Rd, Bay 63-65, Boca Raton,
   FL 33433

LearningRx Learning Center **386.615.6854**
E-mail ....ormondbeach.fl@learningrx.net
   208 Booth Rd, Ste A, Ormond Beach, FL 32174
   Steve Lampkin, Chief Executive Officer

LearningRx Learning Center **321.727.3996**
E-mail ....melbourne.fl@learningrx.net
   225 5th Ave, Ste 7, Indialantic, FL 32903
   Terri Clark, Executive Director

LifeShare Management Group, Inc. **813.891.9474**
Fax 813.891.9058
Web ....www.lifeshareinc.org
   6323 Memorial Highway #A, Tampa, FL 33615
   COA accredited organization.

Lindamood-Bell Learning Processes **954.349.1688**
Fax 954.349.3228
E-mail ....info@lindamoodbell.com
   Weston Town Center, 1835 Main St Ste 201, Weston,
   FL 33326
   Sophia Gelin, Director

Lindamood-Bell Learning Processes **813.253.0453**
Fax 813.253.0454
E-mail ....tampa.center@lindamoodbell.com
   701 S Howard Ave, Ste 204, Tampa, FL 33606
   Tasha Boston, Office Manager

Lindamood-Bell Learning Processes **786.552.6470**
Fax 786.552.6471
   806 Douglas Rd Ste 100, Coral Gables, FL 33134
   Stephanie Zamarno, Office Manager

Manasota BUDS **941.907.0499**
E-mail ....info@manasotabuds.org
   8374 Market St # 113, Bradenton, FL 34202

**Mercy Hospital, Inc. - Comprehensive Rehabilitation
Unit** **305.285.2775**
Fax 305.285.5052
Web ....www.mercymiami.org
   3663 S Miami Ave, Miami, FL 33133
   Sue Sitko, Director
   CARF accredited programs available.

Mount Sinai Medical Center, Inc. **305.674.5957**
Fax 305.604.2741
Web ....www.msmc.com
   4701 North Meridian Avenue, Miami Beach,
   FL 33140
   CARF accredited programs available.

NAMI Florida Inc **850.671.4445**
E-mail ....namifl@namifl.org
   1030 E Lafeyette St Ste 10, Tallahassee, FL 32301
   Judi Evans, Director

National Ctr for Native American Families **727.523.1130**
Fax 727.523.8687
E-mail ....paririe_flower@fndvisions.org
   2196 Main St Ste K, Dunedin, FL 34698
   Olena Voronina, Office Manager

National Multiple Sclerosis Society **904.332.6810**
Fax 904.332.0898
E-mail ....Msnorfla@fln.nmss.org
   4237 Salisbury Rd, Bldg 4 Ste 406, Jacksonville,
   FL 32216

National Multiple Sclerosis Society **800.344.4867**
Fax 407.478.8893
E-mail ....info@Flc.NMSS.org
   2701 Maitland Center Pkwy, Ste 100, Maitland,
   FL 32751
   Pat Chuck, Program Coordinator

Orlando Health Rehabilitation Institute **321.841.4161**
Fax 321.841.4170
Web ....www.orlandohealth.com\rehab
   818 Main Lane, Orlando, FL 32801
   CARF accredited programs available.

Parent Education Network Project **727.523.1130**
E-mail ....pen@fndfl.org
   2735 Whitney Rd, Clearwater, FL 33760

Parent to Parent of Miami Inc **800.527.9552**
E-mail ....info@ptopmiami.org
   7990 SW 117th Ave ,Ste 201, Miami, FL 33183

Parents of the Panhandle Info Ntwrk **850.847.0010**
E-mail ....suzanne@fndfl.org
   541 E Tennessee St Ste 103, Tallahassee, FL 32308
   Suzanne Lane, Coordinator

**PEACE (Parental Encouragement For Autistic Children
Everywhere)** **863.686.1221**
Fax 863.686.0981
Web ....www.peacelakeland.com
E-mail ....nikki73170@aol.com
   1021 Lakeland Hills Blvd, Lakeland, FL 33805-4672
   Nicole Torres, Program Director

Shands Rehab Hospital **352.265.5491**
Fax 352.265.5420
Web ....www.shands.org
   4101 Northwest 89th Boulevard, Gainesville,
   FL 32606
   CARF accredited programs available.

Speech-Language-Hearing Association **800.226.4742**
E-mail ....execdir@gsha.org
   20423 State Road 7 Ste F6-491, Boca Raton,
   FL 33498

Spina Bifida Association **800.722.6355**
E-mail ....mquinone@nemours.org
   807 Childrens Way, Jacksonville, FL 32207
   Maria Quinones, Director

**St. Mary's Medical Center/The Rehabilitation Institute at St.
Mary's Medical Center** **561.882.6036**
Fax 561.882.1077
Web ....www.stmarysmc.com
   901 45th Street, West Palm Beach, FL 33407
   CARF accredited programs available.

**Tampa General Hospital Rehabilitation
Center** **813.844.7610**
Fax 813.844.1477
Web ....www.tgh.org
   Six Tampa General Circle, Tampa, FL 33606-3571
   CARF accredited programs available.

**The Rehabilitation Hospital Lee Memorial Health
System** **239.336.6924**
Fax 239.336.6144
Web ....www.leememorial.org/rehab/index.asp
   2776 Cleveland Avenue, Fort Myers, FL 33901
   CARF accredited programs available.

**The Rehabilitation Institute of South Florida at Memorial
Regional Hospital South** **954.518.5501**
Fax 954.518.2252
Web ....www.mhs.net
   3600 Washington Street, Hollywood, FL 33021
   CARF accredited programs available.

United Cerebral Palsy of Florida **850.878.2141**
E-mail ....rsanders@sunrisegroup.org
   1830 Buford Ct, Tallahassee, FL 32308
   R Sanders, Director

**Winter Haven Hospital Rehabilitation
Services** **863.293.1121**
Fax 863.291.6762
Web ....www.winterhavenhospital.org
E-mail ....brett.probes@mfms.com
   200 Avenue F NE, Main 1 - Rehabilitation Services,
   Winter Haven, FL 33881
   Brett Probes, Director of Hmo Managed Care
   CARF accredited programs available.

SUBSTANCE ABUSE TREATMENT

**Agency for Community Treatment Services,
Inc.** **813.246.4899**
Fax 813.621.6899
Web ....www.actsfl.org
   4612 N 56th St, Tampa, FL 33610
   Porter Johnston, Program Director
   CARF accredited programs available.

Bridgeway Ctr **850.833.7500**
Fax 850.833.7598
Web ....www.bridgewaycenter.org
   137 Hospital Dr NE, Fort Walton Beach,
   FL 32548-5015
   Daniel Cobb, Director

**Broward Sheriff's Office Department of Community Control
Treatment Divisions** **954.535.2373**
Fax 954.535.2398
Web ....www.sheriff.org
E-mail ....al_lamberti@sheriff.org
   4200 NW 16th St, Suite 607, Lauderhill, FL 33313
   Al Lamberti, Chair Person
   CARF accredited programs available.

Ctr For Drug-Free Living **407.245.0010**
Fax 407.245.0011
Web ....www.cfdfc.com
E-mail ....rhankey@cfdfl.com
   5051 North Ln, Orlando, FL 32808
   Rick Hankey, Administrative Director

DISC Village, Inc. **850.575.4388**
Fax 850.576.3317
Web ....www.discvillage.com
E-mail ....discinfo@discvillage.com
   3333 West Pensacola Street, Tallahassee, FL 32304
   Thomas Olk, Executive Director
   CARF accredited programs available.

Drug Free Youth In Town **305.971.0607**
Fax 305.971.4632
Web ....www.dfyit.org
E-mail ....bzohlman@dfyit.org
   16201 Southwest 95th Avenue, Suites 100 and 205,
   Miami, FL 33157
   Barbara Zohlman, Executive Director
   CARF accredited programs available.

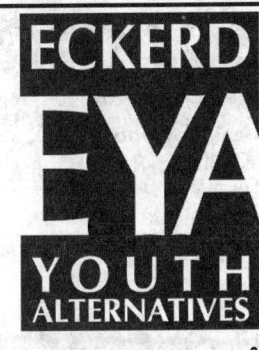

Eckerd **800.914.3937**
Fax 727.442.5911
Web ....www.eckerd.org
E-mail ....admissions@eckerd.org
   100 Starcrest Dr, Clearwater, FL 33758-7450
   David Dennis, President & CEO; Francene Hazel, Director of Admissions
   A full continuum of behavioral health and child welfare programs throughout
   Florida for children and youth from birth through age 23. Behavioral health
   services range from early intervention & prevention to private residential
   treatment centers schools, outdoor therapeutic programs, day treatment,
   residential programs for adjudicated youth, in-home and community-based
   counseling and aftercare services. Child welfare services include case management
   services and child welfare system administration (Eckerd serves as the lead agency
   for community-based child welfare in Pinellas and Pasco counties). For most
   programs, youth are referred through contracts with public agencies. However,
   parents and professionals can refer troubled youth ages 10 – 17 directly to our
   Eckerd Academy at Brooksville program.

Family Counseling Ctr **321.632.5792**
Fax 321.632.5796
Web ....www.sccbrevard.com
E-mail ....phillip@fccbrevard.com
   840 Brevard Ave, Rockledge, FL 32955-2720
   Phillip Kolodziej, President & CEO

First Step of Sarasota, Inc. **941.366.5333**
Fax 941.953.4673
Web ....www.fsos.org
   1970 Main Street, Fifth Floor, Sarasota, FL 34236
   CARF accredited programs available.

Gateway Community Services, Inc. **904.387.4661**
Fax 904.384.5753
Web ....www.gatewaycommunity.com
   555 Stockton St, Jacksonville, FL 32204
   Gary Powers, CEO
   CARF accredited programs available.

Human Services Associates, Inc. **407.422.0880**
Fax 407.284.1050
Web ....www.hsainc.org
   1703 West Colonial Drive, Orlando, FL 32804
   Larry Goldberg, Senior Director
   CARF accredited programs available.

**Management Consulting Svcs, Equine
Therapy** **407.260.8533**
Fax 407.478.0942
E-mail ....jmldbamcs@cs.com
   307 Cranes Roost Blvd, Ste 1018, Altamonte Springs,
   FL 32701
   Janet Leblanc, Director

Phoenix Houses of Florida **813.881.1000**
Fax 813.246.4702
Web ....http://www.phoenixhouse.org/Florida/
   5501 West Waters Avenue, Suite 406, Tampa,
   FL 33634
   Jack Fineberg, Director
   CARF accredited programs available.

Florida

Georgia

Nathan Deal, Governor
203 State Capital
Atlanta, GA 30334
404.656.1776
404.657.7332 (Fax)
www.gov.state.ga.us

Joe Vignati, Juvenile Justice Specialist
55 Park Pl, NE, Ste 410
Atlanta, GA 30303
404.656.5183
404.656.6501 (Fax)
joe.vignati@childrens.ga.gov
www.cycc.state.ga.us

Judge Steve Teske, SAG Chair
Clayton Court House, Annex 3, 3rd Fl
121 S McDonough St
Jonesboro, GA 30236
770.477.3261
steve.teske@co.clayton.ga.us

CRISIS NUMBERS

Child Abuse Reporting . . .404.657.6610

STATE SERVICES

SOCIAL SERVICES

Georgia Dept of Human Resources 404.463.6955
Fax 404.463.2733
Web . . . . .www.dhr.state.ga.us
E-mail . . . . .lmmartin@dhr.state.ga.us
2 Peachtree St NW Ste 3950, Atlanta,
GA 30303-3142
Keith Horton, Acting Director, Child Support Enforcement

Georgia Emergency Management Agency 404.635.7000
Fax 404.635.7205
Web . . . . .www.ohs.state.ga.us
E-mail .charles.english@gema.ga.gov
935 E Confederate Ave SE, Atlanta, GA 30316
Charles English, Director

GENERAL HEALTH SERVICES

Children and Youth with Special Needs GA 404.657.4855
Fax 404.657.2763
E-mail . . . . .gdphinfo@dhr.state.ga.us
Two Peachtree St NW Rm 11 206, Atlanta, GA 30303
Chase Bolds, Manager

Health Dept 770.358.1483
Fax 770.358.1258
Web . . . . .health.state.ga.us/regional/lamar
E-mail . . . . .spfarr@gdph.state.ga.us
118 Academy Dr Ste B, Barnesville, GA 30204-3504
Seth Woodrow, County Environmental Health Manager

Maternal and Child Health GA 404.657.2851
Fax 404.657.7307
E-mail . . . . .gcmih@dhr.ga.gov
2 Peachtree St NW, Ste 11 415, Atlanta, GA 30303

MENTAL HEALTH SERVICES

Rehabilitation Svcs 404.232.3910
Fax 404.232.3912
Web . . . . .www.dol.state.ga.us
E-mail . . . . .annette.mccauley@dol.state.ga.us
148 Andrew Young International Blvd NE, Suite 510,
Atlanta, GA 30303
Annette McCauley, Director

JUSTICE AGENCY

Attorney General's Ofc 404.656.3300
Fax 404.657.8733
Web . . . . .www.ganet.org/ago
E-mail . . . . .samolens@law.ga.gov
40 Capitol Sq SW, Atlanta, GA 30334
Sam Olens, Attorney General

Crime Victim Compensation Program 404.657.1956
Fax 404.463.7652
E-mail . . . . .info@cjcc.ga.gov
104 Marietta St NW Ste 440, Atlanta, GA 30303
Barbara Lynn Howell, Director

Dept of Juvenile Justice .404.508.6500
Fax 404.508.6662
Web . . . . .www.djj.state.ga.us
E-mail . . . . .tinapiper@djj.state.ga.us
3408 Covington Hwy, Decatur, GA 30032
Tina Piper, Director Of Legal Services

Dept Of Juvenile Justice/ Probation 706.422.1922
Fax 706.422.1921
E-mail . . . . .claypowell@djj.state.ga.us
103 Murray Plaza, Chatsworth, GA 30705-2538
Clay Powell, Jpps

Georgia Dept of Corrections 404.656.9772
Fax 404.651.6818
Web . . . . .www.dcor.state.ga.us
E-mail . . . . .gdcinfo@dcor.state.ga.us
2 Martin Luther King Jr. Dr. SE, Atlanta, GA 30334
Katrinka Glass, Program Director

COURTS

Chief Superior Court Judge Middle Circuit 478.237.3260
Fax 478.237.0949
E-mail . . . . .kspalmer@bellsouth.net
125 S Main St, Swainsboro, GA 30401-3699
Honorable Kathy Palmer, Chief Superior Judge

POLICE AND SHERIFF

Georgia Assoc of Chiefs of Police 770.495.9650
Fax 770.495.7872
Web . . . . .www.gachiefs.com
E-mail . . . . .gacp@gachiefs.com
3500 Duluth Park Ln, Ste 700, Duluth,
GA 30096-3243
Frank V. Rotondo, Executive Director

Georgia Bureau Of Investigation 404.244.2501
Fax 404.270.8352
E-mail .vernon.keenan@gbi.ga.gov
3121 Panthersville Rd, Decatur, GA 30034
Vernon Keenan, Director

Georgia Sheriffs' Assoc 770.914.1076
Fax 770.914.1179
Web . . . . .www.georgiasheriffs.org
3000 Hwy 42 N, Stockbridge, GA 30281
James A. Cody, Sr. Executive Vice President

EDUCATION SERVICES

Communities In Schools .404.888.5784
Fax 404.888.5789
Web . . . . .www.cisga.org
E-mail .nshorthouse@cisga.org
600 W Peachtree St NW Ste 1200, Atlanta,
GA 30308-3614
Neil Shorthouse, President

Educ for Homeless Children and Youth GA 404.656.2004
Fax 404.657.1534
E-mail . . . . .jjohnson@doe.k12.ga.us
205 Jesse Hill Jr Dr SE, 1866 Twin Towers E, Atlanta,
GA 30334
J Johnson, Director

Georgia Academy for the Blind 478.751.6083
Fax 478.751.6659
2895 Vineville Ave, Macon, GA 31204
Dorthy Arensman, School Director

Georgia Dept of Education 404.656.2800
Fax 404.651.8737
Web www.doe.k12.ga.us
E-mail . . . . .dstadnick@doe.k12.ga.us
2066 Twin Towers E, Atlanta, GA 30334
Desiree Stadnick, Education Specialist

Georgia School for the Deaf 706.777.2200
Fax 706.777.2204
Web . . . . .www.gsdweb.org
E-mail . . . . .kemoore@doe.k12.ga.us
232 Perry Farm Rd SW, Cave Spring, GA 30124-3018
Kenney Moore, Interim Director

Parents Educ Parents and Prof GA 770.577.7771
Fax 770.577.7774
E-mail .shepard.linda@peppinc.org
PO Box 5128, Douglasville, GA 30154
Linda Shepard, Director

Premier Academy 404.875.9668
Fax 404.875.9732
Web . . . . .www.premier-academy.org
E-mail .ggore@premier-academy.org
444 Angier Ave NE, Atlanta, GA 30308-2602
Gladys Gore, Director

LABOR & WORKFORCE EDUCATION

Comprehensive Rehab 770.928.2112
Fax 770.928.0154
Web . . . . .www.vnaic.org
E-mail . . . . .cpputzel@bellsouth.net
P.O. Box 965222, Marietta, GA 30066
Carroll Putzel

Georgia Dept of Labor **404.232.7300**
Fax 404.656.2683
E-mail .... commissioner@dol.state.ga.us

148 Andrew Young International Blvd NE Ste 600,
Atlanta, GA 30303
Mark Butler, Commissioner

COUNTY SERVICES

Appling County

SOCIAL SERVICES

Georgia Div of Family & Children
Svcs **912.366.1010**
Fax 912.366.1045
  1160 W Parker St, Baxley, GA 31513

GENERAL HEALTH SERVICES

Health Dept **912.367.4601**
Fax 912.367.1096
Web .... www.dhr.state.ga.us
  34 Walnut St, Baxley, GA 31513-0119
Angie Griffin, Nursing Manager

JUSTICE AGENCY

CASA **912.367.0064**
Fax 912.367.0065
E-mail .... tricountycasa@bellsouth.net
  239 NE Park Ave Ste C, Baxley, GA 31513
Denise Graham, Executive Director

COURTS

Juvenile Court **912.366.9000**
Fax 912.367.5883
E-mail .... jajohnson@jalaw.com
  132 W Parker St, Baxley, GA 30513
Honorable Alex Johnson, Director

Atkinson County

SOCIAL SERVICES

Georgia Div of Family & Children
Svcs **912.422.3242**
Fax 912.422.3538
  204 E Legion Ave, PO Box 278, Pearson, GA 31642

GENERAL HEALTH SERVICES

Public Health Dept **912.422.3332**
Fax 912.422.7345
Web .... www.sehdph.org
  63 C Austin Ave, Pearson, GA 31642
Donna Smeltzer, Nursing Manager

Bacon County

SOCIAL SERVICES

Georgia Div of Family & Children
Svcs **912.632.8375**
Fax 912.632.5007
  417 S Dixon St, PO Box 447, Alma, GA 31510

GENERAL HEALTH SERVICES

Health Dept **912.632.4712**
Fax 912.632.7834
  101 N Wayne Street, Alma, GA 31510
Cathy Taylor, Rn, Nursing Manager

COURTS

Superior Court - Waycross Circuit **912.384.0587**
Fax 912.384.0701
  101 Peterson Ave S Ste B2, Douglas, GA 31533
Honorable Dwayne H. Gillis, Superior Court Judge

POLICE AND SHERIFF

Sheriff's Office **912.632.2658**
Fax 912.632.4566
  307 S Dixon St Ste A, Alma, GA 31510
Richard R. Foskey, Sheriff

Baker County

SOCIAL SERVICES

Georgia Div of Family & Children
Svcs **229.734.5247**
Fax 229.734.8442
  101 Sunset Blvd, PO Box 540, Newton, GA 39870

GENERAL HEALTH SERVICES

Health Dept **229.734.5226**
Fax 229.734.6023
Web .... www.health.state.ga.us/regional/baker
  327 Sunset Ave Sw Dept 1, Newton, GA 39870
Cristi Dixon, Rn, Supervisor

COURTS

Juvenile Court **229.294.4460**
Fax 229.294.4951
E-mail .... rechew@gmail.com
  151 Curry St, Pelham, GA 31779
Judge Randall E. Chew, Director

POLICE AND SHERIFF

Sheriff's Ofc **229.734.3003**
Fax 229.734.3022
Web .... www.bakercountysheriffoffice.org
E-mail .... d.meade@sos.state.ga.us
  167 Baker Pl, Newton, GA 39870
Dana Meade, Sheriff

Baldwin County

SOCIAL SERVICES

Georgia Div of Family & Children
Svcs **478.445.4135**
Fax 478.445.6531
  154 Robinson Mill Rd, PO Box 430, Milledgeville,
GA 31061

GENERAL HEALTH SERVICES

Central State Hospital **478.445.4334**
Fax 478.445.0885
Web .... www.centralcityhospital.org
  Yarbrough Rd Crittenden Bldng, Milledgeville,
GA 31062-7525
Carol Boyer, Service Director

Health Dept **478.445.4274**
Fax 478.445.6525
Web .... www.northcentralhealthdistrict.com
  953 Barrows Ferry Rd NE, Milledgeville, GA 31061
Wendy Harris, Nurse Director

MENTAL HEALTH SERVICES

Oconee Community Svcs Board **478.445.4817**
Fax 478.445.4963
Web .... www.oconeecenter.org
E-mail .... oconeeadmin@alltel.net
  131 N Jefferson St, Oconee Center, Milledgeville,
GA 31061
Angela Hicks-hill, Director

JUSTICE AGENCY

Baldwin Inmate Boot Camp **478.445.5218**
Fax 478.445.6874
Web .... www.prisontalk.com
  PO Box 218, Hardwick, GA 31034-0218
Kathy Price, Administrative Director

Ocmulgee CASA **478.452.9170**
Fax 478.452.0592
Web www.baldwin.k12.ga.us
E-mail .... ocasalm@baldwin.k12.ga.us
  100 N ABC St, Milledgeville, GA 31061
Lori Muggridge, Executive Director

COURTS

Juvenile Court **478.445.7060**
Fax 478.445.7059
Web .... www.windstream.net
E-mail .... pspivey@windstream.net
  121 N Wilkinson St, Milledgeville, GA 31061
Philip Spivey, Judge

Banks County

SOCIAL SERVICES

Georgia Div of Family & Children
Svcs **706.677.2272**
Fax 706.677.2196
  432 Evans St, PO Box 159, Homer, GA 30547

GENERAL HEALTH SERVICES

Public Health Dept **706.677.2296**
Fax 706.677.4042
Web www.phdistrict2.org
E-mail .... jdodd@dhr.state.ga.us
  667 Thompson St, Homer, GA 30547-3110
Joann Dodd, Nursing Supervisor

Barrow County

SOCIAL SERVICES

Georgia Div of Family & Children
Svcs **770.868.4222**
Fax 770.868.4235
  16 Lee St, PO Box 546, Winder, GA 30680

GENERAL HEALTH SERVICES

Public Health Dept **770.307.3011**
Fax 770.307.1039
Web .... health.state.ga.us/regional/barrow
E-mail .... behealthy@barrowcountyhealthdepartment.com
  233 E Broad Street A, Winder, GA 30680
Susan Crystal, Nursing Supervisor

COURTS

Dept Of Juvenille Justice **770.868.4010**
Fax 770.868.4025
  32 Lee St, Winder, GA 30680-2015
Cathy Sells, Program Manager

Superior Court **770.307.3035**
Fax 770.867.4800
E-mail .... rmcintyre@barrowga.org
  652 Barrow Park Drive Ste B, Winder, GA 30680
Regina Mcintyre, Clerk Of Superior Court

POLICE AND SHERIFF

Sheriff's Ofc **770.307.3080**
Fax 770.307.3066
Web .... www.barrowsheriff.com
E-mail .... jsmith@barrowsheriff.com
  30 N Broad St, Ste 221, Winder, GA 30680-1964
Jud Smith, Sheriff

Bartow County

SOCIAL SERVICES

Georgia Div of Family & Childrens

Svcs..............................**770.387.3710**
Fax.....................................770.387.3944
  47 Brooks Dr, PO Box 818, Cartersville, GA 30120

JUSTICE AGENCY

CASA............................**770.386.1060**
Fax.....................................770.386.0985
Web...........................www.advochild.org
E-mail.................bartowcasa@advochild.org
  12 South Erwin Street Suite 1 & 4, Cartersville,
  GA 30120
Ava Lipscomb, Program Director

COURTS

Juvenile Court....................**770.387.5039**
Fax.....................................770.387.5044
  135 W Cherokee Ave Ste 333, Cartersville, GA 30120
Honorable Velma C. Tilley, Judge

POLICE AND SHERIFF

Sheriff's Ofc.....................**770.382.5050**
Fax.....................................678.721.3206
Web.................................www.bartow.org
E-mail..................trekastone@bartow.org
  104 Zena Dr, Cartersville, GA 30120
Clark Millsap, Sheriff

Ben Hill County

SOCIAL SERVICES

Child & Family Svcs...............**229.426.5300**
  124 S Grant St, Fitzgerald, GA 31750

GENERAL HEALTH SERVICES

Public Health Dept................**229.426.5288**
Fax.....................................229.426.5291
Web.......................www.southhealthdistrict.com
  251 Appomattox Road, Fitzgerald, GA 31750
Dale Niday, Nursing Supervisor

COURTS

Superior Court....................**229.426.5638**
Fax.....................................229.426.5639
E-mail.................judgechughes@mchsi.com
  255 Appomattox Road, Fitzgerald, GA 31750
Judge Terry Chris Hughes, Judge

POLICE AND SHERIFF

Sheriff's Ofc.....................**229.426.5161**
Fax.....................................229.426.5164
  255 Appomattox Rd, Fitzgerald, GA 31750
Bobby Mclemore, Sheriff

EDUCATION SERVICES

Communities In Schools............**229.423.7933**
Fax.....................................229.423.7221
Web...................................www.cisga.org
E-mail.................beckygay@windstream.net
  401 W. Altamaha Ctr, Fitzgerald, GA 31750
Becky Gay, Director

Berrien County

SOCIAL SERVICES

Georgia Div of Family & Children

Svcs..............................**229.686.5568**
Fax.....................................229.686.3933
  301 S Jefferson St, Nashville, GA 31639

GENERAL HEALTH SERVICES

Public Health Dept................**229.686.2038**
Fax.....................................229.686.9015
Web...............health.state.ga.us/regional/berrien
E-mail.............rhughes@berriencohlthdept.org
  600 A S Jefferson St, Nashville, GA 31639
Regina Hughes, RN, Nursing Supervisor

COURTS

Superior Court - Alapaha Circuit.......**229.686.5506**
Fax.....................................229.543.1032
  201 N Davis St, Nashville, GA 31639
Honorable Dane Perkins, Judge

Bibb County

SOCIAL SERVICES

Georgia Div of Family & Children

Svcs..............................**478.751.6051**
Fax.....................................478.751.6578
  456 Oglethorpe St, Macon, GA 31201

GENERAL HEALTH SERVICES

District Health Dept...............**478.751.6303**
Fax.....................................478.751.6099
Web.................www.northcentralhealthdistrict.org
E-mail.................ctanner@dhr.state.ga.us
  811 Hemlock St, Macon, GA 31201-2144
Carol Tanner, Clinical Director

Health Dept......................**478.745.0411**
Fax.....................................478.749.0101
E-mail.................lhoward@co.bibb.ga.us
  171 Emery Hwy, Macon, GA 31217-3695
Linda Holland, Nursing Supervisor/child Health

MENTAL HEALTH SERVICES

River Edge Behavioral Health Ctr.......**478.751.4519**
Fax.....................................478.752.1040
  175 Emery Hwy Frnt, Macon, GA 31217
Shannon Harvey, Director

JUSTICE AGENCY

Central Georgia CASA..............**478.238.6318**
Fax.....................................478.742.3405
Web................................www.centralgacasa.org
E-mail.............casa@themethodisthome.org
  116 Pierce Ave, Macon, GA 31204-2891
Tracy Willis Kyte, Executive Director

Macon Male Transitional Ctr.......**478.751.6090**
Fax.....................................478.751.6225
  200 Henry st, Macon, GA 31206
Terry Seltzer, Superintendent

Macon Regional Youth Detention

Ctr................................**478.751.3400**
Fax.....................................478.751.4417
Web.............................www.djj.state.ga.us
E-mail.............melissaaaron@djj.state.ga.us
  4164 Riggins Mill Rd, Macon, GA 31217-5440
Melissa Aaron, Director

Macon Youth Development Ctr.............**478.751.3415**
Fax.....................................478.751.3414
Web.............................www.djj.state.ga.us
E-mail.............debbieblasingame@djj.state.ga.us
  4160 Riggins Mill Rd, Macon, GA 31217
Debbie Blasingame, Director

COURTS

Juvenile Court....................**478.621.6448**
Fax.....................................478.621.6368
  601 MULBERRY ST STE 310, Macon, GA 31201-0366
Honorable Quintress J. Gilbert, Director

POLICE AND SHERIFF

Mercer University Police...........**478.301.2970**
Fax.....................................478.301.5578
Web..................................www.mercer.edu
E-mail.................mercerpolice@mercer.edu
  1765 Winship St, Macon, GA 31207-0001
Lt. Cary Barbee, Operations Director

Sheriff's Dept....................**478.746.9441**
Fax.....................................478.621.5681
Web.......................www.co.bibb.ga.us/bibbsheriff
E-mail.................dwalker@co.bibb.ga.us
  668 Oglethorpe St, Macon, GA 31201-6844
Lt. Donald Walker, Junior Deputy Program Senior Lieutenant

EDUCATION SERVICES

Communities In Schools............**229.686.6576**
Fax.....................................229.686.6580
E-mail......constance.thomas@berriencountycollaboratize.org
  1015 Exum Rd, Nashville, GA 31639-2730
Constance Thomas, Director

Bleckley County

SOCIAL SERVICES

Family & Children Svcs.............**478.934.3172**
Fax.....................................478.934.3332
Web.............................www.dhr.state.ga.us
  140 E Peacock St, Cochran, GA 31014-7847
Rebeca Powell, Director

GENERAL HEALTH SERVICES

Public Health Dept................**478.934.6590**
Fax.....................................478.934.8729
  152 N 8th St, Cochran, GA 31014
Debbie Martin, Nursing Supervisor

POLICE AND SHERIFF

Sheriff's Ofc.....................**478.934.4545**
Fax.....................................478.934.3226
E-mail.................bleckleyso@hotmail.com
  112 N 2nd St, Cochran, GA 31014
Harold O. Lancaster, Sheriff

Brantley County

SOCIAL SERVICES

Georgia Div of Family & Children

Svcs..............................**912.462.6171**
Fax.....................................912.462.7255
  127 Bryan St, PO Box 308, Nahunta, GA 31553

COURTS

Juvenile Court....................**912.462.5635**
Fax.....................................912.462.6247
Web...................................www.gsccca.org
E-mail.................debbie.sirmans@gsccca.org
  234 Brantley St, Ste # 200, Nahunta, GA 31553
Debbie Sirmans, Deputy Clerk

POLICE AND SHERIFF

Sheriff's Dept....................**912.462.6141**
Fax.....................................912.462.6597
E-mail.................bcsd@btconline.net
  95 John Wilson St, Nahunta, GA 31553
Robert Thomas, Sheriff

Brooks County

SOCIAL SERVICES

Georgia Div of Family & Children

Svcs..............................**229.263.7567**
Fax.....................................229.263.9014
  201 S Barnes St, Quitman, GA 31643

COURTS

Juvenile Court.............................**229.263.4747**
Fax...229.263.5050
　1 Screven St, Quitman, GA 31643
　Honorable Allen D. Denton, Judge

POLICE AND SHERIFF

Sheriff's Ofc................................**229.263.7558**
Fax...229.263.7559
E-mail.........................shriffdewey@brooksshriff.com
　1 Screven Street, Quitman, GA 31643
　Mike Dewey, Sheriff

Bryan County

SOCIAL SERVICES

Child & Family Svcs.......................**912.653.2805**
　133 W Dubois St, Pembroke, GA 31321

Child &Family Svcs........................**912.756.4441**
　66 Captain Matthew Freeman Dr, Richmond Hill,
　GA 31324

COURTS

Superior Court-Atlantic Circuit.............**912.653.3872**
Fax...912.653.3870
　151 S College St, Pembroke, GA 31321
　Rebecca Crowe, Clerk Of Courts

POLICE AND SHERIFF

Sheriff's Ofc................................**912.653.3800**
Fax...912.653.2880
Web...................................www.gafcp.org
E-mail.................................clyde@gafcp.org
　95 Public Safety Way, Pembroke, GA 31321
　Clyde R. Smith, Sheriff

Bulloch County

SOCIAL SERVICES

Georgia Div of Family & Children
Svcs..**912.871.1333**
Fax...912.681.5990
　41 Pulaski Hwy, PO Box 1103, Statesboro, GA 30459

GENERAL HEALTH SERVICES

Health Dept..................................**912.764.3800**
Fax...912.871.1901
Web.........................health.state.ga.us/regional/bulloch
　1 W Altman St 0, Statesboro, GA 30459
　Tony Flatman, Nurse Manager

COURTS

Juvenile Court..............................**912.681.5996**
Fax...912.871.1707
　1 N Main St, Statesboro, GA 30458-5750
　Bill Martin, Program Manager

Burke County

SOCIAL SERVICES

Georgia Div of Family & Children
Svcs..**706.554.7751**
Fax...706.554.7093
　729 W 6th St, PO Box 390, Waynesboro, GA 30830

GENERAL HEALTH SERVICES

Public Health Dept.........................**706.554.3456**
Fax...706.554.2944
Web.........................health.state.ga.us/regional/burke
　114 Dogwood Dr, Waynesboro, GA 30830
　Regina Richardson, Nursing Supervisor

COURTS

Juvenile Court..............................**706.437.6845**
Fax...706.437.6838
　114 E 6th St, Waynesboro, GA 30830
　Elaine Stokes, Juvenile Probation Parole Specialist

EDUCATION SERVICES

Communities In Schools...................**706.554.7213**
Fax...706.554.9995
　229 E 6th St, Waynesboro, GA 30830-0418
　Deena Sams, Director

Exceptional Students......................**478.589.7310**
Fax...478.589.7038
　234 Harris St, Midville, GA 30411
　Debbie Youmans, Director

Butts County

COURTS

Juvenile Court..............................**770.775.8026**
Fax...770.775.8026
Web................................www.lamarcountysheriff.com
E-mail...........................sheriff@lamarcountysheriff.com
　25 3rd St Ste 15, Jackson, GA 30233-1965
　Honorable Sharon Whitwell, Director

POLICE AND SHERIFF

Sheriff's Ofc................................**770.775.8216**
Fax...770.775.8236
Web...................................www.buttscounty.org
　835 Ernest Biles Dr, Jackson, GA 30233-5103
　Gene Pope, Sheriff

Calhoun County

SOCIAL SERVICES

Georgia Div of Family & Children
Svcs..**229.849.5100**
Fax...229.849.5101
　28239 Main St, PO Box 9, Morgan, GA 39866

GENERAL HEALTH SERVICES

Public Health Dept.........................**229.849.2515**
Fax...229.849.2701
Web.....................health.state.ga.us/regional/calhoun
E-mail.............................csimpson@dhr.state.ga.us
　Highway 45 North 56, Morgan, GA 39866
　Cathy Simpson, Nursing Supervisor

POLICE AND SHERIFF

Sheriff's Dept...............................**229.849.2555**
Fax...229.849.2000
　66 Court St, Morgan, GA 39866
　Josh Hilton, Sheriff

Camden County

SOCIAL SERVICES

Georgia Div of Family & Children
Svcs..**912.729.4583**
Fax...912.729.7969
　800 Charles Gilman Jr Ave, PO Box 68, Kingsland,
　GA 31548

GENERAL HEALTH SERVICES

Public Health Dept.........................**912.882.8515**
Fax...912.882.2072
Web...................www.health.state.ga.us/regional/camden
　905 Dilworth St, Saint Marys, GA 31558
　Debbie Melton, Rn, Nursing Supervisor

JUSTICE AGENCY

CASA...**912.882.3119**
Fax...912.510.8013
Web...................................www.casacamden.org
E-mail..............................casa-director@tds.net
　696 E Williams Ave, Kingsland, GA 31548-6848
　Bridget Wenum, Director

Dept Of Juvenile Justice..................**912.576.5255**
Fax...912.576.8144
　305 E 4th Street, Woodbine, GA 31569
　Robin Taylor, Program Assistant

POLICE AND SHERIFF

Sheriff's Ofc................................**912.510.5100**
Fax...912.510.5145
Web...................................www.camdensheriff.org
E-mail.............................admin@camdensheriff.org
　209 East 4th St, Woodbine, GA 31569
　Tommy Gregory, Sheriff

Candler County

SOCIAL SERVICES

Georgia Div of Family & Children
Svcs..**912.685.2163**
Fax...912.685.3690
　750 S Leroy St, PO Box 46, Metter, GA 30439

GENERAL HEALTH SERVICES

Public Health Dept.........................**912.685.5765**
Fax...912.685.7448
Web.........................health.state.ga.us/regional/candler
　428 North Roundtree, Metter, GA 30439
　June Anderson Rn, Nursing Supervisor

COURTS

Juvenile Court..............................**912.685.5257**
Fax...912.685.2946
E-mail.............................linda.sewell@gsccca.org
　35 SW Broad Ste C, Metter, GA 30439
　Linda Sewell, Clerk

Carroll County

SOCIAL SERVICES

Family & Children Svcs....................**770.830.2050**
Fax...770.830.2106
Web...................................www.dhr.state.ga.us
　165 Independence Dr, Carrollton, GA 30116-9000
　Charlene Harrod, Director

GENERAL HEALTH SERVICES

Public Health Dept.........................**770.836.6667**
Fax...770.836.6722
Web.........................www.health.state.ga.us/regional/carroll
E-mail.............................sbuchanan@dhr.state.ga.us
　1004 Newnan Rd, Carrollton, GA 30116-6428
　Sharon Buchanan, Hiv Coordinator

JUSTICE AGENCY

CASA...**770.838.1964**
Fax...770.838.1964
Web...................................www.carrollcasa.com
E-mail.............................acamp@carrollcasa.com
　123 Newnan St, Carrollton, GA 30117-3225
　Amanda Camp, Executive Director

POLICE AND SHERIFF

Sheriff's Ofc................................**770.830.5888**
Fax...770.830.5894
Web...................................www.carrollsheriff.com
E-mail.............................info@carrollsheriff.com
　1000 Newnan Rd, Carrollton, GA 30116-6427
　Terry E. Langley, Sheriff

EDUCATION SERVICES

Exceptional Students......................**770.830.6766**
Fax...770.830.6848
　423 Alabama St, Carrollton, GA 30117-3002
　Steve Rains, Director

Catoosa County

SOCIAL SERVICES

Child & Family Svcs.......................**706.866.1740**
　700 City Hall Dr, Fort Oglethorpe, GA 30742

GENERAL HEALTH SERVICES

Public Health **706.935.2366**
Fax 706.965.2369
Web ....www.health.state.ga.us/regional/catoosa
E-mail ....aacarroll@dhr.state.ga.us
145 Catoosa Circle, Ringgold, GA 30736
Amy Carroll, Rn, Nursing Supervisor

JUSTICE AGENCY

Juvenile Probation **706.935.4637**
Fax 706.935.2236
Web ....www.djj.state.ga.us
E-mail ....robbgilstrap@djj.state.ga.us
7195 Nashville St, Ringgold, GA 30736-2442
Robb Gilstrap, Juvenile Probation Manager

COURTS

Juvenile Court **706.935.4901**
Fax 706.935.4909
E-mail ....catoosajuvenilecourt@yahoo.com
7694 Nashville Street, Ringgold, GA 30736
Tammy Hardin, Court Administrator

POLICE AND SHERIFF

Sheriff's Dept **706.935.2424**
Fax 706.965.9096
E-mail ....catoosasheriff@catoosa.com
5842 Highway 41, Ringgold, GA 30736
Phillip N. Summers, Sheriff

EDUCATION SERVICES

Communities In Schools **706.858.0529**
Fax 706.861.4855
Web www.catoosak12.org
E-mail ....jelliott@cisga.org
2 Barnhardt Cir, Fort Oglethorpe, GA 30742-3646
Jayme Elliott, Director

Charlton County

SOCIAL SERVICES

**Georgia Div of Family & Children
Svcs** **912.496.2527**
Fax 912.496.4232
401 W Oak St, PO Box 395, Folkston, GA 31537

GENERAL HEALTH SERVICES

Public Health Dept **912.496.2561**
Fax 912.496.2623
Web ....www.health.state.ga.us/regional/charlton
E-mail ....info@sehdph.org
2587 3rd St, Folkston, GA 31537
Brenda Drury, Rn, Nurse Manager

COURTS

Juvenile Court **912.496.2567**
Fax 912.496.4737
Web ....www.gsccca.org
E-mail ....adamsbrooks@windstream.net
3794 Main St, Folkston, GA 31537
John B. Adams, Judge

POLICE AND SHERIFF

Sheriff's Dept **912.496.7321**
Fax 912.496.7612
E-mail ....ccsheriff@windstream.net
1520 3rd st Ste C, Folkston, GA 31537
Ernest Dobie Conner, Sheriff

Chatham County

SOCIAL SERVICES

Family & Children Svcs **912.651.2216**
Fax 912.651.2890
761 Wheaton St, Savannah, GA 31401
Stanley Walthour, Director

GENERAL HEALTH SERVICES

District Health Dept **912.356.2441**
Fax 912.356.2868
1395 Eisenhower Dr, Savannah, GA 31416
Douglas Skelton, Health Director

**Health Promotion And Disease
Prevention** **912.644.5235**
Fax 912.644.5220
Web ....www.gachd.com
24 Oglethorpe Professional Blvd Ste 400, Savannah,
GA 31406-3641
Christina Gibson, Education Director

WIC Admin **912.651.2570**
Fax 912.651.6297
Web ....www.fns.usda.gov
E-mail ....peggy.fouts@fns.usda.gov
1602 Drayton St, Savannah, GA 31401-7526
Jo Manning, District Policy/Procedure Coordinator

MENTAL HEALTH SERVICES

Developmental Svcs **912.644.7500**
Fax 912.644.7549
Web ....www.ccds-sav.org
E-mail ....info@ccds-sav.org
1249 Eisenhower Dr, Savannah, GA 31406-3917
Kathy Thomson, Executive Director

JUSTICE AGENCY

CASA **912.447.8908**
Fax 912.447.0699
Web ....www.savannahcasa.org
E-mail ....info@savannahcasa.org
428 Bull St Ste 205, Savannah, GA 31401-4962
Zadonna Slay, Director

Chatham Multi-Svc Ctr **912.303.1900**
Fax 912.303.1920
Web ....www.djj.state.ga.us
1149 Cornell Ave, Savannah, GA 31406
Patricia Meritt, District Director

**Savannah Regional Youth Detention
Ctr** **912.652.3879**
Fax 912.652.3899
Web ....www.djj.state.ga.us
191 Carl Griffin Dr, Savannah, GA 31405-1362
Rodney Dinkins, Acting Director

COURTS

Juvenile Court **912.652.6700**
Fax 912.652.6741
Web ....www.chathamcounty.org
E-mail ....wparson@chathamcounty.org
197 Carl Griffin Dr, Savannah, GA 31405-1376
Honorable John W. Beam Jr., Director

POLICE AND SHERIFF

**Savannah Chatham Metropolitan Police
Dept** **912.651.6675**
Fax 912.651.6683
Web ....www.savannahga.gov
E-mail ....wlovett@savannahga.gov
201 Habersham Street, Savannah, GA 31412
Willie Lovett, Chief

Sheriff's Dept **912.652.7632**
Fax 912.652.7660
Web ....www.chathamcounty.org
E-mail ....glderryb@chathamcounty.org
1050 Carl Griffin Dr, Savannah, GA 31405-1327
Al St. Lawrence, Sheriff

EDUCATION SERVICES

Communities In Schools **912.644.6450**
Fax 912.644.6491
E-mail ....sdantin@cisga.org
101 E Bay St, Savannah, GA 31401-2052
Stephen P. Dantin, Executive Director

Chattahoochee County

SOCIAL SERVICES

**Georgia Div of Family & Children
Svcs** **706.989.3681**
Fax 706.989.1066
209 McNaughton St, Cusseta, GA 31805

GENERAL HEALTH SERVICES

Public Health Dept **706.989.3663**
Fax 706.989.1243
213 Mcnaughton St, Cusseta, GA 31805
Lisa Tallent, Nursing Supervisor

COURTS

Juvenile Court **706.989.3424**
Fax 706.989.1508
E-mail ....wjernigansr@alltel.net
379 Broad St, Cusseta, GA 31805-0120
Wayne Jernigan Sr., Judge

Chattooga County

SOCIAL SERVICES

**Georgia Div of Family & Children
Svcs** **706.857.0817**
Fax 706.857.0823
102 Hwy 48, Summerville, GA 30747

COURTS

Juvenile Court **706.857.1622**
Fax 706.857.2480
Web ....www.watersprite.com
E-mail ....jerry@watersprite.com
PO Box 427, Summerville, GA 30747-0427
Honorable William Jerry Westbrook, Director

EDUCATION SERVICES

Chattooga Head Start **706.857.7245**
Fax 706.857.5879
201 Penn St, Summerville, GA 30747
Joseph Burrage, Director

Cherokee County

SOCIAL SERVICES

**Georgia Div of Family & Children
Svcs** **770.720.3610**
Fax 770.720.3680
105 Lamar Haley Pkwy, PO Box 826, Canton,
GA 30169

GENERAL HEALTH SERVICES

Public Health Dept **770.345.7371**
Fax 770.345.6978
Web ....www.health.state.ga.us/regional/cherokee
1219 Univeter Rd, Canton, GA 30115-8261
Nancy Stackhouse, Hiv Coordinator

JUSTICE AGENCY

CASA For Children **770.345.3274**
Fax 770.345.3275
E-mail ....info@casacherokee.org
100 North St Ste G22, Canton, GA 30114
Deidre Hollands, Director

COURTS

Juvenile Court **678.493.6240**
Fax 678.493.6244
E-mail ....gail@brjc.net
90 North St Ste 240, Canton, GA 30114-2762
Honorable Ellen Mcelyea, Superior Court Judge

Superior Court-Blue Ridge Circuit **678.493.6100**
Fax 770.479.0467
Web ....www.cherokeega.com
E-mail ....pbaker@cherokeega.com
   90 North St, Ste G170, Canton, GA 30114-2792
Patty Baker, Clerk Of Court

POLICE AND SHERIFF

Sheriff's Dept **678.493.4200**
Fax 678.493.4195
E-mail ....rdgarrison@cherokeega.com
   498 Chattin Dr, Canton, GA 30115-8240
Roger Garrison, Sheriff

Clarke County

SOCIAL SERVICES

Family & Children Svcs **706.227.7002**
Fax 706.227.7925
E-mail ....dmcriss@dhr.state.ga.us
   284 North Ave, Athens, GA 30601
Dawn Criss, Director

GENERAL HEALTH SERVICES

Health Dept **706.583.2772**
Fax 706.389.6897
Web ....www.health.state.ga.us/regional/clarke
   345 N Harris St, Athens, GA 30601
Lynn Beckman, HIV Coordinator

WIC Program **706.583.2859**
Fax 706.543.2034
E-mail ....vjmoody@dhr.state.ga.us
   186 paradise Blvd, Athens, GA 30607
Vicky Moody, Wic Coordinator/director Of Nutritional Services

JUSTICE AGENCY

CASA **706.613.1922**
Fax 706.316.3616
Web ....www.athensoconeecasa.org
E-mail ....info@athensoconeecasa.org
   693 N Pope St, Athens, GA 30601
Christian Orbello, Executive Director

POLICE AND SHERIFF

Sheriff's Dept **706.613.3250**
Fax 706.613.3255
   325 E Washington St, Ste 125, Athens, GA 30601
Ira Edwards Jr., Sheriff

EDUCATION SERVICES

Communities In Schools **706.369.9732**
Fax 706.353.3877
E-mail ....tjohnson@cisga.org
   240 Mitchell Bridge Road, Athens, GA 30603
Tim Johnson, Director

Early Head Start **706.227.7839**
Fax 706.357.5293
   440-2 Bearing Ext, Athens, GA 30606
Dr. Shelly Goodman, Director Of Early Learning

Exceptional Students **706.549.3030**
Fax 706.613.7142
   1250 Oglethorpe Ave, Athens, GA 30606
Najma Hunter, Director

North East Gerogia Resa **706.742.8292**
Fax 706.742.8928
E-mail ....dana.pass@negaresa.org
   375 Winter St, Winterville, GA 30683
Dana Pass, Director

Clay County

SOCIAL SERVICES

Georgia Div of Family & Children
Svcs **229.768.2511**
Fax 229.768.3265
   202 Wilson St, PO Box 189, Fort Gaines, GA 39851

GENERAL HEALTH SERVICES

Public Health Dept **229.768.2355**
Fax 229.768.3356
Web ....www.health.state.ga.us/regional/clay
E-mail ....saskew@dhr.state.ga.us
   147 Wilson St, Fort Gaines, GA 39851
Susan Askew, Nurse Manager

Clayton County

SOCIAL SERVICES

Georgia Div of Family & Children
Svcs **770.473.2300**
Fax 770.478.5948
   877 Battlecreek Rd, Jonesboro, GA 30236

GENERAL HEALTH SERVICES

Board Of Health **678.610.7199**
Fax 404.366.8735
Web ....www.dhr.state.ga.us
   1117 Battlecreek Rd, Jonesboro, GA 30236-2407
Sheralyn Chrisholm, Center Director

JUSTICE AGENCY

Clayton Regional Youth Detention
Ctr **770.473.2100**
Fax 770.473.2101
Web ....www.djj.state.ga.us
   11850 Hastings Bridge Rd, Lovejoy, GA 30250
Antonio Robinson, Director

COURTS

CASA **770.477.3268**
Fax 770.603.4113
Web ....www.claytoncasa.org
E-mail ....clayton.casa@co.clayton.ga.us
   121 S Mcdonough St, Courthouse Annex 3,
   Jonesboro, GA 30236-3651
Requel Stout, Program Assistant

Dept Of Juvenile Justice **770.473.2422**
Fax 770.473.2545
E-mail ....jajuanadewberry@djj.state.ga.us
   737 Veterans Pkwy, Ste 700, Jonesboro, GA 30238
Jajuana Dewberry, Program Manager

Juvenile Court **770.477.3270**
Fax 770.477.3255
Web ....www.co.clayton.ga.us
E-mail ....steven.teske@co.clayton.ga.us
   121 S McDonough St, Jonesboro, GA 30236
Steven Teske, Judge

POLICE AND SHERIFF

Police Dept **770.477.3747**
Fax 770.477.3745
Web ....www.co.clayton.ga.us
   7911 N Mcdonough St, Jonesboro, GA 30236
Gregory Porter, Chief

Sheriff's Ofc **770.471.1122**
Fax 678.479.5358
Web ....www.claytonsheriff.com
E-mail ....kem.kimbrough@co.clayton.ga.us
   9157 Tara Blvd, Jonesboro, GA 30236-4912
Kem Kimbrough, Sheriff

Clinch County

SOCIAL SERVICES

Georgia Div of Family & Children
Svcs **912.487.5263**
Fax 912.487.3599
   101 E Shirley Rd, PO Box 396, Homerville, GA 31634

GENERAL HEALTH SERVICES

Public Health Dept **912.487.2199**
Fax 912.487.3407
Web ....health.state.ga.us/regional/clinch
   285 Sweat St, Homerville, GA 31634-2301
Beth Jones, Rn, Nursing Supervisor

COURTS

Juvenile Court **912.487.2788**
Fax 912.487.3909
Web ....www.georgiacourts.org
   PO Box 316, Homerville, GA 31634-0316
Charles J Steedley, Judge

POLICE AND SHERIFF

Sheriff's Dept **912.487.5316**
Fax 912.487.3602
   115 Court Sq, Homerville, GA 31634
Winston C. Peterson, Sheriff

Cobb County

SOCIAL SERVICES

Georgia Div of Family & Children
Svcs **770.528.5000**
Fax 770.528.5154
   325 Fairground St SE, Marietta, GA 30060

GENERAL HEALTH SERVICES

Health Dept **770.514.2300**
Web ....www.dhr.state.ga.us
   1650 County Services Pkwy Sw, Marietta,
   GA 30008-4010
John Kennedy, Office Manager

JUSTICE AGENCY

CASA Program **770.528.2285**
Fax 770.528.2213
Web ....www.cobbcountycasa.org
E-mail ....carlene.redmond@cobbcounty.org
   1738 SW County Services Pkwy, Marietta,
   GA 30008-4012
Carlene Redmond, Program Coordinator

Marietta Regional Youth Detention
Ctr **770.528.4247**
Fax 770.528.4261
Web ....www.djj.state.ga.us
E-mail ....garymorris@djj.state.ga.us
   1575 County Services Pkwy SW, Marietta, GA 30008
Gary Morris, Director

COURTS

Juvenile Court **770.528.2220**
Fax 770.528.2214
   1738 County Services Pkwy SW, Marietta, GA 30008
Michelle Marchant-wellmon, Director

POLICE AND SHERIFF

Police Dept **770.499.3900**
E-mail ....watch@kenoshapolice.com
   140 N Marietta Pkwy NE, Marietta, GA 30060
John Houser, Police Chief

Sheriff's Ofc **770.499.4600**
Fax 770.499.4705
Web ....www.cobbsheriff.org
   185 Roswell St NE, Marietta, GA 30090-1931
Neil Warren, Sheriff

EDUCATION SERVICES

Communities In Schools **678.503.0901**
Fax 678.503.0902
Web ....www.cismcc.org
E-mail ....info@cismcc.org
   316 Alexander St SE Ste 5, Marietta, GA 30060-2001
Carrol Sey, Director

Georgia

Exceptional Students 770.432.2404
Fax 770.432.6105
Web ....www.glrs.org
E-mail ....donna.ryan@mresa.org
1870 Teasley Dr SE, Smyrna, GA 30080-2474
Donna Ryan, Director

Coffee County

SOCIAL SERVICES

Georgia Div of Family & Children

Svcs 912.389.4286
Fax 912.389.4419
1300 W Baker Hwy, PO Box 1119, Douglas,
GA 31534

GENERAL HEALTH SERVICES

Public Health Dept 912.389.4450
Fax 912.389.4326
Web ....www.sehdth.org
1111 Baker Hwy W, Douglas, GA 31533-2107
Patty Ellis, Nursing Supervisor

COURTS

Juvenile Court.............................912.389.4654
Fax 912.389.4667
212 Bryan St W, Douglas, GA 31533
Marlo A Ross, Judge

POLICE AND SHERIFF

Sheriff's Ofc 912.384.4227
Fax 912.260.2401
Web ....www.coffeesheriff.com
E-mail ....jpope@coffeesheriff.com
825 Thompson Dr, Douglas, GA 31535
Jerry Pope, Sheriff

Colquitt County

SOCIAL SERVICES

Georgia Div of Family & Children

Svcs 229.217.4000
Fax 229.217.4034
449 N Main St, PO Box 3008, Moultrie, GA 31776

GENERAL HEALTH SERVICES

Public Health Dept 229.891.7100
Fax 229.891.7106
Web ....www.health.state.ga.us/regional/colquitt
214 West Central Ave, Moultrie, GA 31768
Dana Reddick, Hiv Coordinator

COURTS

Juvenile Court.............................229.891.7250
Fax 229.891.7254
37 N Main St, Moultrie, GA 31768-3861
Honorable William M. Mcintosh, Judge

POLICE AND SHERIFF

Sheriff's Ofc 229.616.7430
Fax 229.616.7436
200 Veterans Parkway, Moultrie, GA 31776
Al Whittington, Sheriff

Columbia County

SOCIAL SERVICES

Family & Children Svcs 706.541.1640
Fax 706.541.0330
Web ....www.dhr.state.ga.us
E-mail ....jrichards@dhr.state.ga.us
6358 Columbia Rd, Appling, GA 30802
Judy Richards, Director

GENERAL HEALTH SERVICES

Public Health Dept 706.541.1318
Fax 706.541.0753
Web ....www.health.state.ga.us/regional/columbia
E-mail ....lbgraves@dhr.state.ga.us
6420 Pollards Pond Rd, Appling, GA 30802
Linda Graves, Nursing Manager

COURTS

Juvenile Court.............................706.868.3320
Fax 706.868.3325
E-mail ....jflanagan@columbiacountyga.gov
640 Ronald Reagan Dr, Evans, GA 30809-7603
Judge Douglas J. Flanagan, Director

POLICE AND SHERIFF

Sheriff's Ofc 706.541.1043
Fax 706.541.4059
E-mail ....cwhittle@columbiacountyso.org
2273 County Camp Road, Appling, GA 30802
Clay N. Whittle, Sheriff

Cook County

SOCIAL SERVICES

Family & Children Svcs 229.896.3672
Fax 229.896.7709
Web ....www.dhr.state.ga.us
1010 S Hutchinson Ave, Adel, GA 31620-5100
Karen Price, Supervisor

GENERAL HEALTH SERVICES

Health Dept 229.896.3030
Fax 229.896.4751
Web ....www.health.state.ga.us/regional/cook
204 N Parrish Ave, Adel, GA 31620
Velma Bennett, Nursing Supervisor

Coweta County

SOCIAL SERVICES

Georgia Div of Family & Children

Svcs 770.254.7234
Fax 770.254.7500
533 Hwy 29 N, Newnan, GA 30263

GENERAL HEALTH SERVICES

Public Health Dept 770.254.7400
Fax 770.254.7411
Web ....health.state.ga.us/regional/coweta
E-mail ....tadamson@dhr.state.ga.us
137 Jackson St, Newnan, GA 30263-1572
Tina Adamson, HIV Coordinator

JUSTICE AGENCY

Dept Of Juvenile Justice 770.254.7208
Fax 770.254.7286
E-mail ....jeanurrutia@djj.state.dj.us
78 Greenville St, Newnan, GA 30263
Jean Urrutia, Jpo

COURTS

Juvenile Court.............................770.254.3730
Fax 770.252.6413
Web ....www.coweta.ga.us
78 Greenville Street, Newnan, GA 30263
Honorable Joseph P. Macnabb, Judge

POLICE AND SHERIFF

Sheriff's Dept 770.253.1502
Fax 770.254.1043
E-mail ....ccso@coweta.ga.us
560 Greison Trl, Newnan, GA 30263
Michael S. Yeager, Sheriff

EDUCATION SERVICES

Communities In Schools 770.254.2737
Fax 770.254.2828
Web ....www.cowetaschools.org
E-mail ....bgarrison@cisga.org
55 Savannah Street, Newnan, GA 30263-2520
Bonnie Garrison, Director

Exceptional Students 229.546.4367
Fax 229.546.4167
Web ....www.glrs.org
E-mail ....cparker@cpressa.org
245 N Robinson St, Lenox, GA 31637-5137
Claudia Parker, Director

Crawford County

SOCIAL SERVICES

Georgia Div of Family & Children

Svcs 478.836.6030
Fax 478.836.6053
360 N Dugger Ave, PO Box 97, Roberta, GA 31078

POLICE AND SHERIFF

Sheriff's Ofc 478.836.3116
Fax 478.836.3232
21 Hortman Mill Rd, Knoxville, GA 31050
Lewis Walker, Sheriff

Crisp County

SOCIAL SERVICES

Georgia Div of Family & Children

Svcs 229.276.2349
Fax 229.276.2713
107 W 23rd Ave, PO Box 459, Cordele, GA 31010

GENERAL HEALTH SERVICES

Public Health Dept 229.276.2680
Fax 229.276.2683
Web ....health.state.ga.us/regional/crisp
E-mail ....cejenkins@dhr.state.ga.us
111 E 24th Ave, Cordele, GA 31015
Cynthia Jenkins, Nursing Supervisor

EDUCATION SERVICES

Communities In Schools 229.276.3430
Fax 229.276.3436
E-mail ....lsimpson@crisp.k12.ga.usc
2402 Frontage Rd, Cordele, GA 31015
Lisa Simpson, District Social Worker

Exceptional Students 229.273.5653
Fax 229.276.0720
Web www.crisp.k12.ga.us
E-mail ....mseay@crisp.k12.ga.us
PO Box 729, Cordele, GA 31010-0729
Marianne Seay, Director

Dade County

SOCIAL SERVICES

Georgia Div of Family & Children

Svcs 706.657.7511
Fax 706.657.5368
71 Case Ave, PO Box 159, Trenton, GA 30752

GENERAL HEALTH SERVICES

Public Health Dept 706.657.4213
Fax 706.657.7813
Web ....health.state.ga.us/regional/dade
E-mail ....tmfranklin@dhr.state.ga.us
71 Case Ave Ste 8100, Trenton, GA 30752
Tammy Franklin, Nursing Supervisor

POLICE AND SHERIFF

Dade Sheriff's Office **706.657.3233**
Fax 706.657.3825
E-mail ....sheriff@dadesheriff.com
   75 Case Ave, Trenton, GA 30752-2429
   Captain Danny Ellis, Patrol Supervisor

Dawson County

SOCIAL SERVICES

**Georgia Div of Family & Children
Svcs**..**706.265.6598**
Fax 706.265.2085
   424 Hwy 53, PO Box 867, Dawsonville, GA 30534

GENERAL HEALTH SERVICES

Health Dept.....................................**706.265.2611**
Fax 706.265.1636
Web ....health.state.ga.us/regional/dawson
   54 Highway 53 East, Dawsonville, GA 30534
   Nancy Baymiller, Nursing Supervisor

POLICE AND SHERIFF

Sheriff's Dept...............................**706.344.3535**
Fax 706.344.3537
   19 Tucker Ave, Dawsonville, GA 30534
   Billy G. Carlisle, Sheriff

Decatur County

SOCIAL SERVICES

Family & Children Svcs....................**229.248.2420**
Fax 229.248.3955
Web ....www.dhr.state.ga.us
E-mail ....jibridges@dhr.state.ga.us
   505 S Wheat Ave, Bainbridge, GA 39819-4355
   Jackie Bridges, Director

GENERAL HEALTH SERVICES

Public Health Dept.........................**229.248.3055**
Fax 229.248.2648
Web ....health.state.ga.us/regional/decatur
E-mail ....shutchins@dhr.state.ga.us
   928 S West St, Bainbridge, GA 39819
   Sherry Hutchins, Nursing Supervisor

COURTS

Juvenile Court **229.248.3025**
Fax 229.248.3029
   112 West Water Street, Bainbridge, GA 39818-0336
   Honorable Edwin J. Perry Lii, Juvenile Court Judge

POLICE AND SHERIFF

Sheriff's Ofc.................................**229.248.3044**
Fax 229.248.3850
   912 Spring Creek Rd Ste A, Bainbridge, GA 39817
   Wiley Griffin, Sheriff

DeKalb County

SOCIAL SERVICES

Family & Children Svcs....................**404.370.5000**
Fax 404.370.5499
Web ....www.co.dekalb.ga.us
E-mail ....wesolomon@dhr.state.ga.us
   178 Sams St, Decatur, GA 30030-4134
   Walker E Solomon Iii, Director

GENERAL HEALTH SERVICES

East Dekalb Health Ctr....................**770.484.2600**
Fax 770.484.0155
Web ....www.dekalbhealth.net
   2277 Stone Mountain Lithonia Rd, Lithonia,
   GA 30058
   Don Brundage, Acting Director

Kirkwood Health Ctr **404.370.7360**
Fax 404.730.7379
Web ....www.dekalbhealth.net
E-mail ....thedwards@dhr.state.ga.us
   30 Warren St NE, Atlanta, GA 30317
   Theresa Edwards, Clinical Coordinator

North Dekalb Health Ctr **770.454.1144**
Fax 678.530.3426
Web ....www.dekalbhealth.net
   3807 Clairmont Rd, Atlanta, GA 30341
   Yolanda Tapp, Director

**Richardson Health Ctr Refugee Health
Svcs**..**404.294.3818**
Fax 404.508.7844
Web ....www.dekalbhealth.net
   445 Winn Way, Decatur, GA 30030
   Sentayehu Bedane, Director

South Dekalb Health Ctr **404.244.2200**
Fax 404.638.0309
   3110 Clifton Springs Rd, Ste D Physical Health,
   Decatur, GA 30034
   Teresa Edwards, Clinic Coordinator

**T.O.Vinson Health Ctr Children's
Health** **404.508.7771**
Fax 404.294.3116
   440 Winn Way, Decatur, GA 30030
   Hannah Demeke, Nursing Coordinator

MENTAL HEALTH SERVICES

Clifton Springs MH **404.243.9500**
Fax 404.244.2224
   3110 Clifton Springs Rd Ste B, Decatur, GA 30030
   Monica Mcgannon Handma, Lsw, Director

JUSTICE AGENCY

CASA Program **404.378.0038**
Fax 404.373.2407
Web ....www.dekalbcasa.org
E-mail ....dekalbcasa@dekalbcasa.org
   4309 Memorial Drive, Decatur, GA 30032
   Tara Daniels, Director

Dekalb Multi Svc Ctr **404.327.6992**
Fax 404.327.6828
Web ....www.djj.state.ga.us
E-mail ....brucejohnson@djj.state.ga.us
   1833 Lawrenceville Hwy, Decatur, GA 30033-5728
   Bruce Johnson, Assistence Director

**Dekalb Regional Youth Detention
Ctr**...**404.244.2183**
Fax 404.244.5779
   2946 Clifton Springs Rd, Decatur, GA 30034
   Sonya Love, Director

Dept Of Juvenile Justice **404.327.6992**
Fax 404.327.6975
Web ....www.djj.state.ga.us
   1833 Lawrenceville Hwy, Decatur, GA 30033-5728
   A Rainer, District Administrator

COURTS

Juvenile Court.................................**404.294.2700**
Fax 404.294.2702
Web ....www.co.dekalb.ga.us
   4309 Memorial Dr, Decatur, GA 30032-1208
   Judge Desiree S. Peagler, Director

POLICE AND SHERIFF

Decatur Police Dept **404.373.6551**
Fax 404.370.4117
E-mail ....mikebooker@decaturga.com
   420 W Trinity Pl, Decatur, GA 20030
   Mike Booker, Chief

Police Dept Juvenile & Sex Crimes.............**770.724.7710**
Fax 770.724.7735
   1960 W Exchange Plave, Tucker, GA 30084
   Burrell Ellis, CEO

Sheriff's Dept **404.298.8145**
Fax 404.298.8101
E-mail ....tebrown@co.dekalb.ga.us
   4415 Memorial Dr, Decatur, GA 30032-1337
   Thomas E. Brown, Sheriff

Dodge County

SOCIAL SERVICES

**Georgia Div of Family & Children
Svcs**..**478.374.6760**
Fax 478.374.6764
   111 Plaza Ave, PO Box 4219, Eastman, GA 31023

GENERAL HEALTH SERVICES

Public Health Dept.........................**478.374.5576**
Fax 478.374.0234
Web ....www.health.state.ga.us/regional/dodge
E-mail ....tgriffin@dhr.state.ga.us
   1121 Plaza Ave, Eastman, GA 31023-6761
   Terri Griffin, Nursing Supervisor

JUSTICE AGENCY

**Eastman Regional Youth Detention
Ctr**...**478.374.6766**
Fax 478.374.6979
   181 Industrial Blvd, Eastman, GA 31023
   Heath Holloway, Assistant Director

Eastman Youth Development Ctr **478.374.6900**
Fax 478.374.6904
   176 Freaman Graham Blvd, Eastman, GA 31023
   George Smith, Director

COURTS

Superior Court - Oconee Circuit **478.374.2871**
Fax 478.374.3035
   5401 Anson Ave, Eastman, GA 31023
   Honorable Frederick Mullis Jr., Judge

POLICE AND SHERIFF

Sheriff's Dept **478.374.8131**
Fax 478.374.8153
E-mail ....dodgecoso@yahoo.com
   5401 Anson Ave Rm 111, Eastman, GA 31023
   Jeff Hinson, Sheriff

Dooly County

SOCIAL SERVICES

**Georgia Div of Family & Children
Svcs**..**229.268.4111**
Fax 229.268.1703
   1022 E Union St, PO Box 385, Vienna, GA 31092

GENERAL HEALTH SERVICES

Public Health Dept **229.268.4725**
Fax 229.268.1567
Web ....health.state.ga.us/regional/dooly
E-mail ....bgaston@dhr.state.ga.us
   204 W Union St, Vienna, GA 31092-1056
   Barbara Gaston, Rn, Nursing Supervisor

Dougherty County

SOCIAL SERVICES

Commission Social Svcs **229.431.2121**
Fax 229.438.3967
Web ....www.albany.ga.us
   222 Pine Avenue, Albany, GA 31702-5301
   Richard Crowdis, Administrator

GENERAL HEALTH SERVICES

Pulic Health Sw District 229.430.5140
Fax 229.430.5142
Web ....www.health.state.ga.us/regional/dougher ty
E-mail ....dcscott@health.state.ga.us
  1710 S Slappey Dr, Albany, GA 31706
Chanel Dixon, Hiv Coordinator

MENTAL HEALTH SERVICES

Albany Area Community Svc Board 229.430.4042
Fax 229.430.4047
Web ....www.albanycsb.org
E-mail ....fholt@albanycsb.org
  1120 W Broad Ave Ste B4, Albany, GA 31707
Kay Brooks, Executive Director

JUSTICE AGENCY

Dept Of Juvenile Justice 229.430.4238
Fax 229.430.4796
Web ....www.djj.state.ga.us
E-mail ....dianedouglas-harris@djj.state.ga.us
  1500 Gillionville Rd Ste A, Albany, GA 31707-3963
Diane Douglas Harris, District Director

COURTS

Juvenile Court 229.431.2162
Fax 229.434.2665
  225 Pine Avenue Court House, Albany, GA 31702
Honorable Herbie Solomon, Director

POLICE AND SHERIFF

Sheriff's Ofc 229.430.6500
Fax 229.430.6562
  1302 Evelyn Ave, Albany, GA 31702
Kevin Sproul, Sheriff

EDUCATION SERVICES

Even Start 229.888.2414
Fax 229.888.5016
  406 W Highland Ave, Albany, GA 31701-2803
Corrie W Schuette, Even Start Director

Georgia Learning Resource System 229.432.9151
Fax 229.435.1528
Web ....www.glrs.org/southwest
E-mail ....krigsby@glrs.org
  915 S McKinley St, Albany, GA 31701
Kathy Rigsby, Director

Douglas County

SOCIAL SERVICES

Family & Children Svcs 770.489.3000
Fax 770.947.7440
Web ....www.dhr.state.ga.us
  8473 Duralee Ln Ste 100, Douglasville,
  GA 30134-2416
Kay Campbell, Director

GENERAL HEALTH SERVICES

Health Dept 770.949.1970
Fax 770.942.9469
Web ....health.state.ga.us/regional/douglas
  6770 Selman Dr, Douglasville, GA 30134
Carla Ayers, Nursing Supervisor

MENTAL HEALTH SERVICES

Mental Health 770.949.8082
Fax 770.739.7190
Web ....www.cobbcsb.com
  680 Thornton Way, # A, Lithia Springs, GA 30122
Maurice Jones, Director

COURTS

Juvenile Court 770.920.7245
Fax 770.920.7380
E-mail ....pwalker@co.douglas.ga.us
  8700 Hospital Dr, Douglasville, GA 30134
Honorable Peggy H. Walker, Judge

POLICE AND SHERIFF

Sheriff's Dept 770.942.2121
Fax 770.920.7135
Web ....www.sheriff.douglas.ga.us
E-mail ....pmiller@sheriff.douglas.ga.us
  6840 Church St, Douglasville, GA 30134-1788
Phil D. Miller, Sheriff

EDUCATION SERVICES

Communities In Schools 770.651.2039
Fax 770.920.4588
E-mail ....mteal@cisga.org
  9030 Hwy 5, Douglasville, GA 30133
Mitzi Teal, Executive Director

Early County

SOCIAL SERVICES

Georgia Div of Family & Children
Svcs 229.724.2000
Fax 229.724.2005
  11860 Columbia St, PO Box 747, Blakely, GA 39823

GENERAL HEALTH SERVICES

Public Health Dept 229.723.3707
Fax 229.723.8246
Web ....health.state.ga.us/regional/early
E-mail ....award@dhr.state.ga.us
  618 Flowers Dr, Blakely, GA 39823-2804
Aleta Ward, Rn, Nursing Supervisor

MENTAL HEALTH SERVICES

Mental Health 229.724.2206
Fax 229.724.2052
Web ....www.albanycsb.org
  12799 Magnolia St, Blakely, GA 39823
Marian Reardoen, Director

Echois County

SOCIAL SERVICES

Georgia Div of Family & Children
Svcs 229.559.5751
Fax 229.559.6167
  106 Church of God St, Statenville, GA 31648

GENERAL HEALTH SERVICES

Public Health Dept 229.559.5103
Fax 229.559.7256
Web ....www.health.state.ga.us/regional/echols
E-mail ....rhrogers@dhr.state.ga.us
  149 Highway 94 E, Statenville, GA 31648
Rachel Rogers, Rn, Nursing Supervisor

COURTS

Superior Court-Southern Circuit 229.559.5642
Fax 229.559.5792
  110 Highway 94 E, Statenville, GA 31648
Harry Altman, Chief Judge

POLICE AND SHERIFF

Sheriff's Ofc 229.559.5603
Fax 229.559.5678
  109 General Deloch Street, Statenville, GA 31648
Randy Courson, Sheriff

Effingham County

SOCIAL SERVICES

Family & Children Svcs 912.754.6471
Fax 912.754.7638
Web ....www.dhr.state.ga.us
  204 Franklin St, Springfield, GA 31329
Dedra Smith, Director

GENERAL HEALTH SERVICES

Public Health Dept 912.754.6484
Fax 912.754.7623
E-mail ....amoorebarbara@dhr.state.ga.us
  802 Highway 119, South Springfield, GA 31329
Alice Moorebarbara, Nursing Supervisor

COURTS

Juvenile Court 912.754.6223
Fax 912.754.9706
E-mail ....williamwoodrum@djj.state.ga.us
  508 N Pine St, Springfield, GA 31329-4892
Honorable William Woodrum, Chief Judge

Elbert County

SOCIAL SERVICES

Georgia Div of Family & Children
Svcs 706.213.2001
Fax 706.213.2039
  45 Forest Ave, PO Box 1010, Elberton, GA 30635

GENERAL HEALTH SERVICES

Public Health Dept 706.283.3775
Fax 706.283.7155
Web ....health.state.ga.us/regional/elbert
E-mail ....elberthd@yahoo.com
  618 Jones St, Elberton, GA 30635
Tommie Mance, Nursing Supervisor

COURTS

Superior Court Northern Circuit 706.283.2046
Fax 706.213.2079
  45 Forest Ave, Elberton, GA 30635
John Bailey, Superior Court Judge

EDUCATION SERVICES

Communities In Schools 706.283.8838
Fax 706.283.8069
Web ....www.cisga.org
E-mail ....levans@cisga.org
  148 Collage Ave, Elberton, GA 30635-2294
Laura Evans, Director

Emanuel County

SOCIAL SERVICES

Family & Children Svcs 478.289.2400
Fax 478.289.2462
Web ....www.dhr.state.ga.us
E-mail ....kmartin@dhr.state.ga.us
  143 N Anderson Dr,, Swainsboro, GA 30401
Kathy Martin, Director

GENERAL HEALTH SERVICES

Public Health Dept 478.237.7501
Fax 478.289.2501
Web ....health.state.ga.us/regional/emanuel
E-mail ....lchester@dhr.state.ga.us
  50 Highway 56 N, Swainsboro, GA 30401
Lisa Chester, Rn, Nursing Supervisor

JUSTICE AGENCY

Dept Of Juvenile Justice 478.289.2590
Fax 478.289.2592
  101 N Main St, Fl 3, Swainsboro, GA 30401
Jeffrey Alligood, District Director

Evans County

SOCIAL SERVICES

Georgia Div of Family & Children
Svcs 912.739.1222
Fax 912.739.0284
  Courthouse Annex, PO Box 578, Claxton, GA 30417

GENERAL HEALTH SERVICES

Health Dept 912.739.2088
Fax 912.739.3975
Web ....www.health.state.ga.us/regional/evans
4 N Newton St, Claxton, GA 30417
Cindi Hart, Nurse Manager

JUSTICE AGENCY

Claxton Regional Youth Detention
Ctr 912.739.4807
Fax 912.739.7932
Web ....www.djj.state.ga.us
E-mail ....sheiladease@djj.state.ga.us
3609 Bill Hodges Rd, Claxton, GA 30417-6235
Sheila Dease, Director

COURTS

Superior Court-Atlantic Circuit 912.739.3868
Fax 912.739.2504
123 W Main St, Claxton, GA 30417
Kathy Hendix, Clerk Of Court

EDUCATION SERVICES

Exceptional Students 912.739.8888
Fax 912.739.0888
Web ....www.frontiernet.net
E-mail ....jkelley@frontiernet.net
720 Church St, Claxton, GA 30417-5952
Judi Kelley, Director

Head Start 912.739.4576
Fax 912.739.8414
720 Church St, Claxton, GA 30417
Linda Kicklighter, Director

Fannin County

SOCIAL SERVICES

Georgia Div of Family & Children
Svcs 706.632.2296
Fax 706.632.3521
990 E Main St, Ste 10, Blue Ridge, GA 30513

GENERAL HEALTH SERVICES

Health Dept 706.632.3023
Fax 706.632.5257
95 Ouida St, Blue Ridge, GA 30513
Freda Williamson, Rn, Nursing Supervisor

POLICE AND SHERIFF

Sheriff's Ofc 706.632.2044
Fax 706.258.5237
645 W First St, Blue Ridge, GA 30513-7110
Dan Kirby, Sheriff

EDUCATION SERVICES

Head Start-Pre K 706.374.6250
Fax 706.374.5509
8731 Lakewood Hwy, Mineral Bluff, GA 30559
Liz Dobson, Center Director

Fayette County

SOCIAL SERVICES

Family & Children Svcs 770.460.2555
Fax 770.460.2464
Web ....www.dhr.state.ga.us
E-mail ....mhdav@dhr.state.ga.us
905 Highway 85 S, Fayetteville, GA 30215-2005
Ms S Boggs, Director

COURTS

Juvenile Court 770.716.4210
Fax 770.716.4852
1 Center Dr, Fayetteville, GA 30214
Karen Calloway, Associate Judge

POLICE AND SHERIFF

Sheriff's Ofc 770.461.6353
Fax 770.716.4870
E-mail ....whannah@fayettevillega.org
155 Johnson Ave, Fayetteville, GA 30214
Wayne Hannah, Sheriff

Floyd County

SOCIAL SERVICES

Georgia Div of Family & Children
Svcs 706.295.6500
Fax 706.295.6718
450 Riverside Pkwy Ste 110, PO Box 193, Rome, GA 30162

GENERAL HEALTH SERVICES

Health Dept 706.295.6123
Fax 706.802.5141
Web ....www.health.state.ga.us/regional/floyd
16 E 12th St SW, Rome, GA 30161
Pat Townley, Rn, County Nurse Manager

JUSTICE AGENCY

Bob Richards Regional Youth Detention
Ctr 706.295.6035
Fax 706.802.5222
Web ....www.state.ga.us
E-mail ....gailwise@djj.state.ga.us
200 maobay ave, Rome, GA 30165-2397
Gail Wise, Director

CASA 706.235.2272
Fax 706.235.7511
Web ....www.nwga-cac.org
E-mail ....floydgacasa@earthlink.net
PO Box 5143, Rome, GA 30162-5143
Sue Lagermann, Director

Dept Of Juvenile Justice 706.295.6256
Fax 706.295.6740
E-mail ....margaretcawood@djj.state.ga.us
512 Riverside Pkwy NE Ste 500, Rome, GA 30161
Margaret Cawood, Regional Administrator

COURTS

Juvenile Court 706.291.5180
Fax 706.291.5247
E-mail ....papet@floydcountyga.org
3 Government Plz Ste 202, Rome, GA 30161-2836
Honorable Timothy A. Pape, Director

POLICE AND SHERIFF

Sheriff's Dept 706.291.4111
Fax 706.236.2473
2526 New Calhoun Hwy NE, Rome, GA 30161
Tim Burkhalter, Sheriff

Forsyth County

SOCIAL SERVICES

Family & Children Svcs 770.781.6700
Fax 770.781.6742
E-mail ....jtwilson1@dhr.state.ga.us
426 Canton Road, Cummings, GA 30040
John Wilson, Director

GENERAL HEALTH SERVICES

Public Health Dept 770.781.6900
Fax 770.781.6929
Web ....health.state.ga.us/regional/forsyth
E-mail ....nbaymiller@dhr.state.ga.us
428 Canton Highway, Cumming, GA 30040
Nancy Baymiller, Nursing Supervisor

JUSTICE AGENCY

CASA Inc 770.886.4082
Fax 678.648.9486
Web ....www.forsythcountycasa.org
E-mail ....jwalden@forsythco.com
875 Lanier 400 Pkwy, Ste 7, Cumming, GA 30040
Jennet Walden, Director

COURTS

Juvenile Court 770.781.3099
Fax 770.781.3089
Web ....www.forsythco.com
875 Lanier 400 Pkwy, Ste 100, Cumming, GA 30040
Judge J Russell Jackson, Judge

POLICE AND SHERIFF

Sheriff's Ofc 770.781.3077
Fax 770.781.3049
Web ....www.co.forsyth.ga.us
E-mail ....twpaxton@co.forsyth.ga.us
202 Veterans Memorial Blvd, Cumming, GA 30040-2646
Ted Paxton, Sheriff

Franklin County

SOCIAL SERVICES

Georgia Div of Family & Children
Svcs 706.384.4521
Fax 706.384.3212
1133 Hull St, PO Box 279, Carnesville, GA 30521

GENERAL HEALTH SERVICES

Public Health Dept 706.384.5575
Fax 706.384.4217
Web ....www.health.state.ga.us/regional/frankiln
E-mail ....phwindsor@dhr.state.ga.us
6955 Hwy 145 S, Carnesville, GA 30521
Pat Windsor, Rn, Nursing Supervisor

Fulton County

SOCIAL SERVICES

Bright from the Start Georgia 404.656.5957
Fax 404.651.7184
2 Martin Luther King Jr Drive SE, East tower, Ste 754, Atlanta, GA 30334
Bobby Cagle, Commissioner

Southwest Svc Ctr 404.699.4337
515 Fairburn Rd SW, Atlanta, GA 30331
Machel Harris, Economic Support Director

MENTAL HEALTH SERVICES

Center for Health & Rahabilitation 404.730.1650
Fax 404.332.0455
Web ....www.fultoncounty.ga.gov
265 Boulevard NE, Atlanta, GA 30312-1284
Renee Lee Ferguson, Manager

Metro Regional MHDDAD Board 770.414.3052
Fax 770.414.3048
Web ....www.dhr.state.ga.us
E-mail ....trpullum@dhr.state.ga.us
100 Crescent Parkway, Ste. 900, Tucker, GA 30084
Renee Pullum, Administrative Assistant

Northside Behavioral Health Ctr 404.851.8950
Fax 678.320.0383
Web ....www.northside.com
1140 Hammond Dr NE Ste J1075, Atlanta, GA 30328-5558
Cindy Blount, Director

South Fulton MHC 404.762.4042
Fax 404.332.0400
Web ....www.myfultoncountyga.gov
E-mail ....julia.foster-batth@fultoncountyga.gov
1636 Connally Dr, EAST POINT, GA 30344-2558
Julia Foster-Batth, Director

JUSTICE AGENCY

Atlanta Male Transitional Ctr **404.206.5103**
Fax...404.206.5133
  332 Ponce De Leon Ave NE, Atlanta, GA 30308
Stanley Arrington, Superintendent

Juvenile Justice Region LII Ofc **404.559.4227**
Fax...404.669.2957
E-mail ....prebenheidemann@djj.state.ga.us
  1513 E Cleveland Ave, Ste 100A, East Point,
  GA 30344
Tim Suddreth, District Director

Metro Regional Youth Detention
Ctr **404.635.4400**
Fax...404.635.4410
  1300 Constitution Rd SE, Atlanta, GA 30316
Debbie Alexander, Director

COURTS

Georgia Council Of Juvenile Court
Judges **404.657.5020**
Fax...404.657.5038
Web ....www.mindspring.com
E-mail ....ejjohn@mindspring.com
  230 Peachtree St NW, Ste 1625, Atlanta,
  GA 30303-1533
Eric John, Executive Director

EDUCATION SERVICES

Atlanta Area School For The Deaf **404.296.7101**
Fax...404.299.4485
  890 N Indian Creek Dr, Clarkston, GA 30021
Kenneth Moore, Education Director

Chattahoochee YMCA Head Start
Academy **404.792.2740**
Fax...404.794.9086
  2751 Peyton Rd NW, Atlanta, GA 30318
Spring Mcbryde, Director

Communities In Schools Of Atlanta,
Inc. **404.897.2390**
Fax...404.877.1938
Web ....www.cisatlanta.org
E-mail ....ppflum@cisga.org
  600 W Peachtree St NW Ste 1250, Atlanta,
  GA 30308-3627
Patti Pflum, Executive Director

Exceptional Students **404.656.3963**
Fax...404.651.6457
Web ....www.gadoe.org
E-mail ....sboe@k12.state.ga.us
  1870 Twin Towers E, Atlanta, GA 30334-9048
Deborah Gay, Director Of Special Education

Gilmer County

SOCIAL SERVICES

Family & Children Svcs **706.635.2361**
Fax...706.276.2367
Web ....www.dhr.state.ga.us
E-mail ....info@dhr.state.ga.us
  54 Kiker St, Ellijay, GA 30540-3700
Jennifer Brogden, Director

POLICE AND SHERIFF

Sheriff's Ofc **706.635.5775**
Fax...706.635.4172
  1 Broad St Ste 103, Ellijay, GA 30540
Stacy Nicholson, Sheriff

EDUCATION SERVICES

Exceptional Students **706.276.1111**
Fax...706.276.1108
Web ....www.northcentralglrs.org
E-mail ....pamglasgow@ellijay.com
  4731 Old Highway 5 S, Ellijay, GA 30540-7447
Pam Glasgow, Director

Glascock County

SOCIAL SERVICES

Georgia Div of Family & Children
Svcs **706.598.2955**
Fax...706.598.2540
  674 W Main St, PO Box 225, Gibson, GA 30810

GENERAL HEALTH SERVICES

Public Health Dept **706.598.2061**
Fax...706.598.2442
Web ....health.state.ga.us/regional/glascock
E-mail ....njlord@gdph.state.ga.us
  658 West Main Street, Gibson, GA 30810
Nona Lord, Rn, Nursing Supervisor

COURTS

Juvenile Court **706.598.2084**
Fax...706.598.2577
  62 E Main St, Gibson, GA 30810
Thomas B Hammond, Judge

Glynn County

SOCIAL SERVICES

Georgia Div of Family & Children
Svcs **912.262.3200**
Fax...912.262.3056
  4420 Altama Ave Ste 9, PO Box 400, Brunswick,
  GA 31521

GENERAL HEALTH SERVICES

Health Dept **912.264.3961**
Fax...912.265.8837
Web ....www.health.state.ga.us
  2747 4th St, Brunswick, GA 31520
Judy Norman, Admin Operations Coord

JUSTICE AGENCY

Casa Glynn **912.264.4448**
Fax...912.264.4451
Web ....www.gacasa.org
E-mail ....casaglynn@bellsouth.net
  1615 Reyonolds St, Brunswick, GA 31520
Cary Greenfield, Director

Dept Of Juvenile Justice **912.264.7313**
Fax...912.264.7239
Web ....www.djj.state.ga.us
  1513 Gloucester St, Brunswick, GA 31520-7144
Carla Mathis, Program Manager

Juvenile Justice Region V Ofc **912.638.5629**
Fax...912.638.9357
Web ....www.djj.state.ga.us
  221 Mallery St Ste A, Saint Simons Island,
  GA 31522-4720
Adam Kennedy, Regional Administrator

COURTS

Juvenile Court **912.554.7039**
Fax...912.267.5629
  11 Judicial Ln Ste 150, Brunswick, GA 31520
Jill Caldwell, Director Of Juvenile Court Svcs

POLICE AND SHERIFF

Sheriff's Ofc **912.554.7600**
Fax...912.554.7681
Web ....www.glynncounty.org
E-mail ....sheriff@glynncounty.org
  1812 Newcastle St, Brunswick, GA 31520-6409
Wayne V. Bennett, Sheriff

Gordon County

SOCIAL SERVICES

Georgia Div of Family & Children
Svcs **706.624.1200**
Fax...706.624.1206
  639 OOthcalooga St PO Box 217, Calhoun,
  GA 30703

GENERAL HEALTH SERVICES

Public Health Dept **706.624.1444**
Fax...706.624.1450
Web ....health.state.ga.us/regional/gordon
E-mail ....tkirby@dhr.state.ga.us
  310 N River St NW, Calhoun, GA 30701-9408
Tim Kirby, Hiv Coordinator

COURTS

Juvenile Court **706.629.4561**
Fax...706.602.8187
E-mail ....jbearden@gordoncounty.org
  100 Court St, Calhoun, GA 30701
Honorable J. Lane Bearden, Director

Grady County

SOCIAL SERVICES

Georgia Div of Family & Children
Svcs **229.377.3154**
Fax...229.377.9157
  250 2nd Ave SE, PO Box 269, Cairo, GA 39828

GENERAL HEALTH SERVICES

Public Health Dept **229.377.2992**
Fax...229.377.4544
Web ....www.dhr.state.ga.us
E-mail ....pconnell@dhr.state.ga.us
  1030 4th St SE, Cairo, GA 39828-3000
Peggy Connell, Nursing Supervisor

COURTS

Superior Court South Georgia
Circuit **229.377.7349**
Fax...229.378.1032
  250 N Broad St, Cairo, GA 39828
Honorable Jonathan Kevin Chason, Judge

POLICE AND SHERIFF

Sheriff's Ofc **229.377.5200**
Fax...229.377.1339
E-mail ....gradysheriff@gmail.com
  115 16th Ave NE, Cairo, GA 39828
Harry Young, Sheriff

Greene County

SOCIAL SERVICES

Georgia Div of Family & Children
Svcs **706.453.2365**
Fax...706.453.5132
  1951 S Main St, PO Box 460, Greensboro, GA 30642

GENERAL HEALTH SERVICES

Public Health Dept **706.453.7561**
Fax...706.453.9120
Web ....health.state.ga.us/regional/greene
E-mail ....lainsley@dhr.state.ga.us
  1031 Apalachee Road, Greensboro, GA 30642
Leah Ainsley, Nursing Supervisor

POLICE AND SHERIFF

Sheriff's Dept **706.453.3351**
Fax...706.453.3352
Web ....www.greenecountyga.gov
E-mail ....chouston@greenecountyga.gov
  1201 Industrial Blvd, Greensboro, GA 30642-2758
Chris Houston, Sheriff

Gwinnett County

SOCIAL SERVICES

Georgia Div of Family & Children

Svcs **678.518.5500**

Fax 678.518.5505

    1 Justice Squart, 446 W Crogan St, Lawrenceville, GA 30045

GENERAL HEALTH SERVICES

Health Dept Buford Health Ctr **770.614.2401**

Fax 770.614.2449

Web ....www.health.state.ga.us/regional/gwinnett

    2755 Sawnee Ave, Buford, GA 30518-2560

Linda Davis, Nursing Supervisor

Health Dept Lawrenceville Health

Ctr **770.339.4283**

Fax 770.339.2338

Web ....www.emhd.com

    455 Grayson Hwy Ste 300, Lawrenceville, GA 30045

Coco Davis, Nurse Manager

JUSTICE AGENCY

Detention Ctr **770.619.6500**

Fax 770.822.3115

Web ....www.gwinnett.county.com

E-mail ....conwaybu@www.co.gwinnett.ga.us

    2900 University Pkwy, Lawrenceville, GA 30043-4588

R.l.""butch"" Conway, Sheriff

Gwinnett Regional Youth Detention

Ctr **770.995.6921**

Fax 770.339.2341

Web ....www.djj.state.ga.us

    650 Hi Hope Ln, Lawrenceville, GA 30043-4581

Edward Boyd, Director

Juvenile Justice **770.339.5362**

Fax 770.339.5398

Web ....www.djj.state.ga.us

E-mail ....sandradeaton@djj.state.ga.us

    650 Gwinnett Dr, Ste 212, Lawrenceville, GA 30046

Sandra Deaton, Director Federal Programs

COURTS

Juvenile Court **770.619.6300**

Fax 770.619.6093

    115 Stone Mountain St, Lawrenceville, GA 30046

Honorable Robert V. Rodatus, Judge

POLICE AND SHERIFF

Duluth Police Dept **770.476.4151**

Fax 770.623.2782

Web ....www.duluth-ga.com

E-mail ....rbelcher@duluth-ga.com

    3276 Buford Hwy, Duluth, GA 30096-3577

Randall Belcher, Police Chief

Police Dept **770.513.5000**

Fax 770.513.5005

    770 Hi Hope Rd, Lawrenceville, GA 30043

Charles Walters, Chief Of Police

Habersham County

SOCIAL SERVICES

Child & Family Svcs **706.754.2148**

    1045 Grant St, Clarkesville, GA 30523

GENERAL HEALTH SERVICES

Public Health Dept **706.778.7156**

Fax 706.776.7694

Web .....www.health.state.ga.us/regional/habersh am

E-mail ....nengesser@dhr.state.ga.us

    185 Scoggins Dr, Demorest, GA 30535

Norma Engesser, Rn, Nursing Supervisor

COURTS

Juvenile Court **706.754.6308**

Fax 706.754.0047

    555 Monroe St Ste 68, Clarkesville, GA 30523-7816

Judge Robert Cullifer, Judge

Superior Court Judicial Mountain

Circuit **706.754.6274**

Fax 706.754.4722

    555 Monroe St, Clarkesville, GA 30523

Linton K. Crawford Jr., Judge

POLICE AND SHERIFF

Sheriff's Ofc **706.754.6666**

Fax 706.754.1932

E-mail ....hcso@alltel.net

    1000 Detention Dr, Clarkesville, GA 30523

Joey Terrell, Sheriff

Hall County

SOCIAL SERVICES

Georgia Div of Family & Children

Svcs **770.532.5298**

Fax 770.535.6967

    970 McEver Rd Ext, Gainesville, GA 30504

JUSTICE AGENCY

Dept Of Juvenile Justice Field Ofc **770.535.5495**

Fax 770.535.5837

Web ....www.djjstate.ga.us

    869 Rainey St, Gainesville, GA 30501

Gary Sullivan, Jpm

Gainesville Regional Youth Detention

Ctr **770.535.5465**

Fax 770.535.6968

Web ....www.djj.state.ga.us

E-mail ....garypayne@djj.state.ga.us

    450 Crescent Dr, Gainesville, GA 30501-5079

Gary Payne, Director

COURTS

Juvenile Court **770.531.6927**

Fax 770.531.6930

Web ....www.hallcounty.org

E-mail ....mcarden@hallcounty.org

    225 Green St SE, Gainesville, GA 30501

Honorable Mary R. Carden, Judge

EDUCATION SERVICES

Exceptional Students **770.532.9981**

Fax 770.532.6386

Web ....www.pioneerresa.org

E-mail ....alpineprogram@pioneerresa.org

    715 Woodmill Rd, Gainesville, GA 30501

Pam Kirkpatrick, Director

Hancock County

SOCIAL SERVICES

Family & Children Svcs **706.444.1203**

Fax 706.444.1207

Web ....www.dhr.state.ga.us

E-mail ....mjosie@dhr.state.ga.us

    12744 Broad St, Sparta, GA 31087

Myra Josie, Director

GENERAL HEALTH SERVICES

Public Health Dept **706.444.6616**

Fax 706.444.5647

Web ....health.state.ga.us/regional/hancock

    516 Boland St, Sparta, GA 31087

Sherley Tucker, Nursing Supervisor

POLICE AND SHERIFF

Sheriff's Dept **706.444.6471**

Fax 706.444.1279

    67 Spring St, Sparta, GA 31087

Tomyln T. Primus, Sheriff

Haralson County

SOCIAL SERVICES

Georgia Div of Family & Children

Svcs **770.646.3885**

Fax 770.646.9373

    21 Magnolia St, PO Box 324, Buchanan, GA 30113

GENERAL HEALTH SERVICES

Public Health Dept **770.646.5541**

Fax 770.646.8193

Web ....www.health.state.ga.us/regional/haralson

E-mail ....jdguice@dhr.state.ga.us

    133 Buchanan Bypass, Buchanan, GA 30113

Joyce Guice, Rn, Nursing Supervisor

COURTS

Superior Court-Clerk Tallapoosa

Circuit **770.646.2005**

Fax 770.646.8827

    4485 GA Hwy 120, Buchanan, GA 30113

Beckie Robinson, Superior Clerk

Harris County

SOCIAL SERVICES

Family & Children Svcs **706.628.4226**

Fax 706.628.5392

Web ....www.dhr.state.ga.us

    134 N College St, Hamilton, GA 31811

Deborah Cobb, Director

GENERAL HEALTH SERVICES

Public Health Dept **706.628.5037**

Fax 706.628.7196

Web ....health.state.ga.us/regional/harris

    210 Forrest Hill Dr, Hamilton, GA 31811

Kerri Medders, Rn, Nursing Supervisor

COURTS

Superior Court **706.628.4944**

Fax 706.628.7039

    102 N College St, Hamilton, GA 31811

Stacy Haralson, Chief Clerk

Hart County

SOCIAL SERVICES

Georgia Div of Family & Children

Svcs **706.856.2740**

Fax 706.856.2792

    267 E Johnson St, PO Box 518, Hartwell, GA 30643

GENERAL HEALTH SERVICES

Public Health **706.376.5117**

Fax 706.376.5011

Web ....health.state.ga.us/regional/hart

    64 Reynolds St, Hartwell, GA 30643-1315

Rhonda Dyar, Rn, Nursing Supervisor

COURTS

Juvenile Court **706.856.2666**

Fax 706.376.9107

E-mail ....nesmithlawworks@yahoo.com

    130 E Howell St, Hartwell, GA 30643-1894

Christopher Nesmith, Judge

Superior Ct-Northern Circuit 706.376.7189
Fax 706.376.1277
Web ....www.hartcountyga.org
E-mail ....thomashodges@hartcountyga.org
185 W. Franklin St. Rm1 Courthouse Annex, Hartwell, GA 30643
Honorable Thomas L. Hodges, Judge

EDUCATION SERVICES

Communities In Schools 706.376.7449
Fax 706.376.5102
Web ....www.cishart.org
E-mail ....hartpartners@yahoo.com
110 Benson St, Hartwell, GA 30643-1992
Patricia Werner, Director

Head Start-Pre K 706.356.3546
Fax 706.356.1516
84 Hartwell Rd, Lavonia, GA 30553
Sally Turpin, Director

Heard County

SOCIAL SERVICES

**Southern Crescent Agency On
Aging 706.675.6721**
Fax 706.675.0448
Web ....www.scaaa.net
E-mail ....jyshirley@threeriversrc.com
13273 Georgia Hwy 34 E, Franklin, GA 30217
Joy Shirley, Director

GENERAL HEALTH SERVICES

Public Health Dept 706.675.3456
Fax 706.675.6795
Web ....www.health.state.ga.us/regional/heard
7699 US Highway 27, Franklin, GA 30217
Angie Nutt, Nursing Supervisor

EDUCATION SERVICES

Franklin Head Start Ctr 706.675.0303
740 Old Field Rd, Franklin, GA 30217-4724
Elaine Wolfe, Director

Henry County

SOCIAL SERVICES

**Geogia Div of Family & Children
Svcs 770.954.2014**
Fax 770.954.2329
125 Henry Pkwy, McDonough, GA 30253

COURTS

Juvenile Court 770.288.6866
Fax 770.288.6878
44 John Frank Ward Blvd, One Judicial Center, Mcdonough, GA 30253
Patti Johnson, Judge

POLICE AND SHERIFF

Sheriff's Ofc 770.954.2200
Fax 770.288.7094
Web ....www.co.henry.ga.us
E-mail ....dchaffin@co.henry.ga.us
120 Henry Pkwy, Mcdonough, GA 30253-6696
Donald Chaffin, Sheriff

Houston County

SOCIAL SERVICES

**Georgia Div of Family & Children
Svcs 478.988.7600**
Fax 478.988.7617
92 Cohen Walker Dr, Warner Robins, GA 31088

GENERAL HEALTH SERVICES

Public Health Dept 478.218.2000
Fax 478.218.2017
Web ....www.northcentralhealthdistrict.com
98 Cohen Walker Dr, Warner Robins, GA 31088
Christina Sikes, Nurse Manager

JUSTICE AGENCY

CASA 478.396.2185
Fax 478.922.4279
Web ....www.casaofhoustoncounty.org
E-mail ....hccasa@alltel.net
206 Carl Vinson Pkwy, Houston County Juvenile Justice Complex, Warner Robins, GA 31088-5832
Terry Di Diego, Program Coordinator

COURTS

Juvenile Court 478.542.2060
Fax 478.922.4279
Web ....www.houstoncountyga.org
E-mail ....dedwards@houstoncountyga.org
206 Carl Vinson Pkwy, Warner Robins, GA 31088-5832
Honorable Deborah Edwards, Judge

POLICE AND SHERIFF

Sheriff's Ofc 478.542.2080
Fax 478.328.1544
E-mail ....slane@houstoncountyga.org
202 Carl Vinson Pkwy Ste A, Warner Robins, GA 31088
Cullen Talton Jr., Sheriff

EDUCATION SERVICES

Communities In Schools 478.929.5464
Fax 478.929.5427
Web ....www.vhc-cishc.org
E-mail ....info@vhc-cishc.org
2841 Moody Rd, Bonaire, GA 31005
Bobbie Mooris, Director

Ctrville Head Start 478.923.2244
Fax 478.923.2244
1009 Carl Vinson Pkwy, Centerville, GA 31028-1341
Johnnie C Green, Director

Elberta Head Start 478.929.4677
Fax 478.929.4677
Web ....www.acf.hhs.gov
708 Elberta Rd, Warner Robins, GA 31093-1734
Virginia Hilburn, Director

Irwin County

SOCIAL SERVICES

**Georgia Div of Family & Children
Svcs 229.468.2150**
Fax 229.568.2177
108 N Irwin Ave, Ocilla, GA 31774

GENERAL HEALTH SERVICES

Public Health Dept 229.468.5003
Fax 229.468.5028
Web ....www.health.state.ga.us/regional/irwin
407 West 4th St, Ocilla, GA 31774
Rhonda Nixon, Rn, Nursing Supervisor

POLICE AND SHERIFF

Sheriff's Dept 229.468.7459
Fax 229.468.7534
Web ....www.surfsouth.com
E-mail ....irso@surfsouth.com
400 S Irwin Ave, Ocilla, GA 31774-2007
Donnie Youghn, Sheriff

Jackson County

SOCIAL SERVICES

**Georgia Div of Family & Children
Svcs 706.367.3000**
Fax 706.367.3044
456 Athens St, PO Box 526, Jefferson, GA 30549

POLICE AND SHERIFF

Sheriff's Ofc 706.367.6000
Fax 706.367.6034
Web ....www.jacksoncountygov.com
E-mail ....sevans@jacksoncountygov.com
268 Curtis H Spence Dr, Jefferson, GA 30549
Stan Evans, Sheriff

Jasper County

SOCIAL SERVICES

**Georgia Div of Family & Children
Svcs 706.468.6461**
Fax 706.468.1338
226 Funderburg Dr, Monticello, GA 31064

GENERAL HEALTH SERVICES

Public Health Dept 706.468.6850
Fax 706.468.1422
Web ....health.state.ga.us/regional/jasper
E-mail ....scook@gdph.state.ga.us
336 E Greene St, Monticello, GA 31064-1012
Leigh Dover, Nursing Supervisor

POLICE AND SHERIFF

Sheriff's Ofc 706.468.4912
Fax 706.468.4918
E-mail ....croper@jaspercosheriff.com
1551 Hwy 212 West, Monticello, GA 31064
Charles Roper, Sheriff

Jeff Davis County

SOCIAL SERVICES

**Georgia Div of Family & Children
Svcs 912.375.3942**
Fax 912.375.7997
40 E Sycamore St, PO Box 706, Hazlehurst, GA 31539

GENERAL HEALTH SERVICES

Public Health Dept 912.375.2425
Fax 912.375.3845
Web ....www.health.state.ga.us
30 East Sycamore Street, Hazlehurst, GA 31539
Patricia Allis, Nursing Supervisor

COURTS

Juvenile Court 912.375.6615
Fax 912.375.6637
14 Jeff Davis St, Hazlehurst, GA 31539
Honorable Ken W. Smith, Judge

Jefferson County

SOCIAL SERVICES

**Georgia Div of Family & Children
Svcs 478.625.7259**
Fax 478.625.7984
2459 US Hwy 1 N, PO Box 570, Louisville, GA 30434

GENERAL HEALTH SERVICES

Public Health Dept 478.625.3716
Fax 478.625.8201
2501 US Hwy 1 N, Louisville, GA 30434
Janet Pilcher, Rn, Nursing Supervisor

COURTS

Juvenile Court..........................**478.625.3391**
Fax...478.625.9638
112 US Highway 1 Byp N, Louisville, GA 30434
Sherry Mcdonald, Judge

POLICE AND SHERIFF

Sheriff's Ofc..............................**478.625.7538**
Fax...478.625.1441
Web.............................www.jeffersoncountysheriff.us
E-mail................chutchins@jeffersoncountysheriff.us
911 Clarks Mill Rd, Louisville, GA 30434
Charles G. Hutchins, Sheriff

Jenkins County

SOCIAL SERVICES

Family & Children Svcs.................**478.982.1944**
Fax...478.982.2985
Web..................................www.dhr.state.ga.us
618 S Gray St, Millen, GA 30442-5249
Kathy Perry, Director

GENERAL HEALTH SERVICES

Health Dept.............................**478.982.2811**
Fax...478.982.1589
Web................www.health.state.ga.us/regional/jenkins
E-mail..............................pwdrake@gdph.state.ga.us
709 Virginia Avenue, Millen, GA 30442
Pamela Drake, Rn, Clinic Director

EDUCATION SERVICES

Communities In Schools.................**478.982.8004**
Fax...478.982.8222
Web....................................www.jcfec.org
E-mail..................................jcfec@bellsouth.net
527 Barney Ave, Millen, GA 30442
Mandy Underwood, Director

Johnson County

SOCIAL SERVICES

Georgia Div of Family & Children
Svcs......................................**478.864.4210**
Fax...478.864.4214
729 W Court St, PO Box 500, Wrightsville, GA 31096

GENERAL HEALTH SERVICES

Public Health Dept......................**478.864.3542**
Fax...478.864.1777
Web..............health.state.ga.us/regional/johnson
E-mail.............................atanner@dhr.state.ga.us
82 Hilton Holton, Wrightsville, GA 31096
Amelia Tanner, Nursing Supervisor

Jones County

SOCIAL SERVICES

Georgia Div of Family & Children
Svcs......................................**478.986.3126**
Fax...478.986.3127
141 James St, PO Drawer 1689, Gray, GA 31032

GENERAL HEALTH SERVICES

Public Health Dept......................**478.986.3164**
Fax...478.986.3339
Web.................www.health.state.ga.us/regional/jones
E-mail.............................lmharrell@chr.state.ga.us
114 Forest st, Gray, GA 31032
Linda Harreal, Office Manager

Lanier County

SOCIAL SERVICES

Georgia Div of Family & Children
Svcs......................................**229.482.3686**
Fax...229.482.2334
313 Roquemore Cir, Lakeland, GA 31635

GENERAL HEALTH SERVICES

Public Health Dept......................**229.482.3294**
Fax...229.482.2006
Web..............www.health.state.ga.us/regional/lanier
E-mail.............................pturner@dhr.state.ga.us
205 W Murrell Ave, Lakeland, GA 31635-2103
Pat Turner, RN, Nursing Supervisor

Laurens County

SOCIAL SERVICES

Georgia Div of Family & Children
Svcs......................................**478.275.6533**
Fax...478.275.6700
904 Claxton Dairy Rd, PO Box 68, Dublin, GA 31040

GENERAL HEALTH SERVICES

Health Dept.............................**478.275.6545**
Fax...478.275.6575
Web..............health.state.ga.us/regional/laurens
2121 Bellevue Rd Ste B, Dublin, GA 31021
Donna Forth, Rn, Nursing Supervisor

MENTAL HEALTH SERVICES

Community Svcs Board Of Middle
Georgia...................................**478.272.1190**
Fax...478.275.6509
Web...................................www.csbmg.com
E-mail.............................pthomas@csbmg.com
2121A Bellevue Rd Bldg 7, Dublin, GA 31021-9040
Patsy Thomas, Ed.d, Director

JUSTICE AGENCY

CASA......................................**478.275.8100**
Fax...478.275.8130
Web..................................www.tlccasa.org
E-mail.............................tlccasa@bellsouth.net
1347 N Jefferson St, Dublin, GA 31021
Sherri Howard, Executive Director

Dept Of Juvenile Justice................**478.275.6580**
Fax...478.274.7899
100 Corporate Sq Ste B, Dublin, GA 31021
Jeff Alligood, District Director

COURTS

Juvenile Court..........................**478.272.8623**
Fax...478.272.8617
Web..................................www.dlcga.com
E-mail.......................judgetribble@bellsouth.net
101 N Jefferson St, Dublin, GA 31021-6198
Honorable William L. Tribble, Director

POLICE AND SHERIFF

Sheriff's Ofc..............................**478.272.1522**
Fax...478.277.2913
E-mail..............................harrellb@dlcga.com
511 Southern Pines Rd, Dublin, GA 31021
Bill Harrell, Sheriff

EDUCATION SERVICES

Communities In Schools.................**478.274.0394**
Fax...478.274.0394
Web...................................www.cisga.org
E-mail.................................jcurtis@cisga.org
300 N Elm St, Dublin, GA 31021-4800
Jackie Curtis, Director

Lee County

SOCIAL SERVICES

Georgia Div of Family & Children
Svcs......................................**229.759.3000**
Fax...229.759.3004
121 4th St, PO Box 145, Leesburg, GA 31763

GENERAL HEALTH SERVICES

Public Health Dept......................**229.759.3014**
Fax...229.759.3017
Web.........................health.state.ga.us/regional/lee
E-mail.............................dmhager@gdph.state.ga.us
112 Park Street, Leesburg, GA 31763
Dana Hager, Nursing Manager

COURTS

Dept Of Juvenile Justice................**229.759.3010**
Fax...229.759.3168
Web...................................www.djj.state.ga.us
E-mail.............................gordonfisher@djj.state.ga.us
100 Leslie Hwy, Leesburg, GA 31763-4340
Judge Lisa Jones, Director

Liberty County

SOCIAL SERVICES

Family & Children Svcs.................**912.370.2555**
Fax...912.370.2525
Web................................www.thejobsite.org
E-mail.............................dbennett@dhr.state.ga.us
508 N Main St, Hinesville, GA 31313-2512
Deborah Bennett, Director

GENERAL HEALTH SERVICES

Public Health Dept......................**912.876.2173**
Fax...912.368.8033
Web...................................www.gachd.org
1113 E Oglethorpe Hwy, Hinesville, GA 31313
Annette Nu, Hiv Program Manager

JUSTICE AGENCY

CASA......................................**912.876.3816**
Fax...912.876.3726
E-mail.............................atlanticcasa@coastalnow.net
118 E Mlk Dr, Hinesville, GA 31310
Irene Mccall, Director

COURTS

Juvenile Court..........................**912.876.0111**
Fax...912.368.2979
Web...................................www.jojlaw.net
E Court St, Hinesville, GA 31313
Judge Linnie Darden Lii, Judge

Superior Court Atlantic Circuit............**912.368.2250**
Fax...912.368.6622
100 S Main St # 2, Hinesville, GA 31313
Honorable David L. Cavender, Director

POLICE AND SHERIFF

Sheriff's Ofc..............................**912.876.2131**
Fax...912.876.2179
Web..............................www.libertycountyga.com
E-mail.............................sheriff@libertycountyga.com
201 S Main St Ste 1500, Hinesville, GA 31310
Steve Sikis, Sheriff

EDUCATION SERVICES

Exceptional Students....................**912.877.2088**
Fax...912.877.2089
Web...............................www.coastalglrs.org
208 Shipman Ave, Hinesville, GA 31313-2419
Jan Schrum, Director

Lincoln County

SOCIAL SERVICES

Georgia Div of Family & Children
Svcs......................................**706.359.3135**
Fax...706.359.6000
171 N Peachtree St, PO Box 220, Lincolnton, GA 30817

GENERAL HEALTH SERVICES

Public Health Dept **706.359.3154**
Fax 706.359.1939
Web ....www.health.state.ga.us/regional/lincoln
176 North Peachtree, Lincolnton, GA 30817
Brenda Goolsby, Nursing Supervisor

COURTS

Juvenile Court **706.359.5544**
Fax 706.359.5027
E-mail ....bhammond@lincolncountyga.com
210 Humphrey St, Lincolnton, GA 30817
Honorable Thomas B. Hammond, Judge

Long County

SOCIAL SERVICES

Georgia Div of Family & Children
Svcs **912.545.2177**
Fax 912.545.9769
59 N Macon Dr, PO Box 369, Ludowici, GA 31316

GENERAL HEALTH SERVICES

Public Health Dept **912.545.2107**
Fax 912.545.2112
Web ....health.state.ga.us/regional/long
E-mail ....krowell@dhr.state.ga.us
584 N Macon, Ludowici, GA 31316
Kathy Rowell, Rn, Nursing Manager

COURTS

Superior Court-Atlantic Circuit **912.545.2123**
Fax 912.545.2020
E-mail ....frank.middleton@dor.ga.gov
49 McDonald St, Ludowici, GA 31316
Frank S. Middleton, Clerk Of Court

POLICE AND SHERIFF

Sheriff's Ofc **912.545.2118**
Fax 912.545.2120
E-mail ....longso@alltel.net
6 E Academy St, Ludowici, GA 31316
Cecil Nobles, Sheriff

Lowndes County

SOCIAL SERVICES

Georgia Div of Family & Children
Svcs **229.333.5200**
Fax 229.333.7027
206 S Patterson St, PO Box 5166, Valdosta,
GA 31603

COURTS

Juvenile Court **229.333.5252**
Fax 229.333.5272
Web ....www.djj.state.ga.us
2809 N Ashley St, Valdosta, GA 31602-5711
Honorable O. Wayne Ellerbee, Judge

Lumpkin County

SOCIAL SERVICES

Georgia Div of Family & Children
Svcs **706.864.1980**
Fax 706.864.1651
175 Tipton Dr, Dahlonega, GA 30533

GENERAL HEALTH SERVICES

Public Health Dept **706.867.2727**
Fax 706.867.2739
Web www.phdistrict2.org
E-mail ....whbryant@dhr.state.ga.us
60 Mechanicsville Rd, Dahlonega, GA 30533-0543
Wanda Bryant, Rn, Nursing Supervisor

POLICE AND SHERIFF

Sheriff's Ofc **706.864.0414**
Fax 706.864.1032
385 E Main St, Dahlonega, GA 30533
Stacy Jarrard, Sheriff

Marion County

SOCIAL SERVICES

Georgia Div of Family & Children
Svcs **229.649.2311**
Fax 229.649.2428
111 Baker St, .PO Box 473, Buena Vista, GA 31803

GENERAL HEALTH SERVICES

Public Health Dept **229.649.5664**
Fax 229.649.2025
Web ....www.health.state.ga.us/regional/marion
111 N Baker St, Buena Vista, GA 31803
Renee Barrett, Rn, Nursing Supervisor

COURTS

Juvenile Court **229.649.7321**
Fax 229.649.7931
100 Broad St., BuenaVista, GA 31803
Joy Smith, Clerk

McDuffie County

SOCIAL SERVICES

Family & Children Services **706.595.2946**
Fax 706.597.8525
E-mail ....melukich@dhr.state.ga.us
307 Greenway St, Thomson, GA 30824-2721
Mary Beth Lukich, County Director

Georgia Div of Family & Children
Svcs **706.595.2946**
Fax 706.597.8525
307 Greenway St, PO Box 507, Thomson, GA 30824

GENERAL HEALTH SERVICES

Public Health Dept **706.595.1740**
Fax 706.595.8503
Web ....www.health.state.ga.us/regional/mcduffie
E-mail ....klinebarger@dhr.state.ga.us
307 Greenway St, Thomson, GA 30824
Kathy Linebarger, Nursing Supervisor

COURTS

Superior Court- Toombs Circuit **706.595.2126**
Fax 706.595.8930
210 Railroad St, Thomson, GA 30824
Honorable Roger W. Dunaway Jr., Judge

EDUCATION SERVICES

Communities In Schools **706.595.3112**
Fax 706.595.3113
Web ....www.cisga.org
E-mail ....msmith@cisga.org
1119 White Oak Rd, Thomson, GA 30824
Miriam Smith, Executive Director

McIntosh County

SOCIAL SERVICES

Georgia Div of Family & Children
Svcs **912.437.4193**
Fax 912.437.4170
1221 N Way, PO Box 1139, Darien, GA 31305

COURTS

Superior Court Atlantic Circuit **912.437.6641**
Fax 912.437.6673
310 Northway St Ste 100, Darien, GA 31305
Sandra W Bootie-Goodrich, Clerk

Meriwether County

SOCIAL SERVICES

Georgia Div of Family & Children
Svcs **706.672.4244**
Fax 706.674.4342
17234 Roosevelt Hwy, Greenville, GA 30222

GENERAL HEALTH SERVICES

Public Health Dept **706.672.4974**
Fax 706.672.1065
51 Gay Connector, Greenville, GA 30222
Connie Walton, CEO

JUSTICE AGENCY

Dept Of Juvenile Justice **706.846.3117**
Fax 706.846.2375
52 E Main St, Manchester, GA 31816
Wade Moore, District Director

POLICE AND SHERIFF

Sheriff's Ofc **706.672.4489**
Fax 706.672.1560
Web ....www.meriwethercountysheriff.org
E-mail ....contactus@meriwethercountysheriff.org
17400 Roosevelt Hwy, Greenville, GA 30222
Steve Whitlock, Sheriff

Miller County

SOCIAL SERVICES

Family & Children Svcs **229.758.3387**
Fax 229.758.5084
Web ....www.dhr.state.ga.us
E-mail ....jard1@dhr.state.ga.us
69 Thompson Town Rd, Colquitt, GA 39837-5204
James Ard, Director

GENERAL HEALTH SERVICES

Public Health Dept **229.758.3344**
Fax 229.758.5526
Web ....www.health.state.ga.us/regional/miller
250 W Pine St, Colquitt, GA 39837
Alida Ward, Rn, Nursing Supervisor

COURTS

Juvenile Court **229.758.5575**
Fax 229.758.3038
E-mail ....rhrentz@bellsouth.net
PO Box 217, Colquitt, GA 39837-0217
Honorable Ronald H. Rentz, Director

Mitchell County

SOCIAL SERVICES

Family & Children Svcs **229.522.3500**
Fax 229.522.3561
Web ....www.dhr.state.ga.us
E-mail ....tsmithen@dhr.state.ga.us
90 W Oakland Ave, Camilla, GA 31730-1254
Scott Mithen, Acting Director

GENERAL HEALTH SERVICES

Public Health Dept **229.336.2055**
Fax 229.336.1100
Web ....www.health.state.ga.us/regional/mitchell
88 W Oakland Ave, Camilla, GA 31730
Lisa Jenkins, Nursing Supervisor

Monroe County

SOCIAL SERVICES

Georgia Div of Family & Children
Svcs **478.993.3030**
Fax 478.993.3035
107 Martin Luther King Jr Dr, PO Box 734, Forsyth,
GA 31029

GENERAL HEALTH SERVICES

Public Health Dept **478.992.5082**
Fax 478.992.5085
Web .... health.state.ga.us/regional/monroe
E-mail .... jfreeman@dhr.state.ga.us
  106 Martin Luther King Jr Dr, Forsyth, GA 31029
  Janet Freeman, Nursing Manager

JUSTICE AGENCY

**Burrus Correctional Training Ctr and Inmate Boot
Camp** **478.994.7511**
Fax 478.994.7561
Web .... www.middlegatech.edu
  1000 Indian Springs Drive, Forsyth, GA 31029
  Carl Humphrey, Warden

POLICE AND SHERIFF

Sheriff's Ofc **478.994.7287**
Fax 478.993.3071
E-mail .... carekb@forsythcable.com
  36 Langston Avenue, Forsyth, GA 31029
  Lt. K B Ayer, Director

Montgomery County

SOCIAL SERVICES

**Georgia Div of Family & Children
Svcs** **912.583.3722**
Fax 912.583.3739
  103 E Spring St, PO Box 217, Mount Vernon,
  GA 30445

GENERAL HEALTH SERVICES

Public Health Dept **912.583.4602**
Fax 912.583.4085
Web .... health.state.ga.us/regional/montgomery
  218 West Broad Street, Mount Vernon, GA 30445
  Daisy Hainds, Nursing Supervisor

POLICE AND SHERIFF

Sheriff's Ofc **912.583.2521**
Fax 912.583.4701
Web .... www.floridalandlaw.com
E-mail .... ces@floridalandlaw.com
  208 Broad St, Mount Vernon, GA 30445
  Clarence E. Sanders, Sheriff

Murray County

SOCIAL SERVICES

**Georgia Div of Family & Children
Svcs** **706.695.7315**
Fax 706.695.7541
  830 G I Maddox Pkwy, PO Box 1014, Chatsworth,
  GA 30705

GENERAL HEALTH SERVICES

Public Health Dept **706.695.4585**
Fax 706.695.4587
Web .... health.state.ga.us/regional/murray
E-mail .... ljackson@dhr.state.ga.us
  709 Old Dalton Ellijay Rd, Chatsworth,
  GA 30705-2099
  Linda Jackson, Nursing Supervisor

COURTS

Juvenile Court **706.695.5828**
Fax 706.517.8713
E-mail .... mwalker11@windstream.net
  124 N 3rd Ave, Chatsworth, GA 30705
  Mary Walker, Administrator

Muscogee County

SOCIAL SERVICES

**Georgia Div of Family & Children
Svcs** **706.649.7311**
Fax 706.649.1342
  2100 Comer Ave, PO Box 2627, Columbus,
  GA 31902

GENERAL HEALTH SERVICES

Health Dept **706.321.6300**
Fax 706.321.6126
Web .... health.state.ga.us/regional/muscogee
  2100 Comer Ave, Columbus, GA 31904-8725
  Sister Judy Jones, Case Manager

JUSTICE AGENCY

**Columbus Regional Youth Detention
Ctr** **706.565.4374**
Fax 706.565.3595
Web .... www.djj.state.ga.us
E-mail .... frankrodriquez@djj.state.ga.us
  7700 Chattsworth Rd, Midland, GA 31820-4022
  Shasta Thomas, Director

POLICE AND SHERIFF

Sheriff's Ofc **706.653.4225**
Fax 706.653.4234
  100 10th St, Columbus, GA 31902
  John Darr, Sheriff

EDUCATION SERVICES

Woodall Programme **706.748.3166**
Fax 706.748.3171
  4312 Harrison Ave, Columbus, GA 31904
  Geraldine Middleton, Director

Newton County

SOCIAL SERVICES

**Georgia Div of Family & Children
Svcs** **770.784.2490**
Fax 706.784.2479
  4117 Mill St, PO Box 1588, Covington, GA 30015

GENERAL HEALTH SERVICES

Public Health Dept **770.786.9086**
Fax 770.786.0715
E-mail .... julianna.schell@gnrhealth.com
  8203 Hazelbrand Rd NE, Covington, GA 30014-1510
  Julianna Schell, Nursing Supervisor

JUSTICE AGENCY

Alcovy CASA Program **770.385.7450**
Fax 770.385.7448
E-mail .... alcovycasa2@aol.com
  1094B Access Rd, Covington, GA 30014
  Jim Killman, Executive Director

COURTS

Juvenile Court **770.784.2060**
Fax 770.784.2065
Web .... www.ncboc.com
E-mail .... kraines@co.newton.ga.us
  1132 Usher St NW Ste 119, Covington,
  GA 30014-2411
  Honorable Sheri Roberts, Court Judge

POLICE AND SHERIFF

Sheriff's Ofc **678.625.1400**
Fax 678.625.1473
Web .... www.co.newton.ga.us
E-mail .... ibrown@co.newton.ga.us
  15151 Alcovy-Jersey Road, NE, Convington,
  GA 30014
  Isa Brown, Sheriff

Oconee County

SOCIAL SERVICES

**Georgia Div of Family & Children
Svcs** **706.310.2260**
Fax 706.769.8684
  1400 Greensboro Hwy, Watkinsville, GA 30677

COURTS

Juvenile Court **706.769.3940**
Fax 706.769.3948
Web .... www.oconee.ga.us
E-mail .... smcarthur@oconee.ga.us
  23 N. Main St, Watkinsville, GA 30677
  Honorable Sara M. Mcarthur, Juvenile Officer

Oglethorpe County

SOCIAL SERVICES

**Georgia Div of Family & Children
Svcs** **706.743.8152**
Fax 706.743.3019
  231 Union Point St, PO Box 160, Lexington,
  GA 30648

POLICE AND SHERIFF

Sheriff's Ofc **706.743.8102**
Fax 706.743.3969
  115 Buddyfaust rd, Crawford, GA 30630
  Mike Smith, Sheriff

Paulding County

SOCIAL SERVICES

**Georgia Div of Family & Children
Svcs** **770.443.7810**
Fax 770.443.7820
  1387 Industrial Blvd N, PO Box 168, Dallas,
  GA 30132

GENERAL HEALTH SERVICES

Public Health Dept **770.443.7881**
Fax 770.443.7885
Web .... www.health.state.ga.us/regional/paulding
  451 Jimmy Campbell Pkwy, Dallas, GA 30157
  Teresa Knight, Rn, Nursing Supervisor

JUSTICE AGENCY

**Paulding Regional Youth Detention
Ctr** **770.443.1166**
Fax 770.443.1206
Web .... www.djj.state.ga.us
E-mail .... beverlywestbrooks@djj.state.ga.us
  538 Industrial Blvd N, Dallas, GA 30132-8353
  Beverly Westbrooks, Director

COURTS

Juvenile Court **770.443.7532**
Fax 770.443.2029
  280 Constitution Blvd Rm 2106, Dallas, GA 30132
  Sandra Miller, Judge

POLICE AND SHERIFF

Sheriff's Ofc **770.443.3010**
Fax 770.443.3014
Web .... www.paulding.gov
  247 Industrial Way N, Dallas, GA 30132
  Gary Gulledge, Sheriff

Peach County

SOCIAL SERVICES

**Georgia Div of Family & Children
Svcs** **478.825.6428**
Fax 478.825.6693
  700 Spruce St Wing E, PO Box 976, Fort Valley,
  GA 31030

GENERAL HEALTH SERVICES

Public Health Dept **478.825.6939**
Fax 478.825.6792
406 East Church St, Fort Valley, GA 31034
Bertha Ashley, Rn, Nursing Supervisor

COURTS

Superior Court Macon Circuit **478.825.5331**
Fax 478.825.8662
Web ....www.peachcounty.net
E-mail ....joe.wilder@gsccca.org
205 W Church St Ste 120, Fort Valley,
GA 31030-3762
Joe Wilder, Clerk Of Court

EDUCATION SERVICES

Glrs **478.475.8630**
Fax 478.475.8623
Web ....www.mgresa.org
100 College Station Dr, Macon, GA 31206-5100
Carolyn H. Williams, Executive Director

Pickens County

SOCIAL SERVICES

Georgia Div of Family & Children
Svcs **706.692.4701**
Fax 706.692.4700
255 Chambers St, Jasper, GA 30143

GENERAL HEALTH SERVICES

Public Health Dept **706.253.2821**
Fax 706.253.5863
Web ....www.health.state.ga.us/regional/pickens
E-mail ....ssingleton@dhr.state.ga.us
60 Health Way, Jasper, GA 30143-1912
Sandy Singleton, Nursing Supervisor

JUSTICE AGENCY

CASA **706.276.2272**
Fax 706.276.2274
E-mail ....casa@ellijay.com
1 Broad St Ste 201, Ellijay, GA 30540
Diane Scoggins, Executive Director

COURTS

Juvenile Court **706.253.8763**
Fax 706.253.8825
52 N Main St Ste 102, Jasper, GA 30143
Gail Brown, Clerk Of Superior Court

POLICE AND SHERIFF

Sheriff's Ofc **706.253.8900**
Fax 706.253.8930
E-mail ....sheriffpickens@tds.net
2985 Camp Rd Ste 100, Jasper, GA 30143-7718
Donald Craig, Sheriff

Pierce County

SOCIAL SERVICES

Georgia Div of Family & Children
Svcs **912.449.6624**
Fax 912.449.8165
621 Hendry St, PO Box 620, Blackshear, GA 31516

GENERAL HEALTH SERVICES

Public Health Dept **912.449.2032**
Fax 912.449.0409
Web ....www.health.state.ga.us/regional/pierce
E-mail ....lthornton@dhr.state.ga.us
715 Ware St, Blackshear, GA 31516-1723
Lauren Thornton Rn, Nursing Supervisor

COURTS

Superior Court Waycross Circuit **912.449.2020**
Fax 912.449.2106
E-mail ....thomas.sauls@gsccca.org
3550 Highway 84 W, Blackshear, GA 31516
Thomas Sauls, Clerk Of Court

Pike County

SOCIAL SERVICES

Family & Children Svcs **770.567.8427**
Fax 770.567.0784
Web ....www.dhr.state.ga.us
E-mail ....laprice@dhr.state.ga.us
7165 US Hwy 19, Zebulon, GA 30295
Laresa Price, Director

GENERAL HEALTH SERVICES

Public Health Dept **770.567.8972**
Fax 770.567.3531
Web ....health.state.ga.us/regional/pike
E-mail ....dslaugher@dhr.state.ga.us
541 Griffen St, Zebulon, GA 30295
Deidra Slaugher, Nursing Director

COURTS

Juvenile Court **770.567.1784**
Fax 770.567.0581
7820 US Hwy 19, Ste A, Zebulon, GA 30295
Ben Miller Jr., Judge

Polk County

SOCIAL SERVICES

Georgia Div of Family & Children
Svcs **770.749.2232**
Fax 770.749.2262
100 County Loop Rd, PO Box 147, Cedartown,
GA 30125

GENERAL HEALTH SERVICES

Health Dept **770.684.1385**
Fax 770.684.8231
320 Water St, Rockmart, GA 30153-2669
Amanda Loveless, Nursing Supervisor

Public Health Dept **770.749.2270**
Fax 770.749.2298
Web ....www.health.state.ga.us/regional/polk
125 E Ware St, Cedartown, GA 30125
Melinda Ailey, Rn, Nursing Supervisor

COURTS

Juvenile Court **770.749.6723**
Fax 770.749.6729
223 S College st, Cedartown, GA 30125
Rob Monroe, Judge

Superior Courtù Tallapoosa Circuit **770.749.2114**
Fax 770.749.2148
100 Prior St, St 106 Court House No 1, Cedartown,
GA 30125
Judge Richard Sutton, Judge

POLICE AND SHERIFF

Sheriff's Ofc **770.749.2900**
Fax 770.749.2926
1676 Rockmart Hwy, Cedartown, GA 30125
Carolyn Floyd, Sheriff Assistant

Pulaski County

SOCIAL SERVICES

Family & Children Svcs **478.783.6191**
Fax 478.783.6195
Web ....www.dhr.state.ga.us
180 Broad St, Hawkinsville, GA 31036-4716
Lynn Ball, Director

GENERAL HEALTH SERVICES

Public Health Dept **478.783.1361**
Fax 478.892.8362
Web ....www.health.state.ga.us
81 N Lumpkin St, Hawkinsville, GA 31036
Wanda Moore, Nursing Supervisor

Putnam County

SOCIAL SERVICES

Georgia Div of Family & Children
Svcs **706.485.4921**
Fax 706.485.0073
675 Godfrey Hwy, PO Box 3670, Eatonton,
GA 31024

GENERAL HEALTH SERVICES

Public Health Dept **706.485.8591**
Fax 706.485.2018
Web ....www.health.state.ga.us/regional/putnam
E-mail ....chgreen@health.state.ga.us
103 No. Washington Ave, Eatonton, GA 31024
Charolette Green, Rn, Nursing Supervisor

MENTAL HEALTH SERVICES

Dept Of Public Health **478.836.3167**
Fax 478.836.2629
141 Mccray St, Roberta, GA 31078
Mellisa Smith, Nurse Manager

Quitman County

SOCIAL SERVICES

Georgia Div of Family & Children
Svcs **229.334.2427**
Fax 229.334.5606
Main St, PO Box 68, Georgetown, GA 39854

GENERAL HEALTH SERVICES

Public Health Dept **229.334.3697**
Fax 229.334.4389
Web ....health.state.ga.us/regional/quitman
E-mail ....ggary@thecolumbuslibrary.org
105 Main St, Georgetown, GA 39854
Gayle Gary, Rn, Nursing Supervisor

Rabun County

SOCIAL SERVICES

Georgia Div of Family & Children
Svcs **706.782.4283**
Fax 706.782.6193
Hiawasee St, PO Box 787, Clayton, GA 30525

GENERAL HEALTH SERVICES

Public Health Dept **706.212.0289**
Fax 706.212.0296
Web ....health.state.ga.us/regional/rabun
184 S Main Street, Clayton, GA 30525
Connee Martin, Nursing Supervisor

Randolph County

SOCIAL SERVICES

Georgia Div of Family & Children
Svcs **229.732.3742**
Fax 229.732.5412
311 N Webster St, Cuthbert, GA 39840

GENERAL HEALTH SERVICES

Public Health Dept **229.732.2414**
Fax 229.732.5007
Web ....www.health.state.ga.us
E-mail ....dyelverton@dhr.state.ga.us
207 N Webster St, Cuthbert, GA 39840-2506
Donna Yelverton, Nursing Supervisor

Richmond County

SOCIAL SERVICES

Child & Family Svcs **706.721.3000**
520 Fenwick St, Augusta, GA 30903

GENERAL HEALTH SERVICES

District Health Dept **706.667.4326**
Fax 706.667.4365
Web ....www.ecphd.com
1916 N Leg Rd, Augusta, GA 30909
John Nolan, Deputy Director

Health Dept **706.721.5800**
Fax 706.721.5903
Web ....www.health.state.ga.us/regional/richmond
E-mail ....cpbryant@dhr.state.ga.us
950 Laney Walker Blvd, Augusta, GA 30901
Carol Bryant, Clinical Nursing Director

JUSTICE AGENCY

Augusta Regional Youth Detention
Ctr **706.771.4875**
Fax 706.771.4917
Web ....www.djj.state.ga.us
E-mail ....patricksimmons@djj.state.ga.us
3485 Mike Padgett Hwy, Augusta, GA 30906
Patrick Simmons, Director

Augusta Youth Development
Campus **706.792.7500**
Fax 706.792.7507
Web ....www.djj.state.ga.us
E-mail ....jonbrady@djj.state.ga.us
3481 Mike Padgett Hwy, Augusta, GA 30906-3815
Jon Brady, Director

Dept Of Juvenile Justice **706.721.5678**
Fax 706.721.5696
Web ....www.djj.state.ga.us
E-mail ....wendellsmith@djj.state.ga.us
971 Broad St, Augusta, GA 30901-7214
Wendell Smith, Juvenile Program Manager

COURTS

Juvenile Court **706.821.1185**
Fax 706.821.1196
E-mail ....ballen@augustaga.gov
971 Droad St 2nd Floor Ste B, Augusta,
GA 30901-5800
Honorable Benjamin Allen, Director

Superior Court Augusta Circuit **706.821.2357**
Fax 706.821.4208
530 Greene St Rm 503, Augusta, GA 30901-4455
Honorable James G. Blanchard, Director

POLICE AND SHERIFF

Sheriff's Ofc **706.821.1065**
Fax 706.821.1064
E-mail ....bmims@augustaga.gov
401 Walton Way Rm B245, Augusta, GA 30901-5836
Ronald Strength, Sheriff

Rockdale County

SOCIAL SERVICES

Family & Children Svcs **770.388.5025**
Fax 770.785.6828
Web ....www.dhr.state.ga.us
975 Taylor St SW, Conyers, GA 30012-5357
Cindy Norton, CPS Supervisor

JUSTICE AGENCY

CASA **770.761.0202**
Fax 770.761.7765
Web ....www.rockdalecasa.com
E-mail ....rockdalecasa@aol.com
999 Green St SE, Conyers, GA 30012
Lynn Wetzel, Executive Director

COURTS

Juvenile Court **770.278.7777**
Fax 770.388.5035
922 Court St NE, Conyers, GA 30012
Honorable William Schneider, Judge

POLICE AND SHERIFF

Sheriff's Ofc **770.278.8000**
Fax 770.785.2494
Web ....www.rockdalecounty.org
E-mail ....jeffwigington@rockdalecounty.org
911 Chambers Dr NW, Conyers, GA 30012-3401
Jeff Wigington, Sheriff

Schley County

SOCIAL SERVICES

Family & Children Svcs **229.937.2591**
Fax 229.937.5641
Web ....www.dhr.state.ga.us
45 W Oglethorpe St, Ellaville, GA 31806
Debroah Smith, Director

GENERAL HEALTH SERVICES

Public Health Dept **229.937.2208**
Fax 229.937.5089
Web ....www.health.state.ga.us/regional/schley
45 W Oglethorpe St, Ellaville, GA 31806
Vicki Wilder, Rn, Nursing Supervisor

EDUCATION SERVICES

Exceptional Students **229.937.5341**
Fax 229.937.5754
Web ....www.cfresa.org
121 E College St, Ellaville, GA 31806
Dr. Emily A. Collins, Coordinator Of Special Education & School Psychology

Screven County

SOCIAL SERVICES

Family & Children Svcs **912.564.2041**
Fax 912.564.9372
Web ....www.dhr.state.ga.us
E-mail ....atherrington@dhr.state.ga.us
110 Singleton Ave, Sylvania, GA 30467
Anna Herrington, Director

GENERAL HEALTH SERVICES

Public Health Dept **912.564.2182**
Fax 912.564.7887
Web ....health.state.ga.us/regional/screven
416 Pine St, Sylvania, GA 30467
Margaret Hollingsworth, Rncs, Nursing Supervisor

COURTS

Juvenile Court **912.564.2913**
Fax 912.564.7941
Web ....www.djj.state.ga.us
E-mail ....johnturner@djj.state.ga.us
107 N Main St, Sylvania, GA 30467-1818
Judge John R. Turner, Judge

EDUCATION SERVICES

Communities In Schools **912.564.1160**
Fax 912.564.9392
Web ....www.cisga.org
E-mail ....wwarren@cisga.org
205 Mims Rd, Sylvania, GA 30467-1994
Ramona Scewark, Director

Seminole County

SOCIAL SERVICES

Georgia Div of Family & Children
Svcs **229.524.2365**
Fax 229.524.6632
108 W 4th St, Donalsonville, GA 39845

GENERAL HEALTH SERVICES

Public Health Dept **229.524.2577**
Fax 229.524.8986
Web ....www.health.state.ga.us/regional/seminole
E-mail ....brownd@darton.edu
904 N Wiley Ave, Donalsonville, GA 39845-1127
Dottie Brown, Rn, Nursing Supervisor

Spalding County

SOCIAL SERVICES

Georgia Div of Family & Children
Svcs **770.504.2200**
Fax 770.504.2204
178 Earnest Biles Dr, Jackson, GA 30223

Georgia Div of Family & Children
Svcs **770.228.1386**
Fax 770.412.4702
411 E Solomon St, PO Box 1610, Griffin, GA 30223

GENERAL HEALTH SERVICES

Health Dept **770.467.4740**
Fax 770.229.3169
Web ....www.health.state.ga.us/regional/spalding
E-mail ....cktidwell@gdph.state.ga.us
1007 Memorial Dr, Griffin, GA 30224-4445
Cynthia Tidwell, Rn, Nursing Supervisor

MENTAL HEALTH SERVICES

Mcintosh Trail Community Svcs Board
(Admin.) **770.358.5252**
Fax 770.229.3223
Web ....www.mctrail.org
E-mail ....pmccollum@mctrail.org
1501A Kalamazoo Dr, Griffin, GA 30224
Pam Mccollum, Executive Director

COURTS

Juvenile Court **770.467.4730**
Fax 770.467.4733
Web ....www.spaldingcounty.com
E-mail ....hodo_j@bellsouth.net
429 E Solomon St, Griffin, GA 30223-3317
Honorable Ben Miller Jr, Judge

POLICE AND SHERIFF

Sheriff's Ofc **770.467.4282**
Fax 770.467.4268
E-mail ....jstewart@lamarcountysheriff.com
401 Justice Blvd, Griffin, GA 30223
James D. Stewart, Sheriff

EDUCATION SERVICES

Exceptional Students **770.229.3247**
Fax 770.228.7316
E-mail ....dhogan@griffin.net
440 Tilney Ave, Griffin, GA 30224
Dr. Stephanie Gordy, Director

Stephens County

SOCIAL SERVICES

Georgia Div of Family & Children
Svcs **706.282.4505**
Fax 706.282.4502
1000 E Tugalo St, Toccoa, GA 30577

COURTS

Superior Courtù Mountain Circuit **706.886.3598**
Fax 706.886.5710
Web ....www.stephenscountyga.com
70 N ALEXANDER ST STE 202, Toccoa,
GA 30577-6604
Russell W Smith, Director

Stewart County

SOCIAL SERVICES

Family & Children Svcs **229.838.4335**
Fax 229.838.6280
Web ....www.dhr.state.ga.us
E-mail ....rbwatkins@dhr.state.ga.us
   2115 E Broad St, Lumpkin, GA 31815
   Rebecca Watkins, Director

GENERAL HEALTH SERVICES

Public Health Dept **229.838.4859**
Fax 229.838.6053
Web ....health.state.ga.us/regional/stewart
E-mail ....tgthomas6@dhr.state.ga.us
   Highway 27 S, Lumpkin, GA 31815
   Teresa Thomas, Nursing Supervisor

Sumter County

SOCIAL SERVICES

Family & Children Svcs **229.931.2462**
Fax 229.931.2427
Web ....www.dhr.state.ga.us
E-mail ....lulaster@dhr.state.ga.us
   502A S. Lee St, Americus, GA 31709
   Lulean Laster, Director

GENERAL HEALTH SERVICES

Public Health Dept **229.924.3637**
Fax 229.928.8813
Web ....www.health.state.ga.us/regional/sumter
   1601 Mlk Jr Blvd, Americus, GA 31719-2237
   Lanita Brown, Rn, Nursing Supervisor

JUSTICE AGENCY

Sumter Youth Development Ctr **229.931.5800**
Fax 229.931.5861
E-mail ....shawnbanks@djj.state.ga.us
   300 Mcmath Mill Rd, Americus, GA 31709
   Shawn Banks, Director

COURTS

**Southwestern Judicial Circuit Juvenile
Court** **229.928.4569**
Fax 229.928.4572
E-mail ....jones@gnat.net
   605 Spring St, Americus, GA 31709
   Honorable Lisa C. Jones, Judge

POLICE AND SHERIFF

Sheriff's Ofc **229.924.4094**
Fax 229.928.3450
Web ....www.sumter-ga.com
E-mail ....psmith@sumter-ga.com
   352 Mcmath Mill Rd, Americus, GA 31719-8605
   Pete Smith, Sheriff

EDUCATION SERVICES

Communities In Schools **229.924.9443**
Fax 229.931.5711
E-mail ....leapcis@gmail.com
   200 Cotton Ave, Americus, GA 31709-3514
   Kim Fullar, Director

Talbot County

SOCIAL SERVICES

**Georgia Div of Family & Children
Svcs** **706.665.8524**
Fax 706.665.3843
   Jordan City Rd, PO Box 96, Talbotton, GA 31827

GENERAL HEALTH SERVICES

Public Health Dept **706.665.8561**
Fax 706.665.3979
Web ....health.state.ga.us/regional/talbot
E-mail ....swebb@dhr.state.ga.us
   1073 Woodland Hwy, Talbotton, GA 31827
   Gloria Arnoed, Nursing Manager

COURTS

**Superior Court Chattahoochee
Circuit** **706.665.3239**
Fax 706.665.8637
Web ....www.dor.ga.gov
   26 Washington Street, Talbotton, GA 31827
   Judge Wayne Jernigan Sr., Director

POLICE AND SHERIFF

Sheriff's Ofc **706.665.8681**
Fax 706.665.3972
   44 N Washington Ave, Talbotton, GA 31827
   Tom Wimberly, Interim Sheriff

Taliaferro County

SOCIAL SERVICES

**Georgia Div of Family & Children
Svcs** **706.456.2339**
Fax 706.456.2976
   107 Commerce St, PO Box 40, Crawfordville,
   GA 30631

GENERAL HEALTH SERVICES

Health Dept **706.456.2316**
Fax 706.456.2334
   109 Commerce Stre, Crawfordville, GA 30631
   Kenya Smith, Nursing Manager

COURTS

Superior Court Toombs Circuit **706.456.2123**
Fax 706.456.2749
   113 Monuments Street, Crawfordville, GA 30631
   Sandra Greene, Clerk

Tattnall County

SOCIAL SERVICES

**Georgia Div of Family & Children
Svcs** **912.557.7721**
Fax 912.557.7774
   117 N Main St, PO Box 518, Reidsville, GA 30453

GENERAL HEALTH SERVICES

Public Health Dept **912.557.7850**
Fax 912.557.7854
Web ....health.state.ga.us/regional/tattnall
   200-B S Main St, Reidsville, GA 30453
   June Anderson, Nursing Supervisor

JUSTICE AGENCY

**Dept Of Juvenile Justice District Nine
Ofc** **912.557.7910**
Fax 912.557.7917
E-mail ....adamkennedy@jj.ga.us
   108 Braziell St, Reidsville, GA 30453
   Adam Kennedy, District Director

COURTS

Juvenile Court **912.557.6716**
Fax 912.557.4861
E-mail ....georgia.weathers@gsccca.org
   111 N main st, Reidsville, GA 30453
   Ben Brinson, Judge

Taylor County

SOCIAL SERVICES

Family & Children Svcs **478.862.5221**
Fax 478.862.2999
Web ....www.dhr.state.ga.us
   137 Georgia Rd, Butler, GA 31006
   Sekema Harmon, Director

GENERAL HEALTH SERVICES

Public Health Dept **478.862.5628**
Fax 478.862.3177
Web ....health.state.ga.us/regional/taylor
E-mail ....choward@dhr.state.ga.us
   178-1 Charing Rd, Butler, GA 31006
   Cynthia Howard, Rn, Nursing Supervisor

COURTS

**Superior Court Chattahoochee
Circuit** **478.862.5594**
Fax 478.862.5334
   1 Courthouse Square, Butler, GA 31006
   Honorable Frank J. Jordan, Director

POLICE AND SHERIFF

Sheriff's Ofc **478.862.5444**
Fax 478.862.3322
Web ....www.georgiasheriffs.org
E-mail ....jwatson@georgiasheriffs.org
   101 N Ivy, Butler, GA 31006
   Jeff Watson, Sheriff

Telfair County

SOCIAL SERVICES

Family & Children Svcs **229.868.3030**
Fax 229.868.3033
Web ....www.dhr.state.ga.us
E-mail ....nlwilson@dhr.state.ga.us
   35 Brewton St, Mc Rae, GA 31055
   Natalie Conley, Director

GENERAL HEALTH SERVICES

Public Health Dept **229.868.7404**
Fax 229.868.7245
Web ....health.state.ga.us/regional/telfair
   89 Telfair Ave, Mcrae, GA 31055
   Jina Adams, Nursing Supervisor

POLICE AND SHERIFF

Sheriff's Ofc **229.868.6621**
Fax 229.868.7025
E-mail ....jwilliamson@alltel.net
   19 E Oak St, Mc Rae, GA 31055-4338
   Johnny O'Smith, Sheriff

Terrell County

SOCIAL SERVICES

**Georgia Div of Family & Children
Svcs** **229.995.4431**
Fax 229.995.4809
   642 Randolph St SE, PO Box 30, Dawson, GA 31742

GENERAL HEALTH SERVICES

Public Health Dept **229.995.2188**
Fax 229.995.2074
Web ....health.state.ga.us/regional/terrell
   969 Forrester Dr SE, Dawson, GA 39842
   Charlotte Law, Rn, Director

COURTS

Juvenile Court **229.995.5657**
Fax 229.995.6667
E-mail ....law@colliergamble.com
   177 s main, Dawson, GA 39842
   Judge Edward Ross Collier, Director

Thomas County

SOCIAL SERVICES

Georgia Div of Family & Children

Svcs **229.225.4005**

Fax 229.225.5278

   438 Smith Ave, PO Box 2740, Thomasville, GA 31799

GENERAL HEALTH SERVICES

Public Health Dept **229.226.4241**

Fax 229.226.5144

Web ....www.health.state.ga.us/regional/thomas

E-mail ....ttaylor@dhr.state.ga.us

   484 Smith Ave, Thomasville, GA 31792-5535

   Tianne Taylor, Supervisor

JUSTICE AGENCY

Dept Of Juvenile Justice **229.225.4015**

Fax 229.225.5025

Web ....www.djj.state.ga.us

   438C Smith Ave # 12, Thomasville, GA 31792

   Yugonda Stewart, Deputy Juvenile Clerk

Judge Thomas Jefferson Loftiss Ii Regional Youth Detention

Ctr **229.227.2764**

Fax 229.227.2659

Web ....www.djj.state.ga.us

E-mail ....stevenwestberry@djj.state.ga.us

   400 S Pinetree Blvd Bldg 600, Thomasville, GA 31792-7128

   Steven Westberry, Director

COURTS

Juvenile Court **229.226.5308**

Fax 229.228.9108

E-mail ....w4asz@bellsouth.net

   418 North Broad Street, Thomasville, GA 31799

   Honorable Stephen H. Andrews, Director

POLICE AND SHERIFF

Sheriff's Ofc **229.225.3300**

Fax 229.225.3400

E-mail ....thoscoso@rose.net

   921 Smith Ave, Thomasville, GA 31799

   R. Carlton Powell, Sheriff

Tift County

SOCIAL SERVICES

Family & Children Svcs **229.386.3388**

Fax 229.386.7236

   410 2nd St W, Tifton, GA 31794

   Annie Clark, Director

GENERAL HEALTH SERVICES

Public Health Dept **229.386.8373**

Fax 229.386.5075

Web ....health.state.ga.us/regional/tift

E-mail ....pdavis@dhr.state.ga.us

   305 East 12th St, Tifton, GA 31794

   Gracy Muller, Nursing Supervisor

COURTS

Juvenile Court **229.386.3331**

Fax 229.386.3554

   225 Tift Ave N, Tifton, GA 31794

   Engram Moore, Superintendent

POLICE AND SHERIFF

Sheriff's Ofc **229.388.6020**

Fax 229.388.6200

Web ....www.tiftsheriff.net

E-mail ....gary.vowell@tiftcounty.org

   500 Morgan Dr, Tifton, GA 31794-4774

   Gary C. Vowell, Sheriff

Toombs County

SOCIAL SERVICES

Georgia Div of Family & Children

Svcs **912.526.8117**

Fax 912.526.6986

   162 Oxley Dr, PO Box 191, Lyons, GA 30436

JUSTICE AGENCY

Dept Of Juvenile Justice **912.526.8829**

Fax 912.526.5764

Web ....www.djj.state.ga.us

E-mail ....shirleyhayes@djj.state.ga.us

   126 W Grady Ave Ste 1, Lyons, GA 30436-1492

   Shirley Hayes, Juvenile Probation Manager

POLICE AND SHERIFF

Sheriff's Ofc **912.526.6778**

Fax 912.526.7749

   357 NW Broad St Ste 1, Lyons, GA 30436

   Alvie L. Kight Jr., Sheriff

Towns County

SOCIAL SERVICES

Georgia Div of Family & Children

Svcs **706.896.3524**

Fax 706.896.1457

   456 N Main St, PO Box 156, Hiawassee, GA 30546

GENERAL HEALTH SERVICES

Public Health Dept **706.896.2265**

Fax 706.896.1816

Web ....health.state.ga.us/regional/towns

   1104 Jack Dayton Cir, Young Harris, GA 30582

   Roxanne Barrett, Nursing Supervisor

Treutlen County

SOCIAL SERVICES

Georgia Div of Family & Children

Svcs **912.529.3757**

Fax 912.529.4305

   108 Martin Luther King Jr Dr, PO Box 625, Soperton, GA 30457

GENERAL HEALTH SERVICES

Public Health Dept **912.529.4217**

Fax 912.529.4393

Web ....health.state.ga.us/regional/treutlen

E-mail ....mppowell@dhr.state.ga.us

   5614 Third St, Soperton, GA 30457

   Mary P Powell, Rn, Nursing Supervisor

Troup County

SOCIAL SERVICES

Family & Children Svcs **404.657.8000**

Fax 404.657.8215

   84 NW Walton St, Atlanta, GA 30303

   Marie Elder, Director

GENERAL HEALTH SERVICES

Public Health Dept **706.845.4085**

Fax 706.845.4089

Web ....www.health.state.ga.us/regional/troup

   900 Dallis St, Lagrange, GA 30240-4441

   Melody Wegienka, Nursing Supervisor

JUSTICE AGENCY

Troup CASA **706.845.8243**

Fax 706.845.1837

E-mail ....jnelson@troupco.org

   118 Ridley Ave, Lagrange, GA 30240

   June Nelson, Executive Director

COURTS

Juvenile Court **706.883.1735**

Fax 706.883.1738

Web ....www.kmglawfirm.com

E-mail ....michael@kmglawfirm.com

   118 Ridley Ave, Lagrange, GA 30240-2724

   Honorable R. Michael Key, Judge

POLICE AND SHERIFF

Sheriff's Ofc **706.883.1616**

Fax 706.883.1694

E-mail ....dturner@troupco.org

   130 Sam Walker Dr, Lagrange, GA 30240

   Donny Turner, Sheriff

EDUCATION SERVICES

Communities In Schools **706.298.7121**

Fax 706.298.7117

E-mail ....bryantcm@troup.org

   1220 Hogansville Rd, Lagrange, GA 30241

   Brenda Kennedy, Executive Director

Turner County

SOCIAL SERVICES

Family & Children Svcs **229.567.4353**

Fax 229.567.3954

   336 North St, Ashburn, GA 31714

   Melanie Mcswain, Director

GENERAL HEALTH SERVICES

Public Health Dept **229.567.4357**

Fax 229.567.3947

Web ....www.health.state.ga.us/regional/turner

   745 Hudson St, Ashburn, GA 31714

   Jetta Sprayberry, Nursing Supervisor

EDUCATION SERVICES

Communities In Schools **229.567.9066**

Fax 229.567.2877

   330 Gilmore St, Ashburn, GA 31734

   Patricia Day, Director

Twiggs County

SOCIAL SERVICES

Family & Children Svcs **478.945.3258**

Fax 478.945.6508

E-mail ....efdennard@dhr.state.ga.us

   14 Cedar Ln, Jeffersonville, GA 31044

   Evelyn Fowler-dennard, Director

COURTS

Superior Court **478.945.3350**

Fax 478.945.6751

   425 Railroad Street N #120, Jeffersonville, GA 31044

   Patti Grimsley, Clerk Of Court

EDUCATION SERVICES

Communities In Schools **478.945.3127**

Fax 478.945.3078

   952 Main Street, Jeffersonville, GA 31044

   Valya Lee, Superintendent

Union County

SOCIAL SERVICES

Family & Children Svcs **706.781.2381**

Fax 706.745.3560

Web ....www.dhr.state.ga.us

E-mail ....lakelley@dhr.state.ga.us

   163 Blue Ridge Hwy, Blairsville, GA 30512-4443

   Leslie Kelley, Director

GENERAL HEALTH SERVICES

Public Health Dept 706.745.6292
Fax..706.745.6803
Web...................health.state.ga.us/regional/union
E-mail ....jdlance@dhr.state.ga.us
67 Chase Dr, Blairsville, GA 30512
Janice Lance, Nursing Manager

Upson County

SOCIAL SERVICES

Georgia Div of Family & Children
Svcs..706.646.6043
Fax..706.646.6048
711 N Bethel St, Thomaston, GA 30286

GENERAL HEALTH SERVICES

Public Health Dept 706.647.7148
Fax..706.647.3372
Web....................health.state.ga.us/regional/upson
314 E Lee St, Thomaston, GA 30286
Lynn Vickers, Nursing Supervisor

COURTS

Juvenile Court..............................706.647.0028
Fax..706.647.2126
Web.......................................www.upsoncountyga.org
1 Court House Square Main St Ste 150, Thomaston,
GA 30286
Judge Ben Miller, Chief Judge

Walker County

SOCIAL SERVICES

Georgia Div of Family & Children
Svcs..706.375.0726
Fax..706.375.0798
10056 N Hwy 27, PO Box 689, Rock Spring,
GA 30739

GENERAL HEALTH SERVICES

Public Health Dept 706.638.5577
Fax..706.638.5543
Web......................health.state.ga.us/regional/walker
603 East Villanow Street, LaFayette, GA 30728
Michelle Bicknell, Hiv Coordinator

JUSTICE AGENCY

CASA 706.866.8811
Fax..706.866.9003
E-mail ....casas@hotmail.com
510 North Thomas Rd, Fort Oglethorpe, GA 30742
Vicki Scoggins, Executive Director

COURTS

Juvenile Court..............................706.638.3044
Fax..706.639.1776
Web...www.lmjc.net
103 S. Duke Street, LaFayette, GA 30728
Honorable F. Bryant Henry, Judge

POLICE AND SHERIFF

Sheriff's Ofc 706.638.1909
Fax..706.638.6398
E-mail ....walkersheriff01@aol.com
105 S Duke St, La Fayette, GA 30728
Steven B. Wilson, Sheriff

EDUCATION SERVICES

Cloud Springs Head Start 706.861.1831
Fax..706.861.9654
E-mail ....kbrock@fragahs.com
169 Fernwood Dr, Rossville, GA 30741
Kathy Brock, Director

Walton County

SOCIAL SERVICES

Georgia Div of Fam & Children
Svcs..770.207.4000
Fax..770.207.4007
1110 E Spring St, PO Box 927, Monroe, GA 30655

GENERAL HEALTH SERVICES

Public Health Dept 770.207.4125
Fax..770.207.4129
Web...............................www.health.state.ga.us
1404 S Madison Ave, Monroe, GA 30655
Lorri Tanner, Director

POLICE AND SHERIFF

Sheriff's Ofc 770.267.6557
Fax..770.267.1440
E-mail ....jchatman@co.walton.ga.us
1425 S Madison Ave, Monroe, GA 30655
Joe Chatman, Sheriff

Ware County

SOCIAL SERVICES

Georgia Div of Family & Children
Svcs..912.285.6040
Fax..912.287.6626
1200 Plant Ave, PO Box 2048, Waycross, GA 31502

GENERAL HEALTH SERVICES

Public Health Dept 912.283.1875
Fax..912.283.0894
Web ....health.state.ga.us/regional/ware
E-mail ....crbarefield@dhr.state.ga.us
604 Riverside Ave, Waycross, GA 31501
Connie Barefield, Rn, Nursing Supervisor

JUSTICE AGENCY

Dept Of Juvenile Justice 912.285.6096
Fax..912.284.2521
E-mail ....maxsilman@djj.state.ga.us
1724 Old Reynolds St, Waycross, GA 31501
Max Silman, Program Manager

Waycross Regional Youth Detention
Ctr 912.287.6680
Fax..912.287.6681
E-mail ....reneemumford@djj.state.ga.us
3275 Harris Rd, Waycross, GA 31503
Renee Mumford, Director

COURTS

Juvenile Court..............................912.287.4345
Fax..912.287.4347
801 Grove Ave, Waycross, GA 31501-4513
Honorable Jeferry C. Parker, Director

EDUCATION SERVICES

Exceptional Students 912.338.5998
Fax..912.287.6654
Web...www.scglrs.org
E-mail ....cfluker@scglrs.org
1215 Bailey St Ste B, Waycross, GA 31501-6501
Carolyn Fluker, Director

Warren County

SOCIAL SERVICES

Georgia Div of Family & Children
Svcs..706.465.3326
Fax..706.465.2819
224 N Legion Dr, PO Box 166, Warrenton, GA 30828

GENERAL HEALTH SERVICES

Public Health Dept 706.465.2252
Fax..706.465.1410
Web...www.health.state.gov
565 Legion Dr, Warrenton, GA 30828
Virginia Bradshaw, Public Health Nurse

COURTS

Superior Court- Toombs Circuit 706.465.3946
Fax..706.465.1808
Web...www.dhr.state.ga.us
E-mail ....hhinesley@dhr.state.ga.us
521 Main St, Warrenton, GA 30828
Honorable Harold Hinesley, Director

POLICE AND SHERIFF

Sheriff's Ofc 706.465.3340
Fax..706.465.3091
169 Ga Highway 80 N, Warrenton, GA 30828-8851
Joe Peebles, Sheriff

Washington County

SOCIAL SERVICES

Family & Children Svcs 478.553.2350
Fax..478.553.2390
Web...www.dhr.state.ga.us
E-mail ....mjosie@dhr.state.ga.us
1124 South Harris St, Sandersville, GA 31082-6904
Myra Josie, Director

GENERAL HEALTH SERVICES

Public Health Dept 478.552.3210
Fax..478.553.1832
Web...................health.state.ga.us/regional/washington
E-mail ....deryl@cityofwrens.com
201 Morningside Dr, Sandersville, GA 31082
Deryl Scarboro, Rn, Nursing Supervisor

JUSTICE AGENCY

Sandersville Regional Youth Detention
Ctr 478.553.2400
Fax..478.553.2404
Web...www.djj.state.ga.us
E-mail ....haroldtompkins@djj.state.ga.us
423 Industrial Dr, Sandersville, GA 31082-7015
Harold Thompkins, Director

POLICE AND SHERIFF

Sheriff's Ofc 478.552.4795
Fax..478.552.5848
E-mail ....tsmith@mylink.net
1735 Kaolin Rd, Sandersville, GA 31082-6934
Thomas H. Smith, Sheriff

Wayne County

SOCIAL SERVICES

Geogia Div of Family & Children
Svcs..912.427.5866
Fax..912.427.5885
1220 S 1st St, PO Box 267, Jesup, GA 31598

GENERAL HEALTH SERVICES

Public Health Dept 912.427.2042
Fax..912.427.5880
Web...................health.state.ga.us/regional/wayne
240 Peachtree St, Jesup, GA 31598
Stacie Drew, Nursing Supervisor

COURTS

Majistrate Court..............................912.427.5960
Fax..912.427.5962
174 N Brunswick St, Jesup, GA 31546
Dary Browning, Judge

Webster County

SOCIAL SERVICES

Family & Children Svcs **229.828.6265**
Fax 229.828.2032
   Hwy 41, Preston, GA 31824
   Rebecca B. Watkins, Director

GENERAL HEALTH SERVICES

Public Health Dept **229.828.3225**
Fax 229.828.2208
Web .... www.health.state.ga.us
E-mail .... mlstone@dhr.state.ga.us
   6814 Washington Street, Preston, GA 31824
   Michelle Stone, Rn, Nursing Manager

POLICE AND SHERIFF

Sheriff's Ofc **229.828.7503**
Fax 229.828.8870
E-mail .... sheriffwc@gmail.com
   175 Montgomery St, Preston, GA 31824
   Randy Dely, Sheriff

Wheeler County

SOCIAL SERVICES

Family & Children Svcs **912.568.7127**
Fax 912.568.7196
Web .... www.dhr.state.ga.us
E-mail .... nlwilson@dhr.state.ga.us
   44 W 3rd Ave, Alamo, GA 30411
   Natalie Conley, Director

GENERAL HEALTH SERVICES

Public Health Dept **912.568.7161**
Fax 912.568.7770
Web .... www.health.state.ga.us/regional/wheeler
E-mail .... susher@dhr.state.ga.us
   414 Kent Street, Alamo, GA 30411
   Suzanne Usher, Nursing Supervisor

White County

SOCIAL SERVICES

Family & Children Svcs **706.865.3128**
Fax 706.865.9586
   1241 Helen Hwy Ste 200, Cleveland, GA 30528
   Cheryl Dooley, Director

GENERAL HEALTH SERVICES

Public Health Dept **706.865.2191**
Fax 706.865.7745
Web www.phdistrict2.org
E-mail .... cking@dhr.state.ga.us
   1241 Helen Hwy Ste 210, Cleveland, GA 30528-6938
   Cindy King, Nursing Manager

COURTS

**Superior Courtù Northeastern
Circuit** **706.865.2613**
Fax 706.865.7749
E-mail .... dave@whitecounty.net
   59 S Main St Ste B, Cleveland, GA 30528
   Honorable David E. Barrett, Superior Judge

POLICE AND SHERIFF

Sheriff's Ofc **706.865.6370**
Fax 706.865.6977
Web .... www.wcso.com
   1210 Hulsey Rd, Cleveland, GA 30528-6939
   Neal T. Walden, Sheriff

EDUCATION SERVICES

Exceptional Students **706.865.2043**
Fax 706.865.6748
E-mail .... lbrown@pioneerresa.org
   1342 Highway 254, Cleveland, GA 30528
   Laura Brown, Director

Whitfield County

SOCIAL SERVICES

**Georgia Div of Family & Children
Svcs** **706.272.2331**
Fax 706.272.2895
   1142 N Thornton Ave, PO Box 1203, Dalton,
   GA 30722

MENTAL HEALTH SERVICES

**Child And Adolescent Svcs Mental
Health** **706.270.5047**
Fax 706.270.5055
Web .... www.highlandrivers.org
E-mail .... bethbice@highlandrivers.org
   1401 Applewood Dr Ste 4, Dalton, GA 30720-8515
   Beth Bice, Coordinator

JUSTICE AGENCY

**Albert Shaw Regional Youth Detention
Ctr** **706.272.2309**
Fax 706.272.2367
   2735 Underwood Rd NE, Dalton, GA 30721
   Bobby Hughes, Director

COURTS

Juvenile Court **706.278.6558**
Fax 706.272.7018
Web .... www.whitfieldcountyga.us
E-mail .... cblaylock@whitfieldcountyga.us
   205 N Selvidge St Ste G, Dalton, GA 30720-4298
   Honorable Connie Blaylock, Director

Superior Courtù Conasauga Circuit **706.278.0047**
Fax 706.275.9060
Web .... www.gapublicdefender.org
E-mail .... cmorris@whitfieldcountyga.com
   205 N Selvidge St, Dalton, GA 30720
   Honorable Cindy Morris, Judge

POLICE AND SHERIFF

Sheriff's Ofc **706.278.1233**
Fax 706.279.3160
Web .... www.wcso.com
E-mail .... sheriff@wcso.com
   805 Professional Blvd, Dalton, GA 30720-2536
   T. Scott Chitwood, Sheriff

Wilcox County

SOCIAL SERVICES

Family & Children Svcs **229.365.2242**
Fax 229.365.2575
Web .... www.dhr.state.ga.us
E-mail .... rpowell@dhr.state.ga.us
   453 2nd Ave, Rochelle, GA 31079
   Rebecca Powell, Director

GENERAL HEALTH SERVICES

Wilcoxpublic Health Dept **229.365.2310**
Fax 229.365.7825
Web .... www.health.state.ga.us/regional/wilcox
   1000 Second Ave, Rochelle, GA 31079
   Joani Wilson, Nursing Supervisor

COURTS

Superior Court Cordele Circuit **229.467.2442**
Fax 229.467.2886
Web .... www.gajudges.org
   103 Broad St N Ste 102, Abbeville, GA 31001-4256
   Honorable John C. Pridgen, Director

POLICE AND SHERIFF

Sheriff's Ofc **229.467.2322**
Fax 229.467.2330
   126 Main St E, Abbeville, GA 31001
   Stacy C. Bloodsworth, Sheriff

Wilkes County

SOCIAL SERVICES

**Georgia Div of Family & Children
Svcs** **706.678.2814**
Fax 706.678.5325
   48 Lexington Ave, PO Box 126, Washington,
   GA 30673

GENERAL HEALTH SERVICES

Public Health Dept **706.678.2622**
Fax 706.678.3115
Web .... health.state.ga.us/regional/wilkes
E-mail .... jwjackson@dhr.state.ga.us
   204 Gordon St, Washington, GA 30673
   Jennifer Jackson, Rn, Nursing Supervisor

Wilkinson County

SOCIAL SERVICES

Family & Children Svcs **478.946.2224**
Fax 478.946.3821
Web .... www.dfcs.dhr.georgia.gov
E-mail .... efdennard@dhr.state.ga.us
   103 Payne Cir, Mc Intyre, GA 31054-2022
   Fowler Dennard, Director

Worth County

SOCIAL SERVICES

Family & Children's Svcs **229.777.2000**
   503 N Henderson St, Sylvester, GA 31791-0527

GENERAL HEALTH SERVICES

Public Health Dept **229.777.2150**
Fax 229.777.2170
Web .... health.state.ga.us/regional/worth
   1012 W Franklin St, Sylvester, GA 31791
   Gina Connell, Rn, Nursing Supervisor

POLICE AND SHERIFF

Sheriff's Ofc **229.776.8211**
Fax 229.776.8228
   201 N Main St Rm 14, Sylvester, GA 31791
   Freddie Tompkins, Sheriff

SPECIAL SERVICES AGENCIES

ADOPTION AGENCIES

AAA Partners In Adoption Inc **770.844.2080**
Fax 770.844.2075
Web .... www.aaapia.org
E-mail .... aaapia@aol.com
   5665 Highway 9, Ste 103-351, Alpharetta, GA 30004
Melissa Clause, Director

Adoption Info Svc **770.339.7236**
Fax 770.456.5961
Web .... www.adoptioninfosvcs.com
E-mail .... aisteam@adoptioninfosvcs.com
   1840 Old N Cross Rd Ste 100, Lawrenceville, GA 30044-2856
Marcia Parker, Director

Bethany Christian Svcs **770.455.7111**
Fax 770.455.7118
Web .... www.bethany.org
E-mail .... tsmall@bethany.org
   6645 Peachtree Dunwoody Rd NE, Atlanta, GA 30328-1606
Trish Small, Director

Bethany Christian Svcs **706.576.5766**
Fax 706.576.5159
Web .... www.bethany.org/columbus_ga
E-mail .... bcscolumbusga@bethany.org
   5050 Warm Springs Rd Ste 200B, Columbus, GA 31909-6952
Denna Smith, Director

Childkind, Inc. **404.248.1980**
Fax 404.248.1981
Web .... www.childkind.org
   3107 Clairmont Road NE, Suite A, Atlanta, GA 30329
COA accredited organization.

Cradle Of Love **770.955.8550**
Fax 770.953.0807
Web .... www.cradleoflove.org
E-mail .... info@cradleoflove.org
   1501 Johnson Ferry Rd Ste 100, Marietta, GA 30062-6485
Judith Golden, Adoption Supervisor

Family Counseling Ctr **706.868.5011**
Fax 706.868.5023
E-mail .... jkeen@fccsra.org
   3711 Executive Ctr Dr, Augusta, GA 30907-1460
Dawn Jett, Director

Georgia Agape, Inc. **770.452.9995**
Fax 770.457.3623
E-mail .... doug@georgiaagape.org
   3094 Mercer University Dr Ste 200, Atlanta, GA 30341-4141
Doug Mead, Director

Georgia Parent Support Network, Inc. **404.758.4500**
Fax 404.758.6833
Web .... www.gpsn.org
   1381 Metropolitan Parkway, Atlanta, GA 30310-4455
COA accredited organization.

The Giving Tree, Inc. **404.633.3383**
Fax 404.633.3348
Web .... www.thegivingtree.org
E-mail .... receptionist@thegivingtree.org
   1991 N Williamsburg Dr, Decatur, GA 30030-2518
Toni Oliver, Interim Director

ADVOCACY RESOURCES

Ashley Willcott Attorney **770.458.7948**
   227 Sandy Springs Pl Ste D-318, Atlanta, GA 30328
Ashley Willcott, Attorney

Barton Child Law & Policy Clinic **404.727.6664**
E-mail .... rerskin@law.emory.edu
   Emory Law School, 1301 Clifton Rd, Atlanta, GA 30322
Melissa Carter, Director

CASA Paulding **770.505.0065**
Fax 770.443.5940
Web .... www.casapaulding.org
E-mail .... casapaulding@casapaulding.org
   244 Carter Rd, Dallas, GA 30157-5425
Jana M. Stegall, Executive Director

Child Advocacy Center **404.294.2587**
E-mail .... anjenkins@co.dekalb.ga.us
   4309 Memorial Dr, Decatur, GA 30032
Aviance Jenkins, Child Advocate Attorney

Children's Advocacy Ctr **229.245.5362**
Fax 229.245.5360
E-mail .... cacdirector@caclowndes.org
   200 W Moore St, Valdosta, GA 31602
Brenda Hodges, Executive Director

Children's Tree House **706.327.9612**
Fax 706.327.7904
Web .... www.twincedars.org
E-mail .... lmoncries@twincedars.org
   89 St Ste 102, Columbus, GA 31901-3508
Mike Angstandt, Executive Director

Coastal Children's Advocacy Ctr **912.236.1401**
Fax 912.236.0228
E-mail .... ccac@ciscom.com
   PO Box 9926, Savannah, GA 31412-0126
Kris Rice, Executive Director

Georgia CASA (Court Appointed Special Advocates) **404.874.2888**
Fax 404.874.2889
Web .... www.gacasa.org
E-mail .... info@gacasa.org
   1776 Peachtree St NW, Ste 219, Atlanta, GA 30309
Duaine Hathaway, Executive Director

Georgia Supreme Court Comm on Justice for Children **404.601.4117**
E-mail .... tran_lankford@comcast.net
   755 Commerce Dr Ste 800, Decatur, GA 30030
Tran Lankford

Hall-Dawson CASA Program **770.531.1964**
Fax 770.534.5851
E-mail .... casaofhall@bellsouth.net
   PO Box 907471, Gainesville, GA 30501-0908
Connie Stephens, Executive Director

Law Office of Jennifer Watts **404.549.7027**
E-mail .... jenniferwatts06@yahoo.com
   2107 H Decatur Rd # 198, Decatur, GA 30033
Jennifer Watts

Law Offices of Mark Kirchen **678.267.3156**
E-mail .... mark@kirchenlaw.com
   5805 State Bridge Rd Ste G163, Duluth, GA 30097
Mark Kirchen

Office of the Public Defender **770.595.3541**
E-mail .... jroth49@gapublicdefender.org
   307 E 51st St, Savannah, GA 31405
Jill Roth, Manager

Patricia K Buonodono PC **770.977.1330**
E-mail .... femjd@aol.com
   2440 Sandy Plains Rd 6-100, Marietta, GA 30066
Patricia Buonodono

Rainbow House Crc **478.923.5923**
Fax 478.328.0176
Web .... www.rainbowhousecrc.org
E-mail .... ksonderson@rainbowhousecrc.org
   108 Elmwood St, Warner Robins, GA 31093-1804
Kemberlie Sonderson, Executive Director

Safepath Children's Advocacy Ctr, Inc. **770.801.3465**
Fax 770.801.3468
Web .... www.supportsafepath.com
E-mail .... pathsafe@aol.com
   736 Whitlock Ave NW, Ste 600, Marietta, GA 30064-0001
Jinger Robins, Ma, Executive Director

SM Jenkins & Associates **404.242.8839**
E-mail .... smj_law@msn.com
   PO Box 725042, Atlanta, GA 31139
Stacey m Jenkins

Wisotsky Law Inc **706.543.4678**
E-mail .... juliwiso@bellsouth.net
   PO Box 362, Jefferson, GA 30549
Juli Wisotsky

BEHAVIORAL HEALTH TREATMENT

Access Mental Health Agency **704.291.6018**
   250 Georgia Avenue, Atlanta, GA 30312
CARF accredited programs available.

Advance Therapeutic Concepts, Inc. **404.379.4828**
Fax 678.344.7839
E-mail .... advancecon6@aol.com
   2992 Main Street West, Suite 212, Snellville, GA 30078
Carrie Savage, Director
CARF accredited programs available.

Advantage Behavioral Health Systems **706.389.6789**
Fax 706.389.6740
Web .... www.advantagebhs.org
   250 North Avenue, Athens, GA 30601
Cindy Darden, Director
CARF accredited programs available.

Advantage Behavioral Health Systems Child And Adolescent Svcs **706.369.6363**
Fax 706.369.6265
Web .... www.advantagebhs.org
E-mail .... ttellifson@advantagebhs.org
   165 E Dougherty St, Athens, GA 30601-2608
Terry Tellifson, Director

Advantage Counseling Service, Inc. **770.471.0033**
Fax 770.471.4639
Web .... www.acs-counseling.com
E-mail .... rridley@acs-counseling.com
   1299 Battle Creek Rd, Ste 100, Jonesboro, GA 30236
Roy Ridley, Owner
CARF accredited programs available.

Advantage Counseling Service, Inc. **770.281.8811**
Fax 770.281.8812
Web .... www.acs-counseling.com
   2180 Satellite Boulevard, Suite 400, Duluth, GA 30097
CARF accredited programs available.

Ascension Counseling Group, Inc. **770.452.8509**
Fax 866.261.2420
   3301 Buckeye Rd, Ste 205, Atlanta, GA 30341
Phyllis Thompson, Owner & President
CARF accredited programs available.

ASFC Outreach Therapeutic Counseling **770.787.3788**
Fax 770.786.5159
Web .... www.ASFCOutreach.com
   4146 Highway 278 NE, Covington, GA 30014
CARF accredited programs available.

Atlanta Area Psychological **770.953.6401**
Fax 770.953.6015
Web .... www.atlantapsych.com
E-mail .... info@atlantapsych.net
   2520 Windy Hill Rd SE Ste 203, Marietta, GA 30067-8650
Sheila Cannon, MD, Psychiatrist

Atlanta Center for Eating Disorders **770.458.8711**
Fax 770.458.8640
Web ....www.eatingdisorders.cc
4536 Barclay Road, Dunwoody, GA 30338
CARF accredited programs available.

Atlanta Psychiatric Assoc **404.252.4525**
5064 Roswell Rd Ste 102D, Atlanta, GA 30342-2252
Salley Jessee, Md, Psychiatrist

Atlanta Psychiatry & Neurology **770.319.6000**
Fax 770.319.6330
Web ....www.integrativehealthmd.com
3188 Atlanta Rd SE, Smyrna, GA 30080-8256
Jeffrey Klopper, Md, Psychiatrist

Atlanta Psychotherapy **770.389.1925**
Fax 770.389.3077
175 Country Club Drive, Suite 200E, Stockbridge,
GA 30281
Dorothy Watts, Director
CARF accredited programs available.

**AUC DBA Community Healthcare of Georgia/Trading
Faces** **678.422.6050**
Fax 678.422.6044
1115 Mount Zion Road, Suites C and D, Morrow,
GA 30260
CARF accredited programs available.

Avita Partners **678.513.5700**
Fax 678.513.5833
Web ....www.avitapartners.org
4331 Thurmond Tanner Parkway, Flowery Branch,
GA 30542
Allan Harden, Asst Director Human Resource
CARF accredited programs available.

Bagley Youth Development, LLC **404.968.4662**
Fax 404.968.4562
5101 Buffington Road, Suite 3445, College Park,
GA 30349
CARF accredited programs available.

Bedell Medical Practice **770.997.8516**
1631 Phoenix Blvd, College Park, Atlanta, GA 30349
David Bedell, MD, Psychiatrist

**Behavioral Health Services of South
Georgia** **229.671.6100**
Fax 229.671.6755
Web ....www.bhsga.com
E-mail ....rjohnson@bhsga.com
3120 North Oak Street Extension, Suite C, Valdosta,
GA 31602
Roz Johnson, Clinical Director
CARF accredited programs available.

Behavioral Health Svcs Of South Georgia **229.896.4559**
Fax 229.896.8367
E-mail ....vwilliams@bhsga.com
1905 S Hutchinson Ave, Adel, GA 31620-5246
Veronica Williams, Clinic Director

Bidiuc Medical Practice **706.876.1911**
1421 Ross Dr Ste 4, Dalton, GA 30720-3095
Martha Bidiuc, Md, Psychiatrist

Cannon Medical Practice **678.364.0888**
Fax 678.364.0246
21 Eastbrook Bnd Ste 209, Peachtree City, GA 30269
Sheila Cannon, Psychiatrist

Care And Counseling Ctr Of Georgia **404.636.1457**
Fax 404.636.7449
Web ....www.cccgeorgia.org
E-mail ....info@cccgeorgia.org
1814 Clairmont Rd, Decatur, GA 30033
Sandra Mullins, Executive Director

CarePartners of Georgia, Inc. **478.237.2484**
Fax 478.237.7541
109 Roberts Street, Post Office Box 1094,
Swainsboro, GA 30401
CARF accredited programs available.

Carrie Steele-Pitts Home **404.691.5188**
Fax 404.691.3248
Web ....www.csph.org
E-mail ....ollivetteallison@csph.org
667 Fairburn Rd NW, Atlanta, GA 30331-1499

Central State Hospital **478.445.4128**
Web ....www.centralstatehospital.org
E-mail ....bbradley@dhr.state.ga.us
620 Broad St, Milledgeville, GA 31062
Mrs. Betsy Bradley, Accreditation Manager
Joint Commission accredited organization.

Cherokee Ctr For Change, Inc **770.928.7300**
Fax 770.928.7558
E-mail ....cherokeefocus@alltel.net
409 Old Boring Ln, Woodstock, GA 30189
Ita Dore, Director

CHRIS Kids, Inc. **404.486.9034**
Fax 404.486.9053
Web ....www.chriskids.org
3109 Clairmont Road NE, Suite B, Atlanta,
GA 30329-1015
COA accredited organization.

Christian City Home For Children **770.964.3309**
Fax 770.703.2609
Web ....www.christiancity.org
E-mail ....philk@christian-city.org
7345 Red Oak Rd, Union City, GA 30291-2338
Phillip Kouns, Director

Clayton Community Service Board **770.478.2280**
Fax 770.477.9772
Web ....www.claytoncenter.org
112 Broad Street, Jonesboro, GA 30236
Jade Benefield, Director
CARF accredited programs available.

Clayton Ctr - Child & Adolescent Svcs **770.991.7420**
Fax 770.991.7429
E-mail ....tanita.teagle@claytoncenter.org
6315 Garden Walk Blvd, Riverdale, GA 30274-2628
Tanita Teagle, C&A Services Manager

**Clinic for Education, Treatment and Prevention of Addiction,
Inc.** **770.662.0249**
Fax 770.449.5023
Web ....www.cetpa.org
6020 Dawson Boulevard, Suite I, Norcross, GA 30093
CARF accredited programs available.

Coastal Harbor Treatment Center **912.354.3911**
Fax 912.355.1336
Web ....www.coastalharbor.com
E-mail ....deena.schwabe@uhsinc.com
1150 Cornell Ave, Savannah, GA 31406
Deena Schwabe, Director Of Admissions

Coastal Harbor Treatment Center **912.354.3911**
Web ....www.coastalharbor.com
E-mail ....terri.jones@uhsinc.com
1150 Cornell Avenue, Savannah, GA 31406
Ms. Terri Jones, Accreditation Manager
Joint Commission accredited organization.

Cohen Medical Practice **404.266.3247**
Fax 404.364.5316
E-mail ....shelbradco@gmail.com
881 Somerset Dr NW, Atlanta, GA 30327-3732
Sheldon Cohen, Md, Psychiatrist

Community Counseling Solutions, LLC **404.761.2446**
Fax 678.669.2651
2949 Pearl Street, East Point, GA 30344
CARF accredited programs available.

Community Development Systems, Inc. **478.743.8333**
Fax 478.743.8308
Web ....www.cdsga.org
401 Cherry Street, Suite 505, Macon, GA 31201
Gwendolyn Sands, Director
CARF accredited programs available.

**Community Service Board of Middle
Georgia** **478.275.6811**
Fax 478.274.7666
Web ....www.csbmg.com
2121-A Bellevue Road, Building One, Dublin,
GA 31021
CARF accredited programs available.

Compass Pointe Counseling, Inc. **678.521.3092**
Fax 678.669.2247
Web ....Compasspointecounseling.com
3188 Atlanta Road, Smyrna, GA 30080
CARF accredited programs available.

Comprehensive Counseling Solutions, Inc. **770.933.6289**
Fax 404.393.9474
Web ....www.comprehensivecounselingsolutions.com
3330 Cumberland Boulevard, Suite 500, Atlanta,
GA 30339
CARF accredited programs available.

Creative Interventions, Inc. **404.957.8149**
3114 Cherokee Street, Suite 209, Kennesaw,
GA 30144
CARF accredited programs available.

Cumberland Psychiatric Group **678.352.1060**
Fax 678.736.7308
Web ....www.cpg-atlanta.com
E-mail ....comments@cpg-atlanta.com
11111 Houze Rd Ste 225, Roswell, GA 30076-5618
Jayenh Naik, Psychiatrist

DeKalb Community Service Board **404.294.3836**
Fax 404.508.7795
Web ....www.dekcsb.org
445 Winn Way, Fourth Floor, Decatur, GA 30030
CARF accredited programs available.

Devereux Georgia Treatment Network **770.427.0147**
Web ....www.devereux.org
E-mail ....drobins2@devereux.org
1291 Stanley Road, Kennesaw, GA 30152-4359
Mrs. Debra Robinson, Accreditation Manager
Joint Commission accredited organization.

Devereux Georgia Treatment Network **770.427.0147**
Fax 770.427.4030
Web ....www.devereuxga.org
1291 Stanley Rd NW, Kennesaw, GA 30152-4359
Mario Bolivar, Executive Director

Dirksen Medical Practice **706.210.8400**
Fax 706.210.8311
104 Srp Dr, Evans, GA 30809-3319
John Dirksen, Md, Psychiatrist

Downing Clark Center, Inc. **706.629.3282**
Fax 706.629.7892
Web ....www.downingclark.com
1773 Trimble Hollow Road, Adairsville, GA 30103
CARF accredited programs available.

Durden Consulting Services, LLC **478.455.2092**
5910 GA Highway 21 South, Unit 6, Rincon,
GA 31326
CARF accredited programs available.

Dynamic Interventions, Inc. **478.254.6705**
Fax 478.254.6706
Web ....www.dynamic-interventions.com
130 Springfield Boulevard, Macon, GA 31210
CARF accredited programs available.

Eagle Ranch **770.967.8500**
Fax 770.967.3757
Web ....www.eagleranch.org
E-mail ....info@eagleranch.org
5500 Union Church Rd, Flowery Branch,
GA 30542-5216
Eddie Staub, Executive Director

East Central Regional Hospital **706.790.2030**
Web ....ecrh.pmh.dhr.state.ga.us
E-mail ....pshawk@dhr.state.ga.us
100 Myrtle Blvd, Gracewood, GA 30812
Ms. Precious Hawk, Accreditation Manager
Joint Commission accredited organization.

**East Central Regional Hospital At
Gracewood** **706.790.2011**
Fax 706.790.2025
Web ....www.dhr.state.ga.us
100 Middle Blvd, Gracewood, GA 30812
Nan Lewis, Administrator

Evan M Torch, Practice **404.255.7447**
6095 Lake Forrest Dr NW Ste 210, Atlanta,
GA 30328-3845
Evan M. Torch, Md, Psychiatrist

Faith's Home, Inc **770.412.8604**
Fax 770.412.0137
E-mail ....faithshomeinc@aol.com
166 Oakdale Dr, Milner, GA 30257-3013
Larry Herndon, Director

Families United Services, Inc. **678.817.1120**
Fax 770.719.9738
Web ....www.familiesunitedse.com
500 Lanier Avenue West, Suite 904, Fayetteville,
GA 30214
CARF accredited programs available.

Family Empowerment Services, Inc. **678.610.4400**
Fax 678.610.0404
7130 Mount Zion Boulevard, Suite 7, Jonesboro,
GA 30236
CARF accredited programs available.

Family Works, Inc. **770.270.2231**
Fax 770.270.2234
Web ....www.familyworksga.com
1926 Northlake Parkway, Suite 101, Tucker,
GA 30084
CARF accredited programs available.

**Familys Matter Counseling and Psychological
Services** **404.602.0182**
E-mail ....vgrimes@fmcps.org
747 Lauren Parkway, Stone Mountain, GA 30083
Mr. Victor Grimes, Accreditation Manager
Joint Commission accredited organization.

Florence/Mcdonald Ctr **404.816.7171**
Fax 404.636.0849
Web ....www.florencemcdonnellcenter.org
E-mail ....adavis@florencemcdonnellcenter.org
2215 Cheshire Bridge Rd NE, Atlanta,
GA 30324-4234
T Albert Davis, Psychiatrist

Gateway Behavioral Health Services **912.554.8490**
Web ....www.gatewaybhs.org
3441 Cypress Mill Road, Suite 102, Brunswick,
GA 31522
CARF accredited programs available.

Genesis Alliance for Mental Wellness, LLC **404.501.0003**
Fax 404.501.0033
4540 Memorial Drive, Building C, Decatur, GA 30032
CARF accredited programs available.

**Georgia Baptist Children's Home Ellijay Group
Home** **706.276.3488**
Fax 706.276.3489
Web ....www.gbchfm.org
E-mail ....bparish@gbchfm.org
131 Lois Parks Dr, Ellijay, GA 30540
Becky Parish, Director

**Georgia Baptist Childrens Home Independent Living
Program** **770.567.8987**
Fax 770.567.3359
Web ....www.gbchsm.org
E-mail ....ahutcherson@gbchsm.org
2821 US Hwy 19, Meansville, GA 30256-2243
Allison Hutcherson, Administrator

Georgia Center **478.847.2900**
Fax 478.847.2899
Web ....www.rescare.com
211 Goose Hollow Road, Reynolds, GA 31076
Pam Anthony, Director
CARF accredited programs available.

Georgia Pines Community Service Board **229.225.4335**
E-mail ....jjackson@georgiapines.net
1102 Smith Avenue Suite K, Thomasville, GA 31799
Ms. Joni Jackson, Accreditation Manager
Joint Commission accredited organization.

Georgia Regional Hospital at Savannah **912.356.2011**
Web ....www.garegionalsavannah.com
E-mail ....mejones3@dhr.state.ga.us
1915 Eisenhower Drive, Savannah, GA 31406
Ms. Beth Jones, Accreditation Manager
Joint Commission accredited organization.

Georgia Sheriff's Youth Homes **706.845.9771**
Fax 706.845.8168
E-mail ....sgoddard@georgiasheriffsyouth.org
2048 Youngs Mill Rd, Lagrange, GA 30241
Shayne Goddard, Director

Good Shepherd Therapeutic Ctr **706.655.2354**
Fax 706.655.2347
Web ....www.gshepherd.org
E-mail ....ahutcherson@gshepherd.org
390 Bar Best Ranch Rd, Warm Springs,
GA 31830-2418
Alison Hutcherson, Executive Director

Grace Harbour, Inc. **770.716.1444**
Fax 678.669.2693
Web ....www.graceharbour.net
23 Eastbrook Bend, Suite 201, Peachtree City,
GA 30269
CARF accredited programs available.

Grady Memorial Hospital Corporation **404.616.4252**
Web ....gradyhealthsystem.org
E-mail ....fbaker@gmh.edu
80 Jesse Hill, Jr., Drive, S.E., Atlanta, GA 30303
Mrs. Fran Baker, Accreditation Manager
Joint Commission accredited organization.

GRN Community Service Board **770.339.5019**
Fax 770.339.5382
Web ....www.grncsb.com
175 Gwinnett Drive, Lawrenceville, GA 30045
CARF accredited programs available.

Haralson Behavioral Health Services **770.537.2367**
Fax 770.537.1203
405 Alabama Avenue, Bremen, GA 30110
CARF accredited programs available.

**Harris Counseling and Consulting Services,
Inc.** **770.607.7310**
Fax 770.607.7320
17 Felton Place, Suite D, Cartersville, GA 30120
CARF accredited programs available.

Hephzibah Ministries Incorporated **478.477.3383**
Fax 478.474.6370
Web ....www.hephzibah.com
6601 Zebulon Road, Macon, GA 31220-7606
COA accredited organization.

Heritage Foundation, Inc. **229.228.5545**
Fax 229.226.4755
Web ....www.heritageofthomasville.org
228 Gordon Avenue, Thomasville, GA 31792
CARF accredited programs available.

Highland Rivers Community Svcs Board **706.270.5000**
Fax 706.270.5124
Web ....www.highlandrivers.org
1710 Whitehouse Dr Ste 204, Dalton, GA 30720
Ann Davies, Interim Director

Hillside, Inc. **404.875.4551**
Fax 404.892.2201
Web ....www.hside.org
690 Courtenay Drive, Atlanta, GA 30306
CARF accredited programs available.

Hope House, Inc. **706.737.9879**
Fax 706.737.9830
PO Box 3597, Augusta, GA 30914
COA accredited organization.

Hopes of Honorable Youth, LLC **404.797.7126**
E-mail ....hohyouth@yahoo.com
130 W. Wieuca Suite 204 B, Atlanta, GA 30342
Mr. Montaya Wright, Accreditation Manager
Joint Commission accredited organization.

Horizons Family Services, Inc. **478.272.6060**
Fax 478.274.1158
1144 North Jefferson Street, Dublin, GA 31021
CARF accredited programs available.

**Hosanna Youth Facilities dba Hosanna Therapeutic Support
Services** **404.292.3000**
Fax 404.292.3007
4294 Memorial Drive, Suite C, Decatur, GA 30032
CARF accredited programs available.

IMANI Foundation, Inc. **404.584.6288**
Fax 404.584.6292
Web ....www.imaniinc.com
1074 Memorial Drive SE, Atlanta, GA 30316
CARF accredited programs available.

**Integrated Health Resources, LLC dba Behavioral Health
Link** **404.420.3202**
Fax 404.588.2289
Web ....www.behavioralhealthlink.com
260 Peachtree Street NW, Suite 1900, Atlanta,
GA 30303
CARF accredited programs available.

Joseph's Home For Boys **912.681.8526**
Fax 912.681.8701
E-mail ....amyjhb@frontiernet.net
3400 Cypress Lake Rd, Statesboro, GA 30458-8916
Amy Futch, Director

**KidsPeace National Centers of Georgia,
Inc.** **770.437.7200**
Web ....www.kidspeace.org
E-mail ....michael.merritt@kidspeace.org
101 KidsPeace Drive, Bowdon, GA 30108
Mr. Michael Merritt, Accreditation Manager
Joint Commission accredited organization.

Laurel Heights **404.888.7860**
Fax 404.888.6000
Web ....www.laurelheightshospital.com
E-mail ....lawrence.walker@uhsinc.com
934 Briarcliff Rd NE, Atlanta, GA 30306-2655
Lawrence Walker, Director Of Business Development

Laurel Heights Hospital **404.888.7860**
Web ....www.laurelheightshospital.com
E-mail ....mary.c.moore@uhsinc.com
934 Briarcliff Road, Northeast, Atlanta, GA 30306
Ms. Mary Moore, Accreditation Manager
Joint Commission accredited organization.

**Lookout Mountain Community Services
Board** **706.638.5580**
Fax 706.638.5445
Web ....www.lmcs.org
E-mail ....tomf@lmcs.org
501 Mize St, LaFayette, GA 30728
Tom Ford, Executive Director
CARF accredited programs available.

Macon Behavioral Health System **478.477.3829**
E-mail ....james.newton@uhsinc.com
   3500 Riverside Drive, Macon, GA 31210
   Mr. James Newton, Accreditation Manager
   Joint Commission accredited organization.

Malinda Graham and Associates, Inc. **912.877.7928**
Fax 614.388.3712
   445 E.G. Miles Parkway, Suite 108, Hinesville,
   GA 31313
   CARF accredited programs available.

Mary Hall Freedom House, Inc. **770.642.5500**
Fax 770.642.5406
Web ....www.maryhallfreedomhouse.org
E-mail ....barb.newman@mindspring.com
   200 Hannover Park Road, Suite 100, Sandy Springs,
   GA 30350
   Barb Newman, Director of Community Outreach
   CARF accredited programs available.

McIntosh Trail Community Service Board **770.358.8266**
Fax 770.229.3223
Web ....www.mctrail.org
   1501-A Kalamazoo Drive, Griffin, GA 30224
   CARF accredited programs available.

Mel Blount Youth Home **912.537.7758**
Fax 912.537.0825
Web ....www.byhga.org
   582 Mel Blount Rd, Vidalia, GA 30474
   Lesha Blount, Director

Metro Atlanta Counseling Services **678.284.1030**
Fax 678.284.1030
Web ....www.metroatlantacounselingservices.org
   194 Jonesboro Street, Suite D, Jonesboro, GA 30236
   CARF accredited programs available.

Mind, Body & Soul, LLC **678.793.6488**
E-mail ....victoria_linker@yahoo.com
   2221 Peachtree Road, Suite X16, Atlanta, GA 30309
   Ms. Victoria Linker, Accreditation Manager
   Joint Commission accredited organization.

**MLC Counseling Services dba Marvelous Light Consultants,
LLC** **404.286.0054**
Fax 404.286.0064
Web ....www.mlccounselingservices.com/
   4484 Covington Highway, Suite 100A, Decatur,
   GA 30035
   CARF accredited programs available.

**Morningstar Children and Family Services,
Inc.** **912.267.7583**
Fax 912.267.9568
Web ....www.morningstardvs.org
E-mail ....lmoore@morningstartreatmentservices.com
   100 March Dr, Brunswick, GA 31525
   Laura Moore, Director for Community
   CARF accredited programs available.

Murphy Harpst Children's Centers, Inc. **770.748.1500**
Web ....www.murphyharpst.org
E-mail ....jsimmons@murphyharpst.org
   740 Fletcher Street, Cedartown, GA 30125
   Ms. Joanne Simmons, Accreditation Manager
   Joint Commission accredited organization.

Murphy-Harpst Children's Ctr **770.748.1500**
Fax 770.749.1094
Web ....www.murphyharpst.org
E-mail ....ctroutman@murphyharpst.org
   740 Fletcher St, Cedartown, GA 30125-3297
   Chuck Troutman, President/CEO

New Heights Behavioral Consultants, Inc. **770.994.9099**
Fax 770.758.5731
   101 Devant Street, Suite 702, Fayetteville, GA 30214
   CARF accredited programs available.

New Hope Counseling Services, Inc. **678.750.2301**
Fax 678.750.1951
   2064 Eastside Drive, Suite 517, Conyers, GA 30013
   CARF accredited programs available.

New Horizons Community Svc Board **706.596.5583**
Fax 706.596.5589
E-mail ....mjones@newhorizonscsb.org
   2100 Comer Ave, Columbus, GA 31906
   Sherman Whitfield, Director

**Newport Integrated Behavioral Healthcare,
Inc.** **404.289.8223**
Fax 404.289.8224
Web ....www.nibhinc.com
   1810 Moseri Road, Decatur, GA 30032
   COA accredited organization.

**Newport Integrated Behavioral Healthcare,
Inc.** **404.289.8223**
Fax 404.289.8224
Web ....www.nibhinc.com
   4540 Glenwood Road, Decatur, GA 30032
   CARF accredited programs available.

North Georgia Angel House **770.479.9555**
Fax 404.935.9688
Web ....www.angelhousega.com
   2260 Sam Nelson Road, Canton, GA 30114
   CARF accredited programs available.

Northside Hospital, Inc. **404.851.8000**
Web ....www.northside.com
E-mail ....sharon.hester@northside.com
   1000 Johnson Ferry Road, Atlanta, GA 30342-1611
   Ms. Sharon Hester, Accreditation Manager
   Joint Commission accredited organization.

NW Georgia Family Crisis Ctr **706.278.6595**
Fax 706.278.2026
Web ....www.family-haven.org
E-mail ....bhiggins@alltel.net
   136 Nickie Dr, Dalton, GA 30720
   Betty Higgins, Director

NW Georgia Girls' Home **706.226.4862**
Fax 706.278.2522
Web ....www.windstream.net
   508 Chautan Ave, Dalton, GA 30722
   Reita Raughton, Administrator

Oconee Community Service Board **478.445.4817**
Fax 478.445.4963
Web ....www.oconeecenter.org
   131 North Jefferson Street, Milledgeville, GA 31061
   John Prather, Director
   CARF accredited programs available.

OGCC Behavioral Health Services, Inc. **404.691.3270**
Web ....www.ogcbhs.com
   1035 B Research Center Atlanta Drive, Atlanta,
   GA 30331
   COA accredited organization.

Ogeechee Behavioral Health Services **478.289.2522**
E-mail ....flawrence@obhs-ga.org
   223 North Anderson Drive, Swainsboro, GA 30401
   Ms. Faye Lawrence, Accreditation Manager
   Joint Commission accredited organization.

Oshi Behavioral Healthcare Institute **404.389.0882**
Fax 404.389.0885
   4286 Memorial Drive, Decatur, GA 30032
   CARF accredited programs available.

Pathways Ctr **706.845.4045**
Fax 706.845.4049
Web ....www.pathwayscsb.org
E-mail ....jturner@pathwayscsb.org
   122 Gordon Commercial Dr Ste C, Lagrange,
   GA 30240-5754
   Joan Turner, Executive Director

Pathways Transition Programs, Inc. **404.378.2300**
Fax 404.378.2394
Web ....www.pathwaystransitionprograms.com
   120 East Trinity Place, Decatur, GA 30030
   CARF accredited programs available.

Paul Anderson Youth Home **912.537.7237**
Fax 912.537.8734
Web ....www.payh.org
E-mail ....info@payh.org
   1603 McIntosh Street, Vidalia, GA 30474
   Glenda Anderson, Director

Peachford Behavioral Health System **770.455.3200**
Fax 770.454.5589
Web ....www.peachfordhospital.com
E-mail ....matt.crouch@uhsinc.com
   2151 Peachford Rd, Atlanta, GA 30338
   Matt Crouch, CEO

**Peachford Behavioral Health System of
Atlanta** **770.455.3200**
Web ....www.peachfordbhs.com
E-mail ....sharon.stackhouse@uhsinc.com
   2151 Peachford Road, Atlanta, GA 30338
   Ms. Sharon Stackhouse, Accreditation Manager
   Joint Commission accredited organization.

**Phoenix Center Behavioral Health
Services** **478.988.1002**
Fax 478.988.1106
Web ....www.phoenixcenterbhs.com
   940 GA Highway 96, Warner Robins, GA 31088
   CARF accredited programs available.

Pine Woods Retreat, Inc. **912.354.7447**
Fax 912.354.7448
Web ....www.PineWoodsRetreat.org
   1149 Cornell Avenue, Suite 3-A, Savannah,
   GA 31406-2757
   CARF accredited programs available.

**Pineland Mental Health/Developmental Disabilities/Addictive
Disease Services** **912.764.6906**
Fax 912.764.3252
Web ....www.pinelandcsb.org
   Five West Altman Street, Statesboro, GA 30458
   CARF accredited programs available.

**Pineland Mental Health/Mental Retardation/Substance
Abuse** **912.489.8641**
Fax 912.489.5987
Web ....www.pinelandcsb.org
E-mail ....lbradford@pinelandcsb.org
   211 Simons Rd, Statesboro, GA 30458-4322
   Michelle Williams, Specialist

ProActive Management Consulting, LLC **770.319.7468**
Fax 866.416.1767
Web ....www.proactive-management.com
E-mail ....jswafford@proactive-management.com
   2700 Cumberland Pkwy, Ste 120, Atlanta, GA 30339
   Joshua Swafford, Director of Groups and Workshops
   CARF accredited programs available.

Psychiatric Coliseum Hospital Ctr **478.741.1355**
Fax 478.464.8100
Web ....www.gspin.org
E-mail ....info@gspin.org
   340 Hospital Dr, Macon, GA 31217-3838
   Susan Nicholson, Director Of Admissions

Raintree Village, Inc. **229.559.5944**
Fax 229.559.7760
Web ....www.raintreevillage.org
E-mail ....kennyh@raintreevillage.org
   3757 Johnston Rd, Valdosta, GA 31601-2105
   Kenny Holton, Director
   COA accredited organization.

Recovery Outfitters, Inc. dba MASH **800.947.6550**
Fax 678.947.6594
Web ....www.serenityhouse.org
   1300 Peachtree Parkway, Cumming, GA 30041
   CARF accredited programs available.

Georgia

Recovery Place Inc **912.355.1440**
Fax 912.352.0802
Web ....www.recoveryplace.org
E-mail ....acanady@recoveryplace.org
835 E 65th St, Savannah, GA 31405
Allen Canady, Program Director
CARF accredited programs available.

Regeneration Project Georgia, LLC **478.971.4684**
378 Tabor Road, Fort Valley, GA 31030
CARF accredited programs available.

Reunited Counseling and Training, LLC **404.687.9188**
Fax 404.687.9189
Web ....www.reunitedcounseling.com
143 New Street, Decatur, GA 30030
CARF accredited programs available.

Richardson, Halsey & Associates, Inc. **404.298.0050**
5300 Memorial Place Drive, Suite 137, Stone
Mountain, GA 30083
CARF accredited programs available.

Ridgeview Institute **770.434.4567**
Web ....www.ridgeviewinstitute.com
E-mail ....fsartor@ridgeviewinstitute.com
3995 South Cobb Drive, Smyrna, GA 30080
Mr. Frank Sartor, Accreditation Manager
Joint Commission accredited organization.

River Edge Behavioral Health Center **478.751.4586**
Fax 478.752.1040
Web ....www.river-edge.org
175 Emery Highway, Macon, GA 31217
CARF accredited programs available.

River Edge Behavioral Health Center **478.751.4519**
Fax 478.752.1040
Web ....www.river-edge.org
175 Emery Highway, Macon, GA 31217
Shannon Harvey, Executive Director
CARF accredited programs available.

**RJ Shepherd II, Inc., dba Better Home Health Care of
Georgia** **678.547.0495**
Fax 678.547.0496
Web ....www.betterhomehealthcarega.com
4250 Perimeter Park South, Suite 101, Atlanta,
GA 30341
CARF accredited programs available.

Schools **770.887.2461**
Web www.forsyth.k12.ga.us
E-mail ....drondem@forsyth.k12.ga.us
1120 Dahlonega Hwy, Cumming, GA 30040-4536
Debbie Rondem, Director Of Student Support Services

**Serene Reflections For Holistic Behavior Wellness,
LLC** **404.892.2205**
Fax 404.892.2257
1750 Peachtree Street NE, Atlanta, GA 30309
CARF accredited programs available.

Serenity Behavioral Health Systems **706.432.3859**
Fax 706.432.3794
Web ....www.serenitybhs.com
3421 Mike Padgett Highway, Augusta, GA 30906
Chuck Williamson, CEO
CARF accredited programs available.

Solutions Community Services, Inc. **770.646.6806**
Fax 770.646.6809
123 Van Wert Street, Buchanan, GA 30113
CARF accredited programs available.

Southern Behavioral Svcs **478.742.1464**
Fax 478.742.1883
179 Pierce Ave, Macon, GA 31204-2821
Betsy Mills, Lpc, Counsellor

Southern Star Community Services **229.931.2470**
Fax 229.931.2474
Web ....www.sstarga.org
415 North Jackson Street, Americus, GA 31709
CARF accredited programs available.

Southwestern State Hospital **229.227.3020**
E-mail ....dlsmith@dhr.state.ga.us
400 South Pinetree Boulevard, Thomasville,
GA 31792
Mrs. Debra Smith, Accreditation Manager
Joint Commission accredited organization.

St. Francis Hospital, Inc. **706.596.4000**
Web ....www.wecareforlife.com
E-mail ....cornette@sfhga.com
2122 Manchester Expressway, Columbus, GA 31904
Mrs. Elaine Cornett, Accreditation Manager
Joint Commission accredited organization.

**Still Waters Professional Counseling Services,
Inc.** **706.597.1777**
Fax 706.597.0955
959 Augusta Road, Thomson, GA 30824
CARF accredited programs available.

Summerville Professionals **706.733.7029**
Fax 706.733.1376
2301 Wrightsboro Rd, Augusta, GA 30904-6296
Jill Hauenstein, Psychiatrist

Summit Ridge Hospital **678.442.5890**
Fax 678.442.5859
Web ....www.gwinnettmedicalcenter.org
E-mail ....nwarren@gwinnettmedicalcenter.org
250 Scenic Hwy, Lawrenceville, GA 30045-5675
Nancy Warren, Director Of Admissions

Tanner Medical Center / Villa Rica **770.456.3000**
Web ....www.tanner.org
E-mail ....lvalenti@tanner.org
601 Dallas Highway, Villa Rica, GA 30180
Ms. Lynne Valentie, Accreditation Manager
Joint Commission accredited organization.

Tanner Medical Center, Inc. **770.836.9580**
Web ....www.tanner.org
E-mail ....jdaniels@tanner.org
705 Dixie Street, Carrollton, GA 30117
Mrs. Janet Daniels, Accreditation Manager
Joint Commission accredited organization.

Tattnall Counseling Svcs **912.557.6794**
Fax 912.557.6817
E-mail ....cdekle@dhr.state.ga.us
150 Memorial Dr., Reidsville, GA 30453
Cynthia Dekle, Mental Health Coordinator

The ARK Family Counseling Center, Inc. **770.593.0913**
Fax 770.808.3269
4256 Clausell Court, Suite B, Decatur, GA 30035
CARF accredited programs available.

The Bridges Center, Inc. **770.451.6838**
Fax 770.451.7804
Web ....www.thebridgescenter.com
E-mail ....nleath@thebridgescenter.com
3855 Presidential Parkway, Atlanta, GA 30340
Nancia Leath, Clinical Director
CARF accredited programs available.

**The Center for Creative Growth and Human
Development** **706.884.1080**
Fax 706.812.8866
Web ....www.ccghumandevelopment.com
111B Corporate Park East, LaGrange, GA 30240
CARF accredited programs available.

**The Children and Teenagers Foundation,
Inc.** **404.299.2087**
Fax 404.299.3564
Web ....http://www.catfoundation.com
4151 Memorial Drive, Suite 204-A, Decatur,
GA 30032
CARF accredited programs available.

**The Potter's House Family and Children Treatment
Center** **678.987.1020**
Fax 678.987.1019
Web ....http://www.thepottershouseinc.org
1899 Parker Court, Stone Mountain, GA 30087
CARF accredited programs available.

**Toxicology Associates of North Georgia Carrollton,
Inc.** **770.214.9788**
Fax 770.214.9803
2536 Carrollton-villa Rica Highway, Carrollton,
GA 30117
COA accredited organization.

**Toxicology Associates of North Georgia Gwinnett,
Inc.** **770.248.1616**
Fax 770.248.1618
751 Collins Hill Road, Lawrenceville, GA 30043
COA accredited organization.

**Toxicology Associates of North Georgia,
Inc.** **770.612.8264**
Fax 770.612.0716
1700 Cumberland Point Drive, Suite 1, Marietta,
GA 30067
COA accredited organization.

Twin Cedars Youth Svcs, Inc. Bradfield Ctr **706.884.1717**
Fax 706.884.8321
E-mail ....info@twincedars.org
1022 E Depot St, Lagrange, GA 30241-3412
Mike Angstadt, Executive Director

UHS of Anchor, LP **770.991.6044**
Web ....www.southerncrescentbhs.com
E-mail ....connie.whitlock@uhsinc.com
5454 Yorktowne Drive, Atlanta, GA 30349
Mrs. Connie Whitlock, Accreditation Manager
Joint Commission accredited organization.

**Underdue Social Services/Embracing Arms,
Inc.** **770.477.5225**
Fax 770.477.2552
Web ....www.underduesocialservices.com
165 Burke Street, Stockbridge, GA 30281
CARF accredited programs available.

Union Mission, Inc. **912.236.7423**
Fax 912.236.3907
Web ....www.unionmission.org
120 Fahm Street, Savannah, GA 31401
CARF accredited programs available.

United Methodist Children's Home **404.327.5820**
Fax 404.327.5822
Web ....www.umchildrenshome.org
E-mail ....bcochran@umchildrenshome.org
500 S Columbia Dr, Decatur, GA 30030-4197
Beverly O. Cochran, Administrator

Vashti Ctr **229.226.4634**
Fax 229.225.1093
Web ....www.vashti.org
E-mail ....vashti@vashti.org
1815 E Clay St, Thomasville, GA 31792-4797
Ralph Comerford, Executive Director

Village Keepers, Inc **404.761.1500**
Fax 404.559.7899
E-mail ....villagekeepers@bellsouth.net
3020 Bayard Street, East Point, GA 30344
Sheila Joyner-pritchard, Msw, Cpp, Executive Director/CEO

West Central Georgia Regional Hospital **706.568.5203**
Web ....www.wcgrh.org
E-mail ....bemoore@dhr.state.ga.us
3000 Schatulga Road, Columbus, GA 31907-1035
Ms. B. Cheyenne Moore, Accreditation Manager
Joint Commission accredited organization.

WestCare Georgia, Inc. **770.469.8480**
Fax 770.469.1024
Web ....www.westcare.com
2818 Lakewood Avenue, Atlanta, GA 30315
CARF accredited programs available.

Wide Range of Resources, Inc. 478.451.3112
Fax 478.451.0626
　　1776 North Jefferson Street, Suite B, Milledgeville,
　　GA 31061
　　CARF accredited programs available.

Willingway Hospital 912.764.6236
Web ....www.willingway.com
E-mail ....breid@willingway.com
　　311 Jones Mill Road, Statesboro, GA 30458
　　Mrs. Barbara Reid, Accreditation Manager
　　Joint Commission accredited organization.

Yes-U-Can Behavioral Health, Inc. 404.564.9831
Fax 404.564.9837
Web ....http://www.yucinc.com
　　777 Cleveland Avenue, Suite 605, Atlanta, GA 30315
　　CARF accredited programs available.

Young Adult Guidance Center, Inc. 404.792.7616
Fax 404.794.0151
Web ....www.yagc.net
　　1230 Hightower Road NW, Atlanta, GA 30318
　　Marion Simpson, Executive Director
　　CARF accredited programs available.

CHILDREN'S HOSPITAL

Athens Regional Medical Center 706.475.7000
　　1199 Prince Ave, Athens, GA 30606
　　John Drew, Chief Executive Officer

Cobb Memorial Hospital 706.245.5071
　　521 Franklin Springs St, Royston, GA 30662
　　Chuck Adams, Chief Executive Officer

Coffee Regional Medical Center 912.384.1900
　　1101 Ocilla Rd, Douglas, GA 31533
　　George Heck, Chief Executive Officer

Colquitt Regional Medical Center 229.985.3420
　　3131 South Main St, Moultrie, GA 31768

Community Hospital 706.282.4200
　　163 Hospital Dr, Toccoa, GA 30577
　　Ed Gambrell, Administrator

Community Hospital 706.856.6100
　　Gibson and Cade Streets, Hartwell, GA 30643
　　Julie Ridgeway, Director

Crisp Regional Hospital 229.276.3100
　　902 North Seventh St, Cordele, GA 31015
　　Steve Gautney, Chief Executive Officer

DeKalb Medical Center 404.501.1000
　　2701 North Decatur Rd, Decatur, GA 30033
　　Eric Norwood, Chief Executive Officer

Dorminy Medical Center 229.424.7100
　　Perry House Road, Fitzgerald, GA 31750
　　Warren Manley, Director

Dwight David Eisenhower Army
MedicalCtr 706.787.5811
　　300 Hospital Dr, Fort Gordon, GA 30905
　　General Ganble, Commander

East Georgia Regional Medical Center 912.486.1000
　　1499 Fair Rd, Statesboro, GA 30458
　　Jim Rayes, Human Resource Director

Fairview Park Hospital 478.275.2000
　　200 Industrial Blvd, Dublin, GA 31021
　　Don Avery, Chief Executive Officer

Fannin Regional Hospital 706.632.3711
　　2855 Old Highway 5, Blue Ridge, GA 30513
　　David Sanders, Chief Executive Officer

Floyd Medical Center 706.509.5000
　　304 Turner McCall Blvd, Rome, GA 30165
　　Kurt Stuankel, Chief Executive Officer

Gwinnett Medical Center 678.312.4321
　　1000 Medical Center Blvd, Lawrenceville, GA 30046
　　Nick Tea, Director

Hamilton Medical Center 706.272.6000
　　1200 Memorial Dr, Dalton, GA 30720
　　Jeff Myers, Chief Executive Officer

Henry Medical Center 678.604.1000
　　1133 Eagles Landing Pkwy, Stockbridge, GA 30281
　　Charles Scott, Administrator

Houston Medical Center 478.922.4281
　　1601 Watson Blvd, Warner Robins, GA 31093
　　Steven Machen, Administrator

John D Archbold Memorial Hospital 229.228.2000
　　915 Gordon Ave, Thomasville, GA 31792
　　Harry Mustian, President

Kennestone Hospital 770.793.5000
　　677 Church St, Marietta, GA 30060
　　Candice Saunders, Hospital Administrator

MCG Health 706.721.0211
　　1120 15th St, Augusta, GA 30912
　　Ricareo Azziz, Chief Executive Officer

Medical Center 706.571.1000
　　710 Center St, Columbus, GA 31901
　　Lance Duke, Director

Medical Center 706.754.2161
　　541 Historic Highway 441, Demorest, GA 30535
　　Richard Dwozan, President

Medical Center of Central Georgia 478.633.1000
　　777 Hemlock St, Macon, GA 31201
　　Don Saulk, Chief Executive Officer

Memorial University Medical Center 912.350.8000
E-mail ....grineal1@memorialhealth.com
　　4700 Waters Ave, Savannah, GA 31404
　　Alisa Griner, Director

Newton Medical Center 770.786.7053
　　5126 Hospital Dr, Covington, GA 30014
　　James Weadick, Administrator/CEO

Northeast Georgia Medical Center 770.219.3553
　　743 Spring Street NE, Gainesville, GA 30501

Oconee Regional Medical Center 478.454.3500
　　821 North Cobb St, Milledgeville, GA 31061
　　Jean Aycock, Chief Executive Officer

Perry Hospital 478.987.3600
　　1120 Morningside Dr, Perry, GA 31069
　　David Campbell, Administrator

Phoebe Putney Memorial Hospital 229.312.1000
　　417 Third Ave, Albany, GA 31701
　　Joe Warnick, Chief Executive Officer

Piedmont Mountainside Hospital 706.692.2441
　　1266 Highway 515 South, Jasper, GA 30143
　　Linda Stead, Nursing Director

Satilla Regional Medical Center 912.283.3030
　　410 Darling Ave, Waycross, GA 31501
　　Robert Trimm, Chief Executive Officer

South Georgia Medical Center 229.333.1000
　　2501 North Patterson St, Valdosta, GA 31602
　　James McGahee, Chief Executive Officer

Spalding Regional Medical Center 770.228.2721
E-mail ....wadra.mcullough@tenethealth.com
　　601 South Eighth St, Griffin, GA 30224
　　Wadra McCullough, Nursing Director

St Josephs Candler 912.819.6000
　　5353 Reynolds St, Savannah, GA 31405
　　Paul Hinchey, Chief Executive Officer

Tift Regional Medical Center 229.382.7120
　　901 East 18th St, Tifton, GA 31794
　　William Richardson, Chief Executive Officer

Union General Hospital 706.745.2111
E-mail ....rebeccadyer@uniongeneral.org
　　35 Hospital Rd, Blairsville, GA 30512
　　Rebecca Dyer, Chief Executive Officer

University Hospital 706.722.9011
E-mail ....university@helph.org
　　1350 Walton Way, Augusta, GA 30901
　　Jim Davis, Chief Executive Officer

WellStar Cobb Hospital 770.732.4000
　　3950 Austell Rd, Austell, GA 30106
　　Randy Cook, Administrator

WellStar Douglas Hospital 770.949.1500
　　8954 Hospital Dr, Douglasville, GA 30134
　　Ann Smith, Secretary To Administrator

West Georgia Health 706.882.1411
　　1514 Vernon Rd, La Grange, GA 30240
　　Gerald Fulka, President

COUNSELING SERVICES

Carpenter's Way Ranch 706.322.5406
Fax 706.322.5450
Web ....www.carpentersway.org
E-mail ....info@carpentersway.org
　　1645 Hunter Rd, Cataula, GA 31804
　　Bob Lynch, Director

Catholic Charities Of The Archdicese Of
Atlanta 404.881.6571
Fax 404.888.7816
E-mail ....jkrygiel@archatl.com
　　680 W Peachtree St NW, Atlanta, GA 30308-1984
　　Joe Krygiel, Director

Families First 404.853.2844
Fax 404.815.4100
Web ....www.familiesfirst.org
E-mail ....pat@familiesfirst.org
　　1105 W Peachtree St NW, Atlanta, GA 30309
　　Patricia Showell, President & CEO

Families First 404.853.2800
Fax 404.685.0203
Web ....www.familiesfirst.org
E-mail ....kim@familiesfirst.org
　　1105 W Peachtree St NE, Atlanta, GA 30309
　　Kim Anderson, Chief Executive Officer

Family Connections 912.368.7531
Fax 912.368.7563
　　1113 East Oglethorpe Highway, Hinesville, GA 31313
　　Sandra Jenkins, Program Coordinator

Georgia Baptist Children's Home 770.460.6652
Fax 770.460.6685
　　101 Devant St, Fayetteville, GA 30214-7336
　　Sandra Johnson, Program Director

Jewish Family And Career Svcs 770.677.9300
Fax 770.677.9400
Web ....www.jfcs-atlanta.org
　　4549 Chamblee Dunwoody Rd, Atlanta,
　　GA 30338-6210
　　Gary Miller, Executive Director

Sunflower LifeStyle Assessment Center,
LLC 678.715.4683
Fax 678.715.3432
　　8328 Office Park Drive, Suites A & C, Douglasville,
　　GA 30134
　　CARF accredited programs available.

Tapestry Youth Ministries 404.767.5580
Fax 404.767.5581
Web ....www.tapestryyouth.org
　　1773 Hawthorne Ave, Atlanta, GA 30337
　　Rutha Greene, Executive Director

United Methodist Children's Home 706.278.4010
Fax 706.275.6796
Web ....www.mlachapelle@umchildrenshome.org
　　1615 Hickory St # 118, Dalton, GA 30720
　　J. Mike Lachapelle, Supervisor

CRISIS & SHELTER CARE

Administrative Ofc-Emergency Shelter 770.834.9178
Fax 770.834.2566
Web ....www.smipc.net
E-mail ....cces@smipc.net
PO Box 2192, Carrollton, GA 30112-0041
Martha Boyce, Director

Assoc. Against Family Violence 770.960.7153
Fax 770.961.1038
Web ....www.securushouse.org
PO Box 870386, Morrow, GA 30287-0386
Patricia Altemus, Director

Brandon Hall School 770.394.8177
Fax 770.804.8821
Web ....www.brandonhall.org
1701 Brandon Hall Dr, Atlanta, GA 30350
John L Singelton, President

Cherokee Family-Violence Ctr 770.479.1804
Fax 770.720.4834
E-mail ....mrogers@aol.com
130 E Main St, Ste 212, Canton, GA 30114-2784
Meg Rogers, Director

Christian Women's Ctr 770.227.3700
Fax 678.688.3842
174 School Road, Sunny Side, GA 30284
Stephanie Summers, Director

Domestic Violence 770.386.8093
Fax 770.386.4490
Web ....www.tranquilityhouse.cbeyond.com
E-mail ....Director@Tranquilityhouse.Cbeyond.Com
135 W Cherokee Ave Ste 217B, Cartersville,
GA 30120
Sandra Bruce, Director

Family Haven 770.889.6384
Fax 770.205.1350
E-mail ....scoffey@family-haven.org
103 Pilgrim Village Dr, Cumming, GA 30040
Shalon Coffey, Director

Freesa Property-Domestic Violence
Shelter 229.226.0376
Fax 229.226.6685
E-mail ....halcyon@rose.net
PO Box 1838, Thomasville, GA 31799-1838
Chris Marsh, Director

Gateway 770.536.5860
Fax 770.539.9990
Web ....www.gatewaydvcenter.org
E-mail ....gatewayh@bellsouth.net
PO Box 2962, Gainesville, GA 30503-2962
Jessica Butler, Director

Georgia Baptist Children's Homes & Family Ministry,
Inc...770.463.3344
Fax 770.463.8208
Web ....www.gbchfm.org
E-mail ....drelyea@gbchfm.org
9250 Hutchinson Ferry Road, Palmetto, GA 30268
Debbie Relyea, Administrator

Georgia Sheriff's Boys Ranch 229.794.2606
Fax 229.794.3054
Web ....www.georgiasheriffsyouth.org
E-mail ....gsbranch@alltel.net
PO Box 100, Hahira, GA 31632-0100
Beth Tillman, Director

Georgia Sheriff's Youth Homes Cherokee
Estates 706.259.8581
Fax 706.259.9493
Web ....www.georgiasheriffsyouth.org
E-mail ....cherokee_estate@yahoo.com
850 Cherokee Estate Rd NE, Dalton, GA 30721-8807
Nikita Jordan, Director

Gwinnett Children's Shelter 678.546.8770
Fax 678.546.8775
Web ....www.gwinnettchildrenshelter.org
E-mail ....info@gwinnettchildrenshelter.org
3850 Tuggle Rd, Buford, GA 30519
Kim Phillips, Executive Director

Haven House 770.954.1008
Fax 770.954.9203
Web ....www.henryhavenhouse.org
E-mail ....mlacy@henryhavenhouse.org
3234 Jodeco Rd, Mcdonough, GA 30253
Marjorie Lacy, Director

Hospitality House For Women, Inc 706.235.4608
Fax 706.235.4084
Web ....www.hospitalatyhouseforwomen.org
PO Box 5163, Rome, GA 30162-5163
Amy Weaver, Director

International Women's Health 770.413.5557
Fax 678.476.6804
Web ....www.internationalwomenshouse.org
E-mail ....lwh@Bellsouth.Net
PO Box 1327, Decatur, GA 30031-1327
Anna Blau, Director

Methodist Home For Children 229.924.9550
Fax 229.924.8332
E-mail ....judy.tott@themethodisthome.org
100 Millcreek Rd, Americus, GA 31709-9207
Judy Tott, Director

Northern Georgia Mountain Crisis
Network 706.632.8401
Fax 706.632.1007
PO Box 1249, Blue Ridge, GA 30513-0022
Linda Holler, Director

Open Door Home 706.232.6662
Fax 706.235.6230
Web ....www.opendoorhome.org
E-mail ....cgibson@opendoorhome.org
5 Leon St SW, Rome, GA 30165-4099
Carman Gibson, Director

Peace Place 770.307.3633
Fax 770.586.0957
E-mail ....peaceplace@peaceplaceinc.org
PO Box 948, Winder, GA 30680-0948
Char Garrett, Director

Project Safe Inc 706.543.3331
Fax 706.354.6161
Web ....www.project-safe.org
E-mail ....pjctsafe@bellsouth.net
PO Box 7532, Athens, GA 30604-7532
Joan Prittie, Executive Director

Ruth's Cottage 229.387.9697
Fax 229.387.8800
E-mail ....director@ruthscottage.com
107 Magnolia Drive #223, Tifton, GA 31794
Vicki Parsons, Executive Director

Safe Harbor Children's Shelter/Main Ofc 912.267.6000
Fax 912.267.0872
Web ....www.safeharborcenterinc.org
E-mail ....lhartman@safeharborcenterinc.org
2215 Gloucester St, Brunswick, GA 31520-6912
Leslie Hartman, Director

Safe-Domestic Violence Program 706.379.1901
Fax 706.379.1910
Web ....www.safeservices.org
E-mail ....info@safeservices.org
4376 Wren Dr, Blairsville, GA 30512
Kathie Hollis, Director

Share House 770.489.7513
Fax 770.947.7771
E-mail ....dcshare@bellsouth.net
8460 Courthouse Sq E Fl 4, Douglasville, GA 30133
Teresa Smith, Director

The Alcove, Inc...............................770.267.9156
Fax 770.207.9162
E-mail ....alcove_shelter@yahoo.com
507 E Church St, Monroe, GA 30655-2511
Dorothy Morrow, Executive Director

The Bridge 404.792.0070
Fax 404.794.0444
Web ....www.thebridge-atlanta.org
E-mail ....trussell@thebridge-atlanta.org
1559 Johnson Rd NW, Atlanta, GA 30318-4017
Tom Russell, Executive Director

The Ctr For Children And Young Adults 770.333.9447
Fax 770.333.1646
Web ....www.ccyakids.org
2221 Austell Rd SW, Ste A, Marietta, GA 30008
Kim Borna, Executive Director

The Haven 229.244.4477
Fax 229.224.2256
Web ....www.Valdostahaven.Org
E-mail ....Mrowe@Valdostahaven.Org
PO Box 5382, Valdosta, GA 31603-5382
Mandy K Rowe, Director

The Refuge Domestic Violence Shelter 912.538.9936
Fax 912.538.9910
E-mail ....betty@bellsouth.net
128 Church Street, Vidalia, GA 30475
Betty Dell Williams, Director

EDUCATION

Adaptive Learning Ctr 770.509.3909
Fax 770.509.5036
Web ....www.adaptivelearningcenter.org
E-mail ....alckids@alckids.org
736 Johnson Ferry Rd Ste C 245, Marietta, GA 30068
Kathy Ward, Program Director

Atlanta Job Corps Ctr 404.794.9512
Fax 404.794.8426
Web ....www.altjec.org
E-mail ....matthews.annie@jobcorps.org
239 W Lake Ave NW, Atlanta, GA 30314-1894
Annie T. Matthews, Center Director

Atlanta Speech School Katharine Ham Ctr 404.233.5332
Fax 404.266.2175
Web ....www.atlantaspeechschool.org
3160 Northside Pkwy NW, Atlanta, GA 30327
Shelly Carr, Coordinator

Bethesda Home For Boys 912.351.2042
Fax 912.351.2060
Web ....www.bethesdahomeforboys.org
E-mail ....dtribble@bethesdahomeforboys.org
9520 Ferguson Ave, Savannah, GA 31406-6332
David Tribble, Director

Broken Shakle Ranch, Inc....................478.348.6555
Fax 478.348.3652
Web ....www.brokenshakle.org
E-mail ....info@bsranch.org
1542 Francis Bridge Rd, Davisboro, GA 31018
David Cobb, Administrator

Brunswick Job Corps Ctr 912.264.8843
Fax 912.267.7192
Web ....www.jobcorps.org
E-mail ....gainesm@jcdc.jobcorps.org
4401 Glynco Pkwy, Brunswick, GA 31525-6853
Mel Gaines, Center Director

Frazer Ctr Children's Program 404.377.3836
Fax 404.373.0058
Web ....www.thefrazercenter.org
E-mail ....c.turner@thefrazercenter.org
1815 Ponce De Leon Ave NE, Atlanta, GA 30307
Cynthia Turner, Executive Director

Georgia Parent Infant Network For Education Svcs (GAPINES) **404.298.4882**
Fax 404.298.3610
E-mail .... sullivan@doe.k12.ga.us
890 N Indian Creek Dr, Clarkston, GA 30021
Claire H. Sullivan, Education Program Director

Horizon Academy **229.333.5227**
Fax 229.245.2398
E-mail .... sclemons@lowndes.k12.ga.us
1500 Lankford Dr Ste A, Valdosta, GA 31601
Dr Samuel Clemons, Director

Mill Springs Academy **770.360.1336**
Fax 770.360.1341
Web .... www.millsprings.org
E-mail .... sfitzgerald@millsprings.org
13660 New Providence Rd, Alpharetta, GA 30004-3413
Lavone Rippeon, Administrator

Northeast Georgia Speech Ctr **770.534.5141**
Fax 770.534.5141
E-mail .... dianebrower@bellsouth.net
604 Washington St Ste B2, Gainesville, GA 30501
Diane Brower, Med, Ccc-slp, Executive Director

Parent And Child Development Svcs, Inc. **912.238.2777**
Fax 912.238.2773
Web .... www.unionmissions.org
505 E 54th St, Savannah, GA 31405-3515
Deanny Bean, Vice President

Pathways **229.225.3910**
Fax 229.225.5283
E-mail .... jwier@rose.net
208 N Pinetree Blvd, Thomasville, GA 31792
Janine Wier, Director

Safe Homes Crisis Hotline **706.736.2499**
Fax 706.736.8558
Web .... www.augusta-safehome.org
E-mail .... ahall@safehomeofaugusta.org
904 Merry St, Augusta, GA 30904
Aimee Hall, Executive Director

The Howard School **404.377.7436**
Fax 404.377.0884
Web .... www.howardschool.org
E-mail .... mcilella@howardschool.org
1192 Foster St NW, Atlanta, GA 30318-4329
Marifred Cilella, Head Of School

Turner Job Corps Ctr **229.883.8500**
Fax 229.434.0383
Web .... www.turnerjobcorp.org
2000 Schilling Ave, Albany, GA 31705-1524
Rose Walker-Cook, Center Director

FOSTER CARE AGENCIES

Adoptive & Foster Parent Assoc of GA **404.918.1956**
155 W Ridge Pkwy, Ste 305, McDonough, GA 30253
Tony Blash

Christian Adoption Consultants **770.313.8063**
Fax 866.226.0669
E-mail .... info@christianadoptionconsultants.com
1353 Riverstone Pkwy, Ste 120-386, Canton, GA 30114

CSRA-COAC Prnt Sprt Coord Ofc of Adptn **706.863.6241**
3739 Roscommon N, Martinez, GA 30907

Cthlic Chrites ofthe Archdiocese of AT l **404.885.7275**
Fax 404.888.7816
680 W Peachtree St NW, Atlanta, GA 30308
Jutta Hansen, Office Manager

Families First **404.853.2800**
E-mail .... peggy@familiesfirst.org
1105 NE W Peachtree St, Atlanta, GA 30309
Kim Anderson, Director

Independent Adoption Center (IAC) **404.321.6900**
Fax 404.321.6600
E-mail .... staff@adoptionhelp.org
3774 Lavista Rd, Ste 100, Tucker, GA 30084
Ann Wrixon, Director

KidsPeace Bowdon Campus **888.421.5437**
Fax 770.258.9129
Web .... www.kidspeace.org
101 KidsPeace Dr, Bowdon, GA 30108

Lifeline Children's Services Inc **706.571.3346**
E-mail .... lcsga@lifelineadoption.org
1316 Wynnton Ct, Ste A, Columbus, GA 31906
Daniel Taylor, Director

Lowndes Area Adoption Support Group **229.247.8030**
PO Box 372, Valdosta, GA 31603
Cathy Burks, Coordinator

Lutheran Services of Georgia **912.355.9179**
Fax 912.355.1499
E-mail .... llarson@lsga.org
6555 Abercorn St, Ste 200, Savannah, GA 31405
Linda Larson, Office Manager

My Turn Now Georgia **800.603.1322**
2 Peachtree St NE, Ste 8-102, Atlanta, GA 30303
Ann Deibel, Supervisor

Roots Adoption Agency Inc **404.209.7077**
Fax 404.209.7277
Web .... www.galaa.org
1007 Virginia Ave, Ste 100, Hapeville, GA 30354

The Open Door Adoption Agency Inc (TOD) **229.228.6339**
Fax 229.228.4726
E-mail .... opendoor@rose.net
218 E Jackson St, Thomasville, GA 31799
Walter Gilbert, Chief Executive Officer

Tiftarea Foster Care & Adoption In **229.848.2753**
Fax 229.387.6830
E-mail .... cbgraham@gdph.state.ga.us
4504 Lee Anne Dr, PO Box 2307, Tifton, GA 31793
Carlos Graham, Director

HOME MEDICAL EQUIPMENT PROVIDERS

Abilitations **800.850.8602**
Fax 800.845.1535
E-mail .... orders@sportime.com
PO Box 922668, Norcross, GA 30010

Flex-A-Bed **800.648.1256**
E-mail .... info@flexabed.com
1825 Hilldale Rd, La Fayette, GA 30728
Max Morrison, President

Sportaid **770.554.5944**
Fax 770.554.5130
E-mail .... stuff@sportaid.com
78 Bay Creek Rd, Loganville, GA 30052

Weatherly Medical/Consultant, Inc. **912.351.0760**
Fax 912.351.0830
7135 Hodgson Memorial Drive, Suite 1A, Savannah, GA 31406
CARF accredited programs available.

PEDIATRIC HOME CARE

Bayada Nurses **770.992.4660**
Fax 770.992.4430
Web .... www.bayada.com
9755 Dogwood Road, Ste 150, Roswell, GA 30075
Douglas Mcnew, Director

Bayada Nurses **770.297.8901**
Fax 770.297.4774
Web .... www.bayada.com
E-mail .... GAI-TEAM@BAYADA.COM
311 Green Street, Suite 300, Gainesville, GA 30501
Doug Mcnew, Director

Bayada Nurses **678.352.9000**
Fax 678.352.9700
Web .... www.bayada.com
The Pavilion Center, 9755 Dogwood Rd, Suite 140, Roswell, GA 30075
Lawrence Schlava, Director

Bayada Nurses **770.992.4660**
Fax 770.992.4430
Web .... www.bayada.com
1145 Highway 80 West, Suite H, Pooler, GA 31322
Gouboas Mcnew, Director

Cartersville PDN (Recruiting Center) **770.607.4208**
1 Townsley Dr Ste A, Cartersville, GA 30120
Pilar Catlin

Grovetown PDN (Augusta) **706.868.6543**
444 Park West Dr, Grovetown, GA 30813
Dodie Sutton, Mgr.

Interim Healthcare **404.856.6124**
Fax 678.235.3100
3915 Cascade Rd Ste 240, Atlanta, GA 30331
Lauri Sanders, Manager

Interim Healthcare **404.843.2708**
Fax 404.843.1058
6000 Lake Forrest Dr, Atlanta, GA 30328
Pat Gilley, Chief Executive Officer

Interim Healthcare **404.974.3111**
1395 S Marietta Pkwy, Bldg 400 Ste 104, Marietta, GA 30067

Macon PDN **478.841.2772**
E-mail .... hmathis@psahealthcare.com
770 Baconsfield Dr, Bldg 1, Macon, GA 31211
Holly Mathis, Pdn Administrator

Marietta PPEC (Atlanta North) **770.321.6600**
2217 Roswell Rd Ste A-100, Marietta, GA 30062
Cathy Bell, Director

Norcross PDN (Atlanta) **770.263.6373**
310 Technology Pkwy Ste A, Norcross, GA 30092
Christy Carey, Director

Savannah PDN **912.961.1017**
37 W Fairmont Ave Unit 207, Savannah, GA 31406
Marie Evans, Director

SOCIAL SERVICES

Adoption Law Ofc **912.236.7863**
Fax 912.236.7811
420 W Broughton St, Savannah, GA 31401
Birney Bull, Attorney

Alliance for Change Through Treatment, LLC **678.406.9707**
Fax 678.406.9881
Web .... www.actga.com
3548 Habersham at Northlake, Building F, Tucker, GA 30084
CARF accredited programs available.

Armed Svcs YMCA Savannah **912.368.9622**
Fax 912.369.2002
E-mail .... leec@ymcaofcoastalga.org
201 Mary Lou Dr, Hinesville, GA 31313
Lee Coggess, Executive Director

Athens Community Council on Aging **706.549.4850**
Fax 706.549.7786
E-mail .... volunteers@accaging.org
135 Hoyt St, Athens, GA 30601-2646
Jennie Deese, Director

Baxley Wilderness Institute **912.367.3383**
Fax 912.367.3407
Web .... www.amikids.org
1510 Deens Landing Rd, Baxley, GA 31513
James Culverhouse, Executive Director

Ben Massell Dental Clinic **404.881.1858**
Fax 404.885.1581
700 NW 14th St, Atlanta, GA 30318

Brightstar Homes and Services, Inc...........678.491.1561
Fax...770.914.1605
148 Summit View Drive, McDonough, GA 30253
COA accredited organization.

Catholic Charities of the Archdiocese of Atlanta,
Inc....404.881.6571
Fax...404.885.7477
680 W. Peachtree Street, NW, Atlanta, GA 30308
COA accredited organization.

Catholic Diocese Of Savannah..............912.201.4100
Fax...912.201.4101
Web...www.diosav.org
601 E Liberty St, Savannah, GA 31401-5196
Kevin Boland, Bishop

Child & Adolescent After School Svcs.........706.437.6857
Fax...706.437.6858
Web...www.obhs-ga.org
305 Park Dr, Waynesboro, GA 30830-1638
Dan Barnard, Director

Child and Family Guidance of Georgia,
Inc....478.451.5205
Fax...478.451.5024
325 North Cobb Street, Unit B, Milledgeville,
GA 31061
CARF accredited programs available.

Child Care Resource And Referral Of Metro
Atlanta...404.479.4240
Fax...404.479.4166
Web..................................www.qualitycareforchildren.org
E-mail.....................pam.runkle@qualitycareforchildren.org
50 Executive Park South NE Ste 5015, Atlanta,
GA 30329-2214
Pam Runkle, Executive Director

Children's Healthcare of Atlanta..............404.785.7100
Fax...404.785.4449
Web...www.choa.org/rehab
E-mail..........................susannah.kidwell@choa.org
1001 Johnson Ferry Rd NE, Atlanta, GA 30342-1605
Susannah Kidwell, Rehabilitation Services Director

Clinical Intervention Specialists, LLC.........678.422.0723
Fax...678.802.1970
696 Mount Zion Road, Suite C9, Jonesboro,
GA 30236
CARF accredited programs available.

Cobb Office.......................................770.933.0081
1501 Johnson Ferry Rd Ste 100, Marietta, GA 30062

Come Alive Ministries-Barrow...............770.867.3000
Fax...770.867.3000
38 S Broad St Ste 200, Winder, GA 30680-2057
Dee Toliver, Director

Cornerstones Counseling Center, Inc..........706.348.8674
Fax...706.348.8676
Web...cornercc.com
42 North Avenue, Suite 100, Cleveland, GA 30528
CARF accredited programs available.

Creative Community Services, Inc.............770.469.6226
Fax...678.894.4081
Web...www.ccsgeorgia.org
4487 Park Drive, Suite A, Norcross, GA 30093-2964
COA accredited organization.

Ctr For The Visually Impaired...............404.875.9011
Fax...404.607.0062
Web...www.cviga.org
E-mail..sgreen@cviga.org
739 W Peachtree St NW, Atlanta, GA 30308-1137
Cheryl Blewitt, Director Of Client Services

Darsey, Black and Associates, LLC...........912.876.4010
Fax...912.369.2262
215 East Court Street, Hinesville, GA 31313
COA accredited organization.

Developmental Evaluation Clinic............404.508.6413
Fax...404.508.6443
Web...www.dekalbcsb.org
440 Winn Way, Decatur, GA 30030
Carolyn Richardson-atubeh, Director

Douglasville Psychological Outpatient
Svcs...678.838.9336
Fax...678.838.3619
8304 Office Park Dr, Douglasville, GA 30134
Margaret Johns, Office Manager

Edmondson/Telford Ctr For Children.........770.534.5151
Fax...770.534.5754
E-mail..etcenter@bellsouth.net
603 Washington St SW, Gainesville, GA 30501-3535
Heather Hayes, Executive Director

Families First, Inc.............................404.853.2800
Fax...404.759.2207
Web...www.familiesfirst.org
P.O. Box 7948, Station C, Atlanta, GA 30357-0948
COA accredited organization.

Family and Children First, LLC dba Georgia
H.O.P.E....706.279.0405
Fax...706.279.4190
Web...www.gahope.org
P.O. Box 863, Dalton, GA 30722
COA accredited organization.

Family Connection Partnerships.............404.527.7394
Fax...404.527.7443
Web...www.gafcp.org
E-mail..gaye@gafcp.org
235 Peachtree St NE Ste 1600, Atlanta,
GA 30303-1422
Gaye Smith, Director

Family Ties - Mental Health Services.........678.460.0345
Fax...678.460.0350
Web...www.familytiesinc.com
1900 The Exchange, Suite 420, Atlanta, GA 30339
Hugo Mullins, Administrative Director
CARF accredited programs available.

Gateway Behavioral Health Svcs............912.437.7300
Fax...912.437.9499
Web...www.gatewaychs.org
E-mail..vshearer@gatewaybhs.org
1057 SW Commissioners Dr, Darien, GA 31305
Dr. Sheryl Mckinsey, Director

Georgia Assoc Of Homes & Svcs For
Children...404.572.6170
Fax...404.572.6171
Web...www.gahsc.org
E-mail..office@gahsc.org
34 Peachtree St NW Ste 2230, Atlanta,
GA 30303-5014
Normer Adams, Executive Director

Georgia Baptist Children's Homes and Family Ministries,
Inc....770.463.3800
Fax...770.463.6422
Web...www.gbchfm.org
505 Waterworks Road, Palmetto, GA 30268
COA accredited organization.

Georgia Ctr For Child Advocacy............678.904.2880
Fax...678.904.1125
Web...............................www.georgiacenterforchildadvocacy.org
E-mail...................nancyc@georgiacenterforchildadvocacy.org
1485 Woodland Ave SE Bldg B, Atlanta, GA 30316
Nancy Chandler, CEO

Georgia Youth Advocate Program...........800.722.3912
Fax...706.722.3280
Web...www.gyap.org
E-mail..sgadson@nyap.org
343 Telfair St, Augusta, GA 30901-2449
Suette Gadson, Executive Director

Greenbriar Children's Center, Inc.............912.234.3431
Fax...912.238.9149
Web..................................www.greenbriarchildrenscenter.org
3709 Hopkins Street, Savannah, GA 31405
COA accredited organization.

Greenbriar Children's Ctr....................912.234.3431
Fax...912.238.9149
Web..................................www.greenbriarchildrenscenter.org
E-mail.....................gtaylor@greenbriarchildrenscenter.org
3709 Hopkins St, Savannah, GA 31405-3098
Gena P. Taylor, Executive Director

Gwinnett Children's Shelter, Inc.
Web..................................www.gwinnettchildrenshelter.org
P.O. Box 527, Buford, GA 30515-0527
COA accredited organization.

Harbor House...................................706.235.5437
Fax...706.235.7511
E-mail..ggarland@nwga-cac.org
PO Box 5143, Rome, GA 30162-5143
Gail Garland, Executive Director

Inner Harbour Hospitals, Ltd. Excel
Program...770.852.6300
Fax...770.852.6301
Web...www.youthvillages.org
4685 Dorsett Shpals rd, Douglisdille, GA 30135
Sherry Kollmeyer, Human Resourses Director

Intervention and Prevention Services, Inc......229.386.2100
Fax...229.387.7900
128 East First Street, Suite 226, Tifton, GA 31794
COA accredited organization.

Jewish Family & Career Services.............770.677.9381
Fax...770.677.9400
E-mail..aviv@jfcs-atlanta.org
4649 Chamblee Dunwoody Rd, Atlanta, GA 30338
Cori Sackin, Information & Referral Specialist
COA accredited organization.

Jewish Family and Career Services, Inc.
4649 Chamblee Dunwoody Road, Atlanta, GA 30338
COA accredited organization.

KES, Inc....770.484.2489
Fax...770.484.2119
Web...www.kesinc.org
6615 Tribble Street, Lithonia, GA 30058
CARF accredited programs available.

Marcus Autism Ctr............................404.785.9400
Fax...404.785.9416
Web...www.marcus.org
E-mail..don.muller@marcus.org
1920 Briarcliff Rd NE, Marcus Institute, Atlanta,
GA 30329
Don Muller, Director

Northside Psychological Services............770.667.3877
Fax...770.667.3879
Web...www.npsga.com
P.O. Box 250, Alpharetta, GA 30009
COA accredited organization.

O.A.S.I.S. Counseling, Inc.....................770.419.1500
Fax...770.419.1507
Web...www.oasiscounseling.net
E-mail..swhite@oasiscounseling.net
379 Atlanta Street SE, Marietta, GA 30060
Sheila White, Director
CARF accredited programs available.

Open Arms......................................229.431.1121
Fax...229.439.0377
Web...www.openarmsinc.org
E-mail..fstrong@openarmsinc.org
420 Pine Ave, Albany, GA 31701-2403
Fonda Strong, Director

PeaceWay Counseling and Mediation Services, Inc.....................................**229.333.2351**
Fax...229.333.2353
Web.....................................www.peacewaycms.com
    2405 Bemiss Road, Valdosta, GA 31602
Dr. Terrell Andrews
CARF accredited programs available.

Providence Rocky Face Boys Home...........**706.673.3461**
Fax...706.673.3845
    205 Rock Hill Dr, Rocky Face, GA 30740
Kevin Shelton, House Parent

Ridge Creek School...............................**706.864.4730**
Fax...706.864.9109
Web.....................................www.ridgecreekschool.com
    830 Hidden Lake Rd, Dahlonega, GA 30533
Frank Ball, Director

Safe Shelter...**912.629.8888**
Fax...912.629.0028
Web...www.safeshelter.org
E-mail.....................................mail@safeshelter.org
    1052 Mohawk St, Savannah, GA 31419
Cheryl Branch, Director

Savannah Jewish Family Service..............**912.355.8111**
Fax...913.355.8116
E-mail..Larry@Savj.org
    5111 Abercorn St, Savannah, GA 31405
Adam Solender, General-manager

Second Nature Blue Ridge...................**706.212.2037**
Fax...706.212.0354
Web...www.snwp.com
E-mail.................................blueridge@snwp.com
    236 File St, Clayton, GA 30525-3023
Jeff Scott, Clinical Director

Solomon Life Center........................**770.460.1919**
Fax...770.460.1919
Web...www.solomonlife.org
E-mail.......................thesolomonlifecenter@mail.com
    284 Hwy 314, Ste %, Fayetteville, GA 30214
Dr. Myra McKnight, DO, CEO

Solutions Community Services, Inc............**770.574.9386**
Fax...770.574.8373
    305 Monroe Street, Tallapoosa, GA 30176
CARF accredited programs available.

StandUp For Kids- National Headquarters.....**800.365.4543**
Fax...404.954.6610
Web.......................................www.standupforkids.org
E-mail.............................staff@standupforkids.org
    83 Walton St Ste 100, Atlanta, GA 30303
Crystal Bowman, Vice President

The Bridge, Inc.................................**404.792.0070**
Fax...404.794.0444
Web...................................www.thebridge-atlanta.org
    1559 Johnson Road, NW, Atlanta, GA 30318-4017
COA accredited organization.

The Exchange Club Family Resource Ctr.......**706.290.0764**
Fax...706.290.9617
Web.....................................www.exchangeclubsrc.org
E-mail...........................srcenter@bellsouth.net
    5 Professional Ct SW, Ste B, Rome, GA 30165
Jennifer Chandler, Director

The Family Center of Columbus, Inc...........**706.327.3238**
Fax...706.327.5750
    P.O. Box 1825, Columbus, GA 31902-1825
COA accredited organization.

The Methodist Home For Children and Youth......................................**478.751.2800**
Web...............................www.themethodisthome.org
    P.O. Box 2525, Macon, GA 31203
COA accredited organization.

The Social Empowerment Center...........**770.925.2095**
Fax...866.468.1886
Web.....................................www.socialempowermentcenter.com
    504 Indian Trail Rd, Ste 220A, Lilburn, GA 30047
Shelly Hutchinson
CARF accredited programs available.

The United Methodist Children's Home of the North Georgia Conference, Inc.
    500 S. Columbia Drive, Decatur, GA 30030
COA accredited organization.

The Vashti Center, Inc.........................**229.226.4634**
Fax...229.225.1093
Web...www.vashti.org
    1815 East Clay Street, Thomasville, GA 31792
COA accredited organization.

Transitional Family Services..................**770.916.9031**
Fax...770.916.9030
Web...www.tfsga.org
    1830 Water Place, Suite 200, Atlanta, GA 30339
COA accredited organization.

Turning Point, New Directions for Families, Inc......................................**770.716.7977**
Fax...678.868.2354
Web.....................................www.turningpointga.com
    135 Bradford Square, Ste B, Fayetteville, GA 30215
Patricia Mowry, Owner
CARF accredited programs available.

Twin Cedars Youth and Family Services, Inc........................................**706.298.0050**
Fax...706.298.0055
Web...............................http://www.twincedars.org
    P.O. Box 1526, LaGrange, GA 30241
COA accredited organization.

Valdosta State University Speech & Hearing Clinic...................................**229.333.5931**
Fax...229.219.1335
Web...www.valdosta.edu
E-mail.............................emcmjenin@valdosta.edu
    1500 N Patterson St, Valdosta, GA 31698
Dr. Corinne Meyers-jennings, Director

Women's Resource...........................**770.382.7224**
Web...www.bartow.pcc.org
E-mail.......................cindy@womenresourcecenter.org
    20 Douglas St, Cartersville, GA 30120-3222
Cindy Smith, Director

SPECIAL NEEDS

Annandale Village.............................**770.945.8381**
Fax...770.945.8693
Web...www.annandale.org
    3500 Annandale Ln, Suwanee, GA 30024
Adam Pomeranz

Brain Tumor Foundation for Children Inc.....**404.252.4107**
Fax...404.252.4108
E-mail...............................info@braintumorkids.org
    6065 Roswell Rd Ste 505, Atlanta, GA 30328

Children's Healthcare of Atlanta at Scottish Rite.......................................**404.785.3803**
Fax...404.785.9064
Web...www.choa.org
E-mail...............................william.woods@choa.org
    1001 Johnson Ferry Road NE, Atlanta, GA 30342-1600
Bill Woods, Director
CARF accredited programs available.

CSS Corp. dba CSS Healthcare Services.......**770.210.0631**
Fax...770.210.0653
Web...www.csshealthcare.com
    8896 Tara Boulevard, Suite 500, Jonesboro, GA 30236
COA accredited organization.

Down Syndrome Association.................**404.320.3233**
E-mail...............................contactus@atlantadsaa.org
    4355J Cobb Pkwy Ste 213, Atlanta, GA 30339

Dream House...................................**770.717.7410**
Fax...770.923.0659
Web.....................................www.dreamhouseforkids.org
E-mail...............................info@dreamhouseforkids.org
    2092 Scenic Hwy, Ste B, Snellville, GA 30078
Laura Moore, Founder

Easter Seals North Georgia..................**404.214.2006**
E-mail.......................ddavidson@esng.easterseals.com
    1200 Lake Hearn Dr Ste 250, Atlanta, GA 30319
Donna Davidson, Chief Executive Officer

Easter Seals Southern Georgia..............**229.439.7061**
E-mail.......................benglish@swga-easterseals.org
    1906 Palmyra Rd, Albany, GA 31701
Beth English, Chief Executive Officer

Eating Away Autism..........................**678.571.7100**
Web.....................................www.eatingawayautism.com
E-mail.......................stefanie.smith@eatingawayautism.com
    3553 Dexter Way, Marietta, GA 30062-4100
Stefanie T. Smith, Director

Eaton Academy...............................**770.645.2673**
Fax...770.645.2711
Web...www.eatonacademy.org
E-mail...............................Brianu@eatonacademy.org
    1000 Old Roswell Lakes Pkwy, Ste 110, Roswell, GA 30076
Brian L Uitvlugt, V.p.

Elks Aidmore, Inc..............................**770.483.3535**
Fax...770.483.5696
Web...www.elksaidmore.com
    2394 Morrison Road, Conyers, GA 30094
COA accredited organization.

Emory University School of Medicine........**404.727.3507**
Fax...404.727.3728
E-mail.................................jglas03@emory.edu
    Woodruff Memorial Bldg # 6000, PO Box V, Atlanta, GA 30322
Jonathan Glass MD, Director

Epilepsy Foundation of Georgia.............**404.527.7155**
E-mail...............................epilepsy@epilepsyga.org
    6065 Roswell Rd NE Ste 515, Atlanta, GA 30328
Pam Murphy, Executive Director

Families Of Autism/Asperger's Syndrome Care, Educate And Support (FACES)...................**770.207.6346**
Fax...770.207.6283
Web...www.georgiafaces.info
E-mail...............................tjohnson50@aol.com
    501 Nunnally Farm Rd, Monroe, GA 30655-5805
Teresa Johnson, Director

Family Home Care, LLC.......................**770.437.0714**
Web...www.familyhomecare.us
E-mail...............................vlebeau@familyhomecare.us
    1791 Silver Leaf Ct, Marietta, GA 30008
Valentina Lebeau, CEO

Family Voices of Georgia.....................**770.256.2988**
    2460 LeHaven Dr, Tucker, GA 30084

Federation of Families for Children's MH.......**800.832.8645**
E-mail...............................sue.smith@gpsn.org
    1381 Metropolitan Pkwy, Atlanta, GA 30310

Fragile Kids Foundation......................**770.951.6111**
E-mail...............................help@fragilekids.org
    3350 Riverwood Pkwy Ste 1400, Atlanta, GA 30339

Gables Academy..............................**770.465.7500**
Fax...770.465.7700
Web...www.gablesacademy.com
E-mail...............................gablesinfo@bellsouth.net
    811 Gordon St, Stone Mountain, GA 30083-3533
James Meffen, Lii, Director

Georgia Children's Network..................**770.442.8357**
E-mail...............................carolsadler@bellsouth.net
    1105 Rock Pointe Look, Woodstock, GA 30188

Georgia

Georgia Congress of Parents & Teachers 404.659.0214
E-mail .... gapta@bellsouth.net
  114 Baker St NE, Atlanta, GA 30308
Debbie Snyder, Office Manager

Georgia Department of Corrections 706.369.5688
Fax 706.369.5723
  171 Old Fepps Bridge, Athens, GA 30606
Tripp Powers, Administrator

Learning Disabilities Association 404.303.7774
E-mail .... ldaga@bellsouth.net
  2566 Shallowford Rd Ste 104, Atlanta, GA 30345

LearningRx Learning Center 404.252.7246
E-mail .... atlanta-buckhead.ga@learningrx.net
  5252 Roswell Rd, Ste 100 Heritage Park, Atlanta, GA 30342
Beth Ardell, Director

LearningRx Learning Center 770.529.4800
E-mail .... kennesaw.ga@learningrx.net
  3420 Acworth Due West Rd, Ste B, Kennesaw, GA 30144
Kristen Thompson, Director/Owner

Lindamood-Bell Learning Processes 770.850.0612
Fax 770.850.1385
  3200 Cobb Galleria Pkwy, Ste 228, Atlanta, GA 30339

Lindamood-Bell Learning Processes 770.476.7066
Fax 770.476.7177
  3400 McClure Bridge Rd, Bldg C Ste A, Duluth, GA 30096

NAMI Georgia 770.234.0855
E-mail .... nami-ga@nami.org
  3050 Presidential Dr Ste 202, Atlanta, GA 30340
Eric Spencer, Executive Director

National Mental Health Association 404.527.7175
E-mail .... cindy@mhageorgia.org
  100 Edgewood Ave NE Ste 502, Atlanta, GA 30303
Cindy Cohens, Director Of Administrator

Parent to Parent of Georgia Inc 770.451.5484
Fax 770.458.4091
E-mail .... info@p2pga.org
  3805 Presidential Pkwy, Suite 207, Doraville, GA 30340
Debra Tucker, Director

Parent Training & Information Center 800.229.2038
E-mail .... info@parenttoparentofga.org
  3805 Presidential Pkwy, Ste 207, Doraville, GA 30340

Royce Learning Center 912.354.4047
Fax 912.354.4633
Web .... www.roycelearningcenter.com
  4 Oglethorpe Professional Blvd, Savannah, GA 31406
Kathleen Burke-fabrikant, Manager

Shepherd Center, Inc. 404.352.2020
Fax 404.350.3115
Web .... http://www.shepherd.org
  2020 Peachtree Road NW, Atlanta, GA 30309
CARF accredited programs available.

Spina Bifida Association 770.939.1044
E-mail .... info@spinabifidaga.org
  5072 Bristol Industrial Way, Ste F, Buford, GA 30518
Kristen Dicarlo, Executive Director

Statewide Independent Living Council 770.270.6860
E-mail .... ppuckett@silcga.org
  755 Commerce Dr Ste 415, Decatur, GA 30030

The Cottage School 770.641.8688
Fax 770.641.9026
Web .... www.cottageschool.org
E-mail .... jacqued@cottageschool.org
  700 Grimes Bridge Rd, Roswell, GA 30075-4615
Jacque Digieso, Phd, Executive Director

The MS Life Center 678.672.1000
Fax 678.672.1015
E-mail .... mailbox@nmssga.org
  1117 W Perimeter Center, Ste E101, Dunwoody, GA 30338

The Porter Academy 770.594.1313
Fax 770.594.1771
E-mail .... info@porterschool.com
  200 Cox Rd, Roswell, GA 30075
Claudia Porter, Director

The Rehabilitation Institute at Memorial Health University Medical Center 912.350.7099
Fax 912.350.3058
Web .... www.memorialhealth.com
  4700 Waters Avenue, Savannah, GA 31406
CARF accredited programs available.

Tourette Syndrome Association 706.248.9784
E-mail .... tsageorgia@bellsouth.net
  PO Box 6147, Athens, GA 30606

United Cerebral Palsy of Georgia Inc 770.676.2000
Web .... www.ucpga.org
E-mail .... dwilush@ucpga.org
  3300 Northeast Expy Bldg 9, Atlanta, GA 30341
Diane Wilush, Executive Director
COA accredited organization.

VSA Arts of Georgia 404.221.1270
  57 Forsyth St NW, Healey Bldg Ste R1, Atlanta, GA 30303

Walton Rehabilitation Hospital 706.724.7746
Fax 706.724.5752
Web .... www.wrh.com
  1355 Independence Drive, Augusta, GA 30901
CARF accredited programs available.

SUBSTANCE ABUSE TREATMENT

Academy for Family Empowerment Services, Inc. 770.918.8003
Fax 770.918.8800
Web .... www.academyfamempowerment.org
  1261 Commercial Drive, #B, Conyers, GA 30094
CARF accredited programs available.

Focus Counseling and Training, Inc. 770.516.1050
Fax 770.516.1300
Web .... www.focuscounseling.org
  3227 South Cherokee Lane, Suite 1320, Woodstock, GA 30188
CARF accredited programs available.

Gateway Behavioral Health Services 912.264.0979
Fax 912.264.5965
Web .... www.gatewaybhs.org
  3441 Cypress Mill Road, Suite 102, Brunswick, GA 31522
CARF accredited programs available.

Graceway Recovery Residence, Inc 229.446.7800
Fax 229.446.0338
Web .... www.gracewayrecovery.com
E-mail .... liz@gracewayrecovery.com
  412 W Tift Ave, Albany, GA 31701-2246
Liz M. Dixon, Development Director

GRN Community Service Board 770.339.5019
Fax 770.339.5382
Web .... www.grncsb.com
  175 Gwinnett Dr, Lawrenceville, GA 30045
Frank Berry, Director
CARF accredited programs available.

Heritage Foundation, Inc. 229.228.5545
Fax 229.226.4755
Web .... www.heritageofthomasville.org
  228 Gordon Ave, Thomasville, GA 31792
Gloria Jones, Executive Director
CARF accredited programs available.

Lighthouse Care Center of Augusta 706.651.0005
Fax 706.651.9848
Web .... www.psysolutions.com
E-mail .... george.boykin@psysolutions.com
  3100 Perimeter Parkway, Augusta, GA 30909
George Boykin, CEO
CARF accredited programs available.

Odyssey Family Counseling Center 404.762.9190
Fax 404.762.9101
Web .... www.odysseycounseling.org
E-mail .... akelahan@odysseycounseling.org
  1919 John Wesley Ave, Collge Park, GA 30337
Annie Kelahan, Director
CARF accredited programs available.

Salvation Army/ Red Shield Lodge 404.486.2700
Fax 404.486.2737
E-mail .... janeane_schmidt@usn.salvationarmy.org
  400 Luckie St NW, Atlanta, GA 30313-2099
Sgt. Janeane Schmidt, Director

Steppingstones To Recovery LLC 706.733.1935
Fax 706.667.8727
Web .... www.steppingstonestorecovery.net
E-mail .... info@steppingstonestorecovery.net
  2610 Commons Blvd, Augusta, GA 30909
Ken Wilson, Director
CARF accredited programs available.

Hawaii

Neil Abercrombie, Governor
Executive Chambers
State Capitol
Honolulu, HI 96813
808.586.0034
808.586.0006 (Fax)
governor.lingle@hawaii.gov

Edward Chargualaf, Juvenile Justice Specialist
Office of Youth Services, Dept. of Human Services
820 Mililani Street Ste. 817
Honolulu, HI 96813
808.587.5732
808.587.5734 (Fax)
echargualaf@dhs.hawaii.gov

Maryanne Kusaka, SAG Chair
5151 Nonou Rd
Kapaa, HI 96746
808.652.6500
mkusaka@hawaii.rr.com

CRISIS NUMBERS

Child Abuse Reporting . . .808.832.5300

STATE SERVICES

SOCIAL SERVICES

Child Care Program Office Hawaii 808.586.5735
Fax 808.586.5744
820 Mililani St Ste 606, Honolulu, HI 96813

Child Support Enforcement Agency 808.692.8265
Fax 808.692.7060
Web . . . . .www.dhs.hawaii.gov
E-mail . . . . .gkemp@dhs.hawaii.gov
601 Kamokila Blvd Ste 251, Kapolei, HI 96707-2035
Garry Kemp, Administrator

Child Welfare Svcs Branch 808.586.5667
Fax 808.586.4806
Web . . . . .www.dhs.hawaii.gov
810 Richards St Ste 400, Honolulu, HI 96813-4700
Kelle Perez, Administrator

Ofc of Youth Svcs 808.539.4494
Fax 808.539.4486
777 Punchbowl St, Honolulu, HI 96813

Volunteer Guardian Ad Litem 808.538.5930
Fax 808.538.5917
E-mail .robbrede@yahoo.com
777 Punchbowl St, Honolulu, HI 96813
Robert Brede

WIC 808.586.8175
Fax 808.586.8189
Web . . . . .www.doh.hawaii.gov/health/family-child-health/wic/index_html
E-mail .linda.chock@doh.hawaii.gov
235 S Beretania St Ste 701, Honolulu, HI 96813-2419
Linda Chock, Chief

GENERAL HEALTH SERVICES

Child w Special Health Needs Branch HI 808.733.9055
Fax 808.733.9068
E-mail .pauline@hawaiigenetics.org
741 Sunset Ave, Honolulu, HI 96816
Pat Heu, Director

Children with Special Health Needs 808.733.9070
Fax 808.733.9068
741 Sunset Ave, Honolulu, HI 96816
Patricia Heu, Md, Chief Medical Officer

Hawai'i Dept Of Health 808.586.4400
Fax 808.586.4368
Web . . . . .www.hawaii.gov/health
1250 Punchbowl St, Honolulu, HI 96813
Susan Jackson, Deputy Director

Maternal and Child Health Branch HI 808.733.9022
Fax 808.733.8369
E-mail .DOH_MCHB@hotmail.com
741 A Sunset Ave, Rm 206, Honolulu, HI 96816
Barbara Yamashita, Manager

MENTAL HEALTH SERVICES

Child and Adolescent Mental Health Div 808.733.9333
Fax 808.733.9357
Web . . . . .www.camhmis.health.state.hi.us
3627 Kilauea Ave, Rm 101, Honolulu, HI 96816
Stantin Michels, Chief

Developmental Disabilities Div 808.586.5840
Fax 808.586.5844
Web . . . . .www.hawaii.gov/health
1250 Punchbowl St, Room 463, Honolulu, HI 96813
David Fray, Chief

Vocational and Rehab Agency HI 808.692.7719
Fax 808.692.7727
E-mail .jcordova@dhs.hawaii.gov
601 Kamokila Blvd Rm 515, Kapolei State Office Bldg, Kapolei, HI 96707
J Cordova, Director

JUSTICE AGENCY

Attorney General's Ofc .808.586.1500
Fax 808.586.1239
Web . . . . .www.hawaii.gov/ag
E-mail .hawaii@hawaii.gov
425 Queen St, Honolulu, HI 96813-2903
David Louie, Attorney General

Correctional Education Division HI 808.587.1279
Fax 808.587.1280
E-mail .Maureen.L.Tito@Hawaii.Gov
919 Ala Moana Blvd Rm 405, Honolulu, HI 96814
Maureen Tito, Director

Crime Victim Compensation Commission 808.587.1143
Fax 808.587.1146
E-mail .cvcc@hawaii.rr.com
1136 Union Mall Ste 600, Honolulu, HI 96813
Pamela Ferguson-brey, Executive Director

Dept of Corrections/Public Safety 808.587.1340
Fax 808.587.1282
Web . . . . .www.hawaii.gov/psd/
E-mail .tjohnson@parolehq.corr.ca.gov
919 Ala Moana Blvd, 4th Floor, Honolulu, HI 96814
Tommy Johnson, Deputy Director

Dept of Human Svcs/Ofc of Youth Svcs 808.587.5700
Fax 808.587.5734
820 Mililani St Ste 817, Honolulu, HI 96813
David Hipp, Executive Director

District of Hawaii - US Marshal's Ofc 808.541.3000
Fax 808.541.3056
300 Ala Moana Blvd, Honolulu, HI 96850
Gerdin Miyamoto, Us Marshall

Probation Ofc 808.541.1283
Fax 808.541.1345
Web . . . . .www.hip.uscourts.gov
E-mail .selix_mata@hip.uscourts.gov
300 Ala Moana Blvd Rm 2-300, Honolulu, HI 96850-0110
Selix Mata, Chief US Probation Officer

State Dept Of Public Safety 808.587.1288
Fax 808.587.1282
919 Ala Moana Blvd Ste 400, Honolulu, HI 96814-4920
Jodie F. Maesaka-Hirata, Director

COURTS

Ofc of The Administrative Director of The Courts 808.539.4900
Fax 808.539.4855
E-mail .tkeller@pixi.com
417 S King St Rm 206A, Honolulu, HI 96813-2943
Thomas R. Keller, Administrative Director Of The Courts

EDUCATION SERVICES

At-Risk Students Program 808.735.6222
Fax 808.733.9890
Web www.notes.k12.hi.us
E-mail .steve_shiraki@notes.k12.hi.us
641 18th Ave, Bldg. V, Room 201, Honolulu, HI 96816-4444
Steve Shiraki, Program Coordinator

Hawaii Dept of Education 808.586.3232
Fax 808.586.3234
1390 Miller St, Honolulu, HI 96813
Kathryn Matayoshi, Superintendent For Eduacation

Hawaii Dept of Education 808.586.3283
Fax 808.586.3440
E-mail .cara_tanimura@notes.k12.hi.us
1390 Miller St Rm 411, Honolulu, HI 96813
Cara Tanimura, Director

Hawaii

Hawaii Parent Training & Info Ctr 808.536.9684
Fax 808.537.6780
E-mail .... msantana@ldahawaii.org
245 N Kukui St Ste 205, Honolulu, HI 96817
M Santana, Director

School Food Svcs Branch 808.733.8400
Fax 808.735.6262
E-mail .... glenna_owens@notes.k12.hi.us
1106 Koko Head Ave, Honolulu, HI 96816-3710
Glenna Owens, School Food Service Director

COUNTY SERVICES

Hawaii Island

SOCIAL SERVICES

Wheeler/Schofield 808.624.5645
Fax 808.656.1396
782 Santos Dumont Ave, Wheeler Army Airfield,
HI 96854
Tammy Ray, Director

GENERAL HEALTH SERVICES

Health Dept 808.974.6001
Fax 808.974.6000
Web .... www.doh.hawaii.gov
75 Aupuni St #201, Hilo, HI 96720
Aaron Uenu, District Health Supervisor

**Kapiolani Medical Ctr For Women And
Children** 808.983.6000
Fax 808.983.8617
Web .... www.kapiolani.org
1319 Punahou St, Honolulu, HI 96826-1080
Chuck Sted, CEO

JUSTICE AGENCY

**Children's Justice Ctr Of East
Hawaii** 808.933.1505
Fax 808.933.0968
Web .... www.courts.states.hi.us
E-mail .... terri.lum@courts.state.hi.us
1290 Kinoole St, Hilo, HI 96720-4136
Terri Lum, Hawaii County Program Director

COURTS

First Circuit Court/District Court 808.538.5121
Fax 808.538.5233
1111 Alakea St, Honolulu, HI 96813-2897
Iris T. Murayama, Deputy Chief Court Administrator

Teen Court 808.969.7838
Fax 808.961.9140
Web .... www.ywcahawaiiisland.org
E-mail .... aquinn@ywcahawaiiisland.org
1382 Kilauea Ave, Hilo, HI 96720-4231
Amanda Quinn, Teen Court Director

POLICE AND SHERIFF

Police Dept 808.529.3161
Fax 808.529.3030
801 S Beretania St, Honolulu, HI 96813
Louis Kealoha, Chief Of Police

EDUCATION SERVICES

Leeward District Ofc (Admin) 808.692.8000
Fax 808.692.7899
Web www.doe.k12.hi.us
601 Kamokila Blvd Ste 418, Kapolei, HI 96707-2036
Annette Nishipewa, Director

**Special Education - East Hawaii Regional
Ofc** 808.974.4401
Fax 808.974.4588
450 Waianuenue Ave, Bldg C, Hilo, HI 96720
Wade De Sa, Education Specialist

**Special Education -West Hawaii Regional
Ofc** 808.323.0015
Fax 808.323.0022
81-180 Konawaena School Rd, Kealakekua, HI 96750
Linda Price, District Educational Specialist

**Special Education South Hawaii Regional
Ofc** 808.982.4252
Fax 808.982.4292
Web www.notes.k12.hi.us
E-mail .... michael_ogrady@notes.k12.hi.us
15-565 Keaau-Pahoa Rd Bldg B, Keaau, HI 96749
Michael O Grady, Social Worker

Winward District Ofc (Admin) 808.233.5700
Fax 808.233.5709
Web www.doe.k12.hi.us
46-169 Kamehameha Hwy, Kaneohe, HI 96744-3651
Bj Clark English For Second Language Learners (esll), Director

Honolulu Island

SOCIAL SERVICES

**Leeward Child Welfare Svcs
Section** 808.692.7850
Fax 808.692.7832
601 Kamokila Blvd Ste 135, Kapolei, HI 96707-2035
Kristien Tuitama, Unit 1 Supervisor

EDUCATION SERVICES

Public Charter Schools Program 808.586.3570
Fax 808.586.3577
E-mail .... sean_murakami@notes.k12.hi.us
250 S Hotel St, Rm 103, Honolulu, HI 96813
Sean Murakami, Administrative Assisstant

Kauai Island

GENERAL HEALTH SERVICES

Health Dept 808.241.3495
Fax 808.241.3480
3040 Umi St, Lihue, HI 96766
John Hust, Publc Health Administrative Officer

COURTS

Court 808.482.2350
Fax 808.482.2442
Web .... www.courts.state.hi.us
3970 Kaana St Ste 300, Lihue, HI 96766-1283
David M. Lam, Administrator

Fifth Circuit Court 808.482.2300
Fax 808.482.2442
Web .... www.courts.state.hi.us
E-mail .... george.m.masuoka@courts.state.hi.us
3970 Kaana St Ste 207, Lihue, HI 96766-1282
Honorable George Masuoka, Chief Administrating Judge

POLICE AND SHERIFF

Police Dept 808.241.1711
Fax 808.241.1670
Web .... www.kauai.gov
3990 Kaana St Ste 200, Lihue, HI 96766-1268
Darryl Perry, Chief

EDUCATION SERVICES

Kauai District Ofc (Admin) 808.274.3502
Fax 808.274.3508
Web www.doe.k12.hi.us
3060 Eiwa St Ste 305, Lihue, HI 96766-1876
William Arakaki, Complex Area Superintendent

Maui Island

GENERAL HEALTH SERVICES

Maui District Health Ofc 808.984.8208
Fax 808.984.8222
Web .... www.hawaii.gov
54 S High St Rm 301, Wailuku, HI 96793
Gigi Olston, Nursing Supervisor

Public Health Svcs 808.984.8260
Fax 808.243.5118
Web .... www.doh.hawaii.gov
E-mail .... lizbeth.olsten@doh.hawaii.gov
54 S High St Rm 301, Wailuku, HI 96793-2198
Lizbeth Olsten, Nursing Supervisor

COURTS

Family Court, 2nd Circuit 808.244.2770
Fax 808.244.2777
Web .... www.hawaii.gov
2145 Main St Ste 226, Wailuku, HI 96793-1679
Bonnie Brooks, Family Court Director

POLICE AND SHERIFF

Police Dept 808.244.6400
Fax 808.244.6411
Web .... www.mpd.net
E-mail .... phillips@mpd.net
55 Mahalani St, Wailuku, HI 96793-2530
Thomas Phillips, Chief

EDUCATION SERVICES

Maui District Ofc (Admin) 808.984.8001
Fax 808.984.8008
Web www.notes.k12.hi.us
E-mail .... bruce_anderson@notes.k12.hi.us
54 S High St, 4th Fl, Wailuku, HI 96793
Bruce Anderson, Superintendent

Special Education/Special Svcs 808.873.3527
Fax 808.873.3590
Region II, Baldwin & King Kekaulike, Complex,
Kahului, HI 96732
Ruth Anderson, Director

SPECIAL SERVICES AGENCIES

ADOPTION AGENCIES

Adopt International **808.523.1400**
Fax 415.934.0700
Web ....www.adoptinter.org
E-mail ....lynne@adoptinter.org
　　1580 Makaloa Ste 1020, Honolulu, HI 96814
　　Lynne Jacobs, Executive Director

Consuelo Zobel Alger Foundation **808.532.3939**
Fax 808.532.3930
Web ....www.consuelo.org
　　110 N. Hotel Street, Honolulu, HI 96817
　　COA accredited organization.

Foster Family Programs **808.935.2876**
Fax 808.961.4913
Web ....www.ffphawaii.org
E-mail ....lsantos@ffphawaii.org
　　120 Pauahi St Ste 306, Hilo, HI 96720-3048
　　Linda Santos, Director

**Hawaii International Child Placement & Family Svcs,
Inc.** **808.589.2367**
Fax 808.593.2247
Web ....www.h-i-c.org
E-mail ....kristine@h-i-c.org
　　1168 Waimanu St, Honolulu, HI 96814-3403
　　Kristine Altwies Nicholson, Executive Director/CEO

Susannah Wesley Community Center **808.847.1535**
Fax 808.847.0787
Web ....www.susannahwesley.org
　　1117 Kaili Street, Honolulu, HI 96819-3432
　　COA accredited organization.

BEHAVIORAL HEALTH TREATMENT

Alaka'i Na Keiki, Inc. **808.523.7771**
Fax 808.523.1997
Web ....www.alakainakeiki.com
　　1100 Alakea Street, Ninth Floor, Honolulu, HI 96813
　　CARF accredited programs available.

Aloha House, Inc. **808.871.1314**
Fax 808.871.1060
Web ....www.aloha-house.org
　　444 Hana Highway, Suite 201, Kahului, HI 96732
　　CARF accredited programs available.

**Benchmark Behavioral Health Systems - Pearl
City** **808.454.1411**
E-mail ....stephen.blotzke@psysolutions.com
　　2501 Waimano Home Road, Pearl City, HI 96782
　　Mr. Steve Blotzke, Accreditation Manager
　　Joint Commission accredited organization.

Big Island Substance Abuse Council **808.969.9994**
Fax 808.969.7570
　　135 Pu'uhonu Way, Suite 201, Hilo, HI 96720
　　CARF accredited programs available.

Bjornson Medical Practice **808.637.5111**
Fax 603.462.5880
E-mail ....mdypnt@hotmail.com
　　PO Box 385, Kahuku, HI 96731-0385
　　Kristopher Bjornson, Psychiatrist

Bobby Benson Center **808.293.7555**
Fax 808.293.7196
Web ....www.bobbybenson.org
E-mail ....irene@bbcoahu.com
　　56 - 660 Kamehemeha Highway, Kahuku, HI 96731
　　Irene Carpenter, Executive Director
　　CARF accredited programs available.

Brown Medical Practice **808.326.5454**
Fax 808.326.4083
　　75-127 Lunapule Rd Ste 5, Kailua Kona,
　　HI 96740-2119
　　Carol Brown, Psychiatrist

Care Hawaii Inc **808.930.2805**
Web ....www.eyecarehi.com
E-mail ....info@eyecarehi.com
　　1045A Kilauea Ave, Hilo, HI 96720-1468
　　Mr Kevin Hedlund, Director

CARE Hawaii, Inc. **808.533.3936**
Fax 808.791.6198
Web ....www.carehawaii.com
E-mail ....tina@carehawaii.com
　　606 Coral Street, Honolulu, HI 96813
　　Tina Mclaughlin, Executive Director
　　CARF accredited programs available.

Cooney Medical Practice **808.486.3600**
Fax 808.484.9299
　　98-211 Pali Momi St Ste 414, Aiea, HI 96701
　　Jon Cooney, MD, Psychiatrist

Hale Na`au Pono **808.696.4211**
Fax 808.696.5516
Web ....www.wccmhc.org
E-mail ....plaenui@wccmhc.org
　　86 - 226 Farrington Highway, Wai`anae, HI 96792
　　Poka Laenui, Executive Director
　　CARF accredited programs available.

Hawaii Behavioral Health **808.935.7949**
Fax 808.934.8318
Web ....www.hibh.org
　　234 Waianuenue Avenue, Hilo, HI 96720
　　CARF accredited programs available.

Hawaii Families as Allies **808.487.8785**
Fax 808.487.0514
Web ....www.hfaa.net
E-mail ....hfaa@hfaa.net
　　99-209 Moanalua Rd Ste 305, Aiea, HI 96701
　　Linda Mashado, Executive Director

Hawaii Job Corps Ctr **808.259.6001**
Fax 808.259.7907
　　41-467 Hihimanu St, Waimanalo, HI 96795-1423
　　Joanne Espinosa, Center Director

Honolulu Family Guidance Ctr **808.733.9393**
Fax 808.733.9377
Web ....www.state.hi.us/doh/camhd
E-mail ....marie.lee@doh.hawai.gov
　　3627 Kilauea Ave, Room 401, Honolulu, HI 96816
　　Leah Chang, Branch Chief

Kalihi-Palama Health Center **808.845.8578**
Fax 808.841.1265
Web ....www.kphc.org
E-mail ....mdelacruz@kphc.org
　　938 Austin Lane, Suite E, Honolulu, HI 96817
　　Marissa Dela Cruz, Clinical Support Director
　　CARF accredited programs available.

Kauii Family Guidance Ctr **808.274.3883**
Fax 808.274.3889
　　3-3204 Kuhio Hwy Ste 104, Lihue, HI 96766-1135
　　Madelein Hiraganuccio, Branch Chief

**Kids Behavioral Health of Hawaii, Inc. dba Acadia
Hawaii** **808.961.6635**
Fax 808.961.6434
Web ....www.acadiahealthcare.com
　　440 Kapiolani Street, Hilo, HI 96720

Life Foundation **808.521.2437**
Fax 808.521.1279
Web ....www.lifefoundation.org
E-mail ....mail@lifefoundation.org
　　677 Ala Moana Blvd, Ste 226, Honolulu, HI 96813
　　Paul Groesbeck, Executive Director
　　CARF accredited programs available.

Lokahi Treatment Centers **808.883.0922**
Fax 808.883.1022
Web ....www.lokahitreatmentcenters.net
　　68-1845 Waikoloa Road, Suite 224B, Waikoloa,
　　HI 96738
　　CARF accredited programs available.

Loveland Academy, LLC **808.524.4243**
Fax 808.524.7924
Web ....www.lovelandacademyhawaii.com
E-mail ......contact_information@lovelandacademyhawaii.com
　　1506 Pi'ikoi Street, Honolulu, HI 96822
　　Patricia Dukes, Executive Director
　　CARF accredited programs available.

Maui Family Guidance Ctr **808.243.1252**
Fax 808.243.1254
E-mail ....virginia.shaw@doh.hawaii.gov
　　270 Waiehu Beach Rd Ste 213, Wailuku, HI 96793
　　Virginia Shaw, PhD, Branch Chief

North Shore Mental Health, Inc. **808.638.8700**
Fax 808.638.7919
Web ....www.northshorementalhealth.com
　　56-119 Pualalea Street, Kahuku, HI 96731
　　COA accredited organization.

Sutter Health Pacific **808.671.8511**
Web ....www.kahimohala.org
E-mail ....hinesl@kahi.org
　　91-2301 Old Fort Weaver Road, Ewa Beach, HI 96706
　　Sister Linda Hines, Accreditation Manager
　　Joint Commission accredited organization.

**The Alcoholic Rehabilitation Services of Hawaii dba Hina
Mauka** **808.236.2600**
Fax 808.236.2626
Web ....www.hinamauka.org
　　45-845 Po'okela Street, Kaneohe, HI 96744
　　CARF accredited programs available.

The Queen's Medical Center **808.538.9011**
Web ....www.queens.org
E-mail ....ehuey@queens.org
　　1301 Punchbowl Street, Honolulu, HI 96813
　　Ms. Eleanor Huey, Accreditation Manager
　　Joint Commission accredited organization.

**The Salvation Army Family Treatment
Services** **808.732.2802**
Fax 808.734.7470
　　845 22nd Avenue, Honolulu, HI 96816
　　CARF accredited programs available.

**Wai`anae Coast Community Mental Health Center, Inc. dba
Hale Na`au Pono** **808.697.3044**
Fax 808.696.5516
Web ....www.wccmhc.org
　　86 - 226 Farrington Highway, Wai`anae, HI 96792
　　CARF accredited programs available.

CHILDREN'S HOSPITAL

Hilo Medical Center **808.974.4700**
　　1190 Waianuenue Ave, Hilo, HI 96720

Kaiser Permanente Medical Center **808.432.0000**
　　3288 Moanalua rd, Honolulu, HI 96819
　　Janet Liang, Chief Executive Officer

Kauai Veterans Memorial Hospital **808.338.9431**
　　Waimea Canyon Road, Waimea, HI 96796
　　Jerry Walker, Chief Executive Officer

Hawaii

Kona Community Hospital 808.322.9311
79 1019 Kaukapila St, Kealakekua, HI 96750
Kathrine Harder, Administrator

Tripler Army Medical Center 808.433.6661
1 Jarret White rd, Honolulu, HI 96859
General Galliger, Commander

COUNSELING SERVICES

Hugs 808.521.4847
Fax 808.732.4881
Web .... www.hugslove.org
E-mail .... leilani@hugslove.org
3636 Kilauea Ave, Honolulu, HI 96816
Leilani Fernandez, Volunteer Coordinator

LDS Family Svcs 808.945.3690
Fax 808.945.2811
1500 S Beretania St Ste 402, Honolulu,
HI 96826-1937
Sally Lee, Senior Adoption Specialist

CRISIS & SHELTER CARE

Central Oahu Youth Svcs 808.637.9344
Fax 808.637.3050
E-mail .... coysa.shelter@hawaiiantell.net
66-528 Haleiwa Rd, Haleiwa, HI 96712-1525
Lisa Asuncion, Executive Director

Child & Families Services 808.322.7233
Fax 808.322.9287
E-mail .... turningpo001@hawaii.rr.com
PO Box 384, Holualoa, HI 96725-0384
Steve Godrow, Executive Director

Developing Options to Violence 808.532.5100
Fax 808.532.5106
E-mail .... angied@stoptheviolence.org
200 N ginnard blvd, Honolulu, HI 96817
Angie Doi, Program Administrator

Domestic Violence Action Center 808.534.0040
Fax 808.531.7228
Web .... www.stoptheviolence.org
E-mail .... nancik@stoptheviolence.org
PO Box 3198, Honolulu, HI 96801-3198
Nanci Kreidman, Director

Hale Ohana Domestic Violence Shelter 808.959.6118
Fax 808.959.9837
E-mail .... development@cfs-hawaii.org
1266 Kamehameha Ave #A-5, Hilo, HI 96720-8938
Heidi Koop, Director

Hawaii Coalition for the Prevention of Sexual
Assault 808.733.9038
Fax 808.733.9032
741 Sunset Ave Ste A, Room 105, Honolulu,
HI 96816

Hawaii State Coalition On Family Violence 808.832.9316
Fax 808.841.6028
Web .... www.hscadv.org
716 Umi St Ste 210, Honolulu, HI 96819

Hawaii Youth Svcs 808.531.2198
Fax 808.534.1199
Web .... www.hysn.org
E-mail .... jclark@hysn.org
677 Ala Moana Blvd Ste 702, Honolulu,
HI 96813-5416
Judith F. Clark, Executive Director

Kauai YWCA Family Violence Shelter 808.245.8404
Fax 808.246.2799
3094 Elua St, Lihue, HI 96766
Renee Lippmann, Co-Director

Molokai Alternatives To Violence 808.553.3202
Fax 808.553.3036
146 Pauli Rd, Kaunakakai, HI 96748
Alverta Carriera, Director

Pact-Family Peace Ctr - Domestic Violence
Program 808.832.0855
Fax 808.832.0853
1505 Dillingham Blvd Ste 208, Honolulu, HI 96819
Kata Issari, Director

Pu'uhonua Domestic Violence Drop-In Ctr 808.585.7944
Fax 808.585.7955
1505 Dillingham Blvd, Ste 108, Honolulu, HI 96817
Kata Issari, Program Director

Sexual Assault Support Services 808.334.1624
Fax 808.334.0406
E-mail .... ldavis@ywcahawaiiisland.org
75-5706 Hanama Pl, Ste 202, Kailua Kona, HI 96740
Lorraine Davis, Quailty Assurance Director

Turning Point For Families-Domestic
Violence 808.969.7798
Fax 808.961.3204
PO Box 612, Hilo, HI 96721-0612
Howard Garvas, Chief Executive Officer

West Hawaii Domestic Abuse Ctr 808.322.2799
Fax 808.322.9287
PO Box 384, Holualoa, HI 96725-0384
Angie Kalani, Supervisor

Women Helping Women - Domestic Violence
Program 808.242.6600
Fax 808.249.8147
Web .... www.whwmaui.net
1935 Main St Ste 202, Wailuku, HI 96793-1784
Stacy Moniz, Director

EDUCATION

Family Support Hawaii 808.326.7778
Fax 808.326.4063
Web .... www.fsswh.org
E-mail .... info@fsswh.org
75-127 Lunapule Rd Ste 11, Kailua Kona, HI 96740
Paki Story, Executive Director

Susannah Wesley Community Ctr 808.847.1535
Fax 808.847.0787
E-mail .... swcc@hawaii.rr.com
1117 Kaili St, Honolulu, HI 96819-3432
Ronald Higashi, Executive Director

FOSTER CARE AGENCIES

Adoption Assistance 808.564.5499
E-mail .... rabaldino@phrihawaii.org
PO Box 37473, Honolulu, HI 96837

Catholic Charities Hawaii 808.331.8989
Fax 808.327.2729
E-mail .... mgerguson@catholiccharitieshawaii.org
75-166 Kalani St Ste 202, Kailua Kona, HI 96740
Ms Madeleine Ferguson, Prgram Director

Catholic Charities Hawaii (CCH) 808.524.4673
E-mail .... aileen.shin@catholiccharitieshawaii.org
1822 Keeaumoku St, Honolulu, HI 96822
Aileen Shin, Development Director

Child & Family Service (CFS) 808.681.1428
Fax 808.531.0941
E-mail .... adoption@cfs-hawaii.org
200 N Vineyard Blvd, Bldg B, Honolulu, HI 96817

Kauai Adoptive Parents Alliance (KAPA) 808.245.2844
Fax 808.245.8040
E-mail .... pchock@cfs-hawaii.org
2970 Kele St, Ste 203, Lihue Kauai, HI 96766
Lucille Calderon, Administrator

Resources for Life 808.880.1412
59-349 Olomana Rd, Kamuela, HI 96743

The Hanai Coalition Support Group for 808.986.8634
Fax 808.243.8688
E-mail .... randy@mauicjc.org
1773A Wili Pa Loop co Frnds of, the Chldrns Justic
Ctr of Maui, Wailuku, HI 96793

SOCIAL SERVICES

Aliamanu Family Outreach Ctr 808.833.1185
Fax 808.834.3631
Web .... www.asymcahi.org
E-mail .... asymcaamr@aol.com
1875 Aliamanu Dr, Honolulu, HI 96818-1405
Lise Peacock, Director

Catholic Charities Hawai'i 808.524.4673
Fax 808.527.4889
Web .... www.catholiccharitieshawaii.org
1822 Ke'eaumoku Street, Honolulu, HI 96822
COA accredited organization.

Central Adoption Exchange of Hawaii 808.586.5698
Fax 808.586.4806
Web .... www.state.hi.us/dhs
E-mail .... lkazama@dhs.hawaii.gov
810 Richards St Ste 400, Honolulu, HI 96813-4700
Lynn Kazama, Child Welfare Services Program Developement

Child & Family Svc 808.877.6888
Fax 808.877.6860
Web .... www.childandfamilyservice.org
305 E Wakea Ave, Kahului, HI 96732
Sheri Daniels, Administrator

Child and Family Service 808.681.3500
Fax 808.681.5280
Web .... www.childandfamilyservice.org
91-1841 Fort Weaver Road, Ewa Beach, HI 96706
COA accredited organization.

Family Programs Hawaii 808.521.9531
Fax 808.533.1018
Web .... www.familyprogramshi.org
250 Vineyard Street, Honolulu, HI 96813
COA accredited organization.

Hale Kipa, Inc. 808.589.1829
Fax 808.945.9007
Web .... www.halekipa.org
615 Pi'ikoi Street, Suite 203, Honolulu,
HI 96814-3139
COA accredited organization.

Hale Opio Kauai, Inc. 808.245.2873
Fax 808.245.6957
Web .... www.haleopio.org
2959 Umi Street, Lihue, HI 96746
COA accredited organization.

Helping Hands Hawaii 808.536.7234
Fax 808.536.7237
Web .... www.helpinghandshawaii.org
2100 N Nimitz Hwy, Honolulu, HI 96819-2218
Brian Schatz, President

Marimed Foundation for Island Health Care
Training 808.235.1377
Fax 808.235.1074
Web .... www.marimed.org
45-021 Likeke Place, Kaneohe, HI 96744
COA accredited organization.

Maui Family Support Services, Inc. 808.242.0900
Fax 808.249.2800
Web .... www.mfss.org
1844 Wili Pa Loop, Wailuku, HI 96793-1272
COA accredited organization.

Maui Youth and Family Services, Inc. 808.579.8414
Fax 808.579.8426
Web .... www.myfs.org
P. O. Box 790006, Paia, HI 96779
COA accredited organization.

Parent Child Development Ctr 808.696.7657
Fax 808.696.7924
E-mail .... pcdcwaianae@yahoo.com
89-195 Farrington Hwy, Waianae, HI 96792
Susan Merrill, Director

Patch **808.839.1988**
Fax 808.839.1799
Web .... www.patchhawaii.org
E-mail .... patch@patchhawaii.org
　650 Iwilei Rd Ste 205, Honolulu, HI 96817-5318
　Katie Chin, Executive Director

Pearl Harbor YMCA **808.473.3398**
Fax 808.473.5744
Web .... www.asymcahi.org
E-mail .... pearlharbor@asymcahi.org
　1057 North Rd, Honolulu, HI 96818-5005
　Stanley Lum, Executive Director

Sex Abuse Treatment Ctr **808.535.7600**
Fax 808.535.7630
Web .... www.kapiolani.org
　55 Merchant St Fl 22, Honolulu, HI 96813-4333
　Adrianna Ramelli, Director

Sultan Early Intervention Program **808.536.3764**
Fax 808.521.4491
Web .... www.easterslealshawaii.org
E-mail .... info@easterslealshawaii.org
　710 Green St, Honolulu, HI 96813
　John F. Howell, President/CEO

The Institute For Family Enrichment **808.596.8433**
Fax 808.748.3080
Web .... www.tiffe.org
E-mail .... ENQUIRES@TFFI.ORG
　615 Piikoi Street, Suite 105, Honolulu, HI 96814
　LINDA FOX, CLINICAL DIRECTOR
　CARF accredited programs available.

SPECIAL NEEDS

Easter Seals Hawaii **888.241.7450**
E-mail .... INFO@EASTERSEALSHAWAII.ORG
　710 Green St, Honolulu, HI 96813
　Anastasia Keller-Collins, Vice President

Epilepsy Foundation of Hawaii **808.528.3058**
E-mail .... director-efh@hawaiiepilepsy.com
　501 Sumner St, Honolulu, HI 96817

Hawaii Council Developmental Disability **808.984.8218**
E-mail .... mauimatsu@yahoo.com
　54 High St 3rd Fl, Wailuku, HI 96793

Hawaii Down Syndrome Congress **808.949.1999**
E-mail .... hawaiidownsyndrome@hawaii.rr.com
　419 Keoniana St # 804, Honolulu, HI 96815
　Constance Smith, President

Hawaii Families as Allies **866.361.8825**
E-mail .... hfaa@hfaa.net
　99-209 Moanalua Rd Ste 305, Aiea, HI 96701
　Linda Machada, Executive Director

Hawaii Parent Training & Info Center **808.536.9684**
E-mail .... ldah@ldahawaii.org
　245 N Kukui St Ste 205, Honolulu, HI 96817
　Michael Moore, Executive Director

Hawaii State Parent Teacher Student Assn **808.593.2042**
E-mail .... hi_office@pta.org
　PO Box 22878, Honolulu, HI 96823

Kapiolani Deaf Center **808.734.9210**
E-mail .... coryell@hawaii.edu
　4303 Diamond Head Rd, Manono Bldg # 102,
　Honolulu, HI 96816

Learning Disabilities Association **800.533.9684**
E-mail .... ldah@ldahawaii.org
　200 N Vineyard Blvd Ste 310, Honolulu, HI 96817

Mental Health Association **808.521.1846**
E-mail .... info@mentalhealth-hi.org
　1124 Fort St # 205, Honolulu, HI 96813
　Marya Grambs, Director

NAMI Hawaii **808.591.1297**
E-mail .... namihawaii@hawaiiantel.net
　770 Kapiolani Blvd Ste 613, Honolulu, HI 96813

National Multiple Sclerosis Society **808.532.0806**
Fax 808.532.0814
E-mail .... HIH@nmss.org
　418 Kuwili St # 105, Honolulu, HI 96817
　Joyce Nelson, Chief Executive Officer

Special Parent Information Network **808.586.8126**
E-mail .... spin@doh.hawaii.gov
　919 Ala Moana Blvd Ste 101, Honolulu, HI 96814
　Susan Rocco, Coordinator

Speech-Language-Hearing Association **808.528.4742**
E-mail .... hsha_membership@yahoo.com
　PO Box 235888, Honolulu, HI 96823

The Arc in Hawaii **808.737.7995**
E-mail .... info@thearcinhawaii.org
　3989 Diamond Head Rd, Honolulu, HI 96816

United Cerebral Palsy Association of HI **808.532.6744**
E-mail .... ucpa@ucpahi.org
　414 Kuwili St Ste 105, Honolulu, HI 96817
　Donna Fouts, Executive Director

SUBSTANCE ABUSE TREATMENT

Coalition for A Drug Free Hawaii **808.545.3228**
Fax 808.545.2686
Web .... www.drugfreehawaii.org
E-mail .... ashinn@drugfreehawaii.org
　1130 N Nimitz Hwy Rm A259, Honolulu,
　HI 96817-5783
　Alan Shinn, Executive Director

Hawaii

Idaho

http://accessidaho.org

C.L. "Butch" Otter, Governor
Office of the Governor
304 N 8th St Ste. 347 PO Box 83720
Boise, ID 83720
208.334.2100
208.334.3454 (Fax)
www.gov.idaho.gov

Alan F. Miller, Juvenile Justice Specialist
Department of Juvenile Corrections
PO Box 83720
Boise, ID 83720-0285
208.334.5100 Ext. 244
208.334.5120 (Fax)
alanf.miller@idjc.idaho.gov

John Varin, SAG Chair.
PO Box 83720
Fairfield, ID 83720
208.334.2246
208.947.7590 (Fax)
jvarin@idcourts.net

CRISIS NUMBERS

Idaho Care Line 800.926.2588

STATE SERVICES

SOCIAL SERVICES

Child Care Licensing Office Idaho **208.334.5700**
Fax 208.332.7331
450 W States St, 5th Fl, Boise, ID 83720
Bowrie Burgess, Supervisor

Idaho Dept of Health and Welfare **208.334.5500**
Fax 208.334.6558
Web . . . . .www.healthandwelfare.idaho.gov
E-mail . . . . .armstrongr@dhw.idaho.gov
450 W State Fl 9, Boise, ID 83720-0036
Richard Armstrong, Director

Region VI Family & Children's Svcs **208.239.6200**
Fax 208.236.6354
E-mail . . . . .lunneyf@dhw.idaho.gov
1070 Hiline Rd, Pocatello, ID 83201
Francis Lunney, Program Manager

GENERAL HEALTH SERVICES

Childrens Special Health Program ID **208.334.5962**
Fax 208.334.4946
450 W State St, Boise, ID 83720
Jacqui Daniel, Director

Div of Medicaid **208.334.5747**
Fax 208.364.1811
Web . . . . .www.healthandwelfare.idaho.gov
E-mail . . . . .clementl@dhw.idaho.gov
3232 Elder St, Boise, ID 83705-4711
Leslie Clement, Administrator

Maternal and Child Health ID **208.334.5930**
Fax 208.332.7362
E-mail . . . . .princed@dhw.idaho.gov
450 West State St Fl 4, Boise, ID 83720
D Prince, Director

MENTAL HEALTH SERVICES

Developmental Disabilities Program **208.334.5536**
Fax 208.332.7331
Web . . . . .www.welfare.idaho.gov
450 W State St Fl 5, Boise, ID 83720-0001
Chad Carwell, Supervisor

Division of Vocational Rehab ID **208.334.3390**
Fax 208.334.5305
E-mail . . . . .info@vr.idaho.gov
650 W State St, Len B Jordan Bldg Rm 150, Boise,
ID 83720

Idaho Radar Network Ctr **208.426.3471**
Fax 240.221.4292
Web .www.ncadi.samhsa.gov/radar
E-mail . . . . .ggirvan@boisestate.edu
1910 University Dr, Boise, ID 83725
Georgia Girvan, Director

Vocational Rehabilitation Agency ID **208.334.3220**
Fax 208.334.2963
E-mail . . . . .nhanchett@icbvi.idaho.gov
341 W Washington St, Boise, ID 83702
Nanna Hanchett, Director

JUSTICE AGENCY

Attorney General's Ofc **208.334.2400**
Fax 208.854.8071
Web . . . . .www.ag.idaho.gov
700 W Jefferson St, Boise, ID 83720
Lawrence Wasden, Attorney General

Correctional Education Division ID **208.658.2066**
Fax 208.327.7458
E-mail . . . . .gcushman@idoc.idaho.gov
1299 N Orchard St Ste 110, Boise, ID 83706
G Cushman, Director

Idaho Crime Victims Compensation Program . . .**208.334.6000**
Fax 208.332.7559
E-mail . . . . .ggutierr@iic.state.id.us
700 S Colorado Ln, Boise, ID 83712-0041
George Gutierrez, Manager

Idaho Dept of Corrections **208.658.2000**
Fax 208.327.7404
Web . . . . .www.corr.state.id.us
1299 N Orchard St Ste 110, Boise, ID 83706-2266
Brent Reinke, Director

Interstate Compact on Juveniles **208.334.5100**
Fax 208.334.5120
954 W Jefferson St, Boise, ID 83702
Sharon Harrigfeld, Director

COURTS

7th District Court **208.756.2815**
Fax 208.756.4673
E-mail . . . . .sclark@co.bonneville.id.us
206 Courthouse Dr, Salmon, ID 83467
Honorable Steven Clark, Director

Administrative Ofc of the Courts **208.334.2246**
Fax 208.947.7590
Web . . . . .www.idcourts.net
451 W State St, Boise, ID 83702-6057
Patricia Tobias, Administrative Director

POLICE AND SHERIFF

Idaho Chiefs of Police Assoc **208.263.3158**
Fax 208.263.3678
Web . . . . .www.ci.sanpoint.id.us
E-mail . . . . .mlockwood@ci.sanpoint.id.us
1123 Lake St, Sandpoint, ID 83864-1714
Mark Lockwood, President, Chief Of Police

Idaho State Police **208.884.7000**
Fax 208.884.7193
Web . . . . .www.isp.idaho.gov
E-mail . . . . .kernal.russell@isp.state.id.us
700 S. Stratford Dr, Meridian, ID 83642
Kernal Jerry Russell, Director

Idaho State Police Bureau of Criminal
Identification **208.884.7136**
Fax 208.884.7193
E-mail . . . . .dawn.pack@isp.idaho.gov
700 So Stratford St, Ste. 120, Meridan, ID 83642
Dawn Pack, Director

Sheriff's Office **208.934.4422**
Fax 208.934.4260
E-mail . . . . .sheriff@co.gooding.id.us
624 Main St, Gooding, ID 83330-1300
Shaun R. Gough, Sheriff

EDUCATION SERVICES

Deaf & Blind School **208.934.4457**
Fax 208.934.8352
Web . . . . .www.isdb.idaho.gov
1450 Main St, Gooding, ID 83330
Gretchen Spooner, Principal

Homeless Educ Program Office Idaho **208.332.6978**
Fax 208.334.2228
E-mail . . . . .kjseay@sde.idaho.gov
650 W State, PO Box 83720, Boise, ID 83720
Karen Seay, State Coordinator

Idaho Parents Unlimited Inc **208.342.5884**
Fax 208.342.1408
E-mail . . . . .parents@ipulidaho.org
500 S 8th St, PO Box 50126, Boise, ID 83705
Evelyn M, Director

Idaho State Board of Education 208.332.6800
Fax...208.334.2228
E-mail.........................bkmattson@sde.idaho.gov
   650 W State St, Boise, ID 83720
   Bk Mattson, Director

Special Education Team Idaho 208.332.6911
Fax...208.334.2228
E-mail.........................rhenderson@sde.idaho.gov
   650 W State St, Boise, ID 83720
   Richard Henderson, Director

LABOR & WORKFORCE EDUCATION

Idaho Dept of Labor 208.332.3570
Fax...208.334.6430
E-mail.......................roger.madsen@cl.idaho.gov
   317 W Main Street, Boise, ID 83735
   Roger Madsen, Director

COUNTY SERVICES

Ada County

SOCIAL SERVICES

Region IV Dept Of Health And
Welfare.....................................208.334.6800
Fax...208.334.6899
Web..................................www.idahohealth.org
E-mail......................mjoe@idvr.state.id.us
   1720 Westgate Dr Ste D, Boise, ID 83720-0026
   Mary Joe, Program Director

GENERAL HEALTH SERVICES

Central District Health IV Boise 208.375.5211
Fax...208.327.7100
Web..................................www.cdhd.idaho.gov
E-mail......................ggoodman@cdhd.idaho.gov
   707 N Armstrong Pl, Boise, ID 83704-0825
   Gladys Goodman, Rn, Std/hiv Coordinator

JUSTICE AGENCY

CASA Program 208.345.3344
Fax...208.345.3700
Web..............................www.familyadvocate.org
E-mail......................info@familyadvocate.org
   3010 W State St Ste 104, Boise, ID 83703
   Nicole Sirak, Family Advocate Program Executive Director

COURTS

District Court............................208.287.6900
Fax...208.287.6919
Web......................................www.adaweb.net
   200 W Front St, Boise, ID 83702-7399
   Honorable David E. Day, Judge

POLICE AND SHERIFF

Sheriff's Ofc...........................208.577.3000
Fax...208.577.3009
Web..................................www.adasheriff.org
E-mail......................graney@adaweb.net
   7200 Barrister Dr, Boise, ID 83704-9217
   Gary Raney, Sheriff

Adams County

COURTS

3rd District Court 208.253.4233
Fax...208.253.4880
Web..............................www.co.adams.id.us
   201 Industrial Ave, Council, ID 83612-0048
   Honorable James C. Peart, Judge

POLICE AND SHERIFF

Sheriff's Ofc...........................208.253.4227
Fax...208.253.1141
E-mail......................rlgreen@frontiernet.net
   201 Industrial Ave, Council, ID 83612-5283
   Richard L. Green, Sheriff

Bannock County

MENTAL HEALTH SERVICES

Region VI Mental Health 208.234.7900
Fax...208.236.6328
Web..................................www.dhw.idaho.gov
E-mail......................weersr@dhw.idaho.gov
   421 Memorial Dr, Pocatello, ID 83201-4008
   Ritchie Weers, Program Director

JUSTICE AGENCY

CASA/GAL 208.232.2272
Fax...208.478.6978
Web..................................www.nationalcasa.org
E-mail......................casa6th@gmail.com
   836 E Center St Ste A, Pocatello, ID 83201-5874
   Cori Hadley, Director

Juvenile Probation Svcs 208.234.1082
Fax...208.234.1094
   137 S 5th St, Pocatello, ID 83201
   Matt Olsen, Probation Director

COURTS

6th District Court 208.236.7350
Fax...208.236.7013
Web..................................www.bannockcounty.us
   624 E Center St Ste 220, Pocatello, ID 83201-6274
   Honorable Gaylen L. Box, Judge

POLICE AND SHERIFF

Sheriff's Ofc 208.236.7123
Fax...208.236.7192
Web..................................www.co.bannock.id.us
E-mail......................sheriff@co.bannock.id.us
   5800 S 5th Ave, Pocatello, ID 83204-2205
   Lorin W. Nielsen, Sheriff

Bear Lake County

GENERAL HEALTH SERVICES

Southeastern District Health Dept
Montpelier................................208.847.3000
Fax...208.847.2538
Web..................................www.sdhdidaho.org
   455 Washington St Ste 2, Montpelier, ID 83254-1600
   Leslie Talbot, Nursing Supervisor

COURTS

6th District Court 208.945.2208
Fax...208.945.2780
Web......................................www.dcdi.net
E-mail......................blcourtclerk@dcdi.net
   7 E Ctr Fl 2, Paris, ID 83261
   Honorable O. Lynn Brower, Director

POLICE AND SHERIFF

Sheriff's Ofc 208.945.2121
Fax...208.945.2740
Web......................................www.dcdi.net
E-mail......................bearlake@dcdi.net
   50 North Main St, Paris, ID 83261
   Brent R. Bunn, Sheriff

Benewah County

GENERAL HEALTH SERVICES

Benewah Medical Ctr 208.686.1931
Web..................................www.benewahmedicalctr.gov
E-mail......................gcarpent@bmc.portland.ihs.gov
   1115 B Street, Plummer, ID 83851
   Gary Leva, Executive Director

Panhandle District Health Dept Saint
Maries....................................208.245.4556
Fax...208.245.3692
E-mail......................pcuvala@phd1.idaho.gov
   137 N 8th St, Saint Maries, ID 83861-1831
   Peggy Cuvala, Nurse Practioner

JUSTICE AGENCY

Juvenile Probation........................208.245.4065
Fax...208.245.1915
   701 W College Ave Ste 10, Saint Maries, ID 83861
   Marianne Kelly, Director Of Probation Services

COURTS

1st District Court........................208.245.3241
Fax...208.245.3046
Web..................................www.benewahcounty.org
E-mail......................mreynolds@benewahcounty.org
   701 W College Ave, Saint Maries, ID 83861
   Honorable Patrick R. Mcfadden, Director

POLICE AND SHERIFF

Sheriff's Ofc 208.245.2555
Fax...208.245.4898
E-mail......................sherifftharp@benewah-county-sheriff.org
   701 W College Ave Ste 1, Ste 301, Saint Maries,
   ID 83861-1884
   Robert Kirts, Sheriff

Bingham County

SOCIAL SERVICES

Shoshone-Bannock Tribes Social
Svcs.....................................208.478.3863
Fax...208.478.3940
Web..................................www.shoshonebannocktribes.com
E-mail......................mpoog@sbth.nsn.us
   Pima Dr, Fort Hall, ID 83203
   Malissa Poog, Acting Social Services Manager

GENERAL HEALTH SERVICES

Southeastern District Health Dept
Blackfoot.................................208.785.2160
Fax...208.785.6372
   326 Poplar St, Blackfoot, ID 83221-1726
   Wendy Hobley, Public Health Nurse

COURTS

7th District Court 208.782.2680
Fax...208.785.5447
   501 N Maple St Ste 304, Blackfoot, ID 83221
   Shawn Hill, Chief JPO

POLICE AND SHERIFF

Sheriff's Ofc 208.785.4440
Fax...208.785.3033
E-mail......................dljohnson@co.bingham.id.us
   501 N Maple St Ste 405, Blackfoot, ID 83221
   Dave Johnson, Sheriff

Blaine County

JUSTICE AGENCY

Probation................................208.788.5528
Fax...208.788.5541
Web..................................www.blainecounty.org
   219 S 1st Ave Ste 108, Hailey, ID 83333-8768
   Teresa Espedal, Chief JPO

Idaho

COURTS

5th District Court **208.788.5525**
Fax 208.788.5527
E-mail ....relgee@co.blaine.id.us
    201 S 2nd Ave Ste 106, Hailey, ID 83333
    Honorable Robert Elgee, Judge

POLICE AND SHERIFF

Sheriff's Ofc **208.788.5555**
Fax 208.788.3592
E-mail ....wfemling@co.blaine.id.us
    1650 Aviation Drv, Hailey, ID 83333
    Gene Ramsey, Sheriff

Boise County

COURTS

4th District Court **208.392.4452**
Fax 208.392.6712
    419 Main St, Idaho City, ID 83631
    Sue Robinson, Supervising Court Clerk

POLICE AND SHERIFF

Sheriff's Ofc **208.392.4411**
Fax 208.392.4108
E-mail ....broeber@co.boise.id.us
    3851 Hwy 21, Idaho City, ID 83631
    Ben Roeber, Sheriff

Bonner County

GENERAL HEALTH SERVICES

Panhandle District Health Dept **208.263.5159**
Fax 208.263.6963
Web www.phd1.idaho.gov
E-mail ....kmeyer@phd1.idaho.gov
    1020 Michigan St, Sandpoint, ID 83864-1788
    Kristina Meyer, Public Health Nurse

JUSTICE AGENCY

Justice Svcs **208.263.1602**
Fax 208.263.1899
    4105 No. Boyer Ave, Sandpoint, ID 83864
    Debbie Stallcup, Director

COURTS

1st District Court **208.265.1446**
Fax 208.265.1468
Web ....www.co.bonner.id.us
E-mail ....bbuchanan@co.bonner.id.us
    215 S 1st Ave, Sandpoint, ID 83864-1305
    Barbera Buchanan, Magistrate

POLICE AND SHERIFF

Sheriff's Ofc **208.263.8417**
Fax 208.265.4378
Web ....www.bonnerso.org
E-mail ....sheriff@bonnerso.org
    4001 N Boyer Rd, Sandpoint, ID 83864-8066
    Darryl Wheeler, Sheriff

Bonneville County

MENTAL HEALTH SERVICES

Region VII Mental Health **208.528.5700**
Fax 208.528.5747
Web ....www.healthandwelfare.id.gov
E-mail ....rodrique@dhw.idaho.gov
    150 Shoup Ave Ste 17, Idaho Falls, ID 83402-3653
    Randy Rodriquez, Program Manager

JUSTICE AGENCY

Probation **208.528.5600**
Fax 208.528.5608
Web ....www.bonneville.id.us
E-mail ....kremsbur@co.bonneville.id.us
    883 Shoup Ave, Idaho Falls, ID 83402-3404
    Kyla Remsburg, Teen Court Co-Director

POLICE AND SHERIFF

Police Dept **208.529.1200**
Fax 208.529.1153
Web ....www.co.bonneville.id.us
E-mail ....sroof@idahofallsidaho.gov
    605 N Capital Ave, Idaho Falls, ID 83402
    Steve Roof, Chief Of Police

Boundary County

GENERAL HEALTH SERVICES

**Panhandle District Health Dept District I Bonners
Ferry** **208.267.5558**
Fax 208.267.3795
    7402 Caribou St, Bonners Ferry, ID 83805
    Paulette Ketner, Rn, Public Health Nurse

JUSTICE AGENCY

Probation Ofc **208.267.7983**
Fax 208.267.0933
E-mail ....sbrown@boundarycountyid.org
    7167 1st Street 203, Bonners Ferry, ID 83805
    Stacy Brown, Chief Performance Officer

COURTS

1st District Court **208.267.5504**
Fax 208.267.7814
Web ....www.boundary-idaho.com
E-mail ....jjulian@boundarycountyid.org
    6452 Kootenai St, Bonners Ferry, ID 83805
    Honorable Justin Julian, Judge

POLICE AND SHERIFF

Sheriff's Ofc **208.267.3151**
Fax 208.267.3154
Web ....www.boundarysheriff.org
E-mail ....gsprungl@boundarysheriff.org
    6438 Kootenai St, Bonners Ferry, ID 83805
    Greg Sprungl, Sheriff

Butte County

GENERAL HEALTH SERVICES

**Southeastern District Health Dept
Arco** **208.527.3463**
Fax 208.527.3972
Web ....www.sdhdidaho.org
E-mail ....webinfo@phd6.idaho.gov
    178 Sunset Dr, Arco, ID 83213
    Kristy Unruh, Rn, Public Health Nurse

COURTS

7th District Court **208.527.8259**
Fax 208.527.3448
    326 West Grand Ave, Arco, ID 83213
    Honorable Ralph L. Savage, Magistrate

POLICE AND SHERIFF

Sheriff's Ofc **208.527.8553**
Fax 208.527.3916
    256 West Grand Ave, Arco, ID 83213
    Wes Collins, Sheriff

Camas County

COURTS

5th District Court **208.764.2238**
Fax 208.764.2349
    501 Soldier Rd, Fairfield, ID 83327
    Honorable Jason Walker, Judge

POLICE AND SHERIFF

Sheriff's Ofc **208.764.2261**
Fax 208.764.2721
E-mail ....ccso@rtci.net
    119 W Willow St, Fairfield, ID 83327
    David L. Sanders, Sheriff

Canyon County

SOCIAL SERVICES

Children & Family Svcs **208.465.8452**
Fax 208.465.8431
    823 Parkcentre Way, Nampa, ID 83651
    Mary Allen, Supervisor

Health & Welfare **208.454.0421**
Fax 208.454.8351
Web ....www.healthandwelfare.org
E-mail ....rwoods@sco.state.id.us
    3402 Franklin Rd, Caldwell, ID 83605
    Randy Woods, Regional Director

GENERAL HEALTH SERVICES

**Southwest District Health Dept
Caldwell** **208.455.5300**
Fax 208.454.7722
Web ....www.swdh.org
    920 Main St, Caldwell, ID 83605-3748
    Clem Sahleen, Hiv/aids Advocate

MENTAL HEALTH SERVICES

Region III Mental Health **208.459.0092**
Fax 208.454.7714
Web ....www.healthandwelfare.org
E-mail ....hurtt@idhw.state.id.us
    3402 Franklin Rd, Caldwell, ID 83605
    Todd Hurt, Program Manager

JUSTICE AGENCY

Juvenile Corrections Ctr-Nampa **208.465.8443**
Fax 208.465.8484
Web ....www.idjc.idaho.gov
    1650 11th Ave N, Nampa, ID 83687-5000
    Sharon Harrigfeld, Director

Juvenile Probation **208.454.7330**
Fax 208.454.7352
E-mail ....ecatalano@canyonco.org
    222 N 12Th Ave, Caldwell, ID 83605-3554
    Elda Catalano, Supervisor

COURTS

3rd District Court **208.454.7300**
Fax 208.454.6689
Web ....www.canyoncounty.org
    1115 Albany St, Caldwell, ID 83605-3522
    Honorable Debra A. Orr, Director

POLICE AND SHERIFF

Police Dept **208.455.3115**
Fax 208.455.3123
    110 S 5th Ave, Caldwell, ID 83605
    Chris Allgood, Chief

Sheriff's Ofc **208.454.7510**
Fax 208.454.7253
    1115 Albany St, Caldwell, ID 83605
    Chris Smith, Sheriff

EDUCATION SERVICES

Migrant Head Start **208.454.1652**
Fax 208.459.0448
Web ....www.communitycouncilofidaho.org
E-mail ....info@ccimail.org
    317 Happy Day Blvd Ste 250, Caldwell, ID 83607
    Irma Morin, Executive Director

Caribou County

SOCIAL SERVICES

Health & Welfare **208.547.4317**
Fax 208.547.4810
Web ....www.healthandwelfare.org
E-mail ....arambarr@idhw.state.id.us
    184 S Main St, Soda Springs, ID 83276
    Nick Arambarri, Regional Director

GENERAL HEALTH SERVICES

Home & Health **208.547.4375**
Fax 208.547.4398
Web ....www.sdhdidaho.org
E-mail ....ltalbort@phd6.idaho.gov
  55 E 1st S, Soda Springs, ID 83276-1437
  Leslie Talbort, Public Health Nurse

COURTS

6th District Court **208.547.2146**
Fax 208.547.4759
Web ....www.plmw.com
E-mail ....hart@plmw.com
  159 S Main St, Ste 206, Soda Springs, ID 83276
  Honorable David Kress, Judge

POLICE AND SHERIFF

Sheriff's Ofc **208.547.2561**
Fax 208.547.0252
  475 E 2nd S, Soda Springs, ID 83276-1447
  Rick Anderson, Sheriff

Cassia County

SOCIAL SERVICES

Region V Children & Family Svcs **208.678.0974**
Fax 208.677.4002
Web ....www.info-netdhw.com
  2241 Overland Ave, Ste 2, Burley, ID 83318
  Chris Waitley, Supervisor

GENERAL HEALTH SERVICES

South Central District Health Dept
Burley **208.678.8221**
Fax 208.678.7465
  2311 Park Ave, Burley, ID 83318
  Josie, Public Health Nurse

JUSTICE AGENCY

Juvenile Probation **208.878.1230**
Fax 208.878.1009
E-mail ....bray@cassiacounty.org
  1459 Overland Ave, Burley, ID 83318
  Brook Ray, Jpo

COURTS

5th District Court **208.878.0180**
Fax 208.878.1003
  1459 Overland Ave, Burley, ID 83318
  Joseph Larsen, County Clerk

EDUCATION SERVICES

Cassia Head Start **208.678.3669**
Fax 208.678.1580
Web ....www.scheadstart.org
E-mail ....mary@scheadstart.org
  800 E 16th St, Burley, ID 83318-2073
  Mary Marshall, Director

Clark County

POLICE AND SHERIFF

Sheriff's Dept **208.374.5403**
Fax 208.374.5614
E-mail ....clarkeso@mudlake.net
  324 W Main St, Dubois, ID 83423
  Clarke May, Sheriff

Clearwater County

JUSTICE AGENCY

Juvenile Court Svcs **208.476.9725**
Fax 208.476.9749
Web ....www.latah.id.us
E-mail ....acurtis@clearwatercounty.org
  1075 Michigan Ave, Orofino, ID 83544
  Alana Curtis, Director

COURTS

2nd District Court **208.476.5596**
Fax 208.476.8910
  150 Michigan St, Orofino, ID 83544
  Honorable Randall W. Robinson, Magistrate

POLICE AND SHERIFF

Sheriff's Dept **208.476.4521**
Fax 208.476.7835
Web ....www.clearwatercounty.org
E-mail ....sheriff@clearwatercounty.org
  150 Michigan Ave, Orofino, ID 83544
  Chris Goetz, Sheriff

Custer County

COURTS

7th District Court **208.879.2359**
Fax 208.879.6412
Web ....www.co.custer.id.us
E-mail ....croos@co.custer.id.us
  801 Main E, Challis, ID 83226
  Honorable Charles Roos, Judge

POLICE AND SHERIFF

Sheriff's Ofc **208.879.2232**
Fax 208.879.2421
E-mail ....custers@custertel.net
  130 S 9th St, Challis, ID 83226
  Stu Lumpkin, Sheriff

Elmore County

JUSTICE AGENCY

Juvenile Probation **208.587.2141**
Fax 208.587.2150
  195 S 5th E, Mountain Home, ID 83647
  Monica Halliday, Chief JPO

COURTS

4th District Court **208.587.2133**
Fax 208.587.2134
  150 S 4th E, Ste 5, Mountain Home, ID 83647
  George Hicks, Judge

POLICE AND SHERIFF

Sheriff's Ofc **208.587.2100**
Fax 208.587.2118
  2255 E 8 N, Mountain Home, ID 83647
  Rick E. Layher, Sheriff

Franklin County

POLICE AND SHERIFF

Sheriff's Ofc **208.852.1234**
Fax 208.852.2580
E-mail ....dbeckstead@idacom.net
  39 W Oneida St, Preston, ID 83263-1232
  Don B. Beckstead, Sheriff

EDUCATION SERVICES

Bear River Head Start-Daycare Ctr **208.852.3012**
Web ....www.brhd.org
E-mail ....tbarson@utah.gov
  515 S 4th E, Preston, ID 83263-1603
  Todd Barson, Deputy Director

Fremont County

GENERAL HEALTH SERVICES

Eastern Idaho Public Health
District **208.624.7585**
Fax 208.624.1547
Web www.idaho.gov/phd7
  45 S 2nd W, Saint Anthony, ID 83445-2107
  Deon Staker, Rn, Public Health Nurse

JUSTICE AGENCY

Juvenile Corrections Ctr St.
Anthony **208.624.3462**
Fax 208.624.0973
  2220 E 600 N, Saint Anthony, ID 83445
  Skip Greene, Superintendent

COURTS

7th District Court **208.624.7401**
Fax 208.624.4607
E-mail ....kwalker@co.fremont.id.us
  151 W 1st N, Saint Anthony, ID 83445
  Honorable Keith Walker, Judge

POLICE AND SHERIFF

Sheriff's Dept **208.624.4482**
Fax 208.624.4485
Web ....www.co.fremont.id.us
E-mail ....lhumphries@co.fremont.id.us
  146 N 2nd W, Saint Anthony, ID 83445-1435
  Len Humphries, Sheriff

Gem County

GENERAL HEALTH SERVICES

Southwest District Health Dept
Emmett **208.365.6371**
Fax 208.365.4729
  1008 E Locust St, Emmett, ID 83617
  Debra Dobbs, Public Health Nurse

JUSTICE AGENCY

Juvenile Probation **208.365.2127**
Fax 208.365.6114
Web ....www.co.gem.id.us
E-mail ....jschneider@co.gem.id.us
  303 E Main St, Emmett, ID 83617-3034
  Janelle Schneider, Chief JPO

COURTS

3rd District Court **208.365.4221**
Fax 208.365.6172
  415 E Main St Ste 300, Emmett, ID 83617
  Honorable Tyler Smith, Magistrate Judge

POLICE AND SHERIFF

Sheriff's Ofc **208.365.3521**
Fax 208.365.7166
Web ....www.co.gem.id.us
E-mail ....sheriff@co.gem.id.us
  415 E Main St, Emmett, ID 83617
  Charles Roland, Sheriff

Gooding County

GENERAL HEALTH SERVICES

South Central District Health Dept **208.934.4477**
Fax 208.934.8558
Web www.phd5.idaho.gov
E-mail ....manderso@phd5.idaho.gov
  255 N Canyon Dr, Gooding, ID 83330
  Mary Belle Anderson, Rn, Public Health Nurse

JUSTICE AGENCY

Juvenile Probation **208.934.5168**
Fax 208.934.5130
Web ....www.co.gooding.id.us
E-mail ....cjohnson@co.gooding.id.us
  624 Main St Ste 101, Gooding, ID 83330-1300
  Carol A. Johnson, Chief JPO

Idaho

Idaho County

SOCIAL SERVICES

Health & Welfare **208.983.0620**
Fax 208.983.2440
Web ....www.dhw.idaho.gov
E-mail ....beecherr@dhw.idaho.gov
   216 So. C St, Grangeville, ID 83530
Ron Beecher, Regional Director

GENERAL HEALTH SERVICES

North Central District Health Dept
Grangeville **208.983.2842**
Fax 208.983.2845
Web www.phd2.state.id.us
E-mail ....ssickels@phd2.state.id.us
   903 W Main St, Grangeville, ID 83530-5192
Susan Sickels, Rn, Public Health Nurse

JUSTICE AGENCY

Court Services **208.983.0339**
Fax 208.983.0529
E-mail ....nmcdonald@idahocounty.org
   320 W Main St Ste 28, Grangeville, ID 83530-1948
Nadine Mcdonald, Director

COURTS

2nd District Court **208.983.2776**
Fax 208.983.2376
E-mail ....districtcourt@idahocounty.org
   320 W Main St Ste 23, Grangeville, ID 83530
Jeff Payne, Magistrate Judge

POLICE AND SHERIFF

Sheriff's Ofc **208.983.1100**
Fax 208.983.1359
E-mail ....dispatch@idahocounty.org
   320 W Main St Ste 4, Grangeville, ID 83530
Doug Giddings, Sheriff

Jefferson County

JUSTICE AGENCY

Probation Dept **208.745.8244**
Fax 208.745.8293
Web ....www.qwest.net
E-mail ....terridodge@qwest.net
   295 N 3855 E, Rigby, ID 83442-5124
Terri Dodge, Program Coordinator

COURTS

7th District Court **208.745.7736**
Fax 208.745.6636
   210 Courthouse Way Ste 120, Rigby, ID 83442
Chris Boulter, Clerk of the Court

POLICE AND SHERIFF

Sheriff's Ofc **208.745.9210**
Fax 208.745.9212
Web ....www.co.jefferson.id.us
E-mail ....bolsen@co.jefferson.id.us
   200 Courthouse Way, Rigby, ID 83442-5295
Blair R. Olsen, Sheriff

Jerome County

SOCIAL SERVICES

Region V Children & Family Svcs **208.734.4000**
Fax 208.736.2120
   601 Pole Line Rd Ste 6, Twin Falls, ID 83301
Nancy Espinoza, Supervisor

GENERAL HEALTH SERVICES

South Central District Health Dept **208.324.8838**
Fax 208.324.9554
Web www.php5.id.co
E-mail ....manderso@phd5.idaho.gov
   951 E Ave H St, Jerome, ID 83338
Marybelle Anderson, Public Health Nurse

JUSTICE AGENCY

State CASA Program **208.324.6890**
Fax 208.324.2016
Web ....www.safelink.net
   716 Bridge St, Jerome, ID 83338-2332
Tahna Cooper, Executive Director

POLICE AND SHERIFF

Sheriff's Ofc **208.644.2770**
Fax 208.644.2779
Web ....www.jeromecounty.org
E-mail ....dmcfall@jerome.co.id.us
   300 N Lincoln Ave, Ste 206, Jerome, ID 83338
Douglas Mcfall, Sheriff

Kootenai County

JUSTICE AGENCY

CASA Program **208.667.9165**
Fax 208.667.2965
   208 N 4yh St, Coeur D Alene, ID 83814
Sandra Gunn, Director

Juvenile Probation **208.446.1920**
Fax 208.446.1922
E-mail ....kcjv@kcgov.us
   205 N, Coeur D Alene, ID 83814
Sheley Beck, Administrator

COURTS

1st District Court **208.446.1104**
Fax 208.446.1188
   PO Box 9000, Coeur D Alene, ID 83816-9000
Honorable Barry E. Watson, Director

POLICE AND SHERIFF

Sheriff's Ofc **208.446.1300**
Fax 208.446.1307
Web ....www.kcsheriff.com
E-mail ....rwatson@kcgov.us
   5500 N Goverment Way, Coeur D Alene, ID 83816
Rocky Watson, Sheriff

Latah County

SOCIAL SERVICES

Region II Children & Family Svcs **208.882.0562**
Fax 208.882.8575
E-mail ....lyonsj@idhw.state.id.us
   1350 Troy Rd Ste 2, Moscow, ID 83843-3995
Joyce Lyons, Phd, Clinical Supervisor

GENERAL HEALTH SERVICES

North Central District Health Dept
Moscow **208.882.7506**
Fax 208.882.3494
Web www.phd2.state.id.us
E-mail ....mpoluta@phd2.state.id.us
   333 E Palouse River Dr, Moscow, ID 83843-8916
Mary Poluta, HIV Coordinator

JUSTICE AGENCY

Juvenile Probation **208.883.2277**
Fax 208.883.3357
E-mail ....bdulin@latah.id.us
   522 S Adams St, Moscow, ID 83843
Brian Dulin, Director

COURTS

2nd District Court **208.883.2255**
Fax 208.883.2259
Web ....www.latah.id.us
   523 S Adams St, Mosco, ID 83843
Honorable John Judge, Judge

POLICE AND SHERIFF

Sheriff's Dept **208.882.2216**
Fax 208.883.2281
   522 S Adams St, Moscow, ID 83843
Wayne Rausch, Sheriff

Lemhi County

SOCIAL SERVICES

Region VII Children & Family Svcs **208.756.3336**
Fax 208.756.3805
Web ....www.co.custer.id.us
E-mail ....zieskep@dhw.idaho.gov
   1301 Main St Ste 3B, Salmon, ID 83467-4452
Page Zieske, Children Mental Health

JUSTICE AGENCY

Juvenile Probation **208.756.2815**
Fax 208.756.2349
   200 Fulton St, Ste 104, Salmon, ID 83467
Katy Smith, Juvenile Probation Officer

POLICE AND SHERIFF

Sheriff's Dept **208.756.8980**
Fax 208.756.6040
E-mail ....sheriff.lemhicounty@centurytel.net
   206 Courthouse Dr Ste T, Salmon, ID 83467
Lynn Bowerman, Sheriff

Lewis County

GENERAL HEALTH SERVICES

North Central District Health Dept
Kamiah **208.935.2124**
   132 No Hill, Kamiah, ID 83536
Betsy Stemrich, Rn, Public Health Nurse

COURTS

2nd District Court **208.937.2251**
Fax 208.937.9233
Web ....www.lewiscountyid.org
   510 Oak St Rm 1, Nezperce, ID 83543-5065
Honorable Stephen L. Calhoun, Director

POLICE AND SHERIFF

Sheriff's Ofc **208.937.2447**
Fax 208.937.9235
   510 Oak St Rm 5, Nezperce, ID 83543
Brian Brokop, Sheriff

Lincoln County

JUSTICE AGENCY

Juvenile Probation **208.886.7672**
Fax 208.544.7073
E-mail ....lindab@lincolncountyid.us
   117 W Ave A, Shoshone, ID 83352
Linda Boguslawski, Jpo

COURTS

5th District Court **208.886.2173**
Fax 208.886.2458
Web ....www.co.twin-falls.id.us
E-mail ....mingram@co.twin-falls.id.us
   111 W B St Ste C, Shoshone, ID 83352-5364
Honorable Mark A. Ingram, Judge

POLICE AND SHERIFF

Sheriff's Dept **208.886.2250**
Fax 208.886.2851
   111 West B St Ste S, Shoshone, ID 83352
Kevin Ellis, Sheriff

Idaho

Madison County

COURTS

7th District Court 208.356.9383
Fax 208.356.5425
    159 E Main St, Rexburg, ID 83440
    Honorable Mark S. Rammell, Judge

POLICE AND SHERIFF

Sheriff's Dept 208.356.5426
Fax 208.356.6056
Web ....www.madisonsheriff.com
    145 E Main St, Rexburg, ID 83440-1911
    Roy C. Klinger, Sheriff

Minidoka County

GENERAL HEALTH SERVICES

South Central District Health Dept
Rupert 208.436.7185
Fax 208.436.9066
    1218 9th St Ste 15, Rupert, ID 83350
    Lisa Klamm, Rn, Public Health Nurse

COURTS

5th District Court 208.436.7186
Fax 208.436.5857
Web ....www.co.minidoka.id.us
E-mail ....larry.duff@co.minidoka.id.us
    715 G St, Rupert, ID 83350-1612
    Honorable Larry R. Duff, Judge

POLICE AND SHERIFF

Sheriff's Ofc 208.434.2320
Fax 208.436.9561
E-mail ....kevin.halverson@co.minidoka.id.us
    724 H St, Rupert, ID 83350-1615
    Kevin Halverson, Sheriff

Nez Perce County

SOCIAL SERVICES

Nez Perce Tribal Social Svcs 208.843.2463
Fax 208.843.6364
Web ....www.nezperce.org
E-mail ....jackiem@nezperce.org
    311 Agency Rd, Lapwai, ID 83540-0365
    Jackie McArthur, Manager

Region II Dept Of Health & Welfare 208.799.4360
Fax 208.799.3317
    1118 F St, Lewiston, ID 83501
    Maryjo Murdie, Program Manager

GENERAL HEALTH SERVICES

Public Health Idaho North Central
District 208.799.3100
Web ....www.idahopublichealth.com
    215 10th St, Lewiston, ID 83501
    Tara Dudely, Human Resource Director

JUSTICE AGENCY

Juvenile Corrections Ctr - Lewiston 208.799.3332
Fax 208.799.5086
Web ....www.idjc.idaho.gov
E-mail ....kevin.bernatz@idjc.idaho.gov
    140 Southport Ave, Lewiston, ID 83501-4526
    Kevin Bernatz, Superintendent

COURTS

2nd District Court 208.799.3040
Fax 208.799.3058
Web ....www.state.id.us
E-mail ....kmerica@co.nezperce.id.us
    1230 Main St, Lewiston, ID 83501-1975
    Honorable Kent Merica, Judge

POLICE AND SHERIFF

Sheriff's Ofc 208.799.3131
Fax 208.799.3101
E-mail ....dispatch@co.nezperce.id.us
    1150 Wall St, Lewiston, ID 83501
    Dale Buttrey, Sheriff

Oneida County

COURTS

6th District Court 208.766.4116
Fax 208.766.2990
    10 Court St, Malad City, ID 83252
    Honorable David L. Evans, Judge

POLICE AND SHERIFF

Sheriff's Dept 208.766.2251
Fax 208.766.2891
E-mail ....dispatch@oneidasheriff.net
    10 W Court St, Malad City, ID 83252
    Jeffrey P. Semrad, Sheriff

Owyhee County

COURTS

3rd District Court 208.495.2806
Fax 208.495.1226
Web ....www.payettecounty.org
E-mail ....agrober@payettecounty.org
    20381 St Hwy 78, Murphy, ID 83650
    Honorable Ann C Grober, Judge

POLICE AND SHERIFF

Sheriff's Dept 208.495.1154
Fax 208.495.1259
    20381 Hwy 78, Murphy, ID 83650
    Darryl Crandall, Sheriff

Payette County

SOCIAL SERVICES

Region III Children & Family Svcs 208.642.6411
Fax 208.642.7082
E-mail ....blackbuc@dhw.idaho.gov
    515 N 16th St, Payette, ID 83661-2774
    Cami Blackburn, Children & Family Services Supervisor

GENERAL HEALTH SERVICES

Southwest District Health Dept
Payette 208.642.9321
Fax 208.642.1213
    1155 3rd Ave N, Payette, ID 83661-2407
    Diane Markus, Medical Director

COURTS

3rd District Court 208.642.6019
Fax 208.642.6011
    1130 3rd Ave N Rm 104, Payette, ID 83661
    Roy L. Bullington, Jpo

POLICE AND SHERIFF

Sheriff's Dept 208.642.6006
Fax 208.642.6035
Web ....www.payettecounty.org
    1130 3rd Ave N Rm 101, Payette, ID 83661-2473
    Chad Huff, Sheriff

Power County

COURTS

6th District Court 208.226.7619
Fax 208.226.7612
    543 Bannock Ave, American Falls, ID 83211
    Connie Sheppard, Jpo

POLICE AND SHERIFF

Sheriff's Ofc 208.226.2311
Fax 208.226.7783
E-mail ....jjeffries@co.power.id.us
    550 Gifford Ave, American Falls, ID 83211
    Jim Jeffries, Sheriff

Shoshone County

JUSTICE AGENCY

Juvenile Probation 208.556.7861
Fax 208.752.8881
E-mail ....msmith@co.shoshone.id.us
    700 Bank St, Wallace, ID 83873
    Michael G. Smith, Jpo

COURTS

1st District Court 208.752.1266
Fax 208.753.0921
    700 Bank St Ste 300, Wallace, ID 83873
    Honorable Daniel J. Mcgee, Judge

POLICE AND SHERIFF

Sheriff's Dept 208.556.1114
Fax 208.753.8851
Web ....www.co.shoshone.id.us
E-mail ....reynalds@co.shoshone.id.us
    717 Bank St, Wallace, ID 83873-2303
    Chuck Reynalds, Sheriff

Teton County

GENERAL HEALTH SERVICES

Eastern Idaho Public Health Dept 208.354.2220
Fax 208.354.2224
Web www.idaho.gov.phd7
    820 VALLEY CENTRE DR, Driggs, ID 83422-5005
    Cammi Durbin, Rn, Public Health Nurse

COURTS

7th District Court 208.354.2239
Fax 208.354.8496
Web ....www.co.teton.id.us
    150 Courthouse Dr, RM 307, Driggs, ID 83422-5164
    Phyllis Hensen, Clerk

POLICE AND SHERIFF

Sheriff's Ofc 208.354.2323
Fax 208.354.8028
Web ....www.co.teton.id.us
    89 N Main St, Driggs, ID 83422-5164
    Tony Liford, Sheriff

Twin Falls County

SOCIAL SERVICES

Region V Health And Welfare 208.736.3020
Fax 208.736.2116
Web ....www.idhw.state.id.us
E-mail ....hathawaj@idhw.state.id.us
    601 Poleline Rd, Ste 3, Twin Falls, ID 83301
    John Hathaway, Regional Director

GENERAL HEALTH SERVICES

South Central District Health Dept 208.734.5900
Fax 208.734.9502
Web www.phd5.state.id.us
    1020 Washington St N, Twin Falls, ID 83301
    Rene Leblanc, Regional Director

MENTAL HEALTH SERVICES

Region V Mental Health 208.736.2177
Fax 208.736.2113
Web ....www.dhw.idaho.gov
    823 Harrison St, Twin Falls, ID 83301-3997
    Brenda Grupe, Program Manager

Idaho

JUSTICE AGENCY

Idaho Network Of Children's Advocacy

Ctrs **208.737.2600**
Fax 208.737.2603
E-mail ....kerryk@mvrmc.org
2550 Addison Ave E Ste E, Twin Falls, ID 83301
Kerry Koontz, Program Coordinator

Juvenile Probation **208.736.4215**
Fax 208.736.4222
Web ....www.co.twin-falls.id.us
E-mail ....jwilson@co.twin-falls.id.us
2469 Wright Ave, Twin Falls, ID 83301-8273
Jason Wilson, Intensive Probation Officer

COURTS

Trial Court Admin 5th Judicial

District **208.736.4085**
Fax 208.736.4002
Web www.co.twin-falls.id.us/5thdistrict/
427 Shoshone St N., Twin Falls, ID 83303
Honorable Randy S. Stoker, Judge

EDUCATION SERVICES

Felipe Cabral Migrant Head Start

Daycare **208.734.8419**
Fax 208.734.9359
1122 Washington St S, Twin Falls, ID 83301
Jesus Jara, Director

Valley County

SOCIAL SERVICES

Region IV Children & Family Svcs **208.634.2229**
Fax 208.634.3510
299 S 3rd St, McCall, ID 83638-5020
Kris Sal Dana, Child Protection Officer

COURTS

4th District Court **208.382.7178**
Fax 208.382.7184
219 N Main st, Cascade, ID 83611
Doug Miller, Director Of Juvenile Services

Washington County

GENERAL HEALTH SERVICES

Southwest District Health Dept

Weiser **208.549.2370**
Fax 208.549.2371
Web www.phd3.state.id.us
E-mail ....kzanelli@phd3.state.id.us
46 W Court St, Weiser, ID 83672-1941
Karen Zanelli, Public Health Nurse

JUSTICE AGENCY

Juvenile Probation **208.414.0606**
Fax 208.414.0394
256 E Court St Ste C, Weiser, ID 83672
Bahlia Ftender, Chief JPO

COURTS

3rd District Court **208.414.2232**
Fax 208.414.2335
Web ....www.ruralnetwork.net
485 E 3rd St, Weiser, ID 83672
Honorable Gregory F. Frates, Judge

POLICE AND SHERIFF

Sheriff's Ofc **208.414.2121**
Fax 208.414.2536
E-mail ....mwilliams@co.washington.id.us
262 E Court St, Weiser, ID 83672
Marvin E. Williams, Sheriff

SPECIAL SERVICES AGENCIES

ADOPTION AGENCIES

B Joseph Welch **208.342.5693**
Fax 208.342.5749
E-mail ....joseph_welch@qwestoffice.net
447 W Myrtle, Boise, ID 83702
B. Joseph Welch, Attorney

Belnap Law **208.345.3333**
Fax 208.345.4461
1401 Shoreline Dr Ste 2, Boise, ID 83713
Amber Smith, Office Manager

Brady Law Chartered **208.345.8400**
Fax 208.322.4486
Web ....www.bradylawoffice.com
E-mail ....kathleen@bradylawoffice.com
2537 W State St Apt 200, Boise, ID 83702-2200
Kathleen Law, Director

Casey Family Program **208.377.1771**
Fax 208.377.5308
Web ....www.casey.org
E-mail ....mscholl@casey.org
6441 W Emerald St, Boise, ID 83704-8735
Mike Scholl, Director

Casi Foundation For Children **208.376.0558**
Fax 208.376.1931
Web ....www.adoptcasi.org
E-mail ....info@adoptcasi.org
2308 N Cole Rd Ste E, Boise, ID 83704
Neil Gu, President/CEO

Chask **208.267.7854**
Web ....chaskinfo@aol.com
E-mail ....chaskinfo@aol.com
672 Meadow Creek Rd, Bonners Ferry, ID 83805
Tom Bushnell, Director

LDS Family Svcs **208.529.5276**
Fax 208.529.6506
E-mail ....fam-id-idahofalls@ldschurch.org
1600 John Adams Pkwy Ste 102, Idaho Falls,
ID 83401-4300
Claigh Jensen, Lcsw, Counseling Manager

ADVOCACY RESOURCES

Cares Program **208.577.4460**
Fax 208.577.4469
417 S 6th St, Boise, ID 83702
Michael Sexton, Do, Director

BEHAVIORAL HEALTH TREATMENT

Anchor House **208.667.3340**
Fax 208.667.1645
Web ....www.youthranch.org
1609 N Government Way, Coeur D Alene, ID 83814
Mary Christensen, Director

Brooks Medical Practice **208.726.0055**
Fax 504.866.5406
PO Box 5855, Ketchum, ID 83340-5855
Gerald Brooks, MD, Psychiatrist

Centennial Job Corps Ctr **208.442.4500**
Fax 208.442.4506
Web ....www.jobcorps.com
3201 Ridgecrest Dr, Nampa, ID 83687-8399
Michelle Wood, Center Director

Cruzen Medical Practice **208.327.9500**
PO Box 1052, Boise, ID 83701-1052
James John Cruzen, Psychiatrist

Eastern Idaho Behavioral Health Ctr **208.227.2260**
Fax 208.227.2360
2280 E 25th St, Idaho Falls, ID 83404-7542
Kay Seims, Director

Eastern Idaho Health Services **208.529.6210**
Web ....www.eirmc.org
E-mail ....jared.rickabaugh@hcahealthcare.com
3100 Channing Way, Idaho Falls, ID 83404
Mr. Jared Rickabaugh, Accreditation Manager
Joint Commission accredited organization.

Gustafson House **208.542.2905**
Fax 208.522.2427
2935 Rollandet St, Idaho Falls, ID 83402-4654
Shon Shuldberg, Manager

Hope House **208.896.4673**
Fax 208.896.5353
7696 Old Bruneau Hwy, Marsing, ID 83639-8227
Donna Velvick, CEO

Housing Athority **208.345.4907**
Fax 208.345.4909
Web ....www.bcacha.org
E-mail ....dwatson@bcacha.org
1276 W River St Ste 300, Boise, ID 83702-7085
Deanna Watson, Executive Director

Idaho State School And Hospital **208.467.0965**
Fax 208.442.2812
Web ....www.idhw.state.id.us
E-mail ....bosworthj@idhw.state.id.us
1660 11th Ave N, Nampa, ID 83687-5000
Jennifer Bosworth, Nursing Director

Idaho Youth Ranch **208.377.2613**
Fax 208.377.2819
Web ....www.youthranch.org
E-mail ....tpost@youthranch.org
5465 W Irving St, Boise, ID 83706
Steve Woodworth, President

Idaho Youth Ranch **208.532.4117**
Fax 208.532.4532
Web ....www.youthranch.org
E-mail ....lmcarthur@youthranch.org
1275 N 400 E, Rupert, ID 83350-8521
Jim Sockcerter, Program Director

Intermountain Hospital **800.321.5984**
Fax 208.377.5415
Web ....www.intermountainhospital.com
303 Allumbaugh St, Boise, ID 83704-9208
Charles Novack, Clinical Director

Kootenai Behavioral Health Center **208.765.4800**
Fax 208.664.1805
Web ....www.kootenaihealth.org
E-mail ....ajuliano@kmc.org
2003 Kootenai Health Way, Coeur D Alene, ID 83814
Claudia Mirwald, Director

Kootenai Health **208.666.2000**
Web ....www.kmc.org
E-mail ....lolsheski@kmc.org
2003 Kootenai Health Way, Coeur D Alene, ID 83814
Ms. Lorraine Olsheski, Accreditation Manager
Joint Commission accredited organization.

Mental Wellness Centers, Inc. **208.542.1026**
Fax 208.557.7494
2420 East 25th Street, Idaho Falls, ID 83404
CARF accredited programs available.

Project Patch **360.690.8495**
Web ....www.projectpatch.org
E-mail ....chagele@projectpatch.org
25 Miracle Lane, Garden Valley, ID 83622
Mr. Chuck Hagele, Accreditation Manager
Joint Commission accredited organization.

Sane Solutions **208.345.1170**
Fax 208.345.3502
Web ....www.terryrileyhealthservices.org
5400 W Franklin Rd Ste H, Boise, ID 83705-1078
Heidi Hart, Director

SUWS Adolescent And Youth Programs **208.886.2565**
Fax 208.886.2041
Web ....www.suwsyouth.com
E-mail ....krex@suws.com
911 Preacher Creek Rd, Shoshone, ID 83352-5061
Kathy Rex, Executive Director

**Teton Peaks Residential Treatment
Program** **208.227.2230**
Fax 208.227.2363
Web ....www.tetonpeaks.com
2280 E 25th St, Idaho Falls, ID 83404-7542
Kay Seim, Director

CHILDREN'S HOSPITAL

Cascade Medical Center **208.382.4242**
402 Old State Highway, Cascade, ID 83611
Bill Behnke, Chief Executive Officer

Eastern Idaho Regional Medical Center **208.529.6111**
3100 Channing Way, Idaho Falls, ID 83404
Doug Crabtree, Administrator

Elmore Medical Center **208.587.8401**
895 North Sixth East St, Mountain Home, ID 83647
Greg Maurer, Administrator

Gritman Medical Center **208.882.4511**
700 South Main St, Moscow, ID 83843
Kara Besst, Chief Executive Officer

Kootenai Medical Center **208.666.2000**
2003 Kootnai Health Way, Coeur D Alene, ID 83814
John Ness, Chief Executive Officer

Madison Memorial Hospital **208.356.3691**
450 E Main St, Rexburg, ID 83440
Rex Burch, Public Relations

McCall Memorial Hospital **208.634.2221**
1000 State St, McCall, ID 83638
Lee Rhodes, Chief Executive Officer

Mercy Medical Center **208.463.5000**
1512 12th Avenue Rd, Nampa, ID 83686

Minidoka Memorial Hosp & Extended Care **208.436.0481**
1224 Eight St, Rupert, ID 83350
Carla Hanson, Administrator

Portneuf Medical Center **208.239.1000**
777 Hospital way, Pocatello, ID 83201
Norman Steven, Chief Executive Officer

St Alphonsus Regional Medical Center **208.367.2121**
1055 North Curtis Rd, Boise, ID 83706
Sally Jeffcoat, Chief Executive Officer

St Joseph Regional Medical Center **208.743.2511**
415 Sixth St, Lewiston, ID 83501
Kim Syler, Director

St Lukes Magic Valley Regional Med Ctr **208.814.1000**
801 Poleline Rd W, Twin Falls, ID 83301
Jim Angle, Chief Executive Officer

St Lukes Regional Medical Center **208.381.2222**
190 East Bannock St, Boise, ID 83712
David Kate, President

COUNSELING SERVICES

LDS Family Svcs **208.678.8200**
Fax 208.678.8201
255 N Overland Ave, Burley, ID 83318-3430
Jason Nelson, Clinical Supervisor

Lutheran Community Svcs Northwest **208.323.0996**
Fax 208.685.0587
Web ....www.lcsnw.org
E-mail ....cvollet@lcsnw.org
410 S Orchard St Ste 124, Boise, ID 83705-1210
Charles Vollet, Director Of Behavioral Health

CRISIS & SHELTER CARE

Bannock House **208.234.2244**
Fax 208.234.2256
Web ....www.byfhome.org
E-mail ....steve.mead@byfhome.org
620 W Fremont St, Pocatello, ID 83204
Steven Mead, Executive Director

Crisis Intervention Mahoney House **208.756.3146**
Fax 208.756.3146
E-mail ....Lcci@Centurytel.Net
901 Main St, Salmon, ID 83467
Denise Bender, Director

**Domestic Violence Insexual Assault
Center** **208.529.4352**
Fax 208.535.9096
E-mail ....tmcbride@bonneville.id.us
1050 Memorial Dr, Idaho Falls, ID 83402-3410
Tina Mc Bride, Director

Family Crisis Ctr- Domestic Violence **208.356.0065**
Fax 208.356.0717
E-mail ....crisis@ida.net
218 Dividend Drive #5, Rexburg, ID 83440
Margie Harris, Director

Family Safety Network **208.354.8057**
Fax 208.354.8058
E-mail ....familysafetynetwork.info@silverstar.com
120 N 1st St, Driggs, ID 83422
Susan Fenger, Director

**Family Svcs Alliance Southeast Idaho-Domestic
Violence** **208.232.0742**
Fax 208.232.4286
355 S Arthur Ave, Pocatello, ID 83204
Sara Leeds, Director

Hays Shelter Home, Inc. **208.322.6687**
Fax 208.322.3905
E-mail ....sfields@youthranch.org
7221 Poplar St, Boise, ID 83704-7336
Steve Fields, Director

Kinderhaven **208.265.2236**
Fax 208.255.1526
Web ....www.kinderhaven.org.
E-mail ....kinderhaven@verizon.net
101 McGhee Road, Sandpoint, ID 83864
Phyllis Horvath, Executive Director

Oneida Crisis Ctr **208.766.4412**
Fax 208.766.4412
E-mail ....oneidacrisiscenter@atcnet.net
PO Box 174, Malad City, ID 83252
Carol Cauford, Executive Director

Rose Advocates-Domestic Violence **208.414.1231**
Fax 208.414.4151
Web ....www.ruralnetwork.net
E-mail ....dlarsen@ruralnetwork.net
25 W Idaho St, Weiser, ID 83672-2376
Delores Larsen, Director

Syringa House **208.467.5223**
Fax 208.466.6813
E-mail ....nampasyringa@velocitus.net
1723 S Horton St, Nampa, ID 83686
Shelly Hitt, Director

**The Advocates For Survivors-Domestic
Violence** **208.788.4191**
Fax 208.788.4194
E-mail ....info@theadvocatesorg.org
PO Box 3216, Hailey, ID 83333-3216
Tricia Swartling, Director

The Crisis Ctr Of Magic Valley **208.733.0100**
Fax 208.734.9354
E-mail ....gabardi@cableone.net
PO Box 2444, Twin Falls, ID 83303-2444
Deborah Gabardi, Director

EDUCATION

Children's Village Inc **208.667.1189**
Fax 208.664.5735
Web ....www.thechildrensvillage.org
E-mail ....info@thechildrensvillage.org
1350 W Hanley Ave, Coeur D Alene, ID 83815-8638
Patrick Drapeau, Director

Friends Of Children & Families **208.344.9187**
Fax 208.344.9592
Web ....www.focaf.org
E-mail ....ldilley@focaf.org
4709 W Camas St, Boise, ID 83705-5832
Liz Dilley, Director

FOSTER CARE AGENCIES

**A New Beginning Adoption Agency Inc
(ANB)** **208.939.3865**
Fax 208.939.3869
E-mail ....stephanie@adoptanewbeginning.org
9703 W Ustick Rd, Ste 101, Boise, ID 83704
Stephanie Parl, Chief Executive Officer

EmbRACE **208.484.2469**
3262 Scenic Dr, Boise, ID 83703

Idaho Foster & Adopt Parent Assoc **208.629.5976**
PO Box 62, Moreland, ID 83256
Julianne Rinard

Idaho Foster & Adoptive Parent Coalition **208.520.8385**
Fax 208.542.6094
E-mail ....karyledbetter@cableone.net
2164 Brookcliff Dr, Idaho Falls, ID 83402

HOME MEDICAL EQUIPMENT PROVIDERS

OrthoMedical, Inc. **208.785.4595**
Fax 208.785.4595
Web ....www.rentcpm.com
373 West Highway 39, Suite 2, Blackfoot, ID 83221
CARF accredited programs available.

SOCIAL SERVICES

Help Incorporated **208.522.5545**
Fax 208.528.6773
E-mail ....info@helpincidaho.org
1330 Enterprise St Ste 4, Idaho Falls, ID 83402-4318
Melissa Beane, Executive Director

Idaho

Idaho Children's Trust Fund **208.386.9317**
Fax 208.386.9955
Web ....www.idahochildrenstrustfund.idaho.gov
E-mail ....shermanr@dhw.idaho.gov
   304 W State St, Boise, ID 83702
   Roger Sherman, Director

Idaho Legal Aid Svcs **208.345.0106**
Fax 208.342.2561
Web ....www.idaholegalaid.org
E-mail ....rodgere@idaholegalaid.org
   310 N 5th St, Boise, ID 83702
   Rod Gere, Managing Attorney

LDS Family Svcs **208.376.0191**
Fax 208.658.6299
Web ....www.ldsfamilyservices.org
E-mail ....famm-id-boise@ldsfamilyservices.org
   10740 W Fairview Ave Ste 100, Boise, ID 83713-8050
   Debbie Misseldine, Administrative Assistant

LDS Family Svcs **208.232.7780**
Fax 208.232.7782
E-mail ....fam-id-pocatello@ldschurch.org
   1169 Call Creek Dr Ste B, Pocatello, ID 83201-3077
   Steven Dahl, Director

Life Choices Clinic **208.746.9704**
Fax 208.798.7409
E-mail ....officemgr@lifechoicesclinic.info
   2020 12th Ave, Lewiston, ID 83501
   Scott Maynes, Ex Director

Port Of Hope **208.664.3300**
Fax 208.667.3154
E-mail ....port.cda@verizon.net
   218 N 23rd St, Coeur D Alene, ID 83814-5470
   Marlene Scott, Director

Seicaa **208.233.7348**
Fax 208.234.4697
Web ....www.seicaa.org
   825 E Bridger St, Pocatello, ID 83201
   Deb Hemert, Executive Director

The Family Resource Ctr **208.234.1122**
Fax 208.234.1253
Web ....www.byfhome.com
E-mail ....heather.kemp@byshome.com
   403 N Hayes Ave, Pocatello, ID 83204
   Steven Mead, Director

SPECIAL NEEDS

Autism Society Of America/Treasure Valley
Chapter **208.336.5676**
Fax 302.260.9487
Web ....www.asatvc.org
E-mail ....info@asatvc.org
   7842 Rainbow Pl, Nampa, ID 83687-9404

Echo Springs Transition Study Center **208.267.1111**
Fax 208.267.1122
E-mail ....echosprings@meadowcrk.com
   3210 Kootenai Trl Rd, Bonners Ferry, ID 83805
   Rhea Verbanic, Admin Director

Epilepsy Foundation of Idaho **208.344.4340**
E-mail ....efid@epilepsyidaho.org
   310 W Idaho, Boise, ID 83702
   Gretchen Bolton, Director

Glacier Mountain Academy **208.290.6745**
Fax 208.265.8712
E-mail ....glacierm@sisna.com
   1309 Ponderosa Dr, Sandpoint, ID 83864

Idaho Center for Assistive Technology **888.289.3259**
E-mail ....info@idahocat.org
   5420 W Franklin Rd Ste A, Boise, ID 83705

Idaho Council Developmental Disabilities **208.334.2178**
E-mail ....cpisani@icdd.idaho.gov
   700 W Bannock Ste, Boise, ID 83702
   Marilyn Sword, Executive Director

Idaho Elks Rehabilitation Hospital **208.489.4444**
Fax 208.489.4005
Web ....www.idahoelksrehab.org
E-mail ....aburkey@ierh.org
   600 North Robbins Road, Boise, ID 83702
   Anne Burkey, Quality and Compliance Director
   CARF accredited programs available.

Idaho Parents Unlimited Inc **208.342.5884**
E-mail ....parents@ipulidaho.org
   500 S 8th St, Boise, ID 83705
   Kelly Bolen, Director

Idaho PTA **208.344.0851**
E-mail ....idahopta@mindspring.com
   500 W Washington, Boise, ID 83702

ISHA **208.599.2536**
   PO Box 603, Mountain Home, ID 83647

Mountain States Group/Mental Health **208.336.5533**
E-mail ....info@mtnstatesgroup.org
   1607 W Jefferson, Boise, ID 83702
   John Keys, Director

NAMI Idaho **208.673.6672**
E-mail ....namiid@atcnet.net
   PO Box 68, Albion, ID 83311

National Multiple Sclerosis Society **208.388.4253**
Fax 208.388.1907
E-mail ....IDI@nmss.org
   6901 W Emerald St Ste 207, Boise, ID 83704

Saint Alphonsus Rehabilitation Unit **208.367.2660**
Fax 208.367.3454
Web ....www.saintalphonsus.org
   1055 North Curtis Road, Boise, ID 83706
   CARF accredited programs available.

VSA Arts of Idaho **208.342.5884**
E-mail ....evelyn@ipulidaho.org
   1878 W Overland Rd, Boise, ID 83709
   Evelyn Mason, Director

SUBSTANCE ABUSE TREATMENT

Northwest Children's Home **208.743.9404**
Fax 208.746.4955
Web ....www.northwestchildrenshome.org
E-mail ....rwilson@northwestchildrenshome.org
   419 22nd Ave, Lewiston, ID 83501-3812
   Rod Wilson, Assistant Executive Director

Road To Recovery **208.233.9135**
Fax 208.233.9136
Web www.road2recovery.org
E-mail ....info@road2recovery.org
   600 E Oak St Ste B, Pocatello, ID 83201-5090
   Elizabeth Lovell, Director

Salud Y Provecho Counseling **208.454.8632**
Fax 208.459.1661
   317 Happy Day Blvd ,Ste 275, Caldwell,
   ID 83607-1799
   Daniel Ozuna, Director

Idaho

Illinois

Pat Quinn, Governor
207 Statehouse
Springfield, IL 62706
217.782.0244
217.524.4049 (Fax)
govenor@state.il.us
www.illinois.gov/gov

Karrie Reuter, Juvenile Justice Specialist
Dept. of Human Services, Prevention Office
535 West Jefferson, Third Floor
Springfield, IL 62702-5058
217.785.0243
217.557.0515 (Fax)
karrie.reuter@illinois.gov

Hon. George Timberlake, SAG Chair
Jefferson Policy Consultants, LLC
120 N 11st St
Mt Vernon, IL 62864
618.204.5075
618.204.5637 (Fax)
gwtimberlake@jpc.us.com

CRISIS NUMBERS

Child Abuse Reporting . . .217.785.4020

STATE SERVICES

SOCIAL SERVICES

Anna Bixby Women's Ctr- Domestic Violence . . .618.252.8380
Fax 618.252.1707
E-mail . . . . .koalazrule@yahoo.com
213 S Shaw St, Harrisburg, IL 62946-1864
Barb Wingo, Director

Day Care and Early Childhood Of Illinois 217.785.2688
Fax 217.782.6446
406 East Monroe St, Ste 60, Springfield, IL 62701
Connie Burns, Director

Dept of Children and Family Svcs 217.785.2509
Fax 217.785.1052
Web . . . . .www.state.il.us/dcfs/index
406 E Monroe St, Suite 70, Springfield, IL 62701
Erwin Mcerwin, Director, Interstate Compact

GENERAL HEALTH SERVICES

Bur of Maternal & Infant Health IL 312.793.8234
Fax 312.814.3073
E-mail . . . . .glendean.sisk@illinois.go@verizon.net
1112 S Wabash 4th Flr, Chicago, IL 60605
Glendean Sisk, Director

Division of Spec Care for Children IL 217.558.2340
Fax 217.558.0773
E-mail . . . . .dscc@uic.edu
3135 Old Jacksonville Rd, Springfield, IL 62704

Human Services 217.782.2166
Fax 217.785.5247
Web . . . . .www.dhs.state.il.us/chp/ofh/fn/wic.asp
E-mail . . . . .pennyroth@illinois.gov
823 E Monroe, Springfield, IL 62701
Penny Roth, Acting Director

Illinois Dept of Healthcare & Family Svcs 217.782.1200
Fax 217.557.6620
Web . . . . .www.hfs.illinois.gov
201 S Grand Ave E, Springfield, IL 62704
Julie Hamos, Director

Ofc of Health Protection 217.782.3984
Fax 217.524.0802
Web . . . . .www.idph.state.il.us
525 W Jefferson St Fl 3, Springfield, IL 62761
David Culp, Deputy Director

MENTAL HEALTH SERVICES

Div of Rehabilitation Svcs IL 217.782.2094
Fax 217.558.4270
E-mail . . . . .DHS.ORS@illinois.gov
100 S Grand Ave 1st Fl, Springfield, IL 62762

**Illinois Alcohol and Other Drug Abuse Professional
Certification Assoc 217.698.8110**
Fax 217.698.8234
Web . . . . .www.iaodapca.org
E-mail . . . . .info@iaodapca.org
401 E Sangamon Ave, Springfield, IL 62702
Jessica Hayes, Manager

Illinois Div of Mental Health 217.785.6023
Fax 217.785.3066
Web . . . . .www.dhs.state.il.us
319 E Madison St Ste 3B, Springfield, IL 62701-3124
Lorrie Rickman Jones, Phd, Director

JUSTICE AGENCY

Criminal Victims Div 312.814.2581
Fax 312.814.7105
E-mail . . . . .crimevictimservices@atg.state.il.us
100 W Randolph St, 13th Floor, Chicago, IL 60601
Cynthia Hora, Bureau Director

COURTS

Administrative Ofc Of The Courts 217.782.7770
Fax 217.785.9114
Web . . . . .www.court.state.il.us
E-mail . . . . .ccobbs@court.state.il.us
3101 Old Jacksonville Rd, Springfield, IL 62704-6488
Cynthia Cobbs, Director

POLICE AND SHERIFF

Illinois Assoc of Chiefs of Police 217.523.3765
Fax 217.523.8352
Web . . . . .www.ilchiefs.org
E-mail . . . . .ilacp@ilchiefs.org
426 S 5th St, Springfield, IL 62701-1821
Mark Wilkans, Executive Director

Illinois Sheriff's Assoc 217.753.2372
Fax 217.753.2405
Web . . . . .www.ilsheriff.org
E-mail . . . . .isa@ilsheriff.org
658 E. State St., Jacksonville, IL 62650
Greg Sullivan, Executive Director

EDUCATION SERVICES

Homeless Ecducation Program Illinois 217.557.7323
E-mail . . . . .mcullen@isbe.net
100 N 1st St, Springfield, IL 62777
M Cullen, Director

Illinois School for the Deaf 217.479.4200
Fax 217.479.4209
Web www.morgan.k12.il.us/isd
E-mail . . . . .marybeth.lauderdale@illinois.gov
125 S Webster Ave, Jacksonville, IL 62650-1899
Marybeth Lauderdale, Acting Superintendent

Illinois School for the Visually Impaired 217.479.4400
Fax 217.479.4479
Web . . . . .www.isvi.net
E-mail . . . . .merybeth.lauderdale@illinois.gov
658 E State St, Jacksonville, IL 62650
Marybeth Lauderdale, Superintendent

Illinois State Board of Education 217.782.4321
Fax 217.524.4928
E-mail . . . . .state@isbe.net
100 N 1st St, Springfield, IL 62777
Christopher Koch, Administrator

Office of Special Education Illinois 217.782.4870
Fax 217.782.9224
100 N 1st St, Mail Code N 253, Springfield, IL 62777
Elizabeth Hanfelman, Assistant Superintendent

LABOR & WORKFORCE EDUCATION

Office Of Employment & Traning 312.814.6028
Fax 312.814.0999
Web . . . . .www.illinois.gov
E-mail .therese.mcmahon@illinois.gov
100 W Randolph St, 3rd Fl, Chicago, IL 60601
Therese Mcmahon, Deputy Director Workforce Development

Illinois

COUNTY SERVICES

Adams County

GENERAL HEALTH SERVICES

Health Dept **217.222.8440**
Fax 217.222.8508
Web ....www.co.adams.il.us
　330 Vermont St, Quincy, IL 62301-2701
　Nancy Bluhm, Administrator

JUSTICE AGENCY

CASA **217.223.2272**
Fax 217.223.6791
　531 Hampshire St Fl 2, Quincy, IL 62301
　Clairice Hetzler, Executive Director

Juvenile Detention Ctr **217.277.2233**
Fax 217.277.2241
Web ....www.co.adams.il.us
E-mail ....jjones@co.adams.il.us
　200 N 52nd St, Quincy, IL 62305-9114
　John Jones, Superintendent

COURTS

8th Circuit Court **217.277.2100**
Fax 217.277.2116
Web ....www.co.adams.il.us
　521 Vermont St, Quincy, IL 62301
　Honorable Thomas L. Brownfield, Judge

POLICE AND SHERIFF

Sheriff's Ofc **217.277.2200**
Fax 217.277.2214
Web ....www.co.adams.il.us
E-mail ....bfischer@co.adams.il.us
　521 Vermont St Ste 304, Quincy, IL 62301-2934
　Brent Fischer, Sheriff

Alexander County

GENERAL HEALTH SERVICES

Southern Seven Health Dept **618.634.2297**
Fax 618.634.2656
Web ....www.southernseven.org
　37 Rustic Campus Dr, Ullin, IL 62992
　Carolyn Kissiar, Planning Program Coordinator

COURTS

1st Circuit Court **618.734.0107**
Fax 618.734.7003
　2000 Washington Ave Rm 8, Cairo, IL 62914-1717
　Honorable Mark Clarke, Judge

POLICE AND SHERIFF

Sheriff's Ofc **618.734.2141**
Fax 618.734.9030
　2000 Washington Ave Rm 7, Cairo, IL 62914
　Cinothy Brwon, Sheriff

Bond County

GENERAL HEALTH SERVICES

Health Dept **618.664.1442**
Fax 618.664.1744
Web ....www.bchd.us
E-mail ....bchd@bchd.us
　1520 S Fourth St, Greenville, IL 62246
　Penny Dixon, Clinical Coordinator

COURTS

3rd Circuit Court **618.664.3208**
Fax 618.664.2257
Web ....www.bondcountyil.com
　200 W College Ave, Greenville, IL 62246-1088
　Rex Catron, Circuit Clerk

POLICE AND SHERIFF

Sheriff's Ofc **618.664.2151**
Fax 618.664.4689
　403 S 2Nd St, Greenville, IL 62246
　Jeffrey J. Brown, Sheriff

Boone County

COURTS

17th Circuit Court **815.544.0371**
Fax 815.547.9213
Web ....www.boonecountyil.org
　601 N Main St Ste 303, Belvidere, IL 61008-2600
　Honorable John Todd Kennedy, Judge

Brown County

GENERAL HEALTH SERVICES

Public Health Dept **217.773.2714**
Fax 217.773.2512
E-mail ....cskiles@casscomm.com
　120 E Main St, Mount Sterling, IL 62353-1212
　Carrie Skiles, Director Of Daily Services

MENTAL HEALTH SERVICES

Mental Health Ctrs Of Western
Illinois **217.773.3325**
Fax 217.773.2425
Web ....www.macwi.org
E-mail ....roliver@macwi.org
　700 SE Cross St, Mt Sterling, IL 62353-1561
　Roxie Oliver, Executive Director

COURTS

8th Circuit Court **217.773.2713**
Fax 217.773.3648
　200 Court St Rm 5, Mount Sterling, IL 62353-1284
　Keatra Smith, Probation Officer

POLICE AND SHERIFF

Sheriff's Ofc **217.773.2011**
Fax 217.773.4882
E-mail ....browncounty@hotmail.com
　200 Court St Rm 1, Mount Sterling, IL 62353-1233
　Karl Geroesch, Sheriff

Bureau County

COURTS

13th Circuit Court **815.872.2001**
Fax 815.872.0027
Web ....www.bccirclk.gov
　700 S Main St, Princeton, IL 61356
　Honorable Mark Bernebei, Judge

POLICE AND SHERIFF

Sheriff's Ofc **815.875.3344**
Fax 815.875.2452
E-mail ....john.thompson@lumpkincounty.gov
　700 S Main St Ste 14, Princeton, IL 61356-2039
　John E. Thompson, Sheriff

Calhoun County

GENERAL HEALTH SERVICES

Health Dept **618.576.2428**
Fax 618.576.9391
E-mail ....sshireman@ezl.com
　210 French St, Hardin, IL 62047
　Steve Shireman, Administrator

COURTS

8th Circuit Court **618.576.2451**
Fax 618.576.9541
　104 North County Rd, Hardin, IL 62047
　Debbie Tepen, Probation Officer

Carroll County

COURTS

15th Circuit Court **815.244.0230**
Fax 815.244.3869
Web ....www.judici.com
　301 N Main St Ste 203, Mount Carroll,
　IL 61053-1044
　Sherri A. Miller, Clerk Of Court

POLICE AND SHERIFF

Sheriff's Ofc **815.244.9171**
Fax 815.244.2656
E-mail ....lashby@grics.net
　301 N Main St Ste 107, Mount Carroll, IL 61053
　Jeffrey C. Doran, Sheriff

Cass County

GENERAL HEALTH SERVICES

Health Dept **217.452.3057**
Fax 217.452.7245
Web ....www.casscohealth.org
　331 S Main St Frnt, Virginia, IL 62691-1574
　Teresa Smith, Administrator

COURTS

8th Circuit Court-Court House **217.452.7225**
Fax 217.452.7219
Web ....www.state.il.us
　100 E Springfield St, Virginia, IL 62691
　Honorable Bob Hardwick, Jr., Judge

POLICE AND SHERIFF

Sheriff's Ofc **217.452.7718**
Fax 217.452.7211
E-mail ....casssheriff@casscomm.com
　101 N Front St, Virginia, IL 62691
　Bob Fair, Sheriff

Champaign County

GENERAL HEALTH SERVICES

Champaign Urbana Public Health
District **217.352.7961**
Fax 217.352.0126
Web ....www.c-uphd.org
E-mail ....gbird@c-uphd.org
　201 W Kenyon, Champaign, IL 61820
　Julie A. Pryde, Administrator

LDPH Regional Ofc Champaign **217.278.5900**
Fax 217.278.5959
Web ....www.idph.state.il.us
　2125 S 1st St, Champaign, IL 61820-7499
　Brenda Barton, Regional Health Officer

JUSTICE AGENCY

CASA **217.384.9065**
Fax 217.384.6450
Web ....www.chcocasa.org
E-mail ....casa@chcocasa.org
　154 Lincoln Sq Ste C, Urbana, IL 61801-3362
　Rush Record, Executive Director/casa

Juvenile Detention Facility 217.384.3780
Fax 217.384.8617
Web . . . . .www.co.champaign.il.us
E-mail . . . . .ckaiser@co.champaign.il.us
　　400 Art Bartell Rd, Urbana, IL 61802-2879
　　Connie Kaiser, Superintendent

COURTS

6th Circuit Court/Linda S. Frank's Ofc/Circuit
Clerk 217.384.3725
Fax 217.384.3879
Web . . . . .www.cccircuitclerk.com
　　101 E Main St Rm 215, Urbana, IL 61801
　　Honorable Thomas Difanis, Presiding Judge

POLICE AND SHERIFF

Sheriff's Ofc 217.384.1204
Fax 217.384.3023
Web . . . . .www.co.champaign.il.us
E-mail . . . . .dwalsh@co.champaign.il.us
　　204 E Main St, Urbana, IL 61801-2702
　　Daniel J. Walsh, Sheriff

EDUCATION SERVICES

Head Start 217.328.3313
Fax 217.328.2426
Web . . . . .www.ccrpc.org
E-mail . . . . .kliffick@ccrpc.org
　　1776 E Washington St, Urbana, IL 61802
　　Kathleen Liffick, Director

Rantoul-Champaign Ofc Of Special Education
Cooperative 217.892.8877
Fax 217.893.8627
Web www.roe9.k12.il.us
E-mail . . . . .hogans@roe9.k12.il.us
　　201 S Sheldon St, Rantoul, IL 61866-2400
　　Scott Hogan, Director

Special Education 217.351.3841
Fax 217.351.3824
Web . . . . .www.champaignschools.org
　　703 S New St, Champaign, IL 61820
　　Elizabeth Degruy, Director

Special Education 217.586.4947
Fax 217.586.7591
Web www.ms.k12.il.us
E-mail . . . . .cnorthrup@ms.k12.il.us
　　101 N Division St, Mahomet, IL 61853-7032
　　Christine Northrup, Director

Special Education 217.384.3655
Fax 217.337.4973
Web www.usd116.org
E-mail . . . . .sbaker-ory@usd116.org
　　205 N Race St, Urbana, IL 61801-2680
　　Susan Baker-Ory, Assistent Superintendent Of Special Services

Christian County

SOCIAL SERVICES

Dept Of Human Svcs Family Community Resource
Ctr 217.824.3389
Fax 217.287.7334
Web . . . . .www.dhs.state.il.us
E-mail . . . . .robert.tate@illinois.gov
　　1100 N Cheney St, Taylorville, IL 62568
　　Robert Tate, Administrator

GENERAL HEALTH SERVICES

Health Dept 217.824.4113
Fax 217.824.4380
Web . . . . .www.christiancountyhealth.net
E-mail . . . . .gerry.grigsby@christiancountyhealth.org
　　902 W Springfield Rd, Taylorville, IL 62568-1213
　　Gerry Girgsby, Nursing Supervisor

MENTAL HEALTH SERVICES

Civigenics - Taylorville Correctional
Ctr 217.824.4004
Fax 217.824.4371
Web . . . . .www.doc.illinois.gov
　　Illinois Route 29 South, Taylorville, IL 62568
　　Lynn Dexheiner, Warden

Mental Health 217.824.4905
Fax 217.824.3570
Web . . . . .www.ccmha.net
E-mail . . . . .rea@ccmha.net
　　730 N Pawnee St, Taylorville, IL 62568
　　Sue Paso, Clinical Manager

COURTS

4th Circuit Court/Clerk's Ofc 217.824.4966
Fax 217.824.5030
　　101 S Main St Ste 12, Taylorville, IL 62568
　　Julie J Mayer, Clerk Of Court

POLICE AND SHERIFF

Sheriff's Ofc 217.824.4961
Fax 217.824.4963
Web . . . . .www.christiancountysheriff.com
E-mail . . . . .bkettelkamp@christiancountysheriff.com
　　301 W Franklin St, Taylorville, IL 62568-2116
　　Bruce Kettelkamp, Sheriff

Clark County

GENERAL HEALTH SERVICES

Health Dept 217.382.4207
Fax 217.382.4226
Web . . . . .www.clarkcountyhealthdept.org
E-mail . . . . .chayden@clarkcountyhealthdept.org
　　997 N York St, Martinsville, IL 62442
　　Cathy Hayden, Public Health Administrator

COURTS

5th Circuit Court/Circuit Clerk's Ofc 217.826.2811
Fax 217.826.1391
Web . . . . .www.clarkcountyil.org
　　501 Archer Ave Rm 1, Marshall, IL 62441-1275
　　Terry Reynolds, Clerk Of Court

POLICE AND SHERIFF

Sheriff's Ofc 217.826.6393
Fax 217.826.2214
Web www.marshall.k12.il.us
E-mail . . . . .jparsley@marshall.k12.il.us
　　207 N 5th St, Marshall, IL 62441-1201
　　Jerry W. Parsley, Sheriff

Clay County

GENERAL HEALTH SERVICES

Health Dept 618.662.4406
Fax 618.662.2801
Web . . . . .www.claycountyhealthdept.org
E-mail . . . . .jworkman@healthdept.org
　　601 E 12th St, Flora, IL 62839-2335
　　Jeff Workman, Administrator

JUSTICE AGENCY

Probation Ofc 618.665.3060
Fax 618.665.3090
　　110 S Main St, Louisville, IL 62858
　　Curtis Leiv, Chief Performance Officer

POLICE AND SHERIFF

Sheriff's Ofc 618.665.3316
Fax 618.665.3318
E-mail . . . . .claycoso1@wabash.net
　　300 Broadway St, Louisville, IL 62858
　　James C. Sulsberger, Sheriff

Clinton County

GENERAL HEALTH SERVICES

Health Dept 618.594.2723
Fax 618.594.5474
Web . . . . .www.idphnet.com
E-mail . . . . .pclinton@idphnet.com
　　930 Fairfax St Ste A, Carlyle, IL 62231-1848
　　Michael Mcmillan, Administrator

JUSTICE AGENCY

Probation
TTY 618.594.2464
E-mail . . . . .randy.brandmeyer@clintonco.illinois.gov
　　850 Fairfax, Rm 120, Catlyle, IL 62231
　　Randy Brandmeyer

COURTS

4th Circuit Court/Court House 618.594.2464
Fax 618.594.0197
Web . . . . .www.clintonco.illinois.gov
E-mail . . . . .probation@clintonco.illinois.gov
　　850 Fairfax St, Rm 220, Carlyle, IL 62231-1840
　　Randy Brandmeyer, CPO

POLICE AND SHERIFF

Sheriff's Ofc 618.594.4555
Fax 618.594.7199
Web . . . . .www.clintonco.illinois.gov
E-mail . . . . .mike.kreke@clintonco.illinois.gov
　　810 Franklin St, Carlyle, IL 62231-1817
　　Mike Kreke, Sheriff

Coles County

MENTAL HEALTH SERVICES

Life Links 217.238.5700
Fax 217.238.5767
　　750 Broadway Ave E, Mattoon, IL 61938
　　Lynette Ashmore, Executive Director

JUSTICE AGENCY

Probation & Court Svcs .217.348.0535
Fax 217.348.7336
Web . . . . .www.co.coles.il.us
E-mail . . . . .tschumaker@co.coles.il.us
　　651 Jackson Ave Rm 318, Charleston, IL 61920-2093
　　Timothy Schumaker, Court Services Director

COURTS

Peer Court 217.258.7901
Fax 217.258.6715
Web . . . . .www.consolidated.net
E-mail . . . . .kepley@consolidated.net
　　1710 Wabash Ave, C/O Mattoon Police Dept.,
　　Mattoon, IL 61938-3912
　　Gary Kepley, Coordinator

Cook County

SOCIAL SERVICES

Indian Social Svcs St. Augustine's Ctr For American
Indians 773.784.1050
Fax 773.784.1254
Web . . . . .www.ccc.edu
　　4512 N Sheridan Rd, Chicago, IL 60640-5609
　　Father P. Powell, Director

GENERAL HEALTH SERVICES

Chicago Dept Of Public Health 312.747.9870
Fax 312.747.9739
Web . . . . .www.ci.chi.il.us/health
E-mail . . . . .publichealth@ci.chi.il.us
　　333 S State St Lbby 2, Chicago, IL 60604-3955
　　Virginia White, Secretary

Illinois

Evanston Health Dept 847.866.2952
Fax 847.448.8141
Web ....www.cityofevanston.org
E-mail ....ethomas@cityofevanston.org
  2100 Ridge Ave, Evanston Civic Center, Evanston,
  IL 60201-2798
Evonda Thomas, Director Of Health

LDPH Regional Ofc Bellwood 708.544.5300
Fax 708.544.5830
Web ....www.idph.state.il.us
E-mail ....gerald.jackson@illinois.gov
  4212 Saint Charles Rd, Bellwood, IL 60104-1146
Gerald Jackson, Acting Chief

North District Ofc 847.818.2860
Fax 847.818.2464
Web ....www.cookcountypublichealth.com
E-mail ....rsovcik@cookcountygov.com
  2121 Euclid Ave, Rolling Meadows, IL 60008
Regina Sovcik, Rn, Supervisor

Oak Park Dept Of Public Health 708.383.6400
Fax 708.358.5115
Web ....www.oak-park.us
  123 Madison St, Oak Park, IL 60302
Margaret Provost, Director

Skokie Health Dept 847.933.8252
Fax 847.673.8606
Web ....www.skokie.org
  5127 Oakton St, Skokie, IL 60077
Claudia Braden, Public Health Nurse

Southwest District Ofc 708.974.6160
Fax 708.974.6132
E-mail ....zanek@gvc.net
  10220 S 76th Ave, Rm 250, Bridgeview, IL 60455
Josie Zanek, Supervisor

West District Ofc 708.450.5300
Fax 708.450.5301
  1701 S 1st Ave, Maywood, IL 60153
Mary Gibb, Supervisor

MENTAL HEALTH SERVICES

Community Mental Health Council,
Inc 773.734.4033
Fax 773.734.5994
Web ....www.thecouncil-online.org
E-mail ....hsuggs@thecouncil-online.org
  8704 S Constance Ave, Chicago, IL 60617-2746
Hayward Suggs, Sr., Vice President

JUSTICE AGENCY

CASA Program 312.433.4928
Fax 312.433.4927
Web ....www.casacookcounty.org
E-mail ....info@casacookcounty.org
  1100 S Hamilton Ave, 8 West, Chicago, IL 60612
Lanetta Haynes, Program Director

Illinois Youth Ctr Chicago 312.633.5219
Fax 312.633.5229
Web ....www.doc.illinois.gov
  136 N Western Ave, Chicago, IL 60612-2222
Angela Wartowski, Superintendent

Juvenile Detention 312.433.7102
Fax 312.433.6644
Web ....www.cookcountygov.com
E-mail ....rolee@cookcountygov.com
  1100 S Hamilton Ave, Chicago, IL 60612-4207
Robert Lee, Management Anaylist

COURTS

Circuit Court Juvenile Div 312.433.6660
Fax 312.433.5209
Web ....www.courtcounty.gov.com
  2245 W Ogden Ave, Chicago, IL 60612-4267
Michael J. Rohan, Director Of Probation And Court Services

Circuit Court/Ofc Of Dorothy
Brown 312.603.6000
Fax 312.603.5366
Web ....www.cookcountycourt.org
  50 W Washington St Rm 2600, Chicago, IL 60602
Honorable Timothy C. Evans, Chief Judge

POLICE AND SHERIFF

Chicago Police Departmen 3rd
District 312.747.8201
Fax 312.747.5479
  7040 S Cottage Grove Ave, Chicago, IL 60637
Flecher, Commissioner

Chicago Police Dept 312.747.3940
Fax 312.747.3912
  3900 S California Ave, Chicago, IL 60632-1808
Errol Hicks, Youth Investigator

Chicago Police Dept 10th District 312.747.7511
Fax 312.747.7429
Web ....www.chicagopolice.org
  3315 W Ogden Ave, Chicago, IL 60623-2650
Berscott Ruiz, Commander

Chicago Police Dept 12th District 312.746.8309
Fax 312.746.4248
Web ....www.chicagopolice.org
E-mail ....ron.sodini@chicagopolice.org
  100 S Racine Ave, Chicago, IL 60607-2516
D Keane, Commander

Chicago Police Dept 14th District 312.744.8290
Fax 312.744.2422
Web ....www.chicagopolice.org
  2150 N California Ave, Chicago, IL 60647-3925
Walter Green, Commander

Chicago Police Dept 15th District 312.743.1440
Fax 312.743.1366
Web ....www.cityofchicago.org
  5701 W Madison St, Chicago, IL 60644-3950
Walter Green, Commander

Chicago Police Dept 18th District 312.742.5870
Fax 312.742.5771
  1160 N Larrabee St, Chicago, IL 60610
Ken Angronne, Commander

Chicago Police Dept 21st District 312.747.8340
Fax 312.747.5919
Web ....www.chicagopolice.org
  300 E 29th St, Chicago, IL 60616-3217
Richard Elmer, Commissioner

Chicago Police Dept 22nd District 312.745.0710
Fax 312.745.0434
E-mail ....michael.kuemmeth.chicagopolice.gov
  1900 W Monterey Ave, Chicago, IL 60643
Michael Kuemmeth, Commander

Chicago Police Dept 24th District 312.744.5907
Fax 312.744.6928
  6464 N Clark St, Chicago, IL 60626
Zenia Fera, Administrative Manager

Chicago Police Dept 25th District 312.746.8605
Fax 312.746.4353
  5555 W Grand Ave, Chicago, IL 60639
Ronald White, Police Officer

Chicago Police Dept 7th District 312.747.8223
Fax 312.745.6558
Web ....www.chicagopolice.org
  1438 W 63, Chicago, IL 60636-1928
Sheri Mecklenburg, Program Director

Chicago Police Dept 9th District 312.747.8227
Fax 312.747.5329
Web ....www.chicagopolice.org
E-mail ....gkimmons@chicago2016.org
  3120 S Halsted, Chicago, IL 60609-1624
Gyata Kimmons, Director Of Community Relations

Chicago Police Dept Youth Div 312.745.6004
Fax 312.745.6832
E-mail ....robert.harteshimer@chicagopolice.org
  3510 S Michigan Ave, Unit 184, Chicago, IL 60653
Robert Harteshimer, Youth Investigations Division

Sheriff's Ofc 312.603.6444
Fax 312.603.9465
E-mail ....sheriff@cookcountysheriff.org
  50 W Washington St Rm 704, Chicago, IL 60602
Thomas Dart, Sheriff

EDUCATION SERVICES

Albany Park Headstart 773.509.5657
Fax 773.866.1617
  5121 N Kimball Ave, Chicago, IL 60625-4807
Eva Volin, Director

Aunt Marthas Youth Svcs - H St 708.849.6363
Fax 708.849.5785
Web ....www.auntmarthas.org
  14424 S Wentworth Ave, Riverdale, IL 60827-2729
Ms Renee Wheeler, Human Resource

Ceda Head Start Ctr 708.757.1393
Fax 708.758.2523
  1055 Burkley, Ford Heights, IL 60411
Janet Parker, Director

Cedar Northwest Headstart Des
Plaines 847.298.1130
Fax 847.294.1832
E-mail ....khull@cedaorg.net
  1170 N River Rd, Des Plaines, IL 60016
Kate Hull, Center Director

Cedar Oak Park Head Start
Program 708.848.6476
Fax 708.848.1064
E-mail ....bjackson@cedaorg.net
  44 Madison St, Oak Park, IL 60302
Bobbette Jackson, Director

Chicago Heights Saint James
Headstart 708.754.9801
Fax 708.754.1431
  9 W 21st St, Chicago Heights, IL 60411-4011
Vianna-Nolan Peters, Director

Chicago Lawn Head Start 773.925.1085
Fax 773.925.1170
E-mail ....vcorrillo@catholiccharities.net
  3001 W 59th St, Chicago, IL 60629
Virginia Corrillo, Director

Christopher House Logan Square
Headstart 773.235.4073
Fax 773.235.7407
E-mail ....cvelez@christopherhouse.org
  3255 W Altgeld St, Chicago, IL 60647
Carmen Velez, Director

Communities In Schools, Inc. 312.829.2475
Fax 312.829.2610
E-mail ....info@chicagocis.org
  815 W Van Buren St Ste 300, Chicago, IL 60607
Jane Metziger, Executive Director

Country Club Hills Headstart 708.922.1975
Fax 708.922.3895
  17542 Crawford Ave, Country Club Hills, IL 60478
Miracle Moss, Director

Dr Effie O Ellils Head Start Training ...773.533.9011
Fax 773.533.1740
  10 S Kedzie Ave, Chicago, IL 60612-2706
Ellen Jablo, Site Director

Englewood - Messiah Head Start 773.436.5110
Fax 773.436.5341
  1910 W 64th St, Chicago, IL 60636-2604
Delphine Wcittlesey, Director

First Church Of Love Faith Head

Start 773.224.6800

Fax 773.224.8928

   2140 W 79th St, Chicago, IL 60620-5797

   Barbara Mosley, Director

Marcy Newberry Association St.

John 773.379.5533

   5701 W Midway Park, Chicago, IL 60644-1819

   Willie May Cole, Program Director

Nsseo 847.463.8100

Fax 847.463.8114

Web ....www.nsseo.org

   799 W Kensington Rd, Mt Prospect, IL 60056

   Judith Hackett, Director

Oak Park & River Force High School-Special

Education 708.434.3706

Fax 708.434.3921

E-mail ....thalliman@oprfhs.orh

   201 N Scoville Ave, Oak Park, IL 60302

   Dr Tina Halliman, Director Of Special Education

Special Education 847.965.9040

Fax 847.965.0003

Web www.ntdse.k12.il.us

E-mail ....tkendick@ntdse.k12.il.us

   8701 Menard Ave, Morton Grove, IL 60053-3052

   Tarin Kendrick, Superintendant

Special Education Echo Joint

Agreement 708.333.7880

Fax 708.333.9561

Web ....www.specialstudents.org

E-mail ....dwardeja@yahoo.com

   350 W 154th St, South Holland, IL 60473-1229

   Dr. Debra Hooks, Director

Special Education South West

Coop 708.687.0900

Fax 708.687.5695

Web ....www.swcccase.org

E-mail ....goneil@swcccase.org

   6020 151st St, Oak Forest, IL 60452-1841

   Gineen O'Neil, Director

Special Education/Lihigton Area 847.455.3143

Fax 847.451.4892

E-mail ....mmcelherne@lasecfp.org

   10401 Grand Ave, Franklin Park, IL 60131

   Michael Mcelherne Ed.d, Director

Special Education/Special Svcs 847.859.8000

Fax 847.859.8701

Web www.district65.net

E-mail ....lenoirm@district65.net

   1500 Mcdaniel Ave, Evanston, IL 60201-3976

   Martie Lenoir-davis, Director

Special Education/Specialized Svcs 773.553.1800

Fax 773.553.3417

Web ....www.cpsspecialeducation.org

E-mail ....rgsmith@cps.k12.il.us

   125 S Clark St, Fl 8, Chicago, IL 60603

   Richard Smith, Chief Director

Special Education/Student Svcs 708.364.3331

Fax 708.349.0120

Web www.orland135.org

E-mail ....cschultz@orland135.org

   15100 S 94th Ave, Orland Park, IL 60462

   Colleen Schultz, Ed.d, Director Of Special Ed & Student Services

Student Svcs 847.963.3000

Fax 847.963.3145

Web www.ccsd15.net

E-mail ....phelpsc@ccsd15.net

   580 N 1st Bank Dr, Palatine, IL 60067-8110

   Cindy Phelps, Director

Crawford County

GENERAL HEALTH SERVICES

Health Dept 618.544.8798

Fax 618.544.9398

Web ....www.cchd.net

   202 N Bline Blvd, Robinson, IL 62454

   Rhonda Simpson, Infectious Diseases Coordinator

COURTS

2nd Circuit Court/Clerk's Ofc 618.544.3512

Fax 618.546.5628

Web ....www.crawfordcountycentral.com

E-mail ....circuitclerk@crawfordcountycentral.com

   1 Courthouse Square, Robinson, IL 62454

   Angela Reinoehl, Clerk Of Court

POLICE AND SHERIFF

Sheriff's Ofc 618.546.1515

Fax 618.546.0141

E-mail ....sheriff@crawfordcountycentral.com

   203 S Jefferson St, Robinson, IL 62454

   Todd Liston, Sheriff

Cumberland County

GENERAL HEALTH SERVICES

Health Dept 217.849.3211

Fax 217.849.3121

Web ....www.cumberlandhealth.org

E-mail ....info@cumberlandhealth.org

   132 NE Courthouse Sq, Toledo, IL 62468

   Cindy Hanley, Human Resource Manager

POLICE AND SHERIFF

Sheriff's Ofc 217.849.2571

Fax 217.849.2519

   166 Courthouse Square, Toledo, IL 62468

   Stephen Ozier, Sheriff

DeKalb County

GENERAL HEALTH SERVICES

Health Dept 815.758.6673

Fax 815.748.2485

Web ....www.dekalbcountyhealthdepartment.org

   2550 N Annie Glidden Rd, Dekalb, IL 60115-1297

   Bette Chilton, Nursing Director

JUSTICE AGENCY

CASA 815.895.2052

Fax 815.895.3651

Web ....www.casadekalb.org

E-mail ....casadekalb@aol.com

   407 W State St Ste 6, Sycamore, IL 60178-1455

   Jill Olson, Executive Director

COURTS

16th Circuit Court/Court House 815.895.7131

Fax 815.899.0758

   133 W State St, Sycamore, IL 60178

   Honorable Robbin Stuckert, Judge

DeWitt County

COURTS

6th Circuit Court 217.935.7750

Fax 217.935.7759

   201 W Washington St, Clinton, IL 61727

   Lori Berger, Circuit Clerk

POLICE AND SHERIFF

Sheriff's Ofc 217.935.6718

Fax 217.935.3606

Web ....www.police.ci.clinton.il.us

E-mail ....sheriff@police.ci.clinton.il.us

   101 W Washington St, Clinton, IL 61727-1636

   Jered Shofner, Sheriff

Douglas County

GENERAL HEALTH SERVICES

Health Dept 217.253.4137

Fax 217.253.3421

Web ....www.douglascountyhealth.org

E-mail ....clinic@douglascountyhealth.org

   1250 E Us Highway 36, Tuscola, IL 61953

   Susan Hays, Rn, Nursing Director

COURTS

6th Circuit Court 217.253.2352

Fax 217.253.9006

   401 S Center St, Tuscola, IL 61953

   Julie Mills, Circuit Clerk

POLICE AND SHERIFF

Sheriff's Ofc 217.253.3511

Fax 217.253.3144

E-mail ....charlie.mcgrew@douglascountysheriff.com

   920 S Washington St, Tuscola, IL 61953-7506

   Charlie Mcgrew, Sheriff

Dupage County

MENTAL HEALTH SERVICES

Hinsdale Hospital 630.856.9000

Fax 630.856.6000

Web .....www.keepingyouwell.com/facilities/hinsd ale/

E-mail ....barbara.krattochvil@chss.com

   120 N Oak St, Hinsdale, IL 60521

   Barbara Krattochvil, Infection Control Coordinator

JUSTICE AGENCY

CASA 630.221.0889

Fax 630.221.0904

Web ....www.dupagecasa.org

   505 N County Farm Rd, Fl 3C, Wheaton, IL 60187

   Lisa Drake, Executive Director

Illinois Youth Ctr-Warrenville 630.983.6231

Fax 630.983.6213

Web ....www.idoc.state.il.us

   30 West 200 Ferry Rd, Warrenville, IL 60555

   Judy Davis, Superintendent

Juvenile Detention 630.407.2500

E-mail ....bglos@dupageco.org

   420 N County Farm Rd, Wheaton, IL 60187-3996

   Bernard Glos, Superintendent

Probation & Court Svcs 630.407.8400

Fax 630.407.8401

Web ....www.co.dupage.il.us

   503 N County Farm Rd, Wheaton, IL 60187-3942

   Karpy Marge, Director Of Juvinille Services

COURTS

18th Circuit Court 630.407.8700

Fax 630.407.8575

E-mail ....ckachiroubas@dupageco.org

   505 N County Farm Rd, Wheaton, IL 60187

   Chris Kachiroubas, Clerk Of Court

POLICE AND SHERIFF

Police Investigations 630.305.5276

Fax 630.305.5918

Web ....www.naperville.il.us

E-mail ....johnsenj@naperville.il.us

   1350 Aurora Ave, Naperville, IL 60540-6206

   Gary Bolt, Deputy Chief

Sheriff's Ofc 630.407.2400

Fax 630.407.2346

Web ....www.dupageco.org

E-mail ....sheriff@dupageco.org

   501 N County Farm Rd, Wheaton, IL 60187-3986

   Det. Mike Drugan, Detective Agent

EDUCATION SERVICES

School Disrict 200 ....630.682.2000
Fax 630.682.2227
Web www.cusd200.org
E-mail ....lknicker@cusd200.org
　130 W Park Ave, Wheaton, IL 60189-6460
　Linda Knicker, Assistant Superintendant Special Services

Special Education 630.894.0490
Fax 630.894.5960
E-mail ....rjacobson@ndsec.org
　255 E Lake St Ste 300, Bloomingdale, IL 60108
　Dr. Rita Jacobson, Executive Director

Special Education 630.942.5600
Fax 630.942.5601
E-mail ....jnelson@casedupage.com
　22W600 Butterfield Rd Lowr 1, Glen Ellyn, IL 60137
　Jim Nelson, Director

Edgar County

GENERAL HEALTH SERVICES

Public Health Dept 217.465.2212
Fax 217.465.1121
Web ....www.edgarcountypublichealth.org
　502 Shaw Ave, Paris, IL 61944
　Carol Cline, Rn, Nursing Director

COURTS

5th Circuit Court 217.466.7447
Fax 217.466.7443
　115 W Court St, Rm M, Paris, IL 61944
　Karen Halloran, Clerk

POLICE AND SHERIFF

Sheriff's Ofc 217.465.4166
Fax 217.463.2161
　228 N Central Ave, Paris, IL 61944
　Edward Motley, Sheriff

Edwards County

COURTS

2nd Circuit Court 618.445.2016
Fax 618.445.4943
　50 E Main St, Ste 5, Albion, IL 62806-1262
　Honorable David K. Frankland, Director

Effingham County

GENERAL HEALTH SERVICES

Health Dept 217.342.9237
Fax 217.342.9324
Web ....www.effcohealth.org
E-mail ....crystals@effcohealth.org
　901 W Virginia Ave, Effingham, IL 62401
　Crystal Schutzbach, Hiv Coordinator

COURTS

4th Circuit Court 217.342.4065
Fax 217.342.6183
E-mail ....circuitclerk@co.effingham.il.us
　120 W Jefferson Ave Ste 101, Effingham,
　IL 62401-2382
　Becky Jansen, Circuit Clerk

Probation Dept 217.347.7931
Fax 217.347.2001
E-mail ....cmyers@co.effingham.il.us
　120 W Jefferson Ave Ste 102, Effingham, IL 62401
　Cheryl Myers, Chief Managing Officer

Fayette County

GENERAL HEALTH SERVICES

Health Dept 618.283.1044
Fax 618.283.5038
Web ....www.fayettehealthdept.org
　416 W Edwards St, Vandalia, IL 62471-2707
　Dee Sanders, Clinical Director

COURTS

4th Circuit Court 618.283.5009
Fax 618.283.4490
　221 S 7th St Rm 101, Vandalia, IL 62471
　Mary Ruot, Circuit Clerk

POLICE AND SHERIFF

Sheriff's Ofc 618.283.2141
Fax 618.283.5014
Web ....www.leo.gov
E-mail ....alay@leo.gov
　221 S 7th St Rm 500, Vandalia, IL 62471-2755
　Aaron Lay, Sheriff

Ford County

GENERAL HEALTH SERVICES

Ford Iroquois Public Health Dept 217.379.9281
Fax 217.379.2802
Web ....www.fiphd.org
　235 N Taft St, Paxton, IL 60957
　Deeann Schippert, Nursing Director

POLICE AND SHERIFF

Sheriff's Ofc 217.379.9277
Fax 217.379.4801
Web ....www.fcsheriff.com
E-mail ....fcsheriff@fcsheriff.com
　235 N American St, Paxton, IL 60957-1158
　Mark Doran, Sheriff

Franklin County

GENERAL HEALTH SERVICES

Health Dept 618.439.0951
Fax 618.438.3005
Web ....www.bicountyhealth.org
E-mail ....rrice@bicountyhealth.org
　403 E Park St, Benton, IL 62812-1920
　Robyn Rice, Rn, Hiv Coordinator

JUSTICE AGENCY

CASA 618.438.0608
Fax 618.438.6000
E-mail ....casafranklinco@yahoo.com
　202 Public Sq, Benton, IL 62812
　Nicole Garrett, Director

COURTS

2nd Circuit Court 618.439.2011
Fax 618.439.4119
Web ....www.mychoice.net
　On The Square, Benton, IL 62812
　Thomas Tedeschi, Judge

POLICE AND SHERIFF

Sheriffs Ofc 618.438.8211
Fax 618.438.0306
E-mail ....djones.@sherifffranklincounty.com
　403 E Main St, Benton, IL 62812
　Donald R Jones, Sheriff

Fulton County

GENERAL HEALTH SERVICES

Health Dept 309.647.1134
Fax 309.647.9545
Web ....www.fultoncountyhealth.com
E-mail ....cmoshier@fulton.co.org
　700 E Oak St, Canton, IL 61520
　Martha Kepple, Hiv Coordinator

JUSTICE AGENCY

CASA 309.789.6575
E-mail ....casabon@sbcglobal.net
　23441 N Chippewa Dr, Cuba, IL 61427-9344
　Bonnie Krulac, Executive Director

COURTS

9th Circuit Court Juvenile Div 309.547.3041
Fax 309.547.3636
　100 N Main St Rm 207, Lewistown, IL 61542
　James Wilder, JPO

POLICE AND SHERIFF

Sheriff's Ofc 309.547.2277
Fax 309.547.2355
Web ....www.fultonco.org
　268 W Washington Ave, Lewistown, IL 61542-1423
　Jeff Standard, Sheriff

Gallatin County

COURTS

2nd Circuit Court 618.269.3140
Fax 618.269.4324
Web ....www.jodaviess.org
E-mail ....mistyblue80@hotmail.com
　484 Lincoln Blvd, Shawneetown, IL 62984
　Mona L. Moore, Clerk Of Court

POLICE AND SHERIFF

Sheriff's Ofc 618.269.3137
Fax 618.269.3806
E-mail ....sbradley@shawneelink.net
　North Lincoln Blvd, Shawneetown, IL 62984
　Shanon Bradley, Sheriff

Greene County

GENERAL HEALTH SERVICES

Health Dept 217.942.6961
Fax 217.942.3904
Web ....www.greenecountyhealth.com
E-mail ....rflowers@idphnet.com
　310 5th St, Carrollton, IL 62016-1398
　Ruth Ann Flowers, Patient Care Coordinator

COURTS

7th Circuit Court 217.942.3421
Fax 217.942.5431
　519 N Main St Rm 7, Carrollton, IL 62016-1033
　Honorable James W. Day, Director

POLICE AND SHERIFF

Sheriff's Ofc 217.942.6901
Fax 217.942.6041
E-mail ....gcsocc@gcc.net
　403 7Th St, Carrollton, IL 62016
　Robert McMillan, Sheriff

Grundy County

GENERAL HEALTH SERVICES

Health Dept 815.941.3113
Fax 815.941.2389
Web ....www.grundyhealth.com
E-mail ....kshoemaker@grundyhealth.com
　1320 Union St, Morris, IL 60450-2426
　Kay Lynn Shoemaker, Administrator

COURTS

13th Circuit Court **815.941.3256**
Fax 815.941.3265
Web .... www.grundyco.org
   111 E Washington St, Ste 30, Morris, IL 60450-2277
   Honorable Robert Marsaglia, Judge

POLICE AND SHERIFF

Sheriff's Ofc **815.942.6645**
Fax 815.941.3463
E-mail .... sheriff@sheriff1.com
   111 E Illinois Ave, Morris, IL 60450
   Terry Marketti, Sheriff

Hamilton County

GENERAL HEALTH SERVICES

Health Dept **618.643.3522**
Fax 618.643.2390
Web .... www.hamiltoncountyhealthdept.org
E-mail .... health@hamiltonco.us
   100 S Jackson St Rm 5, Mc Leansboro, IL 62859
   Ladonna Lasaper, Rn, Nursing Supervisor

COURTS

2nd Circuit Court **618.643.3224**
Fax 618.643.3455
   100 S Jackson St Rm 3, Mc Leansboro, IL 62859
   Bobbi Oxford, Clerk Of Court

POLICE AND SHERIFF

Sheriff's Ofc **618.643.2511**
Fax 618.643.5114
Web .... www.grundycountysheriff.com
E-mail .... gbrenner@grundycountysheriff.com
   100 S Jackson St Rm 1, Mc Leansboro, IL 62859-1462
   Greg Brenner, Sheriff

Hancock County

GENERAL HEALTH SERVICES

Health Dept **217.357.2171**
Fax 217.357.3562
Web .... www.hancockhealth.com
E-mail .... hchd@adams.net
   671 Wabash Ave, Carthage, IL 62321
   Melita Finney, Health Educator

MENTAL HEALTH SERVICES

Mental Health Centers of Western
Illinois **217.357.3176**
Fax 217.357.6609
Web .... www.mhcwi.org
   607 Buchanan St, Carthage, IL 62321
   Joe Little, Associate Director

COURTS

9th Circuit Court **217.357.2616**
Fax 217.357.2231
   500 Main St, Carthage, IL 62321
   John Neally, Clerk Of Court

Teen Court **217.357.3916**
Fax 217.357.3682
Web www.govo84rl.state.il.us
   500 Main St, Carthage, IL 62321
   Brenda Youngmeyer, Coordinator

POLICE AND SHERIFF

Sheriff's Ofc **217.357.2115**
Fax 217.357.3035
E-mail .... sheriffj@mchsi.net
   98 Buchanan St, Carthage, IL 62321
   John H. Jefferson, Sheriff

Hardin County

GENERAL HEALTH SERVICES

Southern Seven Health Dept **618.285.6215**
Fax 618.285.6218
Web www.southern7.org
E-mail .... s7info@s7hd.org
   5 Ferrell Rd, Rosiclare, IL 62982
   Linda Crossland, Supervisor

COURTS

2nd Circuit Court **618.287.2735**
Fax 618.287.2713
E-mail .... hardincounty@gmail.com
   1 North Main St, Elizabethtown, IL 62931
   Tomm Foster, Judge

POLICE AND SHERIFF

Sheriff's Ofc **618.287.2271**
Fax 618.287.2992
Web .... www.shawneelink.net
   Courthouse Hil, Elizabethtown, IL 62931
   Loyd Cullison, Sheriff

Henderson County

GENERAL HEALTH SERVICES

Health Dept **309.627.2812**
Fax 309.627.2793
E-mail .... phenders@idphnet.com
   206 E Elm St, Gladstone, IL 61437
   Mary Reed, Public Health Administrator

POLICE AND SHERIFF

Sheriff's Ofc **309.867.4291**
Fax 309.867.4127
   113 N warren st, Oquawka, IL 61469
   Steve Haynes, Sheriff

Henry County

JUSTICE AGENCY

Illinois Department Of Juvenile
Justice **309.852.4601**
Fax 309.852.4617
Web .... www.doc.illinois.gov
   2021 Kentville Rd, Kewanee, IL 61443-1768
   Lisa Nordstrom, Superintendent

POLICE AND SHERIFF

Sheriff's Ofc **309.937.3911**
Fax 309.937.2902
E-mail .... sheriff@henrycty.com
   311 W Center St, Cambridge, IL 61238-1240
   Gilbert M. Cady, Sheriff

Iroquois County

COURTS

21st Judicial District **815.432.6950**
Fax 815.432.9333
   550 S 10th St, Watseka, IL 60970
   Barbara King, Juvenile Probation Officer

POLICE AND SHERIFF

Sheriff's Ofc **815.432.6992**
Fax 815.432.7226
Web .... www.iroquois-co.com
E-mail .... sheriff@iroquois-co.com
   550 S 10th St, Watseka, IL 60970-1810
   Derek Hagen, Sheriff

Jackson County

SOCIAL SERVICES

Children And Family Svcs **618.687.1733**
Fax 618.684.2088
   1210 Hanson St, Murphysboro, IL 62966
   Carol Shin, Child Welfare Supervisor

JUSTICE AGENCY

Illinois Youth Ctr- Murphysboro **618.684.8500**
Fax 618.684.8100
Web .... www.egyptiannet.com
E-mail .... wkilquist@egyptiannet.com
   636 Elza Brantley Dr, Murphysboro, IL 62966-6196
   Robert Price, Superintendent

Probation **618.687.7370**
Fax 618.687.4046
   215 N 14th St, Murphysboro, IL 62966-2009
   Edward Tolbert, Director

COURTS

1st Circuit Court **618.687.7300**
Fax 618.684.6378
   1001 Walnut St Rm 3, Murphysboro, IL 62966
   Cindy Svanda, Clerk

POLICE AND SHERIFF

Sheriff's Ofc **618.687.3822**
Fax 618.684.3443
   1001 Mulberry St, Murphysboro, IL 62966
   Robert Burns, Sheriff

EDUCATION SERVICES

Carbondale High School Even Start Rebound
Program **618.549.8232**
Fax 618.351.0288
Web www.cchs165.jacksn.k12.il.us
E-mail .... june.hickey@cchs165.com
   205 N Oakland Ave, Carbondale, IL 62901-1149
   June Hickey, Even Start Director

Jasper County

COURTS

4th Circuit Court **618.783.2524**
Fax 618.783.8626
   100 W Jourdan St Stop 1, Newton, IL 62448
   Sheryl Frederick, Clerk Of Court

POLICE AND SHERIFF

Sheriff's Ofc **618.783.8477**
Fax 618.783.3158
E-mail .... jcso@psbnewton.com
   106 E Morgan St, Newton, IL 62448
   Edward R. Francis, Sheriff

Jefferson County

SOCIAL SERVICES

Children And Family Svcs **618.244.8400**
Fax 618.244.8404
   321A Withers Dr, Mount Vernon, IL 62864
   Don Rose, Child Protection Manager

GENERAL HEALTH SERVICES

Health Dept **618.244.7134**
Fax 618.244.2640
Web .... www.jeffcohealth.com
E-mail .... mstevens@cbnstl.com
   1 Doctors Park Rd Ste F, Mount Vernon,
   IL 62864-6291
   Mark Stevens, Administrator

MENTAL HEALTH SERVICES

Comprehensive Svcs Inc **618.242.1510**
Fax 618.242.6392
Web .... www.jccsinc.info
   Route 37 N, Mount Vernon, IL 62864
   Dan Boihmer, Executive Director

JUSTICE AGENCY

Probation **618.244.8018**
Fax 618.244.8113
   911 Casey Ave, Ste Hi-03, Mount Vernon, IL 62864
   Darla Fitzjerrels, Chief Probational Officer

COURTS

2nd Circuit Court **618.244.8007**
Fax 618.244.8029
Web ....www.jeffil.us
E-mail ....jeffcocircuitclerk@jeffil.us
　100 S 10th St Rm 101, Mount Vernon,
　IL 62864-4012
　John Scott, Clerk Of Court

POLICE AND SHERIFF

Sheriff's Ofc **618.244.8004**
Fax 618.244.9209
E-mail ....dispatch@jeffil.us
　911 Casey Ave, Mount Vernon, IL 62864
　Roger D. Mulch, Sheriff

Jersey County

SOCIAL SERVICES

Children And Family Svcs **618.498.9561**
Fax 618.498.6321
　108 S State St, Jerseyville, IL 62052
　Debra Donham, Child Welfare Supervisor

JUSTICE AGENCY

CASA **618.498.5571**
Fax 618.639.0637
Web ....www.gtec.com
E-mail ....jerseyvillecasa@gtec.com
　201 W Pearl St Ste 4, Jerseyville, IL 62052-1662
　Jamie Buchanan, Program Director

Illinois Youth Ctr-Pere Marquette **618.786.2371**
Fax 618.786.2381
Web ....www.doc.illinois.gov
　17808 State Hwy 100 W, Grafton, IL 62037-2317
　Karen Mckinney, Superintendent

POLICE AND SHERIFF

Sheriff's Ofc **618.498.6881**
Fax 618.498.1911
　114 N Washington St, Jerseyville, IL 62052
　Mark Kallal, Sheriff

Jo Daviess County

COURTS

15th Circuit Court **815.777.0037**
Fax 815.776.9146
Web ....www.jodaviess.org
E-mail ....tstephenson@jodaviess.org
　330 N Bench St Ste 8, Galena, IL 61036-1828
　Timothy Stephenson, Chief Probation Officer

POLICE AND SHERIFF

Sheriff's Ofc **815.777.2141**
Fax 815.777.9284
E-mail ....kturner@jodaviess.org
　330 N Bench St Ste 11, Galena, IL 61036-1828
　Kevin Turner, Sheriff

Johnson County

GENERAL HEALTH SERVICES

Johnson Health Dept **618.658.5011**
Fax 618.658.2547
Web www.southern7hd.org
　515 E Vine St, Vienna, IL 62995
　Marla Goraning, Director

POLICE AND SHERIFF

Sheriff's Ofc **618.658.8264**
Fax 618.658.5951
　113 1/2 N 5th St 5ph, Vienna, IL 62995
　Elry Faulkner, Sheriff

Kane County

SOCIAL SERVICES

Children And Family Svcs **630.844.8400**
Fax 630.844.8405
Web ....www.state.il.us/dcfs
　8 E Galina Ste 100, Aurora, IL 60506-3120
　Erick Cabrera, Child Welfare Supervisor

**Illinois Dept Of Human Svcs Kane/Aurora Family Community
Resource Ctr** **630.844.7400**
Fax 630.844.7499
Web ....www.dhs.state.il.us
E-mail ....carol.adams@illinois.gov
　361 W Old Indian Trl, Aurora, IL 60506-2430
　Carol L. Adams, PhD, Secretary

GENERAL HEALTH SERVICES

Health Dept **630.208.3801**
Fax 630.897.4845
Web ....www.kanehealth.com
　1240 N Highland Ave, Ste 17, Aurora, IL 60506
　Paul Kuehnert, Executive Director

JUSTICE AGENCY

CASA **630.232.4484**
Fax 630.232.4562
Web ....www.casakanecounty.org
E-mail ....gloriabunce@casakanecounty.org
　100 S 3rd St, Ste 460, Geneva, IL 60134
　Gloria Bunce, Executive Director

Illinois Youth Ctr-St. Charles **630.584.0506**
Fax 630.584.1014
　3825 Campton Hills Dr, Saint Charles, IL 60175
　Jay Barger, Program Manager

Juvenile Ctr **630.406.7480**
Fax 630.208.5180
E-mail ....anselmerick@co.kane.il.us
　37 W. 655 Route 38, Saint Charles, IL 60175
　Rick Anselme, Superintendent

Probation Dept **847.742.0050**
Fax 847.742.0626
　80 S Grove Ave, Elgin, IL 60120
　George Torres, Office Manager

POLICE AND SHERIFF

Sheriff's Ofc **630.232.6840**
Fax 630.513.6984
Web ....www.kanesheriff.com
E-mail ....kcsheriffit@aol.com
　37 W 755 Illinois Rd 38, St Charles, IL 60175
　Patrick Perez, Sheriff

EDUCATION SERVICES

**Communities In Schools Of Aurora,
Inc.** **630.844.3713**
Fax 630.844.3715
Web ....www.cisaurora.org
E-mail ....cisaurora1@sbcglobal.net
　407 South, Calumet Aurora, IL 60506
　Theresa Shoemaker, Executive Director

Special Education **630.301.5000**
Fax 630.844.4442
Web www.sd129.org
　80 S River St, Aurora, IL 60506
　Cynthia Latimer, Special Services Chief Officer

**Special Education/School District
246** **847.888.5000**
Fax 847.888.7167
Web www.u-46.org
E-mail ....pamelaharris@u-46.org
　355 E Chicago St, Elgin, IL 60120-6500
　Pamela Harris, Director Of Special Education

**Special Education/School District
300** **847.426.1300**
Fax 847.551.8413
Web www.d300.org
E-mail ....shelley.nacke@d300.org
　300 Cleveland Ave, Carpentersville, IL 60110-1977
　Shelley Nacke, Director Of Special Education

Special Education/Special Svcs **630.299.7902**
Fax 630.299.7904
E-mail ....CLATZ@d131.org
　231 E Indian Trl, Aurora, IL 60505
　Cathrine Lattz, Director

Kankakee County

GENERAL HEALTH SERVICES

Kankakee Health Dept **815.802.9400**
Fax 815.802.9391
Web ....www.kankakeehealth.org
E-mail ....pboudreau@kankakeehealth.org
　2390 W Station St, Kankakee, IL 60901-3000
　Pam Boudreau, Director Of Client Services

JUSTICE AGENCY

Probation **815.937.2955**
Fax 815.937.3933
E-mail ....reinfeldt@co.kankakee.il.us
　470 E Merchant St, Rm 109, Kankakee, IL 60901
　H. Rick Einfeldt, Director

COURTS

21st Circuit Court **815.937.2905**
Fax 815.939.8830
　450 E Court St, Kankakee, IL 60901
　Kathy Bradshaw, Chief Judge

POLICE AND SHERIFF

Sheriff's Ofc **815.802.7100**
Fax 815.802.7101
Web ....www.kankakeecountysheriff.com
E-mail ....sheriff@kankakeecountysheriff.com
　3000 S Justice Way, Kankakee, IL 60901-8449
　Tim F. Bukowski, Sheriff

Kendall County

COURTS

16th Circuit Court **630.553.4183**
Fax 630.553.4964
　807 W John St, Yorkville, IL 60560
　Tina Virney, Probation Supervisor

POLICE AND SHERIFF

Sheriff's Ofc **630.553.7500**
Fax 630.553.1972
Web ....www.co.kendall.il.us
E-mail ....sherifkcso@aol.com
　1102 Cornell Ln, Yorkville, IL 60560-9597
　Richard A. Randall, Sheriff

EDUCATION SERVICES

Del Valle Migrant Head Start **815.436.1092**
Fax 815.436.2217
E-mail ....delvallemh@aol.com
　6550 Plainfield Rd, Oswego, IL 60543
　Maria Acosta, Director

Knox County

GENERAL HEALTH SERVICES

Health Dept **309.344.2225**
Fax 309.344.5049
Web ....www.knoxcountyhealth.org
E-mail ....hbritton@knoxcountyhealth.org
　1361 W Fremont St, Galesburg, IL 61401-2436
　Heidi Britton, Hiv Coordinator

Illinois

JUSTICE AGENCY

Juvenile Court Svcs **309.343.7918**
Fax 309.343.7922
  1319 E 5th St, Galesburg, IL 61401
  John M. Condon, Director Of Court Services

Mary Davis Home **309.343.5112**
Fax 309.343.5036
Web ....www.home.gallatinriver.net
E-mail ....cleair@grics.net
  1319 E 5th St, Galesburg, IL 61401-6698
  Rodney Cleair, Detention Superintendent

COURTS

9th Circuit Court **309.343.3121**
Fax 309.345.6729
Web ....www.knoxcountyil.com
  200 S Cherry St, Galesburg, IL 61401-4912
  Honorable Stephen C. Mathers, Judge

Teen Court **309.345.3800**
Fax 309.345.3897
E-mail ....teenct@ci.galesburg.il.us
  55 W Tompkins St, Galesburg, IL 61401
  Paula Johnson, Executive Director

POLICE AND SHERIFF

Sheriff's Ofc **309.345.3733**
Fax 309.345.3724
Web ....www.galesburg.net
E-mail ....sheriff@ci.galesburg.il.us
  152 S Kellogg St, Galesburg, IL 61401-4706
  David Clague, Sheriff

La Salle County

GENERAL HEALTH SERVICES

La Salle Health Dept **815.433.3366**
Fax 815.433.9522
Web ....www.lasallecounty.org
E-mail ....lchd1@lasallecounty.org
  717 E Etna Rd, Ottawa, IL 61350-1040
  Cathy Larsen, Nursing Director

COURTS

Juvenile Court **815.434.8271**
Fax 815.434.8299
E-mail ....postmaster@lasallecounty.com
  707 E Etna Rd Ste 141, Ottawa, IL 61350
  Joseph M. Carey, Clerk Of Court

POLICE AND SHERIFF

Ottawa Police Dept **815.433.2131**
Fax 815.433.4600
Web ....www.il-ottawa.com
E-mail ....chief@il-ottawa.com
  301 W Lafayette St Ste 2, Ottawa, IL 61350-2077
  Brian Zeilmann, Chief

Sheriff's Ofc **815.433.2161**
Fax 815.434.8393
  707 E Etna Rd Ste 122, Ottawa, IL 61350
  Tom Templeton, Sheriff

Lake County

GENERAL HEALTH SERVICES

Community Health Svcs **847.377.8283**
Web ....www.lakecountyil.gov
  3010 Grand Ave, Waukegan, IL 60085

Health Dept **847.377.8400**
Fax 847.360.9372
Web ....www.lakecountyil.gov
  2400 Belvidere Rd, Waukegan, IL 60085
  Brian Bongner, Hiv Program Coordinator

Prenatal Care Clinic **847.377.8462**
Fax 847.244.3562
Web ....www.co.lake.il.us
E-mail ....jreyes@co.lake.il.us
  2400 Belvidere Rd, Waukegan, IL 60085-6165
  Irene Pierce, Director

JUSTICE AGENCY

CASA **847.808.9154**
Fax 847.808.9328
Web ....www.casalakecounty.com
E-mail ....tzgreenberg@casalakecounty.com
  1020 Milwaukee Ave Ste 312, Deerfield,
  IL 60015-3562
  Terri Greenberg, Executive Director

**Juvenile Probation & Detention
Svcs** **847.377.7800**
Fax 847.634.3833
E-mail ....robertcesar@lakecountyil.gov
  24647 N Milwaukee Ave, Depke Juvenile Justice
  Complex, Vernon Hills, IL 60061
  Robert Cesar, Director

COURTS

19th Circuit Court **847.377.3380**
Fax 847.360.6409
Web ....www.lakecountyil.gov
E-mail ....mmullen@lakecountyil.gov
  18 N County St, Waukegan, IL 60085-4304
  Honorable Margaret Mullen, Judge

19th Circuit Juvenile Court/Intake **847.377.7800**
Fax 847.984.5784
E-mail ....rcesar@lakecountyil.gov
  24647 N Milwaukee Ave, Robert Depke Juvenile
  Justice Complex, Vernon Hills, IL 60061-1576
  Rob Cesar, Director

Juvenile Clerk Of Court **847.634.6104**
  24647 N Milwaukee Ave, Vernon Hills, IL 60061
  Honorable Sarah P. Lessman, Judge

Ni Casa Teen Court **847.546.6450**
Fax 847.546.6760
E-mail ....emcgonigal@nicasa.org
  31979 N Fish Lake Rd, Round Lake, IL 60073-9517
  Elizabeth Mcgonigal, Supervisor

POLICE AND SHERIFF

Sheriff's Ofc **847.377.4050**
Fax 847.360.5796
E-mail ....mcurran@lakecountyil.gov
  25 S Martin Luther King Jr Ave, Waukegan, IL 60085
  Mark C. Curran, Jr, Sheriff

EDUCATION SERVICES

**Deer Park Teaching And Learning
Ctr** **224.632.3380**
Fax 224.632.3700
E-mail ....kellis@dist113.org
  1959 Waukegan Rd, Deerfield, IL 60015-1840
  Karen Ellis, Director

Special Education/Nssed **847.831.5100**
Fax 847.831.5108
Web ....www.nssed.org
  760 Red Oak Ln, Highland Park, IL 60035-3816
  Dr. Tim Thomas, Superintendent

Lawrence County

GENERAL HEALTH SERVICES

Health Dept **618.943.3302**
Fax 618.943.5139
  RR 3 Box 414, Lawrenceville, IL 62439
  Carla Simmons, Hiv Coordinator

JUSTICE AGENCY

Cra-Wa-La Volunteers **618.943.5326**
Fax 618.943.2356
Web ....www.crawalavip.org
E-mail ....goffdm@crawalavip.org
  1300 15th St Ste 5, Lawrenceville, IL 62439-2279
  D. Marie Goff, Executive Director

COURTS

2nd Judicial Circuit **618.943.2815**
Fax 618.943.5205
E-mail ....lchd@wworld.com
  1100 State St, Lawrenceville, IL 62439
  Peggy Frederick, Circuit Clerk

POLICE AND SHERIFF

Sheriff's Ofc **618.943.5766**
Fax 618.943.5768
Web ....www.shawneelink.net
E-mail ....russell@shawneelink.net
  1306 State St, Lawrenceville, IL 62439
  Russell Adams, Sheriff

Lee County

GENERAL HEALTH SERVICES

Health Dept **815.284.3371**
Fax 815.288.1811
Web ....www.lchd.com
E-mail ....cwallace@lchd.com
  309 S Galena Ave Ste 100, Dixon, IL 61021-9185
  Candy Wallace, Rn, Nursing Director

COURTS

15th Circuit Court **815.284.5234**
Fax 815.288.5615
E-mail ....dmccaffrey@countyoflee.org
  309 S Galena Ave Ste 320, Dixon, IL 61021
  Denise A. Mccaffrey, Clerk Of Court

Livingston County

JUSTICE AGENCY

Court Svcs **815.844.5177**
Fax 815.842.1600
E-mail ....lcpcs@mchsi.com
  119-1/2 N Mill St, Pontiac, IL 61764
  Michael Shaughnessy, Director & Cpo

POLICE AND SHERIFF

Sheriff's Ofc **815.844.2774**
Fax 815.844.5124
E-mail ....livingstonsheriff@mchsi.com
  844 W Lincoln St, Pontiac, IL 61764-2325
  Martin Meredith, Sheriff

Logan County

GENERAL HEALTH SERVICES

Dept of Public Health **217.735.2317**
Fax 217.735.1872
Web ....www.lcdph.org
E-mail ....info@lcdph.org
  109 3rd St, Lincoln, IL 62656
  Mary Anderson, Hiv Coordinator

MENTAL HEALTH SERVICES

Logan/Mason Mental Health **217.735.2272**
Fax 217.732.9847
  760 S Postvill dr, Lincoln, IL 62656
  Gene Frioli, Director

POLICE AND SHERIFF

Elkhart Police Dept **217.947.2287**
Fax 217.947.2287
  PO Box 20, Elkhart, IL 62634-0020
  Joe Ludke, Police Chief

Macon County

SOCIAL SERVICES

Children And Family Svcs **217.875.6750**
Fax 217.875.6565
Web .... www.illinois.gov
   2900 N Oakland Ave, Ste B, Decatur, IL 62526
   Pam Waterman, CPS Supervisor

GENERAL HEALTH SERVICES

Health Dept **217.423.6988**
Fax 217.423.5079
Web .... www.maconcountyhealth.org
   1221 E Condit St, Decatur, IL 62521-1476
   Julie Aubert, Administrator

JUSTICE AGENCY

CASA **217.428.8424**
Fax 217.428.8423
Web .... www.nationalcasa.org
E-mail .... maconcasa@sbcglobal.net
   140 S Water St Ste 100, Decatur, IL 62523-1324
   Zincent Rodriguez, Case Executive Director

COURTS

6th Circuit Court **217.424.1454**
Fax 217.425.9292
   253 E Wood St Ste 125, Decatur, IL 62523
   Honorable Ag Webber, Judge

POLICE AND SHERIFF

Sheriff's Ofc **217.424.1332**
Fax 217.424.1491
E-mail .... tschneider@sheriff-macon-il.us
   333 S Franklin St, Decatur, IL 62523
   Thomas Schneider, Sheriff

EDUCATION SERVICES

Anna Waters Head Start Program **217.423.2268**
Fax 217.423.2280
Web .... www.dmcoc.org
E-mail .... rpeople@dmcoc.org
   1126 E Marietta St, Decatur, IL 62521
   Rosy Peoples, Director

Opportunity Corp **217.428.0155**
Fax 217.423.2280
   1122 E Marietta St, Decatur, IL 62521
   Rosy Peoples, Director

Special Education **217.424.3030**
Fax 217.424.3022
E-mail .... dwiley@dpssix.org
   335 E Cerogordo, Decatur, IL 62523
   Deborah Wiley, Director

Macoupin County

GENERAL HEALTH SERVICES

Health Dept **217.854.3223**
Fax 217.854.3225
Web .... www.mcphd.net
E-mail .... khazzard@mcphd.net
   805 N Broad St, Carlinville, IL 62626-1075
   Karen Hazzard, Rn, Nursing Director

MENTAL HEALTH SERVICES

Locust Street Resource Ctr **217.854.3166**
Fax 217.854.9729
Web .... www.mac.mhc.org
   320 S Locust St, Carlinville, IL 62626-1648
   Doug Kilberg, Executive Director

JUSTICE AGENCY

Probation Ofc **217.854.4411**
Fax 217.854.3922
E-mail .... whammann@roe40.k12.il.us
   215 S East St Ste 3, Carlinville, IL 62626
   Wanda Hammann, Chief Performance Officer

POLICE AND SHERIFF

Sheriff's Ofc **217.854.3135**
Fax 217.854.8477
E-mail .... mcsd@frontiernet.net
   215 S East St, Ground Floor, Carlinville, IL 62626
   Don Albrechtt, Sheriff

Madison County

SOCIAL SERVICES

Children And Family Svcs **618.259.8400**
Fax 618.259.8416
E-mail .... llolly@idcfs.state.il.us
   1407 Vaughn Rd, Wood River, IL 62095
   Larry Lolly, Site Supervisor

Children And Family Svcs **618.876.8985**
Fax 618.876.8998
Web .... www.state.il.us
E-mail .... tonny.hempen@illinois.gov
   1925 B Madison Ave, Granite City, IL 62040
   Tonny Hempen, Child Welfare Supervisor

Children And Family Svcs **618.466.7014**
Fax 618.466.9556
   200 N Center Dr Ste D, Alton, IL 62002-5946
   Cindy Lolley, Site And Child Welfare Supervisor

GENERAL HEALTH SERVICES

Health Dept **618.692.8954**
Fax 618.692.8905
Web .... www.madisoncountyhealthdepartment.org
E-mail .... adunstar@co.madison.il.us
   101 E Edwardsville Rd, Wood River, IL 62095-1369
   Alan Dunstar, President

MENTAL HEALTH SERVICES

Community Mental Health Board **618.692.6200**
Fax 618.692.8986
Web .... www.co.madison.il.us
   157 N Main St Rm 380, Edwardsville, IL 60
   Jennifer Roth, Director

JUSTICE AGENCY

Detention Home **618.692.1002**
Fax 618.692.8959
Web .... www.co.madison.il.us
   100 5th Ave, Edwardsville, IL 62025-2575
   Steven M. Bowker, Superintendent

Juvenile Probation **618.692.6255**
Fax 618.656.4591
Web .... www.co.madison.il.us
   157 N Main St Rm 312, Edwardsville, IL 62025-1965
   Judith Dallas, Court Services Director

COURTS

3rd Circuit Court **618.692.6240**
Fax 618.692.0676
Web .... www.co.madison.il.us
E-mail .... circuitclerk@co.madison.il.us
   155 N Main St, Edwardsville, IL 62025-1950
   Matt Melucci, Clerk Of Court

POLICE AND SHERIFF

Sheriff's Ofc **618.692.6087**
Fax 618.656.1210
E-mail .... sbhertz@co.madison.il.us
   405 Randle St, Edwardsville, IL 62025-1953
   Robert Hertz, Sheriff

EDUCATION SERVICES

Collinsville Headstart **618.345.9588**
Fax 618.344.7969
   5 Crestmont Dr, Collinsville, IL 62234
   Debbie Fohr, Center Supervisor

Special Education **618.463.2137**
Fax 618.474.0626
   1854 Rear E Broadway, Alton, IL 62002
   Mark Lambert, Director

Special Education **618.452.7864**
Fax 618.451.6135
   1947 Adams St, Granite City, IL 62040
   Paul Bowler, Director Special Education

Special Education **618.343.2878**
Fax 618.343.2772
Web .... www.kahoks.org
E-mail .... kcarpanter@nv1.cusd10.madison.k12.il.us
   123 W Clay, Collinsville, IL 62234
   Kelly Carpanter, Director

Special Education/Region 3 .... **618.462.1031**
Fax 618.462.1035
Web www.madison.k12.il.us
E-mail .... cpenrod@madison.k12.il.us
   1800 Storey Ln, Cottage Hills, IL 62018-1399
   Cindy Penrod, Director

Marion County

GENERAL HEALTH SERVICES

Health Dept **618.548.3878**
Fax 618.548.3866
Web .... www.marioncountyhealthdept.org
E-mail .... lryan@ussonet.net
   118 Cross Creek Blvd, Salem, IL 62881
   Lori Ryan, Administrator

JUSTICE AGENCY

Court Svcs **618.548.3880**
Fax 618.548.3871
E-mail .... mshoemaker@ussonet.net
   200 E Schwartz St, Salem, IL 62881
   Melinda Shoemaker, Director Of Court Services

COURTS

4th Circuit Court **618.548.3856**
Fax 618.740.0118
   100 E Main St Ste 204, Salem, IL 62881
   Ronda Yates, Clerk Of Court

POLICE AND SHERIFF

Sheriff's Ofc **618.548.2141**
Fax 618.548.0043
Web .... www.ussonet.net
E-mail .... sheriff@ussonet.net
   204 N Washington St, Salem, IL 62881-2907
   Jerry Devore, Sheriff

Marshall County

POLICE AND SHERIFF

Sheriff's Ofc **309.246.2115**
Fax 309.246.2121
E-mail .... 062@yahoo.com
   520 6th St, Lacon, IL 61540
   Rob Russell, Sheriff

Mason County

GENERAL HEALTH SERVICES

Health Dept **309.543.2201**
Fax 309.543.2063
Web .... www.masoncohealth.com
E-mail .... mcht@grics.net
   1002 E Laurel Ave, Havana, IL 62644
   Cindy Abbott, Aids Surveillance Supervisor

COURTS

8th Circuit Court **309.543.6619**
Fax 309.543.4214
E-mail .... masoncourt@grics.net
   125 N Plum St, Havana, IL 62644
   Brenda K Miller, Court Clark

POLICE AND SHERIFF

Forest City Police Dept **309.597.2313**
Fax...309.968.7664
E-mail ....forestcitypd@casscomm.com
   201 N Main St, Forest City, IL 61522
   Glen A Holtslaw, Police Chief

Sheriff's Ofc **309.543.2231**
Fax...309.543.3564
E-mail ....mcso@grics.net
   102 W Market St, Havana, IL 62644-1144
   Wayne Youell, Sheriff

massac County

POLICE AND SHERIFF

Sheriff's Ofc **618.524.2912**
Fax...618.524.3125
   515 Market St, Metropolis, IL 62960
   Ted Holder, Sheriff

McDonough County

GENERAL HEALTH SERVICES

Health Dept **309.837.9951**
Fax...309.837.1100
Web..www.mchdept.com
E-mail ....mcht@mchdept.com
   505 E Jackson St, Macomb, IL 61455-2310
   Cynthia Sheffler, Hiv Coordinator

COURTS

9th Circuit Court **309.837.9278**
Fax...309.833.3547
   130 S Lafayette St Ste 30, Macomb, IL 61455
   Gregory K Mcclintock, Chief Judge

Juvenile Probation Court Svcs **309.837.2307**
Fax...309.833.5570
E-mail ....lchaplin@9thjudicial.org
   130 S Lafayette St Ste 10, Macomb, IL 61455-2239
   Erica Thurman, Juvenile Probation Officer

POLICE AND SHERIFF

Sheriff's Ofc **309.833.2323**
Fax...309.833.1077
   110 S Mcarthur St, Macomb, IL 61455
   Rick Vanbrooker, Sheriff

McHenry County

COURTS

22nd Judicial Court **815.334.4310**
Fax...815.338.8583
   2200 N Seminary Ave, Woodstock, IL 60098
   Kathrine Keefe, Clerk

POLICE AND SHERIFF

Sheriff's Ofc **815.338.2144**
Fax...815.338.9285
Web..www.co.mchenry.il.us
E-mail ....sheriff@co.mchenry.il.us
   2200 N Seminary Ave, Woodstock, IL 60098-2637
   Keith Nygren, Sheriff

EDUCATION SERVICES

Special Education District **815.338.3622**
Fax...815.338.7550
Web..www.sedom.org
E-mail ....kwilhoit@sedom.org
   1200 Claussen Dr, Woodstock, IL 60098-2139
   Kathy Wilhoit, Superintendent

McLean County

GENERAL HEALTH SERVICES

Health Dept **309.888.5450**
Fax...309.888.5439
Web.................................www.mcleancountyil.gov/health
E-mail ....jan.morris@mcleancountyil.gov
   200 W Front St, ste 304, Bloomington, IL 61701
   Jan Morris, Supervisor

POLICE AND SHERIFF

Sheriff's Ofc **309.888.5034**
Fax...309.888.5072
E-mail ....mike.emery@mcleancountyil.gov
   104 West Front, Bloomington, IL 61701
   Mike Emery, Sheriff

EDUCATION SERVICES

Special Education/School District

87 ....**309.827.6031**
Fax...309.827.5717
Web..www.district87.org
   300 E Monroe St, Bloomington, IL 61701-4028
   Rebecca L. Francois, Director Of Special Ed.

Menard County

GENERAL HEALTH SERVICES

Health Dept **217.632.2984**
Fax...217.632.7860
Web..www.menardchd.org
E-mail ....adavis@menardchd.org
   1120 N 4th St, Petersburg, IL 62675
   Alicia Davis, Home Health Administrator

COURTS

8th Circuit Court **217.632.2615**
Fax...217.632.4124
Web..www.menardcountyil.com
   102 S 7th St Ofc 2, Petersburg, IL 62675-1567
   Honorable Thomas J Brannan, Judge

Mercer County

GENERAL HEALTH SERVICES

Health Dept **309.582.3759**
Fax...309.582.3793
Web..www.illinois.gov
E-mail ....dph.pmercer@illinois.gov
   1007 NW 3rd St, Aledo, IL 61231-1317
   Carla Ewing, Public Health Administrator

JUSTICE AGENCY

Family Crisis Ctr **309.582.7233**
Fax...309.582.5675
Web..www.mcfcc.com
E-mail ....marla@mcfcc.com
   110 NW 3rd Ave, Aledo, IL 61231-1503
   Marla Reynolds, Director Of Childrens Advocacy

Probation **309.582.5169**
Fax...309.582.3028
Web..www.mchsi.com
   100 SE 3rd St Stop 11, Aledo, IL 61231-1948
   Vickie M. Hansen, Probation Director

COURTS

14th Circuit Court **309.582.7122**
Fax...309.582.7121
Web..www.mercercountycourthouse.com
   100 SE 3rd St Stop 2, Aledo, IL 61231-1948
   Jeff Benson, Clerk

POLICE AND SHERIFF

Sheriff's Ofc **309.582.5194**
Fax...309.582.5158
Web..www.mercercountyil.org
E-mail ....tthomps3@leo.gov
   906 SW 3rd St, Aledo, IL 61231-1800
   Thomas L. Thompson, Sheriff

Monroe County

GENERAL HEALTH SERVICES

Health Dept **618.939.3871**
Fax...618.939.4459
Web.....................................www.monroecountyhealth.org
E-mail ....jwagner@monroecountyhealth.org
   901 Illinois Ave Ste A, Waterloo, IL 62298-1142
   John Wagner, Nursing Director

COURTS

20th judicial Circuit **618.939.8681**
Fax...618.939.1929
   100 S Main St, Waterloo, IL 62298-1399
   Sandra L Sauget, Clerk Of Court

POLICE AND SHERIFF

Sheriff's Ofc **618.939.8651**
Fax...618.939.4199
E-mail ....sheriff@htc.net
   225 E 3rd St, Waterloo, IL 62298
   Daniel J. Kelley, Sheriff

Montgomery County

JUSTICE AGENCY

Probation Ofc **217.532.9506**
Fax...217.532.9570
Web..www.montgomeryco.com
E-mail ....ulrici@montgomeryco.com
   120 N Main St Rm 102, Hillsboro, IL 62049-1149
   Banee Ulrici, CMO

COURTS

4th Circuit Court **217.532.9546**
Fax...217.532.9614
   120 N Main St Rm 125, Hillsboro, IL 62049
   Mary Webb, Clerk Of Court

POLICE AND SHERIFF

Sheriff's Ofc **217.532.9511**
Fax...217.532.6318
   140 N Main St, Hillsboro, IL 62049
   James Vazzi, Sheriff

Morgan County

GENERAL HEALTH SERVICES

Health Dept **217.245.5111**
Fax...217.243.4773
E-mail ....jackie.barringer@morganhd.com
   345 W State St, Jacksonville, IL 62650
   Jacqueline Barringer, Hiv Coordinator

JUSTICE AGENCY

Probation **217.243.9468**
Fax...217.243.1248
   345 W State St Ste 3, Jacksonville, IL 62650
   Todd Dillard, Director

COURTS

7th Circuit Court **217.243.5419**
Fax...217.243.2009
Web..www.morgancounty-il.com
E-mail ....circlerk@morgancounty-il.com
   300 W State St, Jacksonville, IL 62650
   Honorable Richard T. Mitchell, Circuit Judge

Illinois

POLICE AND SHERIFF

Sheriff's Ofc.............................217.245.4143
Fax...217.243.6998
Web........................www.morgencounty-il.com
E-mail....................rduvendack@net-axess.com
  300 W Court St, Jacksonville, IL 62650-2009
  Randy Duvendack, Sheriff

EDUCATION SERVICES

Special Education/ 4 Rivers...............217.245.7174
Fax...217.245.5533
Web...............................www.frsed.org
  936 W Michigan Ave, Jacksonville, IL 62650-3113
  Gina Eckhouse, Director

Moultrie County

GENERAL HEALTH SERVICES

Health Dept.............................217.728.4114
Fax...217.728.2650
Web......................www.moultriehealth.org
E-mail....................angela@moultriehealth.org
  2 W Adams St, Sullivan, IL 61951-1943
  Angela Hogan, Rn, Mph, Administrator

COURTS

Circuit Clerk..........................217.728.4622
Fax...217.728.7833
E-mail...............cbraden@circuit-clerk.moultrie.il.us
  10 S Main St Ste 7, Sullivan, IL 61951-1973
  Cynthia Braden, Clerk Of Court

POLICE AND SHERIFF

Sheriff's Ofc..........................217.728.4386
Fax...217.728.2489
Web..............................www.one-eleven.net
E-mail................jthomas@moultriesheriff.com
  1605 West Hagerman, Sullivan, IL 61951-1403
  Jeff Thomas, Sheriff

Ogle County

POLICE AND SHERIFF

Sheriff's Ofc..........................815.732.6666
Fax...815.732.7185
Web...............................www.oglecounty.org
  103 Jefferson St, Oregon, IL 61061-1611
  Michael Harn, Sheriff

Peoria County

SOCIAL SERVICES

Children And Family Svcs...............309.671.7900
Fax...309.671.7906
Web..........................www.idcfs.state.il.us
  2001 NE Jefferson Ave, Peoria, IL 61603-3533
  Robert Schiffman, Director

GENERAL HEALTH SERVICES

Peoria Health Dept....................309.679.6000
Fax...309.685.3312
Web...............................www.pcchd.org
  2116 N Sheridan Rd, Peoria, IL 61604
  Curt Fenton, Nursing Director

JUSTICE AGENCY

Juvenile Court Svcs...................309.672.6080
Fax...309.495.4993
Web..........................www.peoriacounty.org
E-mail....................sjones@peoriacounty.org
  324 Main St Ste 424, Peoria, IL 61602-2336
  Sherman Jones, PO

Juvenile Detention....................309.634.4200
Fax...309.634.4204
Web..............................www.wilson-mfg.com
  223 N Maxwell Rd, Peoria, IL 61604-5278
  Mark Bronke, Superintendent

POLICE AND SHERIFF

Sheriff's Ofc..........................309.697.8515
Fax...309.697.3734
Web..........................www.co.peoria.il.us
E-mail....................mmccoy@co.peoria.il.us
  301 N Maxwell Rd, Peoria, IL 61604-5280
  Michael D. Mccoy, Sheriff

EDUCATION SERVICES

Special Education......................309.672.6752
Fax...309.672.6708
Web...............................www.psd150.org
E-mail....................maureen.langhall@psd150.org
  3202 N Wisconsin Ave, Peoria, IL 61603-1260
  Maureen Langhall, Director

Special Education......................309.697.0880
Fax...309.697.0884
Web...............................www.seapco.org
  6000 S Adams St Fl 2, Peoria, IL 61607-2580
  Susan Carrescia, Director

Perry County

GENERAL HEALTH SERVICES

Health Dept.............................618.357.5371
Fax...618.357.3190
Web...............................www.perryhealth.net
E-mail....................clacy@perryhealth.net
  907 S Main St, Pinckneyville, IL 62274-1700
  Cindy Lacy, Home Care Director

JUSTICE AGENCY

Probation...............................618.357.2622
Fax...618.357.5136
Web...............................www.dps.state.nv.us
E-mail....................vmorrow@dps.state.nv.us
  1 Public Sq Rm 9, Pinckneyville, IL 62274-1172
  Vickie Morrow, Supervisor

COURTS

20th Circuit Court....................618.357.6726
Fax...618.357.8336
E-mail....................jimc@onecliq.net
  1 Public Sq Rm 17, Pinckneyville, IL 62274
  Honorable James W. Campanella, Director Judge

POLICE AND SHERIFF

Du Quoin Police Dept..................618.542.2131
Fax...618.542.4014
E-mail....................dq@duquoin.org
  304 E Poplar St, Du Quoin, IL 62832-2357
  Michael Ward, Police Chief

Piatt County

GENERAL HEALTH SERVICES

Health Dept.............................217.762.7911
Fax...217.762.3422
Web......................www.dewittpiatthealth.com
E-mail....................ktrusner@dewittpiatthealth.com
  1020 S Market St, Monticello, IL 61856
  Kathe Trusner, Director Of Nursing

COURTS

6th Circuit Court.....................217.762.4966
Fax...217.762.5906
Web...............................www.piattcounty.org
E-mail....................jshonkwiler@piattcounty.org
  101 W Washington St Ste 204, Monticello,
  IL 61856-1682
  Honorable John P. Shonkwiler, Director

POLICE AND SHERIFF

Sheriff's Ofc..........................217.762.7822
Fax...217.762.3200
Web...............................www.mchsi.com
E-mail....................piattcountysheriff@mchsi.com
  1216 Raymond Rd, Monticello, IL 61856-8269
  David Hunt, Sheriff

Pike County

COURTS

8th Circuit Court.....................217.285.6612
Fax...217.285.4726
  100 E Washington St Stop 3, Pittsfield,
  IL 62363-1445
  Barbara Allensworth, Chief Performance Officer

POLICE AND SHERIFF

Sheriff's Office.......................217.285.5011
Fax...217.285.4496
  204 E Adams St, Pittsfield, IL 62363
  Paul F. Petty, Sheriff

Pope County

COURTS

1st Circuit Court.....................618.683.3941
Fax...618.683.3018
  310 E Main St, Golconda, IL 62938
  Honorable Joseph Liberman, Circuit Court Judge

POLICE AND SHERIFF

Sheriff's Ofc..........................618.683.4321
Fax...618.683.2201
  126 E Decatur, Golconda, IL 62938
  Jerry Suites, Sheriff

Pulaski County

GENERAL HEALTH SERVICES

Southern Seven Health Dept...........618.634.2297
Fax...618.634.9394
Web...............................www.southern7.org
E-mail....................s7info@s7hd.org
  37 Rustic Campus Dr, Ullin, IL 62992
  Cheryl Manus, Director Of Nursing

JUSTICE AGENCY

Juvenile Probation....................618.748.9643
Fax...618.748.9815
  500 Illinois Ave Rm I, Mound City, IL 62963
  Kent Thomas, Jpo

POLICE AND SHERIFF

Sheriff's Ofc..........................618.748.9374
Fax...618.748.9338
  500 Illinois Ave Rm A, Mound City, IL 62963
  Randy Kern, Sheriff

Putnam County

GENERAL HEALTH SERVICES

Health Dept.............................815.925.7326
Fax...815.925.7001
Web...............................www.pchealthdept.org
  220 E High St Ste 102, Hennepin, IL 61327
  Katie Main, Nursing Coordinator

POLICE AND SHERIFF

Sheriff's Ofc..........................815.925.7084
Fax...815.925.7914
  120 N 4th St, Hennepin, IL 61327
  Kevin L. Doyle, Sheriff

Randolph County

SOCIAL SERVICES

Children And Family Svcs 618.443.4317
Fax 618.443.4564
202 W Jackson St, Sparta, IL 62286
Tina Simpson, Child Welfare/CPS Supervisor

GENERAL HEALTH SERVICES

Health Dept 618.826.5007
Fax 618.826.5223
Web ....www.randolphco.org
2515 State St, Chester, IL 62233-1149
Thomas Smith, Administrator

POLICE AND SHERIFF

Ellis Grove Police Dept 618.859.2101
Fax 618.859.2101
101 N Main St, Ellis Grove, IL 62241
Christopher J. Pierman, Police Chief

Sheriff's Ofc 618.826.5484
Fax 618.826.4732
E-mail ....rcso5484@yahoo.com
200 W Buena Vista St, Chester, IL 62233-1919
Michael Hoelscher, Sheriff

Richland County

SOCIAL SERVICES

Children And Family Svcs 618.393.2979
Fax 618.393.2102
E-mail ....aundrea.brooks@illinois.gov
1408 Martin St, Olney, IL 62450-4722
Aundrea Brooks, Child Welfare/CPS Supervisor

GENERAL HEALTH SERVICES

Health Dept 618.392.6241
Fax 618.393.4078
E-mail ....rcho@wobash.net
501 S Whittle Ave, Olney, IL 62450
Deborah Lamb, Rn, Nurse Administrator

COURTS

2nd Circuit Court 618.392.2151
Fax 618.392.5041
103 W Main St Ste 21, Olney, IL 62450
Honorable Larry D. Dunn, Judge

POLICE AND SHERIFF

Sheriff's Ofc 618.395.7481
Fax 618.395.7485
Web ....www.richlandcso.com
E-mail ....rcso@richlandcso.com
211 W Market St, Olney, IL 62450-2205
Andrew Hires, Sheriff

Rock Island

SOCIAL SERVICES

Children And Family Svcs 309.794.3500
Fax 309.794.3511
500 42nd St Ste 5, Rock Island, IL 61201
Jane Norman, Office Manager

GENERAL HEALTH SERVICES

Rock Island Health Dept 309.793.1955
Fax 309.794.7091
Web ....www.co.rock-island.il.us
2112 25th Ave, Rock Island, IL 61201
Wendy Trute, Health Dept Administrator

MENTAL HEALTH SERVICES

**Robert Young Ctr For Community Mental
Health** 309.779.2031
Fax 309.779.2027
Web ....www.trinityqc.com
E-mail ....gittingsj@trinityqc.com
4600 3rd St, Moline, IL 61265-6199
Jeanne Gittings, Project Director

JUSTICE AGENCY

Juvenile Probation Svcs 309.558.3780
Fax 309.558.3365
Web ....www.co.rock-island.il.us
E-mail ....dvanland@co.rock-island.il.us
1504 3rd Ave, Rock Island, IL 61201-8612
David Vanlandegen, Director Of Court Services

**Youth Svcs Bureau-Peer Justice
Program** 309.793.3460
Fax 309.732.0551
Web ....www.ysbri.com
E-mail ....tiffany.clark@ysbri.com
4709 44th St Ste 5, Rock Island, IL 61201-7187
Richard Connor, Executive Director

COURTS

14th Circuit Court 309.558.3538
Fax 309.558.3263
210 15th St, Rock Island, IL 61201
Lisa L. Bierman, Clerk Of Court

POLICE AND SHERIFF

Sheriff's Ofc 309.794.1230
Fax 309.794.9979
1317 3rd Ave, Rock Island Countysherrifs ofc, Rock
Island, IL 61201
Jeffrey Boyd, Sheriff

EDUCATION SERVICES

Project Now Head Start 309.792.4555
Fax 309.792.5829
Web ....www.projectnow.org
E-mail ....mhart@projectnow.org
499 27th St, East Moline, IL 61244-1870
Maureen Hart, Executive Director

Special Education 309.796.2500
Fax 309.796.2911
Web ....www.bhased.org
E-mail ....mweger@bhased.org
4670 11th St, East Moline, IL 61244
Michael Weger, Director

Saline County

JUSTICE AGENCY

Illinois Youth Ctr-Harrisburg 618.252.8681
Fax 618.252.2519
1201 W Poplar St, Harrisburg, IL 62946
Robert Price, Superintendent

Probation Dept 618.252.2701
Fax 618.252.1797
Web ....www.firstcircuitprobation.com
10 E Poplar St, Harrisburg, IL 62946-1452
Marcia Hooten, Secretary

COURTS

1st Circuit Court 618.253.5096
Fax 618.253.3904
Web ....www.state.il.us
10 E Poplar St Ste 24, Harrisburg, IL 62946-1553
Honorable Todd Lambert, Judge

POLICE AND SHERIFF

Sheriff's Ofc 618.252.8661
Fax 618.252.2503
Web ....www.cdavidnelson.com
E-mail ....donald@cdavidnelson.com
1 N Main St Ste 1, Harrisburg, IL 62946-1452
Donald K. Brown, Sheriff

Sangamon County

SOCIAL SERVICES

Div Of Child Support Enforcement 800.447.4278
Fax 217.524.4608
Web ....www.ilchildsupport.com
E-mail ....pam_compton@mail.idpa.state.il.us
509 S 6th St, Marriott Bldg, Springfield, IL 62701
Pam Compton, Acting Administrator

Illinois Dept Of Human Svcs 217.557.1601
Fax 217.557.1647
Web ....www.dhs.state.il.us
100 S Grand Ave E, Springfield, IL 62762
Michelle Saddler, Secretary

GENERAL HEALTH SERVICES

**Div Of Community Health &
Prevention** 217.557.2109
Fax 217.524.5586
823 E Monroe, Springfield, IL 62701
Ivonne Sambolin, Director

Health Dept 217.535.3100
Fax 217.535.3104
Web ....www.scdph.org
2833 S Grand Ave E, Springfield, IL 62703
James D. Stone, MA, Director Of Public Health

JUSTICE AGENCY

Juvenile Detention 217.747.8000
Fax 217.747.8018
E-mail ....terrym@co.sangamon.il.us
2201 S Dirksen Pkwy, Springfield, IL 62703
Terrance Moore, Superintendent

Juvenile Probation 217.753.6780
200 S 9th St Ste 308, Springfield, IL 62701
Kerry Moore, Director Of Juvenile Court Services

COURTS

7th Circuit Court Family Div 217.753.6674
Fax 217.753.6665
Web ....www.sangamoncountycircuitclerk.org
200 S 9th St Fl 7, Springfield, IL 62701-1985
Honorable Patrick Kelley, Chief Judge

POLICE AND SHERIFF

Sheriff's Ofc 217.753.6855
Fax 217.753.6387
E-mail ....nw2473@co.sangamon.il.us
1 Sheriffs Plz, Springfield, IL 62701
Neil M. Williamson, Sheriff

Springfield Police Dept 217.788.8401
Fax 217.788.8323
E-mail ....williamsgl@sandwichfd.org
800 E Monroe Ste 345, Springfield, IL 62701
Greg Williams, Juvenile Division Supervisor

EDUCATION SERVICES

Migrant Head Start 217.524.6318
Fax 217.557.8758
Web ....www.dhs.state.il.us
E-mail ....dhsd60b1@dhs.state.il.us
400 W Lawrerence Ave, Springfield, IL 62762-0001
Molly Joseph Parker, Director

Illinois

Special Education 217.786.3250
Fax 217.786.3652
Web ....www.sased.com
E-mail ....charmsslp@yahoo.com
  2500 Taylor Ave, Springfield, IL 62703-4390
Joe Glassford, Executive Director

Student Support Svcs 217.525.3060
Fax 217.525.3124
Web www.springfield.k12.il.us
E-mail ....leubaker@springfield.k12.il.us
  900 W Edwards St, Fl 3, Springfield, IL 62704
Leu Baker, Director

Schuyler County

COURTS

8th Circuit Court 217.322.4633
Fax 217.322.6164
  102 S Congress St, Rushville, IL 62681
Jane Bauer, Chief Performance Officer

POLICE AND SHERIFF

Sheriff's Ofc 217.322.4366
Fax 217.322.6162
Web ....www.casscomm.com
E-mail ....schuylercoso@casscomm.com
  216 W Lafayette St, Rushville, IL 62681-1404
Don L. Schieferdecker, Sheriff

Scott County

POLICE AND SHERIFF

Sheriff's Ofc 217.742.3141
Fax 217.742.5773
E-mail ....scsd@irtc.net
  32 E Market, Winchester, IL 62694
David King Jr., Sheriff

Shelby County

GENERAL HEALTH SERVICES

Health Dept 217.774.9555
Fax 217.774.2355
  1700 W South 3rd St, Shelbyville, IL 62565
Jennifer Beeson, Communicable Disease Coordinator

POLICE AND SHERIFF

Sheriff's Ofc 217.774.3941
Fax 217.774.2851
Web ....www.consolidated.net
E-mail ....sheriff_miller@consolidated.net
  151 N Morgan St, Shelbyville, IL 62565-1674
Micheal A. Miller, Sheriff

St. Clair County

SOCIAL SERVICES

Dept. of Children and Family Svcs Regional Ofcs - Southern Region 618.583.2600
Fax 618.583.2603
  10 Collinsville Ave, East Saint Louis, IL 62201
Valda Haywood, Regional Administrator

GENERAL HEALTH SERVICES

East Side Health District Clinic 618.874.4713
Fax 618.874.4737
Web ....www.eshd.org
E-mail ....rross@eshd.org
  638 N 20th St, East Saint Louis, IL 62205-1812
Rosalyn Ross, AIDS Director

Health Dept 618.233.7703
Fax 618.233.2506
Web ....www.scchd.org
E-mail ....mark.peters@co.st-clair.il.us
  19 Public Sq Ste 150, Belleville, IL 62220-1695
Mark Peters, Hiv Director

JUSTICE AGENCY

CASA 618.234.4278
Fax 618.234.4360
  110 N High St Ste 2, Belleville, IL 62220
Mechiko White, Director

Court Svcs & Probation 618.277.5690
Fax 618.277.1080
Web ....www.co.st-clair.il.us
E-mail ....probation@co.st-clair.il.us
  11 W Lincoln St, Belleville, IL 62220-2017
Michael Bitner, Director

Detention Ctr 618.397.0791
Fax 618.397.4175
  9006 Lebanon Rd, Belleville, IL 62223
Don Schafer, Superintendent

COURTS

20th Circuit 618.277.6832
Fax 618.277.1562
Web ....www.co.st-clair.il.us
  10 Public Sq, County Building, Belleville, IL 62220-1623
Honorable Walter Brendon, Juvenile Judge

POLICE AND SHERIFF

Sheriff's Ofc 618.277.3500
Fax 618.277.4213
E-mail ....sheriff@norcom2000.com
  700 N 5th St, Belleville, IL 62220
Mearl Justus, Sheriff

EDUCATION SERVICES

Belleville Mac Head Start 618.277.4681
Fax 618.277.5768
E-mail ....hmallor@siue.edu
  1404 E Main St, East Saint Louis, IL 62201
Hazel Mallory, Director

Stark County

POLICE AND SHERIFF

Sheriff's Ofc 309.286.2541
Fax 309.286.6091
E-mail ....sheriff@startkco.illinois.gov
  130 W Jefferson St, Toulon, IL 61483
Jimmie L. Dison, Sheriff

Stephenson County

GENERAL HEALTH SERVICES

Health Dept 815.235.8271
Fax 815.232.7160
Web ....www.stephensonhealth.com
E-mail ....
  10 W Linden St, Freeport, IL 61032-3310
Melinda Cox, Assistant Director Of Nursing

COURTS

15th Circuit Court 815.235.8266
Fax 815.233.1576
E-mail ....bkcurran@hotmail.com
  15 N Galena Ave Ste 12, Freeport, IL 61032-4348
Bonnie Curran, Clerk Of Court

POLICE AND SHERIFF

Dakota Police Dept 815.235.8252
Fax 815.235.8294
  204 W Exchange St, Freeport, IL 61032-4109
Rick Wishard, Police Chief

Sheriff's Ofc 815.235.8290
Fax 815.235.8306
Web ....www.co.stephenson.il.us
E-mail ....dasnyders98@yahoo.com
  15 N Galena Ave, Freeport, IL 61032-4348
David Snyders, Sheriff

Tazewell County

GENERAL HEALTH SERVICES

Health Dept 309.925.5511
Fax 309.925.4381
Web ....www.tazewellhealth.org
E-mail ....tazewell@mtco.com
  21306 State Route 9, Tremont, IL 61568-9294
Sarah Fenton, Rn, Nursing Director

POLICE AND SHERIFF

Deep Creek Police Dept 309.447.6456
  30082 Harding Rd, Deer Creek, IL 61733
George Clark, Plant Manager

Sheriff's Ofc 309.477.2249
Fax 309.346.8886
Web ....www.tazewell.com
E-mail ....rhuston@tazewell.com
  101 S Capitol St, Pekin, IL 61554-4108
Robert M. Huston, Sheriff

EDUCATION SERVICES

Special Education 309.347.5164
Fax 309.346.0440
E-mail ....smasear@tmcsea.org
  300 Cedar St Ste 1, Pekin, IL 61554
Sally Masear, Director

Union County

SOCIAL SERVICES

Dept Of Human Svcs 618.833.2118
Fax 618.833.5608
Web ....www.dhs.state.il.us
E-mail ....sheri.mccans@illinois.gov
  1000 N Main St, Anna, IL 62906-1652
Sheri McCans, Administrator

GENERAL HEALTH SERVICES

Southern Seven Health Dept 618.833.8561
Fax 618.833.6393
  400 Public Sq, Jonesboro, IL 62952
Cheryl Manus, Hiv Coordinator

COURTS

1st Circuit Court 618.833.5913
Fax 618.833.5223
  309 W Market St, Rm 101, Jonesboro, IL 62952-1226
Honorable Mark Boie, Judge

POLICE AND SHERIFF

Sheriff's Ofc 618.833.5500
Fax 618.833.4011
E-mail ....ucso091@mail.com
  307 W Market St, Jonesboro, IL 62952-1202
David Livesay, Sheriff

Vermilion County

GENERAL HEALTH SERVICES

Health Dept 217.431.2662
Fax 217.431.7483
Web ....www.vchd.org
E-mail ....vchd@vchd.org
  200 S College St Ste A, Danville, IL 61832
Sherri Shoemaker, Rn, Common Diseases Coordinator

COURTS

5th Circuit Court 217.554.7700
Fax 217.554.7728
Web ....www.vercounty.org
E-mail ....gardner@vercounty.org
  7 N Vermilion St Ste 1, Danville, IL 61832-5806
Denny Gardner, Circuit Clerk

POLICE AND SHERIFF

Alvin Police Dept **217.765.3511**
　205 E Wood, Alvin, IL 61811
　Gene, Mayor

Belgium Police Dept **217.267.4956**
E-mail ....ghibaudy@sbcglobal.net
　22 Orlea St, Westville, IL 61883-1106
　Dale Ghibaudy, Police Chief

Sheriff's Ofc **217.442.4080**
Fax 217.431.3781
E-mail ....pharts114@aol.com
　2 E South St, Danville, IL 61834
　Patrick Hartshorn, Sheriff

EDUCATION SERVICES

Community Action Agency Family
Ctr **217.443.2705**
Fax 217.442.4952
Web ....www.comaction.org
　56 N Vermilion St, Danville, IL 61832-5802

Wabash County

GENERAL HEALTH SERVICES

Health Dept **618.263.3873**
Fax 618.262.4215
Web ....www.wabashhealth.org
E-mail ....cindy@wabashhealth.org
　130 W 7Th St, Mount Carmel, IL 62863-1439
　Cindy Brown, Administrator

COURTS

2nd Circuit Court **618.262.5362**
Fax 618.263.4441
　401 N Market St Rm 103, P O DRAWER 997, Mount
　Carmel, IL 62863-1582
　Honorable Stephen G. Sawyer, Director

POLICE AND SHERIFF

Sheriff's Ofc **618.262.2706**
Fax 618.262.8954
Web ....www.midwest.net
E-mail ....wabashcountysheriff@hotmail.com
　120 E 4th St, Mount Carmel, IL 62863-2111
　Joe Keeling, Sheriff

Warren County

COURTS

9th Circuit Court **309.734.5179**
Fax 309.734.4151
　100 W Broadway Ste 8, Monmouth, IL 61462-1798
　Courtney Cox, Court Services Director

POLICE AND SHERIFF

Sheriff's Ofc **309.734.8505**
Fax 309.734.4946
　121 N A St, Monmouth, IL 61462
　Martin E. Edwards, Sheriff

Washington County

GENERAL HEALTH SERVICES

Health Dept **618.327.3644**
Fax 618.327.4229
E-mail ....wchd189@yahoo.com
　177 S Washington St, Nashville, IL 62263
　Joyce Carson, Rn, Nursing Supervisor

COURTS

20th Circuit Court **618.327.4800**
Fax 618.327.3583
　101 E Saint Louis St Ste 4, Nashville, IL 62263-1100
　Cynthia Barczewski, Clerk Of Court

POLICE AND SHERIFF

City Of Ashley **618.485.2270**
Fax 618.485.2270
　474 W. Main Street, Ashley, IL 62808
　Lenard Piasecki, Mayor

Wayne County

GENERAL HEALTH SERVICES

Health Dept **618.842.5166**
Fax 618.842.3305
　405 N Basin Rd, Fairfield, IL 62837
　Darlene Kennedy, Nursing Director

COURTS

2nd Circuit Court **618.842.7684**
Fax 618.842.2556
Web ....www.waynecountygovil.com
　307 E Main St, Fairfield, IL 62837
　Honorable Joe Harrison, Judge

POLICE AND SHERIFF

Sheriff's Ofc **618.842.6631**
Fax 618.842.4916
E-mail ....ljackson@waynecountysherrifsdepartment.com
　305 E Court St, Fairfield, IL 62837
　Mike Everett, Sheriff

White County

COURTS

2nd Circuit Court **618.382.2321**
Fax 618.382.2322
　301 E Main St Ste A, Carmi, IL 62821
　Ellen I. Pettijon, Clerk Of Court

POLICE AND SHERIFF

Sheriff's Ofc **618.382.5321**
Fax 618.382.5323
Web ....www.whitecounty-il.gov
　108 N Main Cross St, Carmi, IL 62821
　Doug Maier, Sheriff

Whiteside County

GENERAL HEALTH SERVICES

Health Dept **815.626.2230**
Fax 815.626.3847
Web ....www.whitesidehealth.org
　1300 W 2nd St, Rock Falls, IL 61071
　Beth Fiorini, Administrator

Health Dept **815.772.7411**
Fax 815.772.4723
Web ....www.whitesidehelp.org
E-mail ....jsaunders@whitesidehelp.org
　18929 Lincoln Rd, Morrison, IL 61270-9587
　Jone Saunders, Rn, Aids Services, Coordinator Of Infectious Disease

COURTS

14th Circuit Court **815.772.5188**
Fax 815.772.5187
Web ....www.judici.com
E-mail ....jhauptman@whiteside.org
　200 E Knox St, Morrison, IL 61270-2809
　Honorable John L. Hauptman, Judge

POLICE AND SHERIFF

Sheriff's Ofc **815.772.4044**
Fax 815.772.7944
Web ....www.whiteside.org
E-mail ....kwilhelmi@whiteside.org
　400 N Cherry St, Morrison, IL 61270-2605
　Kelly Wilhelmi, Sheriff

Will County

MENTAL HEALTH SERVICES

Mental Health Youth Svcs **815.727.5065**
Fax 815.727.0136
　501 Ella Ave, Joliet, IL 60433
　Dr. Rita Gray, Program Coordinator

JUSTICE AGENCY

CASA **815.730.7072**
Fax 815.730.7073
E-mail ....casa@casaofwillcounty.org
　3200 Mcdonough St, Joliet, IL 60431
　Rita Facchina, Program Director

Illinois Youth Ctr-Joliet **815.725.1206**
Fax 815.725.9819
Web ....www.idoc.state.il.us
　2848 W McDonough St, Joliet, IL 60436-9757
　John Rita, Superintendent

Juvenile Probation **815.730.7120**
Fax 815.730.7150
　3206 McDonough St, Joliet, IL 60431
　Michael E. Costigan, Director Of Court Services

River Valley Detention Facility **815.730.7070**
Fax 815.730.7176
Web ....www.willcountyillinois.com
E-mail ....dwilson@willcountyillinois.com
　3200 Mcdonough St, Joliet, IL 60431-1088
　Douglas Wilson, Assistant Director Of Juvenile Court Services

EDUCATION SERVICES

Aunt Nancy's Child Care Lincoln Way
Hs **815.464.4285**
Web ....www.auntnancys.net
　201 Colorado Ave, Frankfort, IL 60423-1395

Broadway Early Childhood Ctr **815.727.6239**
Fax 815.727.6361
　350 N Broadway St, Joliet, IL 60435
　Keva Gildon, Director

Catholic Charities St John Head
Start **815.722.6303**
E-mail ....CC-DOJ.ORG
　403 N Hickory St Ste A, Joliet, IL 60435
　Glenn Vancura, Executive Director

Joliet Public School **815.740.3196**
Fax 815.740.5955
Web www.joliet86.org
E-mail ....sthomas@joliet86.org
　420 N Raynor Ave, Joliet, IL 60435-6065
　Sandra L. Thomas, Director

Joliet Township High School **815.727.6986**
Fax 815.727.1277
Web ....www.jths.org
E-mail ....ebrass@jths.org
　201 E Jefferson St, Joliet, IL 60432-2841
　Edna Braff, Director

Special Education **815.741.7777**
Fax 815.741.7779
Web ....www.sowic.org
E-mail ....debb@sowic.org
　1207 N Larkin Ave, Joliet, IL 60435-3436
　Deborah Bernardini, Director

Special Education **815.838.8080**
Fax 815.838.8086
E-mail ....rkovacevich2003@yahoo.com
　1343 E 7th St, Lockport, IL 60441-3894
　Roxanne Kovacevich, Executive Director

Special Education/Administrative

Ofc 815.886.7246
Fax 815.886.2339
Web ....www.vvsd.org
E-mail ....thomasjt@365u.will.k12.il.us
   755 Dalhart Ave, Romeoville, IL 60446-1156
David Hehl, Executive Director

Williamson County

GENERAL HEALTH SERVICES

Health Dept 618.993.8111
Fax 618.993.6455
Web ....www.bicountyhealth.org
E-mail ....lsorensen@bicountyhealth.org
   8160 Express Dr, Marion, IL 62959
Lisa Sorensen, Rn, Nursing Director

LDPH Regional Ofc Marion 618.993.7010
Fax 618.993.7052
Web ....www.idph.state.il.us
E-mail ....brenda.barton@illinois.gov
   2309 W Main St Ste 106, Marion, IL 62959-1196
Brenda Barton, Regional Health Officer

JUSTICE AGENCY

CASA 618.997.1301
Fax 618.998.0006
Web ....www.casawilliamsoncounty.com
E-mail ....casawmsn@yahoo.com
   407 N Monroe Main St, Marion, IL 62959
Vicki Sleyko, Program Director

POLICE AND SHERIFF

Creal Police Dept 618.996.2311
Fax 618.996.8430
E-mail ....phil_jerald@agr.state.il.us
   PO Box 417, Creal Springs, IL 62922-0417
Nick Ryder, Police Chief

Freeman Spur Police Dept 618.942.3594
Fax 618.942.7040
E-mail ....villageoffreemanspur@nychoice.net
   19072 FREEMAN SPUR ROAD, Freeman Spur,
   IL 62841
Curt Spaven, President

Sheriff's Ofc 618.997.6541
Fax 618.997.3405
Web ....www.wcsheriff.com
   200 W Jefferson St, Marion, IL 62959-2415
Bennie Vick, Sheriff

Winnebago County

GENERAL HEALTH SERVICES

Dept Of Public Health 815.720.4000
Fax 815.720.4001
Web ....www.wchd.org
E-mail ....tkisner@wchd.org
   401 Division St, Rockford, IL 61104-2096
Todd Kisner, Director Of Life Ctr

MENTAL HEALTH SERVICES

Ctr For Mental Health 815.966.2273
Fax 815.967.5481
Web ....www.swedishamerican.com
   1401 E State St, Swedish American Hospital,
   Rockford, IL 61104-2315
Debra Wagner, Director

JUSTICE AGENCY

CASA 815.319.6880
Fax 815.319.6881
Web ....www.winnebagocountycasa.org
E-mail ....casaoffice@sbcglobal.net
   403 ELM ST STE 107, Rockford, IL 61101-1250
Roseann Cannariato, Program Director

Juvenile Detention Ctr 815.282.6878
Fax 815.282.8161
Web ....www.co.winnebago.il.us
   5350 Northrock Dr, Rockford, IL 61103-1284
Bill Vedra, Assistant Deputy Superintendent

Juvenile Probation 815.516.2700
Fax 815.516.2701
Web ....www.co.winnebago.il.us
E-mail ....dmeyers@wincoil.us
   420 W State St, Rockford, IL 61101
Dennis Meyers, Director Of Court Services

COURTS

17th Circuit Court 815.319.4500
Fax 815.319.4571
Web ....www.co.winnebago.il.us
E-mail ....jholgrem@co.winnebago.il.us
   400 W State St Ste 108, Rockford, IL 61101-1241
Honorable Janet Holgrem, Director

POLICE AND SHERIFF

Sheriff's Ofc 815.319.6000
Fax 815.962.8551
Web ....www.winnebagosheriff.com
E-mail ....rmeyers@sheriff.co.winnebago.il.us
   650 W State St, Rockford, IL 61102-2201
Richard Meyers, Sheriff

EDUCATION SERVICES

Special Education 815.654.4500
Fax 815.654.4570
Web www.harlem122.org
   8605 N 2nd St, Machesney Park, IL 61115
Caroline Pate-hefpy, Director

Woodford County

GENERAL HEALTH SERVICES

Health Dept 309.467.3064
Fax 309.467.5104
Web ....www.woodfordhealth.org
   1831 S Main St, Eureka, IL 61530-1246
Lynda Mckeown, Rn, Infection Control Coordinator

POLICE AND SHERIFF

Sheriff's Ofc 309.467.2375
Fax 309.467.4092
Web ....www.woodford-county.org
E-mail ....jpierceall@woodford-county.org
   111 E Court St, Eureka, IL 61530-1252
Jim Pierceall, Sheriff

SPECIAL SERVICES AGENCIES

ADOPTION AGENCIES

ABC For Adoptions Ltd 847.821.2901
Fax 847.821.2610
Web ....www.abcforadoption.com
E-mail ....abcadpt@sbcglobal.net
   2275 Half Day Rd Ste 350, Deerfield, IL 60015-1277
Julie Hetherington, Director

Adoption Attorneys 773.509.1818
Fax 773.509.1888
   3247 N Elston Ave, Chicago, IL 60618
Sara Howard, Attorney

Adoption Center for Family Building 847.674.3231
Fax 847.674.8635
Web ....www.centerforfamily.com
E-mail ....info@centerforfamily.com
   8707 Skokie Blvd Ste 208, Skokie, IL 60077-2272
Tobi Ehrenpreis, M.a., Mph, Executive Director

Adoption-Link, Inc. 708.524.1433
Fax 708.524.9691
Web ....www.adoption-link.org
E-mail ....margaret.flemming@adoption-link.org
   1113 South Blvd Ste 2, Oak Park, IL 60302-2840
Margaret Flemming, Director

Angel Adoptions 847.462.8874
Fax 847.462.0906
   40 Crystal st, Cary, IL 60013
Sharon Ahmann, Owner

Bethany Christian Svcs 708.385.4889
Fax 708.385.4088
Web ....www.bethany.org
E-mail ....bcschicago@bethany.org
   6600 W College Dr Ste 207, Palos Heights, IL 60463
Rebecca Macdougall, Director

Bethany Christian Svcs 618.281.5959
Fax 314.781.6161
Web ....www.bethany.org
E-mail ....jcameron@bethany.org
   724 W Bottom Ave, Columbia, IL 62236-1817
Jim Cameron, Director Of Human Resources Of Bethany Christian
Services

Camelot Care Centers, Inc.
Fax 630.773.1988
Web ....www.provcorp.com
   450 E. Devon, Suite 285, Itasca, IL 60143
COA accredited organization.

Chicago Child Care Society 773.643.0452
Fax 773.643.0620
Web ....www.cccsociety.org
   5467 South University Avenue, Chicago, IL 60615
COA accredited organization.

Child Link, Inc. 312.377.4735
Fax 312.377.4888
Web ....www.childlnk.org
   1100 W. Cermak #B404, Chicago, IL 60608-4501
COA accredited organization.

Children's Home & Aid Society 815.899.0137
Fax 815.899.0138
   1430 Dekalb Ave, Sycamore, IL 60178
Margo Sutorius, Chief Executive Officer

Crouse Cobb & Bays 618.344.6300
Fax 618.344.3920
Web ....www.adoptionattorneys.org
E-mail ....debcobb@sbcglobal.net
   515 W Main St, Collinsville, IL 62234-3020
Debbie Crouse, Director

Crouse Cobb Bays 217.345.6099
Fax 217.345.6098
Web ....www.adoptionattorneys.org
   1513 University Dr, Charleston, IL 61920-3203
Kirsten Bays, Partner

Decatur Catholic Charities 217.428.3458
Fax 217.428.4415
   247 W Prairie Ave, Decatur, IL 62523-1220
Michael Odonnell, Director

Epstein & Assoc 815.639.0982
Fax 815.639.0985
E-mail ....laura@attorneyepstein.com
　6072 Brynwood Dr Ste 203, Rockford, IL 61114-5829
　Laura Epstein, Attorney

Family Choices NFPC 618.344.6600
Fax 618.344.3920
Web ....www.familychoices.net
　515 W Main St, Collinsville, IL 62234-3020
　Susan Wolk, Licence Coordinator

Family Choices, NFPC 217.345.6066
Fax 217.345.6098
Web ....www.familychoices.net
　515 West Main Street, Collinsville, IL 62234
　COA accredited organization.

Family Svc Ctr 217.528.8406
Fax 217.528.8542
Web www.service2families.com
E-mail ....fsc@service2families.com
　730 E Vine, Springfield, IL 62703
　Josie Rocco, Executive Director

Journeys Of The Heart Adoption Svcs 630.469.4367
Fax 630.469.4382
Web ....www.journeysoftheheart.net
E-mail ....info@journeysoftheheart.net
　516 N Main St Ste C, Glen Ellyn, IL 60137-5175
　Ann Duwaldt, Adoption Program Coordinator

Lifelink International Adoption 630.521.8281
Fax 630.521.8844
Web ....www.lifelinkadoption.org
　329 S York Rd, Bensenville, IL 60106-2673
　Pat Radley, Director Of Adoptions

One Hope United - Administrative Office 312.922.6733
Fax 312.922.6736
Web ....www.onehopeunited.org
　111 E. Wacker Drive, Suite 325, Chicago, IL 60601
　COA accredited organization.

One Hope United - Hudelson Region 217.789.7637
Fax 217.789.0409
Web ....www.onehopeunited.org
　520 East Capitol, Springfield, IL 62701
　COA accredited organization.

One Hope United - Northern Region 847.245.6500
Web ....www.onehopeunited.org
　P.O. Box 1128, Lake Villa, IL 60046
　COA accredited organization.

Our Children's Homestead 630.369.0004
Fax 630.369.0085
Web ....www.ourchildrenshomestead.org
　387 Shuman Boulevard, Suite 335W, Naperville,
　IL 60563-8137
　COA accredited organization.

Sunny Ridge Family Center, Inc. 630.754.4500
Fax 630.754.4501
Web ....www.sunnyridge.org
　270 Remington Boulevard, Suite C, Bolingbrook,
　IL 60440
　COA accredited organization.

ADVOCACY RESOURCES

Amy Schulz Child Advocacy Ctr 618.244.2100
Fax 618.244.9283
Web ....www.mvn.net
E-mail ....amycenter90@hotmail.com
　500 Fairfield Rd, Mount Vernon, IL 62864-5047
　Ladonna Richards, Director

**Carrie Lynn Children's Ctr/ Children's Advocacy
Project** 815.319.4150
Fax 815.319.4151
Web ....www.carrie-lynn.org
E-mail ....ltomasino@carrie-lynn.org
　826 N Main St, Rockford, IL 61103-6906
　Kathy Pomahac, Director

CASA 217.348.0599
Fax 217.348.7369
E-mail ....edcccasa@co.coles.il.us
　Court House Rm 13, Charleston, IL 61920
　Mamie Richey, Executive Director

**CASA-Children's Advocacy Ctr & Child Protection
Network** 309.888.5656
Fax 309.888.4969
　200 W Front St Ste 500B, Bloomington, IL 61701
　Judy Brucker, Director

Chicago Children's Advocacy Ctr 312.492.3700
Fax 312.492.3760
Web ....www.chicagocac.org
　1240 S Damen Ave, Chicago, IL 60608
　Char Rivett, Executive Director

Child Advocacy Ctr 618.942.3800
Fax 618.942.6941
E-mail ....advocate@wcocac.org
　501 S 14th St, Herrin, IL 62948
　Alyssa Norman, Executive Director

Child Advocacy Ctr 630.208.5160
Fax 630.208.5159
Web ....www.co.kane.il.us
E-mail ....chasseelori@co.kane.il.us
　427 Campbell St, Geneva, IL 60134-2632
　Lori Chassee, Director

Child Advocacy Ctr 815.774.4565
Fax 815.774.4569
Web ....www.willcountychildadvocacy.com
E-mail ....sbloch@willcountyillinois.com
　57 N Ottawa St Ste 506, Joliet, IL 60432-4420
　Sue Bloch, Executive Director

Child Advocacy Ctr 847.885.0100
Fax 847.885.0187
Web ....www.cachelps.org
E-mail ....mparrcac@sbcglobal.net
　640 Illinois Blvd, Hoffman Estates, IL 60169-3325
　Mark Parr, Executive Director

Child Advocacy Ctr 217.422.6294
Fax 217.422.6590
Web ....www.mccac.org
E-mail ....mccac4kids@aol.com
　164 N Edward St, Decatur, IL 62522-2404
　Jean Moore, Executive Director

Children's Advocacy Ctr 815.936.7372
Fax 815.936.9829
　401 N Wall St Ste LL07, Kankakee, IL 60901
　Kristen Jackson, Director

Children's Advocacy Ctr 309.937.5663
Fax 309.937.5665
E-mail ....henrycountycac@hotmail.com
　414 E Center St, Cambridge, IL 61238-1208
　Sally Adams, Coordinator

Children's Advocacy Ctr 309.347.6001
Fax 309.347.6189
Web ....www.tazewell.com
E-mail ....tazewellcac@grics.net
　341 Buena Vista Ave, Pekin, IL 61554-4227
　Barb Strand, Executive Director

Children's Advocacy Ctrs Of Il 217.528.2224
Fax 217.528.3834
Web ....www.cacionline.org
　1131 S 2nd St, Springfield, IL 62704
　Billie Larkin, Executive Director

Children's Ctr 630.407.2750
Fax 630.407.2751
Web ....www.dupageco.org
E-mail ....patrick.dempsey@dupageco.org
　130 N County Farm Rd, Wheaton, IL 60187-3905
　Patrick Dempsey, Director

Children's Legal Rights Journal 708.421.0823
E-mail ....aurelija.juska@gmail.com
　25 E Pearson St, Chicago, IL 60611
　Aurelija Juska

Children's Legal Rights Journal 505.239.1371
E-mail ....mkern18@gmail.com
　2022 N Bissell St Apt 1, Chicago, IL 60614
　Mia Kern

Office of the Public Guardian 312.433.4300
E-mail ....rfharri@cookcounty.com
　2245 W Ogden Ave, Chicago, IL 60612
　Robert Harris, Public Guardian

The Child Advocacy Ctr 217.522.2241
Fax 217.522.2360
　1001 E Monroe St, Springfield, IL 62703
　Joe Goulet, Director

BEHAVIORAL HEALTH TREATMENT

Abraham Lincoln Centre 773.373.6600
Fax 773.373.6612
Web ....www.abelink.org
　3858 South Cottage Grove Avenue, Chicago,
　IL 60653
　CARF accredited programs available.

Adventist Hinsdale Hospital 630.856.6001
Web ....keepingyouwell.com
E-mail ....diane.cesarone@ahss.org
　120 North Oak Street, Hinsdale, IL 60521
　Ms. Diane Cesarone, Accreditation Manager
　Joint Commission accredited organization.

Advocate Christ Medical Center 708.684.8000
Web ....www.advocatehealth.com
E-mail ....colleen.perez@advocatehealth.com
　4440 West 95th Street, Oak Lawn, IL 60453
　Ms. Colleen Perez, Accreditation Manager
　Joint Commission accredited organization.

Advocate Illinois Masonic Medical Center 773.975.1600
Web ....www.advocatehealth.com
E-mail ....patricia.aiello@advocatehealth.com
　836 West Wellington Avenue, Chicago, IL 60657
　Ms. Patricia Aiello, Accreditation Manager
　Joint Commission accredited organization.

Advocate Lutheran General Hospital 847.723.2210
Web ....advocatehealth.com
E-mail ....pamela.hyziak@advocatehealth.com
　1775 Dempster Street, Park Ridge, IL 60068
　Ms. Pamela Hyziak, Accreditation Manager
　Joint Commission accredited organization.

**Alexian Brothers Behavioral Health
Hospital** 847.882.1600
Web ....www.abbhh.org
E-mail ....tara.engstrom@abbhh.net
　1650 Moon Lake Boulevard, Hoffman Estates,
　IL 60169
　Mrs. Tara Engstrom, Accreditation Manager
　Joint Commission accredited organization.

Alexian Brothers Center for Mental Health 847.952.7460
Web ....www.alexiancenter.org
E-mail ....michelle.may@alexian.net
　3350 Salt Creek Lane, #114, Arlington Heights,
　IL 60005
　Ms. Michelle May, Accreditation Manager
　Joint Commission accredited organization.

**Alexian Brothers Northwest Mental Health
Ctr** 866.253.9426
Fax 847.483.7040
Web ....www.alexian.org
E-mail ....freym@alexian.net
　3040 W Salt Creek Ln, Arlington Heights,
　IL 60005-1069
　Mark Frey, CEO

Allendale Association 847.356.2351
Web Allendale4kids.org
E-mail ....cborucki@allendale4kids.org
　Grand Avenue and Offield Drive, Lake Villa, IL 60046
　Mrs. Connie Borucki, Accreditation Manager
　Joint Commission accredited organization.

Alternative Behavior Treatment Centers 847.487.9455
Fax 847.487.9360
Web ....www.abtc-centers.org
27255 N. Fairfield Road, Mundelein, IL 60060
COA accredited organization.

Apollo School 847.827.6231
Fax 847.827.1785
E-mail ....lhall@emsd63.org
10100 Dee Rd, Des Plaines, IL 60016
Leslie Hall, Principal

Ashley Medical Practice 312.938.8774
151 N Michigan Ave, Chicago, IL 60601
Camilla Ashley, Psychiatrist

Asian Human Services, Inc. 773.293.8430
Fax 773.728.4751
Web ....www.ahschicago.org
4753 N Broadway St, Ste 700, Chicago, IL 60640
Abha Pandya, Director
CARF accredited programs available.

Aunt Martha's Youth Service Center, Inc. 708.747.7100
Web ....www.auntmarthas.org
E-mail ....ergonzalez@auntmarthas.org
19990 Governors Highway, Olympia Fields, IL 60461
Mr. Ernie Gonzalez, Accreditation Manager
Joint Commission accredited organization.

Aurora Chicago Lakeshore Hospital 773.878.9700
Web ....www.chicagolakeshorehospital.com
E-mail ....cwhiteside@chicagolakeshorehospital.com
4840 North Marine Drive, Chicago, IL 60640
Ms. Charlotte Whiteside, Accreditation Manager
Joint Commission accredited organization.

Baber Medical Practice 630.859.0120
Fax 630.355.7679
1460 Bond St, Aurora, IL 60505
Riaz Baber, Md, Psychiatrist

Baron Medical Practice 847.432.7007
Fax 847.432.7034
E-mail ....drjeep7@aol.com
2120 Sheridan Rd, Highland Park, IL 60035-2404
Ronald Baron, Md, Psychiatrist

Beacon Therapeutic Diagnostic and Treatment Center 773.298.1243
Web ....www.beacon-therapeutic.org
E-mail ....cthompson@beacon-therapeutic.org
1912 West 103rd Street, Chicago, IL 60643
Ms. Cheryl Thompson, Accreditation Manager
Joint Commission accredited organization.

Beacon Therapeutic Diagnostic And Treatment Ctr 773.298.1243
Fax 773.298.1078
Web ....www.beacon-therapeutic.org
E-mail ....sreyna@beacon-therapeutic.org
1912 W 103rd St, Chicago, IL 60643-2625
Susan Reyna-Guerrero, LCSW, President/CEO

Beacon Theraputic Diagnostic Treatment 773.881.1005
Fax 773.881.1164
106 S Longwood Drive, Chicago, IL 60643
Mary Apichong, Director

Becker House Group Home 847.244.9343
Fax 847.244.9540
448 N Genesee St, Waukegan, IL 60085-4006
Mary Allan Sebasion, Director

Behavioral Health Services 847.377.8299
Web ....www.lakecountyil.gov/Health/BHS.htm
E-mail ....jlaureano@lakecountyil.gov
3010 Grand Avenue, Waukegan, IL 60085
Ms. Jeri Laureano, Accreditation Manager
Joint Commission accredited organization.

Ben Gordon Center 815.756.4875
Web ....www.bengordoncenter.org
E-mail ....bgcbs@bengordoncenter.org
12 Health Services Drive, Dekalb, IL 60115
Ms. Barbara Stagner, Accreditation Manager
Joint Commission accredited organization.

Bethany for Children & Families 309.797.7700
Fax 309.797.2386
Web ....www.bethany-qc.org
P.O. Box 697, Moline, IL 61266-0697
COA accredited organization.

Bloomington High School 309.828.5201
Fax 309.829.0178
1202 E Locust St, Bloomington, IL 61701
Donna Falch, Secretary

Bornstein Medical Practice 847.433.2290
1770 1st St Ste 330, Highland Park, IL 60035-3236
Myron Bornstein, Psychiatrist

Bowers Medical Practice 309.685.7245
4719 N Sheridan Rd, Peoria, IL 61614-5925
Christine Bowers, MD, Psychiatrist

Bridgeway, Inc. 309.837.4876
Fax 309.833.1531
Web ....www.bway.org
900 South Deer Road, Macomb, IL 61455
CARF accredited programs available.

Brown And Associates 630.455.4655
Fax 708.784.1290
E-mail ....brownlcpc@yahoo.com
102 S Washington St Ste B, Hinsdale, IL 60521-4059
Paula Brown, Director

Busch Medical Practice 312.236.2989
Fax 910.396.1845
30 N Michigan Ave Ste 1916, Chicago, IL 60602-3621
Kenneth Busch, Psychiatrist

C4 North 773.365.3000
Fax 773.365.3091
Web www.c4chicago.org
E-mail ....chris.carroll@c4chicago.org
2542 W North Ave, Chicago, IL 60647-5216
Chris Carroll, Director

Catholic Charities 312.602.1468
Web ....www.catholiccharities.net
E-mail ....asamudra@catholiccharities.net
1100 S May St, Chicago, IL 60607-4229
Ajit Samudra, Therapist

Catholic Charities 217.443.1772
Fax 217.443.1701
Web ....www.ccdop.org
E-mail ....tfox@ccdop.org
102 Robinson St, Danville, IL 61832-8515
Trish Fox, Executive Director

Catholic Children's Home, Inc. 618.465.3594
Fax 618.465.4023
Web ....www.catholicchildrenshome.com
1400 State Street, Alton, IL 62002
COA accredited organization.

Center for Human Services, Inc. 309.827.5351
Fax 309.829.6808
108 West Market, Bloomington, IL 61701
CARF accredited programs available.

Center on Deafness 847.559.0110
Web ....Centerondeafness.org
E-mail ....dgomezcod@aol.com
3444 Dundee Road, Northbrook, IL 60062
Ms. Donna Gomez, Accreditation Manager
Joint Commission accredited organization.

Central DuPage Hospital 630.933.1600
Web ....cdh.org
E-mail ....laurel_peterson@cdh.org
25 North Winfield Road, Winfield, IL 60190
Ms. Laurel Peterson, Accreditation Manager
Joint Commission accredited organization.

Central East Alcoholism and Drug Council 217.348.8108
Fax 217.345.6794
Web ....www.ceadcouncil.org
635 Division Street, Charleston, IL 61920
CARF accredited programs available.

Chestnut Health Systems 309.827.6026
Web ....chestnut.org
E-mail ....tlynch@chestnut.org
1003 Martin Luther King Drive, Bloomington, IL 61701
Ms. Victoria Lynch Dahmm, Accreditation Manager
Joint Commission accredited organization.

Chicago Department of Public Health 312.747.9768
Fax 312.747.8836
Web ....cityofchicago.org/health
333 South State Street, Second Floor, Chicago, IL 60604
Micheal Crulich, Director. Professional Services
CARF accredited programs available.

Chicago Lutheran Social Svcs Of Illinois 773.282.7800
Fax 773.282.2163
Web ....www.lssi.org
E-mail ....rboekenhauer@circlefamilycare.org
4840 W Byron St, Chicago, IL 60641-2778
Roger Boekenhauer, Executive Director

Children's Home + Aid 312.424.0200
Fax 312.424.0056
Web ....www.childrenshomeandaid.org
125 S. Wacker Drive, 14th Fl., Chicago, IL 60606
COA accredited organization.

Children's Home Aid Society of IL 312.455.5200
Fax 312.455.5560
Web ....www.chasi.org
E-mail ....abarclay@childrenshomeandaid.org
100 N Western Ave, Chicago, IL 60612-4527
Ann Barclay, Vice President

Circle Family HealthCare Network 773.379.1000
Fax 773.379.1342
Web ....www.cfhcn.org
5002 W. Madison Street, Chicago, IL 60644-4127
COA accredited organization.

Clyde L Choate Mental Health And Developmental Ctr 618.833.5161
Fax 618.833.4191
1000 N Main St, Anna, IL 62906
Cheryl Muckley, Facility Director

Community Counseling 217.245.6126
Fax 217.245.4296
Web ....www.dhs.state.il.us
340 W State St, Jacksonville, IL 62650-2061
Robert Heap, Executive Director

Community Counseling Center 618.462.2331
Fax 618.462.2504
Web ....www.cccnmc.org
2615 Edwards Street, Alton, IL 62002
CARF accredited programs available.

Community Counseling Centers of Chicago 773.765.0810
Web www.c4chicago.org
E-mail ....dennis.peterson@c4chicago.org
4740 North Clark Street, Chicago, IL 60640
Mr. Dennis Peterson, Accreditation Manager
Joint Commission accredited organization.

Community Counseling Ctr Of Fox Valley, Inc **630.966.7400**
Fax 630.897.7539
Web ....www.gatewayfoundation.org
E-mail ....tlgriffi@gatewayfoundation.org
400 Mercy Ln, Aurora, IL 60506-2499
Tracey Griffin-colander, Executive Director

Community Mental Health Council, Inc. **773.734.4033**
Fax 773.734.6447
Web ....www.thecouncil-online.org
8704 South Constance Avenue, Chicago, IL 60617
CARF accredited programs available.

Community Resource and Counseling Center, Inc. **217.379.4302**
Fax 217.379.4304
Web www.4crcc.org
1510 West Ottawa Road, Paxton, IL 60957
CARF accredited programs available.

Community Resource Center **618.533.1391**
Fax 618.533.0012
101 South Locust, Centralia, IL 62801
CARF accredited programs available.

Comprehensive Behavorial Health Center **618.482.7330**
Web cmhc1.org
E-mail ....mjackson@cbhc1.org
505 North 8th Street, East Saint Louis, IL 62207
Mrs. Mary Jackson, Accreditation Manager
Joint Commission accredited organization.

Cornell Interventions-South Wood **773.737.4600**
Fax 773.737.5790
Web ....www.geogroup.com
E-mail ....wcarlson@cornellcompanies.org
5701 S Wood St, Chicago, IL 60636-1646
Walter Carlson, Director

Cornerstone: Foundation For Families **217.222.8254**
Fax 217.222.4512
Web ....www.cornerstone-quincy.org
E-mail ....jwhirner@cornerstone-quincy.org
915 Vermont St, Quincy, IL 62301-3049
John W. Hirner, Msw, Executive Director

Costa Medical Practice **847.236.0901**
420 Lake Cook Rd Ste 118, Deerfield, IL 60015-4914
Petronilo Costa, Psychiatrist

Counseling Center **618.498.9587**
Fax 618.498.6257
Web ....www.medicineshoppe.net
220 East County Road, Jerseyville, IL 62052
CARF accredited programs available.

Counseling Center **217.728.4358**
Fax 217.728.2270
Web ....www.one-eleven.net
E-mail ....mococounccttr@one-eleven.net
12 West Harrison, Sullivan, IL 61951
David Cole, Director
CARF accredited programs available.

Counseling Center of Lake View **773.549.5886**
Web ....................................WWW.CCLAKEVIEW.ORG
E-mail ....hwilliams@cclakeview.org
3225 North Sheffield Avenue, Chicago, IL 60657
Ms. Halley Williams, Accreditation Manager
Joint Commission accredited organization.

Counseling Center, Inc. **618.542.4357**
Fax 618.542.3442
Web ....www.sibs-pccc.com
1016 Madison Street, Suite A, DuQuoin, IL 62832
CARF accredited programs available.

Counseling Services, Inc. **618.833.8551**
Fax 618.833.2911
Web ....www.uccounselingservice.org
204 South Street, Anna, IL 62906
CARF accredited programs available.

Crawford Medical Practice **847.869.3108**
2418 Lincoln St, Evanston, IL 60201-2151
James Crawford, MD, Psychiatrist

Crawford Memorial Hospital **618.544.3131**
Fax 618.546.2619
Web ....www.crawfordmh.org
1000 N Allen St, Robinson, IL 62454
Sandy Burtron, Chief Nursing Officer

Ctr For Positive Change **847.522.7521**
Web ....www.poschange.com
E-mail ....ahoffman@poschange.com
100 S Atkinson Rd Ste 203, Grayslake, IL 60030-7819
Andrew Hoffman, Director

Ctr For Psychiatrist Help **217.245.7275**
Fax 217.245.7427
1515 W Walnut, Jacksonville, IL 62650
Pam B, Office Manager

Ctr On Deafness **847.559.0110**
Fax 847.559.8199
Web ....www.centerondeafness.org
3444 Dundee Rd, Northbrook, IL 60062-2258
Dr. Bonita Simon, Executive Director

Cumberland Associates, Inc. **217.849.3803**
Fax 217.849.3804
120 Courthouse Square, Toledo, IL 62468
CARF accredited programs available.

Cunningham Children's Home of Urbana, IL, Inc. **217.367.3728**
Fax 217.367.2896
Web ....www.cunninghamhome.org
1301 N. Cunningham Avenue, Urbana, IL 61802
COA accredited organization.

Daniel J. Nellum Youth Services, Inc. **773.927.9277**
Fax 773.927.1588
Web ....www.djnellum.org
1458 West 51st Street, Chicago, IL 60609
COA accredited organization.

Delta Center, Inc. **618.734.2665**
Fax 618.734.2665
Web ....www.deltacenter.org
1400 Commercial Avenue, Cairo, IL 62914
CARF accredited programs available.

DePaul Family and Community Services **773.325.7780**
Fax 773.325.7781
2219 North Kenmore, Suite 300, Chicago, IL 60614
CARF accredited programs available.

Dinner Medical Practice **847.432.1334**
350 Sheridan Rd, Highland Park, IL 60035-5352
Arnold Dinner, Psychiatrist

Dresner Medical Ctr **312.337.6888**
150 E Huron St, Ste 1100, Chicago, IL 60611-2948
Bruce Desner, Psychiatrist

Du Bois Medical Practice **815.490.5720**
6066 Strathmoor Dr, Rockford, IL 61107
Carol Du Bois, Psychiatrist

DuPage Interventions **630.325.5050**
Web ....www.abraxasyfs.com
E-mail ....bgregoriev@abraxasyfs.com
11 S 250 Route 83, Hinsdale, IL 60521
Mr. Boris Gregoriev, Accreditation Manager
Joint Commission accredited organization.

Ecker Center for Mental Health **847.695.0484**
Web ....eckercenter.org
E-mail ....rvanderforest@eckercenter.org
1845 Grandstand Place, Elgin, IL 60123
Mr. Rick Vander Forest, Accreditation Manager
Joint Commission accredited organization.

Ecker Ctr For Mental Health Psychiatric Emergency Program **847.888.2211**
Fax 847.695.1265
Web ....www.eckercenter.org
1845 GrandSand Pl, Elgin, IL 60123
Ramona Grosenes, Human Resource

Edelstein Medical Practice **312.332.3699**
Fax 312.332.3698
E-mail ....dredelstein@ameritech.net
30 N Michigan Ave Ste 501, Chicago, IL 60602-3833
David Edelstein, Psychiatrist

Elisabeth Ludeman Center **708.283.3001**
Fax 708.283.3316
114 North Orchard Drive, Park Forest, IL 60466-1297
CARF accredited programs available.

Elmhurst Memorial Hospital **331.221.1000**
Web ....www.emhc.org
E-mail ....cparker@emhc.org
155 East Brush Hill Road, Elmhurst, IL 60126
Dr. Connie Parker, Accreditation Manager
Joint Commission accredited organization.

Exam-Md Clinic **217.442.4055**
601 N Logan Ave, Danville, IL 61832-4320
Surinderpal Kahlon, Md, Psychiatrist

Family Counseling Center, Inc. **618.683.2461**
Fax 618.683.2066
Web ....www.fccinconline.org
125 North Market Street, Golconda, IL 62938
CARF accredited programs available.

Family Counseling Service of Aurora **630.844.2662**
Fax 630.844.3084
Web ....www.aurorafcs.org
70 South River Street, Aurora, IL 60506
COA accredited organization.

Family Guidance Centers at Triangle Center **217.544.9858**
Web ....www.trianglecenter.org
E-mail ....bnottage@fgcinc.org
120 North 11th Street, Springfield, IL 62703-1002
Mr. Brian Nottage, Accreditation Manager
Joint Commission accredited organization.

Family Service and Community Mental Health Center/McHenry **815.385.6400**
Web ....www.familyservicemch.com
E-mail ....lnelson@familyservicemch.org
4100 Veterans Parkway, McHenry, IL 60050
Ms. Lori Nelson, Accreditation Manager
Joint Commission accredited organization.

Family Service and Mental Health Center of Cicero **708.656.6430**
Fax 708.656.6591
Web ....www.cicerofamilyservice.org
E-mail ....jmorgan@cicerofs.org
5341 West Cermak Road, Cicero, IL 60804
John Morgan, Executive Director
CARF accredited programs available.

Fayco Enterprises, Inc. **618.283.0638**
Fax 618.283.3892
Web ....www.fayco.org
1313 Sunset Dr, Vandalia, IL 62471
C. Robert Lindberg, Director

Fayen Medical Practice **312.222.0015**
405 N Wabash Ave, Chicago, IL 60611-3548
Maureen Fayen, Psychiatrist

FHN Family Counseling Center **815.599.7337**
Web ....www.fhn.org
E-mail ....gkoeller@fhn.org
421 W. Exchange St., Freeport, IL 61032
Mrs. Glenda Koeller, Accreditation Manager
Joint Commission accredited organization.

Fox Medical Practice **312.856.0170**
474 Highcrest Dr, Wilmette, IL 60091-2358
Charles Fox, Md, Psychiatrist

Freed Medical Practice 773.525.1276
Fax 773.525.1892
E-mail ....harveyfreed@sbcglobal.net
840 W Chalmers Pl, Chicago, IL 60614-3223
Harvey Freed, MD, Psychiatrist

Freidman Medical Practice 630.510.3966
417 W Roosevelt Rd, Ste 10, Wheaton, IL 60187
Marla Friedman, Md, Psychiatrist

Gateway Foundation, Inc. 312.663.1130
Web ....www.gatewayfoundation.org
E-mail ....nxgantes@gatewayfoundation.org
55 East Jackson Blvd, Suite 1500, Chicago, IL 60604
Mr. Nick Gantes, Accreditation Manager
Joint Commission accredited organization.

Gateway Regional Medical Ctr 618.798.3900
Fax 618.798.3724
Web ....www.gatewayregional.net
2100 Madison Ave, Granite City, IL 62040-4701
Cheryl Patton, Executive Assistant

Grand Prairie Services 708.444.1012
Fax 708.614.7831
Web ....www.gpsbh.org
E-mail ....tmoore@gpsbh.org
17746 South Oak Park Avenue, Tinley Park, IL 60477
Timothy Moore, Associate Clinical Director
CARF accredited programs available.

Great River Recovery Resources, Inc 217.224.6300
Fax 217.224.4329
Web ....www.recoveryres.org
428 S 36th St, Quincy, IL 62301-5978
Ron Howell, Executive Director

Hartgrove Hospital 773.413.1700
Fax 773.413.1805
Web ....www.hartgrovehospital.com
5730 W Roosevelt Rd, Chicago, IL 60644
Carol Kilgallon, Director Of Business Development

Hartgrove Hospital 773.413.1700
E-mail ....tyler.bauer@uhsinc.com
5730 W. Roosevelt. Road, Chicago, IL 60644
Mr. Tyler Bauer, Accreditation Manager
Joint Commission accredited organization.

Healthcare Alternative Systems, Inc. 773.252.3100
Fax 773.252.8945
Web ....www.hascares.org
2755 West Armitage Avenue, Chicago, IL 60647
CARF accredited programs available.

Heartland Health Outreach 312.660.1432
Fax 312.660.1500
Web ....www.heartlandalliance.org
4750 North Sherdian, Chicago, IL 60640
CARF accredited programs available.

Heartland Human Care Services, Inc. 312.660.1300
Fax 312.660.1500
Web ....www.heartlandalliance.org
208 South LaSalle, Suite 1818, Chicago, IL 60604
CARF accredited programs available.

Heartland Human Services 217.347.7179
Web ....www.heartlandhs.org
E-mail ....jbloemker@heartlandhs.org
1200 North Fourth Street, Effingham, IL 62401
Mr. Jeff Bloemker, Accreditation Manager
Joint Commission accredited organization.

Heritage Behavioral Health Center 217.362.6262
Fax 217.362.6290
Web ....www.heritagenet.org
E-mail ....dknaebe@heritagenet.org
151 North Main Street, Decatur, IL 62523
Diana Knaebe, CEO
CARF accredited programs available.

Human Resource Center 217.935.9496
Fax 217.935.4508
1150 Route 54 West, Clinton, IL 61727
CARF accredited programs available.

Human Resources Center of Edgar and Clark Counties 217.465.4118
Fax 217.463.1899
Web ....www.hrcec.org
E-mail ....nelson@hrcec.org
118 East Court Street, Paris, IL 61944
Starr Nelson, Director of Operations
CARF accredited programs available.

Human Resources Development Institute, Inc. 312.441.9009
Fax 312.441.9019
Web ....www.hrdi.org
222 South Jefferson, Chicago, IL 60661
CARF accredited programs available.

Human Service Center 309.671.8005
Web ....www.fayettecompanies.org
E-mail ....pwhite@fayettecompanies.org
600 Fayette Street, Peoria, IL 61603
Ms. Pamela White, Accreditation Manager
Joint Commission accredited organization.

Human Service Center of Southern Metro-East 618.282.6233
Fax 618.282.6220
10257 State Route 3, Red Bud, IL 62278
COA accredited organization.

Human Support Services 618.939.4444
Fax 618.939.4181
Web www.hss1.org
P.O. Box 146, Waterloo, IL 62298-0146
COA accredited organization.

Infant Welfare Society of Chicago 773.782.2800
Fax 773.782.5061
Web ....www.infantwelfare.homestead.com
E-mail ....banmanl@infantwelfare.org
3600 West Fullerton Avenue, Chicago, IL 60647
Lindsay Banman, Director of Healthy Steps for Young Children
CARF accredited programs available.

Institute for Human Resources 815.844.6109
Fax 815.844.3561
Web ....www.ihrpontiac.com
310 East Torrance Avenue, Pontiac, IL 61764
Jenny Larkin, Business Manager
CARF accredited programs available.

Iroquois Mental Health Center 815.432.5241
Fax 815.432.4537
323 West Mulberry Street, Watseka, IL 60970
CARF accredited programs available.

Janet Wattles Center, Inc. 815.968.9300
Web ....www.janetwattles.org
E-mail ....scapone@janetwattles.org
526 West State Street, Rockford, IL 61101
Ms. Sang Capone, Accreditation Manager
Joint Commission accredited organization.

Janet Wattles Ctr 815.544.4849
Fax 815.544.2116
E-mail ....jlodge@janetwattles.org
475 Southtowne Dr, Belvidere, IL 61008-5643
Joan Lodge, Director

Janet Wattles Ctr 815.968.9300
Fax 815.968.5314
E-mail ....fware@janetwattles.org
526 W State, Rockford, IL 61101-1214
Mary-Ann Abobe, Director

Jewish Child and Family Services 312.357.4800
Fax 312.855.3754
Web ....www.jcfs.org
216 West Jackson, Suites 700-800, Chicago, IL 60606-4609
COA accredited organization.

Kenneth Young Center 847.524.8800
Web ....www.kennethyoung.org
E-mail ....joer@kennethyoung.org
1001 Rohlwing Road, Elk Grove Village, IL 60007
Mr. Joe Ruh, Accreditation Manager
Joint Commission accredited organization.

Lagrange Memorial Hospital 708.245.9000
Fax 708.245.5646
Web ....www.keepingyouwell.com
E-mail ....judy.papendrof@ahss.org
5101 Willow Springs Rd, La Grange, IL 60525-2600
Judy Papendrof, Infection Control Coordinator

Larabida Children's Hospital And Research Ctr 773.363.6700
Fax 773.363.7160
Web ....www.larabida.org
E-mail ....pjaudes@larabida.org
East 65th St At Lake Michigan, Chicago, IL 60649
Paula Jaudes, Director/CEO

Leyden Family Service and Mental Health Center 847.451.0330
Web ....www.leydenfamilyservice.org
E-mail ....leyden1001@aol.com
10001 West Grand Avenue, Franklin Park, IL 60131
Ms. Donna Santoro, Accreditation Manager
Joint Commission accredited organization.

Loyola University Behavioral Health Ctr/ Ronald Mcdonald Hospital 708.216.3750
Fax 708.216.6840
Web ....www.loyolamedicine.org
2160 S 1st Ave, Rm 222, Maywood, IL 60153
Thomas Nutter, Md, Medical Director

Lutheran Child And Family Svcs Of Illinois 618.242.2238
Fax 618.242.2279
Web ....www.lcfs.org
E-mail ....gene_svabakken@lcfs.org
17077 N. Illinois, Hwy 37, Mount Vernon, IL 62864
Gene Svabakken, CEO

Maine Center, Inc. 847.696.1570
Fax 847.696.1587
Web ....www.maine-center.org
819 Busse Highway, Park Ridge, IL 60068
CARF accredited programs available.

Maryville Academy 847.294.1999
Fax 847.824.7190
1150 N River Rd, Des Plaines, IL 60016-1290
Sister Catherine M. Ryan, Executive Director

Maryville Academy Scott Nolan Center 847.768.5430
Web ....www.maryvilleacademy.org
E-mail ....borderse@maryvilleacademy.org
555 Wilson Lane, Des Plaines, IL 60016
Mrs. Erin Borders, Accreditation Manager
Joint Commission accredited organization.

McDermott Center dba Haymarket Center 312.226.7984
Fax 312.226.8048
Web ....www.hcenter.org
932 West Washington Boulevard, Chicago, IL 60607-2202
CARF accredited programs available.

Meier Clinics of Illinois, P.C. 630.653.1717
Fax 630.653.9691
Web ....www.meierclinics.org
E-mail ....nancybrown@meierclinics.org
2100 Manchester Road, Suite 1510, Wheaton, IL 60187-4561
Nancy Brown, Medical Director
CARF accredited programs available.

Mental Health and Deafness Resources, Inc. 847.509.8260
Web ....www.mentalhealthanddeafness.org
E-mail ....gfisher@mentalhealthanddeafness.org
614 Anthony Trail, Northbrook, IL 60062
Ms. Gail Fisher, Accreditation Manager
Joint Commission accredited organization.

Illinois

Mental Health and Family Counseling Association, Inc. **217.253.4731**
Fax 217.253.4733
114 W Houghton St, Tuscola, IL 61953
Carol Davis, Director
CARF accredited programs available.

Mental Health Assoc Of IL Valley **309.692.1766**
Fax 309.692.2966
Web ....www.mhaiv.org
E-mail ....lcheek@mhaiv.org
5407 N University St, Peoria, IL 61614-4736
Lori Cheek, Executive Director

Mental Health Association **217.824.9675**
Fax 217.824.3070
Web ....www.ccmha.net
707 McAdam Drive, Taylorville, IL 62568
CARF accredited programs available.

Mental Health Association **217.323.2980**
Fax 217.323.3731
121 East Second Street, Beardstown, IL 62618
CARF accredited programs available.

Mental Health Association, Inc. **217.238.5700**
Web ....www.lifelinksinc.org
E-mail ....dcook@lifelinksinc.org
750 Broadway Avenue East, Mattoon, IL 61938
Mrs. Debra Cook, Accreditation Manager
Joint Commission accredited organization.

Mental Health Board **815.455.2828**
Fax 815.455.2925
Web www.mc708.org
620 Dakota Street, Crystal Lake, IL 60012
sandy lewis, executive director
CARF accredited programs available.

Mental Health Center **217.373.2420**
Fax 217.398.8568
Web ....www.mhcenter.org
1801 Fox Drive, Champaign, IL 61820
shila ferguson, ceo
CARF accredited programs available.

Mental Health Center **217.762.5371**
Fax 217.762.4066
Web ....www.pcmh-thecenter.com
1921 North Market Street, Monticello, IL 61856-8144
CARF accredited programs available.

Mental Health Centers of Central Illinois **217.525.1064**
Fax 217.525.1651
Web ....www.mhcci.org
710 North Eighth Street, Springfield, IL 62702
CARF accredited programs available.

Mental Health Centers of Western Illinois **217.773.3325**
Fax 217.773.2425
Web ....www.mhcwi.org
E-mail ....roliver@mhcwi.org
700 Southeast Cross Street, Mount Sterling, IL 62353
Roxie Oliver, Executive Director
CARF accredited programs available.

Mental Health Ctr **217.373.2430**
Fax 217.373.2444
Web ....www.mhcenter.org
202 W Park Ave, Champaign, IL 61820-3968
Kay Gingretch, Director

Mental Health Services **630.682.7400**
Web ....www.dupagehealth.org
E-mail ....mharring@dupagehealth.org
111 North County Farm Road, Wheaton, IL 60187
Mr. Michael Harrington, Accreditation Manager
Joint Commission accredited organization.

Metropolitan Family Svcs Southwest **708.974.2300**
Fax 708.974.2498
Web ....www.metrofamily.org
E-mail ....bradym@metrofamily.org
10537 S Roberts Rd, Palos Hills, IL 60465-1933
Michael Brady, Executive Director

Mt Sinai/Mile Square **312.850.5800**
Fax 312.850.5839
Web ....www.dhs.state.il.us
E-mail ....dhsasa4@dhs.state.il.us
2040 W Washington Blvd, Chicago, IL 60612-2429
Beverly Hamilton Robinson, Director

Mt. Sinai Hospital & Medical Ctr Child & Adolescent Behavioral Health **773.257.4750**
Fax 773.257.4753
Web ....www.sinai.org
E-mail ....salgyal@sinai.org
1500 S California Ave, Nurses Residence 513, Chicago, IL 60608-1729
Yalut Salgado, Intake Coordinator

Murray Developmental Center **618.532.1811**
Fax 618.532.8171
1535 West McCord, Centralia, IL 62801
rick starr, facility director
CARF accredited programs available.

MYSI Corporation **312.733.8810**
Fax 312.733.8916
Web ....www.mychicago.org
954 W. Washington, Suite 4 East, Chicago, IL 60607
COA accredited organization.

Naperville Psychiatric Venture d/b/a Linden Oaks Hospital **630.305.5500**
Web ....www.edward.org
E-mail ....ksommers@edward.org
852 West Street, Naperville, IL 60540-6400
Ms. Karen Sommers, Accreditation Manager
Joint Commission accredited organization.

Near North Health Service Corporation **312.337.1073**
Web ....www.nearnorthhealth.org
E-mail ....bthomas@nmh.org
1276 North Clybourn Avenue, Chicago, IL 60610
Ms. Berneice Mills-Thomas, Accreditation Manager
Joint Commission accredited organization.

NeuroRestorative Carbondale **800.743.6802**
Fax 501.758.8778
Web ....www.neurorestorative.com
E-mail ....neuroinfo@thementornetwork.com
PO Box 2825, Carbondale, IL 62902
Chris Williamson, State Director
NeuroRestorative Carbondale's Adolescent Integration program provides post acute residential rehabilitation services to adolescents 11-21 years old who have experienced a neurological impairment. Residential services are also provided for children 6-11 years of age through a home host model. Both programs are designed to provide opportunities for intensive transdisciplinary rehabilitation services as well as age appropriate integrated functional community based skill training. Primary goals include fostering reintegration of the adolescent into the family home, increasing their ability to care for themselves, continuing education pursuits with increased abilities, and assisting them in improving their overall social and community integration.

Norman C. Sleezer Youth Home **815.232.8336**
Fax 815.232.8842
Web ....www.sleezeryouthhome.org
P.O. Box 895, Freeport, IL 61032
COA accredited organization.

North Central Behavioral Health System **309.647.1349**
Fax 309.647.1878
Web ....www.ncbhs.org
E-mail ....dmiskowiec@ncbhs.org
229 Martin Ave, Canton, IL 61520-2520
Donald Miskowiec, Chief Executive Officer

North Central Behavioral Health Systems **309.833.2191**
Fax 309.836.2118
Web ....www.ncbhs.org
E-mail ....jreinert@ncbhs.org
301 E Jefferson St, Macomb, IL 61455-2312
John Reinert, Clinical Director

North Central Behavioral Health Systems, Inc. **815.223.0160**
Web ....www.ncbhs.org
E-mail ....mlau@ncbhs.org
2960 Charters Street, La Salle, IL 61301
Dr. Michael Lau, Accreditation Manager
Joint Commission accredited organization.

Northern Illinois Academy **847.391.8000**
Fax 847.391.8001
Web ....www.camelotforkids.org
E-mail ....j.miyi@thecamelotschools.com
1150 N. River Road, Ste. 300 Quigley, Des Plaines, IL 60016
Jung Miyi, Executive Director

Northpointe Resource, Inc **847.872.1700**
Fax 847.872.0037
Web ....www.northpointeresources.org
E-mail ....kkopp@nrthpnrte.org
3441 Sheridan Rd, Zion, IL 60099-3699
Karl Kopp, Executive Director

NorthShore University HealthSystem **847.570.5005**
Web ....www.northshore.org
E-mail ....cbloomfield@northshore.org
1301 Central Street, Suite 300, Evanston, IL 60201
Ms. Christine Bloomfield, Accreditation Manager
Joint Commission accredited organization.

Northwest Community Hospital Youth Center **847.618.1000**
Web ....www.nch.org
E-mail ....cdougherty@nch.org
901 Kirchoff Road, Arlington Heights, IL 60005
Ms. Cindy Dougherty, Accreditation Manager
Joint Commission accredited organization.

Palos Community Hospital **708.923.4000**
Web ....www.paloscommunityhospital.org
E-mail ....jscarano@paloscomm.org
12251 South 80th Avenue, Palos Heights, IL 60463
Mr. John Scarano, Accreditation Manager
Joint Commission accredited organization.

Pillars Community Services **708.698.5500**
Fax 708.698.5090
Web ....www.pillarscommunity.org
333 North La Grange Road, Suite 1, La Grange Park, IL 60526
CARF accredited programs available.

Pilsen-Little Village Community Mental Health Center, Inc. dba Pilsen Wellness Center, Inc. **773.579.0832**
Fax 773.579.0762
Web ....www.pilsenwellnesscenter.org
2319 South Damen, Chicago, IL 60608
CARF accredited programs available.

Pioneer Center for Human Services/Youth Service Bureau **815.338.7360**
Web www.ysb4kids.org
E-mail ....skrause@pioneercenter.org
101 South Jefferson Street, Woodstock, IL 60098
Ms. Susan Krause, Accreditation Manager
Joint Commission accredited organization.

Prairie Counseling Center **618.664.1455**
Fax 618.664.1744
Web ....www.bchd.us
E-mail ....mbarth@bchd.us
503 South Prairie, Greenville, IL 62246
Maxine Barth, Executive Director & Founder
CARF accredited programs available.

Illinois

Prairie Ctr 217.328.4500
Fax 217.328.4535
Web ....www.prairie-center.com
E-mail ....pc@prairiecenter.com
718 W Killarney St, Urbana, IL 61801-1015
Gail Raney, Interim Director

ProCare Centers 708.338.3806
Web ....www.reshealthcare.org
E-mail ....mfonda@reshealthcare.org
1820 South 25th Avenue, Broadview, IL 60153
Mr. Michael Fonda, Accreditation Manager
Joint Commission accredited organization.

Provena Mercy Medical Center 630.859.2222
Web ....www.provenamercy.com
E-mail ....elizabeth.walliser@provena.org
1325 North Highland Avenue, Aurora, IL 60506
Ms. Elizabeth Walliser, Accreditation Manager
Joint Commission accredited organization.

Rehabilitation Institute of Chicago 312.238.2877
Fax 312.238.7594
Web ....www.ric.org
345 East Superior Street, Chicago, IL 60611
CARF accredited programs available.

Remedies Renewing Lives 815.966.1285
Web ....remediesrenewinglives.org
E-mail ....cpiper@remediesrenewinglives.org
516 Green Street, Rockford, IL 61102
Mrs. Cheryl Piper, Accreditation Manager
Joint Commission accredited organization.

Resurrection Behavoiral Health At St. Frances Hospital 847.316.6262
Fax 847.316.2214
E-mail ....mmenasce@reshealthcare.org
355 Ridge Ave, Evanston, IL 60202-3328
Maurice Menasce, Arc Director

Riveredge Hospital 708.771.7000
Web ....www.riveredgehospital.com
E-mail ....sheila.orr@psysolutions.com
8311 West Roosevelt Road, Forest Park, IL 60130
Ms. Sheila Orr, Accreditation Manager
Joint Commission accredited organization.

Riverside Medical Center 815.933.1671
Web ....www.RiversideMC.net
E-mail ....mary-schore@riversidehealthcare.net
350 North Wall Street, Kankakee, IL 60901
Mrs. Mary Schore, Accreditation Manager
Joint Commission accredited organization.

Riverside Medical Ctr Mental Health Unit 815.935.7523
Fax 815.936.8692
Web ....www.riversidehealthcare.org
350 N Wall St, Kankakee, IL 60901-2991
Christine Anthony, Director

Rosecrance, Inc. 815.387.5600
Web ....rosecrance.org
E-mail ....gartnert@rosecrance.net
1021 N. Mulford Road, Rockford, IL 61107
Ms. Toni Gartner, Accreditation Manager
Joint Commission accredited organization.

Roseland Behavioral Health Ctr 312.747.7320
Fax 312.747.6252
Web ....www.cityofchicago.org
E-mail ....neliegames@yahoo.com
200 E 115th St, Chicago, IL 60628-4914
Mamie Robinson, Director

Rush University Medical Center 312.942.5000
Web ....www.rush.edu
E-mail ....karen_tertell@rush.edu
1653 West Congress Parkway, Chicago, IL 60612
Ms. Karen Tertell, Accreditation Manager
Joint Commission accredited organization.

Sequel Schools, LLC 847.391.8000
Web ....www.sequelyouthservices.com
E-mail ....dgoldstein-higgins@sequelyouthservices.com
1150 North River Road, 100 Quigley Bldg., Des Plaines, IL 60016
Ms. Debbie Goldstein-Higgins, Accreditation Manager
Joint Commission accredited organization.

Sinai Psychiatry and Behavioral Health 773.257.5300
Fax 773.257.5330
2653 West Ogden Avenue, Chicago, IL 60608
CARF accredited programs available.

Sinnissippi Centers, Inc. 815.284.6611
Web ....www.sinnissippi.com
E-mail ....larryprindaville@sinnissippi.com
325 Illinois Route 2, Dixon, IL 61021
Mr. Lawrence Prindaville, Accreditation Manager
Joint Commission accredited organization.

Sonia Shankman Orthogenic School 773.702.1203
Fax 773.702.1304
Web ....www.oschool.org
University of Chicago, 1365 East 60th Street, Chicago, IL 60637
COA accredited organization.

Sonia Shankman Orthogenic School At University Of Chicago 773.702.1203
Fax 773.702.1304
Web ....www.oschool.org
1365 E 60th St, Chicago, IL 60637-2856
Pete Myers, Executive Director

Southeastern Illinois Counseling Centers, Inc. 618.395.4306
Web ....www.seicc.org
E-mail ....richswisher@hotmail.com
504 Micah Drive, Olney, IL 62450
Mr. Rich Swisher, Accreditation Manager
Joint Commission accredited organization.

Southern Illinois Regional Social Services, Inc. 618.457.6703
Fax 618.457.8377
Web ....www.sirss.org
604 East College Street, Carbondale, IL 62901
CARF accredited programs available.

Southwest Behavioral Health Ctr 312.747.0881
Fax 312.747.7796
1140 W 79th St, Chicago, IL 60620-3029
Steven Bush, Director

Southwood Interventions 773.737.4600
Web ....cornellcompanies.com
E-mail ....bgregoriev@abraxasyfs.com
5701 South Wood, Chicago, IL 60636
Mr. Boris Gregoriev, Accreditation Manager
Joint Commission accredited organization.

St Mary's Svcs 847.870.8181
Fax 847.870.8325
Web ....www.stmaryservices.com
E-mail ....information@stmaryservices.com
717 W Kirchhoff Rd Fl 2, Arlington Heights, IL 60005-2339
Cindy Anselmo, Supervisor

St. Mary's Hospital 618.436.6519
E-mail ....mary_lynn_szperra@ssmhc.com
400 North Pleasant Avenue, Centralia, IL 62801
Ms. Mary Lynn Szperra, Accreditation Manager
Joint Commission accredited organization.

Stickney Public Health District, Mental Health Division 708.424.9200
Fax 708.499.5427
Web ....www.stickneypublichealthdistrict.org
5635 State Road, Burbank, IL 60459
Dave Lenihan, Director
CARF accredited programs available.

Streamwood Behavioral Healthcare System 630.837.9000
Web ....www.streamwoodhospital.com
E-mail ....sharneice.snyder@uhsinc.com
1400 East Irving Park Road, Streamwood, IL 60107
Mrs. Sharneice Snyder, Accreditation Manager
Joint Commission accredited organization.

Suicide Prevention And Crisis Svc 217.222.1166
Fax 217.223.0461
Web ....www.twi.org
4409 Maine St, Quincy, IL 62305
Michael Rein, Executive Director

Tazwood Mental Health 309.694.6462
Fax 309.694.7812
E-mail ....mpolson@gallatinriver.net
100 N Main St Ste L100, East Peoria, IL 61611-2582
Michael Polson, CEO

Tazwood Mental Health Center, Inc. 309.347.5579
Web ....www.tazwoodmentalhealth.org
E-mail ....crichardson@tazwoodmhc.org
3248 Vandever Ave., Pekin, IL 61554
Mrs. Caterina Richardson, Accreditation Manager
Joint Commission accredited organization.

Tazwood Mental Health Ctr 309.347.5522
Fax 309.347.4264
Web ....www.tazwoodmentalhealth.org
3248 Vandever Ave, Pekin, IL 61554
Michael Polson, CEO

The Advantage Group Foundation Ltd. 815.444.6400
Fax 815.444.6816
422 Tag Way, Crystal Lake, IL 60014
CARF accredited programs available.

The Bridge Youth and Family Services 847.359.7490
Fax 847.359.7525
Web ....www.bridgeyouth.org
721 South Quentin Road, Suite 103, Palatine, IL 60067
COA accredited organization.

The Child, Adolescent and Family Recovery Center, LLC 847.457.6730
Web ....www.adolescentrecoverycenter.org
E-mail ....ryanne.bright@gmail.com
900 North Shore Dr. Suite 140, Lake Bluff, IL 60044
Ms. Ryanne Bright, Accreditation Manager
Joint Commission accredited organization.

The H Group, B.B.T., Inc. 618.937.6483
Fax 618.937.1440
Web ....www.fwhs.org
E-mail ....sara.bond@fwhs.org
902 West Main Street, West Frankfort, IL 62896
Sara Bond, Director of Development
CARF accredited programs available.

The Harbour, Inc. 847.297.8540
1440 Renaissance Drive, Suite 240, Park Ridge, IL 60068
COA accredited organization.

The Helen Wheeler Center for Community Mental Health 815.939.3543
Fax 815.939.3557
275 East Court Street, Suite 102, Kankakee, IL 60901
CARF accredited programs available.

The Josselyn Center 847.441.5600
Fax 847.441.7968
Web ....www.josselyn.org
E-mail ....kschuler@josselyn.org
405 Central Avenue, Northfield, IL 60093
Kelly Schuler, Director of Operations
CARF accredited programs available.

The Larkin Center 847.695.5656
Fax 847.695.0897
Web ....www.larkincenter.org
1212 Larkin Avenue, Elgin, IL 60123-6042
COA accredited organization.

The Pavilion Foundation 217.373.1700
Web.............................www.pavilionhospital.com
E-mail...............regina.harrington@uhsinc.com
　809 West Church Street, Champaign, IL 61820
　Ms. Regina Harrington, Accreditation Manager
　Joint Commission accredited organization.

The Pavilion Foundation 217.373.1700
Fax...217.373.1737
Web.............................www.pavilionhospital.com
E-mail ....info@pavilionhospital.com
　809 W Church St, Champaign, IL 61820-3320
　Bill White, Director Of Psychiatric Services

The South Suburban Council on Alcoholism and Substance
Abuse 708.647.3333
Web......................................www.sscouncil.org
E-mail...............janetcoleman@ameritech.net
　1909 Cheker Square, Hazel Crest, IL 60429
　Ms. Janet Coleman, Accreditation Manager
　Joint Commission accredited organization.

The Youth Campus...............................847.823.5161
Fax...847.823.9291
Web...............................www.theyouthcampus.org
E-mail..................sslomka@theyouthcampus.org
　733 N Prospect Ave, Park Ridge, IL 60068-2764
　Scott Slomka, Director Of Quality Improvement

Thrive Counseling Center 708.383.7500
Fax...708.383.7780
　120 South Marion Street, Oak Park, IL 60302
　CARF accredited programs available.

Timberline Knolls..............................630.257.9600
Web...............................www.timberlineknolls.com
E-mail...............rhayes@timberlineknolls.com
　40 Timberline Drive, Lemont, IL 60439
　Mr. Randy Hayes, Accreditation Manager
　Joint Commission accredited organization.

Transitions of Western Illinois 217.223.0413
Fax...217.223.0461
Web...www.twi.org
　4409 Maine Street, Quincy, IL 62305
　CARF accredited programs available.

Treatment Alternatives for Safe
Communities.....................................312.787.0208
Fax...312.787.9663
Web..www.tasc-il.org
　1500 North Halsted Street, Chicago, IL 60642
　CARF accredited programs available.

TriCity Family Services 630.232.1070
Fax...630.232.1471
Web..........................www.tricityfamilyservices.org
　1120 Randall Court, Geneva, IL 60134
　COA accredited organization.

Trinity Svcs Inc 815.485.6197
Fax...815.485.5975
Web...................................www.trinity-services.org
E-mail...................adykstra@trinity-services.org
　100 Gougar Rd, Joliet, IL 60432
　Art Dykstra, Director

Turning Point Behavioral Health Care
Center 847.933.0051
Fax...847.933.0057
Web..www.tpoint.org
　8324 Skokie Boulevard, Skokie, IL 60077-2545
　CARF accredited programs available.

Vocational Workshop 618.327.4461
Fax...618.327.4477
　781 East Holzhauer Drive, Nashville, IL 62263
　CARF accredited programs available.

Walter Lawson Children's Home 815.633.6636
Fax...815.633.6387
E-mail..jan@wlch.org
　1820 Walter Lawson Dr, Loves Park, IL 61111-2789
　Jan Primuth, Rn, Director Of Nursing

Waukegan IL Hospital Company, LLC 847.249.3900
Web.......................................www.vistahealth.com
E-mail........................marie_r_lee@chs.net
　2615 Washington Street, Waukegan, IL 60085
　Ms. Marie Lee, Accreditation Manager
　Joint Commission accredited organization.

Woodridge Interventions 630.968.6477
Web...abraxasyfs.com
E-mail.........................bgregoriev@abraxasyfs.com
　2221 64th Street, Woodridge, IL 60517
　Mr. Boris Gregoriev, Accreditation Manager
　Joint Commission accredited organization.

World Relief - Chicago, Horizon's Clinic 773.583.9191
Fax...773.583.9410
Web...www.wr.org
　3507 West Lawrence Avenue, Chicago, IL 60625
　Lilian Samaan, Director
　CARF accredited programs available.

Youth Guidance 312.253.4900
Fax...312.253.4917
Web..............................www.youth-guidance.org
　122 South Michigan, Suite 1510, Chicago, IL 60603
　COA accredited organization.

Youth Svc Bureau 217.529.8300
Fax...217.529.8314
Web...www.ysbi.com
E-mail..kw@ysbi.com
　2901 Normandy Rd, Springfield, IL 62703-4358
　Kathleen Wright, Executive Director

CHILDREN'S HOSPITAL

Abraham Lincoln Memorial Hospital 217.732.2161
　200 Stahohut Dr, Lincoln, IL 62656
　Dolian Dodoles, Chief Executive Officer

Advocate BroMenn Medical Center 309.454.1400
　1304 Franklin Ave, Normal, IL 61761
　Colleen Kannaday, Chief Executive Officer

Advocate Christ Medical Center 708.684.8000
　4440 West 95th St, Oak Lawn, IL 60453
　Kenneth Lukhard, Chief Executive Officer

Advocate Condell Medical Center 847.362.2900
　801 South Milwaukee Ave, Libertyville, IL 60048
　Ann Eric Heartty, President

Advocate Good Samaritan Hospital 630.275.5900
　3815 Highland Ave, Downers Grove, IL 60515

Advocate Good Shepherd Hospital 847.381.0123
　450 West Highway 22, Barrington, IL 60010
　Karen Lembert, Chief Executive Officer

Advocate Illinois Masonic Medical Ctr 773.975.1600
　836 W Wellington Ave, Chicago, IL 60657

Advocate Lutheran General Hospital 847.723.2210
　1775 Dempster St, Park Ridge, IL 60068
　Anthony Armada, Head

Alton Memorial Hospital 618.463.7311
　One Memorial Dr, Alton, IL 62002
　Dave Braasch, President

Blessing Hospital 217.223.1200
　Broadway at 11th St, Quincy, IL 62305
　Maureen Kann, President

Carle Foundation Hospital 217.383.3311
　611 West Park St, Urbana, IL 61801
　Pamela Bigler, Nursing Officer

Centegra Memorial Medical Center 815.338.2500
　3701 Doty Rd, Woodstock, IL 60098

Centegra Northern Illinois Medical Ctr 815.344.5000
　4201 Medical Center Dr, McHenry, IL 60050
　Michael Eesley, Chief Executive Officer

Central DuPage Hospital 630.933.1600
　25 North Winfield rd, Winfield, IL 60190
　Mike Vizoda, Chief Executive Officer

CGH Medical Center 815.625.0400
　100 East LeFevre Rd, Sterling, IL 61081
　Ed Anderson, Chief Executive Officer

Childrens Memorial Hospital 773.880.4000
　2300 Childrens Plaza, Chicago, IL 60614

Community Hospital 618.833.4511
　517 North Main St, Anna, IL 62906
　Jim Farris, Chief Executive Officer

Edward Hospital 630.527.3000
　801 South Washington St, Naperville, IL 60540
　Pam Davis, Chief Executive Officer

Elmhurst Memorial Hospital 331.221.1000
　155 E Brush Hill Rd, Elmhurst, IL 60126
　Peter Daniels, Executive Director

Ferrell Hospital 618.273.3361
　1201 Pine St, Eldorado, IL 62930

FHN Memorial Hospital 815.599.6000
　1045 West Stephenson St, Freeport, IL 61032
　Michael Perry, Chief Executive Officer

Genesis Medical Center 309.792.9363
　801 Illinoi Dr, Silvis, IL 61282
　Soo Styrow, President

Good Samaritan Regional Health Center 618.242.4600
　605 North 12th St, Mount Vernon, IL 62864
　Michael Warren, President

Gottlieb Memorial Hospital 708.681.3200
　701 West North Ave, Melrose Park, IL 60160
　Trish Cassidy, Chief Executive Officer

Graham Hospital 309.647.5240
　210 West Walnut St, Canton, IL 61520
　Robert Senneff, Chief Executive Officer

Greenville Regional Hospital 618.664.1230
　200 Healthcare Dr, Greenville, IL 62246

Hamilton Memorial Hospital District 618.643.2361
　611 S Marshall Ave, McLeansboro, IL 62859
　Randy Dauby, President

Hammond Henry Hospital 309.944.6431
　600 North College Ave, Geneseo, IL 61254
　Brab Sloberg, Chief Executive Officer

Harrisburg Medical Center 618.253.7671
　100 Dr Warren Tuttle Dr, Harrisburg, IL 62946
　Vince Ashley, Chief Executive Officer

Heartland Regional Medical Center 618.998.7000
　3333 West DeYoung, Marion, IL 62959
　Suzie Woods, Marketing Director

Hillsboro Area Hospital 217.532.6111
　1200 East Tremont St, Hillsboro, IL 62049
　Rick Brown, Chief Executive Officer

Illini Community Hospital 217.285.2113
　640 West Washington St, Pittsfield, IL 62363
　Kathy Hull, Chief Executive Officer

Illinois Valley Community Hospital 815.223.3300
　925 West St, Peru, IL 61354
　Tommy Hobbs, Administrator

Ingalls Memorial Hospital 708.333.2300
　One Ingalls Dr, Harvey, IL 60426
　Kurt Johnson, Chief Executive Officer

Jackson Park Hospital & Medical Center 773.947.7500
　7531 Stony Island Ave, Chicago, IL 60649
　Nelson Basquez, Vice President

Jersey Community Hospital 618.498.6402
E-mail..lbear@jch.org
　400 Maple Summit Rd, Jerseyville, IL 62052
　Lawrence Bear, President

John H Stroger 312.864.6000
　1869 West Ogdon, Chicago, IL 60612
　Dr. Anthony Tedeschi, Executive Director

Katherine Shaw Bethea Hospital 815.288.5531
E-mail .... dschreiner@ksbhospital.com
 403 East First St, Dixon, IL 61021
 Dave Schreiner, Chief Executive Officer

Kewanee Hospital 309.852.7500
 1051 West South St, Kewanee, IL 61443
 Margaret Gustafson, Chief Executive Officer

Kishwaukee Community Hospital 815.756.1521
 One Kish Hospital Dr, DeKalb, IL 60115
 Kevin Poorten, Chief Executive Officer

Little Company of Mary Hospital 708.422.6200
 2800 West 95th St, Evergreen Park, IL 60805

Loyola University Medical Center 708.216.9000
 2160 South First Ave, Maywood, IL 60153
 Paul Whelton, Chief Executive Officer

Massac Memorial Hospital 618.524.2176
 28 Chick St, Metropolis, IL 62960
 David Suqua, Chief Executive Officer

McDonough District Hospital 309.833.4101
E-mail .... sjdexter@mdh.org
 525 East Grant St, Macomb, IL 61455
 Sue Dexter, Director

Memorial Hospital 618.233.7750
 4500 Memorial Dr, Belleville, IL 62226
 Kim Renth, Office Manager

Memorial Hospital of Carbondale 618.549.0721
 405 West Jackson St, Carbondale, IL 62901
 Barb Nelson, Administrator

Memorial Medical Center 217.788.3000
E-mail .... memorialmedical.com
 701 North First St, Springfield, IL 62781
 Edger Curtis, Chief Executive Officer

Mercy Hospital and Medical Center 312.567.2000
 2525 South Michigan Ave, Chicago, IL 60616
 Sheila Lyne, Chief Executive Officer

Methodist Medical Center of Illinois 309.672.5522
 221 NE Glen Oak Ave, Peoria, IL 61636
 Micheal Ryan, Chief Executive Officer

Metro South Medical Center 708.597.2000
 12935 South Gregory St, Blue Island, IL 60406
 Linda St. Julien, Vice President

Morris Hospital & Healthcare Centers 815.942.2932
 150 West High St, Morris, IL 60450
 Mark Steadham, Chief Executive Officer

Mount Sinai Hospital 773.542.2000
 California Ave at 15th St, Chicago, IL 60608
 Alan Channing, President

North Shore University Skokie Hospital 847.677.9600
 9600 Gross Point Rd, Skokie, IL 60076
 Kristen Murtos, Chief Executive Officer

NorthShore University Hospital 847.570.2000
 2650 Ridge Ave, Evanston, IL 60201
 JP Gallagher, President

Northwest Community Hospital 847.618.1000
 800 West Central Rd, Arlington Heights, IL 60005
 Christine Karolewski, Manager

Northwestern Lake Forest Hospital 847.234.5600
 660 North Westmoreland Rd, Lake Forest, IL 60045
 Thomas Mcafee, Chief Executive Officer

OSF Saint James John W Albrecht Med Ctr 815.842.2828
 2500 West Reynolds, Pontiac, IL 61764
 David Ochs, Chief Executive Officer

OSF St Anthony Medical Center 815.226.2000
 5666 East State St, Rockford, IL 61108
 Ann Hammen, Director of Nursing

OSF St Francis Medical Center 309.655.2000
 530 NE Glen Oak Ave, Peoria, IL 61637
 Keith Steffen, Chief Executive Officer

OSF St Joseph Medical Center 309.662.3311
 2200 East Washington St, Bloomington, IL 61701
 Deborah Smith, Chief Nursing Officer

OSF St Mary Medical Center 309.344.3161
 3333 North Seminary St, Galesburg, IL 61401
 Richard Kowalski, Chief Executive Officer

Ottawa Regional Hospital 815.433.3100
 1100 East Norris Dr, Ottawa, IL 61350
 Maryanne Steven, Nursing Director

Palos Community Hospital 708.923.4000
 12251 South 80th Ave, Palos Heights, IL 60463
 Margaret Wright, Chief Executive Officer

Paris Community Hospital 217.465.4141
 721 East Court St, Paris, IL 61944
 Randy Simmons, President/CEO

Passavant Area Hospital 217.245.9541
 1600 West Walnut St, Jacksonville, IL 62650
 Chester Wynn, Chief Executive Officer

Pekin Hospital 309.347.1151
 600 South 13th St, Pekin, IL 61554
 Kevin Andrews, Chief Executive Officer

Proctor Hospital 309.691.1000
 5409 North Knoxville Ave, Peoria, IL 61614

Provena Covenant Medical Center 217.337.2000
 1400 West Park St, Urbana, IL 61801
 Michael Brown, Chief Executive Officer

Provena Mercy Medical Center 630.859.2222
 1325 North Highland Ave, Aurora, IL 60506
 George Einhorn, Chief Executive Officer

Provena St Jospeh Medical Center 815.725.7133
 333 North Madison St, Joliet, IL 60435
 Jefferey Brickman, Chief Executive Officer

Provena St Marys Hospital 815.937.2400
 500 West Court St, Kankakee, IL 60901
 Michael Arno, Chief Executive Officer

Provena United Samaritans Medical Ctr 217.443.5000
 812 North Logan, Danville, IL 61832

Resurrection Medical Center 773.774.8000
 7435 West Talcott Ave, Chicago, IL 60631
 Sandra Bruce, Chief Executive Officer

Riverside Medical Center 815.933.1671
 350 North Wall St, Kankakee, IL 60901
 Phil Kabie, Chief Executive Officer

Rockford Memorial Hospital 815.971.5000
 2400 North Rockton Ave, Rockford, IL 61103
 Gary Katz, Chief Executive Officer

Rush Copley Medical Center 630.978.6200
 2000 Ogden Ave, Aurora, IL 60504
 Barry Finn, Chief Executive Officer

Rush University Medical Center 312.942.5000
 1653 West Congress Pkwy, Chicago, IL 60612
 Mary Goodwin, Chief Executive Officer

Sarah Bush Lincoln Health Center 217.258.2525
 1000 Health Center Dr, Mattoon, IL 61938
 Tim Ols, Chief Executive Officer

Shriners Hosp for Children at Chicago 773.622.5400
 2211 North Oak Park Ave, Chicago, IL 60707

Silver Cross Hospital 815.740.1100
 1200 Maple Rd, Joliet, IL 60432
 Paul Pawlak, Chief Executive Officer

Sparta Community Hospital 618.443.2177
 818 E Broadway St, Sparta, IL 62286
 Joanne, Chief Executive Officer

St Alexius Medical Center 847.843.2000
 1555 Barrington Rd, Hoffman Estates, IL 60169
 Ed Goldberg, Director

St Anthony Hospital 773.484.1000
 2875 W 19th St, Chicago, IL 60623

St Anthonys Health Center 618.465.2571
 1 Saint Anthonys Way, Alton, IL 62002
 EJ Kuier, Chief Executive Officer

St Anthonys Memorial Hospital 217.342.2121
 503 North Maple St, Effingham, IL 62401
 Dan Woodf, Chief Executive Officer

St Johns Hospital 217.544.6464
 800 East Carpenter St, Springfield, IL 62769
 Robert Ritz, President

St Joseph Hospital 773.665.3000
 2900 North Lake Shore Dr, Chicago, IL 60657
 Roberta Luskin-Hawk, Chief Executive Officer

St Josephs Hospital 618.526.4511
 9515 Holy Cross Ln, Breese, IL 62230
 Mark Koosterman, President/CEO

St Margarets Hospital 815.664.5311
 600 East First St, Spring Valley, IL 61362

St Marys Hospital 217.464.2966
 1800 East Lake Shore Dr, Decatur, IL 62521
 Kevin Kast, Chief Executive Officer

St Marys Hospital 815.673.2311
 111 Spring St, Streator, IL 61364
 Joanne Fenton, Chief Executive Officer

St Marys Hospital 618.436.8000
 400 North Pleasant Ave, Centralia, IL 62801
 Phil Guftafson, Chief Executive Officer

Swedish American Hospital 815.968.4400
 1401 East State St, Rockford, IL 61104

Swedish Covenant Hospital 773.878.8200
 5145 North California Ave, Chicago, IL 60625
 Mark Newton, President

Taylorville Memorial Hospital 217.824.3331
 201 East Pleasant St, Taylorville, IL 62568
 Daniel Raab, Chief Executive Officer

University of Chicago Medical Center 773.702.1000
 5841 South Maryland Ave, Chicago, IL 60637
 John Easton, Director

University of Illinois Medical Center 312.996.7000
 1740 West Taylor St, Chicago, IL 60612

Westlake Hospital 708.681.3000
 1225 W Superior St, Melrose Park, IL 60160
 Bill Brown, Chief Executive Officer

COUNSELING SERVICES

Catholic Charities 309.636.8000
Fax 309.671.1046
 2900 W Heading Ave, Peoria, IL 61604-4868
 Patricia Fox, Executive Director

Children's Home & Aid Society Of Illinois 815.962.1043
Fax 815.962.1272
Web .... www.chasi.org
E-mail .... wheinke@nw.chasi.org
 910 2nd Ave Ste 103, Rockford, IL 61104-2147
 Warren E. Heinke, Vice President

Community Counseling Ctrs Of Chicago 773.769.0205
Fax 773.765.0801
Web www.c4chicago.org
E-mail .... infoc4@c4chicago.org
 4740 N Clark St, Chicago, IL 60640
 Susan Kogan, Site Director

Counseling And Family Svc 309.676.2400
Fax 309.676.6037
Web .... www.cfspeoria.org
E-mail .... dallan@cfspeoria.org
 330 SW Washington St, Peoria, IL 61602
 Doug Allan, Executive Director

Depaul University Family & Community

Services **773.325.7780**
Fax 773.325.7781
Web ....www.depaul.edu/cmhc
E-mail ....wdunn@depaul.edu
   2219 N Kenmore Ave, Rm 300, Chicago, IL 60614
   Winifred Kearns, Lcsw, Associate Director

Hoyleton Youth and Family Svcs **618.875.0673**
Fax 618.875.0861
Web ....www.hoyleton.org
   5601 State St, East Saint Louis, IL 62203
   Kathy Gomez, Supervisor

Illinois Baptist Children's Home **618.242.4944**
Fax 618.242.2568
Web ....www.bchfs.com
E-mail ....bchbabies@sbcglobal.net
   4243 Lincolnshire Dr, Mount Vernon, IL 62864-2157
   Carla Eohono, Director Of Maternity Adoption And Foster Care

Kemmerer Village **217.226.4451**
Fax 217.226.3511
E-mail ....mike@kv.christian.k12.il.us
   941 N 2500 East Rd, Assumption, IL 62510-8026
   Michael Havera, Director

Kenneth Young Center **847.524.8800**
Fax 847.524.8824
Web ....www.kennethyoung.org
E-mail ....mitchb@kennethyoung.org
   1001 Rohlwing Rd, Elk Grove Village, IL 60007-3217
   Mitchell Bruski, Director

Lutheran Child And Family Svcs Of Illinois **618.242.3284**
Fax 618.242.3288
Web ....www.lcfs.org
E-mail ....gene_svabakken@lcfs.org
   800 S 45th St, Mount Vernon, IL 62864-6704
   Gene Svabakken, CEO

Lutheran Child And Family Svcs Of Illinois **217.544.4631**
Fax 217.544.0412
Web ....www.lcfs.org
E-mail ....gene_svabakken@lcfs.org
   431 S Grand Ave W, Springfield, IL 62704-3717
   Gene Svabakken, CEO

Lutheran Child and Family Svcs of Illinois **618.234.8904**
Fax 618.234.0218
Web ....www.lcfs.org
E-mail ....gene_svabakken@lcfs.org
   317 W Main St, Belleville, IL 62220-1317
   Gene L. Svabakken, President/CEO

Midwest Ctr For Children's Development

(MCCD) **815.788.1020**
Fax 815.788.1422
E-mail ....mccd_program@comcast.net
   4701 N Oak St, Crystal Lake, IL 60012
   Amanda Hebling, Director

Spectrum Youth & Family Svcs **847.884.6212**
Fax 847.884.6687
Web ....www.shawnricktownship.org
E-mail ....jlipsch@shawnricktownship.org
   1 Illinois Blvd, Hoffman Estates, IL 60169-3314
   Jerald B. Lipsch, Director

The Cradle **847.475.5800**
Fax 847.475.5871
Web ....www.cradle.org
E-mail ....cradle@cradle.org
   2049 Ridge Ave, Evanston, IL 60201-2794
   Beth Lupo, Intake Coordinator

United Methodist Childrens Home **618.242.1070**
Fax 618.242.9381
Web ....www.umchome.org
E-mail ....glemmon@umchome.org
   2023 Richview Rd, Mount Vernon, IL 62864-2884
   Gary Lemmon, Chief Executive Officer

CRISIS & SHELTER CARE

A Safe Place **847.731.7165**
Fax 847.336.5813
Web ....www.asafeplaceforhelp.org
E-mail ....pdemott@asafeplaceforhelp.org
   2710 17Th Street, Ste 100, Zion, IL 60099
   Phyllis Demott, Director

Apna-Ghar Inc. **773.334.0173**
Fax 773.334.0963
Web ....www.apnaghar.org
E-mail ....info@apnaghar.org
   4753 N Broadway St Ste 632, Chicago,
   IL 60640-4996
   Sanjna Das, Program Director

Between Friends- Domestic Violence **773.274.5232**
Fax 773.262.2543
E-mail ....kdoherty@betweenfriendschicago.org
   PO Box 608548, Chicago, IL 60660-8548
   Ms Kathy Doherty, Director

Cairo Women's Shellter- Domestic

Violence **618.734.4357**
Fax 618.734.4367
Web ....www.midwest.net
E-mail ....Delta1@Midwest.Net
   911 Cedar Street, Cairo, IL 62914
   Jeannie Woods, Director

Catholic Social Svcs of Southern Illinois **618.394.5900**
Fax 618.394.5909
Web ....www.cssil.org
E-mail ....admin@cssil.org
   8601 W Main St Ste 201, Belleville, IL 62223-1719
   Gary Huelsmann, Executive Director

Children's Foundation **309.827.0374**
Fax 309.828.0745
E-mail ....lpieper@tcf.chasi.org
   403 S State St, Bloomington, IL 61701-5556
   Lisa Pieper, CEO

Community Svc Ctr **217.893.1530**
Fax 217.893.8600
   520 E Wabash Ave Ste 1, Rantoul, IL 61866-3019
   Andrew Kulczycki, Director

Connections for Abused Women & their

Children **773.489.9081**
Fax 773.489.6111
E-mail ....cryan@cawc.org
   1116 N Kedzie Ave # 5, Chicago, IL 60651
   Cordelia Ryan, Executive Director

Constance Morris House- Domestic

Violence **708.485.5254**
Fax 708.485.0160
E-mail ....lsiegel@pillarscommunity.org
   333 N La Grange Rd, La Grange Park, IL 60526
   Ms Lynn Siegel, Director

Countering Domestic Violence -Neville

House **309.828.8913**
Fax 309.829.2425
   1013 W Washington St, Bloomington, IL 61701
   Deb White, Program Manager

Crisis Ctr Foundation- Domestic Violence **217.243.4357**
Fax 217.245.9421
E-mail ....donal@jvilleccf.org
   325 9th Ave, Jacksonville, IL 62650-4036
   Dona Leanard, Director

Crisis Ctr Of South Surburbia **708.429.7255**
Fax 708.429.7293
E-mail ....edwardv@crisisctr.org
   7700 Timber Drive, Tinley Park, IL 60477
   Edward Vega, Director

Crosspoint Human Services-Domestic Violence

Shelter **217.443.5566**
Fax 217.709.0377
E-mail ....meithers@humanservice.org
   201 N Hazel St, Danville, IL 61832
   Maretta Withers, Director

Ctr For Prevention Of Abuse- Domestic

Violence **309.691.0551**
Fax 309.272.2918
Web ....www.centreforpreventionofabuse.org
   720 W Joan Ct., Peoria, IL 61614
   Martha Herm, Director

Dove Domestic Violence Programs **217.428.6616**
Fax 217.428.7256
Web ....www.doveinc.org
E-mail ....tducy@doveinc.org
   788 E Clay St, Decatur, IL 62521-2783
   Teri Ducy, Director

Emergency Svcs Ctr **773.538.8800**
Fax 773.538.8835
   5001 S Michigan Ave, Chicago, IL 60615
   Terri Travis-davis, Office Manager

Family Rescue Inc.- Domestic Violence

Program **773.375.1918**
Fax 773.734.1245
E-mail ....j_coffee@familyrescueinc.org
   9204 South Commercial Avenue Ste 407, Chicago,
   IL 60617
   Joyce Coffee, Director

Family Shelter Service- Domestic Violence **630.221.8290**
Fax 630.221.8098
E-mail ....kkuchar@familyshelterservice.net
   605 E Roosevelt Rd, Wheaton, IL 60187-5568
   Karen Kuchar, Executive Director

FHN Family Counseling Ctr **815.777.2836**
Fax 815.777.2849
Web ....www.fhn.org
E-mail ....kshird@fhn.org
   300 Summit St, Galena, IL 61036-1638
   Kimberly Shird, Clinical Supervisor

Freedom House- Domestic Violence **815.872.0087**
Fax 815.872.5044
   440 Elm Pl, Princeton, IL 61356
   Connie Doran, Director

Fulton -Mason Crisis Svc-Domestic

Violence **309.647.7487**
Fax 309.647.8338
E-mail ....martha@netins.net
   1330 E Ash St, Canton, IL 61520
   Martha Daly, Director

Guardian Angel Home **815.729.0930**
Fax 815.744.6087
E-mail ....sschmitz@guardianangelhome.org
   1550 Plainfield Rd, Joliet, IL 60435-3796
   Sheila Schmitz, CEO

Hope Coalition Of East Central Illinois-Domestic

Violence **217.348.5931**
Fax 217.348.0722
E-mail ....hope34@consolidated.net
   701 6th St Ste 2, Charleston, IL 61920
   Mr James Walters, Director

Hope Of Rochelle- Domestic Violence **815.562.4323**
Fax 815.562.5756
E-mail ....Hopecmail@Aol.Com
   PO Box 131, Rochelle, IL 61068-0131
   Ruth Carter, Director

John And Mary Madden/ Paulina Home **312.491.3500**
Fax 312.491.3501
Web ....www.maryvilleacademy.org
   1658 W Grand Ave, Chicago, IL 60622-6309
   Fred Smith, Director

Illinois

Le Penseur Youth And Family Svcs ... 773.375.8637
Fax ... 773.375.8653
Web ... www.lepenseur.org
E-mail ... rsummerrise@lepenseur.org
8550 S Manistee Ave, Chicago, IL 60617
Reginald Summerrise, Director

Life Span, Inc.-Domestic Violence Program ... 847.824.0382
Fax ... 847.824.5311
Web ... www.life-span.org
E-mail ... lifespan@life-span.org
701 Lee St, Des Plaines, IL 60016
Ms Margaret Luft, Director

Maryville St. Margaret Of Scotland ... 773.371.2500
Fax ... 773.371.2531
Web ... www.maryvilleacademy.org
1209 W 98th St, Chicago, IL 60643-1443
Fred Smith, Director

Midwest Youth Svcs ... 217.245.6000
Fax ... 217.245.7000
Web ... www.mchsi.com
E-mail ... youthcntr@mchsi.com
2001 W Lafayette Ave, Jacksonville, IL 62650-1012
Susan Wilson, Executive Director

Mini O'Beirne Crisis Nursery ... 217.525.6800
Fax ... 217.525.4043
1011 N 7th St, Springfield, IL 62702
Kathleen Hayworth, Executive Director

Mujeres Latinas En Accion-Domestic Violence ... 773.890.7676
Fax ... 773.890.7650
E-mail ... maria@mujereslat.org
2124 W 21st Pl, Chicago, IL 60608
Maria Pesqueira, President

Mutual Ground Inc- Domestic Violence ... 630.897.0080
Fax ... 630.897.3536
Web ... www.mututalgroundinc.org
E-mail ... mutualground@ameritech.net
418 Oak Ave, Aurora, IL 60506-3108
Michelle Curry, Executive Director

Oasis Women's Ctr- Domestic Violence ... 618.465.1978
Fax ... 618.465.0749
E-mail ... oasiswc@cbnstl.Com
PO Box 981, Alton, IL 62002
Margarette Trushel, Director

Path-Personal Access To Help ... 309.828.1022
Fax ... 309.827.7485
E-mail ... kzangerle@pathcrisis.org
201 E Grove St Ste 200, Bloomington, IL 61701-5263
Karen Zangerle, Executive Director

People Against Violent Environments ... 618.533.7233
Fax ... 618.533.7255
421 S. Elm St., Centralia, IL 62801
Alice Snyder, Administrative Representative

Project Oz ... 309.827.0377
Fax ... 309.829.8877
Web ... www.projectoz.org
E-mail ... peter@projectoz.org
1105 W Front St, Bloomington, IL 61701
Peter Rankaitis, Executive Director

Quanada-Domestic Violence Program ... 217.222.3069
Fax ... 217.222.4574
Web ... www.quanada.org
E-mail ... megand@quanada.org
2707 Maine St, Quincy, IL 62301-4484
Megan Duesterhaus, Director

Rock River Academy ... 815.877.3440
Fax ... 815.877.4282
3445 Elmwood Rd, Rockford, IL 61101
Jennifer Molawa, Principal

Roundhouse ... 217.359.5276
Fax ... 217.359.6092
311 W White St, Champaign, IL 61820
Kristie Wilson, Program Supervisor

Safe Harbor Family Crisis Ctr ... 309.343.7233
Fax ... 309.343.3956
E-mail ... safeharbor@grics.net
1188 W Main St, Galesburg, IL 61401
Kathy Richardson, Director

Safe Passage Inc-Domestic Violence ... 815.756.5228
Fax ... 815.756.7932
Web ... www.safepassagedv.org
E-mail ... lmoser@safepassagedv.org
1021 State St., DeKalb, IL 60115
Linda Moser, Executive Director

Sarah's Inn ... 708.386.3305
Fax ... 708.386.2657
E-mail ... sarahsinn@sarahsinn.org
5846 West Madison Street, Chicago, IL 60644
Pat Prinzevalle, Executive Director

South Surburban Family Shelter, Inc. ... 708.794.2140
Fax ... 708.794.2145
E-mail ... dbedrosian@ssfs1.org
18139 S. Harwood, Homewood, IL 60430
Diane Bedrosian, Director

The Harbour, Inc. ... 847.297.8540
Fax ... 847.297.8562
E-mail ... randi@theharbour.org
1440 Renaissance Dr Ste 240, Park Ridge, IL 60068
Randi M. Gurian, Executive Director

The Women's Ctr-Domestic Violence ... 618.529.2324
Fax ... 618.529.1802
Web ... www.thewomensctr.org
E-mail ... wced@thewomensctr.org
610 S Thompson St, Carbondale, IL 62901-2740
Cathy McClanahan, Director

Turning Point- Domestic Violence ... 815.338.8081
Fax ... 815.338.8110
11019 NW Hwy 14, Woodstock, IL 60098
Jane Farmer, Director

Victim Svcs Domestic Violence ... 309.837.6622
Fax ... 309.836.3640
E-mail ... diane@wirpc.org
223 S. Randolph St., Macomb, IL 61455
Diane Mayfield, Director

Violence Prevention Ctr of Southwest Illinois ... 618.236.2531
Fax ... 618.235.9521
Web ... www.vpcswi.org
650 N 20th St, Belleville, IL 62222
Jessica Brandon, Executive Director

Youth Outreach Svcs ... 773.777.7112
Fax ... 773.777.7059
Web ... www.yos.org
E-mail ... rickv@yos.org
6417 W Irving Park Rd, Chicago, IL 60634
Rick Velasquez, Chief Executive Officer

Youth Svcs Network, Inc. ... 815.986.1947
Fax ... 815.986.1954
E-mail ... srader@xta.com
3703 N Main St, Ste 105, Rockford, IL 61103-1677
Susan Rader, Administration Director

EDUCATION

Albany Park Communtity Ctr, Inc. ... 773.583.5111
Fax ... 773.583.5062
Web ... www.atcc-chgo.org
3403 W Lawrence Ave Ste 300, Chicago, IL 60625
Harold Rice, Executive Director

Allendale Assoc ... 847.356.2351
Fax ... 847.356.0289
Web ... www.allendale4kids.org
E-mail ... mshahbazian@allendale4kids.org
600 E Grand Ave, Lake Villa, IL 60046-9152
Mary Shahbazian, President

Bloom Township Youth Committee, Inc. ... 708.754.9400
Fax ... 708.755.6024
Web ... www.bloomtownship.org
425 S Halsted St, Chicago Heights, IL 60411-1212
Norma Caratachea, Executive Youth Director

Child's Voice School ... 630.595.8200
Fax ... 630.595.8282
Web ... www.childsvoiceschool.com
E-mail ... info@childsvoiceschool.com
180 Hansen Ct, Wood Dale, IL 60191
Michele Wilkins, Edd, Director

Christopher School ... 773.535.9375
Fax ... 773.535.9567
Web ... www.christopher.cps.k12.il.us
E-mail ... mmcallon@cps.k12.il.us
5042 S Artesian Ave, Chicago, IL 60632-1492
Mary Mcallon, Principal

Ctr For Children's Svcs ... 217.446.1300
Fax ... 217.446.1325
E-mail ... edmichaels@tcfcs.org
702 N Logan Ave, Danville, IL 61832-4323
Ed Michaels, Phd, Director

Glenwood School ... 708.754.0175
Fax ... 708.756.6493
Web ... www.glenwoodschool.org
500 W 187th St, Glenwood, IL 60425-1397
Sam Banks, President & CEO

Golconda Job Corps Ctr ... 618.285.6601
Fax ... 618.285.5296
345 Job Corps Rd, Golconda, IL 62938-9603
David Floyd, Center Director

Hoyleton Youth & Family Svcs ... 618.493.7382
Fax ... 618.493.6390
Web ... www.hoyleton.org
E-mail ... chris.cox@hoyleton.org
350 N Main St, Hoyleton, IL 62803
Chris Cox, Vice President/Coo

Illinois Coalition Against Sexual Assault ... 217.753.4117
Fax ... 217.753.8229
Web ... www.icasa.org
E-mail ... sblack@icasa.org
100 N 16th St, Springfield, IL 62703-1102
Polly Poskin, Executive Director

Jeanine Schultz Memorial School ... 847.696.3315
Fax ... 847.696.3330
E-mail ... jsms334@sbcglobal.net
2101 Oakton St, Park Ridge, IL 60068-1891
Michael Biskupski, Executive Director

John E. Reid & Associates ... 312.583.0700
Fax ... 312.583.0701
Web ... www.reid.com
209 W Jackson Blvd Ste 400, Chicago, IL 60606-6903
Joseph P. Buckley, Executive Director

Joseph Academy ... 847.803.1930
Fax ... 847.803.8669
Web ... www.josephacademy.org
E-mail ... mschack@josephacademy.org
1101 Gregory St, Des Plaines, IL 60016-1231
Michael Schack, Executive Director

Larkin Ctr Home For Children & Adolescents ... 847.695.5656
Fax ... 847.695.0897
Web ... www.larkincenter.org
E-mail ... dgraf@larkincenter.org
1212 Larkin Ave, Elgin, IL 60123-6098
Dennis Graf, Director

Lutheran Child And Family Svcs Of Illinois Toll Free (Central Intake) ... 630.969.6120
Fax ... 708.771.7184
Web ... www.lcfs.org
E-mail ... gene_svabakken@lcfs.org
5211 Carpenter St, Downers Grove, IL 60515-4519
Gene L. Svabakken, President/CEO

Metropolitan Family Svcs **312.986.4000**
Fax 312.986.4334
Web ....www.metrofamily.org
E-mail ....jonesr@metrofamily.org
　1 N Dearborn St, Ste 1000 10th Fl, Chicago,
　IL 60602
　Ricardo Estrada, Chief Executive Officer

NeuroRestorative Carbondale **800.743.6802**
Fax 501.758.8778
Web ....www.neurorestorative.com
E-mail ....neuroinfo@thementornetwork.com
　PO Box 2825, Carbondale, IL 62902
　Chris Williamson, State Director
　NeuroRestorative Carbondale's Adolescent Integration program provides post acute residential rehabilitation services to adolescents 11-21 years old who have experienced a neurological impairment. Residential services are also provided for children 6-11 years of age through a home host model. Both programs are designed to provide opportunities for intensive transdisciplinary rehabilitation services as well as age appropriate integrated functional community based skill training. Primary goals include fostering reintegration of the adolescent into the family home, increasing their ability to care for themselves, continuing education pursuits with increased abilities, and assisting them in improving their overall social and community integration.

Pace Ctr **708.450.2100**
Fax 708.450.1116
E-mail ....tsdir@hotmail.com
　1000 Van Buren St, Maywood, IL 60153-1970
　Terry Smith, Psyd, Director

Pairie Centre Against Saxual Assault **217.744.2560**
Fax 217.744.2563
E-mail ....cws@prairiecasa.org
　3 W Old State Capitol Plz Ste 206, Springfield,
　IL 62701-1574
　Catherine Walters, Executive Director

Philip J. Rock Ctr & School **630.790.2474**
Fax 630.790.4893
Web ....www.project-reach-illinois.org
E-mail ....prc@aol.com
　818 Du Page Blvd, Glen Ellyn, IL 60137-5810
　Arlen E. Beaton, Head Nurse

RAINBOWS **847.952.1770**
Fax 847.952.1774
Web ....www.rainbows.org
E-mail ....bill@rainbows.org
　1360 Hamilton Pkwy, Itasca, IL 60143-1144
　Bill Olbrisch, Community Outreach Director

Rocvale Children's Home **815.654.3050**
Fax 815.633.8057
　4450 N Rockton Ave, Rockford, IL 61103-1526
　Shawn Way, President/CEO

Rush Day School **312.942.6627**
Fax 312.942.6952
Web ....www.rush.edu
E-mail ....jean_l_heideman@rush.edu
　2150 W Harrison St, Chicago, IL 60612
　Jean Heideman, Director

Special Children, Inc. **618.234.6876**
Fax 618.234.6150
Web ....www.specialchildren.net
E-mail ....kathleencullen@sbcglobal.net
　1306 Wabash Ave, Belleville, IL 62220-3370
　Kathleen Cullen, Director

Speed 802 ....**708.481.6100**
Fax 708.481.5713
Web www.speed802.org
E-mail ....gwalters@speed802.org
　1125 Division St, Chicago Heights, IL 60411-2419
　Dr. Genevra Walters, Superintendent

Touch Of Nature-Siuc **618.453.1121**
Fax 618.453.1188
Web ....www.ton.siu.edu
E-mail ....tonec@siu.edu
　1206 Touch Of Nature Rd, 7 Illinois University,
　Makanda, IL 62958
　Geoff Schropp, Program Coordinator For Spectrum

FOSTER CARE AGENCIES

Adoption Information Center of Illinois **312.346.1516**
Fax 312.346.0004
E-mail ....aici@adoptinfo-il.org
　120 W Madison St, Ste 800, Chicago, IL 60602
　Deaudrey Davis, Executive Director

Adopton Ark **847.215.2755**
E-mail ....homestudy@adoptionark.org
　830 S Buffalo Grove Rd, Ste 103-103a, Buffalo Grove,
　IL 60089

Beatrice Caffrey Youth Svcs Inc **773.624.5087**
　4924 S King Dr, Chicago, IL 60615
　Aadil Lateef, Manager

Catholic Charities Diocese of Joliet **815.723.3405**
Fax 815.723.3452
E-mail ....webinfocc@cc-doj.org
　203 N Ottawa St, 2nd Fl Ste A, Joliet, IL 60432
　Harry Wildfeuer, Director Of Children Services

Catholic Charities of the Archdiocese of **312.655.7086**
Fax 312.382.1612
E-mail ....adoptions@catholiccharities.net
　651 W Lake, Chicago, IL 60661
　Norene Chesebro, Director

Catholic Charities Peoria Diocese **309.626.8000**
Fax 309.674.1664
　2900 W Heading Ave, Peoria, IL 61604

Chicago Area Families for Adoption

CAFFA **630.545.4680**
　PMB 108, 1212 Naper Blvd Ste 119, Naperville,
　IL 60540

Children's Home + Aid (CHASI) **618.452.8900**
　2133 Johnson Rd, Ste 104, Granite City, IL 62040
　Renee Koller, Vice President

Family Net Foster & Adoptive Parent Assc **773.721.7977**
Fax 773.721.7977
E-mail ....Famnetfapa@aol.com
　1142 E 82nd Pl, Chicago, IL 60619

Hands Around the World **847.255.8309**
E-mail ....HANDSATW@aol.com
　1417 E Miner St, Arlington Heights, IL 60004
　Albert Walton, Chief Executive Officer

Help2Adapt Adoption Support Group **773.568.7170**
E-mail ....cmoore1968@sbcglobal.net
　9442 Rhodes, Chicago, IL 60619

Jewish Child & Family Svcs (JCFS) **773.467.3700**
Web ....www.jcfs.org
　3145 W Pratt Blvd, Chicago, IL 60645
　Howard Sitron, Director

Lutheran Social Svcs of IL **847.635.6764**
　1001 E Touhy Ave, Ste 50, Des Plaines, IL 60018

Lutheran Social Svcs of IL (LSSI) **309.671.0300**
　3000 W Rohmann Ave, Peoria, IL 61604

Lutheran Social Svcs of IL (LSSI) **847.635.4600**
E-mail ....info@lssi.org
　1001 E Touhy Ave, # 50, Des Plaines, IL 60018
　Pastor Denver Bitner, Chief Executive Officer

Pamark Support Group **708.269.1169**
E-mail ....pamark88@yahoo.com
　1037 S Des Plaines Ave, Unit 306, Forest Park,
　IL 60130

Prevention Family Force Ctr (PFFC) We **773.863.5694**
　3333 W Arthington, Ste 150, Chicago, IL 60624

Project Success-Family Tree Adoption **217.446.3200**
Fax 217.446.3248
E-mail ....MichaelCourtwright@yahoo.com
　101 W North St, Danville, IL 61832

Sunny Ridge Family Ctr Inc (SRFC) **630.754.4500**
Fax 630.668.5144
E-mail ....info@sunnyridge.org
　270 Remington Blvd Ste C, Bolingbrook, IL 60440
　Gary Longman, President

The Adoption Connection Illinois (TAC) **847.433.7820**
　452 Central Ave, Ste 206, Highland Park, IL 60035

The Baby Fold (TBF) **309.454.1770**
E-mail ....krousey@thebabyfold.org
　612 Oglesby Ave, Normal, IL 61761
　Karen Rousey, Program Director

The Cradle **847.475.5800**
E-mail ....cradle@cradle.org
　2049 Ridge Ave, Evanston, IL 60201
　Julie Tye, Executive Director

Volunteers of America of Illinois (VOA) **312.564.2300**
Fax 312.564.2301
　47 W Polk St, Ste 250-2, Chicago, IL 60605
　Nancy Hughes Moyer, Chief Executive Officer

White Oak Foundation **312.666.5721**
E-mail ....lltreesurgeon@aol.com
　525 N Halsted, Ste 203, Chicago, IL 60642

HOME MEDICAL EQUIPMENT PROVIDERS

Anixter Center **773.973.7900**
Fax 773.973.5268
E-mail ....AskAnixter@anixter.org
　2001 N Clybourn Ave 3rd Flr, Chicago, IL 60614

Fastrack Medical Supplies, Inc. **847.982.9440**
Fax 847.982.9442
Web ....fastrackmedical.webs.com
　7301 North Lincoln Avenue, Suite 215, Lincolnwood,
　IL 60712
　CARF accredited programs available.

Illiana Home Med Equip & Supplies **773.778.8800**
E-mail ....info@illianahomemed.com
　3510 W 79th St, Chicago, IL 60652
　Madeleine Singson, Supervisor

Rehab Inst of Chicago Wheelchair & Seat **312.238.1000**
　345 E Superior, Chicago, IL 60611
　Ed Case, Chief Executive Officer

Rehabilitation Institute of Chicago **312.238.1000**
Web ....www.ric.org
　345 E Superior St, Chicago, IL 60611
　Dr. Joann Smith, President

S & E Medical Supply Company, Inc. **847.673.7300**
Fax 847.673.7305
　7434 Skokie Boulevard, Skokie, IL 60077
　CARF accredited programs available.

United Cerebral Palsy of Grtr Chicago **708.444.8460**
Fax 708.429.3981
E-mail ....cdeardorff@ucpnet.org
　7550 West 183rd St, Tinley Park, IL 60477
　Greg Grill, Program Director

University of Illinois at Chicago **312.433.4114**
E-mail ....chicagonorth@uic.edu
　722 W Maxwell St, 3rd Flr Ste 350, Chicago,
　IL 60607
　Sharla Luken, Supervisor

Illinois

University of Illinois at Chicago **312.996.6380**
Fax 312.413.0367
E-mail .... dscc@uic.edu
 1919 W Taylor St mc 618, 8th Flr Room 800,
 Chicago, IL 60612
 Thomas Jerkovitz, Director

PEDIATRIC HOME CARE

Downers Grove (Recruitment Center) **630.829.8410**
 2755-A Curtiss St, Downers Grove, IL 60515

Interim Healthcare **815.725.9091**
Fax 815.725.9094
 310 N Hammes St, Ste 301E, Joliet, IL 60435
 Ceri, Office Manager

Interim Healthcare **708.422.2934**
Fax 708.422.5528
 10735 S Cicero Ave Ste 100, Oswego, IL 60543
 Cheryl Peterson, Nursing Director

Interim Hlthcare (Chicago Oak Park State) **708.383.7223**
Fax 708.383.0989
 1140 W Lake St Ste 202, Oak Park, IL 60301

South Barrington PDN (North Chicago) **847.426.2551**
 33 W Higgins Rd Ste 5050, Barrington, IL 60010
 Cathyline Foynn, Location Director

Tinley Park PDN (South Chicago) **708.429.5551**
 7820 Graphics Dr, Tinley Park, IL 60477
 Kathleen Flynn, Director Of Nursing

SOCIAL SERVICES

Abraham Lincoln Centre Roseland Headst **773.264.7633**
Fax 773.291.0826
E-mail .... bwoods@abelink.org
 7 E 119th St, Chicago, IL 60628-6117
 Barbara Woods, Director

Annie B. Jones Community Services, Inc. **773.667.2100**
Fax 773.667.9578
Web .... www.abj.org
 1507 E. 53rd Street, PMB 336, Chicago, IL 60615
 COA accredited organization.

Arden Shore Child and Family Services **847.549.1730**
Fax 847.549.1731
Web .... www.ardenshore.org
 935 Lakeview Parkway, Suite 105, Vernon Hills,
 IL 60061
 COA accredited organization.

Arrowhead Ranch **309.799.7044**
Fax 309.799.7574
Web .... www.arrowheadranchinc.com
 P.O. Box 370, Coal Valley, IL 61240-0370
 COA accredited organization.

Association House of Chicago **773.772.7170**
Fax 773.384.0560
Web .... www.associationhouse.org
 1116 North Kedzie Avenue, Chicago, IL 60651
 COA accredited organization.

Beatrice Caffrey Youth Service, Inc. **773.624.5087**
Fax 773.624.4892
Web .... www.beatricecaffrey.net
 4924 South King Drive, Chicago, IL 60615
 COA accredited organization.

Behavioral Health Alternatives, Inc. **618.251.4073**
Fax 618.251.6246
 337 East Ferguson Avenue, Wood River, IL 62095
 COA accredited organization.

Bethany For Children & Families **309.797.7700**
Fax 309.797.2386
Web .... www.bethany-qc.org
E-mail .... info@bethany-qc.org
 1830 6th Ave, Moline, IL 61265-2105
 Bill Steinhauser, President

Call for Help, Inc. **618.397.0968**
Fax 618.397.6836
Web .... www.callforhelpinc.org
 9400 Lebanon Road, Edgemont, IL 62203
 COA accredited organization.

Camp Wartburg **618.939.7715**
Fax 618.939.6288
Web .... www.campwartburg.com
E-mail .... wartburgnatc@net
 5705 Lrc Rd, Waterloo, IL 62298
 Bob Polansky, Camp Director

Casa Central Social Services Corporation **773.645.2300**
Fax 773.645.2335
Web .... www.casacentral.org
 1343 North California Avenue, Chicago, IL 60622
 COA accredited organization.

Catholic Charities Children Svcs Div **815.723.3053**
Fax 815.723.2853
Web .... www.dioceseofjoliet.org
 203 N Ottawa St, Ste 2A, Joliet, IL 60432
 Glenn Vancura, Executive Director

**Catholic Charities of the Archdiocese of
Chicago** **312.655.7000**
Fax 312.382.1612
Web .... www.catholiccharities.net
 721 N. LaSalle, Chicago, IL 60654
 COA accredited organization.

Catholic Charities of the Diocese of Peoria **309.636.8000**
Fax 309.674.1664
Web .... www.ccdop.org
 Spalding Pastoral Center 419 NE Madison Avenue,
 Peoria, IL 61603
 COA accredited organization.

Catholic Charities of the Diocese of Peoria **309.636.8000**
Fax 309.674.1664
Web .... www.ccdop.org
 Spalding Pastoral Center 419 NE Madison Avenue,
 Peoria, IL 61603
 COA accredited organization.

**Catholic Charities of the Diocese of Springfield in
Illinois** **217.523.9201**
Fax 217.523.5624
Web .... www.cc.dio.org
 1625 W. Washington Street, Springfield,
 IL 62702-4757
 COA accredited organization.

Catholic Charities, Diocese of Joliet, Inc. **815.723.3405**
Fax 815.723.3452
Web .... www.cc-doj.org
 203 N. Ottawa Street, Joliet, IL 60432

Catholic Charities, Diocese of Rockford, IL **815.965.0623**
Fax 815.965.0628
Web .... www.ccrfd.org
 555 Colman Center Drive - PO Box 7044, Rockford,
 IL 61125
 COA accredited organization.

Catholic Charities, Springfield Diocese **217.525.0500**
Fax 217.525.0554
Web .... www.catholiccharitiesusa.org
E-mail .... zellers_ccspfld@hansoninfosys.com
 120 S 11th St, Springfield, IL 62703-1006
 Danielle Zellers, Director

**Catholic Social Services of Southern
Illinois** **618.394.5900**
Fax 618.394.5909
Web .... www.cssil.org
 8601 W. Main Street, Suite 201, Belleville, IL 62223
 COA accredited organization.

CCR&R John A Logan College **618.985.5975**
Fax 618.985.3528
Web .... www.jalc.edu/ccrr
 700 Logan College Dr, Carterville, IL 62918-2501
 Lori Longuvuville, Director

Centers for New Horizons, Inc. **773.373.5700**
Fax 773.924.1470
Web .... www.cnh.org
 4150 South King Drive, Chicago, IL 60653-2616
 COA accredited organization.

Chaddock **217.222.0034**
Fax 217.222.3865
Web .... www.chaddock.org
 205 South 24th Street, Quincy, IL 62301
 COA accredited organization.

**Chapin Hall Ctr For Children At The University Of
Chicago** **773.753.5900**
Fax 773.753.5940
Web .... www.chapinhall.org
E-mail .... mstagner@chapinhall.org
 1313 E 60th St, Chicago, IL 60637-2830
 Matthew Stagner, Executive Director

Chestnut Health System **618.397.0900**
Fax 618.397.4368
Web .... www.chestnut.org
E-mail .... omercer@chestnut.org
 12 N 64th St Ste 5, Belleville, IL 62223
 Orville Mercer, Executive Director

**Chicago city North Community
Counseling** **773.866.1035**
Fax 773.866.1035
 3525 W Peterson Ave Ste 400, Chicago, IL 60659

Chicago Urban League **773.285.5800**
Fax 773.285.7772
Web .... www.thechicagourbanleague.org
E-mail .... president@thechicagourbanleague.org
 4510 S Michigan Ave, Chicago, IL 60653-3898
 Andrea Zopp, President & CEO

Child & Adolescent Institute at the **847.412.4387**
 Elaine Karsten Childrens Ctr, 255 Revere Dr Ste 200,
 Northbrook, IL 60062

Child Care Assoc Of Illinois **217.528.4409**
Fax 217.528.6498
Web .... www.cca-il.org
 413 W Monroe St Ste 1, Springfield, IL 62704
 Margaret Berglind, President/CEO

Child Care Resource And Referral **815.741.1163**
Fax 815.741.1170
Web .... www.childcarehelp.com
E-mail .... cbzdon@childcarehelp.com
 801 N Larkin Ave Ste 202, Joliet, IL 60435
 Chris Bzdon, Director

Child Care Resource And Referral Network **309.828.1892**
Fax 309.828.0526
Web .... www.ccrrn.com/
E-mail .... referral@ccrrn.com
 207 W Jefferson St Ste 301, Bloomington,
 IL 61701-3969
 Becky Heerdt, Referral Specialist

Children's Home Association of Illinois **309.685.1047**
Fax 309.687.7299
Web .... www.chail.org
E-mail .... jgress@chail.org
 2130 North Knoxville Avenue, Peoria, IL 61603
 Jeff Gress, Director
 COA accredited organization.

ChildServ **773.693.0300**
Fax 773.693.0322
Web .... www.childserv.org
 8765 W. Higgins Road, Suite 450, Chicago, IL 60631
 COA accredited organization.

Community Child Care Connection, Inc. **217.525.2805**
Fax 217.525.2894
Web .... www.cccconnect.org
919 S Spring St, Springfield, IL 62704
Tamara Skube, Director

Community Coordinated Childcare (4-C) **815.344.5510**
Fax 815.344.5520
E-mail .... janf@four-c.org
667 Ridgview Rd, Mchenry, IL 60050
Jan Fox, Director

Coordinated Youth & Human Svcs **618.876.2383**
Fax 618.876.4952
Web .... www.cyhs.com
E-mail .... cindyg@cyhs.com
2016 Madison Ave, Granite City, IL 62040-4657
Cindy Gavilsky, Director

Counseling & Family Services **309.676.2400**
Fax 309.676.6037
Web .... www.cfspeoria.org
330 SW Washington Street, Peoria, IL 61602-1406
COA accredited organization.

Crittenton Centers **309.674.0105**
Fax 309.674.7029
Web .... www.crittentoncenters.org
442 West John Gwynn Jr. Avenue, Peoria, IL 61605
COA accredited organization.

Crosspoint Human Services **217.442.3200**
Fax 217.442.7460
210 Avenue C, Danville, IL 61832
COA accredited organization.

Eastern Illinois University Child Care Resource And
Referral **217.581.6698**
Fax 217.581.7084
Web .... www.eiu.edu
E-mail .... cstld@eiu.edu
600 Lincoln Ave, Charleston, IL 61920
Misty Baker, Director

Egyptian Public and Mental Health
Department **618.273.3326**
Fax 618.273.2808
Web .... www.egyptian.org
1412 U.S. 45 North, Eldorado, IL 62930
COA accredited organization.

Evangelical Child And Family Agency **630.653.6400**
Fax 630.653.6490
Web .... www.evancfa.org
E-mail .... mail@evancfa.org
1530 N Main St, Wheaton, IL 60187-3512
David Lundberg, Director Of Clinical Services
COA accredited organization.

Family Resource Ctr **773.334.2300**
Fax 773.334.8228
Web .... www.f-r-c.org
E-mail .... adoptions@f-r-c.org
5828 N Clark St, Chicago, IL 60660
Richard Pearlman, Executive Director

Family Service Association of Greater Elgin
Area **847.695.3680**
Fax 847.695.4552
Web .... www.fsaelgin.org
22 South Spring Street, Elgin, IL 60120-6410
COA accredited organization.

Family Service Center **217.528.8406**
Fax 217.528.8542
Web www.service2families.org
730 East Vine, Springfield, IL 62703
COA accredited organization.

Family Svc Assoc Of Greater Elgin Area **847.695.3680**
Fax 847.695.4552
Web .... www.fsaelgin.org
E-mail .... lalaforge@fsaelgin.org
22 S Spring St, Elgin, IL 60120
Lisa Laforge, Director

Fola Community Action Services **773.487.4310**
Fax 773.487.4320
8014-8016 S. Ashland Avenue, Chicago, IL 60620
COA accredited organization.

Generation Of Hope **217.893.4673**
Fax 217.893.3126
Web .... www.generationsofhope.org
E-mail .... contact@generationsofhope.org
1530 Fairway Dr, Rantoul, IL 61866
Elaine Gehrmann, Executive Director

Grand Prairie Svcs **708.799.2200**
Fax 708.922.4485
E-mail .... grandprairieservicesgpsbh.org
19530 kedzie ave, Flossmoor, IL 60422
Dr. Ronald Weglarz, Clinical Director

Graywood Enterprises also known as The Graywood
Foundation **217.345.3461**
Fax 217.345.3467
Web .... www.graywood.org
1380 Beech Tree Road, Charleston, IL 61920
CARF accredited programs available.

Guardian Angel Community Services **815.729.0930**
Fax 815.744.6087
Web .... www.guardianangelhome.org
1550 Plainfield Road, Joliet, IL 60435
COA accredited organization.

Habilitative Systems, Inc. **773.261.2252**
Fax 773.854.8300
Web .... www.habilitative.org
E-mail .... ddew@habilitative.org
415 S Kilpatrick, Chicago, IL 60644
Donald Dew, Executive Director
CARF accredited programs available.

Hephzibah Children's Association **708.649.7100**
Fax 708.649.7102
Web .... www.hephzibahhome.org
946 North Boulevard, Oak Park, IL 60301
COA accredited organization.

Hobby Horse House **217.243.7708**
Fax 217.243.5557
E-mail .... escott@agr.state.il.us
208 S Mauvaisterre St, Jacksonville, IL 62650-2550
Ed Scott, Director

Hoyleton Youth and Family Services **618.493.7382**
Fax 618.493.6390
Web .... www.hoyleton.org
P.O. Box 218, Hoyleton, IL 62803

Human Resources Development Institute,
Inc. **312.441.9009**
Fax 312.441.9019
Web .... www.hrdi.org
222 South Jefferson Street, Chicago, IL 60661
COA accredited organization.

Illinois Central Child Care Connection **309.690.7300**
Fax 309.690.7320
Web .... www.salchildcareconnection.org
E-mail .... info@salchildcareconnection.org
3425 N Trees Ln, Peoria, IL 06104
Brenda Smith, Director

Illinois Department of Children & Family Services
406 E. Monroe Street, Springfield, IL 62701-1498
COA accredited organization.

Illinois Mentor **708.679.9137**
Fax 708.503.6267
Web .... www.thementornetwork.com
600 Holiday Plaza, Suite 400, Matteson, IL 60443
COA accredited organization.

Jane Addams Hull House Association **312.906.8600**
Fax 312.235.5287
Web .... www.hullhouse.org
1030 West Van Buren Street, Chicago, IL 60607
COA accredited organization.

JCFS Therapeutic Day School and **773.467.3900**
Fax 773.467.3999
E-mail .... howardfitron@jcfs.org
Yeshiva at the Joy f Knapp Ctr, 3145 W Pratt Blvd,
Chicago, IL 60645
Howard Fitron, Executive Director

Jewish Child & Family Services **773.866.5035**
Fax 773.866.1035
216 W Jackson Ste 800, Chicago, IL 60606
Mary Lentine, Clinical Supervisor

Jewish Child & Family Services **312.444.2090**
Fax 312.855.3754
E-mail .... RobertBloom@JCFS.org
216 W Jackson St Ste 800, Chicago, IL 60606
Howard Sitron, Director

Kemmerer Village **217.226.4451**
Fax 217.226.2102
Web .... www.kemmerervillage.org
941 N. 2500 East Road, Assumption, IL 62510
COA accredited organization.

Lakeside Community Committee **773.224.9217**
Fax 773.224.9468
Web .... www.lakeside-cc.org
7418 S. Cottage Grove Avenue, Chicago, IL 60619
COA accredited organization.

LEEDA Services of Illinois, Inc. **773.274.9760**
Fax 773.274.9763
1607 West Howard Street, Fourth Floor, Chicago,
IL 60626
CARF accredited programs available.

Lutheran Child and Family Services of
Illinois **708.771.7180**
Fax 708.771.7184
Web .... www.lcfs.org
7620 Madison Street, River Forest, IL 60305
COA accredited organization.

Lutheran Social Services of Illinois **847.635.4600**
Fax 847.635.6764
Web .... www.lssi.org
1001 E. Touhy Avenue, Suite 50, Des Plaines,
IL 60018-5816
COA accredited organization.

Lydia Home Association **773.653.2200**
Fax 773.736.6970
Web .... www.lydiahome.org
4300 West Irving Park Road, Chicago, IL 60641-2825
COA accredited organization.

Maryville Academy **847.294.1999**
Fax 847.824.7190
Web .... www.maryvilleacademy.org
1150 North River Road, Des Plaines, IL 60016-1290
COA accredited organization.

Mercy Home for Boys & Girls **312.738.7560**
Fax 312.738.0484
Web .... www.mercyhome.org
1140 West Jackson Boulevard, Chicago, IL 60607
COA accredited organization.

Metropolitan Family Services **312.986.4000**
Fax 312.986.4334
Web .... www.metrofamily.org
1 North Dearborn Avenue, #10, Chicago,
IL 60602-4322
COA accredited organization.

Northwest Suburban Community
Counseling **847.392.8970**
Fax 847.392.8987
1156 W Shure Dr Ste 181, Arlington Heights,
IL 60004
Lili Gray, Director

Illinois

OMNI Youth Services, Inc. **847.353.1500**
Fax 847.353.1759
Web ....www.omniyouth.org
1111 Lake Cook Road, Buffalo Grove, IL 60089
COA accredited organization.

Pediatric Resource Ctr **309.624.9595**
Fax 309.624.9694
Web ....www.uicomp.uic.edu/dept/prc
320 Armstrong, Peoria, IL 61603
Carole Siefken, Supervisor

Peoria Area Blind People's Ctr **309.637.3693**
Fax 309.494.9656
Web ....www.ppeoriablindcenter.org
E-mail ....peoriablindcenter@gmail.com
2905 W Garden St, Peoria, IL 61605-1316
Mabel Van Dusen, Executive Director

Pillars Community Services **708.795.4800**
Fax 708.795.4834
Web ....www.pillarscommunity.org
E-mail ....owilliams@pillarscommunity.org
6918 Windsor Avenue, Berwyn, IL 60402
Ollie Williams, Director
CARF accredited programs available.

Prevent Child Abuse America **312.663.3520**
Fax 312.939.8962
Web ....www.healthyfamiliesamerica.org
E-mail ....jhmurovich@preventchildabuse.org
228 S Wabash Ave, 10th Fl, Chicago, IL 60604
Jim Hmurovich, CEO

Procare Ctrs **708.681.2324**
Fax 708.681.2285
Web ....www.reshealth.org
E-mail ....fperham@reshealthcare.org
1820 S 25th Ave, Broadview, IL 60155-2864
Frank Perham, Director

Project Child Care Resource And Referral **618.244.2210**
Fax 618.244.5209
Web ....www.ric.edu/projectchild
E-mail ....prochild@ric.edu
327 Potomac Blvd, Mt Vernon, IL 62864
Tranae Brockhouse, Director

**Ravenswood Family Community Resource
Ctr** **773.784.0400**
Fax 773.784.7841
Web ....www.ravenswoodcommunities.org
E-mail ....info@ravenswoodcommunity.org
1756 W Wilson, Chicago, IL 60640
Chris Shickles, Executive Director

Response Center Skokie View **847.676.0078**
Fax 847.676.0574
E-mail ....ROBINSTEIN@JCFF.ORG
9304 Skokie Blvd, SKOKIE, IL 60077
Robin Stein, Director

Roger S Bloch Child & Family Counseling **847.568.5200**
Fax 847.568.5250
Goldie Bachmann Luftig Bldg, 5150 Golf Rd, Skokie,
IL 60077
Margaret Vimont, Executive Director

Rosecrance At Alpine **815.391.1000**
Fax 815.387.2590
Web ....www.rosecrance.org
E-mail ....gomeld@rosecrance.net
1601 N University Dr, Rockford, IL 61107-5317
David Gomel, Adolescence Director

Rutledge Youth Foundation, Inc. **217.525.7757**
Fax 217.525.7737
Web ....www.rutledgeyouthfoundation.com
534 West Miller Street, Springfield, IL 62702
COA accredited organization.

SGA Youth & Family Services **312.663.0305**
Fax 312.663.0644
Web ....www.sga-youth.org
11 East Adams Street, Suite 1500, Chicago, IL 60603
COA accredited organization.

Shelter, Inc. **847.255.8060**
Fax 847.590.6184
Web ....www.shelter-inc.org
1616 North Arlington Heights Road, Arlington
Heights, IL 60004
COA accredited organization.

Sinnissippi Ctrs, Inc. **815.625.0013**
Fax 815.625.0197
Web ....www.sinnissippi.com
E-mail ....jim.sarver@sinnissippi.com
2611 Woodlawn Rd, Sterling, IL 61081-4151
Jim Sarver, Director

Sojourn Shelter & Svcs, Inc. **217.726.5100**
Fax 217.726.8664
Web ....www.sojournshelter.org
1800 Westchester Blvd, Springfield, IL 62704-5600
Tami Silverman, Director

SOS Children's Villages Illinois **312.372.8200**
Fax 312.372.8202
Web ....www.sosillinois.org
216 West Jackson Boulevard, Suite 925, Chicago,
IL 60606
COA accredited organization.

South Central Community Services, Inc. **773.483.0900**
Fax 773.483.5701
Web ....www.sccsinc.org
8316 South Ellis Avenue, Chicago, IL 60619
COA accredited organization.

**South Suburban Community Counseling
Ctr** **708.798.1859**
Fax 708.798.9148
3649 W 183rd St Ste 123, Hazel Crest, IL 60429

**Southern Illinois University School of Medicine, Department
of Psychiatry** **217.545.8229**
Fax 217.545.2275
Web ....www.siumed.edu/psych/
P.O. Box 19642, Springfield, IL 62794-9642
COA accredited organization.

**St. Xavier University Ludden Speech & Language
Clinic** **773.298.3561**
Fax 773.298.3007
Web ....www.sxu.edu
E-mail ....klick@sxu.edu
3700 W 103rd St, Chicago, IL 60655-3199
Pamela Klick, Clinical Director

**Teen Dating Violence-Ofc Of The Circuit Court
Clerk** **312.325.9467**
Fax 312.325.9466
Web ....www.cookcountyclerkofcourt.org
555 W Harrison St, Chicago, IL 60607
Kathleen Monahan, Domestic Violence Liaison

Teen Living Programs, Inc. **312.568.5700**
Fax 312.568.5701
Web ....www.teenliving.org
162 W Hubbard St, Ste 400, Chicago, IL 60654
Jeraldine Linaf, Executive Director

The Allendale Association **847.356.2351**
Fax 847.356.0289
Web www.allendale4kids.org
P.O. Box 1088, Lake Villa, IL 60046
COA accredited organization.

The Baby Fold **309.452.1170**
Fax 309.452.0115
Web ....www.thebabyfold.org
P.O. Box 327, Normal, IL 61761-0327
COA accredited organization.

The Center For Children's Services **217.446.1300**
Fax 217.446.1325
Web ....www.tcfcs.org
702 North Logan Avenue, Danville, IL 61832
COA accredited organization.

The Children's Place Association **773.826.1230**
Fax 773.826.7193
Web ....www.childrens-place.org
1436 W. Randolph, Chicago, IL 60607
COA accredited organization.

**The Salvation Army Family & Community
Services** **773.275.6233**
Fax 773.275.6288
4800 N. Marine Drive, Chicago, IL 60640-4220
COA accredited organization.

The Youth Campus **847.823.5161**
Fax 847.823.9291
Web ....www.theyouthcampus.org
733 N. Prospect Avenue, Park Ridge, IL 60068-2764
COA accredited organization.

**Thornton Township Youth Committee,
Inc.** **708.596.6046**
Fax 708.201.1378
Web ....www.thorntontownship.com
14323 South Halsted, Riverdale, IL 60827
COA accredited organization.

Uhlich Children's Home **773.588.0180**
Fax 773.588.7762
Web ....www.ucanchicago.org
E-mail ....vandenberkt@ucanchicago.org
3737 N Mozart St, Chicago, IL 60618-3689
Thomas Vandenberk, Executive Director
COA accredited organization.

United Way Of Metropolitan Chicago **312.906.2350**
Fax 312.876.0199
Web ....www.uw-mc.org
E-mail ....jfroetscher@uw-mc.org
560 W Lake St Fl 4, Chicago, IL 60661-1445
Laura Thrall, President/CEO

Universal Family Connection, Inc. **773.881.1711**
Fax 773.881.3124
Web ....www.ufcinc.org
1350 W. 103rd Street, Chicago, IL 60643
COA accredited organization.

Virginia Frank Child Development Center **773.761.4550**
Fax 773.761.6426
3033 W Touhy ave, Chicago, IL 60645

Voices For Il Children **312.456.0600**
Fax 312.456.0088
Web www.voices4kids.org
E-mail ....info@voices4kids.org
208 S La Salle St Ste 1490, Chicago, IL 60604
Gaylord Gieseke, Vice President

Volunteers Of America Of Il **312.564.2400**
Web ....www.voaillinois.com/
E-mail ....mcomer@voail.org
47 W Polk Ste 250, Chicago, IL 60605
Michelle Comer, Communication Specialist

Volunteers of America of Illinois **312.564.2300**
Fax 312.564.2301
Web ....www.voaillinois.org
47 West Polk Street, Suite 250, Chicago, IL 60605
COA accredited organization.

Webster-Cantrell Hall **217.423.6961**
Fax 217.421.6889
Web ....www.webstercantrell.org
1942 East Cantrell Street, Decatur, IL 62521
COA accredited organization.

West Central Child Care Connection **217.222.2550**
Fax 217.222.3133
Web ....www.wcccc.com
E-mail ....ccrrinfo@wcccc.com
510 Maine St Ste 610, Quincy, IL 62301
Karen Points, Director

**West Suburban Community Counseling
Ctr** **630.705.9639**
Fax 630.392.7832
Two E 22nd St, Ste 120, Lombard, IL 60148

Willowglen Academy - Illinois, Inc. **815.233.6162**
Fax 815.233.6167
Web ....www.willowglen-il.com
  701 W. Lamm Road, Freeport, IL 61032
  COA accredited organization.

Young Womens Christian Assoc Child Care
Solutions **815.484.9442**
Fax 815.484.9456
  4990 E State St, Rockford, IL 61108
  Lisa Bock, Superviser

Youth Outreach Services **773.777.7112**
Fax 773.777.7611
Web ....www.yos.org
  2411 West Congress Parkway, Chicago, IL 60612
  COA accredited organization.

Youth Service Bureau of Illinois Valley **815.433.3953**
Fax 815.433.3980
Web ....www.ysbiv.org
  424 West Madison Street, Ottawa, IL 61350
  COA accredited organization.

SPECIAL NEEDS

Access Living **312.640.2100**
Fax 312.640.2101
E-mail ....cjohnson@accessliving.org
  115 West Chicago Ave, Chicago, IL 60654
  Marca Bristo, Chief Executive Officer

Ada S McKindley Community Srvs **773.602.2660**
E-mail ....mentalhealth@adasmckinley.org
  7640 S Vincennes, Chicago, IL 60620
  George Jones Jr., Executive Director

Adaptive Adventures Adap Sprts for Kids **847.251.8445**
Fax 303.670.8290
E-mail ....joel@adaptiveadventures.org
  2616 Wilmette Ave, Wilmette, IL 60091
  Joel Berman, Executive Director

Addus Healthcare Stockton **800.678.6703**
E-mail ....info@addus.com
  2401 S Plum Grove Rd, Palatine, IL 60067

Advance Ambulance **773.774.8999**
Fax 773.774.4744
  5567 N Elston Ave, Chicago, IL 60603
  Bryan Witek, Owner

Advanced Vision Center **847.891.8003**
Fax 847.891.8045
E-mail ....info@avconline.org
  19 E Schaumburg Rd, Schaumburg, IL 60194
  Claudia Ortiz, Manager

Advocate Lutheran General Hospital/Comprehensive Inpatient
Rehabilitation Unit **847.723.6580**
Fax 847.723.4418
Web ....www.advocatehealth.com
  1775 Dempster Street, Park Ridge, IL 60068
  Janime Gibbons, Manager
  CARF accredited programs available.

AERO Special Education Cooperative **708.496.3330**
Fax 708.496.3920
E-mail ....jgunnell@aerosped.org
  7600 South Mason Ave, Burbank, IL 60459
  James Gunnell, Executive Director

Allendale Association **888.255.3631**
Fax 847.356.0455
Web www.allendale4kids.org
  600 W Grand Ave, PO Box 1088, Lake Villa, IL 60046
  Lisa West, Vp Of Educational Services

Alternative Academic Achievement
Academy **708.206.0000**
Fax 708.957.5324
Web ....www.aaaacademy.org
  14418 S McKinley Ave, Posen, IL 60469
  Freda Mcarthur, Director

American Academy of Pediatrics **847.434.4000**
Fax 847.434.8000
  141 Northwest Point Blvd, Elk Grove Village, IL 60007
  Errol Alden Md, Executive Director

Associates in Therapy & Assessment, LLC **847.295.6141**
Fax 847.295.6176
E-mail ....drhanson@therapyandassessment.com
  21 N Skokie Hwy, Ste 203, Lake Bluff, IL 60044
  David Hanson Psy D

Autism Society Of Illinois **630.691.1270**
Fax 630.932.5620
Web ....www.autismillinois.org
E-mail ....autismill@aol.com
  2200 S Main St Ste 205, Lombard, IL 60148-5365
  Mary Betz, Director

Bear Necessities Pediatric Cancer Founda **312.214.1200**
Fax 312.214.7797
E-mail ....office@bearnecessities.org
  55 W Wacker Dr Ste 1100, Chicago, IL 60601

Blessing Hospital Inpatient Medical Rehabilitation
Unit **217.223.8400**
Fax 217.223.8383
Web ....www.blessinghospital.org
  Broadway at 11th Street, Quincy, IL 62305
  CARF accredited programs available.

Brain Injury Association **800.699.6443**
E-mail ....info@biail.org
  PO Box 64420, Chicago, IL 60664

Brehm Preparatory School **618.457.0371**
Fax 618.529.1248
Web ....www.brehm.org
E-mail ....admissioninfo@brehm.org
  1245 E Grand Ave, Carbondale, IL 62901
  Richard G Collins, Director

Carle Foundation Hospital/Inpatient Rehabilitation
Unit **217.383.3231**
Fax 217.383.3557
Web ....www.carle.com
E-mail ....dawn.henry@carle.com
  611 W Park St, Rogers 3 Rehab, Urbana, IL 61801
  Dawn Henry, Manager
  CARF accredited programs available.

Children's Habilitation Center **708.596.2220**
Fax 708.596.2258
Web ....www.childrenshabilitationcenter.com
  121 West 154th Street, Harvey, IL 60426
  CARF accredited programs available.

Connections Day School South Campus **847.359.8300**
Fax 847.359.8301
Web ....www.counselingconnections.net
  909 E Wilmette Rd, Palatine, IL 60074
  Tom Dempsey, Director

Creative Learning **773.472.1075**
E-mail ....akgon@hotmail.com
  2115 N Sedgwick, Chicago, IL 60614

Decatur Memorial Hospital **217.876.8121**
Fax 217.876.2615
Web ....www.dmhcares.org
  2300 North Edward Street, Decatur, IL 62526
  CARF accredited programs available.

Easter Seals **309.686.1177**
Fax 309.686.2029
Web ....www.ci.easterseals.com
  507 East Armstrong Avenue, Peoria, IL 61603
  CARF accredited programs available.

Easter Seals Central Illinois, Inc. **217.429.1052**
Fax 217.423.7605
Web ....www.easterseals-ci.org
  2715 North 27th Street, Decatur, IL 62526
  CARF accredited programs available.

Easter Seals DuPage and the Fox Valley
Region **630.620.4433**
Fax 630.620.1148
Web ....www.dfvr.easterseals.com
  830 South Addison Avenue, Villa Park, IL 60181
  CARF accredited programs available.

ELIM Christian School **708.389.0555**
Fax 708.389.0671
Web ....www.elimcs.org
  13020 S Central Ave, Palos Heights, IL 60463
  Mike Otte, Principal

Epilepsy Foundation of Greater Chicago **312.939.8622**
E-mail ....info@epilepsychicago.org
  17 N State Ste 1300, Chicago, IL 60602

Epilepsy Resource Center **217.726.1839**
E-mail ....llobue@spfldsparc.org
  232 Brun Ln, Springfield, IL 62702
  L Lobue, Program Manager

Family Matters **866.436.7842**
E-mail ....deinhorn@fmptic.org
  1901 S 4th St, Ste 209, Effingham, IL 62401

Family Matters **217.347.5428**
Fax 217.347.5119
E-mail ....deinhorn@arc-css.org
  1901 S 4th St Ste 209, Effingham, IL 62401
  Deb Einhorn, Executive Director

Family Resource Center on Disabilities **312.939.3513**
E-mail ....michelle.phillips@frcd.org
  20 E Jackson Blvd Rm 300, Chicago, IL 60604
  Michelle Phillips, Executive Director

Family Support Network of Illinois **309.693.8981**
E-mail ....fsn@familysupportnetwork.org
  5739 W Martindale Ln, Peoria, IL 61615
  Charlotte Cronin, Executive Director

Five Star Industries, Inc. **618.542.5421**
Fax 618.542.5556
Web www.5starind.com
  P.O. Box 60, DuQuoin, IL 62832
  COA accredited organization.

Helping Hand School For Children With Autism Helping Hand
Pediatric Outpatient Clinic **708.352.3580**
Fax 708.352.9728
Web ....www.hhrehab.com
E-mail ....sally.campbell@hhrehab.org
  9649 W 55th St, La Grange, IL 60525-3699
  Sally Wilson-Campbell, Director

Illinois Autism **630.889.7398**
E-mail ....gouldkl@comcast.net
  1590 S Fairfield Ave, Lombard, IL 60148

Illinois Center for Autism **618.398.7500**
Fax 618.394.9869
Web ....www.illinoiscenterforautism.org
  548 S Ruby Ln, Fairview Heights, IL 62208
  Susan Szekely, Director

Illinois Congress of PTA **217.528.9617**
E-mail ....il_office@pta.org
  808 S Spring St, Springfield, IL 62705
  Jolene Lowder, Manager

Illinois Spina Bifida Association **773.444.0305**
E-mail ....sbail@sbail.org
  8765 W Higgins Rd Ste 403, Chicago, IL 60631
  Amy Maggio, Executive Director

Institute of Physical Medicine and
Rehabilitation **309.692.8110**
Fax 309.692.8673
Web ....www.ipmr.org
  6501 North Sheridan Road, Peoria, IL 61614
  CARF accredited programs available.

International Dyslexia Association **630.469.6900**
E-mail ....info@readibida.org
  751 Roosevelt Rd Ste 116, Glen Ellyn, IL 60137
  Maria Logan, Office Manager

Janaston Management & Development Corporation **773.261.0075**
Fax 773.261.0084
  4942 West Division, Chicago, IL 60651
  COA accredited organization.

Kiefer School Children's Home Assn of IL **309.687.7236**
Fax 309.687.7299
Web .... www.chail.org
  2130 N Knoxville Ave, Peoria, IL 61603
  Connie Hamann, Vice President

Lawrence Hall Youth Services **773.769.3500**
Fax 773.769.6467
Web .... www.lawrencehall.org
  4833 North Francisco Avenue, Chicago, IL 60625
  COA accredited organization.

Learning Disabilities Association **708.430.7532**
E-mail .... ldaofil@ameritech.net
  10101 S Roberts Rd Ste 205, Palos Hills, IL 60465

Lindamood-Bell Learning Processes **847.412.1841**
Fax 847.412.1842
  3330 Skokie Valley Rd, Ste 207, Highlandpark, IL 60035
  Nicole Serle, Director

Lindamood-Bell Learning Processes **708.660.1860**
Fax 708.660.1861
  137 N Oak Park Ave, Ste 212, Oak Park, IL 60301

Locust Street Resource Center **217.854.3166**
Fax 217.854.3778
  320 S. Locust Street, Carlinville, IL 62626
  COA accredited organization.

Lutherbrook Academy **630.628.1467**
Fax 630.628.5354
Web .... www.lcfs.org
  329 W Lake St, Addison, IL 60101
  Deborah Conn, Director

Marianjoy Rehabilitation Hospital and Clinics **630.909.8000**
Fax 630.909.8001
Web .... www.marianjoy.org
E-mail .... akruse@marianjoy.org
  26W171 Roosevelt Road, Wheaton, IL 60187
  Alison Kruse, Director of Admissions
  CARF accredited programs available.

MDA/ALS Center at the Univ of Illinois **312.996.4780**
Fax 312.413.5780
E-mail .... rowin@uic.edu
  1801 W Taylor St, Neurosciences Ctr Rm 4E, Chicago, IL 60612
  Julie Rowin Md, Director

Memorial Medical Center/Memorial Inpatient Rehab **217.757.7474**
Fax 217.788.5530
Web .... www.memorialmedical.com
  701 North First Street, Mail Box 51, Springfield, IL 62781
  CARF accredited programs available.

Menta Group **630.907.2400**
Fax 630.907.0197
Web .... www.menta.com
  1720 N Randall Rd, Aurora, IL 60506
  Ken Carwell, Director

Mental Health America of Illinois **312.368.9070**
E-mail .... cwoz@mhai.org
  70 E Lake St, Ste 900, Chicago, IL 60601

MPI Educational Assessment, Treatment **815.735.0732**
Fax 815.722.7310
E-mail .... TheMPInstitute@comcast.net
  1415 Maple Rd, Joliet, IL 60432
  Daniel Moran, Director

NAMI Illinois **800.346.4572**
E-mail .... namiil@sbcglobal.net
  218 W Lawrence, Springfield, IL 62704
  Laura Thomas, Director

National Alliance For Autism Research Chicago Regional Ofc **312.832.9900**
Fax 312.832.1990
Web .... www.autismspeaks.org
E-mail .... stimothy@naar.org
  501 N Wells St, Ste Ec, Chicago, IL 60610-6571
  Steve Timothy, Director

National Multiple Sclerosis Society **312.421.4500**
Fax 312.421.4544
  525 W Monroe St, Chicago, IL 60661
  John Blazek, President

National Pediatric Myoclonus Center **217.545.7635**
Fax 217.545.1903
E-mail .... omsusa@siumed.edu
  SIU School of Medicine, Dept of Neurology Div of Ped, Springfield, IL 62794
  Dr. Michael Pranzatelli, Chairman

NeuroRestorative™
Rebuilding Lives After Brain Injury

NeuroRestorative Carbondale **800.743.6802**
Fax 501.758.8778
Web .... www.neurorestorative.com
E-mail .... neuroinfo@thementornetwork.com
  PO Box 2825, Carbondale, IL 62902
  Chris Williamson, State Director

NeuroRestorative Carbondale's Adolescent Integration program provides post acute residential rehabilitation services to adolescents 11-21 years old who have experienced a neurological impairment. Residential services are also provided for children 6-11 years of age through a home host model. Both programs are designed to provide opportunities for intensive transdisciplinary rehabilitation services as well as age appropriate integrated functional community based skill training. Primary goals include fostering reintegration of the adolescent into the family home, increasing their ability to care for themselves, continuing education pursuits with increased abilities, and assisting them in improving their overall social and community integration.

Pathways Awareness **312.893.6620**
E-mail .... friends@pathwaysawareness.org
  150 N Michigan Ave Ste 2100, Chicago, IL 60601
  Sarah Kerndt, Director Of Operations

Reading & Learning Lab **773.325.7745**
E-mail .... Jharri20@depaul.edu
  Schmidt Academic Center Rm212, 2320 N Kenmore Ave, Chicago, IL 60614
  J Harris, Director

Rehabilitation Services of the Illinois Neurological Institute at OSF Saint Francis Medical Center **309.655.3777**
Fax 309.624.8780
Web .... www.ilneuroinstitute.org
  530 Northeast Glen Oak Avenue, Peoria, IL 61637-0001
  CARF accredited programs available.

Schwab Rehabilitation Hospital **773.522.2010**
Fax 773.257.1709
Web .... www.schwabrehab.org
E-mail .... dianne.hunter@sinai.org
  1401 S California Blvd, Chicago, IL 60608
  Dianne Hunter, Director PR
  CARF accredited programs available.

Speech-Language-Hearing Association **312.644.0828**
E-mail .... ckeillor@bostrom.com
  35 E Wacker Dr, Ste 850, Chicago, IL 60601
  Cynthia Keillor, Executive Director

Spinal Cord Injury Association **877.373.0301**
E-mail .... sciinjury@aol.com
  1032 S LaGrange Rd, La Grange, IL 60525
  Mercedes Rauen, Chief Executive Officer

The Camelot Schools **224.402.7422**
Fax 224.402.7407
Web .... www.camelotforkids.org
  5135 Trillium Blvd, Hoffman Estates, IL 60192
  Rella Peeler

Trinity Rehabilitation Services **309.779.5000**
Fax 309.779.3957
Web .... www.trinityqc.com
  2701 17th Street, Rock Island, IL 61201
  Rick Seidler, CEO
  CARF accredited programs available.

Trinity Rehabilitation Services **309.779.5000**
Fax 309.779.3957
Web .... www.trinityqc.com
  2701 17th Street, Rock Island, IL 61201
  CARF accredited programs available.

United Cerebral Palsy of Illinois **217.528.9681**
E-mail .... ucpi@sbcglobal.net
  310 E Adams, Springfield, IL 62701

Unity Parenting & Counseling, Inc. **312.455.0007**
Fax 312.455.0038
Web .... www.unityparentingandcounseling.org
  600 W. Cermack Road, Suite 300, Chicago, IL 60616
  COA accredited organization.

Van Matre HealthSouth Rehabilitation Hospital **815.381.8500**
Fax 815.484.9035
Web .... www.rockfordmemorialhospital.com
  950 South Mulford Road, Rockford, IL 61108
  CARF accredited programs available.

Veterans Healthcare Administration - Edward Hines Jr. VA Hospital **708.202.3800**
Fax 708.202.2725
Web .... www.va.gov
  5000 South Fifth Avenue, Hines, IL 60141-5000
  CARF accredited programs available.

SUBSTANCE ABUSE TREATMENT

Barrington Youth And Family Svcs **847.381.0345**
Fax 847.381.9297
Web .... www.barringtonyouthandfamilyservices.org
E-mail .... contactbys@aol.com
  110 S Hager Ave Ste 103, Barrington, IL 60010-4170
  Rochelle Schulman, Executive Director

Ben Gordon Ctr **815.786.7544**
Fax 815.786.7580
E-mail .... michael@bengordoncenter.org
  100 S Latham St Ste 204, Sandwich, IL 60548
  Michael Flora, CEO

Bobby E. Wright Comprehensive Behavioral Health Center, Inc. **773.722.7900**
Fax 773.722.0644
Web .... www.bobbyewright.org
E-mail .... mwalker@bobbyewright.org
  Nine South Kedzie Avenue, Chicago, IL 60612
  Melvin Walker, Prevention Director
  CARF accredited programs available.

Chestnut Health Systems -- Adolescent Program **309.827.6026**
Fax 309.820.3574
Web .... www.chestnut.org
E-mail .... rhagen@chestnut.org
  1003 Martin Luther King Dr, Bloomington, IL 61701-1429
  Russel Hagen, Executive Director

Comprehensive Services, Inc. **618.242.1994**
Fax 618.242.6392
Web .... www.jccsinc.info
E-mail .... loris@jccsinc.info
  16338 North Illinois Highway 37, Mount Vernon, IL 62864
  Lori Schmider, Director of Mental Health Services
  CARF accredited programs available.

Cornell Interventions 630.325.5050
Fax 630.325.9130
  11 South 250 Route 83, Willowbrook, IL 60527
  Ron Stephan, Intake Counselor

Cornell Interventions-Contact Facility 847.526.0404
Fax 847.526.0472
Web . . . . .www.cornellcompanies.com
E-mail . . . . .jamarks@cornellcompanies.com
  26991 N Anderson Rd, Wauconda, IL 60084-2352
  Joanne Marks, Director

Gateway Youth Care 618.529.1151
Fax 618.549.9540
Web . . . . .www.recovergateway.org
  1080 E Park St, Carbondale, IL 62901-3812
  Steve Wierman, Director

Gateway Youth Care Foundation 217.529.9266
Fax 217.529.9151
Web . . . . .www.gatewayfoundation.org
E-mail . . . . .chenry@gatewayfoundation.org
  2200 Lake Victoria Dr, Springfield, IL 62703-5596
  Cary Henry, Program Manager For Youth Care

North Central Behavioral Health Systems,
Inc 815.224.1610
Fax 815.224.1730
Web . . . . .www.ncbhs.org
  2960 Chartres, Ottawa, IL 61301
  Diane Farrell, Clinical Supervisor

Omni Youth Svcs 847.634.9360
Fax 847.634.9392
Web . . . . .www.omniyouth.org
E-mail . . . . .bmckenna@omniyouth.org
  2900 N Main St, Buffalo Grove, IL 60089-2717
  Brian Mckenna, Director Of Youth And Family Counseling

Prevention First, Inc 217.793.7353
Fax 217.793.7354
Web . . . . .www.prevention.org
E-mail . . . . .karel.ares@prevention.org
  2800 Montvale Dr, Springfield, IL 62704-4291
  Karel Ares, Executive Director

Serenity House Counseling Services, Inc. 630.620.6616
Fax 630.620.7924
Web . . . . .www.serenityhouse.com
E-mail . . . . .serenity@serenityhouse.com
  891 S Rohlwing Rd, Addison, IL 60101-4220
  Deshanna Byrdlong, Hiv Program Manager

Sojourn House, Inc 815.232.5121
Fax 815.233.4591
  565 N Turner Ave, Freeport, IL 61032-3294
  David Manson, Director

Illinois

Indiana

Mitch Daniels, Governor
Office of the Governor
Indianapolis, IN 46204-2797
317.232.4567
317.232.3443 (Fax)
www.in.gov/gov

Ashley Barnett, Juvenile Justice Specialist
Youth Division Director, ICJI
101 W. Washington St. #1170 E
Indianapolis, IN 46204
317.233.3340
317.232.4979 (Fax)
abarnett@cji.in.gov

Mary Wllnitz, SAG Chair
Figment Group, Inc.
2328 N US Hwy 35
LaPorte, IN 46350
219.326.8880
mwellnitz@figmentgroupinc.com

CRISIS NUMBERS

Child Abuse Reporting . . .800.800.5556

STATE SERVICES

SOCIAL SERVICES

Bur of Child Care IN State Fam & SS Admi 317.234.3313
Fax 317.233.6093
402 West Washington St, Indianapolis, IN 46204
Melanie Brizzi, Director

Family and Social Svcs Admin 317.232.4704
Fax 317.232.4490
Web . . . . .www.in.gov/fssa/
E-mail . . . . .zmain@fssa.state.in.us
402 W Washington St Rm W461, Indianapolis, IN 46204
Peter Bisbecos, Director

GENERAL HEALTH SERVICES

Child Special Health Care Srvs IN 317.234.3113
Fax 317.233.1342
E-mail . . . . .kbowen@isdh.in.gov
2 N Meridian St Ste 7B, Indianapolis, IN 46204
K Bowen, Director

Children's Special Health Care Services 317.233.7428
Fax 317.233.1342
E-mail . . . . .kminniear@isdh.in.gov
2 N Meridian St, Indiana State Dept of Health, Indianapolis, IN 46204-3010
Judith Ganser, Md, Mph, Director

Indiana Hospital & Health Assoc 317.633.4870
Fax 317.633.4875
Web . . . . .www.ihconnect.org
E-mail . . . . .sgrover@ihconnect.org
1 American Sq Ste 1900, Indianapolis, IN 46282-0004
Spencer L Grover, Vp

Maternal and Child Health Svcs IN 317.233.1262
Fax 317.233.1300
E-mail . . . . .m.waber@isdh.state.in.us
2 N Meridian St Section 8 C, Indianapolis, IN 46204
Mary Waber, Director

MENTAL HEALTH SERVICES

Com on Rehab Svcs IN 317.234.4475
Fax 317.232.6478
402 W Washington Rm 454, Indianapolis, IN 46207
Greg Mcaloon, Director

Div of Mental Health & Addiction 317.232.7800
Fax 317.233.3472
Web . . . . .www.in.gov/fssa/mental
E-mail . . . . .director@fssa.in.gov
402 W Washington St, Rm W353, Indianapolis, IN 46204-2772
Gina Eckart, Director

JUSTICE AGENCY

Attorney General's Ofc 317.232.6201
Fax 317.232.7979
Web . . . . .www.in.gov/attorneygeneral
302 W Washington St Rm C553, Indianapolis, IN 46204
Greg Zoeller, Attorney General

Dept of Corrections 317.233.6984
Fax 317.232.6798
Web . . . . .www.in.gov/idoc
302 W Washington St, IN Government Center South Room E334, Indianapolis, IN 46204
Bruce Lemmon, Commissioner

Indiana Criminal Justice Institute 317.232.1233
Fax 317.232.4979
Web . . . . .www.in.gov/cji
E-mail . . . . .tjohnson@cji.in.gov
101 W Washington St, Ste 1070, Indianapolis, IN 46204-3407
Tanya Johnson, Juvenile Justice Specialist

Violent Crime Compensation Fund 800.353.1484
Fax 317.233.3912
E-mail . . . . .jfistrovich@cji.in.gov
101 A Washington St, East Tower Ste 1170, Indianapolis, IN 46204
Mary Wilson, Victim Compensation Supervisior

COURTS

Administrative Ofc of Courts 317.232.2542
Fax 317.233.6586
Web . . . . .www.courts.state.in.us
E-mail . . . . .ljudson@courts.state.in.us
115 W Washington St Ste 1080, Indianapolis, IN 46204-3424
Lilia Judson, Executive Director

POLICE AND SHERIFF

Indiana Assoc of Chiefs of Police 317.816.1619
Fax 317.816.1633
Web . . . . .www.iacop.org
E-mail . . . . .mfw@wardmanage.com
10293 N Meridian St Ste 175, Indianapolis, IN 46290-1130
Michael Ward, Executive Director

Indiana Sheriffs Assoc 317.356.3633
Fax 317.356.3996
E-mail . . . . .sluce@indianasheriffs.org
7215 E 21st St Ste E, Indianapolis, IN 46219
Stephen Luce, Executive Director

EDUCATION SERVICES

Div of Exceptional Learners IN 317.232.0570
Fax 317.232.0589
E-mail . . . . .rmarra@doe.in.gov
151 W Ohio St, State House Rm 229, Indianapolis, IN 46204
R Marra, Director

Div of Language Minority & Migrant
Programs 317.232.0555
Fax 317.234.2121
151 W Ohio st, Indianapolis, IN 46204

Indiana Dept of Education 317.232.6610
Fax 317.232.8004
Web . . . . .www.doe.in.gov
E-mail . . . . .webmaster@doe.in.gov
200 W Washington St Ste 229, Indianapolis, IN 46204
Dr. Tony Bennett, Superintendent

Indiana School for the Blind and Visually
Impaired 317.253.1481
Fax 317.251.6511
E-mail . . . . .jdurst@isbvik12.org
7725 N College Ave, Indianapolis, IN 46240-2504
Jim Durst, Superintendent

INSOURCE 574.234.7101
Fax 574.234.7279
E-mail . . . . .rburden@insource.org
1703 S Ironwood, South Bend, IN 46613
Richard Burden, Director

Special Education 765.747.5239
Fax 765.747.5230
Web www.muncie.k12.in.us
E-mail . . . . .jmcshurley@muncie.k12.in.us
2501 N Oakwood Ave, Muncie, IN 47304-2376
Janet Mcshurley, Director

LABOR & WORKFORCE EDUCATION

Indiana Dept of Workforce Development 317.232.1820
Fax 317.233.1670
Web . . . . .www.dwd.is.state.in.us
E-mail . . . . .rstiver@dwd.is.state.in.us
10 N Senate Ave, #300, Indianapolis, IN 46204
Ron Stiver, Commissioner

COUNTY SERVICES

Adams County

SOCIAL SERVICES

Indiana Div of Family & Children **260.724.9169**
Fax 260.724.8265
E-mail ....jean.newton@dcs.in.gov
    720 13th St, Decatur, IN 46733
    Jean Newton, Director

JUSTICE AGENCY

Probation Dept **260.724.5336**
Fax 260.724.5337
Web ....www.co.adams.in.us
E-mail ....tfox@co.adams.in.us
    122 S 3rd St, Decatur, IN 46733-1676
    Tom Fox, Chief Performance Officer

COURTS

Adams Circuit Court **260.724.5307**
Fax 260.724.5308
E-mail ....fschurger@co.adams.in.us
    112 S. Second St, Decatur, IN 46733
    Honorable Frederick A. Schurger, Judge

POLICE AND SHERIFF

Berne Police Dept **260.589.2169**
Fax 260.589.8120
E-mail ....ptaylor@bernepd.org
    1160 W Main St, Berne, IN 46711
    Tim Taylor, Police Chief

Decatur Police Dept **260.724.3123**
Fax 260.724.3957
E-mail ....decaturpolicedept@mchsi.com
    521 N 3rd St, Decatur, IN 46733
    Ken Ketzler, Police Chief

Geneva Police Dept **260.368.7077**
Fax 260.368.7286
    200 E Line St, Geneva, IN 46740
    Robert L Johnson, Police Chief

Monroe Police Dept **260.692.6215**
Fax 260.692.6045
Web ....www.monroepolicedept.org
E-mail ....kmcintosh@monroepolicedept.org
    102 S Polk St, Monroe, IN 46772-9330
    Kevin Mcintosh, Police Chief

Sheriff's Ofc **260.724.5345**
Fax 260.724.5346
E-mail ....sheriff@co.adams.in.us
    313 S 1st St, Decatur, IN 46733
    Shane Rekeweg, Sheriff

Allen County

SOCIAL SERVICES

Div Of Family & Children **260.458.6100**
Fax 260.458.6305
Web ....www.dcs.in.gov
E-mail ....michelle.savieo@dcs.in.gov
    201 E Rudisill Blvd Ste 200, Fort Wayne,
    IN 46806-1756
    Michelle Savieo, Director

GENERAL HEALTH SERVICES

Health Dept **260.449.7561**
Fax 260.449.3010
Web ....www.allencountyhealth.com
E-mail ....info@allencountyhealth.com
    Citizens Sq. Building 200 E Berry St, Ste 360, Fort
    Wayne, IN 46802
    Mindy Waldron, Administrator

JUSTICE AGENCY

CASA Program **260.449.7190**
Fax 260.449.7828
E-mail ....rex.mcfarren@co.allen.in.us
    11801 Lima Rd, Fort Wayne, IN 46818
    Rex Mcfarren, Director

Juvenile Health **260.449.8072**
Fax 260.449.8900
    2929 Wells St, Fort Wayne, IN 46808
    Jamie Mann, Chief Performance Officer

COURTS

Superior Court-Family Relations
Div **260.449.7179**
Fax 260.449.3921
    715 S Calhoun St Rm 208, Fort Wayne, IN 46802
    Lori K. Morgan, Magistrate

POLICE AND SHERIFF

Fort Wayne Police Dept **260.427.1222**
Fax 260.427.1366
Web ....www.fwpd.org
E-mail ....russell.york@ci.ft-wayne.in.us
    1320 E Creighton Ave, Fort Wayne, IN 46803-3502
    Rusty York, Chief

Sheriff's Ofc **260.449.7535**
Fax 260.449.7915
Web ....www.co.allen.in.us
E-mail ....kenneth.fries@co.allen.in.us
    715 S Calhoun St Rm 101, Fort Wayne,
    IN 46802-1805
    Kenneth Fries, Sheriff

EDUCATION SERVICES

Special Education **260.467.1110**
Fax 260.467.1189
    203 E Douglas Ave, Fort Wayne, IN 46802
    Theresa A. Oberley, Director

Special Education **260.431.2040**
Fax 260.431.2047
Web www.sacs.k12.in.us
E-mail ....rmay@sacs.k12.in.us
    4824 Homestead Rd, Fort Wayne, IN 46814-5461
    Roxanne May, Director

Bartholomew County

SOCIAL SERVICES

Div Of Family & Children
Resources **812.376.9361**
Fax 812.378.6370
Web ....www.dcs.in.gov
E-mail ....laura.gentry@dcs.in.gov
    1531 13th St Ste 2700, Columbus, IN 47201-1310
    Heather Angebrandt, Director

GENERAL HEALTH SERVICES

Public Health Nursing **812.379.1555**
Fax 812.379.1559
Web ....www.bartholomewco.com
E-mail ....bbrown@barth.lib.in.us
    1971 State St, Columbus, IN 47201-6965
    Beverly Brown, Hiv/aids Clinic Supervisor

JUSTICE AGENCY

Probation Dept **812.379.1640**
Fax 812.373.2075
    507 3rd St, Columbus, IN 47201
    Brad Barnes, Director

POLICE AND SHERIFF

Clifford Police Dept **812.372.6465**
    PO Box 155, Clifford, IN 47226-0155
    Charlee Deweese, Police Chief

Sheriff's Ofc **812.379.1740**
Fax 812.379.1739
Web ....www.bartholomewco.com
    543 2nd St, Columbus, IN 47201-6713
    Mark Gorbett, Sheriff

Benton County

SOCIAL SERVICES

Family and Child Svcs **765.884.0120**
Fax 765.884.8758
E-mail ....ema4600@yahoo.com
    403 W 5th St, Fowler, IN 47944-1413
    Elva James, Director

GENERAL HEALTH SERVICES

Health Dept **765.884.1728**
Fax 765.884.2026
    706 E 5Th St, Ste 16, Fowler, IN 47944
    Melinda Foley Minks, Public Health Nurse

JUSTICE AGENCY

Probation Dept **765.884.1236**
Fax 765.884.2023
E-mail ....marci_probation@yahoo.com
    706 E 5th St, Fowler, IN 47944-1557
    Marci Maris, Chief Performance Officer

COURTS

Benton Circuit Court **765.884.0370**
Fax 765.884.2027
E-mail ....bcjudge@sbcglobal.net
    706 E 5th St, Fowler, IN 47944-1557
    Honorable Rex W. Kepner, Judge

POLICE AND SHERIFF

Sheriff's Ofc **765.884.0080**
Fax 765.884.2022
    105 S Lincoln Ave, Fowler, IN 47944-1544
    Butch Pritchett, Sheriff

Blackford County

SOCIAL SERVICES

Department of Child Services **765.348.2903**
Fax 765.348.4367
E-mail ....betty.lyons@dcs.in.gov
    1300 W. Water, Hartford City, IN 47348-2201
    Betty Lyons, Director

GENERAL HEALTH SERVICES

Health Dept **765.348.4317**
Fax 765.348.3041
Web ....www.blackfordcounty.com
    506 E Van Cleve St, Hartford City, IN 47348
    Robyn Clamme, Public Health Nurse

JUSTICE AGENCY

Probation Dept **765.348.0720**
Fax 765.348.7213
Web ....www.blackfordcounty.com
    110 W Washington St Ste 1, Hartford City,
    IN 47348-2280
    Aaron Henderson, Chief Performance Officer

COURTS

Blackford Circuit Court **765.348.2901**
Fax 765.348.7213
    110 W Washington St Ste 8, Hartford City,
    IN 47348-2280
    Honorable Dean Young, Director

POLICE AND SHERIFF

Hartford City Police Dept 765.348.4819
Fax 765.348.4003
Web ....www.hartfordcity.net
E-mail ....hcpd@hartfordcity.net
700 N Walnut St, Hartford City, IN 47348-1548
Matthew Felver, Police Chief

Sheriff's Ofc 765.348.0930
Fax 765.348.7237
Web ....www.blackfordcounty.com
E-mail ....jlancaster@blackfordcounty.com
64 N 500 E, Hartford City, IN 47348-9248
John Lancaster, Sheriff

EDUCATION SERVICES

Early Head Start Of Carey Serv 765.348.2523
E-mail ....mdraves@careyservices.com
509 W Franklin St, Hartford City, IN 47348
Mark Draves, Director

Boone County

SOCIAL SERVICES

IN Div of Family & Children 765.482.3023
Fax 765.482.4936
953 Monument Dr, PO Box 548, Lebanon, IN 46052

GENERAL HEALTH SERVICES

Health Dept 765.482.3942
Fax 765.483.4450
E-mail ....cmurphy@co.boone.in.us
116 W Washington St, Ste B 202, Lebanon, IN 46052
Cindy Murphy, Nursing Director

JUSTICE AGENCY

Guardian Ad Litem Program 765.483.5252
Fax 765.483.4420
Web ....www.co.boone.in.us
E-mail ....kkillin@co.boone.in.us
304 Courthouse Sq, Lebanon, IN 46052-2159
Kandi Killin, Director

COURTS

Boone Circuit Court 765.482.0530
Fax 765.483.4420
310 Courthouse Sq, Lebanon, IN 46052
Honorable Steve David, Judge

Superior Court 1 & 2 ....765.482.3510
Fax 765.485.0150
E-mail ....pbogan@co.boone.in.us
212 Courthouse Sq, Lebanon, IN 46052
Penny Bogan, Clerk

POLICE AND SHERIFF

Sheriff's Ofc 765.482.1412
Fax 765.483.3370
1905 Indianapolis Ave, Lebanon, IN 46052
Ken Campbell, Sheriff

Brown County

SOCIAL SERVICES

Family & Children Svcs 812.988.2239
Fax 812.988.1279
Web ....www.dcs.in.gov
E-mail ....debbie.daily@dcs.in.gov
121 Locust Ln, Nashville, IN 47448-7021
Debbie Daily, Director

GENERAL HEALTH SERVICES

Health Dept 812.988.2255
Fax 812.988.5601
Web ....www.browncountyheathdept.org
E-mail ....info@browncountyhealthdept.org
201 Locust Ln, County Office Bldg, Nashville,
IN 47448
Toni Warburton, Public Health Nurse

JUSTICE AGENCY

Guardian Ad Litem Program 812.340.8894
Fax 812.558.0055
E-mail ....galbrowncounty@gmail.com
PO Box 755, Nashville 47448
Sallyann Murphey, Director

Probation Dept 812.988.5505
Fax 812.988.5506
20 E Main St Ste 1., Nashville, IN 47448
Jennifer Acton, Chief Performance Officer

COURTS

Mbrown Circuit Court 812.988.7557
Fax 812.988.5515
20 E Main St, Nashville, IN 47448
Douglas Van Winkle, Magistrate

POLICE AND SHERIFF

Sheriff's Ofc 812.988.6655
Fax 812.988.5618
55 State Route 46 East, Nashville, IN 47448
Rick Followell, Sheriff

Carroll County

SOCIAL SERVICES

Family & Children Svcs 765.564.2409
Fax 765.564.6088
6931 W 300 N, Delphi, IN 46923
Sarah Sailors, Director

GENERAL HEALTH SERVICES

Health Dept 765.564.3420
Fax 765.564.6161
101 W Main St Ste 101, Delphi, IN 46923
Joyce Yoder, Public Health Nurse

JUSTICE AGENCY

Probation Dept 765.564.2460
Fax 765.564.6907
101 W Main St, Fl 3, Delphi, IN 46923
Jeffrey Smith, Case Superior Judge

COURTS

Carroll Circuit Court 765.564.3711
Fax 765.564.1829
101 W Main St, Delphi, IN 46923
Donald Currie, Judge

POLICE AND SHERIFF

Sheriff's Ofc 765.564.2413
Fax 765.564.2418
Web ....www.cacoshrf.com
310 W Main St, Delphi, IN 46923
Tony Burns, Sheriff

Cass County

SOCIAL SERVICES

Family & Children Svcs 574.722.3677
Fax 574.722.2286
Web ....www.dcs.in.gov
E-mail ....brian.brown@dcs.in.gov
300 E Broadway, Ste 502, Logansport, IN 46947
Brian Brown, Director

GENERAL HEALTH SERVICES

Logansport State Hospital 574.722.4141
Fax 574.735.3414
Web ....www.in.gov/jobs
1098 S State Road 25, Logansport, IN 46947
Mark Scuetter, Superintendent

JUSTICE AGENCY

Family Opportunity Ctr/Juvenile
Probation 574.753.7834
Fax 574.753.7638
2496 E County Road 125 N, Logansport, IN 46947
Judi Deak- Hettinger, Director

Clark County

SOCIAL SERVICES

IN Div of Family & Children 812.288.5444
Fax 812.285.0306
1421 Youngstown Shopping Cntr, Jeffersonville,
IN 47130

GENERAL HEALTH SERVICES

Health Dept 812.282.7521
Fax 812.288.2711
Web ....www.digicove.com
E-mail ....clarkisds@digicove.com
1320 Duncan Ave, Jeffersonville, IN 47130-3723
Bridgette Mckerty, Wic Supervisor/nursing Director

JUSTICE AGENCY

Probation Dept 812.285.6300
Fax 812.285.6306
501 E Court Ave Ste 319, Jeffersonville, IN 47130
James Reagan, Chief Performance Officer

POLICE AND SHERIFF

Sheriff's Ofc 812.283.4471
Fax 812.280.5608
Web ....www.clarkcosheriff.com
E-mail ....sheriff@clarkcosheriff.com
501 E Court Ave Ste 159, Jeffersonville,
IN 47130-4029
Danny Rodden, Sheriff

EDUCATION SERVICES

Communities In Schools 812.280.0028
Fax 812.280.0028
E-mail ....cis@cisclark.org
1406 Frederick Ave, Jeffersonville, IN 47130
Cathy Graninger, Executive Director

Clay County

SOCIAL SERVICES

IN Div of Family & Children 812.448.8731
Fax 812.448.1928
1015 E National Ave, Brazil, IN 47834

GENERAL HEALTH SERVICES

Health Dept 812.448.9021
Fax 812.448.9018
E-mail ....hyattk@claycountyin.gov
1214 E National Ave, Ste B110, Brazil, IN 47834
Kimberly Hyatt, Public Health Nurse

COURTS

Clay Circuit Court 812.448.9036
Fax 812.448.8255
609 E National Ave, Brazil, IN 47834
Joseph Trout, Judge

POLICE AND SHERIFF

Sheriff's Dept 812.446.2535
Fax 812.446.0941
Web ....www.claycountyin.gov
E-mail ....mheaton@claycountyin.gov
611 E Jackson St, Brazil, IN 47834-2652
Michael Heaton, Sheriff

Clinton County

SOCIAL SERVICES

IN Dept of Child Protective Svcs 765.654.8571
Fax...765.659.6649
   57 W Washington St, Frankfort, IN 46041
   Sandra Lock, Director

GENERAL HEALTH SERVICES

Health Dept 765.659.6385
Fax...765.659.6387
Web.....................................www.clintonco.com
E-mail...........................pzurfas@clintonco.com
   211 N Jackson St, Frankfort, IN 46041-1936
   Pam Zurfas, Public Health Nurse

JUSTICE AGENCY

Probation Dept 765.659.6355
Fax...765.659.0202
Web.....................................www.clintonco.com
E-mail...........................nancyw@clintonco.com
   207 N Jackson St, Frankfort, IN 46041-1936
   Nancy J. Ward, Chief Performance Officer

COURTS

Clinton Circuit Court 765.659.6345
   355 Courthouse Sq, Frankfort, IN 46041-1964
   Honorable Linley E. Pearson, Director

POLICE AND SHERIFF

Sheriff's Ofc 765.659.6393
Fax...765.659.6304
Web................................www.clintoncountysheriff.com
   301 E Walnut St, Frankfort, IN 46041-2419
   Jeff Ward, Sheriff

Crawford County

SOCIAL SERVICES

IN Div of Family & Children 812.338.2701
Fax...812.338.2704
   304 Indiana Ave, PO Box 129, English, IN 47118

JUSTICE AGENCY

Probation Dept 812.338.3033
Fax...812.338.3196
   717 E State Road 64, English, IN 47118
   James Grizzel, Chief Probation Officer

COURTS

Crawford Circuit Court 812.338.3113
Fax...812.338.2341
   715 Judicial Plaza Drive, English, IN 47118
   Honorable Kenneth L. Lopp, Judge

POLICE AND SHERIFF

Sheriff's Ofc 812.338.2802
Fax...812.338.2585
Web................................www.crawfordcountysheriff.com
   715 Judicial Plaza, English, IN 47118
   Kim Wilkerson, Sheriff

Daviess County

SOCIAL SERVICES

IN Div of Family & Children 812.254.0024
Fax...812.254.9754
   4 NE 21st St, PO Box 618, Washington, IN 47501

GENERAL HEALTH SERVICES

Health Dept 812.254.8666
Fax...812.254.8643
Web.....................................www.daviesshealth.com
E-mail...........................nurse@daviesshealth.com
   303 E Hefron St, Washington, IN 47501-2748
   Jane Norton, Rn, Public Health Nurse

JUSTICE AGENCY

Probation Dept 812.254.8663
Fax...812.254.8649
   200 E Walnut St Ste B05, Washington, IN 47501
   Beth A. O'brian, CPO

COURTS

Daviess Circuit Court 812.254.8670
Fax...812.254.8683
   200 E Walnut St Ste 201, Washington,
   IN 47501-2759
   Honorable Gregor A Smith, Judge

POLICE AND SHERIFF

Sheriff's Dept 812.254.1060
Fax...812.254.9467
   101 NE 4th St, Washington, IN 47501
   Jerry Harbstreit, Sheriff

De Kalb County

SOCIAL SERVICES

IN Div of Family & Children 260.925.2810
Fax...260.925.5542
   934 W 15th St, Auburn, IN 46706

JUSTICE AGENCY

Probation Dept 260.925.2400
Fax...260.925.5942
Web.....................................www.co.dekalb.in.us
E-mail...........................tmcalhany@co.dekalb.in.us
   215 E 9th St Ste 200, Auburn, IN 46706-2362
   Tim A. Mcalhany, Chief Performance Officer

COURTS

**De Kalb Circuit Court Superior
Court** 260.925.2764
   100 S Main St Rm 202, Auburn, IN 46706-2361
   Kirk D Carpenter, Judge

Dearborn County

SOCIAL SERVICES

Family & Children Svcs 812.537.5131
Fax...812.537.8890
Web.....................................www.dcs.in.gov
E-mail...........................sandra.ante@dcs.in.gov
   230 Mary Ave Ste 150, Lawrenceburg,
   IN 47025-2121
   Sandra Ante, Director

GENERAL HEALTH SERVICES

Health Dept 812.537.8826
Fax...812.537.1852
Web.....................................www.dearborn.in.gov
E-mail...........................lfranklin@dearborncounty.in.gov
   215B W High St, Dearborn County Administration
   Bldg, Lawrenceburg, IN 47025
   Lois Franklin, Public Health Nurse

MENTAL HEALTH SERVICES

Community Mental Health Ctr 812.576.1600
Fax...812.576.1602
Web.....................................www.cmhcinc.org
   28208 State Route 1, West Harrison, IN 47060
   Nancy Pieper, North Region Program Director

JUSTICE AGENCY

Probation Dept 812.537.8876
Fax...812.532.2040
   215 W High St, Fl 1, Lawrenceburg, IN 47025
   Stephen Bradley, Chief Performance Officer

COURTS

Dearborn-Ohio Circuit Court 812.537.8865
Fax...812.537.8765
   215 W High St, Lawrenceburg, IN 47025
   Honorable James D. Humphrey, Judge

POLICE AND SHERIFF

Sheriff's Ofc 812.537.8730
Fax...812.537.3629
   301 W High St, Lawrenceburg, IN 47025
   David Lusby, Sheriff

Decatur County

SOCIAL SERVICES

IN Div of Family & Children 812.663.6768
Fax...812.663.5703
   1025 E Freeland, Greensburg, IN 47240

GENERAL HEALTH SERVICES

Health Dept 812.663.8301
Fax...812.663.4174
   801 N Lincoln St, Greensburg, IN 47240
   Sue Colee, Rn, Public Health Nurse

JUSTICE AGENCY

Probation Dept 812.663.6969
Fax...812.527.8007
   150 Courthouse Sq Ste 238, Greensburg, IN 47240
   Deborah S. Schilling, JPO

COURTS

Decatur Circuit Court 812.663.8455
Fax...812.663.7957
E-mail...........................jwesthafer@decaturcounty.in.gov
   150 Courthouse Sq Ste 206, Greensburg, IN 47204
   Honorable John A. Westhafer, Director

POLICE AND SHERIFF

Sheriff's Ofc 812.663.8125
Fax...812.663.6887
Web................................www.decaturcountysheriff.com
   315 S Ireland St, Greensburg, IN 47240
   Daryl Templeton, Sheriff

EDUCATION SERVICES

Head Start 812.663.4450
   422 E Central Ave Ste 3, Greensburg, IN 47240
   Jill Hamer, Director

Delaware County

SOCIAL SERVICES

IN Div of Family & Children 765.751.9565
Fax...765.281.0455
   3600 W Kilgore Ave, Ste 600, Muncie, IN 47304

GENERAL HEALTH SERVICES

Health Dept 765.747.7721
Fax...765.747.7817
Web.....................................www.co.delaware.in.us
   100 W Main St Rm 207, Muncie, IN 47305-2830
   Ann Monroe, Supervisor

JUSTICE AGENCY

CASA 765.747.7875
Fax...765.213.1276
Web.....................................www.delawarecountycasa.org
E-mail...........................casa@co.delaware.in.us
   3812 W Kilgore Ave, Muncie, IN 47304-4811
   Jeff Hansard, Director

Probation Dept 765.747.7793
Fax...765.747.7728
   3412 W Kilgore Ave, Muncie, IN 47304-4842
   Ken S. Mace, CPO

COURTS

Delaware Circuit Court #1 ....765.747.7780
Fax...765.741.5792
   100 W Washington St, Ste 4, Muncie, IN 47305-1752
   Honorable Marianne L. Vorhees, Judge

Indiana

Indiana

POLICE AND SHERIFF

Sheriff's Dept 765.747.7885
Fax 765.741.3391
Web ....www.co.delaware.in.us
100 W Washington St Ste 4, Muncie, IN 47305-1752
Mike Scroggins, Sheriff

Dubois County

SOCIAL SERVICES

IN Div of Family & Children 812.482.2585
Fax 812.482.2588
1045 Wernsing Rd, Jasper, IN 47546

GENERAL HEALTH SERVICES

Health Dept 812.481.7050
Fax 812.481.7069
E-mail ....dchealth@psci.net
1187 S Saint Charles St, Jasper, IN 47546
Donna Oeding, Administrative Director

JUSTICE AGENCY

Probation Dept 812.481.7075
Fax 812.481.7088
E-mail ....probation@duboiscountyin.org
1 Courthouse Sq Rm 106, Jasper, IN 47546
Jennifer Lampert, Chief Performance Officer

COURTS

Dubois Circuit Court 812.481.7020
Fax 812.481.7030
1 Courthouse Sq, Jasper, IN 47546
Honorable William E. Weikert, Judge

POLICE AND SHERIFF

Sheriff's Ofc 812.482.3522
Fax 812.482.9434
E-mail ....terry@psci.net
255 Brucke Strasse, Jasper, IN 47547
Dommy Lampert, Sheriff

Elkhart County

SOCIAL SERVICES

IN Div of Family & Children 574.266.2401
Fax 574.266.2106
1659 Mishawaka St, Elkhart, IN 46514

GENERAL HEALTH SERVICES

Health Dept 574.523.2283
Fax 574.523.2163
Web ....www.elkhartcountyhealth.org
E-mail ....gjaeger@elkhartcountyhealth.org
608 Oakland Ave, Elkhart, IN 46516-2116
Gwen Jaeger, Communicable Disease Director

Maternal & Child Health WIC 574.522.0104
Fax 574.522.1902
1400 Hudson St, Elkhart, IN 46516
Jenny Schrock, Manager/director

JUSTICE AGENCY

Probation Dept Juvenile Div 574.523.2203
Fax 574.523.2280
315 S 2nd St, Elkhart, IN 46516
Robert Gerard, Director

COURTS

Superior Court (1, 2, 4D, 5, 6) 574.523.2231
Fax 574.523.2292
315 S 2nd St Rm F, Elkhart, IN 46516
Honorable Evan Roberts, Judge

EDUCATION SERVICES

Special Education 574.262.5542
Fax 574.262.5548
2720 California Rd, Elkhart, IN 46514
John Hutchings, Ph.d, Director, Student Services Director

Special Education 574.533.3151
Fax 574.534.9159
Web ....www.goshenschools.org
E-mail ....mhamilton@goshenschools.org
704 W Lincoln Ave, Goshen, IN 46526-2418
Mary Beth Hamilton, Director

Fayette County

SOCIAL SERVICES

Children's Svcs 765.825.8732
1503 Eastern Ave, Connorsville, IN 47331

GENERAL HEALTH SERVICES

Health Dept 765.825.4013
Fax 765.825.7189
Web ....www.co.fayette.in.us
E-mail ....cjudd@co.fayette.in.us
401 N Central Ave Ste 1, Connersville,
IN 47331-1981
Carolyn Judd, Rn, Public Health Nurse

JUSTICE AGENCY

Probation Dept 765.825.2813
Fax 765.825.7307
Web ....www.co.fayette.in.us
E-mail ....lsmith@co.fayette.in.us
111 W 4th St Ste 4, Connersville, IN 47331-1973
Laurence H. Smith, Chief Performance Officer

COURTS

CASA 765.827.5227
Fax 765.827.9573
E-mail ....casa@co.fayette.in.us
Fayette County Government Center, 401 N Central
Ave, Connersville, IN 47331-1981
Mona Chilton, Director

Fayette Circuit Court 765.825.1331
Fax 765.825.7307
Web ....www.co.fayette.in.us
E-mail ....danpflum@comcast.net
401 N Central Ave Ste 1, Connersville,
IN 47331-1981
Beth Butsch, Judge

POLICE AND SHERIFF

Sheriff's Ofc 765.825.1110
Fax 765.825.0901
123 W 4th St, Connersville, IN 47331-1901
William Wayson, Sheriff

Floyd County

SOCIAL SERVICES

Children's Svcs 812.949.4056
824 University Woods Dr Ste 10, New Albany,
IN 47150

GENERAL HEALTH SERVICES

Health Dept 812.948.4726
Fax 812.948.2208
Web ....www.dnr.state.in.us
E-mail ....cbissig@dnr.state.in.us
1917 Bono Rd, New Albany, IN 47150-4607
Connie Bissig, Rn, Public Health Nurse

JUSTICE AGENCY

CASA Program 812.949.7305
Fax 812.941.0563
Web ....www.nationalcasa.org
601 E Market St, New Albany, IN 47150
Leslea Townsend, Social Services Director

Probation Dept 812.948.5444
Fax 812.948.4713
E-mail ....ssanders@floydcounty.in.gov
3005 Grant Line Rd Ste 3, New Albany, IN 47150
Virgil L. Seay, Chief Performance Officer

POLICE AND SHERIFF

Sheriff's Ofc 812.948.5400
Fax 812.948.5485
E-mail ....dmills@floydcounty.in.gov
311 Hauss Sq Ste 151, New Albany, IN 47151
Darrell Mills, Sheriff

Fountain County

SOCIAL SERVICES

Family & Children Svcs 765.294.4126
Fax 765.294.4315
981 E State St Ste A, Veedersburg, IN 47987
Sonya Janssen, Director

GENERAL HEALTH SERVICES

Health Dept 765.762.3035
Fax 765.762.6520
E-mail ....fountain/warren@isch.in.gov
113 W Sycamore St, Attica, IN 47918
Melissa Mitchell, Rn, Fountain County Nurse

COURTS

Fountain Circuit Court 765.793.3301
Fax 765.793.6261
Web ....www.k-inc.com
E-mail ....ftncirct@k-inc.com
301 Fourth St, Covinton, IN 47932
Honorable Susan Orr-henderson, Director

POLICE AND SHERIFF

Sheriff's Ofc 765.793.3545
Fax 765.793.5007
216 Union St, Covington, IN 47932
Bill Sanders, Sheriff

Franklin County

SOCIAL SERVICES

Family & Children Svcs 765.647.4081
Fax 765.647.2636
12048 St Marys Rd Ste A, Brookville, IN 47012
Kelly Persinger, Director

GENERAL HEALTH SERVICES

Health Dept 765.647.4322
Fax 765.647.5248
Web ....www.franklincounty.in.gov
E-mail ....fchdnursing@localhealth.in.gov
1010 Franklin Ave Rm 210, Brookville,
IN 47012-1089
Diane Turney, Rn, Public Health Nurse

JUSTICE AGENCY

Probation Dept 765.647.5741
Fax 765.647.2718
Web ....www.franklincounty.in.gov
E-mail ....probation@franklincounty.in.gov
459 Main St Ste 4, Brookville, IN 47012-1475
Brian G. Campbell, Chief Performance Officer

COURTS

Franklin Circuit Court 765.647.4186
Fax 765.647.4970
Web ....www.franklincounty.in.gov
459 Main St Ste 4, Brookville, IN 47012-1475
Honorable J. Steven Cox, Judge

Fulton County

SOCIAL SERVICES

Family & Children Svcs 574.223.3413
Fax 574.223.2634
Web ....www.dcs.in.gov
1920 Rhodes St, Rochester, IN 46975-2662
Andy Turner, Director

GENERAL HEALTH SERVICES

Health Dept....................................574.223.2881
Fax...574.223.2335
Web...........................www.co.fulton.in.us/health
E-mail....................................fulton@isdh.in.gov
　125 E 9th St Ste 4, Rochester, IN 46975
Rhonda Barnett, Public Health Nurse

JUSTICE AGENCY

CASA **574.223.2183**
Fax...574.223.2183
E-mail..........................casafultoncounty@rtcol.com
　401 E 8th St Ste E, Rochester, IN 46975
Tura Thompson, Director

Probation Dept.........................**574.223.4345**
Fax...574.223.9112
Web.................................www.gibsoncounty-in.gov
　815 Main St Rm 106, Rochester, IN 46975-1546
Andrew N. Holland, Chief Performance Officer

COURTS

Fulton Circuit Court......................**574.223.4339**
Fax...574.224.4340
　815 Main St, Fl 3, Rochester, IN 46975
A Christopher Lee, Director

POLICE AND SHERIFF

Sheriff's Ofc.................................**765.647.4138**
Fax...765.647.6991
　371 Main St, Brookville, IN 47012
Ken Murphy, Sheriff

Sheriff's Ofc.................................**574.223.2819**
Fax...574.223.8990
Web...www.rtcol.com
E-mail.......................................wconley@rtcol.com
　200 E 8th St, Rochester, IN 46975-1628
Walker Conley, Sheriff

Gibson County

SOCIAL SERVICES

Family & Children Svcs **812.385.4727**
Fax...812.385.2197
E-mail.............................jan.dotson@dcs.in.gov
　321 S 5th Ave, Princeton, IN 47670
Jan Dotson, Director

GENERAL HEALTH SERVICES

Health Dept.................................**812.385.3831**
Fax...812.386.8027
Web.........................www.gibsoncountyhealth.com
E-mail.........................jschatz@gibsoncounty-in.gov
　800 S Prince St, Courthouse Annex, Princeton,
　IN 47670
Jennifer Schatz, Rn, Public Health Nurse

JUSTICE AGENCY

CASA **812.386.9305**
Fax...812.386.9085
E-mail.............................jjines@gibsoncounty-in.gov
　101 N Main St Ste 1, Princeton, IN 47670
Joy Jines, Director

POLICE AND SHERIFF

Sheriff's Dept.................................**812.385.3496**
Fax...812.385.2814
E-mail.......................gcsd@gibsoncountysheriff.com
　112 E Emerson St, Princeton, IN 47670
George Ballard, Sheriff

Grant County

SOCIAL SERVICES

Dept of Child Svcs **765.668.4500**
Fax...765.668.4516
E-mail..........................joseph.combs@dcs.in.gov
　840 N Miller Ave, Marion, IN 46952
Joseph Combs, Director

JUSTICE AGENCY

CASA Program **765.664.1891**
Fax...765.664.1963
E-mail.........................casa@grantcounty.net
　110 W 4th St, Marion, IN 46952-4018
Leslie Hendricks, Executive Director

COURTS

Superior Court # 2.........................**765.662.1719**
Fax...765.668.6521
　101 E 4th St Ste 210, Marion, IN 46952
Honorable Dana Kenworthy, Director

POLICE AND SHERIFF

Sheriff's Dept.................................**765.662.9836**
Fax...765.668.6538
Web...www.grantcounty.net
E-mail.........................oarchey@grantcounty.net
　214 E 4th St, Marion, IN 46952-4026
Darrel Hiemlich, Sheriff

Greene County

SOCIAL SERVICES

Children's Svcs **812.384.0863**
　104 Cty Rd 70 E, Ste A, PO Box 443, Bloomfield,
　IN 47424

GENERAL HEALTH SERVICES

Health Dept.................................**812.384.4496**
Fax...812.384.2037
E-mail.........................marilyn.crays@co.greene.in.us
　217 E Spring St Ste 1, Bloomfield, IN 47424
Marilyn Crays, Rn, Public Health Nurse

JUSTICE AGENCY

CASA **812.384.2036**
Fax...812.384.2386
Web...www.co.greene.in.us
E-mail.........................casa@co.greene.in.us
　PO Box 231, Bloomfield, IN 47424-0231
Samantha Flath, Director

Probation Dept.........................**812.384.8774**
Fax...812.384.2054
E-mail.........................mike.pate@co.greene.in.us
　1 Main St Ste 202, Bloomfield, IN 47424
Mike Pate, Chief Performance Officer

COURTS

Greene Circuit Court......................**812.384.4325**
Fax...812.384.8458
E-mail.........................eric.allen@co.greene.in.us
　1 E Main St, Bloomfield, IN 47424
Honorable Eric C. Allen, Judge

Superior Court.............................**812.384.3492**
Fax...812.384.8458
Web...www.co.greene.in.us
　1 Main St, PO Box 229, Bloomfield, IN 47424
Honorable Dena Martin, Judge

POLICE AND SHERIFF

Sheriff's Dept.................................**812.384.4422**
Fax...812.384.2024
Web...www.greenecosd.org
　204 County Road 70 East, Bloomfield, IN 47424
Terry D Pierce, Sheriff

Hamilton County

SOCIAL SERVICES

Family & Children Svcs **317.773.2183**
Fax...317.776.3078
Web...www.dcs.in.gov
　938 N 10th St, Noblesville, IN 46060-1801
Christi Tucker, Director

GENERAL HEALTH SERVICES

Health Dept.................................**317.776.8500**
Fax...317.776.8506
Web...............................www.hamiltoncounty.in.gov
　18030 Foundation Dr Ste A, Noblesville, IN 46060
Jim Ginder, Hiv Coordinator

JUSTICE AGENCY

Probation Dept.........................**317.776.9672**
Fax...317.776.8413
Web...www.co.hamilton.in.us
E-mail.........................mlw@co.hamilton.in.us
　1 Hamilton County Sq Ste 29, Noblesville,
　IN 46060-2229
Madonna Wagoner, Director Probation Services

COURTS

Hamilton Circuit Court......................**317.776.9635**
E-mail.........................tsb@co.hamilton.in.us
　1 Hamilton County Sq Ste 337, Noblesville, IN 46060
Peggy Beaver, Clerk Of Court

Hancock County

GENERAL HEALTH SERVICES

Health Dept.................................**317.477.1125**
Fax...317.477.1154
E-mail.........................eburkhardt@hancockcoingov.org
　111 American Legion Pl Ste 150, Greenfield,
　IN 46140-2371
Elizabeth Burkhardt, Rn, Public Health Nurse

JUSTICE AGENCY

Probation Dept.........................**317.477.1135**
Fax...317.477.1182
E-mail.........................waddison@hancockcoingov.org
　9 E Main St Ste 102, 1ST FLOOR COURT HOUSE,
　Greenfield, IN 46140
B. Wayne Addison, Chief Performance Officer

COURTS

Hancock Circuit Court......................**317.477.1107**
Fax...317.477.1711
Web...www.hancockcoingov.org
E-mail.........................rculver@hancockcoingov.org
　9 E Main St Ste 302, Greenfield, IN 46140-2320
Honorable Richard D. Culver, Judge

POLICE AND SHERIFF

Sheriff's Ofc.................................**317.477.1147**
Fax...317.477.1703
E-mail.........................mshepherd@hancockcoingov.org
　123 E Main St, Greenfield, IN 46140
Michael Shepherd, Sheriff

Harrison County

GENERAL HEALTH SERVICES

Health Dept.................................**812.738.3237**
Fax...812.738.4292
Web...www.harrisoncountyhealth.com
E-mail.........................harrisoncountyhealth@yahoo.com
　266 Atwood St, Corydon, IN 47112-1738
Jeanine Fonda, Public Health Nurse

JUSTICE AGENCY

Probation Dept **812.738.3182**
Fax 812.738.1868
E-mail ....eday@harrisoncounty.in.gov
   300 N Capitol Ave, Corydon, IN 47112
Elizabeth Day, Chief Performance Officer

COURTS

Harrison Circuit Court **812.738.2191**
Fax 812.738.7502
   300 N Capitol Ave Ste 103, Corydon, IN 47112
John T Evans, Judge

Hendricks County

GENERAL HEALTH SERVICES

Health Dept **317.745.9222**
Fax 317.745.9383
Web ....www.co.hendricks.in.us
E-mail ....msmith@co.hendricks.in.us
   355 S Washington St Ste 210, Danville,
   IN 46122-1798
Monica Smith, Rn, Nursing Director

JUSTICE AGENCY

Plainfield Educational Re-Entry
Facility **317.839.7751**
Fax 317.838.7548
   501 W Main St, Plainfield, IN 46168-1297
Jennifer French, Superintendent

Probation Dept **317.745.9832**
Fax 317.745.9605
E-mail ....ggreen@co.hendricks.in.us
   1 Courthouse Sq Ste 103, Danville, IN 46122
Gwyn Green, Director Of Probation

POLICE AND SHERIFF

Sheriff's Ofc **317.745.6269**
Fax 317.745.9276
Web ....www.hendricks.in.us
   925 E Main St, Danville, IN 46122
Dave Galloway, Sheriff

Henry County

SOCIAL SERVICES

Family & Children Svcs **765.529.3450**
Fax 765.521.2330
   503 Newyork Ave, New Castle, IN 47362
Michael Fleming, Director

GENERAL HEALTH SERVICES

Health Dept **765.521.7053**
Fax 765.521.7055
Web ....www.henryco.net
E-mail ....dmiller@henryco.net
   1201 Race St, Ste 208, New Castle, IN 47362
Deb Miller, Rn, Director Of Nursing

JUSTICE AGENCY

Probation Dept **765.529.9174**
Fax 765.529.9213
E-mail ....slightfoot@henryco.net
   1215 Race St, Ste 160, New Castle, IN 47362
Susan B. Lightfoot, Chief Performance Officer

COURTS

Henry Circuit Court **765.529.1403**
Fax 765.599.2498
E-mail ....mwillis@henryco.net
   1215 Race St, Justice Center, Ste. 340, New Castle,
   IN 47362
Honorable Mary G. Willis, Judge

Superior Court 1 ....**765.529.6408**
Fax 765.599.2496
Web ....www.henryco.net
   1215 Race St, Justice Center, Ste. 320, New Castle,
   IN 47362
Honorable Michael D. Peyton, Judge

POLICE AND SHERIFF

Sheriff's Dept **765.521.7032**
Fax 765.521.3745
E-mail ....butch.baker@co.henry.in.us
   127 N 12th St, New Castle, IN 47362
Butch Baker, Sheriff

Howard County

JUSTICE AGENCY

CASA Program **765.454.5575**
Fax 765.454.5589
E-mail ....casa2@iquest.net
   104 N Buckeye St Rm 100, Kokomo, IN 46901
Katina Silver, Executive Director

Probation Dept **765.456.2222**
Fax 765.456.2266
E-mail ....don.travis@co.howard.in.us
   701 S Berkley Rd, Kokomo, IN 46901
Donald J. Travis, Chief Performance Officer

COURTS

Howard Circuit Court **765.456.2202**
Fax 765.456.2016
   104 N Buckeye St Rm 310, Kokomo, IN 46901
Honorable Lynn Murray, Judge

POLICE AND SHERIFF

Sheriff Dept **765.456.2020**
Fax 765.456.2145
E-mail ....marty.talbert@co.howard.in.us
   1800 W Markland Ave, Kokomo, IN 46901-6126
Marshall Talbert, Sheriff

Huntington County

GENERAL HEALTH SERVICES

Health Dept **260.358.4831**
Fax 260.358.4899
Web ....www.huntington.in.us
E-mail ....tami.hurlburt@huntington.in.us
   354 N Jefferson St Ste 201, Huntington,
   IN 46750-2769
Tami Hurlburt, Clinic Coordinator

JUSTICE AGENCY

Probation Dept **260.358.4841**
Fax 260.358.4853
E-mail ....jon.kramer@huntington.in.us
   201 N Jefferson St Rm 209, Huntington,
   IN 46750-2842
Jon Kramer, Acting Chief

COURTS

Huntington Circuit Court **260.358.4814**
Fax 260.358.4813
   201 N Jefferson St Rm 301, Huntington,
   IN 46750-2800
Honorable Thomas M. Hankes, Director

POLICE AND SHERIFF

Sheriff's Dept **260.356.8316**
Fax 260.358.4877
   332 E State St, Huntington, IN 46750
Terry Stoffel, Sheriff

Jackson County

SOCIAL SERVICES

IN Div of Family & Children **812.523.9090**
Fax 812.523.3980
   601 N Burkart Blvd, Seymour, IN 47274

GENERAL HEALTH SERVICES

Health Dept **812.522.6667**
Fax 812.522.6672
   801 W 2nd St, Seymour, IN 47274
Jill Brock, Rn, Public Health Nurse

JUSTICE AGENCY

Probation Dept **812.358.6138**
Fax 812.358.5411
E-mail ....jacksoncountyprobation@yahoo.com
   220 E Walnut St Ste 216, Brownstown, IN 47220
Norman Phillips, Chief Performance Officer

COURTS

Jackson Circuit Court **812.358.6133**
Fax 812.358.4689
   111 Main St, Brownstown, IN 47220
Honorable William E. Vance, Director

POLICE AND SHERIFF

Sheriff's Ofc **812.358.2141**
Fax 812.358.4675
Web ....www.indianasheriffs.org
   150 E State Road 250, Brownstown, IN 47220-2000
Mike Carothers, Sheriff

Jasper County

SOCIAL SERVICES

Family & Children Svcs **219.866.4186**
Fax 219.866.0817
Web ....www.dcs.in.gov
E-mail ....sharon.mathew@dcs.in.gov
   215 W. Kellner Blvd, Rensselaer, IN 47978
Sharon Mathew, Director

GENERAL HEALTH SERVICES

Health Dept **219.866.4917**
Fax 219.866.4108
E-mail ....nancy.bailey@co.jasper.in.us
   105 W Kellner Blvd, Rensselaer, IN 47978-2623
Nancy Bailey, Rn, Public Health Nurse

JUSTICE AGENCY

Probation Dept **219.866.4902**
Fax 219.866.3152
Web ....www.co.jasper.in.us
E-mail ....probation@co.jasper.in.us
   105 1/2 W Kellner Blvd, Rensselaer, IN 47978-2623
Michael E. Sinks, Chief Performance Officer

COURTS

Jasper Circuit Court **219.866.4941**
Fax 219.866.4943
   115 W Washington St Ste 204, Rensselaer, IN 47978
Honorable John D. Potter, Judge

POLICE AND SHERIFF

Sheriff's Ofc **219.866.7334**
Fax 219.866.4949
Web ....www.jaspercountypolice.com
   2171 N McKinley Ave, Rensselaer, IN 47978
Terry J Risner, Sheriff

Jay County

SOCIAL SERVICES

Family & Children Svcs **260.726.7933**
Fax 260.726.8589
E-mail ....cwagner@sffa.state.in.us
   1237 W. Botaw, Portland, IN 47371
Joy Woolf, Director

GENERAL HEALTH SERVICES

Health Dept **260.726.8080**
Fax 260.726.2220
Web ....www.jcounty.net
E-mail ....jchdcoleman@hotmail.com
504 W Arch St, Portland, IN 47371-1317
Laura Coleman, Public Health Nurse

COURTS

Jay Circuit Court/CASA **260.726.4044**
Fax 260.726.6941
121 North Court St, Portland, IN 47371
Honorable Brian D. Hutchison, Judge

Jefferson County

SOCIAL SERVICES

Family & Children Svcs **812.265.2027**
Fax 812.265.2927
Web ....www.dcs.in.gov
E-mail ....robert.king@dcs.in.gov
493 W Hutchinson Ln, Madison, IN 47250-7830
Robert G. King, Director

GENERAL HEALTH SERVICES

Health Dept **812.273.1942**
Fax 812.273.1955
Web ....www.localhealth.in.gov
715 Green Rd, Madison, IN 47250-2143
Karen Buchanan, Phn Supervisor

JUSTICE AGENCY

Probation Dept **812.265.8929**
Fax 812.273.1393
E-mail ....jeffcopd@yahoo.com
300 E Main St, Rm 301, Madison, IN 47250
Julie Mitchell, Chief Performance Officer

COURTS

Jefferson Circuit Court **812.265.8930**
Fax 812.265.8946
Web ....www.jeffersoncoin.org
300 E Main St Rm 300, Madison, IN 47250-4500
Karen Mannix, Clerk Of Court

POLICE AND SHERIFF

Sheriff's Dept **812.265.2648**
Fax 812.265.3190
E-mail ....radio@seidata.com
317 Walnut St, Madison, IN 47250-3523
John Wallace, Sheriff

Jennings County

SOCIAL SERVICES

IN Div of Family & Children **812.346.2254**
Fax 812.346.2264
2017 Crestwood Dr, PO Box 1047, North Vernon, IN 47265

GENERAL HEALTH SERVICES

Health Dept **812.352.3024**
Fax 812.352.3030
Web ....www.thehighroad.org
200 E Brown St, County Government Bldg, Vernon, IN 47282
Pam Petry, Rn, Public Health Nurse

JUSTICE AGENCY

Probation Dept **812.346.2720**
Fax 812.346.9262
Web ....www.isdh.state.in.us
953 S State St, North Vernon, IN 47265
Andrew L. Judd, Chief Performance Officer

COURTS

Jennings Circuit Court **812.352.3082**
24 N Pike St, Vernon, IN 47282
Jon W Webster, Judge

POLICE AND SHERIFF

Sheriff's Ofc **812.346.8642**
Fax 812.346.4968
925 S. State St, North Vernon, IN 47265
Steve Hoppock, Sheriff

Johnson County

SOCIAL SERVICES

IN Div of Family & Children **317.738.0301**
Fax 317.738.0388
1784 E Jefferson St, Franklin, IN 46131

GENERAL HEALTH SERVICES

Health Dept **317.346.4365**
Fax 317.736.5264
E-mail ....cbigelow@co.johnson.in.us
86 W Court St, Franklin, IN 46131
Craig Moorman, Health Officer

WIC Div **317.736.6628**
Fax 317.736.4961
Web ....www.co.johnson.in.us
E-mail ....tsmith@co.johnson.in.us
600 Ironwood Dr Ste I, Franklin, IN 46131-8324
Tracy Smith, Rd, Wic Coordinator

JUSTICE AGENCY

CASA Program **317.346.4561**
Fax 317.736.7949
E-mail ....thickman@co.johnson.in.us
5 E Jackson St, Franklin, IN 46131
Tammy Fearin-hickman, Director

Probation Dept **317.736.3000**
Fax 317.736.3755
Web ....www.jdc.co.johnson.in.us
E-mail ....smiller@jdc.co.johnson.in.us
1121 Hospital Rd, Franklin, IN 46131-9026
Suzanne Miller, Chief Performance Officer

COURTS

Circuit Court **317.346.4400**
Fax 317.736.3996
5 E Jefferson St, Franklin, IN 46131
K. Mark Loyd, Judge

POLICE AND SHERIFF

Sheriff's Ofc **317.736.9155**
Fax 317.736.2200
Web ....www.johnsoncountysheriff.com
1091 Hospital Rd, Franklin, IN 46131
Doug Cox, Sheriff

EDUCATION SERVICES

Special Education **317.736.8495**
Fax 317.736.6967
Web www.ssjcs.k12.in.us
E-mail ....pwright@ssjcs.k12.in.us
500 Earlywood Dr, Franklin, IN 46131-9711
Pam Wright, Director

Knox County

SOCIAL SERVICES

IN Div of Family & Children **812.882.3920**
Fax 812.882.4313
1050 Washington Ave, PO Box 235, Vincennes, IN 47591

GENERAL HEALTH SERVICES

Health Dept **812.882.8080**
Fax 812.882.5625
520 S 7th St, Vincennes, IN 47591-1038
Virginia Clark, Administrator

JUSTICE AGENCY

Probation Dept **812.885.2518**
Fax 812.895.4904
E-mail ....jrr-kcp@wvc.net
147 N 8th St, Vincennes, IN 47591
James R. Rees, Chief Performance Officer

COURTS

Knox Superior Court 1 ....**812.885.2517**
Fax 812.895.4890
111 N 7th Ste 20, Vincennes, IN 47591
Honorable W. Timothy Crowley, Judge

POLICE AND SHERIFF

Sheriff's Ofc **812.882.7660**
Fax 812.882.5261
2375 S Old Decker Rd, Vincennes, IN 47591-6122
Micheal Morris, Sheriff

EDUCATION SERVICES

Bicknell Head Start Ctr **812.735.3916**
Fax 812.735.4828
607 Pennsylvania St, Bicknell, IN 47512
Bertha Proctor, Director

Kosciusko County

SOCIAL SERVICES

Family & Children Svcs **574.267.2576**
Fax 574.267.8507
Web ....www.dcs.in.gov
E-mail ....peggy.shively@dcs.in.gov
2307 E Center St Ste B, Warsaw, IN 46580-2713
Peggy A. Shively, CPS Director

GENERAL HEALTH SERVICES

Health Dept **574.372.2349**
Fax 574.269.2023
Web ....www.kcgov.com
E-mail ....bweaver@kcgov.com
100 W Center St Rm 318, Warsaw, IN 46580-2877
William Remington Jr., Md, Health Officer

JUSTICE AGENCY

CASA **574.372.2401**
Fax 574.372.2399
Web ....www.casaofkosciuskocounty.org
E-mail ....casa@kcgov.com
121 N Lake St, Warsaw, IN 46580
Sally Mahnken, Executive Director

Probation Dept **574.372.2412**
Fax 574.372.2438
Web ....www.kcgov.com
E-mail ....tjohnston@kcgov.com
121 N Lake St, Warsaw, IN 46580-2763
Tammy Johnston, Chief Performance Officer

COURTS

Superior Court Circuit Court **574.372.2334**
Fax 574.372.2338
E-mail ....jmcsherry@kcgov.com
121 N Lake St, Fl 162, Warsaw, IN 46580-2785
Jason McSherry, Clerk Of Court

La Porte County

SOCIAL SERVICES

Family & Children Svcs **219.326.5870**
Fax 219.326.5510
Web ....www.fssa.in.gov
E-mail ....terrance.ciboch@dcs.in.gov
1230 W State Road 2, La Porte, IN 46350-5469
Michelle Goebel, Director

GENERAL HEALTH SERVICES

Health Dept **219.326.6808**
Fax 219.325.8628
Web ....www.laportecounty.org
809 State St, Fl 4, La Porte, IN 46350
Jenny Smith, Nursing Supervisor

JUSTICE AGENCY

Camp Summit Boot Camp **219.326.1188**
Fax 219.326.9218
Web ....www.doc.state.in.us
2407 N 500 W, La Porte, IN 46350-9765
Mr Davis, Superintendent

CASA Program **219.324.3385**
Fax 219.362.9114
1005 Michigan Ave, La Porte, IN 46350
Karen Biernacki, Director

COURTS

Superior Court 4 ....**219.874.5611**
Fax 219.878.9523
E-mail ....wboklund@laportecounty.org
300 Washington St Ste 116, Michigan City, IN 46360
William Boklund, Judge

EDUCATION SERVICES

Special Education **219.873.2000**
Fax 219.877.3548
E-mail ....jmccormick@mcas.k12.in.us
408 S Carroll Ave, Michigan City, IN 46360
Joan Mccormick, Director

LaGrange County

SOCIAL SERVICES

Family & Children Svcs **260.463.3451**
Fax 260.463.8316
122 N Detroit St, Lagrange, IN 46761
Wendy Petty, Director

GENERAL HEALTH SERVICES

Health Dept **260.499.4182**
Fax 260.499.4189
304 North Townline Rd Ste 1, Lagrange, IN 46761
T. Anthony Pechin, MD, Health Officer

JUSTICE AGENCY

Probation Dept **260.499.6356**
Fax 260.463.7848
105 N Detroit St Ste 4, Lagrange, IN 46565-1878
Tonda Prince, Jpo

COURTS

Lagrange Circuit Court **260.499.6358**
Fax 260.499.6448
105 N Detroit St Ste 3, Lagrange, IN 46761
Honorable J. Scott Vanderbeck, Judge

POLICE AND SHERIFF

Sheriff's Dept **260.463.7491**
Fax 260.463.8130
0875 S State Rd 9, Lagrange, IN 46761
Terry Martin, Sheriff

Lake County

SOCIAL SERVICES

Div Of Family & Children **219.886.6000**
Fax 219.881.5632
661 Broadway, Gary, IN 46409
James Bisbee, Director

Hammond Ofc **219.937.0232**
Fax 219.931.7987
E-mail ....gloria.jackson@fssa.in.gov
420 Hoffman St, Hammond, IN 46327-1514
Gloria Jackson, Division Manager

Hobart Ofc **219.947.2787**
Fax 219.947.5377
Web ....www.fssa.in.gov
E-mail ....valerie.fletcher@fssa.in.gov
1001 W 37Th Ave, Hobart, IN 46342-2011
Valerie Johnson-Fletcher, Division Manager

GENERAL HEALTH SERVICES

East Chicago Health Dept **219.391.8467**
Fax 219.391.8494
E-mail ....dburns@eastchicago.com
100 W Chicago Ave, East Chicago, IN 46312
Diane Garcia-burns, Rn, Nursing Director

Gary City Health Dept **219.882.5565**
Fax 219.882.8213
Web ....www.ci.gary.in.us
E-mail ....shawkins@ci.gary.in.us
1145 W 5th Ave, Gary, IN 46402-1795
Shirley J Hawkins, Executive Director

Hammond Health Dept **219.755.3655**
Fax 219.755.3668
Web ....www.hmdin.com
2293 N Main St, Crwnpoint, IN 46324-1158
Pat Warner, Interim Public Health Nursing Supervisor

Health Dept **219.755.3655**
Fax 219.755.3668
Web ....www.state.in.us
2293 N Main St, Crown Point, IN 46307-1854
Susan Best, Health Officer

JUSTICE AGENCY

CASA **219.660.6900**
Fax 219.769.7325
E-mail ....etegarden@lpcasa.com
3000 W 93rd Ave, Crown Point, IN 46307
Elizabeth Tegarden, Director

COURTS

Superior Court **219.933.2841**
Fax 219.933.2833
232 Russell St Fl 1, Hammond, IN 46320
Jeffe Villalpando, Judge

Superior Court **219.755.3199**
Fax 219.755.6155
2293 N Main St, Crown Point, IN 46307
Honorable John R Pera, Judge

Superior Court, Civil 2 ....**219.398.2443**
Fax 219.392.0047
Web ....www.lakecountyin.com
E-mail ....cdhawkins@lakecountyin.com
3711 Main St Ste B, East Chicago, IN 46312-2977
Honorable Calvin D Hawkins, Judge

Superior Court, Civil 3 & 4 ....**219.886.3621**
Fax 219.881.6168
Web ....www.gov.in.gov
E-mail ....tphilpot@gov.in.gov
15 W 4th Ave Ste 108, Gary, IN 46402-1260
Thomas Philpot, Clerk Of Court

Superior Court, Juvenile Div **219.660.6900**
Fax 219.736.6209
3000 W 93rd Ave, Crown Point, IN 46307
Honorable Mary Beth Bonaventura, Senior Judge

POLICE AND SHERIFF

Gary Police Dept Juvenile Bureau **219.881.1229**
Fax 219.881.7412
555 Polk St Ste 1023, Gary, IN 46402
Lt. Charles Austin, Commander Juvenile Bureau

Sheriff's Dept **219.755.3400**
Fax 219.755.3371
Web ....www.lakecountysheriff.com
E-mail ....sheriff@lakecountysheriff.com
2293 N Main St, Bldg C, Crown Point, IN 46307
John Buncich, Sheriff

EDUCATION SERVICES

Geminus Head Start **219.757.1826**
8400 Louisiana St, Merrillville, IN 46410
William Kish, Director

Special Education **219.881.5493**
Fax 219.883.4864
E-mail ....efraire@garycsc.k12.in.us
1988 Polk St, Gary, IN 46407-2443
Edmund Fraire, Director

Special Education **219.769.4000**
Fax 219.769.4563
Web ....www.nisec.org
E-mail ....djurasevich@nisec.org
2150 W 97th Pl, Crown Point, IN 46307-2346
Jane Winkoss, Director

Special Education **219.933.2400**
Fax 219.933.2505
Web www.hammond.k12.in.us
E-mail ....cbmanous@hammond.k12.in.us
41 Williams St, Hammond, IN 46320-1948
Connie Manous, Director

Special Education **219.865.1171**
Fax 219.865.1316
Web www.lakecentral.k12.in.us
E-mail ....msledz@lakecentral.k12.in.us
212 E Joliet St, Schererville, IN 46375-2088
Marlene Sledz, Director

Lawrence County

SOCIAL SERVICES

Sicil **812.277.9626**
Fax 812.277.9628
E-mail ....sicil@tiama.com
621 X St, Bedford, IN 47421
Al Tolbert, Director

GENERAL HEALTH SERVICES

Health Dept **812.275.3234**
Fax 812.275.1094
Web ....www.lawrencecountyin.org
2419 Mitchell Rd, Dunn Health Campus, Bedford, IN 47421
Dr. Alan Smith, Health Officer

JUSTICE AGENCY

Probation Dept **812.275.3605**
Fax 812.277.7493
Web ....www.lawrencecounty.in.gov
E-mail ....swedgewood@lawrencecounty.in.gov
918 16th St Ste 600, Bedford, IN 47421-5893
Scott Wedgewood, Assistant Chief Probation Officer

COURTS

Lawrence Circuit Court **812.275.2421**
Fax 812.275.1044
916 15th St Rm 37, Bedford, IN 47421
Andrea Mccord, Judge

POLICE AND SHERIFF

Sheriff's Ofc **812.275.3316**
Fax 812.277.2007
Web ....www.lawrencecountysheriff.org
1420 I St, Bedford, IN 47421
Sam Craig, Sheriff

Madison County

SOCIAL SERVICES

IN Div of Family & Children **765.649.0142**
Fax 765.644.9081
222 E 10th St, Ste D, Anderson, IN 46016

GENERAL HEALTH SERVICES

Health Dept **765.641.9524**
Fax 765.646.9203
E-mail ....swright@madisoncounty.in.gov
　206 E 9th St, County Government Center Annex,
　Anderson, IN 46016
Stephen Wright, Health Officer

JUSTICE AGENCY

Pendleton Juvenile Correctional
Facility **765.778.3778**
Fax 765.778.5211
E-mail ....mdempsey@doc.in.gov
　9310 S State Road 67, Pendleton, IN 46064-8536
Linda Commons, Superintendent

Probation Dept **765.646.9213**
Fax 765.646.9229
Web ....www.madisoncty.com
E-mail ....kholtzleiter@madisoncty.com
　3420 Mounds Rd, Anderson, IN 46017-1873
Katherine Hurd-holtzleiter, Chief JPO

COURTS

Superior Court Juvenile Div **765.641.9627**
Fax 765.608.9711
　16 E 9th St Ste 407, Anderson, IN 46016-1572
Darlene Likens, Clerk Of Court

Marion County

SOCIAL SERVICES

Protection And Advocacy System **317.722.5555**
Fax 317.722.5564
Web ....www.in.gov/ipas
E-mail ....,..........tgallagher@ipas.state.in.us
　4701 N Keystone Ave Ste 222, Indianapolis,
　IN 46205-1561
Thomas Gallagher, Executive Director

GENERAL HEALTH SERVICES

Div of Family & Children **317.931.2920**
Fax 317.232.9472
Web ....www.fssa.state.in.us
　3524 N Meridian St Ste 100, Indianapolis,
　IN 46208-4447
Carolyn Goeke, Director

Public Health Dept **317.221.2380**
Fax 317.221.2307
Web ....www.mchd.com
E-mail ....vcaine@hhcorp.org
　3838 N Rural St, Indianapolis, IN 46205-2930
Virginia A. Caine, Md, Director

JUSTICE AGENCY

Women Prison **317.244.3387**
Fax 317.244.4670
E-mail ....smccauley@doc.in.gov
　2596 N Girls School Rd, Indianapolis, IN 46214-2105
Steve Mccauley, Superintendent

COURTS

Marion Superior Court Juvenile
Div **317.327.6169**
Fax 317.327.6620
　2451 N Keystone Ave, Fl 2, Indianapolis, IN 46218
Honorable Marilynn Mours, Juvenile Court

EDUCATION SERVICES

Special Education **317.233.3111**
Fax 317.234.0956
E-mail ....jnally@idoc.in.gov
　302 W Washington St Rm E201, Indianapolis,
　IN 46204
John Nally, Director

Special Education **317.243.5737**
Fax 317.243.5510
E-mail ....lucy.witte@wayne.k12.in.us
　4730 Gadsden St, Indianapolis, IN 46241
Lucy Witte, Director

Special Education **317.423.8430**
Fax 317.543.3523
Web www.msdlt.k12.in.us
E-mail ....wdriebelbis@msdlt.k12.in.us
　7601 E 56th St, Indianapolis, IN 46226
William Driebelbis, Director

Special Education **317.226.4000**
E-mail ....Warner@ips.k12.in.us
　120 E Walnut St, Indianapolis, IN 46204
Rob Warner, Director

Special Education **317.845.9400**
Fax 317.205.3385
Web www.msdwt.k12.in.us
　8550 Woodfield Crossing Blvd, Indianapolis,
　IN 46240
Karol Farrell, Phd, Director

Special Education **317.227.8636**
Fax 317.243.5744
Web www.wayne.k12.in.us
E-mail ....lucy.witte@wayne.k12.in.us
　1220 S High School Rd, Indianapolis, IN 46241-3127
Lucy Witte, Director Of Special Services

Special Education **317.941.4050**
Fax 317.941.4244
E-mail ....lisa.carrico@fssa.in.gov
　2601 Cold Spring Rd, Indianapolis, IN 46222-2202
Lisa Carriko, Service Line Director Of Youth Services

Marshall County

SOCIAL SERVICES

Family & Children Svcs **574.935.4046**
Fax 574.936.6027
E-mail ....michael.carroll@dcs.in.gov
　2125 N. Oak Dr., Plymouth, IN 46563-1384
Michael J. Carroll, Director

GENERAL HEALTH SERVICES

Health Dept **574.935.8565**
Fax 574.936.9247
E-mail ....susanl@co.marshall.in.us
　112 W Jefferson St Ste 103, Plymouth,
　IN 46563-1764
Susan Lechlitner, Rn, Public Health Nurse

JUSTICE AGENCY

Probation Dept **574.935.8560**
Fax 574.935.4656
E-mail ....maryjanew@co.marshall.in.us
　112 W Jefferson St Ste 102, Plymouth, IN 46563
Mary Jane Walsworth, Chief Performance Officer

COURTS

Marshall Circuit Court **574.935.8780**
Fax 574.936.4703
Web ....www.co.marshall.in.us
　501 N Center St Rm 301, Plymouth, IN 46563-1776
Honorable Curtis Palmer, Judge

Marshall Superior Court 1 ....**574.935.8740**
Fax 574.936.9967
E-mail ....rbowen@co.marshall.in.us
　211 W Madison St Rm 301, Plymouth,
　IN 46563-1780
Honorable Robert O. Bowen, Director

Marshall Superior Court 2 ....**574.935.8763**
Fax 574.935.8700
　211 W Madison St Rm 201, Plymouth, IN 46563
Honorable Dean A. Colven, Judge

POLICE AND SHERIFF

Sheriff's Ofc **574.936.3187**
Fax 574.936.3264
E-mail ....johnv@co.marshall.in.us
　210 W Madison St, Plymouth, IN 46563-1765
Tom Chamberoin, Sheriff

Martin County

SOCIAL SERVICES

IN Div of Family & Children **812.247.2871**
Fax 812.247.2316
　51 Ravine St, PO Box 88, Shoals, IN 47581

GENERAL HEALTH SERVICES

Health Dept **812.247.3303**
Fax 812.247.2009
Web ....www.hoosieruplands.org
　2nd Main St Federal Bldg, Shoals, IN 47581
Julia Albright, Rn, Public Health Nurse

COURTS

Martin Circuit Court **812.247.3652**
Fax 812.247.3901
Web ....www.miamicountyin.gov
　129 Main St, Shoals, IN 47581-5505
Lynne Elllis, Judge

Miami County

SOCIAL SERVICES

IN Div of Family & Children **765.473.6611**
Fax 765.472.3718
　12 S Wabash, Peru, IN 46970

JUSTICE AGENCY

CASA Program **765.472.7894**
Fax 765.472.1412
Web ....www.nationalcasa.org
E-mail ....miamicounty@miamicountyin.gov
　25 Court St, Peru, IN 46970-2247
Kurt Kifer, Director

COURTS

Circuit Court **765.472.3901**
Fax 765.473.7894
E-mail ....rspahr@miamicountyin.gov
　25 N Broadway Ste 310, Peru, IN 46970
Robert Spahr, Judge

POLICE AND SHERIFF

Sheriff's Ofc **765.472.1322**
Fax 765.472.7520
Web ....www.miamicountyin.gov/sheriff
E-mail ....tmiller@miamicountyin.gov
　1104 W 200 N, Peru, IN 46970-2201
Tim Miller, Sheriff

Monroe County

SOCIAL SERVICES

IN Div of Family & Children **812.336.6351**
Fax 812.333.0138
　1717 W 3rd St, Bloomington, IN 47404

GENERAL HEALTH SERVICES

Community Health Svcs **812.332.2901**
Fax 812.330.7902
Web ....www.bhss.com
E-mail ....rdewitt@bloomingtonhospital.org
　333 E Miller Dr, Bloomington, IN 47401
Renee Dewitt, Director Of Community Health

Health Dept **812.349.2543**
Fax 812.339.6481
Web ....www.co.monroe.in.us
E-mail ....pcaubioo@co.monroe.in.us
　119 W 7th St, Bloomington, IN 47404-3926
Kathy Hewitt, Disease Intervention Specialist

Indiana

JUSTICE AGENCY

Probation Dept 812.349.2645
Fax...812.349.2975
E-mail.......................lbrady@co.monroe.in.us
   214 W. 7th St., Ste. 200, Bloomington, IN 47404
Linda M. Brady, Chief Performance Officer

COURTS

Monroe Circuit Court 812.349.2615
Fax...812.349.2791
   301 N College Ave Ste 201, Bloomington, IN 47403
Linda Robbins, Clerk Of Court

EDUCATION SERVICES

Special Education 812.349.4756
Fax...812.330.7811
Web..................................www.mccsc.edu
E-mail...............................khugo@mccsc.edu
   315 E North Dr, Bloomington, IN 47401-6555
Kathleen Hugo, Phd, Director

Special Education 812.876.6325
Fax...812.876.5424
Web..............................www.rbbcsc.k12.in.us
E-mail.....................kwal9456@rbbcsc.k12.in.us
   8045 W State Road 46, Ellettsville, IN 47429-9714
Kelly Walsh, Director

Montgomery County

SOCIAL SERVICES

IN Div of Family & Children 765.362.5600
Fax...765.364.9488
   1635 Eastway Dr, Crawfordsville, IN 47933

GENERAL HEALTH SERVICES

Health Dept 765.364.6440
Fax...765.361.3239
Web............................www.montgomeryco.net
E-mail......................rlang@montgomeryco.net
   110 W South Blvd, Crawfordsville, IN 47933
Rebecca Lang, Rn, Public Health Nurse

JUSTICE AGENCY

Probation Dept 765.364.6460
Fax...765.364.7253
   100 E Main St, Rm 304, Crawfordsville, IN 47933
Kalay Colley, Chief Performance Officer

COURTS

Montgomery Circuit Court 765.364.6450
Fax...765.364.7251
   100 E Main St, Crawfordsville, IN 47933
Honorable Thomas K. Milligan, Judge

Teen Court 765.362.0694
Fax...765.362.5719
E-mail...............................jennifer@mcysb.org
   209 E Pike St, Crawfordsville, IN 47933
Jennifer White, Program Director

POLICE AND SHERIFF

Sheriff's Ofc 765.362.3740
Fax...765.362.1587
   600 Memorial Dr, Crawfordsville, IN 47933
Mark Caspeel, Sheriff

EDUCATION SERVICES

Crawfordsville Head Start 765.361.0863
Fax...765.362.4471
E-mail...............................lori@dke.k12.in.us
   201 E Jefferson St, Crawfordsville, IN 47933
Lori Brewer, Director

Morgan County

SOCIAL SERVICES

IN Div of Family & Children 765.349.5302
Fax...765.349.8319
   1326 S Morton Ave, Martinsville, IN 46151

GENERAL HEALTH SERVICES

Health Dept 765.342.6621
Fax...765.342.1062
Web...........................www.morgancountyhealth.com
E-mail.......................morgancohd@scican.net
   180 S Main St Ste 252, Martinsville, IN 46151-1988
Lori George, Rn, Public Health Nurse

JUSTICE AGENCY

Probation Dept 765.342.1082
Fax...765.342.1106
Web............................www.morgancounty.in.gov
   65 N Jefferson St, Martinsville, IN 46151-1541
Carole A. Kinder, Director Of Court Services

POLICE AND SHERIFF

Sheriff's Dept 765.342.5544
Fax...765.349.5058
E-mail.......................rdowny@morancounty.in.gov
   160 N Park Ave, Martinsville, IN 46151
Robert Downey, Sheriff

Newton County

SOCIAL SERVICES

Dept of Child Svcs 219.285.2206
Fax...219.285.8206
E-mail.......................ron.fisher@dcs.in.gov
   4117 S 240 W, Ste 200-A, Morocco, IN 47963
Ron Fisher, Director

GENERAL HEALTH SERVICES

Health Dept 219.285.2052
Web............................www.newtoncountyin.com
E-mail.......................newtonconurse@localhealth.in.gov
   4117 S 240 W Ste 500, Morocco, IN 47963
Kimberly Durham, Public Health Nurse

COURTS

Newton Circuit Court 219.474.5131
Fax...219.474.6751
   201 N 3rd St, Kentland, IN 47951
Honorable Jeryl F. Leach, Judge

POLICE AND SHERIFF

Sheriff's Dept 219.474.5661
Fax...219.474.5667
E-mail...............................sheriff@ffni.com
   304 E Seymour St, Kentland, IN 47951
Donald Hartman, Sheriff

Noble County

SOCIAL SERVICES

IN Div of Family & Children 260.636.2021
Fax...260.636.3338
   774 Trail Ridge Rd, Ste A, Albion, IN 46701

GENERAL HEALTH SERVICES

Health Dept 260.636.2191
Fax...260.636.2192
Web..............................www.nocohealth.org
   2090 N State Rd 9, Ste C, Albion, IN 46701
Linda Gray, Public Health Nurse

JUSTICE AGENCY

CASA 260.636.6101
Fax...260.636.3759
E-mail.......................neincasa@maplenet.net
   116 West Main Street, Albion, IN 46701
Kristi Bachman, Director

Probation Dept 260.636.3116
Fax...260.636.3117
Web..............................www.nobleco.org
E-mail...............................sbeam@nobleco.org
   101 N Orange St Rm 110, Albion, IN 46701-1049
Stacey Beam, Chief Performance Officer

COURTS

Noble Circuit Court 260.636.2128
Fax...260.636.3053
E-mail...............................dlaur@nobleco.org
   101 N Orange St Rm 300, Albion, IN 46701
Honorable G. David Laur, Director

Ohio County

SOCIAL SERVICES

IN Div of Family & Children 812.438.2530
Fax...812.438.4069
   125 N Walnut, PO Box 196, Rising Sun, IN 47040

GENERAL HEALTH SERVICES

Health Dept 812.438.2551
Fax...812.438.4393
   117 6th St, Rising Sun, IN 47040
Regina Crouch, Public Health Nurse

COURTS

Ohio Circuit Court 812.438.3410
Fax...812.438.2017
   413 Main St, Rising Sun, IN 47040
Honorable James Humphrey, Judge

Orange County

SOCIAL SERVICES

Indiana Dept of Child Svcs 812.723.3616
Fax...812.723.4652
E-mail.......................leslie.rowland@dcs.in.gov
   111 W Main St Ste 2A, Paoli, IN 47454
Leslie Rowland, Director

GENERAL HEALTH SERVICES

Health Dept 812.723.7112
Fax...812.723.7117
E-mail...............................orange@isdh.in.gov
   205 E Main St Ste 9, Paoli, IN 47454
Tammie Johnson, Office Mgr

JUSTICE AGENCY

Probation Dept 812.723.4155
Fax...812.723.4308
Web..............................www.co.orange.in.us
E-mail.......................probation@co.orange.in.us
   1 Court St, Paoli, IN 47454-1399
Dee Pedigo, CPO

COURTS

Orange Circuit Court 812.723.2411
Fax...812.723.4603
Web............................www.courts.state.va.us
E-mail.......................rblanton@courts.state.va.us
   1 Court St, Paoli, IN 47454-1399
Honorable Larry R. Blanton, Judge

Owen County

SOCIAL SERVICES

Family & Children Svcs 812.829.2281
Fax...812.829.9750
Web..............................www.in.gov/dcs
E-mail.......................sonya.seymour@in.gov
   450 E Franklin St, Spencer, IN 47460-1824
Sonya Seymour, Director

GENERAL HEALTH SERVICES

Health Dept 812.829.5017
Fax...812.829.5044
   60 S Main St, Fl 1, Spencer, IN 47460
Lisa Coffman, Public Health Nurse

JUSTICE AGENCY

Probation Dept.........................812.829.5025
Fax.....................................812.829.5051
E-mail.............................occc@ccrtc.com
  60 S Main St, Spencer, IN 47460
  Donna Mcelroy, CPO

COURTS

Owen Circuit Court..................812.829.5030
Fax.....................................812.829.5040
  60 S Main St, Spencer, IN 47460
  Honorable Frank M. Nardi, Judge

POLICE AND SHERIFF

Gosport Police Dept.................812.879.5762
Fax.....................................812.879.9533
  13 S 3rd St, Gosport, IN 47433-7019
  Randall Ganarsdale, Police Chief

Parke County

SOCIAL SERVICES

Family & Children Svcs.............765.569.3156
Fax.....................................765.569.1735
Web...................www.intranet.fssa.state.in.us
E-mail..................katie.edington@dcs.in.gov
  103 S Jefferson St, Rockville, IN 47872
  Katie A. Edington, Director

GENERAL HEALTH SERVICES

Health Dept..........................765.569.6665
Fax.....................................765.569.4061
E-mail....................parkecohealth@yahoo.com
  116 W High St, Rm 12, Rockville, IN 47872-1716
  Melissa Buell, Public Health Nurse

JUSTICE AGENCY

Probation Dept......................765.569.3521
Fax.....................................765.569.4005
Web...www.joint.com
E-mail.............lthompson@parkecounty-in.gov
  116 W High St Rm 201, Rockville, IN 47872-1716
  Laird Thompson, Chief Performance Officer

COURTS

Parke Circuit Court.................765.569.5671
Fax.....................................765.569.4005
Web...www.joink.com
E-mail..........................pcjudge@joink.com
  116 W High St Rm 204, Rockville, IN 47872-1716
  Honorable Sam Swaim, Director

POLICE AND SHERIFF

Sheriff's Dept.......................765.569.5413
Fax.....................................765.569.6869
Web..................www.parkecountysheriff.com
E-mail...............sheriff@parkecountysheriff.com
  458 W Strawberry Rd, Rockville, IN 47872-7095
  Mike Eslinger, Sheriff

Perry County

SOCIAL SERVICES

Dept of Child Svcs..................812.547.7055
Fax.....................................812.547.8507
E-mail....................amy.tempel@dcs.in.gov
  316 E Highway 66, Tell City, IN 47586
  Amy Tempel, Director

GENERAL HEALTH SERVICES

Health Dept..........................812.547.2746
Fax.....................................812.547.0415
E-mail...................pchealthdept@psci.net
  125 S 8th St, Courthouse Annex, Cannelton,
  IN 47520
  Sara Gehlausen, Rn, Public Health Nurse

JUSTICE AGENCY

Probation Dept......................219.474.6081
Fax.....................................219.474.3900
E-mail........michelle.d@newtoncounty-in.us
  301 Seymour St, Kentland, IN 47951
  Michelle Dresbaugh, Chief Performance Officer

Probation Dept......................812.547.8456
Fax.....................................812.547.5424
E-mail...........................jlloyd@psci.net
  2219 Payne St Rm E10, Tell City, IN 47586-2832
  Jamie Lloyd, Probation Officer

COURTS

Perry Circuit Court.................812.547.7048
Fax.....................................812.547.5424
E-mail.........................judge@psci.net
  2219 Payne St Rm E9, Tell City, IN 47586
  Honorable Lucy Goffinet, Judge

POLICE AND SHERIFF

Sheriff's Ofc.........................812.547.2441
Fax.....................................812.547.0410
  119 S 7th St, Cannelton, IN 47520-1209
  Lee Chestnut, Sheriff

Pike County

SOCIAL SERVICES

IN Dept of Child Services...........812.354.9716
Fax.....................................812.354.9811
E-mail..............r.cunningham@dcs.in.gov
  2105 E Main St, Petersburg, IN 47567
  Steve Cunningham, Local Office Director

GENERAL HEALTH SERVICES

Health Dept..........................812.354.8797
Fax.....................................812.354.2532
  801 E Main St, Courthouse, Petersburg,
  IN 47567-1249
  Amy Gladish, Rn, Public Health Nurse

JUSTICE AGENCY

Probation Dept......................812.354.8034
Fax.....................................812.354.6349
E-mail.......................khenry@pikeco.org
  801 E Main St, Petersburg, IN 47567-1249
  Kyler Henry, Jpo

POLICE AND SHERIFF

Sheriff's Ofc.........................812.354.6024
Fax.....................................812.354.6037
E-mail.........jburtton@pikecountysheriffsoffice.com
  100 S 4th St, Petersburg, IN 47567
  Jeremy Burtton, Sheriff

Porter County

SOCIAL SERVICES

IN Div of Family & Children.........219.462.2112
Fax.....................................219.548.5725
  19 E Linconlway, Valparaiso, IN 46383

JUSTICE AGENCY

CASA Program.......................219.763.6623
Fax.....................................219.763.0530
E-mail.............healthyfamilies@verizon.net
  6469 Central Ave, Portage, IN 46368
  Jade Palen, Director

Probation Dept......................219.465.3475
Fax.....................................219.465.3600
Web...www.porterco.org
E-mail.......................akbeier@porterco.org
  1660 S State Road 2, Valparaiso, IN 46385-9039
  Amy Beier, Chief Performance Officer

COURTS

Porter Circuit Court................219.465.3425
Fax.....................................219.465.3647
E-mail.........................d05@porterco.org
  16 Lincolnway Ste 209, Valparaiso, IN 46383
  Honorable Mary R. Harper, Judge

Porter Juvenile Court...............219.465.3603
Fax.....................................219.465.3653
Web...www.porterco.org
E-mail.....................juvcourt@porterco.org
  1660 S State Road 2, Valparaiso, IN 46385-9039
  Pamela Fish, Clerk Of Court

POLICE AND SHERIFF

Sheriff's Ofc.........................219.477.3000
Fax.....................................219.465.0721
Web..................www.portercountysheriff.com
E-mail...............sheriff@portercountysheriff.com
  2755 S State Road 49, Valparaiso, IN 46383
  David Lain, Sheriff

EDUCATION SERVICES

Special Education...................219.464.9607
Fax.....................................219.462.0867
  750 Ransom Rd, Valparaiso, IN 46385-8973
  Diane Mansa, Director

Posey County

SOCIAL SERVICES

Family & Children Svcs.............812.838.4429
Fax.....................................812.838.4507
Web...www.dcs.in.gov
E-mail..................susan.blackburn@dcs.in.gov
  1809 Main St, Mount Vernon, IN 47620-1209
  Susan Blackburn, Director & CPS Supervisor

GENERAL HEALTH SERVICES

Health Dept..........................812.838.1328
Fax.....................................812.838.8561
E-mail...................pchd@localhealth.in.gov
  126 E 3rd St Rm 20, Mount Vernon, IN 47620
  Beverly Emhuff, Rn, Public Health Nurse

JUSTICE AGENCY

Probation Dept......................812.838.1312
Fax.....................................812.838.1345
  300 Main St, Mount Vernon, IN 47620
  Rodney Fetcher, Chief Performance Officer

COURTS

Posey Circuit Clerk.................812.838.1306
Fax.....................................812.838.1307
E-mail...........betty.postletheweight@poseycountygov.org
  300 Main St, Mount Vernon, IN 47620
  Honorable James M. Redwine, Director

Pulaski County

SOCIAL SERVICES

IN Div of Family & Children.........574.946.3312
Fax.....................................574.946.7193
  429 N Sally Dr, PO Box 130, Winamac, IN 46996

GENERAL HEALTH SERVICES

Health Dept..........................574.946.6080
Fax.....................................574.946.6654
E-mail......................pulaski@isdh.in.gov
  125 S Riverside Dr Ste 205, Winamac, IN 46996
  Terri Hansen, Office Manager

JUSTICE AGENCY

Probation Dept......................574.946.6558
Fax.....................................574.946.6741
Web...www.sugardog.com
E-mail.......................pcprob@sugardog.com
  110 E Meridian St Ste 201, Winamac, IN 46996-1645
  Hollie Schultz, Chief Performance Officer

Indiana

COURTS

Pulaski Circuit Court **574.946.3851**
Fax 574.946.6585
  112 E Main St Ste 310, Winamac, IN 46996
  Honorable Michael A. Shurn, Judge

POLICE AND SHERIFF

Sheriff's Ofc **574.946.6655**
Fax 574.946.4234
E-mail ....mgayer@pulaskisheriff.net
  110 E Meridian St, Winamac, IN 46996
  Michael A. Gayer, Sheriff

Putnam County

SOCIAL SERVICES

IN Div of Family & Children **765.653.9780**
Fax 765.653.6663
  121 Ridgeland Rd, Greencastle, IN 46135

GENERAL HEALTH SERVICES

Health Dept **765.653.5210**
Fax 765.653.0211
Web ....www.localhealth.in.gov
  209 W Liberty St Ste 13, Greencastle, IN 46135-1285
  Beth Galze, Administrator

JUSTICE AGENCY

**CASA, Putnam Co. Youth Development
Commission** **765.653.9342**
Fax 765.653.0048
  10 1/2 N Jackson St, Greencastle, IN 46135
  Linda Merkel, Director

Probation Dept **765.653.1257**
Fax 765.653.0234
  1 Court House Square, Fl 3, Greencastle, IN 46135
  Renee Marsteler, Chief Probation Officer

COURTS

Putnam Circuit Court **765.653.5315**
Fax 765.653.4870
Web ....www.co.putnam.in.us
E-mail ....matthew@co.putnam.in.us
  1 Courthouse Square St Ste 30, Greencastle,
  IN 46135-1503
  Honorable Matthew Headley, Judge

POLICE AND SHERIFF

Sheriff's Ofc **765.653.3211**
Fax 765.655.2131
Web ....www.putnam-sheriff.org
  13 Keightly Rd, Greencastle, IN 46135-2227
  Steve Fenwick, Sheriff

Randolph County

SOCIAL SERVICES

Indiana Dept of Child Svcs **765.584.2811**
Fax 765.584.4806
E-mail ....steven.cox@dcs.in.gov
  325 S Oak St Ste 201, Winchester, IN 47394
  Steven Cox, Regional Manager

GENERAL HEALTH SERVICES

Health Dept **765.584.1155**
Fax 765.584.9059
  325 S Oak St Ste 202, Winchester, IN 47394-2247
  Mitchell Jarnagin, Public Health Nurse

JUSTICE AGENCY

Probation Dept **765.584.5805**
Fax 765.584.5816
Web ....www.randolphcounty.us
  216 S Meridian St, Winchester, IN 47394-1811
  Elizabeth Kreig, Chief Performance Officer

COURTS

Randolph Circuit Court **765.584.0465**
Fax 765.584.7186
  123 W Franklin Ste 306, Winchester, IN 47394-1832
  Deb Mcgriss-tharp, Case Director

POLICE AND SHERIFF

Sheriff's Ofc **765.584.1721**
Fax 765.584.5592
Web ....www.randolphcountysheriff.com
  155 E South St, Winchester, IN 47394-2133
  Ken R Hendrickson, Sheriff

Ripley County

SOCIAL SERVICES

IN Div of Family & Children **812.689.6295**
Fax 812.689.1427
  515 S Tangelwood Rd Bldg 1, PO Box 215, Versailles,
  IN 47042

JUSTICE AGENCY

Probation Dept **812.689.6063**
Fax 812.689.6752
Web ....www.ripleycounty.com
E-mail ....schmaltz@ripleycounty.com
  102 W 1st N St, Versailles, IN 47042
  Shannon G. Shmaltz, Chief Performance Officer

COURTS

Ripley Circuit Court **812.689.6226**
Fax 812.689.6104
Web ....www.ripleycounty.com
E-mail ....ctaul@ripleycounty.com
  Courthouse Sq # 2, Versailles, IN 47042
  Honorable Carl H. Taul, Director

POLICE AND SHERIFF

Holton Police Dept **812.689.3269**
Fax 812.689.3269
Web ....www.holtonks.net
  7040 W Versailles St, Holton, IN 47023-9005
  Mr Billy J Moore, Jr., Police Chief

Sheriff's Dept **812.689.5555**
Fax 812.689.5418
Web ....www.ripleycounty.com
E-mail ....sheriff@ripleycounty.com
  210 North Monroe Street, Versailles, IN 47042
  Thomas Grills, Sheriff

Rush County

SOCIAL SERVICES

Dept of Child Services **765.932.2392**
Fax 765.938.1623
  1340 N Cherry St, Rushville, IN 46173
  William Ammerman, Director

JUSTICE AGENCY

Probation Dept **765.932.3748**
Fax 765.932.2357
Web ....www.rushcounty.in.gov
E-mail ....adultprobation@rushcounty.in.gov
  101 E 2nd St, Fl 3, Rushville, IN 46173
  Mark O. Fields, Probation Officer

COURTS

Rush Circuit Court **765.932.2078**
Fax 765.932.2357
  101 E 2nd St, Rushville, IN 46173
  Deborah Richardson, Clerk Of Court

Scott County

SOCIAL SERVICES

Div Of Family & Children **812.752.2503**
Fax 812.752.6114
  1050 W Community Way, Scottsburg, IN 47170
  Joan Kelly, Director

GENERAL HEALTH SERVICES

Health Dept **812.752.8455**
Fax 812.752.6023
E-mail ....scott@isdh.in.gov
  1471 N Gardner St, Scottsburg, IN 47170
  R. Kevin Rogers, Md, Health Officer/director

COURTS

Scott Circuit Court **812.752.8430**
Fax 812.752.8431
  1 E McClain Ave Ste 212, Scottsburg, IN 47170
  Honorable Roger L. Duvall, Judge

POLICE AND SHERIFF

Sheriff's Ofc **812.752.8400**
Fax 812.752.5751
E-mail ....campbell424@verizon.net
  111 S 1st St, Scottsburg, IN 47170-1802
  Dan Mccailn, Sheriff

Shelby County

SOCIAL SERVICES

Family & Children Svcs **317.392.5040**
Fax 317.392.5047
Web ....www.dcs.in.gov
  2535 Parkway Dr Ste 1, Shelbyville, IN 46176
  Tracy Eggleston, CPS Supervisor

GENERAL HEALTH SERVICES

Health Dept **317.392.6470**
Fax 317.392.6472
  1600 E State Road 44 Ste B, Shelbyville, IN 46176
  Cecilia Ortic, Public Health Nurse

JUSTICE AGENCY

Probation Dept **317.392.6490**
Fax 317.392.6307
Web ....www.co.shelby.in.us
  407 S Harrison St, Fl 3, Shelbyville, IN 46176
  Aimee Lykins, Teen Court Coordinator

COURTS

Circuit Court **317.392.6360**
Fax 317.392.6496
  407 S Harrison St Rm 206, Shelbyville,
  IN 46176-2170
  Honorable Charles Oæconnor, Judge

POLICE AND SHERIFF

Sheriff's Dept **317.398.6661**
Fax 317.392.6403
E-mail ....mike.bowley@co.shelby.in.us
  107 W Taylor St, Shelbyville, IN 46176
  Michael D. Bowley, Sheriff

Spencer County

SOCIAL SERVICES

Family & Children Svcs **812.649.9111**
Fax 812.649.5839
E-mail ....connie.branch@dcs.in.gov
  305 Main St, Rockport, IN 47635
  Connie L. Branch, CPS Supervisor

GENERAL HEALTH SERVICES

Health Dept.............................812.649.4441
Fax.......................................812.649.6047
Web.............................www.spencercounty.org
E-mail.........................lvarble@localhealth.in.gov
   200 Main St Ste 1, Rockport, IN 47635-1492
   Lynn Varble, Public Health Nurse

COURTS

Spencer Circuit Court...................812.649.6025
Fax.......................................812.649.6499
Web................................www.siec.k12.in.us
E-mail.........................wroell@siec.k12.in.us
   200 Main St Ste 6, Rockport, IN 47635-1492
   Honorable Wayne A. Roell, Senior Judge

St. Joseph County

SOCIAL SERVICES

Div of Family & Children................574.236.5300
Fax.......................................574.236.5400
Web...............................www.ocse.state.ar.us
E-mail..........................e.smith@ocse.state.ar.us
   401 E Colfax Ave Ste 116, South Bend,
   IN 46617-2885
   Charles E. Smith, Director

GENERAL HEALTH SERVICES

Public Health Dept.......................574.235.9750
Fax.......................................574.245.6576
Web.......................www.stjosephcountyindiana.com
E-mail.....................rchamble@co.st-joseph.in.us
   227 W Jefferson Blvd, 9th Floor, South Bend,
   IN 46601
   R.W. Chamblee, Health Officer

JUSTICE AGENCY

Juvenile Probation Ofc and Detention
Facility..................................574.235.5437
Fax.......................................574.235.5342
   1000 S Michigan St, South Bend, IN 46601
   William Bruinsma, Executive Director

South Bend Juvenile Correctional
Facility..................................574.232.8808
Fax.......................................574.232.9270
   4650 Old Cleveland Rd, South Bend, IN 46628-4324
   Esa Dhmen Krause, Superintendent

POLICE AND SHERIFF

Sheriff's Ofc............................574.245.6540
Fax.......................................574.245.6574
Web.................................www.stjoepros.org
E-mail.......................bmiller@co.st-joseph.in.us
   401 W Sample St, South Bend, IN 46601-2815
   Michael Grzegorek, Sheriff

South Bend Police.......................574.235.9201
Fax.......................................574.235.7522
E-mail.....................sbpd@southbendpolice.com
   701 W Sample St, South Bend, IN 46601
   Darryl Boykins, Chief

EDUCATION SERVICES

Special Education.......................574.283.8130
Fax.......................................574.283.8105
E-mail..........................dkrol@sbcsc.k12.in.us
   215 S Saint Joseph St, South Bend, IN 46601
   Donna Krol, Director

Starke County

SOCIAL SERVICES

IN Div of Family & Children.............574.772.3411
Fax.......................................574.772.3837
   318 E Culver Rd, Knox, IN 46534

GENERAL HEALTH SERVICES

Health Dept.............................574.772.9137
Fax.......................................574.772.8035
Web...............................www.co.starke.in.us
   53 E Washington St Fl 1, Knox, IN 46534
   Frank Lynch, Public Health Nurse

JUSTICE AGENCY

Starke Circuit Court Probation
Dept....................................574.772.9151
Fax.......................................574.772.9159
Web...............................www.co.starke.in.us
E-mail.......................efritz@co.starke.in.us
   53 E Washington St, Fl 2, Knox, IN 46534
   John Thorstad, CPO

COURTS

Starke Circuit Court....................574.772.9146
Fax.......................................574.772.9120
   53 E Washington St, Fl 3, Knox, IN 46534
   Evelian Skronski, Clerk Of Court

POLICE AND SHERIFF

Sheriff's Ofc............................574.772.3771
Fax.......................................574.772.7641
Web...............................www.co.starks.in.us
   108 N Pearl St Ste X, Knox, IN 46534-1113
   Oscar Bowen, Sheriff

Sullivan County

SOCIAL SERVICES

IN Div of Family & Children.............812.268.3905
Fax.......................................812.268.6452
   128 S State St, Sullivan, IN 47882

JUSTICE AGENCY

Probation Dept..........................812.268.4552
Fax.......................................812.268.4870
   100 Court House Sq Rm 303, Sullivan, IN 47882
   Barbara Lance, CPO

POLICE AND SHERIFF

Sheriff's Ofc............................812.268.4308
Fax.......................................812.268.0339
E-mail...................briankinnett@hotmail.com
   24 S State St, Sullivan, IN 47882-1521
   Brian Kinnett, Sheriff

Switzerland County

SOCIAL SERVICES

Family & Children Svcs..................812.427.3232
Fax.......................................812.427.3497
   506 Ferry St, Vevay, IN 47043
   Gary Keith, Director

GENERAL HEALTH SERVICES

Health Dept.............................812.427.3220
Fax.......................................812.427.0235
Web......................................www.ncsl.org
E-mail.......................joyce.johnson@ncsl.org
   1099 Highway 56 Ste 300, Vevay, IN 47043-9128
   Joyce Johnson, Rn, Public Health Nurse

JUSTICE AGENCY

Guardian Ad Litem Program..............812.427.3410
Fax.......................................812.427.4433
   212 W Main St, Vevay, IN 47043
   Cheri Weales, Coordinator

Tippecanoe County

SOCIAL SERVICES

IN Div of Family & Children.............765.742.0400
Fax.......................................765.742.9142
   250 Main St, Ste 301, Lafayette, IN 47901

GENERAL HEALTH SERVICES

Health Dept.............................765.423.9221
Fax.......................................765.423.9154
Web..............................www.tippecanoe.in.gov
E-mail.........................mmuller@tippecanoe.in.gov
   20 N 3rd St, Lafayette, IN 47901-1222
   Marcia Muller, HIV Coordinator

JUSTICE AGENCY

Probation Dept..........................765.423.9347
Fax.......................................765.423.9380
Web..............................www.tippecanoe.in.gov
E-mail........................mrobinson@tippecanoe.in.gov
   301 Main St, Lafayette, IN 47901-1362
   Scott Angspadt, Deputy CPO

POLICE AND SHERIFF

Clark Hill Police Dept..................765.523.2217
Fax.......................................765.523.2217
Web.......................................www.in.gov
   9400 White, Clarks Hill, IN 47930
   Dan Roudebush, Police Chief

Sheriff's Ofc............................765.423.9388
Fax.......................................765.423.4155
E-mail.....................tabrown@tippecanoelaw.in.us
   2640 Duncan Rd, Lafayette, IN 47904-1045
   Tracy Abram, Sheriff

Tipton County

SOCIAL SERVICES

IN Div of Family & Children.............765.675.7441
Fax.......................................765.675.2317
   202 S West St, Tipton, IN 46072

GENERAL HEALTH SERVICES

Health Dept.............................765.675.8741
Fax.......................................765.675.6952
Web..............................www.tiptoncounty.in.gov
E-mail.........................powen@localhealth.in.gov
   1000 S Main St, Tipton, IN 46072-9799
   Bee Welch, Office Manager

JUSTICE AGENCY

Probation Dept..........................765.675.4353
Fax.......................................765.675.7797
Web..............................www.tiptonprobation.com
E-mail......................rickstout@tiptonprobation.com
   101 E Jefferson St, Fl 4, Tipton, IN 46072
   Rick Stout, Chief Performance Officer

COURTS

Tipton Circuit Court....................765.675.2791
Fax.......................................765.675.6436
   101 E Jefferson St, Fl 3, Tipton, IN 46072
   Honorable Thomas R. Lett, Director

Union County

SOCIAL SERVICES

Family & Children Svcs..................765.458.5121
Fax.......................................765.458.6313
E-mail.......................courtney.mathews@dcs.in.gov
   305 N Main St, Liberty, IN 47353
   Courtney Mathews, Director

GENERAL HEALTH SERVICES

Health Dept.............................765.458.5393
Fax.......................................765.458.5582
   6 W South St Ste 2, Liberty, IN 47353
   John Clarkson, Md, Health Officer

JUSTICE AGENCY

Probation Dept..........................765.458.6961
Fax.......................................765.458.6996
   26 W Union St Ste 401, Liberty, IN 07353
   Cyndi Baumbauer, Chief Performance Officer

Indiana

COURTS

Union Circuit Court **765.458.5934**
Fax...765.458.5263
26 W Union St, Liberty, IN 47353
Honorable Matthew R. Cox, Judge

Vanderburgh County

SOCIAL SERVICES

IN Div of Family & Children **812.421.5400**
Fax...812.421.5503
100 E Sycamore St, Evansville, IN 47713

GENERAL HEALTH SERVICES

Health Dept **812.435.2400**
Fax...812.435.5468
Web.............................www.vanderburgh.org
420 Mulberry St, Evansville, IN 47713
Denise Cory, Communicable Disease Director

MENTAL HEALTH SERVICES

SW Indiana Mental Health Ctr **812.423.7791**
Fax...812.422.7558
Web.................................www.southwestern.org
E-mail.........................wwhitehead@swirca.org
415 Mulberry St, Evansville, IN 47713-1298
Willard D. Whitehead Iii, Md, Medical Director

Youth Svc Bureau **812.423.5816**
Fax...812.423.5294
Web.............................www.youthservicebureau.org
E-mail.................csmith@youthservicesbureau.net
734 W Delaware St Ste 206, Evansville, IN 47710
Cynthia Smith, Director

JUSTICE AGENCY

CASA **812.424.5825**
Fax...812.424.5895
E-mail.........................vand.casa@insightbb.com
728 Ct St, Evansville, IN 47708
Suzanne Draper, Executive Director

COURTS

Superior Court Juvenile Div **812.435.5126**
Fax...812.435.5043
Web.............................www.vanderburghgov.org
E-mail.................bniemeier@vanderburghgov.org
1 NW Martin Luther King Jr Blvd Rm 129, Evansville,
IN 47708-1818
Honorable Brett J. Niemeier, Director

POLICE AND SHERIFF

Sheriff's Dept **812.421.6200**
Fax...812.421.6387
3500 N Harland St, Evansville, IN 47711
Eric Williams, Sheriff

EDUCATION SERVICES

Special Education **812.435.8442**
Fax...812.435.8551
Web.............................www.evsc.k12.in.us
E-mail.........................lbass@evsc.k12.in.us
2150 Stringtown Rd, Evansville, IN 47711-3706
Larry K. Bass, Director

Vermillion County

SOCIAL SERVICES

IN Div of Family & Children **765.832.5680**
Fax...765.832.5687
1788 E Hwy 163, PO Box 128, Clinton, IN 47842

GENERAL HEALTH SERVICES

Health Dept **765.832.3622**
Fax...765.832.3684
Web.............................www.localhealth.in.gov
E-mail.............................preely@aol.com
257 Walnut St, Clinton, IN 47842-2261
Penny Bridwell Rn, Public Health Nurse

JUSTICE AGENCY

Probation Dept **765.492.3864**
Fax...765.492.5006
Web.............................www.vermilliongov.us
E-mail.........................ronstateler@vermilliongov.us
255 S Main St,, Newport, IN 47966
Ron G. Stateler, Chief Performance Officer

COURTS

Vermillion Circuit Court **765.492.5320**
Fax...765.492.4325
255 South Main St, Newport, IN 47966
Honorable Bruce V. Stengel, Judge

Vigo County

SOCIAL SERVICES

IN Div of Family & Children **812.234.0100**
Fax...812.234.3182
30 N 8th St, Terre Haute, IN 47807

GENERAL HEALTH SERVICES

Health Dept **812.462.3428**
Fax...812.234.1010
Web.............................www.vigocounty.in.gov
E-mail.........................jkfoulkes@vigocounty.org
147 Oak St, Terre Haute, IN 47807-3438
Joni Foulkes, Administrator

Health Dept **812.462.3431**
Fax...812.231.6242
Web.............................www.vigocounty.org
696 S First St, Terre Haute, IN 47807
Catherine Brown, Md, Pediatrician

COURTS

Probation Dept Juvenile **812.462.3414**
Fax...812.231.5695
E-mail.........................deborah.kesler@vigocounty.org
202 Crawford St, Terre Haute, IN 47807-4616
R.paulette Stagg, Magistrate

POLICE AND SHERIFF

Sheriff's Ofc **812.462.3226**
Fax...812.235.7558
Web.............................www.vigocounty.in.gov
E-mail.........................greg.ewing@vigocounty.in.gov
201 Cherry St, Terre Haute, IN 47807-2940
Greg Ewing, Sheriff

EDUCATION SERVICES

Special Education **812.462.4364**
Fax...812.462.4377
Web.............................www.cbsed.org
E-mail.........................jeb@vigoschools.org
1320 Walnut St, Terre Haute, IN 47807-3931
Jeffrey Blake, Executive Director

Wabash County

SOCIAL SERVICES

Family & Children Svcs **260.563.8471**
Fax...260.563.0578
89 W Canal St, Wabash, IN 46992
Margery Justice, CPS Director

JUSTICE AGENCY

Probation Dept **260.563.8466**
Fax...260.563.8468
E-mail.........................dallas@wabashprobation.com
91 W Hill St, Wabash, IN 46992
Dallas Duggan, Chief Officer

COURTS

Wabash Circuit Court **260.563.0661**
Fax...260.569.1374
Web.............................www.wabashcounty.in.gov
E-mail.........................bmccallen@wabashcounty.in.gov
49 W Hill St, Wabash, IN 46992-3151
Honorable Robert Mccallen III, Director

EDUCATION SERVICES

**Area Agency And Communication Svcs Head
Start** **260.563.5666**
Fax...260.563.0219
Web.............................www.areafive.com
E-mail.........................mmichgaer@areafive.com
105 Olive St, Wabash, IN 46992-2524
Michael Michgaer, Director

Area Agency Head Start **260.982.7885**
E-mail.........................mmeager@areafive.com
20 W Woodring, Laketon, IN 46943
Michael Meager, Director

Warren County

SOCIAL SERVICES

Family & Children Svcs **765.762.6125**
Fax...765.762.8017
Web.............................www.dcs.in.gov
E-mail.........................sonya.janssen@dcs.in.gov
20 W 2nd St, Williamsport, IN 47993-1118
Sonya Janssen, Director

COURTS

Warren Circuit Court **765.762.3604**
Fax...765.764.1692
125 N Monroe St Ste 5, Williamsport, IN 47993
Honorable John A. Rader, Judge

POLICE AND SHERIFF

Sheriff's Ofc **765.764.4367**
Fax...765.762.0315
29 E 2nd St, Williamsport, IN 47993
Russell K Hart, Sheriff

Warrick County

SOCIAL SERVICES

Indiana Dept of Child Svcs **812.897.2270**
Fax...812.897.7024
E-mail.........................judith.harper@dcs.in.gov
1302 Millis Ave, Boonville, IN 47601
Judith A. Harper, Director

GENERAL HEALTH SERVICES

Health Dept **812.897.6105**
Fax...812.897.6410
Web.............................www.warrickcounty.gov
E-mail.........................lbass@warrickcounty.gov
107 W Locust St Ste 107, Boonville, IN 47601-1594
Sharon James, Public Health Nurse

JUSTICE AGENCY

Probation Dept **812.897.6134**
Fax...812.897.6137
E-mail.........................dheal@warrickcounty.gov
1 County Sq Ste 370, Boonville, IN 47601-1862
David Kelley, Judge

COURTS

Judicial Ctr **812.897.8600**
Fax...812.897.6137
Web.............................www.warrickcounty.gov
E-mail.........................clerk@warrickcounty.gov
1 County Sq, Boonville, IN 47601-1862
Sara Topper, Clerk Of Court

Superior Court #1 ....812.897.6140
Fax 812.897.6147
Web ....www.warrickcounty.gov
E-mail ....superior1@warrickcounty.gov
   1 County Sq, Ste 300A, Boonville, IN 47601
   Honorable Keith A. Meier, Judge

POLICE AND SHERIFF

Sheriff's Ofc 812.897.6180
Fax 812.897.3654
Web ....www.warrickcountysheriff.com
E-mail ....bkruse@warrickcountysheriff.com
   100 State Road 62 West, Boonville, IN 47601
   Brett Kruse, Sheriff

Washington County

SOCIAL SERVICES

Family & Children Svcs 812.883.4305
Fax 812.883.9834
E-mail ....nacy.labring@dcs.in.gov
   711 Anson St, Salem, IN 47167-2235
   Nancy Lambring, CPS Supervisor

GENERAL HEALTH SERVICES

Health Dept 812.883.5603
Fax 812.883.5017
Web ....www.washcohealth.com
   806 Martinsburg Rd Ste 100, Salem, IN 47167-5907
   Margaret Scott, Public Health Nurse

JUSTICE AGENCY

Probation Dept 812.883.1446
Fax 812.883.0400
   806 Martinsburg Rd Ste 203, Salem, IN 47167
   Teresa Maise, Chief Performance Officer

COURTS

Superior Court 812.883.4949
Fax 812.883.5488
E-mail ....superior@washingtoncountyin.gov
   801 Jackson St, Salem, IN 47167
   Honorable Frank Newkirk Jr., Judge

Washington Circuit Court 812.883.5302
Fax 812.883.1933
Web ....www.washingtoncounty.in.gov
   99 Public Sq Ste 200, Salem, IN 47167-2060
   Honorable Larry W Medlock, Judge

POLICE AND SHERIFF

Sheriff's Ofc 812.883.5999
Fax 812.883.8615
Web ....www.washingtoncountyindiana.com
E-mail ....wcsheriff@c3bb.com
   801 Jackson St, Salem, IN 47167-1218
   Claud C Combs, Sheriff

Wayne County

SOCIAL SERVICES

Children's Svcs 765.935.0078
   50 S Second St, Richmond, IN 47374-4276

COURTS

Wayne Circuit Court 765.973.9221
Fax 765.973.9250
   301 E Main St, Fl 3, Richmond, IN 47374
   Joanne Stuart, Clerk Of Court

POLICE AND SHERIFF

Sheriff's Dept 765.973.9393
Fax 765.973.9449
Web ....www.co.wayne.in.us
E-mail ....sheriff@co.wayne.in.us
   200 E Main St, Richmond, IN 47374-4209
   P. Matt Strittmatter, Sheriff

EDUCATION SERVICES

Communities In Schools 765.983.2263
Fax 765.939.0508
Web ....www.ciswayneco.org
E-mail ....vivian@parallax.ws
   33 S 7th St, Ste 6, Richmond, IN 47375
   Vivian Ashnawi, Director

Wells County

SOCIAL SERVICES

Family & Children Svcs 260.824.3530
Fax 260.824.8026
Web ....www.dcs.in.gov
E-mail ....jenny.tsakkos@dcs.in.gov
   221 W Market St, Bluffton, IN 46714-1932
   Jenny Tsakkos, Director

GENERAL HEALTH SERVICES

Health Dept 260.824.6489
Fax 260.824.8803
Web ....www.wellscounty.org
E-mail ....dkgerdom@wellscounty.org
   223 W Washington St, Bluffton, IN 46714-1996
   Darlene Gerdom, Rn, Nursing Supervisor

JUSTICE AGENCY

Probation Dept 260.824.6496
Fax 260.824.6519
Web ....www.wellscounty.org
   102 W Market St Ste 404, Bluffton, IN 46714-2050
   Gregory Werich, Chief Performance Officer

COURTS

Wells Circuit Court 260.824.6485
Fax 260.824.6488
Web ....www.wellscounty.org
E-mail ....clerk@wellscounty.org
   102 W Market St Ste 301, Bluffton, IN 46714-2050
   Kenton Kiracose, Judge

POLICE AND SHERIFF

Sheriff's Ofc 260.824.3426
Fax 260.824.6424
Web ....www.wellscounty.org
   1615 W Western Ave, Bluffton, IN 46714-9792
   Monte Fisher, Sheriff

White County

SOCIAL SERVICES

Family & Children Svcs 574.583.5742
Fax 574.583.6754
   715 N Main St, Monticello, IN 47960
   Barbara Bedrick, DCF

GENERAL HEALTH SERVICES

Health Dept 574.583.8254
Fax 574.583.1513
E-mail ....healthdept@whitecountyindiana.us
   315 N Illinois St, Monticello, IN 47960
   Linda Pagels, Rn, Public Health Nurse

COURTS

White Circuit Court 574.583.5032
Fax 574.583.4706
   110 N Main St, Monticello, IN 47960
   Honorable Robert W Thacker, Family Court Judge

POLICE AND SHERIFF

Sheriff's Ofc 574.583.2251
Fax 574.583.6457
   915 Hanawalt St, Monticello, IN 47960-1828
   Patrick Shaser, Sheriff

EDUCATION SERVICES

Area IV Head Start 574.583.8828
Fax 574.583.8846
E-mail ....d.debruyn@areaivagency.org
   904 City Park Loop, Monticello, IN 47960
   Debbie Bebruyn, Director

Whitley County

SOCIAL SERVICES

Children's Svcs 260.244.6531
   115 S Line St, Columbia City, IN 46725

GENERAL HEALTH SERVICES

Health Dept 260.248.3121
Fax 260.248.3129
   220 W Van Buren St Ste 111, Columbia City,
   IN 46725-2056
   Dr. Lisa Hatcher, Health Officer

COURTS

Whitley Circuit Court 260.248.3115
Fax 260.248.3166
   101 W Van Buren St Rm 3, Columbia City,
   IN 46725-2092
   James R. Heuer, Judge

POLICE AND SHERIFF

Sheriff's Ofc 260.248.3171
Fax 260.625.1063
   101 W Market St Ste 1, Columbia City, IN 46725
   Mark E Hodges, Sheriff

SPECIAL SERVICES AGENCIES

ADOPTION AGENCIES

Adoption Support Ctr 317.255.5916
Fax 317.253.8838
E-mail ....info@adoptionsupportcenter.com
   6331 Carrollton Ave, Indianapolis, IN 46220-1754
   Marllys Clements, Executive Director

Americans For African Adoptions, Inc. 317.271.4567
Fax 317.271.8739
Web ....www.africanadoptions.org
E-mail ....info@africanadoptions.org
   8910 Timberwood Dr, Indianapolis, IN 46234-1952
   Cheryl Carter-Shotts, Director

Area IV Agency on Aging & Community Action
Programs 765.447.7683
Fax 765.447.6862
Web ....www.areaivagency.org
   660 N. 36th Street, Lafayette, IN 47903-4727
   COA accredited organization.

Butler & King 317.632.9411
Fax 317.236.0481
   129 E Market St Ste 500, Indianapolis,
   IN 46204-3217
   April Hall, Director

Catholic Charities 574.234.3111
Fax 574.289.1034
Web ....www.diocesefwsb.org
E-mail ....sboffice@fw.diocesefwsb.org
   1817 Miami St, South Bend, IN 46613
   Bob Barb, Director Of Adoptions

Indiana

Catholic Charities of the Diocese of Fort Wayne - South Bend, Inc. **260.422.5625**
Fax 260.422.5657
Web .... www.ccfwsb.org
  315 E. Washington Boulevard, Fort Wayne, IN 46802
COA accredited organization.

Choices, Inc. **317.726.2121**
Fax 317.726.2130
Web .... www.choiceteam.org
  4701 North Keystone Avenue, Suite 150, Indianapolis, IN 46205
COA accredited organization.

Dillon International Adoption **765.965.1195**
E-mail .... denise@dillonadopt.com
  3401 Glen Hills Dr, Richmond, IN 47374
Denise Villan, Director

Families Thru International Adoption **812.479.9900**
Fax 812.479.9901
Web .... www.ftia.org
E-mail .... adopt@ftia.org
  401 SE 6th St, Ste 202, Evansville, IN 47713
Keith Wallace, Executive Director

Families Thru International Adoption, Inc. **812.479.9900**
Fax 812.479.9901
Web .... www.ftia.org
  401 SE 6th Street, Suite 202, Evansville, IN 47713
COA accredited organization.

G.L.A.D. **812.424.4523**
Fax 812.424.3180
E-mail .... glad@gladadoption.com
  5000 N 1st Avenue, Evansville, IN 47710
Nancy VanHoose, Director

Hand In Hand International Adoptions **260.636.3566**
Fax 260.636.2554
Web .... www.hihiadopt.org
E-mail .... indiana@hihiadopt.org
  210A N Orange St, Albion, IN 46701
Vickie Truelove, Director

Indiana Foster Care And Adoption
Associates **317.524.2600**
Fax 317.524.2609
Web .... www.ifcaa.org
E-mail .... info@ifcaa.org
  509 National Ave Ste A, Indianapolis, IN 46227
Christina Morrison, Director

LifeStream Services, Inc.
  P.O. Box 308, Yorktown, IN 47396-0308
COA accredited organization.

Lutheran Social Services of Indiana **260.426.3347**
Fax 260.424.2248
Web .... www.lssin.org
  P.O. Box 11329, Fort Wayne, IN 46857
COA accredited organization.

Specialized Alternatives For Youth **765.287.8477**
Fax 765.287.8372
Web .... www.safy.org
  7701 W Kilgore Ave, Yorktown, IN 47396
Michael Thomas, Treatment Director

The Villages of Indiana **317.775.6500**
Fax 317.775.6397
Web .... www.villageskids.org
  3833 North Meridian Street, Suite 101, Indianapolis, IN 46208
Sharon Pierce, CEO
COA accredited organization.

Villages Healthy Family **219.980.6185**
Fax 219.980.6195
Web .... www.villageskids.org
E-mail .... else_anderson@villages.org
  3229 Broadway Ste 101, Gary, IN 46409-1040
Elsie Anderson, Director

Vincennes University dba Generations **812.888.5880**
Web .... www.generationsnetwork.org/
  PO Box 314, Vincennes, IN 47591
COA accredited organization.

White's Residential And Family Svcs **317.577.5948**
Fax 317.577.5954
Web .... www.whitesrfs.org
E-mail .... kendall.mosberg@whitesrfs.org
  6330 E 75th St, Ste 300, Indianapolis, IN 46250-2708
Kendall Mosburg, Clinical Supervisor

ADVOCACY RESOURCES

Child Advocates Inc **317.205.3055**
  8200 Haverstick Rd Ste 240, Indianapolis, IN 46240
Cynthia Booth, Executive Director

Dr Bill Lewis Center For Children **260.407.5437**
Fax 260.407.5438
  2730 E Way Blvd, Fort Wayne, IN 46805
Rob Pettidone, Supervisor

BEHAVIORAL HEALTH TREATMENT

Adult and Child Mental Health Center, Inc. **317.882.5122**
Web .... adultchild.org
E-mail .... pnovak@adultandchild.org
  222 E. Ohio St. Suite 600, Indianapolis, IN 46204
Dr. Pat Novak, Accreditation Manager
Joint Commission accredited organization.

Aspire Indiana **317.587.0500**
Web .... www.aspireindiana.org
E-mail .... virginia.nelson@aspireindiana.org
  9516 East 148th Street, Noblesville, IN 46060
Mrs. Virginia Nelson, Accreditation Manager
Joint Commission accredited organization.

Atterbury Job Corps Ctr **812.526.5581**
Fax 812.526.9551
  1025 A Hospital Rd., Edinburgh, IN 46124
Lori Winne, Center Director

Bloomington Meadows Hospital **812.331.8000**
E-mail .... brian.wolfe@psysolutions.com
  3600 North Prow Road, Bloomington, IN 47404
Mr. Brian Wolfe, Accreditation Manager
Joint Commission accredited organization.

Brooks School Elementry **317.915.4250**
Fax 317.915.4259
Web www.hse.k12.in.us
E-mail .... bryan@hse.k12.in.us
  12451 Brooks School Rd, Fishers, IN 46037-9745
Bridget Ryan, Director

Campagna Academy **219.322.8614**
Fax 219.322.8436
Web .... www.campagnaacademy.org
E-mail .... bhillman@campagnaacademy.org
  7403 Cline Ave, Schererville, IN 46375-2645
Bruce Hillman, Executive Administrator
COA accredited organization.

Cary Home For Children **765.474.4616**
Fax 765.477.7806
E-mail .... jkinola@tippecanoe.in.gov
  1530 S 18th St, Lafayette, IN 47905-2098
Jason Kinola, Director

Centerstone of Indiana **812.348.7449**
Fax 812.376.4875
Web .... www.centerstone.org
  720 North Marr Road, Suite 400, Columbus, IN 47201
CARF accredited programs available.

Children's Sanctuary, Inc. **260.485.0870**
Fax 260.469.2459
Web .... www.childrenssanctuary.org
  3711 Rupp Drive, Suite 105, Fort Wayne, IN 46815
CARF accredited programs available.

Christian Haven, Inc. **219.956.3125**
Fax 219.956.4128
Web .... www.christianhaven.org
  12501 N State Rd 49, Wheatfield, IN 46392
Patrick Oatis, Executive Director

Columbus Hospital LLC **812.376.1711**
Web .... www.columbusbehavioral.com
E-mail .... kevin.reckelhoff@uhsinc.com
  2223 Poshard Drive, Columbus, IN 47203
Mr. Kevin Reckelhoff, Accreditation Manager
Joint Commission accredited organization.

Community Counseling Ctr **765.659.4771**
Fax 765.659.9473
Web .... www.howardregional.org
  250 Alhambra Ave, Frankfort, IN 46041
Susan Moody, Director

Community Hospital East **317.355.5520**
Web .... www.ecommunity.com
E-mail .... cburgard@ecommunity.com
  1500 North Ritter Avenue, Indianapolis, IN 46219
Ms. Cleo Ann Burgard, Accreditation Manager
Joint Commission accredited organization.

Community Mental Health Center, Inc. **812.537.1302**
Fax 812.537.0194
Web .... www.cmhcinc.org
  285 Bielby Road, Lawrenceburg, IN 47025
Tom Talbog, Ex Director
CARF accredited programs available.

Comprehensive Mental Health, Inc. **574.722.5151**
Web .... wwwFourCounty.org
E-mail .... kbowsher@fourcounty.org
  1015 Michigan Avenue, Logansport, IN 46947
Mrs. Kim Bowsher, Accreditation Manager
Joint Commission accredited organization.

Cooparative School Svcs **219.866.8540**
Fax 219.866.4668
Web .... www.cooperativeschoolservices.org
E-mail .... mail@cooperativeschoolservices.org
  1389 St. Gasper Dr, Rensselaer, IN 47978
Patricia Kim, Director

Correctional Medical Svs **765.593.0111**
Fax 765.521.2098
  1105 W Dunn Ave, Muncie, IN 47303-1729
K Stein, Superintendent

Counseling Ctr **574.722.5151**
Fax 574.722.9523
Web .... www.fourcounty.org
E-mail .... lulrich@fourcounty.org
  1015 Michigan Ave, Logansport, IN 46947
Lawrence Ulrich, Executive Director

Counseling Ctr **574.722.5151**
Fax 574.722.9523
  716 Michigan Ave, Lodansport, IN 46947
Lawrence Ulrich, Executive Director

Counseling Ctr **574.223.8565**
Fax 574.223.8786
Web .... www.fourcounty.org
E-mail .... lulrich@fourcounty.org
  401 E 8th St Ste A, Rochester, IN 46975-1444
Lawrence Ulrich, Executive Director

Counseling Ctr **574.946.4233**
Fax 574.946.4365
Web .... www.fourcounty.org
E-mail .... lulrich@fourcounty.org
  118 N Sally Dr, Winamac, IN 46996-9100
Lawrence Ulrich, Executive Director

Court Svcs **765.423.1172**
Fax 765.423.1422
Web .... www.county.tippecanoe.in.us
  117 N 4Th St, Lafayette, IN 47901-1305
Cindy Hoffman, Director

Crossroad Child & Family Services, Inc. 260.484.4153
Web .... www.crossroad-fwch.org
E-mail .... clink@crossroad-fwch.org
　2525 Lake Avenue, Fort Wayne, IN 46805-5457
Ms. Carma Link, Accreditation Manager
Joint Commission accredited organization.

Ctr For Behavioral Health 317.834.8187
Fax 317.834.8196
Web .... www.the-center.org
E-mail .... dmorrison@the-center.org
　11370 N State Road 67, Mooresville, IN 46158-6368
Dennis P. Morrison, CEO

Ctr For Hospice And Palliative Care 574.243.3100
Fax 574.243.3134
Web .... www.centerforhospite.org
E-mail .... eblenm@Centerforhospice.Org
　111 Sunnybrook Ct, South Bend, IN 46637-3437

Cummins Behavioral Health Systems, Inc. 317.272.3330
Web .... www.cumminbhs.com
E-mail .... lmeadows@cumminsbhs.org
　6655 East US 36, Avon, IN 46123
Ms. Leslie Meadows, Accreditation Manager
Joint Commission accredited organization.

Cummins Mental Health Ctr 765.361.9767
Fax 765.361.0374
Web .... www.cumminshbs.com
E-mail .... amace@cumminsbhs.org
　701 N Englewood Dr, Crawfordsville, IN 47933-9744
Amy Mace, Financial Officer

Damar Svcs, Inc 317.856.5201
Fax 317.856.2333
Web .... www.damar.org
E-mail .... info@damar.org
　6067 Dectaur Blvd, Indianapolis, IN 46221-9704
Danielle Altman, Assistant Director

Damien Center 317.632.0123
Fax 317.632.4362
Web .... www.damien.org
　26 North Arsenal Avenue, Indianapolis, IN 46201
CARF accredited programs available.

David G Crane Inc 317.831.1066
　33 W South St, Mooresville, IN 46158-1731
David Crane, Psychiatrist

David G Crane Inc 812.339.1221
　802 S Washington St, Bloomington, IN 47401-4644
David Crane Md, Psychiatrist

DDSI 317.477.8240
　1278 N State St, Greenfield, IN 46140-1055
Lindsey Huntsman, Director

Deal Medical Practice 317.884.1752
Fax 317.884.1753
　8220 Madison Ave, Indianapolis, IN 46227-6013
Michael Deal, Psychiatrist

Deaton Medical Practice 317.639.6312
Fax 317.298.8301
　333 N Pennsylvania St Ste 612, Indianapolis,
　IN 46204-1828
Rodney Deaton, Psychiatrist

Debra Dineff Counseling Svcs 317.894.1904
　10548 Stillwood Ln, Indianapolis, IN 46239-9393
Debra Dineff, Director

Dianne Martin Inc 317.541.9159
Fax 317.541.9179
　5670 Caito Dr Bldg 5, Ste 125, Indianapolis,
　IN 46226
Dianne Martin, Psychiatrist

Edgewater Systems for Balanced Living,
Inc. 219.885.4264
Fax 219.882.0242
Web .... www.edgewatersystems.org
　1100 West Sixth Avenue, Gary, IN 46402
CARF accredited programs available.

Evansville Psychiatric Children's Center 812.477.6436
E-mail .... tamara.klausmeier@fssa.in.gov
　3300 East Morgan Avenue, Evansville, IN 47715
Lottie Cook, Superintendant; Ms. Tamara Klausmeier, Accreditation
Manager
Joint Commission accredited organization.

Fairbanks Hospital, Inc. 317.849.8222
Web .... www.fairbankscd.org
E-mail .... lmodlik@fairbankscd.org
　8102 Clearvista Parkway, Indianapolis,
　IN 46256-4698
Ms. Liz Modlik, Accreditation Manager
Joint Commission accredited organization.

Family & Chidren's Ctr Counseling & Development
Svcs 574.232.2255
Fax 574.287.9377
Web .... www.fcccds.org
E-mail .... pdhancock@fcccds.org
　611 Lincoln Way E, South Bend, IN 46601-3220
Pat Hancock, Clinical Director

Family & Children's Ctr. Counseling & Development
Services 574.968.9660
Web .... www.fcccds.org
E-mail .... mkowalski@fcccds.org
　315 W. Jefferson, South Bend, IN 46601
Ms. Mary Kowalski, Accreditation Manager
Joint Commission accredited organization.

Family & Children's Services, Inc. 260.744.4326
Fax 260.744.0188
Web .... www.familychildren.org
E-mail .... connie.carman@familychildren.org
　2712 South Calhoun Street, Fort Wayne, IN 46807
Connie Carman, Clinical Director
CARF accredited programs available.

Family And Children Behavior 260.436.0950
Fax 260.436.0893
　4630 W Jefferson Blvd Ste 1, Fort Wayne, IN 46804
Syed Mumtaz, Psychiatrist

Family and Children's Ctr Counseling and Development
Svcs 574.232.2048
Fax 574.288.0827
E-mail .... dwoods@bgcsjc.org
　502 E Sample St, South Bend, IN 46601-3551
Dorene Huddleson, Director

Family Counseling Ctr 260.925.2017
Fax 260.925.9713
　117 Ninth St, Auburn, IN 46706
Judith Williams, Director

Family Svc Society Inc 765.662.9971
Fax 765.651.6556
Web .... www.famservices.com
E-mail .... crose@famservices.com
　101 S Washington St Ste 200, Marion,
　IN 46952-3868
Connie Rose, Executive Administrator

Family Svcs 574.295.6596
Fax 574.522.5363
E-mail .... info@ifitelkhart.com
　101 E Hively Ave, Elkhart, IN 46517
Vanessa Kelleybrew, Director

Fiacable Medical Practice 260.423.3304
Fax 260.426.4284
E-mail .... jpfiac@aol.com
　2426 Lake Ave, Fort Wayne, IN 46805-5406
J Paul Fiacable, Psychiatrist

Good Samaritan Hospital 812.885.3334
Web .... gshvin.org
E-mail .... gwaldroup@gshvin.org
　520 South Seventh Street, Vincennes, IN 47591
Mr. Gerald Waldroup, Accreditation Manager
Joint Commission accredited organization.

Grant-Blackford Mental Health, Inc. 765.662.3971
Web .... www.cornerstone.org
E-mail .... diane.popp@cornerstone.org
　505 Wabash Avenue, Marion, IN 46952
Ms. Diane Popp, Accreditation Manager
Joint Commission accredited organization.

Hale and Associates, LLC 765.236.1964
Fax 765.236.1960
Web .... www.haleandassociatesllc.com
　2738 East 00 NS, Kokomo, IN 46901
CARF accredited programs available.

Hamilton Center, Inc. 812.231.8323
Fax 812.231.8323
Web .... www.hamiltoncenter.org
　620 Eighth Avenue, Terre Haute, IN 47804
CARF accredited programs available.

Hillcrest Washington Youth Home 812.428.0698
Fax 812.429.9655
　2700 W Indiana St, Evansville, IN 47712
Bill Curtis, Administrator

Howard Regional Health System 765.453.8547
Web .... www.howardregional.org
E-mail .... casnyder@howardregional.org
　3500 South Lafountain Street, Kokomo, IN 46902
Ms. Cara Snyder, Accreditation Manager
Joint Commission accredited organization.

Intensive Treatment Programs, Ltd. (ITP) 219.956.3182
Fax 219.956.3174
Web .... www.christianhaven.org
　12501 N State Road 49, Thomas Cottage, Wheatfield,
　IN 46390
Bruce H. Axelrod, Md, Evp, Medical Director

Kids Alive International 219.464.9035
Fax 219.462.5611
Web .... www.kidsalive.org
E-mail .... al@kidsalive.org
　2507 Cumberland Dr, Valparaiso, IN 46383-2503
Al Lackey, President

Life Spring Mental Health 812.981.2594
Fax 812.981.2599
Web .... www.lifespr.com
　2820 Grant Line Rd, New Albany, IN 47150-2426
Misty Scott, Clinical Director

Life Spring Mental Health Ctr Place 3 .... 812.981.4600
Fax 812.981.4602
Web .... www.lifespr.com
E-mail .... aanthony@lifespr.com
　200 Mosier Ave, New Albany, IN 47150-4830
Chuck Anthony, Manager

Life Spring Mental Health Sarkisian House 812.948.0111
Fax 812.948.0118
Web .... www.lifespr.com
E-mail .... info@lifespr.com
　904 E Spring St, New Albany, IN 47150-2945

Lifeline Youth & Family Services, Inc. 260.745.3322
Fax 260.745.0234
Web .... www.lifelineyouth.org
　P.O. Box 80487, Fort Wayne, IN 46898-0487
COA accredited organization.

Lifeline Youth & Family Svc, Inc. 260.745.3322
Fax 260.745.0234
Web .... www.lifelineyouth.org
E-mail .... info@lifelineyouth.org
　7136 Gettysburg Pike, Fort Wayne, IN 46804-0487
Mark Terrell, CEO

LifeSpring, Inc. 812.280.2080
Web .... www.lifespr.com
E-mail .... gduncan@lifespr.com
　460 Spring Street, Jeffersonville, IN 47130
Mr. Greg Duncan, Accreditation Manager
Joint Commission accredited organization.

Meridian Services, Corp. 765.288.1928
Web ....www.meridiansc.org/
E-mail ....garofolg@meridiansc.org
240 North Tillotson Avenue, Muncie, IN 47304
Mr. Gary Garofolo, Accreditation Manager
Joint Commission accredited organization.

Michiana Behavioral Health Center 574.936.3784
Web ....www.michianabhc.com
E-mail ....bryan.lett@psysolutions.com
1800 North Oak Drive, Plymouth, IN 46563
Mr. Bryan Lett, Accreditation Manager
Joint Commission accredited organization.

Midtown Community Mental Health Ctr 317.554.2704
Fax 317.554.2721
Web ....www.wishard.edu
E-mail ....margie.payne@wishard.edu
850 N Meridian St Fl 2, Indianapolis, IN 46204-1191
Margie Payne, CEO

Mulberry Center 812.423.4700
Fax 812.421.2618
414 SE 4th St, Evansville, IN 47713
Ralph Nichols, Administrator

Northeastern Center, Inc. 260.347.2453
Fax 260.347.2456
Web ....www.nec.org
E-mail ....jhollister@nec.org
220 South Main Street, Kendallville, IN 46755
Jerry Hollister, CEO
CARF accredited programs available.

Oaklawn Psychiatric Center, Inc. 574.533.1234
Web ....www.oaklawn.org
E-mail ....julie.frey@oaklawn.org
330 Lakeview Drive, Goshen, IN 46528
Ms. Julie Frey, Accreditation Manager
Joint Commission accredited organization.

Options Treatment Center 317.544.4340
E-mail ....melissa.combs@yfcs.com
5602 Caito Drive, Indianapolis, IN 46226
Ms. Melissa Combs, Accreditation Manager
Joint Commission accredited organization.

Otis R. Bowen Ctr For Human Svcs 574.267.7169
Fax 574.269.3995
Web ....www.bowencenter.org
850 N Harrison St, Oris R. Brown Center for Human,
Warsaw, IN 46580-3199
Kenneth Ogu, Medical Director

Park Center, Inc. 260.481.2700
Fax 260.481.2885
Web ....www.parkcenter.org
909 East State Boulevard, Fort Wayne, IN 46805
CARF accredited programs available.

Porter-Starke Svcs, Inc. 219.531.3500
Fax 219.462.3975
Web ....www.porterstarke.org
E-mail ....apopli@porterstarke.org
601 Wall St, Valparaiso, IN 46383-2512
Anand Popli, Medical Director

PSI Family Services of Indiana, Inc. 219.756.8201
Fax 219.756.8203
Web ....www.psifamilyservices.com
8120 Georgia Street, Suite D, Merrillville, IN 46410
CARF accredited programs available.

R.T.C. Resource Acquisition Corporation 317.783.4003
Web ....resourcetreatmentcenter.com
E-mail ....bobbie.durham@yfcs.com
1404 South State, Indianapolis, IN 46203
Mrs. Bobbie Durham, Accreditation Manager
Joint Commission accredited organization.

Regional Mental Health Center 219.769.4005
Web ....www.regionalmentalhealth.org
E-mail ....sandy.appleby@geminus.org
8555 Taft Street, Merrillville, IN 46410-6199
Ms. Sandy Appleby, Accreditation Manager
Joint Commission accredited organization.

ResCare Residential Program 812.835.4631
Fax 765.653.1965
Web ....www.rcrp.org
1306 South Bloomington, Greencastle, IN 46135
CARF accredited programs available.

Resolute Acquisition Corporation 317.630.5215
E-mail ....melissa.combs@yfcs.com
320 North Tibbs, Indianapolis, IN 46222
Ms. Melissa Combs, Accreditation Manager
Joint Commission accredited organization.

Resolute, Inc. 317.630.5215
Fax 317.630.5221
Web ....www.resolute.com
E-mail ....george@resolute.com
320 N Tibbs Ave, Indianapolis, IN 46222-4064
George Hurd, CEO

Riley Child Psychiatry Clinic 317.274.8162
Fax 317.278.0609
Web ....www.rileyhospital.org
E-mail ....cmcdougl@iupui.edu
702 Barnhill Dr, Rm 4300, Indianapolis, IN 46202
Christopher Mcdougle, Chairman

Saint John's Health System 765.646.8373
E-mail ....ljwood@sjhsnet.org
2015 Jackson Street, Anderson, IN 46016
Ms. Lori Wood, Accreditation Manager
Joint Commission accredited organization.

Southwest Indiana Regional Youth Village 812.886.3000
Fax 812.886.3010
Web ....www.swyouthvillage.org
E-mail ....tbrink@swyouthvillage.com
2290 S Theobald Ln, Vincennes, IN 47591-8027
Barb Tilly, Executive Director

Southwestern Behavioral Healthcare, Inc. 812.436.4231
Web ....southwestern.org
E-mail ....beckhamr@southwestern.org
415 Mulberry Street, Evansville, IN 47713-1298
Mrs. Roxanne Beckham, Accreditation Manager
Joint Commission accredited organization.

Stone Belt Arc, Inc. 812.332.2168
Fax 812.331.6712
Web ....www.stonebelt.org
2815 East Tenth Street, Bloomington, IN 47408
CARF accredited programs available.

Strides To Success, Inc. 317.838.7002
Fax 317.838.7024
Web ....www.stridestosuccess.org
E-mail ....stridestosuccess@aol.com
1350 Terry Dr, Plainfield, IN 46168-9367
Debbie Anderson, Director

Swanson Center 219.879.4621
Fax 219.873.2388
Web ....www.swansoncenter.org
450 Saint John Road, Suite 501, Michigan City,
IN 46360
CARF accredited programs available.

The Children's Campus, Inc. 574.259.5666
Web ....www.childrenscampus.org
E-mail ....kermeti@childrenscampus.org
1411 Lincoln Way West, Mishawaka, IN 46544-1690
Ms. Kris Ermeti, Accreditation Manager
Joint Commission accredited organization.

**The Midwest Center for Youth and
Families** 219.766.2999
Web ....www.midwest-center.com
E-mail ....carol.amore@uhsinc.com
1012 West Indiana Street, Kouts, IN 46347
Mrs. Carol Amore, Accreditation Manager
Joint Commission accredited organization.

**The Otis R. Bowen Center for Human Services,
Inc.** 574.267.7169
Web ....www.bowencenter.org
E-mail ....dan.carey@bowencenter.org
850 North Harrison Street, Warsaw, IN 46581
Mr. Daniel Carey, Accreditation Manager
Joint Commission accredited organization.

The Southern Hills Counseling Center, Inc. 812.482.3020
Fax 812.482.6409
Web ....www.southernhills.org
480 Eversman Drive, Jasper, IN 47546
CARF accredited programs available.

Thelma Marshall Children's Home 219.882.8342
Fax 219.882.8738
2316 Jefferson St, Gary, IN 46407-3044
Tesheza Dixon, Director

United Methodist Youth Home 812.479.7535
Fax 812.479.7203
Web ....www.umyh.com
E-mail ....admin@umyh.com
2521 N Burkhardt Rd, Evansville, IN 47715-2151
Barbara Jessen, Psy.d., Administrator

Valle Vista Hospital, LLC 317.887.1348
Web ....www.vallevistahospital.com
E-mail ....karen.hayden@psysolutions.com
898 East Main Street, Greenwood, IN 46143
Mrs. Karen Hayden, Accreditation Manager
Joint Commission accredited organization.

Wabash Valley Alliance, Inc. 765.464.0401
Web ....wvhmhc.org
E-mail ....gsummers@wvhmhc.org
2900 North River Road, West Lafayette, IN 47906
Ms. Gail Summers, Accreditation Manager
Joint Commission accredited organization.

**Wellstone Regional Hospital Acquisition,
LLC** 812.284.8000
Web ....www.wellstonehospital.com
E-mail ....deanna.new@psysolutions.com
2700 Vissing Park Road, Jeffersonville, IN 47130
Mrs. Deanna New, Accreditation Manager
Joint Commission accredited organization.

Wernle Youth & Family Treatment Center 765.966.2506
Fax 765.939.8303
Web ....www.wernle.org
P.O. Box 1386, Richmond, IN 47375-1386
COA accredited organization.

White's Residential & Family Services, Inc. 260.563.1158
Fax 260.563.1957
Web ....www.whiteskids.org
5233 South 50 East, Wabash, IN 46992
COA accredited organization.

Willowglen Academy - Indiana, Inc. 219.886.1320
Web ....www.phoenixcaresystems.com
E-mail ....lcameron@phoenixcaresystems.com
308 East 21st Avenue, Gary, IN 46407
Mrs. Lorene Cameron, Accreditation Manager
Joint Commission accredited organization.

Wishard Health Services 317.639.6671
Web ....www.wishard.edu
E-mail ....crissy.lough@wishard.edu
1001 West Tenth Street, Indianapolis, IN 46202
Mrs. Crissy Lough, Accreditation Manager
Joint Commission accredited organization.

Women's Bureau 260.424.7977
Fax 260.426.7576
Web ....www.womensbureau.com
3521 Lake Avenue, Suite 1, Fort Wayne, IN 46805
CARF accredited programs available.

Wyandotte House 812.738.3273
Fax 812.738.2912
Web ....www.aye.com
270 Wyandotte Ave, Corydon, IN 47112-2233

Youth Opportunity Center, Inc. **765.289.5437**
Fax 765.213.5094
Web .... www.yocinc.org
　3700 West Kilgore Avenue, Muncie, IN 47304
　　COA accredited organization.

Youth Svcs Bureau **812.948.5481**
Fax 812.948.5427
E-mail .... lpezzarossi@floydcounty.in.gov
　3005 Grant Line Rd Ste 4, New Albany,
　IN 47150-6947
　　Leah Pezzarossi, Executive Director

CHILDREN'S HOSPITAL

Ball Memorial Hospital **765.747.3111**
　2401 University Ave, Muncie, IN 47303
　　Mike Haley, Chief Executive Officer

Bloomington Hospital **812.335.3681**
　601 W 2nd St, Bloomington, IN 47403
　　Mark Moore, Chief Executive Officer

Bluffton Regional Medical Center **260.824.3210**
　303 S Main St, Bluffton, IN 46714
　　Brandon Haushalter, Chief Executive Officer

Bradford Hospital **812.275.1200**
　2900 W 16th St, Bedford, IN 47421
　　Bradford Dykes, Chief Executive Officer

Clairan West Medical Center **314.217.3000**
　1111 N Ronald Reagan Pkwy, Avon, IN 46123

Clarian Health **317.962.2000**
　I-65 at 21st St, Indianapolis, IN 46202
　　Dan Evans, Director

Clarian North Medical Center **317.688.2000**
　11700 N Meridian Ave, Carmel, IN 46032
　　John Goble, Chief Executive Officer

Columbus Regional Hospital **812.379.4441**
　2400 E 17th St, Columbus, IN 47201

Community Hospital **812.537.1010**
　600 Wilson Creed Rd, Lawrenceburg, IN 47025
　　Peter Resnick, Chief Executive Officer

Community Hospital **219.836.1600**
　901 MacArthur Blvd, Munster, IN 46321
　　Don Sesko, Chief Executive Officer

Community Hospital of Bremen **574.546.2211**
　1020 High Rd, Bremen, IN 46506
　　Scott Grayville, President

Crittenton Hospital Medical Center **248.652.5000**
　1101 W University Dr, Muncie, IN 47307
　　Lynn Orfgen, Chief Executive Officer

Daviess Community Hospital **812.254.2760**
　1314 E Walnut St, Washington, IN 47501
　　Gary Kendrick, Chief Executive Officer

Deaconess Hospital **812.450.5000**
　600 Mary St, Evansville, IN 47747
　　Linda White, Chief Executive Officer

Dupont Hospital **260.416.3000**
　2520 E Dupont Rd, Fort Wayne, IN 46825
　　Chad Towner, Chief Executive Officer

Elkhart General Hospital **574.294.2621**
　600 E Blvd, Elkhart, IN 46514

Floyd Memorial Hospital & Health Svcs **812.944.7701**
E-mail .... kwealth@fmhhs.com
　1850 State St, New Albany, IN 47150
　　Mark Shugarman, Chief Executive Officer

General Hospital **812.847.2281**
　RR 1 Box 1000, Linton, IN 47441
　　Jonas Uland, Director

Gibson General Hospital **812.385.3401**
　1808 Sherman Dr, Princeton, IN 47670
　　Mike Lojan, Director

Good Samaritan Hospital **812.882.5220**
　520 S 7th St, Vincennes, IN 47591
　　Rob Mclin, Chief Executive Officer

Goshen General Hospital **574.533.2141**
　200 High Park Ave, Goshen, IN 46526
　　James Dague, Director

Hancock Regional Hospital **317.462.5544**
Web .... www.hancockregional.org
E-mail .... generalinformation@hancockregional.org
　801 N State St, Greenfield, IN 46140
　　Rick Edwards, Chief Executive Officer

Hendricks Regional Health **317.745.4451**
　1000 E Main St, Danville, IN 46122
　　Dennis Dawes, Chief Executive Officer

I U Health **812.723.2811**
　642 W Hospital Rd, Paoli, IN 47454
　　Larry Bailey, Chief Executive Officer

King's Daughters' Hsptl & Hlth Svcs **812.265.5211**
　1 King's Daughters' Dr, Madison, IN 47250

La Porte Regional Hospital **219.326.1234**
　1007 Lincolnway, La Porte, IN 46350
　　Thor Thordarson, Chief Executive Officer

Major Hospital **317.392.3211**
　150 W Washington St, Shelbyville, IN 46176
　　Jack Horner, Chief Executive Officer

Marion General Hospital **765.662.1441**
　441 N Wabash Ave, Marion, IN 46952
　　Paul Usher, President/CEO

Memoiral Hospital & Health Care Center **812.482.2345**
　800 W 9th St, Jasper, IN 47546
　　Ray Snowden, Director

Memorial Hospital **812.663.4331**
　720 N Lincoln St, Greensburg, IN 47240
　　Wenda Simmon, Chief Executive Officer

Memorial Hospital of South Bend **574.647.1000**
　615 N Michigan St, South Bend, IN 46601
　　Craig Gruber, Administrator

Methodist Hospitals **219.886.4000**
　600 Grant St, Gary, IN 46402
　　Inan Mcfadden, Chief Executive Officer

Morgan Hospital & Medical Center **765.342.8441**
　2209 John R Wooden Dr, Martinsville, IN 46151
　　Thomas Lock, Chief Executive Officer

Parkview Hospital **260.373.4000**
　2200 Randallia Dr, Fort Wayne, IN 46805
　　Mike Packnett, Chief Executive Officer

Parkview LaGrange Hospital **260.463.2143**
　207 N Townline rd, Lagrange, IN 46761
　　Mike Packnett, Chief Executive Officer

Parkview Whitley Hospital **260.248.9000**
　353 N Oak St, Columbia City, IN 46725
　　Richard Beemer, Community Relation

Reid Hospital & Health Care Services **765.983.3000**
　1100 Reid Pkwy, Richmond, IN 47374
　　Jackie Webb, Chief Executive Officer

Riverview Hospital **317.773.0760**
　395 Westfield Rd, Noblesville, IN 46060
　　Joyce Wood, Chief Nursing Officer

Schneck Medical Center **812.522.2349**
　411 W Tiption St, Seymour, IN 47274
　　Gary Meyers, Chief Executive Officer

Select Specialty Hsptl-NW Indiana **219.937.9900**
　5454 Hohman Ave 5th Fl, Hammond, IN 46320
　　Kristine Shield, Chief Executive Officer

St Catherine Hospital **219.392.7000**
　4321 Fir St, East Chicago, IN 46312

St John's Hospital **765.649.2511**
Web .... www.saintjohns.stvincent.org
　2015 Jackson St, Anderson, IN 46016
　　Tom Vanosdol, President

St Joseph Hospital **765.452.5611**
　1907 W Sycamore St, Kokomo, IN 46901
　　Kathy Young, President

St Mary Medical Center **219.942.0551**
　1500 S Lake Park Ave, Hobart, IN 46342
　　Janice Ryba, Chief Executive Officer

St Vincent Hospital & Health Center **317.338.2345**
　2001 W 86th St, Indianapolis, IN 46260

St Vincent Randolph Hospital **765.584.0004**
　473 Greenville Ave, Winchester, IN 47394
　　Nicole M, Assistant

St. Elizabeth Health **765.447.6811**
　1701 S Creasy Lane, Lafayette, IN 47905
　　Terrence Wilson, President

St. Mary's Medical Center **812.485.4000**
　3700 Washington Ave, Evansville, IN 47750

St. Mary's Warrick Hospital **812.897.4800**
　1116 Millis Ave, Boonville, IN 47601
　　Carol Godsey, Administrator

Terre Haute Regional Hospital **812.232.0021**
　3901 S 7th St, Terre Haute, IN 47802
　　Brian Bauer, Chief Executive Officer

Union Hospital **812.238.7000**
　1606 N 7th St, Terre Haute, IN 47804
　　Scott Teffeteller, Chief Executive Officer

West Central Community Hospital **765.832.2451**
　801 S Main St, Clinton, IN 47842
　　Terri Hill, Administrator

Wishard Health Services **317.630.7033**
　1001 W 10th St, Indianapolis, IN 46202
　　Lisa Harris, Chief Executive Officer

COUNSELING SERVICES

Adoption Resource Svcs, Inc. **574.293.0229**
Fax 574.534.9676
E-mail .... rcmarco@frontier.com
　218 S 3rd St Ste 2, Elkhart, IN 46516-3158
　　Ruth Mark, Director

Ball State University Speech-Language & Audiology
Clinics **765.285.8160**
Fax 765.285.5623
Web
.... www.bsu.edu/csh/spa/slpclinic/slpclinic.html
E-mail .... sppathaud@bsu.edu
　2000 University Ave, Muncie, IN 47306
　　Mary Jo Germani, Phd, Chairman

Baptist Children's Home **219.462.4111**
Fax 501.631.9169
Web .... www.baptistchildrenshome.org
E-mail .... bchvalpo@frontier.com
　354 West St, Valparaiso, IN 46383-6203
　　Jim Geurink, President

Catholic Charities **812.423.5456**
Fax 812.423.4392
Web .... www.charitiesevv.org
E-mail .... cathchar@evansville.net
　123 NW 4th St Ste 603, COURT BUILDING, STE 603,
　Evansville, IN 47708-1790
　　Gayle Ueblhor, Interim Director

Catholic Family Svcs **219.879.9312**
Fax 219.879.9073
Web .... www.catholic-charities.org
　321 W 11th St, Michigan City, IN 46360
　　Duane Dedelow, Director

Childplace, Inc **812.282.8248**
Fax 812.282.3291
Web .... www.childplace.org
E-mail .... nathans@childplace.org
　2420 E 10th St, Jeffersonville, IN 47130-6000
　　Nathan Samuels, Director

Indiana

Children's Bureau Of Indianapolis 317.264.2700
Fax 317.264.2714
Web .... www.childrensbureau.org
E-mail .... rondcarp@childrensbureau.org
1575 dr Mlk Junior St, Indianapolis, IN 46202-1434
Ron Carpenter, President/CEO

Community Mental Health Ctr 812.427.2737
Fax 812.427.2761
Web .... www.cmhcinc.org
E-mail .... cmhc1107@cmhcinc.org
205 W Main St, Vevay, IN 47043-1178
Nancy Janaszen, Director

Dockside Svcs (Camelot Community Care) 812.273.7103
Fax 812.273.7104
Web .... www.provcorp.com
E-mail .... contact_in@provcorp.com
409 Jefferson St, Madison, IN 47250-3525
Fletcher J. Mccusker, CEO

KidsPeace Foster Care & Family Svcs 877.205.4666
Fax 317.334.1712
Web .... www.fostercare.com
1927 E St Rd 44, Connersville, IN 47331
Ray Culp, National Director Foster Care & Family Services

Lampion Ctr 812.471.1776
Fax 812.469.2000
Web .... www.lampioncenter.com
E-mail .... lkyle@lampioncenter.com
655 S Hebron Ave, Evansville, IN 47714-4048
Lynn Kyle, Executive Director

LDS Social Svcs 317.522.0224
Fax 317.872.1756
E-mail .... pitcherd@ldschurch.org
550 Congressional Blvd, carmel, IN 46032
David Pitcher, Director

CRISIS & SHELTER CARE

Adam Wells Crisis Shelter-Dom Violence 260.728.9800
Fax 260.728.2227
E-mail .... awcc@embarq.net
221 S 4th St, Decatur, IN 46733
Angie Gunset, Director

Albion Fellows Bacon Ctr Domestic Violence 812.422.9372
Fax 812.422.9385
Web .... http://www.albionfellowsbacon.org
650 Judison St, Evansville, IN 47713
Candice Perry, Director

Ark Crisis Prevention Nursery 812.423.9425
Fax 812.423.0319
E-mail .... arkcrisis@sigecom.net
415 Lincoln Ave, Evansville, IN 47713
Angie Richards Cooley, Executive Director

Bethany Charities Domestic Violence 812.232.1447
Fax 812.478.1363
Web .... www.catholiccharitiesterrehaute.org
E-mail .... jetling@catholiccharitiesterrehaute.org
1801 Poplar St, Terre Haute, IN 47803-2240
John Cetling, Director

Coburn Place Safe Haven Dom Violence 317.923.5750
Fax 317.921.1946
E-mail .... julia@coburnplace.org
604 E 38th St Frnt, Indianapolis, IN 46205
Julia Kathary, Director

Community Anti-Violence 260.624.3600
Fax 260.624.3800
455 S. Old 27, Angola, IN 46703
Vallee David, Director

Counsel On Domestic Abuse 812.232.1736
Fax 812.232.0870
1400 Hulman St, Terre Haute, IN 47802
Susan Hall, Director

Crisis Connection 812.482.1555
Fax 812.482.1571
E-mail .... cci@psci.net
332 3rd Avenue, Jasper, IN 47546
Beth Stein, Director

Crisis Ctr Inc. 219.938.7070
Fax 219.938.7502
E-mail .... scaylor@crisiscenterysb.org
101 N Montgomery St, Gary, IN 46403-3921
Shirley Caylor, Executive Director

Elijah Haven Crisis Intervention Ctr Inc 260.463.8700
E-mail .... Marilyn@Ligtel.Com
201 S detroit St, Lagrange, IN 46761-0198
Rose Miller, Director

Family Crisis Shelter Domestic Violence 765.361.6504
Fax 765.362.3315
Web .... www.familycrisisshelter.org
E-mail .... anita.byers@familycrisisshelter.org
PO Box 254, Crawfordsville, IN 47933-0254
Andrew Ford, Director

Family Support Svcs 765.653.4820
Fax 765.653.8045
E-mail .... pcfss@airhop.com
22 W Washington St, Greencastle, IN 46135
Cari Cox, Director

Gary Commision For Women Domestic Violence 219.883.4155
Fax 219.881.5287
Web .... www.ci.gary.in.us
E-mail .... smtaylor@ci.gary.in.us
839 Broadway, Fl 3, Gary, IN 46402
Sharon Mark Taylor, Director

Genesis Domestic Violence Program 765.935.3920
Fax 765.966.0530
E-mail .... genesis765@insightbb.com
15 s 11th st, Richmond, IN 47374
Becky Studebacker, Director

Haven House Domestic Violence 219.931.2090
Fax 219.931.2160
E-mail .... havenhousedvs@aol.com
PO Box 508, Hammond, IN 46325-0508
Lisa Wein, Director

Hoosier Hills Pact Domestic Violence Shelter 812.883.1959
Fax 812.883.0358
E-mail .... cbenson@blueriver.net
108 S Main St, Salem, IN 47167
Connie Benson, Director

Indiana Youth Group (IYG) 317.541.8726
Fax 317.545.8594
Web .... www.indianayouthgroup.org
E-mail .... info@indianayouthgroup.org
2943 E 46th St, Indianapolis, IN 46205
Mary Byrne, Executive Director

Julian Ctr, Inc. Domestic Violence 317.941.2200
Fax 317.926.0364
E-mail .... cmiller@juliancenter.org
2011 N Meridian St, Indianapolis, IN 46202
Karlene Miller, Director

Middle Way House Inc Domestic Violence 812.333.7404
Fax 812.323.9063
Web .... www.middlewayhouse.org
E-mail .... tstrout@middlewayhouse.org
414 W Kirkwood Ave, Bloomington, IN 47404-5149
Toby Strout, Director

N Central Indiana Rural Crisis Ctr Inc 219.866.8281
Fax 219.866.5255
428 N Cullen St., Rensselaer, IN 47978
Frankie Lane, Director

Prevail, Inc. Domestic Violence 317.773.6942
Fax 317.776.3448
E-mail .... prevail@prevailinc.com
1100 S 9Th St, Ste 100, Noblesville, IN 46060
Loretta Moore-sutherland, Director

Promosing Futures 317.773.6342
Fax 317.773.3340
Web .... www.promisingfutures.org
E-mail .... info@promisingfutures.org
294 S 9th St, Noblesville, IN 46060-2728
Stephanie Welberg-lyons, Administrator

RTC Resources, Inc. 317.783.4003
Fax 317.780.4810
Web .... www.yfs.com
E-mail .... jim.bush@yfcs.com
1404 S State Ave, Indianapolis, IN 46203-2000
Jim Bush, Administrator

Safe At Home Domestic Violence 765.521.0647
Fax 765.521.0657
E-mail .... safe.at.home@hotmail.com
101 S Main St, New Castle, IN 47362
Marianne Legge, Director

Safe Passage Inc Domestic Violence 812.933.1990
Fax 812.934.9997
Web .... www.safepassageinc.org
E-mail .... jyorn@safepassageinc.org
125 E George St, Batesville, IN 47006
Jane Yorn, Director

Salvation Army Social Svc Ctr 317.637.5551
Fax 317.687.3711
Web .... www.usc.salvationarmy.org
540 N Alabama St, Indianapolis, IN 46204-1360
Pam Fleck, Director

Sheltering Wings Ctr For Women 317.745.1496
Fax 317.745.1497
E-mail .... info@shelteringwings.org
1251 Sycamore Ln, Danville, IN 46122
Maria Larrison, Director

Stopover 317.635.9301
Fax 317.633.8220
E-mail .... emalone@enn.org
2236 E 10th St, Indianapolis, IN 46201-2006
Elizabeth Malone, Director

The Beaman Home-Domestic Violence 574.267.7701
Fax 574.268.9971
Web .... www.thebeamanhome.org
311 S Lake St, 1515 Provident Dr, Warsaw, IN 46580
Tracie Hodson, Executive Director

The Ctr For Women-Families Domestic Violence 812.944.6743
Fax 812.945.6127
Web .... www.cwfempower.org
E-mail .... Rebecca.Jetton@Cwfempower.Org
213 E Maple St, Jeffersonville, IN 47130
Becky Jetton, Director

The Stepping Stone Domestic Violence 219.879.4616
Fax 219.879.4617
Web .... www.niia.net
E-mail .... steppingstone@niia.net
PO Box 1045, Michigan City, IN 46361-8245
Gerri Jones, Director

The Villages Of Indiana 800.831.4154
Fax 260.422.3655
Web .... www.villageskids.org
2250 Lake Ave Ste 160, Fort Wayne, IN 46805
Sharon Pierce, CEO

Turing Point Domestic Violence Svcs 812.379.5575
Fax 812.379.5576
Web .... www.turningpointdv.org
E-mail .... patricksmith@turningpointdv.org
745 Washington St, Columbus, IN 47202
Patrick Smith, Director

Youth Shelter And Family Svcs, Inc 812.284.5229
Fax 812.284.5301
Web .... www.ccysfs.org
E-mail .... ccadmin@ccysfs.org
118 E Chestnut St, Jeffersonville, IN 47130-3402
Laura Fleming-balmer, Executive Director

Youth Svcs Bureau 812.349.2506
Fax 812.349.2892
Web .... www.youthservicesbureau.net
E-mail .... kmeyer@co.monroe.in.us
   615 S Adams St, Bloomington, IN 47403-2180
   Kim Meyer, Director

YWCA Domestic Violence Program 765.423.4486
Fax 765.742.0079
   605 N 6th St, Lafayette, IN 47901
   Danielle Gaylord, Director

**YWCA Domestic Violence Shelter Crisis
Line** 812.422.1191
Fax 812.422.8705
Web .... www.ywcaevansville.org
E-mail .... ywca@ywcaevansville.org
   118 Vine St, Evansville, IN 47708-1291
   Mary Watson, Shelter Director

YWCA Women's Shelter Outreach Svcs 260.424.4908
Fax 260.420.5202
E-mail .... mraffety@ywcaerew.org
   1610 Spy Run Ave, Fort Wayne, IN 46805
   Mary Jo Raffety, Outreach Director

EDUCATION

Family Svcs, Inc. 765.423.5361
Fax 765.742.8272
Web .... www.fsilafayette.org
E-mail .... sally@fsilafayette.org
   615 N 18th St, Ste 201, Lafayette, IN 47904
   Sally Bryn, President/CEO

**Jewish Community Ctr Assoc Of
Indianapolis** 317.251.9467
Fax 317.251.9493
Web .... www.jccindy.org
E-mail .... info@jccindy.org
   6701 Hoover Rd, Indianapolis, IN 46260
   Ira Jaffee, Msw, Executive Director

**Specialized Alternatives For Families And Youth Of America
(SAFY)** 260.484.4600
Fax 260.484.4002
Web .... www.safy.org
   3730 Allen Ave, Fort Wayne, IN 46805-1812
   Donna Bolinger, Treatment Director

FOSTER CARE AGENCIES

Adoptions of Indiana Inc (AD-IN Inc) 317.574.8950
Fax 317.574.8971
E-mail .... msterchi@ad-in.org
   1980 E 166th St, Ste 325, Carmel, IN 46032
   Meg Sterchi, Director

Catholic Charities-Diocese of Gary 219.844.4883
E-mail .... lkavanaugh@catholic-charities.org
   6919 Indianapolis Blvd, Hammond, IN 46324

Children's Bureau Inc 317.545.5281
Fax 317.547.6378
E-mail .... kcreason@childrensbureau.org
   3801 N Temple Ave, Indianapolis, IN 46205
   Kate Creason, Judge

Compassionate Care General Baptist Fmly 812.749.4152
Fax 812.749.8190
   RR 3 Hwy 64 W Wilder Ctr, PO Box 12B, Oakland
   City, IN 47660

Foster Care Svc 260.925.4142
Fax 260.925.4142
   1016 W 7th St Ste 330, Auburn, IN 46706
   Dona Kinkle, Director

Independent Adoption Center of IN (IAC) 317.887.2015
E-mail .... staff@adoptionhelp.org
   5162 E Stop 11 Rd, Ste 1, Indianapolis, IN 46227
   Kathy Wilkerson, Director

Indiana Foster Care & Adoptive Assoc 800.468.4228
E-mail .... info@ifcaa.org
   509 E National Ave Ste A, Indianapolis, IN 46227
   Christina Morrison, Ex. Dir

Kidz R Special Inc 317.490.3059
Fax 317.858.0082
   9832 Hidden Hills Ln, Indianapolis, IN 46234
   D Ratliff, Chief Executive Officer

Lafayette Adoption Support for Search 765.543.6295
E-mail .... pdebonte@purdue.edu
   1100 N 9th St, Ste 103, Lafayette, IN 47904

Noah, Inc. 317.926.8266
Fax 317.926.8269
   3341 N central Ave, Indianapolis, IN 46205
   CI Day, President

Open Arms Christian Ministries Inc OACM 812.659.2533
Fax 812.659.2477
   Rt 2, Box 37A, Bloomfield, IN 47424
   Martin Corey, Executive Director

**St Elizabeth I Coleman Pregnancy &
Adoption** 317.787.3412
Fax 317.787.0482
E-mail .... rhummel@secindy.org
   2500 Churchman Ave, Indianapolis, IN 46203
   Renee Hummel, Director Of Adoption Programme

St Elizabeth's Regional Maternity Center 812.949.7305
E-mail .... ltownsend@StElizabethCatholicCharities.org
   601 E Market St, New Albany, IN 47150
   Mark Caster, Director

The Villages of Indiana Inc 812.332.1245
Fax 812.333.4717
   2405 N Smith Pike, Bloomington, IN 47404

HOME MEDICAL EQUIPMENT PROVIDERS

**Easter Seals Rehabilitation Center, Inc. dba Assistive
Technology Solutions** 812.479.1411
Fax 812.437.2611
Web .... www.assistive-tech.com
   3701 Bellemeade Avenue, Evansville, IN 47714
   CARF accredited programs available.

Orthodynamics Company, Inc. 317.774.0145
Fax 317.774.0146
Web .... www.od-inc.com
   155 Carey Drive, Noblesville, IN 46060
   CARF accredited programs available.

Scooter Warehouse, Inc. 574.299.8606
Fax 574.299.0538
Web .... www.thescooterwarehouse.com
   4011 South Michigan Street, South Bend, IN 46614
   CARF accredited programs available.

PEDIATRIC HOME CARE

Interim Healthcare 219.736.1135
Fax 219.736.1154
   1575 E 85 Ave, Merrillville, IN 46410
   Linda Stefaniak, Chief Executive Officer

Interim Healthcare 812.537.5546
Fax 812.539.4259
   500 W Eads Pkwy, Lawrenceburg, IN 47025
   Franny Kline, Administrator

Interim Healthcare Ft Wayne Home Care 260.482.9405
Fax 260.482.7180
   310 E Dupont Rd Ste 1, Fort Wayne, IN 46825
   Patrick McGiveney, Owner

Interim Hlthcare Ft Wayne Home Style Sv 260.969.5991
Fax 260.482.7180
E-mail .... lsmart@interimin.com
   310 E Dupont Rd Ste 1, Fort Wayne, IN 46825
   Laura Smart, Director

Interim Hlthcare Indianapolis Staffing 317.956.4024
Fax 317.682.3114
   8803 N Meridian st ste 325, Indianapolis, IN 46260
   Sue Duckwall, Chief Executive Officer

Interim Hlthcare South Bend HomeStyle S 574.252.5186
Fax 574.233.5245
   605 W Edison Rd Ste H, Mishawaka, IN 46545
   Deb Parcell, Owner

Interim Hlthcare South Bend Home Care 574.233.5186
Fax 574.233.5245
   605 W Edison Rd, Mishawaka, IN 46545
   Deb Parcell, Director

SOCIAL SERVICES

4C Of Southern Indiana Inc 812.423.4008
Fax 812.423.3399
Web .... www.child-care.org
E-mail .... 4c@child-care.org
   600 SE 6th St, Evansville, IN 47713
   Jennifer Gronotte, Executive Director

A Better Way Services, Inc. 765.747.9107
Fax 765.281.2740
E-mail .... tc@abetterwaymuncie.org
   806 W Jackson St, Muncie, IN 47305-1551
   Teresa Clemmons, Executive Director

Advocates for Children 812.372.2808
Fax 812.372.2817
E-mail .... casa@apowerfulvoice.org
   1531 13th St, Ste 2107, Columbus, IN 47201
   Therese E. Miller, Executive Director

**Aging and In-Home Services of Northeast Indiana,
Inc.** 260.745.1200
Fax 260.456.1066
Web .... www.agingihs.org
   2927 Lake Avenue, Ft. Wayne, IN 46805
   COA accredited organization.

Bona Vista's Child Care Solutions 765.452.8870
Fax 765.868.4699
Web .... www.bonavista.org
E-mail .... jdunn@bonavista.org
   1425 S Plate St, Kokomo, IN 46902
   Jill Dunn, President

Catholic Charities 260.422.5625
Fax 260.422.5657
Web .... www.ccfwsb.org
E-mail .... djschmidt@ccfwsb.org
   315 E Washington Blvd, Fort Wayne, IN 46802-3123
   Debbie Schmidt, Executive Director

Catholic Charities Diocese of Gary, Inc. 219.886.3549
Fax 219.886.2428
Web .... www.catholic-charities.org
   176 South West Street, Crown Point, IN 46307
   COA accredited organization.

Catholic Charities Indianapolis 317.236.1534
Fax 317.261.3375
Web .... www.CatholicCharitiesIndpls.org
   1400 N. Meridian Street, Indianapolis, IN 46202
   COA accredited organization.

Child Care Answers 317.631.4643
Fax 317.687.6248
Web .... www.childcareanswers.com
E-mail .... marshal@childcareanswers.com
   615 N Alabama St Ste 300, Indianapolis,
   IN 46204-1431
   Marsha Hearn-lindsey, Director

Child Care Resource And Referral 800.554.9331
Fax 765.289.0430
Web .... http://huffer.uwctl.org
E-mail .... clynn@huffermcc.org
   2000 N Elgin St, Muncie, IN 47303-2338
   Terry Dale, Program Director

Indiana

Childhood Connections 812.375.2208
Fax 812.669.0041
Web ....www.childhoodconnections.org
E-mail ....ccinfo@childhoodconnections.org
   923 4th St, Columbus, IN 47201-1314
Rose Ellen Adams, Director

**Children's Bureau Exchange Club Family Resource Ctr,
Inc** 765.643.8022
Fax 765.643.0264
Web ....www.childrensbureau.org
E-mail ....info@childrensbureau.org
   1102 W St, Anderson, IN 46016
Jama Donovon, Director

Community Action Of Southern Indiana 812.288.6451
Fax 812.284.8314
Web www.casi1.org
E-mail ....joyshanks@hotmail.com
   1613 E 8th St, Jeffersonville, IN 47130-4749
Joy Shanks, Director

Community Alliance Service 812.232.3952
Fax 812.232.1731
Web ....www.casyonline.org
E-mail ....info@casyonline.org
   1101 S 13th ST, Terre Haute, IN 47802
Karen Harding, Director

Community Coordinated Child Care, Inc 574.289.7815
Fax 574.289.1922
Web www.4csindiana.org
E-mail ....melanie@4csindiana.org
   3606 E Jefferson Blvd Ste 240, South Bend,
   IN 46615-3050
Melanie Rigdon, Executive Director

Crossroad Child & Family Services, Inc 260.484.4153
Fax 260.484.2337
Web ....www.crossroad-fwch.org
   2525 Lake Avenue, Fort Wayne, IN 46805-5457
COA accredited organization.

Early Childhood Alliance 260.744.0298
Fax 260.744.3473
Web ....www.ecalliance.org
E-mail ....info@ecalliance.org
   3320 Fairfield Ave, Fort Wayne, IN 46807
Madeline Baker, Executive Director

Fall Creek Counseling, Inc. 317.291.6360
Web ....www.fallcreekcounseling.com
   3500 Lafayette Road, Suite 302, Indianapolis,
   IN 46222
COA accredited organization.

Family Services, Inc. 765.423.5361
Fax 765.742.8272
Web ....www.fsilafayette.org
   Howarth Center, 615 North 18th Street, Suite 201,
   Lafayette, IN 47904
COA accredited organization.

Family Svc 812.372.3745
Fax 812.372.5367
Web ....www.familyservicebc.org
   1531 13th St, Ste 2540, Columbus, IN 47201-1305
Kristy Carmichael, Executive Director

Family Svc Assoc 812.232.4349
Fax 812.232.2308
Web ....www.famsvc.org
E-mail ....ffacounselling@gmail.com
   619 Cherry St, Terre Haute, IN 47807-3198
Ronald Benson, Director

First Call For Help 260.744.0700
Fax 260.426.5052
Web ....www.firstcallinfo.org
E-mail ....barbm@uwacin.org
   337 E Berry St, Fort Wayne, IN 46802-2707
Barb Mckee, Information And Resource Manager

First Choice For Women 765.286.6060
Fax 765.286.8798
   600 S Tillotson Ave, Muncie, IN 47304
Amanda Durbin, Office Manager

Gary Neighborhood Svcs, Inc 219.883.0431
Fax 219.883.0919
Web ....www.garyneighsrvc.org
E-mail ....garyneighsrvc@aol.com
   300 W 21st Ave, Gary, IN 46407-2598
Tom Osbourne, Executive Director

Gateway's Assoc 765.649.1900
Fax 765.649.0089
   1215 Jackson St, Anderson, IN 46016
Sarah Krumme, Respite Coordinator

Human Svcs, Inc 812.372.8407
Fax 812.378.4812
Web ....www.hsi-indiana.com
E-mail ....ddebord@hsi-indiana.com
   1585 N Indianapolis Rd, Columbus, IN 47202
Debbie Debord, Executive Director

Huntington Memorial Hospital 260.356.3000
Fax 260.355.3310
Web ....www.parkview.com
E-mail ....darlene.garrett@parkview.com
   2001 Stults Rd, Huntington, IN 46750-1282
Darlene Garrett, Chief Operating Officer

Indiana Youth Institute 800.343.7060
Fax 317.396.2701
Web ....www.iyi.org
E-mail ....iyi@iyi.org
   603 E. Washington St., Ste. 800, Indianapolis,
   IN 46204-2647
Bill Stanczykiewicz, President/CEO

Indiana Youth Svcs Assoc 317.238.6955
Fax 317.238.6978
Web ....www.indysb.org
   445 N Pennsylvania St Ste 945, Indianapolis,
   IN 46204
Cheryl Hall-russell, CEO

Julian Ctr Shelter 317.920.9320
Fax 317.937.7093
Web ....www.juliancenter.org
E-mail ....bwhaley@juliancenter.org
   2011 N Meridian St, Indianapolis, IN 46202
Betsy Whaley, Shelter Director

Lafayette Crisis Ctr 765.423.2255
Fax 765.742.0247
Web ....www.lafayettecrisis.org
   1244 N 15th St, Lafayette, IN 47904
Jane Mccann, Executive Director

**Lutheran Child and Family Services of Indiana/Kentucky,
Inc.** 317.359.5467
Fax 317.322.4095
Web ....www.lutheranfamily.org
   1525 North Ritter Avenue, Indianapolis, IN 46219
COA accredited organization.

Lutheran Social Svcs 260.426.3347
Fax 260.424.2248
Web ....www.lssin.org
E-mail ....amoellering@lssin.org
   330 Madison St, Fort Wayne, IN 46802
Angie Moellering, Director

Madison Ctr/East Bank Day Care 574.234.2747
   403 E Madison St, South Bend, IN 46617-2395
Leslie Kleppe, Owner

New Hope Services, Inc. 812.288.8248
Fax 812.285.8320
Web ....www.newhopeservices.org
   725 Wall Street, Jeffersonville, IN 47130
CARF accredited programs available.

Positive Results Therapies 765.454.5340
Fax 765.456.3503
Web ....www.banabista.org
   1220 Laguna St, Kokomo, IN 46902
Jill Dunn, Ma President

Protect Our Children, Inc. 317.927.7159
Fax 317.927.8910
E-mail ....protectourchildren@pocinc.org
   3961 Broadway St,, Indianapolis, IN 46205
Pamela Page, Director

Right To Life 812.663.8542
E-mail ....pkkoors@emerson.com
   812 E Elmwood Ct S, Greensburg, IN 47240-9531
Pat Course, Director

Samaritan Ctr 812.254.1558
Fax 812.254.8308
Web ....www.gshvin.org/goodsamaritan
   2007 State St, Washington, IN 47501
James Koontz, President/CEO

The Caring Place 219.464.2128
Fax 219.464.2672
Web ....www.thecaringplace.org
   3107 Cascade Dr, Valparaiso, IN 46383-9123
Mary Beth Schultz, Director

The Children's Campus, Inc 574.259.5666
Fax 574.255.6179
Web ....www.childrenscampus.org
E-mail ....infotcc@childrenscampus.org
   1411 Lincolnway W, Mishawaka, IN 46544-1626
Kris Ermeti, Executive Director

**The Exchange Club Ctr For The Prevention Of Child
Abuse** 574.295.2277
Fax 574.295.7642
E-mail ....cyoder@capselkhart.org
   1000 W Hively Ave, Elkhart, IN 46517-1741
Candy Yoder, Vice President

Youth Svc Bureau 574.235.9231
Fax 574.235.5578
Web ....www.ysbsjc.org
E-mail ....bstrycker@sbcglobal.net
   2222 Lincolnway W, South Bend, IN 46628-2514
Bonnie Strycker, Executive Director

Youth Svcs Bureau 219.881.5270
Fax 219.881.0008
E-mail ....qyoung@ci.gary.in.us
   455 Massachusetts St, Gary, IN 46302
Quilla Young, Director

Youth Svcs Ctr 260.449.3561
Fax 260.449.7943
   11805 Lima Rd, Fort Wayne, IN 46818
Christopher Dunn, Director

YWCA Women's Shelter Crisis Hotline 260.447.7233
Fax 260.447.0136
Web ....www.ywca.org/fortwayne
E-mail ....tnoone@ywcaerew.org
   PO Box 11242, Fort Wayne, IN 46856-1242
Debby Beckman, Chief Executive Officer

SPECIAL NEEDS

ASK About Special Kids Help for IN Fmls 317.257.8683
Fax 317.251.7488
E-mail ....familynetw@aboutspecialkids.org
   7275 Shadeland Ave Ste 1, Indianapolis, IN 46250
Joe Bruvaker, Executive Director

Autism Society of Indiana 317.695.0252
E-mail ....susan@broadhorizons.us
   4740 Kings Way Dr Ste 7, Indianapolis, IN 46205

Bona Vista Programs, Inc. 765.457.8273
Fax 765.456.3503
Web ....www.bonavista.org
   1220 East Laguna, Kokomo, IN 46902
CARF accredited programs available.

Brain Injury Association 866.854.4246
E-mail ....info@biai.org
   9531 Valparaiso Ct Ste A, Indianapolis, IN 46268

**Community Hospitals Indianapolis/Hook Rehab Center -
Acute/Neurobehavioral Unit and Outpatient
Svcs...317.355.3843**
Fax 317.351.5485
Web ....www.ecommunity.com
   1500 North Ritter Avenue, Indianapolis, IN 46219
   CARF accredited programs available.

Down Syndrome Association 260.471.9964
E-mail ....dsani4u@aol.com
   PO Box 13611, Fort Wayne, IN 46865
   Kimberley McCoy, Director

**Easter Seals Crossroads Rehabilitation Center,
Inc...317.466.1000**
Fax 317.466.2000
Web ....www.easterealscrossroads.org
   4740 Kingsway Drive, Indianapolis, IN 46205
   CARF accredited programs available.

Easter Seals Wayne/Union Counties 765.855.2482
E-mail ....easterealswu@comcast.net
   1050 E Main St, Centerville, IN 47330
   Kelly Weaver, Director

Epilepsy Foundation of Indiana 800.526.6618
E-mail ....ecgc@fuse.net
   3901 W 86th St Ste 380, Indianapolis, IN 46268

Family Voices Indiana 317.257.8681
   1130 E 77th St, Indianapolis, IN 46240
   Donna G Olsen, Coordinator

Gibault, Inc.............................812.299.1156
Fax 812.298.3290
Web ....www.gibault.org
   6401 South U.S. Highway 41, Terre Haute,
   IN 47802-4749
   COA accredited organization.

IN*SOURCE 574.234.7101
Fax 574.234.7279
E-mail ....insource@insource.org
   1703 S Ironwood Dr, South Bend, IN 46613
   Richard Burden, Director

Indiana Congress of PTA 317.357.5881
E-mail ....indianapta@sbcglobal.net
   2525 N Shadeland Ave # D-4, Indianapolis, IN 46219
   Julie French, Office Manager

**Indiana Developmental Training Center of
Lafayette 877.854.1024**
Fax 765.448.4217
Web ....www.idtc-in.com
E-mail ....admissions@idtc-in.com
   3700 Rome Dr, Lafayette, IN 47905
   John Soderberg, Admissions Director

Indiana Developmental Training Ctr 317.815.0505
Fax 317.815.1645
Web ....www.idtc-in.com
E-mail ....admissions@idtc-in.com
   11075 N Pennsylvania St, Indianapolis,
   IN 46280-1091
   Robert Blondet, Director Of Operations

Indiana Down Syndrome 888.989.9255
E-mail ....lisa@dsindiana.org
   2625 N Meridian St, Ste 249, Indianapolis, IN 46208
   Lisa Tokarz-Guiterrez, Executive Director

LearningRx Learning Center 317.845.1999
E-mail ....indianapolisne.in@learningrx.net
   9767 Fall Creek Rd, Indianapolis, IN 46256

Lindamood-Bell Learning Processes 317.815.1319
Fax 317.815.1490
   710 Adams St Ste A, Carmel, IN 46032
   Shannon Kendall, Center Director

**Maap Svcs For Autism And Asperger
Syndrome 219.662.1311**
Web ....www.aspergersyndrome.org
   PO Box 524, Crown Point, IN 46308-0524
   Susan Moreno, President

Memorial Regional Rehabilitation Center 574.647.6576
Fax 574.647.7074
Web ....www.qualityoflife.org
   615 North Michigan, South Bend, IN 46601
   CARF accredited programs available.

Mental Health America in Indiana Univ 317.638.3501
   1431 N Delaware St, Indianapolis, IN 46202
   Steve McCaffrey, Director

NAMI Indiana 800.677.6442
E-mail ....nami-in@nami.org
   2601 Cold Springs, Indianapolis, IN 46222
   Pam Mcconey, Executive Director

National Multiple Sclerosis Society 317.870.2500
Fax 317.870.2520
E-mail ....Indiana@nmss.org
   3500 Depauw Blvd Ste 1040, Indianapolis, IN 46268
   Leighann Erickson, Director

Parkview Rehabilitation Center 260.373.6450
Fax 260.373.4548
Web ....www.parkview.com
   2200 Randallia Drive, Fort Wayne, IN 46805
   CARF accredited programs available.

Partners in Policymaking 317.232.7770
E-mail ....pip@gpcpd.org
   150 W Market St, Ste 628, Indianapolis, IN 46204
   Suellen Jackson Boner, Director

Rehabilitation Hospital of Fort Wayne 260.435.6100
Fax 260.432.6128
Web ....www.rehabhospital.com
   7970 West Jefferson Boulevard, Fort Wayne,
   IN 46804-4140
   CARF accredited programs available.

Southern Indiana Rehab Hospital 812.941.8300
Fax 812.941.6276
Web ....www.sirh.org
E-mail ....randy.napier@sirh.org
   3104 Blackiston Boulevard, New Albany, IN 47150
   Steven Riggert, Director of Psychology Services
   CARF accredited programs available.

Speech-Language-Hearing Association 317.916.4146
E-mail ....ann@centraloffice1.com
   PO Box 24167, Indianapolis, IN 46224
   Ann Ninness, Executive Director

St. Mary's Rehabilitation Institute 812.485.5620
Fax 812.485.5624
Web ....www.stmarys.org
   3700 Washington Avenue, Evansville, IN 47750
   CARF accredited programs available.

The Arc of Indiana 317.977.2375
E-mail ....jdickerson@arcind.org
   107 N Pennsylvania Ste 800, Indianapolis, IN 46204
   J Dickerson, Executive Director

United Cerebral Palsy Association 800.723.7620
E-mail ....donnar@ucpaindy.org
   6100 N Keystone Ave Ste 254, Indianapolis,
   IN 46220

VSA Arts of Indiana 317.974.4123
E-mail ....jnulty@vsai.org
   1505 N Delaware St, Indianapolis, IN 46202
   Gayle Holtman, President

SUBSTANCE ABUSE TREATMENT

Bloomington Meadows Hospital 812.331.8000
Fax 812.961.2462
Web ....www.psysolutions.com
   3600 N Prow Rd, Bloomington, IN 47404-1616
   Jean Scallon, Administrator

**Cameron Memorial Community Hospital - Cameron Counseling
Center 260.668.7060**
Fax 260.665.8929
Web ....www.cameronmch.com
E-mail ....sbrady@cameronmch.com
   617 N Washington St, Angola, IN 46703
   Sandy Brady, Health Information Management Director
   CARF accredited programs available.

Caring About People, Inc....................260.424.5814
Fax 260.424.6423
Web ....www.caringaboutpeopleinc.org
E-mail ....kobrien@caringaboutpeopleinc.org
   1417 North Anthony Boulevard, Fort Wayne,
   IN 46805
   Kimbra O'brien, Executive Director
   CARF accredited programs available.

Centre of Homeless 574.282.8700
Fax 574.287.5023
   813 S Michigan St, South Bend, IN 46601
   Beth Camilleri, Executive Director

EmberWood Center 317.536.7100
Fax 317.536.7101
Web ....www.communityaddictionservices.org
   1125 Brookside Avenue, Suite I, Indianapolis,
   IN 46202
   Bob Burbacher, president
   CARF accredited programs available.

Family Svcs And Prevention 317.398.0955
Fax 317.398.0956
Web ....www.fspp.org
E-mail ....fspp@fspp.org
   50 W Mckay Rd, # 1, Shelbyville, IN 46176
   Kary Prifogle, Director

Sassi Institute 812.275.7013
Fax 800.546.7995
Web ....www.sassi.com
E-mail ....sassi@sassi.com
   201 Camelot Ln, Springville, IN 47462
   Linda Lazowski, Research Coordinator

The Otis R. Bowen Ctr For Human Svcs 260.248.8176
Fax 260.471.4263
Web ....www.bowencenter.org
   2100 Busch rd, Columbia City, IN 46808-2311
   Scott McAlfiter, Director

Indiana

Iowa

Terry Branstad, Governor
State Capital
Des Moines, IA 50319
515.281.5211
515.281.6611 (Fax)
www.governor.state.ia.us

Dave Kuker, Juvenile Justice Specialist
Division of Criminal and Juvenile Justice Planning
Lucas State Office Building, First Floor
Des Moines, IA 50319
515.281.8078
515.242.6119 (Fax)
dave.kuker@iowa.gov

Jim Morris, SAG Chair
Division of Criminal and Juvenile Justice Planning
1103 Joshua Ave
Creston, IA 50801
641.782.2715
mjmorris_jm@hotmail.com

CRISIS NUMBERS

Child Abuse Reporting . . .800.362.2178

STATE SERVICES

SOCIAL SERVICES

Child Welfare Svcs 515.281.6802
Fax 515.281.6248
Web ....www.dhs.state.ia.us
1305 E Walnut St, Des Moines, IA 50319
Charles Palmer, Director

Division of Children and Family Srvs 515.281.5521
Fax 515.281.6248
1305 East Walnut, Hoover State Office Building, Des Moines, IA 50319
Charles Palmer, Director Of Dept Human Resources.

Iowa Insurance Div 515.281.5705
Fax 515.281.3059
Web ....www.iid.state.ia.us
330 Maple St, Des Moines, IA 50319
Susan Voss, Director

GENERAL HEALTH SERVICES

Bureau of Family Health IA 515.281.3126
Fax 515.242.6013
E-mail ....julie.mcmahon@idph.iowa.gov
5th Flr, Des Moines, IA 50319
Julie McMahon, Director

Child Health Specialty Clinics CHSC 319.356.1117
Fax 319.356.3715
E-mail ....barbara-khal@uiowa.edu
100 Hawkins Dr, Rm 247 CDD, Iowa City, IA 52242
Barbara Khal, Director

Div of Health Promotion and Chronic Disease Prevention 515.242.6383
Fax 515.242.6384
Web ....www.idph.state.ia.us
321 E 12th St, Des Moines, IA 50319
Julie Mcmahon, Division Director

Iowa Dept Of Public Health 515.281.7689
Fax 515.281.4958
Web ....www.idph.state.ia.us
321 E 12Th St, Lucas State Office Building, Des Moines, IA 50319
Dr. Mariannette Miller-Meeks, Director

MENTAL HEALTH SERVICES

Iowa Vocational Rehabilitation Svcs 515.281.4211
Fax 515.281.4703
E-mail ....jane.mccord@iowa.gov
510 E 12th St, Des Moines, IA 50319
Jane Mccord, Administrative Assistant

Vocational Rehabilitation Agency IA 515.281.1333
Fax 515.281.1263
E-mail ....karen.keninger@blind.state.ia.us
524 4th St, Des Moines, IA 50309
Karen Keninger, Director

JUSTICE AGENCY

Attorney General's Ofc 515.281.5164
Fax 515.281.4209
Web ....www.iowaattorneygeneral.org
E-mail ....webteam@ag.state.ia.us
Hoover Building, 1305 E. Walnut St, Des Moines, IA 50319
Tom Miller, Attorney General

Correctional Education Division IA 515.725.5728
Fax 515.725.5798
E-mail ....sandra.smith2@iowa.gov
510 E 12th St Ste 4, Des Moines, IA 50319
Sandra Smith, Director

Criminal & Juvenile Justice Planning Div 515.281.3995
Fax 515.242.6119
Web ....www.state.ia.us/dhr/cjjp
E-mail ....cjjp@max.state.ia.us
321 E 12th St Rm 267, 2ND FLOOR LUCAS STATE OFFICE BLDG, Des Moines, IA 50319-0067
Richard G. Moore, Administrator

Dept of Public Safety 515.725.6250
Fax 515.725.6261
Web ....www.state.ia.us/government/dps/dci/crim hist.htm
E-mail ....hunt@dps.state.ia.us
215 E 9th St Rm 40, DIVISION OF CRIMINAL INVESTIGATION, Des Moines, IA 50319
Tracy Hunt, Human Resource

Governor's Ofc of Drug Control Policy 515.725.0300
Fax 515.725.0304
Web ....www.state.ia.us/government/odcp
E-mail ....mark.schouten@iowa.gov
502 E 9th St, First floor, Des Moines, IA 50319
Mark Schouten, Director

Iowa CASA Program 515.281.7621
Fax 515.281.5975
E-mail ....richard.moore@dia.state.ia.us
321 E 12th St, 4th Fl Lucas State Office Bldg, Des Moines, IA 50319
Dick Moore, Executive Director

Iowa Dept of Corrections 515.725.5701
Fax 515.725.5799
Web ....www.doc.state.ia.us
E-mail ....doc.information@doc.state.ia.us
510 E 12th St, Des Moines, IA 50319-9025
Fred Scaletta, Public/media Relations Director

COURTS

State Court Administrative Ofc 515.281.5241
Fax 515.242.0014
Web ....www.iowacourts.gov
E-mail ....david.k.boyd@iowacourts.gov
1111 E Court Ave, Iowa Judicial Branch Building, Des Moines, IA 50319
David K. Boyd, Administrator

POLICE AND SHERIFF

Iowa State Sheriff's & Deputie's Assoc 712.243.2206
Fax 712.243.4736
Web ....www.sheriffcass.com
E-mail ....webmaster@sheriffcass.com
5 W 7th St, Ste H, Atlantic, IA 50022-1453
Bill Sage, Sheriff

Sheriff's Office 319.892.6100
Fax 319.892.6276
Web ....www.linncounty.org
E-mail ....sheriff@linncounty.org
310 2nd Ave SW, Cedar Rapids, IA 52404-2003
Colonel John C. Stuelke, Chief Deputy Officer

EDUCATION SERVICES

ASK Family Resource Center 515.243.1713
Fax 515.243.1902
E-mail ....info@askresource.org
5665 Greendale Rd, Johnston, IA 50131
Karen Thompson, Executive Director

Bureau of Stu & Family Support Svcs IA 515.281.3176
Fax 515.242.6019
E-mail ....martiy.ikeda@iowa.gov
400 E 14th St, Grimes State Office Bldg, Des Moines, IA 50319
Martiy Ikeda, Bureau Chief

Edu for Homeless Children and Youth IA 515.281.3999
Fax 515.242.6025
E-mail ....sandra.johnson@iowa.gov
400 E 14th St, Grimes State Office Bldg, Des Moines, IA 50319
Sandra Johnson, Director

Iowa Braille School 319.472.5221
Fax 319.472.4371
Web www.iowa-braille.k12.ia.us
1002 G Ave, Vinton, IA 52349-1398
Patrick Clancy, Superintendent

Iowa Department of Education 515.281.5294
Fax 515.242.5988
E-mail ....jason.glass@iowa.gov
400 East 14th St, Grimes State Office Bldg, Des Moines, IA 50319
Jason Glass, Director

Iowa Dept of Education 515.281.5294
Fax 515.242.5988
Web ....www.iowa.gov/educatewww.educateiowa.gov
E-mail ....jason.glass@iowa.gov
400 E 14th St, Des Moines, IA 50319
Jason Glass, Director

Iowa School for the Deaf 712.366.0571
Fax 712.366.3218
3501 Harry Langdon Blvd Ste 1, Council Bluffs, IA 51503
Jeanne Prickett, Edd, Superintendent

LABOR & WORKFORCE EDUCATION

Iowa Workforce Development 515.281.9027
Fax 515.281.9006
E-mail ....anthony.dietsch@iwd.iowa.gov
150 Des Moines St, Des Moines, IA 50309-5500
Anthony A Dietsch, Administrator

COUNTY SERVICES

Adair County

COURTS

5th District Court 641.743.2445
Fax 641.743.2974
Web ....www.iowacourt.gov
400 Public Sq Ste 7, Greenfield, IA 50849-1259
Stacey Armstrong, Clerk

POLICE AND SHERIFF

Sheriff's Ofc 641.743.2148
Fax 641.343.7185
Web ....www.iowatelecom.net
E-mail ....acso@iowatelecom.net
306 E Iowa St, Greenfield, IA 50849-1229
Brad Newton, Sheriff

Adams County

COURTS

5B District Court 641.322.4711
Fax 641.322.4523
Web ....www.iowacourtsonline.org
E-mail ....duane.golden@jb.state.ia.us
500 9th St, Corning, IA 50841-1303
Duane Golden, Judicial Magistrate

POLICE AND SHERIFF

Sheriff's Ofc 641.322.4444
Fax 641.322.3868
E-mail ....sheriff21@frontier.com
901 Davis Ave, Corning, IA 50841
Alan Johannes, Sheriff

Allamakee County

GENERAL HEALTH SERVICES

Community & Home Care 563.568.5660
Fax 563.568.4667
E-mail ....homecare@vmhospital.com
40 1st St SE, Veterens Memorial Hospital, Waukon, IA 52172-2022
Michael Myers, Nurse Administrator

COURTS

1A District Court 563.568.6351
Fax 563.568.6353
110 Allamakee St, Waukon, IA 52172
Honorable John J. Bauercamper, District Judge

POLICE AND SHERIFF

Sheriff's Ofc 563.568.4521
Fax 563.568.4720
E-mail ....dispatch@co.ia.allamakee
110 Allamakee St, Waukon, IA 52172
Timothy J. Heiderscheit, Sheriff

Appanoose County

JUSTICE AGENCY

Juvenile Court Svcs 641.856.6194
Fax 641.856.8935
Appanoose County Courthouse, 1St Floor, Centerville, IA 52544
Bruce Buttel, Juvenile Court Officer

COURTS

8A District Court 641.856.6101
Fax 641.856.2282
Web ....www.jb.state.ia.us
E-mail ....dan.wilson@jb.state.ia.us
201 N 12 Centerville, Centerville, IA 52544
Honorable Daniel P. Wilson, Director

POLICE AND SHERIFF

Sheriff's Ofc 641.437.7100
Fax 641.437.7107
E-mail ....sheriff@sirisonline.com
1125 W Van Buren St, Centerville, IA 52544-3413
Gary D. Anderson, Sheriff

EDUCATION SERVICES

Head Start 641.856.6089
Fax 641.856.6809
Web www.gpaea.k12.ia.us
E-mail ....margaret.hume@gpaea.k12.ia.us
722 N 1st St, Centerville, IA 52544-1224
Margaret Hume, Director

Audubon County

POLICE AND SHERIFF

Sheriff's Ofc 712.563.2631
Fax 712.563.3730
E-mail ....audcoso@iowatelecom.net
318 Leroy St Ste 1, Audubon, IA 50025
Todd W. Johnson, Sheriff

Benton County

SOCIAL SERVICES

Human Svcs 319.472.4746
Fax 319.472.4451
114 E 4th St, Vinton, IA 52349

GENERAL HEALTH SERVICES

Health Dept 319.472.3119
Fax 319.472.2925
Web ....www.co.benton.ia.us
E-mail ....marc@co.benton.ia.us
111 E Forth St, Vinton, IA 52349-0327
Marcus Greenlee, Health Officer And Land Use Administrator

Virginia Gay Hospital -- Home & Health 319.472.6360
Fax 319.472.5976
Web ....www.myvgh.org
E-mail ....bob.hornsby@rivhs.com
309 1st Ave, Vinton, IA 52349-1746
Nancy Farmer, Rn, Director

JUSTICE AGENCY

Juvenile Court Svcs 319.472.3957
Fax 319.472.3957
E-mail ....deanancy78@msn.com
2500 Edgewood Rd. SW, Ste D-200, Cedar Rapids, IA 52404
Sam Moen, Juvenile Court Officer

COURTS

6th District Court 319.472.2766
Fax 319.472.2747
111 E 4th St Stop 4, Vinton, IA 52349-1771
Patrick Grady, Judge

POLICE AND SHERIFF

Sheriff's Ofc 319.472.2337
Fax 319.472.4770
E-mail ....sheriff@bentonsheriff.com
901 D Ave, Vinton, IA 52349
Randall Forsyth, Sheriff

Black Hawk County

SOCIAL SERVICES

Human Services 319.291.2441
Fax 319.291.2619
E-mail ....cblack01@dhs.state.ia.us
1407 Independence Ave, PO Box 7500, Waterloo, IA 50704

GENERAL HEALTH SERVICES

Black Hawk Health Dept 319.291.2413
Fax 319.291.2529
Web ....www.co.black-hawk.ia.us
E-mail ....kemrich@co.black-hawk.ia.us
1407 Independence Ave Fl 5, Waterloo, IA 50703-4396
Kaitlin Emrich, Hiv Division Manager

MENTAL HEALTH SERVICES

Black Hawk-Grundy Mental Health Ctr 319.234.2893
Fax 319.234.0354
Web ....www.bhgmhc.com
E-mail ....teachus@bhgmhc.com
3251 W 9th St, Waterloo, IA 50702-5310
Thomas Eachus, Director

JUSTICE AGENCY

CASA-1st District 319.833.3314
Fax 319.833.3270
Web ....www.co.black-hawk.ia.us
E-mail ....renee.else@dia.iowa.gov
316 E 5th St, Waterloo, IA 50703-4712
Renee Else, Coordinator

Juvenile Court Svcs 319.291.2506
Fax 319.291.2583
Web ....www.iowacourts.gov
E-mail ....ruth.frush@iowacourts.gov
818 Lafayette St, Waterloo, IA 50703-4724
Ruth Frush, Juvenile Court Officer

COURTS

1B District Court **319.833.3331**
Fax 319.833.3251
Web ....www.judicial.state.ia.us
316 E 5th St, Waterloo, IA 50703-4712
Honorable Thomas Bower, Chief Judge

POLICE AND SHERIFF

Sheriff's Ofc **319.291.2587**
Fax 319.291.2541
E-mail ....tthompson@bhcso.org
225 E 6th St, Waterloo, IA 50703
Tony Thompson, Sheriff

Waterloo Police Dept **319.291.4349**
Fax 319.291.4332
Web ....www.waterloopolice.com
E-mail ....wpdrecords@waterloopolice.com
715 Mulberry St, Waterloo, IA 50703
Daniel Trelka, Chief Of Police

Boone County

GENERAL HEALTH SERVICES

Home Care Svcs Hospital **515.432.1127**
Fax 515.432.0706
Web ....www.boonecountyhospital.com
E-mail ....vmccambridge@boonecountyhospital.com
105 S Marshall St Ste B, Boone, IA 50036-4899
Vicki Mccambridge, Rn, Bs, Nursing Director

JUSTICE AGENCY

Juvenile Court Svcs **515.433.0567**
Fax 515.433.0567
E-mail ....marty.mcintyre@iowacourts.gov
201 State St Courthouse, Boone, IA 50036
Marty McIntyre, Juvenile Court Officer

COURTS

2B District Court **515.433.0561**
Fax 515.433.0563
Web ....www.iowa.courts.gov
201 State St Ste 16, Boone, IA 50036-3943
Patricia Freund, Clerk

POLICE AND SHERIFF

Sheriff's Ofc **515.433.0524**
Fax 515.432.8047
E-mail ....bcso@tdsi.net
1019 W MAMIE EISENHOWER AVE, Boone,
IA 50036-3916
Ronald D. Fehr, Sheriff

Bremer County

COURTS

2A District Court **319.352.5661**
Fax 319.352.1054
Web ....www.co.bremer.ia.us
E-mail ....priffel@co.bremer.ia.us
415 E. Bremer Ave, Waverly, IA 50677
Honorable Paul Riffel, Judge

POLICE AND SHERIFF

Sheriff's Ofc **319.352.5400**
Fax 319.352.0233
E-mail ....dhildebrandt@co.bremer.ia.us
111 4th St NE, Waverly, IA 50677
Duane L. Hildebrandt, Sheriff

Buchanan County

SOCIAL SERVICES

Human Svcs **319.334.6091**
Fax 319.334.2063
Web ....www.dhs.state.ia.us
1415 1st St W, Independence, IA 50644-2317
Jason Kilby, Protection Supervisor

POLICE AND SHERIFF

Sheriff's Ofc **319.334.2568**
Fax 319.334.6542
Web ....www.indytel.com
E-mail ....bwolfgram@indytel.com
210 5th Ave NE Ste D, Independence, IA 50644-1980
Bill Wolfgram, Sheriff

Buena Vista County

SOCIAL SERVICES

Human Services **712.749.2536**
Fax 712.749.2569
E-mail ....cbuena01@dhs.state.ia.us
311 E 5th St, Storm Lake, IA 50588

GENERAL HEALTH SERVICES

Health Nurse Svc **712.749.2548**
Fax 712.749.2549
Web ....www.co.buena-vista.ia.us
E-mail ....pbogue@co.buena-vista.ia.us
1709 Richland Dr, Storm Lake, IA 50588-3503
Pam Bogue, Home Health Administrator

JUSTICE AGENCY

CASA-3rd District **712.749.5184**
Fax 712.749.2560
E-mail ....casaslkf@co.buena-vista.ia.us
215 East 5th St, Storm Lake, IA 50588
Kathy Fritz, Coordinator

POLICE AND SHERIFF

Sheriff's Ofc **712.749.2530**
Fax 712.732.3397
Web ....www.bvsheriff.com
E-mail ....gary@bvsheriff.com
411 Expansion Blvd, Storm Lake, IA 50588-3512
Gary Launderville, Sheriff

Butler County

SOCIAL SERVICES

Human Svcs **319.267.2594**
Fax 319.267.2413
Web ....www.dhs.state.ia.us
E-mail ....cmcallister@dhs.state.ia.us
713 Elm St, Allison, IA 50602-7720
Cassie Mcallister, Service Supervisor

GENERAL HEALTH SERVICES

Public Health **319.267.2934**
Fax 319.267.2113
Web ....www.butlercoiowa.org
E-mail ....publichealth@butlercoiowa.org
428 6th St, Allison, IA 50602
Jennifer Becker, Director

COURTS

2A District Court **319.267.2487**
Fax 319.267.2488
428 6th St, Allison, IA 50602
Ronald Peeples, Judicial Magistrate

POLICE AND SHERIFF

Sheriff's Dept **319.267.2410**
Fax 319.267.2135
428 6th St, Allison, IA 50602
Jason S. Johnson, Sheriff

Calhoun County

JUSTICE AGENCY

Juvenile Court Svcs **712.297.5907**
Fax 712.297.5082
416 4th St, Rockwell City, IA 50579
Gregg Jobgen, Juvenile Court Officer

COURTS

2B District Court **712.297.8122**
Fax 712.297.5082
Web ....www.iowacourts.gov
416 4th St Ste 5, Rockwell City, IA 50579-1428
David Gidel, Judicial Magistrate

POLICE AND SHERIFF

Law Enforcement Ctr/ Sheriff **712.297.7583**
Fax 712.297.5000
E-mail ....swad13@hotmail.com
416 4th St Ste 4, Rockwell City, IA 50579
William A. Davis, Sheriff

Carroll County

SOCIAL SERVICES

Human Services **712.792.4391**
Fax 712.792.1516
E-mail ....ccarro01@dhs.state.ia.us
608 N Court Ste C, PO Box 278, Carroll, IA 51401

JUSTICE AGENCY

Juvenile Court Svcs **712.792.5666**
Fax 712.792.5666
225 East 7th Street, Carroll, IA 51401-2413
John Debolt, Juvenile Court Officer

COURTS

2B District Court **712.792.4327**
Fax 712.792.4328
114 E 6th St, Ste 5, Carroll, IA 51401
Honorable Joel E. Swanson, Judge

POLICE AND SHERIFF

Sheriff's Dept **712.792.4393**
Fax 712.792.4564
E-mail ....dbass@co.carroll.ia.us
114 E 6th St Ste 7, Carroll, IA 51401
Douglas R. Bass, Sheriff

Cedar County

GENERAL HEALTH SERVICES

Public Health Nursing **563.886.2226**
Fax 563.886.1218
Web ....www.cedarcountypublichealth.org
E-mail ....awehde@cedarcounty.org
400 Cedar St, Courthouse, Tipton, IA 52772-1748
Amy Wehde, Deputy Director

COURTS

7th District Court **563.886.2101**
Fax 563.886.3594
400 Cedar St, Tipton, IA 52772-1748
Stuart Werling, Judicial Magistrate

POLICE AND SHERIFF

Sheriff's Ofc **563.886.2121**
Fax 563.886.2095
Web ....www.cedarcounty.org
E-mail ....wwethington@cedarcounty.org
711 E South St, Tipton, IA 52772-1977
Warren Wethington, Sheriff

Cerro Gordo County

SOCIAL SERVICES

Human Services **641.424.8641**
E-mail ....ccerro01@dhs.state.ia.us
22 N Georgia Ave Ste 1, Mason City, IA 50401

GENERAL HEALTH SERVICES

Health Dept **641.421.9300**
Fax 641.421.9350
Web ....www.cghealth.com
E-mail ....dps@cghealth.com
22 N Georgia Ave Ste 300, Mason City, IA 50401
Betty Krones, Rn, Hiv Coordinator

JUSTICE AGENCY

Juvenile Court Svcs **641.423.8624**
Fax 641.423.8563
Web . . . . .www.fairview.org
22 N Georgia Ave Ste 101, Mason City,
IA 50401-3435
Jim Wilson, Sub-district Supervisor

COURTS

2A Judicial District Court **641.424.6431**
Fax 641.421.0994
Web .www.co.cerro-gordo.ia.us
E-mail . . . . .jdrew@co.cerro-gordo.ia.us
220 N Washington Ave, Mason City, IA 50401-3220
Honorable James M. Drew, Director

EDUCATION SERVICES

Clear Lake Head Start **641.494.1891**
Fax 641.494.1894
Web . . . . .www.nicao-online.org
E-mail . . . . .dcasto@nicao-online.org
1190 Briarstone Dr, Mason City, IA 50401-4638
Ms Dianne Casto, Director

Cherokee County

COURTS

3A District Court **712.225.6744**
Fax 712.225.6749
Web . . . . .www.iowacourts.gov
520 W Main St Ste F, Cherokee, IA 51012-1700
Cheryl Kaskey, Judicial Magistrate

POLICE AND SHERIFF

Sheriff's Ofc **712.225.6728**
Fax 712.225.1538
111 N 5th St Ste 1, Cherokee, IA 51012
David Scott, Sheriff

Chickasaw County

GENERAL HEALTH SERVICES

Public Health Nursing **641.394.4053**
Fax 641.394.5814
E-mail . . . . .chickphn@iowatelecom.net
260 E Prospect St, New Hampton, IA 50659
Kathy Babcock, Rn, Administrator

POLICE AND SHERIFF

Sheriff's Ofc **641.394.3121**
Fax 641.394.4173
Web . . . . .www.chickasawcoia.org
E-mail . . . . .ccso@iowatelecom.net
116 N Chestnut Ave, New Hampton, IA 50659-1301
Marty Larsen, Sheriff

Clarke County

SOCIAL SERVICES

Human Services **641.342.6516**
Fax 641.342.3371
E-mail . . . . .cclark01@dhs.state.ia.us
109 S Main, Osceola, IA 50213

GENERAL HEALTH SERVICES

Public Health Nursing **641.342.3724**
Fax 641.342.2603
E-mail . . . . .clarkeph@iowatelecom.net
134 W Jefferson St, Osceola, IA 50213-1286
Sandy Eddy, Rn, Administrator

POLICE AND SHERIFF

Sheriff's Ofc **641.342.2914**
Fax 641.342.4071
E-mail . . . . .cccivil@iowatelecom.net
220 Town Line Rd, Osceola, IA 50213
Bill Kearns, Sheriff

EDUCATION SERVICES

Head Start **641.774.8133**
Web www.clarke.k12.ia.us
E-mail . . . . .sseehan@clarke.k12.ia.us
2500 College Dr, Osceola, IA 50213-8288
Stacey Seehan, Teacher Coordinator

Clay County

SOCIAL SERVICES

Human Services **712.262.3586**
Fax 712.262.3621
217 W 5th St, Spencer, IA 51301

JUSTICE AGENCY

Juvenile Court Svcs **712.262.5938**
Fax 712.262.5939
215 W 4th St Ste 1, Spencer, IA 51301
Tony Van Helden, Juvenile Court Officer

COURTS

3rd District Court **712.262.4335**
Fax 712.262.6042
215 W 4th St Ste 4, Spencer, IA 51301-3822
Honorable Frank Nelson Sr, Judge

POLICE AND SHERIFF

Sheriff's Dept **712.262.3221**
Fax 712.262.5448
E-mail . . . . .clayshrf@co.clay.ia.us
3121 W 4th St, Spencer, IA 51301
Randy W. Krukow, Sheriff

Clayton County

GENERAL HEALTH SERVICES

Visiting Nurse Assoc **563.245.1145**
Fax 563.245.2730
E-mail . . . . .nancy.yelden@finleyhospital.org
100 Sandpit Rd, Elkader, IA 52043
Nancy Yelden, Administrator

COURTS

Iowa District Court **563.245.2204**
Fax 563.245.1175
111 High St NE, Elkader, IA 52043
Linny Emrich, Clerk of Court

POLICE AND SHERIFF

Sheriff's Dept **563.245.2422**
Fax 563.245.1630
230 Main St, St. Olas, IA 52072
Mike Tschigi, Sheriff

Clinton County

SOCIAL SERVICES

Human Services **563.242.0573**
Fax 563.242.5079
E-mail . . . . .Cclint01@dhs.state.ia.us
121 6th Ave S, PO Box 1180, Clinton, IA 52733

JUSTICE AGENCY

Juvenile Court Svcs **563.243.3349**
Fax 563.243.4933
121 6th Ave S, Clinton, IA 52732-4104
Kathleen Biscontine, Jpo Iv

COURTS

7 District Court **563.243.6210**
Fax 563.243.0011
Web . . . . .www.clintoncountyattorney.net
E-mail . . . . .david.sivright@iowacourts.gov
612 N 2nd St, Clinton, IA 52732-3840
Honorable David H. Sivright, Director

POLICE AND SHERIFF

Sheriff's Dept **563.242.9211**
Fax 563.242.6307
E-mail . . . . .tarasbertoli@gapa911.us
241 7th Ave N, Clinton, IA 52732
Rick Lincoln, Sheriff

EDUCATION SERVICES

Caei-Dewitt Head Start **563.659.2861**
Fax 563.659.2861
222 12th St, De Witt, IA 52742
Andrea Bayer, Director

Crawford County

JUSTICE AGENCY

Juvenile Court Svcs **712.263.5442**
Fax 712.263.5468
1202 Broadway st, Denison, IA 51442-2637
Glen A. Barngrover, Juvenile Court Officer

COURTS

3rd District Court **712.263.2242**
Fax 712.263.5753
Web . . . . .www.iowacourts.gov
1202 Broadway Ste 1P, Denison, IA 51442-2637
Honorable Duane Hoffmeyer, Chief Judge

POLICE AND SHERIFF

Sheriff's Ofc **712.263.3577**
Fax 712.263.5661
Web .www.crawfordcounty.org
1202 Broadway, Denison, IA 51442-2637
Stein Kuhler, Sheriff

EDUCATION SERVICES

Denison Head Start I And LI **712.263.7105**
Fax 712.263.7100
1826 3rd Ave S, Denison, IA 51442-2133
P Lingle, Director

Dallas County

SOCIAL SERVICES

Human Services **515.993.5817**
Fax 515.993.5829
E-mail . . . . .cdalla01@dhs.state.ia.us
210 N 10th St, Adel, IA 50003

GENERAL HEALTH SERVICES

Public Health **515.993.3750**
Fax 515.993.4949
Web . . . . .www.co.dallas.ia.us
E-mail . . . . .phn@co.dallas.ia.us
902 Court St, Adel, IA 50003
Janice Jensen, Rn, Bsn, Administrator

JUSTICE AGENCY

Juvenile Court Svcs **515.993.5805**
Fax 515.993.4722
801 Court St, Rm 303, Adel, IA 50003
Linda Colby, Director

COURTS

5A District Court **515.993.5816**
Fax 515.993.4752
801 Court St Rm 204, Adel, IA 50003
Honorable Peter A. Keller, Judge

POLICE AND SHERIFF

Sheriff's Dept **515.993.4771**
Fax 515.993.4569
Web . . . . .www.co.dallas.ia.us
201 Nile Kinnick Dr N, Adel, IA 50003-1440
Chad Lenard, Sheriff

Davis County

GENERAL HEALTH SERVICES

Community Health Care **641.664.3629**
Fax 641.664.2494
Web ....www.daviscountyhospital.org
E-mail ....webmaster@daviscountyhospital.org
  105 S Pine St, Bloomfield, IA 52537-1519
Rhonda Northup, Rn, Bsn, Administrator

COURTS

8A District Court **641.664.2011**
Fax 641.664.2041
  100 Courthouse Sq Ste 9, Bloomfield, IA 52537
John D Martin, Judicial Magistrate

POLICE AND SHERIFF

Sheriff's Ofc **641.664.2385**
Fax 641.664.1540
Web ....www.daviscountyiowa.org
E-mail ....divisd@daviscountyiowa.org
  110 W Franklin St, Bloomfield, IA 52537-1614
Dave Divis, Sheriff

Decatur County

GENERAL HEALTH SERVICES

Public Health Nursing **641.446.6518**
Fax 641.446.3616
Web ....www.idph.state.ia.us
E-mail ....sbickel@decaturph.com
  1502 NE Poplar St, Leon, IA 50144-1281
Shelley Bickel, Administrator

COURTS

5B District Court **641.446.4331**
Fax 641.446.3759
  207 N Main St Ste D, Leon, IA 50144
Honorable Sherman W. Phipps, Judge

POLICE AND SHERIFF

Sheriff's Ofc **641.446.4111**
Fax 641.446.6990
  207 N Main St Ste A, Leon, IA 50144
Bert Muir, Sheriff

EDUCATION SERVICES

Building Blocks Early Head Start **641.446.8050**
Fax 641.446.3392
  1601 NW Church St, Leon, IA 50144-1952
Nancy Schnurr, Director

Delaware County

COURTS

1A District Court **563.927.4942**
Fax 563.927.3074
Web ....www.judicial.state.ia.us
  301 E Main St, Manchester, IA 52057
Linny Emrich, Clerk Of Court

POLICE AND SHERIFF

Sheriff's Dept **563.927.3135**
Fax 563.927.6973
E-mail ....jleclere@co.delaware.ia.us
  304 E Delaware St, Manchester, IA 52057-2213
John Leclere, Sheriff

Des Moines County

SOCIAL SERVICES

Human Services **319.754.4622**
Fax 319.457.4628
E-mail ....cdesmo01@dhs.state.ia.us
  560 Division St, Burlington, IA 52601

**Work Force Development/Social
Svcs** **319.753.1671**
Fax 319.753.5855
Web ....www.iowaworkforce.org
  1000 N Roosevelt Ave Ste 9, Burlington,
  IA 52601-1988
Robert Brian, Regional Manager

GENERAL HEALTH SERVICES

Health Department **319.753.8290**
Fax 319.753.8703
  522 N 3rd St, Burlington, IA 52601
Barbara Baker, Director

COURTS

8B District Court **319.753.8272**
Fax 319.753.8253
  513 N Main St Ste 12, Burlington, IA 52601
Honorable Mary Brown, Judge

POLICE AND SHERIFF

Sheriff's Dept **319.753.8212**
Fax 319.754.6910
E-mail ....johnstonem@co.des-moines.ia.us
  512 N Main St Ste 2, Burlington, IA 52601
Mike Johnstone, Sheriff

Dickinson County

SOCIAL SERVICES

Human Svcs **712.336.2555**
  Dickinson Co Courthouse, Ste 2401, Spirit Lake,
  IA 51360

COURTS

3A District Court **712.336.1138**
Fax 712.336.4005
  1802 Hill Ave, ste 2506, Spirit Lake, IA 51360
David A Lester, Judge

POLICE AND SHERIFF

Sheriff's Ofc **712.336.2793**
Fax 712.336.1946
E-mail ....gbaloun@co.dickinson.ia.us
  Courthouse, 19th & Hill, Spirit Lake, IA 51360
Gregory L. Baloun, Sheriff

Dubuque County

SOCIAL SERVICES

Human Services **563.557.8251**
Fax 563.557.9177
E-mail ....CDubuq01@dhs.state.ia.us
  410 Nesler Ctr, PO Box 87, Dubuque, IA 52004

GENERAL HEALTH SERVICES

City Of Dubuque Health Dept **563.589.4181**
Fax 563.589.4299
Web ....www.cityofdubuque.org
E-mail ....health@cityofdubuque.org
  1300 Main St, City Hall Annex, Dubuque, IA 52001
Mary Rose Corrigan, Director

MENTAL HEALTH SERVICES

Hillcrest Mental Health Ctr **563.582.0145**
Fax 888.526.5456
Web ....www.hillcrest-fs.org
  200 Mercy Dr Ste 200, Dubuque, IA 52001-7392
Melissa Anderson, Executive Director

JUSTICE AGENCY

CASA Program **563.582.6219**
Fax 563.582.0914
Web ....www.dia.iowa.gov
E-mail ....shoefer@dia.state.ia.us
  3430 Dodge St Unit 17, Dubuque, IA 52003-5218
Shirley Hoefer, Coordinator

Juvenile Court Svcs **563.589.7831**
Fax 563.589.7842
  350 W 6th St Ste 215, Dubuque, IA 52001
Thomas E. Hoelscher, Juvenile Court Services Officer

COURTS

1A District Court **563.589.4418**
Fax 563.589.7832
  720 Central Avenue, Dubuque, IA 52001
Honorable Lawrence H. Fautsch, Director

POLICE AND SHERIFF

Sheriff's Ofc **563.589.4406**
Fax 563.589.7882
Web ....www.dbqco.org
E-mail ....dvrotsos@dbqco.org
  770 Iowa St, Dubuque, IA 52001
Don Vrotsos, Sheriff

EDUCATION SERVICES

Bluff Street Head Start **563.557.5516**
Fax 563.556.4402
  1499 Bluff St, Dubuque, IA 52001
Kim Halton, Director

Emmet County

SOCIAL SERVICES

Dept Of Human Svcs **712.362.7237**
Fax 515.725.9018
Web ....www.dhs.state.ia.us
E-mail ....epicray@dhs.state.ia.us
  220 S 1St St, Estherville, IA 51334-2110
Ellen Picray, Service Supervisor

GENERAL HEALTH SERVICES

Emmet Public Health **712.362.2490**
Fax 712.362.7160
Web ....www.emmetcountyia.com
  508 S 1 St, Estherville, IA 51334-2429
Cathy Preston, Director

COURTS

3A District Court **712.362.3325**
Fax 712.362.5329
  609 1st Ave N, Estherville, IA 51334
Cynthia Kelly, Clerk Of Court

POLICE AND SHERIFF

Armstrong Police Dept **712.864.3535**
Fax 712.868.4171
  519 6th Street, Armstrong, IA 50514
Craig Merrell, Police Chief

Sheriff's Ofc **712.362.2639**
Fax 712.362.7271
  114 N 6th St Ste 2, Estherville, IA 51334
Mike Martens, Sheriff

EDUCATION SERVICES

Head Start **712.362.5141**
Fax 563.382.9854
  1520 Central Ave, Estherville, IA
Connie Steven-Bruner, Director

Fayette County

SOCIAL SERVICES

Human Services **563.422.5634**
Fax 563.422.5636
E-mail ....cfayet01@dhs.state.ia.us
  PO Box 476, West Union, IA 52175

COURTS

1B District Court **563.422.5694**
Fax 563.422.3137
Web ....www.judicial.state.ia.us
  114 N Vine St, West Union, IA 52175
Larry Woods, Judicial Magistrate

POLICE AND SHERIFF

Sheriff's Ofc 563.422.6067
Fax 563.422.6069
220 N Industrial Pkwy, West Union, IA 52175
Marty Fisher, Sheriff

Floyd County

SOCIAL SERVICES

Human Services 641.228.5713
Fax 641.228.6439
E-mail ....cfloyd01@dhs.state.ia.us
1206 S Main St, PO Box 158, Charles City, IA 50616

JUSTICE AGENCY

Medical Center 641.228.6830
800 Eleventh St, Charles City, IA 50616
Bill Fause, Administrator

COURTS

Juvenile Court Svcs 641.228.7777
Fax 641.228.7772
E-mail ....scott.jenson@jb.state.ia.us
101 S Main St Ste 305, Charles City, IA 50616-2756
Honorable Gerald Magee, Juvenile Judge

POLICE AND SHERIFF

Sheriff's Ofc 641.228.1821
Fax 641.257.6150
E-mail ....fcso@floydcoia.org
101 S Main St Ste 501, Charles City, IA 50616
Rick A. Lynch, Sheriff

Franklin County

COURTS

2A District Court 641.456.5626
Fax 641.456.5628
Web ....www.judicial.state.ia.us
12 1st Ave NW ste 203, Hampton, IA 50441-1752
Deborah Bossman, Clerk Of Court

POLICE AND SHERIFF

Sheriff's Dept 641.456.2731
Fax 641.456.2216
Web ....www.cji.net
E-mail ....lrichtsmeier@cji.net
105 5th St SW, Hampton, IA 50441-1752
Larry L. Richtsmeier, Sheriff

Fremont County

POLICE AND SHERIFF

Sheriff's Dept 712.374.2673
Fax 712.374.2532
E-mail ....cntysheriff@iowatelecom.net
701 Cass St, Sidney, IA 51652
Kevin Aistrope, Sheriff

Greene County

POLICE AND SHERIFF

Sheriff's Dept 515.386.2136
Fax 515.386.3911
Web ....www.greenecountysheriff.net
E-mail ....theater@greenecountysheriff.net
204 S Chestnut St, Jefferson, IA 50129-2204
Thomas Heater, Sheriff

Grundy County

GENERAL HEALTH SERVICES

Public Health 319.824.6312
Fax 319.824.5469
Web ....www.gccourthouse.org
E-mail ....nancyh@gccourthouse.org
704 1/2 H Ave Ste 3, Grundy Center, IA 50638-2008
Nancy Haren, Rn, Administrator

COURTS

1B District Court 319.824.5229
Fax 319.824.3447
Web ....www.grundycounty.org
706 G Ave, Grundy Center, IA 50638
Waynette Saul, Clerk Court

POLICE AND SHERIFF

Sheriff's Dept 319.824.6933
Fax 319.824.5826
Web ....www.grundysheriff.org
E-mail ....rpenning@grundysheriff.org
705 8th St, Grundy Center, IA 50638-1344
Rick D. Penning, Sheriff

Guthrie County

GENERAL HEALTH SERVICES

Health Dept 641.747.3972
Fax 641.747.3839
Web ....www.gcph.com
E-mail ....janell@gcph.com
2002 State St Ste 1, Guthrie Center, IA 50115-8897
Janell Stringham, Rn, Administrator

COURTS

5A District Court 641.747.3415
Fax 641.747.2420
Web ....www.jb.state.ia.us
200 N 5th St, Guthrie Center, IA 50115-1300
Mary Perkins, Judicial Magistrate

POLICE AND SHERIFF

Sheriff's Ofc 641.747.2214
Fax 641.747.3346
E-mail ....gcso391@netins.net
200 N 5th St, Guthrie Center, IA 50115
Marty Arganbright, Sheriff

Hamilton County

SOCIAL SERVICES

Human Services 515.832.9555
Fax 515.832.9560
E-mail ....chamil01@dhs.state.ia.us
2300 Superior St, Webster City, IA 50595

GENERAL HEALTH SERVICES

Public Health Nursing 515.832.9565
Fax 515.832.9660
Web ....www.hamiltoncountypublichealth.org
E-mail ....skroona@hamiltoncountypublichealth.com
821 Seneca St, Webster City, IA 50595-2228
Shelby Kroona, Administrator

JUSTICE AGENCY

Juvenile Court Svcs 515.832.9615
Fax 515.832.8606
2300 Superior St Ste 10, Webster City,
IA 50595-3158
Wendi Dinsdale, Juvenile Court Officer

COURTS

2B District Court 515.832.9600
Fax 515.832.9519
2300 Superior St Ste 9, Webster City, IA 50595
Janelle Groteluschen, Associate Juvenile Judge

POLICE AND SHERIFF

Sheriff's Ofc 515.832.9500
Fax 515.832.9504
Web ....www.wmtel.net
E-mail ....dennis@wmtel.net
2300 Superior St Ste 8, Webster City, IA 50595-3186
Dennis Hegenson, Sheriff

Hancock County

GENERAL HEALTH SERVICES

Health Svc 641.923.3676
Fax 641.923.2631
545 State St, Garner, IA 50438
Kathi Nelson, Rn, Administrator

POLICE AND SHERIFF

Sheriff's Ofc 641.923.2621
Fax 641.923.2460
875 State St, Garner, IA 50438
Scott Dodd, Sheriff

Hardin County

JUSTICE AGENCY

State Training School 641.858.5402
Fax 641.858.2416
3211 Edgington Ave, Eldora, IA 50627
Mark Day, Superintendent

COURTS

2nd District Court 641.858.2328
Fax 641.858.2320
1215 Edington Ave, Eldora, IA 50627
Jean Mcneil Dunn, Judicial Magistrate

POLICE AND SHERIFF

Sheriff's Ofc 641.939.8189
Fax 641.939.8249
Web ....www.co.hardin.ia.us
E-mail ....tsmith@co.hardin.ia.us
1116 14th Ave, Eldora, IA 50627-1731
Timothy Smith, Sheriff

Harrison County

SOCIAL SERVICES

Human Svcs 712.644.2460
Fax 712.644.3395
204 E 6th St, Logan, IA 51546
Tom Bouska, Service Area Manager

GENERAL HEALTH SERVICES

Public Health 712.644.2220
Fax 712.644.3238
116 N 2nd Ave, Logan, IA 51546
Nicole Carritt, Administrator

COURTS

District Court 4 ....712.644.2665
Fax 712.644.2615
E-mail ....jesse.render@iowacourts.gov
111 N 2nd Ave Ste 8, Logan, IA 51546-1367
Jesse Render, Judicial Magistrate

POLICE AND SHERIFF

Sheriff's Office 712.644.2244
Fax 712.644.2274
111 S 1st Ave, Logan, IA 51546
Pat Sears, Sheriff

Henry County

SOCIAL SERVICES

Human Services 319.986.5157
Fax 319.385.8512
E-mail ....chenry01@dhs.state.ia.us
208 W Madison, Mount Pleasant, IA 52641

MENTAL HEALTH SERVICES

Mental Health Ctr 319.385.8051
Fax 319.385.7010
Web ....www.iowarescare.com
E-mail ....jweinand@iowarescare.com
106 N Jackson St Ste 101, Mount Pleasant,
IA 52641-2063
John Weinand, Clinical Director

Iowa

COURTS

8B District Court 319.385.2632
Fax 319.385.4144
E-mail ....henrycountyclerk@iowacourts.gov
100 E Washington St, Mt Pleasant, IA 52641
Honorable Cynthia Danielson, District Court Judge

POLICE AND SHERIFF

Sheriff's Dept 319.385.2712
Fax 319.385.2384
106 E Clay St, Mt Pleasant, IA 52641
Allen Wittmer, Sheriff

Howard County

GENERAL HEALTH SERVICES

Health Dept 563.547.2989
Fax 563.547.4223
Web ....www.rhshc.com
327 8th Ave W, Cresco, IA 52136-1064
Connie Kuennen, Administrator

POLICE AND SHERIFF

Sheriff's Ofc 563.547.3535
Fax 563.547.5325
E-mail ....howardso@cji.net
124 S Park Pl, Cresco, IA 52136
Mike Miner, Sheriff

Humboldt County

POLICE AND SHERIFF

Sheriff's Dept 515.332.2471
Fax 515.332.9040
E-mail ....sheriff@trvnet.net
430 Sumner Ave Ste 2, Humboldt, IA 50548
Dean A. Krueger, Sheriff

Ida County

GENERAL HEALTH SERVICES

Horn Public Health 712.364.7311
Fax 712.364.4064
E-mail ....phn@hornmemorialhospital.org
701E 2nd St, Ida Grove, IA 51445
Patti Andrews, Rn, Nurse Administrator

COURTS

3B District Court 712.364.2628
Fax 712.364.2699
401 Moorehead St, Ida Grove, IA 51445
Cheryl Kaskey, Clerk

POLICE AND SHERIFF

Sheriff's Dept 712.364.3146
Fax 712.364.2746
Web ....www.idacountysheriff.com
E-mail ....sheriffwade@hotmail.com
401 Moorehead St, Ida Grove, IA 51445-1494
Wade A. Harriman, Sheriff

Iowa County

POLICE AND SHERIFF

Sheriff's Dept 319.642.7307
Fax 319.642.3826
E-mail ....iacosh@netins.net
960 Franklyn Ave, Marengo, IA 52301
Rob Rotter, Sheriff

Jackson County

JUSTICE AGENCY

Juvenile Court Svcs 563.652.4249
Fax 563.652.3051
Web ....www.jb.state.ia.us
E-mail ....brian.bopes@jb.state.ia.us
201 W Platt St, Maquoketa, IA 52060-2243
Brian M. Bopes, Juvenile Court Officer

COURTS

**Jackson Clerk Office, 7th District
Court** 563.652.4946
Fax 563.652.2708
Web ....www.jb.state.ia.us
E-mail ....ronald.besch@iowacourts.gov
201 W Platt St, Maquoketa, IA 52060-2243
Ronald Besch, Judicial Magistrate

POLICE AND SHERIFF

Sheriff's Dept 563.652.3312
Fax 563.652.0662
Web ....www.jacksoncountyiowa.com
E-mail ....jcso49@yahoo.com
104 S Niagara St, Maquoketa, IA 52060-2939
Russ D. Kettmann, Sheriff

Jasper County

SOCIAL SERVICES

Human Svcs 641.792.1955
Fax 641.792.5830
115 N 2nd Ave E Ste H, Newton, IA 50208
Tracey Larsen, Income Maintenance Supervisor

JUSTICE AGENCY

Juvenile Court Svcs 641.792.1770
Fax 641.792.0261
115 N 2nd Ave E Ste I, Newton, IA 50208-3241
Douglas Thoma, Juvenile Court Officer

COURTS

5A District Court 641.792.3255
Fax 641.792.2818
Web ....www.iowacourts.gov
101 1st St N, Ste 104, Newton, IA 50208-3227
Honorable Thomas Mott, Associate Judge

POLICE AND SHERIFF

Sheriff's Dept 641.792.5912
Fax 641.792.4202
2300 Law Center Dr, Newton, IA 50208-8255
Michael J. Balmer, Sheriff

Jefferson County

SOCIAL SERVICES

Human Svcs 641.472.5011
Fax 641.472.3519
Web ....www.dhs.state.ia.us
E-mail ....kandrew@dhs.state.ia.us
51 W Hempstead Ave, Fairfield, IA 52556-2832
Karen Andrew, Service Supervisor

COURTS

8A District Court 641.472.3454
Fax 641.472.9472
E-mail ....jefferson.county.clerk@iowacourt.gov
51 W Briggs Ave Ste 5, Fairfield, IA 52556
Benny Waggoner, Judicial Magistrate

POLICE AND SHERIFF

Sheriff's Ofc 641.472.3576
Fax 641.469.3353
E-mail ....jeffcoso@lisco.com
1200 W Grimes Ave, Fairfield, IA 52556-2778
Jerry R. Droz, Sheriff

Johnson County

SOCIAL SERVICES

Human Services 319.356.6050
Fax 319.337.2705
E-mail ....CJOHNS01@dhs.state.ia.us
855 S Dubuque St, Ste 102, Iowa City, IA 52240

GENERAL HEALTH SERVICES

Public Health 319.356.6040
Fax 319.356.6044
Web ....www.johnson/county.com
E-mail ....dbeardsley@co.johnson.ia.us
855 S Dubuque St, Ste 217, Iowa City, IA 52240
Doug Beardsley, Director

MENTAL HEALTH SERVICES

**Community MH Ctr For Mid-Eastern
Iowa** 319.338.7884
Fax 319.338.7006
Web ....www.communitymentalhealthcenter.org
E-mail ....mentalhealth@meimhc.org
507 E College St, Iowa City, IA 52240-5115
Stephen Trefz, Executive Director

JUSTICE AGENCY

Juvenile Court Svcs 319.356.6076
Fax 319.339.6157
Web ....www.jb.state.ia.us
855 S Dubuque St Ste 126, Iowa City, IA 52240-4728
Chris Wyatt, Juvenile Court Supervisor

COURTS

6th District Court 319.356.6060
Fax 319.337.6035
417 S Clinton St Unit 1, Iowa City, IA 52240-4108
Honorable Amanda Potterfield, Judge

EDUCATION SERVICES

Coral Ridge Fam Res Ctr 319.351.1214
Fax 319.351.6914
E-mail ....dmccoy@hacap.org
2441 10th St, Coralville, IA 52241
Dawn Mccoy, Director

Jones County

COURTS

6th District Court 319.462.4341
Fax 319.462.5827
500 W Main St, Anamosa, IA 52205
Sharon Modracak, Clerk

POLICE AND SHERIFF

Sheriff's Dept 319.462.4371
Fax 319.462.4766
Web ....www.co.jones.ia.us
500 W Main St Ste 26, Anamosa, IA 52205-1632
Mark J. Denniston, Sheriff

EDUCATION SERVICES

Anamosa Childrens Ctr 319.462.4343
Fax 319.462.2361
Web ....www.hacap.org
E-mail ....shatfiele@hacap.org
100 Park Ave, Anamosa, IA 52205-1140
Sheri Hatfiele, Director

Keokuk County

SOCIAL SERVICES

Dept Of Human Svcs 641.673.3496
Fax 641.673.5467
Web ....www.dhs.state.ia.us
E-mail ....mdeyoung@dhs.state.ia.us
410 S 11th St, Oskaloosa, IA 52577
Marilyn Deyoung, Income Maintenance Supervisor

GENERAL HEALTH SERVICES

Public Health Ofc 641.622.3575
Fax 641.622.1052
Web ....www.keokukcountyia.com
E-mail ....mwaechter@keokukcountyia.com
101 S Main St, Courthouse, Sigourney,
IA 52591-1482
Marilyn Waechter, Rn, Director

COURTS

8A District Court **641.622.2210**
Fax 641.622.2171
Web .... www.jb.state.ia.us
101 S Main St, Sigourney, IA 52591-1419
Joel Yates, Main Judge

POLICE AND SHERIFF

Sheriff's Ofc **641.622.2727**
Fax 641.622.3304
E-mail .... kcsheriff@iowatelecom.net
204 S Stone St, Sigourney, IA 50268
Jeff Shipley, Sheriff

Kossuth County

JUSTICE AGENCY

Juvenile Court Svcs **515.295.7018**
Fax 515.295.5984
109 W State St Ste 4, Algona, IA 50511-2657
Craig Eckhart, Juvenile Court Officer

COURTS

clerk of court **515.295.3240**
Fax 515.295.2820
Web .... www.judicial.state.ia.us
114 W State St Ste 10, Algona, IA 50511-2613
Judge Don Courtney, Judge

Lee County

SOCIAL SERVICES

Dept Of Human Svcs North Ofc **319.372.3651**
Fax 319.372.8921
Web .... www.dhs.state.ia.us
E-mail .... sgordon@dhs.state.ia.us
933 Ave H, N Lee County Bldg, Fort Madison,
IA 52627
Stacy Gordon, Income Maintenance Supervisor

GENERAL HEALTH SERVICES

Health Dept **319.372.5225**
Fax 319.372.4374
Web .... www.leecounty.org
E-mail .... healthdepartment@leecounty.org
2218 Avenue H Ste A, Fort Madison, IA 52627-4036
Patti Knutson, Hiv Coordinator

JUSTICE AGENCY

Juvenile Court Svcs **319.372.7833**
Fax 319.372.9252
710 Fort Avenue, Fort Madison, IA 52627-2913
Dave Durbala, Juvenile Court Officer

COURTS

8B District Court **319.372.3523**
Fax 319.372.2557
701 Avenue F, Fort Madison, IA 52627
Honorable Michael Shilling, Director Judge

8B District Court **319.524.2433**
Fax 319.524.4699
Web .... www.judicial.state.ia.us
25 N 7th St Ste 301, Keokuk, IA 52632-5547
Honorable Blom Green, Judge

Linn County

SOCIAL SERVICES

Human Svcs **319.892.6700**
Fax 319.892.6899
Web .... www.dhs.state.ia.us
411 3rd St SE Ste 300, Cedar Rapids, IA 52401-1811
Valerie Lovaglia, Director Of Human Services

GENERAL HEALTH SERVICES

Health Dept **319.892.6000**
Fax 319.892.6099
Web .... www.linncounty.org/health
501 13th St NW, Cedar Rapids, IA 52405-3700
Barbara Chadwick, Nursing Supervisor

JUSTICE AGENCY

CASA **319.362.0829**
Fax 319.362.7184
E-mail .... jgericke@dia.state.ia.us
411 3rd St SE Ste 720, Cedar Rapids, IA 52401
Jennifer Gericke, Coordinator

Detention Ctr **319.892.5735**
Fax 319.892.5768
E-mail .... tague.tangborne@linncounty.org
800 Walford Rd, Cedar Rapids, IA 52404
Peg Tangborne, Director

Juvenile Court Svcs **319.398.3545**
Fax 319.398.3972
Web .... www.iowacourts.gov
E-mail .... candice.bennett@iowacourts.gov
2500 Edgewood Rd SW, Ste D-200, Cedar Rapids,
IA 52405
Candice Bennett, Chief

COURTS

6th District Court **319.398.3411**
Fax 319.398.4054
Web .... www.jb.state.ia.us
E-mail .... thomas.koehler@jb.state.ia.us
51 3rd Avenue Brg, Cedar Rapids, IA 52401-1705
Honorable Thomas Koehler, Director

EDUCATION SERVICES

Central City Head Start **319.393.7811**
Fax 319.393.6263
Web .... www.hacap.org
E-mail .... info@hacap.org
1515 Hawkeye Dr, Hiawatha, IA 52233-1102
Jane Drapeaux, Director

Ctr Point Head Start **319.849.1102**
Fax 319.849.1134
Web www.cen-pt-urb.k12.ia.us
E-mail .... hmcgonegle@cen-pt-urb.k12.ia.us
101 Palo Road, Center Point, IA 52213
Heidi Mcgonegle, Director

Grant Area Education Agency **319.399.6700**
Fax 319.399.6457
Web www.aea10.k12.ia.us
E-mail .... rfielder@aea10.k12.ia.us
4401 6th St SW, Cedar Rapids, IA 52404-4432
Ron Fielder, Phd, Chief Administrator

Louisa County

GENERAL HEALTH SERVICES

Public Health Svcs **319.523.3981**
Fax 319.523.8408
E-mail .... lcph@louisacomm.net
805 Highway 61 N, Wapello, IA 52653
Alana Poage, Administrator

COURTS

8B District Court **319.523.4541**
Fax 319.523.4542
E-mail .... melissa.schoonover@iowacourts.gov
117 S Main St, Wapello, IA 52653
Roger Huddle, Judicial Magistrate

POLICE AND SHERIFF

Sheriff's Dept **319.523.3511**
Fax 319.523.4373
12635 County Rd G56, Wapello, IA 52653
Curt Braby, Sheriff

Lucas County

GENERAL HEALTH SERVICES

Public Health Nursing **641.774.4312**
E-mail .... grismorem@lucasco.org
123 S Grand St, Chariton, IA 50049
Mary Grismore, Administrator

COURTS

5B District Court **641.774.4421**
Fax 641.774.8669
916 Braden Ave Ste 4, Chariton, IA 50049
Honorable Arthur Gamble, Judge

POLICE AND SHERIFF

Sheriff's Dept **641.774.5083**
Fax 641.774.1660
E-mail .... longlyd@lucasco.org
1023 Linden Ave, Chariton, IA 50049
Jim Baker, Sheriff

Lyon County

GENERAL HEALTH SERVICES

Health Svcs **712.472.8200**
Fax 712.472.4039
315 1st Ave Ste 208, Rock Rapids, IA 51246
Sherri Boeve, Administrator

POLICE AND SHERIFF

Sheriff's Ofc **712.472.2521**
Fax 712.472.2303
Web .... www.lyoncountyiowa.com
E-mail .... lyon601@hickorytech.net
410 S Boone St, Rock Rapids, IA 51246-1455
Blythe Bloemendaal, Sheriff

Madison County

SOCIAL SERVICES

Community Services **515.462.2931**
Fax 515.462.3076
Web .... www.madisoncoia.us
209 E Madison St, Winterset, IA 50273-2403
John Gresh, Mental Health Director

GENERAL HEALTH SERVICES

Public Health Nursing **515.462.9051**
Fax 515.462.9061
E-mail .... jhoward@i-rule.net
209 e madison, Winterset, IA 50273
Marvin Firch, Board Member

COURTS

5A District Court **515.462.4451**
Fax 515.462.9825
Web .... www.iowacourtsonline.org
Madison County Courthouse, Winterset, IA 50273
Adam Hanson, Judicial Magistrate

POLICE AND SHERIFF

Sheriff's Ofc **515.462.3575**
Fax 515.462.3684
Web .... www.madisoncounty.com
E-mail .... madcosheriff@prairieinet.net
1012 N 1st St, Winterset, IA 50273-1233
Paul D. Welch, Sheriff

Mahaska County

SOCIAL SERVICES

Human Services **641.673.3496**
Fax 641.673.5467
E-mail .... cmahas01@dhs.state.ia.us
410 S 11th St, PO Box 290, Oskaloosa, IA 52577

GENERAL HEALTH SERVICES

Public Health Nursing **641.673.3257**
Fax 641.672.1213
  1225 C Ave E, Oskaloosa, IA 52577
Kim Lambert, Nurse Administrator

JUSTICE AGENCY

Juvenile Court Svcs **641.673.0419**
Fax 641.673.7736
  106 S 1st St Ste 4, Oskaloosa, IA 52577-3143
Patricia Rath, Juvenile Court Officer

COURTS

8th District Court **641.673.7786**
Fax 641.672.1256
E-mail ....james.reilly@jb.state.ia.us
  106 S 1st St Ste 12, Oskaloosa, IA 52577
Honorable James Reilly, Judge

POLICE AND SHERIFF

Sheriff's Dept **641.673.4322**
Fax 641.672.1191
E-mail ....sheriff@mahaskacounty.org
  214 High Ave E Ste 1, Oskaloosa, IA 52577
Paul Degust, Sheriff

Marion County

GENERAL HEALTH SERVICES

Health Dept. **641.828.2238**
Fax 641.842.3442
  2003 N Lincoln, Knoxville, IA 50138
Kim Dorn, Director

COURTS

5A District Court **641.828.2207**
Fax 641.828.7580
  214 E Main St, Knoxville, IA 50138
Carol Sage, Clerk

POLICE AND SHERIFF

Sheriff's Dept **641.828.2220**
Fax 641.828.8453
E-mail ....rgoemaat@co.marion.ia.us
  211 N Godfrey Ln, Knoxville, IA 50138
Ron Goemaat, Sheriff

Marshall County

SOCIAL SERVICES

Human Services **641.752.6741**
Fax 671.752.6746
E-mail ....Cmarsh01@dhs.state.ia.us
  206 W State St, Marshalltown, IA 50158

JUSTICE AGENCY

Juvenile Court Svcs **641.753.3481**
Fax 641.752.5520
Web ....www.jb.state.ia.us
E-mail ....paul.thompson@jb.state.ia.us
  30 S 1st Ave, Ste 205, Marshalltown, IA 50158
Paul Thompson, Juvenile Court Officer

POLICE AND SHERIFF

Sheriff's Dept **641.754.6380**
Fax 641.754.6369
Web ....www.co.marshall.ia.us
E-mail ....sheriff@co.marshall.ia.us
  2369 Jessup Ave, Marshalltown, IA 50158-9845
Ted G. Kamatchus, Sheriff

Mills County

GENERAL HEALTH SERVICES

Public Health Nursing **712.527.9699**
Fax 712.527.4711
  101 Central St, Ste B11, Glenwood, IA 51534
Sheri Bowen, Rn, Administrator

COURTS

District Court 4 ....**712.527.4880**
Fax 712.527.4936
Web ....www.iowacourts.gov
  418 Sharp St Ste 5, Glenwood, IA 51534-1774
Kimberly Carter, Court Clerk

Mitchell County

COURTS

2A District Court **641.732.3726**
Fax 641.732.3728
Web ....www.jb.state.ia.us
E-mail ....bryan.mckinley@jb.state.ia.us
  508 State St, Osage, IA 50461-1250
Honorable Bryan H. Mckinley, Director

POLICE AND SHERIFF

Sheriff's Ofc **641.732.4740**
Fax 641.732.3151
E-mail ....curtis.younker@iowa.gov
  211 S 6th St, Osage, IA 50461-1228
Curtis W. Younker, Sheriff

Monona County

GENERAL HEALTH SERVICES

Public Health Ofc **712.433.1773**
Fax 712.433.9502
E-mail ....mcphns@longlines.com
  610 Iowa Ave, Onawa Courthouse, Onawa, IA 51040
Marjorie Erickson, Executive Director

COURTS

3B District Court **712.423.2491**
Fax 712.423.2744
  610 Iowa Ave, Onawa, IA 51040
Gary Taylor, Judicial Magistrate

POLICE AND SHERIFF

Sheriff's Ofc **712.433.1414**
Fax 712.433.1398
Web ....www.longlines.com
E-mail ....mocoso@longlines.com
  909 7th St, Onawa, IA 51040-1411
Jeffrey Pratt, Sheriff

Monroe County

SOCIAL SERVICES

Human Services **641.932.5187**
Fax 641.932.2114
E-mail ....cmonro01@dhs.state.ia.us
  103 S Clinton, Albia, IA 52531

GENERAL HEALTH SERVICES

Public Health **641.932.7191**
Fax 641.932.5075
Web ....www.mchalbia.com
E-mail ....kwelsh@monroecoia.us
  1801 S B St, Albia, IA 52531-2056
Kathy Welsh, Administrator

COURTS

8A District Court **641.932.5212**
Fax 641.932.3245
Web ....www.iowacourts.gov
E-mail ....countyclerk.monroe@iowacourts.gov
  10 Benton Ave E, Albia, IA 52531-2056
Honorable Annette J. Scieszinski, Presiding District Judge

POLICE AND SHERIFF

Sheriff's Dept **641.932.7815**
Fax 641.932.7381
Web ....www.cosoiowatelecom.net
  103 2nd Ave W Ste 1, Albia, IA 52531-1960
Daniel Johnson, Sheriff

Montgomery County

SOCIAL SERVICES

Human Services **712.623.4838**
Fax 712.623.3569
E-mail ....cmontg01@dhs.state.ia.us
  1109 Highland Ave, PO Box 525, Red Oak, IA 51566

GENERAL HEALTH SERVICES

Public Health **712.623.4893**
Fax 712.623.5714
Web ....www.montgomerycountypublichealth.com
E-mail ....montphns@hotmail.com
  1109 Highland Ave Ste E, Red Oak, IA 51566-1715
Sue Drake, Director

POLICE AND SHERIFF

Sheriff's Dept **712.623.5107**
Fax 712.623.2670
E-mail ....mcso@mchsi.com
  106 W Coolbaugh St, Red Oak, IA 51566
Joe Sampson, Sheriff

Muscatine County

SOCIAL SERVICES

Human Svcs **563.263.9302**
  3210 Harmony Lane, Muscatine, IA 52761

JUSTICE AGENCY

Juvenile Court Svcs **563.263.5903**
Fax 563.262.4180
Web ....www.jb.state.ia.us
E-mail ....dana.echelbarger@iowacourts.gov
  401 E 3rd St, Muscatine, IA 52761-4242
Dana Echelbarger, Juvenile Court Officer

COURTS

7th District Court **563.263.6511**
Fax 563.264.3622
Web ....www.iowacourts.gov
E-mail ....betty.burch@iowacourts.gov
  401 E 3rd St, Muscatine, IA 52761-4118
Betty Burch, Clerk

POLICE AND SHERIFF

Sheriff's Dept **563.262.4190**
Fax 563.262.4194
Web ....www.muscatinejournal.com
E-mail ....rgorr@hotmail.com
  400 Walnut St, Muscatine, IA 52761-4241
Dave White, Sheriff

OBrien County

SOCIAL SERVICES

Human Services **712.957.5135**
Fax 712.957.5155
E-mail ....cobrie01@dhs.state.ia.us
  160 2nd St SE, PO Box 400, Primghar, IA 51245

O'Brien County

SOCIAL SERVICES

Iowa Dept of Human Svcs **712.957.5135**
Fax 712.957.5155
Web ....www.dhs.state.ia.us
E-mail ....cobrie01@dhs.state.ia.us
  160 2nd St SE, Primghar, IA 51245-7703
Jeanne Seecke, Service Supervisor

GENERAL HEALTH SERVICES

Public Health Nursing **712.957.0105**
Fax 712.957.0105
E-mail ....phnurse2@tcaexpress.net
  155 S Hayes Ave, Courthouse, Primghar, IA 51245
Lisa Youngers, Administrator

COURTS

3A District Court............................**712.957.3255**
Fax..712.957.2965
   155 S Hayes Ave, Primghar, IA 51245-7724
   Jeffrey Queck, Judicial Magistrate

POLICE AND SHERIFF

Sheriff's Office............................**712.757.3415**
Fax..712.757.5445
E-mail..............................obcso@tcaexpress.net
   240 1st St NE, Primghar, IA 51245
   Michael J. Anderson, Sheriff

Osceola County

GENERAL HEALTH SERVICES

Community Health Svcs.................**712.754.4611**
Fax..712.754.4612
Web....................www.osceolacommunityhospital.org
E-mail..............................ochsph@hotmail.com
   115 Cedar Ln, # 258, Sibley, IA 51249
   Pam Juber, Rn, Bsw, Administrator

COURTS

3A District Court............................**712.754.3595**
Fax..712.754.2480
E-mail..........................irene.grave@jb.state.ia.us
   300 7th St Ste 2, Sibley, IA 51249
   Irene Grave, Clerk Of Court

POLICE AND SHERIFF

Sheriff's Dept..............................**712.754.2556**
Fax..712.754.2872
E-mail..........................sheriff@oceolacoia.org
   309 6th St, Sibley, IA 51249
   Doug Webber, Sheriff

Page County

GENERAL HEALTH SERVICES

Home Care.................................**712.542.3936**
Fax..712.542.2066
   822 S 17th St, Clarinda, IA 51632-2624
   Karen Marsh, Home Health Secretary

Public Health Nursing....................**712.246.2332**
Fax..712.246.2552
E-mail..............................pcphbd@mchsi.com
   1208 W Nishna Rd Ste B, Shenandoah, IA 51601
   Belinda Debolt, Rn, Administrator

COURTS

District Court 4............................**712.542.3214**
Fax..712.542.5460
Web....................................www.iowacourt.gov
   112 E Main St Ste 3, Clarinda, IA 51632-2111
   James Nye, Judicial Magistrate

POLICE AND SHERIFF

Sheriff's Ofc...............................**712.542.5193**
Fax..712.542.5880
E-mail..........................pagecoso@iowatelecom.net
   323 N 15th St, Clarinda, IA 51632
   Lyle Palmer, Sheriff

Palo Alto County

COURTS

3rd District Court..........................**712.852.3603**
Fax..712.852.2274
Web..................................www.judicial.state.ia.us
   1010 Broadway St, Emmetsburg, IA 50536

POLICE AND SHERIFF

Sheriff's Dept..............................**712.852.3535**
Fax..712.852.3914
E-mail..........................paloaltoso@iowatelecom.net
   2001 East 11th, Emmetsburg, IA 50536
   Dennis J. Goeders, Sheriff

Plymouth County

COURTS

3Rd District Court..........................**712.546.4215**
Fax..712.546.8430
Web....................................www.jb.state.ia.us
E-mail..........................robert.dull@jb.state.ia.us
   215 4th Ave SE, Le Mars, IA 51031-2178
   Honorable Robert Dull, Judge

POLICE AND SHERIFF

Sheriff's Ofc...............................**712.546.8191**
Fax..712.546.8796
E-mail..........................mvanotterloo@co.plymouth.ia.us
   451 14th Ave NE, Le Mars, IA 51031
   Mike Van Otterloo, Sheriff

Pocahontas County

SOCIAL SERVICES

Human Svcs................................**712.335.3565**
Fax..712.335.3929
Web......................................www.iowa.gov
   23 3rd Ave NE, Pocahontas, IA 50574-1614
   Ken Riedel, Service Area Manager

GENERAL HEALTH SERVICES

Public Health Dept........................**712.335.4142**
Fax..712.335.3581
Web..........................www.pcph.pocahontascoia.us
E-mail..........................palexander@pocahontascoia.us
   99 Court Sq Ste 1, COURTHOUSE, Pocahontas,
   IA 50574-1634
   Patricia Alexander, Administrator

POLICE AND SHERIFF

Sheriff's Ofc...............................**712.335.3308**
Fax..712.335.4300
Web....................................www.evertek.net
   99 Court Sq Ste 9, Pocahontas, IA 50574-1629
   Robert Lampe, Sheriff

Polk County

SOCIAL SERVICES

**Bureau Of Student and Family Support
Services**....................................**515.281.3176**
Fax..515.242.6019
Web...................................www.educateiowa.gov
E-mail..........................marty.ikeda@iowa.gov
   Dept Of Education, Grimes State Office Bldg, Des
   Moines, IA 50319
   Marty Ikeda, Chief

GENERAL HEALTH SERVICES

Health Dept................................**515.286.3798**
Fax..515.286.2033
Web...................................www.polkcountyiowa.gov
   1907 Carpenter Ave, Des Moines, IA 50314
   Lori Parson, Nurse Clinic Manager

Visiting Nurse Svcs Of Iowa................**515.288.1516**
Fax..515.288.0437
Web....................................www.vnsdm.org
   1111 9th St Ste 320, Des Moines, IA 50314-2527
   Dave Discher, Interim CEO

JUSTICE AGENCY

Attorney's Office..........................**515.286.2164**
E-mail..........................avitzth@attorney.co.polk.ia.us
   206 6th Ave, Des Moines, IA 50309
   Andrea Vitzthum, Asistance Attorneys

Juvenile Court Svcs.......................**515.286.3960**
Fax..515.286.3029
Web....................................www.jb.state.ia.us
E-mail..........................marilyn.lantz@iowacourts.gov
   2309 Euclid Avn, Des Moines, IA 50310-4757
   Marilyn Lantz, Chief Juvenile Officer

POLICE AND SHERIFF

Des Moines Police Dept....................**515.283.4800**
Fax..515.237.1665
   25 E Robert D Ray Dr, Des Moines, IA 50309
   Judy A. Bradshaw, Chief

Sheriff's Dept..............................**515.286.3800**
Fax..515.286.3410
Web....................................www.co.polk.ia.us
E-mail..........................bill.mccarthy@polkcountyiowa.gov
   2309 Euclid Ave, Des Moines, IA 50310
   Bill Mccarthy, Sheriff

EDUCATION SERVICES

Special Education..........................**515.270.9030**
Fax..515.270.5383
Web....................................www.aea11.k12.ia.us
E-mail..........................rallison@aea11.k12.ia.us
   6500 Corporate Dr, Johnston, IA 50131-1603
   Laura Gillon, Human Resource Director

Pottawattamie County

SOCIAL SERVICES

Human Svcs................................**712.328.4838**
Fax..712.328.4792
   417 E Kanesville Blvd, Council Bluffs, IA 51503
   Thomas Bouska, Service Area Manager

GENERAL HEALTH SERVICES

Council Bluffs Health Dept.................**712.328.4666**
Fax..712.328.4917
Web....................................www.cbhealth.org
E-mail..........................rstolz@councilbluffs-ia.gov
   209 Pearl St, Council Bluffs, IA 51503-0826
   Rachel Stolz, Hiv Coordinator

Visiting Nurse Assoc.......................**712.328.2636**
Web....................................www.thevnacares.org
   822 S Main Ste 102, Council Bluffs, IA 51503
   James Summerfelt, CEO

COURTS

4th District Court..........................**712.328.5604**
Fax..712.328.4810
   227 S 6th St Fl 3, Council Bluffs, IA 51501
   Honorable Greg Steensland, Judge

POLICE AND SHERIFF

Sheriff's Ofc...............................**712.890.2200**
Fax..712.890.2205
Web....................................www.pottcounty.com
E-mail..........................jdanker@pottcosheriff.com
   1400 Big Lake Rd, Council Blfs, IA 51501-0113
   Jeffrey D. Danker, Sheriff

Poweshiek County

GENERAL HEALTH SERVICES

**Grinnell Regional Home Care Public Health
Nursing**....................................**641.236.2385**
Fax..641.236.2599
Web......................................www.grmc.us
E-mail..........................krutledge@grmc.us
   210 4th Ave, Grinnell Regional Home Care, Grinnell,
   IA 50112-1898
   Kim Rutledge, Director

JUSTICE AGENCY

Juvenile Court Svcs.......................**641.236.0655**
Fax..641.236.1456
E-mail..........................steve.bernemann@iowacourts.gov
   927 4th Ave, Rm 230, Grinnell, IA 50112
   Steve Bernemann, Juvenile Court Officer

COURTS

8A District Court **641.623.5644**
Fax 641.623.5320
Web .... www.iowacourts.gov
302 E Main St, Ste 101, Montezuma, IA 50171-1139
Honorable Randy Degeest, Judge

POLICE AND SHERIFF

Sheriff's Dept **641.623.5679**
Fax 641.623.5120
Web .... www.netins.net
E-mail .... tbsheets@netins.net
4802 Barncity Rd, Montezuma, IA 50171-1001
Tom Sheets, Sheriff

Ringgold County

COURTS

5B District Court **641.464.3234**
Fax 641.464.2478
E-mail .... james.pedersen@jb.state.ia.us
109 W Madison St Ste 203, Mount Ayr, IA 50854
James Pedersen, Judicial Magistrate

POLICE AND SHERIFF

Sheriff's Dept **641.464.3921**
Fax 641.464.0626
E-mail .... ringgoldcasa@iowatelecom.net
109 W Madison St Ste 300, Mount Ayr, IA 50854
Michael E. Sobotka, Sheriff

Sac County

GENERAL HEALTH SERVICES

Public Health Nursing **712.662.4785**
Fax 712.662.7862
E-mail .... jduffy@prairieinet.net
116 S State St, Ste A, Sac City, IA 50583
Jackie Duffy, Rn, Administrator

COURTS

Clerk Court **712.662.7791**
Fax 712.662.7978
Web .... www.judicial.state.ia.us
100 NW State St Ste 12, Sac City, IA 50583
Warren Bush, Judicial Magistrate

POLICE AND SHERIFF

Sheriff's Ofc **712.662.7127**
Fax 712.662.7129
E-mail .... sacso@saccounty.org
100 NW State St Ste 13, Sac City, IA 50583
Ken Mcclure, Sheriff

Scott County

SOCIAL SERVICES

Human Svcs **563.326.8680**
Fax 563.328.4108
Web .... www.dhs.state.ia.us
600 W 4th St, Fl 2, Davenport, IA 52801
Gary Lippe, Director

GENERAL HEALTH SERVICES

Health Dept **563.326.8618**
Fax 563.326.8774
Web .... www.scottcountyiowa.com
E-mail .... help@scottcountyiowa.com
600 W 4th St, Davenport, IA 52801
Edward Rivers, Director

JUSTICE AGENCY

Juvenile Court Svcs **563.326.8612**
Fax 563.326.8261
400 W 4th St, Davenport, IA 52801
Scott Hobart, Chief Juvenile Court Officer

COURTS

7th District Court **563.326.8647**
Fax 563.326.8298
Web .... www.judicial.state.ia.us
400 W 4th St, Davenport, IA 52801-1104
Honorable Mark J. Smith, Judge

POLICE AND SHERIFF

Davenport City Police Dept **563.326.7979**
Fax 563.326.6131
416 N Harrison St, Davenport, IA 52802
Frank Donchez, Chief Of Police

Sheriff's Ofc **563.326.8217**
Fax 563.326.8266
Web .... www.scottcountyiowa.com
E-mail .... sheriff@scottcountyiowa.com
400 W 4th St, Davenport, IA 52801-1036
Dennis Conard, Sheriff

EDUCATION SERVICES

Caei-Modular Head Start **563.336.5146**
Fax 563.336.5146
E-mail .... mkundu@iowatrain.org
2804 Eastern Ave, Davenport, IA 52803
Moushumi Kundu, Director

Shelby County

JUSTICE AGENCY

Juvenile Court Svcs **712.755.3891**
Fax 712.755.7487
Web .... www.manchester-ia.org
721 Market St, Harlan, IA 51537-1341
Scott Anderson, Juvenile Court Officer

COURTS

District Court 4 .... **712.755.5543**
Fax 712.755.2667
612 Court St, Harlan, IA 51537-0431
William Early, Judicial Magistrate

POLICE AND SHERIFF

Sheriffs Ofc **712.755.5026**
Fax 712.755.2481
E-mail .... sheriff@shco.org
612 Court St, Harlan, IA 51537
Mark Hervey, Sheriff

Sioux County

SOCIAL SERVICES

Human Services **712.737.2943**
Fax 712.737.3564
E-mail .... csioux01@dhs.state.ia.us
215 Central Avenue SE, PO Box 375, Orange City,
IA 51041

GENERAL HEALTH SERVICES

Community Health Partners - Home &
Health **712.737.2971**
Fax 712.737.8101
Web .... www.siouxcountychp.org
E-mail .... chp@orangecitycomm.net
211 Central Ave SE, Orange City, IA 51041
Deb Vanderplas, Administrator

COURTS

3B District Court **712.737.2286**
Fax 712.737.8908
Web .... www.jb.state.ia.us
E-mail .... james.scott@jb.state.ia.us
210 Central Ave SW, Orange City, IA 51041-0047
Honorable James Scott, Director

POLICE AND SHERIFF

Sheriff's Ofc **712.737.2280**
Fax 712.737.8185
E-mail .... sheriff@siouxcounty.org
4363 Ironwood Ave Ste 1, Orange City, IA 51041
Dan Altena, Sheriff

Story County

SOCIAL SERVICES

Human Services **515.292.2035**
Fax 515.296.2672
E-mail .... cstory01@dhs.state.ia.us
126 S Kellogg, Ste 101, Ames, IA 50010

JUSTICE AGENCY

Juvenile Court Svcs **515.233.3346**
Fax 515.233.3364
E-mail .... shirley.faircloth@iowacourts.gov
126 S Kellogg Ave Ste 202, Ames, IA 50010
Shirley Faircloth, Juvenile Court Officer

POLICE AND SHERIFF

Sheriff's Dept **515.382.6566**
Fax 515.382.7479
Web .... www.storycounty.com
E-mail .... sheriffweb@storycounty.com
1315 S B Ave, Nevada, IA 50201-2806
Paul H. Fitzgerald, Sheriff

Tama County

SOCIAL SERVICES

Dept Of Human Svcs **319.472.4746**
Fax 319.472.4451
Web .... www.dhs.state.ia.us
114 E 4th St, Vinton, IA 52349
Tracy Larson, Service Supervisor

GENERAL HEALTH SERVICES

Health Dept -- Home Care **641.484.4788**
Fax 641.484.5447
Web .... www.tamacounty.org
129 W High St, Toledo, IA 52342-1339
Linda Rosenberger, Rn, Administrator

JUSTICE AGENCY

Juvenile Court Svcs **641.484.2635**
Fax 641.484.3083
100 W High St Ste A, Toledo, IA 52342-1333
Michelle Stubbs, Juvenile Court Officer

COURTS

6th District Court **641.484.3721**
Fax 641.484.6403
100 W High St Ste 5, Toledo, IA 52342-0306
Richard Vandermey, Judicial Magistrate

POLICE AND SHERIFF

Sheriff's Dept **641.484.3760**
Fax 641.484.3254
Web .... www.tamacounty.org
E-mail .... dkucera@so.tamacounty.org
100 N Main St, Toledo, IA 52342-1212
Dennis P. Kucera, Sheriff

Taylor County

GENERAL HEALTH SERVICES

Public Health Nursing **712.523.3405**
Fax 712.523.3402
405 Jefferson St Ste 4, COURTHOUSE, Bedford,
IA 50833
Tami Blunt, Administrator

Iowa

POLICE AND SHERIFF

Sheriff's Dept **712.523.2153**
Fax 712.523.3545
E-mail ....taylorsheriff@frontiernet.net
  403 Jefferson St, Bedford, IA 50833
  Josh Weed, Sheriff

Union County

SOCIAL SERVICES

Human Svcs **641.782.1740**
  304 N Pine St, Creston, IA 50801

GENERAL HEALTH SERVICES

**Greater Regional Home Care Hospice And Public
Health** **641.782.3528**
Fax 641.782.3541
Web ....www.greaterregional.org
E-mail ....louanns@greaterregional.org
  1715 W Prairie St Ste A, Creston, IA 50801-1325
  Louann Snodgrass, Director

JUSTICE AGENCY

Juvenile Court Svcs **641.782.2519**
Fax 641.782.2508
  211/B N Elm St, Creston, IA 50801
  Blake Lauffer, Juvenile Court Officer Iii

COURTS

5B District Court **641.782.7315**
Fax 641.782.8241
Web ....www.iowatelecom.net
E-mail ....mjames@iowatelecom.net
  300 N Pine St Ste 6, Creston, IA 50801-2400
  Marion James, Judicial Magistrate

POLICE AND SHERIFF

Sheriff's Dept **641.782.7717**
Fax 641.782.8404
E-mail ....unioncosheriff@iowatelecom.net
  302 N Pine St Ste 4, Creston, IA 50801
  Rick L. Piel, Sheriff

Van Buren County

GENERAL HEALTH SERVICES

Public Health **319.293.3431**
Fax 319.293.3609
  4Th & Dodge St, Keosauqua, IA 52565-1187
  Lindee Thomas, Rn, Nursing Administrator

COURTS

8A District Court **319.293.3108**
Fax 319.293.3811
  406 Dodge St, Keosauqua, IA 52565
  Steve Westercamp, Judicial Magistrate

POLICE AND SHERIFF

Sheriff's Ofc **319.293.3426**
Fax 319.293.7114
E-mail ....dtedrow@vbcoia.org
  907 Broad St, Keosauqua, IA 52565
  Dan Tedrow, Sheriff

Wapello County

SOCIAL SERVICES

Human Svcs **641.682.8793**
Fax 641.682.7828
Web ....www.dhs.state.ia.us
E-mail ....jmunn@dhs.state.ia.us
  120 E Main St, Ottumwa, IA 52501-2910
  Jane Munn, Income Maintenance Supervisor

GENERAL HEALTH SERVICES

Wapello Community Health **641.682.5434**
Fax 641.682.2245
Web ....www.pcsia.net
E-mail ....wcph@pcsia.net
  108 E Main St, Ottumwa, IA 52501-2910
  Lynelle Diers, Rn, Clinical Director

JUSTICE AGENCY

Juvenile Court Svcs **641.683.0070**
Fax 641.683.0078
Web ....www.jb.state.ia.us
E-mail ....don.wyngarden@jb.state.ia.us
  101 W 4th St, Fl 5, Ottumwa, IA 52501
  Don R. Wyngarden, Juvenile Court Officer

POLICE AND SHERIFF

Sheriff's Dept **641.684.4350**
Fax 641.682.1414
Web ....www.pcsia.net
E-mail ....markm@pcsia.net
  330 W 2nd St, Ottumwa, IA 52501-2505
  Donald C. Kirkendall, Sheriff

Warren County

SOCIAL SERVICES

Human Services **515.961.5353**
Fax 515.961.4420
E-mail ....cwarre01@dhs.state.ia.us
  901 E Iowa Ave, PO Box 729, Indianola, IA 50125

POLICE AND SHERIFF

Sheriff's Dept **515.961.1122**
Fax 515.961.1025
Web ....www.co.warren.ia.us
E-mail ....jiml@co.warren.ia.us
  115 N Howard St Ste A, Indianola, IA 50125-2545
  James W. Lee, Sheriff

Washington County

GENERAL HEALTH SERVICES

Washington Public Health Nursing **319.653.7758**
Fax 319.653.6870
Web ....www.washph.com
  110 N Iowa Ave Ste 300, Washington,
  IA 52353-2037
  Edie Nebel, Rn, Administrator

JUSTICE AGENCY

Juvenile Court Svcs **319.653.2197**
Fax 319.653.3359
  110 N Iowa Ave Ste 420, Washington, IA 52353
  Kim Denning, Juvenile Court Officer

COURTS

8A District Court **319.653.7741**
Fax 319.653.7787
  224 W Main St, Washington, IA 52353
  Julie Johnson, Clerk Of Court

Wayne County

COURTS

5B District Court **641.872.2264**
Fax 641.872.2431
  100 N Lafayette St, Corydon, IA 50060
  John Birdwell, Judicial Magistrate

POLICE AND SHERIFF

Sheriff's Ofc **641.872.1566**
Fax 641.872.1228
  207 N Lafayette St, Corydon, IA 50060
  Donald Keith Davis, Sheriff

Webster County

SOCIAL SERVICES

Human Svcs **515.955.6353**
Fax 515.573.1649
  330 1st Ave N Ste 6, Fort Dodge, IA 50501
  Luann Burgers, Service Supervisor

MENTAL HEALTH SERVICES

**North Central Iowa Mental Health
Ctr** **515.955.7171**
Fax 515.573.7898
E-mail ....jimburr4759@hotmail.com
  720 Kenyon Rd, Fort Dodge, IA 50501-5759
  Jim Burr, Executive Director

JUSTICE AGENCY

Juvenile Court Svcs **515.573.1449**
Fax 515.573.1451
  702 1st Ave S, Ste 5, Fort Dodge, IA 50501
  Honorable Tim Wilaby, Director

COURTS

2B District Court **515.576.7115**
Fax 515.576.0555
Web ....www.webstercountyia.org
  701 Central Ave, Fort Dodge, IA 50501-3813
  Jenelle Grote, Clerk

POLICE AND SHERIFF

Sheriff's Ofc **515.573.1410**
Fax 515.573.2011
E-mail ....bmickelson@webstercountyia.org
  702 1st Ave S Ste 1, Fort Dodge, IA 50501
  Brian Mickelson, Sheriff

EDUCATION SERVICES

Cooper Head Start Classroom **515.574.5602**
Fax 515.574.5518
Web www.fort-dodge.k12.ia.us
E-mail ....mjohnson@fort-dodge.k12.ia.us
  2420 N 14th Ave, Fort Dodge, IA 50501-2154
  Marlene Johnson, Principal

Winnebago County

COURTS

2A District Court **641.585.4520**
Fax 641.585.2615
E-mail ....daron.fritz@jb.state.ia.us
  126 S Clark St Ste 6, Forest City, IA 50436-1706
  Daron Fritz, Judicial Magistrate

Winneshiek County

SOCIAL SERVICES

Winneshiek Human Svcs **563.382.2928**
Fax 563.382.8709
Web ....www.dhs.state.ia.us
E-mail ....cwinne01@dhs.state.ia.us
  2307 US Highway 52, Decorah, IA 52101-7858
  Christine Mcnally, Service Supervisor

GENERAL HEALTH SERVICES

Public Health Nursing **563.382.4662**
Fax 563.387.4121
Web ....www.winneshiekhealth.org
E-mail ....wcphns@winneshiekhealth.org
  305 Montgomery St Ste 3, Decorah, IA 52101
  Krista Vandenbrink, Rn, Administrator

JUSTICE AGENCY

Juvenile Court Svcs **563.382.2966**
Fax 563.382.3471
  1111 Paine St, Decorah, IA 52101

Iowa

COURTS

1A District Court **563.382.2469**
Fax 563.382.0603
Web ....www.iowacourts.gov
E-mail ....mllingreen@co.winneshiek.ia.us
  201 W Main St, Decorah, IA 52101-1713
  Honorable Margaret L. Lingreen, Judge

POLICE AND SHERIFF

Sheriff's Dept **563.382.4268**
Fax 563.382.2042
E-mail ....dpd@decorahia.org
  400 W Claiborne Dr, Decorah, IA 52101
  Leon F. Bohr, Sheriff

Woodbury County

SOCIAL SERVICES

Human Svcs **712.255.0833**
Fax 712.255.2674
E-mail ....cwoodb01@dhs.state.ia.us
  822 Douglas St, Sioux City, IA 51101

GENERAL HEALTH SERVICES

Siouxland District Health Dept **712.279.6119**
Fax 712.255.2601
E-mail ....jliebe@sioux-city.org
  1014 Nebraska St, Sioux City, IA 51105-1435
  Linda Grey, Home Health Administrator

MENTAL HEALTH SERVICES

Siouxland Mental Health Ctr **712.252.3871**
Fax 712.252.3157
Web ....www.siouxlandmentalhealth.com
  625 Court St, Sioux City, IA 51101
  Jim Rixner, Director

JUSTICE AGENCY

CASA **712.279.6602**
Fax 712.279.6469
  822 Douglas St, Ste 202, Sioux City, IA 51101
  Marla Treiber, Coordinator

COURTS

3B District Court **712.279.6611**
Fax 712.279.6021
  620 Douglas St Rm 101, Sioux City, IA 51101
  Honorable Duane Hoffmeyer, Chief Judge

Juvenile Court **712.279.6467**
Fax 712.279.6469
  822 Douglas St, Fl 2, Sioux City, IA 51101
  Honorable Mary Timko, Judge

POLICE AND SHERIFF

Sheriff's Ofc **712.279.6010**
Fax 712.279.6522
  407 7th St, Sioux City, IA 51102
  Glenn Parrett, Sheriff

EDUCATION SERVICES

Special Education **712.222.6000**
Fax 712.222.6115
Web www.nwaea.k12.ia.us
E-mail ....jgorman@nwaea.org
  1520 Morningside Ave, Sioux City, IA 51106
  Jim Gorman, Special Education Director

Worth County

GENERAL HEALTH SERVICES

Worth Public Health Nursing **641.324.1741**
Fax 641.324.2195
Web ....www.westcounty.org
E-mail ....worthph@mchsi.com
  95 9th St N, Northwood, IA 50459
  Theresa Johnson, Rn, Administrator

COURTS

2A District Court **641.324.2840**
Fax 641.324.2360
  1000 Central Ave Ste 2, Northwood, IA 50459
  Douglas Krull, Judicial Magistrate

POLICE AND SHERIFF

Sheriff's Dept **641.324.2481**
Fax 641.324.2611
E-mail ....wcso@worthcounty.org
  1000 Central Ave, Northwood, IA 50459
  Jay Langenbau, Sheriff

Wright County

GENERAL HEALTH SERVICES

Public Health Dept **515.532.3461**
Fax 515.532.3762
  115 1st St SE, Clarion, IA 50525
  Linda Klehm, Rn, Administrator

COURTS

2B District Court **515.532.3113**
Fax 515.532.2343
  115 N Main St, Clarion, IA 50525
  Janelle Groteluschen, Clerk

POLICE AND SHERIFF

Sheriff's Dept **515.532.3722**
Fax 515.532.2189
Web ....www.co.wright.ia.us
E-mail ....pschultz@co.wright.ia.us
  719 2nd St SW, Clarion, IA 50525-1918
  Paul J. Schultz, Sheriff

SPECIAL SERVICES AGENCIES

ADOPTION AGENCIES

Adoption Connection **515.965.8029**
Fax 515.963.4318
Web ....www.adoptioniowa.com
E-mail ....adoptionconnection@adoptioniowa.com
  114 NW 5th St, Ste 103, Ankeny, IA 50023-1711
  Lou Ann Barnes, Director

Bethany Christian Svcs **641.628.3247**
Web ....www.bethany.org
E-mail ....bcpella@bethany.org
  617 Franklin St, Ste 102, Pella, IA 50219
  Marlene Hibma, Branch Director

Catholic Charities **515.296.2759**
Web ....www.catholiccharitiesusa.org
E-mail ....cathchar@midiowa.net
  2210 Lincoln Way, Ames, IA 50014-7106
  Mary Jo Phiffer-Wulf, Director

Child Connect **712.255.9061**
Fax 712.255.3729
  705 Douglas St Ste 652, Sioux City, IA 51101
  Carol Wood, CEO

Eckerd **712.224.4701**
Fax 712.224.4704
Web ....www.eckerd.org
E-mail ....admissions@eckerd.org
  4700 Gordon Dr, Ste 103, Sioux City, IA 51106
  David Dennis, President & CEO; Mindy Louscher, Director
  In the greater Sioux City area of Iowa (Lyon, Osceola, Dickinson, Emmet, Kossuth,
  Palo Alto, Clay, Obrien, Sioux, Plymouth, Cherokee, Buena Vista, Ida, and Woodbury
  counties), Eckerd provides intensive Family Safety Risk & Permanency services
  that help preserve and strengthen families by enhancing parent/caregiver abilities
  to safety care for their children, as well as reunifying children with their families
  or helping children find alternative "forever families" through adoption and
  guardianship.

First Resources **641.842.7462**
  621 N Lincoln St, Knoxville, IA 50138

Four Oaks Family and Children's Services **319.364.0259**
Fax 866.290.5565
Web ....www.fouroaks.org
  5400 Kirkwood Boulevard SW, Cedar Rapids,
  IA 52404
  COA accredited organization.

**Iowa Foster And Adoptive Parents Assoc
(Ifapa)** **515.289.4567**
Fax 515.289.2080
Web ....www.ifapa.org
E-mail ....ifapa@ifapa.org
  6864 NE 14th St Ste 5, Ankeny, IA 50023
  Lynhon Stout, Executive Director

Lutheran Svcs **563.582.0044**
Fax 563.582.7308
Web ....www.lsiowa.org
E-mail ....jim.unsen@lsiowa.org
  2255 John F Kennedy Rd Ste 9, Dubuque,
  IA 52002-2883
  Jim Unsen, Area Manager

Parent Support Group **319.233.4285**
Fax 319.291.2619
Web ....www.cedarnet.org
E-mail ....seedorff_isapa@hotmail.com
  108 Sunset Lane, Elk Run Heights, IA 50707
  Judy Jeffries, Chairperson

ADVOCACY RESOURCES

Crisis Child Care Program **319.653.2141**
Fax 319.653.2142
E-mail ....cgaughan.ymca@yahoo.com
  121 E Main St, Washington, IA 52353-2012
  Cris Gaughan, Director

Iowa Federation Of Families For Children's Mental Health 319.462.2187
Fax 319.538.0238
Web ....www.iffcmh.org
E-mail ....help@iffcmh.org
   106 S Booth St, Anamosa, IA 52205-1834
   Lori Reynolds, Executive Director

Iowa State University 713.824.9201
E-mail ....mbehnken@pgsp.edu
   3821 Marigold Dr, Ames, IA 50014
   Monic Behnken

Mercy Child Advocacy Ctr 712.279.2548
Fax 712.279.5790
Web ....www.mercymedicalcentersiouxcityia.com
   801 5th St, Sioux City, IA 51011
   Barbara Small, Manager

New Opportunities Inc 712.792.9266
Fax 712.792.5723
Web ....www.newopp.org
E-mail ....cjensen@newopp.org
   23751 Hwy 30 E, Carroll, IA 51401
   Chad Jensen, Director

Success St. East High 319.433.2446
Fax 319.433.2447
E-mail ....bottke@cedarnet.org
   214 High St, Waterloo, IA 50703-3996
   Rhonda Bottke, Director

Success Street West 319.433.2780
Fax 319.433.2799
Web ....www.cedarnet.org
E-mail ....bottke@cedarnet.org
   425 1/2 E Ridgeway Ave, Waterloo, IA 50702
   Rhonda Bottke, Program Specilist

BEHAVIORAL HEALTH TREATMENT

Alegent Health Behavioral Svcs 712.246.1901
Fax 712.246.5506
Web ....www.alegent.com
E-mail ....sgraham@alegent.com
   600 S Fremont St Ste 3, Shenandoah, IA 51601-1675
   Shelly Graham, Clinic Office Coordinator

Alegent Health Mercy Hospital 712.328.5000
Web ....www.alegent.com
E-mail ....christine.daley@alegent.org
   800 Mercy Drive, Council Bluffs, IA 51501
   Ms. Chris Daley, Accreditation Manager
   Joint Commission accredited organization.

Boys and Girls Home and Family Services, Inc. 712.293.4700
Web ....www.boysandgirlshome.com
E-mail ....johnsonc@bghome.net
   2101 Court Street, Sioux City, IA 51104
   Ms. Cyndy Johnson, Accreditation Manager
   Joint Commission accredited organization.

Burlington Area Family Practice Ctr 319.754.4242
Fax 319.754.4079
Web ....www.bafpc.com
E-mail ....fpcenter@lisco.com
   1201 W Agency Rd, West Burlington, IA 52655-1645
   Rob Poetting, Director

Calamus Wheatland Schools 563.374.1292
Fax 563.374.1080
   110 E Park Rd, Wheatland, IA 52777
   Lonnie Luepker, Suprentendent

Cedar Rapids Counseling & Psychotherapy 319.362.0632
Web ....www.crcounseling.net
E-mail ....diane@crcounseling.net
   118 2nd St SE Ste 220, Cedar Rapids, IA 52401-1201
   Diane Luther, Therapist

Clarinda Youth Corporation 712.542.3103
Web ....clarindaacademy.org
E-mail ....hherzberg@clarindaacademy.org
   1820 North 16th Street, Clarinda, IA 51632
   Mrs. Heather Herzberg, Accreditation Manager
   Joint Commission accredited organization.

Community Care Inc 563.659.4100
Fax 563.659.1120
Web ....www.communitycareinc.net
E-mail ....benw@communitycareinc.net
   108 Industrial St, De Witt, IA 52742-2063
   William Bonnes, Director

Covenant Clinic 319.272.8922
Fax 319.272.8929
Web ....www.covhealth.com
   2750 Saint Francis Dr, Waterloo, IA 50702
   Valentina Doumanian, Md, Psychiatrist

Crossroads Mental Health Ctr 641.782.8457
Fax 641.782.7048
Web ....www.iowatelecom.net
E-mail ....pprantner@iowatelecom.net
   1003 Cottonwood Rd, Creston, IA 50801-1012
   Pete Prantner, Executive Director

Ctr Associates 641.752.1585
Fax 641.752.9665
Web ....www.centerassoc.com
E-mail ....info@centerassoc.com
   9 N 4th Ave, Marshalltown, IA 50158-1836
   Mike Bergman, Administrator

Family Resources, Inc. 563.326.6431
Fax 563.326.2013
Web ....www.famres.org
   2800 Eastern Avenue, Davenport, IA 52803-2012
   COA accredited organization.

Four Oaks Treatment 641.423.3222
Fax 641.423.1740
Web ....http://www.fouroaks.org
E-mail ....agruenewald@fouroaks.org
   5400 Kirkwood Blvd SW, Cedar Rapids, IA 52404-5298
   Anne Gruenwald, Executive Director

Four Oaks, Inc 319.364.0259
Fax 866.290.5565
Web ....www.fouroaks.org
E-mail ....jernst@fouroaks.org
   5400 Kirkwood Blvd SW, Cedar Rapids, IA 52404-5298
   Jim Ernst, CEO

Hillcrest Family Services 563.583.7357
Web ....www.hillcrest-fs.org
E-mail ....francie.tuescher@hillcrest-fs.org
   2005 Asbury Road, Dubuque, IA 52001
   Ms. Francie Tuescher, Accreditation Manager
   Joint Commission accredited organization.

Horizon Family Svc Agency 319.398.3943
Fax 319.398.3577
Web ....www.horizonfamily.org
E-mail ....lhoward@familyservicesiowa.org
   819 5th St SE, Cedar Rapids, IA 52401-2128
   Bill Gardam, Executive Director

Jackson Recovery Centers, Inc. 712.234.2300
Fax 712.234.2398
Web ....www.jacksonrecovery.com
   800 5th St, Suite 200, Sioux City, IA 51101
   Janelle Tomoson, Program Director
   CARF accredited programs available.

Lutheran Svcs In Iowa Bremwood Campus 319.352.2630
Fax 319.352.0773
Web ....www.lsiowa.org
E-mail ....doug.johnson@lsiowa.org
   106 16th St SW, Waverly, IA 50677-2822
   Doug Johnson, President/CEO

Mental Health Institute 319.334.2583
E-mail ....bdave@dhs.state.ia.us
   2277 Iowa Avenue, Independence, IA 50644
   Dr. Bhasker Dave, Accreditation Manager
   Joint Commission accredited organization.

Mental Health Institute 319.334.2583
Fax 319.334.5252
Web ....www.dhs.state.ia.us
E-mail ....cpaulson@dhs.state.ia.us
   2277 Iowa Ave, Independence, IA 50644-9215
   Carlette Paulson, Nurse Administrator

Mercy Medical Center 515.247.3121
Web ....www.mercydesmoines.org
E-mail ....pmcdermott@mercydesmoines.org
   1111 6th Avenue, Des Moines, IA 50314
   Ms. Pat McDermott, Accreditation Manager
   Joint Commission accredited organization.

Orchard Place 515.285.6781
Web ....orchardplace.org
E-mail ....tguagenti@orchardplace.org
   925 Porter Avenue, Des Moines, IA 50315
   Ms. Tonnie Guagenti, Accreditation Manager
   Joint Commission accredited organization.

Orchard Place 515.285.6781
Fax 515.287.9695
Web ....www.orchardplace.org
E-mail ....chejtmanek@orchardplace.org
   925 Porter Ave, Des Moines, IA 50315-7267
   Carolyn Hejtmanek, Resident Campus Director

Rescare/Touchstone 319.754.4618
Fax 319.754.4193
Web ....www.iowarescare.com
   407 N 4th St, Burlington, IA 52601-5229
   Erika Lybarger, Executive Director

St. Luke's Methodist Hospital 319.369.7211
Web ....www.stlukescr.org
E-mail ....hagenme@crstlukes.com
   1026 A Avenue Northeast, Cedar Rapids, IA 52402
   Ms. Mary Hagen, Accreditation Manager
   Joint Commission accredited organization.

Tanager Place 319.365.9164
Fax 319.365.6411
Web ....www.tanagerplace.org
   2309 C Street SW, Cedar Rapids, IA 52404
   COA accredited organization.

Tanager Place 319.365.9164
Fax 319.365.6411
Web ....www.tanagerplace.org
E-mail ....seddy@dhs.state.ia.us
   2309 C St SW, Cedar Rapids, IA 52404-3707
   Sharon Eddy, Coordinator

The University of Iowa Hospitals and Clinics 319.384.5897
Web ....www.uihealthcare.com
E-mail ....kiley-bybee@uiowa.edu
   200 Hawkins Drive, Iowa City, IA 52242
   Mrs. Kiley Bybee-Francque, Accreditation Manager
   Joint Commission accredited organization.

Woodward Academy 515.438.3481
Web ....www.wwacademy.com
E-mail ....michelle_fenelon@yahoo.com
   1251 334th St., Woodward, IA 50276
   Ms. Michelle Fenelon, Accreditation Manager
   Joint Commission accredited organization.

Youth & Family Resource Services 712.867.4724
Fax 712.867.4505
Web ....www.yfrs.org
E-mail ....nikki.lawson@yfrs.org
   4502 230th St, Wallingford, IA 51365
   Nikki Lawson, SA Program Director
   CARF accredited programs available.

Youth & Shelter Services, Inc.............**515.233.3141**
Fax...515.233.2440
Web...www.yss.org
  420 Kellogg Avenue, Ames, IA 50010
Geoff Taylor Smith, Assistant Director
CARF accredited programs available.

Youth Shelter Care Of North Central Iowa, Inc...**515.955.4222**
Fax...515.955.6828
Web......................................www.yscncia.org
E-mail.............................ysc@frontiernet.net
  301 Avenue M W, Fort Dodge, IA 50501-5623
Laurence Mcluckie, Executive Director

CHILDREN'S HOSPITAL

Alegent Health Community Memorial Hosp...**712.642.2784**
  631 North Eighth St, Missouri Valley, IA 51555
Robert Valentine, Executive Director

Alegent Health Mercy Hospital..............**712.328.5000**
  800 Mercy Dr, Council Bluffs, IA 51503
Marie Knedler, Director

Allen Memorial Hospital.....................**319.235.3941**
  1825 Logan Ave, Waterloo, IA 50703
John Knox, President/CEO

Baum Harmon Mercy Hospital..............**712.957.2300**
  255 North Welch Ave, Primghar, IA 51245
Robert Monical, Administrator

Belmond Medical Center.....................**641.444.3223**
  403 First Street SE, Belmond, IA 50421
Lori Huntley, Administrative Assistant

Central Community Hospital................**563.245.7000**
  901 Davidson Street NW, Elkader, IA 52043
Fran Zichal, Chief Executive Officer

Cherokee Regional Medical Center..........**712.225.5101**
  300 Sioux Valley Dr, Cherokee, IA 51012
John Compstock, Chief Executive Officer

Community Hospital.........................**319.293.3171**
  304 Franklin St, Keosauqua, IA 52565
Linda Goldstein, Office Manager

Community Hospital.........................**641.872.2260**
  417 South East St, Corydon, IA 50060

Floyd Valley Hospital Avera Health..........**712.546.7871**
  714 Lincoln St NE, Le Mars, IA 51031
Michael Donlin, Chief Executive Officer

Franklin General Hospital....................**641.456.5000**
  1720 Central Avenue East, Hampton, IA 50441
Kim Price, Chief Executive Officer

Genesis Medical Center Davenport..........**563.421.1000**
  1227 East Rusholme St, Davenport, IA 52803
Julie Manas, Chief Executive Officer

Great River Medical Center..................**319.768.1000**
  1221 South Gear Ave, West Burlington, IA 52655
Mark Richardson, President

Grinnell Regional Medical Center............**641.236.7511**
  210 Fourth Ave, Grinnell, IA 50112
Todd Linden, President

Guttenberg Municipal Hospital.............**563.252.1121**
  200 Main St, Guttenberg, IA 52052
Kim Gau, Chief Executive Officer

Hawarden Community Hospital.............**712.551.3100**
  1111 11th St, Hawarden, IA 51023
Dawn Anderson, Director

Healthcare System.........................**515.462.2373**
  300 Hutchings St, Winterset, IA 50273

Hegg Memorial Health Center Avera Hlth......**712.476.8000**
  1202 21st Ave, Rock Valley, IA 51247
Glenn Zevenbergen, Chief Executive Officer

Hospital.....................................**641.446.4871**
  1405 NW Church St, Leon, IA 50144
Lynn Milnes, Chief Executive Officer

Hospital.....................................**641.342.2184**
  800 South Fillmore St, Osceola, IA 50213

Hospital.....................................**515.465.3547**
E-mail....................INFO@DALLASCOHOSPITAL.ORG
  610 10th St, Perry, IA 50220
Julie Smith, Purchasing Manager

Iowa Methodist Medical Center.............**515.241.6212**
E-mail..jm@ihs.org
  1200 Pleasant St, Des Moines, IA 50309
Jennifer Perry, Director Of Communications

Jennie Edmundson Hospital.................**712.396.6000**
  933 East Pierce St, Council Bluffs, IA 51503
Becky Henkel, Nursing Director

Jones Regional Medical Center..............**319.462.6131**
  1795 Highway 64 East, Anamosa, IA 52205
Kelly Driscoll, Nursing Officer

Keokuk Area Hospital.......................**319.524.7150**
  1600 Morgan St, Keokuk, IA 52632
Allen Vastrow, Chief Executive Officer

Kossuth Regional Health Center.............**515.295.2451**
E-mail...........................krac@murpheyhealth.com
  1515 S Phillips St, Algona, IA 50511
Scott Curtis, Administration

Manning Regional Healthcare Center........**712.655.2072**
  410 Main St, Manning, IA 51455

Marshalltown Medical & Surgical Center......**641.754.5151**
  3 South Fourth Ave, Marshalltown, IA 50158
Bryan Sid, Chief Executive Officer

Mary Greeley Medical Center................**515.239.2011**
  1111 Duff Ave, Ames, IA 50010
Brian Dieter, Chief Executive Officer

Memorial Hospital..........................**641.743.2123**
  609 SE Kent St, Greenfield, IA 50849
Myrna Erb-Gundeo, Chief Executive Officer

Memorial Hospital..........................**515.332.4200**
  1000 North 15th St, Humboldt, IA 50548
Rob Corerick, Chief Executive Officer

Memorial Hospital..........................**712.265.2500**
  100 Medical Pkwy, Denison, IA 51442
Mark Reinhart, Chief Executive Officer

Mercy Iowa City............................**319.339.0300**
E-mail..................................www.mercyiowacity.org
  500 East Market St, Iowa City, IA 52245
Ronald Reed, President/CEO

Mercy Medical Center.......................**319.398.6011**
  701 Tenth Street SE, Cedar Rapids, IA 52403
Timothy Charles, Chief Executive Officer

Mercy Medical Center.......................**515.247.3121**
  1111 6th Ave, Des Moines, IA 50314
Dave Vellinga, Chief Executive Officer

Mercy Medical Center Clinton...............**563.244.5555**
  1410 N Fourth St, Clinton, IA 52732
Sean Williams, Chief Executive Officer

Mercy Medical Center North Iowa..........**641.428.7000**
  1000 Fourth Street SW, Mason City, IA 50401
James Fitzpatrick, Chief Executive Officer

Mercy Medical Center Sioux City............**712.279.2010**
  801 Fifth St, Sioux City, IA 51101
Robert Peebles, Chief Executive Officer

Orange City Area Hospital..................**712.737.4984**
  1000 Lincoln Circle SE, Orange City, IA 51041

Osceola Community Hospital...............**712.754.2574**
  Ninth Avenue North, Sibley, IA 51249
Janet Dykstra, Chief Executive Officer

Ottumwa Regional Health Center...........**641.684.2300**
  1001 Pennsylvania Ave, Ottumwa, IA 52501
Phil Dionne, Chief Executive Officer

Pocahontas Community Hospital...........**712.335.3501**
  606 NW Seventh, Pocahontas, IA 50574
James Rottman, Chief Executive Officer

Regional Medical Center....................**563.927.3232**
  709 West Main St, Manchester, IA 52057
Lon Dutikofer, President

Sanford Merrill Medical Center.............**712.472.2591**
  801 South Greene St, Rock Rapids, IA 51246

Sioux Center Community Hospital...........**712.722.1271**
  605 S Main Ave, Sioux Center, IA 51250

St Anthony Regional Hospital...............**712.792.3581**
  311 South Clark St, Carroll, IA 51401
Gary Riedman, President

St Lukes Hospital...........................**319.369.7211**
Web.......................................www.stlukescr.org
  1026 A Avenue NE, Cedar Rapids, IA 52402
Ted Townsend, Chief Executive Officer

St Lukes Regional Medical Center...........**712.279.3500**
  2720 Stone Park Blvd, Sioux City, IA 51104
Priscella Stokes, Nursing Director

Trinity Muscatine..........................**563.264.9100**
E-mail............................hthomas@trinitymuscatine.com
  1518 Mulberry Ave, Muscatine, IA 52761
Holly Thomas, Public Relation Coordinator

Trinity Regional Medical Center.............**515.573.3101**
  802 Kenyon Rd, Fort Dodge, IA 50501
Sue Thompson, Chief Executive Officer

Univ of Iowa Hospitals and Clinics...........**319.356.1616**
  200 Hawkins Dr, Iowa City, IA 52242

Van-Dist Medical Center....................**515.832.9400**
  2350 Hospital Dr, Webster City, IA 50595
Thomas Schneider, Director

COUNSELING SERVICES

Catholic Charities..........................**563.588.0558**
Fax...563.557.3140
Web.....................................www.charitiesdbq.com
E-mail.........................dbqcccd@arch.pvt.k12.ia.us
  1229 Mount Loretta Ave, Dubuque, IA 52003-7826
Tracy Morrison, Director

Children's & Family Svcs....................**515.573.2193**
Fax...515.573.2798
E-mail.......................................patc@cfiowa.org
  111 Ave. West, Fort Dodge, IA 50501
Pat Cirks, Regional Supervisor

Families, Inc................................**319.643.2532**
Fax...319.643.5708
Web..www.lcom.net
E-mail...........................mtownsend@familiesinc.net
  101 W Main St, West Branch, IA 52358-9636
Mary Kay Townsend, Executive Director

Forest Ridge Youth Svcs/ Lake Area Foster Parents.......................................**712.362.7026**
Fax...712.362.7254
E-mail............................jen.sievert@yfrs.org
  2047 395th Ave, Estherville, IA 51334
Jen Sievert, Director

Keys To Living..............................**319.377.2161**
Fax...319.377.2094
Web.....................................www.keystoliving.org
E-mail.............................keystoliving@juno.com
  5250 N Park Pl NE Ste 210, Cedar Rapids, IA 52402-6221
Tim Hunter, Executive Director

New Horizon Adoption Agency, Inc..........641.421.7332
Fax..507.526.3548
Web.............................www.nhadoptionagency.com
E-mail.......................................nhaa@bevcomm.net
　103 E State St Ste 623, Mason City, IA 50401-3327
Marlys G. Ubben, Executive Director

Orchard Place Child Guidance Ctr...........515.244.2267
Fax..515.244.1922
Web...............................www.orchardplace.org
E-mail..........................dstout@orchardplace.org
　808 5th Ave, Des Moines, IA 50309-1315
Dave Stout, Lisw, Executive Director

CRISIS & SHELTER CARE

Assault Care Ctr Extending Shltr-Support......515.292.0500
Fax..515.292.0505
　PO Box 1429, Ames, IA 50014-1429
Shelly Mcqueeney, Director

Catholic Charities-Phoenix Hse-Dom
VInce...712.256.2059
Fax..712.256.1186
E-mail.........................dmckee@dmdiocese.org
　300 W Broadway, Ste 223, Council Bluffs,
　IA 51503-9028
Ms Diane Mckee, Program Coordinator

Children And Families Of Iowa..............515.288.1981
Fax..515.288.9109
Web................................www.cfiowa.org
E-mail................................gloriag@cfiowa.org
　1111 University Ave, Des Moines, IA 50314-2363
Gloria Gray, Executive Director

Council Against Dom Abuse-Sexual
Assault...712.225.5003
Fax..712.225.4861
　PO Box 963, Cherokee, IA 51012-0963
Becky C, Director

Crisis Intervention Advocacy-Dom VInce.......515.993.4095
Fax..515.993.2131
E-mail................................johna@ciac91.org
　PO Box 40, Adel, IA 50003
Johna Sullivan, Director

Crisis Intervention Svc....................515.295.8646
Fax..515.295.6959
E-mail................................mary@cishelts.org
　1919 E Maple St, Algona, IA 50511
Mary Ingham, Director

Crisis Intervention Svc....................641.424.9071
Fax..641.424.8915
E-mail................................cis@netconx.net
　206 3rd St NE, Mason City, IA 50401
Ms Mary Ingham, Executive Director

Crisis Intervention Svcs-Domestic
Violence..641.673.0336
Fax..641.676.1997
E-mail................................nancyr@cismc.org
　500 High Ave W, Oskaloosa, IA 52577
Nancy Robertson, Executive Director

Denison Job Corps Ctr.....................712.263.4192
Fax..712.263.6910
　10 Opportunity Dr, Denison, IA 51442
Kevin Fineran, Center Director

Domestic Violence Intervention Program......319.351.1042
Fax..319.466.4624
E-mail................................dvip@dvipiowa.org
　PO Box 3170, Iowa City, IA 52244-3170
Ms Kristie Doser, Director

Domestic/Sexual Assault Outreach Ctr........515.955.2273
Fax..515.955.1958
Web................................www.dsaoc.com
E-mail................................dsaoc@dsaoc.com
　PO Box 773, Fort Dodge, IA 50501-0773
Connie Harris, Director

Family Crisis Ctr-NW Iowa-Domestic
Violence..712.722.4404
Fax..712.722.4407
E-mail................................fccaaker@mtcnet.net
　PO Box 295, Sioux Center, IA 51250-0295
Shari Kastein, Director

Family Resources..........................563.322.1200
Fax..563.322.6104
Web................................www.famres.org
E-mail................................twilson@famres.org
　805 W 35th St, Ste 200, Davenport, IA 52806
Tom Wilson, President

Family Violence Ctr.......................515.243.6147
Fax..515.243.3404
Web................................www.cfiowa.org
E-mail................................sandras@cfiowa.org
　1111 University Avenue, Des Moines, IA 50314
Ms Sandra Smith, Director

Fouroaks Youth Shelter....................319.337.4523
Fax..866.293.6326
Web................................www.fouroaks.org
E-mail................................mchval@fouroaks.org
　1916 Waterfront Dr, Iowa City, IA 52240
Mary Chval, Division Director

Girls And Boys Town Of Iowa................712.323.4011
Fax..712.323.4929
Web................www.girlsandboystown.org/iowa
　1851 madison ave Ste 100, Council Bluffs, IA 51503
Brian Fox, Director Of Family Services

Rural Iowa Crisis Ctr-Dom Violence..........641.782.2706
Fax..641.782.2640
E-mail................................ricc2@iowatelecom.net
　PO Box 384, Creston, IA 50801-0384
Ms Vickie Hodge, Director

Sequel Youth Svcs--Clarinda Academy........712.542.3103
Fax..712.542.2907
Web................................www.clarindaacademy.org
　1820 N 16th St, Clarinda, IA 51632
Mike Mcfarland, Director

The Crittenton Ctr........................712.255.4321
Fax..712.252.4743
Web................................www.crittentoncenter.org
E-mail................................kbruyere@crittentoncenter.org
　303 W 24th St, Sioux City, IA 51104-4025
Marian Burnett, Program Director

Tri-State Coalition Against Dom Violence......319.524.8520
Fax..319.524.0601
E-mail................................tsc@iowatelecom.net
　801 Main St Ste 1B, Keokuk, IA 52632
Sue Prochazka, Director

United Action For Youth....................319.338.9279
Fax..319.337.7999
E-mail................jimswaim@unitedactionforyouth.org
　410 Iowa Ave, Iowa City, IA 52240
Jim Swaim, Director

Waubonsie Mental Health Ctr-Domestic
Violence..712.542.2388
Fax..712.542.2984
E-mail................................Maryanne@Waubonsiemhc.Com
　1800 N 16th St Ste 1, Clarinda, IA 51632
Mary Anne Gibson, Director

Waypoint Svcs-Domestic Violence............319.365.1458
Fax..319.365.2263
E-mail................................waypoint@waypointservices.org
　318 5th St SE, Cedar Rapids, IA 52401
Liz Hoskins, Director

Whittenmyer Youth Ctr.....................563.326.6431
Fax..563.326.2013
Web................................www.samres.org
E-mail................................twilson@famres.org
　2800 Eastern Ave, Davenport, IA 52803-2012
Tom Wilson, Executive Director

Youth Emergency Svcs......................515.243.7825
Fax..515.282.6162
Web................................www.yessiowa.org
E-mail................................fritzm@yessiowa.org
　918 SE 11th St, Des Moines, IA 50309-5324
Jane Katvureck, Operating Business Director

YWCA Womens Resource Ctr-Dom VInce.......319.752.0606
Fax..319.752.0606
Web................................www.ywca.org
　616 N 8th St, Burlington, IA 52601-5037
Ruby McGraw, Director

EDUCATION

Lutheran Svcs.............................712.255.2505
Fax..712.258.0518
Web................................www.lsiowa.org
E-mail................................joy.reuss@lsiowa.org
　2039 S saint argon, Sioux City, IA 51106
Joy Reuss, Director

The Family & Children's Council.............319.234.7600
Fax..319.236.3825
Web................................www.fccouncil.net
E-mail................................jtitzen@fccouncil.net
　500 E 4th St Ste 414, Waterloo, IA 50703
Julie Titzen, Executive Director

Upper Des Moines Opportunities, Inc.........712.859.3885
Fax..712.859.3892
Web................................www.udmo.com
E-mail................................rludwig@udmo.com
　101 Robbins St, Graettinger, IA 51342
Ron Ludwig, Executive Director

FOSTER CARE AGENCIES

Abby's One True Gift Adoptions.............515.987.0565
E-mail................................info@onetruegift.com
　755 Frontier Ave, Ste 102, Waukee, IA 50263

About A Child Adoptions (AAC).............515.221.2231
E-mail................................adopt@aboutachild.org
　729 22nd St, West Des Moines, IA 50265
Carla Tripp, Social Services Director

Allison Area Foster Parent Support Group.....319.352.3600
E-mail................................magnallifapa@msn.com
　2004 11th St SE, Waverly, IA 50677

American Home Finding Association
AHFA...641.682.3449
Fax..641.382.5049
E-mail................................ahfainc@ahfa.org
　217 E 5th St, Ottumwa, IA 52501
Tom Lazio, Director

Avalon Center Adoption Agency.............641.422.0070
Fax..641.422.0060
E-mail................................leah@avaloncenter.us
　22 N Georgia, Ste 102, Mason City, IA 50401
Leah Weber, Executive Director

Bethany Christian Services of NW Iowa.......712.737.4831
Fax..712.737.3238
E-mail................................bcsorangecity@bethany.org
　123 SE Albany Ave, Orange City, IA 51041

Charlton Valley Foster Parents.............515.642.3334
　RR 8, PO Box 78, Bloomfield, IA 52537

First Resources Corporation (FRC)..........641.673.1421
E-mail................................julieseemann@hotmail.com
　1907 17th Ave E, Oskaloosa, IA 52577

Forest Ridge Youth and Family Resources
Services..712.362.5231
　200 6 street, gruver, IA 51334
Chad Jacobson, Director

Iowa City Area Adoptive Families.............319.351.9079
　2840 Brookside, Iowa City, IA 52245

Iowa Foster & Adopt Parents Assoc Inc........800.277.8145
　6864 NE 14th St Ste 5, Ankeny, IA 50021
Marty Laughlin

Iowa KidsNet 800.243.0756
E-mail ....customerservice@iowakidsnet.com
   3125 Cottage Grove, Des Moines, IA 50311
   Joni Boyer, Supervisor

JAMS 641.793.2361
   8124 Main st, Reasnor, IA 50323

Lutheran Services in Iowa (LSI) 712.263.9341
Fax 712.263.6061
E-mail ....susan.salmon@lsiowa.org
   111 W 15th St, Davenport, IA 52803
   Susan Salmon, Office Director

Lutheran Services in Iowa (LSI) 866.409.2351
E-mail ....lsi@lsiiowa.org
   205 S 7th St, Denison, IA 51442
   Susan Salmon, Director

N Central Iowa Foster & Adoptive Parent 641.923.2618
   2315 Rake Ave, Garner, IA 50438

Ours Through Adoption 563.508.3049
E-mail ....rjhess@netexpress.net
   2618 Arlington Ave, Davenport, IA 52803
   Jean Hess, Advocate

Special Needs Adoption Support Group 563.322.7419
E-mail ....melinda.pollmeier@lsiowa.org
   111 W 15th St, Davenport, IA 52803
   Melinda Pollmeier, Site Manager

TLC-Foster & Adoptive Parent Assoc 641.784.6774
   208 S Walnut, Lamoni, IA 50140

West Central Iowa Support Group for 712.792.2025
Fax 713.792.3386
   420 W 19th St, Carroll, IA 51401
   Kathrine Sanderhaiven, Director

PEDIATRIC HOME CARE

Public Health Nursing 641.456.5820
Fax 641.456.5834
E-mail ....wiardac@mercyhealth.com
   1600 Central Ave E, Hampton, IA 50441-1858
   Christa Wiarda, Administrator

SOCIAL SERVICES

Aid To Women 319.364.8967
Fax 319.247.5784
E-mail ....mail@aidtowomen.com
   701 Center Point Rd NE, Cedar Rapids,
   IA 52402-4643
   Katie Sandquist, Director

Brain Injury Association of Iowa 800.444.6443
Fax 800.381.0812
Web ....www.biaia.org
E-mail ....info@biaia.org
   7025 Hickman Road, Suite 7, Urbandale, IA 50322
   Heidi Smith, Director of Programs and Services

Catholic Council for Social Concern, Inc. aka Catholic Charities 515.244.3761
Fax 515.237.5070
Web ....www.catholiccharitiesdm.org
   601 Grand Avenue, Des Moines, IA 50309-2501
   COA accredited organization.

Child Care Resource And Referral Of Northeast Iowa 319.233.0804
Fax 319.274.8841
Web ....www.episervice.org
E-mail ....childcare@episervice.org
   3675 University Ave, Waterloo, IA 50701-5621
   Marilyn Pierce, Director

Child Care Resource And Referral Of Northwest Iowa 712.786.2001
Fax 712.786.3250
   418 S Marion St, Remsen, IA 51050
   Melissa Juhl, Director

Child Care Resource And Referral Of Southwest Iowa 712.755.7381
Fax 712.755.7827
Web ....www.swiowachildcare.org
E-mail ....dmorrison@swiowachildcare.org
   701 10th St, Harlan, IA 51537
   Debra Morrison, Director

Children & Families of Iowa 515.288.1981
Fax 515.288.9109
Web ....www.cfiowa.org
   1111 University Avenue, Des Moines, IA 50314
   COA accredited organization.

Christian Home Association - Children's Square USA 712.322.3700
Fax 712.325.0913
Web ....www.childrenssquare.org
   P.O. Box 8-C, Council Bluffs, IA 51502-3008
   COA accredited organization.

Community Action Agency Of Siouxland 712.274.1610
Fax 712.274.0368
Web ....www.caasiouxland.org
E-mail ....jlogan@caasiouxland.org
   2700 Leech Ave, Sioux City, IA 51106-1129
   Jean Logan, Executive Director

Community Child Care Resource And Referral 563.324.1302
Fax 563.324.7736
Web ....www.iowatrain.org
E-mail ....pchristansen@iacommunityaction.org
   500 E 59th St, Davenport, IA 52807-2623
   Paty Christansen, Director

Families First 319.433.0395
Fax 319.433.3870
Web ....www.families-first.net
E-mail ....lkishmann@families-first.net
   111 Plaza Cir, Waterloo, IA 50701-4651
   Laone Kishmann, Director
   COA accredited organization.

Family Directions Of Iowa 515.255.9490
Fax 515.279.5163
Web ....www.familydirectionsiowa.org
E-mail ....info@familydirectionsiowa.org
   1211 Vine St Ste 1140, West Des Moines, IA 50265
   Sue Renfrow, Director

Foundation 2 ....319.362.1170
Fax 319.297.7406
Web www.foundation2.org
   1714 Johnson Ave NW, Cedar Rapids, IA 52405
   Barb Gay, Director

Hillcrest Family Svcs 319.362.3149
Fax 319.362.8923
Web ....www.hillcrest-fs.org
E-mail ....manderson@hillcrest-fs.org
   317 7th Ave SE Ste 202 C, Cedar Rapids, IA 52401
   Melissa Anderson, Supervisor, Adoptions Coordinator

Horizons, A Family Service Alliance 319.398.3943
Fax 319.398.3577
Web ....www.horizonsfamily.org
   P.O. Box 667, Cedar Rapids, IA 52406
   COA accredited organization.

Iowa Compass 319.353.8777
Fax 319.384.5139
Web ....www.iowacompass.org
E-mail ....jane-gay@uiowa.edu
   100 Hawkins Dr, S295 Cdd, Iowa City,
   IA 52242-1016
   Jane Gay, Director

Iowa Connects 515.966.2565
Fax 515.462.2024
Web ....www.hometown.aol.com/iaconnects/
E-mail ....iaconnects@aol.com
   149 35th Pl, Runnells, IA 50237-7505
   Debbie Hoyt, Director

Lutheran Services in Iowa 515.271.7358
Fax 515.271.7454
Web ....www.lsiowa.org
   3125 Cottage Grove Avenue, Des Moines, IA 50311
   COA accredited organization.

Lutheran Svcs 515.232.7262
Fax 515.232.7416
Web ....www.lsiowa.org
E-mail ....belinda.meis@lsiowa.org
   1323 Northwestern Ave, Ames, IA 50010
   Belinda Meis, Site Manager

Lutheran Svcs 319.233.3579
Fax 319.233.6569
Web ....www.lsiowa.org
   925 E 4th St, Waterloo, IA 50703
   Nancy Beenblosson, Coordinator

Lutheran Svcs 563.263.5170
Fax 563.288.6503
Web ....www.lsiowa.org
E-mail ....linda.cooney@lsiowa.org
   315 Iowa Ave, Ste C, Muscatine, IA 52761
   Doug Johnson, Executive Director

Lutheran Svcs In Iowa 515.274.4946
Fax 515.271.7450
Web ....www.lsiowa.org
E-mail ....douglas.johnson@lsiowa.org
   3125 Cottage Grove Ave, Des Moines,
   IA 50311-3809
   Douglas Johnson, President/ CEO

Matura Action Corp 641.782.8431
Fax 641.782.6287
Web ....www.swiowachildcare.org
E-mail ....jerrysmith@maturaaction.org
   203 W Adams St, Creston, IA 50801
   Jerry Smith, Director

Mid Iowa Community Action, Inc 641.752.7162
Fax 641.752.9724
Web ....www.micaonline.org
   1001 S 18th Ave, Marshalltown, IA 50158-3662
   Arlene Mcatee, Executive Director

Mid-Iowa Family Therapy Clinic, Inc. and Institute for Therapy & Psychological Solutions, LLC 515.465.5739
Fax 515.465.5744
Web ....www.miftc.com
   P.O. Box 416, Perry, IA 50220-0416
   COA accredited organization.

Opportunities Unlimited 712.277.8295
Fax 712.277.8602
Web ....www.opportunitiesunlimited.com
   3439 Glen Oaks Boulevard, Sioux City, IA 51104
   George Wurtzel, Director
   CARF accredited programs available.

Project Concern 563.588.3980
Fax 563.588.3982
Web ....www.pcrta.org
E-mail ....nlewis@pcrta.org
   1789 Elm St Ste B, Dubuque, IA 52001-2256
   Nancy Lewis, Executive Director

Ragtime Industries 641.932.7813
Fax 641.932.7814
   116 North Second Street, Albia, IA 52531
   CARF accredited programs available.

Right To Life 563.556.5960
Fax 563.556.5606
E-mail ....dcrtl@dcrtl.org
   2205 Carter Rd, Dubuque, IA 52001
   Steven Brody, Executive Director

U Of Iowa National Resource Ctr For Fcp 319.335.4965
Fax 319.335.4964
Web ....www.uiowa.edu/~nrcfcp
E-mail ....miriam-landsman@uiowa.edu
   100 MTP4, Room 162, Iowa City, IA 52242-5000
   Miriam Landsman, Executive Director

United Way.................................319.398.5372
Fax..319.398.5381
Web...www.uweci.org
E-mail...lbuntz@uweci.org
317 7th Ave, Cedar Rapids, IA 52401-2479
Lois Buntz, CEO

United Way 211............................515.243.7681
Fax..515.244.8012
E-mail...................schoht@desmoines-redcross.org
2116 Grand Ave, Des Moines, IA 50312
Tim Schoh, Director

White's Iowa Institute dba Quakerdale.......641.497.5294
Fax..641.497.5220
Web...www.quakerdale.org
P.O. Box 8, New Providence, IA 50206
COA accredited organization.

Young House Family Services, Inc............319.752.4000
Fax..319.752.6933
Web...www.younghouse.org
PO Box 845, Burlington, IA 52601
COA accredited organization.

Youth & Shelter Services, Inc................515.233.3141
Fax..515.233.2440
Web...www.yss.org
420 Kellogg Avenue, Ames, IA 50010
CARF accredited programs available.

Youth Emergency Services & Shelter of
Iowa.......................................515.243.7825
Fax..515.282.6162
Web...www.yessiowa.org
918 SE 11th Street, Des Moines, IA 50309
COA accredited organization.

Youth Svcs...............................319.892.5720
Fax..319.892.5719
Web...www.co.linn.ia.us
520 11th St NW, Cedar Rapids, IA 52405-3811
Jeff Lindeman, Director

SPECIAL NEEDS

ASK Resource Center.......................800.450.8667
E-mail...........................f2finfo@askresource.org
5665 Greendale Rd, Ste D, Johnston, IA 50131
Karen Thompson, Executive Director

Autism Society of Iowa.....................515.327.9075
E-mail.............................autism50ia@aol.com
4549 Waterford Dr, West Des Moines, IA 50265
Kris Brofhaman, Owner

Covenant Medical Center Rehabilitation
Program....................................319.272.8000
Fax..319.272.7919
Web...www.covhealth.com
3421 West Ninth Street, Waterloo, IA 50702
CARF accredited programs available.

Easter Seals Iowa..........................515.289.1933
E-mail...........................info@eastersealsia.org
401 NE 66th Ave, Des Moines, IA 50333
Renee Bell, Coordinator

Epilepsy Foundation........................515.238.7660
E-mail...................................efiowa@efncil.com
1111 9th St Ste 275, Des Moines, IA 50314
Jessica Peters, Service-corrdinator

Fed of Families Children's Mental Health.......888.400.6302
E-mail...................................lori@iffcmh.org
106 S Booth, Anamosa, IA 52205

Genesis Medical Center - Davenport/Genesis Regional
Rehabilitation Program.....................563.421.1421
Fax..563.421.1430
Web...www.genesishealth.com
E-mail.............................chin@genesishealth.com
1401 W Central Park, Davenport, IA 52804
Dr. Conway Chin, Medical Director
CARF accredited programs available.

Great River Medical Center, Rehabilitation
Program....................................319.768.4200
Fax..319.768.4215
Web...www.greatrivermedical.org
1221 South Gear Avenue, West Burlington, IA 52655
CARF accredited programs available.

Iowa Compass: Info & Referral.............800.779.2001
E-mail...........................iowa-compass@uiowa.edu
100 Hawkins Dr # 295, Iowa City, IA 52242
Jennifer Britton, Director Of Operations

Iowa PTA...................................800.475.4782
E-mail.................................ia_office@pta.org
5619 NW 86th St Ste 600, Johnston, IA 50131

LearningRx Learning Center.................515.224.4819
E-mail.........................wsdm.ia@learningrx.net
4949 Westown Pkwy Ste 160, West Desmoines,
IA 50263
David Nadler, Director

Mercy Medical Center-Dubuque.............563.589.8000
Fax..563.589.8073
Web...www.mercydubuque.com
250 Mercy Dr, Dubuque, IA 52001
Russell Knight, President and CEO
CARF accredited programs available.

NAMI Iowa..................................800.417.0417
E-mail...............................namiiowa@mchsi.com
5911 Meredith Dr Ste E, Urbandale, IA 50322
Margaret Stout, Executive Director

On With Life, Inc..........................515.965.1339
Fax..515.965.1186
Web...www.onwithlife.org
715 Southwest Ankeny Road, Ankeny, IA 50023-9798
CARF accredited programs available.

Parent Educator Connection Rsrce Ctr for.....515.271.3936
Fax..515.271.4185
E-mail.........................deb.samson@drake.edu
Drake University, 2507 University, Des Moines,
IA 50311

Sioux Land Epilepsy Support Group Inc.......712.281.1741
E-mail...............................slf197@cableone.net
4230 Hickory Ln, Ste 414, Sioux City, IA 51106
Steven Fox, President

Speech-Language-Hearing Association.......515.282.8192
525 SW 5th St Ste A, Des Moines, IA 50309
Dick Goodson, Chief Executive Officer

Spina Bifida Association of Iowa.............515.964.8810
E-mail...........................spinabifidaiowa@yahoo.com
PO Box 1456, Des Moines, IA 50305

St. Luke's Hospital Inpatient Rehabilitation
Unit.......................................319.369.7261
Fax..319.368.5713
Web...www.stlukescr.org
1026 A Avenue NE, Cedar Rapids, IA 52402
Jo Linn, Director
CARF accredited programs available.

The Arc of Cedar Valley.....................319.232.0437
E-mail................................arccv@episervice.org
760 Ansborough Ave, Waterloo, IA 50701
Kim Jensen, Director

The Arc of Iowa.............................800.362.2927
E-mail...............................cwesthoff@arceci.org
3821 71st St Ste A, Urbandale, IA 50322

Tutor/Caregiver For Children With Autism.....515.865.2928
E-mail...........................anniemnovak@yahoo.com
7533 NE 19th Ln, Ankeny, IA 50021-9505
Annie Novak, Autism Interventionist

Younker Rehabilitation at Iowa Health Des Moines c/o Iowa
Methodist Medical Center...................515.241.6435
Fax..515.241.8688
Web...www.iowahealth.org
1200 Pleasant Street, Des Moines, IA 50309-1453
CARF accredited programs available.

SUBSTANCE ABUSE TREATMENT

Center for Alcohol and Drug Services, Inc., IA,
Davenport..................................563.322.2667
Fax..563.322.3671
Web...www.cads-ia.com
E-mail...............................jcowley@cads-ia.com
1523 South Fairmount Street, Davenport, IA 52802
Joseph Cowley, Executive Director
CARF accredited programs available.

Francis Lauer Youth Svcs...................641.423.7362
Fax..641.423.6102
Web...www.francislauer.com
E-mail..............................flys@francislauer.com
50 N Eisenhower Ave, Mason City, IA 50401-7340
Jean Mcaleer, Director

Iowa Substance Abuse Info Ctr.............319.398.5133
Fax..319.398.0476
Web...www.drugfreeinfo.org/
E-mail...............................isaicmail@crlibrary.org
2600 EdgeWood Rd, Cedar Rapids Public Library,
Cedar Rapids, IA 52404-2002
Barbara Gay, Director

South Central Youth And Family Svcs.........515.961.8421
Fax..515.961.7349
Web...www.southcentralshelter.org
E-mail.....................scott@southcentralshelter.org
203 E 4th Ave, Indianola, IA 50125-2910
Scott Thomas, Director

Kansas

www.kansas.gov

Sam Brownback, Governor
State Capitol, # 212S
300 SW 10th Street
Topeka, KS 66612-1590
785.296.3232
785.368.8788 (Fax)
governor@state.ks.us
www.ksgovernor.org

Don Chronister, Juvenile Justice Specialist
Juvenile Justice Authority
714 SW Jackson, Suite 300
Topeka, KS 66603
785.296.4213
785.296.1412 (Fax)
dchronister@jja.ks.gov

Reginald Robinson, SAG Chair
1700 SW College Ave
Topeka, KS 66621
785.670.1674
reggie.robinson@washburn.edu

CRISIS NUMBERS

Child Abuse Reporting . . .800.922.5330

STATE SERVICES

SOCIAL SERVICES

Child Care Lic & Reg Kansas 785.296.1270
Fax 785.296.0803
1000 SW Jackson Ste 200, Topeka, KS 66612
Joe Kroll, Director

Div of Kansas Emergency Management 785.274.1401
Fax 785.274.1426
Web . . . . .www.accesskansas.org/kdem
E-mail .lekrase@agtop.state.ks.us
2800 SW Topeka Blvd, Topeka, KS 66611-1220
Gene Krase, Director

Kansas Attorney General's Ofc 785.296.2215
Fax 785.296.6296
Web . . . . .www.ksag.org
E-mail . . . . .general@ksag.org
120 SW 10th Ave Fl 2, Topeka, KS 66612-1237
Frank Henderson, Director

Kansas Dept of Social and Rehabilitation Svcs . .785.296.3271
Fax 785.296.4685
Web . . . . .www.srsks.gov
E-mail . . . . .patti.cazier@srsks.gov
915 SW Harrison St, 6th Floor, Topeka, KS 66612
Rob Siedlecki, Secretary

GENERAL HEALTH SERVICES

Bureau of Family Health KS 785.291.3368
Fax 785.296.6553
E-mail . . . . .lkenney@kdheks.gov
1000 SW Jackson St Ste 220, Topeka, KS 66612
Linda Kenney, Director

Kansas Dept of Health and Environment 785.296.1500
Fax 785.368.6368
Web . . . . .www.kdhe.state.ks.us
1000 SW Jackson St Ste 120, Topeka, KS 66612-1354
Jason Everhart, Director Of Health

Kansas Health Authority .785.296.3981
Fax 785.296.4813
Web . . . . .www.khpa.ka.gov
E-mail . . . . .andrew.allison@khpa.ks.gov
900 Sw Jackson St, Landon Bldg, Rm 900, Topeka,
KS 66612-1220
Andrew Allison, Phd, Executive Director

**Srvs for Children And Youth With Spec Health Needs
KS** 785.296.1313
Fax 785.296.8616
E-mail . . . . .mshiff@kdheks.gov
1000 SW Jackson St, Ste 220, Topeka, KS 66612
M Shiff, Director

MENTAL HEALTH SERVICES

**Assoc Of Community Mental Health Ctrs Of
Kansas** 785.234.4773
Fax 785.234.3189
Web . . . . .www.acmhck.org
534 S Kansas Ste 330, Topeka, KS 66603
Michael Hammond, Executive Director

Rehabilitation Services KS 785.368.7112
Fax 785.368.7467
E-mail . . . . .michael.donnelly@srs.ks.gov
915 SW Harrison St 9N, Docking State Office Bldg,
Topeka, KS 66612
Micahel Donnelly, Director

JUSTICE AGENCY

Interstate Compact for Juvenile Offenders 785.296.5616
Fax 785.296.1412
Web . . . . .www.jja.ks.gov
E-mail . . . . .kansasicj@jja.ks.gov
714 SW Jackson St Ste 300, Topeka, KS 66603-3722
Curtis Whitten, Commissioner

Kansas Bureau of Investigation 785.296.8277
Fax 785.296.6781
1620 SW Tyler St, Topeka, KS 66612
Sheila Fawyer, Adminstrative Officer

Kansas Dept of Corrections 785.296.3317
Fax 785.296.0759
Web . . . . .www.docnet.dc.state.ks.us/
E-mail . . . . .kdoc@kdoc.dc.state.ks.us
900 SW Jackson 4th Fl, Topeka, KS 66612
Ray Roberts, Secretary Of Corrections

Ofc of Judicial Administration 785.296.2256
Fax 785.296.7076
E-mail . . . . .schwartzh@kscourts.org
301 SW 10th Ave Fl 1, Topeka, KS 66612
Nancy Dixon, Judicial Administrator

COURTS

Adult/Juvenile Probation 785.762.3105
Fax 785.762.2915
E-mail . . . . .ndavenport@8thjd.com
801 N Washington St Ste E, Junction City,
KS 66441-2483
Nikki Davenport, Chief Court Services Officer

Probation Svcs 785.233.8200
Fax 785.291.4959
E-mail . . . . .cleonhart@shawneecourt.org
200 SE 7th St Ste 104, Topeka, KS 66603-3961
Cathy Leonhart, Director

POLICE AND SHERIFF

Kansas Assoc of Chiefs of Police 316.733.7300
Fax 316.733.7301
Web . . . . .www.kacp.cc
E-mail . . . . .kacp@cox.net
655 S Andover Rd, Andover, KS 67002
Doyle M. King, Executive Director

Sheriff's Ofc 785.472.4416
Fax 785.472.5687
E-mail . . . . .tracy.ploutz@leo.gov
212 N Kansas Ave, Ellsworth, KS 67439-3118
Tracy L. Ploutz, Sheriff

EDUCATION SERVICES

Educating Homeless Children and Youth KS 785.296.6714
Fax 785.296.5867
E-mail . . . . .ttoedman@ksde.org
120 SE 10th Ave, Topeka, KS 66612
T Toedman, Director

Families Together Inc Kansas 316.945.7747
Fax 316.945.7795
E-mail . . . . .conine@familiestogetherinc.org
313 N Seneca Ste 114, Wichita, KS 67203
Anittra Beal, Assistant Director

**Kansas Commission for fhe Deaf & Hard of
Hearing** 785.368.8034
Fax 785.368.7467
E-mail . . . . .rebecca.rosenthal@srs.ks.gov
915 SW Harrison St, Suite 9N, Topeka, KS 66612
Rebecca Rosenthal, Director

Kansas Dept of Education 785.296.3201
Fax 785.296.0232
Web . . . . .www.ksde.org
120 SE 10th Ave, Topeka, KS 66612
Jodi Mackey, Director, Nutrition Programs

Kansas State School for the Blind 913.281.3308
Fax 913.281.3104
E-mail . . . . .mburkindine@kssb.net
1100 State Ave, Kansas City, KS 66102
Madeleine Burkindine, Superintendent

Kansas State School for the Deaf 913.791.0573
Fax 913.791.0577
Web . . . . .www.ksdeaf.org
450 E Park St, Olathe, KS 66061
Kevin Milner, Principal

©2011 Dorland Health

Olathe Youth Court...........................913.780.7046
Fax...913.780.8104
Web....www.olatheschools.com/students/studentd evelopment
E-mail.....................jbodenmillernlsc@olatheschools.org
　　315 N Lindenwood Dr, Olathe, KS 66062-1238
　Jennifer Bodenmiller, Facilitator

Parent Advocacy and Support Srvs..........316.685.1821
Fax...316.685.0768
E-mail...info@mhasck.org
　　555 N Woodlawn Ste 3105, Wichita, KS 67208
　Dr. Rose Mary Mohr, Chief Executive Officer

Special Education Services KS................785.291.3097
Fax...785.296.6715
E-mail.......................................dburns@ksde.org
　　120 SE 10th Ave, Topeka, KS 66612
　D Burns, Director

COUNTY SERVICES

Allen County

SOCIAL SERVICES

Social & Rehabilitation Svcs.................620.365.2164
Fax...620.365.5244
E-mail.....................................sf@srskansas.org
　　406 N Buckeye St, Iola, KS 66749-2312
　Ascott Thomtsom, Area Director

GENERAL HEALTH SERVICES

Health Dept....................................620.365.2191
Fax...620.365.3128
E-mail................................dbertone@aceks.com
　　221 S Jefferson Ave, Iola, KS 66749
　Diane Bertone, Administrator

COURTS

31st District Court.........................620.365.1425
Fax...620.365.1429
Web....................www.31judicialdistrict.com
E-mail......................tomsaxton@acdckscoxmail.com
　　1 N Washington Ave Rm B, Iola, KS 66749
　Honorable Thomas M. Saxton, Director

POLICE AND SHERIFF

Sheriff's Ofc...................................620.365.1400
Fax...620.365.1455
E-mail.........................twilliams101@allencosheriff.org
　　1 N Washington, Iola, KS 66749
　Thomas Williams, Sheriff

Anderson County

SOCIAL SERVICES

Social & Rehabilitation Svcs.................785.448.5459
Fax...785.448.3611
Web................................www.stateofks.gov
E-mail.............................susie.grimes@srs.ks.gov
　　504 W Redbud Ln, Garnett, KS 66032-2636
　Susie Grimes, Supervisor

GENERAL HEALTH SERVICES

Health Dept....................................785.448.6559
Fax...785.448.2608
　　407 W 2nd Ave, Garnett, KS 66032
　Jennet Steedley, Clerk

COURTS

District Court...............................785.448.6886
Fax...785.448.3230
E-mail.....................districtcourt@embarqmail.com
　　100 E 4th Ave Rm 6, Garnett, KS 66032
　Kara Reynolds, Clerk At The District Court

POLICE AND SHERIFF

Sheriff's Ofc...................................785.448.5428
Fax...785.448.2686
　　135 E 5th Ave, Garnett, KS 66032
　Scot Brownrig, Sheriff

Atchison County

SOCIAL SERVICES

Social & Rehabilitation Svcs.................913.367.5345
Fax...913.367.1926
　　410 Commercial St, Atchison, KS 66002
　Robert Siedlecki, Regional Director

GENERAL HEALTH SERVICES

Health Dept....................................913.367.5152
Fax...913.367.4580
Web.................................www.aging.ks.gov
E-mail...............................atcht@lmworth.com
　　616 Commercial St, Atchison, KS 66002-2405
　Connie Zeit, Rn, Nursing Supervisor

COURTS

1st District Court..........................913.367.7400
Fax...913.367.1171
Web.............................www.atcodistcourt.org
　　423 N 5th St, Atchison, KS 66002
　Honorable Martin Asher, Judge

POLICE AND SHERIFF

Sheriff's Ofc...................................913.367.0216
Fax...913.367.8244
Web............................www.atchisoncountyks.org
E-mail..........................john.calhoon@atchisonlec.org
　　518 Parallel St, Atchison, KS 66002-1821
　John Calhoon, Sheriff

Barber County

GENERAL HEALTH SERVICES

Health Dept....................................620.886.3294
Fax...620.886.3747
E-mail.........................richard2222@cyberlodg.com
　　117 E Kansas Ave, Medicine Lodge, KS 67104-1404
　Pam Rickard, Administrator

COURTS

30th District Court.........................620.886.5639
Fax...620.886.5854
Web..............................www.ckscoutrs.org
　　118 E Washington Ave Ste 5, Medicine Lodge,
　　KS 67104-1452
　Honorable Matthew Lynch, Magistrate Judge

POLICE AND SHERIFF

Sheriff's Ofc...................................620.886.5678
Fax...620.886.3103
Web................................www.sctelcom.net
E-mail.............................tomsont@sctelcom.net
　　124 E Washington Ave, Medicine Lodge,
　　KS 67104-1421
　Tommy J. Tomson, Sheriff

Barton County

SOCIAL SERVICES

**Kansas Dept of Social and Rehabilitation
Svcs**..620.792.5324
Fax...620.792.5373
　　1305 Patton Rd, Great Bend, KS 67530
　Albert Klaus, Human Serv Associates

GENERAL HEALTH SERVICES

Health Dept....................................620.793.1902
Fax...620.793.1903
Web................................www.greatbend.com
E-mail............................jrose@bartoncounty.org
　　1300 Kansas Ave Ste B, Great Bend, KS 67530-4469
　Janel Rose, Hiv Coordinator

COURTS

20th District Court.........................620.793.1856
Fax...620.793.1860
E-mail.........................skbtdistcrt@cpcis.net
　　1400 Main St Ste 306, Great Bend, KS 67530
　Honorable Hannelore Kitts, Judge

20th Judicial District Court Svcs............620.793.1887
Fax...620.793.1893
E-mail.............................ctservechism@cpcis.net
　　1806 12th St Ste A, Great Bend, KS 67530
　Sabrina Chism, Chief Court Services Officer

POLICE AND SHERIFF

Sheriff's Ofc...................................620.793.1876
Fax...620.793.1885
Web............................www.bartoncounty.org
E-mail.........................sheriff@bartoncounty.org
　　1416 Kansas Ave, Great Bend, KS 67530-4015
　Greg Armstrong, Sheriff

Bourbon County

SOCIAL SERVICES

Social & Rehabilitation Svcs.................620.223.4010
Fax...620.223.0168
　　710 W State 8th St, Ste 3, Fort Scott, KS 66701
　Scott Thompson, Area Director

GENERAL HEALTH SERVICES

Health Dept....................................620.223.4464
Fax...620.223.1686
Web................................www.sekmchd.org
E-mail..............................amaffett@aceks.com
　　221 S Judson, Fort Scott, KS 66701
　Alice Maffet, Supervisor

COURTS

6th District Court..........................620.223.0780
Fax...620.223.5303
　　210 S National, Fort Scott, KS 66701
　Rhonda Cole, Court Clerk

POLICE AND SHERIFF

Sheriff's Ofc...................................620.223.1440
Fax...620.223.0055
Web............................www.bourboncountyks.org
E-mail.........................rgray@bourboncountyks.org
　　204 S National Ave, Fort Scott, KS 66701
　Ron Gray, Sheriff

Brown County

SOCIAL SERVICES

Social And Rehabilitation Svcs..............785.742.7186
Fax...785.742.2929
　　810 Oregon St, Hiawatha, KS 66434-2233
　Betsy Thompson, Area Director

JUSTICE AGENCY

Probation Svcs...............................785.742.7818
Fax...785.742.0036
E-mail..............................vcoy@brdistcrt.org
　　601 Oregon St, Ste 102, Hiawatha, KS 66434
　Vernie L. Coy, Chief Probation Officer

COURTS

22nd District Court 785.742.7481
Fax 785.742.3506
Web .... www.brdistcrt.org
E-mail .... lsmith@brdistcrt.org
  601 Oregon St Ste 102, Hiawatha, KS 66434-2241
Honorable James A. Patton, Judge

POLICE AND SHERIFF

Sheriff's Ofc 785.742.7125
Fax 785.742.3058
  709 Utah St, Hiawatha, KS 66434
John Merchant, Sheriff

Butler County

SOCIAL SERVICES

Social and Rehabilitation Svcs 316.321.4200
Fax 316.321.1230
E-mail .... cyrilla.petracek@srskansas.org
  410 N Haverhill Rd, El Dorado, KS 67042
Cyrilla Petracek, Area Director

GENERAL HEALTH SERVICES

Health Dept 316.321.3400
Fax 316.321.1338
Web .... www.bucoks.com
  206 N Griffith St Ste B, El Dorado, KS 67042
Jamie Downs, Hiv Coordinator

JUSTICE AGENCY

CASA 316.320.0238
Fax 316.322.7797
Web .... www.kansascasa.org
E-mail .... tricountycasa@gmail.com
  204 W Central Ave, El Dorado, KS 67042-2101
Janett Jacobs, Director

Court Svcs 316.322.4153
Fax 316.322.4159
Web .... www.southwind.net
  201 W Pine Ave Ste 102, El Dorado, KS 67042-2911
Bob Keen, Chief Court Services Officer

COURTS

13th District Court 316.322.4370
Fax 316.321.9486
E-mail .... clerkdcbuco@yahoo.com
  201 W Pine Ave Ste 101, El Dorado, KS 67042
Janelle Jessup, Clerk

POLICE AND SHERIFF

Sheriff's Ofc 316.322.4254
Fax 316.320.3189
Web .... www.bucoks.com
  141 S Gordy St, El Dorado, KS 67042-2909
Kelly L Herzet, Sheriff

Chase County

SOCIAL SERVICES

Social & Rehabilitation Svcs 620.273.6369
Fax 620.273.8536
  612 Walnut St, Cottonwood Falls, KS 66845-9798
Maddie Keys, Director

GENERAL HEALTH SERVICES

Health Dept 620.273.6377
Fax 620.273.6593
  301 South Walnut St, Cottonwood Falls, KS 66845
Cheryl Jones, Rn, Administrator

COURTS

5th District Court 620.273.6319
Fax 620.273.6890
E-mail .... csclerk@5thjd.org
  300 Pearl St, Floor 2, Cottonwood Falls, KS 66845
Honorable Douglas P Jones, Judge

POLICE AND SHERIFF

Sheriff's Ofc 620.273.6313
Fax 620.273.6442
E-mail .... dorneker@hotmail.com
  301 S Walnut St, Cottonwood Falls, KS 66845
Richard Dorneker, Sheriff

Chautauqua County

GENERAL HEALTH SERVICES

Health Dept 620.725.5850
Fax 620.725.5856
E-mail .... hucosd@sbcglobal.net
  215 N Chautauqua St, Sedan, KS 67361
Jeanie Beason, Rn, Administrator

COURTS

14th District Court 620.725.5874
Fax 620.725.3027
E-mail .... cqcodct@sbcglobal.net
  215 N Chautauqua St Ste 6, Sedan, KS 67361
Nancy Stevenson, Clerk Of Court

POLICE AND SHERIFF

Sheriff's Ofc 620.725.3108
Fax 620.725.3256
Web .... www.ksok.biz
E-mail .... sheriffcqso@ksok.biz
  215 N Chautauqua St Ste 8, Sedan, KS 67361-1392
Perry Russell, Sheriff

Cherokee County

SOCIAL SERVICES

Social Rehab Svcs 620.429.3014
  215 E Maple, Columbus, KS 66725

GENERAL HEALTH SERVICES

Health Dept 620.429.3087
Fax 620.429.3623
Web .... www.cherokeecountyks.org
E-mail .... hd@cherokeecountyks.org
  110 E Walnut St, Columbus, KS 66725
Betha Elliott, Administrator

POLICE AND SHERIFF

Sheriff's Ofc 620.429.3992
Fax 620.429.1207
E-mail .... sheriffgroves@columbus-ks.com
  915 E Country Rd, Columbus, KS 66725
David Groves, Sheriff

Cheyenne County

GENERAL HEALTH SERVICES

Health Dept 785.332.2381
Fax 785.332.8983
  221 W 1st St, Saint Francis, KS 67756
Mila Bandel, Health Dept Administrator

COURTS

15th District Court 785.332.8850
Fax 785.332.8851
E-mail .... cndist@stfks.net
  212 E Washington St, Saint Francis, KS 67756
Sharon Elliott, Clerk Of The District Court

Clark County

GENERAL HEALTH SERVICES

Health Dept 620.635.2624
Fax 620.635.2870
E-mail .... shotsrus@ucom.net
  913 Highland, P.O. Box 745, Ashland, KS 67831
Mary Ann Cunningham, Administrator

COURTS

16th District Court 620.635.2753
Fax 620.635.2155
Web .... www.ucom.net
E-mail .... cadistct@ucom.net
  913 Highland St, Ashland, KS 67831
Honorable Michael Freelove, Judge

POLICE AND SHERIFF

Sheriff's Ofc 620.635.2802
Fax 620.635.2148
E-mail .... casheriff@ucom.net
  221 W 9th St, Ashland, KS 67831
John M. Ketron, Sheriff

Clay County

GENERAL HEALTH SERVICES

Community Home & Health Svcs 785.632.3193
Fax 785.632.5849
Web .... www.nckcn.com
  820 Spellman Cir, Clay Center, KS 67432-7492
Dana Rickley, Rn, Administrator

COURTS

21st District Court 785.632.3443
Fax 785.632.2651
Web .... www.classicnet.net
E-mail .... mstellner@claycountykansas.org
  724 5th St, Clay Center, KS 67432-2901
Melissa Stellner, Clerk

POLICE AND SHERIFF

Sheriff's Ofc 785.632.5601
Fax 785.632.3278
E-mail .... cdunn@claycountysheriff.us
  539 Lincoln Ave, Clay Center, KS 67432
Chuck Dunn, Sheriff

Cloud County

SOCIAL SERVICES

North Central Kansas CASA, Inc 785.243.8200
Fax 785.243.8191
E-mail .... nckcasa@cloudcountyks.org
  910 W. 11th St., Concordia, KS 66901-3428
Carol Miller, Executive Director

Social & Rehabilitation Svcs 785.243.4671
Fax 785.243.1802
Web .... www.srs.ks.gov
E-mail .... bat@srs.ks.gov
  1501 E 6th Street Trfy, Concordia, KS 66901-2613
Betsy Thompson, Area Director

GENERAL HEALTH SERVICES

Health Dept -- Home & Health 785.243.8140
Fax 785.243.8149
  910 W 11th St, Concordia, KS 66901
Diana Gering, Administrator

POLICE AND SHERIFF

Sheriff's Ofc 785.243.3636
Fax 785.243.8163
  9th & Broadway St, Concordia, KS 66901
Bryan Mark, Sheriff

Coffey County

GENERAL HEALTH SERVICES

Health Dept 620.364.8631
Fax 620.364.2045
E-mail .... cchd@coffeycounty.org
  110 S 6th St Ste 205, Burlington, KS 66839
Lyndsay Payer, Rn, Administrator

COURTS

4th District Court **620.364.8628**
Fax 620.364.8535
E-mail . . . . .debbiecoffeyco@hotmail.com
110 S 6th St Ste 102, Burlington, KS 66839
Honorable Phillip M. Fromme, District Judge

Comanche County

GENERAL HEALTH SERVICES

Health Dept **620.582.2431**
Fax 620.582.2491
E-mail . . . . .cchdjm@unitedwireless.com
207 S Washington St, Coldwater, KS 67029
Shari Jellison, Administrator

COURTS

16th District Court **620.582.2966**
Fax 620.582.2603
201 S New York St, Coldwater, KS 67029
Honorable Loren L. Cronin, Judge

POLICE AND SHERIFF

Sheriff's Ofc **620.582.2511**
Fax 620.582.2261
E-mail . . . . .cmxso1@yahoo.com
408 N Central St, Coldwater, KS 67029
Mike Mcmoran, Sheriff

Cowley County

SOCIAL SERVICES

Social & Rehabilitation Svcs **620.221.6400**
Fax 620.221.0698
1809 Main St, Winfield, KS 67156
Cyrilla Petracek, Area Director

COURTS

19th District Court **620.221.5470**
Fax 620.221.1097
311 E 9th St, Winfield, KS 67156
Honorable Nicholas M. St Peter, Chief Judge

POLICE AND SHERIFF

Sheriff's Dept **620.221.5444**
Fax 620.221.5448
Web . . . . .www.cowleycounty.org
E-mail . . . . .sheriff@cowleycounty.org
911 Loomis, Winfield, KS 67156-0459
Don Read, Sheriff

EDUCATION SERVICES

Health Department **620.221.1430**
Fax 620.221.0389
E-mail . . . . .mmdonals@cowleycounty.org
320 E 9th AVE Ste B, Winfield, KS 67156-2871
Marsha Donals, Hiv Coordinator

Crawford County

SOCIAL SERVICES

Social & Rehabilitation Svcs **620.231.5300**
Fax 620.231.1921
Web . . . . .www.srskansas.org
320 S Broadway St, Pittsburg, KS 66762-5206
Scott Thompson, Director

GENERAL HEALTH SERVICES

Health Dept **620.231.5411**
Fax 620.231.1246
410 E Atkinson Ave, Ste A, Pittsburg, KS 66762
Richard P Feiffer, Executive Administrator

MENTAL HEALTH SERVICES

Community Mental Health Ctr **620.231.5130**
Fax 620.235.7101
911 E Centennial Dr, Pittsburg, KS 66762
Richard H Pfeiffer, Lmsw, Administrator

JUSTICE AGENCY

Probation Svcs **620.232.2460**
Fax 620.232.5646
602 N Locust St, Crawford County Judicial Center, Pittsburg, KS 66762
Mac Young, Chief Court Services Officer

COURTS

Teen Court **620.235.7118**
Fax 620.235.7107
Web . . . . .www.locatnet.com
665 S Highway 69, Pittsburg, KS 66762-8600
Sandy Emerson, Office Manager

POLICE AND SHERIFF

Sheriff's Dept **620.724.8274**
Fax 620.724.8290
225 Enterprise DR, Girard, KS 66743
Eugene Horton, Sheriff

Decatur County

GENERAL HEALTH SERVICES

Health Dept **785.475.8118**
Fax 785.475.8143
E-mail . . . . .decaturhealth@eaglecom.net
902 W Columbia St, Medical Arts Building, Oberlin, KS 67749
Marilyn Gamblin, Rn, Administrator

COURTS

17th District Court **785.475.8108**
Fax 785.475.8170
Web . . . . .www.theclassic.net
E-mail . . . . .dcdcourt@eaglecom.net
120 E Hall St Ste 2, Oberlin, KS 67749-2325
Janet Meitl, Clerk Of Court

POLICE AND SHERIFF

Sheriff's Ofc **785.475.8100**
Fax 785.475.8160
E-mail . . . . .tcsoks55@at.net
120 E Hall St Ste 1, Oberlin, KS 67749
Ken T. Badsky, Sheriff

Dickinson County

GENERAL HEALTH SERVICES

Health Dept **785.263.4179**
Fax 785.263.0335
Web . . . . .www.dkcoks.org
E-mail . . . . .ldavies@dkcoks.org
1001 N Brady St, Abilene, KS 67410-1801
Linda Davies, Administrator

COURTS

8th District Court **785.263.3142**
Fax 785.263.4407
109 E 1st St, Ste 306, Abilene, KS 67410
Cindy Macdonald, Clerk

POLICE AND SHERIFF

Chapman Police Dept **785.922.6463**
Fax 785.922.7000
Web . . . . .www.citiofchapman.org
E-mail . . . . .brownpd@cityofchapman.org
402 N Marshall, Chapman, KS 67431
Mike Brown, Police Chief

Sheriff's Ofc **785.263.4081**
Fax 785.263.1512
Web . . . . .www.dkcoks.org
E-mail . . . . .sheriff@dkcoks.org
109 E 1st St Ste 201, Abilene, KS 67410-2834
Gareth Hoffman, Sheriff

Doniphan County

COURTS

22nd District Court **785.985.3582**
Fax 785.985.2402
E-mail . . . . .dpdc@carsoncomm.com
120 E Chestnutt St, Troy, KS 66087-0295
Janice Kay Wanlass, Clerk Of Court

Douglas County

SOCIAL SERVICES

Lawrence SRS Area Ofc **785.832.3700**
Fax 785.843.0291
E-mail . . . . .ljxb@srs.ks.gov
1901 Delaware St, Lawrence, KS 66044
Lorrie Bezinque, Regional Director

GENERAL HEALTH SERVICES

Health Dept **785.843.3060**
Fax 785.843.3161
Web . . . . .www.ldhealth.org
E-mail . . . . .dpartridge@ldhealth.org
200 Maine St Ste B, Lawrence, KS 66044-1396
Dan Partridge, Administrator/health Officer

Trinity In-Home Care **785.842.3159**
Fax 785.842.7061
Web . . . . .www.trinityinhomecare.com
E-mail . . . . .kelly@trinityinhomecare.com
2201 W 25th St Ste Q, Lawrence, KS 66047
Kelly Evans, Executive Director

JUSTICE AGENCY

Probation Svcs **785.832.5218**
Fax 785.832.5370
Web . . . . .www.douglas-county.com
E-mail . . . . .mroberts@douglas-county.com
111 E 11th St, Douglas County Court Services, Lawrence, KS 66044-2909
Michelle Roberts, Chief Court Services Officer

COURTS

7th District Court **785.832.5218**
Fax 785.832.5370
Web . . . . .www.douglas-county.com
E-mail . . . . .dhamilton@douglas-county.com
111 E 11th St, Judicial Center, Lawrence, KS 66044-2909
Robert Fairchild, Director

POLICE AND SHERIFF

Sheriff's Ofc **785.841.0007**
Fax 785.841.5168
Web . . . . .www.dgso.org
E-mail . . . . .sheriff@dgso.org
111 E 11th St, Lawrence, KS 66044-2909
Ken Mcgovern, Sheriff

Edwards County

GENERAL HEALTH SERVICES

Edwards Health Dept **620.659.3102**
Fax 620.659.3017
Web . . . . .www.edcohealth.com
E-mail . . . . .diana@edcohealth.com
622 W 8th St, Kinsley, KS 67547-2329
Diana Rice, Administrator

COURTS

24th District Court **620.659.2442**
Fax 620.659.2998
Web . . . . .www.edwards.kscoxmail.com
E-mail . . . . .edsbistct@edwards.kscoxmail.com
312 Massachusetts Ave, Kinsley, KS 67547-1090
Llinda Atteberry, Clerk

POLICE AND SHERIFF

Sheriff's Ofc **620.659.3636**
Fax 620.659.3013
312 Massachusetts Ave, Kinsley, KS 67547
Bryant J. Kurth, Sheriff

Elk County

GENERAL HEALTH SERVICES

Health Dept **620.374.2277**
Fax 620.374.3540
127 Pine Courthouse, Howard, KS 67349
Kandy Dowell, Administrator

COURTS

District Court **620.374.2370**
Fax 620.374.3531
E-mail ....ekcourt@yahoo.com
127 N Pine St, Howard, KS 67349
Kristin Hutchison, Judge

POLICE AND SHERIFF

Sheriff's Ofc **620.374.2108**
Fax 620.374.3503
E-mail ....ekso@sktc.net
100 N Cedar, Howard, KS 67349
Douglas Hanks, Sheriff

Ellis County

SOCIAL SERVICES

Hays SRS Area Ofc **785.628.1066**
Fax 785.628.8106
E-mail ....rmf@srs.ks.gov
3000 Broadway Ave, Hays, KS 67601-1917
Rabena Fearl, Acting Director

GENERAL HEALTH SERVICES

Health Dept **785.628.9440**
601 Main St Ste B, Hays, KS 67601
Robert Butch Schlyer, Rn, Hiv Coordinator

COURTS

23rd District Court **785.628.9415**
Fax 785.628.8415
1204 Fort St Ste 302, Hays, KS 67601
Honorable Tom Toepher, District Judge

POLICE AND SHERIFF

Sheriff's Ofc **785.625.1040**
Fax 785.625.1058
E-mail ....elso@ellisco.net
105 W 12th St Ste 103, Hays, KS 67601
Charles E. Harbin, Sheriff

Ellsworth County

GENERAL HEALTH SERVICES

Health Dept **785.472.4488**
Fax 785.472.4489
E-mail ....ellscohd@eaglecom.net
1603 N Aylward Ave, Ellsworth, KS 67439
Ronda Kasiska, Rn, Administrator

COURTS

20th District Court **785.472.4052**
Fax 785.472.5712
E-mail ....ewpas@cpcis.net
210 N Kansas Ave, Ellsworth, KS 67439
Honorable Dale L. Urbanek, Director

Finney County

SOCIAL SERVICES

Social & Rehabilitation Svcs Area
Ofc **620.272.5800**
Fax 620.272.5830
Web ....www.srskansas.org
1710 Palace Dr, Garden City, KS 67846-6268
Jodi Inganza, Social Services Supervisor, 620-272-5800; Robena Farrell,
Area Director; Verna Weber, Assistant Director

GENERAL HEALTH SERVICES

Health Dept **620.272.3600**
Fax 620.272.3606
Web ....www.finneycounty.org
E-mail ....agoss@finneycounty.org
919 W Zerr Rd, Garden City, KS 67846-2795
Ashley Goss, Director

MENTAL HEALTH SERVICES

Mental Health **620.276.7689**
Fax 620.276.6117
Web ....www.areamhd.org
E-mail ....rdalke@areamhc.org
1111 E Spruce St, Garden City, KS 67846
Ric Dalke, Lscsw, Executive Director

JUSTICE AGENCY

Probation Svcs **620.271.6150**
Fax 620.271.6155
Web ....www.finneycounty.org
405 N 8th St, Garden City, KS 67846-5302
Craig Aronson, Chief Court Services Officer

POLICE AND SHERIFF

Sheriff's Ofc **620.272.3700**
Fax 620.272.3777
E-mail ....sheriff@ficolec.org
304 N 9th St Ste 1, Garden City, KS 67846-5366
Kevin C. Bascue, Sheriff

Ford County

SOCIAL SERVICES

Dodge City Social & Rehabilitation
Svcs **620.227.8508**
Fax 620.227.6498
Web ....www.dodgecity.org
1509 Ave P, Dodge City, KS 67801
Shari Campbell, Area Director

GENERAL HEALTH SERVICES

Health Dept **620.227.4545**
Fax 620.227.4738
Web ....www.fordcounty.net
E-mail ....dnoble@fordcounty.net
106 E Spruce St, Dodge City, KS 67801-4910
Debbie Noble, Disease Intervention Specialist

JUSTICE AGENCY

Court Svcs **620.227.4615**
Fax 620.227.4519
100 Gunsmoke St, Court Services, Dodge City,
KS 67801
Dan Pfannenstiel, Chief Court Services Officer

COURTS

16th District Court **620.227.4603**
Fax 620.227.6799
101 W Spruce St, Dodge City, KS 67801
Honorable E. Leigh Hood, Judge

POLICE AND SHERIFF

Sheriff's Ofc **620.227.4501**
Fax 620.227.3284
Web ....www.fordcounty.net
E-mail ....dbush@fordcounty.net
11311 E community, Dodge City, KS 67801
Dean Bush, Sheriff

Franklin County

SOCIAL SERVICES

Social and Rehabilitation Svcs **785.229.8600**
Fax 785.229.8643
E-mail ....lorrie.veecquine@srs.ks.gov
2231 S Elm St, Ottawa, KS 66067-4040
Lorrie Veecquine, Area Director

GENERAL HEALTH SERVICES

Health Dept **785.229.3530**
Fax 785.229.3529
Web ....www.franklincks.org
E-mail ....rhastings@franklincoks.org
1418 S Main St Ste 1, Ottawa, KS 66067-3544
Rebecca Hastings, Rn, Nursing Director

JUSTICE AGENCY

CASA **785.229.8996**
Fax 785.229.8997
E-mail ....scaylor@mail.franklincoks.org
315 S Main St, Fl 3, Ottawa, KS 66067
Sara Caylor, Executive Director

COURTS

4th Judicial District Court **785.242.6000**
Fax 785.242.5970
301 S Main St, Ottawa, KS 66067
John Steelman, Court Administrator

POLICE AND SHERIFF

Sheriff's Ofc **785.229.1200**
Fax 785.229.1210
305 S Main St, Ottawa, KS 66067
Jeff Curry, Sheriff

Geary County

SOCIAL SERVICES

Junction City Social & Rehabilitation
Svcs **785.762.5445**
Fax 785.762.5062
Web ....www.srskansas.org
E-mail ....betsy.thompson@jcks.com
1010 W 6th St, Junction City, KS 66441-2430
Betsy Thompson, Regional Director

MENTAL HEALTH SERVICES

Pawnee Mental Health Svcs **785.762.5250**
Fax 785.762.2144
Web ....www.pawnee.org
814 Caroline Ave, Junction City, KS 66441-5210
Gadria Scott, Office Manager

COURTS

8th District Court **785.762.5221**
Fax 785.762.4420
Web www.8thjd.com
E-mail ....gecdc@8thjd.com
138 E 8th St, Junction City, KS 66441
Honorable Steven Hornbaker, Director

POLICE AND SHERIFF

Sheriff's Ofc **785.238.2261**
Fax 785.762.5085
826 N Franklin St, Junction City, KS 66441
James Jensen, Sheriff

EDUCATION SERVICES

Communities Connection **785.717.4000**
Fax 785.717.4003
Web www.usd475.org
   123 N Eisenhower Dr, Junction City, KS 66441
   Mary Cay Stauffer, Executive Director

Gove County

GENERAL HEALTH SERVICES

Health Dept **785.938.2335**
Fax 785.938.2336
E-mail ....gocohdpt@ruraltel.net
   520 Washington, Gove, KS 67736-0128
   Deena Woodall, Director

COURTS

23rd District Court **785.938.2310**
Fax 785.938.2312
E-mail ....gcdc@ruraltel.net
   420 Broad St, Gove, KS 67736
   Honorable Lois B. Werner, Director

Graham County

COURTS

District Court **785.421.3458**
Fax 785.421.5463
E-mail ....ghdc@ruraltel.net
   410 N Pomeroy Ave Ste 9, Hill City, KS 67642
   Dinna Elliott, Clerk Of Court

POLICE AND SHERIFF

Sheriff's Ofc **785.421.2107**
Fax 785.421.2891
E-mail ....sheriff@ruraltel.net
   410 N Pomeroy Ave Ste 8, Hill City, KS 67642
   Cole Presley, Sheriff

Grant County

POLICE AND SHERIFF

Sheriff's Ofc **620.356.3500**
Fax 620.356.1038
E-mail ....gtso@pld.com
   210 E Central Ave, Ulysses, KS 67880-2502
   Lance Babcock, Sheriff

Gray County

GENERAL HEALTH SERVICES

Health Dept **620.855.2424**
Fax 620.855.7007
E-mail ....rmaddox@grayco.org
   300 S Main, Courthouse, Cimarron, KS 67835
   Rayna Maddox, Rn, Administrator

COURTS

16th District Court **620.855.3812**
Fax 620.855.7037
E-mail ....gycodist@ucom.net
   300 S. Main St, Cimarron, KS 67835
   Honorable Joey E. Duncan, Judge

POLICE AND SHERIFF

Sheriff's Ofc **620.855.3916**
Fax 620.855.3116
E-mail ....jkramer@sheriff.grayco.org
   300 S Main St, Cimarron, KS 67835
   Jim Kramer, Sheriff

Greeley County

COURTS

25th District Court **620.376.4258**
Fax 620.376.2351
   616 2nd St, Tribune, KS 67879
   Honorable Wade M. Dixon, Judge

POLICE AND SHERIFF

Sheriff's Ofc **620.376.4233**
Fax 620.376.2418
   208 E Harper Ave, Tribune, KS 67879
   Mark Rine, Sheriff

Greenwood County

GENERAL HEALTH SERVICES

Greenwood Health Dept **620.583.6632**
Fax 620.583.7709
E-mail ....gw.deina.rockhill@att.net
   200 W 1St St, Eureka, KS 67045
   Deina Rockhill, Community Nurse

COURTS

13th District Court **620.583.8153**
Fax 620.583.6818
E-mail ....info@greenwoodcounty.org
   311 N Main St Ste 10, Eureka, KS 67045-1392
   Honorable Rebecca Lindamood, Judge

POLICE AND SHERIFF

Sheriff's Ofc **620.583.5568**
Fax 620.583.7134
E-mail ....gwso@sbcglobal.net
   311 N Main St Ste A, Eureka, KS 67045
   Mark Kenneson, Sheriff

Hamilton County

GENERAL HEALTH SERVICES

Health Dept **620.384.7875**
Fax 620.384.7503
   304 E Ave A, Syracuse, KS 67878
   Monique Chetum, Health Officer

Harper County

MENTAL HEALTH SERVICES

Horizons Mental Health Ctr **620.842.5881**
Fax 620.842.3768
Web ....www.hmhc.com
E-mail ....garrettm@hmhc.com
   123 N Pennsylvania Ave, Anthony, KS 67003-2935
   L Michael Garrett, Director

COURTS

30th District Court **620.842.3721**
Fax 620.842.6025
E-mail ....courtclerk@cyberlodge.com
   201 N Jennings Ave, Anthony, KS 67003
   Honorable Richard Befort, Magistrate

POLICE AND SHERIFF

Sheriff's Ofc **620.842.5135**
Fax 620.842.3251
E-mail ....sheriff@harpercountyks.gov
   115 E Steadman St, Anthony, KS 67003
   Brad Moore, Sheriff

Harvey County

SOCIAL SERVICES

**Newton Social & Rehabilitation
Svcs** **316.283.3015**
Fax 316.283.6835
   411 Washington Rd, Newton, KS 67114-4358
   Marla Cutsinger, Site Manager

GENERAL HEALTH SERVICES

Health Dept **316.283.1637**
Fax 316.283.0057
Web ....www.harveycounty.com/health
   316 Oak St, Newton, KS 67114
   Joe Miller, Director

Harvey County

MENTAL HEALTH SERVICES

Prairie View, Inc **316.284.6400**
Fax 316.284.6491
Web ....www.pvi.org
E-mail ....info@pvi.org
   1901 E 1st St, Newton, KS 67114
   Dr Gary Fast, Medical Director

COURTS

9th District Court **316.284.6890**
Fax 316.283.4601
E-mail ....richardw@9thdistct.net
   8th & Main, Newton, KS 67114
   Honorable Richard B. Walker, Chief Judge

POLICE AND SHERIFF

Sheriff's Ofc **316.284.6960**
Fax 316.284.6967
   120 E 7th St, Newton, KS 67114
   T Walton, Sheriff

EDUCATION SERVICES

Community Partnership **316.284.6520**
E-mail ....office@hccpinc.org
   816 Oak St, Newton, KS 67114
   Beth Tuszynski, Interim Director

Haskell County

GENERAL HEALTH SERVICES

Health Dept **620.675.8191**
Fax 620.675.2236
Web ....www.haskellcounty.org
E-mail ....vwinger@satantahospital.org
   301 Derby St, Sublette, KS 67877
   Vada Winger, Director

COURTS

26th District Court **620.675.2671**
Fax 620.675.8599
E-mail ....hsdictct@pld.com
   300 S. Inman, Sublette, KS 67877
   Honorable Tom B. Webb, Magistrate Judge

POLICE AND SHERIFF

Sheriff's Ofc **620.675.2280**
Fax 620.675.2638
E-mail ....bar20@pld.com
   300 S. Inman, Sublette, KS 67877
   Troy Briggs, Sheriff

Hodgeman County

GENERAL HEALTH SERVICES

Health Dept **620.357.8736**
Fax 620.357.8846
Web ....www.hgcohealthdept.com
E-mail ....hghealthdept@hotmail.com
   Courthouse, 500 Main, Jetmore, KS 67854
   Karen Haug, Rn, Bsn, Director

COURTS

24th District Court **620.357.6522**
Fax 620.357.6216
E-mail ....hgdistct@sunflowertelco.com
   500 Main St, Jetmore, KS 67854
   Honorable Kenton Gleason, Judge

POLICE AND SHERIFF

Sheriff's Ofc **620.357.8391**
Fax 620.357.8300
Web ....www.hodgemansheriff.us
E-mail ....ronridley@hodgemansheriff.us
   500 Main St, Jetmore, KS 67854
   Ronald Ridley, Sheriff

Jackson County

GENERAL HEALTH SERVICES

Health Dept **785.364.2670**
Fax 785.364.3001
Web .... www.nekhealthdept.org
E-mail .... madreith@hotmail.com
    312 Pennsylvania Ave Ste A, Holton, KS 66436-1872
Jon Anderson, Administrator

COURTS

2nd District Court **785.364.2191**
Fax 785.364.3804
E-mail .... creamer@holtonks.net
    400 New York Ave Ste 311, Holton, KS 66436
Honorable Micheal Ireland, Judge

POLICE AND SHERIFF

Sheriff's Ofc **785.364.2251**
Fax 785.364.4820
E-mail .... sladner@holtonks.net
    210 US Highway 75, Holton, KS 66436
Tim Morse, Sheriff

Jefferson County

GENERAL HEALTH SERVICES

Health Dept **785.863.2447**
Fax 785.863.2652
Web .... www.jfcountyks.com
E-mail .... jchd@jfcounty.com
    1212 Walnut St, US Highway 59, Oskaloosa,
    KS 66066-4200
Brown Beth, Administrator

COURTS

2nd District Court **785.863.2461**
Fax 785.863.2369
Web .... www.kscourts.org
    300 Jefferson St, Oskaloosa, KS 66066
Honorable Gary L. Nafziger, Director

POLICE AND SHERIFF

Sheriff's Ofc **785.863.2765**
Fax 785.863.2993
Web .... www.jeffersoncountykssheriff.com
E-mail .... jherrig@jfcountyks.com
    1360 Walnut St, Oskaloosa, KS 66066-4201
Jeff Herrig, Sheriff

Jewell County

GENERAL HEALTH SERVICES

Health Dept **785.378.4060**
Fax 785.378.4054
Web .... www.nckcn.com
    307 N Commercial St, Mankato, KS 66956-2097
Angelia Murray, Director

POLICE AND SHERIFF

Sheriff's Ofc **785.378.3194**
Fax 785.378.4085
    307 N Commercial St Ste 1, Mankato, KS 66956
Jonas Mcentire, Sheriff

Johnson County

SOCIAL SERVICES

Olathe SRS Area Ofc **913.826.7300**
Fax 913.826.7314
Web .... www.srs.ks.gov
    8915 Lenexa Dr, Overland Park, KS 66214
Phyllis Gilmore, Regional Director

GENERAL HEALTH SERVICES

Health Dept **913.826.1200**
Fax 913.826.1210
Web .... health.jocogov.org
E-mail .... barbara.mitchell@jocogov.org
    6000 Lamar Ave, Ste 140, Mission, KS 66202
Barbara Mitchell, Health Education Division Director

MENTAL HEALTH SERVICES

Mental Health Ctr **913.831.2550**
Fax 913.826.1608
Web .... www.jocogov.org
    6000 Lamar Ave, Ste 130, Mission, KS 66202
David Wiebe, Msw, Executive Director

JUSTICE AGENCY

CASA **913.715.4040**
Fax 913.397.0337
Web .... www.casajwc.com
E-mail .... lrice@casajwc.com
    6901 Shawney Mission Pk, Ste 112, Olathe, KS 66202
Lois Rice, Executive Director

Probation Svcs **913.324.6900**
Fax 913.782.3297
Web .... www.jocogov.org
E-mail .... rise.haneberg@jocogov.org
    18505 W 119th St, Olathe, KS 66061-8004
Rise Haneberg, Chief Court Service Officer

COURTS

Overland Park Court Svcs **913.327.6800**
Fax 913.327.5758
    12400 Foster St, Overland Park, KS 66213
Mary Moss, Director

POLICE AND SHERIFF

Olathe Police Dept **913.782.4500**
Fax 913.971.6927
Web .... www.olatheks.org
E-mail .... jthiessen@olatheks.org
    501 E Highway 56, Olathe, KS 66061-4639
Janet Thiessen, Chief

Sheriff's Office **913.791.5800**
Fax 913.791.5806
Web .... www.jocosheriff.org
E-mail .... frank.denning@jocogov.org
    125 N Cherry St, Olathe, KS 66061-3443
Frank Denning, Sheriff

EDUCATION SERVICES

**Olathe District Schools Special
Svcs** **913.780.7006**
Fax 913.780.8209
Web www.olathe.k12.ks.us
    14160 west boack Rd, Olathe, KS 66062
Deb Chappell, Special Services Executive Director

Special Education **913.239.4044**
Fax 913.239.4154
Web www.bluevalleyk12.org
    15020 Metcalf Ave, Overland Park, KS 66223
Dr Mark Schmidt, Executive Director

Special Education **913.592.7293**
Fax 913.592.7279
Web www.usd230.org
E-mail .... lawsont@usd230.org
    304 S Webster St, Spring Hill, KS 66083-8566
Tom Lawson, Director Of Special Education

Special Education **913.993.8600**
Fax 913.993.8614
Web .... www.smsd.org
E-mail .... debmeyer@smsd.org
    6601 Santa Fe Dr, Shawnee Mission, KS 66202-3925
Deborah Meyer, Special Education Director (lea)

Kearny County

GENERAL HEALTH SERVICES

Health Dept **620.355.6342**
Fax 620.355.7129
E-mail .... kecohd@pld.com
    301 N Kansas St, Lakin, KS 67860
Rosemary Bachman, Rn, Administrator

POLICE AND SHERIFF

Sheriff's Ofc **620.355.6211**
Fax 620.355.6680
E-mail .... jarboe@pld.com
    106 E Washington, Lakin, KS 67860
James Jarboe, Sheriff

Kingman County

GENERAL HEALTH SERVICES

Health Dept **620.532.2221**
Fax 620.532.1083
    125 N Spruce St Stop 2, Kingman, KS 67068
Cindy Chrisman-smith, Rn, Administrator

COURTS

30th District Court **620.532.5151**
Fax 620.532.2952
Web .... www.kmdistrictcourt.kscoxmail.com
E-mail .... stacij@kmdistrictcourt.kscoxmail.com
    130 North Spruce St, Kingman, KS 67068
Honorable James Mathis, Judge

POLICE AND SHERIFF

Sheriff's Ofc **620.532.5133**
Fax 620.532.3216
E-mail .... kms01@hotmail.com
    120 N Spruce St Stop 1, Kingman, KS 67068
Randy Hill, Sheriff

Kiowa County

SOCIAL SERVICES

Social & Rehabilitation Svcs **620.723.3321**
Fax 620.723.2085
    608 E Grant Ave, Greensburg, KS 67054-2708
Srancis Hawpe, Site Director

GENERAL HEALTH SERVICES

Health Dept **620.723.2136**
Fax 620.723.2943
E-mail .... kwcohd@sbcglobal.net
    211 E Florida Ave Stop 7, Greensburg, KS 67054
Mitzi Hesser, Rn, Administrator

COURTS

16th District Court **620.723.3317**
Fax 620.723.2970
Web .... www.kscourts.org
E-mail .... ann.dixson@kiowacountyks.net
    211 E Florida Ave Stop 5, Greensburg,
    KS 67054-2298
Honorable Ann L. Dixson, Judge

POLICE AND SHERIFF

Sheriff's Ofc **620.723.2182**
Fax 620.723.3328
Web .... www.midway.net
E-mail .... kiowsco@midway.net
    200 E Wisconsin Ave, Greensburg, KS 67054-2339
Kendall Lothman, Sheriff

Labette County

SOCIAL SERVICES

Social & Rehabilitation Svcs **620.421.4500**
Fax 620.421.9581
    300 N 17th St, Parsons, KS 67357
Scott Thompson, Area Director

GENERAL HEALTH SERVICES

Parsons Health Dept **620.421.4350**
Fax 620.421.2324
Web . . . . www.labettecounty.com
E-mail . . . . hd@labettecounty.com
 1902 S 59 building C, Parsons, KS 67357
 Debbi Baugher, Adminstrator

POLICE AND SHERIFF

Sheriff's Ofc **620.795.2565**
Fax 620.795.4664
Web . . . . www.labettecounty.com
E-mail . . . . lbso@labettecounty.com
 718 5th St, Oswego, KS 67356
 William C. Blundell, Sheriff

Lane County

COURTS

24th District Court **620.397.2807**
Fax 620.397.5526
Web . . . . www.st-tel.net
E-mail . . . . ledistct@st-tel.net
 144 S Lane, Dighton, KS 67839
 Magistrate Shelley Selfridge, Director

POLICE AND SHERIFF

Sheriff's Ofc **620.397.2452**
Fax 620.397.5933
 144 S Lane, Dighton, KS 67839
 Donald L. Wilson, Sheriff

Leavenworth County

SOCIAL SERVICES

Social & Rehabilitation Svcs **913.680.2200**
Fax 913.680.2125
 515 Limit St Ste 100, Leavenworth, KS 66048-4590
 Phyllis Gilmore, Regional Director

JUSTICE AGENCY

CASA **913.651.6440**
Fax 913.651.6494
Web . . . . www.casa.lvnks.com
E-mail . . . . lv1casa@sbcglobal.net
 100 S 5th St, Leavenworth, KS 66048-2605
 Jennifer Swartz, Director

Probation Svcs **913.684.0750**
Fax 913.684.0752
Web . . . . www.leavenworthcounty.org
E-mail . . . . tweishaar@leavenworthcounty.org
 601 S 3rd St Ste 3026, Leavenworth, KS 66048-2760
 Tom Weishaar, Chief Court Services Officer

COURTS

1st District Court **913.684.0700**
Fax 913.684.0492
 601 S 3rd St, Ste 3051, Leavenworth, KS 66048-2767
 Honorable Frederick Stewart, Director

POLICE AND SHERIFF

Sheriff's Ofc **913.682.1313**
Fax 913.758.4097
Web . . . . www.leavenworthcounty.org
E-mail . . . . dzelner@leavenworthcounty.org
 601 S 3rd St, Ste 2007, Leavenworth, KS 66048-2764
 David Zoellner, Sheriff

Lincoln County

GENERAL HEALTH SERVICES

Health Dept **785.524.4406**
Fax 785.524.5003
Web . . . . www.lchd@att.net
E-mail . . . . lcclerk@lincolncoks.org
 114 W Court St, Lincoln, KS 67455-2202
 Ladonna Reinert, Rn, Director

POLICE AND SHERIFF

Sheriff's Ofc **785.524.4479**
Fax 785.524.4108
 116 N 2nd St, Lincoln, KS 67459
 Russ Black, Sheriff

Linn County

GENERAL HEALTH SERVICES

Health Dept **913.352.6640**
Fax 913.352.6730
E-mail . . . . linn054@yahoo.com
 902 Main St, Pleasanton, KS 66075
 Donna Thomas, Administrator

COURTS

6th District Court **913.795.2622**
Fax 913.795.2004
E-mail . . . . warea@kscourts.org
 318 Chestnut St, Mound City, KS 66056
 Richard M Smith, Judge

POLICE AND SHERIFF

Sheriff's Offc **913.795.2666**
Fax 913.795.2380
E-mail . . . . linncosheriff@earthlink.net
 107 South 4th St, Mound City, KS 66056
 Barry Walker, Sheriff

Lyon County

SOCIAL SERVICES

Emporia SRS Area Ofc **620.342.2505**
Fax 620.342.2808
Web . . . . www.srs.ks.gov
 1701 Wheeler St, Emporia, KS 66801-6147
 Cyrilla Petracek, South Central Regional Director

GENERAL HEALTH SERVICES

Health Dept **620.342.4864**
Fax 620.342.6555
Web . . . . www.flinthillshealth.org
E-mail . . . . rhively@flinthillshealth.org
 420 W 15th Ave, Emporia, KS 66801
 Renee Hively, Rn, Hiv Coordinator

JUSTICE AGENCY

CASA of the Flint Hills **620.343.2744**
Fax 620.343.3070
 25 W 5th Ave, Emporia, KS 66801
 Mickey Edwards, Director

Court Svcs **620.341.3294**
Fax 620.341.3456
E-mail . . . . rsullivan@lyoncounty.org
 430 Commercial St, Emporia, KS 66801
 Robert A. Sullivan, Director

POLICE AND SHERIFF

Sheriff's Dept **620.342.5545**
Fax 620.343.2074
 425 Mechanic St, Emporia, KS 66801
 Jeff Cope, Sheriff

Marion County

GENERAL HEALTH SERVICES

Health Dept **620.382.2550**
Fax 620.382.8823
 230 E Main St, Marion, KS 66861
 Diedre Serene, Administrator

COURTS

8th District Court **620.382.2104**
Fax 620.382.2259
Web www.8thjd.com
E-mail . . . . jhelmer@8thjd.com
 200 S 3rd St Ste 201, Marion, KS 66861-1656
 Honorable Michael F. Powers, Judge

POLICE AND SHERIFF

Sheriff's Ofc **620.382.2144**
Fax 620.382.3441
Web . . . . www.marioncoks.net
E-mail . . . . rcraft@marioncoks.net
 203 S 4th St A, Marion, KS 66861-1511
 Robert Craft, Sheriff

Marshall County

SOCIAL SERVICES

**Marysville Social & Rehabilitation
Svcs** **785.562.5338**
Fax 785.562.3057
 406 N 3rd St Ste 2, Marysville, KS 66508
 Betsy Thompson, Area Director

GENERAL HEALTH SERVICES

Health Dept **785.562.3485**
Fax 785.562.9984
 600 Broadway, Marysville, KS 66508
 Sue Rhodes, Administrator

COURTS

22nd District Court **785.562.5301**
Fax 785.562.2458
Web . . . . www.bluevalley.net
E-mail . . . . mcdc@bluevalley.net
 1201 Broadway Ste 5, Marysville, KS 66508-1844
 Honorable Angela Hecke, Director/Judge

POLICE AND SHERIFF

Frankfort Police Dept **785.562.3141**
 107 S 13th, Marysville, KS 66538
 Daniel Hargrave, Police Chief

Sheriff's Ofc **785.562.3141**
Fax 785.562.2743
E-mail . . . . mss058@yahoo.com
 107 S 13th St, Marysville, KS 66508-1857
 Daniel Hargarez, Sheriff

McPherson County

SOCIAL SERVICES

Social and Rehabilitation Svcs **620.241.3802**
Fax 620.241.0710
Web . . . . www.srs.ks.gov
 218 E Kansas Ave, McPherson, KS 67460-4839
 Christyn Schroeder, Administrative Assistant

GENERAL HEALTH SERVICES

Health Dept **620.241.1753**
Fax 620.241.1756
E-mail . . . . mchd@machealth.org
 1001 N Main St, McPherson, KS 67460
 Fern Hess, Rn, Nursing Supervisor

JUSTICE AGENCY

Court Svcs **620.241.3510**
Fax 620.241.3744
 117 N Maple St, McPherson, KS 67460
 Jennifer Foster, Chief Court Services Officer

COURTS

9th District Court **620.241.3422**
Fax 620.241.1372
E-mail . . . . cindyt@9thdistct.net
 117 N Maple St, McPherson, KS 67460
 Honorable Richard Walker, Chief Judge

POLICE AND SHERIFF

Sheriff's Ofc **620.245.1225**
Fax 620.245.1237
 1177 W Woodside St, Mcpherson, KS 67460
 Larry G. Powell, Sheriff

Kansas

Meade County

COURTS

16th District Court **620.873.8760**
Fax 620.873.8759
   200 N Fowler St, Meade, KS 67864
Honorable Keith Whitney, Judge

POLICE AND SHERIFF

Sheriff's Ofc **620.873.8765**
Fax 620.873.8778
Web . . . . www.meadeso.com
E-mail . . . . mmiller@meadeso.com
   223 N Meade Center St, Meade, KS 67864-6403
Mark Miller, Sheriff

Miami County

SOCIAL SERVICES

Osawatomie Social & Rehabilitation
Svcs **913.755.2162**
Fax 913.755.4228
E-mail . . . . lori.beznique@srs.ks.gov
   616 Brown Ave, Osawatomie, KS 66064-1415
Lori Beznique, Area Director

GENERAL HEALTH SERVICES

Health Dept - Home Health **913.294.2431**
Fax 913.294.9506
E-mail . . . . mchealth@classicnet.net
   1201 Lakemary Dr, Paola, KS 66071
Rita Mckoon, Rn, Administrator

MENTAL HEALTH SERVICES

Mental Health Ctr **913.557.9096**
Fax 913.294.9247
Web . . . . www.elizabethcenter.org
   505 S Hospital Dr, Paola, KS 66071
Gerald Gambrill, Medical Director

COURTS

6th District Court **913.294.3644**
Fax 913.294.2535
   120 S Pearl St, Paola, KS 66071
Honorable Amy Harth, District Court Judge

POLICE AND SHERIFF

Sheriff's Ofc **913.294.4444**
Fax 913.294.9119
   118 S Pearl St, Paola, KS 66071
Frank Kelly, Sheriff

Mitchell County

GENERAL HEALTH SERVICES

North Central Kansas Home Health
Agency **785.738.5175**
Fax 785.738.5053
   310 W 8th St, Beloit, KS 67420
Sondra Hone, Administrator

POLICE AND SHERIFF

Sheriff's Ofc **785.738.3523**
Fax 785.738.3518
E-mail . . . . dord@nckcn.com
   114 S Campbell Ave, Beloit, KS 67420-0338
Douglas R. Daugherty, Sheriff

Montgomery County

SOCIAL SERVICES

Independence Social & Rehabilitation
Svcs **620.331.0350**
Fax 620.331.7667
Web . . . . www.srs.ks.gov
   200 Arco Pl, Ste 220, Independence, KS 67301
Scott Thompson, Area Director

Social & Rehabilitation Svcs **620.251.5750**
Fax 620.251.2434
   602 Union St, Coffeyville, KS 67301
Scott Thompson, Interim Director

GENERAL HEALTH SERVICES

Health Dept **620.251.4210**
Fax 620.251.6708
   908 Walnut St, Coffeyville, KS 67337-5827
Ruth Bardwell, Rn, Administrator

Health Dept **620.331.4300**
Fax 620.331.3491
E-mail . . . . mchd2@sbcglobal.net
   209 E Laurel St, Independence, KS 67301-3136
Chan Han, Md, Medical Consultant

MENTAL HEALTH SERVICES

Mental Health Ctr **620.331.1748**
Fax 620.332.1940
Web . . . . www.fourcounty.com
E-mail . . . . ghennen@fourcounty.com
   3751 W Main St, Independence, KS 67301-8446
Greg Hennen, Executive Director

COURTS

14th District Court **620.330.1070**
Fax 620.331.6120
   300 E Main St Ste 201, Independence, KS 67301
Mary E. Kadel, Court Administraor

POLICE AND SHERIFF

Sheriff's Ofc **620.330.1000**
Fax 620.331.1686
E-mail . . . . stan.veach@atf.gov
   300 E Main St Ste 102, Independence,
   KS 67301-3762
Robert Dierks, Sheriff

Morris County

GENERAL HEALTH SERVICES

Health Dept **620.767.5175**
Fax 620.767.6880
Web . . . . www.centrahealth.com
   221 Hockaday St, Council Grove, KS 66846-1830
Ashley Hinkson, Administrator

COURTS

8th District Court **620.767.6838**
Fax 620.767.6488
Web www.8thjd.com
E-mail . . . . scarlson@shorewest.com
   501 W Main St Ste 13, Council Grove,
   KS 66846-1701
Sondra Carlson, Clerk

POLICE AND SHERIFF

Sheriff's Ofc **620.767.6310**
Fax 620.767.7177
E-mail . . . . mrxso@yahoo.com
   501 W Main St Ste 13, Council Grove, KS 66846
Scott Coover, Sheriff

Morton County

COURTS

26th District Court **620.697.2563**
Fax 620.697.4289
E-mail . . . . mtcodist@elkhart.com
   1025 Morton St, Elkhart, KS 67950
Honorable Roseanna K. Volden, Judge

POLICE AND SHERIFF

Sheriff's Ofc **620.697.4313**
Fax 620.697.2832
Web . . . . www.elkhart.com
E-mail . . . . lyoungers@elkhart.com
   1026 Richard St, Elkhart, KS 67950
Loren W. Youngers, Sheriff

Nehama County

GENERAL HEALTH SERVICES

Health Dept **785.284.2152**
Fax 785.284.3827
E-mail . . . . ncchs@stcglobal.net
   1004 Main St, Sabetha, KS 66534
Jane Sunderland, Director

POLICE AND SHERIFF

Sheriff's Ofc **785.336.2311**
Fax 785.336.2788
   212 N 6th St, Seneca, KS 66538-1718
Richard Vernon, Sheriff

Nemaha County

COURTS

22nd District Court **785.336.2146**
Fax 785.336.6450
E-mail . . . . nmcourt@carsoncomm.com
   607 Nemaha St, Seneca, KS 66538
Patricia Heideman, Clerk Of Court

Neosho County

SOCIAL SERVICES

Chanute SRS Area Ofc **620.431.5000**
Fax 620.431.5055
E-mail . . . . scott.thompson@srs.gov
   1500 W 7th St Ste 4, Chanute, KS 66720
Scott Thompson, Director

GENERAL HEALTH SERVICES

Health Dept **620.431.5770**
Fax 620.431.5772
E-mail . . . . nchd@cableone.net
   320 E Main St, Chanute, KS 66720
Teresa Starr, Administrator

POLICE AND SHERIFF

Sheriff's Ofc **620.244.3888**
Fax 620.244.3887
E-mail . . . . ksa@kansassheriff.org
   42 East State, Erie, KS 66733-0109
Jim Keath, Sheriff

Ness County

GENERAL HEALTH SERVICES

Health Dept **785.798.3388**
Fax 785.798.2389
   202 W Sycamore St Ste 1, Ness City, KS 67560
Eva Petersen, Director

JUSTICE AGENCY

Court Svcs **785.798.3695**
Fax 785.798.3839
E-mail . . . . ccso24th@gbta.net
   202 W Sycamore St, Ness City, KS 67560-1907
Sue Fehrenbach, Chief Officer

COURTS

24th District Court **785.798.3200**
Fax 785.798.3348
Web . . . . www.gbta.net
E-mail . . . . nsdistct@gbta.net
   202 W Sycamore St, Ness City, KS 67560
Joby Henning, Clerk

POLICE AND SHERIFF

Sheriff's Ofc **785.798.3611**
Fax 785.798.2704
    221 W Main St, Ness City, KS 67560
    Bryan Whipple, Sheriff

Norton County

GENERAL HEALTH SERVICES

Norton Health Dept. PRN Home Health
Agency **785.877.5745**
Fax 785.877.5746
    801 N Norton Ave, Norton, KS 67654-1432
    Gina Frack, Administrator

MENTAL HEALTH SERVICES

High Plains Mental Health Ctr **785.877.5141**
Fax 785.877.5142
    211 S Norton Ave, Norton, KS 67654
    Walt Hill, Executive Director

COURTS

17th District Court **785.877.5735**
Fax 785.877.5722
E-mail ....mjatlast@ruraltel.net
    101 S Kansas Ave, Norton, KS 67654
    Honorable Debra Anderson, Judge

POLICE AND SHERIFF

Sheriff's Ofc **785.877.5780**
Fax 785.877.5782
E-mail ....ntso@ruraltel.net
    101 S Norton Ave, Norton, KS 67654
    Troy Thomson, Sheriff

Osage County

SOCIAL SERVICES

Lyndon Social & Rehabilitation
Svcs **785.828.4491**
Fax 785.828.3137
    715 Washington St, Lyndon, KS 66451
    Matt Boddington, Area Director

GENERAL HEALTH SERVICES

Health Dept **785.828.3117**
Fax 785.828.3848
Web ....www.osagecountyhealthdept.com
    103 W 9th St, Lyndon, KS 66451-9559
    Anne Gray, Director

COURTS

4th District Court **785.828.4514**
Fax 785.828.4704
E-mail ....charna@embarqmail.com
    717 Topeka Ave, Lyndon, KS 66451-9792
    Charna Williams, Head Clerk

POLICE AND SHERIFF

Sheriff's Ofc **785.828.3121**
Fax 785.828.3662
E-mail ....info@oscosheriff.org
    131 W Portland St, Lyndon, KS 66451
    Laurie Dunn, Sheriff

Osborne County

COURTS

17th District Court **785.346.2442**
Fax 785.346.5992
Web ....www.ruraltel.net
E-mail ....obcodc@ruraltel.net
    423 W Main St, Osborne, KS 67473-2301
    Sheryl Gorsuch, Clerk

POLICE AND SHERIFF

Sheriff's Ofc **785.346.2001**
Fax 785.346.2345
E-mail ....curt_miner@hotmail.com
    104 S 5th St, Osborne, KS 67473-2304
    Curtis L. Miner, Sheriff

Ottawa County

GENERAL HEALTH SERVICES

Ottawa Health Dept **785.392.2822**
Fax 785.392.3640
    817A Argyle Ave, Minneapolis, KS 67467
    Sandy Cline, Director

COURTS

28th District Court **785.392.2917**
Fax 785.392.3626
Web ....www.nckcn.com
E-mail ....clerkone@nckcn.com
    307 N Concord St Ste 190, Minneapolis,
    KS 67467-2129
    Cheryl Adams, Clerk Of Court

POLICE AND SHERIFF

Delphos Police Dept **785.523.4361**
Fax 785.523.4391
E-mail ....delphos@nckcn.com
    202 W. Second Street., Delphos, KS 67436
    Steve Ringquist, Police Chief

Sheriff's Ofc **785.392.2157**
Fax 785.392.3659
E-mail ....sheriffcoleman@ottawacounty.org
    312 N Ottawa St, Minneapolis, KS 67467
    Keith Coleman, Sheriff

Pawnee County

SOCIAL SERVICES

Social Rehab Svcs **620.285.4630**
    1301 Hwy 264, PO Box 47, Larned, KS 67550

GENERAL HEALTH SERVICES

Health Dept **620.285.6963**
Fax 620.285.3246
E-mail ....MaryBeth@PAWNEE.KSCOXMAIL.COM
    715 Broadway St Stop 6, Larned, KS 67550
    Mary Beth Herrmann, Rn, Director

COURTS

24th District Court **620.285.6937**
Fax 620.285.3665
Web ....www.nckcn.com
    715 Broadway St Fl 3, Larned, KS 67550-3000
    Honorable Julie Fletcher-cowell, Magistrate

POLICE AND SHERIFF

Sheriff's Ofc **620.285.2211**
Fax 620.285.7073
Web ....www.pawneecountysheriff.org
E-mail ....info@pawneecountysheriff.org
    116 W 8th St, Larned, KS 67550-2501
    Scott King, Sheriff

Phillips County

SOCIAL SERVICES

Phillipsburg Social & Rehabilitation
Svcs **785.543.5258**
Fax 785.543.5283
Web ....www.srs.ks.gov
E-mail ....shannon.lindsey@srs.ks.gov
    111 E Highway 36, Phillipsburg, KS 67661-9473
    Shannon Lindsey, Site Manager

GENERAL HEALTH SERVICES

Health Dept **785.543.6850**
Fax 785.543.6852
E-mail ....adminpcht@ruraltel.net
    784 6th St, Courthouse Annex, Phillipsburg,
    KS 67661
    Louette Forrel, Director

MENTAL HEALTH SERVICES

High Plains Mental Health Ctr **785.543.5284**
Fax 785.543.5285
Web ....www.highplainsmentalhealth.com
E-mail ....rex.harman@hpmhc.com
    783 7th St, Phillipsburg, KS 67661-2141
    Rex Harman, Site Manager

COURTS

17th District Court **785.543.6830**
Fax 785.543.6832
E-mail ....plcocdc@ruraltel.net
    301 State St, Phillipsburg, KS 67661
    Debra Grammon, Clerk Of Court

POLICE AND SHERIFF

Sheriff's Ofc **785.543.6885**
Fax 785.543.2289
Web ....www.ruraltel.net
E-mail ....plcotr@ruraltel.net
    301 State St Ste G, Phillipsburg, KS 67661-1940
    Paul Wisinger, Sheriff

Pottawatomie County

GENERAL HEALTH SERVICES

Health Dept **785.457.3719**
Fax 785.457.2144
Web ....www.pottcounty.org
E-mail ....dlind@pottcounty.org
    320 Main St, Westmoreland, KS 66549-9684
    Deb Lind, Hiv Coordinator

COURTS

2nd District Court **785.457.3392**
Fax 785.457.2107
Web ....www.kansas.net
E-mail ....ptcourts@hotmail.com
    106 Main St, Westmoreland, KS 66549-9816
    Honorable Steven M. Roth, Judge

Pratt County

SOCIAL SERVICES

Social & Rehabilitation Svcs **620.672.5955**
Fax 620.672.9391
    400 S Main St Ste B, Pratt, KS 67124
    Cindy Bowen, Site Supervisor

GENERAL HEALTH SERVICES

Health Dept **620.672.4135**
Fax 620.672.1129
    712 S Main St, Pratt, KS 67124
    Debbie Mcgraw, Rn, Director

COURTS

30th District Court **620.672.4102**
Fax 620.672.2902
Web ....www.prattcounty.org
E-mail ....johnna@prattcounty.org
    300 S Ninnescah St, Pratt, KS 67124-2733
    Honorable Robert J. Schmisseur, Judge

POLICE AND SHERIFF

Sheriff's Ofc **620.672.4133**
Fax 620.672.2571
Web ....www.prattcountysheriff.org
E-mail ....vchinn@prattso.org
    303 S Oak St, Pratt, KS 67124-2724
    Vernon Chinn, Sheriff

Rawlins County

COURTS

15th District Court.........................**785.626.3465**
Fax.........................785.626.3350
Web.........................www.kscourts.org
607 Main St Ste F, Atwood, KS 67730-1839
Bessie Persinger, Clerk Of Court

POLICE AND SHERIFF

Sheriff's Ofc.........................**785.626.3865**
Fax.........................785.626.3764
607 Main St Ste G, Atwood, KS 67730
William Finley, Sheriff

Reno County

SOCIAL SERVICES

Hutchison SRS Area Ofc...............**620.663.5731**
Fax.........................620.663.7868
Web.........................www.srskansas.org
E-mail.........................cyrillapatrick@srs.ks.gov
600 Andrew Ave, South Hutchinson, KS 67505
Cyrilla Patrick, Regional Director

GENERAL HEALTH SERVICES

Health Dept.........................**620.694.2900**
Fax.........................620.694.2901
Web.........................www.renogov.org
E-mail.........................judy.seltzer@renogov.org
209 W 2nd Ave, Hutchinson, KS 67501-5232
Judith Seltzer, Rn, Director

JUSTICE AGENCY

CASA - Visions of Hope, Inc..............**620.662.1688**
Fax.........................620.662.4737
E-mail.........................vohinc@hotmail.com
206 W 1st Ave, Hutchinson, KS 67501
Sharon Stokes, Executive Director

Probation Svcs.........................**620.665.8800**
Fax.........................620.665.8886
Web.........................www.renogov.org
E-mail.........................john.pahl@renogov.org
111 W 1st Ave, Hutchinson, KS 67501-5235
John Pahl, Chief Court Services Officer

COURTS

27th District Court.........................**620.694.2972**
Fax.........................620.694.2960
Web.........................www.ourtownusa.net
E-mail.........................dick@ourtownusa.net
206 W 1st Ave, Hutchinson, KS 67501-5204
Honorable Patricia Macke Dick, Judge

POLICE AND SHERIFF

Sheriff's Ofc.........................**620.694.2735**
Fax.........................620.694.2702
E-mail.........................randy.henderson@renogov.com
210 W 1st Ave, Hutchinson, KS 67501
Randy Henderson, Sheriff

Republic County

GENERAL HEALTH SERVICES

Health Dept.........................**785.527.5671**
Fax.........................785.527.2892
1206 18th St, Belleville, KS 66935
Marcia Hansen, Director

POLICE AND SHERIFF

Sheriff's Ofc.........................**785.527.5658**
Fax.........................785.527.2717
1815 M St Ste 5, Belleville, KS 66935-2242
Ronald W. Blad, Sheriff

Rice County

GENERAL HEALTH SERVICES

Health Dept.........................**620.257.2171**
Fax.........................620.257.7856
1486 W US Highway 56, Lyons, KS 67554
Marcai Detmer, Director

COURTS

District Court.........................**620.257.2384**
Fax.........................620.257.3826
E-mail.........................rcdiscrt@hotmail.com
101 W Commercial St Ste 8, Lyons, KS 67554
Jane Hrabik, Clerk

POLICE AND SHERIFF

Sheriff's Ofc.........................**620.257.7876**
Fax.........................620.257.2221
Web.........................www.usacops.com
1482 W US Highway 56, Lyons, KS 67554-9209
Dale Higgins, Sheriff

Riley County

SOCIAL SERVICES

Manhattan SRS Area Ofc.....................**785.776.4011**
Fax.........................785.776.7722
Web.........................www.accesskansas.gov
2709 Amherst Ave, Manhattan, KS 66502
Matt Boddington, Director

GENERAL HEALTH SERVICES

Health Dept.........................**785.776.4779**
Fax.........................785.565.6565
Web.........................www.rileycountyks.gov
2030 Tecumseh Rd, Manhattan, KS 66502-3563
Donna Hart, STD Director

JUSTICE AGENCY

CASA.........................**785.537.6367**
Fax.........................785.565.6445
Web.........................www.casa.manhattanks.org
E-mail.........................sunfcasa@interkan.net
115 N 4th St, Ste 6, Manhattan, KS 66502-6663
Jayme Morris-Hardemann, Executive Director Of Sun Flower Project

COURTS

21st District Court.........................**785.537.6364**
Fax.........................785.537.6382
Web.........................www.co.riley.ks.us
E-mail.........................pmiller@rileycountyks.gov
100 COURTHOUSE PLZ STE 201, Manhattan,
KS 66502-6105
Honorable Paul E. Miller, Chief Judge

POLICE AND SHERIFF

Sheriff's Ofc.........................**785.537.2112**
Fax.........................785.565.6550
Web.........................www.rileycountypolice.org
E-mail.........................contact_rcpd@rileycountypolice.org
1001 S Seth Child Rd, Manhattan, KS 66502
Brad Schoen, Sheriff

Rooks County

GENERAL HEALTH SERVICES

Home & Health Agency.....................**785.425.7352**
Fax.........................785.425.7075
E-mail.........................rooksco@ruraltel.net
426 Main St, Stockton, KS 67669-1930
Lorraine Baughman, Director

POLICE AND SHERIFF

Sheriff's Ofc.........................**785.425.6312**
Fax.........................785.425.6853
115 N Walnut st, Stockton, KS 67669
Randy Axelson, Sheriff

Rush County

GENERAL HEALTH SERVICES

Health Dept.........................**785.222.3427**
Fax.........................785.222.3593
611 Peace St, Lacrosse, KS 67548
Kim Knieling, Rn, Director

COURTS

24th District Court.........................**785.222.2718**
Fax.........................785.222.2748
Web.........................www.gbta.net
E-mail.........................rhdistct@gbta.net
715 Elm, La Crosse, KS 67548
Dale Snyder, Judge

POLICE AND SHERIFF

Sheriff's Ofc.........................**785.222.2578**
Fax.........................785.222.3328
Web.........................www.ks-sheriff.org
E-mail.........................rhso@hotmail.com
715 Elm St, La Crosse, KS 67548
Ward K. Corsair, Sheriff

Russell County

GENERAL HEALTH SERVICES

Health Dept.........................**785.483.6433**
Fax.........................785.483.3118
Web.........................www.ruraltel.net
E-mail.........................russellhd@ruraltel.net
189 W Luray St, Russell, KS 67665-2924
Paula Florian, Rn, Director

COURTS

20th District Court.........................**785.483.5641**
Fax.........................785.483.2448
E-mail.........................russelldistcourt@media-net.net
4th & Main, Russell, KS 67665-0876
Honorable Marty Clark, Magistrate

POLICE AND SHERIFF

Sheriff's Ofc.........................**785.483.2151**
Fax.........................785.483.3681
E-mail.........................sheriff@media-net.net
210 E 4th St, Russell, KS 67665
John Fletcher, Sheriff

Saline County

SOCIAL SERVICES

**Salina Social and Rehabilitation
Svcs**.........................**785.826.8000**
Fax.........................785.827.4199
Web.........................www.srskansas.org
901 Westchester Dr, Salina, KS 67401-7441
Betsy Thompson, Area Director

GENERAL HEALTH SERVICES

Health Dept.........................**785.826.6600**
Fax.........................785.826.6605
125 W Elm St, Salina, KS 67401
Del Myers, Hiv Care Supervisor

MENTAL HEALTH SERVICES

Central Kansas Mental Health Ctr.............**785.823.6322**
Fax.........................785.823.3109
Web.........................www.ckmhc.org
E-mail.........................murray@ckmhc.org
809 Elmhurst Blvd, Saline, KS 67401-7428
Patricia Murray, LCSW, Executive Director

COURTS

28th District Court.........................**785.309.5831**
Fax.........................785.309.5845
300 W Ash St, Salina, KS 67401
Kevin Emerson, Chief Court Services Officer

POLICE AND SHERIFF

Sheriff's Ofc..........................**785.826.6500**
Fax...785.827.1050
Web..www.saline.org
E-mail.....................glen.kochanowski@saline.org
   251 N 10th St, Salina, KS 67401-2149
Glen F. Kochanowski, Sheriff

Scott County

GENERAL HEALTH SERVICES

Health Dept...........................**620.872.5774**
Fax...620.872.2314
Web..www.att.net
E-mail.......................karen.sattler@att.net
   608 S Main St, Scott City, KS 67871-1517
Karen Sattler, Rn, Director

COURTS

25th District Court....................**620.872.7208**
Fax...620.872.3683
E-mail................................scdc@wdsnet.org
   303 Court St Ste 1, Scott City, KS 67871
Honorable James R. Collins, Magistrate Judge

Sedgwick County

SOCIAL SERVICES

Wichita SRS Regional Ofc...............**316.337.6314**
Fax...316.337.6789
Web..www.srskansas.org
E-mail.......................jean.hogan@srs.ks.gov
   230 E William St, Wichita, KS 67201-1620
Jean Hogan, Director

GENERAL HEALTH SERVICES

Dept of Community Health................**316.660.7300**
Fax...316.383.7509
Web..www.fedrickcounty.gov
E-mail.......................cblackburn@sedgwick.gov
   2716 W Central Ave, Wichita, KS 67203-4904
Claudia Blackburn, Director

JUSTICE AGENCY

CASA.......................................**316.866.2920**
Fax...316.866.2923
Web..www.casaofsedgwickcounty.org
E-mail.......................casaofsedgwickcounty.org
   150 N Main Ste1010, Wichita, KS 67202
Ann Duncan, Executive Director

COURTS

18th District Court....................**316.660.5800**
Fax...316.660.5784
Web..www.dc18.org
E-mail.......................blumbrer@dc18.org
   525 N Main St, Wichita, KS 67203
Bernie Lumbreras, Clerk Of Court

POLICE AND SHERIFF

Police Dept...............................**316.268.4111**
Fax...316.268.4566
Web..www.wichita.gov
   455 N Main St Ste 501, Wichita, KS 67202-1684
Norman Williams, Chief Of Police

EDUCATION SERVICES

Communities In Schools.................**316.973.5110**
Fax...316.973.5145
E-mail.......................jfrick@ciswichita.org
   412 S Main, Ste 212, Wichita, KS 67202
Judy Frick, Executive Director

Seward County

SOCIAL SERVICES

Social & Rehabilitation Svcs..............**620.626.3700**
Fax...620.626.3702
E-mail.......................dorothy.wedel@srs.ks.gov
   615 N Kansas Ave, Liberal, KS 67901
Dorothy Wedel, Supervisor

GENERAL HEALTH SERVICES

Health Dept...........................**620.626.3369**
Fax...620.626.3312
Web..www.sewardcountyks.org
E-mail.......................mbrown@sewardcountyks.org
   103 W 2nd St, Liberal, KS 67901-3719
Martha Brown, Rn, Nursing Director

COURTS

26th District Court....................**620.626.3375**
Fax...620.626.3302
Web..www.swko.net
E-mail.......................swcdc@swko.net
   415 N Washington Ave Ste 103, Liberal,
   KS 67901-3462
Koleen Nosekabel, District Clerk

POLICE AND SHERIFF

Sheriff's Dept...........................**620.309.2000**
Fax...620.309.2045
E-mail.......................sheriff@swko.net
   501 N Washington Ave, Liberal, KS 67901
Billy D. Mcbryde, Sheriff

Shawnee County

SOCIAL SERVICES

Topeka SRS Area Ofc.....................**785.296.2500**
Fax...785.296.5895
Web..www.srs.ks.gov
E-mail.......................bat@srs.ks.gov
   500 SW Van Buren St, Topeka, KS 66603-3335
Betsy Thompson, Area Director

GENERAL HEALTH SERVICES

Home & Health Agency...................**785.368.2000**
Fax...785.368.2098
   1615 SW 8th Ave, Topeka, KS 66606

POLICE AND SHERIFF

Sheriff's Ofc..........................**785.368.2200**
Fax...785.368.2338
E-mail.......................richard.barta@snco.us
   320 S Kansas Ave Ste 200, Topeka, KS 66603
Richard Barta, Sheriff

EDUCATION SERVICES

Special Education.........................**785.575.8670**
Fax...785.575.8680
E-mail.......................flannigan@usd345.com
   901 NW Lyman Rd, Topeka, KS 66608-1900
Bill Flannigan, Special Education Coordinator

Special Education.........................**785.339.4000**
Fax...785.339.4025
   5928 SW 53rd St, Topeka, KS 66610
Ann Elloitt, Special Education Coordinator

Sheridan County

GENERAL HEALTH SERVICES

Health Dept...........................**785.675.2101**
Fax...785.675.2236
   940 8th St, Hoxie, KS 67740
Kerri Schippers, Administrator

COURTS

District Court..........................**785.675.3221**
Fax...785.675.2256
   925 9th St, Hoxie, KS 67740
Honorable John Cahoj, Judge

POLICE AND SHERIFF

Sheriff's Ofc..........................**785.675.3481**
Fax...785.675.2294
E-mail.......................sdso@ruraltel.net
   940 8th St, Hoxie, KS 67740
Brian Fenner, Sheriff

Sherman County

SOCIAL SERVICES

Goodland Social & Rehabilitation
Svcs.......................................**785.899.5661**
Fax...785.899.3216
Web..www.srskansas.org
E-mail.......................jd@srskansas.org
   104 W US Highway 24, Goodland, KS 67735-9642
Jeanne Daniels, Acting Area Director

GENERAL HEALTH SERVICES

Health Dept...........................**785.890.4888**
Fax...785.890.4891
Web..www.sherman.kansasgov.com
E-mail.......................shcounty@st-tel.net
   1622 Broadway, Goodland, KS 67735-3053
Jean Kosmatka, Administrator

COURTS

15th District Court....................**785.890.4850**
Fax...785.890.4858
Web..www.st-tel.net
E-mail.......................jack1313@st-tel.net
   813 Broadway Rm 201, Goodland, KS 67735-3056
Honorable Jack L. Burr, Director

POLICE AND SHERIFF

Sheriff's Dept...........................**785.890.4835**
Fax...785.890.4839
Web..www.shermancountysheriff.com
E-mail.......................sheriff@shermancountysheriff.com
   813 1/2 Broadway, Goodland, KS 67735-3093
Kevin Butts, Sheriff

Smith County

GENERAL HEALTH SERVICES

Home Health Agency.....................**785.282.6656**
Fax...785.282.3301
Web..www.ruraltel.net
E-mail.......................schdlaura@ruraltel.net
   119 S Main St, Smith Center, KS 66967-3001
Laura Hageman, Administrator

COURTS

17th District Court....................**785.282.5140**
Fax...785.282.5145
E-mail.......................smcodc@ruraltel.net
   218 S Grant, Smith Center, KS 66967
Honorable Michael Kirchhoff, Judge

POLICE AND SHERIFF

Sheriff's Ofc..........................**785.282.5180**
Fax...785.282.5185
   217 S Jefferson St, Smith Center, KS 66967
Bruce Lehman, Sheriff

Stafford County

GENERAL HEALTH SERVICES

Health Dept...........................**620.549.3504**
Fax...620.549.6593
   610 E 1st Ave, Saint John, KS 67576
Doris Tompkins, Rn, Administrator

Kansas

COURTS

20th District Court **620.549.3295**
Fax 620.549.3298
E-mail ....rsalem@embarqmail.com
    209 N Broadway, Saint John, KS 67576
Renee Salem, Clerk

POLICE AND SHERIFF

Sheriff's Dept **620.549.3247**
Fax 620.549.6409
Web ....www.st.johnks.net
E-mail ....sheriff@stjohnks.net
    209 N Broadway St Ste A, Saint John, KS 67576-2042
Jeffrey D. Parr, Sheriff

Stanton County

GENERAL HEALTH SERVICES

Health Dept **620.492.6443**
Fax 620.492.1440
E-mail ....county@pld.com
    201 N Main St Courthouse, Johnson, KS 67855
K Ellen Kersey, Rn, Administrator

COURTS

26th District Court **620.492.2180**
Fax 620.492.6410
E-mail ....stcourt@pld.com
    201 N. Main st, Johnson, KS 67855
Honorable Bonnie Porks, Director

POLICE AND SHERIFF

Sheriff's Dept **620.492.6866**
Fax 620.492.2585
E-mail ....sheriff@pld.com
    208 N. Chesnut, Johnson, KS 67855
Ed Bezona, Sheriff

Stevens County

COURTS

26th District Court **620.544.2695**
Fax 620.544.2528
E-mail ....svcodist@pld.com
    200 E 6th St Ste 1, Hugoton, KS 67951-2655
Honorable Paula J. Sosa, Director

Sumner County

SOCIAL SERVICES

Social & Rehabilitation Svcs **620.326.7439**
Fax 620.326.8547
Web ....www.srskansas.org
E-mail ....tr@srskansas.org
    1116 W 8th St, Wellington, KS 67152
Terry Rudkin, Supervisor

GENERAL HEALTH SERVICES

Health Dept **620.326.2774**
Fax 620.326.2738
Web ....www.co.sumner.ks.us
E-mail ....lrettig@sumner.ks.us
    217 W 8th St Ste 1, Wellington, KS 67152-3961
Laura Rettig, Administrator

MENTAL HEALTH SERVICES

Mental Health Ctr **620.326.7448**
Fax 620.326.6662
E-mail ....golson@sumnermentalhealth.org
    1601 W 16th St, Wellington, KS 67152
Gregory G. Olson, Ms, CEO

JUSTICE AGENCY

CASA Program **620.326.8919**
Fax 620.326.5576
E-mail ....casaadvocates@hotmail.com
    120 E 9th St, Wellington, KS 67152
Tammy Bradbury, Director

COURTS

30th District Court **620.326.5936**
Fax 620.326.5365
Web ....www.sutv.com
E-mail ....dcclerk@sutv.com
    501 N Washington Ave Ste 202, Wellington,
    KS 67152-4075
Carolyn Jones, Clerk

POLICE AND SHERIFF

Sheriff's Ofc **620.326.8943**
Fax 620.399.1073
    610 E Hillside St, Wellington, KS 67152
Gerald Gilkey, Sheriff

Thomas County

SOCIAL SERVICES

Social and Rehabilitation Svcs **785.462.6760**
Fax 785.462.6985
    1135 S Country Club Dr Ste 1, Colby,
    KS 67701-3666
Sherry Cambell, Director

GENERAL HEALTH SERVICES

Health Dept **785.460.4596**
Fax 785.460.4595
Web ....www.thomascohealth.com
E-mail ....admin@thomascohealth.com
    350 S Range Ave Ste 2, Colby, KS 67701-2966
Kasiah Rothchilde, Administrator

COURTS

15th District Court **785.460.4540**
Fax 785.460.2291
    300 N Court Ave, Colby, KS 67701
Honorable Glen D. Schiffner, District Judge

POLICE AND SHERIFF

Sheriffs Ofc **785.460.4570**
Fax 785.460.3877
    225 N Court Ave, Colby, KS 67701
Rod Taylor, Sheriff

Trego County

POLICE AND SHERIFF

Sheriff's Ofc **785.743.5721**
Fax 785.743.6474
    525 Warren Ave, Wakeeney, KS 67672
Richard Schneider, Sheriff

Wabaunsee County

GENERAL HEALTH SERVICES

Health Dept **785.765.2425**
Fax 785.765.3594
Web ....www.wabaunsee.com
    215 Kansas Ave, Courthouse, Alma, KS 66401-9797
Janet Wertzberger, Rn, Director

COURTS

2nd District Court **785.765.2406**
Fax 785.765.2487
E-mail ....dctalma@embarqmail.com
    215 Kansas Ave, Alma, KS 66401
Honorable Blaine Carter, Magistrate

POLICE AND SHERIFF

Sheriff's Ofc **785.765.2217**
Fax 785.765.2339
Web ....www.wabaunseesheriff.com
E-mail ....wbso@earthlink.net
    215 Kansas Ave, Alma, KS 66401-9797
Doug Howser, Sheriff

Wallace County

GENERAL HEALTH SERVICES

Health Dept **785.852.4272**
Fax 785.852.4249
E-mail ....wchealth@fairpoint.net
    104 E 4th St, Sharon Springs, KS 67758
Brenda Drennan, Director

COURTS

15th District Court **785.852.4289**
Fax 785.852.4271
E-mail ....wacodcc@sunflowertelco.com
    313 Main St, Sharon Springs, KS 67758
Honorable Steve R. Unruh, Judge

POLICE AND SHERIFF

Sheriff's Ofc **785.852.4288**
Fax 785.852.4275
E-mail ....wacoso@sunflowertelco.net
    313 Main St, Sharon Springs, KS 67758
Larry Townsend, Sheriff

Washington County

GENERAL HEALTH SERVICES

Health Dept **785.325.2600**
Fax 785.325.2688
E-mail ....wchealth@truevalley.net
    115 W 3rd St, Washington, KS 66968
Janice Kearn, Rn, Director

POLICE AND SHERIFF

Sheriff's Ofc **785.325.2293**
Fax 785.325.2924
    301 B St, Washington, KS 66968
William Dickson, Sheriff

Wichita County

GENERAL HEALTH SERVICES

Health Dept **620.375.2289**
Fax 620.375.2826
E-mail ....whcohd@sunflowertelco.com
    104 S Indian Rd, Leoti, KS 67861-5039
Marvel Brandt, Clinical Director

POLICE AND SHERIFF

Sheriff's Ofc **620.375.2723**
Fax 620.375.2635
Web ....www.sunflowertelco.com
    411 S 4th St, Leoti, KS 67861-7021
Randy Keeton, Sheriff

Wilson County

GENERAL HEALTH SERVICES

Health Dept **620.378.4455**
Fax 620.378.4647
Web ....www.wlhealthkansas.org
E-mail ....wlhealth@twinmounts.com
    421 N 7th St, Fredonia, KS 66736-1342
Todd Durham, Rn, Administrator

COURTS

31st District Court **620.378.4361**
Fax 620.378.4531
E-mail ....cdc@twinmound.com
    615 Madison St, Fredonia, KS 66736
Honorable David W. Rogers, Dist. Judge

POLICE AND SHERIFF

Sheriff's Ofc **620.378.3622**
Fax 620.378.4510
Web ....www.woodsoncounty.net
E-mail ....dbath@woodsoncounty.net
    925 Pierce St, Fredonia, KS 66736-2258
Daniel L. Bath, Sheriff

Woodson County

GENERAL HEALTH SERVICES

Health Dept **620.625.2484**
Fax 620.625.2146
   109 E Rutledge St, Yates Center, KS 66783-1427
Susan Mueller, Director

POLICE AND SHERIFF

Sheriff's Dept **620.625.2147**
Fax 620.625.8672
Web ....www.woodsoncounty.net
E-mail ....woodsonsherrif.com
   105 W Rutledge St, Yates Center, KS 66783-1493
Shannon Moore, Sheriff

Wyandotte County

SOCIAL SERVICES

Kansas City Social and Rehabilitation Svcs Area
Ofc **913.279.7000**
Fax 913.279.7701
   402 State Ave, Kansas City, KS 66101
Phyllis Gillmore, Area Director

GENERAL HEALTH SERVICES

Health Dept **913.321.4803**
Fax 913.573.6755
Web ....www.wycokck.org
   619 Ann Ave, Kansas City, KS 66101
Greg Stephenson, Hiv/std Services Supervisor

MENTAL HEALTH SERVICES

Wyandot Mental Health Ctr, Inc **913.328.4600**
Fax 913.328.4604
Web ....www.wmhci.org
E-mail ....zevenbergen_p@wmhci.org
   7840 Washington Ave, Kansas City, KS 66112-2152
Peter Zevenbergen, Executive Director

COURTS

29th District Court **913.573.4190**
Fax 913.573.4195
Web ....www.wycokck.org
   711 Armstrong Ave, Kansas City, KS 66101-2701
Honorable Dan Kayhill, Director/Judge

POLICE AND SHERIFF

Sheriff's Ofc **913.573.2861**
Fax 913.573.2972
Web ....www.wycokck.org
E-mail ....dash@wycosheriff.org
   710 N 7th St Ste 20, Kansas City, KS 66101-3093
Donald Ash, Sheriff

EDUCATION SERVICES

Economic Opportunity Foundation - Rosedale
HS **913.722.1628**
Web ....www.acf.hhs.gov
   1444 Southwest Blvd, Kansas City, KS 66103-1829
Susan Reaves, Director

Economic Opportunity Foundation-Bellrose
HS **913.432.5987**
   2924 W 40th Ave, Kansas City, KS 66103-2729
Ms Crystal Primers, Director

SPECIAL SERVICES AGENCIES

ADOPTION AGENCIES

Adoption Connections Inc **316.733.6711**
Fax 316.733.2550
Web ....www.abwaadoptions.org
   105 E Rhondda Ave, Andover, KS 67002-9635
Richard Beckem, Director

American Adoptions **913.383.9804**
Fax 913.383.1615
Web ....www.americanadoptions.com
E-mail ....adoptions@americanadoptions.com
   9101 W 110th St Ste 200, Overland Park,
   KS 66210-1449
Scott Mars, Executive Director

Birthline **620.626.6763**
Web ....www.birthline.net
E-mail ....ctripp@birthline.org
   412 N Washington Ave, Liberal, KS 67901
Carrie Tripp, Executive Director

Bremyer & Wise LLC **620.241.0554**
Fax 620.241.7692
   120 W Kansas Ave, Ste B, Mc Pherson, KS 67460
Julie Silsby, Director

Catholic Charities, Inc. Diocese of Wichita **316.264.8344**
Fax 316.264.4442
Web ....www.wkscatholiccharities.org
   532 N. Broadway, Wichita, KS 67214
COA accredited organization.

Farm **785.539.1017**
Fax 785.539.3097
Web ....www.thefarm.org
   116 S 4th St, Manhattan, KS 66502
Eve Clark, Admn Asst

Kansas Children's Svc League **913.621.2016**
Fax 913.371.0509
Web ....www.kcsl.org
   15717 College Blvd, Lenexa, KS 66219-1360
Patty Mccollum, Director Of Healthy Families

United Methodist Youthville **785.623.4424**
Fax 785.623.4446
E-mail ....kimy@the-farm.org
   205 E 13th St Ste B, Hays, KS 67601
Kim Yoxall, Director

ADVOCACY RESOURCES

CASA **785.762.3907**
Fax 785.762.2915
Web ....casa@8thjd.com
E-mail ....casa@8thjd.com
   801 N Washington St Ste C, Junction City,
   KS 66441-2483
Juliet Follansbee, Executive Director

CASA **785.832.5172**
Fax 785.856.1279
E-mail ....casa@douglas-county.com
   1009 New Hampshire, Ste B, Lawrence, KS 66044
Diana Frederick, Executive Director

CASA of the High Plains, Inc. **785.628.8641**
Fax 785.625.4781
E-mail ....casa@media-net.net
   103 W 13th St Bsmt, Hays, KS 67601-4774
Tony A. Miller, Executive Director

Spirit of the Plains/CASA **620.271.6197**
Fax 620.271.6196
E-mail ....casa@wbsnet.org
   310 E. Walnut St Ste 208, Garden City,
   KS 67846-5306
Susan Escareno, Director

BEHAVIORAL HEALTH TREATMENT

Atchison Valley Hope **913.367.1618**
Web ....valleyhope.com
E-mail ....juanitag@valleyhope.com
   1816 North Second Street, Atchison, KS 66002
Ms. Juanita Gregoire, Accreditation Manager
Joint Commission accredited organization.

Behaviorial Madison Specialist **316.686.5195**
Fax 316.686.8714
   7829 E Rrockhill Bldg 100 Ste 101, Wichita,
   KS 67206-2424
Dr. Shreeja Kumar, Psychiatrist

Bradshaw Medical Practice **785.478.3297**
   3910 Sw Parlington Rd, Topeka, KS 66610-1422
Samuel Bradshaw, Psychiatrist

Camelot of Kansas, Lakeside Academy **316.794.2760**
Fax 316.794.2773
Web ....www.camelotforkids.org
E-mail ....jyi@camelotforkids.org
   24401 West MacArthur Road, Goddard, KS 67052
Jung Mi Yi, Executive Director
CARF accredited programs available.

Comcare Outpatient Mental Health Svcs **316.660.7675**
Fax 316.660.7715
Web ....www.sedgwickcounty.gov
   1919 N Amidon Ave Ste 130, Wichita,
   KS 67203-2118
Dee Staudt, Director

Counseling & Psychological Svc **785.864.2277**
Fax 785.864.2721
   1200 Schwegler Dr, Lawrence, KS 66044
Linda Keeler, Md, Psychiatrist

Ctr For Counseling and Consultation **620.792.2544**
Fax 620.792.7052
Web ....www.thecentergb.org
E-mail ....dyoung@thecentergb.org
   5815 Broadway Ave, Great Bend, KS 67530-3197
Dwight Young, Ms, Mba, Lmlp, Executive Director

Dan Claiborn & Associates **913.438.2100**
Fax 913.438.2119
Web ....www.courtpsychologist.com
E-mail ....danielpsy@aol.com
   10801 W 87th St Ste 300, Overland Park,
   KS 66214-1699
Daniel Claiborn, Administrator

Early Head Start **785.632.5399**
   1021 4th St, Clay Center, KS 67432-2501
Cindy Charbonneau, Family Consultant

East Methodist Youthville Cottage **620.227.6658**
Fax 620.225.0279
Web ....www.youthville.org
E-mail ....lschroeder@youthville.org
   11200 Lariat Way, Dodge City, KS 67801-7328
Lenord Schroeder, Unit Supervisor

Elm Acres Substance Abuse Program **620.231.6129**
Fax 620.231.9893
E-mail ....aljohnson@dccca.org
   1002 E Madison St, Pittsburg, KS 66762-6023
Audrey Johnson, Facility Director

Family Consultation Svc **316.264.8317**
Fax 316.264.0347
Web ....www.fcswichita.org
  560 N Exposition St, Wichita, KS 67203-5993
  Matthew Agnew, Executive Director

Family Psychological Ctr **316.682.2699**
Web ....www.familypsychologicalcenter.com
  1017 N Yale Ave, Wichita, KS 67208-2948
  Fred Dewit, Director

Family Svc and Guidance Ctr of Topeka,
Inc **785.232.5005**
Fax 785.232.4098
Web ....www.fsgctopeka.com
E-mail ....schristenberry@fsgctopeka.com
  325 SW Frazier Ave, Topeka, KS 66606
  Steve Christenberry, Clinical Director

Farm **620.343.6111**
Fax 620.343.1398
Web ....www.the-farm.org
  528 Commercial St, Emporia, KS 66801-4006
  Peggy Martin, President/CEO

Florence Crittenton Services of Topeka,
Inc **785.233.0516**
Fax 785.271.4433
Web ....www.flocritkansas.org
  2649 Southwest Arrowhead Road, Topeka, KS 66614
  CARF accredited programs available.

Fort Larned School Dist Usd 495 ....**620.285.4900**
  120 E 6th St, Larned, KS 67550-3191
  Pat Hayes, Director

Hufford House **620.225.2201**
Fax 620.225.0279
Web ....www.youthville.org
  11200 Lariat Way, Dodge City, KS 67801-7328
  Pat Harman, Director

Iroquois Ctr For Human Development, Inc **620.723.2272**
Fax 620.723.3450
Web ....www.irqcenter.com
  610 E Grant Ave, Greensburg, KS 67054
  C. Sheldon Carpenter, Rmlp, Executive Director

Keys For Networking, Inc -- Kansas Federation of Families For
Children's Mental Health **785.233.8732**
Fax 785.235.6659
Web ....www.keys.org
E-mail ....jadams@keys.org
  211 SW 33rd St, Topeka, KS 66611-2245
  Jane Adams, Executive Director

KVC Behavioral HealthCare, Inc **913.322.4900**
Web ....www.kvc.org
E-mail ....estucky@kvc.org
  21350 West 153rd Street, Olathe, KS 66061
  Mrs. Erin Stucky, Accreditation Manager
  Joint Commission accredited organization.

KVC Hospitals, Inc **913.322.4900**
Web ....www.kvc.org
E-mail ....jhooper@kvc.org
  4300 Brenner Drive, Kansas City, KS 66104
  Mr. Jason Hooper, Accreditation Manager
  Joint Commission accredited organization.

Lakemary Center/Children's Residential Treatment
Program **913.557.4000**
Fax 913.557.4910
Web ....www.lakemaryctr.org
E-mail ....kkilbourn@lakemaryctr.org
  100 Lakemary Drive, Paola, KS 66071
  Bill Craig, Executive Director
  CARF accredited programs available.

Marillac **816.508.3300**
Fax 816.508.3321
Web ....www.marillac.org
E-mail ....marillac@marillac.org
  8000 W 127th St, Overland Park, KS 66213-2714
  Eric Giovanni, Intake Coordinator

Marillac Center Inc **816.508.3300**
Web ....www.marillac.org
E-mail ....sharon.mcgloin@marillac.org
  8000 W. 127th Street, Overland Park, KS 66213
  Ms. Sharon McGloin, Accreditation Manager
  Joint Commission accredited organization.

Mental Health Association of South Central
Kansas **316.685.1821**
Fax 316.685.0768
Web ....www.mhasck.org
  555 North Woodlawn, Suite 3105, Wichita, KS 67208
  CARF accredited programs available.

New Hope Heartland, LLC **843.572.3498**
Web ....www.newhopetreatment.com
E-mail ....ericb@newhopetreatment.com
  619 Fairfield Street, Norwich, KS 67118
  Mr. Eric Baumgartner, Accreditation Manager
  Joint Commission accredited organization.

Pathway Family Services, Inc. **785.271.6657**
Web ....www.pathwayfs.org
  217 Southeast Fourth Street, Topeka, KS 66603
  CARF accredited programs available.

Pawnee Mental Health Services **785.587.4300**
Fax 785.587.4321
E-mail ....robbin.cole@pawnee.org
  2001 Claflin Rd, Manhattan, KS 66502-3415
  Robin Cole, Executive Director

Prairie View, Inc. **316.284.6400**
Web ....www.prairieview.org
E-mail ....bartelkf@pvi.org
  1901 East First Street, Newton, KS 67114
  Mr. Kelvin Bartel, Accreditation Manager
  Joint Commission accredited organization.

Pyxis, Inc. **316.682.8092**
Fax 316.262.4213
Web ....www.pyxispath.com
  334 North Topeka, Wichita, KS 67202
  CARF accredited programs available.

Saint Francis Academy, Inc **785.825.0563**
Fax 785.825.2549
Web ....www.st-francis.org
E-mail ....nealz@st-francis.org
  5097 W Cloud St, Salina, KS 67401-9743
  Neil Zouzsa, Executive Director

Saint Francis Community Services, Inc. **785.825.0541**
Web ....www.st-francis.org
E-mail ....cheryl.rathbun@st-francis.org
  509 East Elm Street, Salina, KS 67401
  Mrs. Cheryl Rathbun, Accreditation Manager
  Joint Commission accredited organization.

Sequel of Kansas, LLC **316.267.5710**
Web ....camelotforkids.org
E-mail ....dgoldstein-higgins@sequelyouthservices.com
  2050 West 11th Street, Wichita, KS 67203
  Ms. Debbie Goldstein-Higgins, Accreditation Manager
  Joint Commission accredited organization.

Shunga Creek Mental Health **785.273.6200**
Fax 785.273.6249
E-mail ....j.woodward@irs.gov
  5040 SW 28th St Ste B, Topeka, KS 66614-2302
  Jim Woodward, Lcsw, Social Worker

Southwest Guidance Ctr **620.624.8171**
Fax 620.624.0114
E-mail ....jkarlan@swguidance.org
  333 W 15th St, Liberal, KS 67901
  Jim Karlan, Executive Director

The Salvation Army Koch Service Center **316.263.2769**
Fax 316.425.6174
Web ....www.salvationarmy-wichita.org
  350 North Market, Wichita, KS 67202-2010
  CARF accredited programs available.

The Shelter, Inc. **785.843.2085**
Fax 785.843.2086
Web ....www.theshelterinc.org
  105 West 11th Street, Lawrence, KS 66044
  CARF accredited programs available.

United Methodist Youthville **620.225.0276**
Fax 620.225.0279
E-mail ....lschroeder@youthville.org
  11200 Lariat Way, Dodge City, KS 67801-7328
  Leonart Schroeder, Campus Director

United Methodist Youthville, Inc. **316.529.9100**
Web ....youthville.org
E-mail ....kherzberg@youthville.org
  4505 E 47th Street South, Wichita, KS 67210
  Mrs. Katie Herzberg, Accreditation Manager
  Joint Commission accredited organization.

Villages, Inc **785.267.5900**
Fax 785.267.1224
Web ....www.thevillagesinc.org
E-mail ....scrawford@thevillagesinc.org
  2219 SW 29th St, Topeka, KS 66611-1908
  Sylvia Crawford, Executive Director

CHILDREN'S HOSPITAL

Atchison Hospital **913.367.2131**
  800 Raven Hill Dr, Atchison, KS 66002
  John Jacobson, Chief Executive Officer

Children's Mercy South **913.696.8000**
  5808 W 110th St, Overland Park, KS 66211
  Randal Oponnell, Director

Clara Barton Hospital **620.653.2114**
  250 W 9th St, Hoisington, KS 67544
  Curt Colson, Chief Executive Officer

Community Health Care System **785.889.4272**
  120 W 8th St, Onaga, KS 66521

Community Hospital **785.325.2211**
  304 E 3rd St, Washington, KS 66968
  Everett Lutjemeier, Chief Executive Officer

Community Hospital **620.355.7111**
  500 Thorpe St, Lakin, KS 67860
  John Loebel, Director

Community Hospital **785.527.2254**
  2420 G St, Belleville, KS 66935

Community Hospital **785.877.3351**
  102 E Holme, Norton, KS 67654

Community Hospital **785.332.2104**
  210 W 1st St, Saint Francis, KS 67756
  Les Lacey, Administrator

Geary Community Hosptial **785.238.4131**
  1102 St Marys Rd, Junction City, KS 66441
  David Bradley, Chief Executive Officer

Goodland Regional Medical Center **785.890.3625**
  220 W 2nd St, Goodland, KS 67735
  Jay Jolly, Chief Executive Officer

Hays Medical Center **785.623.5000**
  2220 Canterbury Dr, Hays, KS 67601
  John Jeter, Chief Executive Officer

Health Care Facility **620.492.6250**
  404 N Chestnut St, Johnson, KS 67855
  Camile, Human Resource Director

Health Center **785.243.1234**
  1100 Highland Dr, Concordia, KS 66901
  Jim Wahlmeier, Director

Heartland Spine & Specialty Hospital **913.754.5000**
  10720 Nall Ave, Overland Park, KS 66211
  Don Burman, Chief Executive Officer

Hospital **620.365.1000**
  101 S 1st St, Iola, KS 66749
  Joyce Heismeyer, Chief Executive Officer

Irwin Army Community Hospital **785.239.7000**
600 Caisson Hill Rd, Junction City, KS 66442

Kiowa District Hospital & Manor **620.825.4131**
810 Drumm St, Kiowa, KS 67070
Alden Vandeveer, Director

Lawrence Memoiral Hospital **785.505.5000**
Web ....www.lmh.org
325 Maine St, Lawrence, KS 66044
Dana Hale, Nursing Director

Medical Center **785.632.2144**
617 Liberty St, Clay Center, KS 67432
Ron Bender, Director

Medical Center **913.294.2327**
2100 Baptiste Dr, Paola, KS 66071
Jerry Wiesner, Chief Operating Officer

Memorial Health System **785.263.2100**
511 NE 10th St, Abilene, KS 67410

Mercy Hospital **620.345.6391**
218 E Pack St, Moundridge, KS 67107
Doyle Johnson, Chief Executive Officer

Mercy Regional Health Center **785.776.3322**
1823 College Ave, Manhattan, KS 66502
Kathleen Soupene, Administrator

Nemaha Valley Community Hospital **785.336.6181**
1600 Community Dr, Seneca, KS 66538
Stan Regehr, Chief Executive Officer

Neosho Memorial Regional Medical
Center **620.431.4000**
629 S Plummer, Chanute, KS 66720
Jennifer Newton, Nursing Director

Newman Regional Health **620.343.6800**
1201 W 12th Ave, Emporia, KS 66801
Robert Driewer, Chief Executive Officer

Ninnescah Valley Health System **620.532.3147**
750 Avenue D W, Kingman, KS 67068
Anita Graber, Foundational Director

Olathe Medical Center **913.791.4200**
20333 W 151st St, Olathe, KS 66061
Frank Devocelle, President

Pratt Regional Medical Center **620.672.7451**
200 Commodore St, Pratt, KS 67124
Susan Page, Chief Executive Officer

Promise Regional Medical Center **620.665.2000**
1701 E 23rd Ave, Hutchinson, KS 67502
Miller, Chief Executive Officer

Providence Medical Center **913.596.4000**
E-mail ....mike.dorsey@providence-health.org
8929 Parallel Pkwy, Kansas City, KS 66112
Mike Dorsey, Chief Executive Officer

Ransom Memorial Hospital **785.229.8200**
1301 S Main St, Ottawa, KS 66067
Lary Felix, Chief Executive Officer

Salina Regional Health Center **785.452.7000**
400 S Santa Fe Ave, Salina, KS 67401
James Barker, Nursing Director

Shawnee Mission Medical Center **913.676.2000**
9100 W 74th St, Overland Park, KS 66204
Shari Hawkins, Nursing Officer

Southwest medical Center **620.624.1651**
315 W 15th St, Liberal, KS 67901
Norman Limbert, Chief Executive Officer

St Catherine Hospital **620.272.2222**
401 E Spuce St, Garden City, KS 67846
Scott Taylor, Chief Executive Officer

St Francis Health Center **785.295.8000**
1700 W 7th St, Topeka, KS 66606
Robert Erickson, Chief Executive Officer

St Rose Andlotory & Surgery Center **620.792.2511**
3515 Broadway St, Great Bend, KS 67530
Leeanne Irsik, Administrator

Stormont-Vail Healthcare **785.354.6000**
1500 SW 10th Ave, Topeka, KS 66604
Carol Perry, Nursing Director

Via Christi Hospital **620.232.0109**
1 Mt Carmel Way, Pittsburg, KS 66762
Pam Newcomer, Administrative Assistant

Via Christi Regional Medical Center **316.268.5000**
E-mail ....hausmann_sherry@viachristi.org
929 N St Francis St, Wichita, KS 67214
Sherry Hausmann, President

Wamego City Hospital **785.456.2295**
711 Genn Dr, Wamego, KS 66547
Shannan Flach, Chief Executive Officer

Wesley Medical Center **316.962.2000**
550 N Hillside, Wichita, KS 67214
Hugh Tappan, Chief Executive Officer

Western Plains Medical complex **620.225.8400**
3001 Avenue A, Dodge City, KS 67801
Kelly, Administrative Assistant

COUNSELING SERVICES

Adoption Option **913.642.7900**
Fax 913.897.0154
E-mail ....hglm@everest.kc.net
7211 W 98th Ter Ste 100, Overland Park,
KS 66212-2257
Hillary Merryfield, Executive Director

Catholic Community Svcs **913.621.3445**
Fax 913.621.4507
Web ....www.catholiccharitiesks.org
E-mail ....jlewis@ccsks.org
2220 Central Ave, Kansas City, KS 66102-4797
Jan Lewis, Director

Comprehensive Counseling/Consultation **785.493.0520**
Fax 785.493.0660
E-mail ....cccllc67401@yahoo.com
204 S Santa Fe Ave, Salina, KS 67401-3932
Marie Frost, Director

Family Care Ctr **785.762.4210**
Fax 785.762.6876
132 N Eisenhower Dr, Junction City, KS 66441-3314
Richard Burnett, Acsw, Lcsw, Director

Kansas Children's Svc League **316.942.4261**
Fax 316.943.9995
Web ....www.kcsl.org
E-mail ....pwischnack@kcsl.org
1365 N Custer St, Wichita, KS 67203-6694
Paula Wischnack, Chief Financial Officer

South Central Mental Health Counseling Ctr,
Inc **316.775.5491**
Fax 316.775.5442
E-mail ....danrice@scmhcc.kscoxmail.com
520 E. Augusta Ave., Augusta, Ks. 67010, Augusta,
KS 67010
Dan Rice, Executive Director

CRISIS & SHELTER CARE

Catholic Charities Harbor House-Domestic
Violence **316.263.6000**
Fax 316.263.8347
E-mail ....lodavis@wkscatholiccharities.org
437 N Topeka St, Wichita, KS 67202
Lisa Odell-davis, Director

Crisis Ctr of Dodge City Meadowlark
House **620.225.6987**
Fax 620.225.3522
E-mail ....brekk1976@yahoo.com
605 CENTRAL AVE, Dodge City, KS 67801
Mia Kolbrick, Executive Director

Crisis Ctr, Inc **785.539.2785**
Fax 785.539.8467
E-mail ....jdavis@carrollsweb.com
PO Box 1526, Manhattan, KS 66505-1526
Judy Davis, Director

Crisis Resource Ctr of Southern Kansas **620.251.3772**
Fax 620.231.2375
Web ....www.srskansas.org
E-mail ....Crlc@Srskansas.Org
1317 W 8Th St, Coffeyville, KS 67337-3507
Rebecca Reedy, Director

Crisis Resource Ctr-SE Kansas-Domestic
Violence **620.231.8692**
Fax 620.231.8693
E-mail ....crlc@srskansas.org
669 S Highway 69, Pittsburg, KS 66762-8600
Rebecca Reedy, Director

Domestic Violence **620.221.7300**
Fax 620.221.2951
Safe Homes Office, Winfield, KS 67156
Leeann Reidiger, Director

Domestic Violence Assoc-Central Kansas **785.827.5862**
Fax 785.827.2410
E-mail ....andreaq@salhelp.org
203 S Santa Fe Ave, Salina, KS 67401
Andrea Quill, Director

Domestic Violence- Sexual Assault Assoc **316.284.6920**
Fax 316.284.6856
E-mail ....janj@dvsainc.org
PO Box 942, Newton, KS 67114-0942
Jan Jones, Director

Family Crisis Svcs **620.275.2018**
Fax 620.275.2761
E-mail ....fcs106@sbcglobal.net
106 W Fulton St, Garden City, KS 67846-5456
Robin Sheldon, Director

Family Life Ctr-Safehouse **316.321.7104**
Fax 316.321.1018
E-mail ....safe.house@flc.kscoxmail.com
115 S Washington St, El Dorado, KS 67042-0735
Darla Carter, Director

Hope Unlimited **620.365.7566**
Fax 620.365.6040
Web ....www.hopeunlimited.org
E-mail ....dbshu@iolaks.com
8 N Washington, Iola, KS 66749
Ms. Dorothy Sparks, Director

Joyce H Williams Ctr - Domestic Violence **913.321.1566**
Fax 913.321.1569
E-mail ....llattimore@hopehouse-ejc.org
1418 Garfield Ave, Kansas City, KS 66104
Ladora Lattimore, Director

Liberal Area Rape Crisis - Domestic Violence
Svcs **620.624.8818**
Fax 620.626.6041
909 N Clay Ave, Liberal, KS 67901
Hope Alvarez, Director

Miracles House **316.264.5900**
Fax 316.265.2881
Web ....www.miracles.org
E-mail ....rwmiracles@aol.com
1250 N Market St, Wichita, KS 67214-2835
Rhonda Walker, CEO

PBP Family Violence Prevention Program **888.966.2932**
Fax 785.966.8383
Web ....www.pbpindiantribe.org
E-mail ....jenniferhale@pbpnation.org
11400 158th Rd, Mayetta, KS 66509
Jennifer Hale, Director

Prairie View at Reflection Ridge **316.729.6555**
Fax 316.634.4794
7570 W 21st St N Ste 1026D, Wichita, KS 67205
Marva Hiebert, Supervisor

Kansas

Kansas

Rape Victim Survivor Svc **785.843.8985**
Fax 785.843.3728
E-mail ....Gadugisafecenter@Sunflower.Com
2518 Ridge Ct Ste 202, Lawrence, KS 66046-4029
Sarah Jane Russel, Director

S O S Inc. **620.343.8799**
Fax 620.343.9460
E-mail ....smoran@soskansas.com
PO Box 1191, Emporia, KS 66801
Susan Moran, Executive Director

Safe Home Inc. **913.432.9300**
Fax 913.432.9302
Web ....www.safehome-ks.org
E-mail ....skatz@safehome-ks.org
6300 W 87th St., Overland Park, KS 66212
Sharon Katz, Executive Director

Sexual Assault-Domestic Violence Ctr Inc **620.663.2522**
Fax 620.665.3609
Web ....www.nbc.kscoxmail.com
E-mail ....sadvc@nbc.kscoxmail.com
335 N Washington St, Ste 240, Hutchinson,
KS 67501-4864
Candace Dixon, Director

Stepstone-Domestic Violence **316.265.1611**
Fax 316.265.0738
Web ....www.csjoseph.org
E-mail ....klambertz@csjoseph.org
1329 S Bluffview Dr, Wichita, KS 67218-3031
Kit Lambertz, Director

Sunflower Family Svcs **785.625.4600**
Fax 785.625.8107
Web ....www.sunflowerfamily.org
E-mail ....teresaw@sunflowerfamily.org
327 E 8th St, Hays, KS 67601-4146
Teresa Witthuhn, Director

**Sunflower House, A Child Abuse Prevention
Ctr** **913.631.5800**
Fax 913.631.5885
Web ....www.sunflowerhouse.org
E-mail ....erin@sunflowerhouse.org
15440 W 65th St, Shawnee, KS 66217-9306
Erin Nova-weiss, Child Assessment Director

Temporary Lodging For Children **913.764.2887**
Fax 913.780.3387
Web ....www.kidstlc.org
E-mail ....drummond@kidstlc.org
480 S Rogers Rd, Olathe, KS 66062-1706
Robert Drummond, CEO

YWCA Battered Women Task Force **785.354.7927**
Fax 785.232.2902
Web ....www.ywcatopeka.org
E-mail ....eileend@ywcatopeka.org
225 SW 12th St, Topeka, KS 66612-1392
Betay Zickenson, Director

EDUCATION

Carpenter Place **316.942.3221**
Fax 316.942.1750
Web ....www.carpenterplace.org
E-mail ....officeadministrator@carpenterplace.org
1501 N Meridian Ave, Wichita, KS 67203
Cory Long, CEO

Heartspring **316.634.8700**
Fax 316.634.0555
Web ....www.heartspring.org
8700 E 29th St N, Wichita, KS 67226
Leigh Horsley, Director Of Development

Kansas Children's Svc League **620.276.3232**
Fax 620.276.3250
Web ....www.kcsl.org
E-mail ....gjones@kcsl.org
705 Ballinger St, Garden City, KS 67846-5919
Julie Wright, Director

FOSTER CARE AGENCIES

**Adoption Concerns Triangle of Topeka
ACT** **785.235.6122**
E-mail ....Waugh5@cox.net
411 SW Greenwood Ave, Topeka, KS 66606
Marilyn Waugh, Director

American Adoptions **913.492.2229**
E-mail ....shawn@americanadoptions.com
9101 W 110th St, Ste 200, Overland Park, KS 66210
Shawn Kane, Director

Caring & Sharing Grandparents **620.663.4134**
2201 S Bonebrake, Hutchinson, KS 67501

Catholic Charities Inc **316.263.0507**
Fax 316.263.5259
425 N Topeka, Wichita, KS 67202

Cindy Beeson **316.442.6736**
PO Box 1042, Arkansas City, KS 67005

Family Voices of Kansas (FV KS) **877.499.5369**
E-mail ....merlin@familiestogetherinc.org

Foster Children **913.248.4455**
E-mail ....halo136@yahoo.com
13405 W 57th St, Shawnee, KS 66216

Kansas ATTACH **316.390.7545**
1650 S Georgetown, Ste 190, Wichita, KS 67218

Kansas Children's Service League **785.625.2244**
2717 Canal Blvd, Ste G, Hays, KS 67601

Kansas Children's Service League **320.356.4180**
921 N College, Ulysses, KS 67880

Kansas Children's Service League **877.530.5275**
1365 N custer, Wichita, KS 67203

Kansas Children's Service League **620.649.2754**
800 Tecuensch, PO Box 808, Satanta, KS 67870

Kansas Children's Service League **620.340.0408**
402 Commercial Ste 123, Emporia, KS 66801

Kansas Children's Service League **620.664.5000**
400 W 2nd St, Ste D, Hutchinson, KS 67501
Micheal Wood, Supervisor

Kansas Children's Service League (KCSL) **877.530.5275**
3545 SW 5th St, Topeka, KS 66606

Kansas Resource Parent Assoc **620.628.4071**
PO Box 273, Canton, KS 67428
Saundra Hiller

KVC Behavioral HealthCare Inc (KVC) **913.322.4900**
E-mail ....adoptionspecialist@kvc.org
21350 W 153rd St, Olathe, KS 66061
Bobby Ecite, Operations Manager

St Francis Academy Adoptive Parent **620.669.3734**
Fax 620.669.3739
501 N Moroe, PO Box 1340, Hutchinson, KS 67501

Youthville (UMY) **316.529.9100**
E-mail ....info@youthville.org
4505 E 47th St S, Wichita, KS 67210
Shelly Duncan, President

PEDIATRIC HOME CARE

Interim Healthcare **620.663.2423**
Fax 620.663.2313
210 E 30th Ste 130, Hutchinson, KS 67502
Toni Cornejo, Branch Manager

Interim Healthcare **913.837.5121**
Fax 913.837.5716
218 Fairlane Dr, Louisburg, KS 66053
Liz Noonan, Director

Interim Healthcare **316.265.4295**
Fax 316.265.4399
E-mail ....jaystehley@interimhealthcare.com
333 S Broadway Ste 200, Wichita, KS 67202
Jay Stehley, Chief Executive Officer

Interim Healthcare **913.381.3100**
Fax 913.381.3181
E-mail ....MNUNN@INTERIMTEAM.COM
8016 State Line Ste 205, Prairie Village, KS 66208
Michelle Nunn, Director

SOCIAL SERVICES

Arc **316.943.1191**
Fax 316.943.3292
Web ....www.arc-sedgwickcounty.org
E-mail ....arc@arc-sedgwickcounty.org
2919 W 2nd St N, Wichita, KS 67203
Kristen Phillips, Executive Assistant

Armed Svcs YMCA Junction City **785.238.2972**
Fax 785.762.2446
Web ....www.asymca.org
E-mail ....asymca@nqks.com
111 E 16th St, Junction City, KS 66441-2517
Meyah Grooms, Asymca Site Director

Birthline Inc **316.265.0134**
339 N Seneca St, Wichita, KS 67203
Burnadett Sanders, Director

Birthline of El Dorado **316.321.7060**
226 W Central Ave Ste 108, El Dorado,
KS 67042-2146
Teresa Fagg, Director

Catholic Charities **620.792.1393**
Fax 620.792.1399
E-mail ....dsnapp@dcdiocese.org
2201 16th St, Great Bend, KS 67530-2412
Debra Snapp, Director

Catholic Charities of Salina Inc **785.825.0208**
Fax 785.826.9708
Web ....www.catholiccharitiessalina.org
E-mail ....ccs@catholiccharitiessalina.org
425 W Iron Ave, Salina, KS 67401-2563
Karen Hauser, Director

Catholic Social Svcs **620.272.0010**
Fax 620.272.0025
E-mail ....dsnapp@dcdiocese.org
603 N 8th St, Garden City, KS 67846
Debbie Snapp, Director

Child Care Links **620.669.0291**
Fax 620.669.0204
Web ....www.childcarelink.org
E-mail ....childcarelinks@sbcglobal.net
21 W 2nd Ave, Hutchinson, KS 67501-5207
Doris Vanek, Executive Director

Child Development Assoc **785.842.9679**
Fax 785.842.1412
Web ....www.dccda.org
E-mail ....ajenny@dccda.org
935 Iowa St Ste 7, Lawrence, KS 66044-1854
Anna Jenny, Director

Child Start **316.682.1853**
Fax 316.689.8713
Web ....www.childstart.org
1069 S Glendale St, Parklane Office Park, Wichita,
KS 67218
Clairissa Maddy, Referal Coordinator

**Childcare Aware Of Northeast & Central
Kansas** **785.357.5171**
Fax 785.357.1813
Web ....www.ercrefer.org
E-mail ....reva@ercrefer.org
1710 SW 10th Ave Ste 215, Topeka, KS 66604-1334
Reva Wywadis, Executive Director

Christian Family Svcs of the Midwest, Inc. **913.383.3337**
Fax 913.381.2547
Web ....www.cfskc.org
E-mail ....mark@cfskc.org
10500 Barkley St Ste 216, Overland Park,
KS 66212-1838
Mark Barone, Executive Director

Colby Community College Child Care Resource And Referral **785.462.3984**
Fax 785.460.4688
Web ....www.colbycc.edu
E-mail ....lyndsey@hacc.info
   1255 S Range Ave, Colby, KS 67701-4099
   Lyndsey Crisenbery, Director

DCCCA, Inc. **785.841.4138**
Fax 785.841.5777
Web ....www.dccca.org
   3312 Clinton Parkway, Lawrence, KS 66047
   COA accredited organization.

Elm Acres Residential Center **620.429.1949**
Fax 620.429.1982
Web ....www.dccca.org
   501 Central Avenue, Columbus, KS 66725
   CARF accredited programs available.

Family Resource Ctr **620.232.9700**
Fax 620.235.3154
Web ....www.ccaftk.org
E-mail ....centerrandr@yahoo.com
   1600 N Locust St, Pittsburg, KS 66762
   Monica Murnan, Executive Director

First Call For Help **620.669.0159**
Fax 620.669.0150
   400 W 2nd Ave Ste A, Hutchinson, KS 67504
   Susie Christopher, Executive Director

Flint Hills Child Care Resource and Referral Agency **785.532.7197**
Fax 785.532.7732
Web ....www.kccto.org
   2323 Anderson Ave Ste 250, Manhattan, KS 66502
   Patty Peschel, Program Coordinator

Hays Area Children's Ctr **785.625.3257**
Fax 785.625.8557
Web ....www.hacc.info
E-mail ....hacc@hacc.info
   94 Lewis Dr, Hays, KS 67601
   Doug Greer, Executive Director

Indian Alcoholism Treatment Svc **316.262.6633**
Fax 316.262.3593
   313 N Seneca St, Ste 109, Wichita, KS 67203-5937
   Gayl Edmunds, Director

Jewish Family Services of Greater Kanas City **913.327.8250**
Fax 913.327.8222
E-mail ....info@jfskc.org
   5801 W 115th St Ste 103, Overland Park, KS 66211
   Don Goldman, Executive Director

Kansas CASA Assoc **785.625.3049**
Fax 785.625.4370
E-mail ....kansascasa@ruraltel.net
   103 E 27th St Ste A, Hays, KS 67601-2957
   Janette Meis, State Director

Kansas Children's Cabinet And Trust Fund **785.368.7044**
Fax 785.296.8694
E-mail ....jrr@srs.ks.gov
   900 SW Jackson Rm 152, Topeka, KS 66612
   Jim Redman, Director

Kansas Children's Service League **316.942.4261**
Fax 316.943.9995
Web ....www.kcsl.org
   1365 N. Custer, Wichita, KS 67203
   COA accredited organization.

Kansas Children's Svc League of Manahttan **785.539.3193**
Fax 785.539.3340
Web ....www.kcsl.org
E-mail ....sallen@kcsl.org
   317 Houston St Ste A, Manhattan, KS 66502-8512
   Sarah Allen, Director

Kaw Valley Ctr **785.242.8965**
Fax 785.242.6947
Web ....www.kvc.org
   1302 S Main St Ste 11, Ottawa, KS 66067
   Megan Edmonds, Director

Kaw Valley Ctr **785.331.4200**
Fax 785.331.4455
Web ....www.kvc.org
E-mail ....ebailey@kvc.org
   1202 E 23rd St Ste C, Lawrence, KS 66046
   Erin Bailey, Director

KidsTLC, Inc. **913.764.2887**
Fax 913.780.3387
Web ....www.kidstlc.org
   480 South Rogers Road, Olathe, KS 66062-1706
   COA accredited organization.

Options **800.794.4624**
Fax 785.625.1742
E-mail ....clnkfs@hotmail.com
   403 E 23rd St, Hays, KS 67601
   Charlotte Linsner, Program Director

Shawnee Regional Prevention & Recovery Svcs **785.266.8666**
Fax 785.266.3833
Web ....www.parstopeka.com
E-mail ....jcalbeck@parstopeka.com
   2209 SW 29th St, Topeka, KS 66611-1908
   John Calbeck, Director

TFI Family Services, Inc. **620.342.2239**
Fax 620.642.0745
Web ....www.the-farm.org
   P.O. Box 2224, Emporia, KS 66801
   COA accredited organization.

The Family Conservancy **913.342.1110**
Fax 913.342.3632
Web ....http://thefamilyconservancy.org/
   626 Minnesota Avenue, Kansas City, KS 66101
   COA accredited organization.

SPECIAL NEEDS

Autism Society of the Heartland **913.706.0042**
E-mail ....ks-johnsoncounty@autismsocietyofamerica.org
   PO Box 860984, Shawnee Mission, KS 66286

Commission on Disability Concerns **800.295.5232**
   900 SW Jackson St Rm 100, Topeka, KS 66612
   Martha Galbhart, Executive Director

Families Together Inc **316.945.7747**
E-mail ....wichita@familiestogetherinc.org
   313 N Seneca St Ste 114, Wichita, KS 67203
   Connie Zienkewicz, Chief Executive Officer

Families Together, Inc **316.945.7747**
Fax 316.945.7795
E-mail ....fmin@feist.com
   3033 W 2nd St, Ste 106, Wichita, KS 67203
   Anita Beal, Assistant Director

Fed of Council for Exceptional Children **913.288.4080**
E-mail ....agaitan798@aol.com
   1920 N 66th, Kansas City, KS 66102

Goodwill Industries **316.744.9291**
E-mail ....info@goodwillks.org
   3636 N Oliver, Wichita, KS 67208
   Emily Compton, President

Kansas Congress of Parents & Teachers **785.234.5782**
E-mail ....kansaspta@gmail.com
   715 SW 10th St, Topeka, KS 66612
   Jackie Waters, President

Learning Disabilities Association **785.273.4505**
E-mail ....marciasu@aol.com
   PO Box 4424, Topeka, KS 66604

Life Enrichment Center, LLC **785.842.2752**
Fax 785.842.2750
E-mail ....lec@lecnetwork.com
   5200 Bob Billings Pkwy, Ste 204, Lawrence, KS 66049

NAMI Kansas **785.233.0755**
E-mail ....namikansas@nami.org
   610 SW Kent 10th St, Topeka, KS 66601
   Rick Cagan, Executive Director

Partners in Policymaking **785.296.2608**
E-mail ....partnersinpolicy@kcdd.org
   915 SW Harrison St Rm 141, Docking State Office Bldg, Topeka, KS 66612
   Keith Tatum, Coordinator

Special Olympics Kansas **913.236.9290**
E-mail ....kso@kso.org
   5280 Foxridge Dr, Mission, KS 66202

Speech-Language-Hearing Association **913.362.0015**
E-mail ....ksha@ksha.org
   6001 Cherokee Dr, Mission, KS 66205

TARC **785.232.0597**
   2701 SW Randolph, Topeka, KS 66611
   Eileen Doran, Director

United Cerebral Palsy of Kansas **316.688.1888**
   5111 E 21st St, Wichita, KS 67208

University of Kansas Medical Center **913.588.5000**
Fax 913.588.6965
E-mail ....adick1@kumc.edu
   39th and Rainbow Blvd, Kansas City, KS 66160
   Arthur Dick Md, Director

Via Christi Rehabilitation Hospital, Inc. **316.634.3400**
Fax 316.660.0061
Web ....www.viachristi.org
   1151 North Rock Road, Wichita, KS 67206
   CARF accredited programs available.

SUBSTANCE ABUSE TREATMENT

Adolescent Ctr For Treatment (ACT) **913.782.0283**
Fax 913.782.0609
   301 N Monroe St, Olathe, KS 66061-3162
   Ken Bishop, Program Manager

First Step House **785.843.9262**
Fax 785.843.9264
E-mail ....l.carter@dccca.org
   315 W 31st St, Lawrence, KS 66044-4651
   Lisa Carter, Director

Norton Valley Hope **785.877.5101**
Fax 785.877.3903
Web ....www.valleyhope.com
E-mail ....moorec@valleyhope.com
   709 W Holme St, West Highway 36, Norton, KS 67654-1251
   Larry Black, Director

Prefered Family Healthcare **316.943.2051**
Fax 316.943.2192
   3540 W Douglas Ave Ste 4, Wichita, KS 67203-5455
   Maccine Kraai, Director

Kentucky

http://kentucky.gov

Steve Beshear
State Capitol, 700 Capitol Ave., Ste. 100
Frankfort, KY 40601
502.564.2611
502.564.2517 (Fax)
HTTP://govenor.ky.gov

Stephanie Reynolds, Juvenile Justice Specialist
1025 Capital Center Drive Third Floor
Frankfort, KY 40601-8205
502.352.0821
502.573.0307 (Fax)
stephanie.reynolds@ky.gov

Nancy Pfaadt, SAG Chair
219 Old Towne Rd
Louisville, KY 40214
502.363.4262
npfaadt@aol.com

CRISIS NUMBERS

Child Abuse Reporting . . .800.752.6200

STATE SERVICES

SOCIAL SERVICES

Dept for Community Based Svcs 502.564.3703
Fax...502.564.6907
Web...www.ky.gov
E-mail..............................michael.cheek@ky.gov
275 E Main St, Frankfort, KY 40621-0001
Michael Cheek, Director Of Protection & Permanency

Div of Child Support 502.564.2285
Fax...502.564.5988
E-mail..............................mark.cornett@ky.gov
730 Schenkel Ln, Frankfort, KY 40601-1402
Mark Cornett, Acting Director

Division of Child Care Kentucky 502.564.2524
Fax...502.564.3464
275 East Main St 3C F, Frankfort, KY 40621
Marybeth Jackson, Director

Kentucky Emergency Management Agency 502.607.1682
Fax...502.607.1622
Web...www.kyem.ky.gov
100 Minuteman Pkwy, Frankfort, KY 40601
John Heltvel, Director

GENERAL HEALTH SERVICES

Cabinet for Health and Family Svcs 502.564.3970
Fax...502.564.9377
Web...www.publichealth.ky.gov
E-mail..............................fran.hawkins@ky.gov
275 E Main St, Frankfort, KY 40621-0001
Fran Hawkins, Ms, Rd, Ld, Wic Director

Com for Child w Spec Health Care Needs KY 502.429.4430
Fax...502.429.7161
E-mail..............................rebecca.cecil@ky.gov
310 Whittington Parkway, Ste 200, Louisville, KY 40222
Rebecca Cecil, Director

Commission for Children with Special Healthcare
Needs 606.546.5109
Fax...606.546.4199
E-mail..............................judy.bargo@ky.gov
110 Johnson Ln, Barbourville, KY 40906
Aisia Dunn, Director

Division of Women's Health 502.564.3236
Fax...502.564.1552
275 E Main St, Frankfort, KY 40621
Joy Hoskins, Director

MENTAL HEALTH SERVICES

Dept for the Blind 502.564.4754
Fax...502.564.2951
E-mail..............................stephen.johnson@ky.gov
209 Saint Clair St, Frankfort, KY 40601-1817
Stephen Johnson, Executive Director

Div of Mental Health & Subatance Abuse 502.564.4448
Fax...502.564.7152
100 Fair Oaks Ln Fl 4, Frankfort, KY 40621
Louis Kurtz, Acting Director

KY Office of Vocational Rehab 502.564.4440
Fax...502.564.6745
E-mail..............................beth.smith@ky.gov
275 E Main St CHR Building, Mail Stop 2 EK, Frankfort, KY 40621
Beth Smith, Executive Director

JUSTICE AGENCY

Attorney General's Ofc 502.696.5300
Fax...502.564.2894
Web...www.ag.ky.gov
E-mail..............................bethany.adkins@law.state.ky.us
State Capitol, Suite118, Frankfort, KY 40601
Bethany Adkins, Attorney

Correctional Education Division KY 502.564.4795
Fax...502.564.0572
E-mail..............................Martha.Stemp@ky.gov
2439 lawrenceburg rd, Frankfort, KY 40601
Martha Stemp, Director

Dept of Juvenile Justice 502.573.2738
Fax...502.573.4308
Web...http://djj.ky.gov
1025 Capital Center Dr, Frankfort, KY 40601
Ronald Haws, Commissioner

Justice and Public Safety 502.564.7554
Fax...502.564.4840
125 Holmes St, Frankfort, KY 40601
Charles Teveden, Deputy Secretary

Kentucky Sheriffs Boys and Girls Ranch 270.362.8660
Fax...270.362.7534
Web...www.kysheriffsranch.com
E-mail..............................info@kysheriffsranch.com
233 Sheriffs Ranch Rd, Gilbertsville, KY 42044
Jerry Wagner, Executive Director

COURTS

Administrative Ofc Of The Courts 502.573.2350
Fax...502.695.1759
100 Mill Creek Park, Frankfort, KY 40601
Laurie Dudjeon, Director

POLICE AND SHERIFF

Kentucky State Police Records Section 502.227.8781
Fax...502.227.8734
1250 Louisville Rd Ste 2, Frankfort, KY 40601
John Carico, Captain

EDUCATION SERVICES

Division of Exceptional Child Svcs KY 502.564.4970
Fax...502.564.6721
E-mail..............................larry.taylor@education.ky.gov
500 Mero St 8th Flr, Frankfort, KY 40601
Larry Taylor, Director

Kentucky Department of Education 502.564.4700
Fax...502.564.5680
E-mail..............................webmaster@education.ky.gov
500 Mero St, Capital Plaza Tower 1st Flr, Frankfort, KY 40601
Terry Holliday, Commissioner Of Education

Kentucky Dept of Education 502.564.4770
Fax...502.564.5680
Web...www.education.ky.gov
E-mail..............................terry.holliday@education.ky.gov
500 Mero St, 1st Flr, Frankfort, KY 40601-1970
Terry Holliday, Commissioner

Kentucky School for the Blind 502.897.1583
Fax...502.897.2850
Web...www.ksb.k12.ky.us
E-mail..............................john.roberts@ksb.kyschools.us
1867 Frankfort Ave, Louisville, KY 40206-3153
John Roberts, Principal

KY Special Parent Involvement Network 502.937.6894
Fax...502.937.6464
E-mail..............................spininc@kyspin.com
10301 B Deering Rd, Louisville, KY 40272
Paulette Logsdon, Director

Ofc of Education Cabinet 502.564.5331
Fax...502.564.7452
275 E Main St Ste 2WB, Frankfort, KY 40601
Bill Monterosso, Executive Director

School for the Deaf 859.239.7017
Fax...859.239.7006
Web...www.ksd.kyschools.us
303 S 2nd St, Danville, KY 40422-2066
Soraya Matthews, Administrator

LABOR & WORKFORCE EDUCATION

Dept for Workforce Investment 502.564.0372
Fax...502.564.5959
E-mail..............................beth.brinly@ky.gov
500 Mero St, Ste 3, Frankfort, KY 40601
Beth Brinly, Commissioner

COUNTY SERVICES

Adair County

SOCIAL SERVICES

Community Based Svcs **270.384.4731**
Fax 270.384.6460
Web ....ky.gov
   703 Jamestown St, Columbia, KY 42728
   Deedee Ward, Supervisor

Family Support **270.384.2163**
Fax 270.384.5875
   703 Jamestown St, Columbia, KY 42728
   Chrytal Caldwell, Field Services Supervisor

GENERAL HEALTH SERVICES

Health Dept **270.384.2286**
Fax 270.384.4800
   801 Westlake Dr, Columbia, KY 42728-1162
   Rhonda Akins, HIV Coordinator & Supervisor

POLICE AND SHERIFF

Sheriffs Ofc **270.384.2776**
Fax 270.384.5049
   500 Public Sq, Columbia, KY 42728
   Harrison Moss, Sheriff

Allen County

SOCIAL SERVICES

Community Based Svcs **270.237.3101**
Fax 270.237.5365
E-mail ....jessica.humthrey@ky.gov
   29 Hillview Dr, Scottsville, KY 42164
   Jessica Humthrey, Supervisor

Family Support **270.237.3661**
Fax 270.237.5365
E-mail ....keith.harwood@ky.gov
   29 Hillview Dr, Scottsville, KY 42164
   Keith Harwood, Field Services Supervisor

GENERAL HEALTH SERVICES

Health Dept **270.237.4423**
Fax 270.237.4777
Web ....www.allencountyhealth.org
   207 E Locust St, Scottsville, KY 42164
   Donnie Fitzpatrick, Director

POLICE AND SHERIFF

Sheriff's Ofc **270.237.3210**
Fax 270.237.3654
Web ....www.acsoky.org
E-mail ....sheriffjcooke@mctc.com
   194 W Wood St, Scottsville, KY 42164-1261
   Jeff Cooke, Sheriff

Anderson County

GENERAL HEALTH SERVICES

Health Dept **502.839.4551**
Fax 502.839.8099
E-mail ....rennae.durr@ky.gov
   1180 Glensboro rd, Lawrenceburg, KY 40342-1108
   Rennae Durr, Nursing Supervisor

POLICE AND SHERIFF

Sheriff's Ofc **502.839.4021**
Fax 502.839.8508
Web ....www.andersoncountysheriff.net
   141 S Main St, Lawrenceburg, KY 40342-1157
   Troy Young, Sheriff

Ballard County

SOCIAL SERVICES

Community Based Svcs **270.335.5173**
Fax 270.335.5373
E-mail ....jane.justice@ky.gov
   117 N 4th St, Wickliffe, KY 42087
   Rose Bryant, Supervisor

Family Support **270.335.5518**
Fax 270.335.5523
E-mail ....david.wolff@ky.gov
   115 N 4th St, Wickliffe, KY 42087
   David Wolff, Field Services Supervisor

GENERAL HEALTH SERVICES

Health Dept **270.665.5432**
Fax 270.665.9166
E-mail ....melissa.ballard@ky.gov
   198 Bluegrass Dr, La Center, KY 42056
   Melissa Ballard, Rn, Nursing Supervisor

POLICE AND SHERIFF

Sheriff's Ofc **270.335.3561**
Fax 270.335.3010
E-mail ....sheriff@brtc.net
   437 Ohio St, Wickliffe, KY 42087
   Todd Cooper, Sheriff

Barren County

SOCIAL SERVICES

Barren River Region - Dept of Community Based
Svcs **270.651.2250**
Fax 270.687.7027
Web ....www.cfc.state.ky.us
E-mail ....joseph.abel@ky.gov
   742 E Main St, Glasgow, KY 42142
   Joe Abel, Service Region Administrator

GENERAL HEALTH SERVICES

Health Dept **270.651.8321**
Fax 270.659.0062
Web ....www.barrencounty.ky.gov
E-mail ....reginas.reid@ky.gov
   318 W Washington St, Glasgow, KY 42141-2405
   Gina Reid, RN, Nursing Supervisor

COURTS

43rd District Court - Judges Ofc **270.651.9839**
Fax 270.659.0092
   204 Court House Sq, Glasgow, KY 42141
   Honorable John T. Alaexander, Judge

POLICE AND SHERIFF

Sheriff's Ofc **270.651.2771**
Fax 270.651.8204
   117 N Public Sq Ste 1B, Glasgow, KY 42141
   Chris Eaton, Sheriff

Bath County

SOCIAL SERVICES

Community Based Svcs **606.674.6308**
Fax 606.674.3920
Web ....www.ky.gov
E-mail ....sharon.kiser@ky.gov
   47 Cedar Creek Ln, Owingsville, KY 40360
   Sharon Kiser, Supervisor

GENERAL HEALTH SERVICES

Family Support **606.674.6344**
Fax 606.674.3920
   47 Cedar Creek Dr, Owingsville, KY 40360
   Bette Adams, Field Services Supervisor

Health Ctr **606.674.2731**
Fax 606.674.9646
Web www.bath.k12.va.us
   680 Oberline St, Owingsville, KY 40360
   Sherry Ingram, Rn, Nursing Supervisor

Bell County

SOCIAL SERVICES

Community Based Svcs **606.337.6171**
Fax 606.337.1329
   211 E Kentucky Ave, Pineville, KY 40977
   Jessica Green, Supervisor

GENERAL HEALTH SERVICES

Family Support **606.337.7055**
Fax 606.337.9967
   124 Kentucky Ave, Pineville, KY 40977
   Betty Bradley, Field Services Supervisor

Health Ctr **606.337.7046**
Fax 606.337.8321
E-mail ....judy.lefevers@education.ky.gov
   310 S Cherry St, Pineville, KY 40977
   Judy Lefevers, Arnp, Nursing Supervisor

Health Ctr Branch Ofc **606.248.2862**
Fax 606.248.2876
   111 N 21st St, Middlesboro, KY 40965
   Judy Lefevers, Arnp, Nursing Supervisor

MENTAL HEALTH SERVICES

Cumberland River Regional MH/MR Board,
Inc. **606.248.4949**
Fax 606.248.6894
Web ....www.cumberlandriver.com
E-mail ....jkishpaugh@cumberlandriver.com
   324 1/2 N 19th St, Middlesboro, KY 40965-1762
   Jason Kishpaugh, Director

POLICE AND SHERIFF

Sheriff's Ofc **606.337.3102**
Fax 606.337.8391
E-mail ....bcsd@wwgaptel.com
   101 Courthouse Sq, Pineville, KY 40977
   Bruce Bennett, Sheriff

EDUCATION SERVICES

Bell Whitley Head Start Preschool **606.549.0481**
Fax 606.549.0481
Web ....www.bell-whitley.org
E-mail ....lisabaker@bell-whitley.org
   535 N 11th St, Williamsburg, KY 40769
   Ms Lisa Baker, Director

Boone County

SOCIAL SERVICES

Community Based Svcs **859.371.6900**
Fax 859.371.0265
   8311 US Highway ste 42, Florence, KY 41042
   Lisa Prewitt, SRA

COURTS

54th District Court **859.334.2230**
Fax 859.334.3969
E-mail ....sandy@mail.aoc.state.ky.us
   6025 Rogers Ln Rm 246, Burlington, KY 41005
   Honorable Michael Collins, District Judge

Kentucky

POLICE AND SHERIFF

Sheriff's Ofc **859.334.2175**
Fax 859.334.2234
Web ....www.boonecountyky.org
E-mail ....mhelmig@boonecountyky.org
   3000 Conrad Lane, Burlington, KY 41005
Michael A. Helmig, Sheriff

Bourbon County

GENERAL HEALTH SERVICES

Family Support **859.987.2455**
Fax 859.987.9041
Web ....www.bourbon.kyschools.us
E-mail ....susie.craycast@bourbon.kyschools.us
   525 High St, Fl 2, Paris, KY 40361
Susie Craycast, Field Services Supervisor

COURTS

14th District Court **859.987.5562**
Fax 859.988.0137
Web ....www.kycourts.net
E-mail ....vanessadickson@kycourts.net
   310 Main St Ste 131, Paris, KY 40361-2065
Honorable Vanessa Mullins Dickson, Judge

POLICE AND SHERIFF

Sheriff's Ofc **859.987.2130**
Fax 859.987.9284
Web ....www.bourbonsheriff.org
E-mail ....mmatthews@bourbonsheriff.org
   301 Main St Ste 104, Paris, KY 40361-2037
Mark L. Matthews, Sheriff

Boyd County

SOCIAL SERVICES

Family Support **606.920.2013**
Fax 606.920.2082
Web ....www.boydcountyky.gov
   1539 Greenup Ave, Ashland, KY 41101-7613
Bonita Blakeby, Field Services Supervisor

MENTAL HEALTH SERVICES

Pathways, Inc **606.324.1141**
Fax 606.329.8195
Web ....www.pathways-ky.org
E-mail ....todd.trumbore@pathways-ky.org
   1212 Bath Ave, Ashland, KY 41105
Todd Trumbore, Substance Abuse Director

JUSTICE AGENCY

CASA of Northeast Kentucky **606.324.6444**
Fax 606.325.7914
Web ....www.childwatchcasa.com
E-mail ....boydcasa@alltel.net
   1544 Winchester Ave Ste 901, Ashland,
   KY 41101-7932
Carol Polley, Director

COURTS

32nd District Court **606.739.8107**
Fax 606.739.0201
   2805 Louisa St, Catlettsburg, KY 41129-1610
Honorable Jerald Reams, Judge

POLICE AND SHERIFF

Sheriff's Dept **606.739.5135**
Fax 606.739.0594
Web ....www.boydcountysheriff.com
E-mail ....sheriff@boydcountysheriff.com
   2800 Louisa St, Catlettsburg, KY 41129
Terry Keelin, Sheriff

EDUCATION SERVICES

Ashland Boe Head Start **606.327.2715**
Fax 606.327.8895
Web ....www.ashland.kyschools.us
E-mail ....jacqui.thornburg@ashland.kyschools.us
   3215 S 29th St, Ashland, KY 41102-5950
Jacqui Thornburg, Director

Boyle County

SOCIAL SERVICES

Community Based Svcs **859.239.7105**
Fax 859.239.7008
   1714 Perryville Rd Ste 550, Danville, KY 40422-1372
Stacy Price, Supervisor

Family Support **859.239.7837**
Fax 859.239.7010
Web ....www.ky.gov
E-mail ....tom.bentley@ky.gov
   1000 E Lexington Ave, Ste 6, Danville,
   KY 40422-1707
Tom Bentley, Field Services Supervisor

GENERAL HEALTH SERVICES

Health Dept **859.236.2053**
Fax 859.236.2863
Web ....www.boylecodept.com
   448 S 3rd St, Danville, KY 40422
Roger Trent, Director

COURTS

50th Circuit Court **859.239.7442**
Fax 859.239.7000
   321 W Main St, Flr 3, Danville, KY 40422
Honorable Jeff Dotson, Judge

POLICE AND SHERIFF

Sheriff's Ofc **859.238.1123**
Fax 859.238.1103
E-mail ....melliott@boyleky.us
   321 W Main St Ste 103, Danville, KY 40422-1848
Marty Elliott, Sheriff

Bracken County

SOCIAL SERVICES

Community Based Svcs **606.735.2195**
Fax 606.735.2214
E-mail ....patty.johnson@ky.gov
   753 Brooksville Powersville Rd, Brooksville,
   KY 41004-8045
Patty Johnson, Supervisor/intake

Family Support **606.735.2193**
Fax 606.735.3716
   753 Brooksville Powersville Rd, Brooksville,
   KY 41004-8045
Jennifer Royce, Field Services Supervisor

GENERAL HEALTH SERVICES

Health Dept **606.735.2157**
Fax 606.735.2159
   429 Frankfort St, Brooksville, KY 41004
Tony Cox, Administrator

POLICE AND SHERIFF

Sheriff's Ofc **606.735.3233**
Fax 606.735.2925
   Sheriff Locust St, Brooksville, KY 41004
Chuck Rechtin, Sheriff

EDUCATION SERVICES

Brooksville Head Start **606.735.3341**
Fax 606.735.3341
Web www.brooksvillekentucky.8k.com
   106 Powell St, Brooksville, KY 41004
Bettie Fissie, Director

Breathitt County

SOCIAL SERVICES

Community Based Svcs **606.666.7506**
Fax 606.666.5991
E-mail ....cathy.gay@ky.gov
   1041 College Ave, Jackson, KY 41339
Cathy Gay, Supervisor And Treatment

Family Support **606.666.2481**
Fax 606.666.9760
   355 Broadway St, Jackson, KY 41339-1040
Lisa Banks, Director

GENERAL HEALTH SERVICES

Health Dept **606.666.5274**
Fax 606.666.4601
E-mail ....sheilag.sharpe@ky.gov
   955 Hwy 30 W, Jackson, KY 41339
Dr. Sheila Sharpe, Director

COURTS

District Court **606.666.5768**
Fax 606.666.4893
   1131 Main St, Jackson, KY 41339
Honorable Kenny Profitt, District Judge

POLICE AND SHERIFF

Sheriff's Ofc **606.666.3805**
Fax 606.666.3806
E-mail ....sheriffbreathitt@hotmail.com
   1137 Main St Ste 206, Jackson, KY 41339-1119
Ray Clemons, Sheriff

Breckinridge County

SOCIAL SERVICES

Community Based Svcs **270.756.2196**
Fax 270.756.1684
E-mail ....flora.wilson@ky.gov
   110 US Highway 60 E, Hardinsburg, KY 40143
Flora Wilson, Supervisor

Family Support **270.756.2156**
Fax 270.756.1120
   110 US Highway 60, Hardinsburg, KY 40143
Jennifer Marshall, Field Services Supervisor

GENERAL HEALTH SERVICES

Health Deptt **270.756.5121**
Fax 270.756.9090
E-mail ....cynthial.bandy@ky.gov
   220 S Hardin, Hardinsburg, KY 40143
Cindy Bandy, Director

EDUCATION SERVICES

Cloverport Head Start **270.788.6428**
Fax 270.788.6640
E-mail ....msimcon@brckridge.kyschool.us
   101 4th St, Cloverport, KY 40111
Mike Simcon, Director

Bullitt County

SOCIAL SERVICES

Community Based Svcs **502.955.6591**
Fax 502.955.8478
E-mail ....Emma.ross@ky.gov
   445 Highway 44 E Ste 203, Shepherdsville,
   KY 40165-6078
Emma Ross, Supervisor

Family Support **502.543.7081**
Fax 502.543.3819
Web ....www.state.ky.gov
E-mail ....sandra.dean@mail.state.ky.gov
   445 Highway 44 E Ste 209, Shepherdsville,
   KY 40165-6079
Sandra Dean, Field Services Supervisor Ii

GENERAL HEALTH SERVICES

Health Dept............................**502.543.2415**
Fax..502.543.2998
E-mail............................edmundm.fitzgibbons@ky.gov
181 Lees Valley Rd, Shepherdsville, KY 40165
Edmund Fitzgibbons, Director

COURTS

Judges Chambers.........................**502.543.2244**
Fax..502.921.2564
Bullitt County Judicial Center, Shepherdsville, KY 40165
Honorable A. Bailey Taylor, Judge

POLICE AND SHERIFF

Sheriff's Dept..............................**502.543.2514**
Fax..502.543.2710
300 S Buckman St, Shepherdsville, KY 40165
David Greenwell, Sheriff

Butler County

SOCIAL SERVICES

Community Based Svcs.................**270.526.3833**
Fax..270.526.3795
333 Gardner Ln, Morgantown, KY 42261
Wanda Nevins, Supervisor

Family Support.............................**270.526.3395**
Fax..270.526.6776
333 Gardner Lane, Morgantown, KY 42261
Theresa Wilson, Field Services Supervisor

GENERAL HEALTH SERVICES

Health Ctr....................................**270.526.3221**
Fax..270.526.6828
E-mail............................monicag.hunt@ky.gov
104 N Warren St, Morgantown, KY 42261-7924
Monica Hunt, Rn, Nursing Supervisor

Caldwell County

SOCIAL SERVICES

Community Based Svcs.................**270.365.7275**
Fax..270.365.7469
E-mail............................jenny.wilkerson@ky.gov
300 Micbeth Dr, Princeton, KY 42445
Jennifer Wilkerson, Supervisor

Family Support.............................**270.365.5524**
Fax..270.365.7469
300 Micbeth Dr, Princeton, KY 42445-0646
Janie Reik, Supervisor

GENERAL HEALTH SERVICES

Health Dept..................................**270.365.6571**
Fax..270.365.3145
310 Hawthorne St, Princeton, KY 42445
Angie Doons, Nursing Supervisor

COURTS

56th District Court / Judges
Chambers....................................**270.365.6656**
Fax..270.365.9171
105 W Court Sq, Princeton, KY 42445-1567
Honorable James R. Ridd III, Judge

POLICE AND SHERIFF

Sheriff's Ofc.................................**270.365.2088**
Fax..270.365.6177
E-mail............................ccso46@caldwellcourthouse.com
100 E Market St, Rm 25, Princeton, KY 42445-1675
Stan Hudson, Sheriff

Calloway County

SOCIAL SERVICES

Community Based Svcs.................**270.753.5362**
Fax..270.759.3084
E-mail............................tena.phillips@ky.gov
205 So 6th St, Murray, KY 42071
Tena Phillips, Supervisor

Family Support.............................**270.753.1871**
Fax..270.753.1817
203 S 6th St, Murray, KY 42071
Carol Lane, Field Services Supervisor

GENERAL HEALTH SERVICES

Health Dept..................................**270.753.3381**
Fax..270.753.8455
602 Memory Ln, Murray, KY 42071-1944
Linda Cavitt, Rn, Nursing Director

JUSTICE AGENCY

CASA..**270.761.0164**
Fax..270.767.0164
E-mail............................casacc@murray-ky.net
1003 Poplar St, Murray, KY 42071
Racquel Strickland, Director

Campbell County

SOCIAL SERVICES

Community Based Svcs.................**859.292.6733**
Fax..859.292.6728
601 Washington Ave Ste 360, Newport, KY 41071-1968
Tracy Barrett, Supervisor

GENERAL HEALTH SERVICES

Health Ctr....................................**859.431.1704**
Fax..859.655.6386
E-mail............................donna.mullen@ky.gov
1098 Monmouth St, Newport, KY 41071-1618
Donna Mullen, Clinic Manager

COURTS

17th District Court.......................**859.292.6322**
Fax..859.292.6361
Web..www.kycourts.net
E-mail............................gregoryc@kycourts.net
600 Columbia St Ste 3, Newport, KY 41071-1892
Greg Copovic, Chief Judge

POLICE AND SHERIFF

Sheriff's Ofc.................................**859.292.3833**
Fax..859.292.3826
E-mail............................jdunn@campbellcountyky.org
1098 Monmouth St, Newport, KY 41071
John D. Dunn Jr., Sheriff

Carlisle County

SOCIAL SERVICES

Community Based Svcs.................**270.628.3434**
Fax..270.628.5438
E-mail............................rose.bryant@ky.gov
178 Hwy 51 N, Bardwell, KY 42023
Rose Bryant, Supervisor

Family Support.............................**270.628.5442**
E-mail............................lisak.record@ky.gov
178 US Highway 51 N, Bardwell, KY 42023
Lisa Record, Field Services Supervisor

GENERAL HEALTH SERVICES

Health Dept..................................**270.628.5431**
Fax..270.628.3811
62 John Robert Dr, Bardwell, KY 42023
Cinda Wilson, Rn, Nursing Supervisor

POLICE AND SHERIFF

Sheriff's Dept..............................**270.628.3377**
Fax..270.628.3392
E-mail............................carlisle1@inbox.com
79 E Court St, Bardwell, KY 42023
Steve Mcchristian, Sheriff

Carroll County

SOCIAL SERVICES

Community Based Svcs.................**502.732.6681**
Fax..502.732.4144
1714 Highland Ave, Carrollton, KY 41008-8775
Paula Fields, Supervisor

Family Support.............................**502.732.4271**
Fax..502.732.8708
1720 Highland Ave, Carrollton, KY 41008
Lewis Ayres, Field Services Supervisor

GENERAL HEALTH SERVICES

Health Dept..................................**502.732.6641**
Fax..502.732.8681
401 11th St, Carrollton, KY 41008
Morgan Bond, Public Health Nurse

COURTS

15th District Court / Circuit Clerks............**502.732.4307**
Fax..502.732.8138
802 Clay St Ste 2, Carrollton, KY 41008
Laman Stark, Carroll County Circuit Clerk

POLICE AND SHERIFF

Sheriff's Dept..............................**502.732.7010**
Fax..502.732.6794
E-mail............................jenniferwillhoite@yahoo.com
440 Main St Ste 1, Carrollton, KY 41008-1064
Jamie Kinman, Sheriff

Carter County

SOCIAL SERVICES

Community Based Svcs.................**606.474.6627**
Fax..606.474.2898
Web..www.ualr.edu
211 W Main St, Grayson, KY 41143-1245
Shannon Hall, Supervisor/on-going

Family Support.............................**606.474.5103**
Fax..606.474.0641
E-mail............................michael.claxon@ky.gov
211 W Main St, Grayson, KY 41143-1245
Michael Claxon, Field Services Supervisor

GENERAL HEALTH SERVICES

Health Ctr....................................**606.474.5109**
Fax..606.474.4217
1710 US Highway 60 E, Grayson, KY 41143
Rita Sexton, Nursing Supervisor

COURTS

37th District Court.......................**606.474.6572**
Fax..606.474.8584
100 E Main St, Grayson, KY 41143-1302
Honorable Rupert Wilhoit, Judge

POLICE AND SHERIFF

Sheriff's Office.............................**606.474.5616**
Fax..606.474.9954
E-mail............................cartercountysheriff@gmail.com
300 W Main St Rm 204, Grayson, KY 41143
Casey Brammell, Sheriff

Kentucky

Casey County

SOCIAL SERVICES

Community Based Svcs **606.787.8369**
Fax 606.787.5485
E-mail ....kathy.hare@ky.gov
59 Hustonville St, Liberty, KY 42539
Sandra Rollins, Administrator

Family Support **606.787.8338**
Fax 606.787.0721
137 Courthouse Sq, Liberty, KY 42539
Allen Thompson, Field Services Supervisor

GENERAL HEALTH SERVICES

Health Dept **606.787.6911**
Fax 606.787.2507
199 Adams St, Liberty, KY 42539
Natasha Bowmer, Nursing Supervisor

COURTS

29th District Court / Clerk's Ofc **606.787.6510**
Fax 606.787.2497
231 Court Square, Liberty, KY 42539
James G Weddle, Circuit Judge

POLICE AND SHERIFF

Sheriff's Ofc **606.787.6821**
Fax 606.787.9632
625 Campbellsville St, Liberty, KY 42539
Jerry Coffman, Sheriff

Christian County

SOCIAL SERVICES

Family Support **270.889.6512**
Fax 270.889.6012
Web ....www.christiancounty.org
E-mail ....kelly.joyce@ky.gov
644 North Dr, Hopkinsville, KY 42240-1853
Kelly Joyce, Field Services Supervisor

GENERAL HEALTH SERVICES

Health Dept **270.887.4160**
Fax 270.887.4165
E-mail ....melissamiller@kypoultry.org
1700 Canton St, Hopkinsville, KY 42240
Mark Pyle, Director

COURTS

3rd District Court / Judges

Chambers **270.889.6544**
Fax 270.889.6003
E-mail ....arnoldl@mail.aoc.state.ky.us
100 Justice Way, Hopkinsville, KY 42240-2137
Honorable Arnold B. Lynch, Judge

Family Court **270.889.6038**
Fax 270.889.6040
Web ....www.courts.ky.gov
E-mail ....jasonfleming@kycourts.net
100 Justice Way, Hopkinsville, KY 42240-2137
Honorable Jason Shea Fleming, Circuit Judge, Family Court

POLICE AND SHERIFF

Sheriff's Ofc **270.887.4143**
Fax 270.887.4032
216 W 7th St, Hopkinsville, KY 42262
Livy Leavell Jr., Sheriff

Clark County

SOCIAL SERVICES

Family Support **859.737.7730**
Fax 859.737.7030
E-mail ....moleta.lambert@ky.gov
1113 Pioneer Dr, Winchester, KY 40391
Moleta Lambert, Field Services Supervisor

GENERAL HEALTH SERVICES

Health Dept **859.744.4482**
Fax 859.744.0338
Web ....www.clarkhealthdept.org
E-mail ....karenb.king@ky.gov
400 Professional Ave, Winchester, KY 40391-1147
Karen King, Rn, Nursing Director

COURTS

25th District Court **859.737.7141**
Fax 859.737.7005
17 Cleveland Ave, Winchester, KY 40392
Honorable Brandy Brown, District Judge

Family Court **859.737.7021**
Fax 859.737.7025
Web ....www.kycourts.net
E-mail ....jeffreywalson@kycourts.net
34 S Main St, winchester, KY 40392
Honorable Jeffrey Walson, Div Iv, Judge

Clay County

SOCIAL SERVICES

Community Based Svcs **606.598.2027**
Fax 606.598.4385
249 Old Hwy 421, Manchester, KY 40962
Helen Adams, Supervisor

GENERAL HEALTH SERVICES

Cumberland Valley Health District **606.598.5564**
Fax 606.598.6615
Manchester Square Shopping Center, Rm 212, Manchester, KY 40962
Lisa Abner, Nursing Director

Health Ctr **606.598.2425**
Fax 606.598.4448
330 Shamrock Rd, Manchester, KY 40962-9201
Linda Madden, Rn, Nursing Supervisor

COURTS

41st District Court / Chambers of District Judge
 .... **606.598.6170**
Fax 606.596.0916
316 Main St Ste 219, Manchester, KY 40962-1282
Honorable Oscar Gayle House, Judge

POLICE AND SHERIFF

Sheriff's Ofc **606.598.3471**
Fax 606.598.5020
102 Richmond Rd Ste 100, Manchester, KY 40962
Kevin Johnson, Sheriff

Clinton County

SOCIAL SERVICES

Community Based Svcs **606.387.6655**
Fax 606.387.7254
E-mail ....carla.grider@hay.gov
801 Tennessee Rd Ste D, Albany, KY 42602
Sue Williams, Secretary

Family Support **606.387.6446**
Fax 606.387.7254
E-mail ....sandra.mcclard@ky.gov
801 Tennessee Rd Ste D, Albany, KY 42602-1074
Sandra McClard, Supervisor

GENERAL HEALTH SERVICES

Health Dept **606.387.5711**
Fax 606.387.7212
E-mail ....donnaj.parish@lcdhd.org
131 FOOTHILLS AVE, Albany, KY 42602-1090
Donna Parish, Nursing Supervisor

COURTS

40th District Court **606.387.6424**
Fax 606.387.8154
100 S Cross St Ste J, Albany, KY 42602
Searlette Latazem, District Judge

POLICE AND SHERIFF

Sheriff's Ofc **606.387.5111**
Fax 606.387.5463
100 S Cross St, Albany, KY 42602
Ricky J. Riddle, Sheriff

Crittenden County

SOCIAL SERVICES

Community Based Svcs **270.965.5246**
Fax 270.965.2424
815 S Main St, Marion, KY 42064
Tammy Givens, Supervisor

Family Support **270.965.2254**
Fax 270.965.2424
E-mail ....angie.curnel@ky.gov
815 S Main St, Marion, KY 42064-1921
Angie Curnel, Field Services Supervisor

GENERAL HEALTH SERVICES

Health Dept **270.965.5215**
Fax 270.965.9078
190 Industrial Dr, Marion, KY 42064
Alfreda Wheeler, Director

POLICE AND SHERIFF

Sheriff's Ofc **270.965.3400**
Fax 270.965.2121
E-mail ....ccso@apex.net
107 S Main St Ste 207, Marion, KY 42064-1500
Wayne Agent, Sheriff

Cumberland County

SOCIAL SERVICES

Community Based Svcs **270.864.3834**
Fax 270.864.4129
E-mail ....markgibson@ky.gov
232 Keen St, Burkesville, KY 42717
Mark Gibson, Supervisor

Family Support **270.864.2556**
Fax 270.864.4129
232 Keene St, Burkesville, KY 42717
Brenda Fruley, Field Services Supervisor

COURTS

Judge Executive **270.864.3444**
Fax 270.864.5377
Web ....www.kactfo.org
600 Court House Square, Burkesville, KY 42717
Honorable Steve D. Hurt, District Judge

Daviess County

SOCIAL SERVICES

Community-Based Svcs & Family Support Green River Region **270.687.7047**
Fax 270.687.7027
Web ....kentucky.gov
311 W 2nd St, Owensboro, KY 42301-0734
Joe Minor, Administrator

GENERAL HEALTH SERVICES

Green River Health District **270.686.7747**
Fax 270.926.9862
E-mail ....debbie.fillman@grdhd.org
1501 Breckridge, Owensboro, KY 42302
Debbie Fillman, Director

Health Ctr.............................**270.686.7744**
Fax..270.926.8677
E-mail.............................judy.payne@grdhd.org
   1600 Breckenridge St, Owensboro, KY 42303
Judy Payne, Rn, Nursing Supervisor

JUSTICE AGENCY

CASA..............................**270.683.2138**
Fax..270.684.3863
E-mail.........................dccasa@mindspring.com
   415 Saint St, Owensboro, KY 42303
Vikki Embry, Program Director

COURTS

6th District Court / Juvenile Court............**270.687.7211**
Fax..270.687.7212
   100 E 2nd St, Judicial Center, Owensboro,
   KY 42303-4108
Honorable Joe Castlen, Judge

POLICE AND SHERIFF

Sheriff's Dept......................**270.685.8444**
Fax..270.685.8454
Web....................................www.mindspring.com
E-mail......................keithrcain@mindspring.com
   212 Saint Ann St Ste 103, Owensboro,
   KY 42303-4148
Keith R. Cain, Sheriff

EDUCATION SERVICES

**Estes Family Resource - Estes Elementary
School**....................................**270.686.1118**
Web..www.adelphia.net
   1675 Leitchfield Rd, Owensboro, KY 42303-0935
Angelia Dean, Director

Exceptional Children................**270.852.7000**
Fax..270.852.7030
Web..www.dcps.org
E-mail..............robin.bush@david.kyschool.us
   1622 Southeastern Pkwy, Owensboro, KY 42303
Robin Bush, Director Of Special Education

Edmonson County

SOCIAL SERVICES

Community Based Svcs..............**270.597.2163**
Fax..270.597.2788
Web..................................www.mail.state.ky.us
E-mail............................mary.lindsey@ky.gov
   1122 S Main St, Lee Williams Building, Brownsville,
   KY 42210
Mary Lindsey, Supervisor

Family Support........................**270.597.2118**
Fax..270.597.2788
   1122 Highway 259 N, Brownsville, KY 42210
Janet Wyrick, Field Services Supervisor

GENERAL HEALTH SERVICES

Health Dept...........................**270.597.2194**
Fax..270.597.3326
Web..............................www.barrenriverhealth.org
   221 Mammoth Cave Rd, Brownsville, KY 42210
Melody Prunty, Rn, Center Coordinator

POLICE AND SHERIFF

Sheriff's Dept........................**270.597.2157**
Fax..270.597.2457
Web..............................www.edmonson.kysheriff.com
   110 E. Jackson St, Brownsville, KY 42210
Wil Cannon, Sheriff

Elliott County

SOCIAL SERVICES

Community Based Svcs...............**606.738.5167**
Fax..606.738.5183
E-mail............................don.holbrook@ky.gov
   854 S Hwy 7, Sandy Hook, KY 41171
Donald Holbrook, Supervisor

Family Support........................**606.738.5193**
Fax..606.738.5183
E-mail...........................melanie.ison@ky.gov
   Hwy 7 South, Sandy Hook, KY 41171
Melanie Ison, Field Services Supervisor

POLICE AND SHERIFF

Sheriff's Ofc.........................**606.738.5422**
Fax..606.738.4669
Web..............................www.caldwellcourthouse.com
E-mail................jstephens@caldwellcourthouse.com
   Main St Courthouse, Sandy Hook, KY 41171
Jim Stephens, Sheriff

Estill County

SOCIAL SERVICES

Community Based Svcs...............**606.723.5146**
Fax..606.723.2915
   102 Mack St, Irvine, KY 40336
Amy Taylor, Supervisor/intake

Family Support........................**606.723.5124**
Fax..606.723.2915
Web...................................www.estillky.com
E-mail.............................beth.ohair@ky.gov
   102 Mack St, Irvine, KY 40336-1310
Beth O'Hair, Field Services Supervisor

GENERAL HEALTH SERVICES

Health Dept...........................**606.723.5181**
Fax..606.723.5254
   365 River Dr, Irvine, KY 40336
Eshia Johnson, Hiv Coordinator

POLICE AND SHERIFF

Sheriff's Ofc.........................**606.723.2323**
Fax..606.723.6166
E-mail....................gfreeman@fayettesheriff.com
   130 Main St Rm 107, Irvine, KY 40336
Gary Freeman, Sheriff

Fayette County

SOCIAL SERVICES

Community Based Svcs...............**859.271.3765**
Fax..859.271.4447
   1165 Centre Pkwy Ste 180, Lexington, KY 40517
Grace Akers, Director

Family Support........................**859.246.2070**
Fax..859.246.2691
   2050 Creative Dr Ste 160, Lexington, KY 40505-4227
Donna Conley, Field Services Supervisor

GENERAL HEALTH SERVICES

Benchmark Family Svcs..............**859.260.1412**
Fax..859.260.1012
Web..............................www.benchmarkfamilyservices.org
E-mail......................ryan.good@benchmarkfs.org
   118 Dennis Dr, Lexington, KY 40503-2917
Ryan Good, Director Of Programs & Development

Health Dept...........................**859.252.2371**
Fax..859.288.2359
Web..............................www.lexintonhealthdepartment.org
E-mail..........................mary.myhre@ky.gov
   650 Newtown Pike, Lexington, KY 40508-1113
Mary Ann Myhre, Executive Director For Public Health

Justice Agency

JUSTICE AGENCY

Attorney's Office.....................**859.226.1882**
E-mail.............brian.mattone@fayettecountyattorney.com
   110 W Vine St, Lexington, KY 40507
Brian Mattone, Ass. County Attorney

POLICE AND SHERIFF

Sheriff's Ofc.........................**859.252.1771**
Fax..859.259.0973
Web..................................www.fayettesheriff.com
E-mail.................................sheriffwit@aol.com
   150 N Limestone Ste 265, Lexington, KY 40507
Kathy Witt, Sheriff

Fleming County

SOCIAL SERVICES

Community Based Svcs...............**606.845.2381**
Fax..606.845.9004
E-mail............................connie.lee@ky.gov
   101-B Clark St, Flemingsburg, KY 41041
Connie Lee, Supervisor/intake

Family Support........................**606.845.7561**
Fax..606.845.9004
E-mail.........................ronela.gruber@ky.gov
   101B Clark St, Flemingsburg, KY 41041
Ronela Gruber, Field Services Supervisor

GENERAL HEALTH SERVICES

Health Dept...........................**606.845.6511**
Fax..606.845.0879
   194 Windsor Rd, Flemingsburg, KY 41041
Stephanie Fryman, Director

POLICE AND SHERIFF

Sheriff's Ofc.........................**606.845.4701**
Fax..606.849.8033
   100 Court Sq, Flemingsburg, KY 41041-1050
Scotty Royse, Sheriff

EDUCATION SERVICES

Head Start............................**606.849.2979**
Fax..606.845.1327
Web..................................www.lvcap.com
E-mail.................................tmiller@lvcap.com
   RR 11 Maysville Rd, Flemingsburg, KY 41041
Toby Miller, Director

Floyd County

SOCIAL SERVICES

Community Based Svcs...............**606.889.1724**
Fax..606.889.1727
Web..www.ky.gov
   311 N Arnold Ave Ste 402, Prestonsburg,
   KY 41653-1279
Angela Baldwin, Supervisor

GENERAL HEALTH SERVICES

Health Dept...........................**606.886.2788**
Fax..606.886.7989
E-mail..........................thursac.sloan@ky.gov
   283 Goble St, Prestonsburg, KY 41653
Thursa Sloan, Director

COURTS

Family Court / Chambers of Judge Paxton
....................................**606.889.1676**
Fax..606.889.1679
E-mail.........................dmarshall@kycourts.net
   127 S Lake Dr Ste 100, Prestonsburg, KY 41653-1981
Dwaght Marshall, Family Court Judge

Kentucky

POLICE AND SHERIFF

Sheriff's Dept **606.886.6171**
Fax 606.886.7973
E-mail ....fcsd@bellsouth.net
  149 S Central Ave Ste 3, Prestonsburg, KY 41653
  John K. Blackburn, Sheriff

Franklin County

SOCIAL SERVICES

**Cabinet for Families and Children - Family
Support** **502.564.3440**
Fax 502.564.4021
  275 E Main St, Frankfort, KY 40621-0001
  Jason Dunn, Director

**Caninet For Health and Family
Services** **502.564.5390**
Fax 502.564.9751
  677 Commanche Trail, Franklin, KY 40601
  Nelson Knight, Regional Administrator

Family Support **502.564.5390**
Fax 502.564.9751
  677 Comanche Trl, Frankfort, KY 40601
  Timika Johnson, Field Services Supervisor

GENERAL HEALTH SERVICES

Health Dept **502.564.7647**
Fax 502.564.9640
E-mail ....paula.alexander@ky.gov
  100 Glenns Creek Rd, Frankfort, KY 40601
  Paula Alexander, Director

Health Dept **502.564.4269**
Fax 502.564.9586
Web ....www.fchd.org
E-mail ....paula.alexander@ky.gov
  100 Glenns Creek Rd, Frankfort, KY 40601-2473
  Paula Alexander, Public Health Director

Health Dept **502.564.7996**
Fax 502.564.4667
E-mail ....dianne.shuntich@ky.gov
  275 E Main St, Mail Slot HS2 W E, Frankfort,
  KY 40621-0001
  Janet Luttrel, Branch Manager

JUSTICE AGENCY

CASA **502.875.0702**
Fax 502.875.0788
E-mail ....casavolcoordinator@fewpb.net
  649 Charity Court, Frankfort, KY 40601
  Ginny Smith, Executive Director

COURTS

48th Judicial District Court **502.564.7073**
Fax 502.564.3711
  669 Chamberlin Ave, Frankfort, KY 40601
  Honorable Kathy R Mangeot, Judge

Family Court **502.564.2278**
Fax 502.564.2311
  669 Chamberlin Ave, Frankfort, KY 40601
  Squire Williams, Judge

POLICE AND SHERIFF

Sheriff's Ofc **502.875.8740**
Fax 502.875.8738
Web ....www.franklincosheriff.com
E-mail ....pat.melton@franklincountyky.com
  669 Chamberlin Ave, Frankfort, KY 40601-1843
  Pat Melton, Sheriff

EDUCATION SERVICES

Crescent Drive Head Start **859.236.1139**
Fax 859.236.1148
  456 Crescent Dr, Danville, KY 40602
  Joann Travis, Director

Fulton County

SOCIAL SERVICES

Community Based Svcs **270.472.1850**
Fax 270.472.2160
  510 Mears St, Fulton, KY 42041
  Lisa Eason, Supervisor

Family Support **270.472.1638**
Fax 270.472.6804
  510 Mears St, Fulton, KY 42041-1411
  Barbara Carrol, Field Services Supervisor

GENERAL HEALTH SERVICES

Health Ctr East **270.472.1982**
Fax 270.472.2553
  350 Browder St, Fulton, KY 42041
  Dawna Fields, Rn, Public Health Nurse

Health Ctr West **270.236.2825**
Fax 270.236.2230
  402 Troy Ave, Hickman, KY 42050
  Donna Fields, Care Coordinator

COURTS

1st District Court **270.236.3944**
Fax 270.236.3729
Web ....www.fultoncountysheriff.net
  114 E Wellington, Hickman, KY 42050
  Honorable Hunter B. Whitesell Ii, District Judge

POLICE AND SHERIFF

Sheriff's Dept **270.236.2545**
Fax 270.236.3373
E-mail ....office@fultoncountysheriff.net
  2216 Myron Corey Dr, Hickman, KY 42050
  Robert Hopper, Sheriff

EDUCATION SERVICES

Fulton City Early Head Start **270.472.2859**
Web ....www.acf.hhs.gov
  212 7th St, Fulton, KY 42041-1333

Gallatin County

SOCIAL SERVICES

Family Support **859.567.7281**
Fax 859.567.2341
Web ....www.gallatincountyky.com
  100 W Market St, Warsaw, KY 41095
  Gloria White, Field Services Supervisor

POLICE AND SHERIFF

Sheriff's Ofc **859.567.5751**
Fax 859.567.7928
  106 W Main Street, Warsaw, KY 41095
  Josh Neale, Sheriff

Garrard County

SOCIAL SERVICES

Family Support **859.792.2701**
Fax 859.792.2049
E-mail ....cindy.wade@ky.gov
  136 Commerce Dr, Lancaster, KY 40444-9767
  Cindy Wade, Field Services Supervisor

GENERAL HEALTH SERVICES

Health Dept **859.792.2153**
Fax 859.792.4719
E-mail ....dorisr.davis@ky.gov
  89 Farra Dr, Lancaster, KY 40444
  Renee Davis, Rn, Clinic Coordinator

MENTAL HEALTH SERVICES

Comprehensive Care Ctr **859.792.2181**
Fax 859.792.6517
Web ....www.bluegrass.org
E-mail ....caltobello@bluegrass.org
  322 Crab Orchard St Ste 1, Lancaster,
  KY 40444-1222
  Christi Altobello, Clinical Director

POLICE AND SHERIFF

Sheriff's Dept **859.792.3591**
Fax 859.792.2570
E-mail ....rgwsher@alltel.net
  15 Public Sq Ste 4, Lancaster, KY 40444-8151
  Ronald G. Wardrip, Sheriff

Grant County

SOCIAL SERVICES

Community Based Svcs **859.824.4471**
Fax 859.824.7910
E-mail ....jennifer.mccomas@ky.gov
  120 N Main St, Williamstown, KY 41097
  Jennifer Mccomas, Supervisor

Family Support **859.824.5202**
Fax 859.824.7910
Web ....www.grantcounty.ky.gov
E-mail ....rebec.stillwell@ky.gov
  120 N Main St, Williamstown, KY 41097-1115
  Rebecca Stillwell, Field Services Supervisor

GENERAL HEALTH SERVICES

Debbie Wright Health Care Ctr **859.824.5074**
Fax 859.824.3220
E-mail ....debbie.wright@ky.gov
  234 Barnes Rd, Williamstown, KY 41097-9482
  Debbie Wright, Rn, Clinic Manager

COURTS

**15th Circuit Court / Ofc of Judge
Bates** **859.824.7516**
Fax 859.824.6494
Web ....www.grantco.org
E-mail ....sbates@grantco.org
  101 N Main St Rm 15, Williamstown, KY 41097-1118
  Honorable Stephen L. Bates, Judge

POLICE AND SHERIFF

Sheriff's Ofc **859.824.3333**
Fax 859.824.3334
  101 N Main St Rm 1, Williamstown, KY 41097
  Chuck Dills, Sheriff

Graves County

SOCIAL SERVICES

Community Based Svcs **270.247.4711**
Fax 270.247.6416
  333 Charles Dr, Mayfield, KY 42066-4900
  Karla High, Supervisor

Family Support **270.247.2862**
Fax 270.247.2007
Web ....www.kentucky.gov
E-mail ....johnr.carrico@ky.gov
  333 Charles Dr, Mayfield, KY 42066-4900
  John A Carrico, Field Services Supervisor

GENERAL HEALTH SERVICES

Health Dept **270.247.3553**
  416 Central Ave, Mayfield, KY 42066
  Jimmye Saunders, Rn, Nursing Supervisor

COURTS

52nd Judicial District **270.247.0580**
Fax 270.247.8221
  100 E Broadway Ste 1, Mayfield, KY 42066-2343
  Deborah Crooks, District Judge

Grayson County

SOCIAL SERVICES

Family Support......................270.259.4041
Fax...............................270.259.0646
Web.....................www.graysoncountyschamber.com
498 S Main St, South Gate Mall, Leitchfield, KY 42754-1024
Victoria Kelly, Field Services Supervisor

GENERAL HEALTH SERVICES

Health Ctr........................270.259.3141
Fax...............................270.259.5388
E-mail......................gigim.meredith@ky.gov
124 E White Oak St, Leitchfield, KY 42754-1447
Gigi Meredith, Clinical Director

POLICE AND SHERIFF

Sheriff's Ofc.....................270.259.3024
Fax...............................270.259.3364
E-mail.............rclemoms@caldwellcourthouse.com
44 Public Sq, Leitchfield, KY 42754
Rick Clemoms, Sheriff

Green County

SOCIAL SERVICES

Community Based Svcs................270.932.7485
Fax...............................270.932.5051
E-mail......................kalion.bagby@ky.gov
605 Columbia Hwy, Greensburg, KY 42743-1115
Kalion Bagby, Supervisor

Family Support......................270.932.7484
Fax...............................270.932.5051
Web.....................www.kentucky.gov
605 Columbia Hwy, Greensburg, KY 42743-1115
Kalon Bagby, Field Services Supervisor

GENERAL HEALTH SERVICES

Health Dept.......................270.932.4341
Fax...............................270.932.6016
Web.....................www.lcdhd.org
220 Industrial Park Rd, Greensburg, KY 42743
Kaylene Bush, Nursing Supervisor

POLICE AND SHERIFF

Sheriff's Dept....................270.932.5641
Fax...............................270.932.3193
E-mail......................greencountyso@alltell.net
203 W Court St Ste 3, Greensburg, KY 42743
Tim Stumph, Sheriff

Greenup County

SOCIAL SERVICES

Community Based Svcs................606.473.7366
Fax...............................606.473.7311
1103 Seaton Ave, Greenup, KY 41144-1132
Carla Tanner, Supervisor

Family Support......................606.473.7311
Fax...............................606.473.9126
1103 Seaton Ave, Greenup, KY 41144
Kim Worthington, Field Services Supervisor

GENERAL HEALTH SERVICES

Health Ctr........................606.473.9838
Fax...............................606.473.6405
Web.....................www.grrenuphealth.net
E-mail......................connied.wilburn@ky.gov
806 Seaton Ave Ste 1, Greenup, KY 41144
Connie Wilburn, Rn, Nursing Supervisor

POLICE AND SHERIFF

Sheriff's Dept....................606.473.9833
Fax...............................606.473.5944
E-mail......................cooper97@wwd.net
Main Street & Harrison Street, Greenup, KY 41144
Keith M. Cooper, Sheriff

Hancock County

SOCIAL SERVICES

Community Based Svcs................270.927.8142
Fax...............................270.927.1294
Web.....................www.csc.state.ky.us
Highway 60 East, Hawesville, KY 42348
Edward Nevitt, Supervisor

POLICE AND SHERIFF

Sheriff's Ofc.....................270.927.6247
Fax...............................270.927.8094
225 Main Cross St, Hawesville, KY 42348
Ralph D. Bozarth, Sheriff

Hardin County

SOCIAL SERVICES

Family Support......................270.766.5029
Fax...............................270.766.5163
916 N Mulberry St Ste 120, Elizabethtown, KY 42701
Ann Wagner, Field Services Supervisor

Protection and Permanency..........270.766.5099
Fax...............................270.766.5155
E-mail......................madeleine.dunaway@ky.gov
916 N Mulberry St Ste 140, Elizabethtown, KY 42701-3628
Madeleine Dunaway, Supervisor

GENERAL HEALTH SERVICES

Health Ctr........................270.765.6196
Fax...............................270.763.0397
E-mail......................debbie.hanson@ky.gov
580 Westport Rd, Elizabethtown, KY 42701-2949
Debbie Hanson, Rn, Clinical Director

COURTS

9th District Court.................270.766.5000
Fax...............................270.769.6505
Web.....................www.kycourts.net
E-mail......................lorettacrady@kycourts.net
120 E Dixie Ave, Elizabethtown, KY 42701-1974
Honorable Kimberly W. Shumate, District Judge

POLICE AND SHERIFF

Sheriff's Ofc.....................270.765.5133
Fax...............................270.737.4574
Web.....................www.hcky.org/hcso
E-mail......................info.hcso@hcky.org
100 Public Sq, Ste 101, Elizabethtown, KY 42701-3408
Charlie Williams, Sheriff

Harlan County

SOCIAL SERVICES

2nd Central.......................606.573.4620
Fax...............................606.573.5391
E-mail......................belindac.smith@mail.state.ky.us
103 S 2nd St, Harlan, KY 40831
Belinda Smith, Family Svcs Ofc Supervisor

Community Based Svcs................606.573.6334
Fax...............................606.573.9848
Web.....................www.harlan.kyschools.us
115 S. Cumberland Ave, Harlan, KY 40831
Melanie Day, Supervisor

Family Support......................606.573.2120
Fax...............................606.573.4789
E-mail......................gary.farmer@harlan.kyschools.us
115 S Cumberland Ave, Harlan, KY 40831
Gary Farmer, Field Services Supervisor

GENERAL HEALTH SERVICES

Health Dept.......................606.573.4820
Fax...............................606.573.6128
E-mail......................bobbiev.crider@ky.gov
402 E Clover St, Harlan, KY 40831-2312
Bobbie Crider, Rn, Nursing Supervisor

MENTAL HEALTH SERVICES

Cumberland River Regional MH/MR Board Inc......................606.848.5444
Fax...............................606.848.5918
Web.....................www.crrvs.org
E-mail......................intake.benham@crccc.net
227 Main St, Benham, KY 40807
Joy Hackler, Director

COURTS

26th District Court................606.573.7209
Fax...............................606.574.9113
E-mail......................jeffreybrock@kycourt.net
129 S 1st St, Harlan, KY 40831
Honorable Jeffrey J. Brock, District Judge

POLICE AND SHERIFF

Sheriff's Dept....................606.573.1313
Fax...............................606.573.2001
E-mail......................marvinlipfrid@harlanonline.net
210 E Central St, Harlan, KY 40831
Marvin Lipfird, Sheriff

EDUCATION SERVICES

Ages Head Start...................606.837.3314
Fax...............................606.837.8964
54 Stillhouse rd, Evarts, KY 40828
Ms Mary Ford, Teacher

Harrison County

SOCIAL SERVICES

Community Based Svcs................859.234.3884
Fax...............................859.234.3465
Web.....................www.ca.uky.edu
1050 US Highway 27 S Ste 6, Cynthiana, KY 41031-5998
Cathy Taylor, Supervisor

Family Support......................859.234.4151
Fax...............................859.234.3465
E-mail......................taffy.taylor@ky.gov
1050 US Highway 27 S Ste 2, Cynthiana, KY 41031
Taffy Taylor, Field Services Supervisor

GENERAL HEALTH SERVICES

Health Ctr........................859.234.2842
364 Oddville Ave, Cynthiana, KY 41031
Debbie Bradford, Rn, Nursing Supervisor

Wedco District Health Dept........859.234.8750
Fax...............................859.234.0054
Web.....................www.wescohealth.org
1050 US Highway 27 South, Cynthiana, KY 41031
Rachel Kendall, Human Resource Director

COURTS

18th District Court................859.234.1914
Fax...............................859.234.6787
115 Court St Ste 1, Cynthiana, KY 41031-1502
Honorable Jay Delaney, Circuit Court Judge

POLICE AND SHERIFF

Sheriff's Dept....................859.234.7135
Fax...............................859.234.5008
E-mail......................hcsd@adelphia.com
113 W Pike St, Cynthiana, KY 41031
Bruce Hampton, Sheriff

Kentucky

Hart County

SOCIAL SERVICES

Community Based Svcs **270.524.7111**
Fax 270.524.2556
E-mail ....tara.wilson@ky.gov
50 Quality St, Munfordville, KY 42765-9475
Tara Wilson, Supervisor

Family Support **270.524.7211**
Fax 270.524.3745
50 Quality St, Munfordville, KY 42765-9475
Elaine Devore, Field Services Supervisor

GENERAL HEALTH SERVICES

Health Dept **270.524.2511**
Fax 270.524.5642
E-mail ....leanne.hennion@ky.gov
500 Aa Whitman Lane, Munfordville, KY 42765
Leanne Hennion, Rn, Manager

Henderson County

SOCIAL SERVICES

Community Based Svcs **270.826.6203**
Fax 270.830.0510
417 S Main St, Henderson, KY 42420

Family Support **270.826.8351**
Fax 270.830.0112
228 N Green St, Henderson, KY 42420
Judy Wilson, Senior Supervisor

GENERAL HEALTH SERVICES

Health Dept **270.826.3951**
Fax 270.827.5527
E-mail ....janie.hardey@grdhd.org
472 Klutey Park Plaza Dr, Henderson, KY 42420
Janie Hardey, Rn, Nursing Supervisor

JUSTICE AGENCY

CASA **270.830.8400**
Fax 270.830.8262
537 S Green St, Henderson, KY 42420
Paula Yevincy, Director

COURTS

51st District Court / Judicial Ctr **270.826.2405**
Fax 270.831.2710
5 N Main St, Henderson, KY 42420
Ruth London, Clerk Of Court

POLICE AND SHERIFF

Sheriff's Ofc **270.826.2713**
Fax 270.827.6022
20 N Main St Ste 112, Henderson, KY 42420
Ed Brady, Sheriff

Henry County

SOCIAL SERVICES

Community Based Svcs **502.845.2922**
Fax 502.845.7402
137 College St, New Castle, KY 40050
Brittany Pidgeon, Supervisor

Family Support **502.845.2110**
Fax 502.845.1856
1427 Campbellsburg Rd, New Castle, KY 40050
Sandra Novobilski, Field Services Supervisor

GENERAL HEALTH SERVICES

Health Dept **502.845.2882**
Fax 502.845.7997
Web ....www.ncd.gov
E-mail ....beverly.aldridge@ky.gov
125 N Property Rd, New Castle, KY 40050
Beverly Aldridge, Rn, Nursing Supervisor

COURTS

Family Court **502.845.2868**
Fax 502.845.6738
Web ....www.courtofjustice.com
E-mail ....timseeley@myway.com
30 N Main St, New Castle, KY 40050-2537
Honorable Timothy E. Seeley, Family Court Judge

POLICE AND SHERIFF

Sheriff's Ofc **502.845.2909**
Fax 502.845.5701
Web ....www.henrycountycareteam.org
E-mail ....dcravens@henrycountycareteam.org
30 N. Main St, Ste C, New Castle, KY 40050
Danny Cravens, Sheriff

Hickman County

SOCIAL SERVICES

Community Based Svcs **270.653.4335**
Fax 270.653.2179
E-mail ....jane.justice@ky.gov
343 Moss Dr, Clinton, KY 42031
Rose Bryant, Supervisor

GENERAL HEALTH SERVICES

Health Ctr **270.653.6110**
Fax 270.653.6523
370 S Washington St, Clinton, KY 42031
Alicia Thompson, Nursing Supervisor

Hopkins County

SOCIAL SERVICES

Community Based Svcs **270.824.7566**
Fax 270.824.7302
1084 Thornberry Dr, Madisonville, KY 42431-1668
Becky White, Supervisor Treatment Team

Family Support **270.824.7555**
Fax 270.824.7588
E-mail ....michael.smith@ky.gov
1086 Thornberry Dr, Madisonville, KY 42431-1668
Michael Smith, Field Services Supervisor

COURTS

4th District Court - Judge Calvet
Ofc **270.824.7513**
Fax 270.824.7323
30 S Main St, Madisonville, KY 42431
Logan Calvert, District Judge

POLICE AND SHERIFF

Sheriff's Ofc **270.821.5661**
Fax 270.825.5014
E-mail ....sheriff@hopcogov.com
56 N Main St, Madisonville, KY 42431-1940
Frank Latham, Sheriff

Jackson County

SOCIAL SERVICES

Community Based Svcs **606.287.7114**
Fax 606.287.4475
Web ....www.csc.state.ky.us
E-mail ....jane.justice@ky.gov
235 Main St N, McKee, KY 40447
Kimberley Collett, Supervisor

Family Support **606.287.7131**
Fax 606.287.4113
E-mail ....kristen.miller@ky.gov
US Highway 421, Vickers Bldg, McKee, KY 40447
Kristen Miller, Field Services Supervisor

GENERAL HEALTH SERVICES

Public Health Ctr **606.287.8421**
Fax 606.287.4199
E-mail ....diane.hisel@ky.gov
Highway 421 S, McKee, KY 40447
Diane Hisel, Rn, Nursing Supervisor

POLICE AND SHERIFF

Sheriff's Dept **606.287.7121**
Fax 606.287.2821
E-mail ....jcso@prtcnet.org
US 421 N, Mc Kee, KY 40447
Venny Teymien, Sheriff

Jefferson County

SOCIAL SERVICES

**Community-Based Svcs & Family Support Kidpa Jefferson
Region** **502.595.4732**
Fax 502.595.4789
Web ....kentuckycommunitybaseservices.gov
E-mail ....becky.murphy@ky.gov
908 W Broadway, Flr 4E, Louisville, KY 40203
Becky Murphy, Administrator

GENERAL HEALTH SERVICES

Health Dept **502.574.6520**
Web ....www.louisvilleky.gov
400 E Gray St, Louisville, KY 40202
Leanne French, MA, Health Education Director

JUSTICE AGENCY

Juvenile Justice **502.595.3161**
Fax 502.595.3073
600 W Cedar St, Louisville, KY 40202
Patricia Davidson, Supervisor

COURTS

30th District Court Administrators
Ofc **502.595.4431**
Fax 502.595.3270
E-mail ....juliehaeyeskycourt.net
600 W Jefferson St Ste 3012, Louisville, KY 40202
Julie Hayes, Court Administrator

Family Court **502.595.4392**
Fax 502.595.3472
Web ....www.kycourts.net
E-mail ....stephengeorge@kycourts.net
700 W Jefferson St Ste 220, Judicial Center, Louisville,
KY 40202
Honorable Stephen George, Chief Family Court Judge

POLICE AND SHERIFF

Sheriff's Dept **502.574.5400**
Fax 502.574.6909
Web ....www.jcso.ky.org
E-mail ....sheriff@jcso.ky.org
531 Court Pl Fl 6, Louisville, KY 40302
John Aubrey, Sheriff

EDUCATION SERVICES

**Dawson Orman Education Ctr Head
Start/Preschool** **502.485.7008**
Fax 502.485.3037
900 S Floyd St, Louisville, KY 40203-2331
Dorcas James, Director

education centre **502.485.3558**
Fax 502.485.6790
3610 Bohne Ave, Louisville, KY 40211-2376
Lisa Meeks, Director

Exceptional Children **502.245.2121**
Fax 502.245.6249
Web ....www.anchorage-school.org
E-mail ....pfarris@anchorage.k12.ky.us
11400 Ridge Rd, Louisville, KY 40223-2444
Phil Farris, Director of Special Educaton

Jessamine County

SOCIAL SERVICES

Cabinet For Families and Children **859.885.9451**
Fax...859.885.4189
   109 S 2nd St, Nicholasville, KY 40356
Melainie Taylor, Ongoing Intake Supervisor

Family Support **859.885.3361**
Fax...859.887.9350
   111 Edgewood Plaza Dr, Nicholasville, KY 40356
Denise Snow, Field Services Supervisor

GENERAL HEALTH SERVICES

Health Dept.....................................**859.885.4149**
Fax...859.885.1863
Web...www.myjachd.com
   215 E Maple St, Nicholasville, KY 40356-1203
Jennifer Wyatt, Director

COURTS

**13th District Court / Ofc of Judge Oliver & Judge
Booth** **859.885.5615**
Fax...859.885.1715
Web...www.jessamineco.com
E-mail..jbooth@jessamineco.com
   107 N Main St, Ste 3, Nicholasville, KY 40356
Honorable Janet C. Booth, District Judge

POLICE AND SHERIFF

Sheriff's Dept **859.885.4139**
Fax...859.887.5317
E-mail..kcorman@jessaminesheriff.org
   101 S 2nd St, Nicholasville, KY 40356
Kevin Corman, Sheriff

Johnson County

SOCIAL SERVICES

Family Support **606.788.7118**
Fax...606.788.7128
E-mail..rhonda.bell@ky.gov
   205 Main St, Paintsville, KY 41240-1122
Rhonda Bell, Field Services Supervisor

GENERAL HEALTH SERVICES

Health Dept.....................................**606.789.2590**
Fax...606.789.8237
E-mail..russellw.briggs@ky.gov
   630 James Trimble Blvd, Paintsville, KY 41240-1026
Russell Briggs, Director

COURTS

24th District Court...........................**606.297.9581**
Fax...606.297.9585
   908 3rd St Ste 120, Paintsville, KY 41240
Honorable Susan Johnson, District Judge

POLICE AND SHERIFF

Sherff's Dept **606.789.3411**
Fax...606.789.2574
Web...www.dailyindependent.com
E-mail..sheriffprice@gmail.com
   339 Main St, Paintsville, KY 41240-1013
Dwayne Price, Sheriff

Kenton County

SOCIAL SERVICES

Community Based Svcs......................**859.292.6549**
Fax...859.292.6527
Web...www.ky.gov
E-mail..tonya.rieger@ky.gov
   624 Madison Ave, Covington, KY 41011-2422
Tonya Reiger, Adoptions Supervisor

Family Support **859.292.6660**
Fax...859.292.6365
E-mail..debbie.fry@ky.gov
   20 E 7th St, Flr 3, Covington, KY 41011
Debbie Fry, Building Manager

**Northern Kentucky Dept of Community Based
Svcs** **859.525.6783**
Fax...859.525.6796
Web...www.ky.gov
E-mail..lisaprewitt@ky.gov
   8311 US Highway 42, Florence, KY 41042
Lisa Prewitt, Regional Administrator

GENERAL HEALTH SERVICES

Health Ctr **859.431.3345**
Fax...859.655.6374
Web...www.kyhealth.org
   2002 Madison Ave, Covington, KY 41011
Joy Woods, Clinic Manager

COURTS

16th District Court...........................**859.292.6576**
Fax...859.292.6503
   230 Madison Ave Rm 4, Covington, KY 41011-1891
Honorable Frank Trusty Ii (5th Fl.), Judge

POLICE AND SHERIFF

Sheriff's Ofc....................................**859.392.1800**
Fax...859.431.8951
Web...www.kcor.org
E-mail..chuck.korzenborn@kentoncounty.org
   303 Court St Ste 409, Covington, KY 41011-1628
Chuck Korzenborn, Sheriff

EDUCATION SERVICES

Exceptional Children........................**859.727.2009**
Fax...859.727.5653
Web...www.erlanger.k12.ky.us
   500 Graves Ave, Erlanger, KY 41018
Laura Hellmann, Director Of Special Education

Exceptional Children........................**859.392.1137**
Fax...859.392.1132
Web...www.covington.kyschools.us
E-mail..ester.brady@covington.kyschools.us
   25 E 7th St, Covington, KY 41011-2401
Ester Brady, Director of Special Education

Ludlow Board of Education **859.261.8210**
Fax...859.291.6811
   525 Elm St, Covington, KY 41016
Rick Smith, Director Of Special Education

Knott County

SOCIAL SERVICES

Community Based Svcs......................**606.785.3106**
Fax...606.785.0970
Web...www.ky.gov
E-mail..elsie.dopson@ky.gov
   50 Professor Clerk Cir, Dixon Building, Hindman,
KY 41822
Elsie Dopson, Family Service Office Supervisor

Family Support **606.785.3137**
Fax...606.785.5699
   Highway 550 W, Hindman, KY 41822
Donna Sparkman, Field Services Supervisor

GENERAL HEALTH SERVICES

Health Ctr **606.785.3144**
Fax...606.785.5512
E-mail..kathyhall@ky.gov
   530 E Main St, Hindman, KY 41834
Kathy Hall, Rn, Clinic Manager

COURTS

Judge Prater's Ofc...........................**606.785.3078**
Fax...606.785.0987
Web...www.tgtel.com
   100 E Maple St, Salyersville, KY 41465
Honorable Dennis Prater, District Judge

EDUCATION SERVICES

Carl D Perkins Head Start...................**606.785.4604**
Fax...606.785.4604
E-mail..a.jones@lklp.net
   238 Highway 160 S, Brinkley, KY 41822
Aleece Jones, Director

Chavies Head Start...........................**606.436.4393**
Fax...606.436.4393
E-mail..a.jones@lklp.net
   165 Carr Creek Hl, Redfox, KY 41847-9020
Aleece Jones, Director

Cowan Head Start.............................**606.633.0718**
Fax...606.633.0718
Web...www.acf.hhs.gov
   81 Sturgill Branch, Redfox, KY 41847
Aleece Jones, Director

Knox County

SOCIAL SERVICES

Family Support **606.546.3121**
Fax...606.545.9104
   209 Knox St, Barbourville, KY 40906-1427
Sandra Fredrick, Field Services Supervisor

GENERAL HEALTH SERVICES

Health Dept.....................................**606.546.3486**
Fax...606.546.2867
E-mail..susan.lifordky.gov
   261 Hospital Dr, Barbourville, KY 40906
Susan Liford, Director

MENTAL HEALTH SERVICES

**Cumberland River Regional MH/MR Board,
Inc**..**606.546.3104**
Fax...606.545.0571
Web...www.crrvs.org
   704 Titzer st, Barbourville, KY 40906
Betty Shields, Director

COURTS

District Court **606.546.3232**
Fax...606.546.7949
   401 Court Sq Ste 202, Barbourville, KY 40906-1471
Honorable John Knox Mills, District Judge

POLICE AND SHERIFF

Sheriff's Ofc....................................**606.546.3181**
Fax...606.546.3196
   401 Court Sq Ste 105, Barbourville, KY 40906-1463
John D. Pickard, Sheriff

Larue County

SOCIAL SERVICES

Community Based Svcs......................**270.358.4176**
Fax...270.358.4133
   105 Howard Ave, Hodgenville, KY 42748
Mary Coates, Supervisor/intake

Family Support **270.358.3176**
Fax...270.358.8569
   105 Howard Ave, Hodgenville, KY 42748
Mary Coates, Field Services Supervisor

GENERAL HEALTH SERVICES

Health Dept.....................................**270.358.3844**
Fax...270.358.5816
   215 E Main St, Hodgenville, KY 42748-1305
Lisa Cox, Rn, Nursing Supervisor

Kentucky

COURTS

Judge Derek Reed's Ofc **270.358.9501**
Fax 270.358.0812
E-mail ....dreed@ky.gov
  209 W High St Ste 13, Hodgenville, KY 42748-1577
Honorable C. Derek Reed, District Judge

POLICE AND SHERIFF

Sheriff's Dept **270.358.3120**
Fax 270.358.9285
E-mail ....kysheriffs@windstream.net
  209 W High St Ste 6, Hodgenville, KY 42748
Bobby Shoffner, Sheriff

Laurel County

SOCIAL SERVICES

**Cumberland Valley Region Dept of Community Based
Svcs** **606.330.2001**
Fax 606.330.2017
E-mail ....sandra.rollins@ky.gov
  85 State Police Rd, London, KY 40741-9008
Sandra Rollins, Regional Administrator

Family Support **606.330.2025**
Fax 606.330.2047
  31 S Laurel Rd, London, KY 40744
Deborah Yaden, Field Services Supervisor

GENERAL HEALTH SERVICES

Health Dept **606.864.5187**
Fax 606.864.8295
E-mail ....mark.hensley@ky.gov
  525 Whitley St, London, KY 40741-2626
Mark Henseley, Director

COURTS

27th District Court **606.330.2055**
Fax 606.330.2084
  305 S Main St, London, KY 40743
Roger Schott, Clerk

Lawrence County

SOCIAL SERVICES

Community Based Serivces **606.638.4360**
Fax 606.638.9188
Web ....www.apps.chfs.ky.gov
  180 Bulldog Ln Ste 2, Louisa, KY 41230-9672
Sally Hensley, Acting Family Service Office Supervisor

Family Support **606.638.4526**
Fax 606.638.0796
E-mail ....karla.wells@ky.gov
  180 Bulldog Ln Ste 1, Louisa, KY 41230-9672
Karla Wells, Field Services Supervisor

GENERAL HEALTH SERVICES

Health Dept **606.638.4389**
Fax 606.638.3008
Web ....www.lchd.ky.gov
  1080 Meadowbrook Ln, Louisa, KY 41230-9657
Shirley Delong, Rn, Nursing Supervisor

COURTS

24th District Court **606.638.4215**
Fax 606.638.3556
E-mail ....susanjohnson@mail.aoc.state.ky.us
  122 S. Main Cross St, Louisa, KY 41230
Honorable Susan Johnson, District Judge

POLICE AND SHERIFF

Sheriff's Ofc **606.638.4368**
Fax 606.638.1316
Web ....www.lawrencecosheriff.org
E-mail ....sheriffroberts@lawrencecosheriff.org
  310 E Main St, Louisa, KY 41230-1159
Garrett Roberts, Sheriff

Lee County

SOCIAL SERVICES

Community Based Svcs **606.464.8801**
Fax 606.464.8448
E-mail ....susan.stepp@ky.gov
  Lake County Court Main St, 2nd Flr, Beattyville,
  KY 41311
Susan Stepp, Supervisor

Family Support **606.464.2404**
Fax 606.464.9909
E-mail ....linda.fugate@kentucky.gov
  256 Main St, Lee County Courthouse, Beattyville,
  KY 41311
Linda Fugate, Field Services Supervisor

GENERAL HEALTH SERVICES

Health Ctr **606.464.2492**
Fax 606.464.5050
  45 Center St, Beattyville, KY 41311
Irsha Wilder, Rn, Nursing Supervisor

POLICE AND SHERIFF

Sheriff's Ofc **606.464.4120**
Fax 606.464.4140
Web ....www.mikrotec.com
  250 Main St, Beattyville, KY 41311
Wendell Childers, Sheriff

Leslie County

SOCIAL SERVICES

Community Based Svcs **606.672.2313**
Fax 606.672.6155
E-mail ....rita.jeffers@ky.gov
  21150 S Main St, Hwy 421 Ste 3, Hyden, KY 41749
Rita Jeffers, Supervisor

Family Support **606.672.2306**
Fax 606.672.6991
Web ....www.lesliecounty.net
  21150 Highway 421, Hyden, KY 41749
Allan Pace, Field Services Supervisor

GENERAL HEALTH SERVICES

Health Dept **606.672.2393**
Fax 606.672.5006
  78 Maple St, Hyden, KY 41749
Jean Hoskins, Rn, Nursing Supervisor

COURTS

41st District Court **606.672.3350**
Fax 606.672.3351
  22030 Main St, Hyden, KY 41749
Honorable Renee H. Muncy, District Judge

POLICE AND SHERIFF

Sheriff's Dept **606.672.2200**
Fax 606.672.4413
E-mail ....leslieso@tds.net
  22010 Main St, Hyden, KY 41749
Paul Howard, Sheriff

Letcher County

SOCIAL SERVICES

Eastern Mountain Svc Region **606.633.1259**
Fax 606.633.9253
E-mail ....jennifer.atkins@ky.gov
  415 Highway 2034 Ste A, Whitesburg,
  KY 41858-9389
Rosemary Parks, Supervisor

Family Support **606.633.9332**
Fax 606.633.9253
E-mail ....rosemary.parks@ky.gov
  415 Highway 2034, Ste 8, Whitesburg,
  KY 41858-9389
Rosemary Parks, Field Services Supervisor

GENERAL HEALTH SERVICES

Health Ctr **606.633.2945**
Fax 606.633.0381
E-mail ....sheila.hogan@ky.gov
  115 E Main St, Whitesburg, KY 41858-7344
Sheila Hogan, Rn, Nursing Supervisor

Lewis County

SOCIAL SERVICES

Community Based Svcs **606.796.2981**
Fax 606.796.3595
E-mail ....pamela.box@ky.gov
  243 Commercial Drive, Vanceburg, KY 41179
Pamela Box, Supervisor

Family Support **606.796.3037**
Fax 606.796.3595
E-mail ....michael.lawson@ky.gov
  243 Commercial Dr, Vanceburg, KY 41179
Michael Lawson, Field Services Supervisor

GENERAL HEALTH SERVICES

Health Dept **606.796.2632**
Fax 606.796.9285
  185 Commercial Dr, Beattyville, KY 41179
Anita Bertram, Director

Lincoln County

SOCIAL SERVICES

**Family Support and Protection
Permanency** **606.365.2171**
Fax 606.365.8285
  144 Frontier Blvd, Stanford, KY 40484
Lavonda Whited, Field Services Supervisor

GENERAL HEALTH SERVICES

Health Dept **606.365.3106**
Fax 606.365.1640
  44 Health Way, Stanford, KY 40484
Diane Miller, Director

POLICE AND SHERIFF

Sheriff's Dept **606.365.2696**
Fax 606.365.7396
  104 N 2nd St, Stanford, KY 40484
Kirt Foldgier, Sheriff

Livingston County

SOCIAL SERVICES

Community Based Svcs **270.928.2158**
Fax 270.928.3120
  108 W. Adair St, Smithland, KY 42081
Tammy Givens, Supervisor

Family Support **270.928.2102**
Fax 270.928.3120
Web ....www.linvingstonco.ky.gov
  104 W Adair St, Smithland, KY 42081
Angela Curnel, Field Services Supervisor

GENERAL HEALTH SERVICES

Health Dept **270.928.2193**
Fax 270.928.2098
E-mail ....linda.belt@ky.gov
  124 State St, Smithland, KY 42081
Linda Belt, Community Health Nurse

POLICE AND SHERIFF

Sheriff's Ofc **270.928.2122**
Fax 270.928.2215
E-mail ....bdavidson@livingstoncoky.com
  351 Court St, Smithland, KY 42081
Bobby Davidson, Sheriff

Logan County

SOCIAL SERVICES

Community Based Svcs **270.726.3516**
Fax...270.726.8392
E-mail.................................missy.perry@ky.gov
  343 W 3rd St, Russellville, KY 42276-1314
Missy Perry, Family Services Office Supervisor

Family Support............................**270.726.9557**
Fax...270.725.9475
  343 W 3rd St, Russellville, KY 42276-1314
Linda Arnold, Field Services Supervisor

GENERAL HEALTH SERVICES

Health Dept.................................**270.726.8341**
Fax...270.726.8399
  151 S Franklin St, Russellville, KY 42276
Kelly Lyne, Nursing Supervisor

COURTS

7th District Court......................**270.726.8080**
Fax...270.726.7893
  200 W 4th St, Russellville, KY 42276
Honorable Sue Carol Browning, District Judge

Lyon County

SOCIAL SERVICES

Community Based Svcs **270.388.2146**
Fax...270.388.0852
E-mail...........................jenny.wilkerson@ky.gov
  620 W. Dale Ave, Eddyville, KY 42038
Jennifer Wilkerson, Supervisor

Family Support............................**270.388.2206**
Fax...270.388.0852
Web...www.kentucky.gov
  620 W Dale Ave, Eddyville, KY 42038
Susan Reik, Field Services Supervisor

GENERAL HEALTH SERVICES

Health Dept.................................**270.388.9763**
Fax...270.388.5941
  211 W Fairview Ave, Eddyville, KY 42038
Angie Dooms, Rn, Nursing Supervisor

POLICE AND SHERIFF

Sheriff's Dept..............................**270.388.2311**
Fax...270.388.2397
  200 E Dale Ave, Eddyville, KY 42038
Kent Murphy, Sheriff

Madison County

SOCIAL SERVICES

Community Based Svcs **502.348.9048**
Fax...502.349.6450
  901 Atkinson Hill Ave A, Bardstown, KY 40004
Robin George, Supervisor Pmp

Community Based Svcs **859.986.8411**
Fax...859.986.4443
  245 Prince Royal Dr, Berea, KY 40403-1471
Layne Caldwell, Supervisor

Family Support............................**859.623.1310**
Fax...859.626.3112
E-mail...................................ken.pillion@ky.gov
  126 S Killarney Ln, Richmond, KY 40475-2310
Ken Pillion, Field Services Supervisor

GENERAL HEALTH SERVICES

Health Dept.................................**859.623.7312**
Fax...859.626.4298
  214 Boggs Ln, Richmond, KY 40476
Nancy Crewe, Director

JUSTICE AGENCY

CASA **859.625.1949**
Fax...859.625.1900
Web...................................www.madisoncasa.org
E-mail............................muters@adelphia.net
  1219 Lexington Rd, Ste B, Richmond, KY 40475
Cynthia Grime, Executive Director

COURTS

25th District Court....................**859.624.4720**
Fax...859.624.4746
  351 W Main St, Richmond, KY 40475-1457
Linda S. Cates, Clerk

Family Court...............................**859.625.0601**
Fax...859.625.5009
  119 N 1st St, Richmond, KY 40476
Honorable Jeffrey Walson, Judge

POLICE AND SHERIFF

Sheriff's Ofc................................**859.623.1511**
Fax...859.623.9520
  135 W Irvine St Ste B01, Richmond, KY 40475-1495
Jerry Combs, Sheriff

EDUCATION SERVICES

Berea Head Start.........................**859.986.9117**
Fax...859.986.2925
  214 W Jefferson St, Berea, KY 40403
Phyllis Adams, Director

Magoffin County

SOCIAL SERVICES

Community Based Svcs **606.349.3123**
Fax...606.349.6033
  125 S Church St, Salyersville, KY 41465
Jerri Conley, Protection & Permanency Supervisor

Family Support............................**606.349.6131**
Fax...606.349.6033
E-mail.............................rhonda.blanton@ky.gov
  125 S Church St, Salyersville, KY 41465
Rhonda Blanton, Field Services Supervisor

Marion County

SOCIAL SERVICES

Community Based Svcs **270.692.3135**
Fax...270.692.4692
E-mail.........................georgane.elmore@ky.gov
  634 W Main St, Lebanon, KY 40033
Georgane Elmore, Supervisor

Family Support............................**270.692.6036**
Fax...270.692.6485
E-mail...................................kitty.smith@att.net
  634 W Main St, Lebanon, KY 40033
Kitty Smith, Field Services Supervisor

GENERAL HEALTH SERVICES

Health Dept.................................**270.692.3393**
  516 N Spalding Ave, Lebanon, KY 40033
Paula Maddingly, Rn, Center Coordinator

POLICE AND SHERIFF

Sheriff's Dept..............................**270.692.3051**
Fax...270.692.4389
E-mail...........................mcso2231@windstream.net
  223 N Spalding Ave Ste 101, Lebanon,
  KY 40033-1584
Jimmy Clements, Sheriff

Marshall County

SOCIAL SERVICES

Community Based Svcs **270.527.1354**
Fax...270.527.5096
E-mail....................................tammi.york@ky.gov
  211 E 7th St, Benton, KY 42025
Tammi York, Supervisor

Family Support............................**270.527.1395**
Fax...270.527.2777
Web...................................www.marshallcounty.org
E-mail.................................david.wolff@ky.gov
  211 E 7th St, Benton, KY 42025-1359
David Wolff, Field Services Supervisor

GENERAL HEALTH SERVICES

Health Dept.................................**270.527.1496**
Fax...270.527.5321
Web...www.mchdt.com
  307 E 12th St, Benton, KY 42025
Reed Conder, Interim Director

COURTS

58th District Court......................**270.527.3390**
Fax...270.527.5865
  80 Judicial Dr, Benton, KY 42025
Carol Fisk, Clerk Of Court

Martin County

SOCIAL SERVICES

Family Support............................**606.298.3577**
Fax...606.298.0311
Web..www.state.ky.us
E-mail................arvie.mcdiana@mail.state.ky.us
  Main St, Inez, KY 41224
Arvie McDiana, Field Services Supervisor

GENERAL HEALTH SERVICES

Health Dept.................................**606.298.7752**
Fax...606.298.0413
E-mail.................................stephen.ward@ky.gov
  136 Rockcastle Rd, Inez, KY 41224
Stephen Ward, Director

POLICE AND SHERIFF

Sheriff's Ofc................................**606.298.2828**
Fax...606.298.2806
  32 E Main St, Inez, KY 41224
Garmon D. Preece, Sheriff

Mason County

SOCIAL SERVICES

Community Based Svcs **606.564.6818**
Fax...606.564.3612
E-mail............................tracie.stafford@ky.gov
  201 Goverment St, Maysville, KY 41056
Kristen Toy, Supervisor

Family Support............................**606.564.6876**
Fax...606.564.3612
E-mail..........................peggy.earlywine@ky.gov
  201 Government St, Maysville, KY 41056
Karen Combs, Field Services Supervisor

JUSTICE AGENCY

Casa..**606.563.7431**
Fax...606.564.8152
E-mail............................casa@maysvilleky.net
  100 W 3rd Street, Maysville, KY 41056-7431
Marty Wallingford, Director

POLICE AND SHERIFF

Sheriff's Ofc................................**606.564.3309**
Fax...606.564.8676
E-mail..patb@lfucg.com
  120 West 3rd, Maysville, KY 41056
Patrick Boggs, Sheriff

Kentucky

McCracken County

SOCIAL SERVICES

Community Based Svcs **270.575.7105**
Fax 270.575.7015
   206 N 8th St, Paducah, KY 42001-1040
   Roy Mccoy, Supervisor

Family Support **270.575.7050**
Fax 270.575.7049
   2855 Jackson St, Hipp Bldg, Ste 1, Paducah,
   KY 42002
   Lisa Holm, Field Services Supervisor

MENTAL HEALTH SERVICES

Four Rivers Behavioral Health **270.442.7121**
Fax 270.443.9692
Web www.4rbh.org
E-mail ....thudspeth@4rbh.org
   425 Broadway St, Paducah, KY 42001-0713
   Terry Hudspeth, CEO

COURTS

District Judge's Ofc **270.575.7261**
Fax 270.575.7066
E-mail ....chrishollowell@kycourts.net
   301 S 6th St Ste 10, Paducah, KY 42003-1700
   Honorable Chris Hollowell, District Judge

Family Court **270.575.7133**
Fax 270.575.7135
E-mail ....cynthiasanderson@kycourts.net
   301 S 6th St Ste 10, Paducah, KY 42003
   Honorable Cynthia E. Sanderson, Family Court Judge

POLICE AND SHERIFF

Sheriff's Ofc **270.444.4719**
Fax 270.444.4743
   301 S 6th St, Paducah, KY 42003
   Jon Hayden, Sheriff

McCreary County

SOCIAL SERVICES

Community Based Svcs **606.376.5365**
Fax 606.376.9538
   Whitley City Plaza, Whitley City, KY 42653
   Panala Stevens, Supervisor Team A

GENERAL HEALTH SERVICES

Health Dept. **606.376.2412**
Fax 606.376.3815
E-mail ....jeanne.gaskin@ky.gov
   South Fork Plaza, Whitley City, KY 42653
   Jeanne Gaskin, Rn, Nursing Supervisor

POLICE AND SHERIFF

Sheriff's Dept **606.376.2322**
Fax 606.376.2347
Web ....www.mccrearysheriff.com
E-mail ....mcso@accesshsd.net
   36 Court Street, Whitley City, KY 42653
   Gus Skinner, Sheriff

McLean County

SOCIAL SERVICES

Family Support **270.273.3599**
Fax 270.273.9962
   290 State Highway 81 N, Calhoun, KY 42327
   Debbie Knight, Field Service Office Supervisor

EDUCATION SERVICES

Audubon Area Head Start **270.278.9693**
Fax 270.278.9693
   110 8th St, Livermore, KY 42352
   Mary Ann Mountain, Director

Meade County

SOCIAL SERVICES

Community Based Svcs **270.422.3942**
Fax 270.422.1194
E-mail ....lisa.parker@ky.gov
   514 Bypass Rd, River Ridge Plaza, Brandenburg,
   KY 40108
   Lisa Parker, Supervisor

Family Support **270.422.3974**
Fax 270.422.1194
   516 Bypass Rd, Brandenburg, KY 40108-1702
   Sandy Snyder, Field Services Supervisor

Menifee County

SOCIAL SERVICES

Community Based Svcs **606.768.2154**
Fax 606.768.6118
   784-A Highway 36, Frenchburg, KY 40322
   Lisa Dennis, Service Region Assistant Administrator

Family Support **606.768.2118**
Fax 606.768.6118
Web ....www.kyfb.com
E-mail ....kcombs@kyfb.com
   Rt 36, Frenchburg, KY 40322
   Kevin Combs, Field Services Supervisor

Mercer County

SOCIAL SERVICES

Family Support **859.734.7724**
Fax 859.733.4917
Web ....www.merceronline.com
E-mail ....lori.baker@ky.gov
   661 Beaumont Plaza, Harrodsburg, KY 40330
   Lori Baker, Field Services Supervisor

GENERAL HEALTH SERVICES

Health Dept **859.734.4522**
Fax 859.734.0568
   900 N College St, Harrodsburg, KY 40330
   Kathy Crown-webber, Director

POLICE AND SHERIFF

Sheriff's Dept **859.734.4221**
Fax 859.734.2460
E-mail ....aspatton@adelphia.net
   224 S. Main St, Harrodsburg, KY 40330
   Ernie Kelty, Sheriff

Metcalfe County

SOCIAL SERVICES

Community Based Svcs **270.432.2721**
Fax 270.432.2722
   100 Tompson St, Edmonton, KY 42129
   Paul Mills, Supervisor

Family Support **270.432.2521**
Fax 270.432.7273
   100 Thompson St, Edmonton, KY 42129
   Mary Rich, Field Services Supervisor

GENERAL HEALTH SERVICES

Metcalfe Health Dept **270.432.3214**
Fax 270.432.4000
   615 W Stockton St, Edmonton, KY 42129
   Julia Davidson, Director Of Nursing

POLICE AND SHERIFF

Sheriff's Dept **270.432.3041**
Fax 270.432.3046
E-mail ....metsher@scrtc.net
   106S main St, Edmonton, KY 42129
   Rondal Shirley, Sheriff

Monroe County

SOCIAL SERVICES

Community Based Svcs **270.487.6701**
Fax 270.487.8138
   201 W. Paige St, Tompkinsville, KY 42167
   James Littl, Supervisor

GENERAL HEALTH SERVICES

health Dept. **270.487.6782**
Fax 270.487.5457
E-mail ....rebecca.tandy@ky.gov
   452 E 4th St, Tompkinsville, KY 42167
   Rebecca Tandy, Director

POLICE AND SHERIFF

Sheriff's Ofc **270.487.6622**
Fax 270.487.6516
Web ....www.caldwellcourthouse.com
E-mail ....jgee@caldwellcourthouse.com
   200 N Main St Ste E, Tompkinsville, KY 42167-1548
   Roger Barlaw, Sheriff

Montgomery County

SOCIAL SERVICES

**Community Based Svcs, Protection and
Permanency** **859.498.6312**
Fax 859.497.0849
   108 E Locust St, Mount Sterling, KY 40353
   Mary Brown, Supervisor

Family Support **859.498.5398**
Fax 859.498.0366
   108 E Locust St, Mount Sterling, KY 40353
   Ron Wells, Supervisor

COURTS

21st District Court **859.498.5966**
Fax 859.498.9341
   1 Court St Ste 5, Mount Sterling, KY 40353
   Tanya Terry, Clerk

POLICE AND SHERIFF

Sheriff's Dept **859.498.8704**
Fax 859.498.8694
   1 Court St Ste 4, Mount Sterling, KY 40353
   Fred D. Shortridge, Sheriff

Morgan County

SOCIAL SERVICES

Community Based Svcs **606.743.3158**
Fax 606.743.3061
E-mail ....brenda.perry@ky.gov
   405 Prestonsburg St, West Liberty, KY 41472-1139
   Brenda Perry, Office Supervisor

Family Support **606.743.3127**
Fax 606.743.3221
E-mail ....williamsv@ky.gov
   324 Glenn Ave, West Liberty, KY 41472
   Vicki Williams, Field Services Supervisor

GENERAL HEALTH SERVICES

Health Ctr **606.743.3744**
Fax 606.743.3750
E-mail ....tamara.montgomery@ky.gov
   493 Riverside Dr, West Liberty, KY 41472-1053
   Tamara Montgomery, Rn, Nursing Supervisor

POLICE AND SHERIFF

Sheriff's Ofc **606.743.3613**
Fax 606.743.3699
E-mail ....mwmcso@mrtc.com
   450 Prestonsburg St, West Liberty, KY 41472
   Mickey Whitt, Sheriff

EDUCATION SERVICES

Ezel Head Start **606.725.4165**
Fax 606.743.1130
　Hwy 460, Ezel, KY 41425
　Charlene Engle, Director

Muhlenberg County

SOCIAL SERVICES

Community Based Svcs **270.338.3072**
Fax 270.338.4311
Web ....www.cscnet.ky.gov
E-mail ....barbara.mcbride@ky.gov
　210 S. Boggess Ave, Greenville, KY 42345
　Barbara Sue McBride, Intake Supervisor

Family Support **270.338.2330**
Fax 270.338.3729
　518 Hopkinsville St, Greenville, KY 42345
　Rhonda Strider, Field Services Supervisor

GENERAL HEALTH SERVICES

Health Dept **270.754.3200**
Fax 270.754.5149
E-mail ....josepho.bean@ky.gov
　105 Legion Dr, Central City, KY 42330
　Joseph O. Bean, Director

COURTS

45th District Court **270.338.0995**
Fax 270.338.0177
　136 S Main, Greenville, KY 42345
　Honorable Brian Crick, District Court Judge

POLICE AND SHERIFF

Sheriff's Dept **270.338.3345**
Fax 270.338.0766
Web ....www.muhlon.com
E-mail ....sheriff@muhlon.com
　100 Main St, Greenville, KY 42345
　Curtis Mcgehee, Sheriff

EDUCATION SERVICES

Bremen Elementary Childcare **270.525.6686**
Fax 270.525.3380
Web www.mberg.k12.ky.us
E-mail ....lking@mberg.k12.ky.us
　5000 Main St, Bremen, KY 42325-2032
　Latricia King, Director

Nelson County

SOCIAL SERVICES

Family Support **502.348.9282**
Fax 502.349.6450
　901 Atkinson Hill Ave Ste A, Bardstown, KY 40004
　Becky Johnson, Field Services Supervisor

GENERAL HEALTH SERVICES

Health Ctr **502.348.3222**
Fax 502.349.1557
E-mail ....tammi.moore@ky.gov
　325 S 3rd St, Bardstown, KY 40004
　Tammi Moore, Rn, Nursing Director

POLICE AND SHERIFF

Sheriff's Ofc **502.348.1840**
Fax 502.348.1874
Web ....www.tqexpress.com
　210 Plaza Dr, Bardstown, KY 40004-2100
　Stephen D Campbell, Sheriff

Nicholas County

SOCIAL SERVICES

Community Based Svcs **859.289.7123**
Fax 859.289.4535
E-mail ....susiecraycraft@ky.gov
　311 Moorefield Rd, Carlisle, KY 40311
　Susie Craycraft, Supervisor Of Family Support Team

Family Support **859.289.7101**
Fax 859.289.4535
E-mail ....susie.craycraft@ky.gov
　311 Moorefield Rd, Carlisle, KY 40311-9551
　Susie Craycraft, Family Support Supervisor

GENERAL HEALTH SERVICES

Health Ctr **859.289.2188**
Fax 859.289.2203
　2320 Concrete Rd, Carlisle, KY 40311
　Terry Sloat, Nursing Supervisor

POLICE AND SHERIFF

Sheriff's Ofc **859.289.3740**
Fax 859.289.3741
E-mail ....ncsheriff1@altiusbb.com
　125 E Main St, Carlisle, KY 40311
　Leonard T. Garrett, Sheriff

Ohio County

SOCIAL SERVICES

Community Based Svcs **270.274.8996**
Fax 270.274.8988
Web ....www.gov.state.ky.us
　947 W 7th St, Beaver Dam, KY 42320
　Shannon Miner, Supervisor

Family Support **270.274.8201**
Fax 270.274.8207
　947 W 7th St, Beaver Dam, KY 42320
　Martha Dockery, Field Services Supervisor

GENERAL HEALTH SERVICES

Health Ctr **270.298.3663**
Fax 270.298.4777
E-mail ....athena.klaas@ky.gov
　1336 Clay St, Hartford, KY 42347
　Athena Klaas, Nursing Supervisor

COURTS

38th District Court **270.298.3238**
Fax 270.298.9565
Web ....www.ky.courts.net
　Community Center, Hartford, KY 42347
　Honorable Renona Carol Browning, District Court Judge

POLICE AND SHERIFF

Sheriff's Ofc **270.298.4444**
Fax 270.298.4440
E-mail ....ocsd@bellsouth.net
　301 South Main Street, Hartford, KY 42347
　David Thompson, Sheriff

Oldham County

SOCIAL SERVICES

Community Based Svcs **502.222.9472**
Fax 502.222.3106
E-mail ....joan.doub@ky.gov
　2206 Commerce Pkwy, Lagrange, KY 40031
　Joan Doub, Supervisor

Family Support **502.222.9191**
Fax 502.222.5813
E-mail ....kanitha.penna@ky.gov
　300 N 1st St, La Grange, KY 40031-1502
　Kanitha Penna, Field Services Supervisor

GENERAL HEALTH SERVICES

Health Dept **502.222.3516**
Fax 502.222.0816
Web ....www.oldhamcohd.com
E-mail ....carla.g.petrzilka@ky.gov
　1786 Commerce Pkwy, La Grange, KY 40031
　Teresa Gamsky, Director

POLICE AND SHERIFF

Sheriff's Dept **502.222.9501**
Fax 502.222.3206
E-mail ....sheriffsteve@hotmail.com
　100 W Jefferson St Ste 2, La Grange, KY 40031
　Steven W. Sparrow, Sheriff

Owen County

SOCIAL SERVICES

Community Based Svcs **502.484.3937**
Fax 502.484.0698
E-mail ....paula.fields@ky.gov
　75 Duke Ave, Owenton, KY 40359-1439
　Paula Fields, Family Service Office Supervisor

GENERAL HEALTH SERVICES

Three Rivers Health District **502.484.3412**
Fax 502.484.0864
Web ....www.trdhd.com
　510 S Main St, Owenton, KY 40359
　Denise Bingham, Nursing Director

POLICE AND SHERIFF

Sheriff's Ofc **502.484.3363**
Fax 502.484.1003
E-mail ....heatherocso@bellsouth.net
　102 N Madison St, Owenton, KY 40359-1561
　Zemer K. Hammond, Sheriff

Owsley County

SOCIAL SERVICES

Community Based Svcs **606.593.5191**
Fax 606.593.7474
E-mail ....susan.stepp@ky.gov
　Mulberry St, Bobrowski Office Bldg, Booneville,
　KY 41314
　Susan Stepp, Supervisor

GENERAL HEALTH SERVICES

Family Support **606.593.5133**
Fax 606.593.7526
　Main St, Booneville, KY 41314
　Sandy King, Field Services Supervisor

Health Center **606.593.5181**
Fax 606.593.7438
　Highway 28, Booneville, KY 41314
　Thelma Spencer, Rn, Nursing Supervisor

Pendleton County

GENERAL HEALTH SERVICES

Family Support **859.654.6123**
Fax 859.654.5868
　510 Wilson St, Falmouth, KY 41040
　Cathy Taylor, Field Services Supervisor

Health Ctr **859.654.6985**
Fax 859.654.6986
E-mail ....susand.binsham@ky.gov
　329 Ky Highway 330 W, Falmouth, KY 41040-7019
　Denise Bingham, Nursing Supervisor

Kentucky

Perry County

SOCIAL SERVICES

Community Based Svcs Regional
Ofc...**606.435.6052**
Fax...606.435.6109
  113 Lovern St Ste 2, Hazard, KY 41701
  Dicey Combs, Service Regional Administrator Assistant

GENERAL HEALTH SERVICES

Family Support...........................**606.435.6043**
Fax...606.435.6125
E-mail...........................michael.colwell@kctcs.edu
  742 High St, Hazard, KY 41701-1372
  Michael Colwell, Field Services Supervisor

Health Ctr.................................**606.436.2196**
Fax...606.439.1813
  239 Lovern St, Hazard, KY 41701
  Pattie Brashear, Nursing Supervisor

Kentucky River Health District............**606.439.2361**
Fax...606.439.0870
E-mail............................karend.cooper@ky.gov
  441 Gorman Hollow Rd, Hazard, KY 41701
  Karen Cooper, Director

COURTS

33rd District Court......................**606.435.6007**
Fax...606.435.6138
  545 Main St Flr 2, Hazard, KY 41701-1774
  Honorable Leigh Anne Stephens, District Judge

POLICE AND SHERIFF

Sheriff's Ofc...............................**606.439.4523**
Fax...606.436.4970
  481 Main St, Hazard, KY 41701
  Les Burgett, Sheriff

Pike County

SOCIAL SERVICES

Community Based Svcs....................**606.433.7596**
Fax...606.433.7526
  131 Summit Dr Ste 400, Pikeville, KY 41501-1580
  Gwen Mullins, Manager

GENERAL HEALTH SERVICES

Family Support...........................**606.433.7760**
Fax...606.433.7100
  295 Hambley Blvd, Pikeville, KY 41501
  Charlotte Wright, Field Services Supervisor

Health Dept...............................**606.437.5500**
Fax...606.433.9690
E-mail...............................paul.hopkins@ky.gov
  119 River Dr, Pikeville, KY 41501-1685
  Paul Hopkins, Director

COURTS

Family Court...............................**606.433.7061**
Fax...606.433.7063
Web...www.kycourts.net
E-mail...................larrythompson@kycourts.net
  164 Main St Ste 400, Pikeville, KY 41501-1182
  Honorable Larry E.thompson, Judge

POLICE AND SHERIFF

Sheriff's Ofc...............................**606.432.6260**
Fax...606.432.6228
Web...www.lrc.ky.gov
E-mail...................charles.keesee@lrc.ky.gov
  146 Main St Ste 204, Pikeville, KY 41501-1184
  Charles E. Keesee, Sheriff

Powell County

SOCIAL SERVICES

Community Based Svcs....................**606.663.2881**
Fax...606.663.4435
  122 N. Main St, Stanton, KY 40380
  Mary Kay Williams-Duff, Family Service Office Supervisor

GENERAL HEALTH SERVICES

Family Support...........................**606.663.2293**
Fax...606.663.9399
  124 N Main St, Stanton, KY 40380
  Della Brouch, Field Services Supervisor

Health Dept...............................**606.663.4360**
Fax...606.663.9790
  376 N Main St, Stanton, KY 40380
  Kathy Keneal, Director

MENTAL HEALTH SERVICES

Comprehensive Care Ctr...................**606.663.2274**
Fax...606.663.2210
E-mail...........................dwrogers@bluegrass.org
  203 N Main St, Stanton, KY 40380
  Don Rogers, Director

COURTS

39th District Court......................**606.663.4141**
Fax...606.663.2710
Web...www.aoc.state.ky.us
E-mail...............kennyprofitt@mail.aoc.state.ky.us
  Powell County Court House, Stanton, KY 40380
  Honorable Kenny Proffit, District Judge

POLICE AND SHERIFF

Sheriff's Ofc...............................**606.663.2226**
Fax...606.663.2910
  524 Washington St, Stanton, KY 40380
  Danny Rogers, Sheriff

Pulaski County

SOCIAL SERVICES

Community-Based Svcs & Family Support - Lake Cumberland
Region......................................**606.677.4178**
Fax...606.677.4206
E-mail...........................sandra.rollins@ky.gov
  67 Eagle Creek Dr Ste 101, Somerset, KY 42501
  Sandra Rollins, Administrator

Family Support...........................**606.677.4103**
Fax...606.677.4143
  650 N Main St Ste 250, Somerset, KY 42501
  Marybeth Mcclendon, Field Services Supervisor

GENERAL HEALTH SERVICES

Health Dept...............................**606.679.4416**
Fax...606.679.4419
Web...www.lcdhd.org
E-mail...........................peggy.dancy@lcdhd.org
  45 Roberts St, Somerset, KY 42501-1295
  Peggy Dancy, Rn, Nursing Supervisor

COURTS

28th District Court......................**606.677.4112**
Fax...606.677.4140
  100 N Main St Ste 3, Somerset, KY 42501
  Honorable Jeffrey Scott Lawless, District Judge

Family Court...............................**606.677.4186**
Fax...606.677.4189
Web...www.kycourts.net
E-mail...................walternaguire@kycourts.net
  50 Public Sq, Fl 2, Somerset, KY 42501
  Honorable Walter F. Naguire, Family Court Judge

POLICE AND SHERIFF

Sheriff's Ofc...............................**606.678.5145**
Fax...606.679.3119
Web...www.pulaskisheriff.com
E-mail...................todd.wood@pulaskisheriff.com
  100 N Main St Ste 5, Somerset, KY 42501-1401
  Todd Wood, Sheriff

Robertson County

SOCIAL SERVICES

Family Support...........................**606.724.5414**
Fax...606.724.2046
  12 McDowell St, Mount Olivet, KY 41064
  Jennifer Royse, Field Services Supervisor

GENERAL HEALTH SERVICES

Health Dept...............................**606.724.5222**
Fax...606.724.5527
  45 McDowell St, Mount Olivet, KY 41064
  Allison Alexander, Rn, Community Health Nurse

POLICE AND SHERIFF

Sheriff's Ofc...............................**606.724.5511**
Fax...606.724.5009
  Courthouse Annex Mt, Olivet, KY 41064
  Randy B. Insko, Sheriff

Rockcastle County

SOCIAL SERVICES

Community Based Svcs....................**606.256.2138**
Fax...606.256.2188
E-mail...........................amyl.yates@ky.gov
  125 W. Main St, Scott Building, Mt Vernon,
  KY 40456
  Amy Yates, Supervisor

GENERAL HEALTH SERVICES

Health Ctr.................................**606.256.2242**
Fax...606.256.5482
  120 Richmond St, Mount Vernon, KY 40456
  Angela Thacker Rn, Nursing Supervisor

POLICE AND SHERIFF

Sheriff's Dept.............................**606.256.2032**
Fax...606.256.5708
E-mail...............rocksheriffdepartment@windstream.com
  205 E Main St Box 2, Mount Vernon, KY 40456
  Mike Peters, Sherrif

Rowan County

SOCIAL SERVICES

Community Based Svcs....................**606.784.4178**
Fax...606.784.7189
Web...www.ky.gov
E-mail...........................anastia.cooper@ky.gov
  120 Normal Ave, Morehead, KY 40351
  Anastia Cooper, Supervisor

Community-Based Svcs North Eastern Regional
Office......................................**606.783.8545**
Fax...606.783.8519
  1415 US Hwy 60 W, Morehead, KY 40351
  Geremia Vincent, Administrator

GENERAL HEALTH SERVICES

Family Support...........................**606.783.8535**
Fax...606.784.7769
  511 Hecks Plz, Morehead, KY 40351
  Kathy Ingle, Field Services Supervisor

Health Dept...............................**606.784.8954**
Fax...606.783.1443
Web...www.gdhd.com
  730 W Main St, Morehead, KY 40351
  Laura Harney, Nursing Supervisor

POLICE AND SHERIFF

Sheriff's Ofc..............................**606.784.5446**
Fax...606.784.1323
E-mail....................j.carter@rowancountysheriff.net
   627 E Main St Ste 6, Morehead, KY 40351-1390
   Jack Carter, Sheriff

Russell County

SOCIAL SERVICES

Community Based Svcs.....................**270.343.3512**
Fax...270.343.6148
   Pierce Building, Jamestown, KY 42629-0888
   Melissa Dudley, Supervisor

Family Support.............................**270.343.3196**
Fax...270.343.5663
E-mail............................melissa.taylor@ky.gov
   S Main St, Bates Bldg, Jamestown, KY 42629
   Melissa Taylor, Field Services Supervisor

GENERAL HEALTH SERVICES

Health Ctr...................................**270.343.2181**
Fax...270.343.2183
   251 Fruit of The Loom Dr, Jamestown, KY 42629
   Beverly Rothman, Rn, Nursing Supervisor

JUSTICE AGENCY

Juvenile Advisory Board....................**270.866.4500**
Fax...270.866.9790
E-mail......................marhays@duo-county.com
   48 Wilson St, Russell Springs, KY 42642
   Honorable Robyn Edmonds Williams, District Judge

COURTS

57th Circuit Court.........................**270.343.2131**
Fax...270.343.2604
   410 Monument Sq Ste 109, Jamestown, KY 42629
   Honorable Vernon Miniard Jr., Circuit Judge

POLICE AND SHERIFF

Sheriff's Ofc...............................**270.343.2191**
Fax...270.343.2195
   410 Monument Sq # 109, Jamestown, KY 42629
   Larry Bennett, Sheriff

Scott County

SOCIAL SERVICES

Family Support.............................**502.863.1381**
Fax...502.863.1069
   1000 W Main St Ste 2, Georgetown, KY 40324-2103
   Julie Burbon, Manager

GENERAL HEALTH SERVICES

Health Ctr...................................**502.863.3971**
Fax...502.863.3986
E-mail........................patsy.gebhardt@ky.gov
   300 E Washington St, Georgetown, KY 40324-1731
   Patsy Gebhardt, Nursing Director

COURTS

14th District Court........................**502.863.4384**
Fax...502.863.4384
   119 N Hamilton St Ste 1, Georgetown,
   KY 40324-1784
   Jim Howard, Court Designated Worker

Shelby County

SOCIAL SERVICES

Kipda Jefferson Region Dept of Community Based
Svcs..**502.647.9245**
Fax...502.647.9256
E-mail.............................nelson.knight@ky.gov
   31 Mount Rushmore Ct, Shelbyville, KY 40065-7805
   Nelson Knight, Regional Administrator

GENERAL HEALTH SERVICES

Health Ctr...................................**502.633.1231**
Fax...502.633.7814
   615 11th St, Shelbyville, KY 40065
   Adriana Cash, Nursing Supervisor

POLICE AND SHERIFF

Sheriff's Ofc...............................**502.633.4324**
Fax...502.633.9677
   501 Main St, Ste 8, Shellbyville, KY 40065
   Mike L. Armstrong, Sheriff

EDUCATION SERVICES

Migrant Even Start.........................**502.647.3533**
Fax...502.647.3581
Web...www.ovec.org
E-mail..............................cbearden@ovec.org
   100 Alpine Dr, Shelbyville, KY 40065-8877
   Carrie Bearden, Director

Simpson County

SOCIAL SERVICES

Community Based Svcs.....................**270.586.8266**
Fax...270.586.0653
Web.....................................www.cscnet.ky.gov
E-mail............................angela.lane@ky.gov
   210 W Cedar St, Franklin, KY 42134
   Angela Lane, Supervisor

Family Support.............................**270.586.4433**
Fax...270.586.6495
E-mail..........................darrin.harwood@ky.gov
   210 W Cedar St, Franklin, KY 42134
   Darrin Harwood, Field Services Supervisor

GENERAL HEALTH SERVICES

Health Dept.................................**270.586.8261**
Fax...270.586.8264
E-mail.............................janee.lewis@ky.gov
   1131 S College St, Franklin, KY 42134
   Jane Lewis, Nursing Supervisor

COURTS

49th District Court........................**270.586.4241**
Fax...270.586.0265
Web................................www.aoc.state.ky.us
E-mail...............marthah@mail.aoc.state.ky.us
   101 N. Court St, Franklin, KY 42135
   Honorable Martha Harrison, District Judge

POLICE AND SHERIFF

Sheriff's Ofc...............................**270.586.7425**
Fax...270.586.9505
E-mail.....................rstarks@simpsoncounty.us
   203 E Kentucky St, Franklin, KY 42135
   Chris Cline, Sheriff

Spencer County

SOCIAL SERVICES

Community Based Svcs.....................**502.477.8807**
Fax...502.477.5679
   73 E. Main St, Taylorsville, KY 40071
   Marjorie Shular, Supervisor

Family Support - Protection and
Permanancy..................................**502.477.2224**
Fax...502.477.5679
   73 E Main St, Taylorsville, KY 40071
   Marjorie Shular, Field Services Supervisor

GENERAL HEALTH SERVICES

Health Dept.................................**502.477.8146**
Fax...502.477.5624
E-mail..........................lindar.johnson@ky.gov
   88 Spears Dr, Taylorsville, KY 40071
   Linda Johnson, Rn, Nursing Supervisor

POLICE AND SHERIFF

Sheriff's Ofc...............................**502.477.3200**
Fax...502.477.3249
   18 E. Main St, Taylorsville, KY 40071
   Steve Coulter, Sheriff

Taylor County

SOCIAL SERVICES

Community Based Svcs.....................**270.465.3549**
Fax...270.789.4095
E-mail..........................kalon.bagby@ky.gov
   1327 E Broadway St Ste A, Campbellsville,
   KY 42718-1599
   Kalen Bagbee, Supervisor Pmp

Family Support.............................**270.465.6621**
Fax...270.789.4095
E-mail..........................gail.whitley@ky.gov
   1327 E Broadway St # A, Campbellsville,
   KY 42718-1599
   Gail Whitley, Field Services Supervisor

GENERAL HEALTH SERVICES

Health Dept.................................**270.465.4191**
Fax...270.789.3873
E-mail....................ruth.bender@dowjones.com
   1880 N Pytass Rd, Campbellsville, KY 42718-1836
   Ruthie Bender, Rn, Nursing Supervisor

POLICE AND SHERIFF

Sheriff's Ofc...............................**270.465.4351**
Fax...270.789.1870
   203 N Court St Ste 6, Campbellsville, KY 42718-2252
   Allen Newton, Sheriff

Todd County

SOCIAL SERVICES

Community Based Svcs.....................**270.265.2543**
Fax...270.265.3543
E-mail............................brian.pharis@ky.gov
   102 N. Williams Lane, Elkton, KY 42220
   Leslie Tinsley, Supervisor

Family Support.............................**270.265.2596**
Fax...270.265.3543
   102 N Williams Ln, Elkton, KY 42220
   Shannon Johnson, Office Supervisor

GENERAL HEALTH SERVICES

Health Dept.................................**270.265.2362**
Fax...270.265.0602
E-mail.......................jenniferm.harris@ky.gov
   205 W Mcreynolds Dr, Elkton, KY 42220
   Jennifer Harris, Director

POLICE AND SHERIFF

Sheriff's Ofc...............................**270.265.9966**
Fax...270.265.2688
Web...www.mchsi.com
   202 E Washington Street, Elkton, KY 42220
   Joey Johnson, Sheriff

Trigg County

SOCIAL SERVICES

Community Based Svcs.....................**270.522.3451**
Fax...270.522.0131
   277 Commerce St, Cadiz, KY 42211
   Brenda Holt, Fsls

Family Support.............................**270.522.6671**
Fax...270.522.0131
   277 Commerce St, Cadiz, KY 42211
   Shanon Johnson, Family Support Supervisor

Kentucky

GENERAL HEALTH SERVICES

Trigg Health Dept **270.522.8121**
Fax 270.522.5384
   196 Main St, Cadiz, KY 42211
Georgia Mcintosh, Public Health Nurse

COURTS

56th District Court **270.522.6270**
Fax 270.522.5828
   41 Main St, Cadiz, KY 42211
Honorable Jill Clark, District Judge

POLICE AND SHERIFF

Sheriff's Dept **270.522.6014**
Fax 270.522.8781
E-mail ....trigcoso@bellsouth.net
   31 Jefferson St, Cadiz, KY 42211
Ray Burnam Ii, Sheriff

EDUCATION SERVICES

Cadiz Family Development **270.522.4035**
Fax 270.522.0522
   117 Lincoln Ave, # 51-B, Cadiz, KY 42211
Aubrey Nehring, Director

Trimble County

SOCIAL SERVICES

Community Based Svcs **502.255.3236**
Fax 502.255.4609
E-mail ....kim.perkinson@ky.gov
   37 Alexander Ave, Bedford, KY 40006
Kimberly Perkinson, Supervisor

Family Support **502.255.3278**
Fax 502.255.4609
E-mail ....sandy.appleman@ky.gov
   37 Alexander Ave, Bedford, KY 40006-1114
Sandy Appleman, Field Services Supervisor

GENERAL HEALTH SERVICES

Health Dept **502.255.7701**
Fax 502.255.3760
   138 Miller Ln, Bedford, KY 40006
Sandra Evans, Rn, Nursing Supervisor

POLICE AND SHERIFF

Sheriff's Ofc **502.255.7138**
Fax 502.255.4882
Web ....www.iglou.com
E-mail ....tcso@iglou.com
   30 Hwy 42 Trimble County, Bedford, KY 40006
Tim Coons, Sheriff

Union County

SOCIAL SERVICES

Community Based Svcs **270.389.2314**
Fax 270.389.0391
   717 US Highway 60 East, Morganfield, KY 42437
Melea Ramin, Supervisor

GENERAL HEALTH SERVICES

Health Dept **270.389.1230**
Fax 270.389.9031
   218 W McElroy St, Morganfield, KY 42437
Jennifer Hagan, Nursing Supervisor

POLICE AND SHERIFF

Sheriff's Dept **270.389.1303**
Fax 270.389.0406
   100 W Main St Ste 122, Morganfield, KY 42437-1468
Mickey Arnold, Sheriff

Warren County

SOCIAL SERVICES

Community Based Svcs **270.746.7447**
Fax 270.746.7456
   1010-1020 State St, Bowling Green, KY 42102
Michelle Jones, Foster Care/adoption Specialist

Family Support **270.746.7850**
Fax 270.746.7035
   1010 State St, Bowling Green, KY 42102-1929
Janet Wyrick, Field Services Supervisor

GENERAL HEALTH SERVICES

Health Dept **270.781.8039**
Fax 270.796.8946
   1109 State St, Bowling Green, KY 42102
Dennis Chaney, Director

JUSTICE AGENCY

CASA of South Central Ky **270.782.5353**
Fax 270.782.6276
E-mail ....director@casaofsck.org
   922 State St, Ste 201, Bowling Green, KY 42101
Will Constable, Director

COURTS

Family Court **270.746.7144**
Fax 270.746.7147
Web ....www.kycourts.net
E-mail ....margareth@kycourts.net
   1001 Center St Ste 108, Bowling Green,
   KY 42101-2184
Honorable Margaret R. Huddleston, Family Court Judge

POLICE AND SHERIFF

Sheriff's Dept **270.842.1633**
Fax 270.781.3180
E-mail ....jerry.gaines@ky.gov
   429 E 10th Ave Ste 102, Bowling Green,
   KY 42101-6802
Jerry Gaines, Sheriff

Washington County

GENERAL HEALTH SERVICES

Health Dept **859.336.3989**
Fax 859.336.9162
   302 E Main St, Springfield, KY 40069-1127
Stacy Willard, Nursing Supervisor

POLICE AND SHERIFF

Sheriff's Ofc **859.336.5400**
Fax 859.336.5402
   124 E Main St, Springfield, KY 40069
Tommy A Bartley, Sheriff

Wayne County

SOCIAL SERVICES

Community Based Svcs **606.348.9361**
Fax 606.348.6388
E-mail ....tracy.patton@ky.gov
   Tradeway Shopping Center, Monticello, KY 42633
Tracy Patton, Supervisor

Family Support **606.348.3321**
Fax 606.348.0366
   1520 N Main St Ste 5, Monticello, KY 42633
Christina Kumer, Field Services Supervisor

GENERAL HEALTH SERVICES

Health Dept **606.348.9349**
Fax 606.348.7464
Web ....www.lcdhd.org
   39 Ji Hill Service Rd, Monticello, KY 42633
Faye Delcamp, Hiv Supervisor

MENTAL HEALTH SERVICES

Adanta Clinic **606.348.9318**
Fax 606.348.6932
Web ....www.adanta.org
E-mail ....dbrown@adanta.org
   735 W COLUMBIA AVE, Monticello, KY 42633-1627
Dianna Brown, Director

POLICE AND SHERIFF

Sheriff's Dept **606.348.5416**
Fax 606.348.3284
   55 N Main St Ste 104, Monticello, KY 42633-1458
Charles Boston, Sheriff

Webster County

SOCIAL SERVICES

Community Based Svcs **270.667.7043**
Fax 270.667.7012
   100 Cedar St, Providence, KY 42450
Melea Ramin, Supervisor

Family Support **270.639.5044**
Fax 270.639.9125
   26 US Hwy 41A S, Dixon, KY 42409
Carla Mooney, Field Services Supervisor

GENERAL HEALTH SERVICES

Health Dept **270.639.9315**
Fax 270.639.7866
E-mail ....carolyn.burnett@ky.gov
   80 Clayton Ave, Dixon, KY 42409
Jennifer Hagin, Nursing Supervisor

COURTS

5th District Court **270.639.9160**
Fax 270.639.6757
   35 US Hwy 41 A, Dixon, KY 42409
Honorable C. Rene Williams, Judge

POLICE AND SHERIFF

Sheriff's Dept **270.639.5067**
Fax 270.639.7018
E-mail ....wcsheriff@bellsouth.net
   25 Main St, Dixon, KY 42409
Frankie Springfield, Sheriff

Whitley County

SOCIAL SERVICES

Community Based Svcs **606.528.4234**
Fax 606.526.9713
E-mail ....barbara.hill@ky.gov
   300 S Kentucky Ave, Corbin, KY 40701
Barbara Hill, Supervisor

Community Based Svcs **606.549.4505**
Fax 606.549.8283
E-mail ....lisa.cain@ky.gov
   1000 S Highway 25 W, Williamsburg, KY 40769-1693
Lisa Cain, Supervisor

Family Support **606.528.5745**
Fax 606.528.2417
Web ....www.kentucky.gov
   408 Roy Kidd Ave, Corbin, KY 40701-1170
Sharon Manning, Field Services Supervisor

GENERAL HEALTH SERVICES

Health Dept **606.549.3380**
Fax 606.549.8940
   114 N 2nd St, Williamsburg, KY 40769
Gail Timperio, Director

Health Dept - Corbin Branch **606.528.5613**
Fax 606.528.8758
E-mail ....tamaraa.johnson@ky.gov
   Cumberland Falls Highway, Corbin, KY 40702
Tamara Johnson, Rn, Nursing Supervisor

COURTS

34th District Court 606.549.5162
Fax 606.549.3393
Web ....www.kycourts.net
E-mail ....danballou@kycourts.net
 PO Box 329, Williamsburg, KY 40769-0329
 Honorable Dan Ballou, Circuit Judge

POLICE AND SHERIFF

Sheriff's Dept 606.549.6006
Fax 606.549.6082
E-mail ....sheriffwcsd@kih.net
 201 Main Ste 4, Williamsburg, KY 40769
 Colan Herrell, Sheriff

EDUCATION SERVICES

Boston Bell / Whitly Early Head Start
Ctr 606.786.7100
 3291 Hwy 1804, Williamsburg, KY 40769
 Lisa Good, Director

Wolfe County

SOCIAL SERVICES

Family Support 606.668.3175
Fax 606.668.7280
 330 Main St, Murphy Bldg, Flr 1, Campton,
 KY 41301
 Shirley Watts, Field Services Supervisor

GENERAL HEALTH SERVICES

Health Ctr 606.668.3185
Fax 606.668.6076
E-mail ....andrea.oliver@ky.gov
 145 Highway 15, Campton, KY 41301
 Andrea Oliver, Clinic Coordinator

POLICE AND SHERIFF

Sheriff's Dept 606.668.3569
Fax 606.668.6147
Web ....www.cji.net
E-mail ....wolfecosd@cji.net
 10 Court Street, Campton, KY 41301
 Chris Carson, Sheriff

Woodford County

SOCIAL SERVICES

Community Based Svcs 859.873.8041
Fax 859.873.8410
 115 Crossfield Dr Ste D, Versailles, KY 40383
 Pat Adams, Supervisor

Family Support 859.873.3191
Fax 859.873.8410
 115 Crossfield Dr Ste D, Versailles, KY 40383
 Sharon Bay, Field Services Supervisor

GENERAL HEALTH SERVICES

Health Dept 859.873.4541
Fax 859.873.7238
 229 N Main St, Versailles, KY 40383
 Melissa Royce, Public Health Director

MENTAL HEALTH SERVICES

Comprehensive Care Ctr 859.873.7316
Fax 859.873.7669
E-mail ....office@vpc1.org
 125 Big Sink Rd Ste B, Versailles, KY 40383
 Rita Soper, Site Supervisor

COURTS

14th District Court 859.873.3711
Fax 859.879.8531
 130 Court St, Versailles, KY 40383
 Tricia Kittinger, Circuit Clerk

POLICE AND SHERIFF

Sheriff's Dept 859.873.3119
Fax 859.873.8371
E-mail ....woodfordcountysherrif@alltell.net
 103 S Main St Ste 114, Versailles, KY 40383
 Wayne Wright, Sherrif

SPECIAL SERVICES AGENCIES

ADOPTION AGENCIES

A Helping Hand Adoption Agency 859.263.9964
Fax 859.263.9957
Web ....www.worldadoptions.org
E-mail ....info@worldadoptions.org
 1510 Newtown Pike, Ste 152, Lexington,
 KY 40511-1255
 Victor Bondarenko, Director

Adopt! Inc. 859.276.6249
Fax 859.276.5570
Web ....www.adoptinc.org
E-mail ....adopt@adoptinc.org
 135 Lackawanna Rd, Lexington, KY 40503-1939
 Brenda Riddle, Executive Director

Adoption Assistance 859.236.2761
Fax 859.936.9945
Web ....www.adoptionassistance.com
E-mail ....adoption@adoptionassistance.com
 510 N Maple Ave, Danville, KY 40422-1173
 Julie Erwin, Director

Adoption Bridges of Kentucky, Inc. 502.585.4369
Fax 502.585.5369
Web ....www.adoptionbridgesofkentucky.org
E-mail ......lindadavis@adoptionbridgesofkentucky.org
 401 W Main St Ste 1710, Louisville, KY 40202-2959
 Linda Davis, Executive Director

Diocesan Catholic Children's Home, Inc. 859.331.2040
Fax 859.344.5022
Web ....www.dcchome.org
 P.O. Box 17007, Fort Mitchell, KY 41017-0007
 COA accredited organization.

Family Connection Ministries 859.498.5230
Fax 859.498.2606
Web ....www.hopehill.org
E-mail ....elvis@hopehill.org
 700 Hope Hill Rd, Hope, KY 40334-7002
 Aleca Elvis, Administrator

For Jamie's Sake 606.327.5511
Fax 606.327.5517
E-mail ....forjamiesake@alltel.net
 1544 Winchester Ave Ste 808, Ashland,
 KY 41101-7931
 Leaann Gollihue, Director

Gateway Juvenile Diversion Project, Inc. dba Gateway
Children's Services 859.498.9892
Fax 859.498.0316
Web
 ....www.gatewaychildrensservices.org/default.html
 37 N. Maysville Street, Mt. Sterling, KY 40353-1315
 COA accredited organization.

Kentucky Cabinet for Health & Family Services, Dept. for
Community Based Services 502.564.6852
Fax 502.564.4653
Web ....http://chfsnet.ky.gov/
 275 East Main Street, 3C-C, Frankfort, KY 40621
 COA accredited organization.

Mary Kendall Adoption Program 270.683.3723
Fax 270.926.0817
Web ....www.kyumh.org
E-mail ....adopt@kyumh.org
 201 Phillips Ct, Owensboro, KY 42303-1313
 Jeannie Howard, Coordinator

Necco & Associates 270.781.8112
Fax 270.781.8114
E-mail ....kathrine@necco.org
 942 Searcy Way, Bowling Green, KY 42103
 Kathrine Tweedy, Director

Reach of Louisville, Inc. 502.585.1911
Fax 502.589.1582
Web ....www.reachoflouisville.com
E-mail ....illbackr@reachoflouisville.com
 501 Park Ave, Louisville, KY 40208-2318
 Dr. Robert Illback, Executive Director

Special Needs Adoption Project (Snap) 859.245.5488
Fax 859.271.3289
Web ....www.cfsnet.ky.gov
E-mail ....johna.bailey@ky.gov
 1165 Centre Pkwy Ste 180, Lexington,
 KY 40517-3229
 John Bailey, Foster Care Supervisor

Specialized Alternatives For Families and
Youth 859.971.2585
Fax 859.971.7594
Web ....www.safy.org
 3150 Custer Dr Ste 103, Lexington, KY 40517
 Lydia Akin, Director

St. Joseph Home For Children 502.893.0241
Fax 502.896.2394
 2823 Frankfort Ave, Louisville, KY 40206
 Pam Cotton, Chief Operating Officer

We Care Child and Family Services, Inc. 270.483.6220
Fax 270.483.6221
Web ....www.wecarefamilies.com
 PO Box 472, Guthrie, KY 42234
 COA accredited organization.

ADVOCACY RESOURCES

CASA 502.595.4911
Fax 502.582.9816
Web ....www.casajc.org
E-mail ....info@casajc.org
 514 W Liberty St Ste 139, Louisville, KY 40202-2800
 Kathy Martin, Director

Child Watch Children's Advocacy Ctr, Inc. 270.443.1440
Fax 270.443.1486
 1118 Jefferson St, Paducah, KY 42002
 Lois Smith, Executive Director

Children's Advocacy Ctr Of The Bluegrass,
Inc. 859.225.5437
Fax 859.225.1102
Web ....www.kykids.org
 183 Walton Ave, Lexington, KY 40508
 Amy Rouse, Executive Director

Children's Law Ctr 859.431.3313
Fax 859.655.7553
Web ....www.childrenslawky.org
E-mail ....childrenslaw@fuse.net
 1002 Russell St, Covington, KY 41011-3053
 Kim Brooks-tandy, Executive Director

BEHAVIORAL HEALTH TREATMENT

ABS Lincs Kentucky **270.886.1919**
Fax 270.886.1335
Web ....www.absfirst.com
E-mail ....patrick.swoopes@absfirst.com
210 W 17th St, Hopkinsville, KY 42240-1912
Patrick Swoopes, Imterm

Adanta Behavioral Health **606.679.4782**
Fax 606.678.5296
Web ....www.adanta.org
E-mail ....bloy@adanta.org
259 Parkers Mill Rd, Somerset, KY 42501-3152
Beverley Loy, Director Of Child And Family Services

Adanta Clinic **270.384.4719**
Fax 270.384.4820
Web ....www.adanta.org
E-mail ....pattypaze@adanta.org
200 E Frazier Ave, Columbia, KY 42728-1915
Patty Paze, Director

Adanta Clinical Svcs **270.465.7424**
Fax 270.465.7993
Web ....www.adanta.org
3020 Old Lebanon Rd, Campbellsville,
KY 42718-9674
Mike Wilson, Clinic Supervisor

Adanta Jamestown Group Home **270.343.5068**
Fax 270.343.5068
E-mail ....dmcclure@adanta.org
272 W Cumberland Ave, Jamestown, KY 42629-2361
Diana Mcclure, Director

Asumendi Medical Practice **502.458.6507**
1000 Cherokee Rd, Louisville, KY 40204
Miren Asumendi, DO, Psychiatrist

Barnabas Home, Inc. **606.364.3640**
Fax 606.364.2534
P.O. Box 209, Annville, KY 40402
COA accredited organization.

Behavioral Health Svcs **502.589.8600**
Fax 502.477.5150
Web ....www.sevencounties.org
E-mail ....spond@sevencounties.org
80 E Main St, Taylorsville, KY 40071
Stephany Pond, Director

Behavioral Health Svcs **502.633.5683**
Fax 502.633.6203
Web ....www.sevencountiesservices.org
E-mail ....smccarty@sevencounties.org
250 Alpine Dr, Shelbyville, KY 40065-8880
Silvia Mccarty, Director

Behavioral Health Svcs **502.589.8920**
Fax 502.447.1967
Web ....www.sevencounties.org
E-mail ....kgoforth@sevencounties.org
1512 Crums Ln, Louisville, KY 40216
Kelly Goforth, Director

Bentley Medical Practice **502.897.7574**
2038 Frankfort Ave, Louisville, KY 40206-2029
Susan Bentley, Psychiatrist

Bluegrass East Comprehensive Care Ctr **859.233.0444**
Fax 859.233.0144
Web ....www.bluegrass.org
E-mail ....gfkiefer@bluegrass.org
201 Mechanic St, Lexington, KY 40507-1004
George Kiefer, Phd, Director

**Bluegrass Regional Mental Health - Mental Retardation
Bd** **859.253.1686**
Web ....www.bluegrass.org
E-mail ....cbfaulkner@bluegrass.org
1351 Newtown Pike, Bldg 1, Lexington,
KY 40511-1277
Ms. Cindy Faulkner, Accreditation Manager
Joint Commission accredited organization.

Bluegrass West Comprehensive Care Ctrs **502.863.4734**
Fax 502.863.4735
Web ....www.bluegrass.org
110 Roach St, Georgetown, KY 40324
Aaren Dowdell, Program Coordinator

Brighton Ctr, Inc **859.581.1111**
Fax 859.581.8033
Web ....www.brightoncenter.com
E-mail ....tweinberg@brightoncenter.com
1315 E 20th St, Covington, KY 41014
Tammy Weinberg, Executive Director

Brooklawn Child and Family Services **502.451.5177**
Fax 502.451.0896
Web ....www.brooklawn.net
2125 Goldsmith Lane, Louisville, KY 40218
COA accredited organization.

Campbell Lodge Boys' Home, Inc. **859.781.1214**
Fax 859.442.3473
Web ....www.clbh.org
5161 Skyline Drive, Cold Spring, KY 41076
COA accredited organization.

Carl D. Perkins Job Corps Ctr **606.886.1037**
Fax 606.886.6048
Web www.jobcorpsregion2.com
478 Meadows Dr, Prestonsburg, KY 41653-1592
Thomas Riley, Center Director

Children's Program **859.734.4653**
Fax 859.734.4664
712 Perryville Rd, Harrodsburg, KY 40330
Steve Layson, Director

Commonwealth of KY **502.564.2687**
Fax 502.564.3852
E-mail ....charles.douglass@ky.gov
275 E Main St, Frankfort, KY 40621-0001
Charles Douglass, Supervisor

Communicare, Inc. Mental Health **270.769.1304**
Fax 270.234.8028
Web ....www.communicare.org
E-mail ....dan@communicate.org
1311 N Dixie Hwy, Elizabethtown, KY 42701-2621
Dan Simpson, Executive Director

Comprehensive Care Ctr **859.744.2562**
Fax 859.252.2855
26 N Highland St, Winchester, KY 40391
Ron Kibbey, Director

Comprehensive Care Ctr **502.223.2182**
Fax 502.223.3338
Web ....www.bluegrass.org
191 Doctors Dr, Frankfort, KY 40601-4101
Jennifer Hardigree, Director

Comprehensive Care Ctr **859.289.7126**
Fax 859.289.7908
E-mail ....ksparks@bluegrass.org
2330 Concrete Rd, Carlisle, KY 40311-9700
Karen Sparks, Director

Ctr For Supported Living **502.495.7800**
Fax 502.495.7816
4400 Breckenridge Ln Ste 115, Louisville,
KY 40218-4082
Jim Covert, Director

Cumberland Hall Kentucky **270.886.1919**
Web ....www.psysolutions.com
E-mail ....daina.higley@psysolutions.com
210 West 17th Street, Hopkinsville, KY 42240
Ms. Daina Higley, Accreditation Manager
Joint Commission accredited organization.

**Cumberland River Regional MH/MR Board,
Inc.** **606.528.7010**
Web ....www.crccc.org
E-mail ....jcaho@crccc.net
1203 American Greeting Road, Corbin, KY 40701
Mr. Danny Jones, Accreditation Manager
Joint Commission accredited organization.

Davis Medical Practice **502.458.8787**
1837 Edenside Ave, Louisville, KY 40204-1521
Kenneth Davis, Psychiatrist

Day Treatment **606.862.6605**
Fax 606.862.6608
Web www.laurel.k12.ky.us
E-mail ....dhauser@laurel.k12.ky.us
65 Marydell Rd, London, KY 40741-8685
Debra Hauser, Program Director

Day Treatment Ctr **859.292.6664**
Fax 859.292.6339
19 E Pike St Unit 1, Covington, KY 41011-2442
Alfred Lehman, Program Director

Day Treatment Ctr **270.766.5053**
Fax 270.766.5052
643 Westport Rd, Elizabethtown, KY 42701-2847
Bruce Davis, Superintendent

Earle C. Clements Job Corps Ctr **270.389.2419**
Fax 270.389.5384
Web ....www.jobcorp.jcdc
2302 US Highway 60 E, Morganfield, KY 42437-6699
Billy K. Cooper, Center Director

Education Ctr at Cropper **502.461.7540**
Fax 502.461.9021
Web ....www.shelby.kyschools.us
8472 Cropper Rd, Pleasureville, KY 40057-7011
Jerry Goodall, Acting Director

Embry Medical Practice **270.765.2503**
107 N Mantle Ave, Elizabeth town, KY 42701-2453
Charles Embry, Psychiatrist

Farabee Medical Practice **859.268.6258**
Fax 606.268.6258
E-mail ....kystamp@msn.com
1025 Dove Run Rd Ste 210, Lexington,
KY 40502-3588
Dale Farabee, Md, Psychiatrist

Father Maloney's Boys' Haven, Inc. **502.458.1171**
Fax 502.451.2161
Web ....www.boyshaven.org
2301 Goldsmith Lane, Louisville, KY 40218
COA accredited organization.

Fernandez Medical Practice **859.263.9305**
Fax 859.264.1169
501 Darby Creek Rd Ste 21, Lexington,
KY 40509-1668
Andre Fernandez, Md, Psychiatrist

Florence Crittenton Home **859.252.8636**
Fax 859.252.5546
E-mail ....flocrit@hotmail.com
519 W 4th St, Lexington, KY 40508-1205
Mary Venezie, Executive Director

**Florence Crittenton Home and Services,
Inc.** **859.252.8636**
Fax 859.252.5546
519 West Fourth Street, Lexington, KY 40508
COA accredited organization.

Foothills Academy, Inc. **606.387.4673**
Fax 606.387.4509
Web ....www.foothillsacademyinc.org
107 Foothills Academy Spur, Albany, KY 42602
COA accredited organization.

Frankfort Group Home **502.227.4569**
Fax 502.227.0167
2790 Bridgeport Benson Rd, Frankfort, KY 40601
Tim Sutton, Superintendent

Frenchburg Job Corps Academy **606.768.2111**
Fax 606.768.3080
E-mail ....dhopwood@fs.fed.us
6969 Tarr Ridge Rd, Frenchburg, KY 40322-8854
Doug Hopwood, Business Community Liason

Great Onyx Civilian Conservation Ctr / Job Corps **270.286.4514**
Fax 270.286.1120
E-mail ....greatonyx@jobcorp.org
3115 Ollie Ridge Rd, Mammoth Cave,
KY 42259-7983
David Haris, Director

Jewish Hospital & St. Mary's HealthCare, Inc. **502.587.4011**
Web ....www.jhsmh.org
E-mail ....jennifer.robards@jhsmh.org
200 Abraham Flexner Way, Louisville, KY 40202-1886
Ms. Jennifer RoBards, Accreditation Manager
Joint Commission accredited organization.

Kentucky Partnership For Families and Children **502.875.1320**
Fax 502.875.1399
E-mail ....kpfc@kypartnership.net
207 Holmes St Ste 1, Frankfort, KY 40601
Carol Cecil, Director

Kinder Haven, Inc. **270.678.1042**
Fax 270.678.7376
3767 Roseville Road, Glasgow, KY 42141
COA accredited organization.

KVC Behavioral HealthCare Kentucky, Inc. **913.322.4900**
Web ....www.kvc.org
E-mail ....ecroney@kvc.org
900 Beasley Street Suite 120, Lexington, KY 40509
Ms. Elizabeth Croney, Accreditation Manager
Joint Commission accredited organization.

Lincoln Trail Behavioral Health System **270.351.9444**
Web ....www.lincolnbehavioral.com
E-mail ....sandra.ray@uhsinc.com
3909 South Wilson Road, Radcliff, KY 40160
Ms. Sandra Ray, Accreditation Manager
Joint Commission accredited organization.

London Group Home **606.330.2040**
Fax 606.330.2071
125 Hickory Rd, London, KY 40743-1330
Lisa Tucker, Director

Mary Kendall Home **270.683.6481**
Fax 270.926.0817
Web ....www.kyumh.org
193 Phillips Ct, Owensboro, KY 42303-3771
Angela Green, Clinical Director

Middlesboro Group Home **606.248.6719**
Fax 606.248.5946
106 Edgewood Rd, Middlesboro, KY 40965
James Hobbs, Superintendent

Mountain Comprehensive Care Ctr **606.886.8572**
Fax 606.886.8577
Web ....www.mtcomp.org
104 S Front Ave, Prestonsburg, KY 41653
Promod Bishnoi, Executive Director

New Pathways for Children, Inc. **270.674.6061**
Fax 270.674.6065
Web ....www.npfc.net/
P.O. Box 10, Melber, KY 42069
COA accredited organization.

North Key Community Care **859.491.1348**
Fax 859.491.7174
E-mail ....bkratzenberg@northkey.org
19 E Pike St Unit 2, Covington, KY 41011
Betty Kratzenberg, Manager

Northkey Community Care **502.732.9331**
Fax 502.732.9333
1714 Highland Ave, Carrollton, KY 41008
Sheila Freeman, Coordinator

Northkey Community Care **859.567.4430**
Fax 859.567.4438
203 W Main St, Warsaw, KY 41095

NorthKey Community Care **859.578.3233**
Web ....www.northkey.org
E-mail ....ngenther@northkey.org
503 Farrell Drive, Covington, KY 41012
Ms. Nan Genther, Accreditation Manager
Joint Commission accredited organization.

Northkey Community Care **859.781.3956**
Fax 859.781.5013
Web ....www.northkey.org
E-mail ....llindeman@northkey.org
1201 S Fort Thomas Ave, Fort Thomas, KY 41075-2421
Lawrence Lindeman, Coordinator

Northkey Community Care **859.525.6808**
Fax 859.525.6342
E-mail ....rlanning@northkey.org
7459 Burlington Pike, Florence, KY 41042-1553
Rose Lanning, Director

Oak Meadow Ranch, Inc. **270.874.2560**
Fax 270.874.2561
290 Burley Avenue, Hopkinsville, KY 42240
COA accredited organization.

Pathways, Inc. **859.498.7546**
Fax 859.498.7547
300 Foxglove Dr, Mount Sterling, KY 40353
Sie Powell, Childrenæs Services Director

Pennyroyal Regional Mental Health-Mental Retardation Board, Inc./Therapeutic Foster Care **270.886.2205**
Fax 270.886.0392
Web ....www.pennyroyalcenter.org
607 Hammond Plaza, Hopkinsville, KY 42240
CARF accredited programs available.

Phelps Day Treatment **606.456.8529**
Fax 606.456.9387
Web ....www.kde.state.ky.us
E-mail ....eblackburn@kde.state.ky.us
11580 S. 632 Rd, Phelps, KY 41553
Eddie Blackburn, Program Director

Pine Knot Civilian Conservation Ctr **606.354.2176**
Fax 606.354.2270
E-mail ....lfredrick@fs.fed.us
Job Corps Rd, US Hwy. 27, Pine Knot, KY 42635-1990
Lori Frederick, Center Director

Ramey-Estep Home, Inc. **606.928.6649**
Fax 606.928.1056
Web ....www.rameyestep.com
E-mail ....reh@rameyestep.com
2901 Pigeon Roost Rd, Rush, KY 41168
Tisha Evans, Human Resource Director

River Valley Behavioral Health **270.689.6500**
Fax 270.689.6701
Web ....www.rvbh.com
1100 Walnut Street, Owensboro, KY 42301
Gayle Dicesare, CEO
CARF accredited programs available.

River Valley Behavioral Health Hospital **270.689.6800**
Fax 270.689.6799
Web ....www.rvbh.com
E-mail ....jimward@rvbh.com
1000 Industrial Dr, Owensboro, KY 42301-8715
Jim Ward, Administrator

Seven Counties Services, Inc. **502.589.8600**
Web ....www.sevencounties.org
E-mail ....tgeftos@sevencounties.org
101 West Muhammad Ali Blvd, Louisville, KY 40202
Mrs. Tish Geftos, Accreditation Manager
Joint Commission accredited organization.

Spectrum Care Academy **270.234.0591**
Fax 270.234.0781
Web ....www.spectrumcareacademy.com
E-mail ....rcundiff@spectrumcareacademy.com
461 Fowler Ln, Spectrum Care Academy, Elizabethtown, KY 42701-8546
Rhea Cundiff, Program / Clinical Director

Spectrum Care Academy **606.864.0899**
Fax 606.862.6783
Web ....www.spectrumcareacademy.com
E-mail ....dschackleford@spectrumcareacademy.com
1551 Lick Fork Rd, London, KY 40741-8121
Doris Schackleford, Interm

Spectrum Care Academy, Inc. **270.384.6444**
Web ....www.spectrumcareacademy.com
E-mail ....barnold@spectrumcareacademy.com
1380 Burkesville St, Columbia, KY 42728
Dr. Ben Arnold, Accreditation Manager
Joint Commission accredited organization.

Stewart Home School **502.227.4821**
Fax 502.227.3013
Web ....www.stewarthome.com
E-mail ....info@stewarthome.com
4200 Lawrenceburg Rd, Frankfort, KY 40601-8936
John Stewart, Md, Resident Physician

Sunrise Children Svcs **502.538.1000**
Fax 502.538.1100
Web ....www.sunrise.org
300 Hope St, Mt Washington, KY 40047
Dr. William Smithwick, President

Sunrise Children's Services **502.538.1000**
Web ....www.sunrise.org
E-mail ....afisher@sunrise.org
300 Hope Street, Ministry Support Center, Mount Washington, KY 40047
Mr. Andrew Fisher, Accreditation Manager
Joint Commission accredited organization.

Ten Broeck Dupont **502.896.0495**
Fax 502.893.8792
Web ....www.thebroookshospitals.com
E-mail ....paul.andrews@psysolutio.com
1405 Browns Ln, Louisville, KY 40207-4608
Paul Andrews, Chief Executive Officer

The Brook Hospital - Dupont **502.896.0495**
E-mail ....sherri.greenhill@psysolutions.com
1405 Browns Lane, Louisville, KY 40207
Mrs. Sherri Greenhill, Accreditation Manager
Joint Commission accredited organization.

The Brook Hospital - KMI **502.426.6380**
Web ....www.TheBrook.com
E-mail ....sherri.greenhill@psysolutions.com
8521 LaGrange Road, Louisville, KY 40242
Ms. Sherri Greenhill, Accreditation Manager
Joint Commission accredited organization.

Western Day Treatment **502.447.9145**
Fax 502.449.4565
Web ....www.sevencounties.org
E-mail ....dkirkbride@sevencounties.org
2501 Rockford Ln, Louisville, KY 40216-2355
Dan Kirkbride, Director

Whitney Young Job Corps Ctr **502.722.8862**
Fax 888.343.1899
8460 Shelbyville Rd, Simpsonville, KY 40067-6572
Will Houston, Center Director

CHILDREN'S HOSPITAL

Baptist Hospital East **502.897.8100**
4000 Kresge Way, Louisville, KY 40207
David Gray, President

Baptist Regional Medical Center **606.528.1212**
1 Trillium Way, Corbin, KY 40701
John Hanson, Chief Executive Officer

Bluegrass Community Hospital **859.873.3111**
360 Amsden Ave, Versailles, KY 40383

Kentucky

Caverna Memorial Hospital 270.786.2191
　1501 S Dixie St, Horse Cave, KY 42749

Central Bapitst Hospital 859.260.6100
　1740 Nicholasville Rd, Lexington, KY 40503
　William Sisfon, Chief Executive Officer

Community Hospital 270.527.4800
　615 Old Symsonia Rd, Benton, KY 42025
　Kathy Long, Chief Executive Officer

Ephraim McDowell Regional Medical Ctr 859.239.1000
　217 S 3rd St, Danville, KY 40422
　Vickey Darnell, Chief Executive Officer

Hardin Memoiral Hospital 270.737.1212
　913 N Dixie Ave, Elizabethtown, KY 42701
　Dennis Johnson, Chief Executive Officer

Harlan ARH Hospital 606.573.8100
　81 Ball Park Rd, Harlan, KY 40831
　Dan Scone, Chief Executive Officer

Harrison Memorial Hospital 859.234.2300
　1210 KY Hwy 36E, Cynthiana, KY 41031
　Wendy Reeder, Director Of Nursing Services

Hazard ARH Regional Medical Center 606.439.6600
　100 Medical Center Dr, Hazard, KY 41701

Highlands Regional Medical Center 606.886.8511
　5000 Kentucky Rt 321, Prestonsburg, KY 41653
　Harold Warman, Chief Executive Officer

Jackson Purchase Medical Center 270.251.4100
　1099 Medical Center Cir, Mayfield, KY 42066
　Fred Pelle, Director

Jennie Stuart Medical Center 270.887.0100
　320 W 18th St, Hopkinsville, KY 42241
　Eric Lee, Chief Executive Officer

King's Daughters Medical Center 606.408.4000
　2201 Lexington Ave, Ashland, KY 41101
　Fred Jackson, Chief Executive Officer

Lake Cumberland Regional Hospital 606.679.7441
　305 Langdon St, Somerset, KY 42501
　Mark Brenzel, Chief Executive Officer

Lourdes Hospital 270.444.2444
　1530 Lone Oak Rd, Paducah, KY 42003
　Steven Grinnell, President

Marcum & Wallace Memorial Hospital 606.723.2115
　60 Mercy Ct, Irvine, KY 40336
　Susan Starling, Chief Executive Officer

Mary Breckinridge Hospital 606.672.2901
　130 Kate Ireland Dr, Hyden, KY 41749
　Mallie Noble, Administrator

McDowell ARH Hospital 606.377.3400
　Rt 122, McDowell, KY 41647
　Russ Barker, Chief Executive Officer

Meadowview Regional Medical Center 606.759.5311
　989 Medical Park Dr, Maysville, KY 41056
　Brad Morse, Chief Executive Officer

Medical Center-Bowling Green 270.745.1000
　250 Park St, Bowling Green, KY 42101
　Connie Smith, Chief Executive Officer

Methodist Hospital 270.827.7700
　1305 N Elm St, Henderson, KY 42420
　Bruce Beagley, Chief Executive Officer

Middlesboro Appalachian Regional Hsptl 606.242.1100
　3600 W Cumberland Ave, Middlesboro, KY 40965
　Michael Slusher, Chief Executive Officer

Muhlenberg Community Hospital 270.338.8000
　440 Hopkinsville St, Greenville, KY 42345
　John Countzler, Administrator

Norton Hospital 502.629.8000
　200 E Chestnut St, Louisville, KY 40202
　Stephen Williams, Chief Executive Officer

Our Lady of Bellefonte Hospital 606.833.3333
　1000 St Christopher Dr, Ashland, KY 41101
　Kevin Halter, Chief Executive Officer

Owensboro Medical Hospital 270.688.2000
　811 E Parrish Ave, Owensboro, KY 42303
　Jeffery Barber, Chief Executive Officer

Pikeville Medical Center 606.218.3500
　911 Bypass Rd, Pikeville, KY 41501
　Juanita Deskins, Chief Executive Officer

Pineville Community Hospital Assoc 606.337.3051
　850 Riverview Ave, Pineville, KY 40977
　Nelson Brookes, Chief Executive Officer

Rockcastle Hsptl & Respiratory Care Ctr ..606.256.2195
　145 Newcomb Ave, Mount Vernon, KY 40456

St Claire Regional Medical Center 606.783.6500
　222 Medical Cir, Morehead, KY 40351
　Mark Neff, Chief Executive Officer

St Elizabeth Health Care 859.212.5200
　4900 Houston Rd, Florence, KY 41042
　Christopher Carle, Administrator

St Elizabeth Medical Center 859.301.2000
　1 Medical Village Dr, Edgewood, KY 41017

St Joseph East 859.967.5000
　150 N Eagle Creek Dr, Lexington, KY 40509
　Amy McIntosh, Administrator

T.J. Samson Community Hospital 270.651.4444
　1301 N Race St, Glasgow, KY
　Bill Kinnard, Chief Executive Officer

Twin Lakes Regional Medical Center 270.259.9400
　910 Wallace Ave, Leitchfield, KY 42754
　Steve Meredith, Chief Executive Officer

University of Kentucky Chandler Hsptl 859.323.5000
　800 Rose St N100, Lexington, KY 40536
　Ann Smith, Chief Executive Officer

Whitesburg Appalahian Regional Hsptl 606.633.3500
　240 Hospital Rd, Whitesburg, KY 41858
　Dana Sparkman, Chief Executive Officer

Williamson ARH Hospital 606.237.1710
　260 Hospital Dr, South Williamson, KY 41503

COUNSELING SERVICES

Benchmark Family Services, Inc. 859.525.1877
Fax 859.525.9008
Web ....www.benchmarkfamilyservices.org
　252 Main St, Florence, KY 41042-2029
　Heather Strunk, Director

Ed Necco & Associates 859.264.8796
Fax 859.264.9957
Web ....www.necco.org
　503A Darby Creek Rd, Lexington, KY 40509-1603
　Eric Morton, Program Director

Lexington Day Treatment 859.246.4370
Fax 859.231.1213
Web ....www.lexingtonky.gov
　1177 Red Mile Pl, Lexington, KY 40504-1172
　Stephanie Hong, Program Director

CRISIS & SHELTER CARE

Appalachian Children's Home, Inc. 606.546.0380
Fax 606.546.3903
Web ....www.achky.org
E-mail ....syeary@barbourville.com
　PO Box 550, Barbourville, KY 40906-0550
　Steve Yeary, Director

**Bethany House Abuse Shelter - Domestic
Violence** 606.679.1553
Fax 606.676.8775
Web ....www.beaconhillbaptist.com
E-mail ....Bethanyhouse_Bb@Newwavecomm.Net
　PO Box 864, Somerset, KY 42502-0864
　Bob Brown, Director

Big Sandy Family Abuse Ctr 606.285.9079
Fax 606.285.3203
E-mail ....iarras@kdva.org
　PO Box 1297, Prestonsburg, KY 41653-5297
　Connie Little, Director

Bluegrass Domestic Violence Program 859.233.0657
Fax 859.519.1938
E-mail ....darlene.thomas@bdvp.org
　4400 Briar Hill Rd, Lexington, KY 40516-9729
　Darlene Thomas, Director

Brass Inc - Domestic Abuse Ctr 270.781.9334
Fax 270.782.3278
Web ....www.barrenriverareasafespace.com
E-mail ....Justiceworkslalcott@Ccol.Net
　2131 Old Louisville Rd, Bowling Green, KY 42101
　Lee Alcott, Director

Bruce Hall Day Treatment 859.936.7502
Fax 859.236.8624
Web www.danville.k12.ky.us
E-mail ....jkirk@danville.k12.ky.us
　152 E Martin Luther King Blvd, Danville,
　KY 40422-1921
　Joey Kirk, Program Director

Cardinal Hill of Northern Kentucky 859.525.1128
Fax 859.525.0351
Web ....www.cardinalhill.org
E-mail ....cw3@cardinalhill.org
　31 Spiral Dr, Florence, KY 41042-1351
　Cynthia Williams, Executive Director

Caring Place Inc - Domestic Violence 270.692.9300
Fax 270.692.9206
　PO Box 945, Lebanon, KY 40033-0945
　Delena Trent, Director

Family Life Abuse Ctr - Domestic Violence 606.256.9511
Fax 606.256.1910
　187 Carpenter Dr, Annville, KY 40402
　Debra Smart, Director

Family Support 270.928.2102
Fax 270.928.3120
Web ....www.linvingstonco.ky.gov
E-mail ....
　104 W Adair St, Smithland, KY 42081
　Angela Curnel, Field Services Supervisor

Father Maloney's Boys' Haven 502.458.1171
Fax 502.451.2161
Web ....www.boyshaven.org
　2301 Goldsmith Ln, Louisville, KY 40218-1018
　Jeff Hadley, Executive Director

Home of the Innocents 502.596.1000
Fax 502.596.1410
Web ....www.homeoftheinnocents.org
　1100 E Market St, Louisville, KY 40206-1838
　Judith Bloor, Vp/director Of Childkind

Kinder Haven, Inc. 270.678.1042
Fax 270.678.6918
E-mail ....mtodd@glasgow-ky.com
　3767 Roseville Rd, Glasgow, KY 42141-2269
　Michael Todd, Director

**LKLP Safehouse - Domestic Violence
Program** 606.439.1552
Fax 606.436.0940
E-mail ....l.valentine@lklp.net
　PO Box 1867, Hazard, KY 41702-1867
　Lois Valentine, Director

Metro Alternative Shelter House 859.254.2501
Fax 859.226.9392
Web ....www.mashbluegrass.org
　536 W 3rd St, Lexington, KY 40508
　Rebecca Macleery, Executive Director

Metro Group - Mash 859.254.2501
Fax 859.226.9392
　536 W 3rd St, Lexington, KY 40508
　Rebecca Macleery, Executive Director

Safe Harbor - Domestic Violence Shelter 606.329.9304
Fax 606.324.6855
Web .... www.safeharborky.org
E-mail .... aperkins@safeharborky.org
   3700 Lands Down Drive, Ashland, KY 41105
   Ann Perkins, Director

Springhaven Inc - Domestic Violence 270.765.4057
Fax 270.766.1081
E-mail .... springhaven@springhaveninc.org
   PO Box 2047, Elizabethtown, KY 42702-2047
   Lisa Holmes, Director

Volunteers of America, KY 502.636.0771
Fax 502.637.8111
Web .... www.voaky.org
   933 Goss Ave, Louisville, KY 40217-1200
   Jane Burks, Director

EDUCATION

Blue Grass Impact East 859.254.3106
Fax 859.253.1177
   1351 Newtown Pike, Lexington, KY 40511
   Aaron Dowdell, Director

Day Treatment 606.337.0957
Fax 606.337.7103
   9788 Old Bell High Rd, Pineville, KY 40977
   Rosie Collins, Program Director

Day Treatment Ctr 859.625.6161
Fax 859.624.4566
   300 Bellevue Dr, Richmond, KY 40475-1261
   Brad Winkler, Program Director

Day Treatment Ctr 270.887.1147
Fax 270.889.6561
E-mail .... dupton@christian.k12.ky.us
   141 Highland School Rd, Hopkinsville,
   KY 42240-2819
   John Reed, Program Director/intake

Day Treatment Ctr 502.429.7217
Fax 502.429.7216
   8711 Lagrange Rd Ste B, Louisville, KY 40242-3801
   Don Stitze, Program Director

De Paul School 502.459.6131
Fax 502.458.0827
Web .... www.depaulschool.org
E-mail .... dpinfo@depaulschool.org
   1925 Duker Ave, Louisville, KY 40205-1099
   Anthony Kemper, Headmaster

Jewish Family Vocational Svcs 502.452.6341
Fax 502.452.6718
   3587 Dutchmans Ln, Louisville, KY 40205-3213
   Judy Tiell, Director

Ju Kevil Memorial Foundation 270.247.5396
Fax 270.247.1233
E-mail .... ljarvis@jukevil.com
   1900 S 10th St, Mayfield, KY 42066
   Leigh Ann Jarvis, Executive Director

Nimco, Inc. 270.273.5000
Fax 270.273.5844
Web .... www.nimcoinc.com
E-mail .... paula@nimcoinc.com
   102 Highway 81 N, Calhoun, KY 42327-2100
   Paula Jones, Director

FOSTER CARE AGENCIES

Adoption Support for Kentucky (ASK) 859.257.3196
E-mail .... adoptky@uky.edu
   1 Quality St, Ste 700, Lexington, KY 40507

Alternative Youth Services dba Kentucky
SAFE 270.846.2163
Fax 270.846.2010
Web .... www.ResCare.com
   980 Morgantown Road, Bowling Green, KY 42102
   CARF accredited programs available.

Buckhorn-KY River Treatment Foster Care 606.487.1023
Fax 606.435.2496
E-mail .... donna.apperson@bucckhorn.org
   100 Airpost Gardens Rd, Ste 189, Hazard, KY 41701
   Donna Apperson, Director

Catholic Charities 270.852.8328
E-mail .... rita.heinc@pastoral.org
   600 Locust St, Owensboro, KY 42301
   Rita Heinc, Director

Family Connection, Inc. 859.498.0373
Fax 859.498.2606
Web .... www.familyconnectioninc.com
   700 Hope Hill Road, Hope, KY 40334
   COA accredited organization.

Foster & Adoptive Families of Fayette 859.299.2749
E-mail .... vsturgeon@iglou.com
   1843 Donco Ct, Lexington, KY 40505
   Virginia Sturgeon, Group Leader

Holly Hill Children's Home 859.635.0500
Fax 859.635.0504
E-mail .... info@hollyhill-ky.org
   9599 Summer Hill Rd, California, KY 41007
   Connie Wong, Executive Director

Home of the Innocents 502.596.1313
Fax 502.596.1414
E-mail .... sstone@homeoftheinnocents.org
   1100 E Market St, Louisville, KY 40206

Kentucky Foster/Adoptive Care Assoc 606.783.0946
   150 Wild Turkey Rd, Morehead, KY 40351
   Judy Gulley

KY Foster & Adptv Parent Trning Support 877.704.3278
   400 N Applied Science Bldg, Murray, KY 42071

KY Foster/Adoptive Care Assoc (KFACA) 606.784.7826
   435 Campbell Dr, Morehead, KY 40351

New Beginnings Family Services, Inc. 502.485.0722
Fax 502.485.0792
Web .... www.newbeginningsinc.com
   1939 Goldsmith Lane, Suite 144, Louisville, KY 40218
   COA accredited organization.

New Hope Foster Homes, Inc. 502.543.1497
Fax 502.543.3307
Web .... www.newhopehomes.org
   240 Raymond Road, Shepherdsville, KY 40165
   COA accredited organization.

Pennyrile Foster & Adoptive Parent Assoc 270.249.0307
   645 Silent Run Church Rd, Nebo, KY 42441
   Shirley Hedges

Western Ky United Methodist Family Svcs 270.443.9004
Fax 270.443.3128
E-mail .... umfs@bellsouth.net
   450 Park Ave, Paducah, KY 42001
   Bill Heaton, Manager

PEDIATRIC HOME CARE

Interim Healthcare 859.578.9191
Fax 859.578.9276
   3005 Dixie Hwy Ste 130, Fort Mitchell, KY 41017
   Laura Hermann, Nursing Director

SOCIAL SERVICES

A Women's Svc 606.523.1113
E-mail .... aawm5@hotmail.com
   601 S Kentucky Ave, Corbin, KY 40701-1641
   Jenny Sanders, Director

Adair Youth Development Ctr 270.384.0822
Fax 270.384.0073
   401 Appleby Dr, Columbia, KY 42728-1083
   Dwane Mills, Superintendent

Adolescent Afterschool Program Unity
House 859.734.7193
Fax 859.734.3070
E-mail .... gabass@bluegrass.org
   222 E Lexington St, Harrodsburg, KY 40330
   Andy Bass, Director

All God's Children, Inc. 859.881.5010
Fax 859.881.1576
Web .... www.kyallgodschildren.org
   P.O. Box 932, Nicholasville, KY 40340
   COA accredited organization.

Alpha Alternatives Crisis Ctr 270.885.3820
Fax 270.885.3171
   1705 S Main St, Hopkinsville, KY 42240-1972
   Kaye Munday, Administrator

Ashland Day Treatment Ctr 606.920.2073
Fax 606.920.2075
   1539 Greenup Ave, Ashland, KY 41105
   John Mullins, Superintendent

Bellewood Presbyterian Home for Children,
Inc. 502.245.4171
Fax 502.245.7447
Web .... www.bellewood.org
   11103 Park Road, Louisville, KY 40223
   COA accredited organization.

Bluegrass Clinical Inhome Services 859.299.0794
Fax 859.299.0967
Web .... www.bluegrass.org
E-mail .... familypreser@bluegrass.org
   201 Mechanic St, Lexington, KY 40511
   Rose Pennington, Program Director

Bowling Green Group Home 270.746.7458
Fax 270.843.1445
   3210 Porter Pike, Bowling Green, KY 42103-9560
   Kendell Williams, Director

Brighton Center, Inc. 859.491.8303
Fax 859.491.8702
Web .... www.brightoncenter.com
   P.O. Box 325, Newport, KY 41072-0325
   COA accredited organization.

Catholic Charities, Diocese of Covington 859.581.8974
Fax 859.581.9595
Web .... www.covingtoncharities.org
   3629 Church Street, Covington, KY 41015-1499
   COA accredited organization.

Catholic Charity 859.253.1993
Fax 859.255.1134
Web .... www.cdlex.org
   1310 W Main St, Lexington, KY 40508
   Ruslyn Case-Compton, Director (bishop)

Child Care Council of Kentucky 859.254.9176
Fax 859.225.5435
Web .... www.childcarecouncilofky.com
E-mail .... bradley.stevenson@ail.state.ky.us
   1460 Newtown Pike, Ste 101A, Lexington, KY 40511
   Bradley Stevenson, Executive Director

Children First 502.584.8505
Fax 502.584.6412
Web .... www.famchild.org
E-mail .... jwhitfield@famchild.org
   560B S 4th St, Louisville, KY 40202-2504
   John Whitfield, Program Director

Children's Home of Northern Kentucky 859.261.8768
Fax 859.291.2431
Web .... www.chnk.org
   200 Home Road, Devou Park, Covington,
   KY 41011-1942
   COA accredited organization.

Choices & Changes Youth Services, Inc. 606.325.8206
Fax 606.324.0288
Web .... www.choicesandchanges.org
1401 Winchester Avenue, Suite 532, Ashland, KY 41101
COA accredited organization.

Community Collaborations For Children 606.526.6303
Fax 606.526.6306
175 Teachtree St, Corbin, KY 40701
Patra Gregory, Program Director

Community Coordinated Child Care 270.360.9911
Fax 270.360.8877
Web www.4cforkids.org
E-mail .... alice.brewer@ky.gov
54 1st St, Elizabethtown, KY 42701
Kathy King, Director

Community Coordinated Child Care 4C 502.636.1358
Fax 502.636.1488
Web www.4cforkids.org
1215 S 3rd St, Louisville, KY 40203
Susan Vessels, Executive Director

Ctr For Women and Families Crisis Hotline 502.581.7200
Fax 502.581.7204
Web .... www.thecenteronline.org
927 S 2nd St Ste A, Louisville, KY 40203-2275
Marta Miranda, President/CEO

Ctr For Women, Children and Families 859.259.1974
Fax 859.254.9465
Web .... www.cwcfky.com
530 N Limestone, Lexington, KY 40508-1674
Eileen Omalley, Director

Day Treatment 270.825.6059
Fax 270.825.6053
E-mail .... jebarlow@hopkins.kyschools.us
5770 Anton Rd, Madisonville, KY 42431-7707
J.e. Barlow, Program Director

Day Treatment 859.635.9113
Fax 859.448.2781
51 Orchard Ln, Alexandria, KY 41001
John Schmidt, Program Director

Day Treatment 606.679.1303
Fax 606.679.0032
Web .... www.pulaski.net
E-mail .... tammy.roberts@pulaski.kyschools.us
67 Parkers Mill Rd, Somerset, KY 42501-3129
Tammy Roberts, Program Director

Eastern Kentucky Child Care Coalition 859.986.5896
Fax 859.986.0801
E-mail .... june.widman@ky.gov
1835 Big Hill Road, Berea, KY 40403
June Widman, Executive Director

Eastern Kentucky Child Care Coalition R&R Lake Cumberland 606.679.0167
Fax 606.678.4836
Web .... www.ekccc.org
E-mail .... carrollannbusher@ekccc.org
2371 Monticello Rd, Somerset, KY 42501-3059
Carrollann Busher, Director Of R&R

Eastern Kentucky University Speech- Language-Hearing Clinic 859.622.4444
Fax 859.622.2247
Web .... www.education.eku.edu/sed/cd/clinic
E-mail .... tami.cranfill@eku.edu
245 Wallace Bldg, Richmond, KY 40475
Jenny Holly, Office Associate

Family & Children's Place 502.893.3900
Fax 502.893.9646
Web .... www.familyandchildrensplace.org
2303 River Road, Suite 200, Louisville, KY 40206
COA accredited organization.

Frenchburg Group Home 606.768.3107
Fax 606.768.2117
E-mail .... tburton@menifee.k12.ky.us
158 Shermill Ln, Denniston, KY 40316
Mitch Adams, Superintendent

Gateway Juvenile Svc Ctr 859.498.9892
Fax 859.498.0316
37 N Maysville St, Mount Sterling, KY 40353
Kaye Jones Templin, Executive Director

Green River Youth Development Ctr 270.526.3826
Fax 270.526.2116
363 Boys Camp Rd, Cromwell, KY 42333-9607
Mark Cook, Superintendent

Holly Hill Children's Services 859.635.0500
Fax 859.635.0504
Web .... www.hollyhill-ky.org
9599 Summer Hill Road, California, KY 41007-9055
COA accredited organization.

Home of the Innocents 502.596.1000
Fax 502.596.1410
Web .... www.homeoftheinnocents.org
1100 East Market Street, Louisville, KY 40206
COA accredited organization.

Jewish Family Services of Central Kentucky 859.269.8244
Fax 502.452.6718
E-mail .... jfs@jewishlexington.org
1050 Chinoe Rd Ste 302, Lexington, KY 40502
Judy Wortman, Director

Lake Cumberland Youth Development Ctr 606.348.4201
Fax 606.348.4953
9000 Highway 1546, Monticello, KY 42633
Jim Gummey, Superintendent

LKLP Community Action Council 606.436.3161
Fax 606.439.2229
Web .... www.lklp.net
E-mail .... msammons@lklp.net
412 Roy Campbell Dr, Hazard, KY 41701
Rick Baker, Executive Director

Louisville Deaf Oral School 502.636.2084
Fax 502.636.9171
Web .... www.thehearinginstitute.org
E-mail .... mkmccubbin@thehearinginstitute.org
111 E Kentucky St, Louisville, KY 40203-2793
Mona Mccubbin, Ms, Executive Director

Maryhurst, Inc. 502.245.1576
Fax 502.254.7906
Web .... www.maryhurst.org
1015 Dorsey Lane, Louisville, KY 40223-2612
COA accredited organization.

MASH Services of the Bluegrass, Inc. 859.254.2501
Fax 859.226.9392
536 West Third Street, Lexington, KY 40508
COA accredited organization.

Mayfield Youth Development Ctr 270.247.3237
Fax 270.247.2605
3179 State Route 45 S, Mayfield, KY 42066
Bryan Bacon, Superintendent

Morehead Youth Development Ctr 606.784.6421
Fax 606.784.0021
495 Forest Hills Dr, Morehead, KY 40351-8899
Kris Mann, Director

New Hope Family Svcs, Inc. 502.543.1497
Fax 502.543.3307
Web .... www.newhopehomes.org
E-mail .... newhopehomes@aol.com
240 Raymond Rd, Shepherdsville, KY 40165-7944
Gwenn Lansing, Executive Director

Northeast Kentucky Area Development Council 606.286.4443
Fax 606.286.6733
Web .... www.nkcaa.net
539 Hitchins Ave, Olive Hill, KY 41164-7508
Connie Offill, Head Start Director

Northern Kentucky Youth Development Ctr 859.356.3172
Fax 859.356.0873
15600 Turner Rd, Crittenden, KY 41030
Martin Strouse, Superintendent

Owensboro Treatment Ctr 270.687.7311
Fax 270.687.7343
Web .... www.kentucky.gov
3001 Leitchfield Rd, Owensboro, KY 42303-2184
Tim Corder, Superintendent

Presbyterian Child Welfare Agency dba Buckhorn Children & Family Services 606.398.7000
Fax 606.398.7912
Web .... www.buckhorn.org
116 Buckhorn Lane, Buckhorn, KY 41721
COA accredited organization.

Purchase Area Child Care Resource and Referral 270.247.7171
Fax 270.251.6110
Web .... www.purchaseadd.org/
E-mail .... beth.carrico@purchaseadd.org
32 E Powell Rd, Mayfield, KY 42066
Jennifer Beck Walker, Executive Director

Ramey-Estep Homes, Inc. 606.928.6648
Fax 606.547.4361
Web .... www.rametestep.com
P.O. Box 39, Rush, KY 41168-0039
COA accredited organization.

St. Joseph Catholic Orphan Society, Inc. 502.893.0241
Fax 502.212.1289
Web .... www.sjkids.org
2823 Frankfort Avenue, Louisville, KY 40206-2639
COA accredited organization.

Sunrise Children Svcs 606.784.5882
Fax 606.780.9128
2495 Cranston Rd, Morehead, KY 40351
Patricia Miller, Program Director

Sunrise Children's Svcs 606.677.1008
Fax 606.677.0883
Web .... www.sunrise.org
225 Hwy 2227, Somerset, KY 42503
Pat Crabtree, Director

The Methodist Home of KY, Inc. dba The Kentucky United Methodist Homes for Children & Youth 859.873.4481
Fax 859.873.8078
Web .... www.kyumh.org
P.O. Box 749, Versailles, KY 40383
COA accredited organization.

Volunteers of America of Kentucky, Inc. 502.636.0771
Fax 502.636.0597
Web .... www.voaky.org
933 Goss Avenue, Louisville, KY 40217
COA accredited organization.

Western Kentucky University Child Care Resource and Referral 270.745.2216
Fax 270.745.7089
Web .... www.wku.edu/ccrr_wku
E-mail .... connie.smith@wku.edu
1906 College Heights Blvd, #11098, Bowling Green, KY 42101
Connie Jo Smith, Director

SPECIAL NEEDS

Autism Society of the Bluegrass 859.299.9000
E-mail .... ky-lexington@autismsocietyofamerica.org
453 Rookwood Pkwy, Lexington, KY 40505

Cardinal Hill Rehabilitation Hospital 859.254.5701
Fax 859.281.1365
Web ....www.cardinalhill.org
  2050 Versailles Rd, Lexington, KY 40504
  Kerry Gillghan, President
  CARF accredited programs available.

Easter Seals Kentucky 800.888.5377
  2050 Versailles Rd, Lexington, KY 40504
  Beth Monarch, Chief Executive Officer

Epilepsy Foundation of Kentuckiana 866.275.1078
E-mail ....dmcgrath@efky.org
  982 E Parkway, Louisville, KY 40217
  Deb McGrath, Executive Director

Find of Louisville 502.587.6500
E-mail ....smduverge@findoflouisville.org
  1151 S 4th St Ste 101, Louisville, KY 40203
  Sandra Duverge, Director

Frazier Rehab Institute 502.582.7490
Fax 502.582.7477
Web ....www.frazierrehab.org
  220 Abraham Flexner Way, Louisville, KY 40202
  CARF accredited programs available.

Kentucky Autism Training Ctr 502.852.4631
Fax 502.852.7148
Web ....www.kyautism.com
E-mail ....rebecca.grau@louisville.edu
  1405 E bernett ave, Louisville, KY 40217-2307
  Rebecca Grau, Assistant Director

Kentucky Disabilities Coalition 502.875.1871
E-mail ....kdcdisabilities@yahoo.com
  869 E Main St, Frankfort, KY 40602
  Sharon Fields, Director

Kentucky Education Rights Center Inc 859.983.9222
E-mail ....kerc@edrights.com
  1323 Moores Mill Rd, Midway, KY 40347

Kentucky Partnership Children w/MH 800.369.0533
E-mail ....kpfc@kypartnership.net
  207 Holmes St 1st Fl, Frankfort, KY 40601
  Carol Cecil, Executive Director

Kentucky PTA 502.226.6607
E-mail ....ky_office@pta.org
  148 consumar Ln, Frankfort, KY 40601
  Teri Gale, President

KY Special Parent Involvement Network 502.937.6894
Fax 502.937.6464
E-mail ....spininc@kyspin.com
  10301 B Deering Rd, Louisville, KY 40272
  Paulette Logsdon, Director

LearningRx Learning Center 859.373.0002
E-mail ....lexingtons.ky@learningrx.net
  185 Pasadena Dr, Ste 115, Lexington, KY 40503
  Aaron, Director

Lourdes Otto J. Diller Rehabilitation Unit 270.444.2780
Fax 270.444.2489
Web ....www.lourdes-pad.org
E-mail ....coverstreet@lourdes-pad.org
  1530 Lone Oak Road, Paducah, KY 42003
  Connie Overstreet, Director of Physician Recruitment & Physicians Services
  CARF accredited programs available.

Mental Health America of Kentucky 888.705.0463
E-mail ....mhaky@mhaky.org
  120 Sears Ave Ste 213, Louisville, KY 40207
  Bruce Scott, Interem Director

Mental Health Association 859.431.1077
E-mail ....mhanky@mhanky.org
  605 Madison Ave, Covington, KY 41011

National Multiple Sclerosis Society 502.451.0014
Fax 502.451.9747
E-mail ....KYW@nmss.org
  11700 Commonwealth Dr Ste 500, Louisville, KY 40299

Parent Outreach 502.584.1239
E-mail ....slawrence@councilondd.org
  1151 S 4th St, Louisville, KY 40203
  April Duval, Executive Director

Southern Kentucky Rehabilitation Hospital 270.782.6900
Fax 270.782.7228
Web ....www.skyrehab.com
  1300 Campbell Lane, Bowling Green, KY 42104
  CARF accredited programs available.

Special Parent Involvement Network 800.525.7746
E-mail ....spininc@kyspin.com
  10301-B Deering Rd, Louisville, KY 40272
  Paulette Logsdon, Director

Spina Bifida Association 866.340.7225
  982 Eastern Pkwy 18, Louisville, KY 40217
  Colleen Payne, Programme Coordinator

The Arc of Kentucky 800.281.1272
E-mail ....arcofky@aol.com
  706 E Main Ste A, Frankfort, KY 40601
  Patty Limsey, Director

The Langsford Learning Center 502.473.7000
Fax 866.223.3443
E-mail ....info@langsfordcenter.com
  2520 Bardstown Rd, Louisville, KY 40205
  Stephen McCrocklin, Director

United Way 2-1-1 ....859.313.5465
E-mail ....dawn.vermey@uwbg.org
  2480 Fortune Dr # 250, Lexington, KY 40509
  David Kitchen, Director

VSA Kentucky 270.781.0872
E-mail ....vsaky@bellsouth.net
  515 E 10th St, Bowling Green, KY 42101
  Delaire Rowe, Executive Director

SUBSTANCE ABUSE TREATMENT

Avenues For Women 502.695.0500
Fax 502.695.0549
E-mail ....cscott@fewpb.net
  73 C Michael DavenPort, Frankfort, KY 40601-4192
  Cheri Scott, Director

Kentucky

Louisiana

Bobby Jindal, Governor
Attn: Constituents Services
P.O. Box 94004
Baton Rouge, LA 70804
225.342.7015
225.342.7099 (Fax)
www.gov.state.la.us

Katherine Guidry, Juvenile Justice Specialist
1885 Wooddale Blvd., Room 1230
Baton Rouge, LA 70806-1511
225.925.4980
225.925.6649 (Fax)
kathy.guidry@lcle.la.gov

William Landry, SAG Chair
1427 South Park
Gonzales, LA 70737
225.647.7836
wlandry@eatel.net

CRISIS NUMBERS

Child Abuse Reporting . . .225.342.6832

STATE SERVICES

SOCIAL SERVICES

Child Care Lic and Reg Section LA 225.342.9905
Fax 225.342.9690
E-mail . . . . .angiebadeaux@la.gov
  PO Box 3078, Baton Rouge, LA 70821
  Angie Badeaux, Director

**Louisiana Dept of Childern And Family
Services 225.342.0286**
Fax 225.342.8636
Web . . . . .www.dss.state.la.us
  627 N 4th St, Baton Rouge, LA 70802-5343
  Ruth Johnson, Secretary Of The Agency

Louisiana Emergency Management Agency . . .225.925.7500
Fax 225.925.7501
Web . . . . .www.gohsep.la.gov
E-mail . . . . .commo1.itd@la.gov
  7667 Independence Blvd, Baton Rouge, LA 70806
  Mark Cooper, Director

Ofc of Community Svcs .318.627.3000
Fax 318.627.3508
  602 Main St, Colfax, LA 71417-1525
  Kim Mccain, Parish Manager

GENERAL HEALTH SERVICES

Children's Special Health Svcs 504.568.5055
Fax 504.568.7529
  1450 Poydras St, New Orleans, LA 70112
  Susan Berry, Administrator

Maternal and Child Health LA 504.568.3504
Fax 504.568.3503
E-mail . . . . .amy.zapata@la.gov
  1450 Poydras St, Fl 21, New Orleans, LA 70112
  Amy Zapata, Director

Ofc of Medicaid 225.342.3891
Fax 225.342.9508
Web . . . . .www.louisianadepartmentofhealthandhospi tal.com
  628 N 4th St, Baton Rouge, LA 70802-5342
  Don Gregory, Director

MENTAL HEALTH SERVICES

Louisiana Rehabilitation Services 225.219.2225
Fax 225.219.2942
E-mail . . . . .mmartin@lwc.la.gov
  950 N 22nd St Ste A, Baton Rouge, LA 70802
  Mark Martin, Director

Ofc for Addictive Disorders 225.342.5988
Fax 225.342.3931
E-mail . . . . .bblanch@dhh.la.gov
  343 3rd St Ste 310, Baton Rouge, LA 70802
  Bill Blanchard, Program Manager

Ofc For Addictive Disorders 225.342.2540
Fax 225.342.3875
Web . . . . .www.addictionsla.com
E-mail . . . . .p.calamari@la.gov
  628 N 4th St, Baton Rouge, LA 70802-5342
  Peter J Calamari, Interim Assistant Secretary

JUSTICE AGENCY

Attorney General's Ofc 225.326.6000
Fax 225.326.6797
Web . . . . .www.ag.state.la.us
E-mail . . . . .admininfo@ag.state.la.us
  1885 N 4TH ST, Baton Rouge, LA 70802-5159
  James Caldwell, Attorney General

Correctional Education Division LA 225.342.6633
Fax 225.342.5556
  PO Box 44314, Baton Rouge, LA 70804
  Michael Moore, Director

Ofc of Juvenile Justice 225.287.7900
Fax 225.287.7969
Web . . . . .www.oyd.louisiana.gov
  7919 Independence Blvd, Baton Rouge,
  LA 70806-6409
  Dr. Mary Livers, Deputy Secretary

COURTS

State Court Admin Ofc 504.310.2550
Fax 504.310.2587
E-mail . . . . .bgundorf@lajao.org
  400 Royal St Ste 4200, New Orleans, LA 70130
  Tim Averill, Administrator

POLICE AND SHERIFF

Kenner Police Dept 504.712.2200
Fax 504.712.2203
E-mail . . . . .kpd@kenner.la.us
  500 Veterans Memorial Blvd, Kenner, LA 70062-5078
  Stephen Caraway, Police Chief

Louisiana Sheriff's Assoc 225.343.8402
Fax 225.336.0343
Web . . . . .www.lsa.org
  1175 Nicholson Dr, Baton Rouge, LA 70802
  Michael Ranatza, Executive Director

Palmetto Police Dept 337.623.4999
Fax 337.623.4814
E-mail . . . . .clerk@palmetto-la.com
  224 E Railroad Ave, Palmetto, LA 71358
  Police Chief David Krull, Police Chief

EDUCATION SERVICES

Educ for Homeless Children and Youth LA . . .225.342.3031
Fax 877.453.2721
E-mail . . . . .laverne.dunn@la.gov
  PO Box 94064, Baton Rouge, LA 70804
  Laverne Dunn, Director

Governors SDFAC Program 225.342.3423
Fax 225.342.7081
E-mail . . . . .don.diaz@la.gov
  150 3rd St, Room 121, Baton Rouge, LA 70801-1303
  Don Diaz, Executive Director

LA Parent Training and Info Center 504.888.9111
Fax 504.888.0246
E-mail . . . . .carceneaux@laptic.org
  201 Evans Rd Bldg 1 Ste 100, Harahan, LA 70123

Louisiana Dept of Education 225.219.5172
Fax 225.342.0781
E-mail . . . . .customerservice@la.gov
  1201 N Third, Baton Rouge, LA 70804
  Renee Greer, Director Of Communications

Louisiana School for the Deaf 225.769.8160
Fax 225.757.3424
Web . . . . .www.lsd.state.la.us
E-mail . . . . .mhara@mail.lsd.state.la.us
  2888 Brightside Dr, Baton Rouge, LA 70820-3509
  Dr. Monita Hara, Director

LABOR & WORKFORCE EDUCATION

Louisiana Dept of Labor .225.342.3001
Fax 225.342.3778
Web . . . . .www.laworks.net
E-mail . . . . .mpitts@lwc.la.gov
  1001 N 23rd St, #2WA, Baton Rouge, LA 70802
  Curt Eysink, Executive Director

Louisiana

348

© 2011 Dorland Health

COUNTY SERVICES

Acadia Parish

SOCIAL SERVICES

Ofc of Community Svcs 337.788.7503
Fax 337.788.7624
Web .... www.sos.louisiana.gov
E-mail .... racinda.latuor@sos.louisiana.gov
  600 N Avenue G, Crowley, LA 70526-4442
  Racinda Latuor, District Manager

GENERAL HEALTH SERVICES

Health Unit 337.788.7507
Fax 337.788.7577
  530 W Mill St, Crowley, LA 70526
  Corine Gilder, Nursing Supervisor

COURTS

15th District Court 337.788.8881
Fax 337.788.1048
E-mail .... blane@acadiaparishclerk.com
  500 N Parkerson Ave, Crowley, LA 70526
  Robert T. Barousse, Clerk Of Court

Professional Home & Health Svcs 337.783.5040
Fax 337.783.5041
  1708 N Parkerson Ave, Crowley, LA 70526
  Shana Coleman, Director Of Nursing

POLICE AND SHERIFF

Church Point Police Dept 337.684.5455
Fax 337.684.2074
  427 N Main St, Church Point, LA 70525-3002
  Albert Venable, Police Chief

Crowley Police Dept 337.788.4114
Fax 337.788.4136
Web .... www.cox-internet.com
E-mail .... kpgibson@cox-internet.com
  426 N Avenue F, Crowley, LA 70526-5045
  K P Gibson, Police Chief

Estherwood Police Dept 337.783.0464
Fax 337.783.0596
E-mail .... esth_vil@bellsouth.net
  124 N lablong street, Estherwood, LA 70534
  Kevin Leblanc, Police Chief

Iota Police Dept 337.779.3345
Fax 337.779.2599
  116 Duson Ave, Iota, LA 70543
  D. Scotty Pousson, Police Chief

Mermentau Police Dept 337.824.3853
Fax 337.824.6973
  107 7th St, Mermentau, LA 70556
  Donnie Bertrand, Police Chief

Rayne Police Dept 337.334.4215
Fax 337.334.6636
  200 Oak St, Rayne, LA 70578
  Carroll Stelly, Police Chief

Allen Parish

SOCIAL SERVICES

Ofc of Family Support 337.639.2961
Fax 337.639.4052
E-mail .... frhea@dss.state.la.us
  213 N 1st St., #A, Oberlin, LA 70655
  Frieda Rhea, Parish Manager

MENTAL HEALTH SERVICES

Mental Health 337.639.3001
Fax 337.639.3008
  402 Industrial Dr, Oberlin, LA 70655
  Scott Morgan, Manager

COURTS

33rd District Court 337.639.2266
Fax 337.639.4310
  400 Main St, Oberlin, LA 70655
  Honorable Joel G. Davis, Director

POLICE AND SHERIFF

Elizabeth Police Dept 318.634.5100
Fax 318.634.7881
E-mail .... elizabethtownhall.net
  230 Poplar Street, Elizabeth, LA 70638
  Shane Ware, Head-police Chief

Fenton Police Dept 337.756.2321
Fax 337.756.2242
E-mail .... info@centurytel.net
  712 3rd Ave, Fenton, LA 70640
  Luther Alfred, Police Chief

Kinder Police Dept 337.738.2600
Fax 337.738.2497
Web .... www.americanpress.com
  807 3rd Ave, Kinder, LA 70648
  Gary Pelican, Police Chief

Oakdale Police Dept 318.335.0290
Fax 318.335.0620
  118 N 10th St, Oakdale, LA 71463-2636
  Scotty Laborde, Police Chief

Oberlin Police Dept 337.639.4922
Fax 337.639.2205
  103 East 6th Ave, Oberlin, LA 70655
  Grady Haynes, Police Chief

Sheriff's Ofc 337.639.4353
Fax 337.639.2855
E-mail .... apso@centurytel.net
  601 Court St, Oberlin, LA 70655
  Harold A. Brady, Sheriff

Ascension Parish

SOCIAL SERVICES

Family Support 225.644.0484
Fax 225.647.9013
Web .... www.dss.state.la.us
E-mail .... gquinta@dss.state.la.us
  1078 E. Worthy Rd., Gonzales, LA 70707
  Gene Quinta, Manager

Ofc of Community Svcs 225.644.4603
Fax 225.647.9413
E-mail .... karen.fletcher@la.gov
  1078 E Worthy St, Gonzales, LA 70737
  Karen Fletcher, District Manager

GENERAL HEALTH SERVICES

Health Unit 225.474.2004
Fax 225.474.2060
Web .... www.louisiana.gov
E-mail .... jan.allred@la.gov
  901 Catalpa St, Donaldsonville, LA 70346-2945
  Jan Allred, Hiv Coordinator

POLICE AND SHERIFF

Gonzales Police Dept 225.647.9540
Fax 225.647.9544
  120 S Irma Blvd, Gonzales, LA 70737-3604
  Sherman Jackson, Police Chief

Sheriff's Ofc 225.621.8322
Fax 225.621.8323
Web .... www.ascensionsheriff.com
E-mail .... jwiley@ascensionsheriff.com
  828 S Irma Blvd Ste 101, Gonzales, LA 70737-3697
  Jeffrey F. Wiley, Sheriff

Assumption Parish

SOCIAL SERVICES

Ofc of Family Support 985.369.6134
Fax 985.369.7779
E-mail .... khall@dss.state.la.us
  108 Robin St., Hwy 308, Napoleonville, LA 70390
  Kathy Hall, Parish Manager

GENERAL HEALTH SERVICES

Assumption Parish Health Unit 985.369.6031
Fax 985.369.2326
Web .... www.assumptionoep.com
  158 Highway 1008, Napoleonville, LA 70390
  Debbie Gonzalez, Nursing Supervisor

POLICE AND SHERIFF

Napoleonville Police Dept 985.369.6365
Fax 985.369.6361
Web .... www.mobiltel.com
E-mail .... lbell@mobiltel.com
  123 Jefferson St, Napoleonville, LA 70390
  Lionell Bell, Police Chief

Sheriff's Ofc 985.369.7281
Fax 985.369.1395
E-mail .... apsosheriff@aol.com
  112 Franklin St., Napoleonville, LA 70390
  Mike J. Waguespack, Sheriff

Avoyelles Parish

SOCIAL SERVICES

Ofc of Family Support 318.253.5941
Fax 318.253.0058
Web .... www.dss.state.la.gov
E-mail .... dssavoyelles@la.gov
  607 Tunica Dr W, Marksville, LA 71351-2630
  Maude Scott, Parish Manager

GENERAL HEALTH SERVICES

Health Unit 318.253.4528
Web .... www.la.gov
  675 Government St, 657, Marksville, LA 71351
  Carmen Villemarant, Supervisor

COURTS

Avoyelles Hospital 318.253.8611
Fax 318.240.6077
Web .... www.avoyelleshospital.com
  4231 Highway 1192, Marksville, LA 71351-4711
  David Micehel, Chief Executive Officer

POLICE AND SHERIFF

Bunkie Police Dept 318.346.2664
Fax 318.346.7634
Web .... www.bunkiepd.com
E-mail .... mfanara@kricket.net
  438 NW Main Street, Bunkie, LA 71322
  Mary Fanara, Police Chief

Cottonport Police Dept 318.876.3488
Fax 318.876.3356
  931 Bryan St, Cottonport, LA 71327
  Gerald Mayeux, Police Chief

Hessmer Police Dept 318.563.4511
Fax 318.563.4010
Web .... www.detelwireless.com
E-mail .... ksmith@detelwireless.com
  4142 Bordelon St, Hessmer, LA 71341
  Kenneth Smith, Police Chief

Mansura Police Dept **318.964.2120**
Fax 318.964.5317
E-mail ....chiefsure@hotmail.com
   1832 Leglise St, Mansura, LA 71350
John Johnson, Police Chief

Marksville Police Dept **318.253.9250**
Fax 318.253.4748
   422 N Main St, Marksville, LA 71351-2411
Ellis Walker, Police Chief

Moreauville Police Dept **318.985.2126**
Fax 318.985.2407
   9898 Bayou Des Glaises Street, Moreauville,
   LA 71355
Scott Lemoine, Police Chief

Sheriff's Ofc **318.253.4000**
Fax 318.253.0826
E-mail ....apso@kricket.net
   675 Government St, Marksville, LA 71351
Doug Anderson, Sheriff

Simmesport Police Dept **318.941.2576**
Fax 318.941.2942
   372 Mission Dr, Simmesport, LA 71369
John Moreau, Police Chief

Beauregard Parish

SOCIAL SERVICES

Ofc of Community Svcs **337.463.2069**
Fax 337.462.1473
E-mail ....dmccullough@dss.state.la.us
   1877 Highway 190 W, DeRidder, LA 70634
Donna Mccullough, Parish Manager

Ofc of Family Support **985.447.0938**
Fax 985.447.0898
Web ....www.dss.state.la.us
E-mail ....mjones@dss.state.la.us
   1000 Plantation Rd Ste B, Thibodaux, LA 70301-4264
Michael Jones, Parish Manager

Ofc of Family Support **337.463.6091**
Fax 337.463.8634
Web ....www.dss.state.la.us
E-mail ....jrhea@dss.state.la.us
   1891 Highway 190 W, DeRidder, LA 70634
Jeanne Rhea, Parish Manager

GENERAL HEALTH SERVICES

Health Unit **337.463.4486**
Fax 337.462.2486
   216 Evangeline St, Deridder, LA 70634
Janet Fontenot, Nursing Supervisor

JUSTICE AGENCY

Casa **337.462.4667**
Fax 337.462.1554
   1118 N Pine St Ste G, DeRidder, LA 70634
Gayle Hodnette, Executive Director

COURTS

36th District Court **337.463.8595**
Fax 337.462.3916
   201 W 1st St, Deridder, LA 70634
Brian S Lestad, Court Clark

POLICE AND SHERIFF

Deridder Police Dept **337.462.8911**
Fax 337.462.8913
   200 S Jefferson St, DeRidder, LA 70634
John Gott, Police Chief

Merryville Police Dept **337.825.6240**
Fax 337.825.1026
   1009 Highway 110 W, Merryville, LA 70653
James Longoria, Police Chief

Bienville Parish

GENERAL HEALTH SERVICES

Health Unit **318.263.2125**
Fax 318.263.2009
   1285 Pine St Ste 102, Arcadia, LA 71001
Amy Gray, Nursing Supervisor

COURTS

2nd District Court **318.263.7412**
Fax 318.263.7414
   100 Courthouse Dr Rm 208, Arcadia, LA 71001-3659
Honorable Glenn Fallin, Director

POLICE AND SHERIFF

Arcadia Police Dept **318.263.8455**
Fax 318.263.2571
E-mail ....vrogers@iamerica.net
   1819 S Railroad Ave, Arcadia, LA 71001
Victor Rogers, Police Chief

Gibsland Police Dept **318.843.6141**
Fax 318.843.9409
E-mail ....gibslandclerkmar@bellsouth.net
   2463 Main Street, Gibsland, LA 71028
Shelton Scott, Police Chief

Ringgold Police Dept **318.894.4699**
Fax 318.894.5990
   2135 Hall St, Ringgold, LA 71068
Lawson Bradley, Police Chief

Sheriff's Ofc **318.263.2215**
Fax 318.263.7418
   100 Courthouse Dr, Arcadia, LA 71001
John E. Ballance, Sheriff

Bossier Parish

GENERAL HEALTH SERVICES

Health Unit **318.741.7314**
Fax 318.741.7441
Web ....www.dhh.louisiana.gov
   3022 Old Minden Rd Ste 100, Bossier City,
   LA 71112-2454
Veronica Attaway, Rn, Nursing Supervisor

COURTS

26th District Court **318.965.2336**
Fax 318.965.3297
Web ....www.bossierclerk.com
E-mail ....bossierclerk@yahoo.com
   204 Burt Blvd, Benton, LA 71006-4901
Joycelyn Shansie, Deputy Clerk

City Court **318.741.8815**
Fax 318.549.4582
E-mail ....wilsont@bossiercity.org
   620 Benton Rd, Bossier City, LA 71111
Honorable Thomas A. Wilson Jr., Judge

POLICE AND SHERIFF

Bossier City Police Dept **318.741.8605**
Fax 318.741.8690
   620 Benton Rd, Bossier City, LA 71111
Shane Mcwilliams, Police Chief

Haughton Police Dept **318.949.6666**
Fax 318.949.6030
   120 W McKinley Ave, Haughton, LA 71037-8935
Rodney Farrington, Police Chief

Plain Dealing Police Dept **318.326.4234**
Fax 318.326.7022
E-mail ....pdealing@centurytel.net
   205 W Palmetto Ave, PlainDealing, LA 71064
Richard Stanford, Police Chief

Sheriff's Dept **318.965.2203**
Fax 318.965.9737
Web ....www.bossiersheriff.com
E-mail ....ldeen@bossiersheriff.com
   204 Burt Blvd, Benton, LA 71006
Larry C. Deen, Sheriff

Caddo Parish

SOCIAL SERVICES

Child & Family Services **318.676.7100**
Fax 318.676.7084
Web ....www.dcfs.louisiana.gov
   1525 Fairfield Ave Ste 850, Shreveport,
   LA 71101-4329
Deborah Renee Clary, Regional Administrator

Family Support **318.676.7600**
Fax 318.676.7317
Web ....www.dss.state.la.us
E-mail ....nedward1@dss.state.la.us
   1525 Fairfield Ave Ste 220, Shreveport,
   LA 71101-4331
Nancy Edwards, Manager

Shreveport Region VII Ofc of Family
Support **888.524.3578**
Fax 318.676.7086
Web ....www.dcss.la.dove
   1525 Fairfield Ave, 330 State Office Bldg, Shreveport,
   LA 71101
Cheryl Rambin, Regional Administrator

GENERAL HEALTH SERVICES

Dept of Health and Hospitals **318.676.7470**
Fax 318.676.7560
Web ....www.louisiana.gov
   1525 Fairfield Ave Ste 569, Shreveport,
   LA 71101-4331
Martha Whyte, Phd, Medical Director

Health Unit **318.676.5222**
Fax 318.676.5221
Web ....www.dhh.la.gov
   1035 Creswell Ave, Shreveport, LA 71101-3997
Belinda Everette, Supervisor

JUSTICE AGENCY

Ofc of Youth Development **318.676.7020**
Fax 318.676.7027
Web ....www.oyd.louisiana.gov
E-mail ....kristi.martin@la.gov
   1525 Fairfield Ave Ste 1053, Shreveport,
   LA 71101-4330
Kristi Martin, District Manager

Volunteer For Youth Justice CASA
Program **318.221.2272**
Fax 318.227.0208
E-mail ....eileen.czerwinski@vyjla.org
   900 Jordan St, Shreveport, LA 71101
Eileen Czerwinski, Case Program Director

COURTS

Juvenile Court **318.226.6751**
Fax 318.226.6942
   1835 Spring St, Shreveport, LA 71101-4298
Honorable Paul Young, Judge

Teen Court **318.425.4413**
Fax 318.227.0208
Web ....www.vyjla.org
E-mail ....shonda.houston@vyjla.org
   900 Jordan St, Shreveport, LA 71101-4310
Chastity Graham, Coordinator

POLICE AND SHERIFF

Blanchard Police Dept **318.929.3700**
Fax 318.929.3408
Web www.caddo911.com
E-mail ....blanpd819@cmaaccess.com
　314 Alexander Ave, Blanchard, LA 71009
　Gary Presswood, Police Chief

Greenwood Police Dept **318.938.5554**
Fax 318.938.5607
E-mail ....dstarcy@greenwoodla.org
　9381 Greenwood Rd, Greenwood, LA 71033-2938
　Davis Starcy, Police Chief

Hosston Police Dept **318.287.3225**
Fax 318.257.3518
Web ....www.idalouisiana.com
　15669 US Highway 7, Hosston, LA 71043
　Ricky Pannell, Police Chief

Ida Police Dept **318.284.3231**
Fax 318.284.3244
Web ....www.idalouisiana.com
　7016 East Ida St, Ida, LA 71044
　Michael Carroway, Police Chief

Mooringsport Police Dept **318.996.7661**
Fax 318.996.7667
E-mail ....mooringsport@bellsouth.net
　122 Croom St, Mooringsport, LA 71060
　Dale Nix Jr, Police Chief

Oil City Police Dept **318.995.6681**
Fax 318.995.6633
　202 Allen St, Oil City, LA 71061
　Tom Bass, Police Chief

Sheriff's Dept **318.675.2170**
Fax 318.681.0888
Web ....www.caddosheriff.org
　501 Texas St Rm 101, Shreveport, LA 71101
　Steve Prator, Sheriff

Shreveport Police Dept **318.673.6900**
Fax 318.673.6914
　1234 Texas Ave, Rm 100, Shreveport, LA 71101
　Willie Shaw, Police Chief

Shreveport Police Dept **318.673.7300**
Fax 318.673.6914
Web ....www.ci.shreveport.la.us
E-mail ....police@ci.shreveport.la.us
　1234 Texas Ave, Shreveport, LA 71101-3345
　Henry Whitehorn, Chief

Vivian Police Dept **318.375.2914**
Fax 318.375.5245
　121 N Pine St, Vivian, LA 71082-2700
　Ryan Nelson, Police Chief

EDUCATION SERVICES

**Caddo Parish Schools-Special
Programs** **318.219.0191**
Fax 318.868.7039
　3004 Knight St, Bldg 6, Shreveport, LA 71105
　Pam Barker, Director Of Special Programs

Calcasieu Parish

GENERAL HEALTH SERVICES

Calcasieu Parish Health Unit **337.478.6020**
Fax 337.475.8613
Web ....www.oph.dhh.state.la.us
E-mail ....pewilliams@dhh.la.gov
　3236 Kirkman St, Lake Charles, LA 70601-8640
　Patrick Williams, Student Supervisor

Ofc of Public Health Region V **337.475.3200**
Fax 337.475.3222
　707 E Prien Lake Rd Ste A, Lake Charles, LA 70601
　Bertram Foch, Md, Regional Administrator

JUSTICE AGENCY

Family and Youth Agency **337.436.9533**
Fax 337.439.9941
Web ....www.fyca.org
E-mail ....david@fyca.org
　220 Louie St, Lake Charles, LA 70601-7250
　Julio Galan, Executive Director

Ofc of Juvenille Justice **337.491.2833**
Fax 337.491.2842
　807 W Bayou Pines, Lake Charles, LA 70601
　Ann Vick, Regional Manager

Office of Juvenile Justice Services **337.721.3900**
Fax 337.721.3907
E-mail ....dbolin@cppj.net
　3615 E Prien Lake Rd, Lake Charles, LA 70615
　Dane Bolin, Director

COURTS

Teen Court **337.437.3363**
Fax 337.437.3390
Web www.14jdc.org
　1000 Ryan St., North Annex, Lake Charles, LA 70602
　Danni Jo Schiel, Coordinator

POLICE AND SHERIFF

Dequincy Police Dept **337.786.4000**
Fax 337.786.6006
　101 S Pine St, Dequincy, LA 70633-3550
　Michael Suchanek, Police Chief

Iowa Police Dept **337.582.3636**
Fax 337.582.1589
E-mail ....policechief@iowala.org
　115 N Thomson Ave, Iowa, LA 70647
　Keith Vincent, Police Chief

Lake Charles Police Dept **337.491.1311**
Fax 337.491.8726
Web ....www.cityoflakecharles.org
　830 Enterprise Blvd, Lake Charles, LA 70602-1564
　Don Dixon, Chief

Sheriff's Ofc **337.491.3700**
Fax 337.494.4522
Web ....www.cpso.org
E-mail ....tmancuso@cpso.com
　5400 Broad St, Lake Charles, LA 70615-4136
　Tony Mancuso, Sheriff

Sulphur Police Dept **337.527.4550**
Fax 337.527.4561
Web ....www.sulphurpolice.com
E-mail ....webmaster@sulphurpolice.com
　500 N Huntington St Ste B, Sulphur, LA 70663-2200
　Chris Abraham, Police Chief

Vinton Police Dept **337.589.3561**
Fax 337.589.2681
　1200 Horridge St, Vinton, LA 70668
　Ricky Fox, Police Chief

Westlake Police Dept **337.433.4151**
Fax 337.433.4578
E-mail ....michael_dickerson@westwegopolice.com
　701 Johnson St, Westlake, LA 70669
　Michael Dickerson, Police Chief

Caldwell Parish

GENERAL HEALTH SERVICES

Caldwell Parish Health Unit **318.649.2393**
　501 Collins Rd, Columbia, LA 71418
　Barbara Hart, Nursing Supervisor

COURTS

37th District Court **318.649.6404**
Fax 318.649.0548
E-mail ....Caldwelljudge@bellsouth.net
　201 Main St., Columbia, LA 71418
　Honorable Don C. Burns, Judge

POLICE AND SHERIFF

Clarks Police Dept **318.649.7218**
Fax 318.649.7215
E-mail ....dreamcity@bellsouth.net
　1714 Hwy 845, Clarks, LA 71415
　Larry Taylor, Police Chief

Columbia Police Dept **318.649.6174**
Fax 318.649.0758
　302 Pearl St Columbia, Columbia, LA 71418
　Clay Bennett, Police Chief

Sheriff's Dept **318.649.2345**
Fax 318.649.5226
E-mail ....cpso@bellsouth.net
　201 Main St, Columbia, LA 71418
　Steven E. May, Sheriff

Cameron Parish

GENERAL HEALTH SERVICES

Health Unit **337.775.5368**
Fax 337.775.5367
Web ....www.dhh.state.la.us
E-mail ....sdupont@dhh.la.gov
　107 Recreation Center Ln, Cameron, LA 70631
　Susan Dupont, RN, Nursing Supervisor

POLICE AND SHERIFF

Sheriff's Dept **337.775.5111**
Fax 337.775.5042
Web ....www.camtel.net
E-mail ....tduhon@camtel.net
　119 Smith Cir., Cameron, LA 70631
　Theos Duhon, Sheriff

Catahoula Parish

SOCIAL SERVICES

**Dept of Children and Family
Services** **318.339.6030**
Fax 318.339.6049
E-mail ....mary.booth@la.gov
　124 Airport Rd, Jonesville, LA 71343
　Mary Booth, Parish Manager

Ofc of Family Support **318.339.6611**
Fax 318.339.6779
E-mail ....ofscata@dss.state.la.us
　1305 Fourth St, Jonesville, LA 71343-2123
　Maude Tollard, Parish Manager

COURTS

7th District Court **318.744.5414**
Fax 318.744.5406
　301 Bushley Street, Harrisonburg, LA 71340
　Honorable Kathy J. Johnson, Director

POLICE AND SHERIFF

Harrisonburg Police Dept **318.744.5794**
Fax 318.744.5381
E-mail ....villageofharrisonburg@yahoo.com
　108 Sicily Street, Harrisonburg, LA 71340
　Joe Cook, Police Chief

Sheriff's Ofc **318.744.5411**
Fax 318.744.5568
　301 Bushley St, Harrisonburg, LA 71340
　James Kelly, Sheriff

Sicily Island Police Dept **318.389.5644**
Fax 318.389.2500
　603 Nemar St, Sicily Island, LA 71368
　Paul Jackson, Police Chief

Louisiana

Claiborne Parish

SOCIAL SERVICES

Ofc of Family Support **318.927.3518**
Fax 318.927.5496
E-mail ....sharmon@dss.state.la.us
  622 E 2nd St, PO Drawer 210, Homer, LA 71040
  Sarah Harmon, Parish Manager

GENERAL HEALTH SERVICES

Claiborne Parish Health Unit **318.927.6127**
Fax 318.927.6362
E-mail ....ewhite@nlahec.org
  624 W Main St, Homer, LA 71040
  Erin White, RN, Nursing Supervisor

COURTS

2nd District Court **318.927.9601**
Fax 318.927.2345
  512 E Main St, Homer, LA 71040
  Honorable Jenifer Ward Clason, Judge

POLICE AND SHERIFF

Homer Police Dept **318.927.4000**
Fax 318.927.4057
  420 E Main St, Homer, LA 71040
  Russell Mills, Police Chief

Sheriff's Office **318.927.2011**
Fax 318.927.9819
  613 E Main St, Homer, LA 71040
  Ken Bailey, Sheriff

Concordia Parish

GENERAL HEALTH SERVICES

Concordia Parish Health Unit **318.757.8632**
Fax 318.757.7654
  905 Mickey Gilley Ave, Ferriday, LA 71334
  Mary Spann, Nursing Supervisor

COURTS

7th District Court **318.336.7121**
Fax 318.336.2128
  4001 Carter St Rm 10, Vidalia, LA 71373
  Honorable Kathy Johnson, Chief Judge

City Court of Vidalia **318.336.6255**
Fax 318.336.9893
E-mail ....citycourt@bellsouth.net
  409 Texas St Rm 101, Vidalia, LA 71373-3333
  Honorable George C. Murray Jr., Judge

Intensive Home & Healthcare **318.336.9030**
Fax 318.336.9497
  901 Carter St, Vidalia, LA 71373
  Ms Margie Googer Rn, Home Health Administrator

POLICE AND SHERIFF

Ferriday Police Dept **318.757.3606**
Fax 318.757.8736
  1302 E Wallace Blvd N, Ferriday, LA 71334
  Kenneth Hedrick, Police Chief

Jonesville Police Dept **318.339.9886**
Fax 318.339.9944
  304 Mound St, Jonesville, LA 71343-2323
  Alder Roy, Police Chief

Ridgecrest Police Dept **318.757.4497**
Fax 318.757.8240
E-mail ....ridgecrestmayors@bellsouth.net
  116 Foster Dr, Ferriday, LA 71334-3668
  Larry Lawrence, Police Chief

Sheriff's Dept **318.336.5232**
Fax 318.336.5021
Web ....www.kricket.net
E-mail ....cpso@kricket.net
  4001 Carter St Rm 6, Vidalia, LA 71373-3021
  Randy J. Maxwell, Sheriff

Vidalia Police Dept **318.336.5254**
Fax 318.336.6261
Web ....www.netscape.net
  602 John Dale Dr, Vidalia, LA 71373-4270
  Arthur K Lewis, Police Chief

De Soto Parish

SOCIAL SERVICES

Ofc of Community Svcs **318.872.6311**
Fax 318.872.8897
Web ....www.ocs.dss.state.la.us
E-mail ....marsha@ocs.dss.state.la.us
  7356 Highway 509, Mansfield, LA 71052
  Marsha McCall, BCSW, Parish Manager

POLICE AND SHERIFF

Mansfield Police Dept **318.872.0520**
Fax 318.872.0539
  700 Franklin St, Mansfield, LA 71052
  John Prepp, Police Chief

Stonewall Police Dept **318.925.9338**
Fax 318.925.9339
E-mail ....townofstonewall@comcast.net
  1318 Highway 171, Stonewall, LA 71078
  Chief Thomas H. Dufrene, Jr., Chief Of Police

East Baton Rouge Parish

SOCIAL SERVICES

Ofc of Community Svcs **225.925.6500**
Fax 225.925.6800
E-mail ....minerva.whitley@la.gov
  160 S Ardenwood Dr, Baton Rouge, LA 70806
  Minerva Whitley, Foster Care/cps Supervisor

**Region II Baton Rouge Ofc of Community
Svcs** **225.922.3099**
Fax 225.922.2922
Web ....www.dss.state.la.us
E-mail ....lwelch@dss.state.la.us
  8549 United Plaza Blvd Ste 210, Baton Rouge,
  LA 70809-0207
  Lisa Welch, Regional Administrator

GENERAL HEALTH SERVICES

Health Unit **225.242.4860**
Fax 225.342.5821
Web ....www.dhh.la.gov
E-mail ....rbaillie@dhh.la.gov
  353 N 12th St, Baton Rouge, LA 70802-4612
  Rita Baillie, RN, Supervisor

MENTAL HEALTH SERVICES

Baton Rouge Mental Health Ctr **225.925.1906**
Fax 225.925.1972
  4615 Government St Bldg 2, Baton Rouge, LA 02412
  Jan Kosfsky, Director

JUSTICE AGENCY

Capital Area CASA Assoc **225.379.8598**
Fax 225.379.3362
Web ....www.casabr.org
E-mail ....info@casabr.org
  848 Louisiana Ave, Baton Rouge, LA 70802
  Liz Betz, Executive Director

Juvenile Detention Svcs **225.354.1280**
Fax 225.354.1303
  8333 Veterans Memorial Blvd, Baton Rouge,
  LA 70805
  Kathline Stuart Richey, Judge

COURTS

Family Court **225.389.4680**
Fax 225.389.4952
Web ....www.familycourt.org
E-mail ....rbullion@familycourt.org
  222 Saint Louis St, Governmental Bldg., Baton Rouge,
  LA 70802-5876
  Ronnie Bullion, Court Administrator

Juvenile Court **225.354.1250**
Fax 225.357.7876
Web ....www.brgov.com
E-mail ....jc@brgov.com
  8333 Veterans Memorial Blvd, Baton Rouge,
  LA 70807-4002
  Honorable Kathleen Stewart Richey, Judges

POLICE AND SHERIFF

Baker Police Dept **225.775.6000**
Fax 225.775.0936
E-mail ....mknats@bakerpd.org
  1320 Alabama St, Baker, LA 70714-2808
  Mike Knats, Police Chief

Baton Rouge Police Dept **225.389.3802**
Fax 225.389.7630
Web ....www.brgov.com
  704 Mayflower St, Baton Rouge, LA 70802
  Dewayne White, Police Chief

Evergreen Police Dept **318.346.9844**
Fax 318.346.9843
  1000 Cotton St, Evergreen, LA 70802
  Charles Mayeaux, Police Chief

Sheriff's Ofc **225.389.5055**
Fax 225.389.5032
Web ....www.ebrso.org
E-mail ....webmaster@ebrso.org
  300 North Blvd., Municiple Bldg., Baton Rouge,
  LA 70821
  Sid Gautreaux, Sheriff

Zachary Police Dept **225.654.9393**
Fax 225.654.1913
  4510 Main St, Zachary, LA 70791
  David Courtney, Police Chief

East Carroll Parish

GENERAL HEALTH SERVICES

East Carroll Parish Health Unit **318.559.2012**
Fax 318.559.3553
Web ....www.la.gov
  403 2Nd St, Lake Providence, LA 71254-2699
  Alisson Tatum, Nursing Supervisor

COURTS

6th District Court **318.559.2399**
Fax 318.559.0037
  400 1st St Ste 3, Lake Providence, LA 71254-2654
  Beatrice A Carter, Clerk Of Court

POLICE AND SHERIFF

Lake Providence Police Dept **318.559.2000**
Fax 318.559.5331
  200 1st St, Lake Providence, LA 71254
  Erin Threats, Police Chief

East Feliciana Parish

SOCIAL SERVICES

Ofc of Community Svcs **225.683.3734**
Fax 225.683.9634
Web ....www.dss.state.la.us
E-mail ....gretchen.williams@la.gov
  12476 Feliciana Dr., Clinton, LA 70722
  Gretchen Williams, Parish Manager

Ofc of Family Support 225.683.5142
Fax 225.683.5088
  9742 Plank Rd, Clinton, LA 70722
  Barbara Stevenson, Parish Manager

GENERAL HEALTH SERVICES

East Feliciana Health Unit 225.683.8551
Fax 225.683.3788
  12080 Marston St, Clinton, LA 70722
  Mary Jane Mccutchion, Rn, Nursing Supervisor

POLICE AND SHERIFF

Clinton Police Dept 225.683.9357
Fax 225.683.6890
E-mail .... clintonclerk@bellsouth.net
  11209 Bank St, Clinton, LA 70722
  Eddie Stewart, Police Chief

Sheriff's Ofc 225.683.8572
Fax 225.683.8823
  Courthouse Square & St. Helena St, Clinton,
  LA 70722
  Talmadge Bunch, Sheriff

Evangeline Parish

SOCIAL SERVICES

Ofc of Community Svcs 337.363.6011
Fax 337.363.7472
  116 SW Rail Rd, Ville Platte, LA 70586
  Kenneth Soileaua, Parish Manager

GENERAL HEALTH SERVICES

Evangeline Parish Health Unit 337.363.1135
Fax 337.363.3899
  1010 W Lasalle St, Ville Platte, LA 70586
  Peggy Duplechain, Hiv/std Coordinator

COURTS

13th District Court 337.363.5516
Fax 337.363.3005
E-mail .... jvidrine@centurytel.net
  200 Court St Ste 104, Ville Platte, LA 70586-4463
  Honorable John Larry Vidrine, Judge

POLICE AND SHERIFF

Basile Police Dept 337.432.6622
Fax 337.432.6641
E-mail .... basilepd@yahoo.com
  1316 S Ryan Avenue, Basile, LA 70515
  Allen Ivory Jr, Police Chief

Mamou Police Dept 337.468.5221
Fax 337.468.3149
  501 Main St, Mamou, LA 70554
  Greg Dupuis, Police Chief

Pine Prairie Police Dept 337.599.2708
Fax 337.599.3093
  1006 Edwin Dr, Pine Prairie, LA 70576
  Todd Ortis, Police Chief

Ville Platte Police Dept 337.363.1313
Fax 337.363.0351
E-mail .... dpk9@hotmail.com
  114 Armand St, Ville Platte, LA 70586
  Neil Lartugie, Police Chief

Franklin Parish

SOCIAL SERVICES

Ofc of Community Svcs 318.435.2188
Fax 318.435.2177
  240 6C West St, Winnsboro, LA 71295
  Tracy Hoggatt, Parish Manager

Ofc of Family Support 318.435.2101
Fax 318.435.2135
E-mail .... tmartin@dss.state.la.us
  2406 West St, Winnsboro, LA 71295
  Johnece Waters, Administrator

GENERAL HEALTH SERVICES

Health Unit 318.435.2143
Fax 318.435.2136
Web .... www.dhh.la.gov
E-mail .... amy.lander@la.gov
  6614 Main St, Winnsboro, LA 71295-2762
  Amy Lander, Nursing Supervisor

COURTS

5th District Court 318.435.7111
Fax 318.435.7109
  6566 Main St, Winnsboro, LA 71295-2701
  Honorable E. Rudolph Mcintyre Jr., Judge

POLICE AND SHERIFF

Baskin Police Dept 318.248.3700
Fax 318.248.2397
E-mail .... baskin@inetsouth.com
  1325 Highway 15, Baskin, LA 71219
  Danny Barber, Police Chief

Gilbert Police Dept 318.435.6506
Fax 318.435.1237
E-mail .... villageofgilbert@att.net
  7564 Gilbert St, Gilbert, LA 71336
  Ty Britt, Police Chief

Sheriff's Ofc 318.435.4505
Fax 318.435.5810
Web .... www.lsa.org
E-mail .... steve@lsa.org
  6556 Main St, Winnsboro, LA 71295-2701
  Steve E. Pylant, Sheriff

Winnsboro Police Dept 318.435.4307
Fax 318.435.7189
  3832 Front St, Winnsboro, LA 71295-2953
  Lester Thomas, Police Chief

Wisner Police Dept 318.724.6568
Fax 318.724.6099
E-mail .... wisnerla@nexusla.net
  9540 Natchez St, Wisner, LA 71378
  Billy Cureington, Police Chief

Grant Parish

GENERAL HEALTH SERVICES

Grant Parish Health Unit 318.627.3133
Fax 318.627.2981
Web .... www.oph.dhh.la.us
E-mail .... foenda.chaendler@la.gov
  340A Webb Smith Dr, Colfax, LA 71417-1910
  Scorlett Freeman, Nursing Supervisor

COURTS

35th District Court 318.627.3244
Fax 318.627.2839
Web www.35jdc.com
  200 Main St Rm 202, Colfax, LA 71417-1859
  Warren Willett, Judge

POLICE AND SHERIFF

Dry Prong Police Dept 318.899.5341
Fax 318.899.1018
  607 Russell Hataway Dr, Dry Prong, LA 71423
  Samuel Allen, Police Chief

Montgomery Police Dept 318.646.3110
Fax 318.646.9696
E-mail .... townhallmont@bellsouth.net
  625 Woodland St, Montgomery, LA 71454
  Floyd Evans, Police Chief

Pollock Police Dept 318.765.1017
Fax 318.765.6691
E-mail .... pollockpolicedept@yahoo.com
  3812 Patterson St, Pollock, LA 71467
  Harris Paul, Police Chief

Sheriff's Dept 318.627.3261
Fax 318.627.3418
E-mail .... cpsheriff@aol.com
  200 Main St, Colfax, LA 71417
  Baxter Welch, Sheriff

Iberia Parish

SOCIAL SERVICES

Ofc of Community Svcs 337.373.0026
Fax 337.373.0150
Web .... www.sos.louisiana.gov
E-mail .... janenne.trahan@sos.louisiana.gov
  705 Bayard St Ste B, New Iberia, LA 70560-5737
  Janenne H. Trahan, Parish Manager

COURTS

16th District Court 337.369.4410
Fax 337.369.4456
Web www.16thjdc-e.com
E-mail .... gwattigny@16jdc.org
  300 S Iberia St Ste 210, New Iberia, LA 70560-4543
  Honorable Keith R.j. Comeaux, Judge

POLICE AND SHERIFF

Jeanerette Police Dept 337.276.6323
Fax 337.276.9527
  811 Canal St Ste A, Jeanerette, LA 70544-5621
  Larry Jones, Police Chief

Sheriff's Dept 337.369.3714
Fax 337.365.5582
Web .... www.iberiaso.org
E-mail .... lackal@iberiaso.org
  300 S Iberia St Ste 120, New Iberia, LA 70560-4584
  Louis Ackal, Sheriff

Iberville Parish

SOCIAL SERVICES

Ofc of Community Svcs 225.687.5243
Fax 225.687.8518
Web .... www.ibervilleparish.com
E-mail .... rware@ibervilleparish.com
  58150 Meriam St, Plaquemine, LA 70764-2721
  Randolph Ware, Director

Ofc of Family Support 225.687.4315
Fax 225.687.8978
Web .... www.dss.state.la.us
E-mail .... mgulato@dss.state.la.us
  23075 Highway 1, Plaquemine, LA 70764-2312
  Mary Gulato, Office Manager

GENERAL HEALTH SERVICES

Iberville Parish Health Unit 225.687.9021
Fax 225.687.1892
  24705 Plaza Dr Ste A, Plaquemine, LA 70764-6827
  Rita Edward, Rn, Nursing Supervisor

COURTS

18th District Court 225.687.5160
Fax 225.687.5260
  58050 Meriam St, Plaquemine, LA 70765
  J G Dupont Jr., Clerk

POLICE AND SHERIFF

Maringouin Police Dept 225.625.2630
Fax 225.625.2359
Web .... www.spillwaycable.com
E-mail .... jsimmion@spillwaycable.com
  77655 Landry Dr, Maringouin, LA 70757
  John Simmion, Police Chief

Plaquemine Police Dept 225.687.9273
Fax 225.687.3260
E-mail .... ogulotta@plaquemine.org
  23540 Railroad Ave, Plaquemine, LA 70765
  Orian Gulotta, Police Chief

Rosedale Police Dept 225.648.2333
Fax 225.648.2335
Web .... www.rosedale.brcoxmail.com
E-mail .... msparks@rosedale.brcoxmail.com
   76535 Rosedale Rd, Rosedale, LA 70772
Mike Sparks, Police Chief

Saint Gabriel Police Dept 225.642.5222
Fax 225.642.9622
E-mail .... kevin.sgpd@stgabriel.us
   1641 LA Hwy 30, Saint Gabriel, LA 70776
Kevin Ambeau, Police Chief

Sheriff's Dept 225.687.5100
Fax 225.687.1947
E-mail .... ipsocid@hotmail.com
   58050 Meriam St, Plaquemine, LA 70764
Brent Allain, Sheriff

White Castle Police Dept 225.545.2484
Fax 225.545.9179
   32535 Bowie St, White Castle, LA 70788-2503
Mario Brown, Police Chief

Jackson Parish

GENERAL HEALTH SERVICES

Health Unit 318.259.6601
Fax 318.259.1146
Web .... www.jacksonparishpolicejury.org
E-mail .... rhonda.vanburen@la.gov
   228 Bond St, Jonesboro, LA 71251-5334
Rhonda Vanburan, Nursing Supervisor

MENTAL HEALTH SERVICES

Jonesboro MH Clinic 318.259.6624
Fax 318.259.4840
E-mail .... jmhc@pineynet.com
   4134 Highway 4, Jonesboro, LA 71251
Stan Mahaffey, Manager

COURTS

2nd District Court 318.259.3442
Fax 318.259.7166
   500 E Court St Rm 202, Jonesboro, LA 71251-3445
Honorable Jimmy Teat, Judge

Jonesboro Meal Site 318.259.8962
   120 Polk Ave, Jonesboro, LA 71251
Ms Nell Stadtlander, Director

POLICE AND SHERIFF

Chatham Police Dept 318.249.2541
Fax 318.249.4436
E-mail .... townofchatham@gmail.com
   1709 Oak St, Chatham, LA 71226
Mickel Wilson, Police Chief

Hodge Police Dept 318.259.4704
Fax 318.259.6670
Web .... www.legis.state.la.us
E-mail .... townofhodge@bellsouth.net
   4693 Quitman Highway, Hodge, LA 71247
Johnny Shively, Police Chief

Jonesboro Police Dept 318.259.2164
Fax 318.259.6321
   100 4th St, Jonesboro, LA 71251
G. Wesley Horton, Police Chief

North Hodge Police Dept 318.259.4272
Fax 318.259.1055
   5204 Quitman Hwy, Hodge, LA 71247
Phillip Moffett, Police Chief

Sheriff's Ofc 318.259.9021
Fax 318.259.8268
   500 E Court St Rm 100, Jonesboro, LA 71251
Andy Brown, Sheriff

Jefferson Davis Parish

SOCIAL SERVICES

Coushatte Tribe Social Svcs 337.584.1433
Fax 337.584.1474
E-mail .... bsylestine@coushattatribela.org
   1984 CC Bel Road, Elton, LA 70532
Milton Hebert, Social Services Director

Ofc of Community Svcs 337.824.9649
Fax 337.824.9526
Web .... www.dss.state.la.us
E-mail .... carroll.gobert@la.gov
   107 N Cutting Ave, Jennings, LA 70546-6205
Carroll Gobert, Parish Manager

GENERAL HEALTH SERVICES

Jefferson Davis Parish Health Dept 337.824.2193
   403 Baker St, Jennings, LA 70546
Renee Duplichan, Head Nurse

COURTS

31st District Court 337.824.3629
Fax 337.824.8985
   300 N State St, Jennings, LA 70546-1389
Ricky Arceneaux, Clerk Of Court

POLICE AND SHERIFF

Jennings Police Dept 337.821.5513
Fax 337.821.5538
   110 N Broadway St, Jennings, LA 70546-5804
Chief Todd Balbor, Police Chief

Lake Arthur Police Dept 337.774.2411
Fax 337.774.3821
E-mail .... lake_arthurpd@yahoo.com
   102 Arthur Ave, Lake Arthur, LA 70549
Cheryl Vincent, Police Chief

Sheriff's Dept 337.821.2100
Fax 337.821.2105
Web .... www.jeffdavis.net
E-mail .... sheriff@jeffdavis.net
   321 E Plaquemine St, Jennings, LA 70546
Richard E. Edwards, Sheriff

Jefferson Parish

SOCIAL SERVICES

Ofc of Family Support 504.838.5111
Fax 504.838.5355
Web .... www.dss.state.la.us
E-mail .... rmartin@dss.state.la.us
   2450 Westbank Expressway, Metarie, LA 70001
Robin Martin, Manager

GENERAL HEALTH SERVICES

**Dept of Children and Family
Services** 504.361.6111
Fax 504.361.6196
Web .... www.dss.state.la.us
   2150 Westbank Expy Ste 201, Harvey, LA 70058
Charlene Williams, Manager

Health Unit 504.349.8802
Fax 504.349.8817
Web .... www.dhh.louisiana.gov
E-mail .... gwhitherspoon@jefferson.lib.la.us
   1855 Ames Blvd, Marrero, LA 70072-3429
Mary Trigds, Facility Manager

MENTAL HEALTH SERVICES

East Jefferson Mental Health Ctr 504.838.5002
Fax 504.838.5284
Web .... www.jphsa.org
   2400 Edenborn Ave, Metairie, LA 70001-1817
Linda Stewart, Manager

**Human Svcs Authority/Children's
Svcs** 504.349.8755
Fax 504.349.8768
Web .... www.jphsa.org
E-mail .... ahenry@jphsa.org
   5001 Westbank Expy, Marrero, LA 70072
Angela Henry, Md, Director Childrenæs Services

JUSTICE AGENCY

CASA Jefferson 504.263.0330
Fax 504.263.1717
Web .... www.jpjc.org/casa
   671 A Whitney Ave, Harvey, LA 70056
Kathy Cheramie, Community Development Coordinator

Department of Juvenile Services 504.364.3750
Fax 504.364.3719
E-mail .... rjuncker@jeffparish.net
   1546-B Gretna Blvd, Harvey, LA 70058-5366
Roy Juncker, Director

Juvenile Probation 504.838.1070
Fax 504.838.1089
E-mail .... scabal@jeffparish.net
   3420 N Causeway Blvd, Metairie, LA 70002
Steve Cabal, Chief Performance Officer

Rivarde Detention Ctr 504.364.2860
Fax 504.364.2859
   1550 Gretna Blvd, Harvey, LA 70058
Chris Brouno, Supervisor

COURTS

Juvenile Court 504.367.3500
Fax 504.361.8033
Web .... www.jpjc.org
E-mail .... jgigenheimer@jpjc.org
   1546 Gretna Blvd, Harvey, LA 70058
John Gigenheimer, Clerk Of Court

POLICE AND SHERIFF

Clarence Police Dept 318.357.0440
Fax 318.356.9700
   6004 Hwy 71, Suite 500, Clarence, LA 71414
Darrell Fredieu, Police Chief

Grand Isle Police Dept 985.787.2204
Fax 985.787.2439
E-mail .... tourism@grand-isle.com
   170 Ludwig Ln, Grand Isle, LA 70358
Euris Dubois, Police Chief

Gretna Police Dept 504.363.1700
Fax 504.363.1725
E-mail .... alawson@gretnapolice.com
   200 5th St, Gretna, LA 70053
Arthur S Lawson, Jr, Police Chief

Harahan Police Dept 504.737.9763
Fax 504.737.6783
   6441 Jefferson Hwy, Harahan, LA 70123
Mack Dickinson, Police Chief

Sheriff's Dept 504.364.5300
Fax 504.363.5711
Web .... www.jpso.com
   1233 Westbank Expy, Bldg B, Harvey, LA 70058
Newell Normand, Sheriff

Welsh Police Dept 337.734.2626
Fax 337.734.2628
   201 W South St, Welsh, LA 70591
Tommy Chaisson, Police Chief

Westwego Police Dept 504.341.5428
Fax 504.341.0301
E-mail .... chiefofpolice@westwegopolice.com
   401 4th ST, Westwego, LA 70094
Dewayne Munch, Police Chief

La Salle Parish

GENERAL HEALTH SERVICES

La Salle Parish Health Unit **318.992.4842**
Fax 318.992.6593
E-mail ....devans@dhh.state.la.us
   1673 N 2Nd St, Jena, LA 71342
   Dana Evans, Rn, Nursing Supervisor

COURTS

28th District Court **318.992.2002**
Fax 318.992.8701
E-mail ....blw@centurytel.net
   1050 Court House St, Jena, LA 71342
   Honorable J. Christopher Peters, District Judge

POLICE AND SHERIFF

Jena Police Dept **318.992.5111**
Fax 318.992.1040
   1810 N 2nd St, Jena, LA 71342
   Paul Smith, Police Chief

Olla Police Dept **318.495.5151**
Fax 318.495.5152
E-mail ....taylor@odmp.org
   1921 Louisiana St, Olla, LA 71465
   Gary Taylor, Police Chief

Sheriff's Dept **318.992.2151**
Fax 318.992.2155
   1st & Court House, Jena, LA 71342
   Carl Smith, Sheriff

Urania Police Dept **318.495.3452**
Fax 318.495.3425
E-mail ....uraniatown@centurytel.net
   2021 E Hartner, Urania, LA 71480
   Wayne Corley, Police Chief

Lafayette Parish

SOCIAL SERVICES

Ofc of Community Svc **337.262.5901**
Fax 337.262.1179
Web ....www.dss.state.la.us
E-mail ....lbriggs@dss.state.la.us
   825 Kaliste Saloom Rd, Ste 104, Lafayette, LA 70508
   Lorrie Briggs, Parish Manager

Ofc of Family Support **337.262.5111**
Fax 337.262.5988
Web ....www.dss.state.la.us
   825 Kaliste Saloom Rd, Bldg. 6STE, Lafayette, LA 70508
   Richard Laseto, Manager

Region IV Ofc of Community Svcs **337.262.5970**
Fax 337.262.1092
   825 Kaliste Saloom Rd Ste 1-218, Lafayette, LA 70508
   Joe Bruno, Regional Administrator

JUSTICE AGENCY

Juvenile Detention Home **337.291.7130**
Fax 337.291.7135
   1613 Surrey St, Lafayette, LA 70501
   Rene Prejean, Administrator

Ofc of Youth Development **337.262.5662**
Fax 337.262.1072
E-mail ....sguillor@oyd.louisiana.gov
   130 Chappuis Dr, Lafayette, LA 70501
   Sharon Guillory, District Manager

COURTS

15th District Court **337.232.8211**
Fax 337.269.5760
   800 S Buchanan St, Lafayette Parish Court Bldg. 4th Floor, Lafayette, LA 70501
   David Blanchet, Judge

City Court **337.291.8720**
Fax 337.291.8023
   105 E CONVENT ST, Lafayette, LA 70501-7944
   Honorable Douglas J. Saloom, Director

Health Care Options Home Health **337.984.3104**
Fax 337.984.4446
   3804 Johnston St Ste 2, Lafayette, LA 70503
   Carol Thomas, Manager

Teen Court **337.232.5977**
Fax 337.232.5975
Web ....www.cox.net
E-mail ....laftc@cox.net
   1112 N University Ave, Lafayette, LA 70506
   Linda Anson, Executive Director

POLICE AND SHERIFF

Broussard Police Dept **337.837.6259**
Fax 337.839.1219
E-mail ....bdecou@broussardpolice.com
   416 E Main St, Broussard, LA 70518
   Brannon Decou, Police Chief

Carencro Police Dept **337.896.6132**
Fax 337.896.1937
   110 Centenal Dr, Carencro, LA 70520
   Carlos Stout, Police Chief

Duson Police Dept **337.873.6736**
Fax 337.873.4967
   801 1st St, Duson, LA 70529
   Frank Andrew, Police Chief

Lafayette Police Dept **337.291.8600**
Fax 337.291.5665
Web ....www.lafayettela.gov
E-mail ....jcraft@lafayettela.gov
   900 E University Ave, Lafayette, LA 70503-2127
   Jim Craft, Police Chief

Scott Police Dept **337.233.3715**
Fax 337.261.0568
E-mail ....cleger@xspedius.net
   129 Lions Club Rd, Scott, LA 70583
   Chad Leger, Police Chief

Sheriff's Ofc **337.232.9211**
Fax 337.236.5697
E-mail ....lpsoinfo@lafayettesheriff.com
   316 W Main St, Lafayette, LA 70501-6880
   Michael W. Neistrom, Sheriff

Youngsville Police Dept **337.856.5931**
Fax 337.856.4904
   304 4th St, Youngsville, LA 70592
   Earl Menard, Police Chief

EDUCATION SERVICES

Special Svcs **337.521.7000**
Fax 337.521.7223
   113 Chaplin Dr, Lafayette, LA 70502
   Burnell Lemoine, Suprentendent

Lafourche Parish

SOCIAL SERVICES

Ofc of Community Svcs **985.447.0945**
Fax 985.447.0875
   1416 Tiger Dr, Thibodaux, LA 70301
   Karen Fletcher, Parish Manager

Region III Ofc of Community Svcs **985.449.5055**
Fax 985.449.5139
Web ....www.dss.state.la.us
   1416 Tiger Dr, Thibodaux, LA 70301-4337
   Vallarie Burriss, Regional Administrator

MENTAL HEALTH SERVICES

Lafourche MH Clinic **985.537.6823**
Fax 985.537.5519
Web ....www.dhh.la.gov
E-mail ....efaust@dhh.la.gov
   157 Twin Oaks Dr, Raceland, LA 70394-2761
   Ed Faust, Manager

JUSTICE AGENCY

Ofc of Youth Development **985.447.0902**
Fax 985.447.0818
Web ....www.oyd.louisiana.gov
E-mail ....rduet@oyd.louisiana.gov
   1077 Highway 3185, Thibodaux, LA 70301-7444
   Robert Duet, Juvenile Services Supervisor

COURTS

17th District Court **985.447.5550**
Fax 985.447.5800
   303 W 3rd St, Thibodaux, LA 70301
   Honorable A. Bruce Simpson, Director

POLICE AND SHERIFF

Golden Meadow Police Dept **985.475.5213**
Fax 985.475.6404
   107 Jervis Dr, Golden Meadow, LA 70357-2715
   Chet Louviere, Police Chief

Leesville Police Dept **337.238.0331**
Fax 337.238.9175
Web ....www.leesvillepd.org
E-mail ....lpd_chief@hotmail.com
   101 W Lee St, Leesville, LA 71446-4039
   Greg Hill, Police Chief

Lockport Police Dept **985.532.9799**
Fax 985.532.7365
E-mail ....wved@lockportpd.com
   710 Church St, Lockport, LA 70374
   Warren A. Vedros Sr, Police Chief

Lincoln Parish

SOCIAL SERVICES

Dept of Children and Family Services **318.251.4101**
Fax 318.251.4104
E-mail ....diane.senn@la.gov
   206 E Reynolds Dr, Ste A2, Ruston, LA 71270
   Diane Senn, Parish Manager

Ofc of Family Support **318.251.4105**
Fax 318.251.4179
Web ....www.dss.state.la.us
E-mail ....cbowden@dss.state.la.us
   206 E Reynolds Dr Ste J, Ruston, LA 71270-2873
   Catherine Bowden, Parish Manager

GENERAL HEALTH SERVICES

Health Unit **318.251.4120**
Fax 318.251.4181
   405 E Georgia Ave, Ruston, LA 71270
   Lynell Washington, Rn, Nursing Supervisor

COURTS

3rd District Court **318.255.4691**
Fax 318.255.3154
   100 W Texas Ave Rm 302, Ruston, LA 71270-4463
   Honorable R. Wayne Smith, Director

POLICE AND SHERIFF

Choudrant Police Dept **318.768.4111**
Fax 318.768.2147
E-mail ....info@choudrant.org
   2629 Hwy 80, Choudrant, LA 71227
   Bobby Joe Milner, Police Chief

Louisiana

Grambling Police Dept **318.247.3771**
Fax 318.247.0760
E-mail ....chiefclark2003@yahoo.com
   2045 Martin Luther King Jr Ave, Grambling,
   LA 71245
   Tommy Clark, Police Chief

Ruston Police Dept **318.255.4141**
Fax 318.251.8609
   501 N Trenton St, Ruston, LA 71273
   Stever Rogers, Chief

Livingston Parish

SOCIAL SERVICES

Department of Children and Family
Svcs **225.686.7257**
Fax 225.686.9886
Web ....www.dss.state.la.us
E-mail ....lhall@dss.state.la.us
   28446 Charlie Watts Rd., Livingston, LA 70754
   Laura Hall, Parish Manager

GENERAL HEALTH SERVICES

Health Unit **225.686.7017**
Fax 225.686.1782
Web ....www.dhh.louisiana.gov
E-mail ....dcarter@dhh.la.gov
   20399 Goverment Blvd, Livingston, LA 70754
   Donna Carter Rn, Nursing Supervisor

COURTS

21st District Court **225.686.7461**
Fax 225.686.0603
Web www.21stjdc.org
   20180 Iowa St, Livingston, LA 70754
   Sara Brumfield, Judicial Administrator

City Court **225.665.5505**
Fax 225.664.2648
Web ....www.dsclerkofcourt.org
   400 Mayor Herbert Hoover Ave, Ward-II City Court,
   Denham Springs, LA 70726-3613
   Honorable Charles W. Borde Jr., Director

POLICE AND SHERIFF

Albany Police Dept **225.567.2115**
Fax 225.567.4902
Web ....www.ci.albany.or.us
E-mail ....rhutchinson@ci.albany.or.us
   29980 Mulberry St, Albany, LA 70711
   Russell Hutchinson, Police Chief

Denham Springs Police Dept **225.665.5106**
Fax 225.667.8353
   447 Lamm St, Denham Springs, LA 70726
   Scott Jones, Police Chief

French Settlement Police Dept **225.698.6100**
Fax 225.698.3007
E-mail ....frenchsettlement@hotmail.com
   16015 LA Highway 16, French Settlement, LA 70733
   Harry Brignac, Police Chief

Killian Police Dept **225.695.3464**
Fax 225.695.3466
   28284 Highway 22, Springfield, LA 70462
   Lloyd Wild III, Police Chief

Port Vincent Police Dept **225.698.6115**
Fax 225.698.9036
E-mail ....portvincent@eatel.net
   18235 La Highway 16, Denham Springs, LA 70726
   Norris Hull, Police Chief

Springfield Police Dept **225.294.3150**
Fax 225.294.2230
Web ....www.townofspringfield.org
E-mail ....springfd@bellsouth.net
   27378 Hwy 42, Springfield, LA 70462
   James Jones, Police Chief

Walker Police Dept **225.664.3125**
Fax 225.664.6470
   13179 Burgess Ave, Walker, LA 70785
   Hunter Grimes, Police Chief

Madison Parish

SOCIAL SERVICES

Ofc of Community Svcs **318.574.5201**
Fax 318.574.2660
Web ....www.dss.state.la.us
   1705 Felicia Ave, Tallulah, LA 71282-8203
   Mary Gilfoil, Parish Manager

JUSTICE AGENCY

Ofc of Juvenille Justice **318.574.3552**
Fax 318.574.2516
   508 E Bayou Dr, Tallulah, LA 71284
   Ruth Stephens, Regional Manager

COURTS

6th District Court **318.574.2712**
Fax 318.574.0534
E-mail ....jcrigler@bellsouth.net
   100 N Cedar St, Tallulah, LA 71282
   Honorable John D. Crigler, Judge

POLICE AND SHERIFF

Tallulah Police Dept **318.574.3230**
Fax 318.574.1444
   500 E Green St, Tallulah, LA 71282-3819
   James Vaughn, Police Chief

Morehouse Parish

SOCIAL SERVICES

Ofc of Community Svcs **318.283.0825**
Fax 318.283.0866
   1045 E Madison Ave, Bastrop, LA 71220
   Kimberly Angrum, Parish Manager

Ofc of Family Support **318.283.0825**
Fax 318.283.0808
   1045 E Madison Ave, Bastrop, LA 71220-4025
   Willie May Hall, Supervisor

COURTS

City Court **318.283.0257**
Fax 318.283.3386
   202 E Jefferson Ave, Bastrop, LA 71220
   Dillop Lester, Director

POLICE AND SHERIFF

Bastrop Police Dept **318.281.1322**
Fax 318.283.3378
Web ....www.cityofbastrop.com
   202 E Jefferson Ave, Bastrop, LA 71220
   Downy Black, Police Chief

Collinston Police Dept **318.874.0911**
Fax 318.874.2196
   4626 Main St, Collinston, LA 71229-6100
   Randy Tappin, Police Chief

Mer Rouge Police Dept **318.647.3490**
E-mail ....merrougecity@suddenlinkmail.com
   217 W Davenport Avenue, Mer Rouge, LA 71261
   Mitch Stephens, Police Chief

Natchitoches Parish

SOCIAL SERVICES

Dept of Children & Family Svcs **318.357.3128**
Fax 318.357.3298
Web ....www.dss.state.la.us
   106 Charlene St, Natchitoches, LA 71457-3429
   Daphne Bonnette, Parish Manager

GENERAL HEALTH SERVICES

Natchitoches Paris Health Unit **318.357.3132**
Fax 318.357.3136
   625 Bienville Cir, Natchitoches, LA 71457
   Rebecca Thompson, Nursing Supervisor

MENTAL HEALTH SERVICES

Natchitoches Mental Health Clinic **318.357.3122**
Fax 318.357.3240
E-mail ....faye.hobley@la.gov
   210 Medical Dr, Natchitoches, LA 71457-6052
   Faye Hobley, Manager

JUSTICE AGENCY

Ofc of Juvenile justice **318.357.3152**
Fax 318.357.3243
   116 South Dr Ste 200, Natchitoches, LA 71457
   Randall Hill, Regional Manager

POLICE AND SHERIFF

Natchez Police Dept **318.352.0920**
Fax 318.352.6266
E-mail ....villageofnatchez@att.net
   181 Main St, Natchez, LA 71456
   Mckindley Hoover, Police Chief

Natchitoches Police Dept **318.352.8101**
Fax 318.357.3853
Web ....www.natchitochesla.gov
   Dispatch 400 Amulet Street, Natchitoches, LA 71457
   Mickey Dove, Police Chief

Powhatan Police Dept **318.352.8549**
Fax 318.352.7791
   291 N. Railroad St, Powhatan, LA 71066
   Raymond Hymes Jr, Police Chief

Robeline Police Dept **318.472.6121**
Fax 318.472.6128
   122 Depot St, Robeline, LA 71469
   Shelby Borders, Officer

Sheriff's Ofc **318.357.7802**
Fax 318.352.7377
Web ....www.cp-tel.net
E-mail ....npsosheriff@cp-tel.net
   220 Church St, Natchitoches, LA 71457
   Victor E. Jones, Jr., Sheriff

Orleans Parish

SOCIAL SERVICES

Region I Ofc of Community Svcs **504.680.9100**
Fax 504.680.9103
   1450 Poydras St, 16th Floor, New Orleans, LA 70112
   Benjamin Francois, Assistant Regional Administrator

Region X Ofc of Community Svcs **504.736.7151**
Fax 504.736.7161
Web ....www.dss.state.la.us
E-mail ....rcorbello@dss.state.la.us
   800 W. Commerce Rd., New Orleans, LA 70181
   Rebecca Corbello, Regional Administrator

GENERAL HEALTH SERVICES

Delgado Health Clinic **504.658.2540**
Fax 504.599.1057
Web ....www.dhh.louisiana.gov
   517 N Rampart St, New Orleans, LA 70112
   Stephanie Taylor, Std/hiv Program Manager

Health Dept **504.658.2500**
Fax 504.658.2520
Web ....www.cityofno.com
E-mail ....kdesalvo@nola.gov
   1300 Perdido St, New Orleans, LA 70112
   Dr. Karen Desalvo, Commissioner Of Health

Ofc of Family Support 504.361.6366
Fax 504.361.6007
Web ....www.dss.state.la.us
E-mail ....lbarbarin@dss.state.la.us
   3510 General Meyer Ave, New Orleans,
   LA 70114-3348
   Lemuel Barbarin, Manager

Ofc of Family Support 504.599.1700
Fax 504.599.1814
Web ....www.dss.state.la.us
E-mail ....bfrancoi@dss.state.la.us
   1661 Canal St., New Orleans, LA 70151
   Benjamin Francois, Manager

JUSTICE AGENCY

CASA **504.522.1962**
Fax 504.522.1897
Web ....www.casaneworleans.org
E-mail ....info@casaneworleans.org
   1340 Poydras St Ste 2120, New Orleans,
   LA 70112-6025
   Karen Henry, Executive Director

Ofc of Youth Development Orleans **504.568.4535**
Fax 504.568.7803
Web ....www.dss.state.la.us
   731 Saint Charles Ave, 2nd Floor, New Orleans,
   LA 70130
   Angela T. Koenig, Regional Manager

POLICE AND SHERIFF

New Orleans Police Dept **504.658.5757**
Fax 504.658.5775
Web ....www.nola.gov
E-mail ....nopdgchiel@nola.gov
   715 S Broad St, New Orleans, LA 70119-7495
   Ronal Serpas, Police Chief

EDUCATION SERVICES

New Orleans Public School System **504.304.4988**
Fax 504.309.4158
Web www.nops.k12.la.us
E-mail ....rosalynne_denis@nops.k12.la.us
   3520 General Degaulle Dr, 5th Floor, New Orleans,
   LA 70114
   Rosalynne Dennis, Phd, Director

Ouachita Parish

SOCIAL SERVICES

Family Support **318.362.5333**
Fax 318.362.3220
Web ....www.dss.state.la.us
E-mail ....tmartin@dss.state.la.us
   1306 North 19th St, Monroe, LA 71201
   Tamara Martin, Manager

Monroe Region VIII Ofc of Family
Support **318.362.3386**
Fax 318.362.3358
   1306 N 19th St, Monroe, LA 71201
   Viki Deckerson, Administrator

Ofc of Community Svcs **318.362.5417**
Fax 318.362.3055
E-mail ....dcfs@la.gov
   1401 Stubbs Ave, Monroe, LA 71207
   Bernadette Huey, Parish Manager

Region VIII Ofc of Community Svcs **318.362.3362**
Fax 318.362.3353
Web ....www.dcss.louisiana.gov
E-mail ....vikidickerson@la.gov
   122 Saint John St Rm 450, Monroe, LA 71201-7371
   Viki Dickerson, Regional Administrator

GENERAL HEALTH SERVICES

Ofc of Public Health **318.361.7201**
Fax 318.362.3163
Web ....www.dhh.la.gov
   1650 Desiard St, 2nd Floor, Monroe, LA 71201
   Susan Wible, Hiv Prevention Coordinator

MENTAL HEALTH SERVICES

Monroe Mental Health Ctr **318.362.3339**
Fax 318.362.3336
E-mail ....dan.bounds@la.gov
   4800 S Grand St, Monroe, LA 71202-6498
   Dan Bounds, Manager

Region VIII Office of Behavior
Health **318.362.3270**
Fax 318.362.3268
Web ....www.dhh.state.la.us
E-mail ....mark.debord@la.gov
   2513 Ferrand St, Monroe, LA 71201
   Mark Deboard, Regional Director

JUSTICE AGENCY

Casa **318.398.0945**
Fax 318.398.0099
Web ....www.casanela.org
E-mail ....cmurray@cfcfnela.org
   622 Riverside Dr, Monroe, LA 71201
   Cindy Murray, Director

Ofc of Youth Development **318.362.5262**
Fax 318.362.5209
E-mail ....clewis@oyd.louisiana.gov
   1907 Washington St, Monroe, LA 71201-6555
   Carolyn Lewis, Regional Manager

Swanson Correctional Ctr for Youth
(SCCY) **318.362.5000**
Fax 318.362.5202
E-mail ....carolyn.atkins@la.gov
   4701 S Grand St, Monroe, LA 71202
   Carolyn Atkins, Facility Director

COURTS

4th District Court **318.327.1444**
Fax 318.327.1462
   301 S Bryant St Rm 104, Monroe, LA 71201
   W J Bill Hodge, Clerk Of Court

City Court of West Monroe **318.396.2767**
Fax 318.396.2738
   2303 N 7th St, West Monroe, LA 71291
   Honorable Jim Norris, Judge

POLICE AND SHERIFF

Monroe Police Dept **318.329.2600**
Fax 318.329.2610
Web ....www.ci.monroe.la.us
E-mail ....sfpdchief@bellsouth.net
   700 Wood St, Monroe, LA 71201
   Quentin Holmes, Chief

Sheriff's Ofc **318.329.1238**
Fax 318.329.1257
Web ....www.opso.net
   400 St. John Street, Monroe, LA 71210
   Richard L. Fewell, Sheriff

Sterlington Police Dept **318.665.4532**
Fax 318.665.0232
   103 High Ave, Sterlington, LA 71280-3272
   Barry Bonner, Police Chief

EDUCATION SERVICES

Special Education **318.338.9997**
Fax 318.338.9987
E-mail ....nvla@bayou.com
   507 Swayze St, New Vision Learning Academy,
   Monroe, LA 71201-8130
   Andrew Mansfield, Director

Special Education **318.388.3751**
Fax 318.387.2090
Web ....www.mcschools.net
E-mail ....vickie.irwin@mcschools.net
   4600 Central Ave, Monroe, LA 71203
   Vicki Irwin, Supervisor

Plaquemines Parish

GENERAL HEALTH SERVICES

Health Dept **504.394.3510**
E-mail ....raymund.ferrer@plaqueminesparish.com
   3706 Main St, Belle Chasse, LA 70037
   Raymund Ferrer, Health Department Supervisor

COURTS

25th District Court **504.297.5222**
Fax 504.297.5229
   301 Main St, Belle Chasse, LA 70037-2725
   Honorable Anthony D. Ragusa Jr.

POLICE AND SHERIFF

Sheriff's Office **504.297.5120**
Fax 504.297.5121
Web ....www.ppso.net
E-mail ....sheriff@ppso.net
   302 Main St, Belle Chasse, LA 70037
   Jiff Hingle, Sheriff

Pointe Coupee Parish

SOCIAL SERVICES

Ofc of Community Svcs **225.638.4846**
Fax 225.638.9945
Web ....www.dss.state.la.us
   1919 Hospital Rd., New Roads, LA 70760
   Alma Brown, Parish Manager

GENERAL HEALTH SERVICES

Health Unit **225.638.7320**
Fax 225.638.3022
Web ....www.dhh.la.gov
E-mail ....agustin@dhh.la.gov
   282 B Hospital Rd, New Roads, LA 70760-2619
   Debbie Coone, Director

COURTS

18th District Court **225.638.5532**
Fax 225.638.4570
   201 E. Main St., New Roads, LA 70760
   Honorable James J. Best, Judge

POLICE AND SHERIFF

Livonia Police Dept **225.637.2520**
Fax 225.637.3189
   3111 La Highway 78, Livonia, LA 70755
   Brad Joffrion, Police Chief

New Roads Police Dept **225.638.5115**
Fax 225.638.5365
E-mail ....kmcdonald@cityofnewroads.net
   101 6th St W, New Roads, LA 70760-3460
   Kevin Mcdonald, Police Chief

Sheriff's Dept **225.638.5400**
Fax 225.638.5403
E-mail ....cchapman@pcpso.org
   215 E Main St, New Roads, LA 70760
   Bud Torres, Sheriff

Rapides Parish

SOCIAL SERVICES

Alexandria Region Support Enforcement
Svcs **318.487.5202**
Fax 318.487.5060
Web ....www.dss.state.la.us
E-mail ....mtradewe@dss.state.la.us
   900 Murray St., Alexandria, LA 71309
   Moody Tradewell, Supervisor

Louisiana

Region VII Ofc of Community Svcs 318.487.5227
Fax 318.484.2178
E-mail ....lsmith@ocs.dss.state.la.us
  900 Murray St Ste A100, Alexandria, LA 71309
   Lillian Smith, Regional Administrator

GENERAL HEALTH SERVICES

Central Louisiana State Hospital 318.484.6200
Fax 318.484.6800
Web ....www.dhh.louisiana.gov
  242 W Shamrock Ave, Pineville, LA 71360
   Edna Clark, Rn, Infection Control Coordinator

Health Unit 318.487.5282
Fax 318.487.5557
Web ....www.lousiana.gov
  5604 Coliseum Blvd Ste A, Alexandria, LA 71303-3709
   Susan Habert, Facility Manager

MENTAL HEALTH SERVICES

Behavioral Health Clinic Of Central Louisiana 318.484.6850
Fax 318.484.6844
  242 W Shamrock Ave, Pineville, LA 71360
   Ingrid Cannella, Clinical Director

Crossroads Regional Hospital 318.445.5111
Fax 318.442.2261
Web ....www.crossroadshospital.org
  110 John Eskew Dr, Alexandria, LA 71301
   Michael Parker, Md, Medical Director

JUSTICE AGENCY

Juvenile Probation Dept 318.445.8282
Fax 318.445.7082
E-mail ....lspottsville9thjdc@yahoo.com
  201 Johnston St., Alexandria, LA 71309
   Larry Spottsville, CPO

Ofc of Youth Development 318.487.5252
Fax 318.487.5767
  1510 Lee St, Alexandria, LA 71301-6234
   Johnny Qualls, Regional Manager

Rapides CASA 318.445.5678
Fax 318.445.7220
Web ....www.rapidescac.org
E-mail ....info@rapidescac.org
  2004 Jackson St, Alexandria, LA 71301
   Wade Bond, Executive Director

COURTS

9th District Court 318.443.6893
Fax 318.484.2704
Web www.9thjdc.org
  701 Murray St Ofc, Alexandria, LA 71301
   Honorable Harry F. Randow, Chief Judge

City Court of Pineville 318.449.5656
Fax 318.473.0960
Web ....www.pinevillecitycourt.org
E-mail ....pterrell@pinevillecitycourt.org
  904 Main St, Pineville, LA 71360
   Honorable Phillip Terrell, Director

POLICE AND SHERIFF

Alexandria Police Dept 318.449.5099
Fax 318.441.6515
Web ....www.alexpolice.com
E-mail ....chief@alex-police.com
  1000 Bolton Ave, Alexandria, LA 71301-6829
   Jane Hay, Chief Assistant

Ball Police Dept 318.640.4673
Fax 318.640.4780
  100 Municipal Dr, Ball, LA 71405
   Danny Caldwell, Police Chief

Boyce Police Dept 318.793.2477
Fax 318.793.9447
  400 Ulster Ave, Boyce, LA 71409
   Preston Burr, Police Chief

Cheneyville Police Dept 318.279.2156
Fax 318.279.2766
  802 Klock St, Cheneyville, LA 71325
   Jeff Jeter, Police Chief

Forest Hill Police Dept 318.748.6300
Fax 318.748.8850
E-mail ....info@foresthill-la.com
  4300 Hwy 112, Forest Hill, LA 71430
   Garland Carroll, Police Chief

Glenmora Police Dept 318.748.4750
Fax 318.748.4649
E-mail ....glenmorapolice@yahoo.com
  1000 7th Ave, Glenmora, LA 71433
   Matt Roland Cloud, Police Chief

Lecompte Police Dept 318.776.9211
Fax 318.776.0154
  1103 Wall St, Lecompte, LA 71346
   Frank Spears, Police Chief

Mcnary Police Dept 318.748.8264
Fax 318.748.8524
E-mail ....mcnaryla1@hotmail.com
  53 W Cady Ave, Glenmora, LA 71433
   Stephen Cloessner, Police Chief

Pineville Police Dept 318.442.6603
Fax 318.442.6636
Web ....www.pineville.net
  910 Main St, Pineville, LA 71360-6408
   Don Weatherford, Police Chief

Sheriff's Ofc 318.473.6700
Fax 318.442.9247
  701 Murray St, Alexandria, LA 71301
   Charles F Wagner Jr., Sheriff

Woodworth Police Dept 318.442.8980
Fax 318.487.6110
Web ....www.centurytel.net
E-mail ....woodworth@centurytel.net
  27 Castor Plunge Road, Woodworth, LA 71485
   James P. Gonzales, Police Chief

EDUCATION SERVICES

Special Education 318.443.4572
Fax 318.473.0356
  4515 Eddie Williams Ave, Alexandria, LA 71302
   Shelly Close, Director

Red River Parish

SOCIAL SERVICES

Ofc of Family Support 318.932.5715
Fax 318.932.3977
Web ....www.ocs.dss.state.la.us
E-mail ....bridget.lynch@ocs.dss.state.la.gov
  5040 Cut Off Road, Coushatta, LA 71019
   Bridget Lynch, Parish Manager

GENERAL HEALTH SERVICES

Red River Health Unit 318.932.4087
Fax 318.932.5415
  2015 Red Oak Rd, Coushatta, LA 71019
   Yashica Turner, Nursing Supervisor

MENTAL HEALTH SERVICES

Red River MH Clinic 318.932.4029
Fax 318.932.5914
E-mail ....larken.doughty@la.gov
  1313 Ringold Ave., Coushatta, LA 71019
   Larkin Doughty, On-Site Manager

POLICE AND SHERIFF

Coushatta Police Dept 318.932.4222
Fax 318.932.3549
  1916 Alonzo St, Coushatta, LA 71019-9411
   Joey Miller, Police Chief

Edgefield Police Dept 318.932.6263
Fax 318.932.6081
  PO Box 371, Coushatta, LA 71019-0371
   Pat Murray, Police Chief

Sheriff's Ofc 318.932.4221
Fax 318.932.6651
  615 E Carrol St, Coushatta, LA 71019
   Johny Norman, Chief Deputy

Richland Parish

SOCIAL SERVICES

Ofc of Community Svcs 318.728.3037
Fax 318.728.4938
  117 Ellington Dr, Rayville, LA 71269
   Ann Brown, Parish Manager

GENERAL HEALTH SERVICES

Health Unit 318.728.4441
Fax 318.728.6291
  21 Lynn Gayle Robertson Rd, Rayville, LA 71269
   Pauline Stewart, Nursing Supervisor

MENTAL HEALTH SERVICES

Richland MH Clinic 318.728.6456
Fax 318.728.4121
  115 Christian Dr, Rayville, LA 71269-
   Mary C. Brooks, Chief Counselor

COURTS

5th District Court 318.728.4111
Fax 318.728.7003
  708 Julia St, Rayville, LA 71269
   Terry A Doughty, Judge

POLICE AND SHERIFF

Delhi Police Dept 318.878.3788
Fax 318.878.9638
  304 Tennessee St, Delhi, LA 71232-2922
   Rufus Carter Steve Harris, Police Chief

Mangham Police Dept 318.248.3100
Fax 318.248.2170
E-mail ....manghampd@inetsouth.com
  306 Main St, Mangham, LA 71259
   Lennie Graham, Police Chief

Rayville Police Dept 318.728.4431
Fax 318.728.9070
  900 Harrison St, Rayville, LA 71269-2102
   Willie Robinson, Police Chief

Sabine Parish

SOCIAL SERVICES

Department Of Children And Family Services 318.256.4104
Fax 318.256.4158
Web ....www.dss.state.la.us
E-mail ....nwright@dss.state.la.us
  195 Marthaville Rd, Many, LA 71449-3359
   Nancy Wright, Parish Manager/foster Care Supervisor

Ofc of Family Support 318.256.4121
Fax 318.256.4142
Web ....www.ocs.dss.state.la.us
E-mail ....blynch@ocs.dss.state.la.us
  910 W Mississippi St, Many, LA 71449-3848
   Bridget Lynch, Parish Manager

GENERAL HEALTH SERVICES

Health Unit........................**318.256.4105**
Fax........................318.256.4144
   1230 W Louisiana Ave, Many, LA 71449
Dawn Leone, Nursing Supervisor

MENTAL HEALTH SERVICES

Many Mental Health Clinic.................**318.256.4119**
Fax........................318.256.4171
E-mail........................sonya.parker@la.gov
   265 Highland Dr, Many, LA 71449-3717
Sonya Parker, Manager

POLICE AND SHERIFF

Converse Police Dept.....................**318.567.3312**
Fax........................318.567.3315
E-mail........................conversevillage@bellsouth.net
   209 West Port Arthur Ave, Converse, LA 71419
John Brock, Police Chief

Many Police Dept.....................**318.256.5617**
Fax........................318.256.4007
   955 San Antonio Ave, Many, LA 71449
Roger Freeman, Police Chief

Pleasant Hill Police Dept.....................**318.796.3680**
Fax........................318.796.3366
   8336 Pearl St, Pleasant Hill, LA 71065
Ray Williams, Police Chief

Zwolle Police Dept.....................**318.645.6141**
Fax........................318.645.6171
   952 S Main Zwolle, Zwolle, LA 71486
Marvin Frazier, Police Chief

Saint Bernard Parish

GENERAL HEALTH SERVICES

Health Unit.....................**504.278.7410**
Fax........................504.278.7324
Web........................www.dhh.louisiana.gov
   3002 Gean Lafitte Pkwy, Chalmette, LA 70043-3624

JUSTICE AGENCY

Juvenile Probation Dept.....................**504.278.4435**
Fax........................504.278.4442
   1100 W Saint Bernard Hwy, Room 201, Chalmette, LA 70043
Randy Dyess, CEO

POLICE AND SHERIFF

Sheriff's Ofc.....................**504.271.2504**
Fax........................504.278.7606
Web........................www.sbso.org
E-mail........................sheriff@sbso.org
   8301 W Judge Perez, Chalmette, LA 70043-4451
Jack A. Stephens, Sheriff

Saint Charles Parish

GENERAL HEALTH SERVICES

Health Unit.....................**985.785.5800**
Fax........................985.785.2104
Web........................www.stcchc.org.
   843 Milling Ave, Luling, LA 70070
Mark Keiser, Facility Director

COURTS

29th District Court.....................**985.783.6632**
Fax........................985.783.2005
   15045 River Rd, Hahnville, LA 70057
Honorable Emile R. St. Pierre, Director

POLICE AND SHERIFF

Sheriff's Dept.....................**985.783.6237**
Fax........................985.783.6497
Web........................www.stcharlessheriff.org
E-mail........................gchamp@stcharlessheriff.org
   15045 River Rd, Hahnville, LA 70057
Greg Champagne, Sheriff

Saint Helena Parish

GENERAL HEALTH SERVICES

Health Unit.....................**225.222.6178**
Fax........................225.222.6466
   52 N 2nd St, Greensburg, LA 70441
Georgette Contreras, Rn, Nursing Supervisor

COURTS

21st District Court.....................**985.748.9445**
Fax........................985.748.6637
Web........................www.21stjdc.org
E-mail........................fins@21stjdc.org
   110 North Bay St, Amie, LA 70422
Honorable Robert H. Morrison Iii, Chief

POLICE AND SHERIFF

Greensburg Police Dept.....................**225.222.3142**
Fax........................225.222.4372
   14516 Highway 37, Greensburg, LA 70441
Lee Carmona, Police Chief

Sheriff's Ofc.....................**225.222.4413**
Fax........................225.222.6908
Web........................www.centurytel.net
E-mail........................nwilliam@centurytel.net
   387 Sitman St, Greensburg, LA 70441
Nathaniel William, Sheriff

Saint James Parish

SOCIAL SERVICES

Ofc of Family Support.....................**225.869.5371**
Fax........................225.869.4990
   1611 Lutcher Ave, Lutcher, LA 70071
Cathy Hall, Parish Manager

COURTS

23rd District Court.....................**225.562.2280**
Fax........................225.562.2246
E-mail........................tom.kliebert@stjamesla.com
   5800 Highway 44, Convent, LA 70723
Honorable Thomas J. Kliebert Jr, Judge

POLICE AND SHERIFF

Sheriff's Dept.....................**225.562.2377**
Fax........................225.562.2380
Web........................www.stjamesla.com
E-mail........................sheriff@stjamesla.com
   5800 La Highway 44, Convent, LA 70723
Willy J. Martin, Jr., Sheriff

Saint John the Baptist Parish

SOCIAL SERVICES

Department Of Children And Family Services.....................**985.652.2938**
Fax........................985.652.4074
   429 W Airline Hwy Ste M, La Place, LA 70068
Lillie Wilson, District Supervisor

GENERAL HEALTH SERVICES

Saint John The Bap Health Unit.............**985.536.2128**
Fax........................985.536.2571
   473 Central Ave, Reserve, LA 70084-5509
Monique Cook, Supervisor

MENTAL HEALTH SERVICES

MH Clinic.....................**985.652.8444**
Fax........................985.652.2450
Web........................www.louisiana.gov
   1809 W Airline Hwy, La Place, LA 70068-3336
Mary Punch, Office Manager

COURTS

40Th District Court.....................**985.497.3331**
Fax........................985.497.3972
Web........................www.stjohnclerk.org
   2393 Highway 18, Edgard, LA 70049
Honorable Madeline Jasmine, Judge

Saint Landry Parish

SOCIAL SERVICES

Ofc of Community Svcs.....................**337.942.0050**
Fax........................337.948.0233
Web........................www.dss.state.la.us
   6069 I 49 S Service Rd Ste C, Opelousas, LA 70570-0786
Richard Morgan, Regional Supervisor

Ofc of Family Support.....................**337.942.0121**
Fax........................337.948.0370
Web........................www.eatel.net
   6069 I 49 S Service Rd Ste A, Opelousas, LA 70570-0786
Wendell Young, Parish Manager

GENERAL HEALTH SERVICES

Health Unit.....................**337.457.2767**
Fax........................337.457.9767
   131 City Ave, Eunice, LA 70535-6401
Debra Credeur, Administrative Coordinator

COURTS

City Court.....................**337.948.2570**
Fax........................337.948.2575
Web........................www.opelousascitycourt.com
E-mail........................wpitre@opelousascitycourt.com
   127 E Grolee St, Opelousas, LA 70570
Wendy Pitre, Juvenile Deputy Clerk

POLICE AND SHERIFF

Arnaudville Police Dept.....................**337.754.5913**
Fax........................337.754.7935
   107 Rue De Jausiers, Arnaudville, LA 70512
Richard Mizzi, Police Chief

Eunice Police Dept.....................**337.457.2626**
Fax........................337.457.6589
   300 S 2nd St, Eunice, LA 70535
Ronald Dies, Police Chief

Grand Coteau Police Dept.....................**337.662.3972**
Fax........................337.662.3098
   438 E Martin Luther King Drive, Grand Coteau, LA 70541
Wilton Guidry, Police Chief

Krotz Springs Police Dept.....................**337.566.3784**
Fax........................337.566.3215
E-mail........................krotzspringPD@att.net
   224 Main St, Krotz Springs, LA 70750
Norman Mouille, Police Chief

Leonville Police Dept.....................**337.879.2601**
Fax........................337.879.7922
   3722 Highway 31, Leonville, LA 70551
Joseph Noel, Police Chief

Opelousas Police Dept.....................**337.948.2513**
Fax........................337.942.5346
   318 N Court St, Opelousas, LA 70570
Perry Gallow, Police Chief

Port Barre Police Dept.....................**337.585.6212**
Fax........................337.585.8108
E-mail........................pbpd@bellsouth.net
   498 Fazion Avenue, Port Barre, LA 70577
Deon Boudreaux, Police Chief

Sheriff's Ofc.....................**337.948.6516**
Fax........................337.942.9729
   108 S Market St, Opelousas, LA 70570
Bobby J. Guidroz, Sheriff

Louisiana

Louisiana

Sunset Police Dept 337.662.5555
Fax 337.662.3912
E-mail ....tsunset@centurytell.com
139 Castille St, Sunset, LA 70584-6218
Alex C. Gullory, Police Chief

Washington Police Dept 337.826.3305
Fax 337.826.7648
109 St Landry Blvd, Washington, LA 70589
Ronelle Broussard, Police Chief

Saint Martin Parish

SOCIAL SERVICES

Ofc of Community Svcs 337.394.6081
Fax 337.394.6335
Web ....www.dcss.state.la.us
E-mail ....dcss@louisiana.gov
1109 South Main, 2nd Floor, Saint Martinville,
LA 70582
Patricia Hebert, Program Manager

GENERAL HEALTH SERVICES

Saint Martin Parish Health Unit 337.394.3097
Fax 337.394.1279
303 W Port St, Saint Martinville, LA 70582-3923
Kathryn Guidry, Nursing Supervisor

POLICE AND SHERIFF

Breaux Bridge Police Dept 337.332.2186
Fax 337.332.8360
Web ....www.breauxbridgelive.com
101 Berard St Ste F, Breaux Bridge, LA 70517-5051
Percy J Hebert, Police Chief

Saint Martinville Police Dept 337.394.3001
Fax 337.394.7982
E-mail ....psmith@stmartinvillepolice.org
105 New Market St, Saint Martinville, LA 70582
Paula Smith, Police Chief

Saint Mary Parish

SOCIAL SERVICES

Chitimacha Human Svcs 337.923.7000
Fax 337.923.2475
E-mail ....karen@chitimacha.gov
3287 Chitimacha Trail, Charenton, LA 70523
Karen Matthews, Director

Ofc of Community Svcs 337.828.5278
Fax 337.828.5905
E-mail ....dss@la.gov
604 2nd St, Franklin, LA 70538
Patricia Mitchell, Parish Manager

GENERAL HEALTH SERVICES

Health Unit 985.380.2441
Fax 985.380.2489
1200 David Dr Ste A, Morgan City, LA 70380
Jesicca Ledford, Nursing Supervisor

COURTS

16th District Court 337.828.4100
Fax 337.413.0850
Web www.16jdc.org
E-mail ....jconery@16jdc.org
500 Main St, 6th Floor, Franklin, LA 70538
Honorable John E. Conery, Director

POLICE AND SHERIFF

Baldwin Police Dept 337.923.4845
Fax 337.923.4840
16215 Highway 182, Baldwin, LA 70514
Gerald Minor, Police Chief

Berwick Police Dept 985.384.7710
Fax 985.384.0346
Web ....www.townofberwick.org
E-mail ....james@townofberwick.org
400 Canton St, Berwick, LA 70342
James Richard, Police Chief

Franklin Police Dept 337.828.1716
Fax 337.828.7346
508 2nd St, Franklin, LA 70538
Sabria Mcguire, Police Chief

Franklinton Police Dept 985.839.4474
Fax 985.839.6838
409 11th Ave, Franklinton, LA 70438
Donald Folse, Police Chief

Morgan City Police Dept 985.380.4605
Fax 985.384.2259
723 Myrtle St, Morgan City, LA 70380
Mark Folse, Police Chief

Patterson Police Dept 985.395.6161
Fax 985.395.8316
1314 Main St, Patterson, LA 70392
Patrick Lasalle, Police Chief

Saint Tammany Parish

SOCIAL SERVICES

Ofc of Family Support 985.893.6215
Fax 985.893.6298
Web ....www.dss.state.la.us
E-mail ....astone@dss.state.la.us
71040 Highway 21, Covington, LA 70433-7160
Ann Stone, Parish Manager

Region IX Ofc of Community Svcs 985.893.6363
Fax 985.893.6366
E-mail ....rcouvillion@dhh.state.la.gov
351 Holiday Blvd, Covington, LA 70433-6109
Ginger Pine, Regional Administrator

MENTAL HEALTH SERVICES

Lurline Smith MH Ctr 985.624.4450
Fax 985.624.4461
Web ....www.dhh.la.gov
E-mail ....kpaul@dhh.la.gov
900 Wilkinson St, Mandeville, LA 70448-3533
Kathleen Paul, Clinic Director

COURTS

22nd District Court 985.809.8700
Fax 985.809.8777
E-mail ....donald.fendlason@sos.louisiana.gov
701 N Columbia St Ste 1, Covington, LA 70433
Honorable Donald M. Fendlason, Director

POLICE AND SHERIFF

Covington Police Dept 985.892.8500
Fax 985.893.0039
E-mail ....rpalmifano@covla.com
200 E Kirkland St, Covington, LA 70433
Richard Palmifano, Police Chief

Folsom Police Dept 985.796.3300
Fax 985.796.3337
E-mail ....folsompolicedepa@belsouth.net
82341 Railroad Ave, Folsom, LA 70437-6188
Ronnie Killingsworth, Police Chief

Madisonville Police Dept 985.845.3393
Fax 985.845.2552
Web ....www.madpd.org
805 Main St, Madisonville, LA 70447-9723
David I Smith, Police Chief

Mandeville Police Dept 985.626.9711
Fax 985.624.3125
Web ....www.cityofmandeville.com
1870 Highway 190, Mandeville, LA 70448-3431
Rick Richard, Police Chief

Pearl River Police Dept 985.863.5711
Fax 985.863.9233
Web ....www.usacops.com
E-mail ....braynor@usacops.com
39470 Willis Alley, Pearl River, LA 70452
Bennie Raynor, Police Chief

Sheriff's Dept 985.892.8181
Fax 985.809.8215
E-mail ....info@stpso.com
701 columbia st, Covington, LA 70433
Rodney J. Strain, Jr., Sheriff

EDUCATION SERVICES

Special Education 985.898.3311
Fax 985.898.3324
706 W 28th Ave, Covington, LA 70433
Sharon Hosch, Supervisor

Tangipahoa Parish

GENERAL HEALTH SERVICES

Health Unit 985.748.2020
Fax 985.748.2029
330 W Oak St, Amite, LA 70422
Darlene, Nursing Supervisor

MENTAL HEALTH SERVICES

Rosenblum Mental Health Clinic 985.543.4080
Fax 985.543.4090
15785 Medical Arts Dr, Hammond, LA 70403
Darlene Jiles, Manager

JUSTICE AGENCY

Ofc of Juvenile Justice 985.543.4096
Fax 985.543.4100
Web ....www.ojj.louisana.gov
E-mail ....roy.wittors@la.gov
42381 Deluxe Plz, Hammond, LA 70403-2821
Roy Wittors, Juvenile Services Supervisor

COURTS

21st District Court 985.748.4146
Fax 985.748.6503
110 N Bay St Ste 100, Amite, LA 70422
Honorable Elizabeth P. Wolfe, Judge

City Court of Hammond 985.542.3455
Fax 985.542.3466
E-mail ....gasaway_g@hammond.org
303 E Thomas St Ste 100, Hammond, LA 70401
Honorable Grace B. Gasaway, Director

POLICE AND SHERIFF

Amite Police Dept 985.748.6169
Fax 985.748.5019
E-mail ....jerrytrabona@i-55.com
101 Oak St, Amite, LA 70422
Jerry Trabona, Police Chief

Hammond Police Dept 985.542.3500
Fax 985.542.3542
Web ....www.hammondpolice.com
E-mail ....rdevall@hammondpolice.com
303 E Thomas St, Hammond, LA 70401
Roddy Devall, Police Chief

Independence Police Dept 985.878.4188
Fax 985.878.8058
E-mail ....policechief@indyla.com
269 E Railroad Ave, Independence, LA 70443
Frank Edwards Iii, Police Chief

Kentwood Police Dept 985.229.6305
Fax 985.229.2658
E-mail ....kpd@kentwoodla.org
308 Avenue G, Kentwood, LA 70444
Greg Newton, Police Chief

Ponchatoula Police Dept....................**985.386.6548**
Fax..985.386.7691
Web......................................www.ponchatoulapolice.com
E-mail...........................chief@ponchatoulapolice.com
　110 W Hickory St, Ponchatoula, LA 70454-3216
　Bry Learson, Police Chief

Roseland Police Dept.........................**985.748.9063**
Fax..985.748.7131
E-mail....................................roseland748@yahoo.com
　62438 Commercial St, Roseland, LA 70456
　Dunn Hannomm, Police Chief

Sheriff's Ofc.......................................**985.748.8147**
Fax..985.748.3224
E-mail...edwardsd@tpso.org
　313 E Oak, Amite, LA 70422
　Daniel Edwards, Sheriff

Tickfaw Police Dept...........................**985.345.4677**
Fax..985.345.0472
　14493 2nd St, Tickfaw, LA 70466
　Joe Starns, Police Chief

Village of Tangipahoa Police Dept............**985.229.4435**
Fax..985.229.4423
　12616 Jackson St, Tangipahoa, LA 70465
　Richard Banks, Police Chief

EDUCATION SERVICES

Special Education.............................**985.542.7195**
Fax..985.542.9947
Web..www.tangischools.org
　1745 SW Railroad Ave Ste 302, Hammond,
　LA 70403-6150
　Virginia Peco, Director

Tensas Parish

GENERAL HEALTH SERVICES

Health Unit.......................................**318.766.3513**
Fax..318.766.9090
Web..www.louisisana.gov
E-mail.............................margaret.a.morgan@la.gov
　1115 Levee St, Saint Joseph, LA 71366
　Margaret Morgan, Administrative Coordinator

POLICE AND SHERIFF

Sheriff's Dept...................................**318.766.3499**
Fax..318.766.3498
　203 Hancock St., Saint Joseph, LA 71366
　Rickey A. Jones, Sheriff

Waterproof Police Dept.....................**318.749.0085**
Fax..318.749.0085
　311 Main St, Waterproof, LA 71375-0248
　Rickey Hollins, Police Chief

Terrebonne Parish

SOCIAL SERVICES

Department of Children and Family
Services...**985.857.3630**
Fax..985.873.2012
Web..www.dss.state.la.us
E-mail..............................sgarrett@dss.state.la.us
　1012 W Tennel Blvd, Houma, LA 70360-2866
　Sandra Garrett, District Supervisor

GENERAL HEALTH SERVICES

Terrebonne Parish Health Unit............**985.857.3601**
Fax..985.857.3607
　600 Polk St, Houma, LA 70360-4154
　Kim Dillard, Rn, Nursing Supervisor

COURTS

32nd District Court............................**985.868.5660**
Fax..985.868.5143
　7856 Main St, Houma, LA 70361
　Honorable George Larke, Judge

POLICE AND SHERIFF

Houma City Police Dept.....................**985.873.6371**
Fax..985.872.4670
Web..www.tpcg.org
E-mail..................................pboudreaux@tpcg.org
　500 Honduras St, Houma, LA 70360-5650
　Patrick Boudreaux, Police Chief

Sheriff's Ofc.....................................**985.876.2500**
Fax..985.857.0274
E-mail......................................bbourgeois@tpso.net
　7856 Main St, Courthouse Annex, Ste 121, Houma,
　LA 70360
　Brnon Bourgeois, Sheriff

Union Parish

SOCIAL SERVICES

Dep Of Children & Family Serv..............**318.251.4105**
Fax..318.251.5065
　206 E Reynolds Ste J, Ruston, LA 71273
　Catherine Bowden, District Manager

GENERAL HEALTH SERVICES

Health Unit.......................................**318.368.3156**
Fax..318.368.3831
　1002 Marion Hwy, Farmerville, LA 71241
　Evelyn Andrews, Supervisor

COURTS

3rd District Court..............................**318.368.3055**
Fax..318.368.3861
E-mail......................................upclerk@bayou.com
　100 E Bayou St Ste 105, Farmerville, LA 71241
　Honorable Cynthia T. Woodard, Judge

POLICE AND SHERIFF

Bernice Police Dept...........................**318.285.9933**
Fax..318.285.0355
E-mail........................bernicepolicedep@bellsouth.net
　424 E 4th St, Bernice, LA 71222
　Ricky Albritton, Police Chief

Farmerville Police Dept......................**318.368.2226**
Fax..318.368.7146
E-mail..echiefc@aol.com
　302 Martin Luther King Dr, Farmerville,
　LA 71241-3009
　Earnest Coulberston, Police Chief

Marion Police Dept............................**318.292.4715**
Fax..318.292.4717
E-mail...............................markdodd@centurytel.net
　398 Main St, Marion, LA 71260
　Mark Dodd, Police Chief

Sheriff's Ofc.....................................**318.368.3124**
Fax..318.368.2728
　100 E Bayou St Ste 101, Farmerville, LA 71241
　Bob Backley, Sheriff

Vermilion Parish

SOCIAL SERVICES

Ofc of Community Svcs.......................**337.898.1430**
Fax..337.898.1413
　2729 Veterans Memorial Dr, Abbeville, LA 70511
　Richman Suire, Parish Manager

GENERAL HEALTH SERVICES

Vermilion Parish Health Unit................**337.893.1443**
Fax..337.893.6680
　2501 Charity St, Abbeville, LA 70510
　Margaret Boudreaux, Nursing Supervisor

COURTS

15th District Court.............................**337.898.1992**
Fax..337.898.9803
　100 N State St, Suite 101, Abbeville, LA 70510
　Diane Broussard, Clerk Of Court

City Court of Abbeville........................**337.893.1513**
Fax..337.893.4731
　208 S State St, Abbeville, LA 70510
　Richard J. Putnam Iii, Judge

POLICE AND SHERIFF

Abbeville Police Dept.........................**337.893.2511**
Fax..337.893.5253
　304 Charity St, Abbeville, LA 70510
　Tony Hardy, Police Chief

Gueydan Police Dept..........................**337.536.9219**
Fax..337.536.9302
　414 Main St, Gueydan, LA 70542
　Stoney Broussard, Police Chief

Kaplan Police Dept.............................**337.643.8600**
Fax..337.643.1737
　413 N Cushing Ave, Kaplan, LA 70548
　Boyd Adams, Police Chief

Maurice Police Dept...........................**337.893.2540**
Fax..337.893.3461
　405 Lastie Ave, Maurice, LA 70555
　Warren Rost, Police Chief

Sheriff's Ofc.....................................**337.898.4409**
Fax..337.740.4510
E-mail.........................mikecouvillon@crt.state.la.us
　101 S State St, Abbeville, LA 70510
　Michael A. Couvillon, Sheriff

Vernon Parish

SOCIAL SERVICES

Ofc of Community Svcs.......................**337.238.7030**
Fax..337.238.6494
　302 Vernon St., Newllano, LA 71461
　Evalyn Annette Brown, Office Manager

Ofc of Family Support.........................**337.238.6414**
Fax..337.238.6464
Web..www.dss.state.la.us
E-mail.....................................jkelly@dss.state.la.us
　300 Vernon St, Newllano, LA 71461
　Sandra Piypon, Supervisor

GENERAL HEALTH SERVICES

Health Unit.......................................**337.238.6410**
Fax..337.238.6447
Web...www.health.state.la.us
　406 W Fertitta Blvd, Leesville, LA 71446-4649
　Wanda Hunt, Nursing Supervisor

MENTAL HEALTH SERVICES

Leesville Mental Health Clinic...............**337.238.6414**
Fax..337.238.7070
　105 Belview Rd, Leesville, LA 71446
　Karen Donahue, Manager

COURTS

30th District Court.............................**337.238.1384**
Fax..337.238.9902
　215 N 4th St, Leesville, LA 71446-4021
　Honorable John C. Ford, Director

POLICE AND SHERIFF

Hornbeck Police Dept.........................**318.565.4659**
Fax..318.565.4228
Web..www.wnonline.net
E-mail.........................townofhornbeck@bellsouth.net
　1083 Hammons St, Hornbeck, LA 71439
　Stieve Holley, Police Chief

Newllano Police Dept.........................**337.239.3849**
Fax..337.239.0031
E-mail.............................newllanopolice@yahoo.com
　109 Stanton St, Newllano, LA 71461
　Danny Hunt, Police Chief

Rosepine Police Dept 337.463.8249
Fax 337.463.8781
   18846 Johny B Hall Memorial Hwy, Rosepine, LA 70659
   James Parrott, Police Chief

Sheriff's Dept 337.238.1311
Fax 337.238.4987
E-mail ....vpso2@bellsouth.net
   203 S 3rd St, Leesville, LA 71446
   John S. Craft, Sheriff

Washington Parish

MENTAL HEALTH SERVICES
Bogalusa Mental Health Clinic 985.732.6610
Fax 985.732.6626
   619 Willis Ave, Bogalusa, LA 70427
   Judy Hooks, Lcsw, Clinic Manager

COURTS
22nd District Court 985.839.7821
Fax 985.839.7851
   Court House Bldg, Corner Washington & Maine, Franklinton, LA 70438
   Honorable Ray Childres, Chief Judge

POLICE AND SHERIFF
Angie Police Dept 985.986.2444
Fax 985.986.2889
E-mail ....angiecityhall@bellsouth.net
   64475 Cherry St, Angie, LA 70426
   Gilbert Hartzog, Chief Of Police

Bogalusa Police Dept 985.732.3611
Fax 985.732.6253
   214 Arkansas Ave, Bogalusa, LA 70427-3810
   Jerry Agnew, Police Chief

Sheriff's Dept 985.839.3434
Fax 985.839.7804
Web ....www.wpsoweb.com
E-mail ....rcrowe@wpsoweb.com
   1002 Main St, Franklinton, LA 70438-1709
   Robert Crowe, Sheriff

Webster Parish

SOCIAL SERVICES
Dept of Children & Family Svcs Child
Welfare 318.371.3004
Fax 318.371.3083
E-mail ....vhaynes@dss.state.la.us
   1232 Sheppard St, Minden, LA 71055-3460
   Vicky Haynes, Parish Manager

Ofc of Family Support 318.371.3012
Fax 318.371.3071
Web ....www.dss.state.la.gov
E-mail ....kwalker@dss.state.la.gov
   223 Pine St, Minden, LA 71055-3235
   Kevin Walker, Supervisor

GENERAL HEALTH SERVICES
Health Unit 318.371.3030
Fax 318.371.3073
Web ....www.dhh.la.gov
E-mail ....dvogel@dhh.la.gov
   1200 Homer Rd, Minden, LA 71055-3082
   Debbie Vogel, Rn, Nursing Supervisor

COURTS
26th District Court 318.371.0366
Fax 318.371.0226
   410 Main St, Minden, LA 71058
   Honorable Bruce Bolin, Judge

POLICE AND SHERIFF
Cotton Valley Police Dept 318.832.4272
Fax 318.832.4856
   478 Resident St, Cotton Valley, LA 71018
   Terry Brown, Police Chief

Cullen Police Dept 318.994.2224
Fax 318.994.3136
Web ....www.cmaaccess.com
E-mail ....mary_hoof@cmaaccess.com
   301 Coyle Ave, Cullen, LA 71021
   Mary Ann Hoof, Police Chief

Dixie Inn Police Dept 318.377.0238
Fax 318.377.9173
E-mail ....dgwdipd@msn.com
   60 Shell St, Minden, LA 71055-9105
   James Edwards, Police Chief

Doyline Police Dept 318.745.2625
Fax 318.745.2658
   624 College St, Doyline, LA 71023
   Robert Hayden, Jr, Police Chief

Dubberly Police Dept 318.371.9528
Fax 318.371.1021
   3465 Hwy 531, Dubberly, LA 71024
   Charles Mims, Police Chief

Minden Police Dept 318.377.1212
Fax 318.371.4222
E-mail ....mindenpd@mindenusa.com
   520 Broadway St, Minden, LA 71058
   Steve Cropter, Police Chief

Sarepta Police Dept 318.847.4333
Fax 318.847.4198
E-mail ....sareptapd@centurytel.net
   24448 Highway 371, Sarepta, LA 71071
   Bill Fields, Police Chief

Sheriff's Dept 318.377.1515
Fax 318.377.5653
Web ....www.webstersheriff.org
   410 Main St, Minden, LA 71058
   Gary Sexton, Sheriff

Springhill Police Dept 318.539.2511
Fax 318.539.4491
   25 Clinic St, Springhill, LA 71075
   Will Lynd, Police Chief

West Baton Rouge Parish

COURTS
18th District Court 225.336.2419
Fax 225.336.2409
   850 8th St, Port Allen, LA 70767
   Honorable J. Robin Free, Judge

POLICE AND SHERIFF
Brusly Police Dept 225.749.2980
Fax 225.749.2366
Web ....www.bruslyla.com
E-mail ....jwhaley@bruslyla.com
   150 E. Francis St., Brusly, LA 70719
   Jamie Whaley, Police Chief

Port Allen Police Dept 225.343.5525
Fax 225.267.4921
Web ....www.portallen.org
E-mail ....chief@portallen.org
   375 Court St, Port Allen, LA 70767-2745
   Fred Smith, Police Chief

Sheriff's Ofc 225.343.9234
Fax 225.344.1004
E-mail ....wbrsheriff@aol.com
   850 8th St, Port Allen, LA 70767-2324
   Michael B. Cazes, Sheriff

West Carroll Parish

SOCIAL SERVICES
Ofc of Family Support 318.428.3252
Fax 318.428.9071
E-mail ....jwaters@dhh.la.gov
   702 E Jefferson St, Oak Grove, LA 71263
   Johnniece Waters, Parish Manager

GENERAL HEALTH SERVICES
Health Unit 318.428.9361
Fax 318.428.7200
Web ....www.dhh.louisiana.gov
E-mail ....pbass@dhh.la.gov
   402 Beale St, Oak Grove, LA 71263
   Peggy Bass, Rn, Nursing Supervisor

COURTS
5th District Court 318.428.4284
Fax 318.428.8265
E-mail ....wcclerk@bellsouth.net
   305 E Main St, Oak Grove, LA 71263-2541
   Kay Bolding, Clerk Of Court

POLICE AND SHERIFF
Oak Grove Police Dept 318.428.3275
Fax 318.428.4556
E-mail ....jmoss@bayou.com
   407 E Main St, Oak Grove, LA 71263
   Johnny Moss, Police Chief

Pioneer Police Dept 318.428.8581
Fax 318.428.2719
   318 Cherry St, Pioneer, LA 71266
   Jamie Wallis, Police Chief

Sheriff's Dept 318.428.2331
Fax 318.428.8889
E-mail ....wcso@westcarrollsheriff.com
   305 E Main St, Oak Grove, LA 71263
   Jerry Philley, Sheriff

West Feliciana Parish

GENERAL HEALTH SERVICES
Health Unit 225.635.3644
Fax 225.635.2167
   5154 Barnette Rd, Saint Francisville, LA 70775
   Dena Tunstall, Clerk

COURTS
20th District Court 225.635.3794
Fax 225.635.3770
   4785 Prosberry St, Saint Francisville, LA 70775
   Honorable George H. Ware Jr., Judge

POLICE AND SHERIFF
Saint Francisville Police Dept 225.635.4177
Fax 225.635.5577
E-mail ....sfpdchief@bellsoutn.net
   11936 Ferdinand St, Saint Francisville, LA 70775
   T Scott Ford, Police Chief

Sheriff's Ofc 225.784.3136
Fax 225.635.6947
Web ....www.wspfo.org
E-mail ....wfone@bellsouth.net
   4789 Prosperity St., Saint Francisville, LA 70775
   J. Austin Daniel, Sheriff

Winn Parish

SOCIAL SERVICES
Dept. of Childern and Family
Services 318.628.2746
Fax 318.628.1995
   1408 E Lafayette St, Winnfield, LA 71483
   Donna Smith, Supervisor

Ofc of Community Svcs **318.648.6805**
Fax 318.648.6905
E-mail .djohnson@dss.state.la.us
   1408 E Lafayette, Winnfield, LA 71483
   Donna Johnson, Parish Manager

GENERAL HEALTH SERVICES

Winn Parish Health Unit **318.628.2148**
Fax 318.628.6822
Web .www.louisianasilverservice.gov
   301 W Main St Rm 101, Winnfield, LA 71483
   Sonda Chandler, Nursing Supervisor

COURTS

8th District Court **318.628.4596**
Fax 318.628.2753
   119 W Main St Rm 103, Winnfield, LA 71483
   Honourable Jacque D Derr, Judge

POLICE AND SHERIFF

Winnfield Police Dept **318.628.3511**
Fax 318.628.4111
   405 S Jones St, Winnfield, LA 71483-3564
   Johnny Carpenter, Police Chief

SPECIAL SERVICES AGENCIES

ADOPTION AGENCIES

Access To Life Adoption Svc **504.832.1503**
Fax 504.828.2079
Web . . . . .www.accesspregnancy.com
   1501 Veterans Memorial Blvd, Metairie,
   LA 70005-2703
   Kay Bongard, Director

Beacon House Adoption Svcs, Inc. **225.753.5551**
Fax 225.753.6866
E-mail . . . . .info@beaconhouseadopt.com
   5917 Jones Creek Rd Ste 100B, Baton Rouge,
   LA 70817
   Ann Hughes, Director

Borchert Law Ofc **985.649.1881**
   1064 Front St, Slidell, LA 70458-2043
   Laura Borchert, Attorney

Catholic Community Svcs **225.336.8700**
Fax 225.336.8703
   1900 S Acadian Thruway, Baton Rouge, LA 70808
   Janice Allen, Director

Daye Bowie & Beresko **318.221.0600**
Fax 318.221.8158
   400 Travis St, Ste 700, Shreveport, LA 71101

Debnam, Terri H. - Law Ofc **318.387.8811**
Fax 318.323.1122
   500 N 7th St, West Monroe, LA 71291
   Terri H Odom, Attorney

Decolores Adoptions Intl **337.855.7398**
Fax 337.217.1280
   2615 Paul White Rd, Lake Charles, LA 70611

Louisiana State Social Svc **318.676.7100**
Fax 318.676.7084
   1525 Fairfield Ave, Shreveport, LA 71101
   Linda Moore, Human Resource

Michael E Theriot, LLC **225.383.9550**
Fax 225.383.9569
Web . . . . .www.batonrougelawyersattorneys.com
E-mail . . . . .directory@batonrougelawyersattorneys.com
   251 Florida St Ste 408, Baton Rouge, LA 70801-1703
   Michael E. Theriot, Attorney

Open Arms Adoption Svcs, Inc. **318.798.7664**
Fax 318.861.1710
Web . . . . .www.adoptinla.com
E-mail . . . . .dmeapc@aol.com
   7330 Fern Ave Ste 204, Shreveport, LA 71105-4973
   Missy Everson, Director

ADVOCACY RESOURCES

Bridge City Correctional Ctr (BCCY) **504.436.4253**
Fax 504.436.0916
   3225 River Rd, Westwego, LA 70094
   Joseph Powe, Facility Director

Child Advocacy Ctr, Inc. **318.448.4006**
Fax 318.448.6427
Web . . . . .www.rapidescac.org
   1506 Albert St, Alexandria, LA 71302
   Wade Bond, Executive Director

Children's Advocacy Ctr **504.364.3857**
Fax 504.364.3703
Web . . . . .www.jeffersoncac.com
E-mail . . . . .jefferson1_child@bellsouth.net
   220 Lavoisier St, Gretna, LA 70053-5842
   Erika Dupepe, Executive Director

Childrens Defense Org New Orleans **504.309.2376**
Fax 504.309.2379
   1452 N Broad St, New Orleans, LA 70119
   Mary Joseph, Director

Hearts of Hope **337.269.1557**
Fax 337.269.1143
Web . . . . .www.theheartsofhope.org
E-mail . . . . .info@theheartsofhope.org
   PO Box 53967, Lafayette, LA 70505-3967
   Jill Dugas, Director

Jetson Correctional Ctr for Youth (JCCY) **225.778.9000**
Fax 225.778.9031
Web . . . . .www.oyd.louisiana.gov
E-mail . . . . .gperkins@oyd.louisiana.gov
   Highway 61, Baker, LA 70714
   Gene Perkins, Facility Director, Unit 3

BEHAVIORAL HEALTH TREATMENT

A Center for Hope and Change, Inc. **318.673.9901**
Fax 318.673.9904
   1925 Centenary Boulevard, Shreveport, LA 71101
   CARF accredited programs available.

Above and Beyond Care Professionals,
LLC **318.934.1919**
Fax 318.934.1921
   1305 Delhi Street, Bossier City, LA 71111
   CARF accredited programs available.

Absolute Health, Inc. **985.652.0078**
Fax 985.652.8360
   1708 Chantilly Drive, Suite A, La Place, LA 70068
   CARF accredited programs available.

Acadia Vermilion Hospital **337.234.5614**
Web . . . . .www.acadiahealthcare.com
E-mail . . . . .jrrodriguez@acadiahealthcare.com
   2520 North University Avenue, Lafayette, LA 70507
   Mr. Joe Rodriguez, Accreditation Manager
   Joint Commission accredited organization.

Accelerated Health Care **318.473.0035**
Fax 318.443.0220
E-mail . . . . .apts100@aol.com
   6410 Masonic Dr, Alexandria, LA 71301-3377
   Mona Lonsberry, Director

Acceptable Health Services, LLC **504.245.2440**
E-mail . . . . .acceptablehealth@bellsouth.net
   5640 Rad Blvd, Ste 740, New Orleans, LA 70126
   Mr. Sonny Okpalobi, Accreditation Manager
   Joint Commission accredited organization.

Allen's Consultation & Training, Inc. **225.778.0992**
Fax 225.778.0994
   1632 Thomas H. Delpit Drive, Baton Rouge,
   LA 70802
   CARF accredited programs available.

American Active Rehab Inc. **504.368.0443**
Fax 504.368.0448
   401 Whitney Avenue, Suite 320, Gretna, LA 70056
   COA accredited organization.

Arshab Medical Practice **504.888.8869**
Fax 504.244.3530
   3351 Severn Ave, Metairie, LA 70002
   M Kaleem Arshab MD, Psychiatrist

Assurance Care Provider, LLC **504.472.0068**
Fax 504.472.0078
   300 Clay Street, Kenner, LA 70062
   CARF accredited programs available.

Baker Medical Corp Ltd **225.775.8500**
Fax 225.775.0289
   3034 Ray Weiland Dr, Baker, LA 70714-3252
   Tracey J, Office Manager

Bayou Oaks Health Services, LLC **985.446.4114**
Fax 985.446.4112
Web .www.bayouoakshealthservices.com
E-mail . . . . .bohs@ymail.com
   206 East 3rd Street, Thibodaux, LA 70301
   Bryan Blanchard, Clinical Director
   CARF accredited programs available.

Behavioral Health Center **318.335.3390**
Fax 318.335.2907
   119 North 13th Street, Oakdale, LA 71463
   CARF accredited programs available.

Behavioral Health Clinic **318.675.1300**
Fax 318.675.1301
   1002 Highland Ave, Ste 201, Shreveport,
   LA 71101-4143
   Larrie Williamson, Md, Psychiatrist

Bergeron Medical Practice **225.922.7885**
   8768 Quarters Lake Rd, Baton Rouge, LA 70809
   William Bergeron, Psychiatrist

Beta Community Services, Inc. **225.929.6355**
Fax 225.929.6354
   936 North Bon Marche' Drive, Baton Rouge,
   LA 70806
   CARF accredited programs available.

Bick Medical Practice **504.891.0094**
   3705 Coliseum St, New Orleans, LA 70115-3708
   John Bick, Psychiatrist

Billings Medical Practice **504.366.9707**
Fax 504.366.7502
   720 Lafayette St, Gretna, LA 70053-6136
   Charles Billings MD, Psychiatrist

Biswas Medical Practice **504.897.6789**
Fax 504.897.6790
   2633 Napoleon Ave, New Orleans, LA 70115
   Minati Biswas MD, Psychiatrist

Blundell Medical Practice **985.845.8101**
Fax 985.845.8130
   205 Holiday Blvd, Covington, LA 70433-5023
   Gordon Blundell, Psychiatrist

Booker Medical Practice **318.227.9600**
Fax 318.227.9601
  851 Olive St, Shreveport, LA 71104-2136
  J Gary Booker Md, Psychiatrist

Boswell Medical Practice **318.949.0882**
Fax 318.949.0882
  PO Box 5258, Bossier City, LA 71171-5258
  Linda Boswell, Psychiatrist

Braud Medical Practice **985.447.1216**
Fax 985.447.1218
E-mail ....mariabraud@yahoo.com
  970 S Acadia Rd Ste C, Thibodaux, LA 70301-4978
  Maria Braud, Psychiatrist

Brentwood Acquisition-Shreveport, Inc. **318.678.7500**
Web ....www.brentwoodhospital.com
E-mail ....tina.haynes@uhsinc.com
  1006 Highland Avenue, Shreveport, LA 71101
  Ms. Tina Haynes, Accreditation Manager
  Joint Commission accredited organization.

Brentwood Outpatient Clinic **318.222.6226**
Fax 318.222.6227
  1002 Highland Ave Ste 200, Shreveport,
  LA 71101-4143
  Guy Brannon, Md, Psychiatrist

Broadway, Inc/K-Bar-B Youth Ranch **985.641.1425**
Fax 985.641.1459
Web ....www.kbarb.com
E-mail ....info@kbarb.net
  31294 Hwy 190, Lacombe, LA 70445
  Jennifer Dexter, Executive Director

Calvin Walker LLC **318.323.0700**
Fax 318.323.9983
  3418 Medical Park Dr, Ste 24, Monroe,
  LA 71203-2358
  Calvin Walker Md, Psychiatrist

Carter Medical Practice **318.340.7999**
Fax 318.322.9213
  1900 Lamy Ln Ste O, Monroe, LA 71201-9207
  Stephen Carter, Psychiatrist

**Center For Hope Children and Family Services,
LLC** **504.439.4823**
Fax 504.243.1716
  5630 Crowder Boulevard, Suite 209, New Orleans,
  LA 70128
  CARF accredited programs available.

Chartwell Ctr **504.899.2478**
Fax 504.899.2416
Web ....www.chartwellcenter.org
E-mail ....chartwell@chartwellcenter.org
  4239 Camp St, New Orleans, LA 70115-2721
  Gwynne Bowman, Director

Chester Medical Practice **504.833.1442**
Fax 504.834.3101
  3500 N Causeway Blvd Ste 1410, Metairie,
  LA 70002-3548
  Charles Chester, Psychiatrist

Claire House **985.395.2424**
Web ....www.clairehouse.com
E-mail ....director@clairehouse.com
  1101 Southeast Blvd, Morgan City, LA 70380-5933
  Kim Lockley, Director

Cochran Medical Practice **504.891.6020**
Fax 504.891.1355
E-mail ....scochran@pol.net
  1426 Amelia St, New Orleans, LA 70115-3622
  Stephen Cochran MD, Psychiatrist

Cognitive Development Center **318.340.1535**
Fax 318.340.1539
  4951 Central Avenue, Monroe, LA 71203
  CARF accredited programs available.

Cognitive Development Center **318.387.1304**
Fax 318.387.1306
E-mail ....fisheradrian@aol.com
  1816 Roselawn Avenue, Monroe, LA 71201
  Yuko Munakata, Director
  CARF accredited programs available.

Cognitive Institute, Inc. **318.871.5566**
Fax 318.871.1076
  809 Polk Street, Mansfield, LA 71052
  CARF accredited programs available.

Community Enrichment Programs, LLC **318.675.0406**
Fax 318.675.0408
  842 Margaret Place, Shreveport, LA 71101
  CARF accredited programs available.

Community Rehabilitation Center **318.325.0072**
Fax 318.325.0070
  509 Bres Avenue, Monroe, LA 71201
  CARF accredited programs available.

**Community Support Services of Louisiana,
Inc.** **318.346.8001**
Fax 318.346.8005
  1140 Shirley Road, Bunkie, LA 71322
  CARF accredited programs available.

Concepcion Medical Practice **337.981.1400**
Fax 337.981.6611
E-mail ....eduardocon@bellsouth.com
  1131 Rue De Belier, Lafayette, LA 70506-6532
  Eduardo Concepcion Md, Psychiatrist

Country Doctors Inc **318.797.1773**
Fax 318.797.1722
  1400 E Bert Kouns Industrial Loop, Shreveport,
  LA 71105
  Laura McClintock, Psychiatrist

Craft Medical Practice **337.893.6131**
Fax 337.893.5527
  318 N Hospital Dr, Abbeville, LA 70510-4041
  David Craft, Psychiatrist

Crossroads Regional Hospital **318.445.5111**
Web ....www.crossroadshospital.com
E-mail ....brian_brunson@msn.com
  110 John Eskew Drive, Alexandria, LA 71303
  Mr. Brian Brunson, Accreditation Manager
  Joint Commission accredited organization.

Cruse Medical Practice **985.493.9304**
Fax 985.493.9305
  604 N Acadia Rd Ste 200, Thibodaux,
  LA 70301-4897
  Maria Cruse, Md, Psychiatrist

Ctr For ADHD Inc **985.624.5305**
Fax 985.624.8643
E-mail ....centerforadhd@bellsouth.net
  2124 Monroe, Mandeville, LA 70448
  R Timothy Brown Md, Psychiatrist

Ctr For Pain Management **337.991.9163**
Fax 337.991.9165
  PO Box 80724, Lafayette, LA 70598-0724
  Charles Bramlet, Psychiatrist

Ctr For Psychiatric and Addictive Medicine **337.233.2400**
Fax 337.232.3656
  800 Kaliste Saloom Rd, Lafayette, LA 70508-4210

Culver Medical Practice **504.455.9990**
Fax 504.455.5715
  4324 Loveland St, Metairie, LA 70006-4122
  R W Culver Md, Psychiatrist

Davis Psychiatric Clinic **504.398.4300**
Fax 504.392.6803
  229 Bellemeade Blvd Ste 404, Gretna,
  LA 70056-7153
  Robert Davis, Psychiatrist

Denney Psychiatry & Pain Mgmt **985.641.5330**
Fax 985.641.6589
  609 Brownswitch Rd, Slidell, LA 70458-1233
  James Denney MD, Psychiatrist

Disney and Associates **337.431.7194**
Fax 337.431.7198
  2711 Ernest Street, Lake Charles, LA 70601
  CARF accredited programs available.

Dopson Medical Practice **318.424.3867**
Fax 318.424.5006
  610 Herndon St, Shreveport, LA 71101-4704
  Clif Dopson Md, Psychiatrist

Down Syndrome Association **504.251.8953**
E-mail ....kscallan@dsagno.org
  PO Box 748, Destrehan, LA 70047

Dupuy Medical Practice **337.233.1165**
Fax 337.234.2595
  101 Feu Follet Rd, Lafayette, LA 70508
  Sidney Dupuy, Psychiatrist

Eastern Louisiana Mental Health System **225.634.0216**
E-mail ....debe.brandom@la.gov
  4502 Highway 951 (also used Highway 10), Jackson,
  LA 70748
  Ms. Deborah Brandom, Accreditation Manager
  Joint Commission accredited organization.

Eckerd **800.914.3937**
Fax 727.442.5911
Web ....www.eckerd.org
E-mail ....admissions@eckerd.org
  1170 Highway 51 North, Ponchatoula, LA 70454
  David Dennis, President & CEO; Francene Hazel, Director of Admissions
  A Juvenile Justice Diversion service to include youth skill-building, mentoring and tracking serving St. Helena, Livingston, Tangipahoa, Washington and St. Tammany parishes in Louisiana. Youth ages 10 – 20 years old are referred by the District 3 Louisiana Office of Youth Development (OYD). Eckerd helps youth stay at home, in school and out of trouble. This is accomplished utilized a team concept which includes the teenager, the parent, the Eckerd counselor, OYD staff and the community.

Eckert Medical Practice **504.862.8120**
Fax 504.865.5770
  6823 Saint Charles Ave, Bldg 90, New Orleans,
  LA 70118-5665
  Rosemarie Eckert Md, Psychiatrist

Ekems Healthcare, Inc **504.248.1581**
Fax 504.248.1583
E-mail ....ekemshealthcarei@bellsouth.net
  8470 Morrison Road suite A, New Orleans, LA 70127
  Mr. Gabriel Ekechukwu, Accreditation Manager
  Joint Commission accredited organization. CARF accredited programs available.

Enhanced Destiny Services **504.821.8184**
Fax 504.821.8185
  2740 Iberville Street, New Orleans, LA 70119
  CARF accredited programs available.

Essential Care Services **504.231.7066**
  4051 Ulloa Street, New Orleans, LA 70119
  CARF accredited programs available.

Exodus Behavioral Health Center, LLC **225.324.2994**
Fax 318.467.2400
  118 Highway 605, Newellton, LA 71357
  CARF accredited programs available.

Extended Care Of Southwest Louisiana 337.436.6111
Fax 337.439.1133
　2837 Ernest St Ste B, Lake Charles, LA 70601-8785
　Sharon Cowmen-Simmin, Director of Nursing

Fairway Counseling, Inc. 318.449.4474
Fax 318.449.4472
Web ....www.fairwayrehab.com
　3434 Independence Drive, Alexandria, LA 71303
　COA accredited organization.

Family Care, Inc. 504.363.7449
Fax 504.363.7077
　3520 General DeGaulle Drive, Suite 4040, New Orleans, LA 70114
　CARF accredited programs available.

Family Ctr 225.765.8648
Fax 225.765.7754
　7777 Hennessy Blvd Ste 6000, Baton Rouge, LA 70808-4370
　John De Back Md, Psychiatrist

Family Focus 225.769.5551
Fax 225.769.5583
Web ....www.familyfocusbr.com
　8303 Ohara Ct, Baton Rouge, LA 70806
　Donna Fargason Md, Psychiatrist

Family New Life Rehabilitation Center, Inc. 318.325.8050
Fax 318.325.5385
Web ....www.fnlrehab.com
　1705 Washington Street, Monroe, LA 71201
　CARF accredited programs available.

Family Services Unlimited, Inc. 318.226.9944
Fax 318.226.9942
　1717 Marshall Street, Shreveport, LA 71101
　CARF accredited programs available.

Feliciana Consultants, Inc. 225.634.5658
Fax 225.634.9947
Web ....www.fci.org
　3613 College Street, Jackson, LA 70748
　CARF accredited programs available.

George Seiden Corp 318.424.4623
Fax 318.424.4678
　1541 Irving Pl, Shreveport, LA 71101-4640
　George Seiden Md, Psychiatrist

Geriatric Psychiatric 504.897.7939
Fax 504.897.7949
　3525 Prytania St, New Orleans, LA 70115
　Ted Bloch Md, Psychiatrist

Ginzburg Medical Practice 504.836.5575
Fax 504.836.5040
E-mail ....haroldginzburg@hotmail.com
　3340 Severn Ave Ste 200, Metairie, LA 70002-7402
　Harold Ginzburg, Psychiatrist

Girls and Boys Town of Louisiana 504.949.9248
Fax 504.949.5735
Web ....www.girlsandboystown.org/louisiana
　700 Frenchmen St, New Orleans, LA 70116-1614
　Dennis Dillon, Executive Director

Glade Medical Practice 504.836.2444
Fax 504.836.2489
　315 Metairie Rd Ste 100, Metairie, LA 70005-4337
　Susan Glade MD, Psychiatrist

Greenpath International, Inc. 504.827.2928
Fax 504.827.2926
Web ....www.gpaddiction.org
　3308 Tulane Avenue, Suite 405, New Orleans, LA 70119
　CARF accredited programs available.

Greenwell Springs Hospital 225.261.2730
Fax 225.261.9080
Web ....www.dhh.la.gov
　23260 Greenwell Springs Rd, Greenwell Springs, LA 70739-0999
　Pat Gonzalez, Executive Director

Greve Medical Practice 504.588.1591
E-mail ....dwgreve@msn.com
　931 Saint Louis St, New Orleans, LA 70112-3417
　Douglas Greve MD, Psychiatrist

Group Medical Practice 225.927.3062
　4521 Jamestown Ave, Baton Rouge, LA 70808
　Glen Estes, Psychiatrist

Group Medical Practice 985.537.2273
Fax 985.537.1985
　4608 Highway 1, Raceland, LA 70394-2623
　Dennis Spires Md, Psychiatrist

Gulf Coast Psychiatry 337.562.8100
Fax 337.562.8356
　1204 W Prien Lake Rd, Lake Charles, LA 70601-8371
　Garrett Ryder, Psychiatrist

Gullapalli Medical Practice 318.329.3933
Fax 318.322.1134
　2404 Duval Dr, Monroe, LA 71201-2986
　Aruna Gullapalli Md, Psychiatrist

HCI Counseling and Rehabilitation Services 225.336.5461
Fax 225.336.5454
　1701 Main Street, Baton Rouge, LA 70802
　CARF accredited programs available.

Helping Hands Counseling, Inc. 337.477.2407
Fax 337.477.2407
Web ....www.mhrsla.org
E-mail ....brianmgwwilliams@mhrsla.org
　3519 Patrick Street, Suite 245, Lake Charles, LA 70605
　CARF accredited programs available.

Helping Hands for Community Development, Inc. 318.227.1113
Fax 318.227.1119
　2405 Line Avenue, Shreveport, LA 71104
　CARF accredited programs available.

Holistic Educational Rehab Center, Inc. 504.367.6630
Fax 504.367.6601
　2100 Belle Chasse Highway, Gretna, LA 70053
　CARF accredited programs available.

Horizon Counseling Center 225.928.4040
Fax 225.928.4111
　2156 Wooddale Boulevard, Suite 100, Baton Rouge, LA 70806
　CARF accredited programs available.

Iberville Rehabilitation Services, Inc. 225.545.0130
Fax 225.545.0131
　33570 Bowie Street, White Castle, LA 70788
　CARF accredited programs available.

Immanuels Healing Center, LLC 318.280.3813
Fax 318.323.0465
　1851 Avenue of America, Suite C, Monroe, LA 71201
　CARF accredited programs available.

Imran Medical Practice 225.766.0773
Fax 225.761.5070
E-mail ....zimran4649@aol.com
　5329 Dijon Dr Ste 107, Baton Rouge, LA 70808-4378
　Zahid Imran MD, Psychiatrist

Institute For Neuropsychiatry 337.474.4552
Fax 337.477.7091
　2829 4th Ave, Lake Charles, LA 70601
　Dale Archer, Psychiatrist

Institute for Neuropsychiatry/Advanced Health Services 337.477.7091
Fax 337.474.4552
Web ....www.ifnlc.com
　2829 Fourth Avenue, Suite 150, Lake Charles, LA 70601
　Art Schafer, Program Director
　CARF accredited programs available.

Integrated Family Services, LLC 504.822.4333
Fax 504.822.4339
Web ....www.jrsla.org
E-mail ....intfam@bellsouth.net
　2714 Canal Street, Suite 314, New Orleans, LA 70119
　Michelle Crossley, Executive Director
　CARF accredited programs available.

Jefferson Psychiatric Assoc 504.889.1448
Fax 504.889.1452
　3340 Severn Ave, Metairie, LA 70002
　S K Smith Md, Psychiatrist

Kennedy Medical Practice 318.212.3846
Fax 318.212.3849
Web ....www.wkhs.com
E-mail ....kkennedy@wkhs.com
　1666 E Bert Kouns Industrial Loop Ste 220, Shreveport, LA 71105-5714
　Kathryn Kennedy Md, Psychiatrist

Kingsley Place Assisted Living-Lake Charles 337.478.4030
Fax 337.478.7854
E-mail ....lakecharles-ed@emeritus.com
　2420 Country Club Rd, Lake Charles, LA 70605
　Christine Bennett, Executive Director

Koy Medical Practice 504.486.9499
E-mail ....akoymed@aol.com
　310 Florida Blvd, New Orleans, LA 70124-1806
　Albert Koy Md, Psychiatrist

Krimerman Medical Practice 504.891.5144
　5920 Constance St, New Orleans, LA 70115-3248
　Eleanor Krimerman, Psychiatrist

Kumari Medical Practice 225.769.1103
Fax 225.761.5155
　4983 Bluebonnet Blvd ste A, Baton Rouge, LA 70809-3086
　Moturu Kumari, Psychiatrist

LA State University-Neurology Dept 318.675.5000
Fax 318.675.6382
　PO Box 33932, Shreveport, LA 71130-3932
　Mary Fitzgerald, Psychiatrist

Lafayette Addictive Disorders Clinic 337.262.5870
Fax 337.262.1272
Web ....www.dhh.la.gov
E-mail ....jben@dhh.la.gov
　302 Dulles Dr, Suite 1, Lafayette, LA 70506
　Joyce Ben, Regional Administrator

Lake Charles Medical & Srgcl 337.433.8400
Fax 337.436.0041
Web ....www.lcmsc.com
　501 Doctor Michael Debakey Dr, Lake Charles, LA 70601-5724
　Alan Sconzert MD, Psychiatrist

Leesville Developmental Ctr 337.239.2687
Fax 337.238.3723
　401 W. Texas St., Leesville, LA 71496
　Ronald Veilion, Md, Administrator

Leesville Surgical & Digestive 337.239.4130
Fax 337.238.4104
　1015 W Fertitta Blvd, Leesville, LA 71446-4646
　Dr Gurughanta, Surgeon

Liberty HealthCare Systems, LLC 318.281.2448
Web ....libertybh.com
E-mail ....lcrymes@libertybh.com
　4673 Eugene Ware Blvd, Bastrop, LA 71220
　Ms. Lisa Crymes, Accreditation Manager
　Joint Commission accredited organization.

Life Care Intervention 318.878.0919
Fax 318.878.0922
Web ....www.delhihospital.com
　203 Ohio St, Delhi, LA 71232-3047
　Gerald Robertson Do, Psychiatrist

Life Care Psychiatric Svcs 337.262.8672
Fax 337.593.9579
   201 Rue Beauregard Blvd Ste 101, Lafayette,
   LA 70508
   Catherine Mcdonald, Director

Louisiana Heart Hospital 985.690.7500
Fax 985.690.7530
Web ....www.louisianahearthospital.com
   64030 Highway 434, Lacombe, LA 70445-3456
   Donnia Frederic, Chief Executive Officer

Louisiana Psychiatric Clinic 225.927.4504
   5225 Capitol Heights Ave, Baton Rouge, LA 70806
   Jerry Sanders Md, Psychiatrist

Love Covers Mental Health Rehabilitation Agency,
LLC 318.861.4357
Fax 318.868.6676
   6000 Fairfield Avenue, Shreveport, LA 71106
   CARF accredited programs available.

Loving Hearts, LLC 337.233.7250
Fax 337.233.7104
   2448 Johnston Street, Suite B, Lafayette, LA 70503
   CARF accredited programs available.

LSU Bogalusa Medical Ctr 985.730.6700
Fax 985.730.6709
Web ....www.lsuhsc.edu
E-mail ....jaugus@lsuhsc.edu
   433 Plaza St, Bogalusa, LA 70427-3729
   Janice Augustine, Director

LSU Healthcare Network 504.412.1100
Fax 504.412.1518
   2820 Napoleon Ave Ste 700, New Orleans,
   LA 70115-6017
   Joseph Ossosky, Psychiatrist

LSU Healthcare Network 504.897.8558
Fax 504.897.8327
E-mail ....mtowns@lsuhsc.edu
   3450 Chestnut St, New Orleans, LA 70115-2443
   Mark Townsend, Psychiatrist

Macdonell United Methodist Children's
Svcs 985.868.8362
Fax 985.868.8474
Web ....www.macdonellchildren.org
E-mail ....gaudet@macdonellchildren.org
   8326 Main St, Houma, LA 70363-4895
   Heidi Hillery, Director

Magnolia Family Services, LLC 985.449.4055
Fax 985.449.4178
Web ....www.magnoliafamilyservices.com
   106 Hickory Street, Thibodaux, LA 70301
   CARF accredited programs available.

Mangat Medical Practice 985.649.2576
Fax 985.649.5346
   1924 Corporate Square Dr Ste D, Slidell,
   LA 70458-3164
   Balminder Mangat Md, Psychiatrist

Mark H Zielinski LLC 225.761.0999
Fax 225.761.8220
   10532 S Glenstone Pl, Baton Rouge, LA 70810
   Mark Zielinski, Psychiatrist

Medicine Clinic 318.388.0218
Fax 318.388.1407
   2106 N 7th St, West Monroe, LA 71291
   Rita Agarwal, Psychiatrist

Mental Health Psychiatry 225.952.9210
Fax 225.952.9214
Web ....www.sugai.com
   4521 Jamestown Ave, Baton Rouge, LA 70808
   Carmen Sugai MD, Psychiatrist

Mental Health Solutions 318.631.1122
Fax 318.866.9622
Web ....www.mentalhealthsolutions.com
   2924 Knight Street, Suite 434, Building 4, Shreveport,
   LA 71105
   CARF accredited programs available.

Mercy Family Ctr 504.838.8283
Fax 877.472.2158
Web ....www.mercyfamilycenter.com
   110 Veterans Memorial Blvd Ste 425, Metairie,
   LA 70005-4959
   Mark Sands, Psychiatrist

Mercy Ministries of America 318.388.2040
Fax 318.322.5310
Web ....www.mercyministries.com
E-mail ....mtroquille@mercyministries.com
   804 Spell St, West Monroe, LA 71292-6224
   Margaret Troquille, Program Director

Metropolitan Circles, LLC 318.636.4194
Fax 318.636.4196
Web ....www.metropolitancircles.com
   3510 Linwood Avenue, Shreveport, LA 71103
   Dazetta Williams, Human Resource Director
   CARF accredited programs available.

Meyers Medical Practice 504.895.5533
E-mail ....cdmmd@bellsouth.net
   3525 Prytania St Ste 518, New Orleans,
   LA 70115-8112
   Christopher Meyers, Psychiatrist

Milestones Mental Health Agency 504.269.0234
Fax 504.269.0206
Web ....www.milestonesmha.com
   4820 Prytania Street, New Orleans, LA 70115
   CARF accredited programs available.

Minden Medical Center 318.377.2321
Web ....www.mindenmedicalcenter.com
E-mail ....lynne.rhodes@lpnt.net
   1 Medical Plaza, Minden, LA 71055
   Ms. Lynne Rhodes, Accreditation Manager
   Joint Commission accredited organization.

Minden Medical Ctr 318.377.2321
Fax 318.371.5606
   1 Medical Plaza, Minden, LA 71055
   George French, Iii, CEO

MMO Westend 337.824.4300
Fax 337.824.4315
   1602 Hwy 90 W, Jennings, LA 70546-5347
   Charles Barmlet, Psychiatrist

Mohamed Medical Practice 504.897.6524
E-mail ....drtalaat@aol.com
   2633 Napoleon Ave Ste 912, New Orleans,
   LA 70115-7406
   Talaat Mohamed, Psychiatrist

Monroe Addictive Disorders Clinic 318.362.5188
Fax 318.362.5215
E-mail ....loria.pierce@la.gov
   3200 Concordia Ave, Monroe, LA 71201-5113
   Loria Pierce, Regional Manager

Murphy Family Ctr 985.727.7993
Fax 985.727.7016
   1445 W Causeway Rd, Mandeville, LA 70471
   Doug Duffourc, Psychiatrist

Nabours Medical Practice 337.474.1010
Fax 337.474.1011
   3700 5th Ave, Lake Charles, LA 70607-2134
   P Keith Nabours MD, Psychiatrist

Nagaraj Medical Practice 504.456.6065
Fax 504.456.6067
   3351 Severn Ave Ste 301, Metairie, LA 70002-7408
   Padmini Nagaraj, Psychiatrist

Natchitoche River 318.472.8701
Fax 318.472.9205
Web ....
E-mail ....mickorsborn@bellsouth.net
   PO Box 486, Provencal, LA 71468

Neuropsychiatric Clinic 337.232.9113
Fax 337.232.0022
   1105 S College Rd Ste A, Lafayette, LA 70503-3094
   David Dawes, Psychiatrist

New Beginnings Behavioral Healthcare,
Inc. 985.542.9949
Fax 985.542.9946
   1417 West Morris Avenue, Suite E, Hammond,
   LA 70403
   CARF accredited programs available.

New Directions 985.893.2970
Fax 985.867.1144
Web ....www.mmoinc.com
   201 Greenbrier Boulevard, Covington, LA 70433
   Will Schuester, Director
   CARF accredited programs available.

New Orleans Psychotherapy 504.362.4122
Fax 504.366.5368
   3520 General Degaulle Dr Ste 5055, New Orleans,
   LA 70114-4000
   Robert Dahmes Md, Psychiatrist

New Way of Southwest Louisiana, LLC 337.363.3703
Fax 337.363.4008
   1769 West Main Street, Ville Platte, LA 70586
   ANGEL THOMAS, OFFICE MANGER
   CARF accredited programs available.

North Oaks Medical Ctr 985.345.2700
Fax 985.230.6482
Web ....www.northoaks.org
E-mail ....pguerra@northoaks.org
   15790 Paul Veggam Dr, Hammond, LA 70403
   Pam Guerra, Infectious Control Coordinator

Northeast Louisiana Psych Svc 318.322.8482
Fax 318.322.5694
   141 Desiard St, Monroe, LA 71201
   Jay Weiss Md, Psychiatrist

Ochsner Clinic 504.842.4111
Fax 504.842.3041
   1514 Jefferson Hwy, New Orleans, LA 70121-2483
   Thomas Lee Keister Md, Psychiatrist

Ochsner Clinic Baton Rouge 225.761.5200
Fax 225.761.5538
   9001 Summa Ave, Baton Rouge, LA 70809-3726
   Cary Bahlinger, Md, Psychiatrist

Ochsner Clinic Foundation Med 985.875.2828
Fax 985.875.2357
   1000 Ochsner Blvd, Covington, LA 70433-8107
   Janet Seligson-Dowie, Psychiatrist

Ochsner For Children-Mandevill 985.875.2340
Fax 985.875.2737
Web ....www.ochsner.org
   2810 E Causeway Approach, Mandeville, LA 70448
   Gabrielle Grant, Office Manager

Ofc for Addictive Disorders-Jefferson
Clinic 504.838.5263
Fax 504.838.5720
Web ....www.jphsa.org
E-mail ....dhicks@jphsa.org
   2400 Evenborn Ave, Metairie, LA 70001
   Darlene Hicks, Nursing Supervisor

Options for Independence 985.868.2620
Fax 985.868.8547
Web ....www.optionsforindependence.com
   1340 West Tunnel Boulevard, Suite 430, Houma,
   LA 70360
   CARF accredited programs available.

Orazio Medical Practice 337.991.9162
Fax 337.991.9165
　119 Rue Fountaine, Lafayette, LA 70508-5744
　Joni Orazio Md, Psychiatrist

Palotta Medical Practice 225.767.1000
　5211 Essen Ln Ste 8A, Baton Rouge, LA 70809-3564
　Joseph Palotta Md, Psychiatrist

Perdigao Medical Practice 504.895.7841
Fax 504.895.7841
E-mail ....hgperdigao@yahoo.com
　1424 Amelia St, New Orleans, LA 70115-3618
　Gunther Perdigao, Psychiatrist

Pinecrest Developmental Ctr 318.641.2000
Fax 318.641.2007
　PO Box 5191, Pineville, LA 71361-5191

Pool Medical Practice 504.835.6320
Fax 504.836.6980
　300 Codifer Blvd, Metairie, LA 70005
　Douglas Pool Md, Psychiatrist

Positive Choices Counseling Services, Inc. 318.336.4700
E-mail ....cabb1004@yahoo.com
　1644 Carter Street, Suite 2, Vidalia, LA 71373
　Mrs. Carolyn Brown, Accreditation Manager
　Joint Commission accredited organization.

Preeminent Healthcare Systems, LLC 337.783.5262
Fax 337.783.5264
　325 N. Avenue F, Crowley, LA 70526
　COA accredited organization.

Professional Psychotherapy 504.729.4414
Fax 504.729.4415
　1529 River Oaks Rd W, New Orleans, LA 70123-2162
　George Daul, Psychiatrist

Promise Hospital 318.425.4096
Fax 318.424.2627
E-mail ....sreed@promisehealthcare.com
　1800 Irving Pl, Shreveport, LA 71101-4608
　Shawn Reed, Interim Director Of Admissions And Case Management

Psychiatric Associates 318.841.2801
Fax 318.841.2800
　1801 Fairfield Ave, Shreveport, LA 71101
　Lloyd Bellah Md, Psychiatrist

Psychiatry Assoc of Baton Rouge 225.769.7575
Fax 225.769.4795
　9229 Bluebonnet Blvd, Baton Rouge, LA 70810-2808
　Burl Forgey MD, Psychiatrist

Raintree Children Svcs 504.899.9045
Fax 504.895.0204
Web ....www.raintreeservices.org
E-mail ....raintreenola@raintreeservices.org
　1233 8th St, New Orleans, LA 70115-3332
　Laura Jensen, Director

Red River Treatment Facility 318.484.6888
Fax 318.487.5703
Web ....www.dhh.la.gov
E-mail ....vgcannella@dhh.la.gov
　Unit 6 D, Pineville, LA 71360
　Vicki Cannella, Manager

Rehab Services of CENLA, LLC 318.473.4328
Fax 337.238.4352
　5417 Jackson Street, Suite D, Alexandria, LA 71303
　CARF accredited programs available.

Rehabilitation Services of Baton Rouge, LLC 225.214.1617
Fax 225.216.0082
　9544 Delcourt Avenue, Baton Rouge, LA 70816
　Sam Presad, director
　CARF accredited programs available.

Rehabilitation Services of Northwest Louisiana, LLC 318.675.0804
Fax 318.425.9030
　2525 Youree Drive, Suite 110, Shreveport, LA 71104
　CARF accredited programs available.

Renaissance Home 318.473.0530
Fax 318.473.8866
Web ....renaissance.home.org
E-mail ....rhy@renaissance.home.org
　6177 Bayou Rapides Rd, Alexandria, LA 71303
　Angela Chustz, Director

Resource Management Services, Inc. 337.437.4014
Fax 337.437.8283
　1333 Common Street, Lake Charles, LA 70601
　CARF accredited programs available.

River Oaks, Inc. 504.734.1740
Web ....www.uhsinc.com
E-mail ....susan.gillespie@uhsinc.com
　1525 River Oaks Road West, New Orleans, LA 70123
　Ms. Susan Gillespie, Accreditation Manager
　Joint Commission accredited organization.

Riversouth Rehabilitation Center, Inc. 318.410.1062
Fax 318.410.1065
　1010 North Ninth Street, Monroe, LA 71201
　CARF accredited programs available.

RTC Providers, Inc. 504.483.0415
Fax 504.483.0416
Web ....www.rtcproviders.com
　330 North Jefferson Davis Parkway, New Orleans, LA 70119
　CARF accredited programs available.

Ruston Mental Health Clinic 318.251.4150
Fax 318.251.4177
　901 White St, Ruston, LA 71273
　Stan Mahaffey, Manager

Savoy Medical Ctr 337.468.5261
Fax 337.468.0278
Web ....www.savoymedicalcenter.com
　801 Poinciana Ave, Mamou, LA 70554-2298
　Natalie Brignac, Infectious Control Coorindator

Sewell Medical Practice 318.868.7740
Fax 318.868.7705
　1002 Highland Ave Ste 400, Shreveport, LA 71101-4143
　Patrick Sewell, Psychiatrist

Simon Medical Practice 225.383.3013
　861 Main St, Baton Rouge, LA 70802-5529
　Dr Tolton, Psychologist

Southeast Louisiana Hospital 985.626.6300
Fax 985.626.6459
E-mail ....canderson@dhh.la.gov
　23515 Highway 190, Mandeville, LA 70448
　Cynthia Anderson, Infectious Control Coordinator

Spectrum Rehab Services, Inc. 225.665.7878
Fax 225.665.7856
Web ....www.spectrumrehab.org
E-mail ....spectrum78@cox.net
　30826 Linder Road, Denham Springs, LA 70726
　Michelle Miner, Owner
　CARF accredited programs available.

St Elizabeth Hospital 225.647.5000
Fax 225.647.6066
Web ....www.steh.com
E-mail ....sara.laiche@steh.com
　1125 W Highway 30, Gonzales, LA 70737-5004
　Sara Laiche, Hr Director

St. Anne General Hospital -- Home Health 985.537.6841
Fax 985.537.8361
　4608 Highway 1, Raceland, LA 70394-2623
　Cathy A Baer, Infectious Control Coordinator

St. Mary Addictive Disorders Clinic 985.380.2455
Fax 985.380.2470
Web ....www.dhh.la.gov
　512 Roderick St Ste 200, Morgan City, LA 70380-2247
　Kent Germaine, Clinic Manager

Strauss Medical Practice 504.899.0236
Fax 504.899.0236
　1325 Amelia St, Ste 100, New Orleans, LA 70115-3625
　Arthur Strauss, Psychiatrist

Stress Treatment Ctr 504.299.9770
Fax 504.299.9768
E-mail ....stresstc40@yahoo.com
　919 Governor Nicholls St, New Orleans, LA 70116-2430
　Arthur Samuels Md, Psychiatrist

Success Counseling Services-North 318.222.4299
E-mail ....brandidjohnston@yahoo.com
　1504 Barksdale Blvd., Bossier City, LA 71111
　Ms. Brandi Johnston, Accreditation Manager
　Joint Commission accredited organization.

Sura Medical Practice 225.767.0460
Fax 225.767.3262
　5425 Brittany Dr, Baton Rouge, LA 70808-9170
　Ashwin Sura Md, Psychiatrist

Taravella Medical Practice 225.767.4668
Fax 225.765.3430
　7777 Hennessy Blvd Ste 302, Baton Rouge, LA 70808-4365
　Ron Taravella, Psychiatrist

The Guidance Center, Inc. 504.278.4006
Fax 504.278.4007
　700 West Judge Perez Drive, Chalmette, LA 70043
　CARF accredited programs available.

The Macro Group, Inc. 318.325.7725
Fax 318.325.7735
　803 Stubbs Avenue, Suite A, Monroe, LA 71201
　CARF accredited programs available.

Todd Medical Practice 225.923.3331
Fax 225.923.3122
E-mail ....info@ktoddmd.com
　7932 Wrenwood Blvd, Baton Rouge, LA 70809
　Kenneth Todd, Psychiatrist

Trinity Community Support Services, LLC 985.871.7770
Fax 985.871.7769
　832 East Boston Street, Unit 16, Covington, LA 70433
　CARF accredited programs available.

Tyler Mental Health 337.262.4190
Fax 337.262.4178
　302 Dulles Dr, Lafayette, LA 70506-3008
　David Regan Md, Psychiatrist

Ulrich Medical Practice 504.525.9011
Fax 504.525.9012
E-mail ....heullrich@bellsouth.net
　2233 Saint Charles Ave, New Orleans, LA 70130
　Helen Ulrich MD, Psychiatrist

Universal Rehabilitation Center 318.342.9979
Fax 318.342.9980
　408 Kansas Lane, Suite C, Monroe, LA 71203
　CARF accredited programs available.

Veronica Griffith LPC, Inc. 225.752.0567
Fax 225.752.0569
　9191 Siegen Lane, Building 1, Baton Rouge, LA 70810
　CARF accredited programs available.

Weinholt Medical Practice 318.322.8462
Fax 318.322.8472
　141 Desiard St, Ste 200, Monroe, LA 71201-7340
　Frank Weinholt Do, Psychiatrist

Williams Consulting Inc 318.998.3511
Fax 318.322.9492
E-mail ....williamsconsulting1@hotmail.com
　1410 Royal Ave, Monroe, LA 71201-5608
　David Williams, Director

Louisiana

Winston Medical Practice 337.593.0830
Fax 337.593.0122
201 Rue Beauregard Ste 100, Lafayette,
LA 70508-3399
Bob Winston, Psychiatrist

CHILDREN'S HOSPITAL

Abbeville General Hospital 337.893.5466
118 N Hospital Dr, Abbeville, LA 70510
Ray Landry, Administrator

American Legion hospital 337.783.3222
1305 Crowley Rayne Hwy, Crowley, LA 70526
Terry Osborne, Chief Executive Officer

Baton Rouge General Medical Center 225.387.7000
3600 Floirida St, Baton Rouge, LA 70806
William Holman, Chief Executive Officer

Beauregard Memorial Hospital 337.462.7100
600 S Pine St, DeRidder, LA 70634
Ted Badger, Chief Executive Officer

Byrd Regional Hospital 337.239.9041
1020 Fertitta Blvd, Leesville, LA 71446
Roger Ledoux, Chief Executive Officer

Children's Hospital 504.899.9511
200 Henry Clay Ave, New Orleans, LA 70118
Steve Worley, Chief Executive Officer

Christus Schumpert Hospital 318.681.4500
1 St Mary Pl, Shreveport, LA 71101
Steven Wright, Chief Executive Officer

Christus St Frances Hospital 318.487.1122
3330 Masonic Dr, Alexandria, LA 71301
Stephen Wright, Chief Executive Officer

Christus St Patrick Hospital 337.436.2511
524 Dr Michael DeBakey Dr, Lake Charles, LA 70601
Nancy Hellyer, Interim Administrator

Dauterive Hospital 337.365.7311
600 N Lewis St, New Iberia, LA 70563

Down Syndrome Association 504.251.8953
E-mail ....kscallan@dsagno.org
PO Box 748, Destrehan, LA 70047

EA Conway Medical Center 318.330.7000
4864 Jackson St, Monroe, LA 71202
Aryon Mcguire, Director

Homer Memorial Hospital 318.927.2024
620 E College St, Homer, LA 71040
Scott Barrilleaux, Chief Executive Officer

Huey P Long Medical Center 318.448.0811
352 Hospital Blvd, Pineville, LA 71360
Gary Crockett, Administrator Director

Iberia Medical Center 337.364.0441
2315 E Main St, New Iberia, LA 70560
John Cucker, Chief Executive Officer

La Salle General Hospital 318.992.9200
187 9th St, Jena, LA 71342
Billy Page, Chief Executive Officer

Lafayette General Surgical Hospital 337.289.8095
1000 W Pinhook Rd, Lafayette, LA 70503
David Callecoz, Chief Executive Officer

Lakeview Regional Medical Center 985.867.3800
95 E Fairway Dr, Covington, LA 70433
Jason Comb, Director

Lane Regional Medical Center 225.658.4000
6300 Main St, Zachary, LA 70791

Leonard J Chabert Medical Center 985.873.2200
1978 Industrial Blvd, Houma, LA 70363
Pam Wright, Nursing Director

LSU Medical Center-University Hospital 318.675.5000
1501 Kings Hwy, Shreveport, LA 71130

Natchitoches Regional Medical Center 318.214.4200
501 Keyser Ave, Natchitoches, LA 71457
Mark Marley, Chief Executive Officer

North Caddo Medical Center 318.375.3235
1000 S Spruce St, Vivian, LA 71082
Stacey Alexander, Director Of Nursing

Ochshner Medical Center 985.649.7070
100 Medical Center Dr, Slidell, LA 70461
Cheryl Woods, Chief Nursing Officer

Ochsner Medical Center 504.842.3000
1514 Jefferson Hwy, Jefferson, LA 70121
Patrick Quinlan, Director

Ochsner Medical Center-West Bank 504.392.3131
2500 Belle Chasse Hwy, Gretna, LA 70056
Travis Capers, Chief Executive Officer

Opelousas General Health System 337.948.3011
539 E Prudhomme St, Opelousas, LA 70570
Gary Keller, Chief Executive Officer

Our Lady of Lake Regional Medical Ctr 225.765.6565
5000 Hennessy Blvd, Baton Rouge, LA 70808
Scott Webster, President

Rapides Regional Medical Center 318.473.3000
211 4th St, Alexandria, LA 71301

Sabine Medical Center 318.256.5691
240 Highland Dr, Many, LA 71449
Chris Beddoe, Chief Executive Officer

Slidell Memorial Hospital 985.643.2200
1001 Gause Blvd, Slidell, LA 70458
Bob Hawley, Chief Executive Officer

St Tammany Parish Hospital 985.898.4000
1202 S Tyler St, Covington, LA 70433
Paddy Ellish, Administrator

Terrebonne General Medical Center 985.873.4141
8166 Main St, Houma, LA 70360
Phyllis Peoples, Administrator

Tulane University Hospital & Clinic 504.988.5263
1415 Tulane Ave, New Orleans, LA 70112
Robert Lynch, Chief Executive Officer

Ville Platte Medical Center 337.363.5684
800 E Main St, Ville Platte, LA 70586
Alan Daughtery, Chief Executive Officer

Women's & Children's Hospital 337.521.9100
4600 Ambassador Caffery Pkwy, Lafayette, LA 70508
Kathy Bobbs, Chief Executive Officer

COUNSELING SERVICES

Ctr For Families, Inc 318.222.0759
Fax 318.221.0216
Web ....www.thecenterforfamilies.com
E-mail ....thecntr@aol.com
864 Olive St, Shreveport, LA 71104-2159
Betsy Williams, Executive Director

Eckerd 800.914.3937
Fax 727.442.5911
Web ....www.eckerd.org
E-mail ....admissions@eckerd.org
1170 Highway 51 North, Ponchatoula, LA 70454
David Dennis, President & CEO; Francene Hazel, Director of Admissions
A Juvenile Justice Diversion service to include youth skill-building, mentoring and tracking serving St. Helena, Livingston, Tangipahoa, Washington and St. Tammany parishes in Lousiana. Youth ages 10 – 20 years old are referred by the District 3 Lousiana Office of Youth Development (OYD). Eckerd helps youth stay at home, in school and out of trouble. This is accomplished utilized a team concept which includes the teenager, the parent, the Eckerd counselor, OYD staff and the community.

Jewish Family Svc 504.831.8475
Fax 504.831.1130
Web ....www.jfsneworleans.org
3330 W Esplanade Ave Ste 600, Metairie, LA 70002
Deena Gerber, Executive Director

CRISIS & SHELTER CARE

Calcasieu Womens Shelter 337.436.4552
Fax 337.436.8327
E-mail ....cws@cwshelter.org
601 W 18th St, Lake Charles, LA 70602
Donna Green, Interim Director

Cane River Children's Svcs 318.352.9349
Fax 318.352.9345
E-mail ....crcs@cp-tel.net
425 Rue de Gabriel, Natchitoches, LA 71457
Jennifer Johnson Karle, Executive Director

Catholic Charities Archdiocese of New
Orleans 504.523.3755
Fax 504.596.3098
E-mail ....jkelly@archdiocese-no.org
1000 Howard Ave Ste 1000, New Orleans,
LA 70113-1942
James Kelly, CEO

Chez Hope, Inc.-Domestic Violence
Program 337.828.4200
Fax 337.828.4202
E-mail ....chezhope@cox-internet.com
801 Main Street, Franklin, LA 70538
Ms. Sami Riley, Director

Christian Acres 318.574.3146
Fax 318.574.4093
E-mail ....cacares@bellsouth.net
301 S Chestnut St, Tallulah, LA 71282
Janet Moore, Administrator

Education Treatment Council Harbor
House 337.433.6739
Fax 337.477.2559
Web ....www.dss.state.la.us
E-mail ....amy@etc-youth.org
PO Box 864, Lake Charles, LA 70602-0864
Amy Dunn, Executive Director

Faith House-Crisis Shelter-Domestic Violence 337.232.8954
Fax 337.232.2770
Web ....www.faithhouseacadiana.com
E-mail ....blacombe@faithhouseacadiana.com
PO Box 93145, Lafayette, LA 70509-3145
Billi Lacombe, Director

Girls and Boys Town of Louisiana 504.392.4501
Fax 504.392.9546
Web ....www.girlsandboystown.org/louisiana
1008 Behrman Hwy, Gretna, LA 70056
Greg Fortenberry, Family Teacher

Hope Haven Ctr/Catholic Charities 504.347.5581
Fax 504.340.2075
1101 Barataria Blvd, Marrero, LA 70072-3024
Robert Guasco, Executive Director

Johnny Gray Jones Regional Youth Shelter 318.747.1459
Fax 318.747.4911
Web ....www.family-to-family.org/
4815 Shed Rd, Bossier City, LA 71111-5416
Debra Hamilton, Executive Director

Livingston Youth & Family Counseling 225.665.7242
Fax 225.665.5451
E-mail ....lyfc@eatel.net
940 Government St, Denham Springs, LA 70726-3633
Ligia Soileau, Executive Director

Natchitoches Ctr for Addictive Disorders 318.357.3283
Fax 318.357.3287
210 Medical Dr, Natchitoches, LA 01457
Judi Trudy Abner, Regional Manager

Our House, Inc. 318.345.5556
Fax 318.345.5550
Web ....www.teen-health.com
E-mail ....ourhouse@comcast.net
203 Smith Ave, Monroe, LA 71203
Ella Mimmers, Executive Director

Southeast Spouse Abuse Program 985.542.8384
Fax 985.429.1288
Web ....www.southeastspouseabuseprogram.com
E-mail ....exdir@southeastspouseabuseprogram.com
1200 Derek Dr # 100, Hammond, LA 70403
Samantha Stone, Director

St. Bernard Battered Women's Program, Inc. 504.277.3178
Fax 504.279.9377
E-mail ....deanobwp@aol.com
2011 Jackson Blvd, Chalmette, LA 70043-4760
Gail Gowland, Director

FOSTER CARE AGENCIES

Down Syndrome Association 504.251.8953
E-mail ....kscallan@dsagno.org
PO Box 748, Destrehan, LA 70047

FAIR Visions Inc (Foster Adoptive 318.340.0230
Fax 318.340.0233
3001 Armand Ste G, Monroe, LA 71202
Tamara Thompson, Program Director

LA Adoption Advisory Board Inc (LAAB) 337.896.5571
Fax 337.896.5571
PO Box 52832, Lafayette, LA 70505

LA Foster & Adoptive Parent Association 337.582.6900
Fax 318.340.0233
E-mail ....kirp50@juno.com
PO Box 332, Baton Rouge, LA 70821
Peggy Kirby, Director

Louisiana Foster & Adoptive Parent Assoc 985.789.0071
PO Box 332, Baton Rouge, LA 70821
Peggy Kirby

Louisiana Mentor 318.448.3747
Fax 318.448.3748
Web ....www.thementornetwork.com
1450 Peterman Dr, Alexandria, LA 71301
Sharon Lair, Program Director

Louisiana State Representative 504.443.1012
E-mail ....LinRWoods@aol.com
25 Osborne Ave, Kenner, LA 70065

Mentor Network 318.410.8823
Fax 318.410.8826
Web ....www.thementornetwork.com
E-mail ....dana.castine@thementornetwork.com
1890 Hudson Cir Ste 12, Monroe, LA 71201-3545
Dana Castine, Director

Natchitoche River 318.472.8701
Fax 318.472.9205
E-mail ....mickorsborn@bellsouth.net
PO Box 486, Provencal, LA 71468

Pride & Hope Ministry Adoptive Parent 985.732.9615
25502 Hwy 21, Angie, LA 70426

SE Louisiana Foster & Adopt Parent Assoc 504.305.3376
PO Box 73302, Metairie, LA 70033
Toni David

St Elizabeth Foundation (SEF) 225.769.8888
Fax 225.769.6874
E-mail ....teri@stelizabethfoundation.org
8054 Summa Ave, Ste A, Baton Rouge, LA 70809
Teri Casso, Director

Vlntrs of American of Greater New Orlean 504.482.2130
Fax 504.482.1922
E-mail ....larceneaux@voagno.org
4152 Canal St, New Orleans, LA 70119
Jim Leblanc, President

Volunteers of American of N Louisiana 318.221.2669
Fax 318.222.6370
E-mail ....lisa@voanorthla.org
360 Jordan St, Shreveport, LA 71101
Chuck Meehan, Chief Executive Officer

PEDIATRIC HOME CARE

Baton Rouge PDN 225.291.1221
4451 Bluebonnet Blvd Ste E, Baton Rouge, LA 70809

Interim Healthcare 985.674.1699
Fax 985.626.7473
235 St Ann Dr Ste 3, Mandeville, LA 70471
Alisia Robinson, Director of Nursing

Interim Healthcare 318.387.8894
Fax 318.387.7380
2106 N 7th St, West Monroe, LA 71291
Robin Buller, Director

Interim Hlthcare (Bossier City Staffing 318.741.3776
Fax 318.742.7094
2323 Old Minden Rd Ste 500, Bossier City, LA 71112
Tricia Firth, Owner

SOCIAL SERVICES

Acadiana Youth, Inc.
Web ....www.acadianayouthinc.org
P.O. Box 92078, Lafayette, LA 70509
COA accredited organization.

Agenda For Child Care Resources 504.586.8509
Fax 504.586.8522
Web ....www.agendaforchildren.org
E-mail ....lcooks@agendaforchildren.org
1720 St. Charles Ave, Thibodaux, LA 70301
Judy Watts, CEO/Executive Director

Catholic Charities 318.445.2401
Fax 318.448.6121
Web ....www.diocesealex.org
E-mail ....frgrem@diocesealex.org
4400 Coliseum Blvd, Alexandria, LA 71303
Father Rickey Gremillion, Director

Catholic Charities 337.439.7436
Fax 337.439.7435
Web ....www.lcdiocese.org
E-mail ....carol.fernandez@lcdiocese.org
1225 2nd St, Lake Charles, LA 70601
Carol Fernandez, Director

Catholic Charities Archdiocese of New Orleans 505.523.3755
Fax 504.523.2789
Web ....www.adoptnola.com;www.ccano.org
1000 Howard Avenue, Suite 1000, New Orleans, LA 70113
COA accredited organization.

Catholic Social Svcs 337.261.5654
Fax 337.261.5660
Web ....www.dol-louisiana.org
E-mail ....paula@diolas.org
1408 Carmel Dr, Lafayette, LA 70501
Paula Milner, Director

Catholic Social Svcs of Houma-Thibodaux 985.876.0490
Fax 985.876.7751
E-mail ....rgorman@htdiocese.org
1220 Aycock St, Houma, LA 70360
Robert Gorman, Director

Centerpoint Community Services/2-1-1 ......318.227.2100
Fax 318.227.0035
Web ....www.centerpt.org
E-mail ....bkeesee@centerpt.org
2121 Fairfield Ave. Ste. 130, Shreveport, LA 71104
Barbara A. Keesee, Homeless Services Director

Children's Bureau of New Orleans 504.525.2366
Fax 504.525.7525
Web ....www.childrens-bureau.com
2626 Canal Street, Suite 201, New Orleans, LA 70119
COA accredited organization.

Children's Trust Fund 225.342.6674
Fax 225.342.2268
Web ....www.lctf.org
E-mail ....jharris1@dss.state.la.us
PO Box 3318, Baton Rouge, LA 70821-3318
Judy Harrison, Director

Covenant House New Orleans Ciaccio Crisis Ctr 504.584.1108
Fax 504.584.1171
Web ....www.covenanthouseno.org
E-mail ....jkelly@covenanthouse.org
611 N Rampart St, New Orleans, LA 70112-3540
James Kelly, Director

Family Service of Greater New Orleans 504.822.0800
Fax 504.822.0831
Web ....www.fsgno.org
2515 Canal Street, Suite 201, New Orleans, LA 70119
COA accredited organization.

Gingerbread House 318.674.2900
Fax 318.674.8141
Web ....www.gingerbreadhousecac.org
1700 Buckner Sq, Shreveport, LA 71101
Jessica Miller, Executive Director

Jewish Childrens Regional Service 504.828.6334
Fax 504.828.5255
E-mail ....ned.jcrs@yahoo.com
3500 N Causeway Blvd Ste 120, Metairie, LA 70010
Ned Goldberg, Exe-direcotr

Kingsley House, Inc. 504.523.6221
Fax 504.523.4450
Web ....www.kingsleyhouse.org
1600 Constance Street, New Orleans, LA 70130
COA accredited organization.

Library Info Svc 225.231.3750
Fax 225.231.3736
Web ....www.ebr.lib.la.us
E-mail ....esmart@ebr.lib.la.us
7711 Goodwood Blvd, Baton Rouge, LA 70806-7625
Emily Smart, Reference Director

Louisiana Baptist Children's Home and Family Ministries 318.343.2244
Fax 318.343.0613
Web ....www.lbch.org
E-mail ....home@lbch.org
  7200 Desiard St, Monroe, LA 71203
  Perry Hancock, President And CEO

Louisiana Department of Children and Family Services, Child Welfare Program 225.342.4073
Fax 225.342.6926
Web ....www.dss.state.la.us
  P.O. Box 3318, Baton Rouge, LA 70821
  COA accredited organization.

Louisiana United Methodist Children and Family Services, Inc 318.255.5020
Fax 318.255.6623
Web ....www.lmch.org
  P.O. Box 929, Ruston, LA 71273-0929
  COA accredited organization.

Northwestern State University Child and Family Network 318.677.3150
Fax 318.677.3169
E-mail ....nancya@nsula.edu
  1800 Warrington Pl, Shreveport, LA 71101-4425
  Nancy Alexander, Director

Ofc for Citizens with Developmental Disabilities 318.362.3396
Fax 318.362.5305
Web ....www.dhh.la.gov
  122 Saint John St, Rm 343, Monroe, LA 71201
  Deanne Groves, Community Services Regional Admin

Partnership In Child Care 225.926.8005
Fax 225.926.8023
E-mail ....jstarks@pic.broxmail.com
  4521 Jamestown Ave Ste 5, Baton Rouge, LA 70808
  Janie Starks, Director

Raintree Children and Family Services 504.899.9045
Fax 504.895.0204
Web ....www.raintreeservices.org
  1233 Eighth Street, New Orleans, LA 70115
  COA accredited organization.

Shreveport Job Corps Ctr 318.227.9331
Fax 318.222.0768
E-mail ....rios.john@dol.gov
  2815 Lillian St, Shreveport, LA 71109-2899
  John Rios, Center Director

SPECIAL NEEDS

Down Syndrome Association 504.251.8953
E-mail ....kscallan@dsagno.org
  PO Box 748, Destrehan, LA 70047

Easter Seals Louisiana 504.523.7325
  305 Baronne St Ste 400, 1010 toman st ste 2000, New Orleans, LA 70112
  Tracy Garner, Chief Executive Officer

Educational Improvement & Assistance 877.453.2721
E-mail ....customerservice@alley.gov
  1201 N 3rd St, Baton Rouge, LA 70802
  Dr. Kerry Laster, Director

Epilepsy Foundation of Louisiana 800.960.0587
E-mail ....dotty@epilepsylouisiana.org
  7762 S Harrells Ferry Rd, Ste F, Baton Rouge, LA 70816
  Dotty Martino, Executive Director

Families Helping Families 504.430.3604
E-mail ....fhf-la@cox.net
  PO Box 626, Thibodaux, LA 70302

Fed Families f/Children's Mental Health 800.224.4010
E-mail ....vboyd@laffcmh.org
  5627 Superior Dr Ste A-2, Baton Rouge, LA 70816
  Verlyn Boyd, Executive Director

LearningRx Learning Center 318.671.0310
E-mail ....bossiercity.la@learningrx.net
  4128 Airline Dr, Bossier City, LA 71111
  Donesa Walker, Director

Louisana Parent Training & Info Center 504.888.9111
Fax 504.888.0246
E-mail ....carceneaux@laptic.org
  201 Evans Rd Bldg 1 Ste 100, Harahan, LA 70123
  Mary Jacob, Executive Director

Louisiana Citizens for Action Now 337.367.7407
E-mail ....kay.marcel@cox.net
  2313 Blue Haven Dr, New Iberia, LA 70563

Louisiana Health & Rehab Center Inc 225.231.2490
E-mail ....soundrajt@aol.com
  214 Ocean Dr, Baton Rouge, LA 70806
  Soundra Temple, Chief Executive Officer

Louisiana Parent-Teacher Association 225.927.7382
E-mail ....la_office@bellsouth.net
  9151 Interline Ave Ste 1A, Baton Rouge, LA 70809
  Sharon Pender, President

Louisiand Occupational Therapy Assn 225.291.4014
E-mail ....lotassoc@aol.com
  PO Box 14806, Baton Rouge, LA 70898

McMains Children's Development Center 225.923.3420
E-mail ....jketcham@mcmainscdc.org
  1805 College Dr, Baton Rouge, LA 70808
  Janet Ketcham, Director

NAMI Louisiana 866.851.6264
E-mail ....namilouisiana@bellsouth.net
  PO Box 40517, Baton Rouge, LA 70835
  Jimmy Jantz, Executive Director

National Multiple Sclerosis Society 504.832.4013
Fax 504.831.7188
E-mail ....LouisianaChapter@nmss.org
  4613 Fairfield St, Metairie, LA 70006
  Rebecca Pennington, Vice President

Parent Training & Information Center 504.888.9111
E-mail ....info@laptic.org
  201 Evans Rd, Bldg 1 Ste 100, Harahan, LA 70123
  Mary Jacob, Executive Director

Pyramid Community Parent Resource Ctr 504.899.1505
E-mail ....pyramidcprc@aol.com
  3132 Napoleon Ave, New Orleans, LA 70125

Special Olympics Louisiana 800.345.6644
E-mail ....pcarpenter@laso.org
  1000 E Morris Ave, Hammond, LA 70403
  Pat Carpenter, President

Speech-Language-Hearing Association 225.922.4512
E-mail ....lsha@pncpa.com
  8550 United Plaza Blvd # 1001, Baton Rouge, LA 70809

Spina Bifida of New Orleans 504.737.5181
E-mail ....sbgno@sbgno.org
  PO Box 1346, Kenner, LA 70063
  Julie Johnson, Coordinator

The Rehab Center of West Jefferson Medical Center 504.349.1345
Fax 504.349.1341
Web ....www.wjmc.org
E-mail ....pat.judd@wjmc.org
  1101 Medical Center Boulevard, Marrero, LA 70072
  Pat Judd, Director - Nursing
  CARF accredited programs available.

The Rehabilitation Center of Thibodaux Regional 985.493.4435
Fax 985.493.4436
Web ....www.thibodaux.com
E-mail ....brenda.parro@thibodaux.com
  602 North Acadia Road, Thibodaux, LA 70301
  Brenda Parro, Education Director
  CARF accredited programs available.

Touro Rehabilitation Center 504.897.8560
Fax 504.897.8393
Web ....www.touro.com
  1401 Foucher Street, M10, New Orleans, LA 70115
  CARF accredited programs available.

United Cerebral Palsy of New Orleans 504.461.4266
E-mail ....info@ucpgno.org
  2200 Veterans Memorial Blvd, Ste 103, Kenner, LA 70062
  Jo Bugg, Executive Director

Univ Ctr f/Excellence in Dev Disability 504.556.7558
E-mail ....sdelvi@lsuhsc.edu
  1900 Gravier St, 8th Fl Rm 817, New Orleans, LA 70112

VSA Arts of Louisiana 225.761.4243
E-mail ....vsalouisiana@bellsouth.net
  2888-D Brightside Ln, Baton Rouge, LA 70820
  Nancy Malbaeux, Director

Willis-Knighton Health System Physical Medicine and Rehabilitation 318.212.4737
Fax 318.212.4347
Web ....www.wkhs.com
  2600 Greenwood Road, Shreveport, LA 71103
  CARF accredited programs available.

Maine

Paul Lepage, Governor
Governor's Office, Rm 236
1 State House Station
Augusta, ME 04333-001
207.287.3531
207.287.1034 (Fax)
governor@maine.gov
www.maine.gov/governor/baldacci/index

Kathryn McGloin, Juvenile Justice Specialist
111 State House Station
Augusta, ME 04333-0111
207.287.1923
207.287.4518 (Fax)
kathryn.mcgloin@maine.gov

Paul K. Vestal, SAG Chair
St. Michael's Center
1066 Kenduskeag Avenue
Bangor, ME 04401-2919
207.941.2855
207.941.2835 (Fax)
pvestal@ccmaine.org

CRISIS NUMBERS

Child Abuse Reporting . . .800.452.1999

STATE SERVICES

SOCIAL SERVICES

Bureau of Family Independence 207.624.8090
Fax 207.624.8124
Web . . . . .www.maine.gov
E-mail . . . . .mike.frey@state.me.us
35 Anthony Dr, Augusta, ME 04333
Mike Frey, Program Administrator

Division of Lic and Reg Srvs Maine 207.287.9300
Fax 207.287.5031
E-mail . . . . .catherinecobb@maine.gov
41 Anthony Ave, 11 State House Station, Augusta,
ME 04333
Catherine Cobb, Director

Maine Dept of Health and Human Svcs 207.287.3707
Fax 207.287.3005
11 State House Sta, 221 State St., Augusta,
ME 04333
Geoffrey Green, Deputy Commissioner Of Operations

GENERAL HEALTH SERVICES

Children with Spec Health Needs ME 207.624.7900
Fax 207.287.5282
E-mail . . . . .james.beougher@maine.gov
2 Anthony Ave, Augusta, ME 04333
Trese Cahill-Low, Acting Director

Family Health Programs ME 207.287.5396
Fax 207.287.5355
E-mail . . . . .mary.colson@maine.gov
286 Water St 7th Flr, 11 State House Station Key Plz,
Augusta, ME 04333
Valerie Ricker, Director

Ofc of Maine Care Svcs 207.287.2674
Fax 207.287.2675
Web . . . . .www.maine.gov
442 Civic Center Dr, Augusta, ME 04333-0001
Stefanie Nadeau, Director

MENTAL HEALTH SERVICES

Div of Vocational Rehab ME 207.623.7943
Fax 207.287.5292
E-mail . . . . .elizabeth.hopkins@maine.gov
45 Commerce Dr, 150 State House Station, Augusta,
ME 04333
Elizabeth Hopkins, Director

Maine Dept of Human Svcs Bureau of Health . . .207.287.8016
Fax 207.287.9058
E-mail . . . . .sheila.pinette@maine.gov
286 Water St, 11 State House Stn 8th Fl Key Plaza,
Augusta, ME 04330
Sheila Pinette, Director

Vocational and Rehab Agency ME 207.623.7956
Fax 207.624.5980
E-mail . . . . .john.m.mcmahon@maine.gov
150 State House Station, Augusta, ME 04333
John McMahon, Director

JUSTICE AGENCY

Crime Victims Compensation Program 207.626.8800
Fax 207.624.7730
Web . . . . .www.state.me.us
111 Sewall St, Augusta, ME 04333-0006
Deborah Shaw Rice, Executive Director

Maine Dept of Corrections 207.287.4362
Fax 207.287.4518
Web . . . . .www.maine.gov
E-mail . . . . .dyana.white@maine.gov
111 State House Sta, Augusta, ME 04333-0111
Dyana White, Administrator Secretary

Maine Dept of Public Safety 207.626.3800
Fax 207.287.3042
Web . . . . .www.maine.gov
E-mail . . . . .john.e.morris@maine.gov
45 Commerce St Ste 1, Augusta, ME 04333-0001
John Morris, Commissioner

State CASA 207.287.5403
Fax 207.287.7553
Web . . . . .www.courts.state.me.us
E-mail . . . . .casamaine@courts.maine.gov
24 Stone St, Augusta, ME 04333
Tracie Adamson, Director Of Family Division

COURTS

Administrative Ofc Of The Courts 207.822.0792
Fax 207.822.0781
125 Presumpscot St Unit 7, Portland, ME 04112
James T. Glessner, Court Administrator

POLICE AND SHERIFF

Maine Chiefs of Police Assoc 207.799.9318
Fax 207.767.2214
E-mail . . . . .rschwar1@maine.rr.com
35 Scamman St, South Portland, ME 04106
Robert M. Schwartz, Executive Director

EDUCATION SERVICES

Educ for Homeless Children and Youth ME 207.624.6637
Fax 207.624.6624
E-mail . . . . .shelley.reed@maine.gov
State House Station 23, Augusta, ME 04333
Shelley Reed, Director

Maine Dept of Education 207.624.6600
Fax 207.624.6700
Web . . . . .www.maine.gov/education
23 State House Station, Augusta, ME 04333
David Stockford, Special Services Director

Maine Parent Federation 207.623.2144
Fax 207.623.2148
E-mail . . . . .parentconnect@mpf.org
PO Box 2067, Augusta, ME 04338

Office of Special Services ME 207.624.6650
Fax 207.624.6651
E-mail . . . . .david.stockford@maine.gov
23 State House Station, Augusta, ME 04333
David Stockford, Director

COUNTY SERVICES

Androscoggin County

SOCIAL SERVICES

Maine Dept of Hlth & Human Svcs 207.795.4300
200 Main St, Lewiston, ME 04240

JUSTICE AGENCY

Juvenile Justice Region II Ofc 207.783.5383
Fax 207.783.5344
Web . . . . .www.maine.gov
E-mail . . . . .cynthia.brann@maine.gov
945 Center St, Ste 3, Auburn, ME 04210
Cynthia Brann, Regional Correctional Administrator

COURTS

8th District Court 207.795.4801
Web . . . . .www.courts.state.me.us
71 Lisbon St, Lewiston, ME 04240-3199
Honorable Paul A. Cote, Jr., District Court Judge

POLICE AND SHERIFF

Sheriff's Ofc 207.784.7361
Fax 207.784.3199
Web ....www.adelphia.net
E-mail ....andyso@roadrunner.com
2 Turner St Unit 9, Auburn, ME 04210-5978
Guy P. Desjardines, Sheriff

EDUCATION SERVICES

Andro Head Start - Turner Primary 207.795.4040
Fax 207.795.4044
Web ....www.androscogginheadstart.org
E-mail ....erubinstein@androkids.com
269 Bates St, Lewiston, ME 04240-7331
Estelle Rubinstein, Director

Aroostook County

SOCIAL SERVICES

Dept of Human Svcs / Caribou 207.493.4050
Fax 207.493.4004
E-mail ....tracy.mccrossin@maine.gov
30 Skyway Dr Unit 100, Caribou, ME 04736-2097
Tracy Mccrossin, Program Administrator

Dept of Human Svcs / Fort Kent 207.834.7700
Fax 207.834.7701
Web ....www.maine.gov
137 Market St, Fort Kent, ME 04743-1447
Wayne Norrow, Business Manager

Indian Social Svcs 207.532.6393
Fax 207.532.7287
Web ....www.maliseets.com
13-2 Clover Court, Littleton, ME 04730
Brenda Commander, Tribal Chief

Micmac Tribal Social Svcs 207.764.1972
Fax 207.764.7667
7 Northern Rd, Presque Isle, ME 04769
Victoria Higgins, Chief

GENERAL HEALTH SERVICES

Micmac Tribal Health Dept 207.764.7219
Fax 207.764.7768
E-mail ....JohnOvellett@ihs.gov
8 Northern Rd, Presque Isle, ME 04769
John Ovellett, Director

MENTAL HEALTH SERVICES

Aroostook Mental Health Ctr 207.498.6431
Fax 207.492.3181
Web ....www.amhc.org
E-mail ....gdisi@amhc.org
43 Hatch Dr, Caribou, ME 04736
Greg Disi, CEO

COURTS

1st District Court 207.834.5003
Web ....www.courts.state.me.us
E-mail ....linda.cyr@courts.maine.gov
139 Market St Ste 101, Fort Kent, ME 04743-1449
Linda Cyr, Clerk Of Court

POLICE AND SHERIFF

Sheriff's Ofc 207.532.3471
Fax 207.532.7319
25 School St, Houlton, ME 04730
James P. Madore, Sheriff

EDUCATION SERVICES

Special Education 207.496.6311
Fax 207.498.3261
Web www.easternaroostookrsu39.org.org
628 Main St, Caribou, ME 04736
Karla Michaud, Director Special Services

Cumberland County

SOCIAL SERVICES

Dept of Human Svcs 207.822.2071
Fax 207.822.2310
Web ....www.maine.gov
161 Marginal Way, Portland, ME 04101-2498
June Cloupier, Business Service Manager

GENERAL HEALTH SERVICES

Public Health Div 207.874.8784
Fax 207.874.8913
Web ....www.portlandmaine.gov
E-mail ....jas@portlandmaine.gov
389 Congress St Rm 307, Portland, ME 04101-3571
Julianne Sullivan, Director Public Health Division

MENTAL HEALTH SERVICES

Behavioral and Developmental Svcs 207.822.0270
Fax 207.822.0295
E-mail ....brian.scanlon@maine.gov
161 Margimal Way, Portland, ME 04101
Brian Scanlon, Team Leader

COURTS

9th District Court 207.822.4200
Web ....www.courts.state.me.us
205 Newbury St, Portland, ME 04101-4160
Honorable Peter Goranites, District Court Judge

POLICE AND SHERIFF

Sheriff's Dept 207.774.1444
Fax 207.828.2373
Web ....www.cumberlandcounty.org
E-mail ....dion@cumberlandcounty.org
36 County Way, Portland, ME 04102-2755
Kevin Joyce, Sheriff

EDUCATION SERVICES

Bridgton Child Development Head Start 207.647.5758
6 Meadow St, Bridgton, ME 04009-1334
Aileen Peaco-burkett, Director

Special Education 207.871.0555
Fax 207.871.0559
Web ....www.spsd.org
E-mail ....coxk@spsd.org
130 Wescott Rd, South Portland, ME 04106-3420
Kathleen Cox, Director

Franklin County

SOCIAL SERVICES

Dept of Health & Human Svcs 207.778.8400
Fax 207.778.8410
Web ....www.maine.gov
E-mail ....barbara.barrows@maine.gov
114 Corn Shop Ln, Farmington, ME 04938-6401
Barbara Barrows, Supervisor

GENERAL HEALTH SERVICES

Health Svcs 207.778.4553
Fax 207.778.4257
Web ....www.wmca.org
E-mail ....rgrant@wmca.org
193 Front St, Farmington, ME 04938
Rebecca Grant, Program Manager

COURTS

Maine District Court XII 207.778.8200
Fax 207.778.8410
129 Main St Ste 1, Farmington, ME 04938
Honorable John Mcelwee, District Court Judge

POLICE AND SHERIFF

Sheriff's Dept 207.778.2680
Fax 207.778.6485
Web ....www.franklincountyso.net
E-mail ....fcsd@verizon.net
123 County Way, Farmington, ME 04938-5200
Dennis C. Pike, Sheriff

Hancock County

SOCIAL SERVICES

Maine Dept of Hlth & Human Svcs 207.667.1600
17 Eastward Ln, Ellsworth, ME 04605

GENERAL HEALTH SERVICES

Downeast Home Health Svc 207.667.5304
Fax 207.667.6117
Web ....www.downeasthealth.org
E-mail ....knorwood@downeasthealth.org
52 Christian Ridge Rd, Ellsworth, ME 04605-3210
Kathie Norwood, Executive Director

COURTS

5th District Court 207.667.7141
Fax 207.664.7507
50 State St Ste 2, Ellsworth, ME 04605
Bruce Mallonee, Judge

POLICE AND SHERIFF

Sheriff's Dept 207.667.7575
Fax 207.667.7516
Web ....www.downeast.net
E-mail ....topdog@hancockcountyso.org
50 State St Ste 10, Ellsworth, ME 04605-1940
William F. Clark, Sheriff

Kennebec County

SOCIAL SERVICES

Region III Health And Human Svcs 207.624.8088
Fax 207.624.5553
35 Anthony Ave, Augusta, ME 04333-0001
Ellen Beerits, Administrator

GENERAL HEALTH SERVICES

Augusta City Health and Welfare 207.626.2325
Fax 207.626.2304
E-mail ....raenae.moore@augustamaine.gov
16 Cony St, Augusta, ME 04330
Raenae Moore, Health & Welfare Director

MENTAL HEALTH SERVICES

Kennebec Valley Mental Health Ctr 207.873.2136
Fax 207.872.4522
Web ....www.kbhmaine.org
67 Eustis Pkwy, Waterville, ME 04901-5173
Josie Shelley, Chief Financial Officer

JUSTICE AGENCY

Juvenile Justice Region II Ofc 207.287.5276
Fax 207.287.5299
Web ....www.state.me.us
320 Water St, Augusta, ME 04338
Susan Gagnon, Regional Correctional Administrator

COURTS

7th District Court 207.287.8075
Fax 207.287.8082
145 State St, Augusta, ME 04330
Michele Lumbert, Clerk

District Court 207.873.2103
Fax 207.873.3207
Web ....www.the-injury-lawyer-directory.com
18 Colby St Ste 1, Waterville, ME 04901-5583
Diane McLaughlin, Chief District Court Judge

POLICE AND SHERIFF

Augusta City Police Dept **207.626.2370**
Fax 207.623.2512
Web .... www.augustamaine.gov
E-mail .... wayne.mccamish@augustamaine.gov
33 Union St, Augusta, ME 04330-6800
B Gregoire, Chief

Knox County

SOCIAL SERVICES

Dept of Health and Human Svcs **207.596.4200**
Fax 207.596.4235
Web .... www.maine.gov
E-mail .... catherine.reynolds@maine.gov
91 Camden St Ste 103, Rockland, ME 04841-2421
Catherine Reynolds, Human Services Administrator

COURTS

6th District Court **207.596.2240**
Fax 207.596.2251
62 Union St, Rockland, ME 04841
Honorable Joseph Field, District Court Judge

POLICE AND SHERIFF

Sheriff's Dept **207.594.0429**
Fax 207.594.0433
Web .... www.knoxso.com
E-mail .... ddennison@knoxcountymaine.gov
327 Park St, Rockland, ME 04841-5302
Donna Dennison, Sheriff

Lincoln County

COURTS

District Court **207.882.6363**
32 High St, Wiscasset, ME 04578
Kelly Cluff, District Court Judge

POLICE AND SHERIFF

Sheriff's Dept **207.882.7332**
Fax 207.882.9872
Web .... www.midcoast.com
E-mail .... sheriff@midcoast.com
42 Bath Road, Wiscasset, ME 04578
Todd B. Brackett, Sheriff

EDUCATION SERVICES

MMCA **207.549.5262**
Fax 207.519.7863
PO Box 182, Whitefield, ME 04353-0182
Joanne Lenox, Center Manager

Oxford County

SOCIAL SERVICES

Maine Dept of Hlth & Human Svcs **207.744.1200**
243 Main St, Ste 6, South Paris, ME 04281

POLICE AND SHERIFF

Sheriff's Ofc **207.743.9554**
Fax 207.743.1510
Web .... www.cji.net
E-mail .... lcherrick@cji.net
26 Western Ave Ste 2, South Paris, ME 04281-1431
Lloyd C. Herrick, Sheriff

Penobscot County

SOCIAL SERVICES

**Indian Human Svcs / Penobscot
Nation** **207.827.7776**
Fax 207.827.2937
Web .... www.penobscotnation.org
E-mail .... sonya.lacoute-dana@penobscotnation.org
12 Wabanaki Way, Old Town, ME 04468-1254
Sonya Lacoute-Dana, Director Human Services

GENERAL HEALTH SERVICES

Public Health Nursing **207.561.4173**
Fax 207.561.4467
396 Griffin Rd, Dept.of Human Services, Bangor,
ME 04401-3002
Jane Mcquarrie, Rn, Phn Supervisor

JUSTICE AGENCY

Probation & Parole **207.941.3130**
Fax 207.941.3132
E-mail .... davidmbarrett@maine.gov
10 Franklin St, Bangor, ME 44401
Dave Barrett, District Supervisor

COURTS

District III **207.368.5778**
Fax 207.368.7724
12 Water St, Newport, ME 04953
Ronda Nelson, Clerk Of Court

District XIII **207.723.4786**
Fax 207.723.3912
207 Penobscot Ave, Millinocket, ME 04462-1430
Honorable Kevin Stitham, District Court Judge

District XIII **207.794.8512**
Fax 207.794.3390
52 Main St, Lincoln, ME 04457
Honorable Kevin Stitham, District Court Judge

POLICE AND SHERIFF

Sheriff's Ofc **207.947.4585**
Fax 207.945.4761
E-mail .... sheriff@penobscot-sheriff.net
85 Hammond St, Bangor, ME 04401
Glenn Ross, Sheriff

EDUCATION SERVICES

Davis Road Head Start **207.262.6091**
Fax 207.945.5501
241 Davis Rd, Bangor, ME 04401-2312
Jean-ann Lawrenson, Director

Dexter Head Start **207.924.3806**
20 Cedar St, Dexter, ME 04930-0552
Donna Bilodeau, Director

Special Education **207.799.3987**
Fax 207.799.2914
Web .... www.capeelizabeth.com
E-mail .... jgolding@capeelizabethschools.org
320 Ocean House Rd, Cape Elizabeth,
ME 04107-2419
Jane Golding, Director Special Services

Piscataquis County

COURTS

13th District Court **207.564.2240**
163 E Main St, Dover Foxcroft, ME 04426-1395
Honorable Kevin Stitham, District Court Judge

POLICE AND SHERIFF

Sheriff's Ofc **207.564.3304**
Fax 207.564.2315
Web .... www.emh.org
E-mail .... jgoggin@emh.org
52 Court St, Dover Foxcroft, ME 04426-1249
John J. Goggin, Sheriff

Sagadahoc County

COURTS

Courts **207.442.0200**
Fax 207.442.0208
Web .... www.maine.gov
101 New Meadows Rd, Bath, ME 04530-6207
Joan M. Kidman, Magistrate

POLICE AND SHERIFF

Sheriff's Dept **207.443.8201**
Fax 207.443.8535
752 High St, Bath, ME 04530
Joe Mary, Sheriff

Somerset County

SOCIAL SERVICES

Maine Dept of Hlth & Human Svcs **207.474.4800**
98 N Avenue, Ste 10, Skowhegan, ME 04976

GENERAL HEALTH SERVICES

Public Health Nursing **207.474.4808**
Fax 207.287.5355
E-mail .... valerie.j.ricker@maine.gov
98 North Ave Ste 10, Skowhegan, ME 04976
Valerie Ricker, Director

POLICE AND SHERIFF

Sheriff's Ofc **207.474.9591**
Fax 207.858.4705
E-mail .... barrydelong@me.gov
131 E Madison Rd, Madison, ME 04950
Barry A. Delong, Sheriff

Waldo County

COURTS

5th District Court **207.338.3107**
Fax 207.338.4273
103 Church St, Belfast, ME 04915-6419
Terri Curtis, Clerk

POLICE AND SHERIFF

Sheriff's Dept **207.338.2040**
Fax 207.338.6784
Web .... www.prexar.com
E-mail .... sheriff@acadia.net
45 Congress St, Belfast, ME 04915-6432
Scott L. Story, Sheriff

Washington County

SOCIAL SERVICES

Maine Dept of Hlth & Human Svcs **207.255.2000**
13 Prescott Dr, Machias, ME 04654

COURTS

4th District Court **207.255.3044**
Fax 207.255.2022
85 Court St, Machias, ME 04654-2109
Honorable John V. Romei, District Court Judge

District IV **207.454.2055**
Fax 207.454.0085
382 South St, Calais, ME 04619-1123
Honorable John Romei, District Judge

POLICE AND SHERIFF

Sheriff's Dept **207.255.4422**
Fax 207.255.8636
Web .... www.washingtoncountymaine.com
E-mail .... sheriff@wcsheriffsoffice.com
83 Court St, Machias, ME 04654
Joseph L. Tibbetts, Sheriff

York County

SOCIAL SERVICES

Dept of Health & Human Svcs **207.490.5418**
Fax 207.490.5499
890 Main St Ste 208, Sanford, ME 04073-3350
Wendy O Blenis, Regional Director

Maine

GENERAL HEALTH SERVICES

SMMC Visiting Nurses 207.985.1000
Fax 207.985.6715
Web ....www.smmc.org
E-mail ....edu.eb@smmc.org
   72 Main St, Kennebunk, ME 04043-7021
   Elaine Brady, Rn, Executive Director

COURTS

York District Court 207.363.1230
Fax 207.363.3783
   11 Chases Pond Rd, York, ME 03909-5798
   Doreen R. Emhoff, Court Clerk

POLICE AND SHERIFF

Sheriff's Ofc 207.324.1113
Fax 207.324.3496
E-mail ....maurice.ouellette@state.me.us
   1 Layman Way, Alfred, ME 04002
   Maurice Ouellette, Sheriff

SPECIAL SERVICES AGENCIES

ADOPTION AGENCIES

Casey Family Svcs 207.772.4110
Fax 207.761.0748
Web ....www.caseyfamilyservices.org
   75 Washington Ave, Ste 300, Portland, ME 04101
   Mark Millar, Director

Iris Network 207.774.6273
Fax 207.774.0679
Web ....www.iris.org
   189 Park Ave, Portland, ME 04102-2909
   James Phipps, Director

Maine Adoption Placement Svc (MAPS) 207.478.9141
Fax 207.941.8942
Web ....www.mapsadopt.org/
E-mail ....kristenh@maps-worldwide.org
   229 State St, Bangor, ME 04401-5319
   Kristen Hirsch, Clinical Director

BEHAVIORAL HEALTH TREATMENT

Alpha One 207.941.6553
Fax 207.941.6410
Web ....www.alphaonenow.org
E-mail ....bangor@alphaonenow.org
   1048 Union St Ste 2, Bangor, ME 04401-8601
   Kelley Mctague, Branch Manager

Balian Medical Practice 207.947.7186
   45 Hogan Rd, Bangor, ME 04401
   Epiphanes Balian, Md, Psychiatrist

Blattner Medical Practice 207.761.5876
   222 Saint John St, Portland, ME 04102-3041
   Francine Blattner, Psychiatrist

Bloom Medical Practice 207.873.1636
Fax 770.979.8305
   67 Silver St, Waterville, ME 04901-6525
   Fred Bloom, MD, Psychiatrist

Brewer Housing Authority 207.989.7551
Fax 207.989.7554
   15 Colonial Cir, Brewer, ME 04412
   Gordon Stitham, Executive Director

Bucknam Road Behavioral Health 207.781.1573
Fax 207.781.1543
   5 Bucknam Rd Ste 1G, Falmouth, ME 04105-1208
   Yvonne De Cory, MD, Psychiatrist

Child Development Svcs 207.764.4490
   560 Main St, Presque Isle, ME 04769-3005
   Dawn Mcpherson, Director

Clemotson Medical Practice 207.415.2700
   81 Bridge St, Yarmouth, ME 04096
   Charles Clemotson, Psychiatrist

Counseling Associates 207.985.6286
Fax 207.967.8847
E-mail ....gchandler2@adelphia.net
   10 Storer St, Kennebunk, ME 04043
   Gail Chandler, Counselor

Counseling Services, Inc. 207.282.1500
Fax 207.282.7509
Web ....www.counselingservices.org
   PO Box 1010, Saco, ME 04072
   COA accredited organization.

Down East Horizons Operating Company 207.288.4234
Fax 207.667.1977
Web ....dehi.org
E-mail ....bboudreau@dehi.com
   1200 State Highway 3, Bar Harbor, ME 04609-7131
   Bill Boudreau, Director

Dr. Lewis S. Libby School 207.745.0412
   13 School St, Milford, ME 04461-3300
   Patti Bradstreet, Director

Dumont Medical Practice 207.422.2020
Web ....www.mainehospital.org
   PO Box 44, Hancock, ME 04640-0044
   Rae Dumont, Psychiatrist

Genesis Residential Treatment Facility 207.777.8944
Fax 207.784.6536
   200 College St, Lewiston, ME 04240-6707
   Donna Martinez, Director

Goodwill Industries of Northern New
England 207.774.6323
Fax 207.761.8460
Web ....www.goodwillnne.org
   353 Cumberland Avenue, Portland, ME 04101
   CARF accredited programs available.

Harbor Family Services 207.725.6505
Fax 207.798.5449
Web ....www.harborfamilyservices.org
   63 Elm Street, Suite A, Topsham, ME 04086
   COA accredited organization.

Kennebec Behavioral Health 207.873.2136
Fax 207.877.8427
Web ....www.kvmhc.org
   67 Eustis Parkway, Waterville, ME 04901
   CARF accredited programs available.

KidsPeace National Ctrs of New England 207.667.0909
Fax 207.667.6348
Web ....www.kidspeace.org
E-mail ....chris.sylvester@kidspeace.org
   Route 180, Ellsworth, ME 04605
   Chris Sylvester, Admissions Supervisor

Loring Job Corps Ctr 207.328.4212
Fax 207.328.4199
Web ....www.jcdcdrc.org
E-mail ....smith.misty@jobcorps.org
   36 Montana Rd, Limestone, ME 04750-6107
   Christy Moore, Center Director

Maine Medical Center 207.662.0111
Web ....www.mmc.org
E-mail ....swasel@mmc.org
   22 Bramhall Street, Portland, ME 04102
   Ms. Lori Swasey, Accreditation Manager
   Joint Commission accredited organization.

Riverview Psychiatric Center 207.624.4600
Fax 207.287.6123
   250 Arsenal St, Augusta, ME 09203
   Mary Louise, Director

Rumford Group Homes, Inc.
Web ....www.rumfordgrouphomes.org
   160 Lincoln Avenue, Rumford, ME 04276
   COA accredited organization.

St. Mary's Regional Medical Center 207.777.8100
Web ....www.stmarysmaine.com
E-mail ....bshew@stmarysmaine.com
   Campus Avenue, Lewiston, ME 04240
   Ms. Betsey Shew, Accreditation Manager
   Joint Commission accredited organization.

Support Solutions Mental Health Clinic 207.294.7458
Fax 207.294.7437
Web ....www.supportsolution.org
   56 Industrial Park Rd, Saco, ME 04072
   Terry Scott, Director
   CARF accredited programs available.

Sweetser 800.434.3000
Fax 207.294.4465
Web ....www.sweetser.org
   50 Moody Street, Saco, ME 04072-0892
   COA accredited organization.

The Acadia Hospital 207.973.6100
Web ....www.acadiahospital.org
E-mail ....dsanford@emh.org
   268 Stillwater Avenue, Bangor, ME 04401
   Ms. Deborah Sanford, Accreditation Manager
   Joint Commission accredited organization.

CHILDREN'S HOSPITAL

Aroostook Medical Center 207.768.4000
   140 Academy St, Presque Isle, ME 04769
   Sylvia Getman, Chief Executive Officer

Blue Hill Memorial Hospital 207.374.3400
   57 Water St, Blue Hill, ME 04614
   Greg Roraff, Chief Executive Officer

Calais Regional Hospital 207.454.7521
E-mail ....crh@calaishospital.org
   24 Hospital Ln, Calais, ME 04619
   Dee Travis, Manager

Cary Medical Center 207.498.3111
   163 Van Buren Rd Ste 1, Caribou, ME 04736
   Kris Doody, Director

Central Maine Medical Center 207.795.0111
   300 Main St, Lewiston, ME 04240
   Laire Covey, President

Down East Community Hospital 207.255.3356
   Upper Court St, Machias, ME 04654
   Jones Doug, Director

Eastern Maine Medical Center 207.973.7000
E-mail ....jhonsonb@enmmc.org
   489 State St, Bangor, ME 04401
   Debra Cary Jhonson, Chief Executive Officer

Franklin Memorial Hospital 207.778.6031
   111 Franklin Health Cmns, Farmington, ME 04938
   Rebecca Ryder, President

Henrietta D Goodall Hospital 207.324.4310
Web ....www.goodallhospital.org
   25 June St, Sanford, ME 04073
   Donna Caty, Director of Nursing

Houlton Regional Hospital 207.532.9471
   20 Hartford St, Houlton, ME 04730
   Tom Moakler, Chief Executive Officer

Maine Medial Center 207.662.0111
   22 Bramhall St, Portland, ME 04102
   Richard Peterson, Director

Maine

MaineGeneral Medical Center 207.872.1000
149 North St, Waterville, ME 04901

Parkview Adventist Medical Center 207.373.2000
329 Maine St, Brunswick, ME 04011
Ted Lewis, President

Penobscot Bay Medical Center 207.596.8000
6 Glen Cove Dr, Rockport, ME 04856
Maura Kelly, Chief Executive Officer

Penobscot Valley Hospital 207.794.3321
7 Transalpine Rd, Lincoln, ME 04457
Dave Shannon, Director

Redington-Fairview General Hospital 207.474.5121
Fairview Ave, Skowhegan, ME 04976
Richard Willett, Chief Executive Officer

Southern Maine Medical Center 207.283.7000
Web .... www.smmc.org
1 Medical Center Dr, Biddeford, ME 04005
Stephen McGeachey, Chief Executive Officer

St Mary's Regional Medical Center 207.777.8100
330 Sabattus St, Lewiston, ME 04240
Rosemary Cummings, Director of Nursing

York Hospital 207.363.4321
15 Hospital Dr, York, ME 03909
Jud Knox, Chief Executive Officer

COUNSELING SERVICES

Adoptive and Foster Families of Maine 207.827.2331
Fax 207.827.1974
Web .... www.affm.net
E-mail .... bette@affm.net
294 Center St Ste 1, Old Town, ME 04468-1570
Bette Hoxie, Director

Maine Educational Opportunity Ctr 207.581.3711
Fax 207.581.2532
Web .... http://meoc.maine.edu
E-mail .... karen.keim@umit.maine.edu
5713 Chadbourne Hall, Orono, ME 04469-5713
David Megquier, Director

CRISIS & SHELTER CARE

Battered Womens Project 207.764.2977
Fax 207.764.8631
Web .... www.batteredwomensproject.org
E-mail .... Bwp@Batteredwomensproject.Org
421 Main St Ste 2, Presque Isle, ME 04769-2660
Donna Baiett, Director

Caring Unlimited - Domestic Violence 207.490.3227
Fax 207.490.2186
Main St, Sanford, ME 04073
Cindy Peoples, Director

Family Violence Project 207.623.8637
Fax 207.621.6372
E-mail .... deborahs@familyviolenceproject.org
PO Box 304, Augusta, ME 04332-0304
Deborah Shepard, Director

Ingraham Helpline 207.774.4357
Fax 207.775.4034
Web .... www.ingraham.org
50 Lydia Lane S, Portland, ME 04106
Michael Tarpinian, Executive Director

Maine Shaw House 207.941.2874
Fax 207.941.2875
136 Union St, Bangor, ME 04401-6327
Sally Tardisf, Director

Preble St. Resource Ctr 207.775.0026
Fax 207.842.3614
Web .... www.preblestreet.org
E-mail .... mswann@preblestreet.org
18 Portland St, Portland, ME 04101-2912
Mark Swann, Director

Safe Voices 800.559.2927
Fax 207.795.6814
E-mail .... info@safevoices.org
PO Box 713, Auburn, ME 04212-0713
Jane Morrison, Director

Spruce Run Assoc 207.945.5102
Fax 207.990.4252
77 Essex St, Bangor, ME 04402
Beverley Wilson, Office Assistant

EDUCATION

Children's Task Force 207.778.6960
Fax 207.779.1029
Web .... www.fcctf.org
E-mail .... fcctf@fcctf.org
113 Church St, Farmington, ME 04938
Renee Blanchet, Executive Director

Community Counseling Ctr 207.874.1030
Fax 207.874.1044
Web .... www.comcc.org
165 lorraine cofter st, Portland, ME 04101-2025
Marrianne Crabs, Interim Director

Deck House School 207.882.7055
Fax 207.882.8151
Web .... www.deckhouseschool.org
E-mail .... admission@deckhouseschool.org
124 Deckhouse Rd, Edgecomb, ME 04556
Dr. Melinda Browne, Program Headmaster

Hyde School 207.443.5584
Fax 207.443.1450
Web .... www.hyde.edu
E-mail .... rsanner@hyde.edu
616 High St, Bath, ME 04530
R Sanner, Director Of Admissions

FOSTER CARE AGENCIES

Adoptive & Foster Families of Maine 800.833.9786
Fax 207.827.1974
E-mail .... bette@affm.net
294 Center St, Ste 1, Old Town, ME 04468
Bette Hoxie, Director

**Maine Adoption Placement Service
(MAPS)** 207.941.9500
Fax 207.775.2255
E-mail .... stephaniem@maps-worldwide.org
229 State St, Bangor, ME 04002
Stephaine Mitchell, Chief Executive Officer

Maine Families with Children from Asia 207.839.2815
E-mail .... bgreenw1@maine.rr.com
597 Parker Farm Rd, West Buxton, ME 04093

SOCIAL SERVICES

Carenet of Mid Coast Maine 207.725.5433
Web .... www.suscom-maine.net
E-mail .... thecenter@carenetme.org
90 Union St, Brunswick, ME 04011-2419
Sue Morley, Director

Catholic Charities Maine 800.781.8550
Web .... www.ccmaine.org
P.O. Box 10660, Portland, ME 04104-6060
COA accredited organization.

Child & Family Opportunities, Inc. 207.667.2995
Fax 207.667.7963
Web .... www.childandfamilyopp.org
E-mail .... judyn@childandfamiliesopp.com
18 Avery Ln, Ellsworth, ME 04605
Martha Bayer, Administrative Support Services Manager

Child Abuse Prevention Council 207.985.5975
Fax 207.985.1758
Web .... www.kidsfreetogrow.org
E-mail .... info@kidsfreetogrow.org
62 Portland Rd Ste 15, Kennebunk, ME 04043-6650
Laurie Dupaul, Executive Director

Child Care Option 207.582.3110
Fax 207.582.3115
Web .... www.skcdc.org
E-mail .... cco@skcdc.org
347 Maine Avenue, Farmingdale, ME 04344
Michelle Pino, Executive Director

**Child Care Resource Dev. Ctr, Child Care
Connections** 207.396.6566
Fax 207.396.6581
Web .... www.childcaremaine.org
E-mail .... lelias@smaaa.org
136 US Rt 1, Scarborough, ME 04074
Linda Elias, Director

Community Care 207.945.4240
Fax 207.990.3660
Web .... www.comcareme.org
P.O. Box 936, Bangor, ME 04402-0936
COA accredited organization.

Community Concepts, Inc. 207.795.4065
Fax 207.784.6882
E-mail .... finderseekers@community-concepts.org
240 Bates St, Lewiston, ME 04240
Koriene Low, Director Of Community Srvs

Family Crisis Svcs 207.767.4952
Fax 207.767.8109
Web .... www.familycrisis.org
E-mail .... lois_r@familycrisis.org
100 Humphreys Rd, Cape Elizabeth, ME 04107
Lois Galgayreckitt, Exec. Director

Jewish Family Services 207.772.1959
Fax 207.772.2234
E-mail .... jca@mainejewish.org
57 Ashmont St, Portland, ME 04101
Karli Efron, Director

KidsPeace Foster Care & Family Svcs 866.642.0003
Fax 207.771.5750
Web .... www.fostercare.com
324 Gannett Dr Ste 300, South Portland,
ME 04106-3269
Ray Culp, Nat'l Director Foster Care & Family Services

**Maine Children's Home For Little
Wanderers** 207.873.4253
Fax 207.873.7548
Web .... www.mainechildrenshome.org
E-mail .... sabrams@mainechildrenshome.org
93 Silver St, Waterville, ME 04901-5923
Sharon Abrams, Executive Director

MAPS Worldwide 207.775.4101
Fax 207.775.2255
Web .... www.mapsadopt.org
100 Brickhill Avenue, South Portland, ME 04106
COA accredited organization.

Mid-Coast Children's Svcs 207.594.8474
Fax 207.594.5227
Web .... www.brmaine.org
E-mail .... mccs@midcoast.com
272 Park St, Rockland, ME 04841-2125
Ruth Southworth, Executive Director

**Mid-Coast Regional Resource Development
Ctr** 207.442.7963
Fax 207.443.7447
Web .... www.midcoastrdc.com
E-mail .... referral@midcaostrdc.com
34 Wing Farm Pkwy, Bath, ME 04530
Jessica Tysen, Executive Director

Saint Andre Home, Inc. 207.282.3351
Fax 207.282.8733
Web .... www.saintandrehome.org
283 Elm Street, Biddeford, ME 04005
COA accredited organization.

Maine

Spurwink Services 207.871.1200
Fax 207.871.1232
Web ....www.spurwink.org
  899 Riverside Street, Portland, ME 04103
  COA accredited organization.

Woodfords Family Services 207.878.9663
Fax 207.878.2259
Web ....www.woodfords.org
  P.O. Box 1768, Portland, ME 04104-1768
  COA accredited organization.

Youth Alternatives Ingraham, Inc. 207.874.1175
Fax 207.874.1181
Web ....www.yimaine.org
  50 Lydia Lane, South Portland, ME 04106
  COA accredited organization.

SPECIAL NEEDS

Able Generation 800.875.2457
Fax 207.549.7942
E-mail ....information@ablegeneration.com
  8 Mills Road, North Whitefield, ME 04353

Autism Society of Maine 800.273.5200
  72B Maine St, Winthrop, ME 04364
  Cathy Dionne, Program Director

Brain Injury Association 207.861.9900
E-mail ....info@biame.org
  325 Main St, Waterville, ME 04901

Learning Disabilities Association 877.208.4029
E-mail ....info@ldame.org
  PO Box 67, Oakland, ME 04963

**Maine Center for Integrated
Rehabilitation** 207.989.2034
Fax 207.989.5971
Web ....www.rehabme.net
  248 State Street, Twin City Plaza, Brewer, ME 04412
  CARF accredited programs available.

Maine Center on Deafness 207.797.7656
E-mail ....info@mcdmaine.org
  68 Bishop St Ste 3, Portland, ME 04103
  Elissa Moine, Chief Executive Officer

Maine Parent Federation 207.588.1933
E-mail ....parentconnect@mpf.org
  PO Box 2067, Augusta, ME 04338
  Janice Lachance, Director

Maine PTA 207.852.6683
E-mail ....tbreen@zoneradio.com
  861 Broadway, Bangor, ME 04402
  Tammie Breen, Board Director

Mainely Parents 800.249.5506
E-mail ....amandal@day-one.org
  188 State St Ste 400, Portland, ME 04101

National Multiple Sclerosis Society 800.344.4867
Fax 207.781.7961
E-mail ....Info@msmaine.org
  170 US Route 1 ste# 200, Falmouth, ME 04105
  Aroyn White, President

Pine Tree Society 207.443.3341
E-mail ....info@pinetreesociety.org
  149 Front St, Bath, ME 04530

Speech-Language-Hearing Association 207.491.5219
E-mail ....sabrinaslp@yahoo.com
  110 N Main St, Strong, ME 04983

United Cerebral Palsy 207.941.2885
E-mail ....office@ucpofmaine.org
  700 Mount Hope Ave Ste 320, Bangor, ME 04401
  Bobbi Yeager, Director

SUBSTANCE ABUSE TREATMENT

Office of Substance Abuse 207.287.2595
Fax 207.287.4334
Web ....www.maineosa.org
E-mail ....guy.cousins@maine.gov
  41 Anthony Ave, Augusta, ME 04333-0011
  Guy Cousins, Director

Maine

Martin O'Malley, Jr., Governor
100 State Circle
Annapolis, MD 21401-1925
410.974.3901
410.974.3275 (Fax)
Governor@gov.state.md.us
www.gov.state.md.us

Jessica Winpigler, Juvenile Justice Specialist
300 E. Joppa Road, Suite 1105
Towson, MD 21286
410.821.2829
410.321.3116 (Fax)
jwinpigler@goccp.state.md.us

Heber Watts, SAG Chair
3628 Sylvan Dr
Baltimore, MD 21207
watts3511@comcast.net

CRISIS NUMBERS

Child Abuse Reporting . . .800.332.6347

STATE SERVICES

SOCIAL SERVICES

Social Svcs Admin **410.767.7216**
Fax 410.333.0127
   311 W Saratoga St, Baltimore, MD 21201
Carnitra D White, Executive Director

GENERAL HEALTH SERVICES

Ctr for Maternal and Child Health MD **410.767.6748**
Fax 410.333.5233
   201 W Preston St, 3rd Flr, Baltimore, MD 21201
Bonnie Birkel, Director

Family Health Admin **410.767.5300**
Fax 410.333.7106
   201 W Preston St, Room 306, Baltimore, MD 21306
Donna Harris, Children With Special Needs Director

Office for Gen & Child w Spec Health Cr MD **410.767.6730**
Fax 410.333.5047
E-mail . . . . pannys@dhmh.state.md.us
   201 W Preston St Rm 424, Baltimore, MD 21201
S Panny, Director

JUSTICE AGENCY

Attorney General's Ofc **410.576.6300**
Fax 410.756.7036
Web . . . . www.oag.state.md.us
E-mail . . . . oag@oag.state.md.us
   200 Saint Paul Pl, Baltimore, MD 21202
Douglas Gansler, Attorney General

Criminal Injuries Compensation Board **410.585.3010**
Fax 410.764.3815
E-mail . . . . clfisher@dpscs.state.md.us
   6776 Reisterstown Rd, Ste 206, Baltimore, MD 21215
Courtney Fisher, Director

Dept of Public Safety & Correctional Svcs **410.585.3300**
Fax 410.764.4182
Web . . . . www.dpscs.state.md.us
E-mail . . . . msaar@dpscs.state.md.us
   6776 Reisterstown Rd, Ste 310, Baltimore,
   MD 21215-2323
Mary Ann Saar, Secretary

Juvenile Srvs Educ Program MD **410.767.0100**
Fax 410.333.2570
E-mail . . . . mmechlinski@msde.state.md.us
   200 West Baltimore St, Baltimore, MD 21201
M Mechlinski, Director

COURTS

Administrative Ofc Of The Courts **410.260.1400**
Fax 410.974.5577
Web . . . . www.mdcourts.gov
E-mail . . . . rocky.mckagan@mdcourts.gov
   580 Taylor Ave, Maryland Judicial Center, Annapolis,
   MD 21401
Roxanne P. Mckagan, Special Assistant

POLICE AND SHERIFF

Maryland Sheriff's Assoc **410.269.4237**
Fax 410.269.7523
Web . . . . www.mdsheriffs.org
E-mail . . . . sheriff@maniscanning.com
   12 Francis St, Annapolis, MD 21401
Michael F. Canning, Executive Director

EDUCATION SERVICES

Div of Spec Edu Early Inter Svcs MD **410.767.0238**
Fax 410.333.8165
   200 W Baltimore St 9th Flr, Baltimore, MD 21201
Carolann Heath, Assistant Superintendent

Maryland Division of Rehabilitation Services . . . **410.554.9442**
Fax 410.554.9412
Web . . . . www.dors.state.md.us
   2301 Argonne Dr, Baltimore, MD 21218-1628
Sue Page, Director

Maryland School for the Blind **410.444.5000**
Fax 410.319.5700
Web . . . . www.mdschblind.org
   3501 Taylor Ave, Nottingham, MD 21236-4499
Dr. Michael Bina, President

Maryland School for the Deaf **301.360.2000**
Fax 301.360.1400
Web . . . . www.msd.edu
E-mail . . . . james.tucker@msd.edu
   101 Clarke Pl, Frederick, MD 21701-6529
James E. Tucker, Superintendent

Maryland State Dept of Education **410.767.0100**
Fax 410.333.6033
E-mail . . . . rpeiffer@msde.state.md.us
   200 W Baltimore St, Baltimore, MD 21201
Ronald Peiffer, Director

Maryland State Dept of Education **410.767.7805**
Fax 410.333.6226
Web . . . . www.marylandpublicschools.org
E-mail . . . . lzang@msde.state.md.us
   200 W Baltimore St Ste 1, Baltimore,
   MD 21201-2594
Linda Zang, Head Start Program Director

Student Family and Sch Support MD **410.767.0100**
Fax 410.333.8010
E-mail . . . . wcohee@msde.state.md.us
   200 W Baltimore St, 4th Flr, Baltimore, MD 21201
Dr. William Cohee, Coordinator

LABOR & WORKFORCE EDUCATION

Dept of Labor Licensing and Regulation **410.230.6001**
Fax 410.333.5355
Web . . . . www.dllr.state.md.us
E-mail . . . . pfrancois@dllr.state.md.us
   1100 N Eutaw St, Baltimore, MD 21201-2201
Paulette Francois, Assistant Secretary

COUNTY SERVICES

Allegany County

SOCIAL SERVICES

Dept of Social Svcs **301.784.7000**
Fax 301.784.7222
E-mail . . . . dpaulman@dhr.state.md.us
   1 Frederick St Ste 100, Cumberland, MD 21502
Richard Paulman, PhD, Director

COURTS

4th Circuit Court **301.777.5922**
Fax 301.777.2100
Web . . . . www.courts.state.md.us
E-mail . . . . gary.leasure@courts.state.md.us
   30 Washington St, Cumberland, MD 21502-2948
Honorable Gary Leasure, Court Judge

POLICE AND SHERIFF

Sheriff's Ofc **301.777.5959**
Fax 301.777.2254
E-mail . . . . crrobertson@allconet.org
   708 Furnace St, Cumberland, MD 21502-1564
Lieutenant Craig Robertson, Sheriff

Maryland

Anne Arundel County

SOCIAL SERVICES

Dept of Social Svcs **410.421.8400**
Fax 410.508.2041
E-mail ....sthompson6@dhr.state.md.us
7500 Ritchie Hwy Rm 106, Glen Burnie,
MD 21061-3749
Sandra Roberts, Aps Supervisor

Glen Burnie Ofc **410.421.8500**
Fax 410.508.2079
7500 Ritchie Hwy, Multi-Purpose Center Room 106,
Glen Burnie, MD 21061
Sharon Meikle, CPS Supervisor

GENERAL HEALTH SERVICES

Health Dept **410.222.7095**
Fax 410.222.7294
Web ....www.aahealth.org
3 Harry S Truman Pkwy, Health Service Bldg,
Annapolis, MD 21401
Douglas Hart, Community Health Director

MENTAL HEALTH SERVICES

**MH Clinic Adolescent & Family
Svcs** **410.222.6785**
Fax 410.222.6888
Web ....mentalhealth.samhsa.gov
122 Langley Rd N Ste A, Glen Burnie,
MD 21060-6531
Howard Pressman, Md, Medical Director

JUSTICE AGENCY

CASA **410.267.7877**
Fax 410.267.9459
Web ....www.aacasa.org
E-mail ....staff@aacasa.org
94 Franklin St, Annapolis, MD 21401-2738
Rebbeca Julian, Executive Director

Dept of Juvenile Justice **410.295.5740**
Fax 410.974.5565
Web ....www.djs.state.md.us
E-mail ....dougm@djs.state.md.us
1623 Forest Dr Ste 101, Annapolis, MD 21403-7700
Doug Mohler, Area Director

POLICE AND SHERIFF

Police Dept **410.222.8181**
Fax 410.222.8602
Web ....www.aacounty.org
8495 Veterans Hwy, Millersville, MD 21108
James Teare, Chief

Sheriff's Ofc **410.222.1571**
Fax 410.222.1583
E-mail ....shwebmail@aacounty.org
7 Church Circle, Annapolis, MD 21401
Ronald S. Bateman, Sheriff

EDUCATION SERVICES

Special Education **410.222.5410**
Fax 410.222.5618
Web ....www.aacps.org
2644 Riva Rd, Annapolis, MD 21401
Mary Tillar, Director

Baltimore County

SOCIAL SERVICES

Dept of Social Svcs **410.853.3800**
Fax 410.853.3850
E-mail ....cdominick@dhr.state.md.us
439 Eastern Blvd, Essex, MD 21221
Carol Dominick, District Manager

Dept of Social Svcs **410.853.3009**
Fax 410.853.3069
130 Chartley Dr, Reisterstown, MD 21136
M Woods, Manager

Dept of Social Svcs **410.853.3400**
Fax 410.853.3401
Web ....www.dhr.state.md.us
E-mail ....dremseur@dhr.state.md.us
7701 Dunmanway, Dundalk, MD 21222
Debbie Remseur, District Manager

Dept of Social Svcs **410.853.3000**
Fax 410.853.3925
Web ....www.baltimorecountymd.gov
E-mail ....tgriffith@zhr.state.md.us
6401 York Rd 3, Baltimore, MD 21212-2130
Timothy Griffith, Director

GENERAL HEALTH SERVICES

Health Dept **410.887.2243**
Fax 410.377.4751
6401 York Rd Ste 3, Baltimore, MD 21212
Gregory Branch, Health Officer

JUSTICE AGENCY

CASA **410.828.0515**
Fax 410.828.0517
E-mail ....casabaltco@aol.com
305 W Chesapeake Ave Ste 117, Towson, MD 21204
Susan Daddio, Executive Director

Dept Of Juvenile Justice **410.512.4040**
Fax 410.296.0567
308 Washington Ave, Towson, MD 21204-4714
Constance Ridgley, Supervisor

COURTS

3rd Circuit Court / Juvenile **410.887.3836**
Fax 410.887.3891
401 Bosley Ave, County Courts Bldg, Towson,
MD 21204
Richard J. Gilbert, Juvenile Master

POLICE AND SHERIFF

Crimes Against Children **410.853.3650**
Fax 410.853.3688
Web ....www.baltimorecountymd.gov
E-mail ....jjohnson@baltimorecountymd.gov
6401 York Rd Ste 1, Baltimore, MD 21212-2127
James Johnson, Chief Of Police

Sheriff's Ofc **410.887.4070**
Fax 410.887.3870
E-mail ....rjfisher@baltimorecountymd.gov
401 Bosley Ave Ground Fl, Towson, MD 21204
R. Jay Fisher, Sheriff

EDUCATION SERVICES

Special Education **410.887.3660**
Fax 410.583.8736
Web ....www.bcps.org
6901 N Charles St, Ste 209, Towson, MD 21204
Kalisha Miller, Director

Baltimore City

SOCIAL SERVICES

Governor's Ofc For Children **410.767.4160**
Fax 410.333.5248
301 W Preston St Ste 1502, Baltimore, MD 21201
Rosemary King Johnston, Executive Director

Protection and Advocacy System **410.727.6352**
Fax 410.727.6389
Web ....www.mdlclaw.org
1800 N Charles St, Flr 4, Baltimore, MD 21201
Virginia Knowlton, Director

GENERAL HEALTH SERVICES

Health Dept **410.396.4398**
Fax 410.396.1617
Web ....www.baltimorecity.gov
E-mail ....obarbot@baltimorecity.gov
1001 E Fayette St, Baltimore, MD 21202
Oxiris Darbot, Commissioner

MENTAL HEALTH SERVICES

**Harford-Belair Community Mental Health
Ctr** **410.426.5650**
Fax 410.426.5143
Web ....www.harfordbelair.org
E-mail ....ttawes@harfordbelair.org
4308 Harford Rd, Baltimore, MD 21214-3116
Teresa Tawes, Ms, Mba, Program Director

On Our Own Inc. **410.444.4500**
Fax 410.444.0239
Web ....www.onourownmd.org/
E-mail ....tonyw21214@aol.com
6301 Harford Rd, Baltimore, MD 21214
Tony Wright, Director

JUSTICE AGENCY

CASA Program of Baltimore City **410.244.1465**
Fax 410.244.1460
Web ....www.casabalt.org
E-mail ....sburger@casabalt.org
511 E Baltimore St, Baltimore, MD 21202-4001
Susan Burger, Director

Dept of Juvenile Justice **443.263.8831**
Fax 443.263.8882
Web ....www.djs.state.md.us
E-mail ....jacksonw@djs.state.md.us
300 N Gay St Fl 2, Baltimore, MD 21202-4819
Delmas Wood, Director

COURTS

District Court **410.878.8000**
E-mail ....lonnie.ferguson@courts.state.md.us
5800 Wabash Ave, Baltimore, MD 21215-3224
Lonnie P. Ferguson Jr., Administrative Clerk

POLICE AND SHERIFF

Sheriff's Ofc **410.396.5826**
Fax 410.396.3545
Web ....www.baltimorecity.gov
E-mail ....john.anderson@baltimorecity.gov
100 N Calvert St Ste 104, Baltimore, MD 21202-1734
John W. Anderson, Sheriff

EDUCATION SERVICES

Special Education **410.396.8900**
Web www.bcps.k12.md.us
E-mail ....khoffman@bcps.k12.md.us
200 E North Ave, Rm 204, Baltimore, MD 21202
Kim Hoffman, Director

Calvert County

SOCIAL SERVICES

Dept of Social Svcs **443.550.6900**
Fax 410.286.7429
E-mail ....ganderso@dhr.state.md.us
200 Duke St, Prince Frederick, MD 20678
Gary Anderson, Director

GENERAL HEALTH SERVICES

Health Dept **410.535.5400**
Fax 410.535.5285
Web ....www.calverthealth.org
E-mail ....pgoodenough@dhmh.state.md.us
975 Solomons Island Rd, Prince Frederick, MD 20678
Penelope Goodenough, Rn, Aids Coordinator

POLICE AND SHERIFF

Sheriff's Ofc **410.535.2800**
Fax 410.535.1770
Web ....www.co.cal.md.us
E-mail ....evansem@co.cal.md.us
 30 Church St, Prince Frederick, MD 20678
Mike Evans, Sheriff

EDUCATION SERVICES

Even Start **410.535.7291**
Fax 410.535.7299
Web www.calvertnet.k12.md.us
E-mail ....judyd@calvertnet.k12.md.us
 1450 Dares Beach Rd, Prince Frederick,
 MD 20678-4206
Ms Judy Devey, Director

Caroline County

SOCIAL SERVICES

Dept of Social Svcs **410.819.4500**
Fax 410.819.4501
 300 Market St, Denton, MD 21629
Osvaldina Gomes Daly, Director

GENERAL HEALTH SERVICES

Health Dept **410.479.8000**
Web ....www.carolinehd.org
 403 S 7th St Ste 218, Denton, MD 21629
Bunie Lewis, Aids/std Director

MENTAL HEALTH SERVICES

Mental Health **410.479.3800**
Fax 410.479.0052
 606 Sunnyside Ave, Denton, MD 21629
Michael Campbell, Lcsw-c, Director/child & Adolescent Coordinator

JUSTICE AGENCY

CASA **410.479.8301**
Fax 410.479.8302
Web ....www.carolinecasa.org
 114 Market St Ste 100, Denton, MD 21629-1066
Katie Parmer, Executive Director

Dept of Juvenile Svcs **410.819.6556**
Fax 410.819.6559
 317 Carter Ave Ste 105, Denton, MD 21629
Taneesha De Shields, Supervisor

COURTS

2nd Circuit Court **410.479.2303**
Fax 410.479.4063
Web ....www.dmv.com
 109 Market St Ste 200, Denton, MD 21629-1062
Honorable Karen A. Murphy Jenson, Judge

Teen Court **410.479.8080**
Fax 410.479.2014
 403 S 7th St Ste 268, Denton, MD 21629
James Gossage, Coordinator Teen Court

EDUCATION SERVICES

EvenStart - Caroline City Public School
....**410.479.1460**
Fax 410.479.0108
Web www.cl.k12.md.us
 204 Franklin St, Denton, MD 21629-1210
Dr. Edward Shirley, Director

Carroll County

SOCIAL SERVICES

Dept of Social Svcs **410.386.3300**
Fax 410.386.3429
Web ....www.dhr.state.md.us
E-mail ....ggiese@dhr.state.md.us
 10 Distillery Rd Ste 100, Westminster,
 MD 21157-5344
George W. Giese, Director

GENERAL HEALTH SERVICES

Health Dept **410.876.2152**
Fax 410.876.4959
 290 S Center St, Westminster, MD 21157-5222
Cindy Bosley, Director Of Nursing

JUSTICE AGENCY

Dept of Juvenile Svcs **410.871.3600**
Fax 410.871.3620
 101 N Court St Ste JS, Westminster, MD 21157
David J. Tucker, Case Management Specialist Supervisor

COURTS

5th Circuit Court **410.386.2326**
Web ....www.mdcourts.gov
E-mail ....michael.galloway@mdcourts.gov
 55 N Court St Ste G8, Westminster, MD 21157-5167
Honorable Michael M. Galloway, Administrative Judge

District Court **410.871.3500**
Fax 410.871.3517
Web ....www.mdcourts.gov
E-mail ....joann.jones@mdcourts.gov
 101 N Court St Ste DC, Westminster,
 MD 21157-5166
Joann Ellinghaus-jones, Administrative Judge

POLICE AND SHERIFF

Sheriff's Ofc **410.386.2900**
Fax 410.876.1152
Web ....www.ccg.carr.org
E-mail ....ktregoning@ccg.carr.org
 100 N Court St, Westminster, MD 21157-5112
Kenneth L. Tregoning, Sheriff

EDUCATION SERVICES

Winchester Elementry School **410.751.3230**
Fax 410.751.3929
 70 Monroe St, Westminster, MD 21157
Joseph Dorsey, Principal

Cecil County

SOCIAL SERVICES

Dept of Social Svcs **410.996.0100**
Fax 410.996.0464
 170 E Main St Ste 1, Elkton, MD 21921
Sue L. Bailey, Msw, LCSW, Assistant Director

GENERAL HEALTH SERVICES

Health Dept **410.996.5550**
Fax 410.996.5179
Web ....www.cecilcountyhealth.org
E-mail ....cchd@cecilcountyhealth.org
 401 Bow St, John M. Byers Health Center, Elkton,
 MD 21921
Mary Ellen Rapposelli, Rn, Msn, Health Promotion Director

JUSTICE AGENCY

Dept of Juvenile Svcs **410.996.2800**
Fax 410.996.2810
Web ....www.djs.state.md.us
 106 E Main St Ste 102, Elkton, MD 21921-5780
Tyra L.kenly, County Supervisor

COURTS

2nd Circuit Court **410.996.5374**
Fax 410.392.6032
Web ....www.courts.state.md.us
E-mail ....robert.lidums@courts.state.md.us
 129 E Main St Rm 108, Elkton, MD 21921-5924
Honorable O. Robert Lidums, Judge

Charles County

SOCIAL SERVICES

Dept of Social Svcs **301.392.6400**
 200 Kent Ave, La Plata, MD 20646
Karen Butler, Director

Local and Regional Ombudsman **301.934.0133**
Fax 301.934.0126
Web ....www.charlescounty.org
E-mail ....sinesk@charlescounty.org
 8190 Port Tobacco Rd, Port Tobacco,
 MD 20677-3126
Kimberly Sines, Budsman

GENERAL HEALTH SERVICES

Health Dept **301.609.6900**
Fax 301.934.7048
Web ....www.dhmh.state.md.us
E-mail ....lfenlon@dhmh.state.md.us
 4545 Crain Hwy, White Plains, MD 20695-3045
Linda Fenlon, Rn, Hiv/aids Coordinator

MENTAL HEALTH SERVICES

Mental Health Ctr **301.609.6700**
Fax 301.609.6741
 4545 Crain Hwy, White Plains, MD 20695
Paul Donato, Phd, Director

COURTS

7th Circuit Court **301.932.3230**
Fax 301.932.3289
 200 Charles St, La Plata, MD 20646
Sharon Hancock, Clerk

POLICE AND SHERIFF

Sheriff's Ofc **301.609.6543**
Fax 301.609.6443
Web ....www.ccso.us
E-mail ....coffeyr@ccso.us
 6915 Crain Hwy, La Plata, MD 20646-3956
Rex Coffey, Sheriff

EDUCATION SERVICES

Eva Turner Head Start **301.645.9720**
Fax 301.645.9720
Web ....www.acf.hhs.gov
E-mail ....mreid@smtccac.org
 1000 Bannister Cir, Waldorf, MD 20602-1699
Mary Reid, Director

Special Education **301.392.7587**
Fax 301.753.2096
Web ....www.ccboe.com
 5980 Radio Station Rd, La Plata, MD 20646
Arden Sotomayor, Acting Director

Dorchester County

SOCIAL SERVICES

Dept of Social Svcs **410.901.4100**
Fax 410.901.1047
 627 Race St, Cambridge, MD 21613-2333
William D Mcdonnell, Director

GENERAL HEALTH SERVICES

Health Dept **410.228.3223**
Fax 410.228.9319
Web ....www.dhmh.state.md.us
 3 Cedar St, Cambridge, MD 21613-2300
Roger Harrell, Health Officer

JUSTICE AGENCY

Dept of Juvenile Svcs **410.228.6452**
Fax 410.228.3342
Web ....www.djs.state.md.us
 310 Gay St Ste 3, Cambridge, MD 21613-1898
Hamilton Brake, Probation Officer

COURTS

1st Circuit Court / Ofc of Judge Brett W. Wilson
....**410.228.6300**
Fax 410.221.5003
 206 High St Ste 1, Cambridge, MD 21613
Honorable Brett W. Wilson, Circuit Court Judge

Maryland

POLICE AND SHERIFF

Sheriff's Ofc **410.228.4141**
Fax 410.228.9869
E-mail .... jphillips@docogonet.com
829 Fieldcrest Rd, Cambridge, MD 21613
James W. Phillips, Jr., Sheriff

Frederick County

SOCIAL SERVICES

Dept of Social Svcs **301.600.4555**
Fax 301.600.4550
E-mail .... dgordy@dhr.state.md.us
100 E All Saints St Ste 100, Frederick, MD 21701
Diane Gordy, Director

GENERAL HEALTH SERVICES

Health Dept **301.600.3342**
Fax 301.600.1403
Web .... www.frederickcountymd.gov
E-mail .... danne@frederickcountymd.gov
350 Montevue Ln, Frederick, MD 21702-8245
Debbie Anne, Aids Coordinator

MENTAL HEALTH SERVICES

Mental Health **301.600.1755**
Fax 301.600.3214
E-mail .... dhubble@fredco-md.net
350 Montevue Ln, Frederick, MD 21701
Karen Hall, Adult & Senior Coordinator

Mental Health Assoc **301.663.0011**
Fax 301.695.4747
E-mail .... sborg@fcmha.org
263 W Patrick St Ste 2, Frederick, MD 21701
Susie Borg, Hotline Director

COURTS

6th Circuit Court **301.600.1975**
Fax 301.600.2245
Web .... www.courts.state.md.us
100 W Patrick St, Frederick, MD 21701-5578
Sandra K Dalton, Clerk

District Court **301.600.2000**
100 W Patrick St, Frederick, MD 21701-5578
Sara Snyder, Administrative Clerk

EDUCATION SERVICES

CDI Head Start **301.600.1024**
Fax 301.600.2723
401 Sagner Ave, Frederick, MD 21701-5719
Stacey Wantz, Director

Even Start **240.236.8450**
Fax 240.236.8451
E-mail .... richard.ramsburg@fcps.org
44 W Frederick St, Walkersville, MD 21793
Mr Richard Ramsburg, Director

Special Education **301.644.5281**
Fax 301.644.5303
Web .... www.fcps.org
E-mail .... daniel.martz@fcps.org
191 SE St, Frederick, MD 21701
Daniel Martz, Director

Garrett County

SOCIAL SERVICES

Dept Of Social Svcs **301.533.3000**
Fax 301.334.5449
Web .... www.dhr.state.md.us
E-mail .... trosser@dhr.state.md.us
12578 Garrett Hwy, Oakland, MD 21550-1159
Thomas Rosser, Assistant Director

JUSTICE AGENCY

Dept of Juvenile Justice **301.334.8608**
Fax 301.334.8687
7000 Thayer Ctr, Oakland, MD 21550
Renee Page, Supervisor

COURTS

4th Circuit Court **301.334.1937**
Fax 301.334.5017
Web .... www.courts.state.md.us
203 S 4th St Rm 205, Oakland, MD 21550-1535
Sondra Beckel, Clerk Of Court

POLICE AND SHERIFF

Sheriff's Dept **301.334.1911**
Fax 301.334.8852
Web .... www.garrettcounty.org
E-mail .... gcso@garrettcounty.org
311 E Alder St, Oakland, MD 21550
Robert Corley, Sheriff

EDUCATION SERVICES

Crellin Head Start **301.334.2206**
Fax 301.334.8555
115 Kendall Dr, Oakland, MD 21550
Ruby King, Director

Friendsville Head Start **301.746.5211**
Fax 301.746.5752
952 Old River Rd, Friendsville, MD 21531
Mary Joe, Director

Harford County

GENERAL HEALTH SERVICES

Health Services **410.638.3060**
Fax 410.638.4927
1 N Main St Ste 2, Bel Air, MD 21014
Cindy Dawson, Rn, Ches, Aids Coordinator

JUSTICE AGENCY

CASA **410.638.4938**
Fax 410.420.6740
E-mail .... casa@harfordcountymd.gov
101 S Main St Ste 303, Bel Air, MD 21014
Ross Diedoardo, Director

Dept of Juvenile Svcs **410.836.4680**
Fax 410.836.4841
2 S Bond St Ste 2, Bel Air, MD 21014-3746
Paul Bowden, Supervisor

Div Parole/Probation **410.836.4650**
Fax 410.838.1407
E-mail .... dlutz@wustl.edu
2 S Bond St Ste 2, Bel Air, MD 21014-3746
Diane Lutz, County Supervisor

COURTS

3rd Circuit Court / Clerks **410.638.3426**
Fax 410.879.6449
E-mail .... james.reilly@mdcourts.gov
20 W Courtland St, Bel Air, MD 21014
Honorable William Carr, Administrative Judge

POLICE AND SHERIFF

Sheriff's Offc **410.836.5444**
Fax 410.879.2782
Web .... www.harfordsheriff.org
45 S Main St, Bel Air, MD 21014
L. Jesse Bane, Sheriff

Howard County

SOCIAL SERVICES

Dept of Social Svcs **410.872.8700**
Fax 410.872.4222
E-mail .... cgallion@dhr.state.md.us
7121 Columbia Gateway Dr, Columbia, MD 21046
Charlene Gallion, Director

GENERAL HEALTH SERVICES

Health Dept **410.313.6300**
Fax 410.313.6303
Web .... www.hchealth.org
7178 Columbia Gateway Dr Ste E, Columbia, MD 21046
Dr. Peter Beilenson, Health Officer

Health Dept **410.313.6202**
Fax 410.313.6212
Web .... www.howardcountymd.gov
7178 Columbia Gateway Dr, Columbia, MD 21046
Dudley Greer, Director

JUSTICE AGENCY

CASA / Voices For Children, Inc **410.740.0933**
Fax 410.740.0975
Web .... www.voicesforchildren.org
E-mail .... info@voicesforchildren.org
5550 Sterrett Pl Ste 215, Columbia, MD 21044-2626
Pamela Grady, Executive Director

Dept of Juvenile Svcs **410.480.7878**
Fax 410.480.7872
Web .... www.djs.state.md.us
3451 Court House Dr, Ellicott City, MD 21043
Timothy Madden, County Supervisor

Parole & Probation **410.480.7920**
Fax 410.480.7910
3451 Court House Dr Ste 101, Ellicott City, MD 21043
Cindy Callan, Field Supervisor

COURTS

District Court **410.480.7700**
Fax 410.480.7701
Web .... www.courts.state.md.us
E-mail .... nancy.mueller@courts.state.md.us
3451 Court House Dr Ste 110, Ellicott City, MD 21043-4377
Nancy E. Mueller, Administrative Clerk

POLICE AND SHERIFF

Sheriff's Ofc **410.313.2150**
Fax 410.313.4237
Web .... www.co.ho.md.us
E-mail .... sheriff1@co.ho.md.us
8360 Court Ave, Ellicott City, MD 21043
James Fitzgerald, Sheriff

EDUCATION SERVICES

Columbia Campus **410.480.4500**
Fax 410.480.4506
E-mail .... james.tucker@msd.edu
108 & Old Montgomery Rd., Columbia, MD 21044
James E. Tucker, Superintendent

Special Education **410.313.5350**
Fax 410.313.5357
Web www.howard.k12.md.us
5451 Beaver Kill Rd, columbia, MD 21044
Patricia Dailey, Director

Kent County

SOCIAL SERVICES

Dept of Social Svcs **410.810.7600**
Fax 410.778.1497
350 High St, Chestertown, MD 21620
Kerri Aphaern-Brown, Director

JUSTICE AGENCY

Carter Youth Facility **410.778.6444**
Fax 410.778.7379
Web .... www.djs.state.md.us
E-mail .... berrym@djs.state.md.us
Scheeler Road, Chestertown, MD 21620
Michael Berry, Director

Maryland

Dept of Juvenile Svcs 410.778.6103
Fax 410.778.6307
  215 Court St, Chestertown, MD 21620
  William Clark, Supervisor

POLICE AND SHERIFF

Sheriff's Ofc **410.778.2279**
Fax 410.778.7488
E-mail ....sheriff@kentgov.org
  104 Vickers Dr Unit B, Chestertown, MD 21620
  John F. Price, Sheriff

Montgomery County

SOCIAL SERVICES

Child Welfare Svcs **240.777.3500**
  1301 Piccard Dr, Flr 4, Rockville, MD 20850
  Agnes Leshner, Network Manager

**Dept of Heath & Human Services Germantown
Ofc** **240.777.3420**
Fax 240.777.3477
Web ....www.dhrstate.md.us
E-mail ....debbie.hackett@montgomerycountymd.gov
  12900 Middlebrook Rd fl 2, Germantown,
  MD 20874-2604
  Deborah Hackett, Supervisor

Dept of Human Svcs **240.777.1245**
Fax 240.777.4636
Web ....www.montgomerycountymd.gov
E-mail ....uma.ahluwahlia@montgomerycountymd.gov
  401 Hungerford Dr, Rockville, MD 20850-4154
  Uma Ahluwahlia, Director

**Dept of Social Svcs Silver Spring
Ofc** **240.777.3100**
Fax 240.777.3070
  8818 Georgia Ave, Silver Spring, MD 20910
  David Carter, Office Manager

GENERAL HEALTH SERVICES

HIV Clinic **240.777.1869**
Fax 240.777.1039
E-mail ....barbara.davis@co.mo.md.us
  2000 Dennis Ave, Silver Spring, MD 20902
  Barbra Davis, Hiv Supervisor

MENTAL HEALTH SERVICES

**Div of Crisis Intervention (& Mental Health Svcs): Crisis
Line** **240.777.4000**
Fax 240.777.4800
Web ....www.montgomerycountymd.gov
  1301 Piccard Dr, Rockville, MD 20850-4320
  Dudley Warner, Director

JUSTICE AGENCY

CASA Program **301.340.7458**
Fax 240.319.7210
Web ....www.casamontgomery.org
E-mail ....mail@casamontgomery.org
  1010 Grandin Ave, Ste B-3, Rockville, MD 20851
  Francha Davis, Executive Director

Dept of Juvenile Svcs **301.650.6760**
Fax 301.587.5601
  8605 Cameron St Ste 502, Silver Spring, MD 20910
  Bernard Hinnant, Office Manager

COURTS

District Court **301.563.8500**
  8552 2nd Ave Rm 235, Silver Spring, MD 20910
  John Bell, Administrative Judge

POLICE AND SHERIFF

Police Dept **240.773.5330**
  2350 Research Blvd, Rockville, MD 20850
  J. Thomas, Chief

Sheriff's Ofc 240.777.7000
Fax 240.777.7148
Web ....www.montgomerycounty.md.gov
  50 Maryland Ave Ste T8, Rockville, MD 20850-2303
  Darren M Topkin, Sheriff

EDUCATION SERVICES

Special Education **301.279.3135**
Fax 301.279.3016
E-mail ....gwendolyn_mason@mcpsmd.org
  850 Hungerford Dr, Rm 225, Rockville, MD 20850
  Gwendolyn Mason, Director

Prince Georges County

SOCIAL SERVICES

Dept of Social Svcs **301.909.2000**
Fax 301.909.2200
Web ....www.dhr.state.md.us
  925 Brightseat Rd, Landover, MD 20785-4725
  Colette Walker Thomas, Deputy Director

GENERAL HEALTH SERVICES

Health Dept **301.883.7879**
  1701 McCormick Dr, Largo, MD 20774
  Angela Crankfield-edmond, Aids Coordinator

Infants & Toddlers Program **301.265.8415**
Fax 301.883.3907
Web ....www.pgcitp.net
E-mail ....itp@co.pg.md.us
  9201 Basil Ct, #440, Largo, MD 20774
  Sharon Leyden, Program Director

JUSTICE AGENCY

CASA **301.209.0491**
Fax 301.209.0492
Web ....www.pgcasa.org
E-mail ....ambinsner@pgcasa.org
  6525 Belcrest Rd Ste G55, Hyattsville,
  MD 20782-2052
  Ann Marie Foley Binsner, Executive Director

Dept of Juvenile Svcs **301.952.2580**
Fax 301.952.2954
  14735 Main St, Ste M0400, Upper Marlboro,
  MD 20772
  David Thompson, Metro Regional Director

POLICE AND SHERIFF

Sheriffs Ofc **301.780.8600**
Fax 301.780.7355
  5303 Chryslerway, Upper Marlboro, MD 20772
  Michael A. Jackson, Sheriff

EDUCATION SERVICES

**Catherine T Reed Before & After Care
Program** **301.429.8907**
Fax 301.918.8559
Web ....www.pgcps.org
E-mail ....ann.chambers@pgcps.org
  9501 Greenbelt Rd, Lanham, MD 20706
  Ann Chambers, Director

Early Childhood Ctr Head Start **301.408.7100**
Fax 301.445.8484
Web ....www.pgcps.org
E-mail ....laura.barbeematthews@pgcps.org
  8908 Rigs Rd, Addelphi, MD 20785
  Laura Barbee Matthews, Director

Prince George's County

SOCIAL SERVICES

Dept of Social Svcs **301.209.5000**
Fax 301.209.5216
Web ....www.co.pg.md.us
E-mail ....klynch@co.pg.md.us
  6505 Belcrest Rd Ste 200, Hyattsville,
  MD 20782-2011
  Karen Lynch, Director

COURTS

7th Circuit Court/Juvenile **301.952.3318**
Fax 301.952.4887
Web ....www.co.pg.md.us
  14735 Main St, #M1408, Upper Marlboro,
  MD 20772
  Tanya James, Supervisor

District Court/Clerk's Ofc **301.952.3318**
Fax 301.937.1335
Web ....www.co.pg.md.us
E-mail ....trhodes@co.pg.md.us
  14735 Main St, Upper Marlboro, MD 20772-3051
  Honorable Thurman H. Rhodes, Administrative Judge

Queen Annes County

SOCIAL SERVICES

Dept of Social Svcs **410.758.8000**
Fax 410.758.8110
Web ....www.dhr.state.md.us
  125 Comet Dr, Centreville, MD 21617
  Cathy Dougherty, Director

JUSTICE AGENCY

Dept of Juvenile Svcs **410.819.4180**
Fax 410.819.4190
Web ....www.djs.state.md.us
E-mail ....gadsbyj@djs.state.md.us
  120 Broadway Ste 9, Centreville, MD 21617-1037
  John Gadsby, Area Director

COURTS

2nd Circuit Court **410.758.0216**
Fax 410.758.4236
E-mail ....sandra.smith@courts.state.md.us
  100 Court House Sq, 2nd Fl, Centreville, MD 21617
  Sandy Smith, Secretary To Judge Ross

POLICE AND SHERIFF

Sheriff Ofc **410.758.0770**
Fax 410.758.1961
E-mail ....sheriff@qac.org
  505 Railroad Ave, Centreville, MD 21617
  Gary R Hoffmann, Sheriff

Somerset County

SOCIAL SERVICES

Dept of Social Svcs **410.677.4200**
Fax 410.677.4300
Web ....www.dhr.state.md.us
E-mail ....pmannion@dhr.state.md.us
  30397 Mount Vernon Rd, Princess Anne,
  MD 21853-1438
  Patricia Mannion, Director

JUSTICE AGENCY

Dept of Juvenile Svcs **410.845.4680**
Fax 410.845.4690
Web ....www.djs.state.md.us
  12155 Elm St Ste B, DISTRICT COURT BLDG, STE B,
  Princess Anne, MD 21853-1348
  Spencer Lee Tracy, Supervisor

POLICE AND SHERIFF

Sheriff's Ofc 410.651.9225
Fax 410.651.1142
Web ....www.direcway.com
E-mail ....scso@intercom.net
  30426 Sam Barnes Rd Ste A, Westover,
  MD 21871-3306
  Robert N. Jones, Sheriff

St. Marys County

SOCIAL SERVICES

Dept of Social Svcs 240.895.7000
Fax 240.895.7099
E-mail ....erussel@dhr.state.md.us
  23110 Leonard Hall Dr, Leonardtown, MD 20650
  Ella May Russell, Director

GENERAL HEALTH SERVICES

Health Dept.........................301.475.4330
Fax 301.475.4350
Web ....www.smchd.org
E-mail ....healthdept@smhd.com
  21580 Peabody St, Leonardtown, MD 20650-2962
  Melanie Gardiner, Aids Coordinator

JUSTICE AGENCY

CASA 301.475.8860
Fax 301.475.3843
Web ....www.center-for-children.org
E-mail ....casamd@center-for-children.org
  23507 Hollywood Rd, Suite 2, Leonardtown,
  MD 20650
  Karin Coeary, Psychologist Director

Talbot County

SOCIAL SERVICES

Dept of Social Svcs 410.770.4848
Fax 410.820.7117
Web ....www.dhr.state.md.us
E-mail ....asharp@dhr.state.md.us
  301 Bay St Unit 5, Easton, MD 21601-2796
  April Sharp, Director

GENERAL HEALTH SERVICES

Health Dept 410.819.5600
Fax 410.819.5690
Web ....www.talbothealth.org
E-mail ....jarichar@dhmh.state.md.us
  100 S Hanson St, Easton, MD 21601-2989
  Judy Richards, Rn, Aids Coordinator

JUSTICE AGENCY

CASA 410.822.2866
Fax 410.820.6620
E-mail ....casa@goeaston.net
  1 S Washington St Ste 2A, Easton, MD 21601
  Robin Davenport, Executive Director

Dept of Juvenile Svcs 410.822.5010
Fax 410.822.5550
  600 Dover Rd Ste 104, Easton, MD 21601
  Tim Haynes, Supervisor

POLICE AND SHERIFF

Sheriff's Ofc 410.822.1020
Fax 410.770.8110
Web ....www.talbotcountymd.gov
E-mail ....sheriff@talbotcountymd.gov
  115 W Dover St Ste 2, PUBLIC SAFETY BUILDING,
  Easton, MD 21601-2673
  Dallas Pope, Sheriff

Washington County

SOCIAL SERVICES

Dept of Social Svcs 240.420.2100
Fax 240.420.2111
E-mail ....kchristof@dhr.state.md.us
  122 N Potomac St, Hagerstown, MD 21740
  Karen Christof, Assistant Director Of Services

MENTAL HEALTH SERVICES

Mental Health Ctr 301.791.3045
Fax 301.714.1212
Web ....www.thementalhealthcenter.net
E-mail ....mlannon@thementalhealthcenter.net
  1180 Professional Ct, Hagerstown, MD 21740-5852
  Mark Lannon, Executive Director

JUSTICE AGENCY

Div of Parole & Probation 240.420.5140
Fax 301.791.5745
  100 W Franklin St, Ste 205, Hagerstown, MD 21740
  Michael Mcdermott, Office Manager

Parent/Child Ctr CASA 301.791.2224
Fax 301.791.5872
E-mail ....pcchage1@verizon.net
  998 Potomac Ave, Hagerstown, MD 21742-3926
  Millie Lowman, Director

COURTS

Circuit Court 301.733.8660
Fax 301.791.1151
  24 Summit Ave, P.O. Box 229, Hagerstown,
  MD 21740
  John Mcdowell, Admistrator Judge

EDUCATION SERVICES

Fountaindale Elementry School 301.766.8156
Fax 301.745.3041
Web www.wcboe.k12.md.us
E-mail ....willithe@wcboe.k12.md.us
  901 Northern Ave, Hagerstown, MD 21742-2727
  Theresa Williamson, Principal

Special Education 301.766.8605
Fax 301.766.2975
Web www.wcboe.k12.md.us
E-mail ....markomic@wcboe.k12.md.us
  820 Commonwealth Ave, Hagerstown,
  MD 21740-6836
  Jeffery Gladhill, Director Special Education

Wicomico County

SOCIAL SERVICES

Maryland Dept of Social Services 410.713.3900
Fax 410.713.3910
E-mail ....wicomdss@dhr.state.md.us
  201 Baptist St, Ste 27, Salisbury, MD 21801

GENERAL HEALTH SERVICES

Health Dept 410.749.1244
Fax 410.543.6568
Web ....www.wicomicohealth.org
  108 E Main St, Salisbury, MD 21801
  Michelle Bailey, Child & Adolescent Director

Health Dept 410.749.1244
Fax 410.543.6568
Web ....www.wicomicohealth.org
  108 E Main St, Salisbury, MD 21801
  Michelle Bailey, Child & Adolescent Director

COURTS

1st Circuit Court 410.548.4822
Fax 410.548.4826
Web ....www.wicomicocounty.org
E-mail ....cbeckstad@wicomicocounty.org
  215 Creekside Dr,,101 N division street, Salisbury,
  MD 21804-2800
  Cathleen Beckstad, Judge

POLICE AND SHERIFF

Sheriff's Ofc 410.548.4891
Fax 410.548.4968
E-mail ....hnelms@wicomicocounty.org
  401 Naylor Mill Rd, Salisbury, MD 21801
  Mike Lewis, Sheriff

Worcester County

SOCIAL SERVICES

Dept of Social Svcs 410.677.6800
Fax 410.677.6810
Web ....www.dhr.state.md.us
E-mail ....pbusgen@dhr.state.md.us
  299 Commerce St, Snow Hill, MD 21863-1005
  Pete Buesgens, Director

Maryland Dept of Social Svcs 410.677.6800
Fax 410.677.6810
  299 Commerce St, Snow Hill, MD 21863

GENERAL HEALTH SERVICES

Health Dept 410.632.1100
Fax 410.632.0906
Web ....www.worcesterhealth.org
E-mail ....tracyt@thmh.state.md.us
  6040 Public Landing Rd, Snow Hill, MD 21863
  Tracy Tilghman, Mental Health Director

COURTS

1st Circuit Court /Ofc of Judge Thomas Groten
....410.632.0600
Fax 410.632.5603
  1 W Market St Rm 228, Snow Hill, MD 21863
  Honorable Thomas C. Groton Iii, Judge

SPECIAL SERVICES AGENCIES

ADOPTION AGENCIES

Children's Choice Inc 410.319.9681
Fax 410.319.9688
Web ....www.thechildrenschoice.org
E-mail ....lallen@childrenschoice.org
  6067 Harford Rd, Baltimore, MD 21214-1329
  Leslie Allen, Director

Cradle of Hope Adoption Ctr, Inc 301.587.4400
Fax 301.588.3091
Web ....www.cradlehope.org/
E-mail ....cradle@cradlehope.org
  8630 Fenton St Ste 310, Silver Spring,
  MD 20910-3816
  Linda Perilstein, Executive Director

Creative Adoptions Inc 301.596.1521
Fax 301.596.0346
Web ....www.creativeadoptions.org
E-mail ....cai@creativeadoptions.org
  8808 Centre Park Dr Ste 208, Columbia, MD 21045
  Philippa J. Street, Executive Director

Employee Assistance Service, OHESS, National Security Agency
Fax 410.712.4216
 9800 Savage Road, Suite 6404, Ft. George G. Meade,
 MD 20755-6404
 COA accredited organization.

Family & Children Svcs of Central
Maryland 410.669.9000
Fax 410.728.2972
Web ....www.fcsmd.org
E-mail ....stanlevi@fcsmd.org
 204 W Lanvale St, Baltimore, MD 21217-4182
 Stan Levi, Director

Mardela Special Care 410.860.5185
Fax 410.742.6452
 23704 Ocean Gtwy, Mardela Springs, MD 21837
 Kathy Dickerson, Program Supervisor

PSI Family Svcs, Inc/Central Location 301.654.3903
Fax 301.654.4021
Web ....www.psifamilyservices.com
E-mail ....eabramowitz@asiworks.com
 7101 Wisconsin Ave Ste 1400, Bethesda, MD 20814
 Elizabeth Abramowitz, President

ADVOCACY RESOURCES

Child Advocacy & Investigation Ctr 410.386.3640
Fax 410.876.1945
E-mail ....wakers@ccg.carr.org
 1232 Tech Court, Westminster, MD 21157
 Walt Akers, Investigative Supervisor

Law Office of Joseph Jose 301.907.4760
E-mail ....jodyjose@mac.com
 3612 Raymond St, Chevy Chase, MD 20815
 Joseph Jose

Legal Aid Bureau Inc 301.560.2125
E-mail ....apetkovsek@mdlab.org
 6811 Kenilworth Ave Ste 500, Riverdale, MD 20737
 Amy Petkovsek

NF Karkowsky Esquire 301.649.5506
E-mail ....karkowskyn@aol.com
 1142 Kersey Rd, Silver Spring, MD 20902
 Nancy Fay Karkowsky, Director

Voices For Children 410.840.2495
Fax 410.840.2497
Web ....www.voicesforchildren-cc.org
E-mail ....vfc@voicesforchildren-cc.org
 255 Clifton Blvd Ste 311, Westminster,
 MD 21157-4787
 Jodi Vanderhorst, Director

BEHAVIORAL HEALTH TREATMENT

Adept 410.761.0725
Fax 410.761.2412
Web ....www.apmandadept.com
E-mail ....apm_adept@yahoo.com
 8028 Ritchie Hwy Ste 308, Pasadena,
 MD 21122-1373
 Michael Bartlinski, Director

Adventist Behavioral Health Eastern
Shore 410.221.0288
E-mail ....ktruitt@ahm.com
 821 Fieldcrest Road, Cambridge, MD 21613
 Mrs. Katherine Truitt, Accreditation Manager
 Joint Commission accredited organization.

Adventist Health Care, Inc. 301.251.4500
Web ....www.adventistbehavioralhealth.com
E-mail ....cpangili@adventisthealthcare.com
 14901 Broschart Road, Rockville, MD 20850
 Ms. Caterina Pangilinan, Accreditation Manager
 Joint Commission accredited organization.

Alliance Inc 410.282.5900
Fax 410.282.3083
Web ....www.allianceinc.org
 7701 Wise Ave, Suite 206, Baltimore, MD 21222
 Suzanne Mauro, Vice President HR
 CARF accredited programs available.

Ambrose Medical Practice 410.884.1555
 5231 W Running Brook Rd, Columbia,
 MD 21044-1741
 Rose Ambrose, MD, Psychiatrist

Arak Medical Practice 410.542.9680
 2208 Arden Rd, Baltimore, MD 21209-4205
 Gladys Arak, Psychiatrist

Arrow Project 410.882.9133
Fax 410.663.7092
Web ....www.arrow.org
E-mail ....infomaryland@arrow.org
 1605 Cromwell Bridge Rd, Parkville, MD 21234-1416
 Mark Tennant, CEO

Baltimore Adolescent Treatment and Guidance Organization,
Inc. (BATGO) 410.383.2801
Fax 410.383.6971
 2901 Druid Park Dr Ste A201, Baltimore,
 MD 21215-8130
 William Dickerson, Director

Beitel Medical Practice 410.221.2266
Fax 410.221.2878
E-mail ....dbeitel@mhamdes.org
 813-1 Chesapeake Dr., Cambridge, MD 21613
 Donna Beitel, Md, Psychiatrist

Berry Elementary School 301.753.1782
Fax 301.638.3659
Web ....www.ccbow.com/berry
E-mail ....jonesm@ccboe.com
 10155 Berry Rd, Waldorf, MD 20603-3710
 Marvin Jones, Principle

Blaes Medical Practice 301.309.8200
Fax 301.309.9667
 208 Monroe St, Rockville, MD 20850-4401
 Peter Blaes, Md, Psychiatrist

Blue Ridge Behavioral Health 301.695.8390
Fax 301.694.7906
Web ....blueridgebehavioralhealth.com
 170 Thomas Johnson Dr Ste 202L, Frederick,
 MD 21702-6200
 Breck Borcherding, Md, Psychiatrist

Board of Child Care of The United Methodist
Church 410.922.2100
Fax 410.496.5620
Web ....www.boardofchildcare.org
 3300 Gaither Road, Baltimore, MD 21244
 COA accredited organization.

Board of Ed 240.236.1250
Fax 240.236.1251
Web ....www.fcps.org
E-mail ....brian.katsef@fcps.com
 103 Prospect St, Ste 555, Middletown, MD 21769
 Brian Katsef, Pychiatrist

Bon Secours Hospital Baltimore, Inc. 410.362.3011
Web ....www.bonsecours.org
E-mail ....cathy_newhouse@bshsi.org
 2000 West Baltimore Street, Baltimore, MD 21223
 Ms. Cathy Newhouse, Accreditation Manager
 Joint Commission accredited organization.

Bronhiem Medical Practice 301.320.3220
Fax 301.320.3220
 6912 Persimmon Tree Rd, Bethesda, MD 20817-4412
 Benjamin Bronheim, Psychiatrist

Brook Lane Health Services 301.733.0330
Web ....www.brooklane.org
E-mail ....sharon.gladfelter@brooklane.org
 13218 Brook Lane Drive, Hagerstown,
 MD 21742-1945
 Ms. Sharon Gladfelter, Accreditation Manager
 Joint Commission accredited organization.

Brook Lane Health Svcs 301.733.0330
Fax 301.733.4038
Web ....www.brooklane.org
E-mail ....david.gonzalez@brooklane.org
 13218 Brooklane Dr, Hagerstown, MD 21742-1435
 David Gonzalez, Medical Director

Calvert Memorial Hospital 410.535.4000
Web ....www.calverthospital.com
E-mail ....npieters@cmhlink.org
 100 Hospital Road, Prince Frederick, MD 20678
 Ms. Nichole Pieters, Accreditation Manager
 Joint Commission accredited organization.

Carroll Hospital Center, Inc. 410.871.6523
Web ....www.carrollhospitalcenter.org
E-mail ....lkmiller@carrollhospitalcenter.org
 200 Memorial Avenue, Westminster, MD 21157
 Ms. Linda Miller, Accreditation Manager
 Joint Commission accredited organization.

Catholic Charities Child and Family
Services 410.252.4700
Web ....www.catholiccharities-md.org
E-mail ....jcarson@catholiccharities-md.org
 2300 Dulaney Valley Road, Timonium, MD 21093
 Ms. Jan Carson, Accreditation Manager
 Joint Commission accredited organization.

Centre For Life Strategies 301.986.1479
Fax 301.680.3756
 4813 Saint Elmo Ave, Bethesda, MD 20814-3009
 Margaret Jensvold, Psychiatrist

Chase Brexton Health Services, Inc. 410.837.2050
Web ....www.chasebrexton.org
E-mail ....eschindler@chasebrexton.org
 1001 Cathedral Street, Baltimore, MD 21201
 Ms. Evangeline Schindler, Accreditation Manager
 Joint Commission accredited organization.

Citizens Assisting & Sheltering The
Abused 301.739.4990
Fax 301.739.2493
Web ....www.casainc.org
E-mail ....casa.incorp@myactv.net
 116 W Baltimore St, Hagerstown, MD 21740
 Vicki Sadehvandi, Executive Director

City of Rockville Police Dept 240.314.8900
Fax 240.314.8929
Web ....www.rockvillemd.gov
E-mail ....dwilkins@rockvillemd.gov
 111 Maryland Ave, Fl 1, Rockville, MD 20850
 Diane Wilkins, Victim Advocate

Cytryn Medical Practice 301.588.8996
 9513 Midwood Rd, Silver Spring, MD 20910-1650
 Leon Cytryn Md, Psychiatrist

Deep Creek Middle School 410.887.0112
Fax 410.391.6534
 1000 S Marlyn Ave, Essex, MD 21221
 Dwan Pinamonti, Principle

Dove Ctr 301.334.6255
Fax 301.245.4525
Web ....www.garrettdovecenter.org
E-mail ....dovecenter@verizon.net
 12978 Garrett Hwy, # 201, Oakland, MD 21550
 Heather-Hanline, Director

Drug Policy Info Clearinghouse 800.666.3332
Fax 301.519.5212
Web ....www.whitehousedrugpolicy.gov
E-mail ....ondcp@ncjrs.gov
 2277 Research Blvd, Rockville, MD 20849
 Gil Kerlikowske, Director

EHP Behavioral Svcs **410.933.9000**
Fax 410.889.2758
  3915 N Charles St, Baltimore, MD 21218
  Stanley Platman, Psychiatrist

Family Support & Education Ctr; The **410.287.1100**
Fax 410.392.9548
E-mail ....jpalmer@cecil.cc.edu
  200 Road B, Hollingsworth Manor, Elkton, MD 21921
  Barbara Istzan, Director

First Step **410.526.7100**
Fax 410.526.7138
Web ....www.firststepmd.com
E-mail ....jperrone@firststepmd.com
  100 Owings Ct Ste 8, Reisterstown, MD 21136-3045
  James Perrone, Director

First Step **410.628.6120**
Fax 410.628.0953
Web ....www.firststepmd.com
E-mail ....jgary@firststepmd.com
  10400 Ridgland Rd Ste 1, Cockeysville,
  MD 21030-2799
  Jeff Gary, Clinical Director

Fishel Watson & Lemaire PA **410.583.2222**
Fax 410.583.2377
  110 E Pennsylvania Ave, Towson, MD 21286-5118
  Theo Lemaire, Director

Frostburg State University **301.687.4000**
Fax 301.687.3065
Web ....www.frostburg.edu/counsil
E-mail ....sdeakin@frostburg.edu
  101 Braddock Rd, Frostburg, MD 21532-2303
  Spencer Deakin, Director

Hannah More School **410.526.5000**
Fax 410.526.7631
Web ....www.hannahmore.org
E-mail ....pkaplan@hannahmore.org
  12039 Reisterstown Rd, Reisterstown,
  MD 21136-3042
  Paul Kaplan, Ba, Msw, Jd, Clinical Director

**House of the Good Shepherd of the City of
Baltimore** **410.247.2770**
Web ....www.goodshepherdcenter.org
E-mail ....mwyman@goodshepherdcenter.org
  4100 Maple Avenue, Baltimore, MD 21227
  Mrs. Michele Wyman, Accreditation Manager
  Joint Commission accredited organization.

Integrative Counseling **410.740.5641**
Fax 410.740.5603
  10440 Little Patuxent Pkwy, Ste 300, Columbia,
  MD 21044-3648
  Jeffrey Crouch, LCLWC

**John L. Gildner Regional Institute for Children&
Adolescents** **301.251.6800**
Web ....www.dhmh.state.md.us/jlgrica/index.html
E-mail ....kbasler@dhmh.state.md.us
  15000 Broschart Road, Rockville, MD 20850
  Mr. Ken Basler, Accreditation Manager
  Joint Commission accredited organization.

Johns Hopkins Bayview Medical Center **410.550.0120**
Web ....www.hopkinsbayview.org
E-mail ....dmoore2@jhmi.edu
  4940 Eastern Avenue, Baltimore, MD 21224-2780
  Ms. Dana Moore, Accreditation Manager
  Joint Commission accredited organization.

Key Point Health Svcs, Inc. **410.788.0300**
Fax 410.869.7244
Web ....www.keypoint.org
E-mail ....lindawilkins@keypoint.org
  500 N Rolling Rd, Catonsville, MD 21228-4134
  Linda Wilkins, Mba, Lcpc, Clinical Director

Lower Shore Clinic **410.341.3420**
Fax 410.341.3397
E-mail ....tuesday.trott@gmail.com
  505 E Main St, Salisbury, MD 21804-5020
  T Trott, Office Manager

Maple Shade Youth & Family Services, Inc. **410.742.7400**
E-mail ....sward@maple-shade.org
  23704 Ocean Gateway, Mardela Springs, MD 21837
  Mrs. Shanda Ward, Accreditation Manager
  Joint Commission accredited organization.

**Maryland Dept Of Juvenile Svcs Backbone Mountain Drug
Treatment Program** **301.359.9190**
Fax 301.359.0811
  124 Camp 4 Rd, Swanton, MD 21561-1329
  Marty Sharpless, Director

Maryland Treatment Centers, Inc. **301.447.2361**
E-mail ....dhoneycutt@atlanticbb.net
  9701 Keysville Rd, US Route 15, Emmitsburg,
  MD 21727
  Dr. Marc Fishman, Accreditation Manager
  Joint Commission accredited organization.

Mental Health Assoc **301.424.0656**
Fax 301.738.1030
Web ....www.mhamc.org
  1000 Twinbrook Pkwy, Rockville, MD 20851
  Sharon E Friedman, Executive Director

Montgomery General Hospital **301.774.8770**
Web ....www.montgomerygeneral.com
E-mail ....bsecrist@montgomerygeneral.com
  18101 Prince Philip Drive, Olney, MD 20832
  Mrs. Betty Secrist, Accreditation Manager
  Joint Commission accredited organization.

Mosaic Community Services, Inc. **443.612.1497**
Fax 410.308.8926
Web ....www.mosaicinc.org
E-mail ....dawn.hurley@mosaicinc.org
  1925 Greenspring Drive, Timonium, MD 21093
  Dawn Hurley, PRP Program Director
  CARF accredited programs available.

Mosaic, Inc. **410.453.9553**
Fax 410.453.9552
Web ....www.mosaicinc.org
  1925 Greenspring Dr Ste D, Lutherville Timonium,
  MD 21093
  Oleg Tachovsky, MSW, MED, Clinical Director

New Foundations **410.576.8600**
Fax 410.576.8666
E-mail ....mark.mclendon@thementornetwork.com
  20 E Franklin St, Baltimore, MD 21202-2204
  Mark Mclendon, Director

**Our House Residential Job Training Ctr For
Youth** **301.519.1019**
Fax 301.990.1560
Web ....www.our-house.org
E-mail ....richard@our-house.org
  19715 Zion Rd, Brookeville, MD 20833-1505
  Richard Bienvenue, Executive Director

Pathways **410.573.5400**
Web ....www.pathwaysprogram.org
E-mail ....hreines@aahs.org
  2620 Riva Road, Annapolis, MD 21401
  Mrs. Helen Reines, Accreditation Manager
  Joint Commission accredited organization.

People's Community Health Center, Inc. **410.467.6040**
Web ....www.peoplesbaltimore.org
E-mail ....rvanek@peopleschc.org
  2524 Kirk Avenue, Baltimore, MD 21218
  Ms. Robon Vanek, Accreditation Manager
  Joint Commission accredited organization.

PSI Family Svcs, Inc **410.277.0221**
Fax 410.277.0229
Web ....www.psifamilyservices.com
  7104 Ambassador Rd, Ste 260, Windsor Mill,
  MD 21244-2740
  Sheila Pandent, Program Director

**Regional Institute For Children & Adolescents
Baltimore** **410.368.7800**
Fax 410.368.7886
E-mail ....sekas@dhmh.state.md.us
  605 S Chapel Gate Ln, Baltimore, MD 21229-3906
  Penny Makris, CEO

**Regional Institute for Children & Adolescents Southern
Maryland** **301.372.1800**
Fax 301.372.1906
  9400 Surratts Rd, Cheltenham, MD 20623-1324
  Holly Sikoryak, MD, Medical Director

**Regional Institute for Children and
Adolescents-Baltimore** **410.368.7800**
Web ....www.dhmh.state.md.us
E-mail ....kmiles@dhmh.state.md.us
  605 South Chapel Gate Lane, Baltimore, MD 21229
  Ms. Kathleen Miles, Accreditation Manager
  Joint Commission accredited organization.

Sheppard Pratt **410.938.3800**
Fax 410.938.4530
Web ....www.sheppardpratt.org
E-mail ....ppinkerton@sheppardpratt.org
  6501 N Charles St, Towson, MD 21204-6819
  Patricia Pinkerton, Vice President/cfo

Sheppard Pratt Health System, Inc. **410.938.4281**
Web ....www.sheppardpratt.org
E-mail ....samrose@sheppardpratt.org
  6501 North Charles Street, Baltimore,
  MD 21285-6815
  Ms. Susan Amrose, Accreditation Manager
  Joint Commission accredited organization.

Sheppard Pratt Mental Health Ctr **410.740.1901**
Fax 410.740.2503
Web ....www.shepardpratt.org
E-mail ....jharvey@waystationinc.org
  9030 State Route 108 Ste A, Columbia, MD 21045
  Janis Harvey, Director

Spring Grove Hospital Center **410.402.6000**
Web ....www.springgrove.com
E-mail ....heilmanc@dhmh.state.md.us
  55 Wade Avenue, Catonsville, MD 21228
  Ms. Cheryl Heilman, Accreditation Manager
  Joint Commission accredited organization.

Susan Fiester MD **301.365.4980**
Fax 301.469.8772
E-mail ....sfiester@sfiester.com
  6 Vendome Ct, Bethesda, MD 20817
  Susan Fiester, Psychiatrist

The Johns Hopkins Hospital **410.955.5000**
Web ....www.hopkinsmedicine.org
E-mail ....sfrankl7@jhmi.edu
  600 North Wolfe Street, Baltimore, MD 21287
  Ms. Susan Franklin, Accreditation Manager
  Joint Commission accredited organization.

The Listening Place **410.313.2630**
Fax 410.313.2633
  3421 Rogers Ave, Ellicott City, MD 21042
  Lt. Roland Dencon, Program Manager

Tuttie's Place **410.277.9170**
Fax 410.277.9174
  3000 Chelsea Ter, Baltimore, MD 21216-1508
  Brenda Boyd, Program Director

University of Maryland Medical Center **410.328.6027**
Web ....www.umm.edu
E-mail ....iconnerney@umm.edu
  22 South Greene Street, Baltimore, MD 21201-1595
  Dr. Ingrid Connerney, Accreditation Manager
  Joint Commission accredited organization.

Villa Maria 410.252.4700
Fax 410.252.3040
Web ....www.catholiccharities-md.org
E-mail ....mgreenbe@catholiccharities-md.org
　2300 Dulaney Valley Rd Ste 2, Lutherville Timonium,
　MD 21093-2736
Mark Greenberg, Lcsw, Administrator

Way Station, Inc. 301.662.0099
Fax 301.694.9932
Web ....www.waystationinc.org
E-mail ....nwoods@waystationinc.org
　230 West Patrick Street, Frederick, MD 21701
Nancy Woods, Director
CARF accredited programs available.

Woodbourne Center, Inc. 410.433.1000
Web ....www.woodbourne.org
E-mail ....swest@woodbourne.org
　1301 Woodbourne Avenue, Baltimore, MD 21239
Ms. Shaliek Maxwell-West, Accreditation Manager
Joint Commission accredited organization.

Youth Svcs Bureau 410.848.2500
Fax 410.876.3016
E-mail ....lynndavis@ccysb.org
　59 Jate Kace Wagner W, Westminster, MD 21157
Lynn Davis, Director

CHILDREN'S HOSPITAL

Anne Arundel Medical Center 443.481.1000
E-mail ....info@aahs.org
　2001 Medical Pkwy, Annapolis, MD 21401

Atlantic General Hospital 410.641.1100
　9733 Healthway Dr, Berlin, MD 21811
Michael Franklin, Chief Executive Officer

Baltimore Washington Medical Center 410.787.4000
　301 Hospital Dr, Glen Burnie, MD 21061
Betsy Tabor, Nursing Department

Calvert Memorial Hospital 410.535.4000
　100 Hospital Rd, Prince Frederick, MD 20678
James Xinis, Chief Executive Officer

Carroll Hospital Center 410.848.3000
　200 Memorial Ave, Westminster, MD 21157
John Sernulka, Chief Executive Officer

Civista Health 301.609.4000
　5 Garrett Ave, La Plata, MD 20646
Noeo Ceribnao, Chief Executive Officer

Franklin Square Hospital Center 443.777.7000
E-mail ....adrienne.kirby@medstar.net
　9000 Franklin Square Dr, Baltimore, MD 21237
Adrienne Kirby, Executive Director

Frederick Memorial Hospital 240.566.3300
　400 W 7th St, Frederick, MD 21701
Thomas Alenchanzel, President

General Hospital 410.740.7890
E-mail ....nsmith@hcgh.org
　5755 Cedar Ln, Columbia, MD 21044
Nancy Smith, Director of Nursing

Greater Baltimore Medical Center 443.849.2000
　6701 N Charles St, Baltimore, MD 21204
John Chessare, Chief Executive Officer

Harbor Hospital 410.350.3200
　3001 S Hanover St, Brooklyn, MD 21225
Dennis Pullen, Chief Executive Officer

Holy Cross Hospital 301.754.7000
　1500 Forest Glen Rd, Silver Spring, MD 20910
Kevin Saxton, Chief Executive Officer

Hospital Association 301.790.8000
　11116 Medical Campus Rd, Hagerstown, MD 21742
Joseph Ross, President

Johns Hopkins Bayview Medical Center 410.550.0100
　4940 Eastern Ave, Baltimore, MD 21224
Richard Benett, President

Johns Hopkins Hospital 410.955.5000
　600 N Wolfe St, Baltimore, MD 21287
Ronald Peterson, Executive Director

Maryland General Hospital 410.225.8000
　827 Linden Ave, Baltimore, MD 21201
Silvia Smith Johnson, Chief Executive Officer

Mercy Medical Center 410.332.9000
　301 St Paul Pl, Baltimore, MD 21202
Thomas Mullen, Director

Montgomery General Hospital 301.774.8882
　18101 Prince Philip Dr, Olney, MD 20832

Ntl Inst of Health Clinical Center 301.496.4000
　9000 Rockville Pike, Bethesda, MD 20892
Francis Collins, Director

Peninsula Regional Medical Center 410.546.6400
　100 E Carroll St, Salisbury, MD 21801
Regina Kundell, Director of Nursing

Prince George's Hospital Center 301.618.2000
　3001 Hospital Dr, Cheverly, MD 20785
Ruby Anderson, Director of Nursing

Shady Grove Adventist Hospital 240.826.6000
　9901 Medical Center Dr, Rockville, MD 20850

Shore Hospital Memorial Hospital 410.822.1000
E-mail ....gwalsh@shorehealth.org
　219 S Washington St, Easton, MD 21601
Derald Walsh, President

Sinai Hospital of Baltimore 410.601.9000
E-mail ....nmeltzer@lifebridgehealth.org
　2401 W Belvedere Ave, Baltimore, MD 21215
Neil Meltzer, President

Southern Maryland Hospital Center 301.868.8000
　7503 Surratts Rd, Clinton, MD 20735
Richard Ardery, Vice President

St Agnes Hospital 410.368.6000
　900 Caton Ave, Baltimore, MD 21229
Bonnie Phipps, Chief Executive Officer

St Joseph Medical Center 410.337.1000
E-mail ....pamelajamieson@catholichealth.net
　7601 Osler Dr, Towson, MD 21204
Peggy Mortenson, Nursing Director

St Mary's Hospital 301.475.8981
　25500 Point Lookout Rd, Leonardtown, MD 20650
Christine Wray, President

Suburban Hospital 301.896.3100
　8600 Old Georgetown Rd, Bethesda, MD 20814
John Hopkins, Owner

Union Hospital 410.398.4000
　106 Bow St, Elkton, MD 21921
Dr. Kenneth Lewis, Chief Executive Officer

Union Memorial Hospital 410.554.2000
　201 E University Pkwy, Baltimore, MD 21218
Ray Chamber, Chief Executive Officer

Univ of Maryland Medical Center 410.328.8667
　22 S Greene St, Baltimore, MD 21201
Jeffery Rivest, Chief Executive Officer

Upper Chesapeake Medical Center 443.643.1000
　500 Upper Chesapeake Dr, Bel Air, MD 21014
Lyle Sheldon, Chief Executive Officer

Western Maryland Regional Hospital 240.964.7000
　12500 Willow Brook, Cumberland, MD 21502
Tom Caldwell, Administrator

COUNSELING SERVICES

Annapolis Youth Svcs Bureau 410.626.1800
Fax 410.626.1922
Web ....www.aaceoc.com
E-mail ....aysb2001@yahoo.com
　92 W Washington St, Annapolis, MD 21401-2432
Sascha Lipczenko, Director

College Park Youth Family Svcs 301.474.1210
Fax 301.474.0717
Web ....www.ci.college-park.md.us
E-mail ....phiggins@collegeparkmd.us
　4912 Nantucket Rd, College Park, MD 20740-1458
Peggy Higgins, Director

Delmarva Family Resources At Charles Hickey
School 410.668.3300
Fax 410.663.7650
　2400 Cub Hill Rd, Parkville, MD 201234
C Wallmen, Director

Dundalk Youth Svc Ctr 410.288.4356
Fax 410.284.7920
Web ....www.dundalkfamilypeace.org
E-mail ....dysc@comcast.net
　2660 Yorkway, Dundalk, MD 21222-4442
Linda Bryan, Executive Director

First Step, Inc. 410.521.4141
Fax 410.521.3993
Web ....www.firststepmd.com
E-mail ....firststepmd@aol.com
　8303 Liberty Rd, Windsor Mill, MD 21244-3125
David Goldman, Executive Director

Greenbelt Cares (Youth and Family Svcs) 301.345.6660
Fax 301.441.8248
Web ....www.greenbeltmd.gov
E-mail ....lpark@greenbeltmd.gov
　25 Crescent Rd, Greenbelt, MD 20770-1891
Elizabeth Park, Phd, Director

Guide Gaithersburg Youth Svcs Bureau 240.683.6580
Fax 240.683.6586
Web ....www.guideprogram.org
　620 E Diamond Ave Ste H, Gaithersburg,
　MD 20877-5328
Nancey Horst, Office Manager

Jewish Family And Children's Svcs 410.466.9200
Fax 410.664.0551
Web ....www.jfs.org
E-mail ....jfs@jfs.baltimore.org
　5750 Park Heights Ave, Baltimore, MD 21215-3930
Barbara Gradet, Executive Director

Lighthouse, Inc 410.788.5483
Fax 410.788.5486
E-mail ....lighthouse60@verizon.net
　60 Mellor Ave, Catonsville, MD 21228-5104
Linda Lombardo, Phd, Director

Northwest Baltimore Youth Svcs, Inc 410.578.8100
Fax 443.524.2628
　3319 W Belvedere Ave Ste 2, Baltimore, MD 21215
Audrey Bennett, Director

Thomas Johnson Middle School 301.918.8680
Fax 301.918.8688
Web ....www.pgcps.org
E-mail ....michael.robinson@pgcps.org
　5401 Barker Pl, Lanham, MD 20706-2499
Dr.Michael Robinson, Headmaster

Youth Svcs Bureau 301.843.2960
Fax 301.645.9169
Web ....www.tcysb.org
E-mail ....info@tcysb.org
　75 Industrial Park Dr, Waldorf, MD 20602-2708
Laurel James, Executive Director

CRISIS & SHELTER CARE

Abused Persons Program (Victims of Spouse Abuse and Their
Dependent Children) Admin 240.777.4195
Fax 240.777.4860
E-mail ....nadja.cabello@montgomerycountymd.gov
　1301 Piccard Dr, Ste 1400, Rockville, MD 20850
Nadja Cabello, Manager

Chrysalis House 410.974.6829
Fax 410.974.6350
Web .... www.chrysalishouses.org
1570 Crownsville Rd, Crownsville, MD 21032-2306
Lorraine Lake, Executive Director

Ctr For Abused Persons - Domestic Violence 301.645.8994
Fax 301.645.8342
E-mail .... ajackson@dhr.state.md.us
2670 Crain Hwy, Ste 303, Waldorf, MD 20601
Ms. Annette Gilbert-jackson, Director

Domestic Violence and Sexual Assault Centre of Healthcare Division 301.618.3154
Fax 301.618.2881
3001 Hospital Dr, Ste 300, Cheverly, MD 20785
Mark Arsenault, Director Of Emergency Services

Domestic Violence Ctr 410.997.0304
Fax 410.997.1397
Web .... www.dvcenter.org
E-mail .... info@dvcenter.org
5457 Twin Knolls Rd Ste 310, Columbia, MD 21045
Krista Mckee, Director

Family and Children Svcs of Central Maryland 410.281.1334
Fax 410.298.4326
Web .... www.fcsmd.org
E-mail .... pthompson@fcsmd.org
7000 Security Blvd, Ste 302, Baltimore, MD 21244
Ms. Patricia Thompson, Director

Family Crisis Ctr Inc-Prince Georges Co 301.779.2100
Fax 301.779.2104
Web .... www.familycrisis-tgco.org
E-mail .... vcallis@familycrisiscenter-pgco.org
3601 Taylor St, Ste 100, Brentwood, MD 20722
Melinda Miles, Director

Family Crisis Ctr of Baltimore Inc. 410.285.4357
Fax 410.285.4361
Web .... www.fcsmd.org
E-mail .... doug@familycrisiscenter.net
PO Box 3909, Dundalk, MD 21222-0809
Mr Douglas Murphy, Director

Family Crisis Resource Ctr 301.759.9246
Fax 301.759.4934
Web .... www.fcrcinc.org
146 Bedford St, Cumberland, MD 21502
Sarabech James, Director

Good Shepherd Ctr 410.247.2770
Fax 410.247.3242
Web .... www.goodshepherdcenter.org
E-mail .... info@goodshepherdcenter.org
4100 Maple Ave, Halethorpe, MD 21227-4099
Terrie Schindler, Director Admissions

Heartly House Inc - Domestic Violence 301.662.8800
Fax 301.663.4334
Web .... www.heartlyhouse.org
PO Box 857, Frederick, MD 21705-0857
Ashley Mancinelli, Chief Executive Officer

Hearts & Homes For Youth, Inc. 301.589.8444
Fax 301.495.0923
Web www.hh4y.org
1320 Fenwick Ln Ste 800, Silver Spring, MD 20910
Rex Smith, President/CEO

House of Ruth Maryland Inc - Domestic Violence 410.889.0840
Fax 410.889.9347
Web .... www.hruth.org
E-mail .... info@hruth.org
2201 Argonne Dr, Baltimore, MD 21218-1627
Sandi Timmins, Executive Director

Life Crisis Ctr Inc 410.749.0771
Fax 410.548.9496
Web .... www.lifecrisiscenter.org
E-mail .... mhughes@lifecrisiscenter.org
PO Box 387, Salisbury, MD 21803-0387
Ms Michelle Hughes, Director

Local Management Board 410.222.7423
Fax 410.222.7674
Web .... www.aacounty.org/localmgmtboard/indexcfm
E-mail .... srbrow00@aacounty.org
1 Harry S Truman Pkwy Ste 103, Annapolis, MD 21401-7037
Dr. Pamela Brown, Executive Director

Mid-Shore Council On Family Violence, Inc. 410.479.1149
Fax 410.479.2064
Web .... www.mscfv.org
E-mail .... jyeager@mscfb.org
322 Market St, DENTON, MD 21629
Jeanne Yeager, Executive Director

Rape Crisis Ctr 410.996.0333
Fax 410.996.0820
E-mail .... abean@dhr.state.md.us
405 Bow St, Elkton, MD 21921
Ms. Ann Bean, Director

Salvation Army Booth House -Domestic Violence 410.685.8878
Fax 410.685.3875
Web .... www.uss.salvationarmy.org
E-mail .... dean_mears@Uss.Salvationarmy.Org
1114 N Calvert St, Baltimore, MD 21202-3875
Dean Mears, Director

Sexual Assault - Spouse Abuse Resource Ctr 410.836.8431
Fax 410.838.9484
Web .... www.sarc-maryland.org
E-mail .... lcn@sarc-maryland.org
PO Box 1207, Bel Air, MD 21014-7207
Luisa Caiazzo-nutter, Director

Walden-Sierra Domestic Violence Program 301.863.6688
Fax 301.997.1321
Web .... www.waldensierra.org
26845 Point Lookout Rd, Leonardtown, MD 20650-4935
Kathy O'Brian, Director

EDUCATION

Arrow Project 410.734.0560
Fax 410.734.0561
Web .... www.arrow.org
E-mail .... infomaryland@arrow.org
2416 Creswell Rd, Bel Air, MD 21015-6508
Mark Tennant, CEO

Catholic Charities Aberdeen Family Ctr 410.273.5650
Fax 410.272.6082
34 N Philadelphia Blvd, Aberdeen, MD 21001-2511
Kaylene Richardson, Director

Chimes School 410.358.8270
Fax 410.358.8271
Web .... www.chimes.org
E-mail .... mschaefer@chimes.org
4810 Seton Dr, Baltimore, MD 21215-3210
Mary Schaefer, Principal

Cumberland Family Support Ctr / Downtown YMCA 301.724.5445
Fax 301.724.0642
E-mail .... janicefsc@msn.com
205 Baltimore Ave, Cumberland, MD 21502-2427
Janice Cannon, Director

Families Foremost Ctr 301.585.3424
Fax 301.585.8382
Web .... www.mhamc.org
E-mail .... swaddy@mhamc.org
1109 Spring St Ste 300, Silver Spring, MD 20910
Shari Waddy, Md, Director

Freestate/ Challenge Academy 410.306.1801
Fax 410.306.1829
Web .... www.ngycp.org
E-mail .... ryoung@mdmildep.org
Bldg. 5469 Proving Grounds, Aberdeen, MD 21005
Col.(Retired) Richard E. Young, Director

Maryland Assoc of Non-Public Special Education Facilities 410.938.4413
Fax 410.938.5130
Web .... www.mansef.org
E-mail .... mansef@aol.com
6501 N Charles St, Towson, MD 21285
Dorie Flynn, Executive Director

Potomac Ridge Behavior Health Systems - Eastern Shore 410.221.0288
Fax 410.228.9588
Web .... www.potomacridge.com
821 Fieldcrest Rd, Cambridge, MD 21613-9423
John Mistrangelo, Director

St. Elizabeth School 410.889.5054
Fax 410.889.2356
Web .... www.stelizabeth-school.org
E-mail .... cmanlove@stelizabeth-school.org
801 Argonne Dr, Baltimore, MD 21218-1998
Christine Manlove, Edd, Executive Director/principal

Waverly Family Ctr, Inc. 410.235.0555
Fax 410.366.7720
Web .... www.goodwillches.org
E-mail .... sthomas@goodwillches.org
829 Montpelier St, Baltimore, MD 21218-3542
Sharon Thomas, Director

Woodstock Job Corps Ctr 410.461.1100
Fax 410.461.5794
E-mail .... rodeny.butler@jobcorps.org
10900 Old Court Rd, Woodstock, MD 21163-1129
Rodeny Butler, Center Director

FOSTER CARE AGENCIES

Adoptions Together 301.439.2900
Fax 301.439.9334
E-mail .... jgoldwater@adoptionstogether.org
10230 New Hampshire Ave, Ste 200, Silver Spring, MD 20903
Janice Golbwater, Executive Director

Adoptive Families & Friends (AFF) 301.371.4903
6134 Cornwell Pl, Frederick, MD 21701

Attachment & Trauma Network (ATN) 240.357.7369
E-mail .... Lorraine@radzebra.org
PO Box 163, Jefferson, MD 21755

Catholic Charities 410.659.4050
Fax 410.659.4060
E-mail .... families@catholiccharities-md.org
2601 N Howard St, Ste 200, Baltimore, MD 21218
Laurie Vovzella-Bell, Director

Center for Adoption Support & Education 301.476.8525
Fax 301.473.8526
E-mail .... caseadopt@adoptionsupport.org
Ste 260, Burtonsville, MD 20866

Children's Choice 410.643.9290
Fax 410.643.9293
1103 Butterworth Ct, Stevensville, MD 21666

Children's Home Treatment Fostor Care 410.368.1306
Fax 410.368.1309
Web .... www.thechildrenshome.net
1531 S Edgewood St Ste D, Halethorpe, MD 21227-1138
George Ealtb, Director

Coalition of Adoption Programs Inc CAPS 301.529.8465
Fax 301.899.0654
E-mail .... janhayes1@verizon.net
3100 Ritchie Rd, Ste J 2nd Fl, Forestville, MD 20747
Jan Hayes, Chief Executive Officer

Day By Day Residential Svc LLC 410.664.1170
Fax 410.664.3079
3304 Oakfield Ave, Gwynn Oak, MD 21207
Janet Uagbor, Executive Director

DC Metro Foster & Adoptive Parent Assoc 301.449.1061
Fax 301.449.5911
7204 Loch Raven Rd, Temple Hills, MD 20748

Latin America Parents Assoc of the 301.431.3407
E-mail .... info@lapa.com
PO Box 4403, Silver Spring, MD 20904

Maryland Foster Parent Assoc 301.994.9344
PO Box 1049, Severna Park, MD 21146
Michelle Burnette, Director

Mentor Maryland 443.543.2192
Fax 443.543.2110
E-mail .... joan.cooper@thementornetwork.com
5720 Executive Dr, Baltimore, MD 21228

The Arc Northern Chesapeake Region TFC 410.836.7177
E-mail .... dross@arcncr.org
4513 Philadelphia Rd, Aberdeen, MD 21001
Diane Ross, Director

The Barker Foundation 301.664.9664
Fax 301.664.9604
E-mail .... info@barkerfoundation.org
7979 Old Georgetown Rd, 1st Fl, Bethesda,
MD 20814
Marilyn Regier, Executive Director

**The Sanctuary at Kingdom Sq TSAKS 1
Chur** 301.333.9033
9171 Central Ave 3rd Fl, Capitol Heights, MD 20743
Maclin Anhony, Pastor

HOME MEDICAL EQUIPMENT PROVIDERS

Autogenesis Inc 410.665.2017
Fax 410.665.1616
E-mail .... autogenesis@sprynet.com
8700 Old Harford Road, Parkville, MD 21234

Capital Hospice Beltsville 301.572.2489
11700 Beltsville Dr Ste 100, Beltsville, MD 20705

Carroll Hospital Center Hospice 410.871.3000
Fax 410.871.7186
E-mail .... mktpr@CarrollHospitalCenter.org
200 Memorial Dr, Westminster, MD 21157
John Sernulka, Chief Executive Officer

Childrens Medical Ministries 301.261.3211
Fax 410.721.4647
E-mail .... childmed@olg.com
PO Box 3382, Crofton, MD 21114
Bill Collins, Executive Director

Greater Baltimore Medical Center 443.849.8200
Fax 443.849.8201
E-mail .... lmulligan@gbmc.org
555 W Towson Blvd, Towson, MD 21204
Lorrie Mulligan, Chief Executive Officer

Hopkins Medical Products 800.835.1995
5 Greenwood Pl, Pikesville, MD 21208
Margie K, Director

Jewish Social Srv Agency 301.838.4200
Web .... www.jssa.org
E-mail .... info@jssa.org
200 Wood Hill Rd, Rockville, MD 20850
Ken Kozloff, Chief Executive Officer

Jewish Social Srv Agency 301.881.3700
6123 Montrose Road, Rockville, MD 20852

PACT helping Children with Special Need 410.298.7000
7000 Tudsbury Road, Baltimore, MD 21244
Audrey Leviton, Executive Director

Rothschilds Orthopedic Appliances 800.532.4473
E-mail .... admin@rothschildslightpro.com
300 mill St Unit D, Salisbury, MD 21801

Voshells Pharmacy Med Equipment 410.644.8400
Fax 410.368.5110
E-mail .... voshellsmail@yahoo.com
3455 Wilkens Ave, Baltimore, MD 21229
Joseph Eorsch, Chief Executive Officer

Washington Area Wheelchair Society 301.495.0277
8220 Mayor Lane, Silver Spring, MD 20910

Western Maryland Home Med Equipment 301.729.4280
Fax 301.729.2944
E-mail .... rhaines@wmhs.com
Braddock Square Shopping Ctr, 12101 Winchester
Road, Cumberland, MD 21502

PEDIATRIC HOME CARE

Bayada Nurses 410.823.0880
Fax 410.823.7905
Web .... www.bayada.com
1001 Cromwell Bridge Road, 3rd Floor, Suite 300,
Towson, MD 21286
Marvin Abramowitz, Director

Bayada Nurses 443.749.1300
Fax 443.749.1306
Web .... www.bayada.com
7310 Ritchie Highway, Empire Towers, Suite 615,
Glen Burnie, MD 21061
Mark Baiada, Director

Bayada Nurses 410.944.5999
Fax 410.944.5994
Web .... www.bayada.com
7175 Security Boulevard, Suite 206, Baltimore,
MD 21244
Ken Wood, Director

SOCIAL SERVICES

Arrow Project 410.677.0741
Fax 410.677.0743
Web .... www.arrow.org
E-mail .... sallen@arrow.org
18 W Main St, Plaza Gateway Bldg 116ing, Salsbury,
MD 21801
Sharlene Allen, Director

Arundel Child Care Connections 410.222.1728
Fax 410.222.1723
Web .... www.mdchildcare.org
E-mail .... welcome@arundelccc.org
77 West St Ste 300, Annapolis, MD 21401-2465

Bethesda Youth Svcs Bureau 301.229.1347
Fax 301.229.1626
Web .... www.ymcadc.org
7425 Macarthur Blvd, Cabin John, MD 20818-1812
Pam Mintz, Coordinator

Bowie Youth and Family Svcs 301.809.3033
Fax 301.809.2303
E-mail .... nbranch@cityofbowie.org
2614 Kenhill Dr, Bowie, MD 20715-2534
Nancy Branch, Director

Catholic Charities 410.561.6363
Fax 410.752.2873
320 Cathedral St Ste 2, Baltimore, MD 21201
William Mccarthy, Executive Director

Center for Social Change, Inc. 410.579.6789
Fax 410.796.1201
Web .... www.centerforsocialchange.org
6600 Amberton Drive, Elkridge, MD 21075
CARF accredited programs available.

Child Care Resource and Referral Ctr 240.777.3130
Fax 301.279.1812
Web .... www.mdchildcare.org
E-mail .... susie.carpio@montgomerycounty.gov
332 W Edmonston Dr, Rockville, MD 20852-1221
Susie Carpio, Director

Child Care Resource Ctr 410.313.1940
Fax 410.313.1430
Web .... www.howardcountymd.gov/children
E-mail .... childcare@co.ho.md.us
3300 N Ridge Rd Ste 380, Ellicott City, MD 21043
Keri Hyde, Director

Contemporary Family Services, Inc. 301.779.8345
Fax 301.779.8417
Web .... www.contemporaryservices.net
6525 Belcrest Road, Suite 300, Hyattsville, MD 20782
COA accredited organization.

Emergency Medical Svcs for Children, NRC 301.244.6300
Fax 301.244.6301
Web .... www.childrensnational.org/emsc
E-mail .... tdbrown@childrensnational.org
801 Roeder Rd, Ste 600, Silver Spring, MD 20910
Tanya Brown, Communications Assoiate

Family and Children's Services of Central Maryland, Inc.
4623 Falls Road, Baltimore, MD 21209
COA accredited organization.

Florence Crittenton Svcs 301.565.9333
Fax 301.565.0872
E-mail .... pjones@crittentonservices.org
815 Silver Spring Ave, Silver Spring, MD 20910
Pamela Jones, Executive Director

Foster Care & Community Programme 410.964.9329
Fax 410.964.9375
Web .... www.fostercare.com
5575 Sperrett Place Ste 200, Columbia, MD 21044
Sandy Rappeport, Program Manager

Healthy Families Frederick 301.696.2058
Fax 301.695.9671
Web .... www.hartlyhouse.org
E-mail .... hffadmin@hartlyhouse.org
22 S Market St Ste 4, Frederick, MD 21701-5572
Robin Shepard, Program Manager

Koba Institute, Inc. 301.562.9370
Fax 301.562.9377
Web .... www.kobainstitute.org
8737 Colesville Rd Ste 601, Silver Spring,
MD 20910-3934
Mimi Stearman, Clinical Director

LDS Family Svcs 301.694.5896
Fax 301.662.8737
Web .... www.ldsfamilyservices.org
E-mail .... fam-md@ldschurch.org
172 Thomas Johnson Dr Ste 200, Frederick,
MD 21702
Kyle Oswald, Director

League for People with Disabilities, Inc. 410.323.0500
Fax 410.323.3298
Web .... www.leagueforpeople.org
1111 East Cold Spring Lane, Baltimore, MD 21239
CARF accredited programs available.

Maryland DHR: Baltimore City 410.361.2201
Fax 410.361.3150
1510 Guilford Ave., #384, Baltimore, MD 21202
COA accredited organization.

San Mar Children's Home, Inc. 301.733.9067
Fax 301.733.3114
Web .... www.sanmarhome.org
8504 Mapleville Road, Boonsboro, MD 21713
COA accredited organization.

**Savage Mountain Youth Ctr Substance
Abuse** 301.463.2244
Fax 301.463.2364
164 Freedom Ln, Lonaconing, MD 21539
Steve Northcraft, Director

Maryland

The Children's Home, Inc. 410.744.7310
Fax 410.455.0071
Web ....www.thechildrenshome.net
205 Bloomsbury Avenue, Catonsville, MD 21228
COA accredited organization.

The Family Tree 410.889.2300
Fax 410.637.8385
Web ....www.familytreemd.org
E-mail ....pcronin@familytreemd.org
2108 N Charles St, Baltimore, MD 21218
Patricia K. Chronin, Executive Director

The Woodbourne Ctr Inc 410.433.1000
Fax 410.433.1459
Web ....www.woodbourne.org
1301 Woodbourne Ave, Baltimore, MD 21239-3399
Stanley Weinstein, Edd, President/CEO

SPECIAL NEEDS

Abilities Network 410.828.7700
E-mail ....info@abilitiesnetwork.org
8503 LaSalle Rd, Towson, MD 21286
Lee Kingham, Executive Director

AbleData 301.608.8912
Fax 301.608.8958
E-mail ....abledata@macrointernational.com
8630 Fenton St Ste 930, Silver Spring, MD 20910

Adventist Community Srvs Inner City 301.680.6438
Fax 301.680.6125
E-mail ....wynelle.stevens@nad.adventist.org
12501 Old Columbia Pike, Silver Spring, MD 20904
Wynelle Stevens, Senior Office Assistant

Adventist HlthCare Mental Hlth Srvs 301.891.5600
Fax 301.891.5596
E-mail ....cmcky@adventisthealthcare.com
Washington Adventist Hospital, 7600 Carrol Ave,
Takoma Park, MD 20912
Charlotte King, Programme Administrator

Asthma & allergy Foundation MD-DC
Chapter 410.484.2054
Fax 410.484.2043
Web ....www.aafa-md.org
E-mail ....staff@aafa-md.org
17 Warren Rd, Ste 13-A, Baltimore, MD 21208
Susan Sweitzer, Executive Director

Autism Society of America 410.655.7933
PO Box 10822, Parkville, MD 21234

Autism Society of America 301.657.0881
E-mail ....info@autism-society.org
4340 East West Hwy, ste 350, Bethesda, MD 20814
Scott Badesch, President

Baptist Family & Children's Services of Maryland,
Inc. 410.872.1050
Fax 410.872.1047
Web ....www.baptistfamily.org
7161A Columbia Gateway Drive, Columbia,
MD 21046
COA accredited organization.

Board of Child Care Strawbridge School 410.922.2100
Fax 410.496.5601
Web ....www.boardofchildcare.org
3300 Gaither Rd, Baltimore, MD 21244
Thomas L Curcio, President/CEO

Brain Injury Association 410.448.2924
E-mail ....info@biamd.org
2200 Kernan Dr, Baltimore, MD 21207
Bryan Puigh, Executive Director

Care Rehab, Inc 410.583.1515
Fax 410.583.9670
1026 Cromwell Bridge Rd, Balitmore, MD 21286
Sharon Guertler, Executive Director

CHADD 301.306.7070
8181 Professional Pl Ste 150, Landover, MD 20785
Russ Shipley, Chief Development & Operation Officer

Chelsea School 301.585.1430
Fax 301.585.9621
Web ....www.chelseaschool.edu
E-mail ....information@chelseaschool.edu
711 Pershing Dr, Silver Spring, MD 20910-4321
Debra Lourie, Director Of Admissions

Chesapeake ADHD Center of Maryland 301.562.8448
Fax 301.562.8449
E-mail ....knadeau@comcast.net
8607 Cedar St, Silver Spring, MD 20910
Kathleen Nadeau, Director

Communication In-Roads 410.583.2477
Fax 410.583.9670
E-mail ....eleventhal@careresources.net
1026 Cromwell Bridge Rd, Ste C, Baltimore,
MD 21286
Sharon Guertler, Executive Director

CureSearch National Childhood Cancer
Fou 626.447.1674
Fax 626.447.6359
E-mail ....info@curesearch.org
440 E Hunnington Dr, Bethesda, MD 20814
John Oehr, Director

Easter Seals 301.588.8700
E-mail ....lreeves@eseal.org
1420 Spring St, Silver Spring, MD 20910
Lisa Reeves, Chief Executive Officer

Ellen Aronis Heard, LLC 301.946.1998
Fax 301.946.5024
E-mail ....ejaheard@verizon.net
9909 Connicticut Ave, Kensington, MD 20895
Ellen Aronis Heard

Epilepsy Foundation 800.492.2523
E-mail ....lkingham@epilepsy-foundation.org
8503 LaSalle Rd, Towson, MD 21286

Family Support Services 410.767.1019
E-mail ....pmiller@msde.state.md.us
200 W Baltimore St 9th Fl, Baltimore, MD 21201
Carol Ann Baglin-Heath, Assistant Superintendent

Frankly Communicating, Inc 410.871.2990
Fax 410.871.2990
E-mail ....heather@franklycommunicating.com
505 Old Westminster Pike, Westminster, MD 21157
Heather Frank, Chief Executive Officer

Genetic and Rare Diseases Information Ct 301.251.4925
Fax 301.251.4911
PO Box 8126, Gaithersburg, MD 20898

HealthSouth Chesapeake Rehabilitation
Hospital 410.546.4600
Fax 410.546.8388
220 Tilghman Road, Salisbury, MD 21804
CARF accredited programs available.

Hearing & Speech Agency 410.318.6780
Fax 410.318.6759
Web ....www.hasa.org
E-mail ....hasa@hasa.org
5900 Metro Dr, Baltimore, MD 21215
Jill Berie, Educational Dir

Interdynamics, Inc 301.306.4590
Fax 301.306.4591
E-mail ....jbranch@interdynamicsinc.com
10001 Derekwood Ln, Ste # 120, Lanham,
MD 20706
Joan Branch, Director

Ivymount Outreach Programs 301.469.0223
Fax 301.469.0778
E-mail ....jmartin@ivymount.org
11614 7 Locks Rd, Rockville, MD 20854

Kennedy Krieger Children's Hospital, Inc. 443.923.9200
Web ....www.kennedykrieger.org
707 North Broadway, Baltimore, MD 21205
Jay Shapiro, Medical Director
CARF accredited programs available.

Kennedy Krieger Institute 888.554.2080
Fax 443.923.7339
Web ....www.kennedykrieger.org
707 N Broadway, Baltimore, MD 21205
Gary Goldstein, Md, President And CEO

Kennedy Krieger School 443.923.7800
Fax 443.923.7850
Web ....www.kennedykrieger.org
3825 Greenspring Ave, Baltimore, MD 21211
Robin P Church, Sr. Ice President

Learning Disabilities Association 888.265.6459
E-mail ....ldamaryland@aol.com
PO Box 268, Huntingtown, MD 20639

Low Vision Center 301.951.4444
E-mail ....terry@lowvisioninfo.org
7701 Woodmont Ave Ste 604, Bethesda, MD 20814
Terry Eison, Chief Executive Officer

Maryland PTA 410.760.6221
E-mail ....office@mdpta.org
5 Central Ave, Glen Burnie, MD 21061
Kay Romero, President

MDA/ALS Center at Johns Hopkins Univ 410.614.3846
Fax 410.614.0659
E-mail ....jrothste@jhmi.edu
855 N Wolfe St Ste 278, Baltimore, MD 21205
Jeffrey D Rothstein Md, Phd Director

Mental Health Association 410.235.1178
E-mail ....info@mhamd.org
711 W 40th St Ste 460, Baltimore, MD 21211
Kari Gorkos, Director, Community Outreach

Modern Eyes, LLC 240.631.2255
Fax 240.631.2299
E-mail ....visiondoc@moderneyes.biz
108 Olde Towne Ave, Ste 106 Cedar Ct,
Gaithersburg, MD 20877
Dr Mark P Borsuk Od, Director

Montgomery Heart Foundation for
Cardiomy 402.502.2578
Fax 443.287.4109
E-mail ....njohnso5@jhmi.edu
1830 E Monument St Ste 7300, Baltimore,
MD 21205

Mt. Washington Pediatric Hospital 410.578.8600
Fax 410.578.0566
Web ....www.mwph.org
1708 West Rogers Ave, Baltimore, MD 21209
Kim Guerin, Director
CARF accredited programs available.

Mt. Washington Pediatric Hospital 410.578.8600
Fax 410.578.0566
Web ....www.mwph.org
1708 West Rogers Avenue, Baltimore,
MD 21209-4596
CARF accredited programs available.

National Multiple Sclerosis Society 443.641.1200
Fax 443.641.1201
E-mail ....info@nmss-md.org
2219 York rd, Ste 302, Timonium, MD 21093
Mark Roeder, President

National Speech/Language Therapy
Center 301.493.0023
Fax 301.493.8230
E-mail ....contact@nationalspeech.com
5606 Shields Dr, Bethesda, MD 20817
Sabra Gelfond, Owner

New Heights Learning & Training Center 410.821.8808
Fax 443.921.0561
E-mail ....NHLTC@aol.com
7604 York Rd Ste C, Towson, MD 21204

Parents' Place of Maryland Inc **800.394.5694**
E-mail .... info@ppmd.org
　801 Cromwell Park Dr Ste 103, Glen Burnie,
　MD 21061
Jose Thomas, Director

Pathfinders for Autism **866.806.8400**
E-mail .... info@pathfindersforautism.org
　303 International Cir, Baltimore, MD 21030
Rebecca Rindi, Executive Director

Pediatric Adolescent Gastroesophageal
Re **301.601.9541**
E-mail .... gergroup@aol.com
　PO Box 486, Silver Spring, MD 20907

Ridge School of the Eastern Shore **410.901.4328**
Fax 410.221.6079
Web .... www.potomacridge.com
E-mail .... bjohnson2@adventisthealthcare.com
　821 Fieldcrest Rd, Cambridge, MD 21613
Bonnie Johnson, Director

Speech-Language-Hearing Association **410.239.7770**
E-mail .... office@mdslha.org
　PO Box 31, Manchester, MD 21102

Stars Dance Studio **301.604.7827**
E-mail .... dancewithstars@verizon.net
　10095 Washington Blvd # 132, Laurel, MD 20723

The Arc of Maryland Inc **410.571.9320**
E-mail .... info@chearcmd.org
　49 Old Solomons Island Rd, Ste 205, Annapolis,
　MD 21401
Kate Fialkowfki, Director

The Benedictine School **410.634.2112**
Fax 410.634.2640
Web .... www.benschool.org
　14299 Benedictine Ln, Ridgely, MD 21660
Nancy Mccloy, Educational Director

The Children's Guild **410.444.3800**
Fax 410.444.0612
Web .... www.childrensguild.org
E-mail .... ross@childrensguild.org
　6802 McClean Blvd, Baltimore, MD 21234
Andrew L Ross, President, CEO

The Coordinating Center **410.987.1048**
E-mail .... bhccord@coordinatingcenter.org
　8258 Veterans Hwy Ste 113, Millersville, MD 21108
Barbara McCord, Communication Marketing Director

The Diener School **301.299.4602**
Fax 301.299.4603
Web .... www.thedienerschool.org
　11510 Falls Rd, Potomac, MD 20854
Jillian Copeland, Director

The Forbush School **410.938.4747**
Fax 410.938.4421
Web .... www.sheppardpratt.org
　6501 N Charles St, Towson, MD 21204
James Truscello, Principal

The Foundation Schools **301.881.0078**
Fax 301.881.8515
Web .... www.foundationschools.org
　6000 Executive Blvd Ste 605, Rockville, MD 20852
Philippe Dupont, Director

The Frost School **301.933.3451**
Fax 301.933.0350
Web .... www.frostcenter.com
　4915 Aspen Hill Rd, Rockville, MD 20853
Kevin Curtin, Director

The Harbour School **410.974.4248**
Fax 410.757.3722
Web .... www.harbourschool.org
　1277 Green Holly Dr, Annapolis, MD 21409
Linda J Jacobs, Director

The James Lawrence Kernan Hospital **410.448.2500**
Fax 410.448.2859
Web .... www.umm.edu/kernan
　2200 Kernan Drive, Baltimore, MD 21207
CARF accredited programs available.

The Jefferson School at Finan Center **301.777.2258**
Fax 301.777.2066
Web .... www.shepheardpratt.org
　10102 Country Club Rd SE, Cumberland, MD 21502
Bonnie Fetzer, Principal

The Kennedy-Krieger Institute **443.923.9200**
　707 N Broadway, Baltimore, MD 21205
Dr. Gary Goldstein, President

The Language and The Voice Experience **301.208.3210**
Fax 301.208.6686
Web .... www.languageandvoiceexperience.net
E-mail .... leslie@languageexperience.net
　5530 Wisconsin Ave, Ste 1528, Chevy Chase,
　MD 20815
Kim McPhee, Assistant Director

The MD Coalition of Family for Children Mental
Health **888.607.3637**
E-mail .... info@mdcoalition.org
　10632 Little Patuxent Pkwy, Ste 234, Columbia,
　MD 21044
Jane Walker, Executive Director

The Parents Place of Maryland **410.768.9100**
Fax 410.768.0830
E-mail .... info@ppmd.org
　801 Cromwell Park Dr Ste 103, Glen Burnie,
　MD 21061
Josie Thomas, Executive Director

The Pathways Schools **301.649.0778**
Fax 301.649.2598
Web .... www.pathwayschools.org
　1106 University Blvd W, Silver Spring, MD 20902
Helen C Williams, Executive Director

Total Rehab Care at Hospital **301.790.8025**
Fax 301.790.9027
Web .... www.wchsys.org
　251 East Antietam Street, 6th Floor, Hagerstown,
　MD 21740
Pam Mcaffey, Director
CARF accredited programs available.

Total Rehab Care Hospital **301.790.8026**
Fax 301.790.9027
Web .... www.wchsys.org
　251 East Antietam Street, Sixth Floor, Hagerstown,
　MD 21740
CARF accredited programs available.

Tourette Syndrome Association **877.295.2148**
E-mail .... tsagw@aol.com
　33 University Blvd E, Silver Spring, MD 20901

United Cerebral Palsy **800.451.2452**
E-mail .... dcoughlin@ucp-cm.org
　11350 McCormick Rd, Ste 1100, Hunts Valley,
　MD 21031
Diane Coughlin, President

United Cerebral Palsy **301.459.0566**
E-mail .... ucppgmc@aol.com
　4409 Forbes Blvd, Lanham, MD 20706
John Garrett, Director Of Operations

United Cerebral Palsy **410.224.4205**
E-mail .... ucpinfo@ucpsm.org
　1919A West St, Annapolis, MD 21401
Mitzi Bernard, Director

Villa Maria School **410.252.6343**
Fax 410.560.1347
Web .... www.vmcontinuum.org
　2300 Dulaney Valley Rd, Lutherville-Timonium,
　MD 21093
Jack Pumprey, Admin Asst

SUBSTANCE ABUSE TREATMENT

Act II Counseling Svcs **301.498.5766**
Fax 301.490.7861
　379 Main St, Laurel, MD 20707
Donna Lund, Director

Adventist Behavioural Health **301.251.4500**
Fax 301.424.3841
Web .... www.adventistbehaviouralhealth.com
E-mail .... ccofone@adventisthealthcare.com
　14901 Broschart Rd, Rockville, MD 20850-3318
Christopher Cofone, Program Director

Crossroads Ctrs **301.696.1950**
Fax 301.698.2661
　203 Broadway St, Ste A-B, Frederick, MD 21701
Jill Maynes, Director

Ctr 4 Clean Start **410.742.3460**
Fax 410.742.5810
　926 Snow Hill Rd, Cottage 200, Salisbury, MD 21804
Tiffany Howard, Director

Echo House Foundation **410.947.1700**
Fax 410.947.5306
Web .... www.echo-house.org
E-mail .... echohousempc@gmail.com
　1705 W Fayette St, Baltimore, MD 21223-1708
Benita Paschall, Executive Director

Epoch Counseling Ctr **410.284.3070**
Fax 410.285.3848
E-mail .... stangires@friendsresearch.org
　1107 N Point Blvd, Ste 205, Dundalk, MD 21224
Sue Tangires, Director

Epoch Counseling Ctr **410.744.5937**
Fax 410.744.4674
　800 Ingleside Ave, Catonsville, MD 21228-1722
Susan Tangires, Director Epoch Counseling

Epoch Counseling Ctr **410.574.2500**
Fax 410.574.4478
Web .... www.friendsresearch.org
　621 Stemmers Run Rd Ste E, Essex, MD 21221-3386
Dana Sohlberg, Center Coordinator

Epoch Counseling Ctr **410.789.2647**
Fax 410.789.8364
Web .... www.friendsresearch.org
　3902 Annapolis Rd, Lansdowne, MD 21227-2249
Mamette Mapa, Center Coordinator

Gaudenzia, Inc. **443.423.1500**
Fax 443.423.1495
Web .... www.gaudenzia.org
E-mail .... gsaler@gaudenzia.org
　4615 Park Heights Ave, Baltimore, MD 21215-6331
Gayle Saler, Director

Glenwood Life Counseling Ctr **410.323.9811**
Fax 410.323.5303
E-mail .... ldonnard@glenwoodlife.org
　516 Glenwood Ave, Baltimore, MD 21212-4294
Lillian Donnard, Director

Green Ridge Youth Ctr Substance Abuse **301.478.3069**
Fax 301.478.3247
Web .... www.djs.state.md.us
E-mail .... treveyj@djs.state.md.us
　10700 Fifteen Mile Creek Rd, Flintstone, MD 21530
Judy Hodell, Director

Institute of Life and Health **301.627.3007**
Fax 301.627.3104
E-mail .... ronald@instituteoflifeandhealth.com
　5311 Water St Ste D, Upper Marlboro,
　MD 20772-3056
Ronald G Medlin, Director

Kolmac Clinic **301.330.7696**
Fax 301.330.5639
E-mail .... kolodner@kolmac.com
　15932 Shady Grove Rd Unit B, Gaithersburg,
　MD 20877-1314
George Kolodner, Director

Kolmac Clinic **301.589.0255**
Fax 301.589.0291
Web ....www.kolmac.com
E-mail ....gkolodner@kolmac.com
　1003 Spring St, Silver Spring, MD 20910-4060
　George Kolodner, Md, Director

Leadership To Keep Children Alcohol Free **301.654.6740**
Fax 301.656.4012
Web ....www.alcoholfreechildren.org
E-mail ....leadership@alcoholfreechildren.org
　7500 Old Georgetown Rd Ste 900, Bethesda,
　MD 20814-6809
　Patrick Vanan, Manager

Meadow Mountain Drug Treatment
Program **301.895.5669**
Fax 301.895.3664
E-mail ....pickrellw@djs.state.md.us
　234 Recovery Rd, Grantsville, MD 21536-2217
　Oesore Wilheon, Director

Meadowbrook **301.733.0330**
Fax 301.739.7380
E-mail ....susan.paytree@brooklane.org
　18714 North Village Shopping Center, Hagerstown,
　MD 21742
　Susan Paytree, Director

Mountain Manor Treatment Ctr **301.662.1407**
Fax 301.662.6989
Web ....www.mactn.vcu.edu
　603A W Patrick St, Frederick, MD 21701-5470
　Richard Sawyer, Director

Mountain Manor Treatment Ctr -
Baltimore **410.233.1400**
Fax 410.233.1666
E-mail ....pwells@mountainmanor.org
　3800 Frederick Ave, Baltimore, MD 21229-3618
　Marc Fishman Md, Medical Director

New Hope Treatment Ctr **410.945.7706**
Fax 410.945.8767
E-mail ....carrie_little@bshsi.com
　2401 W Baltimore St, Baltimore, MD 21223-2134
　Carrie Little, Director

Pathways **410.573.5400**
Fax 410.573.5401
　2620 Riva Rd, Annapolis, MD 21401
　Helen Reines, Director

Sinai Hospital Addictions Recovery
Program **410.601.5355**
Fax 410.578.6281
Web ....www.lifebridgehealth.org
　2401 W Belvedere Ave, Baltimore, MD 21215-5271
　Susan Harrison, Director

Substance Abuse / Eastern Area Treatment
Program **410.887.6465**
Fax 410.687.6005
　9100 Franklin Square Dr, Rosedale, MD 21237
　Richard Thomas, Director

Treatment Resources For Youth (TRY) **410.366.2123**
Fax 410.366.0055
　2517 N Charles St, Baltimore, MD 21218-4602
　Latavia Little, Executive Director

Walden/Sierra Corporation **301.997.1300**
Fax 301.997.1321
Web ....www.waldensierra.org
　26845 Point Lookout Road, Leonardtown, MD 20650
　CARF accredited programs available.

Warwick Manor Behavioral Health, Inc. **800.344.6423**
Fax 410.943.3976
Web ....www.warwickmanor.org
　3680 Warwick Road, East New Market, MD 21631
　Elliott Driscoll, Executive Director
　CARF accredited programs available.

Massachusetts

Deval Patrick, Governor
State House, Room 280
Boston, MA 02133
617.725.4000
617.727.9725 (Fax)
www.mass.gov

Colina Cole, Juvenile Justice Specialist
Ten Park Plaza
Suite 3720
Boston, MA 02116
617.725.3331
617.725.0260 (Fax)
colina.cole@state.ma.us

Robert Gittens, SAG Chair
360 Huntington Avenue
Boston, MA 02115
617.373.5805
617.373.5608 (Fax)
r.gittens@neu.edu

CRISIS NUMBERS

Child Abuse Reporting . . .800.792.5200

STATE SERVICES

SOCIAL SERVICES

Child Care Licensing Office MA **617.988.7815**
Fax 617.988.2451
51 Sleeper St, 4th Flr, Boston, MA 02210
Tresa Glover Smith, Director

Department of Children and Families **617.748.2000**
Fax 617.748.2441
E-mail . . . . .mary.gambon@state.ma.us
24 Farnsworth St, Boston, MA 02210
Mary Gambon, Assistant Commissioner For Adoption, Foster Care And Adolescent Support Services

Massachusetts Executive Ofc of Health & Human
Svcs **617.573.1600**
Fax 617.573.1891
Web . . . . .www.mass.gov.eohhs
E-mail . . . . .mary.skahen@ehs.state.ma
1 Ashburton Pl, Rm 1109, Boston, MA 02108
Judyann Bigby, Md, Secretary

GENERAL HEALTH SERVICES

Bureau of Family Health & Nutrition MA **617.624.6060**
Fax 617.624.5992
E-mail . . . . .sally.fogerty@state.ma.us
250 Washington St 5th Flr, Boston, MA 02108
Ron Benham, Assistant Commissinor

Children with Special Health Needs **800.882.1435**
Fax 617.624.5990
Web . . . . .www.mass.gov/dph/fch/dpech.htm
250 Washington St, 5th Fl, Boston, MA 02108
Ron Benham, Director Of Early Intervention

Div for Perinatal Early Child Spec MA **617.624.6060**
Fax 617.624.6062
E-mail . . . . .Ron.Benham@state.ma.us
250 Washington St 4th Flr, Boston, MA 02108
Ron Benham, Assistant Commisioner

MENTAL HEALTH SERVICES

Dept of Developmental Services **617.727.5608**
Fax 617.624.7577
Web . . . . .www.mass.gov
500 Harrison Ave, Boston, MA 02118
Elin Howe, Commissioner

Rehabilitation Commission **617.204.3600**
Fax 617.727.1354
Web . . . . .www.state.ma.us/mrc
E-mail . . . . .charles.carr@mrc.state.ma.us
27 Wormwood St, Fort Point Pl, Boston, MA 02210-1616
Charles Carr, Commissioner

Voc Rehab Agency MA **617.727.5550**
Fax 617.626.7685
E-mail . . . . .susan.lavin@state.ma.us
48 Boylston St, Boston, MA 02116
Susan Lavin, Director

JUSTICE AGENCY

Correctional Educ Division MA **508.935.0901**
Fax 508.935.0907
PO Box 71 Hodder House, Framingham, MA 01704

Dept of Youth Svcs **617.727.7575**
Fax 617.727.0696
Web . . . . .www.detma.org
E-mail . . . . .edward.dolan@state.ma.us
2743 Wormwood St, Ste 400, Boston, MA 02210-1613
Edward J. Dolan, Deputy Commissioner

Massachusetts Dept of Corrections **508.422.3300**
Fax 508.422.3385
Web .www.magnet.state.ma.us/doc
E-mail . . . . .jim@doc.state.ma.us
50 Maple St, Ste 3, Milford, MA 01757
Luis Spencer, Commissioner

Ofc of The Commissioner of Probation **617.727.5300**
Fax 617.727.8483
Web . . . . .www.jud.state.ma.us
1 Ashburton Pl Rm 405, McCormick Bldg, Boston, MA 02108-1527
Ronald Corbe, Commissioner

Victim Compensation Div **617.727.2200**
Fax 617.742.6262
E-mail . . . . .lian.lowney@state.ma.us
1 Ashburton Pl, Boston, MA 02108
Lian Lowney, Chief

COURTS

Juvenile Court Dept Administrative Ofc **617.788.6550**
Fax 617.788.8965
Web . . . . .www.jud.state.ma.us
E-mail . . . . .jane.strickland@jud.state.ma.us
3 Center Plz Fl 7, Boston, MA 02108-2007
Jane Strickland, Court Administrator

POLICE AND SHERIFF

Massachusetts Chiefs of Police Assoc **508.839.5723**
Fax 508.339.4873
Web . . . . .www.masschiefs.org
E-mail . . . . .info@masschiefs.org
26 Providence Dr, Graston, MA 01519-4028
Wayne Sampson, Executive Director

Massachusetts Deputy Sheriff's Assoc Central
District **617.547.1171**
Fax 617.868.7244
E-mail . . . . .gbreen@sema4usa.com
271 Cambridge St, Cambridge, MA 02141
Gerald E. Breen, Chief Sheriff

EDUCATION SERVICES

MA Dept of Elem & Secondary Education **781.338.3111**
Fax 781.338.3770
75 Pleasant St, Malden, MA 02148
Mitchell Chester, Administrator

Massachusetts Commission for the Deaf and Hard of
Hearing **617.740.1600**
Fax 617.740.1810
Web . . . . .www.mass.gov/mcdhh
E-mail . . . . .mcdhh.office@state.ma.us
150 Mount Vernon St Ste 550, Dorchester, MA 02125-3115
Heide L. Reed, Commissioner

Of for the Educ of Homeless Chi & You MA **781.338.6330**
Fax 781.338.3399
E-mail . . . . .sslautterback@doe.mass.edu
75 Pleasant St, Malden, MA 02148
Peter, Director

Special Educ Planning & Pol Dev Of MA **781.338.3375**
Fax 781.338.3371
E-mail . . . . .specialeducation@doe.mass.edu
75 Pleasant St, Malden, MA 02148
Marcia Mittnacht, Director Of Special Education

COUNTY SERVICES

Barnstable County

GENERAL HEALTH SERVICES

Town of Barnstable Health Div **508.862.4644**
Fax 508.790.6304
Web ....www.town.barnstable.ma.us
E-mail ....health@town.barnstable.ma.us
　200 Main St, Hyannis, MA 02601-4002
　Thomas A. Mckean, Cho, Director

MENTAL HEALTH SERVICES

Pocasset Mental Health **508.564.9600**
Fax 508.564.9700
E-mail ....sjochiam@mvhospital.org
　830 County Rd, Pocasset, MA 02559
　Steven Jochiam, Director

COURTS

Barnstable Juvenile Court **508.362.1389**
Fax 508.362.8224
　3195 Main St, Barnstable, MA 02630
　Charles T. Andrade Jr., Juvenile Court Magistrate

Brighton District Court **617.782.6521**
Fax 617.562.4479
E-mail ....david_d@jud.state.ma.us
　52 Academy Hill Rd, Brighton, MA 02135-3396
　David T. Donnelly, 1st Presiding District Court Judge

POLICE AND SHERIFF

Sheriff's Ofc **508.563.4300**
Fax 508.563.4574
Web ....www.bsheriff.net
E-mail ....jcummings@bsheriff.net
　6000 Sheriffs Pl, Bourne, MA 02532
　James M. Cummings, Sheriff

Berkshire County

SOCIAL SERVICES

**North Adams Dept of Transitional
Assistance** **413.663.1100**
Fax 413.664.9274
　37 Main St Ste 5, North Adams, MA 01247
　Chris Meehan, Director

Pittsfield Area Ofc **413.236.1800**
Fax 413.445.4507
　53 Eagle St Fl 1, Pittsfield, MA 01201
　Laurie Sullivan, Area Director

**Pittsfield Dept of Transitional
Assistance** **413.236.2000**
Fax 413.448.2466
E-mail ....chris_meehan@state.ma.us
　160 North St Ste 201, Pittsfield, MA 01201
　Chris Meehan, Director

GENERAL HEALTH SERVICES

Pittsfield Board of Health **413.499.9411**
Fax 413.448.9798
E-mail ....cnicholas@pittsfieldch.com
　70 Allen St Ste 204, Pittsfield, MA 01201
　Cory Nicholas, Senior Senetarian

MENTAL HEALTH SERVICES

Pittsfield Dept Mental Health **413.395.2000**
Fax 413.395.2018
Web ....www.state.ma.us/dmh
E-mail ....kathryn.casella@dmh.state.ma.us
　333 East St, Ste 4, Pittsfield, MA 01201
　Kathryn Casella, Child/Adolescent Services Supervisor

COURTS

Berkshire Juvenile Court **413.443.8533**
Fax 413.443.8672
　190 North St, Pittsfield, MA 01201
　Daniel Swords, First Justice

**Berkshire Probate and Family
Court** **413.443.9469**
Fax 413.443.3430
　44 Bank Row, Pittsfield, MA 01201
　Daniel Turner, Chief Probation Officer

North Berkshire District Court **413.663.5369**
Fax 413.664.7209
　111 Holden St, North Adams, MA 01247
　Michael Urquhart, Chief Probation Officer

Pittsfield District Court **413.442.5468**
Fax 413.499.7327
　24 Wendell Ave, Pittsfield, MA 01201
　Tom Bartimi, Clerk Magistrate

POLICE AND SHERIFF

Sheriff's Ofc **413.447.7117**
Fax 413.443.0008
　467 Cheshire Rd, Pittsfield, MA 01201
　Thomas Bowler, Sheriff

EDUCATION SERVICES

**Conte Elementary School - Head
Start** **413.496.9494**
Fax 413.496.9494
　200 W Union St, Pittsfield, MA 01201-3999
　Rose Day, Teacher

Bristol County

SOCIAL SERVICES

**Fall River Dept of Transitional
Assistance** **508.646.6200**
Fax 508.675.3441
　1567 N Main St Ste 3, Fall River, MA 02720-2980
　Arn Jorgensen, Director

New Bedford Area Ofc (Social Svcs) **508.910.1000**
Fax 508.990.7321
　100 N Front St, New Bedford, MA 02740
　Dennis Gauthier, Area Director

**New Bedford Dept of Transitional
Assistance** **508.961.2000**
Fax 508.961.2100
　160 W Rodney French Blvd, New Bedford, MA 02744
　Jeffrey Travers, Director

**Taunton Dept of Transitional
Assistance** **508.884.5300**
Fax 508.880.5301
Web ....www.town.freetown.ma.us
E-mail ....aldefresne@town.freetown.ma.us
　21 Spring St Ste 2, Taunton, MA 02780-3457
　Al Defresne, Director

GENERAL HEALTH SERVICES

Attleboro Health Dept **508.223.2222**
Fax 508.222.3046
　77 Park St, Government Center, Attleboro,
　MA 02703
　James P. Mooney, Health Agent

Fall River Health Dept **508.324.2421**
Fax 508.324.2544
Web ....www.fallriverma.org
　1 Government Ctr, Fall River, MA 02722-7700
　Dr Henry Vaillanaourt, Director

Fall River Health Dept **508.324.2410**
Fax 508.324.2429
Web ....www.fallriverma.org
　1 Government Ctr, Fall River, MA 02722-7700
　Henry Vaillancourt, Interim Director

New Bedford Health Dept **508.991.6290**
Fax 508.991.6291
　1213 Purchase St Unit 16, New Bedford, MA 02740
　Marianne Desouza, Director Of The Health Dept

Taunton Health Dept **508.821.1400**
Fax 508.821.1403
　45 School St, Taunton, MA 02780
　Heather Gallant, Director

JUSTICE AGENCY

Southeast Area Ofc **508.828.3800**
Fax 508.880.3516
　60 Hodges Ave, Taunton, MA 02780
　Craig Curtin, Area Director

COURTS

Attleboro District Court **508.222.5900**
Fax 508.226.3916
　88 N Main St, Attleboro, MA 02703
　Mark Sturdy, Court Magistrate

Bristol Juvenile Court **508.676.0090**
Fax 508.676.1213
Web ....www.jri.org
E-mail ....tcomier@jri.org
　289 Rock St Ste 300, Fall River, MA 02720-3245
　Teresa Comier, Assistant Chief Probation Officer

Bristol Probate and Family Court **508.999.5249**
Fax 508.999.1269
Web ....www.bcpfc.com
　505 Pleasant St, New Bedford, MA 02740-5918
　James A. Casey, Chief Probation Officer

Bristol: The Juvenile Div Court **508.222.5350**
Fax 508.222.5930
　100 N Main St, Attleboro, MA 02703
　William Mcgowan, Probation Officer

**Morton Hospital and Medical Ctr Speech, Hearing and
Language** **508.823.3050**
Fax 508.828.5858
Web ....www.mortonhospital.org
　2007 Bay St Ste 100B, Taunton, MA 02780
　Maria Leal, Director Of Admissions

New Bedford District Court **508.999.9700**
Fax 508.991.8540
　75 N 6th St, New Bedford, MA 02740
　Judge Sabra, Chief District Court Judge

Taunton Court District **508.824.4032**
Fax 508.880.8810
　120 Cohannet St, Taunton, MA 02780
　Kevin Cunningham, Judge

Youth Court **508.979.1580**
Fax 508.991.6233
E-mail ....nbppyouth@aol.com
　360 Coggeshall St, New Bedford, MA 02746
　Lisa Tavares, Director

POLICE AND SHERIFF

New Bedford Police Juvenile Div **508.991.6346**
Fax 508.979.1769
E-mail ....matthew.rayner@newbedfordpd.com
　871 Rockdale Ave, New Bedford, MA 02740-2700
　Matt Rayner, Commanding Officer

Sheriff's Ofc **508.995.6400**
Fax 508.995.7835
E-mail . . . . .sheriff@bcso-ma.org
　400 Faunce Corner Rd, North Dartmouth, MA 02747
　Thomas M. Hodgson, Sheriff

EDUCATION SERVICES

Citizens For Citizens Head Start -
Macombe **508.324.7514**
　154 Gifford Rd, Westport, MA 02790-3411
　Anna Gagne, Director

Special Education **508.997.4511**
Fax 508.991.7302
Web . . . . .www.newbedfordschools.org
　455 County St, New Bedford, MA 02740-5106
　Kathleen Turner, Director

Dukes County

GENERAL HEALTH SERVICES

Wampanoag Tribe Health Svc **508.645.9265**
Fax 508.645.3790
Web . . . . .www.wampanoagtribe.net
E-mail . . . . .rmalonson@wampanoagtribe.net
　20 Black Brook Rd, Chilmark, MA 02535-1546
　Ryan Malonson, Director Of Health Services

COURTS

Edgartown District Court **508.627.3751**
Fax 508.627.7070
　81 Main St, Edgartown, MA 02539
　H. Gregory Williams, Presiding District Court Judge

Probate and Family Court **508.627.4703**
Fax 508.627.7664
　81 Main St, Edgartown, MA 02539
　Spencer M Kagan, Presiding Family Court Judge

POLICE AND SHERIFF

Sheriff's Ofc **508.627.5328**
Fax 508.627.8496
E-mail . . . . .mamccormack@dcsoma.org
　149 Main St, Edgartown, MA 02539
　Michael A. Mccormack, Sheriff

Essex County

SOCIAL SERVICES

Lawrence Dept of Transitional
Assistance **978.725.7100**
Fax 978.681.6216
　15 Union St, Lawrence, MA 01840
　Brian Mulholland, Director

North Shore Transitional
Assistance **978.825.7300**
Fax 978.741.4869
　35 Congress St, Bldg B, Salem, MA 01970
　Lisa Griffin, Director

GENERAL HEALTH SERVICES

Beverly Health Dept **978.921.8591**
Fax 978.922.5695
Web . . . . .www.beverlyma.gov
E-mail . . . . .tburke@beverlyma.gov
　90 Colon St, Beverly, MA 01915
　William T. Burke, Director

Health and Inspectional Svcs **978.374.2325**
Fax 978.374.2337
Web . . . . .www.ci.haverhill.ma.us
E-mail . . . . .wpillsbury@cityofhaverhill.com
　4 Summer St Ste 210, CITY HALL, Haverhill,
　MA 01830-5843
　William (bill) Pillsbury, Director

Health Board **978.538.5926**
Fax 978.538.5990
E-mail . . . . .sharon.cameron@peabody-ma.gov
　24 Lowell St, Peabody, MA 01960
　Sharon Cameron, Director

Health Dept **978.281.9798**
Fax 978.281.9729
Web . . . . .www.ci.gloucester.ma.us
E-mail . . . . .jvondras@ci.gloucester.ma.us
　9 Dale Ave Ste 4, Gloucester, MA 01930-3000
　Jack Vondras, Health Director

Salem Board of Health **978.741.1800**
Fax 978.745.0343
Web . . . . .www.salem.com
E-mail . . . . .lramdin@salem.com
　120 Washington St 4th Fl, Salem, MA 01970-3523
　Larry Ramdin, Director

Saugus Health Board **781.231.4115**
Fax 781.231.4109
Web . . . . .www.saugus-ma.gov
E-mail . . . . .fgiacalone@saugus-ma.gov
　298 Central St, TOWN HALL, Saugus, MA 01906
　Frank Giacalone, Director

COURTS

Essex Probate and Family Court **978.744.1020**
Fax 978.741.2957
　36 Federal St, Salem, MA 01970
　Brian Monhagnen, Chief Probation Officer

Gloucester District Court **978.283.2620**
Fax 978.283.8784
Web . . . . .www.remax-gloucesterma.com
E-mail . . . . .rmori@remax-gloucesterma.com
　197 Main St, Gloucester, MA 01930-6098
　Joseph Jennines, District Court Judge

Haverhill District Court **978.373.4151**
Fax 978.521.6886
　45 Ginty Blvd, Haverhill, MA 01830-6187
　William Moynihan, Chief Probation Officer

Lawrence District Court **978.687.7184**
Fax 978.686.2063
　2 Appleton St, Fenton Judicial Center, Lawrence,
　MA 01840
　Kevin Henebury, Chief Performance Officer

Lawrence Div of Essex Probate and Family
Court **978.686.9692**
Fax 978.946.6010
　2 Appleton St Ste 3, Lawrence, MA 01840-1573
　Ryan Marian, Chief Probation Officer

Lynn District Court **781.598.5200**
Fax 781.598.4350
　580 Essex St, Lynn, MA 01901
　Jane Brady Stirgwalt, Clerk Magistrate

Newburyport District Court **978.462.2652**
Fax 978.465.6471
Web . . . . .www.probatecourtiannella.com
　188 State St, Route 1 Traffic Circle, Newburyport,
　MA 01950-6686
　Patricia Kane-Thompson, Chief Probation Officer

Peabody District Court **978.532.3100**
Fax 978.531.8524
　1 Lowell St, Peabody, MA 01960
　Honorable Robert Brennen, District Court Judge

Roxbury District Court **617.427.7000**
Fax 617.442.2786
　85 Warren St, Boston, MA 02119
　David Weingarden, District Court Judge

Salem Juvenile Court **978.745.9660**
Fax 978.745.8932
　45 Congress St, Bldg B, Salem, MA 01970
　Honorable Sally F. Padden, Juvenile Court Judge

Westfield District Court **413.568.8946**
Fax 413.568.4863
　224 Elm St, Westfield, MA 01085
　James Lyons, Chief Probation Officer

POLICE AND SHERIFF

Sheriff's Ofc **978.750.1900**
Fax 978.750.1999
E-mail . . . . .sheriff@eccf.com
　20 Manning Rd, Middleton, MA 01949
　Frank G. Cousins Jr., Sheriff

Franklin County

SOCIAL SERVICES

Greenfield Dept of Transitional
Assistance **413.772.3400**
Fax 413.774.5266
　143 Munson st unit 3, Greenfield, MA 01301
　Yasmin Otero, Reginal Director

MENTAL HEALTH SERVICES

Franklin North Quabbin, Dept of Mental
Health **413.772.5600**
Fax 413.772.5638
　13 Prospect St, Greenfield, MA 01301
　Tom Moriarty, Supervisor

COURTS

Franklin Juvenile Court **413.775.0014**
Fax 413.775.9201
　106 Main St, Greenfield, MA 01301
　Honorable Lilian Meranda, 1st Juvenile Court Justice

Franklin Probate and Family Court **413.774.7011**
Fax 413.774.3829
E-mail . . . . .geoffrey.wilson@jud.state.ma.us
　425 Main St, Greenfield, MA 01302
　Honorable Geoffrey A. Wilson, Chief Family Court Justice

Greenfield District Court **413.774.5533**
Fax 413.774.5328
　425 Main St Ste 40, Greenfield, MA 01301
　William S Mazanes Iii, Presiding District Court Judge

Orange District Court **978.544.8277**
Fax 978.544.5204
　1 Court Sq, Orange, MA 01364
　David Rosas, Judge

POLICE AND SHERIFF

Sheriff's Ofc **413.774.4014**
Fax 413.774.3525
　160 Elm St, Greenfield, MA 01301
　Christopher Donelan, Sheriff

EDUCATION SERVICES

Better Start **413.498.5842**
Fax 413.498.5459
Web www.pioneervalley.k12.ma.us
E-mail . . . . .clarkd@pioneervalley.k12.ma.us
　104 Main St, Greenfield, MA 01301
　Daphne Clark, Director

Hampden County

SOCIAL SERVICES

Holyoke Dept of Transitional
Assistance **413.552.5400**
Fax 413.784.1050
Web . . . . .www.mass.gov/dta
　100 Front St, Holyoke, MA 01040
　Elizabeth Kelley, Assistant Director

Springfield Liberty Street Transitional
Assistance **413.858.1000**
Fax 413.784.1044
E-mail . . . . .mellisa_polish@state.ma.us
　95 Liberty St, Springfield, MA 01103-1011
　Mellisa Polish, Director

Massachusetts

Massachusetts

GENERAL HEALTH SERVICES

Health Board **413.572.6210**
Fax..413.572.6279
Web ....www.cityofwestfield.org
E-mail ....msuckau@cityofwestfield.org
  59 Court St, City Hall, Westfield, MA 01085
  Michael Suckau, Director

Health Dept **413.787.6740**
Fax..413.787.6458
  95 State St Ste 201, Springfield, MA 01103
  Helen Harris, Director

Health Dept **413.594.1660**
Fax..413.594.1673
Web ....www.chicopeema.gov
E-mail ....lsanders@chicopeema.gov
  15 Court St, Chicopee, MA 01020-1885
  Lisa Sanders, Director

MENTAL HEALTH SERVICES

Springfield Mental Health **413.452.2300**
Fax..413.452.2306
  140 High St, Lower Level, Springfield, MA 01105
  Jose Tosado, Supervisor For Adult

COURTS

**Hampden Probate and Family
Court** **413.748.7759**
Fax..413.781.5605
  50 State St, Springfield, MA 01103
  Anne M Geoffrion, 1st Presiding Family Court Justice

Holyoke District Court **413.538.9710**
Fax..413.533.7165
  20 Court Plz, Holyoke, MA 01040-5075
  Honorable Kenneth J. Cote, District Court Judge

Juvenile Court **413.748.7705**
Fax..413.737.4383
  80 State St, Springfield, MA 01103-2025
  Thomas Ginley Jr., Chief Juvenile Probation Officer

Springfield District Court **413.748.8600**
Fax..413.747.4841
E-mail ....bboyle@springfieldcityhall.com
  50 State St, Springfield, MA 01103
  Honorable William J. Boyle, Presiding District Court Judge

POLICE AND SHERIFF

Sheriff's Ofc **413.547.8000**
Fax..413.589.1851
E-mail ....michael.ashe@sdh.state.ma.us
  627 Randall Rd, Ludlow, MA 01056
  Michael J. Ashe, Jr., Sheriff

**Springfield Police Dept - Joseph A. Budd Youth Assessment
Ctr Juvenile Div** **413.787.6361**
Fax..413.787.6350
E-mail ....spd@springfieldpolice.net
  417 Liberty St, Springfield, MA 01104
  William Fipchet, Head Of Police Dept.

EDUCATION SERVICES

Dep Of Youth Serv **413.783.0781**
Fax..413.783.0331
  280 Tinkham Rd, Springfield, MA 01129
  Ruth Rovozee, Regional Director

Eastern Headstart HCS **413.732.3230**
Fax..413.732.3231
  162 Eastern Ave, Springfield, MA 01109-3634
  Mary Caron, Director

**Holyoke Chicopee Springfield Head
Start** **413.788.6522**
Fax..413.788.6679
E-mail ....santosj@headstart.org
  30 Madison Ave, Springfield, MA 01105
  Janis Santos, Executive Director

Hampshire County

GENERAL HEALTH SERVICES

Amherst Health Dept **413.259.3077**
Fax..413.259.2404
Web ....www.amherstma.gov
E-mail ....health@amherstma.gov
  70 Boltwood Walk, Amherst, MA 01002
  Julie Federman, Public Health Director

Health Dept **413.587.1214**
Fax..413.587.1221
Web ....www.northamptonma.gov
  212 Main St Rm 101, Northampton, MA 01060-3167
  Ben Wood, Director

MENTAL HEALTH SERVICES

**Western MA Area Dept of Mental
Health** **413.587.6200**
Fax..413.587.6204
Web ....www.themassgovernment.com
  1 Prince St, Northampton, MA 01060-3600
  Theodore Kirousis, Area Director

JUSTICE AGENCY

**Massachusetts CASA Network / Friends of
Children** **413.584.7120**
Fax..413.584.7833
E-mail ....foc38@verizon.net
  320 Riverside Dr Ste A, Florence, MA 01062-2717
  Jane Lyons, Executive Director

COURTS

**District Court of Eastern
Hampshire** **413.587.3120**
Fax..413.587.3709
  116 Ruffle St, Hadley, MA 01035
  Honorable John M. Payne Jr., 1st Presiding District Court Judge

**Hampshire Div of Probate & Family
Court** **413.586.8503**
Fax..413.586.5670
  33 King St Ste 2, Northampton, MA 01060-3236
  Honorable Gail Perlman, Presiding Family Court Judge

**Hampshire Juvenile Court /
Probation** **413.584.7686**
Fax..413.587.4191
  116 Russel St, Hadley, MA 10135
  Honorable James G Collins, Juvenile Court Judge

Northampton District Court **413.584.8417**
Fax..413.586.1980
  15 Gothic St Ste 11, Northampton, MA 01060-3088
  Michael Goggins, 1st Presiding District Court Judge

POLICE AND SHERIFF

Sheriff's Ofc **413.584.5911**
Fax..413.584.2695
  205 Rocky Hill Rd, Northampton, MA 01060
  Robert J. Garvey, Sheriff

EDUCATION SERVICES

**Community Action - Northhampton Head
Start** **413.582.4212**
Fax..413.527.6409
Web ....www.communityaction.us
  300 Elm St, Northampton, MA 01060
  Annette, Director

Middlesex County

SOCIAL SERVICES

Arlington Area Ofc **781.641.8500**
Fax..781.646.5172
Web ....www.state.ma.us
E-mail ....francis.galligan@state.ma.us
  30 Mystic St, Arlington, MA 02474-1155
  Frank Galligan, Area Director

Dept of Children Services **617.520.8700**
Fax..617.354.0243
  810 Memorial Dr Ste 2, Cambridge, MA 02139
  Richard Ho, Area Director

**Framingham Dept of Transitional
Assistance** **508.661.6600**
Fax..508.727.4718
Web ....www.gettingfoodstamps.org
E-mail ....gettingfoodstamps@projectbread.org
  110 Mount Wayte Ave, Framingham,
  MA 01702-5705
  Paul Sutliff, Director

Health and Human Svcs **617.796.1420**
Fax..617.552.7063
Web ....www.newtonma.gov
  1294 Centre St, Newton Center, MA 02459-1544
  Dori Zaleznik Md, Commissioner Of Health & Human Services

Malden Area Ofc **781.388.7100**
Fax..781.324.2209
Web ....www.mass.us
E-mail ....richard.ho@ago.state.ma.us
  22 Pleasant St, Flr 2, Malden, MA 02148
  Richard Ho, Area Director

GENERAL HEALTH SERVICES

Board of Health **508.460.3751**
Fax..508.460.3625
Web ....www.marlborough-ma.gov
E-mail ....ncleary@ci.marlborough.ma.us
  255 Main St Rm 101, Marlborough, MA 01752-2536
  John Rowe, Chairman, Board Of Health

Cambridge Health Dept **617.665.3800**
Fax..617.665.3888
  119 Windsor St, Cambridge, MA 02139
  Claude Jacob, Chief Public Health Officer

Health Board **617.972.6446**
Fax..617.972.6499
  149 Main St, Watertown, MA 02472
  Steven Ward, Director

Health Board **508.647.6460**
Fax..508.647.6466
Web ....www.natickma.org
E-mail ....health@natickma.org
  13 E Central St, Natick, MA 01760
  James White, Director

Health Board **781.316.3170**
Fax..781.316.3175
Web ....www.town.arlington.ma.us
E-mail ....boh@town.arlington.ma.us
  27 Maple St, Arlington, MA 02476
  Christine Connolly, Director Of Public Health

Health Board **781.862.0500**
Fax..781.861.2780
Web ....www.ci.lexington.ma.us
E-mail ....dfullerton@ci.lexington.ma.us
  1625 Massachusetts Ave, Lexington, MA 02420-3801
  Derrick Fullerton, MPH, Director

Health Dept **978.970.4010**
Fax..978.970.4011
E-mail ....fsingleton@lowellma.gov
  341 Pine St, Lowell, MA 01851-3101
  Frank Singleton, Director

Health Dept **617.394.2255**
Fax..617.387.2139
Web ....www.cityofeverett.com
E-mail ....roberto.santamaria@ci.everett.ma.us
  484 Broadway Rm 20, Everett, MA 02149-3694
  Roberto Santamaria, Director

Medford Health Dept 781.393.2565
Fax 781.393.2562
Web ....www.medford.org
E-mail ....krose@medford.org
  85 George P Hassett Dr, Medford, MA 02155-3256
Karen L. Rose, Director Of Public Health

Wakefield Health Dept 781.246.6375
Fax 781.224.5018
Web ....www.wakefield.ma.us
E-mail ....rclay@wakefield.ma.us
  1 Lafayette St Ste 6, Wakefield, MA 01880-2339
Ruth Clay, Cho, Director

Waltham Health Dept 781.314.3305
Fax 781.314.3319
Web ....www.city.waltham.ma.us
E-mail ....wsweder@city.waltham.ma.us
  119 School St Ste 1, Waltham, MA 02451-4511
Walter Sweder Jr., Director

MENTAL HEALTH SERVICES

Arlington Mental Health / Case
Management 781.641.8100
Fax 781.641.8106
Web ....www.state.ma.us
E-mail ....allen.bachrach@state.ma.us
  20 Academy St, Ste 304, Arlington, MA 02476
Allen Bachrach, Supervisor

COURTS

Ayer District Court 978.772.2100
Fax 978.772.5345
  25 E Main St, Ayer, MA 01432-1699
Susan Reed, Chief Probation Officer

Charlestown District Court 617.242.5400
Fax 617.242.1677
  3 City Sq, Charlestown, MA 02129-3799
Steven Daluka, Probation Officer

Concord District Court 978.369.0500
Fax 978.371.9919
  305 Walden St, Concord, MA 01742
Edward J. Gaffey, Chief Probation Officer

Framingham District Court 508.875.7461
Fax 508.626.2503
  600 Concord St, Framingham, MA 01701
Dan Marciooi, Chief Probation Officer

Juvenile Probate Court 617.494.4100
  121 3rd St, Cambridge, MA 02141-1710

Lowell District Court 978.459.4101
Fax 978.937.2486
  41 Hurd St, Lowell, MA 01852-2295
Gary Mcgee, Chief Probation Officer

Marlborough District Court 508.485.3700
Fax 508.485.1575
  45 Williams St, Marlborough, MA 01752
Sarah Singer, Court Judge

Middlesex Juvenile Court 978.441.3160
Fax 978.441.0578
  89 Appleton St, Lowell, MA 01852
Stephen Alffoppe, Chief Probation Officer

Middlesex Probate and Family
Court 617.768.5800
Fax 617.225.0781
  208 Cambridge St, Cambridge, MA 02141
Sophia OBrian, Chief Probation Office

Somerville District Court 617.666.8000
Fax 617.776.2111
  175 Fellsway W, Somerville, MA 02145-1103
Honorable Maurice Flynn, 1st Presiding District Court Judge

Waltham District Court 781.894.4500
Fax 781.894.4360
  38 Linden St, Waltham, MA 02452-6197
Roland Buoncuore, Acting Chief Probation Officer

Woburn District Court 781.935.4000
Fax 781.932.2593
  30 Pleasant St, Woburn, MA 01801-4184
Marian Hinkle, District Court Judge

POLICE AND SHERIFF

Police Dept / Police Detectives 617.349.3370
Fax 617.349.3327
  125 6th St, Cambridge, MA 02142
Robert Haas, Chief Commissioner

Sheriff's Dept 617.494.4400
Fax 781.960.2901
Web ....www.sdm.state.ma.us
  40 Thorndike St Ste 17, Cambridge, MA 02141
Peter Koutoujian, Sheriff

EDUCATION SERVICES

CTI Headstart Billerica High School 978.663.0091
E-mail ....mfrancione@county.org
  35 River St, Billerica, MA 01821
Maria Francione, Lead Teacher

Feldstein Family Literacy Program 781.388.0663
Web ....www.malden.mec.edu
E-mail ....pfish@malden.mec.edu
  150 Cross St, Malden, MA 02148-7859
Patricia R Fish, Coordinator

Special Education 617.349.6500
Fax 617.349.6355
Web ....www.cpsd.us
E-mail ....aramos@cpsd.us
  159 Thorndike St, Cambridge, MA 02141-1528
Aida Ramos, Executive Director

Nantucket County

COURTS

Nantucket District Court 508.228.0460
Fax 508.325.5759
  16 Broad St Unit 1, Nantucket, MA 02554
Honorable Joseph I. Macy, 1st Presiding District Court Judge

POLICE AND SHERIFF

Sheriff's Dept 508.228.7263
Fax 508.325.5338
Web ....www.nantucket.net
E-mail ....pearlman@islandsheriff.com
  16 Broad St Unit 2 20 S Water St, Nantucket,
MA 02554-3500
James A Pearlman, Sheriff

Norfolk County

GENERAL HEALTH SERVICES

Brookline Health Dept 617.730.2300
Fax 617.730.2296
Web ....www.brooklinema.gov
E-mail ....abalsam@brooklinema.gov
  11 Pierce St, Brookline, MA 02445-7898
Alan Balsam, Director

Health Board 781.340.5008
Fax 781.682.6112
Web ....www.weymouth.ma.us
  75 Middle St, East Weymouth, MA 02189
Daniel Mccormac, Director

Health Board 508.384.5480
Fax 508.384.5449
E-mail ....ggrimaldi@wrentham.ma.us
  79 South St, Wrentham, MA 02093
Debra Dunn, Chairman

Health Board 781.235.0135
Fax 781.235.4685
E-mail ....lizzo@wellesleyma.gov
  90 Washington St, Wellesley Hills, MA 02481-3238
Leonard Izzo, Director

Health Board 781.794.8090
Fax 781.794.8098
Web ....www.braintreegov.org
E-mail ....mmcgrath@braintreema.gov
  90 Pond St, Braintree, MA 02184-5337
Mary Mcgrath, Director

Norwood Health Dept 781.762.1240
Fax 781.278.3000
Web ....www.health.norwood.ma.gov
E-mail ....sv@norwoodma.gov
  566 Washington St, Norwood, MA 02062
Sigalle Reiss, Director

COURTS

Brookline District Court 617.232.4660
Fax 617.739.0734
  360 Washington St, Brookline, MA 02445-6851
Albert Gavagan, Chief Performance Officer

Norfolk Juvenile Court 781.329.1500
Fax 781.329.1640
E-mail ....mitchell_t@jud.state.ma.us
  55 Allied Dr, Dedham, MA 02026
Thomas Mitchell, Chief Performance Officer

Quincy District Court 617.471.1650
Fax 617.773.0530
Web ....www.jud.state.ma.us
  1 Dennis F. Ryan Parkway, Quincy, MA 02169
James Brennan, Acting Cpo

Stoughton District Court 781.344.2131
Fax 781.341.8744
  1288 Central St, Stoughton, MA 02072
Robin Vaughan, Clerk Of Magistrate

Wrentham District Court 508.384.3106
Fax 508.384.5052
  60 East St, Wrentham, MA 02093
Terry Kiley, Chief Probation Officer

POLICE AND SHERIFF

Sheriff's Ofc 781.329.3706
Fax 781.326.1079
  200 West St, Dedham, MA 02027
Michael G. Bellotti, Sheriff

Plymouth County

SOCIAL SERVICES

Brockton Dept of Transitional
Assistance 508.895.7000
Fax 617.727.3569
E-mail ....philip.cummings@state.ma.us
  75 Commercial St, Brockton, MA 02301
Philip Cummings, Director

Plymouth Dept of Transitional
Assistance 508.732.3100
Fax 508.830.9433
  61 Industrial Park Rd Ste 1, Plymouth,
MA 02360-7246
Katherine Green, Director

GENERAL HEALTH SERVICES

Brockton Board of Health 508.580.7175
Fax 508.580.7179
  45 School St, City Hall, Brockton, MA 02301
Louis Tartaglia, Director

COURTS

Brockton District Court 508.587.8000
Fax 508.587.6663
  215 Main St Ste 1, Brockton, MA 02301

Hingham District Court 781.749.7000
Fax 781.830.0229
  28 George Washington Blvd, Hingham, MA 02043
Honorable Patrick Hurley, 1st Presiding District Court Judge

Juvenile Court **508.586.4030**
Fax 508.897.4998
  215 Main St, Ste 207, Brockton, MA 02301
Honorable Kathryn White, Associate Juvenile Court Judge

**Plymouth Div / Probate and Family
Court** **508.897.5400**
Fax 508.583.2545
  215 Main St Ste 3, Brockton, MA 02301
Michael Lafrance, Chief Probation Officer

Plymouth Juvenile Court **508.747.2962**
Fax 508.747.1355
Web ....www.state.ma.us
E-mail ....louis.coffin@state.ma.us
  52 Obery St Ste 4, Plymouth, MA 02360-2199
Honorable Louis Coffin, 1st Presiding Juvenile Court Judge

Suffolk County

SOCIAL SERVICES

**Dept of Transitional Assistance - New Market
Square** **617.989.2200**
Fax 617.427.9214
  1010 Massachusetts Ave, Boston, MA 02118
Agnes Cunio, Director

Fields Corner Area Ofc **617.822.4700**
Fax 617.282.1019
Web ....www.mass.gov/bcs
E-mail ....bill.brown@state.ma.us
  50B Park St, The Esquire Bldg., Boston,
  MA 02122-2629
Bill Brown, Area Director

GENERAL HEALTH SERVICES

Boston Public Health Commission **617.534.5395**
Fax 617.534.5358
Web ....www.bphc.org
  1010 Massachusetts Ave, Flr 6, Boston, MA 02118
Barbara Ferrer, Executive Director

JUSTICE AGENCY

CASA **617.788.6390**
Fax 617.788.8996
Web ....www.casaboston.org
E-mail ....susan.conrad@jud.state.ma.us
  24 New Chardon St, Boston, MA 02114-4703
Susan Conrad, Executive Director

Children's Advocacy Ctr **617.779.2146**
Fax 617.779.2196
E-mail ....cac@suf.state.ma.us
  989 Commonwealth Ave, Boston, MA 02215-1308
Susan Goldfarb, Executive Director

Juvenile Probation **617.788.8571**
Fax 617.788.8973
E-mail ....steven.siciliano@jud.state.ma.us
  24 New Chardon St, Boston, MA 02114-4703
Steven Siciliano, Chief JPO

**Metro Boston Area Ofc / Dept of Youth
Svcs** **617.740.0100**
Fax 617.740.0110
  425 Harvard St, Boston, MA 02124
John Hughes, Director

COURTS

Boston Juvenile Court **617.788.8525**
Fax 617.788.8991
  24 New Chardon St, Boston, MA 02114-4703
Honorable Paul Lewis, Director

Chelsea District Court **617.660.9200**
Fax 617.660.9215
Web ....www.ci.chelsea.ma.us
  120 Broadway, Chelsea, MA 02150-2641
Kevin Murphy, Clerk Magistrate

Dorchester District Court **617.288.9500**
Fax 617.288.7430
  510 Washington St, Boston, MA 02124
Honorable Rosalind Miller, 1st Presiding District Court Judge

Suffolk Probate and Family Court **617.788.8300**
Fax 617.788.8962
Web ....www.state.ma.us
E-mail ....margeret.riley@state.ma.us
  24 New Chardon St, Boston, MA 02114-4703
Margeret Riley, Chief Performance Officer

West Roxbury District Court **617.971.1200**
Fax 617.983.0283
  445 Arborway, Jamaica Plain, MA 02130
Mark Prisco, CPO

POLICE AND SHERIFF

Boston Police Dept **617.343.4500**
Fax 617.343.5003
Web ....www.cityofboston.gov
E-mail ....kearneyk.bpd@cityofboston.gov
  1 Schroeder Plz, Boston, MA 02120-2010
Edward Davis, Comissioner

Boston Police Dept - District E18 .... **617.343.5600**
Fax 617.343.5335
  1249 Hyde Park Ave, Hyde Park, MA 02136
Robert Ciccolo, Captain

Boston Police Dept - District B-3 .... **617.343.4700**
Fax 617.635.4540
Web ....www.cityofboston.gov
E-mail ....joseph.boyle@cityofboston.gov
  1165 Blue Hill Ave, Boston, MA 02124-3914
Joseph Boyle, Captain

Boston Police Dept - District C6 .... **617.343.4730**
Fax 617.343.5320
  101 W Broadway, Boston, MA 02127
John Greland, Captain

Boston Police Dept - District D-4 .... **617.343.4250**
Fax 617.343.5326
Web ....www.ci.boston.ma.us
  650 Harrison Ave, Boston, MA 02118-2423
Paul Ivens, Captain

Boston Police Dept - District D14 .... **617.343.4260**
Fax 617.343.5324
  301 Washington St, Brighton, MA 02135
James Huffey, Captain

Boston Police Dept - District E-5 .... **617.343.4560**
Fax 617.343.5339
Web ....www.cityofboston.gov
E-mail ....hassonj.bpd@ci.boston.ma.us
  1708 Centre St, West Roxbury, MA 02132-1542
James G. Hasson, Captain

Sheriff's Dept **617.704.6505**
Fax 617.704.6581
Web ....www.scsdma.org
E-mail ....jprokovich@scsdma.org
  20 Bradston St, Boston, MA 02118-2705
Andrea J. Cabral, Sheriff

EDUCATION SERVICES

ABCD Walnut Grove Head Start **617.445.8202**
Fax 617.445.6727
Web ....www.bostonabcd.org
  22 Elm Hill Ave, Boston, MA 02121
Lisa Correnti, Director

Capic Head Start - Rose Street **781.284.1334**
Web ....www.capicinc.org
E-mail ....jslibon@capicinc.org
  30 Rose St # A, Revere, MA 02151-4409
Joanne Stone-Lavon, Director

Capic Head Start - Winthrop **617.846.3050**
Fax 617.889.4031
Web ....www.capicinc.org
E-mail ....jslibon@capicinc.org
  45 Pauline St, Winthrop, MA 02152-3011
Joanne Stone-Libon, Director

**East Boston Head Start -
Bennington** **617.569.3948**
  1222 Bennington St, East Boston, MA 02128
Mary Dooley, Director

East Boston Head Start - Elbow **617.567.8855**
Fax 617.567.1477
Web ....www.bostonabcd.org
E-mail ....dooley@bostonabcd.org
  80 Lexington St, Boston, MA 02128
Mary Dooley, Director

Special Education **617.635.8599**
Fax 617.635.8014
Web www.boston.k12.ma.us
  1216 Dorchester Ave, Boston, MA 02125-1504
Dr. Joan Anderson, Senior Director

Worcester County

SOCIAL SERVICES

Dept Children & Families **508.929.2000**
Fax 508.754.9803
  121 Povidence St, Ste 200, Worcester, MA 01604
Donna Hollis, Area Director

**Fitchburg Dept of Transitional
Assistance** **978.665.8700**
Fax 978.345.0935
Web ....www.dta.state.ma.us
E-mail ....maryalyce_cleveland@dta.state.ma.us
  473 Main St, Fitchburg, MA 01420
Maryalyce Cleveland, Director

**Southbridge Dept of Transitional
Assistance** **508.765.2400**
Fax 508.765.0740
  1 North St, Southbridge, MA 01550-2530
R Smith-Miller, Director

GENERAL HEALTH SERVICES

City Of Leominster Health Dept **978.534.7533**
Fax 978.534.8416
Web ....www.leominster.gov
E-mail ....cknuth@leominster-ma.gov
  25 West St Ste 11, CITY HALL, Leominster,
  MA 01453-5699
Christopher J. Knuth, Director

Fitchburg Board Of Health **978.345.9582**
Fax 978.342.9692
Web ....www.ci.fitchburg.ma.us
E-mail ....scurry@ci.fitchburg.ma.us
  718 Main St, Fitchburg, MA 01420
Steven Curry, Director

Health Board **978.297.3537**
Fax 978.297.1616
E-mail ....health@town.winchendon.ma.us
  109 Front St, Winchendon, MA 01475
Steve Callusman, Health Agent

Health Board **781.932.4408**
Fax 781.937.8288
Web ....www.ci.woburn.ma.us
E-mail ....jfralick@citywoburn.com
  10 Common St, Woburn, MA 01801-4139
Jack Fralick Jr., Rs, Health Agent

Health Dept **508.634.2315**
Fax 508.473.1380
Web ....www.milford.ma.us
E-mail ....pmazzuchelli@townofmilford.com
  52 Main St Ste 6, Milford, MA 01757-2611
Paul Mazzuchelli, Health Agent

Worcester Dept.............................508.799.8531
Fax..508.799.8530
Web..................................www.worcesterma.gov
E-mail...........................health@worcesterma.gov
  25 Meade St, Worcester, MA 01610-2715
Patricia Bruchmann, Nursing Director

MENTAL HEALTH SERVICES

Central MA Area Mental Health -

Worcester....................................508.368.3838
Fax..508.363.1500
Web...................................www.mass.gov/dmh
E-mail..............................rich4611@gmail.com
  305 Belmont St, Worcester State Hospital Bryan Bldg,
  Worcester, MA 01604-1681
Richard Brealt, Phd, Director Child/adolescent Services

Dpt of Mental Health.......................508.616.3500
Fax..508.616.3599
  167 Lyman St, Westborough, MA 01581
Susan Wing, Area Director

Fitchburg Mental Health.....................978.353.4400
Fax..978.348.1275
E-mail..........................paula.stylos@state.ma.us
  515 Main St Ste 3, Fitchburg, MA 01420
Paula Stylos, Supervisor of Child Case Mgmt

JUSTICE AGENCY

CASA Project Inc...........................508.757.9877
Fax..508.792.1542
Web.........................www.casaworcestercounty.org
E-mail.......................sscrogin@thecasaproject.org
  100 Grove St Ste 403, Worcester, MA 01605-2630
Sue Ellen Scrogin, Director

Central Area Ofc / Dept of Youth

Svcs...508.792.7611
Fax..508.792.7228
E-mail....................barbara.morton@mail.state.ma.us
  288 Lyman St, Westborough, MA 01581
Barbara Morton, Area Director

Leominster Probation.....................978.537.3846
Fax..978.534.1654
  25 School St, Leominster, MA 01453
Elizabeth Daigneault, CEO

COURTS

Clinton District Court......................978.368.7811
Fax..978.368.7827
  300 Boylston St, Clinton, MA 01510
Bernard J. Oædonnell, Chief Performance Officer

Dudley District Court.......................508.949.3070
Fax..508.949.3078
  West Main St, Dudley, MA 01571
Carol Erkin, Judge

East Brookfield District Court..............508.885.6305
Fax..508.885.7623
Web.................................www.mass.gov
  544 E Main St, East Brookfield, MA 01515-1748
Paul Lasapil, Acting District Court Judge

Gardner District Court......................978.632.2373
Fax..978.630.3902
  108 Matthews St, Gardner, MA 01440
Honorable Patrick A. Fox, 1st Presiding District Court Judge

Leominster District Court...................978.537.3722
Fax..978.537.3970
Web...........................www.leominster-ma.gov
  25 School St, Leominster, MA 01453-3124
Mark E Noonan, District Court Judge

Milford District Court.......................508.473.4541
Fax..508.478.8727
E-mail..........................craig.smith@state.ma.us
  161 West St, Milford, MA 01757
Craig Smith, Clerk Magistrate

Uxbridge District Court.....................508.278.2454
Fax..508.278.2929
  261 S Main St, Uxbridge, MA 01569
Honorable Paul A. Losapio, 1st Presiding District Court Judge

---

Westborough District Court
(Probation).................................508.366.1204
Fax..508.366.8268
  186 Oak St, Westborough, MA 01581-3320
Honorable Paul Waickowski, District Court Judge

Winchendon District Court..................978.632.6326
Fax..978.632.3584
E-mail................daniel.langelier@jud.state.ma.us
  108 Matthews St, Gardner, MA 01440
Arthur Haley, Acting Presiding Justice

Worcester District Court....................508.757.8350
Fax..508.752.6191
  225 Main St, Rm 1025, Worcester, MA 01608
Maureen Chamberlain, Chief Probation Officer

Worcester Juvenile Court...................508.791.7109
Fax..508.757.1230
  225 Main St, Rm 1005, Worcester, MA 01608
Honorable Carol Erskine, 1st Presiding Juvenile Court Judge

Worcester Probate and Family

Court.......................................508.770.0825
Fax..508.798.7923
Web................................www.worcpublib.org
  225 Main St, Worcester, MA 01608-1203
Marjorie T Ursoleo, Chief Probation Officer

POLICE AND SHERIFF

Sheriff's Ofc...............................508.854.1800
Fax..508.856.0465
Web.........................www.worcestercountysheriff.com
  5 Paul X Tivnan Dr, West Boylston, MA 01583-2126
Lewis Evangelidis, Sheriff

Worcester Police Dept......................508.799.8660
Fax..508.799.8637
  9-11 Lincoln Sq, Worcester, MA 01608-1127
Gary Gemme, Chief

SPECIAL SERVICES AGENCIES

ADOPTION AGENCIES

Adoption Resources Assoc.................617.492.8888
  262 Upland Rd, Cambridge, MA 02140-3605

Adoptions With Love, Inc..................617.964.4357
Fax..617.964.2676
Web.............................www.adoptionswithlove.org
  246 wallnut St,Ste # 103, Newton, MA 02460-1580
Amie F Cohen, Director

An Act of Love Adoptions...................617.587.1583
Fax..617.587.1582
Web..............................www.actofloveadoption.com
  99 Summer St Florr 6, Boston, MA 02110
Penny Harrison, Director

Bright Futures Adoption Ctr...............978.263.5400
Fax..978.266.1909
Web...............................www.bright-futures.org
E-mail.........................karen@bright-futures.org
  5 Broadview St, Acton, MA 01720-4240
Karen Cheyney, Director

Casey Family Svcs..........................978.937.1877
Fax..978.937.2262
Web............................www.caseyfamilyservices.org
E-mail.....................acasad@caseyfamilyservices.org
  18 Palmer St, Lowell, MA 01852-1818
Allen Casad, Director

Children's Friend, Inc......................508.753.5425
Fax..587.757.7659
Web................................www.childrensfriend.org
  21 Cedar Street, Worcester, MA 01609
COA accredited organization.

Children's Quarters........................617.726.6010
Fax..617.726.6054
Web...................................www.partners.com
E-mail............................clsmith@partners.org
  36 1st Ave, Charlestown, MA 02129-4557
Christine Smith, Director

China Adoption With Love..................617.731.0798
Fax..617.232.8288
Web...................................www.cawli.org
E-mail...............................info@cawli.org
  251 Harvard St Ste 19 & 20, Brookline,
  MA 02446-5000
Lillian Zhang, Director

Communities For People / Special Family Adoption

Svcs...617.267.1031
Fax..617.267.9293
Web.......................www.communities-for-people.org
  418 Commonwealth Ave, Boston, MA 02215-2801
Joseph Lavey, Executive Director

Dare Family Svcs...........................978.750.0751
Fax..978.750.0749
Web..................................www.darefamily.org
E-mail..........................jaskenase@darefamily.org
  2 Electronics Ave Ste 28, Danvers, MA 01923
Juliet Askenase, Program Director

East End House, Inc.........................617.876.4444
Fax..617.868.3616
Web................................www.eastendhouse.org
  105 Spring Street, Cambridge, MA 02141
COA accredited organization.

Full Circle Adoptions......................413.587.0007
Fax..413.584.1624
Web.............................www.fullcircleadoptions.com
E-mail....................adoption@fullcircleadoptions.com
  39 Main St Ste 31, Northampton, MA 01060-3132
Marla Ruth-allisan, Director

Northeastern Family Institutes.............978.774.0774
Fax..978.531.0312
Web...................................www.nafi/nfi.com
E-mail............................yitzhakbakal@nafi.com
  26 Howley, Peabody, MA 01960
Yitzhak Bakal, Edd, President

Wayside Youth & Family Support Network,

Inc..508.879.9800
Fax..508.875.1348
Web................................www.waysideyouth.org
  1 Frederick Abbott Way, Framingham, MA 01701
COA accredited organization.

ADVOCACY RESOURCES

Affinity Care Management...................508.795.1340
Fax..508.755.6334
Web.................................www.affinitygcm.com
E-mail..........................nancyj@affinitygcm.com
  40 Hunthurst Circle, Worcester, MA 01602
Nancy L. Johnson, Geriatric Care Manager/owner

Associated Advocacy Center - Visions for the Future,
Inc...**508.420.4356**
Fax...508.428.7276
Web...www.aacvisions.org
E-mail...toni@aacvisions.org
   184 Dudley St, Ste 106, Boston, MA 02119
   Toni Saunders, Executive Director

Associated Advocacy Center - Visions for the Future,
Inc...**508.420.4356**
Fax...508.428.7276
Web...www.aacvisions.org
E-mail...toni@aacvisions.org
   24 Widow Coombs Walk, Sandwich, MA 02563
   Toni Saunders, Executive Director

Children's Cove / Cape and Islands Child Advocacy
Ctr..**508.375.0410**
Fax...508.375.0409
E-mail..info@childrenscove.org
   3195 Main St, Barnstable, MA 02630
   Stacy Gallagher, Program Director

CPCS..**978.825.2070**
E-mail...jsong@publiccounsel.net
   1 Salem Grn Ste 408, Salem, MA 01970
   Jane Song

CPCS-CAFLP...**413.442.0052**
E-mail.......................................jrhinehart@publiccounsel.net
   184 North St, Pittsfield, MA 01201
   Jeannie Rhinehart

DFC Boston Legal...................................**617.261.7404**
E-mail..jeanne.hogan@state.ma.us
   24 Farnsworth St, Boston, MA 02210
   Jeanne Hogan

DFC Legal Department.............................**617.261.7404**
E-mail....................................deborah.goldberg@state.ma.us
   15 Union St 2nd Fl, Lawrence, MA 01840
   Deborah Goldberg

Families for Depression Awareness...........**781.890.0220**
Fax...781.890.2411
Web...http://www.familyaware.org
E-mail...info@familyaware.org
   395 Totten Pond Road, Suite 404, Waltham,
   MA 02451
   Julie Totten, President

Family Advocacy Ctr...............................**413.794.9816**
Fax...413.794.4945
Web...www.baystatehealth.com
   50 Maple St, Springfield, MA 01199
   Dr. Stephen Boos, Medical Director

Kid's Place..**413.499.2800**
Fax...413.496.9327
Web...www.kidsplaceonline.org
   63 Wendell Ave, Pittsfield, MA 01201-6305
   Christa Collier, Program Director

Massachusetts Public Health Assoc...........**617.524.6696**
Fax...617.524.5225
Web..www.mphaweb.org
E-mail..jwilkinson@mphaweb.org
   434 Jamaicaway, Jamaica Plain, MA 02130-2009
   Jeffrey Wilkinson, Executive Director

Suffolk Univ Law School Juvenile Justice
Center...**617.305.3206**
E-mail...czza@suffolk.edu
   45 Broomfield St 7th Flr, Boston, MA 02108
   Cheryl Azza

BEHAVIORAL HEALTH TREATMENT

Ablon Medical Practice............................**617.734.3279**
   62 Chestnut Hill Rd, Chestnut Hill, MA 02467-1310
   Steven Ablon, Psychiatrist

Academic & Behavioral Clinic................**617.822.0829**
Web...www.abacinc.net
E-mail...t.betts@abacinc.net
   895 Blue Hill Ave, Boston, MA 02124
   Dr. Terri Betts, Accreditation Manager
   Joint Commission accredited organization.

Accredited Psychiatry............................**617.492.8366**
Fax...617.441.3195
   96 Larchwood Dr, Cambridge, MA 02138-4639
   Harold Burstein, Psychiatrist

AdCare Hospital of Worcester, Inc............**508.799.9000**
Web...www.adcare.com
E-mail..jhillis@adcare.com
   107 Lincoln Street, Worcester, MA 01605-2499
   Mr. Jeff Hillis, Accreditation Manager
   Joint Commission accredited organization.

Addes Medical Practice.........................**413.584.0030**
   118 Main St Ste 101, Northampton, MA 01060-3120
   Ira Addes, Psychiatrist

Addiction Treatment Center of New England,
Inc...**617.254.1271**
Fax...617.782.7668
Web...www.atcne.net
   77 F Warren Street, Brighton, MA 02135
   COA accredited organization.

Allen Medical Practice...........................**508.435.4415**
Fax...508.435.8254
   85 Main St Ste 14, Hopkinton, MA 01748-1156
   Prudence Allen, Psychiatrist

Alonzo Medical Practice.........................**978.373.7010**
Fax...978.373.1678
E-mail...mvyouthcourt@yahoo.com
   116 Summer St, Haverhill, MA 01830-6032
   Juan Roman Alonzo, Md, Psychiatrist

Apogee Intergrated Mental Health..........**508.831.7745**
Web..www.apogeemh.com
   23 Fruit St, Worcester, MA 01609-2126
   Mark Schlickman, Psychiatrist

Appleton Medical Practice......................**617.868.9149**
   11 Hawthorne St, Cambridge, MA 02138-4829
   William Appleton, Psychiatrist

Arbour - Fuller Hospital.........................**508.761.8500**
E-mail....................................christine.paschal@uhsinc.com
   200 May Street, South Attleboro, MA 02703
   Ms. Christine Paschal, Accreditation Manager
   Joint Commission accredited organization.

Arbour Fuller Hospital..........................**508.761.8500**
Fax...508.761.4240
Web..www.arbourhealth.com
   200 May St, Attleboro, MA 02703-5520
   Lisa Pappone, CEO

Arbour Hospital....................................**617.522.4400**
Web..www.arbourhealth.com
E-mail....................................beverly.sadowski@uhsinc.com
   49 Robinwood Avenue, Jamaica Plain, MA 02130
   Ms. Beverly Sadowski, Accreditation Manager
   Joint Commission accredited organization.

Arnold Medical Practice........................**781.575.6788**
   275 Turnpike St, Canton, MA 02021
   Richard Arnold, Psychiatrist

Arons Medical Practice.........................**617.965.6055**
   40 Hampshire St, West Newton, MA 02465-2946
   Elissa Aron, Psychiatrist

Aspel Medical Practice..........................**978.443.6960**
Fax...978.443.6502
   323 Boston Post Rd Ste 13, Sudbury,
   MA 01776-3017
   Bennett Aspel, Md, Psychiatrist

Avery Medical Practice..........................**617.232.8383**
   1141 Beacon St, Brookline, MA 02446
   Irwin Avery, Psychiatrist

Avery Medical Practice..........................**617.964.1164**
   45 Waterston Rd, Newton, MA 02458-2321
   Irwin Avery, MD, Psychiatrist

Banks Medical Practice..........................**781.674.0200**
   114 Waltham St, Lexington, MA 02421
   Amy Banks, MD, Psychiatrist

Barnstable Mental Health Ctr.................**508.362.4141**
   1025 Main St, West Barnstable, MA 02668-1125
   Carol Williamson, Director

Baystate Medical Center.........................**413.794.5960**
Web...www.baystatehealth.com
E-mail..................................deborah.provost@bhs.org
   759 Chestnut Street, Springfield, MA 01199
   Mrs. Deborah Provost, Accreditation Manager
   Joint Commission accredited organization.

Baystate Medical Ctr - Child Behavioral
Health...**413.794.7035**
Fax...413.794.7140
   3300 Main St, # 4AB, Springfield, MA 01199
   Barry Sarzet, Chief

Behavioral Health Network, Inc..............**413.747.0705**
Fax...413.732.0705
Web...www.bhninc.org
   417 Liberty Street, Springfield, MA 01104
   CARF accredited programs available.

Behavioral Medicine Of Boston...............**617.247.3525**
Web..www.bostonbmed.com
E-mail...info@bostonbmed.com
   720 Harrison Ave Ste 808, Boston, MA 02118-2326
   David Leiman, Psychiatrist

Bein Medical Practice............................**978.443.6960**
Fax...978.635.9301
   468 Great Rd, Acton, MA 01720
   Ward Bein, Psychiatrist

Belnap Medical Practice.........................**413.931.5314**
   PO Box 165, Stockbridge, MA 01262-0165
   Barri Belnap, Psychiatrist

Bennett Medical Practice........................**617.738.9204**
Fax...617.738.9204
E-mail...ibennett@ix.netcom.com
   45 Cedar Rd, Chestnut Hill, MA 02467-2209
   Michael Bennett, Md, Psychiatrist

Bennett Medical Practice........................**617.576.6199**
   3 Lancaster St, Cambridge, MA 02140-2806
   William Bennett, Psychiatrist

Bergel Medical Practice.........................**617.739.1812**
   33 Pond Ave Ste B2, Brookline, MA 02445-7128
   Ernest Bergel, Psychiatrist

Berkowitz Medical Practrice.....................**617.244.0503**
Web...www.tristatesleep.com
   125 Brackett Rd, Newton, MA 02458-2613
   David Berkowitz, Psychiatrist

Berlin Medical Practice..........................**413.637.1325**
Fax...413.637.4265
Web...www.richardmberlin.com
E-mail...richard.berlin@gmail.com
   51 Church St Ste 1, Lenox, MA 01240-2648
   Richard Berlin, MD, Psychiatrist

Bertkowitz Medical Practice...................**508.651.1041**
Fax...508.651.0811
   67 Union St, # 404, Natick, MA 01760
   Robert Bertkowitz, MD, Psychiatrist

Bezan Medical Practice..........................**617.969.7722**
   2000 Washington St Ste 302, Newton Lower Falls,
   MA 02462-1602
   Allan Bezan, Md, Psychiatrist

Boston Health Care...............................**508.660.7949**
Fax...508.660.7943
Web...www.bostonhealthcareinc.com
   420 Main St, # 15, Walpole, MA 02081
   Sarah Mourtada, Office Manager

Bournewood Hospital **617.469.0300**
Web ....www.bournewood.com
E-mail ....raymond.robinson@bournewood.com
　300 South Street, Chestnut Hill, MA 02467
　Mr. Raymond Robinson, Accreditation Manager
　Joint Commission accredited organization.

Braintree Public High School **781.848.4000**
Fax 781.848.1541
Web ....www.braintreeschools.org
E-mail ....robert_belmont@braintreeschools.org
　128 Town St, Braintree, MA 02184-5365
　Bob Belmont, Director

Brandon School & Residential Treatment
Ctr **508.655.6400**
Fax 508.650.9431
Web ....www.brandonschool.org
E-mail ....info@brandonschool.org
　27 Winter St, Natick, MA 01760-1099
　Timothy M. Callahan, EDD, Executive Director

Brant Medical Practice **617.964.6982**
Fax 617.969.7803
　30 Lincoln St, Newton Highlands, MA 02461
　Renee Brant, Psychiatrist

Brockton Area Multi-Services, Inc. **508.580.8700**
Fax 508.580.3114
Web ....www.bamsi.org
E-mail ....bmadden@bamsi.org
　10 Christy's Drive, Brockton, MA 02301
　Brian Madden, Director of Operations, Developmental Disabilities
　Services
　CARF accredited programs available.

Brockton Multi Service Center **508.897.2000**
E-mail ....richard.jobin@state.ma.us
　165 Quincy Street, Brockton, MA 02302
　Mr. Richard Jobin, Accreditation Manager
　Joint Commission accredited organization.

Brooks Medical Practice **413.458.9785**
Fax 413.458.9780
E-mail ....rjbrooks@sover.net
　311 Main St, Williamstown, MA 01267-2610
　Robert Brooks, Psychiatrist

Brostoff Medical Practice **781.674.2069**
　10 Muzzey St, Lexington, MA 02421
　Richard Brostoff, Psychiatrist

Brown Medical Practice **617.969.3332**
Fax 617.969.4010
Web ....www.brownmed.com
　303 Highland Ave, West Newton, MA 02465-2513
　Herbert Brown, Psychiatrist

Brownlow Medical Practrice **978.369.3272**
Fax 978.369.4280
　414 Powder Mill Rd, Concord, MA 01742
　Beth Brownlow, Md, Psychiatrist

Bullock Medical Practice **617.247.1388**
Fax 352.795.8378
　909 Beacon St, Boston, MA 02215-3710
　Chris Bullock, Psychiatrist

Cambridge Eating Disorder Center **617.547.2255**
Web ....www.eatingdisordercenter.org
E-mail ....seda@cedcmail.com
　3 Bow Street, Cambridge, MA 02138
　Dr. Seda Ebrahimi, Accreditation Manager
　Joint Commission accredited organization.

Cambridge Psychotherapy **617.661.7315**
　339 Broadway, Cambridge, MA 02139
　Michael Braverman, MD, Psychiatrist

Camoscio Medical Practrice **781.237.8644**
　148 Linden St Ste 206, Wellesley, MA 02482-7970
　Rosemarie Camoscio, Psychiatrist

Cape Cod and Islands Community Mental Health
Center **508.564.9600**
Web ....www.dmh.state.ma.us
E-mail ....marion.stenson@dmh.state.ma.us
　830 County Road, Pocasset, MA 02559
　Ms. Marion Stenson, Accreditation Manager
　Joint Commission accredited organization.

Carl Medical Practrice **508.358.2050**
Fax 508.358.4481
　16 Boston Post Rd, Ste 205, Wayland,
　MA 01778-2435
　Charles Carl, Md, Psychiatrist

Carroll Ctr For The Blind **617.969.6200**
Fax 617.969.6204
Web ....www.carroll.org
E-mail ....oncampus@carroll.org
　770 Centre St, Newton, MA 02458-2597
　Joe Abley, Ma, President

Centerpoint **978.858.3776**
Web ....www.jri.org
E-mail ....cingalls@jri.org
　365 East Street Southgate Building, Tewksbury,
　MA 01876
　Ms. Carolyn Ingalls, Accreditation Manager
　Joint Commission accredited organization.

Children Study Home, Inc **413.783.0567**
Fax 413.783.7980
Web ....www.studyhome.org
E-mail ....thart@studyhome.org
　111 Old Acre Rd, Springfield, MA 01129-1832
　Ty Hart, Director

Childs Medical Practice **617.734.6267**
Fax 617.734.4081
　157 Walnut St, Brookline, MA 02445-7751
　Elizabeth Childs, MD, Psychiatrist

Claycomb Medical Pracitce **978.525.3506**
Fax 978.525.3023
　31 Shore Rd, Gloucester, MA 01930-3916
　J. Barry Claycomb, Md, Psychiatrist

Cohannet Academy **508.977.3730**
E-mail ....blary@jri.org
　60 Hodges Avenue - Goss 3, Taunton, MA 02780
　Mr. Bryan Lary, Accreditation Manager
　Joint Commission accredited organization.

Cohen Medical Practice **413.585.9359**
Fax 413.534.2631
　78 Main St, Northampton, MA 01060
　Donna Cohen, MD, Psychiatrist

Cohen Medical Practice **413.549.5925**
Fax 413.253.9542
　664 Main St Ste 54, Amherst, MA 01002-2428
　Ralph Cohen, MD, Psychiatrist

Community Healthlink **978.840.9354**
Fax 978.840.9389
Web ....www.communityhealthlink.org
E-mail ....ppatterson@communityhealthlink.org
　100 Erdman Way, Leominster, MA 01453
　Paula Patterson, Program Director

Compaine Medical Practice **781.237.9600**
　1 Hollis St Ste 430, Wellesley, MA 02482-4672
　Andrew Compaine, MD, Psychiatrist

Corman Medical Practice **781.643.0310**
Fax 781.687.2198
　94 Pleasant St, Arlington, MA 02476
　Alan Corman, Psychiatrsit

Cossio Medical Practice **617.738.4410**
　64 Welland Rd, Brookline, MA 02445-4504
　Patricia Cossio, MD, Psychiatrist

Counseling & Assessment Clinic of Worcester,
LLC **508.756.5400**
E-mail ....caclinic@verizon.net
　51 Union Street Suite 104, Worcester, MA 01608
　Dr. Jennifer Hylton, Accreditation Manager
　Joint Commission accredited organization.

Craft Medical Assoc. **617.734.5617**
　106 Crafts Rd, Chestnut Hill, MA 02467-1826
　Clifford Briggin, Psychiatrist

Cserr Medical Practice **508.824.6798**
Fax 508.880.8819
E-mail ....bobcserr@mac.com
　707 Green Acres, North Dighton, MA 02764-1394
　Robert Cserr, MD, Psychiatrist

Curran Medical Practice **781.237.7799**
Fax 781.237.9859
　328 Washington St Ste 250, Wellesley Hills,
　MA 02481-6251
　John Curran, Psychiatrist

Curry College **617.333.0500**
Web ....www.curry.edu
　1071 Blue Hill Ave, Milton, MA 02186-2395
　Kenneth Quigly, President

Curtiss Medical Practice **617.566.4776**
　1776 Beacon St, Brookline, MA 02445
　David Curtiss, Md, Psychiatrist

Cutler Medical Practice **508.755.4913**
Fax 508.795.1106
　51 Cedar St, Worcester, MA 01609-2131
　Dr. Scot Cutler, Psychiatrist

D'Afflitti Medical Practice **617.332.9589**
　42 Plainfield St, Waban, MA 02468-1618
　Joseph D'afflitti Md, Psychiatrist

David Medical Practice **617.232.3503**
　1093 Beacon St Ste 303, Brookline, MA 02446-5623
　Paul Daivd, MD, Pschiatristr

Day Medical Practice **617.332.8907**
　108 Lake Ave, Newton Center, MA 02459-2108
　Max Day, Md, Psychiatrist

DCS Mental Health, Inc **781.396.1199**
Fax 781.396.1439
Web ....www.dcsmentalhealth.com
E-mail ....info@dcsmentalhealth.com
　151 Mystic Ave Ste 6, Medford, MA 02155
　Judy Donnelly, Vice President

Devereux Massachusetts **508.886.4746**
Fax 508.886.2274
Web ....www.devereuxma.org
　60 Miles Rd, Rutland, MA 01543-1423
　Kerry Ann Goldsmith, Assistant Executive Director
　COA accredited organization.

Dimock Community Foundation, Inc. **617.442.8800**
Web ....www.dimock.org
E-mail ....sbaran@dimock.org
　45 Dimock Street, Roxbury, MA 02119
　Mr. Shaun Baran, Accreditation Manager
　Joint Commission accredited organization.

Doctor Franklin Perkins School **978.365.7376**
Web ....www.perkinsprograms.org
E-mail ....kflathers@perkinschool.org
　971 Main Street, Lancaster, MA 01523
　Ms. Kerry Flathers, Accreditation Manager
　Joint Commission accredited organization.

Doctor Franklin Perkins School **978.365.7376**
Fax 978.368.8861
Web ....www.perkinsprograms.org
E-mail ....blossom@perkinschool.org
　971 Main St, Lancaster, MA 01523-2595
　Charles P. Conroy, Executive Director

Donald Wexler Inc. **617.864.2266**
Fax 617.354.5790
　3 Concord Ave, Cambridge, MA 02138
　Donald Wexler, Md, Psychiatrist

Dr. John C. Corrigan Mental Health Center 508.235.7200
E-mail ....sheila.mcquillan@dmh.state.ma.us
49 Hillside Street, Fall River, MA 02720
Mrs. Sheila McQuillan, Accreditation Manager
Joint Commission accredited organization.

Draskoczy Medical Practice 781.237.7376
726 Wellesley St, Weston, MA 02493-1000
Paul Draskoczy, MD, Psychiatrist

Dreskin Medical Practice 617.523.3448
5 Longfellow Pl Ste 203, Boston, MA 02114-2839
Jane Dreskin, Psychiatrist

Dundas Medical Practice 781.449.0784
20 Chestnut St Ste 1, Needham, MA 02492-2516
John Dundas, MD, Psychiatrist

Eagleton School 413.528.4385
Fax 413.528.6377
Web ....www.eagletonschool.com
E-mail ....bmitchell@eagletonschool.com
446 Montgomery Rd, Great Barrington, MA 01230
Becky Mitchell

East Middlesex Arc 781.942.4888
Fax 781.942.0820
Web ....www.theemarc.org
E-mail ....mobrien@theemarc.org
20 Gould St, Reading, MA 01867-2927
Mauleen O'Brien, Interim Director

Edelman Medical Practice 508.358.4815
Fax 508.358.5495
58 Glezen Ln, Wayland, MA 01778-1604
Stuart Edelman, Psychiatrist

Egloff Medical Practice 508.548.9526
Web ....www.egloff.org
E-mail ....fegloff@egloff.org
89 Gardiner Rd, Woods Hole, MA 02543-1115
Frank Egloff, Psychiatrist

Eisendrath Medical Pracrtice 617.484.2569
18 Moore St Ste 5, Belmont, MA 02478-2529
Robert Eisendrath, Md, Psychiatrist

Elderly Housing Development 617.464.1075
120 H St, South Boston, MA 02127
Kathleen Stimpson, Director

Ellis Medical Practice 617.232.2008
1101 Beacon St Ste 301E, Brookline, MA 02446-5588
J. Matson Ellis, MD, Psychiatrist

Emerson College 617.824.8595
Fax 617.824.8909
Web ....www.emerson.edu
E-mail ....patty_challan@emerson.edu
120 Boylston St Ste 414, Boston, MA 02116-4624
Patty Challan, Assistant Director

Everett Psychiatric Svc 617.387.2220
Fax 617.394.0538
E-mail ....daniel@danielrutrick.com
617 Broadway, Everett, MA 02149
Daniel Rutrick, Md, Psychiatrist

**Falmouth Public Schools - Lawerence
School** 508.548.0606
Fax 508.457.9778
Web www.falmouth.k12.ma.us
113 Lakeview Ave, Falmouth, MA 02540-2835
Patt Dietlin, Guidence Counselor

Families First 617.868.7687
Fax 617.354.2902
Web ....www.families-first.org
E-mail ....info@families-first.org
99 Bishop Richard Allen Dr Ste 6, Cambridge,
MA 02139-3425
Crista Martinez, Executive Director

Family Continuity Programs 508.862.0600
Fax 508.862.0590
E-mail ....smurati@familycontinuity.org
60 Perseverance Way, Fl 2, Hyannis, MA 02601
Susan Murati, Outpatient Therapist

Family Service Association 508.677.3822
Fax 508.677.3714
Web ....www.frfsa.org
101 Rock Street, Fall River, MA 02720
COA accredited organization.

Family Service of Greater Boston 617.523.6400
Fax 617.523.3034
Web ....www.fsgb.org
31 Heath Street, Jamaica Plain, MA 02130
COA accredited organization.

Family Services of Central Massachusetts 508.756.4646
Fax 508.791.4755
Web ....www.fscm.org
31 Harvard Street, Worcester, MA 01609
COA accredited organization.

Family Svc Assoc of Greater Fall River 508.678.7542
Fax 508.676.3699
Web ....www.frfsa.org
E-mail ....cnegle@frfsa.org
101 Rock St, Fall River, MA 02720-3201
Carol Negle, President/CEO

Feigon Medical Practice 617.323.9141
540 Vfw Pkwy, West Roxbury, MA 02132
Elizabeth Feigon, MD, Psychiatrist

Feldman Medical Practice 617.731.6660
131 Harvard St Ste 6, Brookline, MA 02446-6453
Judith Feldman, Psychiatrist

Fenway Community Health Center, Inc. 617.267.0900
Web ....www.fenwayhealth.org
E-mail ....aanderson@fenwayhealth.org
1340 Boylston Street, Boston, MA 02215
Ms. Alicia Anderson, Accreditation Manager
Joint Commission accredited organization.

Fields Medical Pracrtice 617.489.2423
Fax 858.459.1021
100 Concord Ave, Belmont, MA 02478
Meredith Fields, MD, Psychiatrist

Fisch Medical Practice 617.734.9359
E-mail ....afisch1@rcn.com
149 Buckminster Rd, Brookline, MA 02445-5809
Alan Fisch, Psychiatrist

Foa Fiitness Inc. 781.964.1229
E-mail ....foafitness@hotmail.com
100 Cove Way, Quincy, MA 02169
Olivia Chamberland, Licensed Mental Health Counselor

Fox Medical Practice 978.750.6828
Fax 978.750.6684
Web ....www.bridgewell.org
E-mail ....sfox@bridgewell.org
65 Newbury St, Danvers, MA 01923-1040
Sherman Fox, Md, Psychiatrist

Frader Medical Practice 781.863.0467
Fax 781.863.2743
35 Bedford St Ste 17, Lexington, MA 02420-4440
Marc Frader, MD, Psychiatrist

Franciscan Hospital for Children, Inc. 617.254.3800
Web ....www.fhfc.org
E-mail ....jfexis@fhfc.org
30 Warren Street, Boston, MA 02135-3680
Ms. Jennifer Fexis, Accreditation Manager
Joint Commission accredited organization.

Friedman Medical Pracrtice 617.876.4610
Fax 617.876.1237
E-mail ....friedmanhj@aol.com
6 Garden Ter, Cambridge, MA 02138-1407
Henry Friedman, MD, Psychiatrist

Frim Medical Practice 508.653.7830
220 N Main St Ste 103, Natick, MA 01760-1100
Rosalind Frim, MD, Psychiatrist

Frosch Medical Practice 617.491.5467
Fax 617.527.2734
875 Massachusetts Ave Ste 54B, Cambridge,
MA 02139-3079
James Frosch, Psychiatrist

Germaine Lawrence Incorporated 781.648.6200
Fax 781.646.9106
Web ....www.germainelawrence.org
18 Claremont Avenue, Arlington, MA 02476
COA accredited organization.

Gosnold, Inc. 508.540.6550
Web ....www.gosnold.org
E-mail ....rmartin@gosnold.org
200 Ter Heun Drive, Falmouth, MA 02540
Mr. Richard Martin, Accreditation Manager
Joint Commission accredited organization.

**Grafton Job Corps Career Development
Ctr** 508.839.6904
Fax 508.839.9781
100 Pine St, North Grafton, MA 01536-1847
Peter Lafleur, Center Director

Health & Education Services, Inc. 978.921.1293
Fax 978.921.1294
Web ....www.hes-inc.org
800 Cummings Center, Suite 266T, Beverly,
MA 01915
CARF accredited programs available.

High Point Treatment Center, Inc. 508.224.7701
Web ....www.hptc.org
E-mail ....franmarkle@hptc.org
1233 State Road, Plymouth, MA 02360
Ms. Fran Markle, Accreditation Manager
Joint Commission accredited organization.

Hillcrest Educational Centers, Inc. 413.499.7924
Web ....www.hillcrestec.org
E-mail ....bgoldberg@hillcrestec.org
788 South Street, Pittsfield, MA 01201
Mr. Ben Goldberg, Accreditation Manager
Joint Commission accredited organization.

Home For Little Wanderers; The 617.267.3700
Fax 617.267.8142
Web ....www.thehome.org
E-mail ....aberns@thehome.org
271 Huntington Ave, Boston, MA 02115-4506
Peter Eders, Vice President

Judge Baker Children's Ctr 617.232.8390
Fax 617.232.8399
Web ....www.jbcc.harvard.edu
E-mail ....jweisz@jbcc.harvard.edu
53 Parker Hill Ave, Boston, MA 02120-3225
John Weisz, President

Kolbourne School, Inc 413.229.8787
Fax 413.229.4165
Web ....www.kolbourne.net
E-mail ....jweinstein@kolbourne.net
343 New Marlboro Southfield Rd, New Marlboro,
MA 01230-2199
Mike Kirchner, Chief Financial Officer

L.U.K. Crisis Center, Inc. 978.345.0685
Fax 978.345.8205
Web ....www.luk.org
545 Westminster Street, Fitchburg, MA 01420
COA accredited organization.

Laurel Hill Inn, Ltd. 781.396.1116
Web ....www.laurelhillinn.com
E-mail ....linda@laurelhillinn.com
121 Mystic Street, Medford, MA 02155
Ms. Linda McDonald, Accreditation Manager
Joint Commission accredited organization.

League School of Greater Boston 508.850.3900
Fax...508.660.2442
Web...www.leagueschool.com
E-mail ....jzbyszynski@leagueschool.com
　　300 Providence Hwy, East Walpole, MA 02032-1521
　　John Zbyszynski, Director

Little House; The 617.506.5972
Fax...617.474.1137
E-mail ....ataylor@collegeboundrochester.org
　　275 E Cottage St, Boston, MA 02125-1797
　　Ann Taylor, Site Coordinator

Lynn Community Health Center 781.596.2502
Web...www.lchcnet.org
E-mail ....bobdemp@lchcnet.org
　　269 Union Street, Lynn, MA 01901
　　Mr. Bob Dempkowski, Accreditation Manager
　　Joint Commission accredited organization.

Martha's Vineyard Community Services 508.693.7900
Fax...508.693.7192
Web...www.mvcommunityservices.com
E-mail ....mchavez@mvcommunityservices.com
　　111 Edgartown Road, Vineyard Haven, MA 02568
　　Marcos Chavez, Director of Human Resources
　　CARF accredited programs available.

Massachusetts Society For The Prevention of Cruelty To
Children 413.532.9446
Fax...413.533.0047
Web...www.mspcc.org
E-mail ....mj@mspcc.org
　　230 Maple St Ste B1, Holyoke, MA 01040-5145
　　Mark Jimerson, Office Manager

Massachusetts Society For The Prevention of Cruelty To
Children 978.682.9222
Fax...978.681.9508
Web...www.mspcc.org
E-mail ....pdicori@mspcc.org
　　439 S Union St, Lawrence, MA 01843
　　Peggy Dicori, Regional Administrator

Massachusetts Society For The Prevention of Cruelty To
Children 413.734.4978
Fax...413.737.4684
Web...www.mspcc.org
E-mail ....jstabilec@mspcc.org
　　235 Chestnut St, Springfield, MA 01103
　　Janet Stabile, Clinic Director

Massachusetts Society For The Prevention of Cruelty To
Children 617.983.5800
Fax...617.983.5840
Web...www.mspcc.org
　　157 Green St, Jamaica Plain, MA 02130-2667
　　Denise Duggan, Director

Massachusetts Society For The Prevention of Cruelty To
Children 508.586.2660
Fax...508.584.6281
Web...www.mspcc.org
E-mail ....estrawn@mspcc.org
　　231 Main St, Flr 3, Brockton, MA 02301
　　Evelyn Strawn, Regional Administrator

May Behavioral Health Boston, A Div of The May
Institute 617.325.6700
Fax...617.325.6581
Web...mayinstitute.org
E-mail ....lsolotar@mayinstitute.org
　　2020 Centre St, West Roxbury, MA 02132-3316
　　Laurn Solotar, Executive Director

May Institute Corporate Ofc and National Autism
Ctr 781.440.0400
Fax...781.437.1220
Web...www.mayinstitute.org
E-mail ....wchristian@mayinstitute.org
　　41 Pacella Park Dr, Randolph, MA 02368-1755
　　Walter Christian, President/CEO

McLean Hospital 617.855.3450
Web...www.mcleanhospital.org
E-mail ....mgougeon@partners.org
　　115 Mill Street, Belmont, MA 02478
　　Ms. Michele Gougeon, Accreditation Manager
　　Joint Commission accredited organization.

McLean Hospital 617.855.2000
Fax...617.855.3831
Web...www.mclean.harvard.edu
　　115 Mill St, Belmont, MA 02478-1048
　　Joseph Gold, Clinical Director Of Child & Adolescent Services

Mercy Hospital 413.748.9000
Web...www.mercycares.com
E-mail ....linda.molloy@sphs.com
　　271 Carew Street, Springfield, MA 01104
　　Ms. Linda Molloy, Accreditation Manager
　　Joint Commission accredited organization.

MetroWest Medical Center 508.383.1000
Web...www.mwmc.com
E-mail ....linda.campbell@mwmc.com
　　115 Lincoln Street, Framingham, MA 01702
　　Ms. Linda Campbell, Accreditation Manager
　　Joint Commission accredited organization.

New Bedford Mental Health 508.996.7900
Fax...508.999.1331
E-mail ....lorna.ketin@dmh.state.ma.us
　　888 Purchase St Ste 213, New Bedford, MA 02740
　　Lorna Ketin, Children Coordinator

New England Ctr For Children 508.481.1015
Fax...508.485.3421
Web...www.necc.org
E-mail ....vstrully@necc.org
　　33 Turnpike Rd, Southborough, MA 01772-2108
　　L. Vincent Strully, Jr., Executive Director

New England Medical Ctr Hospitals Div of Child and Adolescent
Psychiatry 617.636.5747
Fax...617.636.4852
Web...www.newenglandmedical.org
E-mail ....psummergrad@tufts-nemc.org
　　750 Washington St, # 1007, Boston, MA 02111
　　Paul Summergrad, MD, Chief, Director of Child And Adolescent Psychiatry

NFI Massachusetts(Northeastern Family
Institute) 978.774.0774
Web...www.nafi.com
E-mail ....mariatebeau@nafi.com
　　26 Hawley St., Peabody, MA 01960
　　Ms. Maria Tebeau, Accreditation Manager
　　Joint Commission accredited organization.

North End Community Health Committee,
Inc. 617.643.8000
Web...www.massgeneral.org
E-mail ....taclifford@partners.org
　　332 Hanover Street, Boston, MA 02113
　　Mr. Timothy Clifford, Accreditation Manager
　　Joint Commission accredited organization.

NorthEast Health Services, LLC 508.880.6666
Fax...508.880.6655
Web...www.northeasthealthservices.com
　　30 Taunton Green, Taunton, MA 02780
　　COA accredited organization.

Northeast Hospital Corporation 978.922.3000
Web...www.nhshealth.org
E-mail ....pdiaz@nhs-healthlink.org
　　85 Herrick Street, Beverly, MA 01915-1777
　　Ms. Patricia Hojnowski-Diaz, Accreditation Manager
　　Joint Commission accredited organization.

Nova Psychiatric Svcs 617.479.4545
Fax...617.479.4555
　　1261 Furnace Brook Pkwy, Ste 30, Quincy, MA 02169
　　Raymond Colella, Md, Psychiatrist

Osiris Family Institute, LLC 617.442.2002
Web...www.osirisinstitute.com
E-mail ....larry@osirisgroup.org
　　184 Dudley Street Suite 107 LL, Roxbury, MA 02119
　　Mr. Larry Higginbottom, Accreditation Manager
　　Joint Commission accredited organization.

Parent Professional Advocacy League / Children Mental
Health 617.542.7860
Fax...617.542.7832
Web...www.ppal.net
E-mail ....info@ppal.net
　　45 Bromfield St 10th Fl, Boston, MA 02108
　　Lisa Lambert, Executive Director

Priority Professional Care, LLC 857.598.4774
Web...www.ppcboston.com
E-mail ....fcharles@ppcboston.com
　　1613 Blue Hill Ave Suite 302, Mattapan, MA 02126
　　Ms. Ferlin Charles, Accreditation Manager
　　Joint Commission accredited organization.

Pyramid Builders Associates 617.516.0280
Web...PyramidBuilders.org
E-mail ....iwilliams@pyramidbuilders.org
　　1960 Washington Street, Boston, MA 02118
　　Mr. Ishman Williams, Accreditation Manager
　　Joint Commission accredited organization.

Robert F. Kennedy Action Corps For Children,
Inc. 617.227.4183
Fax...617.227.2069
Web...www.rfkchildren.org
E-mail ....ekelley@rfkchildren.org
　　11 Beacon St Ste 820, Boston, MA 02108-3014
　　Edward P. Kelley, President/CEO

Seven Hills Behavioral Health, Inc. 508.996.3147
Fax...508.991.4999
Web...sevenhills.org
E-mail ....jroberge@sevenhills.org
　　589 South First Street, New Bedford, MA 02741
　　Jeff Roberge, Director, Career Source
　　CARF accredited programs available.

South Bay Mental Health Center, Inc. 508.580.4691
Fax...508.588.5751
Web...www.southbaymentalhealth.com
　　37 Belmont Street, Brockton, MA 02301
　　CARF accredited programs available.

Stetson School, Inc. 978.355.4541
Fax...978.355.6335
Web...www.stetsonschool.org
E-mail ....rfitzgerald@stetsonschool.org
　　455 South St, PO Box 309, Barre, MA 01005-0309
　　Kathleen Lovenbury, Executive Director
　　Stetson School offers a 40 Week Core Foundation Program to meet the individual needs of youth with sexual or other behavioral problems. We have specialized services for Psychosocial/Psychosexual Assessment, Sexual Abuser, Sexually Reactive, Healthy Sexuality, Youth Extended and an Alternative Learning Program serving adolescents with serious learning problems for IQ's of 55 and up. Services for non sexual behavior disorders now available.

Stevens Children's Home 508.679.0183
Fax...508.679.1950
Web...www.stevenshome.org
E-mail ....info@stevenshome.org
　　24 Main St, Swansea, MA 02777-4620
　　Thomas A. Drooger, Executive Director

Svcnet, Inc. 413.585.1300
Fax...413.582.4252
Web...www.servicenetinc.org
E-mail ....skaras@servicenetinc.org
　　129 King St Ste 1, Northampton, MA 01060-3387
　　Jimfrutikin, Director Of Child & Family Clinic

The Bridge of Central Massachusetts, Inc. 508.755.0333
Fax...508.755.2191
Web...www.thebridgecm.org
　　4 Mann Street, Worcester, MA 01602
　　COA accredited organization.

The Counseling Center of Child Development and Education, Inc..................781.324.2381
Fax...781.324.2343
Web...www.cdedu.us
  10 Cabot Road, Medford, MA 02155
  CARF accredited programs available.

The Italian Home For Children, Inc............617.524.3116
Fax...617.983.5372
Web...www.italianhome.org
  1125 Centre Street, Jamaica Plain, MA 02130
  COA accredited organization.

The Three Rivers Treatment Program.........413.733.4032
E-mail.................................tectonic.inc@comcast.net
  26 Ridgewood Terrace, Springfield, MA 01105
  Ms. Ann Robinson, Accreditation Manager
  Joint Commission accredited organization.

The Whitney Academy, Inc....................508.763.3737
Web...www.whitneyacademy.org
E-mail.................................ballen@whitneyacademy.org
  85 Dr. Braley Road, East Freetown, MA 02717
  Mr. Benjamin Allen, Accreditation Manager
  Joint Commission accredited organization.

Three Rivers Treatment.....................413.733.4032
Fax...413.733.4130
E-mail.................................rterreden@cutchins.org
  26 Ridgewood Ter, Springfield, MA 01105-1315
  Rob Terreden, Director

United Homes For Children.................978.640.0089
Fax...978.640.9652
E-mail.................................emalone@csrox.org
  1147 Main St, Ste 209-210, Tewksbury, MA 01876
  Edward Malone, Director

University of Massachusetts Medical School, Transitions IRTP.................508.856.1439
Web...www.umassmed.edu
E-mail.................................debra.deangelo@umassmed.edu
  305 Belmont Street, 7th Flr C, Worcester, MA 01604
  Ms. Debra DeAngelo, Accreditation Manager
  Joint Commission accredited organization.

Valley View School.........................508.867.6505
Fax...508.867.3300
Web...www.valleyviewschool.org
  91 Oakham Rd, North Brookfield, MA 01535-2031
  Philip G. Spiva, Principal

Walden Behavioral Care.....................781.647.6767
Web...www.waldenbehavioralcare.com
E-mail.................................cobrien@waldenbehavioralcare.com
  9 Hope Avenue, Waltham, MA 02453
  Dr. Colleen O'Brien, Accreditation Manager
  Joint Commission accredited organization.

Wayside Community Counseling Ctr.........508.478.6888
Fax...508.478.9042
  10 Asylum St, Milford, MA 01757-2203
  Louren Berry, Program Director

Westwood Lodge Hospital...................781.762.7764
Fax...781.762.0550
  45 Clapboardtree St, Westwood, MA 02090
  Valerie Packard, Director Of Admissions

Westwood Pembroke Health System.........781.762.7764
Web...www.arbourhealth.com
E-mail.................................stacey.burns@uhsinc.com
  45 Clapboardtree Street, Westwood, MA 02090
  Ms. Stacey Burns, Accreditation Manager
  Joint Commission accredited organization.

Winchendon School; The....................978.297.1223
Fax...978.297.0911
Web...www.winchendon.org
E-mail.................................admissions@winchendon.org
  172 Ash St, Winchendon, MA 01475-1700
  J Kerney, Headmaster

CHILDREN'S HOSPITAL

Anna Jaques Hospital.........................978.463.1000
  25 Highland Ave, Newburyport, MA 01950
  Russell Martin, Director

Baystate Franklin Medical Center.............413.773.0211
  164 High St, Greenfield, MA 01301
  Chuck Gijanto, President

Baystate Mary Lane Hospital.................413.967.6211
  85 S St, Ware, MA 01082
  Joan Sullivan, President

Baystate Medical Center.....................413.794.0000
  759 Chestnut St, Springfield, MA 01199
  Mark Tolosky, Chief Executive Officer

Berkshire Medical Center.....................413.447.2000
  725 N St, Pittsfield, MA 01201
  David Phelps, Chief Executive Officer

Beverly Hospital.............................978.922.3000
  85 Herrick St, Beverly, MA 01915
  Kenneth Hanover, Chief Executive Officer

Boston Medical Center.......................617.638.8000
  1 Boston Medical Ctr Pl, Boston, MA 02118

Cambridge health Alliance...................617.665.1000
  1493 Cambridge St, Cambridge, MA 02139
  Denise Keese, Chief Executive Officer

Cape Cod Hospital...........................508.771.1800
  27 Park St, Hyannis, MA 02601
  Michael Lauf, Chief Executive Officer

Caritas Carney Hospital.....................617.296.4000
  2100 Dorchester Ave, Dorchester, MA 02124

Caritas Holy Family Hospital.................978.687.0151
  70 E St, Methuen, MA 01844
  Lester Schindel, Chief Executive Officer

Cooley Dickinson Hospital...................413.582.2000
  30 Locust St, Northampton, MA 01060
  Craig Melin, Chief Executive Officer

Emerson Hospital...........................978.369.1400
E-mail.................................cschuster@emersonhosp.org
  133 Old Rd to 9 Acre Corner, Concord, MA 01742
  Christine Schuster, President/CEO

Falmouth Hospital...........................508.548.5300
  100 Ter Heun Dr, Falmouth, MA 02540
  Susan Wing, Chief Executive Officer

Good Samaritan Medical Center.............508.427.3000
  235 N Pearl St, Brockton, MA 02301
  Jeff Liebman, Chief Executive Officer

Harrington Memorial Hospital...............508.765.9771
  100 South St, Southbridge, MA 01550

Health Alliance Hospital.....................978.466.2000
  60 Hospital Rd, Leominster, MA 01453
  Patrick Muldoon, Chief Executive Officer

Heywood Hospital...........................978.632.3420
  242 Green St, Gardner, MA 01440
  David Anderson, Chief Executive Officer

Jordan Hospital.............................508.746.2000
  275 Sandwich St, Plymouth, MA 02360

Lawrence General Hospital...................978.683.4000
  1 General St, Lawrence, MA 01842
  Diane Anderson, President

Lowell General Hospital.....................978.937.6000
E-mail.................................ndeschene@lowllgeneral.org
  295 Varnum Ave, Lowell, MA 01854
  Norm Deschene, President

Martha's Vineyard Hospital.................508.693.0410
  1 Hospital Rd, Oak Bluffs, MA 02557
  Tom Lenkowski, Chief Executive Officer

Massachusetts Eye & Ear Infirmary.........617.523.7900
  243 Charles St, Boston, MA 02114

Massachusetts General Hospital.............617.726.2000
  55 Fruit St, Boston, MA 02114
  Peter Slavin, Chief Executive Officer

Mercy Medical Center.......................413.748.9000
  271 Carew St, Springfield, MA 01104
  Daniel Moen, President

MetroWest Medical Center...................508.383.1000
  115 Lincoln St, Framingham, MA 01702
  Andrei Soran, Chief Executive Officer

Milford Regional Medical Center.............508.473.1190
  14 Prospect St, Milford, MA 01757
  Frank Saba, Chief Executive Officer

Morton Hospital & Medical Center...........508.828.7000
  88 Washington St, Taunton, MA 02780

Nantucket Cottage Hospital.................508.825.8100
  57 Prospect St, Nantucket, MA 02554
  Margot Hartmann, Chief Executive Officer

Nashoba Valley Medical Center..............978.784.9000
  200 Groton Rd, Ayer, MA 01432
  Steven Roach, Chief Executive Officer

Newton-Wellesley Hospital..................617.243.6000
  2014 Washington St, Newton Lower Falls, MA 02462
  Elaine Bridge, Chief Nursing Officer

Noble Hospital..............................413.568.2811
  115 W Silver St, Westfield, MA 01086
  Ronald Bryant, Chief Executive Officer

North Adams Regional Hospital..............413.664.5000
  71 Hospital Ave, North Adams, MA 01247
  Bill Frado, Chief Executive Officer

North Shore Medical Center.................978.741.1200
  81 Highland Ave, Salem, MA 01970
  Robert Nortan, President

Norwood Hospital...........................781.769.4000
  800 Washington St, Norwood, MA 02062
  John Holiver, President

Quincy Medical Center.......................617.773.6100
  114 Whitwell St, Quincy, MA 02169
  John Kascanin, Chief Executive Officer

Shriners Hsptl 4 Chldrn at Springfield.......413.787.2000
  516 Carew St, Springfield, MA 01104
  Mark Niederpruem, Administrator

Signature Healthcare Brockton Hospital.......508.941.7000
Web...www.signature-healthcare.org
  680 Centre St, Brockton, MA 02302
  Kim Hollon, Chief Executive Officer

South Shore Hospital........................781.340.8000
  55 Fogg Rd, South Weymouth, MA 02190
  Richard Aubut, President

Southcoast Hospitals Group.................508.679.3131
  363 Highland Ave, Fall River, MA 02720
  Keith Hovan, President

St Anne's Hospital...........................508.674.5741
  795 Middle St, Fall River, MA 02721
  Craig Jesiolowski, President

St Vincent Hospital..........................508.363.5000
  123 Summer St, Worcester, MA 01608
  Derek Wexler, Chief Executive Officer

Sturdy Memorial Hospital....................508.222.5200
  211 Park St, Attleboro, MA 02703
  Linda Shyavitz, President/CEO

Tufts Medical Center........................617.636.5000
E-mail.................................evane@tuftsmedicalcenter.org
  800 Washington St, Boston, MA 02111
  Ellen Vane, Director

UMass Memorial Medical Center.............508.334.1000
  119 Belmont St, Worcester, MA 01605

Winchester Hospital.........................781.729.9000
  41 Highland Ave, Winchester, MA 01890
  Kevin Smith, Chief Executive Officer

Wing Memorial Hospital 413.283.7651
40 Wright St, Palmer, MA 01069
Dr. Cavagnaro, Chief Executive Officer

COUNSELING SERVICES

Bethany Christian Svcs 978.794.9800
Fax 978.683.5676
Web ....www.bethany.org
E-mail ....bcsnandover@bethany.org
820 Turnpike St Ste 101, North Andover,
MA 01845-6125
Debbie Miller, Office Manager

Clearview Ctr Juvenile Sexual Offenders 978.649.9980
Fax 978.649.9127
6 Pondview Pl, Tyngsboro, MA 01879
Kathryn Chapman, MSW, Clinical Director

Hospice & Palliative Care of Cape Cod 508.957.0200
Fax 508.957.0229
Web ....www.hospicecapecod.org
E-mail ....info@hospicecapecod.org
765 Attucks Lane, Hyannis, MA 02601
Melissa Roberts Weidman, Director Of Communications

**Massachusetts Society For The Prevention of Cruelty To
Children** 617.587.1500
Fax 617.587.1582
Web ....www.mspcc.org
E-mail ....msudders@mspcc.org
99 Summer St, Flr 5, Boston, MA 02110
Marylou Sudders, President/CEO

The Bridge, Inc 617.423.9575
Fax 617.482.5459
Web ....www.bridgeovertroubledwater.org
47 West St Fl 3, Boston, MA 02111-1219
Robb Zarges, Executive Director

Thomas F Carr and Associates, Inc 508.650.1811
Fax 508.650.3621
Web ....www.thomascarrlmft.com
E-mail ....tfcarrlmft@aol.com
9 Kinsman Pl, Natick, MA 01760-2732
Thomas F. Carr, President

Trauma Ctr 617.232.1303
Fax 617.232.1280
Web ....www.traumacenter.org
E-mail ....tc_officemanager@traumacenter.org
1269 Beacon St Ste 1, Brookline, MA 02446-5248
Joseph Spinazzola, Executive Director

CRISIS & SHELTER CARE

Alternative House - Domestic Violence 978.937.5777
Fax 978.937.5595
Web ....www.atask.org
E-mail ....altorg1@aol.com
517 Moody St Fl 2, Lowell, MA 01854-4014
Kathy Kelly, Director

Boston Area Rape Crisis Ctr 617.492.8306
Fax 617.492.3291
Web ....www.barcc.org
E-mail ....info@Barcc.Org
99 Bishop Richard Allen Dr, Cambridge,
MA 02139-3425
Gina Scaramella, Executive Director

Brookline Community Mental Health Ctr 617.277.8107
Fax 617.734.6385
Web ....www.brooklinecenter.org
43 Garrison Rd, Brookline, MA 02445-4498
Cynthia Price Dpa, Executive Director

Chauncy Hall Academy 508.898.3280
Fax 508.836.5512
Web ....www.nafi.com
E-mail ....mariatebeau@nafi.com
167 Lyman St, Westborough, MA 01581
Maria Tebeau, Program Director

Children Serv Of Rocksberry 617.445.6655
Fax 617.541.8178
520 Dudley St, Boston, MA 02119
Stepahanie Lewis, Office Manager

Cohannet Academy 508.977.3730
Fax 508.824.7528
Web ....www.jri.org
E-mail ....blary@jri.org
60 Hodges Ave, Ste 3, Taunton, MA 02780
Bryan Lary, Director

Crittenton Womens Union 617.782.7600
Fax 617.254.7966
Web ....www.liveworkthrive.org
10 Perthshire Rd, Brighton, MA 02135
Elizabeth Babcock, President/CEO

Ctr For Human Development 413.781.6556
Fax 413.781.6523
Web ....www.chd.org
E-mail ....jwilliams@chd.org
45 Willow St, Springfield, MA 01103
James Williams, Director

Dare Family Svcs 617.629.2710
Fax 617.629.2713
265 Medford St Ste 500, Somerville, MA 02143
Greg Mcdermott, Director

**Daybreak Resources For Women and
Children** 508.755.5371
Fax 508.767.1301
Web ....www.ywcaworcester.org
E-mail ....gnavickas@ywcaworcester.org
PO Box 3093, Worcester, MA 01613-3093
Ginger Navickas, Director

Dove Inc. - Domesctic Violence 617.770.4065
Fax 617.770.2206
1 Billings Rd Ste 1, Quincy, MA 02169
Sue Chandler, Director

Dove Inc. - Domestic Violence Program 617.471.5087
Fax 866.471.3210
PO Box 690267, Quincy, MA 02269-0267
Sue Chandler, Director

Elizabeth Freeman Ctr 413.499.2425
Fax 413.443.3016
Web ....www.berkshire.net
43 Francis Ave, Pittsfield, MA 01201-5053
Janis Rodriguez, Director

Emerson House 508.540.1554
Fax 508.540.3527
Web ....www.gosnold.org
E-mail ....ashepherd@gosnold.org
558 W Falmouth Hwy, Falmouth, MA 02540
Angela Shepherd, Director

Fall River Deaconess Home 508.674.4847
Fax 508.730.1167
E-mail ....jgolden@deaconesshome.org
603 Rock St, Fall River, MA 02720
John Golden, Director

**Finex House Inc. - Domestic Violence
Program** 617.436.0831
Fax 617.288.1923
Web ....www.geocities.com
E-mail ....finexhouse@yahoo.com
PO Box 300670, Jamaica Plain, MA 02130-0006
Chris Womendez, Director

Germaine Lawrence, Inc. 781.648.6200
Fax 781.646.9106
Web ....www.germainelawrence.org
E-mail ....dhowley@germainelawrence.org
18 Claremont Ave, Arlington, MA 02476-5898
Denise Howley, Edd, Licsw, Deputy Executive Director

Harbor Cove - Domestic Violence 617.884.9799
Fax 617.884.9929
E-mail ....Lynn@Harborcov.Org
PO Box 505754, Chelsea, MA 02150-5754
Lynn Peters, Co-Director

Henry Lee Willis Starting Point Program 508.754.3006
Fax 508.754.2971
Web ....www.willuscenter.org
25 Catharine St, Worcester, MA 01605-2709
Matthew Eppy, Director

Hope House at Cotting School 781.862.7323
Fax 781.861.1179
Web ....www.cotting.org
E-mail ....info@cotting.org
453 Concord Ave, Lexington, MA 02421-8088
David Manzo, Executive Director

Independence House 508.771.6507
Fax 508.778.0143
Web ....www.indhouse.net
E-mail ....ihrape@indhouse.net
160 Bassett Ln, Hyannis, MA 02601-3818
Lysetta Hurge-putnam, Director

Italian Home For Children 617.524.3116
Fax 617.983.5372
E-mail ....chris@italianhome.org
1125 Centre St, Jamaica Plain, MA 02130-3495
Christopher Small, Executive Director

Jeanne Geiger Crisis Ctr 978.465.0999
Fax 978.465.7158
Web ....www.jeannegeigercrisiscenter.org
E-mail ....scdubus@jeannegeigercrisiscenter.org
2 Harris St, Newburyport, MA 01950-2603
Suzanne Dubus, Director

L.U.K. Crisis Ctr Inc. 978.345.0685
Fax 978.345.3602
Web ....www.luk.org
E-mail ....luk@luk.org
545 Westminster St, Fitchburg, MA 01420
Jorbon Venson, CEO

Mcauley Nazareth Home For Boys 508.892.4886
Fax 508.892.9736
E-mail ....maz1901@arizon.net
77 Mulberry St, Leicester, MA 01524
Kim Pare, Executive Director

NELCWIT 413.772.0871
Fax 413.772.2743
E-mail ....info@nelcwit.org
479 Main St, Greenfield, MA 01301
Sarah Dudzic, Director

Rape Crisis Ctr of Central Massachusetts 508.852.7600
Fax 508.852.7870
Web ....www.rapecrisiscenter.org
588 Main St Ste 2, Worcester, MA 01608
Kym Dawkins, Director

Safe Passage 413.586.1125
Fax 413.586.3742
E-mail ....marianne@safepass.org
43 Center St Ste 304, Northampton, MA 01060-3062
Marianne Winters, Executive Director

St. Ann's Home 978.682.5276
Fax 978.688.4932
Web ....st.annshome.org
E-mail ....info@st.annshome.org
100A Haverhill St, Methuen, MA 18440
Denis Grandbois, Msw, Mba, Executive Director

The Second Step Inc - Domestic Violence 617.965.3999
Fax 617.965.3354
Web ....www.thesecondstep.org/
E-mail ....ekirsch@thesecondstep.org
PO Box 600213, Newtonville, MA 02460-0002
Elisabeth Kirsch, Director

Transition House 617.354.2676
Fax 617.497.4836
Web ....www.transitionhouse.org
649 Massachusetts Ave, Ste 6, Cambridge,
MA 02139-3360
Jasmin Khalfanie, Executive Director

Turning Point **978.388.6600**
Fax...978.388.8621
Web...............................www.casamyrna.org
E-mail...................jrobertson@turningpointinc.org
　276 Main St, Amesbury, MA 01913
Jeanne Robertson, Director

Voices Against Violence **508.820.0834**
Fax...508.872.4264
　300 Howard St, Framingham, MA 01702
Mary Gianakis, Director

Wayside Youth & Family Support Network **508.879.9800**
Fax...508.875.1348
Web...............................www.waysideyouth.org
E-mail...............................info@waysideyouth.org
　75 Fountain St, Framingham, MA 01702-6210
Eric L. Masi, CEO

YWCA - Domestic Violence **978.537.2306**
Fax...978.537.3502
Web...............................www.ywcacentralmass.org
E-mail...................scrombie@ywcacentralmass.org
　14 Monument Sq, Suite 401, Leominster, MA 01453
Sarah Crombie, Director

EDUCATION

Arlington School **617.855.2124**
Fax...617.855.2757
Web.................www.spedschools.com/schools/arlington
E-mail...................loughls@mcleanpo.mclean.org
　115 Mill St, Belmont, MA 02478
Suzanne Loughlin, Principal

Baird Ctr **508.224.8041**
Fax...508.224.5989
Web...............................www.thehome.org
E-mail...............................isuenine@thehome.org
　900 Ship Pond Rd, Plymouth, MA 02360-1849
Amani Suenine, Clinical Coordinator

Beacon High School **617.993.5100**
Fax...617.993.5101
Web...............................walkerschool.org/programs/htm
　917 Belmont St, Watertown, MA 02472
Pamela Travers, Director

Beverly School For The Deaf **978.927.7070**
Fax...978.927.6536
Web............www.thechildrencenterforcommunication.org
E-mail...................markcarlson@beverlyschoolforthedeaf.org
　6 Echo Ave, Beverly, MA 01915
Mark Carlson, Director

Boston Public Schools Counseling and Intervention
Ctr **617.635.8123**
Fax...617.635.8117
E-mail...................stephansquillante@boston.k12.ma.us
　515 Hyde Park Ave, Roslindale, MA 02131-3822
Stephan Squillante, Director

Cardinal Christian Ctrs **781.848.6250**
Fax...781.848.0640
Web...............................www.coletta.org
　85 Washington St, Braintree, MA 02184-1719
Patricia Larson, Ba, Msed, Executive Director

Cardinal Cushing Ctrs **781.826.6371**
Fax...781.826.1559
Web...............................coletta.org/cushingschool.html
E-mail...............................mbloom@coletta.org
　405 Washington St, Hanover, MA 02339
Michael Bloom, Executive Director

Carroll School; The **781.259.8342**
Fax...781.259.8852
Web...............................carrollschool.org
E-mail...............................admissions@carrollschool.org
　25 Baker Bridge Rd, Lincoln, MA 01773-3199
Steven Wilkins, Headmaster

Children's Study Home **413.739.5626**
Fax...413.732.5457
Web...............................www.studyhome.org
　44 Sherman St, Springfield, MA 01109-3517
Steve Mccafferty, Executive Director

Corwin-Russell School at Broccoli Hall; The
....**978.369.1444**
Fax...978.369.1026
Web...............................www.corwin-russell.org
E-mail...............................brochall@corwin-russell.org
　142 North Rd Ste Z, Sudbury, MA 01776-1142
Jane-elisabeth Jakuc, Med, Headmaster

Ctr For Audiological Svcs **413.582.1114**
Fax...413.587.0383
Web...............................www.clarkeschool.org
E-mail...............................info@clarkeschool.org
　45 Hill Road, Northampton, MA 01060
Karen Gjerdingen, Director

Educators For Social Responsibility **617.492.1764**
Fax...617.864.5164
Web...............................www.esrnational.org
E-mail...............................educators@esrnational.org
　23 Garden St, Cambridge, MA 02138
Larry Dieringer, Executive Director

Elizabeth Stone House **617.522.3659**
Fax...617.522.0968
Web...............................elizabethstonehouse.org
　PO Box 300039, Jamaica Plain, MA 02130-0001

Elm Park Ctr **508.752.1201**
Fax...508.798.7055
　284 Highland St, Worcester, MA 01602-2130
Janet Mckeag, Director

High Road School of Massachusetts **508.584.0074**
Fax...508.584.3164
　450 Pleasant St, East Bridgewater, MA 02333-1349
Anthony Clancy, Director

Horace Mann School For The Deaf & Hard of
Hearing **617.635.8534**
Fax...617.635.6379
Web...............................mann.boston.k12.ma.us
　40 Armington St, Allston, MA 02134-2404
Joan Corran, ETS

Institute For Learning and Development **781.861.3711**
Fax...781.861.3701
Web...............................www.ildlex.org
E-mail...............................broditi@ildlex.org
　4 Militia Dr, Lexington, MA 02421-3106
Bethany Roditi, Med, Phd, Director Of Education

Learning Prep School **617.965.0764**
Fax...617.527.1514
Web...............................www.learningprep.org
　1507 Washington St, West Newton, MA 02465-2219
John Foster, Interim Director

Lighthouse School **978.251.4050**
Fax...978.251.8950
Web...............................www.lighthouseschool.org
E-mail...............................michaelp@lighthouseschool.org
　25 Wellman Ave, North Chelmsford, MA 01863-1361
Michael Pappafagos, Director

Linden Hill School **413.498.2906**
Fax...413.498.2908
Web...............................www.lindenhs.org
E-mail...............................office@lindenhs.org
　154 S Mountain Rd, Northfield, MA 01360-9701
James Mcdaniel, Headmaster

MAB Community Svcs **508.854.0700**
Fax...508.854.0733
Web...............................www.mabcommunity.org
E-mail...............................bsalisbury@mablind.org
　799 W Boylston St Ste 7, Worcester, MA 01606-3071
Barbara Salisbury, Executive Director

Massachusetts Assoc of 766 Approved Private
Schools **781.245.1220**
Fax...781.245.5294
Web...............................www.maaps.org
E-mail...............................info@maaps.org
　607 North Ave, 15 LAKESIDE OFFICE PARK, Wakefield,
　MA 01880
James Major, Executive Director

Parent/Child Home Program **617.969.5906**
Fax...617.964.3975
Web...............................www.ncscweb.org
E-mail...............................dbrush@ncscweb.org
　492 Waltham St, West Newton, MA 02465-1920
Debbie Brush, Director

Perkins School For The Blind **617.924.3434**
Web...............................www.perkins.org
　175 N Beacon St, Watertown, MA 02472-2790
Steven Rothstein, President

Protestant Guild Learning Ctr **781.893.6000**
Fax...781.893.1171
Web...............................www.protestantguild.org
　411 Waverley Oaks Rd Ste 104, Waltham,
　MA 02452-8449
Thomas Belski, Executive Director

Riverview School **508.888.0489**
Fax...508.833.7001
Web...............................www.riverviewschool.org
　551 Route 6A, East Sandwich, MA 02537-1494
Maureen Brenner, Head Of School

Shriver Job Corps Ctr **978.772.7933**
Fax...978.784.2721
Web...............................www.shriverjcc.org
　270 Jackson Rd, Devens, MA 01434
Tscherina Telesford, Center Director

Southeast Alternative School at Berkeley **508.822.7728**
Fax...508.824.2083
E-mail...............................jbonin@communitycareservices.org
　132 S Main St, Berkley, MA 02779-2000
John Bonin, MED, Director

The Academy at Swift River **800.258.1770**
Fax...413.634.5300
Web...............................www.swiftriver.com
E-mail...............................admissions@swiftriver.com
　151 South St, Cummington, MA 01026
Rhonda Paplo, Director Of Admissions

Walden School **508.626.8581**
Fax...508.875.8080
Web...............................www.tlcdeaf.org
　848 Central St, Framingham, MA 01701-4880
Judy Vreeland, Ma, Executive Director

Walker Home and School **781.449.4500**
Fax...781.444.2268
Web...............................www.walkerschool.org
E-mail...............................rsmall@walkerschool.org
　1968 Central Ave, Needham, MA 02492-1499
Richard Small, Phd, Executive Director

Westover Job Corps Ctr **413.593.5731**
Fax...413.593.4091
Web...............................www.jobcorps.org
　103 Johnson Rd, Chicopee, MA 01022-1067
Cunesha Sanders, Center Director

White Oak School **413.562.9500**
Fax...413.562.9010
Web...............................www.whiteoakschool.org
E-mail...............................ddrake@whiteoakschool.org
　533 North Rd, Westfield, MA 01085-9774
David Drake, Headmaster

Whittier Sweet Health Ctr **617.427.1000**
Fax...617.989.3006
Web...............................www.biat.org
　1125 Tremont St, Boston, MA 02120
Everen Hernandez, Director Of Operations

Willie Ross School For The Deaf 413.567.0374
Fax 413.567.8808
Web ....www.willierossschool.org
E-mail ....williersd@aol.com
  32 Norway St, Longmeadow, MA 01106
  Louis E Abbate, Ed.d, CEO

FOSTER CARE AGENCIES

Adoption Assoc (Counseling & Therapy) 617.965.9369
E-mail ....AdoptionAssociates@yahoo.com
  1163 Walnut St, Ste 2, Newton Highlands,
  MA 02461

Adoption Resources 317.332.2218
Fax 781.487.6719
E-mail ....info@adoptionresources.or@gmail.com
  1430 Main St, Waltham, MA 02451

AdoptionLink Jewish Family Svcs of Great 413.746.2027
Fax 413.746.2024
E-mail ....info@jfswm.org
  15 Lenox St, Springfield, MA 01108
  Robert Marmor, Executive Director

Adoptive Families Together/MSPCC 617.587.1554
E-mail ....pbrady@mspcc.org
  99 Summer St, Boston, MA 02210

Adptn Educ & Support@First Connections 978.287.0221
Fax 978.371.1463
E-mail ....mrowlinson@jri.org
  111 Old Rd to 9 Acre Cor, Concord, MA 01742
  Mary Rowlinson, Adoptions Support Specialist

ARed Thread Adoption Services Inc 781.762.2428
Fax 781.634.5511
E-mail ....redthreadadopt@aol.com
  681 Washington St, Ste 12, Norwood, MA 02062
  Leah O'Leary, Executive Director

Catholic Social Svcs of Fall River Inc 508.674.4681
Fax 508.675.2224
E-mail ....eca@cssdioc.org
  1600 Bay St, PO Box M South Station, Fall River,
  MA 02724
  Aileen Mcnamee, Executive Director

Child & Family Services Inc 508.676.5708
Fax 508.676.1948
  66 Troy St, Fall River, MA 02720

Communities for People Inc 617.628.0415
Fax 617.572.3611
  418 Commonwealth Ave, Boston, MA 02215

Devereux Therapeutic Foster 413.734.2493
Fax 413.734.2495
Web ....www.devereux.org
  425 Union St Ste 119, West Springfield,
  MA 01089-3485
  David Schulteis, Executive Director

Families for Russian & Ukrainian Adptns 978.368.1966
E-mail ....info@fruanewengland.org
  669 Main St, Lancaster, MA 01523

Family Center Pre & Post Adoption 617.628.8815
E-mail ....info@thefamilycenterinc.org
  366 Somerville Ave, Somerville, MA 02143
  Thomas Haynes, Chief Executive Officer

Massachusetts Foster & Adoptive Parent 617.587.1666
  99 Summer St, Boston, MA 02110
  Cheryl Haddad

Raising Our Children's Children 617.541.3561
E-mail ....hjorocc@aol.com
  89 Ruthvn St, Dorchester, MA 02121
  Harriet Jackson-Lyons, Director

Supply Sacks Inc & Furthering Foster 508.350.9811
E-mail ....info@supplysacks.org
  100 Lorraine Dr, East Bridgewater, MA 02333

Valerie Arsenault 978.689.3677
  59 Lyndale Ave, Methuen, MA 01844

HOME MEDICAL EQUIPMENT PROVIDERS

Charm Medical Supply 781.829.9813
Fax 781.829.9836
E-mail ....support@charmmedicalsupply.com
  880 Corporate Park Dr, Pembroke, MA 02359

Mobility Transfer Systems Inc 888.854.4687
E-mail ....thomas@aol.com
  34 Sullivan Rd Unit 32, North Billerica, MA 01862
  Thomas Leoutsakos, Owner

Queset Medical 800.728.8230
  20 Roche Brothers Way, Ste 6-395, North Easton,
  MA 02356
  Andy Shyne, Supervisor

PEDIATRIC HOME CARE

Bayada Nurses 508.830.3904
Fax 508.830.3909
Web ....www.bayada.com
E-mail ....chinds@bayada.com
  385 Court Street, Suite 210, Plymouth, MA 02360
  Connie Hinds, Director

Bayada Nurses 508.540.0071
Fax 508.540.4020
Web ....www.bayada.com
  80 Davis Straits, Building A, Unit 103, Falmouth,
  MA 02540
  Kim Moran, Director

Bayada Nurses 508.830.0999
Fax 508.830.0943
Web ....www.bayada.com
  20 N Park Ave Ste1300, Lower Level, Plymouth,
  MA 02360
  Sandra McLaughlin, Director

Bayada Nurses 617.773.0012
Fax 617.773.0085
Web ....www.bayada.com
E-mail ....MGERRATY@BAYADA.COM
  40 Willard Street, Suite 201, Quincy, MA 02169
  Andrea Langone, Director

Bayada Nurses 617.472.1333
Fax 617.472.0033
Web ....www.bayada.com
E-mail ....dpeterson@bayada.com
  300 Congress Street, Unit 401B, Quincy, MA 02169
  Diane Peterson, Director

Bayada Nurses 508.778.8100
Fax 508.778.5022
Web ....www.bayada.com
E-mail ....staylor@bayada.com
  750 Attucks Ln, Hyannis, MA 02601
  Sandra Taylor, Director

Brockton PDN (Boston) 508.586.9700
E-mail ....dfletcher@psakids.com
  20 Minuteman Way Ste 2, Brockton, MA 02301
  Dorothy Fletcher, Director

Centrus Premier Homecare 978.658.3092
Fax 978.658.4138
Web ....www.centrushomecare.com
E-mail ....nitaylor@maxhealth.com
  226 Lowell St. Suite A3, Wilmington, MA 01887
  Nicole Taylor, Accounts Manager

Interim Healthcare 413.734.6900
Fax 413.730.4282
  442 Westfield St, West Springfield, MA 01089
  Linda Schoenborn, Owner

Interim Healthcare 413.551.7116
Fax 413.551.7128
  31A Church St, Lenox, MA 01240
  Kira Bart, Office Manager

Interim Healthcare 508.771.4117
Fax 508.771.8312
  310 Barnstable Rd Ste 204, Hyannis, MA 02601

Interim Healthcare 508.792.5900
Fax 508.754.5167
  65 James St Ste 201, Worcester, MA 01603

Interim Hlthcare (Danvers Support Svcs) 978.777.9090
Fax 978.777.5520
  72 Atlantic Pl S, South Paotland, MA 04106
  Kristine Rogers, Director

Shrewsbury 508.842.5809
  415 Boston Turnpike Ste 211, Shrewsbury,
  MA 01545
  Dorothy Fletcher, Director

SOCIAL SERVICES

A Woman's Concern 781.284.8747
Fax 781.286.1430
Web ....www.awomansconcern.org
E-mail ....karen@awomansconcern.org
  103 Broadway, Revere, MA 02151-5302
  Karen Cox, Administrator

Adoption Options 800.337.6513
E-mail ....betsy@jfsri.org
  959 Winthrop St, Rehoboth, MA 02769
  Kathy Alter, Director

Berkshire Children and Families 413.448.8281
Fax 413.445.5404
E-mail ....cburns@bcfcma.org
  480 West St, Pittsfield, MA 01201
  Carolyn Burns, Director

Birkshire Ctr For Families & Children 413.584.5690
Fax 413.586.9436
E-mail ....admin@cafshc.org
  220 Russell St, Ste 200, Hadley, MA 01035
  Carolyn Burns, Director

Brightside, Inc.
Web ....www.brightsidecares.com
  2112 Riverdale Street, West Springfield, MA 01089
  COA accredited organization.

Cambridge Family and Children's Svcs 617.876.4210
Fax 617.661.9749
Web ....www.helpfamilies.org
E-mail ....adoption@helpfamilies.org
  60 Gore St, Cambridge, MA 02141
  Denise Maguire, Director

Catholic Charities 413.452.0605
Fax 413.452.0647
Web ....www.diospringfield.org
E-mail ....k.brawner@diospringfield.org
  65 Elliot St, Springfield, MA 01105
  Katherine Bukley-Brawner, Director

Catholic Charity Home Care 508.798.0191
Fax 508.797.5659
Web ....www.ccworc.org
E-mail ....info@ccworc.org
  10 Hammond St, Worcester, MA 01610-1513
  Catherine Loeffler, Executive Director

Child and Family Services, Inc. 508.996.8572
Fax 508.991.8618
Web ....www.child-familyservices.org
  1061 Pleasant Street, New Bedford, MA 02740
  COA accredited organization.

Child Care Choices 617.348.6677
Fax 617.292.4629
Web ....www.childcarechoicesofboston.org
E-mail ....help@bostonabcd.org
  105 Chauncy St Ste 701, 2nd flr, Boston, MA 02111
  Anne Corbin, Director

Child Care Circuit 978.686.4288
Fax 978.927.8083
  190 Hampshire St, Lawrence, MA 01840
  Lois Delorin, Site Director

Massachusetts

Child Care Connection **508.757.1503**
Fax 508.791.4755
Web ....www.cccfscm.org
E-mail ....jgrabell@cccfscm.org
   31 harbard st, Worcester, MA 01609
   Joanne Grabell, Director

Children's Trust Fund **617.727.8957**
Fax 617.727.8997
Web ....www.mctf.org
E-mail ....sbartley@mctf.state.ma.us
   55 Court St Fl 4, Boston, MA 02108-2104
   Suzin Bartley, Executive Director

Community Care For Kids **617.471.6473**
Fax 617.773.5860
Web ....www.semaccrr.org/ccfk/
E-mail ....ereedy@qcap.org
   1509 Hancock St, Quincy, MA 02169
   Lisa Breagy, Program Director

Community Care Services **508.821.7777**
Fax 508.822.2601
Web ....www.communitycareservices.org
E-mail ....tfisher@communitycareservices.org
   70 Main St, Taunton, MA 02780-2778
   Tom Fisher, CEO

Concilo Hispano De Cambridge **617.661.9406**
Fax 617.661.8008
Web ....www.concilohispano.org
E-mail ....jvega@centrolatino.org
   105 Windsor St, Cambridge, MA 02139-3606
   Juan Vegas, Director

Ctr For Family Connections **617.547.0909**
Fax 617.497.5952
Web ....www.kinnect.org
E-mail ....cffc@kinnect.org
   350 Cambridge St, Cambridge, MA 02141-1204
   Joyce Maguire Pavao, Director

**Emerson College - Robbins Speech, Language and Hearing
Ctr** **617.824.8307**
Fax 617.824.8733
Web ....www.emerson.edu
E-mail ....betsy_micucci@emerson.edu
   216 Tremont, Boston, MA 02116
   Betsy Micucci,MA, CCC-SLP, Clinical Director

Family Service, Inc. **978.683.9505**
Fax 978.683.1026
Web ....www.familyserviceinc.com
   430 North Canal Street, Lawrence, MA 01840
   COA accredited organization.

Henry Lee Willis Community Center, Inc. **508.799.0702**
Fax 508.754.0245
Web ....www.williscenter.org
   119 Forest Street, Worcester, MA 01609
   COA accredited organization.

Home Health and Child Care Svcs, Inc. **508.588.6070**
Fax 508.587.3560
Web ....www.hhcc.org
E-mail ....nchiappini@hhcc.org
   15 Jonathan Dr, Brockton, MA 02301
   Nancy Chiappini, Executive Director

**Jewish Family & Childrens Services
Greater** **781.647.5327**
Fax 781.487.6722
E-mail ....info@jfcsboston.org
   Boston Headquarters, 1430 Main St, Waltham,
   MA 02451
   Seymour Friedland, Manager

Jewish Family and Children's Service, Inc. **617.332.2218**
Fax 781.487.6719
Web
............www.adoptionresources.org;www.jfcsboston.org
   1430 Main Street, Waltham, MA 02451
   COA accredited organization.

**Jewish Family Service of the North Shore
Inc** **978.741.7878**
Fax 978.741.8383
E-mail ....info@jfsns.org
   2 East India Square Mall,Ste 200, Salem, MA 01970
   Pam Arseneau, Director

Jewish Family Service of Worcester Inc **508.755.3101**
Fax 508.755.7460
E-mail ....info@jfsworcester.org
   646 Salisbury St, Worcester, MA 01609
   Stephen Slaten, Director

Jewish Family Svc of Metrowest **508.875.3100**
Fax 508.875.4373
Web ....www.jfsmw.org
E-mail ....villageatgordonhouse@verizon.net
   475 Franklin St Ste 101, Framingham,
   MA 01702-6236
   Marc Jacobs, Director

Jewish Family Svcs Inc **413.737.2601**
Fax 413.737.0323
Web ....www.jfswm.org
E-mail ....r.marmor@jfswm.org
   15 Lenox St, Springfield, MA 01108
   Robert Marmor, Executive Director

**Jewish Federation of Greater New
Bedford** **508.997.7471**
Fax 508.997.7730
E-mail ....office@newbedford.org
   467 Hawthorn St, North Dartmouth, MA 02747
   Olea Yorish, Executive Director

Lutheran Community Svcs **508.791.4488**
Fax 508.753.8051
Web ....www.adoptlcs.org
   20 Hamilton St, Worcester, MA 01604-2202
   Julia Nguyen, Director

Massachusetts Citizens For Children **617.742.8555**
Web ....www.masskids.org
E-mail ....info@masskids.org
   14 Beacon St Ste 706, Boston, MA 02108-3732
   Emily Hayes, Office Manager

New England Farm Workers' Council **413.272.2200**
Fax 413.731.5399
Web ....www.partnersforcommunity.org
E-mail ......brenda_montgomery@partnersforcommunity.org
   1628-1640 Main St, Springfield, MA 01103
   Brenda Montgomery, Director

Our Sister's Place, Inc. **508.677.0224**
Fax 508.677.2286
E-mail ....oursistersplace@comcast.net
   PO Box 4236, Fall River, MA 02723-0413
   Alice Costa, Director

Pace Child Care Works **508.999.9930**
Fax 508.984.3559
Web ....www.paceccw.org
E-mail ....pamrkuech@paceccw.org
   105 William St Fl 4, New Bedford, MA 02740
   Pam Kuechler, Director

Portland Street Branch **617.227.6641**
Fax 617.227.1190
E-mail ....lhenderson@jsdsboston.org
   174 Portland St, Boston, MA 02114
   Lesley Henderson, Office Manager

Preschool Enrichment Team **413.736.3900**
Fax 413.734.6848
Web ....www.preschoolenrichmentteam.org
E-mail ....info@preschoolenrichmentteam.org
   293 Bridge St Ste 322, Springfield, MA 01103-1492
   Vicki Van Zee, Executive Director

Project Adventure **978.524.4500**
Fax 978.524.4505
Web ....www.pa.org
   719 cabot st, Beverley, MA 01915
   Dick Prouty, Director

Reed Academy **508.877.1222**
Fax 508.877.7477
E-mail ....reed.academy@verizon.net
   1 Winch St, Framingham, MA 01701-3737
   Edward Cohen, EDD, Special Education Administrator

**Robert F. Kennedy Children's Action Corps Lancaster
School** **978.365.2803**
Fax 978.368.3066
Web ....www.rfkchildren.org
   220 Old Common Rd, Lancaster, MA 01523
   Valerie Paen, Principal

St. Vincent's Home Corp **508.679.8511**
Fax 508.672.2558
Web ....www.stvincentshome.org
E-mail ....jweldon@stvincentshome.org
   2425 Highland Ave, Fall River, MA 02720-4598
   Jack Weldon, Director
   COA accredited organization.

Teen Empowerment Inc. **617.536.4266**
Fax 617.536.4311
Web ....www.teenempowerment.org
E-mail ....stanley@teenempowerment.org
   48 Rutland St, Flr 4, Boston, MA 02118
   Stanley Pollack, Executive Director

**Temporary Home For Women and
Children** **617.720.3611**
Fax 617.723.7486
   41 New Chardon St, Boston, MA 02114-4795
   Pam Fortes, Shelter Director

**The George H. & Irene L. Walker Home for Children,
Inc.** **781.449.4500**
Fax 781.449.5717
Web ....www.walkerschool.org
   1968 Central Avenue, Needham, MA 02492
   COA accredited organization.

The Home for Little Wanderers **617.267.3700**
Fax 617.267.8142
Web ....www.thehome.org
   271 Huntington Avenue, Boston, MA 02115
   COA accredited organization.

The Key Program **508.877.3690**
Fax 508.366.9524
Web ....www.key.org
   670 Old Connecticut Path, Framingham, MA 01701
   William Lyttle, President

The Learning Center for the Deaf **508.879.5110**
Fax 508.875.3355
Web ....www.tlcdeaf.org
   848 Central Street, Framingham, MA 01701
   COA accredited organization.

**University of MA Amherst - Ctr For Language, Speech &
Hearing** **413.545.2565**
Fax 413.545.0803
Web ....www.umass.edu/sphhs/centers/speech
E-mail ....baran@comdis.umass.edu
   358 N Pleasant St, Amherst, MA 01003-9296
   Jane Baran, Phd, Department Director

Warmlines/Freedman Center at MSPP **617.244.4636**
Fax 617.244.1072
Web ....www.warmlines.org
E-mail ....info@warmlines.org
   225 Nevada St, Newtonville, MA 02460-1212
   Elizabeth Basnight, Director

**Wayside Youth & Family Support Network,
Inc.** **508.879.9800**
Fax 508.875.1348
Web ....www.waysideyouth.org
   1 Frederick Abbott Way, Framingham, MA 01701
   COA accredited organization.

Youth Opportunities Upheld, Inc.............508.849.5600
Fax..508.849.5617
Web..www.youinc.org
   81 Plantation Street, Worcester, MA 01604
   COA accredited organization.

SPECIAL NEEDS

Asperger's Association.....................617.393.3824
E-mail...info@aane.org
   85 Main St Ste 101, Watertown, MA 02472

Associated Advocacy Center................888.420.4356
E-mail...tonisvision@aol.com
   24 Widow Coombs Walk, Sandwich, MA 02563

Asthma & Allergy Foundation............781.444.7778
Fax..781.444.7718
Web...................................www.asthmaandallergies.org
E-mail..aafane@aafane.org
   109 Highland Ave, Neeham, MA 02494
   Elain Erenrich Rosenburg, Executive Director

Autism Society of America....................781.237.0272
E-mail........................asamasschapter@hotmail.com
   47 Walnut St, Wellesley Hills, MA 02481
   Joel Smith, Executive Director

Autism Speaks..................................617.924.3300
Fax..617.924.3311
Web...www.autismspeaks.org
E-mail.....................................newengland@naar.org
   11 Mount Euburn St, Ste 1, Watertown, MA 02472
   Amy McEvoy, Manager

Berkshire Hills Music Academy.............413.540.9720
Fax..413.534.3875
Web..www.berkshirehills.org
   48 Woodbridge St, South Hadley, MA 01075
   Ljuba Marsh, Manager

Boston Higashi School........................781.961.0800
Fax..781.961.0888
Web..www.bostonhigashi.org
   800 N Main St, Randolph, MA 02368
   Michael L Kelly, Executive Director

Brain Injury Association.....................508.475.0032
E-mail...biama@biama.org
   30 Lyman St Ste 10, Westborough, MA 01581
   Arlene Korae, Director

Catholic Charities of Mercy Centre.........508.852.7165
Fax..508.856.9755
Web..www.mercycentre.com
   25 W Chester St, Worcester, MA 01605
   Doreen Donovan-Barbara, Manager

Commonwealth Learning Center...........800.461.6671
Fax..781.444.6916
E-mail.....................................info@commlearn.com
   220 Reservoir St, Ste 6, Needham Heights, MA 02494

Commonwealth Learning Center...........978.774.0094
Fax..978.774.1169
E-mail.....................................info@commlearn.com
   130 Sylvan St, Danvers, MA 01923

Community Rehab Care, Inc..................617.244.8480
Fax..617.244.8312
Web..................................www.brain-injury-rehab.com
   305 Centre Street, Newton, MA 02458
   CARF accredited programs available.

Community Resources For People With
Autism...413.529.2428
Fax..413.529.2567
Web................www.communityresearchforautism.org
   116 Pleasant St Ste 366, Easthampton,
   MA 01027-1333
   David Specht, Director

Dearborn Academy...........................781.641.5992
Fax..781.641.5997
Web..www.dearbornacademy.org
   34 Winter St, Arlington, MA 02474
   Howard Rossman, Director

Devereux Massachusetts.....................508.886.4746
Fax..508.886.4773
Web..www.devereuxma.org
   60 Miles Rd, Rutland, MA 01543
   Stephen Yerdon, Director

Easter Seals.....................................800.244.2756
E-mail..easterseals@ma.org
   484 Main St, Worcester, MA 01608
   Adam Shuster, Chief Executive Officer

Epilepsy Foundation..........................617.506.6041
E-mail......................................info@efmarinhme.org
   540 Gallivan Blvd 2nd Fl, Dorchester, MA 02124
   Susan Welby, Program Director

Evergreen Center...............................508.478.2631
Fax..508.634.3251
Web..www.evergreenctr.org
   345 Fortune Blvd, Milford, MA 01757
   Robert F Littleton, Director

Families Organizing for Change.............800.406.3632
E-mail..mfofc@comcast.net
   PO Box 61, Raynham Center, MA 02768

Family TIES of Massachusetts...............781.774.6736
E-mail.......................................mcsummers@fcsn.org
   5 Randolph St, Donovan Health Bldg 3rd Fl, Canton,
   MA 02021
   Mary Summers, Director

Federation for Children W/Special Needs......617.236.7210
Fax..617.572.2094
E-mail...fcsninfo@fcsn.org
   1135 Tremont St Ste 420, Boston, MA 02120
   Rich Robison, Executive Director

Federation for Children with Special Nds......617.482.2915
Fax..617.695.2939
E-mail...fcsninfo@fcsn.org
   95 Berkeley St Ste 104, Boston, MA 02116

Five Star Rehabilitation and Wellness
Services...617.796.8162
Fax..617.796.8291
   400 Centre Street, Newton, MA 02458
   CARF accredited programs available.

Frederic L Chamberlain School..............508.947.7825
Fax..508.947.0944
Web..www.chamberlainschool.org
   1 Pleasant St, Middleboro, MA 02346
   Rhonda Seifert, Administrative Assistant

Greater Boston Arc............................617.783.3900
E-mail...tangelone@arcgb.org
   221 N Beacon St 2nd Fl, Boston, MA 02135

Home Modifications Loan Program..........800.245.6543
E-mail.............................charles.carr@mrc.state.ma.us
   27 Wormwood St, Boston, MA 02210
   Charles Carr, Commissioner

James F Farr Academy.........................617.492.4922
Fax..617.547.8301
Web..www.farracademy.org
E-mail...farr@farracademy.org
   71 Pearl St, Cambridge, MA 02139
   Christy Pappas, Director

Kolburne School................................413.229.8787
Fax..413.229.7708
Web...www.kolburne.net
   343 NW Southfield Rd, Great Barrington, MA 01230
   Jeane K Weinstein

Landmark School...............................978.236.3000
Fax..978.927.7268
E-mail.............................admission@landmarkschool.org
   PO Box 227, Prides Crossing, MA 01965
   Robert Broeudo, President

Latham Centers, Inc............................508.896.5776
Fax..508.896.8310
Web..www.lathamcenters.org
   1646 Route 6A, Main Street, Brewster, MA 02631
   COA accredited organization.

Lindamood-Bell Learning Processes..........781.659.7722
Fax..781.659.2445
   515 Washington St, Norwell, MA 02061
   Christina Seremetis, Director

Lindamood-Bell Learning Processes..........781.643.4567
Fax..781.643.4581
E-mail.........................boston.center@lindamoodbell.com
   4 Water St, Arlington, MA 02476
   Julie Bugdanski, Director

MAPVI..978.897.3005
E-mail.............................judywestgate@comcast.net
   22 Old Marlboro Rd, Maynard, MA 01754

Massachusetts Down Syndrome Congress.....800.664.6372
E-mail...mdsc@mdsc.org
   PO Box 866, Melrose, MA 02176

Massachusetts General Hospital.............617.724.1873
Fax..617.726.5346
E-mail.................................mcudkowicz @partners.org
   CNY Bldg 149 Rm 2274, Charlestown, MA 02129
   Merit E Cudkowicz MD, Director

Massachusetts General Hospital.............617.726.2664
   55 Fruit St, Yawkey Ctr Ste 6B, Boston, MA 02114
   Tanuja Chitnis, Md Center Director

Massachusetts PTA.............................508.347.7055
E-mail...info@masspta.org
   PO Box 421, Rehoboth, MA 02769

Massasoit School...............................781.380.3917
Fax..781.849.8445
Web...www.massasoit.org
   6 Columbian St, Braintree, MA 02184
   Jim Bertram

NAMI Massachusetts..........................800.370.9085
E-mail.........................cindynelson@namimass.org
   400 W Cummings Park Ste 6650, Woburn,
   MA 01801
   Cindy Nelson, Manager

National Multiple Sclerosis Society..........781.890.4990
Fax..781.890.2089
E-mail.........................communications@mam.nmss.org
   101A 1st Ave Ste 6, Waltham, MA 02451

New England Index.............................800.642.0249
E-mail......................................info@disabilityinfo.org
   200 Trapelo Rd, Waltham, MA 02452
   Robert Bass, Director

Parent/Professional Advocacy League........866.815.8122
E-mail...info@ppal.net
   45 Bromfield St 10th Fl, Boston, MA 02108
   Lisa Lambert, President

Radius Pediatric Day School at Plymouth......508.746.4343
Fax..508.747.2853
   123 South St, Plymouth, MA 02360
   Matthew Muratore, Director

Riverview School...............................508.888.0489
Fax..508.833.7001
Web..www.riverviewschool.org
   551 Route 6A, East Sandwich, MA 02537
   Jeanne Pacheco, Director Of Admissions

Schwartz Center for Children.................508.996.3391
Fax..508.996.3397
Web..www.schwartzcenter.org
   One Posa Place, Dartmouth, MA 02747
   Kim Wilmot, Clinical Director
   CARF accredited programs available.

Seven Hills Academy...........................508.755.2340
Fax..508.849.3882
Web...www.sevenhills.org
   81 Hope Ave, Worcester, MA 01603
   Kathrine Cleary, Vice President

Spaulding Rehabilitation Hospital...........617.573.2510
Fax..617.573.2442
Web..www.spauldingrehab.org
   125 Nashua Street, Boston, MA 02114
   CARF accredited programs available.

© 2011 Dorland Health

Spina Bifida Association **888.479.1900**
E-mail ....bpackard@sbamass.org
  733 Turnpike St # 282, North Andover, MA 01845

Statewide Head Injury Program **617.204.3852**
E-mail ....shipu@mrc.state.ma.us
  27 Wormwood St, Fort Point Pl Ste 600, Boston, MA 02210
  Debra Kamen, Director

The Arc **888.343.3301**
E-mail ....mandrade@arcnbc.org
  141 Park St, Attleboro, MA 02703

The Arc of Massachusetts **781.891.6270**
E-mail ....arcmass@arcmass.org
  217 South St, Waltham, MA 02453
  Leo Sarkissian, Chief Executive Officer

**The Doug Flutie, Jr Foundation For
Autism** **508.270.8855**
Fax 508.270.6868
Web ....www.dougflutiejrfoundation.org
E-mail ....info@dougflutiejrfoundation.org
  615 Concord St Ste 7, Framingham, MA 01702-8066
  Douglas Flutie, President And Co-Founder

Tourette Syndrome Association **617.277.7589**
E-mail ....dmerickson84@aol.com
  PO Box 653, Marstons Mills, MA 02648

United Cerebral Palsy **617.926.5480**
E-mail ....ucpboston@ucpboston.org
  71 Arsenal St, Watertown, MA 02472

Urban PRIDE **617.206.4570**
Fax 617.206.4575
E-mail ....c.spinkston@urbanpride.org
  15 N Beacon St Ste NR-2B, Allston, MA 02134
  Charlotte Spinkston, Director

Urban Pride **617.989.3929**
E-mail ....info@urbanpride.org
  184 Dudley St Ste 104LL, Roxbury, MA 02119

VSA Arts of Massachusetts **617.350.7713**
E-mail ....cjwashburn@vsamass.org
  2 Boylston St 2nd Fl, Boston, MA 02116

**Weldon Rehabilitation Hospital at Mercy Medical
Center** **413.748.6800**
Fax 413.748.6970
Web ....www.mercycares.com
  233 Carew Street, Springfield, MA 01104
  CARF accredited programs available.

Whittier Rehabilitation Hospital **978.372.8000**
Fax 978.374.4423
Web ....www.whittierhealth.com
  145 Ward Hill Avenue, Bradford, MA 01830
  CARF accredited programs available.

SUBSTANCE ABUSE TREATMENT

CAB Health and Recovery **978.968.1724**
Fax 978.531.8920
Web ....www.cabhealth.org
  Zero Centennial Drive, Peabody, MA 01960
  Daniel Mccullough, Medical Director
  CARF accredited programs available.

**Massachusetts Society For The Prevention of Cruelty To
Children** **508.775.0275**
Fax 508.790.3988
Web ....www.mspcc.org
E-mail ....estrawn@mspcc.org
  206 Breeds Hill Rd, Hyannis, MA 02601-1881
  Evelyn Strawn, Regional Director

**South Boston Action Ctr and ABCD South Boston Head Start
Ctr** **617.269.5160**
Fax 617.269.1743
  424 W Broadway, Boston, MA 02127
  Anna-jean Mcmahon, Director Head Start

Spectrum Health Systems, Inc. **508.792.5400**
Fax 508.831.0074
Web ....www.spectrumhealthsystems.org
  10 Mechanic Street, Suite 302, Worcester, MA 01608
  CARF accredited programs available.

Michigan

Rick Snyder, Governor
PO Box 30013
Lansing, MI 48909
517.373.3400
517.335.6863 (Fax)
www.michigan.gov/gov

Jeannette Scroggins, Federal Grants Unit Mgr
235 S. Grand Ave, Ste. 403
Lansing, MI 48909
517.335.3541
517.373.2799 (Fax)
Scrogginsj@michigan.gov

Jeriel Heard, SAG Chair
Wayne County Sheriff's Office
3501 Hamtramck Dr
Hamtramck, MI 48211
313.875.7010
313.875.7928 (Fax)
Jheard@co.wayne.mi.us

CRISIS NUMBERS

Child Abuse Reporting . . .517.373.2035

STATE SERVICES

SOCIAL SERVICES

Child Support **517.241.7460**
Fax 517.373.4980
Web . . . . .www.michigan.gov/dhs
E-mail . . . . .stephenm3@michigan.gov
235 S Grand Ave, Suite 1215, Lansing, MI 48933
Marilyn F Stephen, Director

Children's Svcs Admin **517.241.8606**
Fax 517.335.6177
Web . . . . .www.michigan.gov
E-mail . . . . .jamesh@michigan.gov
235 S Grand Avenue # 514, Lansing, MI 48933
Kate Hansley, Adoption Director

Michigan Dept of Human Svcs **313.456.1678**
Fax 313.456.1680
3038 W Grand Blvd, Ste 4-550, Detroit,
MI 48202-6038
Ken Pape, Aids Coordinator

Michigan Emergency Management and Homeland Security Div **517.336.6198**
Fax 517.333.4987
Web . . . . .www.michigan.gov/emd
4000 Collins Rd, Lansing, MI 48910
Thomas Sangs, Director

GENERAL HEALTH SERVICES

Assoc for Local Public Health **517.485.0660**
Fax 517.485.6412
Web . . . . .www.malph.org
E-mail . . . . .mrmalph@aol.com
426 S Walnut St Fl 1, Lansing, MI 48933-2039
Mark J. Bertler, Executive Director

Children with Special Health Needs **517.241.8207**
Fax 517.241.8970
Web . . . . .www.michigan.gov/mdch
320 S Walnut Fl 6, Lansing, MI 48913-0001
Laura Kach, Executive Secretary

Children's Special Health Care Svcs **517.335.8983**
Fax 517.335.9491
Web . . . . .www.michigan.gov/cshcs
E-mail . . . . .startr@michigan.gov
320 S Wallnut St, Lansing, MI 48913
Rebecca Start, Manager

Childrens Spec Health Care Srvs MI **517.241.7186**
Fax 517.241.8970
E-mail . . . . .cshcsfc@michigan.gov
320 S Walnut 6th Flr, Lansing, MI 48913

Mdch Bureau of Maternal, Family & Child Health **517.335.8928**
Fax 517.335.9032
E-mail . . . . .carra@michigan.gov
201 Townsend St Fl 6, Lansing, MI 48913
Alethia Carr, Director

Michigan Dept of Corrections - Bureau of Health Care Svcs **517.373.3629**
Fax 517.335.0871
Web . . . . .www.michigan.gov/corrections
206 E Michigan Ave, Lansing, MI 48933
Dr.clayton straseske, Psycologist

Ofc of Medicaid **517.241.7882**
Fax 517.335.5007
400 S Pine St, 7th Floor Capital Common Center, Lansing, MI 48913
Stephen Fitton, Deputy Director

WIC Div **517.335.8951**
Fax 517.335.8835
E-mail . . . . .biens@michigan.gov
320 S Walnut St Fl 6, Lansing, MI 48913
Stan Bien, Director

MENTAL HEALTH SERVICES

Dep Of Community Health **517.173.3500**
Fax 517.373.4288
Web . . . . .www.michigan.gov/mdch
E-mail . . . . .norris@michigan.gov
201 Townsend St, Capital VW, Lansing, MI 48913
Janet Olszewski, Director

Dept of Correction **517.335.0278**
Fax 517.241.2611
Web . . . . .www.michigan.gov/corrections
E-mail . . . . .patriciac@michigan.gov
206 E Michigan Ave, Lansing, MI 48933
Patricia Curoso, Director

Disability Determination Srv MI **517.241.8450**
Fax 517.373.3773
E-mail . . . . .theresa.wulbrecht@ssa.gov
PO Box 30011, Lansing, MI 48909
Theresa Wulbrecht, Director

MDCH Mental Health Programs **517.335.0196**
Fax 517.335.4798
Web . . . . .www.michigan.gov/mdch
E-mail . . . . .kellyc@michigan.gov
320 S Walnut St, Lewis Cass Bldg, Lansing, MI 48913-0001
Cynthia Kelly, Interim Director

Michigan Commission for the Blind **517.373.2062**
Fax 517.335.5140
E-mail . . . . .jonesl@michigan.gov
201 N Washington Sq 2nd Flr, Lansing, MI 48909
L Jones, Director

Rehabilitation Services MI **517.335.0399**
Fax 517.335.7277
E-mail . . . . .shamsiddeenj@michigan.gov
201 N Washington Sq, PO Box 30010, Lansing, MI 48909
J Shamsiddeen, Director

JUSTICE AGENCY

Correctional Education Division MI **517.335.1388**
Fax 517.241.9717
E-mail . . . . .derosejl@michigan.gov
5656 S Cedar St Ste 100, Lansing, MI 48911

Michigan Crime Victim Svcs Commission **517.373.7373**
Fax 517.334.9462
Web . . . . .www.michigan.gov\crimevictim
E-mail . . . . .mccurcisjames@michigan.gov
320 S Walnut St, Lansing, MI 48913-0001
James McCurcis, Director

Michigan Dept of Corrections **517.373.0720**
Fax 517.373.6883
Web . . . . .www.michigan.gov/corrections
206 E Michigan Ave, Grandview Plaza, Lansing, MI 48933-1431
Dan Haynes, Director

COURTS

Attorney General's Ofc **517.373.1110**
Fax 517.373.3042
Web . . . . .www.michigan.gov/ag
E-mail . . . . .miag@michigan.gov
525 W Ottawa St, Lansing, MI 48933-1067
Bill Schuette, Attorney General

State Court Administrative Ofc **517.373.0130**
Fax 517.373.7517
Web . . . . .www.courts.mi.gov
925 W Ottawa St, Lansing, MI 48909
Chad Schmucker, Administrator

Michigan

POLICE AND SHERIFF

Michigan Assoc of Chiefs of Police **517.349.9420**
Fax 517.349.5823
Web . . . . .www.michiganpolicechiefs.org
2133 University Park Dr Ste 200, Okemos,
MI 48864-5909
Thomas A. Hendrickson, Executive Director

Michigan State Sheriff's Assoc **517.485.3135**
Fax 517.485.1013
Web . . . . .www.misheriff.org
E-mail . . . . .discover@misheriff.org
515 N Capitol Ave, Lansing, MI 48933-1209
Terrence L. Jungel, Executive Director

EDUCATION SERVICES

Educ for Homeless Children and Youth MI **517.241.1162**
Fax 517.335.2886
E-mail . . . . .kies-lowep@michigan.gov
608 W Allegan St, Lansing, MI 48909
Pam Kies-Lowe, Program Coordinator

Michigan Department of Education **517.373.3324**
Fax 517.335.4565
E-mail . . . . .thelens3@michigan.gov
608 W Allegan St, PO Box 30008, Lansing, MI 48909
T Helens, Director

Michigan Schools for the Deaf and Blind **810.257.1400**
Fax 810.257.1403
E-mail . . . . .winklerc@michigan.gov
1667 Miller Rd, Flint, MI 48503-4720
Cecial Winkler, Principal

Of of Spec Edu & Early Inter Svcs MI **517.373.0923**
Fax 517.373.7504
E-mail . . . . .mdeweb@michigan.gov
608 W Allegan, Lansing, MI 48933

COUNTY SERVICES

Alcona County

COURTS

Family Div of Circuit Court **989.724.9470**
Fax 989.724.9479
Web . . . . .www.familydoctors.net
106 Fifth St, Alcona County Bldg, Harrisville,
MI 48740
Honorable Laura A. Frawley, Judge

POLICE AND SHERIFF

Sheriff's Ofc **989.724.6271**
Fax 989.724.6181
Web . . . . .www.alcona-county.net
E-mail . . . . .ellinger@alcona-county.net
214 W Main St, Harrisville, MI 48740-9230
Douglas Atchinson, Sheriff

Alger County

SOCIAL SERVICES

Family Independence Agency **906.387.4440**
Fax 906.387.4710
Web . . . . .www.michigan.gov/dhs
101 Court St, Munising, MI 49862-1103
Doughlas York, Director

COURTS

Family Div of Circuit Court **906.387.2080**
Fax 906.387.4134
E-mail . . . . .billcarmody@algercourthouse.com
101 Court St, Munising, MI 49862
Charles C Nebel, Judge

POLICE AND SHERIFF

Sheriff's Ofc **906.387.4444**
Fax 906.387.5278
E-mail . . . . .rhughes@alerso.com
101 E Varnum St, Munising, MI 49862-1125
Robert Hughes, Sheriff

Allegan County

GENERAL HEALTH SERVICES

Health Dept **269.673.5411**
Fax 269.673.4172
Web . . . . .www.allegancounty.org
E-mail . . . . .rtravis@allegancounty.org
3255 122nd Ave, Ste 200, Allegan, MI 49010
Rashmi Travis, Health Officer

MENTAL HEALTH SERVICES

Mental Health **269.673.6617**
Fax 269.673.2738
Web . . . . .www.accmhs.org
E-mail . . . . .pbrinkley@accmhs.org
3285 122nd Ave, Allegan, MI 49010-9511
Paul M. Brinkley, Acsw, Executive Director

POLICE AND SHERIFF

Sheriff's Ofc **269.673.0500**
Fax 269.673.0406
E-mail . . . . .sheriff@allegancounty.org
112 N Walnut St, Allegan, MI 49010
Blaine A. Koops, Sheriff

Alpena County

COURTS

Family Div of Circuit Court **989.354.9696**
Fax 989.354.9786
719 W Chisholm St Ste 8, Alpena, MI 49707-2452
Honrable Thomas Lacross, Probate/Family Division Judge

EDUCATION SERVICES

Alpena High School **989.358.5200**
Fax 989.358.5205
3303 S 3rd Ave, Alpena, MI 49707
Matt Poli, Principal

Antrim County

GENERAL HEALTH SERVICES

Northwest Michigan Community
Health **231.533.6255**
Fax 231.533.8450
209 Portage Dr, Bellaire, MI 49615-9616
Jane Dinser, Off. Mgr.

COURTS

Family Div of Circuit Court **231.533.6681**
Fax 231.533.6600
E-mail . . . . .albertk@antrimcounty.org
205 E Cayuga St, Bellaire, MI 49615
Honorable Norman R. Hayes, Judge

POLICE AND SHERIFF

Sheriff's Ofc **231.533.8627**
Fax 231.533.5803
Web . . . . .www.antrimcounty.org
E-mail . . . . .911@antrimcounty.org
107 Grove St, Bellaire, MI 49615
Terry L. Johnson, Sheriff

Arenac County

SOCIAL SERVICES

Dept of Human Svcs **989.846.5500**
Fax 989.846.4365
Web . . . . .www.michigan.gov/dhs
3709 Deep River Rd, Standish, MI 48658
Kim Bejcek, Director

GENERAL HEALTH SERVICES

Sterling Area Health Ctr **989.654.2491**
Fax 989.654.2190
Web . . . . .www.sterlinghealth.net
725 E State St, Sterling, MI 48659-9548
Roger Ruslow, Director

COURTS

Family Div of Circuit Court **989.846.9187**
Fax 989.846.9199
120 N Grove St, Standish, MI 48658-0747
Judy Bell, Juvenile Register

POLICE AND SHERIFF

Sheriff's Ofc **989.846.3002**
Fax 989.846.1100
E-mail . . . . .jmoscicski@arenaccountygov.com
126 North Grove St, Standish, MI 48658
James Mosciscki, Sheriff

Baraga County

SOCIAL SERVICES

Dept of Human Svcs **906.353.4700**
Fax 906.353.8415
Web . . . . .www.michigan.gov
E-mail . . . . .willsl@michigan.gov
108 Main Ave, Baraga, MI 49908-9671
Louisa D. Wills, Director

GENERAL HEALTH SERVICES

Health Dept **906.524.6142**
Fax 906.524.6144
Web . . . . .www.wuphd.org
303 Baraga Ave, Lanse, MI 49946
Guy St Germain, Administrator

COURTS

Family Div of Circuit Court **906.524.6390**
Fax 906.524.2052
Web . . . . .www.baragacounty.org
16 N 3rd St, Lanse, MI 49946-1002
Honorable Timothy S. Brennan, Director

Barry County

SOCIAL SERVICES

Dept of Human Svcs **269.948.3200**
Fax 269.948.4101
Web . . . . .www.michigan.gov/dhs
430 Barfield Dr, Hastings, MI 49058
Jerome Calwell, Director

GENERAL HEALTH SERVICES

Barry Eaton Health Dept **517.485.7110**
Fax 269.945.4304
Web . . . . .www.barryeatonhealth.org
1033 Healthcare Dr Ste 1, Charlotte, MI 48813-1089
Robert Schirmer, Md, Medical Director

Health Dept **269.945.9516**
Fax 269.945.4304
Web . . . . .www.hline.org
330 W Woodlawn Ave, Hastings, MI 49058-1035

MENTAL HEALTH SERVICES

Mental Health **269.948.8041**
Fax 269.948.9319
Web . . . . .www.bccmha.org
E-mail . . . . .jmclean@voyager.net
915 W Green St Ste 201, PENNOCK PROFESSIONAL
BLDG, Hastings, MI 49058-1700
Jan Mclean, Executive Director

POLICE AND SHERIFF

Sheriff's Ofc **269.948.4805**
Fax 269.948.4831
1212 W State St, Hastings, MI 49058
Darin Leaf, Sheriff

Bay County

GENERAL HEALTH SERVICES

Health Dept **989.895.4009**
Fax 989.895.4014
Web . . . . .www.co.bay.mi.us
1200 Washington Ave, Bay City, MI 48708
Joel Strasz, Public Health Services Manager

MENTAL HEALTH SERVICES

Bay Arenac Behavioural Health **989.895.2300**
Fax 989.895.2357
Web . . . . .www.babha.org
201 Mulholland St, Bay City, MI 48708-7683
Robert Blackford, Executive Director

COURTS

Family Div of Circuit Court **989.895.4205**
Fax 989.895.4194
1230 Washington Ave Ste 715, Bay City, MI 48708
Honorable Karen A. Tighe, Judge

POLICE AND SHERIFF

Sheriff's Ofc **989.895.4050**
Fax 989.895.4077
503 3rd St, Bay City, MI 48708
John E. Miller, Sheriff

EDUCATION SERVICES

Early Head Start Education Ctr **989.893.9380**
Fax 989.893.9850
Web . . . . .www.nemcsa.org
E-mail .wakefieldb@nemcsa.org
1201 4th St, Bay City, MI 48708-6023
Brenda Wakefield, Director

Benzie County

SOCIAL SERVICES

Dept of Human Svcs **231.882.1330**
Fax 231.882.9078
Web . . . . .www.michigan.gov/dhs
448 Court Pl, Beulah, MI 49617
Kristine Lagios, Director

GENERAL HEALTH SERVICES

Benzie-Leelanau District Health
Dept **231.882.4409**
Fax 231.882.2204
Web . . . . .www.bldhd.org
E-mail . . . . .bldhd@bldhd.org
6051 Frankfort Hwy Ste 100, Benzonia, MI 49616
William A Crawford, Health Officer

POLICE AND SHERIFF

Sheriff's Ofc **231.882.4484**
Fax 231.882.5814
E-mail . . . . .roryheckman@benzieco.net
505 S Michigan Ave, Beulah, MI 49617
Rory Heckman, Sheriff

Berrien County

SOCIAL SERVICES

The Dept Human Svcs **269.934.2000**
Fax 269.934.2115
E-mail . . . . .frankj2@michigan.gov
401 8th St, Benton Harbor, MI 49022-5005
Jerry S Frank, Director

JUSTICE AGENCY

CASA Council For Children **269.556.9640**
Fax 269.556.9643
Web . . . . .www.berrienchild.org
E-mail .jrusow@berrienchild.org
4938 Niles Rd, Saint Joseph, MI 49085-9612
Jamie Rusow, Director

COURTS

Family Div of Circuit Court **269.983.7111**
811 Port St Ste 4, Saint Joseph, MI 49085
Elvin Gonzalez, Director Of Family Court

POLICE AND SHERIFF

Sheriff's Ofc **269.983.7141**
Web . . . . .www.berriencounty.org
E-mail . . . . .lpaulbailey@berriencounty.org
919 Port St, Saint Joseph, MI 49085-1116
L. Paul Bailey, Sheriff

Branch County

SOCIAL SERVICES

Dept of Human Svcs **517.279.4200**
Fax 517.279.9576
Web . . . . .www.michigan.gov/dhs
E-mail . . . . .culps@michigan.gov
388 Keith Wilhelm Dr, Coldwater, MI 49036-9203
Shaun Culp, Director

GENERAL HEALTH SERVICES

Health Dept **517.279.9561**
Fax 517.278.2923
Web . . . . .www.bhsj.org
570 Marshall Rd Ste F, Coldwater, MI 49036-8262
Candy Cox, Hiv Counselor

COURTS

Family Div of Circuit Court **517.279.4316**
Fax 517.279.6410
31 Division St, Coldwater, MI 49036
Honorable Frederick L. Wood, Judge

POLICE AND SHERIFF

Sheriff's Ofc **517.278.2325**
Fax 517.278.5698
E-mail . . . . .wcanon@countyofbranch.com
580 Marshall Rd, Coldwater, MI 49036-9201
Warren C. Canon, Sheriff

Calhoun County

SOCIAL SERVICES

Dept of Human Svcs **269.966.1284**
Fax 269.966.2835
Web . . . . .www.michigan.gov/dhs
190 E Michigan Ave Ste A200, Battle Creek,
MI 49016
Gwain McCree, Director

GENERAL HEALTH SERVICES

Health Dept **269.969.6363**
Fax 269.966.1620
190 E Michigan Ave, Ste A100, Battle Creek,
MI 49014
Gregory Harrington, Medical Director

JUSTICE AGENCY

Health Dept **269.969.6363**
Fax 269.966.1620
190 E Michigan Ave, Ste A100, Battle Creek,
MI 49014
Gregory Harrington, Medical Director

POLICE AND SHERIFF

Sheriff's Dept **269.969.6441**
Fax 269.969.6428
E-mail . . . . .abyam@calhouncountymi.gov
161 E Michigan Ave, Battle Creek, MI 49014
Allen L. Byam, Sheriff

EDUCATION SERVICES

Special Education **269.789.2460**
Fax 269.781.0156
Web . . . . .www.calhounisd.org
E-mail .kesterkel@calhounisd.org
17111 G Dr N, Marshall, MI 49068-9621
Lynne Kesterke, Assistant Superintendent

Cass County

SOCIAL SERVICES

Dept of Human Svcs **269.445.0200**
Fax 269.445.0298
Web . . . . .www.michigan.gov/dhs
E-mail . . . . .kadulskic@michigan.gov
325 M 62, Cassopolis, MI 49031-1056
Christopher Kadulski, Director

GENERAL HEALTH SERVICES

Health Dept **269.445.5280**
Fax 269.445.5278
201 M 62, Cassopolis, MI 49031
Susan Oosterwal, Aids Coordinator

COURTS

Family Div of Circuit Court **269.445.4452**
Fax 269.445.4485
Web . . . . .www.casscountymi.org
E-mail . . . . .sued@cassco.org
60296 M 62, Cassopolis, MI 49031-9749
Honorable Susan L. Dobrich, Family/probate Judge

POLICE AND SHERIFF

Sheriff's Dept **269.445.8644**
Fax 269.445.0036
Web . . . . .www.casscountymi.org
321 M 62 Hwy, Cassopolis, MI 49031-1032
Joseph M. Underwood, Sheriff

Charlevoix County

GENERAL HEALTH SERVICES

Northwest Michigan Community Health
Agency **231.547.6523**
Fax 231.547.1164
220 W Garfield Ave, Charlevoix, MI 49720
Bert Notestine, Aids Coordinator

COURTS

Family Div of Circuit Court **231.547.7214**
Fax 231.547.7256
301 State St Ste 1, Charlevoix, MI 49720-1532
Honorable Frederick Mulhauser, Judge

POLICE AND SHERIFF

Sheriff's Ofc **231.547.4461**
Fax 231.547.6720
E-mail . . . . .schneiderd@charlevoixcounty.org
1000 Grant St, Charlevoix, MI 49720-1674
Donald Schneider, Sheriff

Cheboygan County

SOCIAL SERVICES

Family Independence Agency **231.627.8500**
Fax 231.627.8546
Web .... www.cheboygancounty.net
827 S Huron St, Cheboygan, MI 49721-2209
Kenneth Desarmo, Director

GENERAL HEALTH SERVICES

Health Dept **231.627.8850**
Fax 231.627.9466
Web www.dhd4.org
E-mail .... lrobinson@hline.org
825 S Huron St Ste 1, Cheboygan, MI 49721-2276
Lynn Robinson, Nurse Practitioner

COURTS

Family Div of Circuit Court **231.627.8823**
Fax 231.627.8868
Web .... www.cheboygancounty.net
E-mail .... jrjb@cheboygancounty.net
870 S Main St, Cheboygan, MI 49721-2283
Honorable Robert J. Butts, Director/Judge

POLICE AND SHERIFF

Sheriff's Dept **231.627.3155**
Fax 231.627.8880
E-mail .... sheriff@cheboygancounty.net
870 So. Main St, Cheboygan, MI 49721
Dale V. Clermont, Sheriff

Chippewa County

SOCIAL SERVICES

Dept of Human Svcs **906.635.4100**
Fax 906.635.4173
Web .... www.michigan.gov/fia
E-mail .... stabilec@michigan.gov
463 E 3 Mile Rd, Sault Sainte Marie, MI 49783-9476
Chris Stabile, Director

Indian Social Svcs Inter-Tribal
Council **906.632.6896**
Fax 906.632.1810
Web .... www.itcmi.org
2956 Ashmun St, Sault Sainte Marie, MI 49783-3720
L John Luskins, Executive Director

Sault Sainte Marie Health & Human
Svcs **906.632.5200**
Fax 906.632.5252
Web .... www.saulttribe.net
E-mail .... bcufa@saulttribe.net
2864 Ashmun St, Sault Sainte Marie, MI 49783-3740
Bonnie Cufa, Health Director

GENERAL HEALTH SERVICES

Health Home Care **906.635.1566**
Fax 906.635.1701
Web .... www.hline.localhealth.net
E-mail .... rblashill@chippewahd.com
508 Ashmun St Ste 120, Sault S Marie, MI 49783-1976
Rosemary Blashill, Director

COURTS

Family Div of Circuit Court **906.635.6314**
Fax 906.635.6852
Web .... www.chippewacounty.mi.gov
E-mail .... judgeu@chippewacountymi.gov
319 Court St Unit 8, Sault Sainte Marie, MI 49783-2183
Honorable Lowell R. Ulrich, Director

POLICE AND SHERIFF

Sheriff's Ofc **906.635.6355**
Fax 906.635.6336
Web .... www.chippewacountymi.gov
E-mail .... chippewacoso@cji.net
325 Court St Unit 3, Sault Sainte Marie, MI 49783-2181
Robert Savoie, Sheriff

EDUCATION SERVICES

Algonquin Head Start **906.635.6017**
Web .... www.acf.hhs.gov
2307 Andary Ave, Sault Sainte Marie, MI 49783-1201
Reeney Butler, Director

CLM Community Action Head Start **906.495.2243**
Fax 906.495.2231
E-mail .... rbrown@clmcaa.com
4730 Osborn Pl, Kincheloe, MI 49788-1024
Rhonda Brown, Director

Drummond Island Head Start **906.493.6640**
Web .... www.acf.hhs.gov
29935 East Pine, Drummond Island, MI 49726
Kimberley Cameron, Director

Clare County

SOCIAL SERVICES

Dept of Human Svcs **989.539.4260**
Fax 989.539.5302
Web .... www.michigan.gov/dhs
E-mail .... sweeneyh@michigan.gov
725 Richard Dr, Harrison, MI 48625
Howard Sweeney, Director

GENERAL HEALTH SERVICES

Health Dept **989.539.6731**
Fax 989.539.4449
225 W Main St, Harrison, MI 48625
Sandy Merrifield, Nursing Supervisor

POLICE AND SHERIFF

Frost Township Police Dept **989.539.3233**
Fax 989.539.3233
E-mail .... wcftpd@yahoo.com
2463 E Long Lake Rd, Harrison, MI 48625-8643
William Coon, Police Chief

Sheriff's Ofc **989.539.7166**
Fax 989.539.5721
255 W Main St, Harrison, MI 48625
John Wilson, Sheriff

Clinton County

SOCIAL SERVICES

Dept of Human Svcs **989.224.5500**
Fax 989.224.6418
105 W Tolles Dr, Saint Johns, MI 48879
Kenton Schulze, Director

JUSTICE AGENCY

Juvenile Svcs **989.224.5195**
Fax 989.224.5254
Web .... www.clinton-county.org
E-mail .... olmstedf@clinton-county.org
100 E State St Ste 4200, Saint Johns, MI 48879-1584
Frederick G. Olmsted, Juvenile Officer, Court Director

COURTS

Family Div of Circuit Court **989.224.5190**
Fax 989.224.5102
100 E State St, Ste 4300, Saint Johns, MI 48879
Honorable Lisa Sullivan, Judge

POLICE AND SHERIFF

Sheriff's Dept **989.224.5200**
Fax 989.224.1382
E-mail .... kangask@clinton-county.org
1347 E Townsend Rd, Saint Johns, MI 48879
Wayne Kangas, Sheriff

Crawford County

GENERAL HEALTH SERVICES

Health Dept **989.348.7800**
Fax 989.348.5346
Web www.dhd10.org
202 Meadows Dr, Grayling, MI 49738
Sue Lucksted, Aids Coordinator

COURTS

Family Div of Circuit Court **989.344.3237**
Fax 989.344.3277
Web www.circuit46.org
200 W Michigan Ave 1, Grayling, MI 49738-1746
Honorable Monty Burmeister, Director

POLICE AND SHERIFF

Sheriff's Dept **989.348.4616**
Fax 989.348.6532
E-mail .... sheriff@crawfordsheriff.org
200 W Michigan Ave, Grayling, MI 49738
Kirk A. Wakefield, Sheriff

Delta County

SOCIAL SERVICES

Dept of Human Svcs **906.786.5394**
Fax 906.786.5350
Web .... www.michigan.gov/dhs
E-mail .... sextonr@michigan.gov
2940 College Ave, Escanaba, MI 49829-9597
Russ Sexton, Director

GENERAL HEALTH SERVICES

Delta Public Health Dept **906.786.4111**
Fax 906.786.1962
Web .... www.phdm.org
2920 College Ave, Escanaba, MI 49829-9592
Michael Snyder, Acting Director

COURTS

Family Div of Circuit Court **906.789.5112**
Fax 906.789.5140
310 Ludington St Ste 206, Escanaba, MI 49829
Honorable Robert E. Goebel Jr., Judge

POLICE AND SHERIFF

Sheriff's Dept **906.786.3633**
Fax 906.786.5228
E-mail .... deltasheriff@chartermi.net
111 N 3rd St, Escanaba, MI 49829
Gary A. Ballweg, Sheriff

EDUCATION SERVICES

Escanaba Early Childhood Ctr **906.789.0997**
Fax 906.789.2538
Web .... www.mdsecp.com
1905 S 21st St, Escanaba, MI 49829-1908
Kim Johnson, Director

Dickinson County

GENERAL HEALTH SERVICES

Dickinson Iron District Health Dept **906.774.1868**
Fax 906.774.9910
Web .... www.didhd.org
E-mail .... lmarkham@hline.org
818 Pyle Dr, Kingsford, MI 49802-4455
Steven Markham, Health Officer

COURTS

Family Div of Circuit Court **906.774.1555**
Fax 906.774.1561
705 S Stephenson Ave, Iron Mountain, MI 49801
Wayne Formolo, Juvenile Officer

Eaton County

SOCIAL SERVICES

Dept of Human Svcs **517.543.0860**
Fax 517.543.2125
Web .... www.michigan.gov/dhs
E-mail .... rewad@michigan.gov
1050 Independence Blvd, Charlotte, MI 48813-1032
Don Rewa, Director

GENERAL HEALTH SERVICES

Eaton Health Dept **517.543.2430**
Fax 517.543.0451
1033 Healthcare Dr Ste 1, Charlotte, MI 48813

POLICE AND SHERIFF

Sheriff's Dept **517.543.3512**
Fax 517.543.2922
Web .... www.eatoncounty.org
E-mail .... mraines@eatoncounty.org
1025 Independence Blvd, Charlotte, MI 48813-1031
Michael Raines, Sheriff

EDUCATION SERVICES

Capillary Community Svcs- Head
Start **517.543.2751**
Fax 517.543.3194
Web .... www.cacs-inc.org
1370 N Clinton Trl, Charlotte, MI 48813-8687
Lois Cairns, Site Supervisor

Emmet County

SOCIAL SERVICES

Dept of Human Services **231.348.1600**
Fax 231.347.6211
2229 Summit Park Dr, Petoskey, MI 49770
Bill Denemy, Director

GENERAL HEALTH SERVICES

Heath Department Of Northwest
Michigan **231.347.6014**
Fax 231.347.2861
3434 M 119 Ste A, Harbor Springs, MI 49740
Bert Notestine, Aids Coordinator

Little Traverse Bay Band of Odawa Indians Health
Clinic **231.242.1700**
Fax 231.242.1717
Web .... www.ltbbodawa-nsn.gov/healthclinic.htm
E-mail .... ssierzputowski@ltbbodawa-nsn.gov
1250 Lears Rd, Petoskey, MI 49770-8772
Sharon Sierzputowski, Pac Health Director

Genesee County

SOCIAL SERVICES

Dept of Human Svcs **810.760.2200**
Fax 810.760.2894
Web .... www.michigan.gov/dhs
125 E. Union, Flint, MI 48501
N Reinke, Acting Director

GENERAL HEALTH SERVICES

Health Dept **810.257.3612**
Fax 810.257.3147
Web .... www.gchd.us
E-mail .... mvalacak@gchd.us
630 S Saginaw St Ste 4, Flint, MI 48502-1525
Mark Valacak, Health Officer

MENTAL HEALTH SERVICES

Mental Health **810.257.3742**
Fax 810.257.1328
Web .... www.gencmh.org
E-mail .... drussell@gencmh.org
420 W 5th Ave, Flint, MI 48503-2494
Danis Russell, Executive Director

JUSTICE AGENCY

CASA / Consortium on Child Abuse and
Neglect **810.234.3680**
Fax 810.234.2265
Web .... www.ccan-flint.org
E-mail .... ccan7160@sbcglobal.net
726 Church St, Flint, MI 48502-1108
Pam Morrison, Director

COURTS

Family Div of Circuit Court **810.257.3540**
Fax 810.768.7591
E-mail .... dmelton@co.genesee.mi.us
630 S Saginaw St, Flint, MI 48502-1502
Diane Melton, Director Case Work Service

POLICE AND SHERIFF

Flint Police Dept - East Side Mini
Station **810.766.7304**
Fax 810.766.7317
Web .... www.cityofflint.com
2210 N Franklin Ave, Flint, MI 48506-4434
Cary Wooster, Officer

Flushing City Police Dept **810.659.3119**
Fax 810.659.8059
E-mail .... mhoornstra@flushingcity.com
725 E Main St, Flushing, MI 48433
Mark Hoornstra, Police Chief

Sheriff's Dept **810.257.3426**
Fax 810.257.3077
1002 S Saginaw St, Flint, MI 48502
Robert Pickell, Sheriff

EDUCATION SERVICES

Broome Head Start **810.591.1292**
4119 N Saginaw St, Flint, MI 48505-3995
Matt McKeaver, Director

C/A Fenton Lawn Head Start **810.591.3890**
Fax 810.591.3650
E-mail .... kmyatt@carman.k12.mi.us
1181 W Scottwood Ave, Flint, MI 48507
Kristy Myatt, Director

DTM Head Start Ctr **810.760.7543**
1518 W 3rd Ave, Flint, MI 48504
Lauren Chom, Director

Special Education **810.591.4494**
Fax 810.591.4548
Web .... www.geneseeisd.org
2413 W Maple Ave, Flint, MI 48507-3429
Mr. Jan O. Russell, Director

Gladwin County

SOCIAL SERVICES

Dept of Human Svcs **989.426.3300**
Fax 989.426.3353
Web .... www.michigan.gov/dhs
250 N State St, Gladwin, MI 48624
Kim Bejcek, Director

GENERAL HEALTH SERVICES

Health Dept **989.426.9431**
Fax 989.426.6952
Web .... www.cmdhd.localhealth.net
E-mail .... afegan@cmdhd.localhealth.net
103 N Bowery Ave, Gladwin, MI 48624-1479
Alison Fagen, Health Educator

COURTS

Family Div of Circuit Court **989.426.7451**
Fax 989.426.6936
Web .... www.gladwinco.com
401 W Cedar Ave, Ste 4, Gladwin, MI 48624-2052
Honorable Thomas P. Mclaughlin, Judge

POLICE AND SHERIFF

Sheriff's Ofc **989.426.9284**
Fax 989.426.5517
Web .... www.gladwinco.com
E-mail .... michael.shea@gladwinco.com
501 W Cedar Ave, Gladwin, MI 48624-2064
Michael Shea, Sheriff

Gogebic County

SOCIAL SERVICES

Dept of Human Svcs **906.663.6200**
Fax 906.663.6230
Web .... www.michigan.gov/dhs
301 E Lead St, Bessemer, MI 49911
Bobbie Ferguson, Director

GENERAL HEALTH SERVICES

Health Dept **906.667.0200**
Fax 906.667.0020
Web .... www.gogebic.org
E-mail .... kanderson@gogebic.org
210 N Moore St, Bessemer, MI 49911-1052
Kathy Anderson, Hiv Coordinator

COURTS

Family Court **906.667.0421**
Fax 906.663.4660
Web .... www.gogebic.org
E-mail .... jmassie@gogebic.org
200 N Moore St, Bessemer, MI 49911-1052
Honorable Joel L. Massie, Judge

POLICE AND SHERIFF

Sheriff's Dept **906.667.0203**
Fax 906.663.4090
100 Iron St, Bessemer, MI 49911
Pete Matonich, Sheriff

Grand Traverse County

SOCIAL SERVICES

Dept of Human Svcs **231.941.3900**
Fax 231.941.0037
701 S Elmwood Ave Ste 19, Traverse City, MI 49684
Dawn Mclaughlin, Director

Dept of Human Svcs, Zone 2 Ofc **231.922.5374**
Fax 231.922.5249
Web .... www.michigan.gov
E-mail .... schwartz@michigan.gov
701 S Elmwood Ave Ste 19, Traverse City,
MI 49684-3185
Steven Talarido, Supervisor

GENERAL HEALTH SERVICES

Health Dept **231.922.4831**
Fax 231.922.2719
Web .... www.grandtraverse.org
2325 Garfield Rd N, Ste A, Traverse City, MI 49686
Michael Collins, Medical Director

JUSTICE AGENCY

CASA **231.922.4827**
Fax 231.922.4643
E-mail .... pcv@co.grand-traverse.mi.us
280 Washington St Ste B150, Traverse City,
MI 49684
Linda Fawcett, Director

Michigan

COURTS

Family Div of Circuit Court 231.922.4640
Fax 231.922.4647
280 Washington St Ste 202, Traverse City, MI 49684
Honorable David L. Stowe, Judge

POLICE AND SHERIFF

Sheriff's Ofc 231.995.5001
Fax 231.995.5010
851 Woodmere Ave, Traverse City, MI 49686
Tom Bensley, Sheriff

Gratiot County

POLICE AND SHERIFF

Sheriff's Ofc 989.875.5214
Fax 989.875.3322
Web ....www.co.gratiot.mi.us
E-mail ....rberacy@co.gratiot.mi.us
226 E Center St, Ithaca, MI 48847-1438
Robert L. Beracy, Sheriff

Hillsdale County

SOCIAL SERVICES

Dept of Human Svcs 517.439.2200
Fax 517.439.2272
Web ....www.michigan.gov/dhs
E-mail ....culps@michigan.gov
40 Care Dr, Hillsdale, MI 49242-5039
Shaun Culp, Director

COURTS

Family Div of Circuit Court 517.437.4643
Fax 517.437.4148
Web ....www.co.hillsdale.mi.us
E-mail ....m.nye@co.hillsdale.mi.us
29 N Howell St Ste 5, Hillsdale, MI 49242-1649
Honorable Michael E. Nye, Director

POLICE AND SHERIFF

Sheriff's Dept 517.437.7317
Fax 517.437.0822
Web ....www.hilldalecountysheriff.com
165 W Fayette St, Hillsdale, MI 49242-1014
Stan Burchardt, Sheriff

EDUCATION SERVICES

**Community Action - Camden Head
Start** 517.437.3346
Fax 517.437.3480
Web ....www.co.hillsdale.mi.us
E-mail ....crowe@caajlh.org
23 Care Dr, Hillsdale, MI 49242-5039
Cindy Rowe, Director

Houghton County

SOCIAL SERVICES

Dept of Human Svcs 906.482.0500
Fax 906.487.7726
Web ....www.michigan.gov/dhs
200 Quincy St, Hancock, MI 49930-1817
Leonard Richard, Director

GENERAL HEALTH SERVICES

**Western Upper Peninsula Health
Dept** 906.482.7382
Fax 906.482.9410
E-mail ....shayrynen@hline.org
540 Depot St, Hancock, MI 49930
Sue Hayrynen, Aids Coordinator

MENTAL HEALTH SERVICES

Copper Country Mental Health 906.482.9400
Fax 906.482.9794
E-mail ....admindept@cccmh.org
901 W Memorial Dr, Houghton, MI 49931-2492
Lawrence Pollack, Phd, Executive Director

COURTS

Family Div of Circuit Court 906.482.3120
Fax 906.487.5964
Web ....www.houghtoncounty.net
401 E Houghton Ave, Houghton, MI 49931-2016
Fraser Strome, Director

POLICE AND SHERIFF

Sheriff's Ofc 906.482.0055
Fax 906.487.5949
Web ....www.houghtonsheriff.com
E-mail ....bmclean@houghtonsheriff.com
403 E Houghton Ave, Houghton, MI 49931-2016
Brian J. Mclean, Sheriff

EDUCATION SERVICES

Houghton Head Start 906.482.3663
Fax 906.482.7329
E-mail ....bhk@bhkfirst.org
700 Park Ave, Houghton, MI 49931
Lisa Schmierer, Family Community Coordinator

Huron County

COURTS

Family Div of Circuit Court 989.269.9267
Fax 989.269.0009
E-mail ....goretskc@cohuron.mi.us
250 E Huron Ave Ste 211, County Bldg, Bad Axe,
MI 48413
Honorable David L. Clabuesch, Judge

POLICE AND SHERIFF

Sheriff's Ofc 989.269.9910
Fax 989.269.9811
120 S Heisterman St, Bad Axe, MI 48413
Kelly Hanson, Sheriff

EDUCATION SERVICES

Bad Axe Head Start Ctr 989.269.8451
309 N Outer Dr, Bad Axe, MI 48413-9701
Karen Kubiak, Director

Ingham County

SOCIAL SERVICES

Dept of Human Svcs 517.335.6124
Fax 517.335.6121
Web ....www.michigan.gov/dhs
7109 W Saginaw Hwy, Flr 2, Lansing, MI 48917
James Gale, Director

**Dept of Human Svcs - Urban
Counties** 517.373.3983
Fax 517.241.2555
Web ....www.michigan.gov
E-mail ....yagers@michigan.gov
235 S Grand Ave, Ste 1406, Lansing, MI 48933
Steve Yager, Director

Family Independence Agency 517.887.9400
Fax 517.887.9500
5303 S Cedar St Ste 4, Lansing, MI 48909
Louise wing, Director

GENERAL HEALTH SERVICES

Health Dept 517.887.4311
Fax 517.887.4310
Web ....ww.hdingham.org
E-mail ....hdcdrodgers@ingham.org
5303 S Cedar St Ste 3, Lansing, MI 48911-3800
Ruby Rodgers, Supervisor For Disease Control

Health Dept 517.887.4300
Fax 517.887.4437
Web ....www.hd.ingham.org
5303 S Cedar St Ste 6, Lansing, MI 48911-3859
Dr. Dean Sienko, Director

**Michigan Dept of Community
Health** 517.373.3740
Fax 517.335.3090
Web ....www.michigan.gov/mdch
320 S Walnut St, Lewis Cass Bldg, Lansing, MI 48913
Janet Olszewski, Director

MENTAL HEALTH SERVICES

Mental Health 517.346.8200
Fax 517.346.8245
Web ....www.ceicmh.org
812 E Jolly Rd, Lansing, MI 48910-6825
Robert Sheehan, Executive Director

JUSTICE AGENCY

Bureau of Juvenile Justice 517.335.3489
Fax 517.373.2799
Web ....www.michigan.gov/dhs
235 S Grand Ave, Ste 406, Lansing, MI 48933
John Evans, Director

COURTS

Family Div of Circuit Court 517.483.6339
Fax 517.483.6532
E-mail ....pcole@ingham.org
313 W Kalamazoo St, Lansing, MI 48933-2041
Honorable R. George Economy, Director

POLICE AND SHERIFF

Sheriff's Dept 517.676.8205
Fax 517.676.8299
E-mail ....so_wriggelsworth@ingham.org
630 N Cedar St, Mason, MI 48854
Gene Wriggelsworth, Sheriff

EDUCATION SERVICES

Early LCC Head Start 517.485.3504
820 N Washington Ave Ste 2, Lansing,
MI 48906-5155
Lois Cairnes, Director

Ionia County

SOCIAL SERVICES

Family Independence Agency 616.527.5200
Fax 616.527.1849
E-mail ....larsonp@michigan.gov
920 E Lincoln Ave, Ionia, MI 48846-1393
Phil Larson, Director

GENERAL HEALTH SERVICES

Health Dept 616.527.5341
Fax 616.527.5361
Web ....www.ioniacounty.org
175 E Adams St Ste 1, Ionia, MI 48846
Sugandha Lowhim, Medical Director

COURTS

Family Div of Circuit Court 616.527.5326
Fax 616.527.5321
Web ....www.ioniacounty.org
E-mail ....probate@ioniacounty.org
100 W Main St, Ionia, MI 48846-1651
Honorable Robert Sykes Jr., Judge

POLICE AND SHERIFF

Sheriff's Ofc 616.527.5383
Fax 616.527.9102
133 E Adams St, Ionia, MI 48846
Dwain Dennis, Sheriff

Iosco County

SOCIAL SERVICES

Dept of Human Svcs **989.362.0300**
Fax 989.362.6629
Web ....www.michigan.gov/dhs
E-mail ....hobbsk@michigan.gov
2145 E US 23, East Tawas, MI 48730-9422
Karin Hobbs, Director

MENTAL HEALTH SERVICES

Mental Health **989.362.8636**
Fax 989.362.7800
Web ....www.avcmh.org
E-mail ....floyd.smith@avcmh.org
1199 Harris Ave, Tawas City, MI 48763-9681
Floyd Smith, Executive Director

COURTS

Family Div of Circuit Court **989.362.3991**
Fax 989.984.1035
422 W Lake St, County Bldg, Tawas City, MI 48764
Honorable John D. Hamilton, Judge

POLICE AND SHERIFF

Sheriff's Ofc **989.362.6164**
Fax 989.984.1103
Web ....www.ioscocounty.org
E-mail ....amacgregor@ioscocounty.org
428 W Lake St, Tawas City, MI 48763-5112
Alan Macgregor, Sheriff

Iron County

SOCIAL SERVICES

Dept of Human Svcs **906.265.9958**
Fax 906.265.6390
Web ....www.michigan.gov/dhs
337 Brady Ave, Caspian, MI 49915
Bobbi Ferguson, Acting Director

COURTS

Family Div of Circuit Court **906.875.0626**
Fax 906.875.4924
Web ....www.iron.org
E-mail ....jschwedler@iron.org
2 S 6th St, Ste 22, Crystal Falls, MI 49920
Honorable C. Joseph Schwedler, Judge

Isabella County

SOCIAL SERVICES

Dept of Human Svcs **989.772.8400**
Fax 989.772.8460
Web ....www.michigan.gov
E-mail ....stevensm3@michigan.gov
1919 Parkland Dr, Mount Pleasant, MI 48858
Mark Stevens, Director

Indian Social Svcs Chippewa Indian
Tribe **989.775.4901**
Fax 989.775.4912
7070 E Broadway Rd, Mt Pleasant, MI 48858
Jodie Garner, Protective Services Supervisor

GENERAL HEALTH SERVICES

Saginaw Chippewa Indian Tribe Social
Svcs **989.775.4901**
Fax 989.775.4912
Web ....www.sagchip.org
7070 E broadway st, Mount Pleasant, MI 48858-7950
Judie Garner, Director

POLICE AND SHERIFF

Sheriff's Ofc **989.772.5911**
Fax 989.773.2739
207 Court St, Mount Pleasant, MI 48858
Leo Miodufzewski, Sheriff

Jackson County

SOCIAL SERVICES

Dept OF Human Services **517.780.7400**
Fax 517.780.7160
301 E Louis Glick Hwy, Jackson, MI 49201
Jerome Colwell, Director

Disabilty Connections **517.782.6054**
Fax 517.782.3118
Web ....www.disabiltyconnect.org
E-mail ....caroleb@disabiltyconnect.org
409 Linden Ave, Jackson, MI 49203-4065
Carole Briggs, Rn, Respite Coordinator

GENERAL HEALTH SERVICES

Health Dept **517.788.4420**
Fax 517.788.4373
Web ....www.co.jackson.mi.us
E-mail ....lpinson@co.jackson.mi.us
1715 Lansing Ave Ste 221, Jackson, MI 49202-2193
Lorena Pinson, Md, Mph, Medical Director

COURTS

Family Div of Circuit Court **517.788.4450**
Fax 517.788.4623
312 S Jackson St Ste 1, Jackson, MI 49201
Bonnie Porter, Youth Services Director

Kalamazoo County

SOCIAL SERVICES

Dept of Human Svcs **231.258.1200**
Fax 231.258.4482
Web ....www.michigan.gov/dhs
E-mail ....mclaughlind@michigan.gov
503 N Birch St, Kalkaska, MI 49646-8414
Don McLaughlin, Director

Health and Community Services **269.373.5200**
Fax 269.373.5363
3299 Gull Road, Nazareth, MI 49074
Chris Wagley, Childrens Special Health Care Services Coordinator

MENTAL HEALTH SERVICES

Mental Health **269.553.8000**
Fax 269.553.8012
3299 Gull Road, Nazareth, MI 49074
Jeff Patton, Executive Director

COURTS

Probate Court **269.383.8666**
Fax 269.383.8685
E-mail ....drhals@kalcounty.com
150 E Crosstown Pkwy, Kalamazoo, MI 49001
Honorable Donald R. Halstead, Judge

POLICE AND SHERIFF

Kalamazoo Police Dept **269.337.8123**
Fax 269.337.8245
Web ....www.kalamazoocity.org
E-mail ....publicsafety@kalamazoocity.org
150 E Crosstown Pkwy Ste A, Kalamazoo, MI 49001-2879
Jeff Hadley, Chief Of Police

Sheriff's Dept **269.385.6173**
Fax 269.385.6162
Web ....www.kalcounty.com
1500 Lamont Ave, Kalamazoo, MI 49048-4156
Richard Fuller, Sheriff

EDUCATION SERVICES

Communities In Schools **269.337.1601**
Fax 269.385.5806
Web ....www.kcisfkidsfirst.org
E-mail ....pkingery@kcisfkidsfirst.org
247 N Rose St, Kalamazoo, MI 49007
Pam Kingery, Executive Director

Kalkaska County

GENERAL HEALTH SERVICES

Health Dept **231.258.8669**
Fax 231.258.2805
Web ....www.kalkaskacounty.net/health.asp
625 Courthouse Dr, Kalkaska, MI 49646-8495
Lori Gilinis, Aids Coordinator

POLICE AND SHERIFF

Sheriff's Dept **231.258.8686**
Fax 231.258.3333
E-mail ....kalkaskaso@cji.net
605 N Birch St, Kalkaska, MI 49646
David Israel, Sheriff

Kent County

SOCIAL SERVICES

Catholic Charities West Michigan **616.456.1443**
Fax 616.732.6392
Web ....www.ccwestmi.org
40 Jefferson Ave SE, Grand Rapids, MI 49503-4304
Deb Nykamp, Director

GENERAL HEALTH SERVICES

Health Dept **616.632.7100**
Fax 616.632.7083
Web ....www.accesskent.com
E-mail ....cheryl.clements@kentcountymi.gov
700 Fuller Ave NE, Grand Rapids, MI 49503
Cheryl Clements, Administrative Assistant

JUSTICE AGENCY

CASA **616.632.5112**
Fax 616.632.5181
Web ....www.kentcounty.org
E-mail ....patty.sabin@kentcountymi.gov
180 Ottawa Ave NW, Ste 3500, Grand Rapids, MI 49503
Patty Sabin, Coordinator

COURTS

17th Circuit Court - Family Div **616.632.5106**
Fax 616.632.5134
180 Ottawa Ave NW, Grand Rapids, MI 49503-2703
Marcela Moralez, Kentfields Program Director

Probate Court **616.632.5440**
Fax 616.632.5430
Web ....www.dc.state.fl.us
E-mail ....dmurkowski@mail.crt.state.vt.us
180 Ottawa Ave NW, Ste 2500, Grand Rapids, MI 49503
Honorable David M. Murkowski, Judge

POLICE AND SHERIFF

Police Dept **616.456.3380**
Fax 616.456.3799
1 Monroe Center St NW, Grand Rapids, MI 49503-2948

Sheriff's Dept **616.632.6100**
Fax 616.632.6122
E-mail ....kentsheriff@kentcountymi.gov
701 Ball Ave NE, Grand Rapids, MI 49503
Lawrance Stelma, Sheriff

EDUCATION SERVICES

Even Start Pat **616.819.2107**
1061 Kensington Ave SW, Grand Rapids, MI 49503-4829
Leticia Leffler, Even Start Director

Special Education **616.365.2297**
Fax 616.447.2440
Web ....www.kentisd.org
E-mail ....lucyhoughwaite@kentisd.org
2930 Knapp St NE, Grand Rapids, MI 49525-4518
Lucy Hough-waite, Director Of Special Ed

Keweenaw County

COURTS

Family Div of Circuit Court **906.337.1927**
Fax 906.337.2795
E-mail .... kewprobate@pasty.net
　5095 4th St, Eagle River, MI 49950-9624
　Kathy Mcevers, Juvenile Officer

POLICE AND SHERIFF

Sheriff's Dept **906.337.0528**
Fax 906.337.4278
E-mail .... ksheriff@pasty.com
　5105 4th St, Eagle River, MI 49950
　Ronald J. Lahti, Sheriff

Lake County

SOCIAL SERVICES

Dept of Human Services **231.745.8159**
Fax 231.745.2930
Web .... www.michigan.gov
E-mail .... mccormickj@michigan.gov
　5653 S M 37, Baldwin, MI 49304-7983
　Jim Mccormick, Director

GENERAL HEALTH SERVICES

Health Dept **231.745.4663**
Fax 231.745.2501
Web www.dhd10.org
E-mail .... hjoseph@dhd10.org
　5681 S M 37, Baldwin, MI 49304
　Shelia Miller, Clerical Support

MENTAL HEALTH SERVICES

West Michigan Community Mental
Health **231.745.4659**
Fax 231.845.7095
Web .... www.wmcmhs.org
E-mail .... richv@wmcmhs.org
　1090 Michigan Ave, Baldwin, MI 49304
　Rich Vanden Huevel, Phd, Director

POLICE AND SHERIFF

Sheriff's Ofc **231.745.2712**
Fax 231.745.9008
Web .... www.co.lake.mi.us
E-mail .... sheriff@co.lake.mi.us
　1153 Michigan Ave, Baldwin, MI 49304-7969
　Robert A. Hilts, Sheriff

Lapeer County

SOCIAL SERVICES

Dept of Human Svcs **810.667.0801**
Fax 810.667.0795
Web .... www.michigan.gov/dhs
E-mail .... walleri@michigan.gov
　1505 Suncrest Dr, Lapeer, MI 48446-1137
　Irene Waller, Director

GENERAL HEALTH SERVICES

Health Dept **810.667.0391**
Fax 810.667.0232
E-mail .... rbush@lapeercounty.org
　1800 Imlay City Rd, Lapeer, MI 48446
　Russell Bush, Md, Medical Director

COURTS

Public Court **810.667.0261**
Fax 810.667.0271
　255 Clay St, Lapeer, MI 48446
　Lori Curtiss, Director

POLICE AND SHERIFF

Sheriff's Ofc **810.667.0440**
Fax 810.664.5520
　3231 John Conley Dr, Lapeer, MI 48446-2987
　Ronald J. Kalanquin, Sheriff

Leelanau County

GENERAL HEALTH SERVICES

Grand Traverse Band - Ottawa **231.534.7200**
Fax 231.534.7460
E-mail .... loi.chamabers@gtbindians.com
　2300 N Stallman Rd Ste A, Suttons Bay,
　MI 49682-9158
　Loi Chamabers, Medical Director

Grand Traverse Band of Ottawa - Chippewa Indians Medicine
Lodge **231.534.7750**
Fax 231.534.7565
Web .... www.gtbindians.org
E-mail .... loi.chambers@gtbindians.com
　2605 NW Bay Shore Dr, Suttons Bay, MI 49682
　Loi Chambers, Health Director

COURTS

Family Div of Circuit Court **231.256.9803**
Fax 231.256.9845
　8527 E Goverment Ctr Dr, Ste 203, Suttons Bay,
　MI 49682
　Tom Mayhew, Case Director

POLICE AND SHERIFF

Sheriff's Dept **231.256.8800**
Fax 231.256.2611
Web .... www.co.leelanau.mi.us
E-mail .... sheriff@co.leelanau.mi.us
　8525 E Government Center Dr, Suttons Bay,
　MI 49682-9718
　Mike F. Oltersdorf, Sheriff

Lenawee County

SOCIAL SERVICES

Family Independence Agency **517.264.6300**
Fax 517.264.6357
Web .... www.michigan.gov
E-mail .... satterellij@michigan.gov
　1040 S Winter St Ste 3013, Adrian, MI 49221-3876
　Joe Satterelli, Director

GENERAL HEALTH SERVICES

Health Dept **517.264.5202**
Fax 517.264.0790
Web .... www.lenawehealthdepartment.org
E-mail .... tbacon@hline.org
　1040 S Winter St Ste 2328, Adrian, MI 49221
　Dennis Chernin, Md, Mph, Medical Director

MENTAL HEALTH SERVICES

Mental Health **517.263.8905**
Fax 517.265.8237
Web .... www.lcmha.org
E-mail .... rmyers@lcmha.org
　1040 S Winter St Ste 1022, Adrian, MI 49221-3867
　Roger Myers, Ma, Executive Director

EDUCATION SERVICES

Communities In Schools **517.263.4591**
Fax 517.264.6357
Web .... www.cislenawe.org
E-mail .... cis@cislenawe.org
　1040 S Winter St Ste 3013, Adrian, MI 49221-3876
　Christine Macnaughton, Director

Livingston County

SOCIAL SERVICES

Dept of Human Svcs **517.548.0200**
Fax 517.548.0298
Web .... www.michigan.gov/dhs
E-mail .... fultons@michigan.gov
　2300 E Grand River Ave Ste 1, Howell,
　MI 48843-7577
　Susan Fulton, Director

GENERAL HEALTH SERVICES

Community Coordinating Council
4C **517.548.9112**
Web www.childcare4c.com
E-mail .... childcarel@aol.com
　2710 E Grand River Ave, Ste 6, Howell, MI 48843
　Linda Herbert, Director

Health Dept **517.546.9850**
Fax 517.546.6995
Web .... www.lchd.org
E-mail .... rcook@co.livingston.mi.us
　2300 E Grand River Ave Ste 102, Howell,
　MI 48843-7578
　Rebecca Cook, Hiv Coordinator

Mental Health **517.546.4126**
Fax 517.546.1300
Web .... www.cmhliv.org
E-mail .... macmiller@cmhliv.org
　2280 E Grand River Ave, Howell, MI 48843-8503
　Angus M. Miller, Iv, Executive Director

COURTS

Juvenile Court **517.546.3750**
Fax 517.552.2510
　204 S Highlander Way Ste 2, Howell, MI 48843
　Honorable Carol Hackett Garagiola, Judge

POLICE AND SHERIFF

Sheriff's Ofc **517.546.2440**
Fax 517.546.1744
Web .... www.livingstonsheriff.com
　150 S Highlander Way, Howell, MI 48843
　Robert Bezotte, Sheriff

EDUCATION SERVICES

Special Education **517.546.5550**
Fax 517.546.7047
Web .... www.livingstonesa.org
　1425 W Grand River Ave, Howell, MI 48843-1916
　Dawn Bentley, Director For Special Education

Luce County

SOCIAL SERVICES

Dept of Human Svcs **906.293.5144**
Fax 906.293.3857
Web .... www.michigan.gov/dhs
E-mail .... stabilec@michigan.gov
　500 W McMillan Ave, Newberry, MI 49868
　Chris Stabile, Director

COURTS

Family Div of Circuit Court **906.293.5601**
Fax 906.293.5665
　407 W Harrie St, Luce County Government Bldg,
　Newberry, MI 49868
　Honorable W Clayton Graham, Judge

POLICE AND SHERIFF

Sheriff's Ofc **906.293.8431**
Fax 906.293.3581
　411 W Harrie St, Newberry, MI 49868-1208
　Kevin Erickson, Sheriff

Mackinac County

SOCIAL SERVICES

Dept of Human Svcs......................**906.643.9550**
Fax...906.643.7467
Web.....................................www.michigan.gov/dhs
E-mail...............................desarmok@michigan.gov
　　199 Ferry Ln, Saint Ignace, MI 49781
　　Kenneth Desarmo, Director

GENERAL HEALTH SERVICES

Health Dept...............................**906.643.1100**
Fax...906.643.0239
Web..www.lmasdhd.org
E-mail............................nderusha@lmasdhd.org
　　749 Hombach, Saint Ignace, MI 49781-1868
　　Nick Derusha, Director

COURTS

Family Div of Circuit Court..............**906.643.7303**
Fax...906.643.8861
E-mail......................probate@mackinaccounty.net
　　100 S Marley St Rm 15, Saint Ignace, MI 49781
　　Honorable W Clayton Graham, Judge

POLICE AND SHERIFF

Sheriff's Dept..............................**906.643.1911**
Fax...906.643.9842
Web..www.mackinaccounty.net
E-mail.........................jail49@mackinaccounty.net
　　100 S Marley St, Saint Ignace, MI 49781
　　Scott Strait, Sheriff

Macomb County

SOCIAL SERVICES

Dept of Human Svcs......................**586.412.6150**
Fax...586.412.6142
　　19700 Hall Rd Ste A, Clinton Township, MI 48038
　　Teresa Morin, Children Services Manager

GENERAL HEALTH SERVICES

Health Dept...............................**586.465.8090**
Fax...586.573.2378
Web..www.dhr.state.al.us
　　27690 Van Dyke Ave Ste B, Warren, MI 48093-2842
　　Cheryl Woods, Health Coordinator

Health Dept...............................**586.469.5235**
Fax...586.469.5885
Web...www.macombcountymi.gov
E-mail.................steven.gold@macombcountymi.gov
　　43525 Elizabeth St, Mount Clemens, MI 48043-1034
　　Steven Gold, Health Officer/director

COURTS

Circuit Court Juvenile Div.................**586.469.5195**
Fax...586.469.6276
　　380 N Rose St, Mount Clemens, MI 48043-1523
　　Nicole Faulds, Program Director

EDUCATION SERVICES

Special Education.........................**586.228.3454**
Fax...586.263.6240
Web..www.misd.net
E-mail...................................tkoepke@misd.net
　　44001 Garfield Rd, Clinton Township,
　　MI 48038-1100
　　Tomas Koepke, Phd, Director Of Special Ed Mgmt Services

Manistee County

GENERAL HEALTH SERVICES

Health Dept...............................**231.723.3595**
Fax...231.723.1477
Web...www.dhd10.org
　　385 3rd St, Manistee, MI 49660-1718
　　Linda Vangill, Health Officer

Little River Band of Ottawa.................**231.723.8288**
Fax...231.723.8761
　　375 River St Uppr, Manistee, MI 49660
　　Larry Romanelli, Chief

COURTS

Family Div of Circuit Court..................**231.723.2573**
Fax...231.398.3519
E-mail.....................jsmogoleski@manisteecounty.net
　　415 3rd St, Manistee, MI 49660
　　James Smogoleski, Juvenile Division Director

POLICE AND SHERIFF

Sheriff's Ofc...............................**231.723.8393**
Fax...231.723.1498
　　1525 E Parkdale Ave, Manistee, MI 49660
　　Dale Kowalkowski, Sheriff

Marquette County

SOCIAL SERVICES

Dept of Human Svcs......................**906.228.9691**
Fax...906.228.3393
Web.....................................www.michigan.gov/dhs
　　234 W Baraga Ave, Marquette, MI 49855
　　Richard Miketinac, Director

GENERAL HEALTH SERVICES

Health Dept...............................**906.475.9977**
Fax...906.475.9312
　　184 US Highway 41 E, Negaunee, MI 49866
　　Terri Govern, Hr Director

POLICE AND SHERIFF

Sheriff's Dept..............................**906.225.8435**
Fax...906.225.8485
Web...www.mqtcty.org
E-mail.................................mlovelace@mqtcty.org
　　236 W Baraga Ave, Marquette, MI 49855-4710
　　Mike H. Lovelace, Sheriff

Mason County

GENERAL HEALTH SERVICES

Health Dept...............................**231.845.7381**
Web...www.dhd10.org
E-mail.....................................jwilson@dhd10.org
　　916 Diana St, Ludington, MI 49431
　　James Wilson, Medical Director

POLICE AND SHERIFF

Sheriff's Ofc...............................**231.843.3475**
Fax...231.843.1814
E-mail...............................jfiers@masoncounty.net
　　302 N Delia St, Ludington, MI 49431
　　Jeff Fiers, Sheriff

Mecosta County

GENERAL HEALTH SERVICES

Health Dept...............................**231.592.0130**
Fax...231.796.7864
E-mail..............................bthompson@dhd10.org
　　14485 Northland Dr, Big Rapids, MI 49307-2368
　　Barb Thompson, Hiv Coordinator

COURTS

Family Div of Circuit Court..................**231.592.0135**
Fax...231.592.0191
Web....................................www.co.mecosta.mi.us
E-mail.............................familyct@co.mecosta.mi.us
　　400 Elm St, Big Rapids, MI 49307
　　Honorable Marco Menezes, Judge

POLICE AND SHERIFF

Sheriff's Ofc...............................**231.592.0150**
Fax...231.796.5577
Web...................................www.co.mecosta.mi.us
E-mail.............................tpurcell@co.mecosta.mi.us
　　225 S Stewart Ave, Big Rapids, MI 49307-1841
　　Todd M Purcell, Sheriff

Menominee County

SOCIAL SERVICES

Dept Human Svcs.........................**906.863.9965**
Fax...906.863.7426
Web.....................................www.michigan.gov/dhs
　　2612 10th St, Menominee, MI 49858-1904
　　Russ Sexton, Acting Director

GENERAL HEALTH SERVICES

Health Dept...............................**906.863.4451**
Fax...906.863.7142
Web...www.phdm.org
　　909 10th Ave, Menominee, MI 49858-3014
　　Terry Frankovich, Md, Mph, Health Officer/medical Director

COURTS

Family Div of Circuit Court..................**906.863.2634**
Fax...906.863.9904
Web.................................www.menomineecounty.com
E-mail.......................whupy@menomineecounty.com
　　839 10th Ave Stop 1, Menominee, MI 49858-3054
　　Honorable William A. Hupy, Judge

POLICE AND SHERIFF

Sheriff's Ofc...............................**906.863.4441**
Fax...906.863.2239
E-mail.................................control@menoimeeco.com
　　831 10th Ave, Menominee, MI 49858
　　Ken Marks, Sheriff

Midland County

SOCIAL SERVICES

Dept of Human Svcs......................**989.835.7040**
Fax...989.839.1195
Web...www.michigan.gov
E-mail..............................stevensm@michigan.gov
　　1509 Washington St Ste A, Midland, MI 48640-5612
　　Marks Stevens, Director

GENERAL HEALTH SERVICES

Health Dept...............................**989.832.6655**
Fax...989.837.6524
Web.....................................www.co.midland.mi.us
E-mail............................djacobs@co.midland.mi.us
　　220 W Ellsworth St, Midland, MI 48640-5180
　　Donna Jacobs, HIV Manager

MENTAL HEALTH SERVICES

Community Mental Health For Central
Michigan....................................**989.631.5140**
Fax...989.631.3343
E-mail.........................lindakaufman@earthlink.net
　　218 Fast Ice Dr, Midland, MI 48642
　　Linda Kaufman, Executive Director

COURTS

Family Div of Circuit Court..................**989.832.6880**
Fax...989.832.6607
Web..www.midlandcounty.org
E-mail.............................sburtick@co.midland.mi.us
　　301 W Main St, Ste B, Midland, MI 48640
　　Honorable Dorene S. Allen, Judge

Michigan

Missaukee County

COURTS

Family Div of Circuit Court **231.839.4967**
Fax 231.839.5856
Web .... www.missaukee.org
　111 S Canal, Lake City, MI 49651
　Honorable Charles Parsons, Director

Monroe County

MENTAL HEALTH SERVICES

Monroe Community Mental Health **734.243.7340**
Fax 734.243.5564
E-mail .... jterwilliger@mail.monroecmha.org
　1001 S Raisinville Rd, Monroe, MI 48161-0726
　Jane S. Terwilliger, Msw, Executive Director

JUSTICE AGENCY

CASA **734.850.6040**
Fax 734.850.6099
Web www.bedford.k12.mi.us
E-mail .... brescold@bedford.k12.mi.us
　1623 W Sterns Rd, Temperance, MI 48182-1597
　Deb J Brescol, Executive Director

POLICE AND SHERIFF

Sheriff's Dept **734.240.7401**
Fax 734.240.7480
　100 E 2nd St, Monroe, MI 48162
　Tilman Crutchfield, Sheriff

EDUCATION SERVICES

Special Education **734.242.5799**
Fax 734.242.5807
Web www.misd.k12.mi.us
E-mail .... michelle.brahaney@misd.us
　1101 S Raisinville Rd, Monroe, MI 48161-9047
　Michelle Brahaney, Assistant Superintendent For Special Education

Montcalm County

SOCIAL SERVICES

Dept of Human Svcs **989.831.8400**
Fax 989.831.8496
Web .... www.michigan.gov/dhs
E-mail .... michelles@michigan.gov
　609 N State St, Stanton, MI 48888-9702
　Michelle Seigo, Director

GENERAL HEALTH SERVICES

Mid-Michigan District Health Dept **989.831.5237**
Fax 989.831.5522
E-mail .... bhavlicek@mmdhd.org
　615 N State St, Ste 1, Stanton, MI 48888
　Bonnie Havlicek, HIV Coordinator

COURTS

Family Div of Circuit Court **989.831.7308**
Fax 989.831.7548
　625 N State St, Stanton, MI 48888
　Kristi Romashko, Court Administrator

Montmorency County

SOCIAL SERVICES

Dept of Human Svcs **989.785.4218**
Fax 989.785.2302
Web .... www.michigan.gov/dhs
　11636 M-32 West, Atlanta, MI 49709
　John Kuller, Director

GENERAL HEALTH SERVICES

Montmorency Health Home Care **989.785.4428**
Fax 989.785.2217
Web www.dhd4.org
　12519 State st, Atlanta, MI 49709-9538
　Mary Thompson, Public Health Nurse

Muskegon County

SOCIAL SERVICES

Dept of Human Svcs **231.733.3700**
Fax 231.733.3790
Web .... www.michigan.gov/dhs
E-mail .... johnsonj13@michigan.gov
　2700 Baker St Ste 2, Muskegon, MI 49444
　Jane Johnson, Executive Director

GENERAL HEALTH SERVICES

Health Dept **231.724.6246**
Fax 231.724.6674
Web .... www.muskegonhealth.net
E-mail .... hayeska@co.muskegon.mi.us
　209 E Apple Ave, Muskegon, MI 49442-3406
　Kathy Hayes, Supervisor

JUSTICE AGENCY

Child Abuse Council **231.728.6410**
Fax 231.722.7161
E-mail .... child@childabusecouncil.org
　1781 Peck St Ste 1, Muskegon, MI 49441
　Kristen Collee, Executive Director

POLICE AND SHERIFF

Sheriff's Dept **231.724.6351**
Fax 231.724.6177
E-mail .... roeslerde@co.muskegon.mi.us
　25 W Walton Ave, Muskegon, MI 49440
　Dean Roesler, Sheriff

EDUCATION SERVICES

Fruitport Beach Elementry **231.773.8996**
　2741 Hts Ravenna Rd, Muskegon, MI 49444
　Julie Vanbergen, Principal

Special Education **231.777.2637**
Fax 231.773.1028
E-mail .... kfortino@muskegonisd.org
　630 Harvey St, Muskegon, MI 49442
　Kathy Fortino, Director

Newaygo County

SOCIAL SERVICES

Dept of Human Svcs **231.689.5500**
Fax 231.689.5586
Web .... www.michigan.gov
E-mail .... mccormickj@michigan.gov
　1018 E Newell St, White Cloud, MI 49349-8795
　James Mccormick, Director

GENERAL HEALTH SERVICES

Health Dept **231.689.7300**
Fax 231.689.7382
　1049 E Newell St, White Cloud, MI 49349
　Ann Bianchi, Rd, Wic Director

COURTS

Family Div of Circuit Court **231.689.7275**
Fax 231.689.7015
Web .... www.countyofnewaygo.com
E-mail .... worth@co.newaygo.mi.us
　1092 E Newell St, White Cloud, MI 49349-8795
　Ellsworth Stay, Director

Oakland County

SOCIAL SERVICES

District 4 .... **248.975.5200**
Fax 248.975.5395
　235 N Saginaw St, Pontiac, MI 48342
　J Robinson, Acting Programme Manager

GENERAL HEALTH SERVICES

Family Independence Agency **248.975.4800**
Fax 248.975.4855
　28 North Saganaw, Pontiac, MI 48342
　D Williams, Director

Health Dept - North Ofc **248.858.1280**
Fax 248.858.5639
　1200 N Telegraph Rd, Bldg 36E, Pontiac, MI 48341
　George Miller, Director

Health Dept South Ofc **248.424.7000**
Fax 248.424.7144
E-mail .... schumacherj@co.oakland.mi.us
　27725 Greenfield Rd, Southfield, MI 48076
　Joyce Schumacher, Rn, Aids Coordinator

MENTAL HEALTH SERVICES

CMHSP (Mental Health) **248.858.1210**
Fax 248.858.1855
Web .... www.occmha.org
E-mail .... brownj@occmha.org
　2011 Executive Hills Blvd, Auburn Hills,
　MI 48326-2944
　Jeffery Brown, Executive Director

JUSTICE AGENCY

Probation Programs **248.858.0484**
Fax 248.452.9215
Web .... www.oakgov.com
　1200 N Telegraph Rd Dept 457, Pontiac,
　MI 48341-1045
　Brooks Patterson, County Executive

COURTS

Judge Hallmarks Ofc **248.858.0290**
　1200 N Telegraph Rd, Pontiac, MI 48341
　Lisa Gould, Clerk

POLICE AND SHERIFF

Sheriff's Dept **248.858.5000**
Fax 248.858.2099
Web .... www.oaklandsheriff.com
E-mail .... ocso@oakgov.com
　1200 N Telegraph Rd, Pontiac, MI 48341
　Michael J. Bouchard, Sheriff

EDUCATION SERVICES

**Brandon School District - Head
Start** **248.627.1800**
Fax 248.627.5079
E-mail .... pehde@brandon.k12.mi.us
　209 Varsity Dr, Ortonville, MI 48462
　Pamela Ehde, Director

Farmington Preschool Head Start **248.489.3373**
Fax 248.489.3378
E-mail .... kirsten.jules@farmington.k12.mi.us
　30415 Shiawassee Rd, Farmington, MI 48336
　Kirsten Jules, Director

Oceana County

SOCIAL SERVICES

Family Independence Agency **231.873.7251**
Fax 231.873.7152
Web .... www.michigan.gov
　4081 W Polk Rd, Hart, MI 49420-8177
　James Johnson, Director

GENERAL HEALTH SERVICES

Health Dept **231.873.2193**
Fax 231.873.4248
Web www.dhd10.org
　3986 N Oceana Dr, Hart, MI 49420-8358
　Robin Walicki, Health Counsellor

COURTS

Family Div of Circuit Court **231.873.4605**
Fax 231.873.0252
Web ....www.oceanacountyfoc.com
E-mail ....help@oceanacountyfoc.com
   100 S State St Ste M-10, Hart, MI 49420-1188
   Pat Murphy, Director

POLICE AND SHERIFF

Sheriff's Ofc **231.873.2121**
Fax 231.873.0154
   216 E Lincoln St, Hart, MI 49420
   Bob Farber, Sheriff

Ogemaw County

SOCIAL SERVICES

Dept of Human Svcs **989.345.5135**
Fax 989.345.8590
E-mail ....hobbsk@michigan.gov
   444 E Houghton Ave, West Branch, MI 48661
   Karin Hobbs, Director

COURTS

Family Div of Circuit Court **989.345.0145**
Fax 989.345.5901
Web ....www.ogemawcountymi.gov
   806 W Houghton Ave Ste 203, West Branch,
   MI 48661-1215
   Honorable Shana Lambourn, Director

POLICE AND SHERIFF

Sheriff's Ofc **989.345.3111**
Fax 989.345.7400
E-mail ....ogemawsheriff@ogsh.org
   806 W Wright St, West Branch, MI 48661
   Howie Hanft, Sheriff

Ontonagon County

SOCIAL SERVICES

Family Independence Agency **906.884.4951**
Fax 906.884.6323
Web ....www.michigan.gov
E-mail ....pekurig@michigan.gov
   730 S 7th St, Ontonagon, MI 49953-1451
   Gordon Pekuri, Director

GENERAL HEALTH SERVICES

Health Dept **906.884.4485**
Fax 906.884.2358
Web ....www.hline.org
E-mail ....spiehl@hline.org
   408 Copper St, Ontonagon, MI 49953-1158
   Sarah Piehl, Rn, Nursing Supervisor

COURTS

Family Div of Circuit Court **906.884.4117**
Fax 906.884.2916
   725 Greenland Rd, Ontonagon, MI 49953-1423
   Paula Domitrovich, Juvenile Officer

Osceola County

SOCIAL SERVICES

Independent Living Svcs **231.796.4300**
Fax 231.796.0799
Web ....www.michigan.gov/dhs
E-mail ....dmajor@dhs.state.ia.us
   800 Water Tower Rd, Big Rapids, MI 49307-2161
   Lewis Roubal, Acting Director

GENERAL HEALTH SERVICES

Health Dept **231.832.5532**
Fax 231.832.1020
Web ....www.cmdhd.org
E-mail ....bjohnson@cmdhd.org
   4329 220th Ave, Reed City, MI 49677-8594
   Becky Himes, Rn, Nursing Supervisor

COURTS

Family Div of Circuit Court **231.832.6124**
Fax 231.832.6181
   410 W Upton Ave Ste 3, Reed City, MI 49677
   Marco Menezes, Judge

POLICE AND SHERIFF

Sheriff's Ofc **231.832.2288**
Fax 231.832.6173
E-mail ....james.crawford@bmc.org
   325 W Upton Ave, Reed City, MI 49677
   James Crawford, Sheriff

Oscoda County

SOCIAL SERVICES

Dept of Human Svcs **989.826.4000**
Fax 989.826.3961
Web ....www.michigan.gov/dhs
   200 W 5th St, Mio, MI 48467
   Cynthia Pushman, CEO/Executive Director

GENERAL HEALTH SERVICES

Health Dept **989.826.3970**
Fax 989.343.1895
Web www.dhd2.org
E-mail ....slovelace@dhd2.org
   393 S Mount Tom Rd, Mio, MI 48647-9368
   Sue Lovelace, RN, Nursing Supervisor

POLICE AND SHERIFF

Sheriff's Ofc **989.826.3214**
Fax 989.826.6833
   301 S Morenci Ave, Mio, MI 48647
   Kevin Grace, Sheriff

Otsego County

GENERAL HEALTH SERVICES

**Northwest Michigan Community Health
Agency** **989.732.1794**
Fax 989.732.3285
   95 Livingston Blvd Ste A, Gaylord, MI 49735
   Bert Notestine, Hiv Coordinator

COURTS

Family Div of Circuit Court **989.731.0214**
Fax 989.732.5130
   800 Livingston Blvd Ste 1C, Gaylord, MI 49735
   Honorable Michael K. Cooper, Judge

POLICE AND SHERIFF

Sheriff's Ofc **989.732.3555**
Fax 989.731.7299
Web ....www.otsegocountymi.gov
E-mail ....sheriff69@otsegocountymi.gov
   124 S Court Ave, Gaylord, MI 49735-1309
   James D. Mcbride, Sheriff

Ottawa County

SOCIAL SERVICES

Family Independence Agency **616.394.7220**
Fax 616.394.0029
Web ....www.michigan.gov/dhl
   12185 James St Ste 200, Holland, MI 49424-9698
   Michelle Martin, Director

GENERAL HEALTH SERVICES

Health Dept **616.396.5266**
Fax 616.393.5659
Web ....www.miottawa.org
E-mail ....pheidel@miottawa.org
   12251 James St Ste 500, Holland, MI 49424-8944
   Paul Heidel, Md, Interim Medical Director

Health Dept - Holland

Ofc/Environmental **616.393.5645**
Fax 616.393.5643
Web ....www.miottawa.org
   12251 James St Ste 200, Holland, MI 49424
   Paul Heidel, Md, Medical Director

MENTAL HEALTH SERVICES

Community Mental Health **616.392.1873**
Fax 616.393.5687
Web ....www.co.ottawa.mi.us
E-mail ....mbrashears@co.ottawa.mi.us
   12265 James St, Holland, MI 49424-8613
   Michael Brashears, Executive Director

COURTS

Probation and Juvenile Court **616.786.4110**
Fax 616.738.4624
   12120 Fillmore St, West Olive, MI 49460
   Kevin Bowling, Court Director

POLICE AND SHERIFF

Sheriff's Ofc **616.738.4000**
Fax 616.738.4061
E-mail ....grosema@mi.ottawa.org
   12220 Fillmore St, West Olive, MI 49460
   Gary Rosema, Sheriff

EDUCATION SERVICES

Bright Beginnings Childcare Ctr **616.842.6515**
Fax 616.842.4967
Web ....www.cdsoc.org
E-mail ....sbraspenning@cdsoc.org
   332A N Ferry St, Grand Haven, MI 49417-1122
   Susie Braspenning, Director

**Life Svcs System / Communities In
Schools** **616.396.7566**
Fax 616.396.6893
E-mail ....ddepree@lifeservicessystem.org
   11172 Adams St, Holland, MI 49423
   Deanna Depree, Executive Director

Presque Isle County

SOCIAL SERVICES

Dept of Human Svcs **989.734.2108**
Fax 989.734.2767
Web ....www.michigan.gov/dhs
   1242 W Third St, Rogers City, MI 49779-1206
   Julie Sproul, Acting Director

GENERAL HEALTH SERVICES

**District Health Dept #4 -- Home &
Health** **989.734.4723**
Fax 989.734.3866
   151 E Huron Ave, Rogers City, MI 49779
   Brenda Kamyszek, Public Health Nurse

COURTS

Family Div of Circuit Court **989.734.3268**
Fax 989.734.4420
   151 E Huron Ave, Rogers City, MI 49779
   Donald J Mclennan, Judge

POLICE AND SHERIFF

Sheriff's Dept **989.734.2156**
Fax 989.734.7431
Web www.i2k.net
   267 N Second St, Rogers City, MI 49779-1606
   Robert Paschke, Sheriff

Michigan

Roscommon County

SOCIAL SERVICES

Dept of Human Svcs **989.275.5107**
Fax 989.275.5545
Web .... www.michigan.gov/dhs
    111 Union St, Roscommon, MI 48653-7402
Karen Hobbs, Director

COURTS

Family Div of Circuit Court **989.275.5221**
Fax 989.275.8537
Web .... www.roscommoncounty.net
E-mail .... probatecourt@roscommoncounty.net
    500 Lake St, Roscommon, MI 48653-7664
Honorable Douglas C. Dosson, Judge

POLICE AND SHERIFF

Sheriff's Dept **989.275.5101**
Fax 989.275.5843
E-mail .... sheriff@roscommoncounty.net
    111 S 2nd St, Roscommon, MI 48653
Randall Stevenson, Sheriff

Saginaw County

GENERAL HEALTH SERVICES

Dept of Public Health **989.758.3800**
Fax 989.758.3750
Web .... www.saginawpublichealth.org
E-mail .... tsimon@saginawcounty.com
    1600 N Michigan Ave Ste 304, Saginaw,
    MI 48602-5306
Tonya Simon, Nursing Director

JUSTICE AGENCY

CASA - Program of Child Abuse and Neglect
Council **989.752.7226**
Fax 989.752.2777
Web .... www.cancouncil.org
    1311 N Michigan Ave, Saginaw, MI 48602
Randy Roberts, Coordinator

Juvenile Court Svcs / Family Court **989.799.2821**
Fax 989.799.2171
E-mail .... cmorley@saginawcounty.com
    3360 Hospital Rd, Saginaw, MI 48603
Cindy Morley, Case Director

POLICE AND SHERIFF

Sheriff's Ofc **989.790.5456**
Fax 989.790.5429
E-mail .... wfederspiel@saginawcounty.com
    618 Cass St, Saginaw, MI 48602-2044
William Feder Spiel, Sheriff

EDUCATION SERVICES

Intermediate School District **989.799.4733**
Fax 989.793.1571
Web .... www.sisd.cc
E-mail .... rsyrek@sisd.cc
    6235 Gratiot Rd, Saginaw, MI 48638-5987
Richard Syrek, Superintendent

Special Education **989.777.2520**
Fax 989.399.7479
Web .... www.sisd.cc
    3660 Southfield Dr, Saginaw, MI 48601-5653
Cherry Haswell, Principal

Saint Clair County

SOCIAL SERVICES

Dept of Human Svcs **810.966.2000**
Fax 810.966.2025
Web .... www.michigan.gov/dhs
E-mail .... howep@michigan.gov
    220 Fort St, Port Huron, MI 48060
Kay Andrzejak, Director

GENERAL HEALTH SERVICES

Health Dept **810.987.5300**
Fax 810.985.2150
Web .... www.saintclaircounty.org
    3415 28th St, Port Huron, MI 48060-6931
Annette Mercantate, Director/health Officer

COURTS

Family Div of Circuit Court **810.985.2155**
Fax 810.985.2470
E-mail .... ebrown@stclaircounty.org
    201 McMorran Blvd Rm 2108, Port Huron, MI 48060
Honorable Elwood L. Brown, Judge

POLICE AND SHERIFF

Sheriff's Dept **810.987.1712**
Fax 810.985.3219
Web .... www.stclaircounty.org
    1170 Michigan Rd, Port Huron, MI 48060-4658
Tim Donnellon, Sheriff

Sanilac County

POLICE AND SHERIFF

Sheriff's Ofc **810.648.2000**
Fax 810.648.3170
Web .... www.sanilaccounty.net
    65 N Elk St, Sandusky, MI 48471-1396
Gary Vinicki, Sheriff

EDUCATION SERVICES

CPS Head Start **810.657.9397**
Web .... www.cis.state.mi.us
E-mail .... beverly.sleda@cis.state.mi.us
    4115 E Chandler St, Carsonville, MI 48419-9604
Beverly Sleda, Director

Schoolcraft County

SOCIAL SERVICES

Dept of Human Svcs **906.341.2114**
Fax 906.341.2110
Web .... www.michigan.gov/dhs
    300 Walnut St Rm 175A, Manistique, MI 49854
Douglas York, Acting Director

COURTS

Family Div of Circuit Court **906.341.3641**
Fax 906.341.3627
    300 Walnut St Rm 129, Manistique, MI 49854-1495
Charles Mebel, Family Court Judge

POLICE AND SHERIFF

Sheriff's Ofc **906.341.2122**
Fax 906.341.6154
Web .... www.chartermi.net
E-mail .... scsheriff@chartermi.net
    300 Main St, Manistique, MI 49854-1224
Brent Harris, Sheriff

Shiawassee County

SOCIAL SERVICES

Dept of Human Svcs **989.725.3200**
Fax 989.725.3308
Web .... www.michigan.gov
E-mail .... fultons@michigan.gov
    1720 E M ST STE 1, Owosso, MI 48867-1379
Susan Fulton, Director

GENERAL HEALTH SERVICES

Health Dept **989.743.2355**
Fax 989.743.2357
Web .... www.healthshiawassee.net
E-mail .... rcurnow@shiawassee.net
    110 E Mack St Fl 1, Corunna, MI 48817-1452
Rochelle Curnow, Aids Coordinator

COURTS

Family Div of Circuit Court **989.743.2372**
Fax 989.743.2349
E-mail .... jclatterbaugh@shiawassee.net
    110 E Mack St Fl 2, Corunna, MI 48817
Honorable James R. Clatterbaugh, Judge

EDUCATION SERVICES

CACS Preschool Program & Head
Start **989.723.5849**
Fax 989.723.8151
Web .... www.cacsheadstart.org
E-mail .... kelda.wilson@cacsheadstart.org
    308 W Main St Ste 1, Owosso, MI 48867-2905
Kelda Wilson, Director

St. Joseph County

GENERAL HEALTH SERVICES

Health Dept **269.273.2161**
Fax 269.273.2452
Web .... www.bhsj.org
E-mail .... phillipsj@bhsj.org
    1110 Hill St, Three Rivers, MI 49093-2724
James Phillips, Md, Mph, Medical Director

POLICE AND SHERIFF

Sheriff's Dept **269.467.9045**
Fax 269.467.6201
    650 E Main St, Centreville, MI 49032
Brad Balk, Sheriff

Tuscola County

GENERAL HEALTH SERVICES

Health Dept **989.673.8114**
Fax 989.673.7490
    1309 Cleaver Rd Ste B, Caro, MI 48723
Russell Bush, Medical Director

COURTS

Family Div of Circuit Court **989.672.3850**
Fax 989.672.2057
    440 N State St Dept 1, Caro, MI 48723
Amanda L Roggenbuck, Judge

EDUCATION SERVICES

Cass City Head Start **989.872.5360**
    4869 Seeger St, Cass City, MI 48726-9731
Debbie Romosier, Director

Van Buren County

COURTS

Family Div of Circuit Court **269.657.8237**
Fax 269.657.7573
    212 E Paw Paw St Ste 240, Paw Paw, MI 49079-1473
Honorable Frank D. Willis, Judge

POLICE AND SHERIFF

Sheriff's Dept **269.657.2006**
Fax 269.657.5161
Web .... www.vbco.org
E-mail .... griblerd@vbco.org
    205 S Kalamazoo St, Paw Paw, MI 49079-1525
Dale R. Gribler, Sheriff

Washtenaw County

SOCIAL SERVICES

Dept of Human Svcs **734.481.2000**
Fax 734.481.2059
Web .... www.michigan.gov
    22 Center St, Ypsilanti, MI 48198-5707
Cynthia Martatio, Manager

Human Resources............................**734.481.2000**
Fax...734.481.8386
E-mail......................................maritatoc@michigan.gov
   22 Center St, Ypsilanti, MI 48198
Cynthia Maritato, Director

GENERAL HEALTH SERVICES

Health Dept...................................**734.544.6700**
Fax...734.544.6706
   555 Towner St Ste 1, Ypsilanti, MI 48197-0915
Diana Torres-burgos, Medical Director

JUSTICE AGENCY

Family Court...................................**734.222.6900**
Fax...734.222.6915
   101 E Huron, Ann Arbor, MI 48107
Linda Edwards-brown, Administrator

POLICE AND SHERIFF

Barton Hills Village Police Dept.............**734.663.1284**
   221 Barton Shore Dr, Ann Arbor, MI 48105-1023
Walter Esch, Police Chief

EDUCATION SERVICES

Special Education............................**734.994.8100**
Fax...734.994.2203
Web..www.wash.k12.mi.us
E-mail..................................jburton@wash.k12.mi.us
   1819 S Wagner Rd, Ann Arbor, MI 48103-9715
Jennifer Burton, Director

Wayne County

SOCIAL SERVICES

Dept of Human Svcs.........................**313.295.8000**
Fax...313.295.8126
   25350 Ecorse Rd, Taylor, MI 48180
E Banks, District Secretary

Dept of Human Svcs - Zone 10 Ofc............**313.456.1044**
Fax...313.456.1253
   3040 W Grand Blvd, Ste 5-600, Detroit, MI 48202
Margaret Warner, Wayne County District Manager

Dept of Human Svcs - Zone 9 Ofc.............**313.456.1024**
Fax...313.456.1245
Web...www.michigan.gov
E-mail...willisc@michigan.gov
   2020 W Grand Blvd, Ste 5, Detroit, MI 48202
Clarence Willis Jr., Manager

GENERAL HEALTH SERVICES

**Detroit Dept of Health and Wellness
Promotion**....................................**313.876.4000**
Fax...313.876.0400
Web..................www.ci.detroit.mi.us/health/default.htm
E-mail.................................frankling@detroitmi.gov
   1151 Taylor St, Detroit, MI 48202-1732
Gwen Franklin, Public Health Nursing Division Director

Health Dept...................................**734.727.7000**
Fax...734.727.7043
Web..www.waynecounty.com
   33030 Van Born Rd, Wayne, MI 48184-2453
Vinny Taneja, Deputy Health Director

Taylor Health Ctr.............................**734.955.3900**
Fax...734.955.3910
Web..www.co.wayne.mi.us
E-mail......................................mpaxson@co.wayne.mi.us
   26650 Eureka Rd, Ste B, Taylor, MI 48180
Mary Paxson, Clinic Supervisor

JUSTICE AGENCY

CASA Program.................................**313.833.3093**
Fax...313.833.4649
   1025 E Forest Ave, Ste 118, Detroit, MI 48207
Roland Smith, Director

COURTS

Family Div of Circuit Court...................**313.833.5600**
Fax...313.833.1787
   1025 E Forest Ave, Detroit, MI 48207-1024
Joseph Avore, Juvenile Registrar

POLICE AND SHERIFF

Detroit Police Dept...........................**313.596.1800**
   1300 Beaubien St, Detroit, MI 48226
Ralph L. Godbee Jr., Police Chief

**Detroit Police Dept - Northeastern District
Ofc**..**313.596.1100**
Fax...313.596.1170
   5100 E Nevada St, Detroit, MI 48234
Debra Fair, Commander

**Detroit Police Dept - Northwestern District
Ofc**..**313.596.5600**
Fax...313.596.5615
   11450 Warwick St, Detroit, MI 48228-1388
Ralph Godbee, Chief

**Detroit Police Dept - Southwestern District
Ofc**..**313.596.5300**
Fax...313.596.5310
E-mail......................ewinge@dpdhq.ci.detroit.mi.us
   4700 W Fort St, Detroit, MI 48209-3211
Eric Ewing, Commander

Sheriff's Dept.................................**313.224.2233**
Fax...313.224.2367
   1231 Saint Antoine St, Detroit, MI 48226
Benny N. Napoleon, Sheriff

EDUCATION SERVICES

Ecorse River Rouge Head Start..............**313.928.6200**
Fax...313.928.6201
Web..www.guidance-center.org
   550 Eaton St, River Rouge, MI 48218-1124
Adrianne Sewell, Interim Director

Emmanuel Head Start.........................**313.366.5605**
Fax...313.366.3552
   18440 John R St, Highland Park, MI 48202
Mary Hanna, Director

Renaissance Head Start......................**313.867.0500**
Fax...313.867.5112
   13110 14th St, Detroit, MI 48238-3647
Reginald Ross, Director

St. Vincent & Sarah Fischer Ctr...............**313.535.9200**
Fax...313.535.7804
Web..www.svsfcenter.org
E-mail..........................diane.renaug@svsfcenter.org
   16800 Trinity St, Detroit, MI 48219-3968
Diane Renaug, President/CEO

Wexford County

SOCIAL SERVICES

Dept of Human Svcs.........................**231.779.4500**
Fax...231.779.4574
Web...www.michigan.gov
E-mail.....................................sweeneyh@michigan.gov
   10641 W Watergate Rd, Cadillac, MI 49601-9424
Howard Sweeney, Director

GENERAL HEALTH SERVICES

Health Dept...................................**231.775.9942**
Fax...231.775.5372
   521 Cobb St Ste B, Cadillac, MI 49601
Pattie Schneider, Aids Coordinator

COURTS

Family Div of Circuit Court...................**231.779.9510**
Fax...231.779.9485
Web..www.wexfordcounty.org
   437 E Division St, Cadillac, MI 49601
Honorable Kenneth L. Tacoma, Judge

POLICE AND SHERIFF

Sheriff's Dept.................................**231.779.9211**
Fax...231.779.0218
E-mail.....................................wexford@netonecom.net
   820 S Carmel St, Cadillac, MI 49601
Gary A. Finstrom, Sheriff

EDUCATION SERVICES

Cadillac Head Start...........................**231.775.7871**
   1640 Marty Paul St, Cadillac, MI 49601-9608
Terri Colococco, Director

Michigan

SPECIAL SERVICES AGENCIES

ADOPTION AGENCIES

A A Swartz Adoption Attorneys.............**989.793.0000**
Fax...989.793.7571
Web..www.swartzadoptions.com
   908 Court St Frnt, Saginaw, MI 48602-4115
Christopher Swartz, Director

Adoption Associates, Inc.....................**616.667.0677**
Fax...616.667.0920
Web..www.adoptionassociates.net
E-mail..........................adopt@adoptionassociates.net
   1338 Baldwin St, Jenison, MI 49428-8937
Jane Bareman, Executive Director

Adoption Option Inc..........................**989.839.0534**
Fax...989.839.0537
Web..www.adoptionoptioninc.org
E-mail..leapheart@gmail.com
   4008 W Wackerly St, Midland, MI 48640
Delois Leapheart, Director

Bethany Christian Svcs.......................**616.224.7610**
Web...www.bethany.org
E-mail...info@bethany.org
   901 Eastern Ave NE, Grand Rapids, MI 49503
Bill Blacquiere, President

Bethany Christian Svcs.......................**248.414.4080**
Fax...248.414.4085
Web..www.bethany.org/madisonheights
E-mail.....................................bcsmadisonhts@bethany.org
   30685 Barrington St Ste 140, Madison Heights,
MI 48071
Sheila Mounts, Director

Bethany Christian Svcs.......................**616.396.0623**
Fax...616.396.2315
Web..www.bethany.org/holland
   12048 James St, Holland, MI 49424
Steve Eckert, Director

Bethany Christian Svcs **269.372.8800**
Fax 269.372.8855
Web ....www.bethany.org
E-mail ....bcskalamazoo@bethany.org
   6687 Seeco Dr, Kalamazoo, MI 49009-5970
   Brad Keller, Director

Bethany Christian Svcs **231.995.0870**
Fax 231.995.0871
Web ....www.bethany.org/traverse
E-mail ....bcstraversecity@bethany.org
   1055 Carrage Dr, Traverse City, MI 49684-8878
   Craig Bultsma, Director

Camp Line Law Firm **248.528.1111**
Fax 248.528.5129
   201 W Big Beaver Rd Ste 600, Troy, MI 48084
   Ralph Castelli, Managing Partner

Catholic Social Svcs **906.227.9121**
Fax 906.228.2469
E-mail ....lkearney@dioceseofmarquette.org
   347 Rock St, Marquette, MI 49855-4783
   Deacon Dan Powers, Executive Director

**Central Care Management Organization dba Center for Youth
and Families** **313.875.2092**
Fax 313.875.2192
Web ....www.ccmorg.org
   3031 W. Grand Boulevard, Suite 370, Detroit,
   MI 48202
   COA accredited organization.

Child & Family Svcs **989.356.4567**
Fax 989.354.6100
Web ....www.cfsm.org
E-mail ....dorrl@cfsnemi.org
   1044 US Highway 23 N, Alpena, MI 49707-1262
   Lyle Dorr, Executive Director

Children's Ctr **313.832.3555**
Fax 313.262.0902
Web ....www.thechildrenscenter.com
   79 W Alexandrine Ln, Detroit, MI 48201
   Debora Matthews, Chief Executive Officer

D. A. Blodgett - St. John's **616.451.2021**
Fax 616.451.8936
Web ....www.dablodgett.org
   805 Leonard St. NE, Grand Rapids, MI 49503-1184
   COA accredited organization.

Ennis Ctr For Children **313.342.2699**
Fax 313.342.2180
Web ....www.enniscenter.org
E-mail ....uahart@evergreenserv.org
   20100 Greenfield Rd, Detroit, MI 48235-1803
   Ursala Ahart, Program Director

Ennis Ctr For Children **810.233.4031**
Fax 810.233.0008
Web ....www.enniscenter.org
E-mail ....bob.ennis@enniscenter.org
   129 E 3rd St, Flint, MI 48502-1728
   Bob Ennis, President

Families Through Adoption **616.242.9696**
Web ....www.familiesthroughadoption.org
E-mail ....char@familiesthroughadoption.org
   354 Norwood Ave SE, Grand Rapids, MI 49506
   Char Lanning, Director

Family Counseling & Children's Services **517.265.5352**
Fax 517.263.6090
Web ....www.fccservices.org
   220 N. Main Street, Adrian, MI 49221
   COA accredited organization.

Flint Alternatives - Children **810.250.3800**
Fax 810.250.3836
E-mail ....info@acfinc.org
   2065 S Center Road, Burton, MI 48519
   Yvwaina Richardson, Director

Forever Families Inc **248.344.9606**
Fax 248.344.9604
E-mail ....info@forever-families.org
   42400 Grand River Ave Ste 111, Novi, MI 48375
   Denise Weiss, Director

Frederick F Swegles Ofc **810.984.2228**
Fax 810.984.4249
Web ....www.adoptadvisor.com
E-mail ....rick@adoptadvisor.com
   415 Andrew Murphy Dr, Port Huron, MI 48060-3801
   Frederick F Swegles, Director

GreenPath, Inc. **248.553.5400**
Fax 248.553.2224
Web ....www.greenpath.com
   38505 Country Club Drive, Suite 210, Farmington
   Hills, MI 48331-3429
   COA accredited organization.

Gryphon Place **269.381.1510**
Fax 269.381.0935
Web ....www.gryphon.org
   1104 South Westnedge Avenue, Kalamazoo,
   MI 49008
   COA accredited organization.

Judson Center Inc. **248.549.4339**
Fax 248.837.2013
Web ....www.judsoncenter.org
   4410 West Thirteen Mile Road, Royal Oak,
   MI 48073-6515
   COA accredited organization.

Judson Ctr **734.528.1720**
Fax 734.528.1695
Web ....www.judsoncenter.org
E-mail ....jennifer_trotter@judsoncenter.org
   3840 Packard Rd Ste 170, Ann Arbor, MI 48108-1521
   Jennifer Trotter, Director

Lutheran Adoption Svc - Bay City Branch **989.686.3170**
Fax 989.686.7683
Web ....www.lssm.org
E-mail ....rsalv@lssm.org
   6019 W Side Saginaw Rd, Bay City, MI 48706
   Rebecca Salvner, Supervisor

Matrix Human Services **313.831.1000**
Fax 313.831.4634
Web ....www.matrixhumanservices.org
   120 Parsons Street, Detroit, MI 48201
   COA accredited organization.

**Metropolitan Arts Complex Inc., dba Metro Arts Therapy
Services** **313.863.5554**
Fax 313.863.4711
Web ....www.metropolitanartscomplex.org
   11000 W. McNichols, Suites B1-B4, Detroit,
   MI 48221
   COA accredited organization.

New Light Consultants, Inc. **989.871.6695**
Fax 989.871.3663
Web ....www.newlightconsultants.net
   P.O. Box 359, Millington, MI 48746
   COA accredited organization.

Orchards Children's Svcs **248.258.0440**
Fax 248.258.0487
Web ....www.orchards.org
   30215 Southfield Rd Ste 100, Southfield, MI 48076
   Vicki Orleans, Director Of Adoptions

Pathways, MI **616.396.2301**
Fax 616.396.8070
Web ....www.pathwaysmi.org
   412 Century Lane, Holland, MI 49423
   COA accredited organization.

Spectrum Human Svcs **248.552.8020**
Fax 248.552.8020
Web ....www.spectrumhumanservices.org
   16250 northland dr, ste 250, Southfield,
   MI 48075-3749
   Delisa Glaspie, Program Director

StarrVista **313.387.1235**
Fax 313.387.0760
Web ....www.starrvista.org
   22390 West Seven Mile Road, Detroit, MI 48219
   COA accredited organization.

Wolverine Human Services, Inc. **313.824.4400**
Fax 313.824.4522
Web ....www.wolverinehs.org
   81 Enterprise Drive, Vassar, MI 48768
   COA accredited organization.

ADVOCACY RESOURCES

Andre Bosfe Ctr **231.873.1707**
Fax 231.873.8687
Web ....www.andrebosfecenter.org
E-mail ....heather@andrebosfecenter.org
   302 Hansen St, Hart, MI 49420
   Heather Green, Executive Director

Care House **248.333.0999**
Fax 248.333.1539
Web ....www.carehouse.org
E-mail ....prosen@carehouse.org
   44765 Woodward Ave, Pontiac, MI 48341-5021
   Pat Rosen, Director

Care House **586.463.0123**
Fax 586.783.3515
Web ....www.mccarehouse.org
E-mail ....d.nolan@mccarehouse.org
   131 Market St, Mount Clemens, MI 48043-1762
   Dorie Nolan, Director

CASA **269.445.4431**
Fax 269.445.8978
E-mail ....casscocasa@yahoo.com
   120 N Broadway St., Suite 215, Cassopolis,
   MI 49031-1364
   James Ward, Executive Director

**Child & Family Svcs of The Upper Peninsula,
Inc.** **906.228.4050**
Fax 906.228.2153
Web ....www.cffup.org
E-mail ....info@cffup.org
   706 Chippewa Sq., Ste 200, Houghton, MI 49855
   Norma Semashko, CEO

Feldman & Feldman **269.683.0700**
E-mail ....feldmangreg@comcast.net
   317 Broadway, Niles, MI 49120
   Gregory Feldman, Attorney

Honigman Miller Schwartz & Cohn LLP **313.465.7000**
E-mail ....sdouglas@honigman.com
   660 Woodward Ave, 2290 First National Bldg,
   Detroit, MI 48226
   David Foltyn, CEO

Honigman Miller Schwartz Cohn **313.465.7518**
E-mail ....lara.phillip@honigman.com
   660 Woodward Ave, 2290 First National Bldg,
   Detroit, MI 48226
   Lara Fetsco Phillip, Director

LaFave Smith Ctr for Family & Elder Law **517.485.3595**
E-mail ....lafavesmithlaw@aol.com
   1918 E Michigan Ave, Lansing, MI 48912
   Denise Lafave Smith, Attorney

Law Office of Susan Tarrant **989.249.9102**
E-mail ....sjtarrant@msn.com
   6420 Normandy Dr, Saginaw, MI 48638
   Susan Tarrant, Attorney

Pines Behavioral Health Voice and TTY **517.279.8404**
Fax 517.279.8172
Web ....www.pinesbhs.org
   200 Orleans Blvd, Coldwater, MI 49036-1767
   John Bolton, Executive Director/CEO

Safe Harbor Children's Advocacy Ctr 269.673.3791
Fax 269.686.9481
E-mail .... lantkoviak@safeharborallegan.org
402 Trowbridge St, Allegan, MI 49010-1231
Lori Antkoviak, Executive Director

Univ of Detroit Mercy Law Schl 313.596.0204
E-mail .... paruchd@udmercy.edu
651 E Jefferson Ave, Detroit, MI 48226
Deborah Paruch

Volunteer Advocates For Children 248.332.7173
Fax 248.333.1539
Web .... www.carehouse.org
E-mail .... cludwig@carehouse.org
44765 Woodward Ave, Pontiac, MI 48341-5021
Patricia Rosen, Executive Director

Western Michigan University 269.387.7073
Web .... www.wmich.edu
E-mail .... james.henry@wmich.edu
1000 Oakland Ave, Kalamazoo, MI 49008
Jim Henry, Director

BEHAVIORAL HEALTH TREATMENT

Abaris Behavioral Health - Rochester 248.650.8383
Fax 248.650.4343
Web .... www.abarishealth.com
1202 Walton Boulevard, Suite 212, Rochester, MI 48307
CARF accredited programs available.

ACAC, Inc. 616.957.5850
E-mail .... mdurco19@comcast.net
3949 Sparks Drive SE Suite 103, Grand Rapids, MI 49546
Mr. Michael Durco, Accreditation Manager
Joint Commission accredited organization.

Academy Of The Sacred Heart 248.646.8900
Fax 248.646.4143
Web .... www.ashmi.org
E-mail .... chigh@ashmi.org
1250 Kensington Rd, Bloomfield Hills, MI 48304-3029
Carol High, Director

Access Behavioral Healthcare, LLC 734.453.5603
E-mail .... dw-abh1plymouth@sbcglobal.net
42189 E. Ann Arbor Road, Plymouth, MI 48170
Mr. Donald Warner, Accreditation Manager
Joint Commission accredited organization.

Access Christian Counseling 248.355.4300
Fax 248.355.4393
Web .... www.accesschristiancounsel.com
29260 Franklin Road, Suite 120, Southfield, MI 48034
CARF accredited programs available.

ACCESS Family Counseling Community Mental Health Services 313.945.8138
Fax 313.624.9418
Web .... www.accesscommunity.org
E-mail .... hdeep@accesscommunity.org
6451 Schaefer, Dearborn, MI 48126
Hannan Deep, Director of Communications
CARF accredited programs available.

Addiction Solutions Counseling Center, PC 989.779.9449
Fax 989.779.2922
218 S. Washington, Mt. Pleasant, MI 48858
COA accredited organization.

Advanced Counseling Services, P.C. 734.285.8282
Fax 734.281.4773
Web .... www.advancedcounseling.org
20600 Eureka Road, Ste 819, Taylor, MI 48180
Pat Beach, Provider Relations Director
CARF accredited programs available.

Advocacy Svcs For Kids 269.343.5896
Fax 269.978.0287
Web .... www.askforkids.org
414 E Michigan Ave, Kalamazoo, MI 49007-3888
Dianne Schaeffer, Director

Alcohol Information and Counseling Center 810.667.0243
Fax 810.245.5676
Web .... www.lchd.lapeer.org
E-mail .... tanglebrandt@lapeercounty.org
1800 Imlay City Road, Lapeer, MI 48446
Todd Anglebrandt, AICC Director
CARF accredited programs available.

Alessi Medical Practice 734.222.6222
Fax 732.222.6224
Web .... www.nalessimd.com
E-mail .... office@nalessimd.com
325 E Eisenhower, Ste 6, Ann Arbor, MI 48108
Norman Alessi, Md, Psychiatrist

Allegan General Hospital Psychological Medicine 269.673.8424
Fax 269.686.4239
Web .... http://www.aghosp.org
551 Linn Street, Allegan, MI 49010
CARF accredited programs available.

American Indian Services, Inc. 313.388.4100
Fax 313.388.6566
Web .... www.ameritech.net
1110 Southfield Road, Lincoln Park, MI 48146
CARF accredited programs available.

American Indian Svcs 313.388.4100
Fax 313.388.6566
1110 Southfield Rd, Lincoln Park, MI 48146-2409
Fay Givens, Director

Ann Arbor Consultation Services, Inc. 734.996.9111
Fax 734.996.1950
5331 Plymouth Road, Ann Arbor, MI 48105
Terry Dunivin, Director
CARF accredited programs available.

AOS of Arbor Circle 616.459.7215
Fax 616.451.0020
Web .... www.arborcircle.org
E-mail .... rwiegers@arborcircle.org
1115 Ball Ave NE, Grand Rapids, MI 49505-5904
Jack Green Sieob, Chief Executive Officer

Apex Behavioral Health, PLLC 734.729.3133
Web .... www.apexbehavioralhealth.com
E-mail .... johnsont@apexbh.com
1547 S. Wayne Rd., Westland, MI 48186
Mr. Thomas Johnson, Accreditation Manager
Joint Commission accredited organization.

Arab-American and Chaldean Council 248.559.1990
Fax 248.559.9117
Web .... www.myacc.org
E-mail .... programadvocates@myacc.org
28551 Southfield Rd, Lathrup Village, MI 48076
Robert Ghannam, Special Projects Director
CARF accredited programs available.

Arbor Circle Corporation 616.456.7775
Web .... arborcircle.org
E-mail .... kgietzen@arborcircle.org
1115 Ball Avenue, Grand Rapids, MI 49505
Ms. Kristin Gietzen, Accreditation Manager
Joint Commission accredited organization.

Auburn Counseling Associates, Inc. 810.744.3300
Fax 810.744.1090
Web .... www.auburncounseling.com
E-mail .... swedda@auburncounseling.com
3600 S Dort Hwy, Suite 44, Flint, MI 48507
Susan Wedda, Clinical Director
CARF accredited programs available.

Austad Medical Practice 734.663.3060
303 Riverview Dr, Ann Arbor, MI 48104-1847
Carol Austad, Md, Psychiatrist

Averbach Medical Practice 248.349.2000
Fax 248.349.2112
Web .... www.oaklandbehavioralhealth.com
E-mail .... oaklandhealth@aol.com
23895 Novi Rd Ste 600, Novi, MI 48375-0202
David Aberback, Md, Psychiatrist

Bay Mills Indian Community 906.248.5526
Web .... www.baymills.org/medicalcenter/index.html
E-mail .... abreakie@baymills.org
12124 West Lake Shore Drive, Brimley, MI 49715
Ms. Audrey Breakie, Accreditation Manager
Joint Commission accredited organization.

Bay Psychological Associates, P.C. 989.686.1990
Fax 989.686.0474
1420 Center Avenue, Bay City, MI 48706
CARF accredited programs available.

Bay-Arenac Behavioral Health 989.895.2353
Fax 989.895.2390
Web .... http://www.babha.org/
201 Mulholland Street, Bay City, MI 48708
CARF accredited programs available.

Behavior Educators, Inc. 517.264.1313
Fax 517.266.0553
623 North Broad Street, Adrian, MI 49221
CARF accredited programs available.

Behavioral Resources and Institute for Neuropsychological Services, PLC 616.365.8920
Fax 616.365.8971
Web .... www.brainspotential.com
3351 Eagle Run Drive NE, Suite C, Grand Rapids, MI 49525
CARF accredited programs available.

Beltzman Medical Practice 734.973.1020
Fax 734.973.1074
2004 Hogback Rd, Ann Arbor, MI 48105
David Beltzman, MD, Psychiatrist

Berrien Mental Health Authority 269.925.0585
Fax 269.927.6063
Web .... www.riverwoodcenter.org
1485 M-139, Benton Harbor, MI 49022
CARF accredited programs available.

Biological Psychiatry Center, P.C. 586.773.6020
Fax 586.773.6093
25869 Kelly Road, Suite A, Roseville, MI 48066
COA accredited organization.

Birmingham Maple Clinic 248.646.6659
Fax 248.642.8645
Web .... www.birminghammaple.com
2075 West Big Beaver Road, Suite 520, Troy, MI 48084
COA accredited organization.

Black Family Development, Inc. 313.758.0150
Fax 313.758.0262
Web .... www.blackfamilydevelopment.org
2995 East Grand Boulevard, Detroit, MI 48202
CARF accredited programs available.

Bloom Medical Practice 313.882.8640
E-mail .... vbloom@comcast.net
1007 Three Mile Dr, Grosse Pointe, MI 48230-1412
Victor Bloom, Md, Psychiatrist

Blue Water Counseling 810.985.5125
Fax 810.985.5127
Web .... www.bluewaterclinic.com
1501 Krafft Road, Fort Gratiot, MI 48059
CARF accredited programs available.

Borgess Medical Ctr 269.226.7000
Fax 269.226.5966
Web .... www.borgess.com
1521 Gull Rd, Kalamazoo, MI 49048
Kathy Grueter, Director

Brighton Area Schools-Board Of Ed Ofcs.......810.299.4000
Fax.......810.299.4092
Web.......www.bas.k12.mi.us
E-mail.......grayg@brightonk12.com
125 S Church St, Brighton, MI 48116-2403
Gregory Gray, Superintendent

Brighton Hospital.......810.227.1211
Web.......www.brightonhospital.org
E-mail.......mwhelan@brightonhospital.org
12851 Grand River Road, Brighton, MI 48116
Mrs. Melissa Whelan, Accreditation Manager
Joint Commission accredited organization.

Bucknam Medical Practice.......734.747.7114
Fax.......734.747.6747
E-mail.......wbucknam@hotmail.com
5340 Plymouth Rd, Ann Arbor, MI 48105
William Bucknam, MD, Psychiatrist

C.W. Enterprises LLC.......586.949.7680
Web.......www.thecenterforcounseling.net
E-mail.......lojodo13@hotmail.com
50630 Chesterfield Road, Chesterfield, MI 48051
Mrs. Loni Dobbyn, Accreditation Manager
Joint Commission accredited organization.

Carman Ainsworth Schools.......810.591.7055
Fax.......810.591.3835
Web.......www.carman.k12.mi.us
E-mail.......plinn@carman.k12.mi.us
1197 E Schumacher St, Burton, MI 48529-1558
Pamela Linn, Counselor

Cassandra Klyman.......248.335.7194
Fax.......248.335.5621
E-mail.......cklyman@sbcglobal.net
3060 Chickering Ln, Bloomfield Hills, MI 48302-1408
Cassandra M. Klyman, Md, Psychiatrist

Catholic Charities of Jackson, Lenawee and Hillsdale Counties.......517.782.2551
Fax.......517.783.1986
Web.......www.ccjax.org
1522 Joy Avenue, Jackson, MI 49203
COA accredited organization.

Catholic Family Service of the Diocese of Saginaw, Inc.......989.797.6638
Fax.......989.799.7436
Web.......www.cfssite.org
E-mail.......tconklin@dioceseofsaginaw.org
5800 Weiss Street, Saginaw, MI 48603-2799
Thomas Conklin, Executive Director
CARF accredited programs available.

Catholic Human Services, Inc.......231.947.8110
Fax.......231.947.3522
Web.......www.catholichumanservices.org
1000 Hastings Street, Traverse City, MI 49686-3445
CARF accredited programs available.

Catholic Services of Macomb, Inc.......586.416.2300
Web.......www.csmacomb.org
E-mail.......csmacomb@csmacomb.org
15945 Canal Road, Clinton Township, MI 48038
Mr. Thomas Reed, Accreditation Manager
Joint Commission accredited organization.

Catholic Social Services.......248.333.3700
Fax.......248.333.3718
Web.......www.cssoc.org
1424 East 11 Mile Road, Royal Oak, MI 48067
Jackie Smith, Site Manager
CARF accredited programs available.

Catholic Social Services.......810.987.9100
Fax.......810.987.9105
Web.......www.cssstclair.org
2601 Thirteenth Street, Port Huron, MI 48060
COA accredited organization.

Center for Individual and Family Therapy, PC.......313.291.7000
Fax.......313.291.0942
Web.......www.centerforfamilytherapy.com
21751 Ecorse Road, Taylor, MI 48180
CARF accredited programs available.

Central Therapeutic Services, Inc.......248.559.4340
Fax.......248.559.1451
17600 West Eight Mile Road, Suite 7, Southfield, MI 48075
CARF accredited programs available.

Child and Family Service.......989.790.7500
Fax.......989.790.8037
Web.......www.childandfamilysaginaw.org
2806 Davenport Avenue, Saginaw, MI 48602
CARF accredited programs available.

Christian Mission, Inc.......517.263.7430
E-mail.......christian.mission@frontier.com
1239 Wolf Creek Hwy, Adrian, MI 49221-9401
Jane Clark, Director

Clark and Associates Psychological Services, P.C.......248.559.2673
Fax.......248.559.7944
16250 Northland Drive, Suite 245, Southfield, MI 48075
CARF accredited programs available.

Clarkston Family Counseling Assoc.......248.922.9077
Fax.......248.922.9040
Web.......www.clarkstoncounseling.com
6770 Dixie Hwy Ste 205, Clarkston, MI 48346-2089
Young Kim, Md, Psychiatrist

Community Assessment Referral and Education.......586.541.0033
Fax.......586.541.0034
Web.......www.careofmacomb.com
31900 Utica Road, Fraser, MI 48026
CARF accredited programs available.

Community Care Services.......313.389.7525
Web.......www.comcareserv.org
E-mail.......kmarietti@comcareserv.org
26184 West Outer Drive, Lincoln Park, MI 48146
Mrs. Kelly Marietti, Accreditation Manager
Joint Commission accredited organization.

Community Care Svcs.......734.955.3550
Fax.......734.955.3562
E-mail.......bwalsh@comcareserv.org
26650 Eureka Rd, Ste A, Taylor, MI 48180
William Walsh, Director

Community Care Svcs.......734.697.7880
Fax.......734.697.7377
Web.......www.comcareserv.org
E-mail.......bwalsh@comcareserv.org
25 Owen St, Belleville, MI 48111-2921
Bill Walsh, Director

Community Healing Centers.......269.343.1651
Fax.......269.382.7078
Web.......www.communityhealingcenter.org
E-mail.......sreames@chcmi.org
2615 Stadium Drive, Kalamazoo, MI 49008
Sally Reames, Director
CARF accredited programs available.

Community Mental Health.......616.527.1790
Fax.......616.527.0538
Web.......www.ioniacmhs.org
375 Apple Tree Drive, Ionia, MI 48846
CARF accredited programs available.

Community Mental Health.......269.273.5000
Fax.......269.273.9456
Web.......www.stjoecmh.org
210 South Main Street, Three Rivers, MI 49093
CARF accredited programs available.

Community Mental Health.......616.393.5600
Fax.......616.393.5643
Web.......www.miottawa.org
E-mail.......john@srwmi.org
12265 James Street, Holland, MI 49424
John Snyder, Director
CARF accredited programs available.

Community Mental Health.......586.469.5275
Fax.......586.469.7674
Web.......www.mccmh.net
22550 Hall Road, Clinton Township, MI 48036
CARF accredited programs available.

Community Mental Health Authority.......810.985.8900
Fax.......810.985.7620
Web.......www.sccmh.org
3111 Electric Avenue, Port Huron, MI 48060
CARF accredited programs available.

Community Mental Health Authority.......989.797.3400
Fax.......989.799.0206
Web.......www.sccmha.org
500 Hancock Street, Saginaw, MI 48602
CARF accredited programs available.

Community Mental Health Authority.......810.648.0330
Fax.......810.648.0319
Web.......www.sanilaccmh.org
227 E Sanilac Ave, Sandusky, MI 48471
James Johnson, Executive Director
CARF accredited programs available.

Community Mental Health Authority.......517.546.4126
Web.......www.cmhliv.org
E-mail.......lnewberg@cmhliv.org
2280 East Grand River, Howell, MI 48843
Mr. Lawrence Newberg, Accreditation Manager
Joint Commission accredited organization.

Community Mental Health Authority.......989.723.6791
Fax.......989.725.5061
Web.......www.shiacmh.org
1555 Industrial Drive, Owosso, MI 48867
CARF accredited programs available.

Community Mental Health Authority.......269.948.8041
Fax.......269.948.9319
915 West Green Street, Hastings, MI 49058
CARF accredited programs available.

Community Mental Health Authority.......989.793.3335
Fax.......989.799.0206
Web.......www.sccmha.org
500 Hancock Street, Saginaw, MI 48602
CARF accredited programs available.

Community Mental Health Authority of Clinton-Eaton-Ingham Counties.......517.346.8200
Fax.......517.346.8420
Web.......www.ceicmh.org
812 East Jolly Road, Suite 110, Lansing, MI 48910-6818
CARF accredited programs available.

Community Mental Health for Central Michigan.......989.772.5938
Web.......www.cmhcm.org
E-mail.......cbaybarron@cmhcm.org
301 South Crapo, Suite 100, Mount Pleasant, MI 48858
Ms. Cindy Bay-Barron, Accreditation Manager
Joint Commission accredited organization.

Community Mental Health Services.......810.667.0500
Fax.......810.664.8728
Web.......www.county.lapeer.org/CMH
1570 Suncrest Drive, Lapeer, MI 48446
CARF accredited programs available.

Community Mental Health Services 231.724.1111
Fax 231.724.1300
Web ....www.co.muskegon.mi.us/cmh
376 East Apple Avenue, Muskegon, MI 49442
John North, Director
CARF accredited programs available.

Community Mental Health Services 269.673.3384
Fax 269.686.5201
3283 122nd Avenue, Allegan, MI 49010
CARF accredited programs available.

**Community Supports and Treatment
Services** **734.544.3000**
Web ....www.ewashtenaw.org
E-mail ....greenled@ewashtenaw.org
555 Towner Street, Ypsilanti, MI 48198
Mr. Daryl Greenleaf, Accreditation Manager
Joint Commission accredited organization.

**Comprehensive Youth Services, Inc. dba Clinton Counseling
Center** **586.463.7079**
Fax 586.468.4505
Two Crocker Boulevard, Suite 101, Mount Clemens,
MI 48043-2558
CARF accredited programs available.

Consumer Services, Inc. **517.833.8100**
Fax 517.676.5207
585 Jewett Road, Mason, MI 48854
Diane Williams, Director
CARF accredited programs available.

**Copper Country Community Mental Health Services
Authority** **906.482.9400**
Fax 906.483.0269
Web ....www.cccmh.org
901 West Memorial Drive, Houghton, MI 49930
CARF accredited programs available.

Cornerstone University-Counseling Svcs **616.222.1533**
Web ....www.cornerstone.edu
E-mail ....kerry_postema@cornerstone.edu
1001 E Beltline Ave NE, Grand Rapids,
MI 49525-5897
Kerry Postema, Director

Counseling Associates **248.626.1500**
Fax 248.626.1551
Web ....www.counselingassociates.com
33045 Hamilton Court, Suite W-300, Farmington
Hills, MI 48334
Dr Sidney Grossberg, Director
CARF accredited programs available.

Crisis Center, Inc. (dba Listening Ear) **989.772.2918**
Fax 989.775.3716
Web ....www.listeningear.com
P.O. Box 800, Mt. Pleasant, MI 48804-0800
COA accredited organization.

Crossroads for Youth **248.628.2561**
Fax 248.628.3080
Web ....www.crossroadsforyouth.org
P.O. Box 9, Oxford, MI 48371
COA accredited organization.

Dawn Farm **734.485.8725**
Fax 734.485.6103
Web ....www.dawnfarm.org
6633 Stoney Creek Road, Ypsilanti, MI 48197
CARF accredited programs available.

De Flon Medical Practice **248.647.7577**
30100 Telegraph Rd, Bingham Farms, MI 48025
Cassius De Flon, MD, Psychiatrist

Delta Family Clinic South **810.630.1152**
E-mail ....kawilliams6@juno.com
6195 Miller Road, Suite A, Swartz Creek, MI 48473
Dr. Gerard Williams, Accreditation Manager
Joint Commission accredited organization.

Delta Family Counseling Centers **989.892.4711**
Fax 989.892.4761
200 South Wenona Avenue, Suite 280, Bay City,
MI 48706
CARF accredited programs available.

**Delta Psychological & Neurobehavioral
Services** **989.895.0788**
Fax 989.895.0799
E-mail ....susiedelta@charterinternet.com
114 Tuscola Rd, Bay City, MI 48708
James Olsen, Director
CARF accredited programs available.

**Detroit Central City Community Mental Health,
Inc.** **313.831.3160**
Fax 313.831.2604
Web ....www.dcccmh.org
10 Peterboro, Detroit, MI 48201
CARF accredited programs available.

**Detroit East, Inc. Community Mental Health
Center** **313.331.3435**
Fax 313.924.0605
Web ....www.detroiteastcmh.org
11457 Shoemaker, Detroit, MI 48213
CARF accredited programs available.

Development Centers, Inc. **313.531.2500**
Fax 313.255.3465
Web ....www.develctrs.org
E-mail ....rbowen@develctrs.org
17421 Telegraph Rd, 2nd Fl, Detroit, MI 48219
Rachelle Bowen, Director Administrative Services
CARF accredited programs available.

Dleg/Michigan Rehabilitation Svcs **517.241.5122**
Web ....www.michigan.gov
E-mail ....renauerr@michigan.gov
1048 Pierpont Ste 1, Lansing, MI 48913-0001
Rosanne Renauer, Manager

Don Bosco Hall **313.869.2200**
Fax 313.869.8220
Web ....www.donboscohall.org
2340 Calvert Street, Detroit, MI 48206
COA accredited organization.

Drake Medical Practice **734.668.0099**
400 Maynard St, Ann Arbor, MI 48104
Robert Drake, MD, Psychiatrist

Easter Seals - Michigan, Inc. **248.475.6400**
Fax 248.475.6420
Web ....www.essmichigan.org
2399 East Walton Boulevard, Auburn Hills, MI 48326
CARF accredited programs available.

**Eastern Michigan Counseling Associates,
PC** **810.364.5800**
Fax 810.364.1200
Web ....www.easternmichigancounseling.com
1600 Gratiot Boulevard, Building B, Suite 4,
Marysville, MI 48040
CARF accredited programs available.

**Eastwood Community Clinics dba St. John Providence
Eastwood Clinics** **586.753.0400**
Fax 586.753.0404
Web ....www.stjohn.org/eastwoodclinics
28000 Dequindre Road, Warren, MI 48092-2468
COA accredited organization.

**El Shaddai Counseling and Consultation
Services** **734.240.0372**
Fax 888.277.5583
Web ....www.elshaddaicc.org
105 East Front Street, Suite 204, Monroe, MI 48161
CARF accredited programs available.

Employee Assistance Ctr **616.975.3560**
Fax 616.975.3565
E-mail ....dfogel@eaccares.com
1400 Leonard NE, Grand Rapids, MI 49505
Dan Fogel, Director

Every Woman's Place **231.759.7909**
Fax 231.759.8618
Web ....www.everywomansplace.org
E-mail ....susanj@everywomansplace.org
1221 W Laketon Ave, Muskegon, MI 49441-2866
Susan Johnson, Director

Falit Medical Practice **734.662.1668**
425 E Washington St, Ann Arbor, MI 48104
Harvey Falit, Psychiatrist

**Family and Children's Services of
Mid-Michigan** **989.631.5390**
Fax 989.631.0488
Web ....www.fcs-midland.org
1714 Eastman Avenue, Midland, MI 48640
CARF accredited programs available.

Faust Medical Practice **586.777.1170**
22811 Greater Mack Ave Ste L7, Saint Clair Shores,
MI 48080-2057
Marvin Faust, Md, Psychiatrist

Flint Odyssey House, Inc. **810.238.7226**
Fax 810.239.5518
Web ....www.odysseyvillage.com
529 Martin Luther King Jr. Avenue, Flint, MI 48502
CARF accredited programs available.

Forest View Psychiatric Hospital **616.942.9610**
Web ....www.forestviewhospital.com
E-mail ....marilynn.switzer@uhsinc.com
1055 Medical Park Drive SE, Grand Rapids, MI 49546
Ms. Marilynn Switzer, Accreditation Manager
Joint Commission accredited organization.

Forrest Medical Practice **734.662.6211**
708 W Huron St, Ann Arbor, MI 48103
Elise Forrest, MD, Psychiatrist

Franciscan Life Ctr **616.897.7842**
Fax 616.897.7054
Web ....www.lifeprocesscenter.org
E-mail ....flpc@lifeprocesscenter.org
11650 Downes St NE, Lowell, MI 49331-9489
Sister Colleen Ann Magel, Director

Fuelling Medical Practice **734.455.3361**
496 W Ann Arbor Trl, Plymouth, MI 48170
Craig Fuelling, Psychiatrist

G.R.A.C.E. Center **989.348.2544**
Fax 989.348.7617
Web ....www.gracecentergrayling.org
6459 West M-72, Grayling, MI 49738
CARF accredited programs available.

Genesys Practice Partners, Inc. **810.424.2400**
Web ....WWW.Genesys.org
E-mail ....jherman@genesys.org
8435 Holly Road, Grand Blanc, MI 48439
Ms. JoAnne Herman, Accreditation Manager
Joint Commission accredited organization.

**Gogebic Community Mental Health
Authority** **906.229.6100**
Fax 906.229.6190
Web ....www.gccmh.org
103 West U.S. 2, Wakefield, MI 49968
CARF accredited programs available.

Great Lakes Recovery Centers, Inc. **906.228.9699**
Fax 906.228.0505
Web ....www.glrc.biz
E-mail ....gtoutant@glrc.biz
201 Rublein Street, Suite A, Marquette, MI 49855
Greg Toutant, Executive Director
CARF accredited programs available.

Michigan

Michigan

Growth Works Incorporated **734.455.4095**
Web ....www.growth-works.org
E-mail ....jklotz@growth-works.org
  271 South Main Street, Plymouth, MI 48170
Mrs. Jessica Klotz, Accreditation Manager
Joint Commission accredited organization.

Hannahville Indian Community Health and Human Services **906.466.2782**
Fax 906.466.7454
  N15019 Hannahville B-1 Road, Wilson,
  MI 49896-9612
CARF accredited programs available.

Harbor Oaks Hospital **586.725.5777**
Web ....www.harboroaks.com
E-mail ....bseigel@phc-inc.com
  35031 23 Mile Road, New Baltimore, MI 48047
Mr. Brian Seigel, Accreditation Manager
Joint Commission accredited organization.

Harbor Oaks Hospital **586.725.5777**
Fax 586.725.8181
Web ....www.harboroakshospital.com
E-mail ....info@harboroaks.com
  35031 23 Mile Rd, New Baltimore, MI 48047-3649
Dr. John Adamo, Medical Director

Havenwyck Hospital **248.373.9200**
Fax 248.373.0528
Web ....www.havenwyckhospital.com
E-mail ....cwolschleger@hbch.org
  1525 University Dr, Auburn Hills, MI 48326-2675
Henry F. Woodworth, Md, Medical Director

Havenwyck Hospital **248.373.9200**
Web ....www.havenwyckhospital.com
E-mail ....suzanne.dennis@uhsinc.com
  1525 University Drive, Auburn Hills, MI 48326
Ms. Suzanne Dennis, Accreditation Manager
Joint Commission accredited organization.

Hegira Programs, Inc. **734.458.4601**
Web ....www.hegira.net
E-mail ....dolexa@hegira.net
  8623 N Wayne Road, Suite 200, Westland, MI 48185
Ms. Deborah Olexa, Accreditation Manager
Joint Commission accredited organization.

Hiawatha Community Mental Health Authority dba Hiawatha Behavioral Health **906.341.2144**
Fax 906.341.5793
Web ....www.hbhcmh.org
  125 North Lake Street, Manistique, MI 49854
CARF accredited programs available.

Highfields, Inc. **517.628.2287**
Fax 517.628.3421
Web ....www.highfields.org
  P.O. Box 98, Onondaga, MI 49264
COA accredited organization.

Holy Cross Children's Services **517.423.7255**
Fax 517.423.5442
Web ....www.hccsnet.org
  8759 Clinton-Macon Road, Clinton, MI 49236
CARF accredited programs available.

Home of New Vision **734.975.1602**
Fax 734.975.1604
Web ....www.homeofnewvision.org
  3800 Packard Road, Suite 210, Ann Arbor, MI 48108
CARF accredited programs available.

Hope Network Insight **810.744.3600**
Fax 810.744.2597
Web ....www.insightrecovery.org
  1110 Eldon Baker Drive, Flint, MI 48507
CARF accredited programs available.

Hope Network Southeast **248.334.3454**
Fax 248.334.2737
Web ....www.hopenetwork.org
E-mail ....dgamble@hopenetwork.org
  35 West Huron Street, Suite 302, Pontiac, MI 48342
David Gamble, Center's director
CARF accredited programs available.

Horizon Treatment Services, LLC **248.423.1728**
Web ....www.Horizontreatment.org
E-mail ....msmith@horizontreatment.org
  17515 W. 9 Mile Rd., Suite 720, Southfield, MI 48075
Dr. Monique Smith, Accreditation Manager
Joint Commission accredited organization.

Huron Valley Consultation Center, Inc. **734.662.6300**
Web ....www.huronvalleyconsult.org
E-mail ....mpovermyer@aol.com
  2750 South State Street, Ann Arbor, MI 48104
Ms. Marilyn Overmyer, Accreditation Manager
Joint Commission accredited organization.

Incorporation to Maximize Personal Achievement with Community Training **866.985.5168**
Fax 800.248.1568
Web ....www.impactph.org
  1001 Military Street, Port Huron, MI 48060
CARF accredited programs available.

Intake, Assessment and Referral Center **810.235.9555**
Fax 810.235.9525
  1402 West Court Street, Flint, MI 48503
CARF accredited programs available.

Integro, LLC **517.789.1234**
E-mail ....troumell@integroservices.net
  1200 N West Avenue, Suite 300, Jackson, MI 49202
Mrs. Tracy Roumell, Accreditation Manager
Joint Commission accredited organization.

JEC Counseling **248.253.0176**
Fax 248.253.1570
Web ....www.jeccounseling.com
  91 North Saginaw Street, Suite G101, Pontiac, MI 48342
CARF accredited programs available.

Jewish Family Service **248.592.2300**
Fax 248.592.2326
Web ....www.jfsdetroit.org
  6555 West Maple Road, West Bloomfield, MI 48322
CARF accredited programs available.

JOAK American Homes, Inc. **734.973.7764**
Fax 734.973.7897
Web ....www.joakhomes.com
  3820 Packard Road, Suite 180, Ann Arbor, MI 48108
CARF accredited programs available.

Kairos Healthcare, Inc. **989.777.4357**
Fax 989.777.7257
Web ....www.kairoshealthcare.com
  6379 Dixie Highway, Bridgeport, MI 48722

Kalamazoo Community Mental Health and Substance Abuse Services **269.553.8000**
Fax 269.553.8012
Web ....www.kazoocmh.org
  3299 Gull Road, Nazareth, MI 49074
CARF accredited programs available.

Karalee & Associates, P.C. **734.451.3440**
Web ....www.Karaleeandassociates.com
E-mail ....karaleeandassociates@yahoo.com
  1308 South Main Street, Plymouth, MI 48170
Dr. Karen Maier, Accreditation Manager
Joint Commission accredited organization.

Keepers of the Fire Behavioral Health Program **269.782.4141**
Fax 269.782.8797
  57392 M-51 South, Dowagiac, MI 49047
CARF accredited programs available.

Keweenaw Bay Indian Community Substance Abuse Programs **906.524.4411**
Fax 906.524.4415
  16025 Brewery Road, L'Anse, MI 49946
CARF accredited programs available.

Key Development Center, Inc. **810.220.8192**
Fax 810.220.0402
Web ....www.keycenters.org
  2060 Grand River Annex, Suite 600, Brighton, MI 48114
CARF accredited programs available.

Kingswood Hospital **313.874.6260**
Web ....www.henryford.com
E-mail ....tsamarc1@hfhs.org
  10300 West Eight Mile Road, Ferndale, MI 48220
Ms. Therese Samarco, Accreditation Manager
Joint Commission accredited organization.

Kingswood Hospital **248.398.3200**
Fax 248.691.4963
Web ....www.henryfordhealth.org
  Ferndale Eight Mile Road, Royal Oak, MI 48220
Taft Parsons, Director

Lac Vieux Desert Behavioral Health **906.358.0252**
Fax 906.358.0254
Web ....www.lvdtribal.com
  E23968 Pow Wow Trail, Watersmeet, MI 49969
CARF accredited programs available.

Lakeside Academy **269.381.4760**
Web ....www.lakesideacademy.net
E-mail ....slaidacker@lakesideacademy.net
  3921 Oakland Drive, Kalamazoo, MI 49008
Mr. Steve Laidacker, Accreditation Manager
Joint Commission accredited organization.

LDS Social Svcs **248.553.0902**
Fax 248.553.2632
  37634 Enterprise Ct, Farmington, MI 48331-3440
Lorna Jhanson, Administrative Assistant

Lenawee Community Mental Health Authority **517.263.8905**
Web ....lcmha.org
E-mail ....mperez@lcmha.org
  1040 S. Winter St., Ste.#1022, Adrian, MI 49221
Ms. Melinda Perez, Accreditation Manager
Joint Commission accredited organization.

Lewis and Mikkola Comprehensive Psychological Services, PLLC **248.644.3200**
Fax 248.644.3211
Web ....www.lewisandmikkola.com
  30200 Telegraph, Suite 402, Bingham Farms, MI 48025-4502
CARF accredited programs available.

LifeFocus Mental Health Assessment and Treatment Center **616.451.2777**
Fax 616.451.3888
Web ....www.lifefocusmh.com
  2525 East Paris SE, Suite 111, Grand Rapids, MI 49546
CARF accredited programs available.

Lifespan **248.615.9730**
Fax 248.615.1260
Web ....www.sfish.org
E-mail ....mhoward@sfish.org
  18316 Middlebelt Rd, Livonia, MI 48152-5007
Marisa Howard, Director

Lincoln Behavioral Services **313.450.4500**
Fax 313.450.4514
Web ....www.lbscares.com
  9315 Telegraph Rd, Redford, MI 48239
William Hart, Director
CARF accredited programs available.

List Psychological **989.673.5700**
Fax..989.672.2555
Web...www.centurytel.net
　651 N State St, Caro, MI 48723-1543
　Lisa Sprague, Sr. Assistant

List Psychological Services, PLC **989.672.6160**
Fax..989.672.5649
Web...www.listpsych.com
　443 North State Street, Caro, MI 48723
　COA accredited organization.

LMAS District Health Department **906.293.5107**
Fax..906.293.5453
Web..www.lmasdhd.org
　14150 Hamilton Lake Road, Newberry, MI 49868
　CARF accredited programs available.

Louisiana Homes, Inc. **313.868.8724**
Fax..313.883.5023
　1950 Webb Street, Detroit, MI 48206
　CARF accredited programs available.

M.P.A. Group NFP, Ltd. **989.667.9661**
Fax..989.667.9680
　1217 South Euclid Avenue, Bay City, MI 48706
　CARF accredited programs available.

Manistee Benzie Community Mental Health
Organization **877.398.2013**
Fax..231.723.1504
Web..www.mbcmh.org
　310 North Glocheski Drive, Manistee, MI 49660
　CARF accredited programs available.

Masterpeace Center for Counseling and
Development **517.423.6889**
Fax..517.423.6890
　308 South Maumee Street, Tecumseh,
　MI 49286-2033
　COA accredited organization.

McCullough, Vargas and Associates, Inc. **517.264.2244**
Fax..517.263.3325
　227 N Winter St, Suite 210, Adrian, MI 49221
　CARF accredited programs available.

McLaren Behavioral Health **810.342.5333**
Fax..810.342.5342
Web..www.mclaren.org
　4448 Oakbridge Dr, Flint, MI 48532
　Ken Dayton, Director

McLaren Regional Medical Center **810.342.2000**
Web ....www.mclarenregional.org
E-mail...aprils@mclaren.org
　401 South Ballenger Highway, Flint, MI 48532
　Mrs. April Scrimger, Accreditation Manager
　Joint Commission accredited organization.

Mental Health **231.689.7330**
Fax..231.689.7345
Web..www.newaygocmh.org
E-mail...................................gsnyder@newaygocmh.org
　1049 Newell, White Cloud, MI 49349
　Greg Snyder, Director
　CARF accredited programs available.

Meridian Professional Psychological Consultants,
PC...**517.332.0811**
E-mail...pprs4tish@aol.com
　5031 Park Lake Road, East Lansing, MI 48823
　Ms. Letisha Norris-Powell, Accreditation Manager
　Joint Commission accredited organization.

Methodist Children's Home Society **313.531.4060**
Fax..313.531.1040
Web..www.mchsmi.org
E-mail...btarq@mchsmi.org
　26645 W Six Mile Rd, Redford, MI 48240
　Beth Tarquinio, Executive Director
　CARF accredited programs available.

Michigan Behavior Medicine **248.740.9360**
E-mail.....................................mbm101@comcast.net
　625 East Big Beaver, Suite 101, Troy, MI 48083
　Ms. Rene Joseph, Accreditation Manager
　Joint Commission accredited organization.

Michigan Department of Community Health Corrections
Mental Health Program **734.434.9572**
Fax..734.434.8813
Web..www.michigan.gov
E-mail.................................russellma@michigan.gov
　3201 Bemis Road, Ypsilanti, MI 48197
　Mary Jane Russell, Deputy Director Operations
　CARF accredited programs available.

Michigan Psychiatric & Behavioral Associates,
P.C. **989.922.4900**
E-mail...csoto@mipba.org
　690 South Trumbull Street, Bay City, MI 48708
　Ms. Cindy Soto, Accreditation Manager
　Joint Commission accredited organization.

Mid-South Commission **517.337.4406**
Fax..517.337.8578
Web..www.mssac.com
E-mail.................................gvannorman@mssac.com
　2875 Northwind Dr Ste 215, East Lansing,
　MI 48823-5035
　Gary Vannorman, Executive Director

Monroe Community Mental Health
Authority **734.243.7340**
Web..www.monroecmha.org
E-mail.................................gharris@monroecmha.org
　1001 South Raisinville Road, Monroe, MI 48161
　Mrs. Geralyn Harris, Accreditation Manager
　Joint Commission accredited organization.

Montcalm Ctr For Behavioral Health **989.831.7520**
Fax..989.831.7578
E-mail...rbrown@mcbh.org
　611 N State St, Stanton, MI 48888
　Robert Brown, Executive Director

Montcalm School For Boys **866.244.4321**
Fax..517.629.4650
Web...www.montcalmschools.org
E-mail.................................ostrumn@montcalmschools.org
　13725 26 Mile Rd, Albion, MI 49224-9525
　Norm Ostrum, Director of Admissions

Mott Children's Health Center **810.767.5750**
Fax..810.768.7511
Web..www.mottchc.org
　806 Tuuri Place, Flint, MI 48503
　CARF accredited programs available.

National Council on Alcoholism and Drug Dependence-Greater
Detroit Area **313.369.5411**
Fax..313.369.5415
Web..www.ncadd-detroit.org
　4777 East Outer Drive, Detroit, MI 48234
　CARF accredited programs available.

Network 180 ....**616.336.3765**
Fax..616.336.3593
Web...www.network180.org
E-mail..pauli@network180.org
　728 Fuller Ave NE, Grand Rapids, MI 49503-1918
　Paul Ippel, Phd, Executive Director

New Center Community Services **313.961.3200**
Web...www.newcentercmhs.org
E-mail...........................gmatzelle@newcentercmhs.org
　2051 West Grand Boulevard, Detroit, MI 48208
　Mr. Gregory Matzelle, Accreditation Manager
　Joint Commission accredited organization.

New Oakland Child-Adolescent and Family
Center **248.634.6303**
Fax..248.634.1746
Web..www.newoakland.org
　12850 Fountain Square, Suite 106, Davisburg,
　MI 48350
　CARF accredited programs available.

New Passages Behavioral Health and Rehabilitation
Services **248.338.7458**
Fax..248.338.7513
Web..www.newpassages.org
　70 Lafayette, Pontiac, MI 48342
　CARF accredited programs available.

Niles Riverwood Ctr **269.684.4270**
Fax..269.684.4070
Web..www.riverwoodcenter.org
　115 S Saint Joseph Ave, Niles, MI 49120-2848

North Central Health Center **313.369.1717**
Fax..313.892.0137
Web..www.northcentralhealthcenter.org
　17141 Ryan Road, Detroit, MI 48212
　CARF accredited programs available.

North Country Community Mental Health **231.347.7890**
Fax..231.347.1241
Web..www.norcocmh.org
　One MacDonald Drive, Suite A, Petoskey, MI 49770

North Country Community Mental Health **989.732.7558**
Fax..989.732.8672
Web..www.norcocmh.org
E-mail...ktate@norcocmh.org
　800 Livingston Blvd Ste 2A, Gaylord, MI 49735-8345
　Kevin Tate, Supervisor

North Kent Guidance Services, LLC **616.361.5001**
Fax..616.361.2166
Web..www.nkgs.org
　5250 Northland Drive NE, Suite A, Grand Rapids,
　MI 49525-1040
　CARF accredited programs available.

North Pointe Behavioral Health Care
Systems **906.863.7841**
Fax..906.863.2833
Web..www.nbhs.org
　401 10th Ave, Menominee, MI 49858-3009
　David Block, Director

Northeast Guidance Center **313.824.8000**
Fax..313.824.5559
Web...www.neguidance.org
E-mail...................................smcrill@mentalwellness.org
　12800 East Warren, Detroit, MI 48215
　Sherry Mcrill, Director
　CARF accredited programs available.

Northeast Guidance Ctr **313.245.7000**
Fax..313.245.7009
Web...www.neguidance.org
　20303 Kelly Rd, Ditroit, MI 48225-1206
　Cheryl Coleman, Executive Director

Northeast Michigan Community Mental Health
Authority **989.356.2161**
Fax..989.354.5898
　400 Johnson Street, Alpena, MI 49707
　CARF accredited programs available.

Northern Lakes Community Mental Health
Authority **231.922.4850**
Fax..231.935.3082
Web..www.northernlakescmh.org
　105 Hall Street, Suite A, Traverse City, MI 49684
　CARF accredited programs available.

Michigan

Michigan

Northern Michigan Substance Abuse Svcs,
Inc 989.732.1791
Fax 989.732.7052
Web ....www.nmsas.net
E-mail ....suewinter@nmsas.net
   2090 W M32 Ste C, Gaylord, MI 49735
   Sue Winter, Executive Director

Northpointe Behavioral Healthcare
Systems 906.774.0522
Fax 906.774.1570
Web ....www.nbhs.org
E-mail ....twendt@nbhs.org
   715 Pyle Drive, Kingsford, MI 49802
   Terri Wendt, Director
   CARF accredited programs available.

Oakland Psychological Clinic, P.C. 248.322.0003
Web ....oakpsych.com
E-mail ....kdaldin@opcmail.net
   2550 South Telegraph Road Suite 250, Bloomfield
   Hills, MI 48302
   Ms. Katherine Daldin, Accreditation Manager
   Joint Commission accredited organization.

Old Town Psychological Services 231.941.6550
Fax 231.941.8981
   512 South Union Street, Traverse City, MI 49684
   COA accredited organization.

Pathways Community Mental Health 906.225.7210
Fax 906.225.7204
Web ....http://www.pathwaysup.org
   200 West Spring Street, Marquette, MI 49855
   CARF accredited programs available.

Perfect Solutions, Inc. 248.674.4630
Fax 248.674.7157
Web ....www.perfectsolutionsincorporated.org
E-mail ....psi61995@aol.com
   3650 Dixie Highway, Waterford, MI 48329-4290
   William Thompson, Director
   CARF accredited programs available.

Personal and Family Adjustment Center, PC dba Elm Street
Clinic 248.642.8263
Fax 248.642.6832
Web ....www.elmstreetclinic.com
   700 N. Old Woodward, Suite 300, Birmingham,
   MI 48009
   COA accredited organization.

Perspectives of Troy, P.C. 248.244.8644
Fax 248.244.1330
   888 West Big Beaver Road, Suite 1450, Troy,
   MI 48084
   CARF accredited programs available.

Pine Rest Christian Mental Health Svcs 616.222.3700
Fax 616.222.3707
E-mail ....mark.eastburg@pinerest.org
   4211 Parkway Pl SW Ste 100, Grandville, MI 49418
   Mark Eastberg, President/CEO

Pine Rest Christian Mental Health Svcs 269.343.6700
Fax 269.343.4831
Web ....www.pinerest.org
   1530 Nichols Rd, Kalamazoo, MI 49006-2065
   Jon Weeldreyer, Director

Pine Rest Christian Mental Health Svcs 616.455.5000
Fax 616.222.3724
Web ....www.pinerest.org
E-mail ....mark.eastburg@pinerest.org
   300 68th St SE, Grand Rapids, MI 49548-8207
   Mark Eastberg, Executive Director

Pine Rest Christian Mental Health Svcs 616.847.5145
Fax 616.842.1495
Web ....www.pinerest.org
   1445 Sheldon Rd, Harbor Dunes Center 303, Grand
   Haven, MI 49417
   Megan Zambiasi, Office Manager

Pine Rest Christian Mental Health Svcs 616.455.9200
Fax 616.559.5802
Web ....www.pinerest.org
E-mail ....mark.eastburg@pinerest.org
   300 68th St SE, Grand Rapids, MI 49548-6996
   Mark Eastburg, Executive Director

Pine Rest Christian Residential and Community
Services 616.455.5000
Fax 616.222.4574
Web ....www.pinerest.org
E-mail ....bill.johnson@pinerest.org
   300 68th St SE, Grand Rapids, MI 49548
   Bill Johnson, Director Information Systems
   CARF accredited programs available.

Pines Behavioral Health Services 517.278.2129
Fax 517.279.8172
Web ....www.pinesbhs.org
   200 Orleans Boulevard, Coldwater, MI 49036
   CARF accredited programs available.

Planning for Living Associates, Inc. 989.684.6832
Fax 989.684.4856
   2355 Delta Road, Bay City, MI 48706
   CARF accredited programs available.

Primacare, L.L.C. 734.513.1122
Fax 734.421.1405
   28303 Joy Road, Westland, MI 48185
   COA accredited organization.

Professional Counseling Center 810.984.4202
Fax 810.984.8896
Web ....pccporthuron.com
   520 Superior Street, Port Huron, MI 48060
   Sandra Malawer, Director
   CARF accredited programs available.

PsychSystems P.C. 734.729.7792
Fax 734.729.7938
Web ....www.psychsystemsonline.com
   35640 Michigan Avenue West, Wayne, MI 48184
   CARF accredited programs available.

Public Health, Delta and Menominee Counties Alcohol and
Other Drug Services 906.786.9639
Fax 906.789.8146
Web ....www.phdm.org
   2920 College Avenue, Escanaba, MI 49829
   CARF accredited programs available.

Recovery Pathways, LLC 989.928.3566
Web ....www.recoverypathwaysllc.com
E-mail ....debelakk@gmail.com
   717 E. Midland St., Bay City, MI 48706
   Ms. Kimber Debelak, Accreditation Manager
   Joint Commission accredited organization.

Recovery Technology, LLC 517.780.3336
Fax 517.796.4561
Web ....www.recoverytechnology.org
   1200 North West Avenue, Suite 400, Jackson,
   MI 49202
   CARF accredited programs available.

Renewal Christian Counseling and Ministry
Center 586.783.2950
Fax 586.783.2939
Web ....www.rccmc.org
   24401 Capital Boulevard, Clinton Township,
   MI 48036
   CARF accredited programs available.

Resa 989.224.6831
Fax 989.224.9574
Web ....www.ccresa.org
E-mail ....shinsky_c@ccresa.org
   1013 S US Hwy 27, # A, Saint Johns, MI 48879
   Cindy Shinksky, Associate Superintendent

River's Bend, P.C. 248.585.3239
Web ....www.riversbendpc.com
E-mail ....showey27@yahoo.com
   800 Stephenson Highway, Suite 250, Troy, MI 48083
   Ms. Stephanie Howey, Accreditation Manager
   Joint Commission accredited organization.

Sacred Heart Rehabilitation Center, Inc. 810.392.2167
Fax 810.392.3385
Web ....www.sacredheartcenter.com
   400 Stoddard Road, Richmond, MI 48062
   CARF accredited programs available.

Safehaus Inc. 586.806.4678
Web safehaus123.com
E-mail ....drk@safehaus123.com
   21056 Dean Street, Warren, MI 48091
   Dr. Roman Kolodchin, Accreditation Manager
   Joint Commission accredited organization.

Saginaw Chippewa Indian Tribe - Behavioral Health Program,
Nog-da-win-da-meg 989.775.4850
Fax 989.775.4851
Web ....www.sagchip.org
   2800 South Shepherd Road, Mount Pleasant,
   MI 48858

Saginaw Psychological Services, Inc. 989.799.2100
Fax 989.799.2637
   2100 Hemmeter Road, Saginaw, MI 48603-3944
   CARF accredited programs available.

Samaritan Counseling Services 734.677.0609
Fax 734.677.3072
Web ....www.samaritan.cc
   2890 Carpenter Road, Suite 1600, Ann Arbor,
   MI 48108
   CARF accredited programs available.

Segue, Inc. 517.784.6729
Fax 517.784.7546
Web ....www.segueinc.org
   950 West Monroe Street, Suite 600, Jackson,
   MI 49202
   CARF accredited programs available.

Southfield Mental Health Associates, P.C. 248.557.3606
Fax 248.557.4697
   17320 West 12 Mile Road, Suite 101, Southfield,
   MI 48076
   CARF accredited programs available.

Southwest Counseling Solutions, Inc. 313.841.8900
Fax 313.841.4470
Web ....www.swsol.org
   1700 Waterman, Detroit, MI 48209
   CARF accredited programs available.

St Joseph Mercy Hospital 734.712.3456
Fax 734.712.5697
Web ....www.trinity-health.org
   5301 Mcauley Dr, Ypsilanti, MI 48197
   Thomas Zelnik, Md, Department Of Psychiatry

St. John Providence Macomb-Oakland
Hospital 586.573.5443
Web ....www.stjohnprovidence.org
E-mail ....michelle.bradford@stjohn.org
   11800 East Twelve Mile Road, Warren, MI 48093
   Mrs. Michelle Bradford, Accreditation Manager
   Joint Commission accredited organization.

St. Joseph Mercy Hospital 734.712.3456
Web ....www.sjmercyhealth.org/
E-mail ....halasyal@trinity-health.org
   5301 E Huron River Drive, Ann Arbor, MI 48106
   Dr. Lakshmi Halasyamani, Accreditation Manager
   Joint Commission accredited organization.

Starr Commonwealth **269.968.9287**
Fax 269.966.4123
Web ....www.starr.org
E-mail ....corbins@starr.org
　155 Garfield Ave, Battle Creek, MI 49037-3407
　Andrea Wilcox, Director Of Foster Care

Sterling Area Health Center **989.654.2491**
E-mail ....crashotte@sterlinghealth.net
　725 East State Street, Sterling, MI 48659
　Ms. Claudette Rashotte, Accreditation Manager
　Joint Commission accredited organization.

Summit Pointe **269.966.1460**
Web ....www.summitpointe.org
E-mail ....amv@summitpointe.org
　140 West Michigan Avenue, Battle Creek, MI 49017
　Ms. Annette VanderArk, Accreditation Manager
　Joint Commission accredited organization.

**Summit Pointe Behavioral Health
Resources** **269.979.8333**
Fax 269.979.7766
Web ....www.summitpointe.org
E-mail ....erv@summitpointe.org
　3630 Capital Ave SW Ste 1, Battle Creek,
　MI 49015-7376
　Ervin Brinker, Director

SVRC Industries, Inc. **989.752.6176**
Fax 989.752.3111
Web ....www.svrcindustries.com
　919 Veterans Memorial Parkway, Saginaw, MI 48601
　CARF accredited programs available.

Taylor Psychological Clinic, PC **810.232.8466**
E-mail ....mtaylor1172@sbcglobal.net
　1172 Robert T Longway Blvd, Flint, MI 48503
　Dr. Maxwell Taylor, Accreditation Manager
　Joint Commission accredited organization.

TBI Solutions, LLC **248.355.5800**
Fax 248.355.5801
　24750 Swanson Road, Southfield, MI 48034
　CARF accredited programs available.

**Teaching Family Homes of Upper
Michigan** **906.249.5437**
Fax 906.249.5438
Web ....www.teachingfamilyhomes.org
　1000 Silver Creek Road, Marquette, MI 49855
　CARF accredited programs available.

Team Mental Health Services **313.245.0662**
Fax 313.245.0671
Web ....www.team-mentalhealth.com
　15000 Gratiot, Detroit, MI 48205
　CARF accredited programs available.

The Counseling Centre, P.C. **248.338.2988**
Fax 248.338.1322
　43996 Woodward Avenue, Suite 101, Bloomfield
　Hills, MI 48302
　Bart Anthony, Owner
　CARF accredited programs available.

The Guidance Center **734.785.7700**
Web ....www.guidance-center.org
E-mail ....pcinpak@guidance-center.org
　13101 Allen Road, Southgate, MI 48195
　Ms. Pamela Cinpak, Accreditation Manager
　Joint Commission accredited organization.

The Manor **517.849.2151**
Fax 517.849.2880
Web ....www.the-manor.org
　P.O. Box 98, Jonesville, MI 49250
　COA accredited organization.

The Maple Clinic, Inc. **231.946.9575**
Fax 231.947.5781
　525 South Union Street, Traverse City, MI 49684
　CARF accredited programs available.

**The Montcalm Center for Behavioral
Health** **989.831.7520**
Web ....www.montcalmcenter.org
E-mail ....tquillan@mcbh.org
　611 North State Street, Stanton, MI 48888
　Ms. Tammy Quillan, Accreditation Manager
　Joint Commission accredited organization.

**The University of Michigan Hospitals and Health
Centers** **734.647.2478**
Web ....www.med.umich.edu
E-mail ....phyllisv@umich.edu
　1500 East Medical Center Drive, Ann Arbor,
　MI 48109
　Mrs. Phyllis Voreis, Accreditation Manager
　Joint Commission accredited organization.

Therapeutic Encounters, P.C. **313.832.0870**
Fax 313.832.6024
　3800 Woodward Avenue, Suite 202, Detroit,
　MI 48201
　CARF accredited programs available.

Third Circuit Court - Clinic for Child Study **313.833.2800**
Fax 313.833.2841
Web www.3rdcc.org
　1025 East Forest Avenue, Building C, Detroit,
　MI 48207
　CARF accredited programs available.

**Treatment & Prevention Serv Coordinating
Agency** **989.758.3781**
Fax 989.758.3746
　1600 N Michigan Ave Ste 501, Saginaw, MI 48602
　Amy Murawski, Director

Tri-Care, P.C. dba Northland Clinic **248.559.8190**
Fax 248.559.8776
Web ....www.northland-clinic.com
　20300 Civic Center Drive, Suite 303, Southfield,
　MI 48076
　CARF accredited programs available.

Triad Associates P.C. **248.625.2970**
Fax 248.625.6829
　8062 Ortonville Road, Clarkston, MI 48348
　CARF accredited programs available.

Turning Point Youth Center **989.224.1177**
Fax 989.224.7078
Web ....www.turningpointyouth.net
E-mail ....diana.yount@uhsinc.com
　101 W Townsend Rd, Saint Johns, MI 48879-9200
　Diana Yount, CEO

Tuscola Behavioral Health Systems **989.673.6191**
Fax 989.673.1596
　323 North State Street, Caro, MI 48723
　CARF accredited programs available.

University Psychiatric Centers **313.577.7607**
Fax 313.577.8823
Web ....www.med.wayne.edu/psychiatry
　2751 East Jefferson, Suite 501, Detroit, MI 48207
　CARF accredited programs available.

**Van Buren Community Mental Health
Authority** **269.657.5574**
Fax 269.655.1901
Web ....www.vbcmh.com
E-mail ....cjohnson@vbcmh.com
　801 Hazen St, Suite C, Paw Paw, MI 49079
　Chris Johnson, Director-Human Resources
　CARF accredited programs available.

Volunteers of America Michigan **517.484.4414**
Fax 517.484.5353
Web ....www.voami.org
　21415 Civic Center Drive, Suite 210, Southfield,
　MI 48076
　Diane Cotman, Executive Director, Strategic Thinking
　CARF accredited programs available.

Wentworth and Associates, P.C. **586.997.3153**
Fax 586.997.4956
Web ....www.wentworthandassociates.com
　11111 Hall Road, Suite 303, Utica, MI 48317-5799
　CARF accredited programs available.

**West Michigan Community Mental Health
System** **231.845.6294**
Fax 231.845.7095
　920 Diana Street, Ludington, MI 49431
　CARF accredited programs available.

Whaley Children's Ctr **810.234.3603**
Fax 810.232.3416
Web ....www.whaleychildren.org
　1201 N Grand Traverse St, Flint, MI 48503-1394
　Kevin Roach, President/CEO

**Women's Resource Center of Northern Michigan,
Inc.** **231.347.0067**
Fax 231.347.5805
Web ....www.wrcnm.org
　423 Porter Street, Petoskey, MI 49770
　CARF accredited programs available.

**Woodlands Behavioral Network Health Care (Voice &
TTY)** **269.445.2451**
Fax 269.445.3216
Web ....www.woodlandsbhn.org
　960 M-60 East, Cassopolis, MI 49031
　Kathy Boes, CEO

Woodward Counseling, Inc. **248.333.7222**
Fax 248.333.7254
　35 South Johnson Street, Suite 0-C, Pontiac,
　MI 48341
　CARF accredited programs available.

Wyoming Clinic **616.252.8371**
Fax 616.534.3442
E-mail ....mark.eastburg@pinerest.org
　2215 44th St, Wyoming, MI 49509
　Mark Eastberg, CEO/President

YWCA West Central Michigan **616.459.4681**
Fax 616.459.5423
Web ....wwwywcawcmi.org
　25 Sheldon Boulevard SE, Grand Rapids, MI 49503
　COA accredited organization.

Zeeland Clinic **616.741.3790**
Fax 616.741.3792
Web ....www.pinerest.org
　8333 Felch St Ste 201, Zeeland, MI 49464-2609
　Mellissa Vanorman, Manager

CHILDREN'S HOSPITAL

Allegiance Health **517.788.4800**
E-mail ....georgia.fojtasek@allegiancehealth.org
　205 N East Ave, Jackson, MI 49201
　Georgia Fojtasek, Chief Executive Officer

Alpena Regional Medical Center **989.356.7390**
　1501 W Chisholm St, Alpena, MI 49707
　Carmen Bjella, Chief Executive Officer

Aspirus Keweenaw Hospital **906.337.6500**
E-mail ....cnelson@aspiruskeweenaw.org
　205 Osceola St, Calumet, MI 49913
　Charles Nelson, Chief Executive Officer

Battle Creek Hospital **269.966.8000**
　300 N Ave, Battle Creek, MI 49037
　Dennise Brooks-William, Chief Executive Officer

Bay Regional Medical Center **989.894.3000**
　1900 Columbus Ave, Bay City, MI 48708
　Alice Gerard, Chief Executive Officer

Beaumont Hospital **248.964.5000**
　44201 Dequindre Rd, Troy, MI 48085

Beaumont Hospital **248.898.5000**
E-mail ....www.beaumonthospitals.com
　3601 W 13 Mile Rd, Royal Oak, MI 48073
　Eugene Michalski, Chief Executive Officer

Bell Hospital 906.486.4431
901 Lakeshore Dr, Ishpeming, MI 49849
Rick Ament, Chief Executive Officer

Bixby Medical Center 517.265.0900
818 Riverside Ave, Adrian, MI 49221
Tim Jakacki, President

Borgess-Lee Memorial Hospital 269.782.8681
420 W High St, Dowagiac, MI 49047
Joy Strand, Chief Operating Officer

Botsford Hospital 248.471.8000
28050 Grand River Ave, Farmington Hills, MI 48336
Paul Lacasse, Chief Executive Officer

Bronson LakeView Hospital 269.657.3141
408 Hazen St, Paw Paw, MI 49079
Frank Sardone, Chief Executive Officer

Bronson Methodist Hospital 269.341.6000
601 John St, Kalamazoo, MI 49007
John Hayden, President

Central Michigan Community Hospital 989.772.6700
1221 S Dr, Mount Pleasant, MI 48858
Bill Lawrence, Chief Executive Officer

Charlevoix Area Hospital 231.547.4024
14700 Lake Shore Dr, Charlevoix, MI 49720
Bill Jackson, Chief Executive Officer

Children's Hospital of Michigan 313.745.5437
3901 Beaubien Blvd, Detroit, MI 48201
Michael Duggan, Chief Executive Officer

Community Health Center of Branch Cty 517.279.5400
274 E Chicago St, Coldwater, MI 49036

Covenant Medical Center 989.583.0000
1447 N Harrison St, Saginaw, MI 48602
Spence Maidlow, Administrator

Deckerville Community Hospital 810.376.2835
E-mail ....dch@deckervillehos.org
3559 Pine St, Deckerville, MI 48427
Mike Beeman, Chief Executive Officer

Eaton Rapids Medical Center 517.663.2671
1500 S Main St, Eaton Rapids, MI 48827
Tim Johnson, Chief Executive Officer

Garden City Hospital 734.421.3300
6245 N Inkster Rd, Garden City, MI 48135

Genesys Regional Medical Center 810.606.5000
1 Genesys Pkwy, Grand Blanc, MI 48439=8066
Bepsy Aderholt, Director

Grand View Hospital 906.932.2525
N10561 Grand View Ln, Ironwood, MI 49938
Carol Goffnett, Chief Executive Officer

Gratiot Medical Center 989.463.1101
300 E Warwick Dr, Alma, MI 48801

Hayes Green Beach Memorial Hospital 517.543.1050
321 E Harris St, Charlotte, MI 48813
Matthew Rush, Chief Executive Officer

Henry Ford Macomb Hospital 586.263.2300
15855 19 Mile Rd, Clinton Township, MI 48038
Barbara Rossman, Chief Executive Officer

Henry Ford Wyandotte Hospital 734.246.6000
2333 Biddle Ave, Wyandotte, MI 48192
Josephine Wahl, Chief Nursing Officer

Hillsdale Community Health Center 517.437.4451
168 S Howell St, Hillsdale, MI 49242
Duke Anderson, President

Hurley Medical Center 810.262.9000
1 Hurley Pl, Flint, MI 48503
Patrick Wardell, Chief Executive Officer

Huron Valley-Sinai Hospital 248.937.3300
1 William Carls Dr, Commerce Township, MI 48382
Carrol Warden, Social Worker

Lakeland Regional Medical Center 269.983.8300
E-mail ....lhamel@lakelandregional.org
1234 Napier Ave, Saint Joseph, MI 49085
Loren Hamel Md, Chief Executive Officer

Marquette General Hospital 906.228.9440
580 W College Ave, Marquette, MI 49855
Gary Muller, Chief Executive Officer

McLaren Regional Medical Center 810.342.2000
E-mail ....rachelt@mclaren.org
401 S Ballenger Hwy, Flint, MI 48532
Donald Kooy, President

Memorial Healthcare 989.723.5211
826 W King St, Owosso, MI 48867
Jim Full, President

Memorial Hospital 906.524.3300
770 N Main St, L'Anse, MI 49946

Mercy Health Partners 231.672.2000
1500 E Sherman Blvd, Muskegon, MI 49443
Roger Spoelman, Administrator

Mercy Hospital Cadillac 231.876.7200
400 Hobart St, Cadillac, MI 49601
Christen Brandsma, Nursing Director

Mercy Memorial Hospital 734.240.8400
718 N Macomb St, Monroe, MI 48162
Annette Phillips, Chief Executive Officer

Metro Health Hospital 616.252.7200
5900 Byron Center Ave SW, Wyoming, MI 49519
Michael Faas, Chief Executive Officer

Michigan Affiliated Hospital 517.975.6000
401 W Greenlawn Ave, Lansing, MI 48910
Mickey, CEO Assistant

Mid Michigan Medical Center 989.839.3000
4005 Orchard Dr, Midland, MI 48670
Heidi Lewis, Director of Nursing

MidMichigan Medical Center-Clare 989.802.5000
703 N McEwan St, Clare, MI 48617
Larry Barco, Chief Executive Officer

MidMichigan Medical Center-Gladwin 989.426.9286
E-mail ....ray.stover@midmichigan.org
515 Quarter St, Gladwin, MI 48624
Ray Stover, President

Mount Clemens Regional Medical Center 586.493.8000
1000 Harrington Blvd, Mount Clemens, MI 48043
Mark Ohalla, Chief Executive Officer

Munising Memorial Hospital 906.387.4110
1500 Sand Point Rd, Munising, MI 49862

North Ottawa Community Hospital 616.842.3600
1309 Sheldon Rd, Grand Haven, MI 49417
Shelly Yaklin, President

Northern Michigan Regional Hospital 231.487.4000
416 Connable Ave, Petoskey, MI 49770

NORTHSTAR Health System 906.265.6121
1400 W Ice Lake Rd, Iron River, MI 49935
Bruce Lampage, Chief Executive Officer

Oaklawn Hospital 269.781.4271
200 N Madison St, Marshall, MI 49068
Rob Covert, Chief Executive Officer

Oakwood Hospital & Medical Center 313.593.7000
18101 Oakwood Blvd, Dearborn, MI 48124
Brian Connolly, President

Port Huron Hospital 810.987.5000
1221 Pine Grove Ave, Port Huron, MI 48061
Thomas Defauw, Chief Executive Officer

Portage Health 906.483.1000
E-mail ....jbogan@portagehealth.org
500 Campus Dr, Hancock, MI 49930
James Bogan, Chief Executive Officer

Providence Hospital 248.494.3000
16001 W 9 Mile Rd, Southfield, MI 48075
Dr. Michael Wiemann, President

Schoolcraft Memorial Hospital 906.341.3200
500 Main St, Manistique, MI 49854

South Haven Community Hospital 269.637.5271
955 S Bailey Ave, South Haven, MI 49090
Joanne Urbanski, Chief Executive Officer

Sparrow Hospital 517.364.1000
1215 E Michigan Ave, Lansing, MI 48912
Denise Swan, President/CEO

Spectrum Health 616.774.7444
100 Michigan St NE, Grand Rapids, MI 49503
Richard Breon, President/CEO

Spectrum Health United Hospital 616.754.4691
615 S Bower St, Greenville, MI 48838
Pal Bonif, Chief Executive Officer

St John Hospital & Medical Center 313.343.4000
22101 Moross Rd, Detroit, MI 48236
Diane Radolff, Administrator

St John River District Hospital 810.329.7111
4100 River Rd, East China, MI 48054
Frank Poma, President

St Joseph Mercy Hospital 810.985.1500
2601 Electric Ave, Port Huron, MI 48060
Peter Karadjoff, Chief Executive Officer

St Joseph Mercy Hospital 734.712.3456
5301 McAuley Dr, Ypsilanti, MI 48197
Garry Faja, Chief Executive Officer

St Joseph Mercy Oakland 248.858.3000
44405 Woodward Ave, Pontiac, MI 48341
Jack Weiner, President

St Mary's Health Care 616.685.6090
200 Jefferson Ave SE, Grand Rapids, MI 49503
Phillip Mccorkle, Administrator

Sturgis Hospital 269.651.7824
916 Myrtle, Sturgis, MI 49091
Malanie Mann, Nursing Director

Three Rivers Health 269.278.1145
701 S Health Pkwy, Three Rivers, MI 49093
Bill Russell, Chief Executive Officer

Univ of Michigan Hsptls & Hlth Center 734.936.4000
1500 E Medical Center Dr, Ann Arbor, MI 48109
Doug Strom, Chief Executive Director

West Shore Medical Center 231.398.1000
1465 E Parkdale Ave, Manistee, MI 49660
Jody Botterell, Director

COUNSELING SERVICES

Catholic Charities West Michigan 616.456.1443
Fax 616.732.6391
Web ....www.ccwestmi.org
E-mail ....richardl@cssgr.org
40 Jefferson Ave SE, Grand Rapids, MI 49503-4304
Richard Liberatore, Executive Director

Catholic Social Svcs 810.232.9950
Fax 810.232.7599
901 Chippewa St, Flint, MI 48503-1570
Vickie Schultz, Director

Catholic Svcs 810.664.4557
Fax 810.664.5181
E-mail ....t.reed@csmacomb.org
700 S Main St, Lapeer, MI 48446
Thomas Reed, Director

Catholic Svcs 586.416.2300
Fax 586.416.2311
12434 E 12 Mile Rd Ste 201, Warren, MI 48093-3536
James Henson, Director

Family Counseling & Children's Svcs 517.265.5352
Fax 517.263.6090
Web ....www.fccservices.org
E-mail ....Sharonfccs2@Yahoo.Com
220 N Main St, Adrian, MI 49221-2749
Sharon Hudson, Director

Family Svcs and Children's Aid **517.787.7920**
Fax 517.787.2440
　330 W Michigan Ave, Jackson, MI 49201
　Judy Jove, Executive Director

Integro **517.789.1234**
Fax 517.784.7040
　1200 N West Ave Ste 300, Jackson, MI 49202
　Marilyn Meadowcroft, CEO

New Ctr Community Mental Health Svcs **313.961.3200**
Fax 313.961.3769
Web .... www.newcentercmhs.org
E-mail .... rsanders@newcentercmhs.org
　2051 W Grand Blvd, Detroit, MI 48208
　Roberta Sanders, Executive Director/CEO

Pathways **616.846.5880**
Fax 616.846.6052
Web .... www.pathwaysmi.org
E-mail .... shorsman@pathwaysmi.org
　321 S Beechtree St, Grand Haven, MI 49417-2003
　Sandra Klein Horsman, Supervisor

Sundance Center **269.226.2400**
Fax 269.226.2403
Web .... www.sundancecenter.net
E-mail .... ulla@sundancecenter.net
　813 W South St, Ste 222, Kalamazoo, MI 49007
　Ulla Frederiksen, Director

Youth Corp - REACH **810.233.8700**
Fax 810.233.0263
E-mail .... gcyc@intouchmi.com
　914 Church St, Flint, MI 48502
　Robert A. Edgar, Executive Director

CRISIS & SHELTER CARE

Alliance Against Violence and Abuse Inc **906.789.9207**
Fax 906.789.5640
Web .... www.aavashelter.org
E-mail .... hsatterly@allianceagainstviolence.com
　905 1st Ave S, Escanaba, MI 49829-3705
　Hazel Satterly, Executive Director

Alternatives For Girls **313.361.4000**
Fax 313.361.8938
Web .... www.alternativesforgirls.org
E-mail .... agood@alternativesforgirls.org
　903 W Grand Blvd, Detroit, MI 48208
　Amanda Good, CEO

Arbor Circle Corp **616.451.3001**
Fax 616.451.8779
Web .... www.arborcircle.org
　1115 Ball Ave NE, The Bridge For Runaways, Grand
　Rapids, MI 49505
　Susan Sheppard, Program Manager

Bay Area Women's Ctr **989.686.2251**
Fax 989.686.0906
E-mail .... womenscenter@bawc-mi.org
　3411 E Midland Rd, Bay City, MI 48706
　Kathy Allen, Executive Director

Caring House Inc - Domestic Violence **906.774.1337**
Fax 906.774.0575
E-mail .... coneil@chartermi.net
　1305 S Prospect Ave, Iron Mountain, MI 49801
　Cheryl O'Neil, Director

Catherine Cobb Safe House - Domestic Violence
Program **517.265.6776**
Fax 517.266.0733
E-mail .... Sharonfccs2@Yahoo.Com
　220 N Main St Ste 1, Adrian, MI 49221-2749
　Sharon Hudson, Director

Children's Home of Detroit **313.886.0802**
Fax 313.886.9446
Web .... www.childrenshomeofdetroit.org
E-mail .... mhorwitz@childrenshomeofdetroit.org
　900 Cook Rd, Grosse Pointe, MI 48236-2799
　Michael R. Horwitz, Director

Coalition Against Domestic Violence - Shelter
House **517.278.3356**
Fax 517.279.2054
Web .... www.bccadv.com
E-mail .... shelterhouse@cbpu.com
　220 N Michigan Ave, Coldwater, MI 49036-1529
　Kim Hemker, Director

Common Ground Sanctuary **248.456.8150**
Fax 248.456.8147
Web .... www.commongroundhelps.org
　1410 S Telegraph Rd, Bloomfield Hills, MI 48302
　Tony Rothschild, Executive Director

Communities Overcoming Violent
Encounter **231.843.2541**
Fax 231.843.7897
E-mail .... Cove_Marieed@Verizon.Net
　906 E Ludington Ave, Ludington, MI 49431-2438
　Marie Waite, Director

Comprehensive Youth Svcs Family Youth
Interventions **586.465.1212**
Fax 586.465.4504
Web .... www.familyyouth.com
E-mail .... jbaarck@familyyouth.com
　418 Cass Ave, Mount Clemens, MI 48043-2123
　Jolyne Baarck, Program Director

Council On Domestic Violence - Sexual
Assault **989.835.6771**
Fax 989.835.7449
E-mail .... info@cdvsa.org
　3115 Isabella Rd, Midland, MI 48641
　Sharon Mortenson, Director

Crossroads For Youth **248.628.2561**
Fax 248.628.3080
E-mail .... janet.mcpeek@crossroadsforyouth.org
　930 E Drahner Rd, Oxford, MI 48371
　Dr Janet Mcpeek, President

Ctr For Women In Transition - Domestic
Violence **616.392.2829**
Fax 616.355.9760
E-mail .... charissem@aplaceforwomen.org
　411 Butternut Dr, Holland, MI 49424
　Charisse Mitchell, Director

Diane Peppler Resource Ctr - Domestic
Violence **906.635.0566**
Fax 906.635.2952
E-mail .... perrona@dprcenter.org
　620 E Portage Ave., Sault Sainte Marie, MI 49783
　Amy Perron, Director

Domestic and Sexual Assualt Servies **269.279.5122**
Fax 269.279.1624
Web .... www.dasasmi.org
E-mail .... dasasinfo@dasasmi.org
　PO Box 402, Three Rivers, MI 49093-0402
　Mary Lynn Falbe, Director

Domestic Harmony **517.439.1454**
Fax 517.439.5144
　17 N West St, Hillsdale, MI 49242
　Georgia Mason, Director

Domestic Violence Coalition, Inc **269.655.9008**
Fax 269.655.1428
E-mail .... debnieboer1@aol.com
　303 E Paw Paw St Ste 7, Paw Paw, MI 49079
　Deb Nieboer, Director

Domestic Violence Escape Program **906.932.4990**
Fax 906.932.2040
　PO Box 366, Ironwood, MI 49938-0366
　Pam Orr, Director

Eagle Village, Inc. **231.832.2234**
Fax 231.832.1729
Web .... www.eaglevillage.org
E-mail .... eaglevillage@eaglevillage.org
　4507 170th Ave, Hersey, MI 49639-9736
　Thphey Prudhomme, President/CEO

Eve Inc **517.372.5572**
Fax 517.372.0024
E-mail .... executivedirector@eveinc.org
　PO Box 14149, Lansing, MI 48901-4149
　Susan Schultz, Executive Director

First Step **734.416.1111**
Fax 734.416.5555
Web .... www.firststep.org
E-mail .... fsadsv@aol.com
　44567 Pinetree Dr, Plymouth, MI 48170-3840
　Judy Ellis, Director

Hannahville Indian Community - Victim of Crime
Program **906.466.2932**
Fax 906.466.2933
Web .... www.hannahville.org
E-mail .... kennethmeshigaud@hannahville.org
　N14911 Hannahville Road B-1, Wilson, MI 49896
　Kenneth Meshigaud, Director

Haven-Domestic Violence Shelter **248.334.1284**
Fax 248.334.3161
Web .... www.haven-oakland.org
E-mail .... bmorrison@haven-oakland.org
　30400 Telegraph Rd Ste 101, Bingham, MI 48025
　Beth Morrison, Chief Executive Officer

Interlink Transitional Living & Emergency
Shelter **989.753.3431**
Fax 989.752.5178
　1110 Howard St, Saginaw, MI 48601-2734
　Ronald Spees, CEO

Lapeer Area Citizens Against Domestic
Assault **810.667.4193**
Fax 810.667.4743
E-mail .... lacada@lacada.org
　PO Box 356, Lapeer, MI 48446-0356
　Kim Hebberd, Director

Link Crisis Intervention Ctr **269.927.1422**
Fax 269.927.1433
Web .... www.cfsswmi.org
　2450 M 139, Benton Harbor, MI 49022
　Warren Washington, Executive Director

Listening Ear Crisis Ctr **989.772.2918**
Fax 989.772.5339
Web .... www.listeningear.com
E-mail .... dschuster@listeningear.com
　107 E Illinois St, Mt Pleasant, MI 48858-2503
　Donald Schuster, Director

Livingston Area CNCL Against Spouse
Abuse **517.548.1350**
Fax 517.548.3034
E-mail .... bschrandt@lacasa1.org
　2895 W Grand River Ave, Howell, MI 48843-8538
　Bobette A. Schrandt, Executive Director

MSU Safe Place - Domestic Violence
Program **517.355.1100**
Fax 517.432.6193
E-mail .... Rosen2@Msu.Edu
　G55 E Wilson Hall, East Lansing, MI 48825-1208
　Holly Rosen, Director

OASIS Family Resource Center **231.775.7299**
Fax 231.775.4074
E-mail .... sally.repeck@Cadillacoasis-Frc.Org
　118 S Mitchell St, Cadillac, MI 49601
　Sally Repeck, Director

Ozone House **734.662.2265**
Fax 734.662.9724
Web .... www.ozonehouse.org
　1705 Washtenaw Ave, Ann Arbor, MI 48104-3548
　Katie Doyle, Executive Director

Penrickton Ctr For Blind Children **734.946.7500**
Fax 734.946.6707
Web .... www.penrickton.com
E-mail .... mail@penrickton.com
　26530 Eureka Rd, Taylor, MI 48180
　Kurt Sebaly, Med, Executive Director

Promise Village: Home For Children **248.328.2445**
Fax 248.634.1302
Web .... www.promisevillage.com
E-mail .... info@promisevillage.com
PO Box 210, Davisburg, MI 48350-0210
Timothy Coldiron, Acsw, Phd, Founder/executive Director

Relief After Violent Encounter **616.527.3351**
Fax 616.527.4350
852 E Lincoln Ave, Ionia, MI 48846
Erin Roberts, Director

River House Shelter - Domestic Violence **989.348.3169**
Fax 989.348.1719
Web .... www.riverhouseshelter.org
E-mail .... Director@Riverhouseshelter.Org
1009 N Down River Rd, Grayling, MI 49738
Brooke Hemten Stall, Director

Safe Haven Ministries **616.452.6664**
Fax 616.452.1168
E-mail .... jharkema@safehavenministries.org
3501 Lake Eastbrook Blvd SE, Ste 335, Grand Rapids,
MI 49546
Joe Harkema, Director

Safe House Ctr - Domestic Violence **734.973.0242**
Fax 734.973.7817
E-mail .... barbaran@safehousecenter.org
4100 Clark Rd, Ann Arbor, MI 48105
Barbara Niess, Director

Sexual Assault Prevention-Awareness Ctr **734.998.9368**
Fax 734.998.9380
Web .... www.umich.edu
E-mail .... jsoet@umich.edu
715 N University Ave Ste 202, Ann Arbor,
MI 48104-1605
Johanna Soet, Director

Sexual Assault Svcs - Domestic Violence **269.660.3925**
Fax 269.660.3924
E-mail .... siegelj@trinity-health.org
36 Manchester St W, Battle Creek, MI 49037
Joyce Siegal, Director

**Shelter Inc of Michigan - Domestic
Violence** **989.356.2560**
Fax 989.356.6659
E-mail .... sllewis@shelterincalpena.org
3022 US 23 S Ste D, Alpena, MI 49707
Sandra Pilgrim-Lewis, Director

Siren-Eaton Shelter Inc **517.543.0748**
Fax 517.543.0883
E-mail .... sireneaton@sbcglobal.net
245 S Cochran Ave, Charlotte, MI 48813
Nancy Oliver, Director

Sylvia's Place - Domestic Violence **269.673.8700**
Fax 269.673.8860
E-mail .... admin@sylviasplace.com
151 Brady St, Allegan, MI 49010
Shelly Dietz, Director

The Ark For Runaways **269.343.8765**
Fax 269.343.7323
Web .... www.catholicfamilyservice.org
E-mail .... info@catholicfamilyservices.org
990 W Kilgore Rd, Kalamazoo, MI 49008
Fran Denney, Executive Director

The Harbor **810.982.8584**
Fax 810.982.2676
E-mail .... sallycurry@aol.com
929 Pine St, Port Huron, MI 48060-5252
Sally A. Currie, Program Director

The Manor **517.849.2151**
Fax 517.849.2880
Web .... www.the-manor.org
E-mail .... mgensterblum@the-manor.org
115 East St, Jonesville, MI 49250
Marcia Gensterblum, Clinical Director

Third Level Crisis Intervention Ctr **231.922.4800**
Fax 231.941.5786
Web .... www.thirdlevel.org
E-mail .... khoma@thirdlevel.org
1022 E Front St, Traverse City, MI 49686-2708
Ken Homa, Executive Director

Tribe of Chippewa Indians Victim Svc Prg **906.635.7705**
Fax 906.635.7706
E-mail .... ljump@saulttribe.net
2428 Shunk Rd, Sault Sainte Marie, MI 49783
Lori Jomp, Director

Turning Point Inc - Domestic Violence **586.463.4430**
Fax 586.463.1771
E-mail .... scoats@turningpointmacomb.org
158 S Main St, Mount Clemens, MI 48043
Suzanne Coats, Director

United Way South East Michigan **248.456.8805**
Fax 248.230.8219
Web .... www.uwsem.org
2600 WE Weaver Rd Ste 160, Troy, MI 48084
Judy Muhn, Aree Manager

Victims Assistance Program **313.833.1660**
Fax 313.237.2840
Web .... www.ci.detroit.mi.gov
E-mail .... cooper-reidj419@detroitmi.gov
4707 Saint Antoine St, M167, Detroit, MI 48201
Joann Cooper-reid, Director

Women's Ctr - Harbor House **906.225.1346**
Fax 906.225.1370
E-mail .... ploonsfot@miuplink.com
1310 S Front St, Marquette, MI 49855
Phyllis Loonsfot, Director

Women's Info Svcs - Domestic Violence **231.796.6600**
Fax 231.796.0358
Web .... www.wiseagainstviolence.org
E-mail .... wise@tucker-usa.com
204 West Pere Marquette, Big Rapids, MI 49307
Kelly Samuels, Director

Women's Resource Ctr - Traverse City **231.941.1210**
Fax 231.941.1734
E-mail .... jbullis@wrcgt.com
720 S Elmwood Ave Ste 2, Traverse City,
MI 49684-3005
Jo Bullis, Director

**Women's Resource Ctr of Northern
Michigan** **231.347.1572**
Fax 231.347.7597
423 Porter St, Petoskey, MI 49770
Jan Mancinelli, Director

YWCA Domestic Assault Program **269.385.2869**
Fax 269.978.1211
E-mail .... jashoub@ywcakalamazoo.org
353 E Michigan Ave, Kalamazoo, MI 49007
Jenifer Shoub, Chief Executive Officer

YWCA Domestic Crisis Ctr **616.451.2744**
Fax 616.451.0024
Web .... www.grywcadcc.org
25 Sheldon Blvd SE, Grand Rapids, MI 49503-4295
Eileen Mckeever, Director

YWCA of Greater Flint **810.238.7621**
Fax 810.238.1424
E-mail .... info@ywcaflint.org
310 E 3rd St, Flint, MI 48502
Paul Newman, Chief Executive Officer

EDUCATION

Erickson Learning Ctr **517.347.0122**
Fax 517.347.0288
Web .... www.erickson-learning.org
E-mail .... carynjpe@aol.com
2043 Hamilton Rd, Okemos, MI 48864-2104
Caryn Edwards, Bs, Director

Eton Academy **248.642.1150**
Fax 248.642.3670
Web .... www.etonacademy.org
E-mail .... ppullen@etonacademy.org
1755 E Melton Rd, Birmingham, MI 48009
Pete Pullen, Headmaster

Flint Genesee Job Corps Ctr / WIC **810.232.9102**
Fax 810.232.6835
E-mail .... kizzy.miles@jobcorps.org
2400 N Saginaw St, Flint, MI 48505-4442
Kizzy Miles, Admissions Counselor

Grand Rapids Job Corps Ctr **616.243.6877**
Fax 616.243.1701
Web .... www.jobcorps.org
E-mail .... jablonski.jeffery@jobcorps.org
110 Hall St SE, Grand Rapids, MI 49507-1791
Jeffery Jablonski, Center Director

Michigan Youth / Challenge Academy **269.968.1067**
Fax 269.964.7193
Web .... www.ngycp.org/mi
5500 Armstrong Rd, Bldg 13, Battle Creek, MI 49015
Jim Luce, Director

Traverse Place **810.341.6328**
Fax 810.341.6757
E-mail .... tlt@intouchmi.com
512 S Grand Traverse St, Flint, MI 48502-1207
Robert A. Edgar, Executive Director

FOSTER CARE AGENCIES

Adoption Resource Group **906.482.5954**
E-mail .... sliva@charter.net
1524 Ravineside Dr, Houghton, MI 49931
Micki Sliva, President

Adoptive Family Support Network AFSN **616.458.7945**
Fax 616.458.7545
E-mail .... adoptive@afsn.org
233 E Fulton, Ste 108, Grand Rapids, MI 49503
Brook Banprooyen, Manager

AFC Walnut St **231.258.9478**
Fax 231.258.8997
417 S Walnut St, Kalkaska, MI 49646
Steve Everett, Owner

Aloha Ctr Inc **989.422.6920**
2631 Tower Hill Rd, Houghton Lake, MI 48629
Kelly Presson, Director

Aloha Ctrs Inc **231.328.4695**
Fax 231.328.4802
2439 W Home Lake Road, Houghton Lake, MI 49651
Judy Presson, Director

Atlas Park **810.653.6529**
2099 Atlas Rd, Davison, MI 48423
Roshawn Davis, Manager

Best Care Plus Living Ctr **269.789.0300**
16080 17 1/2 Mile Rd, Marshall, MI 49068
Karen Luna, Director

Bethany Christian Services **231.924.3390**
Fax 231.924.2848
E-mail .... sjordan@bethany.org
6995 W 48th St, Fremont, MI 49412
Dave Glerum, Director

Bethany Christian Services **616.224.7595**
E-mail .... info@bethany.org
901 Eastern Ave NE, Grand Rapids, MI 49501
Jessica Vail, Intake Services Coordinator

Bethany Christian Svcs of SW Michigan **269.372.8800**
6687 Seeco Dr, Kalamazoo, MI 49009
Brad Keller, Branch Manager

Caring Network **269.381.1234**
Fax 616.381.2932
1441 S Westnidge, Kalamazoo, MI 49008
Frances Denny, Executive Director

Catholic Social Svcs 810.987.9100
Fax 810.987.9105
E-mail ....pcogley@cssstclair.org
  2601 13th St, Port Huron, MI 48060
  Pat Cogley, President

Christian Family Services (CFS) 248.557.8390
Fax 248.557.6427
E-mail ....audrey.brown@cfs-michigan.org
  17105 W 12 Mile Rd, Southfield, MI 48076
  Audrey Brown, Director

Corner Stone 517.278.0313
Fax 517.278.7887
  157 W Garfield Ave, Coldwater, MI 49036
  Tracy Hernandez, Owner

Creative Lifestyles 586.775.1608
Fax 510.231.9997
  28330 Little Mack Ave, Saint Clair Shores,
  MI 48081-3508
  Kim Nivens, Manager

DA Blodgett-St John's 616.451.2021
Fax 616.451.8936
  805 Leonard Ave NE, Grand Rapids, MI 49503
  Sharon Loughridge, Director

Dexter Manor 734.426.6910
Fax 734.426.6910
  7394 Black Forest Dr, Dexter, MI 48130-9676
  Mary Zamora, Director

Diems Country Acres 989.845.3783
Fax 989.845.3783
  6787 Ferden Rd, Chesaning, MI 48616-9778
  Kim Schindler, Manager

Eagle Village Inc 231.832.7270
E-mail ....info@eaglevillage.org
  4507 170th Ave, Hersey, MI 49639
  Kathey Prudhomme, Chief Executive Officer

East Bay AIC 231.929.9773
Fax 231.932.8731
  1855 Carlisle Rd, Traverse City, MI 49696-9156
  Paul Stifki, Director

Edmore AFC 989.427.5379
Fax 989.427.5379
E-mail ....dawnia67@yahoo.com
  8782 N Wyman Rd, Edmore, MI 48829-9702
  Dawn Blackler, Director

El Centro of Bethany 616.396.3391
E-mail ....seckert@bethany.org
  12048 James St, Holland, MI 49424
  Jamie Rowl, Office Manager

Faith Assisted Living Home Inc 810.793.4503
Fax 810.793.5200
  320 Dockham Rd, Columbiaville, MI 48421-9654
  Ernestine Herriman, Director

Families on the Move & NA Council on 313.532.0012
E-mail ....vedadthompkins@aol.com
  PO Box 35037, Detroit, MI 48235
  Vedad Thompkins, Director

Family & Children's Services Inc 269.344.0202
  1608 Lake St, Kalamazoo, MI 49001
  Rosemary Gardiner, Chief Executive Officer

Family Adoption Consultants (FAC) 586.726.2988
Fax 586.726.2599
E-mail ....kathyluz@facadopt.org
  45100 Sterritt, Ste 203, Utica, MI 48317
  Kathy Luz, Executive Director

Family Adoption Consultants (FAC) 269.343.3316
Fax 269.343.3359
E-mail ....info@facadopt.org
  421 W Crosstown Pkwy, Kalamazoo, MI 49001

Family Service & Children's Aid FSCA 517.787.7920
Fax 517.787.2440
E-mail ....adoption@strong-families.org
  330 W Michigan Ave, PO Box 6128, Jackson,
  MI 49201
  Judy Jove, Director

Foster/Adoptive Family Resource Center 616.721.8120
Fax 616.660.0449
  181 Broadway Blvd, Battle Creek, MI 49037

Friendly Acres 989.465.1580
  5710 Isabella County Line Rd, Coleman,
  MI 48618-9394
  Marilyn Wilky, Director

Greater Hopes Family Services Inc 616.451.0245
E-mail ....greaterhopes@greaterhopes.org
  1345 Monroe NW, Ste 246, Grand Rapids, MI 49505
  Cathy Raidna, Director

Homes for Black Children (HBC) 313.961.4777
Fax 313.961.2994
E-mail ....hbchildren@aol.com
  511 E Larned St, Detroit, MI 48226
  Jacqelynn Moffett, President/CEO

Love & Logic Support Group 269.660.0448
E-mail ....resourcefamilies@aol.com
  415 S 28t St, Battle Creek, MI 49015

Methodis Children's Home Society 313.531.4060
E-mail ....lkoge@mchsmi.org
  26645 W 6 Mile Rd, Redford, MI 48240
  Beth Tarquinio, Chief Executive Officer

MI Indian Cld Welfare Agcy Anishnabek 906.632.5250
Fax 906.632.5266
E-mail ....acfssecretary@saulttrieve.net
  2218 Shunk Rd, Sault Sainte Marie, MI 49783
  Juanita Bye, Director

Michigan Assoc of Sngl Adoptive Parents 586.758.6909
E-mail ....janetway@bigtlamet.com
  7412 Coolidge, Center Line, MI 48015
  Janet Way, Manager

Michigan Dept of Human Services 313.256.3413
Fax 313.256.1152
  3040 W Grand Blvd Ste 5-650, Detroit, MI 48202

Spaulding for Children (SFC) 248.443.7080
Fax 248.443.7099
Web ....www.spaulding.org
E-mail ....kbaber@spaulding.org
  16250 Northland Dr, Ste 100, Southfield, MI 48075
  Addie Williams, Chief Executive Officer
  COA accredited organization.

Spectrum Human Svcs Independent
Living 734.458.8736
Fax 734.458.8836
E-mail ....info@spectrumhuman.org
  28303 Joy Rd, Westland, MI 48185
  Roger Swaninger, President/CEO

Vista Maria Good Shepherd Center 313.271.3050
Fax 313.336.3460
  20651 W Warren Ave, Dearborn Heights, MI 48127
  Pat Zurlinden, Owner

HOME MEDICAL EQUIPMENT PROVIDERS

AlumiRamp Inc 800.800.3864
E-mail ....sales@alumiramp.com
  855 E Chicago Rd, Quincy, MI 49082
  Doug Cannon, Manager

Balanced Medical Supply 989.846.6328
Fax 989.846.6398
  211 North Main Street, Suite 7, Standish, MI 48658
  CARF accredited programs available.

Beval Medical Equipment and Supplies,
LLC 248.280.1818
Fax 248.786.5362
  4307 West 13 Mile Road, Royal Oak, MI 48073
  CARF accredited programs available.

Viewpoint Mobility 269.344.6282
Fax 269.344.5649
E-mail ....information@viewpointmobility.com
  1815 Palmer Ave, Kalamazoo, MI 49001
  John Doerer, General Manager

PEDIATRIC HOME CARE

Interim Healthcare 248.553.3333
Fax 248.553.3377
E-mail ....interimoc@gmail.com
  41875 11 Mile Rd Ste 205, Novi, MI 48375
  Teresa Tricchard, Chief Executive Officer

Interim Healthcare 810.407.7496
Fax 810.820.8211
E-mail ....interimoc@gmail.com
  601 S Saginaw Ste 313, Flint, MI 48502
  Shelly Lamb, Director

Interim Healthcare 734.404.0300
Fax 734.404.0304
  43050 Ford Rd Ste 110, Canton, MI 48187
  Mohammed Joz, Administrator

Interim Healthcare 989.791.5100
Fax 989.791.8100
  5155 Hampton Pl, Saginaw, MI 48604
  Julie Salter, Chief Executive Officer

SOCIAL SERVICES

4C 586.469.6993
Fax 586.469.6992
Web ....www.msue.msu.edu/macomb
E-mail ....4cr&r@macombcountymi.gov
  21885 Dunham Rd Rm 12, Clinton Township,
  MI 48036-1030
  Mary Frontiero, Director

Advanced Behavioral Medicine 517.548.1537
Fax 517.548.9399
Web ....www.advancedbehavioralmedicine.com
  2901 East Grand River, Howell, MI 48843
  COA accredited organization.

Alpha Women Ctr 231.652.1548
Fax 231.652.1995
  8849 Mason Dr, Newaygo, MI 49337
  Lisa Hubbard, Director

Alpha Women's Ctr 269.948.9013
Web ....www.alphawomenscenter.org
E-mail ....louis@alphawc.org
  838 W Green St, Hastings, MI 49058-1851
  Louis Azona, Director

Alternatives Women's Care Ctr 269.345.0725
Fax 269.345.1032
Web ....www.alternativeskalamazoo.org
E-mail ....cathy@pregnancychoices.com
  4200 W Michigan Ave Ste 100, Kalamazoo,
  MI 49006-5893
  Dave Bos, Director

Another Way Pregnancy Ctr 248.471.5858
E-mail ....anotherwaypc@gmail.com
  33100 Grand River Ave, Farmington, MI 48336
  Karen Jewell, Director

Arenac Ctr 989.846.4573
Fax 989.846.5047
Web ....www.babha.org
E-mail ....pbaker@babha.org
  1000 W Cedar St, Standish, MI 48658-9421
  Pat Baker, Director

Michigan

Michigan

AuSable Valley Community Mental Health 989.362.8636
Fax 989.362.7800
Web ....www.avcmh.org
   P.O. Box 310, Tawas City, MI 48764
   COA accredited organization.

Bethany Christian Services 616.224.7610
Fax 616.224.7611
Web ....www.bethany.org
   P.O. Box 294, Grand Rapids, MI 49501-0294
   COA accredited organization.

Catholic Charities 231.726.4735
Fax 231.722.0789
   1095 3rd St Ste 125, Muskegon, MI 49441
   Pamela Kohn, Director

Catholic Charities of Shiawassee & Genesee
Counties 810.232.9950
Fax 810.232.9110
Web ....www.ccsgc.org
   901 Chippewa Street, Flint, MI 48503
   COA accredited organization.

Catholic Charities West Michigan 616.243.9122
Fax 616.551.5646
Web ....www.ccwestmi.org
   360 Division Avenue, Suite 3A, Grand Rapids,
   MI 49503
   COA accredited organization.

Catholic Family Svcs 989.892.2504
Fax 989.892.1923
   915 Columbus Ave, Bay City, MI 48708
   William Lubold, Clinical Supervisor

Catholic Family Svcs 269.381.9800
Fax 269.381.2932
Web ....www.catholicfamilyservices.org
E-mail ....frandenny@catholicfamilyservices.org
   1819 Gull Rd, Kalamazoo, MI 49048-1611
   Frances Denny, Executive Director

Catholic Social Services 313.883.2100
Fax 313.883.3957
Web ....www.csswayne.org
   9851 Hamilton Avenue, Detroit, MI 48202
   COA accredited organization.

Catholic Social Services 734.971.9781
Fax 734.971.2370
Web ....www.csswashtenaw.org
   4925 Packard Road, Ann Arbor, MI 48108-1521
   COA accredited organization.

Catholic Social Services of the Upper
Peninsula 906.227.9119
Fax 906.228.2469
Web ....www.dioceseofmarquette.org
   347 Rock Street, Marquette, MI 49855
   COA accredited organization.

Catholic Social Svcs 734.971.9781
Fax 734.971.2730
E-mail ....info@csswashtenaw.org
   4925 Packard St, Ann Arbor, MI 48108
   Larry Voight, Director

Catholic Social Svcs 906.774.3323
Fax 906.774.2556
Web ....www.cssup.org
   427 S Stephenson Ave, Ste 215, Iron Mountain,
   MI 49801
   Will Shampo, Director

Catholic Social Svcs 734.240.3850
Fax 734.240.3863
Web ....www.ccmonroe.org
E-mail ....info@ccmonroe.org
   14930 Laplaisance Rd Ste 123, Monroe,
   MI 48161-3878
   Paul Nietman, Interim Executive Director

Catholic Social Svcs 313.883.2100
Fax 313.883.3957
Web ....www.csswc.org
E-mail ....csswc@csswayne.org
   9851 Hamilton Ave, Detroit, MI 48202-1498
   Patrick J. Heron, President

Catholic Svcs 586.416.2300
Fax 586.416.2311
   15945 Canal Rd, Clinton Township, MI 48038
   Jim Hansen, Director

Child & Family Services of Southwestern Michigan,
Inc. 269.925.1725
Fax 269.925.1730
Web ....www.cfsswmi.org
   P.O. Box 8789, Benton Harbor, MI 49023-8789
   COA accredited organization.

Child & Family Svcs 989.790.7500
Fax 989.790.8037
Web ....www.cfsm.org
E-mail ....mbach@cfs-saginaw.org
   2806 Davenport Ave, Saginaw, MI 48602-3734
   Margie Bach, Program Director

Child Advocacy 4C of Central Michigan 989.463.1422
Web ....www.linkforfamilies.org
E-mail ....info@linkforfamilies.org
   525 N State st, Ste 4, Alma, MI 48801
   Audra Sphal, Director

Child and Family Service 989.790.7500
Fax 989.790.8037
Web ....www.childandfamilysaginaw.org
   2806 Davenport Ave, Saginaw, MI 48602
   Margie Bach, Director
   CARF accredited programs available.

Child Care Resources 269.349.3296
Fax 269.349.6822
Web www.ccr4kids.org
E-mail ....elia@ccr4kids.org
   268 Kilgore Ln, Portage, MI 49001
   Renee Diaz, Director Of Operations

Children's Leukemia Foundaiton of
Michigan 248.530.3000
Fax 248.530.3041
Web ....www.leukemiamichigan.org
E-mail ....info@leukemiamichigan.org
   5455 Corporate Dr, Ste 306, Troy, MI 48098
   Kristen West, Vice President, Patient Services

Children's Trust Fund 517.373.4320
Fax 517.241.7038
Web ....www.michigan.gov/ctf
   235 So, Grand Ave, Ste 1411, Lansing, MI 48909
   Michael Foley, Director

Christ Child House 313.584.6077
Fax 313.584.1148
Web ....www.christchildhouse.org
   15751 Joy Road, Detroit, MI 48228-2117
   COA accredited organization.

Claystone Clinical Associates, PLC 616.949.7460
Fax 616.949.3018
Web ....www.claystoneclinical.com
   3330 Claystone Street, SE, Grand Rapids,
   MI 49546-7716
   COA accredited organization.

Community Care Svcs 313.389.7525
Fax 313.389.7510
Web ....www.comcareserv.org
E-mail ....skozak@comcareserv.org
   26184 Outer Dr, Lincoln Park, MI 48146-2084
   Susan Kozak, Director

Cornerstone Farm 231.946.2669
E-mail ....bghoth@coslink.net
   10210 E Shady Ln, Suttons Bay, MI 49682-9452
   Betty Hoth, Director

Cory Place Inc. 989.895.5563
Fax 989.895.7312
Web ....www.coeryplace.org
E-mail ....jmcaffee@bc-times.com
   581 N Scheurmann Rd, Bay City, MI 48708-9174
   Jheri Mcaffee, Executive Director

Counseling Services 810.648.4098
Fax 810.648.2646
Web ....www.sanilachealth.com
   171 Dawson Street, Sandusky, MI 48471
   COA accredited organization.

Counterpoint Runaway 313.563.5005
Fax 313.563.4765
Web ....www.starfishonline.org
   715 Inkster Rd, Shelter and Crisis Center, Inkster,
   MI 48141
   Gloria Gibson, Program Manager

Covenant House Michigan 313.463.2000
Fax 313.463.2001
Web ....www.covenanthousemi.org
E-mail ....sjoseph@covenanthouse.org
   2959 Martin Luther King Jr Blvd, Detroit,
   MI 48208-2475
   Sam Joseph, Executive Director

Delton Women's Ctr 269.623.4061
Fax 269.623.4071
Web ....www.mei.net
E-mail ....rhughes@mei.net
   503 S Grove St, Delton, MI 49046-9485
   Rebecca Hughes, Director

Eagle Village, Inc. 231.832.2234
Web ....www.eaglevillage.org
   4507 170th Avenue, Hersey, MI 49639
   COA accredited organization.

Education and Catechesis 517.342.2485
Fax 517.342.2515
Web ....www.dioceseoflansing.org
E-mail ....prinker@dioceseoflansing.org
   228 N Walnut, Lansing, MI 48933-1530
   Patrick Rinker, Youth Minister

Ennis Center for Children, Inc. 313.342.2699
Fax 313.342.2180
Web ....www.enniscenter.org
   20100 Greenfield Road, Detroit, MI 48235
   COA accredited organization.

Evergreen Children's Svcs 313.862.1000
Fax 313.874.7001
Web ....www.evergreenserv.org
E-mail ....d.evans@evergreenserv.org
   2875 W Grant Blvd Ste 200, Detroit, MI 48202
   Duval Evans, Public Relations

Family & Children Services, Inc. 269.344.0202
Fax 269.344.0285
Web ....www.fcsource.org
   1608 Lake Street, Kalamazoo, MI 49001
   COA accredited organization.

Family & Children's Svcs 989.631.5390
Fax 989.631.0488
Web ....www.cfsm.org
   1714 Eastman Ave, Midland, MI 48640-4216
   Beckey Hockemeyer, Office Manager

Family & Children's Svcs 269.965.3247
Fax 269.966.4135
Web ....www.fcsource.org
E-mail ....rosemaryg@fcsource.org
   535 Emmett St E, Battle Creek, MI 49017-5682
   Rosemary Gardiner, Director

Family Outreach Center, Inc. 616.247.3815
Fax 616.245.0450
Web ....www.familyoutreachcenter.org
   1939 South Division Avenue, Grand Rapids,
   MI 49507
   COA accredited organization.

Family Place...................................313.664.0700
Fax..313.664.0719
  8726 Woodward Ave, Detroit, MI 48202
Denice Glover, Program Director

Family Service & Children's Aid..............517.787.7920
Fax..517.787.2440
Web............................www.strong-families.org
  330 W. Michigan Avenue, Jackson, MI 49201
  COA accredited organization.

Family Service, Inc.............................313.965.2141
Fax..313.961.4612
Web..www.fsiwc.org
  10900 Harper Avenue, Detroit, MI 48213
  COA accredited organization.

Growth Works..................................734.495.1722
Fax..734.495.3068
E-mail..................bspitzberger@growth-works.org
  50430 School House Rd, Canton, MI 48187
Brian Spitzberger, Director

Hegira Programs...............................734.458.4601
Fax..734.458.4611
E-mail.............................cdigiuseppe@hegira.net
  8623 N Wayne Rd Ste 200, Westland,
  MI 48185-1137
Carol Digiuseppe, Director

Huron Behavioral Health......................989.269.9293
Fax..989.269.7544
Web..www.huroncmh.org
  P.O. Box 312, Bad Axe, MI 48413
  COA accredited organization.

Jewish Community Services....................810.767.5922
Fax..810.767.9024
E-mail...jfcs@tm.net
  619 Wallenberg St, Flint, MI 48502
Lynda Yeotis, Executive Director

Jewish Family Service.........................248.592.2300
Fax..248.592.2310
Web......................................www.jfsdetroit.org
E-mail..........................postmaster@jfsdetroit.org
  6555 West Maple Rd, West Bloomfield, MI 48322
Norman Keane, Ex. Dir.

Jewish Family Svcs............................734.769.0209
Fax..734.769.0224
Web......................................www.jfsannarbor.org
E-mail.............................anya@jfsannarbor.org
  2245 S State St Ste 200, Ann Arbor, MI 48104-6184
Anya Abramson, Director

Kent Regional 4C...............................616.451.8281
Fax..616.451.8327
Web......................................www.4cchildcare.org
E-mail.............................debv@4cchildcare.org
  233 Fulton E St Ste 107, Grand Rapids,
  MI 49503-3262
Deb Vandermolen, Executive Director

Livonia Youth Assistance Program...........734.466.2670
Fax..734.466.2190
  33000 Civic Center Dr, Livonia, MI 48154
Susan L. Anderson, Program Supervisor

**Lutheran Child & Family Service of Michigan,
Inc.**...989.686.7650
Fax..989.686.7688
Web..www.lcfsmi.org
  P.O. Box 48, Bay City, MI 48707-0048
  COA accredited organization.

Lutheran Social Services of Michigan.......313.823.7700
Fax..313.823.7985
Web..www.lssm.org
  8131 East Jefferson Avenue, Detroit, MI 48214-2691
  COA accredited organization.

Lutheran Social Svcs..........................906.226.7410
Fax..906.226.9800
Web..www.lsswis.org
E-mail..www.lsswis.org
  290 Rublein St Ste A, Marquette, MI 49855-4067
Richard Kochis, Director

Macomb Oakland Regional Center, Inc........586.263.8700
Fax..586.412.7889
Web..www.morcinc.org
  16200 Nineteen Mile Road, Clinton Township,
  MI 48038-0070
  CARF accredited programs available.

Methodist Childrens Home Society...........313.531.4060
Fax..313.531.9962
Web..www.mchfmi.com
  26645 W 6 Mile Rd, Redford, MI 48240-2399
Lisa Koger, Placement Supervisor

Michigan Indian Child Welfare Agency.......616.454.9221
Fax..616.454.3142
Web..www.micwa.org
  1345 Monroe Ave NW, Ste 220, Grand Rapids,
  MI 49505
Lynn Thompson, Supervisor

Michigan Indian Child Welfare Agency.......517.393.3256
Fax..517.393.0838
Web..www.michigan.gov
E-mail.............................bdurkalee@michigan.gov
  6425 S Pennsylvania Ave Ste 3, Lansing,
  MI 48911-5975
Bill Durkalee, Director

**Michigan State University - Herbert J. Oyer
Speech-Language-Hearing Clinic**...........517.353.8780
Fax..517.353.3176
E-mail..comdis@msu.edu
  101 Oyer Speech And Hearing, East Lansing,
  MI 48824-1220
Frank Boster, Acting Chairperson

Oakland Family Services......................248.858.7766
Fax..248.858.7215
Web......................www.oaklandfamilyservices.org
E-mail..............................info@ofsfamily.org
  114 Orchard Lake Road, Pontiac, MI 48341
Michael Earl, Director
  COA accredited organization.

Oakland Family Svcs..........................248.544.4004
Fax..248.544.4113
Web..www.ofsfamily.org
E-mail..........................Lcoleman@ofsfamily.org
  2351 W. Twelve Mile Rd, Berkeley, MI 48072
Linda Coleman, Office Manager

Oakland Family Svcs..........................248.624.3812
Fax..248.624.0368
Web..www.ofsfamily.org
E-mail..........................jclayton@ofsfamily.org
  2045 E West Maple Rd Ste 407, Walled Lake,
  MI 48390-3801
Jamie Clayton, Director

Ofc For Young Children.......................517.887.4319
Fax..517.887.4310
Web..hd.ingham.org
  5303 S Cedar St, Lansing, MI 48911
Barb Monroe, Coordinator

Orchards Children's Services, Inc...........248.258.0440
Fax..248.258.0487
Web..www.orchards.org
  30215 Southfield Road, Southfield, MI 48076
  COA accredited organization.

Spectrum Child & Family Services...........734.458.8736
Fax..734.513.1148
Web......................................www.spectrumhuman.org
  28303 Joy Road, Westland, MI 48185
  COA accredited organization.

St. Francis Family Svcs.......................248.552.0750
Fax..248.552.9019
Web..www.osfoc.org
  17500 W 8 Mile Rd, Southfield, MI 48075-4330
Kari Mascar, Director

St. Vincent Catholic Charities...............517.323.4734
Fax..517.886.1150
Web..www.stvcc.org
  2800 W. Willow Street, Lansing, MI 48917
  COA accredited organization.

Starfish Family Services......................734.728.3400
Fax..734.728.3500
Web......................................www.starfishonline.org
  30000 Hiveley Road, Inkster, MI 48141
  COA accredited organization.

Starr Commonwealth..........................313.794.4447
Fax..313.794.4484
Web..www.starr.org
E-mail..........................matthewsl@starr.org
  22400 W 7 Mile Rd, Detroit, MI 48219-1849
Linton Matthews, Associate Director

Starr Commonwealth..........................517.629.5591
Fax..517.629.2317
Web..www.starr.org
  13725 Starr Commonwealth Road, Albion, MI 49224
  COA accredited organization.

The Children's Center.........................313.831.5535
Fax..313.831.4443
Web......................................www.thechildrenscenter.com
  79 West Alexandrine, Detroit, MI 48201
  COA accredited organization.

Vista Maria....................................313.271.3050
Fax..313.271.6250
Web..www.vistamaria.org
  20651 West Warren Avenue, Dearborn Heights,
  MI 48127
  COA accredited organization.

Wedgwood Christian Services.................616.942.2110
Fax..616.942.0589
Web..www.wedgwood.org
  3300 36th Street, SE, Grand Rapids, MI 49512
  COA accredited organization.

SPECIAL NEEDS

Assn for Children w/Emotional Disorders.....248.433.2200
E-mail..........................susan@michkids.org
  30233 Southfield Rd Ste 219, Southfield, MI 48076
Susan McParland, Director

Association for Children's Mental Hlth.......517.372.4016
E-mail..........................acmhadmin@spcglobal.net
  6017 W St. John Hwy Ste 200, Lansing, MI 48917
Malisa Parson, Director

Asthma & Allergy Foundation.................248.406.4254
Fax..248.737.8862
Web..www.aafamich.org
E-mail..........................aafamich@sbcglobal.net
  2075 Walnut Lake Rd, West Bloomfield, MI 48323
Kathleen Felice Slonager, Executive Director

Blind Vision Inc...............................248.627.2260
E-mail..........................bkmabma@worldnet.att.net
  2501 Pheasant Run, Ortonville, MI 48462

Borgess Medical Center.......................269.226.8008
Fax..269.226.4923
Web..www.borgess.com
  1521 Gull Road, Kalamazoo, MI 49048
  CARF accredited programs available.

Brain Injury Association of Michigan.........810.229.5880
E-mail..........................info@biami.org
  7305 Grand River Ave Ste 100, Brighton, MI 48114
Michael Dabbs, President

Michigan

Michigan

Center for Dev of Language & Literacy 734.764.8440
E-mail . . . . .ucll@umich.edu
1111 E Catherine St, Ann Arbor, MI 48109
Holly Craig, Director

Children's Hospital of Michigan 313.966.5110
Fax 313.993.0398
Web . . . . .www.childrensdmc.org
3901 Beaubien Boulevard, Detroit, MI 48201
CARF accredited programs available.

Comprehensive Therapy Center 616.559.1054
Fax 616.559.1056
Web . . . . .www.therapycenter.org
2505 Ardmore SE, Grand Rapids, MI 49506
CARF accredited programs available.

Covenant HealthCare Rehabilitation
Program 989.583.2817
Fax 989.583.2843
Web . . . . .www.covenanthealthcare.com
515 North Michigan Avenue, Saginaw, MI 48602
CARF accredited programs available.

Epilepsy Foundation of Michigan 248.351.7979
E-mail . . . . .letters@epilepsymichigan.org
20300 Civic Center Dr, Ste 250, Southfield,
MI 48076

Family Support Network 313.456.4381
E-mail . . . . .d@michigan.gov
3056 W Grand Blvd Ste 3-350, Detroit, MI 48202
Dianna Rizto, Information Specialist

Forest View Psychiatric Hospital 616.942.9610
Fax 616.954.3110
Web . . . . .www.forestviewhospital.com
1055 Medical Park Dr SE, Grand Rapids,
MI 49546-8323
Scott Miles, Director Of Business Development

Gentiva Rehab Without Walls - Michigan 517.323.1124
Fax 517.323.1846
Web . . . . .www.gentiva.com
6105 W Saint Joseph, Ste 211, Lansing, MI 48917
Tammy Goulding, Executive Director
CARF accredited programs available.

Gerstmann Syndrome Support Network 734.479.1517
14246 Heritage Dr, Riverview, MI 48192
Gerald Olseski Jr, Network Dir/spec Ed Co-director

Greater Detroit Agency for Blind & Visually
Impaired 313.272.3900
E-mail . . . . .info@gdabvi.org
16625 Grand River Ave, Detroit, MI 48227
Victor Arbulu, Managing Director

Hope Network Rehabilitation Services 616.940.0040
Fax 616.940.8151
Web . . . . .www.hopenetworkrehab.org
1490 East Beltline SE, Grand Rapids, MI 49506
CARF accredited programs available.

Kids In Motion Pediatric Therapy Services 248.684.9610
Fax 248.684.9611
Web . . . . .www.kimpediatrics.com
2636 South Milford Road, Highland, MI 48357
CARF accredited programs available.

Labor & Economic Growth 877.499.6232
E-mail . . . . .dodhh@michigan.gov
201 N Washington Sq Ste 150, Lansing, MI 48913
Sheryl Emery, Director

Lakeside Comprehensive Rehabilitation,
Inc. 231.873.3577
Fax 231.873.3557
Web . . . . .www.lakesiderehab.com
601 East Main Street, Hart, MI 49420
CARF accredited programs available.

Learning Disabilities Association 517.485.8160
E-mail . . . . .ldamich@sbcglobal.net
200 Museum Dr Ste 101, Lansing, MI 48933

Lindamood-Bell Learning Processes 248.723.5380
Fax 248.723.5390
148 Pierce St, Birmingham, MI 48009
Joe Chen, Director

Mary Free Bed Rehabilitation Hospital 248.553.0010
Fax 248.553.3578
E-mail .wchlphysician@msn.com
28595 Orchard Lake Rd # 200, Farmington Hills,
MI 48334
Deborah F Gelinas Md, Director

Mary Free Bed Rehabilitation Hospital 616.242.0498
Fax 616.242.0302
Web . . . . .www.maryfreebed.com
235 Wealthy Street SE, Grand Rapids, MI 49503
CARF accredited programs available.

Mental Health Asociation in Michigan 248.647.1711
E-mail . . . . .mark@mha-mi.org
30233 Southfield Rd Ste 220, Southfield, MI 48076
Mark Reinstein, Chief Executive Officer

Michigan Alliance for Families 800.552.4821
E-mail . . . . .caryn.ivey@arcmi.org
51 W Hancock, Detroit, MI 48201

Michigan Alliance for Families 517.487.5426
E-mail . . . . .sherri@arcmi.org
1325 S Washington Ave, Lansing, MI 48910
Anissa Vanliew, Manager

Michigan Alliance for Families-Reg 2 . . . . .269.934.9471
Fax 517.487.0303
E-mail . . . . .michelle@arcmi.org
1380 E Napier Ave Ste 4, Benton Harbor, MI 49022
Michelle Miller, Chief Executive Officer

Michigan Head-Pain and Neurological
Institute 734.677.6000
Fax 734.973.7418
Web . . . . .www.mhni.com
3120 Professional Drive, Ann Arbor, MI 48104
Al Lake, Director
CARF accredited programs available.

Munson Medical Center Memory and Attention Training
Center 231.935.6511
Fax 231.935.7344
Web . . . . .www.munsonhealthcare.org
5123 North Royal Drive, Traverse City, MI 49684
CARF accredited programs available.

National Multiple Sclerosis Society 248.350.0020
Fax 248.350.0029
E-mail . . . . .Info@mig.nmss.org
21311 Civic Center Dr, Southfield, MI 48076

New Chapter Learning .616.534.1385
E-mail .info@newchapterlearning.net
West Michigan, Grandville, MI 14906

Origami Brain Injury Rehabilitation
Center 517.336.6060
Fax 517.336.6050
Web . . . . .www.origamirehab.org
3181 Sandhill Road, Mason, MI 48854
CARF accredited programs available.

Ou Care Open Univercity Center For Research Education
Support 248.370.2424
Fax 248.370.4242
Web . . . . .www.oakland.edu/oucares
E-mail . . . . .oucares@oakland.edu
Oakland University 420 B Pawley, Rochester,
MI 48309-4494
Kathy Sweeney, Director

Rainbow Rehabilitation Centers, Inc.- Ypsilanti
Center 734.482.1200
Fax 734.482.5212
Web . . . . .www.rainbowrehab.com
5570 Whittaker Road, Ypsilanti, MI 48197
CARF accredited programs available.

Reading & Language Arts Centers, Inc 248.645.9690
Fax 248.645.2335
E-mail . . . . .info@rlac.com
36700 Woodward Ave Ste 20, Bloomfield Hills,
MI 48304
Nick Smith, Center Coordinator

Rehabilitation Institute of Michigan 313.745.9753
Fax 313.966.8294
Web . . . . .www.RIMrehab.org
261 Mack Avenue, Detroit, MI 48201
CARF accredited programs available.

Sparrow Health System, Rehabilitation
Services 517.364.5264
Fax 517.364.5296
Web . . . . .www.sparrow.org
E-mail . . . . .jeanne.hudson@sparrow.org
1215 East Michigan Avenue, Lansing, MI 48912
Jeanne Hudson, Revenue Cycle Director
CARF accredited programs available.

Special Tree Rehabilitation System 734.941.1142
Fax 734.941.7522
Web . . . . .www.specialtree.com
39000 Chase Road, Romulus, MI 48174
CARF accredited programs available.

Spectrum Health Continuing Care 616.391.5720
Fax 616.391.5721
Web . . . . .www.spectrum-health.org
E-mail . . . . .janis.matthews@spectrum-health.org
4500 Breton SE, Grand Rapids, MI 49508
Sheila Steger, Gift Planning Director
CARF accredited programs available.

Speech-Language-Hearing Association 517.332.5691
E-mail . . . . .msha@ix.netcom.com
790 W Lake Lansing Rd Ste 500A, East Lansing,
MI 48823

The Arc Michigan 517.487.5426
E-mail . . . . .dhoyle@arcmi.org
1325 S Washington Ave, Lansing, MI 48910
Dohn Hoyle, Executive Director

The Autism Society of Michigan 517.882.2800
E-mail . . . . .autism@autism-mi.org
2178 Commons Pkwy, Okemas, MI 48864
Kathy Johnson, President

The Detroit Institute for Children 313.832.1100
Fax 313.832.3025
Web . . . . .www.detroitchildren.org
E-mail . . . . .don.drouillard@detroitchildren.org
5447 Woodward Avenue, Detroit, MI 48202
Don Drouillard, Director of Customer Services and Support Services
CARF accredited programs available.

The Lighthouse, Inc. 989.673.2500
Fax 989.673.2502
Web . . . . .www.lighthouserehab.com
1655 East Caro Road, Caro, MI 48723
CARF accredited programs available.

United Cerebral Palsy of Michigan 517.203.1200
E-mail . . . . .potter@ucpmichigan.org
3401 E Saginaw Ste 216, Lansing, MI 48912

Untd Cerebral Palsy Assc of 248.557.5070
Fax 248.557.0224
E-mail . . . . .ucp@ameritech.net
23077 Greenfield Ste 205, Southfield, MI 48075
Angel Leslynn, Chief Executive Officer

VSA Arts of Michigan 313.832.3303
E-mail . . . . .info@vsami.org
PO Box 2805, Detroit, MI 48202

SUBSTANCE ABUSE TREATMENT

Barry-Eaton District Health Department/Eaton Substance Abuse Program **517.543.2580**
Fax 517.543.8191
Web ....www.barryeatonhealth.org
　　1033 Health Care Drive, Charlotte, MI 48813
　　Jack Jesse, Director of the Substance Abuse Program
　　CARF accredited programs available.

Catholic Charities **734.240.3850**
Fax 734.240.3863
Web ....www.cssdoorway.com
　　14930 LaPlaisance Road, Suite 123, Monroe,
　　MI 48161
　　CARF accredited programs available.

COBAP Substance Abuse Treatment and Prevention Program **313.893.9055**
Fax 313.893.0713
　　17357 Klinger Street, Detroit, MI 48212
　　John W Marks, Director
　　CARF accredited programs available.

Community Programs, Inc. **248.406.0090**
Fax 248.406.0107
Web ....www.communityprograms.org
　　1255 N Oakland Blvd, Ste 200, Waterford, MI 48327
　　Bernie Paige, CEO
　　CARF accredited programs available.

Cristo Rey Counseling Services **517.372.4700**
Fax 517.372.3314
Web ....www.cristoreycounseling.org
　　1717 North High St, Lansing, MI 48906
　　Carol Patterson, Director
　　CARF accredited programs available.

Dawn Farm **734.485.8725**
Fax 734.485.6103
Web ....www.dawnfarm.org
E-mail ....info@dawnfarm.org
　　6633 Stoney Creek Road, Ypsilanti, MI 48197
　　Jason Schwartz, Director
　　CARF accredited programs available.

Detroit Rescue Mission Ministries **313.993.4700**
Fax 313.831.2299
Web ....www.drmm.org
　　150 Stimson Street, Detroit, MI 48201
　　Chad Audi, Director
　　CARF accredited programs available.

Harbor Hall, Inc. **888.880.5511**
Fax 231.347.5422
Web ....www.harborhall.com
E-mail ....tnewt@freeway.net
　　704 Emmet Street, Petoskey, MI 49770
　　Terrance Newton, Executive Director
　　CARF accredited programs available.

Heron Ridge Associates, PLC **248.693.8880**
Fax 248.391.7478
Web ....www.heronridgeassocs.com
　　3694 Clarkston Road, Suite D, Clarkston, MI 48348
　　Tariq Abbasi, Medical Director
　　CARF accredited programs available.

Key Development Center, Inc. **517.545.5890**
Fax 517.545.5891
Web ....http://charityadvantage.com/humandevelop
　　2708 East Grand River, Suite 113, Howell, MI 48843
　　CARF accredited programs available.

Lansing Psychological Associates, P.C. **517.337.6545**
Fax 517.337.3010
　　234 Michigan Avenue, East Lansing, MI 48823
　　Sue Berry, Office Manager
　　CARF accredited programs available.

NCADD **313.861.0666**
Fax 313.861.0413
Web ....www.ncadd-detroit.org
E-mail ....president@ncadd-detroit.org
　　16647 Wyoming St, Detroit, MI 48221-2848
　　Benjamin Jones, Director

NorthPoint Counseling Services **517.647.5337**
E-mail ....dcmitin@yahoo.com
　　7204 - 143 E Grand River Ave, Portland, MI 48875
　　Dennis Mitin, Director
　　CARF accredited programs available.

People's Community Services of Metropolitan Detroit **313.554.3111**
Fax 313.554.3113
Web ....www.pecose.org
E-mail ....tcervenak@pecose.org
　　412 West Grand Boulevard, Detroit, MI 48216
　　Thomas Cervenak, Director
　　CARF accredited programs available.

Proaction Behavioral Health Alliance **616.776.0891**
Fax 616.776.9906
Web ....www.proactionbehavioralhealth.org
E-mail ....tinadee@proactionbehavioralhealth.org
　　330 Eastern Avenue SE, Grand Rapids, MI 49503
　　Tina Dee, Director of Community Relations
　　CARF accredited programs available.

Psychological Consultants of Michigan, P.C. **269.968.2811**
Fax 269.968.2651
Web ....www.psycmi.com
E-mail ....jandert@psycmi.com
　　151 North Ave, Battle Creek, MI 49017
　　Dr Jeff Andert, Director
　　CARF accredited programs available.

Recovery Consultants, Incorporated **248.543.1090**
Fax 248.543.0017
　　2710 West 12 Mile Road, Berkley, MI 48072
　　CARF accredited programs available.

Sault Tribe of Chippewa Indians Health Division - Behavioral Health Program **906.632.0611**
Fax 906.632.5272
Web ....www.saulttribe.org
E-mail ....jbye@saulttribe.net
　　2864 Ashmun Street, Sault Sainte Marie, MI 49783
　　Juanita Bye, Interim Director
　　CARF accredited programs available.

Self Help Addiction Rehabilitation, Inc. **313.894.8444**
Fax 313.894.5542
Web ....www.sharinc.org
E-mail ....dvaughter@sharinc.org
　　1852 West Grand Boulevard, Detroit, MI 48208
　　Dwight Vaughter, Director
　　CARF accredited programs available.

Sobriety House Inc. **313.895.0500**
Fax 313.895.9503
Web ....www.sobrietyhouse.net
E-mail ....sobrietyhouse@sobrietyhouse.net
　　2081 West Grand Boulevard, Detroit, MI 48208
　　Jerome Foster, Director
　　CARF accredited programs available.

Substance Abuse Prevention Group of Greater Battle Creek, Inc. **269.964.3830**
Fax 269.964.3833
Web ....www.spgbservices.com
　　32 East Van Buren Street, Battle Creek, MI 49017
　　CARF accredited programs available.

Ten Sixteen Recovery Network **989.631.0241**
Fax 989.631.0242
Web www.1016.org
　　220 West Main Street, Suite 202, Midland, MI 48640
　　CARF accredited programs available.

The Salvation Army Harbor Light System - Southeastern Michigan **313.361.6136**
Fax 313.361.6210
Web ....www.salmich.org
　　3737 Lawton, Detroit, MI 48208
　　EDWARD ROWLAND, MAJOR
　　CARF accredited programs available.

University Substance Abuse Clinic **269.387.8230**
Fax 269.387.7310
Web ....www.wmich.edu/hhs/unifiedclinics/usac
　　1000 Oakland Dr, Kalamazoo, MI 49008-5361
　　Tom Blackmon, Director, University Substance Abuse Clinic
　　CARF accredited programs available.

Michigan

Minnesota

www.state.mn.us

Mark Dayton, Governor
State Capitol
75 Rev. Dr. MLK Jr., Blvd. Room 130
St. Paul, MN 55155
651.296.3391
651.296.2089 (Fax)
tim.palwenty@state.mn.us
www.governor.state.mn.us

Carrie Wasley, Juvenile Justice Specialist
Office of Justice Programs, Justice and Community Grants
Town Square, Suite 100 444 Cedar Street
St. Paul, MN 55101-5100
651.201.7348
651.284.3317 (Fax)
carrie.wasley@state.mn.us

Richard Gardell, SAG Chair
236 Clifton Ave South
Minneapolis, MN 55403
612.813.5010
richard@180degrees.org

CRISIS NUMBERS

Child Abuse Reporting . . .651.431.2000

STATE SERVICES

SOCIAL SERVICES

Child Care Licensing Office MN 651.296.3971
Fax 651.297.1490
PO Box 64242, Saint Paul, MN 55164
Stephanie Ostwald, Director

Child Support Enforcement 651.431.4403
Fax 651.431.7517
E-mail . . . . .wayland.campbell@state.mn.us
444 Lafayette Road St, Saint Paul, MN 55164-0946
Wayland Campbell, Director

Dept of Human Svcs 651.431.2000
Fax 651.431.7421
Web . . . . .www.state.mn.us
E-mail . . . . .david.godfrey@state.mn.us
540 Cedar St, Saint Paul, MN 55101-2208
David Godfrey, State Medicaid Director

Human Services and Public Health Dept 612.596.9563
Fax 612.348.7645
E-mail . . . . .deborah.huskins@co.hennepin.mn.us
300 So 6Th St, Minneapolis, MN 55487-0001
Deborah Huskins, Director

GENERAL HEALTH SERVICES

Maternal and Child Health Section MN 651.201.3872
Fax 651.201.3590
E-mail . . . . .laurel.briske@state.mn.us
PO Box 64882, Saint Paul, MN 55164
Laurel Briske, Director

Matrenal Child Health /MN Children with Special Health Needs 651.201.3650
Fax 651.201.3655
E-mail . . . . .laurelbriske@state.mn.us
85 E 7th Place, Saint Paul, MN 55164
Laurel Briske, Protection Manager

Minnesota WIC Program 800.942.4030
Fax 651.215.8951
Web . . . .www.health.state.mn.us/divs/fh/wic/inde x.html
E-mail .shawn.matteson@state.mn.us
85 E. 7th Pl, Saint Paul, MN 55101
Betsy Clarke, Director

MENTAL HEALTH SERVICES

Children's Mental Health 651.431.2321
Fax 651.431.7418
Web . . . . .www.dhs.state.mn.us
E-mail .glenace.edwall@state.mn.us
540 Cedar St, Saint Paul, MN 55101
Glenace Edwall, Director

State Operated Svcs .651.431.2367
Fax 651.431.7505
444 lafayette rd n, Saint Paul, MN 55164
Mike Tessneer, CEO

State Services For Blind 651.642.0500
Fax 651.649.5927
E-mail . . . . .richard.strong@state.mn.us
2200 University Ave W, Ste 240, Saint Paul, MN 55114
Richard Strong, Director

Voc Rehab Svcs MN .651.259.7345
Fax 651.297.5159
E-mail . . . . .kim.peck@state.mn.us
332 Minnestoa St, First Natl Bnk Bldg Ste E 200, Saint Paul, MN 55101
Kim Peck, Director

JUSTICE AGENCY

9th District Court 218.333.4212
Fax 218.333.4209
E-mail . . . . .paul.benshoof@courts.state.mn.us
600 Minnesota Ave NW Ste 108, Bemidji, MN 56601-3188
Honourable Paul Benshoof, Director

Attorney General's Ofc 651.296.3353
Fax 651.282.2155
Web . . . . .www.ag.state.mn.us
E-mail . . . . .attorney.general@state.mn.us
445 Minnesota St Ste 1200, 1400 BREAMER TOWER, Saint Paul, MN 55101-2130
Lori Swanson, Attorney General

Community & Juvenile Svcs Div 651.361.7200
Fax 651.642.0414
Web . . . . .www.doc.state.mn.us
1450 Energy Park Dr Ste 200, Saint Paul, MN 55108-5227
Rose Ann Bisch, Interstate Compacts

Correctional Education Division MN 651.361.7244
Fax 651.603.0150
E-mail . . . . .marcie.koetke@state.mn.us
1450 Energy Park Dr Ste 200, Saint Paul, MN 55108
Marcie Koetke, Director

Minnesota Dept of Public Safety 651.201.7000
Fax 651.297.5728
Web . . . . .http://www.dps.state.mn.us/
445 Minnesota St, Ste 1000, Saint Paul, MN 55101
Ramona Dohman, Commissioner Of Public Safety

Ofc of Justice Programs/Crime Victim Svcs 651.201.7300
Fax 651.205.4808
Web . . . . .www.ojp.state.mn.us
445 Minnesota St Ste 2300, Saint Paul, MN 55101-2139
Jeri Boisbert, Director

POLICE AND SHERIFF

Minnesota Chiefs of Police Assoc 651.457.0677
Fax 651.457.5665
Web . . . . .www.mnchiefs.org
E-mail . . . . .info@mnchiefs.org
1951 Woodlane Dr Ste 200, Saint Paul, MN 55125
Dave Pecchia, Executive Director

Sheriff's Ofc 507.377.5205
Fax 507.377.5257
411 S Broadway Ave, Albert Lea, MN 56007-4505
Bob Kindler, Sheriff

EDUCATION SERVICES

Dept of Education 651.582.8751
Fax 651.582.8499
Web . . . . .www.educaiton.mn.state.us
E-mail . . . . .greg.marcus@state.mn.us
1500 Highway 36 W, Saint Paul, MN 55113-4035
Greg Marcus, No Child Left Behind Director

Metro Deaf School 651.224.3995
Fax 651.222.0939
Web . . . . .www.metrodeafschool.org
E-mail . . . . .dsherwood@metrodeafschool.org
1471 Brewster St, St Paul, MN 55108
Diane Sherwood, Program Coordinator

Minnesota Braille and Talking Book Library 507.333.4828
Fax 507.333.4832
Web . . . . .www.webopac.klas.com/mnbph
E-mail . . . . .mn.btbl@state.mn.us
388 6th Ave SE, Faribault, MN 55021-6340
Catherine Durivage, Director

Minnesota Dept of Education 651.582.8200
Fax 651.582.8724
1500 Highway 36 West, Roseville, MN 55113
Brenda Cassellius, Commissioner

Minnesota

438

© 2011 Dorland Health

PACER Center Inc MN 952.838.9000
Fax 952.838.0199
E-mail ....pacer@pacer.org
　8161 Normandale Blvd, Bloomington, MN 55437

Program Evaluation MN 651.582.8282
Fax 651.582.8517
E-mail ....Patricia.k.king@state.mn.us
　1500 Highway 36 W Rm T 31, Roseville, MN 55113
　Patricia King, Director

Special Education Policy MN 651.582.8590
Fax 651.582.8729
E-mail ....barbara.troolin@state.mn.us
　1500 Highway 36 W, Roseville, MN 55113
　Barbara Troplin, Director

LABOR & WORKFORCE EDUCATION

Dept of Employment and Economic
Development 651.259.7114
Fax 651.297.7722
Web ....www.state.mn.us
E-mail ....erik.aamoth@state.mn.us
　332 Minnesota St Ste E200, Saint Paul,
　MN 55101-1351
　Erik Aamoth, Director Of Buisness Services

COUNTY SERVICES

Aitkin County

JUSTICE AGENCY

Community Corrections/
Probation 218.927.7281
Fax 218.927.6223
　204 1st St NW, Aitkin, MN 56431
　Elizabeth Deruyck, Supervisor

COURTS

9th District Court 218.927.7350
Fax 218.927.4535
Web ....www.courts.state.mn.us
　209 NW 2nd St Rm 242A, Aitkin, MN 56431-1257
　Honorable John Solien, Judge

Anoka County

SOCIAL SERVICES

Social Svcs 763.422.7000
Fax 763.422.6987
Web ....www.co.anoka.mn.us
　2100 3rd Ave, Anoka County Government Center,
　Anoka, MN 55303
　Cindy Cesare, Interim Director

GENERAL HEALTH SERVICES

Health Dept 763.323.6071
Fax 763.422.6957
Web ....www.co.anoka.mn.us
E-mail ....susan.carolan@co.anoka.mn.us
　2100 3rd Ave, Anoka, MN 55303-2235
　Susan Carolan, Communicable Disease Supervisor

JUSTICE AGENCY

Juvenile Corrections Dept 763.323.5901
Fax 763.323.5998
　325 E Main St, Anoka, MN 55303
　Don Ilse, Director

POLICE AND SHERIFF

Sheriff's Ofc 763.323.5000
Fax 763.422.7503
E-mail ....sheriff@co.anoka.mn.us
　13301 Hanson Blvd NW, Andover, MN 55304
　James Stuart, Sheriff

EDUCATION SERVICES

Cedar Head Start Ctr 763.434.7253
Fax 763.434.1918
　18900 Cedar Dr NW, Cedar, MN 55011-9513

Special Education 763.506.1353
Fax 763.506.1365
Web www.anoka.k12.mn.us
　2740 Wingfield Ave, Fl 2, Anoka, MN 55303
　Mary Clarkson, Director

Becker County

GENERAL HEALTH SERVICES

White Earth Indian Health Ctr 218.983.4300
Fax 218.983.9369
Web ....www.ihs.gov
E-mail ....brenda.hoverson@ihs.gov
　40520 County Highway 34, Ogema,
　MN 56569-9612
　Brenda Hoverson, Rn, Health Director

COURTS

7th District Court 218.846.7305
Fax 218.847.7620
　913 Lake Ave, Detroit Lakes, MN 56501-3403
　Shelly Jeffers, Court Operations Supervisor

Tribal Court 218.983.3285
Fax 218.983.3641
E-mail ....wecourt@tvutel.com
　26246 Crane Rd, White Earth, MN 56591
　Lori Thompson, Legal Technician

EDUCATION SERVICES

Audubon-Lake Park Head Start 218.439.3301
Fax 218.439.3318
Web ....www.lakeparkaudubon.com
E-mail ....lpigatti@lpa.k12.mn.us
　601 4th St, Audubon, MN 56511-0338
　Ms Leah Pigatti, Director

Beltrami County

SOCIAL SERVICES

Family And Children Svcs 218.679.2122
Fax 218.679.2929
　15816 Main Ave, Redlake, MN 56671
　Paula Woods, Director

Human Svcs 218.333.8300
Fax 218.333.8307
Web ....www.co.beltrami.mn.us
　616 America Ave NW, Ste 330, Bemidji, MN 56601
　Mary Marchel, Director

GENERAL HEALTH SERVICES

Public Health - Red Lake Branch 218.679.3945
Fax 218.679.3040
Web ....www.co.beltrami.mn.us
E-mail ....georgia.downwind@co.beltrami.mn.us
　Highway 1, Redby, MN 56670
　Georgia Downwind, Supervisor

EDUCATION SERVICES

Blackduck Head Start 218.835.6326
Fax 218.835.7218
Web ....www.blackduckmn.com
E-mail ....concessions@ephratafair.org
　289 Summit Ave W, Blackduck, MN 56630
　Terry Leinbach, Director

Benton County

SOCIAL SERVICES

Social Svc Agency 320.968.5087
Fax 320.968.5330
Web ....www.hpretire.com
E-mail ....astruther@hpretire.com
　531 Dewey St, Foley, MN 56329-8413
　Timothy Martin, Director

GENERAL HEALTH SERVICES

Health Dept 320.968.5160
Fax 320.968.5330
E-mail ....dgraning@co.benton.mn.us
　531 Dewey St, Foley, MN 56329
　Diana Graning, Nursing Director

JUSTICE AGENCY

Probation 320.968.5192
Fax 320.968.5347
Web ....www.co.benton.mn.us
　615 Highway 23, Foley, MN 56329
　Tim Huver, Corrections Agent

COURTS

7th District Court 320.968.5205
Fax 320.968.5353
Web ....www.co.benton.mn.us
E-mail ....mjesse@co.benton.mn.us
　615 Highway 23, Foley, MN 56329-9182
　Honorable Michael Jesse, Director

EDUCATION SERVICES

Elk River Head Start 320.253.8110
Fax 320.253.1107
　1250 Johnson Rd, Saint Cloud, MN 56304
　Linda Maron, Director

Big Stone County

GENERAL HEALTH SERVICES

Countryside Public Health 320.839.6135
Fax 320.839.3472
E-mail ....lauch@countryside.co.swift.mn.us
　47 2nd St NW Ste 104, Ortonville, MN 56278
　Elizabeth Auch, Administrator

POLICE AND SHERIFF

Sheriff's Ofc 320.839.3558
Fax 320.839.5980
E-mail ....johnh@bsco.us
　20 2nd St SE, Ortonville, MN 56278
　John Haukos, Sheriff

EDUCATION SERVICES

Clinton Graceville Head Start 320.325.5224
Fax 320.325.5509
Web www.graceville.k12.mn.us
　601 1st St, Clinton, MN 56225
　Kris Giesen, Superintendent

Minnesota

Blue Earth County

GENERAL HEALTH SERVICES

Public Health Nursing **507.304.4319**
Fax 507.304.4387
Web ....www.dhs.state.mn.us
    410 S 5th St, Mankato, MN 56001-4592
Deann Boney, Public Assistance Supervisor

POLICE AND SHERIFF

Mankato Police Dept **507.387.8790**
Fax 507.387.4929
    710 S Front St, Mankato, MN 56001
Todd Miller, Director

Brown County

SOCIAL SERVICES

Family Svcs Ctr **507.354.8246**
Fax 507.359.6542
E-mail ....tom.henderson@co.brown.mn.us
    1117 Center St, New Ulm, MN 56073
Thomas Henderson, Director

GENERAL HEALTH SERVICES

Public Health Nursing **507.233.6820**
Fax 507.233.6819
Web ....www.co.brown.mn.us
E-mail ....karen.moritz@co.brown.mn.us
    1117 Center St, New Ulm, MN 56073-3255
Karen Moritz, Director

COURTS

5th District Court **507.233.6670**
Fax 507.359.9562
Web ....www.courts.state.mn.us
E-mail ....john.rodenberg@courts.state.mn.us
    14 S State St, New Ulm, MN 56073-3154
Honorable John R. Rodenberg, Director

Carlton County

GENERAL HEALTH SERVICES

Human Svcs **218.485.8520**
Web ....www.co.carlton.mn.us
E-mail ....paula.danelski@co.carlton.mn.us
    316 Elm Ave, South Carlton County Family Services
    Center, Moose Lake, MN 55767-7706
Paula Danelski, Office Support

Public Home Health **218.879.4511**
Fax 218.878.2845
Web ....www.co.carlton.mn.us
E-mail ....terri.allen@co.carlton.mn.us
    30 10th St N Ste 1, Cloquet, MN 55720-1633
Terri Allen, Rn, Phn, Health Supervisor

JUSTICE AGENCY

Probation Ofc **218.384.8855**
Fax 218.384.8908
Web ....www.co.st-louis.mn.us
    PO Box 280, Carlton, MN 55718-0280
Terry Fawcette, Director

COURTS

6th District Court **218.384.4281**
Fax 218.384.9182
    301 Walnut Ave, Carlton, MN 55718
Honorable Robert E. Mccaulay, Judge

POLICE AND SHERIFF

Sheriff's Dept **218.384.3236**
Fax 218.384.9183
Web ....www.co.carlton.mn.us
E-mail ....sheriff@co.carlton.mn.us
    317 Walnut Ave, Carlton, MN 55718
Kelly Lake, Sheriff

Carver County

SOCIAL SERVICES

Community Social Services **952.361.1600**
Fax 932.361.1660
Web ....www.co.carver.mn.us
E-mail ....gbork@co.carver.mn.us
    602 E 4th St, Human Services Bldg, Chaska,
    MN 55318-2102
Gary Bork, Director

GENERAL HEALTH SERVICES

Community Health Svcs **952.361.1327**
Fax 952.361.1360
Web ....www.co.carver.mn.us
E-mail ....rwolf@co.carver.mn.us
    600 E 4th St, Carver County Government Center,
    Chaska, MN 55318-2102
Randy Wolf, Director

COURTS

1St District Court **952.361.1420**
Fax 952.361.1491
Web ....www.mncourts.gov/forms
E-mail ....philip.kanning@courts.state.mn.us
    604 E 4th St, Chaska, MN 55318
Honorable Philip T. Kanning, Director

POLICE AND SHERIFF

Sheriff's Dept **952.361.1212**
Fax 952.361.1229
E-mail ....bolson@co.carver.mn.us
    606 E 4Th St, Chaska, MN 55318
Bud Olson, Sheriff

Cass County

SOCIAL SERVICES

**Minnesota Chippewa Tribe Human
Svcs** **218.335.8586**
Fax 218.335.8080
Web ....www.mnchippewatribe.org
E-mail ....ljohnston@mnchippewatribe.org
    15542 State 371 Nw, Cass Lake, MN 56633
Linda Johnston, Human Services Director

Public Health & Human Svcs **218.547.1340**
Fax 218.547.1448
Web ....www.co.cass.mn.us
E-mail ....dorothy.opheim@co.cass.mn.us
    400 Michigan Way, Walker, MN 56484
Dorothy Opheim, Human Services Director

GENERAL HEALTH SERVICES

Cass Lake Indian Hospital **218.335.3200**
Fax 218.335.3300
Web ....www.ihs.gov
    425 7Th St Nw, Cass Lake, MN 56633-3360
Amy Buckanaga, Nursing Director

COURTS

9th District Court **218.547.7200**
Fax 218.547.1904
Web ....www.co.cass.mn.us
E-mail ....cass.prob@co.cass.mn.us
    300 Minnesota Ave, Walker, MN 56484
Honorable John Smith, Director

POLICE AND SHERIFF

Sheriff's Dept **218.547.1424**
Fax 218.547.3394
E-mail ....cass.sheriff@co.cass.mn.us
    300 Minnesota Ave, Walker, MN 56484
Tom Birch, Sheriff

EDUCATION SERVICES

**Central Cass Head Start Family
Resource** **218.947.4813**
Fax 218.947.3472
    320 1St Ave E, Backus, MN 56435
Nicki Lodge, Family and classroom

Chippewa County

GENERAL HEALTH SERVICES

Countryside Public Health **320.269.2174**
Fax 320.269.5187
Web ....www.countrysidepublichealth.org
    719 N 7th St Ste 308, Montevideo, MN 56265
Chris Boike, Team Leader

JUSTICE AGENCY

Community Corrections **320.269.6513**
Fax 320.269.5996
E-mail ....mchristianson@6wcc.com
    129 Nichols Ave, Montevideo, MN 56265
Midge Christianson, Director

COURTS

8th District Court **320.269.7774**
Fax 320.269.7733
E-mail ....paul.nelson@courts.state.mn.us
    629 N 11th St, Montevideo, MN 56265-4809
Honorable Paul A. Nelson, District Judge

POLICE AND SHERIFF

Sheriff's Dept **320.269.2121**
Fax 320.269.7852
E-mail ....sheriff@co.chippewa.mn.us
    629 N 11th St Ste 14, Montevideo, MN 56265
Stacy Tufto, Sheriff

Chisago County

SOCIAL SERVICES

Human Svcs **651.213.5600**
Fax 651.213.5685
    313 N Main St Rm 239, Center City, MN 55012
Jill Briggs, Director Of Public Health

GENERAL HEALTH SERVICES

Community Health Svcs **651.213.5700**
Fax 651.213.5401
E-mail ....jabrigg@co.chisago.mn.us
    6133 402 St, North Branch, MN 55056
Jill Briggs, Director Of Public Health

POLICE AND SHERIFF

Sheriff's Ofc **651.213.6300**
Fax 651.213.6330
E-mail ....tprivar@co.chisago.mn.us
    313 N Main St, Rm 100, Center City, MN 55012
Rick Duncan, Sheriff

Clay County

SOCIAL SERVICES

Social Svcs **218.299.5200**
Fax 218.299.7106
Web ....www.co.clay.mn.us
E-mail ....rhonda.porter@co.clay.mn.us
    715 11th St N Ste 502, Moorhead, MN 56560-2000
Rhonda Porter, Director

GENERAL HEALTH SERVICES

Public Health Dept **218.299.5220**
Fax 218.299.7205
Web ....www.co.clay.mn.us
E-mail ....kathy.anderson@co.clay.mn.us
    715 11th St N Ste 303, Moorhead, MN 56560-2088
Kathy Anderson, Rn, Clinical Supervisor

JUSTICE AGENCY

Community Corrections......................**218.299.5052**
Fax...218.299.7508
Web.............................www.fs.doc.state.mn.us
E-mail.......................sford@fs.doc.state.mn.us
　　919 8th Ave N, Moorhead, MN 56560
　　Shelly Ford, Manager

COURTS

7th District Court...........................**218.299.5065**
Fax...218.299.7307
　　807 11th St N, Moorhead, MN 56560
　　Janice Cossette, Court Administrator

POLICE AND SHERIFF

Sheriff's Dept.................................**218.299.5151**
Fax...218.299.5228
Web...www.co.clay.mn.us
E-mail................bill.berquist@co.clay.mn.us
　　915 9th Ave N, Ste 200, Moorhead, MN 56560
　　Bill Berquist, Sheriff

Clearwater County

GENERAL HEALTH SERVICES

Public Health Nursing.....................**218.694.6581**
Fax...218.694.6594
　　212 Main Ave N, Bagley, MN 56621
　　Bonnie Engen, Public Health Nurse

COURTS

9th District Court...........................**218.694.6177**
Fax...218.694.6213
　　213 Main Ave N Dept 303, Bagley, MN 56621
　　Honorable Paul Rasmussen, Judge

POLICE AND SHERIFF

Sheriff's Ofc..................................**218.694.6226**
Fax...218.694.6964
E-mail.............mike.erickson@co.clearwater.mn.us
　　213 Main Ave N Dept 102, Bagley, MN 56621
　　Mike Erickson, Sheriff

Cook County

SOCIAL SERVICES

**Grand Portage Reservation Tribal Council Human Svcs
Dept**...**218.475.2453**
Fax...218.475.2455
　　6 Casino Drive, Grand Portage, MN 55605
　　Sheryl Konig, Director

GENERAL HEALTH SERVICES

Grand Portage Health Svc...................**218.475.2235**
Fax...218.475.2261
E-mail...........................paulas@grandportage.com
　　62 Upper Rd, Grand Portage, MN 55605-3010
　　Paula Schaefbauer, Health Director

Public Health And Human Svcs..............**218.387.3620**
Fax...218.387.3020
Web..www.co.cook.mn.us
E-mail.....................sue.futterer@co.cook.mn.us
　　411 W 2nd St, Grand Marais, MN 55604-2328
　　Sue Futterer, Social Services Director

JUSTICE AGENCY

Juvenile Probation.........................**218.387.3672**
Fax...218.387.3061
Web..www.co.cook.mn.us
　　411 W 2nd St, Grand Marais, MN 55604-2307
　　Scott Johnson, Probation Officer

POLICE AND SHERIFF

Sheriff's Ofc..................................**218.387.3030**
Fax...218.387.3032
E-mail...........................mark.falk@co.cook.mn.us
　　143 Gunflint Trl, Grand Marais, MN 55604-9712
　　Judy Sivertson, Dispatch Sup/jail Administrator

Cottonwood County

GENERAL HEALTH SERVICES

**Cottonwood-Jackson Community Health
Svcs**...**507.831.1987**
Fax...507.831.1747
　　235 9Th St, Windom, MN 56101-1678
　　Patricia Stewart, Director

COURTS

5th District Court...........................**507.831.4551**
Fax...507.831.1425
　　900 3rd Ave, Windom, MN 56101
　　Honorable Bruce F. Gross, Judge

POLICE AND SHERIFF

Sheriff's Office..............................**507.831.1375**
Fax...507.831.1957
E-mail.............jason.purrington@co.cottonwood.mn.us
　　902 5th Ave Ste 1, Windom, MN 56101
　　Jason Purrington, Sheriff

Crow Wing County

SOCIAL SERVICES

Social Svc Ctr...............................**218.824.1140**
Fax...218.824.1141
E-mail.................beth.wilms@co.crow-wing.mn.us
　　204 Laurel St, Brainerd, MN 56401
　　Beth Wilms, Director

GENERAL HEALTH SERVICES

Health Dept...................................**218.824.1080**
Fax...218.824.1081
Web................................www.co.crow-wing.mn.us
E-mail..............gwen.anderson@co.crow-wing.mn.us
　　204 Laurel St Ste 12, Brainerd, MN 56401-0319
　　Gwen Anderson, Nurse Manager

JUSTICE AGENCY

Community Corrections....................**218.824.1135**
Fax...218.824.1136
　　213 Laurel St, Ste 21, Brainerd, MN 56401
　　Thomas Rosenthal, Director

COURTS

9th District Court...........................**218.824.1310**
Fax...218.824.1311
Web..................................www.courts.state.mn.us
E-mail.....................john.solien@courts.state.mn.us
　　213 Laurel St Ste 11, Brainerd, MN 56401-3563
　　Honorable John Solien, Director

Dakota County

SOCIAL SERVICES

Community Svcs Div Ofc....................**651.554.6000**
Fax...651.554.6043
E-mail...................patrick.coyne@co.dakota.mn.us
　　1 Mendota Rd W Ste 300, Saint Paul,
　　MN 55118-4773
　　Patrick Coyne, Social Service Director

Social Svcs....................................**952.891.7400**
Fax...952.891.7473
Web...www.co.dakota.mn.us
E-mail.......................kopesky@co.dakota.mn.us
　　14955 Galaxie Ave, Apple Valley, MN 55124
　　Joan Granger-kopesky, Deputy Director CFS

GENERAL HEALTH SERVICES

**Employment & Economic
Assistance**....................................**651.554.5611**
Fax...651.554.5709
　　1 Mendota Rd W Ste 100, Saint Paul, MN 55118
　　Ruth Krueger, Director

Public Health................................**952.891.7500**
Fax...952.891.7565
Web...www.co.dakota.mn.us
　　14955 Galaxie Ave, Rm 286, Apple Valley, MN 55124
　　Bonnie B, Director Of Public Health

Public Health Dept.........................**651.554.6100**
Fax...651.554.6130
Web...www.dakotacounty.us
E-mail...................publichealth@co.dakota.mn.us
　　1 Mendota Rd W Ste 410, Saint Paul, MN 55118
　　Bonnie Brueshoff, Deputy Director

JUSTICE AGENCY

Community Corrections....................**651.438.8288**
Fax...651.438.8340
Web...www.co.dakota.mn.us
E-mail...................tim.cleveland@co.dakota.mn.us
　　1560 Highway 55, Hastings, MN 55033-2343
　　Tim Cleveland, Deputy Director Of Adult Services

COURTS

1st District Court...........................**651.438.4325**
Fax...651.438.4302
Web..www.mncourts.gov
　　1560 Hwy 55, Judicial Center, Hastings,
　　MN 55033-2343
　　Edward Lynch, Chief Judge

POLICE AND SHERIFF

Sheriff's Ofc..................................**651.438.4700**
Fax...651.438.4709
　　1580 Highway 55, Hastings, MN 55033-2343
　　Dave Bellows, Sheriff

EDUCATION SERVICES

**Intermediate School District 917 Special
Ed.**..**651.423.8426**
Fax...651.423.8052
Web.............................www.isd917.k12.mn.us
E-mail...................daniel.sullivan@isd917.k12.mn.us
　　1300 145th St E, Rosemount, MN 55068-2932
　　Dr. Daniel Sullivan, Special Education Director

Special Education...........................**651.423.7628**
Fax...651.423.7627
Web..www.district196.org
E-mail...................mary.kreger@district196.org
　　3455 153 St W, Rosemount, MN 55068-4143
　　Mary Kreger, Director

Special Education...........................**651.681.2393**
Fax...651.681.9102
E-mail...................schoepft@isd197.k12.mn.us
　　1897 Delaware Ave, Saint Paul, MN 55118-4338
　　Tom Schoepf, Director

Dodge County

GENERAL HEALTH SERVICES

Public Health................................**507.635.6150**
Fax...507.633.9601
E-mail...................peggy.espey@co.dodge.mn.us
　　42 E Main St, Dodge Center, MN 55927
　　Peggy Espey, Phn, Msn, Director

COURTS

3rd District Court...........................**507.635.6260**
Fax...507.635.6271
　　22 6th St E Dept 12, Mantorville, MN 55955
　　Patricia Ball, Administrator

POLICE AND SHERIFF

Sheriff's Ofc..................................**507.635.6200**
Fax...507.635.6225
Web..www.co.dodge.mn.us
E-mail...................jim.jensen@co.dodge.mn.us
　　22 6th St E Dept 201, Mantorville, MN 55955-2255
　　Jim Jensen, Sheriff

Minnesota

Minnesota

Douglas County

SOCIAL SERVICES

Social Svcs **320.762.2302**
Fax 320.762.3833
Web .... www.co.douglas.mn.us
E-mail .... mike.woods@mail.co.douglas.mn.us
　809 Elm St Ste 1186, Alexandria, MN 56308-1772
Mike Woods, Director

GENERAL HEALTH SERVICES

Public Health Nursing **320.763.6018**
Fax 320.763.4127
E-mail .... sandy.tubbs@mail.co.douglas.mn.us
　725 Elm St Ste 1200, Alexandria, MN 56308
Sandy Tubbs, Director

JUSTICE AGENCY

Community Corrections **320.762.3889**
Fax 320.762.3037
E-mail .... tonya.breitkreutz@mail.co.douglas.mn.us
　305 8th Ave W, Alexandria, MN 56308
Tonya Breitkreutz, Juvenile Agent

COURTS

7th District Court **320.762.3033**
Fax 320.762.8863
Web .... www.courts.state.mn.us
E-mail .... david.battey@courts.state.mn.us
　305 8th Ave W, Alexandria, MN 56308-1759
Honorable David R. Battey, Director

Fairbault County

SOCIAL SERVICES

Human Svcs Of Faribault & Martin
Counties **507.526.3265**
Fax 507.526.2039
　412 N Nicollet St, Blue Earth, MN 56013
Warren Knutson, Director

COURTS

5th Judicial District **507.526.6273**
Fax 507.526.3054
　415 N Main St, Blue Earth, MN 56013
Vicky Driscoll, Court Administrator

POLICE AND SHERIFF

Sheriff's Dept **507.526.5148**
Fax 507.526.3051
Web .... www.frcsd.org
E-mail .... scottc@frcsd.org
　125 W 2nd St, Blue Earth, MN 56013-1202
Mike Gormley, Sheriff

Fillmore County

SOCIAL SERVICES

Social Svcs **507.765.2175**
Fax 507.765.3895
Web .... www.co.fillmore.mn.us
E-mail .... tboyd@co.fillmore.mn.us
　902 Houston St NW Ste 1, Preston, MN 55965-1094
Gail Bunge, Director

GENERAL HEALTH SERVICES

Public Health Nursing **507.765.3898**
Fax 507.765.2139
Web .... www.co.fillmore.mn.us
E-mail .... lstevens@co.fillmore.mn.us
　902 Houston St NW Ste 2, Preston, MN 55965
Lantha Stevens, Public Health Nursing Director

COURTS

3rd District Court **507.765.4483**
Fax 507.765.4571
　100 Fillmore St, Preston, MN 55965
James Attwood, Administrative Coordinator

POLICE AND SHERIFF

Sheriff's Ofc **507.765.3874**
Fax 507.765.2703
Web .... www.co.fillmore.mn.us
E-mail .... djensen@co.fillmore.mn.us
　901 Houston St NW, Preston, MN 55965-1080
Daryl Jensen, Sheriff

Freeborn County

SOCIAL SERVICES

Human Svcs **507.377.5400**
Fax 507.377.5505
Web .... www.co.freeborn.mn.us
E-mail .... brian.buhmann@co.freeborn.mn.us
　203 W Clark St, Albert Lea, MN 56007-2549
Brian Buhmann, Director

GENERAL HEALTH SERVICES

Public Health Nursing **507.377.5100**
Fax 507.377.5272
Web .... www.co.freeborn.mn.us
E-mail .... sue.yost@co.freeborn.mn.us
　411 S Broadway Ave, Albert Lea, MN 56007-4505
Sue Yost, Community Health Administrator

JUSTICE AGENCY

Court Services **507.377.5137**
Fax 507.377.4695
Web .... www.co.freeborn.mn.us
E-mail .... tom.jensen@co.freeborn.mn.us
　411 S Broadway Ave, Albert Lea, MN 56007-4505
Tom Jensen, Director Of Court Services

Goodhue County

SOCIAL SERVICES

Prairie Island Family Svcs **651.385.4185**
Fax 651.385.4183
Web .... www.piic.org
E-mail .... nanderson@piic.org
　5636 Sturgeon Lake Rd, Welch, MN 55089-9635
Nancy Anderson, Family Services Director

Social Svcs **651.385.3232**
Fax 651.385.3191
　426 West Ave, Red Wing, MN 55066
Greg Schoener, Director

GENERAL HEALTH SERVICES

Prairie Island Community Council **651.385.2554**
Fax 651.385.4180
Web .... www.prairieisland.org
　5636 Sturgeon Lake Rd, Welch, MN 55089-9635
Nancy Anderson, Social Services Manager

Public Health **651.385.6100**
Fax 651.385.6472
Web .... www.dhs.state.mn.us
E-mail .... nina.arteson@co.goodhue.mn.us
　512 W 6th St, Red Wing, MN 55066-2855
Nina Arneson, Deputy Director

JUSTICE AGENCY

Minnesota Correctional Facility **651.267.3600**
Fax 651.267.3761
Web .... www.rw.doc.state.mn.us
E-mail .... ozanders@rw.doc.state.mn.us
　1079 Hwy 292, Red Wing, MN 55066-2838
Otis Zanders, Superintendent

COURTS

1st District Court **651.267.4800**
Fax 651.267.4989
　454 W 6th St, Justice Center, Red Wing, MN 55066
Joanne T. Pohl, Probation Director

EDUCATION SERVICES

Colvill Head Start Ctr **651.385.8000**
Fax 651.385.4780
　269 E 5th St, Red Wing, MN 55066
Jill Tenyon, Director

Grant County

SOCIAL SERVICES

Social Svcs **218.685.8200**
Fax 218.685.4978
　28 Central Ave S, Elbow Lake, MN 56531
Stacy Hennen, Director

GENERAL HEALTH SERVICES

Stephen Stravis Grant Public Health Nursing /
Eleah **218.685.5301**
Fax 218.685.6714
　10 1st st NW, ElbowLake, MN 56531
Sandy Tubbs, Rn, Phn, Community Health Administrator

Hennepin County

SOCIAL SERVICES

Child Protection **612.348.3552**
Fax 612.348.9095
Web .... www.co.hennepin.mn.us
E-mail .... deborah.huskins@co.hennepin.mn.us
　525 Portland Ave, Health Services Building, Code
　965, Minneapolis, MN 55415-1533
Deborah Huskins, Department Director

Dept Of Human Svcs & Public
Health **612.348.3456**
Fax 612.348.9908
Web .... www.co.hennepin.mn.us
E-mail .... danial.engstrom@co.hennepin.mn.us
　300 S 6th St, A-1032 Government Center,
　Minneapolis, MN 55487-1308
Daniel Engstrom, Assistence County Officer

Indian Social Svcs Minneapolis American Indian
Ctr **612.879.1700**
Fax 612.879.1795
Web .... www.maicnet.org
E-mail .... sriemers@maicnet.org
　1530 E Franklin Ave, Minneapolis, MN 55404-2192
Sherri Reimers, Director Of Icwa Program

Veteran's Svc **612.348.3300**
Fax 612.596.7676
Web .... www.co.hennepin.mn.us
E-mail .... milton.schoen@co.hennepin.mn.us
　300 South 6th St, 1st Level Southeast 013
　Government Ctr, Minneapolis, MN 55487-0001
Milton Schoen, Area Director

GENERAL HEALTH SERVICES

Bloomington Div Of Public Health **952.563.8900**
Fax 952.563.8997
Web .... www.ci.bloomington.mn.us
　1900 W Old Shakopee Rd, Minneapolis, MN 55431
Karen Zeleznak, Director

Community Health Dept **612.348.3925**
Fax 612.348.3830
Web .... www.co.hennepin.mn.us
E-mail .... mohamed.warsame@co.hennepin.mn.us
　525 Portland Ave, Minneapolis, MN 55415
Child And Teen Check-Up Program, Director

Edina Health Dept **952.927.8861**
Fax 952.826.0390
Web .... www.ci.edina.mn.us
E-mail .... sengelman@ci.edina.mn.us
　4801 W 50th St, Minneapolis, MN 55424-1330
Sherry Engelman, Community Health Administrator

Human Svcs And Public Health **612.348.4464**
Fax 612.348.2856
Web ....www.co.hennepin.mn.us
E-mail ....todd.monson@co.hennepin.mn.us
   300 S 6Th St, Minneapolis, MN 55487
   Todd Monson, Area Director

Minneapolis Health Dept **612.673.2301**
Fax 612.673.3866
Web ....www.ci.minneapolis.mn.us
   250 S 4th St, Rm 5510, Minneapolis, MN 55415
   Gretchen Musicant, Commissioner Of Health

Richfield Health And Safety Dept **612.861.9881**
Fax 612.866.0297
Web ....www.cityofrichfield.org
E-mail ....bosborn@ci.richfield.mn.us
   6700 Portland Ave, Minneapolis, MN 55423-2560
   Betsy Osborn, Community Health Administrator

JUSTICE AGENCY

Court Svcs/Juvenile Probation **612.348.3700**
Fax 612.348.6598
   590 Park Ave, Minneapolis, MN 55415
   Jim Linbera, Director

Dept Of Community Corrections **612.348.8981**
Fax 612.348.6488
Web ....www.co.hennepin.mn.us
E-mail ....gothriel.la-fleur@co.hennepin.mn.us
   300 S 6th St, C2353 Government Center, Mail Code
   533, Minneapolis, MN 55487-0533
   Gothriel (Fred) La Fleur, Director

Government Ctr **612.348.8302**
Web ....www.courts.state.mn.us
E-mail ....herbert.lefler@courts.state.mn.us
   300 S 6th St, Minneapolis, MN 55487-1308
   Honorable Herbert Lefler, Judge

Guardian Ad Litem Program **612.348.6824**
Fax 612.348.4154
Web ....www.courts.state.mn.us
E-mail ....laurie.kusek@courts.state.mn.us
   590 Park Ave, Minneapolis, MN 55415-1578
   Laurie Kusek, Program Manager

Juvenile Detention Ctr **612.348.8122**
Fax 612.348.6992
   510 Park Ave, Minneapolis, MN 55415-1522
   Karen Kuglar, Division Manager

COURTS

4th District Court Juvenile Div **612.348.5022**
Fax 612.348.2131
E-mail ....lucy.wieland@courts.state.mn.us
   300 S 6th St, Minneapolis, MN 55487-1308
   Honorable Lucy Wieland, Chief

POLICE AND SHERIFF

**Minneapolis Police Dept Domestic Violence/Child
Abuse** **612.673.3072**
Fax 612.673.3658
   350 S 5th St Ste 108, Minneapolis, MN 55415-1323
   Lt. Gregory Rhinehardt, Director

Sheriff's Dept **612.348.3744**
Fax 612.348.4208
E-mail ....patrick.mcgowan@co.hennepin.mn.us
   350 S 5th St Ste 6, Minneapolis, MN 55415-1322
   Richard Stanek, Sheriff

EDUCATION SERVICES

**Bloomington School District Special
Education** **952.681.6504**
Fax 952.681.6519
Web www.bloomington.k12.mn.us
E-mail ....emelbye@bloomington.k12.mn.us
   1350 W 106th St, Minneapolis, MN 55431-4152
   Eric Melbye, Director Of Special Services

**Intermediate District 287 Special
Ed.** **763.559.3535**
Fax 763.550.7199
Web www.int287.k12.mn.us
E-mail ....lmkellergautsch@district287.org
   1820 Xenium Ln N, Minneapolis, MN 55441
   Laura Keller-gautsch, Director

**St. Anthony-Newbrighton School District Special
Education** **612.706.1000**
Fax 612.706.1020
E-mail ....ppeterson@stanthony.k12.mn.us
   3303 33rd Ave NE, Minneapolis 55418
   Dr Rod Thompson, Superintendent

Houston County

GENERAL HEALTH SERVICES

Houston Public Health **507.725.5810**
Fax 507.725.2150
E-mail ....heather.myhre@co.houston.mn.us
   611 Vista Dr, Caledonia, MN 55921
   Heather Myhre, Health Educator

COURTS

3rd District Court **507.725.5806**
Fax 507.725.5550
E-mail ....james.fabian@courts.state.mn.us
   304 S Marshall St Rm 204, Caledonia, MN 55921
   Honorable James Fabian, Director

Hubbard County

SOCIAL SERVICES

Social Svc Ctr **218.732.1451**
Fax 218.732.3231
Web ....www.co.hubbard.mn.us
E-mail ....dbessler@co.hubbard.mn.us
   301 Court Ave, Park Rapids, MN 56470-1421
   Daryl Bessler, Director

GENERAL HEALTH SERVICES

**St. Josephs Community Health/Public Health
Nursing** **218.732.4552**
Fax 218.732.1273
E-mail ....raeannmayer@catholichealth.net
   600 Pleasant Ave S, Park Rapids, MN 56470-1431
   Raeann Mayer, Director

COURTS

9th District Court **218.732.3573**
Fax 218.732.0137
   301 Court Ave, Park Rapids, MN 56470
   Loretta Wiebolp, Court Administrator

Isanti County

SOCIAL SERVICES

Family Svcs **763.689.1711**
Fax 763.689.9877
Web ....www.co.isanti.mn.us
E-mail ....penny.messer@co.isanti.mn.us
   1700 E Rum River Dr S Ste A, Cambridge,
   MN 55008-2547
   Kevin Van Hooser, Director

GENERAL HEALTH SERVICES

Public Health Svcs **763.689.4071**
Fax 763.689.8293
Web ....www.isanticountypublichealth.org
E-mail ....kathy.minkler@co.isantic.mn.us
   555 18th Ave SW, Cambridge, MN 55008
   Kathy Minkler, Director

JUSTICE AGENCY

Probation **763.689.3052**
Fax 763.689.8325
Web ....www.co.isanti.mn.us
   555 18th Ave SW, Cambridge, MN 55008-9918
   Tim Macmillan, Director

POLICE AND SHERIFF

Sheriff's Ofc **763.689.2141**
Fax 763.689.3691
   509 18th Ave SW, Cambridge, MN 55008
   Russ Monson, Sheriff

Itasca County

SOCIAL SERVICES

Health & Human Svcs Dept **218.327.2941**
Fax 218.327.5546
E-mail ....lester.kachinske@co.itasca.mn.us
   1209 SE 2nd Ave, Itasca Resource Center, Grand
   Rapids, MN 55744-3982
   Lester Kachinske, Rn, Human Services Director

COURTS

9th District Court **218.327.2870**
Fax 218.327.2897
Web ....www.mncourts.gov
E-mail ....jon.maturi@courts.state.mn.us
   123 NE 4th St, Grand Rapids, MN 55744-2659
   Honorable Jon A. Maturi, Director

EDUCATION SERVICES

Deer River Head Start **218.246.8037**
Fax 218.246.8716
   1006 Comstock Dr, Deer River, MN 56636

Jackson County

GENERAL HEALTH SERVICES

**Cottonwood/Jackson Community Health
Svcs** **507.847.2366**
Fax 507.847.2881
   402 White st, Ste 201, Jackson, MN 56143
   Patricia Stewart, Phn, Administrative Director

COURTS

5th District Court **507.847.4400**
Fax 507.847.5433
Web ....www.courts.state.mn.us
E-mail ....linda.titus@courts.state.mn.us
   405 4th St, Jackson, MN 56143
   Honorable Linda S. Titus, Judge

Kanabec County

GENERAL HEALTH SERVICES

Public Health Nursing **320.679.6330**
Fax 320.679.6333
Web ....www.kanabeccounty.org
E-mail ....wendy.thompson@co.kanabec.mn.us
   905 Forest Ave E Ste 127, Mora, MN 55051-1632
   Wendy Thompson, Director, Outlook

POLICE AND SHERIFF

Sheriff's Dept **320.679.8400**
Fax 320.679.8422
E-mail ....steve.schulz@co.kanabec.mn.us
   18 Vine St N Ste 143, Mora, MN 55051
   Steve Schulz, Sheriff

Kandiyohi County

SOCIAL SERVICES

Family Svcs **320.231.7800**
Fax 320.231.6285
Web ....www.co.kandiyohi.mn.us
E-mail ....jay_k@co.kandiyohi.mn.us
   2200 23rd St NE Ste 1020, Willmar, MN 56201-4964
   Jay Kieft, Director

Minnesota

GENERAL HEALTH SERVICES

Public Health **320.231.7860**
Fax 320.231.7888
2200 23Rd St Ne Ste 1080, Willmar, MN 56201
Ann Stehn, Phn, Director

MENTAL HEALTH SERVICES

Willmar Regional Treatment Ctr **320.231.5100**
Fax 320.231.6623
1801 Technology Dr NE, Willmar, MN 56201-2276
Sandra Buttruff, Administrator

JUSTICE AGENCY

Community Corrections **320.231.6222**
Fax 320.231.6292
Web ....www.co.kandiyohi.mn.us
E-mail ....d_west@co.kandiyohi.mn.us
2200 23rd St NE, Ste 2060, Willmar, MN 56201
Deborah West, Director

POLICE AND SHERIFF

Sheriff's Ofc **320.214.6700**
Fax 320.231.6235
Web ....www.co.kandiyohi.mn.us
E-mail ....3301@co.kandiyohi.mn.us
2201 23rd St NE, Willmar, MN 56201-9500
Daniel Hartog, Sheriff

Kittson County

GENERAL HEALTH SERVICES

**Kittson Memorial Home Health
Care** **218.843.3662**
Fax 218.843.2487
1010 S Birch Ave, Hallock, MN 56728
Cindy Urbaniak, Public Health Nurse

Koochiching County

SOCIAL SERVICES

Community Svcs **218.283.7000**
Fax 218.283.7013
Web ....www.co.koochiching.mn.us
E-mail ....terry.murray@co.koochiching.mn.us
1000 5th St, International Falls, MN 56649-2243
Terry Murray, Director

COURTS

9th District Court **218.283.1160**
Fax 218.283.1162
Web ....www.mncourts.gov
E-mail ....nancy.winger@courts.state.mn.us
715 4th St, International Falls, MN 56649-2438
Nancy Winger, Acting Court Administrator

POLICE AND SHERIFF

Sheriff's Ofc **218.283.4416**
Fax 218.283.1149
715 4th St, International Falls, MN 56649
Brian Youso, Sheriff

Lac Qui Parle County

GENERAL HEALTH SERVICES

Countryside Public Health **320.598.7313**
Fax 320.598.7730
Web ....www.countrysidepublichealth.org
E-mail ....gtobias@countryside.co.swift.mn.us
422 5Th Ave, Ste 305, Madison, MN 56256-5003
Gloria Tobias, Staff Nurse

POLICE AND SHERIFF

Sheriff's Ofc **320.598.3720**
Fax 320.598.7555
600 W 6th St Ste 1, Madison, MN 56256
Graylen Carlson, Sheriff

EDUCATION SERVICES

Dawson Boyd Head Start **320.769.4590**
Fax 320.769.4502
848 Chestnut St, Dawson, MN 56232
Tara Roskens, Director

Lake County

SOCIAL SERVICES

Human Svcs **218.834.8400**
Fax 218.834.8412
Web ....www.co.lake.mn.us
E-mail ....matt.huddleston@co.lake.mn.us
616 3rd Ave, Two Harbors, MN 55616-1518
Matt Huddleston, Coordinator

COURTS

6th District Court **218.834.8330**
Fax 218.834.8397
Web ....www.mncourts.gov
601 3rd Ave, Two Harbors, MN 55616-1517
Michael J Cuzzo, Judge

Lake of the Woods County

SOCIAL SERVICES

Social Svcs **218.634.2642**
Fax 218.634.4520
Web ....www.dhs.state.mn.us
E-mail ....nancy_w@co.lake-of-the-woods.mn.us
206 8Th Ave Se, Baudette, MN 56623
Nancy Wendler, Director

GENERAL HEALTH SERVICES

Lakewood Nursing Svc **218.634.1795**
Fax 218.634.3490
806 Main St W, Baudette, MN 56623
Michelle Brown, Phn, Director

Le Sueur County

GENERAL HEALTH SERVICES

Le Sueur Public Health Nursing Svc **507.357.8246**
Fax 507.357.4223
Web ....www.co.le-sueur.mn.us
88 S Park Ave, Le Center, MN 56057
Cindy Shaughnessy, Director

POLICE AND SHERIFF

Sheriff's Dept **507.357.4440**
Fax 507.357.4627
88 S Park Ave, Le Center, MN 56057
Thomas Doherty, Sheriff

Lincoln County

SOCIAL SERVICES

Dept of Human Svcs **507.694.1452**
Fax 507.694.1859
E-mail ....csorensen@co.lincoln.mn.us
319 N Rebecca St, Ivanhoe, MN 56142
Chris Sorensen, Director

POLICE AND SHERIFF

Sheriff's Dept **507.694.1664**
Fax 507.694.1325
Web ....www.co.lincoln.mn.us
E-mail ....sheriff@co.lincoln.mn.us
322 N Wallace St, Ivanhoe, MN 56142-4104
Jack Vizecky, Sheriff

Lyon County

SOCIAL SERVICES

LLM Human Svcs **507.537.6747**
Fax 507.537.6088
Web ....www.llmhs.com
607 W Main St, Marshall, MN 56258-3021
Chris Sorenson, Director

GENERAL HEALTH SERVICES

Public Health Nursing **507.537.6713**
Fax 507.537.6719
607 W Main St Ste 200, Marshall, MN 56258
Chris Sorensen, Administrator

COURTS

5th District Court **507.537.6734**
Fax 507.537.6150
607 W Main St, Marshall, MN 56258
Karen Bierman, Court Administrator

Mahnomen County

GENERAL HEALTH SERVICES

Public Health Nursing **218.935.2527**
Fax 218.935.5331
Web ....www.co.mahnomen.mn.us
E-mail ....jamie.hennen@co.mahnomen.mn.us
115 E Madison, Mahnomen, MN 56557
Jamie Hennen, Director

COURTS

9th District Court **218.935.5956**
Fax 218.935.2851
Web ....www.courts.state.mn.us
E-mail ....michael.kraker@courts.state.mn.us
PO Box 435, Mahnomen, MN 56557-0435
Honorable Michael J. Kraker, Director

POLICE AND SHERIFF

Sheriff's Dept **218.935.2255**
Fax 218.935.5946
Web ....www.co.mahnomen.mn.us
E-mail ....brad.athmann@co.mahnomen.mn.us
311 N Main St, Mahnomen, MN 56557-4015
Douglas Krier, Sheriff

Marshall County

SOCIAL SERVICES

Social Svcs **218.745.5124**
Fax 218.745.5260
E-mail ....jennifer.anderson@co.marshall.mn.us
208 E Colvin Ave Ste 14, Warren, MN 56762
Jennifer Anderson, Director

GENERAL HEALTH SERVICES

North Valley Home & Health **218.745.5154**
Fax 218.745.4936
109 S Minnesota St, Warren, MN 56762
Gail Larson, Public Health Director

COURTS

9th District Court **218.745.4921**
Fax 218.745.4343
Web ....www.courts.state.mn.us
E-mail ....donald.aandal@courts.state.mn.us
208 E Colvin Ave Ste 18, Warren, MN 56762-1699
Honorable Donald Aandal, Judge

Martin County

COURTS

5th District Court **507.238.3205**
Fax 507.238.1913
Web ....www.co.martin.mn.us
201 Lake Ave Ste 304, Fairmont, MN 56031-1845
Honorable Robert D. Walker, Director

McLeod County

SOCIAL SERVICES

Social Svc Ctr **320.864.3144**
Fax 320.864.5265
1805 Ford Ave N Ste 100, Glencoe, MN 55336
Gary Sprynczynatyk, Director

GENERAL HEALTH SERVICES

Public Health **320.864.3185**
Fax 320.864.1484
Web ....www.co.mcleod.mn.us
  1805 Ford Ave N Ste 200, Glencoe, MN 55336-1371
Diane Hoese, Case Manager

COURTS

1st District Court **320.864.5551**
Fax 320.864.5905
Web ....www.co.mcleod.mn.us
  830 11th St E Ste 106, Glencoe, MN 55336-2200
Patrick Melvin, Administrator

Meeker County

GENERAL HEALTH SERVICES

Public Health Nursing **320.693.5370**
Fax 320.693.5399
Web ....www.mmspublichealth.org
  114 N Holcombe Ave Ste 250, Litchfield, MN 55355
Diane Winter, Director

JUSTICE AGENCY

Court Svcs (Probation) **320.693.5260**
Fax 320.693.4655
  325 N Sibley Ave, Litchfield, MN 55355
Tamra Thompson, Director

COURTS

8th District Court **320.693.5230**
Fax 320.693.5254
  325 N Sibley Ave, Litchfield, MN 55355
Honorable Steven Drange, Judge

POLICE AND SHERIFF

Sheriff's Dept **320.693.5400**
Fax 320.693.5424
Web ....www.co.meeker.mn.us
E-mail ....jeff.norlin@co.meeker.mn.us
  326 N Ramsey Ave, Litchfield, MN 55355-2126
Jeff Norlin, Sheriff

Mille Lacs County

SOCIAL SERVICES

**Mille Lacs Band Of Ojibwe Indian Social
Svcs** **320.532.4754**
Fax 320.532.7583
  17230 Noopiming Dr, Onamia, MN 56359
Don Eubanks, Health And Human Services Commissioner

GENERAL HEALTH SERVICES

Community & Veterans Svcs **320.983.8208**
Fax 320.983.8306
Web ....www.co.mille-lacs.mn.us
  525 2nd St SE, Milaca, MN 56353
Norma Erickson, Rn, Hiv Coordinator

JUSTICE AGENCY

Probation Dept **320.983.8202**
Fax 320.983.8251
E-mail ....warren.liepitz@co.mille-lacs.mn.us
  225 6th Ave SE, Milaca, MN 56353
Warren Liepitz, Director

COURTS

7th District Court **320.983.8313**
Fax 320.983.8384
  225 6th Ave SE, Milaca, MN 56353
George Lock, Court Administrator

Morrison County

SOCIAL SERVICES

Social Svcs **320.632.2951**
Fax 320.632.0225
Web ....www.co.morrison.mn.us
E-mail ....stever@co.morrison.mn.us
  213 1st Ave SE Ste 19, Little Falls, MN 56345-1469
Brad Vold, Director

GENERAL HEALTH SERVICES

Public Health **320.632.6664**
Web ....www.co.morrison.mn.us
E-mail ....bonniep@co.morrison.mn.us
  200 E Broadway, Little Falls, MN 56345
Bonny Paulsen, Director Of Public Health

Mower County

SOCIAL SERVICES

Human Svcs **507.437.9700**
Fax 507.437.9721
Web ....www.co.mower.mn.us
  1301 18th Ave NW, Ste A, Austin, MN 55912-1998
Julie Stevermer, Director

POLICE AND SHERIFF

Sheriff's Dept **507.437.9400**
Fax 507.437.9546
E-mail ....tmamaz@co.mower.mn.us
  201 1st St NE, Austin, MN 55912
Teresa M. Amazi, Sheriff

Murray County

GENERAL HEALTH SERVICES

Public Health Svcs **507.836.6486**
Fax 507.836.8999
E-mail ....jeff.moberg@swmhhs.com
  3001 Maple Rd, Ste 200, Slayton, MN 56172
Jeff Moberg, Public Health Educator

POLICE AND SHERIFF

Sheriff's Ofc **507.836.6168**
Fax 507.836.8704
Web ....www.co.murray.mn.us
E-mail ....stelkamp@co.murray.mn.us
  2558 29th St, Slayton, MN 56172-1408
Steve Telkamp, Sheriff

Nicollet County

SOCIAL SERVICES

Social Svcs **507.934.8559**
Fax 507.931.9562
E-mail ....jtesdahl@co.nicollet.mn.us
  108 S Minnesota Ave Ste 200, Saint Peter,
MN 56082-2559
Joan Tesdahl, Director

JUSTICE AGENCY

Guardian Ad Litem Program **507.934.0278**
Fax 507.934.0279
Web ....www.courts.state.mn.us
  501 S Minnesota Ave, Saint Peter, MN 56082-2507
Alex Miller, Manager

COURTS

5th District Court **507.934.0380**
Fax 507.931.4278
Web ....www.co.nicollet.mn.us
  501 S Minnesota Ave, Saint Peter, MN 56082-2507
Carol Nelick, Court Administrator

POLICE AND SHERIFF

Sheriff's Dept **507.931.1570**
Fax 507.931.1577
Web ....www.co.nicollet.mn.us
E-mail ....dslange@co.nicollet.mn.us
  121 W Myrtle St, Saint Peter, MN 56082-2529
Dave Lange, Sheriff

Nobles County

COURTS

5th District Court **507.372.8263**
Fax 507.372.4994
  1530 Airport Rd, Worthington, MN 56187
Honorable Jeffery L. Flynn, Judge

Norman County

SOCIAL SERVICES

Social Svcs **218.784.5400**
Fax 218.784.7142
Web ....www.co.norman.mn.us
E-mail ....chris.kujava@co.norman.mn.us
  15 2nd Ave E Ste 108, Ada, MN 56510-1389
Chris Kujava, Director

GENERAL HEALTH SERVICES

Norman-Mahnomen Public Health **218.784.5425**
Fax 218.784.7818
Web ....www.co.norman.mn.us
  15 2nd Ave E Ste 107, Ada, MN 56510
Jamie Hennen, Director

COURTS

9th District Court **218.784.5458**
Fax 218.784.3110
E-mail ....lori.wiebolt@courts.state.mn.us
  16 3rd Ave E, Ada, MN 56510
Lori Wiebolt, Court Administrator

Olmsted County

GENERAL HEALTH SERVICES

Human Resources **507.328.6001**
Fax 507.328.7967
Web ....www.co.olmsted.mn.us
E-mail ....adminweb@co.olmsted.mn.us
  151 4th St SE Ste 2, Rochester, MN 55904-3710
David Mueller, County Sheriff

COURTS

3rd District Court **507.206.2481**
Fax 507.285.8996
Web ....www.co.olmsted.mn.us
E-mail ....robert.birnbaum@co.olmsted.mn.us
  151 4th St SE Ste 3, Rochester, MN 55904-3710
Honorable Robert Birnbaum, Judge

EDUCATION SERVICES

**Child Care Resource And Refferral Head
Start** **507.287.1989**
  965 17th Ave SW, Rochester, MN 55902-0911

Special Education **507.328.4310**
Fax 507.328.4207
Web www.rochester.k12.mn.us
  615 7th St SW, Rochester, MN 55902-2052
Karla Bollesen, Director

Otter Tail County

SOCIAL SERVICES

Human Svcs **218.998.8150**
Fax 218.998.8213
Web ....www.co.ottertail.mn.us
  530 W Fir Ave, Fergus Falls, MN 56537-1364
John Dinsmore, Director

Minnesota

GENERAL HEALTH SERVICES

Public Health Dept **218.998.8320**
Fax...218.998.8352
Web.................................www.co.ottertail.mn.us
E-mail.........................dthorson@co.ottertail.mn.us
    560 W Fir Ave, Fergus Falls, MN 56537-1364
    Diane Thorson, Director

POLICE AND SHERIFF

Sheriff's Dept **218.998.8555**
Fax...218.998.8557
E-mail..........................bschlut@co.otter-tail.mn.us
    417 S Court St, Fergus Falls, MN 56537
    Brian Schluter, Sheriff

Pennington County

JUSTICE AGENCY

Dept Of Corrections **218.681.0901**
Fax...218.681.0904
E-mail.............................tiffany.rivard@state.mn.us
    Court House, 101 N Main Ave, Thief River Falls,
    MN 56701
    Tiffany Rivard, Juvenile Probation Officer

COURTS

9th District Court **218.681.0905**
Fax...218.681.0907
E-mail.........................kurt.marben@courts.state.mn.us
    101 Main Ave N, Thief River Falls, MN 56701
    Honorable Kurt Marben, Judge

POLICE AND SHERIFF

Sheriff's Dept **218.681.6161**
Fax...218.683.7006
Web.............................www.penningtonsheriff.org
E-mail....................rkuznia@penningtonsheriff.org
    102 1st St W, Thief River Falls, MN 56701-1911
    Ray Kuznia, Sheriff

Pine County

COURTS

Probation Dep **320.591.1550**
Fax...320.591.1555
E-mail.....................suzanne.bowerman@co.pine.mn.us
    635 Northridge Dr NW, Ste 290, Pine City,
    MN 55063
    Sue Bowerman, Administrative Assistant

Pipestone County

GENERAL HEALTH SERVICES

Pipestone Community Health Dept **507.825.5024**
Fax...507.825.5649
Web...............................www.co.pipestone.mn.us
E-mail................sarah.vanderstoep@co.pipestone.mn.us
    1091 N Hiawatha Ave, Pipestone, MN 56164-1568
    Sarah Vanderstoep, Phn, Co Supervisor

COURTS

5th District Court **507.825.6730**
Fax...507.825.6733
Web...................................www.courts.state.mn.us
E-mail..................david.christensen@courts.state.mn.us
    416 S Hiawatha Ave, Ste 4, Pipestone,
    MN 56164-1568
    Honorable David E. Christensen, Judge

Polk County

SOCIAL SERVICES

Social Svc Ctr **218.281.3127**
Fax...218.281.3926
Web...................................www.co.polk.mn.us
E-mail.........................kent.johnson@co.polk.mn.us
    612 N Broadway Ste 110, Crookston,
    MN 56716-1452
    Kent Johnson, Director

GENERAL HEALTH SERVICES

Public Health **218.281.3385**
Fax...218.281.7376
Web.......................................www.pcphealth.org
    721 S Minnesota St, Ste 1, Crookston, MN 56716
    Sheri Altepeter, Rn, Phn, Director

COURTS

9th District Court **218.281.2332**
Fax...218.281.2204
E-mail.....................kathy.narlock@court.state.mn.us
    816 Marin Ave, Ste 210, Crookston, MN 56716
    Kathy Narlock, Court Administrator

EDUCATION SERVICES

Migrant Head Start **218.281.5832**
Fax...218.281.6676
Web..www.tvoc.org
E-mail....................................dpd@tvoc.org
    102 N Broadway, Crookston, MN 56716-1731
    Dennis Demers, CEO

Pope County

GENERAL HEALTH SERVICES

Public Health **320.634.5720**
Web...................................www.co.pope.mn.us
    211 Minnesota Ave E Ste 100, Glenwood, MN 56334
    Sharon Braaten, Director

COURTS

8th District Court **320.634.5222**
Fax...320.634.5527
    130 Minnesota Ave E Ste 309, Glenwood, MN 56334
    Honorable Jon Stafsholt, Judge

POLICE AND SHERIFF

Sheriff's Ofc **320.634.5411**
Fax...320.634.5457
Web...................................www.co.pope.mn.us
E-mail............................tim.riley@co.pope.mn.us
    130 Minnesota Ave E Ste 137, Glenwood,
    MN 56334-1636
    Tim Riley, Sheriff

Ramsey County

SOCIAL SERVICES

Community Human Svcs Dept **651.266.4444**
Fax...651.266.4439
E-mail.....................monty.martin@co.ramsey.mn.us
    160 Kellogg Blvd E, Saint Paul, MN 55101
    Monte Martin, Director

GENERAL HEALTH SERVICES

Public Health **651.266.2400**
Fax...651.266.2593
Web...................................www.co.ramsey.mn.us
    90 W Plato Blvd Ste 200, Saint Paul, MN 55107
    Rob Fulton, Director of Public Health

Saint Paul Public Health **651.266.1352**
Fax...651.266.1324
Web...................................www.co.ramsey.mn.us
E-mail....................mary.sonnen@co.ramsey.mn.us
    555 Cedar St, Rm 111, Saint Paul, MN 55101
    Mary Sonnen, Chs/Hiv Svcs Coordinator

MENTAL HEALTH SERVICES

Community Mental Health Ctr **651.266.7999**
Fax...651.266.7850
Web...................................www.co.ramsey.mn.us
    1919 University Ave W Ste 200, Saint Paul,
    MN 55104-7655
    Susan Winslow, Clinic Manager

JUSTICE AGENCY

**Community Corrections & Probation Facility- Juvenile
Div** **651.266.5300**
Fax...651.266.5320
    25 7th St W, Saint Paul, MN 55102-1103
    Michael Delton, Director

Corrections **651.266.5343**
Fax...651.266.5320
E-mail.................peter.jessen-howard@co.ramsey.mn.us
    25 West 7th Street, Saint Paul, MN 55102
    Peter Jessen-howard, Assistant Director

Guardian Ad Litem **651.266.5270**
Fax...651.266.5277
Web...................................www.courts.state.mn.us
E-mail.................2ndgalprogram@courts.state.mn.us
    25 7th St W, Ste B212, Saint Paul, MN 55102
    Judy Peterson, Program Director

Park St. Juvenile Probation **651.266.1600**
Fax...651.266.1610
Web...................................www.co.ramsey.mn.us
E-mail...................marypat.dunlap@co.ramsey.mn.us
    555 Park St Ste 200, Saint Paul, MN 55103-2193
    Mary Pat Dunlap, Supervisor

COURTS

Juvenile Court **651.266.5150**
Fax...651.266.5101
Web...................................www.mncourts.gov
E-mail...................gary.bastian@courts.state.mn.us
    25 W 7th St, Saint Paul, MN 55102-1103
    Honorable Gary Bastian, Judge

POLICE AND SHERIFF

Saint Paul Police Dept **651.291.1111**
Fax...651.266.5711
Web...................................www.ci.stpaul.mn.us
    367 Grove St, Saint Paul, MN 55101-2296
    Thomas Smith, Chief Of Police

Sheriff's Dept **651.266.9333**
Fax...651.266.9301
Web...........................www.ramseycountysheriff.org
E-mail....................matt.bostrom@co.ramsey.mn.us
    425 Grove St, Saint Paul, MN 55101-2418
    Matt Bostrom, Sheriff

EDUCATION SERVICES

Battle Creek Head Start **651.730.1663**
Fax...651.714.0851
    2181 Suburban Ave, Saint Paul, MN 55119
    Selina Gant, Center Manager

Special Education **651.767.8321**
Fax...651.228.3626
Web..www.spps.org
    360 Colborne St, Saint Paul, MN 55102-3228
    Mary Kelly, Interim Executive Director

**Special Education (White Bear Lake School District
624)** **651.407.7553**
Fax...651.407.7555
E-mail.....................ksdani@wbl.whitebear.k12.mn.us
    4855 Bloom Ave, Saint Paul, MN 55110-2731
    Kathleen Daniels, Director Of Special Services

Red Lake County

SOCIAL SERVICES

Social Svcs............................**218.253.4131**
Fax.......................................218.253.2926
E-mail.........................dsmills@mail.co.red-lake.mn.us
　125 Edwards Ave SW, Red Lake Falls, MN 56750
Dave Mills, Director

POLICE AND SHERIFF

Sheriff's Dept........................**218.253.2996**
Fax.......................................218.253.2656
Web..........................www.redlakecountysheriff.org
E-mail..........................rlcso1821@yahoo.com
　124 Main St N, Red Lake Falls, MN 56750
Mitch Bernstein, Sheriff

Redwood County

GENERAL HEALTH SERVICES

Public Health Svc.....................**507.637.4041**
Fax.......................................507.637.4046
Web..........................www.mnco.redwood.mn.us
　266 E Bridge St, Redwood Falls, MN 56283
Genie Simon, Director

COURTS

5th District Court.....................**507.637.4020**
Fax.......................................507.637.4021
　250th 3rd And Jefferson St, Redwood Falls,
　MN 56283
Honorable David W. Peterson, Judge

POLICE AND SHERIFF

Sheriff's Dept........................**507.637.4036**
Fax.......................................507.637.4007
Web..........................www.co.redwood.mn.us
E-mail..........................sheriff@co.redwood.mn.us
　303 E 3rd St, Redwood Falls, MN 56283-1611
Randy Hanson, Sheriff

Renville County

GENERAL HEALTH SERVICES

Community Health Svcs.................**320.523.2570**
Fax.......................................320.523.3749
E-mail..................public_health@co.Renville.mn.us
　105 S 5th St Ste 119-H, Olivia, MN 56277
Jill Bruns, Phn, Director/hiv Services Coord

COURTS

8th District Court.....................**320.523.3680**
Fax.......................................320.523.3689
Web..www.mncourts.gov
　500 E Depue Ave, Fl 3, Olivia, MN 56277
Honorable Randall Slieter, Judge

POLICE AND SHERIFF

Sheriff's Dept........................**320.523.1161**
Fax.......................................320.523.3789
Web..............................www.co.renville.mn.us
　105 5th St S Rm 210, Olivia, MN 56277
Scott Hable, Sheriff

Rice County

SOCIAL SERVICES

Social Svcs............................**507.332.6115**
Fax.......................................507.332.6247
Web..................................www.co.rice.mn.us
E-mail...............................mshaw@co.rice.mn.us
　320 3rd St NW Ste 2, Faribault, MN 55021-5197
Mark Shaw, Director

COURTS

3rd District Court.....................**507.332.6107**
Fax.......................................507.332.6199
Web..................................www.co.rice.mn.us
　218 3rd St NW, Faribault, MN 55021
Thomas M Neuville, Judge

POLICE AND SHERIFF

Sheriff's Ofc.........................**507.332.6010**
Fax.......................................507.334.0268
　118 3rd St NW, Faribault, MN 55021
Troy Dunn, Sheriff

Rock County

COURTS

5th District Court.....................**507.283.5020**
Fax.......................................507.283.5017
　204 E Brown St, Luverne, MN 56156
Sandra Hensley, Court Administrator

POLICE AND SHERIFF

Sheriffs Ofc.........................**507.283.5000**
Fax.......................................507.283.5003
　1000 N Blue Mound Ave, Luverne, MN 56156
Evan Verbrugge, Sheriff

Roseau County

SOCIAL SERVICES

Social Svc Ctr........................**218.463.2411**
Fax.......................................218.463.3872
　208 6th St SW, Roseau, MN 56751
David Anderson, Director

COURTS

9th District Court.....................**218.463.2541**
Fax.......................................218.463.1889
　606 5th Ave SW Rm 20, Roseau, MN 56751
Honorable Donna K. Dixon, Judge

Saint Louis County

SOCIAL SERVICES

Bois Forte Human Svcs.................**218.757.0111**
Fax.......................................218.757.0109
E-mail....................................biosforte@nsn.gov
　13071 nett lake rd, Ste B, Nett Lake, MN 55771
Jeneal Goggleye, Director

Hibbing Branch Human Svcs Ofc.........**218.262.6000**
Fax.......................................218.262.6049
E-mail.........................buschea@st-louis.mn.us
　1814 14th Ave E, Hibbing, MN 55746
Ann M. Busche, Director

Northland Branch Social Svcs Ofc.......**218.749.7100**
Fax.......................................218.742.9503
　307 1st St S Ste 212, Virginia, MN 55792
Ann M. Busche, Department Director

Social Svcs............................**218.726.2000**
Fax.......................................218.726.2163
Web..............................www.co.st-louis.mn.us
E-mail.........................buscha@co.st-louis.mn.us
　320 W 2nd St, Government Services Center, Duluth,
　MN 55802
Ann M Busche, Director

GENERAL HEALTH SERVICES

Health Dept...........................**218.725.5210**
Fax.......................................218.725.5282
Web..............................www.stlouiscountymn.gov
　325 W 1st St Ste 300, Duluth, MN 55802
Guy Peterson, Public Health Division Director

Saint Louis Community Health

Board.................................**218.733.2860**
Fax.......................................218.723.4679
Web..........................www.communityhealthboard.org
　404 W Superior St Ste 220, Duluth, MN 55802-1582
Julie Myre, Director

Vermillion Health Clinic...............**218.753.2182**
Fax.......................................218.753.2183
　1610 Farm Rd S, Tower, MN 55790
Jeneal Googleye, Health Services Director

JUSTICE AGENCY

Arrowhead Juvenile Ctr.................**218.625.6700**
Fax.......................................218.722.0018
　1918 N Arlington Ave, Duluth, MN 55811
Kathy Trihey, Superintendent

Arrowhead Regional Corrections.........**218.733.2841**
Fax.......................................218.733.2830
E-mail.........................wrightj@co.st-louis.mn.us
　211 W 2nd St Ste 300, Duluth, MN 55802-1933
Jen Wright, Juvenile Probation Supervisor

COURTS

6th District Court.....................**218.749.7106**
Fax.......................................218.749.7109
Web..............................www.co.st-louis.mn.us
E-mail..................terrence.aronson@courts.state.mn.us
　300 S 5th Ave, Virginia, MN 55792-2665
Honorable Terrence M. Aronson, Director

6th District Court.....................**218.726.2436**
Fax.......................................218.726.2473
Web..www.mncourts.gov
　100 N 5th Ave W Rm 320, Duluth, MN 55802-1207
Honorable David M. Johnson, Judge

POLICE AND SHERIFF

Duluth Police Dept....................**218.730.5400**
Fax.......................................218.730.5911
　411 W 1st St, Rm 330, Duluth, MN 58002
Gordon Ramsey, Chief Of Police

Sheriff's Dept........................**218.726.2337**
Fax.......................................218.726.2171
Web..............................www.co.st-louis.mn.us
E-mail.........................litmanr@co.st-louis.mn.us
　100 N 5th Ave W Rm 103, Duluth, MN 55802-1289
Ross Litman, Sheriff

EDUCATION SERVICES

Babbitt Head Start 2142
Combination...........................**218.827.3215**
　30 South Dr, Babbitt, MN 55706-1108

Duluth Public Schools Special
Education..............................**218.336.8744**
Fax.......................................218.336.8775
Web..............................www.duluth.k12.mn.us
E-mail.........................marci.hoff@duluth.k12.mn.us
　215 N 1st Ave E, Duluth, MN 55802-2069
Marci Hoff, Director Of Special Services

Ely Head Start........................**218.365.3284**
Fax.......................................218.365.4535
Web..www.acf.hhs.gov
　118 S 4th Ave E, Ely, MN 55731-1465
Julie, Director

Eveleth Gilbert Head Start.............**218.744.2211**
Fax.......................................218.744.4381
Web..............................www.isd2154.k12.mn.us
　602 S Summit St, Gilbert, MN 55741

Special Education......................**218.741.9201**
Fax.......................................218.741.5178
　1201 S 13th Ave, Virginia, MN 55792
Reggie Engebritson, Director

Minnesota

Special Education 218.262.0420
Fax...218.262.0458
E-mail ....stacrodo@hibbing.k12.mn.us
800 E 21st St, Rm 104, Hibbing, MN 55746
Nathan Lutzka, Director Of Special Education

Scott County

SOCIAL SERVICES

Human Svcs..............................952.445.7751
Fax...952.496.8551
200 4th Ave W, Governor Center 300, Shakopee, MN 55379
Tim Walsh, Director

Public Health Nursing & Human
Svcs..952.496.8555
Fax...952.496.8825
792 Canterbury Rd S, Ste A160, Shakopee, MN 55379
Merrilee Brown, Rn, Nursing Director

GENERAL HEALTH SERVICES

Public Health Nursing 952.496.8584
Fax...952.496.8825
E-mail ....mbrown@co.scott.mn.us
752 Canterbury Rd S, Shakopee, MN 55379
Merrilee Brown, Director

Shakopee Mdewakanton Dakota Community
Health 952.496.6150
Fax...952.233.4224
Web...www.ccsmdc.org
E-mail ....social@ccsmdc.org
2330 Sioux Trl Nw, Prior Lake, MN 55372-9077
James Lien, Health Administrator

COURTS

1st District Court 952.496.8200
Fax...952.496.8211
Web...www.co.scott.mn.us
200 4th Ave W, Government Center Jc 115, Shakopee, MN 55379-1220
Gregory Ess, Court Administrator

POLICE AND SHERIFF

Sheriff's Dept 952.496.8300
Fax...952.496.8305
E-mail ....kstudnicka@co.scott.mn.us
301 Fuller St S, Shakopee, MN 55379
Kevin Studnicka, Sheriff

EDUCATION SERVICES

Cap Agency Head Start 952.736.8907
E-mail ....linda.donahue@capagency.org
4735 W 123rd St Ste 500, Savage, MN 55378-1491
Linda Donahue, Director

Sherburne County

GENERAL HEALTH SERVICES

Public Health Dept 763.241.2600
Fax...763.241.2698
Web ....www.co.sherburne.mn.us/pubhealth
E-mail ....public.health@co.sherburne.mn.us
13880 Business Ctr Dr, Elk River, MN 55330-1787
Ken Ebel, Social Services Director

POLICE AND SHERIFF

Sheriff's Ofc.................................763.241.2500
Fax...763.441.7303
13880 Business Ctr Dr, Elk River, MN 55330
Joel Brott, Sheriff

Sibley County

GENERAL HEALTH SERVICES

Public Health..............................507.237.4035
Fax...507.237.4031
Web...www.co.sibley.mn.us
111 8th St, Gaylord, MN 55334-4421
Laura Reid, Interim Director

Stearns County

SOCIAL SERVICES

Human Svcs..............................320.656.6000
Fax...320.656.6447
Web...www.co.stearns.mn.us
705 Courthouse Sq, Saint Cloud, MN 56303-4781

GENERAL HEALTH SERVICES

Public Health Dept 320.656.6155
Fax...320.656.6130
Web...www.co.stearns.mn.us
E-mail ....renee.frauendienst@co.stearns.mn.us
705 Courthouse Sq, Rm 307, Saint Cloud, MN 56303
Renee Frauendienst, BSN, PHN, Director Of Public Health Division

MENTAL HEALTH SERVICES

Central Minnesota Mental Health
Ctr 320.252.5010
Fax...320.252.0908
Web...www.cmmhc.org
E-mail ....djbaraga@cmmhc.com
1321 13th St N, Saint Cloud, MN 56303-2614
David Baraga, Md, Director

JUSTICE AGENCY

Community Corrections 320.203.6945
Fax...320.656.6439
E-mail ....mark.sizer@co.stearns.mn.us
705 Courthouse Sq, Rm 445, Saint Cloud, MN 56303
Mark Sizer, Director Of Community Corrections

COURTS

7th District Court 320.656.3620
Fax...320.656.3626
Web...www.co.stearns.mn.us
815 Courthouse Sq, Saint Cloud, MN 56303-4775
Honorable Richard T. Jessen, Judge

POLICE AND SHERIFF

Sheriff's Dept 320.259.3700
Fax...320.259.3703
E-mail ....sheriffsrecords@co.stearns.mn.us
807 Courthouse Sq Ste 1, Saint Cloud, MN 56303
John Sanner, Sheriff

EDUCATION SERVICES

Special Education 320.202.6800
Fax...320.529.4345
E-mail ....studentservices@isd742.org
1000 44th Ave N Ste 100, Saint Cloud, MN 56303
Randy Arnold, Assistant Director

Steele County

SOCIAL SERVICES

Human Svcs Ctr 507.444.7500
Fax...507.451.5947
Web...www.co.steele.mn.us
E-mail ....kelly.harder@co.steele.mn.us
630 Florence Ave, Owatonna, MN 55060-4704
Kelly Harder, Director

GENERAL HEALTH SERVICES

Public Health Nursing 507.444.7650
Fax...507.444.7668
Web...www.co.steele.mn.us
E-mail ....deeann.pettyjohn@co.steele.mn.us
635 Florence Ave, Owatonna, MN 55060-4700
Deann Pettyjohn, Phn, Director

Stevens County

SOCIAL SERVICES

Human Svcs..............................320.208.6600
Fax...320.589.3972
Web...www.co.stevens.mn.us
E-mail ....joaniemurphy@co.stevens.mn.us
400 Colarado Ave Ste 104, Morris, MN 56267
Joanie Murphy, Director

GENERAL HEALTH SERVICES

Stevens Traverse Grant Public
Health 320.208.6670
Fax...320.589.7433
Web...www.co.stevens.mn.us
E-mail ....sandytubbus@co.stevens.mn.us
621 Pacific Ave, Morris, MN 56267-1961
Sandy Tubbus, Director

Swift County

SOCIAL SERVICES

Human Svcs..............................320.843.3160
Fax...320.843.4582
410 21st St S, Benson, MN 56215
Deanna Steckman, Director

GENERAL HEALTH SERVICES

Countryside Public Health 320.843.4546
Fax...320.843.4094
Web.......................www.countrysidepublichealth.org
E-mail ....eauch@countryside.co.swift.mn.us
201 13th St S, Benson, MN 56215-1856
Elizabeth Auch, Administrator

COURTS

8th Judicial District 320.843.2744
Fax...320.843.4124
E-mail ....teresa.fredrickson@court.state.mn.us
301 14th St N Ste 6, Benson, MN 56215
Teresa Fredrickson, Court Administrator

POLICE AND SHERIFF

Sheriff's Dept.............................320.843.3133
Fax...320.843.2299
Web...www.co.swift.mn.us
301 14th St N Ste 4, Benson, MN 56215-2206
John Holtz, Sheriff

EDUCATION SERVICES

Benson Head Start..........................320.843.2710
Fax...320.843.5300
Web www.benson.k12.mn.us
E-mail ....headstart@benson.k12.mn.us
1800 Nevada Ave, Benson, MN 56215-1023
Darcey Klaven, Director

Todd County

SOCIAL SERVICES

Social Svcs..............................320.732.4500
Fax...320.732.4540
Web...www.co.todd.mn.us
E-mail ....frank.sandelin@co.todd.mn.us
212 2nd Ave S Ste 1, Long Prairie, MN 56347-1674
Frank Sandelin, Director

GENERAL HEALTH SERVICES

Public Health **320.732.4440**
Fax 320.732.4445
Web ....www.co.todd.mn.us
E-mail ....cheryl.schneider@co.todd.mn.us
　119 3rd St S Ste 2, Long Prairie, MN 56347-1300
　Cheryl Schneider, Phn, Director

JUSTICE AGENCY

Community Corrections **320.732.6165**
Fax 320.732.6197
　239 Central Ave, Long Prairie, MN 56347
　Katherine Langer, Director

COURTS

7th District Court **320.732.7800**
Fax 320.732.2506
Web ....www.mncourts.gov
　221 S 1st Ave Ste 100, Long Prairie, MN 56347-1351
　Honorable Jay D Carlson, Judge

Traverse County

GENERAL HEALTH SERVICES

Stevens Traverse Grant Public
Health **320.563.4807**
Fax 320.563.0104
Web ....www.co.stevens.mn.us
E-mail ....bettywindomkirsch@co.stevens.mn.us
　202 8th St N, Wheaton, MN 56296-1461
　Sandy Tubbs, Director

COURTS

8th District Court **320.563.4343**
Fax 320.563.4311
　702 2nd Ave N, Wheaton, MN 56296
　Honorable Charles C. Glasrud, Judge

POLICE AND SHERIFF

Browns Valley Police Dept **320.695.2511**
Fax 320.695.2127
Web ....www.hjprovoice.com
　21 3rd St S, Browns Valley, MN 56219
　Randy Huckeby, Police Chief

Sheriff's Dept **320.563.4244**
Fax 320.563.8700
E-mail ....b.plautz@co.traverse.mn.us
　203 7th St N, Wheaton, MN 56296-1462
　Brion Plautz, Sheriff

Wabasha County

SOCIAL SERVICES

Social Svcs **651.565.3351**
Fax 651.565.3084
　411 Hiawatha Dr E, Wabasha, MN 55981
　Terry Smith, Director

GENERAL HEALTH SERVICES

Public Health Svcs **651.565.5200**
Fax 651.565.2637
Web ....www.co.wabasha.mn.us
E-mail ....jbarton@co.wabasha.mn.us
　411 Hiawatha Dr E, Wabasha, MN 55981-1493
　Judy Barton, Director

JUSTICE AGENCY

Court Svcs **651.565.2666**
Fax 651.565.3160
　848 17th St E Ste 5, Wabasha, MN 55981
　Traci Green, Director

COURTS

District Court **651.565.3524**
Fax 651.565.8214
Web ....www.courts.state.mn.us
E-mail ....terry.walters@courts.state.mn.us
　848 17St Ste 4, Wabasha, MN 55981
　Honorable Terrence M. Walters, Judge

Wadena County

SOCIAL SERVICES

Social Svcs **218.631.7605**
Fax 218.631.7616
Web ....www.co.wadena.mn.us
E-mail ....paul.sailer@co.wadena.mn.us
　124 1st St SE Ste 1, Wadena, MN 56482-1572
　Paul M. Sailer, Director

GENERAL HEALTH SERVICES

Public Health Dept **218.631.7629**
Fax 218.631.7632
Web ....www.co.wadena.mn.us
E-mail ....cindy.pederson@co.wadena.mn.us
　22 Dayton Ave SE, Wadena, MN 56482
　Cindy Pederson, Director

JUSTICE AGENCY

Community Corrections **218.631.7618**
Fax 218.631.7620
　415 Jefferson St S, Wadena, MN 56482
　Katherine Langer, Director

POLICE AND SHERIFF

Sheriff's Dept **218.631.7600**
Fax 218.631.7699
E-mail ....dispatch@co.wadena.mn.us
　415 Jefferson St S Ste 101, Wadena, MN 56480
　Michael Carr, Sheriff

Waseca County

GENERAL HEALTH SERVICES

Public Health Nursing **507.835.0686**
Fax 507.835.0687
Web ....www.co.waseca.mn.us
E-mail ....maureen.murray@co.waseca.mn.us
　900 3rd St NE, Waseca, MN 56093-2837
　Cheryl Lewer, Director

JUSTICE AGENCY

Probation & Court Svcs **507.835.0550**
Fax 507.835.0556
E-mail ....steve.peterson@co.waseca.mn.us
　307 N State St, Waseca, MN 56093
　Steve Peterson, Director And Probation Officer

COURTS

3rd District Court **507.835.0530**
Fax 507.837.5317
　307 State St N, Waseca, MN 56093-2947
　Honorable Larry Collins, Judge

POLICE AND SHERIFF

Sheriff's Dept **507.835.0510**
Fax 507.835.0678
Web ....www.co.waseca.mn.us
E-mail ....brad.milbrath@co.waseca.mn.us
　122 3rd Ave NW, Waseca, MN 56093
　Brad Milbrath, Sheriff

Washington County

SOCIAL SERVICES

Community Svcs **651.430.6000**
Fax 651.430.6605
Web ....www.co.washington.mn.us
　14949 62nd St N, Stillwater, MN 55082
　Daniel Papin, Director

GENERAL HEALTH SERVICES

Dept Of Public Health &
Environment **651.430.6655**
Fax 651.430.6730
Web ....www.co.washington.mn.us
E-mail ....phe@co.washington.mn.us
　14949 62nd St N, Stillwater, MN 55082
　Lowell Johnson, Director

MENTAL HEALTH SERVICES

Human Svcs, Inc **651.777.5222**
Fax 651.251.5111
Web ....www.hsicares.org
E-mail ....mkuppe@hsicares.org
　7066 Stillwater Blvd N, Saint Paul, MN 55128
　Mark Kuppe, CEO

JUSTICE AGENCY

Community Corrections **651.430.6900**
Fax 651.430.6947
Web ....www.co.washington.mn.us
　14949 62nd St N, Stillwater, MN 55082
　Tom Adkins, Director

Guardian Ad Litem Program **651.430.6301**
Fax 651.430.6303
E-mail ....dana.ahlness@courts.state.mn.us
　14949 62nd St N, Stillwater, MN 55082
　Dana Ahlness, Program Coordinator

POLICE AND SHERIFF

Minnesota State Sheriffs' Assoc **651.451.7216**
Fax 651.451.8087
Web ....www.mnsheriffs.org
E-mail ....mnsheriff@comcast.net
　1951 Woodlane Dr Ste 200, Saint Paul,
　MN 55125-3048
　James Franklin, Executive Director

Sheriff's Ofc **651.430.7601**
Fax 651.430.7603
Web ....www.wcso.info
E-mail ....Sheriff@co.washington.mn.us
　15015 62nd St N, Stillwater, MN 55082-3801
　William Hutton, Sheriff

EDUCATION SERVICES

Special Education **651.458.6670**
Fax 651.458.6689
Web www.sowashco.k12.mn.us
E-mail ....emetoxen@sowashco.k12.mn.us
　8400 E Point Douglas Rd S, Cottage Grove,
　MN 55016-3324
　Erin Metoxen, Director

Wilkin County

SOCIAL SERVICES

Family Service Agency **218.643.7161**
Fax 218.643.7175
E-mail ....dsayler@co.wilkin.mn.us
　300 5th St S, P.O. Box 369, Breckenridge,
　MN 56520-0369
　Becky Tripp, Social Services Supervisor

GENERAL HEALTH SERVICES

Public Health Nursing **218.643.7122**
Fax 218.643.7166
Web ....www.wilkin.mn.us
　300 5th St S, Breckenridge, MN 56520
　Debra Jacobs, Phn, Director

COURTS

8th District Court **218.643.7172**
Fax 218.643.7167
Web ....www.mncourts.gov
　300 5th St S, Breckenridge, MN 56520-1918
　Diane Fox, Court Administrator

POLICE AND SHERIFF

Sheriff's Dept 218.643.8544
Fax 218.643.9115
Web ....www.co.wilkin.mn.us
E-mail ....sheriff@co.wilkin.mn.us
515 Dacotah Ave, Breckenridge, MN 56520-2017
Tom Matejka, Sheriff

Winona County

SOCIAL SERVICES

Human Svcs 507.457.6500
Fax 507.454.9381
202 W 3rd St, County Office Bldg., Winona,
MN 55987
William Craig Brooks, Director

GENERAL HEALTH SERVICES

Community Health Svcs 507.457.6500
Fax 507.454.9381
Web ....www.co.winona.mn.us
202 W 3rd St, Winona, MN 55987-3431
Merrily Hazelton, Mch, Director

COURTS

3rd District Court 507.457.6385
Fax 507.457.6392
171 W 3rd St, Winona, MN 55987
Renee Patterson, Director

POLICE AND SHERIFF

Sheriff's Dept 507.457.6368
Fax 507.454.5020
201 W 3rd St, Winona, MN 55987
Dave Brand, Sheriff

Wright County

GENERAL HEALTH SERVICES

Public Health 763.682.7456
Fax 763.682.7701
Web ....www.co.wright.mn.us
E-mail ....don.mleziva@co.wright.mn.us
1004 Commercial Dr, Buffalo, MN 55313
Don R Mleziva, Director

POLICE AND SHERIFF

Sheriff's Dept 763.682.1162
Fax 763.682.7610
E-mail ....joe.hagerty@co.wright.mn.us
3800 Braddock Ave NE, Buffalo, MN 55313
Joseph Hagerty, Sheriff

Yellow Medicine County

GENERAL HEALTH SERVICES

Countryside Public Health 320.564.3010
Fax 320.564.2305
415 9th Ave Ste 105, Granite Falls, MN 56241
Linda Norland, Supervisor

COURTS

8th District Court 320.564.3325
Fax 320.564.4435
Web ....www.courts.state.mn.us
415 9th Ave Ste 103, Granite Falls, MN 56241-1367
Honorable Dwayne Knutses, Judge

SPECIAL SERVICES AGENCIES

ADOPTION AGENCIES

Abbys One True Gift Adoptions 952.831.4531
Fax 866.835.1015
E-mail ....celnav123@aol.com
8342 Washburn Ave S, Minneapolis, MN 55431
Dorothy Hecchins, Director

Bethany Christian Svcs 763.553.0344
Fax 763.553.0117
Web ....www.bethany.org/minnesota
E-mail ....bcsplymouth@bethany.org
3025 Harbor Ln N Ste 316, Plymouth, MN 55447
Cindy Kruger, Director

Catholic Charities 507.433.3062
405 4th St NW, Austin, MN 55912
Robert Tereba, Director

Catholic Charities 507.455.2008
E-mail ....kmahaffey@ccwinona.org
577 State Ave Ste 2, Owatonna, MN 55060
Kathy Mahaffey, Support Specialist

Catholic Charities 507.287.2047
Fax 507.287.2050
Web ....www.ccwinona.org
E-mail ....rtereba@ccwinona.org
903 W Center St Ste 220, Rochester,
MN 55902-6278
Robert Tereba, Director

Ceridian LifeWorks 952.853.8100
Web ....www.ceridian.com
3311 East Old Shakopee Road, Minneapolis,
MN 55425
COA accredited organization.

Crossroads Adoption Svcs 952.831.5707
Fax 952.831.5129
Web ....www.crossroadsadoption.com
E-mail ....kids@crossroadsadoption.com
4600 W 77th St, Ste 200, Minneapolis,
MN 55435-4900
Joan Clarkson, Executive Director

European Children's Adoption Svcs 763.694.6131
Fax 763.694.6104
Web ....www.ecasus.org
E-mail ....zina@ecasus.org
6050 Cheshire Ln N, Minneapolis, MN 55446-3541
Zina Bulger, Executive Director

**Hope Adoption & Family Svcs
International** 651.439.2446
Fax 651.439.2071
Web ....www.hopeadoptionservices.org
E-mail ....hope@hopeadoptionservices.org
5850 Omaha Ave N Ste 2, Stillwater, MN 55082
Coleen Gregor, Executive Director

New Horizons Adoption Agency, Inc. 507.878.3200
Fax 507.526.3548
Web ....www.means.net
E-mail ....nhaa@means.net
Frost Benco Building, Highway 254, Frost, MN 56033
Marlyss Ubben, Executive Director

New Life Family Svcs 612.866.7643
Fax 612.866.5990
Web ....www.firstcaremn.com
E-mail ....info@nlfs.org
1515 E 66th St, Minneapolis, MN 55423-2648
Tammy Kocher, Director

North Homes, Inc. 218.327.3000
Fax 218.327.1871
Web ....www.northhomesinc.org
1880 River Road, Grand Rapids, MN 55744
COA accredited organization.

**Path (Professional Assoc Of Treatment
Homes)** 320.654.8807
Fax 320.654.8875
Web ....www.pathinc.org
E-mail ....gwelch@pathinc.org
600 25th Ave S, Ste 104, Saint Cloud,
MN 56301-4820
Gretchen Welch, Regional Director

Permanent Family Resource Ctr 218.998.3400
Fax 218.739.4989
Web ....www.permanentfamily.org
1220 N Tower Rd Ste 101, Fergus Falls, MN 56537
Bridgett Leonard, Director

Summit Adoption Home Studies, Inc. 651.645.6657
Fax 651.645.6713
Web ....www.summitadoption.com
E-mail ....summitadopt@uswest.net
1389 Summit Ave, Saint Paul, MN 55105-2219
Diane Truesdell, Director

Wellspring Adoption Agency 612.379.0980
Fax 612.332.0472
E-mail ....info@adoptionmn.com
111 3rd Ave S Ste 370, Minneapolis, MN 55401
Robert Vincent, Director

ADVOCACY RESOURCES

Childrens Defense Fund - Minnesota HQ 651.227.6121
Fax 651.227.2553
E-mail ....cdf@cdf-mn.org
555 Park St Ste 410, Saint Paul, MN 55103
Sybil Axner, Interim Director

First Witness Child Abuse Resource Ctr 218.727.8353
Fax 218.727.3747
Web ....www.firstwitness.org
E-mail ....info@firstwitness.org
4 W 5th St, Duluth, MN 55806
Susan Mack, Executive Director

Midwest Children's Resource Ctr 651.220.6750
Fax 651.220.6770
Web ....www.childrenmn.org
E-mail ....carolyn.levitt@childrenshc.org
347 Smith Ave N Ste 401, Saint Paul,
MN 55102-3354
Carolyn Levitt, Md, Director

Victim Services 507.328.7270
Fax 507.328.7954
E-mail ....ronayne.jeanne@co.olmsted.mn.us
151 4th St SE, Government Center, Rochester,
MN 55904
Jeanne Ronayne, Victim Services Supervisor

BEHAVIORAL HEALTH TREATMENT

Abbott Northwestern Hospital 612.863.4875
Web ....www.allina.com
E-mail ....lisa.colbert@allina.com
800 East 28th Street, Minneapolis, MN 55407
Ms. Lisa Colbert, Accreditation Manager
Joint Commission accredited organization.

Acute Psychiatric Crisis Intervention Ctr 612.873.3161
Fax 612.904.4232
E-mail ....janet.andrews@hcmed.org
701 Park Ave, Minneapolis, MN 55415-1623
Janet Andrews, Md, Medical Director

Allina Hospitals & Clinics 651.241.0007
Fax 651.241.0121
E-mail ....alan.steed@allina.com
1110 Yankee Doodle Rd, Eagan, MN 55121
C Alan Steed, Director

Anderson Medical Practice 763.588.6086
4920 Killarney Dr, Minneapolis, MN 55422-4810
Floyd Anderson, MD, Psychiatrist

Androff Mary 651.917.9395
Fax 617.244.5727
  2233 Hamline Ave N, Ste 521, Saint Paul,
  MN 55113-5003
  Mary Androff, MD, Psychiatrist

Anoka Hennepin School Dist #11 ....**763.506.1000**
Fax 763.506.1003
Web www.anoka.k12.mn.us
E-mail ....michael.bettendorf@anoka.k12.mn.us
  11299 Hanson Blvd NW, Minneapolis,
  MN 55433-3799
  Michael Bettendorf, School Psychologist

Augustine Medical Practice **952.920.0740**
  6600 France Ave S, Minneapolis, MN 55435
  David Augustine, MD, Psychiatrist

Bar-None Residential Treatment Svcs For
Children **763.753.2554**
Fax 763.753.5999
Web ....www.voamn.org
E-mail ....tthompson@voamn.org
  22426 Saint Francis Blvd, Anoka, MN 55303-9671
  Terry Thompson, Director Of Clinical Services

Beecher Medical Practice **763.420.4250**
  7574 Mariner Pt, Osseo, MN 55311-2617
  Lee Beecher, Psychiatrist

Beecher Medical Practice **952.935.7116**
Fax 952.935.0687
Web ....www.healthprivacy.org
E-mail ....lbeecher@healthprivacy.org
  6600 Excelsior Blvd Ste 121, Minneapolis,
  MN 55426-4746
  Lee Beecher, MD, Psychiatrist

Blue Cross Blue Shield **651.769.6221**
Web ....bluecrossmn.com
  1185 Town Centre Dr, Saint Paul, MN 55123
  Candice Beckham, Director

Boughton Medical Practice **612.339.1248**
E-mail ....bough002@umn.edu
  152 Bank St Se, Minneapolis, MN 55414-1033
  Deborah Boughton, MD, Psychiatrist

Boutin Medical Practice **952.939.6669**
  PO Box 6, Circle Pines, MN 55014-0006
  Arlene Boutin, MD, Psychiatrist

Ceridian **612.616.5654**
  10345 York Ln, Minneapolis, MN 55431-3266
  Sue Monson, Director

Child and Adolescent Behavioral Health
Services **218.330.7406**
E-mail ....gary.binsfeld@state.mn.us
  1701 Technology Drive, Willmar, MN 56201
  Mr. Gary Binsfeld, Accreditation Manager
  Joint Commission accredited organization.

Cigna Behavioral Health **952.996.3810**
Web ....www.cignabehavioral.com
E-mail ....mary.seabloom@cignabehavioral.com
  11095 Viking Dr Ste 350, Eden Prairie,
  MN 55344-7234
  Mary Seabloom, Doctor

Coen Medical Practice **952.746.3330**
Fax 952.545.2652
  5353 Gamble Dr, Minneapolis, MN 55416
  Deborah Coen, MD, Psychiatrist

Community Addiction Recovery
Enterprise **651.431.5020**
E-mail ....karen.e.jones@state.mn.us
  3301 Seventh Avenue North, Anoka, MN 55303
  Ms. Karen Jones, Accreditation Manager
  Joint Commission accredited organization.

Community Svcs **651.554.6425**
Web ....www.co.dakota.mn.us
  1 Mendota Rd W Ste 170, Saint Paul,
  MN 55118-4768
  Patricia Leonard, Director

Counseling Associates **320.843.3454**
Fax 320.843.4692
  640 Atlantic Ave, Benson, MN 56215
  Karla Sundheim, Counsellor

Ctr For Family Counseling **320.253.3540**
Fax 320.253.1475
Web ....cfcinc.biz
E-mail ....rjohnson@cmmhc.com
  2025 Stearns Way Ste 111, Saint Cloud,
  MN 56303-1275
  Randy Johnson, Director

Ctr For Grief Loss & Transcition **651.641.0177**
Web ....www.griefloss.org
E-mail ....cg@griefloss.org
  1133 Grand Ave, Saint Paul, MN 55105-2629
  Karen Heegaard, Director

Curran Medical Practice **952.545.3494**
Fax 952.545.3447
  435 Ford Rd Ste 347, Minneapolis, MN 55426-4911
  John Curran, MD, Psychiatrist

De La Salle High School **612.676.7600**
Fax 612.362.9641
E-mail ....barry.lieske@delasalle.com
  1 De La Salle Dr, Minneapolis, MN 55401
  Barry Lieske, Principal

Dennis M Brekke Ltd **612.991.1769**
  10331 N 108th Pl, Osseo, MN 55369-2638
  Dennis Brekke, Owner

Dessert Medical Practice **651.222.6279**
  325 Cedar St Ste 802, Saint Paul, MN 55101-1012
  Nancy Dessert, Psychiatrist

East Central Area Agency On Aging **320.679.4065**
  100 Park St S, Mora, MN 55051-1431
  Peggy, Director

Epiphany Catholic School **763.754.1750**
Fax 763.862.4350
E-mail ....jmiller@epiphanymn.org
  11001 Hanson Blvd NW, Minneapolis, MN 55433
  Jeri Miller, Director

Face To Face Health **651.772.5603**
  1165 Arcade St, Saint Paul, MN 55106-2615
  Julie, Counselor

Family And Children's Svcs Of The Minneapolis Metro
Area **612.339.9101**
Fax 612.339.9150
Web ....www.thefamilypartnership.org
E-mail ....mgreenman@fcsmn.com
  414 S 8th St, Minneapolis, MN 55404-1081
  Molly Greenman, President

Family Life Mental Health Ctr **763.427.7964**
Fax 763.427.7976
Web ....www.flmhc.org
E-mail ....rchrest@flmhc.org
  1930 Coon Rapids Blvd NW, Minneapolis, MN 55433
  Rosalin Chrest, Executive Director

Family Networks, Inc **952.832.5244**
Fax 952.832.5297
Web ....www.familynetworks.org
E-mail ....ginneee@familynetworks.org
  4530 W 77th St Ste 200, Minneapolis,
  MN 55435-5013
  Ginnee Engberg, PhD, Director

Family Strengths LLC **763.754.8959**
Web ....www.fcsmn.org
  11373 Quincy St NE, Minneapolis, MN 55434-2930
  Paul Sherman, Director

FamilyMeans **651.439.4840**
Fax 651.439.4891
Web ....www.familymeans.org
  1875 Northwestern Avenue South, Stillwater,
  MN 55082-4805
  COA accredited organization.

Fernbrook Family Ctr **507.446.0431**
Fax 507.446.8014
E-mail ....info@fernbrook.org
  115 Landmark Dr NE, Ste 1, Owatonna,
  MN 55060-5704
  Mandy Young, Business Manager

Four Directions Charter School **612.588.0183**
Fax 612.588.1844
Web ....www.fourdirectionsschool.org
  1113 W Broadway Ave, Minneapolis, MN 55411
  Keri Zimmerman, School Social Worker

Fox Medical Practice **612.374.1021**
Fax 612.374.1022
  15 Groveland Ter Ste 201, Minneapolis,
  MN 55403-1154
  Adam Fox, MD, Psychiatrist

Freshwater Education District **218.894.2439**
Fax 218.894.2295
Web www.fed.k12.mn.us
E-mail ....svagle@fed.k12.mn.us
  1100 5th St NE, Staples, MN 56479-3117
  Steve Vagle, Director

Gerard Treatment Programs **507.433.1843**
Fax 507.433.7868
Web ....www.nexustreatment.org
E-mail ....bhenry@nexustreatment.org
  1101 28th St NE, Austin, MN 55912
  Brent Henry, Director

Hazelden Foundation, Recovery Services
Division **612.257.4200**
Web ....www.hazelden.org
E-mail ....merb@hazelden.org
  15251 Pleasant Valley Road, Center City, MN 55012
  Mr. Mike Erb, Accreditation Manager
  Joint Commission accredited organization.

Leo A Hoffmann Ctr **507.934.6122**
Fax 507.934.2594
Web ....www.hoffmanncenter.org
E-mail ....jstevermer@hoffmanncenter.org
  1715 Sheppard Dr, St Peter, MN 56082
  Julie Stevermer, Director

Livinglinks **507.345.8590**
Fax 507.345.3771
E-mail ....judy.conard@livinglinks.org
  1230 N River Dr, Mankato, MN 56001-2280
  Judy Conard, Admistrtive Assistant

Mayo Clinic Adolescent Substance Abuse
Program **507.255.4065**
Fax 507.255.7383
E-mail ....john.huxsahl@mayo.edu
  1216 2nd St SW, Generose Building, 1-B, Rochester,
  MN 55902-1906
  John Huxsahl, MD, Director

Mayo Clinic Health System in Albert Lea **507.373.2384**
Web ....www.almedcenter.org
E-mail ....lauer.tonia@mayo.edu
  404 West Fountain Street, Albert Lea, MN 56007
  Ms. Tonia Lauer, Accreditation Manager
  Joint Commission accredited organization.

Mille Lacs Academy **320.532.4005**
Fax 320.532.4898
  100 Crosier Dr # 1, Onamia, MN 56359-4512
  Paul Smith, Executive Director

Minnesota Assoc For Children's Mental
Health **651.644.7333**
Fax 651.644.7391
Web ....www.macmh.org
E-mail ....info@macmh.org
  165 Western Ave N Ste 2, Saint Paul,
  MN 55102-4613
  Deborah Saxhaug, Executive Director

Minnesota Indian Primary Residential Treatment Center, Inc. (Mash-Ka-Wisen) **218.879.6731**
Fax 218.879.6734
Web ....mashkawisen.com
1150 Mission Road, Sawyer, MN 55780
CARF accredited programs available.

North Homes, Inc. **218.327.3000**
Fax 218.327.1871
E-mail ....james.christmas@northhomesinc.org
1880 River Rd, Grand Rapids, MN 55744-4085
James Christmas, Director

Northwestern Minnesota Juvenile Ctr **218.751.3196**
Fax 218.751.3229
E-mail ....wfrey@minncor.com
1231 5th St NE, Bemidji, MN 56601
William Frey, Superintendent

Northwood Children's Services, Inc. **218.724.8815**
Fax 218.724.0215
Web ....www.northwoodchildren.org
714 West College Street, Duluth, MN 55811-4910
COA accredited organization.

Park Nicollet Health Services **952.993.5000**
Web ....www.parknicollet.com
E-mail ....sannes@parknicollet.com
6500 Excelsior Boulevard, Saint Louis Park,
MN 55426
Ms. Sandra Sannes, Accreditation Manager
Joint Commission accredited organization.

Park Nicollet Health Svcs **952.993.3123**
Fax 952.993.5936
3800 Park Nicollet Blvd, Minneapolis, MN 55416
David Abelson, Chief Executive Officer

Port Group Homes, Inc **218.828.6274**
Fax 218.828.4209
Web ....www.portgrouphomes.org
E-mail ....dmontonye@portgrouphomes.org
115 N 1st St, Brainerd, MN 56401
Desiree Montonye, Executive Director

Professional Assc Of Treatment Homes (Path) Duluth
Ofc **218.722.6106**
Fax 218.722.8356
Web ....www.pathinc.org
306 W Superior St Ste 500, Duluth, MN 55802-5003
Donna Ennis, Regional Area Director

Psychological Svcs **612.348.3723**
Fax 612.348.3452
Web ....www.courts.state.mn.us
E-mail ....lawrence.panciera@courts.state.mn.us
300 S 6th St, C-509 Government Center,
Minneapolis, MN 55487-1308
Lawrence Panciera, Phd, Chief Clinical Psychologist

Saint Cloud Hospital **320.251.2700**
Web ....www.centracare.com
E-mail ....honkompb@centracare.com
1406 Sixth Avenue North, Saint Cloud, MN 56303
Ms. Beth Honkomp, Accreditation Manager
Joint Commission accredited organization.

Sheriff's Youth Programs of Minnesota **651.552.5740**
Fax 651.552.5741
Web ....www.sheriffs-youth-program.org
2925 Buckley Way, Inver Grove Heights,
MN 55076-2018
COA accredited organization.

SMDC Medical Center **218.727.8762**
Web ....www.smdcmedicalcenter.org
E-mail ....barbara.possin@essentiahealth.org
502 East Second Street, Duluth, MN 55805
Ms. Barbara Possin, Accreditation Manager
Joint Commission accredited organization.

The Family Partnership **612.339.9101**
Fax 612.339.9150
Web ....www.everyfamilymatters.org
414 South 8th Street, Minneapolis, MN 55404-1081
COA accredited organization.

United Hospital **651.241.8802**
Web ....allina.com
E-mail ....lenore.day@allina.com
333 North Smith Avenue, Saint Paul, MN 55102
Ms. Lenore Day, Accreditation Manager
Joint Commission accredited organization.

University of Minnesota Medical Center,
Fairview **612.273.3000**
Web ....www.fairview.org
E-mail ....fschaef1@fairview.org
2450 Riverside Avenue, Minneapolis, MN 55455
Ms. Francine Schaefer, Accreditation Manager
Joint Commission accredited organization.

Valley Lake Boys Home, Inc. **218.643.4036**
Fax 218.643.5226
E-mail ....vlboyshome@702com.net
3850 200th Ave, Breckenridge, MN 56520
Joanna Etzler, Program Director

Volunteers Of America Children's Residential Treatment
Ctr **612.870.4300**
Fax 612.870.7448
Web ....www.voamn.org
E-mail ....mfranke@voamn.org
143 E 19th St, Minneapolis, MN 55403
Michael Franke, Director

Woodland Ctrs **320.235.4613**
Fax 320.231.9140
1125 6th St SE, Willmar, MN 56201-4675
David Kerski, Md, Medical Director

CHILDREN'S HOSPITAL

Buffalo Hospital **763.682.1212**
303 Catlin St, Buffalo, MN 55313

Cambridge Medical Center **763.689.7700**
701 S Dellwood St, Cambridge, MN 55008
Dennith Dorane, Chief Executive Officer

Children's Hospitals & Clinics of MN **612.813.6100**
2525 Chicago Ave S, Minneapolis, MN 55404

Children's Hospitals & Clinics of MN **651.220.6000**
345 N Smith Ave, Saint Paul, MN 55102

Community Hospital **218.631.3510**
415 Jefferson St N, Wadena, MN 56482
Goel Beifwenger, President

District One Hospital **507.334.6451**
E-mail ....info@districtonehospital.com
200 State Ave, Faribault, MN 55021
Stephen Pribyl, Chief Executive Officer

Ely-Bloomenson Community Hospital **218.365.3271**
328 W Conan St, Ely, MN 55731
John Fossum, Chief Executive Officer

Fairview Northland Medical Center **763.389.1313**
911 Northland Dr, Princeton, MN 55371
John Harman, Chief Executive Officer

Fairview Range Regional Health Services **218.262.4881**
750 E 34th St, Hibbing, MN 55746
Debra Boardman, Chief Executive Officer

Fairview Red Wing Medical Center **651.267.5000**
701 Fairview Blvd, Red Wing, MN 55066
Scott Wordelman, Director

Fairview Ridges Hospital **952.892.2000**
201 E Nicollet Blvd, Burnsville, MN 55337
Carol Koeppelson, Nursing Director

First Care Medical Services **218.435.1133**
900 Hilligoss Blvd SE, Fosston, MN 56542
Debra Carlson, Chief Nursing Officer

Glencoe Regional Health Services **320.864.3121**
E-mail ....john.braband@grhsonline.org
1805 Hennepin Ave N, Glencoe, MN 55336
John Braband, Director

Granite Falls Municipal Hosp & Manor **320.564.3111**
345 Tenth Ave, Granite Falls, MN 56241
George Gerlach, Chief Executive Officer

Hendricks Community Hospital **507.275.3134**
503 E Lincoln St, Hendricks, MN 56136
Julie Hogi, Director

Hospital **320.762.1511**
111 17th Ave E, Alexandria, MN 56308
Carl Vaagenes, Chief Executive Officer

Immanuel St Joseph's-Mayo Health **507.625.4031**
1025 Marsh St, Mankato, MN 56002
Kevin Burns, Director Of Public Affairs

Johnson Memorial Health Services **320.769.4323**
1282 Walnut St, Dawson, MN 56232
Kathy Johnson, Administrator

Lake Region Healthcare Corp **218.736.8000**
712 S Cascade St, Fergus Falls, MN 56537
Larry Schulb, Director

Lakeview Hospital **651.439.5330**
927 Churchill St W, Stillwater, MN 55082

Life Care Medical Center **218.463.2500**
463 Delmore Ave Ste 2500, Roseau, MN 56751
Keith Okefon, Chief Executive Officer

Madison Hospital **320.598.7556**
900 Second Ave, Madison, MN 56256

Mayo Clinic Health System Austin **507.433.7351**
1000 First Dr NW, Austin, MN 55912
David Ageter, Director

Mayo Clinic Rochester Minn **507.284.2511**
200 SW First St, Rochester, MN 55905
Pamela Johnson, Chairman

Medical Center **612.873.3000**
701 Park Ave S, Minneapolis, MN 55415
Arthur Gonzalez, Chief Executive Officer

Meeker Memorial Hospital **320.693.3242**
612 S Sibley Ave, Litchfield, MN 55355

Melrose Area Hospital CentraCare **320.256.4231**
525 W Main St, Melrose, MN 56352
Julia Draxten, Area Coordinator

Mercy Hospital **218.485.4481**
710 S Kenwood Ave, Moose Lake, MN 55767
Jason Douglas, Chief Executive Officer

New River Medical Center **763.295.2945**
1013 Hart Blvd, Monticello, MN 55362
Eureta Sorenson, Nursing Director

New Ulm Medical Center **507.233.1000**
1324 Fifth St N, New Ulm, MN 56073
Toby Freier, Chief Executive Officer

North Memorial Hospital **763.520.5200**
3300 Oakdale Ave N, Robbinsdale, MN 55422
Larry Taylor, Chief Executive Officer

North Shore Hospital **218.387.3040**
515 W 5th Ave, Grand Marais, MN 55604
Kimber Wraals, Chief Executive Officer

Northfield Hospital **507.646.1000**
2000 North Ave, Northfield, MN 55057

Ortonville Area Health Services **320.839.2502**
450 Eastvold Ave, Ortonville, MN 56278
Richard Ash, Chief Executive Officer

Owatonna Hospital **507.451.3850**
2250 NW 26th St, Owatonna, MN 55060
David Albrecht, Director

Perham Memorial Hospital & Home **218.346.4500**
665 Third St SW, Perham, MN 56573

Queen of Peace Hospital **952.758.4431**
301 Second St NE, New Prague, MN 56071

RC Hospital & Clinics **320.523.1261**
611 E Fairview Ave, Olivia, MN 56277
Glen Haugo, Director

Redwood Area Hospital **507.637.4500**
100 Fallwood Rd, Redwood Falls, MN 56283
James Schulte, Administrator

Ridgeview Medical Center **952.442.2191**
500 S Maple St, Waconia, MN 55387
Bob Stevens, Manager

Sanford Canby Medical Center **507.223.7277**
112 St Olaf Ave S, Canby, MN 56220
Bob Salmon, Chief Executive Officer

Sanford Hospital Luverne **507.283.2321**
1600 N Kniss, Luverne, MN 56156
Tammy Loosbrock, Chief Executive Officer

Sanford Regional Hospital Worthington **507.372.2941**
1018 Sixth Ave, Worthington, MN 56187
Lynn Olsen, Administrator

Sanford Tracy Medical Center **507.629.3200**
E-mail ....stacy.barstad@sanfordhealth.org
251 Fifth St E, Tracy, MN 56175
Stacy Barstad, Chief Executive Officer

Sanford Westbrook Medical Center **507.274.6121**
920 Bell Ave, Westbrook, MN 56183
Stacy Barstad, Chief Executive Officer

Sleepy Eye Medical Center **507.794.3571**
400 Fourth Ave NW, Sleepy Eye, MN 56085
Kevin Sellheim, Director

Springfield Med Ctr Mayo Hlth System **507.723.6201**
625 N Jackson Ave, Springfield, MN 56087

St Francis Healthcare Campus **218.643.3000**
2400 St Francis Dr, Breckenridge, MN 56520
Mary Jacklitch, Marketing Director

St Francis Regional Medical Center **952.428.3000**
1455 St Francis Ave, Shakopee, MN 55379

St John's Hospital **651.232.7000**
1575 Beam Ave, Maplewood, MN 55109
Scott North, Director

St Joseph's Medical Center **218.829.2861**
523 N Third St, Brainerd, MN 56401
Jamy Wiebott, Chief Executive Officer

St Luke's Hospital **218.249.5555**
915 E First St, Duluth, MN 55805
John Strange, Chief Executive Officer

St Mary's Innovis Health **218.847.5611**
1027 Washington Ave, Detroit Lakes, MN 56501
Tom Thompson, Director

St Marys Medical Center **218.780.4000**
407 E Third St, Duluth, MN 55805

Stevens Community Medical Center **320.589.1313**
400 E First St, Morris, MN 56267
John Rau, Administrator

United Hospital District **507.526.3273**
515 S Moore St, Blue Earth, MN 56013
Jeff Lang, Chief Executive Officer

Unity Hospital **763.236.5000**
550 Osborne Rd NE, Fridley, MN 55432
Ken Paulus, Chief Executive Officer

Univ of MN Medical Center **612.672.6000**
2450 Riverside Ave, Minneapolis, MN 55454

US Public Health Service Indian Hosp **218.679.3912**
E-mail ....craig.morin@ihs.gov
Hwy 1, Redlake, MN 56671
Craig Morin, Acting Director

Virginia Regional Medical Center **218.741.3340**
901 Ninth st N, Virginia, MN 55792
Michelle Fleming, Director of Nursing

Winona Health **507.454.3650**
855 Mankato Ave, Winona, MN 55987
Rochelle Schultz, Director

COUNSELING SERVICES

Domestic Abuse Project **612.874.7063**
Fax 612.874.8445
Web ....www.mndap.org
E-mail ....dap@mndap.org
204 W Franklin Ave, Minneapolis, MN 55404-2398
Carol Arthur, Executive Director

Life Skills Education **507.645.2994**
Fax 507.645.2995
Web ....www.lifeskillsed.com
E-mail ....mail@lifeskillsed.com
314 Washington St, Northfield, MN 55057-2025
Suzannah Ciernia, Government Sales

Professional Assoc Of Treatment Homes
(Path) **612.259.1600**
Fax 612.259.1689
Web ....www.pathinc.org
E-mail ....info@pathinc.org
2021 East Hennepin Avenue, Ste 320, Minneapolis,
MN 56716
Mike Peterson, Sw Supervisor

Professional Assoc Of Treatment Homes
(Path) **218.828.3900**
Fax 218.828.3935
Web ....www.pathinc.org
17025 Commercial Park Rd Unit 6, Brainerd,
MN 56401-6254
Nancy Cagle, Social Work Supervisor

Professional Assoc Of Treatment Homes (Path) St. Paul
Ofc **612.259.1700**
Fax 612.259.1789
Web ....www.pathinc.org
E-mail ....rjwhite@pathinc.org
2021 E Hennepin Ave Ste 100, Minneapolis,
MN 55413-1769
Romell White, Office Manager

Psychiatric care **651.554.5955**
Fax 651.554.6565
Web ....www.positivelyminnesota.com
1 Mendota Rd W Ste 170, West Saint Paul,
MN 55118-4768
Patricia Leonard, Director

Soltreks **218.834.4607**
Fax 707.549.3785
Web ....www.soltreks.com
E-mail ....info@soltreks.com
2346 Highway 3, Two Harbors, MN 55616
Lorri Hanna. Ma, Ctrs, Executive Director/president

Spiritdance **612.823.7022**
Fax 610.561.5079
Web ....www.equinecoaching.com
E-mail ....lynn@equinecoaching.com
3808 Pillsbury Ave S, Minneapolis, MN 55409-1223
Lynn Baskfield, Director

St. Joseph's Home For Children **612.204.8250**
Fax 612.827.7954
E-mail ....kkozerski@ccspm.org
1121 E 46th St, Minneapolis, MN 55407-3586
Keith Kozerski, Administrator (interim)

Walk-In Counseling Ctr **612.870.0565**
Fax 612.870.4169
Web ....www.walkin.org
E-mail ....mweeks@walkin.org
2421 Chicago Ave, Minneapolis, MN 55404-3845
Mary Weeks, Executive Director

CRISIS & SHELTER CARE

Advocates Against Domestic Abuse **218.927.2327**
Fax 218.927.2048
Web ....www.charterinternet.com
E-mail ....lhamilton@charterinternet.com
111 2nd St NW, Aitkin, MN 56431
Lisa Hamilton, Director

Advocates For Family Peace-Dom
Violence **218.326.0388**
Fax 218.327.4052
Web ....www.stopdomesticabuse.org
E-mail ....mscaia@stopdomesticabuse.org
1611 NW 4th St, Grand Rapids, MN 55744-2102
Melissa Scaia, Director

Ain Duh Yung Shelter **651.227.4184**
Fax 651.224.5136
Web ....www.aindahyung.com
1089 Portland Ave, Saint Paul, MN 55104-7011
Deb Foster, Executive Director

Alexandra House Inc-Domestic Violence **763.780.2332**
Fax 763.780.9696
Web ....www.alexandrahouse.org
E-mail ....cmoore@alexandrahouse.org
10065 3rd St NE, Blaine, MN 55449
Connie Moore, Director

Arlington House **651.774.3701**
Fax 651.771.3040
Web ....www.arlingtonhouse.com
E-mail ....ggulpranson@breakingfree.net
712 Larpenteur Ave E, Saint Paul, MN 55117-2528
Gary Gulpranson, Executive Director

Battered Womens Legal Advocacy Project **612.343.9842**
Fax 612.343.0786
E-mail ....info@bwlap.org
1611 Park Ave Ste 2, Minneapolis, MN 55404
Rana Fuller, Managing Partner

Bethany Crisis Nursery **218.626.3083**
Fax 218.626.1727
9239 Idaho St, Duluth, MN 55808
Dawn Shykes, Director

Casa De Esperanza-Domestic Violence **651.646.5553**
Fax 651.646.5299
Web ....www.casadeesperanza.org
E-mail ....info@casadeesperanza.org
1515 E Lake St, Minneapolis, MN 55407
Patty Totozintle, Chief Executive Officer

Central Family Resources Dom Abuse
Prog **763.783.4914**
Fax 763.783.4756
1201 89th Ave NE Ste 375, Minneapolis, MN 55434
Dawn Strommen, Director

Central MN Task Force On Battered
Women **320.253.6900**
Fax 320.253.5563
E-mail ....info@annamaries.org
500 11th Ave N, St Cloud, MN 56303
Maxine Barnett, Director

Community Against Domestic Abuse **507.625.8688**
Fax 507.625.9431
E-mail ....cada@hickorytech.net
100 Stadium Ct, Mankato, MN 56002-0466
Julie Ellefson, Director

Community Svc Ctr-Dove Program-Dom
Violence **218.935.5554**
Fax 218.935.2593
2531 310th Ave, Naytahwaush, MN 56566
Ben Bement, Director

Crisis Connection/After Hours Counseling
Svc **612.379.6388**
Fax 612.379.6391
Web ....www.crisis.org
E-mail ....patsy@crisis.org
6400 Penn Ave, Richfield, MN 55423
Patricia Bartley, Executive Director

Crisis Resource Ctr-Steele Co-Domestic
Violence **507.451.1202**
Fax 507.455.2891
E-mail ....crcsteelecounty@qwestoffice.net
125 W Front St, Owatonna, MN 55060
Sara Colby, Director

Domestic Abuse Project 612.673.3526
Fax 612.335.5848
Web .... www.mndap.org
E-mail .... dap@mndap.org
350 S 5th St Ste 113, Minneapolis, MN 55415-1314
Sharon Brice, Director

Evergreen House 218.751.4332
Fax 218.751.3830
Web .... www.evergreenhouse.org
E-mail .... rschueller@evergreenhouse.org
622 Mississippi Ave NW, Bemidji, MN 56601-2943
Rebecca Scheuller, Executive Director

Face To Face Health And Counseling Svcs 651.772.5555
Fax 651.772.5566
Web .... www.facetoface.org
E-mail .... bannettl@face2face.org
1165 Arcade St, Saint Paul, MN 55106-2615
Linda Bennett, Executive Director

Fairview Domestic Abuse Svcs 612.672.2700
Fax 612.672.4002
E-mail .... jseaber1@fairview.org
2450 Riverside Ave, Minneapolis, MN 55454
Joanne Seaberg, Director

Family Safety Network-Cass Co-Dom
Vlnce 218.547.1636
Fax 218.547.6237
E-mail .... familysafety34@hotmail.com
109 S 6th St, Walker, MN 56484
Chris Swenson, Director

Fillmore Family Resources-Dom Violence 507.765.2316
Fax 507.765.2142
Web .... www.familyresources.org
E-mail .... familyresources@mchsi.com
216 Main St SW, Preston, MN 55965
Amy Becker, Director

Freeport West, Inc. Project Solo 612.824.3040
Fax 612.824.0780
2219 Oakland Ave, Minneapolis, MN 55404
Ramona Wilson, Director

Friendship House 651.388.9360
Fax 651.388.9178
E-mail .... kkvols@hope-coalition.org
480 8th St, Red Wing, MN 55066
Kris Kvols, President

Hands Of Hope Resource Ctr-Dom Vlnce 320.632.1657
Fax 320.632.5457
E-mail .... advocates@handsofhope.net
107 2nd St SE Ste 102, Little Falls, MN 56345
Stephaine Och, Director

Hands Of Hope Resource Ctr-Domestic
Violence 320.732.2319
Fax 320.732.2056
Web .... www.handsofhope.net
E-mail .... steph@handsofhope.net
PO Box 171, Long Prairie, MN 56347-0171
Stephenie Och, Director

Head Waters Intervention Ctr 218.732.7413
Fax 218.732.8386
500 Main Ave S, Park Rapids, MN 56470
Becki Leonard, Director

Hispanic Battered Womens Program 218.236.4879
Fax 218.236.6507
E-mail .... mgarcia@702com.net
810 4th Ave S, Moorhead, MN 56560
Maria Garcia, Director

Home Free Shelter - Domestic Violence 763.559.9008
Fax 763.559.6315
Web .... www.homefreeprograms.org
E-mail .... mary@homefreeprograms.org
3405 E Medicine Lake Blvd, Minneapolis,
MN 55441-2396
Mary Monteon, Director

Home-Away Ctrs, Inc. 612.871.7599
Fax 612.871.1881
2119 Pleasant Ave, Minneapolis, MN 55404-2320
Shara Demalignon, Director

Lakes Crisis And Resources Ctr 218.847.8572
Fax 218.847.6113
Web .... www.lakescrisis.com
E-mail .... janl@arvig.net
718 Washington Ave, Detroit Lakes, MN 56501-3012
Jan Logan, Director

Lutheran Social Svc 218.828.4383
Fax 218.829.9726
E-mail .... poleary@lssmn.org
716 E St NE, Brainerd, MN 56401
Patrice Oleary, Program Director

Lutheran Social Svcs 218.626.2726
Fax 218.626.1727
Web .... www.lssmn.org
E-mail .... dawn.shykes@lssmn.org
9239 Idaho St, Duluth, MN 55808-1550
Dawn Shykes, Director

Lutheran Social Svcs 651.644.7739
Fax 651.644.8883
Web .... www.lssmn.org
E-mail .... susan.phillips@lssmn.org
501 Asbury St, Saint Paul, MN 55104-2302
Susan Phillips, Program Director

Migrant Health Svcs-Battered Womens
Prog 218.281.3552
Fax 218.281.2505
303 S Main St Ste 5, Crookston, MN 56716
Leticia Sanchez, Director

Northwoods Coalition for Family Safety 218.444.1393
Fax 218.444.1396
1101 Beltrami Ave NW, Bemidji, MN 56619
Breanna Davis, Director

Outfront Minnesota-Domestic Violence 612.822.0127
Fax 612.822.8786
Web .... www.outfront.org
E-mail .... rwkloek@outfront.org
310 E 38th St Ste 204, Minneapolis, MN 55409-1337
Rebecca Waggoner - Klock, Director

Project Peace-Domestic Violence Program 763.533.0733
Fax 763.533.0861
5637 Brooklyn Blvd Ste 201, Minneapolis, MN 55429
Sue Lantto, Program Director

Range Womens Advocates-Domestic
Violence 218.749.5054
Fax 218.748.6888
Web .... www.rwadvocates.org
301 1st St S, Virginia, MN 55792-2659
Cathy Cerra-Vraa, Director

Safe Haven Shelter For Battered Women 218.728.6481
Fax 218.728.5084
Web .... www.safehavenshelter.org
E-mail .... sutech@safehavenshelter.org
2010 E 7th St, Duluth, MN 55812-1300
Susan Utech, Director

Saint Paul Youth Svc/Crisis 651.771.1301
Fax 651.771.2542
Web .... www.spys.org
E-mail .... nletourneau@spys.org
2100 Wilson Ave, Saint Paul, MN 55119-4034
Nancy Letourneau, Executive Director

Sexual-Domestic Abuse Program 218.384.8927
Fax 218.384.8928
E-mail .... advocateswojo@yahoo.com
317 Chestnut Ave Ste 2, Carlton, MN 55718-2008
Susan Wojocichowski, Director

Shelter House Inc-Domestic Violence 320.235.0962
Fax 320.235.3990
Web .... www.willmarshelter.com
E-mail .... cschmoll@willmarshelter.com
1112 NW Lake Ave, Willmar, MN 56201
Connie Schmoll, Director

Sojourner Project Inc-Domestic Violence 952.933.7433
Fax 952.933.0138
E-mail .... helenchargo@sojournerproject.org
PO Box 272, Hopkins, MN 55343-0272
Helen Chargo, Director

Someplace Safe-Domestic Violence 218.739.3486
Fax 218.739.9305
E-mail .... jijacobs@charterinternet.com
121 Ulest Vasa, Fergus Falls, MN 56538
Jeanne Jacobs, Director

Southwest Crisis Ctr 507.376.4311
Fax 507.372.4311
E-mail .... jojinnaka@knology.net
920 Diagonal Rd, Worthington, MN 56187
Jan Johnson-ojinnaka, Director

Southwest Crisis Ctr-Peace Agency 507.831.2244
Fax 507.831.0146
E-mail .... swcc@frontiernet.net
1043 4th Ave Ste 1, Windom, MN 56101
Ruth Hubbling, Director

The Bridge For Youth 612.377.8800
Fax 612.377.6426
Web .... www.bridgeforyouth.org
E-mail .... info@bridgeforyouth.org
1111 W. 22nd Street, Minneapolis, MN 55405-2705
Dan, Executive Director

The Hope Ctr-Domestic Violence 507.332.0882
Fax 507.332.6999
Web .... www.hopecentermn.org
E-mail .... estaab@hopecentermn.org
1003 7th St NW, Faribault, MN 55021-5297
Erica Staab, Director

The Refuge-Domestic Violence 763.689.3532
Fax 763.689.1636
E-mail .... roxiek@therefugenetwork.org
1700 E Rumriver Rd S, Ste E, Cambridge,
MN 55008-0323
Roxie Karelis, Director

Violence Intervention Project 218.681.5557
Fax 218.681.5626
1911 Greenwood St E, Thief River Falls, MN 56701
Sandy Bentley, Director

Violence Prevention Ctr 218.387.1262
Fax 218.387.2193
21 West 2nd St, Grand Marais, MN 55604
Jodi Yuhasey, Director

Volunteers of America-Regional
Correction 651.488.2073
Fax 651.488.2550
E-mail .... teri.towardski@isd623.org
1771 Kent St, Saint Paul, MN 55113
Teri Towardski, Program Manager

Wilder Comm Assistance Program Domestic
Violence 651.221.0048
Fax 651.224.1578
Web .... www.wilder.org
E-mail .... mfm@wilder.org
919 Lafond Ave, Saint Paul, MN 55104-2108
Michael Mcgrane, Director

Window Victim Svcs-Domestic Violence 320.384.7113
Fax 320.384.6124
E-mail .... exdirwindow@scicable.com
204 Fire Monument Rd, Hinckley, MN 55037-8310
Lisa Lilja, Director

Wings 320.763.6638
Fax 320.763.6639
1417 Broadway, Alexandria, MN 56308
Dorie Twist, Director

Womens Advocates-Domestic Violence.......651.227.9966
Fax.........651.227.4786
E-mail.........rloscalzo@wadvocates.org
588 Grand Ave, Saint Paul, MN 55102-2696
Mary Brown, Women And Childrens Program Manager

Womens Resource Ctr-Domestic Violence......507.452.4440
Fax.........507.452.9518
Web.........www.wrcofwinona.org
E-mail.........lori@wrcofwinona.org
77 E 5th St, Winona, MN 55987-3517
Lori Woodward, Director

Womens Rural Advocacy Proram............507.532.9532
Fax.........507.532.7361
E-mail.........wraplyon@iw.net
700 North 7th Street, Marshall, MN 56258
Karen Brady, Director

Youthlink.........612.252.1200
Fax.........612.252.1201
Web.........www.youthlinkmn.org
E-mail.........huseby@youthlinkmn.org
41 N 12th St, Minneapolis, MN 55403
Heather Huseby, Executive Director

EDUCATION

Children's Home Society And Family Svcs......651.646.7771
Fax.........651.646.8676
Web.........www.chsfs.org
E-mail.........ksvendson@chsfs.org
1605 Eustis St, Saint Paul, MN 55108-1219
Joan Johnson, Director

Groves Academy.........952.920.6377
Fax.........952.920.2068
Web.........www.grovesacademy.org
E-mail.........information@grovesacademy.org
3200 Hwy 100 S, Minneapolis, MN 55416-2175
John Alexander, Head Of School

Hubert H. Humphrey Job Corps Ctr..........651.642.1133
Fax.........651.641.0548
1480 Snelling Ave N, Saint Paul, MN 55108
David Mackenzie, Center Director

KidsPeace Mesabi Academy.........218.258.2274
Fax.........218.258.3579
Web.........www.kidspeace.org
E-mail.........mnadmissions@kidspeace.org
200 Wanless St, Buhl, MN 55713
Karen Moller, Executive Director

Meld.........612.332.7563
Fax.........612.455.2058
Web.........www.parentsasteachers.org
E-mail.........jennifer.barshack@parentsasteachers.org
1700 2nd st NE, Minneapolis, MN 55413-1265
Jennifer Barshack, Manager And State Leader

Minneapolis Crisis Nursery.........763.591.0400
Fax.........763.591.0700
Web.........www.crisisnursery.org
E-mail.........info@crisisnursery.org
5400 Glenwood Ave, Minneapolis, MN 55422-5100
Mary Pat Lee, Executive Director

Northwood Children's Svcs.........218.724.8815
Fax.........218.724.0251
E-mail.........kjohnson@northwoodchildren.org
714 W College St, Duluth, MN 55811
Kim Johnson, Director Of Admissions

FOSTER CARE AGENCIES

ACR Homes Inc.........651.484.5897
Fax.........651.484.5863
E-mail.........acrhomes@acrhomes.com
2437 Rice St, Roseville, MN 55113
Jim Nelson, Director

African American Adoption Agency..........651.659.0460
Fax.........651.644.5306
E-mail.........afadopt@afadopt.org
217 Mackuvin Ave, St. Paul, MN 55103
Marquita Stephens, Executive Director

Bradley House.........507.744.4826
395 4th Ave SW, Lonsdale, MN 55046

Catholic Charities the Diocese of Saint........320.650.1660
Fax.........320.253.7464
E-mail.........mbulson@ccstcloud.org
157 Roosevelt Rd, Ste 200, Saint Cloud, MN 56301

Centrewood Home.........320.352.0252
105 6th St S, Sauk Centre, MN 56378
Gaylette Stillman, Programme Coordinator

Chang Mi Korean Dance & Drum............651.429.0357
E-mail.........mnewmast@ties2.net
2723 Crown Hill Ct, White Bear Lake, MN 55110

Children's Home Society & Family Svcs.......651.646.6393
E-mail.........welcome@chsfs.org
1605 Eustis St, Saint Paul, MN 55108
Maureen Warren, President/CEO

Chosen Ones Adoption Agency..............651.770.5508
E-mail.........info@chosen1s.org
1622 E Sandhurst Dr, Maplewood, MN 55109

Community Involvement Programs..........763.504.1139
Web.........www.cipmn.org
E-mail.........tomr@cipmn.org
4710 Quail Ave N, Minneapolis, MN 55429-3737
Tom Ruff, Director

Country Care.........320.834.4419
Web.........www.gctel.com
E-mail.........shado@gctel.com
23359 Lake Jennie Rd NW, Evansville, MN 56326-8138
Sharon Henneman, Director

Courtwood Home.........218.463.1047
604 Carl Ct, Roseau, MN 56751
Brenda Acker, Director

Dierenfeld Group Foster Home..............507.232.3619
46258 Red Oak Dr, Nicollet, MN 56074-4007
David Dierenfeld, Director

Dignity House.........320.986.2003
13231 State Highway 55, Hoffman, MN 56339
Shirley Hayer, Director

Divine House.........218.233.3186
Fax.........218.233.3228
1001 Center Ave Ste M, Moorhead, MN 56560
Ben Austin, Director

Downey Side.........507.446.8503
E-mail.........owatonnamn@downeyside.org
560 Dunnell Dr, Ste 201, Owatonna, MN 55060
Claudia Flecher, Chief Executive Officer

Downey Side Adoption.........320.240.1433
Fax.........320.240.1532
E-mail.........mschaefer@downeyside.org
1637 N fort ave ste 102, sauk ratics, MN 55379
Marienne Mcguire, Chief Executive Officer

Eagles Haven Foster Home.........218.281.3872
512 Sherman St, Crookston, MN 56716
Melissa Wirth, Programme Superviser

Eagles Landing Foster Home.........218.444.2961
1019 Minnesota Ave Nw, Bemidji, MN 56601-2854

Eaglesview Foster Home.........218.759.7226
523 19th St NW, # B, Bemidji, MN 56601
Pam, Director

Elizabeth's Country Breeze.........218.998.3231
18335 County Highway 10, Elizabeth, MN 56533-9581
Mary Soland, Director

Endeavors At Waterford.........651.683.9545
1249 Merganser Ct, Saint Paul, MN 55123-1005

Eriksmoen Cottages.........952.432.4020
13278 Huron CT, Applevalley, MN 55124
Ron Eriksmoen, Director

Family Services.........320.679.6350
Fax.........320.679.6351
E-mail.........wendy.thompson@co.kanabec.mn.us
905 Forest Ave E, Ste 150, Mora, MN 55051
Wendy Thompson, Executive Director

Fifth Avenue.........218.326.8095
Fax.........856.985.0887
905 SW 5th Ave, Grand Rapids, MN 55744-3517
Marty Kinnenuen, Director

Franklin Foster Home.........952.492.3959
4061 W 173rd St, Jordan, MN 55352
Alaina Gast, Administrator

Hand in Hand International Adoptions.......651.917.0384
Fax.........651.649.0896
E-mail.........minnesota@hihiadopt.org
1360 University Ave W, # 176, Saint Paul, MN 55104

LDS Family Services.........763.560.0900
6120 Earl Brown Dr, Ste 210, Brooklyn Center, MN 55430
Vicki Olson, Office Manager

Lutheran Social Services of Minnesota........507.625.7660
Fax.........507.625.8998
E-mail.........tammy.weisenberger@lssmn.org
710 S 2nd St, North Mankato, MN 56001
Tammy Weisenberger, Director

Lutheran Social Svcs Adoption.............320.251.7700
Fax.........320.251.8898
22 Wilson Ave NE Ste 110, PO Box 6069, Saint Cloud, MN 56302
Kristi Hall, Counsellor

Lutheran Social Svcs Adptn Pregnancy.......218.236.1494
Fax.........218.236.0836
715 11th St N Ste 401, Moorhead, MN 56560
Gene Benson, Operations Manager

Lutheran Social Svcs Adptn Pregnancy.......218.529.2289
Fax.........218.726.1251
E-mail.........adoption@lssmn.org
600 Ordean Bldg, 424 W Superior St, Duluth, MN 55802
Suzanne Aulie, Chief Executive Officer

Lutheran Social Svcs Adptn Pregnancy.......612.879.5230
Fax.........612.871.0354
E-mail.........adoption@lssmn.org
2400 Park Ave, Minneapolis, MN 55404
Marybeth Galey, Nursing Director

Minnesota Adptn Resource Network (MARN).........612.861.7115
E-mail.........info@mnadopt.org
430 Oak Grove St, Ste 404, Minneapolis, MN 55403
Mary Mason, Executive Director

Minnesota Adptn Support & Preservation......612.798.4033
E-mail.........info@mnadopt.org
430 Oak Grove St Ste 404, Minneapolis, MN 55403
Janet Hammer, Adminstrator Coordinator

Minnesota Kinship Caregivers Assoc..........651.917.4640
Fax.........651.917.4641
E-mail.........mkca@mkca.org
161 St Anthony Ave, Ste 940, Saint Paul, MN 55103
Carla Jacobson, Executive Director

MN Dept of Human Svcs.........320.269.6401
Fax.........320.269.6405
719 N 7th St Ste 200, Community Service Bldg, Montevideo, MN 56265
Betty Christensen, Director

New Horizons Adoption Agency Inc (NHAA).........507.526.3518
E-mail.........nhaa@bevcomm.net
302 S Grove St, Blue Earth, MN 56013
Marlys Ubben, Director

North American Council on Adoptable **651.644.3036**
Fax 651.644.9848
E-mail ....info@nacac.org
970 Raymond Ave, Ste 106, Saint Paul, MN 55114
Mary Boo, Assistant Director

PATH (Professional Assoc of Treatment **507.280.0304**
Fax 507.280.8882
124 Elton Hills Ln NW, Ste 200, Rochester,
MN 55901
Jay Kimball, Regional Director Of Southern Region

PATH (Professional Assoc of Treatment **218.333.8000**
Fax 218.751.0253
505 Bemidji Ave N, Ste 2, Bemidji, MN 56601
George Hendrickson, Director

Redeemer Center for Life **763.374.4139**
Fax 763.374.4312
1800 N Glenwood Ave, Minneapolis, MN 55405

Wellspring Adoption Agency **612.333.0489**
Fax 612.332.0472
E-mail ....info@adoptionmn.com
111 3rd Ave S, Ste 370, Minneapolis, MN 55401
Robert Vincent, Director

West Twin Cities Metro **763.545.0293**
E-mail ....dreisner@comcast.net
970 Raymond Ave Ste 106, Saint Paul, MN 55114

Wisconsin Foster & Adoptive Parent Assoc **715.374.2180**
430 Four Mile Creek RD, Brooklyn Park, MN 55445
Sherry Benson

HOME MEDICAL EQUIPMENT PROVIDERS

Altimate Medical **800.342.8968**
Fax 877.342.8968
E-mail ....info@easystand.com
262 West 1st St, 262 West 1st St, Morton, MN 56270
Todd Tholkes, General Manager

PEDIATRIC HOME CARE

Accurate Home Care **763.633.3800**
Fax 763.633.3808
Web ....www.accuratehomecare.com
E-mail ....amynelson@accuratehomecare.com
19021 Freeport St, NW, Ste 400, Elk RIver,
MN 55330
Amy Nelson, Chief Executive Officer

Bayada Nurses **952.935.5581**
Fax 952.935.5920
Web ....www.bayada.com
10709 Wayzata Blvd, Suite 121, Minnetonka,
MN 55305
Lisa Fowler, Division Director

Interim Healthcare **952.993.1650**
Fax 952.993.1654
E-mail ....bingwerson@interimhealthcare.com
3930 Louisiana Ave, South Park Nicolett Hlth Svcs,
Saint Louis Park, MN 55426
Bev Ingwerson, Director

Interim Healthcare **952.886.7133**
7760 France Ave S Ste 1100, Edina, MN 55435

Interim Healthcare **952.883.5550**
Fax 952.883.5015
8170 33rd Ave S, Bloomington, MN 55425
Michelle, Manager

Interim Healthcare **651.917.3634**
Fax 651.917.3620
Univ Crossing, 2200 University Ave # 160, Saint Paul,
MN 55114
Don Lamourdaux, Director

Interim Healthcare **218.722.0053**
Fax 218.722.0318
227 W First St Ste 400, Duluth, MN 55802
Diane Smith, Executive Director

Interim Ventcare **218.740.3433**
Fax 218.740.3435
E-mail ....jvolkman@interimhealthcare.com
4730 Matterhorn Cir, Duluth, MN 55811
Rebecca Volkman, Director Of Nursing

Pediatric Home Service **651.642.1825**
Fax 651.638.0680
Web ....www.pediatrichomeservice.com
E-mail ....maruhs@pediatrichomeservice.com
2800 Cleveland Ave N, Roseville, MN 55113-1126
Michael Ruhs, Director

SOCIAL SERVICES

Catholic Charities **320.650.1550**
Fax 320.650.1528
Web ....www.ccstcloud.org
E-mail ....lwoken@gw.stcdio.org
911 18th St N, St Cloud, MN 56303
Laura Woken, Executive Secretary

**Catholic Charities of the Archdiocese of St. Paul and
Minneapolis** **612.204.8500**
Fax 612.664.8520
Web ....www.cctwincities.org
E-mail ....tmarks@cctwincities.org
1200 Second Avenue South, Minneapolis, MN 55403
Tim Marks, CEO
COA accredited organization.

Catholic Charities/ Seton Svcs **651.603.0225**
Fax 651.641.1005
Web ....www.cctwincities.org
1276 University Ave W, Saint Paul, MN 55104-4101
Mary Ann Sullivan, Director

Central Minnesota Lifecare Ctr **320.351.4025**
519 Sinclair Lewis Ave, Sauk Centre, MN 56378
Ramona Porter, Executive Director

Child Care Resource And Referral **320.629.5164**
Fax 320.629.5107
Web ....www.pinetec.edu/ccrr
E-mail ....ccrr@pinetec.edu
Pine Techical College, Pine City, MN 55063
Wendy Walburg, Program Coordinator

Child Care Resource And Referral, Inc. **507.287.2020**
Fax 507.287.2411
Web www.c2r2.org
E-mail ....maryjos@c2r2.org
126 Woodlake Dr SE, Rochester, MN 55904-5533
Patrick Gannon, Director

Children's Home Society & Family Services **651.646.6393**
Fax 651.646.0436
Web ....www.chsfs.org
1605 Eustis Street, St. Paul, MN 55108-1219
COA accredited organization.

City Life Ctr **612.874.1808**
Fax 612.813.5633
Web ....www.citylifecenter-mn.org
E-mail ....info@citylifecenter-mn.org
2520 Park Ave, Minneapolis, MN 55404-4403
Betty Mcguire, Director

Corner House **612.813.8300**
Fax 612.813.8330
Web ....www.cornerhousemn.org
2502 10th Ave S, Minneapolis, MN 55404-4510
Patricia Harmon, Executive Director

Cornerstone **952.884.0376**
Fax 952.884.2135
E-mail ....susanneis@cornerstonemn.org
1000 E 80th St, Minneapolis, MN 55420
Susan Neis, Director

ECS-Episcopal Community Svcs **612.874.8823**
Fax 612.874.9802
Web ....www.ecsmn.org
E-mail ....mschatzlein@ecsmn.org
1730 Clifton Pl Ste 10, Minneapolis, MN 55403
Mary Schatzlein, Director Of Family Services

Epiphany Caring For Life **612.803.2225**
Web ....www.epiphanycaringforlife.org
1900 111th Ave NW, Minneapolis, MN 55433-3728

Family Services **507.825.6720**
Fax 507.825.6727
E-mail ....nicole.names@co.pipestone.mn.us
1091 N Hiawatha Ave, Pipestone, MN 56164
Nicole Names, CPS Supervisor

**Jewish Family & Childrens Service of
Minneap** **952.546.0616**
Fax 952.593.1778
E-mail ....jfcs@jfcsmpls.org
13100 Wayzata Blvd Ste 400, Minnetonka,
MN 55305
Judy Halper, CEO

Jewish Family Service **651.698.0767**
Fax 651.698.0162
E-mail ....info@jfssp.org
1633 West 7th St, Saint Paul, MN 55102
Rena Waxman, Director

**Lakes And Prairies Community Action
Partnership** **218.299.7026**
Fax 218.299.7547
Web ....www.lakesandprairies.net
715 11th St N Ste 402, Moorhead, MN 56560
Linda Lembke, Director

Lutheran Social Service of Minnesota **651.642.5990**
Fax 651.969.2360
Web ....www.lssmn.org
2485 Como Avenue, St. Paul, MN 55108-1445
COA accredited organization.

Lutheran Social Svcs **612.879.5200**
Fax 612.871.0354
Web ....www.lssmn.org
2400 Park Ave, Minneapolis, MN 55404
Debra Martin-schuler, Mental Health Director

Parent Provider Connection **507.455.2560**
Fax 507.455.9297
E-mail ....resource@parentprovider.org
560 Dunnell Dr Ste 207, Owatonna, MN 55060-4798
Sonya Harris, Director

**PATH (Professional Association of Treatment Homes,
Inc.)** **612.259.1600**
Fax 612.259.1689
Web ....www.pathinc.org
2021 East Hennepin Avenue, Suite 100, Minneapolis,
MN 55413
COA accredited organization.

Prevent Child Abuse Minnesota **651.523.0099**
Fax 651.523.0380
Web ....www.pcamn.org
E-mail ....pcamn@pcamn.org
709 University Ave W Ste 234, Saint Paul,
MN 55104-2881
Karina Forrest-Perkins, Executive Director

Resource For Child Care **651.641.0305**
Fax 651.645.0990
Web ....www.resourcesforchildcare.org
E-mail ....byates@resourceforchildcare.org
10 Yorkton Ct, Saint Paul, MN 55117-1065
Barbara Yates, Executive Director

Teenwise Minnesota **651.644.1447**
Fax 651.644.1417
Web ....www.teenwisemn.org
E-mail ....marilyn@teenwisemn.org
1619 Dayton Ave Ste 111, Saint Paul,
MN 55104-6276
Marilyn Colby Rivkin, Interim Executive Director

Tri-Valley Opportunity Council **701.772.7905**
Fax...701.773.0708
Web......................................www.mnchildcare.org
E-mail..mhams@tvoc.org
　　1424 Central Ave NE, East Grand Forks,
　　MN 56721-1605
　　Maureen Hams, Programming Director

SPECIAL NEEDS

American Council of the Blind **612.730.8100**
E-mail...kgr@isd.net
　　PO Box 7341, Minneapolis, MN 55407

ARC Northland **218.726.4725**
E-mail...........................rengstrom@arcnorthland.org
　　424 W Superior St, 201 Ordean Bldg, Duluth,
　　MN 55802
　　Lars Kuehow, Executive Director

Autism Society of Minnesota **651.647.1083**
E-mail..info@ausm.org
　　2380 Wycliff St Ste 102, Saint Paul, MN 55114

Bethesda Hospital **651.232.2125**
Fax...651.232.2118
Web......................................www.bethesdahospital.org
　　559 Capitol Boulevard, Saint Paul, MN 55103-2101
　　CARF accredited programs available.

Blind Inc **612.872.0100**
E-mail..info@blindinc.org
　　100 E 22nd St, Minneapolis, MN 55404
　　Shawn Mayo, Director

Brain Injury Association **612.378.2742**
E-mail.....................................info@braininjurymn.org
　　34 NE 13th Ave Ste B001, Minneapolis, MN 55413
　　David King, Executive Director

Child Neurology Foundation **952.641.6100**
Fax...952.881.6276
E-mail...................jstone@childneurologyfoundation.org
　　2000 West 98th St, Bloomington, MN 55431
　　John Stone, Director

Clinic for Attention Learning & Memory **612.872.2343**
Fax...612.872.8605
E-mail..gary@calm.us
　　1409 Willow St Ste 600, Minneapolis, MN 55403
　　Gary Johnson, Doctor

Courage Center **763.588.0811**
Fax...763.520.0355
Web...www.courage.org
　　3915 Golden Valley Road, Golden Valley, MN 55422
　　David Phillips, Director
　　CARF accredited programs available.

Discapacitados Abriendose Caminos **651.293.1748**
Fax...651.293.1744
E-mail...............................discapacitados@qwestoffice.net
　　621 Marie Ave, South Saint Paul, MN 55075
　　Ana Perez De Perez, Director

Down Syndrome Association **651.603.0720**
E-mail..dsamn@dsamn.org
　　656 Transfer Rd, Saint Paul, MN 55114
　　Kathleen Forney, Director

Epilepsy Foundation of Minnesota **651.287.2300**
E-mail..info@efmn.org
　　1600 W University Ave ,Ste 300, Saint Paul,
　　MN 55104
　　Vickie Copplin, Chief Executive Officer

Gillette Children's Specialty Healthcare **651.291.2848**
Fax...651.229.1737
Web...www.gillettechildrens.org
　　200 East University Avenue, Saint Paul, MN 55101
　　John Day, Medical Director
　　CARF accredited programs available.

Goodwill/Easter Seals **800.669.6719**
E-mail.....................dtretsven@goodwilleasterseals.org
　　553 Fairview Ave N, Saint Paul, MN 55104

KDWB University Pedaitrics Family Center **612.626.4260**
Fax...612.624.0997
　　717 Delaware St SE, Ste 371, Minneapolis,
　　MN 55414
　　Brianna Cerrato, Clinical Supervisor

Laura Baker School **507.645.8866**
Fax...507.645.8869
Web...www.laurabaker.org
　　211 Oak St, Northfield, MN 55057
　　Sandra Gerdes, Executive Director

Learning Disabilities Association **952.922.8374**
E-mail.....................................info@ldaminnesota.org
　　6100 Golden Valley Rd, Golden Valley, MN 55422
　　Val Kofky, Business Manager

Learning Disabilities Program **651.646.7711**
　　1605 Eustis St, Saint Paul, MN 55108
　　Maxine Walton, Country Specialist

Learning Rx Learning Center **952.949.6900**
E-mail.........................chanhassen.mn@learningrx.net
　　600 Market St, Ste 120, Chanhassen, MN 55317

Learning Rx Learning Center **651.686.1066**
E-mail..............................Eagan.mn@learningrx.net
　　2874 Highway 55, Ste 120, Eagan, MN 55121
　　Brock Henrich, Director

LearningRx Learning Center **763.746.5850**
E-mail........................maplegrove.mn@learningrx.net
　　7270 Forestview Ln N, Ste 100, Maple Grove,
　　MN 55369
　　Baird Johnson, Owner

LearningRx Learning Center **507.206.6757**
E-mail..............................chaco@learningrx.net
　　3780 Market Place Dr NW, Ste 107, Rochester,
　　MN 55901
　　Jennifer Beyst, Director

LearningRx Learning Center **952.226.1115**
E-mail.........................savage.mn@learningrx.net
　　8160 County Rd 42, Ste 800 Marketplace at 42,
　　Savage, MN 55378
　　Rich Frieder, Director

Lindamood-Bell Learning Processes **952.835.0700**
Fax...952.835.2790
　　3300 Edinborough Way, Ste 120, Edina, MN 55435

Mayo Clinic Pediatric MS Center **507.538.2555**
Fax...507.284.2111
　　200 1st St SW, Rochester, MN 55905
　　Nancy L Kuntz, MD Center Director

Mayo Clinic Rehabilitation Unit **507.255.5920**
Fax...507.255.7094
Web.............www.mayoclinic.org/physicalmedicine-rst
E-mail.............................sharonne.hayes@mayo.edu
　　1216 Second Street SW, Rochester, MN 55902
　　Sharonne Hayes, director for diversity
　　CARF accredited programs available.

Mental Health Association **612.331.6840**
E-mail.....................................info@mentalhealthmn.org
　　2021 E Hennepin Ave Ste 412, Minneapolis,
　　MN 55413
　　Ben Ashley-Wurtmann, Ouprevh And Policy Associate

Metro Center for Independent Living **651.603.2019**
E-mail..juliaw@mcil-mn.org
　　1600 University Ave W Ste 16, Saint Paul, MN 55104

**Miland E. Knapp Rehabilitation Medical
Center** **612.873.4333**
Fax...612.904.4303
Web...www.hcmc.org
　　900 South Eighth Street, Minneapolis, MN 55415
　　CARF accredited programs available.

Minnesota Congress PTA **651.999.7320**
E-mail.....................................mnptaofc@mnpta.org
　　1667 Snelling Ave N, Saint Paul, MN 55108
　　Bonni Cannon, President

Minnesota State Council on Disability **651.361.7800**
E-mail.......................council.disability@state.mn.us
　　121 E 7th Pl Ste 107, Saint Paul, MN 55101
　　Joan Willshire, Executive Director

NAMI Minnesota **651.645.2948**
E-mail...nami-mn@nami.org
　　800 Transfer Rd Ste 31, Saint Paul, MN 55114
　　Sue Abidann, Director

National Multiple Sclerosis Society **612.335.7900**
Fax...612.335.7997
E-mail..info@mssociety.org
　　200 12th Ave S, Minneapolis, MN 55415
　　Sarah Danen, Director

Nexus Treatment Centers **763.551.8640**
Fax...763.553.1637
Web...www.nexustreatment.org
　　505 Highway 169 North, Plymouth, MN 55441-6447
　　COA accredited organization.

North Memorial Rehabilitation Services **763.520.5690**
Fax...763.520.1772
Web...www.northmemorial.com
　　3300 Oakdale Avenue North, Robbinsdale,
　　MN 55422
　　CARF accredited programs available.

PACER Center Inc **952.838.9000**
Fax...952.838.0199
Web...www.pacer.org
E-mail..pacer@pacer.org
　　8161 Normandale Blvd, Bloomington, MN 55437
　　Paula Goldberg, Executive Director

Park Nicollet Methodist Hospital **952.993.5000**
Fax...952.993.5485
Web...www.parknicollet.com
　　6500 Excelsior Boulevard, Saint Louis Park,
　　MN 55426
　　CARF accredited programs available.

Partners in Policymaking **651.222.7409**
E-mail..cschoeneck@mngts.org
　　2233 University Ave W Ste 150, Saint Paul,
　　MN 55114
　　Helene Johnson, Executive Director

**Sister Kenny Rehabilitation Institute--Abbott
Northwestern** **612.863.4463**
Fax...612.863.8942
Web...www.sisterkennyinstitute.com
　　800 East 28th Street, Minneapolis, MN 55407
　　CARF accredited programs available.

**SMDC Medical Center - Miller Dwan Rehabilitation
Center** **218.786.2850**
Fax...218.786.5874
E-mail..dfuchs@smdc.org
　　502 East Second Street, Duluth, MN 55805
　　Daniel Fuchs, Director of Development
　　CARF accredited programs available.

Sonday Reading Center **952.920.9280**
Fax...952.929.9291
E-mail.....................karen@sondayreadingcenter.org
　　6950 France Ave S, Ste 22, Edina, MN 55435
　　Karen Sonday, Director

Spina Bifida Association **651.222.6395**
E-mail..jscottthayer@msn.com
　　PO Box 29323, Brooklyn Center, MN 55429

St. Cloud Hospital Rehabilitation Unit **320.251.2700**
Fax...320.255.5773
Web...www.centracare.com
　　1406 Sixth Avenue North, Saint Cloud, MN 56303
　　Deb Eisendtadt, Director
　　CARF accredited programs available.

St. Cloud Hospital Rehabilitation Unit **320.251.2700**
Fax...320.255.5773
Web...www.centracare.com
　　1406 Sixth Avenue North, Saint Cloud, MN 56303
　　CARF accredited programs available.

Minnesota

Student Support Service 651.351.8309
Fax 651.351.8343
E-mail .... lindbergm@stillwater.k12.mn.us
    1875 Greeley St S, Stillwater, MN 55082-6079
    Mary Mesler, Director Of Student Support Service

The Arc of Minnesota 651.523.0823
E-mail .... stevel@arcmn.org
    770 Transfer Rd Ste 26, Saint Paul, MN 55114
    Marlene Thomas, Director

United Cerebral Palsy 651.646.7588
E-mail .... ucpmn@cpinternet.com
    1821 University Ave W, Griggs-Midway Bldg Ste 219
    S, Saint Paul, MN 55104

VSA Minnesota 612.332.3888
E-mail .... info@vsamn.org
    528 Hennepin Ave Ste 305, Minneapolis, MN 55403
    Craig Dunn, Director

SUBSTANCE ABUSE TREATMENT

Adolescent Treatment Ctr Of Winnebago 507.893.3885
Fax 507.893.4223
    550 Cleveland Ave W, Winnebago, MN 56098
    Naomi Ochsendorf, Director

New Connections 651.254.5294
Fax 651.254.1440
Web .... www.newconnections.org
E-mail .... sharer@newconnections.org
    445 Etna St Ste 43, Saint Paul, MN 55106-5848
    Sue Harer, Program Director

Omegon, Inc. 952.541.4738
Fax 952.541.9546
Web .... www.omegon-mn.org
    2000 Hopkins Xrd, Hopkins, MN 55305-2911

Project Turnabout 507.532.3008
Fax 507.532.3058
E-mail .... rforde@projectturnabout.org
    1220 Birch St, Marshall, MN 56258-1500
    Rick Forde, Director

St Cloud Children's Home 320.650.1500
Fax 320.650.1508
Web .... www.saintcloudchildrenshome.org
    1726 7th Ave S, Saint Cloud, MN 56301-5797
    Tim Lieser, Program Director

Minnesota

Mississippi

Haley Barbour, Governor
PO Box 139
550 High St Suite 1900
Jackson, MS 39205-0139
601.359.3150
601.359.3741 (Fax)
governor@governor.state.ms.us
www.governorbarbour.com

Ray Sims, Juvenile Justice Specialist
Dept. of Public Safety
3750 I-55 North Frontage Road
Jackson, MS 39211
601.987.4990
601.987.4154 (Fax)
rsims@mdps.state.ms.us

Alfred Martin, SAG Chair
PO Box 9361
Jackson, MS 39286
601.922.1919
alsyukon2@aol.com

CRISIS NUMBERS

Child Abuse Reporting . . .601.359.4991   Child Abuse Reporting . . .800.222.8000

STATE SERVICES

SOCIAL SERVICES

Child Care Facilities Licensure MS 601.364.2827
Fax 601.364.5058
E-mail . . . . .gaylogan@healthyms.com
143 lefleurs sq., Jackson, MS 39215
Gay Logan, Director

Div of Family and Children's Svcs 601.359.4999
Fax 601.359.4366
750 N State St, Jackson, MS 39205
Linda Millsab, Director

GENERAL HEALTH SERVICES

Childrens Medical Program MS 601.987.3965
Fax 601.987.5560
E-mail . . . . .lclark@msdh.state.ms.us
Ste 3504 Woodrow Wilson Dr, Jackson, MS 39213
L Clark, Director

Maternal and Child Health MS 601.576.7472
Fax 601.576.7825
E-mail . . . . .dbender@msdh.state.ms.us
570 E Woodrow Wilson St, Jackson, MS 39215
D Bender, Director

Ofc of Health Svcs 601.576.7463
Fax 601.576.7825
570 E Woodrow Wilson Ave, Jackson, MS 39215
Danny Bender, Director

MENTAL HEALTH SERVICES

Bureau of Mental Retardation 601.359.1288
Fax 601.359.6295
Web . . . . .www.dmh.state.ms.us.
E-mail . . . . .ed.legrand@dmh.state.ms.us
239 N Lamar St Ste 1101, 1101 ROBERT E LEE
BUILDING, Jackson, MS 39201-1325
Edwin Legrand, Deputy Director

Mississippi State Hospital 601.351.8000
Fax 601.351.8213
Web . . . . .www.msh.state.ms.us
E-mail . . . . .flemija@msh.state.ms.us
3550 Hwy 468 W, P.O. Box 157A, Whitfield,
MS 39193-5529
Jacqueline A. Fleming, Social Services Director

Office of Vocational Rehab MS 601.853.5100
Fax 877.348.1490
1281 Hwy 51 N, Madison, MS 39110
Butch Mcmillian, Director

JUSTICE AGENCY

Attorney General's Ofc .601.359.3680
Fax 601.359.3441
Web . . . . .www.ago.state.ms.us
E-mail . . . . .jkennedy@ago.state.ms.us
550 High St, Jackson, MS 39201-1111
Janet Kennedy, Crime Victim Compensation Program Director

Correctional Education Division MS 601.359.5304
Fax 601.359.6760
E-mail . . . . .kstierle@mdoc.state.ms.us
723 North President St, Jackson, MS 39202
K Stierle, Director

Dept of Public Safety Planning 601.987.4990
Fax 601.987.4154
3750 I-55 N Frontage Rd, Jackson, MS 39211
Mark Allen, Executive Director

Interstate Compact 601.359.4972
Fax 601.359.4970
Web . . . . .www.mdhs.state.ms.us
E-mail . . . . .afriday@mdhs.state.ms.us
750 N State St, Jackson, MS 39202
Andrew Friday, Program Specialist

Mississippi Dept of Corrections 601.359.5600
Fax 601.359.5624
Web . . . . .www.mdoc.state.ms.us
723 N President St Ste 100, Jackson, MS 39202
Christopher B. Epps, Commissioner

POLICE AND SHERIFF

Department of Public Safety, Criminal Info
Ctr 601.933.2600
Fax 601.933.2676
E-mail . . . . .lwaggoner@mdps.state.ms.us
3891 Highway 468 W, Pearl, MS 39208
Larry Waggoner, Director

EDUCATION SERVICES

Homeless Education/Instructional Programs . . .601.359.3499
Fax 601.359.2587
Web www.mde.k12.ms.us
359 N West St, Jackson, MS 39201
Barbara Green, Homeless Coordinator

Mississippi Dept of Education 601.359.3513
Fax 601.359.3242
E-mail . . . . .cblanton@mde.k12.ms.us
359 NW St PO Box 771, Jackson, MS 39205
Tom Burnham, Superintendent

Special Education 601.359.3498
Fax 601.359.2198
359 N West St, Jackson, MS 39201
Ann Moore, State Director

LABOR & WORKFORCE EDUCATION

Mississippi Dept of Employment Security 601.321.6002
Fax 601.321.6004
Web . . . . .www.mdes.ms.gov
1235 Echelon Pkwy, Jackson, MS 39213-8220
Lef Range, Executive Director

COUNTY SERVICES

Adams County

SOCIAL SERVICES

Dept of Human Svcs 601.442.1481
Fax 601.446.5111
150 E Franklin St, Natchez, MS 39120
Patrica Barlow, Director

GENERAL HEALTH SERVICES

Health Dept 601.445.4601
Fax 601.442.8532
Web . . . . .www.msdh.state.ms.us
415 Highway 61 N, Natchez, MS 39120
Thomas Dobbs, Director

COURTS

Youth Court 601.442.6416
Fax 601.445.7960
320 State St, Natchez, MS 39120-3473
Honorable John N. Hudson, Juvenile Court Judge

POLICE AND SHERIFF

Sheriff's Ofc 601.442.2752
Fax 601.442.2911
306 State St, Natchez, MS 39120
Chuck Mayfield, Sheriff

EDUCATION SERVICES

Centreville Head Start 601.645.6342
Fax 601.645.5110
580 Highway 24 W, Centreville, MS 39631
Joyce Handy, Director

Alcorn County

SOCIAL SERVICES

Family and Children's Svcs **662.286.7738**
Fax 662.284.9806
2690 S Harper Rd, Corinth, MS 38834
Deborah Gann, Supervisor

JUSTICE AGENCY

Youth Svcs **662.286.7757**
Fax 662.286.7726
506 Cruise St # D, Corinth, MS 38834
Gail Childers, Youth Services Counselor

COURTS

Chancery Court/District 1 ....**662.286.7700**
Fax 662.286.7706
501 E Waldron St, Corinth, MS 38834
Bobby Morolt, Chancery Clerk

POLICE AND SHERIFF

Sheriff's Ofc **662.286.5521**
Fax 662.286.7773
305 Fulton Dr, Corinth, MS 38834
Charles Rinehart, Sheriff

EDUCATION SERVICES

Corinth Head Start Ctr **662.286.5802**
Fax 662.286.5810
Web ....www.mapheadstart.org
E-mail ....hbugg@mapheadstart.org
2305 Bell School Rd, Corinth, MS 38834-8434
Hester Bugg, Director

Amite County

SOCIAL SERVICES

Dept of Human Svcs **601.657.8066**
Fax 601.657.8068
185 Irene St., Loberty, MS 39645
Carolyn Wooley, Director

GENERAL HEALTH SERVICES

Dept of Health **601.657.8351**
Fax 601.657.9131
Web ....www.msdh.state.ms.us
E-mail ....sheilawilliams@msdh.state.ms.us
1000 Irene St., Liberty, MS 39645
Sheila Williams, Office Manager

COURTS

Chancery Court/District 4 ....**601.657.8022**
Fax 601.657.8288
243 W Main st, Liberty, MS 39645
Honorable Debbra Halford, Chancery Judge

POLICE AND SHERIFF

Sheriff's Ofc **601.657.8057**
Fax 601.657.4199
E-mail ....amiteso@telepak.net
243 S Broad St, Liberty, MS 39645
Timothy A. Perkins, Sheriff

Attala County

SOCIAL SERVICES

Dept of Human Svcs **662.289.1379**
Fax 662.289.1575
717 Fairground Rd, Kosciusko, MS 39090-3258
B Harmon, Director

GENERAL HEALTH SERVICES

Health Dept **662.289.2351**
Fax 662.289.2387
Web ....www.msdh.state.ms.us
E-mail ....cbarber@msdh.state.ms.us
999 Dr Martin Luther King Jr Dr, Kosciusko,
MS 39090-3021
Connie Barber, Office Mgr

Benton County

SOCIAL SERVICES

Dept of Human Svcs **662.224.6245**
Fax 662.224.6308
183 Court St, Ashland, MS 38603
Sondra G Wilburn, Director

COURTS

Chancery Court/District 18 ....**662.224.6300**
Fax 662.224.6303
E-mail ....chanceryclerk@bentoncountyms.gov
190 Ripley Ave, Ashland, MS 38603
Honorable Glen Alderson, Family/youth Court Judges

POLICE AND SHERIFF

Sheriff's Ofc **662.224.8941**
Fax 662.224.6307
E-mail ....bentonso2004@yahoo.com
368 Ripley Ave, Ashland, MS 38603
A.a. Mcmullen, Sheriff

Bolivar County

SOCIAL SERVICES

Dept of Human Svcs **662.843.0294**
Fax 662.843.0120
206 N Pearman Ave, Cleveland, MS 38732
Queen Coleman, Supervisor

Dept of Human Svcs **662.843.8311**
Fax 662.846.0990
212 N Pearman Ave, Cleveland, MS 38732-2634
Mark Couey, Director

GENERAL HEALTH SERVICES

Health Dept **662.843.2706**
E-mail ....nancy.rezinneli@mash.state.ms.us
711 3rd St, Cleveland, MS 38732
Nancy Rezinneli, Nursing Director

JUSTICE AGENCY

Div of Youth Svcs Region II Ofc **662.843.8556**
Fax 662.846.2946
Web ....www.mdhs.state.ms.us
E-mail ....larry.mccalop@mdhs.state.ms.us
204 N. Pearman Ave, Cleveland, MS 38732
Larry Mccalop, Regional Director

POLICE AND SHERIFF

Sheriff's Ofc **662.843.5378**
Fax 662.846.2926
E-mail ....mackhg@cableone.net
2792 Hwy 8, Cleveland, MS 38732
Mack Grimmett, Sheriff

Calhoun County

SOCIAL SERVICES

Dept of Human Svcs **662.412.3169**
Fax 662.412.3176
E-mail ....patriciapatterson@mjhs.ms.gov
237 S Murphree St, Pittsboro, MS 38951
Patricia Patterson, Director

GENERAL HEALTH SERVICES

Health Dept **662.412.3260**
Fax 662.412.3262
235 S Murphree St, Pittsboro, MS 38951
Shaina Kakalef, Coordinating Nurse

POLICE AND SHERIFF

Sheriff's Dept **662.412.3149**
Fax 662.412.3197
E-mail ....ccsd@calhouncoms.net
Hwy 9 South, Pittsboro, MS 38951
Billy M. Gore, Sheriff

Carroll County

SOCIAL SERVICES

Dept of Human Svcs **662.464.5961**
Fax 662.464.5342
205 Lee St, Vaiden, MS 39176
Cathy Whitfield, County Director

GENERAL HEALTH SERVICES

Health Dept **662.237.9224**
Fax 662.237.9354
Web ....www.msdh.state.ms.us
E-mail ....alfio.rausa@msdh.state.ms.us
7225 MS Highway 17 0, Carrollton, MS 38917
Alfio Rausa, District Health Officer

COURTS

Chancery Court **662.237.9274**
Fax 662.237.9642
E-mail ....sugar@duckwood.net
600 Lexington St, Courthouse Sq, Carrollton,
MS 38917
Stanley Mullins, Court Clerk

POLICE AND SHERIFF

Sheriff's Ofc **662.237.9283**
Fax 662.237.6655
Web ....www.mssheriff.org
105 C East Washington St, Carrollton, MS 38917
Jerry Carver, Sheriff

Chickasaw County

SOCIAL SERVICES

Dept of Human Svcs **662.456.3978**
Fax 662.448.8121
101 Castle St, Houston, MS 38851
Melody Hamilton, Acting Social Work Supervisor

Dept of Human Svcs **662.447.5511**
Fax 662.447.5536
234 W Main St Ste 101, Okolona, MS 38860-1439
Samuel Buchanan, Director

GENERAL HEALTH SERVICES

Health Dept Houston Div **662.456.3737**
Fax 662.456.5585
332 N Jefferson St, Houston, MS 38851
Beverly Anderson, Coordinating Nurse

COURTS

Chancery Court/District 14 ....**662.456.2513**
Fax 662.456.5295
E-mail ....wsweeney@chickasawcoms.com
1 Pinson Sq Ste 1, Houston, MS 38851
Wanda Sweeney, Clerk

POLICE AND SHERIFF

Sheriff's Dept **662.456.2339**
Fax 662.456.5291
130 Lancaster Cir, Houston, MS 38851
Jimmy Simmons, Sheriff

Choctaw County

SOCIAL SERVICES

Dept of Human Svcs **662.285.6269**
Fax 662.285.3962
223 W Main St, Ackerman, MS 39735
William Ganann, Director

GENERAL HEALTH SERVICES

Health Dept **662.285.6213**
Fax 662.285.6068
123 Chester St, Ackerman, MS 39735
Charlotte Melms, Coordinating Nurse

COURTS

Chancery Court/District 6 ....**662.285.6329**
Fax 662.285.3444
E-mail ....don_threadgill@yahoo.com
   22 Quinn St, Ackerman, MS 39735
Steve Montgomary, Clerk Of Court

POLICE AND SHERIFF

Sheriff's Ofc **662.285.6129**
Fax 662.285.9040
   122 Jailhouse Rd, Ackerman, MS 39735-5592
Cloyd Halford, Sheriff

Claiborne County

SOCIAL SERVICES

Dept of Human Svcs **601.437.5115**
Fax 601.437.4162
   417 Industrial Ave, Port Gibson, MS 39150-2800
Merdith Hynum, Director

GENERAL HEALTH SERVICES

Health Dept **601.437.5184**
Fax 601.437.5697
   902 Market St, Port Gibson, MS 39150
Lisha Jones, Office Manager

COURTS

Chancery Court/District 17 ....**601.437.4992**
Fax 601.437.3137
E-mail ....gloriadodson@ccmsgov.com
   410 Market St, Port Gibson, MS 39150
Gloria Dodson, Clerk Of Court

POLICE AND SHERIFF

Sheriff's Ofc **601.437.5161**
Fax 601.437.3824
   410 Main St, Port Gibson, MS 39150
Frank Davis, Sheriff

Clarke County

SOCIAL SERVICES

Dept of Human Svcs **601.776.3756**
Fax 601.776.6111
   29 Harris Ave, Quitman, MS 39355
Teresa Nester, Director

GENERAL HEALTH SERVICES

Health Dept **601.776.2149**
Fax 601.776.5029
Web ....www.msstatehealthdept.gov
E-mail ....kathy.posey@msdh.state.ms.us
   426 W Donald St, Quitman, MS 39355-2000
Kathy Posey, Administrator

COURTS

Chancery Court/District 12 ....**601.776.2126**
Fax 601.776.2756
   101 S Archusa Ave, Quitman, MS 39355
Angie Chisholm, Clerk Of Court

Clay County

SOCIAL SERVICES

Dept of Human Svcs **662.494.3843**
Fax 662.494.1747
   360 Washington St, West Point, MS 39773
Amma Stallings, Supervisor

GENERAL HEALTH SERVICES

Ms Health Dept **662.494.4514**
Fax 662.494.1091
Web ....www.msdh.state.ms.us
E-mail ....jerilyn.burroughs@msdh.state.ms.us
   138 S Division St, West Point, MS 39773-2904
Jerilyn Burroughs, Office Manager

JUSTICE AGENCY

Casa/Youth Svcs **662.494.3307**
Fax 662.492.4059
   544 S Division St, West Point, MS 39773
Patricia Cantrell, Youth Center Counselor

COURTS

Chancery Court/District 14 ....**662.494.3124**
Fax 662.492.4059
   205 Court St, West Point, MS 39773
Harmon A Robinson, Chancery Clerk

Coahoma County

SOCIAL SERVICES

Dept of Human Svcs **662.624.3008**
Fax 662.624.3064
E-mail ....viedalewashington@mdhs.ms.gov
   236 sharkey, Clarksdale, MS 38614
Viedale Washington, Regional Director

Dept of Human Svcs **662.624.3050**
Fax 662.624.3038
   917 Ohio Ave, Clarksdale, MS 38614
Vanessa Long, Director

GENERAL HEALTH SERVICES

Health Dept **662.624.8316**
Fax 662.624.2081
Web ....www.msdh.state.ms.us
E-mail ....alfio.rausa@msdh.state.ms.us
   1850 Cheryl St, Clarksdale, MS 38614-7219
Annette Kerson, Office Manager

MENTAL HEALTH SERVICES

Region 1 Mental Health **662.627.7267**
Fax 662.627.5240
Web ....www.regionone.org
   1742 Cheryl St, Clarksdale, MS 38614-7218
Karen Corley, Executive Director

COURTS

Youth Court **662.624.3010**
Fax 662.627.1613
   71 Sunflower Ave, Clarksdale, MS 38614
Honorable Tommy Wilsfort-allen, Youth Court Judge

POLICE AND SHERIFF

Sheriff's Ofc **662.624.3081**
Fax 662.624.3035
   63 Sunflower Ave, Clarksdale, MS 38614
Charles Jones, Sheriff

EDUCATION SERVICES

**Coahoma Opportunities and
Cooperative** **662.624.4887**
Fax 662.624.0115
   115 Issaquena Ave, Clarksdale, MS 38614
Edward Feals, Director

Copiah County

SOCIAL SERVICES

Dept of Human Svcs **601.894.2321**
Fax 601.894.3429
Web ....www.mdhs.state.ms.us
E-mail ....mjefferson@mdhs.state.ms.us
   640 Georgetown St Ste 2, Hazlehurst,
MS 39083-2501
Mary A Jefferson, Director

GENERAL HEALTH SERVICES

Health Dept **601.894.2271**
Fax 601.894.3224
   640 Georgetown St Ste 4, Hazlehurst,
MS 39083-2501
Judy Izzer, Office Manager

COURTS

Chancery Court/District 15 ....**601.894.3021**
Fax 601.894.4081
E-mail ....samos@copiahcounty.org
   122 S Lowe St, Hazlehurst, MS 39083-3015
Steve Amos, Court Clerk

POLICE AND SHERIFF

Sheriff's Ofc **601.894.3011**
Fax 601.892.2133
E-mail ....star1cso@copiahcountyms.gov
   20030 Highway 51, Gallman, MS 39077
Harold Jones, Sheriff

Covington County

SOCIAL SERVICES

Dept of Human Svcs **601.765.6585**
Fax 601.765.5004
E-mail ....tabbott@mdhs.state.ms.us
   107 Arrington Ave. N, Collins, MS 39428
Thomas Abbott, Director

GENERAL HEALTH SERVICES

Covington Health Dept **601.765.4291**
Fax 601.765.2888
Web ....www.ms.gov
   600 S Arrington Ave, Collins, MS 39428
Martha Abercrombie, Office Manager

COURTS

Youth Court **601.765.8356**
Fax 601.765.8248
   501 Main St, Collins, MS 39428
Sheuna Posey, Counselor

POLICE AND SHERIFF

Sheriff's Ofc **601.765.8281**
Fax 601.765.5003
E-mail ....adiehl@covingtoncountyms.gov
   203 1st St., Collins, MS 39428
Angie Diehl, Office Manager

DeSoto County

SOCIAL SERVICES

Dept of Human Svcs **662.429.1480**
Fax 662.429.1487
   3246 Highway 51 S Ste 2, Hernando, MS 38632
Mary Vernon, Supervisor

Dept of Human Svcs **662.429.4461**
Fax 662.449.1407
   2725 Highway 51 S, Hernando, MS 38632-2634
Kennette Hill, Director

COURTS

Court **662.429.1326**
Fax 662.429.4115
   2535 Highway 51 S, Ste 201, Hernando, MS 38632
Celesce Wilson, Judge

POLICE AND SHERIFF

Sheriff's Ofc **662.429.1475**
Fax 662.429.4143
Web ....www.desototimes.com
E-mail ....brasco@desotocountyms.org
   311 W South St, Hernando, MS 38632-2602
Bill Rasco, Sheriff

Forrest County

COURTS

Youth Court **601.545.6185**
Fax 601.545.6110
   110 Alcom St., Hattiesburg, MS 39403
Chris Thomas, Probation Officer

POLICE AND SHERIFF

Sheriff's Ofc 601.544.7800
Fax 601.544.8162
Web ....www.co.forrest.ms.us
E-mail ....bmcgee@co.forrest.ms.us
    316 Forrest St, Hattiesburg, MS 39401-3453
Billy Mcgee, Sheriff

Franklin County

SOCIAL SERVICES

Dept of Human Svcs 601.384.2369
Fax 601.384.3734
    90 Mill Rd., Bude, MS 39630
Carla Mcminns, Director

GENERAL HEALTH SERVICES

Health Dept 601.384.5871
Fax 601.384.3958
Web ....www.msdh.state.ms.us
E-mail ....mattie.covington@msdh.state.ms.us
    140 Mill Road, Bude, MS 39630
Mattie Covington, Office Manager

POLICE AND SHERIFF

Sheriff's Ofc 601.384.2323
Fax 601.384.3770
E-mail ....franklinso@ftc.net
    316 Forrest St, Meadville, MS 39401
James Newman, Sheriff

EDUCATION SERVICES

Head Start Complex 601.384.2818
Fax 601.384.2886
Web ....www.mapheadstart.org
    65 Morgan Fork Church Ln NW, Roxie,
    MS 39661-7128
Shirley W. Hamilton, Director

George County

SOCIAL SERVICES

Dept of Human Svcs 601.947.7551
Fax 601.947.7406
    38 London St Ste B, Lucedale, MS 39452
Angela Hobby, Director

MENTAL HEALTH SERVICES

Region 14 Mental Health 601.947.4274
Fax 601.947.4275
Web ....www.dmh.state.ms.us
E-mail ....carla.brooks@dmh.state.ms.us
    57 Industrial Park Rd, Lucedale, MS 39452-6583
Carla Brooks, Director

POLICE AND SHERIFF

Sheriff's Ofc 601.947.4811
Fax 601.947.0233
E-mail ....sheriff@georgecountyms.gov
    355 Cox St Ste B, Lucedale, MS 39452
Debbie Welford, Acting Sheriff

Greene County

SOCIAL SERVICES

Dept of Human Svcs 601.394.2361
Fax 601.394.4069
    1008 Jackson Ave., Leakesville, MS 39451
Jean Hennington, Director

COURTS

Chancery Court/District 16 ....601.394.2377
Fax 601.394.4445
    400 Main St, Leakesville, MS 39451
Michelle Eubanks, Chancery Court Clerk

POLICE AND SHERIFF

Sheriff's Ofc 601.394.2342
Fax 601.394.5939
E-mail ....greeneso@tds.net
    300 Lafayette St, Leakesville, MS 39451
Kevin Fortinberry, Sheriff

Grenada County

GENERAL HEALTH SERVICES

Health Dept 662.226.3711
Fax 662.227.1168
    1240 Fair Ground Rd, ste a, Grenada, MS 38901
Maxine Brock, Coordinating Nurse

COURTS

Chancery Court/District 3 ....662.226.1821
Fax 662.227.2860
    59 Green St Rm 1, Grenada, MS 38902
Johney Hayward, Court Clerk

POLICE AND SHERIFF

Sheriff's Dept 662.227.2877
Fax 662.227.2872
Web ....www.cji.net
E-mail ....grenadacoso@cji.net
    35 Doak St, Grenada, MS 38901-2609
Alton Strider, Sheriff

Hancock County

SOCIAL SERVICES

Dept of Human Svcs 228.467.4100
Fax 228.466.6224
    3058 Longfellow Rd, Bay Saint Louis, MS 39520
Michelle Henry, Supervisor

Dept of Human Svcs 228.467.4565
Fax 228.467.7530
    3066 Longfellow Rd, Bay Saint Louis, MS 39521
Veronica Breaux, Director

GENERAL HEALTH SERVICES

Health Dept 228.467.4510
Fax 228.466.6227
    3062 Longfellow Rd, Bay Saint Louis, MS 39520
Sharlyne Vuyovich, Office Manager

COURTS

Chancery Court/District 8 ....228.467.5404
Fax 228.466.6236
E-mail ....tim_kellar@hancock.ms.us
    854 Hwy 90 Ste B, Bay Saint Louis, MS 39520-8602
Timothy A. Kellar, Court Clerk

Youth Court 228.467.7945
Fax 228.466.4707
Web ....www.hancockcountyms.gov
    126 Court St, Bay Saint Louis, MS 39520-4516
Honorable Robin Gryder-gibson, Director

POLICE AND SHERIFF

Sheriff's Ofc 228.466.6900
Fax 228.586.1636
    21100 Hwy 603, Kiln, MS 39556
Steve Garber, Sheriff

Harrison County

SOCIAL SERVICES

Dept of Human Svcs 228.897.5600
Fax 228.897.5780
Web ....www.mdhs.state.ms.us
    10260 Larkin Smith Dr, Gulfport, MS 39505
Caroline Delorio, Director

GENERAL HEALTH SERVICES

Health Dept 228.863.1036
Fax 228.864.6084
Web ....www.harrisoncountyhealth.com
    1102 45th Ave, Gulfport, MS 39501-2504
Ann Mauffray, Coordinating Nurse

Health Dept Biloxi Div 228.435.3641
Fax 228.435.4853
Web ....www.msdh.state.ms.us
E-mail ....norma.bond@msdh.state.ms.us
    761 Esters Blvd, Biloxi, MS 39530-3134
Sue Sterns, Office Manager

POLICE AND SHERIFF

Sheriff's Offc 228.865.7092
Fax 228.865.7071
    1801 23rd Ave, Gulfport, MS 39501
Melvin Brisolara, Sheriff

EDUCATION SERVICES

Long Beach Student Education
Services 228.864.8085
Fax 228.867.1783
    111 Quarles St, Long Beach, MS 39560
Madeleine Lord, Director

Special Education 228.832.9344
Fax 228.831.1761
E-mail ....jburr@harrison.k12.ms.us
    16049 Orange Grove Rd, Gulfport, MS 39503-2643
June Burr, Director

Special Education 228.435.4600
Fax 228.435.4601
Web ....www.biloxischools.net
E-mail ....stave.heckaby@biloxischools.net
    1424 Father Ryan Ave, Biloxi, MS 39530
Steve Heckaby, Director Of Exceptional Student Services

Special Services 228.865.4694
Fax 228.865.1911
    700 Pass Rd, Gulfport, MS 39501
Cimmie Switzer, Director

Hinds County

GENERAL HEALTH SERVICES

Clinton Health Dept 601.924.6012
Fax 601.924.6975
    408 Cynthia St, Clinton, MS 39056-3718
Julia Jordan, Coordinating Nurse

Economic Assistance 601.362.9892
Fax 601.364.7615
E-mail ....mmiller@hinds.k12.ms.us
    4777 Medgar Evers Blvd, Jackson, MS 39213
Michael Miller, Director

West Central Public Health District
V 601.978.7864
Fax 601.956.5262
Web www.4healthymississippi.com
    5963 I 55 N, Jackson, MS 39215
Mary Armstrong, Md, Acting Health Officer

MENTAL HEALTH SERVICES

Baptist Behavioral Ctr 601.968.1102
Fax 601.973.1542
Web ....www.mbhs.org
E-mail ....nkobayakawa@mbhs.org
    800 Carlisle St, Jackson, MS 39202-2416
Naomi Kobayakawa, Executive Director

JUSTICE AGENCY

Mississippi Dept of Human Svcs, Div of Youth

Svcs..**601.359.4972**
Fax..601.359.4970
E-mail...........................kpittman@mdhs.state.ms.us
750 N State St, Jackson, MS 39202
Kathy Pittman, Director

COURTS

Youth Court......................................**601.985.3000**
Fax..601.985.3081
Web...www.co.hinds.ms.us
E-mail...........................hpatton@co.hinds.ms.us
940 E Mcdowell Rd, Jackson, MS 39204-5911
Honorable Houston Patton, Director

POLICE AND SHERIFF

Sheriff's Dept...................................**601.974.2901**
Fax..601.968.6705
Web...........................www.stevenpickettyohoe.com
E-mail.......................malcolmmcmillin@yahoo.com
407 E Pascagoula St, Jackson, MS 39201-4206
Malcolm E. Mcmillin, Sheriff

EDUCATION SERVICES

Eulander P. Kendrick Head Start

Ctr..**601.878.5232**
Fax..601.878.2421
642 Morgan Drive, Terry, MS 39170
Amalmeta Roberts, Director

Operation Shoestring....................**601.353.6336**
Fax..601.353.5369
1711 Bailey Ave, Jackson, MS 39203
Robert Langford, Executive Director

Special Education....................**601.857.5222**
Fax..601.857.4964
13192 Hwy 18, Raymond, MS 39154
Dr. Joycelen Whipp, Supervisor

Special Education....................**601.960.8868**
Fax..601.973.8663
Web...www.jackson.k12.ms.us
E-mail.......................tatkins@jackson.k12.ms.us
621 S State St, Jackson, MS 39201-5612
Dr. Tina Atkins, Executive Director

Holmes County

SOCIAL SERVICES

Dept of Human Svcs.....................**662.834.1221**
Fax..662.834.3869
22419 Depot St, Highway 12 E, Lexington,
MS 39095
Mickie Rodgers, Director

GENERAL HEALTH SERVICES

Health Dept...................................**662.834.3142**
Fax..662.834.4906
Web...www.health.ms.gov
E-mail.......................alfio.rausa@msdh.state.ms.us
22545 Depot St, Lexington, MS 39095
Alfio Rausa, Director

COURTS

Chancery Court/District 11...................**662.834.2508**
Fax..662.834.1872
2 Coats Sq, Lexington, MS 39095
Dorothy Jean Ford-smith, Chancery Clerk Of Courts

POLICE AND SHERIFF

Sheriff's Dept...................................**662.834.1511**
Fax..662.834.3362
E-mail.......................holmescoso@yahoo.com
23240 Highway 12, Lexington, MS 39095
Willie E. March, Sheriff

Humphreys County

GENERAL HEALTH SERVICES

Health Dept...................................**662.247.1861**
Fax..662.247.9957
16463 US Hwy 49 N, Ste B, Belzoni, MS 39038
Darla Jones, Office Manager

JUSTICE AGENCY

Youth Court....................................**662.247.2800**
Fax..662.247.3907
E-mail.......................eharbour@youthnetwork.org
102 Castleman St, Belzoni, MS 39038
Eddie J. Harbour, Counsellor

COURTS

Chancery Court/District 9.....................**662.247.1740**
Fax..662.247.0101
102 Castleman St Ste 6, Belzoni, MS 39038-3948
Lawrence Browder, Chancery Clerk Of Courts

POLICE AND SHERIFF

Sheriff's Ofc...................................**662.247.2551**
Fax..662.247.3902
106 Castleman St, Belzoni, MS 39038
Jd Roseman, Sheriff

Issaquena County

SOCIAL SERVICES

Dept of Human Svcs.....................**662.873.6296**
Fax..662.873.9399
129 Court St., Mayersville, MS 39113
Marquetta L Brown, Director

POLICE AND SHERIFF

Sheriff's Ofc...................................**662.873.2781**
Fax..662.873.4500
E-mail.......................rjones@sos.state.ms.us
129 Court St, Mayersville, MS 39113
Richard Jones, Sheriff

Itawamba County

SOCIAL SERVICES

Dept of Human Svcs.....................**662.862.9781**
Fax..662.862.4888
E-mail.......................nhouse@mdhs.state.ms.us
305 W Cedar St, Fulton, MS 38843-1831
Nina House, Director

COURTS

Chancery Court/District 1...................**662.862.3421**
Fax..662.862.3421
201 W Main St Ste 4, Fulton, MS 38843
Lisa Judd, Youth Services Counselor

POLICE AND SHERIFF

Sheriff's Dept...................................**662.862.3401**
Fax..662.862.3404
Web...www.sos.state.ms.us
E-mail.......................cdickinson@sos.state.ms.us
3040 Wiygul St, Fulton, MS 38843-1803
Chris Dickinson, Sheriff

EDUCATION SERVICES

Fulton Head Start Ctr.....................**662.862.3928**
Fax..662.862.2359
Web...www.mapheadstart.org
E-mail.......................bratliff@mapheadstart.org
608 E Elliott Street, Fulton, MS 38843
Bettie Ratliff, Director

Jackson County

SOCIAL SERVICES

Dept of Human Svcs.....................**228.769.3444**
Fax..228.769.3451
5343 Jefferson St, Pascagoula, MS 39563
Brenda Wess, Regional Director

GENERAL HEALTH SERVICES

Health Dept...................................**228.762.1117**
Fax..228.762.5934
Web...www.msdh.state.ms.us
E-mail.......................robert.travnicek@msdh.state.ms.us
4600 vega, Pascagoula, MS 39581-5329
Robert Travnicek, District Health Officer

MENTAL HEALTH SERVICES

Mental Health/Mental Retardation..........**228.696.0030**
Fax..228.712.2783
Web...www.dmh.state.ms.us
E-mail.......................sherman.blackwell@dmh.state.ms.us
4507 Mcarthur St, Singing River Services, Pascagoula,
MS 39567-2351
Sherman Blackwell, Executive Director

JUSTICE AGENCY

CASA..**228.762.7370**
Fax..228.762.7385
Web...www.co.jackson.ms.us
E-mail.......................casa@co.jackson.ms.us
4903 Telephone Rd, Pascagoula, MS 39567-1823
Frances Alsup, Executive Director

Div of Youth Svcs Region VI Ofc.............**228.696.6503**
Fax..228.769.6001
Web...www.mdhs.state.ms.us
E-mail.......................kizzie.wellsdaniels@mdhs.ms.gov
4903 Telephone Rd, Pascagoula, MS 39567-1823
Kizzie Wells-Daniels, Regional Director

COURTS

Youth Court......................................**228.769.3076**
Fax..228.762.7385
Web...www.co.jackson.ms.us
E-mail.......................sharon_sigalas@co.jackson.ms.us
4903 Telephone Rd, Pascagoula, MS 39567-1823
Honorable Sharon Sigalas, Youth Court Judge

POLICE AND SHERIFF

Sheriff's Ofc...................................**228.769.3063**
Fax..228.762.6168
3104 Magnolia St, Pascagoula, MS 39568
Michael Byrd, Sheriff

EDUCATION SERVICES

Special Education....................**228.826.1757**
Fax..228.826.4009
4700 Colonel Vickrey Rd, Vancleave, MS 39565
Tanya Green, Director

Special Education....................**228.938.6488**
Fax..228.938.6528
Web...www.psd.k12.ms.us
E-mail.......................psumrow@psd.k12.ms.us
1006 Communy Ave, Pascagoula, MS 39567-5664
Polly Sumrow, Director

Special Education/Student Svcs.............**228.875.5782**
Fax..228.872.2017
E-mail.......................tcallahan@ossdms.org
2300 Government St, Ocean Springs,
MS 39564-4012
Dr. Teresa Callahan, Director Of Student Services

Jasper County

SOCIAL SERVICES

Dept of Human Svcs **601.764.2151**
Fax 601.764.4869
  37 W 8th Ave # A, Bay Springs, MS 39422
James Sims, Superviser

GENERAL HEALTH SERVICES

Health Dept **601.764.2494**
Fax 601.764.2585
E-mail ....rebecca.james@msdh.state.ms.us
  2761 Highway 15 South, Bay Springs, MS 39422
Rebecca James, Md, District Health Officer

Jefferson County

SOCIAL SERVICES

Dept of Human Svcs **601.786.3571**
Fax 601.786.6005
  235 Medgar Evans Blvd., Fayette, MS 39069
Lillian M Frye, Director

GENERAL HEALTH SERVICES

Health Dept **601.786.3061**
Fax 601.786.3380
  700 Main St, Fayette, MS 39069
June Cotton, Coordinating Nurse

COURTS

Chancery Court/District 17 ....**601.786.3021**
Fax 601.786.6009
  1483 Main St., Fayette, MS 39069
Karen Grover, Youth Services Counselor

POLICE AND SHERIFF

Sheriff's Ofc **601.786.3403**
Fax 601.786.6000
  255 Highway 33, Fayette, MS 39069
Peter E. Walker, Sheriff

Jefferson Davis County

SOCIAL SERVICES

Dept of Human Svcs **601.792.4206**
Fax 601.792.2472
  1185 B Frontage Rd., Prentiss, MS 39474
Kenneth Hall, Acting Director

GENERAL HEALTH SERVICES

Health Dept **601.792.5135**
Fax 601.792.8916
Web ....www.msdh.state.ms.us
E-mail ....beverly.jackson@msdh.state.ms.us
  1185-A Frontage Rd., Prentiss, MS 39474
Beverly Jackson, Office Manager

COURTS

Chancery Court/District 13 ....**601.792.4204**
Fax 601.792.2894
E-mail ....jwdavies53@hotmail.com
  2426 Pearl Ave, Prentiss, MS 39474
John W. Davies, Chancery Court Clerk

POLICE AND SHERIFF

Sheriff's Ofc **601.792.5169**
Fax 601.792.5980
  2330 Columbia Ave, Prentiss, MS 39474
Henry A. Mccullum, Sheriff

Jones County

SOCIAL SERVICES

Dept of Human Svcs **601.426.2266**
Fax 601.426.1232
  923 Sawmill Rd # A, Laurel, MS \39440-3941
Rosa Donaldson, Area Social Work Supervisor

GENERAL HEALTH SERVICES

Health Dept **601.426.3258**
Fax 601.425.1080
  5168 Highway 11, South Laurel, MS 39440
Susan Parker, Rn, Coordinating Nurse

COURTS

Court **601.649.7500**
Fax 601.428.3620
  5170 Highway 11 N, Ellisville, MS 39437
Honorable Gaylon Harper, Director

POLICE AND SHERIFF

Sheriff's Dept **601.425.3147**
Fax 601.428.3152
Web ....www.jonesso.com
E-mail ....sheriff@c-gate.net
  419 Yates Ave, Laurel, MS 39440-3935
Alec Hodge, Sheriff

EDUCATION SERVICES

Early Head Start **601.426.1013**
Fax 601.428.7721
  148 Brown Cir, Laurel, MS 39440
Annie Jackson, Director

Kemper County

SOCIAL SERVICES

Dept of Human Svcs **601.743.5826**
Fax 601.743.9166
  Highway 39 N, De Kalb, MS 39328
Janet Key, Director

GENERAL HEALTH SERVICES

Health Dept **601.743.5865**
Fax 601.743.9964
Web ....www.msdh.state.ms.us
E-mail ....sylvia.grady@msdh.state.ms.us
  Highway 16 West, De Kalb, MS 39328
Sylvia Grady, Office Manager

COURTS

Chancery Court/District 6 ....**601.743.2460**
Fax 601.743.2789
  280 Zeterans St, Dekalb, MS 39328
Sherline Watkins, Chancery Court Clerk

POLICE AND SHERIFF

Sheriff's Ofc **601.743.2255**
Fax 601.743.2266
  14489 Highway 16 W, De Kalb, MS 39328
James Moore, Sheriff

Lafayette County

SOCIAL SERVICES

Dept of Human Svcs **662.234.1861**
Fax 662.236.0228
  819 Jackson Ave E, Oxford, MS 38655-1027
Billy Mcnece, Director

GENERAL HEALTH SERVICES

Health Dept **662.234.5231**
Fax 662.234.7428
  101 Veterans Dr, Oxford, MS 38655-3579
Kay Coleman, Rn, Coordinating Nurse

COURTS

Chancery Court/District 18 ....**662.234.2131**
Fax 662.234.5038
  300 N Lamar Blvd, Oxford, MS 38655
Sherry J. Wall, Chancery Clerk Of Courts

POLICE AND SHERIFF

Sheriff's Ofc **662.234.6421**
Fax 662.236.0203
  711 Jackson Ave E, Oxford, MS 38655
Frankie D. East, Sheriff

Lamar County

SOCIAL SERVICES

Dept of Human Svcs **601.794.1080**
Fax 601.794.1066
E-mail ....bhammer@lamarcounty.com
  207 Main St, Purvis, MS 39475-5439
Barbra Hammer, Director

GENERAL HEALTH SERVICES

Health Dept **601.794.1055**
Fax 601.794.8786
  207 Main St Ste B, Purvis, MS 39475
David Caufield, Director

POLICE AND SHERIFF

Sheriff's Dept **601.794.1005**
Fax 601.794.3914
Web ....www.lamacounty.com
E-mail ....sheriff@lamacounty.com
  205 Main St., #B, Purvis, MS 39475
Danny Rigel, Sheriff

Lauderdale County

SOCIAL SERVICES

Dept of Human Svcs **601.484.5124**
Fax 601.484.5079
Web ....www.mfcf.org
E-mail ....vicki.whitlock@mfcf.org
  5226 Valley St, Meridan, MS 39304
Vicki Whitlock, Area Supervisor Social Work

GENERAL HEALTH SERVICES

Lauderdale Health Dept **601.693.2451**
Fax 601.484.5013
  5224 Valley St, Meridian, MS 39304
Felicia Johnson, Coordinating Nurse

COURTS

Youth Court **601.483.3961**
Fax 601.484.3985
Web ....www.netdoor.com
E-mail ....fmc@netdoor.com
  5400 20th St Ext, Meridian, MS 39307-5320
Honorable Frank M. Coleman, Judge

POLICE AND SHERIFF

Sheriff's Dept **601.482.9806**
Fax 601.484.3954
E-mail ....Sheriff@lauderdalecounty.org
  2001 5th St, Meridian, MS 39301
William D. Sollie, Sheriff

Lawrence County

SOCIAL SERVICES

Dept of Human Svcs **601.587.7632**
Fax 601.587.3008
  1200 Nola Rd, Monticello, MS 39654
Avis Everett, Director

GENERAL HEALTH SERVICES

Health Dept **601.587.2561**
  1230 Nola Rd, Monticello, MS 39654
Carla Bolds, Office Manager

COURTS

Chancery Court/District 13 ....**601.587.7162**
Fax 601.587.0767
  517 E Broad St, Monticello, MS 39654
Saendi Brister, Circuit Clerk Of Courts

POLICE AND SHERIFF

Sheriff's Dept **601.587.2961**
Fax 601.587.4740
E-mail ....sheriffjoelthames@hotmail.com
  1565 Fe Sellers St, Monticello, MS 39654
Joel R. Thames, Sheriff

Leake County

SOCIAL SERVICES

Dept of Human Svcs **601.267.3242**
Fax 601.267.8884
   201 Wm Chipley St, Carthage, MS 39051-4243
Mary Jean Johnson, Director

Leake Family and Childeren Svcs **601.267.8093**
Fax 601.267.8094
   115 N Pearl St, Carthage, MS 39051-0227
Delbra Luckett, Supervisor

GENERAL HEALTH SERVICES

Health Dept **601.267.3072**
Fax 601.267.6277
   204 Chipley St, Carthage, MS 39051
Rebecca James, Md, Director

COURTS

Chancery Court/District 11 ....**601.267.7371**
Fax 601.267.6137
E-mail ....dmerchant@co.leake.ms.us
   Court House, Carthage, MS 39051
Dot Merchant, Chancery Clerk Of Courts

Lee County

SOCIAL SERVICES

Dept of Human Svcs **662.841.9050**
Fax 662.680.5790
   220 S Industrial Rd, Tupelo, MS 38802
Addie Colburn, Director

GENERAL HEALTH SERVICES

Lee Public Health District Ii **662.841.9096**
Fax 662.841.9121
Web ....www.msdh.state.ms.us
   532 S Church St, Tupelo, MS 38804-4708
Roger Riley, Director

North East Public Health District II **662.841.9015**
Fax 662.841.9142
Web ....www.healthymississippi.com
   532 S Church St, Tupelo, MS 38802
Jessie R Taylor, District Health Officer

MENTAL HEALTH SERVICES

Mental Health/Mental Retardation **662.844.1717**
Fax 662.680.6416
E-mail ....robert.smith@dmh.state.ma.us
   2434 S Eason Blvd, Tupelo, MS 38804-6942
Robert Smith, Executive Director

COURTS

Court **662.841.9730**
Fax 662.841.9732
E-mail ....deleotoulos@co.lee.ms.us
   200 W Jefferson St Ste 370, Tupelo, MS 38802
Honorable Charles R. Brett, County Court Judge

Youth Court **662.841.9111**
Fax 662.680.6018
   200 W Jefferson St # 330, Tupelo, MS 38804
David E. Anthony, Youth Services Counselor

Leflore County

SOCIAL SERVICES

Dept of Human Svcs **662.453.3124**
Fax 662.455.7972
   216 Highway 7 S, Greenwood, MS 38930-6058
Dynetha Thornton, Director

Family and Children's Svcs **662.455.7917**
Fax 662.455.7981
   216 Highway 7 S, Greenwood, MS 38930-6058
Judith McCaline, Regional Director

POLICE AND SHERIFF

Sheriff's Dept **662.453.5141**
Fax 662.453.2221
Web ....www.netdoor.com
E-mail ....sheriff@netdoor.com
   3600 County Rd. 540, Greenwood, MS 38935-0905
Frederick L. Banks, Sheriff

Lincoln County

SOCIAL SERVICES

Dept of Human Svcs **601.835.2838**
Fax 601.835.2193
Web ....www.msdh.state.ms.us
E-mail ....mjones@msdh.state.ms.us
   300 E Chickasaw St, Brookhaven, MS 39601-3414
Melinda Jones, Supervisor

GENERAL HEALTH SERVICES

Health Dept **601.833.3314**
Fax 601.833.5150
   1212 Northpark Ln NE, Brookhaven, MS 39601
Tracy Byas, Administrator

COURTS

Chancery Court/District 15 ....**601.835.3411**
Fax 601.835.3423
Web ....www.mssc.state.ms.us
   301 S 2nd St, Brookhaven, MS 39601
Honorable Michael Taylor, Circuit Judge

POLICE AND SHERIFF

Sheriff's Ofc **601.833.5231**
Fax 601.833.4492
E-mail ....steve-rushing@mdoc.state.ms.us
   215 Justice St, Brookhaven, MS 39601
Steve Rushing, Sheriff

Lowndes County

SOCIAL SERVICES

Dept of Human Svcs **662.245.4612**
Fax 662.329.5893
   1604 College St, Columbus, MS 39701-5958
Kessle Hughes, Area Supervisor

GENERAL HEALTH SERVICES

Health Dept **662.328.6091**
Fax 662.328.7355
E-mail ....mtaggart@msdh.state.ms.us
   801 Lehmberg Rd, Columbus, MS 39702
Michelle Taggart, Rn, Coordinating Nurse

COURTS

Youth Court Div **662.245.4622**
Fax 662.245.4617
   1602 College St, Columbus, MS 39701
Honorable Anthoney Nelson, Director

POLICE AND SHERIFF

Sheriff's Ofc **662.328.6788**
Fax 662.244.0769
   527 MLK Drive South, Columbus, MS 39704
C.b. Howard, Sheriff

Madison County

SOCIAL SERVICES

Dept of Human Svcs **601.859.5858**
Fax 601.859.0331
   867 MLK Dr., Canton, MS 39046
Lora Wright, Area Supervisor

Human Svcs **601.859.1276**
Fax 601.859.0321
   867 Martin Luther King Jr. Drive, Canton, MS 39046
Glen Lacey, Director

GENERAL HEALTH SERVICES

Health Dept **601.859.3316**
   309 Park Dr, Canton, MS 39046
Mary Armstrong, Md, District Health Officer

COURTS

Court **601.859.4365**
Fax 601.859.8555
   128 W North St, Canton, MS 39046
Honorable Steve Ratcliff, County Court Judge

POLICE AND SHERIFF

Sheriff's Dept **601.859.2345**
Fax 601.859.6764
Web ....www.madison.co.com
E-mail ....madisonso@madison.co.com
   2941 S Liberty St, Hwy 51 S, Canton,
   MS 39046-8665
Toby Trowbridge, Jr., Sheriff

Marion County

SOCIAL SERVICES

Family and Children's Svcs **601.736.6044**
Fax 601.736.6053
E-mail ....andrea.brown@mdhs.ms.gov
   226 Broad St Ste 1, Columbia, MS 39429
Andrea Brown, Supervisor

GENERAL HEALTH SERVICES

Health Dept **601.736.2676**
Fax 601.731.2417
Web ....www.msdh.state.ms.us
E-mail ....janice.aikens@msdh.state.ms.us
   908 Sumrall Rd, Columbia, MS 39429
Janice Aikens, Officer Manager

COURTS

Chancery Court/District 10 ....**601.736.2691**
Fax 601.444.0206
Web ....www.co.marion.ms.us
E-mail ....cbarnes@Co.Marion.Ms.Us
   250 Broad St Ste 2, Columbia, MS 39429-2962
Cass Barnes, Chancery Clerk Of Courts

POLICE AND SHERIFF

Sheriff's Ofc **601.736.5051**
Fax 601.731.3780
   219 Broad St, Columbia, MS 39429
Berkley Hall, Sheriff

Marshall County

SOCIAL SERVICES

Dept of Human Svcs **662.252.3465**
Fax 662.252.4616
Web ....www.msdh.state.ms.us
E-mail ....mhoey@msdh.state.ms.us
   231 E. College St., Holly Springs, MS 38635
Minnie Hoey, Supervisor

GENERAL HEALTH SERVICES

Health Dept **662.252.4621**
Fax 662.252.7806
Web ....www.msdh.ms.us
   225 S Market St, Holly Springs, MS 38635-3028
Samantha Johnson, Office Manager

JUSTICE AGENCY

Div of Youth Svcs Region I Office **662.252.5661**
Fax 662.252.0596
E-mail ....lynn.pullen@mdhs.state.ms.us
   136 N Alderson, Holly Springs, MS 38635
Lynn Pullen, Regional Director

Mississippi

COURTS

Chancery Court/District 19 ....**662.252.4431**
Fax 662.551.3302
   128 E Van Dorn Court Sq, Holly Springs, MS 38635
   Cw Chuck Thomas, Chancery Clerk Of Courts

POLICE AND SHERIFF

Sheriff's Ofc **662.252.1311**
Fax 662.252.0006
   819 West St, Holly Springs, MS 38635
   Kenny A. Dickerson, Sheriff

EDUCATION SERVICES

Erma Rogers Head Start Ctr **662.838.6290**
Fax 662.838.8216
Web ....www.ics-hs.org
E-mail ....jblackmond@ics-hs.org
   241 Fuller St, Byhalia, MS 38611-7015
   Joyce Blackmond, Director

Head Start Ctr **662.494.4985**
Fax 662.494.4909
Web ....www.ics-hs.org
E-mail ....egriffin@ics-hs.org
   257 W Half Mile St, West Point, MS 39773
   Essie Griffin, Director

Monroe County

SOCIAL SERVICES

Dept of Human Svcs **662.369.2876**
Fax 662.369.7039
Web ....www.msdh.state.ms.us
E-mail ....lsullivan@msdh.state.ms.us
   104 1/2 N Matubba St, Aberdeen, MS 39730-2430
   Loraine Sullivan, Supervisor

GENERAL HEALTH SERVICES

Amory Clinic **662.256.5341**
Fax 662.256.4526
   1300 Highway 25 S, Amory, MS 38821
   Diane Clark, Coordinating Nurse

COURTS

Chancery Court/District 1 ....**662.369.8143**
Fax 662.369.7928
   201 W Commerce St, Aberdeen, MS 39730
   Ronnie Boozer, Chancery Clerk Of Courts

POLICE AND SHERIFF

Sheriff's Ofc **662.369.2468**
Fax 662.369.2470
   700 N Meridian St, Aberdeen, MS 39730
   Andy Hood, Sheriff

Montgomery County

SOCIAL SERVICES

Dept of Human Svcs **662.283.2922**
Fax 662.283.4005
   705 Alberta Dr, Winona, MS 38967-1598
   Shirley Oliver, Director

Dept of Human Svcs **662.283.3430**
Fax 662.283.3510
Web ....www.msdh.state.ms.us
   204 S Front St, Winona, MS 38967-1522
   Mary Leahman, Supervisor

GENERAL HEALTH SERVICES

Health Dept **662.283.3655**
Fax 662.283.2528
Web ....www.msdh.state.ms.us
E-mail ....eloise.forrest@msdh.state.ms.us
   707 Alberta Dr, Winona, MS 38967-1538
   Eloise Forrest, Manager

COURTS

Chancery Court/District 3 ....**662.283.2333**
Fax 662.283.2233
E-mail ....teegolding@montgomeryco.ms
   614 Summit St, Winona, MS 38967
   Talmadge Golding, Chancery Clerk Of Courts

POLICE AND SHERIFF

Sheriff's Ofc **662.283.3343**
Fax 662.283.4000
Web ....www.mssheriff.org
   614 Summit, Winona, MS 38967
   Jerry Nix Jr, Sheriff

Neshoba County

SOCIAL SERVICES

Dept of Human Svcs **601.656.1451**
Fax 601.656.6515
Web ....www.mdhs.state.ms.us
E-mail ....athomas@mdhs.state.ms.us
   1016 Holland Ave, Philadelphia, MS 39350-2160
   Amy Thomas, Supervisor

GENERAL HEALTH SERVICES

Choctaw Health Ctr **601.656.2211**
Fax 601.663.7924
Web ....www.choctaw.org
   210 Hospital Cir, Philadelphia, MS 39350-6781
   Joshua Breedlove, Director

COURTS

Chancery Court/District 6 ....**601.656.3581**
Fax 601.656.5915
E-mail ....ccbookeeper@neshobacounty.net
   401 E Beacon St Ste 107, Philadelphia,
   MS 39350-2954
   Larry Mcmillan, Chancery Clerk Of Courts

Youth Court- Youth Svcs **601.656.2812**
Fax 601.656.3214
   305 W Main St, Philadelphia, MS 39350-2513
   Stacy Durant, Senior Clerk

POLICE AND SHERIFF

Sheriff's Ofc **601.656.1414**
Fax 601.650.3281
   920 Chestnut St, Philadelphia, MS 39350
   Donnie Adkins, Sheriff

EDUCATION SERVICES

Exhibit Hall Head Start **601.656.4731**
Fax 601.656.7265
Web ....www.mapheadstart.org
   234 Carver Ave, Philadelphia, MS 39350-3448
   Elizabeth Moore, Director

Newton County

SOCIAL SERVICES

Dept of Human Svcs **601.635.2798**
Fax 601.635.4081
E-mail ....teresa.parker@msdh.state.ms.us
   14713 Highway 15 South, Decatur, MS 39327
   Teresa Parker, Supervisor

GENERAL HEALTH SERVICES

Health Dept **601.683.3331**
Fax 601.683.7557
   500 Decatur St, Newton, MS 39345
   Millie Smith, Coordinating Nurse

Health Dept **601.635.2337**
Fax 601.635.4016
E-mail ....millie.smith@msdh.state.ms.us
   15776 Highway 15 N, Decatur, MS 39327
   Millie Smith, Coordinating Nurse

COURTS

Chancery Court/District 2 ....**601.635.2367**
Fax 601.635.3479
E-mail ....newpoenchancery@gmail.com
   92 W Broad St, Decatur, MS 39327
   George T. Hayes Jr., Chancery Clerk Of Courts

POLICE AND SHERIFF

Sheriff's Dept **601.635.3501**
Fax 601.635.5768
E-mail ....newtonso@yahoo.com
   300 Access Rd, Decatur, MS 39327
   Jackie Knight, Sheriff

EDUCATION SERVICES

Crossroads Head Start Ctr **601.683.3161**
Fax 601.683.3121
E-mail ....awesley@msdh.state.ms.us
   401 E Railroad St, Newton, MS 39345-2606
   Angie Wesley, Director

Noxubee County

SOCIAL SERVICES

Dept of Human Svcs **662.726.5884**
Fax 662.726.2936
   601 W. Pearl St., Macon, MS 39341
   Sharon Papas, Director

GENERAL HEALTH SERVICES

Health Dept **662.726.4451**
Fax 662.726.5392
Web ....www.missisipihealthdept.com
   480 W Pearl St, Macon, MS 39341
   Jerilyn Burroughs, Office Manager

COURTS

Chancery Court/District 14 ....**662.726.4243**
Fax 662.726.2272
   505 S Jefferson St Ste 4, Macon, MS 39341
   Mary R. Shelton, Chancery Clerk Of Courts

POLICE AND SHERIFF

Sheriff's Ofc **662.726.5133**
Fax 662.726.4166
   505 S Jefferson St Ste 1, Macon, MS 39341
   Albert Walker, Sheriff

Oktibbeha County

GENERAL HEALTH SERVICES

Health Dept **662.323.4565**
Fax 662.323.2667
   203 Yeates St, Starkville, MS 39759
   Veronica Hughes, Office Manager

**Tombigbee Public Health District
IV** **662.323.7313**
Fax 662.324.1011
Web ....www.msdh.state.ms.us
   732 Whitfield St, Starkville, MS 39759-3125
   Bill Fryery, Hiv/std Supervisor

COURTS

Chancery Court/District 14 ....**662.323.5834**
Fax 662.338.1064
E-mail ....monicawbanks@hotmail.com
   101 E Main St, Starkville, MS 39759-2927
   Monica W. Banks, Chancery Clerk Of Courts

Panola County

SOCIAL SERVICES

Dept of Human Svcs **662.487.2098**
Fax 662.487.3592
Web ....www.msdh.state.ms.us
E-mail ....rhonda.jones@msdh.state.ms.us
   203 S Main St, Sardis, MS 38666-1724
   Pina Turner, Supervisor

GENERAL HEALTH SERVICES

Health Dept **662.563.4616**
Fax 662.563.6304
   381 Highway 51 S, Batesville, MS 38606
Freddie Hentz, Office Manager

NW Public Health District I **662.563.5603**
Fax 662.563.6307
Web ....www.msdh.state.ms.us
E-mail ....terry.cousin@msdh.state.ms.us
   240 Tower Rd, Batesville, MS 38606-2724
Terry Cousin, Std Supervisor

MENTAL HEALTH SERVICES

**Communicare Mental Health Region
2** **662.487.2746**
Fax 662.487.2754
Web ....www.communicarems.org
   100 E Frontage Rd, Sardis, MS 38666
Megan Taylor, Mental Health Therapist

Pearl River County

SOCIAL SERVICES

Dept of Human Svcs **601.795.3038**
Fax 601.403.2331
   417 Highway 11 N., Poplarville, MS 39470
Tana Walker, Supervisor

GENERAL HEALTH SERVICES

Health Dept **601.798.6212**
Fax 601.799.2421
Web ....www.msdh.state.ms.us
E-mail ....robert.travnicek@msdh.state.ms.us
   7547 Highway 11, Carriere, MS 39426-8904
Robert Travnicek, District Health Officer

POLICE AND SHERIFF

Sheriff's Ofc **601.403.2300**
Fax 601.403.2344
Web ....www.pearlrivercounty.net
E-mail ....sheriff@pearlrivercounty.net
   200 S Main St Ste 2, Poplarville, MS 39470-2810
David Allison, Sheriff

Perry County

SOCIAL SERVICES

Dept of Human Svcs **601.964.8374**
Fax 601.964.8376
   101 S Main St, New Augusta, MS 39462
Francis Williamson, Director

COURTS

Chancery Court/District 10 ....**601.964.8398**
Fax 601.964.8746
Web ....www.perryco.ms.us
E-mail ....vwalters@perryco.ms.us
   103 S Main St, New Augusta, MS 39462
Vickie Walters, Chancery Clerk Of Courts

POLICE AND SHERIFF

Sheriff's Dept **601.964.8461**
Fax 601.964.8463
E-mail ....perryso@c-gate.net
   103 1st St W, New Augusta, MS 39462
Jimmy D. Smith, Sheriff

Pike County

SOCIAL SERVICES

Dept of Human Svcs **601.684.0195**
Fax 601.249.1079
Web ....www.msdh.state.ms.us
E-mail ....yasmeen.muhammad@msdh.state.ms.us
   1002 Warren Krout Rd, McComb, MS 39648
Yasmeen Muhammad, ASWS, Supervisor

GENERAL HEALTH SERVICES

Health Dept **601.684.1030**
Fax 601.684.5999
Web ....www.msdh.state.ms.us
   114 E Presley Blvd, McComb, MS 39648-5908
Kathy Tiacone, Rn, Coordinating Nurse

COURTS

Youth Court **601.783.2732**
Fax 601.783.5185
Web ....www.co.pike.ms.us
E-mail ....johnp@co.pike.ms.us
   101 N Cherry St, Magnolia, MS 39652-3032
Honorable John Price, Judge

POLICE AND SHERIFF

Sheriff's Dept **601.783.2327**
Fax 601.783.6586
Web ....www.co.pike.ms.us
E-mail ....marks@co.pike.ms.us
   2109 Jessie Hall Memorial Rd, Magnolia, MS 39652
Mark Shepard, Sheriff

Pontotoc County

SOCIAL SERVICES

Dept of Human Svcs **662.489.3970**
Fax 662.489.3918
   341 Ridge Dr, Pontotoc, MS 38863
Kelly Fleming, Supervisor

GENERAL HEALTH SERVICES

Health Dept **662.489.1241**
Fax 662.489.7181
Web ....www.msdh.state.ms.us
E-mail ....paul.byers@msdh.state.ms.us
   341 Ridge Dr, Pontotoc, MS 38863-1214
Paul E Byers, District Health Officer

COURTS

Chancery Court/District 1 ....**662.489.3900**
Fax 662.489.3940
E-mail ....rcollums@pontotoccoms.com
   34 S Liberty St, Pontotoc, MS 38863
Reggie Collums, Chancery Clerk

POLICE AND SHERIFF

Sheriff's Ofc **662.489.3111**
Fax 662.489.3953
   18 S Liberty St, Pontotoc, MS 38863
Neal Davis, Sheriff

Prentiss County

SOCIAL SERVICES

Dept of Human Svcs **662.728.3118**
Fax 662.728.3119
   100 Hotel St, Booneville, MS 38829
Janet Roy, Director

GENERAL HEALTH SERVICES

Health Dept **662.728.3518**
Fax 662.728.2005
Web ....www.msdh.state.ms.us
   615 E Parker Dr, Booneville, MS 38829-5519
Debra Weatherford, Rn, Coordinating Nurse

COURTS

Chancery Court **662.728.8151**
Fax 662.728.2007
E-mail ....bubba@co.prentiss.ms.us
   100 N Main St, Booneville, MS 38829
David Pounds, Chancery Clerk Of Courts

Quitman County

SOCIAL SERVICES

Dept of Human Svcs **662.326.8021**
Fax 662.326.3767
   1054 Martin Luther King Dr., Marks, MS 38646
Luvenia Manon, Director

GENERAL HEALTH SERVICES

Health Dept **662.326.2861**
Fax 662.326.3993
Web ....www.healthyms.com
   235 Chestnut St, Marks, MS 38646-1212
Fredde Hentz, Office Mgr

COURTS

Chancery Court/District 7 ....**662.326.2661**
Fax 662.326.8004
E-mail ....quitmanchancery@hotmail.com
   220 Chestnut St Ste 2, Marks, MS 38646
T.h. Scipper, Chancery Clerk Of Courts

POLICE AND SHERIFF

Sheriff's Ofc **662.326.3131**
Fax 662.326.9550
   233 Chestnut St, Marks, MS 38646
Oliver Parker, Sheriff

Rankin County

SOCIAL SERVICES

Dept Of Human Svcs **601.825.1040**
Fax 601.825.2168
E-mail ....trudy.miller@mdhs.ms.gov
   603 Marquette Rd, Brandon, MS 39043
Trudy Miller, Area Supervisor

Dept of Human Svcs **601.825.7210**
Fax 601.825.7216
E-mail ....sarah.bridge@mdhs.state.ms.us
   603 Marquette Rd, Brandon, MS 39042-3038
Sarah Bridge, Director

GENERAL HEALTH SERVICES

Mississippi Dept of Health **601.576.8090**
Fax 601.576.7909
Web ....www.msdh.state.ms.us
   120 Osborne Building, Jackson, MS 39215
Mary Berrier, State Health Officer

MENTAL HEALTH SERVICES

Mental Health/Mental Retardation **601.824.0342**
Fax 601.824.0349
Web www.region8mhs.org
E-mail ....dvan@region8mhs.org
   613 Marquette Rd, Brandon, MS 39043
Dave Van, Executive Director

JUSTICE AGENCY

Youth Svcs **601.932.5766**
Fax 601.932.6439
Web ....www.rankincounty.org
   3350 Highway 468 W, Pearl, MS 39208-9449
Paul Bowen, Youth Services Counselor

POLICE AND SHERIFF

Sheriff's Ofc **601.825.1480**
Fax 601.824.7120
E-mail ....rtennington@rankincounty.org
   221 N Timber St, Brandon, MS 39042
Ronni Tennington, Sheriff

Scott County

SOCIAL SERVICES

Dept of Human Svcs **601.469.4762**
Fax 601.469.3118
   521 Airport Rd, Forest, MS 39074-4033
Angela Dardner, Director

Region III Social Svcs 601.469.2010
Fax 601.469.3114
  309 Smith Ave Ste B, Forest, MS 39074-4159
Darla Honeysucker, Supervisor

COURTS

Chancery Court/District 2 ....601.469.1922
Fax 601.469.5180
E-mail ....dclark@localink4.com
  100 Main St, Forest, MS 39074
Honorable H. David Clark Ii, Chancery Judge

Youth Court 601.469.1401
Fax 601.469.3118
  521 Airport Rd, Forest, MS 39074-4033
Frederick Payen, Youth Services Counselor

Sharkey County

SOCIAL SERVICES

Dept of Human Svcs 662.873.2655
Fax 662.873.6136
E-mail ....fsampson@mdhs.state.ms.us
  613 Martin LKuther King Jr. St., Rolling Fork,
  MS 39159
Fannie Sampson, Director

GENERAL HEALTH SERVICES

Health Dept 662.873.6202
Fax 662.873.6929
  297 W Race St, Rolling Fork, MS 39159-2621
Dale Clark, Coordinating Nurse

COURTS

Chancery Court/District 9 ....662.873.2755
Fax 662.873.6045
  120 Locust St Ste 6, Rolling Fork, MS 39159-2325
Murindia Williams, Chancery Clerk Of Courts

POLICE AND SHERIFF

Sheriff's Ofc 662.873.4321
Fax 662.873.6135
E-mail ....sheriff@sharkeycounty.ms.gov
  120 Locust St Ste 3, Rolling Fork, MS 39159
Lindsey Adams, Jr., Sheriff

Simpson County

SOCIAL SERVICES

Dept of Human Svcs 601.847.4081
Fax 601.847.4806
  109 W Pine St, Mendenhall, MS 39114
Jeff Wedgeworth, Supervisor

GENERAL HEALTH SERVICES

Health Dept 601.847.2755
Fax 601.847.2670
  405 Main St N, Mendenhall, MS 39114
Karen Herrington, Coordinating Nurse

JUSTICE AGENCY

Youth Svcs 601.847.4761
Fax 601.847.7007
  150 W Court Ave, Mendenhall, MS 39114
Jan Prewitt, Youth Services Counselor

COURTS

Chancery Court/District 13 ....601.847.2626
Fax 601.847.7016
  111 W Pine Ave Ste 3, Mendenhall, MS 39114
Honorable Joedale Walker, Chancery Judge

Smith County

SOCIAL SERVICES

Dept of Human Svcs 601.782.4505
Fax 601.782.4918
Web ....www.health.state.ny.us
E-mail ....stacym@health.state.ny.us
  Highway 37 S, Multi-Purpose Bldg., Raleigh,
  MS 39153
Stacy Mcallen, Director

GENERAL HEALTH SERVICES

Health Dept 601.782.4472
Fax 601.782.9619
Web ....www.sos.state.ms.us
E-mail ....lbreland@sos.state.ms.us
  352 Magnolia Dr, Raleigh, MS 39153
Leon Breland, Coordinating Nurse

COURTS

Chancery Court/District 13 ....601.782.9811
Fax 601.782.4690
Web ....www.smithcounty.ms.gov
  123 Main St, Raleigh, MS 39153-6002
Cindy Austin, Chancery Clerk Of Courts

POLICE AND SHERIFF

Sheriff's Ofc 601.782.4531
Fax 601.782.4003
  200 Courthouse Square, Raleigh, MS 39153
Charlie Crumpton, Sheriff

Stone County

SOCIAL SERVICES

Dept of Human Svcs 601.928.4996
Fax 601.928.6459
E-mail ....cmassey@mdhs.state.ms.us
  648 Fairground St, Wiggins, MS 39577-5700
Carolyn D Massey, Director

GENERAL HEALTH SERVICES

Health Dept 601.928.5293
Fax 601.928.6450
  315A Central Ave E, Wiggins, MS 39577-2715
Marian Cunningham, Rn, Coordinating Nurse

COURTS

Chancery Court/District 8 ....601.928.5266
Fax 601.928.6464
  323 Cavers Ave E Ste C, DRAWER 7, Wiggins,
  MS 39577-2714
Joy Danzey, Court Clerk

POLICE AND SHERIFF

Sheriff's Ofc 601.928.7251
Fax 601.928.6455
  1420 Industrial Park Rd, Wiggins, MS 39577
Mike Farmer, Sheriff

Sunflower County

SOCIAL SERVICES

Dept of Social Svcs 662.887.2795
Fax 662.887.7078
  204 E Baker St, Indianola, MS 38751
Dorothy Manuel, Acting Supervisor

GENERAL HEALTH SERVICES

Ruleville Health Dept 662.756.4881
Fax 662.756.2030
  628 Everett And Elisha Langdon St, Ruleville,
  MS 38771
Sharon Cobb, Rn, Coordinating Nurse

COURTS

Chancery Court/District 9 ....662.887.4703
Fax 662.887.7054
E-mail ....sykes1@capital12.com
  200 Main St, Indianola, MS 38751
Paula S. Sykes, Chancery Clerk Of Courts

POLICE AND SHERIFF

Sheriff's Ofc 662.887.2121
Fax 662.887.4614
  1300 Allen Rd, Indianola, MS 38751-2947
James A. Haywood, Sheriff

Tallahatchie County

SOCIAL SERVICES

Dept of Human Svcs 662.647.5571
Fax 662.647.2204
  200 S Market St, Charleston, MS 38921
Tori Brewer, Director

GENERAL HEALTH SERVICES

Health Dept 662.375.8345
Fax 662.375.7424
Web ....www.health.ms.gov
  208 Wilson St, Sumner, MS 38957
Roberta Braxton, Coordinating Nurse

Health Dept 662.647.3404
Fax 662.647.2689
Web ....www.msdh.state.ms.us
  209 S Pleasant St, Charleston, MS 38921-2325
Anette Wilkerson, Director

COURTS

Chancery Court/District 1 ....662.647.5551
Fax 662.647.3702
E-mail ....anita_greenwood@uml.edu
  1 Court Sq Tllhtchie Cnty, Charleston, MS 38921
Anita Greenwood, Chancery Clerk Of Courts

Tate County

SOCIAL SERVICES

Dept of Human Svcs 662.562.4478
Fax 662.562.7222
Web ....www.sos.state.ms.us
E-mail ....lmcphail@sos.state.ms.us
  1428 Brownsferry Rd., Senatobia, MS 38668
Lisa Mcphail, Director

GENERAL HEALTH SERVICES

Health Dept 662.562.4428
  100 Cutemer Care Dr, Senatobia, MS 38668
Melinda Armstrong, Office Mgr

COURTS

Chancery Court/District 3 ....662.562.5661
Fax 662.560.6205
E-mail ....tateadmin@cgdsl.net
  201 Ward St S Ste C, Senatobia, MS 38668-2659
Wayne Crocket, Chancery Clerk Of Courts

POLICE AND SHERIFF

Sheriff's Dept 662.562.4434
Fax 662.562.7588
Web ....www.cgdsl.net
E-mail ....tateso@cgdsl.net
  1 Justice Dr, Senatobia, MS 38668-2326
Brad Lance, Sheriff

Tippah County

SOCIAL SERVICES

Dept of Human Svcs 662.837.9307
Fax 662.837.1192
  159 Bails Rd, Ripley, MS 38663
Elizabeth Davis, Director

GENERAL HEALTH SERVICES

Health Dept **662.837.3215**
Fax 662.837.9480
129 Hospital St, Ripley, MS 38663-1337
Sherre Mcelwaine, Coordinating Nurse

COURTS

Chancery Court/District 18 ....**662.837.7374**
Fax 662.837.7148
E-mail ....rodneymcbryde@yahoo.com
101 E Spring St, Ripley, MS 38663
Rodney Mcbryde, Chancery Clerk Of Courts

POLICE AND SHERIFF

Sheriff's Ofc **662.837.9336**
Fax 662.837.1191
205 W Spring St, Ripley, MS 38663-1932
Brandon Vance, Sheriff

EDUCATION SERVICES

Chalybeate Head Start **662.223.5522**
Fax 662.223.6621
E-mail ....mmontgomery@mapheadstart.org
4530 CR 201, Walnut, MS 38683
Martha Montgomery, Director

Tishomingo County

SOCIAL SERVICES

Dept of Human Svcs **662.423.7020**
Fax 662.423.7057
1008 Battleground Dr Rm 104, COUNTY
COURTHOUSE, Iuka, MS 38852
Tommy Jean Daugherty, Director

GENERAL HEALTH SERVICES

Health Dept **662.423.6100**
Fax 662.423.1582
1508 Bettydale Dr, Iuka, MS 38852-1111
Tracy Thorndung, Coordinating Nurse

COURTS

Chancery Court/District 1 ....**662.423.7010**
Fax 662.423.7005
E-mail ....pcunnings@pishomrngo.ms.us
1008 Battleground Dr Rm 202, Iuka, MS 38852
Peyton Cummings, Chancery Clerk Of Courts

POLICE AND SHERIFF

Sheriff's Ofc **662.423.7000**
Fax 662.423.9712
1111 Maria Ln, Iuka, MS 38852
Glenn Whitlock, Sheriff

Tunica County

SOCIAL SERVICES

Dept of Human Svcs **662.363.1771**
Fax 662.363.9792
1490 Edwards Ave, Tunica, MS 38676
Jacklyn Mitchner, Director

COURTS

Chancery Court/District 7 ....**662.363.2451**
Fax 662.357.5934
1300 School St, Tunica, MS 38676
Susie White, Chancery Clerk Of Courts

POLICE AND SHERIFF

Sheriff's Dept **662.363.1411**
Fax 662.363.4238
5126 Old Mhoonlanding Rd, Tunica, MS 38676
Kacy Hamp, Sheriff

Union County

SOCIAL SERVICES

Dept of Human Svcs **662.534.1984**
Fax 662.534.1988
923 Fairground Spur Rd, New Albany, MS 38652
John Simpson, Director

Dept of Human Svcs **662.534.1986**
Fax 662.534.1920
814 Hwy 348, New Albany, MS 38652
Shelly Medlin, Supervisor

GENERAL HEALTH SERVICES

Health Dept **662.534.1926**
Fax 662.534.1928
252 Carter Ave, New Albany, MS 38652
Jesse Taylor, District Health Officer

COURTS

Chancery Court/District 1 ....**662.534.1900**
Fax 662.534.1907
E-mail ....jaytidwellmail@yahoo.com
109 E Main St, New Albany, MS 38652-3923
Annette Hickey, Chancery Clerk Of Courts

POLICE AND SHERIFF

Sheriff's Dept **662.534.1941**
Fax 662.534.1993
E-mail ....rtwilhite@yahoo.com
300 Carter Ave, New Albany, MS 38652-3301
Tommy Wilhite, Sheriff

Walthall County

GENERAL HEALTH SERVICES

Walthall Health Dept **601.876.4924**
Fax 601.876.9137
903 Union Rd, Tylertown, MS 39667
Becky Hilburn, Rn, Coordinating Nurse

COURTS

Chancery Court/District 4 ....**601.876.3553**
Fax 601.876.6026
200 Ball Ave Ste B, Tylertown, MS 39667
Melissa Holeman, Youth Services Counselor

Warren County

SOCIAL SERVICES

Dept of Human Svcs **601.636.1597**
Fax 601.634.4819
1100 Grove St, Vicksburg, MS 39181-1829
Andrea Shelton, Area Social-worker Supervisor

Dept of Human Svcs **601.636.1512**
Fax 601.638.0108
1316 Openwood St, Vicksburg, MS 30183
Terri Cozy, Director

GENERAL HEALTH SERVICES

Health Dept **601.636.4356**
Fax 601.636.8557
807 Monroe St, Vicksburg, MS 39183-2593
Susan Johnson, Office Manager

JUSTICE AGENCY

CASA-Child Abuse Prevention Ctr **601.634.0557**
Fax 601.634.0093
Web ....www.vicksburg.com
E-mail ....capctr@vicksburg.com
1529 Walnut St Ste A, Vicksburg, MS 39180-3553
Joel Logue, Case Director

COURTS

Court **601.638.8026**
Fax 601.631.8816
Web ....www.co.warren.ms.us
E-mail ....jprice@co.warren.ms.us
1009 Cherry St, Vicksburg, MS 39183
Honorable John Price, Jr, County Judge

Youth Court **601.630.8004**
Fax 601.630.8010
Web ....www.co.warren.ms.us
E-mail ....rachelh@co.warren.ms.us
100 B. Grove St, Vicksburg, MS 39810
Rachael Hardy, Youth Court Administrator

POLICE AND SHERIFF

Sheriff's Dept **601.636.1761**
Fax 601.634.4803
E-mail ....wcso@vicksburg.com
1000 Grove St, Vicksburg, MS 39180
Martin Pace, Sheriff

EDUCATION SERVICES

Cedars Head Start Ctr **601.636.1360**
Fax 601.636.1332
Web ....www.mapheadstart.org
E-mail ....lpowell@mapheadstart.org
235 Cedars School Cir, Vicksburg, MS 39180-2571
Lavern Powell, Director

Washington County

SOCIAL SERVICES

Dept of Human Svcs **662.335.6051**
Fax 662.334.3554
925 Main St, Greenville, MS 38702
Billy Benson, Director

GENERAL HEALTH SERVICES

Health Dept **662.332.8177**
Fax 662.378.2620
Web ....www.msdh.state.ms.us
1633 Hospital St, Greenville, MS 38703-3222
Princella Pearson, Coordinating Nurse

Health Dept Leland Clinic **662.686.7711**
Fax 662.686.9475
801 N Broad St, Leland, MS 38756-2546
Sue Dobbins, RN, Coordinating Nurse

MENTAL HEALTH SERVICES

Mental Health/Mental Retardation **662.335.5274**
Fax 662.378.3976
E-mail ....gvillexroads@tecinfo.com
1654 E Union St, Greenville, MS 38704
Gilbert S. Macvaugh, Director

Wayne County

SOCIAL SERVICES

Dept of Human Svcs **601.735.4752**
Fax 601.735.6260
1104 Cedar St # A, Waynesboro, MS 39367
Kathy Norsworthy, Director

GENERAL HEALTH SERVICES

Health Dept **601.735.2351**
Fax 601.735.4586
E-mail ....clay.hammack@msdh.state.ms.us
1100 Cedar St # A, Waynesboro, MS 39367
Teresa Sullivan, Office Manager

COURTS

Chancery Court/District 14 ....**601.735.2873**
Fax 601.735.6224
Web ....www.mssc.state.ms.us
609 Azalea Dr, Waynesboro, MS 39367-2616
Marlon West, Counsellor

Mississippi

POLICE AND SHERIFF

Sheriff's Ofc 601.735.3801
Fax 601.735.6262
   613 Court St, Waynesboro, MS 39367-2609
John Stein Farrior, Sheriff

EDUCATION SERVICES

Bryant Turner Head Start Ctr 601.735.9844
Fax 601.735.4974
   215 Mississippi Dr, Waynesboro, MS 39367-2807
Patricia Bruce, Director

Webster County

SOCIAL SERVICES

Dept of Human Svcs 662.258.4771
Fax 662.258.9700
   53 Government Ave, Eupora, MS 39744-2210
Freda Jones, Director

GENERAL HEALTH SERVICES

Health Dept 662.258.3761
Fax 662.258.3150
   57 GOVERNMENT AVE, Eupora, MS 39744-2407
Mattie Dumas, Coordinating Nurse

POLICE AND SHERIFF

Sheriff's Ofc 662.258.7701
Fax 662.258.6069
E-mail ....w1wso@yahoo.com
   87 Government Ave, Eupora, MS 39744
Phillip Smith, Sheriff

Wilkinson County

GENERAL HEALTH SERVICES

Health Dept 601.888.4202
Fax 601.888.4299
Web ....www.healthyms.com
E-mail ....sheila.williams@healthyms.com
   First South St, Woodville, MS 39669
Sheila Williams, Office Manager

COURTS

Chancery Court/District 17 ....601.888.4381
Fax 601.888.6776
E-mail ....TTOLLIVER@BELLSOUTH.NET
   525 Main St, Woodvilleq, MS 39669
Thomas C. Tolliver Jr., Chancery Clerk Of Courts

POLICE AND SHERIFF

Sheriff's Dept 601.888.3511
Fax 601.888.1832
E-mail ....wcsojackson@telepak.net
   1389 HWY 61 S, Woodville, MS 39669
Reginald L. Jackson, Sheriff

Winston County

SOCIAL SERVICES

Dept of Human Svcs 662.773.8096
Fax 662.773.8820
   458 Vance St, Louisville, MS 39339
Joann Clark, Supervisor

Dept of Human Svcs 662.773.8034
Fax 662.773.8839
   458 Vance St, Louisville, MS 39339-9219
Kathy Rogers, Director

COURTS

Chancery Court/District 6 ....662.773.3631
Fax 662.773.8814
E-mail ....pamr@winstoncounty.org
   115 S Court St, Louisville, MS 39339
Pam Real, Chancery Clerk

POLICE AND SHERIFF

Sheriff's Ofc 662.773.5881
Fax 662.773.8831
Web ....www.mdoc.state.ms.us
E-mail ....r.thomas@winstoncounty.org
   115 S Court Ave, Louisville, MS 39339
Randy Thomas, Sheriff

Yalobusha County

GENERAL HEALTH SERVICES

Health Dept 662.473.1424
Fax 662.473.2084
   209 Simmons St, Water Valley, MS 38965-3027
Nicole Davidson, Office Manager

COURTS

Chancery Court/District 2 ....662.473.2091
Fax 662.473.3622
E-mail ....chanceryclark@yolobushacounty.net
   201 Blackmur Dr, Water Valley, MS 38965
Lilly Horan, Clerk

POLICE AND SHERIFF

Sheriff's Ofc 662.473.2722
Fax 662.473.4640
   7076 Cr 436, Water Valley, MS 38965
William Humphreys, Sheriff

Yazoo County

SOCIAL SERVICES

Dept of Human Svcs 662.746.5821
Fax 662.746.2141
   1315 Grady Ave, Yazoo City, MS 39194-3035
Margaret Culpepper, Director

GENERAL HEALTH SERVICES

Health Dept 662.746.3713
Fax 662.746.1033
Web ....www.msdh.state.ms.us
   230 E Broadway St, Yazoo City, MS 39194-4547
Petty Brown, Rn, Coordinating Nurse

MENTAL HEALTH SERVICES

Mental Health Svc 662.746.5712
Fax 662.746.5723
   2303 Gordon Ave, Yazoo City, MS 39194
Millicent Ledbetter, County Director

COURTS

Court 662.746.5214
Fax 662.746.9865
Web ....www.dixie-net.com
E-mail ....dparker@dixie-net.com
   211 E Broadway St Ste 3, Yazoo City,
   MS 39194-4573
Dereck E. Parker, Judge

POLICE AND SHERIFF

Sheriff's Ofc 662.746.5611
Fax 662.746.3890
E-mail ....yazoosheriff@aol.com
   211 East Broadway, Yazoo City, MS 39194
Thomas Vaughan, Sheriff

SPECIAL SERVICES AGENCIES

ADOPTION AGENCIES

Beacon House Adoption Svc, Inc. 228.863.8383
Fax 225.753.6866
E-mail ....msmargie@beaconhouseadopt.com
   440 East Pass Road, Suite B, Gulfport, MS 39507
Margie Mathis, Domestic Adoption Counselor

Bethany Christian Svcs 601.264.4984
Fax 601.264.2648
Web ....www.bethany.org/mississippi
E-mail ....ahurt@bethany.org
   7 Professional Pkwy Ste 103, Hattiesburg,
   MS 39402-2648
Anne Hurt, Director

Mississippi Society for Disabilities/K.I.D.S.
Clinic 601.982.7051
Fax 601.982.1951
   500 E Woodrow Wilson Ave # G, Jackson,
   MS 39216-4538

ADVOCACY RESOURCES

Children First, Inc. 601.371.0451
Fax 601.371.1383
Web ....www.mscourtadvocacy.org
E-mail ....adavis@mscourtadvocacy.org
   2460 Terry Rd., Jackson, MS 39284
Amelia Davis, Director

Emergency Children's Shelter 228.865.7000
Fax 228.865.7012
Web ....www.co.harrison.ms.us
E-mail ....bdaniels@co.harrison.ms.us
   PO Box 7017, Gulfport, MS 39506-7017
Badja Daniels, Shelter Supervisor

BEHAVIORAL HEALTH TREATMENT

Adolescent Offender's Program 601.584.9053
Fax 601.545.5646
Web ....www.pbmhr.com
E-mail ....brian@pbmhr.com
   1204 W 7th St, Hattiesburg, MS 39401-2823
Brian Skully, Director

Baptist Children's Village 601.922.2242
Fax 601.952.2906
Web ....www.baptistchildrensvillage.com
E-mail ....rlee@baptistchildrensvillage.com
   114 Market Ridge Dr, Ridgeland, MS 39157
Rory Lee, Executive Director

CARES Center, Inc. and Mississippi Children's Home
Society 601.352.7784
Web ....www.mchscares.org
E-mail ....terry.hight@mchscares.org
   1900 North West Street, Jackson, MS 39202
Dr. Terry Hight, Accreditation Manager
Joint Commission accredited organization.

Cares Ctr, Inc 601.360.0583
Fax 601.355.3703
Web ....www.mchscares.org
E-mail ....art.ring@mchscares.org
   402 Wesley Ave, Jackson, MS 39202-1000
Arthur Ring, Program Director

Central Mississippi Medical Center 601.376.1000
Web ....www.centralmississippimedicalcenter.com
E-mail ....marcia.hargreaves2@hma.com
 1850 Chadwick Drive, Jackson, MS 39204
 Ms. Marcia Hargreaves, Accreditation Manager
 Joint Commission accredited organization.

Coalition for Children and Youth 601.445.7953
Fax 601.445.7958
 PO Box 1371, Natchez, MS 39121-1371
 Tracy Collines, Aop Director

COPAC, Inc. 601.829.2500
Web ....www.copacms.com
E-mail ....tomk@copacms.com
 3949 Highway 43 North, Brandon, MS 39047
 Mr. Tom Kepner, Accreditation Manager
 Joint Commission accredited organization.

Crossgates River Oaks Hospital 601.825.2811
Web ....www.crossgatesriveroaks.com
E-mail ....rhonda.parker@hma.com
 350 Crossgates Boulevard, Brandon, MS 39042
 Ms. Rhonda Parker, Accreditation Manager
 Joint Commission accredited organization.

**Diamond Grove Center for Children and
Adolescents** 662.779.0119
Fax 662.779.0126
E-mail ....patrick.swoopes@psysolutions.com
 2311 Highway 15 South, Louisville, MS 39339
 Mr. Patrick Swoopes, Accreditation Manager
 Joint Commission accredited organization.

Ellisville State School 601.477.5976
Fax 601.477.5700
Web ....www.ess.state.ms.us
E-mail ....rbratt@ess.state.ms.us
 1101 Highway 11 S, Ellisville, MS 39437-4444
 Renee Bratt, Director

Grenada Lake Medical Center 662.227.7003
Web ....www.glmc.net
E-mail ....molly.brown@glmc.net
 960 Avent Drive, Grenada, MS 38901
 Mrs. Molly Brown, Accreditation Manager
 Joint Commission accredited organization.

Mental Health Ctr 601.792.4872
Fax 601.792.2643
 116 J E Johnson Rd, Prentiss, MS 39474
 Lionell Henderson, Coordinator

Millcreek of Pontotoc 662.488.8878
E-mail ....steve.lancaster@millcreekcenters.com
 1814 Highway 15 North, Pontotoc, MS 38863
 Mr. Steve Lancaster, Accreditation Manager
 Joint Commission accredited organization.

Mississippi Children's Home Society 601.352.7784
Fax 601.968.0021
Web ....www.mchscares.org
 1900 N West St, Jackson, MS 39202
 Christopher Cherney, Executive Director

Mississippi Families as Allies, Inc 601.981.1618
Fax 601.981.1696
Web ....www.msfaacmh.org
E-mail ....info@msfaacmh.org
 5166 Keele St Ste A, Jackson, MS 39206-4319
 Wendy Mahoney, Executive Director

Mississippi State Hospital 601.351.8000
Web ....www.msh.state.ms.us
E-mail ....dana.cline@msh.state.ms.us
 3550 Highway 468 West, Whitfield, MS 39193
 Ms. Dana Cline, Accreditation Manager
 Joint Commission accredited organization.

Parkwood Behavioral Health System 662.895.4900
Web ....parkwoodbhs.com
E-mail ....joyce.tyler@uhsinc.com
 8135 Goodman Road, Olive Branch, MS 38654
 Ms. Joyce Tyler, Accreditation Manager
 Joint Commission accredited organization.

Parkwood Behavioral Health System 662.895.4900
Fax 662.893.7181
Web ....www.parkwoodbhs.com
E-mail ....info@parkwoodbhs.com
 8135 Goodman Rd, Olive Branch, MS 38654-2103
 Everett Bass, Director of Business Development

Pine Belt Mental Healthcare Resources 601.544.4641
Fax 601.582.1607
Web ....www.pbmhr.com
 103 South 19th Avenue, Hattiesburg, MS 39401
 Althea Pierce, Director Information Technology
 CARF accredited programs available.

PSI Crossings 601.483.5452
E-mail ....rae.andreacchio@psysolutions.com
 5000 Highway 39 North, Meridian, MS 39301
 Mr/Mrs Rae Andreacchio, Accreditation Manager
 Joint Commission accredited organization.

Rehabilitation Centers, Inc. 601.849.4221
E-mail ....margaret.stept@millcreekcenters.com
 900 First Avenue, NE, Magee, MS 39111
 Ms. Margaret Stept, Accreditation Manager
 Joint Commission accredited organization.

Specialized Treatment Facility 228.328.6000
Web ....www.stf.state.ms.us
E-mail ....sbush@stf.state.ms.us
 14426 James Bond Road, Gulfport, MS 39503
 Mrs. Shannon Bush, Accreditation Manager
 Joint Commission accredited organization.

CHILDREN'S HOSPITAL

Alliance HealthCare System 662.252.1212
 1430 Hwy 4 E, Holly Springs, MS 38635
 Perry Williams, Chief Executive Officer

Baptist Memorial Hosp 662.538.7631
 200 Hwy 30 W, New Albany, MS 38652
 Walter Grace, Chief Executive Officer

Baptist Memorial Hospital Booneville 662.720.5000
 100 Hospital St, Booneville, MS 38829
 Kyle Armstrong, Administrator

Baptist Memorial Hospital Golden Triang 662.244.1000
 2520 Fifth St N, Columbus, MS 39705
 Paula Cade, Hospital Administrator

Baptist Memorial Hospital N Mississippi 662.232.8100
Web ....www.bmhcc.org
 2301 S Lamar Blvd, Oxford, MS 38655
 Katie Morrissette, Nursing Director

Biloxi Regional Medical Center 228.432.1571
 150 Reynoir St, Biloxi, MS 39530
 Marte Dostwick, Chief Executive Officer

Bolivar Medical Center 662.846.0061
 901 E Sunflower Rd, Cleveland, MS 38732
 Doug Arnold, Chief Executive Officer

Calhoun Health Services 662.628.6611
 140 Burke-Calhoun City Rd, Calhoun City, MS 38916
 James Franklin, Administrator

Community Hospital 662.887.5235
 121 E Baker St, Indianola, MS 38751
 H J Blessidt, Administrative Assistant

Community Hospital 601.765.6711
 701 S Holly St, Collins, MS 39428
 Kristy Evans, Customer Service

Community Hospital 662.323.4320
 400 Hospital Rd, Starkville, MS 39759
 Arthur Kelly, Chief Executive Officer

Community Hospital 662.326.8031
 340 Getwell Dr, Marks, MS 38646
 Richard Manning, Chief Executive Officer

Community Hospital 601.587.4051
 Hwy 84 E, Monticello, MS 39654

Crossgates River Oaks Hospital 601.825.2811
 350 Crossgates Blvd, Brandon, MS 39042
 Jacque Sullins, Chief Nursing Officer

Field Memorial Community Hospital 610.645.5221
 27 Greenfield Ave, Centreville, MS 19003
 Tom Brandi, Owner

Forrest General Hospital 601.288.7000
 6051 US Hwy 49, Hattiesburg, MS 39402
 Evan Dillard, President

Garden Park Medical Center 228.575.7000
 15200 Community Rd, Gulfport, MS 39503
 Brenda Waltz, Chief Executive Officer

General Hospital 601.876.2122
 100 Hospital Dr, Tylertown, MS 39667
 Jimmy Grey, Administrator

General Hospital 601.663.1200
 1001 Holland Ave, Philadelphia, MS 39350
 Lonnie Gilber, Chief Executive Officer

Gilmore Memorial Regional Med Ctr 662.256.7111
 1105 Earl Frye Blvd, Amory, MS 38821
 Duanne Blaylock, Chief Executive Officer

Grenada Lake Medical Center 662.227.7000
 960 Avent Dr, Grenada, MS 38901
 Charles Benteon, Chief Executive Officer

H C Watkins Memorial Hospital 601.776.6925
 605 S Archusa Ave, Quitman, MS 39355
 Clinton Eaves, Chief Executive Officer

Hancock Medical Center 228.467.8600
 149 Drinkwater Blvd, Bay Saint Louis, MS 39521
 Hal Lestwisch, Chief Executive Officer

Hardy Wilson Memorial Hospital 601.894.4541
 233 Magnolia St, Hazlehurst, MS 39083
 Larry Walker, Administrator

Hospital & Clinics 662.834.1321
 239 Bowling Green Rd, Lexington, MS 39095
 Cew Montegomery, Chief Operating Officer

Jeff Anderson Regional Medical Center 601.553.6000
 2124 14th St, Meridian, MS 39301

Kilmichael Hospital 662.262.4311
 301 Lamar Ave, Kilmichael, MS 39747
 Donna Harper, Human Resource Manager

King's Daughters Medical Center 601.833.6011
Web ....www.kdmc.org
 427 Hwy 51 N, Brookhaven, MS 39601
 Alvin Hoover, Chief Executive Officer

Laird Hospital 601.774.8214
 25117 Hwy 15, Union, MS 39365
 Tommy Barlett, Director

Madison Regional Medical Center 601.855.4111
E-mail ....glen.silverman@hma.com
 161 RIVER OAKS DR, Canton, MS 39046
 Glen Silverman, Chief Executive Officer

Magee General Hospital 601.849.5070
 300 Third Ave SE, Magee, MS 39111

Magnolia Regional Health Care 662.293.1000
 611 Alcorn Dr, Corinth, MS 38834
 Rick Napper, Chief Executive Officer

Marion General Hospital 601.736.6303
 1560 Sumrall Rd, Columbia, MS 39429
 Jerry Howell, Administrator

Memorial Hospital 601.384.5801
 40 Union Church Rd, Meadville, MS 39653

Mississippi Baptist Medical Center 601.968.1000
 1225 N State St, Jackson, MS 39202
 Kurt Metnzer, Chief Executive Officer

Montfort Jones Memorial Hospital 662.289.4311
 220 Hwy 12 W, Kosciusko, MS 39090
 John Dawson, Executive Director

N Mississippi Med Ctr West Point **662.495.2300**
835 Medical Center Dr, West Point, MS 39773

N Mississippi Medical Center Eupora **662.258.6221**
70 Medical Plaza, Eupora, MS 39744
Bob Jones, Director

Natchez Community Hospital **610.445.6200**
129 Jefferson Davis Blvd, Natchez, MS 39120

North Mississippi Medical Center **662.377.3000**
830 S Gloster St, Tupelo, MS 38801

North Mississippi Medical Center Iuka **662.423.6051**
1777 Curtis Dr, Iuka, MS 38852
Fred Truesdale, Administrator

North Oak Regional Medical Center **662.562.3100**
401 Getwell Dr, Senatobia, MS 38668
Sonya Graham, Director

Northwest Mississippi Regional Med Ctr **662.627.3211**
1970 Hospital Dr, Clarksdale, MS 38614
John Strayham, Chief Executive Officer

Noxubee General Hospital **662.726.4231**
606 N Jefferson St, Macon, MS 39341
Danny McKay, Administrator

Patient's Choice Med Ctr Claiborne Coun **601.437.5141**
123 McComb Ave, Port Gibson, MS 39150

Patient's Choice Medical Center **662.247.3831**
500 CCC Rd, Belzoni, MS 39038
Paula Lang, Administrator

River Oaks Hospital **601.932.1030**
1030 River Oaks Dr, Flowood, MS 39232

Rush Foundation Hospital **601.483.0011**
1314 19th Ave, Meridian, MS 39301
Wallace Strickland, Chief Executive Officer

S E Lackey Memorial Hospital **601.469.4151**
330 Broad St, Forest, MS 39074
Donna Riser, Chief Executive Officer

Singing River Hospital **228.809.5000**
Web ....www.mysrh.com
2809 Denny Ave, Pascagoula, MS 39581
Mike Crews, Director

South Central Regional Medical Center **610.426.4000**
1220 Jefferson St, Laurel, MS 39440

St Dominic-Jackson Memorial Hospital **601.200.2000**
969 Lakeland Dr, Jackson, MS 39216
Claud Harbarger, President

Trace Regional Hospital **662.456.3700**
Hwy 8 East, Houston, MS 38851
Gary Staten, Chief Executive Officer

Tri-Lakes Medical Center **662.563.5611**
303 Medical Center Dr, Batesville, MS 38606
Vince Brummett, Chief Executive Officer

University of Mississippi Health Care **601.984.1000**
2500 N State St, Jackson, MS 39216

Wayne General Hospital **601.735.5151**
950 Matthew Dr, Waynesboro, MS 39367
Donald Hemeter, Chief Executive Officer

Wesley Medical Center **610.268.8000**
5001 Hardy St, Hattiesburg, MS 39402

Winston Medical Center **662.773.6211**
562 E Main St, Louisville, MS 39339
Lee McCall, Administrative Assistant

CRISIS & SHELTER CARE

Care Lodge Domestic Violence Shelter **601.482.8719**
Fax 601.482.8718
Web ....www.carelodge.com
E-mail ....carelodge@aol.com
1715 23Rd Ave, Meridian, MS 39301
Leslie Payne, Executive Director

Christians In Action **601.346.7119**
Fax 601.346.7059
PO Box 7676, Jackson, MS 39284-7676
Janice Wilder, Executive Director

Domestic Abuse Family Shelter Inc. **601.428.1707**
Fax 601.428.3180
E-mail ....dafss@bellsouth.net
PO Box 273, Laurel, MS 39441-0273
Becky Sims, Director

Domestic Violence Ctr Crisis Hotline/Catholic
Svcs **601.366.0222**
Fax 601.362.8223
E-mail ....gwen.haynes@catholiccharitiesjackson.org
200 N Congress St Ste 100, Jackson, MS 39201
Gwen Bouie-haynes, Project Director

Domestic Violence Project, Inc **662.234.5085**
Fax 662.236.4708
1298 N Lamar Blvd, Oxford, MS 38655
Talunja Eskridge, Director

Gulf Coast Women's Ctr **228.436.3809**
Fax 228.435.0513
E-mail ....smorrison@gcwcfn.org
PO Box 333, Biloxi, MS 39533-0333
Sandra Morrison, Director

Haven House Family Shelter-Domestic
Violence **601.638.0021**
Fax 601.638.0021
E-mail ....havenhl@bellsouth.net
PO Box 57, Vicksburg, MS 39181-0057
Scottie Kiihnl, Director

New Beginnings **662.842.6752**
Fax 662.840.7176
2164 Southridge Dr, Tupelo, MS 38801
Tom Velie, Executive Director

North Mississippi Regional Ctr **662.234.1476**
Fax 662.234.1699
Web ....www.nmrc.state.ms.us
E-mail ....jjohnson@nmrc.state.ms.us
967 Regional Center Dr, Oxford, MS 38655-3551
Eric Dahl, Md, Medical Director

EDUCATION

Mississippi Youth/Challenge Academy **601.558.2324**
Fax 601.558.2400
Web ....www.ms.youthchallenge.org
Bldg 80, Camp Shelby, MS 39407
Earnest Shows, Director

FOSTER CARE AGENCIES

Mississippi Div of Family & Children Ser **662.226.1990**
Fax 662.226.1432
PO Box 945, Grenada, MS 38902
Judy Mclain, Director

Mississippi Div of Family & Children Svc **601.876.3238**
Fax 601.876.6978
PO Box 430, Tylertown, MS 39667
Conya Rogillio, Regional Director

Mississippi Div of Family & Children Svc **662.841.9737**
Fax 662.860.6085
320 S Industrial Rd, Tupelo, MS 38801
Tracy Milone, Director

Mississippi Div of Family & Children Svc **662.323.1573**
Fax 662.323.5862
213 Yeates, Starkville, MS 39760
Angela Nichols, Supervisor

Mississippi Div of Family & Children Svc **601.364.7447**
Fax 601.364.7441
4777 Madar Blvd, Jackson, MS 39213
Maggie Mixoen, Regional Director

Mississippi Div of Family & Children Svc **601.554.4354**
Fax 601.554.4370
1604 W Pine St, PO Box 16209, Hattiesburg,
MS 39403
Jolie Kerenick, Director

Mississippi Div of Family & Children Svs **228.897.5790**
Fax 228.897.5782
10260 Larkin Smith Dr, Gulfport, MS 39503
Teresa Kemp, Chief Executive Officer

Mississippi Foster & Adoptive Parent **601.776.5433**
PO Box 277, Quitman, MS 39355
Becky Watkins

Pine Belt Seedling Support Group **601.606.5064**
1505 Bethel Church Rd, Bassfield, MS 39421
Liz Darver, Director

Southern Christian Svcs/Chldrn & Yth HHA **662.680.9191**
Fax 662.680.9196
E-mail ....hardenad@comcast.net
1800 N Gloster St, Ste A, Tupelo, MS 38804
Patricia Digby, Director

SW Mississippi Foster & Adoptive Parent **601.876.6978**
901- Union Rd, Tylertown, MS 39667

SOCIAL SERVICES

Bethany Christian Svcs **662.327.6740**
Fax 662.327.6533
Web ....www.bethany.org/mississippi
E-mail ....bcscolumbus@bethany.org
116 Lawrence Dr Ste 3, Columbus, MS 39702-5324
Vicki L. Kimbrell, Director

Big Brothers/Big Sisters **601.961.9286**
Fax 601.961.9288
Web ....www.bbbsms.org
E-mail ....www.bbbsms.org
175 E Capitol St Ste 222, Jackson, MS 39201
Joel Waters, Director

Catholic Charities, Inc. **601.355.8634**
Fax 601.960.8493
Web ....www.catholiccharitiesjackson.org
200 N. Congress Street, Suite 100, Jackson,
MS 39201
COA accredited organization.

Children's Defense Fund **601.321.1966**
Fax 601.321.8736
2659 Livingston Rd Ste 200, Jackson, MS 39213
Oleta Fitzgerald, Director

Choose Life **601.206.5816**
Fax 601.427.2339
577 Highway 51 Ste B, Ridgeland, MS 39157-2593
Mike Powell, Director

Ctr for The Prevention of Child Abuse **228.868.8686**
Fax 228.868.8670
Web ....www.msapc.com
E-mail ....tbrinkley@capc.com
2315 17th St Rm 2, Gulfport, MS 39501-2982
Tammy Brinkley, Executive Director

Dream, Developing Resources for Education In
America **601.933.9199**
Fax 601.933.1138
E-mail ....gcrump@dreaminc.org
310 Airport Rd S, Pearl, MS 39208-6649
Glenda Crump, President/CEO

Family First Resource Ctr **601.445.7979**
Fax 601.304.8012
E-mail ....youthco@bellsouth.net
320 State St, Natchez, MS 39120-3473
Marykay Doherty, Chief Financial Officer

Family Resource Ctr **662.844.0013**
Fax 662.844.0560
Web ....www.thefamilyresourcecenterofnems.org
E-mail ....cwebb2@bellsouth.net
425 Magazine St, Tupelo, MS 38804-4733
Christi Web, Director

Mississippi Children's Advocacy Ctr, Inc. 601.969.7111
Fax 601.352.5960
Web ....www.ucmail.com
E-mail ....cdixon@ucmail.com
753 N President St, Jackson, MS 39202-3002
Brenda Luster, Executive Director

North East Mississippi Child Care Resource and Referral
EMCC 662.243.2671
Fax 662.243.2691
Web ....www.msyoucares.com
E-mail ....delfiw@ext.msstate.edu
8731 S. Frontage Rd, Mayhew, MS 39753
Yvonne Shumpert, Onsite Coordinator

SPECIAL NEEDS

Brain Injury Association 601.981.1021
E-mail ....info@msbia.org
PO Box 55912, Jackson, MS 39296
Lai Jenkine, Executive Director

Central Mississippi Autism Support Group 601.594.9314
Fax 601.849.3981
E-mail ....pkdollar@bellsouth.net
149 Dry Creek Rd, Magee, MS 39111-8796
Pam Dollar, Director

Children's Rehabilitation Services 601.984.2940
Fax 601.984.2926
Web ....http://crs.umc.edu
2500 North State Street, Jackson, MS 39216
CARF accredited programs available.

CMDSS 601.397.3696
E-mail ....info@cmdss.org
PO Box 2189, Brandon, MS 39043
Bill Pittman, President

Colation for Citizens with Disabilities 601.969.0601
E-mail ....mspti@mscoalition.com
2 Old River Pl Ste A, Jackson, MS 39202
Mary Troupe, President

Congress of Parents & Teachers Inc 601.352.7383
E-mail ....ms_office@pta.org
PO Box 1937, Jackson, MS 39215

Empower Community Resource Center 662.332.4852
E-mail ....empower@suddenlinkmail.com
2357 Paradise Line, Greenville, MS 38701
Agnes Johnson, Executive Director

Epilepsy Foundation of Mississippi 601.936.5222
E-mail ....tresmsepilepsy@bellsouth.net
2001 Airport Rd Ste 307, Flowood, MS 39232
Tres Townsend, Executive Director

Memorial Hospital at Gulfport, Inpatient Rehabilitation
Unit 228.867.4000
Fax 228.867.5357
Web ....www.gulfportmemorial.com
E-mail ....asteiner@mhg.com
4500 13th St, Gulfport, MS 39502
Amy Steiner, Director Clinical Support Services
CARF accredited programs available.

Mental Health Association 228.864.6274
E-mail ....mhagptms@aol.com
4803 Harrison Cir, Gulfport, MS 39507
Kay Denault, Executive Director

Methodist Rehabilitation Center 601.364.3462
Fax 601.364.3371
Web ....www.methodistonline.org
1350 East Woodrow Wilson Drive, Jackson,
MS 39216
CARF accredited programs available.

MS PTI 601.869.0601
Fax 601.709.0250
E-mail ....mspti@mscoalition.com
5 Old River Pl Ste 101, Jackson, MS 39202

NAMI Mississippi 601.899.9058
E-mail ....namimiss1@aol.com
411 Briarwood Dr, Ste 401, Jackson, MS 39206
Tonya Tate, Executive Director

Parents of Public Schools of Jackson 601.969.6015
E-mail ....annyoung@parents4publicschools.org
200 N Congress St Ste 500, Jackson, MS 39201
Ann Young, Program Coordinator

Safe Kids Mississippi 601.360.0531
E-mail ....mssafekids@bellsouth.net
1304 Vine St, Jackson, MS 39202

Speech-Language-Hearing Association 800.664.6742
E-mail ....mshahelp@mshausa.org
PO Box 22664, Jackson, MS 39225
Deirdre Mcgowan, Executive Director

TEAAM 866.993.2437
E-mail ....takeaction@teaam.org
PO Box 37, Mize, MS 39116

The Arc of Mississippi 601.982.1180
E-mail ....matt@arcms.org
7 Lakeland Cir Ste 600, Jackson, MS 39216
Matt Nalker, Director

University Rehabilitation Center 601.815.3050
Fax 601.815.5845
Web ....http://rehab.umc.edu
777 Lakeland Drive, Jackson, MS 39216
CARF accredited programs available.

Missouri

Missouri

www.mo.gov

Missouri

Jay Nixon, Governor
PO Box 720
Jefferson City, MO 65102
573.751.3222
573.751.1588 (Fax)
www.gov.mo.gov

Vicky Scott, Juvenile Justice Specialist
Dept. of Public Safety
PO Box 749
Jefferson City, MO 65102
573.751.2179
573.751.5399 (Fax)
vicky.scott@dps.mo.gov

Ed Morris, SAG Chair
307 West Route F
Clark, MO 65243
573.687.3713
morrisef@missouri.edu

CRISIS NUMBERS

Child Abuse Reporting . . .573.751.3448

STATE SERVICES

SOCIAL SERVICES

Child Care Licensing Office MO 573.751.2450
Fax 573.526.5345
3418 Knipp Dr Ste F, Jefferson City, MO 65102
Angela Tordoff, Director

Children's Div 573.522.8024
Fax 573.526.3971
Web . . . . .www.dss.mo.gov/cd
615 Howerton Ct, Jefferson City, MO 65109
Candace Shively, Director

Food Stamp Issuance 573.751.3178
Fax 573.522.4333
Web . . . . .www.state.mo.us
E-mail . . . . .rmorris@mail.state.mo.us
PO Box 2320, Jefferson City, MO 65102-2320
Rachel Morris, Assistant Deputy Director

Interstate Compact 573.751.2981
Fax 573.522.2199
E-mail . . . . .mary.c.kliethermes@dss.mo.gov
615 Howerton Ct, Jefferson City, MO 65109
Mary Kay Kliethermes, Coordinator

Missouri Emergency Management Agency 573.526.9100
Fax 573.634.7966
E-mail .paulparmenter@sema.dps.mo.gov
2302 Militia Dr, Jefferson City, MO 65102
Paul Parmenter, Director

GENERAL HEALTH SERVICES

Ctr for Local Public Health Svcs 573.526.0177
Fax 573.751.5350
Web . . . . .www.dhss.mo.gov
E-mail . . . . .anne.lock@dhss.mo.gov
920 Wildwood Dr, Jefferson City, MO 65102-0570
Annie Lock, Director

Division of Com & Public Health MO 573.751.6253
Fax 573.751.6185
E-mail . . . . .info@health.mo.gov
930 Wildwood, Jefferson City, MO 65102
Cindy Wilkinson, Administrator

Ofc of Medicaid 573.751.6922
Fax 573.751.6564
Web . . . . .www.dss.mo.gov
615 Howerton Court, Jefferson City, MO 65102
Ian Mccaslin, Director

MENTAL HEALTH SERVICES

**Div of Mental Retardation and Developemental
Disabilities** 573.751.4054
Fax 573.751.9207
Web . . . . .www.dmh.mo.gov
E-mail . . . . .bernard.simons@dmh.mo.gov
1706 E Elm St, Jefferson City, MO 65101-4130
Bernard Simons, Director

Div of Vocational Rehab MO 573.751.3251
Fax 573.751.1441
E-mail . . . . .patsy.helmig@vr.dese.mo.gov
3024 Dupont Circle, Jefferson City, MO 65109
Tiomthy Gaines, Director

Div of Vocational Rehabilitation 573.751.3251
Fax 573.751.1441
Web . . . . .www.vr.dese.state.mo.us
E-mail .jeanne.loyd@vrdese.mo.us
3024 Dupont Cir, Jefferson City, MO 65109-6188
Jeanne Loyd, Phd, Assistant Commissioner

Rehab Svcs for the Blind MO 573.751.4249
Fax 573.751.4984
E-mail . . . . .Mark.Laird@dss.mo.gov
615 Howerton Court, Jefferson City, MO 65109
Mark Laird, Director

Rehabilitation Svcs for the Blind 573.751.4249
Fax 573.751.4984
615 Howerton Ct, Jefferson City, MO 65109-6806
Mark Laird, Deputy Director

JUSTICE AGENCY

Attorney General's Ofc .573.751.3321
Fax 573.751.0774
Web . . . . .www.ago.mo.gov
E-mail . . . . .chris.koster@mail.ago.state.mo.us
207 W High St, Jefferson City, MO 65101
Chris Koster, Attorney General

Crime Victims Compensation 573.526.6006
Fax 573.526.4940
Web . . . . .www.dps.mo.gov
E-mail .susan.sudduth@dps.mo.gov
301 W High St, Jefferson City, MO 65102
Susan Suddeth, Program Manager

Ctr for Emergency Response and Terrorism 573.526.4768
Fax 573.522.8636
Web . . . . .www.dhss.mo.gov
E-mail .melissa.frier@health.mo.gov
912 Wildwood Dr, Jefferson City, MO 65109-5796
Melissa Frier, Director

Dept of Corrections

Dept of Corrections 573.751.2389
Fax 573.751.4099
Web . . . . .www.dss.state.mo.us
E-mail . . . . .george.lombardi@doc.mo.gov
2729 Plaza Dr, Jefferson City, MO 65109
George Lombardi, Director

Dept of Social Svcs Div of Youth Svcs 573.751.3324
Fax 573.526.4494
Web . . . . .www.dss.state.mo.us
E-mail . . . . .bill.heberly@dss.mo.gov
3418 Knipp Suite A-1, Jefferson City,
MO 65102-0447
Bill Heberly, Interim Director

Div of Offender Rehab Srvs Educ MO 573.526.6534
Fax 573.526.3009
E-mail . . . . .tony.spillers@doc.mo.gov
1717 Industrial Dr, PO Box 236, Jefferson City,
MO 65102
Tony Spillers, Director

Missouri Dept of Public Safety 573.751.4905
Fax 573.751.5399
301 W. High Street, Room 870, Jefferson City,
MO 65102
John Britt, Director

Missouri State Public Defender System 573.526.5210
Fax 573.526.5213
Web . . . . .www.mspd.mo.gov
E-mail . . . . .cat.kelly@mspd.mo.gov
231 E Capitol Ave, Jefferson City, MO 65101-3001
Cat Kelly, Director

COURTS

37th Judicial Circuit 573.226.3315
Fax 573.226.5321
E-mail . . . . .melany.williams@courts.mo.gov
113 Main St., Eminence, MO 65466
Melany D. Williams, Circuit Clerk

State Court Admin 573.751.4377
Fax 573.522.6152
Web . . . . .www.courts.mo.gov
E-mail . . . . .greg.linhares@courts.mo.gov
2112 Industrial Dr, Jefferson City, MO 65109-0952
Greg Linhares, Administrator

POLICE AND SHERIFF

Missouri Police Chiefs' Assoc 573.636.5444
Fax 573.363.6634
Web . . . . .www.mopca.com
E-mail . . . . .slineback@mopca.com
1001 E High St, Jefferson City, MO 65101
Sheldon Lineback, Executive Director

Missouri State Highway Patrol 573.526.6153
Fax 573.751.9382
E-mail ....tim.mcgrail@mshp.dps.mo.gov
  1510 E Elm St, Jefferson City, MO 65101
  Cpt. Timothy P. Mcgrail, Director

Sheriff's Ofc 573.767.5311
Fax 573.767.5412
E-mail ....lcso@marktwain.net
  107 S Washington St, Monticello, MO 63457-1000
  David T. Parrish, Sheriff

EDUCATION SERVICES

Div of Special Education 573.522.8762
Fax 573.526.4404
E-mail ....webreplyspe@dese.mo.gov
  205 Jefferson St, Jefferson City, MO 65102
  Steven Barr, Assistant Commissioner

Div of Special Education MO 573.751.5739
Fax 573.526.4404
E-mail ....lina.browner@dese.mo.gov
  205 Jefferson St, PO Box 480, Jefferson City,
  MO 65102
  Dr. Steven Barr, Administrative Commisioner

Educ for Homeless Children and Youth MO 573.526.3232
Fax 573.526.6698
E-mail ....donna.cash@dse.mo.gov
  PO Box 480, Jefferson City, MO 65102
  Donna Cash, Coordinator For Homeless And Youth

Missouri Dept of Elem & Second Eduction 573.751.4212
Fax 573.751.8613
E-mail ....pubinfo@dese.mo.gov
  205 Jefferson St, Jefferson City, MO 65102
  Dr. Chris Nicastro, Commissioner Of Education

Missouri Parents Act 816.531.7070
Fax 816.531.4777
E-mail ....info@ptimpatt.org
  8301 State Line Rd Ste 204, Kansas City, MO 64114
  Marykay Savage, Director

Missouri School for the Blind 314.776.4320
Fax 314.776.1875
  3815 Magnolia Ave, Saint Louis, MO 63110
  Patricia Yocum, Superintendent

Missouri School for the Deaf 573.592.4000
Fax 573.592.2570
Web www.msd.k12.mo.us
  505 E 5th St, Fulton, MO 65251
  Barbara Garrison, Superintendent

COUNTY SERVICES

Adair County

SOCIAL SERVICES

**Family Support/Children's Div/Senior
Svcs** 660.785.2440
Fax 660.785.2591
Web ....www.dss.mo.gov
E-mail ....michelle.curry@dss.mo.gov
  1612 N Osteopathy, Kirksville, MO 63501-2344
  Michelle Curry, Circuit Manager

GENERAL HEALTH SERVICES

Health Dept 660.665.8491
Fax 660.665.2913
E-mail ....LEBARJ@LPHA.MOPUBLIC.ORG
  1001 S Jamison St, Kirksville, MO 63501
  Jim Lebaron, Administrator

JUSTICE AGENCY

2nd Judicial Circuit Juvenile Ofc 660.665.4224
Fax 660.665.2968
E-mail ....matt.holt@courts.mo.gov
  1400 S Boundary St, Kirksville, MO 63501
  Matt Holt, Juvenile Service Administrator

COURTS

Circuit Clerk Ofc 660.665.2552
Fax 660.665.3420
Web ....www.courts.mo.gov
E-mail ....ldecker@courts.mo.gov
  106 W Washington St, Rm 3, Kirksville,
  MO 63501-2889
  Linda Decker, Clerk

POLICE AND SHERIFF

Sheriff's Ofc 660.665.4644
Fax 660.785.3219
E-mail ....rhardwick@adaircoso.com
  215 N Franklin St, Kirksville, MO 63501-2916
  Robert Hardwick, Sheriff

Andrew County

GENERAL HEALTH SERVICES

Health Dept 816.324.3139
Fax 816.324.6002
Web ....www.andrewcountyhealth.com
E-mail ....COULDW@LPHA.MOPUBLIC.ORG
  106 N 5th St, Savannah, MO 64485
  William Couldry, Director

POLICE AND SHERIFF

Sheriff's Ofc 816.324.3511
Fax 816.324.5110
E-mail ....bryanatkins@andrewcounty.org
  402 W Market St, Savannah, MO 64485
  Bryan Atkins, Sheriff

Atchison County

SOCIAL SERVICES

**Family Support/Children's Div/Senior
Svcs** 660.744.5317
Fax 660.744.6482
  101 Grant St, Rock Port, MO 64482
  Lesoie Riney, Superviser

GENERAL HEALTH SERVICES

Health Dept 660.736.4121
Fax 660.736.5533
Web ....www.lpha.dhss.mo.gov
E-mail ....blacke@lpha.dhss.mo.gov
  421 Main St, Tarkio, MO 64491-1544
  Eleanor Blackney, Rn, Administrator

COURTS

4th Judicial Circuit 660.744.2707
Fax 660.744.6100
Web ....www.courts.mo.gov
  400 S Washington St, Rock Port, MO 64482
  Corey K. Herron, Judge

POLICE AND SHERIFF

Sheriff's Ofc 660.744.6271
Fax 660.744.6274
E-mail ....amail@rpt.coop
  511 W Clay St, Rock Port, MO 64482
  Dennis D. Martin, Sheriff

EDUCATION SERVICES

Head Start Ctr 660.744.2616
Fax 660.744.2615
  16635 US Hwy 136, Rock Port, MO 64482
  Patty Clark, Director

Audrain County

SOCIAL SERVICES

**Family Support/Children's Div/Senior
Svcs** 573.581.3312
Fax 573.581.8001
  3626 S Clark St # A, Mexico, MO 65265
  Kelly Kuda, Circuit Manager

GENERAL HEALTH SERVICES

Health Dept 573.581.1332
Fax 573.581.6652
Web ....www.acchu.org
  605 E Promenade St, Mexico, MO 65265
  Kevin Lawrence, Administrator

POLICE AND SHERIFF

Sheriff's Ofc 573.473.5800
Fax 573.473.5856
Web ....www.audrainsheriff.com
  1100 Littleby Rd, Mexico, MO 65265-6339
  Stuart D. Miller, Sheriff

EDUCATION SERVICES

Audrain Head Start 573.581.1066
Fax 573.582.7701
E-mail ....robyn-higgins@showmeaction.org
  400 Lakeview Rd, Mexico, MO 65265-2362
  Robin Higgins, Counselor

Barry County

GENERAL HEALTH SERVICES

Health Dept 417.847.2114
Fax 417.847.2116
Web ....www.barrycountyhealth.org
E-mail ....brockr@lpha.mopublic.org
  65 Main St, Cassville, MO 65625-9400
  Roger Brock, Director

MENTAL HEALTH SERVICES

**Clark Community Mental Health
Ctr** 417.235.6610
Fax 417.235.8609
Web ....http://www.clarkmentalhealth.com/
E-mail ....comptonf@clarkmentalhealth.com
  1701 N central st, pierce, MO 65708-2316
  Frank Compton, Executive Director

COURTS

39th Judicial Circuit- Juvenile 417.235.6245
Fax 417.235.6254
Web ....www.courts.mo.gov
E-mail ....craig.williams@courts.mo.gov
  102 E Dunn St, Monett, MO 65708-2002
  Keith Parris, Chief Officer

EDUCATION SERVICES

Butterfield Head Start 417.442.7616
Fax 417.442.7616
  Hwy W 9793, Cassville, MO 65625
  Vonna Farris, Lead Teacher/Director

Cassville Head Start I 417.847.2680
Fax 417.847.2680
E-mail ....cassville1@oacac-caa.org
95 Smithson Dr, Cassville, MO 65625-9429
Jerry Dyer, Director

Barton County

SOCIAL SERVICES

Family Support/Children's Div/Senior

Svcs **417.682.3531**
Fax 417.682.6669
Web ....www.dss.mo.gov
E-mail ....chris.j.tannlund@dss.mo.gov
501 W 13th St, Lamar, MO 64759-1775
Chris Tannlund, Director

GENERAL HEALTH SERVICES

Health Dept **417.682.3363**
Fax 417.682.5548
Web ....www.bchdhealth.com
1301 E 12th St, Lamar, MO 64759-2182
Linda Talbott, Director

COURTS

28th Judicial Circuit **417.682.5754**
Fax 417.682.2960
E-mail ....janet.maupin@courts.mo.gov
1004 Gulf St, Lamar, MO 64759
Honorable Charles Curless, Judge

POLICE AND SHERIFF

Sheriff's Ofc **417.682.5541**
Fax 417.682.5805
Web ....www.cji.net
E-mail ....bartoncosd@cji.net
1010 Cherry St, Lamar, MO 64759-1435
Mitchel Shaw, Sheriff

Bates County

SOCIAL SERVICES

Family Support/Children's Div/ **660.679.3174**
Fax 660.679.3894
Web ....www.dss.mo.gov
4 W Ohio St, Butler, MO 64730-2019
Chris Tannlund, County Manager

GENERAL HEALTH SERVICES

Health Dept **660.679.6108**
Fax 660.679.6022
Web ....www.lpha.dhss.mo.gov
E-mail ....welstonj@lpha.dhss.mo.gov
501 N Orange St, Butler, MO 64730-1325
Jody Welston, Director

JUSTICE AGENCY

Juvenile Ofc **660.679.4434**
Fax 660.679.5119
E-mail ....deborah_powell@osca.state.mo.us
1 N Delaware Street, # 3, Butler, MO 64730
Debbie Powell, Deputy Juvenile Officer

COURTS

27th Judicial Circuit **660.679.5171**
Fax 660.679.4446
Web ....www.osca.state.mo.us
E-mail ....debra.hopkins@courts.mo.gov
1 N Delaware St, Butler, MO 64730
Honorable Debra Hopkins, Director

POLICE AND SHERIFF

Sheriff's Ofc **660.679.3232**
Fax 660.679.4147
Web ....www.batescounty.net/
6 W Fort Scott St, Butler, MO 64730-2018
Chad Anderson, Sheriff

EDUCATION SERVICES

Butler Head Start **660.679.5046**
Fax 660.679.5046
225 N Main St, Butler, MO 64730
Judy Moles, Director

Benton County

SOCIAL SERVICES

Family Support/Children's Div/Senior

Svcs **660.438.7357**
Fax 660.438.7997
E-mail ....marshal@dss.mo.gov
1661 Hilltop Dr., Warsaw, MO 65355
Marsha Dinkins, Director

GENERAL HEALTH SERVICES

Health Dept **660.438.2876**
Fax 660.438.5746
1238 Commercial St, Warsaw, MO 65355
Linda Viebrock, Administrator

JUSTICE AGENCY

Juvenile Ofc **660.438.9550**
Fax 660.438.4098
Web ....www.courts.mo.gov
E-mail ....brad.turner@courts.mo.gov
100 West Washington Street, Warsaw, MO 65360
Brad Turner, Chief Deputy Juvenile Officer

COURTS

30th Judicial Circuit **660.438.7712**
Fax 660.438.5755
Circuit Courthouse, Warsaw, MO 65355
Honorable John W. Sims, Circuit Judge

POLICE AND SHERIFF

Sheriff's Ofc **660.438.5252**
Fax 660.438.3053
Web ....www.co.taney.mo.us
E-mail ....ricks@co.taney.mo.us
174 W. Washington St., Warsaw, MO 65355
Rick Sajen, Sheriff

Bollinger County

SOCIAL SERVICES

Family Support Div/Children and Senior

Svcs **573.238.2624**
Fax 573.238.4853
E-mail ....sherri.morris@dss.mo.gov
602 Highway 34 W, Marble Hill, MO 63764
Sherri Morris, County Manager

GENERAL HEALTH SERVICES

Health Dept **573.238.2817**
Fax 573.238.3085
Web ....www.bollingercountyhealth.org
E-mail ....piepeb@lpha.mopublic.org
107 Highway 51 N, Marble Hill, MO 63764
Beverly Piepenbrock, Administrator

POLICE AND SHERIFF

Sheriff's Ofc **573.238.2633**
Fax 573.238.3095
202 High St, Marble Hill, MO 63764-9136
Leo McElrath, Sheriff

Boone County

SOCIAL SERVICES

Family Support/Children's Div **573.882.9180**
Fax 573.884.5110
1500 Vandiver Dr Ste 103, Columbia, MO 65202
Michelle Oberlag, Circuit Manager

Youth Svcs 573.449.2939
Fax 573.449.8766
1240 E Brown School Rd, Northeast Regional Office,
Columbia, MO 65202
Larry Strecker, Regional Administrator

GENERAL HEALTH SERVICES

Columbia Area Health Ofc **573.882.9861**
Fax 573.882.6713
Web ....www.dhss.net
1500 Vandiver Dr Ste 112, Columbia,
MO 65202-3932
Tracy Marshal, Child Care Manager

JUSTICE AGENCY

Juvenile Ofc **573.886.4200**
Fax 573.886.4030
705 E Walnut, Columbia, MO 65201
Rick Gaines, Juvenile Officer

COURTS

13th Circuit Court **573.886.4050**
Fax 573.886.4070
705 E Walnut St Stop 6, Columbia, MO 65201
Gary Oxenhandler, Presiding Judge

POLICE AND SHERIFF

Sheriffs Ofc **573.875.1111**
Fax 573.874.8953
Web ....www.showmeboone.com/sheriff
E-mail ....dcarey@boonecountymo.org
2121 E County Dr, Columbia, MO 65202
Dwayne Carey, Sheriff

Buchanan County

GENERAL HEALTH SERVICES

City Of St Joseph Health Dept **816.271.4636**
Fax 816.271.4764
Web ....www.stjoemo.info/health
E-mail ....dbradley@ci.st-joseph.mo.us
904 S 10th St, Saint Joseph, MO 64503-2405
Debra Bradley, Director

COURTS

5th Judicial Circuit **816.271.1462**
Fax 816.271.1538
Web ....www.courts.mo.gov
E-mail ....daniel.kellogg@courts.mo.gov
411 Jules St Ste 331, Saint Joseph, MO 64501-1735
Honorable Daniel F. Kellogg, Judge

POLICE AND SHERIFF

Sheriff's Ofc **816.236.8812**
Fax 816.901.1758
Web ....www.buchanan.com
501 Faraon St Ste B, Saint Joseph, MO 64501-4101
Mike Strong, Sheriff

Butler County

SOCIAL SERVICES

Family Support/Children's Div/Senior

Svcs **573.840.9200**
Fax 573.840.9273
Web ....www.dss.mo.gov
E-mail ....dennis.french@dss.mo.gov
1903 Northwood Dr, Poplar Bluff, MO 63901-2425
Dennis French, Director

Youth Svcs **573.840.9540**
Fax 573.840.9387
Web ....www.dss.mo.gov
E-mail ....paula.k.shaw@dss.mo.gov
1903 Northwood Dr, Southeast Regional Offices,
Poplar Bluff, MO 63901-2425
Paula Shaw, Regional Administrator

GENERAL HEALTH SERVICES

Health Dept 573.785.8478
Fax 573.785.2825
Web ....www.butlercountyhealth.org
E-mail ....info@butlercountyhealth.org
1619 N Main St, Poplar Bluff, MO 63901-3499
Crystal Robinson, Hiv Coordinator

Southeastern District Health Ofc 573.840.9720
Fax 573.840.9727
E-mail ....elizabeth.harris@dhss.mo.gov
2875 James Blvd, Poplar Bluff, MO 63901
Elizabeth Harris, Regional Manager

JUSTICE AGENCY

Juvenile Ofc 573.686.8054
Fax 573.686.8451
Web ....www.courts.mo.gov
E-mail ....lesi.smith@courts.mo.gov
614 Lindsay Ave, Poplar Bluff, MO 63901-5231
Lesi Smith, Juvenile Officer

Sears Youth Ctr 573.840.9280
Fax 573.840.9352
Web ....www.seattlechildrenshome.org
9400 Sears Ln, Poplar Bluff, MO 63901-9716
Rick Stewart, Facility Manager

COURTS

36th Judicial Circuit 573.686.8082
Fax 573.686.8094
100 N Main St, Poplar Bluff, MO 63901
Honorable Michael Pritchett, Circuit Judge

POLICE AND SHERIFF

Sheriff's Ofc 573.686.8070
Fax 573.778.8016
E-mail ....bc390@bcsheriff.com
200 N Oak St, Poplar Bluff, MO 63901-5147
Mark Dobbs, Sheriff

EDUCATION SERVICES

Broseley Preschool and Daycare 573.328.4141
Fax 573.328.4141
9348 Hwy 51, Broseley, MO 63932
Monica Morgan, Director

Caldwell County

SOCIAL SERVICES

Family Support & Childrens Div 816.583.2166
Fax 816.583.4910
Web ....www.dbi.state.nv.us
E-mail ....kwebb@dbi.state.nv.us
400 W Berry St, Hamilton, MO 64644-1315
Carla L Webb, Director

GENERAL HEALTH SERVICES

Health Dept 816.586.2311
Fax 816.586.2603
Web ....www.lpha.mopublic.org
E-mail ....simss@lpha.mopublic.org
255 W Maine, Kingston, MO 64650
Shelly Sims, Administrator

POLICE AND SHERIFF

Sheriff's Ofc 816.586.2751
Fax 816.586.2103
E-mail ....sherrifsadmin@centurytel.net
54 N Franklin St, Ste 156, Kingston, MO 64650
Jerry Galloway, Sheriff

Callaway County

SOCIAL SERVICES

Children's Division 573.592.4090
Fax 573.592.4097
106 N Hospital Dr, Fulton, MO 65251
Marta Halter, Coordinator

GENERAL HEALTH SERVICES

Health Dept 573.642.6881
Fax 573.642.2098
E-mail ....lynchs@lpha.dhss.mo.gov
4950 County Rd 304, Fulton, MO 65251
Sharon Lynch, Director

JUSTICE AGENCY

Juvenile Ofc 573.642.7992
Fax 573.642.6036
500 Market St Ste 302, Fulton, MO 65251
Rick Gaines, Juvenile Officer

COURTS

13th Judicial Circuit 573.642.0780
Fax 573.642.0700
E-mail ....judy.groner@courts.mo.gov
10 E 5th St Rm 12, Fulton, MO 65251
Judy Groner, Circuit Clerk

POLICE AND SHERIFF

Sheriff's Ofc 573.642.7291
Fax 573.592.2440
1201 State Road O, Fulton, MO 65251
Dennis L. Crane, Sheriff

Camden County

SOCIAL SERVICES

Family Support/Children's Div/Senior
Svcs 573.346.3363
Fax 573.346.0382
Web ....www.dss.mo.gov
E-mail ....donna.farris@dss.mo.gov
146 Rodeo Rd, Camdenton, MO 65020-9378
Donna Farris, Medicaid Director

GENERAL HEALTH SERVICES

Health Dept 573.346.5479
Web ....www.camdenmo.org
1976 N State Highway 5, Camdenton,
MO 65020-2612
Linnie Lee, Hiv Coordinator

JUSTICE AGENCY

Juvenile Ofc 573.317.0099
Fax 573.346.9682
Web ....www.courts.mo.gov
E-mail ....tammy.walden@courts.mo.gov
1180 W Highway 54, Camdenton, MO 65020-0440
Tammy Lea Walden, Juvenile Officer

COURTS

26th Judicial Circuit 573.346.4440
Fax 573.346.5422
Web ....www.camden.mo.org
E-mail ....bruce_coyler@camden.mo.org
1 Courthouse Circle, Suite 8, Camdenton, MO 65020
Bruce Coyler, Associate Judge

POLICE AND SHERIFF

Sheriff's Dept 573.346.2243
Fax 573.346.2063
E-mail ....sheriff@dam.net
1 Court Cir, Suite 13, Camdenton, MO 65020
Dwight Franklin, Sheriff

Cape Girardeau County

GENERAL HEALTH SERVICES

Cape Girardeau Area Health Ofc 573.290.5830
Fax 573.290.5854
216 N Fountain, Cape Girardeau, MO 63701
Gary Harbison, Bureau Chief

Public Health Ctr 573.335.7846
Fax 573.335.5909
Web ....www.cgcohealthdept.com
E-mail ....craigc@lpha.mopublic.org
1121 Linden St, Cape Girardeau, MO 63703-7708
Charlotte Craig, Director

JUSTICE AGENCY

CASA of Southeast Missouri, Inc 573.335.1726
Fax 573.335.8407
E-mail ....pjenkins@capecasa.com
937 Broadway, Ste 201, Cape Girardeau, MO 63701
Linda Nash, Director

Juvenile Ofcs 573.334.6001
Fax 573.331.2989
E-mail ....randall.rhodes@courts.mo.gov
44 N Lorimier St Ste E, Cape Girardeau, MO 63701
Randall Rhodes, Chief Juvenile Officer

Missouri Div of Youth Svcs 573.290.5860
Fax 573.290.5869
E-mail ....anthony.pulliam@dss.mo.gov
609 N Middle St, Cape Girardeau, MO 63701-4840
Anthony Pulliam, Youth Facility Manager

COURTS

32nd Judicial Circuit 573.335.2802
Fax 573.331.2349
44 N Lorimier St Ste 2, Cape Girardeau,
MO 63701-7314
Honorable William L. Syler, Judge

POLICE AND SHERIFF

Police Dept 573.335.6621
Fax 573.335.8571
Web ....www.cityofcapegirardeau.org
E-mail ....ckinnison@cityofcapegirardeau.org
40 S Sprigg St, Cape Girardeau, MO 63703-6289
Carl Kinnison, Chief Of Police

Sheriff's Dept 573.243.3551
Fax 573.204.2909
E-mail ....sjjs01@clas.net
216 N Missouri St, Jackson, MO 63755-1833
John D. Jordan, Sheriff

EDUCATION SERVICES

EMAA Head Start-Girardeau 573.334.5533
Fax 573.334.4416
1111 Linden St, Cape Girardeau, MO 63703
Arin Goggo, Community Director

Carroll County

SOCIAL SERVICES

Family Support/Children's Div/Senior
Svcs 660.542.0656
Fax 660.542.0632
1303 N US Highway 65, Carrollton, MO 64633
Rita Wilson, County Manager

GENERAL HEALTH SERVICES

Health Dept 660.542.3247
Web ....www.carrollplphamo.org
E-mail ....mcatep@lpha.mopublic.org
5 N Ely St, Carrollton, MO 64633-1309
Pat Mcatee, Administrator

JUSTICE AGENCY

Juvenile Ofc 8th Circuit 660.542.0780
E-mail ....kenneth.brown@courts.mo.gov
8 S Main St, Carrollton, MO 64633
Kenneth Brown, Deputy Juvenile Officer

COURTS

8th Judicial Circuit **660.542.1466**
Fax 660.542.1444
E-mail ....cheryl.mansur@courts.mo.gov
   8 S Main St, Carrollton, MO 64633
Cheryl Mansur, Circuit Clerk

POLICE AND SHERIFF

Sheriff's Ofc **660.542.2200**
Fax 660.542.1539
   106 S Folger St, Carrollton, MO 64633
Troy Hofstetter, Sheriff

Carter County

SOCIAL SERVICES

Family Support/Children's Div/Senior
Svcs **573.323.4201**
Fax 573.323.4494
E-mail ....janice.stout@dss.mo.gov
   1306 Broadway St, Van Buren, MO 63965
Janice Stout, County Manager

GENERAL HEALTH SERVICES

Health Dept **573.323.4413**
Fax 573.323.8489
E-mail ....sandad@lpha.mopublic.org
   1611 Health Center Rd, Van Buren, MO 63965
Debbie Sandarciero, Director

JUSTICE AGENCY

Juvenile Ofc **573.323.8945**
Fax 573.323.8665
   1 Ball Park Rd, Van Buren, MO 63965
Stan R. Smith, Chief Juvenile Officer

COURTS

37th Judicial Circuit **573.323.4513**
Fax 573.323.8914
Web ....www.courts.mo.gov
E-mail ....michael.ligons@courts.mo.gov
   105 E. Main St., Van Buren, MO 63965
Honorable Michael Ligons, Judge

POLICE AND SHERIFF

Sheriff's Dept **573.323.4510**
Fax 573.323.4182
E-mail ....carterccso@semo.net
   15 Sicamore, Van Buren, MO 63965
Bruce Banbell, Sheriff

Cass County

SOCIAL SERVICES

Family Support/Children's Div/Senior
Svcs **816.380.3597**
Fax 816.884.4056
E-mail ....patricia.niner@dss.mo.gov
   2500 E Mechanic St, Harrisonville, MO 64701
Patricia L. Niner, Manager

GENERAL HEALTH SERVICES

Health Dept **816.380.8425**
Fax 816.380.8450
Web ....www.cachecountyhealth.com
E-mail ....healthdepartment@cachecounty.com
   300 S Main St, Harrisonville, MO 64701-2354
Tiffany Klaffen, Director

JUSTICE AGENCY

Juvenile Ofc **816.380.8475**
Fax 816.380.8490
Web ....www.courts.mo.gov
E-mail ....bev.newman@courts.mo.gov
   2501 W Mehanic St Ste 200, Harrisonville,
   MO 64701-1777
Beverly Newman, Chief Juvenile Officer

COURTS

17th Judicial Circuit **816.380.8226**
Fax 816.380.8225
Web ....www.courts.state.mo.us
E-mail ....joe_dandurand@osca.state.mo.us
   2501 W Mechanic, Harrisonville, MO 64701
Jacqueline Cook, Presiding Judge

POLICE AND SHERIFF

Sheriff's Dept **816.380.5200**
Fax 816.380.8334
E-mail ....sheriff@cassmosheriff.org
   2501 W Wall St, Harrisonville, MO 64701-1797
Dwight Diehl, Sheriff

EDUCATION SERVICES

Belton Head Start **816.322.0004**
Fax 816.322.0007
   127 Congress St, Belton, MO 64701
Dieidra Leonard, Director

Cedar County

SOCIAL SERVICES

Family Support/Children's Div/Senior
Svcs **417.276.5113**
Fax 417.276.6173
E-mail ....debbie.j.burns@dss.mo.gov
   112 RB Rd, Stockton, MO 65785
Debbie Burns, Director For Family Support

GENERAL HEALTH SERVICES

Health Dept **417.876.5477**
Fax 417.876.5017
   1317 S Hwy 32, El Dorado Springs, MO 64744
Jana Witt, Administrator

POLICE AND SHERIFF

Sheriff's Ofc **417.276.5133**
Fax 417.276.5135
   100 South St., Stockton, MO 65785
David Starbuck, Sheriff

Chariton County

SOCIAL SERVICES

Family Support/Children's Div/Senior
Svcs **660.288.3293**
Fax 660.288.3113
Web ....www.dss.mo.gov
   121 E Jackson St, Keytesville, MO 65261-1215
Margaret Stallman, Chief Executive Officer

GENERAL HEALTH SERVICES

Health Ctr **660.288.3675**
Fax 660.288.3725
Web ....www.lpha.mopublic.org
E-mail ....lincov@lpha.mopublic.org
   206 State St, Keytesville, MO 65261-1163
Vanessa Lincoln, Administrator

JUSTICE AGENCY

Juvenile Ofc **660.288.3840**
Fax 660.288.3866
   306 S Cherry St, Keytesville, MO 65261-1026
Wendy Graskewice, Deputy Juvenile Officer

COURTS

9th Judicial Circuit **660.288.3602**
Fax 660.288.3763
Web ....www.courts.mo.gov
E-mail ....eric.spallo@courts.mo.gov
   306 S Cherry St, Keytesville, MO 65261-1026
Eric Spallo, Circuit Clerk

POLICE AND SHERIFF

Sheriff's Ofc **660.288.3277**
Fax 660.288.3612
E-mail ....cwh640@yahoo.com
   307 S Cherry St, Keytesville, MO 65261-1025
Christopher W. Hughes, Sheriff

Christian County

SOCIAL SERVICES

Family Support/Children's Div **417.581.7511**
Fax 417.581.6515
   4715 N Town Centre Dr, Ozark, MO 65721
Jason Comer, Director

GENERAL HEALTH SERVICES

Health Dept **417.581.7285**
Fax 417.581.6130
E-mail ....pottek@lpha.dhss.mo.gov
   301 E Brick St, Ozark, MO 65721
Karen Potter, Director

JUSTICE AGENCY

Juvenile Ofc **417.581.7274**
Fax 417.581.2995
Web ....www.courts.mo.gov
E-mail ....mike.scofield@courts.mo.gov
   100 W Church Street # 304, Ozark, MO 65721
Michael Scofield, Chief Juvenile Officer

COURTS

38th Circuit Court **417.581.6372**
Fax 417.581.0391
Web ....www.courts.mo.gov
E-mail ....mark.orr@courts.mo.gov
   110 W Elm St, Ozark, MO 65721-9270
Honorable Mark Orr, Judge

POLICE AND SHERIFF

Sheriff's Ofc **417.581.2332**
Fax 417.581.1641
   110 W Elm St Rm 70, Ozark, MO 65721
Joey Kyle, Sheriff

Clark County

SOCIAL SERVICES

Family Support/Children's Div/Senior
Svcs **660.727.3393**
Fax 660.727.1020
   320 W Main St, Kahoka, MO 63445
Teresa Yager, County Manager

GENERAL HEALTH SERVICES

Health Dept **660.727.2356**
Fax 660.727.2927
   670 N Johnson St, Kahoka, MO 63445
Evelena Sutterfield, Director

JUSTICE AGENCY

Juvenile Ofc **660.727.3486**
Fax 660.727.2385
E-mail ....eric.derosear@courts.mo.gov
   510 N Johnson St, Kahoka, MO 63445
Jon Eric Derosear, Chief Juvenile Officer

COURTS

1st Judicial Circuit **660.727.3292**
Fax 660.727.1051
   510 N Johnson St, Kahoka, MO 63445
Mary D. Jones, Circuit Clerk

POLICE AND SHERIFF

Sheriff's Dept **660.727.2915**
Fax 660.727.2445
E-mail ....clarksheriff@hotmail.com
   518 N Lincoln St, Ste 1, Kahoka, MO 63445
Paul Gaudette, Sheriff

Clay County

GENERAL HEALTH SERVICES

Public Health **816.781.1600**
Fax 816.792.1285
Web ....www.clayhealth.com
E-mail ....msteinkamp@clayhealth.com
   800 Hanes Dr, Liberty, MO 64068
   Michelle Steinkamp, Nursing Supervisor

JUSTICE AGENCY

Juvenile Office **816.736.8400**
Fax 816.736.8401
   351 E Kansas St, Liberty, MO 64068
   Jennifer, Probation Officer

POLICE AND SHERIFF

Sheriff's Dept **816.407.3750**
Fax 816.407.3751
Web ....www.claycogov.com
E-mail ....pvescovo@claycogov.com
   12 S Water St, Liberty, MO 64068-1797
   Bob Boyston, Sheriff

EDUCATION SERVICES

Excelsior Springs Head Start **816.630.8884**
Fax 816.630.6864
   416 S Kansas City Ave, Excelsior Springs,
   MO 64024-2113
   Bev Sasek, Director

Clinton County

SOCIAL SERVICES

Family Support/Children's Div/Senior
Svcs **816.539.2146**
Fax 816.539.3120
   108 Bush St, Plattsburg, MO 64477
   Becky Hagen, County Manager

GENERAL HEALTH SERVICES

Health Dept **816.539.2144**
Fax 816.539.3306
Web ....www.clintoncountyhealthdepartment.com
   106 Bush St, Plattsburg, MO 64477
   Dlair Shock, Director

JUSTICE AGENCY

Juvenile Ofc **816.649.1011**
Fax 816.632.5621
Web ....www.courts.mo.gov
E-mail ....adrienne.lloyd@courts.mo.gov
   215 E 2nd St, Cameron, MO 64429-1702
   Adrienne Lloyd, Juvenile Officer

COURTS

43rd Judicial Circuit **816.539.3731**
Fax 816.539.3893
E-mail ....mollylivingston@court.mo.gov
   207 N Main St Ste 7, Plattsburg, MO 64477
   Molly Livingston, Circuit Clerk

POLICE AND SHERIFF

Sheriff's Ofc **816.539.2156**
Fax 816.539.2346
Web ....www.colecounty.org
   207 N Main St Ste 6, Plattsburg, MO 64477-1576
   K. Porter Hensen, Sheriff

EDUCATION SERVICES

Cameron Head Start **816.632.7887**
Web ....www.endpov.com
E-mail ....mduzenberry@endpov.com
   902 W 4th St, Cameron, MO 64429-1419
   Melanie Duzenberry, Director

Cole County

SOCIAL SERVICES

Dept of Social Svcs **573.751.4815**
Fax 573.751.3203
Web ....www.dss.state.mo.us
   615 Howerton Crt, Jefferson City, MO 65109
   Ronald Levy, Director

Family Support/Children's Div/Senior
Svcs **573.751.4688**
Fax 573.526.1370
   1716 4 Seasons Dr Ste 104, Jefferson City, MO 65101
   Venice Wood, Director of Childrens Services

GENERAL HEALTH SERVICES

Health Dept **573.636.2181**
Fax 573.636.3851
Web ....www.colehealth.org
E-mail ....volunteerinfo@colecounty.org
   1616 Industrial Dr, Jefferson City, MO 65109-1471
   Marie Peoples, Director

Ofc of Primary Care and Rural
Health **573.751.6441**
Fax 573.522.8146
Web ....www.health.mo.gov
E-mail ....kristina.klienheider@health.mo.gov
   912 Wild Wood Dr, Jefferson City, MO 65102
   Ben Harvey, Chief

JUSTICE AGENCY

Juvenile Court Svcs **573.636.5177**
Fax 573.634.5162
E-mail ....mcouty@colecounty.org
   400 Stadium Blvd, Jefferson City, MO 65101
   Michael Couty, Administrator

COURTS

19th Judicial Circuit **573.634.9151**
Fax 573.635.0796
   301 E High St Rm 208, Jefferson City, MO 65102
   Marrylue Hemmel, Court Administrator

POLICE AND SHERIFF

Sheriff's Ofc **573.634.9160**
Fax 573.634.2336
Web ....www.mshp.dps.mo.gov
E-mail ....greg.white@mshp.dps.mo.gov
   301 E. High St., Jefferson City, MO 65102
   Greg White, Sheriff

EDUCATION SERVICES

Head Start **573.636.3577**
Fax 573.761.1614
Web ....www.showmeaction.org
   605 Cherry St, Jefferson City, MO 65101-3345
   Lisa Cummings, Director

Head Start-West **573.635.7054**
Fax 573.635.7084
   2010 William St, Jefferson City, MO 65109
   Carmalee Hall, Director

State Schools for Severely
Handicapped **573.751.4427**
Fax 573.751.0276
Web ....www.dese.mo.gov
E-mail ....webreplyspesssh@dese.mo.gov
   205 Jefferson St, Jefferson City, MO 65101-2901
   Archie Derboven, Superintendent

Cooper County

SOCIAL SERVICES

Family Support/Children's Div/Senior
Svcs **660.882.5311**
Fax 660.882.8858
   409 High St, Boonville, MO 65233
   Margaret Stallman, County Manager

GENERAL HEALTH SERVICES

Public Health Dept **660.882.2626**
Fax 660.882.2586
   17040 Klinton Dr, Boonville, MO 65233
   Melanie Hein, Administrator

COURTS

18th Judicial Circuit **660.882.2232**
Fax 660.882.2043
   200 Main St Rm 31, Boonville, MO 65233
   Nancy Fisher, Circuit Clerk

POLICE AND SHERIFF

Sheriff's Ofc **660.882.2771**
Fax 660.882.7075
E-mail ....ccsd590@sbcglobal.net
   200 Main St Rm 3, Boonville, MO 65233-1276
   Jerry Wolfe, Sheriff

EDUCATION SERVICES

Boonville Head Start **660.882.7510**
Fax 660.882.8517
E-mail ....murnelle-king@showmeaction.org
   385 W Ashley Rd, Boonville, MO 65233
   Murnelle King, Director

Crawford County

SOCIAL SERVICES

Health svcs. **573.775.2146**
Fax 573.775.3146
E-mail ....eyvonne.emily@dss.mo.gov
   272 Cushing Rd., Steelville, MO 65565
   Eyvonne Emily, Director

GENERAL HEALTH SERVICES

Nursing Svc/Health Dept **573.775.2555**
Fax 573.775.3826
E-mail ....stulcs@lpha.mopublic.org
   202 W Main St, Steelville, MO 65565
   Shirley Stulce, Administrator

JUSTICE AGENCY

Juvenile Ofc **573.775.2787**
Fax 573.775.2790
   PO Box 859, Steelville, MO 65565-0859
   Raymond Oeth, Deputy Juvenile Officer

COURTS

42nd Judicial Circuit **573.775.2866**
Fax 573.775.2452
Web ....www.crawforcocircuitcourt.com
E-mail ....karen.harlan@courts.mo.gov
   302 Main St., Steelville, MO 65565
   Karen Harlan, Circuit Clerk

POLICE AND SHERIFF

Sheriff's Ofc **573.775.2125**
Fax 573.775.2126
Web ....www.crawfordcountysheriffsdepartment.com
E-mail ....ccsd@misn.com
   302 W Main St, Steelville, MO 65565
   Randy Martin, Sheriff

EDUCATION SERVICES

Cuba Head Start Ctr **573.885.2696**
Fax 573.885.6446
   605 E Washington St, Cuba, MO 65453-1836
   Ella Greenwald, Director

Dade County

SOCIAL SERVICES

Family Support/Children's Div 417.637.5326
Fax 417.637.5113
105 S Grand St, Greenfield, MO 65661
Jane Claas, County Manager

GENERAL HEALTH SERVICES

Health Dept 417.637.2345
Fax 417.637.2507
Web .... www.dadecountyhealthdept.com
E-mail .... allenp1@lpha.mopublic.org
413 W Water St, Greenfield, MO 65661-1353
Pamela Allen, Administrator

JUSTICE AGENCY

Juvenile Ofc 417.276.6700
Fax 417.276.5001
Web .... www.courts.mo.gov
E-mail .... jeani.longstreth@courts.mo.gov
PO Box 665, Stockton, MO 65785-0665
Jeani Longstreth, Chief Juvenile Officer

COURTS

28th Associate Judicial Circuit 417.637.2271
Fax 417.637.5055
Web .... www.osca.state.mo.us
300 W Water St, Greenfield, MO 65661-1351
Mary McGee, Circuit Clerk

POLICE AND SHERIFF

Sheriff's Ofc 417.637.2312
Fax 417.637.2508
Web .... www.mosheriffs.com
E-mail .... steven@mosheriffs.com
201 E Water St, Greenfield, MO 65661-1225
Steven Stapp, Sheriff

Dallas County

SOCIAL SERVICES

Family Support/Children's Div/Senior
Svcs 417.345.7651
Fax 417.345.8509
Web .... www.dss.mo.gov
E-mail .... brad.w.bembry@dss.mo.gov
719 N. Ash St., Buffalo, MO 65622
W. Brad Bembry, Director

GENERAL HEALTH SERVICES

Health Dept 417.345.2332
Fax 417.345.2025
Web .... www.lpha.mopublic.org
E-mail .... eversc2@lpha.mopublic.org
1011 W Main, Buffalo, MO 65622
Cheryl Eversole, Director

JUSTICE AGENCY

Juvenile Ofcs 417.345.6772
Fax 417.345.5110
123 E Main St, Buffalo,, MO 65622
Deborah Butts, Chief Juvenile Officer

COURTS

30th Associate Judicial Circuit 417.345.2243
Fax 417.345.5539
108 N Maple St, Buffalo, MO 65622
Lisa Henderson, Associate Judge

POLICE AND SHERIFF

Sheriff's Ofc 417.345.2441
Fax 417.345.6238
Web .... www.dallascountysheriff.net
E-mail .... mikerackley@dallascountysheriff.net
204 S Poplar St, Buffalo, MO 65622-8600
Mike Rackley, Sheriff

EDUCATION SERVICES

Buffalo Head Start 417.345.2240
Fax 417.345.2240
221 S Elder St, Buffalo, MO 65622
Dana Castele, Office Manager

Daviess County

SOCIAL SERVICES

Family Support/Children's Div 660.663.2189
Fax 660.663.8919
E-mail .... debbie.heldenbrand@dss.mo.gov
201 Ash St, Gallatin, MO 64640
Debbie Heldenbrand, County Manager

GENERAL HEALTH SERVICES

Health Dept 660.663.2414
Fax 660.663.3919
Web .... www.daviesshealthonline.com
E-mail .... alexac1@lpha.mopublic.org
609A S Main St, Gallatin, MO 64640-1447
Cheryl Alexander, Administrator

COURTS

43rd Judicial Circuit 660.663.2932
Fax 660.663.3876
102 N Main St, Gallatin, MO 64640
Pam Howard, Circuit Clerk

POLICE AND SHERIFF

Sheriff's Ofc 660.663.2031
Fax 660.663.2149
102 N Main St, Gallatin, MO 64640
Ben Becerra, Sheriff

DeKalb County

COURTS

43rd Judicial Circuit 816.449.2602
Fax 816.449.2440
Web .... www.courts.mo.gov
109 W Main St, Maysville, MO 64469-8500
Julie Whitsell, Circuit Clerk

POLICE AND SHERIFF

Sheriff's Ofc 816.449.5802
Fax 816.449.5241
Web .... www.sos.mo.gov
E-mail .... wes.raines@sos.mo.gov
Jct. 6-33 Hwy., Maysville, MO 64469-0317
Wes Raines, Sheriff

Dent County

SOCIAL SERVICES

Family Support/Children's Div/Senior
Svcs 573.729.4137
Fax 573.729.7483
800 W Scenic Rivers Blvd, Salem, MO 65560
Janice Stout, County Manager

GENERAL HEALTH SERVICES

Health Dept 573.729.3106
Fax 573.729.3546
601 S Mcarthur St, Salem, MO 65560
Mary Jane Jadwin, Administrator

JUSTICE AGENCY

Juvenile Ofc 573.729.7990
Fax 573.729.8443
112 E 5th St Ste 3, Salem, MO 65560-1412
Joann C. Bayless, Chief Juvenile Officer

COURTS

42nd Judicial Circuit 573.729.3931
Fax 573.729.9414
Web .... www.courts.mo.gov
E-mail .... ruth.williams@courts.mo.gov
112 E 5th St Ste 1, Salem, MO 65560-1412
Ruth Ann Williams, Circuit Clerk

POLICE AND SHERIFF

Sheriff's Ofc 573.729.3241
Fax 573.729.3058
112 E 5th St Ste 7, JUDICIAL BLDG, Salem,
MO 65560-1412
Rick Stallings, Sheriff

Douglas County

SOCIAL SERVICES

Family Support/Children's Div/Senior
Svcs 417.683.4817
Fax 417.683.6151
E-mail .... lane.lakey@dss.mo.gov98
603 NW 12th Ave, Ava, MO 65608
Lane Lakey, County Manager

GENERAL HEALTH SERVICES

Health Dept 417.683.4213
Fax 417.683.4111
Web .... www.dchd.org
603 NW 12th Ave, Ava, MO 65608
Glenna Young, Infectious Disease Nurse

COURTS

44th Associate Judicial Circuit 417.683.4713
Fax 417.683.2794
203 SE 2nd Ave., Ava, MO 65608
Honorable John Moody, Circuit Judge

POLICE AND SHERIFF

Sheriff's Ofc 417.683.1020
Fax 417.683.3100
209 2nd Ave. SE, Ava, MO 65608
Christopher Dagasa, Sheriff

Dunklin County

SOCIAL SERVICES

Family Support/Children's Div/Senior
Svcs 573.888.5981
Fax 573.888.3470
Web .... www.dss.mo.gov
1100 Hwy 25 S. Bypass, Kennett, MO 63857
Amy Helm, Director

GENERAL HEALTH SERVICES

Health Dept 573.717.7317
Fax 573.717.7319
Web .... www.dunklincountyhealth.com
E-mail .... duncohd@semo.net
1051 Jones St, Kennett, MO 63857-3866
Kim Hughes, Nursing Supervisor

Health Dept 573.888.9008
Fax 573.888.1629
Web .... www.semo.net
E-mail .... duncohd@semo.net
410 Teaco Rd, Kennett, MO 63857-3239
Steve Neal, Administrator

JUSTICE AGENCY

Juvenile Ofc 573.888.2962
Fax 573.888.0260
101 S Main, Kennett, MO 63857
Michael Davis, Chief Juvenile Officer

COURTS

35th Judicial Circuit Court **573.888.2456**
Fax 573.888.0319
Web .... www.courts.mo.gov
  Court House Rm 301, Kennett, MO 63857
  Paula Gargus, Clerk

POLICE AND SHERIFF

Sheriff's Dept **573.888.2424**
Fax 573.888.2604
E-mail .... dccourthouse@yahoo.com
  1175 Floyd St, Kennett, MO 63857
  Bob Holder, Sheriff

Franklin County

GENERAL HEALTH SERVICES

Health Dept **636.583.7300**
Fax 636.583.7305
  15 S Oak St, Union, MO 63084
  Charlotte Popper, Nursing Supervisor

JUSTICE AGENCY

Juvenile Ofc **636.583.7333**
Fax 636.583.7337
  120 S Church St, Union, MO 63084
  Gerald H. Poepsel, Juvenile Officer

COURTS

20th Associate Judicial Circuit **636.583.7365**
  401 E Main St, Union, MO 63084
  I Lamke, Judge

POLICE AND SHERIFF

Sheriff's Ofc **636.583.2560**
Fax 636.583.2560
E-mail .... gary_toelke@osca.state.mo.us
  1 Bruns Ln, Union, MO 63084-3221
  Gary F. Toelke, Sheriff

Gasconade County

SOCIAL SERVICES

Family Support/Children's Div **573.437.4188**
Fax 573.437.5776
E-mail .... sherry.smith@dss.mo.gov
  1008 Hwy 28 W, Owensville, MO 65066-3724
  Sherry Smith, Circuit Manager

GENERAL HEALTH SERVICES

Health Dept **573.486.3129**
Fax 573.486.3745
Web .... www.gasconadecountyhealth.com
E-mail .... info@gasconadecountyhealth.com
  300 Schiller St, Hermann, MO 65041-1154
  Sara Michie, Director

COURTS

20th Judicial Circuit **573.486.2632**
Fax 573.486.5812
Web .... www.courts.mo.gov
  119 E 1st St Rm 6, Hermann, MO 65041-1185
  Honorable Gael Wood, Judge

POLICE AND SHERIFF

Sheriff's Ofc **573.486.2424**
Fax 573.486.3693
  119 E 1st St Rm 22, Hermann, MO 65041
  Randy Esphorst, Sheriff

Gentry County

GENERAL HEALTH SERVICES

Family Support/Childrens Div **660.726.3971**
Fax 660.726.3973
Web .... www.dss.mo.gov
  504 N East St, ste 136, Albany, MO 64402
  Leslie Riney, County Manager

COURTS

4th Judicial Circuit **660.726.3618**
Fax 660.726.4102
  PO Box 32, Albany, MO 64402-0027
  Honorable Edward Manring, Chief Judge

POLICE AND SHERIFF

Sheriff's Ofc **660.726.3721**
Fax 660.726.3665
E-mail .... elupfer@albanymo.net
  104 S. Tolk, Albany, MO 64402
  Elmer E. Lupfer, Sheriff

EDUCATION SERVICES

Albany Head Start **660.726.5625**
Fax 660.726.4238
  105 N Van Buren St, Albany, MO 64402-1189
  Dolores Bibley, Director

Greene County

SOCIAL SERVICES

Youth Svcs **417.895.6485**
Fax 417.895.6633
Web .... www.dss.mo.gov
  1735 W Catalpa St Ste B, Springfield,
  MO 65807-1243
  John Creson, Regional Administrator

GENERAL HEALTH SERVICES

Family Support/Children's Div/Senior
Svcs **417.895.6000**
Fax 417.895.5779
E-mail .... heather.ford@dss.mo.gov
  149 Park Central Sq, Springfield, MO 65806-3103
  Heather Ford, Circuit Manager

Health Dept **417.864.1658**
Fax 417.864.1099
Web .... www.springfieldmo.gov
E-mail .... rhilburn@springfieldmo.gov
  227 E Chestnut Expy, Springfield, MO 65802
  Robin Hilburn, Hiv Coordinator

Southwestern District Health Ofc **417.895.6900**
Fax 417.895.6975
Web .... www.health.mo.gov
  149 Park Central Sq Ste 116, Springfield, MO 65801
  Richard Adey, Front Desk Supervisor

JUSTICE AGENCY

Juvenile Court Svcs **417.868.4008**
Fax 417.868.4119
Web .... www.spsmail.org
E-mail .... jaime.stage@missouricourt.com
  1111 N Robberson Ave, Springfield, MO 65802-3893
  Jamie Stage, Teen Court Coordinator

POLICE AND SHERIFF

Sheriff's Dept **417.868.4040**
Fax 417.868.4830
Web .... www.greenecountymo.org
E-mail .... jarnott@greenecountymo.org
  1010 N Boonville Ave, Springfield, MO 65802-3804
  Jim Arnott, Sheriff

EDUCATION SERVICES

Fair Grove Head Start **417.759.6124**
Fax 417.759.6124
  103 N Main St, Fair Grove, MO 65648-8436
  Joyce Dill, Director

Grundy County

SOCIAL SERVICES

Family Support/Children's Div/Senior
Svcs **660.359.3971**
Fax 660.359.5579
  2926 Oklahoma Ave, Trenton, MO 64683-3405
  Sherril Gott, County Manager

GENERAL HEALTH SERVICES

Health Dept **660.359.4196**
Fax 660.359.5470
Web .... www.lpha.mopublic.org
E-mail .... gibsoe@lpha.mopublic.org
  1716 Lincoln St, Trenton, MO 64683-1584
  Elizabeth Gibson, Director

COURTS

3rd Judicial Circuit **660.359.6605**
Fax 660.359.6604
Web .... www.grundycountymo.com
  700 Main St Ste 8, Trenton, MO 64683-2063
  Honorable Jack Peace, Attorney

POLICE AND SHERIFF

Sheriff's Dept **660.359.2828**
Fax 660.359.3761
E-mail .... grucoso@grundycountymo.com
  610 Main St, Trenton, MO 64683
  Rodney Herring, Sheriff

Harrison County

SOCIAL SERVICES

Family Support/Children's Div/Senior
Svcs **660.425.7995**
Fax 660.425.7382
E-mail .... leslie.riney@dss.mo.gov
  2403 Vandivert St, Bethany, MO 64424-2635
  Leslie Riney, County Manager

GENERAL HEALTH SERVICES

Health Dept **660.425.6324**
Fax 660.425.7642
Web .... www.hchdhealth.org
  1700 Bethany Ave, Bethany, MO 64424
  Mike ONeal, Director

COURTS

3rd Judicial Circuit **660.425.6425**
Fax 660.425.6390
Web .... www.courts.mo.gov
E-mail .... jack.peace@courts.mo.gov
  1500 Central, Bethany, MO 64424
  Jack Peace, Judge

POLICE AND SHERIFF

Sheriff's Dept **660.425.3199**
Fax 660.425.7906
Web .... www.cji.net
E-mail .... harrisoncoso@cji.net
  1501 Central St, Bethany, MO 64424-1905
  George Martz, Sheriff

EDUCATION SERVICES

Bethany Head Start Ctr **660.425.3663**
Fax 660.425.8906
  803 S 24th St, Bethany, MO 64424-2631
  Beth Hooker, Director

Henry County

SOCIAL SERVICES

Family Support/Children's Div/Senior
Svcs **660.885.5531**
Fax 660.885.5899
  1661 N 2nd St, Clinton, MO 64735
  Robert Wilcox, Childrens Circuit Manager

GENERAL HEALTH SERVICES

Clinton Health Dept **660.885.8193**
Fax 660.885.7744
Web ....www.lpha.mopublic.org
E-mail ....glassb@lpha.mopublic.org
   306 S 2nd St, Clinton, MO 64735-2106
Bonnie Glass, Administrator

JUSTICE AGENCY

Juvenile Ofc **660.885.7248**
Fax 660.885.8456
Web ....www.courts.mo.gov
E-mail ....rculler@courts.mo.gov
   100 W Franklin St Unit 13, Clinton, MO 64735-2080
Rebecca Culler, Chief Juvenile Officer

COURTS

27th Judicial Circuit **660.885.7248**
Fax 660.885.8456
Web ....www.courts.mo.gov
E-mail ....rebeccaculler@courts.mo.gov
   100 West Franklin St, Clinton, MO 64735
Rebecca Culler, Juvenile Officer

POLICE AND SHERIFF

Sheriff's Dept **660.885.7021**
Fax 660.885.4279
E-mail ....henrysheriff@earthlink.net
   220 S Washington St, Clinton, MO 64735
J. Kent Oberkrom, Sheriff

EDUCATION SERVICES

Clinton Head Start **660.885.3764**
Fax 660.890.6167
   1003 Clark St, Clinton, MO 64735

Hickory County

GENERAL HEALTH SERVICES

Health Dept **417.745.2138**
Fax 417.745.2400
Web ....www.hickorycountymo.net
E-mail ....acarter@hickorycountymo.net
   201 Cedar St, Hermitage, MO 65668
Alisa Carter, Director

COURTS

30th Circuit Court **417.745.6421**
Fax 417.745.6670
E-mail ....john.sims@courts.mo.gov
   Court House Sq, Hermitage, MO 65668
Honorable John W. Sims, Presiding Judge

POLICE AND SHERIFF

Sheriff's Ofc **417.745.6415**
Fax 417.745.6205
E-mail ....hhickory@centurytel.net
   Highway 254, Hermitage, MO 65668
Raymond S. Tipton, Sheriff

Holt County

SOCIAL SERVICES

**Family Support/Children's Div/Senior
Svcs** **660.442.3314**
Fax 660.442.3361
Web ....www.dss.mo.gov
E-mail ....dana.thompson@dss.mo.gov
   1423 State St, Mound City, MO 64470-7218
Leslie Riney, Director

GENERAL HEALTH SERVICES

Health Dept **660.446.2909**
Fax 660.446.2921
Web ....www.lpha.mopublic.org
E-mail ....nelsob@lpha.mopublic.org
   108 S Main St, Oregon, MO 64473
Brenda Nelson, Director

JUSTICE AGENCY

Juvenile Ofc **660.582.4312**
Fax 660.582.4390
Web ....www.courts.mo.gov
E-mail ....rick.bradley@courts.mo.gov
   403 N Market St, rm 307, Maryville, MO 64468-8237
Rick R. Bradley, Juvenile Officer

COURTS

4th Judicial Circuit **660.446.3301**
Fax 660.446.3328
E-mail ....vicki.book@courts.mo.gov
   102 W. Nodaway, Oregon, MO 64473
Vicki Book, Circuit Clerk

POLICE AND SHERIFF

Sheriff's Dept **660.446.3300**
Fax 660.446.2020
E-mail ....Wedlockssheriff@ml.net
   107 S. Main St., Oregon, MO 64473
Scott Wedlock, Sheriff

Howard County

SOCIAL SERVICES

Family Support/Children's Div **660.248.3324**
Fax 660.248.1023
E-mail ....margaret.a.stallman@dss.mo.gov
   103 Furr St, Fayette, MO 65248
Margret Stallman, County Manager

GENERAL HEALTH SERVICES

Public Health Dept **660.248.3100**
Fax 660.248.3275
Web ....www.dhss.mo.gov
   600 W Morrison St Ste 7, Fayette, MO 65248-1075
Sheila Wallace, Rn, Administrator

COURTS

14th Judicial Circuit **660.248.2194**
Fax 660.248.5009
Web ....www.courts.mo.gov
E-mail ....scott.hayes@courts.mo.gov
   1 Courthouse Sq Stop 7, Fayette, MO 65248-1283
Honorable Scott Hayes, Judge

POLICE AND SHERIFF

Fayette Police Dept **660.248.2241**
Fax 660.248.2168
   117 S Main St, Fayette, MO 65248
Jeff Oswald, Police Chief

Sheriff's Ofc **660.248.2477**
Fax 660.248.1444
   100 N Mulberry St, Fayette, MO 65248-1443
Charlie S. Polson, Sheriff

Howell County

SOCIAL SERVICES

**Family Support/Children's Div/Senior
Svcs** **417.256.7121**
Fax 417.256.3473
Web ....www.dss.mo.gov
E-mail ....howell.codfs@dss.mo.gov
   3415 Division Dr, West Plains, MO 65775-5789
Barbara Perry, Circuit Manager

GENERAL HEALTH SERVICES

Health Dept **417.256.7078**
Fax 417.256.1179
Web ....www.lpha.dhss.mo.gov
E-mail ....gillic@lpha.dhss.mo.gov
   411 Garfield Ave, West Plains, MO 65775-2602
Chris Gilliam, Director

JUSTICE AGENCY

Juvenile Ofc **417.256.2432**
Fax 417.256.0520
Web ....www.courts.mo.gov
E-mail ....stan.smith@courts.mo.gov
   111 Walnut Street, West Plains, MO 65775
Stan R. Smith, Chief Juvenile Officer

COURTS

37th Judicial Circuit **417.256.3741**
Fax 417.256.4650
   Court House Courte Sq Rm 6, West Plains,
   MO 65775
Cindy Weeks, Circuit Clerk

POLICE AND SHERIFF

Sheriff's Deptt **417.256.2544**
Fax 417.256.6464
E-mail ....hcso@wpcs.net
   1106 Missouri Ave, West Plains, MO 65659
Mike Shannon, Sheriff

EDUCATION SERVICES

Cabool Head Start **417.962.4086**
Fax 417.962.5476
Web ....www.oaiwp.org
E-mail ....caboolhs@oaiwp.org
   320 Canady Dr, Cabool, MO 65689
Kristy Reese, Director

Iron County

SOCIAL SERVICES

**Family Support/Children's Div/Senior
Svcs** **573.546.7463**
Fax 573.546.6002
   202 Park Dr, Ironton, MO 63650
Eyvonne Emily, County Manager

GENERAL HEALTH SERVICES

Ironton Health Dept **573.546.7121**
Fax 573.546.6979
E-mail ....davisj1@lpha.dhss.mo.gov
   606 W Russell St, Ironton, MO 63650
Heidi Wharton, Administrator

JUSTICE AGENCY

Juvenile Ofc **573.546.7207**
Fax 573.546.1477
E-mail ....Russell.Allen@courts.mo.gov
   250 S Main St, Ironton, MO 63650
Russell Allen, Chief Juvenile Officer

COURTS

42nd Associate Judicial Circuit **573.546.2811**
Fax 573.546.2166
Web ....www.osca.state.mo.us
   250 S Main St, Ironton, MO 63650-1308
Karen Reagan, Clerk

POLICE AND SHERIFF

Sheriff's Dept **573.546.7321**
Fax 573.546.7139
Web ....www.ironcountysheriff.mo.gov
E-mail ....ironsheriff@hotmail.com
   220 S Shepherd St, Ironton, MO 63650-1326
Roger Medley, Sheriff

Jackson County

SOCIAL SERVICES

Children's Svcs **816.929.7800**
Fax 816.929.7898
E-mail ....rebecca.k.jobst@dss.mo.gov
   4900 Swope Pkwy, Kansas City, MO 64130
Rebecca Jobst, Program Manager

Family Support/Children's Div 816.889.2815
Fax 816.889.2258
   615 E 13th St, Kansas City, MO 64106
Margaret Randle, Family Support Division Director

Family Svcs 816.929.7100
Fax 816.929.7101
   4900 Swope Pkwy, Kansas City, MO 64130
Stephanie Fowler, Program Manager .

Fsd Kansas City Regional Ofc 816.889.2500
Fax 816.889.2008
   615 E 13th St, Kansas City, MO 64106
Marge Randle, Im Director

Youth Svcs 816.889.2428
Fax 816.889.3850
Web .... www.dss.mo.gov
   1410 Genessee St Ste 120, Northwest Regional
   Office, Kansas City, MO 64102-1047
Julie Breaux, Administrator

GENERAL HEALTH SERVICES

Health Dept 816.404.6415
Fax 816.404.6418
Web .... www.jacohd.org
E-mail .... jim.kelly@tmcmed.org
   313 S Liberty St, Independence, MO 64050
Jim Kelly, Director

Independence Health Dept 816.325.7182
Fax 816.325.7098
Web .... www.indepmo.org
E-mail .... ljones@indepmo.org
   515 S Liberty St, Independence, MO 64050
Larry Jones, Director

Kansas City Health Dept 816.513.6008
Fax 816.513.6293
Web .... www.kc.mo.org/health
E-mail .... rex_archer@kcmo.org
   2400 Troost Ave Ste 2000, Kansas City,
   MO 64108-2862
Rex Archer, Md, Director

Northwestern District Health Ofc 816.350.5400
Fax 816.350.7764
Web .... www.dhss.mo.gov
   3717 S Whitney Ave, Independence, MO 64055
Patrrick Franklin, Building Manager

JUSTICE AGENCY

CASA 816.842.2272
Fax 816.842.7788
Web .... www.jacksoncountycasa-mo.org
   625 E 26th St, Kansas City, MO 64108
Martha Gershun, Executive Director

Prevention and Diversion Status Offenders
Program 816.881.6570
Fax 816.881.6578
E-mail .... jonni.wright@courts.mo.gov
   501 E 27th St, Kansas City, MO 64108
Jonni Wright, Manager

COURTS

16th Judicial Circuit Court-Family
Div 816.474.3606
Fax 816.435.4793
Web .... www.family-court.org
E-mail .... geoffrey_e_allen@osca.state.mo.us
   625 E 26th St, Kansas City, MO 64108-2719
Honorable Geoffrey E. Allen, Family Court Commissioner

Independence Youth Court 816.325.7750
Fax 816.325.7749
E-mail .... youthct@indepmo.org
   111 E Maple Ave, Independence, MO 64050-3066
Judge Susan Watkins, Director

Lee's Summit Youth Court 816.986.1190
E-mail .... travis.burks@lees-summit.mo.us
   10 NE Tudor Rd, Lees Summit, MO 64086-4530
Mark Wiley, Coordinator

Missouri Court of Appeals Western
District 816.889.3600
Fax 816.889.3668
   1300 Oak St, Kansas City, MO 64106
Terence Lord, Clerk

Raytown Youth Court 816.737.6195
Fax 816.737.6137
Web .... www.raytownpolice.org
E-mail .... clearb@raytownpolice.org
   10000 E 59th St, Raytown, MO 64133-3915
Brad Clear, Detective Agent

POLICE AND SHERIFF

Kansas City Police Dept (Juvenile) 816.234.5150
Fax 816.234.5570
Web .... www.kcpd.org
   1525 Holmes St, Kansas City, MO 64108
James Corwin, Chief Of Police

Sheriff's Dept 816.524.4302
Fax 816.524.4340
E-mail .... msharp@gov.co.jackson.mo.us
   3310 NE Rennau Dr, Lees Summit, MO 64064-2129
Mike Sharp, Sheriff

EDUCATION SERVICES

Ctr School District Special
Education 816.349.3300
Fax 816.349.3431
Web www.center.k12.mo.us
E-mail .... bmckinzie@center.k12.mo.us
   8701 Holmes Rd, Kansas City, MO 64131-2899
Betty Mckinzie, Director Of Special Services

Fort Osage R-1 School District Special
Ed. 816.650.7000
Fax 816.650.3888
Web www.fortosage.k12.mo.us
   2101 N Twyman Rd, Independence, MO 64058
Roxie Lanier, Director Of Special Services

Hickman Mills C-1 Schools Special
Education 816.316.7100
Fax 816.316.7110
Web .... www.hickmanmills.org
E-mail .... susie@hickmanmills.org
   5401 E 103rd St, Kansas City, MO 64037
Susie Fanning, Director

Indepence School District Special
Education 816.521.2700
Fax 816.521.2999
Web www.indep.k12.mo.us
E-mail .... jhinson@indep.k12.mo.us
   218 N Pleasant St, Independence, MO 64050-2655
Jim Hinson, Superintendent

Kansas City School District (Special
Ed.) 816.418.7000
Fax 816.418.5239
Web www.kcmsd.k12.mo.us
E-mail .... chernandez@email.kcmsd.k12.mo.us
   1215 E Truman Rd, Kansas City, MO 64106-2416
Christine Hernandez, Director Of Exceptional Education

Jasper County

SOCIAL SERVICES

Family Support/Childrens Div/Senior
Svcs 417.629.3050
Fax 417.629.3442
   601 Commercial St, Joplin, MO 64802
Jean Rodriquez, Circuit Manager, Childrens Division

GENERAL HEALTH SERVICES

Health Dept 417.358.3111
Fax 417.358.0494
Web .... www.jaspercounty.org
E-mail .... trippl@lpha.dhss.mo.gov
   105 Lincoln St, Carthage, MO 64836-1512
Lauri Fasken-tripp, Hiv Coordinator

Joplin Area Health Ofc 417.629.3085
Fax 417.629.3088
Web .... www.dhss.mo.gov
   1110 E 7th St Ste 12, Joplin, MO 64801-2076
Cathy Rushing, Area Supervisor

Joplin City Health Dept 417.623.6122
Fax 417.624.6453
Web .... www.joplinmo.org
E-mail .... dpekarek@joplinmo.org
   321 E 4th St, Joplin, MO 64801-2262
Daniel Pekarek, Community Health Director

COURTS

29th Judicial Circuit 417.625.4310
Fax 417.782.7172
   601 S Pearl Ave Ste 300, Joplin, MO 64801-2566
David Bally, Judge

POLICE AND SHERIFF

Sheriff's Ofc 417.358.8177
Fax 417.358.5566
   405 E 5th St, Carthage, MO 64836
William Archie Dunn, Sheriff

EDUCATION SERVICES

Carl Junction Head Start 417.649.5746
Fax 417.649.6785
Web .... www.escswa.org
   206 N Roney St, Carl Junction, MO 64834
Beth Ostmeyer, Director

Jefferson County

SOCIAL SERVICES

Family Support/Childrens Div/Senior
Svcs 636.797.9601
Fax 636.797.9780
Web .... www.dss.mo.gov
E-mail .... mary.e.terry@dss.mo.gov
   10325 Business 21, Hillsboro, MO 63050-3587
Tish Naeger, Childrens Services Circuit Manager

GENERAL HEALTH SERVICES

Health Dept 636.789.3372
Fax 636.797.4631
Web .... www.jeffcohealth.org
E-mail .... diehld@lpha.mopublic.org
   405 Main St, Hillsboro, MO 63050-4351
Dennis Diehl, Director

Health Dept 636.282.1010
Fax 636.282.2525
Web .... www.jeffcohealth.org
   1818 Lonedell Rd, Arnold, MO 63010-1050
Sandy Meyer, Nursing Supervisor

COURTS

23rd Judicial Circuit 636.797.5443
Fax 636.797.5073
   300 Main Street, Hillsboro, MO 63050
Nathan Stewart, Judge

POLICE AND SHERIFF

Sheriff's Ofc 636.797.5000
Fax 636.797.6451
Web .... www.jcsd.org
   400 1st St, Hillsboro, MO 63050
Glenn Boyer, Sheriff

Missouri

EDUCATION SERVICES

Antonia Head Start **636.942.3680**
Fax 636.942.2165
Web ....www.acf.hhs.gov
  6283 Old Lemay Ferry Rd, Imperial, MO 63052
  Celestine Chierek, Director

**Fox C6 School District Special
Education** **636.296.8000**
Fax 636.282.5170
  745 Jeffco Blvd, Arnold, MO 63010
  Diane Brown, Phd, Superintendent

**R-7 School District Special
Education** **636.937.9188**
Fax 636.937.9189
E-mail ....ns1383@jr7.k12.mo.us
  1250 Dooling Hollow Rd, Festus, MO 63028
  Nancy Schmitz, Director

Special Education **636.944.3941**
Fax 636.944.5239
E-mail ....mannj@grandviewr2.org
  11470 Highway C, Hillsboro, MO 63050
  Jack Mann, Director of Special Services

Johnson County

GENERAL HEALTH SERVICES

Community Health Svcs **660.747.6121**
Fax 660.747.6087
Web ....www.johnsoncountyhealth.org
E-mail ....halled@lpha.mopublic.org
  429 Burkarth Rd, Warrensburg, MO 64093
  Deborah Haller, Administrator

JUSTICE AGENCY

Juvenile Ofc **660.422.7418**
Fax 660.422.7422
E-mail ....bev.newman@courts.mo.gov
  101 W Market St Ste 101, Warrensburg, MO 64093
  Beverly Newman, Chief Juvenile Officer

COURTS

17th Judicial Circuit **660.422.7413**
Fax 660.422.7417
Web ....www.courts.mo.gov
  101 W Market St, Warrensburg, MO 64093-1744
  Stephanie Elkins, Clerk

POLICE AND SHERIFF

Sheriff's Ofc **660.747.6469**
Fax 816.732.6382
Web ....www.jocomosheriff.org
E-mail ....cheiss@jcfpd.net
  278 SW 871 Rd, Centerview, MO 64019
  Charles M. Heiss, Sheriff

Knox County

GENERAL HEALTH SERVICES

Health Dept **660.397.3396**
Fax 660.397.3579
  217 N 1St St, Edina, MO 63537
  Lori Moots-clair, Director

JUSTICE AGENCY

Juvenile Ofc **660.397.3559**
Fax 660.397.3331
  101 N Main St, Edina, MO 63537
  Jeff Hall, Chief Juvenile Officer

COURTS

2nd Judicial Circuit **660.397.2305**
Fax 660.397.3331
Web ....www.courts.mo.gov
E-mail ....russell.steele@courts.mo.gov
  107 N 4th St Ste 9, Edina, MO 63537-1470
  Honorable Russell E. Steele, Judge

POLICE AND SHERIFF

Sheriff's Dept **660.397.2186**
Fax 660.397.3432
Web ....www.cji.net
E-mail ....knoxcoso@cji.net
  107 N 4th St Ste 3, Edina, MO 63537-1470
  Mike Kite, Sheriff

EDUCATION SERVICES

Edina Head Start Ctr **660.397.3428**
Fax 660.397.3282
E-mail ....edinaheadstart@hotmail.com
  401 N 1st St, Edina, MO 63537-1029
  Annette Whiles, Supervisor

Laclede County

SOCIAL SERVICES

**Family Support/Children's Div/Senior
Svcs** **417.532.3137**
Fax 417.532.3973
Web ....www.dss.mo.gov
E-mail ....laclede.codfs@dss.mo.gov
  2639 S Jefferson Ave, Lebanon, MO 65536-5205
  Sharon Holloway, County Director

JUSTICE AGENCY

Juvenile Ofc **417.532.4961**
Fax 417.532.1863
  200 N Adams Ave, Laclede County Gov. Center,
  Lebanon, MO 65536
  Tammy Lea Walden, Chief Juvenile Officer

POLICE AND SHERIFF

Sheriff's Dept **417.532.2311**
Fax 417.533.3505
Web ....www.llion.org
E-mail ....rwrinkle@llion.org
  240 N Adams Ave, Lebanon, MO 65536-3046
  Richard E. Wrinkle, Sheriff

Lafayette County

SOCIAL SERVICES

**Family Support/Children's Div/Senior
Svcs** **660.259.2294**
Fax 660.259.3834
Web ....www.dss.mo.gov
E-mail ....katie.igo@dss.mo.gov
  736 S Highway 13, Lexington, MO 64067-1514
  Katie Igo, Director/children

GENERAL HEALTH SERVICES

Health Dept **660.259.4371**
Fax 660.259.6250
Web ....www.lpha.dhss.mo.gov
E-mail ....thompj@lpha.dhss.mo.gov
  547 S Highway 13, Lexington, MO 64067-1437
  Jill Thompson, Director

JUSTICE AGENCY

Juvenile Ofc **660.259.4236**
Fax 660.259.6686
E-mail ....amy.meyers@courts.mo.gov
  1108 Main St, Lexington, MO 64067
  Amy Meyers, Chief Juvenile Officer

COURTS

15th Associate Judicial Circuit Div **660.259.6101**
Fax 660.259.6148
Web ....www.lafayettecountymo.com
E-mail ....deana.aversman@courts.mo.gov
  116 S. 10th St., Lexington, MO 64067
  Deana Aversman, Circuit Clerk

POLICE AND SHERIFF

Sheriff's Dept **660.259.3392**
Fax 660.259.2545
E-mail ....lcsheriff@lcsheriff.com
  107 S 11th St, Lexington, MO 64067
  Kerrick Alumbaugh, Sheriff

Sheriff's Dept **660.259.3622**
Fax 660.259.2545
  107 S 11th St, Lexington, MO 64067
  Kerrick Alumbaugh, Sheriff

Lawrence County

SOCIAL SERVICES

**Family Support/Children's Div/Senior
Svcs** **417.678.4138**
Fax 417.678.5721
Web ....www.dss.mo.gov
E-mail ....jane.a.claas@dss.mo.gov
  1419 E Church St, Aurora, MO 65605-2324
  Jane Claas, Family Services Manager

GENERAL HEALTH SERVICES

Health Dept **417.466.2201**
Fax 417.466.7485
Web ....www.lawrencecohealth.com
E-mail ....goodma@lpha.mopublic.org
  105 W North St, Mount Vernon, MO 65712-1017
  Aletha Goodman, Director

COURTS

39th Judicial Circuit **417.466.2471**
Fax 417.466.7899
E-mail ....robert.wiley@courts.mo.gov
  240 N Main St Ste 110, Mount Vernon, MO 65712
  Honorable Robert Wiley, Judge

POLICE AND SHERIFF

Sheriff's Dept **417.466.2131**
Fax 417.466.4222
Web ....www.sofnet.com
E-mail ....bdelay@lawrencecosheriff.com
  300 E Water St, Mount Vernon, MO 65712-1118
  Brad Delay, Sheriff

Lewis County

SOCIAL SERVICES

**Family Support/Children's Div/Senior
Svcs** **573.767.5284**
Fax 573.767.5368
  500 S Washington St, Monticello, MO 63457
  Teresa Yager, Director

GENERAL HEALTH SERVICES

Health Dept **573.767.5312**
Fax 573.767.5301
  101 State Hwy, Monticello, MO 63457
  Diane Lay, Rn, Administrator

JUSTICE AGENCY

Juvenile Ofc **573.767.5210**
Fax 573.767.5452
Web ....www.courts.mo.gov
E-mail ....jeff.hall@courts.mo.gov
  105 E Lafayette, Monticello, MO 63457
  Jeff Hall, Chief Juvenile Officer

COURTS

2nd Judicial Circuit **573.767.5352**
Fax 573.767.5342
Web ....www.courts.mo.gov
E-mail ....jan.geisendorfer@courts.mo.gov
  101 E Lafayette St, Monticello, MO 63457-9997
  Jan Geisendorfer, Circuit Clerk

Lincoln County

GENERAL HEALTH SERVICES

Health Dept 636.528.6117
Fax 636.528.8629
Web ....www.lchdmo.org
E-mail ....bordej@lchdmo.org
5 Health Department Dr, Troy, MO 63379-4551
Jolene Borders, Hiv Program Manager

JUSTICE AGENCY

Div of Youth Svcs/Camp Avery 636.528.8800
Fax 636.528.5179
198 Avery Ln, Troy, MO 63379
Sam Turner, Director

Juvenile Ofc 636.528.4332
Fax 636.528.8188
E-mail ....ernie.painter@courts.mo.gov
45 Business Park Dr, Troy, MO 63379
Ernest M. Painter, Chief Juvenile Officer

COURTS

Justice Ctr 636.528.6300
Fax 636.528.9168
45 Business Park Dr, Troy, MO 63379
Grace Sinclair, Circuit Clerk

POLICE AND SHERIFF

Sheriff's Ofc 636.528.8546
Fax 636.528.6502
65 Business Park Dr, Troy, MO 63379
Mike Krigbaum, Sheriff

Linn County

SOCIAL SERVICES

**Family Support/Children's Div/Senior
Svcs** 660.258.3388
Fax 660.258.2091
E-mail ....pam.j.pope@dss.mo.gov
103 Forest Dr, Brookfield, MO 64628
Pam Pope, County Director

GENERAL HEALTH SERVICES

Health Dept 660.258.7251
Fax 660.258.7105
E-mail ....linnmo2000@yahoo.com
635 S Main St, Brookfield, MO 64628
Gary Routledge, Director

COURTS

9th Judicial Circuit 660.895.5212
Fax 660.895.5277
Web ....www.courts.mo.gov
E-mail ....james.williams@courts.mo.gov
108 North High, Linneus, MO 64653
Honorable James P. Williams, Associate Judge

POLICE AND SHERIFF

Sheriff's Dept 660.895.5312
Fax 660.895.5587
E-mail ....linncoso@yahoo.com
115 West Jackson St, Linneus, MO 64653
Tom Parks, Sheriff

EDUCATION SERVICES

Brookfield A Head Start Ctr 660.258.7571
Fax 660.258.7571
210 W John St, Brookfield, MO 64628-1619
Barbara Buckallew, Director

Livingston County

SOCIAL SERVICES

**Family Support/Children's Div/Senior
Svcs** 660.646.5770
Fax 660.646.3278
Web ....www.dss.mo.gov
E-mail ....deborah.heldendrand@dss.mo.gov
601 W Mohawk Rd Ste B, Chillicothe,
MO 64601-3919
Deborah Heldendrand, County Manager

GENERAL HEALTH SERVICES

Health Ctr 660.646.5506
Fax 660.646.4485
Web ....www.livcohealthcentre.com
E-mail ....Weldos@lpha.mopublic.gov
800 Adam Dr, Chillicothe, MO 64601-3900
Sherry Weldon, Director

JUSTICE AGENCY

Juvenile Ofc 660.646.8000
Fax 660.646.8003
Web ....www.livingstoncountymo.com
E-mail ....david.gann@courts.mo.gov
101 E Washington St, Macon, MO 63552
David Gann, Juvenile Officer

POLICE AND SHERIFF

Sheriff's Dept 660.646.0515
Fax 660.646.0520
E-mail ....sheriff@greenhills.net
901 Webster St, Chillicothe, MO 64601
Steve Cox, Sheriff

EDUCATION SERVICES

Chillicothe R-II Even Start 660.646.1653
E-mail ....pfetter@chillicotheschools.org
209 Henry St, Chillicothe, MO 64601
Pam Fetter, Director

Chilliothe Head Start Ctr 660.646.0083
529 Saint Louis Ave, Chillicothe, MO 64601
Robyn Melte, Director

Macon County

SOCIAL SERVICES

Family Support/Children's Div 660.385.3191
Fax 660.385.5268
1716 Prospect Dr, Macon, MO 63552
Jennifer Gunnels, Supervisor

GENERAL HEALTH SERVICES

Health Dept 660.385.4711
Fax 660.385.2014
E-mail ....rushtj@lpha.dhss.mo.gov
503 N Missouri St, Macon, MO 63530
Judy Rushton, Administrator

Northeastern District Health Ofc 660.385.3125
Fax 660.385.6214
Web ....www.dhss.mo.gov
E-mail ....terri.maley@dhss.mo.gov
708 Patton St, Macon, MO 63552-2505
Terri Maley, Special Health Care Needs Community Health Nurse

JUSTICE AGENCY

Juvenile Ofc 660.385.2715
Fax 660.385.5080
101 East Washington Street, Macon, MO 63552
Cynthia Ayers, Chief Juvenile Officer

COURTS

41st Judicial Circuit 660.385.4631
Fax 660.385.4235
E-mail ....philip.prewitt@courts.mo.gov
101 E Washington, Bldg 2 Ste 1, Macon, MO 63550
Honorable Phlilip E. Prewitt, Associate Judge

POLICE AND SHERIFF

Sheriff's Ofc 660.385.2062
Fax 660.385.5308
E-mail ....mcso@cvalley.net
101 W. Sheridan St, Macon, MO 63552
Robert D. Dawson, Sheriff

EDUCATION SERVICES

DCS Head Start Macon 660.385.5318
Fax 660.385.5319
1307 Maffry Ave, Macon, MO 63552
Dana Kirks, Center Manager

Madison County

SOCIAL SERVICES

**Family Support/Children's Div/Senior
Svcs** 573.783.5596
Fax 573.783.5227
Web ....www.dss.mo.gov
E-mail ....sharron.tinnen@dss.mo.gov
413 Burris St, Fredericktown, MO 63645-7294
Sharron Tinnen, County Manager

GENERAL HEALTH SERVICES

Health Dept 573.783.2747
Fax 573.783.8039
806 W College Ave, Fredericktown, MO 63645
Becky Hunt, Director

POLICE AND SHERIFF

Sheriff's Ofc 573.783.2234
Fax 573.783.8528
124 N Main St, Fredericktown, MO 63645
David R. Lewis, Sheriff

EDUCATION SERVICES

EMAA Head Start Fredericktown 573.783.7112
Fax 573.783.7112
Web ....www.eastmoaa.org
E-mail ....lfrancis@eastmoaa.org
600 S Chamber Dr, Fredericktown, MO 63645-1742
Linda Francis, Director

Maries County

COURTS

25th Associate Judicial Circuit 573.422.3338
Fax 573.422.3976
Web ....www.courts.mo.gov
E-mail ....kerry.rowden@courts.mo.gov
211 4th St, Vienna, MO 65582
Honorable Kerry Rowden, Associate Judge

POLICE AND SHERIFF

Sheriff's Ofc 573.422.3381
Fax 573.422.3100
211 4th St, Vienna, MO 65582
Chris Heitman, Sheriff

Marion County

SOCIAL SERVICES

**Family Support/Children's Div/Senior
Svcs** 573.248.2540
Fax 573.248.2416
E-mail ....teresa.yager@dss.mo.gov
3055 Holman Dr, Hannibal, MO 63401
Teresa Yager, County Manager

GENERAL HEALTH SERVICES

Health Dept 573.221.1166
Fax 573.221.1214
Web ....www.marioncountyhealth.org
E-mail ....MCBRIO@LPHA.MOPUBLIC.ORG
3105 Palmyra Rd, Hannibal, MO 63401
Jean Mcbride, Adminstrator

Missouri

JUSTICE AGENCY

Douglass Community Services..............**573.221.3892**
Fax...573.221.6196
E-mail.............................dave1@douglassonline.org
   711 Grand Ave, C/O Douglass Community Services,
   Hannibal, MO 63401
   Dave Dexheimer, Director

Juvenile Ofc...................................**573.221.1182**
Fax...573.248.1137
   304 Willow St, Hannibal, MO 63401
   Philip Livesay, Chief Juvenile Officer

POLICE AND SHERIFF

Sheriff's Ofc..................................**573.769.2077**
Fax...573.769.2080
   1703 Marion City Rd, Palmyra, MO 63461-3159
   James Fhinn, Sheriff

EDUCATION SERVICES

DCS Head Start-Hannibal.................**573.231.0754**
Fax...573.231.0954
E-mail.............................kathy@douglassonline.org
   2181 Johnson St, Hannibal, MO 63401-5843
   Kathy Newlon, Sr. Manager

McDonald County

SOCIAL SERVICES

Family Support/Children's Div/Senior
Svcs...**417.845.6951**
Fax...417.845.1217
Web...www.dss.mo.gov
E-mail...............................shawn.boyd@dss.mo.gov
   929 N Highway 71, Anderson, MO 64831
   Shawn Boyd, Director

GENERAL HEALTH SERVICES

Health Dept....................................**417.223.4351**
Fax...417.223.4109
Web..............................www.mcdonaldcountyhealth.com
E-mail............................behmp@lpha.mopublic.org
   500 Olin St, Pineville, MO 64856
   Paige Behm, Administrator

COURTS

40th Judicial Circuit.........................**417.223.7515**
Fax...417.223.4125
   602 Main, Pineville, MO 64856
   Honorable Timothy W. Perigo, Presiding Judge

POLICE AND SHERIFF

Sheriff's Ofc..................................**417.223.7429**
Fax...417.223.2331
Web.............................www.mcdonaldcountysheriff.com
   300 East 7th St, Pineville, MO 64856
   Robert Evenson, Sheriff

Mercer County

SOCIAL SERVICES

Family Support/Children's Div/Senior
Svcs...**660.748.3292**
Fax...660.748.3494
E-mail...........................bonnie.walker@dss.mo.gov
   501 W Main St, Princeton, MO 64673-1137
   Bonnie Walker, County Manager Of Family Services

GENERAL HEALTH SERVICES

Health Dept....................................**660.748.3630**
Fax...660.748.3634
E-mail.........................johnsp1@lpha.dhss.mo.gov
   305 W Main St, Princeton, MO 64673
   Phyllis Johnson, Rn, Administrator

COURTS

3rd Judicial Circuit...........................**660.748.4335**
Fax...660.748.4339
   802 E Main St, Princeton, MO 64673
   Honorable Jack N. Peace, Judge

Miller County

SOCIAL SERVICES

Family Support/Children's Div/Senior
Svcs...**573.392.5141**
Fax...573.392.0120
   6 Industrial Dr, Eldon, MO 65026
   Dana Perkins, Circuit Manager, Childrens Services

JUSTICE AGENCY

Juvenile Ofc...................................**573.369.1990**
Fax...573.369.1893
E-mail......................tammy.walden@courts.mo.gov
   2001 Hwy 52, Tuscumbia, MO 65082
   Tammy Walden, Chief Juvenile Officer

COURTS

26th Judicial Circuit.........................**573.369.1980**
Fax...573.369.1894
   2001 Highway 52, Tuscumbia, MO 65082
   Honorable Kenny Hayden, Circuit Judge

POLICE AND SHERIFF

Sheriff's Ofc..................................**573.369.2341**
Fax...573.369.2247
   1999 Highway 52, Tuscumbia, MO 65082
   William M. Abbott, Sheriff

Mississippi County

SOCIAL SERVICES

Family Support/Children's Div/Senior
Svcs...**573.649.3091**
Fax...573.649.5911
Web...www.dss.mo.gov
   718 N Martin St, East Prairie, MO 63845-1211
   Doris Smith, County Manager

GENERAL HEALTH SERVICES

Health Dept....................................**573.683.2191**
Fax...573.683.6539
Web.......................................www.lpha.dhss.mo.gov
E-mail.........................glausm@lpha.dhss.mo.gov
   1200 E Marshall St, Charleston, MO 63834-1336
   Melonie Glaus, RN, Director

COURTS

33rd Judicial Circuit.........................**573.683.2146**
Fax...573.683.7696
Web.......................................www.courts.mo.gov
E-mail.........................leigh.colson@courts.mo.gov
   200 N Main St, Charleston, MO 63834
   Leighann Colson, Circuit Clerk

POLICE AND SHERIFF

Sheriff's Ofc..................................**573.683.2111**
Fax...573.683.2113
Web...www.misscomo.net
E-mail...............................kmoore@misscomo.net
   200 W Commercial St, Charleston, MO 63834-1609
   Keith Moore, Sheriff

EDUCATION SERVICES

East Prairie Head Start.....................**573.649.5005**
Fax...573.649.9298
Web.....................................www.dexterheadstart.org
E-mail...............................hseprairie@daeoc.com
   115 N Lincoln St, East Prairie, MO 63845-1149
   Kristin Byassee, Director

Moniteau County

SOCIAL SERVICES

Family Support/Children's Div/Senior
Svcs...**573.796.3196**
Fax...573.796.3230
E-mail..................................kim.evans@dss.mo.gov
   104 N Gerhart Rd, California, MO 65018
   Kim Evans, County Manager

GENERAL HEALTH SERVICES

Health Ctr.....................................**573.796.3412**
Fax...573.796.8364
   401 S Francis St, California, MO 65018-2204
   Andrea Kincaid, Director

COURTS

26th Judicial Circuit.........................**573.796.2071**
Fax...573.796.2591
   200 E Main St, Ste 6, California, MO 65018
   Honorable Greg Kays, Judge

POLICE AND SHERIFF

Sheriff's Ofc..................................**573.796.2525**
Fax...573.796.4057
Web.................www.moniteaucountysheriffsoffice.org
E-mail..................info@moniteaucountysheriffsoffice.org
   102 E North St, California, MO 65018-1585
   Jeptha Gump, Sheriff

Monroe County

SOCIAL SERVICES

Family Support/Children's Div/Senior
Svcs...**660.327.4185**
Fax...660.327.5668
   315 N Washington St, Paris, MO 65275
   Melinda Macker, County Director

GENERAL HEALTH SERVICES

Health Dept....................................**660.327.4653**
Fax...660.327.4533
   310 Market St, Paris, MO 65275
   Paula Delaney, Administrator

POLICE AND SHERIFF

Sheriff's Ofc..................................**660.327.5175**
Fax...660.327.5188
   300 N Main St Rm 205, Paris, MO 65275-1399
   David Hoffman, Sheriff

Montgomery County

SOCIAL SERVICES

Family Support/Children's Div/Senior
Svcs...**573.564.2258**
Fax...573.564.3167
Web...www.dss.mo.gov
E-mail...............................ann.mullen@dss.mo.gov
   501 Niedergerke Dr, Montgomery City,
   MO 63361-2624
   Vickie Stoneberger, County Manager

GENERAL HEALTH SERVICES

Health Dept....................................**573.564.2495**
Fax...573.564.5059
Web.....................................www.montgomerycountyhealth.org
E-mail...............................riddll@lpha.mopublic.org
   400 Salisbury St, Montgomery City, MO 63361-1213
   Lori Riddle, Rn, Administrator

JUSTICE AGENCY

Juvenile Court Svcs.........................**573.564.3750**
Fax...573.564.2438
   211 E 3rd St Ste 105, Montgomery City, MO 63361
   Melissa Dempsey, Deputy Juvenile Officer

POLICE AND SHERIFF

Sheriff's Ofc............................**573.564.3703**
Fax...573.564.8083
E-mail.........................sheriff@mccountymo.com
211 E 3rd St Ste 209, Montgomery City, MO 63361
Robert Davis, Sheriff

Morgan County

SOCIAL SERVICES

Family Support/Children's Div/Senior

Svcs......................................**573.378.4681**
Fax...573.378.1919
703 N Monroe St, Versailles, MO 65084
Marsha Dinkins, County Manager

GENERAL HEALTH SERVICES

Health Ctr..............................**573.378.5438**
Fax...573.378.2726
Web...............................www.lpha.dhss.mo.gov
E-mail.......................kerksl@lpha.dhss.mo.gov
104 W Lafayette St, Versailles, MO 65084-1346
Lorraine Kerksick, Director

JUSTICE AGENCY

Juvenile Ofc...........................**573.378.4658**
Fax...573.378.2837
211 E Newton St, Versailles, MO 65084
Justin Doyle, Deputy Juvenile Officer

COURTS

26th Judicial Circuit...............**573.378.4413**
Fax...573.378.5356
211 E Newton St Ste 5, Versailles, MO 65084
Cheryl Morris, Circuit Clerk

POLICE AND SHERIFF

Sheriff's Dept.........................**573.378.5481**
Fax...573.378.7171
Web.................................www.morgan-justice.org
E-mail.................jim_petty@morgan-justice.org
211 E Newton St Ste 2, Versailles, MO 65084-1636
Jim Petty, Sheriff

New Madrid County

SOCIAL SERVICES

Family Support/Children's Div/Senior

Svcs......................................**573.748.5533**
Fax...573.748.2729
E-mail....................nada.scruggs@dss.mo.gov
350 US Highway 61, New Madrid, MO 63869
Diaen Danbach, Director

GENERAL HEALTH SERVICES

New Madrid Health Dept.......**573.748.5541**
Fax...573.748.5996
Web..........www.newmadridcountyhealthdepartment.com
E-mail........................deesj@lpha.mopublic.org
406 US Highway 61, New Madrid, MO 63869-1642
Jayne Dees, Director

JUSTICE AGENCY

Juvenile Ofc...........................**573.748.2123**
Fax...573.748.5402
Web...............................www.courts.mo.gov
E-mail....................brian.abbott@courts.mo.gov
450 Main St, New Madrid, MO 63869-1758
Brian Abbott, Chief Juvenile Officer

POLICE AND SHERIFF

Sheriff's Ofc............................**573.748.2516**
Fax...573.748.2540
Web...www.cji.net
E-mail............................tstevens@cji.net
2 Court House Sq, New Madrid, MO 63869-1795
Terry Stevens, Sheriff

Newton County

SOCIAL SERVICES

Family Support/Children's Div/Senior

Svcs......................................**417.455.5100**
Fax...417.455.5152
E-mail.......................shawn.boyd@dss.mo.gov
201 N Washington St, Neosho, MO 64850
Shawn Boyd, Circuit Manager

GENERAL HEALTH SERVICES

Health Dept...........................**417.451.3743**
Fax...417.451.1852
Web...............www.newtoncountyhealth.org
E-mail...............kulpb@newtoncountyhealth.org
812 W Harmony St, Neosho, MO 64850-1627
Bob Kulp, Administrator

JUSTICE AGENCY

Juvenile Ofc...........................**417.451.8236**
Fax...417.451.8280
Web...............................www.courts.mo.gov
E-mail.................cathy.gorham@courts.mo.gov
107 N Jefferson St, Neosho, MO 64850-1543
Cathy Gorham, Chief Juvenile Officer

COURTS

40th Judicial Circuit...............**417.451.8210**
Fax...417.451.8272
101 S Wood St, Neosho, MO 64850
Patty Kruger, Circuit Clerk

POLICE AND SHERIFF

Sheriff's Ofc............................**417.451.8300**
Fax...417.451.8352
E-mail......................ken_copeland@nc-so.org
208 W Coler St, Neosho, MO 64850
Ken Copeland, Sheriff

Nodaway County

SOCIAL SERVICES

Family Support/Children's Div/Senior

Svcs......................................**660.582.3141**
Fax...660.582.3180
Web...............................www.dss.mo.gov
E-mail......................leslie.riney@dss.mo.gov
301 E Summit Dr, Maryville, MO 64468-3619
Leslie Riney, County Manager

GENERAL HEALTH SERVICES

Health Dept...........................**660.562.2755**
Fax...660.562.4995
2332 s main, Maryville, MO 64468
Della Rhoades, Director

COURTS

4th Judicial Circuit.................**660.582.5431**
Fax...660.582.2047
305 N Main St, Maryville, MO 64468-1645
Honorable Glen Dietrich, Associate Circuit Judge

POLICE AND SHERIFF

Sheriff's Ofc............................**660.582.7451**
Fax...660.582.8558
Web.............................www.bransonperry.com
E-mail............................ben@bransonperry.com
404 N Vine St, Maryville, MO 64468-1651
Barren Y White, Sheriff

Oregon County

SOCIAL SERVICES

Family Support/Children's Div/Senior

Svcs......................................**417.778.7251**
Fax...417.778.6773
Highway 19, South Alton, MO 65606
Martha Mills, County Manager

GENERAL HEALTH SERVICES

Health Dept...........................**417.778.7450**
Fax...417.778.6826
Web...............................www.lpha.dhss.mo.gov
E-mail.......................russes@lpha.dhss.mo.gov
4 Market St., Alton, MO 65606
Sheila Russell, Administrator

COURTS

37th Judicial Circuit...............**417.778.7460**
Fax...417.778.7206
Web...............................www.courts.mo.gov
E-mail.................harvey.allan@courts.mo.gov
PO Box 406, Alton, MO 65606-0406
Harvey Allan, Judge

POLICE AND SHERIFF

Sheriff's Ofc............................**417.778.6611**
Fax...417.778.6641
Web.............................www.mosheriffs.com
E-mail............................george@mosheriffs.com
Market Street & Broadway #3, Alton, MO 65606
George Underwood, Sheriff

Osage County

SOCIAL SERVICES

Family Support/Children's Div/Senior

Svcs......................................**573.897.3678**
Fax...573.897.9869
925 E Main St, Linn, MO 65051
Sherry Smith, Childrens Division- 20th Circuit Manager

COURTS

20th Judicial Circuit...............**573.897.3114**
Fax...573.897.4075
Web...............................www.courts.mo.gov
E-mail.............charlene.eisterhold@courts.mo.gov
106 E Main St, Linn, MO 65051-9512
Charlene Eisterhold, Circuit Clerk

POLICE AND SHERIFF

Sheriff's Ofc............................**573.897.3107**
Fax...573.897.0653
106 E Main St, Linn, MO 65051-9512
Carl A. Fowler, Sheriff

EDUCATION SERVICES

Chamois Head Start Ctr.........**573.763.5640**
E-mail...............shelly-weed@showmeaction.org
602 S Poplar St, Chamois, MO 65024
Shelly Weed, Director

Ozark County

SOCIAL SERVICES

Family Support/Children's Div/Senior

Svcs......................................**417.679.4616**
Fax...417.679.3103
Web...............................www.dss.mo.gov
E-mail.......................lane.lakey@dss.mo.gov
735 Highway 160 West, Gainesville, MO 65655
Lane E. Lakey, Director

GENERAL HEALTH SERVICES

Health Dept...........................**417.679.3334**
Fax...417.679.3828
Web...www.ocph.org
304 W 3Rd St, Gainesville, MO 65655
Rhonda Suter, Director

JUSTICE AGENCY

Juvenile Ofc **417.926.3129**
Fax 417.926.6239
Web ....www.courts.mo.gov
E-mail ....jerry.conner@courts.mo.gov
   1400 Industrial Park Drive, Mountain Grove,
   MO 65711
   Jerry Conner, Chief Juvenile Officer

COURTS

44th Judicial Circuit **417.679.4232**
Fax 417.679.4554
   1 Courthouse Square, Gainesville, MO 65655
   Becki Strong, Circuit Clerk

POLICE AND SHERIFF

Sheriff's Dept **417.679.4633**
Fax 417.679.3201
E-mail ....ozarkcountysheriff@centurytel.net
   HCR 1 Box 8-1, Gainesville, MO 65655
   Raymond Pace, Sheriff

Pemiscot County

SOCIAL SERVICES

Family Support/Children's Div/Senior
Svcs **573.333.1060**
Fax 573.333.5008
   911 Highway 84 W, Caruthersville, MO 63830
   Chuck Grubbs, Circuit Manager, Childrens Division

GENERAL HEALTH SERVICES

Health Dept **573.359.1656**
Fax 573.359.0159
E-mail ....wilkersonm@lpha.dhss.mo.gov
   810 E Reed St, Hayti, MO 63851
   Mickey Wilkerson, Rn, Hiv Coordinator

JUSTICE AGENCY

Juvenile Ofc **573.333.4081**
Fax 573.333.2769
Web ....www.courts.mo.gov
E-mail ....brian.abbott@courts.mo.gov
   608 Ward Ave, Suite 4, Caruthersville, MO 63830
   Brian Abbott, Chief Juvenile Officer

COURTS

34th Judicial Circuit **573.333.0187**
Fax 573.333.1272
   610 Ward Ave., Suite 3A, Caruthersville, MO 63830
   Kelly Maners, 34 Circuit Clerk

EDUCATION SERVICES

Caruthersville Head Start **573.333.4536**
Fax 573.333.0877
Web ....www.daeoc.com
   810 Truman Blvd, Caruthersville, MO 63830-1706

Perry County

SOCIAL SERVICES

Family Support/Children's Div/Senior
Svcs **573.547.8372**
Fax 573.547.3803
   300 A Erry Plaza, Perryville, MO 63775
   Terri Mungle, Supervisor

GENERAL HEALTH SERVICES

Health Dept **573.547.6564**
Fax 573.547.3908
Web ....www.perrycountyhealthdepartment.org
   406 N Spring St Ste 1, Perryville, MO 63775
   Judy Laurentius, Director

JUSTICE AGENCY

Juvenile Ofc 32nd Circuit **573.547.1255**
Fax 573.547.2637
E-mail ....randall.rhodes@courts.mo.gov
   15 W Sainte Marie St Ste 8, Perryville,
   MO 63775-1399
   Randall Rhodes, Juvenile Officer Of The Circuit

COURTS

32nd Judicial Circuit **573.547.6581**
Fax 573.547.9323
   15 W Sainte Marie St, Perryville, MO 63775-1301
   Honorable Michael Bullerdieck, Judge

POLICE AND SHERIFF

Sheriff's Ofc **573.547.4576**
Fax 573.547.7461
Web ....www.powrup.net
E-mail ....sheriff@powrup.net
   710 S Kingshighway St, Perryville, MO 63775-2104
   Gary J. Schaaf, Sheriff

EDUCATION SERVICES

EMAA Head Start Perryville **573.547.8496**
E-mail ....cbuchanan@eastmoaa.org
   1416 N Kingshighway St, Perryville, MO 63755
   Christyn Buchanan, Director

Pettis County

SOCIAL SERVICES

Family Support/Children's Div/Senior
Svcs **660.530.5900**
Fax 660.530.5507
   808 Westwood Dr, Sedalia, MO 65301
   Dennis Banbaale, County Manager

GENERAL HEALTH SERVICES

Health Dept **660.827.1130**
Fax 660.827.1141
   911 E 16th St, Sedalia, MO 65301
   Joann Martin, Adminstrator

JUSTICE AGENCY

Juvenile Ofc **660.827.1062**
Fax 660.827.8632
E-mail ....mike.hughes@courts.mo.gov
   403 S Lamine Ave, Sedalia, MO 65301
   Mike Hughes, Chief Juvenile Officer

COURTS

18th Judicial Circuit Court **660.826.5000**
Fax 660.826.4520
Web ....www.osca.state.mo.us
E-mail ....rob_koffman@osca.state.mo.us
   415 S Ohio Ave Ste 102, Sedalia, MO 65301-4445
   Honorable Robert L. Koffman, Judge

POLICE AND SHERIFF

Sheriff's Ofc **660.827.0052**
Fax 660.826.5254
E-mail ....sheriff@pettiscomo.com
   319 S Lamine Ave, Sedalia, MO 65301
   Kevin C. Bond, Sheriff

Phelps County

SOCIAL SERVICES

Family Support/Children's Div/Senior
Svcs **573.368.2340**
Fax 573.368.2383
   1111 Kingshighway St Ste A, Rolla, MO 65401
   Nancy Buchmeier, County Manager

GENERAL HEALTH SERVICES

Health Dept **573.458.6010**
Fax 573.458.6060
Web ....www.phelpscountyhealth.com
E-mail ....jodi.waltman@phelpscounty.org
   200 N Main St Ste G51, Rolla, MO 65401-3070
   Jody Waltman, Administrator

JUSTICE AGENCY

CASA **573.458.6240**
Fax 573.458.6244
Web ....www.casascmo.org
E-mail ....casaphel@fidnet.com
   200 N Main St, Suite 242, Rolla, MO 65401
   Judith Waters, Program Manager

Juvenile Ofc **573.458.6075**
Fax 573.458.6079
E-mail ....kevin.breeden@courts.mo.gov
   200 N Main St, Phelps County Courthouse, Rolla,
   MO 65401
   Kevin Breeden, Juvenile Officer

Pike County

SOCIAL SERVICES

Family Support/Children's Div/Senior
Svcs **573.324.2243**
Fax 573.324.2930
   1610 Business Highway 54 W, Bowling Green,
   MO 63334-1035
   Kristin Gentry, County Manager

GENERAL HEALTH SERVICES

Health Dept **573.324.2111**
Fax 573.324.3057
E-mail ....sellej@lpha.nopublic.org
   1 Health Care Pl, Bowling Green, MO 63334
   Justin Selle, Director

JUSTICE AGENCY

Juvenile Ofc **573.324.3510**
Fax 573.324.6308
Web ....www.courts.mo.gov
E-mail ....don.nacke@courts.mo.gov
   115 W Main St Ste 33, Bowling Green,
   MO 63334-1665
   Don Nacke, Deputy Juvenile Officer

COURTS

45th Judicial Circuit **573.324.3112**
Fax 573.324.3150
   115 W Main St, Bowling Green, MO 63334
   Honorable Dan Dildine, Presiding Judge

POLICE AND SHERIFF

Sheriff's Ofc **573.324.3202**
Fax 573.324.3972
E-mail ....pcsodept@sbcglobal.net
   1600 Business Highway 54 W, Bowling Green,
   MO 63334
   Stephen Korte, Sheriff

EDUCATION SERVICES

DCS Head Start-Bowling Green **573.324.0167**
Fax 573.324.0165
   1903 W Locust St, Bowling Green, MO 63334-1027
   Deanna Mcmorris, Director

DCS Head Start-Louisiana **573.754.5471**
Fax 573.754.6059
E-mail ....aw1008081@onemain.com
   130 Memorial Dr, Louisiana, MO 63353-2418
   Jennifer House, Director

Platte County

SOCIAL SERVICES

Family Support/Children's Div/Senior

Svcs..**816.858.3740**
Fax...816.858.5208
Web...www.dss.mo.gov
E-mail....................debbie.reynolds@dss.mo.gov
233 Marshall Rd, Platte City, MO 64079-9762
Debbie Reynolds, County Manager

GENERAL HEALTH SERVICES

Health Dept.................................816.587.5998
Fax...816.587.6028
1201 East St, Parkville, MO 64152
Jill Harper, Nursing Supervisor

Health Dept.................................816.858.2412
Fax...816.858.2087
Web...........................www.plattecountyhealthdept.com
E-mail...........................lpha@plattehealth.com
212 Marshall Rd, Platte City, MO 64079-9761
Mary Jo Everhart, Administrator/director

JUSTICE AGENCY

Juvenile Ofc................................816.858.3420
Fax...816.858.3411
E-mail...................janet.warner@courts.mo.gov
508 3rd St Ste 85, Platte City, MO 64079
Janet Warner, Head Juvenile Officer

COURTS

6th Judicial Circuit........................816.858.2232
415 3rd St Ste 5, Platte City, MO 64079
Honorable Owens Hull, Juvinile Judge

POLICE AND SHERIFF

Sheriff's Dept...............................816.858.2424
Fax...816.858.3053
E-mail.........................sheriff@plattesheriff.org
415 3rd St Ste 10, Platte City, MO 64079
Richard L. Anderson, Sheriff

Polk County

SOCIAL SERVICES

Family Support/Children's Div/Senior

Svcs..**417.326.6241**
Fax...417.326.6265
Web...www.dss.mo.gov
E-mail.............................bill.hafer@dss.mo.gov
2110 S Springfield Ave, Bolivar, MO 65613-9683
Bill Hafer, Circuit Manager

JUSTICE AGENCY

Juvenile Ofc................................417.326.2498
Fax...417.326.8272
E-mail.....................debbiegiberson@justice.com
102 E Broadway Ste 13, Bolivar, MO 65613-1687
Debbie Giberson, Chief Juvenile Officer

COURTS

30th Judicial Circuit.......................417.326.4912
Fax...417.326.4194
Web...www.courts.mo.gov
E-mail.......................john.sims@courts.mo.gov
102 E Broadway Ste 14, Bolivar, MO 65613-1687
Honorable John W. Sims, Judge

POLICE AND SHERIFF

Sheriff's Ofc................................417.777.9020
Fax...417.777.7684
E-mail...............sb235@polkcountymosheriff.org
113 E Jefferson St, Bolivar, MO 65613
Steve Bruce, Sheriff

Pulaski County

SOCIAL SERVICES

Family Support Childrens Div Senior

Svcs..**573.774.6121**
Fax...573.774.2245
Web...www.dss.mo.gov
E-mail.................carolyn.f.gerber@dss.mo.gov
712 Historic Rt 66 W, Waynesville, MO 65583
Carolyn Gerber, Circuit Manager, Childrens Division

GENERAL HEALTH SERVICES

Health Dept.................................573.736.2217
Fax...573.736.5370
Web...........................www.pulaskcountyihealth.com
E-mail....................brasheard@lpha.dhss.mo.gov
101 12th St, Crocker, MO 65452
Dawna Brashear, Administrator

JUSTICE AGENCY

Juvenile Ofc................................573.774.4730
Fax...573.774.4732
Web...www.courts.mo.gov
E-mail.......................rsheldon@courts.mo.gov
301 Historic Rt. 66 E., Suite 205, Waynesville,
MO 65583
Russell Sheldon, Chief Juvenile Officer

COURTS

25th Judicial Circuit.......................573.774.4755
Fax...573.774.6967
301 Historic Route 66 East, Ste 202, Waynesville,
MO 65583
Honorable Colin P. Long, Judge

POLICE AND SHERIFF

Sheriff's Ofc................................573.774.6196
Fax...573.774.6129
Web...www.pcsheriiff2.com
E-mail.......................jbking@pcsheriiff2.com
301 Historic Route 66 East, Suite 136, Waynesville,
MO 65583
Jb King, Sheriff

EDUCATION SERVICES

Dixon Head Start Ctr.....................573.759.7781
Fax...573.759.7056
306 N Lang Rd, Dixon, MO 65459
Linda Campbell, Director

Putnam County

GENERAL HEALTH SERVICES

Health Dept.................................660.947.2429
Fax...660.947.3870
Web...........................www.putnamcohealthdept.org
E-mail......................klinge@lpha.mopublic.org
103 N 18Th St, Unionville, MO 63565-1607
Ericka Klingner, Medical Director

JUSTICE AGENCY

Juvenile Ofc................................660.359.2347
Fax...660.359.3402
E-mail.......................rita.martz@courts.mo.gov
700 Main St Ste 13, Trenton, MO 64683
Rita Martz, Chief Juvenile Officer

COURTS

3rd Judicial Circuit........................660.947.2071
Fax...660.947.2320
E-mail.........................jbush@courts.mo.gov
1601 Main St Rm 204, Unionville, MO 63565-1600
Honorable Jerri Bush, Judge

POLICE AND SHERIFF

Sheriff's Ofc................................660.947.3200
Fax...660.947.3700
Web...www.nemr.net
E-mail.........................sheriff@nemr.net
Courthouse Room 101, Unionville, MO 63565
Jason Knight, Sheriff

Ralls County

SOCIAL SERVICES

Family Support/Children's Div/Senior

Svcs..**573.985.2911**
Fax...573.985.3996
Web...www.dss.mo.gov
E-mail.......................glenda.coons@dss.mo.gov
209 East 4th St., New London, MO 63459
Teresa Yager, County Manager

GENERAL HEALTH SERVICES

Home Health Agency......................573.985.7121
Fax...573.985.1531
Web...www.ralls.lphamo.org
E-mail.......................taylot2@lpha.mopublic.org
405 W 1st St, New London, MO 63459
Tanya Taylor, Director

POLICE AND SHERIFF

Sheriff's Ofc................................573.985.5611
Fax...573.985.3100
E-mail...............476@rallscountysheriff.com
17630 Highway 19, New London, MO 63459
Paul Forney, Sheriff

EDUCATION SERVICES

DCS Head Start Ralls.....................573.985.3500
Fax...573.985.3500
209 Carstarphen Pl, New London, MO 63459
Maria Cafer, Director

Randolph County

SOCIAL SERVICES

Family Support/Children's Div/Senior

Svcs..**660.263.4330**
Fax...660.263.6560
Web...www.dss.mo.gov
E-mail...................deborah.furnell@dss.mo.gov
1715 S Morley St Ste B, Moberly, MO 65270-3022
Deborah Furnell, Circuit Manager

GENERAL HEALTH SERVICES

Health Dept.................................660.263.6643
Fax...660.263.0333
Web...........................www.randolphcountyhealth.org
423 E Logan St, Moberly, MO 65270-2222
Brook Gibson, Clinic Supervisor

JUSTICE AGENCY

Juvenile Court Svcs.......................660.263.2970
Fax...660.263.1193
223 N Williams St, Moberly, MO 65270
Chanda Bankhead, Chief Juvenile Officer

COURTS

14th Judicial Circuit.......................660.277.4601
Fax...660.277.4611
372 Highway J, Randolph County Justice Center,
Huntsville, MO 65259
Honorable Cynthia Suter, Associate Judge

POLICE AND SHERIFF

Sheriff's Ofc................................660.277.5095
Fax...660.277.5084
E-mail.........................mnichols@rcao.com
372 Highway JJ, Huntsville, MO 65259
Mark Nichols, Sheriff

EDUCATION SERVICES

DCS Head Start-Moberly 660.263.7421
Fax 660.263.2031
E-mail ....carol@douglassonline.org
   707 Sinnock Ave, Moberly, MO 65270-2766
   Carol French, Director

Ray County

SOCIAL SERVICES

Family Support/Children's Div/Senior

Svcs 816.776.6964
Fax 816.776.3503
Web ....www.dss.mo.gov
E-mail ....karla.a.polson@dss.mo.gov
   901 E Lexington St, Richmond, MO 64085-1931
   Karla Polson, County Manager

GENERAL HEALTH SERVICES

Health Dept 816.776.5413
Fax 816.776.2441
E-mail ....coxs@lpha.dhss.mo.gov
   820 E Lexington St, Richmond, MO 64085-1930
   Stacey Cox, Rn, Administrator

JUSTICE AGENCY

Juvenile Ofcs 816.776.5571
Fax 816.776.7046
   100 W Main St Ste 7, Richmond, MO 64085-1755
   Vernon M. Mcclure, Chief Juvenile Officer

COURTS

8th Judicial Circuit 816.776.3377
Fax 816.776.6016
Web ....www.courts.mo.gov
E-mail ....david.busch@courts.mo.gov
   100 West Main Street, Richmond, MO 64085
   David H. Miller, Circuit Judge

POLICE AND SHERIFF

Sheriff's Ofc 816.290.5323
Fax 816.290.5548
   200 W 9th St, Henrietta, MO 64036
   Samuel E. Clemens, Sheriff

Reynolds County

GENERAL HEALTH SERVICES

Div of Family Svcs & Aging 573.648.2401
Fax 573.648.2279
Web ....www.dss.mo.gov
E-mail ....janice.s.stout@dss.mo.gov
   2394 Hwy 21, Centerville, MO 63633
   Janice S Stout, Director

Health Ctr 573.648.2498
Fax 573.648.2510
   2323 Green St, Centerville, MO 63633
   Kathy Zimmerman, Administrator

JUSTICE AGENCY

Juvenile Ofc 573.648.2569
Fax 573.648.8047
E-mail ....debra.thomas@court.mo.us.gov
   PO Box 214, Centerville, MO 63633-0214
   Debra Thomas, Juvenile Officer

COURTS

42nd Judicial Circuit 573.648.2494
Fax 573.648.2503
   Hwy 21 Courthouse Sq, Centerville, MO 63633
   Honorable Edith R. Rutter, Judge

POLICE AND SHERIFF

Sheriff's Ofc 573.648.2491
Fax 573.648.2296
Web ....www.semo.net
   Courthouse Square, Centerville, MO 63665
   Tom Volner, Sheriff

Ripley County

GENERAL HEALTH SERVICES

Health Dept 573.996.2181
Fax 573.996.7632
Web ....www.ripleycountyhealth.com
E-mail ....rcphc@semo.net
   1003 Locust St, Doniphan, MO 63935
   Janice Morrow, Director

JUSTICE AGENCY

Juvenile Ofc 573.996.4015
Fax 573.996.4562
   6 Oak Tree Vlg, Doniphan, MO 63935
   Lesa Smith, Chief Juvenile Officer

COURTS

36th Judicial Circuit 573.996.2013
Fax 573.996.5014
   100 Court House Sq Ste 4, Doniphan,
   MO 63935-1699
   Honorable Thomas David Swindle, Associate Judge

POLICE AND SHERIFF

Sheriff's Ofc 573.996.5555
Fax 573.996.4318
   301 N Lafayette St, Doniphan, MO 63935
   Ron Barnett, Sheriff

EDUCATION SERVICES

Doniphan Head Start 573.996.5252
Fax 573.996.7651
   Highway 160 East, Doniphan, MO 63935
   Brenda Dale, Director

Saint Charles County

SOCIAL SERVICES

Family Support/Children's Div/Senior

Svcs 636.940.3170
Fax 636.940.3190
Web ....www.dss.mo.gov
E-mail ....danielle.abrams@dss.mo.gov
   3737 Harry S Truman Blvd Unit 100, Saint Charles,
   MO 63301-4096
   Danielle Abrams, Circuit Manager

GENERAL HEALTH SERVICES

Health Dept 636.949.7400
Fax 636.949.7403
Web ....www.scchealth.org
   1650 Boones Lick Rd, Saint Charles, MO 63301
   Hope Woodson, Deputy Director

JUSTICE AGENCY

Family court 636.949.7500
Fax 636.949.3028
Web ....www.courts.mo.gov
E-mail ....janelle.walters@courts.mo.gov
   1700 S River Rd, Saint Charles, MO 63303-4123
   Janelle Walters, Coordinator

Juvenile Ofc 636.949.3040
Fax 636.949.3028
   1700 S River Rd, Saint Charles, MO 63303
   Kennech Simmons, Chief Judge

POLICE AND SHERIFF

Sheriff's Ofc 636.949.0809
   101 Sheriff Dierker Ct, O Fallon, MO 63366
   Thomas Neer, Sheriff

EDUCATION SERVICES

Orchard Farm School District Special

Ed. 636.250.5000
Fax 636.250.5444
Web www.ofsd.k12.mo.us
   2165 Highway V, Saint Charles, MO 63301
   Dan Dozier, Superintendent

Saint Clair County

GENERAL HEALTH SERVICES

Health Dept 417.646.8332
Fax 417.646.8159
Web ....www.stclaircountyhealth.net
E-mail ....stephn@lpha.dhss.mo.gov
   530 Arduser Dr, Osceola, MO 64776-6284
   Nancy Stevens, Administrator

JUSTICE AGENCY

Juvenile Ofc 417.646.8591
Fax 417.646.2871
Web ....www.courts.mo.gov
E-mail ....swright@courts.mo.gov
   655 2nd St, Osceola, MO 64776
   Sharon Wright, Deputy Juvenile Officer

COURTS

27th Judicial Circuit 417.646.2226
Fax 417.646.2401
Web ....www.courts.mo.gov
E-mail ....michael.dawson@courts.mo.gov
   655 Second Street, Osceola, MO 64776
   Honorable Michael Dawson, Judge

POLICE AND SHERIFF

Sheriff's Ofc 417.646.2565
Fax 417.646.2852
E-mail ....ron.snodgrass@ago.mo.gov
   360 Chestnut St., Osceola, MO 64776
   Ron Snodgrass, Sheriff

EDUCATION SERVICES

Appleton City Head Start 660.476.5877
Fax 660.476.5877
   216 S Beech St, Appleton City, MO 64724
   Wanda Boch, Director

Saint Francois County

SOCIAL SERVICES

Family Support/Children's Div/Senior

Svcs 573.431.6592
Fax 573.431.7478
   140 Staples Dr, Park Hills, MO 63601
   Cheryl Brien, Circuit Manager

JUSTICE AGENCY

Juvenile Ofc 573.756.5766
Fax 573.756.5752
E-mail ....aceeckoff@courts.mo.gov
   1322 St. Genevieve Ave, Farmington, MO 63640
   Adrian Eckhoff, Chief Juvenile Officer

COURTS

24th Judicial Circuit 573.756.4551
Fax 573.756.3733
E-mail ....vickiweible@courts.mo.gov
   1 N Washington St Ste 102, Farmington, MO 63640
   Vicki Weible, Circuit Clerk

POLICE AND SHERIFF

Sheriff's Dept 573.756.3252
Fax 573.756.9622
Web ....www.sfcsd.org
E-mail ....bullod@sfcsd.org
   1550 Doubet Rd, Farmington, MO 63640-7020
   Daniel R. Bullock, Sheriff

EDUCATION SERVICES

EMAA Farmington Head Start 573.747.0373
E-mail ....bthompson@eastmoaa.org
   135 Vierse Dr, Farmington, MO 63640-1388
   Bev Thompson, Director

EMAA Head Start-Bonne Terre 573.358.5422
Fax 573.358.5422
  2 Savannah Dr, Bonne Terre, MO 63628-1362
Melody Mcdowell, Director

EMAA Head Start-Park Hills 573.431.2658
Web ....www.eastmoaa.org
E-mail ....rkillian@eastmoaa.org
  521 E Main St, Park Hills, MO 63601-2623
Renee Killian, Director

Saint Louis County

SOCIAL SERVICES

Children's Div Jennings Svc Ctr 314.877.2550
Fax 314.877.2551
Web ....www.dss.mo.gov
  8501 Lucas And Hunt Rd, Saint Louis, MO 63136
Susan Shelton, Director

Children's Svcs 314.301.7800
Fax 314.301.7888
Web ....www.dssweb.com
  6821 S Broadway, Saint Louis, MO 63111-3116
Anthony Harper, Unit Manager

Childrens Div South Svc Ctr 314.416.2700
Fax 314.416.2933
  7545 S Lindbergh Blvd Ste 110, Saint Louis, MO 63125
Stacey Ederer, Childrens Division Program Manager

Family Support Div 314.877.3050
Fax 314.877.3071
Web ....www.dss.mo.gov
  4040 7 Hills Dr Ste 141, Florissant, MO 63033
Gwen Belton, Office Manager

Family Support/Children's Div/Senior
Svcs 314.426.9600
Fax 314.426.6035
Web ....www.dss.mo.gov
E-mail ....v.fagyal@dss.mo.gov
  9900 Page Ave Ste 101, Saint Louis, MO 63132-1438
Vicki E. Fagyal, Children's Division Director

FSD St. Louis Regional Ofc 314.933.7000
Fax 314.340.5071
Web ....www.dss.mo.gov
  3101 Chouteau Ave, Saint Louis, MO 63103
Terry Brown, Im Director

Hogan St. Regional Youth Ctr 314.340.7434
Fax 314.340.7487
Web ....www.oa.mo.gov
  1839 Hogan St, Saint Louis, MO 63106-3098

Youth Svcs 314.355.2641
Fax 314.741.8912
  13300 Bellefontaine Rd, Fort Bellefontaine, Saint Louis, MO 63138
Greg Ziezryland, Assistant Regional Administrator

Youth Svcs 636.458.2992
Fax 636.458.5832
  1010 Lodge Rd, Babler Lodge, Chesterfield, MO 63005
Mike Hume, Facility Manager

Youth Svcs-St. Louis Region 314.340.6904
Fax 314.340.7721
Web ....www.dss.mo.gov
E-mail ....donald.pokorny@dss.mo.gov
  111 N 7th St Rm 331, WAINRIGHT BLDG ROOM 331, Saint Louis, MO 63101
Donald Pokorny, Regional Administrator

GENERAL HEALTH SERVICES

Dept of Health 314.612.5100
Fax 314.612.5105
Web ....www.stlouis.missouri.org/citygov/health/
  634 North Grand, Suite 910, Saint Louis, MO 63178
William Kincaid, Md, Phd, Director of Health

Eastern District Health Ofc 314.877.2800
Fax 314.877.2838
Web ....www.dhss.mo.gov/shcn
  220 S Jefferson Ave, Saint Louis, MO 63103
Titus Olajide, Regional Administrator

Health Dept 314.615.0600
Fax 314.615.6435
Web ....www.stlouisco.com
E-mail ....dgunn@stlouisco.com
  111 S Meramec Ave, Clayton, MO 63105
Delores Gunn, Health Director

JUSTICE AGENCY

CASA 314.615.2908
Fax 314.615.0621
E-mail ....info@casastlcounty.org
  121 S Meramec Ave, 2nd Floor, Saint Louis, MO 63105
Allie Chang Ray, Executive Director

Juvenile Detention Ctr 314.615.2996
Fax 314.615.4469
  501 S Brentwood Blvd, Saint Louis, MO 63105
Cheryl Campbell, Director

Juvenile Ofc 314.552.2000
Fax 314.552.2260
  920 N Vandeventer Ave, Saint Louis, MO 63108
Kathryn S. Herman, Juvenile Officer

COURTS

Family Court 314.615.4400
  501 S Brentwood Blvd, Saint Louis, MO 63105-2522
Michael Burton, Administrative Judge

Missouri Court of Appeals Eastern
District 314.539.4300
Fax 314.539.4324
  815 Olive St Rm 304, Saint Louis, MO 63101
Laura Thielmeier Roy, Clerk Of The Court

POLICE AND SHERIFF

Police Dept 314.727.4130
Fax 314.863.0285
Web ....www.clayton.mo.us
  227 S Central Ave, Saint Louis, MO 63105-3505
Detective Ronald Spielman, Juvenile Officer

Sheriff's Dept 314.622.4131
Fax 314.622.4839
  1114 Market St Rm 112, Saint Louis, MO 63101
James W. Murphy, Sheriff

Sheriff's Dept 314.615.4724
Fax 314.615.2548
Web ....www.stlouisco.com
  7900 Carondelet Ave Rm 551, Saint Louis, MO 63105-1720
Jim Buckles, Sheriff

EDUCATION SERVICES

Affton School District Special Ed. 314.638.8770
Fax 314.631.2548
Web www.affton.k12.mo.us
E-mail ....dfrancis@affton.k12.mo.us
  8701 MacKenzie Rd, Saint Louis, MO 63123
Don Francis, EDD, Superintendent

Bayless School District Education 314.631.2244
Fax 314.544.6315
Web www.baylessk12.org
  4530 Weber Rd, Saint Louis, MO 63123
Maureen Clancy, Superintendent

Hancock School District Special Ed. 314.544.1300
Fax 314.631.3712
E-mail ....hancock@k12.mo.us
  9101 S Broadway, Saint Louis, MO 63125
Greg Clark, Superintendent

Hazelwood School District Special
Ed. 314.953.5000
Fax 314.953.5085
Web www.hazelwood.k12.mo.us
E-mail ....sprice@hazelwoodschools.org
  15955 New Halls Ferry Rd, Florissant, MO 63031-1298
Dr. Steve Price, Superintendent

Ladue School District Special Ed 314.994.7080
Fax 314.994.0441
Web www.ladue.k12.mo.us
  9703 Conway Rd, Saint Louis, MO 63124-1698
Marsha Chappelow, Superintendent

Lindbergh School District Special
Ed. 314.729.2480
Fax 314.729.2482
Web ....www.lindberghschools.ws
E-mail ....jsandfort@lindberghschools.ws
  4900 S Lindbergh Blvd, Saint Louis, MO 63126-3299
Jim Simpson, Superintendent

Normandy School District Special
Ed. 314.493.0400
Fax 314.493.0475
Web www.normandy.k12.mo.us
  3855 Lucas And Hunt Rd Ste 100, Saint Louis, MO 63121
Statin Lawrence, Superintendent

Parkway School District Special Ed. 314.415.8100
Fax 314.415.8009
Web www.pkwy.k12.mo.us
  455 N Woods Mill Rd, Chesterfield, MO 63017
Dr. Keith Marty, Superintendent

Ritenour School District Special Ed. 314.493.6010
Fax 314.426.7144
Web www.ritenour.k12.mo.us
E-mail ....comptonc@ritenour.k12.mo.us
  2420 Woodson Rd, Saint Louis, MO 63114
Dr. Sheryl Compton, Superintendent

Riverview Gardens School District Special
Ed 314.869.2505
Fax 314.869.6354
Web ....www.rgsd.org
E-mail ....chomes@rgsd.k12.mo.us
  1370 Northumberland Dr, Saint Louis, MO 63137-1498
Dr. Clive Homes, Phd, Superintendent

Special Education 314.633.5300
Fax 314.633.5452
Web ....www.slps.org
E-mail ....joseph.jones@slps.org
  801 N 11th St, Saint Louis, MO 63101-1015
Joseph Jones, Executive Director

Special School District Special Ed. 314.989.8100
Fax 314.989.8504
Web ....www.ssdmo.org
  12110 Clayton Rd, Saint Louis, MO 63131-2599
John Cary, Superintendent

Student Svcs 314.290.4045
Fax 314.725.0965
Web ....www.ucityschools.org
  8136 Groby Rd, Saint Louis, MO 63130
Bernadette D. White, Executive Director Of Student Services

Sainte Genevieve County

SOCIAL SERVICES

Family Support/Children's Div/Senior

Svcs **573.883.5757**
Fax..................................573.883.7677
Web.............................www.dss.mo.gov
E-mail....................diann.declue@dss.mo.gov
  583 Sainte Genevieve Dr, Sainte Genevieve,
  MO 63670-1745
Diann Declue, Im Supervisor

GENERAL HEALTH SERVICES

Health Dept **573.883.7411**
Fax..................................573.883.5857
Web............................www.lpha.mopublic.org
E-mail....................bells@lpha.mopublic.org
  115 Basler Dr, Sainte Genevieve, MO 63670-7201
Sandi Bell, Director

POLICE AND SHERIFF

Sheriff's Dept **573.883.5820**
Fax..................................573.883.3465
E-mail....................gary.stolzer@sgcso.com
  5 Basler Dr, Sainte Genevieve, MO 63670
Gary Stolzer, Sheriff

EDUCATION SERVICES

EMAA Head Start Weingarten **573.883.3434**
Fax..................................573.883.7879
Web.............................www.eastmoaa.org
E-mail....................sbach@eastmoaa.org
  95 Sainte Genevieve Dr, Sainte Genevieve,
  MO 63670-1754
Susie Boch, Director

Saline County

SOCIAL SERVICES

Div of Family Svcs & Aging **660.886.5562**
Fax..................................660.886.4183
Web.............................www.dese.mo.gov
E-mail....................dennis.danbaale@dese.mo.gov
  1239 Santa Fe Trl Ste 100, Marshall, MO 65340-9168
Dennis Danbaale, Director

GENERAL HEALTH SERVICES

Public Health Ofc **660.886.3434**
Fax..................................660.886.6676
E-mail....................thomal4@lpha.mopublic.org
  1825 S Atchison Ave, Marshall, MO 65340
Lisa Thomas, Administrator

JUSTICE AGENCY

Juvenile Ofc **660.886.8870**
Fax..................................660.886.2378
  357 S Lafayette Ave, Marshall, MO 65340-2055
Amy Meyers, Chief Juvenile Officer

COURTS

15th Judicial Circuit **660.886.2300**
Fax..................................660.831.5360
  19 E Arrow St, Marshall, MO 65340-0597
Sharon Crawford, Circuit Clerk

POLICE AND SHERIFF

Sheriff's Dept **660.886.5511**
Fax..................................660.886.5513
Web.............................www.cdsinet.net
E-mail....................scso@cdsinet.net
  1915 W Arrow St, Marshall, MO 65340-9592
Wally George, Sheriff

Schuyler County

GENERAL HEALTH SERVICES

Health Dept **660.457.3721**
Fax..................................660.457.2238
Web............................www.lpha.mopublic.org
E-mail....................wilsob6@lpha.mopublic.org
  275 S Green, Lancaster, MO 63548
Brenda Wilson, Administrator

POLICE AND SHERIFF

Sheriff's Dept **660.457.3436**
Fax..................................660.457.2254
E-mail....................schlyershf@sbcglobal.net
  Courthouse Hwy 146, Lancaster, MO 63548
Carl Gottman, Sheriff

Scotland County

SOCIAL SERVICES

Family Support/Children's Div/Senior

Svcs **660.465.8549**
Fax..................................660.465.8980
  2 Child Support Ln, Memphis, MO 63555
Rachelle Curry, Director

JUSTICE AGENCY

Juvenile Ofcs **660.465.2978**
Fax..................................660.465.2279
E-mail....................ederosear@centurytel.net
  117 S Market St Ste 209, Memphis, MO 63555-1449
Jon Eric Derosear, Chief Juvenile Officer

COURTS

1st Judicial Circuit **660.465.8605**
Fax..................................660.465.8673
Web.................................www.nemr.net
E-mail....................anita.watkins@courts.mo.gov
  117 S Market St Ste 200, Memphis, MO 63555-1449
Anita Watkins, Circuit Clerk

POLICE AND SHERIFF

Sheriff's Ofc **660.465.2106**
Fax..................................660.465.7005
E-mail....................scsherif@nemr.net
  117 S Market St Ste 3, Memphis, MO 63555
Wayne T. Winn, Sheriff

Scott County

SOCIAL SERVICES

Family Support/Children's Div/Senior

Svcs **573.472.5222**
Fax..................................573.472.5383
Web.............................www.dss.mo.gov
E-mail....................sharon.ray@dss.mo.gov
  106 Arthur Ste B, Sikeston, MO 63801-5454
Sharon Ray, Children Circuit Manager

GENERAL HEALTH SERVICES

Health Dept **573.471.4044**
Fax..................................573.471.7348
  102 Grove Estates Court, Sikeston, MO 63801
Barry Cook, Administrator

JUSTICE AGENCY

Juvenile Ofc **573.472.2554**
Fax..................................573.472.3492
E-mail....................blawson@courts.mo.gov
  205 N New Madrid St, Sikeston, MO 63801-4142
Billie Lawson Jr., Chief Juvenile Officer

COURTS

33rd Judicial Circuit **573.545.3596**
Fax..................................573.545.3597
Web.............................www.osca.state.mo.us
E-mail....................christy.hency@osca.state.mo.us
  131 winchester, benton, MO 63736
Christy Hency, Clerk

POLICE AND SHERIFF

Sheriff's Ofc **573.545.3525**
Fax..................................573.545.4128
E-mail....................walter@charter.net
  131 S. New Madrid St., Benton, MO 63736
Rick Walter, Sheriff

EDUCATION SERVICES

Chaffee Head Start **573.887.6220**
Fax..................................573.887.6635
E-mail....................lwaddle@daeoc.com
  611 N Main St, Chaffee, MO 63740
Lavergne Waddle, Director

Shannon County

SOCIAL SERVICES

Family Support/Children's Div **573.226.3295**
Fax..................................573.226.5422
E-mail....................linda.elam@dss.mo.gov
  Hwy. 19 South & Route F, Eminence, MO 65466
Linda Elam, County Manager

GENERAL HEALTH SERVICES

Home & Health Agency **573.226.3914**
Fax..................................573.226.3240
Web............................www.lpha.mopublic.org
E-mail....................countk@lpha.mopublic.org
  110 Grey Jones Dr, Eminence, MO 65466
Kandra Counts, Home Health Administrator

POLICE AND SHERIFF

Sheriff's Dept **573.226.3615**
Fax..................................573.226.5561
E-mail....................shanso@semo.net
  2nd Street Missouri Ave, Eminence, MO 65466
Steve Blunkall, Sheriff

Shelby County

SOCIAL SERVICES

Family Support/Children's Div **573.633.2550**
Fax..................................573.633.2243
  306 E Main St, Shelbyville, MO 63469
Yvette Collins, Circuit Manager

JUSTICE AGENCY

Juvenile Ofc **573.633.2331**
Fax..................................573.633.2142
Web.............................www.courts.mo.gov
E-mail....................jennifer.fredman@courts.mo.gov
  PO Box 124, Shelbyville, MO 63469-0124
Jennifer Fredman, Deputy Juvenile Officer

COURTS

41st Judicial Circuit **573.633.2151**
Fax..................................573.633.2142
  100 E Main St, Shelbyville, MO 63469
Mike Greenwell, Associate Circuit Judge

POLICE AND SHERIFF

Sheriff's Ofc **573.633.2161**
Fax..................................573.633.2493
Web.............................www.marktwain.net
E-mail....................scshrf@marktwain.net
  100 E Main, Shelbyville, MO 63469
Dennis Perrigo, Sheriff

EDUCATION SERVICES

ADCS Head Start-Shelbin **573.588.2120**
Fax 573.588.1012
Web ....www.centurytel.net
　　116 W Mill St, Shelbina, MO 63468-1419

Stoddard County

SOCIAL SERVICES

Family Support/Children's Div/Senior

Svcs **573.568.2111**
Fax 573.568.3050
Web ....www.dss.mo.gov
E-mail ....dennis.french@dss.mo.gov
　　401 Shawnee St., Bloomfield, MO 63825
　　Dennis French, County Manager/Family Support

GENERAL HEALTH SERVICES

Health Dept **573.568.4593**
Fax 573.568.4736
Web ....www.stoddardcountyhealth.com
E-mail ....pleimd@lpha.dhss.mo.gov
　　1001 N. Highway 25, Bloomfield, MO 63825
　　Debbie Pleimling, Rn, Administrator

JUSTICE AGENCY

Juvenile Ofc **573.568.2159**
Fax 573.568.2103
Web ....www.courts.mo.gov
E-mail ....michael.davis@courts.mo.gov
　　403 S Prairie St, Bloomfield, MO 63825
　　Michael Davis, Chief Juvenile Officer

COURTS

35th Circuit Court **573.568.3118**
Fax 573.568.2271
　　403 S. Prairie St., Bloomfield, MO 63825
　　Honorable Joe Z. Satterfield, Judge

POLICE AND SHERIFF

Sheriff's Dept **573.568.4654**
Fax 573.568.3003
Web ....www.stoddardcasd.com
E-mail ....890@stoddardcasd.com
　　207 South Prairie Street, Bloomfield, MO 63825
　　Carl Hesner, Sheriff

EDUCATION SERVICES

Bell City Head Start **573.733.4244**
E-mail ....hsbc@daeoc.com
　　25925 Spear St, Bell City, MO 63735
　　Beverly Scherer, Director

Dexter Head Start **573.624.8876**
Fax 573.624.1475
E-mail ....fhutchinson@daeoc.com
　　1124 N Outer Rd, Dexter, MO 63841
　　Faye Hutchison, Director

Stone County

SOCIAL SERVICES

Family Support/Children's Div/Senior

Svcs **417.357.6118**
Fax 417.357.8401
Web ....www.dss.mo.gov
E-mail ....kelly.cullers@dss.mo.gov
　　30832 State Highway 413, Galena, MO 65656-8331
　　Kelly Cullers, County Manager

GENERAL HEALTH SERVICES

Health Dept **417.357.6134**
Fax 417.357.6031
Web ....www.stonecountyhealthdepartment.com
　　109 E 4th St, Galena, MO 65656
　　Angela Ford, Rn, Administrator

COURTS

39th Judicial Circuit **417.357.6115**
Fax 417.357.6163
Web ....www.osca.state.mo.us
E-mail ....alan_blankenship@osca.state.mo.us
　　110 F S. Maple, Galena, MO 65656
　　Honorable Alan Blankenship, Manager

POLICE AND SHERIFF

Sheriff's Ofc **417.357.6116**
Fax 417.357.6079
E-mail ....administration@stonecountymo.org
　　110 S. Maple St., Galena, MO 65656
　　Richard L. Hill, Sheriff

EDUCATION SERVICES

Crane Head Start **417.723.5245**
　　707 S Hemphill St, Crane, MO 65633-9161

Sullivan County

SOCIAL SERVICES

Family Support/Children's Div/Senior

Svcs **660.265.4295**
Fax 660.265.4559
　　309 E 3rd St, Milan, MO 63556
　　Pam Pope, Supervisor

GENERAL HEALTH SERVICES

Health Dept **660.265.4141**
Fax 660.265.3891
　　101 Hawthorne Dr, Milan, MO 63556
　　Adam Moore, Director

JUSTICE AGENCY

Juvenile Ofc **660.265.4808**
Fax 660.265.5047
　　109 N Main St Ste 26, Milan, MO 63556-1369
　　Jill Herring, Deputy Juvenile Officer

COURTS

9th Judicial Circuit **660.265.4717**
Fax 660.265.5071
Web ....www.courts.mo.gov
E-mail ....james.spencer@courts.mo.gov
　　109 N Main St Ste 20, Milan, MO 63556-1369
　　Honorable James G. Spencer, Attorney

POLICE AND SHERIFF

Sheriff's Ofc **660.265.3313**
Fax 660.265.4711
　　109 N Main St Ste 9, Milan, MO 63556
　　Roger Smiley, Sheriff

Taney County

SOCIAL SERVICES

Delmina Woods Facility Missouri Div of Youth

Svcs **417.634.3196**
Fax 417.634.4067
　　8872 State Highway H, Forsyth, MO 65653
　　J.d. Barton, Manager

Family Support/Children's Div/Senior

Svcs **417.339.0063**
Fax 417.336.1246
Web ....www.dss.mo.gov
E-mail ....jason.comer@dss.mo.gov
　　2720 Shepherd Of The Hills Expy Ste D1, Branson,
　　MO 65616-3380
　　Jason Comer, Family County Manager

GENERAL HEALTH SERVICES

Health Dept **417.546.4725**
Fax 417.546.4727
Web ....www.taneycohealth.org
E-mail ....berryj@lpha.mopublic.org
　　15479 Highway 160, Forsyth, MO 65653
　　James Berry, Adminstrator

JUSTICE AGENCY

Juvenile Ofc **417.546.3411**
Fax 417.546.2110
　　226 Main Street, Forsyth, MO 65653
　　Michael Scofield, Chief Juvenile Officer

COURTS

38th Judicial Circuit **417.546.7230**
Fax 417.546.6133
　　Taney County Courthouse, Forsyth, MO 65653
　　Brenda Neal, Circuit Clerk

POLICE AND SHERIFF

Sheriff's Dept **417.546.7250**
Fax 417.546.3348
Web ....www.co.taney.mo.us
E-mail ....maggiek@co.taney.mo.us
　　132 David St, Forsyth, MO 65653
　　Jim D. Russell, Sheriff

Texas County

SOCIAL SERVICES

Family Support/Children's Div **417.967.4551**
Fax 417.967.2450
Web ....www.dss.mo.gov
　　16798 Oak Hill Drive Rd Ste 600, Houston,
　　MO 65483-1311
　　Roxie Sponsler, County Manager

GENERAL HEALTH SERVICES

Health Dept **417.967.4131**
Fax 417.967.5700
Web ....www.texascountyhealth.org
　　950 Highway 63, Ste 500, Houston, MO 65483
　　Sheryl Nelson, Wic Coordinator

JUSTICE AGENCY

Juvenile Ofc **417.967.4127**
　　519 N Grand, Houston, MO 65483
　　Russell Shelden, Chief Juvenile Officer

COURTS

25th Judicial Circuit **417.967.3742**
Fax 417.967.4220
Web ....www.osca.state.mo.us
　　210 N Grand Ave Rm 201, Houston,
　　MO 65483-1226
　　Douglas Gaston, Judge

POLICE AND SHERIFF

Sheriff's Dept **417.967.4165**
Fax 417.967.5575
E-mail ....sheriff@fidnet.com
　　519 N Grand Ave, Houston, MO 65483
　　Carl Watson, Sheriff

Vernon County

SOCIAL SERVICES

Family Support/Children's Div/Senior

Svcs **417.448.1100**
Fax 417.448.1348
E-mail ....chris.j.tannlund@dss.mo.gov
　　621 E Highland Ave Ste 1, Nevada, MO 64772
　　Chris Tannlund, County Manager

GENERAL HEALTH SERVICES

Health Dept 417.667.7418
Fax 417.667.4131
Web ....www.vernonhealth.org
301 N Washington St, Nevada, MO 64772-2344
Beth Swopes, Director

JUSTICE AGENCY

Juvenile Ofc 417.667.5015
Fax 417.667.3857
E-mail ....jeani.longstreth@courts.mo.gov
100 W Cherry St Ste 9, Nevada, MO 64772
Jeani Longstreth, Chief Juvenile Officer

COURTS

28th Judicial Circuit 417.448.2525
Fax 417.448.2512
Web ....www.vernoncountymo.org
E-mail ....james.bickel@courts.mo.gov
100 W Cherry St Ste 15, Nevada, MO 64772-3360
Honorable James R. Bickel

POLICE AND SHERIFF

Sheriff's Ofc 417.448.5555
Fax 417.448.2580
Web ....www.vernoncountymo.org
E-mail ....sheriff@vernoncountymo.org
2040 E Hunter St, Nevada, MO 64772-3399
Ron Peckman, Sheriff

EDUCATION SERVICES

Finis Moss Nevada Head Start 417.667.5393
Fax 417.667.8890
Web ....www.wcmcaa.org
E-mail ....mbedford@wcmcaa.org
1025 E Wooter St, Nevada, MO 64772-2761
Melissa Bedford, Director

Warren County

SOCIAL SERVICES

Family Support/Children's Div 636.456.3307
Fax 636.456.4518
513 W Booneslick Rd, Warrenton, MO 63383
Kristen Gentry, County Manager

JUSTICE AGENCY

Juvenile Ofc 636.456.2538
Fax 636.456.1841
Web ....www.warrenton-mo.org
211 E Booneslick St, Warrenton, MO 63383-1918
Bruce Mckinnon, Chief Deputy Juvenile Officer

POLICE AND SHERIFF

Sheriff's Ofc 636.456.4332
Fax 636.456.1811
Web ....www.wcstmo.net
E-mail ....kharrison@warrencountymo.org
104 W Booneslick Rd Ste A, Warrenton, MO 63383-1998
Kevin Harrison, Sheriff

Washington County

SOCIAL SERVICES

Family Support/Children's Div/Senior
Svcs 573.438.2121
Fax 573.438.6254
Web ....www.dss.mo.gov
E-mail ....yvonne.emily@dss.mo.gov
10235 W State Hwy E, Potosi, MO 63664-2027
Yvonne Emily, County Manager

GENERAL HEALTH SERVICES

Health Dept 573.438.2164
Fax 573.438.4759
520 Purcell Dr, Potosi, MO 63664
Franklin Fick, Administrator

COURTS

24th Judicial Circuit 573.438.4171
Fax 573.438.7900
E-mail ....patricia.boyer@courts.mo.gov
102 N Missouri St Ste D, Potosi, MO 63664
Patty Boyer, Circuit Clerk

POLICE AND SHERIFF

Sheriff's Ofc 573.438.5478
Fax 573.438.2079
116 W High St, Potosi, MO 63664
Andy Skiles, Sheriff

EDUCATION SERVICES

Head Start 573.438.1515
Fax 573.438.1515
512 State St, Ste A, Mineral Point, MO 63660
Lavera Saunders, Director

Wayne County

SOCIAL SERVICES

Family Support/Children's Div/Senior
Svcs 573.223.4236
Fax 573.223.7845
E-mail ....linda.s.green@dss.mo.gov
RR 2 Box 26351, Piedmont, MO 63957
Linda Green, Circuit Manager

GENERAL HEALTH SERVICES

Home Health Agency 573.224.3218
Fax 573.224.3164
Web ....www.lpha.mopublic.org
E-mail ....crutcr@lpha.mopublic.org
Highway 67, Greenville, MO 63944
Rae Jean Clutchfield, Administrator

COURTS

42nd Judicial Circuit 573.224.3014
Fax 573.224.3225
E-mail ....kparker@semo.net
109 Walnut St., Greenville, MO 63944
Honorable Kelly Parker, Director

POLICE AND SHERIFF

Sheriff's Ofc 573.224.3219
Fax 573.224.3904
Web ....www.semo.net
E-mail ....pburton@semo.net
100 Maple St, Greenville, MO 63944
Philip Burton, Sheriff

Webster County

GENERAL HEALTH SERVICES

Health Unit 417.859.2532
Fax 417.859.6192
233 E Washington St, Marshfield, MO 65706
Jaci McReynolds, Administrator

COURTS

30th Judicial Circuit Court 417.859.2006
Fax 417.468.3786
Web ....www.courts.mo.gov
E-mail ....john.sims@courts.mo.gov
101 Crittenden Public Square, Marshfield, MO 65706
Honorable John W. Sims, Judge

POLICE AND SHERIFF

Sheriff's Ofc 417.468.2222
Fax 417.859.3614
101 S Crittenden St Rm 32, Marshfield, MO 65706
Lynn Myler, Deputy Clerk

EDUCATION SERVICES

Fordland Head Start 417.767.4596
Web ....www.oacac-caa.org
E-mail ....fordland@oacac-caa.org
871 North St, Fordland, MO 65652-7120
Keith Hyzer, Director

Worth County

COURTS

4th Judicial Circuit 660.564.2210
Fax 660.564.3394
4th & Front St, Grant City, MO 64456
Honorable Joel A. Miller, Associate Judge

Wright County

SOCIAL SERVICES

Family Support/Children's Div/Senior
Svcs 417.926.4142
Fax 417.926.7202
Web ....www.dss.mo.gov
1801 N Talcott Ave, Mountain Grove, MO 65711-1741
Roxie Sponsler, County Manager

GENERAL HEALTH SERVICES

Health Dept 417.741.7791
Fax 417.741.7108
300 S Main St, Suite C, Hartville, MO 65667
Tracy Hardcastle, Rn, Administrator

Health Dept 417.926.0009
Fax 417.926.6096
Web ....www.wrightcountyhealthdept.com
E-mail ....hardct@lpha.dhss.mo.gov
602 E State St Ste B, Mountain Grove, MO 65711-1826
Tracy Hardcastle, Rn, Administrator

COURTS

44th Judicial Circuit 417.741.7121
Fax 417.741.7504
125 Court St, Hartville, MO 65667
Honorable Lynette Veenstra, Judge

POLICE AND SHERIFF

Sheriff's Ofc 417.741.7576
Fax 417.741.6780
Web ....www.dupageco.org
E-mail ....wcsheriff@hotmail.com
125 Court Square, Hartville, MO 65667
Glenn Adler, Sheriff

SPECIAL SERVICES AGENCIES

ADOPTION AGENCIES

Adoption Advocates 816.753.1881
Fax 816.753.5551
Web ....www.altercounseling.com
E-mail ....susan@altercounseling.com
　3100 Broadway St Ste 218, Kansas City,
　MO 64111-2448
　Susan Sarachek, Executive Director

**Adoption By Family Therapy of The
Ozarks** 417.882.7700
Fax 417.887.0457
E-mail ....adoption4family@yahoo.com
　318 Park Central E Ste 420, Springfield,
　MO 65806-2216
　Anne B Summers, Director

Adoption Home Studies of SW MO 417.882.2494
E-mail ....ahsm63@sbcglobal.net
　PO Box 14351, Springfield, MO 65814-0351
　Janis Simkins, Director

Adoption Option 816.224.1525
Fax 913.897.0154
E-mail ....hglm@everest.kc.net
　144 Westwoods Dr, Liberty, MO 64068-1181
　Hillary Merryfield, Executive Director

Adoption Svcs, Inc. 314.567.7500
Fax 314.567.8512
Web ....www.hopehellerphd.com
E-mail ....hopenhellerphd@aol.com
　1133 Olive St, Suite 225, Saint Louis,
　MO 63101-1908
　Hope Heller, Phd, Founder

Affordable Adoption Solutions 573.632.6646
Fax 573.659.8815
Web ....www.adoptionservices.org
　204 E High St, Jefferson City, MO 65101
　Liz Paige, Director

Attachment Consultants-Ozarks 417.881.7151
Fax 417.883.6529
Web ....www.attachmentconsultants.com
E-mail ....ac@attachmentconsultants.com
　304 W Erie St, Springfield, MO 65807-4917
　Jane Rickerd, Director

Brassil & Rohlfing 314.534.5110
Fax 314.534.5190
　4390 Lindell Blvd, Ste 100, Saint Louis, MO 63108
　Tim Brassil, Attorney

Catholic Charities 417.866.0841
Fax 417.866.1140
E-mail ....dmiddleston@ccsomo.org
　601 S Jefferson Ave, Springfield, MO 65803
　Dawna Middleston, Administrative Assistant

Children's Hope Int'l 314.890.0086
Fax 314.427.4288
Web ....www.childrenshope.net
E-mail ....adoption@childrenshopeint.org
　11780 Borman Dr Ste 200, Saint Louis,
　MO 63146-4135
　Dwiatt Gantt, Executive Director

Christian Family Life Ctr 314.721.7128
Web ....www.cflcenter.org
　7445 Cornell Ave, Saint Louis, MO 63130-2915

Collins Webster & Rouse PC 417.782.2222
Fax 417.782.1003
　5957 E 20th St, Joplin, MO 64801-8765
　Richard Collins, President

Dillon International, Inc. 314.576.4100
Fax 314.453.9975
Web ....www.dillonadopt.com
E-mail ....dillonmissouri@dillonadopt.com
　1 1st Missouri Ctr, Ste 115, Saint Louis,
　MO 63141-6085
　Margie Wasielewski, LCSW, Director of Adoptions

Family Resource Center 314.534.9350
Fax 314.531.0372
Web ....www.frcmo.org
　3309 South Kingshighway Boulevard, St. Louis,
　MO 63139
　COA accredited organization.

Family Support Network 314.644.5055
Fax 314.644.5057
Web ....www.familysupportnet.org
　7514 Big Bend Boulevard, St. Louis, MO 63119-2104
　COA accredited organization.

Holt International Children's Svcs 816.822.2169
Fax 816.532.8379
E-mail ....judyy@holtintl.org
　203 Huntington Rd, Kansas City, MO 64113-1430
　Judy Young, Director

Love Basket, Inc. 636.797.4100
Fax 636.789.4978
Web ....www.lovebasket.org
E-mail ....info@lovebasket.org
　10306 Business 21, Hillsboro, MO 63050-5712
　Frank Block, Executive Director

Small World Adoption Foundation, Inc. 636.207.9229
Fax 636.207.9055
Web ....www.swaf.com
E-mail ....staff@swaf.com
　1795 Clarkson Rd Ste 250, Chesterfield,
　MO 63017-4968
　Brenda Henn, Director of Operations

ADVOCACY RESOURCES

Brain Injury Association of Missouri 800.444.6443
Fax 314.426.3290
Web ....biamo.org
E-mail ....info@biamo.org
　10270 Page Avenue, St. Louis, MO 63132
　Maureen Cunningham, Executive Director

CAC of Greater St. Louis 314.516.6798
Fax 314.516.6624
Web ....www.safekidsmo.org
E-mail ....dunnjer@umsl.edu
　1 University Blvd, Saint Louis, MO 63121-4400
　Jerry Dunn, Executive Director

Children's Advocacy Ctr of St. Louis 314.535.3003
Fax 314.535.0756
Web ....www.safekidsmo.org
　4443 W Pine Blvd, Saint Louis, MO 63108
　Jerry Dunn, Executive Director

Missouri CASA Assoc 573.256.1445
E-mail ....bdessem@mocasa.net
　1000 W Nifong Blvd Bldg 1, Ste 200, Columbia,
　MO 65203
　Beth Dessem, Executive Director

Missouri Chapter Children's Ctr 417.623.2292
Fax 417.623.5741
　921 E 34th St Ste A, Joplin, MO 64804
　Chad Adams, Executive Director

**Rainbow House Regional Child Advocacy Ctr,
Inc.** 573.474.6600
Fax 573.474.5992
Web ....www.rainbowhousecolumbia.org
　1611 Towne Dr, Columbia, MO 65202
　Jan Stock, Executive Director

The Child Advocacy Center, Inc. 417.831.2327
Fax 417.831.5122
Web ....www.childadvocacycenter.org
E-mail ....info@childadvocacycenter.org
　1033 E Walnut St, Springfield, MO 65806-2604
　Barbara Brown, Executive Director

Voices for Children 314.552.2352
Fax 314.533.2617
Web ....www.voicesforchildrenstl.org
E-mail ....jhuneke@voicesforchildrenstl.org
　920 N Vandeventer Ave, Saint Louis,
　MO 63108-3530
　Jan Huneke, Executive Director

BEHAVIORAL HEALTH TREATMENT

Alternative Behavioral Care 636.477.6111
Web ....www.alternativebehavioralcare.com
E-mail ....jshiresabc@yahoo.com
　255 Spenser Road, Suite 101, Saint Peters,
　MO 63376
　Ms. Jessica Shires, Accreditation Manager
　Joint Commission accredited organization.

Amicare of Missouri, LLC 573.774.5353
Web ....www.amicarebehavioral.com
E-mail ....rsanchez@pineyridge.net
　1000 Hospital Road, Waynesville, MO 65583
　Mrs. Rachel Sanchez, Accreditation Manager
　Joint Commission accredited organization.

**Annie Malone Children and Family Service
Center** 314.531.0120
Fax 314.531.0125
Web ....www.anniemalone.com
　2612 Annie Malone Drive, St. Louis, MO 63113-2997
　COA accredited organization.

Baird Medical Practice 636.946.5844
　535 Pike St, Saint Charles, MO 63301-2951
　Keim Baird, MD, Psychiatrist

Behavioral Health Response 314.469.4908
Fax 314.469.5087
Web ....www.bhrstl.org
　12647 Olive Boulevard, Suite 200, Saint Louis,
　MO 63141
　Laura Nelson, Director, Department of Health Services
　CARF accredited programs available.

Bernard Campbell Middle School 816.986.3175
Fax 816.986.3245
Web www.bcms.leesummit.k12.mo.us
　1201 NE Colbern Rd, Lees Summit, MO 64086-5816
　Vicki Porter, Director

BJC Behavioral Health 314.206.3712
Web ....www.bjcbehavioralhealth.org
E-mail ....jennifer.haasis@bjc.org
　1430 Olive Street - Suite 400, Saint Louis, MO 63103
　Mrs. Jen Haasis, Accreditation Manager
　Joint Commission accredited organization.

Boonville Valley Hope 660.882.6547
Web ....valleyhope.com
E-mail ....juanitag@valleyhope.com
　1415 Ashley Road, Boonville, MO 65233
　Ms. Juanita Gregoire, Accreditation Manager
　Joint Commission accredited organization.

Boys & Girls Town 573.265.3251
Fax 573.265.5370
E-mail ....vince.hillyer@great-circle.org
　13160 County Rd. 3610, Saint James, MO 65559
　Vincent Hillyer, Executive Director

Boys Hope/Girls Hope 314.298.1250
Fax 314.298.1251
E-mail .... bbradley@bhgh.org
  12120 Bridgeton Square Drive, St Louis, MO 63044
  Bruce B. Bradley, Director Of Childrens Services

Burrell Behavioral Health 417.269.5400
Fax 417.269.7212
Web .... www.coxhealth.com
E-mail .... denise.mills@coxhealth.com
  1300 Bradford Parkway, Springfield, MO 65804
  Denise Mills, Director Corporate Services
  CARF accredited programs available.

CenterPointe Hospital 636.441.7300
Web .... www.centerpointehospital.com
E-mail .... clhotak@cphmo.net
  4801 Weldon Spring Parkway, Saint Charles,
  MO 63304
  Mr. Christopher Lhotak, Accreditation Manager
  Joint Commission accredited organization.

Centrec Care, Inc. 314.205.8068
Web .... centreccare.com
E-mail .... mohammedkabir@centreccare.com
  1224 Fern Ridge Parkway, Suite 305, Saint Louis,
  MO 63141
  Dr. Mohammed Kabir, Accreditation Manager
  Joint Commission accredited organization.

**Change Academy Lake of the Ozarks
(CALO)** 573.365.2221
Web .... caloteens.com
E-mail .... nfuglsang@ca-lo.com
  130 Calo Lane, Lake Ozark, MO 65049
  Ms. Nicole Fuglsang, Accreditation Manager
  Joint Commission accredited organization.

Changes Counseling And Assessment Svc 816.229.2760
E-mail .... achanges@ccglobal.net
  501 NW 5th St 300, Blue Springs, MO 64014-2209
  Angela Prewett, Director

Child Advocacy Services Center Inc. 816.363.1898
Web .... www.childrensplacekc.org
E-mail .... matsond@tcpkc.org
  2 East 59th Street, Kansas City, MO 64113-2116
  Mr. David Matson, Accreditation Manager
  Joint Commission accredited organization.

Columbia College 573.875.8700
Web .... www.ccis.edu
E-mail .... info@ccis.edu
  1001 Rogers St, Columbia, MO 65216
  Gerald Brouder, President

**Community Alternative Svc Program
(CASP)** 417.865.9460
Fax 417.865.6155
E-mail .... gnichols@caspspringfieldmo.org
  721 N Main Ave, Springfield, MO 65802
  Gaye Nichols, Director

Comprehensive Christian Counseling 816.229.8080
  1200 Nw South Outer Rd, Blue Springs,
  MO 64015-3072
  Lauren Kennedy, Director

**Comprehensive Mental Health Services,
Inc.** 816.254.3652
Fax 816.254.9243
Web .... www.thecmhs.com
  10901 Winner Road, Independence, MO 64052-0169
  CARF accredited programs available.

COMTREA 636.931.2700
Fax 636.931.2139
Web .... www.comtrea.org
E-mail .... wecare@comtrea.org
  227 Main St, Festus, MO 63028
  Dr. stephen huss, ceo
  CARF accredited programs available.

Cor Jesu Academy 314.842.4429
Fax 314.849.2649
E-mail .... lpreston@corjesu.org
  10230 Gravois Rd, Saint Louis, MO 63123-4099
  Leah Preston, Director

Corizon Health 314.919.9514
  12647 Olive Blvd Ste 400, Saint Louis,
  MO 63141-6345
  James Friedle, Director

Cottey College 417.667.8181
Web .... www.cottey.edu
E-mail .... syoss@cottey.edu
  1000 W Austin Blvd, Nevada, MO 64772-2763
  Susan Yoss, Coordinator For Student Disabilities

**Cottonwood Residential Treatment
Center** 573.290.5888
E-mail .... marylene.elliott@dmh.mo.gov
  1025 N. Sprigg, Cape Girardeau, MO 63701
  Mrs. Marylene Elliott, Accreditation Manager
  Joint Commission accredited organization.

Cottonwood Residential Treatment Ctr 573.290.5888
Fax 573.290.5895
Web .... www.dmh.mo.gov
  1025 N Sprigg St, Cape Girardeau, MO 63701-4831
  Martha Cassel, Administrator

Counseling Resource Ctr 636.583.7738
Fax 636.583.6745
  104 S McKinley Ave Ste D, Union, MO 63084-1800
  Monica Houttuin, Director

Cox-Burrell - Bramblewood 417.761.5000
Fax 417.761.5491
E-mail .... todd.brizendine@burrellcenter.com
  263 S Essex Rd, Nixa, MO 65714
  Todd Brizendine, Executive Director

Cox-Burrell - Milano House 417.269.0462
Fax 417.269.0465
  1736 N Plantation Dr, Nixa, MO 65714
  Todd Brizendine, Executive Director

Coyote Hill Christian Children's Home 573.874.0179
Fax 573.875.0510
Web .... www.coyotehill.org
  9501 W Coyote Hill Rd, Harrisburg, MO 65256-9598
  Larry Mcdaniel, Executive Director

Crider Health Center 636.332.6000
Fax 636.332.3045
Web .... www.cridercenter.org
  1032 Crosswinds Court, Wentzville, MO 63385
  CARF accredited programs available.

Crider Health Ctr 636.332.6000
Fax 636.332.9981
Web .... www.cridercenter.org
  1032 Crosswinds Ct, Wentzville, MO 63385
  Karl Wilson, Phd, President/CEO

Crittenton 816.765.6600
Fax 816.767.4101
Web .... www.saintlukeshealthsystem.org
  10918 Elm Ave, Kansas City, MO 64134-4199
  Janine Hron, Chief Executive Officer

Crittenton Children's Center 816.765.6600
Web .... www.saintlukeshealthsystem.org
E-mail .... ahuxman@saint-lukes.org
  10918 Elm Avenue, Kansas City, MO 64134-4199
  Mr. Alan Huxman, Accreditation Manager
  Joint Commission accredited organization.

Dean Medical Practice 314.644.6884
E-mail .... jackietodd@earthlink.net
  8008 Carondelet Ave Ste 305, Saint Louis,
  MO 63105-1724
  Jon Todd Dean, Psychiatrist

**East Central Missouri Behavioral Health Services,
Inc.** 573.582.1234
Fax 573.582.7304
Web .... www.arthurcenter.com
  321 West Promenade, Mexico, MO 65265
  CARF accredited programs available.

Epworth Children & Family Services 314.961.5718
Web .... www.epworth.org
E-mail .... mmeehan@epworth.org
  110 North Elm Avenue, Saint Louis, MO 63119
  Dr. Michael Meehan, Accreditation Manager
  Joint Commission accredited organization.

Evangelical Children's Home 314.427.3755
Fax 314.427.2302
Web .... www.newbeginnings-ech.org
E-mail .... mbrennan@echmail.org
  8240 Saint Charles Rock Rd, Saint Louis,
  MO 63114-4598
  Michael Brennan, Executive Director

Excelsior Springs Job Corps Ctr 816.630.5501
Fax 816.637.3813
Web .... www.es.jobcorps.com
E-mail .... wsmith@estigers.k12.mo.us
  701 Saint Louis Ave, Excelsior Springs,
  MO 64024-2615
  Willy Smith, Center Director

Excelsior Springs School Dist 816.630.9284
Fax 816.630.9225
Web www.estigers.k12.mo.us
E-mail .... sdavis@estigers.k12.mo.us
  612 Lynn Rd, Excelsior Springs, MO 64024-1242
  Sarah Davis, Director

Faith Foundation Children's Home 573.783.4400
Fax 573.783.4409
  1800 Madison 257, Fredericktown, MO 63645
  COA accredited organization.

Farzana Medical Practice 314.644.3447
  3115 Hampton Ave, Saint Louis, MO 63139-2303
  Farida Farzana, Md, Psychiatrist

First Presbyterian Church 314.965.0326
Web .... www.kirkwoodpres.org
E-mail .... bdillender@kirkwoodpres.org
  100 E Adams Ave, Saint Louis, MO 63122-4093
  Beth Dillender, Senior Administrator

Florin Medical Practice 314.644.1985
E-mail .... cynthia_florin@yahoo.com
  7750 Clayton Rd Ste 200D, Saint Louis,
  MO 63117-1342
  Cynthia Florin, Psychiatrist

Francis Howell School Dist 636.851.5100
Fax 636.851.4128
Web .... www.fhsdschools.org
E-mail .... philip.bouchard@fhsdschools.org
  1220 Harvest Ridge Dr, Saint Charles,
  MO 63303-5972
  Philip Bouchard, Counsellor

Friesen Medical Practice 314.863.9990
  12412 Powerscourt Dr, Saint Louis, MO 63131
  Darrin Friesen, MD, Psychiatrist

Good Samaritan Boy's Ranch-Attitudes 417.376.2238
Fax 417.865.4527
  1355 S Utah Ave, Brighton, MO 65807
  Kevin Killian, Executive Director
  COA accredited organization.

Great Circle 314.535.7911
Fax 314.535.6632
Web .... www.great-circle.org
E-mail .... vince.hillyer@great-circle.org
  4485 Westminster Pl, St Louis, MO 63108
  Vince Hillyer, President & CEO

Great Circle 573.265.3251
Web ....www.bgtm.org
E-mail ....cindy.burks@bgtm.org
13160 County Rd 3610, Saint James, MO 65559
Ms. Cindy Burks, Accreditation Manager
Joint Commission accredited organization.

Haniel's Home of Hope, Inc. 816.444.7851
Fax 816.523.4099
7558 Prospect Ave, Kansas City, MO 64132
Ibanibo Jack, Executive Director

Hawthorn Children's Psychiatric Hospital 314.512.7800
E-mail ....kristine.norris@dmh.mo.gov
1901 Pennsylvania Avenue, Saint Louis, MO 63133
Ms. Kristine Norris, Accreditation Manager
Joint Commission accredited organization.

Hawthorn Children's Psychiatric Hospital 314.512.7800
Fax 314.512.7812
Web ....www.dmh.missouri.gov
E-mail ....melody.patterson@dmh.mo.gov
1901 Pennsylvania Ave, Saint Louis, MO 63133-1325
Melody Patterson, Nursing Director

Heartland Behavioral Health Services 417.667.2666
Web ....www.heartlandbhs.com
E-mail ....carri.compton-ogle@psysolutions.com
1500 West Ashland, Nevada, MO 64772
Mrs. Carri Compton-Ogle, Accreditation Manager
Joint Commission accredited organization.

Heartland Behavioral Health Svcs 417.667.2666
Fax 417.448.5689
Web ....www.heartlandbhs.com
E-mail ....allison.harder@psysolutions.com
1500 W Ashland St, Nevada, MO 64772-1710
Allison Harder, CEO

Home Court Advantage, Inc. 417.777.6980
Fax 417.777.6981
Web ....www.homecourtboys.com
E-mail ....jack@homecourtboys.com
1211 E Broadway St, Bolivar, MO 65613-2952
Jack Mccrimmon, Executive Director

Hutchens Campus Residential Program 417.466.7844
Fax 417.466.2625
E-mail ....christy.grimes@mbch.org
603 N Main St, Mount Vernon, MO 65712-1074
Christy Grimes, Intake Specialist

Jewish Family & Children's Service 314.993.1000
Fax 314.812.9398
Web ....www.jfcs-stl.org
10950 Schuetz Road, St. Louis, MO 63146
COA accredited organization.

Kansas City Psychiatric and Psychological Services, LLC 816.373.6433
Fax 816.478.9008
4731 South Cochise Drive, Suite 206, Independence, MO 64055
CARF accredited programs available.

Lakeland Regional Hospital 417.865.5581
Web ....lakelandregional.com
E-mail ....mark.moore@yfcs.com
440 South Market Avenue, Springfield, MO 65806
Mr. Mark Moore, Accreditation Manager
Joint Commission accredited organization.

Lakeland Regional Hospital 417.865.5581
Fax 417.865.5964
Web ....www.yfcs.com
E-mail ....keith.furman@yfcs.com
440 S Market Ave, Springfield, MO 65806-2090
Keith Furman, CEO

Lives Under Construction Boys Ranch, Inc. 417.779.5374
Fax 417.779.2106
Web ....www.lucboys.org
E-mail ....kortman@centurytel.net
296 Boys Ranch Rd, Lampe, MO 65681-7205
Ken Ortman, Center Director

Mark Twain Behavioral Health 573.221.2120
Fax 573.221.4380
Web ....www.mtbh.org
E-mail ....hannibal@mtbh.org
917 Broadway Ste 9, Hannibal, MO 63401
Mike Cantrell, CEO

Mattie Rhodes Memorial Society 816.241.3780
Fax 816.471.2521
Web ....www.mattierhodes.org
E-mail ....jfierro@mattierhodes.org
148 N Topping Ave, Kansas City, MO 64123
John Fierro, Executive Director

Missouri Girl's Town Foundation, Inc. 573.642.5345
Fax 573.642.5162
Web ....www.mogirlstown.org
E-mail ....kbecker@mogirlstown.org
8548 Jade Rd, Kingdom City, MO 65262
Kathy Becker, Executive Director
COA accredited organization.

Mother's Refuge 816.356.4797
Fax 816.356.4017
Web ....www.mothersrefuge.org
E-mail ....rzornes@sbcglobal.net
3721 Delridge Rd, Independence, MO 64052-1153
Robert Zornes, Executive Director

New Horizons Community Support Svcs 573.636.8108
Fax 573.635.9892
E-mail ....ccheung@mo-newhorizons.com
2013 William St Ste A, Jefferson City, MO 65109
Chi Cheung, President

New Horizons/Community Support Svcs 573.443.0405
Fax 573.875.2557
Web ....www.mo-newhorizons.com
E-mail ....jheumann@mo-newhorizons.com
1408 Hathman Pl, Columbia, MO 65201-5551
Jan Heaumann, Executive Director

Niles Home for Children 816.241.3448
Fax 816.231.9368
Web ....www.nhc-kc.org
E-mail ....ljohnson@nileshomekc.org
1911 E 23rd St, Kansas City, MO 64127
Louise Johnson, Admissions Coordinator
COA accredited organization.

North Central Missouri Mental Health Ctr 660.359.4487
Fax 660.359.4129
Web ....www.ncmmh.org
E-mail ....lori@ncmmh.org
1601 E 28th St, Trenton, MO 64683-1178
Lori Irvine, Executive Director

Noyes Home for Children 816.232.5650
Fax 816.233.9585
801 N Noyes Blvd, Saint Joseph, MO 64506-2899
Gretchen Herden, Director

Ozanam 816.508.3600
Fax 816.508.3797
Web ....www.ozanam.org
421 East 137 Street, Kansas City, MO 64145
COA accredited organization.

Ozanam Home for Girls and Boys 816.508.3600
Fax 816.508.3797
Web ....www.cornerstoneofcare.org
E-mail ....doug.zimmerman@ozanam.org
421 E 137th St, Kansas City, MO 64145-1487
Doug Zimmerman, President/director (ozanam)

Ozark Ctr - 13 St Transition 417.781.1025
Fax 417.781.0563
E-mail ....pfbaker@freemanhealth.com
2800 W 13th St, Joplin, MO 64801-3650
Paula Baker, Ms, Executive Director

Ozarks Medical Center 417.256.9111
Web ....www.ozarksmedicalcenter.com
E-mail ....mary.fine@ozarksmedicalcenter.com
1100 Kentucky Avenue, West Plains, MO 65775
Mrs. Mary Fine, Accreditation Manager
Joint Commission accredited organization.

Ozarks Medical Ctr 417.257.6762
Fax 417.257.5875
Web ....www.ozarksmedicalcenter.com
E-mail ....carol.eck@ozarksmedicalcenter.com
909 N Kentucky Ave, West Plains, MO 65775
Carol Eck, Executive Director

Pathways 573.364.7551
Fax 573.364.4898
Web ....www.pathwaysonline.org
E-mail ....dduncan@pbhc.org
1450 E 10th St, Rolla, MO 65401-3648
David Duncan, Administrator

Pathways Community Behavioral Healthcare, Inc. 660.885.8131
Fax 660.885.2393
Web ....www.pathwaysonline.org
1800 Community Drive, Clinton, MO 64735
CARF accredited programs available.

Provident Inc. 314.371.6500
Web ....www.providentstl.org
E-mail ....glewis@providentstl.org
2650 Olive Street., Saint Louis, MO 63103
Mr. Gil Lewis, Accreditation Manager
Joint Commission accredited organization.

ReDiscover, Inc. 816.246.8000
Fax 816.246.8207
Web ....www.rediscovermh.org
901 Northeast Independence Avenue, Lee's Summit, MO 64086-5544
CARF accredited programs available.

Research Psychiatric Center 816.444.8172
Web ....researchpsychiatriccenter.com
E-mail ....carmen.kynard@hcahealthcare.com
2323 East 63rd Street, Kansas City, MO 64130
Ms. Carmen Kynard, Accreditation Manager
Joint Commission accredited organization.

Research Psychiatric Ctr 816.444.8161
Fax 816.333.4495
2323 E 63rd St, Kansas City, MO 64130-3495
David Brown, Medical Director

Returning Glory 816.223.9662
Fax 816.524.9329
Web ....www.returningglory.com
E-mail ....info@returningglory.com
34505 E Drinkwater Rd, Lone Jack, MO 64070
Roxanne Van Riessen, Director

Shiloh Christian Children's Ranch 573.588.2191
Fax 573.588.7730
Web ....www.shilohranch.org
601 North Center Street, Shelbina, MO 63468
Mark Adkison, Director

Signature Behavioral Healthcare 816.795.1445
E-mail ....clhotak@cphmo.net
4031 North East Lakewood Way Suite 100, Lees Summit, MO 64064
Mr. Christopher Lhotak, Accreditation Manager
Joint Commission accredited organization.

Southwest Missouri Psychiatry Rehabilitation Ctr 417.876.1000
Fax 417.876.1004
Web ....www.dmh.mo.gov
E-mail ....denise.norbury@dmh.mo.gov
1301 Industrial Pkwy E, El Dorado Springs, MO 64744-6263
Denise Norbury, Regional Executive Officer

Spofford 816.508.3400
Fax 816.508.3425
Web ....www.spoffordhome.org
P.O. Box 9888, Kansas City, MO 64134
COA accredited organization.

SSM DePaul Health Center **314.344.6000**
Web ....SSMDePaul.com
E-mail ....cathy_boschert@ssmhc.com
  12303 DePaul Drive, Bridgeton, MO 63044-2588
  Dr. Patrice Komoroski, Accreditation Manager
  Joint Commission accredited organization.

SSM DePaul Health Ctr **314.344.6000**
  12303 De Paul Dr, Bridgeton, MO 63044-2588
  Gail Reneer, Director

SSM St. Joseph Health Center **314.947.5000**
Web ....www.ssmstjoseph.com
E-mail ....gaspare_calvaruso@ssmhc.com
  300 First Capitol Drive, Saint Charles, MO 63301
  Mr. Gaspare Calvaruso, Accreditation Manager
  Joint Commission accredited organization.

St. Anthony's Medical Center **314.525.1000**
Web ....www.stanthonysmedcenter.com
E-mail ....kevin.sprecher@samcstl.org
  10010 Kennerly Road, Saint Louis, MO 63128
  Mr. Kevin Sprecher, Accreditation Manager
  Joint Commission accredited organization.

St. John's Mercy Medical Ctr **314.251.6000**
Fax 314.251.7578
Web ....www.stjohnsmercy.org
  615 S New Ballas Rd, Saint Louis, MO 63141
  Don Kalicak, Director Behaviroral Health

Steppingstone **816.356.0187**
Fax 816.356.4172
Web ....www.steppingstonekc.org
E-mail ....duanel@sbcglobal.net
  5100 Noland Rd, Kansas City, MO 64133-2610
  Duane Lewis, Resident Director

Swope Health Services **816.922.3166**
Web ....www.swopehealthservices.org
E-mail ....chumphreys@swopecommunity.org
  3801 Blue Parkway, Kansas City, MO 64130
  Mrs. Celia Humphreys, Accreditation Manager
  Joint Commission accredited organization.

The Bridge Home for Children, Inc. **816.333.8711**
Fax 816.333.8799
Web ....www.bhfc.org
E-mail ....dpeters@bhfc.org
  6033 Swope Pkwy, 6029 Swop Pkwy, Kansas City,
  MO 64130-4461

The Light House **816.361.2233**
Fax 816.361.8333
Web ....www.lighthouse-inc.org
E-mail ....eunice@lighthouse-inc.org
  400 W Meyer Blvd, Kansas City, MO 64113-1715
  Eunice Johnson, Program Director

The Salvation Army Children's Shelter **816.285.2480**
Web ....www.salarmy-mokan.org
E-mail ....amanda_buehler@usc.salvationarmy.org
  101 W Linwood, Kansas City, MO 64111
  Mrs. Amanda Buehler, Accreditation Manager
  Joint Commission accredited organization.

Truman Medical Center **816.404.1000**
Web ....www.trumed.org
E-mail ....melinda.smith@tmcmed.org
  2301 Holmes Street, Kansas City, MO 64108
  Ms. Melinda Smith, Accreditation Manager
  Joint Commission accredited organization.

Two Rivers Psychiatric Hospital **816.382.6300**
Fax 816.358.5395
Web ....www.tworivershospital.com
  5121 Raytown Rd, Kansas City, MO 64133
  Kevin Young, CEO

Two Rivers Psychiatric Hospital **816.356.5688**
Web ....www.tworivershospial.com
E-mail ....suzanne.belanger@uhsinc.com
  5121 Raytown Road, Kansas City, MO 64133
  Mrs. Suzanne Belanger, Accreditation Manager
  Joint Commission accredited organization.

University Behavioral Health Youth Svcs **573.777.8300**
Fax 573.777.8390
Web ....www.muhealth.org
  3401 Berrywood Dr Ste 300, Columbia,
  MO 65201-6515
  Joygsna Nair, Md, Medical Director

CHILDREN'S HOSPITAL

Audrain Medical Center **573.582.5000**
  620 E Monroe St, Mexico, MO 65265
  Dave Neuendorf, Chief Executive Officer

Barnes-Jewish Hosp/Washington Univ **314.747.3000**
  1 Barnes-Jewish Hospital Plaza, Saint Louis,
  MO 63110
  Steven Lipstein, President/CEO

Boone Hospital Center **573.815.8000**
  1600 E Broadway, Columbia, MO 65201
  Ann Rothery, Director

Bothwell Regional Health Center **660.826.8833**
  601 E 14th St, Sedalia, MO 65301
  John Dawes, Chief Executive Officer

Callaway Community Hospital **573.642.3376**
  10 S Hospital Dr, Fulton, MO 65251
  Alan Aufderheide, Chief Executive Officer

Cameron Regional Medical Center **816.632.2101**
  1600 E Evergreen, Cameron, MO 64429
  Joe Abrutz, Administrator

Capital Region Medical Center **573.632.5000**
  1125 Madison St, Jefferson City, MO 65101
  Ed Farnsworth, President

Cass Regional Medical Center **816.380.3474**
  2800 E Rock Haven Rd, Harrisonville, MO 64701
  Bhris Lang, Chief Executive Officer

Children's Mercy Hospitals & Clinics **816.234.3000**
  2401 Gillham Rd, Kansas City, MO 64108

Citizens Memorial Hospital **417.326.6000**
  1500 N Oakland Ave, Bolivar, MO 65613
  Donald Bath, Chief Executive Officer

Community Hospital **660.425.2211**
  2600 Miller St, Bethany, MO 64424
  Rich Hamilton, Chief Executive Officer

Cox Health **417.269.3000**
  1423 N Jefferson St, Springfield, MO 65802
  Bob Bezanson, Administrator

Freeman Hospital **417.347.1111**
  1102 W 32nd St, Joplin, MO 64804

Freeman Neosho Hospital **417.451.1234**
  113 W Hickory St, Neosho, MO 64850
  Daxton Holcomb, Chief Executive Officer

General Leonard Wood Army Community
Hos **573.596.0414**
  126 Missouri Ave, Fort Leonard Wood, MO 65473
  Kirk Eggleston, Chief Executive Officer

Hannibal Regional Hospital **573.248.1300**
  6000 Hospital Dr, Hannibal, MO 63401
  John Groffmeier, Chief Executive Officer

Heartland Regional Medical Center **816.271.6000**
  5325 Faraon St, Saint Joseph, MO 64506
  Martha Marklaney, Chief Executive Officer

Hedrick Medical Center **660.646.1480**
  100 Central St, Chillicothe, MO 64601
  Matt Wenzel, Chief Executive Officer

Hermann Area District Hospital **573.486.2191**
  509 W 18th St, Hermann, MO 65041
  Pam Mckinney, Chief Executive Officer

I-70 Community Hospital **660.335.4700**
  105 Hospital Dr, Sweet Springs, MO 65351
  Julie Davenport, Administrator

Jefferson Regional Medical Center **636.933.1000**
  Hwy 61 S, Crystal City, MO 63019
  Jim Newhlhauser, Chief Executive Officer

Lake Regional Hospital **573.348.8000**
  54 Hospital Dr, Osage Beach, MO 65065
  Jennifer, Chief Executive Officer

Liberty Hospital **816.781.7200**
  2525 Glenn Hendren Dr, Liberty, MO 64068
  David Feess, Chief Executive Officer

McCune-Brooks Regional Hospital **417.358.8121**
E-mail ....McCune-Brooks@mbrh.org
  3125 Dr. Russell Smith Way, Carthage, MO 64836
  Bob Copeland, Chief Executive Officer

Medical Center **636.528.8551**
  1000 E Cherry St, Troy, MO 63379
  Pat Bira, Chief Executive Officer

Memorial Hospital **573.547.2536**
  434 N West St, Perryville, MO 63775
  Patrick Carron, President

Memorial Hospital **573.754.5531**
E-mail ....lharness@pcmhmo.org
  2305 Georgia St, Louisiana, MO 63353
  Lorraine Harness, Administrator

Memorial Hospital **660.465.8511**
  450 E Sigler Ave, Memphis, MO 63555
  Marcia Dial, Chief Executive Officer

Memorial Hospital **417.967.3311**
  1333 S Sam Houston Blvd, Houston, MO 65483
  Wes Lurray, Chief Executive Officer

Memorial Hospital **417.876.2511**
  1401 S Park St, El Dorado Springs, MO 64744
  Jana Witt, Chief Executive Officer

Memorial Hospital **417.681.5100**
  29 NW First Ln, Lamar, MO 64759
  Maryls Buckner, Director of Nursing

Memorial Hospital **573.883.2751**
  800 Ste Genevieve Dr, Sainte Genevieve, MO 63670
  Tom Keim, Chief Executive Officer

Memorial Hospital **660.882.7461**
  17651 B Hwy, Boonville, MO 65233
  Allan Waldo, Chief Executive Officer

Memorial Hospital **660.947.2411**
  1926 Oak St, Unionville, MO 63565
  Floyd Bounce, President/CEO

Missouri Baptist Medical Center **314.996.5000**
  3015 N Ballas Rd, Saint Louis, MO 63131

Missouri Baptist Sullivan Hospital **573.468.4186**
  751 Sappington Bridge Rd, Sullivan, MO 63080
  Carmen Wacker, Director Of Nursing

Missouri Delta Medical Center **573.471.1600**
  1008 N Main St, Sikeston, MO 63801
  Jason Schurmps, Chief Executive Officer

Missouri Southern Healthcare **573.624.5566**
  1200 N One Mile Rd, Dexter, MO 63841
  Amy Akers, Chief Executive Officer

Moberly Regional Medical Center **660.263.8400**
  1515 Union Ave, Moberly, MO 65270
  Stephen Lunn, Chief Executive Officer

Nevada Regional Medical Center **417.667.3355**
  800 S Ash st, Nevada, MO 64772
  Judy Fuquay, Director

North Kansas City Hospital **816.691.2000**
  2800 Clay Edwards Dr, North Kansas City, MO 64116

Ozarks Medical Center **417.256.9111**
  1100 Kentucky Ave, West Plains, MO 65775
  Dave Zechman, Chief Executive Officer

Parkland Health Center **573.756.6451**
  1101 W Liberty St, Farmington, MO 63640
  Tom Karl, President

Parkland Health Center-Bonne Terre **573.358.1400**
7245 Raider Rd, Bonne Terre, MO 63628
Thomas Karo, Director

Pemiscot Memorial Health System **573.359.1372**
Hwy 61 & Reed, Hayti, MO 63851

Ranken Jordan Pediatric Specialty Hosp **314.872.6400**
11365 Dorsett Rd, Maryland Heights, MO 63043
Lauri Tanner, President

Regional Medical Center **573.458.8899**
1000 W Tenth St, Rolla, MO 65401
John Deneo, Chief Executive Officer

Sac-Osage Hospital **417.646.8181**
E-mail ....sac-osagehospital.com
Junction Hwys 13 & Business 13, Osceola, MO 64776
Parry Turner, Director of Nursing

Salem Memorial District Hospital **573.729.6626**
Hwy 72 N, Salem, MO 65560
Dennis Pryor, Administrator

Shriners Hospitals for Children St Louis **314.432.3600**
E-mail ....jehoward@shrinenet.org
2001 S Lindbergh Blvd, Saint Louis, MO 63131
Judith Howard, Executive Assistant

Skaggs Regional Medical Center **417.335.7000**
251 Skaggs Rd, Branson, MO 65616
William Mahoney, Chief Executive Officer

Southeast Missouri Hospital **573.334.4822**
1701 Lacey St, Cape Girardeau, MO 63701

SSM Cardinal Glennon Childrens Med Ctr **314.577.5600**
1465 S Grand Blvd, Saint Louis, MO 63104
Joan Aron, Nursing Director

SSM DePaul Health Center **314.344.6000**
12303 DePaul Dr, Bridgeton, MO 63044

SSM St Joseph Hospital West **636.625.5200**
E-mail ....janet_pestle@ssmhc.com
100 Medical Plaza, Lake Saint Louis, MO 63367
Janet Pestle, Director Of Nursing

St Anthony's Medical Center **314.525.1000**
10010 Kennerly Rd, Saint Louis, MO 63128

St Francis Hospital & Health Services **660.562.2600**
2016 S Main St, Maryville, MO 64468
Gray Cox, Administrator

St Francis Medical Center **573.331.3000**
211 St Francis Dr, Cape Girardeau, MO 63703
Steven Vjelich, President/CEO

St John's Hospital **417.820.2000**
1235 E Cherokee St, Springfield, MO 65804
John Swope, Chief Executive Officer

St John's Hospital Aurora **417.678.2122**
500 Porter St, Aurora, MO 65605
Doug Stroemel, President/Administrator

St John's Hospital Lebanon **417.533.6100**
100 Hospital, Lebanon, MO 65536
Mike Gillen, President

St John's Mercy Hospital **636.239.8000**
901 E Fifth St, Washington, MO 63090
Tarry Mclin, President

St John's Mercy Medical Center **314.569.6000**
615 S New Ballas Rd, Saint Louis, MO 63141
Mike Mccurry, Chief Executive Officer

St John's Regional Medical Center **417.781.2727**
2727 McClelland Blvd, Joplin, MO 64804
Scott Watson, Director

St John's St Francis Hospital **417.934.7000**
100 W Hwy 60, Mountain View, MO 65548
John Wade, President

St Luke's Hospital **816.932.2000**
4401 Wornall Rd, Kansas City, MO 64111
Julie Quirin, Chief Executive Officer

St Luke's Hospital **314.434.1500**
232 S Woods Mill Rd, Chesterfield, MO 63017
Gary Olson, President

St Mary's Health Center **573.761.7000**
100 St Marys Medical Plaza, Jefferson City,
MO 65101
Brent Vanconia, President

Truman Medical Center Lakewood **816.404.7000**
7900 Lee's Summit Rd, Kansas City, MO 64139
Charlie Shields, Chief Operating Officer

Twin Rivers Regional Medical Center **573.888.4522**
1301 First St, Kennett, MO 63857
John Graves, Executive Director

University of MO Health Care **573.882.4141**
One Hospital Dr, Columbia, MO 65212

Western Missouri Medical Center **660.747.2500**
403 Burkarth Rd, Warrensburg, MO 64093
Craig Marks, Administrator Director/CEO

Wright Memorial Hospital **660.358.5700**
E-mail ....wrightmemorial@saint-lukes.org
191 Iowa Blvd, Trenton, MO 64683
Gary Wages, Interim CEO

COUNSELING SERVICES

Bethany Christian Svcs **636.536.6363**
Fax 636.536.6262
Web ....www.bethany.org/missouri
E-mail ....bcschesterfield@bethany.org
1 McBride And Son Center Dr Ste 210, Chesterfield,
MO 63005-1407
Donna Nicholson, Director

Bringing Families Together **314.731.3969**
Fax 314.731.3906
Web ....www.bringingfamiliestogether.com
E-mail ....randih@bringingfamiliestogether.com
7151 N Lindbergh Blvd, Hazelwood,
MO 63042-2039
Randi Howard, Executive Director

Children's Place **816.363.1898**
Fax 816.822.7711
Web ....www.childrensplacekc.org
2 E 59th St, Kansas City, MO 64113-2116
David Matson, President/CEO

Family Care Ctr **314.576.6493**
Fax 314.576.7319
763 S New Dallas Rd, Crevevouer, MO 63017-5735
Bridget Laffleur, Executive Director

Heart of America Family Conservancy **816.436.0486**
Fax 816.436.0973
E-mail ....jzimmerman@thefamilyconservancy.org
3100 NE 83rd St Ste 1401, Kansas City,
MO 64119-4467
Joan Zimmerman, Director

LDS Family Svcs **816.461.5512**
Fax 816.461.4907
E-mail ....galep@ldschurch.org
517 W Walnut St Ste 2, Independence,
MO 64050-3738
Paul Gale, Agency Director

Queen of Peace Ctr **314.531.0511**
Fax 314.531.1458
Web ....www.ccstl.org
E-mail ....meversgerd@ccstl.org
325 N Newstead Ave, Saint Louis, MO 63108-2707
Maryann Eversgerd, Director Of Child Development

CRISIS & SHELTER CARE

Boys and Girls Town of Missouri **417.865.1646**
Fax 417.866.1483
Web ....www.bgtm.org
1212 W Lombard St, Springfield, MO 65806
Ann Tucker, Resident Director

CASA Guadalupe-Family Growth Ctr **573.663.2766**
Fax 573.663.2766
E-mail ....Casag@Mcmo.Net
180 County Rd. 700, Ellington, MO 63638
Joann Dawson, Director

**Christos House Domestic Violence
Program** **417.469.1190**
Fax 417.469.1192
Web ....www.townsqr.com
E-mail ....Christos@Townsqr.Com
PO Box 771, West Plains, MO 65775-0771
Sherry Fohey, Director

**Citizens Against Domestic Violence-Sunshine
House** **573.346.9630**
Fax 573.346.9630
E-mail ....cadvvoc@sbcglobal.net
498 W Hwy 54, Camdenton, MO 65020
Angie Fiene, Director

Citizens Against Spouse Abuse **660.827.5559**
Fax 660.827.5548
E-mail ....dircasa1371@hotmail.com
108 E 5th St, Sedalia, MO 65301
Lori Haney, Intrim Director Of Casa

Cope-Domestic Violence Program **417.533.5201**
Fax 417.532.8178
Web ....www.webound.com
E-mail ....cope@webound.com
201 Lawson Ave, Lebanon, MO 65536
Rita Westermann, Director

**Council on Families In Crisis-Dom
Violence** **417.667.7171**
Fax 417.667.4488
415 N Main St, Nevada, MO 64772-2335
Martha Sander, Director

Crisis Intervention Svcs **573.581.3835**
Fax 573.581.2447
E-mail ....mccameyhouse@yahoo.com
300 S Morris St, Mexico, MO 65265
Sherry Levin, Director

Doulos Ministries **417.334.2773**
Fax 417.334.6173
Web ....www.douloscorp.com
E-mail ....jstaples@douloscorp.com
282 Doulos Rd, Branson, MO 65616-9469
Joey Staples, Director

Epworth Children and Family Svcs, Inc. **314.961.5718**
Fax 314.961.3503
Web ....www.epworth.org
110 N Elm Ave, Saint Louis, MO 63119
Becky Appelbaum, Admissions Coordinator

Fair Haven Children's Home **417.862.6675**
Fax 417.862.0993
E-mail ....Barney@fhchome.org
3132 N Fair Haven Loop, Strafford, MO 65757
Barney Crawford, Executive Director

Family Crisis Svcs-Russell Hse **573.364.0579**
Fax 573.364.1824
PO Box 2259, Rolla, MO 65402-2259
Shan Meuch, Executive Director

Family Violence Ctr **417.837.7700**
Fax 417.837.7707
E-mail ....fvc@myharmonyhouse.org
519 E Cherry St, Springfield, MO 65806
Rodney Dwyer, Executive Director

Genesis-New Beginnings-Dom Violence **573.774.4040**
Fax 573.774.4040
E-mail ....pccc@jobe.net
1809 W. Historic 66, Waynesville, MO 65583
Conney Chambers, Director

Missouri

Green Hills Womens Shelton-Dom Violence 660.359.3297
Fax 660.359.3297
E-mail ....taylort@ghcaa.org
1506 Oklahoma Ave, Trenton, MO 64683
Tammy Taylor, Director

Harbor House 417.739.3200
Fax 417.739.3212
E-mail ....acatros1@centurytel.net
13192 State Highway 13, Kimberling City, MO 65686
Allen Catros, Director

Haven House, Inc-Domestic Violence 573.686.4873
Fax 573.686.6416
E-mail ....haven@semo.net
921 W Harper St, Poplar Bluff, MO 63901
Maryann Allen, Director

Havenhouse St. Louis 314.434.5858
Fax 314.434.6541
Web ....www.youthbridge.org
E-mail ....kjsindel@havenhousestl.org
12685 Olive Blvd, Saint Louis, MO 63141-6342
Kathy Sindel, Executive Director

Hope Haven 816.380.2833
Fax 816.380.4712
Web ....www.dps.mo.gov
E-mail ....hopehavened@gmail.com
PO Box 754, Harrisonville, MO 64701-0754
Linda Tessar, Director

House of Hope, Inc-Domestic Violence 660.259.4766
Fax 660.259.6768
Web ....www.cebridge.net
E-mail ....Hoh@Cebridge.Net
301 Broadway St, Lexington, MO 64067-1223
Ann Gosnell-ellison, Director

Kathy Weinman Domestic Violence Program 314.423.1117
Fax 314.423.7537
Web ....www.saintmarthas.org
E-mail ....Mschuller-Baker@Saintmarthas.Org
8001 Natural Bridge Rd, Saint Louis, MO 63121-4401
Michelle Schuller-baker, Director

Life Source Consultants 314.524.4130
Fax 314.524.9844
E-mail ....lifesc@sbcglobal.net
119 Church St Ste 219, Saint Louis, MO 63135-2460
Shirley D. Stevens, Client Services Director

Missouri Baptist's Children's Home/MBCH Children & Family Ministries 314.739.6811
Fax 314.739.6325
Web ....www.mbch.org
11300 Saint Charles Rock Rd, Bridgeton, MO 63044-2721
Russell L. Martin, Mbch Children And Family Ministry, President

New House for Battered Women Crisis Hotline 816.474.6446
Fax 816.474.4157
Web ....www.newhouseshelter.org
660 Brooklyn Ave, Kansas City, MO 64124
Leslie Caplin, Director

Presbyterian Children's Svcs, Inc. 660.263.7044
Fax 660.263.8857
811 S 5th St, Moberly, MO 65270
James Thurman, President

Presbyterian Children's Svcs, Regional Girl's Shelter 417.862.9634
Fax 417.865.6507
E-mail ....leslieschneider@care4kids.org
2740 E Pythian St, Springfield, MO 65802
Leslie Schneider, Director

Rape and Abuse Crisis Svc-Dom Violence 573.634.8346
Fax 573.659.8508
E-mail ....jim@racsjc.org
5717 Chapel Dr, Jefferson City, MO 65102
Jim Clardy, Director

Redevelopment Opportunites for Women 314.588.8300
Fax 314.588.0676
E-mail ....mschnabel@row-stl.org
306 N Tucker, Saint Louis, MO 63101
Meg Snabnal, Director

Regional Family Crisis Ctr - Domestic Violence 573.547.2480
Fax 573.547.6593
E-mail ....wsrfcc@yahoo.com
307 Independence Dr, Perryville, MO 63775
Winnis Sifford, Director

Rose Brooks Ctr-Domestic Violence 816.523.5550
Fax 816.523.8177
E-mail ....susan@rosebrooks.org
PO Box 320599, Kansas City, MO 64132-0599
Susan Miller, Director

Safe House for Women, Inc. 573.335.7745
Fax 573.335.6435
1810 E Plaza Way, Cape Girardeau, MO 63702
Linda Garner, Director

Salvation Army Children's Shelter 816.756.2769
Fax 816.303.0183
101 W Linwood Blvd, Kansas City, MO 64111
Joyce Schau, Executive Director

SE MO Family Violence Council-New Way Shelter 573.358.3913
Fax 573.358.7786
PO Box 465, Bonne Terre, MO 63628-0465
Carla Crocker, Director

St. Louis Crisis Nursery 314.768.3201
Fax 314.338.2206
Web ....www.crisisnurserykids.org
E-mail ....dianne@crisisnurserykids.com
1928 Gravois, Saint Louis, MO 63104
Dianne Mueller, Executive Director

St. Marthas Hall-Domestic Violence 314.533.1313
Fax 314.533.2035
Web ....www.igateway.net
E-mail ....mschiller-baker@igateway.net
PO Box 4950, Saint Louis, MO 63108-0950
Michell Schiller-baker, Director

Synergy Svcs 816.587.4100
Fax 816.587.6691
Web ....www.synergyservices.org
E-mail ....rwinner@synergyservices.org
400 E 6th St, sparksville, MO 64152-3703
Robin Winner, Executive Director

Synergy Svcs Safehaven Shelter 816.452.8910
Fax 816.452.0245
Web ....www.synergyservices.org
E-mail ....rwinners@synergyservices.org
400 E 6th St, Kansas City, MO 64152-3703
Robin Winners, Executive Director

The Kitchen, Inc. 417.837.1500
Fax 417.831.6709
Web ....www.thekitcheninc.org
E-mail ....rorgeron@thekitcheninc.org
1630 N Jefferson Ave, Springfield, MO 65803
Rorie Orgeron, Chief Executive Director

The Lead Institute-Domestic Violence 573.445.5005
Fax 573.445.5088
Web ....www.deaflead.org
E-mail ....slogan@tmail.com
2502 W Ash, Columbia, MO 65203-8104
Stephanie Logan, Director

The Robertson Ctr-Domestic Violence 636.462.2724
Fax 636.462.3176
Web ....www.bridgewaybh.com
E-mail ....Pkulik@Bridgewaybh.Com
PO Box 17, Troy, MO 63379-0017
Pat Kulik, Director

The Shelter-Domestic Violence 573.875.1369
Fax 573.817.1280
Web ....www.socket.net
PO Box 1367, Columbia, MO 65205-1367
Barbara Hodges, Director

The Victim Ctr 417.863.7273
Fax 417.863.9048
E-mail ....hope@thevictimcenter.org
819 N Boonville Ave, Springfield, MO 65802
Nancy Berlin, Director

Turning Point-Domestic Violence 636.456.1186
Fax 636.456.8269
E-mail ....jkarrenbrock@turningpointdvs.com
PO Box 426, Warrenton, MO 63383-0426
Joyce Karrenbrock, Director

Womens Crisis Ctr 417.561.5105
Fax 417.561.8405
Web ....www.centurytel.net
E-mail ....ccrisiscenter@centurytel.net
226 Benton Ave, Rockaway Beach, MO 65615
Becky Vermeire, Director

Womens Support and Community Svcs 314.646.7500
Fax 314.646.8181
Web ....www.safeconnection.org
2165 Hampton Ave, Saint Louis, MO 63139
Susan Kizter, Director

EDUCATION

Children's Therapy Ctr 660.826.4400
Fax 866.495.6424
Web ....www.chs-mo.org
4550 W Main, Sedalia, MO 65301
Ann Graff, Executive Director

Grip-Group Residential Individualized Program 417.498.6852
Fax 417.498.6895
E-mail ....grip@mo-net.com
14422 Business Hwy. 60, Verona, MO 65769
Dave Doner, Program Director

Job Corps 816.861.2353
Fax 816.861.4337
Web ....www.jobcorps.org
2402 Swope Pkwy, Kansas City, MO 64130
Mark Spratt, Director

Lutheran Church Missourie Synod 314.965.9000
Fax 314.996.1016
Web ....www.lcms.org
1333 S Kirkwood Rd, Saint Louis, MO 63122
Matt Harrison, Executive Director

Mingo Job Corp Ctr 573.222.3537
Fax 573.222.2685
E-mail ....samcooper@jobcorps.jcdc.org
4253 State Highway T, Puxico, MO 63960-8225
Sam Cooper, Center Director

Progressive Youth Ctr 314.963.8368
Fax 314.963.8935
Web ....www.pyconline.com
9530 Watson Industrial Park Ste B, Saint Louis, MO 63126
Meg Petri, Executive Director

Sherwood Ctr for the Exceptional Child 816.363.4606
Fax 816.822.1988
Web ....www.sherwoodcenter.org
E-mail ....info@sherwoodcenter.org
7938 Chestnut Ave, Kansas City, MO 64132-3698
Deborah Wood, Ma, Executive Director

Youth Build 314.436.1400
Fax 314.431.0011
E-mail ....jsonn@stlouis.missouri.org
 1919 S Broadway, Saint Louis, MO 63104-4055
 Joyce Sonn, Program Director

FOSTER CARE AGENCIES

Adoption & Fertility Resources 816.781.8550
Fax 816.792.3219
E-mail ....cca144@sbcglobal.net
 1129B W Kansas, Liberty, MO 64068

Adoption Triad Support Network KC 816.505.0328
E-mail ....gapmother@aol.com
 5008 NW Linden Rd, Kansas City, MO 64151
 Carolyn Pooler, Coordinator

Annie Malone Chldrn & Fmly Svc Ctr 314.531.0120
Fax 314.531.0125
E-mail ....amcfsc@anniemalone.com
 2612 Annie Malone Dr, Saint Louis, MO 63113
 A Starks, Chief Executive Officer

Butterfield Youth Services 660.886.2253
Fax 660.886.6601
Web ....www.bys-kids.org
 P.O. Box 333, Marshall, MO 65340-0333
 COA accredited organization.

Children's Home Society of Missouri CHS 314.968.2350
Fax 314.968.4239
E-mail ....annez@chsmo.org
 9445 Litzsinger Rd, Brentwood, MO 63144
 Karen Nolte, Executive Director

Christian Family Svcs of the Midwest Inc 816.451.2077
 5703 N Flora, Gladstone, MO 64118

Community Response 314.361.3304
 5361 Delmar Blvd, Saint Louis, MO 63101

Downey Side 816.531.5465
E-mail ....smiller@downeyside.org
 1 W Armour Blvd, Ste 16, Kansas City, MO 64111
 Dacia Peterson, Regional Director

Foster & Adoptive Care Coalition 314.367.8373
Web ....www.foster-adopt.org
E-mail ....debbiegenung@foster-adopt.org
 1750 S Brentwood Blvd Ste 210, Saint Louis,
 MO 63144
 Melanie Scheetz, Director

Hope Chest for Kids Inc 573.449.7804
 4187 W Harper Rd, Clark, MO 65243
 Theresa Foltz, Director

Lutheran Fmly & Chldrn Svcs of MO (LFCS) 314.534.1515
Fax 314.534.1588
Web ....www.oscsmo.org
 8631 Delmar Blvd, Saint Louis, MO 63124
 Alan Erdnan, Director

Midwest Foster Care & Adption Assoc Inc 816.350.0215
Fax 816.350.0085
 3210 Lees Summit Rd, Independence, MO 64055

Missouri Foster Care & Adoption Assc 417.862.8081
Fax 417.862.8081
E-mail ....mfcaastatepres@centurytel.net
 225 S Troy, Springfield, MO 65802

Missouri Foster Care & Adoption Assoc 636.250.3367
E-mail ....judyb327@aol.com
 3737 Harry S Truman Blvd, 5943 Hwy V, Saint
 Charles, MO 63301
 Judy Bexter-Mueller, President

Parkland Foster & Adoptive Families 573.358.3512
Fax 573.756.6007
 408 N Allen St, Bonne Terre, MO 63628

St Louis Arc 314.569.2211
 1177 N warson Rd, Ste 200, Saint Louis, MO 63132
 Kathy Meath, Chief Executive Officer

Urban Behavioral HealthCare Institute 314.577.5000
Fax 314.577.5003
Web ....www.urbanbehav.com
 1104 South Jefferson, St. Louis, MO 63104
 COA accredited organization.

HOME MEDICAL EQUIPMENT PROVIDERS

HealthMEDX Inc 417.582.1816
 5100 N Towne Centre Dr, Ozark, MO 65721
 Jim Atteberry, Chief Executive Officer

Paraquad, Inc. 314.289.4200
Fax 314.289.4201
Web ....www.paraquad.org
 5240 Oakland Avenue, Saint Louis, MO 63110
 CARF accredited programs available.

Southwest Technologies 800.247.9951
 1746 Levee Rd, North Kansas City, MO 64116

PEDIATRIC HOME CARE

Advantage Nursing Services 866.383.3535
Fax 314.997.2404
Web ....www.advantage-nursing.com
 2127 Innerbelt Business Ctr Dr, Ste 100, Corporate
 Headquarters, St. Louis, MO 63114

Bayada Nurses 314.849.1188
Fax 314.849.5187
Web ....www.bayada.com
E-mail ....ddecker@bayada.com
 13131 Tesson Ferry Road, Suite 221, St. Louis,
 MO 63128
 Dan Decker, Director

Interim Healthcare 816.478.2277
Fax 816.478.2279
 14500 E 42nd St Ste 200, Independence, MO 64055

SOCIAL SERVICES

Abortion Alternatives 636.724.1200
Fax 636.946.0447
Web ....www.birthrightstl.org
 205 N 5th St, Saint Charles, MO 63301
 Glenda Amey, Executive Director

Abortion Alternatives 314.298.0945
Web ....www.birthrightstlouis.org
 3435 Bridgeland Dr Ste A, Bridgeton,
 MO 63044-2638
 Joyce Receniello, Director

Abortion Alternatives 636.946.4900
 625 N Euclid Ave, Saint Louis, MO 63108
 Glenda Stevens, Director

Adoption Exchange 314.291.3313
Fax 314.291.3373
Web ....www.adoptex.org
E-mail ....dani@adoptex.org
 3437 Bridgeland Dr, Bridgeton, MO 63044-2604
 Jennifer Beavers, Coordinator

Armed Svcs YMCA Pulaski 573.329.4513
Web ....www.ound.com/asymca
E-mail ....ymca@ound.com
 29 Young St, Fort Leonard Wood, MO 65473-1034
 Linda Bright, Executive Director

**BFT Holding Corp/Bringing Families
Together** 314.731.3969
Fax 314.731.3906
Web ....www.bringingfamiliestogether.com
 7151 North Lindbergh Boulevard, Hazelwood,
 MO 63042
 COA accredited organization.

**Catholic Charities of Kansas City-St. Joseph,
Inc.** 816.221.4377
Fax 816.221.9116
Web ....www.catholiccharities-kcsj.org
 20 West 9th Street, Kansas City, MO 64105-1704
 COA accredited organization.

**Catholic Charities, Archdiocese of St.
Louis** 314.367.5500
Fax 314.367.5128
Web ....www.ccstl.org
 4532 Lindell Boulevard, St. Louis, MO 63108
 COA accredited organization.

Child Abuse Prevention Association, Inc. 816.252.8388
Fax 816.252.1337
Web ....www.childabuseprevention.org
 503 East 23rd Street, Independence, MO 64055
 COA accredited organization.

Child Care Connections 660.385.1378
Fax 660.385.1387
Web ....www.moccrrn.org
E-mail ....joanne@moccrrn.org
 1119 S Missouri St Ste C, Macon, MO 63552-1485
 Joanne Nelson, Director

Child Day Care Assoc of St. Louis 314.531.1412
Fax 314.531.4184
Web ....www.childcarestl.org
E-mail ....sharon@childcarestl.org
 4236 Lindell Blvd Ste 300, Saint Louis,
 MO 63108-2948
 Sharon Ackermann, Controller

**Children's Foundation of Mid America,
Inc.** 314.989.9727
Fax 314.989.9709
Web www.care4kids.org
 1220 North Lindbergh, St. Louis, MO 63132
 COA accredited organization.

Children's Home Society 636.940.1119
Fax 636.940.8298
Web ....www.chsmo.com
 2424 Muegge Rd, Saint Charles, MO 63303-3150
 Kateri Chapman-kramer, Director

Children's Home Society of Missouri 314.968.2350
Fax 314.968.4239
Web ....www.chsmo.com
 9445 Litzsinger Road, St. Louis, MO 63144
 COA accredited organization.

Children's Trust Fund 573.751.5147
Fax 573.751.0254
Web ....www.oa.mo.gov
E-mail ....ctf@oa.mo.gov
 301 W High St, Room 840, Jefferson City, MO 65101
 Kurk Schreiber, Executive Director

Christian Family Svcs 314.968.2216
Fax 314.968.2335
Web ....www.cfserve.org
E-mail ....sawtrey@cfserve.org
 7955 Big Bend Blvd, Saint Louis, MO 63119-2703
 Steve Awtrey, Executive Director

Cornerstones of Care 816.561.1791
Fax 816.753.1119
Web ....www.cornerstonesofcare.org
 4901 Main Street, Suite 450, Kansas City, MO 64112
 COA accredited organization.

Covenant House Missouri 314.533.2241
Fax 314.454.0005
Web ....www.covenanthousemo.org
E-mail ....swagener@covenanthousemo.org
 2727 N Kings Hwy, Saint Louis, MO 63108-2213
 Suzanne Wagener, Lcsw, Executive Director

Crossroads Family Ministries 660.438.9140
 314 W Main St, Warsaw, MO 65355

Missouri

Developmental Disability Resource Board 636.939.3351
Fax 636.939.3988
Web ....www.ddrb.org
156 Saint Peters Centre Blvd, Saint Peters,
MO 63376-1695
Keri Riley, Administrative Assistant

ECH Every Child's Hope 314.427.3755
Fax 314.426.0764
Web www.ech1858.org
8240 St. Charles Rock Road, St. Louis, MO 63114
COA accredited organization.

Family Haven - A Community &
Partnership 314.423.7770
Fax 314.423.5458
Web ....www.usc.salvationarmy.org
10740 Page Ave, Saint Louis, MO 63132-1016
Leslie Marna, Administrator

Gillis Center 816.508.3500
Fax 816.508.3535
Web ....www.gillis.org
8150 Wornall Road, Kansas City, MO 64114
COA accredited organization.

Healthy Families Counseling & Support 816.468.6336
Fax 816.468.0289
Web ....www.healthyfamilieskc.org
3100 NE 83rd Street, Suite 1401, Kansas City,
MO 64119
COA accredited organization.

Jewish Family & Childrens Service 314.812.9333
Fax 314.812.9388
E-mail ....transstrat@yahoo.com
10950 Schuetz Rd, Saint Louis, MO 63146
Lori Goldberg

Jewish Family & Childrens Service 314.993.1000
Fax 314.812.9399
E-mail ....jfcs@jfcs-stl.org
10950 Schuetz Rd, Saint Louis, MO 63146
Louis Albert, Director

Kings Day Care Ctr- Foster/Respite
Program 314.727.7015
E-mail ....thekingsday@sbcglobal.net
848 Kingsland Ave, Saint Louis, MO 63130-3112
Carol Mitchel, Director

Lutheran Family and Children's Services of
Missouri 314.787.5100
Fax 314.994.7405
Web ....www.lfcsmo.org
8631 Delmar Boulevard, St. Louis, MO 63124
COA accredited organization.

MBCH Children and Family Ministries 314.739.6811
Fax 314.739.6325
Web ....www.mbch.org
11300 St. Charles Rock Road, Bridgeton,
MO 63044-2793
COA accredited organization.

Medical Center 636.528.8551
Fax
Web
1000 E Cherry St, Troy, MO 63379
Pat Bira, Chief Executive Officer

Missouri Alliance for Children and Families,
LLC 573.556.8090
Fax 573.632.2761
Web ....www.ma-cf.org
PO Box 104265, Jefferson City, MO 65110-4265
COA accredited organization.

Missouri Baptist Children and Family
Ministries 816.795.8878
Fax 816.795.6637
Web ....www.mbch.org
E-mail ....shirley.gibson@mbch.org
5155 Raytown Rd Ste 105, Kansas City, MO 64133
Shirley Gibson, Assistant Director

Missouri BRANCH 816.333.1172
Fax 816.333.1776
8080 Ward Pkwy Ste 350, Kansas City, MO 64114
Richard Odiam, Director

Missouri Department of Social Services-Children's
Division 573.522.8024
Web ....www.dss.mo.gov/cd
P.O. Box 88, Jefferson City, MO 65103-0088
COA accredited organization.

Missouri DSS-Childrens Div-Circuit 3 ....660.425.7995
2403 Vandivert Street, Bethany, MO 64424
COA accredited organization.

New Hope Care, Inc. 573.431.7336
Fax 573.431.7136
Web ....www.newhoperc.com
E-mail ....jkienzle@newhoperc.com
2280 Pimville Rd, Park Hills, MO 63601
Jack Kienzle Med, Executive Director

Our Little Haven 314.533.2229
Fax 314.533.3098
Web ....www.ourlittlehaven.org
4316 Lindell, St. Louis, MO 63108
COA accredited organization.

Preferred Family Healthcare, Inc. 660.665.1962
Fax 660.665.3989
Web ....www.pfh.org
E-mail ....pberg@pfh.org
900 East LaHarpe, Kirksville, MO 63501
Pat Berg, Director
CARF accredited programs available.

Prince Hall Family Support Ctr 314.877.2000
Fax 314.877.2444
Web ....www.mo.gov
E-mail ....valerie.davis@dss.mo.gov
4411 N Newstead Ave, Saint Louis, MO 63115-2534
Valerie Davis, Director

Saints Joachim and Ann Care Service 636.441.1302
Fax 636.447.6283
Web ....www.jacares.org
4116 McClay Road, St. Charles, MO 63304
COA accredited organization.

Southeast Missouri State University Speech and Hearing
Clinic 573.651.2050
Fax 573.651.2155
E-mail ....mjcook@semo.edu
1 University Plaza, #2600, Cape Girardeau,
MO 63701
Martha Cook, Clinic Coordinator

St. Louis Crisis Nursery 636.947.0600
Fax 636.947.1455
E-mail ....info@crisisnurserykids.com
315 1st Capitol Dr, Saint Charles, MO 63301
Dianne Mueller, Executive Director

St. Louis Crisis Nursery 314.953.8030
Fax 314.953.8033
Web ....www.crisisnurserykids.com
E-mail ....dianne@crisisnurserykids.com
11037 Breezy Point Ln, Saint Louis, MO 63136-6114
Dianne Mueller, Executive Director

St. Louis Respite Voucher Program 314.421.0090
Fax 314.421.2525
Web ....www.stldd.org
E-mail ....stldd@stldd.org
2334 Olive St, Saint Louis, MO 63103
Michelle Darden, Executive Director

St. Vincent Home for Children 314.261.6011
Fax 314.385.1467
Web ....www.saintvincenthome.org
7401 Florissant Road, St. Louis, MO 63121
COA accredited organization.

Synergy Services, Inc. 816.587.4100
Fax 816.587.6691
Web ....www.synergyservices.org
400 East Sixth Street, Parkville, MO 64152
COA accredited organization.

Truman State University Speech and Hearing
Clinic 660.785.4669
Fax 660.785.7424
Web ....www.truman.edu
E-mail ....chelton@truman.edu
222 Barnett Hall, Truman State University, Kirksville,
MO 63501
Connie Ikerd, Secretary

University of Missouri Speech and Hearing
Clinic 573.882.3873
Fax 573.884.8686
Web ....www.missouri.edu
E-mail ....brinkmanb@health.missouri.edu
303 Lewis Hall, Columbia, MO 65211-4280
Barbara Brinkman, Ma, Ccc-slp, Clinical Director

Watkins Mill Youth Svcs 816.781.8786
Fax 816.580.3825
25610 Park Rd N, Watkins Mill Park Camp, Lawson,
MO 64062
Nikki Hamre, Facility Manager

Wyman Center, Inc. 636.938.5245
Fax 636.938.5289
Web ....www.wymancenter.org
600 Kiwanis Drive, Eureka, MO 63025
COA accredited organization.

Youth In Need 636.946.5600
Fax 636.946.2900
Web ....www.youthinneed.org
E-mail ....jbraun@youthinneed.org
1815 Boones Lick Rd, Saint Charles, MO 63301-2247
James Braun, Executive Director
COA accredited organization.

YWCA Child Care Center 816.232.4481
Fax 816.232.4494
Web ....www.ywcasj.org
E-mail ....jbrown@ywcasj.org
304 N 8th St, Saint Joseph, MO 64501-1988
Jean Brown, Executive Director

SPECIAL NEEDS

Ability Arts 573.875.2782
E-mail ....director@abilityarts.org
PO Box 1763, Columbia, MO 65205

Applied Learning Processes 816.942.6808
Fax 816.942.6898
E-mail ....info@appliedllearningprocesses.com
430 E Blue Ridge Blvd, Kansas City, MO 64145

Asthma & Allergy Foundation 816.333.6608
Fax 816.333.6684
Web ....www.aafakc.org
E-mail ....info@aafakc.org
400 E Red Bridge Rd Ste 214, Kansas City, MO 64131
Melissa Bondon, Executive Director

Asthma & Allergy Foundation 314.645.2422
Fax 314.645.2022
Web ....www.aafastl.org
E-mail ....aafa@aafastl.org
1500 S Big Bend, St 1S, St Louis, MO 63117
Joy Krieger, Director

Brain Injury Association 314.426.4024
E-mail ....info@biamo.org
10270 Page Ave Ste 100, Saint Louis, MO 63132
Maureen Cunningham, Director

Easter Seals Missouri Inc 636.779.2299
E-mail ....cbyrd@mo.easterseals.com
13975 Manchester Rd, Ballwin, MO 63011

Educational Therapy Center 816.584.8860
E-mail ....info@etctutoring.org
6004 B NW 9 Hwy, Kansas City, MO 64152
Lorie Wolf, Administrator

Epilepsy Foundation 816.444.2800
E-mail ....staylor@efha.org
6400 Troost Ste 300 B, Kansas City, MO 64132
Darla Tonmpleton, Director

Family Voices of Missouri Inc 417.619.2609
E-mail ....fvmo@mchsi.com
811 N Fremont Ave, Springfield, MO 65802

Hanger Prosthetics and Orthotics 314.567.6844
Web ....www.hanger.com
9719 Olive Blvd, St. Louis, MO 63146
Fred Schaumburg, Manager, Certified Prosthetist

Howard Park Center 636.227.2339
Fax 636.227.8711
Web ....www.howardparkcenter.org
15834 Clayton Rd, Ballwin, MO 63011
Dawn Casey, Executive Director

Mental Health Association 314.773.1399
1905 S Grand Blvd, Saint Louis, MO 63104
Mark Utterback, President

Missouri Congress of Parents & Teachers 573.445.4161
E-mail ....office@mopta.org
2100 I-70 Dr SW, Columbia, MO 65202
Linda Thiele, Coordinator Of Administrative Services

Missouri Parents Act 816.531.7070
Fax 816.531.4777
E-mail ....msavage@ptimpact.org
8301 State Line Rd Ste 204, Kansas City, MO 64114
Mary Savage, Director

Missouri Rehabilitation Center 417.466.3711
Fax 417.461.5730
Web ....http://www.muhealth.org/
600 North Main Street, Mount Vernon, MO 65712
CARF accredited programs available.

MO-FEAT 314.993.0806
E-mail ....info@mofeat.org
2388 Schuetz Rd Ste A-49, Saint Louis, MO 63146

MPACT Missouri Parents Act 816.531.7070
Fax 816.531.4777
8301 State Line Rd, Ste 204, Kansas City, MO 64114
Mary K Savage, Executive Director

National Alliance on Mental Illness 573.634.7727
E-mail ....namimockj@yahoo.com
3405 W Truman Blvd, Jefferson City, MO 65109
Cynthia Keele, Executive Director

National Multiple Sclerosis Society 314.781.9020
Fax 314.781.1440
E-mail ....info@gatewaymssociety.org
1867 Lackland Hill Pkwy, Saint Louis, MO 63146

National Multiple Sclerosis Society 913.432.3926
Fax 913.432.6912
E-mail ....Info@nmsskc.org
7611 State Line Rd Ste 100, Kansas City, MO 64114

Ozark Neuro Rehab Center 417.269.9300
Fax 417.269.0582
3550 South National, Suite 200, Springfield, MO 65807
CARF accredited programs available.

Planning Cncl Developmental Disabilities 573.751.8611
E-mail ....susan.pritchard-green@dmh.mo.gov
PO Box 687, Jefferson City, MO 65102
Susan Pritchard, Director

Poplar Bluff Regional Medical Center 573.727.2360
Fax 573.727.2460
Web ....www.poplarbluffregional.com
2620 North Westwood Boulevard, Poplar Bluff, MO 63901
CARF accredited programs available.

Sharing Our Strengths 800.444.0821
215 W Pershing Rd, Kansas City, MO 64108
Jenny Hatfield-Callen, Match Coordinator

Special Health Care Needs 573.751.6246
E-mail ....info@dhss.mo.gov
930 Wildwood, Jefferson City, MO 65102
Gary Harbison, Director

Special Healthcare Needs Family Partnership 573.369.2359
E-mail ....huffl@lpha.mopublic.org
21252 Hwy 52, Tuscumbia, MO 65082
Lucreitia Huff, Coordinator

Special Svcs 573.897.2991
Fax 573.897.4760
E-mail ....jennieames@hotmail.com
1006 E. Jefferson St., Linn, MO 65051
Jennie Ames, Executive Director

Speech-Language-Hearing Association 888.729.6742
E-mail ....msha@showmemsha.org
2000 E Broadway, Columbia, MO 65201

St. John's Hospital - Inpatient Rehabilitation Unit 417.820.2973
Fax 417.820.7148
1235 East Cherokee, Springfield, MO 65804
CARF accredited programs available.

St. John's Mercy Rehabilitation Hospital 314.251.6268
Fax 314.881.4188
14561 North Outer Forty, Chesterfield, MO 63017
CARF accredited programs available.

St. John's Mercy Rehabilitation Hospital 636.368.4000
Fax 314.881.4188
14561 North Outer Forty, Chesterfield, MO 63017
CARF accredited programs available.

St. Louis Children's Hospital 314.454.6000
Fax 314.454.2380
Web ....www.stlouischildrens.org
One Children's Place, Saint Louis, MO 63110
CARF accredited programs available.

The RehabCare Center at Regional Medical Center 573.458.7886
Fax 573.458.8352
Web ....www.pcrmc.com
E-mail ....jmorland@pcrmc.com
1000 W 10th St, Rolla, MO 65401
Suzanne Paule, Director of Foundation and Public Relations
CARF accredited programs available.

The Rehabilitation Institute of Kansas City 816.751.7700
Fax 816.751.7985
Web ....www.rehabkc.org
3011 Baltimore Avenue, Kansas City, MO 64108
CARF accredited programs available.

United Cerebral Palsy Association 314.994.1600
E-mail ....forkoshr@ucpstl.org
8645 Old Bonhomme Rd, Saint Louis, MO 63132
Rick Forkosh, President

Washington Univ School of Medicine 314.362.6981
Fax 314.362.2826
E-mail ....pestronk @neuro.wustl.edu
660 S Euclid, PO Box 8111, Saint Louis, MO 63110
Alan Pestronk MD, Director

SUBSTANCE ABUSE TREATMENT

Act Missouri 573.635.6669
Fax 573.635.7257
Web ....www.actmissouri.org
E-mail ....info@actmissouri.org
428 E Capitol Ave, 2nd Floor, Jefferson City, MO 65101
Chuck Daugherty, Director Of Contracts/collaboration

Bridgeway Counseling Svcs 636.757.2300
Fax 636.949.5168
Web ....www.bridgewaybh.com
E-mail ....sglenn@bridgewaybh.com
1601 Old South River Road, Saint Charles, MO 63303
Stacy Glenn, Clinical Supervisor

Family Counseling Ctr of Missouri, Inc 573.443.2204
Fax 573.875.6607
Web ....www.fccmo.org
E-mail ....info@fccmo.org
117 N Garth Ave, Columbia, MO 65203-4103
Al Tacker, Phd, Executive Director

Preferred Family Healthcare: Enhanced Primary Recovery Plus Program 660.665.1963
Fax 660.665.3989
Web ....www.pfh.org
E-mail ....nscott@pfh.org
900 E Laharpe St, Kirksville, MO 63501-4520
Naomi Scott, Executive Director

Montana

Brian Schweitzer, Governor
PO Box 200801
State Capital
Helena, MT 59620-0801
406.444.3111
406.444.5529 (Fax)
governor@mt.gov
www.governor.mt.gov

Julie Fischer, Juvenile Justice Specialist
3075 N Montana Ave
PO Box 201408
Helena, MT 59620
406.444.2056
jfischer2@mt.gov

Pam Kennedy Carbonari, SAG Chair
P.O. Box 2445
Kalispell, MT 59903
406.758.7704
406.755.6052 (Fax)
pkennedy@kalispell.com

CRISIS NUMBERS

Child Abuse Reporting . . .866.820.5437

STATE SERVICES

SOCIAL SERVICES

Child and Family Svcs **406.841.2400**
Fax 406.841.2487
E-mail ....cfsd@mt.gov
E-mail ....childandfamilyservicesdiv@mt.gov
301 S Park, 5th Floor, Helena, MT 59601-5231
Jackie Stoeckel, Foster Care Director, 406.841.2402; Kandice Morse, ICPC/ICAMA Director, 406.841.2417; Heidi Lutz, Adoption Director, 406.841.2419; Sarah Corbally, Administrator

Foster Care **406.444.1675**
Fax 406.444.5956
E-mail ....bstimatz@state.mt.us
1400 E Broadway St, Helena, MT 59601-5231
Betsy Stimatz, Program Officer

Human and Community Svcs Div **406.444.1788**
Fax 406.444.2547
Web ....www.dphhs.state.mt.us
E-mail ....mjstandert@mt.gov
111 Jackson St, Helena, MT 59620-2925
Mary Jane Standert, Head Start Collaboration Director

GENERAL HEALTH SERVICES

Childrens Spec Health Srvs MT **406.444.3622**
Fax 406.444.2750
E-mail ....cscott@mt.gov
1218 E 6th Ave, Helena, MT 59620
Corliss Scott, Director

Family and Community Health Bureau MT ...**406.444.4572**
Fax 406.444.2606
E-mail ....jdotson@mt.gov
1218 E Sixth Ave, PO Box 202951, Helena, MT 59620
J Dotson, Director

Health Care Resources Bureau/Childrens Health Insurance Plan **406.444.6971**
Fax 877.418.4533
Web ....www.chip.mt.gov
E-mail ....jforba@state.mt.us
1400 E Broadway St, Room 201, Helena, MT 59601
Jackie Forba, Chief

Montana Dept of Public Health & Human Svcs ..**406.444.5622**
Fax 406.444.1970
Web ....www.dphhs.mt.gov
111 N Sanders St, Helena, MT 59604
Anna Whiting-sorrell, Director

WIC **406.444.5533**
Fax 406.444.0239
E-mail ....jbowsher@mt.gov
1400 E Broadway St, #P, Helena, MT 59601
Joan Bowsher, Program Manager

MENTAL HEALTH SERVICES

Drug And Alcohol Agency **406.444.3964**
Fax 406.444.4435
Web ....www.dphhsmt.gov
E-mail ....jcassidy@mt.gov
555 Fuller Ave, Helena, MT 59601-3394
Joan Cassidy, Director

Montana Vocational Rehab **406.444.2590**
Fax 406.444.3632
E-mail ....pewilliams@mt.gov
111 Sanders, Helena, MT 59604
Pe Williams, Director

JUSTICE AGENCY

Attorney General's Ofc **406.444.2026**
Fax 406.444.3549
Web ....www.doj.state.mt.us
E-mail ....contactdoj@mt.gov
215 N Sanders St, Helena, MT 59601-4574
Steve Bullock, Attorney General

CASA of Montana **406.443.2448**
Fax 406.449.7095
Web ....www.casagal.org
E-mail ....info@casagal.org
120 Reeders Alley, Helena, MT 59601
Ellen Bush, Executive Director

Correctional Educ Division Montana **406.444.3930**
Fax 406.444.4920
E-mail ....webadmin@mt.gov
5 S Last Chance Gulch, Helena, MT 59620
Jeane Ward, Administrative Assistant

Crime Victims Unit **406.444.3653**
Fax 406.444.9680
Web ....www.doj.mt.gov
E-mail ....kmatson@mt.gov
2225 11th Ave, Helena, MT 59601
Kathy Matson, Program Officer

Montana Board of Crime Control **406.444.3604**
Fax 406.444.4722
5 S Last Chance Gulch, Helena, MT 59620
Don Merritt, Acting Director

Montana Dept of Justice Div of Criminal Investigation **406.444.3874**
Fax 406.444.2759
Web ....www.doj.state.mt.us
E-mail ....mbatista@mt.gov
2225 11th Avenue, Helena, MT 59620
Mike Batista, Director

Montana Human Rights Bureau **406.444.2884**
Fax 406.444.2798
Web ....www.montanadiscrimination.com
E-mail ....kkountz@montanadiscrimination.com
1625 11th Ave Ste 2, Helena, MT 59601-4668
Katherine Kountz, Bureau Chief

COURTS

Ofc of The Court **406.444.2621**
Fax 406.444.0834
215 N Sanders St, Justice Building Room 315, Helena, MT 59601
Beth McLaughlin, Administrator

Youth Court Svcs **406.433.3011**
Fax 406.433.6985
Web ....www.richland.com/richlandprobation
E-mail ....krasmussen@mt.gov
300 12th Ave NW, Suite 4, Sidney, MT 59270
Kale Rasmussen, Probation Officer

POLICE AND SHERIFF

Montana Assoc of Chiefs of Police **406.444.3916**
Fax 406.444.4169
Web ....www.state.mt.us
E-mail ....kolsen@state.mt.us
2550 Prospect Ave, Helena, MT 59601
Kevin Olsen, Director

Montana State Sheriff's Assoc **406.443.5669**
Fax 406.443.1592
E-mail ....jimesmith@mt.net
34 W 6th Ave Ste 2E, Helena, MT 59601-5075
Kathy Mcgowan, Director

EDUCATION SERVICES

Deaf/Blind Specialist **406.444.4426**
Fax 406.444.3924
E-mail ....froman@state.mt.us
1300 11th Ave, Helena, MT 59601-3916
Francisco Roman, Director

Dept of Education Svcs **406.444.3693**
Fax 406.444.1373
1300 11th Ave, Helena, MT 59620
Nancy Coopersmith, Assistant Superintendent

Div of Special Education Montana **406.444.5661**
Fax 406.444.3924
E-mail ....tharris@mt.gov
1300 11th Ave, Helena, MT 59601-2501
Tim Harris, Director

Educ for Homeless Children and Youth MT **406.444.2036**
Fax 406.444.3924
E-mail . . . . tteichrow@mt.gov
　　1300 11th Ave, PO Box 202501, Helena, MT 59620
　　T Teichrow, Director

Montana Office of Public Instruction **406.444.3693**
Fax 406.444.2955
　　PO Box 202501, Helena, MT 59620
　　Susan Court, Health Specialist

Parents, Lets Unite for Kids MT **406.255.0540**
Fax 406.255.0523
E-mail . . . . info@pluk.org
　　516 N 32nd St, Billings, MT 59101
　　Roger Holt, Director

LABOR & WORKFORCE EDUCATION

Dept of Labor and Industry **406.444.4100**
Fax 406.444.3037
E-mail . . . . gwright@state.mt.us
　　1327 Lockey St, Helena, MT 59624
　　Gary Wright, Bureau Chief

COUNTY SERVICES

Beaverhead County

SOCIAL SERVICES

Ofc Of Public Assistance **406.683.3773**
Fax 406.683.3774
Web . . . . www.co.beaverhead.mt.us
E-mail . . . . mbeattie@co.beaverhead.mt.us
　　2 S Pacific St Ste 9, Dillon, MT 59725-2799
　　Mark Beattie, Director

GENERAL HEALTH SERVICES

Public Health Dept **406.683.4771**
Fax 406.683.3188
　　41 Barrett St, Dillon, MT 59725-3519
　　Mary Leavitt, Family Planning Nurse

COURTS

5th Judicial District Court **406.683.3725**
Fax 406.683.3728
E-mail . . . . dkaatz@mt.gov
　　2 S Pacific St Ste 5, Dillon, MT 59725
　　Loren Tucker, Judge

POLICE AND SHERIFF

Sheriff's Ofc **406.683.3700**
Fax 406.683.3778
E-mail . . . . bvhdsheriff@bmt.net
　　2 S Pacific St Ste 16, Dillon, MT 59725
　　Jay Hansen, Sheriff

Big Horn County

SOCIAL SERVICES

Bureau of Indian Affairs Social
Svcs **406.638.2676**
Fax 406.638.2084
Web . . . . www.bia.gov
　　2 Weaver Dr, Crow Agency, MT 59022-0069
　　Debra Stiffarm-Rattler, Social Service Supervisor

JUSTICE AGENCY

Youth Court Svcs **406.665.9815**
Fax 406.665.9708
E-mail . . . . jhicks@mt.gov
　　317 N Custer, Hardin, MT 59034
　　James Hicks, Chief Performance Officer

POLICE AND SHERIFF

Sheriff's Ofc **406.665.9780**
Fax 406.665.9797
E-mail . . . . bhcextsh@mcn.net
　　121 W 3rd St, Hardin, MT 59034
　　Laurence Bighair, Sheriff

EDUCATION SERVICES

Crow Tribe Head Start Program **406.638.3710**
Fax 406.638.3767
E-mail . . . . central@crownations.net
　　PO Box 249, Crow Agency, MT 59022-0249
　　Anita Birdinground, CEO

Blaine County

SOCIAL SERVICES

Bureau of Indian Affairs **406.353.2902**
Fax 406.353.4206
Web . . . . www.bia.gov
　　Ft. Belknap Agency, Harlem, MT 59526
　　Judy Gray, Superintendant

Public Assistance **406.665.8700**
Fax 406.665.8752
　　23 8th St W, Hardin, MT 59034
　　Tanya Watson, Director

GENERAL HEALTH SERVICES

Fort Belknap Health Ctr **406.353.3100**
Fax 406.353.3227
　　456 Gros Ventre St, Harlem, MT 59526
　　Steve Fox, Service Unit Director

Public Health **406.357.2345**
Fax 406.357.3891
Web . . . . www.co.blaine.mt.gov
E-mail . . . . fhodgson@co.blaine.mt.us
　　420 Ohio, Chinook, MT 59523
　　Frances Hodgson, Rn, County Health Nurse

JUSTICE AGENCY

Youth Court Svcs **406.357.2369**
Fax 406.357.2370
E-mail . . . . astewart@mt.gov
　　420 Ohio Street, Chinook, MT 59523
　　Ann Stewart, Chief Performance Officer

POLICE AND SHERIFF

Sheriff's Ofc **406.357.3260**
Fax 406.357.2824
E-mail . . . . ghuestis@co.blaine.mt.us
　　400 Ohio St., Chinook, MT 59523
　　Glenn A. Huestis, Sheriff

Broadwater County

GENERAL HEALTH SERVICES

Health Svcs **406.266.5209**
Fax 406.266.3940
E-mail . . . . licampbell@mt.gov
　　124 N Cedar St, Townsend, MT 59644-2300
　　Dianna Hall, WIC

POLICE AND SHERIFF

Sheriff's Ofc **406.266.3441**
Fax 406.266.3762
Web . . . . www.broadwatercountysheriff.com
　　519 Broadway St, Townsend, MT 59644
　　Brenda K. Ludwig, Sheriff

Carbon County

SOCIAL SERVICES

Ofc of Public Assistance **406.446.1302**
Fax 406.446.1680
Web . . . . www.dphhs.mt.gov
　　206 N Broadway, Red Lodge, MT 59068
　　Nancy Ambrose, County Director

JUSTICE AGENCY

Youth Court Svcs **406.446.1560**
Fax 406.446.2968
E-mail . . . . phellerud@mt.gov
　　5 9th Street East, Red Lodge, MT 59068
　　Pam Hellerud, Probation Officer

POLICE AND SHERIFF

Sheriff's Ofc **406.446.1234**
Fax 406.446.1239
E-mail . . . . trieger@co.carbon.mt.us
　　104 N Broadway, Red Lodge, MT 59068
　　Thomas Rieger, Sheriff

Carter County

GENERAL HEALTH SERVICES

Dahl Memorial Health Ctr **406.775.8739**
Fax 406.775.6479
E-mail . . . . progers@midrivers.com
　　221 Sandy St, Ekalaka, MT 59324
　　Patti Rogers, Nursing Director

Cascade County

SOCIAL SERVICES

Ofc of Public Assistance **406.454.5640**
Fax 406.454.5697
　　201 1st St S, Great Falls, MT 59405
　　Nancy Loncki, Director

GENERAL HEALTH SERVICES

Health Dept **406.454.6950**
Fax 406.454.6959
E-mail . . . . cchd@co.cascade.mt.us
　　115 4th St S, Great Falls, MT 59401
　　Keith Echols, Clinic Manager

JUSTICE AGENCY

CASA/GAL **406.454.6738**
Fax 406.454.6736
Web . . . . www.casacangreatfalls.squarespace.com
E-mail . . . . lgoffcasa@gtfalls.com
　　325 2nd Ave N, Great Falls, MT 59401-2517
　　Lisa Goff, Executive Director

Great Falls Youth Transition Ctr **406.452.1792**
Fax 406.452.8745
E-mail . . . . kmcguire@state.mt.us
　　4212 3rd Ave S, Great Falls, MT 59405-1603
　　Ken Mcguire, Program Director

Youth Court Svcs **406.454.6880**
Fax 406.454.6885
E-mail . . . . ddronen@mt.gov
　　325 2nd Ave N, Suite 110, Great Falls, MT 59401
　　Dennis Dronen, Chief JPO

POLICE AND SHERIFF

Great Falls City Police Dept **406.771.1180**
Fax 406.453.8141
E-mail . . . . cgrove@ci.great-falls.mt.us
　　112 1st St S, Great Falls, MT 59403
　　Corky Grove, Chief

Montana

Sheriff's Dept 406.454.6820
Fax 406.454.6948
Web ....www.ccso.psemail.com
E-mail ....bedwards@ccso.psemail.com
　3800 Ulm North Frontage Rd Stop 3, Great Falls,
　MT 59404-5903
　Bob Edwards, Sheriff

EDUCATION SERVICES

North Central Leaning Resource
Ctr 406.727.6303
Fax 406.727.6304
E-mail ....espin@mcn.net
　1601 2nd Ave N Ste 234, Great Falls, MT 59401
　Lauri Ingebrightson, Director

Chouteau County

SOCIAL SERVICES

Ofc of Public Assistance 406.622.5432
Fax 406.622.3472
　1020 13th St, Fort Benton, MT 59442
　Nancy Lonki, County Director

GENERAL HEALTH SERVICES

Public Health Dept 406.622.3771
Fax 406.622.3411
Web ....www.co.chouteau.mt.us/health
E-mail ....angjohnson@mt.gov
　1020 13th St, Fort Benton, MT 59442
　Angel Johnson, Rn, Nursing Director

Custer County

GENERAL HEALTH SERVICES

Health Dept 406.874.3377
Fax 406.874.3459
E-mail ....w.richards@co.custer.mt.us
　2000 Clark Street, Miles City, MT 59301
　Wendy Richard, Director

MENTAL HEALTH SERVICES

Eastern Montana Community Mental Health
Ctr 406.234.0234
Fax 406.234.0235
Web ....www.emcmhc.org
E-mail ....flanemhc@mcn.net
　2508 Wilson St, Miles City, MT 59301
　Frank Lane, Executive Director

JUSTICE AGENCY

Pine Hills Youth Correctional
Facility 406.232.1377
Fax 406.232.7432
Web ....www.mt.gov
　4 N Haynes Ave, Miles City, MT 59301-5600
　Sandy Fogle, Director Of Nursing

Youth Court Svcs 406.874.3418
Fax 406.874.3337
E-mail ....mphillips@mt.gov
　1010 Main St Ste 19, Miles City, MT 59301-3419
　Matt Phillips, Chief JPO

COURTS

16th Judicial District Court 406.874.3326
Fax 406.874.3451
　1010 Main St Ste 19, Miles City, MT 59301-3419
　Honorable Gary L. Day, District Court Judge

Daniels County

GENERAL HEALTH SERVICES

Health Dept 406.487.5000
Fax 406.487.2471
　105 5th Ave E, Scobey, MT 59263
　Kim Wolfe, Director Of Nursing

POLICE AND SHERIFF

Sheriff's Ofc 406.487.2691
Fax 406.487.2699
　106 Railroad Ave East, Scobey, MT 59263
　M. Skip Baldrey, Sheriff

Dawson County

SOCIAL SERVICES

Ofc of Public Assistance 406.377.4314
Fax 406.377.5917
Web ....www.dawsoncountymontana.org
　121 S Douglas St, Glendive, MT 59330-1621
　Donna Lemieux, Supervisor

MENTAL HEALTH SERVICES

Eastern Montana Mental Health
Ctr 406.377.6075
Fax 406.377.8013
Web ....www.emcmhc.org
　204 N Kendrick Ave, Glendive, MT 59330
　Carole Diede, Day Treatment Director

COURTS

7th Judicial District Court 406.377.2666
Fax 406.377.7280
　207 W Bell St, Glendive, MT 59330
　Honorable Richard Simonton, District Court Judge

Deer Lodge County

SOCIAL SERVICES

Ofc of Public Assistance 406.563.3448
Fax 406.563.7279
E-mail ....mbeattie@state.mt.us
　307 E Park Ave Ste 305, Anaconda, MT 59711-2357
　Mark Beattie, Director

GENERAL HEALTH SERVICES

Health Dept 406.563.7863
Fax 406.563.2387
E-mail ....adlcph@rfwave.net
　115 W Commercial Ave, Anaconda, MT 59711-2246
　Linda Best, Health Nurse

Montana State Hospital 406.693.6000
Fax 406.693.7069
E-mail ....sbeausoleil@mt.gov
　300 Garnet Way, Warm Springs, MT 59756
　Susan Beausoleil, Director

JUSTICE AGENCY

Youth Court Svcs 406.563.4030
Fax 406.563.4028
　800 Main St, Anaconda, MT 59711-2950
　Marylyn Shovlin, Chief Performance Officer

Fallon County

POLICE AND SHERIFF

Sheriff's Dept 406.778.2879
Fax 406.778.2815
Web ....www.midrivers.com
E-mail ....fcso@midrivers.com
　10 West Fallon Ave, Baker, MT 59313
　Tim J. Barkley, Sheriff

Fergus County

SOCIAL SERVICES

Ofc of Public Assistance 406.538.7468
Fax 406.538.8419
　312 Birch St Ste 1, Lewistown, MT 59457
　Barb Gilskey, County Director

GENERAL HEALTH SERVICES

Nurses Ofc 406.535.7433
Fax 406.535.7434
Web ....www.fergus.mt.us
　712 W Main St, Courthouse, Lewistown,
　MT 59457-2561
　Carri Craig, Department Head

JUSTICE AGENCY

CASA/GAL 406.538.2242
Fax 406.538.2242
E-mail ....olden@tien.net
　505 W Main St Ste 309, Lewistown, MT 59457-5703
　Jon A. Oldenburg, Director

Flathead County

SOCIAL SERVICES

Public Assistance 406.751.5900
Fax 406.751.5929
Web ....www.dphhs.mt.gov
E-mail ....tharmon@mt.gov
　121 Financial Dr Ste A, Kalispell, MT 59901-1616
　Tammy Harmon, Director

GENERAL HEALTH SERVICES

Health Dept 406.751.8100
Fax 406.751.8102
Web ....www.flatheadhealth.org
　1035 1st Ave W, Kalispell, MT 59901
　Alice Dall, Administrative Assistant

JUSTICE AGENCY

CASA For Kids-A Child's Voice In
Court 406.755.7208
Fax 406.755.7270
Web ....www.flatheadcasa.com
E-mail ....casafvmt@centurytel.net
　1203 US Highway 2 West, Kalispell, MT 59901
　Jamie Campbell, Program Director

Youth Court Svcs/11th Judicial
District 406.758.5541
Fax 406.758.5860
Web ....www.co.flathead.mt.us
E-mail ....nnyman@flathead.mt.gov
　800 S Main St, Kalispell, MT 59901-5435
　Nick Nyman, Chief Performance Officer

POLICE AND SHERIFF

Sheriff's Dept 406.758.5585
Fax 406.758.5862
　920 S Main St, Kalispell, MT 59901-5435
　Chuck Curry, Sheriff

Gallatin County

SOCIAL SERVICES

Ofc of Public Assistance 406.582.3010
Fax 406.582.3114
Web ....www.dphhs.mt.gov
E-mail ....dpingrey@mt.gov
　237 W Main St, Bozeman, MT 59715
　Deb Pingrey, Director

GENERAL HEALTH SERVICES

Health Dept 406.582.3100
Fax 406.582.3112
Web ....www.gallatin.mt.gov/health/index.htm
E-mail ....ssmith@co.gallatin.mt.us
　12 N 3rd Ave, Human Resource Bldg, Bozeman,
　MT 59715-3402
　Shanda Smith, Ryan White Case Manager

JUSTICE AGENCY

Guardian Ad Litem Program 406.582.2051
Fax 406.582.2077
Web ....www.co.gallatin.mt.us
E-mail ....guardian@co.gallatin.mt.us
  615 S 16th Ave Ste 313, Bozeman, MT 59715-4117
Anita Nybo, Director

Youth Court Svcs 406.582.2180
Fax 406.582.2177
E-mail ....gmassey@mt.gov
  615 S 16th Ave Ste 100, Bozeman, MT 59715-4117
Gwen Massey, Chief Performance Officer

COURTS

18th Judicial District Court 406.582.2165
Fax 406.582.2176
Web ....www.gallatin.mt.gov
  615 S 16th Ave Ste 302, Bozeman, MT 59715-4117
Jennifer Brandon, District Court Judge

POLICE AND SHERIFF

Sheriff's Dept 406.582.2125
Fax 406.582.2126
E-mail ....jimcashell@co.gallatin.mt.us
  615 S 16th Ave Ste 220, Bozeman, MT 59715
James R. Cashell, Sheriff

Garfield County

GENERAL HEALTH SERVICES

Health Dept 406.557.2500
Fax 406.557.2950
Web ....www.garfieldcountyhealthcenter.com
  332 Leavitt Ave, Jordan, MT 59337
Mega Weeding, County Health Nurse

POLICE AND SHERIFF

Sheriff's Dept 406.557.2540
Fax 406.557.2567
E-mail ....gcsheriff@midrivers.com
  352 Leavitt Ave, Jordan, MT 59337
Frank Edwards, Sheriff

Glacier County

SOCIAL SERVICES

Bureau of Indian Affairs 406.338.7515
Fax 406.338.7726
Web ....www.blackfeetagencybia.gov
E-mail ....roberta.lane@deq.state.or.us
  PO Box 880, Browning, MT 59417-0880
Roberta Lane, Lead Social Services Rep.

Ofc of Public Assistance 406.873.4113
Fax 406.873.2488
  505 E Main St, Cut Bank, MT 59427-3015
Katie Bremner, Director

JUSTICE AGENCY

Youth Court Svcs 406.873.3620
Fax 406.873.5627
E-mail ....tstiner@mt.gov
  512 E Main St Ste 7, Cut Bank, MT 59427
Tasha Stiner, Jpo

POLICE AND SHERIFF

Sheriff's Ofc 406.873.2711
Fax 406.873.4218
Web ....www.co.glacier.mt.us
E-mail ....sheriff@co.glacier.mt.us
  28 6th Ave SE, Cut Bank, MT 59427-3025
Vernon Billedeaux, Sheriff

EDUCATION SERVICES

Blackfeet Tribal 406.338.7370
Fax 406.338.7030
Web ....www.inaksim.com
E-mail ....susanc@inaksim.com
  615 S Piegan, Browning, MT 59417
Susan Carlson, Director

Golden Valley County

POLICE AND SHERIFF

Sheriff's Dept 406.568.2321
Fax 406.568.2598
E-mail ....gvcso@midrivers.com
  107 Kemp St., Ryegate, MT 59074
Floyd R. Fisher, Sheriff

Granite County

POLICE AND SHERIFF

Sheriff's Dept 406.859.3251
Fax 406.859.3252
Web ....www.co.granite.mt.us
  115 E. Kearny, Philipsburg, MT 59858
Stephen T. Immenschuh, Sheriff

Hill County

SOCIAL SERVICES

Ofc of Public Assistance 406.265.4348
Fax 406.265.6919
E-mail ....sbriese@mt.gov
  48 2nd Ave Ste 200, Havre, MT 59501
Shirley Briese, Director

GENERAL HEALTH SERVICES

Health Dept 406.265.5481
Fax 406.265.6976
Web ....www.hillcountyhealth.com
E-mail ....brichardson@co.hill.mt.us
  302 4th Ave, Havre, MT 59501-3654
Bruce W. Richardson, Health Officer

Rocky Boy Clinic 406.395.4486
Fax 406.395.4408
Web ....www.rbclinic.rockyboy.org
E-mail ....dee@rbclinic.rockyboy.org
  Clinic Rd, Elder, MT 59521
D. Althouse, Md, Medical Director

Jefferson County

GENERAL HEALTH SERVICES

Jefferson Health Dept 406.225.4007
Fax 406.225.4108
Web ....www.jeffco.mt.gov
E-mail ....nmathis@jeffco.mt.gov
  214 S Main St, Boulder, MT 59632
Noel Mathis, Director

COURTS

5th District Court 406.225.4042
Fax 406.225.4044
Web ....www.montanacourts.org
E-mail ....mcraft@mt.gov
  201 Centennial St, Boulder, MT 59632
Honorable Loren Tucker, District Court Judge

POLICE AND SHERIFF

Sheriff's Dept 406.225.4075
Fax 406.225.4145
Web ....www.co.jefferson.mt.us
E-mail ....cdoolittle@co.jefferson.mt.us
  110 S Washington, Boulder, MT 59632
Craig D. Doolittle, Sheriff

Lake County

SOCIAL SERVICES

Ofc of Public Assistance 406.883.7820
Fax 406.883.5320
Web ....www.dphhs.mt.gov
E-mail ....mbecker@mt.gov
  826 Shoreline Dr, Polson, MT 59860-9472
Marilyn Becker, Director

GENERAL HEALTH SERVICES

Health Dept 406.883.7288
Fax 406.883.7290
E-mail ....lindavis@state.mt.us
  802 Main St Ste A, Polson, MT 59860-3200
Linda Davis, RN, HIV/AIDS Coordinator

Tribal Health Dept 406.745.3525
Fax 406.745.4719
Web ....www.thhs.cskt.org
E-mail ....yconko@thhs.cskt.org
  880 Mission Drive, Saint Ignatius, MT 59865
Kevin Howitt, Director

JUSTICE AGENCY

Youth Court Svcs 406.883.7264
Fax 406.883.7270
  106 4th Ave E, Polson, MT 59860
Barbara Monaco, Chief Performance Officer

COURTS

20th Judicial District Court 406.883.7256
Fax 406.883.8582
Web ....www.lakecounty-mt.org
  106 4th Ave E, Polson, MT 59860-2171
Honorable C.b. Mcneil, District Court Judge

Lewis & Clark County

SOCIAL SERVICES

Ofc of Public Assistance 406.444.1700
Fax 406.444.1751
  3075 N Montana Ave, Helena, MT 59601-0552
Dave Morey, Director

Protection and Advocacy System 406.449.2344
Fax 406.449.2418
E-mail ....bernie@mtadv.org
  1020 Chestnut St, Helena, MT 59601
Bernadette Franks Ongoy, Executive Director

GENERAL HEALTH SERVICES

Dept of Public Health and Human Svcs 406.444.9656
Fax 406.444.4435
Web ....www.mt.gov
E-mail ....jcassidy@mt.gov
  555 Fuller Ave, Helena, MT 59620-2905
Joan Cassidy, Bureau Chief

Health Dept 406.443.2584
Fax 406.457.8990
Web ....www.co.lewis-clark.mt.us/health
E-mail ....junderhill@co.lewis-clark.mt.us
  1930 9th Ave, Helena, MT 59601-9753
Jeanne Underhill, Case Manager

JUSTICE AGENCY

CASA Advocates for Kids 406.457.0797
Fax 406.457.0797
Web ....www.casagal.org
E-mail ....bcollins-casa@qwestoffice.net
  133 Reeders Aly, Helena, MT 59601-6286
Bill Collins, Director

Ofc of Juvenile Probation 406.447.8228
Fax 406.447.8421
E-mail ....stregiega@mt.gov
  228 E Broadway St Rm 306, Helena, MT 59601
Sharon Tregidga, Chief

COURTS

1st Judicial District Court **406.447.8205**
Fax 406.447.8421
Web .... www.methfreemt.org
228 E Broadway St Rm 201, Helena, MT 59601-4263
Honorable Jeffrey M. Sherlock, District Court Judge

POLICE AND SHERIFF

Helena Police Dept **406.447.8479**
Fax 406.442.3965
Web .... www.ci.helena.mt.us
221 Breckenridge St, Helena, MT 59601
Troy Mcgee, Chief

Sheriff's Ofc **406.447.8235**
Fax 406.449.8452
Web .... www.co.lewis-clark.mt.us
E-mail .... ldutton@co.lewis-clark.mt.us
221 Breckenridge St, Helena, MT 59601-4230
Leo Dutton, Sheriff

Liberty County

GENERAL HEALTH SERVICES

Liberty Medical Ctr **406.759.5194**
Fax 406.759.5105
418 West Monroe Ave, Chester, MT 59522
Anna Earl, Md, Health Officer

POLICE AND SHERIFF

Sheriff's Dept **406.759.5171**
Fax 406.759.5520
Web .... www.co.liberty.mt.us
E-mail .... sheriff@co.liberty.mt.us
101 Adams St, Chester, MT 59522
Richard A. Burrows, Sheriff

Lincoln County

SOCIAL SERVICES

Ofc of Public Assistance **406.293.3791**
Fax 406.293.5549
899 Farm To Market Rd, Libby, MT 59923
Tammy Harmon, Director

GENERAL HEALTH SERVICES

Health Dept **406.293.2660**
Fax 406.293.9284
Web .... www.lincolncountymt.us
E-mail .... k@libby.org
418 Main Ave, Libby, MT 59923-1848
Karol Spas-otte, Rn, Public Health Nurse

Nurse's Svcs North Ofc **406.296.2023**
Fax 406.296.2550
Web .... www.libby.org
E-mail .... shotsrus@libby.org
66121 Montana Hwy 37, Eureka, MT 59917
Micki Carvey, County Nurse

JUSTICE AGENCY

Youth Court Svcs **406.293.7781**
Fax 406.293.6917
E-mail .... khageness@mt.gov
418 Main Ave, Libby, MT 59923
Kindra Hageness, CPO

POLICE AND SHERIFF

Sheriff's Ofc **406.293.4112**
Fax 406.293.3171
Web .... www.lincolncountysomt.com
E-mail .... ro@lcso.mt.gov
512 California Ave, Libby, MT 59923-1942
Roby Bowe, Sheriff

Madison County

GENERAL HEALTH SERVICES

Public Health **406.843.4295**
Fax 406.843.5231
Web .... www.madison.mt.gov
E-mail .... madcophd@3rivers.net
7 Placer Loop, Virginia City, MT 59755
Sara Googe, Md, Health Officer

POLICE AND SHERIFF

Sheriff's Dept **406.843.5301**
Fax 406.843.5351
E-mail .... kmiller@madison.mt.gov
100 W Wallace, Virginia City, MT 59755
David J. Schenk, Sheriff

McCone County

GENERAL HEALTH SERVICES

Health Dept **406.485.2444**
Fax 406.485.3603
E-mail .... mcconeph@midrivers.com
605 Sullivan Ave, Circle, MT 59215
Sue Good-Brown, RN, Nurse Director

POLICE AND SHERIFF

Sheriff's Dept **406.485.3405**
Fax 406.485.3464
Web .... www.mccone.mt.gov.
E-mail .... mcso@midrivers.com
905 D Ave, Circle, MT 59215-0201
Dave I. Harris, Sheriff

Meagher County

GENERAL HEALTH SERVICES

Mountain View Medical Ctr **406.547.3321**
Fax 406.547.3589
Web .... www.mvmc.org
16 W Main St, White Sulphur Springs, MT 59645
Aaron Rogers, CEO

POLICE AND SHERIFF

Sheriff's Ofc **406.547.3397**
Fax 406.547.3721
Web .... www.meagherco.org
E-mail .... sheriff@meagherco.org
101 W Crawford, White Sulphur Springs, MT 59645
Rick E. Seidlitz, Sheriff

Mineral County

GENERAL HEALTH SERVICES

Health Dept **406.822.3564**
Fax 406.822.3745
Web .... www.co.mineral.mt.us
E-mail .... pstevens@co.mineral.mt.us
1208 6th Ave E, Superior, MT 59872
Preggy Stevens, Director

Ofc of Public Assistance **406.822.4551**
Fax 406.822.3217
Web .... www.dphhs.mt.gov
E-mail .... mbecker@mt.gov
305 Main, Superior, MT 59872
Marilyn Becker, County Director

Missoula County

SOCIAL SERVICES

Ofc of Public Assistance **406.329.1200**
Fax 406.329.1270
2677 Palmer St, Suite 100, Missoula, MT 59808
Chris Mitchell, Director

GENERAL HEALTH SERVICES

Health Dept **406.258.4770**
Fax 406.258.4857
Web .... www.co.missoula.mt.us
E-mail .... eleahy@co.missoula.mt.us
301 W Alder St, Missoula, MT 59802
Ellen Leahy, Director

JUSTICE AGENCY

CASA **406.542.1208**
Fax 406.542.8288
Web .... www.casamissoula.org
E-mail .... casamissoula@gmail.com
100 Ryman St Ste 600, Missoula, MT 59802
Lanette Diaz, Executive Director

Youth Court Svcs **406.258.4735**
Fax 406.258.4892
Web .... www.missoulayouthcourt.org
E-mail .... gwelch@mt.gov
311 Woody St, Missoula, MT 59802-4143
Glen Welch, Chief Performance Officer

COURTS

4th Judicial District Court **406.258.4780**
Fax 406.258.4899
Web .... www.co.missoula.mt.us
E-mail .... jlarson@co.missoula.mt.us
200 W Broadway St, Missoula, MT 59802-4216
Honorable John W. Larson, District Court Judge

POLICE AND SHERIFF

Sheriff's Dept **406.258.4810**
Fax 406.721.8575
200 W Broadway St, Missoula, MT 59802
Carl Ibsen, Sheriff

EDUCATION SERVICES

**The Missoula Area Education
Cooperative** **406.523.4861**
Fax 406.258.3973
Web .... www.co.missoula.mt.us
E-mail .... lmaas@co.missoula.mt.us
438 W Spruce St, Missoula, MT 59802-4106
Linda Maas, Director

Musselshell County

JUSTICE AGENCY

Youth Court Svcs **406.323.1714**
Fax 406.323.1877
E-mail .... sapalmer@mt.gov
32 Main St, Roundup, MT 59072
Sallie Palmer, Chief Performance Officer

COURTS

14th Judicial District Court **406.323.1701**
Fax 406.323.1710
506 Main St, Roundup, MT 59072
Honorable Randal I. Spaulding, Judge

POLICE AND SHERIFF

Sheriff's Dept **406.323.1402**
Fax 406.323.2566
E-mail .... squids@midrivers.com
820 Main St, Roundup, MT 59072
Woodrow Weitzeil, Sheriff

Park County

GENERAL HEALTH SERVICES

Health Dept **406.222.4140**
Fax 406.222.4199
Web .... www.parkcounty.org/health.html
414 E Callender St, Livingston, MT 59047-2799
Suzanne Brown, Rn, Public Health Nurse

POLICE AND SHERIFF

Sheriff's Dept 406.222.4172
Fax 406.222.4175
Web . . . . .www.parkcounty.org
E-mail . . . . .alutes@parkcounty.org
   414 E Callender St Ste 2, Livingston, MT 59047-2700
   Allan Lutes, Sheriff

Petroleum County

POLICE AND SHERIFF

Sheriff's Ofc 406.429.6551
Fax 406.429.6328
   201 E. Main st, Winnett, MT 59087
   Bill Caffell, Sheriff

Phillips County

COURTS

17th Judicial District Court 406.654.1062
Fax 406.654.2363
E-mail . . . . .kking@mt.gov
   314 S 2nd Ave W, Malta, MT 59538
   Honorable John C. Mckeon, District Court Judge

POLICE AND SHERIFF

Sheriff's Dept 406.654.2350
Fax 406.654.1213
E-mail . . . . sheriff@co.phillips.mt.us
   314 S 2nd Ave. West, Malta, MT 59538
   Tom Miller, Sheriff

Pondera County

SOCIAL SERVICES

Ofc of Public Assistance 406.271.4020
Fax 406.271.4074
E-mail . . . . .darmiller@mt.gov
   20 4th Ave SW, Courthouse, Conrad, MT 59425
   Darlene Miller, Director

GENERAL HEALTH SERVICES

Health Dept 406.271.3247
Fax 406.271.3248
Web www.3rivers.net
   809 Sunset Blvd Ste 7, Conrad, MT 59425-1700
   Cynthia Grubb, Rn, County Health Nurse

JUSTICE AGENCY

Youth Court Svcs 406.271.4026
Fax 406.271.4081
Web . . . . .www.ponderacountymontana.org
E-mail . . . . .tsteiner@mt.gov
   20 4th Ave SW Ste 301, Conrad, MT 59425-2340
   Tasha Steiner, Chief Performance Officer

POLICE AND SHERIFF

Sheriff's Ofc 406.271.4060
Fax 406.271.2039
   20 4th Ave SW, Conrad, MT 59425
   Jeff Pruttis, Undersheriff

Powder River County

GENERAL HEALTH SERVICES

Powder River Health Dept 406.436.2651
Fax 406.436.2652
Web . . . . .www.dphhs.mt.gov
   507 N Lincoln, Broadus, MT 59317
   Christine Drivdahl-Smith, Director

Powder River Public Health 406.436.2297
Fax 406.436.2315
Web . . . . .www.rangeweb.net
E-mail . . . . .prpublichealth@rangeweb.net
   507 N Lincoln, Broadus, MT 59317
   Jaci Phillips, Public Health Nurse

POLICE AND SHERIFF

Sheriff's Ofc 406.436.2333
Fax 406.436.2866
Web . . . . .www.prco.mt.gov
E-mail . . . . .jblain@prco.mt.gov
   Courthouse Sq, Broadus, MT 59317
   John Blain, Sheriff

Powell County

SOCIAL SERVICES

Ofc of Public Assistance 406.846.3680
Fax 406.846.3257
Web . . . . .www.state.mt.us
E-mail . . . . .mbrown@state.mt.us
   409 Missouri Ave, Deer Lodge, MT 59722-1078
   Mary Pat Brown, Supervisor

JUSTICE AGENCY

Montana State Prison Cd Program 406.846.1320
Fax 406.846.2966
   500 W Conley Ave, Deer Lodge, MT 59722
   Blair Hopkins, Program Director

Prairie County

POLICE AND SHERIFF

Sheriff's Ofc 406.635.5738
Fax 406.635.4126
Web . . . . .www.prairie.mt.gov
E-mail . . . . .sheriff@prairie.mt.gov
   217 West Park Street, Terry, MT 59349
   William Klunder, Sheriff

Ravalli County

SOCIAL SERVICES

Ofc of Public Assistance 406.363.1944
Fax 406.363.2138
Web . . . . .www.dphhs.mt.gov
   310 N 3rd St, Hamilton, MT 59840-2406
   Patty West, County Director

GENERAL HEALTH SERVICES

Public Health Nursing 406.375.6670
Fax 406.375.6349
Web . . . . .www.ravallicounty.mt.gov
E-mail . . . . .jgriffin@ravallicounty.mt.gov
   205 Bedford St Ste L, Hamilton, MT 59840-2853
   Judy Griffin, Public Health Director

JUSTICE AGENCY

Youth Court Svcs 406.375.6805
Fax 406.375.6806
   220 S 3rd St, Hamilton, MT 59840-2722
   Clint Arneson, Clerk

COURTS

21st Judicial District Court 406.375.6710
Fax 406.375.6721
Web . . . . .www.rc.mt.gov
E-mail . . . . .jhaynes@rc.mt.gov
   205 Bedford St Ste D, Hamilton, MT 59840
   Honorable James Haynes, Ste. B, Judge

POLICE AND SHERIFF

Sheriff's Dept 406.375.4060
Fax 406.375.4065
Web . . . . .www.ravalli.mt.gov
E-mail . . . . .choffman@ravalli.mt.gov
   205 Bedford St Ste G, Hamilton, MT 59840-2853
   Chris Hoffman, Sheriff

Richland County

GENERAL HEALTH SERVICES

Health Dept 406.433.2207
Fax 406.433.6895
Web . . . . .www.richland.org
   1201 W Holly Ste #1, Sidney, MT 59270
   Judy Lapan, Ms, Mba, Director

COURTS

7th Judicial District Court 406.433.5939
Fax 406.433.6879
Web . . . . .www.lawlibrary.state.mt.us
E-mail . . . . .kirigoin@mt.gov
   201 W Main St, Sidney, MT 59270-4035
   Honorable Katherine M. Irigoin, District Court Judge

POLICE AND SHERIFF

Sheriff's Ofc 406.433.2919
Fax 406.433.4025
Web . . . . .www.midrivers.com
E-mail . . . . .daischb@midrivers.com
   300 12th Ave, Ste 1, Sidney, MT 59270-4027
   Brad D. Daisch, Sheriff

Roosevelt County

SOCIAL SERVICES

Bia Social Svcs 406.768.5337
Fax 406.768.5437
   500 Medicine Bear Rd., Poplar, MT 59255
   Fayda Simmons, Supervisor

Ofc of Public Assistance 406.653.1210
Fax 406.653.2057
Web . . . . .www.dphhs.mt.gov
   400 2nd Ave S, COURTHOUSE BLDG, Wolf Point,
   MT 59201
   Leni Loendorf, County Director

GENERAL HEALTH SERVICES

Roosevelt Health Dept 406.653.6223
Fax 406.653.6210
Web . . . . .www.dphhs.mt.gov
   124 Custer St Ste B, Wolf Point, MT 59201-1640
   Bonnie Webber, Director

JUSTICE AGENCY

Youth Court Svcs 406.653.6263
Fax 406.653.6207
E-mail . . . . .ronkemp@mt.gov
   400 2nd Ave S, Wolf Point, MT 59201
   Ron Kemp, Chief JPO

POLICE AND SHERIFF

Sheriff's Dept 406.653.6216
Fax 406.653.6205
E-mail . . . . .jqgr1@hotmail.com
   416 1/2 2nd Ave S Ste A, Wolf Point,
   MT 59201-1603
   Freedom Crawford, Sheriff

Rosebud County

SOCIAL SERVICES

Child & Family Svcs 406.346.7918
Fax 406.346.7166
   121 N 11th Ave., Forsyth, MT 59327

Northern Cheyenne Tribe Human
Svcs 406.477.8321
Fax 406.477.8333
Web . . . . .www.ncheyenne.net/tribalgovmt.htm
E-mail . . . . .deagle@deapmt.org
   600 Cheyenne Ave, Lame Deer, MT 59043
   Leroy Stang, Chairman

Ofc of Public Assistance 406.346.2563
Fax 406.346.7166
Web .... www.dphhs.mt.gov
   121 N 11th st, Forsyth, MT 59327
Tonya Watson, County Director

GENERAL HEALTH SERVICES

Health Dept 406.346.2156
Fax 406.346.4266
Web .... www.rosebudcountypublichealth.com
   121 N 11Th Ave, Forsyth, MT 59327
Ginger Roll, Rn, Public Health Nurse

Public Health 406.748.2800
Fax 406.748.2659
   417 Willow Ave, Human Resource Bldg., Colstrip,
   MT 59323
Carol Ashley, Rn, Public Health Nurse

JUSTICE AGENCY

CASA 406.477.8340
Fax 406.477.6111
Web .... www.cheyennenation.com
E-mail .... john_robinson43@hotmail.com
   708 Cheyenne Ave., Lame Deer, MT 59043
John J Robinson, Chief Judge

Sanders County

SOCIAL SERVICES

DPHHS - Child & Family Svcs 406.827.4317
Fax 406.827.9870
   2504 Tradewinds Way Ste 4, Thompson Falls,
   MT 59873-9707

Ofc of Public Assistance 406.827.4395
Fax 406.827.5395
Web .... www.dphhs.mt.gov
   2504 Tradewinds Way, Thompson Falls, MT 59873
Marilyn Becker, County Director

GENERAL HEALTH SERVICES

Public Health Nursing 406.827.6931
Fax 406.827.6988
Web .... www.sanderscounty.mt.gov
E-mail .... cmorgan@sanderscounty.mt.gov
   1111 Main St, Courthouse, Thompson Falls,
   MT 59873
Cindy Morgan, Public Health Nurse

Sheridan County

GENERAL HEALTH SERVICES

Public Health Nursing 406.765.3410
Fax 406.765.3495
E-mail .... kjensen@co.sheridan.mt.us
   100 W Laurel Ave, Courthouse, Plentywood,
   MT 59254
Kathleen Jensen, Rn, Public Health Nurse

COURTS

District Court 406.765.3404
Fax 406.765.2602
   100 W Laurel Ave, Plentywood, MT 59254
Honorable David Cybulski, District Court Judge

POLICE AND SHERIFF

Sheriff's Ofc 406.765.1200
Fax 406.765.3552
   100 W Laurel Ave, Plentywood, MT 59254
Patrick Ulrickson, Sheriff

Silver Bow County

SOCIAL SERVICES

Public Assistance 406.496.4900
Fax 406.496.4901
E-mail .... mbeattie@mt.gov
   700 Casey St Ste A, Butte, MT 59701-5286
Mark Beattie, Director

GENERAL HEALTH SERVICES

Health Dept 406.497.5020
Fax 406.723.7245
Web .... www.co.silverbow.mt.us
E-mail .... thocking@co.silverbow.mt.us
   25 W Front St, Butte, MT 59701-2801
Terri Hocking, RN, Public Health Nursing Director

Walgreens-OptionCare 406.782.3221
Fax 406.782.3321
Web .... www.walgreens.com
   800 West Platinum St., Suite D, Butte, MT 59701
Kimberly Putzke, General Manager

JUSTICE AGENCY

Youth Court Probation 406.497.6376
Fax 406.497.6383
   155 W Granite St Ste 305, Butte, MT 59701
Glen Granger, CPO

COURTS

2nd Judicial District Court 406.497.6350
Fax 406.497.6358
   155 W Granite St Ste 313, Butte, MT 59701-9256
Honorable Kurt Krueger, District Court Judge

POLICE AND SHERIFF

Sheriff's Ofc 406.497.1120
Fax 406.497.1181
E-mail .... jpwalsh@bsb.mt.gov
   225 N Alaska St, Butte, MT 59701-9211
John P. Walsh, Sheriff

EDUCATION SERVICES

Butte Head Start 406.723.4078
Fax 406.723.5620
Web .... www.montana.com
E-mail .... butteheadstart@montana.com
   1000 S Arizona St, Butte, MT 59701
Barb Brophy, Director

Stillwater County

SOCIAL SERVICES

Ofc of Public Assistance 406.322.5331
Fax 406.322.4076
Web .... www.dphhs.mt.gov
   43 N 4th St, Columbus, MT 59019
Kathy Lee, Social Service Specialist

GENERAL HEALTH SERVICES

Columbus Clinic 406.322.4542
Fax 406.322.5418
   407 A St, Columbus, MT 59019
Richard Klee, Md, Health Officer

POLICE AND SHERIFF

Sheriff's Dept 406.322.5326
Fax 406.322.5328
   400 N 3rd St, Columbus, MT 59019
Clifford D. Brophy, Sheriff

Sweet Grass County

GENERAL HEALTH SERVICES

Health Dept 406.932.5449
Fax 406.932.3027
Web .... www.dphhs.mt.gov
E-mail .... caure@state.mt.us
   115 West 5th St, Suite 1, Big Timber, MT 59011
Carol Aure, Public Health Nurse

POLICE AND SHERIFF

Sheriff's Dept 406.932.5143
Fax 406.932.4777
E-mail .... sgsheriff@mtintouch.net
   200 W 1st Ave, Big Timber, MT 59011
Dan Tronrud, Sheriff

Teton County

GENERAL HEALTH SERVICES

Health Dept 406.466.2562
Fax 406.466.5292
Web .... www.tetoncomt.org/healthdept
   905 4th St NW, Choteau, MT 59422-9123
Lora Wier, RN, Public Health Nurse

POLICE AND SHERIFF

Sheriff's Ofc 406.466.5781
Fax 406.466.5787
   26 1st St SE, Choteau, MT 59422
Keith Van Seetten, Sheriff

Toole County

GENERAL HEALTH SERVICES

Health Dept 406.424.5169
Fax 406.424.2425
E-mail .... tc@3rivers.net
   402 1st St S, Shelby, MT 59474
Krifti Akleftad, Public Health Nurse

COURTS

9th Judicial District Court 406.424.8360
Fax 406.424.8361
E-mail .... enichols@mt.gov
   226 1st Street S # 302, Shelby, MT 59474
Honorable Laurie Mckinnon, Judge

POLICE AND SHERIFF

Sheriff's Dept 406.434.5585
Fax 406.434.7265
Web www.3rivers.net
E-mail .... tcsheriff@3rivers.net
   235 Deer Lodge Ave, Public Safety Bldg., Shelby,
   MT 59474-2009
Donna Matoon, Sheriff

Treasure County

POLICE AND SHERIFF

Sheriff's Dept 406.342.5211
Fax 406.342.5212
Web .... www.rangeweb.net
E-mail .... tcco@rangeweb.net
   307 Rapelje, Hysham, MT 59038
Wayne Robison, Sheriff

Valley County

SOCIAL SERVICES

Public Assistance 406.228.4022
Fax 406.228.4030
   501 Court Sq Ste 9, Glasgow, MT 59230-2405
Leni Loendorf, Director

GENERAL HEALTH SERVICES

Health Dept 406.228.6261
Fax 406.228.6242
Web .... www.co.valley.mt.us
E-mail .... vbell@valleycountymt.net
   501 Court Sq, Glasgow, MT 59230
Vickie Bell, Rn, Public Health Nurse

JUSTICE AGENCY

Youth Court Svcs 406.228.6265
Fax 406.228.6265
E-mail .... msorenson@mt.gov
   501 Court Sq Ste 4, Glasgow, MT 59230-2405
Melanie Sorenson, JPO

COURTS

17th Judicial District Court 406.228.6268
Fax 406.228.6212
   501 Court Sq Ste 6, Glasgow, MT 59230-2405
Honorable John Mckeon, Judge

POLICE AND SHERIFF

Sheriff's Ofc **406.228.4333**
Fax 406.228.4601
E-mail ....vcsheriff@valleycountysheriff.net
   501 Court Sq Ste 10, Glasgow, MT 59230
   Glen Meier, Sheriff

Wibaux County

POLICE AND SHERIFF

Sheriff's Dept **406.796.2415**
Fax 406.796.2625
E-mail ....zsheriff@midrivers.net
   203 S Wibaux St, Wibaux, MT 59353
   Shane Harrington, Sheriff

Yellowstone County

SOCIAL SERVICES

Child Protective Svcs **406.657.3120**
Fax 406.657.3178
Web ....www.mt.gov
   2525 4th Ave N Ste 309, Billings, MT 59101-1312

Indian Social Svcs **406.247.7988**
Fax 406.247.7566
E-mail ....louise.reyes@bia.gov
   316 N 26th St Ste 4051, Billings, MT 59101
   Louise Reyes, Indian Services Officer

Yellowstone Public Assistance **406.237.0520**
Fax 406.237.0572
   111 N 31st St, Billings, MT 59101
   Brenda Rush, Director

GENERAL HEALTH SERVICES

Billings Area Indian Health Svc **406.247.7107**
Fax 406.247.7122
   2900 4th Ave N, Billings, MT 59101
   Charlene Johnson, Nurse Program Officer

Health Dept **406.247.3200**
Fax 406.247.3202
Web ....www.riversdownhealth.org
   123 S 27th St Ste C, Billings, MT 59101-4200
   Lil Anderson, Rn, Health Officer/CEO

Riverstone Health **406.247.3350**
Fax 406.247.3389
Web ....www.ycchd.org
E-mail ....debbieh@ycchd.org
   123 S 27th St Ste C, Billings, MT 59101
   Debbie Hedrick, Phs Community Health Services Director

**Rocky Mountain Bureau of Indian Affairs Social
Svc** **406.247.7988**
Fax 406.247.7566
Web ....www.doi.gov/bureau-indian-affairs.html
E-mail ....edward.parisian@bia.gov
   316 N 26th St Ste 1418, Billings, MT 59101-1339
   Edward Parisian, Regional Director

JUSTICE AGENCY

CASA/GAL **406.259.1233**
Fax 406.254.1273
Web ....www.yellowstonecasa.org
E-mail ....angela@yellowstonecasa.org
   3203 3rd Ave N, Ste 203, Billings, MT 59103
   Angela Campbell, Executive Director

Juvenile Probation Dept **406.256.2838**
Fax 406.256.2966
Web ....www.mt.gov
E-mail ....dward@co.yellowstone.mt.gov
   217 N. 27th St. Rm 607, Billings, MT 59107
   Dave Ward, Chief/JPO

COURTS

13th Judicial District Court **406.256.2862**
Fax 406.256.2995
Web ....www.yellowstonecounty.com
E-mail ....rfagg@co.yellowstone.mt.us
   217 N 27th St, Billings, MT 59101
   Honorable Russell C. Fagg, Judge

POLICE AND SHERIFF

Billings Police Dept **406.657.8460**
Fax 406.657.8417
Web ....www.ci.billings.mt.us
E-mail ....stjohnr@ci.billings.mt.us
   220 N 27th St, Billings, MT 59101-1938
   Rich St.john, Chief

Sheriff's Ofc **406.256.2929**
Fax 406.256.2934
Web ....www.co.yellowstone.mt.gov
   219 N. 26th St, Billings, MT 59101
   Mike Linder, Sheriff

EDUCATION SERVICES

Special Education **406.252.4022**
Fax 406.252.7140
Web ....www.metnet.mt.gov
E-mail ....lorth@metnet.mt.gov
   1932 US Highway 87 E, Billings, MT 59101-6651
   Leonard Orth, Director

SPECIAL SERVICES AGENCIES

ADOPTION AGENCIES

Catholic Charities **406.771.7805**
Fax 406.791.5220
   410 Central Ave Ste 601, Great Falls, MT 59401
   Rosemary Miller, Director

Catholic Social Svcs of Montana **406.728.5429**
Web ....www.cssmt.org
E-mail ....betsy@cssmt.org
   420 W Pine St, Missoula, MT 59802-4118
   Rose Mary Miller, Director

LDS Family Svcs **406.443.1660**
Fax 406.495.1418
Web ....www.ldsfamilyservices.org
E-mail ....fam-mt@ldschurch.org
   2620 Colonial Dr Ste D, Helena, MT 59601-8042
   Cary Shelton, Director

Lutheran Social Svcs **406.245.9949**
Fax 406.259.9185
Web ....www.lssmt.org
E-mail ....lssmt@imt.net
   2429 Mission Way, Billings, MT 59102
   Tom Peterman, Executive Director

The Dan Fox Home For Kids **406.443.4730**
Fax 406.442.0248
Web ....www.missoulayouthhomes.com
   616 Helena Ave Ste 104, Helena, MT 59601
   Erin Williams, Director

ADVOCACY RESOURCES

Childrens Defense Fund - Montana **406.761.6233**
Fax 406.761.6233
E-mail ....kdavis@childrensdefence.org
   163 Woodland Estates Rd, Great Falls, MT 59404
   Kristina Davis, State Director

Tribal Program for Indian Children **406.675.2700**
Fax 406.275.2749
Web ....www.cskt.org
E-mail ....jamess@cskt.org
   51383 Highway 93 North, Pablo, MT 59855
   James Steele Jr., Tribal Chairman

BEHAVIORAL HEALTH TREATMENT

A.W.A.R.E., Inc. **406.563.8117**
Fax 406.563.7133
Web ....www.aware-inc.org
E-mail ....canderson@aware-inc.org
   205 East Park Street, Anaconda, MT 59711
   Carter Anderson, Mental Health Residential Service Director
   CARF accredited programs available.

Acadia Montana **406.494.4183**
Web ....www.acadiamontana.com
E-mail ....vmarshall@acadiahealthcare.com
   55 Basin Creek Road, Butte, MT 59701
   Ms. Valerie Marshall, Accreditation Manager
   Joint Commission accredited organization.

Billings Clinic **406.657.4000**
Web ....www.billingsclinic.com
E-mail ....cbohnet@billingsclinic.com
   2800 10th Avenue North, Billings, MT 59107
   Mrs. Cheryl Bohnet, Accreditation Manager
   Joint Commission accredited organization.

Braun Medical Practice **406.439.5334**
   7020 Four Mile Rd, Butte, MT 59701
   Bennett Braun, Psychiatrist

Bryson Counseling And Consulting **406.863.4949**
Fax 406.863.4809
   100 2Nd St E, Whitefish, MT 59937-2410
   Steven Bryson, Director

Crystal Creek Lodge **406.338.3660**
Fax 406.338.7660
Web ....www.blackfeetcd.org
   450 Old Hospital Hill, Browning, MT 59417
   CARF accredited programs available.

Drury Medical Practice **406.257.1336**
Fax 406.257.1353
Web ....www.wmmhc.org
E-mail ....ndrury@wmmhc.org
   410 Windward Way, Kalispell, MT 59901-2680
   Noel Drury, Psychiatrist

Echeverri Medical Practice **406.245.3526**
   208 N 29th St, Billings, MT 59101
   Eeva Echeverri, Md, Psychiatrist

Finsaas Medical Practice **406.532.9770**
Fax 406.541.3034
Web ....www.wmmhc.org
E-mail ....tfinsaas@wmmhc.org
   1305 Wyoming St, Missoula, MT 59801-1725
   Torgeir Finsaas, Md, Psychiatrist

Florence Crittenton Home and Svcs **406.442.6950**
Fax 406.442.6571
Web ....www.florencecrittenton.org
E-mail ....bburton@florencecrittenton.org
   901 N Harris St, Helena, MT 59601-3000
   Barbara Burton, Executive Director

**Fort Belknap Chemical Dependency
Program** **406.353.8317**
Fax 406.353.2884
   Tribal Way, Fort Belknap Agency, Harlem, MT 59526
   CARF accredited programs available.

Fowlie Medical Practice **406.585.7111**
Web ....www.fowlie.yourmd.com
E-mail ....pfowly@fowlie.yourmd.com
   321 E Main St, Bozeman, MT 59715
   Patricia Fowly, Psychiatrist

Intermountain Children's Home 406.442.7920
Web ....www.intermountain.org
E-mail ....julieo@intermountain.org
500 South Lamborn, Helena, MT 59601
Mrs. Julie Ouzts, Accreditation Manager
Joint Commission accredited organization.

Intermountain Children's Home 406.442.7920
Fax 406.442.7949
Web ....www.intermountain.org
E-mail ....tina@intermountain.org
500 S Lamborn St, Helena, MT 59601-5499
Tina Johnson, Residential Service Director

Montana Academy 406.858.2339
Web ....www.montanaacademy.com
E-mail ....gretchenb@montanaacademy.com
9705 Lost Prairie Road, Marion, MT 59925
Ms. Gretchen Boyer, Accreditation Manager
Joint Commission accredited organization.

Rimrock Foundation 406.248.3175
Fax 406.248.3821
Web ....www.rimrock.org
1231 North 29th Street, Billings, MT 59101
CARF accredited programs available.

Rocky Mountain Treatment Center 406.727.8832
E-mail ....clinicaldirector@rockymountaintc.net
920 Fourth Avenue North, Great Falls, MT 59401
Mr. Brian Linnell, Accreditation Manager
Joint Commission accredited organization.

Rosebud Counseling Svcs 406.671.5441
Fax 406.477.8060
E-mail ....karlamcd2003@yahoo.com
PO Box 887, Lame Deer, MT 59043-0887
Karla Mcdonald-Moore, Director

Shodair Children's Hospital 406.444.7500
Web ....www.shodairhospital.org
E-mail ....elivers@shodair.org
2755 Colonial Drive, Helena, MT 59601
Ms. Ellen Livers, Accreditation Manager
Joint Commission accredited organization.

**Summit Ranch dba Summit Preparatory
School** 406.758.8100
Fax 406.758.8150
Web ....www.summitprepschool.org
1605 Danielson Road, Kalispell, MT 59901
COA accredited organization.

**Support and Techniques for Empowering People
(STEP)** 406.248.2055
Fax 406.248.1493
Web ....www.step-inc.org
E-mail ....silvian@step-inc.org
624 Grand Ave Ste 1, Billings, MT 59101-3151
Silvia Novle, Human Resource Director

Yellowstone Boys and Girls Ranch, Inc. 406.655.2100
Fax 406.655.2110
Web ....www.ybgr.org
1732 South 72nd Street West, Billings,
MT 59106-3599
COA accredited organization.

Youth Dynamics, Inc. 406.245.6539
Fax 406.245.9647
2334 Lewis Avenue, Billings, MT 59102
CARF accredited programs available.

Youth Home 406.728.2662
Fax 406.543.0356
Web ....www.youthhomes.com
E-mail ....info@youthhomes.com
515 S Reserve Ste 1, Missoula, MT 59801
Erin Williams, Executive Director

CHILDREN'S HOSPITAL

Benefis Healthcare Hospital 406.455.5000
1101 26th St S, Great Falls, MT 59405
John Goodnow, Administrator

Clark Fork Valley Hospital 406.826.4800
10 Kruger Rd, Plains, MT 59859
Dr. Greg Hanson, Chief Executive Officer

Dahl Memorial Healthcare Assn 406.775.8730
215 Sandy St, Ekalaka, MT 59324
Nadine Comore, Chief Executive Officer

Frances Mahon Deaconess Hospital 406.228.3500
621 S Third St, Glasgow, MT 59230

Glendive Medical Center 406.345.3306
202 Prospect Dr, Glendive, MT 59330
Scott Duke, Chief Executive Officer

Holy Rosary Healthcare 406.233.2600
2600 Wilson St, Miles City, MT 59301

Liberty Medical Center 406.759.5181
315 W Madison Ave, Chester, MT 59522
Ron Gleason, Chief Executive Officer

Marcus Daly Memorial Hospital 406.363.2211
1200 Westwood Dr, Hamilton, MT 59840
John Bartos, Chief Executive Officer

North Valley Hospital 406.863.3500
1600 Hospital Way, Whitefish, MT 59937
Jason Spring, Chief Executive Officer

Northern Montana Hospital 406.265.2211
30 13th St, Havre, MT 59501
Dave Henrey, Chief Executive Officer

Northern Rockies Medical Center 406.873.2251
802 Second St SE, Cut Bank, MT 59427
Cherie Taylor, Chief Executive Officer

Roosevelt Medical Center 406.787.6401
818 Second Ave E, Culbertson, MT 59218
Audrey Stoneberg, Chief Executive Officer

Sidney Health Center 406.488.2100
216 14th Ave SW, Sidney, MT 59270

St James Healthcare 406.723.2500
400 S Clark St, Butte, MT 59702
Chuck Wright, Chief Executive Officer

St John's Lutheran Hospital 406.293.0100
350 Louisiana Ave, Libby, MT 59923
Bill Patten, Chief Executive Officer

St Joseph Hospital 406.883.5377
6 Thirteenth Ave E, Polson, MT 59860
James Kiser, Chief Executive Officer

St Peter's Hospital 406.442.2480
2475 Broadway St, Helena, MT 59601
John Solatin, Chief Executive Officer

St Vincent Healthcare 406.237.7000
1233 N 30th st, Billings, MT 59101
Jason Barker, Chief Executive Officer

Trinity Hospital 406.653.6500
315 Knapp St, Wolf Point, MT 59201
Margaret Norgaard, Chief Executive Officer

COUNSELING SERVICES

Choices Counseling 406.543.2220
Web ....www.choicesmissoula.com
E-mail ....pnord@missoulachoices.com
126 E Broadway St, Suite 18, Missoula, MT 59802
Penny Nord, Director

Lutheran Social Svcs of Montana 406.761.4341
Fax 406.761.7528
Web ....www.lssmt.org
E-mail ....kathryns@lssmt.org
501 Central Ave Ste 201, Great Falls, MT 59401-3125
Kathryn Sabol, Executive Director

CRISIS & SHELTER CARE

Bitter Root Detention Home 406.363.0619
Fax 406.375.0228
E-mail ....bitterrootstaff@youthhomes.com
196 Providence Way, Hamilton, MT 59840-3062
Ramey Kodadek, Program Director

Building Bridges, Inc. 406.827.9853
Fax 406.827.9854
Web ....www.buildingbridgesinc.net
E-mail ....jfairbanks@blackfoot.net
100 Graves Creek Rd, Thompson Falls,
MT 59873-9400
Jill Fairbanks, Admissions & Program Head Director

Coalition Against Domestic Violence 406.433.7421
Fax 406.433.7426
Web ....www.ncadv.org
E-mail ....rccadv@midriver.com
913 SW 6th St, Sidney, MT 59270-3716
Helen Schmitt, Director

Custer Network Against Domestic Abuse 406.234.0542
Fax 406.234.9125
E-mail ....Cnada2000@Yahoo.Com
2000 Clark St, Miles City, MT 59301-2726
Caroline Fleming, Director

Dawson Co. Domestic Violence Program 406.377.6477
Fax 406.377.1286
E-mail ....dcdv@midriver.com
122 W Bell St, Glendive, MT 59330
Susan Anderson, Director

Elk Mountain Academy 208.266.1122
Fax 406.847.0024
Web ....www.elkmountainacademy.org
63 Serenity In, Heron, MT 59844
Barbi Flanders, Executive Director

Family Violence Program 406.827.3218
Fax 406.827.9111
E-mail ....sccff@blackfoot.net
303 East Main,, Thompson Falls, MT 59873
Gayle Seratt, Executive Director

Fort Belknap Domestic Violence Program 406.353.2205
Fax 406.353.4875
Web ....www.ihs.gov
E-mail ....julie.adoney@mail.ihs.gov
RR 1 Box 66, Harlem, MT 59526-9705
Julie Adoney, President

Help Line 406.822.4262
E-mail ....mchelpline@blackford.net
301 S 2nd Ave E, Superior, MT 59801-1839
Sally Miller, Director

Hi- Lines Help for Abused Spouses 406.278.3342
Fax 406.278.5137
Web ....www.hlhas.mcn.net
E-mail ....Hlhas@Mcn.Net
300 N Virginia St Ste 307, Conrad, MT 59425-1662
Connie Huffman, Director

**Kairos Youth Svcs, Inc. Runaway Attention
Home** 406.761.2135
Fax 406.761.5469
1201 7th Ave NW, Great Falls, MT 59404-2229
James P. Corrigan, Executive Director

Montana Youth Homes 406.449.3038
Fax 406.449.3069
Web ....www.rmdc.net
E-mail ....emcbay@rmdc.net
200 Miller St, Helena, MT 59601-5738
Emily Mcbay, Executive Director

Safe Harbor, Inc 406.676.0800
Fax 406.676.0805
Web ....www.ronan.net
E-mail ....Safe@Ronan.Net
48581 Clarice Paul Ln, Ronan, MT 59864
Deeann Richardson, Director

Safe Space Domestic Violence Program 406.782.9807
Fax...406.782.9807
Web...www.safespace.org
E-mail.....................................tgeraghty@safespace.org
PO Box 594, Butte, MT 59703-0594
Tonya Geraghty, Director

Shodair Children's Hospital 406.444.7500
Fax...406.444.7536
Web..www.shodairhospital.org
E-mail...cbates@shodair.org
2755 Colonial Dr, Helena, MT 59601-4926
Christine Bates, Nursing Director

Supporters of Abuse Free Environments 406.363.2793
Fax...406.363.0382
E-mail...safe@Cybernet1.Com
150 Morningstar Way, Hamilton, MT 59840
Stacey Umhey, Director

Victim Program 406.293.7781
Fax...406.293.6614
Web...www.Libbymt.Com
E-mail...Info@Libbymt.Com
418 Mineral Ave, Libby, MT 59923-1956
Carol Ramos, Director

Womens Help Line 406.293.3223
Fax...406.293.3951
724 Louisiana Ave, Libby, MT 59923
Barbara Goffnick, Director

EDUCATION

Chrysalis, Inc. 406.889.5577
Fax...406.889.5576
E-mail...office@chysalisschool.net
77 TRAILS END RD, Eureka, MT 59917-9332
Mary Alexine, Admissions Program Head

Explorations 406.827.3863
Fax...406.827.4072
Web..www.explorationsmt.com
E-mail...explorations@blackfoot.net
119 S. Hill Rd., Trout Creek, MT 59874
Penny James-Riddell, Admissions/Director

Kicking Horse Job Corps Ctr 406.644.2217
Fax...406.644.2343
E-mail...camel.charles@jobcorps.org
33091 Mollmann Pass Trl, Ronan, MT 59864-9899
Charles Camel, Center Director

Monarch School 406.847.5095
Fax...406.847.5014
Web..www.monarchschool.com
E-mail...ranelh@monarchschool.com
26 Aspen Ln, Heron, MT 59844
Patrick Mckenna, Executive Director

Prickly Pear Cooroperative 406.227.7322
Fax...406.227.8039
Web...www.ehps.k12.mt.us
E-mail...vkauffman@ehps.k12.mt.us
2525 Lake Helena Dr, East Helena, MT 59635-3342
Vaughn Kauffman, Director

Summit Preparatory School 406.758.8100
Fax...406.758.8150
Web..www.summitprepschool.org
E-mail...jjohnson@summitprepschool.org
1605 Danielson Rd, Kalispell, MT 59901-7252
Rick Johnson, Msw, Executive Director

Trapper Creek Job Corp 406.821.3286
Fax...406.821.3290
E-mail...lgubik@fs.fed.us
5139 W Fork Rd, Darby, MT 59829-9609
Linda Gubik, Director

FOSTER CARE AGENCIES

A New Arrival 406.684.5312
Fax...406.684.5315
Web...www.anewarrival.com
E-mail...info@anewarrival.com
204 South Main St, Twin Bridges, MT 59754
Julie, Office Manager

Adoptive Parents Assoc 406.457.4845
E-mail...twilac@intermountain.org
500 South Lamborn, Helena, MT 59601

Catholic Social Services of Montana 406.442.4130
E-mail...rosemary@cssmt.org
1301 11th Ave PO Box 907, Helena, MT 59624
Rosemay Miller, Director

Dan Fox Family Care Program 406.721.2704
E-mail...ewilliams@youthhomes.com
PO Box 7616, Missoula, MT 59807

PEDIATRIC HOME CARE

Interim Healthcare 406.252.8794
Fax...406.248.6575
3312 Second Ave N, Billings, MT 59101
Mark Cassel, Director

SOCIAL SERVICES

Child Care Partnership 406.443.4608
Fax...406.443.6186
Web..www.childcarepartnerships.org
901 N Benton Ave, Helena, MT 59601
Sheila Reep, Administrator

Child Care Resources 406.728.6446
Fax...406.549.1189
Web..www.childcareresources.org
E-mail...ccr@childcareresources.org
105 E Pine St, Missoula, MT 59802
Kelly Rosenleaf, Director

District 7 Human Resources Development Council
....406.247.4732
Fax...406.248.2943
Web...www.hrdc7.org
7 N 31st St, Billings, MT 59101
Denise Jordon, Executive Director

Family Connections 406.761.6010
Fax...406.453.8976
Web..www.childcaresolutionsmt.org
202 2nd AveSsouth, Ste 201, Great Falls, MT 59405
Kim Richter, Executive Director

Healing Horse Equine Svcs, LLC 406.327.8830
Fax...406.549.2151
510 S 4th St W, Missoula, MT 59801
Victor Liberman, Director

Pretty Shield Foundation 406.259.4040
Fax...406.652.3640
E-mail...psf@180com.net
3122 Brayton St, Billings, MT 59102-2026
William F. Snell, Jr., Chairperson

The Nurturing Ctr Inc 406.756.1414
Fax...406.756.1410
Web..www.nurteringcenter.org
E-mail...info@nurturingcenter.org
146 3rd Ave W, Kalispell, MT 59901-4428
Eileen Donohoue, Executive Director

SPECIAL NEEDS

A.W.A.R.E., Inc. 800.432.6145
Web..www.dphhs.mt.gov
E-mail...lnoonan@aware-inc.org
205 East Park Avenue, Anaconda, MT 59711
Larry Noonan, Executive Chief Officer

Benefis Health System, Rehabilitation
Unit 406.455.2293
Fax...406.455.2947
Web...www.benefis.org
500 15th Avenue South, Second Floor, Great Falls,
MT 59405
CARF accredited programs available.

Brain Injury Association 406.541.6442
E-mail...biam@biamt.org
1280 S 3rd W Ste 4, Missoula, MT 59801
Kristen, Director

Easter Seals 406.761.3680
E-mail...michelleb@esgw.org
4400 Central Ave, Great Falls, MT 59405
Michelle B, Chief Executive Officer

Family Support Network 406.256.7783
E-mail...fsntoo@aol.com
1002 Kent St W Ste 1, Billings, MT 59102
Windy Ochs, Director

Fragile X Resource of Montana 406.763.4268
Web...www.fragilex.org
E-mail...gatewaymary@gmail.com
12345 Gooch Hill Rd, Gallatin Gateway, MT 59730
Mary DeBernardis, Founder

IDEA PTA 406.728.1124
E-mail...lotus@bigsky.net
PO Box 7724, Missoula, MT 59807

Kalispell Regional Medical Center - Inpatient Rehabilitation
Unit 406.756.4720
Fax...406.751.5430
Web...www.krmc.org
320 Sunnyview Lane, Kalispell, MT 59901
CARF accredited programs available.

Learning Disabilities Association 406.259.3110
E-mail...mark@learningclinic.com
3544 Toboggan Rd, Billings, MT 59101
Mar Taylor, President

Montana Association for the Blind 406.442.9411
E-mail...l.glueckert@milp.us
34 N Last Chance gulch Ste 500, Helena, MT 59624
Laura Glueckert, Administrative Manager

National Multiple Sclerosis Society 406.252.5927
Fax...406.252.5956
E-mail...MTT@nmss.org
1629 Avenue D Ste 2C, Billings, MT 59102

Parents Let's Unite for Kids 406.255.0540
Web...www.pluk.org
E-mail...plukinfo@pluk.org
516 N 32nd St, Billings, MT 59101
Roger Holt, Executive Director

Rehabilitation Institute of Montana at Community Medical
Center 406.728.4100
Fax...406.327.4496
Web..www.communitymed.org
2827 Fort Missoula Road, Missoula, MT 59804
CARF accredited programs available.

Rehabilitation Institute of Montana at Community Medical
Center 406.728.4100
Fax...406.327.4496
Web..www.communitymed.org
2827 Fort Missoula Rd, Missoula, MT 59804
Jeanne Elliott, Director
CARF accredited programs available.

St. Patrick Hospital and Health Sciences
Center 406.543.7271
Fax...406.329.5693
Web..www.saintpatrick.org
E-mail...info@saintpatrick.org
500 W Broadway, Missoula, MT 59802
Tom Schussler, Director of Facilities
CARF accredited programs available.

St. Vincent Healthcare **406.657.7000**
Fax 406.237.7190
Web ....www.svh-mt.org
   1233 North 30th Street, Billings, MT 59107-5200
   CARF accredited programs available.

STEP **888.866.3822**
   1501 W 14th St Ste 210, Billings, MT 59102
   Marsha Sampson, Project Coordinator

VSA Arts of Montana **406.549.2984**
E-mail ....alaynusa@montana.com
   200 N Adams, Missoula, MT 59807

Yellowstone Arc **406.652.5510**
   602 W 18th St, Billings, MT 59102
   Beverly Owens, Volunteer

SUBSTANCE ABUSE TREATMENT

Abortion Education Helpline **406.782.2927**
E-mail ....newhopecenter@yahoo.com
   320 S Idaho St, Butte, MT 59701-2408
   Mary Anne Casagranda, Director

Crow Nation Wellness Center **406.638.3361**
Fax 406.638.3460
Web ....www.crownations.net
   1010 South 7650 East, Crow Agency, MT 59022
   Alberta Goggles, Director
   CARF accredited programs available.

Crystal Creek Lodge **406.338.6330**
Fax 406.338.7660
Web ....www.blackfeetcd.org
   Old Hospital Hill, Post Office Box 450, Browning, MT 59417
   CARF accredited programs available.

Nebraska

Dave Heineman, Govenor
PO Box 94848
Lincoln, NE 68509-4848
402.471.2244
402.471.6031 (Fax)
gov.heineman@gov.ne.gov

Lisa Stamm, Juvenile Justice Specialist
PO Box 94946
Lincoln, NE 68509-4946
402.471.3687
402.471.2837 (Fax)
lisa.stamm@nebraska.gov

Mark Benne, SAG Chair
PO Box 50
Madison, NE 68748
402.454.3955
safety@cableone.net

CRISIS NUMBERS

Boys Town Hotline . . . . . . .800.448.3000   Child Abuse Reporting . . .800.652.1999   Child Abuse Reporting . . .402.595.1324

STATE SERVICES

SOCIAL SERVICES

Child Enforcement Svcs 402.471.1400
Fax 402.471.7311
  220 S 17th St, Lincoln, NE 68509
  Byron Van Patten, Administrator Of Child Support

Economic & Family Support Svcs 402.471.9200
Fax 402.471.9597
Web . . . . .www.hhss.ne.gov
E-mail . . . . .daryl.wusk@hhss.ne.gov
  301 Centennial Mall S, Lincoln, NE 68508-2529
  Daryl Wusk, Office Administrator

Licensure Unit Nebraska .402.471.9278
Fax 402.471.7763
  301 Centennial Mall S, Lincoln, NE 68509
  Lannelle Eastburn, Manager

GENERAL HEALTH SERVICES

Childrens Spec Health Care NE 402.471.9401
Fax 402.471.6352
E-mail . . . . .ginger.goomis@nebraska.go@verizon.net
  PO Box 95026, Lincoln, NE 68509
  Bibianne Chanumont, Director

Lifespan Health Svcs Unit NE 402.471.2907
Fax 402.471.7049
E-mail . . . . .lifespan.health@dhhs.ne.gov
  PO Box 95026, Lincoln, NE 68509
  Paula Eurek, Director

MENTAL HEALTH SERVICES

Nebraska Commission for Blind & Vis
  Impaired 402.471.2891
Fax 402.471.3009
E-mail . . . . .kathy.stevens@nebraska.gov
  4600 Valley Rd Ste 100, Ste 100, Lincoln, NE 68510
  Kathy Stevens, Administrator

Vocational Rehabilitation Svcs 402.471.3644
Fax 402.471.0788
E-mail . . . . .mark.schultz@nebraska.gov
  301 Centennial Mall S, 6th Floor, Lincoln, NE 68509
  Mark Schultz, Assistant Commissioner

JUSTICE AGENCY

Attorney General's Ofc 402.471.2682
Fax 402.471.3297
Web . . . . .www.ago.state.ne.us
E-mail . . . . .nedoj@nebbraska.gov
  2115 State Capitol Bldg, Lincoln, NE 68509
  John Bruning, Attorney General

CASA State Assoc 402.477.2788
Fax 402.477.1720
E-mail . . . . .joann@nebraskacasa.org
  315 S 9th St Ste 213, Lincoln, NE 68508
  Gwen Hurst-Anderson, State Director

Commission on Law Enforcement & Criminal
  Justice 402.471.2194
Fax 402.471.2837
Web . . . . .www.ncc.ne.gov
E-mail .nsteeves@crimecom.state.ne.us
  301 Centennial Mall S, Lincoln, NE 68508-2529
  Mike Behm, Director

Correctional Education Division NE 402.479.5723
Fax 402.479.5623
E-mail . . . . .bob.houston@nebraska.gov
  Folson Prospector Pl Bldg 1, Lincoln, NE 68509
  Robert Houston, Director

Dept of Correctional Svcs 402.471.2654
Fax 402.479.5119
  Folsom W Prspector Bldg 1, Lincoln, NE 68522
  Robert Houston, Director

Nebraska Supreme Court Probation Admin 402.471.4140
Fax 402.471.2197
E-mail . . . . .dminardi@nebraska.gov
  1445 K St, Lincoln, NE 68508-2731
  Deb Minardi, Deputy Administrator

COURTS

Administrative Ofc Of The Courts 402.471.3730
Fax 402.471.2197
Web . . . . .www.supremecourt.ne.gov
E-mail . . . . .janice.walker@nebraska.gov
  Supreme Court, Room 1213, Lincoln, NE 68508
  Janice K. Walker, State Court Administrator

POLICE AND SHERIFF

Nebraska Sheriff's Assoc .402.434.3785
Fax 402.476.2469
Web . . . . .www.mesheriffsassoc.org
E-mail . . . . .nesheriffsassoc@windstream.net
  1700 N 17th St Bldg 114, Lincoln, NE 68508
  Amy Prenda, Executive Director

Nebraska State Patrol, Sex Offender Registry . .402.471.8640
Fax 402.471.8496
E-mail . . . . .nsp.sor@nebraska.gov
  3800 NW 12th St, Lincoln, NE 68507
  Andy Hart, Client Analyst

EDUCATION SERVICES

Educ for Homeless Children and Youth NE 402.471.2968
Fax 402.471.0117
E-mail . . . . .roger.reikofski@nebraska.gov
  301 Centennial Mall S, PO Box 94987, Lincoln,
  NE 68509
  Roger Reikofski, Director

Nebraska Ctr for the Education of Children Who Are Blind or
  Visually Impaired 402.873.5513
Fax 402.873.3463
Web . . . . .www.ncecbvi.org
E-mail . . . . .sgittinger@esu4.org
  824 10th Ave, Nebraska City, NE 68410-1370
  Sally Gittinger, Administrator

Nebraska Dept of Education 402.471.5020
Fax 402.471.4433
E-mail . . . . .denise.fisher@nebraska.go@verizon.net
  301 Centennial Mall S, PO Box 94987, Lincoln,
  NE 68509
  Denise Fisher, Director

Nebraska Dept of Education 402.471.3240
Fax 402.471.0117
Web . . . . .www.education.ne.gov
E-mail . . . . .mary.duffy@nebraska.gov
  301 Centennial Mall S, Lincoln, NE 68508-2529
  Mary Duffy, Gifted Educator

Office of Special Education NE 402.471.2471
Fax 402.471.5022
E-mail . . . . .gary.sherman@nebraska.gov
  301 Centennial Mall S, PO Box 94987, Lincoln,
  NE 68509
  Gary Sherman, Director

LABOR & WORKFORCE EDUCATION

Ofc of Workforce Svcs 402.471.9000
Web . . . . .www.dol.nebraska.gov
E-mail . . . . .catherine.lang@nebraska.gov
  550 S 16th St, Lincoln, NE 68508-2601
  Catherine D Lang, Commissioner Of Labour

Nebraska

COUNTY SERVICES

Adams County

SOCIAL SERVICES

Dept of Health and Human Svcs **402.462.1800**
Fax 402.462.1870
   300 N Saint Joseph Ave, Ste 204, Hastings, NE 68902
Yolanda Nunico, Administrator

JUSTICE AGENCY

District 10 Probation Ofc **402.461.7225**
Fax 402.461.7226
   300 N Saint Joseph Ave Ste 210, Hastings, NE 68901
Robert Horton, Chief Performance Officer

COURTS

Court **402.461.7143**
Fax 402.461.7144
Web ....www.courts.ne.gov
E-mail ....michael.offner@courts.nebraska.gov
   Corner of 5th & Denver, Hastings, NE 68901
Honorable Michael L. Offner, Judge

POLICE AND SHERIFF

Sheriff's Ofc **402.461.7181**
Fax 402.461.7270
Web ....www.adamscounty.org
E-mail ....gmagee@adamscounty.org
   500 W 4th St Ste 126, Hastings, NE 68901-7501
Gregg A. Magee, Sheriff

Antelope County

SOCIAL SERVICES

Dept of Health and Human Svcs **402.887.4196**
Fax 402.887.4536
Web ....www.dhhs.ne.gov
E-mail ....melodee.drenkow@hhss.ne.gov
   501 M St Ste 10, Neligh, NE 68756-1466
Melodee Drenkow, Social Services Supervisor

Banner County

POLICE AND SHERIFF

Sheriff's Ofc **308.436.5271**
Fax 308.436.4180
   204 State St Ste 1, Harrisburg, NE 69345
Stanley Mcknight, Sheriff

Blaine County

POLICE AND SHERIFF

Sheriff's Ofc **308.547.2222**
Fax 308.547.2228
Web ....www.blaine.nacone.org
E-mail ....tsierks986bcso@yahoo.com
   145 Lincoln Ave, Brewster, NE 68821-9700
Tim L. Sierks, Sheriff

Boone County

GENERAL HEALTH SERVICES

Health Ctr **402.395.2191**
Fax 402.395.5165
Web ....www.boonecohealth.org
E-mail ....bchchr@boonecohealth.org
   723 W Fairfield St, Albion, NE 68620
Victor Lee, Administrator

POLICE AND SHERIFF

Sheriff's Ofc **402.395.2144**
Fax 402.395.6517
   217 S 5th St, Albion, NE 68620
Dave Spagel, Sheriff

Box Butte County

SOCIAL SERVICES

Dept of Health and Human Svcs **308.763.2900**
Fax 308.763.2910
Web ....www.dhhs.ne.gov
   624 Yellowstone Ave, Alliance, NE 69301-3436
Connie Green, On-site Supervisor

POLICE AND SHERIFF

Sheriff's Dept **308.762.6464**
Fax 308.762.5162
Web ....www.telecomwest.net
E-mail ....bbcoso@telecomwest.net
   512 Niobrara Ave, Alliance, NE 69301-3422
Tammy Mowry, Sheriff

Boyd County

POLICE AND SHERIFF

Sheriff's Ofc **402.775.2331**
Fax 402.775.2419
   401 Thayer St, Butte, NE 68722
David J. Derickson, Sheriff

Brown County

POLICE AND SHERIFF

Sheriff's Ofc **402.387.1440**
Fax 402.387.0719
E-mail ....bruce@threeriver.net
   142 W 4th St, Ainsworth, NE 69210-1636
Bruce Patftein, Sheriff

Buffalo County

SOCIAL SERVICES

Nebraska Dept of Human Svcs **308.865.5592**
Fax 308.865.5583
Web ....www.nebraska.gov
E-mail ....pat.rappahold@dhhs.ne.gov
   24 W 16th St, Kearney, NE 68848
Pat Rappahold, Supervisor

GENERAL HEALTH SERVICES

Mid-Nebraska Community Action **308.865.5675**
Fax 308.865.5681
Web ....www.mnca.net
E-mail ....mnca@mmca.net
   16 W 11th St, Kearney, NE 68847-7440
Karen Lueck, Director

JUSTICE AGENCY

District 9 Probation Ofc **308.236.1251**
Fax 308.233.3664
   215 W 18th St, Kearney, NE 68848-
Clay Schutz, Chief Performance Officer

COURTS

Court **308.236.1228**
Fax 308.236.1243
E-mail ....gjorgensen@buffalogov.org
   1512 Central Ave, Kearney, NE 68847-6020
Honorable Gerald R. Jorgensen Jr., Judge

Burt County

POLICE AND SHERIFF

Sheriff's Dept **402.374.2900**
Fax 402.374.2901
Web ....www.huntel.net
E-mail ....burtcosheriff@huntel.net
   111 N 13th St Ste 1, Tekamah, NE 68061-1094
Robert D. Pickell, Sheriff

Butler County

GENERAL HEALTH SERVICES

Health Dept **402.367.1200**
Fax 402.367.1350
Web ....www.bchccnet.org
   372 S 9th St, David City, NE 68632
Donald Naiberk, Administrator

Health Dept **402.367.1200**
Fax 402.367.1350
Web ....www.bchccnet.org
   372 S 9th St, David City, NE 68632
Donald Naiberk, Administrator

POLICE AND SHERIFF

Sheriff's Ofc **402.367.7400**
Fax 402.367.3222
Web ....www.neb.rr.com
E-mail ....mhecker@neb.rr.com
   451 N 5th St Ste 1, David City, NE 68632-1667
Mark A. Hecker, Sheriff

Cass County

JUSTICE AGENCY

District 5 Probation **402.296.9363**
Fax 402.296.9333
   346 Main St, Room 102, Plattsmouth, NE 68048
Jeff Leach, Probation Officer

POLICE AND SHERIFF

Sheriff's Ofc **402.296.9370**
Fax 402.296.9390
Web ....www.casshome.com
   336 Main St, Plattsmouth, NE 68048
William C. Brueggemann, Sheriff

Cedar County

SOCIAL SERVICES

Nebraska Dept of Health & Human

Svcs **402.254.7426**
Fax 402.254.7427
Web ....www.dhhs.ne.gov
E-mail ....marilyn.kudera@dhhs.ne.gov
   107 Broadway, Courthouse, Hartington, NE 68739
Marilyn Kudera, Supervisor

COURTS

District 6 Court **402.254.7441**
Fax 402.254.7447
Web ....www.nebraska.gov
E-mail ....douglas.luebe@nebraska.gov
   101 S Broadway Ave, Hartington, NE 68739-4618
Honorable Douglas L. Luebe, County Judge

POLICE AND SHERIFF

Sheriff's Ofc **402.254.6884**
Fax 402.254.2351
Web ....www.co.cedar.ne.us
E-mail ....sheriff@hartel.net
   101 E Centre St, Hartington, NE 68739-6006
Larry D. Koranda, Sheriff

Chase County

SOCIAL SERVICES

Nebraska Dept of Health & Human

Svcs **308.882.4791**
Fax 308.882.3031
Web ....www.dhhs.ne.gov
E-mail ....kerry.hopkins@hhss.state.ne.us
   130 W 4th St, Imperial, NE 69033-2050
Kerry Hopkins, Supervisor

Nebraska

POLICE AND SHERIFF

Sheriff's Dept 308.882.4748
Fax 308.882.5679
Web www.chase3000.com
E-mail ....sheriff@chase3000.com
    921 Broadway, Imperial, NE 69033-3012
    Kevin Mueller, Sheriff

Cherry County

POLICE AND SHERIFF

Sheriff's Ofc 402.376.1890
Fax 402.376.1892
Web ....www.co.cherry.ne.us
E-mail ....clerk@cherry.nacone.org
    365 N Main St, Valentine, NE 69201
    Rusty Osburn, Sheriff

Cheyenne County

SOCIAL SERVICES

Nebraska Dept of Health & Human
Svcs 308.254.6900
Fax 308.254.6914
    1820 Illinois St, Sidney, NE 69162
    Denise Prohs, Supervisor

COURTS

Court 308.254.2929
Fax 308.254.2312
E-mail ....rendin.roland@courts.ne.gov
    1000 10th Ave, Sidney, NE 69162-1612
    Honorable Rendin Roland, County Judge

POLICE AND SHERIFF

Sheriff's Dept 308.254.2922
Fax 308.254.7895
    1000 10th Ave, Sidney, NE 69162
    John D Jenson, Sheriff

Clay County

SOCIAL SERVICES

Nebraska Dept of Health & Human
Svcs 402.762.3465
Fax 402.762.3065
Web ....www.dhhs.ne.gov
    100 S Alexander Ave, Clay Center, NE 68933-1401
    Sheila Williamson, Supervisor

JUSTICE AGENCY

CASA 402.463.1030
Fax 402.463.1054
E-mail ....casab@windstream.net
    2727 W 2nd St, Suite 410, Hastings, NE 68901
    Ruann Ruth, Director

POLICE AND SHERIFF

Sheriff's Dept 402.762.3528
Fax 402.762.3852
E-mail ....clsodispatch@datacc.net
    104 E Edgar St, Clay Center, NE 68933
    Jeff K. Franklin, Sheriff

Colfax County

COURTS

Court 402.352.8511
Fax 402.352.8535
    411 E 11th St, Schuyler, NE 68661
    Honorable Patrick R. Mcdermott, Judge

POLICE AND SHERIFF

Colfax Co. Sheriff's Office 402.352.8526
Fax 402.352.8545
E-mail ....colfx15@megavision.com
    411 E 11th St, Schuyler, NE 68661-1921
    Sheriff Paul Kruse, Sheriff

Cuming County

GENERAL HEALTH SERVICES

Goldenrod Hills Community Action
Inc. 402.529.3513
Fax 402.529.3209
Web ....www.goldenrodhillscommunityaction.org
E-mail ....ghcs@gpcom.net
    1119 Avenue E, Wisner, NE 68791
    Robin Snyder, Executive Director

COURTS

District Court 402.372.6004
Fax 402.372.6017
E-mail ....merna.recker@nebraska.gov
    200 S Lincoln Rm 200, West Point, NE 68788
    Honorable Richard Krepela, County Judge

POLICE AND SHERIFF

Sheriff's Dept 402.372.6019
Fax 402.372.6018
E-mail ....ccso@cableone.net
    200 S Lincoln St Rm 203, West Point,
    NE 68788-1800
    Brad Boyum, Sheriff

Custer County

JUSTICE AGENCY

District 8 ....308.872.6189
Fax 308.872.6901
E-mail ....custerprob@kdsi.net
    1030 S D St, Broken Bow, NE 68822
    Jeff Kawata, Probation Officer

COURTS

District 8 Court 308.872.5761
Fax 308.872.6052
E-mail ....gary.washburn@courts.ne.gov
    431 S 10th Ave Rm 6, Broken Bow, NE 68822
    Honorable Gary G. Washburn, County Judge

POLICE AND SHERIFF

Sheriff's Dept 308.872.6418
Fax 308.872.6585
Web ....www.cornhusker.net
E-mail ....sheriff@custercounty.org
    116 S 11th Ave, Broken Bow, NE 68822-1902
    Dan Osmond, Sheriff

Dakota County

SOCIAL SERVICES

Nebraska Dept of Health & Human
Svcs 402.241.0032
Fax 402.987.3376
Web ....www.dhhs.ne.gov
E-mail ....cricket.phelps@hhss.state.ne.us
    1401 Pine St, Dakota City, NE 68731-5090
    Cricket Phelps, Supervisor

GENERAL HEALTH SERVICES

Health Dept. 402.987.2164
Fax 402.987.2163
Web ....www.dakotacountyne.org
    1601 Broadway St, Dakota City, NE 68731
    Pam Devries, Director

COURTS

District 6 Court 402.987.2145
Fax 402.987.2185
E-mail ....kurt.rager@nebraska.gov
    1601 Broadway St, Dakota City, NE 68731-5065
    Honorable Kurt T. Rager, Judge

Dawes County

SOCIAL SERVICES

Nebraska Dept of Health & Human
Svcs 308.432.6151
Fax 308.432.6004
    1033 E 3rd St, Chadron, NE 69337
    Connie Green, Supervisor

JUSTICE AGENCY

District 1 Probation Ofc 308.432.0121
Fax 308.432.0122
Web ....www.courts.ne.gov
E-mail ....gary.hoffman@courts.ne.gov
    451 Main St Ste B, Chadron, NE 69337-2698
    Gary Hoffman, CPO

COURTS

District 12 Court 308.432.0116
Fax 308.432.0118
    451 Main St Ste d, Chadron, NE 69337
    Lori Miskinins, Clark Magistrate

POLICE AND SHERIFF

Sheriff's Dept 308.432.3025
Fax 308.432.0115
E-mail ....sheriff@dawescountysheriffs.com
    451 Main St Ste F, Chadron, NE 69337
    Karl J. Dailey, Sheriff

Dawson County

JUSTICE AGENCY

District 11 Probation Ofc 308.324.5615
Fax 308.324.5616
Web ....www.courts.ne.gov
E-mail ....kurt.stevens@courts.ne.gov
    700 N Washington St Rm L, Lexington,
    NE 68850-1940
    Kurt Stevens, Intense Supervision Probation Officer

POLICE AND SHERIFF

Sheriff's Ofc 308.324.3011
Fax 308.324.3006
E-mail ....sheriff@dawsoncountynet.net
    709 N Grant St, Lexington, NE 68850
    Gary W. Reiber, Sheriff

Deuel County

POLICE AND SHERIFF

Sheriff's Dept 308.874.3305
Fax 308.874.2994
    3rd & Vincent, Chappell, NE 69129
    Adam J. Hayward, Sheriff

Dixon County

POLICE AND SHERIFF

Sheriff's Dept 402.755.5608
Fax 402.755.5654
E-mail ....dixonso@gpcom.net
    302 3rd St, Ponca, NE 68770-7050
    Dean Chase, Sheriff

Dodge County

SOCIAL SERVICES

HHS Developmental Disabilities
System 402.727.3245
Fax 402.727.3298
    1959 E Military Ave, Northern Service Area, Fremont,
    NE 68025
    Jane Cleveland, Administrator

Nebraska

Nebraska Dept of Health & Human

Svcs.................................**402.727.3200**
Fax.................................402.727.2972
Web.................................www.dhhs.ne.gov
   124 E 5th St, Fremont, NE 68025-5022
   Todd Reckling, Director

GENERAL HEALTH SERVICES

Three Rivers Immunization Clinic.............**402.727.5396**
Fax.................................402.727.5399
Web.................................www.threeriverspublichealth.org
   33 W 4th St Ste 2, Fremont, NE 68025
   Brandy Tumbleson, Executive Director

JUSTICE AGENCY

CASA.................................**402.727.2795**
Fax.................................402.727.2807
   435 N Park St, Ste 302, Fremont, NE 68025-5015
   Dawn Peters, Director

District 16 Probation Ofc.................**402.727.2790**
Fax.................................402.727.2793
E-mail.................................dentonwork@yahoo.com
   320 N Main St, Fremont, NE 68025-5058
   Bob Denton, Chief Probation Officer

COURTS

Court.................................**402.727.2755**
Fax.................................402.727.2762
   428 N Broad St Fl 3, Fremont, NE 68025-4962
   Honorable Kenneth Vampola, Judge

POLICE AND SHERIFF

Sheriff's Ofc.................................**402.727.2702**
Fax.................................402.727.2714
E-mail.................................dodgecoso@68025.com
   428 N Broad St Fl 1, Fremont, NE 68025
   Steve Hespen, Sheriff

Douglas County

SOCIAL SERVICES

Dept of Children & Family Svcs.............**402.595.1055**
Fax.................................402.595.2946
E-mail.................................maria.lavicky@hhss.state.ne.us
   1313 Farnam St FL 3, Omaha, NE 68102
   Maria Lavicky, Supervisor

Dept of Health and Human Svcs Developmental Disabilities

System.................................**402.595.2700**
Fax.................................402.595.1240
E-mail.................................cindy.brinker@hhss.ne.gov
   1821 N 73rd St, Local Field Office #6, Omaha,
   NE 68114
   Cindy Brinker, Administrator

GENERAL HEALTH SERVICES

Health Dept.................................**402.444.7471**
Fax.................................402.444.6267
Web.................................www.douglascountyhealth.com
   401 Civic Ctr, 1819 Farnam St, Omaha, NE 68183
   Adi M. Pour, Phd, Health Director

MENTAL HEALTH SERVICES

CMHC.................................**402.444.7449**
Fax.................................402.996.8171
E-mail.................................john.sheehan@douglascounty-ne.gov
   4102 Woolworth Ave, Omaha, NE 68105-1899
   John Sheehan, Fache, Director

JUSTICE AGENCY

District 18ùJuvenile Probation

Ofcs.................................**402.444.7835**
Fax.................................402.444.4231
   319 S 17th St Fl 4, Omaha, NE 68102-1911
   James G. Fahy, Chief Probation Officer

Intensive Supervision Probation.............**402.444.5420**
Fax.................................402.444.5566
   4236 Redman Ave, Omaha, NE 68111-1448
   Timothy Sprakel, Coordinator

Probation Midtown Ofc.................**402.444.7852**
Fax.................................402.444.7999
   8303 Spring Plz, Omaha, NE 68124-3227
   Gina Volenec, Supervisor

Region 4 Probation Dept.................**402.444.7166**
Fax.................................402.444.3336
E-mail.................................ron.broich@nebraska.gov
   1701 Farnam Rm 164, Omaha, NE 68183-1001
   Ronald Broich, Chief Performance Officer

COURTS

Juvenile Court.................................**402.444.7121**
Fax.................................402.444.6896
   1701 Farnam St # 600, Omaha, NE 68108
   Honorable Elizabeth G. Crnkovich, Judge

Teen Court.................................**402.431.9272**
Fax.................................402.431.0444
E-mail.................................srall@mac-bsa.org
   12401 W Maple Rd, Omaha, NE 68164
   Stephanie E. Rall, Coordinator

POLICE AND SHERIFF

Sheriff's Dept.................................**402.444.3578**
Fax.................................402.444.7342
   3601 N 156th St, Criminal Investigation Bureau,
   Omaha, NE 68116
   Timothy Dunning, Sheriff

EDUCATION SERVICES

Educational Services Unit No.3.............**402.597.4930**
Fax.................................402.597.4811
Web.................................www.esu3.org
E-mail.................................ggaden@esu3.org
   6949 S 110th St, La Vista, NE 68128-5722
   Greg Gaden, Director

Dundy County

COURTS

Court.................................**308.423.2374**
Fax.................................308.423.2325
Web.................................www.courts.ne.gov
E-mail.................................edward.steenburg@courts.ne.gov
   700 Chief Street, Benkelnlan, NE 69021-0378
   Honorable Edward Steenburg, Circuit Judge

POLICE AND SHERIFF

Sheriff's Dept.................................**308.423.2393**
Fax.................................308.423.2325
Web.................................www.bwtelcom.net
E-mail.................................dundycosheriff@bwtelcom.net
   701 Chief St, Benkelman, NE 69021
   Justin Nichols, Sheriff

Fillmore County

SOCIAL SERVICES

Dept of Health and Human Svcs.............**402.759.3718**
Fax.................................402.759.4456
Web.................................www.dhhs.ne.gov
E-mail.................................ellen.moeller@dhhs.ne.gov
   160 N 9th St, Geneva, NE 68361-2016
   Nancy Bettin, Office Supervisor

MENTAL HEALTH SERVICES

Blue Valley Mental Health Ctr.................**402.759.4761**
Fax.................................402.759.4768
Web.................................www.bvbh.net
E-mail.................................bgreen@bvbh.net
   831 F St, Geneva, NE 68361-2533
   Becky Green, Substance Abuse Counselor

POLICE AND SHERIFF

Sheriff's Dept.................................**402.759.4441**
Fax.................................402.759.4429
E-mail.................................burgess@fillmorecounty.org
   900 G St, Geneva, NE 68361
   William L. Burgess, Sheriff

Franklin County

POLICE AND SHERIFF

Sheriff's Dept.................................**308.425.6231**
Fax.................................308.425.3261
   405 15th Ave Ste 9, Franklin, NE 68939-1331
   Jerry L. Archer, Sheriff

EDUCATION SERVICES

Head Start.................................**308.425.9908**
   713 15th Ave, Franklin, NE 68939-1511
   Niki Gemar, Director

Frontier County

POLICE AND SHERIFF

Sheriff's Dept.................................**308.367.4411**
Fax.................................308.367.4268
E-mail.................................nb03200@curtis-ne.com
   308 Center Ave, Curtis, NE 69025
   Daniel D. Rupp, Sheriff

Gage County

MENTAL HEALTH SERVICES

Blue Valley Behavioral Health Ctr.............**402.228.3386**
Fax.................................402.228.2004
Web.................................www.bvbh.net
E-mail.................................webmail@bvbh.net
   1123 N 9th St, Beatrice, NE 68310-2041
   Jon Day, Lcsw, Lmhp, Executive Director

COURTS

Court.................................**402.223.1323**
Fax.................................402.223.1374
   612 Grant St Ste 17, Beatrice, NE 68310-2946
   Honorable Steven Bruce Timm, County Judge

POLICE AND SHERIFF

Sheriff's Dept.................................**402.223.5222**
Fax.................................402.223.5223
E-mail.................................gcso@copmail.com
   612 Lincoln St Ste 1, Beatrice, NE 68310
   Millard Guftuffson, Sheriff

Garden County

POLICE AND SHERIFF

Sheriff's Dept.................................**308.772.3540**
Fax.................................308.772.4143
E-mail.................................mquinn@gardencountysheriff.org
   611 Main St, Oshkosh, NE 69154
   Michelle Quinn, Sheriff

Garfield County

POLICE AND SHERIFF

Sheriff's Ofc.................................**308.346.5150**
Fax.................................308.346.5064
   250 S 8th Ave, Burwell, NE 68823
   Larry D. Donner, Sheriff

Gosper County

POLICE AND SHERIFF

Sheriff's Dept.................................**308.785.2420**
Fax.................................308.785.2036
E-mail.................................gosperso@atcjet.net
   507 Smith Ave, Elwood, NE 68937
   Dennis Ocken, Sheriff

Greeley County

POLICE AND SHERIFF

Sheriff's Ofc **308.428.2395**
Fax 308.428.4905
E-mail ....dweeks962@yahoo.com
　101 Killdeer Avenue, Greeley, NE 68842
　Dave Weeks, Sheriff

Hall County

SOCIAL SERVICES

**Child and Adult Protection and Safety
Svcs** **308.385.6123**
Fax 308.385.6132
Web ....www.hhss.ne.gov
E-mail ....yolanda.nuncio@hhss.ne.gov
　208 N Pine St, Grand Island, NE 68801-5926
　Yolanda Nuncio, Service Area Administrator

GENERAL HEALTH SERVICES

Central District Health Dept **308.385.5188**
Fax 308.398.4700
E-mail ....tanderson@cdhe.ne.gov
　1137 S Locust St, Grand Island, NE 68801
　Teresa Anderson, Director

Central Health Ctr **308.384.7625**
Fax 308.384.8904
Web ....www.centralhealthcenter.org
E-mail ....chcurbanec@hamilton.net
　217 E Stolley Park Rd Ste E, Grand Island, NE 68802
　Laura Urbanec, Director

JUSTICE AGENCY

District 9 Probation **308.385.6216**
Fax 308.385.6234
　117 E 1st St Ste 1, Grand Island, NE 68801
　Clay Schutz, Chief Performance Officer

COURTS

District 9 Court **308.385.5135**
Fax 308.385.5138
　111 W 1st St Ste 1, Grand Island, NE 68801
　Honorable Philip M. Martin Jr., Judge

POLICE AND SHERIFF

Sheriff's Dept **308.385.5200**
Fax 308.385.5209
Web ....www.hcgi.org
E-mail ....jerryw@hcgi.org
　131 S Locust St, Grand Island, NE 68801
　Jerry Watson, Sheriff

Hamilton County

GENERAL HEALTH SERVICES

Aurora Memorial Health Inc. **402.694.3171**
Fax 402.694.3177
Web ....www.memorialcommunityhealth.org
　1423 7th St, Aurora, NE 68818
　Sabrina Dickey, Clinic Director

POLICE AND SHERIFF

Sheriff's Dept **402.694.6936**
Fax 402.694.6930
E-mail ....countysheriff@hamilton.net
　715 12th St, Aurora, NE 68818-2306
　Kirk W. Handrup, Sheriff

EDUCATION SERVICES

Aurora Head Start Ctr **402.694.4090**
Fax 402.694.4091
E-mail ....kathy@genie.esu10.k12.ne.us
　208 16th St # 2, Aurora, NE 68818-3009

Harlan County

POLICE AND SHERIFF

Sheriff's Dept **308.928.2147**
Fax 308.928.2592
Web ....www.megavision.com
E-mail ....hclaw@megavision.com
　706 2nd St, Alma, NE 68920-2092
　Chris Becker, Sheriff

Hayes County

POLICE AND SHERIFF

Sheriff's Ofc **308.286.3364**
Fax 308.286.3368
　502 Troth Street, Hayes Center, NE 69032
　Tom Dow, Sheriff

Hitchcock County

POLICE AND SHERIFF

Sheriff's Dept **308.334.5444**
Fax 308.334.5351
E-mail ....sheriff967@mccook.net
　229 E D St, Trenton, NE 69044-1713
　D. Bryan Leggott, Sheriff

Holt County

COURTS

Court **402.336.1662**
Fax 402.336.1663
　204 N 4th St, Oneill, NE 68763
　Honorable Alan L. Brodbeck, Judge

EDUCATION SERVICES

Atkinson Head Start **402.925.2058**
Fax 402.325.2233
E-mail ....atkhs@inetnebr.com
　406 E 2nd St, Atkinson, NE 68713
　Tanya Schroder, Director

Hooker County

POLICE AND SHERIFF

Sheriff's Ofc **308.546.2290**
Fax 308.546.2490
　303 NW 1st St, Mullen, NE 69152
　Lynn O. Nichols, Sheriff

Howard County

POLICE AND SHERIFF

Sheriff's Dept **308.754.5433**
Fax 308.754.5517
E-mail ....hccc@howardcountyso.org
　612 Indian St Ste 13, Saint Paul, NE 68873
　Harold Schenk, Sheriff

Jefferson County

GENERAL HEALTH SERVICES

Blue Valley Community Action **402.729.2278**
Fax 402.729.2801
Web ....www.bvca.net
E-mail ....changinglives@bvca.net
　620 5th St, Fairbury, NE 68352
　Richard Nation, CEO

MENTAL HEALTH SERVICES

Blue Valley Behavioral Health Ctr **402.729.2272**
Fax 402.729.2273
Web ....www.bvbh.net
E-mail ....vswartz@bvbh.net
　521 E Ste 120, Fairbury, NE 68352
　Virginia Swartz, Phd, Mental Health Counselor

POLICE AND SHERIFF

Sheriff's Ofc **402.729.2284**
Fax 402.729.2904
E-mail ....jcso@diodecom.net
　606 3rd St Ste 3, Fairbury, NE 68352
　Nels L. Sorensen, Sheriff

Johnson County

GENERAL HEALTH SERVICES

Family Health Svcs **402.335.2988**
Fax 402.335.3747
E-mail ....sharon.rickman@fhsi.org
　1179 Webster St, Tecumseh, NE 68450-2484
　Sharon Rickman, Director

POLICE AND SHERIFF

Sheriff's Ofc **402.335.3307**
Fax 402.335.2737
E-mail ....jcsocommunications@windstream.net
　222 N 4th St, Tecumseh, NE 68450
　Scott Walton, Sheriff

Kearney County

JUSTICE AGENCY

District 10 Probation **308.832.1745**
Fax 308.832.0636
Web ....www.courts.ne.gov
E-mail ....tina.luz@nebraska.gov
　424 N Colorado Ave Ste 6, Minden, NE 68959-1662
　Tina Luz, Probation Officer

POLICE AND SHERIFF

Sheriff's Dept **308.832.2805**
Fax 308.832.0946
　246 N Colorado Ave, Minden, NE 68959
　D. Scott White, Sheriff

Keith County

SOCIAL SERVICES

Dept of Health and Human Svcs **308.284.8080**
Fax 308.284.8083
Web ....www.dhhs.ne.gov
E-mail ....steve.mayer@dhhs.ne.gov
　201 E 5th St, Ogallala, NE 69153-2161
　Steve Mayer, Information Technology Director

JUSTICE AGENCY

Probation Ofc **308.284.2081**
Fax 308.284.2082
Web ....www.megavision.com
E-mail ....info@megavision.com
　511 N Spruce St Ste 201, Ogallala, NE 69153-2146
　Lonni Solchert, Director

COURTS

District 11 Court **308.284.3693**
Fax 308.284.6825
E-mail ....lori.hill@nebraska.gov
　511 N Spruce St Ste 201, Ogallala, NE 69153
　Edward D. Steenburg, County Judge

POLICE AND SHERIFF

Sheriff's Ofc **308.284.3641**
Fax 308.284.6171
E-mail ....jstevens@kc911.net
　103 E 5th St, Ogallala, NE 69153
　Jeff Stevens, Sheriff

Keya Paha County

POLICE AND SHERIFF

Sheriff's Ofc **402.497.3201**
Fax 402.497.3203
Web ....www.co.keya-paha.ne.us
　310 Court House Drive, Springview, NE 68778
　Jeff Kirsch, Sheriff

Nebraska

Kimball County

POLICE AND SHERIFF

Sheriff's Dept...........................**308.235.3615**
Fax...308.235.3131
Web...www.kcso.com
E-mail..........................kcso71@embarqmail.com
　114 E 3rd St Ste 12, Kimball, NE 69145-1456
　Harry Gillway, Sheriff

Knox County

SOCIAL SERVICES

Dept of Health and Human Svcs.............**402.288.4291**
Fax...402.288.4272
　310 Bridge Street, Center, NE 68724
　Tami Hilfinker, Supervisor, CPS

GENERAL HEALTH SERVICES

Santee Clinic...............................**402.857.2300**
Fax...402.857.2315
　110 S Visiting Eagle St, Niobrara, NE 68760-7201
　Mike Henry, Health Director

POLICE AND SHERIFF

Sheriff's Ofc...............................**402.288.4261**
Fax...402.288.4263
E-mail...................................kcso@gpcom.net
　206 Main St, Center, NE 68724-9705
　Don Henery, Sheriff

Lancaster County

SOCIAL SERVICES

HHS Developmental Disabilities
System.....................................**402.471.4400**
Fax...402.471.4403
Web...www.dhhs.ne.gov
E-mail..........................sara.kramer@dhhs.ne.gov
　1033 O St Ste 519, Lincoln, NE 68508-3672
　Sara Kramer, Administrator

GENERAL HEALTH SERVICES

Family Svc.................................**402.441.7949**
Fax...402.441.6466
Web.....................www.familyservicelincoln.org
E-mail................jkirchner@familyservicelincoln.org
　501 S 7th St, Lincoln, NE 68508
　Barry Gourley, Executive Director

Health Dept................................**402.471.9270**
Fax...402.471.6446
Web...www.hhss.nebraska.gov
E-mail........................peggy.trouba@nebraska.gov
　301 Centennial Mall S, Lincoln, NE 68508-2529
　Peggy Trouba, Wic Coordinator

Lincoln-Lancaster Health Dept.............**402.441.8000**
Fax...402.441.6205
Web...www.lincoln.ne.gov
E-mail.........................ttimmons@lincoln.ne.gov
　3140 N St, Lincoln, NE 68510-1514
　Tim Timmons, HIV/AIDS Coordinator

JUSTICE AGENCY

Attorney's Ofc.............................**402.441.7321**
Fax...402.441.7336
E-mail..........................jkelly@lancaster.ne.gov
　575 S 10th St, Lincoln, NE 68508
　Joe Kelly, County Attorney

CASA......................................**402.474.5161**
Fax...402.474.5188
　210 N 14th St Ste 3, Lincoln, NE 68508
　Deb Vandyke-Reis, Interim Program Director

Juvenile Probation.........................**402.441.7364**
Fax...402.441.6052
E-mail............................lorigriggs@cega.com
　575 S 10th St, Rm 2301, Lincoln, NE 68508
　Lori Griggs, Chief Performance Officer

Protection & Safety Div....................**402.471.9272**
Fax...402.471.9034
E-mail....................todd.reckling@nebraska.gov
　301 Centennial Mall S, Lincoln, NE 68509
　Todd Reckling, Administrator

COURTS

Juvenile Court.............................**402.441.6928**
Fax...402.441.6930
E-mail...............................temmert@nebraska.gov
　575 S 10th St, Lincoln, NE 68508
　Teresa Emmert, Court Administrator

POLICE AND SHERIFF

Sheriff's Ofc...............................**402.441.6500**
Fax...402.441.8320
Web...www.lincoln.ne.gov
E-mail........................twagner@lancaster.ne.gov
　575 S 10th St, Justice & Law Enforcement Center,
　Lincoln, NE 68508-2810
　Terry T. Wagner, Sheriff

Lincoln County

SOCIAL SERVICES

Nebraska Dept of Health & Human
Svcs.......................................**308.535.8200**
Fax...305.535.8368
　200 S Silber Ave, 2nd Floor, North Platte, NE 69101
　Kathleen Kalliham, District Administrator

GENERAL HEALTH SERVICES

West Central District Health Dept...........**308.696.1201**
Fax...308.696.1204
Web...www.wcdhd.org
E-mail........................vanderheidens@wcdhd.org
　111 N Dewey St, North Platte, NE 69101-5439
　Shannon Vanderhaeiden, Director

JUSTICE AGENCY

District 11 Probation Dept..................**308.534.4350**
Fax...308.535.3526
　110 E 3rd St, North Platte, NE 69101
　Lonnie Folchert, Probation Officer

POLICE AND SHERIFF

Sheriff's Ofc...............................**308.535.9599**
Fax...308.535.9594
Web.....................www.co.lincoln.countysheriff.com
　302 N Jeffers St, North Platte, NE 69101-3900
　Jerome Kramer, Sheriff

Loup County

POLICE AND SHERIFF

Sheriff's Ofc...............................**308.942.3435**
Fax...308.942.6015
　408 4th St, Taylor, NE 68879
　T Araus, Sheriff

Madison County

MENTAL HEALTH SERVICES

Region 4 Behavioral Health Svcs.............**402.370.3100**
Fax...402.370.3125
Web...www.region4bhs.org
E-mail........................igansebom@region4bhs.org
　206 W Monroe Ave, Norfolk, NE 68701-6442
　Ingrid Gansebom, Reg. Administrator

JUSTICE AGENCY

CASA of NE................................**402.371.9599**
Fax...402.844.3406
Web...www.nebraskacasa.org
E-mail..............................casa@telebeep.com
　2501 Lakeridge Dr Ste 104A, Norfolk,
　NE 68701-2558
　Ruth Matthews-mott, Director

COURTS

Court......................................**402.454.3311**
Fax...402.454.3438
E-mail..................donna.farrell-taylor@courts.ne.gov
　1313 North Main Street, Madison, NE 68748
　Honorable Donna Farrell-taylor, County Judge

POLICE AND SHERIFF

Sheriff's Dept..............................**402.454.2110**
Fax...402.454.3816
E-mail...................mcso@madisoncountysheriff.com
　1313 N Main St, Madison, NE 68748
　Vern J. Hjorth, Sheriff

McPherson County

POLICE AND SHERIFF

Sheriff's Dept..............................**308.587.2445**
Fax...308.587.2599
Web...www.apcom.net
E-mail.....................mcphersonsheriff@apcom.net
　500 Anderson St, Tryon, NE 69167
　John Hower, Sheriff

Merrick County

JUSTICE AGENCY

District 3 Probation Dept...................**308.946.2094**
Fax...308.946.5135
E-mail........................scline@ncc.state.ne.us
　1707 16th Ave, Central City, NE 66826
　Sara Cline, Juvenile Intake

COURTS

Court......................................**308.946.2812**
Fax...308.946.3838
　1510 18th St, Central City, NE 68826
　Honorable Linda Castersenfs, County Judge

POLICE AND SHERIFF

Sheriff's Dept..............................**308.946.2345**
Fax...308.946.2444
E-mail...........................merikso@ccconline.net
　1821 16th Ave, Central City, NE 68826
　Kevin Campbell, Sheriff

Morrill County

SOCIAL SERVICES

Health & Human Svcs.......................**308.262.1900**
Fax...308.262.1903
E-mail........................connie.green@dhhs.ne.gov
　514 Main St, Bridgeport, NE 69336
　Connie Green, Office Manager

POLICE AND SHERIFF

Sheriff's Ofc...............................**308.262.0408**
Fax...308.262.0352
Web...www.dor.state.ne.us
　113 L St, Bridgeport, NE 69336
　Cardenas, Sheriff

EDUCATION SERVICES

Bridgeport Head Start......................**308.262.0507**
　401 N Main, Bridgeport, NE 69336
　Goldie Muzquiz, Director

Nance County

POLICE AND SHERIFF

Sheriff's Dept **308.536.2452**
Fax...308.536.2453
E-mail.............................nancesheriff@hamilton.net
  209 Esther St, Fullerton, NE 68638-3133
  Paul J. Kruse, Sheriff

Nemaha County

SOCIAL SERVICES

Nebraska Dept of Health & Human
Svcs **402.274.4021**
Web.......................................www.dhhs.ne.gov
E-mail...........................colleen.faigner@nebraska.gov
  1908 O St, Auburn, NE 68305-2347
  Colleen Faigner, Supervisor

GENERAL HEALTH SERVICES

Health Dept **402.274.3993**
Fax...402.274.3967
Web..www.sedhd.org
E-mail.......................................kay@sedhd.org
  2511 Snyder Ave, Auburn, NE 68305
  Kay Oestmann, Rn, Director

MENTAL HEALTH SERVICES

Blue Valley Behavioral Health **402.274.4373**
Fax...402.274.5442
E-mail..kdye@bvbh.net
  820 Central Ave Ste 4, Auburn, NE 68305
  Jon Day, Lcsw, Lmhp, Executive Director

POLICE AND SHERIFF

Sheriff's Ofc **402.274.3139**
Fax...402.274.5066
  1805 N St, Auburn, NE 68305
  Brent Lottman, Sheriff

EDUCATION SERVICES

Auburn Head Start Senca **402.274.4160**
E-mail..........................headstartaub@windstream.net
  1806 O St, Auburn, NE 68305-2345
  Sue James, Director

Nuckolls County

SOCIAL SERVICES

HHS Developmental Disabilities
System **402.879.3101**
Fax...402.879.4505
  213 E 3rd St, Superior, NE 68978-1810
  Annice Utecht, Service Coordinator

POLICE AND SHERIFF

Sheriff's Ofc **402.225.2831**
Fax...402.225.3014
Web..........................www.nuckollscounty.ne.gov
E-mail........................nuckollstreasurer@alltel.net
  150 S Main St, Nelson, NE 68961-6100
  James Marr, Sheriff

Otoe County

SOCIAL SERVICES

Deparment of Health and Human
Svcs **402.873.6671**
Fax...402.873.6875
  970 Wild Wood Ln, Nebraska City, NE 68410
  Lisa Kechely, Local Office Administrator

HHS Developmental Disabilities
System **402.873.6671**
Fax...402.873.5453
Web.................................www.hhs.state.ne.us
  917 Wildwood Ln Ste A, Nebraska City,
  NE 68410-1370
  Maggie Thoms, Supervisor

MENTAL HEALTH SERVICES

Blue Valley Mental Health Svcs **402.873.5505**
Fax...402.873.6374
Web..www.bvbh.net
E-mail..kdye@bvbh.net
  1903 4th Corso, Nebraska City, NE 68410-2601
  Jon Day, Lcsw, Lmhp, Executive Director

JUSTICE AGENCY

District 5 Probation Dept **402.873.9570**
Fax...402.873.9573
  1021 Central Ave Rm 202, Nebraska City,
  NE 68410-2356
  Judi York, Supervisor

COURTS

Court **402.873.9575**
Fax...402.873.9030
  1021 Central Ave, Nebraska City, NE 68410
  Jeffery Funke, County Court Judge

POLICE AND SHERIFF

Sheriff's Ofc **402.873.9560**
Fax...402.873.6130
E-mail..sgress@hotmail.com
  1021 Central Ave, Nebraska City, NE 68410
  James M. Gress, Sheriff

Pawnee County

POLICE AND SHERIFF

Sheriff's Ofc **402.852.2969**
Fax...402.852.2969
  625 6th St, Pawnee City, NE 68420
  Jayme Reed, Sheriff

Perkins County

POLICE AND SHERIFF

Sheriff's Dept **308.352.4564**
Fax...308.352.4149
E-mail..............................sheriff@perkinscoso.com
  200 Lincoln Ave, Grant, NE 69140
  James Brueggeman, Sheriff

Phelps County

SOCIAL SERVICES

Dept of Health and Human Svcs **308.995.8658**
Fax...308.995.4404
Web...www.hhss.ne.gov
E-mail...........................brenda.bender@hhss.ne.gov
  701 5th Ave, Holdrege, NE 68949
  Brenda Bender, Supervisor

JUSTICE AGENCY

District 10 ....**308.995.4890**
Fax...308.995.6562
  715 5th Ave Ste 4, Holdrege, NE 68949
  Jolene Ritterbush, Probation Officer

COURTS

Court **308.995.6561**
Fax...308.995.6562
  715 5th Ave, Holdrege, NE 68949
  Honorable Robert A. Ide, County Judge

POLICE AND SHERIFF

Sheriff's Dept **308.995.5692**
Fax...308.995.2375
E-mail..............................webmaster@phelpso.org
  715 5th Ave, Ste 20, Holdrege, NE 68949
  Gene Samuelson, Sheriff

Pierce County

SOCIAL SERVICES

Nebraska Dept of Health & Human
Svcs **402.329.4927**
Fax...402.329.6853
Web...www.nebraska.gov
E-mail...........................sharon.hjorth@nebraska.gov
  111 W Court St Rm 15, Pierce, NE 68767-1276
  Sharon Hjorth, Supervisor

POLICE AND SHERIFF

Sheriff's Ofc **402.329.6346**
Fax...402.329.6620
  111 W Court St Rm 7, Pierce, NE 68767-1276
  Rick Eberhardt, Sheriff

Platte County

SOCIAL SERVICES

Dept of Health and Human Svcs **402.564.1113**
Fax...402.564.7947
Web.......................................www.dhhs.ne.gov
  2365 39th Ave, Columbus, NE 68601-2219
  Sarah Hjorth, Child & Family Services Supervisor

JUSTICE AGENCY

District 3 Probation Ofc **402.563.4910**
Fax...402.564.1620
E-mail.............................jschaefer001@neb.rr.com
  2610 14th Street # 15, Columbus, NE 68601-4960
  Jim Schaefer, Probation Officer

COURTS

Court **402.563.4905**
Fax...402.562.8158
Web...www.megavision.com
E-mail..............................jdgskor@megavision.com
  2610 14th St, Columbus, NE 68601
  Honorable Frank Skorupa, County Judge

EDUCATION SERVICES

Columbus Even Start Family Literacy
Program **402.564.1124**
Fax...402.564.0710
Web...www.cennecs.org
E-mail.........................sobermiller@cennecs.org
  3286 53rd Ave, Columbus, NE 68601-1516
  Susan Obermiller, Director

Polk County

POLICE AND SHERIFF

Sheriff's Ofc **402.747.2231**
Fax...402.747.5981
Web...www.pcsheriff.com
E-mail..........................sheriff@pcsheriff.com
  251 N Main St, Osceola, NE 68651-5512
  Dwaine Ladwig, Sheriff

Red Willow County

SOCIAL SERVICES

Nebraska Dept of Health & Human
Svcs **308.345.8420**
Fax...308.345.8444
  108 W D St, 2nd Floor, McCook, NE 69001
  Anne Lincoln, Director

Nebraska

GENERAL HEALTH SERVICES

Health Department **308.345.1790**
Fax 308.345.1794
E-mail ....rwchealth@mccooknet.com
1400 W 5th St, Mc Cook, NE 69001-2593
Darcey Hansen, Rn, Bsn, Director Rwchd

Red Willow Health Dept **308.345.6130**
Fax 308.345.1794
E-mail ....rwchealth@mccooknet.com
1400 W 5th St Ste 1, Mc Cook, NE 69001
Darcey Henson, Director

JUSTICE AGENCY

District 11 Probation Ofc **308.345.4070**
Fax 308.345.2015
E-mail ....info@probation.com
502 Norris Ave, Mc Cook, NE 69001-2000
James Taylor, Isp Officer

COURTS

Court **308.345.1905**
Fax 308.345.1904
Web ....www.courts.ne.gov
E-mail ....anne.paine@courts.ne.gov
502 Norris Ave, McCook, NE 69001-0199
Honorable Anne Paine, County Judge

POLICE AND SHERIFF

Sheriff's Ofc **308.345.1850**
Fax 308.345.1503
502 Norris Ave Ste 1, Mc Cook, NE 69001-2000
Gene Mahon, Sheriff

Richardson County

SOCIAL SERVICES

Dept of Health and Human Svcs **402.245.4431**
Fax 402.245.4085
Web ....www.hhss.ne.gov
E-mail ....coleen.fiegener@HHSS.ne.gov
1700 Stone St, Falls City, NE 68355-2025
Coleen Fiegener, Office Manager/Social Service Supervisor

JUSTICE AGENCY

Probation Ofc **402.245.3484**
Fax 402.245.3043
1700 Stone St, Ste 106, Falls City, NE 68355
Rick Deklotz, Probation Officer

COURTS

Court **402.245.2812**
Fax 402.245.3352
1700 Stone St Ste 205, Falls City, NE 68355
Honorable Curtis L. Maschman, County Judge

POLICE AND SHERIFF

Sheriff's Ofc **402.245.2479**
Fax 402.245.3327
E-mail ....richcojail@sentco.net
1700 Stone St, Falls City, NE 68355
Randy Houser, Sheriff

EDUCATION SERVICES

Falls City Head Start School **402.245.4983**
Web ....www.sentco.net
E-mail ....fcscheadstart@sentco.net
320 W 14th St, Falls City, NE 68355-2549
Anita Kimpston, Director

Rock County

COURTS

Court **402.684.3601**
Fax 402.684.2741
E-mail ....cathy.reiman@nebraska.gov
PO Box 249, Bassett, NE 68714-0249
Cathy Reiman, Court Magistrate

POLICE AND SHERIFF

Sheriff's Dept **402.684.3811**
Fax 402.684.2884
E-mail ....jim9812@hotmail.com
400 State St, Bassett, NE 68714
James Anderson, Sheriff

Saline County

SOCIAL SERVICES

Dept of Health and Human Svcs **402.826.2196**
Fax 402.826.5940
E-mail ....betty.daubendiek@hhss.ne.gov
1005 E Highway 33 Ste 1, Crete, NE 68333-2546
Betty Daubendiek, Office Manager

JUSTICE AGENCY

District 1 Probation Ofc **402.821.2042**
Fax 402.821.3631
E-mail ....stephaniecavalier@nebraska.gov
12th Probation District, Wilber, NE 68465
Stephanie Cavalier, Probation Officer

POLICE AND SHERIFF

Sheriff's Ofc **402.821.2111**
Fax 402.821.2987
911 South Main St, Wilber, NE 68465
Alan J. Moore, Sheriff

EDUCATION SERVICES

Crete Public Schools Even Start **402.826.5228**
Fax 402.826.5218
Web ....www.creteschools.org
E-mail ....conniel@creteschools.org
920 Linden Ave, Crete, NE 68333-2292
Connie Lentell, Even Start Director

Sarpy County

SOCIAL SERVICES

Dept of Health and Human Svcs **402.595.2600**
Fax 402.595.2532
E-mail ....stephanie.anderson@hhss.ne.gov
1261 Golden Gate Dr Ste 1E, Papillion, NE 68046

GENERAL HEALTH SERVICES

**Alegent Midlands Community
Hospital** **402.593.3000**
Fax 402.593.3812
Web ....www.alegent.org
E-mail ....christin.ryan@alegent.org
11111 S 84th St, Papillion, NE 68046
Christin Ryan, Imunization Asst

JUSTICE AGENCY

CASA Program **402.593.2259**
Fax 402.593.2158
E-mail ....casa@sarpy.com
1210 Golden Gate Dr, Papillion, NE 68046
Georgie Scurfield, Executive Director

District Juvenile Probation **402.593.2222**
Fax 402.593.2221
Web ....www.sarpy.com
E-mail ....jyork@sarpy.com
1210 Golden Gate Dr Ste 3140, Papillion,
NE 68046-2844
Jodi York, CPO

COURTS

Court **402.593.5775**
Fax 402.593.2193
1210 Golden Gate Dr Ste 3142, Papillion, NE 68046
Honorable Robert C. Wester, Director

POLICE AND SHERIFF

Sheriff's Dept **402.593.2290**
Fax 402.593.4323
Web ....www.sarpy.com
1208 Golden Gate Dr, Papillion, NE 68046-2838
Jeffery Davis, Sheriff

EDUCATION SERVICES

Special Education **402.293.4000**
Fax 402.291.7982
Web ....www.bellevuepublicschools.org
1600 Highway 370, Bellevue, NE 68005-3591
Matt Fenster, Director Of Student Services

Saunders County

SOCIAL SERVICES

**Nebraska Dept Of Health & Human
Svcs** **402.443.4252**
Fax 402.443.4588
Web ....www.dhhs.ne.gov
E-mail ....linda.soukup@hhss.state.ne.us
355 E 4th St, Wahoo, NE 68066-1920
Linda Soukup, Supervisor

GENERAL HEALTH SERVICES

**Saunders 3 Rivers Satellite Ofc Health
Dept** **402.443.4603**
Fax 402.443.1412
Web www.3riverspublicealph.org
E-mail ....schdpt@yahoo.com
754 W 9th St, Wahoo, NE 68066-1517
Linda Fritz, Administrator

MENTAL HEALTH SERVICES

Blue Valley Mental Heath Ctr **402.443.4414**
Fax 402.443.3462
Web ....www.bvbh.net
E-mail ....kdye@bvbh.net
355 E 4th St, Wahoo, NE 68066-1960
Jon Day, Lcsw, Lmhp, Executive Director

JUSTICE AGENCY

District 3 Probation Dept **402.443.4976**
Fax 402.443.5091
E-mail ....pvandevoorde@alltel.net
112 E 7th St, Wahoo, NE 68066-1701
Shane Stutvman, Acting Chief Probation Officer

COURTS

Court **402.443.8119**
Fax 402.443.8121
387 N Chestnut Ste 5, Wahoo, NE 68066
Gerald Round, County Judge

POLICE AND SHERIFF

Sheriff's Ofc **402.443.3718**
Fax 402.443.5118
Web ....www.saunderscounty.ne.gov
E-mail ....kstukenholtz@co.saunders.ne.us
387 N Chestnut St, Wahoo, NE 68066-1861
Kevin Stukenholtz, Sheriff

Scotts Bluff County

GENERAL HEALTH SERVICES

Health Dept **308.436.6636**
Fax 308.436.6638
E-mail ....bwineman@scottsbluffcounty.org
1825 10Th St, Gering, NE 69341
Bill Wineman, Director

Panhandle Community Svcs **308.632.2540**
Fax 308.632.2752
Web ....www.pcswn.com
E-mail ....jtracy@pcswn.com
975 Crescent Dr, Gering, NE 69341-1712
Jeff Tracy, Clinic Director

JUSTICE AGENCY

District 10 Probation Ofc **308.436.6655**
Fax 308.436.6658
Web .... www.nebraska.gov
E-mail .... linda.buehler@nebraska.gov
   1825 10th St Ste 13, Gering, NE 69341-2456
   Linda Buehler, CPO

Intensive Supervision Probation **308.436.3343**
Fax 308.436.3347
   1725 10th St Ste 3, Gering, NE 69341-2466
   Roger Witcofski, Intensive Supervision Officer

POLICE AND SHERIFF

Sheriff's Ofc **308.436.6667**
Fax 308.436.4794
E-mail .... moverman@scottsbluffcounty.org
   1825 10th St Ste 15, COUNTY ADMINISTRATION
   BUILDING, Gering, NE 69341-2444
   Mark Overman, Sheriff

EDUCATION SERVICES

Early Head Start **308.632.1999**
   513 W 24th St, Scottsbluff, NE 69361
   Donna Jenny, Director

Seward County

SOCIAL SERVICES

Dept of Health and Human Svcs **402.643.6614**
Fax 402.643.6552
Web .... www.dhhs.ne.gov
E-mail .... carla.crook@nebraska.gov
   3477 Redwood Rd, Seward, NE 68434-7651
   Carla Crook, CPS Supervisor

JUSTICE AGENCY

Probation Ofc **402.643.2562**
Fax 402.643.4277
   529 Seward St Ste 101, Seward, NE 68434-2062
   Shane Tutzman, Probation Officer

COURTS

Court **402.643.3214**
Fax 402.643.2950
Web .... www.nebraska.gov
E-mail .... grouse@nlc.state.ne.us
   529 Seward Street, Seward, NE 68434
   Honorable Gerald E. Rouse, County Judge

POLICE AND SHERIFF

Sheriff's Ofc **402.643.2359**
Fax 402.643.4852
E-mail .... sheriffjoeyocum@netscape.net
   261 S 8th St, Seward, NE 68434-2417
   Joseph O. Yocum, Sheriff

Sheridan County

JUSTICE AGENCY

District 1 Probation Ofc **308.327.5655**
Fax 308.327.5618
Web .... www.courts.ne.gov
E-mail .... linda.michaelson@courts.ne.gov
   310 Sprague St., Rushville, NE 69360
   Linda Michaelson, Probation Officer

POLICE AND SHERIFF

Sheriff's Ofc **308.327.2161**
Fax 308.327.2812
   303 1/2 E 2nd St, Rushville, NE 69360
   Terry E. Robbins, Sheriff

Sherman County

POLICE AND SHERIFF

Sheriff's Ofc **308.745.1511**
Fax 308.745.1820
Web .... www.co.sherman.ne.us
E-mail .... shermancoso@sherman.nacone.org
   630 O St, Loup City, NE 68853-8003
   Michael Janulewicz, Sheriff

Sioux County

GENERAL HEALTH SERVICES

Legend Butte Health Svcs **308.665.1770**
Fax 308.665.1420
   11 Paddock St, Crawford, NE 69339
   Harold Kruegger, Administrator

POLICE AND SHERIFF

Sheriff's Ofc **308.247.9280**
Fax 308.247.9910
   325 Main St, Harrison, NE 69346-1751
   James H. Costello, Sheriff

Stanton County

POLICE AND SHERIFF

Sheriff's Ofc **402.439.2212**
Fax 402.439.2229
Web .... www.stanton.net
E-mail .... scso@stanton.net
   804 Ivy, Stanton, NE 68779
   Michael S. Unger, Sheriff

Thayer County

GENERAL HEALTH SERVICES

Health Svcs **402.768.6041**
Fax 402.768.4669
Web .... www.thayercountyhealth.com
   120 Park Ave, Hebron, NE 68370-2019
   Audra Loontjer Capek, Clinical Manager

Thurston County

SOCIAL SERVICES

Omaha Tribe of Nebraska Child Protection

Svcs **402.837.5331**
Fax 402.837.5362
Web .... www.omahatribe.com
E-mail .... mspears@omahatribe.com
   PO Box 429, Macy, NE 68039-0429
   Marla Spears, Director

Winnebago Tribe of Nebraska Child and Family

Svcs **402.878.2379**
Fax 402.878.2228
   107 Bluff Ave, Winnebago, NE 68071
   Anitrna Mallory, Director

POLICE AND SHERIFF

Sheriff's Ofc **402.385.3018**
Fax 402.385.2518
E-mail .... thurstonso@huntel.net
   106 S 5th St, Pender, NE 68047
   Shelly Terez, Sheriff

Valley County

SOCIAL SERVICES

Nebraska Dept of Health & Human

Svcs **308.728.3685**
Fax 308.728.7771
Web .... www.dhhs.ne.gov
E-mail .... kathy.fiorelli@dhhs.ne.gov
   213 S 15th St, Ord, NE 68862-1705
   Kathy Fiorelli, Supervisor

JUSTICE AGENCY

District 8 Probation Ofc **308.728.3575**
Fax 308.728.3783
Web .... www.hhss.ne.gov
   125 S 15th St, Ord, NE 68862
   Tara Sprigler-Price, Chief Probation Officer

POLICE AND SHERIFF

Sheriff's Ofc **308.728.3906**
Fax 308.728.5320
E-mail .... valleycounty@cornhusker.net
   125 S 15th St Ste 102, Ord, NE 68862-1444
   Casey Hurlburt, Sheriff

Washington County

SOCIAL SERVICES

Dept of Health and Human Svcs **402.426.2329**
Fax 402.426.8960
E-mail .... david.prokesh@hhss.ne.gov
   1555 Colfax St Ste 5, Blair, NE 68008-2007
   David Prokesh, Administrator

JUSTICE AGENCY

District 16 Probation Ofc **402.426.2250**
Fax 402.426.6984
   1555 Colfax St Ste 8, Blair, NE 68008-2007
   Patty Lyon, Probation Officer

Wayne County

JUSTICE AGENCY

District 7 Probation Ofc **402.375.1250**
Fax 402.375.4808
   521 Lincoln St, Wayne, NE 68787-1833
   Kathryn Liebers, Chief

Webster County

POLICE AND SHERIFF

Sheriff's Ofc **402.746.2722**
Fax 402.746.3225
Web .... www.co.webster.ne.us
E-mail .... sheriffschmitz@gpcom.net
   641 N Cedar St, Red Cloud, NE 68970-2326
   Troy Schmitz, Sheriff

Wheeler County

POLICE AND SHERIFF

Sheriff's Ofc **308.654.3232**
Fax 308.942.3127
Web .... www.nntc.net
E-mail .... wcso@nntc.net
   3rd & Commercail, Bartlett, NE 68622
   Adrian A. Lindsay, Sheriff

York County

SOCIAL SERVICES

Dept of Health and Human Svcs **402.362.4471**
Fax 402.362.3042
Web .... www.dhhs.ne.gov
E-mail .... rose.harnly@dhhs.ne.gov
   824 N Lincoln Ave, York, NE 68467-2444
   Rose Harnly, Supervisor

GENERAL HEALTH SERVICES

Four Corners Health Dept **402.362.2621**
Fax 402.362.2687
Web .... www.fourcorners.ne.gov
E-mail .... questions@fourcorners.ne.gov
   2101 N Lincoln Ave, York, NE 68467-1027
   Vicky Duey, Executive Director

Nebraska

MENTAL HEALTH SERVICES

Blue Valley Mental Heath Ctr 402.362.6128
Fax 402.362.7012
Web ....www.bvbh.net
   722 S Lincoln Ave Ste 1, York, NE 68467
Jon Day, Lcsw, Lmhp, Executive Director

JUSTICE AGENCY

District 5 Probation 402.362.6540
Fax 402.362.4388
   510 N Lincoln Ave, York, NE 68467
Shane Sputzman, Isp Officer

COURTS

District 5 Court 402.362.4925
Fax 402.362.2577
   510 N Lincoln Ave, York, NE 68467
Kathy Barnes, Clerk Of Magistrate

POLICE AND SHERIFF

Sheriff's Dept 402.362.4927
Fax 402.362.2651
E-mail ....dradcliff@windstream.net
   510 N Lincoln Ave, York, NE 68467
Dale E. Radcliff, Sheriff

SPECIAL SERVICES AGENCIES

ADOPTION AGENCIES

Adoption Consultants 308.340.6242
Fax 308.345.2812
Web ....www.adoptionconsultantsinc.org
E-mail ....nancy@adoptionconsultantsinc.org
   205 Apache Dr, Mc Cook, NE 69001-2231
Nancy Morris, Director

Cline Williams Wright Johnson 402.474.6900
Fax 402.474.5393
Web ....www.clinewilliams.com
E-mail ....lbush@clinewilliams.com
   233 S 13th St Ste 1900, Lincoln, NE 68508-2095
Laurie Bush, Administrative Coordinator

Family Service Association of Lincoln 402.441.7949
Fax 402.441.6466
Web ....www.familyservicelincoln.org
   501 South 7th Street, Lincoln, NE 68508-2920
COA accredited organization.

Holt International Children's Svcs 402.934.5031
Fax 402.934.5034
Web ....www.holtintl.org
E-mail ....info@holtintl.org
   10685 Bedford Ave Ste 300, Omaha, NE 68134-3684
Celeste Snodgrass, Branch Manager

Nebraska Children's Home Society 402.451.0787
Fax 402.898.7750
Web ....www.nchs.org
E-mail ....ckrueger@nchs.org
   4939 S 118th St, Omaha, NE 68137-2213
Carol Krueger, Director Of Social Services

Nebraska Children's Home Society 402.483.7879
Fax 402.483.7870
Web ....www.nchs.org
E-mail ....dharstick@nchs.org
   4700 Valley Rd, Lincoln, NE 68510-4846
Dara Harstick, Office Manager

ADVOCACY RESOURCES

Asst Public Defendr 402.444.3877
E-mail ....nicholas.wurth@douglascounty-ne.gov
   H05 Civic Ctr, Omaha, NE 68183
Nicholas Wurth, Director

Child Advocacy Ctr 402.476.3200
Fax 402.476.5330
E-mail ....lynn@smvoicese.org
   5205 Garland St, Lincoln, NE 68504
Lynn Ayers, Director

Dier Osborn & Cox PC 308.995.8621
E-mail ....nnelsen@qwestoffice.net
   815 4th Ave, Holdrege, NE 68949
Natalie G Nelsen, Director

Eastern Nebraska Action Partnership 402.453.5656
Fax 402.451.3057
Web ....www.goca.org
E-mail ....exec@gocaomaha.org
   2406 Fowler Ave, Omaha, NE 68111-2013
Karen Shephard Raven, Director

Family & Juvenile Law Omaha - Christensen & Madra 402.934.6232
E-mail ....jackie@famandjuvlaw.com
   209 S 19th St Ste 675, Omaha, NE 68102
Jackie Madara-campbell, Managing Partner

Family Resource Ctr 308.262.1600
Fax 308.262.1581
   1309 R St, Bridgeport, NE 69336-4040
Donna Kesterson, Immunizations Clinic Director

Hastings Family Planning 402.463.5687
Fax 402.463.5021
Web ....www.hastingsfamilyplanning.com
   422 N Hastings Ave Ste 204, Hastings,
   NE 68901-5109
Barb Harrington, Executive Director

Headstart Child $ Family Development Programme Inc 402.462.4187
Fax 402.462.4568
   123 N Marian Rd, Hastings, NE 68901
Deb Ross, Executive Director

Heartland CASA 308.385.5125
   410 W 2nd St Ste 7, Grand Island, NE 68801
Amy Bennette, Executive Director

Incontro Law Office PC LLO 402.933.7456
E-mail ....cnovak@incontrolaw.com
   1904 Farnam St Ste 400, Omaha, NE 68102
Candice Novak

Indian Ctr, Inc. 402.438.5231
Fax 402.438.5236
E-mail ....ctyndall@aol.com
   1100 Military Rd, Lincoln, NE 68521
Clyde Tyndall, Executive Director

NDHHS 402.595.3244
E-mail ....tammi.burk@nebraska.gov
   CPS-IA, 7110 F St, Omaha, NE 68117
Tammi Burk

Pollack & Ball LLC 402.476.7474
E-mail ....tina_marroquin@yahoo.com
   1003 H St, Lincoln, NE 68508
Tina Marroquin, Manager

Project Harmony 402.595.1326
Fax 402.595.1329
Web ....www.projectharmony.com
E-mail ....gklein@projectharmony.com
   7110 F St, Omaha, NE 68117
Gene Klein, Director

Shamburg Wolf McDermott Depue 308.384.1635
E-mail ....expelter2@unl.edu
   308 N Locust St Ste 501, Grand Island, NE 68802
Mark Porto, Attorney

Southeast Nebraska Community Action Council 402.862.2411
Fax 402.862.2428
Web ....www.senca.org
E-mail ....awynn@neb.rr.com
   802 Fourth St., Humboldt, NE 68376
Amy Wynn, Headstart Director

BEHAVIORAL HEALTH TREATMENT

A Counseling Ctr 402.573.7277
Fax 402.573.7360
   3323 N 109th Plz, Omaha, NE 68164-2908
George Young, Psychiatrist

Alegent Health Immanuel Medical Center 402.572.2291
Web ....www.alegent.com
E-mail ....christine.daley@alegent.org
   6901 North 72nd Street, Omaha, NE 68122
Ms. Christine Daley, Accreditation Manager
Joint Commission accredited organization.

Arbor Family Counseling 402.330.4700
Fax 402.330.8815
   11605 Arbor St Ste 106, Omaha, NE 68144
Maureen O'Donnell, Director

Behave'n Day Center, Inc. 402.926.4373
Fax 402.926.3898
Web ....www.behavenkids.com
   8922 Cuming Street, Omaha, NE 68114
CARF accredited programs available.

Behavioral Health Specialists, Inc 402.370.3140
Fax 402.370.3373
Web www.4bhs.org
E-mail ....cbarnes@4bhs.org
   900 W Norfolk Ave, Norfolk, NE 68701
Connie Barnes, Executive Director
Joint Commission accredited organization.

Bellevue Public Schools 402.293.4721
Web ....www.bellevuepublicschools.org
E-mail ....bellevuepublicschools@hotmail.com
   12501 S 25th St, Bellevue, NE 68123-5526
Laura Jackson, Principal

Beneficial Behavioral Health Services, Inc. 402.697.3923
Fax 402.697.3924
Web ....http://www.behaviortherapyomaha.com
   4732 South 131st Street, Omaha, NE 68137
CARF accredited programs available.

Beneficial Behavioral Health Services, Inc. 402.697.3923
Fax 402.697.3924
Web ....www.bbhsi.org
E-mail ....steve_taylor@bbhsi.org
   12165 West Center Road, Suite 70, Omaha,
   NE 68144
Steven Taylor, Operations Director
CARF accredited programs available.

Blue Valley Behavioral Health, Inc. 402.228.3386
Web ....www.bvbh.net
E-mail ....charmon@bvbh.net
   1123 North 9th Street, Beatrice, NE 68310
Ms. Connie Harmon, Accreditation Manager
Joint Commission accredited organization.

Boys and Girls Home of Nebraska 402.494.4185
Fax 402.494.3925
E-mail ....sheehanr@bghome.net
   100 Futures Dr, South Sioux City, NE 68776-3920
Robert Sheehan, President

Boys Town 402.498.1111
Web ....www.girlsandboystown.org
E-mail ....info@boystown.org
   14100 Crawford St, Boys Town, NE 68010
   Father Steven Boes, Executive Director

Boys Town National Research Hospital 402.498.6525
Web ....www.boystownhospital.org
E-mail ....pat.allgeier@boystown.org
   555 North 30th Street, Omaha, NE 68131
   Ms. Pat Allgeier, Accreditation Manager
   Joint Commission accredited organization.

**Catholic Charities of the Archdiocese of Omaha,
Inc.** 402.554.0520
Fax 402.554.0365
Web ....www.ccomaha.org
   3300 North 60th Street, Omaha, NE 68104
   COA accredited organization.

Cedars Youth Svcs 402.434.5437
Fax 402.437.8833
Web ....www.cedars-kids.org
E-mail ....jblue@cedars-kids.org
   6601 Pioneer Blvd, Lincoln, NE 68506
   James R. Blue, President/CEO

CenterPointe, Inc. 402.475.8717
Fax 402.475.6728
Web ....www.centerpointe.org
   2633 P Street, Lincoln, NE 68508
   CARF accredited programs available.

Child Guidance Center 402.475.7666
Web ....child-guidance.org
E-mail ....ccrumpacker@child-guidance.org
   2444 'O' Street, Lincoln, NE 68510
   Dr. Carol Crumpacker, Accreditation Manager
   Joint Commission accredited organization.

Child Guidance Ctr 402.475.7666
Fax 402.476.9623
Web ....www.child-guidance.org
   2444 O St, Lincoln, NE 68510
   Carol Crumpacker, Director

Columbus Family Support 402.563.2466
Fax 402.563.2427
Web ....www.omnibehavioralhealth.com
E-mail ....mgreen@omnibehavioralhealth.com
   2919 15th St, Columbus, NE 68601
   Mike Green, Director

Continuum Eap 402.476.0186
Fax 402.476.2757
Web www.4continuum.com
   1135 M St Ste 400, Lincoln, NE 68508-2196
   Christian Brennan, Director

Creighton University 402.280.3955
Web ....www.creighton.edu
E-mail ....psullivan@creighton.edu
   11111 Mill Valley Rd, Omaha, NE 68154-3933
   Patricia Sullivan, Director

Ctr for Psychological Svcs, PC 308.234.6029
Fax 308.237.4792
Web ....www.centerpsych.com
E-mail ....center13@verizon.net
   4111 4th Ave Ste 32, Kearney, NE 68845
   Susie Coons, Officer Manager

Davis Medical Practice 402.637.0101
   PO Box 540973, Omaha, NE 68154-8973
   Terry Davis, Psychiatrist

Developmental Services of Nebraska, Inc. 402.435.2800
Web ....www.dsnonline.org
E-mail ....clasley@cii.us.com
   5701 Thompson Creek Blvd, Suite 200, Lincoln,
   NE 68516
   Ms. Carla Lasley, Accreditation Manager
   Joint Commission accredited organization.

Developmental Svcs of Nebraska, Inc. 402.435.2800
Fax 402.435.8801
E-mail ....slefevre@dsnonline.org
   5701 Thompson Creek Blvd Ste 200, Lincoln,
   NE 68516-5661
   Scott Lefevre, CEO

Epworth Village, Inc. 402.362.3353
Web ....www.epworthvillage.org
E-mail ....angie@epworthvillage.org
   2119 Division Avenue, York, NE 68467
   Ms. Angela Walker, Accreditation Manager
   Joint Commission accredited organization.

Families Care, Inc 308.237.1102
Fax 308.234.5712
Web ....www.families-care.net
E-mail ....arohan@region3.net
   4009 6th Ave Ste 55, Kearney, NE 68845-2393
   Anne Rohan, Executive Director

**Father Flanagan's Boys' Home dba Boys
Town** 402.498.1111
Fax 402.498.1925
Web ....www.boystown.org
   13603 Flanagan Boulevard, Boys Town, NE 68010
   COA accredited organization.

Frontier House 308.532.4730
Fax 308.532.4737
   114 S Chestnut St, North Platte, NE 69101
   Larry D. Brown, Regional Administrator

**Girls and Boys Town Behavioral Health
Svcs** 402.498.6615
Fax 402.498.6768
Web ....www.girlsandboystown.org
   555 N 30th St, Omaha, NE 68131-2136
   Dennis Vollmer, Behavioral Health Access Center Director

Hastings Regional Center 402.462.1971
E-mail ....marj.colburn@nebraska.gov
   4200 West Second Street, Hastings, NE 68901
   Ms. Marjorie Colburn, Accreditation Manager
   Joint Commission accredited organization.

Heartland Counseling Services, Inc. 402.494.3337
Fax 402.494.3356
   917 West 21st Street, South Sioux City, NE 68776
   CARF accredited programs available.

Heartland Family Service 402.553.3000
Fax 402.553.3133
Web ....www.heartlandfamilyservice.org
   2101 So. 42nd Street, Omaha, NE 68105
   COA accredited organization.

Human Services, Inc. 308.762.7177
Fax 308.762.2161
Web ....www.house-of-photography.com
   419 West 25th Street, Alliance, NE 69301
   CARF accredited programs available.

Improved Living, Inc 402.371.5631
Fax 402.371.3645
E-mail ....jeanfili@conpoint.com
   106 W Norfolk Ave, Norfolk, NE 68701-5340
   Jean Franchetti, Executive Director

Jewish Family Svcs 402.330.2024
Fax 402.697.7019
E-mail ....kgustafson@jewishomaha.org
   333 S 132nd St, Omaha, NE 68154-2106
   Karen Gustafson, Executive Director

Lincoln Regional Center 402.471.4444
Web ....dhhs.ne.gov/beh/rc/lrcserv.htm
E-mail ....stacey.werthsweeney@nebraska.gov
   West Prospector Place & Folsom Street, Lincoln,
   NE 68509
   Mrs. Stacey Werth Sweeney, Accreditation Manager
   Joint Commission accredited organization.

Lincoln Regional Ctr 402.471.4444
Fax 402.479.5124
Web ....www.nebraska.gov
E-mail ....bill.gibson@nebraska.gov
   801 W Prospector Pl, Lincoln, NE 68522-2299
   Bill Gibson, Director/CEO

Lutheran Family Svcs of Nebraska 402.435.2910
Fax 402.435.2949
Web ....www.lfsneb.org
E-mail ....jfisher-erickson@lfsneb.org
   2900 O St Ste 200, Lincoln, NE 68510-1469
   Julie Fisher-Erickson, Director

**Mid-Plains Center for Behavioral Healthcare Services,
Inc.** 308.395.1040
Fax 308.395.1060
Web ....www.midplainscenter.org
   615 North Elm Street, Grand Island, NE 68801
   COA accredited organization.

NOVA Therapeutic Community, Inc. 402.455.8303
Fax 402.455.7050
Web ....www.novatc.org
   3483 Larimore Avenue, Omaha, NE 68111
   CARF accredited programs available.

O'Neill Valley Hope 402.336.3747
Web ....valleyhope.com
E-mail ....juanitag@valleyhope.com
   1421 North 10th Street, Oneill, NE 68763
   Ms. Juanita Gregoire, Accreditation Manager
   Joint Commission accredited organization.

Oasis Counseling International 402.379.2030
Fax 402.379.3933
Web ....www.ocinternational.org
   333 West Norfolk Avenue, Suite 201, Norfolk,
   NE 68701
   CARF accredited programs available.

OMNI Behavioral Health 402.926.3385
Web ....www.omnibehavioralhealth.com
E-mail ....ktevis@omnibehavioralhealth.com
   5115 F Street, Omaha, NE 68117
   Mrs. Kristine Tevis, Accreditation Manager
   Joint Commission accredited organization.

Panhandle Mental Health Center 308.635.3171
Fax 308.635.7026
Web ....www.pmhc.net
   4110 Avenue D, Scottsbluff, NE 69361
   David Singer, Director
   CARF accredited programs available.

People's Family Health Svcs 308.534.3075
Fax 308.534.6104
E-mail ....pfhs@inebraska.com
   102 S Elm St Ste A, North Platte, NE 69101-5169
   Racheal Stahr, Executive Director

Ponca Tribe of Nebraska 402.371.8834
Fax 402.371.7564
Web ....www.poncatribe-ne.org
E-mail ....greggh@poncatribe-ne.org
   1800 Syracuse Ave, Norfolk, NE 68701-2458
   Greg Hansen, Interim Director Of Social Services

Region 3 Behavioral Health Services 308.237.5113
Fax 308.236.7669
Web www.region3.net
   4009 Sixth Avenue, Suite 65, Kearney, NE 68845
   Beth Bexter, Director
   CARF accredited programs available.

Region 4 Behavioral Health System 402.370.3100
Fax 402.370.3125
Web www.region4bhs.org
E-mail ....igansebom@region4bhs.org
   206 Monroe Avenue, Norfolk, NE 68701
   Ingrid Gansebom, Network Director
   CARF accredited programs available.

Nebraska

Nebraska

Region 6 Behavioral Healthcare 402.444.6573
Fax 402.444.7722
Web .... www.regionsix.com
3801 Harney Street, Omaha, NE 68131
CARF accredited programs available.

Region II Human Services 308.534.0440
Fax 308.534.8775
110 North Bailey, North Platte, NE 69101
CARF accredited programs available.

Region V Systems 402.441.4343
Fax 402.441.4335
Web www.region5systems.net
1645 N Street, Lincoln, NE 68508
CJ Johnson, Director
CARF accredited programs available.

**Saint Monica's Adolescent Girls Treatment Group
Home** 402.441.3768
Fax 402.441.3770
Web .... www.stmonicas.com
120 Wedgewood Dr, Lincoln, NE 68510-2431
Mary Barry, Director

South Central Behavioral Services, Inc. 308.237.5951
Fax 308.234.4018
Web .... www.scbsne.com
3810 Central Avenue, Kearney, NE 68848
CARF accredited programs available.

**Summit Care and Wellness Treatment and Counseling,
PC** 402.435.2273
Fax 402.435.2274
Web .... www.summitcareandwellness.com
1700 South 24th Street, Lincoln, NE 68502
CARF accredited programs available.

**The HUB - Central Access Point For Young
Adults** 402.471.8526
Fax 402.471.8527
Web .... www.hublincoln.org
835 South 12th Street, Lincoln, NE 68508
CARF accredited programs available.

The Omaha Home for Boys 402.457.7000
Fax 402.457.7162
Web .... www.omahahomeforboys.org
4343 North 52nd Street, Omaha, NE 68104
COA accredited organization.

**The Salvation Army Omaha Social
Services** 402.898.5900
Fax 402.898.7503
Web .... www.salvationarmyomaha.org
3612 Cuming Street, Omaha, NE 68131-1998
COA accredited organization.

Uta Halee Girls Village 402.457.1300
Web .... www.utahalee-cooper.org
E-mail .... cmeyer@utahalee-cooper.org
10625 Calhoun Road, Omaha, NE 68112
Ms. Cindy Meyer, Accreditation Manager
Joint Commission accredited organization.

Youth Rehabilitation and Treatment Ctr 308.865.5313
Fax 308.865.5323
Web .... www.hhs.state.ne.us
2802 30th Ave, Kearney, NE 68845
Jana Peterson, Director

CHILDREN'S HOSPITAL

**Alegent Health Bergan Mercy Medical
Center** 402.398.6060
7500 Mercy Rd, Omaha, NE 68124

Alegent Health Memorial Hospital 402.352.2441
104 West 17th St, Schuyler, NE 68661
Connie Peters, Director

Antelope Memorial Hospital 402.887.4151
102 West Ninth St, Neligh, NE 68756

Bryan LGH Medical Center 402.489.0200
1600 South 48th St, Lincoln, NE 68506
Kim Russel, President/CEO

Childrens Hospital and Medical Center 402.955.5400
8200 Dodge St, Omaha, NE 68114
Gary Perkins, Chief Executive Officer

Community Hospital 402.274.4366
2022 13th St, Auburn, NE 68305
Marty Fattig, Chief Executive Officer

Community Hospital 308.882.7111
600 West 12th St, Imperial, NE 69033
Lola Jones, Chief Executive Officer

Community Medical Center 402.245.2428
3307 Barada St, Falls City, NE 68355
Ryan Larsen, Chief Executive Officer

Creighton Area Health Services 402.358.5700
1503 Main St, Creighton, NE 68729
Mark Schulte, Chief Executive Officer

Faith Regional Health Services 402.371.4880
2700 West Norfolk Ave, Norfolk, NE 68701
Jim Sinek, Chief Executive Officer

Fremont Area Medical Center 402.721.1610
450 East 23rd St, Fremont, NE 68025
Pat Booth, Chief Executive Officer

Good Samaritan Hospitals 308.865.7100
10 East 31st St, Kearney, NE 68847
Mike Schnieders, Chief Executive Officer

Great Plains Regional Medical Center 308.696.8000
601 West Leota St, North Platte, NE 69101
Jane Goodwin, Marketing Director

Kimball Health Services 308.235.1952
505 South Burg St, Kimball, NE 69145
Kenneth Hunter, Chief Executive Officer

Mary Lanning Memorial Hospital 402.463.4521
715 North St Joseph Ave, Hastings, NE 68901
Bradeley Neet, Director

Nebraska Medical Center 402.552.2000
987400 Nebraska Medical Center, Omaha, NE 68198
Glenn Fosdick, Chief Executive Officer

Ogallala Community Hospital 308.284.4011
2601 N Spruce St, Ogallala, NE 69153

St Elizabeth Regional Medical Center 402.219.8000
555 S 70th St, Lincoln, NE 68510
Robert Lanik, Chief Executive Officer

St Francis Medical Center 308.384.4600
2620 West Faidley Ave, Grand Island, NE 68803
Dann Mcelligott, Chief Executive Officer

St Marys Community Hospital 402.873.3321
1314 Third Ave, Nebraska City, NE 68410

COUNSELING SERVICES

Child Saving Institute Crisis Ctr 402.553.6000
Fax 402.553.2428
Web .... www.childsaving.org
E-mail .... lblunt@childsaving.org
4545 Dodge, Omaha, NE 68132-3229
Lisa Blunt, Chief Operations Officer

Heartland Family Svc 402.553.3000
Fax 402.553.3133
Web .... www.heartlandfamilyservice.org
E-mail .... info@heartlandfamilyservice.org
2101 S 42nd St, Omaha, NE 68105-2909
John Jeanetta, President/CEO

Nebraska Christian Svcs 402.334.3278
Fax 402.697.5147
E-mail .... cindy.arterburn@swestcc.org
2600 S 124th St, Omaha, NE 68144-2707
Cindy Arterburn, Executive Director

CRISIS & SHELTER CARE

Crisis Ctr Dom Vlnce Prog 308.382.8250
Fax 308.382.1559
E-mail .... Crisis@Cccusa.Net
2251 N Webb Rd, Grand Island, NE 68802
Shellie Pointer, Director

**Ctr for Sexual Assault and Domestic Violence Survivors Crisis
Hotline** 402.564.2155
Fax 402.563.1719
3103 13th St, Columbus, NE 68601
Jonathan Niles, Director

Domestic Abuse-Sexual Assault Svcs 308.345.1612
Fax 308.345.4177
322 Norris Ave, Mc Cook, NE 69001
Donna Goad, Director

Domestic Violence Emergency Svcs 308.436.2787
Fax 308.436.2817
Web .... www.dovesprogram.com
E-mail .... hilarykw@earthlink.net
2035 10th Street., Gering, NE 69341
Hilary Wasserburger, Director

Epworth Village Inc. 402.362.3353
Fax 402.362.3248
Web .... www.epworthvillage.org
2119 N Division Ave, York, NE 68467
Thomas G. Mcbride, Director

Family Rescue Svcs-Domestic Violence 308.432.4113
Fax 308.432.3573
E-mail .... frs@bbc.net
300 W 2nd St, Chadron, NE 69337
Ann Beseke, Director

Friendship Home-Domestic Violence 402.437.9302
Fax 402.437.9310
E-mail .... amye@friendshiphome.org
PO Box 30268, Lincoln, NE 68503-0268
Amy Evans, Executive Director

Girls and Boys Town of Grand Island 308.381.4444
Fax 308.381.6124
Web .... www.boystown.org/grandisland
E-mail .... reedd@boystown.org
3230 W Wildwood Dr, Grand Island, NE 68801-9609
David Reed, Program Director

Hastings Regional Ctr 402.462.1971
Fax 402.460.3144
Web .... www.dhhs.ne.gov
E-mail .... william.gibson@nebraska.gov
4200 W 2nd St, Hastings, NE 68901-9701
William Gibson, CEO

**Haven House Family Svcs Ctr-Domestic
Violence** 402.375.5433
Fax 402.833.5526
PO Box 44, Wayne, NE 68787-0044
Nancy Cederlind, Director

Heartland Family Svc-Dom Abuse Prog 402.553.3000
Fax 402.553.3133
E-mail .... info@heartlandfamilyservices.org
2101 S 42nd st, Omaha, NE 68105
Dawn Bashara, Director

Northcentral Quad Co-Domestic Violence 402.376.2045
Fax 402.376.2478
E-mail .... ncqc@qwest.net
421 E 3rd St, Valentine, NE 69201-1913
Linda Monroe, Director

**Panhandle Community Svcs Youth Shelter
Hotline** 308.635.7777
Fax 308.635.1564
Web .... www.pcswn.com
2426 Broadway, Scottsbluff, NE 69361-1605
Vickie Lawton, Director

Parent-Child Protective Svcs Inc............**308.324.2336**
Fax..308.324.2812
Web....................................www.cozadtel.net
E-mail.........................pccjennifer@cozadtel.net
1001 North Washington Street, Lexington, NE 68850
Jennifer Soncksen, Director

Rape and Domestic Abuse Program..........**308.532.0624**
Fax..308.534.5596
101 S Chestnut St ste 2, NorthPlatte, NE 69101
Jeanie Gilbert, Director

Spousal Abuse-Sexual Assault Crisis Ctr.......**402.463.5810**
Fax..402.463.0103
E-mail.....................jsegelke@hastingssasa.com
220 S Burlington Ave Ste 4, Hastings, NE 68902
Jolynn Segelke, Director

The Shelter- Domestic Violence Program......**402.558.5700**
Fax..402.829.9208
Web.......................................www.ccomaha.org
E-mail...............................francesh@ccomaha.org
PO Box 4346, Omaha, NE 68104-0346
Frances Hauptman, Director

Utah Halee Girls' Village.....................**402.457.1300**
Fax..402.457.1405
Web..............................www.utahalee-cooper.org
10625 Calhoun Rd, Omaha, NE 68112
Mary Fraser Meints, CEO

Voice of Hope............................**402.476.2110**
Fax..402.476.3592
E-mail.........................info@voicesofhopelincoln.org
2545 N St, Lincoln, NE 68510
Marcie Metzger, Director

Wesley Ctr Crisis Nursery....................**402.644.4749**
Fax..402.371.0575
Web......................................www.conpoint.com
E-mail.............................wcenter@conpoint.com
406 W Phillip Ave, Norfolk, NE 68701-5250
Tracy Olson, Director

Y.E.S. Youth Emergency Svcs, Inc.............**402.345.5187**
Fax..402.345.6704
Web......................................www.yesomaha.org
E-mail................................info@yesomaha.org
2679 Farnam St, Omaha, NE 68031
Cindy Housley, Director Of Shelter Services

EDUCATION

Alpha School..............................**402.444.6557**
Fax..402.444.6574
Web.......................................www.ebdkids.org
E-mail..................................creid@ebdkids.org
1615 S 6th St, Omaha, NE 68108-3714
Clint Reid, Director

Apex Foster Care, Inc.......................**402.571.5400**
Fax..402.571.5412
Web..............................www.apexfostercare.com
E-mail.........................aspeck@apexfostercare.com
9945 Maple St, Omaha, NE 68134-7002
Marlon Brewer, Placement Specialist

Mary Our Queen School....................**402.333.8663**
Fax..402.334.3948
3405 S 119th St, Omaha, NE 68144
Lisa Nelson, Principal

Pine Ridge Civilian Conservation Ctr.........**308.432.3316**
Fax..308.432.4145
15710 Highway 385, Chadron, NE 69337
Clyde Franklin, Center Director

Wegner School............................**402.498.1820**
Fax..402.498.1825
E-mail.................gehringerr@girlsandboystown.org
14124 Norton Dr, Boys Town, NE 68010
Robert Gehringer, Superintendent

FOSTER CARE AGENCIES

Adoption Links Worldwide.................**402.556.2367**
Fax..402.556.2401
E-mail...............................mkoepsell@alww.org
5017 Leavenworth St, Ste 1, Omaha, NE 68106

Adoption Triad Midwest....................**402.493.8047**
E-mail................................NRS1985@aol.com
2411 S 123rd S, Omaha, NE 68144
Elaine Holder, President

Central Service Area.......................**402.370.3120**
Fax..800.782.8844
E-mail...........................mike.pulse@nebraska.gov
209 North 5th St, Norfolk, NE 68702
Mike Pulse, Director

Christian Heritage Children's Home.........**402.421.5437**
Fax..402.421.5438
Web...www.chne.org
14880 Old Cheney Road, Walton, NE 68461
COA accredited organization.

Eastern Service Area.......................**402.595.2850**
1313 Farnam Mall 3rd Fl, Omaha, NE 68102

Eastern Service Area.......................**402.471.7000**
1050 N Street, Ste 250, Lincoln, NE 68508

Fos Adopt Support Group...................**402.489.1295**
6001 Sunrise Rd, Lincoln, NE 68510

NE Foster & Adoptive Parent Assoc Inc......**402.768.6803**
315 S 9th St Ste 10, Lincoln, NE 68508
Lynne Weidel

Nebraska Foster Adoptive Parent Assoc......**402.476.2273**
Fax..402.476.2273
2431 Fairfield St Ste C, Lincoln, NE 68521
Pamela Allen, Executive Director

North American Cncl Adoptable Children.....**308.382.4495**
Fax..308.385.0407
E-mail..................................oldmill@kdsi.net
712 West Koenig, Grand Island, NE 68801
David Rehovsky, Director

Southwest Service Area.....................**308.324.6633**
Fax..308.324.8065
800 North Washington PO Box E, Lexington, NE 68850
Nathan Bush, Chief Executive Officer

Voices for Children in Nebraska.............**402.597.3100**
Fax..402.597.2705
E-mail.....................kmoore@voicesforchildren.com
7521 Main St Ste 103, Omaha, NE 68127
Carolyn Rooker, Director

Wester Service Area.......................**308.436.6500**
1600 10th St, Gering, NE 69341

PEDIATRIC HOME CARE

Interim Healthcare........................**402.421.7930**
Fax..402.421.7931
6040 S 58th St Ste A, Lincoln, NE 68516
Lynette Helling, Chief Executive Officer

Interim Healthcare........................**402.392.1818**
Fax..402.392.0167
11207 W Dodge Rd Ste 100, Omaha, NE 68154
Paula Christensen, Director

SOCIAL SERVICES

Cedars Youth Services......................**402.434.5437**
Fax..402.437.8833
Web.....................................www.cedars-kids.org
6601 Pioneers Boulevard, Suite 1, Lincoln, NE 68506
COA accredited organization.

Child Saving Institute, Inc...................**402.553.6000**
Fax..402.553.2428
Web......................................www.childsaving.org
4545 Dodge Street, Omaha, NE 68132
COA accredited organization.

Children and Families Foundation...........**402.476.9401**
Fax..402.476.9486
Web.............................www.nebraskachildren.org
E-mail........................info@nebraskachildren.org
215 Centennial Mall S Ste 200, Lincoln, NE 68508-1813
Mary Jo Pankoke, Director

Community Action Partnership of Lancaster and Saunders Counties.............................**402.471.4515**
Fax..402.471.4844
Web...............................www.lincoln-action.org
E-mail................info@communityactionwork.org
210 O St, Lincoln, NE 68508-2322
Vi See, Executive Director

Heartland Family Svc Care Connection.......**402.552.7000**
Fax..402.552.7016
Web..........................www.heartlandfamilyservice.org
E-mail................rstricklett@heartlandfamilyservice.org
2101 S 42nd St, Omaha, NE 68105-2909
Rachael Stricklett, Program Director

Hispanic Community Ctr....................**402.474.3950**
Fax..402.474.3842
2032 U ST, Lincoln, NE 68503
Marien Ruiz, Director

Lutheran Family Services of Nebraska, Inc.......**402.342.7038**
Fax..402.342.6408
Web...www.lfsneb.org
124 S. 24th Street, Suite 230, Omaha, NE 68102-1246
COA accredited organization.

Midwest Child Care Assoc...................**402.551.2379**
Fax..402.551.7198
Web.....................................www.childcarene.org
E-mail....................jphelan@midwestchildcare.org
7701 Pacific St Ste 200, Omaha, NE 68114
Janet Phelan, Executive Director

Nebraska Children's Home Society..........**402.451.0787**
Fax..402.898.7750
Web..www.nchs.org
4939 S. 118th Street, Omaha, NE 68137
COA accredited organization.

Nebraska Family Support Network..........**402.345.0791**
Fax..402.345.0938
E-mail.........................dstroud@nefamilysupport.org
3568 Dodge Ste 2, Omaha, NE 68131
Dawn Stroud, Administrative Assistant

Northwest Community Action...............**308.432.3393**
Fax..308.432.5799
Web...www.ncap.org
E-mail..........................ncaplorye@yahoo.com
270 Pine St, Chadron, NE 69337-2296
Lorie Mcleod, Director

Voices for Children In Nebraska.............**402.597.3100**
Fax..402.597.2705
Web............................www.voicesforchildren.com
E-mail...................voices@voicesforchildren.com
7521 Main St Ste 103, Omaha, NE 68127-3984
Carolyn Rooker, Director

Women In Community Svcs, Inc. (WICS Residence)................................**402.477.5256**
Fax..402.477.5289
E-mail........................wicshome@windstream.net
1935 D St, Lincoln, NE 68502
Tauni Waddington, Director

SPECIAL NEEDS

Acute Rehabilitation Unit at Regional West Medical Center **308.630.1440**
Fax 308.630.2045
Web ....www.rwhs.org
4021 Avenue B, Scottsbluff, NE 69361
CARF accredited programs available.

Alegent Health Immanuel Rehabilitation Center **402.572.2295**
Fax 402.572.2393
Web ....www.alegent.org
6901 North 72nd Street, Omaha, NE 68122
CARF accredited programs available.

Answers 4 Families **800.746.8420**
E-mail ....info@answers4families.org
206 S 13th st ste 1000, Lincoln, NE 68588
Charlie Lewis, Project Director

Autism Society of Nebraska **402.637.5670**
E-mail ....autismsociety@autismnebraska.org
PO Box 83559, Lincoln, NE 68501

Boys Town National Research Hospital - West **402.778.6000**
Fax 402.778.6001
Web ....www.boystownhospital.org
E-mail ....peb@boystown.org
14000 Hospital Rd, Boys Town, NE 68010-7513
Patrick Brookhouser, Director

BryanLGH Medical Center Inpatient Rehabilitation Unit **402.481.9326**
Fax 402.481.9392
Web ....www.bryanlgh.org
2300 South 16th Street, Lincoln, NE 68502-3704
CARF accredited programs available.

Congress of Parents & Teachers **402.884.4048**
E-mail ....nebraskapta@hotmail.com
13304 W Center Rd Ste 221, Omaha, NE 68144

Easter Seals Nebraska **800.650.9880**
E-mail ....kcarlson@ne.easterseals.com
638 N 109th Plz, Omaha, NE 68154
Karen Carlson, Chief Executive Officer

Educational Therapy, Inc **402.498.8708**
Fax 402.445.0433
E-mail ....kat.edchvrpy@yahoo.com
4405 N 156 Ave Cir, Omaha, NE 68116
Mary Nicholf, Director

Families for Effective Autism Treatment **402.489.9572**
E-mail ....info@featofnebraska.com
PO Box 84154, Lincoln, NE 68501
Jennifer Korinek, President

Independent Living Council **402.438.7979**
E-mail ....nesilc@alltel.net
215 Centennial Mall S Ste 210, Lincoln, NE 68508

Learning Disabilities Association **402.348.1567**
E-mail ....ldaofneb@yahoo.com
3135 N 93rd St, Omaha, NE 68134

Madonna Rehabilitation Hospital **402.489.7102**
Fax 402.483.9460
Web ....www.madonna.org
5401 S St, Lincoln, NE 68506
Marsha Lommel, CEO
CARF accredited programs available.

Methodist Hospital Rehabilitation Center - Omaha **402.354.4400**
Fax 402.354.5268
Web ....www.bestcare.org
8303 Dodge Street, Omaha, NE 68114
CARF accredited programs available.

NAMI Nebraska **877.463.6264**
E-mail ....naminebraska@nami.org
415 S 25 Ave, Omaha, NE 68131
Jonah Deppe, Executive Director

National Multiple Sclerosis Society **800.344.4867**
Fax 402.505.6277
E-mail ....NEN@nmss.org
328 S 72nd St, Omaha, NE 68114

Nebraska Family Support Network **402.345.0791**
E-mail ....nfsn@nefamilysupport.org
3568 Dodge St Ste 2, Omaha, NE 68131
Judy Domina, Executive Director

Parent to Parent Network **877.379.9926**
201 S Miller, Norfolk, NE 68702
Robert Gereaux, Executive Director

People First of Nebraska **308.872.6490**
E-mail ....peoplefirstofnebr@lycos.com
345 S G St, Broken Bow, NE 68822

PTI Nebraska **402.346.0525**
Fax 402.934.1479
E-mail ....info@pti-nebraska.org
6805 Grover St, Omaha, NE 68106
Glenda Davis, Executive Director

Speech-Language-Hearing Association **402.476.9573**
E-mail ....angie@nslha.org
455 S 11th St Ste A, Lincoln, NE 68508
Angie Carman, Director

The Arc of Nebraska **402.475.4407**
E-mail ....arcneb@inebraska.com
1672 Van Dorn St, Lincoln, NE 68502

The Nebraska Medical Center **402.559.9369**
Fax 402.559.8685
E-mail ....dlynes@nebraskamed.com
987740 Nebraska Medical Center, Omaha, NE 68198
Denise Lynes, Nicu Case Manager

The Ollie Webb Center Pilot Parents **402.346.5220**
1941 S 42nd St Ste 122, Omaha, NE 68105
Annie Anderson, Director

UCP of Nebraska **800.729.2556**
E-mail ....ucp@ucpnebraska.org
920 S 107th Ave, Omaha, NE 68114
Carol Hahn, Executive Director

SUBSTANCE ABUSE TREATMENT

Catholic Charities **402.827.0570**
Fax 402.827.0580
Web ....www.ccomaha.org
E-mail ....mikep@ccomaha.org
1490 N 16th St, Omaha, NE 68102
Mike Phillips, Director

O'Neill Valley Hope **402.336.3747**
Fax 402.336.3096
Web ....www.valleyhope.com
E-mail ....info@valleyhope.com
1421 N 10th St, Oneill, NE 68763
Monte Miller, Program Director

The Bridge, Inc **402.462.4677**
Fax 402.462.4699
E-mail ....bridgeincthe@yahoo.com
907 S Kansas Ave, Hastings, NE 68901-7024
Charlotte Hamburger, Director

Well Link, Inc **402.379.3622**
Fax 402.644.4593
Web ....www.womenslifeline.org
E-mail ....reneeob@womenslifeline.org
305 N 9th St, Norfolk, NE 68701-3915
Renee Otto-berglund, Program Director

Nevada

Brian Sandoval, Governor
State Capital
101 North Carson Street
Carson City, NV 89701
775.684.5670
775.684.5683 (Fax)
govern@gov.state.nv.us

Pauline E. Salla, Juvenile Justice Specialist
475 W Haskell St, Box 7
Winnemucca , NV 89445
775.623.6555
775.623.6559 (Fax)
psalla@dcfs.state.nv.us

John Hambrick, SAG Chair
11216 Dell Cliff's Ct
Las Vegas, NV 89144
702.499.6169
702.242.3406 (Fax)
J16212@yahoo.com

CRISIS NUMBERS

Child Abuse Reporting . . .775.684.4400

STATE SERVICES

SOCIAL SERVICES

Child Care Licensing Office Nevada 775.684.4463
Fax 775.684.4455
4126 Technology Way 3rd Flr, Carson City, NV 89706
D Comeaux, Director

Div of Welfare and Supportive Svcs 775.684.0500
Fax 775.684.0711
Web . . . . .www.dwss.nv.gov
E-mail . . . . .rgilliland@dwss.state.nv.gov
1470 College Pkwy, Carson City, NV 89706-7924
Romaine Gilliland, Administrator

Nevada Dept of Health and Human Svcs 775.684.4000
Fax 775.684.4010
Web . . . . .www.dhhs.nv.gov
E-mail . . . . .nvdhhs@dhhs.nv.gov
4126 Technology Way Ste 100, Carson City, NV 89706
Michael Willden, Director

GENERAL HEALTH SERVICES

Maternal and Child Health NV 775.684.4285
Fax 775.684.4245
E-mail . . . . .rwhiteley@health.nv.gov
4150 Technology Way Ste 101, Carson City, NV 89706
Richard Whiteley, Director

Nevada State Medical Assoc 775.825.6788
Fax 775.825.3202
Web . . . . .www.nsmadocs.org
E-mail . . . . .lmatheis@nsmadocs.org
3660 Baker Ln Ste 101, Reno, NV 89509-5497
Lawrence P Matheis, Executive Director

MENTAL HEALTH SERVICES

Div of Mental Health and Developmental
Svcs 775.684.5943
Fax 775.684.5964
Web . . . . .www.mhds.state.nv.us
4126 Technology Way, ste 201 fl 2, Carson City, NV 89706-2023
Deborah McBride, Agency Director

Rehabilitation Division Nevada 775.684.4040
Fax 775.684.4184
1370 S Curry St, Carson City, NV 89703
Maureen Cole, Director

Substance Abuse Prevention And Treatment
Agency 702.486.8250
Fax 702.486.8253
Web . . . . .www.health.nv.gov
E-mail . . . . .kgdavis@sapta.nv.gov
4220 S Maryland Pkwy, Ste 806D, Las Vegas, NV 89119
Kim Davis, Office Manager

JUSTICE AGENCY

Educ and Vocational Training NV 775.887.3236
Fax 775.887.3253
E-mail . . . . .mhall@doc.nv.gov
5500 Snyder Ave Bldg 17, Carson City, NV 89701

Juvenile Svcs 702.486.5095
Fax 702.486.5089
Web . . . . .www.dcfs.state.nv.us
E-mail . . . . .dprice@dcfs.state.nv.us
620 Belrose St Ste 107, Las Vegas, NV 89107-2256
Dan Prince, Deputy Administrator

Victims Of Crime Program 702.486.2740
Fax 702.486.2825
E-mail . . . . .bnix@voc.nv.gov
2200 S Rancho Dr Ste 130, Las Vegas, NV 89102
Bryan Nix, Coordinator

COURTS

Administrative Ofc of the Courts 775.684.1700
Fax 775.684.1723
Web . . . . .www.nvcourts.state.nv.us
E-mail . . . . .rsweet@nvcourts.state.nv.us
201 S Carson St Ste 250, Carson City, NV 89701-4780
Robin Sweet, Director

POLICE AND SHERIFF

Las Vegas Police Dept 702.828.3111
Fax 702.828.0144
E-mail . . . . .sheriff@lvmpd.com
3141 Sunrise Ave, Las Vegas, NV 89101
Douglas C. Gillespie, Sheriff

EDUCATION SERVICES

Educ for Homeless Children and Youth NV 775.687.9235
Fax 775.687.9250
E-mail . . . . .kstephens@doe.nv.gov
700 E 5th St, Carson City, NV 89701
K Stephens, Director

Navada Department Of Education 702.486.6458
Fax 702.486.6450
9890 S Maryland Pkwy Ste 221, Las Vegas, NV 89183
Dr. Jerry Barbee, Administrator

Nevada Department of Education 775.687.9217
Fax 775.687.9202
E-mail . . . . .krheault@doe.nv.gov
700 E 5th St, Carson City, NV 89701
Keith Rheault, Superintendent

Nevada PEP 702.388.8899
Fax 702.388.2966
E-mail . . . . .pepinfo@nvpep.org
20101 S Jones Blvd, Las Vegas, NV 89146
Karen Paycher, Executive Director

Office of Special Edu Elem & Sec Edu NV 775.687.9171
Fax 775.687.9123
E-mail . . . . .rfitzpatrick@doe.nv.gov
700 E 5th St Ste 113, Carson City, NV 89701
R Fitzpatrick, Director

LABOR & WORKFORCE EDUCATION

Nevada Dept of Employment Training and
Rehabilitation 775.684.3911
Fax 775.684.3908
Web . . . . .www.nvdetr.org
E-mail . . . . .tjohnson@nvdetr.org
500 E 3rd St Ste 200, Carson City, NV 89713-0001
Terry Johnson, Director

Nevada

COUNTY SERVICES

Carson City

SOCIAL SERVICES

Bia Indian Social Svcs **775.887.3514**
Fax 775.885.6857
311 E Washington St, Carson City, NV 89701-4065
Norma Moyle, Msw, Social Worker

GENERAL HEALTH SERVICES

Carson City Health Dept **775.887.2190**
Fax 775.887.2248
Web .... www.carson.org
E-mail .... mworks@carson.org
900 E Long St, Carson City, NV 89706-3129
Marena Works, Rn, Nursing Supervisor

WIC **775.684.5942**
Fax 775.684.4246
E-mail .... mwalker@health.nv.gov
4126 Technology Way St 102, Carson City,
NV 89706
Michelle Walker, Program Manager

JUSTICE AGENCY

Attorney General's Ofc **775.684.1100**
Fax 775.684.1108
Web .... www.ag.state.nv.us
E-mail .... aginfo@ag.state.nv.us
100 N Carson St, Carson City, NV 89701-4717
Catherine Cortez Masto, Attorney General

Carson City Juvenile Probation **775.887.2033**
Fax 775.887.2036
1545 E 5th St, Carson City, NV 89701
John Simms, Chief

CASA **775.882.6776**
Fax 775.887.2513
Web .... casaofcc.org
E-mail .... casaofcc@earthlink.net
1545 E Fifth St, Carson City, NV 89701-5023

COURTS

1st Judicial District Court **775.887.2082**
Fax 775.887.2177
885 E Musser St Ste 3031, Carson City, NV 89701
Honorable William Maddox, Judge

Juvenile Court **775.887.2038**
Fax 775.887.2513
Web .... www.ci.carson-city.nv.us
E-mail .... kluif@ci.carson-city.nv.us
1545 E Fifth St, Carson City, NV 89701-5098
Kristine Luif, Special Master

POLICE AND SHERIFF

Sheriff's Ofc **775.887.2020**
Fax 775.887.2026
Web .... www.ccsheriff.com
E-mail .... kfurlong@ci.carson-city.nv.us
911 E MUSSER ST, Carson City, NV 89701-3706
Ken Furlong, Sheriff

EDUCATION SERVICES

Special Education **775.283.2350**
Fax 775.283.2390
Web .... www.carson.cityschool.com
E-mail .... kcroskery@carsoncityschool.com
710 W 4th St, Carson City, NV 89703
Keith Croskery, Director Of Special Education

Churchill County

GENERAL HEALTH SERVICES

Community Health Nursing **775.423.4434**
Fax 775.423.0422
Web .... www.health.nv.gov
E-mail .... rlorentzen@health.nv.gov
485 W B St Ste 101, Fallon, NV 89406-2765
Rose Lorentzen, Public Health Nurse

Fallon Tribal Health Ctr **775.423.3634**
Fax 775.423.1453
E-mail .... healthdirector@fpst.org
1001 Rio Vista Dr, Fallon, NV 89406
Lani Miguel, Acting Tribal Director

MENTAL HEALTH SERVICES

Fallon Mental Health Ctr **775.423.7141**
Fax 775.423.4020
Web .... www.ruralclinics.nv.gov
E-mail .... rkendall@ruralclinics.nv.gov
151 N Maine St, Fallon, NV 89406-2902
Ray Kendall, CEO

JUSTICE AGENCY

Juvenile Probation **775.423.6587**
Fax 775.423.6888
E-mail .... ccjpo@churchillcounty.org
335 N Broadway, Fallon, NV 89406
Devere Karlson, Chief Performance Officer

COURTS

3rd Judicial District Court **775.423.6088**
Fax 775.423.8578
Web .... www.churchillcounty.org
E-mail .... distct-lawclk@churchillcounty.org
73 N Maine St Ste B, Fallon, NV 89406-2958
Honorable David A. Huff, Director

EDUCATION SERVICES

Special Education **775.423.5187**
Fax 775.423.8680
601 Discovery Dr, Fallon, NV 89406
Will Jensen, Director

Clark County

SOCIAL SERVICES

Child And Family Svcs **702.455.7200**
Fax 702.647.1535
Web .... www.clarkcountynv.gov
E-mail .... tmorton@clarkcountynv.gov
121 S Martin Luther Blvd, Las Vegas, NV 89106
Tom Morton, Director

District Welfare Ofc **702.486.1675**
Fax 702.455.6494
Web .... www.welfare.state.nv.us
700 Belrose St, Las Vegas, NV 89107-2235
Rachelle Church, MSW

Div Of Children And Family Svcs
Treatment **702.486.6100**
Fax 702.486.7759
Web .... www.dcfs.state.nv.us
6171 W Charleston Blvd, Bldg 7, Las Vegas,
NV 89146
Patricia Merryfield, Deputy Administrator For Treatment Services (Bldg 8)

Social Svcs Welfare Dept **702.455.4270**
Fax 702.455.5950
Web .... www.clarkcounty.nv.gov
1600 Pinto Ln, Las Vegas, NV 89106-4184
Tim Burch, Director

GENERAL HEALTH SERVICES

Helen J. Stewart School **702.799.5588**
Fax 702.799.5592
E-mail .... patriciaschultz@interact.ccsd.net
2375 E Viking Rd, Las Vegas, NV 89169-3357
Patricia Schultz, Principal

Nursing And Clinic Svcs **702.759.1000**
Fax 702.383.1446
Web .... www.southernnevadahealthdistrict.org
625 Shadow Ln, Las Vegas, NV 89106-4118
Bonnie Sorenson, Director Of Nursing

JUSTICE AGENCY

8th District Juvenile Justice Svcs **702.455.5200**
Fax 702.455.5216
Web .... www.accessclarkcounty.com
601 N Pecos Rd, Las Vegas, NV 89101-2408
Fritz Reese, Assistant Director

Spring Mountain Youth Camp **702.455.5555**
Fax 702.455.5250
Web .... www.mccarran.com
2400 Angel Peak Pl, Las Vegas, NV 89124
Michael Whelihan, Camp Manager

Youth Parole **702.486.5080**
Fax 702.486.5087
620 Belrose St Ste 107, Las Vegas, NV 89107
Brett Allen, Acting Chief

COURTS

8th Judicial District Court **702.671.4528**
Fax 702.671.4548
Web .... www.clarkcountynv.gov
200 Lewis, Las Vegas, NV 89155
Steven D Grierson, Court Executive Officer

Family Div **702.455.5306**
Fax 702.455.5551
601 N Pecos Rd, Las Vegas, NV 89101
Honorable, Dept Judge

North Las Vegas Justice Court **702.455.7801**
Fax 702.455.7832
Web .... www.clark.nv.gov
E-mail .... tmarsh@clark.nv.gov
2428 N Martin L King Blvd, North Las Vegas,
NV 89032-3700
Terry Marsh, Court Administator

Teen Court/Trial By Peers **702.387.6011**
Fax 702.387.7867
Web .... www.clarkcountybar.org
725 S 8th St, Las Vegas, NV 89101
Kelly Thomas Boyers, Executive Director

POLICE AND SHERIFF

Las Vegas Metropolitan Police
Dept **702.828.3111**
Fax 702.828.3073
Web .... www.lvmpd.com
E-mail .... t3629w@lvmpd.com
3141 E Sunrise Ave, Las Vegas, NV 89101
Lt. Brian Evans, Sexual Abuse Section

School District Police Dept **702.799.7830**
Fax 702.799.7837
Web .... www.ccsdpd.com
120 Corporate Park Dr, Henderson, NV 89074
Phil Arroyo, Acting Chief

EDUCATION SERVICES

Cdi Head Start Learning
Ctr-Henderson **702.566.1048**
Fax 702.566.4503
180 Westminster Way, Henderson, NV 89015
Florence Liu, Director

Special Education.........................702.799.7461
Fax...702.799.3760
Web...www.ccsd.net
E-mail..........................kwilliams@interact.ccsd.net
  2625 E Saint Louis Ave, Las Vegas, NV 89104-4200
  Karen Williams, Regional Director For School Based Programs

Douglas County

GENERAL HEALTH SERVICES

Community Health Nursing................**775.782.9038**
Fax...775.782.9875
  1133 Spruce St, Gardnerville, NV 89410-5114
  Terese Litterer, Supervisor

MENTAL HEALTH SERVICES

Douglas Mental Health....................**775.782.3671**
Fax...775.782.6639
Web.............................www.ruralclinics.nv.gov
E-mail..........................kbent@ruralclinics.nv.gov
  1538 US Highway 395 N, Gardnerville,
  NV 89410-5207
  Kathleen Bent, Clinic Director

COURTS

9th District Court.........................**775.782.9820**
Fax...775.782.9954
  1625 8th St, Minden, NV 89423
  Honorable Michael Gibbons, District Judge

POLICE AND SHERIFF

Sheriff's Ofc..............................**775.782.9900**
Fax...775.783.6401
Web.............................www.co.douglas.nv.us
E-mail..........................rpierini@co.douglas.nv.us
  1625 8th St, Minden, NV 89423
  Ron P. Pierini, Sheriff

Elko County

COURTS

4th Judicial District Court..................**775.753.4600**
Fax...775.753.4610
Web.............................www.elkocountynv.net
E-mail..........................clerk@elkocountynv.net
  540 Court St, Elko, NV 89801
  Honorable J. Michael Memeo, District Court Judge

Esmeralda County

POLICE AND SHERIFF

Sheriff's Ofc..............................**775.485.6373**
Fax...775.485.3524
E-mail..........................kelgan@frontiernet.net
  233 Crook St, Goldfield, NV 89013
  Kenneth N. Elgan, Sheriff

Eureka County

GENERAL HEALTH SERVICES

Eureka Medical Clinic......................**775.237.5313**
Fax...775.237.5073
Web.............................www.nvhealthcenter.org
E-mail..........................dgibson@nvrhc.org
  250 S Main, Eureka, NV 89316
  Duke Gibson, Director

JUSTICE AGENCY

Probation Dept............................**775.237.5450**
Fax...775.237.6044
  701 S Main St, Eureka, NV 89316
  Steve Zimmerman, Jpo

POLICE AND SHERIFF

Sheriff's Ofc..............................**775.237.5701**
Fax...775.237.5704
Web.............................www.eurekanv.org
E-mail..........................kjones@eurekanv.org
  411 N Main St, Eureka, NV 89316-0736
  Kenneth E Jones, Sheriff

Humboldt County

SOCIAL SERVICES

**Winnemucca District Ofc Div Of Child And Family
Svcs**......................................**775.623.6555**
Fax...775.623.6559
Web.............................www.dcfs.state.nv.us
  475 W Haskell St, Box 7, Winnemucca, NV 89445
  Pauline Salla, Social Services Chief

JUSTICE AGENCY

Probation Dept............................**775.623.6382**
Fax...775.623.6386
E-mail..........................esampson@wmnv.net
  737 E Fairgrounds Rd, Winnemucca, NV 89445
  Edward Sampson, Chief JPO

COURTS

6th Judicial District Court..................**775.623.6371**
Fax...775.623.6457
  25 W 5th St, Rm 212, Winnemucca, NV 89445
  Michael Montero, District Judge

POLICE AND SHERIFF

Sheriff's Ofc..............................**775.623.6419**
Fax...775.623.2192
Web.............................www.hcsonv.com
E-mail..........................h101@hcsonv.com
  50 W 5th St, Winnemucca, NV 89445-3150
  Ed Kilgore, Sheriff

Lander County

GENERAL HEALTH SERVICES

Lander Community Health Nursing...........**775.635.2386**
Fax...775.635.9203
Web.............................www.nvhd.state.nv.us
E-mail..........................rnewgard@health.nv.gov
  150 Palmer St, Battle Mountain, NV 89820-1930
  Reita Newgard, Community Health Nurse

MENTAL HEALTH SERVICES

Battle Mountain Mental Health Ctr...........**775.635.5753**
Fax...775.635.8028
Web.............................www.ruralclinics.nv.gov
E-mail..........................canderson1@ruralclinics.nv.gov
  10 E 6th St, Battle Mountain, NV 89820-2081
  Christian Anderson, Director

POLICE AND SHERIFF

Sheriff's Ofc..............................**775.635.1100**
Fax...775.635.2577
  2 State Route 305 S, Battle Mountain, NV 89820
  Ron Unger, Sheriff

Lincoln County

GENERAL HEALTH SERVICES

Community Health Nursing..................**775.726.3123**
Fax...775.726.3874
Web.............................www.health.nv.gov
E-mail..........................mjlucht@health.nv.gov
  360 Lincoln St, Caliente, NV 89008
  Mary Jean Lucht, Health Nurse

POLICE AND SHERIFF

Sheriff's Dept.............................**775.962.5151**
Fax...775.962.5384
  1050 Sr322, Pioche, NV 89043
  Kerry Lee, Sheriff

Lyon County

GENERAL HEALTH SERVICES

Community Health Nursing..................**775.463.6539**
Fax...775.463.6534
Web.............................www.health.nv.gov
E-mail..........................jhakin@health.nv.gov
  26 Nevin Way, Yerington, NV 89447-2327
  Joycelynn Hakin, RN, Community Health Nurse

MENTAL HEALTH SERVICES

Silver Springs Mental Health Ctr............**775.577.0319**
Fax...775.577.9571
Web.............................www.ssshospitaldistrictnv.com
E-mail..........................darren@ssshospitaldistrictnv.com
  3595 US Highway 50, Silver Springs, NV 89429-9303
  Darren Anderson, Acting Supervisor

Yearington Mental Health Ctr...............**775.463.3191**
Fax...775.463.4641
  215 W Bridge St Ste 5, Yerington, NV 89447
  Winonna Holloway, Lead Clinitian

JUSTICE AGENCY

Juvenile Probation Dept....................**775.463.6641**
Fax...775.463.2204
  31 S Main St, Yerington, NV 89447
  Roger W. Sayre, Chief Performance Officer

COURTS

3rd Judicial District Court..................**775.463.6503**
Fax...775.463.3643
  31 S Main St, Yerington, NV 89447
  Nikki Bryan, Clerk

POLICE AND SHERIFF

Sheriff's Dept.............................**775.463.6600**
Fax...775.463.6610
E-mail..........................sheriff@lion-county.org
  30 Nevin Way, Yerington, NV 89447
  Allen Beil, Sheriff

Mineral County

GENERAL HEALTH SERVICES

Community Health Nursing..................**775.945.3657**
Fax...775.945.2039
E-mail..........................wnixon@health.md.gov
  331 1st St, Hawthorne, NV 89415
  Wanda Nixon, Community Health Nurse

Schurz Indian Health Ctr...................**775.773.2345**
Fax...775.773.2425
Web.............................www.ihs.gov
E-mail..........................steve.fox@mail.ihs.gov
  1025 Hospital Rd., Schurz, NV 89427
  Steven Fox Jr, Service Unit Director

MENTAL HEALTH SERVICES

Hawthorne Mental Health Ctr...............**775.945.3387**
Fax...775.945.2307
  1000 C Street, Hawthorne, NV 89415
  Kathy Trujillo, Administrative Assistant

JUSTICE AGENCY

Probation Dept............................**775.945.3393**
Fax...775.945.0719
  525 W 9th St, Hawthorne, NV 89415
  Curtis Schlett, Chief Performance Officer

Nye County

MENTAL HEALTH SERVICES

Pahrump Mental Health....................**775.751.7406**
Fax...775.751.7409
E-mail..........................shaut@ruralclinics.nv.gov
  240 Humahuaca St, Pahrump, NV 89048
  Susan Haut, Clinic Director

Nevada

Tonopah Mental Health **775.482.6742**
Fax 775.751.7409
Web ....www.nvaging.net
   825 S Main st, Pahrump, NV 89041
   Theresa Lambrect, Clinic Director

JUSTICE AGENCY

Probation Dept **775.751.7007**
Fax 775.751.7017
   1510 E Basin Ave Ste 106, Pahrump, NV 89060
   Tom Metscher, Chief JPO

COURTS

5th District Court **775.751.4210**
Fax 775.751.4218
E-mail ....lmulvey@co.nye.nv.us
   1520 E Basin Ave Ste 105, Pahrump, NV 89060
   Honorable Robert W. Lane, Judge

5th District Court/Judges

Chambers **775.482.8141**
Fax 775.482.7345
Web ....www.nyecounty.net
E-mail ....jdavis@co.nye.nv.us
   101 Rader Road, Tonopah, NV 89049
   Honorable John P. Davis, District Judge

POLICE AND SHERIFF

Sheriff's Ofc **775.482.8110**
Fax 775.482.8195
Web ....www.co.nye.nv.us
E-mail ....ademeo@co.nye.nv.us
   101 Radar Road, Tonopah, NV 89049
   Tony Demeo, Sheriff

Pershing County

GENERAL HEALTH SERVICES

Public Health Dept **775.273.2041**
Fax 775.273.4900
Web ....www.health.nv.gov
E-mail ....lcooper@health.nv.gov
   535 Western Ave, Lovelock, NV 89419
   Laura Cooper, Practitioner

MENTAL HEALTH SERVICES

Lovelock Mental Health Ctr **775.273.1036**
Fax 775.273.1109
Web ....mhds.state.nv.us
   775 Cornell Ave, Lovelock, NV 89419
   Annie Perkins, Clinic Director

COURTS

6th Judicial District Court **775.273.2410**
Fax 775.273.2434
Web ....www.pershingcounty.net
   400 Main St, Lovelock, NV 89419
   Honorable Richard Wagner, Director

POLICE AND SHERIFF

Sheriff's Dept **775.273.2641**
Fax 775.273.7635
Web ....www.pershingcounty.net
E-mail ....rmachado@pershingcounty.net
   395 9th St, Lovelock, NV 89419
   Richard Machado, Sheriff

Washoe County

GENERAL HEALTH SERVICES

Health Dept **775.328.2400**
Fax 775.328.2279
Web ....www.washoecounty.us
   1001 E 9th St, Reno, NV 89512-2845
   Janet Smith, Admin Secretary

Pyramid Lake Tribal Health Ctr **775.574.1018**
Fax 775.574.1028
   705 Highway 446, Nixon, NV 89424
   Cindy Curly, Health Director

JUSTICE AGENCY

Dept Of Juvenile Svcs Detention
Ctr **775.325.7800**
Fax 775.325.7923
   650 Ferrari Mcleod Blvd, Reno, NV 89512
   Carey Stewart, Director

Youth Parole **775.688.1421**
Fax 775.688.2662
E-mail ....smcbride@dcfs.nv.gov
   560 Mill St, Ste 250, Reno, NV 89502-1089
   Steve McBride, Unit Manager

COURTS

2nd Judicial District Court Family
Div **775.325.6726**
Fax 775.328.3475
   1 S Sierra St, Fl 3, Reno, NV 89501
   Victoria Van Meter, Court Master, Domestic Violence

POLICE AND SHERIFF

Detectives **775.785.8605**
Fax 775.785.8607
   1 East 1st Street, Reno, NV 89501
   Michael Pohlman, Chief Of Police

Police Dept **775.334.2175**
Fax 775.334.2157
Web ....www.reno.com
   455 E 2nd St, Reno, NV 89502-1020
   Steven Pitts, Chief Of Police

Sheriff's Dept **775.328.3002**
Fax 775.328.6308
E-mail ....dabalaam@mail.co.washoe.nv.us
   911 E Parr Blvd, Reno, NV 89512
   Michael Haley, Sheriff

EDUCATION SERVICES

Picollo School **775.851.5650**
Fax 775.851.5652
Web www.washoe.k12.nv.us
E-mail ....mburak@washoe.k12.nv.us
   900 Foothill Rd, Reno, NV 89511-9427
   Matt Burak, Principal

Special Education **775.857.3161**
Fax 775.861.4497
   380 Edison Way, Reno, NV 89502
   Scott Reynolds, Director

White Pine County

SOCIAL SERVICES

Div Of Child And Family Svcs **775.289.1640**
Fax 775.289.1652
Web ....www.dcfs.state.nv.us
E-mail ....lrobb@dcfs.state.nv.us
   740 Park Ave, Ely, NV 89301-2797
   Larry Robb, Social Services Manager

JUSTICE AGENCY

Juvenile Probation Dept **775.289.3766**
Fax 775.289.8557
Web ....www.mwpower.net
E-mail ....lgust@mwpower.net
   995 Campton St, Ely, NV 89301
   Lynette Gust, Probation Officer

SPECIAL SERVICES AGENCIES

ADOPTION AGENCIES

A Celebrity Adoptions **702.459.6696**
Fax 702.346.0330
Web ....www.premieradoption.org
E-mail ....cmurray@premieradoption.org
   590 W Mesquite Ave, Las Vegas, NV 89106-4600
   Catharine Murray, Director

A Childs Dream **702.399.3274**
Fax 360.598.3454
Web ....www.achildsdream.org
E-mail ....mjkadoptic@achildsdream.org
   4550 W Oakey Blvd, # 111B, Las Vegas, NV 89102
   Micheal Kotzin, Director

Adoption Exchange **702.436.6335**
Fax 702.436.6304
Web ....www.adoptex.org
   4310 South Caneron St 12, Las Vegas, NV 89103
   Kathleen Fischer, Director

Children's Adoption Svcs **775.785.8600**
Fax 775.337.4478
   350 S Center St, Ste 280, Reno, NV 89501-2118
   Kevin Schiller, Division Director

Jewish Family Svc Agency/ Adoption
Options **702.732.0304**
Fax 702.794.2033
Web ....www.jfsalv.org
E-mail ....christinap@jfsalv.org
   4794 S Eastern Ave Ste C, Las Vegas, NV 89119-6145
   Christina Primack, Executive Director

Koinonia Foster Homes **775.826.1113**
Fax 775.826.0248
   1355 Airmotive Way, Reno, NV 89502
   Sandra Arguello, Associate Clinical Director

Trinity Children And Family Svcs **702.222.0792**
Fax 702.222.9572
Web ....www.trinityys.org
   2760 Lake Sahara Dr Ste 108, Las Vegas, NV 89117
   Edwina Munday-keller, Director

ADVOCACY RESOURCES

Family Support Council **775.782.8692**
Fax 775.782.1942
Web ....www.family-support.org
E-mail ....amonroe@family-support.org
   1255 Waterloo Ln Ste A, Gardenerville, NV 89410
   Adrianne Monroe, Executive Director

Legal Aid Center of Southern Nevada **702.386.1070**
E-mail ....efinsten@lacsn.org
   800 S 8th St, Las Vegas, NV 89101
   Erin Finsten, Attorney

Legal Aid Ctr of S Nevada **702.386.1070**
E-mail ....xplantalv@gmail.com
   800 S 8th St, Las Vegas, NV 89101
   Barbara Buckley, Executive Director

Nevada Early Intervention Svcs **775.688.1341**
Fax 775.688.2984
Web ....www.nvhd.state.nv.us
   2667 Enterprise Rd, Reno, NV 89512-1666
   Janelle Mulvenon, Clinic Manager

Nevada

BEHAVIORAL HEALTH TREATMENT

Adolescent Treatment Ctr **775.688.1633**
Fax 775.688.1640
480 Galletti Way, Bldg 8N, Sparks, NV 89431
Ryan Gustafson, Director-program Manager 1

Barney Medical Practice **702.242.0485**
6284 S Rainbow Blvd Ste 110, Las Vegas,
NV 89118-3245
Deborah Barney, Psychiatrist

Bridge Counseling Associates **702.474.6450**
Fax 702.474.6463
Web .... www.bcalv.com
E-mail .... jharris@bcalv.com
1701 W Charleston Blvd Ste 400, Las Vegas,
NV 89102-2320
Jackie Harris, Director

Community Counseling Center **702.369.8700**
Web .... www.CCCofSN.org
714 East Sahara Avenue, Suite 101, Las Vegas,
NV 89104
COA accredited organization.

**Community Counseling Center, Carson
City** **775.882.3945**
Web .... www.communitycc.org
E-mail .... meadowmary@aol.com
205 South Pratt Avenue, Carson City, NV 89701
Ms. Mary Bryan, Accreditation Manager
Joint Commission accredited organization.

**CRC ED Treatment, Inc. dba Center for Hope of the
Sierras** **775.828.4949**
Fax 775.322.4556
1453 Pass Drive, Reno, NV 89509
CARF accredited programs available.

Desert Willow Treatment Center **702.486.8900**
E-mail .... santangelo@dcfs.nv.gov
6171 W Charleston Boulevard, Building #17, Las
Vegas, NV 89146
Dr. Linda Santangelo, Accreditation Manager
Joint Commission accredited organization.

Girls And Boys Town Of Nevada **702.642.7070**
Fax 702.649.3906
Web .... www.boystown.org
E-mail .... thomas.waite@boystown.org
821 N Mojave Rd, Las Vegas, NV 89101
Tom Waite, Executive Director

Montevista Hospital **702.364.1111**
E-mail .... linda.hall@psysolutions.com
5900 West Rochelle Avenue, Las Vegas,
NV 89103-3327
Ms. Linda Hall, Accreditation Manager
Joint Commission accredited organization.

New Frontier Treatment Center **775.423.1412**
Web .... www.newfrontiernv.us
E-mail .... ccoad@cccomm.net
1490 Grimes Street, Fallon, NV 89406
Mrs. Lana Henderson, Accreditation Manager
Joint Commission accredited organization.

PSI Solutions Montevista Hospital **702.364.1111**
Fax 702.364.8183
Web .... www.ardenthealth.com
5900 W Rochelle Ave, Las Vegas, NV 89103-3327
William Bauer, Medical Director

Seven Hills Behavioral Institute, Inc. **702.646.5000**
Web .... www.sevenhillssbi.com
E-mail .... vvariale@sevenhillssbi.com
3021 W. Horizon Ridge Parkway, Henderson,
NV 89052
Mr. Vincenzo Variale, Accreditation Manager
Joint Commission accredited organization.

Spring Mountain Treatment Center **702.873.2400**
Fax 702.873.2710
Web .... www.springmountaintreatmentcenter.com
E-mail .... joanne.libertelli@uhsinc.com
7000 Spring Mountain Rd, Las Vegas,
NV 89117-3816
Bonnie Winkleman, Psyd, Clinical Director

Spring Mountain Treatment Center **702.873.2400**
Web .... www.springmountaintreatmentcenter.com
E-mail .... petti.ebrahimi@uhsinc.com
7000 Spring Mountain Road, Las Vegas, NV 89117
Mrs. Petti Ebrahimi, Accreditation Manager
Joint Commission accredited organization.

Willow Springs Center **775.858.4515**
Web .... www.willowspringscenter.com
E-mail .... sadie.tate@psysolutions.com
690 Edison Way, Reno, NV 89502
Ms. Sadie Tate, Accreditation Manager
Joint Commission accredited organization.

Willow Springs Ctr **775.858.3303**
Fax 775.858.4585
690 Edison Way, Reno, NV 89502-4135
James Scratt, Executive Director/CEO

CHILDREN'S HOSPITAL

Banner Churchill Community Hospital **775.423.3151**
801 East Williams Ave, Fallon, NV 89406
Walker Beck, Chief Executive Officer

Carson Tahoe Regional Healthcare **775.882.1361**
1600 Medical Pkwy, Carson City, NV 89703

Renown Regional Medical Center **775.982.4100**
E-mail .... www.renown.org
1155 Mill St, Reno, NV 89502
James Miller, Chief Executive Officer

St Marys Regional Medical Center **775.770.3000**
235 West Sixth St, Reno, NV 89503

St Rose Dominican Hospital Siena **702.616.5000**
3001 St Rose Pkwy, Henderson, NV 89052
Rod Davis, Chief Executive Officer

Sunrise Hospital and Medical Center **702.731.8000**
3186 Maryland Pkwy, Las Vegas, NV 89109
Slycia Young, Chief Executive Officer

University Medical Center **702.383.2000**
1800 West Charleston Blvd, Las Vegas, NV 89102

COUNSELING SERVICES

LDS Family Svcs **702.385.1072**
Fax 702.385.3053
E-mail .... fam-nv@ldsfamilyservices.org
4455 Allen Lane Ste 130, Las Vegas, NV 89031-7010
Bobby Turner, Director

CRISIS & SHELTER CARE

Advocates To End Domestic Violence **775.883.7654**
Fax 775.883.0364
Web .... www.aedv.org
E-mail .... carsonadvocates@aol.com
32 Sierra Circle, Carson City, NV 89703
Lisa Lee, Director

Alternative Living Environment **775.463.4009**
Fax 775.463.4453
400 N Main St Ste A, Yerington, NV 89447-3343
Vicki Straw, Director

Comittee Against Domestic Violence **775.738.6524**
Fax 775.738.2976
E-mail .... harborhs@ctins.com
PO Box 2531, Elko, NV 89803-2531
Yvette Waters, Director

Comittee Against Family Violence **775.623.3974**
Fax 775.623.3974
Web .... www.dop.nv.gov
PO Box 583, Winnemucca, NV 89446-0583
Bonnie Hackel, Director

Committee To Aid Abused Women **775.329.4150**
Fax 775.785.7550
E-mail .... caaw@gbis.com
1735 Vassar St, Reno, NV 89502
Joni Kaiser, Executive Director

Domestic Violence Intervention Program **775.423.1313**
Fax 775.423.9699
125 W Center St, Fallon, NV 89406
Linda East, Director

Family Support Svcs-Domestic Violence **775.782.8692**
Fax 775.782.1942
Web .... www.family-support.org
E-mail .... amonroe@family-support.org
PO Box 810, Minden, NV 89423-0810
Adrian Monroe, Director

Lander Comitte Against Family Svcs **775.635.2117**
Fax 775.635.2146
190 W 3rd St, Battle Mountain, NV 89820
Edward Sampson, Chief

**Mineral Advocates To End Domestic
Violence** **775.945.2472**
Fax 775.945.1434
721 East St, Hawthorne, NV 89415
Cydell G Welt, Director

EDUCATION

China Spring Youth Camp **775.265.5350**
Fax 775.265.7159
Web .... www.co.douglas.nv.us
225 China Spring Drive, Minden, NV 89423
Wendy Garrison, Director

John F. Miller School **702.799.7401**
Fax 702.799.0118
1905 Atlantic St, Las Vegas, NV 89104
Jean Trudell, Principal

Miley Achievement Ctr **702.799.5631**
Fax 702.799.5642
245 N Pecos Rd, Las Vegas, NV 89101
Cheryl Joyce, Principal

Nevada Early Intervention Svcs **775.753.1214**
Fax 775.753.1374
1020 Ruby Vista Dr Unit 102, Elko, NV 89801
Martha Schott-bernius, Supervisor

Nevada Early Intervention Svcs **702.486.7670**
Fax 702.486.7686
Web .... www.nvhd.state.nv.us
E-mail .... eracoma@nvhd.state.nv.us
1161 S Valley View Blvd, Las Vegas, NV 89102-1854
Dr. Estella Racoma, Medical Director

New Horizons Academy **702.876.1181**
Fax 702.365.7807
Web .... www.nhalv.org
E-mail .... mayvillej@nhalv.org
6701 W Charleston Blvd, Las Vegas, NV 89146-1049
Jody Mayville, Executive Director

Variety School **702.799.7938**
Fax 702.799.8506
2601 Sunrise Ave, Las Vegas, NV 89101
Patricia Schepers, Principal

FOSTER CARE AGENCIES

Catholic Charities Southern Nevada **702.385.2662**
Fax 702.384.0677
E-mail .... adoptionservices@catholiccharities.com
1501 Las Vegas Blvd North, Las Vegas, NV 89101

Child Focus Inc 702.436.1624
Fax 702.367.1624
E-mail ....yourfriends@childfocusnv.org
    4310 Cameron St Ste 13, Las Vegas, NV 89103
    Ellen Lloyd, Director

Eagle Quest Of Nevada Inc 702.375.1488
Fax 702.396.4193
Web ....www.eaglequestofnevada.com
E-mail ....rtippetts@eaglequestofnevada.com
    4612 Evan Ridge Ct, Las Vegas, NV 89129-1624
    Ray Tippetts, Director

FAS Support Group of Southern Nevada 702.643.7574
Fax 702.367.2047
E-mail ....coy4125@aol.com
    1643 Hinson St, Las Vegas, NV 89102

Foster Care Adoption Association Nevada 702.657.6470
Fax 702.657.9326
E-mail ....simmslawfirm@aol.com
    1918 Night Shadow Ave, North Las Vegas, NV 89031
    Marsha Simms, Director

KidsPeace Foster Care & Community
Programs 702.576.0533
Fax 702.369.5605
Web ....www.fostercare.com
Web ....www.kidspeace.org
    1785 E Shara Ave, Las Vegas, NV 89104

The Sierra Assoc of Foster Families 775.828.9977
    3376 Lakeside Ct, Reno, NV 89510
    Mary Sondgroth

HOME MEDICAL EQUIPMENT PROVIDERS

Ability Center 702.434.3030
Fax 702.434.3014
E-mail ....kmiller@AbilityCenter.com
    6001 South Decatur Blvd Ste N, Las Vegas, NV 89118

PEDIATRIC HOME CARE

Interim Healthcare 702.369.5533
Fax 702.369.2018
    5506 S Fort Apache Rd Ste 100, Las Vegas, NV 89148
    Jan Durham, Supervisor

Interim Healthcare 775.883.4455
Fax 775.841.1133
    1950 College Pkwy, Ste 101, Carson City, NV 89701

SOCIAL SERVICES

Child Haven 702.455.5444
Fax 702.385.2999
Web ....www.accessclarkcounty.com
E-mail ....tmorton@co.clark.nv.us
    701 N Pecos Rd, Las Vegas, NV 89101-2400
    Thomas D Morton, Director Of Family Services

Family Counseling Service/CCCS of Northern
Nevada 775.329.0623
Fax 775.337.2971
Web ....www.fcsnv.org
    575 East Plumb Lane, Reno, NV 89502
    COA accredited organization.

Nevada Pep, Inc 702.388.8899
Fax 702.388.2966
Web ....www.nvpep.org
E-mail ....pepinfo@nvpep.org
    2101 W Jones, Ste 120, Las Vegas, NV 89146-3106
    Karen Taycher, Executive Director

ReStart 775.324.2622
Fax 775.324.0446
Web ....www.restartreno.org
    335 Record Street, #155, Reno, NV 89512
    COA accredited organization.

Step 2, Inc 775.787.9411
Fax 775.327.6055
Web http://www.step2reno.org
    1435 N. Virginia Street, Reno, NV 89503
    COA accredited organization.

The Children's Cabinet, Inc 800.753.5500
Fax 775.856.6208
Web ....www.childrenscabinet.org
    1090 S Rock Blvd, Reno, NV 89502
    Mike Gomi, Executive Director

WestCare Nevada, Inc 702.385.3642
Fax 702.307.0269
Web ....www.westcare.com
    401 South Martin Luther King Boulevard, Las Vegas,
    NV 89106
    CARF accredited programs available.

SPECIAL NEEDS

Autism Society of Northern Nevada 775.786.9315
    3490 Southampton Dr, Reno, NV 89509

Disability Resources Inc 775.329.1126
E-mail ....danadr@nvbell.net
    50 E Greg St Ste 102, Sparks, NV 89431
    Robin Krueger, Chief Executive Officer

Down Syndrome Organization of Southern
Nevada 702.648.1990
E-mail ....dsosn@dsosn.org
    5300 Vegas Dr, Las Vegas, NV 89108
    Deann Cline, Executive Director

Easter Seals Sierra Nevada 800.228.7102
E-mail ....info@eastersealsnv.org
    6100 Neil Rd Ste 201, Reno, NV 89511

Easter Seals Southern nevada 702.870.7050
E-mail ....bpatchett@eastersealssn.org
    6200 W Oakey Blvd, Las Vegas, NV 89146
    Brian Patchett, Director

Family TIES of Nevada 866.326.8437
E-mail ....info@familytiesnv.org
    3100 Mill St Ste 117, Reno, NV 89502
    Melanie Kauffman, Executive Director

Lindamood-Bell Learning Processes 702.228.6942
Fax 702.254.4196
E-mail ....monica.daggs@lindamood.com
    10655 Park Run Dr, Ste 180, Las Vegas, NV 89144
    Monica Daggs, Director

NAMI Nevada 775.322.1346
    1170 Curti Dr, Reno, NV 89502

National Multiple Sclerosis Society 702.736.1478
Fax 702.736.2487
E-mail ....NVL@nmss.org
    5463 S Durango Dr Ste D, Las Vegas, NV 89113

National Multiple Sclerosis Society 775.329.7180
Fax 775.827.3167
E-mail ....ms@cal.mmss.org
    4600 Kietzke Ln Ste K225, Great Basin Sierra Office,
    Reno, NV 89502
    Linda Lott, Director

Nevada Community Enrichment Program 702.259.1903
Fax 702.259.1907
Web ....www.accessiblespace.org
E-mail ....tbaumann@accessiblespace.org
    6375 West Charleston Boulevard, Suite L200/WCL,
    Las Vegas, NV 89146
    Jodi Sabal, Director
    CARF accredited programs available.

Nevada P.E.P 775.448.9950
Fax 775.448.9603
E-mail ....nvpep@vegas.infi.net
    4600 Kietzke Ln Ste C-128, Reno, NV 89502
    Retta Germoty, Director

Nevada Parent-Teacher Association 800.782.7201
E-mail ....office@nevadapta.org
    6175 Spring Mountain Rd Ste 1B, Las Vegas,
    NV 89146
    Kimberly Pate, President

Nevada Parents Encouraging Parents 702.388.8899
Fax 702.388.2966
E-mail ....pepinfo@nvpep.org
    2101 S Jones Blvd, Ste 120, Las Vegas, NV 89146
    Natalie Filipic, Operations Director

Opportunity Village 702.259.3707
E-mail ....guthrie@opportunityvillage.org
    6300 W Oakey Blvd, Las Vegas, NV 89146
    Ed Guthrie, Executive Director

Speech-Language & Hearing Association 702.452.9029
    PO Box 7313, Reno, NV 89510

Spina Bifida & Hydrocephalus Assn 702.796.7242
    3106 Laentrada St, Henderson, NV 89014

Sunrise Hospital and Medical Center/Rehabilitation
Unit 702.731.8319
Fax 702.892.3623
Web ....www.sunrisehospital.com
    3186 South Maryland Parkway, Rehab Unit - 3rd
    Floor, Las Vegas, NV 89109
    CARF accredited programs available.

VSA Arts of Nevada 775.826.6100
E-mail ....tammy@vsanevada.org
    250 Court St, Reno, NV 89501

SUBSTANCE ABUSE TREATMENT

Community Counseling Ctr 775.882.3945
Fax 775.882.6126
E-mail ....meadowmary@aol.com
    205 S Pratt Ave, Carson City, NV 89701
    Mary Bryan, Executive Director

Lovelock Counseling Ctr/ New Frontier 775.423.1412
Fax 775.423.4054
    1490 Grines St, Fallon, NV 89406
    Lana Handerson, Director

New Hampshire

John Lynch, Governor
State House
107 N Main St Room 208
Concord, NH 03301
603.271.2121
603.271.7680 (Fax)
www.state.nh.us/governor

Pam Sullivan, Juvenile Justice Specialist
1056 N River Rd
Manchester, NH 03104
603.625.5471 x366
603.624.0512 (Fax)
psullivan@dhhs.state.nh.us

David Kemper, SAG Chair
41 Captain Lovewell Lane
Ctr Ossipee, NH 03814
603.569.6330
dkemper@roadrunner.com

CRISIS NUMBERS

Child Abuse Reporting . . .603.271.6556

STATE SERVICES

SOCIAL SERVICES

Child Care Licensing New Hampshire 603.271.4264
Fax...603.271.4782
129 Pleasant St, Concord, NH 03301
Denise Corvino, Director

Interstate Compact On Juveniles 603.625.5471
Fax...603.625.1110
Web..www.dhhs.state.nh.us
1056 River Rd, Manchester, NH 03104-1958
Jay Apicelli, Interim Director

New Hampshire Dept of Health & Human Svcs Div of Human Svcs 603.271.4286
Fax...603.271.4810
Web..www.dhhs.state.nh.us
129 Pleasant St, Concord, NH 03301
Jose Montero, Director Of Public Health

New Hampshire Emergency Management Agency 603.271.2231
Fax...603.223.3609
Web....................www.nh.gov/safety/divisions/bem
33 Hazen Dr, Concord, NH 03305
Christopher Pope, Director

GENERAL HEALTH SERVICES

Child w Spec Health Care Needs NH 603.271.4488
Fax...603.271.4902
E-mail.............................ecollins@dhhs.state.nh.us
129 Pleasant St- Thayer Bldg, Concord, NH 03301
Elizabeth Collins, Director

Maternal and Child Health Section NH 603.271.4451
Fax...603.271.4519
E-mail..................................ptilley@dhhs.state.nh.us
29 Hazen Dr, Concord, NH 03301
Patricia Tilley, Administrator

MENTAL HEALTH SERVICES

Bureau of Developmental Svcs 603.271.5034
Fax...603.271.5166
Web..www.dhhs.state.nh.us
105 Pleasant St, Concord, NH 03301
Matthew Ertas, Director

New Hampshire Board of Mental Health Practice 603.271.6762
Fax...603.271.3950
Web..www.nh.gov/mhpb
E-mail..................................bdmhp@dhhs.state.nh.us
117 pleasant St, Concord, NH 03301-2621
David Draiteman, Chairman

NH Dept. of Alcohol Tobacco and Other Drugs Clearinghouse and Lending Library 603.271.2677
Fax...603.271.6105
105 Pleasant St, Concord, NH 03301
Nancy Jackson-Reno, Helath Promotion Advisor

Vocational Rehabilitation NH 603.271.3471
Fax...603.271.7095
E-mail.............................cynthia.wisell@ed.state.nh.us
21 S Fruit St Ste 20, Concord, NH 03301
Cyndy Wisell, Director

JUSTICE AGENCY

Attorney General's Ofc 603.271.3658
Fax...603.271.2110
Web..www.state.nh.us
E-mail..................................valerie.hall@doj.nh.gov
33 Capitol St, Concord, NH 03301-6397
Valerie Hall, Victim Assistance Compensation

CASA of NH, Inc. 603.626.4600
Fax...603.623.6362
Web..www.casanh.org
E-mail..................................speakup@casanh.org
138 Coolidge Ave, Manchester, NH 03102
Marcia Sink, Executive Director

Correctional Edu Division NH 603.271.1855
Fax...603.271.0401
E-mail.............................daniel.t.tanquay@nhdoc.state.nh.us
PO Box 14, Concord, NH 03302
Daniel Tanquay, Director

Dept of Corrections 603.271.5600
Fax...603.271.5643
E-mail..................................info@nhdoc.state.nh.us
105 Pleasant St, Concord, NH 03301-3852
William L. Wrenn, Commissioner

Governor's Commission on Disability 603.271.2773
Fax...603.271.2837
Web..www.nh.gov/disability
E-mail..................................disability@nh.gov
57 Regional Dr Ste 3, Concord, NH 03301
John Richard, Director

New Hampshire Dept of Safety 603.271.2559
Fax...603.271.3903
Web..www.nh.gov/safety/
E-mail..................................john@nh.gov
33 Hazen Dr, Concord, NH 03305-0001
John Barthelmas, Commissioner

COURTS

Administrative Ofc Of The Courts 603.271.2521
Fax...603.513.5454
E-mail..................................aoc@courts.state.nh.us
2 Charles Doe Dr, Concord, NH 03301-6147
D. Joan Bishop, Director Of Education

POLICE AND SHERIFF

New Hampshire Assoc of Chiefs of Police 603.744.5423
Fax...603.744.9238
12 Pinnacle Hill Rd, New Hampton, NH 03256
Merritt Salmon, Chief Of Police

EDUCATION SERVICES

Bureau of Special Education NH 603.271.3741
Fax...603.271.1099
E-mail..................................braymond@ed.state.nh.us
101 Pleasant St, Concord, NH 03301
Bara Raymond, Director

Educ for Homeless Children and Youth NH 603.271.3840
Fax...603.271.2760
E-mail..................................LElliott@ed.state.nh.us
101 Pleasant St, Concord, NH 03301
L. Elliott, Director

New Hampshire Dept of Education 603.271.3494
Fax...603.271.1953
Web..www.ed.state.nh.us
E-mail..................................evandyke@ed.state.nh.us
101 Pleasant St, Concord, NH 03301-3852
Elaine Vandyke, Nutrition Director

New Hampshire Dept of Education 603.271.3495
Fax...603.271.1953
E-mail..................................pbutler@ed.state.nh.us
101 Pleasant St, Hugh J Gallen State Off Park,
Concord, NH 03301
Pat Butler, Administrative Assistant

New Hampshire Svcs for the Blind & Visually Impaired 603.271.3537
Fax...603.271.3816
Web..www.ed.state.nh.us
21 S Fruit St Ste 20, Concord, NH 43301
William Finn, Administrator

Parent Information Center NH 603.224.7005
Fax...603.224.4365
E-mail..................................mlewis@picnh.org
151A Manchester St, Concord, NH 03301
Kevin Lew-Hanson, Director

New Hampshire

LABOR & WORKFORCE EDUCATION

Workforce Opportunity Council, Inc. **603.229.3303**
Fax 603.228.8557

Web ....www.nhworks.org
E-mail ....mpower@nhworkforce.org
  64 Old Suncook Rd, Concord, NH 03301-7317
Michael Power, President

COUNTY SERVICES

Belknap County

SOCIAL SERVICES

Dept Of Health And Human Svcs - Laconia
Ofc **603.524.4485**
Fax 603.528.4105
Web ....www.dhhs.state.nh.us
  65 Beacon St W, Laconia, NH 03246-3428
Karen Salome, Public Health Nurse

MENTAL HEALTH SERVICES

Genesis Behavioral Health **603.524.1100**
Fax 603.528.0760
Web ....www.genesisbh.org
  111 Church St, Laconia, NH 03246-3417
Maggie Pritchard, Executive Director

COURTS

Laconia District Court **603.524.4128**
Fax 603.524.5535
  26 Academy St, Laconia, NH 03246
Honorable Michelle Brown, Clerk Of Court

Teen Court **603.524.9457**
Fax 603.524.6618
Web ....www.co.monroe.in.us
E-mail ....eouellette@co.monroe.in.us
  306 Union Ave, Laconia, NH 03246-2812
Elisha Ouellette, Director

POLICE AND SHERIFF

Sheriff's Ofc **603.527.5454**
Fax 603.527.5469
Web ....www.belknapcounty.org
E-mail ....cwiggin@belknapcounty.org
  42 County Dr, Laconia, NH 03246-2900
Craig Wiggin, Sheriff

Carroll County

GENERAL HEALTH SERVICES

Ossipee Family Planning Prenatal
Program **603.539.7552**
Fax 603.539.6186
Web ....www.bm-cap.org
  127 Route 28, Ossipee, NH 03864-7300
Rachael Deveau, HIV Coordinator

White Mountain Community Health
Ctr **603.447.8900**
Fax 603.447.4846
Web ....www.whitemountainhealth.org
E-mail ....whitemountainhealth.org
  298 White Mountain Hwy, Conway, NH 03818
Margie Riforgiaglo, Rn, Nurse

MENTAL HEALTH SERVICES

Mental Health Svcs **603.569.1884**
Fax 603.569.1882
Web ....www.northerhs.org
E-mail ....Bastles@northernhs.org
  70 Bay St, Wolfeboro, NH 03894-4320
B Astles, Area Director

POLICE AND SHERIFF

Bartlett Police Dept **603.356.5868**
Fax 603.356.7286
Web ....www.bartlettnh.org
  56 Town Hall Road, Intervale, NH 03845
Tim Connifey, Police Chief

Sheriff's Ofc **603.539.2284**
Fax 603.539.7506
E-mail ....christopher.conley@carrollcountynh.net
  95 Water Village Rd, Ossipee, NH 03864
Christopher Conley, Sheriff

EDUCATION SERVICES

Conway Head Start **603.447.5161**
  73 W Main St, Conway, NH 03818
Joanne L Pandora, Director

Cheshire County

GENERAL HEALTH SERVICES

Keene Health And Inspections
Dept **603.352.5440**
Fax 866.690.8364
Web ....www.ci.keene.nh.us
  3 Washington St, Keene, NH 03431
Medard Kopczynski, Assistant City Manager/health Director

MENTAL HEALTH SERVICES

Monadnock Family Svcs **603.357.4400**
Fax 603.357.6859
  64 Main St Ste 301, Keene, NH 03431
Robit Roone, Executive Director

COURTS

Jaffrey/Petersborough District
Court **603.532.8698**
Fax 603.532.6807
E-mail ....JulianneD.Lodef
  84 Peterborough St, Jaffrey, NH 03452
Julianne D. Lodef, Clerk Of Court

Keene District Court **603.352.2559**
Fax 603.271.3972
E-mail ....hlane@courts.state.nh.us
  3 Washington St, Keene, NH 03431-3137
Honorable Howard B. Lane, Director

POLICE AND SHERIFF

Dublin Police Dept **603.563.8411**
Fax 603.563.5041
E-mail ....james.letourneau@wku.edu
  1122 Main St, Dublin, NH 03444
James Letourneau, Police Chief

Sheriff's Ofc **603.352.4238**
Fax 603.355.3020
Web ....www.co.cheshire.nh.us
  12 Court St, Keene, NH 03431-3402
Richard A. Foote, Sheriff

Coos County

GENERAL HEALTH SERVICES

Berlin Health Dept **603.752.1272**
Fax 603.752.5238
  168 Main St, City Hall, Berlin, NH 03570
Yvette Leighton, Rn, Nursing Supervisor

Family Health **603.752.2040**
Fax 603.752.7797
Web ....www.coosfamilyhealth.org
E-mail ....awoods@ccfhs.org
  133 Pleasant St, Berlin, NH 03570-2006
Adelle Woods, Director

MENTAL HEALTH SERVICES

Northern Human Services Mental Health
Cntr **603.752.7404**
Fax 603.752.5194
Web ....www.northernhs.org
E-mail ....ccotton@northernhs.org
  3 12th St Ste 2, Berlin, NH 03570-3860
Charles Cotton, Director

Northern Human Svcs **603.237.4955**
Fax 603.237.4882
Web ....www.northernhs.org
E-mail ....ccotton@northernhs.org
  55 Colby St, Colebrook, NH 03576-3047
Charles Cotton, Area Director

COURTS

Colebrook District Court **603.237.4229**
  17 Bridge St, Colebrook, NH 03576-3032
Honorable Paul D. Desjardins, Judge

Lancaster Family Div **603.788.4485**
  55 School St Ste 201, Lancaster, NH 03584
Parry Peterson, Court Clerk

POLICE AND SHERIFF

Sheriff's Ofc **603.788.5598**
Fax 603.788.2437
  55 School St Ste 202, Lancaster, NH 03584
Gerald P. Maicou, Sheriff

EDUCATION SERVICES

Berlin Head Start **603.752.5464**
Fax 603.752.4713
  610 Sullivan St, Berlin, NH 03570-3226
Shirley Frenette, Director

Colebrook Area Head Start **603.237.8190**
  53 Park St, Colebrook, NH 03576
Lee Teacher, Director

Grafton County

GENERAL HEALTH SERVICES

Ammonoosuc Family Health Svcs **603.444.2464**
Fax 603.444.5209
  25 Mount Eustis Rd, Littleton, NH 03561
Ed Shanahala, Director

Lebanon Health Inspector **603.448.1524**
Fax 603.448.0684
Web ....www.lebcity.com
E-mail ....calvin.hunnewell@lebcity.com
  51 N Park St, Lebanon, NH 03766-1317
Calvin Hunnewell, Health Officer

Mt. Mooselaukee Health Ctr **603.764.5704**
Fax 603.764.5705
Web ....www.achs-inc.org
E-mail ....teresa.brooks@achs-inc.org
  333 NH Route 25, Warren, NH 03279-4431
Teresa Brooks, Manager

Plymouth Family Planning **603.536.3584**
Fax 603.536.1365
  258 Highland St Ste 18A, Plymouth, NH 03264-3612
Susan Wnuk, Director

COURTS

Family Div At Plymouth 603.536.7609
Fax 603.536.3241
Web ....www.courts.state.nh.us
E-mail ....scarbon@courts.state.nh.us
26 Green St, Plymouth, NH 03264-1606
Honorable Susan B. Carbon, Director

Haverhill District Court 603.787.6626
E-mail ....tmckenna@courts.state.nh.us
3785 Dartmouth College Hwy Unit 10, North
Haverhill, NH 03774-4936
Honorable Timothy J. Mckenna, District Court

POLICE AND SHERIFF

Sheriff's Dept 603.787.2111
Fax 603.787.2005
Web ....www.graftoncountysheriff.net
E-mail ....dispatch@graftoncountysheriff.net
3785 Dartmouth College Hwy Unit 6, North
Haverhill, NH 03774-4936
Douglas Butile, Sheriff

Hillsborough County

SOCIAL SERVICES

Div Of Human Svcs Manchester District
Ofc 603.668.2330
Fax 603.668.5442
Web ....www.dhhs.state.nh.us
195 McGregor St Ste 110, Manchester,
NH 03102-3749
Kathy Finnigan, Supervisor

GENERAL HEALTH SERVICES

Child Health Svcs 603.668.6629
Fax 603.622.7680
Web ....www.childhealthservices.org
1245 Elm St, Manchester, NH 03101-1308
Lisa Dibrigida, Director

Manchester Health Dept 603.624.6466
Fax 603.628.6004
Web ....www.manchesternh.gov/health
1528 Elm St Ste 1, Manchester, NH 03101-1356
Tim Soucy, Mph, Public Health Director

Nashua Community Health Dept 603.589.4500
Fax 603.594.3452
Web ....www.nashuanh.gov
E-mail ....bagleyb@nashuanh.gov
18 Mulberry St, Nashua, NH 03060
Bobbie Bagley, Clinical Manager

MENTAL HEALTH SERVICES

Monadnock Family Svcs 603.924.7236
Fax 603.924.4245
Web ....www.mfs.org
9 Vose Farm Rd, Peterborough, NH 03458
Mary Seebart, Director

COURTS

Manchester District Court 603.624.6510
Web ....www.courts.state.nh.us
35 Amherst St, Manchester, NH 03101
Honorable Norman E. Champagne, Judge

Merrimack District Court 603.424.9916
4 Baboosic Lake Rd, Merrimack, NH 03054
Honorable Gregory E. Michael, Alternate Judge

Milford District Court 603.673.2900
Web ....www.probatecourt.org
E-mail ....mcrocker@courts.state.nh.us
180 Elm St, Milford, NH 03055
Honorable Martha Crocker, Judge

POLICE AND SHERIFF

Manchester Police Dept 603.668.8711
Fax 603.628.6137
351 Chestnut St, Manchester, NH 03101
David J Mara, Police Chief

Nashua Police Dept 603.594.3500
Fax 603.594.3615
E-mail ....connellyd@nashuapd.com
0 Panther Drive, Nashua, NH 03061
Don Connelly, Chief

EDUCATION SERVICES

Special Education 603.424.6211
Fax 603.424.6240
Web www.merrimack.k12.nh.us
2 Brentwood Dr, Merrimack, NH 03054-3654
David St. Jean, Director

Special Education 603.886.8500
Fax 603.886.0163
Web ....www.rsec.org
E-mail ....jkoch@rsec.org
94 State Route 101A, Amherst, NH 03031-2211
Judy Koch, Executive Director

Special Education 603.624.6300
Fax 603.624.6337
Web ....www.mansd.org
E-mail ....kburkush@mansd.org
195 McGregor St, Manchester, NH 03102
Karen Burkush, Assistant Superintendent Of Special Education

Special Education 603.673.6709
Fax 603.673.9883
Web www.sau40.com
E-mail ....jweick@sau40.com
5 Elm St, Milford, NH 03055-4810
Johanna Weick, Director

Merrimack County

SOCIAL SERVICES

Children, Youth And Families Ofc 603.271.6556
Fax 603.271.6565
Web ....www.dhhs.state.nh.us
E-mail ....dcyf.centralintake@dhhs.state.nh.us
27 Hazen Dr, Concord, NH 03301-7315
Elizabeth Carr, Supervisor

Div Of Health & Human Svcs Concord District
Ofc 603.271.6200
Fax 603.271.6451
Web ....www.dhhs.state.nh.us
E-mail ....rgay@dhhs.state.nh.us
40 Terrill Park Dr Unit 1, Concord, NH 03301-7325
Richard Gay, Program Manager

GENERAL HEALTH SERVICES

Concord Health Dept 603.225.8580
Fax 603.225.8586
Web ....www.onconcord.com
E-mail ....eblack@concordnh.gov
37 Green St, Concord, NH 03301-4253
Eugine Black, Health Officer

New Hampshire State Hospital 603.271.5200
Fax 603.271.5395
36 Clinton St, Concord, NH 03301
Robert McLeod, Chief Executive Officer

MENTAL HEALTH SERVICES

Community Svcs Council Of New
Hampshire 603.225.9694
Fax 603.225.4158
Web ....www.cscnh.org
E-mail ....joel.green@cscnh.org
79 Sheep Davis Rd, Concord, NH 03302
Joel Green, Chief Executive Officer

JUSTICE AGENCY

Judicial Council 603.271.3592
Fax 603.271.1112
25 Capitol St Rm 424, Concord, NH 03301
Nina C. Gardner, Director

COURTS

Franklin District Court 603.934.3290
Web ....www.court.state.nh.us
7 Hancock Ter, Franklin, NH 03235
Honorable Edward M. Gordon, Judge

POLICE AND SHERIFF

Sheriff's Dept 603.796.6600
Fax 603.225.5630
Web ....www.merrimackcosheriff.org
E-mail ....cjordan@merrimackcosheriff.org
163 N Main St Ste 1, Concord, NH 03301-5001
Scott Hillard, Sheriff

EDUCATION SERVICES

Office of Student Services 603.485.5104
Fax 603.485.2840
5 Memorial Dr, Hooksett, NH 03106

Special Education 603.435.6701
Fax 603.435.7087
Web www.pittsfield.k12.nh.us
23 Oneida St, Pittsfield, NH 03263-3403
Tobi Chassie, Director Of Student Services

Special Education 603.934.0207
Fax 603.934.3462
Web www.franklin.k12.nh.us
E-mail ....aholton@franklin.k12.nh.us
119 Central St, Franklin, NH 03235-1131
Anne Holton, Director

Special Education 603.435.8432
Fax 603.435.7358
Web www.pittsfield.k12.nh.us
E-mail ....tchassie@pittsfield.k12.nh.us
34 Bow St, Pittsfield, NH 03263-3421
Toby Chassie, Coordinator

Special Education 603.526.2051
Fax 603.526.2145
Web ....www.atkearsarge.org
E-mail ....lelliott@kearsarge.org
114 Cougar Court, New London, NH 03257-7804
Larry Elliott, Director

Special Education Unit 24 ....603.428.3269
Fax 603.428.3850
258.Western Ave, Henniker, NH 03242
Diane Lurvey, Director

Rockingham County

JUSTICE AGENCY

Derry Juvenile Svcs 603.432.7462
Fax 603.432.0239
1 Commons Dr, # B, Londonderry, NH 03053
Margaret Lafleur, Juvenile Probation And Parole Supervisor

COURTS

Family Division 603.421.0077
10 Courthouse Ln, Derry, NH 03038
Robin Pinelle, Clerk

Family Divison At Brentwood 603.642.6314
Web ....www.courts.state.nh.us
10 Route 25, Brentwood, NH 03833
Honorable Peter G Hood, Judge

Hampton District Court 603.474.2637
Fax 603.474.2924
130 Ledge Rd, Seabrook, NH 03874
Mark Weaver, Judge

Plaistow District Court 603.382.4651
Fax 603.382.4952
   14 Elm St, Plaistow, NH 03865
Theresa McCafferty, Clerk Of Court

Portsmouth District Court 603.431.2192
Fax 603.431.6402
E-mail ....sdevries@courts.state.nh.us
   111 Parrott Ave, Portsmouth, NH 03801-4490
Sharon N. Devries, Special Justice

Salem District Court 603.893.4483
Fax 603.894.7066
   35 Geremonty Dr, Salem, NH 03079
Honorable John A. Korbey, Judge

POLICE AND SHERIFF

Chester Police Dept 603.887.2080
Fax 603.887.2090
Web ....www.gsinet.net
E-mail ....chstrpol@gsinet.net
   84 Chester St, Chester, NH 03036-4305
William Burke, Police Chief

Sheriff's Ofc 603.679.2225
Fax 603.679.1877
   101 North Rd, Exeter, NH 03833
Michael Downing, Sherrif

EDUCATION SERVICES

Special Education 603.382.6119
Fax 603.382.3334
E-mail ....edwina.lovett@timberlane.net
   30 Greenough Rd, Plaistow, NH 03865
Edwina Lovett, Director Of Pupil Personal Services

Special Education 603.775.8645
Fax 603.775.8643
Web www.sau16.org
E-mail ....tandre@sau16.org
   30 Linden St, Exeter, NH 03833-2622
Tara Andre, Director

Special Education 603.926.3658
Fax 603.929.2189
Web ....www.winnacunnet.org
E-mail ....levans@winnacunnet.org
   1 Alumni Dr, Hampton, NH 03842-2282
Linda Evans, Director

Special Education 603.893.7040
Fax 603.893.7080
Web www.sau57.org
   38 Geremonty Dr, Salem, NH 03079-3313
Patricia Stone, Special Education Coordinator

Special Education 603.329.6326
Fax 603.329.6329
Web www.hampstead.k12.nh.us
E-mail ....gallagherk@hampstead.k12.nh.us
   21 Emerson Ave, Hampstead, NH 03841-2265
Karen Gallagher, Director Of Special Education

Strafford County

SOCIAL SERVICES

**Dept Of Health & Human Svcs Rochester District
Ofc** 603.332.9120
Fax 603.332.5204
Web ....www.dhhs.state.nh.us
E-mail ....meldridg@dhhs.state.nh.us
   150 Wakefield St Ste 22, Rochester, NH 03867
Mary Eldridge, Manager Of Administration

GENERAL HEALTH SERVICES

Rochester Health Dept 603.332.3976
Fax 603.509.1912
E-mail ....thomas.abbott@rochesternh.net
   31 Wakefield St, Rochester, NH 03867
Thomas Abbott, Health Officer

Somersworth Health Dept 603.692.9520
Fax 603.692.9575
Web ....www.somersworth.com
E-mail ....tmetizer@somersworth.com
   1 Government Way, Somersworth, NH 03878-3248
Tim Metizer, Senior Officer

JUSTICE AGENCY

**Juvenile Svcs Dover Juvenile
Probation** 603.742.9153
Fax 603.742.5558
   61 Locust St, # 129, Dover, NH 03820
Richard Long, Juvenile Probation Parole Officer

COURTS

Dover District Court 603.742.7202
Fax 603.742.5956
Web ....www.courts.state.nh.us
   25 Saint Thomas St, Dover, NH 03820
Justice Stephen Morrison, Judge

Rochester District Court 603.332.3516
Fax 603.332.3150
Web ....www.courts.state.nh.us
   76 N Main St, Rochester, NH 03867-1932
Honorable Daniel M. Cappiello, Judge

POLICE AND SHERIFF

Sheriff's Ofc 603.742.4960
Fax 603.743.4921
E-mail ....sheriff.estes@casscountytx.org
   259 County Farm Rd, Dover, NH 03820
Wayne M. Estes, Sheriff

EDUCATION SERVICES

Special Education 603.332.3678
Fax 603.335.7367
Web ....www.rochesterschools.com
E-mail ....pray.s@rochesterschools.com
   150 Wakefield St Ste 8, Rochester, NH 03867
Sharon Pray, Coordinator

Special Education 603.868.5100
Fax 603.868.6668
Web ....www.orcsd.org
E-mail ....mnadeau@orcsd.org
   36 Coe Dr, Durham, NH 03824-2206
Meredith Nadeau, Special Education Director

Special Education 603.755.2627
Fax 603.755.9334
Web www.sau61.org
   356 Main St, Farmington, NH 03835-3769
Walter Anacki, Director Of Pupil Personnel Services

Sullivan County

SOCIAL SERVICES

**Claremont District Ofc Children And Youth
Svcs** 603.542.9544
Fax 603.542.1707
   17 Water St Ste 301, Claremont, NH 03743
Mark Rissola, Family Services Supervisor

COURTS

Claremont District Court 603.542.6064
   1 Police Ct Ste 2, Claremont, NH 03743-3629
Honorable John J. Yazinski, Presiding Judge

Newport District Court 603.863.1832
Web ....www.courts.state.nh.us
E-mail ....etenney@courts.state.nh.us
   55 Main St Ste 2, Newport, NH 03773-1519
Honorable Edward B. Tenney Ii, District

POLICE AND SHERIFF

Newport Police Dept 603.863.3232
Fax 603.863.8152
Web ....www.newportpolicenh.com
   59 Main St, Newport, NH 03773

Sheriff's Dept 603.863.4200
Fax 603.863.0012
Web ....www.nhvt.net
E-mail ....sheriff@nhvt.net
   14 Main St, Newport, NH 03773
Michael L. Prozzo Jr., Sheriff

SPECIAL SERVICES AGENCIES

ADOPTION AGENCIES

Bethany Christian Svcs 603.483.2886
Fax 603.483.0161
Web ....www.bethany.org/newengland
E-mail ....bcscandia@bethany.org
   183 High Street, Candia, NH 03034
Jan Lessard, Director

Casey Family Svcs 603.224.8909
Fax 603.224.2584
Web ....www.caseyfamilyservices.org
E-mail ....erennells@caseyfamilyservices.org
   105 Loudon Rd Bldg 2, Concord, NH 03301-5613
Ed Rennells, Director

Edward T Clancy Law Ofc 603.742.4600
Fax 603.742.4930
Web ....www.clancylaw.net
   4 4th St Ste 2, Dover, NH 03820-2987
Edward Clancy, Director

ADVOCACY RESOURCES

Claremont Child And Family Ctr 603.542.5449
Fax 603.542.5455
Web ....www.wcbh.org
   18 Bailey Ave, Claremont, NH 03743
Laurie White, Director

BEHAVIORAL HEALTH TREATMENT

Anna Philbrook Ctr 603.271.5900
Fax 603.271.5962
E-mail ....cbatchelder@dhhs.state.nh.us
   36 Clinton St, Concord, NH 03301-2359
Chester Batchelder, Superintendent

Auburn Village School 603.483.2769
Fax 603.483.5144
E-mail ....rpedro@sau15.net
   11 Eaton Hill Rd, Auburn, NH 03032
Ron Pedro, Principal

Bricketts Mill Counseling 603.329.4379
   10 Bricketts Mill Rd Ste E2, Hampstead,
   NH 03841-2396
Stephanie Young, Director

New Hampshire

Casey Medical Practice 603.749.9900
Fax...603.749.9901
   383 Central Ave Ste 318, Dover, NH 03820-6420
   Jennifer Casey, Psychiatrist

Colby Sawyer College 603.648.6544
Web..............................www.colby-sawyer.edu
E-mail ....lbarnes@colby-sawyer.edu
   541 MAIN ST, New London, NH 03257-7818
   Linda Barnes, Director

Community Council of Nashua, NH 603.889.6147
Web..www.gnmhc.org
E-mail ....collinsm@ccofnashua.org
   7 Prospect Street, Nashua, NH 03060
   Ms. Monica Collins, Accreditation Manager
   Joint Commission accredited organization.

Counseling Ctr Of Newport 603.863.1951
Fax...603.863.8043
Web..www.wcbh.org
   167 Summer St Ste 4, Newport, NH 03773
   Laurie White, Director

Coursin Medical Practice 603.225.5299
   6 Hills Ave, Concord, NH 03301-4803
   David Coursin, Psychiatrist

Ctr For Behavioral Change 603.293.0395
   PO Box 7198, Laconia, NH 03247-7198
   Harriet Redmond, MD, Psychiatrist

Dartmouth Hitchcock 603.695.2900
Fax...603.695.2919
Web.......................www.dartmouth-hitchcock.org
E-mail ....amy.huelle@hitchcock.org
   100 Hitchcock Way, Manchester, NH 03104-4125
   Amy Huelle, Nutritionist

Doctors Professionals Svc 603.526.9655
   PO Box 1995, New London, NH 03257-1995
   Charles Batt, Psychiatrist

Easter Seals 603.621.3599
Web...www.easterseals.com
E-mail ....jtuddle@eastersealsnh.org
   1 Mammoth Rd, Manchester, NH 03109-4301
   John Tuddle, Director

Edward Jacobs Phd And Associates 603.437.2069
Fax...603.437.5588
E-mail ....ehjpsych@aol.com
   12 Parmenter Rd Unit C3, Londonderry, NH 03053-3279
   Edward Jacobs, Owner/Director

Evans Medical Practice 603.528.2573
Fax...603.528.2558
   PO Box 7235, Laconia, NH 03247-7235
   Michael Evans, Psychiatrist

Family Strength 603.228.3266
Fax...603.228.2990
Web...www.familystrength.org
E-mail ....ccrane@familystrength.org
   85 N State St, Concord, NH 03301
   Carolyn Crane, Administrative Manager

Fellowship Housing Opportunities 603.225.0977
Web...www.fellowshiphousing.org
E-mail ....pcannon@fellowshiphousing.org
   36 Pleasant St, Concord, NH 03301-4055
   Paige Cannon, Executive Director

Hunter School 603.786.3666
Fax...603.786.2221
Web...www.hunterschool.org
E-mail ....info@hunterschool.org
   768 Doetown Road, Rumney, NH 03266
   James Kemmerer, Executive Director

Lakeview NeuroRehabilitation Center 603.539.7451
Web...www.lakeviewsystem.com
E-mail ....mradloff@lakeview.ws
   244 Highwatch Road, Effingham, NH 03882
   Ms. Michelle Radloff, Accreditation Manager
   Joint Commission accredited organization.

Pavilion at Portsmouth Regional Hospital 603.436.0600
Fax...603.433.6497
Web...www.portsmouthhospital.com
   333 Borthwick Ave Ste 100, Portsmouth, NH 03801-4198
   Anne Jamieson, Chief Executive Officer

Portsmouth Psychiatric Assosiates 603.431.3220
Fax...603.436.4713
   404 The Hl, Portsmouth, NH 03801-7722
   Paul Fallon, MD, Psychiatrist

River Bend Community Mental Health 603.934.3400
Fax...603.934.3459
Web...www.riverbendcmhc.org
E-mail ....ggoodman@riverbendcmhc.org
   53 Kendall St, Franklin, NH 03235
   Glenna Goodman, BA, Director

Shortridge Academy 603.755.3096
Fax...603.755.9096
Web...www.shortridgeacademy.com
   619 Governors Rd, Milton, NH 03851-4757
   Adam Rainer, Founder

CHILDREN'S HOSPITAL

Androscoggin Valley Hospital 603.752.2200
   59 Page Hill Rd, Berlin, NH 03570
   Russell Keene, Chief Executive Officer

Catholic Medical Center 603.668.3545
   100 McGregor St, Manchester, NH 03102
   Alyson Picman Giles, President

Cheshire Medical Center 603.354.5400
   580 Court St, Keene, NH 03431
   Arthur Nichols, Administrator

Concord Hospital 603.225.2711
   250 Pleasant St, Concord, NH 03301
   Michael Greene, President

Cottage Hospital 603.747.9000
   Swiftwater Rd, Woodsville, NH 03785
   Maria Ryan, Chief Executive Officer

Dartmouth Hitchcock Medical Center 603.650.5000
E-mail ....dartmouthhitchcockmedicalcenter@hitchcock.org
   One Medical Center Dr, Lebanon, NH 03756
   Nancy Formella, Director

Elliot Hospital 603.669.5300
   One Elliot Way, Manchester, NH 03103
   Doug Dean, President

Exeter Hospital 603.778.7311
   5 Alumni Dr, Exeter, NH 03833
   Kevin Callahan, Chief Executive Officer

Frisbie Memorial Hospital 603.332.5211
   11 Whitehall Rd, Rochester, NH 03867

Lakes Region General Hospital 603.524.3211
   80 Highland St, LACONIA, NH 03246
   Thomas Clairmont, Chief Executive Officer

Littleton Regional Hospital 603.444.9000
   600 Saint Johnsbury Rd, Littleton, NH 03561
   Warren West, Director

Monadnock Community Hospital 603.924.7191
   452 Old Street Rd, Peterborough, NH 03458
   Peter Gofline, Chief Executive Officer

New London Hospital 603.526.2911
   273 County Rd, New London, NH 03257
   Trish Sweezey, Nursing Manager

Parkland Medical Center 603.432.1500
   One Parkland Dr, Derry, NH 03038
   Tina L, Chief Executive Officer

Portsmouth Regional Hospital 603.436.5110
   333 Borthwick Ave, Portsmouth, NH 03801
   Anne Jamieson, Chief Executive Officer

Southern New Hampshire Medical Center 603.577.2000
   8 Prospect St, Nashua, NH 03060
   Thomas Wilhelmsen, Chief Executive Officer

St Joseph Hospital 603.882.3000
E-mail ....dross@sjhnh.org
   172 Kinsley St, Nashua, NH 03061
   David Ross, Executive Director

Upper Connecticut Valley Hospital 603.237.4971
   181 Corliss Lane, Colebrook, NH 03576

Weeks Medical Center 603.788.4911
   173 Middle St, Lancaster, NH 03584
   Scott Howe, Chief Executive Officer

Wentworth Douglass Hospital 603.742.5252
   789 Central Ave, Dover, NH 03820
   Gregory Walker, Administrator

COUNSELING SERVICES

New Hampshire

FOSTER CARE AGENCIES

Greater Nashua Foster Adoptive Parent As 603.882.1815
Fax..603.595.9731
E-mail...dnbnoel@aol.com
8 Iroquois Rd, Nashua, NH 03060

LDS Family Services 603.889.0148
Fax..603.889.4358
E-mail..........................fam-nh@ldsfamilyservices.org
547 Amherst St Ste 404, Nashua, NH 03063
Edward Van Gass, Clinical Supervisor

New Hampshire Foster & Adoptive Parent 877.964.3272
PO Box 2820, Concord, NH 03302
Paul Desmarais

HOME MEDICAL EQUIPMENT PROVIDERS

Direct Home Medical 888.505.0212
E-mail...........................adam@directhomemedical.com
142 Lowell Rd Ste 17-392, Hudson, NH 03051

PEDIATRIC HOME CARE

Interim Healthcare...........................603.298.7411
Fax..603.298.7413
E-mail.........................rtrombley@interimhealthcare.com
One Glen Rd Box 34, West Lebanon, NH 03784
Rachel Trombley, Director

Interim Healthcare...........................603.668.6956
Fax..630.668.6959
608 Chestnut St, Manchester, NH 03105
Richard Peterson, Chief Executive Officer

Interim Healthcare...........................603.436.4155
Fax..603.431.0571
875 Greenland Rd, B 7 - Orchard Park, Portsmouth,
NH 03801
Rcik Peterson, President/CEO

Interim Healthcare...........................603.524.7212
Fax..603.524.7219
277 Union Ave, Gilford, NH 03246
Rick Peterson, Chief Executive Officer

Interim Healthcare...........................603.352.7290
Fax..603.352.6926
403 Winchester St, Keene, NH 03431
Rick Peterson, Chief Executive Officer

Interim Healthcare...........................603.880.4412
Fax..603.595.4665
E-mail...........................info@interimhealthcare.com
76 Northeastern Blvd Ste 33A, Nashua, NH 03062
Richard Peterson, Owner

SOCIAL SERVICES

Child and Family Services of New Hampshire
Web..www.cfsnh.org
464 Chestnut St., P.O. Box 448, Manchester,
NH 03105-0448
COA accredited organization.

Child Care Project 603.646.3233
Fax..603.646.0197
Web..www.dartmouth.edu/~ccp
E-mail...........................child.care.project@dartmouth.edu
17 1/2 Lebanon St Ste 2, Hanover, NH 03755-2184
Jeff Robbins, Director

Hope Ctr 603.624.4673
Fax..423.569.2402
222 Cedar St, Manchester, NH 03103
George Rosado, Executive Director

SPECIAL NEEDS

Autism Society of New Hampshire 603.679.2424
E-mail...info@nhautism.com
PO Box 68, Concord, NH 03302

Brain Injury Association 603.225.8400
E-mail...mail@bianh.org
109 N State St Ste 2, Concord, NH 03301

Crotched Mountain School 603.547.3311
Fax..603.547.3232
Web.....................................www.crotchedmountain.org
E-mail.................bill.cossaboon@crotchedmountain.org
One Verney Dr, Greenfield, NH 03047
William H Cossaboon, Principal

Easter Seals New Hampshire 603.623.8863
E-mail...........................lgammon@eastersealsnh.org
555 Auburn St, Manchester, NH 03103
Elin Preanor, Chief Executive Officer

Education-A-Must Inc 603.437.6286
Fax..603.434.0371
E-mail...Education7@aol.com
PO Box 216, East Derry, NH 03041
Dorothy French

Families for Children's Mental Health 603.785.7948
E-mail...gsffcmh@aol.com
340 Commercial St 2nd Fl, Manchester, NH 03101

Granite State Independent Living 603.228.9680
E-mail...gsil@info.com
21 Chenell Dr, Concord, NH 03301
Clyde Terry, Chief Executive Officer

Greater Laconia Community Services, Inc 603.524.8811
Fax..603.524.0288
E-mail...glcs@cyberportal.net
635 Main St, Laconia, NH 03246
kevin Welford, Director

Independent Living Counsil 603.271.0476
E-mail...info@silcnh.org
57 Regional Dr, Concord, NH 03301

Institute on Disability/UCE 603.228.2084
E-mail...mary.schuh@unh.edu
56 Old Suncook Rd Ste 2, Concord, NH 03301
Mary Schuh, Associate Director

International Dyslexia Association 603.229.7355
E-mail...information@nhida.org
PO Box 3724, Concord, NH 03302

Lakeview NeuroRehabilitation Center 800.473.4221
Fax..603.539.8815
Web.....................................www.lakeviewsystem.com
E-mail...admitnh@lakeview.ws
244 Highwatch Road, Effingham, NH 03882
Kim Giles, Licsw, Director Of Admissions
CARF accredited programs available.

Lakeview NeuroRehabilitation Center 603.539.7451
Fax..603.539.8815
E-mail...tmerka@lakeview.ws
244 Highwatch Rd, Effingham, NH 03882
Tony Merka, Chief Executive Officer

Monadnock Developmental Services, Inc 603.352.1304

National Spinal Cord Injury Association 603.479.0560
54 Wentworth Ave, Londonderry, NH 03053

NDHHS 800.492.0407
E-mail...info@ndhhs.org
57 Regional Dr, Concord, NH 03301

New Hampshire Challenge 603.742.0500
E-mail...........................nhchallenge@comcast.net
PO Box 579, Dover, NH 03821

New Hampshire Family Voices 603.271.4525
93 Pleasant St, Concord, NH 03301
Martha Jean Madison, Co-Director

Northeast Rehabilitation Hospital 603.893.2900
Fax..603.893.1628
Web.....................................www.northeastrehab.com
70 Butler Street, Salem, NH 03079
CARF accredited programs available.

Parent Information Center 603.224.7005
Fax..603.224.4365
E-mail...admin@picnh.org
151 A manchester st, Concord, NH 03301
Kevin Lew-Hanson, Director

Parent to Parent 603.448.6393
E-mail...p2pnh@valley.net
12 FLYNN STREET, LEBANON, NH 03755
Phillil Eller, Director

Speech-Language-Hearing Association 603.228.5949
E-mail...nhslha@aol.com
PO Box 1538, Concord, NH 03302

SUBSTANCE ABUSE TREATMENT

New Jersey

www.state.nj.us

Chris Christie, Governor
PO Box 001
125 W State St
Trenton, NJ 08625
609.292.6000
609.292.3454 (Fax)
www.state.nj.us/governor

Kylthia Roberts, Juvenile Justice Specialist
PO Box 107
1001 Spruce St., Ste. 202
Trenton, NJ 08625
609.341.5019
609.943.4617 (Fax)
kylthia.roberts@njjjc.org

Jean Krauss, SAG Chair
134 Orchid Ct
Toms River, NJ 08753
732.557.0686
jeankrauss134@comcast.net

CRISIS NUMBERS

Child Abuse Reporting . . .877.652.2873

STATE SERVICES

SOCIAL SERVICES

Child Care & Youth Res Licensing NJ 609.777.5942
Fax 609.826.3972
  PO Box 717, Trenton, NJ 08625
  Gary Sefchik, Director

Dept of Human Svcs 609.292.3717
Fax 609.292.3824
Web . . . . .www.state.nj.us/humanservices/index.html
E-mail . . . . .dhs_commissioner@dhs.state.nj.us
  222 S Warren St, Trenton, NJ 08625-2306
  Jennifer Velez, Commissioner

Div of Youth and Family Svcs 609.292.6920
Fax 609.292.7513
Web . . . . .www.dhs.state.nj.us
  50 E. State St., Capital Center, Trenton, NJ 08625
  Eugine Marimon, Deputy Director Of Operations

Human Services 609.633.6932
Fax 609.777.1229
Web . . . . .www.dhs.state.nj.us
  222 S Warren St, Trenton, NJ 08625-2306
  Lori Woodworth, Director

GENERAL HEALTH SERVICES

Div of Medical Assistance & Health Svcs 609.588.2600
Fax 609.588.3583
Web . . . . .www.dhs.state.nj.us
  7 Quakerbridge Plz, Trenton, NJ 08625-1241
  Valerie Garr, Director

Family Health Svcs NJ 609.292.4043
Fax 609.292.3580
  50 E State St, PO Box 364, Trenton, NJ 08625
  Gooria M Rodriguez, Director

Spec Child Health & Early Inter Srvs NJ 609.777.7778
Fax 609.292.9288
E-mail . . . . .marilyn.gorney-daley@doh.state.nj.us
  50 E State St, Trenton, NJ 08625
  Marilyn Gorney-Daley, Director

MENTAL HEALTH SERVICES

Com for the Blind Visually Impaired NJ 973.648.3333
Fax 973.648.7364
E-mail . . . . .greg.patty@dhs.state.nj.us
  153 Halsey St 6th Flr, PO Box 47017, Newark,
  NJ 07101
  Greg Patty, Director

Div of Mental Health and Children's Svcs
  Admin 732.745.3280
Fax 732.296.7971
Web . . . . .www.co.middlesex.nj.us
E-mail . . . . .wanda.dillon@co.middlesex.nj.us
  1 John F Kennedy Sq, New Brunswick,
  NJ 08901-2149
  Wanda Dillon, Director Of Children S Services

Div of Vocational Rehabilitation Svcs 609.292.5987
Fax 609.292.8347
Web . . . . .www.dol.state.nj.us
E-mail . . . . .allis.hunnicutt@dol.state.nj.us
  1 John Fitch Pl 12 th Floor, Trenton, NJ 08625
  Allis Hunnicutt, Director

Division of Addiction Services 609.292.5760
Fax 609.292.3816
E-mail . . . . .raquel.jeffers@dhs.state.nj.us
  120 South Stockton Street, Trenton, NJ 08625
  Raquel Maxon-jeffers, Assistant Commissioner

Ofc of Child Behavioral Health Svcs 609.292.4741
Fax 609.396.6960
Web . . . . .www.state.nj.us/dcf/behavioral/
E-mail . . . . .nadevhda.robinson@dcf.state.nj.us
  50 E State St 4th Fl Ste 215, 625, Trenton,
  NJ 08608-1715
  Jeffery Guenzel, Director

JUSTICE AGENCY

Attorney General's Ofc 609.292.4925
Fax 609.292.3508
Web . . . . .www.njpublicsafety.com
E-mail . . . . .paula.dow@lps.state.nj.us
  25 Market St, Trenton, NJ 08625-0080
  Paula Dow, Attorney General

CASA of New Jersey 609.695.9400
Fax 609.695.0040
Web . . . . .www.casaofnj.org
E-mail . . . . .rita@casaofnj.org
  945 W State St Ste A, Trenton, NJ 08618-5347
  Rita Gulden, Executive Director

Juvenile Justice Commission 609.292.1400
Fax 609.943.4615
Web . . . . .www.state.nj.us
E-mail . . . . .rosanne.fairbanks@njjjc.org
  1001 Spruce St Ste 202, Trenton, NJ 08638-3957
  Roseanne Fairbanks, Director Of Administration

Office of Educational Srvs NJ 609.292.8054
Fax 609.777.4143
E-mail . . . . .patty.friend@doc.state.nj.us
  PO Box 863, Trenton, NJ 08625
  Patty Friend, Director

Probation Dept 908.475.6948
Fax 908.475.6951
E-mail . . . . .brenda.beacham@judiciary.state.nj.us
  413 2nd St, Belvidere, NJ 07823
  Brenda Beacham, CEO

Victims of Crime Compensation Board 973.648.2107
Fax 973.648.3937
Web . . . . .www.njvictims.org
E-mail . . . . .marsetta.lee@vccb.org
  50 Park Pl Fl 5, Newark, NJ 07102-4301
  Marsetta Lee, Director

COURTS

Administrative Ofc of the Courts 609.984.0275
Fax 609.984.6968
E-mail . . . . .jennifer.amos@judiciary.state.nj.us
  25 Market St, Trenton, NJ 08625
  Glenn A Grant, Acting Administrative Director Of The Courts

Probation Division 856.661.2500
Fax 856.379.2421
E-mail . . . . .louis.narvaez@judiciary.state.nj.us
  Executive Campus, Bldg #5 & #6, PO Box 8107,
  Cherry Hill, NJ 08002
  Louis R. Narvaez, Vicinage Chief Probation Officer

POLICE AND SHERIFF

NJ State Police 609.882.2000
Fax 609.882.6523
E-mail . . . . .fuentes.joseph@gw.njsp.org
  1 River Dr, Trenton, NJ 08628
  Joe Fuentes, Superintendent

EDUCATION SERVICES

Communities In Schools of New Jersey, Inc. 973.242.0706
Fax 973.242.2928
Web . . . . .www.cis.org
E-mail . . . . .wallen@cisnj.org
  155 Washington St Ste 201, Newark, NJ 07102-3016
  William A. Allen, State Director

Dept of Education 609.292.4450
Fax 609.777.4099
Web . . . . .www.state.nj.us/education
  100 River View Executive Plaza, Trenton, NJ 08625
  Tonya Hall-coston, Early Childhood Coordinator

Educ for Homeless Children and Youth NJ 609.984.4974
Fax 609.292.1211
E-mail . . . . .danielle.anderson-thomas@doe.state.nj.us
  100 Riverview Executive Pova, Trenton, NJ 08625
  Danielle Anderson Thomas, Coordinator

Marie H. Katzenbach School for the Deaf 609.530.3112
Fax 609.530.5791
Web ....www.mksd.org
E-mail ....dennis_russell@mksd.state.nj.us
  320 Sullivan Way, Trenton, NJ 08628-3495
Dr. Angel Ramos, Superintendent

New Jersey Dept of Education 609.633.0665
Fax 609.984.5347
E-mail ....vocinfo@doe.state.nj.us
  100 Riverview Plaza, Trenton, NJ 08625
Marie Barry, Director

Office of Special Education Programs NJ 609.984.1286
Fax 609.984.8422
E-mail ....peggy.mcdonald@doe.state.nj.us
  100 River New Plz, Rte 29, Trenton, NJ 08625
Peggy McDonald, Interim Director

Statewide Parent Advocacy Network Inc 973.642.8100
Fax 973.642.8080
E-mail ....diana.autin@spannj.org
  35 Halsey St 4th Flr, Newark, NJ 07102
Diana Autin, Director

Statewide Praent Advoc Network Inc 973.642.8100
Fax 973.642.8080
E-mail ....diana.autin@spannj.org
  35 Halsey St 4th Flr, Newark, NJ 07102
Diana Autin, Co-Director

LABOR & WORKFORCE EDUCATION

New Jersey Dept of Labor and Workforce
  Development 609.292.2323
Fax 609.633.9271
E-mail ....constituent.realtions@dol.state.nj.us
  1 John Fitch Plz, Fl 13, Trenton, NJ 08625
Harold J. Wirths, Commissioner

COUNTY SERVICES

Atlantic County

SOCIAL SERVICES

Dept Of Family & Community
  Development 609.348.3001
Fax 609.343.2374
Web ....www.aclink.org
E-mail ....karen.enous@dol.state.nj.us
  1333 Atlantic Ave, Atlantic City, NJ 08401-7212
Karen B. Enous, Director

GENERAL HEALTH SERVICES

City Health Dept 609.347.5663
Fax 609.347.5662
Web ....www.cityofatlanticcity.org
  1301 Bacharach Blvd, Fl 4, Atlantic City, NJ 08401
Ronald Cash, Mpp, Mpa, Director

Health Dept 609.645.5972
Fax 609.645.5931
Web ....www.aclink.org
E-mail ....diamond_patricia@aclink.org
  201 Shore Rd, Northfield, NJ 08225-2319
Patricia Diamond, Mpj, Director, Health Officer

JUSTICE AGENCY

Law Guardian/Child Abuse 609.441.3773
Fax 609.441.3477
E-mail ....sonia.wagner@opd.state.nj.us
  1300 Atlantic Ave Ste ME22, Citycenter Center,
  Atlantic City, NJ 08401-7207
Sonia Wagner, Assistant Deputy Public Defender

Ofc Of Public Defender 609.625.9111
Fax 609.625.4260
  5914 Main St Ste 201, Mays Landing, NJ 08330
Robert J. Moran, Deputy Public Defender

Probation Dept 609.343.2288
Fax 609.347.9193
Web ....www.judiciary.state.nj.us
E-mail ....robert.scull@judiciary.state.nj.us
  1201 Bacharach Blvd, Atlantic City, NJ 08401
Lee Mooney, Assistant Chief

COURTS

Family Court 609.345.6700
Fax 609.343.2290
E-mail ....floreine.alexander@judiciary.state.nj.us
  1201 Bacharach Blvd, Atlantic City, NJ 08401
Floreine Alexander, Family Division Manager

POLICE AND SHERIFF

Sheriff's Ofc 609.909.7289
Fax 609.909.7292
Web ....www.atlanticcountysheriff.org
E-mail ....mcgettigan_jim@yahoo.com
  4997 Unami Blvd, Mays Landing, NJ 08331-2054
James Mcgettigan, Sheriff

EDUCATION SERVICES

Adriatic Avenue Head Start Ctr 609.343.0290
Fax 609.449.1327
Web ....www.acf.hhs.gov
  1410 Adriatic Ave, Atlantic City, NJ 08401-2380
Leah Scarbrogh, Director

Dover Avenue Headstart 609.347.8404
Fax 609.343.0290
Web ....www.acf.hhs.gov
  4001 Atlantic Ave, Atlantic City, NJ 08401-5910
Maria Gomez, Director

Bergen County

SOCIAL SERVICES

Board Of Social Svcs 201.368.4200
Fax 201.368.8710
Web ....www.bcbss.com
E-mail ....jroll@bcbss.com
  216 State Rt 17 N, Rochelle Park, NJ 07662
Janice Roll, Director

Youth And Family Svcs 201.996.8900
Fax 201.342.1375
E-mail ....marisol.naranjo@dhs.state.nj.us
  125 State St Fl 2, Hackensack, NJ 07601-5453
Marisol Naranjo, District Manager

GENERAL HEALTH SERVICES

Bergenfield Board Of Health 201.387.4055
Fax 201.385.7386
Web ....www.bergenfieldborough.com
E-mail ....health@bergenfield.com
  198 N Washington Ave, Borough Hall, Bergenfield,
  NJ 07621
David Volte, Bs, Ma, Health Officer

Closter Board Of Health 201.784.0600
Fax 201.784.0371
E-mail ....closter.health@verizon.net
  295 Closter Dock Rd, Municipal Building, Closter,
  NJ 07624-2618
Sam Yanovich, Health Officer

Elmwood Park Dept Of Health 201.796.1072
  182 Market St Ste 1, Municipal Building, Elmwood
  Park, NJ 07407
Deborah Ricci, Health Officer

Englewood Dept Of Health 201.568.3450
Fax 201.568.5738
  73 S Van Brunt St, Englewood, NJ 07631
Xavier Cruz, Health Officer

Fair Lawn Health Dept 201.794.5327
Fax 201.475.2975
Web ....www.fairlawn.org
E-mail ....health@fairlawn.org
  8-01 Fair Lawn Ave Ste 1, Fair Lawn, NJ 07410-1839
Carol Wagner, Health Officer

Fort Lee Dept Of Health 201.592.3500
Fax 201.585.1901
Web ....www.fortlee.com
E-mail ....s-wielkocz@fortleenj.org
  309 Main St, Memorial Health Building, Fort Lee,
  NJ 07024
Stephen S. Wielkocz, MA, Health Officer

Health Counseling Ctr 201.336.3350
Fax 201.487.4956
Web ....www.co.bergen.nj.us
E-mail ....jfalcone@co.bergen.nj.us
  120 S River St, Hackensack, NJ 07601
Joann Falcone, Director

Health Dept 201.634.2600
Fax 201.986.1068
Web ....www.bergenhealth.org
E-mail ....healthdept@co.bergen.nj.us
  327 E Ridgewood Ave, Paramus, NJ 07652-4819
Hansel Asmar, Health Officer

Mid-Bergen Regional Health
  Commission 201.599.6290
Fax 201.262.7783
Web ....www.midbergenregional.org
E-mail ....sam.yanovich@midbergen-regionalheath.org
  930 River Rd, New Milford, New Milford,
  NJ 07646-3043
Sam Yanovich, Ms, Health Officer

North Bergen Health Dept 201.392.2084
Fax 201.392.2153
Web ....www.hudsoncountynj.org
E-mail ....rcensullo@northbergen.org
  1116 43rd St, North Bergen, NJ 07047-2795
Richard Censullo, Director/ Health Officer

Northwest Bergen Regional Health
  Commission 201.445.7217
Fax 201.445.4001
Web ....www.nwbrhc.org
E-mail ....armusella@yahoo.com
  20 W Prospect St, Waldwick, NJ 07463-1739
Angela R. Musella, Health Officer

Palisades Park Dept Of Health 201.585.4106
Fax 201.585.4107
Web ....www.bergenhealth.org
E-mail ....ppbdhealth@aol.com
  275 Broad Ave Ste 1, Palisades Park, NJ 07650-1579
Jad Mihalinec, Ma, Health Officer

Paramus Dept Of Health 201.265.2100
Fax 201.225.9014
Web ....www.paramusborough.org
E-mail ....jhopper@paramusborough.org
  Borough Hall, Jockish Square, Paramus, NJ 07652
John Hopper, Health Officer

Teaneck Health Dept **201.837.1600**
Fax 201.837.4817
E-mail ....health@teanecknj.gov
   818 Teaneck Rd Ste 1, MUNICIPAL BUILDING,
   Teaneck, NJ 07666-4581
   Ken Katter, Health Officer

Washington TWP Board Of Health **201.666.8512**
Fax 201.782.1760
E-mail ....dglevy@bellatlantic.net
   350 Hudson Ave Ste A, Township Of Washington,
   NJ 07676-4758
   Daniel Levy, Mpa, Health Officer

MENTAL HEALTH SERVICES

Mental Health Board **201.634.2750**
Fax 201.634.3002
Web ....www.co.bergen.nj.us
   327 E Ridgewood Ave, Paramus, NJ 07652-4819
   Michelle Hart Loughlyn, Administrator

JUSTICE AGENCY

Conklin Youth Ctr **201.646.2756**
Fax 201.646.2729
   125 Essex St, Hackensack, NJ 07601
   Joanne Eckert, Director

Juvenile Detention Ctr **201.599.6185**
Fax 201.599.6266
   296 E Ridgewood Ave, Paramus, NJ 07652
   Bob Day, Director

Ofc Of Public Defender **201.996.8030**
Fax 201.996.8034
Web ....www.opd.state.nj.us
   60 State St Fl 3, Hackensack, NJ 07601-5468
   Louis Acevedo, Deputy Public Defender

Probation Dept **201.527.4000**
Fax 201.527.4040
   133 River St, Hackensack, NJ 07601
   John Fuhrman, Chief Performance Officer

POLICE AND SHERIFF

Hackensack Police Dept **201.646.7777**
Fax 201.646.7590
E-mail ....cpadilla@hackensack.org
   225 State St, Hackensack, NJ 07601
   Captain Tom Padilla, Acting Officer Incharge

Sheriff's Ofc **201.646.3020**
Fax 201.752.4164
   10 Main St 204, Hackensack, NJ 07601
   Micheal Sauzino, Sheriff

EDUCATION SERVICES

School Based Youth Svcs **201.646.0722**
Fax 201.646.1558
Web ....www.hackensackschools.org
E-mail ....d.polifrone@hackensackschools.org
   1st And Beech St, Hackensack Drop In Center, Room
   161, Hackensack, NJ 07601
   Dominick Polifrone, Director

Burlington County

SOCIAL SERVICES

Board Of Social Svcs **609.261.1000**
Fax 609.261.9530
   795 Woodlane Rd, Westampton, NJ 08060
   Daniel Boas, Director

Youth And Family Svcs **800.847.1753**
Fax 856.787.3890
Web ....www.state.nj.us
   1000 Howard Blvd Ste 300, Mount Laurel,
   NJ 08054-2320
   Nina Roller, District Manager

GENERAL HEALTH SERVICES

Health Dept **609.265.5548**
Fax 609.265.3152
Web ....www.co.burlington.nj.us
E-mail ....rgogats@co.burlington.nj.us
   15 Pioneer Blvd, Raphael Meadow Health Center,
   Mount Holly, NJ 08060-3825
   Robert Gogats, Public Health Coordinator

JUSTICE AGENCY

Ofc Of Public Defender **609.518.3060**
Fax 609.518.3072
Web ....www.thedefenders.com
   100 High St Fl 2, Mount Holly, NJ 08060-1458
   Kevin Walker, Chief

Probation Dept **609.518.2885**
Fax 609.518.2886
Web ....www.judiciary.state.nj.us
E-mail ....edwin.lee@judiciary.state.nj.us
   50 Rancocas Rd, Ground Floor, Mount Holly,
   NJ 08060
   Edwin Lee Jr, Chief Performance Officer

POLICE AND SHERIFF

Sheriff's Dept **609.265.5127**
Fax 609.265.5767
E-mail ....jstanfield@co.burlington.nj.us
   49 Rancocas Rd, Rm 210, Mount Holly, NJ 08060
   Jean Stanfield, Sheriff

EDUCATION SERVICES

Bccap-Lumberton Headstart Ctr **609.267.9527**
Fax 609.267.4434
Web ....www.bccap.org
E-mail ....cbuffett@bccap.org
   100 Rte 38 & Maple Grove Blvd., Lumberton,
   NJ 08016
   Christina Buffett, Director

Bccap Head Start Child Development
Ctr **856.764.2562**
Fax 856.764.1862
E-mail ....cvera@bccap.org
   2431 Burlington Ave, Delanco, NJ 08075-5047
   Clemencia Vera, Superintendent

School Based Youth Svcs **609.893.8141**
Fax 609.894.0153
Web ....www.drenk.org
E-mail ....lwilliams@drenk.org
   148 Arneys Mount Rd, Pemberton, NJ 08068
   Jen Rodir, Director

Special Education **609.265.5938**
Fax 609.265.5922
   2 Academy Drive, Westampton, NJ 08060
   Deborah Magee, Supervisor Of Child Study

Camden County

SOCIAL SERVICES

Board Of Social Svcs **856.225.8800**
Fax 865.225.7797
Web ....www.oel.state.nj.us
E-mail ....ccbss@oel.state.nj.us
   808 Market St, Camden, NJ 08102
   Robert Ellis, Director

GENERAL HEALTH SERVICES

Communicable Disease **856.374.6141**
Fax 856.374.6358
Web ....www.camdencounty.com
   512 Lakeland Rd Ste 501, DIPIRO, Blackwood,
   NJ 08012
   Stephen Walter, Director

Health Dept **856.374.6037**
Fax 856.374.6034
Web ....www.camdencounty.com
E-mail ....ccho@camdencounty.com
   Dipiero Center 512 Lakeland Rd, Blackwood,
   NJ 08012
   Robert Smith, Director

JUSTICE AGENCY

Law Guardian **856.346.8008**
Fax 856.346.8017
   20 Clementon Rd E Ste 301N, Gibbsboro,
   NJ 08026-1179
   Sarah Miner, Interim Deputy Public Defender

Ofc Of Public Defender **856.614.3500**
Fax 856.614.3503
E-mail ....thedefenders@opd.state.nj.us
   101 Haddon Ave Ste 2, Camden, NJ 08103
   Sue Williford, Chief Investigator

Ofc Of Youth Svcs **856.757.7644**
Fax 856.757.7114
   713-715 Broadway, Camden, NJ 08103
   Foday Kamara, Director

COURTS

Family Court **856.379.2200**
Fax 856.379.2265
E-mail ....charles.rand@judiciary.state.nj.us
   101 S 5th St, Rm 270, Camden, NJ 08103
   Honorable Charles Rand, Director

POLICE AND SHERIFF

Sheriff's Dept **856.225.5473**
Fax 856.225.5595
Web ....www.camdencounty.com
E-mail ....sheriff@camdencounty.com
   520 Market St, Courthouse Room 100, Camden,
   NJ 08102-1300
   Charles Billingham, Sheriff

EDUCATION SERVICES

Atco Head Start **856.767.1616**
   113 New Jersey Ave, Atco, NJ 08004-2611
   Ms. Washington, Director

Blackwood Headstart Ctr **856.232.4943**
   35 E Church St, Camden, NJ 08105-2413
   Terry Loerch, Director

Collingswood Headstart Ctr- **856.869.3378**
Fax 856.964.2484
   710 Collings Ave, Collingswood, NJ 08107
   Melissa Thompson, Director

Cui Headstart **856.966.0408**
Fax 856.966.6299
   538 S Broadway st, Camden, NJ 08103-1244
   Dorothy Washington, Director

Florence Road Headstart Ctr **856.875.1417**
   156, Norcross, Berlin, NJ 08009
   Dorothy Washington, Director

School Based Youth Svcs **856.541.0253**
Fax 856.541.1989
Web www.camden.k12.nj.us
E-mail ....sshields@camden.k12.nj.us
   1700 Park Blvd, Camden High School, Camden,
   NJ 08103-2806
   Sharon Shields, Project Manager

Cape May County

SOCIAL SERVICES

Board Of Social Svcs **609.886.6200**
Fax 609.889.9332
   4005 Route 9 S, Social Services Building, Rio Grande,
   NJ 08242
   Dennis Seer, Director

Youth And Family Svcs 609.463.9652
Fax 609.463.9689
   601 S Route 9, Bldg B, Cape May Court House, NJ 08210
Michelle Rupe, District Manager

GENERAL HEALTH SERVICES

Health Dept 609.465.1187
Fax 609.465.3933
E-mail ....thomaske@njlincs.net
   4 Moore Rd, DN-601, Cape May Court House, NJ 08210
Kevin L. Thomas Ma Ho, Public Health Coordinator

JUSTICE AGENCY

Ofc Of Public Defender 609.465.3101
Fax 609.465.3830
Web ....www.opd.state.nj.us
E-mail ....francis.tomlinson@opd.state.nj.us
   201 S Main St, Cape May Court House, NJ 08210-2289
Francis Tomlinson, Chief Investigator

Probation Div 609.465.1095
Fax 609.463.6470
E-mail ....capekidsmailbox@judiciary.state.nj.us
   9 N Main St, Cape May Court House, NJ 08210
Roberta Sandrow-Scull, Interim Director

COURTS

Children In Court Unit 609.463.6600
Fax 609.463.6623
   4 Moore Rd, Cape May Court House, NJ 08210-1654
Honorable Kyran Connor, Director

POLICE AND SHERIFF

Sheriff's Dept 609.463.6430
Fax 609.463.6464
Web ....www.cmcshriffs.net
E-mail ....sheriff@cmcshriffs.net
   4 Moore Rd, Dn 301, Cape May Court House, NJ 08210-1654
Gary Schaffer, Sheriff

EDUCATION SERVICES

School Based Youth Svcs 609.884.3475
Fax 609.884.0546
Web ....www.lcmr.capemayschools.com
E-mail ....vsmith@lcmr.capemayschools.com
   687 Route 9, Cape May, NJ 08204-4637
Vicki Smith, Director Youth Services

Cumberland County

SOCIAL SERVICES

Board Of Social Svcs 856.691.4600
Fax 856.692.7635
E-mail ....krodrigu@xbp.dhs.state.nj.us
   275 N Delsea Dr Ste 1, Vineland, NJ 08360
Kathy Rodriguez, Interim Director

Youth And Family Svcs 856.453.3830
Fax 856.453.3904
E-mail ....Betty.Musso@dcf.state.nj.us
   40 E Broad St Ste 400, Bridgeton, NJ 08302
Betty Musso, District Manager

GENERAL HEALTH SERVICES

City Of Vineland Dept Of Health 856.794.4131
Fax 856.794.1159
Web ....www.vinelandcity.org
E-mail ....gsartorio@vinelandcity.org
   640 E Wood St, Vineland, NJ 08360-3713
George Sartorio, Health Officer

JUSTICE AGENCY

Ofc Of Public Defender 856.453.1568
Fax 856.453.1407
   14 E Commerce St, Bridgeton, NJ 08302
Dinaz Akhtar, Deputy Public Defender

Probation Dept (Child Support) 856.453.4600
Fax 856.451.4450
Web ....www.childsupport.state.nj.us
   60 W St Brodway, Bridgeton, NJ 08302
Susan Sasser, Acpo, Child Support

COURTS

Family Court 856.453.4534
Fax 856.459.1382
Web ....www.judiciary.state.nj.us
   Broad And Fayette St's, Bridgeton, NJ 08302
Jason Corter, Family Divison Manager

POLICE AND SHERIFF

Sheriff's Dept 856.451.4449
Fax 856.453.1902
Web ....www.mindspring.com
E-mail ....robertau@co.cumberland.nj.us
   220 N Laurel St, Bridgeton, NJ 08302-1516
Robert Austino, Sheriff

EDUCATION SERVICES

School Based Youth Svcs (Teen Ctr) 856.451.4440
Fax 856.451.5815
   111 N West Ave, Bridgeton High School, Teen Ctr, Bridgeton, NJ 08302
Lopez Miguel, Coordinator

Special Education 856.453.0422
Fax 856.455.9523
E-mail ....danielma@co.cumberland.nj.us
   19 Landis Ave, Bridgeton, NJ 08302-4317
Dr. Richard Stepura, Executive County Superintendent

Essex County

SOCIAL SERVICES

Bloomfield District Ofc 973.680.3587
Fax 973.680.3552
Web ....www.state.nj.us
E-mail ....pbruce-el@bloomfield.k12.nj.us
   650 Bloomfield Ave Ste 3, Bloomfield, NJ 07003-2544
Patricia Bruce-el, Manager

Newark South District Ofc 973.648.2400
Fax 973.648.8473
Web ....www.dhs.state.nj.us
   153 Halsey St, Fl 4, Newark, NJ 07102
Wendy Griffin, District Manager

North District Ofc II 973.648.2960
Fax 973.648.7229
Web ....www.dcf.state.nj.us
   153 Halsey St, Fl 4Dl2, Newark, NJ 07101
Reginald Dickerson, Manager

School Based Youth Svcs 973.622.1100
Fax 973.624.6780
E-mail ....mmess@essextech.org
   91 W Market St, Teen Powerhouse, Newark, NJ 07104
Mary Ellen Mess, Director

Youth And Family Svcs: Newark Central District Ofc 973.648.4200
Fax 973.648.7326
   153 Halsey St, Newark, NJ 07102-2807
Lori Saunders, District Manager

GENERAL HEALTH SERVICES

Belleville Health Dept 973.450.3390
Fax 973.450.4550
Web ....www.bellevillenj.org
   152 Washington Ave, Fl 3, Belleville, NJ 07109
Susan Portuese, Health Officer

Bloomfield Board Of Health 973.680.4024
Fax 973.680.4825
Web ....www.bloomfieldtwpnj.com
E-mail ....health@mailbloomfieldtwpnj.com
   1 Municipal Plz, Rm 111, Bloomfield, NJ 07003
Michael Fitzpatrick, Health Officer

Community Nursing Svc 973.509.4970
Fax 973.509.1479
   205 Claremont Ave, Montclair, NJ 07042
Jackie Messineo, Supervisor

Dept Of Health 973.497.9401
Fax 973.497.9407
E-mail ....ecdohceha@admin.essexcountynj.org
   115 Clifton Ave, 3 Fl, North New Jersey, NJ 07104
Michael Festa, Phd, Health Officer

East Orange Dept Of Health 973.266.5490
Fax 973.266.5402
   143 New St, East Orange, NJ 07017-4194
Rochelle D. Williams-evans, Health Officer

Irvington Township Dept Of Health 973.399.6645
Fax 973.371.1489
Web ....www.irvington.net
E-mail ....atifho@gmail.com
   Municipal Building-Civic Square, Irvington, NJ 07111
Atif Nazir, Health Officer

Livingston Dept Of Health 973.535.7961
Fax 973.535.3234
Web ....www.livingstonnj.org
   204 Hillside Ave, Livingston, NJ 07039
Louis E. Anello, Director Of Health

Maplewood Health Dept 973.762.8120
Fax 973.762.1934
Web ....www.maplewoodtownship.nj.us
E-mail ....healthofficer@twp.maplewood.nj.us
   574 Valley St, Maplewood, NJ 07040-2669
Robert D. Roe, Mph, Health Officer

Millburn Board Of Health 973.564.7087
Fax 973.564.7569
Web ....www.twp.millburn.nj.us
E-mail ....lanello@milburntwp.org
   375 Millburn Ave, Town Hall, Millburn, NJ 07041-1377
Louis E. Anello, Health Officer

Montclair Health Dept 973.509.4970
Fax 973.509.1479
Web ....www.montclairnjusa.org
   205 Claremont Ave, Montclair, NJ 07042
Susan Portuese, Director Of Health And Human Services

Nutley Health Dept 973.284.4976
Fax 973.661.9411
Web ....www.nutleynj.org
E-mail ....trestaino@nutleynj.org
   149 Chestnut St, Nutley, NJ 07110-2393
Tom Restaino, Health Officer

West Caldwell Health Dept 973.226.2303
Fax 973.226.2396
Web ....www.westcaldwell.com
E-mail ....health@westcaldwell.com
   30 Clinton Rd, Borough Hall, Caldwell, NJ 13904
Peter N. Tabbot, Mph, Health Officer

West Orange Dept Of Health 973.325.4124
Fax 973.325.4005
Web ....www.westorange.org
E-mail ....jf2@njlincs.net
   66 Main St, Municipal Building, West Orange, NJ 07052-5404
Theresa Denova, Health Officer

MENTAL HEALTH SERVICES

Mental Health Board **973.571.2800**
Fax 973.571.2807
Web ....www.essexcountynj.org
E-mail ....jpsdc@aol.com
204 Grove Ave, Cedar Grove, NJ 07009-1436
Joseph N. Divincenzo, County Executive

JUSTICE AGENCY

CASA **973.693.6785**
Fax 973.693.6791
Web ....www.casaessex.org
212 Washington St, # 912, Newark, NJ 07102
Karen Burns, Executive Director

Div Of Youth And Family Svcs **973.624.3678**
Fax 973.643.7996
E-mail ....slea@dhs.state.nj.us
33 Washington St, Newark, NJ 07102
Shelley Lea, Lead Administrator Of Western Regional Operations

Law Guardian/Child Abuse **973.648.4572**
Fax 973.648.3220
E-mail ....guadalupe.casillas@opd.j.nj.us
31 Clinton St, 2nd Fl, Newark, NJ 07102
Guadaulpe Casillas, Deputy Public Defender

Ofc Of Public Defender **973.648.3470**
Fax 973.648.2028
31 Clinton St Ste 4, Newark, NJ 07102-3729
Ill Abraham Drake, Deputy Public Defender

COURTS

Family Court **973.693.6814**
Fax 973.693.6721
Web ....www.state.nj.us
E-mail ....rich.brown@judiciary.state.nj.us
212 Washington St, Newark, NJ 07102-2904
Rich Brown, Family Crisis Intervention Liason Supervisor

POLICE AND SHERIFF

Sheriff's Dept **973.621.4105**
Fax 973.621.4066
Web ....www.essexsheriff.com
50 W market st, Zederans Courts Bldg, 2nd Fl,
Newark, NJ 07102
Armando B. Fontoura, Sheriff

EDUCATION SERVICES

Alberta Bey Ctr Head Start **973.282.0190**
300 Chancellor Ave, Newark, NJ 07102
Diane Benstein, Director

Broadway Mini Mall Head Start **973.485.4906**
Fax 973.481.2186
724 Broadway, Newark, NJ 07104
Alma Vincent, Manager

Carmel Towers I LI Head Start **973.824.0271**
440 Elizabeth Ave Ste 1, Newark, NJ 07112-2667

Friendly Fuld Neighborhood Ctr
Inchea **973.642.3143**
Fax 973.623.2080
Web ....www.acf.hhs.gov
555 Martin Luther King Jr Blvd, Newark,
NJ 07102-1244
Kim Wady, Supervisor

School Based Youth Svcs - The
Bridge **973.399.7797**
Fax 973.372.6545
E-mail ....bcanady@oel.state.nj.us
1253 Clinton Ave, Irvington, NJ 07111
Beverly Canady, Site Manager

Special Education **973.395.4677**
Fax 973.395.4696
Web ....www.doe.state.nj.us
E-mail ....mark.lanzi@doe.state.nj.us
7 Glenwood Ave Ste 404, East Orange,
NJ 07017-1041
Mark Lanzi, Supervisor Of Child Study

Gloucester County

SOCIAL SERVICES

division Of Social Svcs **856.582.9200**
Fax 856.582.6587
E-mail ....esmith@co.gloucester.nj.us
400 Holly Dell Dr, Sewell, NJ 08080-9198
Edward Smith, Superintendent

Youth And Family Svcs **856.853.5525**
Fax 856.853.1152
215 Crown Point Rd Ste 400, Thorofare, NJ 08086
San Payne, District Manager

GENERAL HEALTH SERVICES

Health Dept **856.218.4101**
Fax 856.218.4109
Web ....www.gloucestercountynj.gov
E-mail ....vpreesada@co.gloucester.nj.us
204 E Holly Ave, Sewell, NJ 08080
Virginia Preesada, Health Officer

JUSTICE AGENCY

Div Of Youth And Family Svcs **866.492.8320**
Fax 856.582.5183
Web ....www.dcf.state.nj.us
309 Fries Mill Rd Ste 11, Sewell, NJ 08080-9209
Christine M. Mozes, Director, Regional Operations

Ofc Of Public Defender **856.853.4188**
Fax 856.853.4197
65 Newton Ave, Eastwood Professional Building,
Woodbury, NJ 08096
P. Jeffrey Witner, Deputy Public Defender

Probation Dept **856.232.9777**
Fax 856.374.8936
Web ....www.ocgov.com
E-mail ....miles@ocgov.com
5 Pts Plaza Hurfvillerd, Deptford, NJ 08096
Robert O. Miles, CPO

COURTS

Family Court **856.686.7400**
Fax 856.686.7585
70 Hunter St, Woodbury, NJ 08096
Mark Strock, Director

POLICE AND SHERIFF

Sheriff's Ofc **856.384.4600**
Fax 856.384.4679
Web ....www.co.gloucester.nj.us
E-mail ....cmorina@co.gloucester.nj.us
70 Hunter St, Woodbury, NJ 08096-4606
Carmel M. Morina, Sheriff

EDUCATION SERVICES

Special Education **856.468.6500**
Fax 856.468.9115
E-mail ....dolores.walther@doe.state.nj.us
1492 Tanyard Rd, Sewell, NJ 08080-4222
Dr. Dolores Walther, Supervisor Of Child Study

Hudson County

SOCIAL SERVICES

Bayonne District Ofc **201.243.5000**
Fax 201.339.1462
Web ....www.state.nj.us
690 Broadway, Bayonne, NJ 07002
Robert Rubinsky, District Manager

North Hudson District Ofc **201.865.4101**
Fax 201.864.4014
Web ....www.dep.state.nj.us
E-mail ....linda.gibbons@dep.state.nj.us
1 Harmon Meadow Blvd, Fl 4, Secaucus, NJ 07094
Linda Stack, District Manager

Youth And Family Svcs: Jersey City District
Ofc **201.795.0423**
Fax 201.217.7012
438 Summit Ave Fl 4, Jersey City, NJ 07306
Harold Daman, District Manager

GENERAL HEALTH SERVICES

Bayonne Board Of Health **201.858.6112**
Fax 201.858.6111
Web ....www.bayonnenj.org
E-mail ....bb1@njlincs.net
630 Ave C, Bayonne, NJ 07002
Brigid Breivogel, Health Officer

Harrison Board Of Health **973.268.2441**
Fax 973.482.2924
Web ....www.townofharrison.com
E-mail ....kcomer@townofharrison.com
326 Harrison Ave, Harrison, NJ 07029-1752
Karen L. Comer, Ms, Ches, Health Officer

Hoboken Health Dept **201.420.2375**
Fax 201.420.7862
Web ....www.hobokennj.org
124 Grand St, Hoboken, NJ 07030
Frank S. Sasso, Ms, Msw, Health Officer

Hudson Regional Health
Commission **201.223.1133**
Fax 201.223.0122
Web ....www.hudsonregional.org
E-mail ....rf@hudsonregional.org
595 County Ave, Bldg 1, Secaucus, NJ 07094
Robert Ferraiuolo, Mpa, Health Officer

Union City Dept Of Health **201.348.5608**
Fax 201.348.6916
3715 Palisade Ave, Union City, NJ 07087
Richard Zenzullo, Health Officer

West NJ Dept Of Health **201.295.5070**
Fax 201.295.0769
Web ....www.westnewyorknj.org
E-mail ....wnjhealthdept@aol.com
428 60th St, Rm 31, West New York, NJ 07093
Vincent A. Rivelli, Ms, Health Officer

MENTAL HEALTH SERVICES

Mental Health Ctr **201.339.9200**
Fax 201.339.7842
E-mail ....jkadian@bayonnementalhealth.org
601 Broadway, Bayonne, NJ 07002
Joseph Kadian, Director

JUSTICE AGENCY

CASA **201.795.9856**
Fax 201.795.3336
E-mail ....bsavage@hudsoncountycasa.org
442 Hoboken Ave, Jersey City, NJ 07306
Beverly Savage, Executive Director

Ofc Of Public Defender **201.795.8922**
Fax 201.795.8966
438 Summit Ave Fl 5, Jersey City, NJ 07306
Martha Royster, Deputy Public Defender

Probation Dept **201.795.6827**
Fax 201.795.6603
Web ....www.judiciary.state.nj.us
595 Newark Ave, Rm 406, Jersey City, NJ 07306
Anthony Casale, Vicinage Cpo

POLICE AND SHERIFF

Jersey City Police Dept **201.547.5424**
Fax 201.547.5341
E-mail ....jwisely@jcpd.org
139 Cator Ave, Jersey City, NJ 07305-2801
Captain J. Wisely, Commander Juvenile Division

EDUCATION SERVICES

Bayonne Headstart 2 ....**201.437.2209**
Fax 201.437.0320
557 Kennedy Blvd, Bayonne, NJ 07002
Rosemary Simnowitz, Director

Bethany Headstart Class 1 ....**201.432.8908**
Web ....www.jerseycityheadstart.com
E-mail ....aduke.bennett@jerseycityheadstart.com
2015 John F Kennedy Blvd, Jersey City,
NJ 07305-1527
Dr Aduke A. Bennett, Director

Hunterdon County

SOCIAL SERVICES

Hunterdon Youth Svcs **908.782.1046**
Fax 908.788.8367
PO Box 2397, Flemington, NJ 08822-2397
Judith G. Fredericks, Executive Director

Youth And Family Svcs **908.782.8784**
Fax 908.782.9488
Web ....www.state.nj.us
84 Park Ave, Bldg 1, Flemington, NJ 08822
Kathy Straley, District Manager

GENERAL HEALTH SERVICES

Health Dept **908.788.1351**
Fax 908.782.7510
Web ....www.co.hunterdon.nj.us/health
314 State Hwy 12 W, Bldg 1, Flemington, NJ 08822
John W. Beckley, Mph, Health Officer

JUSTICE AGENCY

Ofc Of Public Defender **908.782.1082**
Fax 908.782.9337
Web ....www.opd.state.nj.us
84 Park Ave Ste G102, Flemington, NJ 08822-1174
Peter Abatemarco, Deputy Public Defender

Probation Dept **908.237.5900**
Fax 908.237.5868
E-mail ....brenda.beacham@judiciary.state.nj.us
65 Park Ave, Flemington, NJ 08822
Brenda Beacham, Assistant Cpo

COURTS

Family Court **908.237.5920**
Fax 908.237.5918
Web ....www.judiciary.state.nj.us
E-mail ....peter.buchsbaun@judiciary.state.nj.us
65 Park Ave, Flemington, NJ 08822-1128
Honorable Peter A. Buchsbaun, Director

POLICE AND SHERIFF

Sheriff's Ofc **908.788.1166**
Fax 908.806.4624
E-mail ....fbrown@co.hunterdon.nj.us
8 Court St, Flemington, NJ 08822
Frederick W Brown, Sheriff

Mercer County

SOCIAL SERVICES

Protection And Advocacy System **609.292.9742**
Fax 609.777.0187
Web ....www.drnj.org
210 S Broad St 3rd floor, Trenton, NJ 08608-2407
Joseph Young, Director

Youth And Family Svcs **609.292.5100**
Fax 609.633.9602
Web ....www.state.nj.us
120 So Stockton St, Ste 2, Trenton, NJ 08625
Rasel Palmer, District Manager

GENERAL HEALTH SERVICES

City Of Trenton Div Of Health **609.989.3242**
Fax 609.989.3898
E-mail ....jbrownley@trentonnj.org
218 N Broad St, Trenton, NJ 08608
James A Brownley, Health Officer

Communicable Diseases Control **609.826.5964**
Fax 609.826.4874
Web ....www.nj.gov/dacksalsh/health
135 E Estate St, Trenton, NJ 08619
Christina Tan, Md, Ms, Assistant Commissioner

**East Windsor Township Div Of
Health** **609.443.4000**
Fax 609.443.8303
16 Lanning Blvd, Hightstown, NJ 08520
Jeffery Plunkett, Health Officer

Ewing Township Health Dept **609.883.2900**
Fax 609.883.0215
Web ....www.ewingtownship.com
E-mail ....alee@ewingtwp.com
2 Jake Garzio Dr, Trenton, NJ 08628
Allen Lee, Health Officer

**Hamilton Township-Division Of
Health** **609.890.3820**
Fax 609.890.6093
E-mail ....jplunkett@hamiltonnj.com
2100 Greenwood Ave, Hamilton, NJ 08609
Jeffery J. Plunkett, Ba, Med, Health Officer

**Hopewell Township Dept Of
Health** **609.737.0120**
Fax 609.737.6836
Web ....www.hopewelltwp.org
E-mail ....gguarino@hopewelltwp.org
201 Washington Crossing Pennington Road,
Titusville, NJ 08560
Gary A. Guarino, Health Officer

Lawrence Township Health Dept **609.844.7089**
Fax 609.895.1668
Web ....www.lawrencetwp.com
2207 Lawrence Rd, Lawrence Township, NJ 08648
Carol Chamberlain, Health Officer

Princeton Health Commission **609.497.7608**
Fax 609.924.7627
Web ....www.princetonboro.org
E-mail ....dhenry@princetonboro.org
1 Monument Dr, Princeton, NJ 08542
David Henry, Mph, Health Officer

**West Windsor Township Health
Dept** **609.799.2400**
Fax 609.799.2044
Web ....www.westwindsor.nj.org
E-mail ....bhary@westwindsortwp.com
271 Clarksville Rd, Princeton Junction,
NJ 08550-5333
Robert Hary, Health Officer

MENTAL HEALTH SERVICES

**Greater Trenton Community Mental Health
Ctr** **609.396.6788**
Fax 609.989.1245
1001 Spruce st, Trenton, NJ 08638
John Monahan, CEO

Ofc Of Addiction Svcs **609.989.6897**
Fax 609.989.5218
Web ....www.mercercounty.org
E-mail ....mbillek@mercercounty.org
640 S Broad St, Rm 230, Trenton, NJ 08611
Marygrace Billek, Director

JUSTICE AGENCY

Dept of Public Defender **609.292.7087**
Fax 609.777.1795
25 Market St, Fl CN850, Trenton, NJ 08625
John Richardson Bowser, Deputy Public Defender

Div Of Youth And Family Svcs **609.777.2000**
Fax 609.777.2001
E-mail ....ecrummy@dhs.state.nj.us
PO Box 717, Trenton, NJ 08625-0717
Eileen Crummy, Director

**Mental Health And Guardianship
Advocacy** **609.292.1780**
Fax 609.984.3396
25 Market St, Trenton, NJ 08611
Patrick Reilly, Director

Ofc Of Public Defender **609.292.4081**
Fax 609.777.0892
210 S Broad St, Fl 2, Trenton, NJ 08608
Vernon Clash, Deputy Public Defender

POLICE AND SHERIFF

Sheriff's Ofc **609.989.6111**
175 South Broad St, Trenton, NJ 08650
John Kemler, Sheriff

EDUCATION SERVICES

**Div Of District and School
Improvement** **609.292.6874**
Fax 609.341.2070
Web ....www.doe.state.nj.us
E-mail ....james.mcbee@doe.state.nj.us
100 Riverview Plaza, Rte 29, Trenton, NJ 08625-0500
James McBee, Director

Ofc Of Special Education Programs **609.633.6833**
Fax 609.984.8422
Web ....www.state.nj.us/education
100 Riverview Plaza, Trenton, NJ 08625
Peggy McDonald, Acting Director

Special Education **609.588.5873**
Fax 609.588.5849
1075 Old Trenton Rd, Trenton, NJ
Carmen Fanucci, Supervisor Of Child Study

Middlesex County

SOCIAL SERVICES

Board Of Social Svcs **732.745.3500**
Fax 732.745.4558
Web ....www.middlesexcwa.newark.rockers.edu
E-mail ....angela.mackaronis@co.middlesex.nj.us
181 How Ln, New Brunswick, NJ 08901-3641
Angela Mackaronis, Director

Perth Amboy District Ofc **732.293.5060**
Fax 732.293.4954
Web ....www.judiciary.state.nj.us
E-mail ....edna.rosa@judiciary.state.nj.us
458 Florida Grove Rd, Perth Amboy, NJ 08861-3729
Edna Rosa, Acting Manager

**Youth And Family Svcs: Edison District
Ofc** **732.980.9312**
Fax 732.980.0328
53 Knightsbridge Rd, Piscataway, NJ 08854
Peter Mancusi, District Manager

GENERAL HEALTH SERVICES

Edison Township Div Of Health 732.248.7290
Fax 732.248.0494
Web .... www.edisonnj.org
E-mail .... health@edisonnj.org
  100 Municipal Blvd, Municipal Complex, Edison,
  NJ 08817-3369
  Lisa Gulla, Mph, Health Officer

Health Dept 732.745.3100
Fax 732.745.2568
Web .... www.co.middlesex.nj.us/publichealth
  75 Bayard St, Fl 5, New Brunswick, NJ 08901
  Kathy Antonitis, Acting Director

Middle-Brook Regional Health
Commission 732.356.8090
Fax 732.356.1249
Web .... www.middlebrookhealth.org
E-mail .... ksumner@middlebrookhealth.org
  1200 Mountain Ave, Middlesex, NJ 08846
  Kevin G. Sumner, MPH, Health Officer

Piscataway Township Health Dept 732.562.2323
Fax 732.743.2500
Web .... www.piscatawaynj.org
E-mail .... asimpf@piscatawaynj.org
  455 Hoes Ln, Piscataway, NJ 08854-4147
  Andrew C. Simpf, Jr., Health Officer

South Brunswick Board Of Health 732.329.4000
Fax 732.329.4168
Web .... www.sbtnj.net
E-mail .... sp1@njlincs.net
  540 Ridge Rd, Monmouth Junction, NJ 08852-2677
  Stephen J. Papenberg, Health Officer

Woodbridge Township Dept Of
Health 732.855.0600
Fax 732.855.0887
E-mail .... dennis.green@twp.woodbridge.nj.us
  2 G Frederick Plz, Woodbridge, NJ 07095
  Dennis Green, Health Officer/director

MENTAL HEALTH SERVICES

Mental Health Clinic 732.442.1666
Fax 732.442.9512
  570 Lee St, Perth Amboy, NJ 08861-3053
  Laurie Sneider, Executive Director

POLICE AND SHERIFF

New Brunswick Police Dept 732.745.5200
Fax 732.514.0643
E-mail .... jcatanese@newbrunswick.com
  25 Kirkpatrick St Fl 1A, New Brunswick, NJ 08903
  Keith Mangrola, Director

Sheriff's Ofc 732.745.3366
Fax 732.745.4055
Web .... www.co.middlesex.nj.us
E-mail .... sheriff@co.middlesex.nj.us
  701 Livingston Ave, New Brunswick, NJ 08901
  Mildred Scott, Sheriff

EDUCATION SERVICES

School Based Youth Svcs 732.745.3000
Fax 732.214.1285
  1000 somerset st, New Brunswick High School, New
  Brunswick, NJ 08901
  James Christman, Interim Principal

Special Education 732.249.2900
Fax 732.296.0683
E-mail .... denise.wilkins@co.middlesex.nj.us
  1501 Livingston Ave, North Brunswick, NJ 08902
  Denise Wilkins, Supervisor Of Child Study

Monmouth County

SOCIAL SERVICES

Div Of Social Svcs 732.431.6000
Fax 732.431.6267
E-mail .... jhutcheson@co.monmouth.nj.us
  3000 Kozloski Rd, Freehold, NJ 07728
  John Hutcheson, Director

Youth And Family Svcs 732.988.2161
Fax 732.988.7025
Web .... www.dhs.state.nj.us
  630 Bangs Ave Ste 2, Asbury Park, NJ 07712-6946
  Charles Freer, District Manager

GENERAL HEALTH SERVICES

Colts Neck Township Health Dept 732.462.5470
Fax 732.431.3173
Web .... www.colts-neck.nj.us
E-mail .... coltsneckhd@optonline.net
  124 Cedar Dr, Colts Neck, NJ 07722-1673
  Thomas Frank, Health Officer

Freehold Township Health Dept 732.294.2060
Fax 732.462.2340
Web .... www.twp.freehold.nj.us
E-mail .... mjahn@twp.freehold.nj.us
  1 Municipal Plz, Freehold, NJ 07728-3099
  Margaret Jahn, Health Officer

Hazlet Health Dept 732.264.5541
Fax 732.264.9531
  1766 Union Ave, Hazlet, NJ 07730
  Robert N. Scapicio, Ma, Health Officer

Health Dept 732.431.7456
Fax 732.409.7579
Web .... www.visitmonmouth.com/health
E-mail .... mmeddis@co.monmouth.nj.us
  3435 US Highway 9, Freehold, NJ 07728-3285
  Micheal A Meddis, Public Health Coordinator

Long Branch Dept Of Health 732.571.5665
Fax 732.222.1516
Web .... www.visitlongbranch.com
  344 Broadway, Long Branch, NJ 07740
  David Roach, Mph, Health Officer

Manalapan Township Dept Of
Health 732.446.8345
Fax 732.446.1576
Web .... twp.manalapan.nj.us
E-mail .... health@twp.manalapan.nj.us
  120 Route 522 & Taylor Mills Road, Town Hall,
  Manalapan, NJ 07726
  William David Richardson, Mph, Health Officer

Middletown Health Dept 732.615.2095
Fax 732.671.8697
Web .... www.middletownnj.org
E-mail .... rdebenebetto@middletownnj.org
  1 Kings Hwy, Middletown, NJ 07748-2502
  Richard Debenebetto, Health Officer

Regional Health Commission 732.493.9520
Fax 732.493.9521
Web .... www.mcrhc.org
E-mail .... info@mcrhc.org
  1540 W Park Ave Ste 1, Asbury Park, NJ 07712-3192
  Sandra Vansant, Health Officer

MENTAL HEALTH SERVICES

Mental Health Board 732.431.7200
Fax 732.308.3700
Web .... www.co.monmouth.nj.us
  3000 Kozloski Road, Freehold, NJ 07728
  Berry Johnson, Administrator

JUSTICE AGENCY

Ofc Of Public Defender 732.308.4320
Fax 732.308.2378
  7 Broad St, Freehold, NJ 07728
  Sharon, Coordinator

Probation Dept 732.677.4800
Fax 732.677.4818
E-mail .... bkennedy-sinacore@co.monmouth.nj.us
  30 Mechanic St, Freehold, NJ 07728
  Bonnie Kennedy-Sinacore, CPO

COURTS

Children In Court Team 732.677.4310
Fax 732.677.4365
  Superior Courthouse, Monmouth, 72 Monument Pl,
  Freehold, NJ 07728
  Fern Varasano, Team Leader

POLICE AND SHERIFF

Sheriff's Ofc 732.431.7139
Fax 732.294.5965
Web .... www.monmouthsheriff.org
E-mail .... sgolden@mcsonj.org
  50 E Main St, Freehold, NJ 07728
  Shaun Golden, Sheriff

Morris County

SOCIAL SERVICES

Board of Social Svcs 973.326.7800
Fax 973.326.7808
  340 W Hanover Ave, Morristown, NJ 07960
  Gary Denamen, Director

Youth And Family Svcs 973.927.0931
Fax 973.927.3757
  855 State Route 10 Ste 101, Randolph, NJ 07869
  Suzanne Alvino, District Manager

GENERAL HEALTH SERVICES

Denville Div Of Health 973.625.8300
Fax 973.627.8371
Web .... www.denvillenj.org
  1 Saint Marys Pl, Denville, NJ 07834
  Steven Ward, Administrator

Dover Health Dept 973.366.2200
Fax 973.366.6167
Web .... www.dover.nj.us
E-mail .... doverhealth@dover.nj.us
  37 N Sussex St, Dover, NJ 07801
  Donald N. Costanzo, Health Officer

East Hanover Board Of Health 973.428.3035
Fax 973.428.2986
Web .... www.easthanovertownship.com
E-mail .... carlo.dilizia@njlincs.net
  411 Ridgedale Ave, East Hanover, NJ 07936-1487
  Carlo Dilizia, Ma, Health Officer

Hanover Township Health Dept 973.428.2485
Fax 973.515.3772
Web .... www.hanovertownship.com
E-mail .... gvanorden@hanovertownship.com
  1000 State Route 10, Whippany, NJ 07981-1006
  George Van Orden, Phd, Health Officer

Jefferson Township Health Dept 973.697.1500
Fax 973.697.8090
E-mail .... pgarv@jeffersontownship.net
  1033 Weldon Rd, Lake Hopatcong, NJ 07849-2399
  Cindee Degennaro, Ma, Health Officer

Lincoln Park Health Dept 973.270.2040
Fax 973.270.2041
E-mail .... patp@bolp.org
  34 Chapel Hill Rd, Lincoln Park, NJ 07035
  Pasquale A. Pignatelli, Jr., Mpa, Health Officer

Madison Health Dept **973.593.3079**
Fax 973.593.3072
Web ....www.rosenet.org
E-mail ....norgalisj@rosenet.org
   28 Walnut St Ste 1, Madison, NJ 07940-1638
   James H Norgalis, Health Officer

Montville Township Health Dept **973.331.3316**
Fax 973.331.9287
Web ....www.montvillenj.org
E-mail ....jwozniak@montvillenj.org
   195 Changebridge Rd, Montville, NJ 07045-9498
   John A. Wozniak, Jr Meh, Health Officer

Morristown Div Of Health **973.796.1975**
Fax 973.292.6730
Web ....www.townofmorristown.org
E-mail ....d-oconnell@townofmorristown.org
   200 South Street, Morristown, NJ 07963
   Darlene O Connell, Health Officer

Parsippany Board Of Health **973.263.7160**
Fax 973.299.1349
Web ....www.parsippany.net
   1130 Knoll Rd, Lake Hiawatha, NJ 07034
   Carlo Dilizia, Health Officer

**Pequannock Township Board Of
Health** **973.835.5700**
Fax 973.835.4328
Web ....www.peqtwt.org
E-mail ....pcorreale@peqtwt.org
   530 Newark Pompton Tpke, Pompton Plains,
   NJ 07444-1798
   Peter Correale, Health Officer

**Randolph Township Board Of
Health** **973.989.7050**
Fax 973.989.7076
Web ....www.randolphnj.org
E-mail ....mcaputo@randolphnj.org
   502 Millbrook Ave, Randolph, NJ 07869-3713
   Mark Caputo, Health Officer

**Rockaway Township Dept Of
Health** **973.983.2848**
Fax 973.983.2497
Web ....www.rockawaytownship.org
E-mail ....health@rockawaytownship.org
   65 Mount Hope Rd, Rockaway, NJ 07866-1699

Roxbury Township Health Dept **973.448.2028**
Fax 973.252.6079
Web ....www.roxburynj.us
E-mail ....mcaputo@roxburynj.us
   72 Eyland Ave, Succasunna, NJ 07876-1622
   Mark Caputo, Health Officer

Washington Township Health Dept **908.876.3650**
Fax 908.876.5138
Web ....www.wtmorris.org
E-mail ....ccooke-gibbs@wtmorris.net
   43 Schooleys Mountain Rd, Long Valley, NJ 07853
   Cristianna Cooke-gibbs, Mph, Health Officer

JUSTICE AGENCY

CASA **973.998.7590**
Fax 973.998.7589
Web ....www.casamsc.org
E-mail ....info@casamsc.org
   18 Cattano Ave, Morristown, NJ 07960
   Lisa Firkser, Executive Director

Ofc Of Public Defender **973.631.6260**
Fax 973.631.6271
E-mail ....dolores.mann@opd.state.nj.us
   2150 Headquarters Plz, Fl 3, Morristown, NJ 07960
   Dolores Mann, Deputy Public Defender

Probation Dept **973.656.3500**
Fax 973.656.3531
E-mail ....mike.glasgo@judiciary.state.nj.us
   PO Box 910, Morristown, NJ 07963-0910
   Mike Glasgo, CPO

COURTS

Family Court **973.656.4010**
Fax 973.656.4039
E-mail ....greg.lambard@judiciary.state.nj.us
   PO Box 910, Morristown, NJ 07963-0910
   Greg Lambard, Family Division Director

POLICE AND SHERIFF

Sheriff's Dept **973.285.6600**
Fax 973.605.8312
E-mail ....sheriff@gti.net
   60 Washington St, Morristown, NJ 07960
   Edward Rochford, Sheriff

Ocean County

SOCIAL SERVICES

Board Of Social Svcs **732.349.1500**
Fax 732.244.8075
E-mail ....ocbss@xbp.dhs.state.nj.us
   1027 Hooper Ave, Toms River, NJ 08754
   Mary Fran-mcfadden, Director

**Providence House -Domestic
Violence** **732.350.2120**
Fax 732.350.2725
Web ....www.catholiccharitiestrenton.org
E-mail ....mpettrow@cctrenton.org
   88 Schoolhouse Rd Ste 1, Manchester Township,
   NJ 08759-3051
   Mary Pettrow, Director

Youth And Family Svcs **732.255.0700**
Fax 732.255.0845
Web ....www.dhs.state.nj.us
E-mail ....michelle.kennedy@dhs.state.nj.us
   1510 Hooper Ave Ste 210, Toms River,
   NJ 08753-2228
   Michelle Kennedy, District Manager

GENERAL HEALTH SERVICES

Health Dept **732.341.9700**
Fax 732.678.0033
Web ....www.ochd.org
E-mail ....dregenye@ochd.org
   175 Sunset Ave, Toms River, NJ 08754
   Dan Regenye, Communicable Disease Director

Long Beach Island Health Dept **609.492.1212**
Fax 609.492.9215
E-mail ....lbihd@lbihealth.com
   11601 Long Beach Blvd, Beach Haven, NJ 08008
   Timothy Hilferty, Health Officer

MENTAL HEALTH SERVICES

Ocean Mental Health Svcs **732.349.5550**
Fax 732.505.1517
Web ....www.oceanmentalhealth.org
E-mail ....charleslangan@oceanmentalhealth.org
   160 Atlantic City Blvd, Bayville, NJ 08721-1229
   Charles Langan, PhD, Executive Director

JUSTICE AGENCY

Juvenile Probation Ofc **732.831.7999**
Fax 732.831.7992
Web ....www.co.ocean.nj.us
   100 E Water St, Toms River, NJ 08753-7518
   James J. Kelly, Chief Probation Division Manager

Ofc Of Public Defender **732.286.6400**
Fax 732.286.6432
   236 Main St, Toms River, NJ 08753-7469
   Claude Rogatis, Assistant Chief For Investigations

Toms River Township **732.341.1000**
Fax 732.505.1886
   33 Washington St, Toms River, NJ 08753
   Kathleen Adams, Director

COURTS

Criminal Court **732.929.2173**
Fax 732.288.7233
E-mail ....honorable.Daniels@judiciary.state.nj.us
   120 Hooper Ave, Rm 17, Toms River, NJ 08753
   Honorable Daniels, Judge

POLICE AND SHERIFF

Sheriff's Ofc **732.929.2044**
Fax 732.349.1909
E-mail ....wpolhemus@co.ocean.nj.us
   120 Hooper Ave, Toms River, NJ 08754
   William Polhemus, Sheriff

EDUCATION SERVICES

Brick Headstart **732.477.1155**
Fax 732.477.6513
   503 Adamston Rd, Toms River, NJ 08753
   Barbara Bruce, Director

School Based Youth Svcs **609.296.5074**
Fax 609.812.9643
   520 Nugentown Rd, Tuckerton, NJ 08087
   Carol Turano, Director

School Based Youth Svcs **732.363.7272**
Fax 732.905.5644
E-mail ....lakewoodschbase@aol.com
   855 Somerset Ave, Lakewood, NJ 08701
   Maryann Arkis, Director

Special Education **732.929.2078**
Fax 732.244.4073
Web ....www.doe.state.nj.us
E-mail ....carmen.fanucci@doe.state.nj.us
   212 Washington St, Toms River, NJ 08753-7566
   Carmen L. Fanucci, Supervisor Of Child Study

Passaic County

SOCIAL SERVICES

**City Of Paterson Dept Of Human
Resources** **973.321.1242**
Fax 973.321.1225
Web ....www.patcity.com
E-mail ....ccorrea@patcity.com
   125 Ellison St Ste 1, Paterson, NJ 07505-1310
   Millie Izqueredr, Program Director

Youth And Family Svcs **973.977.4525**
Fax 973.742.0952
Web ....www.state.nj.us
   22 Mill St Ste 1, Paterson, NJ 07501-1893
   Adrien Dupree, District Manager

GENERAL HEALTH SERVICES

City Of Paterson Health Clinic **973.321.1277**
Fax 973.321.1246
Web ....www.patcity.gov
E-mail ....tweigle@patersonnj.gov
   176 Broadway, Fl 1, Paterson, NJ 07505
   Trevor Weigle, Health Officer

Clifton Board Of Health **973.470.5758**
Fax 973.470.5768
Web ....www.cliftonnj.org
   900 Clifton Ave, Clifton, NJ 07013
   John Biegel, Health Officer

Dept Of Health **973.881.4396**
Fax 973.225.0222
Web ....www.passaiccountynj.org
E-mail ....josephs@passaiccountynj.org
   317 Pennsylvania Ave, Paterson, NJ 07503
   Joseph Surowiez, Health Officer

Passaic City Health Dept 973.365.5603
Fax.....................973.365.2242
Web.....................www.cityofpassaic.com
E-mail.....................jbiegel@cityofpassaicnj.gov
   330 Passaic St, Passaic, NJ 07055-5815
John Biegel, Health Officer

Pompton Lakes Board Of Health 973.835.0400
Fax.....................973.835.9960
Web.....................www.njpublic.com
E-mail.....................pompton.nurse@njpublic.com
   25 Lenox Ave, Municipal Building, Pompton Lakes,
NJ 07442-1729

West Milford Township Health
Dept 973.728.2720
Fax.....................973.728.2847
Web.....................www.westmilford.org
E-mail.....................healthdirector@westmilford.org
   1480 Union Valley Rd, West Milford, NJ 07480-1338
William Walllace, Health Officer

MENTAL HEALTH SERVICES

Mental Health Clinic Of Passaic 973.471.8006
Fax.....................973.471.1630
Web.....................www.mhcp.org
E-mail.....................sschreiber@mhcp.org
   111 Lexington Ave, Passaic, NJ 07055-5297
Sybil Schreiber, Phd, Director

JUSTICE AGENCY

Ofc Of Public Defender 973.977.4150
Fax.....................973.977.1917
   66 Hamilton St, Fl 3, Paterson, NJ 07505
John B. Dwyer, Deputy Public Defender

Probation Office 973.247.8632
Fax.....................973.247.8621
   63-65 Hamilton St, Paterson, NJ 07505
Gordon Muth, Chief Performance Officer

Youth Svc Bureau 973.321.1264
Fax.....................973.595.7460
   60 Temple St, Paterson, NJ 07522
Alonzo Moody, Director

COURTS

Family Court.....................973.247.8441
Fax.....................973.247.8444
Web.....................www.judiciary.state.nj.us
   401 Grand St, Rm 819, Paterson, NJ 07505
Judge Capalsela, Presiding Judge

POLICE AND SHERIFF

Sheriff's Dept 973.389.5919
Fax.....................973.389.9350
Web.....................www.pasaiccountynj.org
   435 Hamburg Tpke Ste C, Wayne, NJ 07470-2067
Charles Mayers, Sheriff

EDUCATION SERVICES

Communities In Schools 973.472.2478
Fax.....................973.472.5474
Web.....................www.unitedpassaic.org
E-mail.....................info@unitedpassaic.org
   41 Myrtle Ave, Passaic, NJ 07055-2924
Ed Lyons, Director

Ctr For Family Resources 973.853.2020
   41 Henry Rd, Ringwood, NJ 07456
Danielle Babula, Director

Ctr For Family Resources 973.962.0055
Fax.....................973.962.1129
Web.....................www.head.com
   10 morris ave, Ringwood, NJ 07456
Elaine Roel, Executive Director

School Based Youth Svcs 973.321.0541
Fax.....................973.720.9553
E-mail.....................phowe@patcity.com
   61-127 Preakness Ave, John F. Kennedy High School,
Paterson, NJ 07522
Paula Howe, Director

School Based Youth Svcs 973.473.2408
Fax.....................973.473.6883
Web.....................www.dhs.state.nj.us
E-mail.....................valerie.colleti@dhs.state.nj.us
   185 Paulison Ave, Passaic, NJ 07055-4809
Valerie Colleti, Director

Special Education 973.569.2110
Fax.....................973.754.0241
   501 River St, Paterson, NJ 07524
Timolin Hollins, Office Manager

Salem County

SOCIAL SERVICES

Board of Social Svcs 856.299.7200
Fax.....................856.299.3245
E-mail.....................kathy.lockbaum@verizon.net
   147 S Virginia Ave, Penns Grove, NJ 08069-1797
Kathy Lockbaum, Director

GENERAL HEALTH SERVICES

Health Dept 856.935.7510
Fax.....................856.935.8483
Web.....................www.cshealth.org
   98 Market St Ste 1, Salem, NJ 08079
Nancy Gerrity, Health Officer

MENTAL HEALTH SERVICES

Health Care Commons, Inc 856.299.3200
Fax.....................856.299.7183
Web.....................www.hcommons.com
E-mail.....................e.stalter@hcommons.com
   500 S Pennsville Auburn Rd, Penns Grove,
NJ 08069-2943
Eric Stalter, Clinical Director

JUSTICE AGENCY

Ofc Of Public Defender 856.935.2212
Fax.....................856.935.9249
Web.....................www.opd.state.nj.us
E-mail.....................opd@opd.state.nj.us
   199 E Broadway, Salem, NJ 08079-2000
Nathan Davis, Assistant Chief

Probation Dept 856.935.7510
Fax.....................856.935.3825
Web.....................www.judiciary.state.nj.us
   85 Market St, Salem, NJ 08079-1910
Curtis J. Hurff, Vacpo, Chief Performance Officer

POLICE AND SHERIFF

Sheriff's Ofc 856.935.7510
Fax.....................856.935.8880
E-mail.....................chuck.miller@salemcountynj.gov
   94 Market St, Salem, NJ 08079
Charles M. Miller, Sheriff

EDUCATION SERVICES

School Based Youth Svcs 856.935.7365
Fax.....................856.935.5027
   166 Salem-Woodstown Rd, Salem, NJ 08079
Lorraine Green, Director

Somerset County

SOCIAL SERVICES

Board Of Social Svcs 908.526.8800
Fax.....................908.231.9010
E-mail.....................kunzmanj@co.somerset.nj.us
   73 E High St, Somerville, NJ 08876
Joseph Kuzmann, Director

Youth And Family Svcs 908.526.5030
Fax.....................908.704.7301
   92 E Main St, Somerville, NJ 08876-2949
Carmen Diaz, District Manager

GENERAL HEALTH SERVICES

Bernards Township Health Dept 908.204.3070
Fax.....................908.204.3075
Web.....................www.bernardshealth.org
E-mail.....................lforgione@bernards.org
   262 S Finley Ave, Basking Ridge, NJ 07920-1430
Lucy A. Forgione, Health Officer

Branchburg Township Dept Of
Health 908.526.1300
Fax.....................908.231.7882
Web.....................www.branchburg.nj.us
E-mail.....................healthdept@branchburg.nj.us
   1077 US Hwy 202 N, Branchburg, NJ 08876
Cynthia Weaver, Health Officer

Bridgewater Township Div Of
Health 908.725.5750
Fax.....................908.707.1235
E-mail.....................health@bridgewaternj.gov
   100 Commons Way, Bridgewater, NJ 08807
Chris O. Poulsen, Director

Franklin Township Health Dept 732.873.2500
Fax.....................732.214.0969
E-mail.....................galanowsky@co.somerset.nj.us
   935 Hamilton St Ste 2, Somerset, NJ 08873-3675
Walter Galanowsky, Health Officer

Health Dept.....................908.231.7155
Fax.....................908.704.8042
Web.....................www.co.somerset.nj.us/health
E-mail.....................healthdiv@co.somerset.nj.us
   27 Warren St, Somerville, NJ 08876
John A. Horensky, Ms, Director

Montgomery Township Board Of
Health 908.359.8211
Fax.....................908.359.4308
Web.....................www.twp.montgomery.nj.us
E-mail.....................health@twp.montgomery.nj.us
   2261 US Highway 206, Municipal Bldg., Belle Mead,
NJ 08502-4012
Stephanie Carey, Health Officer

MENTAL HEALTH SERVICES

Richard Hall Community Mental Health
Ctr 908.725.2800
Fax.....................908.704.1790
Web.....................www.co.sumerset.nj.us
   500 N Bridge St, Bridgewater, NJ 08807-2135
Micheal Frost, Administrator

JUSTICE AGENCY

Ofc Of Public Defender 908.704.3020
Fax.....................908.704.3028
E-mail.....................thomas.hofgesang@opd.state.nj.us
   75 Veterans Memorial Dr E Ste 201, Somerville,
NJ 08876
Thomas Hofgesang, Chief Investigator

Probation Dept 908.231.7111
Fax.....................908.704.8604
   20 N Bridge St, Somerville, NJ 08876
John Higgins, Vice President, Nursing

POLICE AND SHERIFF

Sheriff's Dept 908.231.7140
Fax.....................908.526.2558
E-mail.....................provenzano@co.somerset.nj.us
   20 Grove St, Somerville, NJ 08876
Frank J. Provenzano, Sr., Sheriff

EDUCATION SERVICES

Special Education **908.541.5700**
Fax 908.722.6902
Web ....www.co.somerset.nj.us
E-mail ....paul/bilik@doe.state.nj.us
27 Warren St., Somerville, NJ 08876
Diane Mari, Supervisor Of Child Study

Sussex County

SOCIAL SERVICES

Div Of Social Svcs **973.383.3600**
Fax 973.383.3627
Web ....www.sussex.nj.us
E-mail ....scdfs@oel.state.nj.us
83 Spring St, Newton, NJ 07860
Carol Novrit, Director

Youth And Family Svcs **973.383.8400**
Fax 973.579.3213
20 E Clinton St, Newton, NJ 07860
Michelle J. Richard, Director

GENERAL HEALTH SERVICES

Sussex Couty Home Stead **973.948.5400**
Fax 973.948.3056
Web ....www.sussex.nj.us
129 Morris Tpke, Newton, NJ 07860
Marguerite Bransky, Director

Vernon Township Board of Health **973.764.4055**
Fax 973.764.4291
Web ....www.vernontwp.com
E-mail ....healthdir@vernontwp.com
21 Church St, Vernon, NJ 07462
Gene S. Osias, MSW, Health Director

JUSTICE AGENCY

Probation Dept **973.579.0600**
Fax 973.579.0641
E-mail ....michael.lasko@judiciary.state.nj.us
43-47 High St, Newton, NJ 07860
Michael Lasko, Vicinage Asst Chief Probation Officer

COURTS

Family Court **973.579.0630**
Fax 973.579.0719
E-mail ....edward.gannon@judiciary.state.nj.us
43-47 High St, Newton, NJ 07860
Honorable Edward V. Gannon, Director

POLICE AND SHERIFF

Sheriff's Dept **973.579.0850**
Fax 973.579.7884
Web ....www.sussexcountysheriff.com
39 High St, Newton, NJ 07860-1725
Michael Strada, Sheriff

EDUCATION SERVICES

School Based Youth Svcs **973.579.7725**
Fax 973.579.7493
105 N Church Rd, Sussex County Technical School, Sparta, NJ 07871
Suzanne Sarner, Director

Special Education **973.579.6996**
Fax 973.579.6476
262 White Lake Rd, Sparta, NJ 07871-3223

Union County

SOCIAL SERVICES

Dept Of Human Svcs **908.527.4808**
Fax 908.527.4875
Web ....www.ucnj.org
E-mail ....smettlen@ucnj.org
10 Elizabethtown Plz, Union County Administration Building, Elizabeth, NJ 07207
Shanon Mettlen, Hiv Grant Coordinator

Div Of Social Svcs **908.965.2700**
Fax 908.965.2752
Web ....www.oel.state.nj.us
E-mail ....cgillon@oel.state.nj.us
342 Westminster Ave, Elizabeth, NJ 07208-3290
Charles J. Gillon, Director

Family And Children's Svcs **908.352.7474**
Fax 908.965.3227
Web ....www.facsnj.org
E-mail ....wwebb@facsnj.org
40 North Ave, Elizabeth, NJ 07208-2402
William Webb, Director

GENERAL HEALTH SERVICES

City Of Elizabeth Div Of Health **908.820.4060**
Fax 908.820.4290
E-mail ....health@elizabethnj.org
50 Winfield Scott Plz, City Hall Of Elizabeth G-12, Elizabeth, NJ 07201
John Surmay, Health Officer

Clark Health Dept **732.428.8405**
Fax 732.388.1490
Web ....www.ourclark.com
E-mail ....nogonowski@hotmail.com
430 Westfield Ave, Clark, NJ 07066-1732
Nancy A. Raymond, Health Officer

Linden Board Of Health Dept **908.474.8409**
Fax 908.474.1836
E-mail ....health@linden-nj.org
301 N Wood Ave Ste 1, Linden, NJ 07036
Nancy Koblis, Health Officer

Plainfield Health Div **908.753.3084**
Fax 908.753.3679
Web ....www.plainfield.com
E-mail ....mark.colicchio@doh.state.nj.us
510 Watchung Ave, Plainfield, NJ 07060-1721
Mark Colicchio, Acting Health Officer

Summit Board of Health **908.277.6464**
Fax 908.277.0185
512 Springfield Ave, Summit, NJ 07901-2607
Megan Avallone, Director/health Officer

Union Township Board Of Health **908.851.8507**
Fax 908.851.4673
Web ....www.uniontownship.com
E-mail ....jf1@njlincs.net
1976 Morris Ave, Union, NJ 07083-3579
John J. Ferraioli, Health Officer

Westfield Regional Health Dept **908.789.4070**
Fax 908.789.4076
Web ....www.westfieldnj.gov/health
E-mail ....health@westfieldnj.gov
425 E Broad St, Westfield, NJ 07090
Megan Avallone, Health Officer

MENTAL HEALTH SERVICES

Office of Disabilities **908.527.4807**
Fax 908.558.2562
E-mail ....cnewman@cunj.org
10 Elizabethtown Plz, County Administration Building, Elizabeth, NJ 07202-3451
Charlie Newman, Director

JUSTICE AGENCY

Ofc Of Public Defender **908.820.3070**
Fax 908.820.3958
Web ....www.opd.state.nj.us
65 Jefferson Ave, Elizabeth, NJ 07201
Jerri Reed Harris, Chief Investigator

COURTS

Family Court **908.527.4438**
Fax 908.659.3499
Web ....www.jcpenney.com
E-mail ....karen.cassidy@judiciary.state.nj.us
2 Broad St, Elizabeth, NJ 07201-2202
Honorable Karen M. Cassidy, Presiding

POLICE AND SHERIFF

Sheriff's Ofc **908.527.4450**
Fax 908.527.4490
E-mail ....rfroehlich@ucnj.org
10 Elizabethtown Plaza, 1St Floor, 1 Administration Bldg, Elizabeth, NJ 07202-3451
Ralph Froehlich, Sheriff

EDUCATION SERVICES

Battle Hill School **908.851.6481**
2600 Killian Pl, Union, NJ 07083
Micelle Osborne-Warren, Principal

Connecticut Farms School Head School Program **908.851.6471**
Fax 908.687.7332
711 Stuyvesant Ave, Union, NJ 07083
Monica Topal -Mcgrovern, Director

School Based Youth Svcs (Yes Program) **908.436.6644**
Fax 908.351.4572
E-mail ....lperry@trinitas.org
225 Williamson St, Trinitas Hospital, Elizabeth, NJ 07202
Lisa Perry, Director

Special Education **908.654.9860**
Fax 908.654.9869
Web ....www.unioncountynj.org
E-mail ....heather.mills@doe.state.nj.us
300 N Ave E, Westfield, NJ 07090
Heather Mills-Pevonis, Supervisor Of Child Study

Warren County

SOCIAL SERVICES

Social Svcs **908.475.6301**
Fax 908.475.1533
E-mail ....socialservices@co.warren.nj.us
501 2nd St, Belvidere, NJ 07823
Lorraine Scheibner, Director

Youth And Family Svcs **908.689.7000**
Fax 908.835.1225
E-mail ....mary.parkinson@dhs.state.nj.us
415 E Washington, Washington, NJ 07882-1761
Kethy Sgraley, District Manager

GENERAL HEALTH SERVICES

Public Health Nurse Agency **908.689.6000**
Fax 908.689.8330
Web ....www.co.warren.nj.us
E-mail ....judithleone@warren.nj.us
162 E Washington Ave, Washington, NJ 07882-1849
Judith Leone Rn, Bsn, Division Head

MENTAL HEALTH SERVICES

Mental Health Board **908.475.6080**
Fax 908.475.6085
Web ....www.co.warren.nj.us
E-mail ....humanservices@co.warren.nj.us
202 Mansfield St, Belvidere, NJ 07823-1827
Shannon Brennan, Mental Health Administrator

COURTS

Family Div **908.475.6167**
Fax 908.475.6175
Web ....www.judiciary.state.nj.us
413 Second Street Courthouse, Belvidere, NJ 07823
Jackie Ford Condelli, Assistant Div Manager

POLICE AND SHERIFF

Sheriff's Ofc **908.475.6309**
Fax 908.475.6360
413 2nd St Ste 1, Belvidere, NJ 07823
David P. Gallant, Sheriff

SPECIAL SERVICES AGENCIES

ADOPTION AGENCIES

A Bright Beginning Child Care **732.448.0400**
Fax 732.448.0400
1440 How Ln Ste 1B, North Brunswick,
NJ 08902-4600
Sandy Ino, Director

A Loving Choice Adoption Associates **732.224.0924**
Fax 732.842.1740
E-mail ....alovingchoice@comcast.net
25 Monroe Avenue, PO Box 6712, Shrewsbury,
NJ 07702-4017
Cathleen Mcnee, Administrator

Adoptions From The Heart **856.665.5655**
Fax 856.665.5855
Web ....www.adoptionfromtheheart.org
E-mail ....adoption@adoptionfromtheheart.org
451 Woodland Ave, Cherry Hill, NJ 08002-2225
Maxine Chalker, Director

Atlanticare Behavioral Health **856.374.7666**
Fax 856.374.9628
Web ....www.atlanticare.org
E-mail ....pat.ross@atlanticare.org
121 Johnson Rd Ste 5, Blackwood, NJ 08012-1758
Pat Ross, Program Director

Bethany Christian Svcs **856.672.9780**
Fax 856.672.9782
Web ....www.bethany.org/ftwash/
E-mail ....jchantz@bethany.org
739 S White Horse Pike Ste 5, Audubon,
NJ 08106-1648
Jennifer Chantz, Director

Better Living Adoption Svcs **908.654.0277**
Fax 908.654.0414
Web ....www.betterlivingadoptionservices.com
E-mail ....betterlivingadoptionsservices@comcast.net
560 Springfield Ave Ste C, Westfield, NJ 07090-1024
Barbara Fraley, Director

Brodsky And Marla Weinstein Law Ofcs **732.431.1333**
Fax 732.303.0626
2 Buck Ln Ste 6, Marlboro, NJ 07746
Marla Weinstein, Attorney

Catholic Charities Youth Svc **732.249.3881**
Fax 732.249.3630
Web ....www.catholiccharitiesusa.org
E-mail ....mparisi@ccdom.org
115 Commercial Ave, New Brunswick,
NJ 08901-2748
Melissa Parisi, Director

Children's Aid And Family Svcs **201.226.0300**
Fax 201.226.9262
Web ....www.cafsnj.org
E-mail ....rjones@cafsnj.org
240 FRISCH CT FL 1, Paramus, NJ 07652-5250
Robert Jones, Phd, President/CEO

Cofsky & Zeidman **856.429.5005**
Fax 856.429.6328
E-mail ....dcc@209law.com
209 N Haddon Ave Ste A, Haddonfield, NJ 08033
Donald Cofsky Esq., Attorney

Holt International Children's Svcs **609.882.4972**
Fax 609.883.2398
Web ....www.holtintl.org
E-mail ....info@holtintl.org
340 Scotch Rd Ste 2, Trenton, NJ 08628
Murielle S Elfman, Director

**Homestudies & Adoption Placement Svcs
(HAPS)** **201.836.5554**
Fax 201.836.0204
Web ....www.haps.org
E-mail ....info@haps.org
668 American Legion Drive, 2nd Floor, Teaneck,
NJ 07666-2419
Lorraine Kolankowski, Executive Director

ADVOCACY RESOURCES

CASA **908.689.5515**
E-mail ....tracy@casashaw.org
150 Boulecard, Ste 4B, Washington, NJ 07882
Tracy Heisler, Director

Child Advocacy Ctr **609.265.5881**
Fax 609.265.5906
E-mail ....prosecutors@co.burlington.nj.us
118 High Street, Mount Holly, NJ 08060
Mary Anne Wisnitewski, Director

CHS Gertiaric Care, Inc. **856.985.1180**
Fax 856.985.8629
Web ....www.chsgeriatric.com
E-mail ....chs@chsgeriatric.com
3000 Atrium Way, Suite 223, Mt. Laurel, NJ 08054
Carol H. Solomon, President/geriatric Care Manager

Family Svc Assoc **609.569.0239**
Fax 609.569.1942
Web ....www.fsasj.org
E-mail ....jerome.j.johnson@att.net
3073 English Creek Ave Ste 3, Egg Harbor Township,
NJ 08234
Jennie Echo, Vice President

Prosecutor's Ofc And Child Advocacy Ctr **908.965.3865**
Fax 908.965.3872
Web ....www.ucnj.org
E-mail ....jesmerado@ucnj.org
123 Westfield Ave, Elizabeth, NJ 07208-3117
John Esmerado, Supervisor

Youth Svcs Commission **856.663.3998**
Fax 856.663.7182
Web ....www.cpachvi.org
E-mail ....dcrone@cpachvi.org
6991 N Park Dr, Fl 3, Pennsauken, NJ 08109
Ashley Maxwell, Jmdt Coordintor

BEHAVIORAL HEALTH TREATMENT

A Anxiety & Depression Associate **973.471.8888**
721 Clifton Ave Ste 2C, Clifton, NJ 07013-1880
Dilip Shah, Md, Psychiatrist

American Institute For Counseling **732.469.6444**
Fax 732.469.6445
Web ....www.aiccounselors.com
1952 Us Highway 22, Bound Brook, NJ 08805
Miriam Borton, MD, Psychiatrist

Aroga Medical Assoc **609.279.1339**
Fax 609.279.1359
Web ....www.arogaonline.com
188 Tamarack Cir, Skillman, NJ 08558-2021
Edward Bilotti, Psychiatrist

AtlantiCare Behavioral Health **609.645.7600**
Web ....www.atlanticare.org
E-mail ....lenore.hildebrandt@atlanticare.org
2511 Fire Road, Unit B10 Bellevue Commons, Egg
Harbor Township, NJ 08234
Ms. Lenore Hildebrandt, Accreditation Manager
Joint Commission accredited organization.

Awad Medical Practice **732.591.9100**
Fax 732.219.0184
470 State Route 79 Ste 9, Morganville,
NJ 07751-4701
Maher Awad, Md, Psychiatrist

Badaracco Medical Practice **973.783.5033**
Fax 973.746.2604
88 Norwood Ave, Montclair, NJ 07043-1937
Marie Badaracco, Md, Psychiatrist

Bancroft Rehabilitation Services **856.429.0010**
Web ....www.bancroftneurohealth.org
E-mail ....jdeluca@bnh.org
425 Kings Highway East, Haddonfield, NJ 08033
Mrs. Jennifer DeLuca, Accreditation Manager
Joint Commission accredited organization.

**Bayonne Community Mental Health
Center** **201.339.9200**
E-mail ....jkadian@bayonnementalhealth.org
601 Broadway, Bayonne, NJ 07002
Mr. Joseph Kadian, Accreditation Manager
Joint Commission accredited organization.

BBH Bayshore Behavioral Health **732.255.9411**
Fax 732.255.9424
1749 Hooper Ave Ste 102, Toms River,
NJ 08753-8130
Donald Oh, Psychiatrist

Behar Medical Practice **908.273.9525**
E-mail ....lonnybehar@aol.com
7 Union Pl, Summit, NJ 07901
Lonny Behar, Md, Psychiatrist

Bergen Regional Medical Center **201.967.4000**
Web ....www.bergenregional.com
E-mail ....smendelowitz@bergenregional.com
230 East Ridgewood Avenue, Paramus, NJ 07652
Ms. Susan Mendelowitz, Accreditation Manager
Joint Commission accredited organization.

Bethany Baptist Church **856.784.1550**
Fax 856.486.7770
Web ....www.bethanybaptistchurch.com
1115 E Gibbsboro Rd, Clementon, NJ 08021-1213
Priscilla Smith, Youth Administrator

Bhatiya Medical Practice **732.449.0290**
1540 State Route 138 Ste 208, Belmar,
NJ 07719-3765
Savji Bhatiya, MD, Psychiatrist

Black Medical Practice **609.822.9518**
Fax 609.822.2184
2 S Oxford Ave, Ventnor City, NJ 08406
Edward Black, Md, Psychiatrist

Blackinton Medical Practice **609.465.0018**
PO Box 456, Cape May Court House, NJ 08210-0456
Charles Blackinton, Psychiatrist

Bloom Medical Practice **973.746.0447**
517 Park St, Montclair, NJ 07043-1942
Lawrence Bloom, MD, Psychiatrist

Board Of Education **609.476.2267**
Fax 609.476.4205
Web ....www.estellmanorschool.com
E-mail ....guidancecounselorkuppel@msn.com
128 Cape May Ave, Estell Manor, NJ 08319-1735
Jill Kuppel, Guidance Counselor

Bonnie Brae **908.647.0800**
Web .... www.bonnie-brae.org
E-mail .... klewis@bonnie-brae.org
3415 Valley Road, Liberty Corner, NJ 07938
Dr. Kathy Lewis, Accreditation Manager
Joint Commission accredited organization.

Borough Of Westwood **201.664.7100**
Fax 201.664.5340
E-mail .... rhuffman@westwood.org
101 Washington Ave, Westwood, NJ 07675
Robert Huffman, Adminstrator

Borthwick Medical Practice **609.688.9800**
Fax 609.921.8355
34 Chambers St, Princeton, NJ 08542
James Borthwick, MD, Psychiatrist

Boyajian Medical Practice **201.567.0870**
361 Cumberland St, Englewood, NJ 07631-4704
Levon Boyajian, MD, Psychiatrist

Brandon Medical Practice **973.376.8687**
1 Exeter Rd, Short Hills, NJ 07078-1405
Raplh Brandon, Md, Psychiatrist

Breckinridge Medical Practice **973.912.9200**
Fax 314.251.4197
116 Millburn Ave, Millburn, NJ 07041
Doris Breckinbridge, Psychiatrist

Brentwood Ctr-Psychotherapy **973.625.9128**
23 Diamond Spring Rd Ste 8, Denville, NJ 07834-2750
Leon Schul, Psychiatrist

Brick Township Board Of Education **732.785.3000**
Fax 732.920.5907
Web .... www.brickschools.org
E-mail .... dkuch@brickschools.org
101 Hendrickson Ave, Brick, NJ 08724-2585
Donna Kuch, Guidence Counselor

Buchan Medical Practice **732.244.2222**
718 Bernice Ct, Toms River, NJ 08753-3347
Shahin Buchan, Psychiatrist

Burlington Township Board Of Education-Young's School **609.386.3520**
Fax 609.239.3532
Web .... www.burltwpsch.org
E-mail .... dmccracken@burltwpsch.org
1203 Neck Rd, Burlington, NJ 08016-3909
Dana Mccracken, Guidence Counselor

Burstein Medical Practice **732.462.5270**
505 Stillwells Corner Rd, Freehold, NJ 07728-2965
Allan Burstein, Psychiatrist

Burton Medical Practice **201.567.4633**
163 Engle St, Ste 205, Englewood, NJ 07631-2530
Anna Burton, MD, Psychiatrist

CAEC, Inc. **856.983.3328**
Fax 856.983.6677
Web .... www.raproom.org
E-mail .... lynne@raproom.org
1003 Lincoln Dr W Ste A, Marlton, NJ 08053-1532
Lynne Scheiter, Director

Cape Counseling Services **609.778.6100**
Web .... www.capecounseling.org
E-mail .... kreeves@capecounseling.org
1129 Route 9, Cape May Court House, NJ 08210
Ms. Kathy Reeves, Accreditation Manager
Joint Commission accredited organization.

Care Plus NJ, Inc. **201.265.8200**
Web .... www.careplusnj.org
E-mail .... joem@careplusnj.org
610 Valley Health Plaza, Paramus, NJ 07652
Mr. Joseph Masciandaro, Accreditation Manager
Joint Commission accredited organization.

Carrier Clinic **908.281.1000**
Web .... carrierclinic.org
E-mail .... ckosztyo@carrierclinic.com
252 Route 601, Belle Mead, NJ 08502
Ms. Carol Kosztyo, Accreditation Manager
Joint Commission accredited organization.

Castillo Medical Practice **856.768.1818**
95 Route 73rd st, Voorhees, NJ 08043-9532
Edwin Castillo, Psychiatrist

Catholic Charities **908.782.7905**
Fax 908.782.5934
E-mail .... mrezeli@ccdom.org
6 Park Ave, Flemington, NJ 08822
Martha Rezeli, Director

Catholic Charities **732.738.1323**
Fax 732.738.3896
Web .... www.ccdom.org
26 Safran Ave, Edison, NJ 08837
Wesley Moore, Site Manager

Catholic Charities - Diocese of Metuchen **732.324.8200**
Web .... www.ccdom.org
E-mail .... ndixon@ccdom.org
319 Maple Street, Perth Amboy, NJ 08861
Ms. Nora Dixon, Accreditation Manager
Joint Commission accredited organization.

Catholic Charities of the Archdiocese of Newark **973.266.7998**
Fax 973.266.7950
Web .... www.ccsnewark.org
590 North Seventh Street, Newark, NJ 07107
CARF accredited programs available.

Cedar Glen Professional Assoc **609.896.1122**
Fax 609.896.2688
E-mail .... jgreen@cedarglenpa.com
170 Cold Soil Rd, Princeton, NJ 08540-4202
Jeffery Green, Psychiatrist

Charles Medical Practiice **973.672.2555**
Fax 973.672.2529
E-mail .... ellischarlesdoc@aol.com
90 Washington St Ste 209, East Orange, NJ 07017-1050
Ellis Charles, Md, Psychiatrist

Children's Aid and Family Services, Inc. **201.261.2800**
Fax 201.634.3672
Web .... www.cafsnj.org
200 Robin Road, Paramus, NJ 07652
COA accredited organization.

Christian Health Care Center **201.848.5200**
Web .... www.chccnj.org
E-mail .... scil@chccnj.org
301 Sicomac Avenue, Wyckoff, NJ 07481
Ms. Sara Cilderman, Accreditation Manager
Joint Commission accredited organization.

Ciora Medical Practice **201.569.6100**
E-mail .... acciora@hotmail.com
214 Engle St Ste 23, Englewood, NJ 07631-2418
Cristian Ciora, MD, Psychiatrist

Clever Medical Practice **732.345.9100**
25 Bridge Ave Ste 205, Red Bank, NJ 07701-1182
Marcia Sue Clever, Psychiatrist

Community Access Unlimited, Inc. **908.354.3040**
Fax 908.354.2665
Web .... www.caunj.org
80 West Grand Street, Elizabeth, NJ 07202
CARF accredited programs available.

Counseling Ctrs Of Delware Valley **856.985.4300**
11000 W Lincoln Dr Ste 5, Marlton, NJ 08053-3431

CPC Behavior Health Care **732.842.2000**
Fax 732.219.0474
Web .... www.cpcbhc.org
270 State Route 35, Red Bank, NJ 07701-5920
John Mans, Executive Director

CPC Behavioral Healthcare, Inc. **732.935.2220**
Web .... www.cpcbhc.com
E-mail .... mmarinaccio@cpcbhc.org
10 Industrial Way East, Eatontown, NJ 07724
Mrs. Maria Marinaccio, Accreditation Manager
Joint Commission accredited organization.

CPC Behavioral Healthcare- High Point Schools **732.591.1750**
Fax 732.591.2516
Web .... www.cpcbhc.org
E-mail .... kdec@cpcbhc.org
1 High Point Center Way, Morganville, NJ 07751-4213
Tina Behr, Director

Craig Medical Practice **973.895.4752**
Fax 973.895.4458
20 Oak Dr, Randolph, NJ 07869-4809
Thomas Craig, MD, Psychiatrist

Crecca Medical Practice **732.280.2099**
2640 Highway 70 Ste 2A, Manasquan, NJ 08736-2610
Peter Crecca, Psychiatrist

Crossroads Programs, Inc. **609.880.0210**
Fax 609.880.0230
Web .... www.crossroadsprograms.org
610 Beverly-Rancocas Road, Willingboro, NJ 08046
COA accredited organization.

Daytop Village of New Jersey **973.543.5656**
Fax 973.543.7502
Web .... www.daytopnj.org
80 West Main Street, Mendham, NJ 07945
CARF accredited programs available.

De La Torre Medical Practice **973.746.0795**
27 Valley Rd, Montclair, NJ 07042-2708
L S De Latorre, MD, Psychiatrist

De Mercurio Medical Practice **856.985.1664**
562 Lippincott Dr, Marlton, NJ 08053-4810
Robert De Mercurio, DO, Psychiatrist

De Ritter Medical Practice **732.560.9770**
73 West Ave, Somerville, NJ 08876
Lois Deritter, Psychiatrist

Depression Specialist **732.842.1270**
62 Highfield Ct, Little Silver, NJ 07739-1810
David Reskof, MD, Psychiatrist

Deron School **973.509.2777**
Fax 973.509.2515
Web .... www.deronschool.org
E-mail .... ealter@deronschool.org
130 Grove St, Montclair, NJ 07042-4022
Eric. Alter, Director

Deshande Medical Practice **609.799.9020**
666 Plainsboro Rd Ste 1271, Plainsboro, NJ 08536-3046
Kaylani Deshpande, MD, Psychiatrist

Drenk Behavioral Health Ctr **609.267.5656**
Fax 609.267.8892
Web .... www.drenk.org
1289 Route 38 Ste 203, Hainesport, NJ 08036-2730
Harry Marmorstein, President

Duarte Medical Practice **908.522.1820**
24 Beechwood Rd, Summit, NJ 07901
B Duarte, Md, Psychiatrist

East Orange General Hospital **973.672.8400**
Web .... evh.org
E-mail .... sanguilianob@evh.org
300 Central Avenue, East Orange, NJ 07018
Ms. Barbara Sanguiliano, Accreditation Manager
Joint Commission accredited organization.

Eisenberg Medical Practice **908.753.0916**
Fax 301.652.9051
10 Shawnee Dr Ste B, Watchung, NJ 07069-5803
S Eisenberg, MD, Psychiatrist

Elferbein Medical Practice **973.228.8943**
204 Eagle Rock Ave, Roseland, NJ 07068
Emmanuel Elferbein, Psychiatrist

Fair Lawn Mental Health **201.797.2660**
Fax 201.797.5025
Web ....www.careplusnj.org
17-07 Romaine St, Fair Lawn, NJ 07410
Tara Augustine, Director Of Children Services

Fairbanks Medical Practice **201.384.2242**
65 N Maple Ave, Englewood, NJ 07450
J Fairbanks, Psychiatrist

Family Guidance Center Corporation **609.586.0668**
Fax 609.586.4759
Web ....www.fgccorp.org
1931 Nottingham Way, Hamilton, NJ 08619
COA accredited organization.

Family Svc Bureau Of Newark **973.412.2056**
Fax 973.484.3452
Web ....www.newcommunity.org
274 S Orange Ave, Fl 2, Newark, NJ 07103
Arti Kakkar, Executive Director

Fardman Medical Practice **732.970.9077**
Fax 732.970.9088
481 State Route 79, Morganville, NJ 07751-4060
E Fardman Md, Psychiatrist

Feldman Medical Practice **973.376.7774**
16 Holly Dr, Short Hills, NJ 07078-1318
Russett Feldman, Md, Psychiatrist

Ferretti Medical Practice **201.963.6363**
Fax 201.963.0827
142 Palisade Ave Ste 210, Jersey City, NJ 07306-1108
James Ferretti, Md, Psychiatrist

Fiore Medical Practice **201.569.9059**
75 Grand Ave, Englewood, NJ 07631-4355
Vicki Fiore, Md, Pychiatirst

Fisher Medical Practice **201.871.1676**
155 County Rd Ste 15, Cresskill, NJ 07626-2200
William Fisher, Psychiatrist

Forensic Psychiatry **973.467.8987**
75 Main St, Millburn, NJ 07041
Richard Sostowski, Psychiatrist

Formento Medical Practice **732.431.1610**
85 South St, Freehold, NJ 07728-2317
Juan Formento, Md, Psychiatrist

Francisco Medical Practice **908.879.2112**
PO Box 642, Chester, NJ 07930-0642
Rowena Francisco, Psychiatrist

Freehold Counseling Ctr **732.780.7387**
Fax 732.780.5157
37 Court St, Freehold, NJ 07728
Patricia Smith, Program Coordinator

Friedberg Medical Practice **201.871.4778**
Fax 201.767.6926
151 E Palisade Ave, Englewood, NJ 07631
Eugene Friedberg, Psychiatrist

Fuchs Medical Practice **609.585.4200**
396 White Horse Ave Ste 3, Trenton, NJ 08610-1431
Susan Fuchs, Psychiatrist

Guidance Ctr **856.825.6810**
Fax 856.327.4281
Web ....www.ccgcnj.org
2038 Carmel Rd, Millville, NJ 08332
Dieter Hovermann, Executive Director

Hampton Behavioral Health Center **609.267.7000**
Web ....www.hamptonhospital.com
E-mail ....karen.johnson@uhsinc.com
650 Rancocas Rd, Westampton, NJ 08060
Ms. Karen Johnson, Accreditation Manager
Joint Commission accredited organization.

Hampton Behavioral Health Ctr **609.267.7000**
Fax 609.518.2190
650 Rancocas Rd, Mount Holly, NJ 08060-5613
Kristene Jones, Director Of Admissions

Hecht Medical Practice **908.730.9019**
6 Leigh St, Clinton, NJ 08809-1310
George Hecht, Psychiatrist

High Focus Centers **908.363.1023**
Web ....highfocuscenters.com
E-mail ....kcerretta@highfocuscenters.com
47 Maple Street, Suite 401, Summit, NJ 07901
Ms. Kimberly Cerretta, Accreditation Manager
Joint Commission accredited organization.

Hoboken Universal Medical Center **201.792.8200**
Fax 201.792.8452
Web ....www.hobokenumc.com
506 3rd St, Hoboken, NJ 07030-1970
Michael Swerdlow, Phd, Director

Hoboken University Medical Center **201.418.1000**
Web ....www.HobokenUMC.com
E-mail ....ashah@hobokenumc.com
308 Willow Avenue, Hoboken, NJ 07030
Ms. Anjly Shah, Accreditation Manager
Joint Commission accredited organization.

Hope House **973.361.5555**
Fax 973.361.7354
Web ....www.hopehousenj.org
P.O. Box 851, Dover, NJ 07802-0851
COA accredited organization.

Integrity, Inc. **973.623.0600**
Fax 973.623.1862
Web ....www.integrityhouse.org
103 Lincoln Park, Newark, NJ 07102
CARF accredited programs available.

Jersey City Medical Center **201.915.2000**
Web ....www.libertyhcs.org
E-mail ....wlester@libertyhcs.org
355 Grand Street, Jersey City, NJ 07302
Ms. Wren Lester, Accreditation Manager
Joint Commission accredited organization.

Jersey Shore University Medical Center **732.776.4900**
Web ....www.meridianhealth.com
E-mail ....apalisi@meridianhealth.com
1945 Route 33, Neptune, NJ 07754-0397
Ms. Andrea Palisi, Accreditation Manager
Joint Commission accredited organization.

Kennedy University Hospital **856.566.5200**
Web ....www.kennedyhealth.org
E-mail ....p.wallace@kennedyhealth.org
1099 White Horse Road, Voorhees, NJ 08043
Ms. Patricia Wallace, Accreditation Manager
Joint Commission accredited organization.

Life Excel **732.920.7933**
Fax 732.920.2966
Web ....www.thecentercares.com
35 Beaverson Blvd Ste 1D, Brick, NJ 08723-7854
Vinod Bhashyam, Md, Psychiatrist

Lutheran Social Ministries **609.386.7171**
Fax 609.386.7191
Web ....www.lsmnj.org
E-mail ....msager@lsmnj.org
6 Terri Ln Ste 300, Burlington, NJ 08016-4911
Maryann Sager, Director Of Adoption

Maryville Incorporated **856.629.0244**
Fax 856.629.0741
Web ....www.maryvillenj.org
1903 Grant Avenue, Williamstown, NJ 08094
CARF accredited programs available.

Mental Health Association **973.509.9777**
Fax 973.509.9888
Web ....www.mhaessex.org
33 South Fullerton Avenue, Montclair, NJ 07042
CARF accredited programs available.

Merit Mountainside DBA Mountainside
Hospital **973.429.6000**
Web ....mountainsidehosp.com
E-mail ....karen.palatella@mountainsidehosp.com
1 Bay Avenue, Montclair, NJ 07042
Ms. Karen Palatella, Accreditation Manager
Joint Commission accredited organization.

Monmouth Medical Center **732.222.5200**
Web ....www.sbhcs.com
E-mail ....pkeating@sbhcs.com
300 Second Avenue, Long Branch, NJ 07740
Ms. Patricia Keating, Accreditation Manager
Joint Commission accredited organization.

Morristown Medical Center **973.971.5450**
Web ....www.atlantichealth.org
E-mail ....ing-marie.meacham@atlantichealth.org
100 Madison Avenue, Morristown, NJ 07962-1956
Ms. Ing-Marie Meacham, Accreditation Manager
Joint Commission accredited organization.

Mount Carmel Guild Behavioral
Healthcare **973.639.6508**
Fax 973.596.4105
Web ....www.catholichealthandhumanservices.com
E-mail ....anita_holland@ccsnewark.org
58 Freeman, Newark, NJ 07105-4168
Phillip Frese, Administrator

My Father's House, Inc. **856.742.0900**
Fax 856.742.0811
Web ....www.myfathershouseinc.org
104 North Kings Street, Glouster City, NJ 08030
CARF accredited programs available.

NAMI NJ Alliance For The Mentally Ill **732.940.0991**
Fax 732.940.0355
Web ....www.naminj.org
E-mail ....info@naminj.org
1562 US Highway 130, North Brunswick, NJ 08902
Sylvia Axelrod, Executive Director

New Hope Foundation **732.946.3030**
Fax 732.946.9012
Web ....www.newhopefoundation.org
80 Conover Rd, Marlboro, NJ 07746
Tony Comberford, Director
CARF accredited programs available.

New Jersey Health Care System **973.676.1000**
Fax 973.395.7122
Web ....www.va.gov
151 Knollcroft Rd, Building 57, Lyons, NJ 07939
Maryjo Apice, Assistant Director
CARF accredited programs available.

New Jersey Psychiatric Associates **908.719.2222**
Fax 908.719.4747
Web ....www.psychnj.org
E-mail ....psychnj@optonline.net
8 White Tail Ln, Bedminster, NJ 07921
Deborah Wilson, Executive Director

Newark Beth Israel Medical Center **973.926.7000**
Web ....www.saintbarnabas.com
E-mail ....pmicchelli@sbhcs.com
201 Lyons Avenue, Newark, NJ 07112
Ms. Pam Micchelli, Accreditation Manager
Joint Commission accredited organization.

Newark Beth Israel Medical/ Behavioral Health Ctr,
CMHC **973.926.7026**
Fax 973.926.2862
E-mail ....mprowe@sbhcs.com
210 Lehigh Ave, Newark, NJ 07112
Joanne Reilly, Director

Newpoint Behavioral Healthcare **856.845.8050**
Fax 856.845.0688
E-mail ....vincents@newpointbhc.org
404 Tatum St, Woodbury, NJ 08096
John Zukauskas, Executive Director

Newton Medical Center 973.383.2121
Web ....www.nmhnj.org
E-mail ....mfox@nmhnj.org
　　175 High Street, Newton, NJ 07860
　　Mrs. Maryanne Fox, Accreditation Manager
　　Joint Commission accredited organization.

**Newton Memorial Hospital Ctr For Mental
Health** 973.383.1533
Fax 973.383.9309
Web ....www.nmhnj.org
　　175 High St, Newton, NJ 07860
　　Roger Cherney, Director Of Social Services & Admissions

**North Hudson Community Action
Corporation** 201.866.2727
Web ....NHCAC.org
E-mail ....michaels@nhcac.org
　　800-31st Street, Union City, NJ 07087
　　Mr. Michael Shababb, Accreditation Manager
　　Joint Commission accredited organization.

**Preferred Behavioral Health of New Jersey,
Inc.** 732.458.1700
Fax 732.785.3296
Web ....www.preferredbehavioral.org
　　700 Airport Road, Lakewood, NJ 08701
　　CARF accredited programs available.

Princeton HealthCare System 609.497.4000
Web ....www.princetonhcs.org
E-mail ....krauch@princetonhcs.org
　　253 Witherspoon Street, Princeton, NJ 08540
　　Ms. Kathy Rauch, Accreditation Manager
　　Joint Commission accredited organization.

Princeton House 856.779.8455
Fax 856.779.2988
Web ....www.princetonhcs.org
E-mail ....donna.kiley@princetonhcs.org
　　375 Kings Hwy N, Cherry Hill, NJ 08034-1013
　　Donna Kiley, Director

Recovery Services of New Jersey, Inc. 609.625.4900
Web ....discoverlighthouse.com
E-mail ....lorettak@lhrecovery.com
　　5034 Atlantic Avenue, Mays Landing, NJ 08330
　　Ms. Loretta Kettell, Accreditation Manager
　　Joint Commission accredited organization.

**Richard Hall Community Mental Health
Center** 908.725.2800
E-mail ....schmitt@co.somerset.nj.us
　　500 North Bridge Street, Bridgewater, NJ 08807
　　Ms. Priscilla Schmitt, Accreditation Manager
　　Joint Commission accredited organization.

Riverview Medical Center 732.741.2700
Web ....www.meridianhealth.com
E-mail ....ccutone@meridianhealth.com
　　One Riverview Plaza, Red Bank, NJ 07701
　　Mrs. Catherine Cutone, Accreditation Manager
　　Joint Commission accredited organization.

Saint Clare's Health System 973.983.2233
Web ....www.saintclares.org
E-mail ....dscott@saintclares.org
　　25 Pocono Road, Denville, NJ 07834
　　Ms. Donna Scott, Accreditation Manager
　　Joint Commission accredited organization.

Saint Peter's Healthcare System 732.745.8555
Web ....saintpetersuh.com
E-mail ....jgscott@saintpetersuh.com
　　254 Easton Avenue, New Brunswick, NJ 08903-0591
　　Ms. Joan Scott, Accreditation Manager
　　Joint Commission accredited organization.

Sequel of New Jersey - Capital Academy 856.635.0200
Web ....camelotforkids.org
E-mail ....dgoldstein-higgins@sequelyouthservices.com
　　1770 Mt Ephraim Avenue, Haddon Township,
　　NJ 08104
　　Ms. Debbie Goldstein-Higgins, Accreditation Manager
　　Joint Commission accredited organization.

**Somerset Home for Temporarily Displaced
Children** 908.526.6605
Fax 908.526.6999
Web ....www.somersethome.org
　　P.O. Box 6871, Bridgewater, NJ 08807-0871
　　COA accredited organization.

Somerset Medical Center 908.685.2200
Web ....somersetmedicalcenter.com
E-mail ....jguzik@somerset-healthcare.com
　　110 Rehill Avenue, Somerville, NJ 08876-2598
　　Ms. Joan Guzik, Accreditation Manager
　　Joint Commission accredited organization.

South Jersey Healthcare 856.575.4500
Fax 856.451.8318
Web ....www.sjhealthcare.net
　　333 Irving Ave, Bridgeton, NJ 08302
　　Dade Moore, Director/mental Health

St Clare's Hospital 973.316.1800
Fax 973.316.1815
Web ....www.saintclares.org
E-mail ....jzaccone@saintclares.org
　　130 Powerville Rd, Boonton, NJ 07005-8705
　　Suellyn Ellerbe, Vice President

St. Francis Medical Center 609.599.5000
Web ....www.stfrancismedical.com
E-mail ....jpribila@stfrancismedical.org
　　601 Hamilton Avenue, Trenton, NJ 08629
　　Mrs. Juliana Pribila, Accreditation Manager
　　Joint Commission accredited organization.

St. Mary's Hospital 973.365.4300
Web ....www.smh-passaic.org
E-mail ....ricciardellij@smh-passaic.org
　　350 Boulevard, Passaic, NJ 07055
　　Mrs. Jayne Ricciardelli, Accreditation Manager
　　Joint Commission accredited organization.

Steininger Behavioral Care Svcs 856.482.8747
Fax 856.482.8420
Web ....www.sbcs.us
E-mail ....len.altamura@sbcs.us
　　499 Cooper Landing Rd, Cherry Hill, NJ 08002-2504
　　Leonard A. Altamura, President & CEO

Summit Oaks Hospital 908.522.7000
E-mail ....jim.gallagher@psysolutions.com
　　19 Prospect Street, Summit, NJ 07901
　　Mr. James Gallagher, Accreditation Manager
　　Joint Commission accredited organization.

**The Lester A. Drenk Behavioral Health Center,
Inc.** 609.267.5656
Web ....www.drenk.org
E-mail ....gsuschke@drenk.org
　　1289 Route 38 West, Suite 203, Hainesport,
　　NJ 08036
　　Mrs. Gerilyn Suschke, Accreditation Manager
　　Joint Commission accredited organization.

The Lighthouse 609.625.4900
Fax 609.625.4568
Web ....www.lighthouseatmayslanding.com
E-mail ....info@lhrecovery.com
　　5034 Atlantic Ave, Mays Landing, NJ 08330-2022
　　Kenneth Sandler, CEO

Therapist Group 732.246.1969
　　223 State Route 18 Ste 102, East Brunswick,
　　NJ 08816-1913
　　David Kassoff, MD, Psychiatrist

Trinitas Regional Medical Center 908.994.5754
Web ....WWW.TRINITAS.ORG
E-mail ....bcountryman@trinitas.org
　　225 Williamson Street, Elizabeth, NJ 07207
　　Mrs. Bernadette Countryman, Accreditation Manager
　　Joint Commission accredited organization.

UCPC Behavioral Health 908.756.6870
Fax 908.756.5566
Web ....www.ucpcbhc.org
　　117 Roosevelt Ave, Plainfield, NJ 07060-1331
　　Richard Rogers, Director

UCPC Behavioral Health Care 908.756.6870
E-mail ....juliekrup04@aol.com
　　117-119 Roosevelt Avenue, Plainfield, NJ 07060
　　Ms. Julie Krupinski, Accreditation Manager
　　Joint Commission accredited organization.

**UMDNJ - University Behavioral
HealthCare** 732.235.5500
Web ....ubhc.umdnj.edu
E-mail ....coyne@umdnj.edu
　　671 Hoes Lane, Piscataway, NJ 08855
　　Dr. Andrew Coyne, Accreditation Manager
　　Joint Commission accredited organization.

Underwood - Memorial Hospital 856.845.0100
Web ....www.umhospital.org
E-mail ....brookj@umhospital.org
　　509 North Broad Street, Woodbury, NJ 08097
　　Ms. Jane Brook, Accreditation Manager
　　Joint Commission accredited organization.

Union Association of the Children's Home 609.267.1550
Fax 609.261.5672
Web ....www.childrens-home.org
　　243 Pine Street, Mt. Holly, NJ 08060
　　COA accredited organization.

University Behavioral Health Care 732.235.5500
Fax 732.235.4594
Web ....www.umdnj.edu
E-mail ....kosseff@umdnj.edu
　　671 Hoes Ln W, Piscataway, NJ 08854-8021
　　Christopher Kosseff, President/CEO

**Vineland Children's Residential Treatment
Center** 856.696.6550
E-mail ....michael.dindak@dcf.state.nj.us
　　2000 Maple Avenue, Vineland, NJ 08361
　　Mr. Mike Dindak, Accreditation Manager
　　Joint Commission accredited organization.

Virtua Health, Inc. 888.847.8823
Web ....www.virtua.org
E-mail ....ckaplan@virtua.org
　　401 Route 73 North, 50 Lake Center Drive, Suite 402,
　　Marlton, NJ 08053
　　Ms. Caryn Kaplan, Accreditation Manager
　　Joint Commission accredited organization.

VisionQuest - New Jersey 609.894.4856
Web ....www.VQ.com
E-mail ....louis.kassa@vq.com
　　Route 70 & Route 72, New Lisbon, NJ 08064
　　Mr. Louis Kassa, Accreditation Manager
　　Joint Commission accredited organization.

Volunteers of America Delaware Valley 856.854.4660
Fax 856.854.0651
Web ....www.voadv.org
　　235 White Horse Pike, Collingswood, NJ 08107
　　Daniel Lombardo, CEO
　　CARF accredited programs available.

Willowglen Academy New Jersey, Inc. 973.579.3700
Web ....www.willowglen-nj.com
E-mail ....asingh@willowglen-nj.com
　　8 Wilson Drive, Sparta, NJ 07871
　　Ms. Anu Singh, Accreditation Manager
　　Joint Commission accredited organization.

Youth Consultation Service 973.482.8411
Web ....www.ycs.org
E-mail ....jfox@ycs.org
284 Broadway, Newark, NJ 07104
Ms. Jaime Fox, Accreditation Manager
Joint Commission accredited organization.

CHILDREN'S HOSPITAL

Atlantic Care Regional Medical Center 609.345.4000
Web ....www.altanticare.org
1925 Pacific Ave, Atlantic City, NJ 08401
Margaret Belfield, Administrator

Bayonne Medical Center 201.858.5000
29th E 29 St Avenue East, Bayonne, NJ 07002
Dan Kane, Chief Executive Officer

Bayshore Community Hospital 732.739.5900
727 North Beers St, Holmdel, NJ 07733
Michael Swartz, Chief Executive Officer

Capital Health Mercer 609.394.4000
446 Bellevue Ave, Trenton, NJ 08618
Al Maghazehe, Chief Executive Officer

Capital Health Regional Medical Center 609.394.6000
750 Brunswick Ave, Trenton, NJ 08638
Al Maghazehe, Director

Centrastate Medical Center 732.431.2000
901 West Main St, Freehold, NJ 07728
John Gribbin, Chief Executive Officer

Chilton Memorial Hospital 973.831.5000
97 West Parkway, Pompton Plains, NJ 07444
Deborah Zastocki, Chief Executive Officer

Christ Hospital 201.795.8200
Web ....www.christhospital.org
176 Palisade Ave, Jersey City, NJ 07306
Bill Atkinson, Director of Nursing

Clara Maass Medical Center 973.450.2000
One Clara Maass Dr, Belleville, NJ 07109
Mary Clyne, Director

Community Medical Center 732.557.8000
99 Route 37 West, Toms River, NJ 08755
Stephanie Bloom, Chief Executive Officer

Cooper University Hospital 856.342.2000
One Cooper Plaza, Camden, NJ 08103
John Sheridan, Chief Executive Officer

Englewood Hospital and Medical Center 201.894.3000
350 Engle St, Englewood, NJ 07631
Douglas Juack, Chief Executive Officer

Hackensack University Medical Center 201.996.2000
E-mail ....lguarino@humeb.com
30 Prospect Ave, Hackensack, NJ 07601
Louis Guarino, Admin Director Of Nursing

Hoboken University Medical Center 201.418.1000
308 Willow Ave, Hoboken, NJ 07030
Michael Swerdlow, Director Of Family And Youth Services

Holy Name Medical Center 201.833.3000
718 Teaneck Rd, Teaneck, NJ 07666

Hunterdon Medical Center 908.788.6100
2100 Westcott Dr, Flemington, NJ 08822
Robert Wise, Chief Executive Officer

Jersey Shore University Medical Center 732.775.5500
1945 Route 33, Neptune, NJ 07754
Steven Middleson, President

Kennedy Memorial Hospitals University 856.488.6500
2201 Chapel Ave W, Cherry Hill, NJ 08002
Martin Bieber, Chief Executive Officer

Liberty Health Jersey City Center 201.915.2000
355 Grand St, Jersey City, NJ 07302

Liberty Health Meadowlands Hosp
Medical 201.392.3100
55 Meadowland Pkwy, Secaucus, NJ 07094

Memorial Hospital 856.935.1000
Web ....www.mhschealth.com
310 Woodstown Rd, Salem, NJ 08079
Richard Grogan, Chief Executive Officer

Memorial Hospital 856.935.1000
Web ....www.mhschealth.com
310 Woodstown Rd, Salem, NJ 08079
Richard Grogan, Chief Executive Officer

Monmouth Medical Center 732.222.5200
300 Second Ave, Long Branch, NJ 07740
Frank Vozos, Chief Executive Officer

Morristown Memorial Hospital 973.971.5000
E-mail ....denise.brock@atlantichealth.org
100 Madison Ave, Morristown, NJ 07962
Dr. David Shulkin, Chief Executive Officer

Mountainside Hospital 973.429.6000
1 Bay Ave, Montclair, NJ 07042
John Fromhold, President/CEO

Newark Beth Israel Medical Center 973.926.7000
201 Lyons Ave, Newark, NJ 07112
John Brennan, Chief Executive Officer

Newton Medical Center 973.383.2121
175 High St, Newton, NJ 07860
Tom Senker, President

Ocean Medical Center 732.840.2200
425 Jack Martin Blvd, Brick, NJ 08724

Our Lady of Lourdes Medical Center 856.757.3500
1600 Haddon Ave, Camden, NJ 08103
Alexander Hatala, Chief Executive Officer

Overlook Hospital 908.522.2000
99 Beauvoir Ave, Summit, NJ 07902
Alan Lieber, Chief Executive Officer

Palisades Medical Center 201.854.5000
7600 River Rd, North Bergen, NJ 07047

Raritan Bay Medical Center 732.442.3700
Web ....www.rbmc.com
530 New Brunswick Ave, Perth Amboy, NJ 08861
Michael Dagnes, Chief Executive Officer

Riverview Medical Center 732.741.2700
1 Riverview Plaza, Red Bank, NJ 07701
Denise Crisanti, Administrative Assistant

Robert Wood Johnson University Hosp 732.828.3000
1 Robert Wood Johnson Pl, New Brunswick, NJ 08901
Stephen Jones, Chief Executive Officer

Shore Memorial Hospital 609.653.3500
1 East New York Ave, Somers Point, NJ 08244
Ron Johnson, President

Somerset Medical Center 908.685.2200
110 Rehill Ave, Somerville, NJ 08876
Kenneth Bateman, President/CEO

South Jersey Healthcare Regional Medica 856.641.8000
1505 West Sherman Ave, Vineland, NJ 08360
Chev Kaletkowski, Chief Executive Officer

St Barnabas Medical Center 973.322.5000
94 Old Short Hills Rd, Livingston, NJ 07039
John Vonamo, Chief Executive Officer

St Josephs Regional Medical Center 973.754.2000
703 Main St, Paterson, NJ 07503
Williams McDonald, Chief Executive Officer

St Marys Hospital 973.365.4300
350 Blvd, Passaic, NJ 07055

St Michaels Medical Center 973.877.5000
111 Central Ave, Newark, NJ 07102
Dave Ricci, Chief Executive Officer

St Peters University Hospital 732.745.8600
254 Easton Ave, New Brunswick, NJ 08901
Ron Rak, Chief Executive Officer

Trinitas Hospital 908.994.5000
225 Williamson St, Elizabeth, NJ 07202
Gary Horan, Chief Executive Officer

Underwood Memorial Hospital 856.845.0100
509 North Broad St, Woodbury, NJ 08096
Eileen K Cardile, Chief Executive Officer

University Hospital 973.972.4300
150 Bergen St, Newark, NJ 07103

Valley Hospital 201.447.8000
223 North Van Dien Ave, Ridgewood, NJ 07450
Audrey Myers, Chief Executive Officer

Virtua Memorial 609.267.0700
175 Madison Ave, Mount Holly, NJ 08060
Richard Miller, Chief Executive Officer

COUNSELING SERVICES

Cape Counseling Svcs 609.465.4100
Fax 609.465.2588
Web ....www.capecounseling.org
1129 Route 9 S, Cape May Court House, NJ 08210
Greg Speed, Chief Executive Officer

Catholic Charities 732.257.6100
Fax 732.324.8200
Web ....www.ccdom.org
288 Rues Ln, East Brunswick, NJ 08816-3699
Marianne Majewski, Executive Director

Catholic Charities 732.826.9160
Fax 732.826.8342
Web ....www.ccdom.org
E-mail ....lgesumaria@ccdom.org
271 Smith St, Perth Amboy, NJ 08861
Linda Gesumaria, Manager

Children's Home Society Of New Jersey 609.695.6274
Fax 609.394.5769
Web ....www.chsofnj.org
E-mail ....dpressma@chsofnj.org
635 S Clinton Ave Ste 206, Trenton, NJ 08611-1831
Donna C. Pressma, CEO

Family Gudiance Center And Family Children Svcs Of Central
NJ 609.924.2098
Fax 609.924.7826
Web ....www.familyguidancecentercorp.org
120 John St Ste 6, Princeton, NJ 08542-3121
Joni Sampson, Center Director

Jewish Family Svcs 908.352.8375
Fax 908.352.8858
E-mail ....info@jfscentralnj.org
655 Westfield Ave, Elizabeth, NJ 07208-1398
Tom Beck, Executive Director

Jfk Johnson Rehabilitation Institute Dept. Of Speech Pathology
And Audiology 732.321.7063
Fax 732.767.2905
Web ....www.solarishealthsystems.org
65 James St, Edison, NJ 08818
Anne Eckert, Ma, Mba, Ccc-a, Director

Ofc Of Children Svcs 973.742.0063
Fax 973.742.0952
Web ....www.ci.newark.nj.us
E-mail ....backielk@ci.newark.nj.us
22 Mill St, Paterson, NJ 07501
Karen Backiel, Interim Manager

Spence-Chapin Svcs To Families And
Children 908.522.0043
Fax 908.598.1506
Web ....www.spence-chapin.org
E-mail ....bmerley@spence-chapin.org
57 Union Pl Ste 212, Summit, NJ 07901
Brenda Merley, Office Manager

The Community Counseling Center of Moorestown
VNA 877.862.8001
Fax 856.552.1301
Web ....www.moorestownvna.org
E-mail ....services@moorestownvna.org
300 Harper Drive, Moorestown, NJ 08057
Diana Mears Ritz, Director

United Family And Children's Society 908.755.4848
Fax 908.755.3655
Web ....www.unitedfamily.org
E-mail ....treedy@unitedfamily.org
305 W 7th St, Plainfield, NJ 07060-1511
Tom Reedy, Director

CRISIS & SHELTER CARE

Alternatives To Domestic Violence 201.336.7575
Fax 201.336.7555
Web ....www.co.bergen.nj.us
E-mail ....dcohen@co.bergen.nj.us
1 Bergen County Plz, Fl 2, Hackensack, NJ 07601
David Cohen, Director

Anchor House 609.396.8329
Fax 609.396.1239
Web ....www.anchorhousenj.org
E-mail ....anchorhouse@comcast.net
482 Centre St, Trenton, NJ 08611
Kim Mcnear, Executive Director

Catholic Charities Family Growth Program 609.394.5157
Fax 609.394.3010
Web ....www.cctrenton.org
39 N Clinton Ave, Fl 3, Trenton, NJ 08609
Ronald Gering, Director

Crossroads 856.786.1276
Fax 856.786.3760
2216 Lenola Rd, Riverton, NJ 08077-3114
Cheryl Conway, Executive Director

Ctr For Family Svcs. 856.964.1990
Fax 856.964.0242
Web ....www.centerffs.org
E-mail ....ehenderson@centerffs.org
584 Benson St, Camden, NJ 08103
Eileen Henderson, Vice President

Domestic Abuse & Sexual Assault Crisis Ctr 908.453.4121
Fax 908.453.3706
Web ....www.darcc.org
E-mail ....sallan@besafewc.org
PO Box 423, Belvidere, NJ 07823-0423
Pam Farago, Executive Director

Domestic Abuse Svcs, Inc. 973.579.2386
Fax 973.579.3277
E-mail ....info@dasi.org
105 Main St, Newton, NJ 07860
Jamie Bernard, Director

English Community Center 973.881.0280
Fax 973.881.0126
Web ....www.fatherenglish.org
E-mail ....admin@fatherenglish.org
435 Main St, Paterson, NJ 07501
Robert Vesota, Director

Ewing Residential Treatment Ctr 609.530.3350
Fax 609.530.3467
1610 Stuyvesant Ave, Trenton, NJ 08618-3299
William May, CEO

Family Violence Program 973.484.1704
Fax 973.484.7682
E-mail ....cynthiah@babylonfamilyservices.org
755 S Orange Ave, Newark, NJ 07106
Cynthia House, Program Director

Jersey Battered Womens Svc 973.455.1256
Fax 973.605.5898
Web ....www.jbws.org
E-mail ....psly@jbws.org
PO Box 1437, Morristown, NJ 07962-1437
Patty Sly, Director

Manavi Inc.-Domestic Violence Program 732.435.1414
Fax 732.435.1411
E-mail ....manavi@manavi.org
PO Box 3103, New Brunswick, NJ 08903-3103
Maneesha Kelkar, Ex Director

Millburn-Short Hills Red Cross Chapter 973.379.4198
Fax 973.379.5797
Web ....www.usa.redcross.org
E-mail ....balloraredcoss@comcast.net
389 Millburn Ave, Millburn, NJ 07041-1326
Barbara Allora, Director

Ocean's Harbor House 732.929.0660
Fax 732.929.3094
E-mail ....admin@oceansharborhouse.org
2445 Windsor Ave, Toms River, NJ 08754
Sid Colvin, Executive Director

Project Protect Domestic Violence Program 908.355.1995
Fax 908.355.2010
1130 31 E Jersy St, Elizabeth, NJ 07201
Jan Lillien, Director

Providence House-Willingboro Domestic Violence 856.824.0599
Fax 856.824.9340
Web ....www.cctrenton.org
E-mail ....jmetz@cctrenton.org
950 S Chester Ave Ste A, delran, NJ 08075-1272
Jean Metz, Director

Renfrew Ctr 201.652.5114
Fax 201.652.6253
Web ....www.renfrewcenter.com
174 Union St Ste 101, Ridgewood, NJ 07450
Silvia Pascarella, Director

Resource Ctr For Women And Their Families 908.359.0003
Fax 908.359.8881
E-mail ....info@resourcecenterforsomerset.org
427 Homestead Rd, Ste 2, Hillsborough, NJ 08844
Paloma Amar-coleman, Director

Somerset Home For Temporarily Displaced Children 908.526.6605
Fax 908.526.6999
Web ....www.somersethome.org
E-mail ....mail@somersethome.org
49 Brahma Avenue, Bridgewater, NJ 08807
Jeffrey Fetzko, Executive Director

St. Peter's Village 973.627.0212
Fax 973.627.3338
170 Diamond Spring Rd, Denville, NJ 07834
Kelly Mcnamara, Executive Director

The Safe House-Domestic Violence 973.759.2378
Fax 973.844.4950
Web ....www.sbhcs.com
E-mail ....sscioscia@sbhcs.com
PO Box 1887, Bloomfield, NJ 07003-1887
Sue Scioscia, Director

Womanspace Inc.-Domestic Violence Program 609.394.2532
Fax 609.394.5417
E-mail ....ehy@womanspace.org
1860 US Highway 1, Lawrence Township, NJ 08648
Ellen Yeagle, Director

Women Aware Inc.-Domestic Violence 732.249.4900
Fax 732.249.4901
Web ....www.womenaware.net
E-mail ....padams@womenaware.net
250 Livingston Ave, New Brunswick, NJ 08901
Phyllis Adams, Director

Women Rising Inc.-Domestic Violence 201.333.5700
Fax 201.333.9305
Web ....www.womenrising.org
E-mail ....jeileen@womenrising.org
270 Fairmount Ave, Jersey City, NJ 07306-4712
Joan Eileen Cunning, Director Of Domestic Violence

Womens Ctr 856.963.5668
Fax 864.964.4998
311 Market St, Camden, NJ 08102
Helena Toma, Director

Womens Ctr 973.881.1450
Fax 973.881.0617
Web ....www.njaconline.org
1027 Madison Ave, Paterson, NJ 07513
Susan Fleinch, Director

Womens Ctr-Domestic Violence 856.691.3713
Fax 856.825.8119
E-mail ....nbaez@centerffs.org
PO Box 930, Millville, NJ 08332
Naida Baez, Director

EDUCATION

Alpine Learning Group 201.612.7800
Fax 201.612.7710
Web ....www.alpinelearninggroup.org
E-mail ....lmoran@alpinelearninggroup.org
777 Paramus Rd, Paramus, NJ 07652-1710
Bridget Taylor, Executive Director

Arc-Kohler School 908.518.0021
Fax 908.518.0636
Web ....www.arckohlerschool.org
1137 Globe Ave, Mountainside, NJ 07092-2903
Frank Caragher, Acting Principal

Bonnie Brae 908.647.0800
Fax 908.647.5021
Web ....www.bonnie-brae.org
E-mail ....wpowers@bonnie-brae.org
3415 Valley Rd, Liberty Corner, NJ 07938-0825
Donna Crane, Educational Director

Cerebral Palsy of Monmouth & Ocean Counties 732.493.5900
Fax 732.493.5980
Web ....www.ladacin.org
E-mail ....patricia.carlesimo@ladacin.org
1701 Kneeley Blvd, Asbury Park, NJ 07712-7622
Patricia Carlesimo, Director

Children's Day School Of Family Guidance Ctr 609.882.2288
Fax 609.882.7806
Web ....www.fgccorp.org
E-mail ....jim.rigel@fgccorp.org
1925 Pennington Rd, Trenton, NJ 08618
James Rigel, Director

Collier School 732.946.4771
Fax 732.946.3519
Web ....www.collieryouthservices.org
E-mail ....jmcmerty@collieryouthservices.org
160 Conover Road, Wickatunk, NJ 07765
Debbie Drago, Director

Covenant House New Jersey Rights Of Passage Program 609.348.1421
Fax 609.348.1122
Web ....www.nineline.org
E-mail ....jrottman@covenanthouse.org
3529 Pacific Ave, Atlantic City, NJ 08401-6151
Jill Rottman, Executive Director

Creative Achievement Academy 856.691.6667
Fax 856.794.3280
120 W Wood Street, Vineland, NJ 08360
Sharon Bruno, Director

Crescent Hill Academy 856.662.7300
Fax 856.662.1099
7512 N Crescent Blvd, Pennsauken, NJ 08110
Alfred Minicozzi, Director

Ctr School 732.249.3355
Fax 732.249.1928
Web ....www.thecenterschool.com
E-mail ....marcie@thecenterschool.com
319 N 3rd Ave, Highland Park, NJ 08904-2495
Marcie Fiorentino, Director

David Gregory School 201.967.9772
Fax 201.967.7071
E-mail ....mlupinski@davidgregoryschool.com
347 N Farview Ave, Paramus, NJ 07652-4632
Marie Lupinski, Director

Devereux New Jersey Treatment Network 856.599.6400
Fax 856.599.6401
Web ....www.devereuxnj.org
286 Mantua Grove Rd Bldg 4, Paulsboro,
NJ 08066-1738
Maureen F. Walsh, Executive Director

Durand Academy 856.845.0666
Fax 856.848.7659
Web ....www.duranac.org
E-mail ....r.cristofoletti@durandac.org
230 N Evergreen Ave Ste 1, Woodbury,
NJ 08096-1800
Raymond Cristofoletti, Director

Edison Job Corps Ctr 732.985.4800
Fax 732.985.8551
Web ....http://edison.jobcorps.gov
500 Plainfield Ave, Edison, NJ 08817
Jibu Kuruvilla, Center Director

Education Academy 609.693.3322
Fax 609.693.5454
Web ....www.theeducationacademy.com
E-mail ....educationacademy@comcast.net
505 N Main St (Rt 9), Lanoka Harbor, NJ 08734
Roland J. Lewis, Director

Green Brook Academy, Inc 732.469.8677
Fax 732.469.0035
E-mail ....gbainfo@aol.com
151 Vossleer Ave, Bound Brook, NJ 08805
Constance Dougherty, Director

High Point School 973.574.0344
Fax 973.574.0344
E-mail ....hpsofbergency@aol.com
46 Spring St, Lodi, NJ 07644-2312
Marc Fanaroff, Director

High Road Schools- Kids 1 ....732.390.0303
Fax 732.390.5577
Web www.kids1inc.com
E-mail ....dwinikur@kids1inc.com
3071 Bordentown Ave, Parlin, NJ 08859-1168
Annette Hockenjos, Executive Director

Hunterdon Learning Ctr 908.832.7200
Fax 908.832.9772
Web ....www.hunterdonlearning.com
E-mail ....trlloyd@hunterdonlearning.com
37 Hoffmans Crossing Rd, Califon, NJ 07830-4223
Toby Loyd, Director

Institute For Educational Achievement 201.262.3287
Fax 201.262.9479
Web ....www.ieaschool.org
E-mail ....dawn.townsend@ieaschool.org
381 Madison Ave, New Milford, NJ 07646-1302
Dawn Townsend, Director

JCC On The Palisades Therapeutic Nursery 201.569.7900
Fax 201.569.7448
Web ....www.jcconthepalisades.org
E-mail ....alewinson@jcconthepalisades.org
411 E Clinton Ave, Tenafly, NJ 07670-2397
Avi A. Lewinson, Executive Director

Kingsway Learning Ctr 856.428.8108
Fax 856.428.7520
Web ....www.kingswaylc.com
E-mail ....kingswaylc@aol.com
144 Kings Hwy W, Haddonfield, NJ 08033
David Panner, Ma, Executive Director

Kingsway Learning Ctr At Morrestown 856.234.4442
Fax 856.234.0484
Web ....www.kingswaylearningcenter.org
E-mail ....dpanner@kingswaylearningcenter.org
244 W Route 38, Moorestown, NJ 08057-3200
David J. Panner, Executive Director

Larc School 856.933.3725
Fax 856.933.3158
Web ....www.larcschool.org
E-mail ....info@larcschool.org
1089 Creek Rd, Bellmawr, NJ 08031
Susan Weiner, Executive Director

Millburn Regional Day School 201.498.8137
Fax 973.912.8887
Web ....www.bergen.org
70 Spring St, Millburn, NJ 07041
Angela Cupo, Principal

Montgomery Academy 908.234.2840
Fax 908.234.2817
Web ....www.montgomeryacademyonline.org
St Johns Dr, Andover, NJ 07934
Zaida Gomez, Secretary

Mt Carmel Guild Academy 973.325.4400
Fax 973.669.8450
E-mail ....roz_monica@ccsnewark.org
100 Valley Way, West Orange, NJ 07052
James Badavas, Principal

Newgrange School And Education Ctr 609.688.1280
Fax 609.430.3030
Web ....www.thenewgrange.org
E-mail ....info@thenewgrange.org
526 S Olden Ave, Trenton, NJ 08629
Gordan Sherman, Executive Director

Palisades Learning Ctr 201.576.9890
Fax 201.225.0168
E-mail ....jpkahn1017@aol.com
140 North State Route 17, Paramus, NJ 07652
Jeffrey P. Kahn, Director

Pg Chambers School 973.829.8484
Fax 973.829.8485
Web ....www.chamberschool.org
E-mail ....seamans@chambersschool.org
15 Halko Dr, Cedar Knolls, NJ 07927-1380
Susan Seamans, Executive Director

**School For Children With Hidden
Intelligence/SCHI** 732.886.0900
Fax 732.886.7603
Web ....www.schischool.org
E-mail ....oeisemann@schischool.org
345 Oak St, Lakewood, NJ 08701-5347
Osher Eisemann, Director

Somerset Hills School 732.469.6900
Fax 732.469.0024
Web ....www.somersethills.org
E-mail ....info@somersethills.org
1275 Bound Brook Rd, Ste 1, Middlesex,
NJ 08846-1486
Christopher Kimmins, Director

**Spring Run School/Ctr For Educational
Advancement** 908.782.1480
Fax 908.782.5370
E-mail ....jritchie@ceaemployment.com
11 Minneakoning Rd, Flemington, NJ 08822
John Ritchie, Principal

**St. John Of God Community Svcs/Archishop Damiano
School** 856.848.4700
Fax 856.384.1512
Web ....www.sjogcs.org
1145 Delsea Dr, Westville, NJ 08093
Muncie Buckalew, Director

Stepping Stone School 908.995.1999
Fax 908.995.1994
Web ....www.ptd.net
45 County Road 519, Bloomsbury, NJ 08804-3430
Frank Jiorle, Director

Summit Speech School 908.508.0011
Fax 908.508.0012
Web ....www.summitspeech.org
E-mail ....info@summitspeech.org
705 Central Ave Ste 1, New Providence,
NJ 07974-1196
Pamela Paskowitz, Executive Director

The Gramon School 973.808.9555
Fax 973.227.8626
Web ....www.gramon.org
E-mail ....kgerritz@gramon.org
24 Dwight Pl, Fairfield, NJ 07004-3304
Kalle Gerritz, Edd, Director

The Leaguers, Inc 973.373.2397
Fax 973.373.8786
Web www.leag281.aol.com
E-mail ....veronica_ray@theleaguers.org
731 Clinton Ave, Newark, NJ 07108-1227
Veronica Ray, Executive Director

The Rugby School at Woodfield 732.681.6900
Fax 732.681.4867
Web ....www.rugbyschool.org
E-mail ....poppled@aol.com
1604 Woodfield Ave, Wall Township, NJ 07719
Delores Desanto, Assistant Director

The Winston School 973.379.4114
Fax 973.379.3984
Web ....www.winstonschool.org
E-mail ....plewis@winstonschool.org
30 East Ln, Short Hills, NJ 07078-3243
Peter Lewis, Head Of School

Washington Academy 973.239.6555
Fax 973.239.6335
Web ....www.washingtonacademy.com
E-mail ....schwartz@washingtonacademy.com
520 Pompton Ave, Cedar Grove, NJ 07009-1724
Jack Schwartz, Director

Y.A.L.E. School 856.482.5252
Fax 856.779.7721
Web ....www.yaleschool.com
E-mail ....evonderschmidt@yaleschool.com
2127 Church Rd, Cherry Hill, NJ 08002-1250
Ed Vonderschmidt, Director

FOSTER CARE AGENCIES

Catholic Charities Archdiocese of Newark 201.246.7378
Fax 201.991.3771
499 Belgrove Dr Ste 2, Kearny, NJ 07032

**Concerned Parents for Adoption North
Ame** 609.799.3269
12 Reed Dr North, Princeton Junction, NJ 08550

Concerned Persons for Adoption 973.659.9772
494 Rt 10 W Whippany Rd, Whippany, NJ 07981

Drenk Behavioral Health Ctr 973.677.7005
Fax 973.677.1381
E-mail ....kfennell@drenk.org
7 Glenwood Ave Ste 400, East Orange,
NJ 07017-1041
Karen Fennell, Director

Family Options 732.936.0770
Fax 732.936.0094
E-mail ....info@famopt.org
45 Riverside Ave, Red Bank, NJ 07701
Dina Vecchione, Executive Director

Family Svc Foster Care 856.778.8231
Fax 856.778.1180
E-mail ....debw@famserv.org
15 W Main St, Moorestown, NJ 08057
Deb Wolff, Program Supervisor

Foster & Adoptive Family Services 800.222.0047
Fax 609.520.1515
4301 Route 1 S, Monmouth Junction, NJ 08852
Mary Jane, Executive Director

New Jersey

Golden Cradle Adoption Services Inc 856.428.1180
Fax 856.428.1007
E-mail ....adoptions@goldencradle.org
  95 W Gate Dr, Cherry Hill, NJ 08034
  Jared Rolsky, Director

Infertility Adoption Counseling Center 609.737.8750
E-mail ....JMantellMSW@iaccenter.com
  2 Tree Farm Rd Ste A200, Pennington, NJ 08534

Morristown Post Adoption Support Group 973.267.8698
E-mail ....janenast@aol.com
  65 South St, Morristown, NJ 07960
  Jane Nast, Director

Stars of David Chaverim 856.866.0055
  681 Cornwallis Dr, Medford, NJ 08055

Voice of Choice Foster Parent Assoc 717.991.2692
  PO Box 1800, Bellmawr, NJ 08099

HOME MEDICAL EQUIPMENT PROVIDERS

Amer Cancer Society Chinese American Af 732.224.8868
Fax 732.224.8821
  801 Broad St, Shrewsbury, NJ 07702

Lingraphicare America, Inc. 888.274.2742
Fax 609.683.7104
Web ....www.lingraphica.com
  103 Carnegie Center, Suite 204, Princeton, NJ 08542
  CARF accredited programs available.

Matheny School and Hospital 908.234.0011
Fax 908.781.8862
  65 Highland Avenue, Peapack, NJ 07977
  CARF accredited programs available.

Tylers Gift Foundation 201.933.4677
E-mail ....info@tylersgift.com
  201 Jay St, Wood Ridge, NJ 07075

PEDIATRIC HOME CARE

Bayada Nurses 973.340.6400
Fax 973.340.6981
Web ....www.bayada.com
E-mail ....pas@bayada.com
  45 East Madison Avenue, Suite 9, Clifton, NJ 07011
  Denise Kelaman, Director

Bayada Nurses 856.354.1000
Fax 856.354.9425
Web ....www.bayada.com
  20 Brace Road, Suite 202, Cherry Hill, NJ 08034
  Bruce Costo, Director

Bayada Nurses 732.240.0244
Fax 732.240.0442
Web ....www.bayada.com
E-mail ....cmamola@bayada.com
  1144 Hooper Avenue, Suite 203, Toms River,
  NJ 08753
  Cathy Mamola, Director

Bayada Nurses 732.442.3370
Fax 732.442.3307
Web ....www.bayada.com
  285 McClellan Street, Perth Amboy, NJ 08861
  Paula Sanchez, Nursing Director

Bayada Nurses 856.327.5103
Fax 856.327.5108
Web ....www.bayada.com
  10 East Main St, Ste I, Riverview Commerce Center,
  Millville, NJ 08332
  Iris Lueder, Director

Bayada Nurses 201.867.8667
Fax 201.867.8644
Web ....www.bayada.com
E-mail ....Hudoffice@bayada.com
  3196 Kennedy Boulevard, Kennedy Medical Center,
  Union City, NJ 07087
  Wanda Netayer, Director

Bayada Nurses 973.538.3005
Fax 973.538.8830
Web ....www.bayada.com
  520 Speedwell Ave, Morris Plains, NJ 07950

Bayada Nurses 973.328.1790
Fax 973.328.1731
Web ....www.bayada.com
E-mail ....dov-team@bayada.com
  25-27 Dickerson Street, Suite 101, Dover, NJ 07801
  Susana Sueldo, Director

Bayada Nurses 856.231.0200
Fax 856.231.9030
Web ....www.bayada.com
  1000 Lenola Rd, Suite 102, Maple Shade, NJ 08052
  Ramona Phillips, Director

Bayada Nurses 856.722.9900
Fax 856.722.9901
Web ....www.bayada.com
  521 Fellowship Road, Suite 160, Mount Laurel,
  NJ 08054
  Meretich Miller, Director

Bayada Nurses 856.690.0946
Fax 856.690.9551
Web ....www.bayada.com
E-mail ....mcomegys@bayada.com
  760 South Delsea Drive, Suite 300, Vineland,
  NJ 08360
  Mike Comegys, Director

Bayada Nurses 973.743.6075
Fax 973.743.5722
Web ....www.bayada.com
  652 Bloomfield Avenue, Bloomfield, NJ 07003
  Marlene Boemi, Director

Bayada Nurses 732.863.5000
Fax 732.863.5605
Web ....www.bayada.com
  303 West Main Street, 1st Floor, Freehold, NJ 07728
  Jessica Wishkoff, Director

Bayada Nurses 732.240.0244
Fax 732.240.0442
Web ....www.bayada.com
  1144 Hooper Avenue, Suite 201a, Toms River,
  NJ 08753
  Cathy Manola, Director

Bayada Nurses 201.377.6000
Fax 201.377.6083
Web ....www.bayada.com
E-mail ....dbrown1@bayada.com
  150 Warren Street, Jersey City, NJ 07302
  Donnett Brown, Executive Director

Bayada Nurses 609.601.2200
Fax 609.601.9009
Web ....www.bayada.com
E-mail ....acc_team@bayada.com
  Central Square Unit 31, 199 New Road, Linwood,
  NJ 08221
  Mary Klvea, Director

Bayada Nurses 201.343.7100
Fax 201.343.3895
Web ....www.bayada.com
  90 Main Street, Hackensack, NJ 07601

Bayada Nurses 609.219.9600
Fax 609.219.0111
Web ....www.bayada.com
  2000 Lenox Dr Ste 104, Lawrenceville, NJ 08648
  Robin Rodriguez, Director

Bayada Nurses 609.601.6511
Fax 609.272.9900
Web ....www.bayada.com
  3069 English Creek Ave Ste 221, Linwood, NJ 08231
  John, Manager

Bayada Nurses 201.339.1330
Fax 201.339.1396
Web ....www.bayada.com
E-mail ....bayoffice@bayada.com
  473 Broadway Bayonne Plaza, Suite 400, Bayonne,
  NJ 07002
  Christine Rios, Director

Bayada Nurses 609.926.4600
Fax 609.926.0051
Web ....www.bayada.com
  35 Central Square, Linwood, NJ 08221
  Maryann Prudhomme, Director

Bayada Nurses 201.488.1262
Fax 201.343.0629
Web ....www.bayada.com
  90 Main Street, Suite 202, Hackensack, NJ 07601
  Marlana F, Administrator Director

Bayada Nurses 973.538.3000
Fax 973.984.0450
Web ....www.bayada.com
  40 Maple Ave, P.O. Box 1212, Morristown, NJ 07962
  Mark Bayada, Director

Bayada Nurses 732.418.2273
Fax 732.418.8894
Web ....www.bayada.com
  1460 Livingston Avenue, Building 400, Third Floor,
  North Brunswick, NJ 08902
  Kelley McNulty, Director

Bayada Nurses 856.772.2010
Fax 856.772.0150
Web ....www.bayada.com
  2140 Voorhees Town Center, Upper Level, Voorhees,
  NJ 08043

Bayada Nurses 908.687.6363
Fax 908.687.6544
Web ....www.bayada.com
E-mail ....info@bayada.com
  324 Chestnut Street, Union, NJ 07083
  Miriam Mercado, Director

Bayada Nurses 856.795.0110
Fax 856.354.2243
Web ....www.bayada.com
  1415 Route 70, Suite 412, Cherry Hill, NJ 08034
  Sonja Morrow, Director

Bayada Nurses 856.327.6800
Fax 856.327.6820
Web ....www.bayada.com
  1601 North Second Street, Executive Suites, Suite
  D-8, Millville, NJ 08332
  Ann Clark, Director

Bayada Nurses 856.256.2800
Fax 856.256.9500
Web ....www.bayada.com
E-mail ....wttoffice@bayada.com
  100 Kings Way East, Suite D1, Sewell, NJ 08080
  John Barbaccia, Director

Bayada Nurses 609.407.6801
Fax 609.407.6808
Web ....www.bayada.com
  2 West Glendale Avenue, Pleasantville, NJ 08232
  Kathy Reeves, Director

Interim Healthcare 908.206.8637
Fax 908.756.5915
  2414 Morris Ave Ste 106, Union, NJ 07083
  Barbara Stanton, Administrator

Interim Healthcare 908.756.1515
Fax 908.756.5915
  265 Durham Ave, South Plainfield, NJ 07080
  Candice Martino, Nursing Director

Interim Healthcare 201.864.3838
Fax 201.864.0093
  3133 Central Ave, Ste 209, Union City, NJ 07087
  Rosemary Hall, Director

Interim Healthcare 856.783.0312
Fax 856.783.8049
　113 W Whitehorse Rd Ste 9, Ste 1200, Voorhees,
　NJ 08043
　Susan Trotman, Administrator

Interim Healthcare 609.584.0251
Fax 609.586.9805
　IBIS Plaza, 3525 Quakerbridge Rd Ste 1500,
　Mercerville, NJ 08619
　Sue Trontman, Administrator

Interim Healthcare 732.341.0330
Fax 609.586.9805
　3525 Quakerbridge Rd Ste 1500, Hamilton, NJ 08619
　Susan Trotman, Administrator

Sparta PDN 973.579.5355
　34-B White Lake Rd, Sparta, NJ 07871
　Jennifer Blanchard, Director

SOCIAL SERVICES

Abortion Alternative-Birthrght 201.845.4646
Fax 201.845.4646
Web ....www.birthright.org
　19 W Pleasant Ave, Maywood, NJ 07607-1320
　Kathy Semsey, Director

Alternatives, Inc. 908.685.1444
Fax 908.685.2660
Web ....www.alternativesinc.org
E-mail ....ngood@alternativesinc.org
　600 1st Ave Ste 1, Raritan, NJ 08869-1346
　Nancy Good, President

Bergen Ctr For Child Development 201.385.4857
Fax 201.385.4997
Web ....www.bccdsite.org
E-mail ....eyeager@bccdschool.com
　140 Park St, Haworth, NJ 07641
　Elizabeth Yeager, Director

Catholic Charities 973.279.7100
Fax 973.523.1150
Web ....www.catholiccharities.org
　24 Degrasse St, Paterson, NJ 07505
　Diane Silvernagel, Executive Director

Catholic Charities 732.324.8200
Fax 732.826.3549
Web ....www.ccdom.org
　319 Maple St, Perth Amboy, NJ 08861-4197
　Mary Ann Majewski, Director

Catholic Charities Adoption And Maternity
Svcs 609.386.6221
Fax 609.386.6993
E-mail ....nmorrell@cctrenton.org
　115 W Pearl St, Burlington, NJ 08016-1319
　Nancy Morrell, Supervisor

Catholic Charities Diocese Of Metuchen 908.927.0869
Fax 908.927.9653
Web ....www.childcaresoluation.com
E-mail ....dmartin@ccdom.org
　92 E Main St Ste 304, Somerville, NJ 08876-1917
　Diane Martin, Director

Catholic Charities, Diocese of Trenton 609.394.5181
Fax 609.695.6978
Web ....www.catholiccharitiestrenton.org
　383 West State Street, Trenton, NJ 08607
　COA accredited organization.

Catholic Charity 856.691.1841
Fax 856.692.6575
E-mail ....john.desparrois@vhscd.org
　810 E Montrose St, Vineland, NJ 08360-4731
　John Desparrois, Director

Catholic Family And Community Svcs 973.523.9595
Fax 973.333.6217
Web ....www.cscsadoptions.org
E-mail ....adopcscs@optionline.net
　476 17th Ave, Paterson, NJ 07504-1123
　Father Thomas Mcgrath, Director

Ccs-Mt. Carmel Guild Preschool 973.639.6622
Fax 973.639.6626
Web ....www.ccsnewark.org
E-mail ....katherine_thornton@ccsnewark.org
　236 Hoover Ave, Bloomfield, NJ 07003
　Katherine Thornton, Principal

Center For Family Services, Inc. 856.964.1990
Fax 856.964.1992
Web ....www.centerffs.org
　584 Benson Street, Camden, NJ 08103
　COA accredited organization.

Child And Family Resources Inc. 973.398.1730
Fax 973.398.0319
Web ....www.childandfamily-nj.org
　111 Howard Blvd Ste 201, Mount Arlington,
　NJ 07856
　Rebekka Zydel-Lupianez, Executive Director

Child Care Connection 609.989.7770
Fax 609.989.8060
Web ....www.childcareconnection-nj.org/
E-mail ....childcarecon@att.net
　1001 Spruce St Ste 201, Trenton, NJ 08638
　Nancy Thompson, Executive Director

Child Care Resources 732.918.9901
Fax 732.918.9902
Web ....www.ccrnj.org
E-mail ....thayes@ccrnj.org
　3301 C Route 66, Neptune, NJ 07754
　Theresa Hayes, Director

Choices Of The Heart 856.374.2445
Fax 856.232.6288
　132 Ganttown Rd, Blackwood, NJ 08012-1677
　Rita Walz, Director

Community Access Unlimited 908.354.3040
Fax 908.354.2665
Web ....www.caunj.org
E-mail ....info@caunj.org
　80 W Grand St Ste 1, Elizabeth, NJ 07202-1471
　Sidney Blanchard, Executive Director

Community Action Agency 856.451.8100
Fax 856.455.7288
Web ....www.tricountycaa.org
　110 Cohansey St, Bridgeton, NJ 08302
　Michael Cudemo, Director Of Planning

Community Coordinated Child Care 973.923.1433
Fax 973.923.1311
Web ....www.ccccunion.org
E-mail ....referral@ccccunion.org
　225 Long Ave Ste 15, Hillside, NJ 47205
　Pat Mennuti, Executive Director

Community Treatment Solutions 856.642.9090
Fax 856.642.9303
Web ....www.ctsnj.org
　236 W. Route 38, Suite 100, Moorestown, NJ 08057
　COA accredited organization.

Cornerstone Womens Resource 856.453.0030
E-mail ....info@cornerstonewrc.org
　105 Manheim Ave Ste 12, Bridgeton, NJ 08302
　Sue Smith, Executive Director

Court Appointed Special Advocates (CASA) of Atlantic and
Cape May Counties 609.601.7800
Fax 609.601.7900
E-mail ....staff@atlanticcapecasa.org
　321 Shore Road, Somers Point, NJ 08244
　Angela Waters, Executive Director

Covenant House New Jersey 973.621.8705
Fax 973.621.8005
Web ....www.covenanthousenj.org
E-mail ....jrottmann@covenanthouse.org
　330 Washington St, Newark, NJ 07102-2690
　Jill Rottmann, Executive Director

Covenant House New Jersey Crisis Ctr 609.348.4070
　...................................609.348.1122
Web ....www.nineline.org
E-mail ....jrottmann@covenanthouse.org
　929 Atlantic Ave, Atlantic City, NJ 08401-7401
　Jill Rottmann, Executive Director

Eclc Of New Jersey 973.635.1705
Fax 973.635.0548
Web ....www.eclcofnj.org
E-mail ....blitinger@eclcofnj.org
　100 Passaic Ave, Chatham, NJ 07928
　Bruce Litinger, Director

Edison Prep 609.777.3292
Fax 609.777.2974
　1212 Edgewood Ave, Trenton, NJ 08618-5212

First Choice Women's Resources 973.655.9806
Fax 973.655.1091
E-mail ....chrissy@1stchoice.org
　180 Bloomfield Ave Ste A, Montclair, NJ 07042
　Melissa, Director

First Way 609.871.1431
　215 Sunset Rd Ste 304, Willingboro, NJ 08010
　Irene Fattorini, Director

Gateway Community Action Partnership 856.935.0944
Fax 856.935.0920
E-mail ....urivera@tricountycaa.org
　14 New Market St, Salem, NJ 08079
　Utausha Rivera, Child Care Assistant Director

Githens Ctr 609.261.1667
Fax 609.261.1844
E-mail ....githenscp@aol.com
　40 Cedar St, Mount Holly, NJ 08060
　Dr. Robert Andrew, Executive Director

Jewish Family & Childrens Service 609.987.8100
Fax 609.987.0574
E-mail ....info@jfcsonline.org
　707 Alexander Rd Ste 102, Princeton, NJ 08540
　Linda Meisel, Director
　COA accredited organization.

Jewish Family & Childrens Service Ocean
Co 732.363.8010
Fax 732.363.2097
E-mail ....JFCS@ocjf.org
　301 Madison Ave, Lakewood, NJ 08701
　Rita Sason, Director

Jewish Family & Childrens Service of
SthrnNJ 856.424.1333
Fax 856.424.7384
E-mail ....jweiss@jfedsnj.org
　1301 Springdale Rd Ste 150, Cherry Hill, NJ 08003
　Jennifer Weiss, Director

Jewish Family & Service of Somerset
Hunterdo 908.725.7799
Fax 908.725.0284
E-mail ....JFSofSHW@verizon.net
　150 West High St, Somerville, NJ 08876
　Jerry Starr, Director

Jewish Family & Vocational Services of 732.777.1940
Fax 732.777.1889
E-mail ....office@jfvs.org
　32 Ford Ave 2nd Fl, Milltown, NJ 08850
　Sara Levine, Director

Jewish Family Service 201.837.9090
Fax 201.837.9393
E-mail ....info@jfsbergen.org
　1485 Teaneck Rd, Teaneck, NJ 07666
　Lisa Fedder, Director

Jewish Family Service 201.604.9991
Fax 201.604.9995
　921 Bergen Ave Ste 627, Jersey City, NJ 07306
　Rueben Rotman, Executive Director

Jewish Family Service & Riskin Childrens 973.777.7638
Fax 973.777.9311
E-mail ....j.jfs@fjsclifton.org
Center of Clifton Passaic, 199 Scoles Ave, Clifton, NJ 07012
Esther East, Director

Jewish Family Service of Atlantic & Cape May 609.822.1108
Fax 609.822.1106
607 N Jerome Ave, Margate City, NJ 08402
Andrea Steinberg, Director

Jewish Family Service of MetroWest 973.765.9050
Fax 973.765.0195
Web ....www.jfsmetrowest.org
256 Columbia Turnpike, Suite 105, Florham Park, NJ 07932
COA accredited organization.

Jewish Family Service of North Jersey 973.595.0111
Fax 973.595.5477
E-mail ....info@jfsnorthjersey.org
One Pike Dr, Wayne, NJ 07470
Leah Kaufman, Executive Director

Jewish Family Svc Of Metrowest 973.765.9050
Fax 973.765.0195
Web ....www.jfsmetrowest.org
E-mail ....rrotman@jfsmetrowest.org
256 Columbia Tpke, Ste 105, Florham Park, NJ 07932
Reuben Rotman, Executive Director

Jewish Family Svcs 732.774.6886
Fax 732.774.8809
Web ....www.jfcsmonmouth.org
E-mail ....paulf@jfcsmonmouth.org
705 Summerfield Ave, Asbury Park, NJ 07712-6900
Paul Freedman, Director

JFVS Branch 609.395.7979
52 Concordia Shopping Center, Monroe Township, NJ 08831
Sarah Levine, Director

Livingston BRANCH 973.740.1233
Fax 973.740.1590
570 West Mt Pleasant Ave Ste 203, Livingston, NJ 07039

Middle Earth 908.725.7223
Fax 908.722.5401
Web ....www.mddlearthnj.org
E-mail ....mddlearth@aol.com
520 N Bridge St, Bridgewater, NJ 08807
Dan Puntillo, Executive Director

New Bridge Svcs Inc. 973.316.9333
Fax 973.316.5790
Web ....www.newbridge.org
E-mail ....awasser-malmud@newbridge.org
390 Main Rd, Montville, NJ 07045-9785
Andrea Wasser-malmud, Services Director

New Jersey National Guard Challenge Youth 609.562.0570
Fax 609.562.0581
Web ....www.ngycp.org
5910 W 16th St, Fort Dix, NJ 08640-5326
Victoria Ragucci, Director

North Hudson Community Action Corp Health Ctr 201.866.9320
Web ....www.nhcac.org
5301 Broadway, West New York, NJ 07093
Christopher Irizarry, President

North Jersey 4C's 973.684.1904
Fax 973.684.0468
Web www.nj4c.com
2 Market St, 3rd Fl, Paterson, NJ 07514
Marianne Mirko, Executive Director

Ofc For Children 201.336.7150
Fax 201.336.7155
E-mail ....ofcreception@co.bergen.nj.us
1 Bergen County Plz, Fl 2, Hackensack, NJ 07601
Phyllis Strohmeyer, Director

Office of Youth Services 908.704.6333
Fax 908.253.0180
Web ....www.co.somerset.nj.us/hservices/youthservices/index.html
P.O. Box 3000, Somerville, NJ 08876
COA accredited organization.

Parents Anonymous Of NJ 609.585.7666
Fax 609.585.7686
Web ....www.pa-of-nj.org
E-mail ....panjstress@aol.com
127 US Highway 206 Ste 10, Trenton, NJ 08610-4300
Donny Bellamy, Assistant Executive Director

Princeton House 732.729.3600
Fax 732.435.0222
Web ....www.princetonhcs.org
E-mail ....kcochrane@princetonhcs.org
1460 Livingston Ave Bldg 100-1, North Brunswick, NJ 08902-1877
Karen Cochrane, Director

Programs For Parents 973.744.4050
Fax 973.744.6809
E-mail ....ahempel@programsforparents.org
500 Bloomflied Ave, MONTCLAIR BLDG, Montclair, NJ 07042-2700
Beverly Lynn, CEO

Robins' Nest, Inc. 856.881.8689
Fax 856.881.5508
Web ....www.robinsnestinc.org
42 South Delsea Drive, Glassboro, NJ 08028
COA accredited organization.

Senior Care Options, Inc. 732.872.8882
Fax 732.872.7540
Web ....www.seniorcareoptionsinc.com
E-mail ....scoptions@comcast.net
PO Box 385, Navesink, NJ 07752
Lisa Curtis, Lcsw, C-aswcm, Director

Teen Svc Ctr 609.345.8336
Fax 609.345.8373
Web ....www.atlanticcare.org
E-mail ....craig.cochran@atlanticcare.org
1400 N Albany Ave, Atlantic City, NJ 08401-1208
Craig Cochran, Ma, Director

The ARC 856.935.3600
Fax 856.935.9612
Web ....www.arcsalem.com
E-mail ....shirley@arcsalem.com
150 Route 45, Salem, NJ 08079
Shirley Brooks, Associate Executive Director

The Arc Of Monmouth 732.493.1919
Fax 732.493.3604
Web ....www.arcofmonmouth.org
E-mail ....info@arcofmonmouth.org
1158 Wayside Rd, Asbury Park, NJ 07712-3148
Mary E. Scott, Ma, Executive Director

The Community YMCA 732.290.9040
Fax 732.566.0433
Web ....www.cymca.org
166 Main Street, Matawan, NJ 07747
COA accredited organization.

Urban League 201.451.8888
Fax 201.451.4158
Web ....www.ulohc.org
E-mail ....ewatson@oel.state.nj.us
253 Mlk Dr, Jersey City, NJ 07305
Elenora Wattson, President/CEO

Visiting Homemaker Service 201.656.6001
Web ....www.vhshc.org
E-mail ....case@vhshc.org
586 Newark Avenue, Jersey City, NJ 07306
John Buck, Executive Director

Volunteers of America - Northern New Jersey 732.827.2444
Fax 732.827.2450
Web ....www.voa-gny.org
205 West Milton Avenue, Rahway, NJ 07065
COA accredited organization.

Voorhees Pediatric Facility 856.346.3300
Fax 856.346.4537
Web ....www.forkidscare.com
E-mail ....sgoldberg@forkidscare.com
1304 Laurel Oak Rd, Voorhees, NJ 08043-4310
Scott Goldberg, Executive Director

West Bridge Academy 973.429.8110
Fax 973.748.6105
60 West St, Bloomfield, NJ 07003
Viviana Litovsky, Director

Wynona's House 973.926.3111
Fax 973.926.0842
Web ....www.sbhcs.com
E-mail ....bwood@sbhcs.com
201 Lyons Ave, Bldg J-3, Newark, NJ 07112
Barbara Wood, Executive Director

SPECIAL NEEDS

ADDvantages Learning Center 856.482.0756
E-mail ....addvantages@aol.com
1101 N Kings Hwy, Cherry Hill, NJ 08034

Allegro School 973.267.8060
Fax 973.267.5872
Web ....www.allegroschool.org
125 Ridgedale Ave, Cedar Knolls, NJ 07927
Deborah Lewinson, Director

Alliance f/Betterment of Citizens w/Dis 609.581.8375
E-mail ....lowell@abcdnj.org
127 Route 206 Ste 18, Hamilton Township, NJ 08610

ARC Dorothy B Hersch High School 732.493.3563
Fax 732.493.3427
Web ....www.arcofmonmouth.org
1158 Wayside Rd, Tinton Falls, NJ 07712
Mary Scott, Executive Director

ASPEN 732.321.0880
E-mail ....info@aspennj.org
9 Aspen Cir, Edison, NJ 08820
Lori Shery, President

Association for Special Children & Fam 973.728.8744
E-mail ....ascfamily@hotmail.com
1810 Macopin Rd, Hewitt, NJ 07421
Anglea Abdul, Director

Asthma & Allergy Foundation 856.224.9547
E-mail ....aafasepa@verizon.net
32 Casperson St, Gibbstown, NJ 08027
Debi Maines, Executive Director

Autism New Jersey 609.588.8200
E-mail ....information@autismnj.org
500 Horizon Dr # 530, Robbinsville, NJ 08691
Linda Meyer, Executive Director

Bacharach Institute for Rehabilitation 609.652.7000
Fax 609.652.7487
Web ....www.bacharach.org
61 West Jimmie Leeds Road, Pomona, NJ 08240
Beth Hoffman, VP for Clinical Svcs
CARF accredited programs available.

Balaban & Associates, LLC 201.833.0655
Fax 201.833.4025
E-mail ....jplasner@optonline.net
1415 Queen Anne Rd, Teaneck, NJ 07666
Dr. Joseph Plasner, Director

Bancroft Neuro Health 856.429.5637
Fax 856.429.1613
Web ....www.bancroft.org
　425 Kings Hwy E, Haddonfield, NJ 08033
　Stephen Bruce, Director

Banyan School 973.439.1919
Fax 973.439.1396
Web ....www.banyanschool.com
E-mail ....msaunders@banyanschool.com
　12 Hollywood Ave, Fairfield, NJ 07004
　Mary Jo Saunders, Director

Benway School 973.633.3837
Fax 973.633.3805
E-mail ....hcarline@benwayschool.org
　620 Belly Rd, Wayne, NJ 07470-6315
　Harry Carline, Principal

Bonnie Brae School 908.647.4703
Fax 908.647.5021
Web ....www.bonnie-brae.org
　3415 Valley Rd, Liberty Corner, NJ 07938
　William Powers, Director

Brookfield Schools 856.795.8228
Fax 856.795.3009
Web ....www.brookfieldschools.org
　1009 Berlin Rd, Cherry Hill, NJ 08034
　Dorothy K Van Horn, Superintendent

Celebrate the Children 973.989.4033
Fax 973.895.7451
Web ....www.celebratethechildren.org
E-mail ....celebratethechildren.org
　345 S Main St, Wharton, NJ 07885
　Monica Osgood, Director

Cerebral Palsy Ctr 973.772.2600
Fax 973.772.5171
Web ....www.pcecpc.org
　1481 Main Ave, Clifton, NJ 07011
　William G Weiss, Director

Cerebral Palsy of New Jersey 888.322.1918
E-mail ....info@cpofnj.org
　1005 Whitehead Rd Ste 1, Ewing Township,
　NJ 08638
　Jack Mugde, Director

Chapel Hill Academy 973.784.4787
Fax 973.784.4788
Web ....www.chapelhillacademy.net
E-mail ....tom.c@chapelhillacademy.net
　31 Chapel Hill Academy, Lincoln Park, NJ 07045
　Thomas Celli, Director

Children's Home Mary A Dobbins School 609.267.1550
Fax 609.261.5672
Web ....www.childrens-home.org
　243 Pine St, Mount Holly, NJ 08060
　Roy Leitstein, Director

Children's Specialized Hospital 908.233.3720
Fax 908.889.8521
Web ....www.childrens-specialized.org
　330 South Ave, Fanwood, NJ 07023
　Pamela Venckus, Manager

Childrens Cardiomyopathy Foundation 866.808.2873
Fax 201.227.7016
E-mail ....info@childrenscardiomyopathy.org
　PO Box 547, Tenafly, NJ 07670

CHN Therapeutic School & Preschool 973.450.3123
Fax 973.450.3025
　570 Belleville Ave, Belleville, NJ 07109
　Elizabeth Callahan

Community High School 201.862.1796
Fax 201.862.1791
Web ....www.communityschoolnj.org
　1135 Teaneck Rd, Teaneck, NJ 07666
　Dennis Cohen, Director

Concordia Learning Ctr St Joseph's Schoo 201.876.5432
Fax 201.876.5431
Web ....www.sjsnj.org
　761 Summit Ave, Jersey City, NJ 07307
　Judy Ortman, Ex. Dir.

Congenital Heart Information Network 609.822.1572
Fax 609.822.1574
E-mail ....mb@tchin.org
　101 N Washington Ave Ste 1A, Margate City,
　NJ 08402
　Mona Barmash, Chief Executive Officer

Department for Persons with Disabilities 973.697.4395
Fax 973.697.9603
Web ....www.dpd.org
　P.O. Box 2539, Oak Ridge, NJ 07438
　COA accredited organization.

Deron School of New Jersey 908.206.0444
Web ....www.deronschool.org
　1140 Commerce Ave, Union, NJ 07083
　Kenneth Alter

Durand Academy & Community Services 856.845.0666
Fax 856.848.7659
Web ....www.durandac.org
　230 N Evergreen Ave, Woodbury, NJ 08096
　Raymond Cristofoletti, CEO

East Mountain School 908.281.1416
Fax 908.281.1663
Web ....www.carrier.org
E-mail ....ppharamia@carrier.com
　252 Route 601, PO Box 147, Belle Mead, NJ 08502
　Phillip A Haramia, Director

Eden Institute 609.987.0099
Fax 609.987.0243
Web ....www.edenservices.org
　One Eden Way, Princeton, NJ 08540
　Thomas P Mccool, CEO

Eduational Partnership for Instructing
Children 201.576.0600
Fax 201.576.0699
Web ....www.epicschool.org
　238 Farview Ave, Paramus, NJ 07652
　Christine Grogan, Manager

Elite Healtcare Inc. 201.862.1300
Fax 201.837.2074
Web ....www.elite-healthcare.com
E-mail ....npessar@elite-healthcare.com
　131 Main Street Suite 180, Hackensack, NJ 07601
　Nechama Pessar, Director Of Nursing

Epilepsy Foundation 800.336.5843
E-mail ....ejoice@efnj.com
　1 AAA Dr Ste 203, Robbinsville, NJ 08691
　Andrea Racioppi, Associate Director

Essex Valley School 973.244.7890
Fax 973.244.7894
Web ....www.essexvalleyschool.org
E-mail ....alichtenstein@essexvalleyschool.org
　1 Henderson Dr, Caldwell, NJ 07006
　Alan Lichtenstein, Director

FACES Autism Support Network 609.412.3750
E-mail ....facesgroup@comcast.net
　PO Box 2341, Ventnor, NJ 08406

Family Support Center 732.528.8080
E-mail ....jacqui.moskowitz@fscnj.or@gmail.com
　2516 Route 35 N, Manasquan, NJ 08736
　Jacqui Moskowitz, Director

Hawkswood School 732.542.2525
Fax 732.542.2445
Web ....www.sfconline.org
　270 Industrial Way West, Eatontown, NJ 07724
　Vincent J Renda, Manager

HollyDELL School 856.582.5151
Fax 856.582.5055
Web ....www.hollydell.org
　610 Hollydell Dr, Sewell, NJ 08080
　Gracanne Ryan, Director

Holmstead School 201.447.1696
Fax 201.447.4608
Web ....www.holmstead.org
E-mail ....pwhitewhead@holmstead.org
　14 Hope St, Ridgewood, NJ 07450
　Patricia G Whitehead, Director

Horizon School Div Cerebral Palsy of NJ 973.535.1999
Fax 973.535.1268
Web ....www.cpnj.org
　71-77 Okner Pkwy, Livingstone, NJ 07039
　Carolyn Garafola, Director

Hypertrophic Cardiomyopathy
Association 973.983.7429
Fax 973.983.7870
E-mail ....support@4hcm.org
　328 Green Pond Rd, Hibernia, NJ 07842
　Lisa Salberg, Chief Executive Officer

JCC Therapeutic Nursery 201.569.7900
Fax 201.569.7448
Web ....www.jccotp.org
　411 E Clinton Ave, Tenafly, NJ 07670
　Lois Mendelson, CEO

Jewish Family & Children's Service of Southern New
Jersey 856.424.1333
Fax 856.424.7384
Web ....www.jfcssnj.org
　1301 Springdale Road, Suite 150, Cherry Hill,
　NJ 08003-2729
　COA accredited organization.

LADACIN Network 732.493.5900
Fax 732.493.4980
Web ....www.ladacin.org
　1701 Kneeley Blvd, Asbury Park, NJ 07712
　Patricia Carlesimo, Director

Lakeview School 732.549.5580
Fax 732.494.6038
Web ....www.cpamc.org
　10 Oak Dr, Roosevelt Park, Edison, NJ 08837
　Lynn Sikorski, Director

Learning Disabilities Association 973.265.4303
E-mail ....ldanj@optonline.net
　PO Box 492, Towaco, NJ 07082

LearningRx Learning Center 908.834.0606
E-mail ....chester.nj@learningrx.net
　350 Main St, Chester, NJ 07930
　James Goryeb, Owner

LearningRx Learning Center 973.544.8170
E-mail ....shorthills.nj@learningrx.net
　788 Morris Ave, Short Hills, NJ 07078

Lindamood-Bell Learning Processes 973.644.2202
Fax 973.644.2409
　10 Park Pl, Ste 360, Morristown, NJ 07960

Lord Stirling School 908.766.1786
Fax 908.766.9443
Web ....www.lordstirlingschool.org
　99 Lord Stirling Rd, Basking Ridge, NJ 07920
　Joseph E Gorga, Executive Director

McAuley School for Exceptional Children 908.754.4114
Fax 908.754.3312
Web ....www.mcauleyschool.org
　107 Wester Ave, Watchung, NJ 07060
　Gina Donath, Director

Mental Health Association 973.571.4100
E-mail ....info@mhanj.org
　88 Pompton Ave Ste 1, Verona, NJ 07044
　Carolyn Beauchanp, Chief Executive Officer

Mentor Rehabilitative & Support Services 856.533.4100
E-mail ....paula.blum@thementornetwork.com
   505 S Lenola Rd, Blason Office Plaza II Ste 217,
   Moorestown, NJ 08057
   Paula Blum, CEO

National Multiple Sclerosis Society 201.967.5599
Fax 201.967.7085
E-mail ....info@njm.nmss.org
   1 Kalisa Way Ste 205, Paramus, NJ 07652
   Jim Roberts, President

National Multiple Sclerosis Society 732.660.1005
Fax 732.660.1338
E-mail ....info@njm.nmss.org
   246 Monmouth Rd, Oakhurst, NJ 07755
   Allison Cerco, Program Director

Natl Federation of the Blind 866.632.1940
E-mail ....nfbnj@yahoo.com
   254 Spruce St, Bloomfield, NJ 07003

New Jersey Center for Autism 856.455.7200
Fax 856.455.2765
Web ....www.devereux.org
   198 Roadstown Rd, Bridgeton, NJ 08302
   Pam Cooper

New Jersey Centre For Tourette Syndrome 908.575.7350
E-mail ....info@njcts.org
   50 Division St Ste 205, Somerville, NJ 08876
   Saith Rice, Director

**New Jersey Ctr For Outreach And Svcs For The Autism
Community (COSAC)** 609.883.8100
Fax 609.883.5509
Web ....www.autismnj.org
   1450 Parkside Ave, Ste 22, Trenton, NJ 08638-2951
   Dr. Linda Meyer, Director

New Jersey Parent-to-Parent 800.372.6510
E-mail ....parent2parent@spannj.org
   30 Halsey St, Newark, NJ 07102

New Jersey Parents Caucus 973.989.8866
E-mail ....kathyw@njparentcaucus.org
   236 S Salem St, Randolph, NJ 07869

New Road Schools of New Jersey 732.238.7700
Fax 732.238.7868
Web ....www.newroadschool.com
   3071 A Bordentown Ave, 1st Fl, Parlin, NJ 08859
   Annette Hockenjos

Newgrange School & Educational Center 609.584.1800
Fax 609.584.6166
Web ....www.thenewgrange.org
   526 S Olden Ave, Hamilton, NJ 08629
   Robert Hegedus

Oakwood School 732.747.8746
Fax 732.933.0545
Web ....www.oakwoodschool.net
   62 Hance Ave, Eatontown, NJ 07724
   Robert E White, Director

Palisades Learning Center 201.262.2270
Fax 201.262.1289
   304 E Midland Ave, Paramus, NJ 07652
   Jeffrey P Kahn, Director

Parent Advocacy Network 973.642.8100
E-mail ....span@spannj.org
   35 Halsey St 4th Fl, Newark, NJ 07102
   Al Pelham, Business Manager

Parents of Autistic Children 732.785.1099
E-mail ....info@poac.net
   1999 Route 88, East Brick, NJ 08724
   Gary Weitzen, Chief Executive Officer

Parents of Blind Children 973.377.0976
E-mail ....blindchildren@verizon.net
   23 Alexander Ave, Madison, NJ 07940
   Carol Castellano, President

**Pediatric And Adolescent Psychiatry
Associates** 973.605.5000
Fax 973.898.9305
Web ....www.feelgoodandfocused.com
E-mail ....contact@feelgoodandfocused.com
   210 Malapardis Rd, Cedar knoll, NJ 07927
   Merritt Hubsher, Director

Pineland Learning Center 856.378.5020
Fax 856.378.5025
Web ....www.pinelandschool.org
   520 N 4th St Bldg 1, Vineland, NJ 08360
   John L Reed, Director

Princeton Child Development Institute/PC 609.924.6280
Fax 609.924.4119
Web ....www.pcdi.org
E-mail ....info@pcdi.org
   300 Cold Soil Rd, Princeton, NJ 08540
   Edward C Fenske, Executive Director

PSE&G Children's Specialized Hospital 908.301.5561
Fax 908.301.5522
Web ....www.childrens-specialized.org
   200 Somerset Street, New Brunswick, NJ 08901
   CARF accredited programs available.

Quality Health Care, Inc. 866.672.7707
Fax 973.672.7708
Web ....www.qualityhealthcarenurses.com
E-mail ....qualityhealth@aol.com
   167 S Harrison St, East Orange, NJ 07018
   Gwen Watford-Miller, Director Of Clinical Services

Ranch Hope/Strang School 856.935.1555
Fax 856.935.0152
Web ....www.ranchhope.org
   45 Sawmill Rd, Alloway, NJ 08001
   Valerie Quackenbush, Principal

REED Academy 973.772.1188
Fax 973.772.7760
Web ....www.reedacademy.org
   85 Summit Ave, Garfield, NJ 07026
   Dr. Cachus, Director

Rehabilitation Specialists 201.478.4200
Fax 201.791.2280
Web ....http://www.rehab-specialists.com
   18-01 Pollitt Drive, Suite 1A, Fair Lawn, NJ 07410
   CARF accredited programs available.

Rock Brook School 908.431.9500
Fax 908.431.9503
Web ....www.rock-brook.org
E-mail ....info@rock-brook.org
   109 Orchard Rd, Skillman, NJ 08558-2611
   Mary Caterson, Director

SEARCH Day Program 732.531.0454
Fax 732.531.5934
Web ....www.members.aol.com/searchday
   73 Wickapecko Dr, Asbury Park, NJ 07712
   Katherine Solana, Director

Self-Help Group Clearinghouse 973.989.1122
E-mail ....ed@selfhelpgroups.org
   375 E McFarlan St, Dover, NJ 07801
   Ed Madara, Director

Somerset Hills Learning Institute 908.719.6400
Fax 908.719.6401
Web ....www.somerset-hills.org
E-mail ....info@somerset-hills.org
   1810 Burnt Mills Rd, Bedminster, NJ 07921
   Kevin J Brothers, Ececutive Director

SPARC 201.656.3779
E-mail ....sparkleofucp@yahoo.com
   721 Broadway, Bayonne, NJ 07002

Speech-Language-Hearing Association 908.359.5308
E-mail ....info@njsha.com
   203 Towne Centre Dr, Hillsborough, NJ 08844

Spina Bifida Association 908.782.7475
E-mail ....info@thesern.org
   84 Park Ave Ste G-106, Flemington, NJ 08822
   Julia McConnell, Chief Executive Officer

Statewide Parent Advocacy Network 973.642.8100
Fax 973.642.8080
E-mail ....diana.autin@spannj.org
   35 Halsey St 4th Flr, Newark, NJ 07102
   Diana Autin, Co-Executive Director

**Statewide Prnt Advcy Ntwrk of New
Jersey** 973.642.8100
Fax 973.642.8080
   35 Halsey St, Newark, NJ 07102
   Albert Pelham, Office Manager

Stepping Stone School 908.995.1999
Fax 908.995.1994
Web ....www.sstoneschool.com
   45 County Rd 519, Bloomsbury, NJ 08804
   Frank Jiorle, Executive Director

Summit Speech School 908.508.0011
Fax 908.508.0012
Web ....www.summitspeech.org
E-mail ....info@summitspeech.org
   705 Central Ave, New Providence, NJ 07974
   Pamela A Paskowitz, Director

The Arc of New Jersey 732.246.2525
E-mail ....info@arcnj.org
   985 Livingston Ave, North Brunswick, NJ 08902
   Thomas Baffuto, Executive Director

The Bridge Academy 609.844.0770
Fax 609.844.0773
Web ....www.banj.org
   1958 B Lawrence Rd, Lawrenceville, NJ 08648
   Susan Morris, Director

The Calais School 973.884.2030
Fax 973.884.0460
Web ....www.thecalaisschool.org
E-mail ....davidleither@thecalaisschool.org
   45 Highland Ave, Whippany, NJ 07981
   David Leitner, Director

The Children's Institute 973.509.3050
Fax 973.509.3060
Web ....www.tcischool.org
   One Sunset Ave, Verona, NJ 07044
   Bruce Ettinger, Director

The Children's Therapy Center 201.797.7440
Fax 201.797.1039
Web ....www.thechildrenstherapycenter.org
E-mail ....mleiken@thechildrenstherapycenter.org
   29-01 Berkshire Rd, Fair Lawn, NJ 07140
   Marvin Leiken, Director

The Daniel Jordan Fiddle Foundation 877.444.1149
   PO Box 1149, Ridgewood, NJ 07451

The Education Academy 609.693.3322
Fax 609.693.5454
Web ....www.theeducationacademy.com
   505 N Main St Route 9, Lanoka Harbor, NJ 08734
   Roland J Lewis, Director

The Felician School for Exceptional Chil 973.777.5355
Fax 973.777.0725
Web ....www.fsec.org
   260 S Main St, PO Box 530, Lodi, NJ 07644
   Mary Ramona Borkowski

The Forum School 201.444.5882
Fax 201.444.4003
Web ....www.theforumschool.com
E-mail ....info@theforumschool.com
   107 Wyckoff Ave, Waldwick, NJ 07463
   Alice Keener, Director

The Midland School...........................908.722.8222
Fax..908.722.1547
Web...............................www.midlandschool.org
E-mail...........................info@MidlandSchool.org
  94 Readington Rd, North Branch, NJ 08876
  Philip M Gartlan, Director

The Newmark Schools........................908.753.0330
Fax..908.753.0860
Web...........................www.newmarkeducation.com
E-mail.......................nsinfo@newmarkeducation.com
  365 Emerson Ave, Plainfield, NJ 07062
  Cynthia Allman, Executive Director

The Parent Advocacy Center of New
Jersey..732.220.0055
Fax..732.220.0038
E-mail............................nancyfcohen@yahoo.com
  107 Cedar Grove Ln, Ste 104, Somerset, NJ 08873

The Phoenix Ctr, Inc........................973.542.0743
Fax..973.542.0687
Web...............................www.phoenixcenterinc.net
E-mail....................drgibbia@phoenixcenterinc.com
  16 Monsignor Owens Pl, Nutley, NJ 07110-3712
  Dr. Geraldine A. Gibbia, Executive Director

Titusville Academy...........................609.737.7733
Fax..609.737.3343
Web...................................www.titusac1.org
  86 River Dr, Titusville, NJ 08560
  Deborah R Zerbib

Tools To Learn................................201.692.8185
E-mail..................................info@toolstolearn.com

Total Learning Center.......................732.922.6655
Fax..732.922.1019
E-mail..................info@thetotallearningcenter.com
  3455 Rte 66 Neptune, Neptune, NJ 07753
  Marge Weiner, Director

UMDNJ-Division of Developmental-Behavioral
Pediatrics.....................................973.972.8930
Fax..973.972.0812
  183 South Orange Avenue, UBHC Building F-level,
  Newark, NJ 07305

VSA Arts of New Jersey.....................732.745.3885
E-mail.....................................info@vsanj.org
  703 Jersey Ave, New Brunswick, NJ 08901
  Vanessa Young, Executive Director

Willowglen Academy.........................973.579.5117
Fax..973.579.6124
Web...............................www.willowglen-nj.com
  8 Wilson Dr, Sparta, NJ 07871
  Susan Hackett, Principal

YALE School...................................856.482.5252
Fax..856.779.7721
  Executive Offices, 2127 Church Rd, Cherry Hill,
  NJ 08002
  Ed Vonderschmidt, Exective-director

You & Me School..............................732.548.7610
Fax..732.548.7751
Web.......................www.njrehab/pediatricrehab.htm
  2050 Oak Tree Rd, Edison, NJ 08820
  Claudia Somerer, Director

Youth Consultation Services...............973.854.3640
Fax..973.854.3641
Web.....................................www.ycs.org
  60 Evergreen Pl 9th Fl, East Orange, NJ 07018
  Barbara Markell

SUBSTANCE ABUSE TREATMENT

Center for Urban Education, Inc.............973.282.0615
Fax..973.282.1179
Web...............................www.cuehouse.org
E-mail...............................petibone@aol.com
  561 Elizabeth Avenue, Newark, NJ 07112
  John Pinkard, Jr, Director of business Administration/Developement
  CARF accredited programs available.

Daytop Village of New Jersey...............973.543.5656
Fax..973.543.7502
Web...............................www.daytopnj.org
  80 W Main St, Mendham, NJ 07945
  James Curtin, Senior Vice President
  CARF accredited programs available.

Family Connections...........................973.675.3817
Fax..973.673.5782
Web...............................www.familyconnectionsnj.org
E-mail...............................psabreen@att.net
  395 S Center St, Orange, NJ 07050-3205
  Paula Sabreen, Lcsw, Executive Director

High Focus Ctrs...............................201.291.0055
Fax..201.291.0888
Web...............................www.highfocuscenters.com
  40 Eisenhower Dr, Paramus, NJ 07652-1404
  Kim Lenox, Director

New Hope Foundation.......................732.308.0113
Fax..732.308.0115
Web.................http://www.newhopefoundation.org/
E-mail..................skuncken@newhopefoundation.org
  2 Monmouth Ave, Ste 2A, Freehold, NJ 07728
  Samantha Kuncken, Director

Newark Renaissance House..................973.623.3386
Fax..973.623.8877
Web...................................www.nrh.org
  50 Norfolk St, Newark, NJ 07103-3228
  Jordan Kunish, Director

Seashore Family Services of New Jersey......732.920.2700
Fax..732.262.0707
Web...............................www.seashorefamilyservices.org
E-mail...............................rflecha@sfsnj.org
  270 Chambers Bridge Road, Suite 10, Brick, NJ 08723
  Roberto Flecha, Executive Director
  CARF accredited programs available.

West Bergen Mental Healthcare Inc..........201.444.3550
Fax..201.652.1613
Web...............................www.westbergen.org
E-mail...............................anarula@westbergen.org
  120 Chestnut St, Ridgewood, NJ 07450
  Amarjot Narula, West Bergens Medical Director
  CARF accredited programs available.

New Mexico

Susana Martinez, Governor
490 Old Santa Fe Trail, Room 400
Santa Fe, NM 87501
505.476.2200
505.476.2226 (Fax)
www.governor.state.nm.us

Gerri Dupree, Juvenile Justice Specialist
PO Drawer 5160
Santa Fe, NM 87502
505.827.6325
505.476.0225 (Fax)
gerrik.dupree@state.nm.us

David Schmidt, SAG Chair
NM Council on Crime & Delinquency
2319 Mountain Road, NW
Albuquerque, NM 87104
505.235.9351
505.242.3360 (Fax)
nmccd@aol.com

CRISIS NUMBERS

Child Abuse Reporting . . .800.797.3260   Child Abuse Reporting . . .505.841.6100

STATE SERVICES

SOCIAL SERVICES

Child Care Licensing Office New Mexico 505.827.4185
Fax 505.827.7361
PO Drawer 5160, Santa Fe, NM 87502
Jeanette Martinez, Director

Dept of Children, Youth and Families 505.827.7610
Fax 505.476.0225
Web . . . . .www.cyfd.org
1120 Paseo De Peralta Fl 2, Santa Fe, NM 87502
Bill Dunbar, Cabinet Secretary

Human Services Dept. 505.827.7250
Fax 505.827.7203
Web . . . . .www.hsd.state.nm.us
2009 S Pacheco St, Santa Fe, NM 87505-5473

Youth And Family Services 505.827.8008
Fax 505.476.0225
Web . . . . .www.cyfd.org
E-mail . . . . .david.martinez1@state.nm.us
1120 Paseo Be Peralta, Santa Fe, NM 87502
David Martinez, Director

GENERAL HEALTH SERVICES

Children Medical Svcs 505.476.8868
Fax 505.476.8896
2040 S Pacheco, Santa Fe, NM 87505
Susan Chacon, Chief Executive Officer

Family Health Bureau NM 505.476.8905
Fax 505.476.8959
E-mail . . . . .monica.montoya@state.nm.u@sbcglobal.net
2040 S Pacheco St, Santa Fe, NM 87505
Monica Montoya, Director

Medical Assistance Div 505.827.3106
Fax 505.827.3185
Web . . . . .www.state.nm.us
2025 S Pacheco, Santa Fe, NM 87505
Julie Weinberg, Director

Public Health Div 505.827.2389
Fax 505.827.2329
Web . . . . .www.state.nm.us/health
1190 S Saint Francis Dr, Santa Fe, NM 87505
Maggi Gallaher, Director

MENTAL HEALTH SERVICES

Div of Vocational Rehabilitation 505.954.8500
Fax 505.954.8562
Web . . . . .www.state.nm.us
E-mail . . . . .ralph.vigil@state.nm.us
435 Saint Michaels Dr Ste D, Santa Fe,
NM 87505-7679
Ralph Vigil, Acting Director

New Mexico Commission for the Blind 505.841.8844
Fax 505.841.8850
E-mail . . . . .Evelyn.Blair@state.nm.us
2200 Yale Blvd SE, Albuquerque, NM 87106
Evelyn Blair, Director

JUSTICE AGENCY

Attorney General's Ofc 505.827.6000
Fax 505.827.6685
Web . . . . .www.nmag.gov
E-mail . . . . .gking@ago.state.nm.us
408 Galisteo St., Santa Fe, NM 87504
Gary King, Attorney General

Crime Victim Reparation Commission 505.841.9432
Fax 505.841.9437
Web . . . . .www.cvrc.state.nm.us
E-mail . . . . .cvrc@state.nm.us
8100 Mountain Rd NE Ste 106, Albuquerque,
NM 87110-7800
Kristy Ring, Executive Director

Juvenile Justice Div 505.827.7629
Fax 505.827.8408
Web . . . . .www.state.nm.us
1120 Paseo De Peralta, Santa Fe, NM 87501
Pablo Sagillo, Director

COURTS

Administrative Ofc Of The Courts 505.827.4800
Fax 505.827.4824
Web . . . . .www.nmcourts.gov
237 Don Gaspar Ave, Rm 25, Santa Fe,
NM 87501-2178
Arthur W. Pepin, Director

POLICE AND SHERIFF

Dept of Public Safety 505.827.9192
Fax 505.827.3388
Web . . . . .www.dps.state.nm.us
4491 Cerrillos Rd, Santa Fe, NM 87504-1628
Regina Chacon, Assistant Bureau Chief

New Mexico Sheriff's and Police Assoc 505.888.3714
Fax 505.888.0185
Web . . . . .www.nmspa.org
E-mail . . . . .jburleson@nmspa.org
3500 Comanche Rd NE, Bldg ASTE, Albuquerque,
NM 87107
Jim Burleson, Executive Director

EDUCATION SERVICES

Bureau of Indian Education 505.563.5255
Fax 505.563.5281
E-mail . . . . .bjames@bia.edu
1011 Indian Sch Rd NW Ste 332, Albuquerque,
NM 87104
B James, Director

New Mexico School for the Deaf 505.476.6300
Fax 505.476.6315
Web www.nmsd.k12.nm.us
1060 Cerrillos Rd, Santa Fe, NM 87505
Ronald Stern, Superintendent

Parents Reaching Out to Help 505.247.0192
Fax 505.247.1345
1920 B Columbia Dr SE, Albuquerque, NM 87106
Johnny Wilson, Director

Public Education Dept 505.827.5800
Fax 505.827.6696
Web . . . . .www.ped.state.nm.us
300 Don Gaspar Ave, Santa Fe, NM 87501
Patrick Werito, Education Adminstrator

Special Education Bureau New Mexico 505.827.1457
Fax 505.954.0001
120 S Federal Place Rm 206, Santa Fe, NM 87501
Denise Koscielniak, Director

LABOR & WORKFORCE EDUCATION

Ofc of Workforce Training and Development . . .505.827.6827
Fax 505.827.6812
Web . . . . .www.state.nm.us
E-mail . . . . .lmary@state.nm.us
1596 Pacheco St Ste 201, Santa Fe, NM 87505-3960
Len Malry, Executive Director

COUNTY SERVICES

Bernalillo County

SOCIAL SERVICES

Dept of Human Svcs 505.841.7700
Fax 505.841.7754
Web ....www.state.nm.us
E-mail ....julie.linsey@state.nm.us
  1041 Lamberton Pl NE, Albuquerque, NM 87107
  Julie Linsey, Director

Dept of Human Svcs 505.222.9200
Fax 505.222.9650
Web ....www.hsd.state.nm.us
E-mail ....jmascaren@hsd.state.nm.us
  4330 Cutler NE, Albuquerque, NM 87176
  Joel Mascaren, Director

New Mexico Children, Youth And Families Dept. Protective Svcs Div 505.841.7800
Fax 505.841.7886
  1031 Lamberton Pl NE, Albuquerque, NM 87107
  Lisa Madrid, Regional Manager

South West Regional Bureau of Indian Affairs Social Svcs 505.563.3522
Fax 505.563.3058
  1001 Indian School Road NW, Albuquerque, NM 87104
  Don Selwyn, Deputy Director for Indian Services

GENERAL HEALTH SERVICES

Health Ofc 505.841.4100
Fax 505.841.4147
Web ....www.govhealth.gov
  1111 Stanford Dr NE, Albuquerque, NM 87106
  Margy Winebar, Director

Indian Health Hospital 505.248.4000
Fax 505.248.4088
  801 Vassar Dr NE, Albuquerque, NM 87106-2799
  Charles North, Md, Clinical Director

Northwest Valley Public Health Ofc 505.897.5700
Fax 505.897.1010
Web ....www.health.state.nm.us
E-mail ....priscilla.pulakos@state.nm.us
  7704 2nd St NW, Albuquerque, NM 87107-6708
  Priscilla Pulakos, PHN, Nurse Manager

Public Health Ofc 505.873.7477
Fax 505.452.4048
  2001 N Centro Familiar Blvd SW Ste 1, Albuquerque, NM 87105
  Carolyn Salazar, Acting Nurse Manager

Southeast Public Health Ofc 505.841.8928
Fax 505.841.8936
Web ....www.doh.state.nm.us
  7525 Zuni Rd SE Ste B, Albuquerque, NM 87108
  Linda Hellyer, Nurse Manager

JUSTICE AGENCY

CASA 505.841.7388
Fax 505.841.7653
Web ....www.nmcourts.com
E-mail ....albdsmm@nmcourts.com
  5100 2nd St NW, Albuquerque, NM 87107-4009
  Susan Mcdonald, Program Director

CASA-Network 505.217.0220
Fax 505.766.1818
Web ....www.nmcan.org
E-mail ....nmcasa@swcp.com
  707 Broadway Blvd NE Ste 101, Albuquerque, NM 87102-2300
  Brian Oæconnell, State Director

COURTS

2nd Judicial District Court 505.841.7425
Fax 505.841.7446
Web ....www.nmcourts.gov
E-mail ....juanitad@nmcourts.gov
  400 Lomas Blvd NW, Albuquerque, NM 87102-2222
  Juanita Duran, Clerk Of Court

POLICE AND SHERIFF

Albuquerque Police Dept 505.768.2020
E-mail ....rschultz@cabq.gov
  400 Roma Ave NW Ste 1, Albuquerque, NM 87102-5322
  Ray Schultz, Chief

Albuquerque Police Dept-Valley Area 505.761.8800
Fax 505.761.8896
Web ....www.cabq.gov
E-mail ....ctramirez@cabq.gov
  5408 2nd St NW, Albuquerque, NM 87107-4012
  Chris Ramirez, Director Of Communications

Sheriff's Ofc 505.468.7100
Web ....www.bernco.gov
E-mail ....sheriff@bernco.gov
  400 Roma NW, Albuquerque, NM 87102
  Darren White, Sheriff

Chaves County

SOCIAL SERVICES

Children, Youth And Families Protective Div 575.624.6071
Fax 575.624.6190
Web ....www.cysd.nm.us
E-mail ....virgina.villarreal@state.nm.us
  4 Grand Avenue Plz Ste A, Roswell, NM 88201
  Virgina Villarreal, County Office Manager

GENERAL HEALTH SERVICES

Dexter Public Health Ofc 505.734.5582
Fax 505.734.5816
Web ....www.health.state.nm.us
E-mail ....becky.trujjill@health.state.nm.us
  206 South Monroe, Dexter, NM 88230
  Becky Trujjill, Nurse Manager

MENTAL HEALTH SERVICES

Counseling Associates, Inc. 575.623.1480
Fax 575.622.3325
E-mail ....ann.anderson@cai-nm.com
  110 E Mescalero Rd, Roswell, NM 88201
  Marti Everitt, Executive Director

JUSTICE AGENCY

5th District Probation 505.623.2920
Fax 505.624.6059
  4 Grand Avenue Plz Ste C, Roswell, NM 88201-6479
  Daniel Schwertner, Cheif

Cibola County

SOCIAL SERVICES

New Mexico Dept Of Human Svcs 505.287.8836
Fax 505.285.6278
E-mail ....dave.klumpenhower@state.nm.us
  900 Mount Taylor Ave, Grants, NM 87020
  David Klumpenhower, Director

Pueblo Of Laguna Social Svcs 505.552.9712
Fax 505.552.6484
Web ....www.lagunatribe.org
E-mail ....malarid@lagunatribe.org
  Old Highway 66, Laguna, NM 87026
  Marie Alarid, Director

Ramah Navajo Social Svcs 505.775.3221
Fax 505.775.3520
E-mail ....lerettanmartinez@yahoo.com
  PO Box 250, Pinehill, NM 87357-0250
  Leretta Martinez, Acting Director Of Social Services

GENERAL HEALTH SERVICES

Cibola Public Health Ofc 505.285.4601
Fax 505.287.9367
  515 W High St, Grants, NM 87020-2558
  Lou Mazon, Rn, Public Health Nurse Manager

Indian Health Hospital 505.552.5300
Fax 505.552.5490
Web ....www.ihs.gov
E-mail ....martin.kileen@ihs.gov
  80 B Veteran blvd, San Fidel, NM 87049
  Martin Kileen, Clinical Director

COURTS

13th District Court 505.287.8831
Fax 505.285.5755
  515 W High St, Grants, NM 87020
  Honorable Camille M. Olguin, Judge

Pueblo of Laguna Tribal Court 505.552.6687
Fax 505.552.7186
  31 Rodeo Dr, Laguna, NM 87026
  Peggy Bird, Chief Judge

POLICE AND SHERIFF

Sheriff's Ofc 505.876.2040
Fax 505.876.2090
E-mail ....jvaldez_cosd@yahoo.com
  515 W High St, Grants, NM 87020
  Johnny Valdez, Sheriff

Colfax County

SOCIAL SERVICES

Children, Youth And Families Protective Div 575.445.2358
Fax 575.445.2410
E-mail ....rcristin@cyfd.state.nm.us
  1900 Hospital Dr, Raton, NM 87740-2029
  Richard Cristin, Chief Financial Officer

COURTS

8th District Court 505.445.5585
Fax 505.445.2626
Web ....www.nmcourts.com
E-mail ....taod@nmcourts.com
  PO Box 160, Raton, NM 87740-0160
  Honorable Sam B. Sanchez, Director

POLICE AND SHERIFF

Sheriff's Ofc 505.445.5561
Fax 505.445.2988
  440 Hereford Ave, Raton, NM 87740
  Pat Casias, Sheriff

De Baca County

GENERAL HEALTH SERVICES

Debaca Public Health Ofc 505.355.2362
Fax 505.355.7942
Web ....www.state.nm.us
E-mail ....nancy.giannini@state.nm.us
  514 Avenue C, Fort Sumner, NM 88119
  Nancy Giannini, RN, Public Health Nurse Manager

POLICE AND SHERIFF

Sheriff's Ofc 505.355.7433
Fax 505.355.3322
  514 Ave C, Fort Sumner, NM 88119
  James Butterfield, Sheriff

Dona Ana County

JUSTICE AGENCY

Juvenile Probation/Parole **575.524.6360**
Fax 575.524.6013
  750 A Motal Blvd, Las Cruces, NM 88007
  Jay Wisner, Chief JPO

COURTS

3rd Judicial District Court **575.523.8200**
Fax 575.523.8290
  201 W Picacho Ave, Las Cruces, NM 88005
  Honorable James Martin, Division VI

Eddy County

SOCIAL SERVICES

Children, Youth & Families Artesia
Ofc **505.748.1221**
Fax 505.748.3789
E-mail ....vicky.cobb@state.nm.us
  2215 W Main St, Artesia, NM 88210-3721
  Vicky Cobb, County Office Manager

GENERAL HEALTH SERVICES

Eddy Public Health Artesia Ofc **505.746.9819**
Fax 505.748.9755
Web ....www.health.state.pa.us
  111 N 1st St, Artesia, NM 88210-2101
  Anthony Landreth, Public Health Nurse

Grant County

SOCIAL SERVICES

Children, Youth And Families Protective
Div **575.538.2945**
Fax 575.388.5498
E-mail ....richard.anderson@state.nm.us
  3082 32nd St Byp Ste A, Silver City, NM 88061-7875
  Andy Anderson, County Office Manager

COURTS

6th District Court **575.538.3250**
Fax 575.388.5439
  201 N Cooper St, Silver City, NM 88061
  Honorable Henry R. Quintero, Director

Teen Court **505.538.8085**
Fax 505.534.1711
E-mail ....lafleur@zianet.com
  2610 N Silver St, Silver City, NM 88061
  Rebecca Lafleur, Director

Guadalupe County

COURTS

4th District Court **505.472.3888**
Fax 505.472.4451
  1448 HISTORIC ROUTE 66 STE 5, Santa Rosa,
  NM 88435-2375
  Honorable Euginos Mathis, Director

Los Alamos County

GENERAL HEALTH SERVICES

Los Alamos Public Health Ofc **505.662.4038**
Fax 505.662.3899
E-mail ....megan.pfeffer@state.nm.us
  1183 Diamond Dr Ste D, Los Alamos,
  NM 87544-5302
  Megan Pfeffer, Nurse Manager

POLICE AND SHERIFF

Sheriff's Ofc **505.662.8028**
Fax 505.663.3501
E-mail ....marco.lucero@lac.losalamos.nm.us
  2500 Trinity Dr, Los Alamos, NM 87544
  Marco Lucero, Sheriff

McKinley County

SOCIAL SERVICES

Children, Youth And Families Protective
Svcs **505.863.9556**
Fax 505.722.6976
Web ....www.cyfd.state.nm.us
E-mail ....bsandoval@cyfd.state.nm.us
  1720 E Aztec Ave Ste A, Gallup, NM 87301-4925
  Bart Sandoval, Regional Manager

Indian Social Svcs Of Zuni Pueblo **505.782.7000**
Fax 505.782.7202
E-mail ....betnez@ashiwi.org
  1203 B State Hwy 53, Zuni, NM 87327
  Betty Nez, Diretor

New Mexico Dept Of Human Svcs **505.726.7600**
Fax 505.726.7650
  3006 E Hwy 66, Gallup, NM 87301-4605
  Edna Ashley, Director

GENERAL HEALTH SERVICES

Indian Medical Ctr **505.722.1000**
Fax 505.722.1543
Web ....www.ihs.gov
E-mail ....bennie.yazzie@ihs.gov
  516 Nizhoni Blvd, Gallup, NM 87301-5748
  Bennie Yazzie, Md, Director/CEO

POLICE AND SHERIFF

Sheriff's Ofc **505.863.1410**
Fax 505.722.9317
E-mail ....fbegay@co.mckinley.nm.us
  300 W Nizhoni Blvd, Gallup, NM 87301
  Felix Begay, Sheriff

Mora County

GENERAL HEALTH SERVICES

Health Ctrs of Northern New
Mexico **505.666.2288**
Fax 505.666.2186
  604 Catron Ave, Wagon Mound, NM 87752
  Joni Bost, Nursing Manager

Otero County

GENERAL HEALTH SERVICES

Indian Health Hospital **505.464.4441**
Fax 505.464.4422
Web ....www.userinstinct.com
  301 Sage Ave, Mescalero, NM 88340
  Todd Bulman, Clinical Director

Quay County

SOCIAL SERVICES

Children, Youth And Families Protective
Div **575.461.0110**
Fax 575.461.4173
  107 W Aber St, Tucumcari, NM 88401
  Tom Cassidy, County Office Manager

Rio Arriba County

SOCIAL SERVICES

Human Svcs Dept **505.588.7103**
Fax 505.588.7369
Web ....www.state.nm.us/hsd
E-mail ....antonette.cordova@state.nm.us
  410 Paseo De Onate, Suite B, Espanola, NM 87532
  Antonette Cordova, Director

Jicarilla Apache Behavorial Health

Dept **505.759.3162**
Fax 505.759.3588
Web ....www.csvanw.org
E-mail ....mcarrasco@jbhd.org
  12924 Seneca Dr, Dulce, NM 87528
  Monica Carrasco, Director

New Mexico Dept Of Human Svcs **505.753.2271**
Fax 505.753.5826
Web ....www.state.nm.us
E-mail ....antenette.cordava@state.nm.us
  228 Paseo De Onate, Espanola, NM 87532-3549
  Antenette Cordava, Director

Northern Pueblos Agency Social
Svcs **505.753.1435**
Fax 505.753.1404
  1 Mile N Espanola-Taos Hwy, Espanola, NM 87533
  Raymond Fry, Superintendent

POLICE AND SHERIFF

Sheriff's Ofc **505.753.3329**
Fax 505.753.9812
Web ....www.rio-arriba.org
  1122 Johnny Roybal Industrial Pk Rd, Espanola,
  NM 87532-3453
  Thomas Rodella, Sheriff

Roosevelt County

COURTS

9th District Court **505.356.4464**
Fax 505.359.2140
  109 W 1st St, Ste 202, Portales, NM 88130
  Honorable Drew D. Tatum, Division V

San Juan County

SOCIAL SERVICES

New Mexico Dept Of Human Svcs **505.566.9600**
Fax 505.566.9658
E-mail ....deannau.grace@state.nm.us
  101 W Animas St, Farmington, NM 87401
  Elizabeth Jakeway, Director

GENERAL HEALTH SERVICES

Dzilth-Na-O-Ddith-Hle Phs Indian Health
Ctr **505.960.1801**
Fax 505.368.8009
E-mail ....carenda.robinson@ihs.gov
  6 Rd 7586, Bloomfield, NM 87413
  Carenda Robinson, Administrator

MENTAL HEALTH SERVICES

Navajo Tribe Dept. Of Behavioral Health - Shiprock Outpatient
Treatment Program **505.368.1050**
Fax 505.368.1055
  North Hwy 491 Pinion St, Shiprock, NM 87420
  Richard Westbrook, Senior Office Specialist

POLICE AND SHERIFF

Sheriff's Ofc **505.334.6107**
Fax 505.334.6745
Web ....www.sjcounty.net
E-mail ....sjcso@sjcounty.net
  211 S Oliver Dr, Aztec, NM 87410-2416
  M Mccloskey, Sheriff

EDUCATION SERVICES

Special Education **505.334.3695**
Fax 505.599.4388
  1607 W Aztec Blvd, Aztec, NM 87410

Special Education..........................505.368.5163
Fax...505.368.5502
Web..................................www.centralschools.org
　US HWY 64 Old High School Rd, Shiprock,
　NM 87420
　Olivia Kien, Director

Special Education..........................505.599.8617
Fax...505.599.8810
Web..www.fms.k12.nm.us
E-mail...........................pvaldez@fms.k12.nm.us
　1400 E 20th St A, Farmington, NM 87401-9024
　Phyl Valdez, Director

San Miguel County

SOCIAL SERVICES

New Mexico Dept Of Human Svcs.............505.425.6741
Fax...505.454.0256
E-mail.............................seth.conkle@state.nm.us
　2536 Ridge Runner Rd, Las Vegas, NM 87701
　Seth Conkle, County Director

GENERAL HEALTH SERVICES

San Miguel Public Health Ofc................505.425.9368
　18 Gallegos Rd, Las Vegas, NM 87701

MENTAL HEALTH SERVICES

New Mexico Behavorial Health Svcs/ Community Base
Svcs...505.454.5100
Fax...505.454.0397
　700 Friedman Ave, Las Vegas, NM 87701
　Corrine Dominguez, Director

JUSTICE AGENCY

4th District Probation.......................505.425.3543
Fax...505.425.7927
　2518 Ridge Runner Rd, Las Vegas, NM 87701
　Teresa Martinez, Chief Performance Officer

POLICE AND SHERIFF

Sheriff's Ofc...................................505.425.7589
Fax...505.425.8799
E-mail.........................smsheriff@newmexico.com
　26 NM 283, Las Vegas, NM 87701-6006
　Benjie Vigil, Sheriff

Sandoval County

SOCIAL SERVICES

Jemez Pueblo Social Svcs...................505.834.7117
Fax...505.834.7103
Web...www.csvanw.org
　5123 Hwy 4, Jemez Pueblo, NM 87024
　Henrietta Gachupin, Program Administrator

New Mexico Dept Of Human Svcs.............505.867.3357
Fax...505.867.9492
Web..www.state.nm.us
E-mail.............................susan.sewell@state.nm.us
　830 S Camino Del Pueblo, Bernalillo,
　NM 87004-5927
　Susan Sewell, Director

Pueblo De Zia Social Svcs...................505.867.3304
Fax...505.867.3308
E-mail..............................tammylpino@yahoo.com
　135 Capitol Square Dr, San Ysidro, NM 87053-6013
　Marcellus Medina, Governor

Santo Domingo Pueblo Tribal Social
Svcs...505.465.2214
Fax...505.465.2688
Web...www.nmia.com
E-mail..............................dbailon@nmia.com
　Tesuque St, Santo Domingo Pueblo, NM 87052
　Doris Bailon, Director

GENERAL HEALTH SERVICES

Public Health Ofc.............................505.867.2291
Fax...505.867.0107
Web..www.state.nm.us
　1500 Idalia Rd Blvd Bidg B, Bernalillo, NM 87004
　Esther Acosta, Nursing Manager

JUSTICE AGENCY

CASA...505.720.7030
Fax...505.271.0022
Web...www.nationalcasa.org
　PO Box 44184, Rio Rancho, NM 87174-4184
　Tammy Hanks, Executive Director

Juvenile Probation/Parole.................505.867.9559
Fax...505.867.9655
　4359 Jager Dr NE Ste C, Rio Rancho, NM 87144
　Carlton Liggins, Chief Performance Officer

COURTS

13th District Court...........................505.867.2376
Fax...505.867.5161
　1500 Idalia Rd, Bernalillo, NM 87004
　Teresa Valencia, Chief Clerk

POLICE AND SHERIFF

Sheriff's Ofc...................................505.867.7526
Fax...505.867.7608
Web.....................................www.sandovalcounty.com
　1500 Iolia, Bernalillo, NM 87124
　Doug Wood, Sheriff

Santa Fe County

SOCIAL SERVICES

Children, Youth And Families Protective
Div...505.827.7450
Fax...505.827.7440
Web..www.state.nm.us
E-mail....................matthewa.esquibel@state.nm.us
　1920 5th St, Santa Fe, NM 87505-3467
　Mat Esquibel, County Office Manager

New Mexico Ofc Of Emergency
Management....................................505.476.9600
Fax...505.476.9695
Web..www.nmdhsem.org
　13 Bataan Blvd, Santa Fe, NM 87508-4695
　Michael Duvall, Cabinet Secretary

GENERAL HEALTH SERVICES

Indian Health Hospital.......................505.988.9821
　1700 Cerrillos Rd, Santa Fe, NM 87505
　Bret Smoker, Clinical Director

Santa Fe Public Health Ofc..................505.476.2600
Fax...505.476.2692
Web...www.nmhealth.org
　605 Letrado St, Santa Fe, NM 87505
　Steven Mckinsey, Nurse Manager

JUSTICE AGENCY

1st District Probation.......................505.476.2300
Fax...505.476.2320
　1920 5th St, Santa Fe, NM 87505-3467
　Susan Sisneros, Regional Administrator

CASA Program..................................505.820.1500
Fax...505.992.8846
E-mail..................................info@casafirst.org
　4066 W San Francisco, Santa Fe, NM 87501
　Janice Quinn, Director

POLICE AND SHERIFF

Sheriff's Dept.................................505.986.2455
Fax...505.986.2410
E-mail..................shfconcerns@co.santa-fe.nm.us
　35 Camino Justicia, Santa Fe, NM 87508
　Robert Jarcia, Sheriff

EDUCATION SERVICES

Special Education............................505.467.2503
Fax...505.989.5568
　1300 Camino Sierra, Santa Fe, NM 87505-1007
　Patricia Elmer, Director

Sierra County

COURTS

7th District Court............................505.894.7167
Fax...505.894.7168
Web...www.nmcourts.com
E-mail..............................mattr@nmcourts.com
　PO Box 3009, Truth Or Consequences,
　NM 87901-7009
　Honorable Matthew G. Renolds, Division II

Taos County

SOCIAL SERVICES

Children, Youth And Families Protective
Div...575.758.8871
Fax...575.751.0719
　1308 Gusdorf Rd, Taos, NM 87571
　Melissa Quinpana, County Office Manager

JUSTICE AGENCY

CASA Program..................................505.758.0106
Fax...505.751.7621
E-mail.............................tccasa@taosnet.com
　126 Cavalry Rd, Taos, NM 87571-1664
　Rachel Cox, Director of Volunteers

Torrance County

SOCIAL SERVICES

New Mexico Dept of Human Svcs.............505.832.5026
Fax...505.832.4882
Web..www.state.nm.us
E-mail.........................belinda.garland@state.nm.us
　109 Tulane Ave, Moriarty, NM 87035
　Belinda Garland, Director

GENERAL HEALTH SERVICES

Torrance Public Health Ofc..................505.384.2351
Fax...505.384.2626
Web...www.doh.state.nm.us
E-mail....................audrey.rodriquez@state.nm.us
　300 S 8th St, Estancia, NM 87016
　Audrey Rodriguez, Rn, Public Health Nurse

JUSTICE AGENCY

7th District Probation.......................505.384.2780
Fax...505.384.1827
E-mail.............................dwightcurry@state.nm.us
　214 S 5th St, Estancia, NM 87016
　Dwight Curry, Jpo Supervisor

POLICE AND SHERIFF

Sheriff's Ofc...................................505.246.4773
Fax...505.384.1277
E-mail.................mwells@torrancecountynm.org
　205 9th St, Estancia, NM 87016
　Heath White, Sheriff

Union County

SOCIAL SERVICES

New Mexico Dept Of Human Svcs.............505.374.9401
Fax...505.374.2853
Web..www.state.nm.us
E-mail.............................pam.hyde@state.nm.us
　834 Main St Ste 1, Clayton, NM 88415-2900
　Pamela Hyde, Director

COURTS

8th District Court **505.374.9577**
Fax...505.374.2089
   PO Box 310, Clayton, NM 88415-0310
   Honorable John M. Paternoster, Director

POLICE AND SHERIFF

Sheriff's Ofc **505.374.2583**
Web..............................www.charterinternet.com
E-mail.......................bskriggs@charterinternet.com
   200 Court St, Ste C, Clayton, NM 88415
   Bill Skriggs, Sheriff

Valencia County

SOCIAL SERVICES

New Mexico Dept of Human Svcs **505.864.5200**
Fax...505.864.5247
E-mail.......................................anna.roibal@state.nm.us
   5th & Becker, Belen, NM 87002
   Anna Roibal, Administrative Secretary

COURTS

13th District Court **505.865.4639**
Fax...505.865.8801
Web..................................www.13districtcourt.com
   1835 Hwy 314, Los Lunas, NM 87031
   Honorable John W. Pope, Division I

POLICE AND SHERIFF

Sheriff's Ofc **505.866.2400**
Fax...505.866.2027
Web..................................www.co.valencia.nm.us
E-mail...............................shr@co.valencia.nm.us
   453 Luna Ave, Los Lunas, NM 87031
   Louis Burkhard, Sheriff

SPECIAL SERVICES AGENCIES

ADOPTION AGENCIES

Adoption Assistance Agency **505.821.7779**
Fax...505.821.4111
Web...................................www.adoptionassistance.org
E-mail.........................info@adoptionassistance.org
   2800 Eubank Blvd NE, Albuquerque, NM 87112
   Sharon Allcorn, Clinical Director

Connections Plus Case Mgmt **505.897.7154**
Fax...505.890.1055
E-mail.....................connectionsplus@comcast.net
   5821 Avenida La Mirada NW, Albuquerque, NM 87193
   Kathleen Dewitt, Director

New Mexico Solutions **505.268.0701**
Fax...505.232.9055
Web..............................www.newmexicosolutions.com
   707 Broadway Blvd NE Ste 500, Albuquerque, NM 87102-2367
   Dr. David Laye MD, Director

ADVOCACY RESOURCES

Cristen Conley Attorney at Law **505.933.8795**
E-mail..........................conderson@juno.com
   PO Box 134, Albuquerque, NM 87103
   Cristen Conley, Director

Gerber & Bateman **505.986.8530**
E-mail..........................alytrain@yahoo.com
   2009 Botulph Rd Ste 400, Santa Fe, NM 87505
   Amber Train

BEHAVIORAL HEALTH TREATMENT

Albuquerque Children's Home **505.898.5520**
Fax...505.899.4341
Web..www.acch4kids.org
E-mail.......................................ewhite@acch4kids.org
   5700 Winter Haven Dr NW, Albuquerque, NM 87120-2643
   Everett White, Director

All Faiths Receiving Home, Inc. **505.271.0329**
Fax...505.271.4957
Web..www.allfaiths.org
   1709 Moon Street NE, Albuquerque, NM 87112
   COA accredited organization.

Baca Medical Practice **505.872.2929**
Fax...505.872.9503
   5808 McLeod Rd NE Ste K, Albuquerque, NM 87109-2468
   George Baca, Psychiatrist

Connections Inc **505.863.3377**
Fax...505.722.5622
Web..www.cnetco.com
E-mail.......................................connections@cnetco.com
   100 E Aztec Ave, Gallup, NM 87301-6256
   Larry Winn, Director

E L Rocky Mountain Management & Services, LLC **505.762.6091**
E-mail.......................................ijgurule@hotmail.com
   712 Rencher, Clovis, NM 88101
   Mrs. Inez Lovato, Accreditation Manager
   Joint Commission accredited organization.

Ewing Medical Practice **505.255.6002**
Fax...505.255.7890
   2741 Indian School Rd NE, Albuquerque, NM 87106-2653
   David Ewing, Md, Psychiatrist

Grace House **505.885.3681**
Fax...505.885.4259
E-mail.......................................wlaw@gracehouse.net
   2412 Tulip St, Carlsbad, NM 88220-6170
   Will Law, Director

Hogares, Inc **505.345.8471**
Fax...505.342.5414
E-mail.......................................narcher@hogaresinc.com
   1218 Griegos Rd NW, Albuquerque, NM 87107-3752
   Nancy Jo Archer, Executive Director

La Familia Placement Svcs **505.766.9361**
Fax...505.766.9157
Web..www.la-familia-inc.org
E-mail.......................................ceo@la-familia-inc.org
   707 Broadway Blvd NE Ste 103, Albuquerque, NM 87102-2300
   Beverly Nomberg, CEO

Los Alamos Family Council, Inc. **505.662.3264**
Fax...505.662.9707
Web..www.lafamilycouncil.com
   1505 15th St Ste C, Los Alamos, NM 87544-3000
   Joyce Baery, Executive Director

Mesilla Valley Hospital **575.382.3500**
Web..www.psysolutions.com
E-mail.......................................katherine.lamkin@psysolutions.com
   3751 Del Rey Boulevard, Las Cruces, NM 88012
   Ms. Katherine Lamkin, Accreditation Manager
   Joint Commission accredited organization.

New Mexico Behavioral Health Institute at Las Vegas **505.454.2404**
E-mail.......................................louie.trujillo@state.nm.us
   3695 Hot Springs Boulevard, Las Vegas, NM 87701
   Mr. Louie Trujillo, Accreditation Manager
   Joint Commission accredited organization.

New Sunrise Regional Treatment Center **505.552.5500**
Fax...505.552.5530
   Post Office Box 219, Acoma Reservation, San Fidel, NM 87049
   CARF accredited programs available.

Outcomes Inc. **505.243.2551**
Fax...505.243.0446
Web..outcomenm.org
E-mail.......................................sn@outcomesnm.org
   1503 University Blvd NE, Albuquerque, NM 87102-1708
   Steve Nuanez, Chief Executive Officer

Peak Behavioral Health Services, LLC **575.589.3000**
Web..www.peakbehavioral.com/
E-mail.......................................sylvia.huerta@psysolutions.com
   5045 McNutt Road, Santa Teresa, NM 88008
   Ms. Sylvia Huerta, Accreditation Manager
   Joint Commission accredited organization.

Presbyterian Medical Services **505.982.5565**
Web..www.pms-healthierstate.org
E-mail.......................................joahnna_bell@pmsnet.org
   1422 Paseo de Peralta, Santa Fe, NM 87504-2267
   Mrs. Joahnna Bell, Accreditation Manager
   Joint Commission accredited organization.

Rancho Valmora **505.425.6057**
Fax...505.425.3522
Web..www.ranchovalmora.com
E-mail.......................................ranchovalmora@starband.net
   3 Miles East Of Watrous State Rd 97, Valmora, NM 87750-9700
   Angel Burch, Admissions Coordinator

RCI **505.255.5501**
Fax...505.255.9971
Web..www.rci-nm.org
E-mail.......................................angelav@rci-nm.org
   1111 Menaul Blvd NE, Albuquerque, NM 87107-1614
   Kathleen Cates, Interim CEO

San Cristobal Ranch Academy **575.776.2524**
Fax...575.776.2513
Web..www.sancristobalacademy.org
   176 Camino Del Medio, San Cristobal, NM 87564
   David Johnson, President And Executive Director

Sequel of New Mexico, LLC **505.924.6330**
Web..www.camelotforkids.org
E-mail..........................dgoldstein-higgins@sequelyouthservices.com
   5400 Gibson Blvd, Albuquerque, NM 87108
   Ms. Debbie Goldstein-Higgins, Accreditation Manager
   Joint Commission accredited organization.

Sequoyah Adolescent Treatment Center **505.222.0375**
Web..www.nmsatc.org/
E-mail.......................................whgardner@comcast.net
   3405 W Pan American Freeway NE, Albuquerque, NM 87107
   Dr. W. Gardner, Accreditation Manager
   Joint Commission accredited organization.

Sequoyah Adolescent Treatment Ctr **505.222.0300**
Fax...505.222.0301
E-mail.......................................henry.gardner@state.nm.us
   3405 W Pan American Fwy NE, Albuquerque, NM 87107
   W. Henry Gardner, Phd, Executive Director

University of New Mexico Health Sciences Center **505.272.2111**
Web..www.hospitals.unm.edu
E-mail.......................................cljaco@salud.unm.edu
   2211 Lomas Blvd NE, Albuquerque, NM 87106
   Ms. Cathy Jaco, Accreditation Manager
   Joint Commission accredited organization.

Villa Santa Maria, Inc. 505.281.3609
Fax 505.281.0124
Web ....www.villasantamaria.org
E-mail ....attachkids@aol.com
19 Cirquela Rd, Cedar Crest, NM 87008
Joseph Mcguill, Executive Director

Wonder Way 505.873.3138
E-mail ....sacww@earthlink.net
9217 Galaxia Way NE, Albuquerque, NM 87111
Sally Carlon, Director

**Youth and Family Centered Services of New Mexico,
Inc** 505.836.7330
Web ....www.deserthills-nm.com
E-mail ....michael.girlamo@yfcs.com
5310 Sequoia NW, Albuquerque, NM 87120
Mr. Michael Girlamo, Accreditation Manager
Joint Commission accredited organization.

CHILDREN'S HOSPITAL

Cibola General Hospital 505.287.4446
1016 Roosevelt Ave, Grants, NM 87020
Shiela Cox, Human Resource Manager

General Hospital 575.374.2585
300 Wilson St, Clayton, NM 88415
Don Weidenann, Chief Executive Officer

Holy Cross Hospital 575.758.8883
1397 Weimer Rd, Taos, NM 87571
Peter Hoffsteder, Chief Executive Officer

Lea Regional Medical Center 575.492.5000
5419 North Lovington Hwy, Hobbs, NM 88240
Tim Thornell, Chief Executive Officer

Memorial Medical Center 575.522.8641
2450 South Telshor Blvd, Las Cruces, NM 88011
Paul Heizog, Chief Executive Officer

Mescalero Public Health Service Indian 505.671.4441

Mountainview Regional Medical Center 575.556.7600
4311 East Lohman Ave, Las Cruces, NM 88011
Dengn Park, President

Presbyterian Hospital 505.841.1234
1100 Central Ave SE, Albuquerque, NM 87106
Jim Hinton, Chief Executive Officer

Rehoboth McKinley Hospital 505.863.7000
Web ....www.rnch.org
1901 Red Rock Dr, Gallup, NM 87301
Karen Lautermilch, Chief Executive Officer

San Juan Regional Medical Center 505.609.2000
801 West Maple ST, Farmington, NM 87401
Rick Wallace, Chief Executive Officer

U S Public Health Service Indian Hosp 505.786.5291
New Mexico State Rd 371, Crownpoint, NM 87313
Virtual Davis, Chief Executive Officer

U S Public Health Service Indian Hospital 505.782.4431
Route 301 North B Street, Zuni, NM 87327

University Hospital 505.272.2111
2211 Lomas Boulevard NE, Albuquerque, NM 87106
Steven Mckernan, Chief Executive Officer

Veterans Affairs Medical Center 505.265.1711
1501 San Pedro SE, Albuquerque, NM 87108
George Marnell, Director

COUNSELING SERVICES

LDS Family Svcs 505.327.6123
Fax 505.327.9562
Web ....www.ldsfamilyservices.org
E-mail ....fam-nm-farmington@ldschurch.org
925 Cannery Ct Ste A, Farmington, NM 87401-4058
David Holmes, Manager

New Mexico Parent And Child Resources 505.268.4973
Fax 505.268.5056
E-mail ....adesiderio@nmpcr.org
3500 Indian School Rd NE, Albuquerque, NM 87106-1143
Anne Desiderio, Director

CRISIS & SHELTER CARE

Crisis Ctr Of Northern New Mexico 505.753.1656
Fax 505.753.7743
Web ....www.crisis-centers.org
577 El Llano Rd, Espanola, NM 87532
Ms Carol Merriweather, Director

**Home For Women And Children-Domestic
Violence** 505.368.5124
Fax 505.368.5129
E-mail ....shiprockwomen1@yahoo.com
North Highway 491, Shiprock, NM 87420
Gloria Champion, Director

Laguna Family Shelter Program 505.552.9701
Fax 505.552.6053
Web ....www.lagunatribe.org
5 RIO SAN JOSE, Laguna, NM 87026
Ken Thomas, Director

**Northern Indian Peace Keepers-Dom
VInce** 505.753.4790
Fax 505.753.5233
Web ....www.eightnorthernpueblos.com
706 La Joya St Ste A1, Espanola, NM 87532-2877
Mr Elias Bigil, Director

Rape Crisis Ctr Of Central New Mexico 505.266.7711
Fax 505.268.5046
Web ....www.rapecrisiscnm.org
9741 Candelaria Blvd NE, Albuquerque, NM 87112

Robertas Place-Domestic Violence 505.287.7724
Fax 505.876.2534
E-mail ....sally.sanchez@state.nm.us
103 Goltz Dr, Grants, NM 87020
Ms. Sally Sanchez, Director

Santa Fe Youth Development Program 505.473.4154
Fax 505.471.7062
Web ....www.santafecounty.org
4250 Airport Rd, Santa Fe, NM 87507-2844

Youth Development Crisis Shelter 505.877.0371
Fax 505.877.6767
E-mail ....llopez@ydinm.com
1706 Bentero Familier, Albuquerque, NM 87105-5549
Louis Lopez, Program Director

Youth Shelters 505.983.0586
Fax 505.424.0949
Web ....www.youthshelters.org
E-mail ....info@youthshelters.org
PO Box 28279, Santa Fe, NM 87592-8279
Karen Rowell, Executive Director

EDUCATION

National Indian Youth Council 505.247.2251
Fax 505.247.4251
Web ....www.niyc-alb.org
E-mail ....nration@niyc-alb.org
318 SE Elm St, Albuquerque, NM 87102
Norman Ration, Executive Director

**New Mexico Boys Ranch, A Div Of New Mexico Boys And Girls
Ranches, Inc.** 505.881.3363
Fax 505.888.1595
Web ....www.theranches.org
E-mail ....info@theranches.org
6209 Hendrix Rd Ne, Albuquerque, NM 87110-1334
Nikki Kull, Executive Director

Santa Fe Mountain Ctr 505.983.6158
Fax 505.983.0460
Web ....www.santafemc.org
E-mail ....jenn@santafemc.org
1524 Bishops Lodge Rd, Tesuque, NM 87574
Sky Gray, Director

FOSTER CARE AGENCIES

CYFD PSD 505.827.7602
Fax 505.827.4474
PO Drawer 5160 Pera Bldg #219, Santa Fe, NM 87502

Families for Children 505.881.4200
6209 Hendrix Rd NE, Albuquerque, NM 87110
Michael Kull, President

New Mexico Parent and Child Resources In 505.858.3028
Fax 505.268.4973
3500 Indian School Rd Ne, Albuquerque, NM 87106

Operation Identity 505.293.3144
13101 Blackstone NE, Albuquerque, NM 87111

Rio Arriba & Los Alamos FPA 505.662.6269
1080 Sioux St, Los Alamos, NM 87544
Tony Montoya, Father

The Adoption Exchange 505.247.1769
Fax 505.888.5978
2920 Carlisle NE Ste G, Albuquerque, NM 87110
Bill Ryan, Manager

HOME MEDICAL EQUIPMENT PROVIDERS

Southwest Footprints 575.392.1063
Fax 575.392.7750
1200 East Bender Road, Hobbs, NM 88240
CARF accredited programs available.

PEDIATRIC HOME CARE

Interim Healthcare 575.391.0121
Fax 575.397.6060
726 E Michigan St Ste 130, Hobbs, NM 88240
Betty Sigala, Customer Service

Interim Healthcare 575.396.1394
Fax 575.397.6060
726 E Michigan Ste 130, hobbs, NM 88240
Irma Minjares, Director

SOCIAL SERVICES

Catholic Charities 505.424.9789
Fax 505.424.9792
E-mail ....rosecando@ccaffnm.org
4985 Airport Rd, Santa Fe, NM 87507-1802
Rose Cando, Administrator

Catholic Charities 505.724.4670
Fax 505.254.2623
Web ....www.ccasfnm.org
6001 Marble NE, Albuquerque, NM 87110
COA accredited organization.

Childhaven 505.325.5358
Fax 505.327.1482
Web ....www.childhaven.org
E-mail ....erinh@childhaven.org
807 W Apache St, Farmington, NM 87401
Erin Hourihan, Executive Director

Choices For Families, Inc. 505.884.0208
Fax 505.884.1545
E-mail ....directorchoices@aol.com
2727 San Pedro Dr NE Ste 113, Albuquerque, NM 87110
Michelle Otero, Director

New Mexico

Community Action Agency Of Southern NM, Inc **505.523.1639**
Fax 505.527.9028
Web ....www.caasnm.org
E-mail ....stacycox@hotmail.com
  320 Wyatt Dr, Las Cruces, NM 88001-3673
Stacy Cox, Executive Director

Discovery Child Development Center, Inc. **575.382.0338**
Fax 575.382.5838
Web ....www.discoverychild.net
  3300 Del Rey Boulevard, Las Cruces, NM 88012
COA accredited organization.

Family Resource Ctr **505.566.3825**
Fax 505.566.3826
Web ....www.newmexicokids.org
  3539 E 30th St, Farmington, NM 87402-8801
Bev Michael, Director

High Desert Family Services, Inc. **505.823.4530**
Fax 505.797.3956
Web ....www.highdesertfs.com
  7001 Prospect Place NE, Suite 100, Albuquerque, NM 87110
CARF accredited programs available.

Jewish Family Service **505.291.1818**
Fax 505.291.0332
E-mail ....info@jfsnm.org
  5520 Wyoming Blvd NE Ste 200, Albuquerque, NM 87109
Michael Gemme, Director

La Familia, Inc. **505.766.9361**
Fax 505.243.2252
Web ....www.la-familia-inc.org
  707 Broadway NE, Suite 103, Albuquerque, NM 87102
COA accredited organization.

LDS Family Svcs **505.345.3046**
Fax 505.343.1898
E-mail ....schougaardc@ldschurch.org
  4400 Presidential Pl NE, Ste C, Albuquerque, NM 87109
Chad Schougaard, Director

Mosaic **505.287.9333**
Fax 505.287.9336
Web ....www.mosaic.org
E-mail ....michelle.staley@mosaicinfo.org
  920 Lobo Canyon Rd, Grants, NM 87020-2173
Michelle Staley, Early Intervention Coordinator

Namaste Child and Family Development Ctr **505.865.6176**
Fax 505.865.3268
Web ....www.namasteinc.org
E-mail ....namaste@nm.net
  2112 N Main St, Clovis, NM 88101
Carol Reinhart, Executive Director

New Mexico Family Network **505.265.0430**
Fax 505.255.6578
Web ....www.pbdc.org
E-mail ....spianci@nmfamilynetwork.org
  1101 Cardenas Dr NE Ste 202, Albuquerque, NM 87110
Sergio Pianci, Executive Director

Pecos Valley Cooperative (Rcc #8) **505.746.2731**
Fax 505.748.6160
Web www.pvrec8.org
E-mail ....scaleron@pvrec8.com
  2218 W Grand Ave, Artesia, NM 88210
Sylvia Calderon, Respite Coordinator

SPECIAL NEEDS

Abrazos Family Support Services **505.867.3396**
E-mail ....jeanettet@epicsproject.org
  PO Box 788, Bernalillo, NM 87004

Brain Injury Association **505.292.7414**
E-mail ....info@braininjurynm.org
  3234 Candle Area NE, Albuquerque, NM 87107
Delsy Roach, Executive Director

Family Voices Inc **888.835.5669**
E-mail ....kidshealth@familyvoices.org
  2340 Alamo SE Ste 102, Albuquerque, NM 87106

Info Ctr for New Mexicans w/Disabilities **505.272.8549**
E-mail ....infonet@unm.edu
  2300 Menaul NE, Albuquerque, NM 87107

Lovelace Rehabilitation Hospital **505.727.4781**
Fax 505.727.7572
Web ....www.lovelace.com
  505 Elm Street NE, Albuquerque, NM 87102
CARF accredited programs available.

MDA/ALS Ctr at the Univ of NM **505.272.3160**
Fax 505.272.6692
  1 University of New Mexico, Albuquerque, NM 87131
Sarah Youssof MD, Director

Multicultural Evaluation and Consultation Associates, LLC **575.526.1161**
Fax 575.523.1108
Web ....www.mecatherapies.com
E-mail ....edward@mecatherapies.com
  1350 Hillrise Circle, Las Cruces, NM 88011
Edward Flores, Director of Community-Based Services
CARF accredited programs available.

NAMI New Mexico **800.953.6745**
E-mail ....naminm@aol.com
  PO Box 3086, Albuquerque, NM 87190
Trinidade Jesusarguello, President

National Multiple Sclerosis Society **505.243.2792**
Fax 505.244.0629
E-mail ....NMX@nmss.org
  4125 Carlisle Blvd NE Ste A, Albuquerque, NM 87107

New Mexico Autism Society **505.332.0306**
E-mail ....nmautism@nmautismsociety.org
  PO Box 30955, Albuquerque, NM 87190

New Mexico Congress of PTA **505.881.0712**
E-mail ....nmpta@aol.com
  3315 Louisiana NE, Albuquerque, NM 87110

New Mexico Family Network **800.273.7232**
  1101 Cardenas Dr NE Ste 202, Albuquerque, NM 87110

Parents Reaching Out **505.247.0192**
  1920B Columbia SE, Albuquerque, NM 87106
Johnny Wilson, Director

Speech-Language-Hearing Association **800.292.8465**
E-mail ....nmsha@comcast.net
  PO Box 90846, Albuquerque, NM 87199

The Arc of New Mexico **505.883.4630**
E-mail ....rshuman@arcnm.org
  3655 Carlisle NE, Albuquerque, NM 87110
Randy Costales, Director

VSA Arts of New Mexico **505.345.2872**
E-mail ....info@vsartsnm.org
  4904 4thst NW, Albuquerque, NM 87107
Marj Neset, Executive Director

New York

Andrew Cuomo, Govenor
Executive Chambers
State Capitol
Albany, NY 12224
518.474.8390
518.474.1513 (Fax)
www.ny.gov

Jacquelyn Greene, Juvenile Justice Specialist
4 Tower Place
Albany, NY 12203
jacquelyn.greene@dcjs.state.ny.us

Joseph Cocozza, SAG Chair
345 Delaware Ave
Delmar, NY 12054
518.439.7415
jcocozza@prainc.com

CRISIS NUMBERS

Child Abuse Reporting . . .518.474.8740	Child Abuse Reporting . . .800.342.3720	Covenant House 800.999.9999

STATE SERVICES

SOCIAL SERVICES

Child Care Licensing Office New York 518.474.9454
Fax 518.474.9617
52 Washington St Rm 309 S, Rensselaer, NY 12144
Janice Molnar, Deputy Commissioner

New York State Ofc of Children and Family
Svcs **518.473.7793**
Fax 518.486.7550
Web . . . . .www.ocfs.state.ny.us
E-mail . . . . .donna.quirk@ocfs.state.ny.us
52 Washington St, Rensselaer, NY 12144-2834
Donna Quirk, Executive Secretary

Social Svcs **518.853.4646**
Fax 518.853.8327
Web .www.montgomeryny.com
64 Broadway, Fonda, NY 12068
Michael Mahon, Commissioner

State Central Registry **518.474.1567**
PO Box 4480, Albany, NY 12204

GENERAL HEALTH SERVICES

Bureau of Family and Com Health NY **518.474.2084**
Fax 518.473.8673
E-mail . . . . .rmd07@health.state.ny.us
Corning Tower Rm 208, Albany, NY 12237
Rachael Delonj, Director

Bureau of Maternal & Child Health **518.402.5706**
Fax 518.474.3914
E-mail . . . . .dohweb@heatlh.state.ny.us
ESP Corning Tower Rm 1805, Albany, NY 12237
Rachel Delong, Director

Child Morbidity and Mortality Prevention **518.473.3511**
Fax 518.474.1420
Web . . . . .www.health.state.ny.us
E-mail . . . . .jjr04@health.state.ny.us
Empire State Plz, Corning tower Rm 2162, Albany,
NY 12237-0001
James Raucci, Director

Div of Family Health **518.473.7922**
Fax 518.473.2015
1 Empire State Plz, Room 890, Albany, NY 12237
Barbara McTatu, Director

MENTAL HEALTH SERVICES

Dept of Mental Health **315.435.3355**
Fax 315.435.3279
Web . . . . .www.ongov.net
E-mail . . . . .ocdmh@ongov.net
421 Montgomery St, 10th Floor, Syracuse, NY 13202
Robert Long, Director

Dept of Mental Health/Mental Retardation/Substance Abuse
Svcs **212.219.5400**
Fax 212.219.5555
Web . . . . .www.nyc.gov/health
93 Worth St, Rm 410, New York, NY 10013
Adam Karpati, Deputy Commissioner

Office Of Children family Services **518.473.7793**
Fax 518.486.7550
E-mail . . . . .info@ocfs.state.ny.us
52 Washington St, Rensselaer, NY 12144
Gladys Carrion, Commissioner

State Com for the Blind & Vis Hand NY **518.474.6812**
Fax 518.486.5819
E-mail . . . . .brian.daniels@dfa.state.ny.us
52 Washington St, Rensselaer, NY 12144
Brian Daniels, Director

The Office For People With Developmental
Disabilities **518.473.1997**
Fax 518.473.1271
Web . . . . .www.opwdd.ny.gov
44 Holland Ave, Albany, NY 12229
Courtney Burke, Commissioner

Voc & Educ Svcs for Ind with Dis NY **518.474.1711**
Fax 518.474.5652
E-mail . . . . .vesidadm@mail.nysed.gov
99 Washington Ave, 1 Commerce Plaza Rm 1609,
Albany, NY 12234

JUSTICE AGENCY

Attorney General's Ofc **518.474.7330**
Fax 518.473.9909
E-mail . . . . .ag@ny.gov
State Capitol, Room 220, Albany, NY 12224
Eric Schneiderman, Attorney General

Correctional Education Division NY **518.457.8142**
Fax 518.457.1914
E-mail . . . . .nydocsedu@docs.state.ny.u@sbcglobal.net
1220 Washington Ave, Harriman State Campus Bldg
2, Albany, NY 12226

Crime Victims Board **718.923.4325**
Fax 718.923.4347
E-mail . . . . .tinastanford@ovs.state.ny.us
55 Hanson Pl, Rm 1000, Brooklyn, NY 11217
Tina Stanford, Director

Div of Criminal Justice Svcs **518.457.3670**
Fax 518.485.0909
Web . . . . .www.criminaljustice.state.ny.us
4 Tower Pl Ste 7, Albany, NY 12203-3764
Jonathan Gradess, Executive Director

New York State CASA Association Inc **518.426.5354**
Fax 518.426.5348
Web . . . . .www.casanys.org
E-mail . . . . .page@casanys.org
911 Central Ave, #117, Albany, NY 12206
Penny Page, Executive Director

New York State Div of Children and Family
Svcs **212.961.4121**
Fax 212.961.4109
Web . . . . .www.dfa.ocfs.state.ny.us
163 W 125th St, 14th Floor, New York, NY 10027
Gladys Carown, Commissioner

NYS Dept of Correctional Svcs **518.457.7329**
Fax 518.457.0108
Web . . . . .docf.state.ny.us
1220 Washington Ave Bldg 2, Albany, NY 12236
Daniel Martuscello, Director Of Personnel

COURTS

Administrative Ofc Of The Courts **518.474.1038**
Fax 518.473.5514
4 Empire State Plz Ste 2001, Albany, NY 12223-1400
Honorable Ann U. Pal, Administrative Judge

Family Court **518.853.8133**
Fax 518.853.8148
E-mail . . . . .pcortese@courts.state.ny.us
58 Broadway, Fonda, NY 12068
Laurie Furnare, Secretary

POLICE AND SHERIFF

New York State Assoc of Chiefs of Police **518.355.3371**
Fax 518.356.5767
Web . . . . .www.nychiefs.org
E-mail . . . . .nysacop@nycap.rr.com
2697 Hamburg St, Schenectady, NY 12303-3783
John Grebert, Executive Director

New York State Sheriffs' Assoc **518.434.9091**
Fax 518.434.9093
Web . . . . .www.nysheriffs.org
E-mail . . . . .sheriff@nysheriffs.org
27 Elk St, Albany, NY 12207-1002
Peter R. Kehoe, Executive Director

EDUCATION SERVICES

Advocates for Children of New York Inc **212.947.9779**
Fax 212.947.9790
E-mail . . . . .ksweet@advocatesforchildren.org
151 W 30th St 5th Flr, New York, NY 10001
Kim Sweet, Director

New York

Communities In Schools of New York **212.407.6264**
Fax 212.407.6266
Web . . . . .www.pace.edu
E-mail . . . . .rblash@pace.edu
  390 Park Ave, New York, NY 10022
  Roy Blash, Executive Director

Dept of Education **518.474.3852**
Fax 518.486.5631
Web . . . . .www.nysed.gov
  89 Washington Ave, Albany, NY 12234-1000
  John King, Commissioner Of Education

Educ for Homeless Children and Youth NY **800.388.2014**
Fax 212.807.6872
E-mail . . . . .info@nysteachs.org
  151 W 30th St 5th Flr, New York, NY 10001

Hebrew Academy For Special Children **718.851.6100**
Fax 718.437.6654
Web . . . . .www.hasc.net
E-mail . . . . .julie.ben-zvi@hasc.net
  1311 55th St, Brooklyn, NY 11219-4299
  Julie Benzvi, Program Director

New York State Education Dept Educ Bldg **518.474.5844**
Fax 518.473.4909
E-mail . . . . .commissioner@mail.nysed.gov
  89 Washington Ave Rm 111, Albany, NY 12234
  John King, Director

New York State School for the Blind at
  Batavia **585.343.5384**
Fax 585.344.5557
Web . . . . .www.nysed.gov
E-mail . . . . .csanger@mail.nysed.gov
  2A Richmond Ave, Batavia, NY 14020-1499
  Mathis Calvin, Superintendent

Resources for Children w Spec Needs NY **212.677.4650**
Fax 212.254.4070
E-mail . . . . .info@resourcesnyc.org
  116 E 16th St 5th Flr, New York, NY 10003
  Rachel Howard, Director

United We Stand of New York **718.302.4313**
Fax 718.302.4315
E-mail . . . . .uwsofny@aol.com
  91 Harrison Ave, Brooklyn, NY 11206
  Lourdes Rivera-Putz, Director

LABOR & WORKFORCE EDUCATION

Office Of Temporary And Disabilites
  Assistance **518.474.9222**
Fax 518.474.5281
  40 N Pearl St 11th F, Albany, NY 12243
  Russell Sykes, Deputy Commissioner

COUNTY SERVICES

Albany County

SOCIAL SERVICES

Dept For Children, Youth And
Families **518.447.7500**
Fax 518.447.7766
Web . . . . .www.dfa.state.ny.us
  112 State St, Fl 4, Albany, NY 12207
  Marian Logan, Director

Dept Of Social Svcs **518.447.7300**
Fax 518.447.7664
  162 Washington Ave, Albany, NY 12210
  Vincent Colonno, Commisioner

New York State Ofc Of Children & Family Svcs Albany Regional
Ofc **518.486.7078**
Fax 518.486.7625
E-mail . . . . .kerri.barber@ocfs.state.ny.us
  52 Washington St, Rensselaer, NY 12144
  Kerri Barber, Family & Children Services Director

New York State Of Alcholic & Substances Of Abuse
Services **518.457.2061**
Fax 518.457.5474
Web . . . . .www.oasas.state.ny.us
E-mail . . . . .Commissioner@oasas.state.ny.us
  1450 Western Ave, Albany, NY 12203
  Arlene Gonzalez-Sanchez, Commissioner

GENERAL HEALTH SERVICES

Health Dept **518.447.4580**
Fax 518.447.4698
Web . . . . .www.albanycounty.com/departments/health
  175 Green St, Albany, NY 12202
  Anna Scavo, Director

WIC **518.402.7093**
Fax 518.402.7348
Web . . . . .www.health.state.ny.us
  150 Broadway, Fl 6, Albany, NY 12204
  Barbara Krueger, Associate Director

MENTAL HEALTH SERVICES

Mental Health **518.447.4550**
Fax 518.447.2045
Web . . . . .www.albanycounty.com
  175 Green St 260 S Pearl St, Albany, NY 12202-2011
  Moira Manning, Supervisor

JUSTICE AGENCY

Juvenile Secure Detention **518.456.9399**
Fax 518.456.8290
  838 Albany Shaker Rd, Albany, NY 12211-1054
  Eugene Terry, Facility Director

Ofc of Children & Family Svcs Aftercare/Intake Ofc Capitol
District **518.438.8044**
Fax 518.489.8852
Web . . . . .www.ocfs.state.ny.us
E-mail . . . . .johnejohnson@ocfs.state.ny.us
  79 Ryckman Ave, Albany, NY 12202-2526
  John Johnson, Director

Probation Dept **518.487.5200**
Fax 518.487.5204
  60 S Pearl St, Albany, NY 12207
  Williams Connors, Deputy Director

COURTS

Family Court **518.285.8600**
Fax 518.462.4248
Web . . . . .www.courts.state.ny.us
E-mail . . . . .ddugan@courts.state.ny.us
  30 Clinton Ave, Albany, NY 12207-2203
  Honorable W. Dennis Dugan, Judge

Opp Incann Klose Head Start **518.432.9622**
Fax 518.434.2828
  295 Colonie St Ste 1, Albany, NY 12210-1532
  Michael Macmillian, Court Services & Probation Director, CPO

POLICE AND SHERIFF

Albany Police Deptù Juvenile Unit **518.447.8780**
Fax 518.447.7840
  I Mortin Ave, Albany, NY 12202
  Detective Lt. Kevin Connelley, Juvenile Officer

Sheriff's Ofc **518.487.5400**
Fax 518.487.5037
E-mail . . . . .jcampbell@albanycounty.com
  16 Eagle St Rm 312, Albany, NY 12207-1011

EDUCATION SERVICES

Acoi Early Learning Ctr **518.463.0655**
Fax 518.434.2828
Web . . . . .www.acoi.com
E-mail . . . . .bbarth@acoi.com
  25 Monroe St Ste 100, Albany, NY 12210-2729
  Ms Bridget Barth, Director

Special Education **518.486.6366**
Fax 518.473.5387
Web www.p12.nysed.gov/specialed
E-mail . . . . .jdeloren@mail.nysed.gov
  89 Washington Ave, Rm # 309, Education Bldg.,
  Albany, NY 12234-0001
  James De Lorenzo, State Wide Coordinator Over All Regional Offices

Allegany County

SOCIAL SERVICES

Social Svcs **585.268.9622**
Fax 585.268.9479
  7 Court St, County Office Bldg, Belmont, NY 14813
  Vicki Grant, Commissioner

GENERAL HEALTH SERVICES

Health Dept **585.268.9250**
Fax 585.268.9264
Web . . . . .www.alleganyco.com
E-mail .healthinfo@alleganyco.com
  7 Court St Rm 17, Belmont, NY 14813
  Laurie Ballengee, Public Health Director

MENTAL HEALTH SERVICES

Community Svcs **585.593.1991**
Fax 585.593.7104
Web . . . . .www.co.allegany.ny.us
  45 N Broad St, Wellsville, NY 14895-1224
  Robert W. Anderson, Phd, Director

The Counseling Ctr Allegany Rehabilitation
Associates **585.593.6300**
Fax 585.593.7071
E-mail . . . . .wholbrook@araservices.com
  4220 State Route 417W, Wellsville, NY 14895
  Wendy Holbrook, Office Manager

COURTS

Family Court **585.268.5816**
Fax 585.268.7090
  7 Court St, Belmont, NY 14813
  Kathryn Brownell, Chief Clerk

POLICE AND SHERIFF

Belmont Police Dept **585.268.5522**
Fax 585.268.7005
Web . . . . .www.belmontpd.org
E-mail . . . . .villageofbelmont@yahoo.com
  1 Schuyler St, Belmont, NY 14813-1014
  Chris Finnemore, Police Chief

Sheriff's Ofc **585.268.9200**
Fax 585.268.9484
Web ....www.alleganyco.com
    4884 State Route 19 S, Belmont, NY 14813-9506
    Rick Whitney, Sheriff

Bronx County

MENTAL HEALTH SERVICES

Bronx Psychiatric Ctr **718.931.0600**
Fax 718.862.4889
Web ....www.omh.state.ny.us
E-mail ....lcarmichael@omh.state.ny.us
    1500 Waters Pl, Bronx, NY 10461
    Mr. Carmicheal, Director

Bronx-Lebanon Hospital Ctr **718.584.5035**
Fax 718.562.9426
E-mail ....tcaery@bronx-leb.org
    401 E St 10067 2nd Fl, Bronx, NY 10458
    Theresa Caery, Director

Bronx-Lebanon Hospital Ctr **718.590.1800**
Fax 718.901.6251
Web ....www.bronxleb.org
E-mail ....jmarcian@bronxleb.org
    1650 Selwyn Ave Apt 6B, Bronx, NY 10457-7688
    Jennifer Marciano, Administrative Director, Aids Program

Jewish Assoc For Svcs For The Aged
Inc **718.365.4044**
Fax 718.563.0715
Web ....www.jasa.org
    1 Fordham Plz Ste 232, Bronx, NY 10458-5871
    Danielle Palmisino, Director

JUSTICE AGENCY

Boys Intake **718.597.3842**
Fax 718.597.3550
    1101 Beach Ave, Bronx, NY 10474
    Antonio Fonseca, Acting Director

POLICE AND SHERIFF

Bronx Precinct 40 .... **718.402.2270**
Fax 718.402.3195
    257 Alexander Ave, Bronx, NY 10454-1133
    Elias Nikas, Deputy Inspector

Bronx Precinct 41 .... **718.542.4771**
Fax 718.542.7158
Web ....www.cammarata.com
    1035 Longwood Ave, Bronx, NY 10459-5204
    Captain Philip Rivera, Captain

Bronx Precinct 43 .... **718.542.0888**
Fax 718.842.1931
    900 Fteley Ave, Bronx, NY 10473-4006
    Dones, Police Officer

Bronx Precinct 45 .... **718.822.5411**
Fax 718.822.5458
    2877 Barkley Ave, Bronx, NY 10465
    Kathy Greene, Captain

Bronx Precinct 46 .... **718.220.5211**
    2120 Ryer Ave, Bronx, NY 10457
    R Faraz, Director

Bronx Precinct 47 .... **718.920.1211**
Fax 718.920.1200
    4111 Laconia Ave, Bronx, NY 10466-4901
    Dent Cremont, Commander

Bronx Precinct 50 .... **718.543.5700**
Fax 718.543.0957
    3450 Kingsbridge Ave, Bronx, NY 10463
    Eddy Rodriguez, Community Affairs Officer

EDUCATION SERVICES

Eastside House Mott Haven Community
Ctr **718.292.4151**
Web ....www.eastsidehouses.org
E-mail ....harris@eastsidehouses.org
    375 E 143rd St, Bronx, NY 10454-1258
    Ms. Harris, Director

Broome County

SOCIAL SERVICES

Social Svcs **607.778.8850**
Fax 607.778.3506
    3642 Main St, Binghamton, NY 13905
    Sandi Sanzo Director, Medical Service/child-teen Health Program Director

GENERAL HEALTH SERVICES

Health Dept **607.778.3930**
Fax 607.778.2838
Web ....www.co.broome.ny.us
E-mail ....cedwards@co.broome.ny.us
    225 Front St, Binghamton, NY 13905-2424
    Melissa Brennen, Clinic Director

MENTAL HEALTH SERVICES

Community Mental Health Svcs **607.778.1152**
Fax 607.778.1164
E-mail ....amack@co.broome.ny.us
    229-231 State St, Binghamton, NY 13901-3102
    Abby Mack, Director

Greater Binghamton Health Ctr **607.797.0680**
Fax 607.797.4315
E-mail ....jsteen@omh.state.ny.us
    114 Clinton St, Binghamton, NY 13905
    James Steen, Director

United Health Svcs Hospitals Inc **607.762.2340**
Fax 607.762.3298
Web ....www.uhs.net
E-mail ....edwin_rivera@uhs.org
    33 Mitchell Ave Ste 204, Binghamton, NY 13903
    Ed Wynn Rivera, Lcswr, Clinic Manager

JUSTICE AGENCY

Dept of Probation **607.778.2121**
Fax 607.778.6137
E-mail ....lwilmot@co.broome.ny.us
    45 Hawley St, Binghamton, NY 13902-1766
    Lorraine S. Wilmot, Director

Ofc of Children & Family Svc Aftercare/Intake Ofc Binghampton
Satellite **607.721.8454**
Fax 607.721.8459
Web ....www.oag.state.ny.us
    44 Hawley St Fl 6, Binghamton, NY 13901-4402
    Faye Welch, Supervisor

Youth Bureau **607.778.2085**
Fax 607.778.2044
Web ....www.gobroomecounty.com
    60 Hawley St, Binghamton, NY 13902
    Joanna Kamin, Executive Director

COURTS

Family Court **607.778.2156**
Fax 607.778.2439
E-mail ....rconnerton@courts.state.ny.us
    65 Hawley St, Binghamton, NY 13902
    Honorable Rita Connerton, Judge

POLICE AND SHERIFF

Sheriff's Ofc **607.778.1911**
Fax 607.778.2104
Web ....www.co.broome.ny.us
    153 Lt Vanwinkle Dr, Binghamton, NY 13905-1338
    David E. Harder, Sheriff

Cattaraugus County

SOCIAL SERVICES

Social Svcs **716.373.8065**
Fax 716.701.3721
Web ....www.co.cattaraugus.ny.us
    1 Leo Moss Dr Ste 6010, Olean, NY 14760
    Kathy Mcgoldrick, Director Of Social Services

GENERAL HEALTH SERVICES

Health Dept **716.373.8050**
Fax 716.701.3737
Web ....www.co.cattaraugus.ny.us
E-mail ....jmcandrew@cattco.org
    1 Leo Moss Dr Ste 4010, Olean, NY 14760-1175
    Julie Mcandrew, Hiv Manager

Seneca Nation **716.945.1790**
Fax 716.945.1565
Web ....www.sni.org
    90 Ohi yo way, Salamanca, NY 14779
    Robert Porter, President

MENTAL HEALTH SERVICES

Counselling Centre **716.373.8040**
Fax 716.701.3729
Web ....www.cattco.org
E-mail ....dmiller@cattco.org
    1 Leo Moss Dr Ste 4308, Olean, NY 14760-1100
    Dawn Miller, Director

COURTS

Family Court **716.373.8035**
Fax 716.373.0449
    1 Leo Moss Dr Ste 1140, Olean, NY 14760
    Denise Filjones, Deputy Clerk

EDUCATION SERVICES

Cattaraugus Wyoming Counties Project Head
Start **716.372.5959**
Fax 716.372.3825
E-mail ....ikatzenstein@headstartnetwork.com
    210 Elm St, Olean, NY 14760
    Ira Katzenstein, Director

Cattaraugus Wyoming Counties Project Head
Start **716.945.5281**
Fax 716.945.0588
E-mail ....ikatzenstein@headstartnetwork.com
    79 River St, Salamanca, NY 14779-1414
    Ira Ketzenstein, Director

Head Start **716.532.5927**
Fax 716.532.2101
    64 E Main St, Gowanda, NY 14070
    Christine Ellington, Director

Head Start **716.492.4720**
Fax 716.492.3298
Web ....www.headstartnetwork.com
    11713 Route 16, Delevan, NY 14042
    Ira Katzenstein, Director

Cayuga County

SOCIAL SERVICES

Dept Of Health And Human Svcs **315.253.1451**
Fax 315.253.1409
Web ....www.co.cayuga.ny.us
    160 Genesee St Ste 2A, CAYUGA COUNTY OFFICE BLDG, Auburn, NY 13021-3409
    Elane Daly, Director

GENERAL HEALTH SERVICES

Cayuga Health Dept Home Health **315.253.1301**
Fax 315.253.1465
Web ....www.dfa.state.ny.us
E-mail ....andrea.andersen@dfa.state.ny.us
    8 Dill St, Auburn, NY 13021-3606
    Andrea Andersen, Director

New York

Health Dept 315.253.1560
Fax 315.253.1156
Web ....www.co.cayuga.ny.us/healthdept
    8 Dill St, Auburn, NY 13021
    Joan Knight, Prevention Director

MENTAL HEALTH SERVICES

Mental Health 315.253.2746
Fax 315.253.1077
Web ....www.co.cayuga.ny.us
E-mail ....mentalhealth@co.cayuga.ny.us
    146 N St, Auburn, NY 13021-1889
    Kathrine O'Connell, Director

JUSTICE AGENCY

Willowview Non-Secure Detention (Grow
Unit) 315.258.2122
Fax 315.258.2149
    7432 County House Rd, Auburn, NY 13021-8216
    Tom Wilson, Program Manager

COURTS

Youth Court 315.253.9795
Fax 315.253.3255
Web ....www.cayugacounseling.org
E-mail ....ccsinc@cayugacounseling.org
    17 E Genesee St, Ste 2, Auburn, NY 13021-4045
    Lisa Biljanoski, Coordinator

POLICE AND SHERIFF

Sheriff's Dept 315.253.1222
Fax 315.253.3022
Web ....www.co.cayuga.ny.us
    7445 County House Rd, Auburn, NY 13021-8297
    David Gould, Sheriff

Chautauqua County

SOCIAL SERVICES

Social Svcs 716.753.4421
Fax 716.753.4422
Web ....www.chautauqua-ny.com
    7 N Erie St, Mayville, NY 14757
    Christine Schuyler, Commissioner

GENERAL HEALTH SERVICES

Health Dept 716.363.3660
Fax 716.363.3629
Web ....www.co.chautauqua.ny.us
    1136 central Ave, Dunkirk, NY 14048
    Kathy Burgess, Supervisor

Health Dept 716.661.8111
Fax 716.661.8171
Web ....www.co.chautauqua.ny.us
    110 E 4th St, Jamestown, NY 14701
    Kathy Burdgess, Supervisor

MENTAL HEALTH SERVICES

Mental Hygiene 716.753.4104
Fax 716.753.4230
    7 N Erie St, H.R.C. Building, 1st Floor, Mayville,
    NY 14757
    Patricia Brinkman, Director Of Community Hygiene

JUSTICE AGENCY

Probation Dept 716.661.8011
Fax 716.661.8018
Web ....www.co.chautauqua.ny.us
E-mail ....shieldsl@co.chautauqua.ny.us
    110 E 4th St, South County Office Building,
    Jamestown, NY 14701
    Linda Shields, Director

COURTS

Family Court 716.753.4351
Fax 716.753.4350
Web ....www.courts.state.ny.us
E-mail ....fbaggian@courts.state.ny.us
    2 Academy St Ste 5, Gerace Office Building, Mayville,
    NY 14757
    Frank Baggiano, Clerk

POLICE AND SHERIFF

Sheriff's Dept 716.753.4900
Fax 716.753.4987
    15 E. Chautauqua St, Mayville, NY 14757
    Joseph A. Gerace, Sheriff

EDUCATION SERVICES

Cattaraugus Territory Even Start 716.532.3341
Fax 716.532.3269
    12861 Route 438, Irving, NY 14081
    Larry Wheeler, Director

Head Start Connection South 716.483.5779
Fax 716.483.0203
Web ....www.chautauquaopportunities.com
E-mail ....bmulkin@shautopp.org
    2887 Fluvanna Townline Rd, Jamestown,
    NY 14701-9755
    Beth Mulkin, Director

Chemung County

MENTAL HEALTH SERVICES

Mental Hygeine 607.737.5501
Fax 607.737.5500
Web ....www.co.chemung.ny.us
    425 Pennsylvania Ave, Elmira, NY 14904-1762
    Jennifer Stinson, Director Of Administrative Services

COURTS

Youth Court 607.737.5802
Fax 607.732.6514
Web ....www.ci.elmira.ny.us
E-mail ....jbrannon@ci.elmira.ny.us
    317 E Church St Ste 3, Elmira, NY 14901-2789
    Luanne Straufer, Coordinator

POLICE AND SHERIFF

Sheriff's Ofc 607.737.2987
Fax 607.737.2930
E-mail ....cmoff@co.chemung.ny.us
    203 William St, Elmira, NY 14901
    Christopher Moff, Sheriff

Chenango County

GENERAL HEALTH SERVICES

Health Dept 607.337.1660
Fax 607.337.1709
Web ....www.co.chenango.ny.us
E-mail ....susanz@co.chenango.ny.us
    5 Court St, County Office Building, Norwich,
    NY 13815-1654
    Susan Zeipner, Communicable Disease Coordinator

COURTS

Family Court 607.337.1824
Fax 607.337.1835
E-mail ....hsullivan@courts.state.ny.us
    5 Court St, County Office Bldg, Norwich, NY 13815
    Honorable W. Howard Sullivan, Judge

Clinton County

SOCIAL SERVICES

Social Svcs 518.565.3300
Fax 518.561.8101
Web ....www.clintoncountygov.com
    13 Durkee St, Plattsburgh, NY 12901-2981
    Chris Allen, Social Services Director

GENERAL HEALTH SERVICES

Health Dept 518.565.4840
Fax 518.565.4717
Web ....www.clintonhealth.org
E-mail ....smithn@co.clinton.ny.us
    133 Margaret St, Plattsburgh, NY 12901-2968
    Nancy Smith, Hiv Coordinator

MENTAL HEALTH SERVICES

Mental Health And Addiction Serv 518.565.4060
Fax 518.566.0168
E-mail ....gillettes@co.clinton.ny.us
    16 Ampersand Dr, Plattsburgh, NY 12901
    Sherrie Gillette, Director

JUSTICE AGENCY

Dept Of Probation/Ati 518.565.4640
Fax 518.565.4651
E-mail ....marcouxd@co.clinton.ny.us
    34 Court St, Old Jail Bldg., Plattsburgh, NY 12901
    David Marcoux, Director

COURTS

Family Court 518.565.4658
Fax 518.565.4688
    137 Margaret St Ste 311, Plattsburgh,
    NY 12901-2964
    Honorable Timothy J. Lawliss, Director

POLICE AND SHERIFF

Sheriff's Dept 518.565.4300
Fax 518.565.4333
    25 Mccarthy Dr, Plattsburgh, NY 12901
    David Favro, Sheriff

EDUCATION SERVICES

Acap Inc Head Start Ausable Forks
Site 518.873.3207
Fax 877.873.6848
    PO Box 112, Au Sable Forks, NY 12912-0112
    Mickey Hooper, Director

Cumberland Head Elementary
School 518.563.8321
Fax 518.563.8343
Web www.bcsdk12.org
    1187 Cumberland Head Rd, Plattsburgh,
    NY 12901-6952
    Diane Fox, Administrator

Columbia County

SOCIAL SERVICES

Social Svcs 518.828.9411
Fax 518.822.9089
Web ....www.govt.co.columbia.ny.us
E-mail ....lcutsky@govt.co.columbia.ny.us
    25 Railroad Ave, Hudson, NY 12534-2301
    Lynn Cutsky, Income Maintenance Director

JUSTICE AGENCY

Probation Dept 518.828.4126
Fax 518.828.2957
Web ....www.govt.co.columbia.ny.us
E-mail ....mbenvenuto@govt.co.columbia.ny.us
    610 State St, Hudson, NY 12534-2514
    Mike Benvenuto, Director

COURTS

Family Court 518.828.0315
Fax 518.828.1603
    401 Union St Ste 3, Hudson, NY 12534
    Honorable Paul Czajka, Judge

Cortland County

SOCIAL SERVICES

Social Svcs................................**607.753.5248**
Fax..607.753.5282
Web..................................www.cortland-co.org
E-mail.....................tiffani.parker@dfa.state.ny.us
   60 Central Ave, County Office Building, Cortland,
   NY 13045-2746
   Tiffani Parker, Director of families & Children

Youth Bureau.............................**607.753.5067**
Fax..607.758.5580
Web........................www.cortland-co.org/youth
E-mail.............................elann@cortland-co.org
   60 Central Ave, Cortland County Office Bldg.,
   Cortland, NY 13045-2746
   Emanuel Lann, Director

GENERAL HEALTH SERVICES

Health Dept...............................**607.753.5036**
Fax..607.753.5209
Web..................................www.cortland-co.org
E-mail.......................cfeuerherm@cortland-co.org
   60 Central Ave, Cortland, NY 13045
   Catherine Feuerherm, Director Of Public Health

MENTAL HEALTH SERVICES

Mental Health.............................**607.758.6100**
Fax..607.758.6116
Web..................................www.cortland-co.org
   7 Clayton Ave, Cortland, NY 13045-2501
   Dr Jason Stepkovitch, Director

COURTS

Family Court...............................**607.753.5353**
Web..................................www.cortland-co.org
   46 Greenbush St Ste 301, Cortland, NY 13045
   Laurie Case, Chief Clerk

Delaware County

SOCIAL SERVICES

Social Svcs................................**607.832.5300**
Fax..607.746.6310
   111 Main St Ste 4, Delhi, NY 13753-1233
   Sylvia Armanno, Assistant Director Of Services & Deputy
   Commissioner

MENTAL HEALTH SERVICES

Children And Family Svcs (Mental
Health)......................................**607.865.8255**
Fax..607.865.7252
   132 Delaware St Ste 2A, Walton, NY 13856
   Patricia Thomson, Csw, Director

Mental Health.............................**607.865.6522**
Fax..607.865.7424
E-mail.................patricia.thomson@co.delaware.ny.us
   1 Hospital Rd, Walton, NY 13856
   Patricia Thomson, Csw, Director

JUSTICE AGENCY

Probation Dept............................**607.746.2075**
Fax..607.746.2916
E-mail.................scott.glueckert@co.delaware.ny.us
   280 Phoebe Ln Ste 2, Delhi, NY 13753
   Scott Glueckert, Director

COURTS

Family Court...............................**607.746.2298**
Fax..607.746.2288
   3 Court St Ste 1, Delhi, NY 13753
   Honorable Carl F. Becker, Judge

Dutchess County

SOCIAL SERVICES

Social Svcs................................**845.486.3000**
Fax..845.486.3090
   60 Market St, Poughkeepsie, NY 12601
   Robert Allers, Commissioner

GENERAL HEALTH SERVICES

Health Dept...............................**845.486.3400**
Fax..845.486.3447
Web..www.dcny.gov
E-mail.......................mcaldwell@co.dutchess.ny.us
   387 Main St, Poughkeepsie, NY 12601
   Antonia Brewer, Director Of Public Health Nursing/ Home Health Care

Health Dept Communicable Disease
Section......................................**845.486.3402**
Fax..845.486.3561
Web............................www.health.co.dutchess.ny.us
   387 Main St, Poughkeepsie, NY 12601-3368
   Michael Caldwell, Commissioner Of Health

MENTAL HEALTH SERVICES

Dept Of Mental Hygiene...................**845.486.3700**
Fax..845.486.3727
   9 Mansion St, Poughkeepsie, NY 12601
   Karen Troken, Director

Hudson Valley Mental Health Inc............**845.677.4050**
Fax..845.677.4056
   131 County House Rd, Millbrook, NY 12545
   Elizabeth Willis, Director

Hudson Valley Mental Health Inc............**845.877.4100**
Fax..845.877.4112
   7 Market St, Dover Plains, NY 12522
   Bob Rizzo, Director

Mental Health Assoc......................**845.473.2500**
Fax..845.473.4870
Web..www.mhadc.com
E-mail..........................jbrownstein@mhadc.com
   253 Mansion St, Poughkeepsie, NY 12601-2623
   Jacqueline Brownstein, Director

JUSTICE AGENCY

Probation Dept............................**845.486.2600**
Fax..845.486.2676
Web............................www.co.dutchess.ny.us
E-mail.............................mstill@co.dutchess.ny.us
   50 Market St Ste 1, Poughkeepsie, NY 12601-3258
   Mary Ellen Still, Director

POLICE AND SHERIFF

Police Dept................................**845.451.4000**
Fax..845.451.4156
E-mail.................rknapp@cityofpoughkeepsie.com
   62 Civic Center Plz, Poughkeepsie, NY 12601
   Ronald Knapp, Chief Of Police

EDUCATION SERVICES

Astor Early Childhood Program............**845.832.3331**
Fax..845.832.0509
E-mail.......................gcaddell@astorservices.org
   6423 Route 55, Wingdale, NY 12594
   Ms Grace Caddell, Director

Erie County

SOCIAL SERVICES

Child Protection Svcs......................**716.858.6691**
Fax..716.858.1501
   478 Main St, Rm 327, Buffalo, NY 14202
   Robert Deisc, CPS Director

Commission For The Blind And Visually Handicapped Buffalo
Ofc..**716.847.3516**
Fax..716.847.3983
Web..................................www.ocfs.ny.state.us
E-mail........................len.hanel@ocfs.ny.state.us
   295 Main St, Rm 590, Buffalo, NY 14203
   Lynn Hanel, District Manager

New York State Ofc Of Children & Family Svcs Buffalo Regional
Ofc..**716.847.3145**
Fax..716.847.3742
   295 Main St, Ellicott Square Bldg., Rm 545, Buffalo,
   NY 14203
   Dana Whitcomb, Regional Director

MENTAL HEALTH SERVICES

Buffalo Psychiatric Ctr....................**716.816.2445**
   400 Forest Ave, Buffalo, NY 14213
   Debbie Dycha, Director

Community Concern Of Western New York
Inc...**716.947.5025**
Fax..716.947.5909
Web..............................www.communityconcern.org
E-mail.....................mail@communityconcern.org
   6722 Erie Rd, Derby, NY 14047-9670
   Jerry Bartone, Director

Medical Ctr................................**716.898.3255**
Fax..716.898.3658
Web..www.ecmc.edu
E-mail.............................mhamann@ecmc.edu
   462 Grider St, Buffalo, NY 14215-3098
   Marty Hamann, Director

Mental Health.............................**716.858.8530**
Fax..716.858.6264
Web.....................www.erie.gov/health/mentalhealth/
E-mail.............................endressp@erie.gov
   95 Franklin St Rm 1237, Buffalo, NY 14202-3904
   Philip Endress, Commissioner

Mental Health Svcs.......................**716.831.1856**
Fax..716.831.0263
Web..www.brylin.org
E-mail...............hartnetc@spectrumhumanservices.org
   2309 Ettert Rd Ste 9, Tonawanda, NY 14150
   Christopher Hartnet, Director

Mid-Erie Counseling And Treatment
Svcs...**716.893.0062**
Fax..716.893.0070
E-mail.............................lusser@mid-erie.org
   463 William St, Buffalo, NY 14204-1649
   Christie Lusser, Supervisor

JUSTICE AGENCY

Probation Dept............................**716.858.8205**
Fax..716.858.8194
E-mail.............................dina.connors@erie.gov
   1 Niagara Plz Ste 111, Buffalo, NY 14202
   Bryan Mclaughlin, Director

Youth Detention Svcs......................**716.923.4000**
Fax..716.893.5548
E-mail.................................rustd@erie.gov
   810 E Ferry St, Buffalo, NY 14211-1139
   David Rust, Deputy Commissioner

COURTS

Family Court...............................**716.845.7400**
Fax..716.845.7546
   1 Niagara Plz Ste 419, Buffalo, NY 14204
   Honorable Rosalie Bailey, Judge

Lancaster Youth Bearue...................**716.683.4444**
Fax..716.683.4447
E-mail.................mindymuench@lancasterny.com
   200 Oxford Ave, Lancaster, NY 14086
   Mindy Muench, Coordinator

New York

Village of Depew **716.683.1400**
Fax 716.683.1398
  85 Manitou St, Depew, NY 14043-3756
  Steven Hoffman, Mayor

POLICE AND SHERIFF

Sheriff's Ofc **716.858.7608**
Fax 716.858.7680
  10 Delaware Ave, Buffalo, NY 14202
  Timothy B. Howard, Sheriff

EDUCATION SERVICES

Cao Head Start **716.852.1262**
Web ....www.caoec.org
E-mail ....pmcbrid3e@caoec.org
  62 Republic St, Buffalo, NY 14204-2727
  Phyllis Mcbride, Director

Cao Southtowns Head Start **716.947.0085**
Fax 716.947.0099
  7008 Erie Rd Ste 6, Derby, NY 14047
  Kaitlyn Perkins, Site Director

Community Action **716.881.5150**
Fax 716.885.2927
  70 Harvard Pl, Buffalo, NY 14209
  Elle Mason Hare, Executive Director

Friendship Baptist Church **716.847.1020**
Fax 716.847.0260
E-mail ....friendship@roadrunner.com
  402 Clinton St, Buffalo, NY 14204
  Darris Dickson Clark, Pastor

Head Start-Weinburg Campus **716.639.3330**
Fax 716.639.3341
Web ....www.wnyptot.com
  2700 N Forest Rd Ste 108, Getzville, NY 14068-1527
  David Cunkelman, Chief Executive Officer

Essex County

SOCIAL SERVICES

Social Svcs **518.873.3441**
Fax 518.873.3467
Web ....www.dfa.state.ny.us
E-mail ....Sueann.Caron@dfa.state.ny.us
  7551 Court St, Government Center, Court St,
  Elizabethtown, NY 12932
  Sueann Caron, Director

GENERAL HEALTH SERVICES

Public Health Dept **518.873.3500**
Fax 518.873.3811
Web ....www.co.sx.ny.us/publichealth
E-mail ....snicola@co.essex.ny.us
  132 Water St, Elizabethtown, NY 12932
  Sarina Nicola, Director Of Patient Services

COURTS

Family Court **518.873.3320**
Fax 518.873.3626
Web ....www.courts.state.ny.us
E-mail ....mlawliss@courts.state.ny.us
  7559 Court St, Elizabethtown, NY 12932
  Michael Lawliss, Clerk

EDUCATION SERVICES

Acap Inc Head Start Ticonderoga
Site **518.585.6300**
Fax 518.585.6718
E-mail ....mickey.hooper@acf.hhs.gov
  12 Father Jogues Place, Ticonderoga, NY 12883
  Mickey Hopper, Director

Franklin County

SOCIAL SERVICES

Social Svcs **518.483.6770**
Fax 518.481.1614
  355 W Main St, Malone, NY 12953
  Steve Rondeau, Case Work Supervisor

St. Regis Mohawk Tribe **518.358.2272**
Fax 518.358.3203
Web ....www.stregismohawktribe.com
E-mail ....jwhalen@srmt-nsn.gov
  412 State Route 37, Hogansburg, NY 13655-3109
  Jeff Whalen, Director Of Human Services

GENERAL HEALTH SERVICES

Public Health Dept **518.481.1710**
Fax 518.483.9378
Web ....www.franklincounty.org
E-mail ....kstrack@co.franklin.ny.us
  125 Catherine St, Malone, NY 12953-2343
  Katie Sarrell-Strack, Public Health Director

MENTAL HEALTH SERVICES

Community Svcs **518.891.2280**
Fax 518.891.2621
Web ....www.citizenadvocates.net
E-mail ....suzannegoolden@citizenadvocates.net
  70 Edgewood Rd, Saranac Lake, NY 12983-1706
  Suzanne Goolden, Director

Northstar Mental Health Svcs **518.483.3261**
Fax 518.483.3383
Web ....www.citizenadvocates.net
E-mail ....jayulrich@citizenadvocates.net
  209 Park St, Malone, NY 12953-1228
  Jay Ulrich, Director

COURTS

Family Court **518.481.1742**
Fax 518.481.5453
E-mail ....rmain@nycourts.gov
  355 W Main St Ste 3223, Malone, NY 12953-1853
  Honorable Robert G. Main Jr., Judge

POLICE AND SHERIFF

Sheriff's Ofc **518.483.3304**
Fax 518.483.3205
E-mail ....kmulverhill@co.franklin.ny.us
  45 Bare Hill Rd, Malone, NY 12953
  Kevin Mulverhill, Sheriff

EDUCATION SERVICES

Caffc Chateaugay Head Start **518.497.6218**
Fax 518.497.6218
Web ....www.jceo.org
  9 River St, Chateaugay, NY 12920-2000
  Stacy McDonald, Associate Director

Vesid **518.483.3530**
Fax 518.483.3552
Web ....www.vesid.nysed.gov
  209 W Main St Ste 3, Malone, NY 12953
  Michelle Snail, Regional Associate Of Special Education

Fulton County

SOCIAL SERVICES

Social Svcs **518.736.5640**
Fax 518.762.0080
  4 Daisy Ln, Johnstown, NY 12095
  Amy Meade, Director Of Adult And Child Services

GENERAL HEALTH SERVICES

Nursing Svcs **518.773.3444**
Fax 518.725.7582
E-mail ....khogan@co.fulton.ny.us
  847 County Highway 122, Gloversville, NY 12078
  Karen Hogan, Clinical Director

Public Health Dept **518.736.5720**
Fax 518.762.1382
Web ....www.fultoncountypublichealth.com
E-mail ....d.frederick@co.fulton.ny.us
  2714 State Highway 29, Johnstown, NY 12095
  Denise Fredrick, Public Health Director

MENTAL HEALTH SERVICES

Mental Health **518.773.3531**
Fax 518.773.9103
Web ....www.county.fulton.ny.us
  57 E Fulton St, Gloversville, NY 12078-3212
  Ernest Gagnon, Director

JUSTICE AGENCY

Probation Dept **518.773.3565**
Fax 518.773.7958
  64 E Fulton St, Gloversville, NY 12078
  Michael Mckirkpatrick, Director

COURTS

Family Court **518.762.3840**
Fax 518.762.9540
  11 N William St, Johnstown, NY 12095
  Edward Skoda, Judge

Genesee County

MENTAL HEALTH SERVICES

Genesee Council On Alcohol And Substance
Abuse **585.343.1124**
Fax 585.343.1197
Web ....www.gcasa.net
  430 E Main St, Batavia, NY 14020
  David Markham, Executive Director

COURTS

Family Court **585.344.2550**
Fax 585.344.8520
Web ....www.co.genesee.ny.us
E-mail ....eadams@co.genesee.ny.us
  1 W Main St, Courts Facility Bldg., Batavia,
  NY 14020-2019
  Honorable Eric Adams, Judge

POLICE AND SHERIFF

Sheriff's Dept **585.345.3000**
Fax 585.344.3102
Web ....www.co.genessee.ny.us
E-mail ....gmaha@co.genesee.ny.us
  165 Park Rd, Batavia, NY 14020-1283
  Gary T. Maha, Sheriff

Greene County

SOCIAL SERVICES

Social Svcs **518.719.3700**
Fax 518.719.3695
Web ....www.dfa.state.ny.us
  411 Main St, Catskill, NY 12414
  Fran Delgaudio, Social Services Director

GENERAL HEALTH SERVICES

Public Health Nursing **518.719.3600**
Fax 518.719.3781
Web ....www.discovergreene.com
E-mail ....mostoyich@discovergreen.com
  411 Main St, Fl 3, Catskill, NY 12414
  Marie Ostoyich, Public Health Director

MENTAL HEALTH SERVICES

Mental Health Ctr **518.622.9163**
Fax 518.622.8592
E-mail ....mgraham@discovergreene.com
  905 Greene County Office Bldg, Cairo,
  NY 12413-2868
  Maggie Graham, Director Of Community Services

POLICE AND SHERIFF

Sheriff's Ofc **518.943.3302**
Fax 518.943.6832
Web ....www.discovergreene.com
E-mail ....sheriff@discovergreene.net
   80 Bridge St, Catskill, NY 12414-1433
Richard H. Hussey, Sheriff

EDUCATION SERVICES

Early Childhood Learning Ctr **518.299.3207**
Fax 518.299.3018
   11630 Main St, Prattsville, NY 12468
Deborah Sutch, Director

Hamilton County

SOCIAL SERVICES

Social Svcs **518.648.6131**
Fax 518.648.5257
   79 White Birch Ln, Indian Lake, NY 12842
Beth King, Medicaid Assistance Director

GENERAL HEALTH SERVICES

Public Health **518.648.6141**
Fax 518.648.6143
Web ....www.hamiltoncountypublichealth.org
   79 White Birch Ln, Indian Lake, NY 12842-1409
Beth Ryan, Director Of Public Health

MENTAL HEALTH SERVICES

Community Svcs **518.648.5355**
Fax 518.648.6437
E-mail ....rkleppang.hccs@frontiernet.net
   83 White Birch Ln, Indian Lake, NY 12842-1409
Robert Kleppang, Director

JUSTICE AGENCY

Probation Dept **518.648.5040**
Fax 518.648.0359
E-mail ....probation@hamiltoncountyny.gov
   White Birch Ln, Indian Lake, NY 12842
Amy Kristiansen, Probation Director

COURTS

Family Court **518.648.5411**
Fax 518.648.6286
E-mail ....pfeldstein@courts.state.ny.us
   79 White Birch Ln, Indian Lake, NY 12842-0780
Honorable S. Peter Feldstein, Judge

Herkimer County

GENERAL HEALTH SERVICES

Public Health Nursing Svcs **315.867.1176**
Fax 315.867.1444
Web ....www.herkimercountypublichealth.org
E-mail ....dward@herkimercounty.org
   301 N Washington St Ste 2300, Herkimer,
   NY 13350-2910
Diane Ward, Hiv Coordinator

MENTAL HEALTH SERVICES

Mental Health Svcs **315.867.1465**
Fax 315.867.1469
E-mail ....escudder@herkimercounty.org
   301 N Washington St Ste 2470, Herkimer, NY 13350
Edgar Scudder, Director

JUSTICE AGENCY

Probation Dept **315.867.1158**
Fax 315.867.1194
Web ....www.herkimercounty.org
E-mail ....jsohnn@herkimercounty.org
   109 Mary St Ste 1202, Herkimer, NY 13350-2921
Josephine M Sohnn, Director

COURTS

Family Court **315.867.1139**
Fax 315.867.1369
Web ....www.courts.state.ny.us
   301 N Washington St, Herkimer, NY 13350-1216
John Brennan, Judge

Jefferson County

SOCIAL SERVICES

Social Svcs **315.782.9030**
Fax 315.785.3346
Web ....www.co.jefferson.ny.us
   250 Arsenal St, Watertown, NY 13601
Laura Cerow, Commissioner

GENERAL HEALTH SERVICES

Public Health Svc **315.786.3710**
Fax 315.786.3761
Web ....www.co.jefferson.ny.us
E-mail ....publichealth@co.jefferson.ny.us
   531 Meade St, Watertown, NY 13601-1225
Jean Bilow, Rn, Director Of Public Health

MENTAL HEALTH SERVICES

Behavioral Health Clinic **315.493.3300**
Fax 315.493.3306
Web ....www.carthagehospital.com
E-mail ....cahadmin@carthageareahospital.com
   3 Bridge St, Ste 7, Carthage, NY 13619
Joel Millard, Administrator

Community Svcs **315.785.3283**
Fax 315.785.5182
   175 Arsenal St Rm 102, Watertown, NY 13601
Roger Ambrose, Director

Mercy Care Ctr **315.782.7400**
Fax 315.782.7432
   218 Stone St, Watertown, NY 13601-3211
Paula Edwards, Director Of Nursing

JUSTICE AGENCY

**Ofc Of Children & Family Svcs Aftercare/Intake Ofc Watertown
Satellite** **315.785.2426**
Fax 315.785.2425
E-mail ....robert.wieliczka@ocfs.state.ny.us
   317 Washington St, State Office Building, 4th Floor,
   Watertown, NY 13601
Mark Roser, Aftercare Supervisor

POLICE AND SHERIFF

Sheriff's Ofc **315.786.2660**
Fax 315.786.2684
E-mail ....johnb@co.jefferson.ny.us
   753 Waterman Dr, Watertown, NY 13601
John P. Burns, Sheriff

Kings County

GENERAL HEALTH SERVICES

Community Educational Svcs **718.722.7510**
Fax 718.722.7530
Web ....www.health.nyc.gov
   25 Chapel St Ste 1006, Brooklyn, NY 11201-1955
Yvonne Sinclair, Director

MENTAL HEALTH SERVICES

**Brooklyn Ctr For Families In Crisis,
Inc.** **718.282.0010**
Fax 718.693.4490
Web ....www.bklynctr.org
E-mail ....bcfcarkin@aol.com
   1309-1311 Foster Avenue, Brooklyn, NY 11230
Leslie Arkin, Director

**Brooklyn Ctr For Psychotherapy,
Inc.** **718.622.2000**
Fax 718.398.3328
E-mail ....bcp300@aol.com
   300 Flatbush Ave, Brooklyn, NY 11217
Mark Soloman, Director

Brooklyn Psychiatric Ctrs, Inc. **718.875.7510**
Fax 718.643.3455
Web ....www.bpcinc.org
E-mail ....bryantp@bpcinc.org
   189 Montague St Ste 436, Brooklyn, NY 11201-3604
Patricia Bryant- Reed, Director

Brooklyn Psychiatric Ctrs, Inc. **718.257.3400**
Fax 718.257.0178
Web ....www.bpcinc.org
E-mail ....charless@bpcinc.org
   1310 Rockaway Pkwy, Brooklyn, NY 11236-2339
Sheryl Almen-charles, Director

**Jewish Board Of Family & Children's
Svcs** **718.238.6444**
Fax 718.238.5165
E-mail ....plotenderg@jbfcs.org
   9435 Ridge Blvd, Brooklyn, NY 11209-6750
Pam Lotenberg, Director

JUSTICE AGENCY

Barbara Blum **718.832.5738**
Fax 718.369.2492
   262 9th St, Brooklyn, NY 11215
Angela Williams, Program Director

Clinton Ave House **718.789.2911**
Fax 718.789.2796
Web ....www.lssny.org
E-mail ....tarozqueta@lssny.org
   521 Clinton Ave, Brooklyn, NY 11238-2201
Tesa Arozqueta, Director

Crossroads Juvenile Ctr **718.495.8160**
Fax 718.495.8254
E-mail ....eduardo.marcial@acs.nyc.gov
   17 Bristol St, Brooklyn, NY 11212
Eduardo Marcial, Executive Director

**New York City Police Dept Youth Svcs
Section** **718.834.8855**
Fax 718.834.9443
   189 Montague St Ste 600, Brooklyn, NY 11201-3612
Karin Azadania, Deputy Inspector

COURTS

Family Court Liaison **718.855.3384**
Fax 718.797.3578
E-mail ....joann.defrancesco@ocfs.state.ny.us
   330 J St, Brooklyn, NY 11201
Joann Defrancesco, Court Liaison Supervisor

POLICE AND SHERIFF

Brooklyn 62nd Precinct **718.236.2611**
Fax 718.236.2759
   1925 Bath Ave, Brooklyn, NY 11214
Captain Paul Babick, Police Chief

Brooklyn 63rd Precinct **718.258.4411**
Fax 718.258.0559
   1844 Brooklyn Ave, Brooklyn, NY 11210-4240
Michael Deddo, Captain

Brooklyn 68th Precinct **718.439.4211**
Fax 718.439.4455
   333 65th St, Brooklyn, NY 11220
J Grant, Youth Officer

Brooklyn 69th Precinct **718.257.6211**
Fax 718.257.6214
Web ....www.health.nyc.gov
E-mail ....tfrieden@health.nyc.gov
   9720 Foster Ave, Brooklyn, NY 11236-2123
Lt. T Friedman, Operations Coordinator

New York

Brooklyn 70th Precinct **718.851.5511**
Fax 718.436.7811
　154 Lawrence Ave, Brooklyn, NY 11230
　Monte Forte, Deputy Inspector

Brooklyn 71st Precinct **718.735.0511**
Fax 718.735.5791
　421 Empire Blvd, Brooklyn, NY 11225-3217
　Peter Fimometti, Commander

Brooklyn 72nd Precinct **718.965.6311**
Fax 718.965.6358
　830 4th Ave, Brooklyn, NY 11232
　Raul Pintos, Director

Brooklyn 73rd Precinct **718.495.5411**
Fax 718.495.5427
Web ....www.assembly.state.ny.us
　1470 E New York Ave, Brooklyn, NY 11212-5007
　Samuel Wright, Director

Brooklyn 75th Precinct **718.827.3511**
Fax 718.827.3627
　1000 Sutter Ave, Brooklyn, NY 11208
　Jeffery Maddery, Director

Brooklyn 76th Precinct **718.834.3212**
Fax 718.834.3200
　191 Union St, Brooklyn, NY 11231
　Lewis Gomez, Captain

Brooklyn 78th Precinct **718.636.6411**
Fax 718.636.6462
Web ....www.assembly.state.ny.us
　65 6th Ave, Brooklyn, NY 11217-2110
　Inspector Argenziano, Commanding Officer

Brooklyn 79th Precinct **718.636.6611**
Fax 718.636.6627
E-mail ....borbeckx@assembly.state.ny.us
　263 Tompkins Ave, Brooklyn, NY 11216

Brooklyn 81st Precinct **718.574.0411**
Fax 718.574.8722
Web ....www.assembly.state.ny.us
　30 Ralph Ave, Brooklyn, NY 11221-3607
　Juanita Holmes, Inspector, Commanding Officer

Brooklyn 83rd Precinct **718.574.1605**
Fax 718.574.1860
　480 Knickerbocker Ave, Brooklyn, NY 11237-5132
　D Diaz, Community Affairs Officer

Brooklyn 84th Precinct **718.875.6811**
Fax 718.624.6983
E-mail ....avelc@assembly.state.ny.us
　301 Gold St, Brooklyn, NY 11201
　M. Dipaolo, Deputy Inspector

Brooklyn 90th Precinct **718.963.5311**
Fax 718.963.5393
　211 Union Ave, Brooklyn, NY 11211-7417
　Michael Kemper, Deputy Inspector

Brooklyn 94th Precinct **718.383.3879**
Fax 718.383.8120
　100 Meserole Ave, Brooklyn, NY 11222
　Terence Herson, Officer

EDUCATION SERVICES

CCNS St Malachy's Head Start **718.647.0966**
Fax 718.647.0089
　220 Hendrix St, Brooklyn, NY 11207
　Petra Padilla, Director

Family Head Start **718.859.7720**
Fax 718.434.0849
　3017 Glenwood Rd, Brooklyn, NY 11210
　Masie Chi, Principal

Family Head Start **718.332.8524**
Fax 718.332.6250
　293 Neptune Ave, Brooklyn, NY 11235-6812
　Peraro Benenfield, Director

Special Education **718.722.4544**
Fax 718.722.2032
Web ....www.nysed.gov/vesid
　55 Hanson Pl, Rm 545, Brooklyn, NY 11217
　Rebecca Cort, Assistant Commissioner

Lewis County

SOCIAL SERVICES

Social Svcs **315.376.5400**
Fax 315.376.4112
　5274 Outer Stowe St, Lowville, NY 13367
　Jenny Jones, Social Services Director

GENERAL HEALTH SERVICES

Public Home Health Agency **315.376.5453**
Fax 315.376.5435
Web ....www.lewiscountypublichealth.org
　7785 N State St, Lowville, NY 13367
　Carol Baluck, Patient Services Director

MENTAL HEALTH SERVICES

Mental Health Svcs **315.376.5450**
Fax 315.376.7221
Web ....www.lewismh.org
E-mail ....jearl@lewiscountyny.org
　7550 S State St Ste 7, Lowville, NY 13367-1596
　Jennifer Earl, Director

COURTS

Family Court **315.376.5345**
Fax 315.376.5189
Web ....www.courts.state.ny.us
E-mail ....cmerrel@courts.state.ny.us
　7660 N State St, Lowville, NY 13367
　Honorable Charles C. Merrel, Director

Livingston County

SOCIAL SERVICES

Social Svcs **585.243.7300**
Fax 585.243.7344
　1 Murray Hill Dr, Mount Morris, NY 14510-1153
　Marian Hilderbrant, Medicaid Assistance Director

GENERAL HEALTH SERVICES

Health Dept **585.243.7270**
Fax 585.243.7287
Web ....www.co.livingston.ny.us/pubhlth.htm
E-mail ....dept-of-health@co.livingston.ny.us
　2 Murray Hill Dr, Mount Morris, NY 14510
　Mary Margaret Stallone, Director Preventive Services

MENTAL HEALTH SERVICES

Mental Health Svcs **585.243.7250**
Fax 585.243.7264
Web ....www.co.livingston.ny.us
　4600 Millennium Dr, Geneseo, NY 14454-1197
　Gail Long, Director

JUSTICE AGENCY

Probation Dept **585.243.7190**
Fax 585.243.7169
Web ....www.co.livingston.ny.us
E-mail ....eerhard@co.livingston.ny.us
　6 Court St Rm 101, Geneseo, NY 14454-1043
　Edward Erhard, Probation Director

COURTS

Family Court **585.243.7070**
Fax 585.243.7076
E-mail ....liv_family_court@courts.state.ny.us
　2 Court St, Geneseo, NY 14454
　Robert M. Lewis, Chief Clerk

EDUCATION SERVICES

Migrant Even Start **585.658.7960**
Fax 585.658.7969
Web ....www.migrant.net
E-mail ....rlynch@gvboces.org
　27 Lackawanna Ave, Mount Morris, NY 14510-1001
　Robert Lynch, Director

Madison County

SOCIAL SERVICES

Oneida Indian Nation **315.829.8335**
Fax 315.829.8392
Web ....www.oneida-nation.org
　577 Main St, Oneida, NY 13421
　Kim Jacobs, Director Of Member Relations

Social Svcs **315.366.2211**
Fax 315.366.3039
Web ....www.healthymadisoncounty.org
E-mail ....inez.degroat@madisoncounty.org
　133 North Court St., Social Services Building,
　Wampsville, NY 13163
　Inez Degroat, Deputy Commissioner

GENERAL HEALTH SERVICES

Public Health Dept **315.366.2361**
Fax 315.366.2566
Web ....www.healthymadisoncounty.org
E-mail ....cheryl.baska@co.madison.ny.us
　138 N Court St, Wampsville, NY 13163
　Cheryl Geiler, Prevention Services Director

MENTAL HEALTH SERVICES

Mental Health **315.366.2327**
Fax 315.366.2599
Web ....www.healthymadisoncounty.org
E-mail ....james.yonai@co.madison.ny.us
　138 N Court St, Wampsville, NY 13163
　James Yonai, Phd, Mental Health Director

COURTS

Family Court **315.366.2291**
Fax 315.366.2828
E-mail ....bdistefa@courts.state.ny.us
　N Court St,, Bldg 3, Wampsville, NY 13163
　Honorable Biago J. Distefano, Judge

Oneida City Youth Court **315.363.9111**
Fax 315.363.4754
Web ....www.oneidacity.com
　108 Main St, Oneida, NY 13421
　Troy Tiller, Investgator

POLICE AND SHERIFF

Sheriff's Dept **315.366.2318**
Fax 315.366.2286
　138 North Court St, Wampsville, NY 13163
　Allan Riley, Sheriff

Monroe County

SOCIAL SERVICES

Commission For The Blind & Visually Handicapped Rochester
Outstation **585.238.8110**
Fax 585.238.8278
Web ....www.ocfs.state.ny.us
E-mail ....tom.sullivan@ocfs.state.ny.us
　259 Monroe Ave, Rm 303, Rochester,
　NY 14607-3664
　Tom Sullivan, Director

Social Svcs **585.753.6000**
Fax 585.753.6325
Web ....www.co.monroe.ny.us
　111 Westfall Rd, Ste 1, Rochester, NY 14620-4647
　Joseph Martino, Deputy Director

GENERAL HEALTH SERVICES

Health Dept **585.753.2991**
Fax 585.753.5115
Web ....www.monroecounty.gov
　111 Westfall Rd, Rochester, NY 14620
　Andrew S. Doniger, Md, Director

Monroe Community Hospital **585.760.6500**
Fax 585.760.6066
Web ....www.monroehosp.org
　435 E Henrietta Rd, Rochester, NY 14620
　Todd Spring, Director

MENTAL HEALTH SERVICES

Genese Mental Health **585.922.7770**
Fax 585.922.7246
Web ....www.rochestergeneral.org
　224 Alexander St, Rochester, NY 14607
　Bill Brien, Director

Mental Health Of Patient **585.368.6700**
Fax 585.368.6767
　100 Pinewild Dr, Rochester, NY 14606
　James Myer, Director

University Of Rochester Medical Ctr/Strong Memorial Hospital **585.279.4900**
Fax 585.461.9504
　2613 W Henrietta Rd, Rochester, NY 14623-2327
　Kim Haooy-Heccric, Administrator

JUSTICE AGENCY

CASA **585.428.5297**
Fax 585.428.2780
Web ....www.casarochester.org
E-mail ....casa@casarochester.org
　99 Exchange Blvd, Hall Of Justice, Room 332,
　Rochester, NY 14614
　Laurie Holmes, Director

Ofc Of Children & Family Aftercare/Intake Ofc Rochester Satellite **585.238.8210**
Fax 585.238.8213
　259 Monroe Ave Rm 309, Rochester, NY 14607
　Jimmie Winkfield, Supervisor

Ofc of Probation Community Corrections **585.428.5765**
Fax 585.428.2552
Web ....www.monroecounty.gov
E-mail ....lesliebarnes@monroecounty.gov
　33 Fitzhugh St N Ste 2000, Rochester,
　NY 14614-1233
　Leslie S. Barnes, Assistant Administrator

Probation Dept **315.366.2351**
Fax 315.366.2730
Web ....www.co.madison.ny.us
E-mail ....karen.birch@co.madison.ny.us
　North Court St, Wampsville, NY 13163
　Karen J. Birch, Director

COURTS

Family Court **585.428.5429**
Fax 585.428.2597
Web ....www.courts.state.ny.us
E-mail ....gail.donofrio@yale.edu
　99 Exchange Blvd Ste 360, Rochester,
　NY 14614-2127
　Honorable Gail A. Donofrio, Judge

POLICE AND SHERIFF

Sheriffs Ofc **585.753.4175**
Fax 585.753.4524
　130 Plymouth Ave S, Rochester, NY 14614
　Patrick O"Flynn, Sheriff

EDUCATION SERVICES

Abc Inc. Head Start **585.482.8914**
Fax 585.654.4844
　1772 Clifford Ave, Rochester, NY 14609

Abc Inc. Head Start **585.325.5116**
Web ....www.abcinfo.org
E-mail ....mderhan@abcinfo.org
　30 Hart St, Rochester, NY 14605-1708
　Mustachan Derhan, Director

Montgomery County

GENERAL HEALTH SERVICES

Public Health **518.853.3531**
Fax 518.853.8218
Web ....www.po.montgomery.ny.us
E-mail ....kconboy@co.montgomery.ny.us
　20 Park St, County Annex, Fonda, NY 12068
　Kim Conboy, Public Health Director

MENTAL HEALTH SERVICES

Mental Health Svcs **518.841.7333**
Fax 518.841.7336
　427 Guy Park Ave, Amsterdam, NY 12010
　Leigh Novak, Manager

St Mary's Hospital- Childrens Svcs **518.843.7520**
Fax 518.843.7537
Web ....www.smha.org
　8 Northampton Rd, Amsterdam, NY 12010
　John Kelly, Director

JUSTICE AGENCY

Probation Dept **518.853.8380**
Fax 518.853.8228
Web ....www.co.montgomery.ny.us
E-mail ....lsitterly@co.montgomery.ny.us
　64 Broadway, Fonda, NY 12068
　Lucille Sitterly, Director

POLICE AND SHERIFF

Sheriff's Ofc **518.853.5500**
Fax 518.853.4096
Web ....www.co.montgomery.ny.us
E-mail ....mamato@co.montgomery.ny.us
　200 Clark Drive, Fultonville, NY 12072
　Michael J. Amato, Sheriff

Nassau County

SOCIAL SERVICES

Commission For The Blind And Visually Handicapped Hempstead Ofc **516.564.4311**
Fax 516.292.7448
　50 Clinton St, Ste 208, Hempstead, NY 11550
　Robin Gilman-capon, Regional Coordinator

GENERAL HEALTH SERVICES

Health Dept **516.571.2260**
Fax 516.571.3369
Web ....www.co.nassau.ny.us/health
E-mail ....shelly.schechter@dfa.state.ny.us
　240 Old Country Rd Fl 4, Mineola, NY 11501-4245
　Shelly Schechter, Director

MENTAL HEALTH SERVICES

Dept Of Mental Health Mental Retardation And Developmental Disabilities **516.227.7057**
Fax 516.227.7076
　60 Charles Lindbergh Blvd Ste 200, Uniondale,
　NY 11553
　James Dolan .jr, Director

South Nassau Communities

Hospital **516.377.5400**
Fax 516.377.5385
Web ....www.omh.state.ny.us
E-mail ....janice.scalero@omh.state.ny.us
　2277 Grand Ave, Baldwin, NY 11510-3148
　Janice Scalero, Director

JUSTICE AGENCY

Juvenile Detention Ctr **516.571.9260**
Fax 516.571.9690
Web ....www.djj.state.fl.us
E-mail ....maureen.hutcheon@djj.state.fl.us
　61 Carman Ave, Westbury, NY 11590-5755
　Robbins Laqueta, Director

Probation Dept **516.571.4676**
Fax 516.571.5611
Web ....www.nassaucountyny.gov
E-mail ....jfowle@nassaucountyny.gov
　400 County Seat Dr, Mineola, NY 11501-4823
　John Fowle, Acting Director Of Probation

Project 29 ....**516.483.3400**
Fax 516.483.3402
E-mail ....jmel@ltiny.org
　29 Richardson Pl, Hempstead, NY 11550-5021
　Mel Jackson, Director

COURTS

Advanced Prosthetics & Orthotics, Inc. **516.365.7225**
Fax 516.365.7112
　50 Maple Pl, Manhasset, NY 11030
　Michael Joyce, Director

Glen Cove Youth Court **516.676.0109**
Fax 516.676.1570
　13 Glen St, C/O City Court, Glen Cove,
　NY 11542-2704
　Stacey Timans-Newman, Chief Clerk

POLICE AND SHERIFF

Sheriff's Dept **516.572.4100**
Fax 516.572.4300
Web ....www.nassaucountyny.gov
E-mail ....mstosato@nassaucountyny.gov
　100 Carman Ave, East Meadow, NY 11554-1160
　Michael J Stosato, Acting Sheriff

EDUCATION SERVICES

Freeport Head Start **516.546.8251**
Fax 516.546.8255
　74 N Main St, Freeport, NY 11520
　Lorenzo Sistiunk, Supervisor

New York County

SOCIAL SERVICES

Admin For Children's Svcs **212.341.0900**
Fax 212.341.0916
Web ....www.nyc.gov
　150 William St Fl 2, New York, NY 10038-2614
　Joe Cardiri, Legal Counsel

Commission For The Blind & Visually Handicapped New York City Ofc **212.825.5710**
Fax 212.383.1350
Web ....www.dfa.state.ny.us
　80 Maiden Ln 23 Fl, New York, NY 10038
　Arnold Kramer, District Manager

Dept Of Social Svcs **212.331.6000**
Fax 212.331.6214
Web ....www.ci.nyc.ny.us
E-mail ....doarr@hra.nyc.gov
　180 Water St, Fl 25, New York, NY 10038
　Robert Doar, Commissioner

Div Of Child Support Enforcement New York City

Operations **212.961.8269**
Fax 212.961.8273
  317 Lenox Ave, New York, NY 10027-4450
  Kevin Boyoe, Deputy Director

Manhattan Acs **212.676.7055**
Fax 212.676.7060
  110 William St, Fl 20, New York, NY 10038
  Ralph Ortiz Jr., Bureau Director

New York City Dept Of Youth Svcs **212.442.5900**
Fax 212.442.9180
Web ....www.nyc.gov/dycd
  156 William St, New York, NY 10038-5323
  Jeanne Mullgrave, Commissioner

New York City-Bureau Of Day Care **212.676.2444**
Fax 212.676.2424
Web ....www.health.nyc.gov
  2 Lafayette St, Fl 22, New York, NY 10007
  Frank Cresciullo, Assistant Commissioner

New York State Ofc Of Children & Family Svcs New York City

Regional Ofc **212.383.1788**
Fax 212.383.1811
E-mail ....info@ocff.ny.us
  80 Maiden Ln Fl 24, New York, NY 10038
  Gladys Carrion, Commissioner

Ofc Of Youth Development Buffalo

Ofc **716.847.3323**
Fax 716.847.3324
  545 Ellicott Sq. Building, 295 Main St, Buffalo,
  NY 14203
  Richard John, Director

GENERAL HEALTH SERVICES

Dept Of Health **212.788.5261**
Fax 347.396.4135
Web ....www.health.nyc.gov
E-mail ....tfarley@health.nyc.gov
  125 Worth St Ste 514, Rm 331, New York, NY 10013
  Thomas Farley, Commissioner Of Health

Elgibility Program **212.273.0047**
Fax 212.643.3896
  330 W 34th St, New York, NY 10001
  Maria Quezada, Director

JUSTICE AGENCY

Lenox House **212.926.1236**
Fax 212.234.1350
E-mail ....lenox1house@aol.com
  131 W 132nd St, New York, NY 10027
  Anisa Kirne, Director

Manhatten Intake Ofc **212.961.4116**
Fax 212.961.4109
  163 W 125th St, New York, NY 10027
  Kenneth Tussaint, Family Advocate

New York City Dept Of Juvenile

Justice **212.925.7779**
Fax 212.442.8552
Web ....http://www.nyc.gov/html/djj/home.html
  150 William St, New York, NY 10038-3945
  William Soto, Director Of MCCU

New York City Dept Of Probation **212.361.8977**
Fax 212.361.8985
Web ....www.nyc.gov
E-mail ....vschiraldi@probation.nyc.gov
  33 Beaver St, Fl 23, New York, NY 10004
  Vincent Schiraldi, Commissioner

New York City-CASA **212.334.4010**
Fax 212.334.4018
Web ....www.casa-nyc.org
E-mail ....afeldman@casa-nyc.org
  50 Broadway Fl 4, New York, NY 10004-3856
  Amy Feldman, Executive Director

Queens Outreach Haven **718.358.6300**
Fax 718.358.3709
  4353 Robinson St, Flushing, NY 11355-3042
  Michelle Benefield, Director

COURTS

Family Court Of NYC **646.386.5200**
Fax 212.748.5272
Web ....www.nycourthelp.gov
  60 Lafayette St Rm 5C1, New York, NY 10013
  Evely Hasanoeddin, Clerk Of Court

Harlem Youth Court **212.360.4100**
Fax 212.397.0985
Web ....www.courtinnovation.org
E-mail ....khickman@courts.state.ny.us
  170 E 121st St, New York, NY 10035-3523
  Keith Hickman, Director

EDUCATION SERVICES

Childrens Aid Society PS 8 ....**212.740.8655**
Fax 212.740.7420
Web ....www.childrensaidsociety.org
  465 W 167th St, New York, NY 10032-4351
  Esther Olvera, Director Of Headstart

CPFLH Head Start **212.926.8264**
Fax 212.283.4740
  529-531 W 155th St, New York, NY 10032-7803
  Janice Gray, Director

East Harlem Head Start **212.348.2343**
Fax 212.876.0711
Web ....www.childrensaidsociety.org
E-mail ....moriac@childrensaidsociety.org
  130 E 101st St, New York, NY 10029-6106
  Moria Cappio, Director

Niagara County

SOCIAL SERVICES

Social Svcs **716.439.7602**
Fax 716.439.7609
Web ....www.niagaracounty.com
E-mail ....burt.marshall@niagaracounty.com
  20 East Ave, Lockport, NY 14094-3708
  Burt Marshall, Director Of Social Services And Cps

GENERAL HEALTH SERVICES

Health Dept **716.278.1900**
Fax 716.278.1936
Web ....www.niagaracounty.com
  1001 11Th St, Trott Building, Niagara Falls,
  NY 14301
  Mary Huczel, Hiv/std Supervisor

Health Dept **716.439.7435**
Fax 716.439.7440
Web ....www.niagaracounty.com
E-mail ....dan.stapleton@niagaracounty.com
  5467 Upper Mountain Rd Ste 100, Lockport,
  NY 14094-1894
  Daniel Stapleton, Public Health Director

Health Dept Lockport Ofc **716.439.7430**
Fax 716.439.7483
Web ....www.niagaracounty.com
E-mail ....lenora.teixeira@niagaracounty.com
  5467 Upper Mountain Rd Ste 100, Lockport,
  NY 14094-1894
  Lenora Teixeira, Communicable Disease Coordinator

MENTAL HEALTH SERVICES

Dept of Mental Health **716.278.1940**
Fax 716.278.1943
Web ....www.niagaracounty.com
  1001 11th St, Niagara Falls, NY 14301-1201
  Carol Ross, Program Director

Mental Health **716.439.7410**
Fax 716.439.7418
Web ....www.niagaracounty.com
E-mail ....antoinette.lech@niagaracounty.com
  5467 Upper Mountain Rd Ste 200, Lockport,
  NY 14094-1895
  Antoinette Lech, Csw, Community Services Director

JUSTICE AGENCY

Orchard House **716.778.5515**
Fax 716.778.9232
  5331 W Lake Rd, Burt, NY 14028
  Nancy Jones, Detention Case Manager

Youth Bureau **716.434.3071**
Fax 716.434.3672
Web ....www.dhs.state.tx.us
E-mail ....mjunk23@aol.com
  201 Willow St, Lockport, NY 14094-4839
  Melissa Junke, Executive Director

COURTS

Family Court **716.439.7172**
Fax 716.439.7170
E-mail ....jbatt@courts.state.ny.us
  175 Hawley St, Fl 2, Lockport, NY 14094
  Honorable John Batt, Director

POLICE AND SHERIFF

Sheriff's Ofc **716.438.3393**
Fax 716.438.3357
Web ....www.niagarasheriff.com
E-mail ....james.voutour@Niagaracounty.com
  5526 Niagara St Extention, Lockport, NY 14095
  James Voutour, Sheriff

Oneida County

SOCIAL SERVICES

Social Svcs **315.798.5738**
Fax 315.798.5218
Web ....www.ocgov.net
  800 Park Ave, Utica, NY 13501
  Colleen Fahy-olney, Social Services Director

GENERAL HEALTH SERVICES

Clinical Svcs **315.798.5748**
Fax 315.798.1057
Web ....www.oneidacounty.org
  406 Elizabeth St, Utica, NY 13501-2306
  Susan Blatt, Md, Medical Director

Health Dept **315.798.6400**
Fax 315.798.5022
Web ....www.ocgov.net
E-mail ....gjones@ocgov.net
  185 Genesee St, Utica, NY 13501
  Gayle Jones, Public Health Director

MENTAL HEALTH SERVICES

Dept Of Mental Health **315.798.5903**
Fax 315.798.6445
Web ....www.oneidacounty.com
E-mail ....lnelson@ocgov.net
  235 Elizabeth St, Utica, NY 13502
  Linda Nelson, Commissioner

JUSTICE AGENCY

The Peacemaker Program Inc. **315.724.1718**
Fax 315.724.1375
E-mail ....info@thepeacemakerprogram.org
  502 Court St Ste 234, The Peacemaker Program Inc.,
  Utica, NY 13502
  Steve Robinson, Director

Youth Bureau 315.798.5027
Fax 315.798.6438
Web ....www.ocgov.net
E-mail ....lsoldato@ocgov.net
    209 Elizabeth St, Utica, NY 13501-2939
    Robert Roth, Youth Bureau Director

POLICE AND SHERIFF

Sheriff's Ofc 315.765.2222
Fax 315.765.2205
Web ....www.oneidacountysheriff.us
    6065 Judd Rd, Oriskany, NY 13424
    Robert Mashil, Sheriff

EDUCATION SERVICES

New York State Schools For Deaf 315.337.8400
Fax 315.336.8859
Web ....www.nysd.org
    401 Turin St, Rome, NY 13440-3314
    Carriann Ray, Superintendent

Onondaga County

SOCIAL SERVICES

Commission For The Blind And Visually Handicapped Syracuse
Ofc 315.423.5417
Fax 315.423.5416
Web ....www.vision.ny.gov
E-mail ....john.scott@ocfs.state.ny.us
    100 S Salina St Ste 105, Syracuse, NY 13202-1808
    John Scott, District Manager

New York State Ofc Of Children & Family Svcs Syracuse
Regional Ofc 315.423.1200
Fax 315.423.1198
Web ....www.ocfs.state.ny.us
E-mail ....jack.klump@dfa.state.ny.us
    100 S Salina St, The Atrium Bldg, Syracuse, NY 13202
    Jack Klump, Family & Children Svcs Director

Social Svcs 315.435.2985
Fax 315.435.2113
E-mail ....ava.kerznowski@dfa.state.ny.us
    421 Montgomery St, Civic Center, Syracuse,
    NY 13202
    Ava Kerznowski, Income Maintenance Director

GENERAL HEALTH SERVICES

Health Dept 315.435.3252
Fax 315.435.5720
Web ....ocgov.net
    421 Montgomery St, 9th flr, Syracuse,
    NY 13202-2906
    Cynthia Morrow, Health Commissioner

Health Dept 315.435.3280
Fax 315.435.5720
Web ....www.ongov.net/health
E-mail ....hldroth@ongov.net
    421 Montgomery St, Rm 80, Syracuse, NY 13202
    Diane Rothermel, Disease Control Director

MENTAL HEALTH SERVICES

Dept Of Mental Health 315.435.7707
Fax 315.435.7710
    530 Cedar St, Syracuse, NY 13210
    Soe Ellen Harris, Director

Onondaga Pastoral Counseling Ctr
Inc 315.472.4471
Fax 315.472.8869
Web ....www.opcc-ny.org
E-mail ....jholm@liberty-resources.org
    1045 Jim St, Syracuse, NY 13203-1811
    Jean Holm, Manager

Suny Health Science Ctr-University
Hospital 315.464.3100
Fax 315.464.3178
E-mail ....dewanm@upstate.edu
    713 Harrison St, Syracuse, NY 13210
    Mantosh Dewan, Director

JUSTICE AGENCY

CASA 315.422.5638
Fax 315.471.4924
Web ....www.communityalternatives.org
    115 E Jefferson St Ste 300, Syracuse, NY 13202-2018
    Marsha Weissman, Executive Director

Hillbrook Detention Facility 315.435.1421
Fax 315.435.2671
    4949 Velasko Rd, Syracuse, NY 13215-1930
    James Dzarnika, Director

New York State Div Of Children And Family
Svcs 315.423.5488
Fax 315.423.5499
Web ....www.ocfs.state.ny.us
    100 S Salina St Ste 105, The Atrium, Syracuse,
    NY 13202-1808
    Denise Dyer, Youth Development Coordinator

Probation Dept 315.435.2380
Fax 315.435.3329
Web ....www.ongov.net
E-mail ....algiacchi@ongov.net
    421 Montgomery St, Fl 6, Syracuse, NY 13202
    Al Giacchi, Commissioner

COURTS

All Metro Health Care 315.453.5537
Fax 315.453.7138
E-mail ....ituttle@all-metro.com
    526 Old Liverpool Rd Ste 1, Liverpool,
    NY 13088-6249
    Irene Tuttle, Director Clinical Services

Family Court 315.671.2000
Fax 315.671.1163
    401 Montgomery St, Rm 101, Syracuse, NY 13202
    Sherree Jackson, Chief Clerk

Youth Court 315.295.0397
Fax 315.475.0769
E-mail ....youthcourt@newjusticeservices.org
    1153 W Fayette St, C/O New Justice Services,
    Syracuse, NY 13204
    John McCoulough, Executive Director

POLICE AND SHERIFF

Sheriff's Ofc 315.435.3044
Fax 315.435.2942
E-mail ....sheriffwalsh@hotmail.com
    407 S State St, Syracuse, NY 13202
    Kevin Walsh, Sheriff

Syracuse Police Dept 315.442.5200
Fax 315.442.5198
Web ....www.ci.syracuse.ny.us
E-mail ....fchmarak@ci.syracuse.ny.us
    511 S State St Ste 400, Syracuse, NY 13202-2181
    Lt. Frank Chmarak, Family Services Division

Ontario County

SOCIAL SERVICES

Social Svcs 585.396.4060
Fax 585.396.4980
Web ....www.co.ontario.ny.us/social-services
    3010 County Complex Dr, Canandaigua, NY 14424
    Eileen Tiberio, Children & Family Services Director Of Services

GENERAL HEALTH SERVICES

Community Health Svcs 585.396.4343
Fax 585.396.4551
Web ....www.ontariocountypublichealth.com
E-mail ....mary.beer@co.ontario.ny.us
    3019 County Complex Dr, Canandaigua,
    NY 14424-9505
    Mary Beer, Public Health Director

JUSTICE AGENCY

Probation Dept 585.396.4222
Fax 585.396.4187
    3010 County Complex Dr, Canandaigua, NY 14424
    Sharon Donovan, Director

Youth Care Facility 585.394.0180
Fax 585.394.4623
Web ....www.hillside.com
    3093 County Complex Dr, Canandaigua, NY 14424
    Terry Lefrois, Supervisor

COURTS

Family Court 585.396.4272
Fax 585.396.4576
E-mail ....ontariofamilycourt@courts.state.ny.us
    27 N Main St, Canandaigua, NY 14424
    Lynda Wood, Chief Clerk

Youth Court 585.396.4519
Fax 585.396.8821
Web ....www.partnershipoc.org
    8 Coy st, Canandaigua, NY 14424-9502
    Debbie Holland, Coordinator

Orange County

SOCIAL SERVICES

Social Svcs 845.291.4000
Fax 845.291.4201
Web ....www.orangecountygov.com
    11 Quarry Rd, Goshen, NY 10924
    David Jolly, Commissioner

GENERAL HEALTH SERVICES

Health Dept 845.291.2332
Fax 845.291.2341
Web ....www.co.orange.ny.us
E-mail ....svanzetta@co.orange.ny.us
    124 Main St, Goshen, NY 10924-2199
    Shirley Vanzetta, Rn, Nursing Director

MENTAL HEALTH SERVICES

Dept Of Mental Health 845.858.1456
Fax 845.858.1459
Web ....www.orangecountygov.com
    146 Pike St, Port Jervis, NY 12771-1808
    Lacey Trimble, Director

Dept Of Mental Health 845.568.5260
Fax 845.568.5213
Web ....www.orangecountygov.com
    141 Broadway, Newburgh, NY 12550
    Joseph Perales, Director

Mental Health Dept 845.291.2600
Fax 845.291.2628
Web ....www.co.orange.ny.us
E-mail ....cashman@orangecountygov.com
    30 Harriman Dr, Goshen, NY 10924
    Chris Ashman, Commissioner

JUSTICE AGENCY

Youth Bureau 845.615.3620
Fax 845.346.1170
E-mail ....cchichester@co.orange.ny.us
    18 Seward Ave, Ste 102, Middletown, NY 10940
    Carol Chichester, Executive Director

New York

COURTS

Family Court **845.291.3030**
Fax 845.291.3054
Web ....www.nycourts.gov
   285 Main St, Goshen, NY 10924
   Honorable Andrew P. Bivona, Judge

POLICE AND SHERIFF

Sheriff's Dept **845.291.7900**
Fax 845.294.1590
E-mail ....cdubois@co.orange.ny.us
   110 Wells Farm Rd, Goshen, NY 10924
   Carl E. Dubois, Sheriff

Orleans County

GENERAL HEALTH SERVICES

Health Dept **585.589.3278**
Fax 585.589.2873
Web ....www.orleansny.com
E-mail ....msahukar@orleansny.com
   14012 State Route 31, Albion, NY 14411-9301
   Mary Janet Sahukar, Director Of Patient Services

MENTAL HEALTH SERVICES

Community Svcs **585.589.7066**
Fax 585.589.6395
Web ....www.orleansny.com
E-mail ....jgraziano@orleansny.com
   14014 State Route 31, Albion, NY 14411-9301
   James Graziano, Lcsw, Director

JUSTICE AGENCY

Probation Dept **585.590.4100**
Fax 585.590.4103
   13925 State Route 31 Ste 200, Albion, NY 14411
   Lucille Taylor-welch, Director

COURTS

Family Court **585.589.4457**
Fax 585.589.0632
Web ....www.courts.state.ny.us
E-mail ....ldower@courts.state.ny.us
   1 S Main St Ste 1, Albion, NY 14411-1448
   Honorable James P. Punch, Judge

POLICE AND SHERIFF

Sheriff's Dept **585.590.4137**
Fax 585.590.4178
E-mail ....oscher@orleansny.com
   13925 State Route 31 Ste 400, Albion, NY 14411
   Scott Hess, Sheriff

Oswego County

SOCIAL SERVICES

Social Svcs **315.963.5000**
Fax 315.963.5600
   100 Spring St, Mexico, NY 13114
   Gregg Heffner, Acting Director Of Social Services

GENERAL HEALTH SERVICES

Health Dept **315.349.3545**
Fax 315.349.3435
Web ....www.oswegocountypublichealth.com
   70 Bunner St, Oswego, NY 13126-3357
   Dennis Norfleet, Director Of Public Health

COURTS

Family Court **315.349.3350**
Fax 315.349.3457
Web ....www.oswegocounty.com
   39 Churchill Rd, Oswego, NY 13126
   Honorable. Kimberly M Seager, Judge

Youth Court **315.349.3451**
Fax 315.349.3231
Web ....www.oswegocounty.com
E-mail ....brian@oswegocounty.com
   70 Bunner St, Oswego, NY 13126-3357
   Kathleen Finland, Executive Director

POLICE AND SHERIFF

Sheriff's Ofc **315.349.3307**
Fax 315.349.3483
Web ....www.oswegocounty.com
E-mail ....sheriff@oswegocounty.com
   39 Churchill Rd, Oswego, NY 13126
   Reuel A. Todd, Sheriff

Otsego County

SOCIAL SERVICES

Social Svcs **607.547.1700**
Fax 607.547.1721
Web ....www.otsegocounty.com
E-mail ....lincolnd@otsegocounty.com
   140 County Highway W, Meadows Office Building,
   Cooperstown, NY 13326
   Cindy Lane, Assistance Director

GENERAL HEALTH SERVICES

Dept Of Health **607.547.6458**
Fax 607.547.4385
Web ....www.otsegocounty.com
E-mail ....cusworthd@otsegocounty.com
   140 County Highway 33, Ste 3, Cooperstown,
   NY 13326
   Diane Cusworth, Director Of Public Services

MENTAL HEALTH SERVICES

Community Svcs **607.433.2334**
Fax 607.433.1364
E-mail ....dalesandros@otsegocounty.com
   242 Main St, Oneonta, NY 13820
   Susan Dalesandro, Director

COURTS

Family Court **607.547.4264**
Fax 212.457.2956
E-mail ....otsegofamilycourt@courts.state.ny.us
   32 Chestnut St, Cooperstown, NY 13326
   Karen Nichols, Clerk Of Court

POLICE AND SHERIFF

Sheriff's Ofc **607.547.4271**
Fax 607.547.6413
Web ....www.otsegocounty.com
E-mail ....Sheriff@otsegocounty.com
   172 County Highway 33 W, Cooperstown, NY 13326
   Richard J. Devlin Jr., Sheriff

Putnam County

GENERAL HEALTH SERVICES

Health Dept Nursing Svcs **845.278.6558**
Fax 845.278.6085
Web ....www.putnamcountyny.com
   1 Geneva Rd, Terravest Corporate Park, Brewster,
   NY 10509
   Barbara Ilardi, Hiv Educator

POLICE AND SHERIFF

Sheriff's Ofc **845.225.4300**
Fax 845.228.5227
Web ....www.pcsd.org
E-mail ....dsmith@pcsd.org
   3 County Ctr, Carmel, NY 10512-1323
   Donald B. Smith, Sheriff

Queens County

SOCIAL SERVICES

Queens Acs **718.557.1745**
Fax 718.480.4413
E-mail ....marsha.kellam@dfa.state.ny.us
   165-15 Archer Ave, Jamaica, NY 11433-1109
   Marsha Kellam, Bureau Director

GENERAL HEALTH SERVICES

Queens Health Dept **718.476.7636**
Fax 718.476.7131
   3433 Junction Blvd, Fl 2, Jackson Heights, NY 11372
   Dr. Diana Nielsen, Director

MENTAL HEALTH SERVICES

Behaviorial Health **718.899.0592**
Fax 718.335.9114
   3334 80th St, Jackson Heights, NY 11372-1341
   Andy Phillips, Director

Rensselaer County

SOCIAL SERVICES

Social Svcs **518.283.2000**
Fax 518.283.7884
Web ....www.rensco.com
E-mail ....scott.steanburg@dfa.state.ny.us
   133 Bloomingrove Dr, Troy, NY 12180-8553
   Scott Steanburg, Child Protective Services Coordinator

GENERAL HEALTH SERVICES

Health Dept **518.270.2626**
Fax 518.270.2638
Web ....www.rensco.com
   1600 7th Ave, County Government Center, Troy,
   NY 12180
   Lisa Devito-casale, Nursing Director

MENTAL HEALTH SERVICES

Dept Of Mental Health **518.463.8869**
Fax 518.463.8733
Web ....www.rensco.com
E-mail ....ckapola@rensco.com
   1641 3rd St, Rensselaer, NY 12144-1539
   Carol Kapola, Director

Mental Health Dept **518.270.2800**
Fax 518.270.2723
E-mail ....kmaciol@rensco.com
   1600 7th Ave, Ned Pattison Government Center,
   Troy, NY 12180
   Katherine Maciol, Acsw, Commissioner

JUSTICE AGENCY

Probation Dept **518.270.8440**
Fax 518.273.8101
   500 Broadway, Troy, NY 12180
   Laura Bauer, Director

Unified Family Svcs/Youth **518.270.2960**
Fax 518.270.2956
Web ....www.rensco.com
E-mail ....phoyt@rensco.com
   1600 7th Ave, Troy, NY 12180
   Pierce Hoyt, Deputy Commissioner

POLICE AND SHERIFF

Sheriff's Ofc **518.270.5448**
Fax 518.270.5447
E-mail ....jmahar@rensco.com
   4000 Main St, Troy, NY 12180
   Jack Mahar, Sheriff

Richmond County

SOCIAL SERVICES

Staten Island Acs 718.720.2700
Fax 718.720.2842
E-mail ....rafael.ortiz@dfa.state.ny.us
　350 Saint Marks Pl, Fl 5, Staten Island, NY 10301
　Rafael Ortiz Jr, Borough Commissioner

MENTAL HEALTH SERVICES

**Staten Island University Hospital Outpatient Mental
Health** 718.226.2274
Fax 718.226.2658
E-mail ....robert_schaer@siuh.edu
　392 Seguine Ave, Staten Island, NY 10309-3906
　Robert Schaer, Manager

**Staten Island University Hospital Outpatient Mental
Health** 718.226.8910
Fax 718.226.8467
Web ....www.siuh.edu
E-mail ....robert_schaer@siuh.edu
　450 Seaview Ave, Staten Island, NY 10305-3401
　Robert Schaer, Manager

Rockland County

SOCIAL SERVICES

Social Svcs 845.364.3100
Fax 845.364.3109
Web ....www.co.rockland.ny.us
　50 Sanitorium Rd, Bldg L, Pomona, NY 10970
　Barbara Gavin, Child Protective Services Director

GENERAL HEALTH SERVICES

Health Dept 845.364.2513
Fax 845.364.2628
Web ....www.co.rockland.ny.us
E-mail ....quinn@co.rockland.ny.us
　50 Sanitorium Rd, Bldg D, Pomona, NY 10970
　Nellie Quinn, Director Of Nursing

MENTAL HEALTH SERVICES

Mental Health Dept 845.364.2378
Fax 845.364.2381
E-mail ....rcdmh@co.rockland.ny.us
　50 Sanitorium Rd, Bldg F, Pomona, NY 10970
　Mary Ann Walsh-tozer, Commissioner

JUSTICE AGENCY

Probation Dept 845.638.5544
Fax 845.638.5648
　11 New Hempstead Rd Ste 201, New City, NY 10956
　Kathy Cower-bernstein, Director

Youth Bureau 845.638.5166
Fax 845.638.5377
　18 New Hempstead Rd Ste 400, Sain Office Bldg,
　New City, NY 10956
　Marianne Mccarney, Assistant Director

COURTS

Family Court 845.638.5300
Fax 845.638.5319
　1 S Main St Ste 300, New City, NY 10956-3554
　Honorable Linda Christopher, Director

Youth Court 845.359.1775
Fax 845.359.3721
E-mail ....orangetownpolice@yahoo.com
　26 W Orangeburg Rd, Orangeburg, NY 10962-1706
　Peter Maher, Executive Director

Youth Court 845.639.5846
Fax 845.639.5924
Web ....www.town.clarkstown.ny.us
E-mail ....e_malloy@town.clarkstown.ny.us
　20 Maple Ave, New City, NY 10956-5011
　Eileen Malloy, Coordinator

Youth Court 845.786.2242
Fax 845.786.3120
E-mail ....dko611@yahoo.com
　79 Route 210, Stony Point, NY 10980-1750
　Kevin O'connor, Detective

POLICE AND SHERIFF

Sheriff's Dept 845.638.5400
Fax 845.638.5161
Web ....www.co.rockland.ny.us
E-mail ....kralikj@co.rockland.ny.us
　55 New Hempstead Rd, New City, NY 10956-3627
　James Kralik, Sheriff

EDUCATION SERVICES

Bais Mikroh Head Start 845.425.4880
Fax 845.425.1062
Web ....www.baismikroh.org
　221 Viola Rd, Monsey, NY 10952-1732
　Yakov Horowitz, Administrator

Saratoga County

SOCIAL SERVICES

Social Svcs 518.884.4140
Fax 518.884.4199
Web ....www.co.saratoga.ny.us
　152 W High St, Ballston Spa, NY 12020
　Patrick Maxwell, Director Of Social Services

GENERAL HEALTH SERVICES

Public Health Nursing 518.584.7460
Fax 518.583.1202
Web ....www.saratogacountyny.gov
　31 Woodlawn Ave Ste 1, Saratoga Springs,
　NY 12866-2198
　Terryayne Stortz, Director Prevention Services

JUSTICE AGENCY

Probation Dept 518.884.4120
Fax 518.884.4258
　152 W High St, Ballston Spa, NY 12020
　John Adams, Director

COURTS

Youth Court 518.581.1230
Fax 518.581.1240
　36 Phila St, Saratoga Springs, NY 12866
　Heather, Director

POLICE AND SHERIFF

Sheriff's Ofc 518.885.2450
Fax 518.885.2453
Web ....www.govt.co.saratoga.ny.us
E-mail ....james@govt.co.saratoga.ny.us
　6010 County Farm Rd, Ballston Spa, NY 12020-2229
　James D. Bowen, Sheriff

EDUCATION SERVICES

Corinth Head Start 518.654.7090
　331 Main St, Corinth, NY 12822
　Bernie Jones, Director

Schenectady County

SOCIAL SERVICES

Children And Family Svcs 518.388.4570
Fax 518.382.1256
　106 Erie Blvd, Schenectady, NY 12305
　Jean Nicholas, CPS Supervisor

Social Svcs 518.388.4470
Fax 518.382.0310
　797 Broadway, Schenectady, NY 12305
　Land Acre, Principal

GENERAL HEALTH SERVICES

Health Dept 518.386.2824
Fax 518.382.5418
Web ....www.schenectadycounty.com
　107 Nott Ter, Ste 302, Schenectady, NY 12308
　Stephanie L. Scuderi, Director Of Patient Services

MENTAL HEALTH SERVICES

Northeast Parent & Child Society 518.381.8911
Fax 518.377.4292
Web ....www.neparentchild.org
E-mail ....yette.kelly@neparentchild.org
　530 Franklin St, Schenectady, NY 12305
　Yette Kelly, Director

JUSTICE AGENCY

The Center For Community Justice 518.346.1281
Fax 518.346.1311
E-mail ....cneal@thecenterforcommunityjustice.org
　144 Barrett St, Schenectady, NY 12305
　Connie Neal, Director

Youth Bureau 518.386.2211
Fax 518.344.2807
E-mail ....ed.kosiur@schenectadycounty.com
　797 Broadway, Fl 3, Schenectady, NY 12305
　Ed Kosiur, Director

COURTS

Family Court 518.285.8435
Fax 518.393.1565
　620 State St, Schenectady, NY 12305
　Christine Clark, Honorable Judge

Youth Court 518.386.4570
Fax 518.386.4515
Web ....www.niskayuna.org
E-mail ....kwetzel@niskayuna.org
　1 Niskayuna Cir Ste 1, Schenectady, NY 12309-4343
　Geoffrey Stroebel, Coordinator

POLICE AND SHERIFF

Sheriff's Dept 518.388.4300
Fax 518.388.4593
Web ....www.nycap.rr.com
　320 Veeder Ave, Schenectady, NY 12307-1304
　Dominick Dagastino, Sheriff

EDUCATION SERVICES

**Communities In Schools Academy Of Steimetz,
Inc.** 518.370.8183
Fax 518.881.3602
　880 Oakwood Ave, Schenectady, NY 12303
　Diane Wilkinson, Director

Schoharie County

SOCIAL SERVICES

Social Svcs 518.295.8334
Fax 518.295.8492
Web ....www.schohariecounty-ny.gov
E-mail ....seniorcouncil@co.schoharie.ny.us
　284 Main St, Ste 210, Schoharie, NY 12157
　Paul J. Brady, Commissioner

MENTAL HEALTH SERVICES

Mental Health Ctr 518.295.8336
Fax 518.295.8724
Web ....www.omh.state.ny.us
　284 Main St, Fl 3, Schoharie, NY 12157
　Joseph Patterson, Director Of Community Services

COURTS

Family Court 518.295.8383
Fax 518.295.8451
E-mail ....gbartlett@co.schoharie.ny.us
　290 Main St, Schoharie, NY 12157
　Honorable George R. Bartlett Iii, Judge

Schuyler County

SOCIAL SERVICES

Dept Of Social Svcs **607.535.8303**
Fax 607.535.8377
Web ....www.co.schuyler.ny.us
  323 Owego St. Unit 3, Human Services Complex, Montour Falls, NY 14865
  Beverly K. Clickner, Deputy Commissioner

GENERAL HEALTH SERVICES

Health Serv **607.535.8140**
Fax 607.535.8157
Web ....www.co.schuyler.ny.us
  106 S Perry St, Watkins Glen, NY 14891
  George Rotes, Director of Public Health

MENTAL HEALTH SERVICES

Community Svcs **607.535.8282**
Fax 607.535.8284
E-mail ....groets@co.schuyler.ny.us
  106 S Perry St, Watkins Glen, NY 14891
  George Roets, Csw, Director

JUSTICE AGENCY

Probation Dept **607.535.8165**
Fax 607.535.8173
E-mail ....crosno@co.schuyler.ny.us
  105 9th St Unit 10, Watkins Glen, NY 14891
  Christopher Rosno, Director

COURTS

Family Court **607.535.7760**
Fax 607.535.4918
Web ....www.courts.state.ny.us
E-mail ....jargetsinger@courts.state.ny.us
  105 9th St Unit 35, Watkins Glen, NY 14891-1435
  Honorable J.c. Argetsinger, Judge

Youth Court **607.535.6236**
Fax 607.535.6810
Web ....www.schuylercounty.gov
E-mail ....alawton@co.chuyler.ny.us
  323 Owego St, Ste 128, Montour Falls, NY 14865
  Adam Lawton, Coordinator

Seneca County

GENERAL HEALTH SERVICES

Health Dept **315.539.1980**
Fax 315.539.1054
Web ....www.co.seneca.ny.us/public
E-mail ....slivigne@co.seneca.ny.us
  31 Thurber Dr, Waterloo, NY 13165
  Scott Livigne, Mental Health Director

JUSTICE AGENCY

Probation Dept **315.539.1740**
Fax 315.539.3646
E-mail ....dterry@co.seneca.ny.us
  1 Dipronio Dr, Waterloo, NY 13165-1680
  David E. Terry, Director

Youth Bureau **315.539.1790**
Fax 315.539.4251
Web ....www.co.seneca.ny.us
E-mail ....mwhirtley@co.seneca.ny.us
  1 Dipronio Dr, Waterloo, NY 13165-1680
  Michael Whirtley, Executive Director

COURTS

Family Court **315.539.4917**
Fax 315.539.3267
E-mail ....dbender@courts.state.ny.us
  48 W Williams St, Waterloo, NY 13165-1338
  Honorable Dennis F. Bender, Director

EDUCATION SERVICES

Cimmunity Action Agency **315.539.5647**
Fax 315.539.4313
Web ....www.cscaa.com
  23 Center St, Waterloo, NY 13165
  Rose Rathborn, Director

St. Lawrence County

SOCIAL SERVICES

Social Svcs **315.379.2111**
Fax 315.379.2278
Web ....www.co.st-lawrence.ny.us
  6 Judson St, Canton, NY 13617-1196
  Chris Rediehs, Commissioner

GENERAL HEALTH SERVICES

Public Health **315.386.2325**
Fax 315.386.2203
Web ....www.co.st-lawrence.ny.us
E-mail ....scryderman@co.st-lawrence.ny.us
  80 State Highway 310 Ste 2, Canton, NY 13617-1476
  Rebecca Trejos, Communicable Disease Nurse

MENTAL HEALTH SERVICES

Community Svcs **315.386.2048**
Fax 315.386.2435
Web ....www.co.st-lawrence.ny.us
E-mail ....rayen@co.st-lawrence.ny.us
  80 State Highway 310 Ste 1, Canton, NY 13617-1493
  Ruth Ayen, Director

St. Lawrence Psychiatric Ctr **315.541.2001**
Fax 315.541.2041
  1 Chimney Point Dr, Ogdensburg, NY 13669
  Sam Bastien, Director

JUSTICE AGENCY

Youth Bureau **315.379.9464**
Fax 315.386.8636
Web ....www.co.st-lawrence.ny.us
E-mail ....jsevick@co.st-lawrence.ny.us
  80 State Highway 310 Ste 4, Canton, NY 13617-1494
  Joanne Sevick, Executive Director

COURTS

Family Court **315.379.2410**
Fax 315.386.3197
  48 Court St, Canton, NY 13617
  Rhonda Poupore, Chief Clerk

Steuben County

GENERAL HEALTH SERVICES

Public Health Nursing **607.664.2438**
Fax 607.664.2166
Web ....www.steubencony.org
E-mail ....publichealth@co.steuben.ny.us
  3 Pulteney Sq E, Bath, NY 14810
  Victoria Fuerst, Director Of Public Health/patient Services

MENTAL HEALTH SERVICES

Mental Health Svcs **607.776.6577**
Fax 607.664.2161
Web ....www.co.steuben.ny.us
E-mail ....roberta@co.steuben.ny.us
  115 Liberty St, Bath, NY 14810-1508
  Robert W. Anderson, Phd, Director

JUSTICE AGENCY

Probation Dept **315.379.2230**
Fax 315.386.1030
  48 Court St, Canton, NY 13617
  Edward Gauthier, Probation Director

Probation Dept **607.664.2330**
Fax 607.664.2165
Web ....www.co.steuben.ny.us
  3 Pulteney Sq E Ste 17, Bath, NY 14810-1500
  Eugene Greeley, Probation Director

Steuben Detention Ctr **607.776.2383**
Fax 607.776.0668
Web ....www.glovehouse.org
  983 County Route 113, Bath, NY 14810
  John Treahy, President & CEO

Youth Bureau **607.664.2119**
Fax 607.664.2189
Web ....www.co.steuben.ny.us
  3 Pulteney Sq E, Bath, NY 14810
  Jack Wheeler, Youth Program Administrator

COURTS

Family Court **607.664.2136**
Fax 607.776.7857
Web ....www.courts.state.ny.gov
  3 E Pulteney Sq, Bath, NY 14810-1500
  Pamela Gardner, Chief Clerk

POLICE AND SHERIFF

Sheriff's Dept **607.776.3347**
Fax 607.776.7671
Web ....www.co.steuben.ny.us
E-mail ....orewayj@co.steuben.ny.us
  7007 Rumsey St Extention, Bath, NY 14810
  Joel Oreway, Sheriff

Suffolk County

SOCIAL SERVICES

Social Svcs **631.854.9166**
Fax 631.854.9196
Web ....www.co.suffolk.ny.us
E-mail ....karen.yorysh@dfa.state.ny.us
  3455 Vetteren Memorial Hwy, Ronkonkoma, NY 11779
  Karen Yorysh, Child Placement Services Bureau Director

Social Svcs **631.854.9700**
Fax 631.854.9996
Web ....www.co.suffolk.ny.us
  3085 Veterans Memorial Hwy, Meridan Plaza, Ronkonkoma, NY 11779-7659
  Gregory Blass, Commissioner

GENERAL HEALTH SERVICES

Dolan Family Health Ctr **631.425.5250**
Fax 631.425.0140
Web ....www.hunthosp.org
  284 Pulaski Rd, Greenlawn, NY 11740
  Kathy Giffuni, Rn, Nursing Manager

Martin Luther King Jr Community Health Ctr **631.854.1700**
Fax 631.854.1783
  1556 Straight Path, Wyandanch, NY 11798-3299
  Laura Shortmeyer, Hiv Coordinator

North Brookhaven Family Health Ctr - Coram **631.854.2301**
Fax 631.854.2104
Web ....www.co.suffolk.ny.us
  82 Middle Country Rd, Coram, NY 11727-4411
  Margaret Culhane, RN, FNP, HIV Coordinator

Riverhead Health Ctr **631.852.1800**
Fax 631.852.1807
  300 Center Dr, Riverhead, NY 11901
  Mathew Elgutt, Hiv Coordinator

MENTAL HEALTH SERVICES

Brookhaven Memorial Hospital Medical

Ctr **631.852.1070**
Fax 631.852.1119
    550 Montauk Hwy, Shirley, NY 11967
    Karen Shaughness, Director

Community Mental Hygiene Svcs **631.852.1856**
Fax 631.852.2570
E-mail .... james.graziano@suffolkcountyny.gov
    100 Center Dr, Riverhead, NY 11901
    Jim Graziano, Director

Community Mental Hygiene Svcs **631.852.1440**
Fax 631.852.1448
    300 Center Dr. County Center, Riverhead, NY 11901
    Marlene Neknez, Director

JUSTICE AGENCY

Casa **631.853.4260**
Fax 631.853.7908
Web .... www.eacinc.org
    Room 470, Central Islip, NY 11722
    Marie Carson, Director

Juvenile Probation **631.853.4246**
Fax 631.853.5341
    400 Carleton Ave, Fl 3, Central Islip, NY 11722
    Denise Giacoppo, Supervising Probation Officer

Probation Dept **631.852.5100**
Fax 631.852.5103
Web .... www.suffolkcountyny.gov
E-mail .... gerard.cook@suffolkcountyny.gov
    Yaphank Ave Bldg C0110, Yaphank, NY
    Gerard J Cook, Director

Youth Bureau **631.853.8270**
Fax 631.853.8271
E-mail .... lou.medina@suffolkcountyny.gov
    100 Veterans Memorial Hwy, Fl 3, Hauppauge,
    NY 11788
    Louis A. Medina, Executive Director

COURTS

Family Court **631.852.3905**
Fax 631.852.2851
    889 E Main St Ste 308, Riverhead, NY 11901
    Giooen Patrick, Clerk

Family Court **631.853.4647**
Fax 631.853.5704
    400 Carleton Ave, Central Islip, NY 11722
    Vincent Iraia, Probation Director

Youth Court **631.271.5547**
Fax 631.271.1360
E-mail .... youthcourt@optonline.net
    423 Park Ave, Huntington, NY 11743
    Maria Danisi, Director

Youth Court **631.727.3200**
Fax 631.727.2497
    200 Howell Ave, Riverhead, NY 11901
    Det. Evelyn Hobsen, Director

POLICE AND SHERIFF

Missing Persons Unit **631.852.6194**
Fax 631.852.6192
    30 Yaphank Ave, Yaphank, NY 11980
    Richard Dormer, Commissioner

Sheriff's Ofc **631.852.2200**
Fax 631.852.1898
Web .... www.suffolkcountyny.gov
E-mail .... vincent.demarco@suffolkcountyny.gov
    100 Center Dr, Riverhead, NY 11901-3390
    Vincent Demarco, Sheriff

EDUCATION SERVICES

Bay Area Head Start **631.395.4853**
Fax 631.395.4894
E-mail .... li@headstart.org
    161 Margin Dr E, Shirley, NY 11967
    Carol Smith, Director

Special Education **631.884.8530**
Fax 631.884.8540
E-mail .... sberman@mail.nysed.gov
    887 Kellum St, Lindenhurst, NY 11757
    Eileen Taylor, Supervisor

Sullivan County

SOCIAL SERVICES

Social Svcs **845.292.0100**
Fax 845.292.1320
Web .... www.co.sullivan.ny.us
E-mail .... alicia.frankel@scgnet.us
    16 Community Ln, Liberty, NY 12754-2851
    Alicia Frankel, Director

COURTS

Family Court **845.794.3000**
Fax 845.794.0199
    100 North St, County Government Center,
    Monticello, NY 12701
    Christina Benson, Probation Director

POLICE AND SHERIFF

Sheriff's Ofc **845.794.7100**
Fax 845.794.0810
E-mail .... michael.schiff@co.fullidan.ny.us
    8 Bushnell Ave, Monticello, NY 12701
    Michael A. Schiff, Sheriff

Tioga County

SOCIAL SERVICES

Social Svcs **607.687.8300**
Fax 607.687.8093
    State Route 38, Owego, NY 13827
    Gail Barton, Services Director

GENERAL HEALTH SERVICES

Health Dept **607.687.8600**
Fax 607.687.2916
Web .... www.tiogacounty.ny.com
E-mail .... peetersh@co.tioga.ny.us
    1062 State Route 38, Owego, NY 13827
    Johannes A Peters, Public Health Director

MENTAL HEALTH SERVICES

Mental Hygiene **607.687.0200**
Fax 607.687.0248
Web .... www.co.tioga.ny.us
    1062 State Rt 38, Owego, NY 13827
    Sue Romanczuk, Director Of Community Services

JUSTICE AGENCY

Probation Dept **607.687.8535**
Fax 607.687.0804
Web .... www.co.tioga.ny.us
E-mail .... bennettj@co.tioga.ny.us
    20 Court St Ste 1, Owego, NY 13827-1515
    Joy Bennett, Director

COURTS

Family Court **607.687.1730**
Fax 607.687.3240
    20 Court St, Owego, NY 13827
    Sgueglia Vincent, Honorable Judge

Tompkins County

SOCIAL SERVICES

Social Svcs **607.274.5252**
Fax 607.274.5673
Web .... www.co.tompkins.ny.us
    320 W State St, Ithaca, NY 14850-5432
    Maryanne Banks, Children Services Director

GENERAL HEALTH SERVICES

Health Dept **607.274.6674**
Fax 607.274.6680
Web .... www.tompkins-co.org
    55 Brown Rd, Ithaca, NY 14850
    Brenda Crosby, Administrator

Health Dept **607.274.6600**
Fax 607.274.6620
Web .... www.tompkins-co.org
    55 Brown Rd, Ithaca, NY 14850
    Allison Rice, Hiv Coordinator

MENTAL HEALTH SERVICES

Mental Health Svcs **607.274.6300**
Fax 607.274.6316
Web .... www.tompkins-co.org
    201 E Green St, Ithaca, NY 14850-5635
    Robert Deluca, Csw, Commissioner

COURTS

Family Court **607.277.1517**
Fax 607.277.5027
E-mail .... jsherman@courts.state.ny.us
    320 N Tioga St, Ithaca, NY 14850-4206
    Honorable M. John Sherman, Director

POLICE AND SHERIFF

Sheriff's Ofc **607.257.1345**
Fax 607.266.5436
Web .... www.tompkins-co.org
    779 Warren Rd, Ithaca, NY 14850-1255
    Peter J Meskill, Sheriff

EDUCATION SERVICES

Caroline After School Program **607.539.7422**
    2439 Slaterville Rd, Slaterville Springs, NY 14881
    Nancy Helms, Director

Dryden Head Start **607.844.4490**
Fax 607.844.4354
    3 Farmhouse, Dryden, NY 13053
    Jennifer Citron, Director

Ulster County

SOCIAL SERVICES

Social Svcs **845.334.5000**
Fax 845.334.5301
E-mail .... marijane.knudsen@co.ulster.ny.us
    667 Ulster Ave, Kingston, NY 12401-1959
    Marijane Knudsen, Assistance Director

GENERAL HEALTH SERVICES

Health Dept **845.340.3150**
Fax 845.340.3086
Web .... www.co.ulster.ny.us
    300 Flatbush Ave, Kingston, NY 12401-2740
    Lamar Hasbrouck, Public Health Director

MENTAL HEALTH SERVICES

Mental Health Dept **845.883.9747**
Fax 845.883.9751
    560 Route 299 E, Highland, NY 12528
    Bruce Barrick, Director

Mental Health Dept **845.647.3266**
Fax 845.647.1103
    50 Center St, Ellenville, NY 12428-1315
    Bruce Barrick, Director

Mental Health Svcs 845.340.4000
Fax 845.340.4094
E-mail ....mbec@co.ulster.ny.us
   239 Golden Hill Ln, Kingston, NY 12401-6441
Lamar Hansberg, Director

JUSTICE AGENCY

Probation Dept 845.340.3200
Fax 845.340.3220
   733 Broadway, Kingston, NY 12401
Melanie Mullins, Director

Youth Bureau 845.334.5264
Fax 845.334.5587
Web ....www.co.ulster.ny.us
E-mail ....afoy@co.ulster.ny.us
   304 Flacbush Ave, Kingston, NY 12401-1953
Arlene Foy Reynolds, Director

COURTS

Ellenville Youth Court 845.647.7080
Fax 845.647.7171
E-mail ....ellenvilleyouthcourt@yahoo.com
   2 Elping Court, Ellenville, NY 12428-1320
Charlie J. Dechon, Coordinator

Family Court 845.340.3600
Fax 845.340.3626
   16 Lucas Ave, Kingston, NY 12401
Honorable Marianne Mizel, Judge

POLICE AND SHERIFF

Sheriff's Dept 845.338.3640
Fax 845.340.3718
Web ....www.co.ulster.ny.us
E-mail ....jboc@co.ulster.ny.us
   380 Blvd, Kingston, NY 12401-6404
Paul Vanblarbum, Sheriff

Warren County

SOCIAL SERVICES

Social Svcs 518.761.6300
Fax 518.761.6314
   1340 State Route 9, Lake George, NY 92845
Sheila Weaver, Social Services Director

GENERAL HEALTH SERVICES

Public Health Nursing 518.761.6580
Fax 518.761.6422
Web ....www.co.warren.ny.us
E-mail ....jonesg@co.warren.ny.us
   1340 State Route 9, Lake George, NY 12845-3434
Ginelle Jones, Assistant Director Of Public Health

Warren Health Svcs 518.761.6415
Fax 518.761.6562
Web ....www.co.warren.ny.us
   1340 State Route 9, Lake George, NY 12845-3484
Dan Durkee, Health Education Director

MENTAL HEALTH SERVICES

Glens Falls Hospital 518.926.7100
Fax 518.926.7069
Web ....www.glensfallshospital.org
   1 Lawrence St Ste 1, Glens Falls, NY 12801-3618
Jamie Powers, Director

**Glens Falls Hospital Outpatient Mental
Health** 518.926.3210
Fax 518.926.3215
Web ....www.glensfallshospital.org
   100 Park St, Glens Falls, NY 12801
Dave Alloway, Director

JUSTICE AGENCY

Detention Home 518.793.6954
Fax 518.743.9014
   46 Gurney Ln, Queensbury, NY 12804-8250
Nancy Warnock, Director

COURTS

Family Court 518.761.6500
Fax 518.761.6230
   1340 State Route 9, Lake George, NY 12845
Timothy Breen, Judge

POLICE AND SHERIFF

Sheriff's Ofc 518.743.2500
Fax 518.743.2519
Web ....www.sheriff.co.warren.ny.us
E-mail ....wcso@sheriff.co.warren.ny.us
   1400 State Route 9, Lake George, NY 12845-3435
Larry J. Cleveland, Sheriff

Washington County

SOCIAL SERVICES

Social Svcs 518.746.2300
Fax 518.746.2360
   383 Broadway, Washington County Municipal
Center, Fort Edward, NY 12828
Karen Baker, Social Services Director

GENERAL HEALTH SERVICES

Public Health Dept 518.746.2400
Fax 518.746.2410
E-mail ....phunt@co.washington.ny.us
   415 Lower Main St, Hudson Falls, NY 12839
Patty Hunt, Public Health Director

MENTAL HEALTH SERVICES

**Warren-Washington Assoc For Mental Health
Inc** 518.747.8243
Fax 518.747.2253
Web ....www.wwamh.org
   3043 State Route 4, Hudson Falls, NY 12839-9632
Wendy Berry, Director

COURTS

Family Court 518.746.2501
Fax 518.746.2503
Web ....www.courts.state.ny.us
E-mail ....spritzker@courts.state.ny.us
   383 Broadway, Fort Edward, NY 12828
Stan L Pritzker, Director

POLICE AND SHERIFF

Sheriff's Ofc 518.746.2475
Fax 518.746.2483
Web ....www.co.washington.ny.us
E-mail ....rleclaire@co.washington.ny.us
   399 Broadway, Fort Edward, NY 12828-1021
Roger W. Leclaire, Sheriff

Wayne County

SOCIAL SERVICES

Social Svcs 315.946.4881
Fax 315.946.7581
   77 Water St, Lyons, NY 14489
Marylee Lippert, Income Maintenance Director

GENERAL HEALTH SERVICES

Public Health Dept 315.946.5749
Fax 315.946.5767
Web ....www.co.wayne.ny.us
E-mail ....lmichielson@co.wayne.ny.us
   1519 Nye Rd Ste 200, Lyons, NY 14489-9112
Dian Devlin, Public Hlth Director

JUSTICE AGENCY

Probation Dept 315.946.7448
Fax 315.946.7427
E-mail ....rstevens@co.wayne.ny.us
   7376 Route 31 Ste 1100, Lyons, NY 14489
Rick Stevens, Director

COURTS

Family Court 315.946.5420
Fax 315.946.5456
Web ....www.nycouthouse.gov
E-mail ....waynefamilycourt@courts.state.ny.us
   54 Broad St, Rm 106, Lyons, NY 14489
Honorable John B. Nefbitt, Judge

Westchester County

SOCIAL SERVICES

Dept. of Social Services 914.813.6000
Fax 914.813.6464
   100 E 1st St, Mount Vernon, NY 10550
S Natoli, Director

Peekskill 914.862.5078
Fax 914.862.5179
Web ....www.westchestergov.com
   750 Washington St, Peekskill, NY 10566
David Kingsly, Manager

Social Svcs 914.995.5000
Fax 914.995.3285
   112 E Post Rd, Fl 2, White Plains, NY 10601
Donald Wiede, Preventive Services Director

Yonkers 914.231.2000
Fax 914.231.2184
E-mail ....charles.little@cityofyonkers.com
   131 Wardurton Ave, Yonkers, NY 10701
Charles Little, Manager

GENERAL HEALTH SERVICES

Dept Of Health 914.813.5000
Fax 914.813.5014
   145 Huguenot St Fl 8, New Rochelle, NY 10801
*Caren Halbfinger, Director Of Health Education And Public
Information*

MENTAL HEALTH SERVICES

Mental Health Dept 914.995.5220
Fax 914.995.4265
Web ....www.westchestergov.com
   112 E Post Rd Ste 219, White Plains, NY 10601-5113
Grant Mitchell, Commissioner

JUSTICE AGENCY

Mount Vernon Probation 914.813.7933
Fax 914.813.7922
   24 S 3rd Ave, Mount Vernon, NY 10550
Steven Haight, Supervisor

Probation Dept 914.995.3500
Fax 914.995.6261
   111 Dr Martin Luther King Blvd Fl 7, White Plains,
NY 10601
Rocco A. Pozzi, Commissioner Of Probation

Woodfield Cottage 914.231.1103
Fax 914.231.1148
E-mail ....althomas@leakeandwatts.org
   20 Hammond House Rd, Valhalla, NY 10595
Al Thomas, Program Director

Yonkers Probation 914.231.2900
Fax 914.231.2906
Web ....www.cityofyonkers.com
E-mail ....richard.localio@cityofyonkers.com
   53 S Broadway, Fl 2, Yonkers, NY 10701
Richard Localio, Supervisor, Family Court Probation

Youth Bureau 914.654.2045
Fax 914.654.2046
Web ....www.newrochelleny.com
E-mail ....kjohnson@newrochelleny.com
   515 North Ave, New Rochelle, NY 10801-3405
Kelly Johnson, Executive Director

New York

COURTS

Family Court.....................**914.824.5500**
Fax.....................914.995.8647
　111 Dr Martin Luther King Blvd, White Plains, NY 10601
　Honorable Kathy E. Davidson, Supervising Judge

POLICE AND SHERIFF

Mount Vernon Police Dept..................**914.665.2534**
Fax.....................914.665.2571
　2 Roosevelt Sq, Mount Vernon, NY 10550-2061
　Lt. Adinara, Detective Supervisor

New Rochelle Police Dept...................**914.654.2300**
Fax.....................914.632.0249
　475 North Ave, New Rochelle, NY 10801
　Patrick J. Carroll, Commissioner

Westchester Sheriff Dept...................**914.995.3053**
Fax.....................914.995.4095
E-mail.....................teb1@westchestergov.com
　110 Dr Martin Luther King Blvd Ste L217, White Plains, NY 10601
　Thomas Belfoire, Commissioner

White Plains Police Dept...................**914.422.6111**
Fax.....................914.422.6314
　77 S Lexington Ave, White Plains, NY 10601
　James Bradley, Chief Executive Officer

Yonkers Police Dept.....................**914.377.7293**
Fax.....................914.377.7295
　127 N Broadway, Yonkers, NY 10701
　Captain Cave, Head Chief

EDUCATION SERVICES

Special Education.....................**914.245.0010**
Fax.....................914.245.2952
Web.....................www.vesid.nysed.gov
E-mail.....................christineafner@mail.nysed.gov
　1950 Edgewater St, Yorktown Heights, NY 10598
　Christine Afner, Supervisor

Wyoming County

SOCIAL SERVICES

Ofc on Aging.....................**585.786.8833**
Fax.....................585.786.8832
E-mail.....................aproper@wyomingco.net
　8 Perry Ave, Warsaw, NY 14569
　Angie Proper, Deputy Director

Social Svcs.....................**585.786.8900**
Fax.....................585.786.8927
　2410 R19 S, Warsaw, NY 14569
　David Ramsey, Commissioner

GENERAL HEALTH SERVICES

Health Dept.....................**585.786.8890**
Fax.....................585.786.3537
E-mail.....................CMIRDY@WYOMINGCO.NET
　5362 Mungers Mill Rd, Silver Springs, NY 14550
　Cathy Mirdy, Director Of Patient Services

MENTAL HEALTH SERVICES

Mental Health.....................**585.786.8871**
Fax.....................585.786.8874
Web.....................www.wyomingco.net
E-mail.....................ssnell@wyomingco.net
　338 N Main St, Warsaw, NY 14569-1045
　Stephen Snell, Csw-r, Mental Health Director

COURTS

Family Court.....................**585.786.3148**
Fax.....................585.786.3800
Web.....................www.courts.state.ny.us
　147 N Main St, Warsaw, NY 14569-1123
　Honorable Michael F. Griffith, Director

POLICE AND SHERIFF

Sheriff's Dept.....................**585.786.8989**
Fax.....................585.786.8961
Web.....................www.wyomingco.net
　151 N Main St, Warsaw, NY 14569-1123
　Farris Heimann, Sheriff

Yates County

GENERAL HEALTH SERVICES

Public Health.....................**315.536.5160**
Fax.....................315.536.5145
Web.....................www.yatescounty.org
E-mail.....................dminor@yatescounty.org
　417 Liberty St Ste 2120, Penn Yan, NY 14527-1124
　Deborah Minor, Dph, Director Of Public Health

JUSTICE AGENCY

Probation Dept.....................**315.536.5155**
Fax.....................315.536.5508
　415 Liberty St, Penn Yan, NY 14527
　Sharon Dawes, Probation Director

COURTS

Family Court.....................**315.536.5127**
Fax.....................315.536.5190
　415 Liberty St, Penn Yan, NY 14527
　Honorable W. Patrick Falvey, Judge

POLICE AND SHERIFF

Sheriff's Dept.....................**315.536.5172**
Fax.....................315.536.5191
Web.....................www.yatescountysheriff.org
E-mail.....................sheriff@yatescountysheriff.org
　227 Main St, Penn Yan, NY 14527-1719
　Ronald G. Spike, Sheriff

SPECIAL SERVICES AGENCIES

ADOPTION AGENCIES

Adoption Annex.....................**516.385.6171**
Web.....................www.adoptionannex.org
　100 Quentin Roosevelt Blvd Ste 103, Garden City, NY 11530-4843

Adoption S.T.A.R. (Support, Training, Advocacy And Resources), Inc......................**716.639.3900**
Fax.....................716.639.3700
Web.....................www.adoptionstar.com
E-mail.....................info@adoptionstar.com
　47 Plaza Dr, Buffalo, NY 14221-2335
　Michelle Fried, Director

Adoptive Parents Committee Inc...........**516.223.9584**
Web.....................www.adoptiveparents.org
E-mail.....................apcli@hotmail.com
　44 Linden St, Massapequa, NY 11758-5126
　Triston, Director

Baker Victory Svcs.....................**716.828.9500**
Fax.....................716.828.9798
Web.....................www.ourladyofvictory.org
E-mail.....................npal1653342@aol.com
　780 Ridge Rd, Buffalo, NY 14218-1629
　Nancy Pankow, Director

Bethany Christian Services.....................**518.371.1336**
Fax.....................518.371.4262
Web.....................www.bethany.org
　2 Crestmont Dr, Clifton Park, NY 12065
　Cindy Fabozzi, Director

Bethany Christian Svcs.....................**585.288.6760**
　969 Monroe Ave, Rochester, NY 14620
　Nancy Dykstra, Director

Bethany Christian Svcs.....................**212.714.3550**
Fax.....................201.703.4376
Web.....................www.bethany.org/manhattan_ny
E-mail.....................bcsmanhattan@bethany.org
　292 5th Ave, Ste 421, New York, NY 10001
　Nancy Dykstra-powers, Director

Bethany Christian Svcs.....................**845.987.1453**
Fax.....................201.444.5420
Web.....................www.bethany.org/warwickny
E-mail.....................bcswarwickny@bethany.org
　16 Maple Ave, Warwick, NY 10990-1027
　Nancy Dykstra-powers, Director

Child & Family Adoption.....................**845.691.4520**
　102 Vineyard Ave, Highland, NY 12528

Child Development Support Corporation......**718.398.2050**
Fax.....................718.230.0112
Web.....................www.cdscny.org
　352-358 Classon Ave, Brooklyn, NY 11238
　Marcia Riddick, Executive Director

Children At Heart Adoption Svcs Inc..........**518.664.5988**
Fax.....................518.664.1220
Web.....................www.childrenatheart.com
E-mail.....................cahadoptions@aol.com
　145 N Main St, Mechanicville, NY 12118-1619
　Janice Bergeron, Director

Children Of The World.....................**516.935.1235**
Fax.....................516.933.8532
Web.....................www.cwaany.org
E-mail.....................herscovici77@yahoo.com
　27 Hillvale Rd, Syosset, NY 11791-6916
　Justin Herscovici, Director

Edwin Gould Academy.....................**212.828.2173**
Fax.....................212.828.1076
Web.....................www.edwingouldacademy.org
E-mail.....................jgolden@edwingouldacademy.org
　55 E 110th St, New York, NY 10029
　Jim Golden, Director

Family Connections.....................**607.756.6574**
Fax.....................607.756.0373
Web.....................www.adoptfamilyconnections.org
E-mail.....................info@adoptfamilyconnectoins.org
　156 Port Watson St, Cortland, NY 13045
　Anita Stevens, Executive Director

Family Focus Adoption Svcs.................**718.224.1919**
Fax.....................718.225.8360
E-mail.....................ffasmaris@familyfocusadoption.org
　5440 Little Neck Pkwy Ste 4, Little Neck, NY 11362-2205
　Maris Blechner, Executive Director

Graham Windham.....................**212.529.6445**
Fax.....................212.614.9811
Web.....................www.graham-windham.org
　33 Irving Place, New York, NY 10003
　COA accredited organization.

Harlem-Dowling Children's Svcs.............**212.749.3656**
Fax.....................212.678.1094
Web.....................www.harlemdowling.org
E-mail.....................dworrell@harlemdowling.org
　2090 Adam Clayton Powell Jr Blvd Fl 3, New York, NY 10027-4992
　Dorthy Worrell, Director

Hillside Children's Ctr 716.848.6400
Fax 716.848.6424
Web ....www.hillside.com
131 Orchard Park Rd, Buffalo, NY 14224
Jeff Ribbeck, Clinical Mentor

Hillside Children's Ctr 716.439.5400
Fax 716.439.5430
Web ....www.hillside.com
E-mail ....bbirkmeyer@hillside.com
66 Stevens St, Lockport, NY 14094-4230
Bonnie Birkmeyer, Director

Hillside Childrens Svcs 585.786.5900
Fax 585.786.3937
96 W Buffalo St, Warsaw, NY 14569
John Myer, Service Leader

Jewish Child Care Association 212.558.9900
Fax 212.558.9991
Web ....www.jccany.org
120 Wall Street, 12th Floor, New York, NY 10005
COA accredited organization.

Liberty Resources, Inc....................315.425.1004
Fax 315.479.7884
Web ....www.liberty-resources.org
E-mail ....info@liberty-resources.org
1045 James St Ste 100, Syracuse, NY 13202
Carl M. Coyle, Executive Director

Little Flower Children And Family Svcs 631.929.6200
Fax 631.929.6121
Web ....www.littleflowerny.org
E-mail ....lograndg@lfchild.org
2450 N Wading River Rd, Wading River,
NY 11792-1402
Grace Logrande, Executive Director

Salvation Army Foster Home 212.807.6100
Fax 212.620.3096
Web ....www.use.salvationarmy.org
E-mail ....susan_pope@use.salvationarmy.org
132 W 14th St, New York, NY 10011-7301
Susan Pope, Assistant Director

Scarsdale § Edgemont Family Counseling
Service 914.723.3281
Fax 914.725.6046
Web ....www.sfcsinc.org
14 Harwood Court, Suite 405, Scarsdale, NY 10583
COA accredited organization.

Seamen's Society For Children And
Families 718.313.1111
Fax 718.313.1657
E-mail ....nancy@roots-wings.org
57 Willoughby St Ste 3, Brooklyn, NY 11201-5255
Nancy Vamaro, President/CEO

Seamen's Society For Children And Families (Administrative
Ofc) 718.447.7740
Fax 718.720.2321
E-mail ....jerry@roots-wings.org
50 Bay St, Staten Island, NY 10301-2511
Nancy Vonlermo, President/CEO

Spence-Chapin Services to Families and
Children 212.369.0300
Fax 212.369.8589
Web ....www.spence-chapin.org
410 East 92nd Street, New York, NY 10128
COA accredited organization.

St. Christopher Ottilie 718.935.9466
Fax 718.237.2778
Web ....www.st-christopher-ottilie.org
E-mail ....cwagner@svdprvc.org
570 Fulton St, Brooklyn, NY 11217
Carmen Wagner, Director

The ABSW Child Adoption, Counseling And Referral
Svc 212.831.5181
Fax 212.831.5350
E-mail ....abswnyc@aol.com
1969 Madison Ave, New York, NY 10035
Gloria Scott, President

Therapeutic Foster Boarding Home
Program 845.344.3166
390 Crystal Run Rd, Middletown, NY 10941
Jene Cavanaugh, Director

V.I.D.A. Voice For International Development And
Adoptions 518.828.4527
Fax 518.828.0688
Web ....www.vidaadopt.org
E-mail ....vidaadopt@aol.com
354 Allen St, Hudson, NY 12534-2440
Deguerre A. Blackburn, Phd, Acsw, Executive Director

ADVOCACY RESOURCES

Admin for Children's Svcs 212.442.3030
E-mail ....regina.schaefer@dfa.state.ny.us
150 William St, New York, NY 10038
Regina Schaefer

Brooklyn Borough President 718.802.3700
E-mail ....askmarty@brooklynnbp.nyc.gov
209 Joralemon St, Brooklyn, NY 11201
Marty Markowitz, President

Burnham Youth Safe Ctr 518.781.3785
Fax 518.781.3787
13640 State Route 22, Canaan, NY 12029-3504
Donelle Hauser, Coordinator

Carmella House 518.439.7327
Fax 518.436.6616
121 Waldenmaier Rd, Feura Bush, NY 12067-1830
Sherlyn Costa, Program Supervisor

Child Abuse Prevention Ctr 845.454.0595
Fax 845.454.0129
Web ....www.preventchildabusedutchess.net/firms
E-mail ....kmurphy@thecpca.com
249 Hooker Ave, Poughkeepsie, NY 12603-3327
Kathline Murphy, Exec. Director

Child Advocacy Ctr 845.808.1400
Fax 845.808.1926
E-mail ....cac@putnamcounty.ny.gov
121 Main St, Brewster, NY 10509
Marla Behler, Coordinator

Child Advocacy Ctr 315.732.3990
Fax 315.732.2804
E-mail ....oneidacac@yahoo.com
930 York St, Utica, NY 13502-3930
Jim Brognano, Grade A Supervisor

Child Advocacy Ctr Of Niagara 716.285.0045
Fax 716.285.8991
Web ....www.cacofniagara.org
E-mail ....laura.kelemen@nfmmc.org
501 10th St, Niagara Falls, NY 14301
Laura Kelemen, Executive Director

Child Welfare Organization Project 212.348.3000
E-mail ....mikearsham@aol.com
80 E 110th St # 1E, New York, NY 10029
Sabra Jackson, Manager

Children's Advocacy Ctr 716.886.5437
Fax 716.886.5888
556 Franklin St, Buffalo, NY 14202
Judith Olin, Csw, Director

Children's Ctr 585.753.5940
Fax 585.753.5939
355 Westfall Rd, Rochester, NY 14620
Michael Marinan, Director

Children's Rights 212.683.2210
E-mail ....evargas@childrensrights.org
330 7th Ave 4gh Fl, New York, NY 10001
Susan Lambiase, Executive Director

Children's Rights Inc 212.683.2210
E-mail ....mcohen@childrensrights.org
330 7th Ave, 4th Fl, New York, NY 10001
Melissa Cohen, Attorney

Childrens Defense Fund - New York 212.697.2323
Fax 212.697.0566
15 Maiden Ln Ste 1200, New York, NY 10038
Rev. Emma Jordan-Simpson, Director

Emmett House 518.462.0516
Fax 518.462.0479
593 River Rd, Glenmont, NY 12077
Wayne Burt, Program Supervisor

Evan B. Donaldson Adoption Institute 212.925.4089
Fax 775.796.6592
Web ....www.adoptioninstitute.org
E-mail ....info@adoptioninstitute.org
120 E 38th St, New York, NY 10016-2602
Adam Pertman, Executive Director

Girls Education & Mentoring 212.926.8089
E-mail ....info@gems-girls.org
2988 W 149th St, New York, NY 10039
Rachel Lloyd, Executive Director

Hope For Youth 631.841.1650
Fax 631.841.2765
E-mail ....sodonnahue@hfyny.org
366 Broadway, Brunswick Hospital Center, Bldg 5,
Amityville, NY 11701-2711
Suzanne O'donnahue, Director

House Of The Good Shepherd 315.733.6537
Fax 315.798.9022
Web ....www.hgs-utica.com
1606 Sunset Ave, Utica, NY 13502-5404
Ted Wheelock, Program Director

Justice For Children Advocacy Ctr 585.344.8576
Fax 585.344.8586
E-mail ....cmmarvel@rochester.rr.com
108 Bank St, Batavia, NY 14020-2216
Colleen Marvel, Coordinator

Legal Aid Bureau of Buffalo 716.853.9555
237 Main St Ste 1602, Buffalo, NY 14203
Jeffrey Piore, Director

Legal Aid Bureau of Buffalo Inc 716.853.9555
E-mail ....chalvorsen@legalaidbuffalo.org
237 Main St, Buffalo, NY 14203
Charles Halvorsen

Legal Aid Society 718.298.8900
E-mail ....jjrao@legal-aid.org
153-01 Jamaica Ave 3rd Fl, Jamaica Estates,
NY 11432
Jess Rao, Attorney

Legal Aid Society 718.250.4274
E-mail ....vphillips@legal-aid.org
111 Livingston St 8th Fl, Brooklyn, NY 11201
Vincent Phillips

Legal Aid Society 212.312.2260
E-mail ....lntrentacosti@legal-aid.org
60 Lafayette St Rm 9A, New York, NY 10013
Lisa Trentacosti, Socialworker

Legal Aid Society for Juvenile Rights
Practice 718.579.7900
E-mail ....sfbodack@legal-aid.org
900 Sheridan Ave Room 6C-12, Bronx, NY 10451
Sarah Bodack, Manager

Legal Aid Society for Juvenile Rights
Practice 718.579.7974
E-mail ....eblue@legal-aid.org
900 Sheridan Ave Room 6C-12, Bronx, NY 10451
Evanjeline Blue

Legal Aid Society for Juvenile Rights
Practice **718.298.8900**
E-mail ....nbowler@legal-aid.org
153-01 Jamaica Ave 3rd Flr, Jamaica Estates,
NY 11432
Norah Bowler, Attorney

Legal Aid Society for Juvenile Rights
Practice **212.312.2260**
E-mail ....mfayora@legal-aid.org
60 Lafayette St Room 9A, New York, NY 10013
Yvonne Hobbs, Office Manager

Legal Aid Society for Juvenile Rights
Practice **212.312.2260**
E-mail ....rbelnavis@legal-aid.org
60 Lafayette St Rm 9A, New York, NY 10013
Connie Belnavis, Support Specialist

Legal Aid Society for Juvenile Rights
Practice **718.579.7900**
E-mail ....jadiamon@legal-aid.org
900 Sheridan Ave Room 6C-12, Bronx, NY 10451
Jesse Diamond, Attorney

Legal Aid Society for Juvenile Rights
Practice **212.312.2260**
E-mail ....amscalia@legal-aid.org
60 Lafayette St Room 9A, New York, NY 10013
Ann Marie Scalia, Judge

Legal Aid Society for Juvenile Rights
Practice **212.312.2260**
60 Lafayette St Room 9A, New York, NY 10013
Nanette Schrandt, Director Jsu

Legal Aid Society for Juvenile Rights
Practice **718.237.3100**
E-mail ....kballinger@legal-aid.org
111 Livingston St 8th Flr, New York, NY 10101
Kelly Ballinger, Law Guardian

Legal Aid Society for Juvenile Rights
Practice **718.237.3100**
E-mail ....pcbirnberg@legal-aid.org
111 Livingston St 8th Flr, Brooklyn, NY 11201
Paula Birnberg, Attorney

Legal Aid Society for Juvenile Rights
Practice **212.312.2260**
E-mail ....bgacunis@legal-aid.org
60 Lafayette St Room 9A, New York, NY 10013
Benji Acunis, Attorney

Legal Aid Society for Juvenile Rights
Practice **718.579.7900**
E-mail ....legalaidsociety@legal-aid.org
900 Sheridan Ave Room 6C-12, Bronx, NY 10451
Don Mitchell, County Incharge

Legal Aid Society for Juvenile Rights
Practice **212.312.2260**
60 Lafayette St Room 9A, New York, NY 10013
Annemarie Scalia, Director

Legal Aid Society for Juvenile Rights
Practice **718.237.3100**
111 Livingston St 8th Flr, Brooklyn, NY 11201
Robert Stevenson, Office Manager

Legal Aid Society for Juvenile Rights
Practice **718.298.8900**
E-mail ....lkavgente@legal-air.org
153-01 Jamaica Ave 3rd Flr, Jamaica Estates,
NY 11432
Lynda Avgente, Attorney Supervisor

Legal Aid Society for Juvenile Rights
Practice **212.312.2260**
60 Lafayette St Room 9A, NEW YORK, NY 10013
Ada Dicarlo, Parrel Legal

Legal Aid Society for Juvenile Rights
Practice **718.237.3100**
E-mail ....anarmstrong@legal-aid.org
111 Livingston St 8th Flr, Brooklyn, NY 11201
Andrea Armstrong

Legal Aid Society for Juvenile Rights
Practice **212.312.2260**
E-mail ....DMEwell@legal-aid.org
60 Lafayette St Room 9A, New York, NY 10013
Jeanne Barenholtz, Director

Legal Aid Society for Juvenile Rights
Practice **212.312.2260**
E-mail ....ascaliat@legal-aid.org
60 Lafayette St Room 9A, New York, NY 10013
Annmarie Scalia, Director

Legal Aid Society Juvenile **718.579.7900**
E-mail ....kfcalabrese@legal-aid.org
900 Sheridan Ave Rm 6C-12, Bronx, NY 10470
Kristen Calabrese, Manager

Legal Aid Society Juvenile Rights Practice **718.579.7900**
900 Sheridan Ave Rm 6C-12, Bronx, NY 10451
Dawne Mitchell, Attorney Incharge

Legal Aid Society Juvenile Rights Practice **718.579.7900**
E-mail ....dmitchell@legal-aid.org
900 Sheridan Ave Rm 6c-12, Bronx, NY 10451
Dawn Mitchell, Attorney

Legal Aid Society Juvenile Rights Practice **718.579.7900**
E-mail ....sasuckoo@legal-aid.org
900 Sheridan Ave Rm 6C-12, Bronx, NY 10450
Stacy Suckoo

Legal Aid Society Juvenile Rights Practice **718.579.7900**
E-mail ....rlstegman@legal-aid.org
900 Sheridan Ave Rm 6C-12, Bronx, NY 10451
Rebecca Stegman, Director

Legal Aid Society Juvenile Rights Practice **212.312.2341**
E-mail ....amscalia@legal-aid.org
60 Lafayette St Rm 9A, New York, NY 10013
Annmarie Scalia, Director

Legal Aid Society Juvenile Rights Practice **212.312.2260**
E-mail ....rfmittler@legal-aid.org
60 Lafayette St Rm 9A, New York, NY 10013
Renee Mittler, Supervisor

Legal Aid Society Juvenile Rights Practice **718.981.3253**
E-mail ....lhferng@legal-aid.org
60 Bay St 2nd Fl, Staten Island, NY 10301
Joan Ferng

Legal Aid Society Juvenile Rights Practice **212.312.2260**
E-mail ....annmariescalia@legal-aid.org
60 Lafayette St Rm 9A, New York, NY 10013
Annmarie Scalia, County Incharge

Legal Aid Society Juvenile Rights Practice **718.579.7900**
E-mail ....joweedle@legal-aid.org
900 Sheridan Ave Rm 6C-12, Bronx, NY 10451
Jamien Weddle

Legal Aid Society Juvenile Rights Practice **718.237.3100**
E-mail ....lrkatzman@legal-aid.org
111 Livingston St 8th Fl, Brooklyn, NY 11201
Lauren Katzman, Director

Legal Aid Society Juvenile Rights Practice **718.237.3100**
E-mail ....khourya@staff.abanet.org
111 Livingston St 8th Fl, Brooklyn, NY 11201
Dena Kesselman, Director

Legal Aid Society Juvenile Rights Practice **718.237.3100**
E-mail ....pipetrakopoulos@legal-aid.org
111 Livingston St 8th Fl, Brooklyn, NY 11201
Polixene Petrakopoulos, Attorney

Legal Aid Society Juvenile Rights Practice **718.298.8900**
153-01 Jamaica Ave 3rd Fl, Jamaica Estates,
NY 11432
Melinda Fraser, Office-manager

Legal Aid Society Juvenile Rights Practice **718.517.3420**
E-mail ....mlthomas@legal-aid.org
153-01 Jamaica Ave 3rd Fl, Jamaica Estates,
NY 11432
Megan Thomas

Legal Aid Society Juvenile Rights Practice **646.340.1912**
E-mail ....jxnewton@legal-aid.org
111 Livingston St 8th Fl, Brooklyn, NY 11201
Jack Newton

Legal Aid Society Juvenile Rights Practice **212.577.3300**
E-mail ....tbmoser@legal-aid.org
199 Water St 3rd Fl, New York, NY 10038
Teresa Moser

Legal Aid Society Juvenile Rights Practice **718.237.4527**
E-mail ....ecate@legal-aid.org
111 Livingston St 8th Fl, Brooklyn, NY 11201
Elizabeth Cate

Legal Aid Society Juvenile Rights Practice **212.577.3300**
E-mail ....cvmerkine@legal-aid.org
199 Water St 3rd Fl, New York, NY 10038
Clair Merkine

Legal Aid Society Juvenile Rights Practice **212.577.3300**
E-mail ....cachambers@legal-aid.org
199 Water St 3rd Fl, New York, NY 10038
Cara Chambers, Supervisor

Legal Aid Society Juvenile Rights Practice **212.312.2280**
E-mail ....kameyer@legal-aid.org
60 Lafayette St, Rm 9A, New York, NY 10013
Katherine Meyer

Legal Aid Society Juvenile Rights Practice **718.237.3100**
E-mail ....brgoldstein@legal-aid.org
111 Livingston St 8th Fl, Brooklyn, NY 11201
Byrin Goldstein

Legal Aid Society Juvenile Rights Practice **718.237.3100**
E-mail ....mfmeltzer@legal-aid.org
111 Livingston St 8th Fl, Brooklyn, NY 11201
Molly Frank-Meltzer

Legal Aid Society Juvenile Rights Practice **212.577.3300**
199 Water St 3rd Fl, New York, NY 10038
Steven Banks, Attorney In Chief

Legal Aid Society Juvenile Rights Practice **212.312.2260**
60 Lafayette St Rm 9A, New York, NY 10013
Annmarie Scalia, Attorney In Charge

Legal Aid Society Juvenile Rights Practice **718.517.3420**
E-mail ....jlebright@legal-aid.org
153-01 Jamaica Ave 3rd Fl, Jamaica Estates,
NY 11432
Joann Lebright

Legal Aid Society Juvenile Rights Practice **718.250.3100**
E-mail ....lamasco@legal-aid.org
111 Livingston St 8th Fl, Brooklyn, NY 11201
Lori Masco

Legal Aid Society Juvenile Rights Practice **718.237.3100**
E-mail ....sshandhari@legal-aid.org
111 Livingston St 8th Fl, Brooklyn, NY 11201
Sandeep Kandhari, Manager

Legal Aid Society Juvenile Rights Practice **718.579.7900**
E-mail ....bjstock@legal-aid.org
900 Sheridan Ave Rm 6C-12, Bronx, NY 10451
John Mitchell, Attorney In Charge

Legal Aid Society Juvenile Rights Practice **212.577.3300**
E-mail ....lfreeman@legal-aid.org
199 Water St 3rd Fl, New York, NY 10038
Lisa Freeman, Attorney

Legal Aid Society Juvenile Rights Practice **212.312.2260**
E-mail ....amscalia@legal-aid.org
60 Lafayette St Rm 9A, New York, NY 10013
Ann Scalia, Supervisor

Legal Aid Society Juvenile Rights Practice **718.517.3420**
E-mail ....mrduprey@legal-aid.org
153-01 Jamaica Ave 3rd Fl, Jamaica, NY 11432
Michelle Duprey, Attorney

New York

Legal Aid Society Juvenile Rights Practice 718.579.7900
E-mail ....mljacobs@legal-aid.org
900 Sheridan Ave Rm 6C-12, Bronx, NY 10451
Michelle Jacobs, Attorney

Legal Aid Society Juvenile Rights Practice 718.237.3100
E-mail ....amdicorleto@legal-aid.org
111 Livingston St 8th Fl, Brooklyn, NY 11201
Angela Dicorleto, Attorney Officer

Legal Aid Society Juvenile Rights Practice 718.298.8900
E-mail ....gmhesser@legal-aid.org
153-01 Jamaica Ave 3rd Fl, Jamaica, NY 11432
Gwyneth Hesser, Attorney

Legal Aid Society Juvenile Rights Practice 212.577.3399
E-mail ....lmclarke@legal-aid.org
199 Water St 3rd Fl, New York, NY 10038
Lucinda Clarke

Legal Aid Society Juvenile Rights Practice 212.312.2260
E-mail ....amscalia@legalaid.org
60 Lafayette St Rm 9A, New York, NY 10013
Ann Marie Scalia, Director

Legal Aid Society Juvenile Rights Practice 212.312.2260
E-mail ....egpark@legal-aid.org
60 Lafayette St Rm 9A, New York, NY 10013
Grace Park, Attorney

Legal Aid Society Juvenile Rights Practice 718.579.7900
E-mail ....ajhulkower@legal-aid.org
900 Sheridan Ave Rm 6C-12, Bronx, NY 10457
Adira Hulkower

Legal Aid Society Juvenile Rights Practice 718.579.7929
E-mail ....cmolina@legal-aid.org
900 Sheridan Ave, Bronx, NY 10451
Cesar Molina

Legal Aid Society Juvenile Rights Practice 718.579.7900
E-mail ....bspray@legal-aid.org
900 Sheridan Ave Rm 6C-12, Bronx, NY 10451
Bethany Pray, Manager

Legal Aid Society Juvenile Rights Practice 212.312.2260
E-mail ....amscalia@legal-aid.org
60 Lafayette St Rm 9A, New York, NY 10013
Annmarie Scalia, Director

Legal Aid Society Juvenile Rights Practice 718.298.3420
E-mail ....drterry@legal-aid.org
153-01 Jamaica Ave 3rd Fl, Jamaica Estates, NY 11432
Dodd Terry

Legal Aid Society Juvenile Rights Practice 718.298.8910
E-mail ....bperry@legal-aid.org
153-01 Jamaica Ave 3rd Fl, Jamaica Estates, NY 11432
Bob Perry, Attorney

Legal Aid Society Juvenile Rights Practice 718.579.7900
E-mail ....alkirwan@legal-aid.org
900 Sheridan Ave Rm 6C-12, Bronx, NY 10451
Antoinette Kirwan, Director

Legal Aid Society Juvenile Rights Practice 718.517.3420
E-mail ....sclawson@legal-aid.org
153-01 Jamaica Ave 3rd Fl, Jamaica Estates, NY 11432
Simone Lawson

Legal Aid Society Juvenile Rights Practice 718.579.7900
E-mail ....jmcrafton@legal-aid.org
900 Sheridan Ave Rm 6C-12, Bronx, NY 10451
Jessica Crafton, Attorney Officer

Legal Aid Society Juvenile Rights Practice 718.237.3100
E-mail ....aperahia@legal-aid.org
111 Livingston St 8th Fl, Brooklyn, NY 11432
Arthur Perahia, Lawyer

Legal Aid Society Juvenile Rights Practice 212.312.2260
E-mail ....amscalia@legal-aid.org
60 Lafayette St, NEWYORK, NY 10013
Ann Marie Scalia, Director

Legal Aid Society Juvenile Rights Practice 718.237.3100
E-mail ....abserlin@legal-aid.org
111 Livingston St 8th Fl, Brooklyn, NY 11201
Amy Serlin, Attorney

Legal Aid Society Juvenile Rights Practice 718.527.3402
E-mail ....eskaplan@legal-aid.org
153-01 Jamaica Ave 3rd Fl, Jamaica, NY 11432
Emily Kaplan

Legal Aid Society Juvenile Rights Practice 718.579.7900
E-mail ....lgdelplato@legal-aid.org
900 Sheridan Ave Rm 6C-12, Bronx, NY 10451
Lina Delplato, Attorney

Legal Aid Society Juvenile Rights Practice 212.312.2260
E-mail ....azzarrabi@legal-aid.org
60 Lafayette St Rm 9A, New York, NY 10013
Azaden Zarrabi, Lawyer

Legal Aid Society Juvenile Rights Practice 212.577.3300
E-mail ....mesopher@legal-aid.org
199 Water St 3rd Fl, New York, NY 10038
Meredith Sopher, Attorney

Legal Aid Society Juvenile Rights Practice 718.237.3100
E-mail ....lmmaslauskas@legal-aid.org
111 Livingston St 8th Fl, Brooklyn, NY 11201
Laura Maslauskas, Director

Legal Aid Society Juvenile Rights Practice 212.577.3520
E-mail ....ahausknecht@legal-aid.org
199 Water St 3rd Fl, New York, NY 10013
Amy Hausknecht

Legal Aid Society Juvenile Rights Practice 718.579.7900
E-mail ....jholmes@legal-aid.org
900 Sheridan Ave Rm 6C-12, Bronx, NY 10451
Jaqueline Holmes, Data-Entry

Legal Aid Society Juvenile Rights Practice 718.237.3100
E-mail ....slshaw@legal-aid.org
111 Livingston St 8th Fl, Brooklyn, NY 11201
Sophia Shaw, Paralegal Supervisor

Legal Aid Society Juvenile Rights Practice 718.579.7900
E-mail ....bethomsen@legal-aid.org
900 Sheridan Ave Rm 6C-12, Bronx, NY 10451
Bettina Thomsen, Manager

Legal Aid Society Juvenile Rights Practice 212.312.2260
E-mail ....amscalia@legal-aid.org
60 Lafayette St Rm 9A, New York, NY 10013
Annmarie Scalia, Attorney Incharge

Legal Aid Society Juvenile Rights Practice 718.237.3100
E-mail ....cswise@legal-aid.org
111 Livingston St 8th Fl, Brooklyn, NY 11201
Don Ryan, Executive Director

Legal Aid Society Juvenile Rights Practice 212.577.3300
199 Water St 3rd Fl, New York, NY 10038
Tamara Steckler, Incharge Of Juvnile Practice

Legal Aid Society Juvenile Rights Practice 718.237.3100
111 Livingston St 8th Fl, Jamaica, NY 11451
Camara Watkins, Director

Legal Aid Society Juvenile Rights Practice 212.577.3300
E-mail ....tsteckler@legal-aid.org
199 Water St 3rd Fl, New York, NY 10038
Tamara Steckler, Attorney Incharge

Legal Aid Society Juvenile Rights Practice 718.579.7900
900 Sheridan Ave Rm 6C-12, Bronx, NY 10451
Dawn Mitchell, Attorney Incharge

Legal Aid Society Juvenile Rights Practice 718.981.0219
E-mail ....rwarren@legal-aid.org
60 Bay St 2nd Fl, Staten Island, NY 10301
Rosalyn Warren

Legal Aid Society Juvenile Rights Practice 718.237.3100
E-mail ....jbchazen@legal-aid.org
111 Livingston St 8th Fl, Brooklyn, NY 11201
Jonathan Chazen, Attorney

Legal Aid Society Juvenile Rights Practice 718.237.3100
E-mail ....ramantri@legal-aid.org
111 Livingston St 8th Fl, Brooklyn, NY 11201
Resham Mantri

Legal Aid Society Juvenile Rights Practice 212.312.2260
E-mail ....amscalia@legal-aid.org
60 Lafayette St Rm 9A, New York, NY 10013
Annmarie Scalia, Incharge

Legal Aid Society Juvenile Rights Practice 212.312.2260
E-mail ....anscalia@legal-aid.org
60 Lafayette St Rm 9A, New York, NY 10013
Annmarie Scalia, Attorney Incharge

Legal Aid Society Juvenile Rights Practice 718.579.7900
E-mail ....ldasilva@legal-aid.org
900 Sheridan Ave Rm 6c-12, Bronx, NY 10451
Leah Dasilva, Attorney

Legal Aid Society Juvenile Rights Practice 718.237.3100
E-mail ....kaostheimer@legal-aid.org
111 Livingston St 8th Fl, Brooklyn, NY 11201
Kimberlee Ostheimer

Legal Aid Society Juvenile Rights Practice 718.237.3100
111 Livingston St 8th Fl, Brooklyn, NY 11201

Legal Aid Society Juvenile Rights Practice 212.577.3300
E-mail ....lswinston@legal-aid.org
199 Water St 3rd Fl, New York, NY 10038
Leslie Winston, Social Worker

Legal Aid Society Juvenile Rights Practice 718.237.3100
E-mail ....lpodemski@legal-aid.org
111 Livingston St 8th Fl, Brooklyn, NY 11201
Lisa Podemski, Attorney

Legal Aid Society Juvenile Rights Practice 212.312.2260
E-mail ....jdthomas@legal-aid.org
60 Lafayette St Rm 9A, New York, NY 10013
Jessica Thomas, Attorney

Legal Aid Society Juvenile Rights Practice 212.312.2260
E-mail ....nbmenon@legal-aid.org
60 Lafayette St Rm 9A, New York, NY 10013
Nisha Menon, Attorney

Legal Aid Society Juvenile Rights Practice 718.517.3420
E-mail ....malindafrasermm@legal-aid.org
153-01 Jamaica Ave 3rd Fl, Jamaica Estates, NY 11432
Malinda Fraser, Office Manager

Legal Aid Society Juvenile Rights Practice 718.237.3100
E-mail ....ekitay@legal-aid.org
111 Livingston St 8th Fl, Brooklyn, NY 11201
Emily Kitay, Supervisor

Legal Aid Society Juvenile Rights Practice 718.298.8900
E-mail ....mfrazier@legal-aid.org
153-01 Jamaica Ave 3rd Fl, Jamaica, NY 11432
Melinda Frazier, Attorney

Legal Aid Society Juvenile Rights Practice 212.312.2260
E-mail ....mmomarra@legal-aid.org
60 Lafayette St Rm 9A, New York, NY 10013
Margaret Omarra, Supervisor

Legal Aid Society Juvenile Rights Practice 718.298.8900
E-mail ....tjburrows@legal-aid.org
153-01 Jamaica Ave, 3rd Fl, Jamaica, NY 11432
Thomas Burrows, Lawyer

Legal Aid Society Juvenile Rights Practice 718.579.7900
E-mail ....eepowers@legal-aid.org
900 Sheridan Ave Rm 6C-12, Bronx, NY 10451
Elizabeth Powers, Manager

Legal Aid Society Juvenile Rights Practice 212.312.2260
60 Lafayette St, Rm 9A, New York, NY 10013
Annmarie Scalia, Director

Legal Aid Society Juvenile Rights Practice 718.579.7900
E-mail ....zcneeley@legal-aid.org
900 Sheridan Ave Rm 6C-12, Bronx, NY 10451
Zachary Neely, Manager

Legal aid Society Juvenile Rights Practice 718.981.2019
E-mail ....fabrickman@legal-aid.org
60 Lafayette St Rm 9A, Staten Island, NY 10301
Frances Brickman

Legal Aid Society Juvenile Rights Practice 718.312.2260
E-mail ....tvcurtis@legal-aid.org
60 Lafayette St Rm 9A, New York, NY 10013
Tom Curtis

Legal Aid Society Juvenile Rights Practice 718.579.7900
E-mail ....aewhite@legal-aid.org
900 Sheridan Ave Rm 6C-12, Bronx, NY 10451
Dawne Mitchell, Attorney Incharge

Legal Aid Society Juvenile Rights Practice 718.579.7900
E-mail ....madellaquila@legal-aid.org
900 Sheridan Ave Rm 6C-12, Bronx, NY 10451
Mark Dellaquila, Attorney

Legal Aid Society Juvenile Rights Practice 718.237.3100
E-mail ....laross@legal-aid.org
111 Livingston St 8th Fl, Brooklyn, NY 11201
Martin Feinman, Attorney Inchrage

Legal Aid Society Juvenile Rights Practice 718.579.7900
E-mail ....hpsquatrigalia@legal-aid.org
900 Sheridan Ave Rm 6C-12, Bronx, NY 10451
Heather Squatrigalia, Staff Attorney

Legal Aid Society Juvenile Rights Practice 212.577.3361
199 Water St 3rd Fl, New York, NY 10038
Tamara Steckler, Attorney Incharge

Legal Aid Society Juvenile Rights Practice 718.579.7900
E-mail ....necavanavgh@legal-aid.org
900 Sheridan Ave Rm 6C-12, Bronx, NY 10451
Dawn Mitchell, Director

Legal Aid Society Juvenile Rights Practice 718.237.3100
111 Livingston St 8th Fl, Brooklyn, NY 11201
Martin Feinman, Attorney In Charge

Legal Aid Society Juvenile Rights Practice 718.579.7900
900 Sheridan Ave Rm 6C-12, Bronx, NY 10451

Legal Aid Society Juvenile Rights Practice 718.237.3100
E-mail ....shreisberg@legal-aid.org
111 Livingston St 8th Fl, Brooklyn, NY 11201
Sara Reisberg, Attorney

Legal Aid Society Juvenile Rights Practice 212.312.2260
E-mail ....cccamp@legal-aid.org
60 Lafayette St Rm 9A, New York, NY 10013
Annmarie Scalia, Director

Legal Aid Society Juvenile Rights Practice 718.237.3100
E-mail ....aewolff@legal-aid.org
111 Livingston St 8th Fl, Brooklyn, NY 11201
Alexzander Wolff, Director

Legal Aid Society Juvenile Rights Practice 718.579.7900
900 Sheridan Ave Rm 6C-12, Bronx, NY 10451
Dawn Mitchell, Director

Legal Aid Society Juvenile Rights Practice 718.579.7961
E-mail ....hbgraham@legal-aid.org
900 Sheridan Ave Rm 6C-12, Bronx, NY 10451
Holly Graham, Manager

Legal Aid Society Juvenile Rights Practice 718.298.8900
E-mail ....mjchiv@legal-aid.org
153-01 Jamaica Ave 3rd Fl, Jamaica, NY 11432
Maria Chiv, Attorney

Legal Aid Society Juvenile Rights Practices 718.298.8900
E-mail ....iicomo@legal-aid.org
153-01 Jamaica Ave 3rd Fl, Jamaica, NY 11432
Irena Como, Attorney

New York Presbyterian Child Advocacy Ctr 212.305.6474
Fax 212.305.9742
722 W 168th St Moore Haven Ave, Rm 820, New York, NY 10032
Jocelyn Brown, Director Of Child Support Clinic

NYC Admin for Children's Svc 212.442.5132
E-mail ....eden.hauslaib@dfa.state.ny.us
150 William St 18th Fl, New York, NY 10038
Eden Hauslaib, Counsellor

The Center for HIV Law and Policy 212.430.6733
E-mail ....mkaplan@hivlawandpolicy.org
65 Broadway, Ste 832, New York, NY 10006
Catherin Hanffen, Executive Director

The Legal Aid Society 212.577.3300
199 Walter St, New York, NY 10038
Steve Benques, CEO

The Legal Aid Society 718.579.7912
E-mail ....velight@legal-aid.org
900 Sheridan Ave Rm 6-C12, Bronx, NY 10451
Tamara Steckler, Director

The NY Centre for Children 212.517.3012
Fax 212.517.6738
Web ....www.newyorkcenterforchildern.org
E-mail ....info@newyorkcenterforchildern.org
333 E 70th St Frnt 1, New York, NY 10021-8658
Christine Krowther, Administrative Director

Univ of Rochester Dept of Pediatrics 585.275.4600
E-mail ....mszilagyi@monroecounty.gov
451 E henrietta 2nd Fl, Rochester, NY 14620
Moria Szilagyi, Medical Director

Urban Justice Ctr 917.881.5729
E-mail ....sharonjlyoo@hotmail.com
123 William St 16th Fl, New York, NY 10038
Sharon Yoo

BEHAVIORAL HEALTH TREATMENT

Abastillas Medical Practice 845.229.6331
Fax 845.229.6353
4350 Albany Post Rd, Hyde Park, NY 12538-3609
B F Abastillas, Md, Psychiatrist

Abidi Medical Practice 516.294.9036
300 Garden City Plz Ste 324, Garden City, NY 11530-3331
Oana Abidi, Psychiatrist

Abrams Medical Practice 212.465.3287
E-mail ....drbethabrams@yahoo.com
307 E 49th St, New York, NY 10017
Beth Abrams, Psychiatrist

Abt Medical Practice 212.874.2724
Fax 212.874.4010
185 W End Ave Ste 1C, New York, NY 10023
Renee Abt, Md, Psychiatrist

Ackerman Medical Practice 516.365.2070
75 Plandome Rd Fl 1-1, Manhasset, NY 11030-2301
Norman Ackerman, MD, Psychiatrist

Adelphi University 516.877.3646
Fax 516.877.3139
Web ....www.adelphi.edu
1 South Ave, Garden City, NY 11530-4299
Carrol Phelen, Executive Director

Adirondack Psychiatric 518.891.5927
27 Rickerson Pond Rd, Saranac Lake, NY 12983-2609
Ruth Cassin, Md, Psychiatrist

Advanced Ctr For Psychotherapy, Inc. 718.658.1123
Fax 718.658.7091
Web ....www.jamaicahospital.org
17810 Wexford Ter Apt 1F, Jamaica, NY 11432-3003
Alicia Lascave, Director

Afl Assoc 718.273.5768
452 Tompkins Ave, Staten Island, NY 10305-1760
Prospero Lim, Psychiatrist

Ahmad Medical Practice 631.475.2311
107 N Ocean Ave Ste L, Patchogue, NY 11772-2012
Shafi Ahmad, Psychiatrist

Ahmad Medical Practice 212.585.1111
Fax 212.562.8541
E-mail ....samoon.ahmad@med.nyu.edu
800 5th Ave, New York, NY 10065
Samoon Ahmad, Psychiatrist

Ahola Medical Practice 212.877.3775
E-mail ....av38@columbia.edu
680 Westend Ave, Suit 1A, New York, NY 10025
Joanne Ahola, Md, Psychiatrist

Aidinoff Medical Practice 212.535.9415
16 E 79th St Fl 5, New York, NY 10075-0150
Seth Aidinoff, Psychiatrist

Al - Tariq Medical Practice 845.344.2573
41 Dolson Ave Ste 9, Middletown, NY 10940-6440
Quazi Al - Tariq, MD, Psychiatrist

Albrecht Medical Practice 315.446.1564
7000 E Genesee St, Fayetteville, NY 13066
Janette Albrecht, MD, Psychiatrist

Almeleh Medical Practice 212.355.4250
E-mail ....jackalm@verizon.net
340 E 52nd St Ste 1F, New York, NY 10022-6775
Jack Almeleh Md, Psychiatrist

Alpert Medical Practice 518.439.5630
Fax 518.765.4036
Web ....www.alpert.yourmd.com
E-mail ....info@albertvein.com
1240 New Scotland Rd Ste 204, Slingerlands, NY 12159-9222
James Alpert, Psychiatrist

Ambrosino Medical Practice 718.445.5846
Fax 718.445.3507
16403 33rd Ave, Flushing, NY 11358-1439
Salvatore Ambrosino, Md, Psychiatrist

Andreski Medical Practice 518.438.1033
527 Western Ave, Albany, NY 12203
Stephen Andreski, MD, Psychiatrist

Andrew Sheldon Ctr Mental Health-Yonkers 914.965.1109
Fax 914.965.9705
35 Dock St, Yonkers, NY 10701
Anna Sandbank, Clinical Coordinator

Andrew Sheldon Mental Health Div 914.949.7680
Fax 914.949.3525
19 Greenridge Ave, White Plains Clinic Administration, White Plains, NY 10605-1201
Rosas Bautista, Executive Director

Andrews Medical Practice 516.933.5446
Fax 516.933.5446
1171 Old Country Rd Ste 6, Plainview, NY 11803-5022
Gary Andrews, Psychiatrist

Arc 585.271.0660
Fax 585.442.1911
Web ....www.arcmonroe.org
2060 Brighton Henrey Rd, Rochester, NY 14623
Barbara Wale, President

Arms Acres 845.225.3400
Fax 845.704.6173
Web ....www.armsacres.com
E-mail ....pwallace-moore@libertymgt.com
75 Seminary Hill Rd, Carmel, NY 10512-1921
Patrice Wallice-moore, Director

Arms Acres, Inc. 845.225.3400
Web ....www.armsacres.com
E-mail ....bklein@libertymgt.com
75 Seminary Hill Road, Carmel, NY 10512
Ms. Barbara Klein, Accreditation Manager
Joint Commission accredited organization.

Aronoff Medical Practice 212.799.8257
Fax 702.871.7844
E-mail ....aronom@worldnet.att.net
60 Riverside Dr Apt 16D, New York, NY 10024-6171
Michael Aronoff, MD, Psychiatrist

Aronson Medical Practice 212.534.5735
Fax 516.466.9289
250 E 87th St, New York, NY 10128
Morton Aronson, Psychiatrist

Associates In Psychiatry 315.471.7634
Fax 212.213.1374
   108 W Jefferson St, Syracuse, NY 13202
Jeannine Bordonaro, Psychiatrist

Astor Services for Children & Families 845.871.1000
Web .... www.astorservices.org
E-mail .... lcard@astorservices.org
   6339 Mill Street, Rhinebeck, NY 12572-5005
Ms. Lauren Card, Accreditation Manager
Joint Commission accredited organization.

Astrocare, Inc. 718.467.7200
Fax 718.467.7115
Web .... www.psch.org
   1669 Bedford Ave, Brooklyn, NY 11225-2009
Guillermo Velez, Director

August Aichhorn R.T.F. 212.316.9353
Web .... www.aichhorn.org
E-mail .... mpawel@aichhorn.org
   23 West 106th Street, New York, NY 10025
Dr. Michael Pawel, Accreditation Manager
Joint Commission accredited organization.

Baker Victory Services, Inc. 716.828.9515
Web .... www.bakervictoryservices.org
E-mail .... khauser@olv-bvs.org
   780 Ridge Road, Lackawanna, NY 14218
Ms. Kristin Hauser, Accreditation Manager
Joint Commission accredited organization.

Balas Medical Practice 212.996.3984
   1235 Park Ave, New York, NY 10128-1759
Anna Balas, MD, Psychiatrist

Balter Medical Practice 212.861.5671
   544 E 86th St, New York, NY 10028
Leon Balter, MD, Psychiatrist

Barasch Medical Practice 212.410.3681
   1060 5th Ave, New York, NY 10128-0104
Alan Barasch, MD, Psychiatrist

Barash Medical Practice 212.722.3122
   425 E 86th St, New York, NY 10028
Harvey Barash, Md, Psychiatrist

Barbuto Medical Practice 212.744.5538
Fax 212.744.4767
   945 5th Ave, New York, NY 10021
Joseph Barbuto, MD, Psychiatrist

Bardinelli Medical Practice 914.946.8525
Fax 914.934.3122
   510 N Broadway, White Plains, NY 10603-3217
Anthony Bardinelli, Psychiatrist

Baretz Medical Practice 845.634.7377
   120 N Main St Ste 205, New City, NY 10956-3743
Roger Baretz, Psychiatrist

Bark Medical Practice 845.359.7553
   117 Constitution Dr, Orangeburg, NY 10962-2733
Nigel Bark, Psychiatrist

Barris Medical Practice 718.544.0932
   7531 141st Pl, Flushing, NY 11367-2836
Robert Barris, MD, Psychiatrist

Bauman Medical Practice 212.799.4668
   265 W 14th St, New York, NY 10011
Daniel Bauman, MD, Psychiatrist

Becker Medical Practice 516.466.4760
Fax 516.466.4761
   9 Cedar Dr, Great Neck, NY 11021-1954
Eugene Becker, MD, Psychiatrist

Begum Medical Practice 845.359.7804
   48 S Constitution Dr, Tappan, NY 10983-1619
Mona Begum, Psychiatrist

Behling Medical Practice 631.689.2500
Fax 718.442.2289
   100 S Jersey Ave Unit 3, East Setauket,
   NY 11733-2035
Mary Behling, Psychiatrist

Behr Medical Practice 516.482.1980
Fax 516.829.4368
E-mail .... raybehr@verizon.net
   81A Arleigh Rd, Great Neck, NY 11021-1442
Raymond Behr, Psychiatrist

Bellevue Hospital Center 212.562.3718
E-mail .... emily.mescon@bellevue.nychhc.org
   462 First Avenue, New York, NY 10016
Mrs. Emily Mescon, Accreditation Manager
Joint Commission accredited organization.

Bellevue Hospital Ctr 212.562.4132
Fax 212.562.4036
Web .... www.hac.org
E-mail .... lcurtis@bhc.org
   462 1st Ave Frnt 1, New York, NY 10016-9198
Linda Curtis, Executive Director

Benedictine Hospital 845.338.2500
Web .... www.hahv.org
E-mail .... tinesha.schell@hahv.org
   105 Mary's Avenue, Kingston, NY 12401
Mrs. Tinesha Schell, Accreditation Manager
Joint Commission accredited organization.

Berger Medical Practice 212.996.7621
   200 E 89th St, New York, NY 10128
Dirk Berger, MD, Psychiatrist

Berk Medical Practice 516.627.7607
E-mail .... norlandberk@hotmail.com
   1025 Northern Blvd Ste 100, Roslyn, NY 11576-1506
Norland Berk, MD, Psychiatrist

Berkman Medical Practice 212.579.6670
Web .... www.hr.duke.edu
   565 W End Ave, New York, NY 10024
Kathy Berkman, Psychiatrist

Berkshire Farm Ctr And Svcs For Youth 518.781.4567
Fax 518.781.4577
Web .... www.berkshirefarm.org
E-mail .... hflagg@berkshirefarm.org
   13640 State Route 22, Canaan, NY 12029-3504
Harith Flagg giacchetta, Chief Executive Officer

Berliner Medical Practice 718.461.6990
Fax 718.460.1543
   4161 Kissena Blvd Ste C, Flushing, NY 11355-3105
Neil Berliner, MD, Psychiatrist

Berman Medical Practice 914.946.5644
Fax 703.836.6470
   499 N Broadway, White Plains, NY 10603-3255
Harvey Berman, Psychiatrist

Berman Medical Practice 516.374.4417
   8 Payne Cir, Hewlett, NY 11557-2735
Sheldon Berman, MD, Psychiatrist

Bernick Medical Practice 212.249.0717
   11 E 68th St, New York, NY 10065-4955
Raymond Bernick, MD, Psychiatrist

Bernstein Medical Practice 518.489.4183
Fax 212.598.7605
   135 Woodlawn Ave, Albany, NY 12208-2912
Jeffery Bernstein, MD, Psychiatrist

Beth Israel Medical Ctr 212.420.4230
Fax 212.420.4332
Web .... www.bethisraelny.org
E-mail .... nmaruyama@bethisraelny.org
   317 E 17th St, New York, NY 10003-3804
Nancy Maruyama, Psychiatrist

Better Days Ahead 585.325.3145
Fax 585.325.3188
Web .... www.mharochester.org
E-mail .... pwoods@mharochester.org
   320 Goodman St N, Rochester, NY 14607
Patricia Woods, Director Of Mental Health Association

Beverley Mack Harry Consulting Svcs, Inc. 718.363.0100
Fax 718.363.3005
Web .... www.bmhtherapy.org
E-mail .... casemanager@bmhtherapy.org
   738 Crown St, Fl 1, Brooklyn, NY 11213
Beverly Mack, President

Bezahler Medical Practice 212.777.8015
E-mail .... h.bezahler@yahoo.com
   14 E 4th St, Apt 601, New York, NY 10012-1141
Harvey Bezahler, Md, Psychiatrist

Bezirganian Medical Svcs 607.273.0253
   211 N Geneva St, Ithaca, NY 14850-4135
Sophia Bezirganian, Psychiatrist

Bikur Cholim, Inc. 845.425.5252
Fax 845.678.6060
Web .... www.bikurcholim.org
E-mail .... schechter@bikurcholim.org
   25 Robert Pitt Dr Ste 101, Monsey, NY 10952-3366
Iisaac Shasta, Director

Billick Medical Practice 212.570.5300
Web .... billick.com
E-mail .... stephen@billick.com
   144 W 12th St, New York, NY 10011-8202
Stephen Billick, MD, Psychiatrist

Birger Medical Practice 212.831.3837
   155 E 91st St, New York, NY 10128
Daniel Birger, Psychiatrist

Bittman Medical Practice 212.599.1718
   25 Tudor City Pl Apt 1004, New York,
   NY 10017-6839
Betsy Bittman, MD, Psychiatrist

Bjork Medical Practice 212.219.3680
Fax 212.925.4777
E-mail .... db@darlabjork.com
   91 Franklin St, New York, NY 10013-3408
Darla Bjork, MD, Psychiatrist

Blau Medical Practice 914.834.9139
E-mail .... sbmd9@yahoo.com
   9 Center Ave, Larchmont, NY 10538-2503
Stephen Blau, Psychiatrist

Blaustein Medical Practice 212.666.3470
E-mail .... abfg1@verizon.net
   350 Central Park W, New York, NY 10025
Alvin Blaustein, Psychiatrist

Bleuler Psychotherapy Ctr Inc 718.275.6010
Fax 718.275.6062
Web .... www.bleulerpsychotherapycenter.org
E-mail .... bpc1949@verizon.net
   10470 Queens Blvd, Forest Hills, NY 11375
John Rossland, Executive Director

Blitman Medical Practice 212.289.2080
   103 E 86th St, New York, NY 10028-1058
Judy Blitman, Psychiatrist

Bluestein Medical Practice 212.947.7111
   19 W 34th St, New York, NY 10001
Steven Bluestein, Md, Psychiatrist

Blum Medical Practice 516.487.8052
E-mail .... martin.blum@erols.com
   53 Arleigh Rd, Great Neck, NY 11021-1442
Martin Blum, Psychiatrist

Blumenfield Medical Practice 914.472.5035
   16 Donellan Rd, Scarsdale, NY 10583-2008
Michael Blumenfield, Pyschiatrist

Blumenthal Medical Practice 212.628.4458
   315 E 65th St, New York, NY 10065
Allan Blumenthal, Md, Psychiatrist

Body Mind Wellness Ctr 585.425.7415
Fax 585.223.5792
E-mail .... framirez99@aol.com
   326 Garnsey Rd, Pittsford, NY 14534
Frederick Remington, Md, Psychiatrist

New York

Bolling Medical Practice 212.281.9939
203 W 138th St, New York, NY 10030-2102
John Bolling, Psychiatrist

Borbely Medical Practice 212.222.1678
Fax 212.531.3851
E-mail ....anfborbely@aol.com
675 W End Ave Apt 1A, New York, NY 10025-7366
Antal Borbely, MD, Psychiatrist

Borenstein Medical Practice 315.853.6899
Fax 315.853.2309
2 Fountain St, Ste 202, Clinton, NY 13323-1725
Neal Borenstein, MD, Psychiatrist

Borner Medical Practice 718.857.1733
45 Plaza St W, Brooklyn, NY 11217
Irmgard Borner, Psychiatrist

Bose Medical Practice 212.787.9041
Fax 212.662.6967
E-mail ....jbose@psychoanalysis.net
20 W 74th St, New York, NY 10023-2401
Joerg Bose, MD, Psychiatrist

Brachman Medical Practice 718.596.2991
160 Clinton St, Brooklyn, NY 11201-4618
Irwin Brachman, Md, Psychiatrist

Brand Medical Practice 212.614.9700
E-mail ....brooklyndb@aol.com
17 W 9th St, New York, NY 10011
David Brand, Md, Psychiatrist

Brandt Medical Practice 212.996.0698
Fax 212.348.8403
1095 Park Ave, New York, NY 10128-1154
Stephanie Brandt, Psychiatrist

Brandt Medical Practice 212.986.0640
E-mail ....maxbrandt@aol.com
35 E 38th St Apt 1A, New York, NY 10016-2528
Max Brandt, Psychiatrist

Bremer Medical Practice 585.381.6270
10 Office Park Way, Pittsford, NY 14534
Brenda Bremer, Psychiatrist

Brent Medical Practice 212.289.7595
157 E 86th St, New York, NY 10028
Richard Brent, MD, Psychiatrist

Brockman Medical Practice 212.496.1507
Fax 212.721.5727
E-mail ....rb37@columbia.edu
15 W 81st St, New York, NY 10024-6022
Richard Brockman, MD, Psychiatrist

Brockner Medical Practice 212.772.9732
Fax 212.744.2121
Web ....www.psychoanalysis.org
124 E 84th St Apt 1D, New York, NY 10028-0918
Nora Brockner, MD, Psychiatrist

Broden Medical Practice 212.722.4648
Fax 212.650.3464
E-mail ....abroden@optonline.net
1070 Park Ave, New York, NY 10128-1000
Alexander Broden, MD, Psychiatrist

Broden Medical Practice 914.723.8708
11 Hillview Dr, Scarsdale, NY 10583-7531
Alexander Broden, Psychiatrist

Brody Medical Practice 914.762.4440
210 Cedar Dr E, Briarcliff Manor, NY 10510-2604
David Brody, Psychiatrist

Brody Medical Practice 631.424.8494
Fax 631.920.8501
45 Balsam Dr, Huntington Station, NY 11746-7724
Paul Brody, Psychiatrist

Bronx Children's Psychiatric Center 718.239.3621
E-mail ....bcsweah@omh.state.ny.us
1000 Waters Place, Bronx, NY 10461-2799
Ms. Emily Harf, Accreditation Manager
Joint Commission accredited organization.

Bronx Children's Psychiatric Ctr 718.742.6019
Fax 718.742.6016
Web ....www.omh.state.ny.us
595 Gerard Ave, Bronx, NY 10453
Jeff Greenlinger, Acting Progam Director

Bronx Children's Psychiatric Ctr 718.239.3639
Fax 718.239.3669
E-mail ....cmyers@omh.state.ny.us
1000 Waters Pl, Bronx, NY 10461
Chris Myers, Md, Director

Bronx-Lebanon Hospital Center 718.590.1800
Web ....www.bronxcare.org/contactus.html
E-mail ....mriggins@bronxleb.org
1650 Grand Concourse, Bronx, NY 10457
Ms. Marion Riggins, Accreditation Manager
Joint Commission accredited organization.

Brookdale Hospital Medical Ctr 718.240.5000
E-mail ....mmalhotra@brookdale.edu
1 Brookdale Plz, Brooklyn, NY 11212-3198
Madhu Malhotra, Md, Director

Brooklyn Children's Center 718.221.4500
E-mail ....rosemary.culotta@omh.ny.gov
1819 Bergen Street, Brooklyn, NY 11233
Ms. Rosemary Culotta, Accreditation Manager
Joint Commission accredited organization.

Brooks Medical Practice 914.428.2040
56 Doyer Ave Ste 1C, White Plains, NY 10605-1643
Leslie Brooks, Psychiatrist

Brooks Medical Practice 212.744.6555
Fax 212.744.6555
9 E 75th St Ste 1A, New York, NY 10021-2634
Robert Brooks, Psychiatrist

Bross Medical Practice 212.744.7166
E-mail ....arbyemdy@aol.com
31 E 72nd St, New York, NY 10021-4131
Robert Bross, Psychiatrist

Brower Medical Practice 212.772.8620
Fax 212.918.7912
226 E 70th St, New York, NY 10021
Ross Brower, Md, Psychiatrist

Brown Medical Practice 212.678.6878
372 Central Park W, New York, NY 10025-8201
Richard Brown, MD, Psychiatrist

Brown Medical Practice 212.737.0821
30 E End Ave, New York, NY 10028
Dr. Richard Brown, Psychiatrist

Brown Medical Practice 212.799.1413
Fax 732.235.7677
156 W 86th St Apt 1A, New York, NY 10024-4029
Donald Brown, Psychiatrist

Brunswick Hospital Ctr Brunswick Hall 631.789.7000
Fax 631.789.8571
Web ....www.brunswickhospital.com
E-mail ....akhan@brunswickhospital.org
366 Broadway, Amityville, NY 11701
Abid Khan, Medical Director

Brunswick Medical Practice 212.355.4225
E-mail ....rbrunswick@hayesbrunswick.com
30 E 60th St Ste 1002, New York, NY 10022-1042
Roger Brunswick, Psychiatrist

Buckingham Medical Practice 212.986.0997
244 Madison Ave, New York, NY 10016-2810
Ian Buckingham, Psychiatrist

Builders For The Family & Youth Of The Diocese In Brooklyn, Inc 718.779.1600
Fax 718.803.0895
Web ....www.ccbq.org
E-mail ....hanham@ccbq.org
3722 82nd St, Jackson Heights, NY 11372-7032
Lee-ann Hanham, Director

Bukberg Medical Practice 212.614.0312
3 E 10th St, New York, NY 10003
Judith Bukberg, Psychiatrist

Bukholts Medical Practice 718.332.2001
2601 Emmons Ave, Brooklyn, NY 11235
Benjamin Bukholts, Psychiatrist

Bulgarelli Medical Practice 212.807.1054
455 W 23rd St, New York, NY 10011
Christopher Bulgarelli, MD, Psychiatrist

Burlingham Medical Practice 212.396.3766
119 E 83rd St, New York, NY 10028
Eleanor Burlingham, Psychiatrist

Busch Medical Practice 212.734.0257
E-mail ....fnb80@aol.com
10 E 78th St Ste 5A, New York, NY 10075-1734
Fredrick Busch, Psychiatrist

C Care Corp 212.267.3653
128 Mott St, New York, NY 10013-5540
Qi Hu, MD, Psychiatrist

C/O Northern Westchester Counseling Ctr 914.666.4646
Fax 914.666.5002
Web ....www.mhawestchester.org
E-mail ....lgoodman@mhawestchester.org
344 E Main St Ste 301, Mount Kisco, NY 10549-3036
Lawrence Goodman, Program Director

Caldwell Medical Practice 212.799.7984
Fax 619.543.3746
1 Lincoln Plz, New York, NY 10023
Arline Caldwell, Psychiatrist

Cale Medical Practice 518.383.0600
E-mail ....drcale@nycap.rr.com
634 Plank Rd, Clifton Park, NY 12065-2019
Randy Cale, Psychiatrist

Caligor Medical Practice 212.996.5285
Fax 914.722.4041
E-mail ....ec8@columbia.edu
19 E 3rd St, New York, NY 10003
Eve Caligor, Psychiatrist

Canino Medical Practice 212.877.4180
Web ....www.iancanino.com
28 W 71st St, New York, NY 10023
Ian Canino, Psychiatrist

Capello Medical Practice 718.386.6642
6051 Fresh Pond Rd, Maspeth, NY 11378-3541
Louis Capello, MD, Psychiatrist

Capital District Psychiatric Ctr 518.447.9611
Fax 518.434.0041
Web ....www.omh.state.ny.us
E-mail ....lcampbell@omh.state.ny.us
75 New Scotland Ave, Albany, NY 12208-3474
Lou Campbell, Psychiatrist

Carol A Ipsen Md Pc 518.439.5624
Fax 518.765.4036
Web ....www.carolipsenmd.com
1240 New Scotland Rd Ste 204, Slingerlands,
NY 12159-9222
Carol Ipsen, Psychiatrist

Cartagine Chiropractic & Wellness 516.678.3322
Fax 516.678.8087
Web ....www.cartaginechiropractic.com
E-mail ....rcartagine@optonline.net
119 N Park Ave Ste 201, Rockville Centre,
NY 11570-4113
Rosemarie Cartagine, Director

Casarino Medical Practice 212.873.1600
Fax 509.357.4092
15 W 72nd St, New York, NY 10023
Dr. John Casarino, MD, Psychiatrist

Castroll Robert 631.444.2570
Fax 631.444.8962
Stony Brook Medical Park # BLDNG, 2500 Mesconsit
Hwy, Stony Brook, NY 11794-0001
Sashi Sukland, Psychitrist

New York

Catholic Charities 607.689.0272
Web ....www.catholiccharitiesusa.org
1277 Taylor Rd, Owego, NY 13827
Judy Groves, Director

Catholic Charities 718.779.1234
Fax 718.779.7775
Web ....www.ccbq.org
6120 Woodside Ave, Woodside, NY 11377
Joanne Fahey, Director

Catholic Charities Mental Health Svcs 516.623.3322
Fax 516.623.3526
Web ....www.catholiccharities.org
E-mail ....dennis.malloy@catholiccharities.org
333 N Main St, Freeport, NY 11520-1231
Marlin Destesano, Coordinator

Cayuga Home for Children 315.253.5383
Fax 315.253.7278
Web ....www.cayugahome.org
101 Hamilton Avnenue, Auburn, NY 13021
COA accredited organization.

Celian Medical Practice 212.758.4654
60 Sutton Pl S, New York, NY 10022-4168
Charles Celian, Psychiatrist

**Central NY Developmental Disabilities Svcs
Ofc** 315.336.2300
Fax 315.339.5456
Web ....www.omr.state.ny.us/central.htm
101 W Liberty St, Rome, NY 13440-5717
Dr. Todd Podkowka, Medical Director

Central Westchester Family Mental Health 914.949.6761
Fax 914.949.3224
141 N Central Ave, Hartsdale, NY 10530
Aaron Newman, Director

Central Yonkers Family Mental Health 914.423.4433
Fax 914.423.9434
487 S Broadway, Yonkers, NY 10705
Erin Newman, Director

Cerra Medical Practice 212.246.2370
30 W 60th St Apt 1P, New York, NY 10023-7906
Luis Cerra, MD, Psychiatrist

Chabus Medical Practice 212.477.5698
E-mail ....bchabus@chpnet.org
155 E 29th St, New York, NY 10016
Brent Chabus, Psychiatrist

Chalfin Medical Practice 212.995.9764
Fax 718.962.7717
E-mail ....rchalfinmd@earthlink.net
30 E 10th St, New York, NY 10003
Robert Chalfin, Md, Psychiatrist

Chalif Medical Practice 631.271.7133
191 E Main St Ste 2, Huntington, NY 11743-2987
Lawrence Chalif, Psychiatrist

Chanin Medical Practice 718.387.4200
132 Graham Ave, Brooklyn, NY 11206-2621
Lubh Chanin, MD, Psychiatrist

Chapin Medical Practice 212.534.5671
30 E 95th St, New York, NY 10128
Joanna Chapin, Psychiatrist

Charles Medical Practice 716.883.2782
E-mail ....rocharl@pol.net
142 N Pearl St, Buffalo, NY 14202-1108
Roderick Charles, Md, Pyschiatrist

Charles Tolk Pc 212.683.2458
E-mail ....chastolkmd@aol.com
200 E 33rd St, New York, NY 10016
Charles Tolk, MD, Psychiatrist

Chelebian Medical Practice 585.394.5690
527 N Main St, Canandaigua, NY 14424-1021
Jack Chelebian, MD, Psychiatrist

Chen Medical Practice 718.755.6450
833 58th St, # 3R, Brooklyn, NY 11220
Xu Zhang Chen, Md, Psychiatrist

Child & Adolescent Psych 845.342.5716
PO Box 7339, Newburgh, NY 12550-9267
Richard Hahn, Psychiatrist

Child & Adolescent Treatment Svcs Inc 716.881.2405
Fax 716.881.2425
E-mail ....mgrover@catswny.org
1487 Main St, Buffalo, NY 14209
Mary Grover, Director

Child & Adolescent Treatment Svcs, Inc. 716.835.4011
Fax 716.835.0253
3350 Main St, Buffalo, NY 14214
Patricia Jones, Supervisor

Child & Adolescent Treatment Svcs, Inc. 716.853.1335
Fax 716.853.1598
Web ....www.catswny.org
E-mail ....izannitt@catswny.org
430 Niagara St Ste 2, Buffalo, NY 14201-1886
Irene Zannitt, Branch Director

Children's Aid Society 212.534.8596
130 E 101st St 3rd Fl, New York, NY 10029
Kelly Collins, Director

Children's Home 845.452.1420
Fax 845.452.1488
Web ....www.childrenshome.us
10 Childrens Way, Poughkeepsie, NY 12601-1499
Walter Joseph, Executive Director

Children's Home Of Kingston 845.331.1448
Fax 845.334.9507
Web ....www.chkingston.org
E-mail ....gmccann@chkingston.org
26 Grove St, Kingston, NY 12401-3399
Gwendolyn Mccann, Executive Director

Children's Home Of Wyoming Conference 607.772.6904
Fax 607.723.2617
Web ....www.childrenshomewyomconf.org
E-mail ....tgilmore@chowc.org
1182 Chenango St, Binghamton, NY 13901-1653
Tina Gilmore, Director

Children's Village 212.932.9009
Fax 212.932.1756
Web ....www.childrensvillage.org
E-mail ....dgaffney@childrenvillage.org
2090 Adam Clayton Powell Jr Blvd Fl 9, New York,
NY 10027-4990
Danielle Gaffney, Director

Chua Medical Practice 845.338.2979
117 Albany Ave, Kingston, NY 12401-2509
Streamson Chua, Psychiatrist

**Citizens' Committee For Children Of New York,
Inc** 212.673.1800
Fax 212.979.5063
Web ....www.cccnewyork.org
E-mail ....jmarch@cccnewyork.org
105 E 22nd St Rm 700, New York, NY 10010-5496
Jennifer March-joly, Acting Executive Director

Clare Medical Practice 212.787.2622
50 Central Park W, New York, NY 10023-6028
Gloria Clare, Md, Psychiatrist

**Clear View School/Day Treatment
Program** 914.941.9513
Fax 914.941.2339
Web ....www.clearviewschool.org
480 Albany Post Rd, Briarcliff Manor, NY 10510
William Barnes, Executive Director

Cohen Medical Practice 212.686.4130
200 E 33rd st, New York, NY 10016
Ingram Cohen, Md, Psychiatrist

Cohen Medical Practice 212.595.6473
E-mail ....rucohenmd@verizon.net
277 W End Ave, New York, NY 10023
Ruth Cohen, MD, Psychiatrist

Cohen Medical Practice 212.289.6800
Fax 212.662.4506
64 E 94th St Apt 1A, New York, NY 10128-0700
Arnold Cohen, MD, Psychiatrist

Cohen Medical Practice 212.744.2182
Fax 212.319.7824
E-mail ....skcmd@aol.com
950 Park Ave, New York, NY 10028-0320
Sandra Cohen, Psychiatrist

Cohen Medical Practice 914.946.8076
Fax 914.946.8076
10 Old Mamaroneck Rd Ste 1B, White Plains,
NY 10605-1724
Arnold Cohen, Psychiatrist

Coleman Medical Practice 315.255.1382
23 Woodland Dr, Port Washington, NY 11050-1136
Stephen Coleman, Psychiatrist

Collins Medical Practice 914.967.9383
Fax 501.202.1958
107 Theodore Fremd Ave, Rye, NY 10580-2824
Thomas Collins, Psychiatrist

Collins Medical Practice 212.362.0173
239 Central Park W, New York, NY 10024-6038
Lucy Collins, Psychiatrist

**Community Action Bedford Stuyvesant
Clinic** 718.388.0390
Fax 718.486.5741
Web ....www.chnnyc.org
E-mail ....rsalamanca@chnnyc.org
94-98 Manhattan Ave, Brooklyn, NY 11206
Rafael Salamanca, Director

**Community Assoc Of Progressive Dominicans,
Inc.** 212.781.5500
Fax 212.927.6089
Web ....www.acdp.org
E-mail ....hreeton@acdp.org
3940 Broadway Fl 2, New York, NY 10032-1534
Howard Reeton, Director

Coney Island Hospital 718.616.3000
Web ....www.coneyislandhospital.com
E-mail ....battagll@nychhc.org
2601 Ocean Parkway, Brooklyn, NY 11235
Ms. Laura Battaglia, Accreditation Manager
Joint Commission accredited organization.

Conifer Park 518.793.7273
Fax 518.798.5004
Web ....www.coniferpark.com
55 Elm St, Glens Falls, NY 12801
William Bean, Director

Conifer Park Inc. 518.399.6446
Web ....Libertymgt.com
E-mail ....jgluchowski@libertymgt.com
79 Glenridge Road, Glenville, NY 12302
Ms. Jeanne Gluchowski, Accreditation Manager
Joint Commission accredited organization.

Conigliaro Medical Practice 212.243.5045
Fax 212.734.9733
22 W 21st St Fl 10, New York, NY 10010-6938
Vincenzo Conigliaro, Psychiatrist

Constantino Medical Practice 631.476.7275
1000 Main St Ste 5, Port Jefferson, NY 11777-2250
E. Constantino, Psychiatrist

Consumer Svcs 315.361.9131
Fax 315.361.4526
E-mail ....w.cesare@csomc.org
1019 Northside Shopping Ctr, Oneida,
NY 13421-4901
William Cesare, Director

Cooper Medical Practice 845.425.4713
55 College Rd, Monsey, NY 10952-2826
Steven Cooper, Psychiatrist

Cornell University **607.255.5208**
Fax 607.254.5244
E-mail ....lb77@cornell.edu
110 Ho Plz, Ithaca, NY 14853-3102
Lisa Berki, Administrator

Cottrol Medical Practice **212.969.0586**
935 Saint Nicholas Ave, New York, NY 10032
Cheryl Cottrol, Psychiatrist

Covenant House New York Crisis Shelter **212.613.0300**
Fax 212.947.2478
Web ....www.nineline.org
E-mail ....info@covenanthouseny.org
460 W 41st St, New York, NY 10014-1004
Jeriome Kileane, Executive Director

Creative Insights **518.257.2018**
Fax 518.525.2779
E-mail ....gpjs@berk.com
1University Place, Rensselaer, NY 12144
Patricia Schuler, Director

Crestwood Children's Ctr Inc **585.429.2700**
Fax 585.429.2800
Web ....www.hillside.com
E-mail ....bconrad@hillside.com
2075 Scottsville Rd, Rochester, NY 14623-2098
Barbara Conrad, President

Crow Medical Practice **212.744.7003**
15 W 72nd St, New York, NY 10023
John Crow, Psychiatrist

Ctr For Attention Deficit **718.544.7912**
Web ....www.drbarryholzer.yourmd.com
E-mail ....bholzer@drbarryholzer.yourmd.com
13718 Jewel Ave Ste 1A, Flushing, NY 11367-1962
Barry Holzer, Md, Psychiatrist

Dabbs Medical Practice **212.534.5220**
E-mail ....dabstam@aol.com
125 E 87th St, New York, NY 10128
E Gerald Dabbs, Psychiatrist

Daley Medical Practice **516.747.6828**
Fax 718.224.7587
E-mail ....drrobertdaley@aol.com
515 Herricks Rd, New Hyde Park, NY 11040
Robert Daley, MD, Psychiatrist

Dalsimer Medical Practice **212.595.0412**
Fax 925.283.5732
490 W End Ave, New York, NY 10024
Andrew Dalsimer, MD, Psychiatrist

Davidson Medical Practice **212.247.7359**
27 W 72nd St, New York, NY 10023-3498
Leah Davidson, MD, Psychiatrist

Daytop Village Inc Brightside Manor
House **845.876.4060**
Fax 845.876.6349
Web ....www.daytopvillage.org
E-mail ....mclifford@daytopvillage.org
248 Fox Hollow Rd, Rhinebeck, NY 12572
Michael Clifford, Director

Daytop Village, Inc. **212.354.6000**
Fax 212.869.0929
Web ....www.daytop.org
248 Fox Hollow Road, Rhinebeck, NY 12572
CARF accredited programs available.

De Corse Medical Practice **914.762.5595**
1133 Pleasantville Rd, Briarcliff Manor,
NY 10510-1634
Marie De Corse, Psychiatrist

De La Chapelle Medical Practice **212.988.6789**
530 E 72nd St, New York, NY 10021
Alain De La Chapelle, Psychiatrist

Deitz Medical Practice **212.722.9777**
Fax 203.377.3071
E-mail ....jdeitzmd@aol.com
17 E 96th St, New York, NY 10128-0783
Jeffrey Deitz, Psychiatrist

Delaware Valley Job Corps Ctr **845.887.5400**
Fax 845.887.4762
9367 State Route 97, Callicoon, NY 12723
Curtis Price, Center Director

Deliyannides Medical Practice **212.595.1595**
2 W 86th St, New York, NY 10024
Deborah Deliyannides, MD, Psychiatrist

Dendy Medical Practice **516.621.1448**
32 Plantingfield Rd, Roslyn Heights, NY 11577-1819
Errol Dendy, MD, Psychiatrist

Denea Medical Practice **518.584.8888**
433 Broadway Ste 203, Saratoga Springs,
NY 12866-2367
Russell Denea, Psychiatrist

Dent Medical Practice **212.288.7643**
182 E 79th St, New York, NY 10075
Katherine Dent, MD, Psychiatrist

Derosis Medical Practice **718.796.0308**
4625 Douglas Ave, Bronx, NY 10471-3530
Louis Derosis, Md, Psychiatrist

Detommasi Medical Practice **518.482.7759**
17 Woodlawn Ave, Albany, NY 12208-3225
Anthony Detommasi, Psychiatrist

Deutsch Medical Practice **212.860.3393**
185 E 85th St, New York, NY 10028
Leonard Deutsch, Psychiatrist

Deutsch Medical Practice **212.249.9390**
115 E 82nd St, New York, NY 10028
Alexander Deutsch, Psychiatrist

Deutscher Medical Practice **212.501.0726**
E-mail ....lisadeutscher@gmail.com
440 W End Ave, New York, NY 10024-5358
Lisa Deutscher, Md, Psychiatrist

Devereux New York **845.758.1899**
Fax 845.758.1817
Web ....www.devereuxny.org
E-mail ....jokeefe@devereux.org
40 Devereux Way, Red Hook, NY 12571-2268
John Oaekeefe, Executive Director

Di Bianco Medical Practice **914.238.5300**
60 Commodore Rd, Chappaqua, NY 10514-2628
Joseph Di Bianco, Psychiatrist

Di Gangi Medical Practice **212.628.1349**
175 E 70th St, New York, NY 10021-5162
M Di Gangi, MD, Psychiatrist

Diabetes Ctr **914.698.7500**
Fax 914.698.7523
E-mail ....diabetes@scientist.com
1160 Greacen Pkwy, Mamoroneck, NY 10543
Anne Bernstein, Psychiatrist

Diamond Medical Practice **516.248.5005**
233 7th St, Ste 101, Garden City, NY 11530-5747
Steven Diamond, Psychiatrist

Diamond Medical Practice **212.988.6656**
440 E 79th St, New York, NY 10075
Leonard Diamond, Psychiatrist

Dixon Medical Practice **914.345.9131**
PO Box 780, Elmsford, NY 10523-0780
Carla Dixon, Psychiatrist

Doft Medical Practice **212.677.2493**
E-mail ....edbary@aol.com
55 E 9th St, Ste 12F, New York, NY 10003-6328
Martin Doft, Md, Psychiatrist

Dolan Medical Practice **914.476.1208**
22 Edgecliff Ter, Yonkers, NY 10705-1606
Anna Dolan, Psychiatrist

Donovan House **518.885.8220**
Fax 518.885.1633
30 E High St, Ballston Spa, NY 12020
Sister Charla Commins, Executive Director

Dorfman Medical Practice **718.768.6630**
137 Garfield Pl, Brooklyn, NY 11215
Vernon Dorfman, MD, Psychiatrist

Douglas Ingram Pc **212.289.4022**
E-mail ....dhingrammd@aol.com
4 E 89th St, New York, NY 10128
Douglas Ingram, Psychiatrist

Doyle Medical Practice **718.997.6500**
Fax 608.280.7204
136 Ascan Ave, Forest Hills, NY 11375-5946
Thomas Doyle, Psychiatrist

Draghi Medical Practice **212.688.5999**
409 E 50th St, New York, NY 10022
Suzanne Draghi, Psychiatrist

Drassinower Medical Practice **914.682.0448**
15 Lake St Ste 1, White Plains, NY 10603-4051
Samuel Drassinower, Psychiatrist

Dreisinger Medical Practice **718.652.5959**
2355 Westervelt Ave, Bronx, NY 10469-6315
Albert Dreisinger, Psychiatrist

Dudley Medical Practice **212.222.5122**
466 W 144th St, New York, NY 10031-4722
Richard Dudley, Psychiatrist

Dunkell Medical Practice **212.628.2236**
1065 Lexington Ave, New York, NY 10021-3237
Samuel Dunkell Md, Psychiatrist

Dvorak Medical Practice **518.456.6500**
1067 Madison Ave, Albany, NY 12208-2656
Nancy Dvorak, Psychiatrist

Easton Medical Practice **212.532.8823**
151 E 31st St, New York, NY 10016
Jonathan Easton, Md, Psychiatrist

Eating Disorders Clinic **212.543.5752**
E-mail ....edru@nysti.columbia.edu
1051 Riversite, New York, NY 10032
B Timothy Walsh, Md, Psychiatrist

Edleman Medical Practice **631.424.6949**
Fax 631.421.9216
33 Walt Whitman Rd Ste 236, Huntington Station,
NY 11746-4294
Robert Edleman, Psychiatrist

Educational Equity Concepts, Inc **212.243.1110**
Fax 212.627.0407
Web ....www.edequity.org
E-mail ....information@edequity.org
100 5th Ave Fl 8, New York, NY 10011
Barbara Sprung, Director

Eichler Medical Practice **516.484.4379**
15 Linwood Dr, Roslyn, NY 11576-2200
Seth Eichler, MD, Psychiatrist

Eisen Medical Practice **516.482.1191**
230 Middle Neck Rd, Ste 2, Great Neck,
NY 11021-1113
Arthur Eisen, Psychiatrist

Eisenman Medical Practice **914.472.4822**
156 Brewster Rd, Scarsdale, NY 10583-2022
Sheldon Eisenman, Psychiatrist

Ellis Medicine Ellis Hospital **518.243.4000**
Web ....www.ellishospital.org
E-mail ....frankos@ellishospital.org
1101 Nott Street, Schenectady, NY 12308
Ms. Susan Franko, Accreditation Manager
Joint Commission accredited organization.

Elmcrest Children's Ctr **315.446.6250**
Fax 315.445.2667
Web ....www.elmcrest.org
E-mail ....jgeglia@elmcrest.org
960 Salt Springs Rd, Syracuse, NY 13224-1696
Joe Geglia, Executive Director

New York

Elmhurst Hospital Center **718.334.4000**
E-mail ....casianos@nychhc.org
79-01 Broadway, Elmhurst, NY 11373
Ms. Sonia Casiano, Accreditation Manager
Joint Commission accredited organization.

Elmira Psychiatric Center **607.737.4739**
Web
......www.omh.state.ny.us/omhweb/facilities/elpc/facility.htm
E-mail ....maryjo.owen@omh.ny.gov
100 Washington Street, Elmira, NY 14901-2898
Ms. Mary Jo Owen, Accreditation Manager
Joint Commission accredited organization.

Elmira Psychiatric Ctr **607.737.4711**
Fax 607.737.9080
Web ....www.omh.state.ny.us
E-mail ....elmirapc@omh.state.ny.us
100 Washington St, Elmira, NY 14901-2849
Mark Stephany, Executive Director

Elmwood Franklin School **716.877.5035**
Fax 716.877.9680
Web ....www.elmwoodfranklin.org
E-mail ....jcianciosa@elmwoodfranklin.org
104 New Amsterdam Ave, Buffalo, NY 14216-3399
Joy Cianciosa, Director

Emad Medical Practice **315.735.0940**
1627 Genesee St, Utica, NY 13501-4732
Jamal Emad, Md, Psychiatrist

Enable **315.455.7591**
Fax 315.455.1087
Web ....www.enablecny.org
1603 Court St, Syracuse, NY 13208-1896
Sara Wall-Bollinger, Director

Engel Medical Practice **718.855.8911**
115 Henry St, Brooklyn, NY 11201
Lenore Engel, MD, Psychiatrist

Entelis Medical Practice **212.369.1628**
Web ....www.columbia.edu
E-mail ....cfe1@columbia.edu
1150 5th Ave, New York, NY 10128-0724
Charles Entelis, MD, Psychiatrist

Evangelista Medical Practice **718.939.3755**
14031 Oak Ave, Flushing, NY 11355-3558
Osvaldo Evangelista, Psychiatrist

Family And Children's Assoc **516.623.1644**
Fax 516.623.3125
E-mail ....info@familyandchildrens.org
175 Nassau Rd, Roosevelt, NY 11575-2016
Lary Weissberger, Director

Family Care Certified Svc **516.932.7799**
Fax 516.932.1415
Web ....www.familyhomecare.com
E-mail ....mberger@familyhomecare.com
120 W John St, Hicksville, NY 11801-1020
Loretta Jost, Director

Fass Medical Practice **585.256.1105**
527 Linden St, Rochester, NY 14620-2422
Margot Fass, Md, Psychiatrist

Fayer Medical Practice **212.628.6208**
E-mail ....gooddoc20@aol.com
161 E 74th St Lowr A, New York, NY 10021-3399
Steven Fayer, Psychiatrist

FEGS At Ctr Moriches **631.874.2700**
Fax 631.874.3786
Web ....www.fegs.org
E-mail ....rmarino@fegs.org
220 Main St Ste 1, Center Moriches, NY 11934-3516
Rosemarie Marino, Clinic Manager

FEGS Health & Human Services System **212.366.8400**
Fax 212.366.8441
Web ....www.fegs.org
E-mail ....info@fegs.org
315 Hudson Street, New York, NY 10013
Gail A. Magaliff, Chief Executive Officer

Feigelson Medical Practice **585.624.9310**
Fax 585.624.2788
234 Parrish Rd, Honeoye Falls, NY 14472-9715
Janet Feigelson, Psychiatrist

Feinberg Medical Practice **718.520.7200**
E-mail ....shalomf@aol.com
10420 Queens Blvd, Forest Hills, NY 11375
S Shalom Feinberg, Md, Psychiatrist

Feinstein Medical Practice **607.257.6262**
206 Hanshaw Rd, Ithaca, NY 14850-2210
Howard Feinstein, Psychiatrist

Feirstein Medical Practice **212.427.0419**
1235 Park Ave, New York, NY 10128-1759
Ira Feirstein, Psychiatrist

Feldshuh Medical Practice **212.689.4320**
Web ....www.benfeldshuh.com
150 E 37th St, New York, NY 10016
Benjamin Feldshuh, Psychiatrist

Ferran Medical Practice **212.924.2673**
1 Washington Square Vlg, New York, NY 10012-1601
Ernesto Ferran, MD, Psychiatrist

Filiaci Medical Practice **212.777.5013**
Fax 212.777.2054
11 5th Ave, New York, NY 10003-4342
Carlo Filiaci, Md, Psychiatrist

Fine Medical Practice **516.295.2277**
949 Central Ave Ste 205, Woodmere,
NY 11598-1204
Leslie Fine, Md, Psychiatrist

Finger Lakes Parent Network, Inc **607.776.2164**
Fax 607.776.4327
Web ....www.flpn.org
E-mail ....flpninc25@verison.net
25 W Steuben St, Bath, NY 14810-1511
Patti Dinardo, Executive Director

Finger Medical Practice **718.897.8595**
Fax 631.661.2515
10225 67th Dr, Forest Hills, NY 11375
Mark Finger, MD, Psychiatrist

Finger Medical Practice **212.686.0599**
120 E 36th St Ste 1H, New York, NY 10016-3423
Mark Finger, MD, Psychiatrist

Finkel Medical Practice **212.289.2077**
108 E 91st St Ofc 2, New York, NY 10128-1658
Jay Finkel, MD, Psychiatrist

Finkelstien Medical Practice **718.884.6300**
Fax 914.472.8363
E-mail ....fbfmd@fbfinkelstein.com
3333 Henry Hudson Pkwy, Bronx, NY 10463
Frank Finkelstien, Psychiatrist

Finnerty Medical Practice **917.796.3523**
Fax 212.330.6359
E-mail ....molly.finnerty@omh.ny.gov
119 W 57th St Ste 620, New York, NY 10019-2302
Molly Finnerty, Md, Psychiatrist

Fischel Medical Practice **212.486.6486**
Web ....www.fosper.org
E-mail ....rfischel@fosper.org
225 E 63rd St, New York, NY 10065
Robert Fischel, Psychiatrist

Fishman Medical Practice **516.791.5551**
Fax 516.791.1622
1 Ivy Pl, Valley Stream, NY 11581-2613
Jirina Fishman, Md, Psychiatrist

Flax Medical Practice **845.362.2557**
Fax 845.638.6992
E-mail ....drflax@aol.com
11 Medical Park Dr Ste 102, Pomona,
NY 10970-3559
James Flax, Psychiatrist

Flynn Medical Practice **518.371.8899**
Fax 518.371.8803
PO Box 486, Clifton Park, NY 12065-0486
Robert Flynn, Psychiatrist

Fogarty Medical Practice **914.738.1534**
1055 Grant Ave, Pelham, NY 10803-3439
Thomas Fogarty, Psychiatrist

Fogelman Medical Practice **845.354.1141**
Fax 845.623.4520
971 Route 45 Ste 108, Pomona, NY 10970-3529
John Fogelman, Psychiatrist

Foote Medical Practice **718.231.6964**
Fax 718.920.6538
3302 Steuben Ave, Bronx, NY 10467-2806
Jay Foote, Pyschiatrist

Fordham Tremont Community Mental Health Ctr
(CMHC) **718.960.0300**
Fax 718.901.1345
Web ....www.fordhamtremont.org
E-mail ....msullivan@fordhamtremont.org
2021 Grand Concourse Fl 10, Bronx, NY 10453-4304
Martha Adams Sullivan, Executive Director

Forensic Mental Health **716.858.8095**
120 W Eagle St Fl 1, Buffalo, NY 14202-3895
Michael Ranney, Director

Forester Medical Practice **212.249.7253**
51 E 73rd St, New York, NY 10021
Bruce Forester, Psychiatrist

Forester Medical Practice **914.337.4444**
55 Northway, Bronxville, NY 10708-2325
Bruce Forester, Pyschiatrist

Foster Adoptive Parent **716.769.7587**
Web ....
E-mail ....
2125 Mann Rd, Clymer, NY 14724

Four Winds - Saratoga **518.584.3600**
Web ....fourwindshospital.com
E-mail ....jgacek@fourwindshospital.com
30 Crescent Avenue, Saratoga Springs, NY 12866
Ms. Jacqueline Gacek, Accreditation Manager
Joint Commission accredited organization.

Four Winds - Saratoga **518.584.3600**
Fax 518.583.2265
Web ....www.fourwindshospital.com
E-mail ....rgreenbaum@fourwindshospital.com
30 Crescent Ave, Saratoga Springs, NY 12866-5100
Robert Greenbaum, Phd, Executive/clinical Director

Four Winds, Inc. **914.763.8151**
Web ....www.fourwindshospital.com
E-mail ....jmcnamara@fourwindshospital.com
800 Cross River Road, Katonah, NY 10536
Ms. Julie Mcnamara, Accreditation Manager
Joint Commission accredited organization.

Fox Medical Practice **212.674.8622**
515 E 72nd St, New York, NY 10021
Herbert Fox, MD, Psychiatrist

Fraier Medical Practice **914.969.2550**
480 N Broadway Ste 3, Yonkers, NY 10701-1990
Ronald Fraier, Psychiatrist

Frank Medical Practice **212.986.2500**
Fax 212.305.1249
104 E 40th St Rm 802, New York, NY 10016-1810
David Frank, MD, Psychiatrist

Fras Medical Practice **607.722.3023**
33 Avon Rd, Binghamton, NY 13905-4201
Ivan Fras, Psychiatrist

Fredland Medical Practice **212.722.9136**
121 E 95th St, New York, NY 10128-1723
Mio Fredland, MD, Psychiatrist

Friedes Medical Practice 631.329.2293
Fax 631.329.3135
  PO Box 1893, East Hampton, NY 11937-0907
  Stephen Freides, Psychiatrist

Friedman Medical Practice 212.496.1777
Fax 212.496.4007
E-mail ....cfriedman1@aol.com
  30 W 86th St Apt 1F, New York, NY 10024-3600
  Cathy Friedman, Psychiatrist

Friedman Medical Practice 212.799.5723
Fax 212.877.6030
E-mail ....mefriedman@gmail.com
  205 W End Ave, New York, NY 10023
  Michelle Friedman, Psychiatrist

Frogel Medical Practice 516.482.5377
  78 Oxford Blvd, Great Neck, NY 11023-2329
  Marvin Frogel, Psychiatrist

Fromberg Medical Practice 212.535.3728
Fax 212.517.8820
  50 E 72nd St, New York, NY 10021-4246
  Vivian Fromberg, Psychiatrist

Fuchs Medical Practice 212.988.0798
  239 E 79th St, New York, NY 10075
  Ruth Fuchs, MD, Psychiatrist

Fule Medical Practice 718.435.0158
  3918 7th Ave, Brooklyn, NY 11232-3202
  Ofelia Fule, Psychiatrist

Furer Medical Practice 212.534.7988
  166 E 93rd St, New York, NY 10128-3711
  Manuel Furer, Psychiatrist

Furer Medical Practice 212.427.2692
  150 E 90th St, New York, NY 10128-2328
  Walter Furer, MD, Psychiatrist

Furstenberg Medical Practice 212.923.1030
Fax 212.923.1427
  610 W 173rd St, New York, NY 10032
  Sylvia Furstenberg, DO, Psychiatrist

Fyer Medical Practice 212.734.2749
  50 E 89th St, New York, NY 10128-1225
  Abby Fyer, MD, Psychiatrist

Fyer Medical Practice 212.861.2586
Fax 212.439.6357
  242 E 72nd St, New York, NY 10021-4574
  Minna Fyer, Psychiatrist

Glendale Mental Health 718.456.7001
Fax 718.456.9470
Web ....www.ccbq.org
  6729 Myrtle Ave, Ridgewood, NY 11385-7063
  Steven Kampton, Director

Glens Falls Hospital 518.926.1000
Web ....www.glensfallshospital.org
E-mail ....carehart@glensfallshosp.org
  100 Park Street, Glens Falls, NY 12801
  Ms. Carrie Arehart, Accreditation Manager
  Joint Commission accredited organization.

Good Shepherd Svcs Family Reception Ctr 718.788.0666
Fax 718.965.0365
Web ....www.goodshepherds.org
E-mail ....lee_turner@goodshepherds.org
  441 4th Ave, Brooklyn, NY 11215-3903
  Lee Turner, Program Director

Goodhope Youth Home 607.387.5562
Fax 607.387.3537
Web ....www.htva.net
E-mail ....ghyh@clarityconnect.com
  4010 Mcintyre Rd, Trumansburg, NY 14886-9637
  John A. Gaines, IV, Executive Director

**Graham-Windham Svcs For Families And
Children** 212.529.6445
Fax 212.614.9811
Web ....www.graham-windham.org
E-mail ....jensenp@graham-windham.org
  33 Irving Pl Fl 4, New York, NY 10003-2385
  Paul Jensen, President/ CEO

Greater Binghamton Health Center 607.773.4082
Web
  ......www.omh.state.ny.us/omhweb/facilities/bipc/facility.htm
E-mail ....cheryl.minnier@omh.ny.gov
  425 Robinson Street, Binghamton, NY 13904
  Ms. Cheryl Minnier, Accreditation Manager
  Joint Commission accredited organization.

Greater Birmingham Health Ctr 607.773.4082
Fax 607.773.4387
Web ....www.omh.state.ny.us
E-mail ....bidomrd@omh.state.ny.us
  425 Robinson St, Binghamton, NY 13904-1775
  Margaret Dugan, Director

**Greenwich House Counseling Ctr Mental Health
Project** 212.255.8980
Fax 212.647.1509
Web ....www.greenwichhouse.org
E-mail ....rgrossman@greenwichhouse.org
  122 W 27th St Fl 3, New York, NY 10001-6274
  Rosalie Grossman, Hiv Director

Hamilton-Madison House Inc 212.720.4540
Fax 212.732.9297
Web www.hmh100.com
  253 South St, New York, NY 10002-7827
  Peter Yee, Executive Director

Harlem Hospital Center 212.939.1340
E-mail ....shahims@nychhc.org
  506 Lenox Avenue, New York, NY 10037-1802
  Dr. Sara Shahim, Accreditation Manager
  Joint Commission accredited organization.

Helpline 716.282.5432
Fax 716.433.3847
Web ....www.mhanc.com
E-mail ....cblacklock@mhanc.com
  36 Pine St, Lockport, NY 14094-3632
  Cheryl Blacklock, Executive Director

**Herbert G Birch School For Exceptional
Children** 718.591.8100
Fax 718.969.2941
Web ....www.hgbirch.org
E-mail ....ellen.mollen@birchfamilyservices.org
  7164 168th St, Fresh Meadows, NY 11365-3242
  Ellen Mollen, Principal

Hope For Youth, Inc. 631.691.5100
Fax 631.691.5104
Web ....www.hfyny.org
E-mail ....dhegarty@hfyny.org
  201 Dickson Ave, Amityville, NY 11701
  Dr. David Hegarty, Executive Director

Hospital Center 718.245.5315
E-mail ....natalie.german@nychhc.org
  451 Clarkson Avenue, Brooklyn, NY 11203
  Ms. Natalie German, Accreditation Manager
  Joint Commission accredited organization.

House Of The Good Shepherd 315.235.7600
Fax 315.235.7609
Web ....www.hgs-utica.com
E-mail ....billh@hgs-utica.com
  1550 Champlin Ave, Utica, NY 13502-4894
  William Holicky, Executive Director

Hudson River HealthCare, Inc 914.734.8800
Web ....www.hrhcare.org
E-mail ....dmiller@hrhcare.org
  1037 Main Street, Peekskill, NY 10566
  Dr. Daniel Miller, Accreditation Manager
  Joint Commission accredited organization.

Hutchings Psychiatric Center 315.426.3600
E-mail ....humrpfl@omh.state.ny.us
  620 Madison Street, Syracuse, NY 13210
  Ms. Patricia Bronson, Accreditation Manager
  Joint Commission accredited organization.

Institute for Community Living, Inc. 212.385.3030
Fax 212.385.0845
Web ....www.iclinc.net
  40 Rector Street, Eighth Floor, New York, NY 10006
  CARF accredited programs available.

Interfaith Medical Center 718.613.4001
Web ....www.interfaithmedical.com
E-mail ....bmarshall@interfaithmedical.com
  1545 Atlantic Avenue, Brooklyn, NY 11213
  Ms. Barbara Marshall, Accreditation Manager
  Joint Commission accredited organization.

JBFCS Boro Park 718.435.5700
Fax 718.854.5495
Web ....www.jbfcs.org
E-mail ....fwilbur@jbfcs.org
  1273 53rd St 1st Fl, Brooklyn, NY 11219
  Faye Wilbur, Director

JBFCS South Brooklyn 718.339.5300
Fax 718.339.9082
Web ....www.jbfcs.org
E-mail ....jcoyle@jbfcs.org
  333 Ave X, Brooklyn, NY 11223
  Jeffery Coyle, Director

Jewish Board Of Family & Children's Svcs 718.601.2280
Fax 718.601.2281
E-mail ....kcwalinski@jbfcs.org
  521 W 239th St, Bronx, NY 10463
  Karen Cwolinski, Director

Jewish Board Of Family & Children's Svcs 718.372.3300
Fax 718.996.8758
  2928 W 36th St, Brooklyn, NY 11224
  Tonya Harrah, Director

Jewish Board Of Family & Children's Svcs 718.676.4210
Fax 718.676.4216
Web ....www.jbfcs.org
  2020 Coney Island Ave, Brooklyn, NY 11223-2329
  Inna Litrovnik, Director

Jewish Board Of Family & Children's Svcs 718.761.9800
Fax 718.370.1142
Web ....www.jbfcs.org
  2795 Richmond Ave Ste 31, Staten Island,
  NY 10314-5857
  Valerie Mitchell-fadil, Deputy Executive Director

**Jewish Board Of Family And Children's Svcs,
Inc** 212.582.9100
Fax 212.956.5676
Web ....www.jbfcs.org
  135 W 50 St 6th Fl, New York, NY 10020-3320
  Paul Levine, President/CEO

**JGB Mental Health And Mental Retardation Svcs
Inc** 212.769.6259
Web ....www.jgb.org
E-mail ....gdursch@omh.state.ny.us
  15 W 65th St, New York, NY 10023-6601
  Goldie Dursch, Director

John T. Mather Memorial Hospital 631.473.1320
Web ....www.matherhospital.org
E-mail ....mgordon@matherhospital.org
  75 North Country Road, Port Jefferson,
  NY 11777-2190
  Mrs. Maryanne Gordon, Accreditation Manager
  Joint Commission accredited organization.

Joseph P Addabbo Family Health Ctr Inc 718.945.7150
Fax 718.945.2596
Web ....www.addabbo.org
  6200 Beach Channel Dr, Fl 2, Arverne, NY 11692
  Peter Nelson, Executive Director

New York

Karen Horney Clinic Inc **212.838.4333**
Fax 212.838.7158
Web ....www.karenhorneyclinic.org
E-mail ....theclinic@karenhorneyclinic.org
329 E 62nd St Ofc 1, New York, NY 10021
Dr. Henry Paul, Executive Director

Kingsbrook Jewish Medical Ctr **718.604.5000**
Fax 718.604.5527
Web ....www.kingsbrook.org
585 Schenectady Ave Ste 1, Brooklyn,
NY 11203-1809
Pinkha Sov, Director

**Lake Grove Schools-Mountain Lake Children's
Residence** **518.523.4300**
Fax 518.523.5322
386 River Rd, Lake Placid, NY 12946-3213
Carol Prevost, Executive Director

Lake Shore Behavioral Health **716.882.3151**
Fax 716.886.4002
Web ....www.lake-shore.org
625 Delaware Ave Ste 204, Buffalo, NY 14202-1007
Elmira Sulejmanovic, Director

Lake Shore Behavioral Health Inc **716.822.2117**
Fax 716.822.8165
3176 Abbott Rd, orchard park, NY 14127
Kathleen Delano, Director

Lasalle School, Inc **518.242.4731**
Fax 518.242.4747
Web ....www.lasalle-school.org
391 Western Ave, Albany, NY 12203
William Wolff, Executive Director

League for the Hard of Hearing **917.305.7800**
Fax 917.305.7888
Web ....www.chchearing.org
50 Broadway Fl 6, New York, NY 10004-3810
Lori Hannon, Director

Leake & Watts Services, Inc. **914.375.8700**
Fax 917.963.7048
Web ....www.leakeandwatts.org
463 Hawthorne Avenue, Yonkers, NY 10705
COA accredited organization.

Lenox Hill Hospital **212.434.3365**
Fax 212.702.7579
Web ....www.lenoxhillhospital.org
E-mail ....jgorsky@lenoxhill.net
210 E 64 St, 4th Fl, New York, NY 10065
Joshua Gorsky, Clinical Director

**Lexington Center for Recovery, Inc./Methadone Maintenance
Treatment Program** **845.486.2850**
Fax 845.486.2770
Web ....www.lexingtonctr.org
116 Radio Circle, Suite 307, Mt. Kisco, NY 10549
COA accredited organization.

Life Line **585.275.5151**
Fax 585.760.8260
E-mail ....cborsa@thehealthassociation.org
1 Mount Hope Ave Ste 2, Rochester, NY 14620-1059
Carol Borsa, Director

Lincoln Hall, Inc. **914.248.7474**
Fax 914.248.8391
Web ....www.lincolnhall.org
E-mail ....jflavin@lincolnhall.org
145 Route 202, Lincolndale, NY 10540
Jack Flavin, Executive Director

Long Island Jewish Medical Center **516.470.7000**
Web ....www.lij.edu
E-mail ....lcary@nshs.edu
270-05 76th Avenue, New Hyde Park, NY 11040
Mrs. Lisa Cary, Accreditation Manager
Joint Commission accredited organization.

Lutheran Clinic **718.854.1851**
Fax 718.437.5239
Web ....www.lmcmc.com
514 49th St, Brooklyn, NY 11220-2010
Thomas Cruise, Director

Maimonides Developmental Ctr **718.283.1900**
Fax 718.635.7062
Web ....www.maimonides.org
931 49th St, Brooklyn, NY 11219
Pam Bryer, President

Maimonides Medical Center **718.283.6000**
Web ....www.maimonidesmed.org
E-mail ....sgoldberg@maimonidesmed.org
4802 Tenth Avenue, Brooklyn, NY 11219-2916
Ms. Susan Goldberg, Accreditation Manager
Joint Commission accredited organization.

Maimonides Medical Ctr- Childrens Svcs **718.283.8128**
Fax 718.635.7290
920 48th St, Brooklyn, NY 11219
Allen Hilfer, Director

Manhattan Psychiatric Ctr **212.961.8700**
Fax 212.866.2760
163 W 125th St, Fl 11 & Fl 12, New York, NY 10027
Lucy Borges Smith, Director

Maplebrook School **845.373.9511**
Fax 845.373.7092
Web ....www.maplebrookschool.org
E-mail ....maplebrookschool@aol.org
5142 Route 22, Amenia, NY 12501-5357
Donna Konkolics, Director

Martin D. Porres Group Home **718.527.0606**
Fax 718.723.1528
Web ....www.mdp.org
E-mail ....profrano@mdp.org
13625 218th St, Springfield Gardens,
NY 11413-2299
Br. Phillip Rofrano, Executive Director
COA accredited organization.

MBCS Outpatient Mental Health **212.795.9888**
Fax 212.795.9899
Web ....www.jbfcs.org
E-mail ....ppayne@jbfcs.org
549 W 180th St, New York, NY 10033
Patricia Payne, Director

Mcquade Children's Svcs **845.561.0436**
Fax 845.561.5720
Web ....www.mcquade.org
E-mail ....lpearson@mcquade.org
623 Blooming Grove Tpke, New Windsor, NY 12553
Lois Pearson, Director Of Treatment Services

Mental Patient's Liberation Alliance **800.654.7227**
Fax 315.732.5625
Web ....www.recoveryisreal.org
E-mail ....georgeebert@yahoo.com
13 Hopper St, Bronx, NY 10458
George Ebert, Director

MercyFirst **516.921.0808**
Fax 516.921.4542
Web ....www.mercyfirst.org
525 Convent Road, Syosset, NY 11791-3864
COA accredited organization.

Metropolitan Hospital **212.423.6501**
Fax 212.423.8535
E-mail ....meryl.weinberg@nycc.org
1901 1st Ave, New York, NY 10029
Meryl Weinberg, Sr. Vice President

Metropolitan Hospital Center **212.423.6501**
E-mail ....patricia.jones@nychhc.org
1901 First Avenue, New York, NY 10029
Ms. Patsy Jones, Accreditation Manager
Joint Commission accredited organization.

Mohawk Valley Psychiatric Center **315.738.3800**
Web
.....www.omh.state.ny.us/omhweb/facilities/mvpc/facility.htm
E-mail ....mvnrcac@omh.state.ny.us
1400 Noyes Street, Utica, NY 13502
Ms. Cecilia Corts, Accreditation Manager
Joint Commission accredited organization.

Mount Sinai Medical Ctr **212.241.7181**
Web ....www.msnyuhealth.org
1 Gustave L Levy Pl Fl 12, New York, NY 10029
Andrew Aaronson, Director

Mt Vernon Family Mental Health Clinic **914.668.8938**
Fax 914.668.2545
6 Gramatan Ave Ste 401, Mount Vernon, NY 10550
Ann Bramer, Clinic Supervisor

**New York City Health And Hospitals Corporation Gouverneur
Hospital Diagnostic And Treatment Ctr** **212.238.7050**
Fax 212.925.7532
227 Madison St, New York, NY 10002-7537
Dr. Nardochi, Director

**New York City Health and Hospitals Corporation Harlem
Hospital Ctr** **212.939.1000**
Fax 212.939.3536
506 Malcolm X Blvd Fl 5, New York, NY 10037
Carol Roberts-matthews, Administrator

**New York City Health And Hospitals Corporation Queens
Hospital Ctr** **718.883.2710**
Fax 718.883.6167
8268 164th Pl, Jamaica, NY 11432-1825
Meyer Rao, Psychiatrist

**New York Flushing Hospital And Medical
Ctr** **718.670.5562**
Fax 718.670.4571
14601 45th Ave, Flushing, NY 11355
Daniel Chen, Psychiatrist

New York Presbyterian Hospital **212.305.5977**
Fax 212.305.8394
635 W 165th St, New York, NY 10032
John Sash, Clinic Director

New York Psychiatric Institute **212.942.8500**
Fax 212.567.2019
26 Sherman Ave, New York, NY 10040-1602
Diana Dragatsi, Director

NewYork-Presbyterian Hospital **212.746.5454**
Web ....www.nyp.org
E-mail ....pkeill@nyp.org
525 E. 68th St., New York, NY 10065
Ms. Patricia Keill, Accreditation Manager
Joint Commission accredited organization.

**North Shore Child And Family Guidance
Ctr** **516.626.1971**
Fax 516.626.8043
Web ....www.northshorechildguidance.org
480 Old Westbury Rd, Roslyn Heights, NY 11577
Andrew Malekoff, Executive Director

Northeast Parent & Child Society **518.346.1284**
Fax 518.377.8714
Web ....www.neparentchild.org
530 Franklin Street, Schenectady, NY 12305
COA accredited organization.

Ogdensburg Mental Clinic **315.394.0101**
Fax 315.394.0097
109 Ford St, Ogdensburg, NY 13669-1419
Patrick Lyons, Director

Opportunities **315.598.4717**
Fax 315.592.7533
Web ....www.oco.org
239 Oneida St, Fulton, NY 13069-1228
Diane Cooper-Carrier, Executive Director

Oswego Hospital **315.349.5566**
Web ....oswegohealth.org
E-mail ....mglass@oswegohealth.org
   110 West Sixth Street, Oswego, NY 13126
   Ms. Margaret Glass, Accreditation Manager
   Joint Commission accredited organization.

Parson's Child & Family Ctr **518.426.2600**
Fax 518.447.5234
Web ....www.parsonscenter.org
E-mail ....schimmr@parsonscenter.org
   60 Academy Rd, Albany, NY 12208-3198
   Raymond Schimmer, Chief Executive Officer

Parsons Child and Family Ctr **518.463.0050**
Fax 518.436.0699
   1450 Western Ave, Ste 102, Albany, NY 12203
   Kathleen Naughter, Director

Peekskill Community Health Ctr **914.734.8800**
Fax 914.734.8745
E-mail ....hhargrove@nrhcare.org
   1037 Main St Ste C, Peekskill, NY 10566
   Heidi Hargrove, Operations Manager

Phelps Memorial Hospital Ctr **914.366.3000**
Fax 914.366.1017
   701 N Broadway, sleepyhollow, NY 10591-1096
   Steve Safin, Chief Executive Officer

Phoenix Houses of New York, Inc...........**646.505.2000**
Web ....www.phoenixhouse.org
   164 West 74th Street, New York, NY 10023
   CARF accredited programs available.

Postgraduate Ctr for Mental Health Inc **212.560.6711**
Fax 212.889.5501
Web ....www.pgcmh.org
E-mail ....jjennings@pgcmh.org
   344 W 36th St, New York, NY 10018-6486
   JoElla Jennings, Director

Puerto Rican Family Institute Inc **718.275.0983**
Fax 718.275.7973
   9131 Queens Blvd Ste 618, Elmhurst, NY 11373
   Esther Huer, Director

Puerto Rican Family Institute Mental Health
Dept **212.229.6905**
Fax 212.691.5635
Web ....www.prfi.org
   145 W 15th St, New York, NY 10011-6701
   Jolanda Winn, Program Director

Queens Child Guidance Ctr **718.657.7100**
Fax 718.657.7137
Web ....www.ccny.org
   8956 162nd St, Jamaica, NY 11432
   Annie John, Clinic Administrator

Queens Children's Psychiatric Center **718.264.4600**
E-mail ....john.holmes@omh.ny.gov
   74-03 Commonwealth Boulevard, Bellerose,
   NY 11426
   Mr. John Holmes, Accreditation Manager
   Joint Commission accredited organization.

Queens Children's Psychiatric Ctr **718.264.4500**
Fax 718.264.4954
   7403 Commonwealth Blvd, Bellerose, NY 11426
   Tom Mcolvin, Director

Queens Hospital Center **718.883.2351**
Web ....www.nyc.gov/hac.org
E-mail ....frasera@nychhc.org
   82-68 164th Street, Jamaica, NY 11432
   Ms. Anne Fraser, Accreditation Manager
   Joint Commission accredited organization.

Richmond Medical Center **718.818.1234**
Web ....www.rumcsi.org
E-mail ....lgiacomoni@rumcsi.org
   355 Bard Avenue, Staten Island, NY 10310
   Mrs. Lora Giacomoni, Accreditation Manager
   Joint Commission accredited organization.

Riverdale Mental Health Ctr, Child And Adolescent Drug Abuse
Program **718.796.5300**
Fax 718.548.1161
Web ....www.rmha.org
E-mail ....rmb@rmha.org
   5676 Riverdale Ave, Ste 102, Bronx, NY 10471
   Robert Brewster, Deputy Executive Director

Rochester General Hospital **585.922.4000**
Web ....www.rochestergeneral.org
E-mail ....cindy.bileschi@rochestergeneral.org
   1425 Portland Avenue, Rochester, NY 14621
   Ms. Cynthia Bileschi, Accreditation Manager
   Joint Commission accredited organization.

Rochester Mental Health Center **585.922.2500**
E-mail ....cindy.bileschi@rochestergeneral.org
   490 East Ridge Road, Rochester, NY 14621
   Ms. Cynthia Bileschi, Accreditation Manager
   Joint Commission accredited organization.

Rochester Mental Health Ctr **585.922.2500**
Fax 585.922.2646
Web ....www.viahealth.org
E-mail ....lynn.volringer@viahealth.org
   490 E Ridge Rd, Rochester, NY 14621
   Lynn Volringer, Adminstrator

Rochester Psychiatric Ctr **585.241.1200**
Fax 585.241.1424
E-mail ....mzuber@omh.state.ny.us
   1111 Elmwood Ave, Rochester, NY 14620
   Mike Zuber, Executive Director

Rockland Children's Psychiatric Center **845.680.4040**
E-mail ....john.dixon@omh.ny.gov
   2 First Avenue, Orangeburg, NY 10962
   Mr. John Dixon, Accreditation Manager
   Joint Commission accredited organization.

Sagamore Children's Psychiatric Center **631.370.1701**
E-mail ....scqassf@omh.state.ny.us
   197 Half Hollow Road, Dix Hills, NY 11746
   Mr. Stephen Ferrante, Accreditation Manager
   Joint Commission accredited organization.

Sagamore Children's Psychiatric Ctr **631.370.1700**
Fax 631.370.1714
   197 Half Hollow Rd, Huntington Station, NY 11746
   Dennis Dubey, Executive Director

Seafield Center, Inc...........................**631.288.1122**
Web ....www.seafieldcenter.com
E-mail ....mepley@seafieldcenter.com
   7 Seafield Lane, Westhampton Beach, NY 11978
   Mr. Mark Epley, Accreditation Manager
   Joint Commission accredited organization.

Services for the UnderServed **212.633.6900**
Fax 646.486.0022
Web ....www.susinc.org
E-mail ....dcolonna@susinc.org
   305 Seventh Avenue, Tenth Floor, New York,
   NY 10001
   Donna Colonna, CEO
   CARF accredited programs available.

Skills Unlimited Inc **631.567.3320**
Fax 631.567.3285
Web ....www.skillsunlimited.org
E-mail ....info@skillsunlimited.org
   405 Locust Ave, Oakdale, NY 11769-1695
   Richard Kassnove, Director

South Beach Psychiatric Center **718.667.2300**
Web ....www.omh.state.ny.us/
E-mail ....sbnrnmt@omh.state.ny.us
   777 Seaview Avenue, Staten Island, NY 10305
   Ms. Natalie Toomey, Accreditation Manager
   Joint Commission accredited organization.

South Brooklyn Medical Administrative Services,
Inc...**718.788.2594**
Fax 718.788.5848
Web
.http://hometown.aol.com/sobro685/myhomepage/business.html
   685 Third Avenue, Brooklyn, NY 11232
   COA accredited organization.

South Nassau Communities Hospital **516.632.3999**
Web ....www.southnassau.org
E-mail ....rragusa@snch.org
   1 Healthy Way, Oceanside, NY 11572
   Ms. Ruth Ragusa, Accreditation Manager
   Joint Commission accredited organization.

St Catherine's Ctr For Children **518.453.6700**
Fax 518.453.6712
Web ....www.st-catch.org
E-mail ....hhayes@st-cath.org
   40 N Main Ave Ste 3, Albany, NY 12203-1481
   Helen M. Hayes, Executive Director

St Colman's Home **518.273.4911**
Fax 518.273.3312
E-mail ....pbvm@stcolmans.com
   11 Haswell Rd, Watervliet, NY 12189-1302
   Mother Mary Carmel Fuda, Executive Director

St Joseph's Villa Of Rochester **585.865.1550**
Fax 585.865.5219
   3300 Dewey Ave, Rochester, NY 14616-3795
   Joseph G. Gullo, Director Of Intake

St Luke's-Roosevelt Hospital Ctr **212.523.4068**
Fax 212.523.4069
Web ....www.chpnet.org
E-mail ....hmcquist@chpnet.org
   411 W 114th St, New York, NY 10025
   Hunter Mcquistion, Director

St. Agatha Home / Turning Point **845.623.3461**
Fax 845.623.6244
Web ....www.nyfoundling.org
E-mail ....jscott@nyfoundling.org
   235 N Main St Ste 14, Spring Valley, NY 10977
   Joseph Scott, Director

St. Barnabas Hospital **718.960.6108**
Web ....stbarnabashospital.org
E-mail ....debra_kramer@stbarnabas-ny.org
   4422 Third Avenue, Bronx, NY 10457
   Ms. Debra Kramer, Accreditation Manager
   Joint Commission accredited organization.

St. James Mercy Hospital **607.324.8703**
Web ....www.stjamesmercy.org
E-mail ....nkhork@sjmh.org
   411 Canisteo Street, Hornell, NY 14843
   Mrs. Nancy Khork, Accreditation Manager
   Joint Commission accredited organization.

St. John's Episcopal Hospital - South Shore **718.869.7400**
Web ....www.ehs.org
E-mail ....sbehar@ehs.org
   327 Beach 19th Street, Far Rockaway, NY 11691
   Ms. Sharon Behar, Accreditation Manager
   Joint Commission accredited organization.

St. John's Residence For Boys **718.945.2800**
Fax 718.945.4662
Web ....www.stjohnsresidence.org
E-mail ....thomas.trager@dfa.state.ny.us
   144 Beach 111th St, Rockaway Park, NY 11694-2592
   Dr. Thomas N Trager, Executive Director

St. Joseph's Hospital **914.378.7839**
Web ....www.saintjosephs.org
E-mail ....fran.casola@saintjosephs.org
   127 South Broadway, Yonkers, NY 10701
   Ms. Frances Casola, Accreditation Manager
   Joint Commission accredited organization.

New York

New York

St. Joseph's Villa of Rochester **585.865.1550**
Web ....www.stjosephsvilla.org
E-mail ....rlustig@stjosephsvilla.org
3300 Dewey Avenue, Rochester, NY 14616
Dr. Robert Lustig, Accreditation Manager
Joint Commission accredited organization.

St. Lawrence Psychiatric Center **315.541.2279**
E-mail ....aimee.dean@omh.ny.gov
One Chimney Point Drive, Ogdensburg, NY 13669
Ms. Aimee Dean, Accreditation Manager
Joint Commission accredited organization.

St. Lawrence Psychiatric Ctr **315.287.2811**
Fax 315.287.4743
Web ....www.omh.state.ny.us
E-mail ....shutcheson@omh.state.ny.us
28 William St, Gouverneur, NY 13642-1405
Sara Hutcheson, Program Director

St. Luke's-Roosevelt Hospital Center **212.523.4000**
Web ....www.wehealny.org
E-mail ....ejohansson@chpnet.org
1000 10th Avenue, New York, NY 10019
Ms. Eva Johansson, Accreditation Manager
Joint Commission accredited organization.

St. Mary's Hospital **518.770.7592**
Web ....www.smha.org
E-mail ....cameronw@smha.org
427 Guy Park Avenue, Amsterdam, NY 12010
Mr. William Cameron, Accreditation Manager
Joint Commission accredited organization.

Staten Island University Hospital **718.226.9000**
Web ....www.siuh.edu
E-mail ....klefkovic@siuh.edu
475 Seaview Avenue, Staten Island, NY 10305
Ms. Karen Lefkovic, Accreditation Manager
Joint Commission accredited organization.

Stony Lodge Hospital, Inc. **914.941.7400**
Web ....www.stonylodgehospital.com
E-mail ....shannonstroppel@optimum.net
40 Croton Dam Road, Ossining, NY 10562
Ms. Shannon Stroppel, Accreditation Manager
Joint Commission accredited organization.

Strong Memorial Hospital **585.275.2121**
Fax 585.273.1118
Web ....www.urmc.rochester.edu
601 Elmwood Ave, Rochester, NY 14642-0001
Steven Golstein, CEO

Summit Park Hospital **845.364.2700**
Web ....www.co.rockland.ny.us
E-mail ....fellaa@co.rockland.ny.us
50 Sanitorium Road, Pomona, NY 10970
Mrs. Anne Fella, Accreditation Manager
Joint Commission accredited organization.

Summit School **845.358.7772**
Web ....www.summitschoolqueens.com
E-mail ....dbrizer@summitnyack.com
339 N Broadway, Nyack, NY 10960-1522
David Brizer, Psychiatrist

Syracuse Community Health Center, Inc. **315.476.7921**
Web ....www.schcny.com
E-mail ....cdj1@schcny.com
819 South Salina Street, Syracuse, NY 13202
Ms. Crystal Jordan, Accreditation Manager
Joint Commission accredited organization.

Terrace Group Home **585.336.8130**
Fax 585.336.8150
160 Northaven Ter, Rochester, NY 14621
Jim Boyer, Director

**The Cabrini Mental Health Ctr Outpatient Psychiatry
Clinc** **212.995.7288**
227 E 19th St, Fl 7, New York, NY 10003
Frank Badillo, Director

The Charlton School **518.399.8182**
Web ....www.thecharltonschool.org
P.O. Box 47, Burnt Hills, NY 12027
COA accredited organization.

**The Children's Home of Poughkeepsie, NY,
Inc.** **845.452.1420**
Fax 845.452.1488
Web ....www.childrenshome.us
10 Children's Way, Poughkeepsie, NY 12601
COA accredited organization.

The Children's Home RTF, Inc. **607.656.9004**
Web ....www.stillwaterrtf.org
E-mail ....psmith@stillwaterrtf.org
638 Squirrel Hill Road, Chenango Forks, NY 13746
Mr. Paul Smith, Accreditation Manager
Joint Commission accredited organization.

The Dale Assoc Inc **716.693.9961**
Fax 716.693.4402
89 B River Rd, North Tonawanda, NY 14120
Patricia Copeland, Director

The Family Foundation School **845.887.5213**
Web ....www.thefamilyschool.com
E-mail ....cscott@thefamilyschool.com
431 Chapel Hill Road, Hancock, NY 13783
Mr. Christopher Scott, Accreditation Manager
Joint Commission accredited organization.

The House of the Good Shepherd **315.235.7600**
Web ....www.hgs-utica.com
E-mail ....nanettec@hgs-utica.com
1550 Champlin Avenue, Utica, NY 13502
Ms. Nanette Conney, Accreditation Manager
Joint Commission accredited organization.

The Institute for Family Health **212.633.0800**
Web www.Institute2000.org
E-mail ....rlecky@institute2000.org
16 East 16th Street, New York, NY 10003
Mr. Richard Lecky, Accreditation Manager
Joint Commission accredited organization.

The Kildonan School **845.373.8111**
Fax 845.373.9793
Web ....www.kildonan.org
425 Morse Hill Rd, Amenia, NY 12501-5209
Ben Powers, Headmaster

The Long Island Home **631.264.4000**
Web ....www.south-oaks.org
E-mail ....cmoran@south-oaks.org
400 Sunrise Highway, Amityville, NY 11701
Adm. Christine Moran, Accreditation Manager
Joint Commission accredited organization.

**The Mount Sinai Adolescent Health Ctr Of Mount Sinai
Hospital** **212.423.3000**
Fax 212.423.2920
Web ....www.mountsinai.org
E-mail ....angela.diaz@mountsinai.org
312 E 94th St, New York, NY 10128-5604
Angela Diaz, Md, Director

The Mount Sinai Medical Center **212.241.6500**
Web ....www.mountsinai.org
E-mail ....marianne.coughlin@mountsinai.org
100th Street and Fifth Avenue, New York,
NY 10029-6574
Ms. Marianne Coughlin, Accreditation Manager
Joint Commission accredited organization.

The Neighborhood Ctr Inc **315.272.2730**
Fax 315.337.0675
E-mail ....sandra@neighborhoodctr.org
195-199 W Dominick St, Rome, NY 13440
Sandra Soroka, Director

The Neighborhood Ctr Inc **315.272.2700**
Fax 315.732.2229
628-632 Mary St, Utica, NY 13501
Sandra Soroka, Director

Timothy Hill Children's Ranch **631.369.1234**
Fax 631.369.0130
Web ....www.timothyhillranch.org
E-mail ....thud@timothyhillranch.org
298 Middle Rd, Riverhead, NY 11901-2034
Thaddaeus Hill, Executive Director

Toomey Residential And Community Svcs **315.424.1845**
Fax 315.424.7567
E-mail ....jdamore@ccoc.us
1654 W Onondaga St, Syracuse, NY 13204-3318
Judy D'amore, Executive Director

Transitional Svcs Assoc- Kaydeross House **518.587.4277**
Fax 518.583.1196
Web ....www.tsa-inc.org
57 Kirby Rd, Saratoga Springs, NY 12866
Sharon Andersen, Program Director

**Transitional Svcs for New York -- Crisis & Counseling
Ctr** **718.526.8400**
Fax 718.297.8658
90-27 Suthin Blvd, Jamaica, NY 11435
Mark Burnstein, Director

**Warren Washington Assoc For Mental
Health** **518.747.2284**
Fax 518.747.2253
Web ....www.wwamh.org
E-mail ....peter@wwamh.org
3043 State Route 4, Hudson Falls, NY 12839-9632
Peter Groff, Chief Executive Officer

Westchester Medical Center **914.493.7000**
Web ....www.worldclassmedicine.com
E-mail ....mcfarlanev@wcmc.com
100 Woods Road, Valhalla, NY 10595
Ms. Vanessa McFarlane, Accreditation Manager
Joint Commission accredited organization.

**Western New York Children's Psychiatric
Center** **716.677.7000**
E-mail ....wcasdtp@omh.state.ny.us
1010 East and West Road, West Seneca, NY 14224
Mr. David Privett, Accreditation Manager
Joint Commission accredited organization.

William George Agency For Children Svcs **607.844.6460**
Fax 607.844.4053
Web ....www.georgejuniorrepublic.com
380 Freeville Rd, Freeville, NY 13068-9684
Brad Herman, Msw, Executive Director

CHILDREN'S HOSPITAL

Adirondack Medical Center **518.891.4141**
Web ....www.amccares.org
2233 State Route 86, Saranac Lake, NY 12983
Margaret Sorensen, Chief Nursing Officer

Albany Medical Center **518.262.3125**
43 New Scotland Ave, Albany, NY 12208
Maryallen Plass, Chief Nursing Officer

Arnot Ogden Medical Center **607.737.4100**
600 Roe Ave, Elmira, NY 14905
Anthony Cooper, Chief Executive Officer

Auburn Memorial Hospital **315.255.7011**
17 Lansing St, Auburn, NY 13021
Scott Balluchi, Chief Executive Officer

Aurelia Osborn Fox Memorial Hospital **607.432.2000**
1 Norton Ave, Oneonta, NY 13820
John Remillard, Chief Executive Officer

Bassett Medical Center **607.547.3456**
1 Atwell Rd, Cooperstown, NY 13326
William Stamp, Director

Bellevue Hospital Center **212.562.4141**
462 First Ave 27 St, New York, NY 10016
Linda Curtiz, Chief Executive Officer

Benedictine Hospital **845.338.2500**
105 Marys Ave, Kingston, NY 12401
David Lundquist, Chief Executive Officer

Beth Israel Medical Center 212.420.2000
First Avenue , 16th St, New York, NY 10003
Harris Magner, Chief Executive Officer

Bon Secours Community Hospital 845.858.7000
160 East Main St, Port Jervis, NY 12771
Jeff Reilley, Vice President

Brookdale Hospital Medical Center 718.240.5000
Linden Blvd at Brookdale Plz, Brooklyn, NY 11212

Brooks Memorial Hospital 716.366.1111
529 Central Ave, Dunkirk, NY 14048
Jonathan Lawrence, Chief Executive Officer

Buffalo General Hospital 716.859.5600
Web ....www.kaleidahealth.org
100 High ST, Buffalo, NY 14203
Marybeth Campo, Director of Nursing

Carthage Area Hospital 315.493.1000
1001 West St, Carthage, NY 13619
Baker Walter, Administrator

Chenango Memorial Hospital 607.337.4111
179 North Broad St, Norwich, NY 13815
Dr. Drake Lamen, President/CEO

Columbia Memorial Hospital 518.828.7601
71 Prospect Ave, Hudson, NY 12534
Jane Ehrlich, Director

Community Hospital 585.786.2233
400 North Main St, Warsaw, NY 14569
Leon Kuczmarski, Chief Executive Officer

Coney Island Hospital 718.616.3000
2601 Ocean Parkway, Brooklyn, NY 11235

Corning Hospital 607.937.7200
176 Denison Parkway East, Corning, NY 14830
Shirley Magana, President/CEO

Cortland Regional Medical Center 607.756.3500
134 Homer Ave, Cortland, NY 13045
Brian Mitter, Chief Executive Officer

Crouse Hospital 315.470.7111
736 Irving Ave, Syracuse, NY 13210

CVPH Medical Center 518.561.2000
75 Beekman St, Plattsburgh, NY 12901
Stephens Mundy, Chief Executive Officer

Eastern Nygra Hospital Lockport Site 716.514.5700
521 East Avenue, Lockport, NY 14094
Clare Haar, Chief Executive Officer

Edward John Noble Hosp of Gouverneur 315.287.1000
77 West Barney St, Gouverneur, NY 13642

Elmhurst Hospital Center 718.334.4000
E-mail ....nychhc.org
79 01 Broadway, Elmhurst, NY 11373
Chris Constantino, Director

Faxton St Lukes Healthcare 315.624.6000
1676 Sunset Ave, Utica, NY 13502
Scott Perra, Chief Executive Officer

FF Thompson Hospital 585.396.6000
350 Parrish St, Canandaigua, NY 14424
Jennifer Vezault, Head Of Dept.

Flushing Hospital Medical Center 718.670.5000
45th Ave at Parsons Blvd, Flushing, NY 11355
Bruce Flanz, Chief Executive Officer

Franklin Hospital 516.256.6000
900 Franklin Ave, Valley Stream, NY 11580
Joseph Manopella, Chief Executive Officer

Hospital Center 718.245.3131
451 Clarkson Ave, Brooklyn, NY 11203
Antonio Martin, President

Hospital for Special Surgery 212.606.1000
535 East 70th St, New York, NY 10021
Louis Shapiro, Chief Executive Officer

Hudson Valley Hospital Center 914.737.9000
1980 Crompond Rd, Cortlandt Manor, NY 10567
Ruth Johnson, Human Resource Director

Huntington Hospital 631.351.2200
270 Park Ave, Huntington, NY 11743
Kevan Lawlor, Director

Interfaith Medical Center 718.613.4000
1545 Atlantic Ave, Brooklyn, NY 11213
Patricia Cahill, Vice President, Nursing

Jacobi Medical Center 718.918.5000
E-mail ....william.walsh@nvhn.net
1400 Pelham Pkwy S, Bronx, NY 10461
Bill Walsh, Vice President

Jamaica Hospital Medical Center 718.206.6000
8900 Van Wyck Expwy, Richmond Hill, NY 11418
Jacqueline Holley, Nursing Director

Jones Memorial Hospital 585.593.1100
191 North Main St, Wellsville, NY 14895
Tracy Gates, Chief Executive Officer

Kingston Hospital 845.331.3131
396 Broadway, Kingston, NY 12401
David Lundquist, Chief Executive Officer

Lawrence Hospital Center 914.787.1000
55 Palmer Ave, Bronxville, NY 10708
Edward Dinan, Chief Executive Officer

Lenox Hill Hospital 212.434.2000
100 East 77th St, New York, NY 10021
Frank Danza, Executive Director

Lincoln Medical And Mental Health Centre 718.579.5000
234 East 149th St, Bronx, NY 10451
Joan Caiazzo, Associate Director

Long Beach Medical Center 516.897.1000
E-mail ....dmelzer@lbmc.org
455 East Bay Dr, Long Beach, NY 11561
Douglas Melzer, Chief Executive Officer

Long Island College Hospital 718.780.1000
339 Hicks St, Brooklyn, NY 11201
Dominick Stanzione, President

Long Island Jewish Medical Center 718.470.7000
270 05 76th Ave, New Hyde Park, NY 11040

Lutheran Medical Center 718.630.7000
150 55th St, Brooklyn, NY 11220
Wendy Goldstein, President/CEO

Maimonides Medical Center 718.283.6000
4802 Tenth Ave, Brooklyn, NY 11219
Pam Brier, President

Massena Memorial Hospital 315.764.1711
One Hospital Dr, Massena, NY 13662
Charles Fahd, Chief Executive Officer

Medical Center 914.493.7000
100 Wood Rd, Valhalla, NY 10595
Michael Israel, Chief Executive Officer

Medina Memorial Hospital 585.798.2000
200 Ohio St, Medina, NY 14103
Jim Sinner, Chief Executive Officer

Mercy Hospital 716.826.7000
565 Abbott Rd, Buffalo, NY 14220
Cj Urlaub, Chief Executive Officer

Metropolitan Hospital Center 212.423.6262
1901 First Ave, New York, NY 10029
Meryl Weinberg, Director

Montefiore Medical Center 718.920.4321
111 East 210th St, Bronx, NY 10467
Steven Sasyer, President

Montefiore Medical Center N Division 718.920.9000
600 East 233rd St, Bronx, NY 10466
Steven Safyer, Chief Executive Officer

Mount Sinai Medical Center 212.241.6500
One Gustave L Levy Place, New York, NY 10029
Dr. Kenneth Davis, Chief Executive Officer

New York Methodist Hospital 718.780.3000
506 Sixth St, Brooklyn, NY 11215

New York Presbyterian Univ Hosp of Colu 212.746.5454
525 East 68th St, New York, NY 10065
Herbert Pardes, President

North Central Bronx Hospital 718.519.5000
3424 Kossuth Ave, Bronx, NY 10467
Barbera Rofado, Administrator

North Shore University Hospital 516.562.0100
300 Community Dr, Manhasset, NY 11030
Susan Somerville, Executive Director

Northern Westchester Hospital 914.666.1200
400 East Main St, Mount Kisco, NY 10549
Joel Seligman, President

Nyack Hospital 845.348.2000
E-mail ....dfreedd@nyackhospital.org
160 N Midland Ave, Nyack, NY 10960
David Freed, Chief Executive Officer

NYU Langone Medical Center 212.263.7300
550 First Ave, New York, NY 10016
Robert Grossman, Chief Executive Officer

Olean General Hospital 716.373.2600
515 Main St, Olean, NY 14760
Timothy Finan, Chief Executive Officer

Oneida Healthcare Center 315.363.6000
321 Genesee St, Oneida, NY 13421
Karen Perry, Manager

Orange Regional Medical Center 845.343.2424
E-mail ....sbatulis@ormc.org
60 Prospect Ave, Middletown, NY 10940
Scott Batulis, Chief Executive Officer

Oswego Hospital 315.349.5511
110 West Sixth St, Oswego, NY 13126
Ann Gilpin, President

Our Lady of Lourdes Memorial Hospital 607.798.5111
169 Riverside Dr, Binghamton, NY 13905
David Patak, Chief Executive Officer

Putnam Hospital Center 845.279.5711
670 Stoneleigh Ave, Carmel, NY 10512
Dianna Mcgregor, Chief Executive Officer

Queens Hospital Center 718.883.3000
82 68 164th St, Jamaica Estates, NY 11432
Julius Wool, Executive Director

Rochester General Hospital 585.922.4000
1425 Portland Ave, Rochester, NY 14621
Mark Clement, Chief Executive Officer

Rome Memorial Hospital 315.338.7000
1500 North James St, Rome, NY 13440
Basil Ariglio, President

Roswell Park Cancer Institute 716.845.2300
E-mail ....ASKRTCI@ROSWELLPARK.ORG
Elm and Carlton St, Buffalo, NY 14263
Dr. Donald Trump, President

Samaritan Medical Center 315.785.4000
830 Washington St, Watertown, NY 13601
Thomas Carman, Chief Executive Officer

Seton Health St Marys Hospital 518.268.5000
1300 Massachusetts Ave, Troy, NY 12180
Scott Stgeorge, Chief Executive Officer

Sisters of Charity Hospital 716.862.1000
2157 Main St, Buffalo, NY 14214
Peter Burkman, Chief Executive Officer

South Nassau Community Hospital 516.632.3000
One Healthy Way, Oceanside, NY 11572

Southampton Hospital 631.726.8200
240 Meeting House Lane, Southampton, NY 11968
Robert Chaloner, Chief Executive Officer

Southside Hospital 631.968.3000
301 East Main St, Bay Shore, NY 11706
Winnie Mack, Chief Executive Officer

New York

St Barnabas Hospital 718.960.9000
   4422 3rd Ave, Bronx, NY 10457
   Dr. Scott Cooper, President

St Elizabeth Medical Center 315.798.8100
   2209 Genesee St, Utica, NY 13501
   Richard Ketcham, Chief Executive Officer

St Francis Hospital and Health Centers 845.483.5000
   241 North Rd, Poughkeepsie, NY 12601
   Robert Savage, Chief Executive Officer

St James Mercy Hospital 607.324.8000
   411 Canisteo St, Hornell, NY 14843
   Mary Larowe, Chief Executive Officer

St Johns Episcopal Hospital 718.869.7000
E-mail ....ntoebbe@ehs.org
   327 Beach 19th St, Far Rockaway, NY 11691
   Nelson Toebbe, Chief Executive Officer

St Josephs Medical Center 914.378.7000
   127 South Broadway, Yonkers, NY 10701
   Michael Spicer, President

St Lukes Cornwall Hospital 845.561.4400
   70 Dubois St, Newburgh, NY 12550

St Lukes Roosevelt Hospital Center 212.523.4000
   1111 Amsterdam Ave, New York, NY 10025

St Peters Hospital 518.525.1550
   315 South Manning Blvd, Albany, NY 12208
   Steven Boyle, Chief Executive Officer

Staten Island University Hospital 718.226.9000
   475 Seaview Ave, Staten Island, NY 10305
   Donna Proske, Coordinator

Stony Brook University Medical Center 631.689.8333
   State University of New York, Stony Brook, NY 11794
   Steven Strongwater, Chief Executive Officer

SUNY Upstate Medical University 315.464.5540
   750 East Adams St, Syracuse, NY 13210
   John McCabe, Chief Executive Officer

United Health Services Hospitals 607.763.6000
   3357 St Harrison St, Binghamton, NY 13790
   Mathew Salanger, Chief Executive Officer

United Memorial Medical Center 585.343.6030
   127 North St, Batavia, NY 14020
   Mark Schoell, Chief Executive Officer

University Hospital of Brooklyn SUNY 718.270.1000
E-mail ....debra.carey@downstatehospital
   445 Lenox Rd, Brooklyn, NY 11203
   Debra Carey, Chief Executive Officer

University of Rochester Medical Center 585.275.2100
   601 Elmwood Ave, Rochester, NY 14642

Vassar Brothers Medical Center 845.454.8500
   45 Reade Place, Poughkeepsie, NY 12601
   Daniel Harrison, Chief Executive Officer

White Plains Hospital Center 914.681.0600
   Davis Avenue and Post Road, White Plains, NY 10601
   John Schlander, Chief Executive Officer

Winthrop University Hospital 516.663.0333
   259 First St, Mineola, NY 11501
   John Collins, President

COUNSELING SERVICES

Arc 518.377.2186
Fax 518.377.2189
Web ....www.arcschenectady.org
E-mail ....lscrotta@arcschenectady.org
   214 State St, Schenectady, NY 12305-1887
   Lisa Scrotta, Director

Catholic Charities 716.856.4494
Fax 716.856.2005
Web ....www.ccwny.org
E-mail ....revj.sicari@ccwny.org
   525 Washington St, Buffalo, NY 14203-1796
   Katrina D, Director

Catholic Youth Organization 718.448.4949
Fax 718.448.0576
   120 Anderson Ave, Staten Island, NY 10302
   Mike Neely, Director

Central Nassau Guidance And Counseling Svcs,
Inc. 516.822.6111
Fax 516.396.0553
E-mail ....bbartell@centralnassau.org
   950 S Oyster Bay Rd, Hicksville, NY 11801-3511
   Barbara Bartell, Lcsw, Acsw, Executive Officer

Children's Aid Society, Adoption/Foster Home
Div 212.949.4800
Fax 212.680.8216
E-mail ....rbarry@childrensaidsociety.org
   150 E 45th St, New York, NY 10017-3192
   Richard Barry, CEO

Co-Op City Svcs 718.320.3082
Fax 718.379.4348
Web ....www.jbfcs.org
E-mail ....pthomas@jbfcs.org
   135 Einstein Loop Rm 46, Bronx, NY 10475-4961
   Pierre Thomas, Director

Coalition For Hispanic Family Svcs 718.497.6090
Fax 718.497.9495
Web ....www.hispanicfamilyservicesny.org
E-mail ....mgonzales@hispanicfamilyservicesny.org
   315 Wyckoff Ave Ste 4, Brooklyn, NY 11237-5842
   M. Gonzales, Director

Community Counseling And Mediation 718.802.0666
Fax 718.858.9493
Web ....www.ccmnyc.org
E-mail ....knachman@ccmnyc.org
   1 Hoyt St Fl 7, Brooklyn, NY 11201
   Emory Brooks, Executive Director

Family Svc Of Westchester 914.948.8004
Fax 914.948.0299
Web ....www.sfw.org
   1 Summit Ave, White Plains, NY 10606-3003
   Susan Wayne, President/CEO

Inwood House 212.861.4400
Fax 212.535.3775
Web ....www.inwoodhouse.com
E-mail ....lbryant@inwoodhouse.com
   320 E 82nd St, New York, NY 10028-4118
   Linda Bryant, Executive Director

New York Community Trust 212.686.0010
Fax 212.532.8528
Web ....www.ny.communitytrust.org
   909 3rd Ave Fl 22, New York, NY 10022
   Lori Slutsky, Director

Puerto Rican Family Institute 718.299.3045
Fax 718.716.2605
Web ....www.prfi.org
   4123 3rd Ave, Bronx, NY 10457
   Lourdes Sanchez, Program Director

St Vincent's Mental Health Svcs 718.522.6011
Fax 718.522.1560
   333 Atlantic Ave, Brooklyn, NY 11201
   Bremaine Saylea, Doctor

The Spence-Chapin-Svcs To Families And
Children 212.369.0300
Fax 212.369.8589
Web ....www.spence-chapin.org
E-mail ....eforhman@spence-chapin.org
   410 E 92nd St, New York, NY 10128-6883
   Emily Forhman, Executive Director

CRISIS & SHELTER CARE

Adirondack Saratoga RC - Glens Falls 518.792.6545
Fax 518.792.8586
E-mail ....ferrisg@usa.redcross.org
   74 Warren St, Glens Falls, NY 12801
   Gary Ferris, Director

Aid To Victims Of Violence 607.753.3639
Fax 607.753.8774
Web ....www.cortlandywca.org
   14 Clayton Ave, Cortland, NY 13045-2502
   Linda Shutts, Director

Allen Women's Resource Ctr 718.739.6200
Fax 718.739.2818
E-mail ....dmccune@allenwomens.Org
   11031 Merrick Blvd, Jamaica, NY 11433
   D Mccune, Executive Secretary

Alternatives For Battered Women 585.232.5200
Fax 585.232.3955
E-mail ....cathym@abwrochester.org
   PO Box 39601, Rochester, NY 14604-9601
   Catherine Mozzota, Director

Astor Home For Children 845.871.1000
Fax 845.876.2020
Web ....www.astorservices.org
E-mail ....jmcguirk@astorservices.org
   6339 Mill St, Rhinebeck, NY 12572-1495
   Dr. James McGuirk, Director

Catholic Charities 607.334.3532
Fax 607.336.5779
Web ....www.catholiccharitiesbc.org
E-mail ....jsereno@ccofcc.com
   3 Ohara Dr, Norwich, NY 13815-2000
   Daniel Auwarter, Director

Catholic Charities 518.234.3581
Fax 518.234.8423
Web ....www.catholiccharitiessc.org
E-mail ....ccsc@csdsl.net
   489 W Main St, Cobleskill, NY 12043-4641
   Dan Denofio, Executive Director

Catholic Charities- Domestic Violence Victims
Assistance 518.842.3384
Fax 518.627.0152
E-mail ....Lisa.Ghenoiu@Cc-Fmc.Org
   1 Kimball St, Amsterdam, NY 12010
   John Nasso, Director

Cattaraugus Somestic Violence Program 716.945.1041
Fax 716.945.1301
Web ....www.ccaction.org
E-mail ....amaitland@ccaction.org
   25 Jefferson St, Salamanca, NY 14779
   Amy Maitland, Director

Cayuga/Seneca Community Action Agency - Domestic Violence
Intervention Program 315.255.1703
Web ....www.cscaa.com
E-mail ....ladidio@cscaa.com
   65 State St, Auburn, NY 13021-3427
   Laurie Didio, Director

Chautauqua Opportunities 716.366.3333
Fax 716.366.7366
Web ....www.chautauquaopportunities.com
E-mail ....rkeller@chautopp.org
   17 W Courtney St, Dunkirk, NY 14048-2754
   Roberta Keller, Executive Director

Children's Home 315.788.7430
Fax 315.785.5637
Web ....www.nnychildrenshome.com
E-mail ....krichmond@nnychildrenshome.com
   1704 State St, Watertown, NY 13601
   Karen Richmond, Executive Director

Circulo De La Hispanidad- Domestic
Violence 516.431.1135
Fax 516.431.2307
Web ....www.cdlh.org
E-mail ....sbrewster@cdlh.org
   26 W Park Ave, Long Beach, NY 11561-2049
   Sarah Brewster, Director

Coalition Against Domestic Violence 516.465.4700
Fax 516.465.4740
Web ....www.cadvnc.org
E-mail ....contacts@cadvnc.org
  15-10 Grumman Road West, Bethpage, NY 11714
  Sharon Hoahing, Director Of Operations

Columbia- Greene Domestic Violence
Program 518.943.9211
Fax 518.943.4719
Web ....www.cagcny.org
E-mail ....bpalmateer@cagcny.org
  53 S Jefferson Ave, Catskill, NY 12414-2109
  Barbara Palmateer, Director

Compass House 716.886.0935
Fax 716.886.8387
Web ....www.compasshouse.org
E-mail ....sylviahnadler@roadrunner.com
  370 Linwood Ave, 1451 Main Street, Buffalo,
  NY 14209
  Lisa Freeman, Assistant Executive Director

Cornerstone Manor 716.854.8181
Fax 716.852.5428
Web ....www.buffalocitymission.org
  150 E North St, Buffalo, NY 14203
  Ellen Grant, Director

Crime Victims And Sexual Violence Ctr 518.447.7100
Fax 518.447.7102
Web ....www.albanycounty.com
E-mail ....cvsvc@albanycounty.com
  112 State St Rm 1100, Albany, NY 12207-2022
  Karen Ziegler, Director

Crime Victims Assistance Program 845.340.3443
Fax 845.340.3223
E-mail ....cvap@co.ulster.ny.us
  5 Pearl St, Kingston, NY 12401
  Madeleine Miller, Sr. Counselor

Crime Victims Treatment Ctr 212.523.4728
Fax 212.523.4781
E-mail ....sxenarios@cvtc-slr.org
  411 Amsterdam Ave, New York, NY 10025
  Ms Susan Xenarios, Director

Ctr Against Domestic Violence 718.254.9134
Fax 718.254.9132
E-mail ....jkahan@centeragainstdv.org
  25 Chapel St Ste 904, Brooklyn, NY 11201
  Judith Kahan, Chief Executive Officer

Domestic Violence Assistance 585.589.3159
Fax 585.589.3154
E-mail ....deann.cork@dva.state.ny.us
  14016 State Route 31, Albion, NY 14411
  Deann Cork, Director

Domestic Violence Intervention Program 212.410.9080
Fax 212.410.9117
Web ....www.vipmujeres.org
  PO Box 1161, New York, NY 10035-0810
  Cecilia Gaston, Director

Domestic Violence Program Of Herkimer
Co 315.866.0458
Fax 315.894.6313
Web ....www.cvb.state.ny.us
  61 West St, Ilion, NY 13357-1723
  Jackie Ward, Director

Domestic Violence Project 518.793.9496
Fax 518.793.9499
E-mail ....Ccdvp@Spa.Net
  35 Broad St, Glens Falls, NY 12801
  Rachel Gartner, Director

Domestic Violence Project 518.453.6650
Fax 518.453.6792
Web ....www.ccrcda.org
E-mail ....ken.raymond@rcda.org
  40 N Main Ave, Albany, NY 12203
  Kenneth Raymond, CEO

Domestic Violence Svcs 518.583.0280
Fax 518.583.2215
  480 Broadway, Ste LL2.0, Saratogasprings, NY 12866
  Maggie Frank, Director

Dorothy Day House 315.476.0617
Fax 315.295.2382
Web ....www.ccoc.us
E-mail ....mholmes@ccoc.us
  1654 W Onondaga St, Syracuse, NY 13204
  Melody Holmes, Director

Emergency Housing Group 845.343.7115
Fax 845.342.3175
Web ....www.emergencyhousinggroup.org
E-mail ....ehgceo@warwick.net
  38 Seward Ave, Bldg 14, Middletown, NY 10940
  John Harper, Director

Family Counseling Svcs Of Northern NY 315.782.4483
Fax 315.785.9210
Web ....www.fcsnny.org
E-mail ....fcs_ftass@imcnet.net
  120 Washington St Ste 510, Watertown,
  NY 13601-3477
  Collene Alexander, Executive Director

Family Svcs 845.452.1110
Fax 845.452.1119
Web ....www.familyservicesny.org
E-mail ....swest@familyservicesny.org
  29 N Hamilton St, Poughkeepsie, NY 12601
  Sue West, President

Fordham Tremont Mental Health Ctr 718.960.3000
Fax 718.583.6610
E-mail ....smcdonald@fordhamtremont.org
  2021 Grand Concourse, 7th Floor, Bronx, NY 10453
  Martha Sullivan, Executive Director

Gateway 607.584.7800
Fax 607.584.7801
Web ....www.catholiccharitiesbc.org
  86-88 Walnut St, Binghamton, NY 13905
  Sandra Olson, Division Director

Grace Smith House 845.471.3038
Fax 845.471.3039
E-mail ....susanp@gracesmithhouse.org
  Southern Dutchess, Poughkeepsie, NY 12602
  Susan Pomeroy, Director

Green Chimneys Children's Svcs 212.491.5911
Fax 212.368.8975
Web ....www.greenchimneys.org
  456 W 145th St, New York, NY 10031
  Jeremy Filwiler, Director

Haven House 716.884.6002
Fax 716.884.2354
Web ....www.childfamilybny.org
E-mail ....Kjoyce@Child-Family.Org
  451 Ellicott Station, Buffalo, NY 14201
  Katey Joyce, Director

Henry Street Shelter 212.475.6400
Fax 212.533.4004
Web ....www.henrystreet.org
E-mail ....fdrayton@henrystreet.org
  130 Baruch Place, NewYork, NY 10002
  Frances Drayton, Director

Hillside Children's Ctr 607.275.0067
Fax 607.275.9760
Web ....www.hillside.com
  120 W State St Ste 3, Ithaca, NY 14850-5441
  Trudy Pantella, Program Manager

Hope Store 914.747.0828
Fax 914.747.3825
E-mail ....chorton@northernwestchestershelter.org
  39 Washington Ave Fl 2, Pleasantville, NY 10570
  Carlla Horton, Director

Hudson River Housing 845.454.5176
Fax 845.485.1641
Web ....www.hudsonriverhousing.org
E-mail ....pkellett@hudsonriverhousing.org
  313 Mill St, Poughkeepsie, NY 12601
  Patrice Kellett, Director Of Youth Services

Joseph's House & Shelter 518.272.2544
Fax 518.272.9370
Web ....www.josephshouseandshelter.org
E-mail ....tneitzel@josephshousetroy.org
  74 Ferry St, Troy, NY 12180-4116
  Tracy Neitzel, Director

Liberty Resources- Victims Of Violence 315.363.0048
Fax 315.363.0052
E-mail ....tsvanepps@liberty-resources.org
  218 Liberty St Ste 1, Oneida, NY 13421-1679
  Tammy Van Epps, Supervisor

Long Island Crisis Ctr 516.679.1111
Fax 516.781.8306
Web ....www.longislandcrisiscenter.org
E-mail ....lleonard@longislandcrisiscenter.org
  2740 Martin Ave Unit 2, Bellmore, NY 11710
  Linda Leonard, Director

Mechanicville Domestic Violence Advocacy
Program 518.664.4008
Fax 518.664.9457
E-mail ....Mquillinan@Mechanicvilleacsc.Org
  6 S Main St, Mechanicville, NY 12118
  Megan Quillinan, Director

Mercy House 518.434.3531
Fax 518.426.1276
  12 St Josephs Ter, Albany, NY 12210
  Mokaya Bosire, Director

Mowhawk Valley Community Action
Agency 315.339.5640
Fax 315.339.2981
Web ....www.mvcaa.com
E-mail ....aturner@mvcaa.com
  207 N James St, Rome, NY 13440-5886
  Amy Turner, Executive Director

My Sisters Place Inc 914.683.1333
Fax 914.683.1412
Web ....www.mysistersplaceny.org
E-mail ....kcheekslomax@mysistersplaceny.org
  1 Water St Ste 300, White Plains, NY 10601
  Karen Cheeks-lomax, Executive Director

Ofc Of Domestic Violence And Emergency Intervention
Svcs 212.331.4500
Fax 212.331.4486
Web ....www.hra.nyc.gov
E-mail ....noelc@hra.nyc.gov
  180 Water St, Rm 2407, New York, NY 10038
  Cecile Noel, Deputy Commissioner

Opportunities 315.376.8202
Fax 315.376.8421
  8265 State Route 812, Lowville, NY 13367
  Scott Mathis, Director

Opportunities Youth Svcs 315.342.7532
Fax 315.342.7554
Web ....www.oco.org
E-mail ....youthservices@oco.org
  75 1st Ave, Midtown Plaza, Oswego, NY 13126
  Sarah Irlend, Division Director

Project Safe 518.374.0166
Fax 518.374.2497
  1344 Albany St, Schenectady, NY 12304-2716
  Delores Edmonds-mcintosh, Executive Director

Putnam N. Westchester Women's Resource
Ctr 845.628.9284
Fax 845.628.9272
Web ....www.pnwwrc.org
E-mail ....Info@pnwwrc.org
  935 S Lake Blvd, Ste 2, Mahopac, NY 10541-3222
  Ann Ellsworth, Director

New York

Reachout **315.265.2422**
Fax 315.265.1752
Web.............................www.reachouthotline.org
E-mail.......................hollis@reachouthotline.org
   PO Box 5051, Potsdam, NY 13676-5051
   Hollis Easter, Director

Renewal House **315.379.9845**
Fax 315.379.9014
E-mail.........................renewalhouse@verizon.net
   3 Chapel St, Canton, NY 13617
   Ilene Burke, Director

Ridgewood Bushwick Ctr **718.381.9653**
Fax 718.381.9680
E-mail..................................evullo@rbscc.org
   1474 Gates Ave, Brooklyn, NY 11237
   Elena Vullo, Director

Safe Against Violence **607.746.1720**
Fax 607.746.1605
Web.............................www.health.state.ny.us
E-mail................dosav@delawareopportunities.org
   35430 State Highway 10, Hamden, NY 13782-1112
   Dorothy Strachman, Director

Safe Space **212.226.3536**
Fax 718.526.3180
Web..............................www.safespacenyc.org
E-mail........................cmolner@safespacenyc.org
   8974 162 St 11432, New York, NY 10012
   Christine Molner, President/CEO

Sakhi for South Asian Women **212.714.9153**
Fax 212.564.8745
E-mail.............................contactus@sakhi.org
   Greeley Square Station, New York, NY 10001
   Tiloma Jayasinghe, Director

Salvation Army Domestic Violence
Program **716.664.6567**
Fax 716.484.2793
Web.............................www.use.salvationarmy.org
E-mail...............stacey.tanner@use.salvationarmy.org
   83 S Main St, Jamestown, NY 14701
   Stacey Tanner, Director

Salvation Army Emergency Shelter **716.884.4798**
Fax 716.888.6294
E-mail..............carolyn_hillman@use.salvationarny.org
   960 Main St, Buffalo, NY 14203
   Carolyn Hillman, Director

Samaritan House Domestic Violence **914.683.1185**
Fax 914.922.9930
   33 Church St, White Plains, NY 10601-1902
   John Rubin, Director

Sanctuary For Families **212.349.6009**
Fax 212.349.6810
E-mail.................................cnash@sffny.org
   105 Chamber St Ste 5A, New York, NY 10007
   Carolyn Nash, Director

Sex Crime Victim Ctr **518.447.7100**
Fax 518.447.7102
E-mail..............................cvsvc@albanycounty.com
   112 State St Rm 1100, Albany, NY 12207
   Karen Ziegler, Director

Sexual Assault & Crime Victims Assistance
Program **518.271.3512**
Fax 518.271.3163
Web......................................www.nehealth.com
E-mail......................krockenburgerg@nehealth.com
   2215 Burdett Ave, Troy, NY 12180-2466
   Gene Krockenburger, Director

SOS Shelter **607.748.7453**
Fax 607.748.5166
Web......................................www.sosshelter.org
E-mail.............................paterickson@hotmail.com
   1201 Park St, Endicott, NY 13761
   Patricia Erickson, Director

Spanish Action League Domestic Violence
Program **315.475.6153**
Fax 315.474.5767
   700 Oswego St, Syracuse, NY 13204-3116
   Rita Paniagua, Director

Stillwater **607.656.9004**
Fax 607.656.9076
Web......................................www.stillwaterrtf.org
E-mail..........................kwright@stillwaterrtf.org
   638 Squirrel Hill Rd, Chenango Forks, NY 13746
   Karen Wright, Director

Stop Domestic Violence **518.962.8949**
Fax 518.962.8948
Web..www.bhsn.org
E-mail..................................skelley@bhsn.org
   Main Line, Westport, NY 12993
   Susan Kelley, Director

Stop Domestic Violence/Bhsn **518.563.6904**
Fax 518.563.9958
Web..www.bhsn.org
E-mail..................................skelley@bhsn.org
   22 Us Oval, Ste 218, Plattsburgh, NY 12903-5902
   Susan Kelley, Director

Suicide Prevention And Crisis Svcs,Inc. **716.834.3131**
Fax 716.834.9881
Web..............................www.crisisservices.org
E-mail..........................dfabian@crisisservices.org
   2969 Main St, Buffalo, NY 14214-1003
   Doug Fabian, Executive Director

The Ctr For Youth Svcs **585.473.2464**
Fax 585.271.8134
Web..............................www.centerforyouth.net
E-mail......................espaull@centerforyouth.net
   905 Monroe Ave, Rochester, NY 14620-1707
   Elaine Spaull, Ph.d, Executive Director

The Family Violence Project **518.725.4310**
Fax 518.725.2556
Web......................www.thefamilycounsellingcenter.org
   11-21 Broadway St, Gloversville, NY 12078-3968
   Paul Moyer, Director

The Net Shelter And Domestic Abuse
Program **607.776.3407**
Fax 607.776.1238
E-mail......................jeaton@arbordevelopment.org
   16 W William St, Bath, NY 14810
   Jeffrey Eaton, Director

The Safe Homes Project **718.788.6947**
Fax 718.369.6151
Web......................................www.safehomesproject.org
E-mail................Catherine_Hodes@Goodshepherds.Org
   305 Seventh Ave 9th Fl, New York, NY 10001
   Catherine Hodes, Director

The Salvation Army **315.475.1688**
Fax 315.475.6307
Web......................................www.use.salvationarmy.org
E-mail.........................lwright@use.salvationarmy.org
   677 S Salina St Ste 1, Syracuse, NY 13202-3513
   Linda M. Wright, Executive Director

The Salvation Army Genesis House **585.235.2660**
Fax 585.235.2752
   35 Ardmore St, Rochester, NY 14611
   William Gutschow, Director

The Westchester Youth Svcs/Children's
Village **914.693.0600**
Fax 914.693.0671
Web..............................www.childrensvillage.org
E-mail.................jkohomban@childrensvillage.org
   1 Echo Hills, Dobbs Ferry, NY 10522
   Jeremy Kohomban, CEO

Town Of Huntington Youth Bureau **631.351.3061**
Fax 631.271.1360
E-mail..............mgeorgiou@town.huntington.ny.us
   423 Park Ave, Huntington, NY 11743-2803
   Maria Georgiou, Executive Director

Transtition Ctr For Domestic Violence **718.327.7660**
Fax 718.327.4230
Web..www.jbfcs.org
E-mail..................................lyoung@jbfcs.org
   PO Box 900629, Queens, NY 11690-0629
   Leslie Samuel-young, Director

Victim Resource Ctr **315.331.1171**
Fax 315.331.1189
E-mail..................................Vrc132@Verizon.Net
   132 Harrison St, Newark, NY 14513
   Romana Palmer, Executive Director

Victim Resource Ctr (Rape Crisis Ctr) **315.425.0818**
Fax 315.425.8942
Web..............................www.verahouse.org
E-mail.............................info@Verahouse.Org
   6181 Thompson Rd Ste 100, Syracuse,
   NY 13206-1420
   Randi Bregman, Executive Director

Westhab Special Needs Housing **914.376.0063**
Fax 914.376.5078
   20 South Broadway 12rd Fl, Yonkers, NY 10701
   M. Rita Brown, Director

Westhab, Inc. **914.345.2800**
Fax 914.345.3139
Web..www.westhab.org
E-mail.............................bob.miller@westhab.org
   85 Executive Blvd, Elmsford, NY 10523-1387
   Robert Miller, President/CEO

EDUCATION

Adirondack Experience, Inc. **518.523.1718**
Fax 518.523.8045
Web..www.adkexp.com
E-mail..............................john@adkexperience.com
   162 Adirondack Loj Rd, Lake Placid, NY 12946-4202
   John Marshall, Director

Adirondack Leadership Expeditions **518.897.5011**
Fax 518.897.5017
Web..............................www.adirondackleadership.com
E-mail..............................admissions@adkle.com
   82 Church St, Saranac Lake, NY 12983
   Ed Caooahan, Executive Director

APEX (Asian Professional
Extension)-Hotline **212.748.1225**
Fax 212.748.1250
Web..www.apex-ny.org
   80 Maiden Ln 11th Fl, New York, NY 10001-5012
   Michael Lee, Executive Director

Arc **607.535.6934**
Fax 607.535.2666
Web..............................www.arcofschuyler.org
   203 12th St, Watkins Glen, NY 14891
   James Wilson, Executive Director

Arc **607.776.4146**
Fax 607.776.9366
   1 ARC WAY, Bath, NY 14810
   Bernard Burns, Director

Arc **518.295.8130**
Fax 518.295.8969
   121 Opportunity Dr, Schoharie, NY 12157
   Desiree Loucks-Baer, Program Director

Aspira Of New York, Inc **212.564.6880**
Fax 212.564.7152
Web..www.aspira.org
E-mail..................................aspira@ny.org
   630 9th Ave, Room 302, New York, NY 10018
   Hector Gesualdo, Executive Director

Assoc For The Help Of Retarded Children New York
City **212.780.2500**
Fax 212.780.2353
Web..www.ahrcnyc.org
E-mail..................................ahrcnyc@dti.net
   83 Maiden Ln, New York, NY 10038-4736
   Michael Goldfarb, Executive Director

Assoc To Benefit Children/ Cassidy's Place.....212.831.1322
Fax....212.426.9488
Web....www.a-b-c.org
E-mail....info@a-b-c.org
419 E 86th St, New York, NY 10028-6402
Diana Vasquez, Director

Buffalo Hearing And Speech At Fredonia......716.672.2731
Fax....716.672.2739
E-mail....dmorlock@askbhsc.org
75 Chestnut St, Fredonia, NY 14063
Debra Morlock, Director

Cardinal Hayes School For Special...........845.677.6363
Fax....845.677.6691
Web....www.cardinalhayeshome.org
60 St.Joseph Dr, Millbrook, NY 12545
Fred Apers, Executive Director

Children Annex....845.336.2616
Fax....845.336.4153
Web....www.childrensannex.org
E-mail....centerforstectrumservices.org
70 Kukuk Ln, Kingston, NY 12401-6943
Susan Buckler, Administrative Director

Children's Creative Response To Conflict.......845.353.1796
Fax....845.358.4924
Web....www.crc-ny.org
E-mail....inquiries@crc-global.org
521 N Broadway, Nyack, NY 10960-1215
Pricilla Prutzman, Director

Cleary School For The Deaf....631.588.0530
Fax....631.588.0016
Web....www.clearyschool.org
E-mail....kenm@clearyschool.org
301 Smithtown Blvd, Nesconset, NY 11767-2077
Kenneth Moreson, Superintendent

Cortland Youth Bureau/Zap....607.753.3021
Fax....607.753.3023
35 Port Watson St, Cortland, NY 13045
John Mcnerny, Director

Creekside Boces Monroe #1....585.383.2239
Fax....585.383.2274
Web....www.monroe.edu
41 OConnor Rd, Fairport, NY 14450
Dan White, Superintendent

Epic Program, Inc....716.332.4100
Fax....716.332.4101
Web....www.epicforchildren.org
E-mail....richardss@epicforchildren.org
1000 Main St, Buffalo, NY 14202-1102
Shelley Richards, Progam Director

Gow School....716.652.3450
Fax....716.652.3457
Web....www.gow.org
E-mail....admissions@gow.org
2491 Emery Rd, South Wales, NY 14139
Bradley Rogers Jr., Headmaster

Hunter College Ctr For Communication Disorders....212.481.4464
Fax....212.481.3029
Web....www.hunter.cuny.edu
E-mail....csclinic@hunter.cuny.edu
425 E 25th St, New York, NY 10010-2547
Donald Vogel, Director

Institute For Special Ed....718.519.7000
Fax....718.231.9314
Web....www.nyise.org
E-mail....bkappen@nyise.org
999 Pelham Pkwy N, Bronx, NY 10469-4905
Dr. Bernadette Kappen, Executive Director

Just Kids: Early Childhood Learning Ctr.......631.924.0008
Fax....631.924.1243
Web....www.justkidsschool@aol.com
E-mail....justkidseclc@optonline.net
35 Longwood Rd, Middle Island, NY 11953
Steven Held, Director

Kennedy Child Study Ctr....212.988.9500
Fax....212.570.6690
Web....www.kenchild.org
E-mail....lperry@kenchild.org
151 E 67th St, New York, NY 10065-5998
Larry Perry, Principal/executive Director

Lavelle School For The Blind....718.882.1212
Fax....718.882.0005
Web....www.lavelleschool.org.
E-mail....fsimpson@lavelleschool.org
3830 Paulding Ave, Bronx, NY 10469-1299
W.f. Simpson, Superintendent

Learning Leaders....212.213.3370
Fax....212.213.0787
Web....www.learningleaders.org
E-mail....mduitz@learningleaders.org
80 Maiden Ln Fl 11, New York, NY 10038-4729
Mindy Duitz, President

Lexington School For The Deaf....718.350.3300
Fax....718.899.9846
Web....www.lexnyc.org
E-mail....generalinfo@lexnyc.org
30th Ave & 75th St, Jackson Heights, NY 11370
Ronnie Hollander, Principal

Long Island Jewish Medical Ctr Hearing And Speech Ctr....718.470.8910
Fax....718.347.8241
430 Lakeville Rd, New Hyde Park, NY 11042
Mark Goldstein, Medical Director

Mary Cariola Childrens Ctr....585.271.0761
Fax....585.442.3143
Web....www.marycariola.org
E-mail....dom@marycariola.org
1000 Elmwood Ave Ste 100, Rochester, NY 14620
Denise O'Brien-Miller, Executive Director

Mill Neck Manor School for the Deaf..........516.922.4100
Fax....516.922.4172
Web....www.millneck.org
E-mail....frostmill@aol.com
40 Frost Mill Rd, Mill Neck, NY 11765
Mark Prowatzke, Executive Director

New Directions Youth And Family Svcs......716.433.4487
Fax....716.433.7030
Web....www.ndyfs.org
6395 Old Niagara Rd, Lockport, NY 14094-1421
Jim Coder, Executive Director

Norman Howard School....585.334.8010
Fax....585.334.8073
275 Pinnacle Rd, Rochester, NY 14623
Joseph Martino, Executive Director

Pathfinder Village, Inc....607.965.8377
Fax....607.965.8655
Web....www.pathfindervillage.org
E-mail....info@pathfindervillage.org
3 Chenango Rd, Edmeston, NY 13335-2314
Kelly Meyers, Admissions Coordinator

Reece School....212.289.4872
Fax....212.423.9652
E-mail....thereeceschool@hotmail.com
25 E 104th St, New York, NY 10029
Thomas Colasuonno, Executive Director

Rochester School For The Deaf....585.544.1240
Fax....585.544.0495
Web....www.rsdeaf.org
E-mail....info@rsdeaf.org
1545 Saint Paul St, Rochester, NY 14621-3197
Harold Mowl Jr., Superintendent

School Of The Holy Childhood....585.359.3710
Fax....585.359.3722
Web....www.holychildhood.org
E-mail....dsyta@holychildhood.org
100 Groton Pkwy, Rochester, NY 14623
Diane Syta, Chief Financial Officer

St. Anne Institute....518.437.6500
Fax....518.437.6555
160 N Main Ave, Albany, NY 12206
Richard Riccio, Executive Director

St. Joseph's School For The Deaf....718.828.9000
Fax....718.792.6631
E-mail....stjosephs@sjsdny.org
1000 Hutchinson River Pkwy, Bronx, NY 10465
Debra Arles, Executive Director

Stephen Gaynor School....212.787.7070
Fax....212.787.3312
Web....www.stephengaynor.org
E-mail....ysiegel@stephengaynor.org
148 W 90th St, New York, NY 10032
Yvette Siegel, Education Director

Substance Abuse Program....585.786.8970
Fax....585.786.8985
Web....www.partnersforprevention.com
E-mail....jmcalver@frontiernet.net
338 N Main St, Warsaw, NY 14569-1045
Julie Calvert, Program Coordinator

The Children's School For Early Development....914.347.3227
Fax....914.347.4216
E-mail....cscdwarch@bestweb.net
40 Saw Mill River Rd, Ste 4, Hawthorne, NY 10532
Frances Porcaro, Ma, Director

The Lowell School....718.445.4222
Fax....718.353.6942
Web....www.thelowellschool.com
E-mail....dproujansky@thelowellschool.com
2420 Parsons Blvd, Whitestone, NY 11357-3444
Dede Proujansky, Ba, Ms, Executive Director

The Mary McDowell Ctr For Learning.........718.625.3939
Fax....718.625.1456
Web....www.marymcdowell.org
E-mail....deborahe@mmcl.net
20 Bergen St, Brooklyn, NY 11201-6302
Deborah Edel, Director Of Admissions

V C S, Inc....845.634.5729
Fax....845.634.7839
Web....www.volunteercounselingservice.org
E-mail....dmurnion@volunteercounselingservice.org
77 S Main St, New City, NY 10956-3511
Deborah Murnion, Executive Director

Vera House Inc....315.425.0818
Fax....315.425.8942
Web....www.verahouse.org
E-mail....rbregman@verahouse.org
6181 Thompson Rd Ste 100, Syracuse, NY 13206-1444
Randy Bregman, Executive Director Of Administration

Westchester Exceptional Children's School....914.277.5533
Fax....914.277.7219
520 Route 22, North Salem, NY 10560-2714
Linda Murphy, Ms, Director

Winston Preparatory School....646.638.2705
Fax....646.638.2706
E-mail....sbezsylko@winstonprep.edu
126 W 17th St, New York, NY 10011
Scott Bezsylko, Bs, Ma, Executive Director

FOSTER CARE AGENCIES

Adapting to Adoption....917.254.2508
E-mail....ljaffeata@gmail.com
19 W 34th St, Penthouse Level, New York, NY 10001
Leanne Jaffe, Psychotherapist

Adoption Foster Family....607.334.5596
234 County Rd 10A, Norwich, NY 13815
Jerry Barnes, Manager

New York

Adoption Group **845.427.3955**
E-mail ....snowanddike@yahoo.com
   PO Box 156, Chester, NY 10918

Adoptive Families **607.936.4706**
E-mail ....lwakeman@stny.rr.com
   750 State St 414, Beaver Dams, NY 14812

Adoptive Families Capitol Region Inc **518.448.5295**
   PO Box 656, Wynantskill, NY 12198

Adoptive Families of Westchester **914.779.1509**
   11 Bristol Pl, Yonkers, NY 10710

Adoptive Families Older Children Inc **718.380.7234**
   14932A Union Turnpike, Flushing, NY 11367

**Adoptive Family Network Central New
York** **315.458.7379**
   112 Windsor Dr, North Syracuse, NY 13212
   Terry Hochins, Chief Executive Officer

Adoptive Parents Committee Inc **212.304.8479**
E-mail ....maholly@aol.com
   PO Box 3525, Church St Station, New York,
   NY 10008
   Mark Holly, President

**Adoptive Parents Committee New York
City** **212.304.8479**
E-mail ....nycapc@hotmail.com
   PO Box 3525, New York, NY 10008

Adoptive Parents Community **914.997.7859**
E-mail ....apchudson@hotmail.com
   PO Box 625, Hartsdale, NY 10530

Camp Mu Ji Gae Inc **518.426.2600**
E-mail ....campmujigae@hotmail.com
   60 Academy Rd, Albany, NY 12208
   Linda Smith, Director

Capital District Foster Adoptive Parents **518.370.0589**
E-mail ....gwashbu1@nycap.rr.com
   4 Arden Rd, Scotia, NY 12302
   George Washbu, Director

Catholic Charities Oneida Madison Counti **315.724.2158**
E-mail ....mtimian@ccharityom.org
   1408 Genesee St, Utica, NY 13502
   Kathy Eichenlaub, Director

Catholic Family Center **585.262.7100**
E-mail ....aeichas@cfrochester.org
   87 North Clinton Ave 3rd Fl, Rochester, NY 14604
   Ann Eichas, Director

**Catholic Guardian Facility And Home
Bureau** **914.375.3746**
   23 Mention Ave, Yonkers, NY 10704
   John Frein, Chief Executive Officer

Catholic Guardian Society Home Bureau **212.371.1000**
Fax 212.755.4233
E-mail ....kdooley-polcha@cgshb.org
   1011 First Ave 7th Fl, New York, NY 10022
   John Frein, Executive Director

Center Kids The Family Project Lesbian G **212.620.7310**
Fax 212.924.2657
E-mail ....centerkids@gaycenter.org
   208 West 13th St, New York, NY 10011
   Shanequa Anderson, Coordinator

Children of the World Adoption Agency In **516.935.1235**
Fax 516.933.8532
E-mail ....cwaa@attglobal.net
   27 Hillvale Rd, Syosset, NY 11791
   Justin Herscovici, Chief Executive Officer

Childrens Aid Society **212.949.4800**
   150 East 45th St, New York, NY 10017
   Rodney Lee, Director

Community Counseling and Mediation **718.802.0666**
Fax 718.858.9493
E-mail ....danielsj@ccmnyc.org
   1 Hoyt St 7th Fl, Brooklyn, NY 11201
   George Daniels, Director

Dare to Care **607.748.5127**
E-mail ....ampurdy5127@aol.com
   640 Underwood Rd, Vestal, NY 13850
   Annmarie Purdy, President

Downey Side Families for Youth **212.714.2200**
Fax 212.714.9518
   470 7th Ave, New York, NY 10001
   Terence, Director

Dunbar Association Inc **315.476.4269**
Fax 315.471.6821
E-mail ....dunbarfamsvc@aol.com
   1453 South State St, Syracuse, NY 13205
   Louella William, Director

Edwin Gould Services Children and Famili **212.437.3500**
Fax 212.437.3598
E-mail ....afeatherstone@egscf.org
   151 Lawrence St 5th Floor, Brooklyn, NY 10006
   Arbury Featherstone, Director

Episcopal Social Service **718.401.5162**
   500 Bergen Ave, 2nd Fl, Bronx, NY 10455

Families for Russian Ukrainian Adoption **845.338.0127**
E-mail ....jlawson1@hvc.rr.com
   PO Box 834, Port Ewen, NY 12466

Families for the Future Inc **518.882.6569**
   4114 Jockey St, Ballston Lake, NY 12019

Families Through Adoption **315.733.6984**
E-mail ....davesne@adelphia.net
   10172 Campbell Rd, Sauquoit, NY 13456

**Families with Children from Camboida
Roc** **585.482.6571**
   401 Thomas Ave, Rochester, NY 14617

Families with Children From China **607.255.7274**
E-mail ....pm11@cornell.edu
   1421 Mecklenberg Rd, Ithaca, NY 14850

Families With Children From China **212.579.0115**
E-mail ....GreaterNYFCC@aol.com
   PO Box 237065, New York, NY 10023

Families with Children from China Roches **585.507.9299**
Fax 866.527.1315
E-mail ....President@fcc-rochester.org
   PO Box 93355, Rochester, NY 14692

Families with Children from Vietnam **585.787.9038**
E-mail ....dwikiera@aol.com
   1303 Hatch Rd, Webster, NY 14580

Family and Childrens Society Broome Cty **607.729.6206**
Fax 607.729.1858
   257 Main St, Binghamton, NY 13905
   Dianne Kubik, Associate Director

Forestdale Foster Adoptive Parents Assoc **718.263.0740**
   67 35 112th St, Forest Hills, NY 11375
   Anstiss Agnew, Director

Foster Adoptive Parent **716.769.7587**
   2125 Mann Rd, Clymer, NY 14724

Foster Adoptive Parent Advis **716.614.5905**
E-mail ....klyczek@niagaracc.suny.edu
   3111 Saunders Settlement Rd, Sanborn, NY 14132
   James Klyczek, President

Foster Adoptive Parent Suppo **716.694.8170**
E-mail ....trskjs@aol.com
   164 Broadmoor Dr, Tonawanda, NY 14150

Foster Adoptive Parents **845.225.1836**
   8 Iris Ct, Carmel, NY 10512

Foster Adoptive Parents **315.492.1882**
   3305 Cedarvale Rd, Nedrow, NY 13120

Foster Adoptive Parents **845.356.0922**
   One Jacqueline Rd, Monsey, NY 10952

Foster Adoptive Parents A **518.643.6849**
E-mail ....anna3md@aol.com
   1029 Rt 22 B, Plattsburgh, NY 12901

Foster Adoptive Parents Su **315.781.2762**
E-mail ....ronsaracino@gmail.com
   3402 Woodworth Rd, Geneva, NY 14456

Foster Adoptive Support Gr **315.497.2680**
Fax 315.678.2774
   12740 Maurer Rd, Cato, NY 13033

**Foster and Adoptive Family Support
Services** **315.724.2989**
Fax 315.724.4407
E-mail ....dac2547@aol.com
   2 Lowell Dr, New Hartford, NY 13413

Foster Parents **607.748.5362**
E-mail ....RMPT33@aol.com
   9512 State Route 176, Endicott, NY 13760

Foster Parents Assoc **315.393.1261**
E-mail ....sking2@twcny.rr.com
   320 Pine St, Ogdensburg, NY 13669

Foster Parents Assoc **716.792.9001**
   5695 East Main Rd, Brocton, NY 14716
   Mary Grace, Foster Parent

Friends in Adoption Long Island Supp Grp **631.878.6511**
   3 Brenda Ln, Manorville, NY 11949

Friends of Children from Asia **518.674.5802**
E-mail ....gvfalco@aol.com
   3164 NY Route 43, Averill Park, NY 12018

Gateway Longview Inc **716.883.4531**
Fax 716.883.0645
   605 Niagara St, Buffalo, NY 14201
   James Sampson, Chief Executive Officer

Grandparents Advocacy Project Inc **718.863.4776**
Fax 718.239.2815
E-mail ....keggap@optonline.net
   1595 Metropolitan Ave #6G, Bronx, NY 10462
   Ke Gibson, Director

Greater Rochester Committee For Single A **585.271.5996**
E-mail ....sbayer3@frontiernet.net
   100 Hollywood Ave, Rochester, NY 14618

Hearts Homes Post Adoption Services **315.479.3616**
Fax 315.479.1182
   677 South Salina St, Syracuse, NY 13202
   Linda Wright, Executive Director

Hillside Childrens Center **585.350.2504**
Fax 585.350.2598
E-mail ....lmaynard@hillside.com
   100 Metro Park Ste 102, Rochester, NY 14623

Hillside Chilren Center **585.654.4456**
   1337 East Main St, Rochester, NY 14609
   Sandy Gossin, Operations Manager

Home Again Adoption Support Group Inc **718.776.4224**
   205 21 113 Rd, Saint Albans, NY 11412
   Maude A Chavis, President

JCCA Ametz **212.558.9949**
E-mail ....ametz@jccany.org
   120 Wall St, New York, NY 10005

Jewish Child Care Association **212.425.3333**
Fax 212.558.9993
E-mail ....ametz@jccany.org
   120 Wall St 12th Fl, New York, NY 10005

Jewish Family Service of Rochester **585.461.0110**
   441 EastAve, Rochester, NY 14607
   Janet Sunkin, Director

Kids Peace **716.675.7065**
Fax 716.675.7060
E-mail ....info@kidspeace.org
   4184 Seneca St Ste 212, West Seneca, NY 14224
   Linda McCarcan, Program Manager

**KidsPeace Foster Care & Community
Programs** **800.726.5565**
Lockport 716.438.2080
Scotia 800.201.3005
West Seneca 800.451.3425
Kingston 866.360.0911
Ithaca 866.412.9727
Elmsford 877.205.4645
Fax 716.675.7060
Web ....www.fostercare.com
Web ....www.kidspeace.org
    4184 Seneca St, Ste 213, West Seneca, NY 14224

Kitchen Table Support Group Inc **518.406.5170**
E-mail ....mpilczuk@aol.com
    809 Plank Rd, Clifton Park, NY 12065
    Michael Pilczuk, Owner

Latin America Parents Association **718.236.8689**
E-mail ....info@lapa.com
    PO Box 339 340, Brooklyn, NY 11234

Little Flower Children Family Services **718.875.3500**
Fax 718.260.8863
E-mail ....info@lfchild.org
    186 Joralemon St, Brooklyn, NY 11201
    Grace Logrande, Chief Executive Officer

LOFT Kids **914.245.4381**
    1370 Baptist Church Rd, Yorktown Heights,
    NY 10598

Love the Children of Rochester Inc **585.727.3148**
E-mail ....connie.ltcrochester.org@gmail.com
    238 Bayway Dr, Webster, NY 14580
    Connie Nowakowski, President

Love the Children of Western New York **716.626.4367**
E-mail ....dbrady@adelphia.net
    69 Telfair Dr, Williamsville, NY 14221

Lutheran Service Society of New York **716.631.9212**
Fax 716.631.9209
E-mail ....luthsvc@aol.com
    6680 Main St PO Box 1963, Williamsville, NY 14231
    Susan Lichtenthal, Director

Lutheran Social Services of NY Inc **212.870.1100**
Fax 212.870.1172
    475 Riverside Dr Ste 1244, New York, NY 10115
    Ronald Drews, Director

MercyFirst **718.232.1500**
    6301 12th Ave, Brooklyn, NY 11219
    Jacqueline McKelvey, Vice President

Monroe Dept Of Human Services **585.753.6000**
Fax 585.753.6649
    111 Westfall Rd Rm 442, Rochester, NY 14620

New Alternatives for Children Inc **212.696.1550**
E-mail ....info@nac-inc.org
    37 West 26th St, New York, NY 10010
    Arlene Goldsmith, Executive Director

**New Beginnings Single Parent Support
Grp** **516.747.2204**
E-mail ....newbeginn@aol.com
    87 Mineola Blvd, Mineola, NY 11501
    Tim Sutfin, Director

New York Council Adoptable Children **212.714.2788**
Fax 212.714.2838
    589 Eighth Ave 15th Fl, New York, NY 10018
    Ernesto Loperna, Executive Director

**New York Foster & Adoptive Parents
Assoc** **718.725.3657**
Fax 718.725.2104
    PO Box 120151, Jamaica, NY 11412
    Mary Norwood

New York State Adoption Service **716.278.8699**
    20 E Ave, Lockport, NY 14095
    Burt Marshell, Director

New York State Adoption Service **518.481.1824**
    355 West Main St, Malone, NY 12953
    Lowell Tennyson, Director

New York State Adoption Service **518.447.5542**
    112 State Street 3rd Fl, Albany, NY 12207

New York State Adoption Service **212.676.7491**
    150 Williams St 6th Fl, New York, NY 10038

New York State Adoption Service **315.539.1800**
    1 DiPronio Dr, Waterloo, NY 13165
    Diana Fegley, Director

New York State Adoption Service **716.373.8070**
    1701 Lincoln Ave Ste 6010, Olean, NY 14760
    Kathy Boldrick, Director

New York State Adoption Service **315.785.3337**
    250 Arsenal St, Watertown, NY 13601

New York State Adoption Service **607.756.3486**
    60 Central Ave, Cortland, NY 13045
    Kristine Monroe, Commissioner

New York State Adoption Service **516.227.8273**
    60 Charles Lindbergh Blvd, Uniondale, NY 11553

New York State Adoption Service **716.858.2679**
    95 Franklin St, Buffalo, NY 14202

New York State Adoption Service **315.366.2443**
    North Court St PO Box 637, Wampsville, NY 13163
    Melissa Maine, Deputy Commissioner

New York State Adoption Service **914.995.5303**
    112 East Post Rd 4th Fl, White Plains, NY 10601

New York State Adoption Service **845.334.5174**
    1091 Development Ct, Kingston, NY 12401
    Roberto Rodriguez, Commissioner Of Social Services

New York State Adoption Service **518.565.5320**
    13 Durkee St, Plattsburgh, NY 12901
    Jay Lepage, Commissioner

New York State Adoption Service **607.274.5259**
    320 West State St, Ithaca, NY 14850
    Debbie Mckane, Supervisor

New York State Adoption Service **518.736.5615**
    4 Daisy Lane, Johnstown, NY 12095
    Amy Meade, Director

New York State Adoption Service **518.873.3441**
E-mail ....toni.teuschler@dfa.state.ny.us
    7551 Court St, Elizabethtown, NY 12932
    Toni Teuschler, Home Finder And Adoption Worker

New York State Adoption Service **585.589.7000**
    14016 Route 31 West, Albion, NY 14411
    Thomas Kuryla, Commissioner

New York State Adoption Service **607.337.1564**
    5 Court St, Norwich, NY 13815
    Bette Osborne, Commissioner

New York State Adoption Service **315.963.5534**
E-mail ....carol.vincent@dfa.state.ny.us
    100 Spring St PO Box 1320, Mexico, NY 13114
    Carol Vincent, Senior Case Worker

New York State Adoption Service **631.854.9477**
    3455 Memorial Hwy, Hauppauge, NY 11779-8900
    Anjela Pandolfo, Supervisor

New York State Adoption Service **607.737.5413**
    425 Pennsylvania Ave Box 588, Elmira, NY 14902

New York State Adoption Service **315.435.3815**
    421 Montgomery St 7th Fl, Syracuse, NY 13202

New York State Adoption Service **845.486.3068**
    60 Market St, Poughkeepsie, NY 12601
    Coleen Mahoney, Director

New York State Adoption Service **315.253.1397**
E-mail ....christine.bertot@dfa.state.ny.us
    160 Genesee St, Auburn, NY 13021
    Christine Bertot, Director

New York State Adoption Service **518.388.4399**
E-mail ....lori.pirrone@esa.state.ny.us
    106 Erie Blvd, Schenectady, NY 12305
    Lori Pirrone, Superintendent

New York State Adoption Service **607.547.6490**
E-mail ....joyce.boyd@dfa.state.ny.us
    197 Main St, Cooperstown, NY 13326
    Joyce Boyd, Commissioner Social Services

New York State Adoption Service **518.884.4157**
    152 W High St, Ballston Spa, NY 12020
    Stacy McVaigh, Supervisor

New York State Adoption Service **315.379.2190**
    6 Judson St, Canton, NY 13617
    Diane Wilby, Deputy Commissioner

New York State Adoption Service **585.344.2580**
    5130 East Main St Rd Ste 3, Batavia, NY 14020
    Kirk Patrick, Commissioner Of Social Services

New York State Adoption Service **315.531.3417**
    417 Liberty St Ste 2122, Penn Yan, NY 14527
    Dan Zeigler, Deputy Commissioner

New York State Adoption Service **518.295.8751**
    284 Main St, Schoharie, NY 12157
    Paul Brady, Commissioner

New York State Adoption Service **845.364.3535**
    Mental Health Complex Bldg C, Pomona, NY 10970

New York State Adoption Service **716.661.8234**
    110 East Fourth St, Jamestown, NY 14701

New York State Adoption Service **716.396.4111**
    3010 County Complex, Canandaigua, NY 14424

New York State Adoption Service **315.946.9733**
    77 Water St, Lyons, NY 14489

New York State Adoption Service **585.268.9425**
    7 Court St, Belmont, NY 14813

New York State Adoption Service **845.808.1500**
    110 Old Route 6 Bld 2, Carmel, NY 10512
    Michael Piazza, Commissioner

New York State Adoption Service **315.731.3480**
E-mail ....dneal@dfa.state.ny.us
    800 Park Ave, Utica, NY 13501
    Debbie Neal, Director

New York State Adoption Service **518.761.6315**
    1340 State Route 9, Lake George, NY 12845
    Anne O'Neil, Adoption Case Worker

New York State Adoption Service **518.746.2341**
    383 Broadway, Fort Edward, NY 12828

**New York State Children and Family
Services** **845.708.2498**
    11 Perlman Dr, Spring Valley, NY 10977
    Leora Neal, Adoption Specialist

**North Country Adoptive Parents Group
Inc** **315.686.3732**
    820 Rees St, Clayton, NY 13624

North Country Foster Adoptive Family Net **315.783.5562**
    27875 Wilson Ln, Chaumont, NY 13622
    Linda Simerson, Director

Northern New York Families **315.347.2178**
    68 Streeter Rd, DeKalb Junction, NY 13630
    Gary Berk, Director

NYS Foster Adoptive Parents Association **718.725.2103**
Fax 718.725.2104
    PO Box 120151, Saint Albans, NY 11412

**Onondaga Foster Adoptive Parents
Associa** **845.361.4777**
E-mail ....tpconklin@frontiernet.net
    962 Scothchman Collabar Rd, Bear Mountain,
    NY 10911

Onondaga Foster Adoptive Parents
Support 315.622.6004
E-mail ....millanese1@aol.com
16 Glenburn Rd, Liverpool, NY 13090

Otsego Adopt Inc 315.858.0304
E-mail ....dmiller14@stny.rr.com
PO Box 323, Springfield Center, NY 13468

Otsego Special Needs Adption
Information 607.263.5093
PO Box 712, Morris, NY 13808

Rochester African American Adoption Grp 595.334.9699
2126 Lehigh Station Rd, Pittsford, NY 14534

SAFFE 315.364.5161
1868 Atwater Rd, King Ferry, NY 13081

Salvation Army Foster Adoptive Parents A 212.227.8266
275 Cherry St # 17B, New York, NY 10002

SCO Family of Services 516.759.1844
Fax 516.674.3171
E-mail ....rdavenport@scony.org
1 Alexander Pl, Glen Cove, NY 11542
Ruth Davenport, General Manager

Single Mothers By Choice 212.988.0993
E-mail ....smc-office@pipeline.com
Gracie Square Station, PO Box 1642, New York, NY 10028

South Shore Adoptive Parents Group 631.968.4079
1551 Manatuck Blvd, Bay Shore, NY 11706

Southern Tier Adoptive Families 607.785.7003
PO Box 930, Vestal, NY 13851

St Vincents Services 718.422.2321
E-mail ....Henry.Floyd@svs.org
205 Montaque St, Brooklyn, NY 11201
Elissa Grossinger, Director

Stars of David FEGS Long Island Chapter 516.496.7550
6900 Jericho Trnpk Ste 306, Syosset, NY 11791
Kathy Rosenthal, Vice President

State Vincents Services Foster Adoptive 718.529.8193
111 14 131 St, South Ozone Park, NY 11420

Voice for International Development
Adop 518.282.4527
Fax 518.282.0688
E-mail ....vidaadopt@aol.com
354 Allen St, Hudson, NY 12534

Wide Horizons for Children Inc 516.922.0751
71 West Main St, Oyster Bay, NY 11771

You Gotta Believe 718.372.3003
E-mail ....ygbpat@msn.com
1728 Mermaid Ave, Brooklyn, NY 11224
Patrick O'Brien, Executive Director

HOME MEDICAL EQUIPMENT PROVIDERS

Adaptivemall.com 800.371.2778
Fax 315.429.8862
E-mail ....info@adaptivemall.com
Bergeron Health Care, 15 S Second St, Dolgeville, NY 13329

Agape Parents Fellowship Inc Buffalo 716.827.5407
Fax 716.827.5913
E-mail ....info@agapeparentsfellowship.org
3280 South Park Ave, Lackawanna, NY 14218
Donna Roberts, Executive Director

ALS Assoc Greater NY Chapter 212.619.1400
Fax 212.619.7409
E-mail ....als@als-ny.org
42 Broadway Ste 1724, New York, NY 01004
Dorina Gordon, Chief Executive Officer

American Home Patient Syracuse 315.438.3121
Fax 315.438.3122
6700 Thompson Road, Mattydale, NY 13211
Cindy Falk, Director

Americare Certified Special Srvs Inc 718.535.3100
Fax 718.872.1817
5923 Strickland Ave, Brooklyn, NY 11234

Apria Healthcare Syracuse 315.463.5217
Fax 315.463.5218
E-mail ....contact_us@apria.com
6103 E Molloy Rd, East Syracuse, NY 13057
Chris Haffer, Branch Manager

Arimed Orthotics & Prosthetics 718.875.8754
Fax 718.875.6177
302 Livingston St, Brooklyn, NY 11217
Tim Evans, Chief Executive Officer

Aspire of Western New York 716.838.0047
Fax 716.838.5925
E-mail ....info@aspirewny.org
Center for Learning, 4635 Union Road, Cheektowaga, NY 14225
Cathy Voyer, Director

Asthma Freedom Inc Buffalo 716.688.5922
Fax 716.688.5922
3845 Tonawanda Creek Rd, East Amherst, NY 14051

Audionics Queens 718.224.6100
Fax 718.224.8395
210 08 Northern Blvd, Bayside, NY 11361

Baker Victory Services Buffalo 716.828.9500
780 Ridge Road, Lackawanna, NY 14218
James Casion, Chief Executive Officer

Beltone New England LLC Bronx 718.678.8277
Fax 718.678.8278
E-mail ....jcortes@beltonene.com
2017 Williamsbridge Road, Bronx, NY 10461
John Cortes, Director

BorBas Surgical Supply Brooklyn 718.677.9066
Fax 718.677.9065
2046 Bath Ave, Brooklyn, NY 11214
Konstatine Bas, Manager

Brooklyn Audiology Assoc PC Brooklyn Ht ...718.855.4330
E-mail ....info@hearingaidexperts.co@msn.com
142 Joralemon St Ste 8B, Brooklyn, NY 11201

Brooklyn Audiology Assoc PC Sheepshead 718.449.9800
E-mail ....info@hearingaidexperts.co@msn.com
1400 Ave Z Ste 203, Brooklyn, NY 11235
Richard Kaner, Director

Care One Home Medical Equipment 212.491.1234
Fax 212.491.3565
E-mail ....ben@care1homemedical.com
2230 1st Ave, New York, NY 10029
Ben Allison, President

Center For Hearing And Communications 917.305.7700
Fax 917.305.7888
E-mail ....info@chchearing.org
50 Broadway 6th Flr, New York, NY 10004
Carmela Chesse, Administrator

Chelsea Mobility & Med Equipment 212.255.5522
Fax 212.255.4686
E-mail ....chelsea.nme@gmail.com
327 8th Ave, New York, NY 10001
Michael L, Director

Childrens Hearing Inst & NY Cochlear 646.438.7819
Fax 646.438.7844
E-mail ....jbrown@nyee.edu
Childrens Hearing Institute, 380 2nd Ave 9th Flr, New York, NY 10010
Joseph Brown, Executive Director

CNY Prosthetics Center 315.476.9697
Fax 315.476.9694
E-mail ....sheila@cnyprocenter.com
1124 E Fayette St, Syracuse, NY 13210

Creative Orthotics and Prosthetics Inc 716.635.5034
Fax 716.635.5035
E-mail ....buffalo@creativeoandp.com
4949 Harlem Rd Ste 405, Amherst, NY 14226
F. Laurie, Office Administrator

CWI Medical Healthcare Supplies 631.844.0055
E-mail ....info@CWIMedical.com
200 Allen Blvd, Farmingdale, NY 11735
Shirley Lam, Owner

CWI Medical Queens 631.753.8390
Fax 631.753.8394
E-mail ....info@cwimedical.com
200 Allen Blvd, Farmingdale, NY 11735
Shirley Lam, Chief Executive Officer

Disabled Childrens Relief Fund 516.377.1605
Fax 516.377.3978
PO Box 89, Freeport, NY 11520

Extended Home Care 212.356.4200
Fax 212.563.9264
360 West 31st St, Ste 304, New York, NY 10001

GEM Wheelchair & Scooter Srv 718.969.8600
Fax 718.969.8300
E-mail ....mywheelsturning@aol.com
176 39 Union Turnpike, Flushing, NY 11366

Hanger Orthotics and Prosthetics 716.882.7938
Fax 716.882.7974
205 Lynwood Ave, Buffalo, NY 14209
Adam Archibee, Practice Manager

Hanger Prosthetics And Orthotics 315.492.6608
Fax 315.492.6159
E-mail ....387200@hanger.com
6620 Fly Rd, Ste 203, East Syracuse, NY 13057
Ramona Fields, Practice Manager

Harmony Hearing and Speech Center 718.641.3817
E-mail ....Harcbl@aol.com
161 24 84th St, Howard Beach, NY 11414

Hear 2 Learn Syracuse 315.701.5710
Fax 315.701.5711
E-mail ....admin@hear-2-learn.com
6575 Kirkville Rd, East Syracuse, NY 13057
Arlene Marko, Director

Home Medical Specialties Queens 718.418.2000
Fax 718.326.1400
5644 59th St, Maspeth, NY 11378
Mary, Chief Executive Officer

Home Technologies Inc Queens 718.658.6161
Fax 718.291.9324
E-mail ....hometechinc@msn.com
83 37 Parsons Blvd, Jamaica Estates, NY 11432

Hospice of the Finger Lakes Syracuse 315.255.2733
1130 Corporate Dr, Auburn, NY 13021
Theresa Kline, Executive Director

Intl Mission for the Disabled Inc 718.353.3791
Fax 718.353.5695
E-mail ....imdusa@imdusa.org
135 53 Northern Blvd, 3rd Flr, Flushing, NY 11354

Jerome Belson Hlth Care Ctr Cerebral Pa 718.665.7565
Fax 718.665.7595
245 E 149th St, Bronx, NY 10451
Ira Goldberg, Director

King Medical Equip Company Bronx
Morris 718.904.9422
Fax 718.904.9516
E-mail ....kingmed1955@hotmail.com
1040 Morris Park Ave, Bronx, NY 10461

King Medical Equipment Company 718.828.1510
Fax 718.829.4849
E-mail ....kingmed1955@hotmail.com
1969 Westchester Ave, Bronx, NY 10462
Ted Stevens, Vice President

Lawrence Home Care of Westchester 914.961.2818
Fax 914.961.2982
69 Main St, Tuckahoe, NY 10707
Renee Levesque, Administrator

Lehneis Orthotics and Prosthetics Assoc 718.645.3880
Fax 516.621.7223
445 Kings Highway, Brooklyn, NY 11223

LightHouse Inernational 212.821.9200
Fax 212.821.9707
E-mail .... kcampbell@lighthouse.org
111 E 59th St, New York, NY 10022
Karen Campbell, Director Of Social Services

Linda Buch Gherardi Hlth Care Center 718.778.8587
Fax 718.735.8938
E-mail .... pmonsanto@cpofnys.org
921 E New York Ave, Brooklyn, NY 11203
Pauline Monsanto, Supervisor Director

Medstar Surgical Queens 718.460.2900
Fax 718.460.1900
E-mail .... info@medstarsurgical.com
1540 128th St, College Point, NY 11356
Zeb Pirzada, Chief Executive Officer

Metropolitan Brace & Limb Bronx 718.824.3595
Fax 718.824.4404
E-mail .... info@mblny.com
1402 Castle Hill Ave, Bronx, NY 10462

MH Mandelbaum Orthotic & Prosthetic Services,
Inc. 631.473.8668
Fax 631.473.8691
Web .... www.mhmoandp.com
E-mail .... marty@mhmoandp.com
116 Oakland Avenue, Port Jefferson, NY 11777
M Mandelbaumartin, President/CPO

Mt Carmel Pharmacy Bronx 718.364.6100
Fax 718.365.6421
E-mail .... mtcarmelrx@aol.com
705 E 187th St, Bronx, NY 10458

Muscular Dystrophy Assoc Buffalo 716.626.0035
Fax 716.626.4229
E-mail .... buffalo@mdausa.org
5500 Main St 343, Williamsville, NY 14221
Terrance Roberts, Director

Muscular Dystrophy Assoc Syracuse 315.451.8269
Fax 315.451.4107
E-mail .... syracuse@mdausa.org
6315 Fly Rd 3102 E, Syracuse, NY 13057
Kristin Rogers, Executive Director

National Seating & Mobility 716.674.0783
Fax 716.674.0784
E-mail .... Buffalo@nsm-seating.com
19B Ransier Dr, West Seneca, NY 14224
Mark Sigeti, Manager

New York Eye & Ear Infirmary Manhattan 212.979.4000
310 E 14th St, New York, NY 10003
Michelle Morris, Manager

New York State Commission for the Blind 416.847.3516
Fax 716.847.3983
Ellicott Square Bldg, 295 Main St Rm 590, Buffalo,
NY 14203

New York State Commission for the Blind 315.423.5421
The Atrium, 100 S Salina St Ste 105, Syracuse,
NY 13202

Olmsted Ctr for the Visually Impaired 716.882.1025
Fax 719.882.5577
E-mail .... info@olmstedcenter.org
1170 Main St, Buffalo, NY 14209
Ronald Maier, President

Omni Rehabilitation Center 718.998.1415
Fax 718.802.1550
Flatbush Facility, 1651 Coney Island Ave, Brooklyn,
NY 11230

Pelham Audiology Assoc PC 718.822.4100
Fax 718.829.1350
1934 Williamsbridge Road, Bronx, NY 10461

Pesach Tikvah Door of Hope 718.875.6900
Fax 718.875.6999
E-mail .... info@pesachtikvah.org
18 Middleton St, Brooklyn, NY 11206
Arthur Heimowitz, Director

Rehab Technologies of Syracuse Inc 315.426.9920
Fax 315.426.1254
E-mail .... info@rehabtechny.com
Erie Medical Plaza, 1101 Erie Blvd East Ste 209,
Syracuse, NY 13210
Terry Hall, Office Manager

ReMed 800.735.8078
187 Winchester St, Rochester, NY 14615

Shield Inst Bronx Early Learning Center 718.299.7600
Fax 718.299.8995
E-mail .... lcosta@shield.org
1800 Andrews Ave, Bronx, NY 10453
Lourdes Costa, Principal

Spina Bifida Assoc of Western New York 716.446.5595
E-mail .... info@sbawny.org
137 Warner Ave, North Tonawanda, NY 14120

St Josephs Home Care Syracuse 315.458.4600
Fax 315.458.4644
7246 Janus Park Dr, Liverpool, NY 13088
Melissa Allard, Director

St Marys Healthcare System for Children 718.281.8800
E-mail .... info@stmaryskids.org
2901 216th St, Bayside, NY 11360
Jeff Freichs, Director

Syracuse Univ Gebbie Speech Lang Hearin 315.443.4485
Fax 315.443.1113
E-mail .... jsford@syr.edu
805 South Crouse Ave, Syracuse, NY 13244
Janet Ford, Director

Total Care Health Industries, Inc. 516.326.4999
Fax 516.326.6196
Web .... www.tchomemedical.com
40 Nassau Terminal Road, New Hyde Park, NY 11040
CARF accredited programs available.

United Cerebral Palsy of NYC 877.827.2666
E-mail .... info@ucpnyc.org
160 Lawrence Ave, Early Childhood Programs,
Brooklyn, NY 11230
Juliana Mejia, Project Coordinator

United Cerebral Palsy of NYC 718.652.9790
Fax 718.547.9108
E-mail .... bellman@ucpnyc.org
1770 Stillwell Ave, Bronx, NY 10469
Beverley Ellman, Director

United Cerebral Palsy of NYC 212.677.7400
Fax 212.529.2071
E-mail .... projectconnect@ucpnyc.org
122 East 23rd St, New York, NY 10010
Amy Bittenger, Director

United Spinal Association 718.803.3782
Fax 718.803.0414
E-Mail .... info@unitedspinal.org
75 20 Astoria Blvd, Jackson Heights, NY 11370
Paul Gobin, Chief Executive Officer

USA Techguide 718.803.3782
Fax 718.803.0414
E-mail .... techguide@usatechguide.org
75 20 Astoria Blvd, Jackson Heights, NY 11370
Paul Tobin, President/CEO

Val-U-Care 888.622.3304
244 5th Ave Ste 2005, New York, NY 10001
Monique Gordier, Sales Manager

Wenzelite Rehab Supplies 516.998.4600
99 Seaview Blvd, Port Washington, NY 11050

Western NY Developmental Disabilities 716.517.2000
Fax 716.674.7488
1200 East & West Road, West Seneca, NY 14224

Wheelchair Medic Queens 718.352.1623
Fax 718.352.3239
E-mail .... info@wheelchairmedic.com
102 Duane Road Bldg 102, Bayside, NY 11359

PEDIATRIC HOME CARE

Allen Health Care Services 718.657.2400
Fax 718.657.8950
Web .... www.allenhealth.com
E-mail .... intake@allenhealth.com
175-20 Hillside Ave., Jamaica, NY 11432
Marie Andreacchio, President

Bayada Nurses 212.354.9400
Fax 212.278.0600
Web .... www.bayada.com
252 West 38th Street, Room 1505, New York,
NY 10018
Terry Casler, Director

Bayada Nurses 516.408.7922
Fax 516.408.7935
Web .... www.bayada.com
825 East Gate Boulevard, Ste 201, Garden City,
NY 11530
Angelica Dimartino, Director

Bayada Nurses 914.631.2027
Fax 914.631.6826
Web .... www.bayada.com
1 Central Avenue, Suite 202, Tarrytown, NY 10591
Iris Cognevich, Director

Interim Healthcare 315.437.4500
Fax 315.437.1632
3300 James St Ste 201, Syracuse, NY 13206
Melanie, Director

Interim Healthcare 631.689.8920
Fax 631.689.8955
Web .... www.interimhealthcare.com
207 Hallock Rd, Stony Brook, NY 11790
Ellen Hamburger, Office Administrator

Interim Healthcare 716.283.3828
Fax 716.283.3848
7703 Niagara Falls Blvd, Niagara Falls, NY 14304
Judy Ketteman, Vice President

Interim Healthcare 518.877.3811
Fax 518.877.3812
315 Ushers Rd, Ballston Lake, NY 12019

Interim Healthcare 518.610.8145
Fax 518.610.8144
1042 B Kinderhook St, Valatie, NY 12184
Lisa Evans, Co-President

Interim Healthcare 585.454.4930
Fax 585.325.6059
347 East Ave, Rochester, NY 14604
Elise Bamser, Human Resource Manager

Interim Healthcare 607.722.6461
Fax 607.771.0116
38 Front St Ste D, Binghamton, NY 13905
Sally Hoffman, Administrator

Interim Healthcare 845.425.2655
Fax 845.425.2696
508 Airport Executive Park, Nanuet, NY 10954
Lisa Narvaez, Director

Interim Healthcare 914.946.2810
Fax 914.946.2031
E-mail .... tammyroyster@interimhealthcare.com
19 Court St Ste 206, White Plains, NY 10601
Tammy Royster, Director

Interim Healthcare 518.452.3655
Fax 518.452.0765
E-mail .... levans@interimhealthcr.com
1735 Central Ave, Albany, NY 12205
Lisa Evans, Co-President

Interim Healthcare 518.798.6811
Fax 518.798.6879
99 Ridge St, Glens Falls, NY 12801

New York

New York

Interim Healthcare 716.852.5900
Fax 716.852.5913
360 Delaware Ave 3rd Fl North, Buffalo, NY 14202
Judy Ketteman, Administrator

Maxim Healthcare Services 716.881.2800
Fax 866.941.4302
Web ....www.maximhomecare.com
E-mail ....zamiller@maximhomecare.com
392 Pearl Street, Suite 400, Buffalo, NY 14202
Zach Miller, Health Care Recruiter

SOCIAL SERVICES

A Women's Care Ctr 585.865.0360
Web ....www.rochesterwomencare.com
E-mail ....ttclay@rochester.rr.com
3252 Lake Ave, Rochester, NY 14612-5449
Theresa Claybaugh, Director

Alternatives For Children 631.331.6400
Fax 631.331.6865
Web www.alternatives4children.org
14 Research Way, East Setauket, NY 11733
Marie Ficano, Director

Anderson Ctr For Autism (Formerly Anderson
School) 845.889.4034
Fax 845.889.8206
Web ....www.andersonschool.org
E-mail ....info@andersonschool.org
4885 Route 9, Staatsburg, NY 12580-6028
Eliza Bozenski, Supervisor Of Community And Education Supports

Andrus Children's Center 914.965.3700
Fax 914.965.3883
Web ....www.andruschildren.org
1156 North Broadway, Yonkers, NY 10701
COA accredited organization.

Armed Svcs YMCA Watertown/Fort Drum 315.782.3100
Fax 315.782.0802
Web ....www.watertownymca.org
E-mail ....ymca_pschmitt@yahoo.com
119 Washington St, Watertown, NY 13601-3323
Peter Schmitt, Executive Director

Astor Child Guidance Ctr 718.231.3400
Fax 718.655.3503
Web ....www.astorservices.org
750 Tilden St, Bronx, NY 10467-6099
Andrew Kuntz, Director Of Outpatient Services

Berkshire Farm Center and Services for
Youth 518.781.4567
Web ....www.berkshirefarm.org
13640 Route 22, Canaan, NY 12029-3500
COA accredited organization.

Boys Town 718.636.2130
Fax 718.636.5735
535 Bergen St, Brooklyn, NY 11217-2406
Lataje Jackson, Program Director

Boys Town Of New York - Dean Street Ofc 718.636.3110
Fax 718.636.2979
E-mail ....warner.graham@boystown.com
525 Dean St, Brooklyn, NY 11217
Warner Graham, Program Director

BRANCH 718.793.7890
Fax 718.275.0143
97 45 Queens Blvd Ste 1018, Rego Park, NY 11374

BRANCH Pleasantville Cottage School 914.769.0164
Fax 914.741.4596
1075 Broadway, Pleasantville, NY 10570
Joanna Kibel, Director

Bronx Program Office BRANCH 718.742.8550
Fax 718.993.4345
555 Bergen Ave, Bronx, NY 10455
Dennis Samuels, Manager

Brooklyn Program BRANCH 718.758.7800
Fax 718.258.2800
870 East 29th St, Brooklyn, NY 11210

Buffalo State College Speech-Language- Hearing
Clinic 716.878.3530
Fax 716.878.3526
Web ....www.buffalostate.edu
E-mail ....joneskb@buffalostate.edu
1300 Elmwood Ave, Buffalo, NY 14222
Karen Bailey Jones, Ma, Director

Capital District Child Care Coordinating
Council 518.426.7181
Fax 518.426.9649
Web ....www.cdcccc.org
E-mail ....pskinner@cdcccc.org
91 Broadway St, Menands, NY 12204
Patricia Skinner, Executive Producer

Captain Youth And Family Svcs 518.371.1185
Fax 518.383.7997
Web ....www.captainyfs.com
E-mail ....info@captainyfs.com
5 Municipal Plz Ste 3, Clifton Park, NY 12065-3992
Sue Malinowski, Executive Director

Cassadaga Job Corps Academy 716.595.8760
Fax 716.595.2844
8115 Glasgow Rd, Cassadaga, NY 14718-9619
Ann Anderson, Center Director

Catholic Charities 315.424.1871
Fax 315.424.6079
Web ....www.ccoc.us
1654 W Onondaga St, Syracuse, NY 13204
Ellen Ketchum, Director Of Counceling

Catholic Charities 315.470.1415
Fax 315.478.4619
240 E Onondaga St, Syracuse, NY 13202
Joseph Slavik, Director

Catholic Charities 516.733.7000
Fax 516.733.7099
E-mail ....catholiccharities@cc.com
90 Cherry Ln, Hicksville, NY 11801
Laura Cassell, Director

Catholic Charities 607.729.9166
Fax 607.729.2062
Web ....www.catholiccharitiesbc.org
E-mail ....laccardi@ccbc.net
232 Main St, Binghamton, NY 13905
Lori Accardi, Executive Director

Catholic Charities 607.756.5992
Fax 607.756.5999
Web ....www.ccocc.org
E-mail ....mwalsh@ccocc.org
33-35 Central Ave., Cortland, NY 13045
Marie L. Walsh, Executive Director

Catholic Charities of Buffalo, New York 716.218.1400
Fax 716.362.6143
Web ....www.ccwny.org
741 Delaware Avenue, Buffalo, NY 14209
COA accredited organization.

Catholic Charities Of Delaware And Otsego
Counties 607.432.0061
Fax 607.431.9303
E-mail ....ccdo-ccrr@stny.rr.com
176 Main St, Oneonta, NY 13820
Tracey Martindale, Administrative Assistant

Catholic Charities Of Rome 315.337.8600
Fax 315.337.2433
212 W Liberty St, Rome, NY 13440
Brenda Webb, Office Manager

Catholic Charities, Diocese of Brooklyn and
Queens 718.722.6000
Fax 718.722.6096
Web ....www.ccbq.org
191 Joralemon Street, Brooklyn, NY 11201
COA accredited organization.

Catholic Family Center 585.546.7220
Fax 585.546.6396
Web ....www.cfcrochester.org
87 N. Clinton Avenue, Rochester, NY 14604-1407
COA accredited organization.

Central Referral Svcs 716.842.8613
Fax 716.851.5414
E-mail ....dougfrank@centralreferral.org
45 Elm St, Buffalo, NY 14203
Douglas W. Frank, Executive Director

Cerebral Palsy Assoc Of The Rochester
Area 585.334.6000
Fax 585.334.1646
3399 Winton Rd S, Rochester, NY 14623
Diane, Director of Clinical Services

Child Abuse Prevention 518.474.9613
Fax 518.402.6824
E-mail ....ay6910@dfa.state.ny.us
52 Washington St, # 331, Rensselaer, NY 12144
Judy Richards, Director

Child And Family Resource, Inc. 315.536.1134
Fax 315.536.9918
Web ....www.cfresources.org
E-mail ....pyfrc@adelphia.net
100 E Main St Ste 2, Penn Yan, NY 14527-1668
Julie Mccoy, Director

Child And Family Resources 315.568.0945
Fax 315.568.0978
Web ....www.csresources.com
E-mail ....julie.mccoy@csresources.com
115 Fall St, Seneca Falls, NY 13148
Julie Mccoy, Executive Director

Child and Family Services
330 Delaware Avenue, Buffalo, NY 14202
COA accredited organization.

Child Care Coalition Of The Niagra
Frontier 716.877.6666
Fax 716.877.6205
Web ....www.wnychildren.org
E-mail ....sblock@wnychildren.org
2635 Delaware Ave Ste A, Buffalo, NY 14216-1706
Susan Block, Executive Director

Child Care Coordinating Council 607.535.7964
Fax 607.535.8942
Web ....www.scccccc.org
E-mail ....scchildcarecc@stny.rr.com
235 S. Catharine Street., Montour Falls, NY 14865
Debbie Macdonald, Executive Director

Child Care Coordinating Council 607.336.2809
Fax 607.336.5827
Web www.6cs.org
E-mail ....director1.cccccc@frontiernet.net
24 Conkey Ave, Norwich, NY 13815-1760
Donna Adams, Executive Director

Child Care Coordinating Council Of The North Country,
Inc. 518.561.4999
Fax 518.561.6956
Web ....www.ccccnc.org
E-mail ....nground@primelink1.net
194 Us Oval, Plattsburgh, NY 12901
Jamie Basilier, Executive Producer

Child Care Council 845.294.4012
Fax 845.294.4045
Web ....www.childcarecouncilor.org
40 Matthews St Ste 103, Goshen, NY 10924-1986
Elizabeth Kuriplach, Executive Director

Child Care Council Of Columbia And Green
Counties 518.822.1944
Fax 518.822.8233
Web ....www.familyofwoodstockinc.org
E-mail ....cccg@familyofwoodstockinc.org
160 Fairview Ave Ste 270, Hudson, NY 12534
Suzanne Holdridge, Assistant Program Director

Child Care Council Of Dutchess Inc 845.473.4141
Fax 845.473.4161
Web www.childcaredutchess.org
E-mail meagen@childcaredutchess.org
70 Overocker Rd, Poughkeepsie, NY 12603
Jeanne Wagner, Executive Director

Child Care Council Of Nassau, Inc. 516.358.9288
Fax 516.358.9287
Web www.childcarenassau.org
E-mail childcare@childcarenassau.org
925 Hempstead Tpke Ste 400, Franklin Square, NY 11010
Jan Barbieri, Executive Director

Child Care Council Of Soffolk 631.462.0303
Fax 631.462.1617
E-mail info@childcaresoffolk.org
60 Calvert Ave Ste 1, Commack, NY 11725
Janet Walerstein, Executive Director

Child Care Council Of Westchester, Inc. 914.761.3456
Fax 914.761.1957
Web www.childcarewestchester.org
E-mail childcare@cccwny.org
313 Central Park Ave, Scottsdale, NY 10583
Kathy Halas, Executive Director

Child Care Council, Inc 845.292.7166
Fax 845.292.1755
Web www.scchildcare.com
E-mail info@scchildcare.com
7 Community Ln, Liberty, NY 12754
Donna Willi, Executive Director

Child Care Council, Inc. 315.343.2344
Fax 315.343.0442
157 W 1st St, Oswego, NY 13126
Pam Ouderkirk, Refferal Specialist

Child Care Council, Inc. 607.734.3941
Fax 607.737.7293
Web www.chemchildcare.com
E-mail rkrusen@chemchildcare.com
571 E Saint Joseph Blvd, Elmira, NY 14901-3230
Ruth Krusen, Executive Producer

Child Care Resourece Of Rockland, Inc. 845.425.0009
Fax 845.425.5312
Web www.childcarerockland.org
E-mail info@rocklandchildcare.org
235 N Main St Ste 11, Spring Valley, NY 10977-4014
Jane Brown, Executive Director

Child Care Solutions 315.446.1220
Fax 315.446.2010
Web www.childcaresolutionscny.org
E-mail ccs@childcaresolutionscny.org
6724 Thompson Rd Ste 1, Syracuse, NY 13211
Peggy Liuzzi, Executive Director

Child Care, Inc. 212.929.4999
Fax 212.929.5785
Web www.centreforchildreninitiatives.org
322 8th Ave, Fl 4, New York, NY 10001
Carmen Vega, Office Adminstrative Assistant

Child Development Support Corporation 718.398.6738
Fax 718.399.6504
Web www.cdscnyc.org
E-mail dcscdsc1@aol.com
352-358 Classon Ave, Fl 2, Brooklyn, NY 11238
Anita Franklin, Director Of Childcare Services

Child Find of America Inc. 800.716.3468
Alternate 845.883.6060
Fax 845.883.6614
Web www.childfindofamerica.org
E-mail dlinder351@aol.com
PO Box 277, New Paltz, NY 12561
Donna Linder, Executive Director

Children's Home of Wyoming Conference 607.772.6904
Fax 607.723.2617
Web www.chowc.org
1182 Chenango Street, Binghamton, NY 13901-1696
COA accredited organization.

Chinese American Planning Council 212.941.0030
Fax 212.226.5351
Web www.cpc-nyc.org
E-mail dchen888@hotmail.com
165 Eldriege St, New York, NY 10002
David Chen, Executive Director

Citizen's Advice Bureau 718.365.0910
Fax 718.365.0697
Web www.bronxworks.org
E-mail cmclaughlin@cabny.org
60 E Cremont Ave, Bronx, NY 10453-3538
Carolyn Mclaughlin, Executive Director

Coalition On Child Abuse And Neglect 516.747.2966
Fax 516.747.5065
Web www.coalitionagainstchildabuse.org
E-mail cscott@coalitiononchildabuse.org
15 Grumman Rd W Ste 900, Bethpage, NY 11714-5766
Cynthia Scott, Executive Director

Committee For Hispanic Children And Families 212.206.1090
Fax 212.206.8093
Web www.chcfinc.org
110 William St Fl 18, New York, NY 10038-3937
Elba Montalvo, Executive Director

Community Action Program 518.234.2568
Fax 518.234.3507
Web www.sccapinc.org
E-mail admin@sccapinc.org
795 E Main St Ste 5, Cobleskill, NY 12043
Phil Alotta, Executive Director

Community Child Care Clearinghouse Of Niagara 716.285.8572
Fax 716.286.9243
Web www.childcareofniagara.com
E-mail ccrrniagara@prodigy.net
1521 Main St, Niagara Falls, NY 14305-2521
Angela Burns, Director

Community For Hispanic Children And Families Inc 212.206.1090
Fax 212.206.8093
Web www.chcfinc.org
E-mail chcfinc@chcfinc.org
110 William St Rm 1802, New York, NY 10038
Elba Montalvo, Executive Director

Community Maternity Svcs 518.482.8836
Fax 518.482.5805
Web www.cccms.org
E-mail smal@cccms.org
27 N. Main Avenue, Albany, NY 12203-1416
Sr. Mary Ann Logiudice, Rsm, Executive Director

Community Mediation Svcs 718.523.6868
Fax 718.523.8204
Web www.mediatenyc.org
8964 163rd St, Jamaica, NY 11432-5070
Mark Kleiman, Executive Director

Community Svc Society 212.254.8900
Fax 212.260.6218
Web www.cssny.org
E-mail info@cssny.org
105 E 22nd St Rm 303, New York, NY 10010
David R. Jones, President And CEO

Cortland Area Child Care Council 607.753.0106
Fax 607.753.0119
Web www.cortlandchildcare.org
E-mail anne@cortlandchildcare.org
111 Port Watson St, Cortland, NY 13045-3178
Anne Weithers, Executive Director

Cross-Road Foundation Inc 718.556.3474
Fax 718.556.3471
Web www.crossroadfoundation.org
E-mail crossroad15@verizon.net
15 Treadwell Ave, Staten Island, NY 10302-1241
Neil Hudder, Director

Ctr For Comprehensive Health Practice, Inc. 212.360.7400
Fax 212.348.7253
1900 2nd Ave, New York, NY 10029
Annie Mendelsohn, Site Manager

Ctr For Family & Youth 518.462.4630
Fax 518.427.1462
Web www.ctrfamyouth.com
E-mail dbosworth@ctrfamyouth.com
135 Ontario St, ste 6240, Albany, NY 12206
David A. Bosworth, Executive Director

Ctr For Family And Divorce Mediation 212.799.4302
Fax 212.721.1012
Web www.divorcemediation.com
E-mail kennethneumann@teenmediation.org
111 W 90th St, New York, NY 10024
Kenneth Neumann, Director

Day Care Council Of New York, Inc 212.206.7818
Fax 212.206.7836
Web www.dccnyinc.org
E-mail dcc12w21@dccnyinc.org
12 W 21st St Fl 3, New York, NY 10010
Andrea Anthony, Executive Director

Delaware Opportunites, Inc. Child And Family Development Div 607.746.1620
Fax 607.746.1605
E-mail daycare@delawareopportunities.org
35430 State Highway 10, Hamden, NY 13782
John Eberhard, Executive Director

Dominican Sisters Family Health Svcs 914.941.1710
Fax 914.941.0518
Web www.dsfhs.org
299 N Highland Ave, Ossining, NY 10562-2327
Mary Zatajeski, Executive Director

East Side House Settlement 718.665.5250
Fax 718.585.1433
Web www.eastsidehouse.org
E-mail jas@eastsidehouse.org
337 Alexander Ave, Bronx, NY 10454
John Sanchez, Executive Director

Embracing Options 585.235.0690
Fax 585.235.0011
E-mail embracingoptions@hisbranches.org
342 Arnett Blvd, Rochester, NY 14619
Althea Pitts-Swailf, Executive Director

Family And Children Assoc, Inc. 516.485.4600
Fax 516.489.2602
Web www.familyandchildrens.org
E-mail ncohan@familyandchildrens.org
129 Jackson St, Hempstead, NY 11550-2412
Nancy Cohan, Team Director

Family And Children's Svc Of The Capital Region, Inc 518.462.6531
Fax 518.462.0181
Web www.fcscr.org
E-mail kpickett@fcscr.org
650 Warren St, Albany, NY 12208
Keith Pickett, Executive Director

Family Counseling Svc 315.789.2613
Fax 315.789.2524
E-mail familycounseling@fcssl.org
671 Exchange St, Geneva, NY 14456-3498
Bonnie Deier, Director

Family Nurturing Ctr Of Central NY, Inc. 315.738.9773
Fax 315.738.1486
Web www.fnccny.org
E-mail delefante@fnccny.org
209 Elizabeth St, Fl 4, Utica, NY 13501
Donna Lataur-Elefante, Executive Director

New York

Family Of Woodstock **845.679.2485**
Fax 845.679.8490
Web ....www.familyofwoodstockinc.org
E-mail ....fowh@familyofwoodstockinc.org
   16 Rock City Rd, Woodstock, NY 12498-1295
   Tamara Cooper, Program Director

Family Of Woodstock, Inc. **845.331.5197**
Fax 845.331.0526
Web ....www.familyofwoodstockinc.org
E-mail ....info@familyofwoodstockinc.org
   39 John St, Kingston, NY 12402
   Michael Berg, Executive Director

Family Service League, Inc. **631.427.3700**
Fax 631.427.9149
Web ....www.fsl-li.org
   790 Park Avenue, Huntington, NY 11743
   COA accredited organization.

Family Services of Westchester **914.937.2320**
Fax 914.937.4902
Web ....www.fsw.org
   One Gateway Plaza, Port Chester, NY 10573
   COA accredited organization.

Family Violence Prevention Council **607.778.2153**
Fax 607.778.3788
Web ....www.gobroomecounty.com
E-mail ....jcyganozich@co.broome.ny.us
   36-42 Main St, Binghamton, NY 13905
   Janette Cyganozich, Coordinator

Federation Of Protestant Welfare
Agencies **212.777.4800**
Fax 212.673.4085
Web ....www.fpwa.org
E-mail ....fgoldman@fpwa.org
   281 Park Ave S, New York, NY 10010-6125
   Fatima Goldman, Executive Director

FEGS Health & Human Services System **212.366.8400**
Fax 212.366.8441
E-mail ....info@fegs.org
   315 Hudson St, New York, NY 10013
   Gail Magaliff, CEO

Forest Hills Day Care Center BRANCH **718.263.5730**
Fax 718.793.7225
E-mail ....nacanielova@jccany.org
   108 05 68th rd, Forest Hills, NY 11375
   Abbe Naeanielova, Director

Free Abortion Alternatives **718.994.3500**
Fax 718.884.9211
Web ....www.abortion-options.com
   4377 Bronx Blvd, Bronx, NY 10466
   Kathy Keoh, Director

Friends For Life **315.468.6798**
   2010 W Genesee St Ste 201, Syracuse, NY 13219
   Helen Daley, Office Manager

Girls And Boys Town Of New York **212.725.4260**
Fax 212.725.4385
Web ....www.boystown.org/new-york
E-mail ....btnycontact@boystown.org
   444 Park Ave S Rm 801, New York, NY 10016
   Cynthia Armijo, Site Director

Girls And Boys Town of New York - The Willoughby
School **718.596.3354**
Fax 718.596.3595
   167 Willoughby St, Brooklyn, NY 11201
   Damian Kinsey, Director

Glenmont Job Corps Ctr **518.767.9371**
Fax 518.767.2106
   822 River Rd, Glenmont, NY 12077-4108
   Korey Adams, Center Director

Good Shepherd Services **212.243.7070**
Fax 212.243.8085
Web ....www.goodshepherds.org
   305 Seventh Avenue, 9th Fl., New York, NY 10001
   COA accredited organization.

Gustavus Adolphus Child And Family Svcs **716.665.2116**
Fax 716.720.9379
Web ....www.lutheran-jamestown.org
   200 Gustavus Ave, Jamestown, NY 14701
   Karl Wiggins, Executive Director

Hale House **212.663.0700**
Fax 212.749.2888
Web ....www.halehouse.org
E-mail ....info@halehouse.org
   152 W 122nd St, New York, NY 10027-5598
   Tammy Lewis, Family Advocate

Harmony Heights **516.922.4060**
Fax 516.922.4133
Web ....www.harmonyheightsschool.com
E-mail ....eb@harmonyheightsschool.com
   57 Sandy Hill Rd, Oyster Bay, NY 11771-3110
   Ellen Benson, Executive Director

HeartShare Human Services of New York, Roman Catholic
Diocese Brooklyn **718.422.4200**
Fax 718.522.4506
Web ....www.heartshare.org
   12 Metrotech Center, 29th Floor, Brooklyn,
   NY 11201
   COA accredited organization.

Hetrick-Martin Institute **212.674.2400**
Fax 212.674.8650
Web ....www.hmi.org
E-mail ....tcrever@hmi.org
   2 Astor Pl Fl 3, New York, NY 10003-6998
   Thomas Crever, Executive Director

HIAS Inc **212.967.4100**
Fax 212.967.4483
E-mail ....info@hias.org
   333 Seventh Ave 17th Fl, New York, NY 10001
   Gideon Aronoff

Hillside Family of Agencies **585.350.2509**
Fax 585.350.2599
Web ....www.hillside.com
   1180 Monroe Avenue, Rochester, NY 14620
   COA accredited organization.

Homecare Planning Solutions **718.838.3838**
Fax 718.838.3839
Web ....www.hpsny.com
E-mail ....info@hpsny.com
   946 McDonald Avenue, Brooklyn, NY 11218

Hudson Valley Region 2-1-1 ....**845.471.1900**
Fax 845.471.1933
Web ....www.unitedwaydutchess.org
E-mail ....mckann@unitedwaydutchess.org
   75 Market St, Poughkeepsie, NY 12601-4015
   Megan Mckann, Resource Specialist

Huntington Family Ctrs **315.476.3157**
Fax 315.476.3860
Web ....www.huntingtonfamilycenters.org
E-mail ....dpaniski@hfcsyr.org
   405 Gifford St, Syracuse, NY 13204-3290
   David Paniski, Director

Iroquois Job Corps **585.798.7000**
Fax 585.798.7046
Web ....www.jobcorps.gov
E-mail ....melissa.volpe@jobcorps.org
   11780 Tibbits Rd, Medina, NY 14103-9725
   Melissa Volpe, Center Director

JCCA - Jewish Child Care Assoc Child/ Adolescent Guidance
Ctr **718.859.4500**
Fax 718.859.4013
   858 E 29th Ave, Brooklyn, NY 11210
   Robert Cizma, Brooklyn Preventive Services Director

Jefferson Lewis Childcare Project **315.782.8475**
Fax 315.788.8251
Web ....www.capcjc.org
   518 Davidson St, Watertown, NY 13601
   Melinda Gault, Executive Director

Jewish Board Of Family & Children
Services **718.761.9800**
Fax 718.370.1142
   2795 Richmond Ave, Staten Island, NY 10314
   Valerie Mitchell, Director

Jewish Board of Family & Children's Services,
Inc. **212.582.9100**
Fax 212.582.9139
Web ....www.jbfcs.org
   135 West 50th Street, New York, NY 10020
   COA accredited organization.

Jewish Family Service **845.471.9817**
Fax 845.471.3233
E-mail ....jfs@jewishdutchess.org
   110 S Grand Ave, Poughkeepsie, NY 12603
   Linda Tafapolsky, Psycologist

Jewish Family Services **845.341.1173**
Fax 845.342.6436
E-mail ....support@JFSorange.org
   720 Route 17M, Middletown, NY 10940
   Sonia Wagner, Director

Jewish Family Services **845.338.2980**
Fax 845.331.4875
E-mail ....jfs.ulster@gmail.com
   280 Wall St, Floor 2, Kingston, NY 12401
   Sharon Murray-Cohen, Executive Director

Jewish Family Services of Northeastern
NY **518.482.8856**
Fax 518.489.5839
E-mail ....jfsneny@banet.net
   877 Madison Ave, Albany, NY 12208
   Miriam Adler, Director

Jewish Family Svcs **716.883.1914**
Fax 716.883.7637
Web ....www.jfsbuffalo.org
   70 Barker St, Buffalo, NY 14209
   Marleen Schillinger, Executive Director

Joan A. Males Family Support Svcs **716.822.0919**
Fax 716.822.5098
Web ....www.literacybuffalo.org
   60 Dingens St, Buffalo, NY 14206-2308
   Andrew Mattle, Executive Director

Kingbridge Heights Community Ctr **718.884.0700**
Fax 718.884.0858
Web ....www.khcc-nyc.org
   3101 Kingsbridge Ter, Bronx, NY 10463
   Debroah L. Harris, Chairwoman

Lake Grove Schools-Lake Grove School **631.585.8776**
Fax 631.737.5564
E-mail ....arnette_leftenant@lgstc.org
   Morisches Rd, Lake Grove, NY 11755
   Arnette Leftenant, Executive Director

Language And Learning Assoc **914.381.4477**
Fax 914.381.6971
   550 Mamaroneck Ave Ste 102, Harrison, NY 10528
   Rosalind Rothman, BS, MA, ED., Director

LaSalle School **518.242.4731**
Fax 518.242.4747
Web ....www.lasalle-school.org
   391 Western Avenue, Albany, NY 12203
   COA accredited organization.

Leeway School **631.589.8060**
Fax 631.589.0908
   335 Johnson Ave, Sayville, NY 11782-1199
   Penny Lewis, Executive Director

Legal Aid Society-Juvenile Rights Div **212.440.4300**
Fax 212.577.3520
Web ....www.legal-aid.org
   199 Water St Frnt 3, New York, NY 10038-3526
   Tamara Stecklar, Attorney

Little Flower Children's Svcs **718.260.8840**
Fax 718.875.6613
Web ....www.littleflowerny.org
　44 Court St Fl 4, Brooklyn, NY 11201
　Greg Logrande, Executive Director

Little Sisters Of The Assumption Family Health
Svc **212.987.4422**
Fax 212.348.8284
Web ....www.littlesisters.org
　333 E 115th St, New York, NY 10029
　Gary Carter, Executive Director

McCloskey Svcs **914.997.8000**
Fax 914.997.2166
Web ....www.cardinalmccloskeyservices.org
　2 Holland Ave, White Plains, NY 10603-3318
　Margaret Roth, Adoption Coordinator

Mental Health Assoc in Tompkins, The **607.273.9250**
Fax 607.272.5343
Web ....www.mhaedu.org
E-mail ....info@mhaedu.org
　614 W State St, Ithaca, NY 14850-5222
　Beth Jenkins, Executive Director

Mid Brooklyn Office **718.676.4210**
Fax 718.676.4216
　2020 Coney Island Ave, Brooklyn, NY 11223
　Inna Lidrovnik, Director

Montefiore Child Protection Ctr **718.920.5833**
Fax 718.405.6149
Web ....www.montefiore.org
E-mail ....kamarant@montefiore.org
　3314 Steuben Ave, Bronx, NY 10467-2806
　Karel Amaranth, Executive Director

Mt. Hope Family Ctr **585.275.2991**
Fax 585.454.2972
Web ....www.rochester.edu
E-mail ....s.toth@worldnet.att.net
　187 Edinburgh St, Rochester, NY 14608-2415
　Cheree Toth, Director

Ncpca-New York State **518.445.1273**
Fax 518.436.5889
Web ....www.preventchildabuseny.org
E-mail ....cdeyss@preventchildabuseny.org
　133 eok St, Albany, NY 12207
　Christine S. Deyss, Ms, Executive Director

New Directions Youth & Family Services,
Inc. **716.433.4487**
Fax 716.433.7030
Web ....www.ndyfs.org
　6395 Old Niagara Road, Lockport, NY 14094
　COA accredited organization.

New Directions Youth And Family Svcs **716.358.3636**
Fax 716.358.3676
E-mail ....jcoder@ndyfs.org
　356 Main Street Er, Randolph, NY 14772
　James W. Coder, Executive Director

New Hope Family Svcs **315.437.8300**
Fax 315.437.9107
E-mail ....newhopefamily@aol.com
　3519 James St, Syracuse, NY 13206-2766
　Judy Geyer, Executive Director

New York Council On Adoptable Children **212.475.0222**
Fax 212.714.2838
Web ....www.coac.org
　589 8th Ave Fl 15, New York, NY 10018-3084
　Ernesto Loperena, Executive Director

New York Society For The Prevention Of Cruelty To
Children **212.233.5500**
Fax 212.791.5227
Web ....www.nyspcc.org
E-mail ....mpulito@nyspcc.org
　161 William St Fl 9, New York, NY 10038-5312
　Mary Pulito, Executive Director

New York University Child Study Ctr **212.263.6622**
Fax 212.263.0990
Web ....www.aboutourkids.org
　577 1st Ave, New York, NY 10016
　Dr Glenn Sax, Director

Newburgh Office BRANCH **845.562.8372**
Fax 845.562.5114
E-mail ....jfsrobin@hvc.rr.com
　68 Stewart Ave, Newburgh, NY 12550

Niagara Community Action Program **716.285.9681**
Fax 716.285.9693
E-mail ....lauried@prodigy.net
　1521 Main St, Niagara Falls, NY 14305-2521
　Ms. S. Shears, Executive Director

Northeast Parent And Child Society, Inc. **518.346.1284**
Fax 518.377.8714
Web ....www.neparentchild.org
E-mail ....jim.johans@neparentchild.org
　1 Genium Plz, Schenectady, NY 12304-4607
　Dr. James Johans, Executive Director

NYS Child Care Coordinating Council, Inc. **518.690.4217**
Fax 518.690.2887
　230 Washington Avenue Ext Ste 3, Albany,
　NY 12203-6321
　Marsha Basloe, Executive Director

Ohel Children's Home And Family Svcs **718.851.6300**
Fax 718.851.1672
Web ....www.ohelfamily.org
E-mail ....dm@ohelfamily.org
　4510 16th Ave, Brooklyn, NY 11204-1101
　David Mandel, Executive Director

Orleans Community Action Committee Child Care Resource
And Referral **585.343.7727**
Fax 585.343.4063
Web ....www.caoginc.org
E-mail ....ccrrgen@ocacinc.org
　5073 Clinton Street Rd, Batavia, NY 14020-1126
　Bonnie Malicky, Director Of Youth & Family Services

Parsons Child and Family Center **518.426.2600**
Fax 518.447.5234
Web ....www.parsonscenter.org
　60 Academy Road, Albany, NY 12208-3198
　COA accredited organization.

Pelham Office **718.882.5000**
Fax 718.798.7633
　750 Astor Ave, Bronx, NY 10467
　Julie List, Director

Phase: Piggy Back, Inc. **212.234.4623**
Fax 212.234.2008
Web ....www.phasepiggyback.org
E-mail ....npauls@phasepiggyback.org
　262 W 145th St, New York, NY 10031-5101
　Nellie Pauls, Clinical Director

Project Extreme **516.897.4448**
Fax 707.982.7248
E-mail ....projectextremeay@aol.com
　335 Central Ave, Lawrence, NY 11559
　Rabbi Ay Weinberg, Executive Director

Rockland Jewish Family Service **845.354.2121**
Fax 845.354.2928
E-mail ....info@rjfs.org
　450 West Nyack Rd Ste 2, West Nyack, NY 10994
　Maria Dowling, Director

Rosalie Hall **718.920.9800**
Fax 718.920.9896
Web ....www.rosaliehallny.org
E-mail ....info@rosaliehallny.org
　4150 Bronx Blvd, Bronx, NY 10466-2656
　Steven Parker, Executive Director

Saint Dominic's Home **845.359.3400**
Fax 845.359.4235
Web ....www.stdominicshome.org
　500 Western Highway, Blauvelt, NY 10913
　COA accredited organization.

SCO Family of Services **516.671.1253**
Fax 516.671.2988
Web ....www.sco.org
　1 Alexander Place, Glen Cove, NY 11542
　COA accredited organization.

SCO Family Of Svcs **516.671.1253**
Fax 516.671.2899
E-mail ....gnayowith@sco.org
　1 Alexander Pl, Glen Cove, NY 11542
　Gale Nayowith, Executive Director

Soundview Throgs Neck Community Mental Health
Center **718.842.1400**
Fax 718.328.3349
　1967 Turnbull Ave Ste 26, Bronx, NY 10473
　Thomas Betzler, Director

South Bronx Job Corps Ctr **718.731.7700**
Fax 718.731.3543
Web ....www.jobcorps.com
E-mail ....rondell.pachato@jobcorps.org
　1771 Andrews Ave, Bronx, NY 10453-6803
　Rondell Pachato, Center Director

Southern Brooklyn Family Services **718.339.5300**
Fax 718.339.9082
　333 Ave X, Brooklyn, NY 11223
　Stephanie Coyle, Chief Executive Officer

St Mary's Children And Family Svcs **516.921.0808**
Fax 516.496.3690
Web ....www.mercyfirst.org
E-mail ....jmccaffery@mercyfirst.org
　525 Convent Rd, Syosset, NY 11791
　Jerry Mccaffery, CEO

St. Anne Institute **518.437.6501**
Fax 518.437.6555
Web ....www.stanneinstitute.org
　160 North Main Avenue, Albany, NY 12206
　COA accredited organization.

St. Catherine's Center for Children **518.453.6700**
Fax 518.453.6712
Web ....www.st-cath.org
　40 North Main Avenue, Albany, NY 12203
　COA accredited organization.

St. Lawrence Child Care Council **315.393.6474**
Fax 315.394.6809
Web ....www.nymail.com
E-mail ....slccc@nymail.com
　318 Ford St, Ogdensburg, NY 13669-1404
　Bruce Stewart, Executive Director

St. Vincent's Svcs **718.522.3700**
Fax 718.875.8536
Web ....www.janetsvs.org
E-mail ....robert.harris@dfa.state.ny.us
　66 Boerum Pl, Brooklyn, NY 11201-5705
　Robert M Harris, President

Steuben Child Care Project **607.776.2126**
Fax 607.776.4873
Web ....www.proactioninc.com
E-mail ....hibbardc@proactioninc.org
　117 E Steuben St Ste 11, Bath, NY 14810-1636
　Carla Hibbard, Director

Strong Family Marriage Therapy Svcs **585.275.8321**
Fax 585.271.7706
　University Of Rochester, 300 Crittenden Blvd,
　Rochester, NY 14642-8409
　Jenny Speice, Phd, Clinic Director

The Center For Family Life And Recovery **315.735.2236**
Fax 315.735.9177
Web ....www.cflrinc.org
E-mail ....casandra@mvcaa.org
　401 Columbia St, Ste 200, Utica, NY 13502
　Casandra Sheets, Chief Executive Officer

New York

The Children's Health Fund **212.535.9400**
Fax 212.535.7488
Web ....www.childrenshealthfund.org
E-mail ....info@chfund.org
215 W 125th St Ste 301, New York, NY 10027
Irwin Redlener, President

The Children's Village **914.693.0600**
Fax 914.517.6825
Web ....www.childrensvillage.org
Echo Hills, Dobbs Ferry, NY 10522
COA accredited organization.

**The Exchange Club Ctr For Family Unity,
Inc.** **716.945.6401**
Fax 716.945.6404
4039 Route 219, Ste 205, Salamanca, NY 14779
Corrie Phetterplace, Executive Director

**The Exchange Club Ctr For The Prevention Of Child
Abuse** **914.997.2642**
Fax 914.997.1241
7 Holland Ave, White Plains, NY 10603
Laura B. Schwartz, Executive Director

The Mediation Ctr **845.471.7213**
Fax 845.471.7264
Web ....www.dutchessmediation.org
E-mail ....jbmiller29@aol.com
147 Union St, Poughkeepsie, NY 12601
Jody Miller, Executive Director

The New York Foundling Hospital **212.633.9300**
Fax 212.886.4008
Web ....www.nyfoundling.org
590 Avenue of the Americas, New York, NY 10011
COA accredited organization.

The Salvation Army Territorial Youth Dept **845.620.7359**
Fax 845.620.7740
Web ....www.salvationarmy.org
440 W Nyack Rd, West Nyack, NY 10994
Steve Hedgren, Territorial Commander

**The Salvation Army, Syracuse Area
Services** **315.479.1320**
Fax 315.475.6307
Web ....www.sasyr.org
677 South Salina Street, Syracuse, NY 13202
COA accredited organization.

Trinity Institution - Homer Lerkins Ctr **518.449.5155**
Fax 518.689.0379
15 Trinity Pl, Albany, NY 12202
Harris Oberlander, Executive Director

UCP **845.336.7235**
Fax 845.336.7248
E-mail ....pcarroad@cpulster.org
250 Tuytenbridge Rd, katrine, NY 12449
Pamela Carroad, Executive Director

**UJA Federation Of Jewish Philanthropies Of
NY** **212.980.1000**
Fax 212.836.1778
Web ....www.ujafedny.org
E-mail ....donercenter@ujafedny.org
130 E 59th St, New York, NY 10022-1375
John Ruskay, CEO

**United Cerebral Palsy Of Queens Children's Ctr
School** **718.380.3000**
Fax 718.380.3214
Web ....www.queenscp.org
E-mail ....nglass@queenscp.org
8225 164th St, Jamaica, NY 11432-1120
Nancy Glass, Director

United Neighborhood Houses **212.967.0322**
Fax 212.967.0792
Web ....www.unhny.org
E-mail ....nwackstein@unhny.org
70 W 36th St, Fl 5, New York, NY 10018
Nancy Wackstein, Executive Director

United Way Of Long Island **631.940.3700**
Fax 631.940.2552
Web ....www.unitedwayli.org
E-mail ....info@unitedwayli.org
819 Grand Blvd Ste 1, Deer Park, NY 11729-5780
Elizabeth Eberhardt, Director Of Information And Referral

Vanderheyden Hall, Inc. **518.283.6500**
Fax 518.283.7156
Web ....www.vanderheydenhall.org
E-mail ....lmappes@vanderheydenhall.org
614 Cooper Hill Rd, Wynantskill, NY 12198
Linda Mappes, Executive Director

Western New York Child Care Council, Inc. **585.654.4720**
Fax 585.654.4721
Web ....www.childcarecounsel.com
595 Blossom Rd Ste 120, Rochester, NY 14610
Barbara Anne Mattle, CEO

SPECIAL NEEDS

Abilities **516.465.1400**
Fax 516.747.5400
201 IU Willets Road, Albertson, NY 11507
Rose Sanicola, Administrator

Ability Builders for Children LLC **718.239.8239**
Fax 718.770.7686
E-mail ....admin@abilitybuildersforchildren.com
3175 E Tremont Ave, 2nd Flr, Bronx, NY 10461
Oliver Trinidad, Director

Abraham House Bronx **718.292.9321**
Fax 718.292.5925
E-mail ....Information@AbrahamHouse.org
340 Willis Ave, Bronx, NY 10454
Andre Pabon, Executive Director

Abundant Life Agency Inc **718.735.7151**
Fax 718.735.7141
827 Clarkson Ave, Brooklyn, NY 11203
Olive Archer, Director

Abundant Life Tabernacle Ministries Inc **718.292.8734**
Fax 718.993.4470
E-mail ....zoe144@earthlink.net
2692 Third Ave, Bronx, NY 10454
Jaspero Rolle, Chief Executive Officer

Achilles Track Club New York **212.354.0300**
Fax 212.354.3978
E-mail ....kids@achillesinternational.org
42 West 38th St Ste 400, New York, NY 10018
Richard Traum, Director

Adams Mark Buffalo Niagara **716.845.5100**
E-mail ....jamesburke@adamsmark.com
120 Church St, Buffalo, NY 14202
Jim Burke, General Manager

Adaptive Snowsports Greek Peak **607.785.8101**
E-mail ....jcappellett@stny.rr.com
208 Meeker Road, Vestal, NY 13850
James Cappellett, President

Adaptive Sports Foundation **518.734.5070**
Fax 518.734.6740
E-mail ....asfwindham@mhcable.com
100 Silverman Way, Windham, NY 12496
Cherisse Young, Chief Executive Officer

ADD Coach Academy **800.915.7702**
Fax 888.316.6137
Web ....www.addca.com
E-mail ....info@addca.com
1971 W ave 106, Slingerlands, NY 12203
David Giwerc, Director

Advanced Care Inc Queens **631.391.9670**
Fax 800.734.2273
931 Conklin St Unit D, Farmingdale, NY 11735

Advocates for Children of NY **212.947.9779**
Fax 212.947.9790
E-mail ....aespada@advocatesforchildren.org
151 W 30th St 5th Flr, New York, NY 10001
Ana Espada

Affinia Dumont Hotel Manhattan **212.481.7600**
Fax 212.889.8856
E-mail ....generalmanagers@affinia.com
150 East 34th St, New York, NY 10016
Alex Spektor, General Manager

Agape Christian Center Queens **718.418.2749**
59 02 Summerfield St, Ridgewood, NY 11385

AHRC Health Services Bronx **718.730.1004**
Fax 718.892.6469
1500 Pelham Parkway S, Bronx, NY 10461
Debbie Sorkin, Chief Executive Officer

AHRC Home Care Services Inc New York **212.780.2500**
83 Maiden Lane, New York, NY 10038

Aides at Home Inc Queens **718.639.9365**
Fax 718.639.9394
91 31 Queens Blvd Ste 402, Elmhurst, NY 11373
Roslyn Wilkins, President

AIDS Center **718.896.2500**
E-mail ....nat@acqc.org
Far Rockaway, 1600 Central Ave, Far Rockaway,
NY 01603
Nat Liengsiriwat, Supervisor

AIDS Family Services Buffalo **716.881.4612**
Fax 716.881.4618
E-mail ....afs@afsbflo.org
1092 Main St, Buffalo, NY 14209
Julie Rosado, Executive Director

All in 1 SPOT with Theratalk **718.767.0071**
Fax 718.767.0086
E-mail ....theratalk@aol.com
150-50 14 Rd, Whitestone, NY 11357

American Fndtn for Blind Information Ctr **212.502.7600**
E-mail ....afbinfo@afb.net
11 Penn Plz Ste 300, New York, NY 10001

American Foundation for the Blind **800.232.5463**
E-mail ....afbinfo@afb.net
11 Penn Plz Ste 300, New York, NY 10001

Autism Society of Albany **518.355.2191**
E-mail ....info@albanyautism.org
101 State St, Schenectady, NY 12305
Jeanine Kruiswijk, Executive Director

Autism Society of Manhattan **212.628.0669**
E-mail ....gdzuckerman@yahoo.com
370 E 76th St # C1208, New York, NY 10021
Carrie Zuckerman, President

Autism Society of Western New York **716.633.2275**
E-mail ....info@autismwny.org
19 Limestone Dr Ste 1, Williamsville, NY 14221
Katheleen Eiss, President

Autismconcepts.com **845.978.3182**
Fax 845.355.2104
Web ....www.autismconcepts.com
E-mail ....info@autismconcepts.com
59 Mullock Rd, Middletown, NY 10940-6196
Crystal Brown, Owner

Brain Injury Association **518.459.7911**
E-mail ....info@bianys.org
10 Colvin Ave, Albany, NY 12206
Judith Avnver, Executive Director

Care At Home - Diocese of Brooklyn, Inc. **718.907.4700**
Fax 718.965.7020
Web ....www.cahny.com
E-mail ....RMBorg@cahny.com
168 Seventh Street, Brooklyn, NY 11215
Rose Marie Borg, Executive Director

Cerebral Palsy Associations 212.947.5770
E-mail ....information@cpofnys.org
　330 W 34th St 15th Fl, New York, NY 10001
　Sue Constantino, President

Childrens Brain Tumor Foundation 212.448.1595
Fax 212.448.1022
E-mail ....info@cbtf.org
　274 Madison Ave Ste 1004, New York, NY 10016
　Joe Fay, Chief Executive Officer

Congress of Parents & Teachers Inc 518.452.8808
E-mail ....pta.office@nyspta.org
　1 Wembley Ct, Albany, NY 12205
　Rick Longhurst, Executive Administrator

**Ctr for Autism and Related Disorders
(Card)** 585.377.6590
Fax 585.377.6605
Web ....www.centerforautism.com
　6 N Main St Ste 110, Fairport, NY 14450-1581
　Denise Rhine, Sr. Managing Supervisor

Dove Rehab Services 516.935.3683
Fax 516.935.0365
E-mail ....info@doverehab.com
　270 Duffy Ave Unit G, Hicksville, NY 11801
　Renee

Easter Seals New York 518.244.6053
E-mail ....essofny@aol.com
　29 W 36th St 4th Fl Rm 404, New York, NY 10018

EBL Coaching 646.342.9380
Fax 212.937.2305
E-mail ....info@eblcoaching.com
　17 E 89th St, New York, NY 10128
　Emily Levy, Director

Edenwald Ctr 914.769.7150
Fax 914.773.6170
Web ....www.jccany.org
E-mail ....jcca@jccany.org
　1075 Broadway, Pleasantville, NY 10570
　Beverly Lemmon, Director Of Permanency

Epilepsy Foundation of Long Island 516.739.7733
E-mail ....t.hopkins@epil.org
　506 Stewart Ave, Garden City, NY 11530
　Thomas Hopkins, Director

Families Together in New York State Inc 518.432.0333
E-mail ....info@ftnys.org
　737 Madison Ave, Albany, NY 12208
　Page Pearce, Director

Family Empowerment Council Inc 845.343.8100
E-mail ....brussell@familyempowerment.org
　225 Dolson Ave Ste 403, Middletown, NY 10940

Gersh Education Services 631.385.3342
Fax 631.427.6332
Web ....www.gershacademy.org
　21 Ste hollow 2nd Fl, Huntington, NY 11743
　Dan Selmer, Program Director

Green Chimneys School 845.279.2995
Fax 845.279.3077
Web ....www.greenchimneys.org
E-mail ....dlester@greenchimneys.org
　400 Doansburg Rd, Brewster, NY 10509
　Duncan Lester, Aed Operations
　COA accredited organization.

Hallen School 914.636.6600
Fax 914.633.4089
Web ....www.hallenschool.net
　97 Centre Ave, New Rochelle, NY 10801
　Priscilla Feir, Director

Helen Hayes Hospital 845.786.4000
Fax 845.786.4022
Web ....http://www.helenhayeshospital.org
　Route Nine West, West Haverstraw, NY 10993
　CARF accredited programs available.

Jacobs Neurological Institute 877.878.7367
E-mail ....jray@thejni.org
　219 Bryan St, Buffalo, NY 14222
　Bianca Weinstock-guttman, Center Director

League Treatment Ctr Joan Fenichel Thera 718.643.5300
Fax 718.643.0640
Web ....www.leaguetreatment.org
　30 Washington St, Brooklyn, NY 11201
　Hannah Achtenberg Kinn, Exective-director

Learning Disabilities Association 518.608.8992
E-mail ....statelda@ldanys.org
　1190 Troy-Schenectady Rd, Rm 225, Latham,
　NY 12110

Lindamood-Bell Learning Processes 516.625.5133
Fax 516.625.1407
　20 Roosevelt Ave, Roslyn, NY 11576
　Daryl Martin, Center Director

Lindamood-Bell Learning Processes 212.644.0650
Fax 212.644.0654
E-mail ....jan.egan@lindamoodbell.com
　110 E 55th St, New York, NY 10022
　Jennifer Egan, Director

Memorial Sloan-Kettering Cancer Center 212.639.2000
Web ....www.mskcc.org
　1275 York Ave, New York, NY 10065

Mental Health Association 518.434.0439
E-mail ....info@mhanys.org
　194 Washington Ave Ste 415, Albany, NY 12210
　Glenn Liebman, Chief Executive Officer

**MindWorks Mental Health Counseling,
PLLC** 914.574.6363
Fax 914.574.6364
E-mail ....athaler@mindworkscenter.com
　2 Overhill Rd Ste 320, Scarsdale, NY 10583

**Mount Sinai Medical Center/Mount Sinai Rehabilitation
Center** 212.659.9328
Fax 212.731.7206
Web ....www.mssm.edu/rehab/
　One Gustave L. Levy Place, Department of
　Rehabilitation, New York, NY 10029
　CARF accredited programs available.

National Multiple Sclerosis Society 631.864.8337
Fax 631.864.8342
E-mail ....Pmastrota@nmssli.org
　40 Marcus Dr Ste 100, Melville, NY 11747
　Pam Mastrota, Director

National Multiple Sclerosis Society 212.463.7787
Fax 212.986.7981
E-mail ....info@msnyc.org
　733 3rd Ave 3rd Fl, New York, NY 10017
　Carolyn Cronin, President

National Multiple Sclerosis Society 585.271.0801
Fax 585.442.2817
E-mail ....chapter@msupstateny.org
　1650 South Ave Ste 100, Rochester, NY 14620
　Stephanie Mincer, Chapter President

Natl Alliance for the Mentally Ill 518.462.2000
E-mail ....info@naminys.org
　260 Washington Ave, Albany, NY 12210
　Donald Capone, Executive Director

New Interdisciplinary School 631.924.5583
Fax 631.924.5687
Web ....www.niskids.org
E-mail ....nis@ighl.org
　430 Sills Rd, Yaphank, NY 11980
　Helen C Wiilder, Director

New York Autism Network (Nyan) 518.442.2574
Fax 518.442.4834
Web ....www.albany.edu/psy/autism/autism.html
E-mail ....card@albany.edu
　1535 Western Ave, University Albany, Department
　Of Psychology, Albany, NY 12203-3513
　Kristin Christodulu, Director

New York Institute for Special Education 718.519.7000
Fax 718.881.4219
Web ....www.nyise.org
　999 Pelham Pkwy, Bronx, NY 10469
　Bernadette M Kappen, Director

New York State Partners in Policymaking 585.546.1700
E-mail ....steel@advocacycenter.com
　590 South Ave, Rochester, NY 14620
　Joyce Steel, Manager

NYSARC Inc 518.439.8311
E-mail ....brandtm@nysarc.org
　393 Delaware Ave, Delmar, NY 12054
　Mark Brandt, Executive Director

Occupational Therapy Association 518.462.3717
E-mail ....nysota@aol.com
　119 Washington Ave 2nd Fl, Albany, NY 12210

Parent Network 716.853.1570
Fax 716.853.1574
E-mail ....parentnetworkcenter@webt.com
　250 Delaware Ave, Ste 3, Buffalo, NY 14202

Parent Network of WNY 716.332.4100
Fax 716.332.4171
E-mail ....kmw@parentnetworkwny.org
　1000 Main St, Buffalo, NY 14202
　Sue Barlow, Executive Director

Parent to Parent 518.359.3006
E-mail ....p2pnys@adelphia.net
　PO Box 1296, Tupper Lake, NY 12986
　Janice Fitzgerald, Executive Director

Parent to Parent of New York State 518.381.4350
Fax 518.382.1959
　500 Balltown Rd, Schenectady, NY 12304

Pediatric Keratoplasty Association 914.493.1599
Fax 914.493.7445
E-mail ....pedkera@aol.com
　Dept of Ophthalmology, Westchester Medical Center,
　Valhalla, NY 10595
　Dr. Gerald Zaidman, Director

Ramapo for Children 845.876.8403
Fax 845.876.8414
E-mail ....office@ramapoforchildren.org
　Rt 52 Salisbury Tpke, Rhinebeck, NY 12572
　Mike Kunin, Director

Resources for Children w/ Special Needs 212.677.4650
E-mail ....information.services@resourcesmyc.org
　116 E 16th St 5th Fl, New York, NY 10003
　Rachel Howard, Director

**Rusk Institute of Rehabilitation Medicine, NYU Hospital
Center** 212.263.5147
Fax 212.263.8460
Web ....www.ruskinstitute.org
E-mail ....steven.flanagan@nyumc.org
　400 East 34th Street, New York, NY 10016
　Steven Flanagan, Medical Director
　CARF accredited programs available.

Sinergia/Metropolitan Parent Center 212.643.2840
Fax 212.643.2871
E-mail ....information@sinergiany.org
　2082 Lexington Ave, New York, NY 10032
　Michael Mitchell, Director

Sinergia/Metropolitan Parent Center 212.643.2840
E-mail ....information@sinergiany.org
　2082 lexington ave, New York, NY 10035
　Myrta Cuadra-Lash, Executive Director

Spina Bifida Association of Nebraska 518.399.9151
E-mail ....sbaneny@aol.net
　123 Saratoga Rd, Scotia, NY 12302
　Karen Wentworth, Executive Director

St. Charles Hospital and Rehabilitation

Center **631.474.6000**
Fax 631.474.6371
Web ....www.stcharles.org
   200 Belle Terre Road, Port Jefferson, NY 11777
   Marilyn Fabbricante, Director - Public & External Affairs
   CARF accredited programs available.

Stony Brook University Hospital **631.689.8333**
E-mail ....info@pediatricmscenter.org
   Dept of Neurology, HSC-T12-020, Stony Brook,
   NY 11794
   Lauren Krupp, MD Center Director

Sunnyview Rehabilitation Hospital **518.382.4523**
Fax 518.382.4570
Web ....www.sunnyview.org
   1270 Belmont Avenue, Schenectady, NY 12308
   CARF accredited programs available.

SUNY Upstate Medical University **315.464.4243**
Fax 315.464.7328
E-mail ....shefnerj@upstate.edu
   750 E Adams St, Syracuse, NY 13210
   Jeremy M Shefner Md, Phd Director

The Advocacy Center **585.546.1700**
Fax 585.546.7069
E-mail ....klein@advocacycenter.com
   590 South Ave, Averill Court, Rochester, NY 14620
   Paul Shew, Executive Director

The Brain Clinic **212.268.8900**
E-mail ....nurosvcs@aol.com
   19 W 34th St Penthouse, New York, NY 10001
   James Lawrence Thomas, Director

The Center for Kinesthetic Education **212.414.2921**
Fax 212.414.2921
E-mail ....info@wellnessCKE.net
   151 W 30th St # 200, New York, NY 10001

The Children's Home of Kingston, New

York **845.331.1448**
Fax 845.334.9507
Web ....www.chkingston.org
   26 Grove Street, Kingston, NY 12401
   COA accredited organization.

The Eleanor & Lou Gehrig MDA/ALS Ctr **212.305.1319**
Fax 212.305.8398
E-mail ....afscenter@columbia.edu
   710 W 168th St 9th Fl, New York, NY 10032
   Hiroshi Mitsumoto MD, Director

The Family Foundation School **845.887.5213**
Fax 845.887.4939
E-mail ....info@thefamilyschool.com
   431 Chapel Hill Rd, Hancock, NY 13783
   Emmanuel Argiros, Owner

The Family Resource Network Inc **607.432.0001**
E-mail ....familyrn@dmcom.net
   46 Oneida St, Oneonta, NY 13820
   Pam Larson, Executive Director

The Study Shack **212.628.9129**
E-mail ....janie@thestudyshack.com
   1490 2nd Ave # 1A, New York, NY 10075
   Janie Teller, Owner

The Winifred Masterson Burke Rehabilitation

Hospital **914.597.2500**
Fax 914.597.2588
Web ....www.burke.org
E-mail ....tboelsen@burke.org
   785 Mamaroneck Ave, White Plains, NY 10605
   Toni Boelsen, Director of Community Relations
   CARF accredited programs available.

Tourette Syndrome Association Inc **718.224.2999**
E-mail ....ts@tsa-usa.org
   42-40 Bell Blvd Ste 205, Bayside, NY 11361
   Judith Ungar, President

United We Stand OF New York **718.302.4313**
E-mail ....uwsofny@aol.com
   91 Harrison Ave, Brooklyn, NY 11206
   Lourdes Rivera-Putz, Executive Director

Unity Health System, Acute Rehabilitation and Brain Injury

Program **585.368.3360**
Fax 585.368.3838
Web ....www.unityhealth.org
E-mail ....lvella@unityhealth.org
   89 Genesee Street, Rochester, NY 14611
   Louise Vella, Director S T A R
   CARF accredited programs available.

Univ of Rochester Medical Center **585.275.2559**
Fax 585.273.1255
E-mail ....Charles_Thornton@urmc.rochester.edu
   601 Elmwood Ave, Rochester, NY 14642
   Roxanne Cannaozzo, Secretary Of Director

University of Rochester, Strong Memorial Hospital

Rehabilitation Unit **585.275.3272**
Fax 585.442.2949
Web ....http://www.urmc.rochester.edu/strong-mem
   601 Elmwood Avenue, Physical Medicine and
   Rehabilitation, Rochester, NY 14642
   CARF accredited programs available.

VESID **518.486.7462**
E-mail ....egervais@mail.nysed.gov
   89 Washington Ave, Rm 309 EB, Albany, NY 12234
   Noel Granger, Supervisor

VSA Arts of New York City **718.225.6305**
E-mail ....bbvsanyc@msn.com
   18-05 215th St Ste 15N, Bayside, NY 11360

Westchester School for Special Children **914.376.4300**
Fax 914.965.7059
Web ....www.westchesterschool.org
   45 Park Ave, Yonkers, NY 10703
   Leonard Spano, Executive Director

Women and Children's Hospital of Buffalo **716.878.7000**
Web ....www.wchob.org
   219 Bryant St., Buffalo, NY 14222
   Sheryl Klass, Director

YAI/Ntnl Inst for People with Dsblts **212.273.6100**
Fax 212.268.1083
E-mail ....staff@yai.org
   460 W 34th St, New York, NY 10001
   Steve Freeman, Chief Executive Officer

SUBSTANCE ABUSE TREATMENT

Champlain Valley Family Ctr **518.561.8480**
Fax 518.566.6382
Web ....www.champlainvalleyfamilycenter.org
E-mail ....cwille@westelcom.com
   20 Ampersand Dr, Plattsburgh, NY 12901-6500
   Connie Willie, Director

George K Authur Community Svcs **716.896.1325**
Fax 716.892.2080
   2056 Genesee St, Buffalo, NY 14211-1937
   Michael Tritto, Director

Park Ridge **585.368.4719**
Fax 585.272.0704
Web ....www.unityhealth.org
   2000 Winton Rd S Bldg 2, Rochester, NY 14618-3922
   Anthony Klein, Site Coordinator

Phoenix Academy of Yorktown **914.962.2491**
Fax 914.962.0559
   3151 Stony St, Shrub Oak, NY 10588
   Jose Rosario, Director

Phoenix House **718.276.9001**
Fax 718.978.4279
Web ....www.phoenixhouse.org
E-mail ....bugwu@phoenixhouse.org
   21804 140th Ave, Springfield Gardens,
   NY 11413-2654
   Benet Ugwu, Director

Seafield Svcs **631.424.2900**
Fax 631.598.5716
Web ....www.seafieldcenter.com
E-mail ....dhenry@seafieldcenter.com
   37 John St, Amityville, NY 11701-2930
   Diane Henry, Director

Seafield Svcs **516.747.5644**
Fax 516.747.2556
   110 Main St Fl 1, Mineola, NY 11501-4000
   Kieran Dwyer, Director

Seafield-Riverhead Svcs **631.369.7800**
Fax 631.369.7898
Web ....www.seafieldcenter.com
E-mail ....gsmith@seafieldcenter.com
   212 W Main St, Riverhead, NY 11901-2841
   Gail Smith, Director

Stutzman Addiction Treatment Center **716.882.4900**
Fax 716.882.4426
Web ....www.oasas.state.ny.us/atc/stutz-home.htm
E-mail ....susanlisker@oasas.state.ny.us
   360 Forest Avenue, Buffalo, NY 14213
   Susan Lisker, Director
   CARF accredited programs available.

North Carolina

Beverly Perdue, Governor
Office of the Governor
20301 Mail Service Center
Raleigh, NC 27699-0301
919.733.4240
919.733.2120 (Fax)
governor.office@ncmail.net
www.governor.state.nc.us

Kimberly Wilson, Juvenile Justice Specialist
Governor's Crime Commission
1201 Front Street, Ste. 200
Raleigh, NC 27609
919.733.4564
919.733.4625 (Fax)
kwilson@ncgccd.org

Sandra Reid, SAG Chair
301 Old Farm Dr
Graham, NC 27253
336.278.6460
sreid@elon.edu

CRISIS NUMBERS

Child Abuse Reporting . . .800.442.4453

STATE SERVICES

SOCIAL SERVICES

Division of Child Development NC 919.662.4499
Fax 919.661.4845
319 Chapanoke Rd, Ste 120, Raleigh, NC 27603
Deb Cassidy, Director

NCDHHS Public Affairs 919.855.4840
Fax 919.733.7447
Web . . . . .www.nc.dhhs.gov
101 Blair Dr, Raleigh, NC 27699
Renee Mccoy, Director

North Carolina Div Of Social Svcs 919.733.3055
Child Support 919.255.3800
Child Protective Services .919.733.4622
Fax 919.334.1018
Web . . . . .www.dhhs.state.nc.us/dss/
2401 Mail Service Ctr, 325 N Salisbury St, Raleigh,
NC 27699-2400

North Carolina Emergency Management
Agency 919.733.3867
Fax 919.733.7554
Web . . . . .www.nccrimecontrol.org
E-mail . . . . .dhoell@ncem.org
116 W Jones St, Raleigh, NC 27603
Doug Hoell, Director

GENERAL HEALTH SERVICES

Child w Spec Health Needs NC 919.553.1322
E-mail . . . . .dianne.tyson@ncmail.net
1928 Mail Srv Cntr, Raleigh, NC 27699
Dianne Tyson, Director

Dept of Health and Human Svcs Div of Public
Health 919.707.5425
Fax 919.870.4803
Web . . . . .www.injuryfreenc.ncdhhs.gov/index.htm
E-mail . . . . .jane.miller@dhhs.nc.gov
5505 Six Force Rd, Raleigh, NC 27609
Jane Ann Miller, Public Health Consultant

Div of Environmental Health 919.733.2870
Fax 919.715.3242
Web . . . . .www.deh.enr.state.nc.us
E-mail . . . . .terry.pierce@ncmail.net
2728 Capital Blvd, Raleigh, NC 27604
Terry Pierce, Director

Div of Medical Assistance 919.855.4100
Fax 919.733.6608
E-mail . . . . .gwen.lawrence@dhhs.nc.gov
1985 Umstead Dr, Raleigh, NC 27603-2035
Dr. Craigan Gray, Director

Div of Public Health 919.707.5000
Fax 919.870.4829
Web . . . . .www.ncpublichealth.com
5601 Forks Rd, 1st Floor, Raleigh, NC 27609
Jeffrey Engel, State Health Director

North Carolina Hospital Assoc 919.677.2400
Fax 919.677.4200
Web . . . . .www.ncha.org
2400 Weston Pkwy, Cary, NC 27513
Christie Johnson, Administrative Assistant

North Carolina Medical Board 919.326.1100
Fax 919.326.1130
Web . . . . .www.ncmedboard.org
E-mail . . . . .info@ncmedboard.org
1203 Front St, Raleigh, NC 27609
David Henderson, Executive Director

Rural Health & Development 919.733.2040
Fax 919.733.8300
Web . . . . .www.dhhs.state.nc.us
E-mail . . . . .john.price@dhhs.nc.gov
311 Ashe Ave, Raleigh, NC 27606-2102
John Price, Director

Womens and Childrens Health Section NC 919.707.5512
Fax 919.870.4828
E-mail . . . . .kevin.ryan@ncmail.net
1916 Mail Service Center, Raleigh, NC 27699
Kevin Ryan, Director

MENTAL HEALTH SERVICES

Div of Svcs for the Blind .919.733.9822
Fax 919.733.9769
Web . . . . .www.dhhs.state.nc.us
E-mail . . . . .eddie.weaver@dhhs.nc.gov
301 Ashe Ave Bldg MSC, Raleigh, NC 27699-0001
Eddie Weaver, Director

Div of Svcs for the Blind NC 919.733.9822
Fax 919.733.9769
E-mail . . . . .eddie.weaver@dhhs.nc.gov
2601 Mail Service Center, Raleigh, NC 27699
Eddie Weaver, Director

Div of Vocational Rehabilitation Svcs 919.855.3500
Fax 919.733.7968
E-mail . . . . .linda.harrington@dvrs.nc.gov
2801 Mail Service Ctr, Raleigh, NC 27699-2800
Linda Harrington, Director

JUSTICE AGENCY

Buncombe Regional Juvenile Detention Ctr 828.251.6168
Fax 828.251.6182
E-mail . . . . .debby.burchfield@ncmail.net
20 Lees Creek Rd, Asheville, NC 28806-4712
Debby Burchfield,lcsw, Facility Director

Correctional Educ Division NC 919.838.3642
Fax 919.838.4764
E-mail . . . . .ugm01@doc.state.nc.us
831 W Morgan St, Raleigh, NC 27601

Crime Victim Compensation Program 919.733.7974
Fax 919.715.4209
Web .www.nccrimecontrol.org/vcs
4703 Mail Service Ctr, Raleigh, NC 27699
Janice Carmichael, Director

Dept of Corrections 919.716.3700
Fax 919.716.3794
E-mail . . . . .info@doc.state.nc.us
214 W Jones St, Raleigh, NC 27699
Theddis Beck, Secretary Of Corrections

Dept Of Juvenile Justice .828.697.4895
Fax 828.697.5610
E-mail . . . . .rodney.wesson@djjdp.nc.gov
200 N Grove St Ste 36, Hendersonville,
NC 28792-5027
Brad Renegar, Court Counselor Services

Dept Of Juvenile Justice And Delinquency
Prevention 704.852.3123
Fax 704.852.3252
Web . . . . .www.juvjus.state.nc.us
E-mail . . . . .carol.mcmanus@djjdp.nc.gov
325 N Marietta St, Suite 2140, Gastonia,
NC 28052-2331
Carol Mcmanus, Chief Court Counselor

Governor's Crime Commission 919.733.4564
Fax 919.733.4625
1201 Front St Ste 200, Raleigh, NC 27609
Gwendolyn Burrell, Executive Director

POLICE AND SHERIFF

North Carolina Sheriff's Assoc 919.783.8899
Fax 919.783.5272
Web . . . . .www.ncsheriffs.org
E-mail . . . . .ncsa@ncsheriffs.net
323 W Jonesboro St, Raleigh, NC 27603-1764
Edmond Caldwell, Jr., Vice President

North Carolina

EDUCATION SERVICES

Asheville City Schools **828.350.7000**
Fax 828.255.5131
Web www.asheville.k12.nc.us
E-mail ....paul.perrotta@asheville.k12.nc.us
   85 Mountain Street, Asheville, NC 28801
   Paul Perrotta, Special Education

Communities In Schools of North Carolina,
   Inc. **919.832.2700**
Fax 919.832.5436
Web ....www.cisnc.org
   222 N Person St Ste 101, Raleigh, NC 27601-1067
   Linda Harrell, President

Exceptional Children Division NC **919.807.3969**
Fax 919.807.3243
E-mail ....lbynum@dpi.state.nc.us
   6356 Mail Service Center, Raleigh, NC 27699
   L Bynum, Director

Exceptional Childrens Asst Ctr Inc NC **704.892.1321**
Fax 704.892.5028
E-mail ....chawkins@ecacmail.org
   907 Barra Row Ste 102/103, Davidson, NC 28036
   Connie Hawkins, Director

Homeless Edu Program North Carolina **336.315.7491**
Fax 336.315.7457
E-mail ....homeless@serve.org
   PO Box 5367, Greensboro, NC 27435
   Diana Bowman, Director

NC Dept of Public Instruction **919.807.3430**
Fax 919.807.3445
E-mail ....mwertis@dpi.state.nc.us
   301 N Wilmington St, Raleigh, NC 27601
   M Wertis, Director

LABOR & WORKFORCE EDUCATION

NC Commission on Workforce Development ...**919.733.3016**
Fax 919.733.6918
   316 W Edenton St, main service centre, Raleigh,
   NC 27603-1058
   Joseph A Jr., Commissioner

COUNTY SERVICES

Alamance County

SOCIAL SERVICES

Social Svcs Dept **336.570.6532**
Fax 336.570.6771
E-mail ....susan.osborne@alamance-nc.com
   319 N Graham Hopedale Rd Ste C, Burlington,
   NC 27217
   Susan Osborne, Director

MENTAL HEALTH SERVICES

Alamance-Caswell Lme **336.513.4200**
Fax 336.513.4203
Web ....www.acmhddsa.org
E-mail ....sclinkscale@acmhddsa.org
   319 N Graham Hopedale Rd Fl A, Burlington,
   NC 27217-2992
   Selena Clinkscale, Administrative Assistant

EDUCATION SERVICES

Exceptional Children's Program **336.570.6060**
Fax 336.570.0811
Web www.abss.k12.nc.us
   1712 Vaughn Rd, Burlington, NC 27217-2916
   Bill Hussey, Director

Alexander County

SOCIAL SERVICES

Social Svcs **828.632.1080**
Fax 828.632.1359
Web .....www.dhhs.state.nc.us/dss/local/dir_alex.htm
E-mail ....cholman@alexandercountync.gov
   604 7th St SW, Taylorsville, NC 28681-2443
   Cyntha Holman, Director

GENERAL HEALTH SERVICES

Health Dept **828.632.9704**
Fax 828.632.9008
Web ....www.co.alexander.nc.us/health
   338 1st Ave SW, Ste 1, Taylorsville, NC 28681
   Leeanne Whismant, Health Director

JUSTICE AGENCY

Alexander Juvenile Detention Ctr **828.632.1141**
Fax 828.632.1151
E-mail ....kimberly.cowart@ncmail.net
   928 NC Highway 16 S, Taylorsville, NC 28681-8941
   Kimberly Cowart, Director

EDUCATION SERVICES

Head Start **828.632.3809**
Fax 828.632.3717
Web www.alexander.k12.nc.us
E-mail ....deinstein@alexander.k12.nc.us
   5860 ES Highway 6490 W, Taylorsville, NC 28681
   Debroah Ferguson, Director

Alleghany County

GENERAL HEALTH SERVICES

Health Dept **336.372.5641**
Fax 336.372.7793
   157 Health Services Rd, Sparta, NC 28675-3000
   Danny Staley, Health Director

POLICE AND SHERIFF

Sheriff's Ofc **336.372.4455**
Fax 336.372.8639
Web ....www.skybest.com
E-mail ....acsdrecords@skybest.com
   40 Alleghany St, Sparta, NC 28675
   David Edwards, Sheriff

Anson County

SOCIAL SERVICES

Social Svcs **704.694.9351**
Fax 704.695.1608
Web ....www.co.anson.nc.us
E-mail ....lcrandell@email.co.anson.nc.us
   118 N Washington St, Wadesboro, NC 28170-2255
   Larry Crandell, Director

GENERAL HEALTH SERVICES

Health Dept **704.694.5188**
Fax 704.694.9067
Web ....www.co.anson.nc.us
E-mail ....cgibson@county.anson.nc.us
   110 E Ashe St, Wadesboro, NC 28170-2702
   Carol Ann Gibson, Health Director

Ashe County

GENERAL HEALTH SERVICES

Health Dept **336.246.9449**
Fax 336.246.8163
   413 McConnell St, Jefferson, NC 28640-9772
   Beth Lovette, Health Director

Avery County

SOCIAL SERVICES

Social Svcs Dept **828.733.8230**
Fax 828.733.8245
Web ....www.averyco.dss.com
   175 Linville St, Newland, NC 28657
   Tom Hughes, Director

GENERAL HEALTH SERVICES

Health Dept **828.733.6031**
Fax 828.733.6034
   545 Schultz Cir, Newland, NC 28657
   Vivian Greene, Supervisor

JUSTICE AGENCY

Dept Of Juvenile Justice **828.733.9524**
Fax 828.733.9664
E-mail ....lisa.garland@djjdt.nc.gov
   200 Old Montezuma Rd, Newland, NC 28657
   Lisa Garland, Chief Court Counselor

COURTS

24th District Court **828.733.2900**
Fax 828.733.8410
Web ....www.aoc.state.nc.us
E-mail ....a.lyerly@aoc.state.nc.us
   200 Monotezuma St, Newland, NC 28657
   Honorable Alexander Lyerly, Judge

POLICE AND SHERIFF

Sheriff's Ofc **828.733.2071**
Fax 828.733.1382
E-mail ....kevin.frye@ncmail.net
   300 Schultz Cr., Newland, NC 28657
   Kevin Frye, Sheriff

Beaufort County

SOCIAL SERVICES

Social Svcs **252.975.5500**
Fax 252.975.5555
E-mail ....sanya.temon@beaufort.nc.gov
   632 W 5th St, Washington, NC 27889
   Sonya Toman, Director

GENERAL HEALTH SERVICES

Health Dept **252.946.1902**
Fax 252.946.8430
Web ....www.bchd.net
E-mail ....roxanne.holloman@bchd.net
   1436 Highland Dr, Washington, NC 27889-3222
   Roxanne Holloman, Health Director

MENTAL HEALTH SERVICES

Tideland Area Mental Health **252.946.8061**
Fax 252.946.5499
   1308 Highland Dr, Washington, NC 27889
   Janet Joyner, Area Director

JUSTICE AGENCY

Dept Of Juvenile Justice **252.946.1173**
Fax 252.974.1162
   132 N Market St, Washington, NC 27889
   Mark Leggett, Chief Court Counselor

POLICE AND SHERIFF

Sheriff's Ofc **252.946.7111**
Fax 252.946.0993
Web ....www.sheriff.co.beaufort.nc.us
E-mail ....jordan@sheriff.co.beaufort.nc.us
   210 N Market St, Washington, NC 27889-4950
   Robert A. Jordan, Sheriff

© 2011 Dorland Health

EDUCATION SERVICES

Belhaven Head Start **252.943.3006**
Fax 252.943.2420
E-mail ....amills@mccai.org
   193 E Pantego St, Belhaven, NC 27810-1434
   Annie Mills, Center Director

Bertie County

SOCIAL SERVICES

Social Svcs Dept **252.794.5320**
Fax 252.794.5344
   110 Jasper Bazemore Ave, Windsor, NC 27983
   Morris L. Rascoe, Director

GENERAL HEALTH SERVICES

Health Dept **252.794.5322**
Fax 252.794.5321
   102 Rhodes Ave, Windsor, NC 27983
   Jerry Parks, Health Director

COURTS

6th District Court **252.794.3039**
Fax 252.794.2482
Web ....www.co.bertie.nc.us
   108 Dundee St, Windsor, NC 27983
   Honorable W. Rob Lewis, Director

Bladen County

SOCIAL SERVICES

Social Svcs Dept **910.862.6800**
Fax 910.862.6801
Web ....www.bladenco.org
E-mail ....jkoenig@bladenco.org
   208 E McKay St, Elizabethtown, NC 28337
   June Koenig, Director

GENERAL HEALTH SERVICES

Health Dept **910.862.6900**
Fax 910.862.6859
   300 Mercer Mill Rd, Elizabethtown, NC 28337
   Wayne Stewart, Health Director

COURTS

Teen Court **910.862.4591**
Fax 910.862.6939
Web ....www.ncsu.edu
E-mail ....johnice_autry@ncsu.edu
   450 Smith Circle Dr, Elizabeth town, NC 28337
   Johnice Autry, Coordinator

POLICE AND SHERIFF

Sheriff's Ofc **910.862.6960**
Fax 910.862.6949
Web ....www.bladenco.org
E-mail ....pbenston@bladenco.org
   201 W King St, Elizabethtown, NC 28337-9578
   Prentis Benston, Sheriff

Brunswick County

SOCIAL SERVICES

Social Svcs **910.253.2077**
Fax 910.253.2071
E-mail ....pconnelly@brunsco.net
   60 Govt Ctr Dr NE, Bolivia, NC 28422
   Patricia Connelly, Director

GENERAL HEALTH SERVICES

Health Dept **910.253.2250**
Fax 910.253.2387
   25 Courthouse Dr NE, Bolivia, NC 28422
   Pauline Robinson, Rn, Communicable Disease Coordinator

POLICE AND SHERIFF

Caswell Beach Police Dept **910.278.1555**
Fax 910.278.7311
Web ....www.caswellbeach.org
E-mail ....jcarroll@caswellbeach.org
   1100 Caswell Beach Rd, Oak Island, NC 28465-8437
   Judith Carroll, Police Chief

Sheriff's Ofc **910.253.2777**
Fax 910.253.4370
   70 Stamp Act Dr, Bolivia, NC 28422
   John Ingram, Sheriff

Buncombe County

SOCIAL SERVICES

Social Svcs Dept **828.250.5500**
Fax 828.250.6235
Web ....www.buncombecounty.org
E-mail ....mandy.stone@buncombecounty.org
   40 Coxe Ave, Asheville, NC 28802-3308
   Mandy Stone, Director

GENERAL HEALTH SERVICES

Health Dept **828.250.5000**
Fax 828.250.6173
Web ....www.buncombecounty.org
E-mail ....gibbie.harris@buncombecounty.org
   35 Woodfin St, Asheville, NC 28801-3072
   Gibbie Harris, Director

JUSTICE AGENCY

Guardian Ad Litem **828.251.6130**
Fax 828.251.6235
Web ....www.nccourts.org
E-mail ....jean.l.moore@nccourts.org
   31 College Pl, Bldg. D Suite 204, Asheville,
   NC 28801-2483
   Jean Moore, District Administrator

**Juvenile Crime Prevention Council-Western
Area** **828.258.5888**
Fax 828.250.3821
Web ....www.djjdp.nc.gov
E-mail ....linda.garney@ncmail.net
   741 Old Us 70 Hwy, Swannanoa, NC 28778-3314
   Linda Garney, Consultant

COURTS

Teen Court **828.250.4297**
Fax 828.258.6423
Web ....www.main.nc.us
E-mail ....executive@main.nc.us
   20 S Spruce St Ste 103, Asheville, NC 28801-3700
   Karen Kowalski, Executive Director

POLICE AND SHERIFF

Sheriff's Dept **828.255.5000**
Fax 828.250.4471
Web ....www.buncombesheriff.org
E-mail ....jack.duncan@buncombecounty.org
   202 Haywood St, Asheville, NC 28801-2619
   Jack Duncan, Sheriff

EDUCATION SERVICES

Exceptional Childrens Program **828.255.5921**
Fax 828.255.5923
Web www.buncombe.k12.nc.us
E-mail ....jana.griggs@bcsemail.org
   175 Bingham Rd, Asheville, NC 28806-3800
   Jana Griggs, Director Of Exceptional Childrens Program

Burke County

SOCIAL SERVICES

Social Svcs Dept **828.439.2000**
Fax 828.439.2137
Web ....www.dhhs.state.nc.us
E-mail ....dgsmith@co.burke.nc.us
   700 E Parker Rd, Morganton, NC 28655
   David Smith, Director

GENERAL HEALTH SERVICES

Home Health Agency **828.439.4400**
Fax 828.439.4444
Web ....www.co.burke.nc.us
E-mail ....david.rust@ncmail.net
   700 E Parker Rd, Morganton, NC 28655
   David L. Rust Jr., Health Director

MENTAL HEALTH SERVICES

Broughton Hospital **828.433.2111**
Web ....www.broughtonhospital.org
E-mail ....tom.mahle@broughtonhospital.org
   1000 S Sterling St, Morganton, NC 28655
   Tom Mahle, Director

Cabarrus County

SOCIAL SERVICES

Social Svcs Dept **704.920.1400**
Fax 704.920.1401
   1303 S Cannon Blvd, Kannapolis, NC 28083
   Ben Rose, Director

JUSTICE AGENCY

Dept of Juvenile Justice **704.786.5611**
Fax 704.792.1993
Web ....www.juvjus.state.nc.us
E-mail ....scott.stoker@ncmail.net
   77 Union St S, Concord, NC 28025
   Scott Stoker, Chief Court Counselor

EDUCATION SERVICES

Communities In Schools **704.788.1007**
Fax 704.786.3615
Web ....www.vnet.net
E-mail ....ciscabco@vnet.net
   120 Marsh Ave NW, Concord, NC 28025-4889

Exceptional Children's Program **704.786.6191**
Fax 704.786.6141
Web www.cabarrus.k12.nc.us
E-mail ....vshandor@cabarrus.k12.nc.us
   4401 Old Airport Rd, Concord, NC 28025-7188
   Victor Shandor, Director

Caldwell County

SOCIAL SERVICES

Social Svcs Dept **828.426.8200**
Fax 828.426.8398
E-mail ....jedwards@caldwellcountync.org
   2345 Morganton Blvd SW Ste A, Lenoir, NC 28645
   Joyce Edwards, Director

GENERAL HEALTH SERVICES

Home & Health **828.426.8401**
Fax 828.426.8441
Web ....www.caldwellcountync.org
   2345 Morganton Blvd, Lenoir, NC 28645-5313
   Denise Michaud, Health Director

JUSTICE AGENCY

Dept Of Juvenile Justice **828.757.1351**
Fax 828.757.1443
   208 Mulberry St, Lenoir, NC 28645
   Ronn Abernathy, Chief Court Counselor

North Carolina

COURTS

25th District Court **828.759.3502**
Fax 828.759.3501
Web ....www.nccourts.org
E-mail ....robert.m.brady@nccourts.org
216 Main St, Lenoir, NC 28645-1376
Honorable Robert Brady, Chief District Court Judge

POLICE AND SHERIFF

Sheriff's Ofc **828.757.1338**
Fax 828.757.1381
Web ....www.co.sioux.ne.us
2351 Morganton Blvd SW, Lenoir, NC 28645-4973
Alen Jones, Sheriff

EDUCATION SERVICES

Communities In Schools **828.759.2852**
Fax 828.759.2853
Web ....www.cisnet.org/caldwell
E-mail ....ciscaldwell@bellsouth.net
616 Ashe Ave NW, Lenoir, NC 28645-5152
Deborah Eller, Director

Camden County

SOCIAL SERVICES

Social Svcs **252.331.4787**
Fax 252.335.1009
E-mail ....sholley@camdencountync.gov
117 N Hwy 343, Camden, NC 27921
Sylvia Holley, Director

GENERAL HEALTH SERVICES

Health Dept **252.338.4460**
Fax 252.338.4475
Web ....www.arhs-nc.org
E-mail ....jmelko@arhs-nc.org
160B US Highway 158 E, Camden, NC 27921-7521
Juanita Melko, Hiv Coordinator

POLICE AND SHERIFF

Sheriff's Dept **252.338.1919**
Fax 252.333.1603
Web ....www.camdencountync.gov
E-mail ....tperry@camdencountync.gov
Hwy 343 N 117, Camden, NC 27921
Tony E. Perry, Sheriff

Carteret County

SOCIAL SERVICES

Social Svcs **252.728.3181**
Fax 252.728.3631
210 Craven St, Beaufort, NC 28516
David Atkinson, Director

GENERAL HEALTH SERVICES

Health Dept **252.728.8550**
Fax 252.222.7739
E-mail ....cchd@carteretcountygov.org
3820 A Bridges Street, Morehead City,
NC 28557-2979
Dr. J. T. Garrett, Ed.d., Mph, Health Director

Caswell County

SOCIAL SERVICES

Social Svcs **336.694.4141**
Fax 336.694.1816
Web ....www.caswellcountync.gov
E-mail ....dmoorefield@caswellcountync.gov
175 Church St, Yanceyville, NC 27379-9378
Diane Morfield, Director

GENERAL HEALTH SERVICES

Health Dept **336.694.4129**
Fax 336.694.7030
Web ....www.cchd.caswellnc.us
189 County Park Rd, Yanceyville, NC 27379
Fred Moore, Director

COURTS

9-A District Court **336.694.4171**
Fax 336.694.7338
Web ....www.nccourts.org
E-mail ....mark.gallaway@nccourts.org
139 8th Church St, Yanceyville, NC 27379
Honorable Mark Gallaway, Chief District Judge

Catawba County

SOCIAL SERVICES

Social Svcs Dept **828.695.5600**
Fax 828.695.2497
E-mail ....jeller@catawbacountync.gov
3030 11th Avenue Dr SE, Hickory, NC 28602
John Eller, Director

GENERAL HEALTH SERVICES

Health Dept **828.695.5800**
Fax 828.695.4410
3070 11th Avenue Dr SE, Hickory, NC 28602
Linda Greene, Hiv Health Coordinator

JUSTICE AGENCY

Dept Of Juvenile Justice **828.466.5671**
Fax 828.466.5674
Web ....www.djjdp.nc.gov
E-mail ....ronn.abernathy@ncmail.net
1175 S Brady Ave, Newton, NC 28658
Ronn Abernathy, Chief Court Counselor

COURTS

25th District Court **828.466.6100**
Fax 828.465.8975
E-mail ....clc@catawbacountync.gov
100 B SW Blvd, Newton, NC 28658
Honorable Robert M. Brady, Chief District Court Judge

POLICE AND SHERIFF

Sheriff's Ofc **828.464.5241**
Fax 828.465.8471
Web ....www.catawbacountync.gov
E-mail ....coy@catawbacountync.gov
100-B Southwest Blvd, Newton, NC 28658
Coy Reid, Sheriff

EDUCATION SERVICES

Exceptional Children Program **828.464.8333**
Fax 828.464.0925
Web ....www.catawbaschools.net
E-mail ....juli_white@catawbaschools.net
10 E 25th St, Newton, NC 28658-2763
Juli White, Director Of Exceptional Childrens Program

Exceptional Children's Program **828.322.2855**
Fax 828.322.1834
Web ....www.hickoryschools.net
E-mail ....rohrlo@hickoryschools.net
432 4th Ave SW, Hickory, NC 28602-2805
Lorane Rohr, Director Of Ec

Chatham County

SOCIAL SERVICES

Social Svcs **919.542.2759**
Fax 919.542.6355
Web ....www.dhhs.state.nc.us
E-mail ....sandra.coletta@ncmail.net
102 Camp St, Pittsboro, NC 27312
Sanda Colleta, Director

GENERAL HEALTH SERVICES

Health Dept **919.542.8220**
Fax 919.542.2473
Web ....www.chatamcounty.org
E-mail ....pam.mccall@chatamnc.com
80 E St, Pittsboro, NC 27312
Pam Mccall, Nursing Director

COURTS

15th District Court **919.542.3240**
Fax 919.542.1402
Web ....www.nccourts.org
E-mail ....joseph.m.buckner@nccourts.org
Courthouse Circle 12 East St, Pittitboro, NC 27312
Honorable Joseph M. Buckner, Director

Cherokee County

SOCIAL SERVICES

Social Svcs **828.837.7455**
Fax 828.837.9789
Web ....www.cherokeecounty-nc.gov
E-mail ....lisa.davis@cherokeecounty-nc.gov
4800 W Hwy, Murphy, NC 28906-2940
Donna Crawford, Director

GENERAL HEALTH SERVICES

Health Dept **828.837.7486**
Fax 828.837.3983
228 Hilton St, Murphy, NC 28906
Jim Higgins, Health Director

JUSTICE AGENCY

Guardian Ad Litem Program **828.837.8003**
Fax 828.837.0967
40 Peachtree St, Murphy, NC 28906
Heather Phillips, Program Supervisor

COURTS

30th District Court **828.837.8500**
Fax 828.837.8178
Web ....www.cherokeecounty-nc.org
E-mail ....danny.davis@cherokeecounty-nc.org
75 Peachtree St Ste 201, Murphy, NC 28906-2948
Roger Gibson, Clerk Of Court

POLICE AND SHERIFF

Sheriff's Ofc **828.837.2589**
Fax 828.837.6590
Web ....www.cherokeecounty-nc.gov
E-mail ....keith.lovin@cherokeecounty-nc.gov
577 Regal Ste, Murphy, NC 28906-2949
Ronald K. Lovin, Sheriff

Chowan County

SOCIAL SERVICES

Social Svcs Dept **252.482.7441**
Fax 252.482.7041
Web ....www.dhhs.state.nc.us
E-mail ....ben.rose@ncmail.net
113 E King St, Edenton, NC 27932-1957
William B. Rose, Director

JUSTICE AGENCY

Juvenile Home **252.482.0329**
Fax 252.482.7813
110 Sub Station Rd, Edenton, NC 27932-2065
Kim Richardson, Program Manager

COURTS

Teen Court **252.482.4436**
Fax 252.482.7309
E-mail ....wkoonce@ecps.k12.nc.us
113 E. King Street, Suite 300, Edenton, NC 27932
Willie Koonce, Director Of Testing & Accountability

Clay County

SOCIAL SERVICES

Social Svcs **828.389.6301**
Fax 828.389.6427
E-mail .... debbie.mauney@clay.nc.gov
    55 Riverside Cir, Hayesville, NC 28904
Debbie Mauney, Director

GENERAL HEALTH SERVICES

Health Dept **828.389.8052**
Fax 828.389.8533
Web .... www.clayhdnc.us
E-mail .... janicepatterson@clayhdnc.us
    Riverside Circle, Hayesville, NC 28904
Janice Patterson, Health Director

Cleveland County

SOCIAL SERVICES

Social Svcs Dept **704.487.0661**
Fax 704.484.1051
E-mail .... karen.ellis@clevelandcounty.com
    130 S Post Rd Ste 3, Shelby, NC 28151
Karen Ellis, Director

GENERAL HEALTH SERVICES

Health Dept **704.484.5100**
Fax 704.484.5114
    315 E Grover St, Shelby, NC 28150
Marsha Harris, Hiv Case Manager

JUSTICE AGENCY

Dept Of Juvenile Justice **704.480.5648**
Fax 704.480.5662
E-mail .... sara.brunner@ncmail.net
    408 E Marion St, Shelby, NC 28150-4614
Sara Brunner, Chief Court Counselor

Guardian Ad Litem Program **704.484.4771**
Fax 704.480.5487
E-mail .... dawn.scoggins@nccourts.org
    100 Justice Pl, Shelby, NC 28150
Dawn Scoggins, Programme Supervisor

COURTS

27th District Court **704.484.4851**
Fax 704.480.5487
Web .... www.nccourts.org
E-mail .... a.paksoy@nccourts.org
    100 Justice Pl Ste 104A, Shelby, NC 28150-4662
Honorable Ali B. Paksoy, Judge

POLICE AND SHERIFF

Sheriff's Dept **704.484.4817**
Fax 704.476.3047
Web .... www.clevelandcounty.com
E-mail .... alan.norman@clevelandcounty.com
    100 Justice Place, Shelby, NC 28151
Alan Norman, Sheriff

Columbus County

SOCIAL SERVICES

Social Svcs **910.642.2800**
Fax 910.641.3970
E-mail .... pmccormick@columbus.co.org
    40 Gov Complex Rd, Whiteville, NC 28472
Gerald Fogle, Director

GENERAL HEALTH SERVICES

Health Dept **910.640.6615**
Fax 910.640.7502
E-mail .... kim.l.smith@columbusco.org
    304 Jefferson St, Miller Building, Whiteville,
    NC 28472
Kimberly Smith, Director

JUSTICE AGENCY

Dept Of Juvenile Justice **910.641.3080**
Fax 910.641.0245
E-mail .... olaf.thorson@ncmail.net
    310 Jefferson St, Whiteville, NC 28472
Olaf Thorson, Chief Court Counselor

Guardian Ad Litem Program **910.641.3095**
Fax 910.641.3096
    704 N Thompson St, Whiteville, NC 28472
Christy Robbins, Program Supervisor

POLICE AND SHERIFF

Sheriff's Ofc **910.642.6551**
Fax 910.642.4321
E-mail .... cbatten@columbusco.org
    805 Washington St, Whiteville, NC
Chris Batten, Sheriff

Craven County

GENERAL HEALTH SERVICES

Health Dept **252.636.4920**
Fax 252.636.4970
    2818 Neuse Blvd Ste 15, New Bern, NC 28562
Scott Harrelson, Director

MENTAL HEALTH SERVICES

East Carolina Behavrioal Health **252.636.1510**
Fax 252.633.1237
Web .... www.ecbhlme.org
E-mail .... rwilson@neusecenter.org
    800 Cardinal Rd, New Bern, NC 28562
Roy P. Wilson Jr., Area Director

JUSTICE AGENCY

Dept Of Juvenile Justice **252.514.4718**
Fax 252.638.4857
    509 Broad St, New Bern, NC 28563-1556
Mary Mallard, Director

Guardian Ad Litem **252.514.4701**
Fax 252.633.3367
E-mail .... gail.c.horne@nccourts.org
    509 Broad St, New Bern, NC 28563
Gail Horne, District Administrator

Cumberland County

MENTAL HEALTH SERVICES

**Cumberland Area Mental Health
Program** **910.323.0601**
Fax 910.323.0096
Web .... www.ccmentalhealth.org
E-mail .... hdebnam@mail.ccmentalhealth.org
    711 Executive Pl Ste B, Fayetteville, NC 28305-5388
Hank Debnam, Area Director

JUSTICE AGENCY

**Cumberland Regional Juvenile Detention
Ctr** **910.486.1399**
Fax 910.486.1411
E-mail .... gene.hallock@ncmail.net
    1911 Coliseum Dr, Fayetteville, NC 28306-3060
Eugene S. Hallock, Director

Dept Of Juvenile Justice **910.678.2922**
Fax 910.321.3737
Web .... www.stateofnc.djjdp
E-mail .... michael.stricland@ncmail.net
    117 Dick St Ste 23, Fayetteville, NC 28301-5749
Michael Strickland, Chief Court Counselor

Guardian Ad Litem Program **910.678.2921**
Fax 910.678.2941
Web .... www.nccourts.org
E-mail .... valerie.haynes@nccourts.org
    117 Dick Street, Fayetteville, NC 28302
Valerie Hayne, District Administrator

(continued)

POLICE AND SHERIFF

Sheriff's Dept **910.677.5400**
Fax 910.677.5571
Web .... www.ccsonc.org
E-mail .... sheriff@ccsonc.org
    131 Dick St, Fayetteville, NC 28301-5725
Earl Butler, Sheriff

EDUCATION SERVICES

Exceptional Children's Program **910.678.2440**
Fax 910.678.2620
Web www.ccs.k12.nc.us
E-mail .... rubenreyes@ccs.k12.nc.us
    PO Box 2357, Fayetteville, NC 28302-2357
Ruban Reyes, Executive Director

Currituck County

SOCIAL SERVICES

Social Svcs **252.232.3083**
Fax 252.232.2167
    2793 Caratoke Hwy, Currituck, NC 27929
Kathlyn S Romm, Director

GENERAL HEALTH SERVICES

Health Dept **252.232.2271**
Fax 252.232.2442
Web .... www.arhs-nc.org
    2795 Currituck Hwy, Currituck, NC 27929
Jerry Parks, Health Director

POLICE AND SHERIFF

Sheriff's Ofc **252.453.8204**
Fax 252.453.2238
Web .... www.co.currituck.nc.us
E-mail .... sjohnson@co.currituck.nc.us
    407 Maple Rd, Maple, NC 27956-9714
Susan D. Johnson, Sheriff

Dare County

SOCIAL SERVICES

Social Svcs Dept **252.475.5500**
Fax 252.473.6165
E-mail .... burrusj@dcdss.org
    107 Eseterre St, Manteo, NC 27954
Jay F. Burrus, Director

POLICE AND SHERIFF

Sheriff's Dept **252.475.5980**
Fax 252.473.6371
E-mail .... dougdoughtie@darenc.com
    962 Marshall C. Collins Drive, Manteo, NC 27954
Jd Doughtie, Sheriff

Davidson County

SOCIAL SERVICES

Social Svcs **336.242.2500**
Fax 336.249.7588
E-mail .... dale.moorefield@davidsoncountync.gov
    913 Greensboro St, Lexington, NC 27292
Dale Moorefield, Director

GENERAL HEALTH SERVICES

Health Dept **336.242.2300**
Fax 336.242.2485
Web .... www.davidsoncountync.gov
    915 Greensboro St, Lexington, NC 27292-2699
Nancy Stout, Rn, Hiv Coordinator

JUSTICE AGENCY

Dept Of Juvenile Justice **336.249.2197**
Fax 336.236.4270
    40 Vance Cir, Lexington, NC 27292
Krista Hiatt, Chief Court Counselor

POLICE AND SHERIFF

Sheriff's Ofc 336.242.2100
Fax 336.249.6968
Web ....www.co.davidson.nc.us
E-mail ....dgrice@co.davidson.nc.us
  110 W Center St, Lexington, NC 27292-3010
David Grice, Sheriff

EDUCATION SERVICES

Communities In Schools Of Lexington,
Inc. 336.242.1520
Fax 336.242.1520
E-mail ....cis@triad.rr.com
  6 E 4th St Ste B, Lexington, NC 27293
Christina Howell, Executive Director

Exceptional Children's Program 336.249.8182
Fax 336.249.1062
Web www.davidson.k12.nc.us
  215-C County School Road, Lexington, NC 27292
Rob Mcouat, Director Of Exceptional Childrens Program

Thomasville City School 336.474.4200
Fax 336.475.0356
Web www.tcs.k12.nc.us
E-mail ....tobink@tcs.k12.nc.us
  400 Turner St, Thomasville, NC 27360
Kieth Tobin, Assistant Superintendent

Davie County

SOCIAL SERVICES

Social Svcs Dept 336.751.8800
Fax 336.751.1639
E-mail ....becky.finney@co.davie.nc.us
  228 Hospital St, Mocksville, NC 27028-2039
Rebecca J. Finney, Director

POLICE AND SHERIFF

Sheriff's Ofc 336.751.6238
Fax 336.751.5470
  140 S Main St Ste 106, Mocksville, NC 27028
Andy Stokes, Sheriff

Duplin County

SOCIAL SERVICES

Social Svcs 910.296.2200
Fax 910.296.2323
Web ....www.duplincounty.org
E-mail ....eric.bush@duplincountync.com
  423 N Main St, Kenansville, NC 28349
Eric Bush, Director

GENERAL HEALTH SERVICES

Health Dept 910.296.2130
Fax 910.296.2139
Web ....www.duplincountync.com
E-mail ....rosek@duplincountync.com
  340 Seminary St, Kenansville, NC 28349
Rose Kornegay, Hiv Coordinator

JUSTICE AGENCY

Dept Of Juvenile Justice 910.296.1941
Fax 910.296.1886
E-mail ....tracy.arrington@ncmail.net
  112 Duplin St, Kenansville, NC 28349
Tracy Arrington, Chief Court Counselor

COURTS

4th District Court 910.296.1686
Fax 910.296.2313
Web ....www.nccourts.org
  112 Duplin St, Kenansville, NC 28349
Katie Harrell, Clerk of Court

POLICE AND SHERIFF

Sheriff's Ofc 910.296.2150
Fax 910.296.2156
E-mail ....blakew@duplincounty.org
  112 W Hill St, Kenansville, NC 28349
Blake Wallace, Sheriff

EDUCATION SERVICES

East Coast Migrant Head Start 910.267.1114
Fax 910.267.1730
Web ....www.ecmhsp.org
E-mail ....sharris-harper@ecmhsp.org
  2669 Hwy 403 W, Faison, NC 28341
Maria Balcierra, Director

Durham County

SOCIAL SERVICES

Social Svcs 919.560.8000
Fax 919.560.8103
Web ....www.durhamcountync.gov
E-mail ....trobinson@durhamcountync.gov
  220 E Main St, Durham, NC 27701-3606
Terri Robinson, Director

GENERAL HEALTH SERVICES

Health Dept 919.560.7600
Fax 919.560.7652
Web ....www.co.durham.nc.us
  414 E Main St, Durham, NC 27701
Arleen Sena, Md, Mph, Medical Director

Lincoln Community Health Ctr 919.956.4000
Fax 919.956.4535
  1301 Fayetteville St, Durham, NC 27707
Evelyn Schmidt, Director

MENTAL HEALTH SERVICES

Mental Health 919.560.7100
Fax 919.560.7240
Web ....www.durhamcenter.org
  501 Willard St, Durham, NC 27701
Ellen Hollimon, Director

JUSTICE AGENCY

Dept Of Juvenile Justice 919.972.2001
Fax 919.560.6193
Web ....www.djjdp.nc.gov
E-mail ....donald.pinchback@ncmail.net
  201 N. Roxboro St, Durham, NC 27701
Donald Pinchback, Chief Court Counselor

Guardian Ad Litem Program 919.564.7290
Fax 919.560.3307
  201 N Roxboro St, Fl 3, Durham, NC 27701
Shirley Harley-smith, District Administrator

COURTS

14th District Court 919.564.7070
Fax 919.560.3341
Web ....www.durhamcountync.gov
E-mail ....rchaney@durhamcountync.gov
  201 E Main St Ste 675, Durham, NC 27701-3646
Honorable Richard G. Chaney, Director

Teen Court 919.682.1960
Fax 919.530.1907
  123 Market st, Durham, NC 27701
Sabrina Cates, Program Director

POLICE AND SHERIFF

Sheriff's Dept 919.560.0900
Fax 919.560.0854
Web ....www.shf.co.durham.nc.us
E-mail ....sheriff@shf.co.durham.nc.us
  201 E Main St, Durham, NC 27701-3646
Worth L. Hill, Sheriff

Edgecombe County

SOCIAL SERVICES

DSS, Rocky Mount Ofc 252.985.4101
Fax 252.985.1615
E-mail ....marva.scott@co.edgecombe.nc.us
  301 S Fairview Rd, Rocky Mount, NC 27801-6975
Marva Scott, Director

Social Svcs Dept 252.641.7611
Fax 252.641.7980
Web ....www.co.edgecombe.nc.us
E-mail ....marva.scott@co.edgecombe.nc.us
  3003 N Main St, Tarboro, NC 27886-1922
Marva Scott, Director

GENERAL HEALTH SERVICES

Health Dept 252.641.7511
Fax 252.641.7504
  2909 N Main St, Tarboro, NC 27886
Lesley Honer, Communicable Disease Supervisor

MENTAL HEALTH SERVICES

Edgecombe-Nash Area Mental
Health 252.937.8141
Fax 252.443.9574
Web ....www.thebeaconcenter.net
E-mail ....nancy.hunt@en.ncmh.org
  500 Nash Medical Arts Mall, Rocky Mount,
  NC 27804-1417
Nancy Hunt, Area Director

JUSTICE AGENCY

Dept Of Juvenile Justice 252.977.1795
Fax 252.985.2695
Web ....www.djjdp.nc.gov
E-mail ....maxine.evans.armwood@ncmail.net
  305 Cokey Rd, Rocky Mount, NC 27801-5636
Maxine Evans-Armwood, Chief Court Counselor

EDUCATION SERVICES

Communities In Schools 252.442.9991
Fax 252.442.6876
Web ....www.cisnc.org/rmcis
  201 S Pearl St, Rocky Mount, NC 27804-5731
Sandra Jones, Executive Director

Forsyth County

SOCIAL SERVICES

Social Svcs Dept 336.703.3800
Fax 336.727.2850
Web ....www.co.forsyth.nc.us
  741 Highland Ave, Winston Salem, NC 27101

POLICE AND SHERIFF

Police Dept 336.773.7760
Fax 336.773.7996
Web ....www.ncpolicechief.org
E-mail ....secondvp@ncpolicechief.org
  725 N Cherry St, Winston Salem, NC 27101-1418
Scott Cunningham, Chief Of Police

EDUCATION SERVICES

Kernersville Head Start 336.996.1998
Fax 336.996.1998
  512 W Mountain St, Kernersville, NC 27284-2514
Lilliane Mcqueen, Director

Franklin County

SOCIAL SERVICES

Social Svcs 919.496.5721
Fax 919.496.8137
  107 Industrial Dr Ste A, Louisburg, NC 27549
Nicki Griffin, Director

North Carolina

GENERAL HEALTH SERVICES

Health Dept **919.496.8110**
Fax 919.496.8140
   107 Industrial Dr Ste C, Louisburg, NC 27549-2371
   Chirs Szwagiel, Health Director

JUSTICE AGENCY

Guardian Ad Litem Program **919.497.3010**
Fax 919.497.5504
Web www.district9gal.org
   113 S Main St, Louisburg, NC 27549
   Mary Jo Vanhorne, District Administrator

POLICE AND SHERIFF

Sheriff's Dept **919.496.2186**
Fax 919.496.5429
Web ....www.fcncso.org
   285 T Kemp Rd, Louisburg, NC 27549-6708
   C Elliott Pinnell Jr., Sheriff

Gaston County

SOCIAL SERVICES

Social Svcs **704.862.7500**
Fax 704.862.7885
E-mail ....kmoon@co.gaston.nc.us
   330 N Marietta St, Gastonia, NC 28052
   Keith Moon, Director

GENERAL HEALTH SERVICES

Health Dept **704.853.5000**
Fax 704.853.5252
E-mail ....martha.keever@co.gaston.nc.us
   991 W Hudson Blvd, Gastonia, NC 28052
   Joyce Floyd, Hiv Program Supervisor

JUSTICE AGENCY

Gafton Detention **704.922.7832**
Fax 704.922.1090
   PO Box 452, Dallas, NC 28034-0452
   Angelia Wilson, Director

Guardian Ad Litem Program **704.852.3260**
Fax 704.852.3065
E-mail ....joanne.s.cranke@nccourts.org
   325 N Marietta St, Ste 2147, Gastonia, NC 28052
   Joanne Cranke, District Administrator

COURTS

27th District Court **704.852.3100**
Fax 704.852.3267
Web ....www.co.gaston.nc.us
   325 N Marietta St, Gastonia, NC 28052-2331
   Honorable Dennis J. Redwing, Director

POLICE AND SHERIFF

Sheriff's Ofc **704.869.6880**
Fax 704.869.6815
   425 N Marietta St, Gastonia, NC 28053-1578
   Allen Cloniger, Sheriff

EDUCATION SERVICES

Communities In Schools **704.867.3512**
Fax 704.864.2985
Web ....www.afcay.org
E-mail ....alliancegastonia@afcay.org
   218 E Franklin Blvd, Gastonia, NC 28052
   Kathy Kenzig, Director

Dept Of Exceptional Children's
Program **704.866.6100**
Fax 704.866.6191
Web www.gaston.k12.nc.us
   215 W 3 Ave, Gastonia, NC 28053
   Sadie Broome, Director

Gates County

SOCIAL SERVICES

Social Svcs **252.357.0075**
Fax 252.357.2132
Web ....www.dhhs.state.nc.us
   122 Main St, Gatesville, NC 27938-9328
   Colleen Turner, Director

GENERAL HEALTH SERVICES

Health Dept **252.357.1380**
Fax 252.357.2251
Web ....www.arhs-nc.org
E-mail ....dboslau@arhs-nc.org
   29 Medical Center Rd, Gates, NC 27937-9816
   Dana Boslau, Nursing Supervisor

Graham County

SOCIAL SERVICES

Social Svcs **828.479.7911**
Fax 828.479.7928
Web ....www.dhhs.state.nc.us
   196 Knight St, Robbinsville, NC 28771-9701
   Lisa Rogers, Director

GENERAL HEALTH SERVICES

Health Dept **828.479.7900**
Fax 828.479.6956
E-mail ....kristen.shuler@@graien.nc.gov
   21 S Main St, Robbinsville, NC 28771
   Kristen Schuler, Hiv/aids Coordinator

POLICE AND SHERIFF

Sheriff's Ofc **828.479.3352**
Fax 828.479.3427
Web ....www.main.nc.us
E-mail ....anderson.mickey50@yahoo.com
   300 Rodney Orr Bypass, Robbinsville, NC 28771
   Mickey Anderson, Sheriff

Granville County

SOCIAL SERVICES

Social Svcs **919.693.1511**
Fax 919.603.5090
   107 Lanier St, Oxford, NC 27565-0966
   Lou Bechtel, Director

GENERAL HEALTH SERVICES

Granville-Vance Health District **919.693.2141**
Fax 919.693.8517
   101 Hunt Dr, Oxford, NC 27565
   Dr. Rodwell Derake, Health Director

MENTAL HEALTH SERVICES

Alcohol And Drug Abuse Treatment
Ctr **919.575.7928**
Fax 919.575.7260
   1003 12th St, Butner, NC 27509-1626
   Lisa Haire, Director

POLICE AND SHERIFF

Sheriff's Ofc **919.693.3213**
Fax 919.603.1315
Web ....www.granvillecounty.org
E-mail ....sheriff@granvillecounty.org
   143 Williamsboro St, Oxford, NC 27565
   Brindell Wilkins, Sheriff

Greene County

GENERAL HEALTH SERVICES

Health Dept **252.747.8183**
Fax 252.747.4040
Web ....www.co.greene.nc.us
E-mail ....mrhodes@co.greene.nc.us
   227 Kingold Blvd Ste B, Snow Hill, NC 28580-1303
   Michael Rhodes, Health Director

POLICE AND SHERIFF

Sheriff's Dept **252.747.3411**
Fax 252.747.5079
Web www.1comnet.com
E-mail ....lsmith@co.greene.nc.us
   301 N Greene St, Snow Hill, NC 28580-1411
   Lemmie Smith, Sheriff

Guilford County

SOCIAL SERVICES

Social Svcs Dept **336.641.3000**
Fax 336.641.6099
Web ....www.co.guilford.nc.us
E-mail ....rwilla1@co.guilford.nc.us
   1203 Maple St, Greensboro, NC 27260
   Robert Williams, Director

GENERAL HEALTH SERVICES

Health Dept **336.641.7777**
Fax 336.641.6971
Web ....www.co.guilford.nc.us
E-mail ....mgreen@co.guilford.nc.us
   1203 Maple St, Greensboro, NC 27405-6910
   Merle Green, Health Director

MENTAL HEALTH SERVICES

Guilford Ctr For Behavioral Health And Disability
Svcs **336.641.4981**
Fax 336.641.7761
Web ....http://www.guilfordcenter.com/
E-mail ....bpierce@guilfordcenter.com
   201 N Eugene St, Greensboro, NC 27401-2218
   Anthony Ward, Area Director

Mental Health Ctr **336.845.7946**
Fax 336.845.7601
Web ....www.co.guilfordnc.us
   211 S Centennial St, High Point, NC 27260
   Anthony Ward, Area Director

Mental Health Development Disabilities And Substance Abuse
Program **336.641.3630**
Fax 336.641.4973
Web ....www.guilfordcenter.com
E-mail ....scampbell@guilfordcenter.com
   201 N Eugene St, Greensboro, NC 27401-2221
   Susan Campbell, Director

POLICE AND SHERIFF

Sheriff's Ofc **336.641.3694**
Fax 336.641.6729
Web ....www.co.guilford.nc.us
E-mail ....bbarnes@co.guilford.nc.us
   400 W Washington St, Greensboro, NC 27401-2349
   BJ Barnes, Sheriff

EDUCATION SERVICES

Communities In Schools Of Greater Greensboro
Inc **336.691.1268**
Fax 336.691.1270
Web ....www.greensboro.communitiesinschools.org
E-mail ....jw_cisgg@bellsouth.net
   122 N Elm St Ste 301, Greensboro, NC 27402
   Jimmi Williams, Executive Director

North Carolina

Council House Child Development Ctr......................336.378.7723
Fax......................336.378.1391
602 Hyde Dr Apt B, Greensboro, NC 27406-3027
Dana Bailey, Director

Exceptional Children's Svcs...............336.370.2323
Fax......................336.370.2324
Web......................www.gcsnc.com
E-mail......................chandlb@gcsnc.com
120 Franklin Blvd, Greensboro, NC 27403-4606
Betty Ann Chandler, Executive Director

Halifax County

GENERAL HEALTH SERVICES
Health Dept......................252.583.5021
Fax......................252.583.2975
19 N Dobbs St, Halifax, NC 27839
Debbie Barrow, Rn, Hiv Coordinator

POLICE AND SHERIFF
Sheriff's Dept......................252.583.8201
Fax......................252.583.2698
Web......................www.halifaxnc.com
E-mail......................frazierj@halifaxnc.com
355 Ferrell Ln, Halifax, NC 27839
Jeff P. Frazier, Sheriff

Harnett County

GENERAL HEALTH SERVICES
Health Dept......................910.893.7550
Fax......................910.893.9429
Web......................www.harnett.org
E-mail......................jbuie@harnett.org
307 W Cornelius Harnett Blvd, Lillington, NC 27546-9335
Janice Buie, Hiv Coordinator

JUSTICE AGENCY
Community Home Care And Hospice......................910.892.7548
Fax......................910.892.7372
Web......................www.community-companies.com
400 E H St, Erwin, NC 28339
Gail Booker, Patient Care Coordinator

Dept Of Juvenile Justice......................910.893.2114
Fax......................910.814.1262
E-mail......................marsha.woodall@djjdp.nc.gov
22 W Front St, Lillington, NC 27546
Marsha Woodall, Chief Court Counselor

POLICE AND SHERIFF
Sheriff's Dept......................910.893.9111
Fax......................910.893.6450
Web......................www.harnett.org
E-mail......................lrollins@harnett.org
175 Bain St, Lillington, NC 27546
Larry W. Rollins, Sheriff

EDUCATION SERVICES
Elizabethtown Head Start......................910.862.3880
Fax......................910.862.7570
601 David St, Elizabethtown, NC 28337
Aquenetta Robinson, Director

Haywood County

SOCIAL SERVICES
Social Svcs Dept......................828.452.6620
Fax......................828.452.6673
486 E Marshall St, Waynesville, NC 28786
Ira Dove, Director

GENERAL HEALTH SERVICES
Health Dept......................828.452.6675
Fax......................828.452.6730
Web......................www.main.haywoodnc.net
E-mail......................crocco@haywoodnc.net
2177 Asheville Rd, Waynesville, NC 28786-3139
Carmine F. Rocco, Health Director

POLICE AND SHERIFF
Sheriff's Ofc......................828.452.6666
Fax......................828.452.6699
Web......................www.gov.co.haywood.nc.us
1620 Brown Ave, Waynesville, NC 28786-4980
Bobby Suttles, Sheriff

EDUCATION SERVICES
Mountain Projects Head Start...............828.456.4546
Fax......................828.456.4536
Web......................www.mountainprojects.org
E-mail......................hcrawford@mountainprojects.org
489 B Pigeon, Waynesville, NC 28786-3593
Holly Crawford, Director

Henderson County

SOCIAL SERVICES
Social Svcs Dept......................828.697.5500
Fax......................828.698.5110
1200 Spartanburg Hwy, Ste 300, Hendersonville, NC 28792
Liston B. Smith, Director

GENERAL HEALTH SERVICES
Health Dept......................828.692.4223
Fax......................828.697.4709
Web......................www.hendersoncountync.org
E-mail......................lindaw@hendersoncountync.org
1200 Spartanburg Hwy Ste 100, Hendersonville, NC 28792-6443
Linda Weldon, Rn, Communicable Disease Nurse

POLICE AND SHERIFF
Sheriff's Dept......................828.697.4596
Fax......................828.697.4613
Web......................www.hendersoncountync.org
E-mail......................rdavis@hendersoncountync.org
201 N Main St, Hendersonville, NC 28792
Rick Davis, Sheriff

Hertford County

SOCIAL SERVICES
Social Svcs......................252.358.7830
Fax......................252.358.7806
Web......................www.dhhs.state.nc.us
704 N King St, Winton, NC 27986
Adonica Hantton, Director

GENERAL HEALTH SERVICES
Health Dept......................252.358.7833
Fax......................252.358.7869
Web......................www.co.hertford.nc.us
801 N King St, Winton, NC 27986
Curtis Dixon, Director

JUSTICE AGENCY
Juvenile Home......................252.358.0433
Fax......................252.358.0334
114 Oak Villa Rd, Winton, NC 27986
Roxanna White, Program Manager

Hoke County

SOCIAL SERVICES
Social Svcs Dept......................910.875.8725
Fax......................910.875.1068
Web......................www.dhhs.state.nc.us
E-mail......................della.sweat@ncmail.net
314 S. Magnolia Street, Raeford, NC 28376
Dalla Sweac, Director

COURTS
16th District Court......................910.878.4100
Fax......................910.878.4101
E-mail......................william.c.mcilwain@nccourts.org
304 N Main St, Raeford, NC 28376
Honorable William C. Mcilwain, Chief District Court Judge

Hyde County

SOCIAL SERVICES
Social Svcs......................252.926.4476
Fax......................252.926.3711
Web......................www.hydecounty.org
E-mail......................gloria.spencer@ncmail.net
1430 Main St, Swanquarter, NC 27885
Gloria C Spencer, Director

GENERAL HEALTH SERVICES
Health Dept......................252.926.4200
Fax......................252.926.3702
Web......................www.hydehealth.com
E-mail......................wsmith@hydehealth.com
1151 Main St, Swanquarter, NC 27885
Wesley T Smith, Health Director

POLICE AND SHERIFF
Sheriff's Ofc......................252.926.3171
Fax......................252.926.3713
1223 Main Street, Swan Quarter, NC 27885
David T. Mason, Sheriff

Iredell County

SOCIAL SERVICES
Social Svcs Dept......................704.873.5631
Fax......................704.878.5419
E-mail......................sbyzette@co.iredell.nc.us
549 Eastside Dr, Statesville, NC 28625
Smith Byzette, Director

GENERAL HEALTH SERVICES
Health Dept......................704.878.5300
Fax......................704.878.5311
E-mail......................lwilliard@co.iredell.nc.us
318 Turnersburg Hwy, Statesville, NC 28625
Lora Williard, Rn, Hiv Coordinator

JUSTICE AGENCY
Dept Of Juvenile Justice......................704.878.4247
Fax......................704.878.4337
110 Stockton St, Ste G, Statesville, NC 28677
Krista Hiatt, Chief Court Counselor

COURTS
22nd District Court......................704.832.6602
Fax......................704.832.6611
221 E Water St, Statesville, NC 28677
Dale L Graham, Chief Court Judge

POLICE AND SHERIFF
Sheriff's Dept......................704.878.3180
Fax......................704.878.5094
230 N Tradd St, Statesville, NC 28687
Phillip H. Redmond, Sheriff

Jackson County

SOCIAL SERVICES

Social Svcs.............................**828.586.5546**
Fax..828.586.6270
Web...........................www.dss.co.jackson.nc.us
E-mail...............rcochran@dss.jackson.nc.us
   15 Griffin St, Community Services Bldg, Sylva,
NC 28779-8630
Robert Cochran, Director

GENERAL HEALTH SERVICES

Health Dept.........................**828.586.8994**
Fax..828.586.3493
Web...www.jacksonnc.org
E-mail.....................paulacarden@jacksonnc.org
   538 Scotts Creek Rd Ste 100, Sylva, NC 28779-5281
Paula Carden, Interim County Health Director

JUSTICE AGENCY

Dept Of Juvenile Justice..................**828.586.5756**
Fax..828.631.9846
E-mail...................chuck.mallonee@ncmail.net
   8 Colonial Sq Ste 100, Sylva, NC 28779-5147
Chuck Mallonee, Chief Court Counselor

POLICE AND SHERIFF

Sheriff's Dept.........................**828.586.8901**
Fax..828.631.1113
E-mail..................jamesmashe@hotmail.com
   399 Grindstaff Cove Rd, Sylva, NC 28779
Jimmy Ashe, Sheriff

Johnston County

SOCIAL SERVICES

Social Svcs Dept.....................**919.989.5300**
Fax..919.989.5324
Web.....................................www.co.johnstonnc.com
E-mail.......................earl.marett@johnstonnc.com
   714 North St, Smithfield, NC 27577-4067
G. Earl Marett, Director

GENERAL HEALTH SERVICES

Health Dept.........................**919.989.5200**
Fax..919.989.5208
   517 N Brightleaf Blvd, Smithfield, NC 27577
Marilyn Pearson, Md, Health Director

POLICE AND SHERIFF

Sheriff's Ofc.........................**919.989.5010**
Fax..919.989.5039
E-mail................................info@jcso.org
   120 S. 3rd St, Smithfield, NC 27577
Steve Bizzell, Sheriff

Jones County

SOCIAL SERVICES

SOCIAL SERVICES.....................**252.448.2581**
Fax..252.448.5651
E-mail.......................tsimmons@jonesdss.com
   418 Hwy 58 N, Trenton, NC 28585
Thelma Simmons, Director

COURTS

Teen Court.............................**910.275.0044**
Fax..910.275.9999
E-mail.........................dsc4@earthlink.net
   106 South Street, Kenansville, NC 28349
Thomasina Williams, President

Lee County

SOCIAL SERVICES

Social Svcs.............................**919.718.4690**
Fax..919.718.4634
Web...www.leecountync.gov
E-mail...............brenda.potts@leecountync.gov
   530 Carthage St, Sanford, NC 27330-4105
Brenda Potts, Director

GENERAL HEALTH SERVICES

Health Dept.........................**919.718.4640**
Fax..919.718.4632
Web...www.leecountync.gov
E-mail...................wraynor@leecountync.gov
   106 Hillcrest Dr, Sanford, NC 27330
Wayne Raynor, Interim Director

POLICE AND SHERIFF

Sheriff's Ofc.........................**919.775.5531**
Fax..919.718.4562
   1401 Elm St, Sanford, NC 27331
Tracy Car, Sheriff

EDUCATION SERVICES

Communities In Schools.................**919.718.5426**
Fax..919.776.6244
Web...www.cisleecounty.org
E-mail...............cisleedirector@windstream.net
   143 Charlotte Ave, Sanford, NC 27330
Heather Little, Director

Lenoir County

SOCIAL SERVICES

Social Svcs.............................**252.559.6400**
Fax..252.559.6380
Web...www.dss.co.lenoir.nc.us
   130 W King St, Kinston, NC 28501-4830
Susan Moora, Director

JUSTICE AGENCY

Dobbs Youth Development Ctr.............**252.522.0511**
Fax..252.526.4609
Web...www.juvjus.state.nc.us
E-mail...................glenn.elmore@ncmail.net
   3060 Dobbs Farm Rd, Kinston, NC 28504-8987
Glenn Elmore, Director

POLICE AND SHERIFF

Sheriff's Ofc.........................**252.559.6106**
Fax..252.527.3854
Web...www.co.camden.ga.us
E-mail...................wsmith@co.camden.ga.us
   130 S Queen St, Kinston, NC 28501
William E. Smith, Sheriff

Lincoln County

GENERAL HEALTH SERVICES

Health Dept.........................**704.735.3001**
Fax..704.732.9034
   151 Sigmon Rd, Lincolnton, NC 28092
Margaret B. Dollar, Med, Health Director

POLICE AND SHERIFF

Sheriff's Dept.........................**704.732.9050**
Fax..704.732.9016
Web...www.lincolnsheriff.org
E-mail...............sheriffcarpenter@lincolnsheriff.org
   700 John Howel Memorial Dr, Lincolnton,
NC 28092-3151
David Carpenter, Sheriff

EDUCATION SERVICES

Communities In Schools.................**704.736.0303**
Fax..704.736.9429
   107 S Abernethy St, Lincolnton, NC 28092-3805

Macon County

SOCIAL SERVICES

Social Svcs.............................**828.349.2124**
Fax..828.349.2401
Web...www.maconnc.org
E-mail...................jkimsey@maconnc.org
   1832 Lakeside Dr, Franklin, NC 28734-6778
Jane C Kimsey, Director

GENERAL HEALTH SERVICES

Health Dept.........................**828.349.2420**
Fax..828.349.2501
Web...www.maconnc.org
E-mail...................jbruckner@maconnc.org
   1830 Lakeside Dr, Franklin, NC 28734-6778
Jim Bruckner, Director

JUSTICE AGENCY

Guardian Ad Litem.....................**828.349.2409**
Fax..828.349.2408
Web...www.nccourts.org
   5 W Main St, Franklin, NC 28734-3005
Shannon Cowan, Supervisor

Madison County

GENERAL HEALTH SERVICES

Health Dept.........................**828.649.3531**
Fax..828.649.9078
Web...........www.madisoncountypublichealthnow.com
   493 Medical Park Dr, Marshall, NC 28753
Carolyn Moser, Health Director

POLICE AND SHERIFF

Sheriff's Ofc.........................**828.649.2721**
Fax..828.649.2485
Web...www.newriver.usmc.mil
E-mail...................johnl@newriver.usmc.mil
   33 Baileys Branch Road, Marshall, NC 28753
James E Harwood, Sheriff

EDUCATION SERVICES

Communities In Schools - Board Of
Education.............................**828.649.9276**
Fax..828.649.9334
Web...www.madison.k12.nc.us
E-mail...................tfields@madison.k12.nc.us
   5738 US Highway 25-70, Marshall, NC 28753
Tom Fields, Communties Info Incharge

Martin County

GENERAL HEALTH SERVICES

Health Dept.........................**252.793.1619**
Fax..252.793.1644
Web...www.mtwdistricthealth.org
E-mail...............kathleen.dedore@mtwdistricthealth.org
   210 W Liberty St, Williamston, NC 27892-1769
Kathleen Dedore-jones, Director

POLICE AND SHERIFF

Sheriff's Ofc.........................**252.789.4500**
Fax..252.789.4529
Web...www.martincountyncgov.com
E-mail...................dgibbs@martincountyncgov.com
   305 E Main St, Williamston, NC 27892
Dan W. Gibbs, Sheriff

McDowell County

SOCIAL SERVICES

Social Svcs.............................**828.652.3355**
Fax..828.652.9167
Web...www.dhhs.state.nc.us
E-mail...................phillip.hardin@ncmail.net
   145 E Court St, Marion, NC 28752-4042
Phillip Hardin, Director

North Carolina

GENERAL HEALTH SERVICES

Health Dept **828.652.6811**
Fax 828.652.9376
Web ....www.rpmhd.org
E-mail ....jwalker@rpmhd.org
408 Spaulding Rd, Marion, NC 28752-5212
Jackie Walker, Hiv Coordinator

JUSTICE AGENCY

Guardian Ad Litem Program **828.652.4632**
Fax 828.652.2641
Web ....www.nccourts.org
E-mail ....jim.sain@nccourts.org
60 E Court St, Marion, NC 28752-4041
Michelle Rink, Program Supervisor

EDUCATION SERVICES

Communities In Schools **828.652.1040**
Fax 828.652.9840
Web www.mcdowell.k12.nc.us
E-mail ....marcie.lewis@mcdowell.k12.nc.us
176 Lukin St, Marion, NC 28752-5245
Marcie Lewis, Director For The Principal

Head Start **828.652.3229**
Fax 828.652.5110
E-mail ....peggy.freeman@mcdowell.k12.nc.us
2111 Sugar Hill Rd, Marion, NC 28752-5078
Peggy Freeman, Director

Mecklenburg County

SOCIAL SERVICES

Children, Youth And Families **704.336.4740**
Fax 704.336.7429
720 E 4th St, Ste 502, Charlotte, NC 28202
Paul Risk, Director

Social Svcs **704.336.3150**
Fax 704.336.3361
Web ....www.mecklenburgcountync.gov
E-mail ....richard.jacobsen@mecklenburgcountync.gov
301 Billingsley Rd, Charlotte, NC 28211-1096
Richard W Jacobsen, Director

GENERAL HEALTH SERVICES

Health Dept **704.304.6701**
Fax 704.523.4921
Web ....www.machealth.org
E-mail ....maria.bonaiuto@carolinenshealthcar.org
5727 W Park Dr, Charlotte, NC 28217-1097
Maria Bonaiuto, Dental Health Director Of School Health Services

MENTAL HEALTH SERVICES

**Area Developmental Disabilities & Substance Abuse
Svcs** **704.336.2023**
Fax 704.336.4383
Web ....www.co.mecklenburg.nc.us
429 Billingsley Rd, Charlotte, NC 28211
Carlos Hernandez, Interim Director

JUSTICE AGENCY

Dept Of Juvenile Justice **704.330.4338**
Fax 704.330.5265
E-mail ....laura.mcfern@ncmail.net
720 E 4th St Ste 400, Charlotte, NC 28202-2865
Laura Mcfern, Chief Court Counselor

POLICE AND SHERIFF

**Charlotte Police Dept Youth Svcs
Div** **704.336.2811**
Fax 704.336.4529
Web ....www.cmpd.org
601 E Trade St, Charlotte, NC 28202-3000
Angela Haywood, Domestic Violence

Sheriff's Ofc **704.336.2543**
Fax 704.336.6118
Web ....www.mecklenbergcountync.gov
832 E 4th St, Charlotte, NC 28202
Daniel Bailey, Sheriff

EDUCATION SERVICES

Exceptional Children's Program **980.343.6960**
Fax 980.343.5433
Web www.cms.k12.nc.us
E-mail ....j.rhyne@cms.k12.nc.us
700 E Stonewall St Ste 404, Charlotte,
NC 28202-1167
Jane Rhyne, Assistant Superintendent

Mitchell County

SOCIAL SERVICES

Social Svcs Dept **828.688.2175**
Fax 828.688.4940
347 Longview Dr, Bakersville, NC 28705
Paula Holtsclaw, Director

GENERAL HEALTH SERVICES

Health Dept **828.688.2371**
Fax 828.688.3866
130 Forest Service Dr Ste A, Bakersville, NC 28705
Stacie Mckinney, Nursing Supervisor

EDUCATION SERVICES

Communities In Schools **828.467.0970**
Web ....www.cismitchell.org
E-mail ....gilchrists@aol.com
2206 Carters Ridge Rd, Spruce Pine, NC 28777-8529
Lori Gilchrist, Executive Director

Montgomery County

SOCIAL SERVICES

Social Svcs **910.576.6531**
Fax 910.576.5016
Web ....www.montgamerycounty.nc.com
E-mail ....jim.sanders@tev.com
102 E Spring St Ste D, Troy, NC 27371-3057
James Sanders, Director

GENERAL HEALTH SERVICES

Health Dept **910.572.1393**
Fax 910.572.8177
Web ....tammie.bell@ncmail.net
E-mail ....tammie.bell@ncmail.net
217 S Main St, Troy, NC 27371
July Clark, Acting Health Director

COURTS

19th District Court **910.576.4211**
Fax 910.576.5020
E-mail ....m.sabiston@nccourts.org
108 E Main St, Troy, NC 27371
Honorable Michael A. Sabiston, District Judge

EDUCATION SERVICES

Candor Head Start **910.974.9673**
Fax 910.974.4256
218 Albemarle Rd, Troy, NC 27371
Laura Moses, Administrator

Moore County

SOCIAL SERVICES

Social Svcs Dept **910.947.2436**
Fax 910.947.1618
Web ....www.co.moore.nc.gov
E-mail ....jbensen@moorecountync.gov
1036 Carriage Oaks Drive, Carthage, NC 28327
John Bensen, Director

GENERAL HEALTH SERVICES

Health Dept **910.947.3300**
Fax 910.947.1663
Web ....www.moorecountync.gov
705 Pinehurst Ave, Carthage, NC 28327
Robert Whitman, Director

MENTAL HEALTH SERVICES

Sandhills Area Mental Health Ctr **910.673.9111**
Fax 910.673.0081
E-mail ....victoriaw@sandhillscenter.org
1163 7 Lakes Dr N, West End, NC 27376
Victoria Whitt, Area Director

JUSTICE AGENCY

**Dept Of Juvenile Justice & Delequency
Prevention** **910.947.2886**
Fax 910.947.2528
E-mail ....lisa.kennedy@djjdp.nc.gov
205 Dowd St, Carthage, NC 28327
Lisa Kennedy, Administrative Assistant

COURTS

Teen Court **910.295.6853**
Fax 910.295.9183
Web ....www.daymarkrecovery.org
E-mail ....mark@mooreyouthservices.org
205 Memorial Drive, Pinehurst, NC 28374
Brenda Brown, Support Supervisior

POLICE AND SHERIFF

Sheriff's Ofc **910.947.2931**
Fax 910.947.1668
Web ....www.moorecountync.gov
E-mail ....lcarter@moorecountync.gov
101 Courthouse Square, Carthage, NC 28327
Lane Carter, Sheriff

EDUCATION SERVICES

Aberdeen Head Start **910.944.0457**
Fax 910.944.3567
333 Glasco St, Aberdeen, NC 28315
Maxine Howe, Administrator

**Communities In Schools/Andi Korte's
Ofc** **910.692.9010**
Web ....www.cisnc.org
E-mail ....andikorte@yahoo.com
231 W Pennsylvania Ave, Southern Pines, NC 28387
Andi Korte, Executive Director

Nash County

SOCIAL SERVICES

Social Svcs **252.459.9818**
Fax 252.459.9833
Web ....www.nashcountync.gov
E-mail ....melbia.batts@nashcountync.gov
120 W Washington St Ste 1005, Nashville,
NC 27856-1376
Melbia Batts, Director

GENERAL HEALTH SERVICES

Health Dept **252.459.9819**
Fax 252.459.9834
Web ....www.co.nash.nc.us
E-mail ....william.hill@ncmail.net
214 S Barnes St, Nashville, NC 27856
William W. Hill Jr., Health Director

EDUCATION SERVICES

East Coast Migrant Head Start **252.235.2503**
Fax 252.235.2503
Web ....www.acf.hhs.gov
E-mail ....galante@ecmhsp.org
4562 Us Hwy 264 Alt, Bailey, NC 27807
Annette Galante, Director

New Hanover County

SOCIAL SERVICES

Social Svcs Dept **910.798.3400**
Fax 910.798.3491
　1650 Greenfield St, Wilmington, NC 08402
　Wanda Marino, Assistant Director Of Social Work Services

MENTAL HEALTH SERVICES

**Southeastern Area Mental Health
Program** **910.251.6440**
Fax 910.251.6557
Web .... www.secmh.org
E-mail .... corriher@secmh.org
　2023 S 17th St, Wilmington, NC 28401-6694
　Arthur Constantini, Area Director

JUSTICE AGENCY

Guardian Ad Litem Progam **910.251.2733**
Fax 910.251.5806
Web .... www.nccourts.org
E-mail .... liz.k.jones@nccourts.org
　272 N Front St Ste 215, Wilmington,
　NC 28401-4066
　Liz Kachris-jones, 5th District Administrator

**New Hanover Regional Juvenile Detention
Ctr** **910.675.0594**
Fax 910.675.2542
Web .... www.ccncems.org
E-mail .... jim.speight@ncmail.net
　3830 Juvenile Center Dr, Castle Hayne,
　NC 28429-6105
　Jeff Fritz, Director

COURTS

5th District Court **910.341.1120**
Fax 910.341.4071
Web .... www.nccourts.org
E-mail .... sherri.h.turna@nccourts.org
　316 Princess St, Ste 328, Wilmington,
　NC 28401-4283
　Honorable Sandra Ray Criner, Judge

POLICE AND SHERIFF

Sheriff's Dept **910.798.4200**
Fax 910.798.4163
　3950 Juvenile Center Dr, Castle Hayne, NC 28429
　Edward Mcmahon, Sheriff

EDUCATION SERVICES

**Communities In Schools Of Cape
Fear** **910.343.1901**
Fax 910.343.8566
E-mail .... ciscf@bellsouth.net
　20 N 4th St, Wilmington, NC 28401
　Louise Hicks, CEO

Special Education Program **910.763.5431**
Fax 910.254.4445
Web www.nahcs.k12.nc.us
E-mail .... william.trant@nhcs.net
　6410 Carolina Beach Rd, Wilmington, NC 28412
　William Trant, Director Of Special Education

Northampton County

SOCIAL SERVICES

Social Svcs Dept **252.534.5811**
Fax 252.534.0061
Web .... www.northamptonnc.com
E-mail .... d.wentzy@ncmail.net
　9467 NC Hwy 305, Jackson, NC 27845
　D. A. Wentzy, Phd, Director

GENERAL HEALTH SERVICES

Health Dept **252.534.5841**
Fax 252.534.1045
E-mail .... nhdadmin@ncol.net
　9495 NC 305 Hwy, Jackson, NC 27845
　Sue Gay, Health Director

JUSTICE AGENCY

Dept Of Juvenile Justice **252.534.6711**
Fax 252.574.3122
E-mail .... clarence.high.jr@djjdp.nc.gov
　102 Jefferson St, Jackson, NC 27845
　Clarence High, Chief Court Counselor

POLICE AND SHERIFF

Sheriff's Ofc **252.534.2611**
Fax 252.534.1408
　105 Jefferson St, Jackson, NC 27845
　Wardie P. Vincent, Sheriff

Onslow County

SOCIAL SERVICES

Social Svcs Dept **910.989.0230**
Fax 910.989.0713
　1915 Onslow Drive Ext., Jacksonville,
　NC 28541-1379
　Roger Penrod, Agency Director

GENERAL HEALTH SERVICES

Health Dept **910.347.2154**
Fax 910.347.7941
Web .... www.co.onslow.nc.us
　612 College St, Jacksonville, NC 28540-5396
　Cynthia Bandy, Hiv Coordinator

JUSTICE AGENCY

Guardian Ad Litem **910.346.5335**
Fax 910.346.1966
E-mail .... iris.derrick@nccourts.org
　625 Court St, Jacksonville, NC 28540-4732
　Iris Derrick, District Administrator

Youth Svcs **910.455.1202**
Fax 910.938.1566
Web .... www.onslowcountync.gov
E-mail .... amy_dail@co.onslow.nc.gov
　220 Georgetown Rd, Jacksonville, NC 28540-4146
　Angie Robeles, Supervisor

POLICE AND SHERIFF

Sheriff's Dept **910.455.3113**
Fax 910.455.0048
Web .... www.co.onslow.nc.us
E-mail .... sheriff@co.onslow.nc.us
　701 Mill Ave, Jacksonville, NC 28540-4823
　Edward E. Brown, Sheriff

Orange County

SOCIAL SERVICES

Social Svcs Dept **919.968.2000**
Fax 919.969.3048
Web .... www.co.orange.nc.us
　113 Mayo St, Hillsborough, NC 27278-2438
　Nancy Coston, Director

GENERAL HEALTH SERVICES

Health Dept **919.245.2400**
Fax 919.644.3312
　300 W Tryon St, Hillsborough, NC 27278
　Rosemary Summers, Dp, Health Director

Health Dept **919.968.2022**
Fax 919.968.2013
Web .... www.co.orange.nc.us
　2501 Homestead Rd, Chapel Hill, NC 27516-9087
　Sue Rankin, Nursing Coordinator

JUSTICE AGENCY

Dept Of Juvenile Justice **919.245.2215**
Fax 919.644.3039
E-mail .... peggy.hamlet@djjdp.nc.gov
　110 E. King St, Hillsborough, NC 27278
　Peggy Hamlett, Chief Court Counselor

POLICE AND SHERIFF

Sheriff's Ofc **919.644.3050**
Fax 919.732.6403
Web .... www.co.orange.nc.us
E-mail .... sheriff@co.orange.nc.us
　106 E Margaret Ln, Hillsborough, NC 27278-2526
　Lindy Pendergrass, Sheriff

EDUCATION SERVICES

Communities In Schools **919.967.6677**
Fax 919.962.1772
Web .... www.cisoc-nc.org
E-mail .... cisoc_ed@bellsouth.net
　151 E Rosemary St Ste 205, Chapel Hill, NC 27504
　Sheila Sholes, Director

**Efland Cheeks Elementary Head
Start** **919.563.5112**
Fax 919.563.3137
Web www.orange.k12.nc.us
E-mail .... lisa.napp@orange.k12.nc.us
　4401 Fuller Rd, Efland, NC 27243-9735
　Lisa Napp, Director

**Ephesus Elementary Prekindergarten Head
Start** **919.929.8715**
Fax 919.967.5705
E-mail .... vcreamer@chccs.k12.nc.us
　1495 Ephesus Church Rd, Chapel Hill, NC 27517
　Victoria Creamer, Director

Pasquotank County

SOCIAL SERVICES

Social Svcs Dept **252.338.2126**
Fax 252.338.7512
E-mail .... melissa.stokely@pcdss.com
　709 Roanoke Ave, Elizabeth City, NC 27909
　Mellissa Stokely, Director

GENERAL HEALTH SERVICES

Health Dept **252.338.4400**
Fax 252.338.4456
Web .... www.ahc_nc.org
　711 Roanoke Ave, Elizabeth City, NC 27907
　Jerry Parks, Health Director

JUSTICE AGENCY

Dept Of Juvenile Justice **252.331.4759**
Fax 252.331.4788
Web .... www.djjdp.nc.gov
E-mail .... sherri.ellington@ncmail.net
　1305 McPherson Street, Elizabeth City, NC 27909
　Sherry Ellington, Chief Court Counselor

Guardian Ad Litem Program **252.331.4755**
Fax 252.331.4789
E-mail .... kathleen.foreman@nccourts.org
　1305 McPherson St Ste D, Elizabeth City, NC 27909
　Kathleen Foreman, District Administrator

POLICE AND SHERIFF

Sheriff's Ofc **252.338.2191**
Fax 252.338.1667
E-mail .... sheriff@co.pasquotank.nc.us
　200 E Colonial Ave, Elizabeth City, NC 27909
　Randy W. Cartwright, Sheriff

Pender County

SOCIAL SERVICES

Social Svcs......................................910.259.1240
Fax...910.259.1418
Web...............................www.pender-county.com
E-mail.......................shiverr@pender-county.com
810 S Walker St, Burgaw, NC 28425-5000
Reta M Shiver, Dpa, Director

GENERAL HEALTH SERVICES

Health Dept...................................910.259.1230
Fax...910.259.1258
E-mail................healthdirector@pendercountync.gov
803 S Walker St, Burgaw, NC 28425
Amber Parker, Health Director

POLICE AND SHERIFF

Sheriff's Ofc...................................910.259.1212
Fax...910.259.1509
E-mail..................carson.smith@pendersheriff.com
605 E Fremont St, Burgaw, NC 28425
Carson H. Smith Jr., Sheriff

EDUCATION SERVICES

East Coast Migrant Head Start-Long
Creek..910.259.7491
Fax...910.259.7495
23280 Nc Hwy 210 W, Rocky Point, NC 28435
Jackie Hand, Director

Perquimans County

JUSTICE AGENCY

Perquimans Juvenile Detention Ctr...........252.426.2541
Fax...252.426.2546
E-mail.......................michael.cayton@ncmail.net
125 Jessup St, Hertford, NC 27944-8107
Michael Cayton, Director

POLICE AND SHERIFF

Sheriff's Dept................................252.426.5615
Fax...252.426.4019
E-mail...............etilley@perquimanscountync.gov
110 N Church St, Hertford, NC 27944
Eric V. Tilley, Sheriff

Person County

SOCIAL SERVICES

Social Svcs...................................336.599.8361
Fax...336.597.9339
E-mail...........................c.paylor@personcounty.net
355 S Madison Blvd Ste B, Roxboro, NC 27573
Carlton Paylor, Director

GENERAL HEALTH SERVICES

Health Dept...................................336.597.2204
Fax...336.597.4804
355 S Madison Blvd Ste A, Roxboro, NC 15986
Janet Clayton, Health Director

Pitt County

SOCIAL SERVICES

Social Svcs Dept............................252.902.1111
Fax...252.413.1066
1717 W 5th St, Greenville, NC 27834
Gwen Burns, Assistant Director

GENERAL HEALTH SERVICES

Health Dept...................................252.902.2300
Fax...252.413.1446
Web...............................www.pittcountync.gov
201 Government Cir, Greenville, NC 27828
John Morrow, Md, Health Director

JUSTICE AGENCY

Dept Of Juvenile Justice...................252.695.7350
Fax...252.695.7346
Web...............................www.juvjus.state.nc.us
E-mail.......................brian.stewart@djjdp.nc.gov
110 S EVANS ST STE A, Greenville, NC 27835-1160
Brian Stewart, Chief Court Counselor

Juvenile Crime Prevention Council...........252.355.9013
Fax...252.439.1807
Web...............................www.juvjus.state.nc.us
E-mail...............................jesse.riggs@nc.gov
404 Saint Andrews Dr, Greenville, NC 27834
Jesse Riggs, Area Consultant

Pitt Regional Juvenile Detention
Ctr...252.830.6590
Fax...252.830.3355
451 W Belvoir Rd, Greenville, NC 27834
Stanley Melvin, Director

COURTS

3rd District Court............................252.695.7100
Fax...252.830.3144
100 W 3rd Street, Greenville, NC 27858
Sara Beth Fulford Rhodes, Superior Court Clerk

Teen Court....................................252.758.0268
Fax...252.758.8810
E-mail.............................mwest@mceonline.org
400 Martin Luther King, Jr. Dr, Greenville, NC 27836
Katherine Lennox, Director

POLICE AND SHERIFF

Sheriff's Dept................................252.902.2800
Fax...252.830.4636
Web...............................www.cnsheriffs.net
E-mail...............sheriffmanning@cnsheriffs.net
100 W 3rd St, Greenville, NC 27858-1806
Neil Elks, Sheriff

EDUCATION SERVICES

East Carolina Vocational Head Start
Ctr...252.707.8022
Fax...252.707.8067
901 Staton Rd, Greenville, NC 27834
Freida Dixon, Supervisor

East Coast Migrant Head
Start-Fountain...............................252.749.4011
Fax...252.749.1508
Web...............................www.ecmhsp.org
E-mail...........................mbelltiara@ecmhsp.org
7656 Nc Highway 222, Fountain, NC 27829-9202
Maria Belltiara, Director

Exceptional Children's Program.............252.830.4200
Fax...252.830.4239
Web...............................www.pitt.k12.nc.us
E-mail.............................keeterc@pitt.k12.nc.us
1717 W 5th St, Greenville, NC 27834-1601
Cathy Keeter, Director

Polk County

SOCIAL SERVICES

Social Svcs...................................828.859.5825
Fax...828.859.9703
E-mail...........................srhodes@polknc.org
330 Carolina Dr Ste A, Tryon, NC 28782
Sue Rhodes, Director

GENERAL HEALTH SERVICES

Health Dept...................................828.894.8271
Fax...828.894.8678
Web...............................www.rpmhd.org
161 Walker St, Columbus, NC 28722-9433
Jimmy Hines, Health Director

Randolph County

SOCIAL SERVICES

Social Svcs...................................336.683.8000
Fax...336.683.8131
Web...............................www.co.randolph.nc.us
E-mail...............bwduncan@co.randolph.nc.us
1512 N Fayetteville St, Asheboro, NC 27203-3894
Beth Duncan, Director

GENERAL HEALTH SERVICES

Health Dept...................................336.318.6200
Fax...336.318.6234
Web...............................www.co.randolph.nc.us
2222 S Fayetteville St Ste B, Asheboro, NC 27205
Mary Cooper, Health Director

JUSTICE AGENCY

Dept Juvenile Justice.......................336.318.6990
Fax...336.318.6705
Web...............................www.djjdp.nc.gov
176 E Salisbury St Ste 104, Asheboro,
NC 27203-5571
Emily Coltrane, Chief Court Counselor

POLICE AND SHERIFF

Sheriff's Ofc...................................336.318.6699
Fax...336.318.6618
E-mail...............armcneill@co.randolph.nc.us
727 Mcdowell Rd, Asheboro, NC 27205
Maynard Reid, Sheriff

EDUCATION SERVICES

Communities In Schools.....................336.625.0008
Fax...336.625.0008
E-mail...............cisrc@randolph.k12.nc.us
1011 Sunset Avenue, Asheboro, NC 27203
Sandi Norman, Executive Director

Exceptional Children's Program.............336.318.6100
Fax...336.318.6166
Web...............................www.randolph.k12.nc.us
E-mail...............cvoncannon@randolph.k12.nc.us
2222 S Fayetteville St Ste C, Asheboro,
NC 27205-7368
Carol Von Cannon, Director

Exceptional Children's Program.............336.625.5104
Fax...336.625.9238
Web...............................www.asheboro.k12.nc.us
E-mail...............ghicks@asheboro.k12.nc.us
PO Box 1103, Asheboro, NC 27204-1103
Gail Hicks, Director Of The Exeptinoal Childrens Program

Richmond County

SOCIAL SERVICES

Social Svcs...................................910.997.8480
Fax...910.997.8447
Web...............................www.dhhs.state.nc.us
E-mail...............tammy.schrenker@ncmail.net
125 Caroline St, Rockingham, NC 28379-3567
Tammy Shrenker, Director

JUSTICE AGENCY

Richmond Juvenile Detention Ctr...........910.997.9195
Fax...910.997.9205
E-mail...............Kathy.bethea.djjpp@nc.gov
269 Cartledge Creek Rd, Rockingham, NC 28379
Kathy Bethany, Director

POLICE AND SHERIFF

Sheriff's Dept................................910.895.3232
Fax...910.997.8384
01 Court St, Rockingham, NC 28379-3595
James Clemmons, Sheriff

Robeson County

JUSTICE AGENCY

Dept Of Juvenile Justice **910.671.3350**
Fax 910.671.6231
E-mail .... lance.dritt@djjdp.nc.gov
　800 N Walnut St, Lumberton, NC 28358
　Lance Dritt, Chief Court Counselor

Guardian Ad Litem **910.671.3077**
Fax 910.737.4083
E-mail .... tulisha.j.pridgen@nccourts.org
　108 W 8th St, Lumberton, NC 28358
　Tulisha Pridgen, District Administrator

POLICE AND SHERIFF

Sheriff's Ofc **910.671.3106**
Fax 910.608.2274
　120 Legend Rd, Lumberton, NC 28358-8936
　Kennith Feely, Sheriff

Rockingham County

SOCIAL SERVICES

Social Svcs **336.342.1394**
Fax 336.634.1847
Web .... www.rockingham.nc.us
E-mail .... ljohnson@co.rockingham.nc.us
　411 State Highway 65, Wentworth, NC 27375
　Larry Johnson, Director

GENERAL HEALTH SERVICES

Health Dept **336.342.8143**
Fax 336.342.8356
Web .... www.co.rockingham.nc.us
E-mail .... gmartin@co.rockingham.nc.us
　371 Nc 65 Ste 204, Wentworth, NC 27375
　Glenn Martin, Health Director

JUSTICE AGENCY

Dept Of Juvenile Justice **336.634.5707**
Fax 336.634.5709
Web .... www.juvjus.state.nc.us
E-mail .... rusty.stlad@djjdt.nc.gov
　170 Hwy 65, Reidsville, NC 27320
　Rusty Slatd, Chief Court Counselor

COURTS

Teen Court **336.342.5756**
Fax 336.349.1115
E-mail .... tprice@co.rockingham.nc.us
　335 County Home Road, Wentworth, NC 27375
　Teresa Price, Director

Rowan County

SOCIAL SERVICES

Social Svcs **704.216.8330**
Fax 704.638.3041
Web .... www.rowancountync.gov
　1813 E Innes St, Salisbury, NC 28146
　Sandra Wilkes, Director

Social Svcs Dept **704.216.8440**
Fax 704.638.3134
E-mail .... pat.spears@rowancountync.gov
　1813 E Innes St, Salisbury, NC 281446-2448
　Pat Spears, Program Director

GENERAL HEALTH SERVICES

Health Dept **704.216.8777**
Fax 704.638.3129
Web .... www.co.rowan.nc.us
E-mail .... patty.yost@rowancountync.gov
　1811 E Innes St, Salisbury, NC 28146-6030
　Patty Yost, Nursing Supervisor

JUSTICE AGENCY

Dept Of Juvenile Justice **704.639.7515**
Fax 704.639.7747
Web .... www.djjdp.nc.gov
E-mail .... kecia.barnes@djjdp.nc.gov
　210 N Main St, Salisbury, NC 28144
　Keisha Barnes, Chief Court Counselor

Guardian Ad Litem Program **704.639.7517**
Fax 704.639.7708
Web .... www.rowanguardian.org
E-mail .... rowanguardian@yahoo.com
　310 N Main St, Salisbury, NC 28144
　Jeanne Dixon, District Administrator

COURTS

Teen Court **704.633.5636**
Fax 704.636.8117
　1322 S Fulton St, Salisbury, NC 28144
　Karen Carpenter, Program Director

POLICE AND SHERIFF

Sheriff's Ofc **704.216.8700**
Fax 704.216.8674
Web .... www.co.rowan.nc.us
　232 N Main St Ste 129, Salisbury, NC 28144-4366
　Kevin Auten, Sheriff

EDUCATION SERVICES

East Spencer Head Start **704.636.9639**
Web .... www.acf.hhs.gov
E-mail .... cmorrison@acf.hhs.gov
　1300 W Bank St, Salisbury, NC 28144-3910
　Carol Morrison, Director

**Exceptional Children's Dept of Rowan's Salisbury
Schools** **704.639.3064**
Fax 704.639.3072
E-mail .... vailcp@rss.k12.nc.us
　417 N Main St, Salisbury, NC 28145
　Dr. Crystal Vail, Director

Rutherford County

SOCIAL SERVICES

Dept. of Social Services **828.287.6165**
Fax 828.287.6350
E-mail .... john.carroll@rutherfordcountync.gov
　389 Fairground Rd, Spindale, NC 28160-2204
　John Carroll, Mhdl, Agency Director

POLICE AND SHERIFF

Sheriff's Dept **828.287.6247**
Fax 828.287.6196
Web .... www.blueridge.net
E-mail .... chirs.francis@countync.gov
　198 N Washington St, Rutherfordton,
　NC 28139-2440
　Chirs Francis, Sheriff

Sampson County

SOCIAL SERVICES

Social Svcs **910.592.7131**
Fax 910.592.4297
E-mail .... sarah.w.bradshaw@ncmail.net
　405 County Complex Rd, Clinton, NC 28328-4781
　Sarah Bradshaw, Director

GENERAL HEALTH SERVICES

Health Dept **910.592.1131**
Fax 910.592.1901
E-mail .... wrobinson@sampsonnc.com
　360 County Complex Rd Ste 200, Clinton, NC 28328
　Wanda Robinson, Director

Scotland County

SOCIAL SERVICES

Social Svcs **910.277.2500**
Fax 910.277.2402
Web .... www.scotlandcounty.org
E-mail .... jknott@scotlandcounty.org
　1405 W Blvd, Government Complex, Laurinburg,
　NC 28353
　Joseph Knot, Director

GENERAL HEALTH SERVICES

Health Dept **910.277.2440**
Fax 910.277.2450
Web .... www.scotlandcountyhealth.org
E-mail .... rsapp@scotlandcounty.org
　1405 West Blvd, Laurinburg, NC 28352-9170
　Ron Sapp, Director

JUSTICE AGENCY

Dept Of Juvenile Justice **910.277.3222**
Fax 910.277.3181
　212 Biggs St, Rm 14, Laurinburg, NC 28352
　Randy Jones, Chief Court Counselor

POLICE AND SHERIFF

Sheriff's Ofc **910.276.3385**
Fax 910.610.1590
　212 Biggs Street, Laurinburg, NC 28352
　Shep Jones, Sheriff

Stanly County

GENERAL HEALTH SERVICES

Health Dept **704.982.9171**
Fax 704.982.8354
E-mail .... dennisjoyner@co.stanly.nc.us
　1000 N 1st St Ste 3, Albemarle, NC 28001
　Dennis Joyner, Director

POLICE AND SHERIFF

Sheriff's Dept **704.986.3719**
Fax 704.986.3733
Web .... www.co.stanly.nc.us
　223 S 2nd St, Albemarle, NC 28001-5701
　Rick Burris, Sheriff

Stokes County

SOCIAL SERVICES

Social Svcs **336.593.2861**
Fax 336.593.9362
E-mail .... kpreston@co.stokes.nc.us
　1010 Highway 8 & 89 N, Danbury, NC 27016
　Kristy Preston, Director

GENERAL HEALTH SERVICES

Health Dept **336.593.2400**
Fax 336.593.9361
Web .... www.co.stokes.nc.us
E-mail .... slenhart@co.stokes.nc.us
　1009 N Main, Danbury, NC 27016
　Scott Lenhart, Health Director

POLICE AND SHERIFF

Sheriff's Ofc **336.593.8787**
Fax 336.593.3361
Web .... www.co.stokes.nc.us
E-mail .... sheriff@co.stokes.nc.us
　1012 Main St, Danbury, NC 27016
　Mike Marshall, Sheriff

North Carolina

Surry County

SOCIAL SERVICES

Social Svcs Dept **336.401.8800**
Fax 336.401.8860
E-mail ....wayne.black@ncmail.net
118 Hamby Rd, Dobson, NC 27017-8471
Wayne Black, Director

GENERAL HEALTH SERVICES

Health Dept **336.401.8400**
Fax 336.401.8599
E-mail ....thughes@doc.state.nc.us
118 Hamby Rd, Dobson, NC 27017-8471
Theresa Hughes, Rn, Hiv Coordinator

JUSTICE AGENCY

Guardian Ad Litem **336.386.4090**
Fax 336.386.4614
Web ....www.nccourts.org
E-mail ....linda.a.devine@nccourts.org
114 W Atkins St, Dobson, NC 27017
Linda Devine, District Administrator

POLICE AND SHERIFF

Sheriff's Dept **336.401.8900**
Fax 336.401.8909
E-mail ....gammonsm@co.surry.nc.us
218 N Main St, Dobson, NC 27017
Graham H. Atkinson, Sheriff

Swain County

GENERAL HEALTH SERVICES

Health Dept **828.488.3198**
Fax 828.488.8672
545 Center St, Bryson City, NC 28713
Tricia Carver, Hiv Coordinator

COURTS

30th District Court **828.488.2288**
Fax 828.488.9360
Swain County Courthouse, Bryson City, NC 28713
Honorable Richlyn Holt, Judge

EDUCATION SERVICES

Communities In Schools **828.488.7505**
Fax 828.488.9953
E-mail ....mbarker@dnet.net
234-A Bryson Walk, Bryson City, NC 28713
Melissa Barker, Director

Transylvania County

GENERAL HEALTH SERVICES

Health Dept **828.884.3135**
Fax 828.884.3140
Web ....www.transylvaniacounty.org
98 E Morgan St, Brevard, NC 28712
Sharon Cameron, Rn, Nursing Supervisor

COURTS

29th District Court **828.884.3120**
Fax 828.883.2161
E-mail ....HumanResources@nccourts.org.
7 E Main St Rm 101, Brevard, NC 28712
Honorable Mark E Powell, Judge

EDUCATION SERVICES

Communities In Schools **828.885.7390**
Fax 828.877.5643
Web ....www.citcom.net
E-mail ....cistc@citcom.net
225 Rosenwald Lane, Brevard, NC 28712
Jana Jacobs, Director

Tyrrell County

SOCIAL SERVICES

Social Svcs Dept **252.796.3421**
Fax 252.796.1732
102 N. Road St, Columbia, NC 27925
Sandra K. Walker, Director

Union County

GENERAL HEALTH SERVICES

Health Dept **704.296.4800**
Fax 704.296.4887
Web ....www.co.union.nc.us
E-mail ....templeaycoth@co.union.nc.us
1224 W Roosevelt Blvd, Monroe, NC 28110-2820
Temple Aycoth, Rn, Hiv Coordinator

JUSTICE AGENCY

Dept Of Juvenile Justice **704.289.4169**
Fax 704.283.3972
Web ....www.djjdp.nc.gov
E-mail ....jimmy.craig@ncmail.net
500 N Main St, Monroe, NC 28112
Jimmy Craig, Chief Court Counselor

POLICE AND SHERIFF

Sheriff's Dept **704.283.3789**
Fax 704.292.2700
Web ....www.co.union.nc.us
E-mail ....eddiecathey@co.union.nc.us
3344 Presson Rd, Monroe, NC 28112-9140
E.g. Cathey, Sheriff

Vance County

SOCIAL SERVICES

Social Svcs Dept **252.492.5001**
Fax 252.438.5997
Web ....www.vancecounty.com
E-mail ....kay.fields@vance.nc.gov
350 Ruin Creek Rd, Henderson, NC 27536-5941
Kay Fields, Director

GENERAL HEALTH SERVICES

Health Dept **252.492.7915**
Fax 252.492.4219
Web ....www.gvdhd.org
E-mail ....acurrin@gvdhd.org
115 Charles Rollins Rd, Henderson, NC 27536-2939
Audrey Currin, Rn, Hiv Coordinator

POLICE AND SHERIFF

Sheriff's Ofc **252.738.2200**
Fax 252.738.2220
Web ....www.vancecounty.org
E-mail ....sheriff@vancecounty.org
156 Church St Ste 004, Henderson, NC 27536-5574
Peter White, Sheriff

Wake County

SOCIAL SERVICES

Child Support Enforcement **919.255.3800**
Fax 919.212.3840
E-mail ....daisie.blue@dhhs.nc.gov
3301 Terminal Dr Ste 125, Raleigh, NC 27604-3896
Daisie Blue, Director

JUSTICE AGENCY

Attorney General's Ofc **919.716.6400**
Fax 919.716.6750
Web ....www.ncdoj.com
E-mail ....ncago@ncdoj.gov
114 W Edenton St, Raleigh, NC 27603-1712
Roy Cooper, Attorney General

Dept Of Juvenile Justice **919.715.3333**
Fax 919.835.3412
Web ....www.juvjus.state.nc.us
316 Fayetteville Street Mall, Raleigh, NC 27601
Maxine Armwood, Chief Court Counselor

**Wake Regional Juvenile Detention
Ctr** **919.212.3104**
Fax 919.212.3112
Web ....www.ncmail.net
E-mail ....sheila.l.davis@ncmail.net
700 Beacon Lake Dr, Raleigh, NC 27610-1373
Sheila L. Davis, Director

POLICE AND SHERIFF

Sheriff's Dept **919.856.6900**
Fax 919.856.6874
Web ....www.co.wake.nc.us
E-mail ....donnie.harrison@co.wake.nc.us
330 S Salisbury St, Raleigh, NC 27601-1729
Donnie Harrison, Sheriff

Warren County

SOCIAL SERVICES

Social Svcs Dept **252.257.5000**
Fax 252.257.5610
E-mail ....jef.woodard@ncmail.net
307 N Main St, Warrenton, NC 27589
Jef Woodard, Director

GENERAL HEALTH SERVICES

Health Dept **252.257.1185**
Fax 252.257.2897
Web ....www.warrencountync.com
E-mail ....asmith@co.warren.nc.us
544 W Ridgeway St, Warrenton, NC 27589-1716
Andy Smith, Director

COURTS

9th District Court **252.257.3261**
Fax 252.257.5529
109 S Main St, Warrenton, NC 27589
Honorable Daniel Finch, District Judge

Washington County

GENERAL HEALTH SERVICES

**Martin Tyrrell Washington District Health
Dept** **252.793.3023**
Fax 252.791.3159
Web ....www.mtwdistricthealth.org
E-mail ....billiehs@yahoo.com
198 Nc Highway 45 N, Plymouth, NC 27962-9232
Billie Patrick, Hiv/aids Coordinator

Watauga County

GENERAL HEALTH SERVICES

Health Dept **828.264.6635**
Fax 828.265.3101
Web ....www.apphealth.com
126 Poplar Grove Connector, Boone, NC 28607
Pam Rush, Nursing Supervisor

POLICE AND SHERIFF

Sheriff's Ofc **828.264.3761**
Fax 828.265.7617
E-mail ....len.hagaman@wat.gov.org
184 Hodges Gap Rd, Boone, NC 28607
Len D. Hagaman, Sheriff

Wayne County

GENERAL HEALTH SERVICES

Cherry Hospital 919.731.3200
Fax 919.731.3785
Web ....www.dhhs.nc.gov
E-mail ....philip.cook@dhhs.nc.gov
201 Stevens Mill Rd, Goldsboro, NC 27530
Phillip Cook, Director

Health Dept 919.731.1000
Fax 919.731.1232
Web ....www.wchd.net
E-mail ....jamesroosen@waynegov.com
301 N Herman St, Goldsboro, NC 27530
James Roosen, Director

MENTAL HEALTH SERVICES

East Pointe Human Svcs 919.731.1133
Fax 919.731.1333
Web ....www.eastpointe.net
E-mail ....kjones@eastpointe.net
100 S James St, Goldsboro, NC 27530
Kenneth Jones, Director

JUSTICE AGENCY

Dept Of Juvenile Justice 919.731.7916
Fax 919.731.5691
Web ....www.djjdp.nc.gov
E-mail ....joe.testino@ncmail.net
109 Ormond Ave, Goldsboro, NC 27530
Joe Testino, Chief Court Counselor

Juvenile Home 919.734.7761
Fax 919.734.7061
Web ....www.ncdnpe.org
1703 Oberry Center Rd, Goldsboro, NC 27530-9527
Kevin Hicks, Program Manager

COURTS

Communities In Schools 919.735.1432
Fax 919.734.9994
E-mail ....sdavis@ciswayne.org
308 N William St, Goldsboro, NC 27530
Sudie Davis, Executive Director

EDUCATION SERVICES

Exceptional Children's Program 919.705.6027
Fax 919.736.5030
Web ....www.waynecountyschools.org
E-mail ....jwalston@wcps.org
801 N Lionel St, Goldsboro, NC 27530
Jane Walston, Director

Wilkes County

GENERAL HEALTH SERVICES

Health Dept 336.651.7450
Fax 336.651.7472
Web ....www.wilkescounty.net
E-mail ....blovette@wilkescounty.net
306 College St, Wilkesboro, NC 28697-2854
Beth Lovett, Director

POLICE AND SHERIFF

Sheriff's Dept 336.903.7600
Fax 336.903.7606
E-mail ....stopcrime@wilkes.net
201 Curtis Bridge Rd, Wilkesboro, NC 28697
Dane C. Mastin, Sheriff

EDUCATION SERVICES

Communities In Schools 336.651.7830
Fax 336.651.7833
Web ....www.cisnc.org/wilkes
E-mail ....chipmang@wilkes.k12.nc.us
613 Cherry St, North Wilkesboro, NC 28659-4229
Glenda Chipman, Executive Director

Wilson County

GENERAL HEALTH SERVICES

Health Dept 252.237.3141
Fax 252.293.8300
Web ....www.wilson-co.com
1801 Glendale Dr SW, Wilson, NC 27893
Felix Meyer, Health Director

COURTS

7th District Court 252.291.7500
Fax 252.291.8049
115 Nash St E, Wilson, NC 27894
Andrew Whitley, Clerk

POLICE AND SHERIFF

Sheriff's Office 252.237.2118
Fax 252.399.2871
E-mail ....cwoodard@wilson-co.com
100 Green St E, Wilson, NC 27893
Calvin Woodard, Sheriff

Yadkin County

GENERAL HEALTH SERVICES

Health Dept 336.679.4203
Fax 336.679.6358
Web ....www.yadkincountync.gov
E-mail ....mpowell@yadkincounty.gov
217 E Willow St, Yadkinville, NC 27055
Martha Powell, Rn, Hiv/aids Coordinator

EDUCATION SERVICES

Boonville Head Start 336.367.5301
Fax 336.367.3637
E-mail ....kdj93003@hotmail.com
3801 River Rd, Boonville, NC 27011-8341
Kathryn Jenkins, Director

Yancey County

SOCIAL SERVICES

Social Svcs Dept 828.682.2470
Fax 828.682.1602
E-mail ....alice.elkins@ncmail.net
447 E Hwy 19E, Burnsville, NC 28714
Alice Elkins, Director

GENERAL HEALTH SERVICES

Health Dept 828.682.6118
Fax 828.682.6262
Web ....www.trhd.dst.nc.us
E-mail ....linda.cinnane@trhd.dst.nc.us
202 Medical Campus Dr, Burnsville, NC 28714-9004
L Inda Cinnane, Health Director

SPECIAL SERVICES AGENCIES

ADOPTION AGENCIES

A Caring Heart Case Management, Inc. 252.206.1266
Fax 252.206.1268
1901 Tarboro Street SW, Suite 300, Wilson,
NC 27893
COA accredited organization.

A Child's Hope 919.839.8800
Fax 919.839.8900
Web ....www.achildshope.com
E-mail ....pherring@hermcb.com
2 Hannover Sq, Ste 1860, Raleigh, NC 27601
Parker Herring, Director

Amazing Grace Adoptions 919.858.8998
Fax 919.858.8997
Web ....www.agadoptions.org
E-mail ....agadopt@bellsouth.net
1215 Jones Franklin Rd Ste 202, Raleigh,
NC 27606-3351
Donnas Kinton, Executive Director

Amy S Davis 704.784.9440
Fax 704.721.5175
Web ....www.amysdavislaw.com
235 Cabarrus Ave E, Concord, NC 28025-3409
Amy S. Davis, Attorney

Another Choice For Black Children 704.394.1124
Fax 704.394.3843
Web ....www.anotherchoice.net
E-mail ....info@anotherchoice.net
2340 Beatties Ford Rd, Charlotte, NC 28216-4314
Ruth Amerson, Director

Bethany Christian Svcs 919.510.9511
Fax 919.510.9512
Web ....www.bethany.org/raleigh
E-mail ....bcsraleigh@bethany.org
4008 Barrett Dr Ste 206, Raleigh, NC 27609
Melanie Switzer, Director

Bethany Christian Svcs 704.541.1833
Fax 704.542.1311
Web ....www.bethany.org/ncarolina
E-mail ....bcscharlotte@bethany.org
10720 Carmel Commons Blvd # 370, Charlotte,
NC 28226
Cynthia Long, Director

Bridging The Gap, LLC 252.758.1300
Fax 252.758.0015
205 D Plaza Drive, Greenville, NC 27858
COA accredited organization.

Carolina Adoption Svcs, Inc. 336.275.9660
Fax 336.273.9804
Web ....www.carolinaadoption.org
E-mail ....cas@carolinaadoption.org
301 N Elm St Ste 500, Greensboro, NC 27401-2189
Rosemary Martin, Executive Director
COA accredited organization.

Catholic Social Svcs 704.370.3262
Fax 704.370.3377
E-mail ....ekthurbee@charlottediocese.org
1123 S Church St, Charlotte, NC 28203-4003
Gerry Carter, Director

Central Children's Home of North Carolina,
Inc. 919.693.7617
Fax 919.693.3963
Web ....www.cch-nc.org
211 W. Antioch Drive, Oxford, NC 27565
COA accredited organization.

Children's Home Society 828.874.0257
604 Meadow St, Greensville, NC 28612
Keane Tutterow, Chief Executive Officer

Children's Home Society of North Carolina 336.274.1538
Fax 336.274.7347
Web ....www.chsnc.org
P.O. Box 14608, Greensboro, NC 27415-4608
COA accredited organization.

North Carolina

Children's Homes 704.484.2558
Fax 704.484.2042
Web ....www.chccinc.org
P.O. Box 2053, Shelby, NC 28151
COA accredited organization.

Christian Adoption Svcs 704.847.0038
Fax 704.841.1538
Web ....www.christianadopt.org
E-mail ....cas@christianadopt.org
624 Matthews Mint Hill Rd Ste 134, Matthews,
NC 28105-1845
James Woodward, Executive Director

Christian World Adoption 828.693.7007
Fax 828.693.8113
Web ....www.cwa.org
E-mail ....cwa@cwa.org
777 S Allen Rd, Flat Rock, NC 28731-9439
Anita Thomas, Office Manager

Cumberland Community Action Program,
Inc. 910.485.6131
Fax 910.485.1897
Web ....www.ccap-inc.org
P.O. Box 2009, Fayetteville, NC 28302-2009
COA accredited organization.

Family Guidance Center, Inc. 828.322.1400
17 Highway 70, S.E., Hickory, NC 28602
COA accredited organization.

Family Preservation Services of North Carolina,
Inc. 704.344.0491
Fax 704.344.0493
Web ....www.FPScorp.com
4601 Park Road, Suite 400, Charlotte, NC 28209
COA accredited organization.

Frank Adoption Ctr 919.510.9135
Fax 919.510.9137
Web ....www.frankadopt.org
E-mail ....info@frankadopt.org
2840 Plaza Pl Ste 102, Raleigh, NC 27612
Mischalina Miller, Director

Homes For Children 828.898.5465
Fax 828.898.6140
Web ....www.grandfatherhome.org
P.O. Box 98, Banner Elk, NC 28604
COA accredited organization.

Independent Adoption Ctr 919.676.6288
Fax 919.676.6707
Web ....www.adoptionhelp.org
E-mail ....info@adoptionhelp.org
184 Wind Chime Ct Ste 101, Raleigh,
NC 27615-6485
Gina Hayes, Coordinator

KidsPeace Foster Care & Family Svcs 919.872.1121
Fax 919.872.6671
Web ....www.fostercare.com
3109 Poplarwood Ct Ste 310, Raleigh,
NC 27604-1025
Ray Culp, National Director Foster Care & Family Services

New Life Christian Adoptions 919.779.1004
Fax 919.779.1544
Web ....www.nlcadopt.org
E-mail ....newlife@nlcadopt.org
500 Benson Rd Ste 201, Garner, NC 27529-3947
John Wheeler, Director

NuVizions, LLC 252.332.2297
Fax 252.332.2416
101 W. Main Street, Ahoskie, NC 27910
COA accredited organization.

Onslow Carteret Behavioral Healthcare
Services 910.219.8000
Fax 910.219.8072
Web ....www.ocbhs.org
165 Center Street, Jacksonville, NC 28546
COA accredited organization.

Professional Parenting 828.236.2877
Fax 828.236.9825
Web ....www.bariumsprings.org
E-mail ....tammy.detz@bariumsprings.org
38 Garfield St, Asheville, NC 28803-2327
Tammy Detz, Director

Rooted and Grounded, Incorporated 252.332.4409
Fax 252.332.5099
124 East Main Street, Ahoskie, NC 27910
COA accredited organization.

Southeastern Center for Mental Health, Developmental
Disabilities & Substance Abuse Services 910.332.6888
Fax 910.332.6880
Web ....www.secmh.org
P.O. Box 4147, Wilmington, NC 28406
COA accredited organization.

Southeastern Regional Mental Health, Developmental
Disabilities and Substance Abuse Services 910.738.5261
Fax 910.738.8230
Web ....www.srmhc.org
450 Country Club Road, Lumberton, NC 28360
COA accredited organization.

Step By Step Care, Inc. 336.378.0109
Web ....www.stepbystepcare.org
709 E. Market St., Suite 100B, Greensboro,
NC 27401
COA accredited organization.

The Enola Group 828.433.2862
Fax 828.438.6483
Web ....www.enolagroup.org
PO Box 250, Morganton, NC 28680-0250
COA accredited organization.

W.E.B. DuBois Community Development
Corporation 919.556.0709
Fax 919.556.5160
Web ....www.duboiscdc.org
P.O. Box 1828, Wake Forest, NC 27588
COA accredited organization.

WOTP Programs, Inc. 704.536.0555
Fax 704.332.3121
Web ....www.wotpprograms.com
1100 Harding Place, Charlotte, NC 28204

Yahweh Center Children's Village 910.675.3533
Fax 910.675.3405
Web ....www.yahwehcenter.org
P.O. Box 10399, Wilmington, NC 28404
COA accredited organization.

ADVOCACY RESOURCES

Awake 828.586.3574
Web ....www.awakecacenter.org
E-mail ....r.schaeffer@sylvanc.net
563 W Main St Ste 10, Sylva, NC 28779
Robin Schaeffer, Director

Child Advocacy Ctr Family Svc Inc. 704.864.7704
Fax 704.862.0239
E-mail ....fsi@tricounty.co
214 E Franklin Blvd, Gastonia, NC 28052
Phil Deluca, Coordinator

Children's Ctr 828.885.7286
Fax 828.885.7288
150 S. Johnson St, Brevard, NC 28712
Kathy Williams, Director

Council for Children Inc 704.372.7961
601 E 5th St Ste 510, Charlotte, NC 28202
Loftis, Director

Crossroads: Children's Advocacy Ctr 336.228.0813
Fax 336.228.7087
Web ....www.webcrossroads.org
E-mail ....center@webcrossroads.org
1206 Vaughn Rd Ste B, Burlington, NC 27217
Deana Joy, Director

Family Ctr 828.247.0366
Fax 828.247.1870
Web ....www.frrc.org
E-mail ....shbright_fr@bellsouth.net
652 S Broadway St, Forest City, NC 28043-4247
Sherri Bright, Executive Director

Guardian ad Litem Program 704.686.0085
E-mail ....nita.k.stanley@nccourts.org
700 E 4th St, Ste 300, Charlotte, NC 28202
Nita Stanley, Attorney

Open Gates 252.465.8015
Fax 252.465.8058
E-mail ....gcso805sro@yahoo.com
PO Box 180, Sunbury, NC 27979-0180
Aron Martin, Director

Our House 336.667.5555
Fax 336.667.0677
203 E Main St, Wilkesboro, NC 28697
Shelby Parsons, Chairman

Paul W Freeman Jr 336.667.7565
E-mail ....pwfoff@wilkes.net
201 E Main St, Wilkesboro, NC 28697
Paul Freeman Jr, Attorney

Program in Conflict Studies and
DisputeResolution 336.217.5103
E-mail ....swhayes@uncg.edu
5900 Summit Ave, Ste 104, Browns Summit,
NC 27214
Sherrill W Hayes

Samarkand Youth Development Ctr 910.673.3756
Fax 910.673.5633
Web ....www.juvjus.state.nc.us
E-mail ....donald.burns@ncmail.net
3600 Samarkand Road, Eagle Springs, NC 27242
Don Burns, Campus Manager

Tedi Bear: Children's Advocacy Ctr 252.744.8334
Fax 252.744.8335
2303 Executive Cir, Greenville, NC 27834
Julie Ocker, Project Coordinator

BEHAVIORAL HEALTH TREATMENT

1st & 10 Group Home, Inc. 910.299.0096
Fax 910.299.0010
210 McKoy Street, Clinton, NC 28328
CARF accredited programs available.

1st Choice Health Services 336.905.7688
2107 Chester Ridge Drive, High Point, NC 27262
CARF accredited programs available.

3 D's Forever, Inc. dba Step Down 336.854.5789
Fax 336.854.5789
3012 Branderwood Drive, Greensboro, NC 27406
CARF accredited programs available.

A Better Path, Inc. 336.578.6115
Fax 336.578.3159
309 South Beaumont Avenue, Burlington, NC 27217
CARF accredited programs available.

A Brighter Tomorrow Group Home 336.509.5559
Fax 336.378.9478
2214 Atlanta Street, Greensboro, NC 27406-4002
CARF accredited programs available.

A Caring Alternative, LLC 828.437.3000
Fax 828.437.4999
Web ....www.caringalternative.com
203 East Union Street, Morganton, NC 28655
CARF accredited programs available.

A Caring Home, Inc. **704.525.2840**
E-mail .... acaringhomeinc@att.net
　8616 Nations Ford Road, Charlotte, NC 28217-5126
　Ms. Tamra Carver, Accreditation Manager
　Joint Commission accredited organization.

A Greater Power with Inn Residential Level II Group
Home **252.459.8777**
E-mail .... prophetessfostr@aol.com
　3784 Old County Home Road, Nashville, NC 27856
　Ms. Wilhelmenia Debro, Accreditation Manager
　Joint Commission accredited organization.

A New Beginning Adult and Youth Services,
Inc. **910.205.8970**
Fax 910.205.8948
　202 East Main Street, Hamlet, NC 28345
　CARF accredited programs available.

A New Frontier, LLC **919.937.9925**
Fax 919.937.9927
Web .... www.anewfrontierllc.com
　3711 University Drive, Suite B, Durham, NC 27707
　CARF accredited programs available.

A New Horizon, Inc. **252.758.6555**
Fax 252.756.5966
Web www.anewhorizon1.com
　1990 Alan Rd Ste B, Greenville, NC 27834
　Ashley Cheeseman, Clinical Director
　CARF accredited programs available.

A New Start Support Services, LLC **919.550.2629**
　935 Shotwell Road, Suite 104A, Clayton, NC 27520
　CARF accredited programs available.

A Place of Their Own, LLC **336.697.7453**
Fax 336.697.5884
　5629 Burlington Road, McLeansville, NC 27301
　CARF accredited programs available.

A Positive Life, Inc. **910.223.7300**
Fax 910.323.3206
　3108 Dyke Street, Fayetteville, NC 28306
　CARF accredited programs available.

A Special Touch, Inc. **910.602.2769**
Fax 910.285.8959
　5925 NC Highway 11, Willard, NC 28478
　CARF accredited programs available.

A Sure House, Inc. **336.773.7627**
Fax 336.773.7627
　1265 Arbor Road, Winston-Salem, NC 27104-1105
　CARF accredited programs available.

A United Community, LLC **919.878.1590**
Fax 919.878.1593
Web .... www.unitednc.com
　4921 Professional Court, Raleigh, NC 27609
　CARF accredited programs available.

A+ Absolute Care, Inc. **252.430.0112**
Fax 252.430.0113
Web .... www.aplusabsolutecare.com
　943 G West Andrews Avenue, Henderson, NC 27536
　CARF accredited programs available.

A-1 Community Support, LLC **252.433.0255**
Fax 252.430.6222
Web http://a-1communitysupport.com
　560 Dabney Drive, Suite B, Henderson, NC 27536
　CARF accredited programs available.

Abundant Health and Human Services,
Inc. **252.335.9400**
Fax 252.335.9404
Web .... www.abundanthealthservices.net
　401 South Griffin Street, Suite 175, Elizabeth City,
　NC 27909
　CARF accredited programs available.

Access Family Services and Compass Adult
Care **704.521.4977**
Fax 704.521.8541
Web .... accessfamilyservices.com
　2633 West Boulevard, Charlotte, NC 28208

ACI Support Specialists, Inc. **919.329.5671**
Fax 919.329.5669
Web .... www.acisupport.com
　1027 Highway 70 W, Suite 109, Garner,
　NC 27529-2501
　Rita Barnes, Director of Support Services
　CARF accredited programs available.

Adess Residential Services, Inc. **336.549.1580**
Fax 336.282.6911
　5402 Courtfield Drive, Greensboro, NC 27455
　CARF accredited programs available.

Adolescent Alternatives **336.370.9876**
Fax 336.292.6711
　612 Pasteur Drive, Suite 300, Greensboro, NC 27403
　CARF accredited programs available.

Adolescent Alternatives **336.451.1113**
Fax 336.292.6711
　612 Pasteur Drive, Suite 300, Greensboro, NC 27403
　CARF accredited programs available.

Advanced Placement BHHS, Inc. **336.722.1862**
Fax 336.722.1863
Web .... www.aplacement.org
　2295 East 14th Street, Suite 400, Winston-Salem,
　NC 27105
　CARF accredited programs available.

Advantage Behavioral Healthcare, Inc. **910.640.1038**
Fax 910.640.1465
　732 Davis Avenue, Whiteville, NC 28472
　CARF accredited programs available.

Agape Home Incorporated **336.884.1475**
Fax 336.884.1482
　211 West Lexington Avenue, Suite 103, High Point,
　NC 27262
　CARF accredited programs available.

Agape Services, Inc. **704.225.0584**
Fax 704.225.1479
Web .... www.agapeservicesinc.net
E-mail .... marymassey@agapeservicesinc.net
　1505 Skyway Dr, Monroe, NC 28110
　Mary Massey, Agency Director
　CARF accredited programs available.

Alberta Professional Services **336.273.2640**
Fax 336.273.6522
Web .... www.albertakids.org
　1155 Revolution Mill Drive, Studio 5, Greensboro,
　NC 27405
　CARF accredited programs available.

Alcohol and Drug Services **336.333.6860**
Fax 336.275.1187
Web .... http://www.adsyes.org
　301 East Washington Street, Suite 101, Greensboro,
　NC 27401
　CARF accredited programs available.

Alexander Children's Ctr **704.366.8712**
Fax 704.362.8464
Web .... www.alexanderyouthnetwork.org
E-mail .... cbass@alexanderyouthnetwork.org
　6220 Thermal Rd, Charlotte, NC 28211-5630
　Craig Bass, Director

Alexander Youth Network **704.366.8712**
Web .... alexanderyouthnetwork.org
E-mail .... jgreene@alexanderyouthnetwork.org
　6220 Thermal Road, Charlotte, NC 28211
　Ms. Jennifer Greene, Accreditation Manager
　Joint Commission accredited organization.

All God's Children of Burlington, LLC **336.227.9594**
　619 Lincoln Street, Burlington, NC 27217
　CARF accredited programs available.

All My Children Home, Inc. **704.435.6727**
Fax 704.435.6730
　711 East Main Street, Cherryville, NC 28021
　Jonne Miller, Director
　CARF accredited programs available.

Allied Behavioral Management, Inc. **910.640.2021**
Fax 910.640.2022
　603 Pecan Lane, Whiteville, NC 28472
　CARF accredited programs available.

Alpha Community Support Services, LLC **910.318.6757**
Fax 910.610.1030
　114 South Hancock Street, Rockingham, NC 28379
　CARF accredited programs available.

Alpha Management Services, Inc. **919.419.0043**
Fax 919.489.4372
Web .... http://www.alpha-community.org/index.htm
E-mail .... elizabeth.lamothe@amshco.com
　Two Consultant Place, Durham, NC 27707
　Elizabeth Lamothe, Executive Director
　CARF accredited programs available.

Alternative Behavioral Solution, Inc. **336.370.9400**
Fax 336.297.0103
　157 Blue Bell Road, Greensboro, NC 27406
　CARF accredited programs available.

Alternative Care Treatment Systems, Inc. **910.826.3694**
Fax 910.826.3695
Web .... www.actsinc.net
　907 Hay Street, Suite 200, Fayetteville, NC 28305
　CARF accredited programs available.

Alternative Life Programs, Inc. **919.383.0891**
Fax 919.384.0108
Web .... www.alternativelifeprograms.com
　2726 Croasdaile Drive, Suite 210, Durham,
　NC 27705
　CARF accredited programs available.

Amani Residential Human Services **252.799.0600**
Fax 252.799.0644
　312 West Boulevard, Williamston, NC 27892
　CARF accredited programs available.

Amazing Graces, Inc. **919.581.8652**
Fax 919.583.9496
　201 West Ash Street, Suite 5, Goldsboro, NC 27530
　CARF accredited programs available.

Annas Resources, P.C. **919.942.8422**
Fax 919.942.8409
Web .... www.annasresources.org
　976 Martin Luther King, Jr. Boulevard, Suite 250,
　Chapel Hill, NC 27514
　CARF accredited programs available.

Another Level Counseling & Consultation **704.548.5298**
Fax 704.548.9529
Web .... www.anotherlevelservices.com
　1927 JN Pease Place, Suite 104, Charlotte, NC 28262
　CARF accredited programs available.

Anuvia Prevention and Recovery Center,
Inc. **704.376.7447**
Fax 704.376.3384
Web .... www.anuvia.org
　100 Billingsley Road, Charlotte, NC 28211
　CARF accredited programs available.

Applied Behavioral Concepts for Families,
LLC **252.442.2000**
Fax 252.442.2507
　1828 Willow Glynn Road, Rocky Mount, NC 27712
　CARF accredited programs available.

ARP/Phoenix, Inc..........................**828.254.2700**
Fax...828.254.1524
Web..www.arpnc.org
257 Biltmore Avenue, Suite 200, Asheville, NC 28801
Tom Britton, Director
CARF accredited programs available.

Asheville Ctr For Group & Family Therapy......**828.274.5757**
Fax...828.274.4316
1270 Hendersonville Rd, Ste 8, Asheville, NC 28803
Pam White, Therapist

Aspirations and Miracles Community Support, LLC...**252.442.0012**
Fax...252.442.0013
1621 Eastern Avenue, Rocky Mount, NC 27801
CARF accredited programs available.

Aspire Youth and Family, Inc...............**828.627.1329**
Fax...828.627.1307
33 Sharon Lynne Way, Clyde, NC 28721
CARF accredited programs available.

AssistedCare Management Group, Inc.........**910.332.2346**
Web..www.assistedcare.net
E-mail..........................heather.weeks@assitedcare.net
1003 Old Waterford Way, Suite 2C, Leland, NC 28451
Ms. Heather Weeks, Accreditation Manager
Joint Commission accredited organization.

Associate Behavioral Services, Inc............**910.914.0006**
Fax...910.914.0008
Web....................http://associatebehavioralservices.webs.
18 Whiteville Mini Mall, Whiteville, NC 28472
CARF accredited programs available.

Associated Family and Life Services, LLC......**919.824.4966**
Fax...919.572.6808
3417 South Alston Avenue, Durham, NC 27707
CARF accredited programs available.

At Home Personal Care Services, Inc..........**252.321.9300**
Fax...252.321.9390
Web..www.athomepcs.org
119 Heritage Crossing, Snow Hill, NC 28580
CARF accredited programs available.

Auldern Academy...........................**919.837.2336**
Fax...919.837.5284
Web..www.auldern.com
E-mail....................auldern.admissions@threesprings.com
990 Glovers Grove Church Rd, Siler City, NC 27344-6517
James Samuels, Director Of Admissions And Business Development

B & D Behavioral Health Services............**919.753.1080**
Fax...919.753.1089
Web..www.behavioralhealth.com
249 East North Carolina Highway 54, Suite 320, Durham, NC 27713
CARF accredited programs available.

B & J's Family Services, Inc....................**704.272.7258**
Fax...704.272.7158
35 West Passaic Street, Peachland, NC 28170

Barium Springs Home for Children..........**704.872.4157**
Fax...704.838.1541
Web..www.bariumsprings.org
P.O. Box 1, Barium Springs, NC 28010
COA accredited organization.

Behavior Education and Resource Specialists, Incorporated................................**252.537.6799**
Fax...252.537.6793
Web..www.bearsinc.org
1609 East 10th Street, Roanoke Rapids, NC 27870
CARF accredited programs available.

Behavioral Enrichment Services, Inc..........**704.968.1864**
E-mail..bes.inc@hotmail.com
10130 Mallard Creek Rd Ste 306, Charlotte, NC 28262
Mrs. Lashea Headen, Accreditation Manager
Joint Commission accredited organization.

Behavioral Health and Wellness Care Services, Inc........................................**336.292.4604**
Fax...336.292.4604
Web..bhwcareservices.org
3721 West Market Street, Suite C, Greensboro, NC 27403
CARF accredited programs available.

Behavioral Health Care Of Cape Fear Valley Health Systems.................................**910.609.3600**
Fax...910.615.3798
Web....................................www.capefearvalley.com
E-mail..............................jflom@capefearvalley.com
3425 Melrose Rd, Fayetteville, NC 28304-1608
Dr. Jonathan Flom, Medical Director

Bertha's Place, Inc...........................**980.721.9416**
Fax...704.843.5889
3412 Green Meadow Drive, Charlotte, NC 28269
CARF accredited programs available.

Bethesda Care dba Keston Care.............**919.967.0507**
Web..kestoncare.com
E-mail..rokess@aol.com
11312 US 15/501 N, Chatham Crossing, Ste. 400, Chapel Hill, NC 27517
Ms. Roxanne Kessler, Accreditation Manager
Joint Commission accredited organization.

Beyond Expectations Comprehensive Services, Inc........................................**336.896.2046**
Fax...336.896.2047
8025 North Point Boulevard, Suite 230, Winston-Salem, NC 27106
CARF accredited programs available.

Blessed Alms...............................**336.997.0971**
E-mail................................blessedalmsinc@bellsouth.net
4321 Rehoeeth Church Rd., Greensboro, NC 27406
Mr. Bobby Cunningham, Accreditation Manager
Joint Commission accredited organization.

Body Whole Health and Counseling, Inc.......**252.293.9966**
Fax...252.293.9967
Web.................www.bodywholehealthcounseling.com
103 Brentwood Center Lane, Wilson, NC 27896
CARF accredited programs available.

Braasch Medical Practice....................**919.782.4980**
E-mail..erb@nctherapy.com
3726 Camley Ave, Raleigh, NC 27612-4320
Ernest Braasch, MD, Psychiatrist

BranMarc, Inc. Family Services..............**704.867.7117**
Fax...704.867.7794
Web........................www.branmarc.com/welcome.htm
621 Huntsman Court, Gastonia, NC 28054
CARF accredited programs available.

Bridgebuilders Family and Youth Svcs, Inc........................................**704.537.5760**
Fax...704.537.5761
5500 Executive Center Dr, Ste 103, Charlotte, NC 28212
Jennifer Clark, Director of Human Resources
CARF accredited programs available.

Bridges of Hope, Inc.........................**252.321.1621**
Fax...252.321.6002
Web..................................www.bridgesofhopeinc.com
214 East Arlington Boulevard, Suite A, Greenville, NC 27858
CARF accredited programs available.

Bridging to Success, Inc......................**704.637.7562**
Fax...704.596.4191
223 West 12th Street, Salisbury, NC 28215-5359
CARF accredited programs available.

BriteSmilz Family and Community Connections, LLC.......................................**252.537.7575**
Fax...252.537.9008
1165 Gregory Drive, Roanoke Rapids, NC 27870
CARF accredited programs available.

Britton and Crump, Inc......................**919.286.2100**
Fax...919.286.2107
Web......................................www.brittonandcrump.com
1007 Broad Street, Durham, NC 27705
CARF accredited programs available.

Brown Medical Practice.....................**336.538.2505**
1236 Huffman Mill Rd, Burlington, NC 27215-8700
Alycia Brown, Psychiatrist

Brynn Marr Hospital........................**910.577.1400**
Web..www.brynnmarr.org
E-mail................................cynthia.waun@uhsinc.com
192 Village Drive, Jacksonville, NC 28546
Ms. Cynthia Waun, Accreditation Manager
Joint Commission accredited organization.

Brynn Marr Hospital........................**910.577.1400**
Fax...910.577.7365
Web..www.brynnmarr.org
E-mail....................aanderson@premierbehavioral.com
192 Village Dr, Jacksonville, NC 28546-7299
Arnold C. Anderson, Director Of Residential Services

Building Futures............................**919.556.0534**
100 Holden Road, Suite F, Youngsville, NC 27596
CARF accredited programs available.

Burston's Consulting and Counseling Services, LLC.......................................**336.613.5515**
Fax...336.634.0449
1117 South Main Street, Reidsville, NC 27320
CARF accredited programs available.

Cambridge Behavioral Health Services, PLLC.......................................**252.353.4250**
Fax...252.353.4228
Web..................................www.cambridgebehavioral.com
E-mail.............fayebordeaux@cambridgebehavioral.com
622 South Memorial Drive, Greenville, NC 27834
Faye Bordeaux, Clinical Director
CARF accredited programs available.

Cardinal Therapeutic Home Services.........**910.867.8889**
Fax...910.487.3061
1540 Purdue Dr, Ste 200, Fayetteville, NC 28303
Ray Strong
CARF accredited programs available.

Carelink Solutions, Inc......................**336.327.2088**
E-mail........................monica_stimpson@yahoo.com
402 S. Cox Street, Asheboro, NC 27203
Ms. Monica Stimpson, Accreditation Manager
Joint Commission accredited organization.

Caring Arms Youth and Family Services, Inc........................................**704.510.1600**
Fax...704.510.9222
Web..www.caringarmsyfs.com
520 Collins Aikman Drive, Suite 206, Charlotte, NC 28262
CARF accredited programs available.

Caring Arms, Inc............................**919.884.1300**
Fax...919.294.4125
Web..www.Caringarmsinc.com
115 Market Street, Suite 204-B, Durham, NC 27701
CARF accredited programs available.

Caring Hands and Supplementary Enrichment Education, LLC..............................**919.479.6806**
Web..www.careingh.com
E-mail..............................tamikkahinton@yahoo.com
3209 Guess Road, Durham, NC 27705
Ms. Tamikka Hinton, Accreditation Manager
Joint Commission accredited organization.

Caring Touch Home Health Care, LLC.........910.521.9175
Web..................www.caringtouchhomehealthcare.com
E-mail...........................jmclambmpa@intrstar.net
799 James Lynn Drive, Pembroke, NC 28372
Mrs. Jennifer McLamb, Accreditation Manager
Joint Commission accredited organization.

Carmel Counseling Ctr.......................704.849.0686
Fax..704.815.1972
1145 Pineville Matthews Rd, Matthews, NC 28105
David Dixon, Director

Carobell......................................910.326.7600
Fax..910.326.9988
Web...www.carobell.org
E-mail..............................carobell@carobell.com
198 Cinnamon Dr, Hubert, NC 28539-4441
Vanessa Ervin, Emra, President

**Carolina Center for Counseling and Clinical Services,
Inc.**...704.861.2234
Fax..704.861.2235
Web.......................................www.carolinacenter.org
227 Wilmot Drive, Gastonia, NC 28054-4048
COA accredited organization.

Carolina Community Services, Inc.............704.853.8817
Fax..704.853.8920
201 West Second Street, Suite E, Gastonia, NC 28052
CARF accredited programs available.

Carolina Comprehensive Services, LLC.......919.847.0550
Web.......................................Carolinacomprehensive.com
E-mail...........................ron@carolinacomprehensive.com
312 West Millbrook Rd Suite 137, Raleigh, NC 27609
Mr. Ron Kilgore, Accreditation Manager
Joint Commission accredited organization.

Carolina Counseling Ctr......................704.542.2226
Fax..704.542.3298
1106 Weeping Willow Ln, Matthews,
NC 28105-2824
Wayne Robertson, MD, Psychiatrist

Carolina Outreach, LLC.......................919.933.1560
Fax..919.933.1854
Web.......................................www.carolinaoutreach.com
E-mail...........................timbrooks@carolinaoutreach.com
2670 Durham - Chapel Hill Boulevard, Durham,
NC 27707-2829
Tim Brooks, Co-Director
CARF accredited programs available.

**Carolina Professional Mental Health Associates,
Inc.**...910.739.1876
Fax..910.739.1893
Web...www.cpmha.com
109 North Court Square, Lumberton, NC 28358
CARF accredited programs available.

Carolina Solution Incorporated..............704.201.4472
128 West Elwood Avenue, Raeford, NC 28376
CARF accredited programs available.

Carolina Staffing and Homehealth...........252.237.7898
Fax..919.881.0278
2305 Wellington Drive Southwest, Suite A, Wilson,
NC 27893
CARF accredited programs available.

Carolinas Home Care Agency, Inc.............910.642.3700
Fax..910.642.5146
603 South Canal Street, Whiteville, NC 28472
CARF accredited programs available.

Carolinas Medical Center.....................704.355.7359
Web.......................................www.carolinashealthcare.org
E-mail...........................stephen.avant@carolinashealthcare.org
1000 Blythe Boulevard, Charlotte, NC 28232
Mr. Stephen Avant, Accreditation Manager
Joint Commission accredited organization.

Carring Arms, Inc.............................252.747.7615
Fax..252.747.7615
Web...www.cartes.freeuk.com
920 Highway 903 South, Snow Hill, NC 28580
CARF accredited programs available.

Carter Behavior Health Services.............252.353.5577
Fax..252.353.8577
1708 East Arlington Boulevard, Greenville, NC 27858
CARF accredited programs available.

Carter's Circle of Care, Inc..................336.271.5817
E-mail...........................ronjay1978@yahoo.com
2031 Martin Luther King Jr. Dr, Ste, E,D,, Greensboro,
NC 27406
Mr. Ronald Carter, Accreditation Manager
Joint Commission accredited organization.

Carteret Counseling Services, Inc............252.247.1109
Fax..252.247.1107
3820 B Bridges Street, Morehead City, NC 28577
CARF accredited programs available.

Case Management Care, Inc...................336.292.5478
Fax..336.617.5948
Web.....................http://www.casemanagementcare.net
612 Pastuer Drive, Suite 203, Greensboro, NC 27403
CARF accredited programs available.

Catawba Valley Behavioral Healthcare.......828.695.5900
Fax..628.695.4256
Web...www.cvbh.org
3050 11th Avenue Drive SE, Hickory, NC 28602

CC & A Family Services, Inc. #2..............336.854.9553
Fax..336.464.2188
1005 Benjamin Parkway, Greensboro, NC 27408
CARF accredited programs available.

CCDP, Inc.....................................252.638.9046
Fax..252.638.9026
E-mail...........................ccdp4@earthlink.net
1900 C Brittany Place, New Bern, NC 28560
Donne Davis, Executive Director
CARF accredited programs available.

Center for Behavioral Health Care, PA.......919.776.0303
Fax..919.776.0377
Web.....................www.centerforbehavioralhealth.com
E-mail
.........vicki.stephenson@centerforbehavioralhealth.com
138 South Streele Street, Second Floor, Sanford,
NC 27330-4201
Vicki. Stephenson, Program Director
CARF accredited programs available.

Center for Youth Development, LLC..........919.598.1515
Fax..919.598.9725
2515 NC Highway 55, Suite A, Durham, NC 27713
CARF accredited programs available.

Central Care Division, LLC....................336.635.2000
Fax..336.635.2003
405 North Bridge Street, Eden, NC 27288-5647

Central Community Services, LLC.............252.430.6633
Fax..919.693.4930
848 Dabney Drive, Henderson, NC 27536
CARF accredited programs available.

Centre for New Hope II, LLC..................919.945.0580
Fax..919.945.0585
Web.....................www.centrefornewhope.com
101 East Weaver Street, Suite G4, Carrboro,
NC 27510
CARF accredited programs available.

**Changing Hearts Instead of Losing Lives,
Inc.**...252.791.0909
Fax..252.791.0902
713 Forest Road, Plymouth, NC 27962
CARF accredited programs available.

Chaparral Youth Services.....................910.827.1169
Fax..910.521.7286
56 Three Hunts Drive, Pembroke, NC 28372
CARF accredited programs available.

Child Medical Evaluation Program...........919.843.9365
Fax..919.843.9368
Web.......................................www.med.unc.edu/cmet
C B 3415, Chapel Hill, NC 27599-0001
Molly Berkoff, Md, Associate Medical Director

**Children Under Construction Treatment Center Barnes,
Inc.**...910.551.5481
Fax..919.934.8611
42 Jewel Lane, Four Oaks, NC 27524
CARF accredited programs available.

Children's Advocacy Network, LLC...........704.833.0154
Fax..704.833.7076
Web...www.canllc.org
E-mail...........................childadvnet@bellsouth.net
1552 Union Road, Suite E, Gastonia, NC 28054
Linda Corbett, Co-Owner
CARF accredited programs available.

Children's Developmental Services..........828.251.6091
Fax..828.251.6911
E-mail...........................maggie.panther@dhhs.nc.gov
852 Merrimon Ave, Asheville, NC 28804
Maggie Panther, Director

Children's Homes.............................704.871.2289
Web.......................................www.chomesofiredell.net
PO Box 451, Statesville, NC 28687
COA accredited organization.

Clinical Psychology Associates...............919.469.9888
2000 Regency Pkwy Ste 204, Cary, NC 27518-8507
Lawrence Greenburg, Psychiatrist

Clinical Psychology Svcs......................919.929.7527
Web.......................................www.nataliesadlermd.com
E-mail...........................nsadler@mindspring.com
200 N Greensboro St, Carrboro, NC 27510-1804
Natalie Sadler, Psychiatrist

CNC Access, Inc. dba ResCare HomeCare.......828.466.6023
Fax..828.433.6025
Web...www.cncaccess.com
301 10th Street NW, Suite F-106, Conover,
NC 28613
CARF accredited programs available.

CNC/Access...................................828.433.8181
Fax..828.433.9406
Web...www.cncaccess.com
617 South Green Street, Morganton, NC 28655

Coastal Horizons Center, Inc..................910.790.0187
Fax..910.790.0189
Web.......................................www.coastalhorizons.org
615 Shipyard Boulevard, Wilmington, NC 28412
CARF accredited programs available.

Coastal Horizons Center, Inc..................910.343.0145
Fax..910.341.5779
Web.......................................www.coastalhorizons.org
615 Shipyard Boulevard, Wilmington, NC 28412
Sarah Boyce, Asst CEO
CARF accredited programs available.

Coastal Residential Services, Inc.............910.938.9550
Fax..910.938.5912
Web.....................www.coastalresidentialservicesinc.com
120 Henderson Drive, Jacksonville, NC 28540
CARF accredited programs available.

Coastal Southeastern United Care...........910.796.3350
209 Market Street, Suite B, Wilmington, NC 28401
CARF accredited programs available.

Coastal Therapeutic Services.................252.945.9600
Fax..252.948.0702
3005A South Memorial Drive, Greenville, NC 27834
CARF accredited programs available.

Coastal Therapeutic Services 252.948.0701
Fax 252.948.0702
   212 Stewart Parkway, Washington, NC 27889
   CARF accredited programs available.

Coleman Medical Practice 910.254.2022
   313 Walnut St, Wilmington, NC 28401
   Elisabeth Coleman, Md, Psychiatrist

Collaborative Hope, LLC 980.253.0830
Fax 704.295.1109
   1011 Palmer Plaza Lane, Charlotte, NC 28211-1185
   CARF accredited programs available.

Colvard Medical Practice 919.781.3141
E-mail ....david@divepsych.com
   3725 National Dr Ste 228, Raleigh, NC 27612-4879
   David Colvard, Psychiatrist

**Community Based Learning Alternatives Center Services,
Inc.** 919.989.1786
Fax 919.989.1791
   1300 West Market Street, Smithfield, NC 27577
   CARF accredited programs available.

Community Care Services, LLC 704.330.8787
Fax 704.332.8788
   1801 North Tryon Street, Suite 321, Charlotte,
   NC 28206
   CARF accredited programs available.

Community Connections Healthcare Svcs 919.783.8080
Fax 919.783.8040
Web ....www.cchs-nc.com
E-mail ....alesha@cchs-nc.com
   343 E Six Forks Rd, Ste 190, Raleigh, NC 27609
   Alesha McCoy, Manager
   CARF accredited programs available.

Community Connections, Inc. 336.882.6549
Fax 336.882.6549
   808 West English Road, High Point, NC 27262
   CARF accredited programs available.

Community Enrichment Services, LLC 919.848.4013
Fax 919.341.5135
Web ....communityenrichmentnc.com
   174 Mine Lake Court, Suite 100, Raleigh, NC 27615
   CARF accredited programs available.

Community Health Council, Inc 910.567.6194
Web ....www.commwellhealth.org
E-mail ....ksmith@commwellhealth.org
   3331 Easy Street, Dunn, NC 28334
   Ms. Karen Smith, Accreditation Manager
   Joint Commission accredited organization.

Community Innovations, Inc. 910.642.5697
Fax 910.642.8039
Web ....www.communityinnovations.com
   3210 Fairhill Drive, Raleigh, NC 27612
   CARF accredited programs available.

**Community Outreach for Youth and Family Services,
Inc.** 919.321.2387
Fax 800.873.6013
Web ....communityoutreachservices.com
   5318 Highgate Drive, Suite 231, Durham, NC 27713
   CARF accredited programs available.

Community Resource Solutions, LLC 704.868.4132
Fax 919.528.5746
Web ....www.communityresourcesolutions.net
   813-A South Oakland Street, Gastonia, NC 28054
   CARF accredited programs available.

Community Specialized Services, Inc. 704.795.7600
Fax 704.795.7601
Web ....www.communityspecializedservices.org
   15 Spencer Avenue NW, Concord, NC 28025
   CARF accredited programs available.

Community Support Svcs Para-Professi 989.631.6691
Web ....cscsm.org
   122 N Elm St, Greensboro, NC 27401
   Connie Grove, Office Manager

Community Treatment Alternatives, Inc. 704.323.9266
   5410 Frederick Street, Indian Trail, NC 28079
   CARF accredited programs available.

**Community-Based Developmental
Services** 910.488.5820
Fax 910.488.5837
   3274 Rosehill Road, Suite 2, Fayetteville, NC 28301
   CARF accredited programs available.

Companion Home Care 910.608.3511
Fax 910.608.3530
   3317 North Carolina Highway 211 West, Lumberton,
   NC 28358
   CARF accredited programs available.

Comprehensive Behavior Health Services 252.824.1188
Fax 252.824.1189
   2109 A Saint Andrews Street, Colonial Plaza, Tarboro,
   NC 27886
   CARF accredited programs available.

Comprehensive Community Care, Inc. 919.402.0323
Fax 919.402.9435
Web ....www.compcarenc.com
   3308 Durham Chapel Hill Boulevard, Suite 160,
   Durham, NC 27707
   CARF accredited programs available.

Comprehensive Interventions, Inc. 252.792.8035
Fax 252.792.8045
Web ....www.comprehensiveinterventions.com
   607 Washington St, Williamston, NC 27892
   Besiree Rodgers, CEO
   CARF accredited programs available.

ComServ, Inc. 828.757.0209
Fax 828.757.0309
Web ....www.comserve.org
   619 Pennton Avenue, Lenoir, NC 28645
   CARF accredited programs available.

Concern of Durham, Inc. 919.489.5652
Fax 919.490.6288
Web ....www.concernofdurham.org
   3001 Academy Drive, Suite 230, Durham, NC 27707
   Gail Yashar, Director
   CARF accredited programs available.

Concordia Support Services, LLC 910.826.8253
Fax 910.826.8254
Web ....www.concordiasptsvc.com
   2315 Bloom Avenue, Suite 2, Fayetteville, NC 28304
   CARF accredited programs available.

Connections BWB Incorporated 704.596.5553
Web ....connectionsbwb.com
E-mail ....shari.wright@connectionsbwb.com
   8430 University Executive Park Drive Suite 655,
   Charlotte, NC 28262
   Mrs. Shari Wright-Harley, Accreditation Manager
   Joint Commission accredited organization.

Consumer Solutions, LLC 919.518.4004
Fax 919.359.1171
   7106 Cornwallis Road, Garner, NC 27529
   CARF accredited programs available.

Continuum Care Services, Inc. 704.784.0753
Web ....www.continuumcareservices.com
E-mail ....ebonique2000@yahoo.com
   284 Executive Park Drive Suite 150, Concord,
   NC 28025
   Ms. Ebonique Morman, Accreditation Manager
   Joint Commission accredited organization.

Cooper Medical Practice 919.846.0444
   6512 Six Forks Rd Ste 505, Raleigh, NC 27615-6527
   Claire Cooper, Psychiatrist

Coordinated Health Services 919.465.0910
Fax 919.465.0918
Web ....http://coordinatedhealthservicesinc.com
   1224 Copeland Oaks Drive, Morrisville, NC 27560
   CARF accredited programs available.

Corine's Care Management, Inc. 252.747.5705
Fax 252.747.5705
Web ....www.corinescare.org
   369 B Highway 13 South, Snow Hill, NC 28580
   CARF accredited programs available.

Cornerstone 919.508.0777
Fax 919.508.0725
Web ....www.co.wake.nc.us
E-mail ....pcraft@co.wake.nc.us
   220 Snow Ave, Raleigh, NC 27603
   Michael Yonk, Program Director

**Cornerstone Treatment Facility Program,
Inc.** 919.522.0315
   703B West 3rd Avenue, Red Springs, NC 28377
   CARF accredited programs available.

Cornerstone Treatment Facility, Inc. 704.695.0601
Fax 704.695.0607
Web ....www.ncprtf.com
   129 Wallace Road, Wadesboro, NC 28170
   CARF accredited programs available.

Corpus Christi Services, Inc. 910.735.2988
Fax 910.735.2987
   210 East Second Street, Suite 105, Lumberton,
   NC 28358-5620
   CARF accredited programs available.

Counseling Ctr Of Greensboro 336.274.2100
Fax 336.274.6366
   101 S Elm St Ste 325, Greensboro, NC 27401
   Sherel Lawson, Director

Counseling Group 828.322.8736
Fax 828.322.7890
E-mail ....suzanne_trollan@thecounselinggroup.com
   106 3rd Ave NE, Hickory, NC 28601
   Suzanne Trollan, Co-owner

Covenant Community Partners 919.401.8000
Fax 919.401.8005
   1803 Chapel Hill Road, Durham, NC 27707
   CARF accredited programs available.

CRE Care Management 704.864.2927
Fax 704.864.2947
   1541 Delta Drive, Gastonia, NC 28052

**Creative Learning Centers Community Support
Services** 336.286.9016
Fax 336.286.9016
   2820 Lawndale Drive, Suite 210, Greensboro,
   NC 27408
   CARF accredited programs available.

**Creative Solutions Child & Family Counseling,
LLC** 910.371.9030
Fax 910.371.9060
Web ....www.creativesolutionsla.com
   324 Village Road, Suite I, Leland, NC 28451
   CARF accredited programs available.

Ctrview Psychiatric Associates 919.859.1014
   5540 Centerview Dr, Ste 423, Raleigh, NC 27606
   Ian Lev, Md, Psychiatrist

D-POM, LLC 252.824.1255
Fax 252.824.1120
Web ....www.dpom.org
   316 Russell Drive, Princeville, NC 27886
   CARF accredited programs available.

Danek Medical Practice 919.968.9855
E-mail ....info@bizadvertizing.com
   109 Conner Dr, Chapel Hill, NC 27514
   Julia Danek, Psychiatrist

Day Treatment Programs 336.634.3209
Fax 336.634.3260
Web www.rock.k12.nc.us
   401 Moss Street, Reidsville, NC 27320
   CARF accredited programs available.

Day Treatment, LLC **252.367.6733**
　605 East Ash Street, Goldsboro, NC 27530
　CARF accredited programs available.

DAYMARK Recovery Services, Inc. **704.939.1100**
　Fax 704.939.1120
　Web ....www.daymarkrecovery.org
　E-mail ....bwest@daymarkrecovery.org
　284 Executive Park Dr, Ste 100, Concord, NC 28025
　Billy West, Director
　CARF accredited programs available.

Daymark Recovery Svcs **704.633.3616**
　Fax 704.633.5902
　E-mail ....rwerstlein@daymarkrecovery.org
　2129 Statesville Blvd, Salisbury, NC 28147
　Bob Werstlein, Phd, Director

Deliverance Outreach dba Restored Hope **828.277.1706**
　Fax 828.505.2116
　41 Imperial Court, Asheville, NC 28803
　CARF accredited programs available.

Denker Medical Practice **919.678.1011**
　E-mail ....drdenker@nc.rr.com
　1020 Southhill Dr Ste 320, Cary, NC 27513-8629
　Michelle Denker, Psychiatrist

Department of Social Services/Family NET **828.695.6500**
　Fax 828.695.4729
　Web ....www.familynetofcatawba.org
　1985 Tate Boulevard SE, Suite 300, Hickory, NC 28602
　CARF accredited programs available.

DirecCare Behavioral Services, Inc. **910.738.1818**
　Fax 910.738.1817
　506 East 22nd Street, Lumberton, NC 28358
　CARF accredited programs available.

DirectCare Community Base Services, LLC **828.286.4466**
　Fax 828.286.4450
　132 West Main Street, Forest City, NC 28043
　CARF accredited programs available.

Dispute Settlement Ctr **828.697.7055**
　Fax 828.697.8528
　Web ....www.dschc.org
　E-mail ....disputesettlement@att.net
　101 S Grove St, Hendersonville, NC 28792
　Jane Wilson, Director

Diverse Family Services **919.225.9338**
　Fax 919.572.0044
　2402 South Miami Boulevard, Suite 108, Durham, NC 27703

Dixon Social Interactive Services, Inc. **252.353.0100**
　Fax 252.353.0600
　113 A West Fire Tower Road, Winterville, NC 28590
　CARF accredited programs available.

Dorothea Dix Hospital Child Psychiatry Outpatient Clinic **919.733.5344**
　Fax 919.733.9441
　2108 Umstead Dr, Raleigh, NC 27603
　Karen Poulos, Md, Co-Director

Down Home Intervention Services, Inc. **252.414.5361**
　Fax 252.792.7593
　Web ....www.downhomeinterventionservices.com
　239 Green Street, Williamston, NC 27892
　CARF accredited programs available.

Dream Makers Assisted Living Services, LLC **336.793.1508**
　Fax 336.793.2045
　1001 South Marshall Street, Box 69, Suite 227, Winston-Salem, NC 27101
　CARF accredited programs available.

DREAM Provider Care Services **252.946.0585**
　Fax 252.946.0580
　216 Stewart Parkway, Washington, NC 27889
　CARF accredited programs available.

Dreams and Vision, LLC **704.566.9734**
　5004 Glenview Court, Charlotte, NC 28215
　CARF accredited programs available.

E B Frink Middle School **252.566.2001**
　Web www.lenoir.k12.nc.us
　E-mail ....mmcclung@lenoir.k12.nc.us
　102 Martin Luther King Jr Dr, La Grange, NC 28551-1499
　Melissa Mcclung, Director

Eastern Carolina Case Management, LLC **252.353.1114**
　Fax 252.353.1119
　Web ....www.easterncarolinacm.com
　154 Beacon Dr Ste I, Winterville, NC 28590
　Jaime Marcum, Regional Manager
　CARF accredited programs available.

Eastern Psychiatric Associate **910.815.0260**
　E-mail ....epa@bentsenmd.com
　3807 Peachtree Ave, Ste 101, Wilmington, NC 28403-5729
　B Steven Bentsen, Md, Psychiatrist

Echelon Consulting, Inc. dba Echelon Care **704.594.9143**
　Fax 704.594.9915
　520 Collins Aikman Drive, Suite 200, Charlotte, NC 28269
　CARF accredited programs available.

Eckerd **800.914.3937**
　Fax 727.442.5911
　Web ....www.eckerd.org
　E-mail ....admissions@eckerd.org
　500 E-Ku-Sumee Dr, Candor, NC 27229
　David Dennis, President & CEO; Francene Hazel, Director of Admissions
　Eckerd provides fully licensed and accredited, short-term juvenile justice residential services for troubled and at-risk boys and girls throughout the state of North Carolina, as well as family preservation and reunification services in Anson, Hoke, Johnston, Cumberland, Harnett, Lee, Montgomery, Moore, Richmond and Scotland counties. Teen parenting education services are provided in Vance County. Fully licensed and accredited. Youth are primarily referred through contracts with public agencies.

Eder Medical Practice **919.546.8885**
　Fax 614.444.7924
　E-mail ....seder@nc.rr.com
　4020 Westchase Blvd, Raleigh, NC 27607
　Susan Eder, Psychiatrist

ELDO, Inc. **910.762.3120**
　Fax 910.762.3115
　E-mail ....eldoinc@hotmail.com
　1805 Castle Street, Wilmington, NC 28403
　Yolanda Randolph, Director
　CARF accredited programs available.

Elegant Ladies of the Future, Inc. **252.237.3147**
　3720 Martha Lane, Wilson, NC 27896
　CARF accredited programs available.

Eliada Homes, Inc. **828.254.5356**
　Web ....www.eliada.org
　P.O. Box 16708, Asheville, NC 28816
　COA accredited organization.

Elite Care, Inc. **252.814.6957**
　132 West Main Street, Williamston, NC 27892

Elite Community Health, LLC **704.864.9668**
　Fax 704.864.1788
　Web ....www.elitecommunityhealth.com
　2409 East Ozark Avenue, Gastonia, NC 28054-1421
　CARF accredited programs available.

Elohim Counseling and Resource Center, Inc. dba The River House **252.756.0450**
　Fax 252.353.9076
　4051 South Memorial Drive, Suite D, Greenville, NC 27834
　CARF accredited programs available.

Elon Homes and Schools for Children **336.584.0091**
　Fax 336.584.4026
　Web ....www.elonhomes.org
　201 South O'Kelly Avenue, Elon, NC 27244
　COA accredited organization.

Embrace Us, Inc. **336.510.4969**
　Fax 336.547.3968
　307 South Swing Road, Greensboro, NC 27409
　CARF accredited programs available.

Emmanuel Residential Facility **252.355.4131**
　Fax 252.355.4337
　208 Country Club Drive, Greenville, NC 27834
　CARF accredited programs available.

Empowerment Quality Care Services, LLC **704.790.3340**
　5736 North Tryon Street, Suite 130, Charlotte, NC 28213
　CARF accredited programs available.

ENC Behavioral Health Care **252.439.2275**
　Fax 252.439.2353
　2080 A Park Place, West Arlington Boulevard, Greenville, NC 27834
　CARF accredited programs available.

Enterpro STC Services dba Carolina Care Health Services **704.379.1850**
　E-mail ....wgibson@enterprostc.com
　1100 South Mint St., Charlotte, NC 28203
　Ms. Wendy Gibson, Accreditation Manager
　Joint Commission accredited organization.

Envisions of Life, LLC **336.887.0708**
　Fax 336.887.1085
　Web ....www.envisionsoflife.com
　204 Kelly Place, High Point, NC 27262
　COA accredited organization.

Essence of Care **336.272.3095**
　Fax 800.658.1059
　1400 Battleground Avenue, Suite 134 A, Greensboro, NC 27408
　CARF accredited programs available.

Esteem Family Life Center **910.997.4926**
　Fax 910.997.4927
　1219 Rockingham Road, Suite 10, Rockingham, NC 28379
　CARF accredited programs available.

Ethel's Footprints **336.226.4103**
　Fax 336.226.5547
　219 Albany Street, Burlington, NC 27215
　CARF accredited programs available.

Evergreen Behavioral Management, Inc. **910.641.0600**
　Fax 910.641.0606
　Web ....www.evergreenbehavioral.com
　1409 Pinckney Street, Whiteville, NC 28472
　CARF accredited programs available.

Excel Therapeutic Services, Inc. **252.940.0799**
　Fax 252.940.0949
　156 West 15th Street, Washington, NC 27889
　CARF accredited programs available.

North Carolina

Extended Reach Day Treatment 910.484.0095
Web .... www.extendedreach.org
E-mail .... extended_reach08@yahoo.com
2716 Custer Avenue, Fayetteville, NC 28312
Ms. Andrea Hall, Accreditation Manager
Joint Commission accredited organization.

FACT Specialized Services 910.346.3744
Fax 910.346.5344
127 Center Street, Jacksonville, NC 28546
CARF accredited programs available.

Faith Counseling and Clinical Consultation Services, PLLC 252.482.1770
Fax 252.482.1773
103 East King Street, Edenton, NC 27932
CARF accredited programs available.

Faith in Families, Inc. 336.653.9584
232 Gilmer Street, Suite 206, Reidsville, NC 27320
CARF accredited programs available.

Faith Works Community Services, Inc. 252.799.3000
Fax 252.792.8104
223 Washington Street, Williamston, NC 27834
CARF accredited programs available.

Falcon Crest Residential Care, Inc. 336.226.2575
Fax 336.226.2474
108 South Maple Street, Graham, NC 27253
CARF accredited programs available.

Families Together, Inc. 828.258.0031
Fax 828.258.0038
Web .... www.familiestogether.net
E-mail .... jlatek@familiestogether.net
68 Grove Street, Asheville, NC 28801
Jackie Latek, Regional Director
CARF accredited programs available.

Family & Youth Services, Inc. 919.680.2345
Fax 919.680.8685
102 East Main Street, Durham, NC 27701
CARF accredited programs available.

Family Advantage, LLC 252.536.0600
Fax 252.536.0600
3104 Highway 301 North, Garysburg, NC 27831
CARF accredited programs available.

Family Alternatives, Inc. 910.739.6624
Fax 910.739.6781
Web .... www.familyalternatives.com
103 North Elm Street, Lumberton, NC 28358-6541
CARF accredited programs available.

Family and Community Resources 252.753.5100
Fax 252.753.5121
3707 N Main St, Suite H, Farmville, NC 27828
Kim Anderson, Director
CARF accredited programs available.

Family Connections, LLC 919.572.5305
Fax 919.321.0683
Web .... http://www.familyconn.com
2310 South Miami Boulevard, Suite 239, Durham, NC 27703
CARF accredited programs available.

Family Connexions 919.718.1355
Fax 919.718.1366
Web .... www.familyconnexions.com
329 Carthage Street, Sanford, NC 27330
CARF accredited programs available.

Family First Community Services LLC 704.364.3989
Fax 704.364.3974
Web .... www.familyfirstcommunity.com
3705 Latrobe Drive, Suite 340, Charlotte, NC 28211
CARF accredited programs available.

Family First Support Center Inc 919.635.3344
Fax 919.635.3388
Web www.familyfirst1.com
E-mail .... info@familyfirst1.com
110 SW Center St, Mount Olive, NC 28365
Howard Calhoun, Administrative Director
CARF accredited programs available.

Family First Support Center, Inc. 919.271.2668
Fax 919.635.3344
110 Southwest Center Street, Mount Olive, NC 28365
CARF accredited programs available.

Family First, Inc. 704.825.0020
Fax 704.825.0021
Web .... www.familyfirstnc.org
32 North Main Street, Belmont, NC 28012
CARF accredited programs available.

Family Homecare Services, LLC 704.272.7034
Fax 704.272.8391
219 North Main Street, Troy, NC 27371
CARF accredited programs available.

Family Intensive Homecare 252.747.2190
Fax 252.747.2498
107 Southeast Second Street, Snow Hill, NC 28580
CARF accredited programs available.

Family Intervention & Prevention Services 919.340.1626
Fax 919.340.1627
Web www.fips4hope.com
211 Court Street, Louisburg, NC 27549
CARF accredited programs available.

Family Legacy Mental Health Services, Inc. 919.834.2000
Fax 919.834.2001
Web .... www.familylegacyinc.com
204 North Person Street, Raleigh, NC 27610
CARF accredited programs available.

Family Legacy Mental Health Services, Inc. 919.667.4263
Fax 919.844.6491
Web .... www.familylegacyinc.com
6612 Six Forks Road, Suite 204, Raleigh, NC 27615
CARF accredited programs available.

Family Mental Health P.A. 828.349.6185
Fax 828.349.6112
486 West Palmer Street, Franklin, NC 28744
CARF accredited programs available.

Family Pillars, Inc. 828.572.1846
Fax 828.572.1846
230 Morganton Boulevard, Suite A, Lenoir, NC 28645
CARF accredited programs available.

Family Quality Care Services, Inc. 919.237.2225
Fax 919.237.2226
1812 Liberty Street, Durham, NC 27703
CARF accredited programs available.

Favor Youth Services, Inc. 704.866.9177
Fax 704.866.9176
1568 Union Road, Suite A, Gastonia, NC 28054
CARF accredited programs available.

FFC Institute for Change, Inc. 910.642.6915
Fax 910.642.3960
333 Jefferson Street, Whiteville, NC 28472
CARF accredited programs available.

Fidelity First Health Care Services, LLC 910.343.1003
Fax 910.343.1007
3825 Market Street, Suite 6, Wilmington, NC 28403-1426
CARF accredited programs available.

Finding Your Way Homes, Inc. 704.851.9033
Fax 704.851.3207
Web .... www.findingyourwayhomes.com
280 Sandy Ridge Church Road, Morven, NC 28119
CARF accredited programs available.

First Genesis Corporation 336.292.1555
201 Muirs Chapel Road, Greensboro, NC 27410
CARF accredited programs available.

First Genesis Group Home Inc 336.274.4447
E-mail .... bisbeeplace1903@yahoo.com
1903 Delmar Drive, Greensboro, NC 27406
Mr. Jeff Carrington, Accreditation Manager
Joint Commission accredited organization.

Florence Crittenton Svcs 704.372.4663
Fax 704.334.8169
Web .... www.fcsnc.org
E-mail .... mthompson@fcsnc.org
1300 Blythe Blvd, Charlotte, NC 28203-5872
Marilyn Thompson, President And CEO

FOCUS Behavioral Health Services, LLC 828.433.4567
Fax 828.439.8191
Web .... www.focusbhsllc.com
110 South Sterling Street, Morganton, NC 28655
CARF accredited programs available.

Focus Point, Inc. 704.363.1309
Fax 704.782.9299
102 North Yates Street, Gastonia, NC 28052
CARF accredited programs available.

Fonseca Family Services 919.683.1500
Fax 919.683.1004
Web .... www.fonsecafamilyservices.org
1111 Fayetteville Street, Durham, NC 27701-3918
CARF accredited programs available.

Forever Young Group Care, LLC 910.864.9148
Fax 910.864.8548
6541 Raeford Road, Fayetteville, NC 28304
CARF accredited programs available.

Foundations Strong, LLC 336.508.2847
Fax 336.307.3906
1677 Banbridge Road, Kernersville, NC 27284
CARF accredited programs available.

Freedom House Recovery Center, Inc. 919.942.2803
Fax 919.942.2126
Web .... www.rtpnet.org/freedom
104 New Stateside Drive, Chapel Hill, NC 27516
CARF accredited programs available.

Future Innovations, LLC 910.843.6600
Fax 910.843.6887
Web .... www.futureinnv.com
703 West Third Avenue, Red Springs, NC 28377
CARF accredited programs available.

G & D Residential Services, LLC 336.254.6770
Fax 336.272.8083
620-G Guilford College Road, Greensboro, NC 27410
CARF accredited programs available.

Gaston Adolescent Center, Inc. 704.691.7561
635 Cox Road, Suite B, Gastonia, NC 28054
CARF accredited programs available.

Genesis House, Inc. 704.852.3778
Fax 704.853.8751
Web .... www.genesishousemhdd.com
1528 Union Road, Gastonia, NC 28054
CARF accredited programs available.

Genesis Professionals, LLC 336.289.7235
Fax 336.289.7235
Web .... www.genesisprofessionals.com
E-mail .... paris.littlejohn@genesisprofessionals.com
175 Northpoint Avenue, High Point, NC 27264
Paris Littlejohn, Executive Director
CARF accredited programs available.

Genesis Youth & Family Services, LLC 704.940.0036
9700 Research Drive, Suite 122, Charlotte, NC 28262
CARF accredited programs available.

GET Services, Inc 252.522.2293
Fax 252.522.2295
211 East New Bern Road, Kinston, NC 28504
CARF accredited programs available.

Getting Ready, Inc.......................252.289.5890
Fax...252.243.4948
 2303A Madison Drive, Wilson, NC 27893
 CARF accredited programs available.

Golden Opportunity Homes, Inc.........910.488.8777
Fax...910.482.4665
Web...............................www.goldopp.com
 321 Dick Street, Suites 103 and 104, Fayetteville,
 NC 28301
 CARF accredited programs available.

Golden Rule Enhanced, Inc..............704.535.5499
Fax...704.532.5953
Web.....................www.goldenruleenhanced.com
 4822 Albemarle Road, Suite 112, Charlotte,
 NC 28205
 CARF accredited programs available.

Good Deeds............................910.848.2273
Web.........................gooddeedsnotwords.com
E-mail.............................nekay2k@aol.com
 381 Northwoods Drive, Raeford, NC 28376
 Ms. Shanicha McNeil, Accreditation Manager
 Joint Commission accredited organization.

Good Kids Therapeutic Resources.........919.491.3299
E-mail....................mwilliams@goodkidsnc.com
 200 Wilson St, Williamston, NC 27892
 Ms. Mary Williams, Accreditation Manager
 Joint Commission accredited organization.

Grandfather Home for Children..........828.898.5465
Web...........................www.grandfatherhome.org
E-mail.................s.knowles@grandfatherhome.org
 158 Grandfather Home Drive, Banner Elk, NC 28604
 Ms. Stephanie Knowles, Accreditation Manager
 Joint Commission accredited organization.

Greater Metrolina Mental Health Services......704.865.5613
Fax...704.865.5614
Web......................www.greatermetrolina.org
 609 South New Hope Road, Suite 103, Gastonia,
 NC 28054
 CARF accredited programs available.

Guess Community Services, Inc...........336.545.5995
Fax...336.545.5996
 3818 North Elm Street, Suite E, Greensboro,
 NC 27455-2778
 CARF accredited programs available.

H.E.L.P., LLC..........................704.837.0620
Fax...704.837.0768
Web.................................www.helpllcnc.org
 5104 Reagan Drive, Suite 12, Charlotte, NC 28206
 CARF accredited programs available.

HabCare Facilities, Inc.................252.794.1944
Fax...252.794.1931
 129 East Granville Street, Windsor, NC 27983-7595
 CARF accredited programs available.

**Haire Enterprises, Inc. dba Community Re-Entry
Program**................................910.488.7517
Fax...910.484.3950
 400 Westwood Shopping Center, Fayetteville,
 NC 28314-1644
 CARF accredited programs available.

Hamilton Services, LLC.................336.389.1142
Fax...336.373.3996
Web..........................www.hamiltonservices.biz
 1050 Revolution Mill Drive, Studio 3, Greensboro,
 NC 27405-5041
 CARF accredited programs available.

Hand Up Homes for Youth, Inc............828.439.8191
Fax...828.439.2622
Web......................www.handuphomesforyouth.com
 310 Burke Drive, Morganton, NC 28655
 Pam Douglas, Programme Director
 CARF accredited programs available.

Heading in the Right Direction, Inc.........828.505.8306
 45 Eye View Drive, Candler, NC 28715
 CARF accredited programs available.

**Healthcare Solutions Network of North
Carolina**...............................828.684.4228
Web.....................healthcaresolutionsnetwork.net
E-mail.........................j.thoen@hcsnetwork.net
 170 Old Naples Rd., Hendersonville, NC 28792
 Mr. John Thoen, Accreditation Manager
 Joint Commission accredited organization.

HealthCore Resource Inc................919.872.1178
Fax...919.872.1170
Web.................................www.hcresource.com
E-mail.........................lebling@hcresource.com
 1001 Navaho Dr, Ste 210, Raleigh, NC 27609
 Lindsey Ebling, Community Support Director
 CARF accredited programs available.

Heartfelt Alternatives, Inc..............919.844.7770
Fax...919.844.7771
Web....................www.heartfelt4families.com
 8394 Six Forks Road, Suite 201, Raleigh,
 NC 27615-7813
 CARF accredited programs available.

Hearthstone Youth & Family Services, Inc......336.694.0906
Fax...336.694.5920
 474 North Carolina Highway 62 South, Yanceyville,
 NC 27379
 CARF accredited programs available.

**Helping Hands Care Management Services,
Inc.**...................................910.285.5221
Fax...910.285.5647
Web.....................................www.hhcms.org
 517 South Norwood Street, Wallace, NC 28466
 CARF accredited programs available.

**Helping Hands Community Support Services,
Inc.**...................................910.455.7696
Fax...910.455.5434
 118 Chaney Avenue, Jacksonville, NC 28546
 CARF accredited programs available.

Helping Hands Healthcare Services, Inc.......704.568.7817
Fax...704.568.7818
Web..................www.helpinghandhealthcare.com
 100 Alley Drive, Mount Gilead, NC 27306
 CARF accredited programs available.

Highsmith Support Agency, Inc...........910.259.4065
Fax...910.259.4063
 112 West Courthouse Avenue, Burgaw, NC 28425
 CARF accredited programs available.

HomeCare Management Corporation........828.754.3665
Fax...828.757.3195
Web............................www.homecaremgmt.org
 315 Wilkesboro Boulevard, NE, Suite 2-A, Lenoir,
 NC 28645
 COA accredited organization.

Homes Of A New Hope, Inc...............919.604.5812
Fax...919.938.9416
 126 Jethro Circle, Smithfield, NC 27576
 CARF accredited programs available.

Hope Catchers, LLC....................910.822.3333
Fax...910.822.3336
Web.....................www.hopecatchers@earthlink.net
 5851 Ramsey Street, Suite 102, Fayetteville,
 NC 28311
 CARF accredited programs available.

Hope Community Support, LLC............704.922.8322
Fax...704.957.0331
 1012 East Philadelphia Church Road, Dallas,
 NC 28034
 CARF accredited programs available.

HOPE Foundations, LLC.................919.713.0267
Fax...919.713.0268
Web.............................www.hopefoundations.com
 3712 Benson Drive, Suite 101, Raleigh, NC 27609

Hope In The Carolina, LLC..............910.296.6244
Fax...910.296.6246
Web............................www.hopeinthecarolina.com
 149 Limestone Road, Suite 1, Kenansville, NC 28349
 CARF accredited programs available.

Hope Services, LLC....................919.215.8852
Fax...910.458.4327
Web.............................www.hopeservices4u.com
 2900 Kidd Road, Raleigh, NC 27610
 CARF accredited programs available.

Hope Street, LLC......................336.375.5985
Fax...336.375.0253
 2007 Lynn Road, Greensboro, NC 27405
 CARF accredited programs available.

**Horizon Group Homes, Inc. dba Family First
Services**................................704.694.2232
Fax...704.694.3522
 123 East Martin Street, Suite 200, Wadesboro,
 NC 28170
 CARF accredited programs available.

House of Care, Inc.....................919.493.6871
Fax...919.493.6878
E-mail.......................houseofcare2@yahoo.com
 3020 Pickett Road, Suite 141, Durham, NC 27705
 ogo onwuka, director
 CARF accredited programs available.

Human Resources Unlimited, Inc..........252.635.1232
Fax...252.635.5164
 116 Market Street, New Bern, NC 28560
 CARF accredited programs available.

ICAN & Associates, Inc.................910.860.9787
Fax...910.860.3903
 6112 Louise Street, Fayetteville, NC 28314
 CARF accredited programs available.

Independently Moving, LLC.............919.416.0000
Fax...919.416.0002
 1530 North Gregson Street, 2C, BB&T Building,
 Durham, NC 27701
 CARF accredited programs available.

Ingram Health Services/Manna House Inc......910.422.2273
Fax...910.422.9889
 108 South Hickory Street, Rowland, NC 28340
 CARF accredited programs available.

Inner Peace Life Development Center, LLC.....910.816.0114
 1618 West Fifth Street, Lumberton, NC 28358
 CARF accredited programs available.

Inner Wealth Residential...............919.201.1626
Fax...919.794.4781
Web.............................www.innerwealthhomes.com
 Two Isaacs Way, Durham, NC 27703
 CARF accredited programs available.

InnerVision, Inc.......................704.377.5042
Web.............................www.innervisionnc.org
 PO Box 31083, Charlotte, NC 28231
 COA accredited organization.

Innovative Cognitive Services, Inc.........910.521.3009
Fax...910.521.3010
Web.............................www.innovativecognitive.com
 410C South Jones Street, Pembroke, NC 28372
 CARF accredited programs available.

**Innovative Compliance Solutions dba New Hope Group
Home**...................................704.879.4219
Fax...704.817.9945
Web.............................www.newhopehome.org
 3915 South New Hope Road, Gastonia, NC 28056
 CARF accredited programs available.

Inspirationz Group Home 336.788.8579
Fax 336.788.1069
  607 Hillhaven Drive, Winston-Salem, NC 27107-6223
  CARF accredited programs available.

Inspiring Hope, PLLC 910.739.5518
Fax 910.739.5520
Web ....www.inspiringhopepllc.com
  325 East Fourth Street, Lumberton, NC 28358
  CARF accredited programs available.

Integrated Family Services, PLLC 252.862.4411
Fax 252.862.4414
Web ....www.integratedfamilyservices.net
  228 East Main Street, Ahoskie, NC 27910
  CARF accredited programs available.

Integrated Family Solutions, LLC 919.510.5110
Fax 919.510.5291
Web www.ifs4families.com
  5300 Six Forks Road, Suite 213, Raleigh, NC 27609
  TONJA AUSTIN, MANAGER
  CARF accredited programs available.

Integrated Programs and Services, Inc. 919.648.2918
Fax 919.735.9163
Web ....www.ipasinc.net
  715 East Simmons Street, Goldsboro, NC 27530
  CARF accredited programs available.

Internal Family Relations, Inc. 252.337.7516
Fax 252.337.7517
Web ....www.internalfamilyrelations.org
  122 Gumberry Road, Camden, NC 27921
  CARF accredited programs available.

IQUOLIOC Therapeutic Services, Inc. 910.355.2000
Fax 910.355.6900
Web ....www.iquolioc.org
E-mail ....cristinaespinar@iquolioc.org
  675 Bell Fork Rd, Jacksonville, NC 28540
  Cristina Espinar, HR/QA/QI Director
  CARF accredited programs available.

**It Takes A Village Youth and Family
Services** 704.790.3342
Fax 704.790.3343
  5736 North Tryon Street, Suite 221C, Charlotte, NC 28213
  CARF accredited programs available.

J Iverson Riddle Developmental Ctr 828.433.2731
Fax 828.433.2799
  300 Enola Rd, Morganton, NC 28655
  Arthur Robarge, Director

Jabez Management, LLC 336.361.9579
E-mail ....empoweredgirls@bellsouth.net
  122 N. Main Street, Reidsville, NC 27323
  Ms. Sharon Sellars, Accreditation Manager
  Joint Commission accredited organization.

Jackson Family Homes, Inc. 704.817.7539
Fax 704.702.9955
  2734 Freedom Drive, Charlotte, NC 28208
  CARF accredited programs available.

**JMJ Enterprise LLC d/b/a Fresh Start Home for
Children** 336.271.6982
Web ....jmjenterprise.net
E-mail ....tylerlee6@earthlink.net
  1929 Murrayhill Rd, Greensboro, NC 27403
  Ms. Tracy Martin, Accreditation Manager
  Joint Commission accredited organization.

Johari Family Services 910.897.3000
Fax 910.897.3004
  42 East Main Street, Coats, NC 27521
  CARF accredited programs available.

Just In Time Youth Services, Inc. 336.270.4578
Fax 336.270.4578
  111 Dogwood Drive, Burlington, NC 27215
  CARF accredited programs available.

Keep Hope Alive Human Services, LLC 252.353.8003
Fax 252.353.9912
  3219 Landmark Street, Suite 6, Greenville, NC 27834
  CARF accredited programs available.

Key Behavior Essentials, LLC 919.846.6800
Fax 919.846.6807
Web ....www.keybehavioressentials.webs.com
  8300 Falls of Neus Road, Suite 108, Raleigh, NC 27615
  CARF accredited programs available.

**Keystone Charlotte, LLC dba The Keys of
Carolina** 704.554.9874
Fax 704.554.9641
Web ....www.thekeysofcarolina.com
  1715 Sharon Road West, Charlotte, NC 28210
  CARF accredited programs available.

**KidsPeace National Centers of North America,
Inc** 919.872.6447
Web ....www.kidspeace.org
E-mail ....espissza@kidspeace.org
  3109 Poplarwood Court , Suite 310, Raleigh, NC 27604
  Mr. Ed Spisszac, Accreditation Manager
  Joint Commission accredited organization.

Kingdom Healthcare, Inc. 919.496.3053
Fax 919.833.0198
  81 Egypt Church Road, Louisburg, NC 27549
  CARF accredited programs available.

KMG Holding, Inc. Dba The Lighthouse 919.412.9711
Fax 919.882.6311
  1521 Ranch Road, Clayton, NC 27520
  CARF accredited programs available.

Krystal's House 252.747.2988
Fax 252.747.4330
  208 North Greene Street, Snow Hill, NC 28580
  CARF accredited programs available.

L&M Management Services, Inc. 919.732.6010
Fax 919.732.6176
  236 Orange Grove Street, Hillsborough, NC 27278
  CARF accredited programs available.

Le'Chris Health Systems, Inc. 252.636.6105
Fax 252.636.6109
Web ....www.lechris.com
  1405 South Glenburnie Road, New Bern, NC 28562
  CARF accredited programs available.

Leading Into New Communities, Inc. 910.762.4635
Web ....www.lincnc.org
E-mail ....tray@lincnc.org
  907 Castle Street, Wilmington, NC 28402
  Ms. Tracey Ray, Accreditation Manager
  Joint Commission accredited organization.

Life Enhancement Svcs 704.342.9595
  500 E Morehead St, Ste 110, Charlotte, NC 28202
  Herb Gray, CEO
  CARF accredited programs available.

Life Opportunities, Inc. 910.843.1105
Fax 910.843.1295
  303 East Fourth Avenue, Red Springs, NC 28377
  CARF accredited programs available.

Life Touch, LLC 252.527.2000
Fax 525.527.6200
  1879 Highway 258 North, Kinston, NC 28504
  CARF accredited programs available.

Life Turn 336.342.2609
Fax 336.342.5012
  3008 Highway 150 East, Reidsville, NC 27320
  CARF accredited programs available.

LIFE, Inc. 919.778.1900
Fax 919.736.7790
Web ....www.lifeincorporated.com
  2609 Royall Avenue, Goldsboro, NC 27534
  CARF accredited programs available.

**Light To My Path Therapeutic Services,
Inc.** 910.548.0732
Fax 910.455.1921
  99 Village Drive, Suite 15, Jacksonville, NC 28546
  CARF accredited programs available.

**Lighthouse Counseling Center and Associated Therapeutic
Services, LLC** 910.485.2463
Fax 910.485.5412
  2800 Breezewood Avenue, Suite 100, Fayetteville, NC 28303
  CARF accredited programs available.

Living Well Centre, Inc. 919.489.2254
Fax 919.403.1551
Web ....www.livingwellcentre.com
  1804 Martin Luther King Junior Parkway, Suite 210, Durham, NC 27707
  CARF accredited programs available.

Lois' House 252.234.9996
Fax 252.237.1413
  3301 A West Nash Street, Wilson, NC 27896
  CARF accredited programs available.

Loving Care Supervised Living Group 252.937.1096
Fax 252.937.2396
  3041 Zebulon Place, Rocky Mount, NC 27804
  CARF accredited programs available.

Lydia's Home, LLC 336.855.6937
Fax 336.299.7060
  2704 Grimsley Street, Greensboro, NC 27403
  CARF accredited programs available.

Lyngrett Enterprises, Inc. 252.521.2246
Fax 252.523.7772
  110 South Queen Street, Suite 108, Kinston, NC 28501
  CARF accredited programs available.

Mag's House II, Inc. 336.255.5152
Fax 336.643.9189
  1104 West Meadowview Road, Greensboro, NC 27406
  CARF accredited programs available.

Majestic Solutions, LLC 336.907.1034
Fax 336.274.7669
  2344 Brentwood Street, High Point, NC 27263
  CARF accredited programs available.

Makin' Choices, Inc. 910.483.2002
Fax 910.483.4004
  107 Davis Street, Fayetteville, NC 28305
  CARF accredited programs available.

Making Changes, Inc. 252.258.5303
Fax 252.281.5006
  2405 Nash Street NW, Suite D, Wilson, NC 27896-1634
  CARF accredited programs available.

Mary's Loving Arms, LLC 252.522.1071
Fax 252.522.1071
  1573 Savannah Heights Drive, Kinston, NC 28530-8315
  CARF accredited programs available.

**Matrix Mental Health Alliance dba CriSyS,
LLC** 704.566.3410
Fax 704.537.1226
Web ....www.thesantegroup.org
  5820 East W.T. Harris Boulevard, Suite 211, Charlotte, NC 28215
  CARF accredited programs available.

McCloud & Associates, Inc. 252.355.6272
Fax 252.355.0116
  2423 Mills Street, Winterville, NC 28590
  CARF accredited programs available.

McLeod Addictive Disease Center, Inc. **704.332.9001**
Fax 704.332.0124
Web .... www.mcleodcenter.com
  145 Remount Road, Charlotte, NC 28203
  CARF accredited programs available.

McMillan Home Care, Inc. **910.735.0301**
Fax 910.735.0334
  120 Eden Avenue, Lumberton, NC 28359
  CARF accredited programs available.

McWilliams Center for Counseling, Inc. **704.868.7001**
Fax 704.852.4401
Web .... www.mcwilliamscenter.com
  936 North Marietta Street, Suite A, Gastonia,
  NC 28054
  CARF accredited programs available.

Meadows Place, LLC **919.477.3120**
  8224 Lowell Valley Drive, Bahama, NC 27503
  CARF accredited programs available.

Melange Health Solutions, LLC **704.567.8690**
Fax 704.536.6030
Web .... http://www.melangehs.com
E-mail .... ghawkins@melangehs.com
  107 Scaleybark Road, Charlotte, NC 28209-2608
  Gardner Hawkins, Managing Director
  CARF accredited programs available.

Midstate Health Systems, Inc **910.484.3717**
Web .... www.midstatehealthsystems.com
E-mail .... midstatehealthsystems@yahoo.com
  3721 Legion Rd, Hope Mills, NC 28348
  Ms. Sera Gilmore, Accreditation Manager
  Joint Commission accredited organization.

Milestone Child and Family Services, Inc. **252.522.2800**
Fax 888.524.1157
Web .... www.milestonecfs.com
  2906 Hull Road, Kinston, NC 28504
  CARF accredited programs available.

Millers Alternative Living **910.289.3727**
Fax 910.289.2273
  291 East Charity Road, Rose Hill, NC 28458
  CARF accredited programs available.

Miracle Houses, Inc. **704.369.1445**
Fax 704.535.4476
  5500 Executive Center Drive, Suite 201, Charlotte,
  NC 28212
  CARF accredited programs available.

Miss Daisy's Gentlemen of Future **252.363.5446**
E-mail .... tjohnsongrace@yahoo.com
  304 Fairview Ave., Wilson, NC 27893
  Ms. Tonya Johnson, Accreditation Manager
  Joint Commission accredited organization. CARF accredited programs available.

Monae Supportive Services, Inc. **252.321.8488**
Fax 252.321.2209
  108 Firetower Road, Suite H, Winterville, NC 28590
  CARF accredited programs available.

Mountain Area Residential Facilities, Inc. **828.299.3636**
Fax 828.299.3302
E-mail .... marfinc108@charterinternet.com
  108 Cedar Ridge Drive, Ashville, NC 28803
  Jeanne Cagle, Director
  CARF accredited programs available.

MQA Support Services, LLC **919.710.0258**
Fax 919.439.0215
Web .... mqasupportllc.com
  4014 Shipyard Boulevard, Wilmington, NC 28403
  CARF accredited programs available.

MQA Support Services, LLC **919.637.7567**
Fax 919.439.0215
Web .... mqasupportllc.com
  4018 Oleander Drive, Wilmington, NC 28403
  Ahada Jones, Clinical Director
  CARF accredited programs available.

Murdoch Ctr **919.575.1000**
Fax 919.575.1007
E-mail .... aleckmyers@dhhs.nc.gov
  1600 E C St, Butner, NC 27509
  Aleck Myers, Director

Murray Fork Home Care **910.480.4181**
Fax 910.480.4182
Web .... www.srmhc.org
E-mail .... sprevatte@srmhc.org
  1555 Cain Road, Suite 201, Fayetteville, NC 28303
  Sharen Prevatte, Area Director
  CARF accredited programs available.

My B.R.O.T.H.E.R.S. HOUSE, Inc. **704.532.4770**
Fax 704.532.4774
  4822 Albermarle Road, Suite 105, Charlotte,
  NC 28205
  CARF accredited programs available.

**My Savior Family Care Home, Inc. dba People of
Purpose** **252.695.6417**
Fax 252.752.0024
Web .... www.mysavior-peopleofpurpose.com
  755 Johns Hopkins Drive, Greenville, NC 27834
  CARF accredited programs available.

Native Angels Home Care Agency, Inc. **910.272.6400**
Fax 910.321.6077
Web .... www.nativeangels.biz
  201 East Livermore Drive, Pembroke, NC 28372
  CARF accredited programs available.

Nature's Reflections **919.477.2728**
Fax 919.477.3938
  2604 Carver Street, Suite C, Durham, NC 27705
  CARF accredited programs available.

Nazareth Children's Home, Inc. **704.279.5556**
Fax 704.279.5439
Web .... www.nazch.com
  P.O. Box 1438, Rockwell, NC 28138-1438
  COA accredited organization.

NeoGenesis LLC **252.355.9151**
Fax 252.355.9153
  1645 Arlington Boulevard, Suite B, Greenville,
  NC 27858
  CARF accredited programs available.

New Beginning Youth Facility **336.302.0801**
E-mail .... kspinks@triad.rr.com
  2106 Newell St., Ramseur, NC 27316
  Mrs. Kimesha Spinks, Accreditation Manager
  Joint Commission accredited organization.

**New Beginnings Therapeutic Resources,
PLLC** **919.489.5870**
Fax 919.287.2544
Web .... www.newbeginningsnc.com
  3326 Durham-Chapel Hill Boulevard, Building C,
  Suite 220, Durham, NC 27707
  CARF accredited programs available.

New Beginnings With Love, Inc. **252.823.8448**
Fax 252.641.5683
  3503 North Main Street, Tarboro, NC 27886
  CARF accredited programs available.

New Beginnings Youth Facility **336.622.9439**
Fax 336.622.9439
  2106 Newell Street, Ramseur, NC 27316
  CARF accredited programs available.

New Beginningz, Inc. **910.904.2840**
Fax 910.904.2847
Web .... www.newbeginningz.com
  2194-A Hillcrest Plaza, Raeford, NC 28376
  CARF accredited programs available.

New Dimension Group **910.289.2610**
Fax 910.289.4410
  416 West Ridge Street, Rose Hill, NC 28458
  CARF accredited programs available.

New Hope Family and Youth Services, LLC **252.445.4357**
Fax 252.445.2550
Web .... www.newhopefamilyandyouthservices.com
  102 Southwest Railroad Street, Enfield, NC 27823
  CARF accredited programs available.

New Hope Residential Facility Inc. **910.864.0070**
Fax 910.864.9700
  235 Westlake Drive, Suite 201, Fayetteville,
  NC 28314
  CARF accredited programs available.

New Horizon Group Home, LLC **910.536.3502**
Fax 910.674.4488
  905 North Cedar Street, Lumberton, NC 28359
  CARF accredited programs available.

New Leaf Academy of North Carolina **828.697.5029**
Fax 828.697.9722
Web .... www.newleafacademy.com
  2075 North Rugby Road, Hendersonville, NC 28791
  CARF accredited programs available.

New Leaf Adolescent Care, Inc. **704.405.8890**
Fax 704.405.8893
Web .... www.newleafinc.info
  200 East Arrowhead Drive, Office 5, Charlotte,
  NC 28213
  CARF accredited programs available.

New Life Community Services, LLC **252.215.1172**
Fax 252.215.1173
  104 West Firetower Road, Winterville, NC 28590
  CARF accredited programs available.

New Life Services, Inc. **910.671.4067**
Fax 910.671.0383
Web .... www.newlifeservices.org
  2003 Godwin Avenue, Suite C, Lumberton,
  NC 28358
  CARF accredited programs available.

New Place, Inc. **704.567.8984**
Fax 704.567.8954
  6612 East Harris Boulevard, Suite D, Charlotte,
  NC 28215
  CARF accredited programs available.

New Possibilities Home For Children, LLC **336.261.3427**
  813 Trail One, Burlington, NC 27215
  CARF accredited programs available.

**New River Service Authority dba New River Behavioral
HealthCare** **828.264.9007**
Fax 828.264.9468
Web .... http://www.newriver.org/
  895 State Farm Road, Suite 508, Boone, NC 28607
  CARF accredited programs available.

Next Level Adolescent Services **252.349.8999**
  1107 Holloway Street, Durham, NC 27701
  CARF accredited programs available.

NextStep Family Counseling **704.536.9310**
Fax 704.536.9311
  5500 Executive Center Drive, Suite 202, Charlotte,
  NC 28214
  CARF accredited programs available.

Nia Children and Family Services **252.291.5585**
Fax 252.291.5585
  504 East Green Street, Wilson, NC 27893
  CARF accredited programs available.

No Bounds Care, Inc. **704.548.2445**
Fax 704.548.2448
  520 Collins-Aikman Drive, Suite 208, Charlotte,
  NC 28262
  CARF accredited programs available.

Noir Enterprises, llc **828.654.9452**
E-mail .... respect162027922@aol.com
  5030 Hendersonville Hwy Suite A, Fletcher,
  NC 28732
  Ms. Gloria Rollins, Accreditation Manager
  Joint Commission accredited organization.

North Carolina

North Carolina MENTOR **919.790.8580**
Fax 919.790.8065
Web .... www.nc-mentor.com;www.thementornetwork.
3125 Poplarwood Ct, Ste 300, Raleigh, NC 27604
Charles Davis, Director
CARF accredited programs available.

**North Carolina Tarheel/ Challenge
Academy** **910.525.5520**
Fax 910.525.5821
Web .... www.ngycp.org
600 Ne Main St, Salemburg, NC 28385
Bill Autry, Director

**NOVA, Inc. dba NOVA Behavioral Healthcare
Corporation** **252.522.4233**
Fax 252.522.0703
Web .... www.novabehavioralhealthcare.com
105 West Caswell Street, Kinston, NC 28501
CARF accredited programs available.

NuDay Case Management, Inc. **336.831.2788**
Fax 336.831.2787
Web .... www.nudaycm.com
E-mail .... nwilliamson@nudaycm.com
3820 N Patterson Ave, Winston-Salem, NC 27105
Nancy Williamson, Director
CARF accredited programs available.

O'Berry Neuro-Medical Treatment Ctr **919.581.4000**
400 Old Smithfield Rd, Goldsboro, NC 27530
Deborah Exum, Director

Old Vineyard Behavioral Health Services **336.794.3550**
Web .... www.oldvineyard.net
E-mail .... kelly.thacker@uhsinc.com
3637 Old Vineyard Road, Winston Salem,
NC 27104-4842
Ms. Kelly Thacker, Accreditation Manager
Joint Commission accredited organization.

Old Vineyard Youth **336.794.3550**
Fax 336.794.4319
Web .... www.oldvineyard.net
E-mail .... kathryn.murray@uhsinc.com
3637 Old Vineyard Rd, Winston Salem,
NC 27104-4842
Lee Staton, Director of Admissions
JCAHO Accredited Acute/In-Patient and Psychiatric Residential Treatment Facility.
PHP/IOP services for adults also provided.

Onas' Place **828.225.3606**
Fax 828.225.3607
Web .... http://onasplace.com
39 Choctaw Street, Asheville, NC 28801
CARF accredited programs available.

One to One With Youth, Inc. **919.731.2119**
Fax 919.739.4989
Web .... www.onetooneonline.org
307 East Beech Street, Goldsboro, NC 27530-2818
CARF accredited programs available.

Open Arms Group Homes, Inc. **704.865.6470**
Fax 704.865.6404
620 East Price Street, Gastonia, NC 28054

**Open Arms Residential and Community Supports,
Inc.** **252.795.5200**
Fax 252.795.5006
606 West Green Street, Robersonville, NC 27871
CARF accredited programs available.

Our Hands of Hope, Inc. **704.263.4922**
Fax 704.263.4922
Web .... http://www.ourhandsofhope.com/
148 Hunters Point Drive, Dallas, NC 28034
CARF accredited programs available.

Outreach Management Services, LLC **704.854.9828**
Fax 704.854.9882
Web .... www.outreachms.com
1723 Armstrong Park Drive, Gastonia, NC 28054
CARF accredited programs available.

P&G Community Support Team, Inc. **919.637.9091**
4406 Wake Forest Road, Suite C, Raleigh, NC 27609
CARF accredited programs available.

Parkway Behavioral Health **828.254.5008**
Web .... www.parkwaybh.com
E-mail .... rclontz@parkwaybh.com
31 College Place, Ste B-100, Asheville, NC 28801
Rob Clontz, Practice Manager

**Partnership for a Drug-Free NC, Inc. dba Insight Human
Services** **336.725.8389**
Fax 336.725.6628
Web .... www.drugfreenc.org
665 West Fourth Street, Winston-Salem, NC 27101
CARF accredited programs available.

Paths to Success, LLC **704.873.4505**
Fax 704.873.4580
Web .... www.pathstosuccessnc.com
215 South Tradd Street, Statesville, NC 28677
CARF accredited programs available.

Pathways To Life, Inc. **252.695.0269**
Fax 252.413.0526
Web .... www.pwstolife.com
E-mail .... pathways@pwstolife.com
1202 East Firetower Road, Greenville, NC 27858
Lamont Chappell, Director
CARF accredited programs available.

Pearl's Angel Care, Inc. **910.487.2500**
Fax 910.487.2501
E-mail .... pearlangelcare@nc.rr.com
231 West Lake Drive, Fayetteville, NC 28314
veronica lambright, clinical director
CARF accredited programs available.

Peggy's Home Health Care **252.795.5207**
Fax 252.795.5207
413 Modica Street, Robersonville, NC 27871
CARF accredited programs available.

People Achieving Living Skills, Inc. **910.897.4311**
Fax 910.897.4342
200 North 13th Street, Suite 3B, Erwin, NC 28334
CARF accredited programs available.

**People Helping People of North Carolina,
LLC** **336.760.1330**
Fax 336.760.1341
Web .... www.phpofnc.com
4550 Country Club Road, Winston-Salem, NC 27104
Deb Sudnickovich, Director

Perfect Foundation, Inc. **919.693.3898**
Fax 919.693.5633
104 Belle Street, Oxford, NC 27565
CARF accredited programs available.

Personalized Therapy, Inc. **252.353.4968**
Fax 252.353.4967
Web .... www.personalizedtherapy.net
2317-B Executive Circle, Greenville, NC 27834
CARF accredited programs available.

Phoenix Counseling Center **704.689.2908**
Fax 704.854.4860
2505 Court Drive, Gastonia, NC 28054
CARF accredited programs available.

Piedmont Behavioral Resources, Inc. **704.487.6226**
Fax 704.487.6286
201 West Marion Street, Suite 207, Shelby,
NC 28150
CARF accredited programs available.

Pine Village Treatment Services **910.864.7004**
Fax 910.864.3002
1206 Hope Mills Road, Fayetteville, NC 28304
CARF accredited programs available.

PORT Human Services **252.830.7540**
Fax 252.752.0074
Web .... www.porthumanservices.org
4300 Sapphire Court, Suite 110, Greenville,
NC 27834
CARF accredited programs available.

**Positive Connection Community Service,
Inc.** **252.793.5131**
412 East Third Street, Plymouth, NC 27962
CARF accredited programs available.

Positive Future, LLC **252.426.7537**
Fax 252.426.1877
Web .... positivefuturenc.com
141 Ocean Highway N, Hertford, NC 27944
CARF accredited programs available.

Positive Outlook Services , LLC **252.492.9410**
Web ....
E-mail .... cwpositiveoutlook@yahoo.com
120 E Belle street, Henderson, NC 27536
Ms. Cassandra Williams, Accreditation Manager
Joint Commission accredited organization. CARF accredited programs available.

Precious Haven, Inc. **910.868.6092**
Fax 910.868.8882
7762 Hazelwood Drive, Fayetteville, NC 28314
CARF accredited programs available.

Precision Health Care Services, Inc. **252.327.1815**
Fax 252.520.0034
Web .... www.precisionhealthnc.net
2902 B North Heritage Street, Kinston, NC 28501
CARF accredited programs available.

Preferred Alternatives, Inc. **910.483.5744**
Fax 910.483.5494
Web .... www.preferredalternatives.org
941 South McPherson Church Road, Fayetteville,
NC 28303
CARF accredited programs available.

Premier Behavioral Services, Inc. **910.671.1111**
Fax 910.671.4454
2003 Godwin Avenue, Suite B, Lumberton,
NC 28358
Dr. S. Augustine, CEO
CARF accredited programs available.

Premier Family Health Care Services, LLC **252.519.2273**
Fax 252.535.2399
1704 Highway 158, Roanoke Rapids, NC 27870
CARF accredited programs available.

Premier Healthcare Services, Inc. **910.878.0121**
Fax 910.878.0123
Web www.nclevel4.com
1892 Turnpike Road, Raeford, NC 28376
CARF accredited programs available.

Preparing Adults and Children to Excel **336.887.1150**
Web .... www.paceyourway.com
200 Hillstone Drive, Suite D, Jamestown, NC 27282
CARF accredited programs available.

Prestige, Inc. **910.483.6416**
Fax 910.483.5924
1711 Ramsey Street, Suite B, Fayetteville, NC 28301
CARF accredited programs available.

Pride in North Carolina, Inc. **919.467.4745**
Fax 919.467.5299
117 Edinburgh South, Suite 205, Cary, NC 27511
CARF accredited programs available.

Primary Health Choice, Inc. **910.865.8280**
219 West Broad Street, Saint Pauls, NC 28384
CARF accredited programs available.

Professional Care Management, Inc. **704.567.6800**
Fax 704.567.6811
Web .... www.pcmnc.com
3421-H St. Vardell Lane, Charlotte, NC 28217
CARF accredited programs available.

Professional Care Services Providers, LLC 910.738.7752
Fax 910.618.0401
Web ....www.procareproviders.com
4320 Fayetteville Road, Lumberton, NC 28358
CARF accredited programs available.

Program Resource Institute, Inc. 910.891.7062
Fax 910.892.3764
108 North Orange Avenue, Dunn, NC 28334
CARF accredited programs available.

Progressive Care Services, Inc. 252.985.3216
Fax 252.985.3210
3216 Zebulon Road, Rocky Mount, NC 27804
CARF accredited programs available.

Psychological Services 828.586.6600
Fax 828.586.6601
Web ....www.jacksoncountyps.org
98D Cope Creek Road, Sylva, NC 28779
CARF accredited programs available.

Purpose Driven Support Services, LLC 910.624.7825
890 South Kerr Avenue, Suite 260, Wilmington,
NC 28403
CARF accredited programs available.

Quality Care Developmental Services, Inc. 704.798.2851
Fax 704.645.8038
328 Old Concord Road, Salisbury, NC 28144
CARF accredited programs available.

Quality Care Solutions, Inc. 919.790.7775
Fax 919.790.9755
Web ....www.qcsolutions.org
E-mail ....mandrakel@q-csolutions.org
1127 Cedar Hurst Drive, Suite 270, Raleigh,
NC 27609
Mandrake Lewis, Director
CARF accredited programs available.

Quality Family Services 704.536.0005
Fax 866.228.3276
Web ....www.qfsmail.com
5103 Monroe Road, Charlotte, NC 28205

Quality Home Care Services, Inc 704.394.8968
Web ....www.qhcsnc.org
E-mail ....lisawigfall@yahoo.com
3552 Beatties Ford Road, Charlotte, NC 28216
Ms. Lisa Wigfall, Accreditation Manager
Joint Commission accredited organization.

Quality Mental Health, Inc. 704.753.9687
Fax 704.753.3917
210 Mulberry Street, Suite D, Lenoir, NC 28645
CARF accredited programs available.

Quest Therapeutic and Personal Care, Inc. 704.712.6122
Fax 704.919.3463
1914 JN Pease Place, Suite 107, Charlotte,
NC 28262-4504
CARF accredited programs available.

Rachel's House 252.794.8503
Fax 252.794.8504
1212 Charles Street, Windsor, NC 27983
CARF accredited programs available.

Reaching Your Goals, Inc. 919.832.6150
Fax 919.832.6151
Web ....www.reachingyourgoalsinc.com
211 East Six Forks Road, Suite 201, Raleigh,
NC 27609
CARF accredited programs available.

Reintegration Targeting Inc. 704.334.2600
Web ....www.reintegrationtargetinginc.com
E-mail ....mcole@reintegrationtargetinginc.com
2210 North Tyron Street Suite A, Charlotte,
NC 28206-2772
Ms. Marionette Cole, Accreditation Manager
Joint Commission accredited organization.

Removing Mountains, LLC 919.493.7600
Fax 919.493.4477
Web ....www.removingmountains.com
4011 University Drive, Suite 204, Durham, NC 27707
CARF accredited programs available.

Residential & Supportive Services, LLC 910.293.4919
Fax 910.293.4533
Web ....www.rassnc.com
E-mail ....hannon@rassnc.com
206 North Front Street, Warsaw, NC 28398-0586
Lf Shannon, Executive Director
CARF accredited programs available.

**Residential Adolescent Adult Services and Training,
Inc.** 919.329.2630
Fax 919.329.2631
Web ....www.raastinc.com
304 West Millbrook Road, Suite F, Raleigh, NC 27609
CARF accredited programs available.

Residential Services, Inc. 919.942.7391
Web ....www.rsi-nc.org
E-mail ....lguillen@rsi-nc.org
111 Providence Road, Chapel Hill, NC 27514
Mrs. LeAnna Guillen, Accreditation Manager
Joint Commission accredited organization.

Resolutions for Care Network, Inc. 252.332.2026
Fax 252.332.2096
109 Loftin Lane, Ahoskie, NC 27910
CARF accredited programs available.

Resource and Referral Center 336.454.1140
Fax 336.454.1180
Web ....www.guilfordcountyresourceandreferralcen
725-B West Main Street, Jamestown, NC 27283
CARF accredited programs available.

Resourceful Solutions II, LLC 704.563.3336
Fax 704.563.3356
Web ....www.resourcefulsolutions.vpweb.com
4917 Albemarle Road, Suite 206, Charlotte,
NC 28205-6654
CARF accredited programs available.

ReStart Inc. 252.355.4725
2602 Courtier Drive, Greenville, NC 27834
COA accredited organization.

Restoration Family Services, Inc. 919.550.0808
Fax 919.550.0998
442 East Main Street, Suite A, Clayton, NC 27520
renee jones, director
CARF accredited programs available.

Right Foundation, Inc. 910.485.0041
Fax 910.485.0071
100 Hay Street, Suite 802, Fayetteville, NC 28301
CARF accredited programs available.

Riverbend Services, Inc. 910.618.9260
Fax 910.737.6505
6688 Elizabethtown Road, Lumberton, NC 28358
CARF accredited programs available.

Riverside Community Supports, Inc. 252.862.4111
Fax 252.862.4211
121 East Main Street, Ahoskie, NC 27910
CARF accredited programs available.

**RJ Shepherd, Inc. dba Better Home Health
Care** 910.424.2929
Fax 910.424.2967
1207 Walter Reed Road, Fayetteville, NC 28304
CARF accredited programs available.

Rockwell Development Center, Inc. 704.987.2096
Fax 704.987.2096
Web ....www.rockwelldevelopmentcenter.com
120 Rockwell Loop, Mooresville, NC 28115
COA accredited organization.

S & T WeCare, Inc. 910.826.2273
Fax 910.483.9600
501 Helen Street, Fayetteville, NC 28303
CARF accredited programs available.

S. Carr Rehabilitation and Associates, Inc. 336.540.8829
Fax 336.282.0580
3521 Battleground Avenue, Greensboro, NC 27410
CARF accredited programs available.

S.T.E.P's Developmental Academy, Inc. 704.668.1218
Fax 704.532.0144
4822 Albemarle Road, Suite 100, Charlotte,
NC 28205
CARF accredited programs available.

Samaritans Network, Inc. 252.799.0300
Fax 252.799.0314
300 South Pearl Street, Williamston, NC 27892
CARF accredited programs available.

Sandhills Alternative Academy, LLC 910.417.4922
Fax 910.417.4923
Web ....http://www.salt-academy.com/index.html
504-A East Broad Avenue, Rockingham, NC 28379
CARF accredited programs available.

SBH- Wilmington, LLC 910.371.2500
Web ....www.strategicbh.com
E-mail ....dginn@strategicbh.com
2050 Mercantile Drive, Leland, NC 28451
Mr. Doug Ginn, Accreditation Manager
Joint Commission accredited organization.

Second Chance Recovery 252.442.0100
Fax 252.442.0106
Web ....www.second-chancerecovery.com
203 South Grace Street, Rocky Mount, NC 27804
CARF accredited programs available.

Securing Resources for Consumers, Inc. 919.405.2700
Fax 919.405.2750
3209 Yorktown Avenue, Suite 171, Durham,
NC 27713
CARF accredited programs available.

Serenity Counseling & Resource Center 336.617.8910
Fax 336.617.8909
Web ....www.serenitycounselingrc.com
2211 West Meadowview Road, Suite 10, Greensboro,
NC 27407
CARF accredited programs available.

Shadows Community Support Center 252.795.6662
Fax 252.795.6696
Web ....www.shadowscsc.org
7356 Highway 64 East Alternate, Robersonville,
NC 27871
CARF accredited programs available.

Sigma Health Services 919.848.9108
Fax 919.848.9109
Web ....www.sigmahealthservices.com
8368 Six Forks Road, Suite 102, Raleigh, NC 27615
CARF accredited programs available.

Sims Consulting & Clinical Services, Inc. 704.630.6634
Fax 866.828.5520
Web ....www.simsconsulting.net
204 East Innes Street Suite 280, Salisbury, NC 28144
COA accredited organization.

Singleton Care Inc. 336.790.0290
Fax 336.790.0290
1 Centerview Drive, Suite 307, Greensboro,
NC 27407
CARF accredited programs available.

Skillful Behaviors, Inc.- McDowell 828.659.9245
Fax 828.652.1619
P.O. Box 1029, Marion, NC 28752
COA accredited organization.

North Carolina

Smartseeds, Inc. **910.797.7354**
Fax 206.666.2303
   110 East Main Street, Suite 205, Clinton,
   NC 28328-4060
   CARF accredited programs available.

Solid Foundation Facilities, Inc. **252.209.8932**
Fax 252.209.8933
E-mail .... shander.meadows@solid-foundation.org
   1313 West First Street, Ahoskie, NC 27910
   Shander Meadows, Clinical Director
   CARF accredited programs available.

Solutions Community Support Agency,
LLC **336.436.0074**
Fax 336.436.0232
   236 North Mebane Street, Suite 123, Burlington,
   NC 27217
   CARF accredited programs available.

Sophia B. Pierce & Associates, Inc. **910.488.8477**
Fax 910.822.1951
E-mail .... c611club@aol.com
   1422 Murchison Road, Fayetteville, NC 28301
   Barbara Mcwhite, Director
   CARF accredited programs available.

Southeastern United Care, LLC **910.521.0009**
Fax 910.521.0077
Web .... www.seunitedcare.com
   30 Drakes Branch Drive, Pembroke, NC 28372

Southwestern Child Care Resource And
Referral **828.586.5561**
Fax 828.586.4039
E-mail .... ansley.vickie@swcdcinc.org
   1528 Webster Road, Webster, NC 28788
   Vickie Ansley, Director

Special K Enrichment, Inc. **704.395.9387**
Fax 704.395.9436
Web .... www.skeinc.org
   2211 Executive Street, Suite G, Charlotte, NC 28208
   CARF accredited programs available.

Special K Services, Inc. **336.275.4594**
Fax 336.275.6825
Web .... www.specialkinc.com
   825 Nestleway Drive, Greensboro, NC 27406
   CARF accredited programs available.

Specialized Children's Care, Inc. **336.834.1890**
Fax 336.632.0368
   515 Guilford College Road, Greensboro, NC 27409
   CARF accredited programs available.

Spirit of Excellence Community Outreach dba Guardian
Care **910.938.2003**
Fax 910.938.2018
   1690 Wilmington Highway, Jacksonville, NC 28546
   CARF accredited programs available.

Stephens Outreach Center, Inc. **910.738.7865**
Fax 910.738.7876
   2105-B Elizabethtown Road, Lumberton, NC 28358
   CARF accredited programs available.

Stepz-2-Greater Heights, LLC **919.583.8017**
Fax 919.583.8635
   223-1 West Walnut Street, Goldsboro, NC 27530
   CARF accredited programs available.

Stevens Healthcare Agency, Inc. **910.938.7200**
Fax 910.938.7201
   824 Gum Branch Road, Suite N, Jacksonville,
   NC 28540
   CARF accredited programs available.

Strategic Interventions, Inc. **828.659.3418**
Fax 888.398.8072
   P.O. Box 1149, Nebo, NC 28655
   COA accredited organization.

Structured Family Interventions, LLC **919.416.0800**
Fax 919.416.0804
Web www.sfi4families.com
   1530 North Gregson Street, Suite 3A, Durham,
   NC 27701
   CARF accredited programs available.

Successful Transitions, LLC **336.275.7973**
Fax 336.272.1325
Web .... www.successfultransitionsllc.com
   301 North Elm Street, Suite 510, Greensboro,
   NC 27401
   CARF accredited programs available.

Sunlight Behavior Center, Inc. **910.864.2443**
Fax 910.864.2804
Web .... www.sunlightbehaviorcenter.org
   2030 Hoke Loop Road, Fayetteville, NC 28314
   COA accredited organization.

Sunpath, LLC **704.478.6093**
Fax 704.973.9287
Web .... www.sunpathllc.com
   415 West Main Avenue, Gastonia, NC 28052
   CARF accredited programs available.

Sunrise Clinical Associates, PLLC **919.493.5013**
Fax 919.493.5026
   3326 Durham Chapel Hill Boulevard, Suite C-100,
   Durham, NC 27707
   CARF accredited programs available.

Sunrise Pointe, LLC **336.226.8004**
Fax 336.792.4310
   631 Spence Street, Burlington, NC 27217
   CARF accredited programs available.

Sunrise Therapy and Support Services,
LLC **919.690.8400**
Fax 919.690.8401
Web .... www.sunrisetherapy.org
   911 Linden Avenue, Suite 109, Oxford, NC 27565
   CARF accredited programs available.

Sunshine Center, Inc. **910.734.8549**
Fax 910.738.7079
   4140 Fayetteville Road, Lumberton, NC 28358

Support, Incorporated **704.865.3525**
Fax 704.865.3520
Web .... www.supportinc.org
   175 West Franklin Boulevard, Gastonia, NC 28052
   Jeffrey Williams, Director
   CARF accredited programs available.

Suws Of The Carolinas **888.828.9770**
Fax 828.668.7959
Web .... www.suwscarolinas.com
E-mail .... admissions@suwscarolinas.com
   363 Graphite Rd, Old Fort, NC 28762-9455
   Graham Shannonhouse, Executive Director

T & D Empowerment Center, LLC **919.294.8708**
   2609 North Duke Street, Suite 401, Durham,
   NC 27704
   CARF accredited programs available.

Taft's Creative Service Council, Inc. **910.630.1946**
Fax 910.487.9537
   413 Country Club Drive, Fayetteville, NC 28301
   CARF accredited programs available.

Tanglewood Arbor/Mobile Crisis Mangement
Team **910.618.5606**
Fax 910.618.5604
Web .... www.srmhc.org
   207 West 29th Street, Lumberton, NC 28358

Tanyi's Respite and Habilitation Services,
Inc. **704.484.2450**
Fax 704.484.3001
   113 North Lafayette Street, Shelby, NC 28150
   CARF accredited programs available.

Teaching Alternative Strategies and Knowledge
Incorporated **919.758.8797**
Fax 919.720.4193
Web .... www.taskincorporated.com
   3200 Spring Forest Road, Suite 206, Raleigh,
   NC 27616-2811
   CARF accredited programs available.

The Alamance Academy, LLC **336.437.4382**
Fax 336.270.6105
   147 East Fifth Street, Burlington, NC 27215
   CARF accredited programs available.

The Aya Center **919.402.8738**
Fax 919.403.6106
Web .... www.theayacenter.com
E-mail .... hanifomar@theayacenter.com
   3500 Westgate Dr, Ste 101, Durham, NC 27707
   Hanif Omar, CES Program Director
   CARF accredited programs available.

The Aya Center **919.402.8738**
Fax 919.403.6106
Web .... http://www.theayacenter.com/
   3500 Westgate Drive, Suite 701, Durham, NC 27707
   CARF accredited programs available.

The Brunson Group, Inc. **919.261.8566**
Fax 919.266.5469
   7417 Knightdale Boulevard, Unit 101, Knightdale,
   NC 27545
   CARF accredited programs available.

The Children's Home, Inc. **336.721.7600**
Fax 336.721.7676
Web .... www.tchome.org
   1001 Reynolda Road, Winston-Salem, NC 27104
   COA accredited organization.

The Circle of Courage Support Services,
LLC **910.338.0001**
E-mail .... cocss@aol.com
   3137 Wrightville Ave, Wilmington, NC 28403
   Ms. LaRonda Woods-Freeman, Accreditation Manager
   Joint Commission accredited organization.

The Empowerment Center **336.312.5528**
E-mail .... kylemack1964@hotmail.com
   1 Centerview Drive, Suite 102, Greensboro,
   NC 27407
   Mr. Kyle McEachirn, Accreditation Manager
   Joint Commission accredited organization.

The HOPE Centre for Advancement, LLC **919.383.0426**
Fax 919.383.0619
   701 Morreene Road, Durham, NC 27705
   CARF accredited programs available.

The Masonic Home for Children at Oxford,
Inc. **919.693.5111**
Fax 919.693.2479
Web .... www.mhc-oxford.org
   600 College Street, Oxford, NC 27565
   COA accredited organization.

The May Frances Partnership in Caring,
Inc. **252.215.1262**
Fax 252.215.1263
   313 Clifton Street, Suite H, Greenville, NC 27858
   CARF accredited programs available.

The Renfrew of North Carolina **704.366.1264**
Web .... www.renfrewcenter.com
E-mail .... hrussock@renfrewcenter.com
   6633 Fairview Road, Charlotte, NC 28210
   Mr. Hayes Russock, Accreditation Manager
   Joint Commission accredited organization.

The Right Choice MWM, Inc. **704.537.3650**
Fax 704.537.3646
Web .... www.therightchoicemwm.com
   8825 University East Drive, Suite 210, Charlotte,
   NC 28215
   CARF accredited programs available.

The Right Trax, Inc............................919.662.7630
Web...............................www.therighttraxinc.com
883 U.S. Highway 70 West, Garner, NC 27529
CARF accredited programs available.

The Salaam Project, LLC.....................336.491.5423
Fax...336.889.5129
Web..............................www.thesalaamproject.com
927 East Dayton Avenue, High Point, NC 27262
CARF accredited programs available.

Therapeutic Supportive Services, Inc..........252.327.7930
Fax...252.413.6856
200 Eastbrook Drive, Suite D, Greenville, NC 27858
CARF accredited programs available.

Timber Ridge Treatment Center.............704.279.1199
Web...www.trtc.net
E-mail...tomhibb@nc.rr.com
665 Timber Trail, Gold Hill, NC 28071
Mr. Thomas A. Hibbert, Accreditation Manager
Joint Commission accredited organization.

Top Priority Care Services, LLC.............336.896.1323
Fax...336.896.1327
Web..........................www.topprioritycareservices.com
7990 North Point Boulevard, Suite 204,
Winston-Salem, NC 27106
CARF accredited programs available.

Total Care & Concern, Inc......................704.321.1635
Web.............................www.totalcareandconcern.org
E-mail.....................alishandra@totalcareandconcern.org
1428 Orchard Lake Drive, Charlotte, NC 28270
Ms. Alishandra Bethea, Accreditation Manager
Joint Commission accredited organization.

Total Miracle Kids, Inc........................704.854.8399
Fax...704.854.8410
212 West Second Avenue, Units A & F, Gastonia,
NC 28052
CARF accredited programs available.

Touchstone Residential Services.............919.380.9558
Fax...919.380.9987
1222 Copeland Oaks Drive, Morrisville, NC 27560
CARF accredited programs available.

Transcend Enhancement Services...........901.401.2772
Fax...910.221.0806
Web...................................www.TranscendNC.com
1033 Quailwood Drive, Fayetteville, NC 28314
CARF accredited programs available.

Triad Coordinated Services, Inc..............336.808.3490
Fax...336.808.3506
5009 High Point Road, Suite 113, Greensboro,
NC 27407
CARF accredited programs available.

Triangle Comprehensive Health Services,
Inc....919.751.0277
Fax...919.751.0278
Web...................................www.tchs1705@yahoo.com
1705 North Berkeley Boulevard, Goldsboro,
NC 27534
CARF accredited programs available.

Triangle Family Services.....................919.839.2286
Fax...919.839.2264
Web...www.tfsnc.org
P.O. Box 33393, Raleigh, NC 27636-3393
COA accredited organization.

Triangle Medical Services, Inc................910.904.2965
Fax...910.904.2931
4005 Fayetteville Road, Raeford, NC 28376
CARF accredited programs available.

Trinity Comprehensive Services, Inc..........252.212.0222
Fax...252.937.5806
301 South Church Street, Suite 160, Rocky Mount,
NC 27804
CARF accredited programs available.

Trinity House, Inc............................336.697.5506
Fax...336.697.5503
Web.................................www.trinityhousellc.com
1803 Lochwood Drive, Greensboro, NC 27406
CARF accredited programs available.

Trinity III, Inc................................704.482.0901
Fax...704.482.2081
Web...................................www.trinity3inc.net
921 North Lafayette Street, Shelby, NC 28150
CARF accredited programs available.

Trinity Services, LLC.........................910.461.1761
109 West Franklin Street, Suite 10, Rockingham,
NC 28379
CARF accredited programs available.

Triumph, LLC.................................919.256.0824
Fax...919.256.0833
Web...................................www.triumphcares.com
E-mail..........................kpeterson@triumphcares.com
c/o Saguaro Management and Accounting, Inc., 3210
Fairhill Dirve, Raleigh, NC 27612
Kate Peterson, Eastern Regional Director
CARF accredited programs available.

True Behavioral Healthcare, Inc................704.842.6354
Fax...704.842.6393
Web...................................www.truekids.com
2505-B Court Drive, Gastonia, NC 28054
CARF accredited programs available.

TT & T Services, Inc..........................910.739.0050
Fax...910.739.0077
Web..........................http://www.ttandtservices.net
4719/4721 Fayetteville Road, Lumberton, NC 28358
CARF accredited programs available.

Turning Point Family Care, PLLC.............919.493.0959
Fax...919.493.0970
Web...................................www.tpacenter.org
4300 Garrett Road, Suite A, Durham, NC 27707
CARF accredited programs available.

Turning Point Homes, Inc....................704.660.6854
Fax...704.662.0866
Web...................................www.Turning.com
201 North Church Street, Suite M, Mooresville,
NC 28115
CARF accredited programs available.

Ultimate Support Services, LLC.............910.343.1188
Fax...910.254.1088
Web...................................www.ussllc1.com
419 Grace Street, Wilmington, NC 28401
CARF accredited programs available.

Unified Behavioral Health, Inc................252.940.7260
Fax...252.940.7261
Web...................................www.unifiedbh.com
214 West Third Street, Washington, NC 27889
CARF accredited programs available.

Unique Family Services dba Kings Children and Adolescents
Services.......................................910.738.7479
Fax...910.738.7961
307 Martin Luther King Drive, Lumberton, NC 28358

Unique Home Care, Inc........................336.246.6991
Web.................................uniquehomecareinc.com
E-mail.............................uniquecareinc@yahoo.com
1320 Hwy 221 North, Jefferson, NC 28640
Mrs. Donna Badger, Accreditation Manager
Joint Commission accredited organization.

United Family Network, Inc....................919.749.2767
Fax...919.567.1325
Web...................................www.Ufnnc.org
9609 Kennebec Road, Willow Springs, NC 27592
CARF accredited programs available.

United Health Rehabilitation Services, LLC.....336.271.6800
E-mail.............................uhrs2009@gmail.com
1314 Headquarters Drive, Greensboro, NC 27405
Ms. Lori Johnson, Accreditation Manager
Joint Commission accredited organization.

United Treatment Facility, Inc................704.569.9192
Fax...704.566.7794
Web...................................www.unitedtreatment.com
2121 Shamrock Drive, Charlotte, NC 28205-2132
CARF accredited programs available.

United Youth Care Services. Inc..............336.370.9232
Fax...336.274.7200
Web...www.uycs.org
1207 Fourth Street, Greensboro, NC 27405
CARF accredited programs available.

Unity Healing Center.........................828.497.3958
E-mail.............................timothy.fowler@ihs.gov
448 Sequoyaqh Trail Drive, Cherokee, NC 28719
Mr. Timothy Fowler, Accreditation Manager
Joint Commission accredited organization.

Universal Mental Health Services, Inc..........828.759.2228
Fax...828.759.0159
Web...www.umhs.net
E-mail...info@umhs.net
839 Wilkesboro Blvd, Lenoir, NC 28645
Amy England, Agency Director
CARF accredited programs available.

Uplift Comprehensive Services............252.794.3834
Fax...919.882.8377
Web...................................www.upliftnc.org
PO Box 1123, Windsor, NC 27983
COA accredited organization.

Uprising Homes, Inc..........................252.794.5234
Fax...252.794.5231
1101 South King Street, Windsor, NC 27983
CARF accredited programs available.

Upward Change Health Services.............919.682.5300
807 East Main Street, Suites 4-100, Durham,
NC 27701
CARF accredited programs available.

VisionOne Health Services, Inc.............704.323.7617
Web...................................www.myvisiononehealth.com
E-mail.............................antoinelassiter@gmail.com
4822 Albemarle Road, Ste 112A, Charlotte,
NC 28205
Mr. Antoine Lassiter, Accreditation Manager
Joint Commission accredited organization.

Visions In View, Inc..........................252.482.2186
Fax...252.482.5271
407 South Broad Street, Edenton, NC 27932
CARF accredited programs available.

Visions of Hope, Inc..........................919.876.6211
Fax...919.876.6212
Web...................................www.visionsofhopeonline.com
E-mail.............................smarks@visionsofhopeonline.com
5886 Faringdon Place, Raleigh, NC 27609
Sally Marks, Executive Director of Visions of Hope
CARF accredited programs available.

Visions Residential Healthcare Services.......910.482.3513
Fax...910.482.3571
E-mail...adhccare@aol.com
549 Stacy Weaver Drive, Fayetteville, NC 28311
Annie Hasan, Executive Director
CARF accredited programs available.

W & B Health Care, Inc.......................910.843.1997
E-mail...rennerthome@aol.com
130 S. Main Street, Red Springs, NC 28377
Ms. Sandra Wilson, Accreditation Manager
Joint Commission accredited organization.

Wake Forest University Health Sciences, Amos Cottage Therapeutic Day Program 336.713.7400
Fax 336.713.7850
Web ....www.brennerchildrens.org
3325 Silas Creek Parkway, Winston-Salem, NC 27103
CARF accredited programs available.

Walker's Group Home 252.432.6308
2130 NC18/US64, Morganton, NC 28655
CARF accredited programs available.

WeCARE Residential Facility, Inc. 252.830.9600
Fax 252.830.4700
1761 Roosevelt Spain Road, Greenville, NC 27834
CARF accredited programs available.

Well Care LLC 910.452.1555
Web ....www.wellcarehealth.com
E-mail ....troberts@wellcarehealth.com
2715 Ashton Drive, Suite 200, Wilmington, NC 28412
Ms. Traci Roberts, Accreditation Manager
Joint Commission accredited organization.

Wellness Solution Center 919.682.6909
Web ....www.wscofdurham.com
E-mail ....lvance@wscofdurham.com
1100 North Miami Blvd Suite 601, Durham, NC 27703
Ms. Lucinda Vance, Accreditation Manager
Joint Commission accredited organization.

Wellness Supports, LLC 919.782.8730
Fax 919.782.8731
Web ....www.wellnesssupports.com
8390 Six Forks Road, Suite 201, Raleigh, NC 27615
Wendy Wenzel, Dirctor
CARF accredited programs available.

Whitaker PRTF 919.575.7927
Web ....www.dhhs.state.nc.us/mhddsas/whitaker.htm
E-mail ....jeff.lenker@dhhs.nc.gov
1003 12th Street, Butner, NC 27509
Mr. Jeff Lenker, Accreditation Manager
Joint Commission accredited organization.

White Alternative Services, Inc. 910.483.1146
Fax 910.483.1149
Web ....www.whitealternative.com
214 Lisbon Street, Clinton, NC 28328
Kristi Montero, Choral Director
CARF accredited programs available.

Wilson's Constant Care, LLC 336.703.9650
Fax 336.703.9793
1228 North Highland Avenue, Winston-Salem, NC 27101
CARF accredited programs available.

Wilson's Professional Care, LLC 336.403.1414
Fax 336.885.7745
Web ....www.wilsonsprofessionalcare.com
2415 Penny Road, Suite 102, High Point, NC 27265-8121
CARF accredited programs available.

Woodbranch Child and Family Support Services, Inc. 910.277.2600
Fax 910.277.6200
910 South Main Street, Laurinburg, NC 28352
CARF accredited programs available.

Woodbridge Alternatives, Inc. 910.488.9570
Fax 910.822.0111
Web ....www.woodbridgealternative.com
E-mail ....abrewer@woodbridgealternative.com
1480 Pamalee Drive, Fayetteville, NC 28302
Amie Brewer, Personnel Director
CARF accredited programs available.

Word of Life Outreach of Cape Fear, Inc. 910.371.5300
Fax 910.371.5302
Web ....www.wolocapefear.org
10225 Blackwell Road, Leland, NC 28451
CARF accredited programs available.

WOTP Programs, Inc. 704.536.0555
Fax 704.625.0067
Web ....www.wotpprograms.com
1100 Harding Place, Charlotte, NC 28204
CARF accredited programs available.

WrightCare Alternative Services 919.241.4064
Fax 919.267.3773
122 Faucette Mill Road, Hillsborough, NC 27278
CARF accredited programs available.

Wrights Care Services, LLC 336.542.2884
204 Muirs Chapel Road, Suite 105, Greensboro, NC 27410
CARF accredited programs available.

WTB New Vision, Inc. 336.723.7185
Fax 336.724.4545
Web ....www.wtbnewvision.org
102 West Third Street, Suite 330, Winston-Salem, NC 27101
CARF accredited programs available.

Yelverton's Enrichment Services, Inc. 252.522.4200
Fax 252.522.4209
5976 U.S. Highway 258 South, Suite C, La Grange, NC 28551
CARF accredited programs available.

Your Choice Health Services 919.957.0700
Fax 919.957.9300
3739 Wake Forest Highway, Durham, NC 27703
CARF accredited programs available.

Youth and Family Alliance, Inc. 910.251.5858
Fax 910.251.5893
2600 New Village Way, Raleigh, NC 28405
Lisa Loeffel, Clinical Director
CARF accredited programs available.

Youth Enrichment Group Home, Inc. 336.382.6658
Fax 877.846.8962
4299 Harbor Ridge Drive, Greensboro, NC 27406
CARF accredited programs available.

Youth Extensions, LLC 919.246.5664
Fax 919.321.0351
3501 South Alston Avenue, Suites A-B, Durham, NC 27713
CARF accredited programs available.

Youth Focus, Inc. 336.274.5909
Fax 336.274.3622
Web ....www.youthfocus.org
715 North Eugene Street, Greensboro, NC 27401
COA accredited organization.

Youth Haven Services, Inc. 336.349.2233
Fax 336.634.0444
Web ....www.youthhavenservices.com
1309 Coach Road, Reidsville, NC 27320
Jenna Lackard, Executive Director
CARF accredited programs available.

Youth Image, Inc. 828.433.4485
Fax 828.433.4486
107 Kela Drive, Morganton, NC 28655
CARF accredited programs available.

Youth Opportunities, Incorporated 336.724.1412
Fax 336.724.1464
Web ....www.youthopp.org
206 North Spruce Street, Winston-Salem, NC 27101
CARF accredited programs available.

Youth Services, Inc. 910.285.6099
Fax 910.285.6321
410 East Cavenaugh Street, Wallace, NC 28466
CARF accredited programs available.

Youth Unlimited, Inc. 336.883.1361
Fax 336.883.0065
Web ....www.youthunklimited.cc
PO Box 485, High Point, NC 27261-0485
COA accredited organization.

Youth/Adult Care Management, Inc. 704.933.3505
Fax 704.933.3525
Web ....www.youthadultcaremanagement.com
1605 Old Earnhardt Road, Kannapolis, NC 28083
CARF accredited programs available.

CHILDREN'S HOSPITAL

Alamance Regional Medical Center 336.538.7000
1240 Huffman Mill Rd, Burlington, NC 27216
John Currins, President

Ashe Memorial Hospital 336.846.7101
200 Hospital Ave, Jefferson, NC 28640
R D Williams, Chief Executive Officer

Betsy Johnson Regional Hospital 910.892.7161
E-mail ....kenbryan@bjrh.org
800 Tilghman Dr, Dunn, NC 28334
Ken Bryan, Chief Executive Officer

Blue Ridge Regional Hospital 828.765.4201
125 Hospital Dr, Spruce Pine, NC 28777
Keith Holpsclaw, President/CEO

Caldwell Memorial Hospital 828.757.5100
321 Mulberry St SW, Lenoir, NC 28645
Mark B Batts Md, Doctor Of Medicine

Cape Fear Valley Hospital 910.615.4000
1638 Owen Dr, Fayetteville, NC 28304

Carolina East Medical Center 252.633.8111
2000 Neuse Blvd, New Bern, NC 28560
Ray Legette, Chief Executive Officer

Carolinas Medical Center 704.355.2000
1000 Blythe Blvd, Charlotte, NC 28203
Michael Carwati, Chief Executive Officer

Carolinas Medical Center Lincoln 980.212.2000
433 Ecalister, Lincolnton, NC 28092

Carolinas Medical Center NE 704.403.3000
920 Church St North, Concord, NC 28025
Phyllis Wingate-Jones, Chief Executive Officer

Carolinas Medical Center Union 704.283.3100
600 Hospital Dr, Monroe, NC 28112
Michael Lutes, President

Carteret General Hospital 252.808.6000
3500 Arendell St, Morehead City, NC 28557
Fred Odell, Chief Executive Officer

Catawba Valley Medical Center 828.326.3000
810 Fairgrove Church Rd SE, Hickory, NC 28602
J Anthony Rose, Chief Executive Officer

Chowan Hospital 252.482.8451
211 Virginia Rd, Edenton, NC 27932
Jeff Sackrison, President

Cleveland Regional Medical Center 704.487.3000
201 East Grover St, Shelby, NC 28150
Brian Quinn, Chief Executive Officer

Columbus Regional Healthcare System 910.642.8011
500 Jefferson St, Whiteville, NC 28472
Henry Hawthrone, President

Davis Regional Medical Center 704.873.0281
218 Old Mocksville Rd, Statesville, NC 28625
Andy Davis, Chief Executive Officer

Duke University Medical Center 919.684.8111
E-mail ....victor.dzau@duke.edu
2301 Erwin Rd, Durham, NC 27710
Victor Dzau, Director

First Health Moore Regional Hospital 910.715.1000
155 Memorial Dr, Pinehurst, NC 28374
John Campbell, Director

FirstHealth Richmond Memorial Hospital 910.417.3000
925 Long Dr, Rockingham, NC 28379
John Jackson, Chief Executive Officer

Forsyth Medical Center 336.718.5000
3333 Silas Creek Pkwy, Winston-Salem, NC 27103
Cynthia Charles, Marketing Publishing Director

Gaston Memorial Hospital **704.834.2000**
2525 Court Dr, Gastonia, NC 28054

Harris Regional Hospital **828.586.7000**
68 Hospital Rd, Sylva, NC 28779
Mike Poore, Chief Executive Officer

Heritage Hospital **252.641.7700**
111 Hospital Dr, Tarboro, NC 27886
Wick Becker, Chief Executive Officer

High Point Regional Hospital **336.878.6000**
601 North Elm St, High Point, NC 27262
Jeffery Miller, Chief Executive Officer

Hoots Memorial Hospital **336.679.2041**
624 West Main St, Yadkinville, NC 27055
Fred Soule, President

Iredell Memorial Hospital **704.873.5661**
557 Brookdale Dr, Statesville, NC 28677
Ed Rush, Chief Executive Officer

Johnston Health **919.934.8171**
509 North Bright Leaf Blvd, Smithfield, NC 27577
Chuck Elliott, Chief Executive Officer

Kings Mountain Hospital **980.487.5000**
706 West King St, Kings Mountain, NC 28086
Brian Gwen, Chief Executive Officer

Lenoir Memorial Hospital **252.522.7000**
100 Airport Rd, Kinston, NC 28501
Debbie Lanier, Administrative Assistant

Lexington Memorial Hospital **336.248.5161**
250 Hospital Dr, Lexington, NC 27292

Margaret R Pardee Memorial Hospital **828.696.1000**
800 North Justice St, Hendersonville, NC 28791
Jerry Maier, Chief Executive Officer

Memorial Hospital **252.847.4100**
2100 Stantonsburg Rd, Greenville, NC 27834
Dave Mcrae, Chief Executive Officer

Mission Hospital **828.213.1111**
509 Biltmore Ave, Asheville, NC 28801
Ron Paules, Chief Executive Officer

Morehead Memorial Hospital **336.623.9711**
E-mail ....cmartin@morehead.org
117 East Kings Hwy, Eden, NC 27288
Carl Martin, Chief Executive Officer

Moses H Cone Memorial Hospital **336.832.7000**
1200 North Elm St, Greensboro, NC 27401
Judy Schanal, President

Nash Health Care **252.443.8000**
2460 Curtis Ellis Dr, Rocky Mount, NC 27804
Lawrence Chewning, Chief Executive Officer

New Hanover Regional Medical Center **910.343.7000**
2131 South 17th St, Wilmington, NC 28401
Jack Barto, Chief Executive Officer

North Carolina Specialty Hospital **919.956.9300**
3916 Ben Franklin Blvd, Durham, NC 27704
Randi Shults, Chief Executive Officer

Onslow Memorial Hospital **910.577.2345**
317 Western Blvd, Jacksonville, NC 28540
Ed Piper, Chief Executive Officer

Park Ridge Hospital **828.684.8501**
E-mail ....jimm.bunch@ahss.org
100 Hospital Dr, Hendersonville, NC 28792
Jimm Bunch, Chief Executive Officer

Presbyterian Hospital **704.384.4000**
200 Hawthorne Ln, Charlotte, NC 28204
Mark Billings, Chief Executive Officer

Presbyterian Hospital Matthews **704.384.6500**
1500 Matthews Township Pkwy, Matthews,
NC 28105

Randolph Hospital **336.625.5151**
364 White Oak St, Asheboro, NC 27203
Robert Morrison, Chief Executive Officer

Rex Healthcare **919.784.3100**
4420 Lake Boone Trail, Raleigh, NC 27607
David Strong, President

Roanoke Chowan Hospital **252.209.3000**
500 South Academy St, Ahoskie, NC 27910
Sue Lassiter, Chief Executive Officer

Sampson Regional Medical Center **910.592.8511**
607 Beaman St, Clinton, NC 28328
David Masterson, Director

Scotland Memorial Hospital **910.291.7000**
500 Launchwood Dr, Laurinburg, NC 28352
Greg Wood, Chief Executive Officer

Southeastern Regional Medical Center **910.671.5000**
300 West 27th St, Lumberton, NC 28358
Joann Anderson, Chief Executive Officer

Stanly Regional Medical Center **704.984.4000**
301 Yadkin St, Albemarle, NC 28001
Al Taylor, President

Thomasville Medical Center **336.472.2000**
207 Old Lexington Rd, Thomasville, NC 27360
Kathy Johnson, Chief Executive Officer

University of North Carolina Hospitals **919.966.4131**
101 Manning Dr, Chapel Hill, NC 27514

Wake Forest University Baptist Med Cent **336.716.2011**
Medical Center Blvd, Winston-Salem, NC 27157
Dr. John Mcconnell, Chief Executive Officer

Wake Medical Center **919.350.8000**
3000 New Bern Ave, Raleigh, NC 27610
William Atkinson, Chief Executive Officer

Watauga Medical Center **828.262.4100**
336 Deerfield Rd, Boone, NC 28607
Richard Starks, President

Wayne Memorial Hospital **919.736.1110**
2700 Wayne Memorial Dr, Goldsboro, NC 27534
William Paugh, Chief Executive Officer

Wilkes Regional Medical Center **336.651.8100**
1370 West D St, North Wilkesboro, NC 28659

Wilson Medical Center **252.399.8040**
1705 Tarboro St Sw, Wilson, NC 27893

COUNSELING SERVICES

Catholic Charities Of The Diocese Of Raleigh-Raleigh Regional
Ofc **919.790.8533**
Fax 919.790.8836
Web ....www.raldioc.org/csm/
E-mail ....mharawayr@raldioc.org
3000 Highwoods Blvd Ste 128, Raleigh,
NC 27604-1027
Rick Miller Haraway, Regional Director

Center For Family Violence Program **252.758.4400**
Fax 252.752.4197
E-mail ....dlucas@c4fvp.org
823 Evans St, Greenville, NC 27834-3267
Diana Lucas, Director

Child Abuse Prevention Svcs, Inc **828.254.2000**
Fax 828.254.2605
E-mail ....childadvocacy@buncombe.main.nc.us
50 S French Broad Ave Ste 152, Asheville,
NC 28801-3251
Bill McGuire, Director

CNC /Access **336.227.0440**
Fax 336.227.0821
236 N Mebane St Ste 102, Burlington, NC 27215
Tempia Foster, Director

Eckerd **800.914.3937**
Fax 727.442.5911
Web ....www.eckerd.org
E-mail ....admissions@eckerd.org
500 E-Ku-Sumee Dr, Candor, NC 27229
David Dennis, President & CEO; Francene Hazel, Director of Admissions
Eckerd provides fully licensed and accredited, short-term juvenile justice
residential services for troubled and at-risk boys and girls throughout the state
of North Carolina, as well as family preservation and reunification services in
Anson, Hoke, Johnston, Cumberland, Harnett, Lee, Montgomery, Moore, Richmond
and Scotland counties. Teen parenting education services are provided in Vance
County. Fully licensed and accredited. Youth are primarily referred through
contracts with public agencies.

Family Svcs, Inc. **336.722.8173**
Fax 336.724.6491
Web ....www.fsifamily.org
E-mail ....arenna@fsifamily.org
1200 S. Broad St, Winston Salem, NC 27101
Al Renna, Chief Executive Officer

Joanne Koster, PLLC **252.756.3433**
Fax 252.756.7533
Web ....www.greenvillecounselors.com
E-mail ....jkoster@embarqmail.com
620-A Lynndale Court, Greenville, NC 27858
Joanne Koster, Psychotherapist

CRISIS & SHELTER CARE

A Battered Women's Residence and Resource
Center **704.852.6000**
Fax 704.852.6004
E-mail ....cathy.cloninger@co.gaston.nc.us
330 N Marietta St, Gastonia, NC 28052-2332
Cathy Cloninger, Director

Albemarle Hopeline-Domestic Violence **252.338.5338**
Fax 252.338.2952
E-mail ....hopeline@raleigh.twcbc.com
1802 W Ehringhaus St, Elizabeth City, NC 27909
Pat Youngblood, Director

Amys House-Domestic Violence **704.736.0112**
Fax 704.736.0171
PO Box 476, Lincolnton, NC 28093-0476
Vicky Lingerfelt, Director

Catholic Social Svcs Host Homes **336.725.4678**
Fax 336.727.9333
Web ....www.cssnc.org
E-mail ....dvhaley@charlottediocese.org
621 W 2nd St, Winston-Salem, NC 27101
Duwey V. Haley, Director

Coastal Horizons Ctr, Inc. **910.392.6936**
Fax 910.392.0628
Web ....www.coastalhorizonscenter.org
E-mail ....afeath@coastalhorizons.org
615 Shipyard Blvd, Wilmington, NC 28412-6431
Amy L. Feath, Crisis Intervention Services Director

Coat Shelter **252.638.4509**
Fax 252.638.1298
E-mail ....cws@embarqmail.com
1333 S Glenburnie Rd, New Bern, NC 28561
Martha Hardison, Director

CVAN **704.788.1108**
Fax 704.788.1109
Web .... www.dhr.state.nc.us
E-mail .... mmargaret@dhr.state.nc.us
PO Box 1749, Concord, NC 28026-1749
Mary Margaret, Director

Dom Violence-Rape Crisis Ctr-Scotland Co **910.276.5505**
Fax 910.276.3600
PO Box 2130, Laurinburg, NC 28353
Betty P. Mcgee, Executive Director

Domestic Violence **252.523.5573**
Fax 252.523.9888
E-mail .... Sproctorsafe@Yahoo.Com
834 Hardee Rd, Kinston, NC 28504
Sue Proctor, Director

Domestic Violence **828.369.5544**
Fax 828.524.4535
E-mail .... reach@reachofmaconcounty.org
1895 old murphy rd, Franklin, NC 28744
Ann Vanharlingen, Director

Domestic Violence **919.774.8923**
Fax 919.775.7114
Web .... www.haveninleecounty.org
E-mail .... tina@haveninleecounty.org
160 Charlotte Ave, Sanford, NC 27330-4318
Tina McNeill, Director

Domestic Violence Coalition **704.694.4499**
Fax 704.694.4515
E-mail .... karendv129@yahoo.com
304 E Wade, Wadesboro, NC 28170
Karen Baucon, Director

Domestic Violence Program **252.726.2336**
Fax 252.726.8996
E-mail .... Ccdvp@Bizec.Rr.Com
PO Box 2279, Morehead City, NC 28557-2279
Glenda Riggs, Director

Domestic Violence Shelter And Svcs Inc **910.343.0703**
Fax 910.343.9388
Web .... www.domesticviolence-wilm.org
E-mail .... dvexecdir@earthlink.net
2901 Market St, Wilmington, NC 28403
Mary Ann Lama, Director

Durham Crisis Response Ctr-Dom Vlnce **919.403.9425**
Fax 919.490.9726
E-mail .... abelle@durhamcrisisresponse.org
206 N Dillard St, Durham, NC 27701
Aurelia Sands, Director

Families First **910.642.5996**
Fax 910.641.0253
E-mail .... Ffirst1995@Embarqmail.Com
812 Pinckney St, Whiteville, NC 28472
Vicky Pait, Director

Family Abuse Svcs **336.226.5982**
Fax 336.226.7303
E-mail .... sparker@familyabuseservices.org
1950 Martin St, Burlington, NC 27217
Lynn Rouffeau, Executive Director

Family Crisis Ctr **336.629.4159**
Fax 336.629.0523
E-mail .... info@familycrisis.com
239 E Academy St, Asheboro, NC 27203
Dare Spicer, Director

Family Guidance Ctr **828.322.1400**
Fax 828.322.8958
Web .... www.embarqmail.com
E-mail .... familyguidance@embarqmail.com
17 US Highway 70 SE, Hickory, NC 28602-5255
Ann Peele, Director

Family Svcs **336.694.5655**
Fax 336.694.9056
E-mail .... doris.boyd@yahoo.com
144 Court Sq, Yanceyville, NC 27379
Ms Doris Boyd, Director

Family Svcs Inc-Domestic Violence **336.722.8173**
Fax 336.724.6491
E-mail .... jshepherd@fsifamily.org
1200 S Broad St, Winston Salem, NC 27101
Joetta Shepherd, Director

**Family Svcs Of The Piedmont-Carpenter
House** **336.889.6161**
Fax 336.387.9167
Web .... www.familyservice.org
1401 Long St, High Point, NC 27262-2541
Tom Cambell, Chief Executive Officer

Family Svcs- Domestic Violence **336.679.2072**
Fax 336.679.2236
E-mail .... goadyveddi@yahoo.com
106 E Elm St, Yadkinville, NC 27055
Tonia Swaim-goad, Domestic Violence Supervisor

Family Violence And Rape Crisis Svcs **919.542.5445**
Fax 919.542.6414
Web .... www.fvrc.org
E-mail .... Kathy@Fvrc.Org
PO Box 1105, Pittsboro, NC 27312-1105
Kathy Hodges, Co-Executive Director

Family Violence Coalition Of Yancey Co **828.682.5655**
Fax 828.682.5655
Web .... www.main.nc.us
E-mail .... fvc@yanceycountync.gov
621 W Main St, Burnsville, NC 28714-2737
Samantha Phipps, Director

Friend To Friend-Domestic Violence **910.947.3333**
Fax 910.947.1849
E-mail .... Friend@Pinehurst.Net
111 Mc Neill Street, Carthage, NC 28327
Anne Friesen, Director

Hawthorne Heights **828.488.6512**
Fax 828.488.9267
Web .... www.mountainyouthresource.org
E-mail .... dkeller@mountainyouthresource.org
155 Patterson Ave, Bryson City, NC 28713-6773
Darlene Keller, Director

Help Mate **828.254.2968**
Fax 828.254.0720
E-mail .... vcollin@helpmateonline.org
68 Grove St, Ste C, Asheville, NC 28802
Valerie Collins, Executive Director

Help, Inc **336.342.3331**
Fax 336.342.6377
E-mail .... aboles@co.rockingham.nc.us
335 County Home Road, Wentworth, NC 27375
Angie Boles, Executive Director

Hope **910.754.5726**
Fax 910.754.9049
Web .... www.hopeharborhome.org
E-mail .... lcarlson@Hopeharborhome.Org
1053 Old Ocean Highway, Bolivia, NC 28422
Lynn Carlson, Director

Interact Domestic Violence Program **919.828.7501**
Fax 919.828.8304
1012 Overlin Rd, Raleigh, NC 27605
Leigh Duque, Director

Mainstay Domestic Violence Program **828.693.3840**
Fax 828.696.8104
Web .... www.mainstayhelp.org
E-mail .... tanyab@mainstayhelp.org
133 5th Ave W, Hendersonville, NC 28792-5083
Tanya Blackford, Director

Mecklenburg Womens Commision **704.336.3210**
Fax 704.336.4198
E-mail .... rlhall@ci.charlotte.nc.us
700 N Tryon St, Charlotte, NC 28202
Marie White, Division Director

My Sisters Place-Domestic Violence **828.649.2582**
Fax 828.649.2446
Web .... www.mysisterplace.org
E-mail .... Helpmate_Mad@Yahoo.Com
103 S Main St, Marshall, NC 28753
Joyce Cody, Director

Oasis Inc-Domestic Violence Program **828.264.1532**
Fax 828.264.1538
E-mail .... director@oasisinc.org
225 3rd St Ste 4, Boone, NC 28607
Jennifer Herman, Director

Onslow Womens Ctr Inc-Dom Violence **910.347.4000**
Fax 910.347.7960
E-mail .... onslowwomenscenter@earthlink.net
226 New Bridge St, Jacksonville, NC 28540-4737
Suzanne Wilbert, Director

Option **828.438.9444**
Fax 828.437.0323
E-mail .... inc6400@bellsouth.net
412 E. Meeting St., Morganton, NC 28655
Kristy Graf, Director

Outer Banks Hotline-Domestic Violence **252.473.5121**
Fax 252.473.9895
Web .... www.obhotline.org
E-mail .... bryant@obhotline.org
602 Amandas St, Manteo, NC 27954
Lynn Bryant, Director

Prevention Of Abuse In The Home **828.245.8595**
Fax 828.247.1456
E-mail .... pathshelter@bellsouth.net
358 E Main St, Forest City, NC 28043
Sherry Bright, Executive Director

Rape-Child-Family Abuse Crisis Council **704.636.4718**
Fax 704.642.0345
Web .... www.familycrisiscouncil.org
131 W Council St, Salisbury, NC 28144-4320
Lucritia Crent, Director

Reach **828.837.2097**
Fax 828.835.3434
Web .... www.webworkz.com
E-mail .... Reachinc@Verizon.Net
84 Valley River Ave, Murphy, NC 28906-2955
Ms Vicky Taylor, Director

Reach -Dom Violence **828.456.7898**
Fax 828.452.0960
E-mail .... reachofhaywood@att.net
1085 N Main St, Waynesville, NC 28786-3591
Julia Freeman, Director

Roanoke-Chowan Safe-Domestic Violence **252.332.1933**
Fax 252.332.2450
E-mail .... Rcsafe2000@Yahoo.Com
123 loftin lane, Ahoskie, NC 27910
Tamie Mccarter, Director

Safe Haven **910.259.8989**
E-mail .... Shopinc1@Eastnc.Twcbc.Com
1411 Highway 117S, Burgaw, NC 28425
Ted Proukol, Director

Safe Haven - Dom Vlnce **336.597.8699**
Fax 336.597.9318
Web .... www.embarqmail.com
E-mail .... Personsafe1@Embarqmail.Com
201 N. Main Street, Roxboro, NC 27573
Annette Hampton, Director

Safe Space Inc-Domestic Violence **919.497.5599**
Fax 919.497.1761
E-mail .... lrudolph@ncsafespace.org
113 S Main St, Louisburg, NC 27549
Linda Rudolph, Director

Safeplace - Domestic Violence **828.765.4044**
Fax 828.765.4011
E-mail .... pikedh@aol.com
51 Poplar Dr, Spruce Pine, NC 28777
David Pike, Director

Shelter Home **828.758.0888**
Fax 828.758.8949
E-mail .... director@shelterhomecc.org
　PO Box 426, Lenoir, NC 28645
Sharon Poarch, Executive Director

Southeastern Family Violence Ctr **910.739.8622**
Fax 910.739.1180
E-mail .... Sfvc@Nc.Rr.Com
　108 W 9th St, Lumberton, NC 28358
Hollie Oxendine, Director

Steps To Hope-Domestic Violence **828.894.2340**
Fax 828.894.3702
E-mail .... Steps@stepstohope.org
　60 Ward St., Columbus, NC 28722
Rachem Ramsey, Director

Swain-Qualla Safe Inc-Domestic Violence **828.488.9038**
Fax 828.488.1620
E-mail .... sqsafe@dnet.net
　171 Patterson Ave, Bryson City, NC 28713
Lisa Barker, Director

Timber Ridge Treatment Ctr, Inc. **704.279.1199**
Fax 704.279.7668
Web .... www.trtc.net
　665 Timbre Trail, Gold Hill, NC 28071
Tom Hibbert, CEO

Trinity Place **828.253.7233**
Fax 828.253.2476
E-mail .... amylilanhobson@juno.com
　12 Ravenscroft Dr, Asheville, NC 28801
Amy Hobson, Program Director

Turning Point **704.283.9150**
Fax 704.225.8857
E-mail .... nherndon@unioncountyturningpoint.org
　530 Patton Ave, Monroe, NC 28110
Naiomi Herndon, Director

U Care Inc-Domestic Violence **910.596.0931**
Fax 910.596.0574
E-mail .... Ucare@Intrstar.Net
　102 N. Road St, Columbia, NC 27925
Pamela Gonzales, Director

**United Family Svc Shelter-Battered
Women** **704.332.2513**
Fax 704.332.5403
E-mail .... jpayler@ussclp.org
　PO Box 220312, Charlotte, NC 28222-0312
Jane Payler, Coordinator

Victim Assistance-Domestic Violence Unit **704.336.4126**
Fax 704.336.4416
　720 E 4th St Ste 204, Charlotte, NC 28202
Amanda Wilson, Director

Wesley Shelter, Inc. **252.291.2344**
Fax 252.291.1436
Web .... www.wesleyshelter.org
E-mail .... lwhite@wesleyshelter.org
　106 E Vance St, Wilson, NC 27894
Lynn White, Director

EDUCATION

Christian School Assoc **919.731.4844**
Fax 919.731.4847
Web .... www.nccsa.org
E-mail .... joehaas@nccsa.org
　101 Millbrook Village Drive, Goldsboro, NC 27533
Joe Haas, Executive Director

Ed Tech **252.946.5382**
Fax 252.946.7964
Web www.beaufort.k12.nc.us
　820 Bridge St, Beaufort County Schools, Washington,
　NC 27889
Willard Bryant, Principal

Kittrell Job Corps Ctr **252.438.6161**
Fax 252.492.9630
Web .... www.jobcorps.doleta.gov
E-mail .... graham.ty@jobcorps.org
　1096 US Highway #1 South, Kittrell, NC 27544
Ty Grahan, Center Director

Lyndon B. Johnson Job Corp Ctr **828.524.4446**
Fax 828.369.7338
　3170 Wayah Rd, Franklin, NC 28734-8120
Arthur Phalo, Center Director

Schenck Job Corps **828.862.6100**
Fax 828.877.3028
Web .... www.jobcorps.com
E-mail .... gagner@jcdc.jobcorps.org
　98 Schenck Dr, Pisgah Forest, NC 28768-7713
Tammy Wentlend, Center Director

Stone Mountain School At Camp Elliott **828.669.8639**
Fax 828.669.2521
Web .... www.stonemountainschool.com
E-mail .... info@stonemountainschool.com
　126 Camp Elliott Rd, Black Mountain,
　NC 28711-9003
Jake Weld, Executive Director

FOSTER CARE AGENCIES

Access Family Svc **910.763.3166**
Fax 910.763.3169
　4000 Shipyard Blvd Ste 130, Wilmington, NC 28403
Mary Mack, Director

Adoption Triad Dialogue Group **336.605.3011**
E-mail .... fportnoy@bellsouth.net
　602 Meadow St, Greensboro, NC 27405
Francie Portnoy, Facilitator Of The Group

Beautitude House Christian Counseling **828.926.5591**
E-mail .... counseling@beautitudehouse.org
　470 Twin Brook Dr, Waynesville, NC 28785
Matthew Bradley, Director

Capital Area Families for Adoption **919.782.3836**
Fax 919.783.9418
　2725 Townedge Ct, Raleigh, NC 27612

Catholic Social Services of the Diocese **704.370.3227**
E-mail .... CSSadopt@AOL.com
　1123 South Church St, Charlotte, NC 28203
Linda Franks, Purchasing Manager

Grafted Families **704.660.3909**
E-mail .... lucarini@juno.com
　113 Drawbridge Ct, Mooresville, NC 28117

LDS Family Services **704.541.5626**
E-mail .... fam-nc@ldsfamilyservices.org
　7621 Little Ave Ste 420, Charlotte, NC 28226
Cheri Simmons, Administrative Assistant

Lutheran Family Services in the Carolina **919.861.2837**
　616 Hutton St, Raleigh, NC 27606
John Burns, Executive Director

N Carolina Foster & Adoptive Parent Assc **919.367.9302**
　2609 Atlantic Ave, Ste 105, Raleigh, NC 27604
Stacey Darbee

Newlife Christian Adoptions **919.779.1004**
Fax 919.779.1544
E-mail .... newlife@nlcadopt.org
　500 Benson Rd Ste 201, Garner, NC 27529
John Wheeler, Director

Roots and Wings **336.322.5437**
Fax 336.322.5439
E-mail .... rootsandwings@esinc.net
　1200 North Main St, Roxboro, NC 27573

**Southmountain Children and Family
Services** **828.584.1105**
Fax 828.584.8910
Web .... www.southmountain.org
　7330 Myrtle Drive, Nebo, NC 28761
COA accredited organization.

The Gladney Center for Adoption **252.355.6267**
Fax 817.922.5955
　235 Commerce St, Greenville, NC 27858
Frank Garrett, Director

Transracial Families of the North Carolina **919.405.2152**
E-mail .... info@transracial.org
　22 Cedar Hill Dr, Durham, NC 27713

HOME MEDICAL EQUIPMENT PROVIDERS

A Brighter Future, Inc. **910.321.6006**
Fax 910.321.6007
Web .... www.abrighterfutureinc.com
　4140 Ferncreek Drive, Fayetteville, NC 28314
CARF accredited programs available.

PEDIATRIC HOME CARE

Bayada Nurses **828.263.5350**
Fax 828.263.5354
Web .... www.bayada.com
E-mail .... boooffice@bayada.com
　240 Highway 105 Extension, Suite 201, Boone,
　NC 28607
Dan Wanta, Director

Bayada Nurses **704.982.7070**
Fax 704.982.7078
Web .... www.bayada.com
E-mail .... rkelly@bayada.com
　731 North Second Street, Suite C, Albemarle,
　NC 28001
Brup Kelly, Director

Bayada Nurses **336.331.1000**
Fax 336.750.0444
Web .... www.bayada.com
E-mail .... vhienkle@bayadanurse.com
　1605 Westbrook Plaza Drive, Suite 101, Winston
　Salem, NC 27103
Vena Hienkle, Director

Bayada Nurses **828.681.5100**
Fax 828.687.9898
Web .... www.bayada.com
　200 Ridgefield Ct., Suite 214, Asheville, NC 28806
Mark Bayada, President

Bayada Nurses **336.629.9919**
Fax 336.629.9929
Web .... www.bayada.com
　1207 South Cox Street, Asheboro, NC 27203
Suzanne Cook, Director

Bayada Nurses **336.852.2000**
Fax 336.851.2008
Web .... www.bayada.com
　2306 W Meadowview Road, Suite 111, Greensboro,
　NC 27407
Rob Varner, Director

Bayada Nurses **828.437.5454**
Fax 828.437.5559
Web .... www.bayada.com
　305 South Green Street, Suite 200, Morganton,
　NC 28655
Tom Minowicz, Director

Bayada Nurses **336.322.3200**
Fax 336.322.3035
Web .... www.bayada.com
　610 N Madison Blvd Ste A, Roxboro, NC 27573
Shelby Batto, Director

Bayada Nurses **704.226.0100**
Fax 704.291.9072
Web .... www.bayada.com
　1606 East Roosevelt Blvd, Suite 207, Monroe,
　NC 28110
Alicia Hopkins, Director

Bayada Nurses.................................**704.669.4000**
Fax...704.669.2535
Web...www.bayada.com
  1105-3 East Dixon Blvd, Shelby, NC 28152
  Joe Seidel, Director

Bayada Nurses.................................**336.651.8833**
Fax...336.651.8831
Web...www.bayada.com
  46 Boone Trail, Suite B, North Wilkesboro, NC 28659
  Allison Swisher, Director

Bayada Nurses.................................**704.797.2993**
Fax...704.797.8899
Web...www.bayada.com
  130 North Arlington Street, The Loflin Center, Suite
  B, Salisbury, NC 28144
  Kevin Cheek, Director

Bayada Nurses.................................**336.627.8900**
Fax...336.627.8901
Web...www.bayada.com
  810 S Van Buren Rd, Suite A, Eden, NC 27288
  Courtney Hodgen, Director

Bayada Nurses.................................**828.327.3800**
Fax...828.327.3303
Web...www.bayada.com
  1985 Tate Boulevard SE, Suite 417, Hickory,
  NC 28602
  Dan Noel, Director

Bayada Nurses.................................**336.632.9000**
Fax...336.851.5655
Web...www.bayada.com
  2306 W Meadowview Rd, Suite 115, Greensboro,
  NC 27407
  Shannon McCarson, Division Director

Bayada Nurses.................................**919.785.2900**
Fax...919.785.3191
Web...www.bayada.com
  One Crosspointe Plaza, 5505 Creedmoor Road,
  Raleigh, NC 27612

Bayada Nurses.................................**336.835.8500**
Fax...336.835.3510
Web...www.bayada.com
  1814 North Bridge St, Elkin, NC 28621
  Allison Swisher, Director

Bayada Nurses.................................**336.855.5220**
Fax...336.855.0963
Web...www.bayada.com
  2306 W Meadowview Road, Suite 115, Greensboro,
  NC 27407

Bayada Nurses.................................**704.920.1150**
Fax...704.920.1151
Web...www.bayada.com
  280 Concord Parkway South, Suite 110B, Concord,
  NC 28027
  Joann Reed, Director

Bayada Nurses.................................**704.289.6000**
Fax...704.291.9072
Web...www.bayada.com
  E-mail..................................hkuzara@bayada.com
  1606 East Roosevelt Blvd, Ste 210, Monroe,
  NC 28110
  Heather Kuzara, Executive Director

Bayada Nurses.................................**704.797.8000**
Fax...704.797.8899
Web...www.bayada.com
  130 North Arlington Street, The Loflin Center, Suite
  A, Salisbury, NC 28144

Bayada Nurses.................................**704.884.7000**
Fax...704.884.2135
Web...www.bayada.com
  1361 East Garrison Blvd, Suite B, Gastonia, NC 28054
  Shawn Widerick, Director

Bayada Nurses.................................**828.327.3300**
Fax...828.327.3303
Web...www.bayada.com
  1985 Tate Blvd. S.E., Suite 417, Hickory, NC 28602
  Jennifer Bainey, Director

Bayada Nurses.................................**828.696.1900**
Fax...828.696.8880
Web...www.bayada.com
  711 Yarborough Street, Unit B, Hendersonville,
  NC 28739
  Beth Kater, Director

Bayada Nurses.................................**919.785.9090**
Fax...919.785.2984
Web...www.bayada.com
  5505 Creedmoor Road, Suite 205, Raleigh,
  NC 27612
  Gill Burns, Director

Bayada Nurses.................................**704.971.4600**
Fax...704.971.4601
Web...www.bayada.com
  9009 J.M. Keynes Drive, Suite 12, Charlotte,
  NC 28262
  Mark Bayada, Chief Executive Officer

Bayada Nurses.................................**336.236.1000**
Fax...336.236.1040
Web...www.bayada.com
  E-mail................................lex-team@bayada.com
  200 S State Street, Suite 2, Lexington, NC 27292
  Brian Huckabe, Director

Bayada Nurses.................................**910.486.5001**
Fax...910.486.5002
Web...www.bayada.com
  2944 Breezewood Avenue, Suite 102, Fayetteville,
  NC 28303
  Dineen Morton, Director

Bayada Nurses.................................**336.694.9111**
Fax...336.694.9112
Web...www.bayada.com
  Bright Leaf Center, 2254 NC Highway 86N,
  Yanceyville, NC 27379
  Shelbia Battla, Director

Bayada Nurses.................................**704.295.1200**
Fax...704.714.5389
Web...www.bayada.com
  7300 Carmel Executive Park Dr, Suite 100, Charlotte,
  NC 28213
  Melissa Allman, Director

Bayada Nurses.................................**704.873.7722**
Fax...704.873.8831
Web...www.bayada.com
  1321 Dixie Drive, Suite E, Statesville, NC 28677
  Ben Trammell, Client Services Manager

Bayada Nurses.................................**704.795.5000**
Fax...704.795.5025
Web...www.bayada.com
  212 LePhillip Court, Suite 202, Concord, NC 28025
  Melissa Brown, Director

Bayada Nurses.................................**704.688.2500**
Fax...704.548.9518
Web...www.bayada.com
  E-mail................................khusn@bayada.com
  8801 J.M. Keynes Drive, Suite 140, Charlotte,
  NC 28262
  Kelly Husn, Director

Bayada Nurses.................................**828.452.0010**
Web...www.bayada.com
  50 South Main Street, Waynesville, NC 28786
  Jason Fox, Director

Cary PDN (Raleigh).........................**919.481.6712**
  MacGregor Center, 121 Edinburgh S Ste 203, Cary,
  NC 27511
  Mary Rollins, Regional Director

Charlotte PDN................................**704.335.9797**
  4530 Park Rd Ste 105, Charlotte, NC 28204
  Marcie Gilreaph, Director

Fayetteville NC PDN........................**910.323.1811**
  Omni Centre Complex Bldg II, 351 Wagoner Dr Ste
  412, Fayetteville, NC 28303
  Mary Rollins, Regional Dir.

Interim Healthcare.........................**252.758.7665**
Fax...252.758.0429
  1805-D W Arlington Blvd, Greenville, NC 27834

Interim Healthcare.........................**910.483.6144**
Fax...910.483.6049
E-mail...................srosol@interimhealthcare.com
  2401 Robeson St, Fayetteville, NC 28305
  Samantha Rosol, Rn

Interim Healthcare.........................**910.343.5244**
Fax...910.341.3246
  2007 Dawson St Extension, Wilmington, NC 28403
  Debbie Cobb, Nursing Manager

Interim Healthcare.........................**252.332.7665**
Fax...252.332.5882
  112 S Maple St, Ahoskie, NC 27910
  Kathy Vincon, Supervisor

Interim Healthcare.........................**910.738.1628**
Fax...910.671.4538
  4311-A Ludgate Ave, Lumberton, NC 28358

Interim Healthcare.........................**910.296.0012**
Fax...910.296.0409
  PO Box 513, Kenansville, NC 28349
  Shanon Shaler, Customer Service

Interim Healthcare.........................**910.755.8044**
Fax...910.755.7626
  117 Holden Beach Rd Ste 101A, Charlotte, NC 28459
  Jayne Sanderson, Supervisor

Interim Healthcare.........................**252.526.9792**
Fax...252.526.9794
  400 Glenwood Ave Ste 1, Kinston, NC 28501

Interim Healthcare.........................**252.243.7665**
Fax...252.243.4966
  1705 Medical Park Dr, Wilson, NC 27893

Interim Healthcare.........................**910.259.7075**
Fax...910.259.7075
  126 Fremont St, Burgaw, NC 28425
  Alice Sholar, Branch Manager

Interim Healthcare.........................**252.443.7222**
Fax...252.443.1341
  2483 Hurt Dr, Rocky Mount, NC 27804

Interim Healthcare.........................**704.861.1156**
Fax...704.861.1951
  2551 Pembroke Rd, Gastonia, NC 28052
  Tammy Hogue, Supervisor

Interim Healthcare.........................**336.273.4600**
Fax...336.370.0790
  2100T W Cornwallis Dr, Greensboro, NC 27408
  Kim McClure, Manager

Interim Healthcare.........................**704.487.5750**
  The Charleston Place Ste 304, 201 W Marion St Ste
  206, Shelby, NC 28150
  Laurie Mercer, Office Manager

Interim Healthcare.........................**336.768.6997**
Fax...336.768.7122
  3325 Healy Dr Ste A, Winston-Salem, NC 27103

Interim Healthcare.........................**919.681.2474**
Fax...919.681.2225
  Duke University Medical Ctr, Durham, NC 27710
  Kathy Merideth, Director

Interim Healthcare.........................**828.274.2082**
Fax...828.274.3201
  1550 Hendersonville Rd Ste 202, Asheville, NC 28803
  Mitch Huff, Office Manager

Interim Healthcare.........................**704.784.3483**
Fax...704.784.3499
  139 Union St, Concord, NC 28025
  Margaret Webb, Chief Executive Officer

Interim Healthcare **252.338.7665**
Fax 252.338.9584
　1023 S US Hwy 17 Ste 3, Elizabeth City, NC 27909

Interim Healthcare **910.640.2885**
Fax 910.640.2985
E-mail ....tellis@interimheathcare.com
　305 Liberty St, Whiteville, NC 28472
　Tina Ellis, Director Of Support Services

Interim Healthcare **910.642.6211**
Fax 910.642.6903
　310 Liberty St, 310 Liberty St, Whiteville, NC 28472
　Steve Smith, Director

Interim Healthcare **919.420.0336**
Fax 919.420.0172
　6310 Chapel Hill Rd Ste 280, Raleigh, NC 27607
　Lara Ewing, Operations Manager

Interim Healthcare **252.537.1500**
Fax 252.537.3348
　PO Box 237, Roanoke Rapids, NC 27870

Interim Healthcare **704.372.8230**
Fax 704.348.2672
　131 Providence Rd, Charlotte, NC 28207
　Julie Conrad, Director

Interim Healthcare **252.793.1000**
Fax 252.793.1567
　383 Hwy 64 W Ste 10, Plymouth, NC 27962
　Lisa Hill, District Manager

Interim Healthcare **910.862.8790**
Fax 910.862.7763
　207 S Poplar St, Elizabethtown, NC 28337
　Donna Kersey, Manager

Interim Healthcare **828.324.2121**
Fax 828.324.9435
Web ....www.interimhealth.com
　858 Second St NE Ste 301, Hickory, NC 28601
　Tammy Hogue, Regional Director

Interim Healthcare **919.735.8665**
Fax 919.734.6463
　1306B Wayne Memorial Dr, Goldsboro, NC 27534

Winston Salem PDN **336.760.8599**
　1386 Westgate Center Dr Ste A, Winston-Salem,
　NC 27102
　Brian Kowalski, Director

Winterville PDN (Greenville) **252.756.7233**
E-mail ....rhoggard@psakids.com
　108 W Firetower Rd Unit B, Winterville, NC 28590
　Renee Hoggard, Location Director

SOCIAL SERVICES

Agape Of NC, Inc. **336.855.7107**
Fax 336.855.8160
　302 College Rd, Greensboro, NC 27410-5106
　Thomas E. Slaughter, Director

Albemarie Child Care Resource And
Referral **252.333.3206**
Fax 252.333.1201
Web ....www.albemarlessp.org
E-mail ....rsabados@albemarlessp.org
　1403 Parkview Dr, Elizabeth City, NC 27909-6533
　Regina Sabados, Office Manager

Armed Svcs YMCA Fayetteville **910.436.0500**
Fax 910.436.0018
Web ....www.asymca.org
E-mail ....lgratesasymca@earthlink.net
　208 Thorncliff Dr, Fayetteville, NC 28303-5259
　Lynne Grates, Executive Director

Autism Services **704.392.9220**
Fax 704.392.9221
Web ....www.autismservices.org
　2211 Executive Street, Suite A, Charlotte, NC 28208
　COA accredited organization.

Brunswick Academy of Total Learning,
Inc. **910.754.3618**
Fax 910.755.7777
　344 Mulberry Street, Shallotte, NC 28470
　CARF accredited programs available.

CARING for Children, Inc. **828.298.0186**
Fax 828.298.2478
Web www.caring4children.org
　P.O. Box 19113, Asheville, NC 28815
　COA accredited organization.

Carolina Family Alliance, Inc. **704.536.9378**
Fax 704.536.9359
Web ....www.carolinafamilyalliance.com
　4915 Albemarle Road, Charlotte, NC 28205
　COA accredited organization.

Carolina Family Comprehensive Services,
Incorporated **704.548.9600**
Fax 704.548.9666
Web ....www.cfcs-inc.net
　P.O. Box 681105, Charlotte, NC 28216
　COA accredited organization.

Catholic Social Services of the Diocese of Charlotte, NC,
Inc. **704.370.3228**
Fax 704.370.3377
Web ....www.cssnc.org
　1123 South Church Street, Charlotte,
　NC 28203-4003
　COA accredited organization.

CCR&R Partnership For Children **252.727.0445**
Fax 252.727.0460
Web ....www.carteretkids.org
E-mail ....cjackson@carteretkids.org
　3328 Bridges St Ste A, Morehead City, NC 28557
　Constance Sowers, Office Manager

Challenges and Choices Behavioral Services,
Inc. **336.854.5330**
Fax 336.854.5331
Web ....www.ccbehavioral.com
　3407C West Wendover Avenue, Greensboro,
　NC 27407
　CARF accredited programs available.

Child Advocacy Council **252.793.5437**
Fax 252.793.1526
Web ....www.twpfc.org
E-mail ....keverson@mchsi.com
　125 W Water St # B, Plymouth, NC 27962-1305
　Kay Everson, Executive Director

Child Care Avenues Inc. **910.997.2273**
Fax 910.997.5432
Web ....www.richmondsmartstart.org/cca.htm
E-mail ....mvancebrown@richmondsmartstart.org
　315 S Lawrence St, Rockingham, NC 28379-3611
　Martha Vance-Brown, Executive Director

Child Care Choices/Partnership For
Children **919.202.0002**
Fax 919.202.0902
Web ....www.pfcjc.org
E-mail ....obogle@dockpoint.net
　1406 S Pollock St, Selma, NC 27576-3400
　Dwight Morris, Executive Director

Child Care Connections **336.513.0063**
Fax 336.226.1152
　2322 River Rd, Burlington, NC 27217
　Cindy Watkins, Director

Child Care Connections **704.487.7397**
Fax 704.487.6220
Web ....www.ccckidsbiz.org
　327 Market St Ste A, Shelby, NC 28151
　Karen Coster, Parent Referal Specialist

Child Care Connections/Smart Start **704.630.9085**
Fax 704.603.3398
Web ....www.rowan-smartstart.org
　1839 Jake Alexander Blvd W, Salisbury,
　NC 28147-1144
　David Rechui, Director

Child Care Resource And Referral **828.632.3799**
Fax 828.632.6411
　1565 NC Hwy W, Taylorsville, NC 28681
　Susan Cogdill, Director

Child Care Resource And Referral **910.296.2000**
Fax 910.296.1497
Web ....www.dpcfc.org
　149 Limestone Rd, Kenansville, NC 28349
　Joan Williams, Executive Director

Child Care Resource And Referral **910.938.0336**
Fax 910.938.0068
Web ....www.onslowkids.org
E-mail ....dawnrochelle@onslowkids.org
　301 NW Dr, Jacksonville, NC 28546-6339
　Dawn Rochelle, Executive Director

Child Care Resource And Referral Of
Brunswick **910.755.3362**
Fax 910.755.3376
Web ....www.smartstart-bruns.org
E-mail ....ccrrparents@smartstart-bruns.org
　5140 Sellers Rd, Shallotte, NC 28470
　Carol King, Director

Child Care Resource Of Alleghany **336.372.2846**
Fax 336.372.7705
Web ....www.danaservices.com
E-mail ....ccralleghany@yahoo.com
　994 N Main St, Sparta, NC 28675-8609
　Angie Wagner, Director

Child Care Search **704.348.2181**
Fax 704.376.7865
　4601 Park Rd Ste 500, Charlotte, NC 28209
　Denise Squier, Supervisor

Child Care Svcs Assoc **919.967.3272**
Fax 919.967.7683
Web ....www.childcareservices.org
E-mail ....info@childcareservices.org
　1201 S Briggs Ave ste 200, Durham, NC 27703

Child Connections **252.975.4647**
Fax 252.975.4722
Web ....www.beaufortcountykids.org
E-mail ....beverly@beaufortcountykids.org
　979 Washington Square Mall, Washington,
　NC 27889-3532
　Beverly Marslender, Director

Child Resource And Referral **252.672.5921**
Fax 252.672.5922
　2111 S Neuse Blvd, New Bern, NC 28560
　Pat Morrow, Director

Children And Family Resource Ctr Ccr&R **828.692.3847**
Fax 828.698.5532
Web ....www.childrenandfamily.org
E-mail ....noahw@childrenandfamily.org
　851 Case St, Hendersonville, NC 28792-6503
　Noah Wood, Coordinator

Children's Center of Surry, Inc. **336.386.9144**
Fax 336.386.9147
Web ....www.childrenscenterofsurry.org
　PO Box 692, Dobson, NC 27017
　COA accredited organization.

Choices In Child Care **828.426.2422**
Fax 828.426.4329
E-mail ....ksmithccc@bellsouth.net
　602 Morganton Blvd SW, Lenoir, NC 28645-5823
　Helen Wilke, Executive Director

North Carolina

Community Intervention Center, Inc. 252.321.7710
Fax 252.317.0516
Web ....www.cicenter.org
  605-A Lynndale Court, Greenville, NC 27858
  CARF accredited programs available.

Community Living & Choices 704.852.4428
Fax 704.852.4473
  4011 River Falls Drive, Lowell, NC 28098
  COA accredited organization.

Community Support Agency 910.655.0698
Fax 910.655.0611
  2957 Old Stage Highway Building #1 Suite 1, Delco,
  NC 28436
  COA accredited organization.

Cozie's Supervised Living, Inc. 336.622.2754
Fax 336.622.1420
  442 North Greensboro Street, Liberty, NC 27298
  CARF accredited programs available.

Crisis Ctr 252.237.5156
Fax 252.291.7408
  PO Box 8026, Wilson, NC 27893-1026
  Nancy Sallenger, Director

Crist Clinic For Women 910.353.2115
Fax 910.355.2422
E-mail ....cristclinic@bizec.rr.com
  250 Memorial Dr, Jacksonville, NC 28546-6332
  Sharon Cannon, Office Manager

Crossnore School, Inc. 828.733.4305
Fax 828.733.3250
Web ....www.crossnoreschool.org
  P.O. Box 249, Crossnore, NC 28616
  COA accredited organization.

Down East Partnership For Children Child Care Resource And
Referral 252.985.4300
Fax 252.985.4319
Web ....www.depc.org
E-mail ....info@depc.org
  215 Lexington St, Rocky Mount, NC 27801
  Carol Crocker, Operations Director

Early Childhood Partnership 336.786.1880
Fax 336.786.1879
Web ....www.surrychildren.org
E-mail ....mwestmoreland@smartstart-nc.org
  817 W Pine St, Mount Airy, NC 27030
  Marty Westmoreland, Executive Director

Family Life Council 336.333.6890
Fax 336.333.6891
Web ....www.flcgso.com
E-mail ....info@flcgso.com
  301 E Washington St Ste 204, Greensboro,
  NC 27401
  Rebecca Starnes, Executive Director

Family Service of the Piedmont, Inc. 336.387.6161
Fax 336.387.9167
Web ....www.safeandhealthyfamilies.com
  902 Bonner Drive, Jamestown, NC 27282
  COA accredited organization.

Family Services 336.249.0237
Fax 336.243.7685
Web ....www.fsdc.org
  P.O. Box 607, Lexington, NC 27292
  COA accredited organization.

Family Services, Inc. 336.722.8173
Fax 336.724.6491
Web ....www.fsifamily.org
  1200 South Broad Street, Winston-Salem, NC 27101
  COA accredited organization.

Family Svcs Of Piedmont 336.387.6161
Fax 336.387.9167
Web ....www.safeandhealthyfamilys.com
E-mail ....thomas.bonney@familyservice-piedmont.org
  315 E Washington St, Greensboro, NC 27401-2911
  Thomas Bonney, President And CEO

First Call For Help 910.397.0497
Fax 910.392.0628
  615 Shipyard Blvd, Wilmington, NC 28412
  Celine Adair, Open House Clinical Supervisor

Florence Crittenton Services 704.372.4663
Fax 704.334.8169
Web ....www.fcsnc.org
  P.O. Box 36392, Charlotte, NC 28236
  COA accredited organization.

For Kids Only Child Development Center,
Inc. 910.754.7777
Fax 910.755.7777
  344 Mulberry Street, Shallotte, NC 28470
  CARF accredited programs available.

Foster's Care Facility, LLC 336.885.0602
Fax 336.885.0603
  213 Lindsay Street, Suite 201, High Point, NC 27262
  COA accredited organization.

Free Will Baptist Children's Home, Inc. 252.235.2161
Fax 252.235.2625
Web ....www.fwbchildrenshome.org
  P.O. Box 249, Middlesex, NC 27557
  COA accredited organization.

Green Light Counseling, Inc. 336.274.1237
Fax 336.274.1236
Web ....www.greenlightcounseling.com
  415 North Edgeworth, Suite 205, Greensboro,
  NC 27401
  CARF accredited programs available.

Halifax Warren Child Care Resource And
Referral 252.535.4715
Fax 252.537.9732
Web ....www.hwss.org
E-mail ....mjames@hwss.org
  1139 Roanoke Ave, Roanoke Rapids, NC 27870-3703
  Magda Baligh, Deputy Director

Haven House, Inc. 919.833.3312
Fax 919.833.3512
Web ....www.havenhousenc.org
  706 Hillsborough Street, Suite 200, Raleigh,
  NC 27603
  COA accredited organization.

Holy Angels, Inc. 704.825.4161
Fax 704.825.0401
Web ....www.holyangelsnc.org
  6600 Wilkinson Boulevard, Belmont, NC 28012
  CARF accredited programs available.

Independent Opportunities, Inc. 704.547.8521
Fax 704.547.8522
  1977 JN Pease Place, Suite 102, Charlotte, NC 28262
  COA accredited organization.

Jenny C. Carrington, Inc. dba ABC Human
Services 704.869.6480
Fax 704.869.6477
Web ....www.abchumanservices.com
  P.O. Box 550234, Gastonia, NC 28055
  COA accredited organization.

Jewish Family Services 336.852.4829
Fax 336.852.4346
E-mail ....bgamburg@shalomgreensboro.org
  5509C W Friendly Ave, Greensboro, NC 27410
  Betsy Gamburg, Director

Jewish Family Services of Greater
Charlotte 704.364.6594
Fax 704.364.6596
E-mail ....info@JFSCharlotte.org
  5007 Providence Rd Ste 105, Charlotte, NC 28226
  Stephanie Starr, Executive Director

JFS of Western North Carolina 828.253.0701
Fax 828.254.7666
  236 Charlotte St, Asheville, NC 28801
  Alison Gilreath

Kare 828.456.8995
Fax 828.456.8905
Web ....www.karehouse.org
E-mail ....tkeilberg@karehouse.org
  1159 N Main St, Waynesville, NC 28786
  Tara Keilberg, Director

Kidsource CCR&R 336.985.2676
Fax 336.985.3302
Web ....www.stokespfc.com
E-mail ....kidsource@stokespfc.com
  PO Box 2319, King, NC 27021-2319
  Shannon Cox, Program Manager

LDS Family Svcs 704.535.2436
Fax 704.541.9284
E-mail ....fam-nc@ldschurch.org
  7621 Little Ave Ste 420, Charlotte, NC 28226-8368
  Paul Garrett, Director

Lutheran Family Svcs 919.832.2620
Fax 919.832.9876
Web ....www.lfscarolinas.org
  616 Hutton St, Raleigh, NC 27606-1817
  Ted Goins, Chief Executive Officer

Meridian Behavioral Health Services, Inc. 828.631.3973
Fax 828.631.9280
  P.O. Box 2187, Sylva, NC 28779
  COA accredited organization.

Methodist Home for Children 919.833.2834
Fax 919.755.1833
Web ....www.mhfc.org
  1041 Washington Street, Raleigh, NC 27605-1259
  COA accredited organization.

My Peace Keeper, Inc. 704.531.5656
Fax 704.531.9711
Web ....mypeacekeeper.org
  P.O. Box 25332, Charlotte, NC 28229-5332
  COA accredited organization.

New Lite Living Choices, Inc. 704.547.1900
Fax 704.547.1937
Web ....www.new-lite.com
  3634 Vest Mill Road, Winston Salem, NC 27103
  COA accredited organization.

North Carolina Family Health Start
Foundation 919.828.1819
Fax 919.828.1446
Web ....www.nchealthystart.org
E-mail ....information@nchealthystart.org
  1300 Saint Marys St Ste 204, Raleigh,
  NC 27605-1276
  Janice Freedman, Director

Northampton Partnership For Children 252.534.9921
Fax 252.534.1568
Web ....www.northamptonsmartstart.org
E-mail ....cwccrr@mchsi.com
  125 W Jefferson St, Jackson, NC 27845
  Cynthia Brown, Executive Director

Onipa Psychological and Consulting Services,
PLLC 919.231.2109
Fax 919.231.2152
Web ....www.onipa.com
  PO Box 46768, Raleigh, NC 27620
  COA accredited organization.

Partnership For Children 704.694.4036
Fax 704.694.4010
Web ....www.ansonsmartstart.org
E-mail ....acpfc@alltel.net
  117 S Green St, Wadesboro, NC 28170
  Elaine Scarborough, Director

Partnership For Children 336.694.1538
Fax 336.694.7666
Web ....www.caswellchildren.org
E-mail ....ccp4child@esinc.net
  1084 NC Hwy 86 North, Yanceyville, NC 27379
  Sandra Hudsteth, Executive Director

Partnership For Children 910.862.3335
Fax 910.862.7031
E-mail ....dcpsced@yahoo.com
228-B W Broad St, Elizabethtown, NC 28337
Lillian Bryant, Executive Director

Partnership For Children 910.592.9399
Fax 910.592.9304
Web ....www.scpfc.org
211 W Main St, Clinton, NC 28328
Victoria Byrd, Executive Director

Partnership For Children 336.342.9676
Fax 336.342.9962
Web ....www.rockinghamkids.org
87/65 Reidsville, Wentworth, NC 27375
Heather Kilpatrick, Executive Director

Partnership For Children 336.751.2113
Fax 336.751.9677
Web ....www.daviesmartstart.org
E-mail ....peburton@davidsonccc.edu
965 Yadkinville Rd, Mocksville, NC 27028-2033
Marybeth Scebold, Director

Partnership For Children 252.398.4124
Fax 252.398.3965
E-mail ....cbnhpsc@ambarqmail.com
711 E. Vance St., Murfreesboro, NC 27855
Cynthia Brown, Director

Partnership For Children 704.982.2038
Fax 704.983.8981
Web ....www.stanelypartnership.org
E-mail ....bwhitley@stanlypartnership.org
1000 North 1st Street, Suite 8, Albemarle, NC 28001
Barbara Whitley, Executive Director

Partnership For Children 252.206.4235
Fax 252.206.4245
Web ....www.wilsonpfc.org
E-mail ....jim.hawley@wilsonpfc.org
109 Park Ave W, Wilson, NC 27893-3844
Jim Hawley, Director

Partnership For Children 828.733.2899
Fax 828.733.9122
Web ....www.averypartnership.org
E-mail ....clindecamp@yahoo.com
414 Pineola Street, Newland, NC 28657
Sara Wackey, Director

Partnership For Children Child Care Resource And
Referral 336.599.3773
Fax 336.599.3999
Web ....www.personpartnershipforchildren.org/
E-mail ....jbatten@esinc.net
111 S Main St, Roxboro, NC 27573-5522
Judy Batten, Executive Director

Partnership For Children Of Lenoir & Greene
Counties 252.526.5000
Fax 252.939.1313
E-mail ....k.sylvester@lgpfc.com
1465 Us Highway 258 N, Kinston, NC 28504
Keith Sylvester, Executive Director

Partnership For Children Of Lincoln And Gaston
Counties 704.922.0900
Fax 704.922.0996
Web ....www.pfclg.org
E-mail ....parentinfo@pfclg.com
120 Roechling St, Dallas, NC 28034
Steve Eaton, Executive Director

Partnership For Young Children 704.878.9980
Fax 704.878.9961
Web ....www.iredellsmartstart.org
132 E Broad St, Statesville, NC 28677
Marta Koesling, Executive Director

Peterkin and Associates, Inc. 910.323.1817
Fax 910.323.2607
Web ....www.peterkinandassociates.com
131 Hay Street, Suite 201, Fayetteville, NC 28301
COA accredited organization.

Primary Care Solutions, Inc. 704.537.1022
Fax 704.569.0822
Web ....www.primarycareinc.com
5700 Executive Center Drive, Suite 101, Charlotte,
NC 28212
COA accredited organization.

ProCure Therapeutic Agency, Inc. 704.919.3542
Fax 704.919.3543
Web ....www.procureagency.com
1914 JN Pease Place, Charlotte, NC 28262
COA accredited organization.

Promise Place 252.636.3381
E-mail ....jean.hood.promise@gmail.com
1401 Park Ave, New Bern, NC 28560
Jaen Hood, Executive Director

Rainbow Center, Inc. 336.667.3333
Fax 336.667.8749
Web ....www.rainbowcenterforchildren.org
507 Courthouse Drive, Wilkesboro, NC 28697-2926
COA accredited organization.

Room At the Inn of the Carolinas, Inc. 336.996.3788
Fax 336.996.7567
Web ....www.roomattheinnofthecarolinas.org
P.O. Box 484, Colfax, NC 27235
COA accredited organization.

Sipe's Orchard Home 828.256.5056
Fax 828.256.4031
Web ....www.sipesorchardhome.org
4431 County Home Road, Conover, NC 28613
COA accredited organization.

Skill Creations, Inc. 919.734.7398
Fax 919.735.5064
Web ....www.skillcreations.com
P.O. Box 1664, Goldsboro, NC 27533-1664
COA accredited organization.

Smart Start 336.679.7833
Fax 336.679.6692
E-mail ....carolync@yadkinchild.org
246 E. Main Street, Yadkinville, NC 27055
Carolyn Choplin, Executive Director

Social Svcs 252.745.4086
Fax 252.745.7384
E-mail ....bjohnson@pamlicodss.net
828 Alliance Main St, Bayboro, NC 28515-9419
Debbie Green, Human Services Program Manager

Stars Of David International Inc/ Jewish Family
Svcs 919.676.2200
Fax 919.676.2122
Web ....www.shalomraleigh.org
E-mail ....info@shalomraleigh.org
8210 Creedmoor Rd Ste 104, Raleigh, NC 73613
Barry Schwartz, Executive Director

The Child Advocacy Commission 910.791.1057
Fax 910.791.2441
Web ....www.childcarenetwork.org
E-mail ....cacnc@childadvocacywilm.com
1401 South 39th St, Wilmington, NC 28403
Eliabeth Mandell, Director

The Children's Council Child Care Resource And
Referral 828.262.5424
Fax 828.264.8008
Web ....www.thechildrenscouncil.org
E-mail ....ccwci@bellsouth.net
225 Birch St Ste 3, Boone, NC 28607
Brian Cornell, Director

The Exchange Club Ctr For The Prevention Of Child
Abuse 336.748.9028
Fax 336.748.9030
E-mail ....cynthia.hanger@exchangescan.org
500 W Northwest Blvd, Winston Salem,
NC 27105-6526
Cynthia Napoleon-hanger, Executive Director

The Healing Place 828.692.0495
Fax 828.692.0433
Web ....www.thehealingplace.info
E-mail ....healingp@brinet.com
522 5th Avenue West, Hendersonville, NC 28793
Angie Alley, Executive Director

The Health Adventure 828.254.6373
Fax 828.257.4521
Web ....www.thehealthadventure.org
2 S Pack Square, Asheville, NC 28801
Paige Wheeler, Director

The Janice Mae Hawkins Foundation, Inc. 910.864.3426
Fax 910.864.1457
204 S. Reily Road, Fayetteville, NC 28314
COA accredited organization.

The Soul Focus 910.343.8438
Fax 910.341.7945
2539 Castle Hayne Road, F1, Wilmington,
NC 28401-2691
COA accredited organization.

Thompson Child and Family Focus 704.536.0375
Fax 704.531.9266
Web ....www.thompsoncff.org
6800 St. Peter's Lane, Matthews, NC 28105
COA accredited organization.

UNC Hospital Child Beacon And Family
Program 919.966.9314
Fax 919.966.9315
Web ....www.med.unc.edu\beacon
E-mail ....diana_bass@med.unc.edu
101 Manning Dr, Chapel Hill, NC 27514
Diana Bass, Director

United Family Services, Inc. 704.332.9034
Fax 704.373.1604
Web ....www.unitedfamilyservices.org
601 East 5th Street, Suite 400, Charlotte,
NC 28202-3095
COA accredited organization.

United Way 828.433.0681
Fax 828.433.7421
Web ....www.bcuw.org
E-mail ....slearned@bcuw.org
301 E Meeting St, Morganton, NC 28655
Sally Learned, Exec. Director

United Way Info And Referral 336.438.2000
Fax 336.438.2009
Web ....www.uwalamance.org
E-mail ....rpruitt@uwalamance.org
803 Hermitage Rd, Burlington, NC 27215-3513
Ruth Pruitt, Info/referral Coordinator

United Way Info And Referral Svcs 704.487.1111
Fax 704.482.9662
Web ....www.uwcluvco.org
E-mail ....jane.hoyle@unitedway.org
132 W Graham St, Shelby, NC 28150-5360
Jane Hoyle, Info/Referral Specialist

Volunteer Ctr/Info And Referral 828.324.4357
Fax 828.324.4358
Web ....www.ccunitedway.com
E-mail ....cabee@ccunitedway.com
800 17th St NW, Ste UW, Hickory, NC 28601
Cheryl Abee, Info/referral Director

Wayne Child Care Resource And Referral/Partnership For
Children 919.735.3371
Fax 919.735.3194
Web ....www.pfcw.org
E-mail ....info@pfcw.org
800 N William St, Goldsboro, NC 27530
Charles Ivey, Executive Director

Waynesboro Family Clinic, PA 919.734.6676
Fax 919.734.9050
Web ....www.waynesborofamilyclinic.com
1706 Wayne Memorial Drive, Goldsboro, NC 27534
COA accredited organization.

North Carolina

Work Family Resource Ctr, Inc.............336.761.5100
Fax......................................336.761.5107
E-mail...................mail@workfamilyresource.org
  530 N Spring St, Winston Salem, NC 27101-3383
  Katura Jackson, Executive Director

Youth Quest Inc......................919.942.1625
Fax......................................919.869.1387
Web...............................www.youthquestinc.org
  1162 Belfair Way, Chapel Hill, NC 27517
  COA accredited organization.

SPECIAL NEEDS

Abilitations Childrens Therapy & Wellness.....919.844.6611
E-mail....................................jennifer@actwc.com
  11030 Raven Ridge Rd Ste 101, Raleigh, NC 27614
  Jennifer Mock, Director

Autism Society of North Carolina............919.743.0204
E-mail.......................jhkeel@autismsociety-nc.org
  505 Oberlin Rd Ste 230, Raleigh, NC 27605

Baptist Children's Homes of North Carolina,
Inc.....................................336.474.1200
Fax......................................336.474.7776
Web....................................www.bchfamily.org
  P.O. Box 338, Thomasville, NC 27361
  COA accredited organization.

Brain Injury Association...................919.833.9634
E-mail......................................bianc@bianc.net
  PO Box 10912, Raleigh, NC 27605

Cape Fear Valley Rehabilitation Center.......910.609.6087
Fax......................................910.609.7711
Web.................................www.capefearvalley.com
  1638 Owen Drive, Fayetteville, NC 28304
  CARF accredited programs available.

Carolina Support Services, Inc...............252.752.2002
Fax......................................252.754.2008
  925 C and D Conference Drive, Greenville, NC 27858
  COA accredited organization.

Carolinas Rehabilitation....................704.355.4300
Fax......................................704.355.4231
Web.............................www.carolinashealthcare.org
  1100 Blythe Boulevard, Charlotte, NC 28203
  Robert Larison, President
  CARF accredited programs available.

Community CarePartners, Inc. dba CarePartners Rehabilitation
Hospital..................................828.274.2400
Fax......................................828.277.4890
Web....................................www.carepartners.org
  68 Sweeten Creek Road, Asheville, NC 28803
  CARF accredited programs available.

Congress of Parents & Teachers.............800.255.0417
E-mail....................................office@ncpta.org
  3501 Glenwood Ave, Raleigh, NC 27612
  Deborah Horton, Executive Director

Epilepsy Foundation.....................800.451.0694
E-mail..............................pgibson@wfubmc.edu
  1920 W 1St, Winston-Salem, NC 27104
  Patricia Gibson, Executive Director

Exceptional Childrens Assistance Ctr........704.892.1321
Fax......................................704.892.5028
E-mail....................................ecac@ecacmail.org
  907 Barra Row, Ste 102 & !03, Davidson, NC 28036
  Connie Hawkins, Director

FIRST....................................828.277.1315
E-mail...................................first@firstwnc.org
  PO Box 802, Nashville, NC 28802

First in Families of North Carolina...........866.740.4135
E-mail...................................amber@fifnc.org
  3803 Computer Dr, Bldg B Ste 205, Raleigh,
  NC 27609

Group Homes, Inc........................336.599.9421
Fax......................................336.599.7220
  PO Box 721, Roxboro, NC 27573
  COA accredited organization.

Hope Parent Resource Center..............828.438.6540
E-mail.............................vbdieter@charter.net
  300 Enola Rd, Morganton, NC 28655

Learning Disabilities Association............919.493.5362
E-mail...............................ldanc@mindspring.com
  9650 Strickland Rd, Ste 103-224, Raleigh, NC 27615

Lindley Habilitation Services, LLC...........336.855.3757
Fax......................................336.855.3363
Web.............................www.lindleyhabilitation.com
  4249 Piedmont Parkway, Suite 103, Greensboro,
  NC 27410
  COA accredited organization.

MDA/ALS Center at Carolinas Medical Ctr......704.446.1900
Fax......................................704.446.6255
E-mail...........benjamin.brooks@carolinashealthcare.org
  1010 Edgehill Rd N, Charlotte, NC 28203
  Benjamin R Brooks Md, Director

Moses H. Cone Memorial Hospital Rehabilitation
Center...................................336.832.4000
Fax......................................336.832.7464
Web...................................www.mosescone.com
  1200 North Elm Street, Greensboro, NC 27401
  CARF accredited programs available.

Mountain Youth Resources, Inc.............828.586.8958
Fax......................................828.586.0649
Web..............................www.mountainyouthresources.org
  P.O. Box 99, Webster, NC 28788
  COA accredited organization.

NAMI North Carolina.....................919.788.0801
E-mail...................................mail@naminc.org
  309 W Millbrook Rd Ste 121, Raleigh, NC 27609
  Gloria Harrison, Healthline Manager

National Multiple Sclerosis Society..........919.834.0678
Fax......................................919.834.9822
E-mail......................................NCT@nmss.org
  3101 Industrial Dr Ste 210, Raleigh, NC 27609

National Multiple Sclerosis Society..........336.299.4136
Fax......................................336.855.3039
E-mail......................................ncc@nmss.org
  2211 W Meadowview Rd Ste 30, Greensboro,
  NC 27407
  Elizabeth Green, President

National Multiple Sclerosis Society..........704.525.2955
Fax......................................704.248.9249
  9801-I Southern Pine Blvd, Charlotte, NC 28273
  Jennifer Lee, President

New Hanover Regional Medical Center Rehabilitation
Hospital..................................910.343.7835
Fax......................................910.343.3232
Web.....................................www.nhrmc.org
  2131 South 17th Street, Wilmington, NC 28402
  CARF accredited programs available.

North Carolina Baptist Hospital.............336.713.8031
Fax......................................336.713.8077
Web............................www.wfubmc.edu/rehab
  Medical Center Boulevard, Winston-Salem,
  NC 27157
  CARF accredited programs available.

North Carolina Baptist Hospital/Inpatient Rehabilitation
Programs.................................336.716.8455
Fax......................................336.716.8459
Web............................www.wfubmc.edu/rehab
  Medical Center Boulevard, Winston-Salem,
  NC 27157
  CARF accredited programs available.

Parents Together.........................910.924.5301
  4505 Shattalon Dr, Winston-Salem, NC 27106

Pediatric Brain Tumor Foundation...........828.665.6891
Fax......................................828.665.6894
  302 Ridgefield Ct, Asheville, NC 28806
  Diane Traynor, Chief Executive Officer

Ralph Scott Lifeservices, Inc................336.227.1011
Fax......................................336.226.6465
Web...www.rsli.org
  408 West Trade Street, Burlington, NC 27217
  COA accredited organization.

Recording for the Blind & Dyslexic...........919.599.4104
E-mail..............................eboyd@rfbdvanc.org
  25 Birnham Ln, Durham, NC 27707

Regional Rehabilitation Center Memorial
Hospital..................................252.847.4715
Fax......................................252.847.7552
Web.......................www.rehabilitation.uhseast.com
  2100 Stantonsburg Road, Greenville,
  NC 27835-6028
  CARF accredited programs available.

SOAR....................................828.456.3435
Fax......................................828.456.3449
E-mail..............................admissions@soarnc.org
  PO Box 388, Balsam, NC 28707
  Kylie Cyr, Administrative Instructer

Speech Hearing & Language Association.......919.833.3984
E-mail...................................info@mtsshla.org
  PO Box 28359, Raleigh, NC 27611
  Kathy Cox, President

Spina Bifida Association....................800.847.2262
E-mail.............................sbanc@mindspring.com
  3915 Grace Ct, Indian Trail, NC 28079

Student Learning Recovery.................919.303.3090
E-mail.............................icansee3d@yahoo.com
  522 E Williams St, Apex, NC 27502

Summit Support Services of Ashe, Inc........336.846.4491
Fax......................................336.846.4927
  P.O. Box 381, Jefferson, NC 28640
  COA accredited organization.

The Arc of North Carolina.................800.662.8706
E-mail...................................drichard@arcnc.org
  343 E Six Forks Rd Ste 320, Raleigh, NC 27609
  Dave Richard, Executive Director

The Brain Trainer.......................704.541.1373
Fax......................................704.541.7995
Web.............................www.thebrain-trainer.com
E-mail....................angela@thebrain-trainer.com
  11030 Golf Links Dr, Ste 204, Charlotte, NC 28277
  Dr. Vicki Parker, Slp, Director

The Simple Life Services, Inc................704.868.8328
Fax......................................704.868.8332
Web.........................www.thesimplelifeservices.com
  520 Union Road, Gastonia, NC 28054-4450
  COA accredited organization.

UNC hospital...........................919.966.4131
  101 Manning Dr, Chapel Hill, NC 27514

University of North Carolina Health Care
System...................................919.966.2016
Fax......................................919.966.0221
Web...................................www.unchealthcare.org
  101 Manning Drive, Chapel Hill, NC 27514
  CARF accredited programs available.

WakeMed Rehab.........................919.350.8852
Fax......................................919.350.7130
Web....................................www.wakemed.org
  3000 New Bern Ave, Raleigh, NC 27610
  Denton Arledge, Director - Information Technology
  CARF accredited programs available.

SUBSTANCE ABUSE TREATMENT

CommuniCare, Inc..........................**910.829.9017**
Fax..910.485.4752
Web..www.cccommunicare.org
E-mail..............................shallock@cccommunicare.org
  711-B Executive Place, Fayetteville, NC 28305
  Sarah Hallock, Director
  CARF accredited programs available.

Eckerd...**800.914.3937**
Fax..727.442.5911
Web..www.eckerd.org
E-mail..................................admissions@eckerd.org
  500 E-Ku-Sumee Dr, Candor, NC 27229
  David Dennis, President & CEO; Francene Hazel, Director of Admissions
  Eckerd provides fully licensed and accredited, short-term juvenile justice
  residential services for troubled and at-risk boys and girls throughout the state
  of North Carolina, as well as family preservation and reunification services in
  Anson, Hoke, Johnston, Cumberland, Harnett, Lee, Montgomery, Moore, Richmond
  and Scotland counties. Teen parenting education services are provided in Vance
  County. Fully licensed and accredited. Youth are primarily referred through
  contracts with public agencies.

Mary Frances Corporation...................**252.641.1111**
Fax..252.641.0297
  1212 Recovery Road, Tarboro, NC 27886
  Patricia Synder, Supervisor
  CARF accredited programs available.

McLeod Addictive Disease Center, Inc.........**704.332.9001**
Fax..704.332.0124
Web...www.mcleodcenter.com
E-mail....................jolennadenison@mcleodcenter.com
  145 Remount Road, Charlotte, NC 28203
  Jolenna Denison, Marketing Director
  CARF accredited programs available.

Palmer Prevention Inc......................**910.618.1135**
Fax..910.739.3822
E-mail...............................palmerteencourt@aol.com
  2501 E. Elizabeth town, Lumberton, NC 28359
  Thomas Norton, Executive Director

Self Concepts Clinical Counseling Services,
Inc....**704.852.3874**
Fax..704.852.7060
Web...www.myselfconcept.com
  1558 Union Road, Suite A, Gastonia, NC 28054
  CARF accredited programs available.

SouthLight, Inc..............................**919.787.6131**
Fax..919.571.2932
Web...www.southlight.org
E-mail...............................scottr@southlight.org
  3125 Poplarwood Court, Suite 203, Raleigh,
  NC 27604
  Earl London, Program Director
  CARF accredited programs available.

North Dakota

Jack Dalrymple, Governor
600 E. Boulevard Avenue, Dept. 101
Bismark, ND 58505-0001
701.328.2200
701.328.2205 (Fax)
governor@nd.gov
www.nd.gov

Terry Traynor, Juvenile Justice Specialist
Division of Juvenile Services
1661 Capitol Way
Bismark, ND 58501
701.328.7321
701.328.7308 (Fax)
ttraynor@ndaco.org
www.ndaco.org

Lisa Jahner, SAG Chair
1661 Capitol Way
Bismark, ND 58501
701.328.7320
701.328.7308 (Fax)
ljahner@ndaco.org
www.ndaco.org

CRISIS NUMBERS

Child Abuse Reporting . . .701.328.2316

STATE SERVICES

SOCIAL SERVICES

Child Care Licensing Office North Dakota 701.328.2316
Fax 701.328.3538
E-mail . . . . .TMUHLHAUSER@ND.GOV
  600 East Blvd Ave Dept 325, Bismarck, ND 58505
  Tara Muhlhauser, Director

Child Support Enforcement 701.328.3582
Fax 701.328.6575
Web . . . . .www.childsupportnd.com
E-mail . . . . .jfleming@nd.gov
  1600 E Century Ave Ste 7, Bismarck, ND 58503
  Jim Fleming, Director

North Dakota Dept of Human Svcs 701.328.2310
Fax 701.328.1544
Web . . . . .www.nd.gov/bhf
E-mail . . . . .dhfeo@nd.gov
  600 E Boulevard Ave Dept 325, Bismarck, ND 58505
  Carol K. Olson, Executive Director

Vocational Rehabilitation 701.328.8950
Fax 701.328.8969
E-mail . . . . .rcusack@nd.gov
  1237 W Divide Ave, Prairie Hills Plaza Suite 1B,
  Bismarck, ND 58501
  Russell Cusack, Director

GENERAL HEALTH SERVICES

Children's Special Health Svcs 701.328.2436
Fax 701.328.1645
Web . . . . .www.ndhealth.gov/cshs
E-mail . . . . .dohcshsadm@nd.gov
  600 E Boulevard Ave Dept 301, Bismarck, ND 58505
  Tammy Gallup-millner, Division Director

Ctr for Rural Health 701.777.3848
Fax 701.777.6779
Web . . . . .www.medicine.nodak.edu/crh
  501 N Columbia Rd, UND School of Medicine, Grand
  Forks, ND 58203-2817
  Gary Hart, Director

Dept of Health 701.328.2372
Fax 701.328.4727
Web . . . . .www.ndhealth.gov
E-mail . . . . .dmeschke@nd.gov
  600 E Boulevard Ave Dept 301, Bismarck,
  ND 58505-0200
  Darin Meschke, It Coordinator

Family Health 701.328.2493
Fax 701.328.1412
E-mail . . . . .kmertz@nd.gov
  600 E Blvd Ave Dept 301, Bismarck, ND 58505
  Kim Mertz, Director

MENTAL HEALTH SERVICES

Mental Health And Substance Abuse Svcs 701.328.8920
Fax 701.328.8969
Web . . . . .www.state.nd.us
E-mail . . . . .dhsmhsas@state.nd.us
  1237 W Divide Ave Ste 1C, Bismarck,
  ND 58501-1208
  Joanne Haoesel, Director

JUSTICE AGENCY

Attorney General's Ofc 701.328.2210
Fax 701.328.2226
E-mail . . . . .ndag@nd.gov
  600 E Boulevard Ave Dept 125, Bismarck, ND 58505
  Wayne Stenehjem, Attorney General

Crime Victims Compensation Program 701.328.6195
Fax 701.328.6186
E-mail . . . . .pcoughli@nd.gov
  3100 Railroad Avenue, Bismarck, ND 58501
  Paul J. Coughlin, Administrator ND Crime Victims Compensation

DOCR, Div of Juvenile Svcs 701.328.6390
Fax 701.328.6651
  3100 Railroad Ave, Bismarck, ND 58502
  Lisa Bjergaard, Director

COURTS

Administrative Ofc Of The Courts 701.328.4216
Fax 701.328.2092
E-mail . . . . .sholewa@ndcourts.gov
  600 E Boulevard Ave Dept 180, Bismarck, ND 58505
  Sally Holewa, Administrator

POLICE AND SHERIFF

Bureau Of Criminal Investigation 701.328.5500
Fax 701.328.5510
Web . . . . .www.ag.state.nd.us
E-mail . . . . .jkemmet@state.nd.us
  4205 State St, Bismarck, ND 58503
  Jerald Kemmet, Director

EDUCATION SERVICES

Educ for Homeless Children and Youth ND 701.328.4646
Fax 701.328.0203
E-mail . . . . .tbitz@nd.gov
  600 E Boulevard Ave Dept 201, Bismarck, ND 58505
  Terry Bitz, Director

ND Dept of Public Instruction 701.328.2260
Fax 701.328.2461
E-mail . . . . .alrichardon@nd.gov
  600 E Blvd Ave Dept 201, Bismarck, ND 58505
  Amanda Richardson, Clerk

North Dakota Vision/School for the Blind 701.795.2700
Fax 701.795.2727
Web . . . . .www.ndvisonservices.com
  500 Stanford Rd, Grand Forks, ND 58203
  Carmen Grove-suminski, Superintendent

Office of Special Educ ND 701.328.2277
Fax 701.328.4149
E-mail . . . . .adollar@nd.gov
  600 E Boulevard Ave, Dept 201, Bismarck, ND 58505
  Alison Dollar, Director

School Health Programs .701.328.4138
Fax 701.328.4770
Web . . . . .www.state.nd.us
E-mail . . . . .vfischer@nd.gov
  600 E Blvd Ave, 9th Fl, Bismarck, ND 58505
  Valerie Fisher, Director

LABOR & WORKFORCE EDUCATION

Job Svc North Dakota 701.328.2836
Fax 701.328.1612
Web . . . . .www.state.nd.us
E-mail . . . . .mdaley@state.nd.us
  1000 E Divide Ave, Bismarck, ND 58506-1926
  Maren Daley, Executive Director

North Dakota

COUNTY SERVICES

Adams County

GENERAL HEALTH SERVICES

Health Unit..............................**701.567.2720**
Fax...701.567.4799
E-mail..............................mank4@hotmail.com
   609 2nd Ave N, Hettinger, ND 58639
Katie Manning, Rn, Supervisor

Barnes County

SOCIAL SERVICES

Social Svc...............................**701.845.8521**
Fax...701.845.4281
E-mail......................SSEW@CO.BARNES.ND.US
   230 4th St NW Rm 103, Valley City, ND 58072
Heather Pautz, County Director

GENERAL HEALTH SERVICES

Health Dist.............................**701.845.8518**
Fax...701.845.8542
Web.................................www.co.barnes.nd.us
   230 4th St NW Rm 102, Valley City, ND 58072
Theresa Will, Rn, Nursing Director

COURTS

District Court.........................**701.845.8525**
Fax...701.845.8544
Web....................................www.ndcourts.gov
   230 4th St NW Rm 303, Valley City, ND 58072
John T Paulson, District Court Judge

POLICE AND SHERIFF

Sheriff's Offc..........................**701.845.8530**
Fax...701.845.0002
   218 2nd Ave NE, Valley City, ND 58072
Randy Mcclaslin, Sheriff

Benson County

SOCIAL SERVICES

Social Svc Board.....................**701.473.5302**
Fax...701.473.5330
Web...www.state.nd.us
E-mail.....................................polson@nd.us
   108 East 4th St, Minnewaukan, ND 58351
Paul Olson, Director

GENERAL HEALTH SERVICES

Lake Rigion District Health......**701.473.5444**
Fax...701.473.2564
E-mail...........................bensphn@stellanet.com
   201 Main St W Apt 5, Minnewaukan, ND 58351
Shelly Aabrekke, RN, Staff Nurse

Bottineau County

SOCIAL SERVICES

Social Svc Board.....................**701.228.3613**
Fax...701.228.3600
Web...............................www.co.bottineau.nd.us
E-mail....................kelly.jensen@co.bottineau.nd.us
   314 5th St W Ste 1, Bottineau, ND 58318-1271
Kelly Jensen, Director

GENERAL HEALTH SERVICES

Health Unit.............................**701.228.3101**
Fax...701.228.3788
Web...www.fdhu.org
E-mail........................smbrandvold@nd.gov
   314 5th St W Ste 7, Bottineau, ND 58318-1204
Susan Brandvold, Rn, County Nurse

COURTS

Juvenile Court........................**701.228.2375**
Fax...701.228.2336
Web....................................www.ndcourts.gov
E-mail..............................rgense@ndcourts.gov
   314 5th St W Ste 12, Bottineau, ND 58318
Launee Lawyer-hamnes, Juvenile Court Officer

Bowman County

SOCIAL SERVICES

Social Svc Board.....................**701.523.3285**
Fax...701.523.5871
E-mail.................................06burj@nd.gov
   104 1st St NW Ste 8, Bowman, ND 58623-4342
Shonda Schwartz, Director

Burke County

GENERAL HEALTH SERVICES

Health Unit.............................**701.377.2316**
Fax...701.377.2326
Web...www.fdhu.org
E-mail..................................mburud@nd.gov
   103 Main St NE, Bowbells, ND 58721
Melissa Burud, Public Health Nurse

POLICE AND SHERIFF

Sheriff's Dept.........................**701.377.2311**
Fax...701.377.2177
   103 Main Street SE, Bowbells, ND 58721
Barry Jager, Sheriff

Burleigh County

SOCIAL SERVICES

West Central Human Svc Ctr.......**701.328.8888**
Fax...701.328.8900
Web..................................www.discovernd.com
E-mail..................................saut@state.nd.us
   1237 W Divide Ave Ste 5, Bismarck, ND 58501
Tim Sauter, Director

GENERAL HEALTH SERVICES

Bismarck Burleigh Public Health.......**701.355.1540**
Fax...701.221.6883
Web..www.bismark.org
E-mail..................................pflander@nd.gov
   500 E Front Ave Ste 1, Bismarck, ND 58504-5689
Paula Flanders, Rn, Administrator/director Of Nursing

JUSTICE AGENCY

**Bismarck Parole And Probation Central
Ofc**..**701.328.6190**
Fax...701.328.6186
Web...www.state.nd.us
E-mail............................wemmer@state.nd.us
   3100 Railroad Ave, Bismarck, ND 58501-5011
Warren Emmer, Director

Div Of Juvenile Svcs................**701.328.3940**
Fax...701.328.3968
   921 S 9th St 110, Bismarck, ND 58504
Sally Walker, Administration Assistant

COURTS

District Court.........................**701.222.6682**
Fax...701.222.6689
Web....................................www.ndcourts.com
   514 E Thayer Ave, Bismarck, ND 58502
Honorable Phonna Anderson, Judge

Juvenile Court........................**701.222.6709**
Fax...701.222.6699
Web....................................www.ndcourts.gov
E-mail..........................cpeterson@ndcourts.gov
   514 E Thayer Ave, Bismarck, ND 58501-4413
Cory Peterson, Director

Teen Court.............................**701.258.2240**
Fax...701.258.2245
Web...www.tap7.com
E-mail.................................mandyr@tap7.com
   2105 Lee Ave, Bismarck, ND 58504-6728
Mandy Reinhart, Coordinator

POLICE AND SHERIFF

Police Youth Bureau................**701.222.6738**
Fax...701.355.1925
Web....................................www.bismarck.org
   700 S 9th St, Bismarck, ND 58504-5821
Lt. Dan Donlin, Director

Cass County

SOCIAL SERVICES

Social Svc Board.....................**701.241.5761**
Fax...701.239.6820
E-mail................................08hogk@state.nd.us
   1010 Second Avenue, South Fargo, ND 58108
Dhip Ammerman, Executive Director

Southeast Human Svc Ctr.........**701.298.4500**
Fax...701.298.4400
Web...www.state.nd.us
E-mail..........................nmckenzie@state.nd.us
   2624 9th Ave S, Fargo, ND 58103-2367
Nancy Mckenzie, Director

GENERAL HEALTH SERVICES

Health Dept............................**701.241.1360**
Fax...701.241.8559
Web.............................www.cityoffargo.com/health
   401 3rd Ave N, Fargo, ND 58102
Ruth Bachmeier, Director Of Public Health

JUSTICE AGENCY

**Div Of Juvenile Svcs Dept Of
Corrections**..............................**701.239.7100**
Fax...701.356.2058
   461 34th St S Ste C, Fargo, ND 58103
Anthony Kozojed, Deputy Director

COURTS

District Court.........................**701.451.6900**
Fax...701.451.6937
Web....................................www.ndcourts.gov
   211 9th St S, Fargo, ND 58108
Rod Olsen, Trial Court Administration

Juvenile Court........................**701.451.6980**
Fax...701.451.6996
   1010 2nd Ave S, Fargo, ND 58102
Karen Kringlie, Director

Youth Court............................**701.271.3253**
Fax...701.235.7359
Web...www.lssnd.org
E-mail.................................lpipkin@lssnd.org
   1325 11th St S, Fargo, ND 58103-4126
Laurel Pipkin, Coordinator

POLICE AND SHERIFF

Fargo Police Dept...................**701.235.4493**
Fax...701.241.8272
Web....................................www.fargopolice.com
E-mail........................kternes@cityoffargo.com
   222 4th St N, Fargo, ND 58102-4818
Keith Ternes, Chief

North Dakota

Sheriff's Dept **701.241.5800**
Fax 701.241.5805
Web ....www.co.cass.nd.us
E-mail ....laneyp@casscountynd.gov
    211 9th St. S, Fargo, ND 58108
    Paul Laney, Sheriff

Cavalier County

SOCIAL SERVICES

Social Svc Board **701.256.2175**
Fax 701.256.2179
Web ....www.cavaliercounty.us
E-mail ....34denj@nd.gov
    324 7th Avenue, Langdon, ND 58249
    Jill Denault, Lisw, Director

GENERAL HEALTH SERVICES

Health District **701.256.2402**
Fax 701.256.5765
Web ....www.cavaliercountyhealth.com
    901 3rd St Ste 11, Langdon, ND 58249-2457
    Terri Gustafson, Rn, Administrator/director Of Nursing

COURTS

District Court **701.256.2540**
Fax 701.256.3468
E-mail ....lfontaine@ndcourts.gov
    901 3rd St Ste 1, Langdon, ND 58249
    Honorable Laurie A. Fontaine, Judge

Dickey County

SOCIAL SERVICES

Social Svc Board **701.349.3271**
Fax 701.349.3277
E-mail ....wlarson@nd.gov
    205 15th Street North, Ellendale, ND 58436
    Wanda Larson, Director

GENERAL HEALTH SERVICES

Health Unit **701.349.4348**
Fax 701.349.3277
E-mail ....rholm@nd.gov
    205 15TH St N, Ellendale, ND 58436
    Sharon Vanorny, Rn, Director Of Nursing

Divide County

SOCIAL SERVICES

Social Svcs **701.965.6521**
Fax 701.965.6529
    300 2nd Ave N., Crosby, ND 58730
    Shauna McFarland, Director

Eddy County

SOCIAL SERVICES

Social Svc Boards **701.947.5314**
Fax 701.947.2960
    22 9th St S, New Rockford, ND 58356
    John Mogren, Director

Emmons County

SOCIAL SERVICES

Social Svc Board **701.254.4502**
Fax 701.254.4503
    100 SW 4th St., Linton, ND 58552
    Michelle Masset, Director

GENERAL HEALTH SERVICES

Public Health Unit **701.254.4027**
Fax 701.254.4057
    118 E Spruce Ave, Linton, ND 58552
    Beverly Voller, RN, Administrator/Director Of Nursing

Foster County

SOCIAL SERVICES

Social Svcs **701.652.2221**
Fax 701.652.2207
Web ....www.fostercounty.com
E-mail ....jmogren@nd.gov
    1000 N Central Ave, Carrington, ND 58421-0080
    John Mogren, Director

Golden Valley County

SOCIAL SERVICES

Social Svc Board **701.872.4121**
Fax 701.872.3141
Web ....www.state.nd.us
E-mail ....17fedr@state.nd.us
    70 SE 1st Street, Beach, ND 58621
    Doug Wegh, Director

GENERAL HEALTH SERVICES

**Billings & Golden Valley Counties Health
Unit** **701.872.4533**
Fax 701.872.4533
E-mail ....marsha_schmidt@yahoo.com
    53 Central Ave S, Beach, ND 58621
    Marsha Schmidt, RN, Public Health Nurse

Grand Forks County

SOCIAL SERVICES

Social Svc Board **701.787.8535**
Fax 701.772.1426
Web ....www.state.nd.us
E-mail ....18berk@state.nd.us
    151 South 4th Street, Grand Forks, ND 58206
    Keith Berger, Director

GENERAL HEALTH SERVICES

Public Health Dept **701.787.8100**
Fax 701.787.8145
Web ....www.grandforksgov.com
E-mail ....dshields@grandforksgov.com
    151 S 4th St, Ste N301, Grand Forks, ND 58201
    Don Shields, Director

JUSTICE AGENCY

Div Of Juvenile Svcs **701.795.3839**
Fax 701.795.3838
E-mail ....kdavis@nd.gov
    311 S 4th St Ste 119, Grand Forks, ND 58201
    Kari Davis, Case Manager

**Grand Forks Parole And Probation District
Ofc** **701.795.3873**
Fax 701.795.3897
    311 S 4St Ste 101, Grand Forks, ND 58201-4756
    John Knutson, Supervisor

COURTS

District Court **701.787.2730**
Fax 701.787.2731
Web ....www.ndcourts.gov
E-mail ....ljahnke@ndcourts.gov
    124 S 4th St, Grand Forks, ND 58201-4736
    Honorable Lawrence E. Jahnke, Judge

POLICE AND SHERIFF

Police Dept **701.787.8000**
Fax 701.780.8253
Web ....www.grandforksgov.com
E-mail ....jpackett@grandforksgov.com
    122 S 5th St, Grand Forks, ND 58201-4647
    John Packett, Police Chief

EDUCATION SERVICES

Special Education **701.746.2230**
Fax 701.746.2475
Web ....www.gfschools.org
E-mail ....tori.johnson@gfschools.org
    2400 47th Ave S, Grand Forks, ND 58201-3405
    Tori Johnson, Director

Grant County

SOCIAL SERVICES

Social Svc Board **701.622.3706**
Fax 701.622.3045
Web ....www.state.nd.us
    106 2nd Avenue East, Carson, ND 58529
    Vicki Zimmerman, Director

GENERAL HEALTH SERVICES

Health Unit **701.622.3591**
Fax 701.622.3005
Web ....www.nd.gov
E-mail ....hpeltz@custerhealth.com
    PO Box 164, Carson, ND 58529-0164
    Heidi Peltz, RN, Staff Nurse

POLICE AND SHERIFF

Elgine Police Dept **701.584.2177**
Fax 701.456.7680
    305 North Main Street, Elgin, ND 58533
    Randall Hoffman, Police Chief

Griggs County

SOCIAL SERVICES

Social Svc Board **701.797.2127**
Fax 701.797.2172
Web ....www.state.nd.us
E-mail ....marcia.beglau@griggscountynd.gov
    808 Rolling Avenue SW, Cooperstown, ND 58425
    Marcia Beglau, Director

Hettinger County

SOCIAL SERVICES

Social Svcs **701.824.3276**
Fax 701.824.2820
Web ....www.state.nd.us
E-mail ....21wegd@nd.gov
    309 Millionaire Ave, Mott, ND 58646-7267
    Douglas J Wegh, Director

GENERAL HEALTH SERVICES

Health Unit **701.824.3215**
Fax 701.824.3216
Web ....www.ndhealth.gov
E-mail ....jolson@nd.gov
    309 Millionaire Ave, Mott, ND 58646
    Jodi Olson, Public Health Nurse

Kidder County

SOCIAL SERVICES

Social Svc Board **701.475.2551**
Fax 701.475.2298
E-mail ....22dewj@nd.gov
    120 East Broadway, Steele, ND 58482
    Jolene Dewitz, Director

GENERAL HEALTH SERVICES

District Health Unit **701.475.2582**
Fax 701.475.2652
E-mail ....mstrand@state.nd.us
    422 2nd Ave NW, Steele, ND 58482-7320
    Mary Ellen Strand, Rn, Nursing Director

McHenry County

SOCIAL SERVICES

Social Svc Board **701.537.5944**
Fax 701.537.5417
E-mail ....35herm@nd.gov
    407 South Main, Towner, ND 58788
    Mary Hermanson, Director

GENERAL HEALTH SERVICES

First District Health Unit **701.537.5732**
Fax 701.537.0804
Web ....www.fdhu.org
E-mail ....nbryn@nd.gov
    112 Main St S, PO Box 517, Towner, ND 58788
    Nancy Bryn, RN, Public Health Nurse

McIntosh County

SOCIAL SERVICES

Social Svc Board **701.288.3343**
Fax 701.288.2186
    112 1st Street Northeast, Ashley, ND 58413
    Brooke Kosiak, Director

GENERAL HEALTH SERVICES

District Health Unit **701.288.3957**
Fax 701.288.3671
E-mail ....tmmeidinger@nd.gov
    511 3rd Ave NW, Ashley, ND 58413
    Tami Meidinger, Nursing Director

McKenzie County

SOCIAL SERVICES

Social Svc Board **701.444.3661**
Fax 701.444.6436
Web ....www.state.nd.us
    201 W 5th Street, Watford City, ND 58854
    Amy Fast, Director

GENERAL HEALTH SERVICES

District Health Unit **701.444.3449**
Fax 701.842.6985
Web ....www.umdhu.org
E-mail ....mwashburn@umdhu.org
    109 5th St SW., Watford City, ND 58854
    Marcia Washburn, Rn, Public Health Nurse

COURTS

District Court **701.857.6600**
Fax 701.857.6649
E-mail ....bmclees@ndcourts.gov
    315 3rd St SE, Minot, ND 58702
    Honorable William W. Mclees, Judge

McLean County

GENERAL HEALTH SERVICES

Health Unit/WIC **701.463.2641**
Fax 701.463.7228
Web ....www.nd.gov
E-mail ....aheer@nd.gov
    141 N Main St Ste 3, Garrison, ND 58540
    Amy Heer, Rn, Bsn, Director

Mercer County

POLICE AND SHERIFF

Hazen Police Dept **701.748.2414**
Fax 701.748.2400
    146 E Main St, Hazen, ND 58545
    Charles Dahl, Chief Of Police

Morton County

GENERAL HEALTH SERVICES

Custer Health -- Home Health
Agency **701.667.3370**
Fax 701.667.3371
Web ....www.custerhealth.com
    210 2nd Ave NW, Mandan, ND 58554
    Jocelyn Koch, Nursing Director

JUSTICE AGENCY

Mandan Parole And Probation Ofc **701.667.3401**
Fax 701.667.3224
    210 2nd Ave NW, Mandan, ND 58554-3124
    Rick, Supervisor

North Dakota Youth Correctional
Ctr **701.667.1400**
Fax 701.667.1414
    701 16th Ave SW, Mandan, ND 58554
    Ron Crouse, Director

COURTS

District Court **701.667.3357**
Fax 701.667.3385
    210 2nd Ave NW, Mandan, ND 58554-3124
    Honorable Thomas J. Schneider, Director

Mountrail County

SOCIAL SERVICES

Social Svc **701.628.2925**
Fax 701.628.3175
E-mail ....buigley@co.mountrail.md.us
    18 2nd Avenue SE, Stanley, ND 58784
    Brian Quigley, Director

Three Affiliated Tribes Social Svcs **701.627.4781**
Fax 701.627.3805
Web ....www.mhanation.com
E-mail ....reneem@mhanation.com
    404 Frontage Rd, Three Affiliated Tribes, New Town,
    ND 58763-9404
    Renee Mayer, Director Of Tribal Social Services

GENERAL HEALTH SERVICES

Indian Health Ctr **701.627.4701**
Fax 701.627.4318
    1 Minni Tohe Dr, New Town, ND 14304
    Dawn Berg, Service Unit Director

Nelson County

SOCIAL SERVICES

Social Svcs **701.247.2945**
Fax 701.247.2943
E-mail ....20begm@nd.gov
    210 B Ave W Ste 301, Lakota, ND 58344
    Marcia Beglau, Director

GENERAL HEALTH SERVICES

Nelson-Griggs District Health Unit **701.322.5624**
Fax 701.322.5111
E-mail ....julieferry@nd.gov
    116 Main St, McVille, ND 58254
    Julie Ferry, RN, Public Health Nurse

Oliver County

SOCIAL SERVICES

Social Svc Board **701.794.3212**
Fax 701.794.3476
Web ....www.state.nd.us
E-mail ....33isal@state.nd.us
    115 Main Street, Center, ND 58530
    Steve Reiser, Director

GENERAL HEALTH SERVICES

Health Unit **701.794.3105**
Web ....www.nd.gov
E-mail ....jklayson@nd.gov
    PO Box 375, Center, ND 58530-0375
    Jan Klayson, RN, Supervisor

Pembina County

SOCIAL SERVICES

Social Svc Board **701.265.8441**
Fax 701.265.8058
Web ....www.state.nd.us
E-mail ....jdenault@nd.gov
    300 Boundary Rd W, Ste 3, Cavalier, ND 58220
    Jill Denault, Lsw, Director

GENERAL HEALTH SERVICES

Public Health Department **701.265.4248**
Fax 701.265.5193
Web ....www.beembinecountynd.gov
E-mail ....jchaput@nd.gov
    301 Dakota St W Unit 2, Cavalier, ND 58220
    Jeanne Chaput, Administrator

COURTS

District Court **701.265.8783**
Fax 701.265.4514
    301 Dakota St W Unit 3, Cavalier, ND 58220
    Honorable Laurie A. Fontaine, Judge

Pierce County

SOCIAL SERVICES

Social Svc Board **701.776.5818**
Fax 701.776.2516
E-mail ....35herm@nd.gov
    820 S Main Ave, Rugby, ND 58368
    Mary Hermanson, Director

GENERAL HEALTH SERVICES

Health Unit **701.776.6783**
Fax 701.776.7609
Web ....www.nd.gov
E-mail ....dschiff@nd.gov
    240 SE 2nd St ,Ste 3, COURTHOUSE, Rugby,
    ND 58368-1830
    Deb Schiff, Public Health Nurse

POLICE AND SHERIFF

Sheriff's Ofc **701.776.5245**
Fax 701.776.6818
    110 Industrial Rd, Rugby, ND 58368
    Matt Lunde, Sheriff

Ramsey County

SOCIAL SERVICES

Social Svcs **701.662.7050**
Fax 701.662.7095
    524 4th Ave NE, Unit 19, Devils Lake, ND 58301
    Edward D Forde, Director

GENERAL HEALTH SERVICES

Lake Region District Health Unit **701.662.7035**
Fax 701.662.7097
    524 4th Ave NE Unit 9, Devils Lake, ND 58301
    Karen Pederson-Halle, Nursing Director

JUSTICE AGENCY

Div Of Juvenile Svcs **701.662.4846**
Fax 701.662.1375
E-mail ....dlundy@nd.gov
    304 4th St NE Ste 2, Devils Lake, ND 58301
    David Lundy, Case Manager

North Dakota

Juvenile Court Svcs..........................701.662.1307
Fax...701.662.1306
   524 4th Ave NE Unit 10, Devils Lake, ND 58301
Karen Olson, Juvenile Court Director

COURTS

District Court...................................701.662.1300
Fax...701.662.8539
Web...www.ndcourts.gov
E-mail...............................dfoughty@ndcourts.com
   524 4th Ave NE Unit 10, Devils Lake,
   ND 58301-2490
Honorable Donovan Foughty, Director

Ransom County

SOCIAL SERVICES

Social Svcs......................................701.683.6133
Fax...701.683.4491
E-mail.....................wendy.jacobson@co.sargent.nd.us
   205 5th Ave W, Lisbon, ND 58054-0950
Wendy Jacobson, Director

GENERAL HEALTH SERVICES

Health Dept.....................................701.683.5823
Fax...701.683.0034
Web..www.nd.gov
E-mail.......................................dbergstr@nd.gov
   403 Elm Street, Lisbon, ND 58054
Deb Bergstrom, RN, Nursing Director

Renville County

SOCIAL SERVICES

Social Svcs......................................701.756.6374
Fax...701.756.7158
   205 Main Street, Mohall, ND 58761
Tami Chrest, Director

GENERAL HEALTH SERVICES

Health Unit.....................................701.756.6383
Fax...701.756.6837
Web..www.fdhu.org
E-mail...taberle@nd.gov
   205 Main St E, Mohall, ND 58761
Tami Aberle, Rn, Public Health Nurse

Richland County

GENERAL HEALTH SERVICES

Health Dept.....................................701.642.7735
Fax...701.642.7746
Web........................www.richlandcountyhealth.org
   413 3rd Ave N, Wahpeton, ND 58075
Debra Flack, Rn, Director Of Nursing/administrator

JUSTICE AGENCY

Juvenile Court Svcs..........................701.671.1515
Fax...701.671.1527
Web...www.ndcourts.com
E-mail...............................csheeley@ndcourts.com
   413 3rd Ave N Ofc 2, Wahpeton, ND 58075-4427
Charles Sheeley, Juvenile Court Director

Wahpeton Parole And Probation
Ofc...701.671.1517
Fax...701.671.1519
E-mail......................................gnankive@state.nd.us
   709 Dakota Ave Ste D, Wahpeton, ND 58075-4333
Jerry Nankivel, Parole Officer

Rolette County

SOCIAL SERVICES

Bureau Of Indian Affairs.....................701.477.3191
Fax...701.477.6628
Web..www.bia.gov
E-mail............................patrickhemmy@bia.com
   Highway 5 Fish Lake Rd, Belcourt, ND 58316
Patrick Hemmy, Superintendent

Bureau Of Indian Affairs Indian Social
Svcs...701.477.6147
Fax...701.477.8973
Web..www.bia.gov
E-mail......................jennifer.champagne@bia.gov
   Bia 7 Social Services Bldg, Belcourt, ND 58316
Jennifer Champagne, Acting Director

Social Svcs......................................701.477.3141
Fax...701.477.5979
Web..www.state.nd.us
E-mail...............................bmathiason@state.nd.us
   212 2nd Avenue NE, Rolla, ND 58367
Bav Mathiason, Director

GENERAL HEALTH SERVICES

Public Health District......................701.477.5646
Fax...701.477.9578
   211 1st Ave NE, Rolla, ND 58367
Barbara Frydenlund, Rn, Administrator

Sargent County

SOCIAL SERVICES

Social Svcs......................................701.724.6241
Fax...701.724.3323
   355 S Main St Ste 7, Forman, ND 58032
Wendy Jacobson, Director

Sheridan County

SOCIAL SERVICES

Social Svcs......................................701.363.2281
Fax...701.363.2702
Web............................www.co.sheridan.nd.us
E-mail...28redr@nd.gov
   215 2nd Street East, McClusky, ND 58463
Steve Reiser, Director

GENERAL HEALTH SERVICES

Health Unit.....................................701.363.2506
Fax...701.363.2806
Web..www.fdhu.org
E-mail..sebach@nd.gov
   215 2nd St E, Mcclusky, ND 58463
Susan Ebach, Rn, Director

Sioux County

SOCIAL SERVICES

Social Svc Board..............................701.854.3821
Fax...701.854.3854
E-mail.....................................43gilv@state.nd.us
   300 2nd Avenue, Fort Yates, ND 58538
Vince Gillette, Director

Social Svcs General Assistance...............701.854.3491
Fax...701.854.3637
E-mail.......................marilyn.keerseagle@bia.gov
   Proposal Ave Bldg 194, Yates, ND 58538
Marilyn Keepseagle, Supervisory Social Services Rep

Standing Rock Agency Social Svcs.............701.854.3431
Fax...701.854.2119
Web..www.westriv.com
E-mail...cps1@westriv.com
   5532 Warrior St, Fort Yates, ND 58538
Lori Sager, Director

MENTAL HEALTH SERVICES

Standing Rock Sioux Tribe Chemical
Prevention.....................................701.854.7219
Fax...701.854.7650
E-mail.................................duanesilk@hotmail.com
   9307 Highway 24, Fort Yates, ND 58538
Duane Silk, Director

POLICE AND SHERIFF

Sheriff's Ofc...................................701.854.3481
Fax...701.854.3854
   303 2nd Ave, Fort Yates, ND 58538
Frank Landeis, Sheriff

Stark County

SOCIAL SERVICES

Social Svc Board..............................701.456.7675
Fax...701.456.7777
Web..www.starkcountynd.com
E-mail...45berl@nd.gov
   664 12th St W, Dickinson, ND 58601-3511
Maureen Haman, Director

JUSTICE AGENCY

Dickinson Parole And Probation
Ofc...701.227.7420
Fax...701.227.7421
   135 Sims St Ste 205, Dickinson, ND 58601
Barney Tomanek, Director

COURTS

District Court...................................701.227.3150
Fax...701.227.3156
Web...www.ndcourts.com
E-mail...............................wherauf@ndcourts.gov
   51 3rd St E, Dickinson, ND 58601-5254
Honorable William A. Herauf, Judge

POLICE AND SHERIFF

Sheriff's Dept.................................701.456.7610
Fax...701.456.7692
   66 W Museum Drive, Dickinson, ND 58601
Clarence Tuhy, Sheriff

Steele County

SOCIAL SERVICES

Social Svcs......................................701.524.2584
Fax...701.524.1103
E-mail...46dahs@nd.gov
   600 S Washington, Finley, ND 58230

POLICE AND SHERIFF

Sheriff's Ofc...................................701.524.2742
Fax...701.524.1715
Web..www.steelecountynd.com
E-mail.......................................wbeckman@nd.gov
   201 Washington Ave, Finley, ND 58230
Wayne Beckman, Sheriff

Stutsman County

SOCIAL SERVICES

Social Svc Board..............................701.252.7172
Fax...701.252.1561
E-mail.....................................47danc@state.nd.us
   116 1st St E, Jamestown, ND 58401
Sandy Bendewald, Director

GENERAL HEALTH SERVICES

Central Valley Health District...............701.252.8130
Fax...701.252.8137
Web......................www.centralvalleyhealthdistrict.com
   122 2Nd St Nw, Jamestown, ND 58402
Robin Iszler, Administrator

JUSTICE AGENCY

DOCR, Div Of Juvenile Svcs **701.253.3655**
Fax 701.952.3650
E-mail ....nnygaard@ne.gov
   214 6th Ave NE Ste A, Jamestown, ND 58401
Nicole Nygaard, Juvenile Corrections Specialist

Jamestown Community
Corrections **701.952.2038**
Fax 701.952.2868
E-mail ....dhorn@daktel.com
   109 1st St W, Jamestown, ND 58401-4102
Dell Horn, Director

Jamestown Parole Ofc **701.253.3227**
Fax 701.253.3216
   221 1st Ave N, Jamestown, ND 58401-3165
Kathy Jaskowski, Community Corrections Agent

Tompkins Corrections Unit **701.253.3755**
Fax 701.253.3757
E-mail ....choornae@nd.gov
   PO Box 1915, Jamestown, ND 58402-1915
Chad Hoornaert, Parole Officer

COURTS

District Court **701.252.9044**
Fax 701.251.1006
Web ....www.ndcourts.gov
   511 2nd Ave SE, Jamestown, ND 58401-4210
Brian Washburn, Juvenile Court Director

POLICE AND SHERIFF

Sheriff's Ofc **701.252.9000**
Fax 701.251.6298
   205 6th St SE Ste 102, Jamestown, ND 58401
C Kaiser, Sheriff

Towner County

SOCIAL SERVICES

Social Svcs **701.968.4355**
Fax 701.968.4359
E-mail ....36fore@nd.gov
   315 2nd St, Cando, ND 58324
Edward D Forde, Director

GENERAL HEALTH SERVICES

Medical Center **701.968.2542**
Fax 701.968.2519
E-mail ....jacm@tcmedcenter.com
   Highway 281, North Cando, ND 58324
Jack Mctaggert, Administrator

Public Health District **701.968.4353**
Fax 701.968.4354
Web ....www.ndhealth.gov/localhd/tcphd/
E-mail ....townerph@nd.gov
   404 5th Ave, Ste 3, Cando, ND 58324
Sherry Walters, Director

POLICE AND SHERIFF

Sheriff's Ofc **701.968.4350**
Fax 701.968.4351
E-mail ....townersh@nd.gov
   315 2nd St, Cando, ND 58324
Vaughn Klier, Sheriff

Traill County

SOCIAL SERVICES

Social Svc Board **701.636.5220**
Fax 701.636.5221
Web ....www.co.traill.nd.us
E-mail ....kim.jacobson@co.trail.nd.us
   114 West Caledonia Avenue, Hillsboro, ND 58045
Kim Jacobson, Director

Walsh County

SOCIAL SERVICES

Social Svcs **701.352.5111**
Fax 701.352.5060
E-mail ....walshcss@nd.gov
   516 Cooper Ave Ste 101, Grafton, ND 58237
Twila Novak, Director

GENERAL HEALTH SERVICES

Health Unit **701.352.5139**
Fax 701.352.5074
E-mail ....wkratoch@nd.gov
   638 Cooper Ave Ste 3, Grafton, ND 58237-1511
Wanda Kratochvil, Rn, Director Of Nursing

Ward County

SOCIAL SERVICES

Social Svcs **701.852.3552**
Fax 701.857.0756
Web ....www.co.ward.nd.us
   400 22nd Ave NW, Minot, ND 58703
Robert Kondos, Director

JUSTICE AGENCY

Minot Parole And Probation Ofc **701.857.7683**
Fax 701.857.7721
   108 Burdick Expy E Ste 1, Minot, ND 58701-4474
Steve Hall, Chief Officer

COURTS

Teen Court **701.839.7221**
Fax 701.839.1747
Web www.caoregion2.org
E-mail ....janell@caoregion2.org
   2020 8th Ave SE, Minot, ND 58701-5035
Janell Roy, Coordinator

POLICE AND SHERIFF

Sheriff's Dept **701.857.6500**
Fax 701.857.6520
Web ....www.co.ward.nd.us
E-mail ....steve.kukowski@co.ward.nd.us
   315 3rd Street SE, Minot, ND 58701
Steve Kukowski, Sheriff

Wells County

SOCIAL SERVICES

Social Svc Board **701.547.3694**
Fax 701.547.3348
Web ....www.mylocalgov.com/wellscountynd/index. asp
E-mail ....jogren@nd.gov
   600 Railway St N, Fessenden, ND 58438
John Mogren, Director

GENERAL HEALTH SERVICES

Health Unit **701.547.3756**
Fax 701.547.2535
E-mail ....kvolk@nd.gov
   600 North Railway St, Fessenden, ND 58438
Karen Volk, Administrator/director Of Nursing

Williams County

SOCIAL SERVICES

Northwest Human Svc Ctr **701.774.4600**
Fax 701.774.4620
   316 2nd Ave W, Williston, ND 58801
Marilyn Rudolph, Regional Director

Social Svc Board **701.774.6300**
Fax 701.572.9794
Web ....www.state.nd.us
E-mail ....53saxm@state.nd.us
   110 W Broadway, Ste 202, Williston, ND 58801-6056
Michon C. Sax, Director

GENERAL HEALTH SERVICES

Uppermissouri Dist Health Unit **701.774.6400**
Fax 701.577.8536
Web ....www.umdhu.org
   110 W Broadway Ste 101, Williston, ND 58801
Javayne Oyloe, Interim Executive Officer

JUSTICE AGENCY

Div Of Juvenile Svcs **701.774.4348**
Fax 701.774.4313
Web ....www.nd.gov
   322 Main St, Ste 103, Williston, ND 58801
Ashile Granrud, Juvenile Corrections Specialist

COURTS

District Court **701.774.4367**
Fax 701.774.4363
   205 E Broadway, Williston, ND 58802
Judge David W Nelson, Director

SPECIAL SERVICES AGENCIES

ADOPTION AGENCIES

Adoption Option **701.451.4900**
Fax 701.451.5057
Web ....www.thevillagefamily.org
E-mail ....sgrundysen@thevillagefamily.org
   1201 25th St S, Fargo, ND 58103-2311
Sue Grundysen, Director

Catholic Charities North Dakota **701.235.4457**
Fax 701.356.7993
Web ....www.catholiccharitiesnd.org
   5201 Bishops Boulevard, Suite B, Fargo,
ND 58104-7605
COA accredited organization.

Catholic Charities- Grand Forks ND **701.775.4196**
Fax 701.775.0129
Web ....www.catholiccharitiesnd.org
   311 S 4th St Ste 105, Grand Forks, ND 58201-4782
Donna Byzewski, Guardian Supervisor

Christian Family Life Svcs **701.237.4473**
Fax 701.235.1703
Web ....www.cflsadoption.org
E-mail ....info@cflsadoption.org
   203 8th St S, Fargo, ND 58103-1824
Ann Dahl, Director

Family Life Services, Inc. dba Family Life Credit
Services **701.237.9247**
Fax 701.234.9557
Web ....www.familylifecredit.org
   P.O. Box 720, West Fargo, ND 58078
COA accredited organization.

Path **701.839.8887**
Fax 701.839.8990
Web ....www.pathinc.org
E-mail ....kberg@pathinc.org
   2000 Burdick Expy E, Minot, ND 58701
Karen Berg, Regional Director

North Dakota

Path...701.775.7725
Fax..701.775.7880
Web...www.pathinc.org
E-mail..bsundeen@pathinc.org
   301 N 3rd St Ste 200, Grand Forks, ND 58203
   Barry Sundeen, Supervisor

Path...701.572.7650
Fax..701.572.7656
Web...www.pathinc.org
E-mail...kberg@pathinc.org
   1135 2ND AVE W STE 202, Williston,
   ND 58801-4175
   Karen Berg, Regional Director

Path...701.225.3310
Fax..701.225.2208
Web...www.pathinc.org
E-mail..jtishmack@pathinc.org
   135 Sims St Ste 204, Dickinson, ND 58601-5148
   Janice Tishmack, Regional Director

Path...701.251.9150
Fax..701.251.9130
Web...www.pathinc.org
E-mail..nhorton@pathinc.org
   300 2nd Ave NE Ste 202, Jamestown,
   ND 58401-3373
   Nancy Horton, Regional Director

Professional Assoc Of Treatment Homes
(Path)...701.280.9545
Fax..701.280.9520
Web..www.pathinc.org
E-mail.......................................bmetcalfe@pathinc.org
   1112 Nodak Dr S, Ste 200, Fargo, ND 58103-2366
   William Metcalfe, Executive Director

ADVOCACY RESOURCES

Childrens Defense Fund - N Dakota..........701.400.1827
   PO Box 655, Bismarck, ND 58502

BEHAVIORAL HEALTH TREATMENT

Altru Health System.........................701.780.5000
Web...www.altru.org
E-mail...jholth@altru.org
   1200 South Columbia Road, Grand Forks,
   ND 58206-6002
   Ms. Janelle Holth, Accreditation Manager
   Joint Commission accredited organization.

Altru Health Systems - Outpatient Psychiatry
Svcs..701.780.6697
Fax..701.780.6937
Web...www.altru.org
   860 S Columbia Rd, Bldg 1, Grand Forks, ND 58201
   Mike Dewald, Area Manager

Center for Solutions PC.....................701.968.2568
Web...Centerforsolutions.org
E-mail.............................bobs@centerforsolutions.org
   7448 68th Avenue NE, Cando, ND 58324
   Mr. Robert Spencer, Accreditation Manager
   Joint Commission accredited organization.

Centre, Inc..................................701.746.6303
Fax..701.746.7713
Web...www.centreinc.org
E-mail...thomasko@centreinc.org
   201 S 4th St, Grand Forks, ND 58201-4737
   Thomas Kopp, Program Manager

Community Living Svcs, Inc.................701.232.3133
Fax..701.478.4140
   111 University Dr N, Fargo, ND 58102
   Jim Berglie, Director

Dakota Boys & Girls Ranch..................701.224.1789
Web..www.dakotaranch.org
E-mail...................................a.iverson@dakotaranch.org
   1227 N 35th St, Bismarck, ND 58501-7722
   Amanda Iverson, Director Of Admissions

Dakota Boys and Girls Ranch Association......701.852.3628
Fax..701.839.5541
Web..www.dakotaranch.org
   6301 19th Avenue NW, Minot, ND 58703
   Gene Kaseman, President
   CARF accredited programs available.

Dickinson Family Counseling Ctr............701.483.9720
Fax..701.483.9721
E-mail.........................dickinsonfamilycc@hotmail.com
   11 2nd Ave E # B, Dickinson, ND 58601-5218
   Robert Bear, Owner

Eckert Youth Homes.........................701.572.7262
Fax..701.572.8783
E-mail...eyh2@nemontel.net
   1102 7th Ave E, Williston, ND 58801
   Don Pitman, Director

Lake Oahe Group Home Of Standing Rock
Nation...701.854.2094
Fax..701.854.3643
   PO Box 176, Fort Yates, ND 58538-0176
   Leslie Gibb, Administrator

North Dakota State Hospital................701.253.3964
E-mail...deissinger@nd.gov
   2605 Circle Drive, Jamestown, ND 58401-6905
   Ms. Debra Eissinger, Accreditation Manager
   Joint Commission accredited organization.

Prairie St. John's...........................701.476.7200
Web...www.prairie-stjohns.com
E-mail...............................jennifer.faul@psysolutions.com
   510 4th Street South, Fargo, ND 58103
   Ms. Jenn Faul, Accreditation Manager
   Joint Commission accredited organization.

Pride Manchester House.....................701.223.5600
Fax..701.223.5611
Web...www.prideinc.org
   2600 Manchester Street, Bismarck, ND 58504
   COA accredited organization.

Ruth Meiers Adolescent Residential
Center...701.795.3870
Fax..701.795.3899
E-mail...mulrich@nd.gov
   770 South 14th Street, Grand Forks, ND 58201
   Muriel Ulrich, Tax Director
   CARF accredited programs available.

Saint Alexius Medical Center...............701.530.7600
Web...www.primecare.org
E-mail...................................kaschneider@primecare.org
   900 East Broadway, Bismarck, ND 58502
   Ms. Karen Schneider, Accreditation Manager
   Joint Commission accredited organization.

Trinity Health..............................701.857.5000
Web...www.trinityhealth.org
E-mail...............................alyce.killmer@trinityhealth.org
   One Burdick Expressway West, Minot, ND 58702
   Ms. Alyce Killmer, Accreditation Manager
   Joint Commission accredited organization.

CHILDREN'S HOSPITAL

First Care Health Center....................701.284.7500
   115 Vivian St, Park River, ND 58270
   Louise Dryburgh, Director

Heart of America Medical Center............701.776.5261
   800 Main Ave South, Rugby, ND 58368
   Jeff Lingerfelt, Chief Executive Officer

Innovis Health..............................701.364.8000
   3000 32nd Ave S, Fargo, ND 58103
   Greg Goasner, Chief Medical Operator

Memorial Hosp..............................701.265.8461
   301 Mountain St E, Cavalier, ND 58220

Mercy Hospital.............................701.662.2131
   1031 Seventh St NE, Devils Lake, ND 58301
   James Marshal, Chief Executive Officer

Mercy Hospital.............................701.845.6400
   570 Chautauqua Blvd, Valley City, ND 58072
   Keith Heuser, Chief Executive Officer

Mercy Medical Center......................701.774.7400
   1301 W 15th Ave, Williston, ND 58801

Oakes Community Hospital..................701.742.3291
   1200 North Seventh St, Oakes, ND 58474
   Lee Boyles, Chief Executive Officer

Presentation Medical Center...............701.477.3161
   213 Second Ave NE, Rolla, ND 58367
   Holly Chill, Human Resource

Public Health Service Indian Hosp..........701.477.6111
   2 blocks North of Hwy 5, Belcourt, ND 58316
   Allen Davis, Chief Executive Officer

Sanford Health MeritCare Hosp.............701.234.6000
   801 Boadway N, Fargo, ND 58122
   Dennis Millirons, President Medical Center

St Alexius Medical Center..................701.530.7000
E-mail...................................rschmidt@primecare.org
   900 East Broadway, Bismarck, ND 58501
   Rosanne Schmidt, Nursing Director

St Joseph Hospital and Health Center.........701.456.4000
   30 Seventh St W, Dickinson, ND 58601
   Karen Z, Administrator

St Lukes Hospital..........................701.965.6384
   702 First Street SW, Crosby, ND 58730
   Les Urvand, Administrator

Trinity Hospitals...........................701.857.5000
   1 Burdick Expy West, Minot, ND 58701

COUNSELING SERVICES

Lutheran Social Svcs Of North Dakota.......701.772.7577
Fax..701.772.5001
Web...www.lssnd.org
E-mail..jregimbal@lssnd.org
   412 Demers Ave, Grand Forks, ND 58201-4508
   Janell Regimbal, Director Of Youth Services

CRISIS & SHELTER CARE

Charles Hall Youth Svcs....................701.255.2773
Fax..701.255.6261
E-mail............gayla.sherman@charleshallyouthservices.com
   513 E Bismarck Expy, Bismarck, ND 58504
   Gayla Sherman, Executive Director

Domestic Violence Crisis Ctr...............701.852.2258
Fax..701.838.7053
E-mail...dvcc@minot.com
   3331 Burdick Expy E, Minot, ND 58701
   Ms. Dena Filler, Director

Domestic Violence Program..................701.628.3233
Fax..701.628.3234
Web..www.ag.ndsu.edu
E-mail..Creese@Ag.Ndsu.Edu
   101 S Main St, #2, Stanley, ND 58784
   Ms Colleen Reese, Director

Domestic Violence-Rape Crisis Ctr...........701.225.4506
Fax..701.225.4506
Web...www.lovewithoufear.org
E-mail.......................................Dvrcc@Ndsupernet.Com
   PO Box 1081, Dickinson, ND 58602-1081
   Darianne Johnson, Director

Family Crisis Shelter-Domestic Violence.......701.572.0757
Fax..701.572.7239
E-mail.............................lana.fcs@midconetwork.com
   723 Main st, Williston, ND 58802-1893
   Lana Bonnet, Director

Kedish House Domestic Violence Program.....701.349.4729
Fax..701.349.3562
E-mail...skbrady@drtel.net
   51 1st Street, Ellendale, ND 58436
   Ms Sharron Brady, Director

North Dakota

Lutheran Social Svcs 701.232.8905
Fax...701.232.3537
Web...www.lssnd.org
E-mail..................................mweiler@lssnd.org
   1505 5th Ave S, Fargo, ND 58103
   Mary Weiler, Ms, Director

Mclean Family Resource Ctr-Domestic
Violence..**701.462.8643**
Fax...701.462.8680
Web...www.westriv.com
E-mail..................................mfrc@westriv.com
   718 Main Ave, Washburn, ND 58577
   Ms Janelle Olson, Director

Rape And Abuse Crisis Ctr **701.293.7273**
Fax...701.293.9424
Web...www.raccsm.com
E-mail..................................greg@raccfm.com
   317 8th Street North, Fargo, ND 58102
   Greg Diehl, Director

Safe Alternatives For Abused Families **701.662.7378**
Fax...701.662.2380
E-mail..................................saaf@gondtc.com
   312 5th Ave NE Studio C, Devils Lake, ND 58301
   Ms Janel Taylor, Director

Safe Shelter-Domestic Violence **701.251.2300**
Fax...701.251.9095
E-mail..................................sshel@qweftoffice.net
   112 6th St SE, Jamestown, ND 58401
   Ms. Lynne Tally, Director

FOSTER CARE AGENCIES

Family To Family Foster Adoptive Parent **701.795.3016**
Fax...701.795.3050
   151 South 4th St Ste 401, Grand Forks, ND 58201
   Kate Kenna, Director

Jamestown Area Foster Adopt Support
Team **701.252.5437**
E-mail..................................bobthu@msn.com
   2534 SE 87th Ave, Jamestown, ND 58401

NACAC Subsidy Representative **701.277.2741**
   7316 Ellis Ln, Horace, ND 58047

The Adoption Option **701.255.1165**
Fax...701.255.7647
   411 North 4th St Ste 10, Bismarck, ND 58501
   Gary Wolski, Director

The Adoption Option **701.235.7341**
   1325 11 Street South, Fargo, ND 58103
   Bob Sanderson, Director

HOME MEDICAL EQUIPMENT PROVIDERS

Developmental Center Adaptive Equipment
Services **701.352.4583**
Fax...701.352.4410
Web............http://www.nd.gov/dhs/locations/developm
   701 West Sixth Street, Grafton, ND 58237
   CARF accredited programs available.

Innovative Products Inc **800.950.5185**
   830 S 48th St, Grand Forks, ND 58201
   Jims Speike, Director

SOCIAL SERVICES

Catholic Charities ND **701.852.2854**
Fax...701.852.6573
Web...www.catholiccharitiesnd.org
   216 S Broadway Ste 103, Minot, ND 58701-3852
   Brian Oswald, Guardian Worker

Dakota Boys & Girls Ranch Fargo Youth
Home **701.237.3123**
Fax...701.237.4063
Web...www.dakotaboysranch.org
E-mail..................................tim.eissinger@dakotaboysranch.org
   1641 31st Ave S, Fargo, ND 58103-5934
   Tim Eissinger, Med, Lsw, Administrator I,program Director

Firstlink **701.293.6462**
Fax...701.235.2476
Web...www.myfirstlink.org
E-mail..................................cmiller@eyestreet.com
   4357 13th Ave S, Fargo, ND 58103
   Cindy Miller, Executive Director

Lutheran Social Services of North Dakota **701.235.7341**
Fax...701.271.3270
Web...www.lssnd.org
   P.O. Box 389, Fargo, ND 58107
   COA accredited organization.

Lutheran Social Svcs Child Care Resource And
Referral **888.223.1510**
Fax...701.223.0440
Web...www.ndchildcare.org
E-mail..................................lreinicke@lssnd.org
   1616 Capitol Way, Bismarck, ND 58501-2100
   Linda Reinicke, Program Director

Social Svc Board **701.667.3395**
Fax...701.667.3384
E-mail..................................kenneth.gerhardt@mortonnd.org
   200 2nd Ave NW, Mandan, ND 58554-3124
   Kenneth Gerhardt, Director

The Village Family Service Center **701.451.4900**
Fax...701.451.5058
Web...www.thevillagefamily.org
   1201 25th Street South, Fargo, ND 58103
   COA accredited organization.

SPECIAL NEEDS

Autism Society of North Dakota **701.281.8254**
   628 6th Ave, Alice, ND 58031

Brain Injury Association **701.845.1124**
   129 3rd Ave NE, Valley City, ND 58072
   Mary Simonson, Executive Director

Easter Seals Goodwill of North Dakota **800.247.0698**
E-mail..................................ghauge@esgwnd.org
   211 collena ave, Mandan, ND 58554
   Gordon Hauge, Chief Executive Officer

Family Voices of North Dakota Inc **888.522.9654**
E-mail..................................fvnd@drtel.net
   PO Box 163, Edgeley, ND 58433

Great Plains Autism Spectrum **800.233.1737**
E-mail..................................ndcpd@minotstateu.edu
   500 University Ave W, Minot, ND 58707
   Connie Irey, Project Director

Medcenter One Rehabilitation Center **701.323.6000**
Fax...701.323.6189
Web...www.medcenterone.com
   300 North Seventh Street, Bismarck, ND 58501
   CARF accredited programs available.

Mental Health America of North Dakota **701.391.8824**
E-mail..................................srhelgeland@gmail.com
   523 N 4TH St, Bismarck, ND 58502
   Susan Helgeland, Executive Director

MeritCare Hospital **701.280.4611**
Fax...701.461.5764
Web...www.meritcare.com
   1720 South University, Rehab 5C, Fargo, ND 58122
   CARF accredited programs available.

Pathfinder Family Center **701.837.7500**
E-mail..................................ndpath01@srt.com
   1600 SW 2nd Ave Ste 30, Minot, ND 58701

Pathfinder Family Center **701.852.9426**
Fax...701.838.9324
E-mail..................................ndpath01@minot.ndak.net
   1600 2nd Ave SW # 19, Minot, ND 58701

Red River Valley Asperger Network **701.566.1675**
   PO Box 281, West Fargo, ND 58078
   Joanne Vieweg, President

St. Alexius Medical Center Inpatient Rehabilitation
Unit...**701.530.4890**
Fax...701.530.4482
Web...www.st.alexius.org
   900 East Broadway, Bismarck, ND 58502-5510
   CARF accredited programs available.

The Arc of Bismarck **701.258.7949**
E-mail..................................joyce@apsimail.com
   1211 Park Ave, Bismarck, ND 58504

The Arc of North Dakota **701.772.6191**
   PO Box 12420, Grand Forks, ND 58208
   Diane Shepard, Chief Executive Officer

SUBSTANCE ABUSE TREATMENT

Heartview Foundation **701.222.0386**
Fax...701.255.4891
E-mail..................................heartview@heartview.org
   101 E Broadway Ave, Bismarck, ND 58501-3840
   Kurt Snyder, Executive Director

Mercy Medical Ctr **701.774.7409**
Fax...701.774.4188
Web...www.mdmercy.com
   1301 15th Ave W, Williston, ND 58801-3821
   Mathew Grimshaw, Chief Executive Officer

Prairie Learning Ctr **701.597.3419**
Fax...701.597.3004
Web...www.prairielearningcenter.org
E-mail..................................plc@westriv.com
   7785 Saint Gertrude Ave, Raleigh, ND 58564-4103
   Nichole Delatlane, Program Director

Trinity Addiction Svcs **701.857.2480**
Fax...701.857.3692
Web...www.trinityhealth.org
   407 3rd St SE, Minot, ND 58701-4470
   Meredithe Lester, Clinical Supervisor

Ohio

ohio.gov

John Kasich, Governor
77 South High Street, 30th Floor
Columbus, OH 43215-6117
614.466.3555
614.466.9354 (Fax)
www.governor.ohio.gov

Kristi Oden, Juvenile Justice Specialist
Department of Youth Services
51 N High Street, Sixth Floor
Columbus, OH 43215-4242
614.644.7738
614.644.0308 (Fax)
kristi.oden@dys.state.oh.us

Judge David E. Stucki, SAG Chair
PO Box 1
Brewster, OH 44613
330.844.1211
judgestucki@gmail.com

CRISIS NUMBERS

Child Abuse Reporting . . .800.442.4453

STATE SERVICES

SOCIAL SERVICES

Ofc of Families & Children **614.466.1213**
Fax 614.466.6185
  50 W Town St, Columbus, OH 43215
  Sandra Holt, Deputy Director

Ohio Dept of Insurance **614.644.2658**
Fax 614.644.3744
Web .... www.insurance.ohio.gov
  50 W Town St Ste 300, Columbus, OH 43215
  Mary Taylor, Lutinent Governer

Ohio Emergency Management Agency **614.889.7150**
Fax 614.889.7183
Web .... www.ema.ohio.gov
  2855 W Dublin Granville Rd, Columbus, OH 43235
  Nancy Bragani, Executive Director

Ohio Rehabilitation Svcs Commission **614.438.1200**
Fax 614.438.1257
Web .... www.rsc.ohio.gov
E-mail .... kevin.miller@rsc.state.oh.us
  400 E Campus View Blvd, Columbus,
  OH 43235-4604
  Kevin Miller, Director

GENERAL HEALTH SERVICES

Bureau for Child & Med Handicaps **614.466.1547**
Fax 614.728.3616
  246 N High St 2nd Flr, Columbus, OH 43216
  Jessica Foster, Director

Health Dept **937.382.3829**
Fax 937.382.7027
Web .... www.clincohd.com
E-mail .... bderge@clincohd.com
  111 S Nelson Ave Ste 1, Wilmington,
  OH 45177-2067
  Angie Putman, Nursing Director

Maternal and Child Health Ohio **614.466.5332**
Fax 614.564.2433
E-mail .... karen.hughes@odh.ohio.gov
  246 N High St, Columbus, OH 43215
  Karen Hughes, Director

Ofc of Medicaid **614.466.4443**
Fax 614.752.3986
Web .... www.ohio.gov
E-mail .... jhon.mccarthy@jfs.ohio.gov
  50 West Town Street, Floor 4, Columbus, OH 43215
  Jhon McCarthy, Director

Ofc of Primary Care & Rural Health **614.644.8508**
Fax 614.995.4235
Web .... www.gw.odh.state.oh.us
E-mail .... jmariott@gw.odh.state.oh.us
  246 N High St, 6th Floor, Columbus, OH 43215
  Joel Marriotti, Chief

Ohio State Medical Board **614.466.3934**
Fax 614.728.5946
Web .... www.med.ohio.gov
  30 E Broad St Fl 3, Columbus, OH 43215-6127
  Richard Whitehouse, Director

MENTAL HEALTH SERVICES

Alcohol & Drug Addiction Svcs **614.466.3445**
Fax 614.752.8645
Web .... www.odadas.ohio.gov
E-mail .... orman.hall@ada.ohio.gov
  280 N High St Fl 12, Columbus, OH 43215
  Orman Hall, Director

Board Of MR/DD **937.544.2574**
Fax 937.544.2223
Web .... www.odmrdd.state.oh.us
E-mail .... adamsmrdd@yahoo.com
  3964 Wheat Ridge Rd, West Union, OH 45693-9457
  Scott Aman, Superintendent

Ohio Dept of Mental Health **614.466.2596**
Fax 614.752.9453
Web .... www.mh.state.oh.us
E-mail .... questions@mh.ohio.gov
  30 E Broad St Fl 8, Columbus, OH 43215-3430
  Marion Sherman, Medical Director

Ohio Rehabilitation Services Commssion **614.438.1200**
Fax 614.785.5010
  150 E Campus View, Columbus, OH 43235
  Kevin Miller, Director

JUSTICE AGENCY

Attorney General's Ofc **614.466.4320**
Fax 614.466.5087
Web .... www.ag.state.oh.us
  30 E Broad St Fl 17, Columbus, OH 43215-3414
  Michael Dewine, Attorney General

Correctional Education Div OH **740.845.3240**
Fax 740.845.3387
E-mail .... denise.justice@odrc.state.oh.us
  1580 State Rt 56, London, OH 43140
  Denise L. Justice, Superintendent

Dept of Corrections **614.752.1150**
Fax 614.752.1171
  770 W Broad St, Columbus, OH 43222
  Gary Bohr, Director

Dept of Youth Svcs **614.466.8783**
Fax 614.387.2606
Web .... www.dys.ohio.gov
E-mail .... WEBMASTER@DYS.OHIO.GOV
  51 N High St, Suite 300, Columbus, OH 43215
  Martha Spohn, Deputy Asst. Director, Division Of Institutions

Ohio State CASA **614.224.2272**
Fax 614.228.6446
Web .... www.ohiocasa.org
E-mail .... ohiocasa@ohiocasa.org
  150 E Mound St, Ste 210, Columbus,
  OH 43215-5748
  Jackie Wilson, Executive Director

Victims of Crime Compensation Program **614.466.5610**
Fax 614.995.5412
  150 E Gay St Fl 25, Columbus, OH 43215
  Mike Dewine, Attorney General

COURTS

Family And Juvenile Court **937.599.7282**
Fax 937.599.7243
E-mail .... mbrady@co.logan.oh.us
  101 S Main St Rm 6, Bellefontaine, OH 43311-2055
  Ed Uhlman, Juv TX Court PO

Supreme Court of Ohio **614.387.9000**
Fax 614.387.9259
  65 S Front St, Columbus, OH 43215
  Steven Hollon, Administrative Director

POLICE AND SHERIFF

Buckeye State Sheriff's Assoc. **614.431.5500**
Fax 614.431.5665
Web .... www.buckeyesheriffs.org
E-mail .... bssa@buckeyesheriffs.org
  6230 Busch Blvd Ste 260, Columbus,
  OH 43229-1870
  Robert A. Cornwell, Executive Director

Ohio Assoc of Chiefs of Police **614.761.0330**
Fax 614.761.9509
Web .... www.oacp.org
  6277 Riverside Dr Ste 2N, Dublin, OH 43017-5067
  Donna Braxton, Executive Director

EDUCATION SERVICES

Dept of Education **877.644.6338**
Fax 614.387.0964
Web .... www.education.ohio.gov
E-mail .... kathe.shelby@ode.state.oh.us
  25 S Front St, Columbus, OH 43215-4183
  Kathe Shelby, Director

Educ for Homeless Children and Youth OH 614.466.4161
Fax 614.752.1622
E-mail ....tom.dannis@ode.state.oh.u@sbcglobal.net
25 S Front St Mail Stop 404, Columbus, OH 43215
Tom Dannis, Consultant For Homeless Children

Office for Exceptional Children Ohio 614.466.2650
Fax 614.387.0968
E-mail ....crystal.ginn@ode.state.oh.us
25 S Front St 2nd Flr, Mail Stop 202, Columbus,
OH 43215
Kathy Shelby, Director

Ohio Coalition for the Edu of Chil w Dis 740.382.5452
Fax 740.383.6421
E-mail ....ocecd@ocecd.org
165 W Center St Ste 302, Marion, OH 43302
Margaret Burley, Director

Ohio Department of Education 877.644.6338
Fax 614.728.9300
25 S Front St, Columbus, OH 43215
Cathy Shelby, Director

Ohio School for the Deaf 614.728.4030
Fax 614.995.3448
Web ....www.ohioschoolforthedeaf.org
500 Morse Rd, Columbus, OH 43214
Edward E. Corbett Jr., Superintendant

Ohio State School for the Blind 614.752.1152
Fax 614.752.1713
5220 N High St, Columbus, OH 43214
Cynthia Johnson, Interim Superintendent

LABOR & WORKFORCE EDUCATION

Ofc of Workforce Development 614.466.9505
Fax 614.995.1298
E-mail ....oconnl@odjfs.state.oh.us
4020 E 5th Ave, Columbus, OH 43219-1811
Linda OConnor, Deputy Director

Ohio

COUNTY SERVICES

Adams County

POLICE AND SHERIFF

Sheriff's Ofc 937.544.2314
Fax 937.544.6201
E-mail ....kinnyrogers@yahoo.com
110 W Main St Rm 43, West Union, OH 45693-1390
Kinny Rogers, Sheriff

Allen County

SOCIAL SERVICES

Child Support Enforcement 419.224.7133
Fax 419.222.6135
Web ....www.allencountyohio.com
200 W Market St, Lima, OH 45801
Lisa Markle, Director

PCSA 419.227.8590
Fax 419.229.2296
E-mail ....ferris@odjfs.state.oh.us
123 W Spring St, Lima, OH 45801
Scott Ferris, Executive Director

GENERAL HEALTH SERVICES

Family Planning 419.228.6154
Fax 419.229.2082
Web ....www.allencountyhealthdepartment.org
E-mail ....bdershem@allenhealthdept.org
219 E Market St, Lima, OH 45801-2825
Becky Dershem, Rn, Nursing Director

Health Dept 419.228.4457
Fax 419.224.4161
Web ....www.gw.odh.state.oh.us
E-mail ....kluhn@allenhealthdept.org
219 E Market St, Lima, OH 45801-4913
Kathy Luhn, Rd, Nutrition/wic Director

JUSTICE AGENCY

Juvenile Detention Ctr 419.998.5240
Fax 419.222.7403
E-mail ....bcarroll@allencountyohio.com
1000 Wardhill Ave, Lima, OH 45805
Berlin Carroll, Director Of Treatment And Detention Services

COURTS

Juvenile Court 419.227.5531
Fax 419.222.7403
E-mail ....acjc@allencountyohio.com
1000 Wardhill Ave, Lima, OH 45802
Doug Schweingruber, Senior Probation Officer

POLICE AND SHERIFF

Lima Police Dept 419.227.4444
Fax 419.221.5109
117 E Market St, Lima, OH 45801
Kevin Martin, Chief Of Police

Sheriff's Ofc 419.227.3535
Fax 419.227.2004
Web ....www.allencountyohio.com
E-mail ....dbeck@allencountyohio.com
333 N Main St, Lima, OH 45801-4434
Sam Uricrish, Sheriff

EDUCATION SERVICES

LACCA 419.227.9953
Fax 419.227.7626
E-mail ....jfox@lacca.org
540 S Central Ave, Lima, OH 45804
Jaclyn Fox, Director

Ashland County

GENERAL HEALTH SERVICES

Health Dept 419.282.4317
Fax 419.282.4333
Web ....www.ashlandhealth.com
E-mail ....ashlandhealth@ashlandhealth.com
1763 State Rout 60, Ashland, OH 44805-2114
Daniel R. Daugherty, Health Commissioner/Medical Director

JUSTICE AGENCY

Juvenile Detention Ctr 419.289.3988
Fax 419.281.8710
E-mail ....ashlandjuveniledet@zoominternet.net
1260 Center St, Ashland, OH 44805-4139
Duane Botdorf, Director

COURTS

Family And Juvenile Court 419.289.0000
Fax 419.281.5699
142 W 2nd St Ste 2, Ashland, OH 44805-2140
Duane Botdorf, Director Of Youth Detention Center

POLICE AND SHERIFF

Sheriff's Ofc 419.289.3911
Fax 419.289.0207
Web ....www.ashlandcounty.org
E-mail ....sheriff@ashlandcounty.org
1205 E Main St, Ashland, OH 44805-2810
E. Wayne Risner, Sheriff

Ashtabula County

SOCIAL SERVICES

CDJFS/CSEA 440.998.1110
Fax 440.998.1538
Web ....www.jfs.ohio.gov
E-mail ....arcarp@odjfs.state.oh.us
2924 Donahoe Dr, Ashtabula, OH 44004-4540
Patrick Arcaro, Director

PCSA 440.998.1811
Fax 440.992.6828
3914 C Ct, Ashtabula, OH 44005
Nick Kerosky, Director

GENERAL HEALTH SERVICES

Conneaut City Health Dept 440.593.3087
Fax 440.593.6026
Web ....www.ashtabulacountyhealth.com
327 Mill St, Conneaut, OH 44030-2439
Gary Huston, Do, Medical Director

Family Planning Clinic 440.992.5953
Fax 440.998.5202
Web ....www.fpaneo.org
E-mail ....mwp@fpaneo.org
510 W 44th St Ste 2, Ashtabula, OH 44004-6889
Mary Wynn Peaspanen, Executive Director

Health Dept 440.576.6010
Fax 440.576.5527
Web ....www.ashtabulacountyhealth.com
E-mail ....ashtcohd@odh.ohio.gov
12 W Jefferson St, Jefferson, OH 44047-1028
Christin Kettunen, Nursing Director

JUSTICE AGENCY

Youth Detention Ctr 440.992.3390
Fax 440.992.7835
3816 Donahoe Dr, Ashtabula, OH 44004
Kathy Thompson, Director

COURTS

Family And Juvenile Court 440.994.6000
Fax 440.994.6020
3816 Donahoe Dr, Ashtabula, OH 44004
Jim Howell, Assistant Director Youth Detention Center

POLICE AND SHERIFF

Sheriff's Ofc 440.576.9046
Fax 440.576.5915
E-mail ....whjohnson@co.ashtabula.oh.us
25 W Jefferson St, Jefferson, OH 44047-1027
William R. Johnson, Sheriff

Athens County

SOCIAL SERVICES

CDJFS 740.592.4477
Fax 740.797.2447
Web ....www.athenscountygoverment.com
184 N Lancaster St, Athens, OH 45701
Jack R. Frech, Director

Children Services 740.592.3061
Fax 740.593.3880
Web ....www.athenschildrenservices.com
18 Stonybrook Dr, Athens, OH 45701
Andrea Reik, Executive Director

GENERAL HEALTH SERVICES

Athens-Terry WIC Program 740.797.2352
Fax 740.797.2465
Web ....www.wic.com
88 N Plains Rd Ste 1, The Plains, OH 45780-1160
Jody Shrever, Director

MENTAL HEALTH SERVICES

Athens-Hocking-Vinton Alcohol, Drug & Mental Hlth Recovery Board 740.593.3177
Fax 740.592.1996
Web www.317board.org
E-mail ....earl@ahv317.co.athens.oh.us
7990 Dairy Ln, Athens, OH 45701-9391
Earl L Cecil, Executive Director

JUSTICE AGENCY

CASA/GAL 740.592.3255
Fax 740.594.2096
E-mail ....casagal45701@yahoo.com
1 S Court St, Athens, OH 45701
Rebecca Robison-miller, Director

Hocking Valley Community Residential Ctr 740.753.4400
Fax 740.753.4448
111 W Twenty Nine Dr, Nelsonville, OH 45764
Tamara Bauman, Executive Director

COURTS

Juvenile Court 740.592.3256
Fax 740.592.3268
1 S Court St Rm 2, Athens, OH 45701-2824
Honorable Robert W. Stewart, Director

POLICE AND SHERIFF

Sheriff's Ofc 740.593.6633
Fax 740.594.1374
13 W Washington St, Athens, OH 45701
Patrick Kelley, Sheriff

EDUCATION SERVICES

State Support Team Region 16 ....740.594.4235
Fax 740.592.5690
Web ....www.snowcrestassoc.org
E-mail ....president@snowcrestassoc.org
507 Richland Ave Ste 200, Athens, OH 45701-3700
Rick Edwards, Superintendent

Auglaize County

SOCIAL SERVICES

Child Support Enforcement 419.739.6510
Fax 419.739.6511
Web ....www.odjfs.state.oh.us
E-mail ....morrom@odjfs.state.oh.us
12 N Wood St, Wapakoneta, OH 45895
Michael Morrow, Director

COURTS

Family And Juvenile Court 419.739.6778
Fax 419.739.6779
209 S Blackhoof, Wapakoneta, OH 45895-1998
David Thornberry, Juvenile Probation Officer

EDUCATION SERVICES

Special Education 419.738.9224
Fax 419.738.9199
E-mail ....hc_graf@woco-k12.org
1045 Dearbaugh Ave Ste 1, Wapakoneta, OH 45895
Marlene Graf, Serrc Director

Belmont County

GENERAL HEALTH SERVICES

Health Dept 740.695.1202
Fax 740.695.8890
Web ....www.belmontcountyhealth.org
E-mail ....george.cholak@odh.ohio.gov
68501 Bannock Rd, Saint Clairsville, OH 43950-9736
George L. Cholak, Md, Health Comm/medical Director

JUSTICE AGENCY

Sargus Juvenile Detention Ctr 740.695.9750
Fax 740.695.6001
E-mail ....cshrieve@belcc.com
210 Fox Shannon Pl, Saint Clairsville, OH 43950
Cory Shreve, Administrator

COURTS

Family And Juvenile Court 740.695.2121
Fax 740.699.2143
E-mail ....jshunk@belcojuvct.com
101 W Main St, Saint Clairsville, OH 43950-1264
Jennifer Shunk, Court Programs / Finance Director

POLICE AND SHERIFF

Sheriff's Ofc 740.695.7933
Fax 740.695.9662
E-mail ....sheriff@belmontsheriff.com
68137 Hammond Rd, Saint Clairsville, OH 43950
Fred Thompson, Sheriff

EDUCATION SERVICES

Flushing Head Start 740.633.8964
Fax 740.665.0869
Web ....www.cacbelmont.org
E-mail ....smallory@cacbelmont.org
327 High Morris Town St, Saint Clairsville, OH 43950
Shirley Johnson Mallory, Director

Brown County

SOCIAL SERVICES

Child Support Enforcement 937.378.6414
Fax 937.378.2552
Web ....www.odjfs.state.oh.us
E-mail ....smiths@odjfs.state.oh.us
740 Mount Orab Pike Ste 1, Georgetown, OH 45121-1147
Susan Smith, Director

GENERAL HEALTH SERVICES

Health Dept 937.378.6892
Fax 937.378.4301
E-mail ....browcohd@odh.ohio.gov
826 Mount Orab Pike, Georgetown, OH 45121
Gina K. Spiller, Rn, Director Of Nursing

COURTS

Family And Juvenile Court 937.378.6726
Fax 937.378.4729
E-mail ....margaret_clark@fccourts.org
510 E State St Ste 1, Georgetown, OH 45121
Honorable Margaret A. Clark, Judge

Butler County

SOCIAL SERVICES

PCSA 513.887.4055
Fax 513.887.4260
Web ....www.bccsb.org
E-mail ....nottk@odjfs.state.oh.us
300 N Fair Ave, Hamilton, OH 45011-4250
Jeff Sanders, Director

GENERAL HEALTH SERVICES

Family Svcs Of Middletown 513.423.4637
Fax 513.424.7131
1311 Columbia Ave, Middletown, OH 45042
Maurice Maxwell, Executive Director

Hamilton City Health Dept 513.785.7080
Fax 513.785.7065
Web ....www.ci.hamilton.oh.us
E-mail ....hamicihd@odh.ohio.gov
345 High St Fl 3, Hamilton, OH 45011-6072
Shawn Dempsey, Health Director

Health Dept 513.863.1770
Fax 513.863.4372
Web ....www.butlercountyohio.org
E-mail ....boh@butlercountyohio.org
301 S 3rd St, Hamilton, OH 45011-2913
Jenny Bailer, Nursing Director

Middletown City Health Dept 513.425.1818
Fax 513.425.7852
Web ....www.ci.middletown.oh.us
E-mail ....mchd@cityofmiddletown.org
1 Donham Plz, Middletown, OH 45042-1901
Paul Jennewine, Do, Medical Director

Middletown Community Health Ctr 513.425.8305
Fax 513.425.1810
Web ....www.ci.middletown.oh.us
E-mail ....healthshare@horanassoc.com
930 9th Ave, Middletown, OH 45044-5530
Laura Senter, Nursing Director

COURTS

Family And Juvenile Court 513.887.3318
Fax 513.887.3698
280 N Fair Ave, Juvenile Justice Center, Hamilton, OH 45011-4222
Teri Lenhoff, Director Of Clerk Services

POLICE AND SHERIFF

Sheriff's Ofc 513.785.1300
Fax 513.785.1071
Web ....www.butlersheriff.org
E-mail ....webmaster@butlersheriff.org
705 Hanover St, Hamilton, OH 45011-3789
Richard K. Jones, Sheriff

Carroll County

SOCIAL SERVICES

Child Support Enforcement 330.627.5357
Fax 330.627.3346
7 E Main St, Carrollton, OH 44615
Shelley Martin, Director

PCSA 330.627.7313
Fax 330.627.4969
55 E Main St, Carrollton, OH 44615
Kate Offenberger, Director

GENERAL HEALTH SERVICES

Health Dept 330.627.4866
Fax 330.627.3040
Web ....www.carroll-lhd.org
E-mail ....mkampbell@carroll-ohd.org
301 Moody Ave SW, Carrollton, OH 44615
Mellini Kampbell, Md, Health Comissioner

COURTS

Family And Juvenile Court 330.627.2323
Fax 330.627.6004
E-mail ....p.beamer@carrollcountyohio.us
119 S Lisbon St Ste 202, Carrollton, OH 44615
Patricia Beamar, Chief Deputy Juvenile

POLICE AND SHERIFF

Sheriff's Ofc 330.627.2141
Fax 330.627.2143
E-mail ....dwilliams@carrollcountysheriff.org
43 2nd St SE, Carrollton, OH 44615-1408
Dale Williams, Sheriff

Champaign County

GENERAL HEALTH SERVICES

Health Dept 937.484.1605
Fax 937.484.1622
E-mail ....jeff.webb@odh.ohio.gov
1512 S US Hwy68 Ste Q100, Urbana, OH 43078
Jeff Webb, Director Of Environmental Health

© 2011 Dorland Health

MENTAL HEALTH SERVICES

Board Of Menatl Retardation/Developmental Disabilities 937.653.5217
Fax 937.653.7516
E-mail ....dkabbes@yahoo.com
　1250 E. Route 36, Urbana, OH 43078
　Dee Dee Kabbes, Superintendent

COURTS

Family And Juvenile Court 937.484.1027
Fax 937.484.1026
　200 N Main St Ste 319, Urbana, OH 43078-1673
　Jana Champ, Clerk Of Court

POLICE AND SHERIFF

Sheriff's Ofc 937.652.1313
Fax 937.484.1056
Web ....www.lio.champaign.oh.us
E-mail ....sheriff@ctcn.net
　214 N Main St, Urbana, OH 43078-1661
　Brent A. Emmonds, Sheriff

Clark County

GENERAL HEALTH SERVICES

Health Dept 937.390.5600
Fax 937.390.5625
Web ....www.ccchd.com
　529 E Home Rd, Springfield, OH 45503-2710
　Katheryn Mckee, Md, Medical Director

POLICE AND SHERIFF

Sheriff's Ofc 937.521.2050
Fax 937.328.2515
Web ....www.clarkcountysheriff.com
E-mail ....genekelly@clarkcountysheriff.com
　120 N Fountain Ave Ste B, Springfield,
　OH 45502-1163
　Gene A. Kelly, Sheriff

Clermont County

GENERAL HEALTH SERVICES

Health District 513.732.7499
Fax 513.732.7936
Web ....www.clermonthealthdistrict.org
E-mail ....cchealth@co.clermont.oh.us
　2275 Bauer Rd Ste 300, Batavia, OH 45103
　Dina Elliot Rn, Bsn, Nursing Director

JUSTICE AGENCY

CASA 513.735.7233
Fax 513.735.7283
Web ....www.casaforclermontkids.org
E-mail ....exe.director@casaforclermontkids.org
　313 E Main St, Batavia, OH 45103-3001
　Amanda List, Executive Director

Juvenile Detention Ctr 513.732.7154
Fax 513.732.7707
　2340 Clermont Center Dr Ste 100, Batavia,
　OH 45103-1955
　Tom Delgrande, Superintendent

POLICE AND SHERIFF

Sheriff's Ofc 513.732.7500
Fax 513.732.7515
E-mail ....clermontsheriff@co.clermont.oh.us
　4470 State Route 222, Batavia, OH 45103
　Albert J. Rodenberg Jr., Sheriff

EDUCATION SERVICES

Bethel Head Start 513.734.4025
Fax 513.734.0444
　101 Fossyl Dr, Bethel, OH 45106-1394
　Cindy Walriven, Director

CNE Head Start 513.625.7075
Fax 513.625.3325
Web ....www.cneschools.org
E-mail ....yvonne_t@cneschools.org
　2792 US Highway 50, Batavia, OH 45103-8532
　Yvonne Tucker, Director

Felicity Head Start 513.876.2113
Fax 513.876.2560
Web ....www.felicityfranklinschools.org
E-mail ....karenn@felicityfranklinschools.org
　415 Washington Street, Felicity, OH 45120
　Karen Nelcamp, Director

Clinton County

SOCIAL SERVICES

Child Support Enforcement 937.382.5726
Fax 937.383.2400
E-mail ....familyservices@cinci.rr.com
　1025 S South St Ste 400, Wilmington, OH 45177
　Judy Eschmann, Director

Children Sevices 937.382.5935
Fax 937.382.1165
Web ....www.odjfs.state.oh.us
　1025 S South St Ste 300, Wilmington,
　OH 45177-2788
　Judy Eschmann, Director

COURTS

Family And Juvenile Court 937.382.2391
Fax 937.383.0823
Web ....www.ccclerk.org
　46 S South St, Fl 2, Wilmington, OH 45177
　Honorable G. Allen Gano, Judge

POLICE AND SHERIFF

Sheriff's Ofc 937.382.1611
Fax 937.382.7530
　1645 Davids Dr, Wilmington, OH 45177
　Ralph D. Fizer Jr., Sheriff

Columbiana County

GENERAL HEALTH SERVICES

East Liverpool City Health Dept 330.385.7900
Fax 330.386.7403
Web ....www.eastliverpool.com
E-mail ....elhealthnurse@gmail.com
　126 W 6th St, East Liverpool, OH 43920-2960
　Jelayne Dray, Rn, Nursing Director

East Palestine City Health Dept 330.426.4367
Fax 330.426.7066
Web ....www.eastpalestineohio.org
　PO Box 231, East Palestine, OH 44413-0231
　Gary Clark, Manager

Lisbon Community Health Ctr 330.424.5686
Fax 330.424.4012
Web ....www.caaofcc.org
E-mail ....weir@caaofcc.org
　7880 Lincole Pl, Lisbon, OH 44432-8322
　Beth Weir, Director

JUSTICE AGENCY

Guardian Ad Litem Program 330.424.4071
Fax 330.424.6670
Web ....www.core.com
E-mail ....coljuv@core.com
　260 W Lincoln Way, Lisbon, OH 44432-1179
　Ann Weigle, Director

Louis Tobin Attention Ctr 330.424.9809
Fax 330.424.0429
　8363 County Home Rd, Lisbon, OH 44432
　Lori Paskevitch, Administrator

POLICE AND SHERIFF

Sheriff's Ofc 330.424.1104
Fax 330.424.3795
E-mail ....rstone@ccclerk.org
　105 S Market, Lisbon, OH 44432
　Raymond L Stone, Sheriff

EDUCATION SERVICES

East Liverpool Head Start 330.386.4899
Web ....www.eastliverpool.com
E-mail ....maryspooner@eastliverpool.com
　500 Maryland St, East Liverpool, OH 43920-2121
　Mary Spooner, Director

Coshocton County

SOCIAL SERVICES

CDJFS/CSEA 740.622.1020
Fax 740.622.5591
Web ....www.coshoctonjfs.org
E-mail ....millet03@odjfs.state.oh.us
　725 Pine St, Coshocton, OH 43812-2318
　Terry W. Miller, Director

GENERAL HEALTH SERVICES

Coshocton City Health Dept 740.622.1736
Fax 740.623.4559
Web ....www.coshoctoncityhall.com
E-mail ....coshcihd@odh.ohio.gov
　400 Browns Ln, Coshocton, OH 43812
　Wendy Redmond, Health Commissioner/medical Director

Health Dept 740.622.1426
Fax 740.295.7576
Web ....www.coshoctonhealth.net
E-mail ....coshcohe@odh.ohio.gov
　724 S 7th St Rm 125, Coshocton, OH 43812-2391
　Rebecca J Beiter, Rn, Nursing Director

COURTS

Family And Juvenile Court 740.622.8969
Fax 740.623.6514
Web ....www.coshoctoncounty.net
　426 Main St, Coshocton, OH 43812-1511
　Shelby Miller, Intensive/diversion Probation Officer

POLICE AND SHERIFF

Sheriff's Ofc 740.622.2411
Fax 740.622.4487
E-mail ....sheriffrogers@coshoctoncounty.net
　328 Chestnut St, Coshocton, OH 43812
　Tim Rogers, Sheriff

EDUCATION SERVICES

Head Start 740.622.3667
　3201 County Road 16, Coshocton, OH 43812
　Stephen Troendly, Executive Director

Crawford County

SOCIAL SERVICES

Child Support Enforcement 419.562.0773
Fax 419.562.2018
Web ....www.odifs.state.oh.us
　224 Norton Way, Bucyrus, OH 44820-1831
　Thomas O Leary, Director

GENERAL HEALTH SERVICES

Galion City Health Dept 419.468.1075
Fax 419.468.8618
E-mail ....scroffla@odh.ohio.gov
　113 Harding Way E, Galion, OH 44833
　Steve Novack, Medical Director

Health Dept 419.562.5871
Fax 419.562.2048
Web ....www.crawfordhealth.com
E-mail ....cchd@crawford-co.org
130 N Walnut St, Ste B, Bucyrus, OH 44820
Cynda Brause, Nursing Director

COURTS

Family And Juvenile Court 419.562.1896
Fax 419.562.6538
E-mail ....juvcrt17@bright.net
112 E Mansfield St Ste 101, Bucyrus, OH 44820
Honorable Steven D. Eckstein, Director

Cuyahoga County

SOCIAL SERVICES

Children and Family Services 216.431.4500
Fax 216.881.4807
Web ....http://cfs.cuyahogacounty.us/
3955 Euclid Avenue, Rm 223W, Cleveland,
OH 44115
COA accredited organization.

Department of Job Family Services 216.987.6387
Fax 216.987.8183
Web ....www.cuyahogacounty.us
1641 Payne Ave, Rm 520, Cleveland, OH 44114
Jaqueline Ward, Director

GENERAL HEALTH SERVICES

Cleveland Health Dept 216.664.4370
Fax 216.664.2197
Web ....www.odhgateway.state.oh.us
E-mail ....aavery@metrohealth.org
1925 Saint Clair Ave NE, Mural Building, Cleveland,
OH 44114-2080
Ann Avery, Medical Director

Health Dept 216.201.2000
Fax 216.676.1311
Web ....www.ccbh.net
E-mail ....ccbh@ccbh.net
5550 Venture Dr, Parma, OH 44130
Anna Mandalakas, Md, Medical Director

Lakewood Dital Statistics 216.529.7690
Fax 216.529.5910
Web ....www.ditalstatslakewoodoh.net
E-mail ....health.dept@lakewoodoh.net
12805 Detroit Ave, Lakewood, OH 44107
Dorothy M. Buckon, Rn, Director Of Human Servicess

Northern Ohio Hemophilia
Foundation 216.834.0051
Fax 216.834.0055
Web ....www.nohf.org
E-mail ....lynnecapretto@nohf.org
5000 Rockside Rd Ste 320, Independence,
OH 44131-2153
Lynne Capretto, Executive Director

Shaker Heights City Health Dept 216.491.1480
Fax 216.491.1439
Web ....www.shakeronline.com
E-mail ....health.department@shakeronline.com
3400 Lee Rd, Shaker Heights, OH 44120-3408
Scott H. Frank, Md, Ms, Health Comm/medical Director

MENTAL HEALTH SERVICES

Board Of And Developmental
Disabilities 216.241.8230
Fax 216.861.0253
Web ....www.ccbmrdd.org
E-mail ....ryan_t@ccbmrdd.org
1275 Lakeside Ave E, Cleveland, OH 44114-1132
Terrence Ryan, Superintendent

Mental Health Board 216.241.3400
Fax 216.363.1000
Web ....www.adamhscc.org
E-mail ....denihan@adamhscc.org
2012 W 25th St 6th Fl, Cleveland, OH 44113-3149
William M. Deniham, CEO

JUSTICE AGENCY

Justice Affairs 216.443.7265
Fax 216.698.6524
310 W Lakeside Ave, # 795A, Cleveland, OH 44113
Norberto Colon, Director

Juvenile Detention Ctr 216.443.3300
Fax 216.443.5019
Web ....www.juvenile.cuyahogacounty.us
E-mail ....lmunks@cuyahogacounty.us
2209 Central Ave, Cleveland, OH 44115-3113
Len Munks, Superintendent

Youth Svcs Regional Ofc 216.787.3350
Fax 216.787.3692
E-mail ....carla.brown@dys.ohio.gov
615 W Superior Ave Ste 860, Cleveland, OH 44113
Carla Brown, Regional Administrator

COURTS

Juvenile Court 216.443.8400
Fax 216.443.3413
2163 E 22nd St, Cleveland, OH 44115
Marita Kavalec, Court Administrator

West Park YMCA 216.941.5410
Fax 216.941.1351
15501 Lorain Ave, Cleveland, OH 44111
Monic Hill, Executive Director

POLICE AND SHERIFF

Sheriff's Ofc 216.443.6000
Fax 216.348.4353
E-mail ....tgrossman@cuyahogacounty.us
1215 W 3rd St, Cleveland, OH 44113
Bob Reed, Sheriff

EDUCATION SERVICES

Avon Head Start 216.883.8550
Fax 216.883.8550
10902 Avon Ave, Cleveland, OH 44105-4219
Ms Rosonya Bogarty, Director

Bingham Childcare Ctr 216.621.1782
Fax 216.621.0515
2421 Central Ave, Cleveland, OH 44115
Fadoik, Director

Broadway YMCA Head Start 216.341.3266
Fax 216.391.8282
11300 Miles Ave, Cleveland, OH 44105-5368
Mary Jackson, Director

Buckeye Head Start 216.751.1409
Fax 216.391.8282
12100 Buckeye Rd, Cleveland, OH 44120
Tonya Williams, Director

Carl B Stokes Head Start 216.692.4010
Web ....www.ceogc.org
E-mail ....nbowling@ceogc.org
1883 Torbenson Dr, Cleveland, OH 44112-1308
Natisha Bowling, Director

Ceogc Head Start Ctr 216.541.7878
14209 Euclid Ave, Cleveland, OH 44112
Brenda Vann, Director

Ceogc Puritas Head Start 216.476.3201
Fax 216.476.3205
E-mail ....kdemarco@ceogc.org
14402 Puritas Ave, Cleveland, OH 44135-2800
Kelley Demarco, Director

Faith Presbyterian Head Start 216.228.8918
E-mail ....wsemfaith@sbcglobal.net
12601 Detroit Ave, Lakewood, OH 44107
Kathy Wasikowski, Director

Special Education 216.524.2770
Fax 216.524.2885
Web ....www.esc-cc.org
E-mail ....bob.mengerink@ese-cc.org
5811 Canal Rd Ste 130, Cleveland, OH 44125-3442
Robert Menerink, Superintendent

Darke County

COURTS

Family And Juvenile Court 937.547.7350
Fax 937.547.1945
Web ....www.darkeprobatejuvenile.org
300 Garst Ave Ste 1, Greenville, OH 45331-2389
Paul Garrett, Chief Performance Officer

POLICE AND SHERIFF

Sheriff's Ofc 937.548.3399
Fax 937.548.9235
Web ....www.darkecountysheriff.org
E-mail ....tspencer@darkecountysheriff.org
5185 County Home Rd, Greenville, OH 45331-9753
Toby Spencer, Sheriff

Defiance County

SOCIAL SERVICES

Child Support Enforcement 419.784.2123
Fax 419.782.7680
Web ....www.odjfs.state.oh.us
E-mail ....schapperts@odjfs.state.oh.us
1300 E 2nd St Ste 204, Defiance, OH 43512-2171
Sandra Schappert, Director

GENERAL HEALTH SERVICES

Health Dept 419.784.3818
Fax 419.782.4979
Web ....www.defiancecohealth.org
E-mail ....healthcommish@defiance-county.com
1300 E 2nd St Ste 100, Defiance, OH 43512-2484
Kim Moss, Health Commissioner

COURTS

Family And Juvenile Court 419.782.4181
Fax 419.783.4811
E-mail ....jddunbar@defiance-county.com
221 Clinton St, Defiance, OH 43512
Janet Dunbar, Court Administrator

EDUCATION SERVICES

Family Resource Ctr Head Start 419.784.2152
Fax 419.784.0702
644 Clinton St, Defiance, OH 43512
Becky Michael, Director

Delaware County

GENERAL HEALTH SERVICES

Health Dept 740.368.1700
Fax 740.368.1736
Web ....www.delawarehealth.org
E-mail ....nshapiro@delawarehealth.org
1 And 3 W Winter St, Fl 2, Delaware, OH 43015
Nancy Shapiro, Assistant Health Commissioner Personal Health

JUSTICE AGENCY

Freedom Ctr 740.881.3337
Fax 740.881.3389
Web ....www.dys.state.oh.us
E-mail ....marci.sutherland@dys.state.oh.us
8101 Dublin Rd, Delaware, OH 43015-8892
Marci Sutherland, Superintendent

Scioto Juvenile Correctional

Facility **740.881.3250**
Fax 740.881.6944
Web ....www.dys.ohio.gov
E-mail ....gwen.randle@dys.ohio.gov
　5993 Home Rd, Delaware, OH 43015-9477
　Gwen Randle, Superintendent

COURTS

Family And Juvenile Court **740.833.2600**
Fax 740.833.2599
　140 N Sandusky St, Delaware, OH 43015
　Lisa Risinger, Intake Department Director

POLICE AND SHERIFF

Sheriff's Ofc **740.833.2860**
Fax 740.833.2859
E-mail ....sheriff@co.delaware.oh.us
　149 N Sandusky St, Delaware, OH 43015-1732
　Walter Davis, Sheriff

Erie County

GENERAL HEALTH SERVICES

Health Dept **419.626.5623**
Fax 419.626.8778
Web ....www.eriecohealthohio.org
E-mail ....pschade@eriecohealthohio.org
　420 Superior St, Sandusky, OH 44870
　Peter T Schade, Do, Health Commissioner/medical Director

JUSTICE AGENCY

CASA **419.621.0324**
Fax 419.621.8788
E-mail ....ohcasakids@bex.net
　141 E Water St, # 208, Sandusky, OH 44870
　Terry Stephan, Executive Director

Juvenile Justice Ctr **419.627.7611**
Fax 419.627.6673
Web ....www.eriecounty.oh.gov
E-mail ....kcollins@eriecounty.oh.gov
　1338 Tiffin Ave, Sandusky, OH 44870-2049
　Krista Collins, Superintendent

COURTS

Family And Juvenile Court **419.627.7782**
Fax 419.627.6600
E-mail ....www.eriecounty.oh.gov
　323 Columbus Ave, 4th Fl, Sandusky, OH 44870
　Tammy Barbato, Court Services Director

Fairfield County

SOCIAL SERVICES

PCSA **740.653.4060**
Fax 740.687.7070
E-mail ....bowler@odjfs.state.oh.us
　239 W Main St, Lancaster, OH 43130-3739
　Rich Bowlen, Director

GENERAL HEALTH SERVICES

Health Dept **740.653.4489**
Fax 740.653.6626
Web ....www.myfdh.org
　1587 Granville Pike, Lancaster, OH 43130
　Gwen Shafer, Nursing Director

Job & Family Svcs **740.653.1701**
Fax 740.687.6810
Web ....www.myworkfamily.com
E-mail ....bopet@odjfs.state.oh.us
　239 W Main St, Lancaster, OH 43130-3739
　Michael Orlando, Director

Fayette County

SOCIAL SERVICES

CSEA **740.335.0745**
Fax 740.333.3572
Web ....www.odjfs.state.oh.us
E-mail ....harrisonl@odjfs.state.oh.us
　133 S Main St, Washington Court House, OH 43160
　Leslie Harrison, Supervisor

Job & Family Svcs **740.335.0350**
Fax 740.333.3572
Web ....www.fayette-co-oh.com
E-mail ....hellenthall@odjfs.state.oh.us
　133 S Main St Rm 100, Washington Court House,
　OH 43160
　Lori Hellenthal, Director

GENERAL HEALTH SERVICES

Health Dept **740.335.5910**
Fax 740.333.3528
Web ....www.fayette-co-oh.com
E-mail ....fayecohd@odh.ohio.gov
　317 S Fayette St, Washington Court House,
　OH 43160-2235
　Nancy Stegbauer, Rn, Nursing Director

COURTS

Family And Juvenile Court **740.335.0640**
Fax 740.333.3598
E-mail ......nancydrake.hammond@fayette-co-oh.com
　110 E Court St, Washington Court House, OH 43160-
　David Bender, Judge

EDUCATION SERVICES

Head Start-Jeffersonville **740.335.7138**
Fax 740.335.0051
Web ....www.adelphia.net
E-mail ....jlewis@adelphia.net
　41 Colonial Dr, Jeffersonville, OH 43128
　Jacquline Lewis, Director

Franklin County

SOCIAL SERVICES

Adoptions **614.341.6000**
Fax 614.341.6090
Web ....www.fccs.co.franklin.oh.us
E-mail ....krtoler@fccs.co.franklin.oh.us
　855 W Mound St, Columbus, OH 43223-2208
　Kim Toler, Director Of Adoption

Area Agency On Aging Region 6 ....**614.645.7250**
Fax 614.645.3884
Web ....www.coaaa.org
E-mail ....coaaa@coaaa.org
　174 E Long St, Columbus, OH 43215
　Cindy Farson, Director

East Region Children's Svcs **614.575.3500**
Fax 614.575.3600
　205 N Hamilton Rd, Columbus, OH 43213-1388
　Christine Kade, Director

Franklin Conty childrens Services **614.275.2571**
Fax 614.275.2755
Web ....www.co.franklin.oh.us
E-mail ....edfenner@fccs.co.franklin.oh.us
　855 W Mound St, Columbus, OH 43223
　Anne O'Lery, Acting Director

West Region Children's Svcs **614.278.5800**
Fax 614.278.5896
Web ....www.franklincountyohio.org
　1919 Frank Rd, Columbus, OH 43223-3731
　Alissa Cash, Director

GENERAL HEALTH SERVICES

Bexley City **614.235.8694**
Fax 614.559.4201
Web ....www.bexley.org
E-mail ....robert@bexley.org
　2242 E Main St, Columbus, OH 43209-2399
　Debbie, Assistant To The Mayor

Columbus City Health Dept **614.645.7417**
Fax 614.645.0070
Web ....www.publichealth.columbus.gov
　240 Parsons Ave, Columbus, OH 43215
　Teresa Long, Director

Columbus Health Dept **614.645.7002**
Fax 614.645.1753
Web ....www.publichealth.columbus.gov
E-mail ....healthcommissioner@columbus.gov
　240 Parsons Ave, Columbus, OH 43215-5331
　Martha Simmons, Maternal & Child Health Perinatal Service Director

Health Dept **614.462.3160**
Fax 614.462.6672
Web .....www.franklincountyohio.gov/board_of_hea lth
E-mail ....fcbh@franklincountyohio.gov
　280 E Broad St, Fl 2 Rm 200, Columbus, OH 43215

Woods At Parkside **419.352.8402**
Fax 419.353.9680
Web ....www.thewoodsatparkside.com
　1840 E Gypsy Ln, Bowling Green, OH 43402
　Michael Lemon, Medical Director

JUSTICE AGENCY

CASA **614.462.7450**
Fax 614.462.5070
Web ....www.casacolumbus.org
E-mail ....casa@casacolumbus.org
　373 S High St Fl 15, Columbus, OH 43215
　Marilyn Berlekamp, Executive Director

Criminal Justice Svcs Ofc **614.466.7782**
Fax 614.466.0308
Web ....www.ocjs.ohio.gov
　1970 W Broad St, Ste 429, Columbus, OH 43223
　Karhlton Moore, Director

Dept Of Youth Svcs Columbus Regional

Ofc **614.466.4676**
Fax 614.752.7492
E-mail ....steve.curl@dys.ohio.gov
　899 E Broad St, Columbus, OH 43205
　Steve Curl, Administrator

COURTS

Teen Court **614.462.3130**
Fax 614.462.5388
　373 S High St Fl 4, Columbus, OH 43215
　Peggy Betts, Coordinator

POLICE AND SHERIFF

Columbus Division Of Police **614.645.4600**
Fax 614.645.8648
Web ....www.columbuspolice.org
　120 Marconi Blvd, Columbus, OH 43215-2376
　Commander Thomas Fischer, Juvenile Bureau

EDUCATION SERVICES

Board of Developmental

Disabilities **614.475.0564**
Fax 614.342.5804
　2879 Johnstown Rd, Columbus, OH 43219
　Rebecca Love, Director

Broad Street Infant And Toddler

Ctr **614.221.6102**
Fax 614.884.3582
E-mail ....sbrown@columbusearlylearning.org
　760 E Broad St, Columbus, OH 43205
　Shannon Brown, Director

Ohio

C Ray Williams Head Start 614.866.7133
4737 Etna Rd, Columbus, OH 43213-2064
Ms Renee Silverman, Director

CDC Godman Guild Head Start 614.297.8634
Web . . . . .www.cdcheadstart.org
E-mail .ccarter@cdcheadstart.org
303 E 6th Ave, Columbus, OH 43201-2888
Carmen Carter, Director

CDC Linden Head Start 614.263.9516
E-mail .indouta@cdcheadstart.org
1254 Briarwood Ave, Columbus, OH 43211-1300
Idia Ndouta, Director

CDCFC Poindexter Head Start 614.252.1901
Web . . . . .www.cdcheadstart.org
E-mail .rpritchard@cdcheadstart.org
240 N Champion Ave, Columbus, OH 43203-1561
Rebecca Pritchard, Director

CDCFC Rosewind Head Start 614.297.8755
Web . . . . .www.cdcheadstart.org
E-mail .mallen@cdcheadstart.org
1400 Brooks Ave Ste 1, Columbus, OH 43211-2900
Mozelle Allen, Director

Cdi St Agnes Head Start 614.274.8822
2350 W Mound St, Columbus, OH 43204
Joyce Grimes, Director

Cdi St Phillips Head Start 614.252.1191
166 Woodland Ave, Columbus, OH 43203-1774
Brandy Cromer, Director

Communities In Schools Columbus 614.268.2472
Fax 614.268.4260
Web . . . . .www.ciskids.org
E-mail . . . . .burban@ciskids.org
510 E North Broadway St, Columbus,
OH 43214-4114
Mark D. Phelan, Chairman

Fulton County

COURTS

Family And Juvenile Court
Probation 419.337.9244
Fax 419.337.9284
Web . . . . .www.fultoncountyoh.com
E-mail .sreed@fultoncountyoh.com
210 S Fulton St Ste B1, Wauseon, OH 43567-1325
Stacey Reed, Chief Performance Officer

POLICE AND SHERIFF

Archbold Police Dept 419.445.9991
Fax 419.445.0021
Web . . . . .www.policearchbold.com
E-mail .archpdcf@policearchbold.com
405 E Lutz Rd, Archbold, OH 43502-1252
Mr Martin Schmidt, Police Chief

Gallia County

SOCIAL SERVICES

PCSA 740.446.4963
Fax 740.446.2063
E-mail .moorer03@odjfs.state.oh.us
83 Shawnee Ln, Gallipolis, OH 45631
Russ V Moore, Executive Director

GENERAL HEALTH SERVICES

Health Dept 740.441.2018
Fax 740.441.2045
Web . . . . .www.gw.odh.state.oh.us
E-mail .melissa.conkle@odh.ohio.gov
499 Jackson Pike Ste D, Gallipolis, OH 45631-1399
Mellissa Conkle, Nursing Director

MENTAL HEALTH SERVICES

Gallia-Jackson-Meigs Alcohol, Drug & Mental Health Svcs
Board 740.446.3022
Fax 740.446.6814
Web . . . . .www.gjmboard.org
E-mail . . . . .info@gjmboard.org
53 Shawnee Ln, Gallipolis, OH 45631
Ron Adkins, Executive Director

POLICE AND SHERIFF

Sheriff's Ofc 740.441.2054
Fax 740.441.4804
Web . . . . .www.galliasheriff.org
E-mail . . . . .sheriff@gallianet.net
18 Locust St Ste 1289, Gallipolis, OH 45631
Joseph Browning, Sheriff

Geauga County

GENERAL HEALTH SERVICES

Health Dept 440.279.1950
Fax 440.286.1290
Web . . . . .www.geaugacountyhealth.org
E-mail .info@geaugacountyhealth.org
470 Center St Bldg 8, Chardon, OH 44024
Chris Pintchuk, Nursing Director

COURTS

Family And Juvenile Court 440.279.1830
Fax 440.285.8751
Web . . . . .www.geaugacourts.org
231 Main St Ste 200, Chardon, OH 44024-1288
Beth Williams, Senior Probation Officer

POLICE AND SHERIFF

Sheriff's Ofc 440.279.2009
Fax 440.286.3251
Web . . . . .www.sheriff.geauga.oh.us
E-mail .geaugaso@co.geauga.oh.us
12450 Merritt Dr, Chardon, OH 44024-9010
Daniel C. Mcclelland, Sheriff

Greene County

SOCIAL SERVICES

PCSA 937.562.6600
Fax 937.562.6650
Web . . . . .www.greenecsp.org
601 Ledbetter Rd, Xenia, OH 45385
Alice Maddox, Executive Director

GENERAL HEALTH SERVICES

Health Dept 937.374.5600
Fax 937.374.5675
Web . . . . .www.gcchd.org
360 Wilson Dr, Xenia, OH 45385
Robert P. Dillaplain, Md, Medical Director

MENTAL HEALTH SERVICES

Board Of MR/DD 937.562.6500
Fax 937.562.6539
E-mail . . . . .johnlarock@aol.com
245 N Valley Rd, Xenia, OH 45385-9301
Jill Larock, Director Of Community Services

JUSTICE AGENCY

Juvenile Detention Ctr 937.562.4101
Fax 937.562.4118
2100 Greene Way Blvd, Xenia, OH 45385
Gary Niedenthal, Superintendent

Miami Valley Juvenile Rehabilitation
Ctr 937.562.4150
Fax 937.562.4170
E-mail .bhershey@co.greene.oh.us
2100 Greene Way Blvd, Xenia, OH 45385
Gary Neidenthal, Director

Residential Treatment (Boys) 937.562.7644
Fax 937.562.7644
701 Dayton Xenia Rd, Xenia, OH 45384
Chleo Watts, Director

COURTS

Family And Juvenile Court 937.562.4000
Fax 937.562.4010
Web . . . . .www.co.greene.oh.us
E-mail .tgevedon@co.greene.oh.us
2100 Greene Way Blvd, Xenia, OH 45385-2677
Timothy Gevedon, Restitution Director/CPO

POLICE AND SHERIFF

Sheriff's Ofc 937.562.4800
Fax 937.562.4880
E-mail .gfischer@co.greene.oh.us
120 E Main St, Xenia, OH 45385
Gene Fischer, Sheriff

Guernsey County

SOCIAL SERVICES

Area Agency On Aging Region 9 . . . . .740.432.6600
Fax 740.432.1060
Web www.aaa9.org
E-mail . . . . .aaa9@aaa9.org
60788 Southgate Rd Rm 1, Byesville,
OH 43723-9533
Jim Embly, Director

PCSA 740.439.5555
Fax 740.439.5521
274 Highland Ave, Cambridge, OH 43725
Nicole Caldwell, Executive Director

GENERAL HEALTH SERVICES

Cambridge District Ofc 740.432.3012
Fax 614.564.2468
107 N 6th St, Cambridge, OH 43725
Lawissa Kidrick, Administrator

JUSTICE AGENCY

CASA 740.439.5697
Fax 740.432.7245
Web . . . . .www.yourradioplace.com
E-mail .casadirector@guernseycounty.org
801 Wheeling Ave Rm D102, Cambridge,
OH 43725-2302
Jean Stevens, Program Director

EDUCATION SERVICES

Beatty Avenue Head Start 740.439.3493
Fax 740.432.8037
E-mail . . . . .ppayton@acf.hhs.gov
1127 Beatty Ave, Cambridge, OH 43725-1921
Patricia Payton, Director

Hamilton County

GENERAL HEALTH SERVICES

Braxton F. Cann Medical Ctr 513.263.8750
Fax 513.263.8787
5818 Madison Rd, Cincinnati, OH 45227
Brenda Waldron, Clinic Manager

Cincinnati City Health Dept 513.357.7280
Fax 513.357.7498
Web . . . . .www.cincinnati-oh.gov/health
E-mail .brenda.frye@cincinnati-oh.gov
3101 Burnet Ave, Cincinnati, OH 45229-3098
Brenda Frye, Administrative Assistant

Cincinnati City Health Dept AIDS
Ctr 513.357.7346
Fax 513.357.7307
Web . . . . .www.cincinnati-oh.gov/departments.html
E-mail .eric.washington@cincinnati-oh.gov
3101 Burnet Ave, Cincinnati, OH 45229-3098
Eric Washington, Interim Director

Elm Street Health Ctr 513.352.3092
Fax 513.352.1429
 1525 Elm St, Cincinnati, OH 45202
 Debby Dreyfus, Clinic Manager

Health District 513.946.7800
Fax 513.946.7890
Web ....www.hamiltoncountyhealth.org
E-mail ....tim.ingram@hamilton-co.org
 250 William Howard Taft Rd Fl 2, Cincinnati,
 OH 45219-2630
 Mary Sacco, Msn, Rn, Director Of Nursing

Northside Health Ctr 513.357.7600
Fax 513.352.3939
 3917 Spring Grove Ave, Cincinnati, OH 45223
 Brenda Waldron, Clinic Manager

Norwood City Health Dept 513.458.4600
Fax 513.458.4606
Web ....www.norwoodhealth.org
E-mail ....ccorbin@norwoodhealth.org
 2059 Sherman Ave, Norwood, OH 45212-2633
 Chandra Corbin, Rn, Nursing Director

Price Hill Health Ctr 513.357.2700
Fax 513.357.2750
 2136 W 8th St, Cincinnati, OH 45204
 Debroah Dreyfus, Clinic Manager

Sharonville City Health Dept 513.563.1722
Fax 513.563.0084
Web ....www.sharonville.org
E-mail ....bwebb@cityofsharonville.com
 10900 Reading Rd, Cincinnati, OH 45241-2559
 Barry Webb, Md, Medical Director

Springdale City Health Dept 513.346.5725
Fax 513.346.3975
Web ....www.springdale.org/depart/health/health .htm
E-mail ....cmitrione@springdale.org
 11700 Springfield Pike, Cincinnati, OH 45246
 Barry Webb, Md, Medical Director

St. Bernard City Health Dept 513.242.7709
Fax 513.482.7480
E-mail ....lschmitt@cityofstbernard.org
 110 Washington Ave, Cincinnati, OH 45217-1399
 Robert Evans, Environmental Director

WIC Program 513.821.6946
Fax 513.821.6513
Web ....www.cincinnati-oh.gov
E-mail ....betsy.buchanan@cincinnati-oh.gov
 7162 Reading Rd, Cincinnati, OH 45237-2897
 Betsy Buchanan, Director

MENTAL HEALTH SERVICES

Mental Health Board 513.946.8600
Fax 513.946.8610
E-mail ....patrickt@hamilton.mhrsb.state.oh.us
 2350 Auburn Ave Fl 1, Cincinnati, OH 45219-2854
 Patrick Tribbe, Executive Director

Summit Health Care 513.948.3600
Fax 513.948.3080
Web ....www.mh.state.oh.us
E-mail ....banksl@mh.state.oh.us
 1101 Summit Rd, Cincinnati, OH 45237-2621
 Liz Banks, CEO

JUSTICE AGENCY

Good Samaritan Hospital 513.862.1400
Fax 513.872.3435
Web ....http://www.trihealth.com/gsh/gsh_index.aspx
 375 Dixmyth Ave, Cincinnati, OH 45220-2489
 Dave Dornheggen, Chief Operating Officer

Hillcrest Training School 513.552.1200
Fax 513.552.1290
Web ....www.dys.ohio.gov
 246 Bonham Rd, Cincinnati, OH 45215-2099
 Rotterman, Superintendent

Prokids/CASA 513.281.2000
Fax 513.487.6444
Web ....www.prokidscasa.org
E-mail ....info@prokidscasa.org
 2605 Burnet Ave, Cincinnati, OH 45219
 Tracy Cook, Executive Director

Youth Ctr 513.946.2600
Fax 513.946.2675
E-mail ....dwayne.bowman@juvcourt.hamilton-co.org
 2020 Auburn Ave, Juvenile Detention, Cincinnati,
 OH 45219-3025
 Dwayne Bowman, Superintendent

COURTS

Family And Juvenile Court 513.946.9200
Fax 513.946.9240
 800 Broadway St Fl 1, Cincinnati, OH 45202-1333
 Frank Yux, Executive Director Of Court Services

POLICE AND SHERIFF

Cincinnati Police 513.352.3536
Fax 513.352.2949
Web ....www.cincinnati-oh.gov
 310 Ezzard Charles Dr, Cincinnati, OH 45214-2805
 Gloria, Manager

Sheriff's Ofc 513.946.6400
Fax 513.946.6402
E-mail ....sleis@sheriff.hamilton-co.org
 1000 Sycamore St Ste 110, Cincinnati, OH 45202
 Simon Leis, Jr., Sheriff

EDUCATION SERVICES

**Camp Washington Child Development
Ctr** 513.541.9080
Fax 513.541.2840
 1054 Heywood St, Cincinnati, OH 45225
 Julie Controveros, Director

Special Education 513.563.0045
Fax 513.563.0588
Web ....www.hccanet.org
E-mail ....poth_r@hccanet.org
 1301 Bonnell St, Fl 3, Cincinnati, OH 45215
 Rita Poth, Director

Hancock County

SOCIAL SERVICES

Child Support Enforcement 419.424.1365
Fax 419.424.7288
 7814 County Road 140, Findlay, OH 45839
 Don Kissh, Administrator

GENERAL HEALTH SERVICES

Findlay City Health Dept 419.424.7105
Fax 419.424.7189
Web www.ci.findlay.oh.us/health1.htm
E-mail ....health@ci.findlay.oh.us
 318 Dorney Plz Ste 206, Findlay, OH 45840-3346
 Stephen D. Mills, DO, Health Commissioner/Medical Director

COURTS

Juvenile Court 419.424.7066
Fax 419.424.7081
 308 Dorney Plz, Findlay, OH 45840
 Honorable Allan H. Davis, Judge

POLICE AND SHERIFF

Sheriff's Ofc 419.424.7097
Fax 419.424.7078
E-mail ....meheldman@co.hancock.oh.us
 200 W Crawford St, Findlay, OH 45840
 Michael Heldman, Sheriff

Hardin County

SOCIAL SERVICES

Child Support Enforcement 419.674.2269
Fax 419.673.1417
Web ....www.odjfs.state.oh.us
E-mail ....perkip@odjfs.state.oh.us
 175 W Franklin St, Ste 220, Kenton, OH 43326
 Laura Rogers, Director

Job & Family Svcs 419.675.1130
Fax 419.674.2340
Web ....www.hardincountyjfs.org
E-mail ....norman@odjfs.state.oh.us
 175 W Franklin St, Ste 150, Kenton, OH 43326
 Robert Norman, Director

GENERAL HEALTH SERVICES

Health Dept 419.673.6230
Fax 419.673.8761
Web ....www.kentonhardinhealth.com
E-mail ....cindy.keller@odh.ohio.gov
 175 W Franklin St, Ste 120, Kenton, OH 43326
 Cindy Keller, Nursing Director

MENTAL HEALTH SERVICES

Board Of MR/DD 419.674.4158
Fax 419.673.1741
Web ....www.simonkentonharco.com
E-mail ....mkieffer@dbscorp.net
 707 N Ida St, Kenton, OH 43326-1060
 Mark Kieffer, Superintendant

COURTS

Juvenile Court 419.674.2233
Fax 419.675.2941
E-mail ....cindybeverly@hardinohio.us
 1 Court House Sq Ste 200, Kenton, OH 43326
 Wade Melton, Program Director

Harrison County

SOCIAL SERVICES

Child Support Enforcement 740.942.2900
Fax 740.942.8135
Web ....www.odrc.state.oh.us
E-mail ....david.watson@odrc.state.oh.us
 538 N Main St Ste E, Cadiz, OH 43907-1281
 David Watson, Director

COURTS

Family And Juvenile Court 740.942.2088
Fax 740.942.8483
 100 W Market St Dept 202, Cadiz, OH 43907-1132
 Laurie Mcafee, Probation Officer

Henry County

SOCIAL SERVICES

Child Support Enforcement 419.592.4633
Fax 419.592.7433
Web ....www.odjfs.state.oh.us
E-mail ....gruenhagena@odjfs.state.oh.us
 1809 Oakwood Ave, Napoleon, OH 43545
 Alan Gruenhagen, Director

GENERAL HEALTH SERVICES

Health Dept 419.599.5545
Fax 419.599.1714
Web ....www.henrycohd.org
E-mail ....healthdt@henrycohd.org
 1843 Oakwood Ave, Napoleon, OH 43545-9243
 Julie Laus, Nursing Director

Ohio

COURTS

Family And Juvenile Court

Probation 419.599.5951

Fax 419.599.0179

660 N Perry St Ste 401, Napoleon, OH 43545

Honorable Denise Mccully, Judge

POLICE AND SHERIFF

Sheriff's Ofc 419.592.8010

Fax 419.592.6915

Web ....www.henrycountysheriff.com

E-mail ....jnye@henrycountysheriff.com

123 E Washington St, Napoleon, OH 43545-1645

John J. Nye, Sheriff

Highland County

SOCIAL SERVICES

PCSA 937.393.3111

Fax 937.393.3299

E-mail ....jacobw0@odjfs.state.oh.us

1575 N High St, Hillsboro, OH 45133

Windy Jacobs, Director

GENERAL HEALTH SERVICES

Health Department 937.393.1941

Fax 937.393.5137

Web ....www.highlandcountyhealthdepartment.com

E-mail ....highcohd@odh.ohio.gov

1487 N High St Ste 400, Hillsboro, OH 45133-8496

Karen Oglesby, Rn, Nursing Director

JUSTICE AGENCY

Cuyahoga Hills Juvenile Correctional

Facility 216.464.8200

Fax 216.464.3540

4321 Green Rd, Cleveland, OH 44128

Katie Needham, Superintendent

COURTS

Family And Juvenile Court 937.393.9982

Fax 937.393.0926

E-mail ....juvenilecourt@co.highland.oh.us

105 N High St Ste 2, Hillsboro, OH 45133-1076

Honorable Kevin Greer, Judge

EDUCATION SERVICES

Belfast Head Start Ctr 937.764.1591

8831 St Rt 785, Hillsboro, OH 45133

Vonda Newkirk, Director

Special Education 937.393.1904

Fax 937.393.0496

Web www.ohioregion14.org

E-mail ....lbarnhouse@ohioregion14.org

5350 W New Market Rd, Hillsboro, OH 45133-7722

Lisa Barnhouse, Region 14 Hopewell Center

Hocking County

GENERAL HEALTH SERVICES

Health Dept 740.380.3030

Fax 740.385.2252

Web ....www.hockingcountyhealthdepartment.com

E-mail ....ktaulbee@hockingchd.com

132 Hocking Mall, Logan, OH 43138-1001

Kelly Taulbee, Nursing Director

POLICE AND SHERIFF

Sheriff's Ofc 740.385.2131

Fax 740.380.2121

E-mail ....lnorth@hockingsheriff.org

25 E 2nd St, Logan, OH 43138

Lanny North, Sheriff

Holmes County

GENERAL HEALTH SERVICES

Hospice & Home Health 330.674.5035

Fax 330.674.2528

Web ....www.holmescounty.com/health

E-mail ....shofstetter@holmeshealth.org

931 Wooster Rd, Millersburg, OH 44654-1535

Maurice Mullet, Administrator/medical Director

COURTS

Family And Juvenile Court 330.674.5841

Fax 330.674.5820

1 E Jackson St Ste 201, Millersburg, OH 44654-1249

Honorable Thomas C. Lee, Judge

POLICE AND SHERIFF

Sheriff's Ofc 330.674.1936

Fax 330.674.8504

E-mail ....twz@holmescountysheriff.org

8105 Trl 574, Holmesville, OH 44633

Timothy W, Zimmerly, Sheriff

Huron County

GENERAL HEALTH SERVICES

Bellevue City Health Dept 419.483.3404

Fax 419.483.9109

Web ....www.huroncohealth.com

3000 Santika Industrial Pkwy, Bellevue,
OH 44811-9431

Stephanie Gibson, Medical Director

General Health District 419.668.1652

Fax 419.668.5423

Web ....www.huroncohealth.com

180 Milan Ave Ste 8, Norwalk, OH 44857

Christina Cherry, Nursing Director

COURTS

Juvenile Court 419.668.1616

Fax 419.663.0944

E-mail ....hcjpc@accnorwalk.com

2 E Main St Rm 101, Norwalk, OH 44857

Honorable Timothy Cardwell, Judge

Jackson County

GENERAL HEALTH SERVICES

Health Dept 740.286.5094

Fax 740.286.8809

Web ....www.jchd.us

E-mail ....chughes@jchd.us

200 E Main St, Bj Allison Health Center, Jackson,
OH 45640

Cindy Hughes, Rn, Director Of Nursing

COURTS

Juvenile Court 740.286.6405

Fax 740.288.4836

350 Portsmouth St Ste 101, Jackson, OH 45640

John Dioguardi, Chief Probation Officer

POLICE AND SHERIFF

Sheriff's Ofc 740.286.6464

Fax 740.286.5635

E-mail ....jshasteen@jacksonso.org

350 Portsmouth St, Ste 103, Jackson, OH 45640

John L. Shasteen, Sheriff

Jefferson County

SOCIAL SERVICES

CDJFS 740.282.0961

Fax 740.282.7425

Web ....www.jcdjfs.com

125 S 5th St, Steubenville, OH 43952-2811

Elizabeth Ferron, Director

GENERAL HEALTH SERVICES

Health Dept 740.283.8530

Fax 740.283.8536

Web ....www.jchealth.com

E-mail ....becky@jchealth.com

500 Market St, # Basement, Steubenville, OH 43952

Becky Howe, Nursing Director

COURTS

Juvenile Court 740.283.8558

Fax 740.283.8694

16001 State Route 7, Steubenville, OH 43952

J. Douglas Knight, Program Director

POLICE AND SHERIFF

Sheriff's Ofc 740.283.8600

Fax 740.283.8598

16001 State Rt. 7, Steubenville, OH 43952

Fred J. Abdalla, Sheriff

Knox County

GENERAL HEALTH SERVICES

Health Dept 740.392.2200

Fax 740.392.9613

Web ....www.knoxhealth.com

E-mail ....jfletcher@knoxhealth.com

11660 Upper Gilchrist Rd, Mount Vernon,
OH 43050-9084

Jacqueline Fletcher, Nursing Director

COURTS

Family And Juvenile Court 740.393.6796

Fax 740.393.6832

111 E High St Fl 1st, Mount Vernon, OH 43050

Diane Randall, Chief Deputy Clerk

POLICE AND SHERIFF

Sheriff's Ofc 740.393.6800

Fax 740.397.5277

Web ....www.rrohio.com

E-mail ....sheriffbarber@rrohio.com

11540 Upper Gilchrist Rd, Mount Vernon,
OH 43050-9084

David B. Barber, Sheriff

EDUCATION SERVICES

Ctrburg Head Start 740.625.9500

119 S Preston St, Centerburg, OH 43011-7090

Deb Sykes, Director

Lake County

GENERAL HEALTH SERVICES

Health Dept 440.350.2543

Fax 440.350.2548

Web ....www.lcghd.org

33 Mill St, Painesville, OH 44077

Robert M. Curran, Md, Medical Director

JUSTICE AGENCY

Youth Detention Ctr 440.350.3161

Fax 440.350.2724

53 E Erie St, Painesville, OH 44077-3907

Rick Sivula, Superintendent

COURTS

Juvenile Justice Ctr 440.350.3000

Fax 440.350.2724

53 E Erie St, Juvenile Justice Center, Painesville,
OH 44077

Honorable William W. Weaver, Director

POLICE AND SHERIFF

Sheriff's Ofc 440.350.5620

Fax 440.350.5590

104 E Erie St, Painesville, OH 44077

Daniel A. Dunlap, Sheriff

Lawrence County

GENERAL HEALTH SERVICES

Health Dept 740.532.3962
Fax 740.532.1014
Web ....www.lcohd.org
　2122 S 8th St, Ironton, OH 45638
　Eileen Payton, Nursing Director

Ironton City Health Dept 740.532.2172
Fax 740.532.4186
　2120 S 8th St, Ironton, OH 45638
　James Medows, Md, Medical Director

COURTS

Family And Juvenile Court 740.533.4341
Fax 740.533.4412
　111 S 4th St Rm 2, Ironton, OH 45638
　Honorable David Payne, Judge

POLICE AND SHERIFF

Sheriff's Ofc 740.533.4373
Fax 740.532.7525
　115 S 5th St, Ironton, OH 45638
　Jeffery S. Lawless, Sheriff

EDUCATION SERVICES

Dawson-Bryant Head Start 740.532.8258
Fax 740.533.6013
E-mail ....lcremeans@headstartworks.org
　1 Hornet Ln, Ironton, OH 45638-2994
　Lee Ann Cremeans, Director

Licking County

SOCIAL SERVICES

Child Support Enforcement 740.670.5998
Fax 740.670.5900
Web ....jfs.ohio.gov/county.licking
E-mail ....lccsea@odjfs.state.oh.us
　65 E Main St, Newark, OH 43055
　Nancy Johnson, Director

**Department of Job and Family
Services** 740.670.8795
Fax 740.670.8993
Web ....www.msmisp.com/lcdjfs
　P.O. Box 5030, Newark, OH 43058-5030
　COA accredited organization.

GENERAL HEALTH SERVICES

Health Dept 740.349.6535
Fax 740.349.6510
Web ....www.lickingcohealth.org
E-mail ....health@lickingcohealth.org
　675 Price Rd NE, Newark, OH 43055
　Charles Marty, Md, Medical Director

MENTAL HEALTH SERVICES

Board Of MR/DD 740.349.6588
Fax 740.344.2757
Web ....www.lcbmrdd.org
　116 N 22Nd St, Newark, OH 43055
　Nancy Neely, Director

COURTS

Probate And Juvenile Court 740.670.5624
Fax 740.670.5881
　Courthouse Sq, First Fl, Newark, OH 43055
　Debra Depaso, Director Of Diversion

POLICE AND SHERIFF

Sheriff's Ofc 740.670.5500
Fax 740.670.5581
E-mail ....rthorpe@lcounty.com
　155 E Main St, Newark, OH 43055
　Randy Thorp, Sheriff

Logan County

SOCIAL SERVICES

Child Support Enforcement 937.599.7232
Fax 937.599.3176
E-mail ....kellok@odjfs.state.oh.us
　120 E Sandusky Ave, Bellefontaine, OH 43311-2045
　Kim Martin, Director

Children Services 937.599.7290
Fax 937.599.7296
　1855 State Route #47 West, Bellefontaine, OH 43311
　Melanie Engle, Executive Director

GENERAL HEALTH SERVICES

Health Dept 937.592.9040
Fax 937.592.6746
Web ....www.co.logan.oh.us/healthdistrict
E-mail ....cirick@odh.ohio.gov
　310 S Main St, Bellefontaine, OH 43311-1720
　Cindy Irick, Rn, Bsn, Nursing Director

MENTAL HEALTH SERVICES

**Board Of Mental Retardation And Developmental
Disabilities** 937.592.0015
Fax 937.592.5615
Web ....www.co.logan.oh.us/mrdd
E-mail ....lbarber@mrdd.co.logan.oh.us
　1851 State Rte. 47 W, Bellefontaine, OH 43311
　Joseph Mancuso, Superintendent

**Logan-Champaign Mental Health, Drug & Alcohol Svcs
Board** 937.465.1045
Fax 937.465.3914
Web ....www.bhg.org/boards/lc.htm
E-mail ....dhiggins@bhg.org
　123 N Detroit St, West Liberty, OH 43357
　David Higgins, Executive Director

POLICE AND SHERIFF

Sheriff's Ofc 937.592.5731
Fax 937.651.6283
Web ....www.co.logan.oh.us
E-mail ....a.smith@co.logan.oh.us
　284 County Rd 32 S, Bellefontaine, OH 43311-9302
　Andrew Smith, Sheriff

Lorain County

SOCIAL SERVICES

CDJFS/CSEA 440.284.4500
Fax 440.323.3422
Web ....www.lcdjfs.com
E-mail ....lchs@eshores.com
　42485 N Ridge Rd, Elyria, OH 44035-1045
　Mary Lou Golski, Director

GENERAL HEALTH SERVICES

Elyria City Health Dept 440.323.7595
Fax 440.284.1558
Web ....www.elyriahealth.com
E-mail ....elyriahealth@elyriahealth.com
　202 Chestnut St, Elyria, OH 44035-5398
　Linda Moore, RN, Nursing Director

Health Dept 440.322.6367
Fax 440.322.0911
Web ....www.loraincountyhealth.com
E-mail ....twilcox@loraincountyhealth.com
　9880 S Murray Ridge Rd, Elyria, OH 44035
　Tanas Wilcox, Nursing Director

Lorain City Health Dept 440.204.2300
Fax 440.246.6894
Web ....www.lorainhealth.com
E-mail ....loracihd@odh.ohio.gov
　1144 W Erie Ave, Lorain, OH 44052-1445
　Craig J. Chapple, MD, Medical Director

JUSTICE AGENCY

Detention Home For Girls 440.326.4040
Fax 440.323.0188
　9967 S Murray Ridge Rd, Elyria, OH 44035
　Lori Oconnor, Superintendent

Voices For Children/CASA 440.329.5158
Fax 440.328.2210
Web ....www.vfclc.org
E-mail ....timgreen@vfclc.org
　225 Court St, Elyria, OH 44035-5512
　Timothy Green, Program Director

COURTS

Family And Juvenile Court 440.329.5000
Fax 440.329.5271
　225 Court St, Elyria, OH 44035-5512
　Honorable Paulette J. Lilly, Director

POLICE AND SHERIFF

Sheriff's Ofc 440.329.3709
Fax 440.329.3792
Web ....www.loraincountysheriff.com
E-mail ....sheriff@loraincountysheriff.com
　9896 Murray Ridge Rd, Elyria, OH 44035-6957
　Phil R. Stammitti, Sheriff

Lucas County

GENERAL HEALTH SERVICES

Northwest District Health Ofc 419.245.2840
Fax 419.245.2400
E-mail ....kim.sander@odh.ohio.gov
　1 Government Ctr Ste 1320, Toledo, OH 43604-2203
　Kim Sander, Administrator

JUSTICE AGENCY

CASA/GAL 419.213.6753
Fax 419.213.6785
E-mail ....cmarti@co.lucas.oh.us
　1801 Spielbusch Ave, Toledo, OH 43604
　Carol Martin, Program Director

**Dept Of Youth Svcs Toledo Regional
Ofc** 419.245.3040
Fax 419.245.2784
E-mail ....dawn.kerschner@dys.ohio.gov
　1 Government Ctr, Ste 1016, Toledo, OH 43604
　Dawn Kerschner, Administrator

Youth Treatment Ctr 419.213.6161
Fax 419.259.2450
E-mail ....thobbs@nboh.com
　225 11th St, Toledo, OH 43604-5523
　Tara Hobbs, Administrator

POLICE AND SHERIFF

Sheriff's Ofc 419.213.4900
Fax 419.255.3096
E-mail ....jtelb@co.lucas.oh.us
　1622 Spielbusch Ave, Toledo, OH 43604
　James A. Telb, Phd, Sheriff

Toledo Police 419.245.3200
Fax 419.936.2308
Web ....www.toledo.oh.gov
E-mail ....michael.navarre@toledo.oh.gov
　525 N Erie St Ste 2, Toledo, OH 43604-3345
　Michael J. Navarre, Chief Of Police

EDUCATION SERVICES

Alternate Learning Ctr 419.255.7033
E-mail ....mgorsha@eopa.org
　3939 Wrenwood Rd, Toledo, OH 43623-1762
　Mitchell Gorsha, Director, Information Systems

Madison County

GENERAL HEALTH SERVICES

Health Dept **740.852.3065**
Fax 740.852.5418
Web ....www.co.madison.oh.us
E-mail ....syoung@co.madison.oh.us
   306 Lafayette St, London, OH 43140-9069
   Susan Young, Rn, Nursing Director

COURTS

Family And Juvenile Court **740.852.0760**
Fax 740.852.7134
   1 N Main St Rm 8, London, OH 43140
   Tammy Stoops, Intensive Probation Officer

EDUCATION SERVICES

Fairhaven Head Start Ctr **740.852.5412**
   1501 State Route 38 SE, London, OH 43140-9218
   Mary Jo Daniels, Director

Mahoning County

GENERAL HEALTH SERVICES

Board Of Health **330.270.2855**
Fax 330.270.2860
Web ....www.mahoninghealth.org
E-mail ....dianacolaianni@mahoningcounty.org
   50 Westchester Dr Ste 101, Youngstown, OH 44515
   Diana Colaianni, Nursing Director

Campbell City Health Dept **330.755.1451**
Fax 330.750.2953
   351 Tenney Ave, Campbell, OH 44405-1698
   Carol Zamary, Rn, Nursing Director

Job & Family Svcs **330.740.2600**
Fax 330.740.2523
Web ....www.jfs.ohio.gov
   345 Oak Hill Ave Ste 320, Youngstown,
   OH 44502-1454
   John K Zachariah, Director

MENTAL HEALTH SERVICES

Mental Health Board **330.746.2959**
Fax 330.746.4323
Web ....www.mahoningcountyoh.gov
E-mail ....rmarian@mahoningcountyoh.gov
   25 E Boardman St, Ste 211, Youngstown, OH 44503
   Ronald A. Marian, Executive Director

JUSTICE AGENCY

Martin P. Joyce Detention Ctr **330.740.2261**
Fax 330.740.2003
   300 E Scott St, Youngstown, OH 44505
   Jason Lanzo, Detention Director

COURTS

Family And Juvenile Court **330.740.2278**
Fax 330.740.2272
Web ....www.mahoningcountyoh.gov
E-mail ....tdellick@mahoningcountyoh.gov
   300 E Scott St, Youngstown, OH 44505-2963
   Honorable Theresa Dellick, Judge

Teen Court **330.451.7407**
Fax 330.451.7104
E-mail ....jasalapck@co.stark.oh.us
   110 Central Plz S, Ste 625, Canton, OH 44702
   Joyce Salapack, Probation Dept. Director

POLICE AND SHERIFF

Sheriff's Ofc **330.480.5020**
Fax 330.480.5089
E-mail ....rwellington@mahoningcountyoh.gov
   110 5th Ave, Justice Center, Youngstown,
   OH 44503-1110
   Randall A. Wellington, Sheriff

Marion County

SOCIAL SERVICES

PCSA **740.389.2317**
Fax 740.389.3499
Web ....www.odjfs.state.oh.us
E-mail ....ringej@odjfs.state.oh.us
   1680 Marion Waldo Rd, Marion, OH 43302-7426
   Jacquilin Ringer, Executive Director

GENERAL HEALTH SERVICES

Marion City Health Dept **740.387.3604**
Fax 740.383.2251
Web ....www.marionhealthdept.com
E-mail ....maricihd@odh.ohio.gov
   233 W Center St, City Hall, 3rd Floor, Marion,
   OH 43302-3643
   Fredrick Winegarner, Md, Health Commissioner/med Director

Marion Public Health **740.387.6520**
Fax 740.383.2546
Web ....www.marionpublichealth.org
   98 Mckinley Park Blvd, Marion, OH 43302
   Kathy Dixon, Md, Health Commissioner/medical Director

COURTS

Family Court **740.223.4060**
Fax 740.382.3798
Web ....www.co.marion.oh.us
E-mail ....rfragale@co.marion.oh.us
   222 W Center St, Marion, OH 43302-3646
   Robert Fragale, Director

Medina County

GENERAL HEALTH SERVICES

Health Dept **330.723.9511**
Fax 330.723.9659
Web ....www.medinahealth.org
E-mail ....medicohd@odh.ohio.gov
   4800 Ledgewood Dr, Medina, OH 44256
   Daniel Raub, Do, Health Commissioner/medical Director

Health Dept **330.723.9688**
Fax 330.723.9659
Web ....www.medinahealth.org
E-mail ....lstrebler@medinahealth.org
   4800 Ledgewood Dr, Medina, OH 44256-7666
   Lisa Strebler, Rn, Nursing Director

JUSTICE AGENCY

Juvenile Detention Ctr **330.764.8408**
Fax 330.764.8412
   655 Independence Dr, Medina, OH 44256
   Ron Staller, Superintendent

COURTS

Family And Juvenile Court **330.725.9710**
Fax 330.725.9173
   93 Public Sq Ste 112, Medina, OH 44256
   Honorable John J. Lohn, Judge

POLICE AND SHERIFF

Sheriff's Ofc **330.725.0028**
Fax 330.764.8123
E-mail ....nhassinger@medinaco.org
   555 Independence Dr, Medina, OH 44256
   Neil Hassinger, Sheriff

Meigs County

SOCIAL SERVICES

**Dept of Job & Family Svcs-Children Svcs
Div** **740.992.2117**
Fax 740.992.7500
Web ....www.meigsdjfs.net
   175 Race St, Middleport, OH 45760
   Christopher Shank, Job & Family Svcs Director

GENERAL HEALTH SERVICES

Meigs Health Dept **740.992.6626**
Fax 740.992.0836
Web ....www.meigscountyhealth.com
E-mail ....meigcohd@odh.ohio.gov
   112 E Memorial Dr Ste A, Pomeroy, OH 45769-9569
   Doug Hunter, Medical Director

MENTAL HEALTH SERVICES

Board Of MR/DD **740.992.6681**
Fax 740.992.6438
E-mail ....joyssameigs@suddenlinkmail.com
   1310 Carleton St, Syracuse, OH 45779
   Joy Stewart, Services & Support Administrator

COURTS

Family And Juvenile Court **740.992.6205**
Fax 740.992.6727
E-mail ....judgescottpowell@yahoo.com
   100 E 2nd St Rm 203, Pomeroy, OH 45769-1095
   Honorable L. Scott Powell, Judge

POLICE AND SHERIFF

Sheriff's Ofc **740.992.3371**
Fax 740.992.2654
E-mail ....robert.beegle531@hotmail.com
   104 E 2nd St, Pomeroy, OH 45769
   Robert Beegle, Sheriff

Mercer County

SOCIAL SERVICES

Child Support Enforcement **419.586.7961**
Fax 419.586.2151
Web ....www.odjfs.state.oh.us
E-mail ....snidek@odjfs.state.oh.us
   220 W Livingston St Ste B 181, Celina,
   OH 45822-1671
   Angela Nickell, Director

POLICE AND SHERIFF

Sheriff's Ofc **419.586.7724**
Fax 419.586.1979
E-mail ....jeff.grey@mercercountysheriff.org
   4835 State Rd 29, Celina, OH 45822
   Jeff Grey, Sheriff

Miami County

SOCIAL SERVICES

CDJFS/CSEA **937.440.3471**
Fax 937.335.2225
Web ....www.co.miami.oh.us
   2040 N County Road 25A, Troy, OH 45373-1325
   Carol A. Morgan, Director

PCSA **937.335.4103**
Fax 937.339.7533
E-mail ....cannoj01@odjfs.state.oh.us
   510 W Water St 210, Troy, OH 45373
   June Cannon, Executive Director

GENERAL HEALTH SERVICES

Piqua City Health Dept **937.778.2060**
Fax 937.778.0050
Web ....www.piquaoh.org
   201 W Water St, Piqua, OH 45356-2235
   Scott Swabb, Do, Medical Director

JUSTICE AGENCY

David L. Brown Youth Ctr **937.339.1858**
Fax 937.335.7904
E-mail ....dlbycexdir@dlbyc.org
   291 S Childrens Home Rd, Troy, OH 45373
   Diana Karnehm, Director

West Central Juvenile Detention

Ctr **937.440.5651**
Fax 937.335.3843
Web ....www.woh.rr.com
E-mail ....wray@woh.rr.com
   2044 N County Road 25A, Troy, OH 45373-1325
   William Ray, Director Of Detention

COURTS

Family And Juvenile Court **937.440.5970**
Fax 937.440.3531
Web ....www.co.miami.oh.us
   201 W Main St, Troy, OH 45373
   Lance Ray, Detention Director

POLICE AND SHERIFF

Sheriff's Ofc **937.440.6085**
Fax 937.440.6077
Web ....www.miamicountysheriff.org
E-mail ....charles.cox@miamicountyso.com
   201 W Main St, Troy, OH 45373-3239
   Charles A. Cox, Jr., Sheriff

Monroe County

GENERAL HEALTH SERVICES

Health Dept **740.472.1677**
Fax 740.472.2508
Web ....www.mchealthdept.com
E-mail ....mchealth@odh.oh.gov
   118 Home Ave, Woodsfield, OH 43793
   Karen Aulg, Nursing Director

COURTS

Juvenile Court **740.472.5790**
Fax 740.472.2520
   101 N Main St Rm 39, Woodsfield, OH 43793
   Deirdre Ollom, Court Services Director/probation Officer

Montgomery County

SOCIAL SERVICES

Catholic Social Svcs-Miami Valley **937.223.7217**
Fax 937.222.6750
Web ....www.cssmv.org
E-mail ....cssmv@cssmv.org
   922 W Riverview Ave, Dayton, OH 45402-6400
   Laura Roesch, Director

Children Services **937.276.6121**
Fax 937.277.1127
Web ....www.odjfs.state.oh.us
E-mail ....bullag@odjfs.state.oh.us
   3304 N Main St, Dayton, OH 45405-2709
   Gayle Bullard, Executive Director

GENERAL HEALTH SERVICES

Community Child Health Ctr East **937.258.6330**
Fax 937.252.1242
   25 Thorpe Dr, Dayton, OH 45420-1823
   Rhonda Neeley, Rn, Nurse Case Manager

Community Child Health Ctr South **937.866.6406**
Fax 937.866.6798
   31 N Locust St, Dayton, OH 45449
   Raj Gupta, Medical Director

Community Child Health Ctr West **937.496.7155**
Fax 937.275.4245
   2166 N Gettysburg Ave, Dayton, OH 45406-3514
   Anette Rutter, Rn, Nurse Case Manager

Dayton District Health Ofc **937.285.6250**
Fax 937.285.6306
Web ....www.odh.ohio.gov
   1 S Main St, Fl 4, Dayton, OH 45402
   Barb Farrell, Administrator

Oakwood City Health Dept **937.298.0600**
Fax 937.297.2940
Web ....www.mvcc.net
E-mail ....rgarrison@mvcc.net
   30 Park Ave, Dayton, OH 45419-3400
   Richard Garrison, Health Commissioner

Public Health **937.225.4395**
Fax 937.496.3070
Web ....www.phdmc.org
E-mail ....montcohd@odh.ohio.gov
   117 S Main St, Reibold Bldg, Dayton,
   OH 45402-2005
   Fred Steed, Ms, Community Health Services Director

JUSTICE AGENCY

CASA Program **937.225.5491**
Fax 937.224.3693
Web ....www.nationalcasa.org
E-mail ....fellerg@mcohio.org
   380 W 2nd St, Dayton, OH 45402-2005
   Gina Feller, Director

Ctr For Adolescent Svcs **937.687.9427**
Fax 937.687.0112
E-mail ....hamningr@mcohio.org
   333 Access Rd, New Lebanon, OH 45345-9384
   Richard Hamning, Director

Dept Of Youth Svcs Dayton Regional

Ofc **937.285.6525**
Fax 937.285.6708
   1133 S. Edwin C. Moses Blvd, Ste. 400, Dayton,
   OH 45408
   Larry T. Lewis, Administrator

Detention Ctr **937.225.7324**
Fax 937.225.5903
E-mail ....carterj@mcohio.org
   380 W 2nd St, Dayton, OH 45402
   Jimmie Carter, Director

COURTS

Family And Juvenile Court **937.496.3347**
Fax 937.496.7272
   380 W 2nd St, Dayton, OH 45422
   Honorable Anthony Capizzi, Judge

POLICE AND SHERIFF

Dayton Police Dept **937.333.2677**
Fax 937.333.1321
   335 W 3rd St Ste 100, Dayton, OH 45402
   Wanda Smith, Assistant Chief Of Police

Sheriff's Ofc **937.225.4192**
Fax 937.225.4764
   345 W 2nd St, Dayton, OH 45402
   Dave Vore, Sheriff

EDUCATION SERVICES

Special Education **937.236.9965**
Fax 937.233.0161
Web ....www.mcesregionalcenter.com
   4801 Springfield St, Dayton, OH 45431
   Donald H. Sheer Jr., Director

Morgan County

MENTAL HEALTH SERVICES

Health Dept **740.962.4572**
Fax 740.962.3271
E-mail ....rclark@odh.ohio.gov
   4275 N SR 376 NW, Mcconnellsville, OH 43756
   Richard D. Clark, Director

COURTS

Family And Juvenile Court **740.962.2861**
Fax 740.962.1380
Web ....www.morgancounty-oh.gov
E-mail ....dan.favreau@morgancounty-oh.gov
   19 E Main St, Mc Connelsville, OH 43756
   Honorable D.w. Favreau, Director

EDUCATION SERVICES

Chesterhill Head Start-Little Red

School **740.554.5001**
Fax 740.962.2039
E-mail ....ece@coadinc.org
   1757 Mill St, Chesterhill, OH 43728
   Stephanie Nolen, Director

Morrow County

GENERAL HEALTH SERVICES

Health Dept **419.947.1545**
Fax 419.946.6807
Web ....www.morrowcountyhealth.org
E-mail ....mchdpip@odh.ohio.gov
   619 W Marion Rd Rm 143, Mount Gilead, OH 43338
   Cathy Zuercher, Nursing Director

MENTAL HEALTH SERVICES

Board Of MR/DD **419.947.7045**
Fax 419.947.1187
Web ....www.whetstoneserves.com
E-mail ....nfoglesong@whetstoneserves.com
   406 Bank St, Mount Gilead, OH 43338-1300
   Nancy Foglesong, Director

POLICE AND SHERIFF

Sheriff's Ofc **419.946.6991**
Fax 419.946.2406
E-mail ....sbrenneman@morrowcountysheriff.com
   101 Home Rd, Mount Gilead, OH 43338
   Steve Brenneman, Sheriff

Muskingum County

SOCIAL SERVICES

Child Support Enforcement

Agency **740.455.7146**
Fax 740.453.5660
Web ....www.jobandfamily.com
E-mail ....duranv@odjfs.state.oh.us
   1830 East Pike, Zanesville, OH 43701-4619
   Vince Durant, Deputy Director

Dept of Children's Svcs **740.455.6710**
Fax 740.455.6719
E-mail ....boyer02@odjfs.state.oh.us
   205 N 7th St, Zanesville, OH 43701
   David Boyer, Executive Director

ODJFS **740.454.0161**
Fax 740.454.0067
Web ....www.jobandfamily.com
E-mail ....cochrr01@odjfs.state.oh.us
   445 Woodlawn Ave, Zanesville, OH 43701-4941
   Randy Cochrane, Director

GENERAL HEALTH SERVICES

Health Dept **740.454.9741**
Fax 740.455.6726
Web ....www.zmchd.org
E-mail ....coreyh@zmchd.org
   205 N 7th St Rm 1, Zanesville, OH 43701-3791
   Corey Hamilton, Medical Director

COURTS

Family And Juvenile Court **740.453.0351**
Fax 740.453.1066
   1860 East Pike, Zanesville, OH 43701-4619
   Honorable Joseph Gormley, Director

Ohio

POLICE AND SHERIFF

Sheriff's Ofc......................740.452.3637
Fax...................................740.455.7902
Web.................www.ohiomuskingumsheriff.org
E-mail..............information@ohiomuskingumsheriff.org
28 N 4th St, Zanesville, OH 43701-3410
Matthew Lutz, Sheriff

EDUCATION SERVICES

Alps Head Start Ctr....................740.454.6251
Fax...................................740.454.7369
Web......................................www.ccri.org
E-mail............................jjohnson@ccri.org
1580 Adams Ln, Zanesville, OH 43701-2606
Jerry Johnson, Director

Noble County

GENERAL HEALTH SERVICES

Health Dept..........................740.732.4958
Fax...................................740.732.5043
Web................................www.noblecohd.org
E-mail........................noblecohd@noblecohd.org
44069 Marietta Rd, Caldwell, OH 43724
Madeline Watson Rn, Bsn, Nursing Director

Ottawa County

GENERAL HEALTH SERVICES

Health Dept..........................419.734.6800
Fax...................................419.734.6888
Web................................www.ottawahealth.org
1856 E Perry St, Port Clinton, OH 43452-1497
Sandy Walton, Rn, Msn, Nursing Director

Paulding County

SOCIAL SERVICES

Child Support Enforcement...............419.399.8464
Fax...................................419.399.8465
201 E Caroline St Ste 1, Paulding, OH 45879
Brian Gorrell, Director

GENERAL HEALTH SERVICES

Health Dept..........................419.399.3921
Fax...................................419.399.3494
Web.................www.pauldingcountyhealth.com
E-mail........................paulcohd@odh.ohio.gov
800 E Perry St, Paulding, OH 45879
Judy Fisher, Rn, Nursing Director

Perry County

SOCIAL SERVICES

PCSA.................................740.342.3836
Fax...................................740.342.5531
E-mail........................glassr@odjfs.state.oh.us
526 Mill St, New Lexington, OH 43764
Rick L. Glass, Executive Director

GENERAL HEALTH SERVICES

Health Dept..........................740.342.5179
Fax...................................740.342.5540
Web................................www.perryhealth.gov
E-mail........................perrcohd@odh.ohio.gov
212 S Maine St, New Lexington, OH 43764-1241
Don Pingle, Rn, Nursing Director

MENTAL HEALTH SERVICES

Board Of Developmental
Disabilties...........................740.342.3542
Fax...................................740.342.1081
Web................................www.perrymrdd.org
499 N State St, New Lexington, OH 43764
David Couch, Superintendent

POLICE AND SHERIFF

Sheriff's Ofc......................740.342.4123
Fax...................................740.342.5521
E-mail............sheriffbarker@perrycountysheriff.org
110 W Brown St, New Lexington, OH 43764
William R. Barker, Sheriff

Pickaway County

GENERAL HEALTH SERVICES

General Health District..............740.477.9667
Fax...................................740.474.5523
Web......................................www.pchd.org
465 E Ohio St, Circleville, OH 43113
Elaine Miller, Rn, Nursing Director

JUSTICE AGENCY

Circleville Juvenile Correctional
Facility..............................740.477.2500
Fax...................................740.420.9816
640 Island Rd, Circleville, OH 43113
Baker Christofer, Superintendent

POLICE AND SHERIFF

Sheriff's Office......................740.477.6000
Fax...................................740.474.1798
600 Island Rd, Circleville, OH 43113
Dwight E. Radcliff, Sheriff

Pike County

GENERAL HEALTH SERVICES

General Health District..............740.947.7721
Fax...................................740.947.1109
Web................................www.pike-health.org
E-mail........................lmurphy@pike-health.org
14050 Us 23 North, Waverly, OH 45690
Linda Murphy, Assistant Administrator

COURTS

Family And Juvenile Court............740.947.5914
Fax...................................740.941.3086
E-mail............pikecountyjuvenilecourt@yahoo.com
230 Waverly Plz Ste 600, Waverly, OH 45690
Jerome Catanzaro, Judge

Portage County

GENERAL HEALTH SERVICES

Health Dept..........................330.296.9919
Fax...................................330.297.3597
E-mail........................pchd@portageco.com
449 S Meridian St, Ravenna, OH 44266
Kelly Engelhart, Rn, Nursing Director

Kent City Health Dept................330.678.8109
Fax...................................330.678.2082
E-mail..................................gailb@apk.net
325 S Depeyster St, Kent, OH 44240
John Ferlito, Commissioner

Ravenna City Health Dept............330.296.4478
Fax...................................330.296.4038
530 N Freedom St, Ravenna, OH 44266
Susan Mischka, Bsn, Rn, Director Of Nursing

MENTAL HEALTH SERVICES

Mental Health & Recovery Board.........330.673.1756
Fax...................................330.673.1330
Web................www.mental-health-recovery.org
E-mail..........haroldf@mental-health-recovery.org
155 E Main St, Kent, OH 44240-2524
Harold Farrier, Interim Director

JUSTICE AGENCY

Portage-Geauga Detention Ctr...........330.297.5233
Fax...................................330.297.1533
Web................................www.portageco.com
E-mail........................trehnert@portageco.com
8000 Infirmary Rd, Ravenna, OH 44266-8049
Thomas Rehnert, Director

POLICE AND SHERIFF

Sheriff's Ofc......................330.296.5100
Fax...................................330.297.3402
8240 Infirmary Rd, Ravenna, OH 44266
David Wdoak, Sheriff

Preble County

SOCIAL SERVICES

PCSA.................................937.456.1135
Fax...................................937.456.5591
Web................................www.odjfs.state.oh.us
E-mail........................sorrell@odjfs.state.oh.us
1500 Park Ave, Eaton, OH 45320-8680
Becky Sorrell, Director

MENTAL HEALTH SERVICES

Health Dept..........................937.472.0087
Fax...................................937.456.6382
Web................www.preblecountyhealth.org
E-mail........................prebcohd@odh.ohio.gov
615 Hillcrest Dr, Eaton, OH 45320-8561
Melissa Wallace, Health Commisioner

JUSTICE AGENCY

Treatment Alternatives To Street Crime
(TASC)..............................937.456.3443
Fax...................................937.456.3062
E-mail........................pcjuvtasc@voyager.net
225 N Barron St, Eaton, OH 45320-1703
Michelle Davis, Director

COURTS

Family And Juvenile Court............937.456.8136
Fax...................................937.456.5803
101 E Main St 2nd fl, Eaton, OH 45320
Honorable Wilfrid G. Dues, Judge

POLICE AND SHERIFF

Sheriff's Ofc......................937.456.6301
Fax...................................937.456.2524
Web................www.preblecountysheriff.org
E-mail........................msimpson@preblecountysheriff.org
1139 Preble Dr, Eaton, OH 45320-9266
Michael L. Simpson, Sheriff

Putnam County

SOCIAL SERVICES

CDJFS/PCSA..........................419.523.4580
Fax...................................419.523.6130
Web......................................www.jfs.ohio.gov
E-mail........................diamok@odjfs.state.oh.us
1225 E 3rd St, Ottawa, OH 45875-2062
Kim Diamond, Director

GENERAL HEALTH SERVICES

Health Dept..........................419.523.5608
Fax...................................419.523.4171
Web................................www.putnamhealth.com
E-mail........................sherri.recker@odh.ohio.gov
256 E Williamstown Rd, Ottawa, OH 45875-1870
Sherri Recker, Rn, Nursing Director

COURTS

Family And Juvenile Court............419.523.3012
Fax...................................419.523.9291
245 E Main St, Ste 204, Ottawa, OH 45875
Honorable Michael A. Borer, Judge

POLICE AND SHERIFF

Sheriff's Ofc 419.523.3208
Fax 419.523.6851
Web ....www.sheriffoff.com
  1035 Heritage Trl, Ottawa, OH 45875-8524
  James Beutler, Sheriff

Richland County

SOCIAL SERVICES

Child Support Enforcement 419.774.5700
Fax 419.524.1507
Web ....www.jfs.ohio.gov
  161 Park Ave E, Mansfield, OH 44902-1780
  Jerry Faunders, Director

GENERAL HEALTH SERVICES

Health Dept 419.774.4500
Fax 419.774.4557
Web ....www.richlandhealth.org
E-mail ....avincent@richlandhealth.org
  555 Lexington Ave, Mansfield, OH 44907-1599
  Amy Vincent, Rn, Nursing Director

Shelby City Health Dept 419.342.5226
Fax 419.347.1193
Web ....www.shelbyohio.org
E-mail ....j.smith@shelbyohio.org
  43 W Main St, Shelby, OH 44875
  Jim Smith, Health Commissioner

COURTS

CASA 419.774.6385
Fax 419.774.5555
E-mail ....casa@rcjcoh.us
  411 S Diamond St, Mansfield, OH 44902-7812
  Brenda Bumpus, GAL/CASA Program Coordinator

Family And Juvenile Court 419.774.5578
Fax 419.774.5555
E-mail ....court@rcjcoh.us
  411 S Diamond St, Mansfield, OH 44902-7812
  Honorable Ron Spon, Director/Judge

POLICE AND SHERIFF

Sheriff's Ofc 419.774.5881
Fax 419.522.8153
Web ....www.richlandcountyoh.us
E-mail ....ssheldon@richlandcountyoh.us
  597 Park Ave E, Mansfield, OH 44905-2848
  J. Steve Sheldon, Sheriff

EDUCATION SERVICES

State Support Team Region 7 ....419.747.4808
Fax 419.747.3806
E-mail ....csanyi.george@ncoserrc.k12.oh.us
  1495 W Longview Ave Ste 200, Mansfield, OH 44906
  George Csanyi, Director

Ross County

GENERAL HEALTH SERVICES

Health District 740.779.9652
Fax 740.779.0744
Web ....www.rosscountyhealth.com
  475 Western Ave, Ste 5A, Chillicothe, OH 45601
  Kathy Wakefield, Rn, Nursing Director

JUSTICE AGENCY

Roweton Youth Ctr 740.702.2210
Fax 740.702.2213
  102 Cattail Rd, Chillicothe, OH 45601
  Robert Gallagher, Facility Director

Scor Juvenile Detention Ctr 740.773.4169
Fax 740.773.3714
  182 Cattail Rd, Chillicothe, OH 45601
  Michael T. Oyer, Superintendent

COURTS

Family And Juvenile Court 740.774.1177
Fax 740.774.3711
Web ....www.rossprobatejuvenile.com
  2 N Paint St Ste A, Chillicothe, OH 45601-3109
  Donald E. Darby, Court Mediator/Personnel Director

POLICE AND SHERIFF

Sheriff's Ofc 740.773.1186
Fax 740.773.1248
Web ....www.rosssheriff.com
  28 N Paint St Ste A, Chillicothe, OH 45601-3100
  George W Lavender, Sheriff

Sandusky County

GENERAL HEALTH SERVICES

Health Dept 419.334.6377
Fax 419.334.6380
Web ....www.sanduskycohd.org
E-mail ....info@sanduskycohd.org
  2000 Countryside Dr Ste 2, Fremont,
  OH 43420-8561
  Francis Aona, MD, Health Commissioner

Scioto County

GENERAL HEALTH SERVICES

Health Dept 740.354.3241
Fax 740.354.8623
Web ....www.odh.ohio.gov
E-mail ....sciocohd@odh.ohio.gov
  602 7th St Rm 210, Portsmouth, OH 45662-3951
  Ruth Montavon, Nursing Director

Portsmouth City Health Dept 740.353.5153
Fax 740.351.0694
Web ....www.ci.portsmouth.oh.us
E-mail ....rmaloy@odh.ohio.gov
  605 Washington St, Portsmouth, OH 45662-3919
  Raeleen Maloy, Nursing Director

JUSTICE AGENCY

Ohio River Valley Juvenile Correctional
Facility 740.354.7000
Fax 740.354.7036
Web ....www.dys.ohio.gov
  4696 Gallia Pk, Franklin Furnace, OH 45629-8600
  Mr Pigman, Superintendent

COURTS

Family And Juvenile Court 740.355.8306
Fax 740.353.1095
  602 7th St Rm 201, Portsmouth, OH 45662
  Honorable James W. Kirsch, Judge

POLICE AND SHERIFF

Sheriff's Ofc 740.353.5649
Fax 740.355.8237
Web ....www.sciotocountysheriff.com
E-mail ....scso@sciotocountysheriff.com
  1025 16th St, Portsmouth, OH 45662-2912
  Marty Donini, Sheriff

Seneca County

GENERAL HEALTH SERVICES

Health District 419.447.3691
Fax 419.448.5782
E-mail ....senecohd@odh.ohio.gov
  71 S Washington St Ste 1102, Tiffin, OH 44883
  Michael G. Scherer, Do, Medical Director

JUSTICE AGENCY

CASA 419.448.1442
Fax 419.448.6663
Web ....www.casa-ssw-ohio.com
E-mail ....casa@senecacounty.com
  21 Court St, Tiffin, OH 44883-2302
  Rebecca Herner, Executive Director

Youth Ctr 419.447.7852
Fax 419.448.5061
  3484 S Eden Township Road, Tiffin, OH 44883
  Matthew Wolph, Director

POLICE AND SHERIFF

Sheriff's Ofc 419.447.3456
Fax 419.447.5746
E-mail ....sheriff@senecacountyso.org
  3040 S State Route 100, Tiffin, OH 44883-8868
  William Eckelberry, Sheriff

EDUCATION SERVICES

Fostoria Early Childhood Ctr 419.435.8426
Fax 419.435.6596
Web ....www.wsos.com
  801 Kirk St Ste 1, Fostoria, OH 44830-1788
  Shirley Behstein, Center Supervisor

Shelby County

SOCIAL SERVICES

CDJFS/PCSA 937.498.4981
Fax 937.498.7396
E-mail ....beyt01@odjfs.state.oh.us
  227 S Ohio Ave, Sidney, OH 45365-3003
  Thomas Bey, Executive Director

GENERAL HEALTH SERVICES

Health Dept 937.498.7249
Fax 937.498.7013
Web ....www.shelbycountyhealthdept.org
E-mail ....sschd@odh.ohio.gov
  202 W Poplar St, Sidney, OH 45365
  Margie Eilerman, Rn, Nursing Director

COURTS

Family And Juvenile Court 937.498.7255
Fax 937.498.7260
  100 E Court St, Sidney, OH 45365
  Bridget Davis, Case Director

Stark County

GENERAL HEALTH SERVICES

Alliance City Health Dept 330.821.7373
Fax 330.821.9517
Web ....www.cityofalliance.com/health/
E-mail ....rflint@alliancecityhealth.org
  537 E Market St, Alliance, OH 44601-2514
  Sharon Andreani, Bsn, Rn, Director Of Nursing

Canton City Health Dept 330.489.3231
Fax 330.489.3335
Web ....www.cantonhealth.org
E-mail ....info2@cantonhealth.org
  420 Market Ave N, Canton, OH 44702-1544
  James Adams, Health Commissioner

Health Dept 330.493.9904
Fax 330.493.9920
Web ....www.starkhealth.org
E-mail ....mccoyl@starkhealth.org
  3951 Convenience Cir NW Ste 100, Canton,
  OH 44718-2686
  Lynn Mccoy, Bsn, Rn, Nursing Director

Massillon City Health Dept **330.830.1710**
Fax 330.830.1798
Web .www.massillonohio.com/health
E-mail . . . . .massillonhealthdept@massillonohio.com
 845 8th St NE, Rear BUILDING, Massillon, OH 44646
 Terri Argent, Health Commissioner

MENTAL HEALTH SERVICES

Mental Health & Recovery Svcs

Board **330.455.6644**
Fax 330.455.4242
Web . . . . .www.starkmhrsb.org
 800 Market Ave N Ste 1150, Canton, OH 44702
 John Aller, Executive Director

JUSTICE AGENCY

Indian River Juvenile Correctional

Facility **330.837.4211**
Fax 330.837.4740
 2775 Indian River Rd SW, Massillon, OH 44646
 James Darnell, Superintendent

COURTS

Family And Juvenile Court **330.451.7415**
Fax 330.451.7837
 110 Central Plz S Ste 670, Canton, OH 44702
 Honorable Jim D. James, Senior Judge

POLICE AND SHERIFF

Canton Police Dept **330.649.5800**
Fax 330.489.3290
Web . . . . .www.cityofcanton.com
 221 3rd St SW, Canton, OH 44702
 Capt. Bruce Lawver, Incharge Of Police Trainee Academy

Summit County

SOCIAL SERVICES

Child Support Enforcement **330.643.2765**
Fax 330.643.2745
 175 S Main St, Akron, OH 44308
 Jennifer Bheam, Director

GENERAL HEALTH SERVICES

Akron Health Dept **330.375.2363**
Fax 330.375.2486
Web . . . . .www.schd.org
E-mail . . . . .health@schd.org
 177 S Broadway St, Akron, OH 44308-1799
 Chris Partis, Hiv Coordinator

Barberton Health District **330.745.6067**
Fax 330.745.5681
Web . . . . .www.scht.org
 571 W Tuscarawas Ave Ste 200, Barberton,
 OH 44203
 Leanne Beavers, Rn, Bsn, Director Of Nursing

Health Dept **330.923.4891**
Fax 330.923.7558
Web . . . . .www.schd.org
 1100 Graham Road Cir, Stow, OH 44224-2992
 Gillian Solem, Msn, Nursing Director

Northeast District Health Ofc **330.643.1300**
Fax 330.643.1346
Web . . . . .www.odh.ohio.gov
 161 S High St Ste 400, Akron, OH 44308-1666
 Marsha Felber, Administrator

MENTAL HEALTH SERVICES

Alcohol, Drug Addiction And Mental Health Svcs

Board **330.762.3500**
Fax 330.252.3024
Web . . . . .www.admboard.org
E-mail . . . . .adm@admboard.org
 100 W Cedar St Ste 300, Akron, OH 44307-2597
 Gerald Craig, Executive Director

Board Of MRDD **330.634.8000**
Fax 330.634.8081
Web . . . . .www.summitdd.org
 89 E Howe Rd, Tallmadge, OH 44278
 Tom Armstrong, Superintendent

JUSTICE AGENCY

CASA/GAL **330.643.2928**
Fax 330.643.8682
Web . . . . .www.summitcasa.org
E-mail . . . . .info@summitcasa.org
 650 Dan St, Akron, OH 44310
 Beth Cardina, Program/executive Director

Dept Of Youth Svcs Akron Regional

Ofc **330.643.3040**
Fax 330.643.1436
Web . . . . .www.dys.state.oh.us
E-mail . . . . .joe.marsilio@dys.state.oh.us
 161 S High St Ste 100, Akron, OH 44308-1615
 Joe Marsilio, Administrator

Juvenile Detention Svcs **330.643.2960**
Fax 330.643.5305
 650 Dan St, Akron, OH 44310
 Robert Bickett, Court Administrator

COURTS

Family And Juvenile Court **330.643.2915**
Fax 330.643.2894
E-mail . . . . .lteodosio@cpcourt.summitoh.net
 650 Dan St, Akron, OH 44310-3909
 Honorable Linda Tucci Teodosio, Judge

POLICE AND SHERIFF

Sheriff's Ofc **330.643.2181**
Fax 330.434.2701
Web . . . . .www.sheriff.summitoh.net
 53 University Ave Fl 4, Akron, OH 44308-1608
 Drew Alexander, Sheriff

Trumbull County

SOCIAL SERVICES

CDJFS **330.675.2000**
Fax 330.399.7824
Web . . . . .www.hs.co.trumbull.oh.us
E-mail . . . . .mahont01@odjfs.state.oh.us
 280 N Park Ave, Warren, OH 44481
 Tom Mahoney, Director

Child Support Enforcement **330.675.2732**
Fax 330.675.2746
Web . . . . .www.odjfs.state.oh.us
E-mail .trumbullcsea@odjfs.state.oh.us
 106 High St NW, Warren, OH 44481-1003
 Cathy Corson, Supervisor

Children Services **330.372.2010**
Fax 330.372.3446
Web . . . . .www.neonet.net
E-mail . . . . .tigerm@odjfs.state.oh.us
 2282 Reeves Rd NE, Warren, OH 44483-4300
 Nick Kerosky, Executive Director

GENERAL HEALTH SERVICES

Girard City Health Dept **330.545.6048**
Fax 330.539.7209
Web . . . . .www.cityofgirard.com
 100 W Main St Ste 3, Girard, OH 44420
 James Dobson, Health Commissioner

Health Dept **330.675.2489**
Fax 330.675.2494
Web . . . . .www.tcbh.org
E-mail . . . . .hemokosh@co.trumbull.oh.us
 176 Chestnut Ave NE, Warren, OH 44483-5803
 Deborah Mokosh, Nursing Director

Niles City Health Dept **330.544.9000**
Fax 330.544.9030
Web . . . . .www.nilesema.com
E-mail . . . . .ksalapata@nilesema.com
 34 W State St, Niles, OH 44446-5036
 William S. Eddy, Do, Health Commissioner/medical Director

Warren City Health Dept **330.841.2596**
Fax 330.841.2911
Web . . . . .www.warren.org/health.htm
 418 Main Ave SW Ste 205, Warren, OH 44481-1060
 Cheryl Strother, Nursing Director

COURTS

Juvenile And Family Court Ctr **330.675.2606**
Fax 330.675.2619
Web . . . . .www.co.trumbull.oh.us
 220 Main Ave SW, Warren, OH 44481-1011
 Honorable Pamela A. Rintala, Judge

POLICE AND SHERIFF

Sheriff's Ofc **330.675.2508**
Fax 330.675.7041
 150 High St NW, Warren, OH 44481-1003
 Thomas L. Altiere, Sheriff

EDUCATION SERVICES

State Support Team Region 5 . . . .**330.544.4315**
Fax 330.544.1000
 5555 Youngstown Warren Rd Unit 696, Niles,
 OH 44446
 Michele Dimuzio, Director

Tuscarawas County

SOCIAL SERVICES

Child Support Enforcement **330.343.0099**
Fax 330.364.4854
 154 2nd St NE, New Philadelphia, OH 44663
 Traci Berry, Director

GENERAL HEALTH SERVICES

Health Dept **330.343.5555**
Fax 330.343.1601
Web . . . . .www.tuschealth.org
 897 E Iron Ave, Dover, OH 44622-2030
 Linda Fanning, Executive Director

MENTAL HEALTH SERVICES

Tuscarawas-Carroll Alcohol, Drug Addiction, & Mental Health

Svcs Board **330.364.6488**
Fax 330.364.3307
Web . . . . .www.adamhtc.org
E-mail . . . . .office@adamhtc.org
 1260 Monroe St NW Ste 27N, New Philadelphia,
 OH 44663
 Dave Schaffer, Executive Director

EDUCATION SERVICES

Special Education **330.343.3355**
Fax 330.343.3357
Web . . . . .www.ecoserrc.org
E-mail . . . . .jim@ecoserrc.k12.oh.us
 141 McDonald Dr NW, New Philadelphia,
 OH 44663-6300
 James E. Martinek, Serrc Director

Union County

GENERAL HEALTH SERVICES

Health Dept **937.642.0801**
Fax 937.642.1568
Web . . . . .www.uchd.net
E-mail . . . . .unioncohd@odh.ohio.gov
 940 London Ave Ste 1100, Marysville, OH 43040
 Joseph Linscott, Do, Medical Director

JUSTICE AGENCY

Juvenile Detention Central Ohio Youth

Ctr **937.642.1015**
Fax....................................937.642.5900
E-mail.........................vmjordan@coyc.org
  18100 State Route 4, Marysville, OH 43040-8550
  Victoria Jordan, Superintendent

COURTS

Family And Juvenile Court **937.645.3029**
Fax....................................937.645.3160
  215 W 5th St Rm 109, Marysville, OH 43040
  Honorable Charlotte Coleman Eufinger, Judge

POLICE AND SHERIFF

Sheriff's Ofc **937.645.4100**
Fax....................................937.645.4171
Web.....................www.co.union.oh.us/sheriff
E-mail.........................jpatton@co.union.oh.us
  221 W 5th St, Marysville, OH 43040-1111
  Malcolm J Pattom, Sheriff

Van Wert County

SOCIAL SERVICES

Child Support Enforcement **419.238.9566**
Fax....................................419.238.5336
E-mail.................dyann.bayeat@odrc.state.oh.us
  114 E Main St Fl 3, Van Wert, OH 45891-1748
  Dyann M. Bayeat, Deputy Director

GENERAL HEALTH SERVICES

Health Dept **419.238.0808**
Fax....................................419.238.9571
Web.....................www.vanwertcountyhealth.org
  140 Fox Rd Ste 402, Van Wert, OH 45891
  Pamela Herminghuysen, Nursing Director

COURTS

Juvenile Court **419.238.1118**
Fax....................................419.238.7315
  108 E Main St, Van Wert, OH 45891
  Honorable Rex D. Fortney, Judge

POLICE AND SHERIFF

Sheriff's Ofc **419.238.3866**
Fax....................................419.238.9531
  113 N Market St, Van Wert, OH 45891
  Stan D. Owens, Sheriff

Vinton County

COURTS

Family And Juvenile Court **740.596.5480**
Fax....................................740.596.3438
E-mail.................court.probate@vintoncounty.com
  100 E Main St, Rm 12, Mc Arthur, OH 45651
  Honorable N. Robert Guerillo, Judge

Warren County

SOCIAL SERVICES

Human Services **513.695.1420**
Fax....................................513.695.2940
E-mail.................dbishop@co.warren.oh.us
  416 S East St, Lebanon, OH 45036
  Doris Bishop, Director

PCSA **513.695.1546**
Fax....................................513.695.2957
E-mail.................jacobp02@odjfs.state.oh.us
  416 S East St, Fl 3, Lebanon, OH 45036
  Patricia Jacobs, Executive Director

GENERAL HEALTH SERVICES

Health District **513.695.1228**
Fax....................................513.695.2941
Web.....................www.co.warren.oh.us/health
  416 S East St Unit 1, Cnty Ofc Bldg, Lebanon,
  OH 45036
  Lori Smyth, Rn, Nursing Director

JUSTICE AGENCY

Juvenile Detention Ctr **513.695.1392**
Fax....................................513.695.1394
  570 Justice Dr, Lebanon, OH 45036
  Tony Miller, Superintendent

COURTS

Family And Juvenile Court **513.695.1161**
Fax....................................513.695.2948
  570 Justice Dr, Lebanon, OH 45036-2361
  Laura Sutherland, Director Of Judicial Administration

POLICE AND SHERIFF

Sheriff's Ofc **513.695.1280**
Fax....................................513.695.1286
E-mail.........................tariss@wcsooh.org
  550 Justice Dr Ste 2, Lebanon, OH 45036-2377
  Larry Sims, Sheriff

Washington County

SOCIAL SERVICES

Child Support Enforcement **740.373.9324**
Fax....................................740.373.9447
Web.....................www.odjfs.state.oh.us
E-mail.........................brucem@odjfs.state.oh.us
  205 Putnam St Rm 4,fl 4, Marietta, OH 45750-3017
  Margie A. Bruce, Director

Job & Family Svcs **740.373.5513**
Fax....................................740.374.7692
E-mail.........................thomasb@odjfs.state.oh.us
  1115 Gilman Ave, Marietta, OH 45750
  Thomas Balengee, Director

PCSA **740.373.3485**
Fax....................................740.373.1856
Web.....................www.odjfs.state.oh.us
E-mail.........................copend01@odjfs.state.oh.us
  204 Davis Ave, Marietta, OH 45750-1417
  Dave Copen, Executive Director

GENERAL HEALTH SERVICES

Belpre City Health Dept **740.423.7592**
Fax....................................740.423.4967
Web.....................www.cityofbelpre.com
E-mail.........................belprehd@wirefire.com
  715 Park Dr, Belpre, OH 45714-1022
  Michael Brockett, Md, Medical Director

Family Health Svc Clinic **740.374.8501**
Fax....................................740.374.3555
  696 Wayne St, Marietta, OH 45750
  Kathleen Boersma, Rn, Director

Health Dept **740.374.2782**
Fax....................................740.376.7074
Web.....................www.washco-ohhealth.org
  342 Muskingum Dr, Marietta, OH 45750-1435
  Dr. Daley, Md, Medical Director

JUSTICE AGENCY

Juvenile Ctr **740.374.7453**
Fax....................................740.374.3581
  1699 Colegate Dr, Marietta, OH 45750
  Brian Hesson, Director

COURTS

Family And Juvenile Court **740.373.6623**
Fax....................................740.376.7425
Web.....................www.washingtongov.org
E-mail.........................juvenilecourt@washingtongov.org
  205 Putnam St Rm 12, Marietta, OH 45750-3017
  Tim Currin, Intensive Probation Officer

POLICE AND SHERIFF

Sheriff's Ofc **740.376.7070**
Fax....................................740.373.6108
Web.....................www.washingtoncountysheriff.org
E-mail.........................webmaster@washingtoncountysheriff.org
  309 4th St, Marietta, OH 45750-2002
  Larry R. Mincks, Sheriff

Wayne County

SOCIAL SERVICES

CDJFS **330.287.5800**
Fax....................................330.287.5899
  356 W North St, Wooster, OH 44691
  Richard Owens, Director

Child Support Enforcement **330.287.5600**
Fax....................................330.287.5623
Web.....................www.odjfs.state.oh.us
E-mail.........................butlem@odjfs.state.oh.us
  201 E Liberty St Ste 202, Wooster, OH 44691-4365
  Deborah C Watkins, Director

GENERAL HEALTH SERVICES

Health Dept **330.264.9590**
Fax....................................330.262.2538
Web.....................www.wayne-health.org
  203 S Walnut St, Wooster, OH 44691
  Robin Farnsworth, Nursing Director

JUSTICE AGENCY

Linda Martin Attention Ctr **330.264.9050**
Fax....................................330.262.9058
  6807 Non Pariel Rd, Wooster, OH 44691-8385
  Leon Horton, Administrator

POLICE AND SHERIFF

Sheriff's Ofc **330.287.5750**
Fax....................................330.287.5769
E-mail.........................wcso@wcjustice-center.org
  201 W North St, Wooster, OH 44691
  Thomas G. Maurer, Sheriff

Williams County

JUSTICE AGENCY

Northwest Ohio Juvenile Detention

Ctr **419.428.2322**
Fax....................................419.428.6303
Web.....................www.nwojdc.org
  3389 County Rd., 24-25, Stryker, OH 43557
  Brian Patrick, Superintendent

COURTS

Juvenile Court/Probation **419.636.2934**
Fax....................................419.636.3200
E-mail.........................sbird@wmsco.org
  1 Courthouse Sq, Fl 1, Bryan, OH 43506
  Honorable Steven R. Bird, Probate/juvenile Court Judge

Wood County

SOCIAL SERVICES

Child Support Enforcement **419.354.9000**
Fax....................................419.354.9371
Web.....................www.co.wood.oh.us
E-mail.........................childsupport@co.wood.oh.us
  1940 E Gypsy Lane Rd, Bowling Green,
  OH 43402-9396
  Frank Mclaughlin, Director

Ohio

COURTS

Juvenile Court..............................**419.352.3554**
Fax...419.352.6084
E-mail..........................dwoessner@co.wood.oh.us
  1032 S Dundridge Rd, Bowling Green, OH 43402
Honorable David Woessner, Judge

Wyandot County

GENERAL HEALTH SERVICES

Health Dept.................................**419.294.3852**
Fax...419.294.6424
Web......................................www.wyandothealth.com
E-mail.....................wchealthdept@co.wyandot.oh.us
  127 A So Sandusky Ave, Rm A, Upper Sandusky,
  OH 43351
Darlene Steward Rn, Director Of Nursing

COURTS

Family And Juvenile Court................**419.294.2545**
Fax...419.209.0251
  109 S Sandusky Ave Rm 33, Upper Sandusky,
  OH 43351
Honorable Kathleen Aubry, Judge

POLICE AND SHERIFF

Sheriff's Ofc................................**419.294.2362**
Fax...419.294.1719
E-mail..........................mhetzel@co.wyandot.oh.us
  125 E Wyandot Ave, Upper Sandusky, OH 43351
Michael R. Hetzel, Sheriff

SPECIAL SERVICES AGENCIES

ADOPTION AGENCIES

Adopt America Network.................**419.726.5100**
Fax...419.726.5089
E-mail....................adoption@adoptamericanetwork.org
  1500 N Superior St Ste 303, Toledo, OH 43604
Wendy Porel, Executive Director

Adoption Assessors Ltd..................**419.873.0095**
  1011 Sandusky St, Toledo, OH 43623
Shelia Post, Director

Adoption By Gentle Care..................**614.469.0007**
Fax...614.621.2229
Web.............................www.adoptionbygentlecare.org
  370 S 5th St Ste 2, Columbus, OH 43215-4707
John E. Cameron, Director

Adoption Circle............................**614.237.7222**
Fax...614.237.8484
Web..................................www.adoptioncircle.org
E-mail..............................info@adoptioncircle.org
  400 S 5th St Ste 304, Columbus, OH 43215-5430
Nancy Burley, Executive Director

Adoption Connection......................**513.489.1616**
Fax...513.766.3338
Web..............................www.adoptioncincinnati.org
  8487 Ridge Rd, Cincinnati, OH 45236
Cherry McCarthy, Director

Buckeye Ranch-Columbus................**614.384.7700**
Fax...614.384.7701
Web....................................www.buckeyeranch.org
E-mail........................srichard@buckeyeranch.org
  697 E Broad St, Columbus, OH 43215-3948
Steve Richard, Director

Building Blocks Adoption Svcs.............**330.725.5521**
Fax...330.725.0672
Web..www.bbas.org
E-mail.....................................denise@bbas.org
  52 Public Sq, Medina, OH 44256-2255
Denise Hubbard, Executive Director

Catholic Charities........................**440.992.2121**
Fax...440.992.5974
Web..www.doyccac.org
  4200 Park Avenue, 3rd Floor, Ashtabula, OH 44004
COA accredited organization.

Cincinnati Area Senior Services, Inc...........**513.721.4330**
Fax...513.559.4493
Web..www.cassdelivers.org
  2368 Victory Parkway, Suite 300, Cincinnati,
  OH 45206
COA accredited organization.

Family Adoption Consultants...............**330.468.0673**
Fax...330.468.0678
Web...www.facadopt.org
  8536 Crow Dr Ste 220, MACEDONIA PROFESSIONAL
  BUILDING, Macedonia, OH 44056-1900
R Baker, Director

Flanagan Lieberman Hoffman.............**937.223.5200**
Fax...937.223.3335
E-mail..............................ccrafka@flhslaw.com
  15 W 4th St, Dayton, OH 45402
Crista Crafka, Office Manager

Lutheran Social Svcs......................**513.326.5430**
Fax...513.612.6555
Web................................www.graceworks.org/adoptions
E-mail..................adoption.cincinnati@graceworks.org
  11370 Springfield Pike, Cincinnati, OH 45246-4202
Ed Petry, Adoptions Manager

Lutheran Social Svcs of Northwestern
Ohio...**419.243.9178**
Fax...419.243.4450
Web..www.lssnwo.org
E-mail.................................nyunker@lssnwo.org
  2149 Collingwood Blvd, Toledo, OH 43620
Nancy Yunker, President & CEO

NE OH Adoption Svcs......................**330.856.5582**
Fax...330.856.5586
E-mail......................................cdeal@noas.org
  5000 E Market St Ste 26, Warren, OH 44484-2259
Cynthia Deal, Executive Director

Pathway Caring for Children.............**330.493.0083**
Fax...330.493.3689
Web...www.pathwaycfc.org
  6370 Wise Avenue NW, North Canton, OH 44720
COA accredited organization.

Specialized Alternatives For Youth..........**614.729.2024**
Fax...614.729.2030
Web..www.safy.org
E-mail................................devriesk@safy.org
  4615 Hilton Corporate Dr, Columbus, OH 43232
Kristy Devries, Director

Specialized Alternatives For Youth..........**614.854.0944**
Fax...614.854.0947
Web..www.safy.org
E-mail................................devriesk@safy.org
  4615 Hilton Corporate Dr, Columbus,
  OH 43232-1094
Kristy Devries, Director

Specialized Alternatives For Youth/Safy......**937.853.9061**
Fax...937.853.9069
Web..www.safy.org
E-mail..................................vetterm@safy.org
  255 S Dixie Dr, Dayton, OH 45409
Laurie Rammel, Office Manager

Specialized Alternatives For Youth/Safy......**937.497.7239**
Fax...937.497.7238
Web..www.safy.org
  211 N Main Ave, Sidney, OH 45365-2705
Kelly Davis, Treatment Director

Youth Advocate Services...................**614.258.9927**
Fax...614.258.5719
Web...www.yasohio.org
  825 Grandview Avenue, Columbus, OH 43215
COA accredited organization.

ADVOCACY RESOURCES

Care House.................................**937.512.1670**
Fax...937.512.1675
Web...www.thecarehouse.org
E-mail...................carehouse@childrendayton.org
  741 Valley St, Dayton, OH 45404-1957
Libby Nicholson, Director

Child Protection Ctr......................**740.779.7431**
Fax...740.779.7432
Web..www.adena.org
  138 Marietta Rd Ste E, Chillicothe, OH 45601-9494
Julie Oats, Executive Director

Children's Advocacy Ctr...................**419.292.2927**
Fax...419.292.2929
Web..www.fcapc.org
E-mail...............................cjenkins@fcapc.org
  2460 cherry st, Toledo, OH 43608-3930
Christie Jenkins, Director

Childrens Defense Fund - Cleveland Ofc.......**216.298.4480**
Fax...216.298.4481
  1422 Euclid Ave Ste 972, Hanna Bldg, Cleveland,
  OH 44115
Renuka Mayadev, Executive Director

Childrens Defense Fund - Ohio HQ...........**614.221.2244**
Fax...614.221.2247
  395 E Broad St Ste 330, Columbus, OH 43215
Renuka Mayadev, Executive Director

Legal Aid Society Juvenile Rights Practice......**513.361.8820**
E-mail.............................lkennedy@lascinti.org
  10 Journal Square, Hamilton, OH 45011
Leslie Kennedy

Legal Aid Society of SW Ohio.................**513.362.2799**
E-mail...............................ssmith@lascinti.org
  10 Journal Sq, Hamilton, OH 45011
Sarah Smith, Manager

Michael J Davis Attorney at Law.............**513.398.9500**
E-mail................................lawmjd@cinci.rr.com
  8093 Columbia Rd, Ste 103, Mason, OH 45040
Michael Davis, attorney

Ohio Domestic Violence Network.............**614.781.9651**
Fax...614.781.9652
Web..www.odvn.org
E-mail..................................info@odvn.org
  4807 Evanswood Dr Ste 201, Columbus,
  OH 43229-6282
Nancy Neylon, Director

Southern Consortium For Children..........**740.593.8293**
Fax...740.592.4170
Web...www.scchildren.com
E-mail.................................strout@frognet.net
  20 E Circle Dr Ste 37206, Athens, OH 45701-7206
Steve Trout, Director

Village House/Kic Start....................**419.334.4582**
  350 Rawson Ave, Fremont, OH 43420
Linda Mcgilton, Director

BEHAVIORAL HEALTH TREATMENT

A Renewed Mind **419.720.9247**
Fax 419.878.3658
　1822 Cherry Street, Toledo, OH 43608
　CARF accredited programs available.

Access Ohio **614.225.0400**
E-mail ....bendy@columbus.rr.com
　99 N Brice Rd Suite 360, Columbus, OH 43213
　Ms. Belinda Stevens, Accreditation Manager
　Joint Commission accredited organization.

Adriel School, Inc. **937.465.0010**
Fax 937.465.8690
Web ....www.adriel.org
　414 North Detroit Street, West Liberty, OH 43357
　CARF accredited programs available.

Akron Children's Hospital **330.543.1000**
Web ....www.akronchildrens.org
E-mail ....lephlin@chmca.org
　One Perkins Square, Akron, OH 44308-1082
　Ms. Laura Ephlin, Accreditation Manager
　Joint Commission accredited organization.

Alternative Paths, Inc. **330.725.9195**
Fax 330.725.9187
Web ....www.alternativepaths.org
　246 Northland Drive, Suite 200A, Medina, OH 44256
　CARF accredited programs available.

Amethyst, Inc. **614.242.1284**
Fax 614.242.1285
Web ....www.amethyst-inc.org
E-mail ....lucas@866uswomen.org
　527 South High Street, Columbus, OH 43215
　Paula Lucas, Executive Director
　CARF accredited programs available.

**Appleseed Community Mental Health Center,
Inc.** **419.281.3716**
Fax 419.281.4605
Web ....www.appleseedmentalhealth.com
　2233 Rocky Lane, Ashland, OH 44805
　CARF accredited programs available.

Applewood Centers Inc. **216.696.5800**
Web ....applewoodcenters.org
E-mail ....reavisl@wingspancg.org
　2525 East 22nd St, Cleveland, OH 44115-3266
　Ms. Laurie Reavis, Accreditation Manager
　Joint Commission accredited organization.

Arrowsmith Medical Practice **440.331.4990**
　22255 Center Ridge Rd Ste 308, Rocky River,
　OH 44116-3972
　Margaret Arrowsmith, Psychiatrist

ATS Behavioral Health, Inc. **937.223.1781**
Fax 937.424.8656
　1320 Woodman Drive, Suite 105, Dayton, OH 45432
　CARF accredited programs available.

Bayshore Counseling Services **419.626.9156**
Fax 419.621.0099
　1218 Cleveland Road, Suite B, Sandusky, OH 44870
　CARF accredited programs available.

Beech Brook **216.831.2255**
Web ....www.beechbrook.org
E-mail ....nroettger@beechbrook.org
　3737 Lander Road, Cleveland, OH 44124
　Ms. Nikki Roettger, Accreditation Manager
　Joint Commission accredited organization.

Behavioral Connections **419.352.5387**
Web ....www.behavioralconnections.org
E-mail ....vmoyer1@bc.wcnet.org
　280 S. Main St., Bowling Green, OH 43402
　Dr. Valerie Moyer, Accreditation Manager
　Joint Commission accredited organization.

Bellefaire Jewish Children's Bureau **216.932.2800**
Web ....www.bellefairejcb.org
E-mail ....reavisl@bellefairejcb.org
　22001 Fairmount Boulevard, Shaker Heights,
　OH 44118
　Ms. Laurie Reavis, Accreditation Manager
　Joint Commission accredited organization.

**Bellflower Center for Prevention of Child Abuse,
Inc.** **216.229.2420**
Fax 216.229.2474
Web ....www.bellflowercenter.org
　11811 Shaker Boulevard, Suite 220, Cleveland,
　OH 44120
　Jackie Pennington, Administrator
　CARF accredited programs available.

Belmont Pines Hospital **330.759.2700**
Web ....www.belmontpines.com
E-mail ....lisa.cocca@uhsinc.com
　615 Churchhill-Hubbard Road, Youngstown,
　OH 44505
　Ms. Lisa Cocca, Accreditation Manager
　Joint Commission accredited organization.

Berkowitz Medical Practice **513.671.1820**
Web ....www.tristatesleep.com
　1275 E Kemper Rd, Cincinnati, OH 45246-3901
　David Berkowitz, MD, Psychiatrist

BHC Fox Run Hospital **740.695.2131**
Web ....www.foxruncenter.com
E-mail ....mikel.smith@psysolutions.com
　67670 Traco Drive, Saint Clairsville, OH 43950
　Mr. Michael Smith, Accreditation Manager
　Joint Commission accredited organization.

Blick Clinic, Inc. **330.762.5425**
Fax 330.762.2877
Web ....www.blickclinic.org
　640 West Market Street, Akron, OH 44303
　CARF accredited programs available.

Butler Behavioral Health Services **513.881.7189**
Fax 513.881.7188
Web ....www.bbhs.org
　1490 University Boulevard, Hamilton, OH 45011
　CARF accredited programs available.

Cambridge Counseling Center, Inc. **740.435.9766**
Fax 740.432.4966
Web ....www.cambridgecounselingcenter.org
　317 Highland Avenue, Cambridge, OH 43725
　Susan Lych, Director
　CARF accredited programs available.

Canton Boys Group Home **330.453.7420**
Fax 330.455.9778
　711 Cleveland Ave SW, Canton, OH 44702-2160
　Lora Bomestar, Director

Carol S Colbert Inc **440.461.0042**
Fax 440.461.5033
　6009 Landerhaven Dr Ste F, Cleveland,
　OH 44124-4192
　Patrick Enders MD, Psychiatrist

Catherine Holladay Inc **419.624.8330**
Fax 419.625.3967
　1717 E Perkins Ave Ste 200, Sandusky,
　OH 44870-7922
　Catherine Holladay Do, Psychiatrist

Center for Behavioral Health, Inc. **330.783.9690**
Fax 330.783.9693
Web ....www.centerforbehavioralhealth.com
　725 Boardman-Canfield Road, Building D,
　Youngstown, OH 44512
　Dr Steven King, Medical Director
　CARF accredited programs available.

Centerpoint **513.221.4673**
Fax 513.872.5783
Web ....www.centerpointhealth.org
　2602 Victory Parkway, Cincinnati, OH 45206
　CARF accredited programs available.

Central Clinic **513.558.9015**
Fax 513.558.3880
Web ....www.centralclinic.org
　311 Albert Sabin Way, Cincinnati, OH 45229
　Dr. Walter Smithson, Clinic Director
　CARF accredited programs available.

Central Oh Mental Health Ctr **740.369.7688**
Fax 740.363.6415
Web ....www.comhc.net
　824 Bowtown Rd, Delaware, OH 43015-9661
　Mark Travis, Director

Century Health Inc **419.425.5050**
Fax 419.423.6464
Web ....www.centuryhealth.net
E-mail ....bbasu@centuryhealth.net
　1918 N Main St, Findlay, OH 45840
　Basanti Basu, Medical Director
　CARF accredited programs available.

Child & Adolescent Psychiatry **330.433.1300**
Fax 330.494.0828
Web www.4kidhelp.com
E-mail ....lreynolds@ncmf.com
　6513 Frank Ave NW, North Canton, OH 44720-7265
　Lee Reynolds, Psychiatrist

Child and Adolescent Behavioral Health **330.454.7917**
Fax 330.452.8860
Web ....www.childandadolescent.org
　919 Second Street, N.E., Canton, OH 44704
　COA accredited organization.

Child Care Choices **937.667.1799**
Fax 937.667.0819
Web ....www.child-care-choices.org/
E-mail ....betsy-childcarechoice@bizwoh.rr.com
　4817 State Rte 202, Tipp City, OH 45371-1311
　Elizabeth Russ, Director

Child Focus, Inc. **513.752.1555**
Fax 513.688.8155
Web ....www.child-focus.org
E-mail ....bvelilla@child-focus.org
　555 Cincinnati-Batavia Pike, Cincinnati, OH 45244
　Berta Velilla, Director of Early Learning Programs
　CARF accredited programs available.

Child Guidance & Family Solutions **330.762.0591**
Web ....www.cgfs.org
E-mail ....bartt@cgfs.org
　312 Locust Street, Akron, OH 44302
　Dr. Timothy Bartlett, Accreditation Manager
　Joint Commission accredited organization.

Children's Services Association **419.352.7588**
E-mail ....melaniek@crc.wcnet.org
　1045 Klotz Road, Bowling Green, OH 43402
　Ms. Melanie Kneessi, Accreditation Manager
　Joint Commission accredited organization.

Chittiprolu Medical Practice **614.789.0078**
　6350 Frantz Rd Ste J, Dublin, OH 43017-5397
　Jagan Chittiprolu Md, Psychiatrist

Churchill Counseling Services, Inc. **330.759.3040**
Fax 330.759.3070
Web ....www.churchillcounseling.com
　4531 Belmont Avenue, Youngstown, OH 44505
　CARF accredited programs available.

**Cincinnati Children's Hospital Medical
Center** **513.636.3333**
Web ....www.cincinnatichildrens.org
E-mail ....maryanne.morris@cchmc.org
　3333 Burnet Avenue, Cincinnati, OH 45229-3039
　Ms. Mary Anne Morris, Accreditation Manager
　Joint Commission accredited organization.

Clemens Medical Practice **216.381.4850**
Fax 216.371.4373
E-mail ....naclemens@cs.com
　1611 S Green Rd Ste 301, Cleveland,
　OH 44121-4192
　Norman Clemens MD, Psychiatrist

Ohio

Clermont Recovery Center, Inc. 513.735.8100
Fax 513.735.8103
Web ....www.recoveryctr.org
  1088 Wasserman Way, Suite C, Batavia, OH 45103
  CARF accredited programs available.

Cleveland Center for Eating Disorders, Inc. 216.765.0500
Fax 216.765.0521
Web ....www.eatingdisorderscleveland.org
  25550 Chagrin Boulevard, Suite 200, Cleveland,
  OH 44122
  CARF accredited programs available.

Cleveland Christian Home 216.416.4277
Fax 216.416.4273
  11401 Lorain Ave, Cleveland, OH 44111
  Tonya Smell Swanson, Director

Coleman Professional Services 330.673.1347
Fax 330.678.3677
Web ....www.coleman-professional.com
  5982 Rhodes Road, Kent, OH 44240
  CARF accredited programs available.

Columbus Area, Inc. 614.252.0711
Fax 614.251.7766
Web ....www.columbus-area.com
  1515 East Broad Street, Columbus, OH 43205
  CARF accredited programs available.

Columbus Colony Elderly Care 614.891.5055
Web ....www.columbuscolony.org
  1150 Colony Dr, Westerville, OH 43081-3624
  Linda Bergel, Director

Community Behavioral Health, Inc 513.785.4784
E-mail ....cconnolly@communitybehavioralhealth.org
  520 Eaton Ave, Hamilton, OH 45013
  Mr. Chris Connolly, Accreditation Manager
  Joint Commission accredited organization.

Community Counseling & Crisis Center 513.523.4149
Fax 513.523.4145
Web ....www.communitycounselingandcrisiscenter.o
  110 South College Avenue, Oxford, OH 45056
  CARF accredited programs available.

Community Counseling Center 440.998.4210
E-mail ....wendy.charles@cccohio.com
  2801 C Court, Ashtabula, OH 44004
  Ms. Wendy Charles, Accreditation Manager
  Joint Commission accredited organization.

Community Counseling Services, Inc. 419.562.2000
Fax 419.562.1296
Web ....www.communitycounseling.info
  2458 Stetzer Road, Bucyrus, OH 44820
  CARF accredited programs available.

Community Health Center 330.434.4141
Web ....www.commhealthcenter.org
E-mail ....cdbcd1@aol.com
  725 East Market Street, Akron, OH 44305
  Dr. Nancy Keogh, Accreditation Manager
  Joint Commission accredited organization.

Community Mental Health Svc 740.695.9344
Web ....www.cmhs.net
  68353 Bannock Rd, Saint Clairsville, OH 43950-9736
  Karen Barger Mercer, Director

Community Mental Healthcare, Inc. 330.343.6631
Fax 330.343.8188
Web ....www.cmhdover.org
  201 Hospital Drive, Dover, OH 44622
  CARF accredited programs available.

Community Solutions Association 330.394.9090
Fax 330.394.8163
  320 High Street NE, Warren, OH 44481
  CARF accredited programs available.

Community Support Services, Inc. 330.996.9141
Fax 330.253.0377
Web ....www.cssbh.org
E-mail ....temesgenfasil@cssbh.org
  150 Cross Street, Akron, OH 44311
  Fasil Temesgen, Director
  CARF accredited programs available.

Community Teaching Homes 419.868.1178
Fax 419.868.1989
Web ....ct-homes.org
  6715 Dorr Street, Toledo, OH 43615
  CARF accredited programs available.

**Community Teaching Homes, Behavioral Health
Services** 419.836.2167
Fax 419.836.2177
Web ....www.ct-homes.org
  6715 Door Street, Toledo, OH 43615
  Diane Jaeger, Director
  CARF accredited programs available.

**Comprehensive Behavioral Health Associates,
Inc.** 330.797.4050
Fax 330.799.1262
  104 Javit Court, Austintown, OH 44515
  CARF accredited programs available.

Comprehensive Counseling Service 513.424.0921
Fax 513.424.4810
Web ....www.comprehensivecounselingservice.com
  1659 South Breil Blvd, Middletown, OH 45044
  Deanna Proctor, Director
  CARF accredited programs available.

Comprehensive Group 614.538.2860
  6013 Winstead Rd, Columbus, OH 43235-3330
  Alan Resor, Phsychiatrist

Comprehensive Psychiatry Group, Inc. 330.726.9570
Web ....www.cpgboardman.com
E-mail ....smarlin.cpg@gmail.com
  955 Windham Court, Youngstown, OH 44512
  Mr. Scott Marlin, Accreditation Manager
  Joint Commission accredited organization.

Comprehensive Psychiatry Specialists 330.884.1900
Fax 330.884.1928
  955 Windham Ct Ste 2, Youngstown,
  OH 44512-5035
  Scott Marlin, Administrator

Concord Counseling Services, Inc. 614.882.9338
Fax 614.882.3401
Web ....www.concordcounseling.org
E-mail ....connieemerson@concordcounseling.org
  774 Park Meadow Road, Westerville, OH 43081
  Connie Emerson, Director
  CARF accredited programs available.

Connecting Point 419.475.8681
Fax 419.475.5413
Web ....www.connectingpoint.org
E-mail ....jdeckebach@connectingpoint.org
  3151 Chollett Dr, Toledo, OH 43606-1839
  Jeffrey Deckeback, CEO

Consumer Advocacy 937.652.4555
Fax 937.652.4945
  1150 Scioto Street, Suite 200, Urbana, OH 43078
  Kristin Dunn, Director
  CARF accredited programs available.

Cornell Abraxas 419.747.3322
Web ....abraxasyfs.com
E-mail ....aclose@cornellcompanies.com
  2775 State Route 39, Shelby, OH 44875
  Ms. Amy Close, Accreditation Manager
  Joint Commission accredited organization.

Counseling Center, Inc. 937.492.6970
Fax 937.492.6971
Web ....www.scccinc.org
E-mail ....coberlies@scccinc.org
  500 East Court Street, Sidney, OH 45365
  Christian Oberlies, Clinical Director
  CARF accredited programs available.

Craig and Frances Lindner Center of HOPE 513.536.4673
Web ....lindnercenterofhope.org
E-mail ....daniela.nelson@lindnercenter.org
  4075 Old Western Row Road, Mason, OH 45040
  Ms. Daniela Nelson, Accreditation Manager
  Joint Commission accredited organization.

Crew Medical Practice 513.559.1191
  124 E Mcmillan St, Cincinnati, OH 45219-2607
  Carl Crew, MD, Psychiatrist

**Crisis Intervention and Recovery Center,
Inc.** 330.452.9812
Web ....circstark.org
E-mail ....deborahfk@circstark.org
  832 McKinley Avenue NW, Canton, OH 44703
  Ms. Deborah Foster-Koch, Accreditation Manager
  Joint Commission accredited organization.

Crisis Intervention Ctr 330.452.6000
Fax 330.454.4357
E-mail ....berniej@circstark.org
  2421 13th St NW, Canton, OH 44708-3189
  Bernie Jesiolowski, Executive Director

Ctr For Cognitive Therapy 614.459.4490
E-mail ....intake@ccbtcolumbus.com
  4624 Sawmill Rd, Columbus, OH 43220-2247
  Brooke Thorner, Md

Ctrville High School 937.439.3500
Fax 937.439.3574
Web www.centerville.k12.oh.us
E-mail ....eileen.booher@centerville.k12.oh.us
  500 E Franklin St, Dayton, OH 45459-5714
  Eileen Booher, Principal

Cuyahoga Community College 216.987.5000
Fax 216.987.5388
Web ....www.tri-c.edu
  11000 W Pleasant Valley Rd, Cleveland,
  OH 44130-5199
  Janice Taylor Herd, Director

D & E Counseling Center, Inc. 330.793.2487
Fax 330.793.4559
Web ....www.dandecenter.com
  142 Javit Court, Youngstown, OH 44515
  COA accredited organization.

Directions for Youth & Families 614.294.2661
Fax 614.294.3247
Web ....www.dfyf.org
  1515 Indianola Avenue, Columbus, OH 43201
  COA accredited organization.

Disability & Impairment Eval 440.975.1225
  5370 Som Center Rd, Willoughby, OH 44094-6636
  Joel Steinberg, Psychiatrist

Doukides Medical Practice 419.824.9993
  4027 N Holland Sylvania Rd Ste 1, Toledo,
  OH 43623-2599
  Panos Doukides, Md, Psychiatrist

Dublin Counseling Center 614.889.5722
Fax 614.889.9335
Web ....www.dublincounselingcenter.org
  299 Cramer Creek Court, Dublin, OH 43017
  CARF accredited programs available.

Eastway Corporation 937.496.2000
Fax 937.463.2958
Web ....www.eastway.org
  600 Wayne Ave, Dayton, OH 45410
  Derek Pope, Facility Manager
  CARF accredited programs available.

Educational Service Center 937.767.1303
Fax 937.767.1025
Web ....www.greene.esc.org
360 East Enon Road, Yellow Springs, OH 45387
terry thomas, suprintendent
CARF accredited programs available.

ENA, Inc. (dba Necco) 740.313.0400
Fax 740.313.0433
Web ....www.necco.org
P.O. Box 568, South Point, OH 45680
COA accredited organization.

Excel Academy 740.323.1102
Fax 740.323.5821
Web ....www.excelacademyohio.org
116 West Church Street, Newark, OH 43055
CARF accredited programs available.

Fairless High School 330.767.3444
Fax 330.767.3447
11885 Navarre Rd SW, Navarre, OH 44662
Philip Glasgow, Guidance Counselor

**Family Life Counseling and Psychiatric
Services** 419.774.9969
Fax 419.756.5642
Web ....www.flcps.com
151 Marion Avenue, Mansfield, OH 44903
CARF accredited programs available.

Family Pride of Northeast Ohio, Inc. 440.286.1553
Fax 440.286.1318
Web ....www.fpinhome.org
100 Parker Court, Chardon, OH 44024-1141
CARF accredited programs available.

Family Recovery Center 330.424.1468
Fax 330.424.9844
Web ....www.familyrecovery.org
964 North Market Street, Lisbon, OH 44432
CARF accredited programs available.

**Farooqui Medical Practice-Corrections Reception
Ctr** 614.877.7011
Fax 614.877.7038
PO Box 300, Orient, OH 43146-0300
Asim Farooqui MD, Psychiatrist

Firelands Counseling 419.332.5524
Fax 419.332.7581
E-mail ....krohd@firelands.com
675 Bartson Rd, Fremont, OH 43420-9672
Dawn Kroh, Director

**Firelands Counseling and Recovery
Services** 419.557.5177
Fax 419.557.5179
Web ....www.firelands.com
1925 Hayes Avenue, Sandusky, OH 44870
CARF accredited programs available.

First Call For Help, Inc. 419.599.1660
Fax 419.592.8336
Web ....www.firstcallnwo.org
600 Freedom Drive, Napoleon, OH 43545
CARF accredited programs available.

**Foundations Behavioral Health Services,
Inc.** 419.584.1000
Fax 419.584.1825
4761 State Route 29, Celina, OH 45822
CARF accredited programs available.

Foy Medical Practice 419.335.3732
Fax 419.335.3462
Web ....www.fsno.org
7320 State Route 108, Wauseon, OH 43567

Franciscan University Of Steubenville 740.284.7217
Fax 740.284.7036
Web ....www.franciscan.edu
E-mail ....jloizzo@franciscan.edu
1235 University Blvd, Steubenville, OH 43952-1796
Joe Loizzo, Director

Franklin Cty Residential Serv Inc 614.844.3800
Fax 614.844.5913
E-mail ....mgroll@fcres.com
1021 Checkrein Ave, Columbus, OH 43229-1106
Mark Groll, Director

FRS Counseling, Inc. 937.393.4562
Fax 937.393.2056
313 Chillicothe Avenue, Hillsboro, OH 45133
CARF accredited programs available.

G.L.A.D. HOUSE, Inc. 513.641.5530
Fax 513.482.7042
Web ....www.gladhouse.org
4721 Reading Road, Bldg A, Cincinnati, OH 45237
COA accredited organization.

Gateways 513.861.0035
Fax 513.681.0108
Web ....www.gatewaysrecovery.com
3131 Harvey Avenue, Suite 201, Cincinnati,
OH 45229
CARF accredited programs available.

Goodwill Easter Seals Miami Valley 937.461.4800
Fax 937.461.8458
Web ....www.gesmv.org
1511 Kuntz Road, Dayton, OH 45404
CARF accredited programs available.

Greenleaf Family Center 330.376.9494
Fax 330.376.4525
Web ....www.greenleafctr.org
212 East Exchange Street, Akron, OH 44304
COA accredited organization.

Greentree Counseling Center, Inc. 330.372.2200
Fax 330.372.2600
3915 East Market Street, Building Four, Warren,
OH 44484
CARF accredited programs available.

Hamilton Choices, LLC 513.765.5500
Fax 513.765.5555
Web ....www.choicesteam.org
644 Linn Street, Suite 900, Cincinnati, OH 45203
CARF accredited programs available.

Harbor 419.479.4449
Fax 419.479.3230
Web ....www.harbor.org
4334 Secor Road, Toledo, OH 43623
CARF accredited programs available.

Harbor Behavioral Health 419.241.6191
Fax 419.255.5623
Web ....www.harbor.org
123 22nd St Ste 1, Toledo, OH 43604
Yvette Kane, Office Superintendent

Harbor Behavioral Health 419.475.4449
Fax 419.479.3833
Web ....www.harbor.org
E-mail ....dshreeve@harbor.org
4334 Secor Rd, Toledo, OH 43623-4234
Dale Shreeve, CEO

Harbor Behavioral Health Care 419.782.4196
Fax 419.782.4302
206 Perry St, 6825 St bought N, Defiance,
OH 43512-2118
Monica Thomas, Office Manager

Health Recovery Services, Inc. 740.592.6724
Fax 740.592.6728
Web ....www.healthrecserv.org
224 Columbus Road, Athens, OH 45701
CARF accredited programs available.

Hittle House LLC 614.443.5454
Fax 614.737.5248
Web ....www.hittlehouse.com
774 Internet Drive, Columbus, OH 43207
COA accredited organization.

House of New Hope 740.345.5437
Fax 740.745.3429
Web ....www.houseofnewhope.org
E-mail ....ibshrink@houseofnewhope.org
8135 Mount Vernon Rd, Saint Louisville, OH 43071
Dr. Jeffrey Greene, Executive Director
CARF accredited programs available.

Huckleberry House, Inc. 614.294.8097
Fax 614.294.6109
Web ....www.huckhouse.org
1421 Hamlet Street, Columbus, OH 43201
COA accredited organization.

IKRON Corporation 513.621.1117
Fax 513.621.2350
Web ....www.ikron.org
E-mail ....rstrunk@ikron.org
2347 Vine St, Cincinnati, OH 45219
Randy Strunk, Executive Director
CARF accredited programs available.

Integrated Services of Appalachian Ohio 740.594.6807
Fax 740.594.9967
Web ....www.integratedservice.org
11 Graham Drive, Athens, OH 45701
CARF accredited programs available.

Jefferson Behavioral Health System 740.264.7751
Fax 740.264.2422
E-mail ....cnoutpat@jbhsorg.com
3200 Johnson Road, Steubenville, OH 43952
Jean Spillan, Director
CARF accredited programs available.

**Jewish Family Service Association of
Cleveland** 216.504.2600
Fax 216.504.0551
Web ....www.jfsa-cleveland.org
24075 Commerce Park Road, Beachwood, OH 44122
CARF accredited programs available.

Jewish Family Services 614.231.1890
Fax 614.231.4978
Web ....www.jfscolumbus.org
1070 College Avenue, Columbus, OH 43209
CARF accredited programs available.

John Lein Deckers Office 740.695.4805
47865 Resorvior Rd, Saint Clairsville, OH 43950
John Lenbecker, Therapist

**Keystone Richland Center, LLC dba Foundations for
Living** 419.589.5511
Fax 419.589.7599
Web ....www.keystoneyouth.com
1451 Lucas Road, Mansfield, OH 44903
CARF accredited programs available.

L & P Services, Inc. 740.376.0930
Fax 740.376.0933
207 Colegate Drive, Suites A and D, Marietta,
OH 45750
CARF accredited programs available.

LHS Family and Youth Services 419.693.1520
Fax 419.693.3295
Web ....www.familyandyouth.org
E-mail ....hlblackmon@familyandyouth.org
2411 Seaman St, Toledo, OH 43605
Harry Blackmon, Executive Director
CARF accredited programs available.

Liberty Center Connections, Inc. 330.264.8498
Fax 330.264.3777
Web ....www.stepsatlibertycenter.org
104 Spink Street, Wooster, OH 44691
COA accredited organization.

LifeSpan, Inc. 513.868.3210
Fax 513.868.3249
Web ....www.lifespanohio.org
1900 Fairgrove Avenue, Hamilton, OH 45011
COA accredited organization.

Ohio

Lifessentials Counseling **937.222.5496**
Web ....www.lifessentialscounseling.com
E-mail ....lifessentials@sbcglobal.net
131 N Ludlow St., Suite 1212, Dayton, OH 45402
Mrs. Nettie Putnam, Accreditation Manager
Joint Commission accredited organization.

Lighthouse Youth Services, Inc. **513.221.3350**
Fax 513.221.3665
Web ....www.lys.org
401 East McMillan Street, Cincinnati, OH 45206
CARF accredited programs available.

Lutheran Social Services of Northwestern Ohio,
Inc. **419.243.9178**
Fax 419.243.4450
Web ....www.lssnwo.org
2149 Collingwood Boulevard, Toledo,
OH 43620-1696
COA accredited organization.

Magnolia Clubhouse, Inc. **216.721.3030**
Fax 216.721.0105
Web ....www.magnoliaclubhouse.org
E-mail ....lori@magnoliaclubhouse.org
11101 Magnolia Drive, Cleveland, OH 44106
Lori D'angelo, Executive Director
CARF accredited programs available.

Maryhaven **614.445.8131**
Fax 614.444.3541
Web ....www.maryhaven.com
1791 Alum Creek Drive, Columbus, OH 43207
CARF accredited programs available.

Marymount Hospital **216.581.0500**
Web ....www.marymount.org
E-mail ....vedick@ccf.org
12300 McCracken Road, Garfield Heights, OH 44125
Ms. Victoria Edick, Accreditation Manager
Joint Commission accredited organization.

Maumee Valley Guidance Center **419.782.8856**
Web ....www.maumeeguidancecenter.org/
E-mail ....mvgccp@defnet.com
211 Biede Ave., Defiance, OH 43512
Ms. Connie Planson, Accreditation Manager
Joint Commission accredited organization.

Mended Reeds Mental Health, Inc. **740.532.6220**
Fax 740.532.1715
Web ....www.mendedreeds.org
P.O. Box 108, Ironton, OH 45638
COA accredited organization.

Mental Health & Recovery Center **937.383.4441**
Fax 937.383.2348
953 South South Street, Wilmington, OH 45177
CARF accredited programs available.

Mental Health & Recovery Svcs **419.213.4600**
Fax 419.244.4707
Web ....www.co.lucas.oh.us
E-mail ....netmail@ocmarsb.mh.state.oh.us
701 Adams St Ste 800, Toledo, OH 43604-6630
Scott Sylak, Executive Director

Mental Health and Counseling Services,
Inc. **740.594.5045**
Fax 740.594.5642
90 Hospital Drive, Athens, OH 45701-2301
CARF accredited programs available.

Mental Health Clinic, Inc. **937.548.1635**
Fax 937.548.1500
Web ....www.dcmhc.org
212 East Main Street, Greenville, OH 45331
CARF accredited programs available.

Mental Health Services for Clark and Madison Counties,
Inc. **937.629.3046**
Web ....www.mhscc.com
E-mail ....vicki.wartner@mhscc.com
1345 Fountain Boulevard, Springfield, OH 45504
Ms. Vicki Wartner, Accreditation Manager
Joint Commission accredited organization.

Mental Health Services for Homeless Persons,
Inc. **216.623.6555**
Fax 216.623.6539
Web ....www.mhs-inc.org
1744 Payne Avenue, Cleveland, OH 44114
CARF accredited programs available.

Meridian Services, Inc. **330.797.0070**
Fax 330.797.9148
Web ....www.meridianservices.org
E-mail ....vbrancaccio@meridianservices.org
527 North Meridian Road, Youngstown, OH 44509
Vince Brancaccio, Director of Residential Services
CARF accredited programs available.

Mid-Ohio Psychological Services, Inc. **740.687.0042**
Fax 740.687.6677
Web ....www.mopsohio.com
624 East Main Street, Lancaster, OH 43130
Bradley Hedges, Executive Director
CARF accredited programs available.

Mid-Western Children's Home **513.877.2141**
Fax 513.877.2151
Web ....www.mid-western.org
E-mail ....barry.boverie@mid-western.org
4581 Long Spurling Rd, Pleasant Plain, OH 45162
Barry Boverie, Executive Director

Minority Behavioral Health Group **330.996.4600**
Fax 330.643.0767
1293 Copley Road, Akron, OH 44320
COA accredited organization.

Moundbuilders Guidance Center, Inc. **740.788.3400**
Fax 740.788.3401
65 Messimer Drive, Newark, OH 43055
CARF accredited programs available.

Murtis Taylor Human Services System **216.283.4400**
Fax 216.283.3636
Web ....www.murtistaylor.org
13422 Kinsman Road, Cleveland, OH 44120
CARF accredited programs available.

Nationwide Children's Hospital, Inc. **614.722.5950**
Web ....nationwidechildrens.org
E-mail ....rayburna@chi.osu.edu
700 Children's Drive, Columbus, OH 43205
Ms. Anamarie Rayburn, Accreditation Manager
Joint Commission accredited organization.

Neil Kennedy Recovery Clinic **330.744.1181**
Web ....www.nkrc.org
E-mail ....candy.kacvinsky@gatewayrehab.org
2151 Rush Boulevard, Youngstown, OH 44507
Ms. Candice Kacvinsky, Accreditation Manager
Joint Commission accredited organization.

Netcare Corporation **614.274.9500**
Fax 614.279.0925
Web ....www.netcareaccess.org
199 South Central Avenue, Columbus, OH 43223
CARF accredited programs available.

New Directions, Inc. **216.591.0324**
Web ....www.newdirect.org
E-mail ....stager@newdirect.org
30800 Chagrin Boulevard, Cleveland, OH 44124
Ms. Susan Tager, Accreditation Manager
Joint Commission accredited organization.

New Horizons Youth and Family Center **740.687.0835**
Fax 740.687.9391
Web ....www.nhyfc.com
1592 Granville Pike, Lancaster, OH 43130
CARF accredited programs available.

North Coast Behavioral Health Care
System **330.467.7131**
Fax 330.467.2420
Web ....www.mh.state.oh.us
E-mail ....guggenheimp@mh.state.oh.us
1756 Sagamore Rd, Northfield, OH 44067-1086
Paul Guggenhiem, CEO

North Community Counseling Centers,
Inc. **614.267.7003**
Fax 614.267.7013
Web ....www.northcommunity.com
E-mail ....info@northcommunity.com
1495 Morse Road, Suite B-3, Columbus, OH 43229
David Kittredge, Director
CARF accredited programs available.

North East Ohio Health Services dba Connections: Health,
Wellness, Advocacy **216.831.6466**
Fax 216.766.6084
Web ....www.connectionscleveland.org
24200 Chagrin Boulevard, Beachwood, OH 44122
CARF accredited programs available.

North Point Consulting and Behavioral Health
Services **740.782.0092**
Fax 740.782.1510
40060 National Road, Bethesda, OH 43719
CARF accredited programs available.

Northcoast Behavioral Health Care
System **419.381.1881**
Fax 419.389.1967
Web ....www.mh.state.oh.us
930 S Detroit Ave, Toledo, OH 43614-2701
Dr. Michael Scheramic, CEO

Northeast Ohio Behavioral Health, Ltd. **330.494.5155**
Fax 330.494.6868
Web ....www.neobh.com
4510 Dressler Road, NW, Canton, OH 44718
COA accredited organization.

Northwest Mental Health Services dba Northwest Counseling
Services **614.457.7876**
Fax 614.457.7896
Web ....www.northwestcounselingservices.org
1560 Fishinger Road, Columbus, OH 43221-2108
CARF accredited programs available.

Oesterlen Services For Youth, Inc. **937.399.6101**
Fax 937.399.6609
Web ....www.oesterlen.org
1918 Mechanicsburg Road, Springfield, OH 45503
COA accredited organization.

Ohio Chemical Dependency Professionals
Sports **614.387.1110**
Fax 614.387.1109
Web ....www.ocdp.ohio.gov
E-mail ....field@ocdp.state.oh.us
77 S High St 16th Fl, Columbus, OH 43215-4132
Robert Field, Director

Ohio Hospital for Psychiatry **614.449.9664**
E-mail ....marcia.berch@bca-corp.com
880 Greenlawn Avenue, Columbus, OH 43223
Ms. Marcia Berch, Accreditation Manager
Joint Commission accredited organization.

Ohio Mentor, Inc. **216.525.1885**
Fax 216.525.1894
Web ....www.thementornetwork.com
E-mail ....angelobonhutto@thementornetwork.com
9800 Rockside Road, Suite 800, Valley View,
OH 44125
Angelo bonhutto, prg addmin
CARF accredited programs available.

Options for Families and Youth **216.267.7070**
Fax 216.267.7075
Web ....www.ofycares.org
5131 West 140th Street, Brook Park, OH 44142
CARF accredited programs available.

Pamela Drake MD **330.337.0088**
Fax 330.337.3099
   12680 Salem Warren Rd, Salem, OH 44460
   Pamela Drake Md, Psychiatrist

Pathways Counseling and Growth Center **440.323.5707**
Fax 440.323.3016
E-mail ....pathwayscounselingctr@yahoo.com
   312 Third Street, Elyria, OH 44035
   Ralph Thompson, Executive Director
   CARF accredited programs available.

Pathways, Inc. **440.918.1000**
Fax 440.918.1029
Web ....www.pathwaysinc.org
   7350 Palisades Parkway, Mentor, OH 44060
   Don Joss, Director
   CARF accredited programs available.

Phoenix Rising Behavorial Healthcare And Recovery,
Inc. **330.493.4553**
Web ....www.phoenixrisingbhr.org
E-mail ....michelleb@phoenixrisingbhr.org
   4974 Higbee ave, suite 209, Canton, OH 44718
   Ms. Michelle Litton-Betts, Accreditation Manager
   Joint Commission accredited organization.

Pomegranate Health Systems of Central
Ohio **614.223.1650**
Web ....www.phs-kids.com
E-mail ....dr.s@phs-kids.com
   765 Pierce Drive, Columbus, OH 43223
   Dr. Kasiraja Sathappan, Accreditation Manager
   Joint Commission accredited organization.

Psycare, Inc **330.759.2310**
Fax 330.759.0018
E-mail ....doug900@psycare.com
   2980 Belmont Ave, Youngstown, OH 44505
   Doug Darnall, Director

PsyCare, Inc. **330.759.2310**
Web ....www.psycare.com
E-mail ....mbhayer@sbcglobal.net
   2980 Belmont Avenue, Youngstown, OH 44505
   Ms. Mary Beth Hayer, Accreditation Manager
   Joint Commission accredited organization.

Rakesh Ranjan MD and Associates, Inc **216.587.6727**
E-mail ....jhupp@charakresearch.com
   12300 McCraken Road, Suite 137, Garfield Heights,
   OH 44105
   Mr. Joe Hupp, Accreditation Manager
   Joint Commission accredited organization.

Ravenwood Mental Health Center **440.285.3568**
Web ....www.geauga.org
E-mail ....klaricr@ravenwoodmhc.org
   12557 Ravenwood Drive, Chardon, OH 44024
   Ms. Renee Klaric, Accreditation Manager
   Joint Commission accredited organization.

Recovery Centers Inc. **937.352.2900**
Fax 937.352.2930
Web ....www.greenehealth.org/wrc/
   515 Martin Drive, Xenia, OH 45385
   CARF accredited programs available.

Recovery Resources **216.431.4131**
Fax 216.923.1244
Web ....www.recres.org
   3950 Chester Avenue, Cleveland, OH 44114
   CARF accredited programs available.

Recovery Services of Northwest Ohio, Inc. **419.782.9920**
Fax 419.784.2523
   511 Perry Street, Defiance, OH 43512
   CARF accredited programs available.

Rehabilitation Service of North Central Ohio,
Inc. **419.756.1133**
Fax 419.756.6149
Web ....www.therehabcenter.org
E-mail ....lfeldman@therehabcenter.org
   270 Sterkel Boulevard, Mansfield, OH 44907
   Lynn Feldman, CCD Director
   CARF accredited programs available.

Reinbows At Serenity Springs Equine Ctr **330.488.6330**
Web ....www.reinbows.org
E-mail ....serenityspgs@aol.com
   6370 Mapleton St SE, East Canton, OH 44730-9566
   Renee Weaver, Director

Rescue Incorporated **419.255.9585**
Web ....www.rescuemhs.com
E-mail ....jeppard@rescuemhs.com
   3350 Collingwood Boulevard, Toledo, OH 43610
   Ms. Janet Eppard, Accreditation Manager
   Joint Commission accredited organization.

Residential Treatment Ctr **330.484.6471**
Fax 330.484.8112
   815 Faircrest St SW, Canton, OH 44706-4844
   David Vanderwall, Superintendent

River Centre Clinic **419.885.8800**
Fax 419.885.8600
Web ....www.river-centre.org
   5465 Main Street, Sylvania, OH 43560
   CARF accredited programs available.

Rocking Horse Children's Health Center **937.324.1111**
Web ....www.rockinghorsecenter.org
E-mail ....kbodey@rockinghorsecenter.org
   651 S. Limestone St., Springfield, OH 45505
   Ms. Karen Bodey, Accreditation Manager
   Joint Commission accredited organization.

Rogers Boys Group Home **330.227.3238**
Fax 330.227.9255
E-mail ....donaldw@sconet.state.oh.us
   7221 Depot St, Rogers, OH 44455
   Brandon Settles, Director

Rosemont Center, Inc. **614.471.2626**
Fax 614.478.3234
Web ....www.rosemont.org
   2440 Dawnlight Avenue, Columbus, OH 43211
   COA accredited organization.

Samaritan Behavioral Health, Inc. **937.276.8333**
Fax 937.276.8336
Web ....www.sbhihelp.com
   601 Edwin C. Moses Boulevard, Fourth Floor, Dayton,
   OH 45417
   CARF accredited programs available.

Shaker Clinic, LLC **216.751.4762**
E-mail ....rich.warden@bca-corp.com
   20600 Chagrin Blvd. Suite 620, Shaker Heights,
   OH 44122
   Mr. Richard Warden, Accreditation Manager
   Joint Commission accredited organization.

Shawnee Mental Health Center, Inc. **740.354.7702**
Fax 740.353.6206
Web ....www.shawneemhc.org
   901 Washington Street, Portsmouth, OH 45662
   CARF accredited programs available.

Signature Health, Inc. **440.953.9999**
Fax 440.918.3839
Web ....signaturehealthinc.com
   38879 Mentor Avenue, Suite C, Willoughby,
   OH 44094
   CARF accredited programs available.

Snouffer Center **740.369.4482**
   250 South Henry Street, Delaware, OH 43015-2978
   CARF accredited programs available.

Solutions Behavioral Healthcare, Inc. **330.723.9600**
Fax 330.722.1446
Web ....www.solutionsbh.org
   246 Northland Drive, Suite 140, Medina, OH 44256
   CARF accredited programs available.

South Community, Inc. **937.293.8300**
Fax 937.534.1353
Web ....www.southcommunity.com
   3095 Kettering Boulevard, Dayton, OH 45439
   CARF accredited programs available.

Southeast, Inc. **614.225.0980**
Web ....www.southeastinc.com
E-mail ....reynoldsd@southeastinc.com
   16 West Long Street, Columbus, OH 43215
   Mr. Richard Reynolds, Accreditation Manager
   Joint Commission accredited organization.

Southern Ohio Behavioral Health, LLC **740.533.0055**
Fax 740.533.1511
Web www.sobh45638.com
E-mail ....dowdy5@hotmail.com
   2113 South Seventh Street, Ironton, OH 45638
   Mike Dowdy, Director
   CARF accredited programs available.

Southwest General Health Center **440.816.8469**
Web ....www.swgeneral.com
E-mail ....pkost@swgeneral.com
   18697 East Bagley Road, Middleburg Heights,
   OH 44130
   Ms. Penny Kost, Accreditation Manager
   Joint Commission accredited organization.

Specialty Care Counseling Services, Ltd **330.399.1221**
E-mail ....zalaom@aol.com
   2000 East Market Street, Warren, OH 44483
   Mrs. Nivine Sedra, Accreditation Manager
   Joint Commission accredited organization.

St. Aloysius Orphanage **513.242.7600**
Fax 513.242.2845
Web ....www.stalsorphanage.org
   4721 Reading Road, Cincinnati, OH 45237
   COA accredited organization.

St. Joseph Orphanage **513.741.3100**
Fax 513.231.1438
Web ....www.stjosephorphanage.org
E-mail ....info@sjokids.org
   5400 Edalbert Drive, Cincinnati, OH 45239
   Robert Wehr, Director
   CARF accredited programs available.

Starr Columbus Hannah Neil Ctr **614.491.5784**
Fax 614.491.7246
Web ....www.starr.org
E-mail ....kitsonm@starr.org
   301 Obetz Rd, Columbus, OH 43207-4036
   Okpara Rice, Executive Director

Step By Step Academy, Inc. **614.436.7837**
Fax 614.436.8704
Web ....www.stepbystepacademy.org
E-mail ....mroot@stepbystepacademy.org
   445 E Dublin Granville Rd, Bldg G, L and R,
   Worthington, OH 43085
   Marla Root, Director
   CARF accredited programs available.

Summit Psychological Associates, Inc. **330.535.8181**
Fax 330.535.9303
Web ....www.summit-psychological.com
   37 North Broadway Street, Akron, OH 44308
   James Orlando, Director
   CARF accredited programs available.

TCN Behavioral Health Services, Inc. **937.376.8700**
Fax 937.376.0113
Web ....www.tcn-bhs.org
E-mail ....tom.otto@wright.edu
   452 West Market Street, Xenia, OH 45385
   Tom Otto, Director
   CARF accredited programs available.

Ohio

The Buckeye Ranch **614.384.7700**
Fax 614.875.2366
Web ....www.buckeyeranch.org
E-mail ....nick.rees@buckeyeranch.org
   5665 Hoover Rd, Grove City, OH 43123-9280
   Nick Rees, President & CEO

The Buckeye Ranch, Inc. **614.875.2371**
Web ....www.buckeyeranch.org
E-mail ....robert.petersiii@buckeyeranch.org
   5665 Hoover Road, Grove City, OH 43123
   Mr. Robert Peters, Accreditation Manager
   Joint Commission accredited organization.

**The Center for Child and Family Advocacy,
Inc.** **419.592.0540**
Fax 419.592.4514
   219 East Washington Street, Napoleon, OH 43545
   CARF accredited programs available.

**The Center for Individual and Family Services,
Inc.** **419.756.1717**
Fax 419.774.5955
Web ....www.richlandthecenter.comorwww.cifscen
   741 Scholl Road, Mansfield, OH 44907
   CARF accredited programs available.

The Children's Home of Cincinnati **513.272.2800**
Fax 513.272.2807
Web ....www.thechildrenshomecinti.org
   5050 Madison Road, Cincinnati, OH 45227
   COA accredited organization.

**The Counseling Center of Wayne and Holmes
Counties** **330.264.9029**
Fax 330.263.7251
Web ....www.ccwhc.org
E-mail ....kearney@ccwhc.org
   2285 Benden Drive, Wooster, OH 44691
   Kay Earney, Director of Health Information,
   CARF accredited programs available.

The Counseling Center, Inc. **740.354.6685**
Fax 740.353.3002
Web ....www.thecounselingcenter.org
E-mail ....ehughes@thecounselingcenter.org
   1634 11th Street, Portsmouth, OH 45662
   Ed Hughes, Executive Director
   CARF accredited programs available.

The Counseling Source, Inc. **513.984.9838**
Fax 513.984.8075
Web ....www.thecounselingsource.com
   10921 Reed Hartman Highway, Suite 133, Cincinnati,
   OH 45242
   CARF accredited programs available.

The Crossroads Center **513.475.5300**
E-mail ....butter6508@yahoo.com
   311 Martin Luther King Drive, Cincinnati, OH 45220
   Dr. C. Pashi, Accreditation Manager
   Joint Commission accredited organization.

The Giving Tree, Inc. **419.734.2942**
Fax 419.734.4922
Web ....www.givingtreecounseling.com
   335 Buckeye Boulevard, Port Clinton, OH 43452
   CARF accredited programs available.

The Lighthouse, Inc. **740.689.2558**
Fax 740.689.2616
   PO Box 215, Lancaster, OH 43130
   COA accredited organization.

The Marsh Foundation **419.238.1695**
Fax 419.238.1747
Web ....www.marshfoundation.org
   1229 Lincoln Highway, Van Wert, OH 45891
   CARF accredited programs available.

The MetroHealth System **216.778.7800**
Web ....www.metrohealth.org
E-mail ....cjakovcic@metrohealth.org
   2500 MetroHealth Drive, Cleveland, OH 44109-1998
   Mrs. Cheryl Jakovcic, Accreditation Manager
   Joint Commission accredited organization.

The Nord Center **440.233.7232**
Fax 440.204.4383
Web ....www.nordcenter.org
E-mail ....wbierie@nordcenter.org
   6140 South Broadway, Lorain, OH 44053
   Willliam Bierie, Executive Director
   CARF accredited programs available.

The Ohio State University Hospital **614.293.9700**
Web ....www.medicalcenter.osu.edu
E-mail ....tammie.hayes@osumc.edu
   410 West Tenth Avenue, Columbus, OH 43210
   Ms. Tammie Hayes, Accreditation Manager
   Joint Commission accredited organization.

The Recovery Center **740.687.4500**
Fax 740.687.4595
Web ....www.therecoverycenter.org
E-mail ....tsaunders@therecoverycenter.org
   1856 Cedar Hill Road, Lancaster, OH 43130
   Trisha Saunders, Executive Director
   CARF accredited programs available.

The Toledo Hospital **419.291.7460**
Web ....www.promedica.org
E-mail ....jan.butterfield@promedica.org
   2142 North Cove Boulevard, Toledo, OH 43606
   Mrs. Jan Butterfield, Accreditation Manager
   Joint Commission accredited organization.

The Twelve of Ohio, Inc. **330.837.3555**
Fax 330.837.0513
Web www.the12inc.org
   P.O. Box 376, Massillon, OH 44648
   COA accredited organization.

The University of Toledo Medical Center **419.383.3407**
Web ....utmc.utoledo.edu
E-mail ....margaret.mcfadden@utoledo.edu
   3000 Arlington Avenue, Toledo, OH 43614
   Ms. Margaret McFadden, Accreditation Manager
   Joint Commission accredited organization.

**The Village Network - Boys' Village
Campus** **330.264.3232**
Fax 330.202.3878
Web ....www.thevillagenetwork.com
E-mail ....rrodman@thevillagenetwork.com
   3011 Akron Rd, Wooster, OH 44691-7904
   James T. Miller, Executive Director

**Thompkins Child and Adolescent Services,
Inc.** **740.826.7650**
Fax 740.826.4966
Web ....www.thompkinstreatment.org
E-mail ....chriscaples@thompkinstreatment.org
   172 South Friendship Drive, New Concord,
   OH 43762
   Christopher Caples, Director of Residential Services
   CARF accredited programs available.

Thompkins Child And Adolescent Svcs **740.432.2377**
Fax 740.432.5669
Web ....www.tcasinc.org
E-mail ....tcasinc@frognet.net
   2007 E Wheeling Ave, Cambridge, OH 43725-2158
   Chuck Larrick, Executive Director

Travco Behavioral Health, Inc. **330.286.0050**
Fax 330.286.0055
   4030 Boardman-Canfield Road, Suite 200C, Canfield,
   OH 44406
   CARF accredited programs available.

Trillium Family Solutions **330.454.7066**
Fax 330.437.0016
Web ....www.trilliumfs.org
   624 Market Avenue, N., Canton, OH 44702
   COA accredited organization.

Twin Valley Behavioral Healthcare **614.752.0333**
Fax 614.752.0087
Web ....www.mh.state.oh.us
   2200 W Broad St, Columbus, OH 43223-1297
   Karen Woods, CEO

Unison Behavioral Health **419.693.0631**
Fax 419.936.7650
Web ....www.unisonbhg.org
   1425 Starr Ave, Toledo, OH 43605-2456
   Larry Hamme, PhD, Chief Clinical Officer

Unison Behavioral Health Group **419.242.9577**
Web ....unisonbhg.org
E-mail ....tbutler@unisonbhg.org
   544 East Woodruff Avenue, Toledo, OH 43604
   Ms. Theresa Butler, Accreditation Manager
   Joint Commission accredited organization.

United Methodist Children's Home **614.885.5020**
Fax 614.885.4058
Web ....www.umchohio.org
E-mail ....admin@umchohio.org
   1033 High St, WORTHINGTON, OH 43085-4054
   William Wilkins, Chief Executive Officer

Valley Counseling Services, Inc. **330.399.6451**
Fax 330.394.6233
Web ....www.vcsinc.org
   150 East Market Street, Warren, OH 44481
   CARF accredited programs available.

ViaQuest Behavioral Health of Ohio, LLC **614.889.5837**
Fax 614.889.5847
Web ....www.viaquestbh.com
   525 Metro Place North, Suite 300, Dublin, OH 43017
   CARF accredited programs available.

WellSpring **937.325.5564**
Fax 937.325.8727
Web ....www.fsafamilyserviceagency.org
   15 East Pleasant Street, Springfield, OH 45506
   COA accredited organization.

West Side Ecumenical Ministry **216.651.2037**
Fax 216.651.4145
Web ....www.wsem.org
   5209 Detroit Avenue, Cleveland, OH 44102
   CARF accredited programs available.

Western Reserve Counseling Service, Inc. **440.352.8954**
Fax 440.352.0351
   One Victoria Square, Suite 105, Painesville,
   OH 44077
   CARF accredited programs available.

Westwood Behavioral Health Center, Inc. **419.238.3434**
Fax 419.238.1955
Web ....www.westwoodbehavioralhealth.com
   1158 Westwood Drive, Van Wert, OH 45891
   CARF accredited programs available.

**Windsor Laurelwood Center for Behavioral
Medicine** **440.953.3000**
Web ....www.uhsinc.com
E-mail ....dan.aranda@uhsinc.com
   35900 Euclid Avenue, Willoughby, OH 44094
   Mr. Dan Aranda, Accreditation Manager
   Joint Commission accredited organization.

WomenSafe, Inc. **440.286.7154**
Fax 440.286.1037
Web ....www.womensafe.org
   12041 Ravenna Road, Chardon, OH 44024
   CARF accredited programs available.

Woodland Centers, Inc. 740.446.5500
Fax 740.441.4402
Web ....www.woodlandcenters.org
　3086 State Route 160, Gallipolis, OH 45631
　CARF accredited programs available.

Worthington Center Management Company,
Incorporated 740.423.4225
Fax 740.423.4228
　2515 Washington Boulevard, Belpre, OH 45714
　CARF accredited programs available.

Wright State University-School of Professional Psychology
Duke E. Ellis Human Development
Institute 937.775.4300
Fax 937.775.4323
Web ....www.wright.edu/sopp
　9 N Edwin C. Moses Blvd, Dayton, OH 45402
　Mary Ann Drewry, Executive Director
　CARF accredited programs available.

Your Human Resource Center of Wayne and Holmes
Counties 330.264.9597
Fax 330.264.0946
Web ....www.yhrc.org
　2587 Back Orrville Road, Wooster, OH 44691
　CARF accredited programs available.

Zepf Center 419.841.7701
E-mail ....kcesen@zepfcom.com
　6605 West Central Avenue, Toledo, OH 43617
　Ms. Kathi Cesen, Accreditation Manager
　Joint Commission accredited organization.

CHILDREN'S HOSPITAL

Akron Childrens Hospital 330.543.1000
　One Perkins Square, Akron, OH 44308

Aultman Hospital 330.452.9911
　2600 Sixth Street SW, Canton, OH 44710
　Edward Roth, Chief Executive Officer

Barnesville Hospital Assoc 740.425.3941
　639 West Main St, Barnesville, OH 43713
　Richard Doan, Chief Executive Officer

Bellevue Hospital 419.483.4040
Web ....www.bellevuehospital.com
　1400 West Main St, Bellevue, OH 44811
　Janet Runner, Nursing Director

Berger Hospital 740.474.2126
　600 North Pickaway St, Circleville, OH 43113
　Tim Tolburn, Director

Childrens Medical Center of Dayton 937.641.3000
Web ....www..childrendayton.org
　One Childrens Plaza, Dayton, OH 45404
　Davis Kinsaul, Chief Executive Officer

Cincinnati Childrens Hospital Med Ctr 513.636.4200
　3333 Burnet Ave, Cincinnati, OH 45229
　Michael Fischer, Chief Executive Officer

Cleveland Clinic 216.444.2200
　9500 Euclid Ave, Cleveland, OH 44195
　Debbie Jones, Nursing Director

Community Hospital 419.238.2390
　1250 South Washington St, Van Wert, OH 45891
　Mark Minick, President

Community Hospital 419.354.8900
E-mail ....gorisj@woodcountyhospital.org
　950 West Wooster St, Bowling Green, OH 43402
　Stan Korduvki, Chief Executive Officer

Community Memorial Hospital 419.542.6692
　208 North Columbus St, Hicksville, OH 43526
　Mel Fahs, Chief Executive Officer

Community Regional Medical Center 440.960.4000
　3700 Kolbe Rd, Lorain, OH 44053
　maxine, marketing assistant

Dunlap Community Hospital 330.682.3010
　832 South Main St, Orrville, OH 44667
　Marsha Suppan, President/CEO

East Liverpool City Hospital 330.385.7200
Web ....www.elch.org
　425 West Fifth St, East Liverpool, OH 43920
　Ken Cochran, President/CEO

EMH Regional Medical Center 440.329.7500
　630 East River St, Elyria, OH 44035
　Don Shelton, Chief Executive Officer

Fairfield Medical Center 740.687.8000
　401 N Ewing St, Lancaster, OH 43130

Fairview Hospital 216.476.7000
　18101 Lorain Ave, Cleveland, OH 44111
　Janice Murphy, Chief Executive Officer

Firelands Regional Medical Center 419.557.7400
　1111 Hayes Ave, Sandusky, OH 44870
　Charles Start, President

Fort Hamilton Hospital 513.867.2000
Web ....www.ketteringhealthnetwork.com
　630 Eaton Ave, Hamilton, OH 45013
　Jennifer Swenson, President

Fostoria Community Hospital 419.435.7734
　501 Van Buren St, Fostoria, OH 44830
　Dan Schwanke, President

General Hospital 937.378.7500
　425 Home St, Georgetown, OH 45121
　Joan Phillips, Chief Executive Officer

Genesis Health Care Hospital 740.454.5000
　2951 Maple Ave, Zanesville, OH 43701
　Matt Perry, President

Grandview Medical Center 937.723.3200
　405 Grand Ave, Dayton, OH 45405
　Richard Haas, Chief Executive Officer

H B Magruder Memorial Hospital 419.734.3131
　615 Fulton St, Port Clinton, OH 43452
　Mike Long, Chief Executive Officer

Hillcrest Hospital 440.312.4500
　6780 Mayfield Rd, Mayfield Heights, OH 44124
　Geoffrey Leimgruver, Chief Executive Officer

Holzer Medical Center 740.446.5000
　100 Jackson Pike, Gallipolis, OH 45631
　James Phillippe, Chief Executive Officer

Joint Township District Memorial Hosp 419.394.3335
　200 St Clair St, Saint Marys, OH 45885
　Kevin Harlan, Chief Executive Officer

Kettering Medical Center 937.298.4331
　3535 Southern Blvd, Dayton, OH 45429
　Fred Manchur, Chief Executive Officer

Lakewood Hospital 216.521.4200
　14519 Detroit Ave, Lakewood, OH 44107
　Jan Murphy, Chief Executive Officer

Licking Memorial Hospital 740.348.4000
　1320 West Main St, Newark, OH 43055
　Robert Montagnese, Chief Executive Officer

Marietta Memorial Hospital 740.374.1400
　401 Matthew St, Marietta, OH 45750
　Scott Cantley, Chief Executive Officer

Marion General Hospital 740.383.8400
　1000 McKinley Park Dr, Marion, OH 43302
　John Sanders, President

Mary Rutan Hospital 937.592.4015
　205 Palmer Ave, Bellefontaine, OH 43311
　Mindy Goble, Chief Executive Officer

McCullough Hyde Memorial Hospital 513.523.2111
E-mail ....bhahamann@mhmh.org
　110 N Poplar St, Oxford, OH 45056
　Bryan Hahamann, Chief Executive Officer

MedCentral Hospital 419.526.8000
　335 Glessner Ave, Mansfield, OH 44903

Medical Center Sycamore 937.866.0551
　4000 Miamisburg Centerville Rd, Miamisburg,
　OH 45342
　Mark Smith, Chief Executive Officer

Memorial Hospital 419.332.7321
Web ....www.memorialhcs.org
　715 South Taft Ave, Fremont, OH 43420
　Wes Azwel, Interim CEO

Mercy Allen Hospital 440.775.1211
　200 West Lorain St, Oberlin, OH 44074
　Chris, Switchboard Head

Mercy Hospital of Tiffin 419.455.7000
　45 St Lawrence Dr, Tiffin, OH 44883
　Dale Thornton, Chief Executive Officer

Mercy Hospital of Willard 419.964.5000
　110 East Howard St, Willard, OH 44890

Mercy Medical Center 330.489.1000
　1320 Mercy Drive NW, Canton, OH 44708
　Tom Cecconi, Chief Executive Officer

Mercy St Charles Hospital 419.696.7200
E-mail ....robert_gospodarek@mhsnr.com
　2600 Navarre Ave, Oregon, OH 43616
　Robert Gospodarek, President

Mercy St Vincent Medical Center 419.251.3232
E-mail ....nancy_sahadi@mahsnr.org
　2213 Cherry St, Toledo, OH 43608
　Imran Andrabi, Chief Executive Officer

Metro Health Medical Center 216.778.7800
　2500 MetroHealth Dr, Cleveland, OH 44109
　Mark Moran, Chief Executive Officer

Nationwide Childrens Hospital 614.722.2000
　700 Childrens Dr, Columbus, OH 43205
　Dr. Steve Allen, Chief Executive Officer

Pomerene Hospital 330.674.1015
　981 Wooster Rd, Millersburg, OH 44654
　Tony Snyder, Chief Executive Officer

Riverside Methodist Hospital Ohio Healt 614.566.5000
　3535 Olentangy River Rd, Columbus, OH 43214
　Bruce Hagan, Chief Executive Officer

Salem Community Hospital 330.332.1551
Web ....www.salemhosp.com
　1995 East State St, Salem, OH 44460
　Howard Rohleder, Director

Southern Ohio Medical Center 740.354.5000
　1805 27th ST, Portsmouth, OH 45662
　Randy Arnett, Chief Executive Officer

Southwest General Health Center 440.816.8000
　18697 Bagley Rd, Middleburg Heights, OH 44130
　Anne Selden, Chief Executive Officer

St Elizabeth Health Center 330.746.7211
　1044 Belmont Ave, Youngstown, OH 44504

St John Medical Center 440.835.8000
　29000 Center Ridge Rd, Westlake, OH 44145
　Cliff Coker, Chief Executive Officer

St Joseph Health Center 330.841.4000
　667 Eastland Avenue SE, Warren, OH 44484
　Renee Jones, Nursing Director

St Lukes Hospital 419.893.5911
　5901 Monclova Rd, Maumee, OH 43537
　Dan Wakenan, Chief Executive Officer

Toledo Hospital 419.291.4000
　2142 North Cove Blvd, Toledo, OH 43606
　Kevin Webd, Chief Executive Officer

Trinity Hospital 740.283.7000
　380 Summit Ave, Steubenville, OH 43952
　Fred Brower, President

Union Hospital 330.343.3311
　659 Boulevard, Dover, OH 44622
　Bruce James, Chief Executive Officer

University Hospitals Case Medical Centr 216.844.1000
11100 Euclid Ave, Cleveland, OH 44106

University Hospitals Geauga Med Ctr 440.269.6000
13207 Ravenna Rd, Chardon, OH 44024
M Steven Jones, Chief Executive Officer

Wayne Hospital 937.548.1141
835 Sweitzer St, Greenville, OH 45331
Wayne Deschambeau, Chief Executive Officer

Wilson Memorial Hospital 937.498.2311
915 West Michigan St, Sidney, OH 45365
Tom Bucker, Chief Executive Officer

Wooster Community Hospital 330.263.8100
1761 Beall Ave, Wooster, OH 44691
wiliam

Wyandot Memorial Hospital 419.294.4991
885 North Sandusky Ave, Upper Sandusky,
OH 43351

COUNSELING SERVICES

Applewood Ctrs 216.696.5800
Fax 216.696.6592
Web ....www.applewoodcenters.org
E-mail ....mfalls@applewoodcenters.org
2525 E 22nd St, Cleveland, OH 44115-3202
Melanie Falls, Director

Applewood Ctrs, Inc 440.934.9930
Fax 440.934.9645
Web ....www.applewoodcenters.org
E-mail ....mmunn@applewoodcenters.org
5255 N Abbe Rd Ste 1, Elyria, OH 44035-1451
Mary Munn, Director Of Operations

Catholic Charities 330.393.4254
Fax 330.393.4050
175 Laird Ave NE, Warren, OH 44483
Paula Smigrocky, Director

Children's Rights Council 419.473.8955
Fax 419.473.8984
E-mail ....crcofnwohio@aol.com
4069 W Sylvania Ave, Toledo, OH 43623
Margaret Wuwert, Executive Director

Directions For Youth And Families 614.294.2661
Fax 614.294.3247
Web ....www.dfyf.org
E-mail ....svotaw@dfyf.org
1414 E Broad St, Columbus, OH 43205-1505
Steve Votaw, CEO/Executive Director

Family Resource Ctrs 419.222.1168
Fax 419.222.7610
E-mail ....powellc@frcohio.com
799 S Main St, Lima, OH 45804-1519
Charles Powell, Director

Family Svc Of NW Ohio 419.244.5511
Fax 419.321.6459
E-mail ....jjones@fsno.org
701 Jefferson, Toledo, OH 43604-1484
James E. Jones, President/CEO

LDS Family Svcs 614.836.2466
Fax 614.836.1865
Web ....www.lds.org
E-mail ....sullivanr@ldschurch.org
4431 Marketing Pl, Groveport, OH 43125-9556
Richard Sullivan, Director

Pathways Counseling Ctr, Inc. 419.523.4300
Fax 419.523.6188
E-mail ....rwilliams@pathwaysputnam.org
835 N Locust St, Ottawa, OH 45875-1216
Robert Williams, Executive Director

CRISIS & SHELTER CARE

Abuse And Rape Crisis Shelter-Warren Co 513.695.1185
Fax 513.695.2433
E-mail ....arcs-hoffman@cinci.rr.com
27 N East St, Lebanon, OH 45036
Janet Hoffman, Director

**Adelante Inc-Hispanic Family Violence
Program** 419.244.8440
Fax 419.244.1660
E-mail ....sonia.troche@adelantelrc.org
520 Broadway St, Toledo, OH 43604
Sonia Troche, Director

Alive Inc-Domestic Violence Shelter 740.283.3444
Fax 740.283.3559
E-mail ....aliveinc@sbcglobal.net
PO Box 866, Steubenville, OH 43952-5866
Jodi Scheetz, Director

Alliance Area Domestic Violence Shelter 330.823.7223
Fax 330.823.6033
Web ....www.neo.rr.com
E-mail ....aadvs@neo.rr.com
1641 S Arch Ave, Alliance, OH 44601
Kim Stanley, Director

Battered Women's Shelter 330.374.0740
Fax 330.374.0119
Web ....www.scmcbws.org
E-mail ....info@scmcbws.org
759 W Market St, Akron, OH 44303-1015
Terri Heckman, Executive Director

Buckeye Region Anti-Violence Org 614.294.7867
Fax 614.294.3980
E-mail ....bravo@bravo-ohio.org
870 N Pearl St, Columbus, OH 43215
Gloria Mccauley, Director

Choices For Victims Of Domestic Violence 614.224.4663
Fax 614.224.7222
Web ....www.choicesdvcols.org
E-mail ....gheller@choicesdvcols.org
475 E Mound St Fl 2, Columbus, OH 43215
Gail Heller, Lisw, Director

Coalition Against Dom Vlnce 740.775.5396
Fax 740.779.9592
E-mail ....executivedirector@horizonview.net
62 North Poing St, Chillicothe, OH 45601
Bud Scharfeder, Interm Director

Council On Rural Svcs Programs 937.778.5220
Fax 937.778.8970
Web ....www.corsp.org
E-mail ....shathaway@corsp.org
201 Robert M Davis Pkwy, Ste B, Piqua, OH 45356
Shirley Hathaway, Executive Director

Crime Victims Svcs-Domestic Violence 419.523.1111
Fax 419.523.3900
E-mail ....victim@crimevictimservice.org
338 E 3rd St, Ottawa, OH 45875
David Voth, Director

Crisis Care-Domestic Violence 419.238.4641
Fax 419.232.4357
E-mail ....k_boaz@embarqmail.com
PO Box 266, Van Wert, OH 45891-0266
Kathy Boaz, Director

Ctr For New Beginnings-Dom Violence 740.349.8719
Fax 740.345.1704
Web ....www.thewoodland.org
E-mail ....Thufford@Thewoodland.Org
60 N 1st St, Newark, OH 43055
Tricia Hufford, Director

Domestic Violence Program Of Bowling 419.352.5387
Fax 419.352.5439
Web ....www.bc.wcnet.org
E-mail ....jbroadwe@bc.wcnet.org
280 S Main, Bowling Green, OH 43402-0029
Julie Broadwell, Manager

Eve Inc-Domestic Violence Program 740.374.5820
Fax 740.373.5321
E-mail ....evedirector@suddenlinkmail.com
303 6th St, Marietta, OH 45750
Anelle Edwards, Director

Every Woman's House-Domestic Violence 330.263.6021
Fax 330.264.3777
E-mail ....douglasb@steps-ewh.org
104 Spink St, Wooster, OH 44691
Bobbi Douglas, Director

Family And Child Abuse Prevention Ctr 419.244.3053
Fax 419.244.1100
E-mail ....scorpening@fcapc.org
2460 Cherry St, Toledo, OH 43608
Saran Corpening, Director

Family And Child Abuse Prevention Ctr 419.734.3266
Fax 419.732.1037
Web ....www.fcapc.org
E-mail ....vtodd@fcapc.org
323 Buckeye Blvd Ste 1, Port Clinton,
OH 43452-1586
Diana Laubenthal, Supervisor

Family Crisis Network-Domestic Violence 419.586.1133
Fax 419.584.0456
Web ....www.bright.net
E-mail ....Familycrisisnetwork@Bright.Net
117 W Fayette St, Celina, OH 45822-2107
Kathy Mescher, Director

Family Svc Agency 330.782.5664
Fax 330.782.1614
E-mail ....familyserviceagency.com
535 Marmion Ave, Youngstown, OH 44502
David Arnold, Director

Family Violence Prevention Ctr-Green Co 937.376.8526
Fax 937.376.8529
E-mail ....info@violencefreefutures.org
380 Bellbrook Ave, Xenia, OH 45385-3638
Debbie Matheson, Interim Director

Forbes House-Domestic Violence Program 440.357.1018
Fax 440.392.0012
Web ....www.forbeshouse.org
32 Kensington Avenue, Painesville, OH 44077
Michael Kruger, Executive Director

Harbor House Inc-Domestic Violence 330.343.2778
Fax 330.343.6863
Web ....www.harbor-house.com
E-mail ....Mhenry@Harbor-House.Com
PO Box 435, New Philadelphia, OH 44663-0435
Marilyn Henry, Director

Help Hotline 330.747.2696
Fax 330.747.4055
Web ....www.helphotline.org
E-mail ....dpiccirilli@helphotline.org
PO Box 46, Youngstown, OH 44501-0046
Dwayne Piccirilli, Executive Director

Juvenile Residential Ctr Of NW Ohio 419.353.4406
Fax 419.353.4502
Web ....www.wcnet.org
E-mail ....bansberg@wcnet.org
1012 S Dunbridge Rd, Bowling Green,
OH 43402-9295
Bridget Ansberg, Director

**Lutheran Homes Society Family And Youth
Div** 419.693.1520
Fax 419.693.3295
Web ....www.familyandyouth.org
2411 Seaman St, Toledo, OH 43605-1519
Harry L. Blackmon, Ms, Lpc, Executive Director

My Sister's Place 740.594.8337
Fax 740.594.7122
E-mail ....msplace@Frontier.com
PO Box 1158, Athens, OH 45701-1158
Kate Mcguckin, Lpcc, Director

New Choices-Domestic Violence Program 937.498.7261
Fax 937.498.7404
PO Box 4182, Sidney, OH 45365-4182
Kerry Mauer-Enneking, Director

Open Arms Domestic Violence Shelter 419.422.4766
Fax 419.422.0248
E-mail ....aritz@openarmsfindlay.org
PO Box 496, Findlay, OH 45839-0496
Ashley Ritz, Director

Parmadale/ Catholic Charities 440.845.7700
Fax 440.845.5910
E-mail ....cxgyekenyesi@clevelandcatholiccharities.org
6753 State Rd, Cleveland, OH 44134-4596
Cheryl Gyekenyesi, Director Of Intake

Partnership Against Dom Vlnce 740.947.1611
Fax 740.947.8744
14534 US Highway 23, Waverly, OH 45690
Annette Jenkins, Director

Safe Harbour Domestic Violence Shelter 419.626.2200
Fax 419.626.6052
Web ....www.safeharbourshelter.org
247 Columbus Ave, Sandusky, OH 44870
Linda Mitchell, Director

**Safer Futures-Women's Shelter-Domestic
Violence 330.296.2100**
Fax 330.298.9180
E-mail ....cbeaty@portagefamilies.org
143 Gougler Ave, Kent, OH 44240
Carole Beaty, Director

Serenity House-Domestic Violence 740.446.6752
Fax 740.446.3014
E-mail ....serenityhous@yahoo.com
11 Hickory Lane, Gallipolis, OH 45631
Mellisa Kimmel, Director

Sojourner House-Domestic Violence 330.747.4040
Fax 330.480.4382
Web ....www.burdmangroup.com
E-mail ....mgavins@burdmangroup.com
284 Broadway, Youngstown, OH 44504
Malinda Gavins, Director

Some Place Safe-Domestic Violence 330.393.3003
Fax 330.393.5288
Web ....www.someplacesafe.org
E-mail ....someplacesafe@Someplacesafe.Org
1540 Tod Ave NW, Warren, OH 44485-1907
Cheryl Tarantino, Director

**Southern Ohio Transforce On Domestic
Violence 740.456.8217**
Fax 740.456.8218
E-mail ....endviolence@roadrunner.com
2315 Grant St, Portsmouth, OH 45662
Lou Ann Hoffer, Director

The Domestic Violence Ctr 216.651.8484
Fax 216.651.8575
E-mail ....calexander@dvccleveland.org
3146 Scranton Rd, Cleveland, OH 44109
Cathleen Alexander, Director

The Domestic Violence Shelter 419.774.5843
Fax 419.526.5320
Web ....www.thedvshelter.com
E-mail ....Shelter@Thedvshelter.Com
PO Box 1524, Mansfield, OH 44901-1524
Catherine Ezawa, Director

Transitions-Domestic Violence Program 740.454.3214
Fax 740.454.2042
PO Box 156, Zanesville, OH 43702-0156
Barabara Davis, Director

Victim Assistance Program 419.663.3839
Fax 419.663.3844
Web ....www.accnorwalk.com
E-mail ....egorby@accnorwalk.com
12 E Main St Ste 100, Norwalk, OH 44857-1543
Eva Gorby, Director

Washington Court Hse 740.335.3101
Fax 740.335.9181
201 S Main St, Washington Court House, OH 43160
Katie Bottorff, Director

EDUCATION

Akron Speech & Reading Ctr 330.666.1161
Fax 330.665.1862
Web ....www.akroneducationcampus.com
700 Ghent Rd, Akron, OH 44333-2698
Ardath Franck, Director

Alliance For Heathy Youth 330.864.1359
Fax 330.864.1540
Web www.all4youth.org
E-mail ....info@all4youth.org
1815 W Market St Ste 107, Akron, OH 44313-7018
Cheryl Biddle, Director

Catholic Charity Svc 216.391.2030
Fax 216.391.8946
E-mail ....mdee@dioceseofcleveland.org
3135 Euclid Ave Ste 202, Cleveland, OH 44115-2524
Maureen Dee, Vice President Of Chemical Dependency Programs

Children's Home of Cincinnati, Ohio 513.272.2800
Fax 513.272.2807
Web ....www.olympuscenter.org
E-mail ....ejohnson@thechildrenshomecinti.org
5050 Madison Rd, Cincinnati, OH 45227-1493
Wesley Young Acsw, Executive Director

Cincinnati Job Corps Ctr 513.651.2000
Fax 513.651.2004
1409 Western Ave, Cincinnati, OH 45214
Beverly Williams, Center Director

Dayton Job Corps Ctr 937.268.6571
Fax 937.267.3822
Web ....www.mtctrains.com
3849 Germantown Pike, Dayton, OH 45417-2199
Charles Howard, Center Director

Friendly Inn Settlement House 216.431.7656
Fax 216.431.8189
E-mail ....fish2@acclink.com
2386 Unwin Rd, Cleveland, OH 44104-1099
Geraldine H. Burns, Lisw, Mssa, Executive Director

Gibault Springfield, Ohio 937.327.3720
Fax 937.327.3742
Web ....www.gibault.org
E-mail ....james.sinclair@gibault.org
525 E Home Rd, Springfield, OH 45503
James M. Sinclair, CEO/Executive Director

Jackson Vinton Community Action, Inc........740.384.5119
Fax 740.384.5405
Web ....www.jackson-vinton.com
118 S New York Ave, Wellston, OH 45692
Cheryl Thiessen, Executive Director

Judge FW Nicholas Residential Treatment 937.496.7100
Fax 937.496.7315
5581 Dayton Liberty Rd, Dayton, OH 45418-1403
Bill Draugelis, Superintendent

Julie Billiart School 216.381.1191
Fax 216.381.2216
4982 Clubside Rd, Lyndhurst, OH 44124
Jodi Johnston, Principal

Marburn Academy 614.433.0822
Fax 614.433.0812
Web ....www.marburnacademy.org
E-mail ....marburnadmission@marburnacademy.org
1860 Walden Dr, Columbus, OH 43229-3627
Scott Burton, Med, Admissions Director/dean

Marimor School 419.221.1262
Fax 419.225.5184
E-mail ....ebaldridge@acbdd.org
2550 Ada Rd, Lima, OH 45801
Esther Baldridge, Ba, Med, Superintendent

Mary Immaculate School 419.474.1688
Fax 419.479.3062
3835 Secor Rd, Toledo, OH 43623
Shelli Staudt, Principal

**Monarch Svcs For Children & Adolescents With
Autism 216.320.8945**
Fax 216.320.8756
Web ....www.bellefairejcb.org
E-mail ....mandelld@bellefairejcb.org
22001 Fairmount Blvd, Cleveland, OH 44118-4819
Debra Mandell, Director Of School

Positive Education Program 216.361.4400
Fax 216.361.8600
Web ....www.pepcleve.org
3100 Euclid Ave, Cleveland, OH 44115
Frank A Fecser, Phd, Executive Director

**Society For The Prevention Of Violence
(SPV) 216.591.1876**
Fax 216.591.1879
E-mail ....spvmail@att.net
4645 Richmond Rd, Warrenville, OH 44128
David Volosin, Executive Director

Springer School 513.871.6080
Fax 513.871.6428
Web ....www.springer-ld.org
E-mail ....info@springer-ld.org
2121 Madison Rd, Cincinnati, OH 45208-3288
Shelly Weisbacher, Ma, Executive Director

St. Rita School For The Deaf 513.771.7600
Fax 513.326.8264
Web ....www.srsdeaf.org
1720 Glendale Milford Rd, Cincinnati, OH 45215
Gregory R. Ernst, Executive Director

Starr Commonwealth 419.238.4051
Fax 419.238.5571
Web ....www.starr.org
E-mail ....kitsonm@starr.org
15145 Lincoln Hwy, Van Wert, OH 45891-9619
Mike Kitson, Assistant Director Of Intake

The Grand River Academy 440.275.2811
Fax 440.275.1825
Web ....www.grandriver.org
E-mail ....academy@grandriver.org
3042 College St, Austinburg, OH 44010
Sam Corabi, Director Of Admissions

The Langsford Ctr 513.531.7400
Fax 513.531.7471
Web ....www.weteachreading.com
E-mail ....jeff@langsfordcenter.com
9402 Towne Square Ave Ste B, Cincinnati,
OH 45242-6909
Jeff Graham, Executive Director

FOSTER CARE AGENCIES

**Adopting Children Today Information
Opti 937.277.6101**
Fax 937.277.2962
E-mail ....ACTIONadpt@aol.com
6000 Philadelphia Dr, Dayton, OH 45415

Adoption Cluster Support Group 216.381.2611
E-mail ....michelemvm@msn.com
3955 Euclid Ave 3rd Fl, Cleveland, OH 44115

Adoption Network Cleveland 216.325.1000
E-mail ....betsie.norris@adoptionnetwork.org
4614 Prospect Ave Ste 550, Cleveland, OH 44103
Betsie Norris, Director

Adoption STAR Inc 513.631.6590
Fax 716.639.3700
E-mail ....michele@adoptionstar.com
11918 Foxgate Way, Loveland, OH 45140
Michelle Fried, Director

Advantage Adoption and Foster Care Inc 419.528.4411
43 East 4th St, Mansfield, OH 44902

Bair Foundation 614.846.6265
Fax 614.846.4133
Web ....www.bair.org
    665 E Dublin Granville Rd Ste 300, Columbus,
    OH 43229-3245
    Kristina Hudson, Interim Director

Bellefaire Jewish Childrens Bureau 216.932.2800
Fax 216.320.8747
E-mail ....andersonk@bellefairejcb.org
    22001 Fairmount Blvd, Shaker Heights, OH 44118
    Karen Anderson, Supervisor

Caring for Kids Inc 330.928.0044
Fax 330.928.0303
E-mail ....info@cfkadopt.org
    650 Graham Rd, Ste 101, Cuyahoga Falls, OH 44221
    Patricia Ameling, Director

Catholic Charities Diocese of Toledo 419.244.6711
Fax 494.244.4860
    1933 Spielbusch Ave, Toledo, OH 43604
    Bishop Leonard Blair, Bishop

Cherub International Adoption Services I 937.748.4812
Fax 937.748.4889
E-mail ....cherubint@aol.com
    1827 West Tamarron Ct, Springboro, OH 45066

Children Svcs Foster Parent 614.959.4235
    5477 Glasgow Pl, Columbus, OH 43235

Christian Childrens Home of Ohio 330.345.7949
E-mail ....portergd@ccho.org
    2685 Armstrong Rd, Wooster, OH 44691
    Gary Parter, Chief Executive Officer

Concern for Children Inc 330.678.0090
Fax 330.678.0090
E-mail ....pburnskent@excite.com
    746 Grove Ave, Kent, OH 44240
    Patricia Burns, Program Coordinator

Dayton Area Minority Adoptive Parents In 937.372.4720
    191 Coddington Ave, Xenia, OH 45385

Down Syndrome Assoc of Greater
Cincinnat 513.761.5400
Fax 513.554.4486
E-mail ....dsagc@dsagc.com
    644 Linn St, Ste 1128, Cincinnati, OH 45203
    Collette Maddy, Director

Focus On Youth, Inc. 513.644.1030
Fax 513.644.1025
Web ....www.focusonyouth.com
E-mail ....adodds@focusonyouth.com
    8904 Brookside Ave, West Chester, OH 45069-3139
    Cindy Skinner, Director

Foreign Adoptive Children Eastern
Suburb 440.729.2535
    11875 Laurel Rd, Chesterland, OH 44026

Foster & Adoptive Support Team 513.844.1583
E-mail ....fastbutlercounty@hotmail.com
    842 Louise Ave, Fairfield, OH 45014
    Deanna Henderson, President

Foster Parent Assoc. 330.876.0283
    7630 State Route 5, Kinsman, OH 44428

House of Samuel Inc 740.439.5634
Fax 740.439.0505
E-mail ....JimBarrhos@hotmail.com
    420 North Eigth, Cambridge, OH 43725
    Jim Barrhos, Director

Jewish Family Service Adoption
Connectio 513.469.1188
Fax 513.766.3358
E-mail ....adoption@jfscinti.org
    8487 Ridge rd, Cincinnati, OH 45236
    Sherry Caplan, Marketing Director

Loving Choice Adoption and Maternity
Ser 330.455.0374
Fax 330.455.2101
E-mail ....lovingchoice@csstark.org
    625 Cleveland Ave NW, Canton, OH 44702
    Daniel Fuline, Chief Executive Officer

Miami Valley Adoption Coalition 937.547.1021
E-mail ....mvac@embarqmail.com
    4923 Timberlawn Ct, Greenville, OH 45331
    Marjie Schaaf, President

North American Cncl of Adoptable Childre 614.299.0177
    1371 Virginia Ave, Columbus, OH 43212

Ohio Family Care Association 614.222.2712
E-mail ....Office@OFCAonline.org
    823 1/2 Long St, Columbus, OH 43203

Parenthesis Family Advocates 614.751.9112
E-mail ....adavey@parenthesisonline.com
    6500 Taylor Rd, Reynoldsburg, OH 43068
    Arlene Davey, Director

Phoenix Homes, Inc.
    233 North Main Street, Delphos, OH 45833
    COA accredited organization.

Single Parents by Adoption 513.661.5170
    2547 Talbott Ave, Cincinnati, OH 45211

Specialized Alternatives Families Youth 800.532.7239
E-mail ....safy@safy.org
    10100 Elida Rd, Delphos, OH 45833
    Ben Brooks, Chief Executive Officer

HOME MEDICAL EQUIPMENT PROVIDERS

Falls Welding & Fabricating/Medical Prod 800.231.6444
    608 Grant St, Akron, OH 44311
    Rof Hogan, Chief Executive Officer

Invacare Corp 800.333.6600
    1 Invacare Way, Elyria, OH 44035

KLC Services Inc 866.532.3534
    4038 Weaver Ct E, Hilliard, OH 43026
    Mark Reep, Director

Medical Resources 740.201.3300
    8377 C Green Meadows Dr N, Lewis Center,
    OH 43035
    Randy Reichenbach, Vice President

Specialy Medical Supply 800.380.8539
E-mail ....sales@specialymedicalsupply.com
    5991 Meijer Dr Ste 23, Milford, OH 45150

SpinKids Pediatric Med Equipment 614.564.1402
Fax 614.564.1401
    330 West Spring St Ste 303, Columbus, OH 43215

PEDIATRIC HOME CARE

Cincinnati Children's Home Care Services 513.636.4663
Fax 513.636.7152
Web ....www.cincinnatichildrens.org/homecare
E-mail ....homecareservices@cchmc.org
    3333 Burnet Avenue 5017, Cincinnati, OH 45229
    Susan Wade-murphy, Rn, Senior Clinical Director

Interim Healthcare 614.888.3130
Fax 614.888.3686
    784 Morrison Rd, Gahanna, OH 43230
    Fran Baby, Director

Interim Healthcare 740.432.2966
Fax 740.439.2599
    2146 Southgate Pkwy, Cambridge, OH 43725
    Lisa Moore, Administrator

Interim Healthcare 419.228.2535
Fax 419.227.9244
    3745 Shawnee Rd, Ste 108, Lima, OH 45806
    Tammy Barfield, Vice President

Interim Healthcare 740.373.3800
Fax 740.373.3705
E-mail ....wmorrisinterim@yahoo.com
    1017 Pike St, Marietta, OH 45750
    Wanda Morris, Executive Director

Interim Healthcare 513.984.1110
Fax 513.984.1442
    8050 Hosbrook Rd Ste 406, Cincinnati, OH 45236
    Julie Brown, Barnch Manager

Interim Healthcare 740.453.5130
Fax 740.453.8889
Web ....www.interimhealthcare.org
    1100 F Brandywine Blvd, Zanesville, OH 43701
    Deb Studer, Manager

Interim Healthcare 419.422.5328
Fax 419.422.6478
    1710 Manor Hill Rd Ste 2, Findlay, OH 45840
    Krista Finsel, Branch Manager

Interim Healthcare 740.387.0301
Fax 740.387.0320
    125 Executive Dr Ste 200, Marion, OH 43302
    Anthony Voegele, Branch Manager

Interim Healthcare 937.642.9032
Fax 937.642.9033
    441 Allenby Dr, Marysville, OH 43040
    Holly, Administrator

Interim Healthcare 740.653.5990
Fax 740.653.8301
    2670 N Columbus St Ste B, Lancaster, OH 43130
    Paula Sprouse, Administrator

Interim Healthcare 330.677.8010
Fax 330.677.3220
    184 Currie Hall Pkwy Ste 1, Kent, OH 44240
    Jan Pajk, Executive Director

Interim Healthcare 740.266.4101
Fax 740.266.4103
E-mail ....pcoronainterim@yahoo.com
    4039 Sunset Blvd, Steubenville, OH 43952
    Pamela Corona, Customer Service

Interim Healthcare 937.291.5330
Fax 937.291.5336
    30 W Rahn Rd Ste 2, Dayton, OH 45429
    Jennifer Hall, Director

Interim Healthcare 513.892.3200
Fax 513.896.3792
    7185 Liberty Centre Dr, West Chester, OH 45069
    Sherryl Hasting, Chief Executive Officer

Interim Healthcare 216.524.0400
Fax 216.524.2136
    4600 Rockside Rd Ste 107, Independence, OH 44131
    Jan Pajk, Vice President

Interim Healthcare 740.385.3623
Fax 740.385.3624
    12873 Grey St, Logan, OH 43138
    Pam Pote, Director

Interim Healthcare 740.472.9000
Fax 740.472.9002
    230 S Main St, Woodsfield, OH 43793
    Chris Strawn, Supervisor

Interim Healthcare 330.836.5571
Fax 330.836.5721
    3040 W Market St, Akron, OH 44333
    Jeniffer N, Administrator

Interim Healthcare 740.592.4901
Fax 740.592.4909
    2099 E State St, Ste D, Athens, OH 45701

Interim Healthcare 740.349.8700
Fax 740.366.0191
    900 Sharon Valley Rd, Newark, OH 43055
    Michael Norman, Branch Manager

Interim Healthcare **740.635.0045**
Fax 740.635.0470
  253 N Lincoln Ave, Ste 200, Bridgeport, OH 43912
  Becky Evert, General Manager

Interim Healthcare **937.292.7871**
Fax 937.292.7857
  921 Rush Ave, Bellefontaine, OH 43311
  Tammy Bergfeld, Vice President

Interim Healthcare **330.498.0081**
Fax 330.498.0084
Web ....www.interimhealthcare.com
  1001 S Main St, North Canton, OH 44720
  Marilyn Williams, Branch Manager

Interim Healthcare **419.578.4698**
Fax 419.578.4925
  3103 Executive Pkwy Ste 208, Toledo, OH 43606
  Michelle Patton, Vice President

Interim Healthcare **419.782.4777**
Fax 419.782.8264
  1018 Ralston Ave Ste 108, Defiance, OH 43512
  Becky Schrag, Chief Executive Officer

Interim Healthcare **877.759.2106**
Fax 740.623.2956
  420 Downtown Plaza, Coshocton, OH 43812
  Cindi Harriman, Office Manager

Interim Healthcare **937.399.0171**
Fax 937.399.2125
  425 W Harding Rd Ste B, Springfield, OH 45504
  Jennifer Hall, Director

Interim Healthcare **330.343.3760**
Fax 330.343.3840
E-mail ....interim@healthcare.com
  1320 4th St NW Unit D, New Philadelphia,
  OH 44663
  Cindi Harriman, Branch Manager

Interim Healthcare **740.964.2904**
Fax 740.964.2908
E-mail ....Dakers@interin-health.com
  350 S Main St, Ste B, Pataskala, OH 43062
  Michael Norman, Office Manager

Interim Healthcare **740.392.4211**
Fax 740.392.4209
  112 Harcourt Rd Ste 2, Mount Vernon, OH 43050
  Angela Chadwick, Executive Director

Interim Healthcare **740.354.5550**
Fax 740.354.5670
  4130 Gallia St, Portsmouth, OH 45662
  Amelissa Williams, Chief Executive Officer

Maxim Pediatric Services **614.880.1253**
Fax 614.880.1233
Web ....http://www.maximhomecare.com/
E-mail ....jafuller@maxhealth.com
  200 East Campus View Blvd. Suite 160, Columbus,
  OH 43235
  Jarrett Fuller, Accounts Manager

SSC **216.573.0900**
Fax 216.573.5963
Web ....www.bayada.com
  Liberty Plaza, 5000 Rockside Road, Suite 320,
  Independence, OH 44131
  Ales Kleman, Director

SOCIAL SERVICES

4C **513.221.0033**
Fax 513.221.0393
Web www.4cforchildren.org
E-mail ....psemail@4c-cinci.org
  1924 Dana Ave, Cincinnati, OH 45207-1212
  Sallie Westheimer, Exectuive Director

4C Miami Valley **937.220.9660**
Fax 937.220.9661
Web www.4cforchildren.org
E-mail ....agency@4cforchildren.org
  1000 N keowee St, Dayton, OH 45404-2223
  Tammy Vaunghn, Director

Action For Children **614.224.0222**
Fax 614.224.5437
Web ....www.actionforchildren.org
  78 Jefferson Ave, Columbus, OH 43215
  Diane Bennett, Executive Director

Action For Children **740.369.0649**
Fax 740.369.5252
Web ....www.actionforchildren.org
E-mail ....actionforchildren@rrohio.com
  39 W Winter St, Delaware, OH 43015-1934
  Mary Cusak, President

Among Women Cornerstone **440.284.1010**
Fax 440.324.5333
Web ....www.amongwomen.org
E-mail ....nport@cornerstoneamongwomen.org
  364 Griswold Rd, Elyria, OH 44035-3537
  Donna Fondle, Director

Ashland Care Ctr **419.281.1111**
E-mail ....duciah@ashlandcarecentre.org
  119 Sooan ave, Ashland, OH 44805
  Ducia Hamm, Executive Director

Beech Acres Parenting Center **513.231.6630**
Fax 513.624.0134
Web ....www.beechacres.org
  6881 Beechmont Avenue, Cincinnati,
  OH 45230-2093
  COA accredited organization.

Berea Children's Home & Family Services **440.234.2006**
Fax 440.234.0787
Web ....www.bchfs.org
  202 East Bagley Road, Berea, OH 44017
  COA accredited organization.

Board of Developmental Disabilities **740.349.6588**
Fax 740.344.2787
Web ....lcounty.com
  116 North 22nd Street, Newark, OH 43055
  CARF accredited programs available.

Catholic Charities **740.282.3631**
Fax 740.282.3327
  422 Washington St, Steubenville, OH 43952
  Michele Santin, Director

Catholic Charities Family Ctr **440.366.1106**
Fax 440.366.5645
Web ....www.clevelandcatholiccharities.org/
E-mail ....mlwellman@clevelandcatholiccharities.org
  628 Poplar St, Elyria, OH 44035-4065
  Mary Lou Wellman, Director

Catholic Charities of Southwestern Ohio **513.241.7745**
Fax 513.241.4333
Web ....www.catholiccharitieswo.org
  100 East Eighth Street, Cincinnati, OH 45202
  COA accredited organization.

Catholic Charities Regional Agency **330.744.3320**
Fax 330.744.3677
Web ....www.ccregional.org
  2401 Belmont Avenue, Youngstown, OH 44505
  COA accredited organization.

Catholic Social Services **614.221.5891**
Fax 614.228.1125
Web ....www.colscss.org
  197 East Gay Street, Columbus, OH 43215
  COA accredited organization.

Catholic Social Services of the Miami
Valley **937.223.7217**
Fax 937.222.6750
Web ....www.cssmv.org
  922 W. Riverview Avenue, Dayton, OH 45402
  COA accredited organization.

Catholic Svc League, Inc. **440.992.2121**
Fax 440.992.5974
E-mail ....marka@doyccac.org
  4200 Park Ave Fl 3, Ashtabula, OH 44004-6887
  Aynn Zalewski, Director

Child Care Choices **419.468.7581**
Fax 419.468.5764
Web ....www.childcarechoices.org
E-mail ....director@childcarechoices.org
  601 South St, Galion, OH 44833-3306
  Dawn Fraizer, Director

Child Care Resource Ctr **440.960.7187**
Fax 440.960.7191
Web ....www.ccrcinc.com
E-mail ....edirector@ccrinc.com
  5350 Oberlin Ave Ste 2, Lorain, OH 44053-3483
  Jennifer Dodge, Executive Director

Children Services **330.451.8077**
Fax 330.451.8706
Web ....www.starkdjfs.org
  221 3rd Street SE, Canton, OH 44702
  COA accredited organization.

Children Services **419.774.4100**
Fax 419.774.4114
Web ....www.richlandcountychildrenservices.org
  731 Scholl Road, Mansfield, OH 44907
  COA accredited organization.

Children Services Board **330.372.2010**
Fax 330.372.3446
Web ....www.trumbullcsb.com
  2282 Reeves Road, NE, Warren, OH 44483
  COA accredited organization.

Children's Advantage **330.296.5552**
Fax 330.296.6126
Web ....www.childrensadvantage.org
  520 North Chestnut Street, Ravenna, OH 44266
  COA accredited organization.

Children's and Family Service dba Family Service
Agency **330.782.5664**
Fax 330.782.1614
Web ....www.familyserviceagency.com
  535 Marmion Avenue, Youngstown, OH 44502
  COA accredited organization.

Children's Services Board **937.599.7290**
Fax 937.599.7296
Web ....www.logancountychildrenservices.org
  1855 S.R. 47 West, Bellefontaine, OH 43311
  COA accredited organization.

Christian Children's Home of Ohio, Inc. **330.345.7949**
Fax 330.345.5218
Web ....www.ccho.org
  PO Box 765, Wooster, OH 44691
  COA accredited organization.

Cleveland Christian Home **216.671.0977**
Fax 216.688.4158
Web ....www.cchome.org
  2202 Prame Avenue, Cleveland, OH 44109
  COA accredited organization.

Coad Child Care Resourece Network Sda
10 ....**740.373.6996**
Fax 740.373.6829
Web ....www.coadinc.org
E-mail ....ece@coadinc.org
  1500 Greene St Unit B, Marietta, OH 45750
  Mareen Boggs, Director

Community Mental Health **740.374.6989**
Fax 740.374.7236
　118 Putnam St, Marietta, OH 45750-2923
　Leah Jaquith, Director

Community Services **330.455.0374**
Fax 330.455.2101
Web ....www.communityservicesofstark.org
　625 Cleveland Avenue NW, Canton, OH 44702
　COA accredited organization.

Crossroads: Adolescent Counseling

Service **440.255.1700**
Fax 440.205.2417
Web ....www.crossroads-lake.org
　8445 Munson Road, Mentor, OH 44060
　COA accredited organization.

Domestic Violence Task Force **937.393.8118**
Fax 937.393.8135
E-mail ....jchristie@co.highland.oh.us
　135 N High St Ste A, Hillsboro, OH 45133-1177
　Julie Christie, Director

Drost Family Center BRANCH **216.292.3999**
Fax 216.932.9213
　24075 Commerce Park, Beachwood, OH 44122
　Susan Bichsel, Chief Executive Officer

Elizabeth's New Life Ctr **937.226.7414**
Fax 937.226.1682
Web ....www.elizabethnewlife.org
E-mail ....vkoob@elizabethnewlife.org
　359 Forest Ave Ste 203, Dayton, OH 45405-5215
　Vivian Koob, Director

Family & Community Services, Inc. **330.297.7027**
Fax 330.296.2684
Web ....www.portagefamilies.org
　705 Oakwood Street, Suite 221, Ravenna, OH 44266
　COA accredited organization.

Family Resource Center of Northwest Ohio,
Inc. **419.222.1168**
Fax 419.222.2158
Web ....www.frcohio.com
　530 South Main Street, Lima, OH 45804
　COA accredited organization.

Family Service Association **740.283.4763**
Fax 740.283.2929
　P.O. Box 1027, Steubenville, OH 43952
　COA accredited organization.

Family Service Association **937.222.9481**
Fax 937.222.3710
Web ....www.fsadayton.org
　184 Salem Avenue, Dayton, OH 45406
　COA accredited organization.

Family Service of Northwest Ohio **419.244.5511**
Fax 419.321.6459
Web ....www.fsno.org
　701 Jefferson Avenue, Suite 301, Toledo, OH 43604
　COA accredited organization.

First Step Ctr For Family **330.491.0896**
Fax 330.491.1298
E-mail ....ccstart@sbcglobal.net
　3112 Cleveland Ave NW, Canton, OH 44709
　Deborah Kampman, Director

Graceworks Lutheran Services **937.534.7918**
Fax 937.534.7930
Web ....www.graceworks.org
　3131 South Dixie Drive, #300, Dayton, OH 45439
　COA accredited organization.

Jewish Family Service **330.867.3388**
Fax 330.867.3396
E-mail ....jfs@jewishakron.org
　750 White Pond Dr, Akron, OH 44320
　Gizelle Williams, Executive Director

Jewish Family Service Assoc of Cleveland **216.378.8660**
Fax 216.378.8662
E-mail ....imikhae@jfsa-cleveland .org
　Community Care at Home, 3569 South Green Rd
　Ste 316, Beachwood, OH 44122
　Irina Mikhalev

Jewish Family Service of Toledo **419.885.2561**
Fax 419.724.0413
E-mail ....jff@jewishtoledo.org
　6505 Sylvania Ave, Sylvania, OH 43560
　Nancy Newbury, Director

Jewish Family Services **330.452.6444**
Fax 330.452.4487
E-mail ....cantonjfs@aol.com
　2631 Harvard Ave NW, Canton, OH 44709
　Gail Arenstein, Director

Jewish Family Services **614.559.0122**
Fax 614.231.4978
E-mail ....jmarshall@@jfscolumbus.org
　1070 College Ave, Columbus, OH 43209
　Jennifer Marshall, Chief Operating Officer

Jewish Family Services **614.231.1890**
Fax 614.231.4978
E-mail ....info@jfscolumbus.org
　1070 College Ave, Columbus, OH 43209
　June Gutterman, CEO

Jewish Family Services **330.746.7929**
Fax 330.746.7939
E-mail ....alvinw@idmi.net
　517 Gypsy Ln, Youngstown, OH 44504
　Alvin Weisberg, Director

National Youth Advocate Program, Inc. **614.487.8758**
Fax 614.487.3819
Web ....www.nyap.org
　1801 Watermark Drive, Suite 200, Columbus,
　OH 43215
　COA accredited organization.

National Youth Advocate Program, Inc. **877.NYAP.CAN**
Fax 614.487.8760
Web ....www.nyap.org
E-mail ....info@nyap.org
　1801 Watermark Dr, Suite 200, Columbus,
　OH 43215

Northwestern Ohio Community Action
Commission **419.784.2150**
Fax 419.782.5648
Web ....www.nocac.org
E-mail ....dgerkin@nocac.org
　1933 E 2nd St, Defiance, OH 43512-2503
　Deb Gerkin, Director

Pastoral Counseling Service **330.996.4600**
Fax 330.643.0767
　282 W. Bowery Street, Akron, OH 44307
　COA accredited organization.

Pathways **740.345.6166**
Fax 740.349.9894
Web ....www.pathwayscentralohi.com
E-mail ....mailco.org@pathwayslc.org
　1627 Bryn Mawr Dr, Newark, OH 43055-1505
　Kirstin Mccloud, Executive Director

Personal & Family Counseling Services of Tuscarawas Valley,
Inc. **330.343.8171**
Fax 330.343.8439
Web www.pfcs1.org
　1433 Fifth Street NW, New Philadelphia, OH 44663
　COA accredited organization.

Right to Life **937.547.3113**
　206 Wagner Ave, Greenville, OH 45331-2533
　Virgil Unrast, President

Right To Life **937.653.6745**
Web ....www.ctcn.net
E-mail ....davidgeorge@ctcn.net
　122 Miami St, Urbana, OH 43078
　David George, Director

Safy/Specialized Alternatives For Families &
Youth **419.427.3320**
Fax 419.427.1697
Web ....www.safy.org
E-mail ....amandah@safy.org
　1624 Tiffin Ave Ste D, Findlay, OH 45840-6852
　Amanda Howard, Director

Shelter Care, Inc. **330.630.5600**
Fax 330.630.5810
Web ....www.sheltercareinc.org
　32 South Avenue, Tallmadge, OH 44278
　COA accredited organization.

Specialized Alternatives for Families & Youth
(SAFY) **419.695.8010**
Fax 419.695.0004
Web ....www.safy.org
　10100 Elida Road, Delphos, OH 45833
　COA accredited organization.

St. Stephen's Community House **614.294.6347**
Fax 614.294.0258
Web ....www.saintstephensch.org
　1500 East 17th Avenue, Columbus, OH 43219
　COA accredited organization.

St. Vincent Family Center **614.252.0731**
Fax 614.252.8468
Web ....www.svfc.org
　1490 East Main Street, Columbus, OH 43205
　COA accredited organization.

Starting Point **216.575.0061**
Fax 216.575.0102
Web ....www.starting-point.org
　4600 Euclid Ave, Ste 500, Cleveland, OH 44106-1399
　Billie Osborne-sears, Executive Director

The Mayerson Ctr For Safe And Healthy
Children **513.636.7233**
Fax 513.636.0204
　3333 Burnet Ave, # 5, Cincinnati, OH 45229
　Robert Shapiro, Medical Director

The Ohio Assoc Of Child Caring Agencies,
Inc. **614.461.0014**
Fax 614.228.7004
Web ....www.oacca.org
E-mail ....pwyman@oacca.org
　50 W Broad St Ste 3200, Columbus, OH 43215-5929
　Penny M. Wyman, Executive Director

The Woodlands, Serving Central Ohio, Inc. **740.349.7066**
Fax 740.345.6028
Web ....www.thewoodland.org
　195 Union Street, Suite B-1, Newark, OH 43055
　COA accredited organization.

United Way 211 ....**419.246.4636**
Fax 419.246.4614
Web ....www.unitedwaytoledo.org
E-mail ....jeanette.hrovatich@unitedwaytoledo.org
　1 Stranahan Sq Ste 160, Toledo, OH 43604-1467
　Jeanette Hrovatich, Interim Director

Violence Prevention Project **937.225.5623**
Fax 937.496.7689
E-mail ....hunts@mcohio.org
　41 N. Perry St, Ste. 212, Dayton, OH 45401
　Sandra Hunt, Director

Westark Family Services **330.832.5043**
　42 1st St NE, Massillon, OH 44646
　Nancy Maier, Director Of Detention

Witness Victim Svc Ctr **216.443.7345**
Fax 216.443.7365
Web ....www.uws.org
E-mail ....jkronenberg@cuyahogacounty.us
　310 W Lake Side Ave, Cleveland, OH 44113
　Janet Kronenberg, Manager

Womanline of Dayton, Inc....................937.223.3446
Fax...937.223.3484
Web...............................www.womanlinedayton.org
301 East Sixth Street, Dayton, OH 45402
COA accredited organization.

Women's Ctr...................................937.382.2424
Fax...937.383.6908
Web...............................www.ccwcsupport.org
815 S South St, Wilmington, OH 45177-2755
Tara Wheeldon, Director

Youth Development Corporation of
America..740.313.0400
Fax...740.313.0393
Web...................................www.ydca.org
P.O. Box 568, South Point, OH 45680
COA accredited organization.

SPECIAL NEEDS

Achievement Centers for Children...........216.292.9700
Fax...216.292.9721
E-mail...................sally.farwell@achievementctrs.org
4255 Northfield Rd, Cleveland, OH 44128
Sally Farwell, Director

Achievement Ctrs for Children Adv Camp......440.238.6200
Fax...440.238.1858
E-mail........................tim.fox@achievementctrs.org
15000 Cheerful Lane, Strongsville, OH 44136
Tim Fox, Vice President

Akron General Edwin Shaw Rehab, LLC.......330.784.1271
Fax...330.733.2975
Web...............................www.edwinshaw.com
330 Broadway Street East, Cuyahoga Falls, OH 44221
CARF accredited programs available.

Association of Pupil Services Admin.........330.239.1901
E-mail...................opperman@highlandschools.org
3880 Ridge Rd, Medina, OH 44256

Autism Society of Ohio.....................614.487.4726
E-mail...........................askaso@autismohio.org
1335 Dublin Rd Ste 205-C, Columbus, OH 43214

Brain Injury Association.....................614.481.7100
E-mail...................................help@biaoh.org
855 Grandview Ave Ste 225, Columbus, OH 43215

Cerebral Palsy Association..................614.228.8300
E-mail...................cpohio@midohio.twcbc.com
995 Goodale Blvd, Columbus, OH 43212

Cincinnati Children's Hospital Medical Center - A4C1
Rehab...513.636.7480
Fax...513.636.7360
Web...............................www.CCHMC.org
3333 Burnet Avenue, MLC-4009, Cincinnati,
OH 45229-3039
CARF accredited programs available.

Cincinnati Health Care for the Homeless.......513.352.6364
Fax...513.352.6379
40 E McMicken Ave, Cincinnati, OH 45202
Jackie Campbell, Program Manager

Cleveland Clinic Children's Hospital for
Rehabilitation...............................216.448.6400
Fax...216.448.6341
Web...........www.clevelandclinic.org/childrenshospita
2801 Martin Luther King Jr. Drive, Cleveland,
OH 44104-3815
CARF accredited programs available.

Cleveland Hearing and Speech Center........216.231.8787
Fax...216.231.7141
Web...................................www.chsc.org
11206 Euclid Avenue, Cleveland, OH 44106
CARF accredited programs available.

Daybreak, Inc.................................937.395.4600
Fax...937.395.4610
Web...............................www.daybreakdayton.org
605 S. Patterson Boulevard, Dayton, OH 45402
COA accredited organization.

DDC Clinic for Special Needs Children........440.632.1668
Fax...440.632.1697
E-mail...................................info@ddcclinic.org
14567 Madidson Rd, Middlefield, OH 44062
Patty Gallaher, Business Administrator

Drake Center, Inc............................513.418.4711
Fax...513.418.5979
Web...............................www.drakecenter.com
151 West Galbraith Road, Cincinnati,
OH 45216-1096
CARF accredited programs available.

Easter Seal Society of Mahoning, Trumbull, and Columbiana
Counties.....................................330.743.1168
Fax...330.743.1616
Web...............................www.mtc.easterseals.com
299 Edwards Street, Youngstown, OH 44502
CARF accredited programs available.

Easter Seals Central and Southeast Ohio,
Inc..614.228.5523
Fax...614.228.8249
Web...................www.eastersealscentralohio.org
3830 Trueman Court, Hilliard, OH 43026
CARF accredited programs available.

Epilepsy Association.........................216.579.1330
E-mail...........................info@epilepsyinfo.org
2831 Prospect Ave, Cleveland, OH 44115

Epilepsy Council of Cincinnati Inc............877.804.2241
E-mail.....................................ecgc@fuse.net
895 Central Ave Ste 550, Cincinnati, OH 45202
Kathy Stewart, Executive Director

Flower Rehabilitation Center.................419.824.1584
Fax...419.882.8847
5150 Harroun Road, Sylvania, OH 43560
CARF accredited programs available.

Forum Health Hillside Rehabilitation
Hospital......................................330.841.3720
Fax...330.841.3647
Web...............................www.forumhealth.org
8747 Squires Lane NE, Warren, OH 44484
CARF accredited programs available.

Humility of Mary Health Partners, St. Elizabeth Health Center,
Acute Rehabilitation Unit...................330.480.3999
Fax...330.480.3748
Web...............................www.hmpartners.org
E-mail...........................michael_kavic@hmis.org
1044 Belmont Avenue, Youngstown, OH 44501
Michael Kavic, Program Director
CARF accredited programs available.

LearningRx Learning Center..................330.668.9711
E-mail.......................bath.oh@learningrx.net
81 Springside Dr Ste A, Akron, OH 44333
Chris Schroeder, Director/Owner

Linking Employment, Abilities and Potential
(LEAP)..216.696.2716
Fax...216.687.1453
Web...................................www.leapinfo.org
E-mail...........................mhogan@leapinfo.org
2545 Main Ave, Cleveland, OH 44113-3102
Melanie Hogan, Executive Director

MDA/ALS Center at Ohio State University......614.293.4981
Fax...614.293.6111
E-mail.....................................kissel.2 @osu.edu
1580 Dodd Dr, Columbus, OH 43210
John T Kissel MD, Co-Director

MetroHealth Rehabilitation Institute of
Ohio..216.778.5516
Fax...216.778.7393
Web...................................www.metrohealth.org
2500 MetroHealth Drive, Cleveland, OH 44109
CARF accredited programs available.

Miami Valley Hospital - Rehabilitation Institute of
Ohio..937.208.8000
Fax...937.208.9137
Web...................................www.mvh.org
One Wyoming Street, Dayton, OH 45409
CARF accredited programs available.

NAMI Ohio....................................614.224.2700
E-mail...........................amiohio@amiohio.org
747 E Broad St, Columbus, OH 43205
Terry Russell, Director

National Multiple Sclerosis Society..........419.897.9533
Fax...419.897.9733
E-mail...........................NWOhio@amplex.net
401 Tomahawk Dr, Maumee, OH 43537
Maureen Mohney, Program Coordinator

National Multiple Sclerosis Society..........513.769.4400
Fax...513.769.6019
E-mail...........................Info@Ohg.nmss.org
4440 Lake Forest Dr Ste 120, Cincinnati, OH 45242

Nationwide Children's Hospital..............614.722.6500
Fax...614.722.4768
Web...................www.nationwidechildrens.org/rehab
700 Children's Drive, Columbus, OH 43205-2696
CARF accredited programs available.

OCECD-PTI Region 1.........................740.382.5452
Fax...740.383.6421
E-mail...................................ocecd@ocecd.org
165 W Center St Ste 302, Marion, OH 43302
Margaret Burley, Executive Director

Ohio Congress of Parents & Teachers.........614.781.6344
E-mail...................................office@ohiopta.org
40 Northwoods Blvd, Columbus, OH 43235
Sue Owen, Executive Director

Ohio Family and Children First..............614.752.4044
E-mail...................................info@ohiofcf.org
30 E Broad St 8th Fl, Columbus, OH 43215
Angela Sausser-Short, Director

Project Woman...............................937.328.5308
Fax...937.328.5324
Web...................................www.projectwomanohio.org
1316 East High Street, Springfield, OH 45505
COA accredited organization.

Speech-Language-Hearing Association.......800.866.6742
E-mail...................................oslhaoffice@donet.com
PO Box 309, Germantown, OH 45327

St. Rita's Medical Center - Rehab Unit.........419.227.3361
Fax...419.226.9705
Web...................................www.stritas.org
730 West Market Street, Lima, OH 45801
CARF accredited programs available.

The Arc of Ohio..............................614.487.4720
E-mail...................................arcohio@rrohio.com
1335 Dublin Rd Ste 205-C, Columbus, OH 43215

The Coghlin Rehabilitation Center at the University of Toledo
Medical Center..............................419.383.5040
Fax...419.383.3184
Web...................................www.utmc.utoledo.edu
3000 Arlington Avenue, Mail Stop #1100, Toledo,
OH 43614
Chasity O'neill, Director of Development, Office of Institutional A
CARF accredited programs available.

The Ohio State University Medical Center, Rehabilitation Services **614.293.4734**
Fax 614.293.3284
Web ....www.medicalcenter.osu.edu
  1228 Dodd Hall, 480 Medical Center Drive,
  Columbus, OH 43210
  CARF accredited programs available.

VSA Arts of Ohio **614.241.5325**
E-mail ....info@vsao.org
  77 S High St 2nd Fl, Columbus, OH 43215
  Erin Hoppe, Executive Director

SUBSTANCE ABUSE TREATMENT

Bassett House **740.594.8108**
Fax 740.593.3890
E-mail ....jpadget@hrs.org
  10050 Bassett Rd, Athens, OH 45701-3626
  John Padget, Phd, Director

Consolidated Care, Inc. **937.465.8065**
Fax 937.465.0442
Web ....www.ccibhp.com
E-mail ....shartley@ccibhp.com
  1521 North Detroit Street, West Liberty,
  OH 43357-9794
  Sarah Hartley, Director
  CARF accredited programs available.

Day-Mont Behavioral Health Care, Inc. **937.824.3306**
Fax 937.222.3019
Web ....www.daymont.org
  1520 Germantown Street, Dayton, OH 45408
  CARF accredited programs available.

Gateway Outreach Ctr **419.586.4030**
Fax 419.586.3268
Web ....www.gatewayoutreachcenter.org
  800 Pro Dr, Celina, OH 45822-1360
  Matthew Ronan, Clinical Director

Lake Area Recovery Ctr **440.998.0722**
Fax 440.992.1699
Web ....www.larc.cc
E-mail ....kkinney@larc.cc
  2801 Ct Unit 1, Ashtabula, OH 44004
  Kathleen Kinney, Director

Lake-Geauga Recovery Centers, Inc. **440.255.0678**
Fax 440.255.6348
Web ....www.lgrc.us
E-mail ....jmclaughlin@lgrc.us
  9083 Mentor Avenue, Mentor, OH 44060
  Janis Mclaughlin, Director
  CARF accredited programs available.

Lutheran Social Svcs **419.334.3431**
Fax 419.334.4230
Web ....www.lssnwo.org
  512 E State St, Fremont, OH 43420-4259
  Rebecca Serrick, Director

Marion Area Counseling Center Inc **740.387.5210**
Fax 740.383.3472
Web ....www.maccsite.com
E-mail ....byoung@maccsite.com
  320 Executive Dr, Marion, OH 43302
  Beverly Young, Executive Director
  CARF accredited programs available.

Mental Health Recovery Centers **513.261.6031**
Fax 513.695.2309
  100 Campus Loop Road, Suite A, Franklin, OH 45005
  CARF accredited programs available.

New Directions Inc Alcoholism Treatment **216.591.0324**
Fax 216.591.1243
Web ....www.newdirect.org
E-mail ....cmoore@newdirect.org
  30800 Chagrin Blvd, Cleveland, OH 44124-5927
  Mike Matoney, Executive Director

NKRC **330.609.5441**
Fax 330.609.5448
E-mail ....vmb@gatewayrehab.org
  160 Clifton Dr NE, Warren, OH 44484
  Vince Brancacio, Director

Nkrc Austintown **330.792.4724**
Fax 330.792.1848
Web ....www.nkrc.org
E-mail ....vmb@gatewayrehab.org
  5211 Mahoning Ave, # 307, Youngstown, OH 44515
  Vince Brancaccio, Mssa, Lisw, Program Director

North Central Mental Health Services, Inc. **614.299.6600**
Fax 614.421.3111
Web ....www.ncmhs.org
E-mail ....druck@ncmhs.org
  1301 North High Street, Columbus, OH 43201
  Don Wood, CEO
  CARF accredited programs available.

Pickaway Area Recovery Svcs **740.477.1745**
Fax 740.477.2779
E-mail ....pars@rrohio.com
  319 Logan St, Circleville, OH 43113-2213
  Barry Bennett, Executive Director

Recovery & Prevention Resources of Delaware and Morrow Counties, Inc. **740.369.6811**
Fax 740.363.8742
Web ....www.rprdm.org
E-mail ....janet.chandler@rprdm.org
  118 Stover Drive, Delaware, OH 43015-8601
  Janet Chandler, Associate Director
  CARF accredited programs available.

School of Medicine-Student Affairs **937.775.2934**
Fax 937.775.3322
Web ....www.med.wright.edu
E-mail ....gary.leroy@wright.edu
  190 White Hall, Dayton, OH 45401-1751
  Gary Leroy, Associate Dean For Student Affairs

Scioto Paint Valley Mental Health Center **740.775.1260**
Fax 740.775.1845
Web ....www.spvmhc.org
E-mail ....gkreuchauf@spvmhc.org
  4449 State Route 159, Second Floor, Chillicothe,
  OH 45601
  Gary Kreuchauf, Executive Director
  CARF accredited programs available.

Talbert House **513.751.7747**
Fax 513.751.8107
Web ....www.talberthouse.org
  2600 Victory Parkway, Floors 1, 3, and 4, Cincinnati,
  OH 45206
  Eloise Cobb-lakes, Director
  CARF accredited programs available.

The Counseling Center **330.424.9573**
Fax 330.424.7140
Web ....www.colmhc.org
E-mail ....rsikorszky@colmhc.org
  40722 State Route 154, Lisbon, OH 44432
  Roger Sikorszky, Executive Director
  CARF accredited programs available.

Oklahoma

Mary Fallin, Governor
2300 N. Lincoln Blvd.
Room 212
Oklahoma City, OK 73105
405.521.2342
405.521.3353 (Fax)
governor@gov.state.ok.us
www.gov.ok.gov

Anna Kelly, Juvenile Justice Specialist
Office of Juvenile Affairs
PO Box 268812
Oklahoma City, OK 73126-8812
405.530.2804
405.530.2913 (Fax)
anna.kelly@oja.ok.gov

John Selph, SAG Chair
Volunteers of America Oklahoma
9605 E 61st St
Tulsa, OK 74133
918.307.3030
918.307.1520 (Fax)
jselph@voaok.org

CRISIS NUMBERS

Child Abuse Reporting . . .800.522.3511

STATE SERVICES

SOCIAL SERVICES

Child Care Services Oklahoma 405.521.3561
Fax 405.522.2564
  2400 N Lincoln Blv POB 25352, Sequoyah Memorial
  Office Bldg, Oklahoma City, OK 73125
  Lesli Blazer, Director

Child Support Enforcement Div 405.522.5871
Fax 405.522.2753
Web ....www.childsupport.org
E-mail ....gary.dart@okdhs.org
  2409 N Kelley Ave, Oklahoma City, OK 73111
  Gary Dart, Director

Head Start Assoc 405.949.1495
Fax 405.949.0955
Web ....www.okacaa.org
E-mail ....kfloyd@okacaa.org
  2800 NW 36th St Ste 221, Oklahoma City,
  OK 73112-7468
  Kay C. Floyd, Ma, Director

Oklahoma Dept of Human Svcs 405.521.3777
Fax 405.521.4373
  Child Welfare Unit, Oklahoma City, OK 73105
  Deborah Smith, Director

GENERAL HEALTH SERVICES

Children w Spec Health Care Needs OK 405.521.3679
Fax 405.521.4158
E-mail ....hrms@okdhs.org
  PO Box 25352, Oklahoma City, OK 73125

Dept of Health 405.271.5600
Fax 405.271.3431
Web ....www.health.ok.gov
  1000 NE 10th St, Oklahoma City, OK 73117
  Terry Cline, Commissioner

Major Co. Health Dept 580.227.3362
Fax 580.227.2836
E-mail ....joyeg@health.ok.gov
  501 E Broadway, Fairview, OK 73737-2207
  Lanette Terry, Nursing Supervisor

Maternal and Child Health Srv OK 405.271.4480
Fax 405.271.2994
E-mail ....SuzannaD@health.ok.gov
  1000 NE 10th St Rm 809, Oklahoma City, OK 73117
  Suzanna Dooley, Chief

Oklahoma Heath Care Authority 405.522.7300
Web ....www.okhca.org
  2401 NW 23Rd St, Ste 1A, Oklahoma City, OK 73107
  Mike Fogarty, CEO

WIC Service 405.271.4676
Fax 405.271.5763
Web ....www.health.ok.gov
E-mail ....terryb@health.ok.gov
  2401 NW 23rd St, Ste 70, Oklahoma City,
  OK 73107-2475
  Terry Bryce, Interim State Director

MENTAL HEALTH SERVICES

Dept of Rehabilitation Svcs 405.951.3400
Fax 405.951.3529
Web ....www.okdrs.gov
E-mail ....mobrian@okdrs.gov
  3535 NW 58th St Ste 500, Oklahoma City,
  OK 73112-4824
  Michael O'Brian, Director

Developmental Disabilities Div 405.521.6267
Fax 405.522.3037
Web ....www.okdhs.org
E-mail ....james.nicholson@okdhs.org
  2400 N Lincoln Blvd, Oklahoma City, OK 73105
  Jim Nicholson, Director

Oklahoma Dept of Rehabilitation Svcs 405.951.3400
Fax 405.951.3529
E-mail ....jharlan@okdrs.gov
  3535 NW 58th St Ste 500, Oklahoma City, OK 73112
  J Harlan, Director

JUSTICE AGENCY

Attorney General's Ofc 405.521.3921
Fax 405.522.4535
Web ....www.oag.state.ok.us
  313 NE 21st St, Oklahoma City, OK 73105-3207
  Drew Edmondson, Attorney General

Commission on Children & Youth 405.606.4900
Fax 405.524.0417
Web ....www.okkids.org
  1111 N Lee Ave, Ste 500, Oklahoma City, OK 73103
  Lisa Smith, Director

Correctional Educ Division OK 405.962.6106
Fax 405.962.6171
E-mail ....pam.humphrey@doc.state.ok.us
  2901 N Classen Ste 200, Oklahoma City, OK 73106
  Pam Humphrey, Director

Crime Victims Compensation Board 405.264.5006
Fax 405.264.5097
E-mail ....victimservices@dac.state.ok.us
  421 NW 13th St Ste 290, Oklahoma City, OK 73103
  Suzanne Breedlove, Director Victim Services

Dept of Corrections 405.425.2500
Fax 405.425.2578
Web ....www.doc.state.ok.us
E-mail ....leslie.robinson@doc.state.ok.us
  3400 N Martin Luther King Ave, Oklahoma City,
  OK 73111
  Justin Jones, Director

Dept of Public Safety 405.425.2424
Fax 405.425.2600
Web ....www.dps.state.ok.us
E-mail ....comment@dps.state.ok.us
  3600 N Martin Luther King Ave, Oklahoma City,
  OK 73111-4200
  Clint Dickson, Administrator Of Department Services

Juvenile Svcs Divison 405.530.2800
Fax 405.530.2892
Web ....www.oja.ok.gov
E-mail ....len.morris@oja.ok.gov
  3812 N Santa Fe Ave Ste 400, Oklahoma City,
  OK 73118-8500
  Robert E. Gene Christian, Executive Director

Juvenile Svcs Unit 405.713.6700
Fax 405.713.6733
Web ....www.oja.ok.gov
  5905 N Classen Ct Ste 301, Oklahoma City,
  OK 73118
  James Eakins, Juvenile Services Supervisor

Oklahoma CASA Assoc 405.524.8999
Fax 405.524.7222
Web ....www.oklahomacasa.org
E-mail ....casa@oklahomacasa.org
  3813 N. Santa Fe Ave., Suite 202, Oklahoma City,
  OK 73154
  Sheryl Marseilles, Executive Director

Oklahoma Emergency Management Agency ...405.521.2481
Fax 405.521.4053
Web ....www.oem.ok.gov
  2401 N Lincoln Blvd, Will Rogers Sequoia Tunnel,
  Oklahoma City, OK 73105
  Albert Ashwood, Director

COURTS

Administrative Ofc Of The Courts 405.521.2450
Fax 405.521.6815
  1915 N Stiles Ave Ste 305, Oklahoma City, OK 73105
  Michael Evans, Administrator

District Court, 3rd Judicial District 580.688.3617
Fax 580.688.2900
E-mail ....mike.warren@oscn.net
  114 W Hollis St Rm 3-1, Hollis, OK 73550-3053
  Honorable Winford Mike Warren, Judge

Oklahoma

POLICE AND SHERIFF

Sheriff's Ofc **580.625.4549**
Fax 580.625.4261
E-mail .... bvrso@ptsi.net
215 Avenue E, Beaver, OK 73932
Reuben Parker Jr., Sheriff

EDUCATION SERVICES

Dept of Education **405.521.3301**
Fax 405.521.6205
Web .... www.sde.state.ok.us
2500 N Lincoln Blvd Rm 121, Oklahoma City,
OK 73105-4503
Janet Barresi, State Suprindentant

Educ for Homeless Children and Youth OK **405.521.2846**
Fax 405.521.6205
E-mail .... erin_clapper@sde.state.ok.us
2500 N Lincoln Blvd, Oliver Hodge Memorial Educ
Bld, Oklahoma City, OK 73105

okhlahoma School for the Blind **918.781.8200**
Fax 918.781.8300
Web www.osb.k12.ok.us
E-mail .... csheppard@osb.k12.ok.us
3300 Gibson St, Muskogee, OK 74403-2849
Carolyn Sheppard, Principal

Oklahoma School for the Deaf **580.622.4900**
Fax 580.622.4959
E-mail .... lhawkins@osd.k12.ok.us
1100 E Oklahoma Ave, Sulphur, OK 73086
Larry Hawkins, Superintendent

Oklahoma State Dept of Education **405.521.3301**
Fax 405.521.6205
2500 N Lincoln Blvd, Oklahoma City, OK 73105
Janet Barresi, Superintendent

Special Education Svcs OK **405.521.3351**
Fax 405.522.2066
E-mail .... misty_kimbrough@sde.state.ok.us
2500 N Lincoln Blvd Rm 412, Oklahoma City,
OK 73105
Misty Kimbrough, Assistant Superintendant

LABOR & WORKFORCE EDUCATION

Employment and Training Div **405.557.7100**
Fax 405.557.7256
Web .... www.oesc.state.ok.us
E-mail .... glen.robards@oesc.state.ok.us
2401 N Lincoln Ave, Oklahoma City, OK 73160-8933
John Brock, Director

COUNTY SERVICES

Adair County

SOCIAL SERVICES

Child Welfare Svcs **918.696.3118**
Fax 918.696.7759
Section Line Rd. Route 1, Stilwell, OK 74960
Bob Ryals, Intake Supervisor

Dept Of Human Svcs **918.696.7736**
Fax 918.696.5419
Section Line Rd RR 1, Stilwell, OK 74960
Joan Clay, Director

GENERAL HEALTH SERVICES

Health Dept **918.696.7292**
Fax 918.696.5360
600 W Hickory St, Stilwell, OK 74960-3622
Marybeth Marie, Administrative Director

JUSTICE AGENCY

Juvenile Svcs Unit **918.696.3116**
Fax 918.696.6606
E-mail .... jack.roberts@oja.ok.gov
Section Line Rd, Stilwell, OK 74960
Jack Roberts, Intake Prob. Officer

COURTS

15th District Court **918.696.7633**
Fax 918.696.5365
220 W Division St Ste 201, Stilwell, OK 74960
Paula Sam Mccarter, Clerk Of Court

POLICE AND SHERIFF

Sheriff's Ofc **918.696.2106**
Fax 918.696.3477
600 Paul Mead Rd, Stilwell, OK 74960
Austin Young, Sheriff

Alfalfa County

SOCIAL SERVICES

Dept Of Human Svcs **580.596.3335**
Fax 580.596.2414
Web .... www.okdhs.org
E-mail .... karen.tucker@okdhs.org
101 S Grand Ave, Cherokee, OK 73728
Karen Tucker, Director

COURTS

4th District Court **580.596.2224**
Fax 580.596.2556
Web .... www.okstate.edu
E-mail .... loren.angle@okstate.edu
300 S Grand Ave Ste 10, Cherokee, OK 73728-2548
Honorable Loren E. Angle, Director

POLICE AND SHERIFF

Sheriff's Ofc **580.596.3269**
Fax 580.596.2254
E-mail .... alssoco@att.net
300 S Grand Ave Ste 3, Cherokee, OK 73728-2548
Charles Tucker, Sheriff

Atoka County

SOCIAL SERVICES

Oklahoma Dept of Huamn Services **580.889.3394**
Fax 580.889.3451
401 North Greathouse Dr, Atoka, OK 74525

GENERAL HEALTH SERVICES

Health Dept **580.889.2116**
Fax 580.889.7698
Web .... www.health.ok.gov
E-mail .... nadinew@health.ok.gov
1006 W 13th St, Atoka, OK 74525-3435
Nadine Witt, Nursing Supervisor

COURTS

25th District Court **580.889.3565**
E-mail .... rick.branam@oscn.net
200 E Court St Ste 210E, Atoka, OK 74525
Honorable Richard E. Branam, Judge

EDUCATION SERVICES

Caney Head Start **580.889.6758**
402 N. Perkins, Caney, OK 74533
Melissa Smith, Teacher

Choctaw Nation Head Start **580.889.7054**
Fax 580.889.7054
E-mail .... azurline@choctawnation.com
711 Greathouse Dr., Atoka, OK 74525
Anita Zurline, Director

Beaver County

SOCIAL SERVICES

Oklahoma Dept of Human Services **580.625.3441**
Fax 580.625.4921
111 West 2nd St, Beaver, OK 73932

GENERAL HEALTH SERVICES

Health Dept **580.625.3693**
Fax 580.625.3680
Web .... www.health.ok.gov
E-mail .... terri@health.ok.gov
Highway 270 S, Beaver, OK 73932
Terri Salisbury, Administrator

COURTS

1st District Court **580.625.3191**
111 W 2nd St, Beaver, OK 73932
Sharon Raven, Clerk

Beckham County

SOCIAL SERVICES

Dept Of Human Svcs **580.928.4000**
Fax 580.928.4080
312 E Madden Ave, Sayre, OK 73662
Craig Mahl, County Director

GENERAL HEALTH SERVICES

Health Dept **580.225.1173**
Fax 580.225.7612
Web .... www.ok.gov/health
E-mail .... joemi@health.ok.gov
400 E 3rd St, Elk City, OK 73644-4720
Jo Miller, Rn, Public Health Nurse

Health Dept **580.928.5551**
Fax 580.928.9279
115 S 4th St, Sayre, OK 73662-2924
Karen Weaver, Administrative Director

COURTS

District Court **580.928.3330**
Fax 580.928.9278
E-mail .... michelle.roper@oscn.net
302 E. Main St, Sayre, OK 73662
Honorable Michelle Kirby Roper, Associate District Judge

Teen Court **580.225.6247**
Fax 580.225.3234
321 W 5th St, Elk City, OK 73648
Cheryl Mingle, Director

POLICE AND SHERIFF

Sheriff's Ofc **580.928.2121**
Fax 580.928.2262
E-mail .... sheriffjay@hotmail.com
108 S 3rd St, Sayre, OK 73662-3001
Scott L. Jay, Sheriff

EDUCATION SERVICES

Elk City Head Start **580.225.4103**
Fax 580.225.4103
Web .... www.acf.hhs.gov
1700 W 8th St, Elk City, OK 73644-6151
Mary Garcia, Director

Blaine County

SOCIAL SERVICES

Dept Of Human Svcs **580.623.2000**
Fax 580.623.2064
　410 W Main St, Watonga, OK 73772-4297
　Steve Torres, Director

GENERAL HEALTH SERVICES

Health Dept **580.623.7977**
Fax 580.623.7980
　521 W 4th St, Watonga, OK 73772-2853
　Jay Smith, Administrative Director

COURTS

4th District Court **580.623.5970**
Fax 580.623.4781
E-mail ....mmoore@dasnr.okstate.edu
　212 N Weigle Ave, Watonga, OK 73772
　Cynthia Scheffer, Court Clerk

POLICE AND SHERIFF

Sheriff's Ofc **580.623.5111**
Fax 580.623.7221
Web ....www.pldi.net
E-mail ....blaineso@pldi.net
　205 N Burford Ave, Watonga, OK 73772-3828
　Ricky G. Ainsworth, Sheriff

EDUCATION SERVICES

Cheyene Arapaho Head Start **580.886.2817**
Fax 580.886.2829
　73724 Canton Cntn Lake, Canton, OK 73724
　Shelene Washington, Director

Bryan County

SOCIAL SERVICES

Dept Of Human Svcs **580.931.2500**
Fax 580.931.2599
　4302 Highway 70W, Durant, OK 74702
　Rita Hart, County Director

GENERAL HEALTH SERVICES

Health Dept **580.924.4299**
Fax 580.924.1651
E-mail ....jtettle@health.ok.gov
　1524 Chuckwa Dr, Durant, OK 74702
　Jenny Tettle, Nursing Supervisor

JUSTICE AGENCY

Juvenile Svcs Unit **580.924.8432**
Fax 580.931.0217
　405 W Main St, Durant, OK 74701
　Cassie Stafford, Supervisor

COURTS

19Th District Court **580.924.1446**
Fax 580.931.0577
　402 W Evergreen St Fl 3, Durant, OK 74701
　Mark Campbell, Judge

POLICE AND SHERIFF

Sheriff's Dept **580.924.3000**
Fax 580.924.0259
　402 W Evergreen St Ste A1, Durant, OK 74701
　Bill Sturch, Sheriff

EDUCATION SERVICES

Big Five Head Start I & II **580.924.4907**
　PO Box 1577, Durant, OK 74702-1577

Choctaw Nation Head Start **580.847.2767**
Fax 580.847.2058
　820 N Perry St, Bennington, OK 74723-0010
　Betty Trammell, Director

Caddo County

SOCIAL SERVICES

**Indian Child Welfare Southern Plains Regional
Ofc** **405.247.1608**
Fax 405.247.2895
　PO Box 368, Anadarko, OK 73005-0368
　Sallie Allen, Acting Regional Social Worker

**Indian Social Svcs Kiowa Tribe Of
OK** **580.654.2300**
Fax 580.654.2406
Web ....www.kiowatribe.net
E-mail ....cory_z_kiowa@yahoo.com
　PO Box 369, Carnegie, OK 73015-0369
　Walter Ahhaitty, Director

GENERAL HEALTH SERVICES

Bia Southern Plains Regional Ofc **405.247.6673**
Fax 405.247.2242
　1 Mile North of City, Hwy 281, Anadarko, OK 73005
　Dan Deerinwater, Regional Director

Health Dept **405.247.2507**
Fax 405.247.9503
Web ....www.health.state.ok.us/chds/caddo
　216 W Broadway St, Anadarko, OK 73005
　Keith Reede, Administrative Director

JUSTICE AGENCY

Juvenile Svcs Unit **405.247.2501**
Fax 405.247.2443
Web ....oja.state.ok.us
　105 E Oklahoma St, Anadarko, OK 73005
　Billy Brown, Social Service Supervisor

COURTS

6th District Court **405.247.3393**
Fax 405.247.4127
　201 W Oklahoma Avenue, Anadarko, OK 73005
　Honorable S. Wyatt Hill, Associate Court Judge

POLICE AND SHERIFF

Sheriff's Ofc **405.247.6666**
Fax 405.247.5559
E-mail ....gene.cain@anadarko.org
　201 W Oklahoma Ave, Anadarko, OK 73005
　Gene H. Cain, Sheriff

Canadian County

SOCIAL SERVICES

**Cheyenne-Arapaho Tribes Social
Svcs** **405.262.0345**
Fax 405.422.3167
Web ....www.c-a-tribes.org
　PO Box 38, Concho, OK 73022-0038
　Adrian Prairiechief, Director

Dept Of Human Svcs **405.295.2700**
Fax 405.295.2727
　314 W Rogers St, El Reno, OK 73036
　Cheryl Thornton, Director

Indian Child Welfare **405.422.7539**
Fax 405.422.3167
　100 Redmoon Cir, Concho, OK 73022-0038
　Mary Davenport, Director Of Social Services

GENERAL HEALTH SERVICES

Health Dept **405.354.4872**
Fax 405.354.5623
Web ....www.health.state.ok.us/chds/canadian
E-mail ....jays@health.ok.gov
　1023 E Vandament Ave, Yukon, OK 73099-4949
　Jay Smith, Administrative Director

JUSTICE AGENCY

Children's Justice Center **405.262.0202**
Fax 405.262.0259
Web ....www.canadiancokids.com
　7905 East Highway 66, El Reno, OK 73036
　CARF accredited programs available.

Juvenile Svcs Unit **405.262.9220**
Fax 405.262.0039
　7905 E US Highway 66, El Reno, OK 73036-9225
　Belinda Hannon, Supervisor

COURTS

26Th District Court **405.262.1070**
Fax 405.422.2411
Web ....www.canadiancounty.org
　301 N Choctaw Ave Ste 9, El Reno, OK 73036-2468
　Gary Miller, District Judge

POLICE AND SHERIFF

Sheriff's Ofc **405.262.3434**
Fax 405.422.2430
Web ....www.ccsheriff.net
　208 W Rogers St, El Reno, OK 73036-2459
　Randell Edwards, Sheriff

Carter County

SOCIAL SERVICES

Child Welfare Svcs **580.490.6060**
Fax 580.490.6088
E-mail ....regina.benson@okdhs.org
　925 W Broadway St, Annex Building, Ardmore,
　OK 73401-4567
　Regina Benson, Child Welfare Supervisor

GENERAL HEALTH SERVICES

Health Dept **580.223.9705**
Fax 580.223.8736
Web ....www.health.ok.gov
　405 S Washington St, Ardmore, OK 73401-7044
　Caroline Jones, Hiv Coordinator

JUSTICE AGENCY

CASA **580.226.0009**
Fax 580.226.0099
Web ....www.brightok.net
E-mail ....casa_child@yahoo.com
　20 B St SW Ste 401, Ardmore, OK 73401-6415
　Lynn Riley, Director

COURTS

20th District Court **580.223.5253**
Web ....www.odcr.com
E-mail ....karen.bolino@oscn.net
　20 B St SW Ste 203, Ardmore, OK 73401
　Karen Bolino, Clerk Of Court

POLICE AND SHERIFF

Sheriff's Dept **580.223.6014**
Fax 580.221.5528
　100 S Washington St, Ardmore, OK 73401
　Ken Grace, Sheriff

EDUCATION SERVICES

Fox Head Start **580.673.2206**
　Fox Public School, Fox, OK 73435
　Jennifer Ruth, Director

Cherokee County

SOCIAL SERVICES

Dept Of Human Svcs **918.207.4500**
Fax 918.207.4630
Web ....www.okdhs.org
　1298 West 4th Street, Tahlequah, OK 74464-5034
　Steven Edwards, County Director

GENERAL HEALTH SERVICES

Health Dept **918.456.8826**
Fax 918.458.6533
912 S College Ave, Tahlequah, OK 74464-4705
Kelli Rader, Rn, Nursing Supervisor

JUSTICE AGENCY

CASA Of Cherokee Country **918.456.8788**
Fax 918.456.6041
E-mail ....cccncasa@sbcglobal.net
304 W Keetoowah St, Tahlequah, OK 74464-3824
Jo Prout, Executive Director

COURTS

15th District Court **918.456.0691**
Fax 918.458.6587
E-mail ....mark.dobbins@oscn.net
213 W Delaware St Ste 302, Tahlequah,
OK 74464-3601
Honorable Mark Dobbins, Associate District Judge

POLICE AND SHERIFF

Sheriff's Ofc **918.456.2583**
Fax 918.458.6594
213 W Delaware St Ste 201, Tahlequah,
OK 74464-3600
Norman Fisher, Sheriff

Choctaw County

SOCIAL SERVICES

Dept Of Human Svcs **580.317.2900**
Fax 580.317.2964
2565 E 2070 Rd, Hugo, OK 74743
Freda House, County Director

GENERAL HEALTH SERVICES

Health Dept **580.326.8821**
Fax 580.326.8823
Web ....www.health.ok.gov
103 S 4th St, Hugo, OK 74743
June Matlock, Coordinating Nurse

COURTS

17th District Court **580.326.3384**
Fax 580.326.7415
300 E Duke St Ste 9, Hugo, OK 74743
Honorable James R. Woolfe, Judge

POLICE AND SHERIFF

Sheriff's Ofc **580.326.5600**
Fax 580.326.7683
305 E Jefferson St, Hugo, OK 74743-4405
Lewis E. Collins, Sheriff

EDUCATION SERVICES

Ft Towson Head Start Ctr **580.873.2259**
Fax 580.873.9285
E-mail ....forttownsonheadstart@yahoo.com
Hwy 70 Cemtary Rd, Fort Towson, OK 74735
Carolyn Hampton, Director

Cimarron County

SOCIAL SERVICES

Dept Of Human Svcs **580.544.2512**
Fax 580.544.2707
Web ....www.okdhs.org
E-mail ....alejo.pena@okdhs.org
1 Courthouse Square, Boise City, OK 73933
Alejo Pena, County Director

COURTS

1st District Court **580.544.2221**
Fax 580.544.2006
1 Courthouse Sq, Boise City, OK 73933
Priscilla Johnson, Court Clerk

POLICE AND SHERIFF

Sheriff's Ofc **580.544.2020**
Fax 580.544.2494
1 Courthouse Square, Boise City, OK 73933
Keith Borth, Sheriff

EDUCATION SERVICES

Boise City Head Start **580.544.2230**
Fax 580.544.2913
1104 N Logan, Boise City, OK 73933
Latonia Cayton, Director

Cleveland County

SOCIAL SERVICES

Child Welfare Svcs **405.573.8300**
Fax 405.573.8460
E-mail ....pam.sadler@ok.org
631 E Robinson St, Norman, OK 73071
Pam Sadler, Assistant County Director

Dept Of Human Svcs **405.912.2000**
Fax 405.912.2041
Web ....www.okdhs.org
E-mail ....sue.durrett@okdhs.org
2507 N Shields Blvd, Oklahoma City,
OK 73160-3305
Karen Blaiser, Director

GENERAL HEALTH SERVICES

Health Dept **405.321.4048**
Fax 405.329.1273
Web ....www.health.state.ok.ou/chds/cleveland
250 12th Ave NE, Norman, OK 73071
Shari Kinney, Administrative Director

Health Dept **405.794.1591**
Fax 405.794.2385
Web ....www.health.ok.gov
E-mail ....junew@health.ok.gov
424 S Eastern Ave, Oklahoma City, OK 73160-5223
June Wagner, Nursing Supervisor

JUSTICE AGENCY

CASA **405.360.5295**
Fax 405.360.7014
E-mail ....clevcocasa@aol.com
1650 W Tecumseh Rd Ste 400, Norman, OK 73069
Kathleen Romero, Executive Director

Juvenile Svcs **405.360.4310**
Fax 405.579.7408
1650 W Tecumseh Rd Ste 300, Norman,
OK 73069-8269
Lisa Madewell, Juvenile Justice Supervisor

Moore Alcohol And Drug Ctr, Inc **405.799.3379**
Fax 405.799.0917
Web ....www.coxinet.net
E-mail ....lisawilliams@coxinet.net
624 NW 5th St, Moore, OK 73160-3924
Walt Hedrick, Director

COURTS

21st District Court **405.321.6402**
Fax 405.366.0287
Web ....www.oscn.net
E-mail ....tom.lucas@oscn.net
200 S Peters Ave Rm 10, Norman, OK 73069-6070
Honorable Tom Lucas, Director

POLICE AND SHERIFF

Sheriff's Dept **405.321.8600**
Fax 405.366.5705
E-mail ....dbeggs@okclev.cogov.net
203 S Jones Ave, Norman, OK 73069
Joe Wester, Sheriff

EDUCATION SERVICES

Csbi Head Start /Early Head Start **405.701.2141**
Fax 405.701.2112
1111 E Main St, Norman, OK 73071
Angie Nuanally, Director Early Head Start

Moore Head Start **405.912.9993**
Fax 405.912.2366
312 N Janeway Ave, Oklahoma City, OK 73160-3918

Coal County

SOCIAL SERVICES

Dept Of Human Svcs **580.927.2379**
Fax 580.927.2342
Web ....www.okdhs.org
E-mail ....alice.curry@okdhs.org
1 N Main St, Coalgate, OK 74538-2832
Alice Curry, Director

GENERAL HEALTH SERVICES

Health Dept **580.927.2367**
Fax 580.927.3037
Web ....www.dcs.state.ok.gov
1404 S Highway 75, Coalgate, OK 74538
Tammy Gearhart, Nursing Supervisor

COURTS

25th District Court **580.927.2281**
Fax 580.927.2339
4 N Main St Ste 9, Coalgate, OK 74538
Honorable Richard E. Branam, District Judge

POLICE AND SHERIFF

Sheriff's Dept **580.927.3227**
Fax 580.927.2438
4 N Main St Ste 8, Coalgate, OK 74538
Roy Deck, Sheriff

EDUCATION SERVICES

Coalgate Head Start **580.927.3446**
Web ....www.seniorcorps.org
210 N Main St, Coalgate, OK 74538
Mary Eddings, Teacher

Comanche County

SOCIAL SERVICES

**Comanche Tribe Of Oklahoma Social
Svcs** **580.492.3794**
Fax 580.492.3742
584 Nw Bingo Rd Hc 32, Elgin, OK 73507
Sandra Mithlo, Director

GENERAL HEALTH SERVICES

Health Dept **580.248.5890**
Fax 580.585.6621
1010 S Sheridan, Lawton, OK 73505
Keith Reed, Administrator

JUSTICE AGENCY

Juvenile Svcs Unit **580.355.7277**
Fax 580.357.5719
1715 SW 11th St Ste 2, Lawton, OK 73501-7338
Greg Delaney, District Supervisor

COURTS

**District Court 5th Judicial District Juvenile
Div** **580.357.4881**
Fax 580.355.0306
315 SW 5th St Rm 200, Lawton, OK 73501-4326
Rick Lowe, Director

POLICE AND SHERIFF

Sheriff's Ofc **580.353.4280**
Fax 580.585.5327
E-mail ....comcosher@yahoo.com
315 SW 5th St Rm 102, Lawton, OK 73501
Kenny Stradley, Sheriff

EDUCATION SERVICES

First Start **580.355.4333**
Fax 580.355.4366
　　2003 NW Lincoln Ave, Lawton, OK 73507

Cotton County

SOCIAL SERVICES

Oklahoma Dept of Human Services **580.875.4000**
Fax 580.875.4048
E-mail .... jeff.zachary@okdhs.org
　　1501 South 7th St, Walters, OK 73572

GENERAL HEALTH SERVICES

Health Dept **580.875.6121**
Fax 580.875.6128
Web .... www.health.ok.gov
E-mail .... keithr@health.ok.gov
　　1501A S 7th St, Walters, OK 73572-2463
　　Keith Read, Administrator/director

JUSTICE AGENCY

Juvenile Svcs Unit **580.875.3286**
Fax 580.875.3426
　　301 N Broadway St Rm 3, Walters, OK 73572-1271
　　Gene Christen, Director

COURTS

5th District Court **580.875.3137**
Fax 580.875.2288
Web .... www.okbar.org
E-mail .... michaelf@okbar.org
　　301 N Broadway St Rm 3, Walters, OK 73572-1271
　　Honorable Michael C. Flanagan, Judge

POLICE AND SHERIFF

Sheriff's Ofc **580.875.3383**
Fax 580.875.3888
　　301 N Broadway St Rm 10, Walters, OK 73572-1271
　　Paul Jeffrey, Sheriff

Craig County

SOCIAL SERVICES

Dept Of Human Svcs **918.713.5000**
Fax 918.713.5080
E-mail .... samuel.westfall@okdhs.org
　　310 N Wilson St, Vinita, OK 74301
　　Sam Westfall, Director

GENERAL HEALTH SERVICES

Health Dept **918.256.7531**
Fax 918.256.3823
Web .... www.health.ok.gov
　　115 E Delaware Ave, Vinita, OK 74301-4204
　　William Pierson, Administrative Director

Creek County

SOCIAL SERVICES

Dept Of Human Svcs **918.746.3300**
Fax 918.746.3397
Web .... www.ohfa.org
E-mail .... toy.obrien@ohfa.org
　　17 S Elm St, Sapulpa, OK 74066-4207
　　Toy O'Brien, Director

JUSTICE AGENCY

Juvenile Svcs Unit **918.224.9011**
Fax 918.224.5986
E-mail .... john.metcalfe@oja.ok.gov
　　10 S Water St, Sapulpa, OK 74066-4232
　　John Metcalfe, Supervisor

COURTS

24th District Court **918.227.2525**
Fax 918.227.5030
　　222 E Dewey Ave Ste 201, Sapulpa, OK 74066-4237
　　Amanda Vanorsdol, Court Clerk

POLICE AND SHERIFF

Sheriff's Dept **918.224.4964**
Fax 918.227.6324
Web .... www.creekcountysheriff.com
E-mail .... stevetoliver@aol.com
　　316 E Lee, Sapulpa, OK 74067
　　Steve Toliver, Sheriff

Custer County

SOCIAL SERVICES

Dept Of Human Svcs **580.331.1900**
Fax 580.331.1966
　　190 S 31st St, Clinton, OK 73601
　　Sherwana Gathers, Director

GENERAL HEALTH SERVICES

Clinton Health Ctr **580.323.2884**
Fax 580.323.2579
　　2501 NE Route 66, Clinton, OK 73601
　　Pedro Lopez, Clinical Director

Health Dept **580.323.2100**
Fax 580.323.2282
E-mail .... nicholsm@health.state.ok.us
　　3030 Custer Ave, Clinton, OK 72601
　　Marcia Nichols, Rn, Nursing Supervisor

JUSTICE AGENCY

Juvenile Svcs Unit **580.323.4331**
Fax 580.323.5934
　　422 Avant Ave, Clinton, OK 73601
　　Jerry Skinner, Juvenile Justice Specialist Iv

COURTS

2nd District Court **580.323.3233**
Fax 580.331.1121
　　675 B St, Arapaho, OK 73620
　　Jill Weedon, Judge

POLICE AND SHERIFF

Sheriff's Ofc **580.323.1616**
Fax 580.323.6262
　　603 B St, Arapaho, OK 73620
　　Bruce Peoples, Sheriff

Delaware County

SOCIAL SERVICES

Dept Of Human Svcs **918.253.4213**
Fax 918.253.6534
　　Highway 59 S, Jay, OK 74346
　　Susan Gillilend, Director

GENERAL HEALTH SERVICES

Health Dept **918.253.4511**
Fax 918.253.8419
Web .... www.health.ok.gov
　　Hwy 59 West, Jay, OK 74346
　　Jane Ann Nichols, Administrative Director

JUSTICE AGENCY

Juvenile Svcs Unit **918.253.8920**
Fax 918.253.6346
　　1431 N main St, Jay, OK 74346
　　John Depoe, Assistant District Supervisor

COURTS

13th District Court **918.253.4420**
Fax 918.253.5739
　　327 N 5th St, Jay, OK 74346
　　Caroline Weaver, Clerk Of Court

POLICE AND SHERIFF

Sheriff's Ofc **918.253.4531**
Fax 918.253.4594
　　327 South 5th, Jay, OK 74346
　　Jay Blackfox, Sheriff

EDUCATION SERVICES

Colcord Head Start **918.326.4139**
Fax 918.326.4139
Web .... www.neocaa.org
E-mail .... dspillman@neocaa.org
　　100 Spencer Street, Colcord, OK 74338
　　Dug Spillman, Director

Dewey County

SOCIAL SERVICES

Oklahoma Dept of Human Services **580.328.5546**
Fax 580.328.5524
　　Broadway and Ruble St, Taloga, OK 73667

COURTS

4th District Court **580.328.5521**
Fax 580.328.5658
E-mail .... rick.bozarth@oscn.net
　　105 S Broadway, Taloga, OK 73667
　　Honorable Rick Bozarth, Director

POLICE AND SHERIFF

Sheriff's Dept **580.328.5558**
Fax 580.328.5559
E-mail .... clay_sander@hotmail.com
　　Broadway & Ruble Sts, Taloga, OK 73667
　　L Clay Sander, Sheriff

Ellis County

SOCIAL SERVICES

Dept Of Human Svcs **580.885.7546**
Fax 580.885.7490
E-mail .... linda.semmel@okdhs.org
　　103 N Washington, Arnett, OK 73832
　　Linda Semmel, County Director

COURTS

2nd Judicial District Court **580.885.7255**
Fax 580.885.7506
E-mail .... dona.fox@oscn.net
　　100 S Washington, Arnett, OK 73832
　　Honorable Joe L. Jackson, Judge

POLICE AND SHERIFF

Sheriff's Ofc **580.885.7377**
Fax 580.885.7647
　　100 S Washington St, Arnett, OK 73832
　　Dewayne Miller, Sheriff

Garfield County

SOCIAL SERVICES

Dept Of Human Svcs **580.548.2100**
Fax 580.548.2199
　　2405 Mercer Dr, Enid, OK 73702
　　Marie Holsten, Director

JUSTICE AGENCY

Enid Adventure Program **580.234.0002**
Fax 580.233.7251
Web .... www.okcc.state.ok.us
E-mail .... toddc@okcc.state.ok.us
　　3601 E Randolph Ave, Enid, OK 73701-9412
　　Todd Chambers, Director/Supervisor

Juvenile Svcs Unit **580.242.3452**
Fax 580.233.0659
　　601 S Harding St Ste C, Enid, OK 73703-6323
　　Rhonda Smith, Juvenile Supervisor

Oklahoma

COURTS

4th District Court **580.237.0232**
Fax 580.249.5951
Web .... www.oscn.net
   114 W Broadway Ave Ste 301, Enid, OK 73701-4024
   Honorable Norman Grey, Judge

POLICE AND SHERIFF

Sheriff's Ofc **580.237.0244**
Fax 580.237.0256
E-mail .... garfield_county@yahoo.com
   114 W Broadway Enid, Enid, OK 73702
   Bill Winchester, Sheriff

EDUCATION SERVICES

Enid Head Start **580.234.5740**
   815 S 5th St, Enid, OK 73701-7537
   Becky Hutson, Director

Enid Wilson Head Start **580.234.6170**
Fax 580.234.8566
Web .... www.oppertunity-einc.org
E-mail .... gwilliam@oppertunity-einc.org
   740 N 10th St, Enid, OK 73701-3431
   Gwen Williams, Director

Garvin County

SOCIAL SERVICES

Dept Of Human Svcs **405.238.6461**
Fax 405.238.9554
   1304 S Chickasaw, Pauls Valley, OK 73075
   Pat Bain, County Director

GENERAL HEALTH SERVICES

Health Dept **405.238.7346**
Fax 405.238.1134
   1809 S Chickasaw St, Pauls Valley, OK 73075
   Lori Fisher, Admintrative Assistant

JUSTICE AGENCY

Juvenile Svcs Unit **405.238.5547**
Fax 405.238.3231
E-mail .... dotti.willis@oja.ok.gov
   119 W Paul, Pauls Valley, OK 73075
   Dotti Willis, Juvenile Justice Specialist

COURTS

21st District Court **405.238.5596**
Fax 405.238.1138
   201 W Grant Ave Rm 3, Pauls Valley, OK 73075
   Honorable John A. Blake, Associate Judge

POLICE AND SHERIFF

Sheriff's Ofc **405.238.7591**
Fax 405.238.3224
Web .... www.garvincountysheriff.net
E-mail .... larryrhodes@garvincountysheriff.com
   201 W Grant Ave Rm 4, Pauls Valley, OK 73075-3234
   Larry Rhodes, Sheriff

Grady County

SOCIAL SERVICES

Dept Of Human Svcs **405.574.7400**
Fax 405.574.7544
E-mail .... calvin.kelley@okdhs.org
   1707 Frisco Ave, Chickasha, OK 73018
   Calvin Kelley, County Director

GENERAL HEALTH SERVICES

Health Dept **405.224.2022**
Fax 405.224.4877
   2116 W Iowa Ave, Chickasha, OK 73018
   Mike Milton, Administrative Director

COURTS

6th District Court **405.224.5314**
Fax 405.224.3012
   326 W Choctaw Ave, Chickasha, OK 73018
   Honorable John E. Herndon, District Judge

POLICE AND SHERIFF

Sheriff's Ofc **405.222.1000**
Fax 405.222.5044
Web .... www.gradycosheriff.com
E-mail .... artkell@gradycosheriff.com
   215 N 3rd St, Chickasha, OK 73018
   Art Kell, Sheriff

EDUCATION SERVICES

Chickasha Headstart **405.224.5831**
Fax 405.222.4303
   1301 S 7TH ST, Chickasha, OK 73018-4454
   Rebecca Donnovan, Director

Grant County

SOCIAL SERVICES

Dept Of Human Svcs **580.395.3312**
Fax 580.395.2815
E-mail .... marie.holsten@okdhs.org
   112 E Guthrie St Ste 303, Medford, OK 73759
   Marie Holsten, Director

COURTS

4th District Court **580.395.2828**
E-mail .... jack.hammontree@oscn.net
   112 E Guthrie St Ste 202, Medford, OK 73759-1245
   Honorable Jack Hammontree, Judge

POLICE AND SHERIFF

Sheriff's Ofc **580.395.2356**
Fax 580.395.2548
Web .... www.grantcosheriff.com
   219 N 1st St, Medford, OK 73759-1203
   Roland Hula, Sheriff

Greer County

SOCIAL SERVICES

Human Svcs **580.782.1000**
   130 N Oklahoma, Mangum, OK 73554

GENERAL HEALTH SERVICES

Health Dept **580.782.5531**
Fax 580.782.5483
   2100 N Louis Tittle, Mangum, OK 73554
   Karen Weaver, Administrative Director

JUSTICE AGENCY

Juvenile Svcs Unit **580.782.3128**
Fax 580.782.7985
   116 E Pierce St, Mangum, OK 73554
   Sarah Peirce, Supervisor

COURTS

3rd District Court **580.782.3665**
Fax 580.782.4026
   106 E jefferson, Mangum, OK 73554
   Honorable Richard Darby, District Judge

POLICE AND SHERIFF

Sheriff's Dept **580.782.3065**
Fax 580.782.2302
E-mail .... greercoso@cableone.net
   105 S Pennsylvania Ave, Mangum, OK 73554-4224
   Devin Huckabay, Sheriff

Harmon County

SOCIAL SERVICES

Dept Of Human Svcs **580.688.3361**
Fax 580.688.2367
   114 W Hollis St, 1st Floor Room 6, Hollis, OK 73550
   Cindy Clayton, County Director

GENERAL HEALTH SERVICES

Health Dept **580.688.3348**
Fax 580.688.2645
E-mail .... karenxw@health.ok.gov
   1104 N 7th St, Hollis, OK 73550-1445
   Karen Weaver, Administrative Director

POLICE AND SHERIFF

Sheriff's Ofc **580.688.3306**
Fax 580.688.9218
   105 W Jones St, Hollis, OK 73550-3003
   Kirk Wade, Under Sheriff

Harper County

SOCIAL SERVICES

Dept Of Human Svcs **580.735.2541**
Fax 580.735.6119
   1001 N Hoy, Buffalo, OK 73834
   Linda Semmel, Director

GENERAL HEALTH SERVICES

Health Dept **580.921.2029**
Fax 580.921.2033
E-mail .... terri@health.ok.gov
   7th And Oklahoma, Ste 9, Laverne, OK 73848
   Terri Salsbury, Administrative Director

COURTS

1st District Court **580.735.2010**
Fax 580.735.2787
   311 1st St, Buffalo, OK 73834
   Honorable G. Wayne Olmstead, Associate District Judge

POLICE AND SHERIFF

Sheriff's Dept **580.735.2213**
Fax 580.735.2122
Web .... www.pldi.net
E-mail .... harpso@pldi.net
   311 SE 1st St, Buffalo, OK 73834
   Marty Drew, Sheriff

Haskell County

SOCIAL SERVICES

Oklahoma Dept of Human Services **918.967.4658**
Fax 918.967.8647
E-mail .... gale.sipes@okdhs.org
   #9 Highway East, Stigler, OK 74462

GENERAL HEALTH SERVICES

Health Dept **918.967.3304**
Fax 918.967.2368
   1407 NE D St, Stigler, OK 74462
   William R. Pierson, Administrative Director

COURTS

16th District Court **918.967.3323**
Fax 918.967.2819
E-mail .... robin.rea@ofcn.net
   202 E Main St Ste 9, Stigler, OK 74462
   Robin Rea, Clerk Of Court

POLICE AND SHERIFF

Sheriff's Ofc **918.967.2400**
Fax 918.967.8184
E-mail .... hcso515@yahoo.com
   1304 E Industrial St, Stigler, OK 74462
   Brian Haoe, Sheriff

Oklahoma

EDUCATION SERVICES

Choctaw Nation Head Start 918.967.2897
Fax...918.967.4930
E-mail.........................rgood@choctawnation.com
208 S City Lake Rd, Stigler, OK 74462
Rebecca Good, Head Start Supervisor

Hughes County

SOCIAL SERVICES

Dept Of Human Svcs 405.379.7231
Fax...405.379.2376
Web...www.okdhs.org
E-mail.........................donald.holliman@okdhs.org
801 Kingsberry Rd, Holdenville, OK 74848-9212
Donald Holliman, Director

GENERAL HEALTH SERVICES

Health Dept.................................405.379.3313
Fax...405.379.7223
200 McDougal Dr, Holdenville, OK 74848
Mary Hughes, Nursing Supervisor

COURTS

22nd District Court.........................405.379.3384
Fax...405.379.3204
E-mail.........................ashley.stanford@oscn.net
200 N Broadway St Ste 10, Holdenville,
OK 74848-3401
Patty Tilley, Clerk

POLICE AND SHERIFF

Sheriff's Ofc...............................405.379.2203
Fax...405.379.3204
200 N Broadway St, Ste 1, Holdenville, OK 74848
Houston Yeager, Sheriff

Jackson County

SOCIAL SERVICES

Oklahoma Dept of Human Services 580.480.3400
Fax...580.480.3500
E-mail.........................rick.steen@okdhs.org
201 South Main St, Altus, OK 73521

GENERAL HEALTH SERVICES

Health Dept.................................580.482.7308
Fax...580.477.2763
Web...www.health.ok.gov
E-mail.........................karenxw@health.ok.gov
401 W Tamarack Rd, Altus, OK 73521-1529
Karen Weaver, Administrative Director

POLICE AND SHERIFF

Sheriff's Dept.............................580.482.0408
Fax...580.482.2505
600 S Main St, Altus, OK 73521
Roger Levick, Sheriff

Jefferson County

SOCIAL SERVICES

Dept Of Human Svcs 580.228.3581
Fax...580.228.3626
400 E Highway 70, Waurika, OK 73573
Jeff Zachary, Director

GENERAL HEALTH SERVICES

Health Dept.................................580.228.2313
Fax...580.228.3200
Web...www.health.ok.gov
E-mail.........................autumnj@health.ok.gov
107 E Anderson Ave, Waurika, OK 73573-3000
Autumn James, Public Health Nurse

COURTS

5th District Court.........................580.228.2961
Fax...580.228.2185
220 N Main St Rm 302, Waurika, OK 73573-2237
Carolyn Watkins, Court Clerk

POLICE AND SHERIFF

Sheriff's Dept.............................580.228.2375
Fax...580.228.2233
Web...www.olets.state.ok.us
E-mail.........................sowaurika@olets.state.ok.us
218 N Main St, Waurika, OK 73573-2234
Michael Bryant, Sheriff

Johnston County

SOCIAL SERVICES

Dept Of Human Svcs 580.371.4000
Fax...580.371.4050
E-mail.........................jan.stowers@okdhs.org
1 Box 94 Suite 4, Tishomingo, OK 73460
Jan Stowers, County Director

GENERAL HEALTH SERVICES

Health Dept.................................580.371.2470
Fax...580.371.3347
Web...www.health.ok.gov
1080 S Byrd St, Tishomingo, OK 73460-3265
Mendy Spohn, Administrative Director

JUSTICE AGENCY

Juvenile Svcs Unit.........................580.371.3586
Fax...580.371.3766
E-mail.........................lys.hulse@oja.ok.gov
209 E Wilson St, Tishomingo, OK 73460
Lys Hulse, Juvenile Justice Specialist

COURTS

20th District Court........................580.371.3281
Fax...580.371.2199
403 W Main St Ste 201, Tishomingo,
OK 73460-1753
Cassandra Slover, Court Clerk

POLICE AND SHERIFF

Sheriff's Ofc..............................580.371.2646
Fax...580.371.9819
E-mail.........................johnstonsheriff@hotmail.com
110 N Capital Ave, Tishomingo, OK 73460
Tom Winkler, Sheriff

EDUCATION SERVICES

Chickasaw Nation Head Start...............580.371.3216
Fax...580.371.3854
1201 W Ray Branum Rd, Tishomingo, OK 73460
Danny Wells, Director

Kay County

SOCIAL SERVICES

Dept Of Child Welfare......................580.362.2548
Fax...580.362.4880
801 W South St, Newkirk, OK 74647
Andrea Gifford, Supervisor

GENERAL HEALTH SERVICES

Health Dept.................................580.762.1641
Fax...580.762.4539
Web...www.healthok.gov
433 Fairview Ave, Ponca City, OK 74601
Annette Connor, Administrative Director

JUSTICE AGENCY

Juvenile Svcs Unit.........................580.762.3281
Fax...580.765.3051
615 E Hartford Ave, Ponca City, OK 74601
Teena Stone, Assistant District Supervisor

COURTS

8th District Court.........................580.362.3350
Fax...580.362.1129
Web...www.courthouse.kay.ok.us
201 S Main St Ste A, Newkirk, OK 74647-4528
Honorable D.w. Boyd, Judge

POLICE AND SHERIFF

Sheriff's Ofc..............................580.362.2517
Fax...580.362.3259
110 S Maple Ave, Newkirk, OK 74647
Everett Vanhoesen, Sheriff

Kingfisher County

SOCIAL SERVICES

Dept Of Human Svcs 405.375.3867
Fax...405.375.6493
Web...www.okdhs.org
E-mail.........................steve.torres@okdhs.org
102 W Coronado, Kingfisher, OK 73750
Steve Torres, County Director

GENERAL HEALTH SERVICES

Health Dept.................................405.375.3008
Fax...405.375.5975
Web...www.health.ok.gov
124 E Sheridan Ave Ste 101, Kingfisher,
OK 73750-3200
Jay Smith, Administrative Director

COURTS

4th District Court.........................405.375.3813
Fax...405.375.4249
Web...www.odcr.com
101 S Main St Ste 24, Kingfisher, OK 73750
Honorable Robert E Davis, Judge

POLICE AND SHERIFF

Sheriff's Dept.............................405.375.4242
Fax...405.375.4359
119 S Main St, Kingfisher, OK 73750
Dennis Banther, Sheriff

Kiowa County

SOCIAL SERVICES

Dept Of Human Svcs 580.726.6500
Fax...580.726.6549
Web...www.okdhs.org
E-mail.........................mona.wheeler@okdhs.org
430 S Main St, Hobart, OK 73651-4018
Mona Wheeler, CWS Supervisor

GENERAL HEALTH SERVICES

Health Dept.................................580.726.3316
Fax...580.726.5701
Web...www.dcs.state.ok.us
431 W Elm St, Hobart, OK 73651-1615
Kathy Sanford, Coordinating Nurse

COURTS

3rd District Court.........................580.726.5125
Fax...580.726.2340
E-mail.........................norman.russell@oscn.net
316 S Main St, Ste 5, Hobart, OK 73651-4040
Honorable Norman L. Russell, Director/Judge

POLICE AND SHERIFF

Sheriff's Dept.............................580.726.3265
Fax...580.726.5847
301 S Jefferson St, Hobart, OK 73651-4011
Russ Tate, Sheriff

Latimer County

SOCIAL SERVICES

Human Svcs 918.465.5800
1809 Hwy 270 East, Wilburton, OK 74578

GENERAL HEALTH SERVICES

Health Dept 918.465.5673
Fax 918.465.4956
Web ....www.latimer.health.ok.gov
   201 W Main St, Wilburton, OK 74578-4010
Lynda Long, Nursing Supervisor

COURTS

16th District Court 918.465.2011
Fax 918.465.3328
   109 N Central St Ste 200, Wilburton, OK 74578
Honorable Bill Welch, Judge

EDUCATION SERVICES

Choctaw Nation Head Start 918.465.5360
E-mail ....drowe@choctawnation.com
   1016 Hwy 2 N, Wilburton, OK 74578-3215
De Ann Rowe, Director

LeFlore County

SOCIAL SERVICES

Dept Of Human Svcs 918.649.2300
Fax 918.649.2481
Web ....www.okdhs.org
E-mail ....sevilla.vance@okdhs.org
   511 S Harper, Poteau, OK 74953
Sevilla Vance, County Director

GENERAL HEALTH SERVICES

Health Dept 918.647.8601
Fax 918.647.2741
Web ....www.ok.gov
E-mail ....jilll@health.ok.gov
   1212 Reynolds, Poteau, OK 74953
Jill Larcade, Rn, Nursing Supervisor

JUSTICE AGENCY

Juvenile Svcs Unit 918.647.9154
Fax 918.647.3106
Web ....www.ja.ok.gov
   109 Beard Ave Ste 111, Poteau, OK 74953
Jim Spray, Social Service Supervisor

COURTS

16th District Court 918.647.3181
Web ....www.odcr.com
   100 S Broadway St, Poteau, OK 74953
Melba Hall, Clerk

POLICE AND SHERIFF

Sheriff's Ofc 918.647.2317
Fax 918.647.2774
Web ....www.crawford-county.org
E-mail ....crawfordcountysheriff@crawford-county.org
   100 S Broadway St, Poteau, OK 74953-3318
Bruce Curnutt, Sheriff

EDUCATION SERVICES

Bokoshe Headstart 918.969.2451
   22796 Tennessee St, Bokoshe, OK 74930
Debra Restine, Director

Fort Coffee Head Start 918.962.3443
   16112 Community Rd, Spiro, OK 74959
Michael Welker, Director

Lincoln County

SOCIAL SERVICES

Indian Child Welfare Sac And Fox Nation Of
Oklahoma 918.968.3526
Fax 918.968.4837
   920883 S Hwy 99 Bldg A, Stroud, OK 74079
Marilyn Spoon, Social Services Director

GENERAL HEALTH SERVICES

Health Dept 405.258.2640
Fax 405.258.2696
Web ....www.health.ok.gov
E-mail ....debrab@health.ok.gov
   101 Meadow Ln, Chandler, OK 74834-8786
Debra Beloncik, Rn, Nursing Supervisor

JUSTICE AGENCY

Juvenile Svcs Unit 405.258.2035
Fax 405.258.0277
   121 W 10th Ste B, Chandler, OK 74834
Jeff Linde, Supervisor

COURTS

23rd District Court 405.258.1309
Fax 405.258.3067
E-mail ....cindy.kirby@oscn.net
   811 Manvel Ave Ste 9, Chandler, OK 74834-3800
Cindy Kirby, Court Clerk

POLICE AND SHERIFF

Sheriff's Ofc 405.258.1191
Fax 405.258.2027
   811 Manvel Ave Ste 14, Chandler, OK 74834-3800
Charlie Dougherty, Sheriff

EDUCATION SERVICES

Agra Head Start 918.375.2556
Fax 405.257.5737
   112 S Main, Agra, OK 74824
Nicki Azlon, Director

Logan County

SOCIAL SERVICES

Dept Of Human Svcs 405.264.2700
Fax 405.264.2781
Web ....www.okdhs.org
E-mail ....kevin.gregory@okdhs.org
   1414 S Division St, Guthrie, OK 73044-5008
Donna Kays, County Director

GENERAL HEALTH SERVICES

Health Dept 405.282.3485
Fax 405.282.5389
   215 Fairgrounds Rd Ste A, Guthrie, OK 73044
Jay Smith, Mph, Administrative Director

JUSTICE AGENCY

Juvenile Svcs Unit 405.282.6020
Fax 405.282.7015
Web ....www.oja.ok.gov
E-mail ....jeff.linde@oja.ok.gov
   201 W Oklahoma Ave Ste 314, Guthrie,
   OK 73044-3138
Jeff Linde, Supervisor

COURTS

9th District Court 405.282.0546
Fax 405.282.7661
E-mail ....phillip.corley@oscn.net
   301 E Harrison Ave Ste 201, Guthrie, OK 73044-4955
Honorable Phillip Corley, Judge

POLICE AND SHERIFF

Sheriff's Ofc 405.282.4100
Fax 405.260.3227
E-mail ....logancountyso@aol.com
   216 S Broad St, Guthrie, OK 73044-4939
Jim Bauman, Sheriff

Love County

SOCIAL SERVICES

Dept of Human Svcs 580.276.3383
Fax 580.276.5413
Web ....www.okdhs.org
E-mail ....blaine.dudley@okdhs.org
   311 S Hwy 77 Ste A, Marietta, OK 73448-3453
Blaine Dudley, Director

GENERAL HEALTH SERVICES

Health Dept 580.276.2531
Fax 580.276.3884
Web ....www.health.ok.gov
E-mail ....mendys@health.ok.gov
   200 Ce Colston Dr, Marietta, OK 73448-1201
Mendy Spohn, Administrative Director

COURTS

20th District Court 580.276.3373
   405 W Main St Ste 201, Marietta, OK 73448
Honorable Charles E. Roberts, Judge

POLICE AND SHERIFF

Sheriff's Dept 580.276.3150
Fax 580.276.2822
   408 W Chickasaw St, Marietta, OK 73448
Joe Russell, Sheriff

Major County

SOCIAL SERVICES

Dept of Human Svcs 580.227.3759
Fax 580.227.2712
E-mail ....sarah.tucker@okdhs.org
   1425 N Main # 3, Fairview, OK 73737
Karen Tucker, Director

JUSTICE AGENCY

Juvenile Svcs Unit 580.227.2207
Fax 580.227.2712
   1425 North Main #4, Fairview, OK 73737
Paula Gard, Juvenile Justice Specialist Ii

COURTS

4th District Court 580.227.4690
Fax 580.227.1275
E-mail ....shauna.hoffman@oscn.net
   500 E Broadway St, Ste 5, Fairview, OK 73737
Shauna Hoffman, Clerk

POLICE AND SHERIFF

Sheriff's Ofc 580.227.4471
Fax 580.227.4473
Web ....www.nwt.tec.ok.us
E-mail ....mcsheriff@nwt.tec.ok.us
   500 Block E Broadway, Fairview, OK 73737
Steve Randolph, Sheriff

Marshall County

SOCIAL SERVICES

Dept of Human Svcs 580.795.8100
Fax 580.795.8141
Web ....www.okdhs.org
   111 Highway 70, Madill, OK 73446-1024
Jan Stowers, Director

GENERAL HEALTH SERVICES

Health Dept 580.795.3705
Fax 580.795.3892
Web ....www.ok.gov/health
   310 West Lillie Boulevard, Madill, OK 73446
Rhonda Dennis, Administrative Director

Oklahoma

COURTS

20th District Court **580.795.3278**
Fax 580.795.2169
E-mail .... richard.miller@oscn.net
   1 County Court House St Ste 202, Madill, OK 73446
   Honorable Richard A. Miller, Associate District Judge

POLICE AND SHERIFF

Sheriff's Dept **580.795.2221**
Fax 580.795.7524
   207 N 4th St, Madill, OK 73446-2259
   Robert V. Wilder, Sheriff

Mayes County

SOCIAL SERVICES

Dept Of Human Svcs **918.824.4900**
Fax 918.824.4980
   501 S Elliott St, Pryor, OK 74361
   Debbie Luna, Director

GENERAL HEALTH SERVICES

Health Dept **918.825.4224**
Fax 918.825.3817
Web .... www.health.state.ok.us
   111 NE 1st St, Pryor, OK 74361-2400
   Marybeth Murray, Director

JUSTICE AGENCY

Juvenile Svcs Unit **918.825.5460**
Fax 918.825.5495
   1498 S Elliott St, Pryor, OK 74361
   Linda Rothe, District Supervisor

POLICE AND SHERIFF

Sheriff's Dept **918.825.3535**
Fax 918.825.2059
E-mail .... captainparent@mayescountysheriff.org
   1 Court Pl Ste 150, Pryor, OK 74361
   Frank Cantey, Sheriff

McClain County

SOCIAL SERVICES

Dept Of Human Svcs **405.527.6511**
Fax 405.527.2085
Web .... www.okdhs.org
E-mail .... pat.bain@okdhs.org
   1930 S Green Ave, Purcell, OK 73080-0467
   Pat Bain, Director

GENERAL HEALTH SERVICES

Health Dept **405.527.6541**
Fax 405.527.4775
Web .... www.health.state.ok.us/chds.mcclain
E-mail .... sharik@health.ok.gov
   919 N 9th Ave Ste 3, Purcell, OK 73080-2028
   Shari Kinney, Rn, Administrative Director

JUSTICE AGENCY

Juvenile Svcs Unit **405.527.6755**
Fax 405.527.0021
   323 W Main St Ste A, Purcell, OK 73080
   Debbie Sugg, Supervisor

COURTS

21st District Court **405.527.3221**
Fax 405.527.7164
   121 N 2nd Ave Ste 231, Purcell, OK 73080-4241
   Gerg Dixon, District Judge

POLICE AND SHERIFF

Sheriff's Ofc **405.527.2141**
Fax 405.527.9055
   121 N 2nd Ave, Ste 121, Purcell, OK 73080
   Don L. Hewett, Sheriff

McCurtain County

SOCIAL SERVICES

Dept of Human Svcs **580.208.3400**
Fax 580.208.3500
E-mail .... terry.martin@okdhs.org
   1300 SE Adams St, Idabel, OK 74745-5239
   Terry Martin, Director

GENERAL HEALTH SERVICES

Health Dept **580.286.6620**
Fax 580.286.2012
Web .... www.health.ok.gov
E-mail .... rhondasd@health.ok.gov
   1400 S Lynn Ln, Idabel, OK 74745-6858
   Rhonda Dennis, Administrative Director

JUSTICE AGENCY

Juvenile Svcs Unit **580.286.7616**
Fax 580.286.2014
   16 N Central Ave, Idabel, OK 74745-4648
   Chuck Manning, Juvenile Justice Specialist

COURTS

17th District Court **580.286.3693**
Fax 580.286.7095
E-mail .... info@oscn.net
   108 N Central Ave Ste 2, Idabel, OK 74745
   Vicki Justus, Court Clerk

POLICE AND SHERIFF

Sheriff's Dept **580.286.3331**
Fax 580.286.7410
E-mail .... mccurtainso@yahoo.com
   200 N Central Ave, Idabel, OK 74745
   John Tadlock, Sheriff

EDUCATION SERVICES

Broken Bow Head Start Ctr **580.584.6946**
Fax 580.584.2087
Web .... www.okacaa.org
   1008 N Park Dr, Broken Bow, OK 74728-2150
   Judy Jones, Director

Broken Bow Head Start III **580.584.6956**
Fax 580.326.7584
E-mail .... annetta@pine-net.com
   409 N Broadway St, Broken Bow, OK 74728-2941
   Annetta Burris, Director

Choctaw Nation Head Start **580.981.2634**
Fax 580.981.2634
   105 W 10th St, Wright City, OK 74766
   Debra Dailey, Director

McIntosh County

SOCIAL SERVICES

Dept Of Human Svcs **918.689.1200**
Fax 918.689.1265
E-mail .... ronda.glenn@okdhs.org
   Hospital Road and Highway 69, Eufaula, OK 74432
   Ronda Glenn, County Director

GENERAL HEALTH SERVICES

Health Dept **918.689.7774**
Fax 918.689.7775
Web .... www.ok.gov/health
E-mail .... billp@health.ok.gov
   29 Hospital Rd, Eufaula, OK 74432
   William R. Pierson, Administrative Director

JUSTICE AGENCY

Juvenile Svcs Unit **918.689.5691**
Fax 918.689.7230
E-mail .... keeper.johnson@oja.ok.gov
   110 N 1st St, Eufaula, OK 74432-3052
   Keeper Johnson, Supervisor

COURTS

18th District Court **918.689.2282**
Fax 918.689.2995
   110 N First Street, Eufaula, OK 74432-2449
   Honorable James Pratt, Director

EDUCATION SERVICES

Checotah Creek Nation Head Start **918.473.0605**
Fax 918.473.3706
   302 B St, Checotah, OK 74426-5226
   Juliette Haikey, Director

Murray County

SOCIAL SERVICES

Dept Of Human Svcs **580.622.2186**
Fax 580.622.3734
Web .... www.okdhs.org
E-mail .... blaine.dudley@okdhs.org
   1019 W Wyandotte Ave, Sulphur, OK 73086-4421
   Blaine Dudley, County Director

JUSTICE AGENCY

Juvenile Svcs Unit **580.622.4410**
Fax 580.622.3266
   921 W 11th St, Ste 2B, Sulphur, OK 73086
   Allan Miller, Supervisor

COURTS

20th District Court **580.622.3223**
Fax 580.622.2979
E-mail .... tim.colbert@oscn.net
   10th W And Wyandotte St, Sulphur, OK 73086
   Honorable Timothy K. Colbert, Director

POLICE AND SHERIFF

Sheriff's Dept **580.622.5110**
Fax 580.622.3804
   700 W 10th St, Sulphur, OK 73086
   Darin Rogers, Sheriff

EDUCATION SERVICES

Davis Head Start **580.369.3266**
   701 E Benton Ave, Davis, OK 73030

Muskogee County

SOCIAL SERVICES

Dept Of Human Svcs **405.199.4543**
Fax 918.684.5377
Web .... www.okdhs.org
E-mail .... mike.jackson@okdhs.org
   1110 NE 12th St, Oklahoma City, OK 73117
   Mike Jackson, Director

GENERAL HEALTH SERVICES

Bureau Of Indian Affairs - Muskogee Regional
Ofc **918.781.4600**
Fax 918.781.4604
Web .... www.bia.gov
   3100 W Peak Blvd, Muskogee, OK 74401-8203
   Charles Head, Acting Interm Regional Director

COURTS

15th District Court **918.682.7873**
Fax 918.684.1696
E-mail .... mike.norman@oscn.net
   220 State St, Muskogee, OK 74401
   Honorable Mike Norman, Judge

POLICE AND SHERIFF

Sheriff's Ofc **918.687.0202**
Fax 918.687.9658
E-mail .... sheriffpearson@hotmail.com
   220 State St Ste 151, Muskogee, OK 74403
   Charles Pearson, Sheriff

Oklahoma

EDUCATION SERVICES

Cherokee Nation Head Start-Webbers Falls.............................**918.464.2959**
Fax...918.464.2920
E-mail.......................ehsnrcinfo@zerotothree.org
404 Gibson St, Webbers Falls, OK 74470
Mary Thomson, Director

Eastside Head Start.......................**918.683.9245**
3900 Eufaula Ave, Muskogee, OK 74401

Noble County

SOCIAL SERVICES

Oklahoma Dept of Human Services............**580.336.5581**
Fax...580.336.4795
205 15th St, Perry, OK 73077

GENERAL HEALTH SERVICES

Health Dept................................**580.336.2257**
Fax...580.336.2480
Web.....................www.health.state.ok.us/chds/noble
E-mail.......................oconnor@health.state.ok.us
300 E Fir St, Perry, OK 73077-4902
Annette Oæconnor, Administrative Director

COURTS

8th District Court...........................**580.336.5187**
300 Courthouse Dr #14, Perry, OK 73077-6649
Hillary Vorndran, Clerk

POLICE AND SHERIFF

Sheriff's Dept...............................**580.336.3517**
Fax...580.336.3510
E-mail.......................changer10@sbcglobal.net
721 Cedar, Perry, OK 73077-6649
Charlie Hanger, Sheriff

Nowata County

SOCIAL SERVICES

Dept Of Human Svcs.......................**918.273.2327**
Fax...918.273.1748
309 E Delaware Ave, Nowata, OK 74048
Samuel Westfall, Director

POLICE AND SHERIFF

Sheriff's Ofc................................**918.273.2287**
Fax...918.273.1936
E-mail.............................hallett@mtcnet.net
229 N Maple St, Nowata, OK 74048
James H. Hallett, Sheriff

Okfuskee County

SOCIAL SERVICES

Human Svcs................................**918.623.3100**
119 S First St, Okemah, OK 74859

GENERAL HEALTH SERVICES

Health Dept................................**918.623.1800**
125 N 2nd St, Okemah, OK 74859-2696
Cindy Casey, Administrative Assistant

COURTS

24th District Court.........................**918.623.0525**
Fax...918.623.2687
209 N 3rd St Ste 31, Okemah, OK 74859
Honorable Lawrence Parish, District Judge

POLICE AND SHERIFF

Sheriff's Ofc................................**918.623.1122**
Fax...918.623.9417
E-mail.............................jchoate@lakewebs.net
209 N 3rd St Ste 15, Okemah, OK 74859
Jack D. Choate, Sheriff

Oklahoma County

SOCIAL SERVICES

Dept of Human Svcs.......................**405.644.5700**
Fax...405.644.5772
Web.....................................www.okdhs.org
E-mail.......................gayle.casey@okdhs.org
401 SW 25th St, Oklahoma City, OK 73109-5923
Gayle Casey, Director

Dept Of Human Svcs: Southeast Ofc.......................**405.739.8000**
Fax...405.739.8158
Web.....................................www.okdhs.org
E-mail.......................vicki.williams@okdhs.org
9901 SE 29th St, mid set, Oklahoma City, OK 73130-7401
Nancy Thompson, County Director

GENERAL HEALTH SERVICES

Health Dept................................**405.427.8651**
Fax...405.427.3233
Web.....................................www.cchdoc.com
921 NE 23rd St, Oklahoma City, OK 73105
Gary Cox, Director Of County Health

JUSTICE AGENCY

CASA..**405.713.6456**
Fax...405.713.6610
Web.............................www.okcountycasa.org
E-mail.......................jjleelim@oklahomacounty.org
5905 N Classen Ct, Ste 302, Oklahoma City, OK 73118
Lee Ann Limber, Executive Director

COURTS

Juivenelle Office...........................**405.713.6400**
Fax...405.713.6741
5905 N Classen Ct Ste 203, Oklahoma City, OK 73118-5943
Honorable Richard Kirby, Director

POLICE AND SHERIFF

Oklahoma City Police Dept.................**405.297.1000**
Fax...405.297.1360
E-mail.............................bill.citty@okc.gov
701 Colcord Dr, Oklahoma City, OK 73102-2281
Bill Citty, Chief Of Police

Sheriff's Office.............................**405.869.2511**
Fax...405.713.1908
Web.....................www.oklahomacounty.org/sheriff
E-mail.......................johwhe@oklahomacounty.org
201 N Shartel Ave, Oklahoma City, OK 73102-2227
John Whetsel, Sheriff

EDUCATION SERVICES

Armstrong Head Start Ctr.................**405.277.3530**
Fax...405.232.9074
309 SW 5th St, Luther, OK 73054
Maa-uatchet Ra, Director

Dana Brown Cooper Head Start.............**405.733.0289**
Fax...405.737.2163
9300 NE 10th St, Oklahoma City, OK 73130
Carol Moning, Director

Edmond Head Start.......................**405.359.7155**
Fax...405.359.5963
E-mail.............................adminhs@coxinet.net
717 Churchill Rd, Edmond, OK 73034-5016
Audrea Smith, Director

Okmulgee County

SOCIAL SERVICES

Oklahoma Dept of Human Services............**918.752.2000**
Fax...918.752.2090
E-mail.......................gail.hazelwood@okdhs.org
5005 North Wood Dr, Okmulgee, OK 74447

GENERAL HEALTH SERVICES

Health Dept................................**918.756.1883**
Fax...918.756.6770
1304 R D Miller Dr, Okmulgee, OK 74447
William Peirson, Director

MENTAL HEALTH SERVICES

Creoks Mental Health Clinic.................**918.756.9250**
Fax...918.756.9187
Web.............................www.creoksbehavioralhealthservice.com
E-mail.......................joe.saddoris@lottery.ok.gov
1803 S Wood Dr, Okmulgee, OK 74447-5019
Joe Saddoris, Executive Director

JUSTICE AGENCY

Creek Nation CASA Project-Safehouse.......................**918.756.2545**
Fax...918.752.0611
E-mail.......................casaokm@sbcglobal.net
1501 S Creek Ave, Okmulgee, OK 74447-7863
Kimberley Deer, Interim Executive Director

Juvenile Svcs Unit.........................**918.756.2422**
Fax...918.758.0646
1018 E 4th St, Okmulgee, OK 74445
Keeter Johnson, Supervisor

COURTS

24th District Court.........................**918.756.3042**
Fax...918.758.1237
E-mail.......................duane.woodliff@oscn.net
314 W 7th St Ste 205, Okmulgee, OK 74447-5029
Honorable Duane Woodliff, Judge

POLICE AND SHERIFF

Sheriff's Dept...............................**918.756.4311**
Fax...918.758.1208
E-mail.............................ocso@geotec.net
315 W 8th St Ste 102, Okmulgee, OK 74447-5006
Eddie Rice, Sheriff

EDUCATION SERVICES

Creek Nation Head Start.....................**918.652.3822**
Fax...918.652.3818
23725 Wilson Rd, Henryetta, OK 74437-1485
Norma Colub, Director

Osage County

SOCIAL SERVICES

Oklahoma Dept of Human Services............**918.287.5800**
Fax...918.287.5914
E-mail.......................shirley.roberts@okdhs.org
550 Kihekah, Pawhuska, OK 74056

JUSTICE AGENCY

Juvenile Svcs Unit.........................**918.287.3358**
Fax...918.287.3165
E-mail.......................teena.stone@oja.ok.gov
1000 W Main, Ste. 103, Pawhuska, OK 74056
Michelle Duncan, Supervisor

POLICE AND SHERIFF

Sheriff's Ofc................................**918.287.3535**
Fax...918.287.6011
900 St Paul Ave, Pawhuska, OK 74056
Ty Koch, Sheriff

Ottawa County

SOCIAL SERVICES

Dept Of Human Svcs.......................**918.541.2400**
Fax...918.541.2516
2114 Denver Harner Dr, Miami, OK 74354
Rebecca Thulin, Director

GENERAL HEALTH SERVICES

Health Dept.............................918.540.2481
Fax...918.541.9390
Web......................................www.health.ok.gov
　1930 N Elm St, Miami, OK 74354-5400
　Bill Pierson, Director

North Eastern Tribal Health
System.....................................918.542.1655
Fax...918.540.1685
Web.....................................www.nthsclinic.com
E-mail...........................sharon.dawes@ihs.gov
　2301 Eight Tribe Trl, Miami, OK 74354
　Sharon A. Dawes, Health Program Director

JUSTICE AGENCY

Juvenile Svcs Unit......................918.542.2169
Fax...918.542.2894
Web...www.oja.ok.gov
E-mail...........................john.depoe@oja.ok.gov
　2110 E Steve Owens Blvd Ste B, Miami, OK 74354
　John Depoe, Social Service Supervisor

COURTS

13th District Court......................918.542.2801
Fax...918.542.8482
　102 E Central Ave Ste 203, Miami, OK 74354
　Honorable Robert Haney, Judge

POLICE AND SHERIFF

Sheriff's Ofc.............................918.542.2806
Fax...918.542.3189
Web......................................www.datalinkok.com
　28 B St SE, Miami, OK 74354
　Terry Durborrow, Sheriff

EDUCATION SERVICES

Commerce Head Start...................918.675.5556
Fax...918.675.5556
Web...www.neocaa.org
　124 N Vine St, Commerce, OK 74339-1429
　Angie Burgess, Director

Pawnee County

SOCIAL SERVICES

Oklahoma Dept of Human Services............918.762.3606
Fax...918.762.3476
E-mail...........................donna.kays@okdhs.org
　501 Fifth St, Pawnee, OK 74058

GENERAL HEALTH SERVICES

Health Dept.............................918.358.2546
Fax...918.358.5141
　1390 W Cherokee St Ste A, Cleveland, OK 74020
　Nancy Arnold, District Nursing Supervisor

Health Dept.............................918.762.3643
Fax...918.762.3228
　639 7th St, Pawnee, OK 74058
　Annette Oconnor, Administrative Director

JUSTICE AGENCY

CASA......................................918.762.3776
Fax...918.762.2498
E-mail...........................helen@pawneecasa.org
　500 Harrison St, Pawnee, OK 74058-2599
　Helen Norris, Project Director

Ofc Of Juvenile Affairs.................918.762.2571
Fax...918.762.3645
Web.....................................www.oja.state.ok.us
E-mail...........................consch@oja.state.ok.us
　500 Harrison St Rm 105, Pawnee, OK 74058-2580
　Connie Schones, Probation Officer

COURTS

14th District Court......................918.762.2547
　500 Harrison St Rm 300, Pawnee, OK 74058
　Janet Dallas, Clerk

POLICE AND SHERIFF

Sheriff's Ofc.............................918.762.2565
Fax...918.762.3335
Web.................www.pawneecountysheriff.com
　500 Harrison St, Rm B-1, Pawnee, OK 74058
　Mike Waters, Sheriff

Payne County

SOCIAL SERVICES

Dept Of Human Svcs.....................405.707.3700
Fax...405.707.3790
　711 E Krayler Ave, Stillwater, OK 74075
　Harl Hentges, County Director

GENERAL HEALTH SERVICES

Health Dept.............................918.225.3377
Fax...918.225.3402
E-mail...........................annetteg@health.ok.gov
　1026 N Linwood, Cushing, OK 74023
　Annette Oconnor, Director

Health Dept.............................405.372.8200
Fax...405.743.2619
Web...............www.health.state.ok.us/chds/payne
　1321 W 7th Ave, Stillwater, OK 74074
　Annette Oconnor, Administrative Director

Iowa Tribe Of Oklahoma Social
Svcs.......................................405.547.2402
Fax...405.547.1060
　3355 88 E 750 Rd, Perkins, OK 74059
　Janice Kurak, Chairman

JUSTICE AGENCY

CASA Program...........................405.624.2242
Fax...405.624.2250
E-mail...........................info@casaforkids.com
　315 W 6th Ave Ste 205, Stillwater, OK 74074
　Carmen Miller, Program Director

Juvenile Svcs Unit......................405.743.1545
Fax...405.372.3550
Web...www.oscn.net
E-mail...........................clmckey@yahoo.com
　2319 W 7Th Pl, Stillwater, OK 74074-1902

COURTS

9th District Court.......................405.372.4774
E-mail...........................lisa.lambert@oscn.net
　606 S Husband St, Stillwater, OK 74074-4044
　Lisa Lambert, Clerk

POLICE AND SHERIFF

Sheriff's Ofc.............................405.372.4522
Fax...405.372.1440
Web.....................................www.paynecounty.org
　606 S Husband St Ste 106, Stillwater,
　OK 74074-4044
　R B Hauf, Sheriff

EDUCATION SERVICES

Early Bird Head Start...................918.225.1029
Fax...918.225.1029
　111 W Vine St, Cushing, OK 74023-2141
　Wava Anderson, Director

Pittsburg County

SOCIAL SERVICES

Dept Of Human Svcs.....................918.421.6100
Fax...918.421.6212
Web...www.okdhs.org
E-mail...........................lynn.childres@okdhs.org
　1900 S Main St, Mcalester, OK 74501-7404
　Lynn Childres, County Director III

GENERAL HEALTH SERVICES

Health Dept.............................918.423.1267
Fax...918.423.2948
　1400 E College Ave, Mcalester, OK 74501
　Michael Echelle, Director

JUSTICE AGENCY

CASA Southeast Oklahoma.................918.426.5779
Fax...918.426.4807
E-mail...........................casasock@sbcglobal.net
　1230 S Main St, McAlester, OK 74502
　Aaron Williams, Director

Juvenile Svcs Unit......................918.423.8270
Fax...918.426.5883
Web...www.oja.ok.gov
E-mail...........................wayne.garner@oja.ok.gov
　104 E Carl Albert Pkwy, Mcalester, OK 74501
　Wayne Garner, Assistant District Supervisor

COURTS

18th District Court......................918.423.4859
Fax...918.429.0945
　115 E Carl Albert Pkwy Ste 18, McAlester, OK 74502
　Honorable James Bland, Associate Judge

POLICE AND SHERIFF

Sheriff's Dept...........................918.423.5858
Fax...918.423.6117
E-mail...........................pittsburgdispatch@yahoo.com
　1210 N West St, McAlester, OK 74501
　Joel Kerns, Sheriff

Pontotoc County

SOCIAL SERVICES

Dept Of Human Svcs.....................580.310.7050
Fax...580.310.7127
Web...www.okdhs.org
E-mail...........................ronald.magar@okdhs.org
　1628 E Beverly St Ste 104, Ada, OK 74820-2699
　Ronnie Magar, Director

GENERAL HEALTH SERVICES

Health Dept.............................580.332.2011
Fax...580.332.9537
　2330 Arlington St, Ada, OK 74820
　Michael E Kelly, Administrator

JUSTICE AGENCY

CASA......................................580.332.1441
Fax...580.332.2441
E-mail...........................casa_ada2@yahoo.com
　514 E 10th St, Ada, OK 74820-5223
　Gwen Gjovig, Director

Juvenile Svcs Unit......................580.436.4102
Fax...580.436.3352
Web...www.oja.ok.gov
　1628 E Beverly St Ste 113, Ada, OK 74820-2654
　Kinny Thomas, District Supervisor

COURTS

22nd District Court......................580.332.5763
Fax...580.332.5766
E-mail...........................martha.kilgore@oscn.net
　120 W 13th St, Ada, OK 74820
　Honorable Martha Kilgore, Director

POLICE AND SHERIFF

Sheriff's Ofc.............................580.332.4168
Fax...580.332.5970
　117 W 13th St, Ada, OK 74820
　John Christian, Sheriff

Oklahoma

Oklahoma

Pottawatomie County

SOCIAL SERVICES

Absentee Shawnee Tribe Substance Abuse
Program **405.275.4030**
Fax 405.878.4540
Web ....www.astribe.com
E-mail ....cwalker@astribe.com
2025 S Gordon Cooper Dr, Shawnee,
OK 74801-8648
Wade, Health Director

Indian Social Svcs Citizen Pottawatomi
Nation **405.275.3121**
Fax 405.878.4659
1601 S Gordon Cooper Dr, Shawnee, OK 74801
Rocky Barrett, Chairman

Kickapoo Tribe Of Oklahoma Social
Svcs **405.964.2075**
Fax 405.964.6211
Web ....www.kickapootribeofoklahoma.com
E-mail ....kwilson@kickapootribeofoklahoma.com
400 S Highway 102, McLoud, OK 74851
Christine Wilson, Social Services Director

GENERAL HEALTH SERVICES

Health Dept **405.273.2157**
Fax 405.275.5167
Web ....www.health.state.ok.us/
1904 S Gordon Cooper Dr, Shawnee, OK 74801
Tina Johnson, Bsn, Rn, Administrative /director

Kickapoo Tribal Health Ctr **405.964.2081**
Fax 405.964.2722
407 N Hwy 102, McLoud, OK 74851
Janetta Mahtapene, Health Director

JUSTICE AGENCY

Juvenile Svcs Unit **405.275.3219**
Fax 405.878.9534
500 N Pennsylvania Ave, Shawnee, OK 74801
Jeff Mader, Assistant District Supervisor

COURTS

23rd District Court **405.273.3624**
Fax 405.878.5525
325 N Broadway Ave Ste 301, Shawnee,
OK 74801-6938
John Canavan, Judge

POLICE AND SHERIFF

Sheriff's Ofc **405.273.1727**
Fax 405.275.3576
Web ....www.pottcoso.com
E-mail ....k.shirey@pottcoso.com
325 N Broadway Ave Ste 102, Shawnee,
OK 74801-6938
Michael Booth, Sheriff

EDUCATION SERVICES

Crossroads-Tecumseh Head Start **405.598.5114**
515 N 3rd St, Tecumseh, OK 74873
Andrea Wolmack, Director

Pushmataha County

SOCIAL SERVICES

Dept Of Human Svcs **580.298.3361**
Fax 580.298.2129
Web ....www.okdhs.org
E-mail ....freda.house@okdhs.org
104 SE B St, Antlers, OK 74523-4020
Freda House, County Director

GENERAL HEALTH SERVICES

Health Dept **580.298.6624**
Fax 580.298.2743
Web ....www.ok.gov
E-mail ....rhondasd@health.ok.gov
318 W Main St, Antlers, OK 74523-2034
Rhonda Dennis, Administrative Director

JUSTICE AGENCY

Juvenile Svcs Unit **580.298.5568**
Fax 580.298.3829
E-mail ....kinny.thomas@oja.ok.gov
205 Sw 2nd St, Antlers, OK 74523-3805
Kinny Thomas, District Supervisor

Little Dixie Community Action CASA
Program **580.298.2921**
Fax 580.298.3111
Web ....www.ldcaa.org
E-mail ....kluginbill@ldcaa.org
603 SW B St, Antlers, OK 74523-3830
Karla Luginbill, Director

COURTS

17th District Court **580.298.2274**
Fax 580.298.3696
302 SW B St, Antlers, OK 74523
Honorable Jana Wallace, Judge

POLICE AND SHERIFF

Sheriff's Ofc **580.298.2475**
Fax 580.298.6300
207 Sw 3rd St, Antlers, OK 74523-3809
Jimmy Duncan, Sheriff

Roger Mills County

SOCIAL SERVICES

Dept Of Human Svcs **580.497.3393**
Fax 580.497.2632
480 E Broadway, Cheyenne, OK 73628
Craig Mahl, Director

COURTS

2nd District Court **580.497.3361**
Fax 580.497.2167
500 E Broadway, Cheyenne, OK 73628
Jan Bailey, Clerk Of Court

POLICE AND SHERIFF

Sheriff's Ofc **580.497.2417**
Fax 580.497.3341
E-mail ....rogermillsso@hotmail.com
500 E Broadway, Cheyenne, OK 73628
Joe L. Hay, Sheriff

Rogers County

SOCIAL SERVICES

Oklahoma Dept of Human Services **918.283.8300**
Fax 918.283.3445
2020 Holly Rd, Claremore, OK 74017

GENERAL HEALTH SERVICES

Health Dept **918.341.3166**
Fax 918.341.3715
Web ....www.health.ok.gov
E-mail ....angela@health.state.ok.us
2664 N Highway 88, Claremore, OK 74017-0409
Angela Rhoten, Nursing Coordinator

Indian Health Hospital **918.342.6200**
Fax 918.342.6409
Web ....www.ihs.gov
101 S Moore Ave, Claremore, OK 74017-5091
Robert Guy, Director Of Social Services

JUSTICE AGENCY

CASA **918.343.1515**
Fax 918.343.0808
Web ....www.ocasaa.com
E-mail ....tricountycasa@tulsacoxmail.com
E. Will Rogers Blvd, Claremore, OK 74018
Angela Henderson, Director

Juvenile Svcs Unit **918.341.6776**
Fax 918.341.5629
2020 Holly Rd, Ste B, Claremore, OK 74017-8510
Linda Rothe, District Supervisor

POLICE AND SHERIFF

Sheriff's Ofc **918.341.3535**
Fax 918.342.9725
E-mail ....sheriff@rogerscosheriff.com
201 S Cherokee Ave, Claremore, OK 74017
Scott Walton, Sheriff

Seminole County

SOCIAL SERVICES

Oklahoma Dept of Human Services **405.257.7400**
Fax 405.257.7480
206 E Second St, Wewoka, OK 74884

GENERAL HEALTH SERVICES

Health Dept **405.257.5401**
Fax 405.257.5484
Web ....www.conservation.ok.gov
200 S Brown St, Wewoka, OK 74884-2622
Tina Johnson, Bsn, Rn, Administrative Director

Health Dept **405.382.4369**
Fax 405.382.0298
Web ....www.ok.gov/health
E-mail ....robinls@health.ok.gov
1900 Boren Blvd, Seminole, OK 74868-2049
Robin Harris, Administrative Assistant

COURTS

22nd District Court **405.257.6236**
Fax 405.257.2631
E-mail ....timothy.olsen@oscn.net
120 S Wewoka Ave, Wewoka, OK 74884
Timothy Olsen, Judge

POLICE AND SHERIFF

Sheriff's Ofc **405.257.5445**
Fax 405.257.5509
E-mail ....seminolecountyone@yahoo.com
110 S Wewoka Ave, Wewoka, OK 74884-2638
Shannon Smith, Sheriff

Sequoyah County

SOCIAL SERVICES

Dept Of Human Svcs **918.776.8000**
Fax 918.776.8112
Web ....www.okdhs.org
1611 South Kerr Blvd, Sallisaw, OK 74955
Joy Walker, County Director

GENERAL HEALTH SERVICES

Health Dept **918.775.6201**
Fax 918.775.7749
612 N Oak St, Sallisaw, OK 74955-2827
Doris Spencer, Hiv Coordinator

COURTS

15th District Court **918.775.4411**
Fax 918.775.1223
E-mail ....jeff.payton@oscn.net
120 E Chickasaw Ave Ste 205, Sallisaw, OK 74955
Honorable Jeff Payton, District

POLICE AND SHERIFF

Sheriff's Dept.............................918.775.1214
Fax..918.775.1219
   119 S Oak St, Sallisaw, OK 74955
Ron Lockhart, Sheriff

Stephens County

SOCIAL SERVICES

Dept Of Human Svcs........................580.251.8300
Fax..580.251.8396
Web...www.okdhs.org
E-mail.............................victria.lynch@okdhs.org
   1805 W Plato Rd, Duncan, OK 73533-1244
Victria Lynch, Director

JUSTICE AGENCY

Juvenile Svcs Unit.........................580.252.0180
Fax..580.252.3284
   1003 W Walnut Ave, Duncan, OK 73533
Abby Kimbro, Assistant District Supervisor

COURTS

5th District Court.........................580.470.2000
Fax..580.470.2029
E-mail...............................connie.elam@oscn.net
   101 S 11th St Rm 301, Duncan, OK 73533-4758
Connie Elam, Clerk

POLICE AND SHERIFF

Sheriff's Dept.............................580.255.3131
Fax..580.255.3133
Web...www.texhoma.net
E-mail...............................scso2@texhoma.net
   101 S 11th St Rm 104, Duncan, OK 73533-4799
Wayne Mckinney, Sheriff

Texas County

SOCIAL SERVICES

Dept Of Human Svcs........................580.338.8592
Fax..580.338.2988
Web...www.okdhs.org
E-mail...............................alejo.pena@okdhs.org
   1000 NE 4th St, Guymon, OK 73942-5426
Alejo Pena, County Director

GENERAL HEALTH SERVICES

Health Dept................................580.338.8544
   1410 N. East St, Guymon, OK 73942
Terri Salisbury, Administrative Director

JUSTICE AGENCY

Juvenile Svcs Unit.........................580.338.8490
Fax..580.338.7349
E-mail...............................joerobinson@oja.ok.gov
   506 N Roosevelt St, Guymon, OK 73942
Joe Robinson, Social Service Supervisor

COURTS

1St District Court.........................580.338.3003
Fax..580.338.3819
E-mail...............................greg.zigler@oscn.net
   319 N Main St Rm 1, Guymon, OK 73942-4843
Honorable Greg A. Zigler, Judge

POLICE AND SHERIFF

Sheriff's Ofc.............................580.338.4000
Fax..580.338.1622
Web...www.ptsi.net
E-mail...............................tcso@ptsi.net
   1102 S Ellison St, Guymon, OK 73942-5627
Rick Cavdell, Sheriff

Tillman County

SOCIAL SERVICES

Oklahoma Dept of Human Services...........580.335.6800
Fax..580.335.6850
   125 North Ninth, Frederick, OK 73542

GENERAL HEALTH SERVICES

Health Dept................................580.335.2163
Fax..580.335.2165
   1500 N Main St, Frederick, OK 73542
Kallie Clemmer, Rn, Public Health Nurse

COURTS

3Rd District Court.........................580.335.3023
Fax..580.335.5613
   201 N Main, Frederick, OK 73542
Daralene Kidwell, Court Clerk

POLICE AND SHERIFF

Sheriff's Ofc.............................580.335.3013
Fax..580.335.7135
   1200 S Main St, Frederick, OK 73542-6812
Bobby Whitington, Sheriff

Tulsa County

SOCIAL SERVICES

Child Welfare Svcs.........................918.581.2033
Fax..918.581.2074
   444 S Houston Ave, Tulsa, OK 74127
Nancy Robison, County Director

Family Medical Care Tulsa..................918.493.7800
Fax..918.493.7888
Web...www.fmct.com
E-mail...............................fhamilton@fmct.com
   7600 S Lewis Ave, Tulsa, OK 74136-6836
Frank Hamilton, Md, Director

GENERAL HEALTH SERVICES

Health Dept................................918.582.9355
Fax..918.595.4586
Web...www.tulsa-health.org/
   5051 S 129th East Ave, Tulsa, OK 74134-7004
Bruce Dart, Director

JUSTICE AGENCY

CASA.......................................918.584.2272
Fax..918.584.5740
   700 S Boston Ave Ste 230, Tulsa, OK 74119
Pamela Dose, Executive Director

COURTS

14th District Court Juvenile Ctr..........918.596.5971
E-mail...............................robert.perugino@oscn.net
   315 S Gilcrease Museum Rd, Tulsa, OK 74127
Honorable Robert Perugino, Director

POLICE AND SHERIFF

Sheriff's Dept.............................918.596.5701
Fax..918.596.5697
Web...www.tcso.org
   500 S Denver Ave, Tulsa, OK 74103
Stanley Glanz, Sheriff

Tulsa City Police Dept.....................918.596.9328
Fax..918.596.9330
Web...www.cityoftulsa.org
   600 Civic Ctr Ste 201, Tulsa, OK 74103
Greg Smith, Corporate Officer

EDUCATION SERVICES

Cella Clinton Head Start...................918.746.9320
Fax..918.746.9332
Web...www.tulsaschools.org
   1740 N Harvard Ave, Tulsa, OK 74115-4911
Marcus Paul, Director

Wagoner County

SOCIAL SERVICES

Child Welfare Svcs.........................918.614.5000
Fax..918.614.5129
   102 NE 7th St, Wagoner, OK 74467
Shane Greer, CWS Supervisor

GENERAL HEALTH SERVICES

Health Dept................................918.486.2845
Fax..918.486.7748
   28596 E 141St St S, Coweta, OK 74429
Linda Hattaway, Administrative Director

Wagoner....................................918.485.3022
Fax..918.485.2799
Web...www.wagoner.health.ok.gov
E-mail...............................lindah@health.ok.gov
   212 N Pierce Ave, Wagoner, OK 74467-4128
Linda Hattaway, Administrator

JUSTICE AGENCY

Juvenile Svcs Unit.........................918.485.5613
Fax..918.485.0080
   403 E Cherokee St, Wagoner, OK 74467
Troy Bowline, Assistant District Supervisor

COURTS

15th District Court........................918.485.4508
Fax..918.485.5836
   307 E Cherokee St Ste 4, Wagoner, OK 74477
Honorable Darrell Shepherd, Judge

POLICE AND SHERIFF

Sheriff's Dept.............................918.485.3124
Fax..918.485.7795
   307 E Cherokee St Ste 12, Wagoner, OK 74467
Bob Colbert, Sheriff

Washington County

SOCIAL SERVICES

Oklahoma Dept of Human Services...........918.338.5700
Fax..918.336.5777
   5205 Jacqueline Lane, Bartlesville, OK 74006

GENERAL HEALTH SERVICES

Health Dept................................918.335.3005
Fax..918.335.3012
Web...www.health.ok.gov
E-mail...............................cwilson@health.ok.gov
   3838 State St, Bartlesville, OK 74006-2528
Christy Wilson, Nursing Supervisor

MENTAL HEALTH SERVICES

Grand Lake Mental Health Ctr, Inc.........918.337.8080
Fax..918.337.8099
Web...www.glmhc.net
   700 SW Penn st, Bartlesville, OK 74003
Carrie Harlan, Administrator

JUSTICE AGENCY

Juvenile Svcs Unit.........................918.333.6262
Fax..918.333.6274
E-mail...............................tracie.goad@oja.ok.gov
   1368 SE Washington Blvd Ste A, Bartlesville,
   OK 74006
Tracie Goad, Social Service Supervisor

POLICE AND SHERIFF

Sheriff's Ofc.............................918.337.2800
Fax..918.337.2890
Web...www.countycourthouse.org
E-mail...............................pballard@countycourthouse.org
   420 S Johnstone Ave Ste 110, Bartlesville,
   OK 74003-6602
Rick Silver, Sheriff

Oklahoma

Oklahoma

EDUCATION SERVICES

Bartlesville Public Schools Even Start 918.337.6229
Fax 918.337.6225
Web .... www.dps-ok.org
E-mail .... bradleyld@dps-ok.org
   1536 S Keeler Ave, Bartlesville, OK 74003-5722
Lori Bradley, Even Start Director

Washita County

SOCIAL SERVICES

Oklahoma Dept of Human Services 580.832.3391
Fax 580.832.3516
E-mail .... Belinda.Maldonado@OKDHS.org
   106 Lowber Lane, Cordell, OK 73632

GENERAL HEALTH SERVICES

Health Svcs 580.832.5062
Fax 580.832.5106
   1121 N Market St, Cordell, OK 73632-2641
John Thur, Administrator

COURTS

Court Clerk 580.832.3836
Fax 580.832.4123
   111 E Main St Ste 3, Cordell, OK 73632-4831
Carol Corbett, Court Clerk

POLICE AND SHERIFF

Sheriff's Dept 580.832.2370
Fax 580.832.2946
E-mail .... washitaso@hotmail.com
   215 E 1st St, Cordell, OK 73632-4819
Larry Burrows, Sheriff

EDUCATION SERVICES

Burns Flat-Dill City Head Start 580.674.3787
Fax 580.674.3787
E-mail .... cadchobart@sbcglobal.net
   113 W 4Th St, Dill City, OK 73641-9521
Lynda Vaughn, Director

Cordell Head Start 580.832.2454
Fax 229.276.0222
   606 E 3rd St, Cordell, OK 73632-4408
Carol Hines, Director

Woods County

SOCIAL SERVICES

Oklahomas Dept of Human Services 580.430.3100
Fax 580.480.3164
   509 Barnes, Alva, OK 73717
Karen Tucker, County Director

GENERAL HEALTH SERVICES

Health Dept 580.327.3192
Fax 580.327.2703
E-mail .... dsanderson@health.ok.gov
   901 14th St Ste B, Alva, OK 73717-2513
Darlene Sanderson, Administrative Director

JUSTICE AGENCY

Juvenile Svcs Unit 580.327.3451
Fax 580.327.2082
   509 Barnes, Alva, OK 73717-1817
Tammy Tuxhorn, Worker

COURTS

4Th District Court 580.327.3119
E-mail .... ray.linder@oscn.net
   407 Government St, Alva, OK 73717
Honorable Ray Dean Linder, Judge

POLICE AND SHERIFF

Sheriff's Ofc 580.327.3434
Fax 580.327.1219
Web .... www.countycourthouse.org
   407 Government St Ste 1, Alva, OK 73717-2260
Rudy Briggs Jr., Sheriff

Woodward County

SOCIAL SERVICES

Human Svcs 580.254.6000
   2119 W Main, Woodward, OK 73801

GENERAL HEALTH SERVICES

Health Dept 580.256.6416
Fax 580.254.6802
   1631 Texas St, Woodward, OK 73801
Terri Salisbury, Rn, Administrator

JUSTICE AGENCY

Juvenile Svcs Unit 580.256.2344
Fax 580.254.2350
Web .... www.okdhs.org
   3421 Lakeside Ln, Woodward, OK 73801-3965
Robert Adams, Assistant District Supervisor

COURTS

4th Judicial District 580.256.3413
Fax 580.254.6807
E-mail .... jenny.hopkins@oscn.net
   1600 Main St Ste 4, Woodward, OK 73801
Jenny Hopkins, Court Clerk

POLICE AND SHERIFF

Sheriff's Dept 580.256.3264
Fax 580.254.6815
   1600 Main St Ste 1, Woodward, OK 73801
Gary Stanley, Sheriff

SPECIAL SERVICES AGENCIES

ADOPTION AGENCIES

Adoption Affiliates 918.664.2275
Fax 918.627.3693
   6136 E 32nd Pl, Tulsa, OK 74135-5406
Jan Couve, Executive Director

Bair Foundation, Inc. 405.759.2670
Fax 405.759.2669
   1601 Greenbriar Pl Ste A, Oklahoma City, OK 73159
Tara Base, State Director

Bair Foundation, Inc. 918.298.5059
Fax 918.298.3869
Web .... www.thebairfoundation.org
E-mail .... jmcfarmond@bair.org
   2921 E 91st St, Tulsa, OK 74137-3322
Joanne McFarmond, Director

Bethany Adoption Svc 405.789.5423
Fax 405.787.6913
E-mail .... jack.petty@bethany.org
   6666 NW 39th Expy, Bethany, OK 73008
Jack Petty, Executive Director

Catholic Charities Counseling 580.237.7352
   528 W Broadway Ave, Enid, OK 73701

Christian Svcs Of Oklahoma 405.216.5240
Fax 405.285.0294
Web .... www.christian-adoption.org
E-mail .... hollytowers@christian-adoption.org
   501 E 15th St Ste 500A, Edmond, OK 73013-5051
Holly Towers, Director

Credit Counseling Centers of Oklahoma, Inc. 918.744.5611
Fax 918.744.0232
Web .... www.cccsofok.org
   P.O. Box 4450, Tulsa, OK 74159-0450
   COA accredited organization.

Deaconess Pregncy & Adopt Svc 405.949.4200
Fax 405.720.8686
   7101 N W Expy Ste 325, Oklahoma City, OK 73132
Dierdre Mccool, Director

Dillon International, Inc. 918.749.4600
Fax 918.749.7144
Web .... www.dillonadopt.com/
E-mail .... info@dillonadopt.com
   3227 E 31st St Ste 200, Tulsa, OK 74105-2435
Deniese Dillon, Executive Director

Eagle Ridge 918.485.3554
Fax 918.485.8371
Web .... www.eagleridgeok.org
E-mail .... wmannon@eagleridgeok.org
   109 S Harrill Ave, Wagoner, OK 74467-5317
Wendy Mannon, Executive Director

Family Development and Intervention Services 405.767.1126
Fax 405.242.6454
   5131 N. Classes Boulevard, Suite 110, Oklahoma City, OK 73118
   COA accredited organization.

Heritage Family Svcs 918.491.6767
Fax 918.491.6717
Web .... www.heritagefamilyservices.org
E-mail .... m.nomura@hfs.org
   5110 S Yale Ave Ste 525, Tulsa, OK 74135
Mike Nomura, Co-Director

Safy Of Oklahoma 405.942.5570
Fax 405.942.5603
Web .... www.safy.org
E-mail .... browns@safy.org
   1209 Sovereign Row, Oklahoma City, OK 73108-1824
Sandy Brown, Treatment Director

Safy-Lawton Ofc 580.536.9129
Fax 580.536.9132
Web .... www.safy.org
E-mail .... evanss@safy.org
   6217 West Gore Blvd, Lawton, OK 73505
Suzi Evans, State Director

Shadow Mountain 405.631.4567
Fax 405.631.4593
Web .... www.psysolutions.com
E-mail .... beverly.aghoon@uhsinc.com
   5350 S Western Ave Ste 555, Oklahoma City, OK 73109-4533
Beverly Ahgoon, Director

Small Miracles, International 405.732.7295
Fax 405.732.7297
Web .... www.smiint.org
E-mail .... smi@ionet.net
   1148 S Douglas Blvd, Oklahoma City, OK 73130-5237
Margaret Orr, Director

Tri-City Substance Abuse Center, Inc.........**405.382.1112**
Fax...405.382.5747
　P.O. Box 230, Seminole, OK 74868
　COA accredited organization.

Wesley Youth, Inc.................................**918.689.2999**
Fax...918.689.3560
　119 McKinley St, Eufaula, OK 74432
　Jan Sills, Director

Western Plains Youth And Family Svcs........**918.429.0845**
Fax...918.429.0588
E-mail...............................mcalester@wpyss.org
　505 S 3rd St, McAlester, OK 74501-5819
　Wendy Vann, District Supervisor

Western Plains Youth And Family Svcs........**405.528.2011**
Fax...405.528.1750
Web...................................www.wpyfs.org
E-mail................................kevans@wpyfs.org
　201 NE 50th St, Oklahoma City, OK 73105-1811
　Kevin Evans, Director

ADVOCACY RESOURCES

CASA..**580.482.4600**
Fax...580.482.4602
Web.............................www.oklahomacasa.org
E-mail............................3jdcasa@sbcglobal.net
　123 W Commerce St Ste 230, Altus, OK 73521-3800
　Amber Pascua, Director

CASA Program................................**918.686.8199**
Fax...918.683.0745
E-mail..................casaforchildren@sbcglobal.net
　215 State St, Ste 815, Muskogee, OK 74401
　Kathryn Eaton, Director

Child Abuse Network, Inc....................**918.624.0200**
Fax...918.624.0222
Web.........................www.childabusenetwork.org
　2829 S Sheridan Rd, Tulsa, OK 74129
　Barbara Findeiss, Director

Child Advocacy Ctr.........................**580.242.1153**
Fax...580.242.5190
Web.................www.garfieldcountycarecampus.org
E-mail.............advocacycouncil@thecarecampus.com
　1002 E Broadway Ave, Enid, OK 73701-4409
　Carole Wade, Director

Child Advocacy Ctr Of Southern
Oklahoma....................................**580.226.7283**
Fax...580.226.7378
E-mail..............................coxlinc@yahoo.com
　814 16th Ave NW, Ardmore, OK 73401
　Dorothy Burge, Exec. Director

Lawton Adventure Program..................**580.357.5435**
Fax...580.357.5696
Web...................................www.swosu.edu
E-mail......................lenson.hearn@swosu.edu
　709 SW C Ave, Lawton, OK 73501-4311
　Lenson Hearn, Administrator

Mary Abbott Children's House..............**405.579.5800**
Fax...405.579.5942
E-mail............................online@abbott-house.org
　231 E Symmes St, Norman, OK 73069
　Ann Way, Executive Director

Special Advocacy Network...................**918.253.8598**
Fax...918.253.8735
E-mail........................dccsan@brightok.net
　337 Main St, Jay, OK 74346
　Jennifer Lawson, Director

The Saville Ctr- Child Advocacy Ctr..........**405.377.5670**
Fax...405.377.1880
E-mail......................saville@savillecenter.org
　1523 W 9th Ave, Stillwater, OK 74074-5469
　Brandi White, Executive Director

BEHAVIORAL HEALTH TREATMENT

21 Days 2 Change, LLC.....................**405.255.9574**
Fax...405.286.1380
　3033 Northwest 63rd, Suite 200E, Oklahoma City,
　OK 73116
　CARF accredited programs available.

A Chance to Change Foundation............**405.840.9000**
Fax...405.840.9017
Web...................................www.achancetochange.org
　5228 Classen Circle, Oklahoma City, OK 73118
　CARF accredited programs available.

A New View, Inc..............................**405.818.8364**
Fax...405.293.9047
Web.........................www.anewviewcounseling.org
　2905 Harr Drive, Suite 102, Midwest City, OK 73110
　CARF accredited programs available.

Access 2 Counseling.........................**405.537.2228**
Web...........................www.access2counseling.com
　6701 Broadway Extension, Suite 210, Oklahoma City,
　OK 73116-8237
　CARF accredited programs available.

ACE DUI School, Inc. dba Addiction Recovery
Center..**918.398.7979**
Fax...918.289.0116
Web.................www.addictionrecoveryservices.org
　4528 S. Sheridan Road, Suite 101, Tulsa, OK 74145
　COA accredited organization.

Advance Counseling, PC.....................**405.844.8085**
Fax...405.285.2186
　1015 Waterwood Parkway, Suite H2, Edmond,
　OK 73007
　CARF accredited programs available.

Advanced Therapy Associates...............**405.242.5070**
　2525 Northwest Expressway, Suite 624 A, Oklahoma
　City, OK 73112
　CHRISTINE MCGLASHEN, DIRECTOR
　CARF accredited programs available.

Advantage Community Resources LLC........**405.206.0177**
E-mail......................victoria_linker@yahoo.com
　11032 Quail Creek Road, Suite # 175, Oklahoma
　City, OK 73120
　Ms. Victoria Linker, Accreditation Manager
　Joint Commission accredited organization.

AHS Hillcrest Medical Center, LLC............**918.579.1000**
Web...................................www.hillcrest.com
E-mail......................brpayne@hillcrest.com
　1120 South Utica Avenue, Tulsa, OK 74104-4090
　Mrs. Brandi Payne, Accreditation Manager
　Joint Commission accredited organization.

Alliance of Tulsa, Inc.........................**918.747.0155**
Web...................................www.allianceoftulsa.com
E-mail......................jimlovett@yahoo.com
　5214 E. 71st Street Suite 1400, Tulsa, OK 74136
　Mr. Jim Lovett, Accreditation Manager
　Joint Commission accredited organization.

Alpha Assessment and Counseling...........**580.234.8865**
Fax...580.234.8361
　121 West Maple Avenue, Enid, OK 73701
　CARF accredited programs available.

Area Youth Shelter, Inc.......................**580.436.6130**
Fax...580.436.6135
Web...................................www.oays.org
　901 West 18th Street, Ada, OK 74820
　CARF accredited programs available.

Associated Centers for Therapy, Inc..........**918.492.2554**
Fax...918.494.9870
Web...................................www.actcares.org
　7010 South Yale, Suite 215, Tulsa, OK 74136
　Larry Marks, Executive Director
　CARF accredited programs available.

Associated Therapeutic Services PC.........**580.242.4673**
Fax...580.242.4679
Web...................................www.atscounseling.com
　1625 West Owen K. Garriott, Suite F, Enid, OK 73703
　CARF accredited programs available.

Aurora Counseling Services Incorporated.....**405.664.8443**
Fax...405.631.2780
　6803 South Western Avenue, Suite 401, Oklahoma
　City, OK 73139
　CARF accredited programs available.

Beacon Pointe................................**405.848.5620**
Fax...405.848.5619
　10400 North Vineyard, Suite E, Oklahoma City,
　OK 73120
　CARF accredited programs available.

Bethesda Family Services Foundation........**918.224.6349**
Fax...918.224.7951
Web...................................www.bfsf.org
　1807 South Main, Sapulpa, OK 74066
　CARF accredited programs available.

Better Life Counseling Services, Inc...........**405.735.9732**
Fax...405.735.9643
　9700 South Pennsylvania Avenue, Oklahoma City,
　OK 73159
　CARF accredited programs available.

BetterLife Counseling Services, Inc............**405.735.9732**
E-mail......................betterlife@coxinet.net
　9700 South Pennsylvania Avenue, Oklahoma City,
　OK 73159
　Mr. Isaac Olorunnisomo, Accreditation Manager
　Joint Commission accredited organization.

Bill Willis Community Mental Health and Substance Abuse
Center..**918.207.3000**
Fax...918.207.3064
　1400 South Hensley Drive, Tahlequah, OK 74465
　CARF accredited programs available.

Blue Sky Behavioral Health, Inc...............**918.681.1113**
Fax...918.681.1116
　502 E Cincinnati Ave, Muskogee, OK 74403
　Patricia Vaught, Executive Director
　CARF accredited programs available.

Briggs Family and Youth Association........**405.521.8635**
Fax...405.521.8652
Web...................................www.bfya.org
　1211 North Shartel Avenue, Suite 600, Oklahoma
　City, OK 73103
　CARF accredited programs available.

Building Up People.........................**405.549.0925**
　4801 North Classen, Suite 233, Oklahoma City,
　OK 73118
　CARF accredited programs available.

Byte and Associates, LLC.....................**405.222.4786**
Fax...405.222.1615
Web.................www.byteandassociatescounseling.com
E-mail......................byteandassociates@sbcglobal.net
　117 S Kevin St, Chickasha, OK 73018
　Andrew Byte, Director for the Incident Command System
　CARF accredited programs available.

Calming Connections, LLC...................**918.790.2292**
Fax...918.790.2291
　204 East Choctaw, Sallisaw, OK 74955
　CARF accredited programs available.

Carl Albert Community Mental Health
Center..**918.426.7800**
Web...................................odmhsas.org
E-mail......................clgarvin@odmhsas.org
　1101 East Monroe, McAlester, OK 74501
　Ms. Carol Lynn Garvin, Accreditation Manager
　Joint Commission accredited organization.

Cedar Ridge 405.605.6111
Web . . . . .cedarridgebhs.com
E-mail . . . . .katie.landers@uhsinc.com
  6501 NE 50th Street, Oklahoma City, OK 73141
Mrs. Katie Landers, Accreditation Manager
Joint Commission accredited organization.

Center for Positive Change, Inc. 405.265.2800
Fax 405.265.2553
Web .www.cpcfamilyservices.com
E-mail . . . . .cpcyukon@coxinet.net
  1607 Professional Circle, Yukon, OK 73099
Frank Barrett, Executive Director
CARF accredited programs available.

Center for Psychological Development 580.920.2069
Fax 903.892.2265
  142 West Main, Durant, OK 74701
CARF accredited programs available.

Center for Therapeutic Interventions 918.384.0002
Fax 918.384.0004
Web . . . . .www.ctitulsa.org
  4845 South Sheridan, Suite 510, Tulsa, OK 74145
CARF accredited programs available.

Central Oklahoma Behavioral Health
Services 405.528.1690
  600 Northwest 23rd, Suite 108, Oklahoma City,
  OK 73103
CARF accredited programs available.

Central Oklahoma Community Mental Health
Center 405.360.5100
Fax 405.573.3958
Web . . . . .www.cocmhc.org
  909 East Alameda Street, Norman, OK 73071
Larry Gross, Director
CARF accredited programs available.

Central Oklahoma Family Medical Center,
Inc. 580.925.3286
E-mail . . . . .sara.lytle@cofmc.org
  527 West Third Street, Konawa, OK 74849
Mrs. Sara Lytle, Accreditation Manager
Joint Commission accredited organization.

Challenge Counseling Services, Inc. 405.604.5344
Fax 405.604.5345
Web .www.challengecounseling.com
  6803 Southwestern Avenue, Suite 309, Oklahoma
  City, OK 73139
CARF accredited programs available.

Cherokee Nation Behavioral Health 918.207.3898
Fax 918.458.7601
E-mail . . . . .bj-boyd@cherokee.org
  2051 Mahaney Ave, Tahlequah, OK 74464
Dr. B.j. Boyd, Director

Child & Family Wellness Center 918.225.0750
E-mail . . . . .tonyc@hughes.net
  355004 E 750 Rd, Cushing, OK 74023
Mr. Tony Clyburn, Accreditation Manager
Joint Commission accredited organization.

Children's Recovery Center of Oklahoma 405.364.9004
Web . . . . .www.odmhsas.org
E-mail .eamelton@odmhsas.org
  320 12th Avenue Northeast, Norman, OK 73071
Mrs. Elizabeth Melton, Accreditation Manager
Joint Commission accredited organization.

Choices Counseling Center, Inc. 405.702.6677
Fax 405.702.6680
Web . . . . .www.choicesok.com
  4401 North Classen Boulevard, Suite 100, Oklahoma
  City, OK 73118
CARF accredited programs available.

Choices for Life Foster Care, Inc. 405.751.0800
Fax 405.751.6488
Web . . . . .www.cflfostercare.com
  4101 Perimeter Center Drive, Suite 250, Oklahoma
  City, OK 73112-2309
COA accredited organization.

Choices Institute 580.234.8880
Web . . . . .www.choicesinstitute.net
E-mail .ellenrn2@yahoo.com
  529 N. Grand, Enid, OK 73701
Mrs. Ellen Huffmaster, Accreditation Manager
Joint Commission accredited organization.

Chrysalis Institute, LLC 405.912.5145
Fax 405.912.5147
Web .http://chrysalisinstitute.com
  1922 North Eastern, Moore, OK 73160
CARF accredited programs available.

Chrysalis Institute, LLC 405.735.5263
Fax 405.735.5265
Web . . . . .www.mariposacounseling.com
  1922 North Eastern, Moore, OK 73160
CARF accredited programs available.

Citizen's Advisory Committee Youth Shelter,
Inc. 918.423.8845
Fax 918.423.8898
  904 North Ninth Street, McAlester, OK 74501
CARF accredited programs available.

Clear View Professional Counseling, Inc. 405.388.8458
  2525 Northwest Expressway, Suite 608-B, Oklahoma
  City, OK 73112
CARF accredited programs available.

Committee of Concern, Inc. 580.323.3322
Fax 580.323.6233
  600 Avant, Clinton, OK 73601
CARF accredited programs available.

Community Children's Shelter and Family Service Center,
Inc. 580.226.1838
Fax 580.223.7856
Web .www.childrenshelter.org
  15 Monroe NE, Ardmore, OK 73401
CARF accredited programs available.

Community Counselors Group, Inc. 918.297.3400
Fax 918.297.3401
  310 1/2 South 11th Street, Hartshorne, OK 74547
CARF accredited programs available.

Community Pathways Unlimited, Inc. 405.842.4911
Fax 405.842.5807
  4045 Northwest 64th Street, Suite 520, Oklahoma
  City, OK 73116
CARF accredited programs available.

Concepts in Counseling, LLC 405.205.8326
  3535 Northwest 58th Street, Suite 870, Oklahoma
  City, OK 73112
CARF accredited programs available.

Core Life Counseling Center, LLC 580.237.3432
E-mail .acbrownlpc@yahoo.com
  412 North Van Buren, Enid, OK 73703
Ms. Anita Brown, Accreditation Manager
Joint Commission accredited organization.

Cornerstone Clinical Services, Inc. 580.595.7000
Web . . . . .www.ccsok.net
E-mail .ryanpayne@ccsok.net
  807 SW F Ave, Lawton, OK 73501
Mr. Ryan Payne, Accreditation Manager
Joint Commission accredited organization.

Cornerstone Counseling and Consulting,
Inc. 405.231.3150
Fax 405.231.3157
Web . . . . .http://cornerstonecounselinginc.org
  312 Northeast 28th Street, Suite 101, Oklahoma City,
  OK 73105
CARF accredited programs available.

Council of Youth Services 918.682.2841
Fax 918.686.6859
Web . . . . .www.mccys.org
E-mail .mwinters@mccys.org
  4009 Eufaula Avenue, Muskogee, OK 74403
Mark Winters, Director
CARF accredited programs available.

Counseling Center of SE Oklahoma 580.298.2830
Fax 580.298.6723
Web .www.oklahomatherapy.com
E-mail . . . . .derrel.levey@oklahomatherapy.com
  107 South High, Antlers, OK 74523
Derrel Levy, Director
CARF accredited programs available.

Counseling Solutions and Interventions,
Inc. 405.601.6710
Fax 405.601.6711
  1330 North Classen Boulevard, Suite 214, Oklahoma
  City, OK 73106
CARF accredited programs available.

Counseling, Inc. 405.527.1785
Fax 405.527.1084
Web . . . . .www.multi-county-counseling-inc.com
  112 West Main Street, Purcell, OK 73080
CARF accredited programs available.

Covenant Youth & Family Services, Inc. 405.521.1755
Fax 405.521.1138
  3005 NW 63rd Street, Oklahoma City, OK 73116
COA accredited organization.

CREOKS Behavioral Health Services, Inc. 918.756.9411
Fax 918.756.2126
Web . . . . .www.creoks.org
  323 West 6th Street, Okmulgee, OK 74447
CARF accredited programs available.

Crossroads Youth and Family Services,
Inc. 405.292.6440
Fax 405.292.6442
Web . . . . .www.crossroadsyfs.com
  1333 West Main Street, Norman, OK 73069
Kate Butler, Dir. of Human Resources; Lisa Winters, Executive Director;
Marla Parish, Dir. of Administrative Services; Mike Templeton, Dir. of
Programs and Services; Terran Manning, Dir. of Residential Services
CARF accredited programs available.

D & D Counseling Services, Inc. 918.647.2262
  3111B North Broadway, Poteau, OK 74953
CARF accredited programs available.

Dallas Restorative Family Services 405.245.7590
Fax 405.285.7495
  920 South Boulevard, Suite 103, Edmond, OK 73034

Dancer Medical Practice 405.377.1206
  1301 W 6th Ave, Ste 210, Stillwater, OK 74074-4381
Alison Dancer, MD, Psychiatrist

Daybreak Family Services 918.561.6000
Web . . . . .www.daybreakfamilyservices.com
E-mail .dpeters@daybreakok.com
  1516 S. Boston Ave. Suite 1, Tulsa, OK 74119
Mr. David Peters, Accreditation Manager
Joint Commission accredited organization.

Demson Counseling and Associates, Inc. 405.553.9997
Fax 405.553.9928
Web .www.demsoncounseling.com
  1330 North Classen Boulevard, Suite 215, Oklahoma
  City, OK 73106
CARF accredited programs available.

Discovery Uttuwah LLC 918.485.1573
E-mail .suesdiscovery@yahoo.com
  118 So. Main, Wagoner, OK 74467
Ms. Sue Billups, Accreditation Manager
Joint Commission accredited organization.

Distinctive Adolescent and Adult Guidance Counseling Services..................405.812.8623
Fax.................................405.793.7150
Web...................................dagcs.org
　8901 South Santa Fe, Suite E, Oklahoma City, OK 73139
　CARF accredited programs available.

Diversified Family Services, Inc...............580.225.4337
Fax.................................580.225.4338
　1021 East Highway 66, Elk City, OK 73644
　CARF accredited programs available.

Eagle Ridge Institute.......................405.840.1359
Fax.................................405.840.5086
Web......................www.eaglereidgeinstitute.com
　601 Northeast 63rd Street, Oklahoma City, OK 73105
　CARF accredited programs available.

Edmond Family Counseling, Inc...............405.341.3554
Fax.................................405.341.3511
Web......................www.edmondfamilycounseling.org
　1251 North Broadway, Suite C, Edmond, OK 73034
　CARF accredited programs available.

Edmond Medical Ctr.........................405.359.5253
Fax.................................405.359.5262
Web......................www.edmondhospital.com
E-mail..............michael.spaulding@hcahealthcare.com
　1 S Bryant Ave, Edmond, OK 73034-6398
　Michael Spaulding, Director

Edwin Fair Community Mental Health Center, Inc...................580.762.7561
Fax.................................580.762.2576
Web...................................www.efcmhc.com
　1500 North Sixth Street, Ponca City, OK 74601
　Edwin Fair, psychiatrist director
　CARF accredited programs available.

Effective Transitions, Inc.....................405.286.3900
Fax.................................405.286.3911
Web...................................www.etiok.com
　245-A West Wilshire, Oklahoma City, OK 73116
　CARF accredited programs available.

Elite Counseling LLC.........................580.478.3645
Web......................www.elitecounselingllc.com
E-mail......................elitecounseling@yahoo.com
　403 North Clarence Nash Boulevard, Watonga, OK 73772
　Ms. Melissa Sankey, Accreditation Manager
　Joint Commission accredited organization.

Enid Counseling and Diagnostic Center, Inc...................580.242.5544
Fax.................................580.233.8905
　230 West Maple, Enid, OK 73701
　CARF accredited programs available.

Eufaula Lake Family Developmental Center..................918.452.3133
Fax.................................918.452.3939
Web...................................ELFDC.com
　Route 1, Box 131-C, Eufaula, OK 74432
　CARF accredited programs available.

Evolution: Changing Paths through Talk Therapy, LLC..................405.912.7730
E-mail...................................evolution@att.net
　121 West Main Street, Suite 103, Moore, OK 73160
　Judy Lindstrom, Clinical Director
　CARF accredited programs available.

Evolution: Changing Paths through Talk Therapy, LLC..................405.826.6052
　121 West Main Street, Suite 103, Moore, OK 73160
　CARF accredited programs available.

Family and Children's Consultants, Inc........405.943.7500
Fax.................................405.943.7501
　3516 Northwest 50th Street, Oklahoma City, OK 73112
　CARF accredited programs available.

Family Enrichment, LLC.....................405.753.4269
Fax.................................405.753.4270
　5005 North Pennsylvania Avenue, Suite 103, Oklahoma City, OK 73112
　CARF accredited programs available.

Family Focus Counseling Services, LLC........405.602.0835
Fax.................................405.602.0936
　3824 North Meridian Avenue, Suite 104, Oklahoma City, OK 73112
　CARF accredited programs available.

Family Options.............................405.604.9790
E-mail...................................okcbrown@aol.com
　2914 Epperly Drive, Del City, OK 73115
　Mr. Lee Brown, Accreditation Manager
　Joint Commission accredited organization.

Firm Foundations Visitation and Counseling Center, Inc...................580.427.3476
Fax.................................580.427.3477
　221 A West 14th, Ada, OK 74820
　CARF accredited programs available.

First United Methodist Church..............918.587.9481
Fax.................................918.584.5228
　1115 S Boulder Ave, Tulsa, OK 74119-2492
　Connie Cole Jeske, Executive Minister

FOCIS Counseling Services, Inc...............405.528.1748
Fax.................................405.528.1802
Web......................fociscounselingservices.com
　2220 North Classen Boulevard, Suite E, Oklahoma City, OK 73106
　CARF accredited programs available.

Fresh Start Counseling Services, Inc...........405.607.6670
Fax.................................405.607.6671
　4801 North Classen, Suite 159, Oklahoma City, OK 73118
　CARF accredited programs available.

Future and Hope Outreach, LLC..............405.413.9102
　927 North Flood, Suite 106, Norman, OK 73069
　CARF accredited programs available.

Gateway to Prevention and Recovery, Inc.....405.273.1170
Fax.................................405.275.5132
Web......................www.gatewaytoprevention.org
　1010 East 45th Street, Shawnee, OK 74804
　CARF accredited programs available.

Grand Lake Mental Health Center, Inc.........918.273.1841
Fax.................................918.273.1843
Web...................................www.glmhc.net
　114 West Delaware, Nowata, OK 74048
　CARF accredited programs available.

Great Plains Youth and Family Services, Inc...................580.726.3383
Fax.................................580.726.3384
　901 South Broadway, Hobart, OK 73651
　CARF accredited programs available.

Green Country Behavioral Health Services, Inc...................918.682.8407
Fax.................................918.682.4636
E-mail...................................jwoolridge@gcbhs.org
　619 North Main, Muskogee, OK 74401
　Jeanette Woodridge, Project Director
　CARF accredited programs available.

Health Concepts Family Services Outpatient Behavioral Health..................918.872.6135
E-mail......................victoria_linker@yahoo.com
　1843 SE 15th Street, Tulsa, OK 74104
　Ms. Victoria Linker, Accreditation Manager
　Joint Commission accredited organization.

Health Network, LLC.........................918.333.0222
Web...................................okcounseling.com
E-mail......................victoria_linker@yahoo.com
　1366 A Southeast Washington Blvd, Bartlesville, OK 74006
　Ms. Victoria Linker, Accreditation Manager
　Joint Commission accredited organization.

HOPE Community Services, Inc...............405.632.1900
Fax.................................405.632.1976
Web...................................www.hopecsi.org
　105 Southeast 45th Street, Oklahoma City, OK 73129
　CARF accredited programs available.

Hope Counseling Services, Inc...............405.942.4740
Fax.................................405.208.4574
　2915 North Classen Boulevard, Suite 325, Oklahoma City, OK 73106
　CARF accredited programs available.

Human Skills and Resources, Inc...............918.747.6377
Fax.................................918.747.8594
Web...................................www.humanskills.org
　2140 South Harvard Avenue, Tulsa, OK 74114
　CARF accredited programs available.

Improving Lives Counseling Services, Inc....918.812.6010
E-mail......................improvinglivescounseling@yahoo.com
　7049 Frankoma Road, # 6, Admin. Bldg., Tulsa, OK 74131
　Mr. Kneale Ewing, Accreditation Manager
　Joint Commission accredited organization.

Infant Parent Intervention Center, Inc.........405.415.2300
Fax.................................405.415.2301
　4801 North Classen, Suite 102, Oklahoma City, OK 73118
　CARF accredited programs available.

Infinity Counseling, PLLC...................405.615.4464
Fax.................................405.801.2900
Web...................................www.infinitycounseling.com
　330 West Gray, Suite 409, Norman, OK 73069
　CARF accredited programs available.

Integrated Comprehensive Health Care (ICHC), LLC..................405.290.7744
E-mail...................................kc4u@live.com
　8101 W. 10th Street, Suite 7 & 8, Oklahoma City, OK 73127
　Mr. Keith Combs, Accreditation Manager
　Joint Commission accredited organization.

Integrated Health Solutions.................405.225.6563
　6801 South Western, Suite 206, Oklahoma City, OK 73139
　CARF accredited programs available.

Integris Mental Health.......................405.427.2441
Fax.................................405.427.4703
Web...................................www.integrishealth.com
E-mail......................diane.bedell@integris-health.com
　2601 Spencer Rd, Spencer, OK 73084-3699
　Diane Bedell, CEO/Administrater

Integrity Pathways.........................918.682.9292
Fax.................................918.682.0054
　1805 N York Ste G, Muskogee, OK 74403
　Tasha Grayson, Director
　CARF accredited programs available.

Jack Brown Youth Regional Treatment Center..................918.453.5519
Fax.................................918.458.0499
Web...................................www.cherokee.org
　17091 South Muskogee, Tahlequah, OK 74464
　CARF accredited programs available.

Jennifer M Smith MCP, LPC, PLC..............918.978.1109
E-mail...................................jsmithcounseling@att.net
　1002 E. Virginia suite B, Stillwater, OK 74075
　Ms. Jennifer Smith, Accreditation Manager
　Joint Commission accredited organization.

Oklahoma

Jim Taliaferro Community Mental Health Center **580.248.5780**
E-mail ....judyw@odmhsas.org
602 SW 38th st, Lawton, OK 73505
Mrs. Judy Wallace, Accreditation Manager
Joint Commission accredited organization.

Jordan's Crossing, Inc. **405.604.9644**
Fax 405.604.9689
Web ....www.jordanscrossinginc.org
301 West I-240 Service Road, Oklahoma City, OK 73139
CARF accredited programs available.

Journey Within Myself Counseling Services, LLC **405.204.1476**
Fax 405.525.0530
14018 North Western Avenue, Edmond, OK 73013
CARF accredited programs available.

Kiamichi Council on Alcoholism and/or Other Drug Abuse, Inc. **580.286.3301**
Fax 580.286.6385
104 Northeast Avenue A, Idabel, OK 74745
CARF accredited programs available.

Kiamichi Youth Services, Inc. **580.286.6671**
Fax 580.286.5747
E-mail ....debbie.forshee@ysoc.org
116 Southeast Avenue N, Idabel, OK 74745
Debbie Forshee, Executive Director
CARF accredited programs available.

Kid's Place **918.682.4204**
Fax 918.682.4430
Web ....www.nccac.net
E-mail ....amatthews@nccac.net
400 Court St, Muskogee, OK 74401
Ann Matthews, Director

Latino Community Development Agency **405.236.0701**
Fax 405.236.0737
Web ....www.latinoagencyokc.org
420 Southwest 10th Street, Oklahoma City, OK 73109
CARF accredited programs available.

Laureate Psychiatric Clinic and Hospital **918.481.4000**
Web ....www.laureate.com
E-mail ....vdgraham@saintfrancis.com
6655 South Yale Avenue, Tulsa, OK 74136
Ms. Valorie Graham, Accreditation Manager
Joint Commission accredited organization.

Life Connection Counseling Ctr **918.496.9588**
7145 S Braden Ave, Tulsa, OK 74136-6302
Brent Sharp, Psychiatrist

Life Management Counseling and Consulting, Inc. **580.351.1188**
Fax 580.351.1313
E-mail ....lifemanagment@att.net
621 Southwest D Ave, 1st Fl, Lawton, OK 73501
Jennifer Glover-Gallaher, Dierctor
CARF accredited programs available.

Lifeline Mental Health Services, Inc. **405.740.3233**
Fax 405.396.2864
700 West 15th Street, Suite 2, Edmond, OK 73012
CARF accredited programs available.

Lifespan Counseling Professionals **580.931.9901**
Fax 580.931.9953
212 West Evergreen, Durant, OK 74701
CARF accredited programs available.

Lifeworks Counseling Solutions, LLC **580.515.1010**
E-mail ....dj7777@hotmail.com
311 West Main Street, Canton, OK 73724
Ms. Darla Perry, Accreditation Manager
Joint Commission accredited organization.

Logan Community Services, Inc. **405.282.5524**
Fax 405.282.4652
Web ....www.logancommunityservices.com
E-mail ....ajgriffin@logancommunityservices.com
4710 South Division Street, Guthrie, OK 73044
A J Griffin, Executive Director
CARF accredited programs available.

Love and Hope Counseling Services, LLC **405.528.4673**
Fax 405.528.4674
4030 North Lincoln Boulevard, Oklahoma City, OK 73105
CARF accredited programs available.

LXE Counseling Services, LLC **580.380.1844**
6202 South Lewis, Suite H, Tulsa, OK 74136-1064
CARF accredited programs available.

Marie Detty Youth and Family Service Center **580.250.1123**
Fax 580.248.0171
Web ....www.mariedetty.com
317 C Avenue, Lawton, OK 73501
CARF accredited programs available.

Massey Counseling and Consulting **918.429.7853**
23 East Choctaw, Suite 3, McAlester, OK 74501
CARF accredited programs available.

Maximus Counseling Services, Inc. **405.601.1154**
Fax 405.601.1183
E-mail ....fsomade_maximuscounseling@yahoo.com
5714 South Western Avenue, Oklahoma City, OK 73109
Mickey O'keefe, Executive Director
CARF accredited programs available.

Mead Family Services **580.564.1660**
Fax 580.564.2475
Web ....treatmentservices.org
5912 U.S. Highway 70 North, Mead, OK 73449
CARF accredited programs available.

Mental Health Services of Southern Oklahoma **580.223.5070**
Fax 580.223.5617
Web ....www.mhsso.org
2530 South Commerce, Building A, Ardmore, OK 73401
CARF accredited programs available.

Mid-Del Youth and Family Center, Inc. **405.733.5437**
Fax 405.732.7741
Web ....www.mid-delyouth.org
316 South Midwest Boulevard, Midwest City, OK 73110
Jeremy Wente, Director
CARF accredited programs available.

Millennium Community Services, LLC **405.573.9905**
Fax 405.573.0404
448 36th Avenue NW, Suite 101, Norman, OK 73072
CARF accredited programs available.

Montgomery Individual and Family Therapy, LLC **918.852.9644**
10306 North 138th Avenue, Suite 1014, Owasso, OK 74055
CARF accredited programs available.

Moore Youth and Family Services, Inc./Moore Alcohol and Drug Center, Inc. **405.799.3379**
Fax 405.799.0912
624 Northwest Fifth Street, Moore, OK 73160
CARF accredited programs available.

Morning Star Mental Health, Inc. **918.650.9500**
Fax 918.650.9559
504 West Broadway, Henryetta, OK 74437

Neurologic Rehabilitation Institute at Brookhaven Hospital **918.438.4257**
Fax 918.438.8016
Web ....www.brookhavenhospital.com
E-mail ....wecanhelp@brookhavenhospital.com
201 S Garnett Rd, Tulsa, OK 74128-1805
Liz Lamers, Utilization Review Director

New Beginnings Counseling Services, Inc. **405.601.2307**
Fax 405.601.3317
625 Northwest 13 Street, Suite D, Oklahoma City, OK 73103
CARF accredited programs available.

New Day Recovery Youth and Family Services, Inc. **405.525.0452**
Fax 405.525.0515
Web ....www.newdayokc.org
4420 N. Lincoln Boulevard, Oklahoma City, OK 73105
COA accredited organization.

New Discoveries Youth and Family Services, Inc. **405.232.1401**
Fax 405.232.1402
628 Northeast Fourth, Oklahoma City, OK 73104
CARF accredited programs available.

New Horizon Youth and Family Services, LLC **405.216.5608**
Fax 405.216.5272
E-mail ....nhyfs@coxinet.net
1729 West 33rd Street, Suite B, Edmond, OK 73013
Karen Young, Director
CARF accredited programs available.

New Life Youths and Family Counseling Services, Inc. **405.605.5601**
Fax 405.605.7914
Web ....www.nlcounseling.com
6801 South Western Avenue, Suite 200, Oklahoma City, OK 73139
CARF accredited programs available.

New Restoration Counseling Center **405.601.6717**
Fax 405.604.5515
E-mail ....sweetiecdenise@msn.com
243 W Wilshire Blvd Ste B, Oklahoma City, OK 73116
Willie Denise Barr, Owner & President
CARF accredited programs available.

Norman Addiction Information and Counseling **405.321.0022**
Fax 405.360.4918
Web ....www.naichelp.org
215 West Linn Street, Norman, OK 73069
CARF accredited programs available.

Norman Counseling Clinic **405.809.2004**
E-mail ....nccdoc@psychtestcorp.com
2416 Tee Circle, Norman, OK 73069
Dr. Donald Hume, Accreditation Manager
Joint Commission accredited organization.

NorthCare Direction for Life **405.858.2700**
Fax 405.858.2720
Web ....www.northcare.com
4436 Northwest 50th Street, Oklahoma City, OK 73112
CARF accredited programs available.

Northern Oklahoma Youth Services Center & Shelter, Inc. **580.762.8341**
Fax 580.762.9967
E-mail ....noys@sbcglobal.net
2203 N Ash St, Ponca City, OK 74601
Vearl Caid, Executive Director
CARF accredited programs available.

Oklahoma

Northwest Center for Behavioral Health (NCBH) **580.256.8615**
E-mail ....rwhite@odmhsas.org
　　1222 10th Street, Suite 211, Woodward, OK 73801
　　Mr. Richard White, Accreditation Manager
　　Joint Commission accredited organization.

Northwest Ctr For Behavioral Health **405.282.1830**
Fax 405.282.1861
　　1923 S Division St, Guthrie, OK 73044
　　Mark Hayes, Coordinator

Northwest Ctr For Behavioral Health **580.234.3791**
Fax 580.237.7711
Web ....www.odmhsas.org
E-mail ....dee-white@kingfisherhospital.com
　　702 N Grand St, Enid, OK 73701-3221
　　Dee White, Executive Director

Northwest Family Services, Inc. **580.327.2900**
Fax 580.327.1337
Web ....www.northwestfamily.net
　　620 Flynn Street, Alva, OK 73717
　　JOHN JONES, EXECUTIVE DIRECTOR
　　CARF accredited programs available.

Oasis Counseling Center, Inc. **405.605.3093**
Fax 405.601.5689
Web ....www.myoasishelp.com
　　4911 North Portland Avenue, Suite 111, Oklahoma City, OK 73112
　　CARF accredited programs available.

Oklahoma Counseling Services, Inc. **918.286.2535**
Web ....www.okcounseling.com
E-mail ....victoria_linker@yahoo.com
　　3100 S. Elm Place, Suite B, Broken Arrow, OK 74012
　　Ms. Victoria Linker, Accreditation Manager
　　Joint Commission accredited organization.

Oklahoma Families First, Inc. **405.360.2133**
Fax 405.360.4821
Web ....www.offibhs.org
　　2227 West Lindsey Street, Suite 1550, Norman, OK 73069
　　CARF accredited programs available.

Oklahoma Family Counseling Services **405.822.8458**
　　428 South Mustang Road, Yukon, OK 73099
　　CARF accredited programs available.

Oklahoma Play Therapy Counseling Center **580.484.5683**
Web ....www.okplaytherapy.com
E-mail ....okplaytherapy@suddenlink.net
　　502 W. Randolph, Enid, OK 73701
　　Ms. Connie O'Brien, Accreditation Manager
　　Joint Commission accredited organization.

Oklahoma Prevention Resource Ctr **405.522.3810**
Fax 405.522.8316
Web ....www.odmhsas.org/oprc.htm
E-mail ....njanssen@odmhsas.org
　　2401 NW 23rd St Ste 82, Oklahoma City, OK 73107
　　Norma Janssen, Manager

Oklahoma United Methodist Circle of Care, Inc. **405.530.2078**
Fax 405.525.5897
Web ....www.circleofcare.org
　　1501 NW 24th Street, Oklahoma City, OK 73106
　　COA accredited organization.

Open Arms Behavioral Health, LLC **580.355.5242**
Fax 580.355.5245
Web ....www.ccmhonline.net
　　3811 West Gore Boulevard, Suite 10, Lawton, OK 73505
　　CARF accredited programs available.

Open Arms Behavioral Health, LLC **580.695.3469**
Fax 580.250.6640
　　3811 West Gore Boulevard, Suite 10, Lawton, OK 73505
　　CARF accredited programs available.

Options Unlimited Counseling and Consulting **405.272.1610**
Fax 405.272.1630
　　214 Southwest 30th, Oklahoma City, OK 73109

Palmer Continuum of Care, Inc. **918.832.7763**
Fax 918.292.8250
Web ....www.palmer-tulsa.org
　　3015 East Skelly Drive, Suite 270, Tulsa, OK 74105
　　CARF accredited programs available.

Parkside, Inc. **918.582.2131**
Web ....www.parksideinc.org
E-mail ....rcarbuhn@parksideinc.org
　　1620 East 12th Street, Tulsa, OK 74120
　　Ms. Rita Carbuhn, Accreditation Manager
　　Joint Commission accredited organization.

Pathways Professional Counseling, Inc. **405.842.7284**
Fax 405.418.0324
Web ....www.pathwaysokc.com
　　2212 Northwest 50th Street, Suite 241C, Oklahoma City, OK 73112
　　CARF accredited programs available.

Pennington Creek Lifehouse **580.310.4164**
E-mail ....trat19@hotmail.com
　　705 W Main, Tishomingo, OK 73460
　　Mr. Tyson Ratzlaff, Accreditation Manager
　　Joint Commission accredited organization.

People Inc **918.775.7787**
Fax 918.775.0328
Web ....www.peopleinc.org
　　205 South J.T. Stites, Sallisaw, OK 74955
　　CARF accredited programs available.

Positive Changes **405.636.1463**
Web ....positivechangesokc.com
E-mail ....positive8835@sbcglobal.net
　　744 S.E. 25th Street, Oklahoma City, OK 73129
　　Mrs. Laura Balliett-Box, Accreditation Manager
　　Joint Commission accredited organization.

Professional Counseling and Consulting Services, P.C. **918.420.5238**
Fax 918.420.5717
　　400 East Wyandotte, McAlester, OK 74501
　　CARF accredited programs available.

Professional Counseling Solutions, PLLC **580.335.3320**
E-mail ....moreydebbie@gmail.com
　　1500 North Main, Frederick, OK 73542
　　Ms. Debbie Morey, Accreditation Manager
　　Joint Commission accredited organization.

Promises, Inc. **405.620.2094**
Fax 405.270.0956
　　505 Northeast 46th Street, Oklahoma City, OK 73105
　　CARF accredited programs available.

Providence of Oklahoma **580.924.6363**
Fax 580.924.0379
Web ....www.provcorp.com
E-mail ....rbutler@provcorp.com
　　134 North 12th Street, Durant, OK 74701
　　Roeathea Butler, Clinical Director
　　CARF accredited programs available.

Psychiatric Solutions of Oklahoma **918.492.8200**
Web ....www.shadow-mtn.com
E-mail ....thyland@psysolutions.com
　　6262 South Sheridan Road, Tulsa, OK 74133
　　Mr. Tom Hyland, Accreditation Manager
　　Joint Commission accredited organization.

Public Strategies, Inc. **405.848.2171**
Fax 405.848.2078
Web ....www.publicstrategies.com
　　301 N.W. 63rd, Suite 600, Oklahoma City, OK 73116
　　COA accredited organization.

Pure Hope Corporation **405.715.1616**
Fax 405.715.1617
　　1413 South Boulevard, Edmond, OK 73034
　　CARF accredited programs available.

Quest MHSA, LLC **580.298.3001**
Fax 580.298.5357
Web ....www.questmhsa.com
　　903 West Main, Antlers, OK 74523
　　CARF accredited programs available.

Red River Counseling Center, LLC **580.317.3726**
Fax 580.326.9028
　　1717 1/2 West Jackson Street, Hugo, OK 74743
　　CARF accredited programs available.

Red Rock Behavioral Health Services **405.425.0355**
Fax 405.425.0343
Web ....www.red-rock.com
　　4400 North Lincoln Boulevard, Oklahoma City, OK 73105
　　CARF accredited programs available.

Red Rock Behavioral Health Svcs **405.424.7711**
Fax 405.425.0441
Web ....www.redrock.com
　　4400 N Lincoln Blvd, Oklahoma City, OK 73105
　　Al S. Friedman, CEO

Redefine U **918.708.5220**
　　2511 South Muskogee Avenue, Tahlequah, OK 74464
　　CARF accredited programs available.

Rivers Edge Mental Health Associates **580.225.8899**
　　1800 West First Street, Suite 104, Elk City, OK 73664
　　CARF accredited programs available.

ROCMND Area Youth Services, Inc. **918.256.7518**
Fax 918.256.6771
　　1520 North Industrial Road, Vinita, OK 74301
　　CARF accredited programs available.

Roland Family Counseling Center **918.427.1311**
Fax 918.427.0013
　　100 East Ray Fine Boulevard, Suite M, Roland, OK 74954
　　CARF accredited programs available.

Rolling Hills Hospital **580.436.3600**
Fax 580.436.3958
Web ....www.rollinghillshospital.com
E-mail ....john.baker@havenbehavioral.com
　　1000 Rolling Hills Ln, Ada, OK 74820-9415
　　John Baker, CEO

Rural Area Counseling Center **405.379.3505**
Fax 405.379.3546
　　223 North Broadway, Holdenville, OK 74848

Sequel of Oklahoma, LLC **405.548.1280**
Web ....camelotforkids.org
E-mail ....dgoldstein-higgins@sequelyouthservices.com
　　3301 North Martin Luther King Avenue, Oklahoma City, OK 73111
　　Ms. Debbie Goldstein-Higgins, Accreditation Manager
　　Joint Commission accredited organization.

Shadow Mountain Behavioral Health Svcs **918.492.8200**
Fax 918.497.4952
Web ....www.shadow-mtn.com
　　6262 S Sheridan Rd, Tulsa, OK 74133-4099
　　Mike Kistler, Chief Executive Officer

Signature Transformation Counseling Service, LLC **405.824.9252**
Fax 405.729.2892
　　433 Wilshire Boulevard, Suite B, Oklahoma City, OK 73116
　　CARF accredited programs available.

Oklahoma

Solutions for Life Counseling Services 580.234.4700
E-mail ....kathyandrews70@yahoo.com
309 W. Cherokee, Enid, OK 73701
Mrs. Kathy Andrews, Accreditation Manager
Joint Commission accredited organization.

Southeastern Oklahoma Family Services 580.341.8522
Fax 580.226.5998
907 Holiday Drive, Ardmore, OK 73401
CARF accredited programs available.

Southeastern Oklahoma Social Services,
Inc. 918.302.0389
Fax 918.302.3809
512 East Chickasaw, McAlester, OK 74501
CARF accredited programs available.

Southeastern Psychiatric Services 918.423.3700
E-mail ....spsmcalester@yahoo.com
100 S. Main, Suite B, McAlester, OK 74501
Ms. Karen Bowden, Accreditation Manager
Joint Commission accredited organization.

Southern Oklahoma Treatment Services, Inc. dba Mead Family
Services 580.745.9610
Fax 580.745.9650
Web ....www.treatmentservices.org
5912 U.S. Highway 70 North, Mead, OK 73449
CARF accredited programs available.

Southern Plains Treatment Services 405.217.8400
Fax 405.217.8405
Web ....www.splains.org
310 12th Avenue NE, Norman, OK 73071
CARF accredited programs available.

SouthWest Counseling Services, PLLC 580.323.9100
E-mail ....scs06@sbcglobal.net
703 Frisco Ave., Clinton, OK 73601
Mr. William Walker, Accreditation Manager
Joint Commission accredited organization.

Southwest Foster Care Of Oklahoma 405.848.0011
Web ....www.southwestfostercare.com
E-mail ....candacetucker.swfc@coxinet.net
4801 North Classen Blvd Suite 135, Oklahoma City,
OK 73118
Mrs. Candace Tucker, Accreditation Manager
Joint Commission accredited organization.

Southwest Oklahoma Counseling, Inc. 580.323.9800
Fax 580.323.3389
725B South Eighth, Clinton, OK 73601
CARF accredited programs available.

Specialized Outpatient Services, Inc. 405.810.1766
Fax 405.810.0331
Web ....www.okcsos.com
5208 Classen Circle, Oklahoma City, OK 73118
CARF accredited programs available.

Speck Homes, Inc. 405.239.7101
Fax 405.239.7106
E-mail ....speck@speckhomesinc.com
605 NW 13th St Ste C, Oklahoma City, OK 73103
Glenn Koch, Director

St. Anthony Hospital 405.272.7000
Web ....www.saintslinks.sah-okc.ssmhc.com
E-mail ....marti_jourden@ssmhc.com
1000 North Lee Street, Oklahoma City, OK 73101
Ms. Marti Jourden, Accreditation Manager
Joint Commission accredited organization.

Stonebridge Therapeutic & Psychological Services,
PC 405.708.3640
Fax 888.499.3569
Web ....www.stonebridgeok.com
1900 North MacArthur Boulevard, Suite 108,
Oklahoma City, OK 73127
CARF accredited programs available.

Street School, Inc. 918.833.9800
Fax 918.833.9858
Web ....www.streetschool.org
E-mail ....mcginlo@tulsaschools.org
1135 South Yale Avenue, Tulsa, OK 74112
Lori Mcginnis-madland, Director
CARF accredited programs available.

SummerCrest, Inc. 918.686.6876
Fax 918.686.6826
3300 Chandler Road, Suite 109, Muskogee,
OK 74403
CARF accredited programs available.

Sunbeam Family Services, Inc. 405.528.7721
Fax 405.528.7731
Web ....www.sunbeamfamilyservices.org
P.O. Box 61237, Oklahoma City, OK 73146-1237
COA accredited organization.

Sundance Counseling and Mental Health
Services 405.321.3719
Fax 405.364.3209
Web ....http://www.sundancecs.com
932 North Flood Avenue, Norman, OK 73071
CARF accredited programs available.

SW Behavioral Health Ctr 580.536.0077
Fax 580.510.2725
Web ....www.swmconline.com
E-mail ....lanya.doyle@hcahealthcare.com
1602 SW 82nd St, Lawton, OK 73505
Lanya Doyle, Program Director

Tenkiller Behavioral Services, Inc. 918.457.4999
Fax 918.457.4104
27753 South Welling Road, Welling, OK 74471
CARF accredited programs available.

The 4UN Counseling Center 405.801.2488
Fax 405.801.2588
210 East Main, Suite 210, Norman, OK 73069
CARF accredited programs available.

The Holloway Group, Inc. 405.603.8450
Fax 405.603.8455
Web ....www.thehollowaygroup.org
6613 North Meridian Avenue, Oklahoma City,
OK 73118
CARF accredited programs available.

The Mental Health Center, Inc. 580.286.5184
Fax 580.286.5185
17 South Central, Idabel, OK 74745
CARF accredited programs available.

The Office of Counseling Services 405.214.0933
647 North Kickapoo, Shawnee, OK 74801-6917
CARF accredited programs available.

The Parent Child Center of Tulsa, Inc. 918.599.7999
Fax 918.599.8054
Web ....www.parentchildcenter.org
1421 S. Boston Avenue, Tulsa, OK 74119
COA accredited organization.

The Referral Ctr For Alcohol And Drug Svc Of Central
Oklahoma 405.525.2525
Fax 405.525.3108
Web ....www.trc.ok.com
E-mail ....burkdx2@yahoo.com
1215 NW 25th St, Oklahoma City, OK 73106-5629
Don Burk, Director

Therapeutic Services, Inc. P.C. 918.742.6050
Fax 918.742.8430
Web ....www.therapeuticservicesok.com
5569 South Lewis Avenue, Tulsa, OK 74105
CARF accredited programs available.

Tox Integrated Guidance, Inc. 405.605.4903
Fax 405.605.4904
1330 North Classen Boulevard, Suite G10, Oklahoma
City, OK 73106
CARF accredited programs available.

Transitions, Inc. 405.810.0054
Fax 405.810.8977
6051 North Brookline, Suite 112, Oklahoma City,
OK 73112
CARF accredited programs available.

Tri-City Youth & Family Center, Inc. 405.390.8131
Fax 405.390.8134
14625 Northeast 23rd, Choctaw, OK 73020
CARF accredited programs available.

University of Oklahoma Health Sciences Center/Section of
Developmental and Behavioral Pediatrics 405.271.5700
Fax 405.271.2931
Web ....http://devbehavpeds.ouhsc.edu/
1100 Northeast 13th Street, Oklahoma City,
OK 73117-1099
CARF accredited programs available.

Valeria E. Milstead-Benabdallah, LCSW,
PC 405.604.0180
Fax 405.228.0181
1330 North Classen Boulevard, Suite 307, Oklahoma
City, OK 73106-6834
CARF accredited programs available.

Waynoka Mental Health Authority dba Northwest Substance
Abuse Treatment Center 580.824.0674
Fax 580.824.0676
1095 South Nickerson Street, Waynoka, OK 73860
CARF accredited programs available.

White Horse Ranch, LLC 580.994.5649
Fax 580.994.2739
Web ....www.whitehorseranch.org
1601 Wilkie Road, Mooreland, OK 73852
CARF accredited programs available.

Wichita Counseling Center 580.536.5102
Fax 580.536.5102
6217 West Gore Boulevard, Lawton, OK 73505
CARF accredited programs available.

Willow Crest Hospital, Inc. 918.542.1836
Web ....www.willowcresthospital.com
E-mail ....tellison@willowcresthospital.com
130 A Street South West, Miami, OK 74354
Ms. Toby Ellison, Accreditation Manager
Joint Commission accredited organization.

YCO, Inc. 580.214.2342
Web ....www.youthcareok.com
E-mail ....dfawnd@sbcglobal.net
3535 NW 58th Street, Suite 800 E, Oklahoma City,
OK 73112
Ms. D'Fawn Downs, Accreditation Manager
Joint Commission accredited organization.

Youth and Family Center, Inc. 405.527.2424
Fax 405.527.6406
118 South Second St, Purcell, OK 73080
Donna Mcclung, Executive Director
CARF accredited programs available.

Youth and Family Services 918.335.1111
Fax 918.335.1119
2200 Southeast Washington Boulevard, Bartlesville,
OK 74006
CARF accredited programs available.

Youth and Family Services for Hughes and Seminole Counties,
Inc. 405.257.5491
Fax 405.257.5492
219 North Wewoka Avenue, Wewoka, OK 74884
CARF accredited programs available.

Youth and Family Services of North Central Oklahoma,
Inc. 580.233.7220
Fax 580.237.7550
Web ....www.yfsenid.org
E-mail ....yfss@yfsenid.org
605 West Oxford, Enid, OK 73701
Justin Simmons, Director
CARF accredited programs available.

Youth and Family Services, Inc. 405.262.6555
Fax 405.262.6557
7565 East Highway 66, El Reno, OK 73036
Dee Blose, Director
CARF accredited programs available.

Youth Services 580.323.3322
Fax 580.323.6233
600 Avant, Clinton, OK 73601
cody brittain, director
CARF accredited programs available.

Youth Services 580.924.6263
Fax 580.924.6775
1105 Lynnwood, Durant, OK 74701
CARF accredited programs available.

Youth Services 580.255.8800
Fax 580.255.8842
16 South Seventh Street, Duncan, OK 73533
CARF accredited programs available.

Youth Services 405.235.7537
Fax 405.528.5754
Web .... www.ysoc.org
201 Northeast 50th Street, Oklahoma City,
OK 73105
CARF accredited programs available.

Youth Services, Inc. 918.756.7700
Fax 918.756.3347
Web .... www.annemoroneyyouthservices.com
1950 North Okmulgee, Okmulgee, OK 74447
CARF accredited programs available.

Youth Services, Inc. 580.326.3382
Fax 580.326.3383
101 West Jefferson, Hugo, OK 74743
Tiffany Gail, Director
CARF accredited programs available.

Youth Services, Inc. 405.377.3380
Fax 405.377.3499
Web .... www.pcys.org
E-mail .... janetf@pcys.org
2224 West 12th Street, Stillwater, OK 74074
Janet Irwin-fultz, Director
CARF accredited programs available.

Youth Services, Inc. 918.647.4196
Fax 918.647.5741
Web .... www.lcys.org
320 Dewey Avenue, Poteau, OK 74953
CARF accredited programs available.

Youth Svcs 405.377.3380
Fax 405.377.3499
E-mail .... pcysoffice@pcys.org
2224 W 12th Ave, Stillwater, OK 74074-5154
Janet Fultz, Director

YWCA Oklahoma City 405.948.1770
Fax 405.943.7177
Web .... www.ywcaokc.org
2460 West I-44 Service Road, Oklahoma City,
OK 73112
CARF accredited programs available.

**Zen Gee Counseling & Psychological Services,
LLC** 580.298.5062
Fax 580.298.5072
Web .... www.embracingchange.info
608 Highway 271 North, Antlers, OK 74523
CARF accredited programs available.

**Zen Gee Counseling & Psychological Services,
LLC** 580.513.2932
Fax 580.298.5072
608 Highway 271 North, Antlers, OK 74523
CARF accredited programs available.

CHILDREN'S HOSPITAL

Baptist Medical Center of Ok 405.949.3011
3300 NW Expressway, Oklahoma City, OK 73112
Chris Hammas, Chief Executive Officer

Bristow Medical Center 918.367.2215
700 West 7th St Ste 6, Bristow, OK 74010
Jan Winter, Chief Executive Officer

Choctaw Nation Health Care Center 918.567.7000
One Choctaw Way, Talihina, OK 74571

Cleveland Area Hospital 918.358.2501
1401 West Pawnee St, Cleveland, OK 74020
Jim Clough, Chief Executive Officer

Community Hospital 580.735.2555
Highway 64 North, Buffalo, OK 73834
Karen Ives, Chief Executive Officer

Cordell Memorial Hospital 580.832.3339
1220 North Glen English St, Cordell, OK 73632
Charles Greene, Administrator

Craig General Hospital 918.256.7551
735 N. Foreman St, Vinita, OK 74301
Rex Walk, Chief Executive Officer

Creek Nation Community Hospital 918.623.1424
309 North 14th St, Okemah, OK 74859
Edwin McLemore, Administrative Assistant

Harmon Memorial Hospital 580.688.3363
400 E Chestnut St, Hollis, OK 73550
Shelia Lewis, Chief Executive Officer

Hillcrest Medical Center 918.579.1000
E-mail .... kdscott@hillcrest.com
1120 South Utica St, Tulsa, OK 74104
Jason Fahrlander, Chief Executive Officer

Integris Baptist Regional Health Center 918.542.6611
200 Second Ave SW, Miami, OK 74354
Joel Hart, Administrator

Medical Center of Southeastern OK 580.924.3080
1800 University Blvd, Durant, OK 74701
Patricia Dorris, Chief Executive Officer

Memorial Hospital 918.696.3101
1401 West Locust, Stilwell, OK 74960
Alan L Adams, Administrator

Memorial Hospital and Physician Group 580.335.7565
319 East Josephine, Frederick, OK 73542
Al Allee, Chief Executive Officer

Mercy Health Center 405.755.1515
4300 West Memorial Rd, Oklahoma City, OK 73120
Jim Gebhart, President

Muskogee Regional Medical Center 918.682.5501
300 Rockefeller Dr, Muskogee, OK 74401
Kevin Fowler, Chief Executive Officer

Oklahoma State University Medical Ctr 918.587.2561
744 West Ninth St, Tulsa, OK 74127
Jane Slater, Chief Executive Officer

OU Medical Center 405.271.4700
1200 Everett Dr, Oklahoma City, OK 73104
Pole Eslyn, Chief Executive Officer

Purcell Municipal Hospital 405.527.6524
1500 North Green Ave, Purcell, OK 73080
Jim Berry, Chief Executive Officer

Reynolds Army Community Hospital 580.458.3000
4301 Mow Way Rd, Fort Sill, OK 73503

Southwestern Medical Center 580.531.4700
5602 SW Lee Blvd, Lawton, OK 73505
Mary Westman, Chief Nursing Officer

St Francis Hospital 918.434.2200
6161 South Yale Ave, Tulsa, OK 74136

St John Medical Center 918.744.2345
1923 South Utica Ave, Tulsa, OK 74104
Charles Anderson, President

St Marys Regional Medical Center 580.233.6100
305 South Fifth St, Enid, OK 73701
Stan Tatum, Administrator

Tahlequah City Hospital 918.456.0641
1400 E Downing St, Tahlequah, OK 74464

Tulsa Spine and Specialty Hospital 918.388.5701
6901 South Olympia Ave, Tulsa, OK 74132
Terry Woodbeck, Chief Executive Officer

Valley View Regional Hospital 580.332.2323
E-mail .... dgould@vvrh.com
430 North Monta Vista, Ada, OK 74820
Kent Rogers, Chief Executive Officer

Wagoner Community Hospital 918.485.5514
1200 West Cherokee, Wagoner, OK 74467
Jimmy Leapard, Chief Executive Officer

COUNSELING SERVICES

Oklahoma Families First, Inc 580.226.9388
Fax 580.226.9395
E-mail .... chillierd@familiesfirstinc.org
1301 Crossroads Dr Ste A, kiowa, OK 73401-2503
Christy Hillierd, Director Of Therapeutic Family Counseling

Oklahoma Families First, Inc. 580.924.9441
Fax 580.924.9459
Web .... www.offibhs.org
E-mail .... travis.gameson@offibhs.org
4216 Commercial Ln, Durant, OK 74701-7785
Travis Gameson, Director

Sunbeam Family Svcs 405.528.7721
Fax 405.528.7731
Web .... www.sunbeamfamilyservices.org
E-mail .... webmaster@sunbeamfamilyservices.org
616 NW 21st St, Oklahoma City, OK 73146
Ray Bitsche, Executive Director

CRISIS & SHELTER CARE

Care Cottage 580.320.5437
Fax 580.332.2441
E-mail .... adacarecottage@yahoo.com
514 E 10th St, Ada, OK 74820-5223
Gwen Gjovig, Director

Cherokee Nation Youth Svcs 918.458.4440
Fax 918.458.7655
E-mail .... lindavann@cherokee.org
21834 S. Jules Valdez Road, Tahlequah, OK 74465
Linda Vann, Associate Director

Community Crisis Ctr 918.540.2432
Fax 918.542.1027
E-mail .... ccci@table1.net
17 north maine, miami, OK 74354
Niovionni Cox, Director

Crisis Control Ctr 580.924.3030
Fax 580.924.3493
E-mail .... nwalker@netcommander.com
115 N 12th Ave Ste C, Durant, OK 74701-4767
Norita Walker, Executive Director

Dayspring Villa-Domestic Violence 918.245.4075
Fax 918.245.3995
Web .... www.dayspringvilla.com
E-mail .... wlively@dayspringvilla.com
7802 W 7th St, Tulsa, OK 74127
Wilma Lively, Director

Domestic Violence Intervention Svcs, Inc. 918.224.9290
Fax 918.248.7140
424 E Hobson Ave, Sapulpa, OK 74066-3504

**Domestic Violence Prog-North Ctrl
Oklahoma** 580.762.2873
Fax 580.762.3603
E-mail .... dvtn@co.org
208 S 13th St, Ponca City, OK 74601
Amanda Doran, Director

Oklahoma

Domestic Vlnce Intervention-Call Rape 918.744.7273
Fax 918.744.4432
E-mail .... Tredmon@Dvis.Org
4300 S Harvard Ave, Tulsa, OK 74135
Tracey Redmon, Executive Director

Family Crisis And Counseling 918.336.1188
Fax 918.336.2933
Web .... www.onenet.net/
E-mail .... safe@onenet.net
615 SE Frank Phillips Blvd, Bartlesville, OK 74003-3918
Barbra Turner, Executive Director

Family Crisis Ctr, Inc 580.436.3504
Fax 580.436.5047
E-mail .... fccsharell@sbcglobal.net
605 E. 12th St, Ada, OK 74820
Sharell Campton, Director

Family Resource Ctr-Domestic Violence 405.382.5979
Fax 405.382.5978
Web .... ww.familyrc.org
E-mail .... familyrc@sbcglobal.net
212 East Oak, Seminole, OK 74868
Laura Allison, Director

Family Shelter Of Southern Oklahoma 580.226.3750
Fax 580.226.6470
E-mail .... thefamilyshelter@dwoodbridze.net
117 B St SW, Ardmore, OK 73401
Debra Woodbridze, Director

Marie Detty Youth And Family Svc Ctr 580.248.6450
Fax 580.248.6486
317 C Ave, Lawton, OK 73502
Dianne Owens, Director

Mcalester Care Ctr-Domestic Violence 918.423.0032
Fax 918.426.4150
Web .... www.kibois.org
E-mail .... deidre.harris@kibois.org
PO Box 3324, Mcalester, OK 74502-1404
Nancy Sparks, Director

New Directions, Inc. 580.357.6141
Fax 580.250.0246
E-mail .... ndadminasst@mariedety.com
PO Box 1684, Lawton, OK 73502-1684
Leah Stout, Director

Safenet Svcs Inc-Domestic Violence 918.341.1424
Fax 918.341.1471
E-mail .... info@safenetservices.org
2235 N Highway 88, Claremore, OK 74018
Donna Grabow, Director

Southeastern Oklahoma Svcs Sos, Inc 580.286.7583
Fax 580.286.2599
Web .... www.mchep.osrhe.edu
106 W Main St, Antlers, OK 74523
Lasonya Butler, Director

Southwestern Youth Svcs 580.482.2809
Fax 580.482.2820
Web .... www.swys.org
E-mail .... swys7867@sbcglobal.net
1313 N Forrest St, Altus, OK 73521-2734
Veronica Damron, Director

The Tulsa Day Ctr For Homeless 918.583.5588
Fax 918.583.6745
415 W Archer St, Tulsa, OK 74103
Sandra Lewis, Director

Thunderbird Youth Academy 918.824.4850
Fax 918.824.4858
Web .... www.ngycp.org
417 S Elliott St, Pryor, OK 74361
Jack Ritchie, Program Director

Willow Crest Hospital & Moccasin Bend Ranch 918.542.1836
Fax 918.542.8730
130 A St SW, Miami, OK 74354
Camelia Willis, Director Of Patient Services

Women's Resource Ctr. 405.364.9424
Fax 405.364.4888
E-mail .... wrc@wrcweb.net
501 Alameda St Ste E, Norman, OK 73071-5465
Joann Smith, Executive Director

Women's Svc And Family Resource Ctr 405.222.1818
Fax 405.224.4406
E-mail .... wsfrc@sbcglobal.net
1628 S 17th St, Chickasha, OK 73018
Debbie Gitthens, Director

Youth And Family Resource Ctr 405.275.3340
Fax 405.275.3343
Web .... www.hopehouseonline.org
E-mail .... scm@hopehouseonline.org
326 W 11th St, Shawnee, OK 74801
Susan Morris, Director

Youth Svcs 580.255.8800
Fax 580.255.8842
E-mail .... ythsvc@sbcglobal.net
16 S 7th Street, Duncan, OK 73533
John Herdt, Director

EDUCATION

Guthrie Job Corps Ctr 405.282.9930
Fax 405.282.6743
Web .... www.guthriejcc.com
E-mail .... mayberry.priscilla@jobcorps.org
3106 W University Ave, Guthrie, OK 73044
Priscilla Mayberry, Center Director

Talking Leaves Job Corps Ctr 918.456.9959
Fax 918.207.3489
Web .... www.tljc.org
E-mail .... littlejohn.j@jobcoprs.org
5700 Bald Hill Rd., Tahlequah, OK 74465
Jay Littlejohn, Center Director

Tulsa Job Corps Ctr 918.585.9111
Fax 918.732.5303
E-mail .... thee.wayne@jobcorps.org
1133 N Lewis Ave, Tulsa, OK 74110-4730
Wayne Thee, Center Director

FOSTER CARE AGENCIES

Choices For Life 918.248.4340
724 S Mission St, Sapulpa, OK 74066
Melanie Johnson, Director

Cimarron Valley Therapeutic 580.765.0076
2553 Olivewood Ct, Ponca City, OK 74604
Sharon Sisco, Director

Circle Of Care Child Share 405.579.1232
407 S University Blvd, Norman, OK 73069

Crisis Pregnancy Outreach 918.296.3377
Fax 866.336.4948
E-mail .... cherylbauman@earthlink.net
11323 S Vine St, Jenks, OK 74037
Cheryl Bauman, Director

Foster Care Assoc of Oklahoma Inc 405.387.5052
E-mail .... lana.73@gmail.com
Route 1 Box 188, Wellston, OK 74881
Lana Freeman, President

Oklahoma Family Connections Inc 405.282.3539
Fax 405.282.3755
PO Box 367, Guthrie, OK 73044

Oklahoma Post Adoption Triad Support Grp 918.369.1279
E-mail .... s.franklin565@yahoo.com
5202 S Hudson Ave, Tulsa, OK 74105
Samantha Franklin, Director

One Church One Child of Oklahoma Inc 405.424.0225
E-mail .... 1church1child@sbcglobal.net
3129 North MLK Blvd, Oklahoma City, OK 73111
Valarie Howard, Executive Director

HOME MEDICAL EQUIPMENT PROVIDERS

Limbs for Life Foundation 405.843.5174
Fax 405.843.5123
E-mail .... cgavras@limbsforlife.org
218 E Main St, Oklahoma City, OK 73104
Craig Gavras, Executive Director

PEDIATRIC HOME CARE

Interim Healthcare 405.848.3555
Fax 405.842.4629
5600 N May Ste 145, Oklahoma City, OK 73112
Sharon Collins, General Manager

Interim Healthcare 918.331.0900
Fax 918.331.0735
1025 Swan Dr Ste 306, Bartlesville, OK 74006

Interim Healthcare 918.749.9933
Fax 918.747.9315
2828 E 51 St, Ste 102, Tulsa, OK 74105

SOCIAL SERVICES

Agape Pre-School And Childcare Ctr 918.341.0870
Fax 918.341.0870
Web .... www.agapechildrenscenter.org
E-mail .... kschmitz@agapechildrenscenter.org
29506 S Highway 66, Claremore, OK 74019
Karen Schmitz, Owner

Birth Choice 405.262.0003
Fax 405.632.4347
400 W London St, El Reno, OK 73036
Barbara Doyle, Director

Birth Choice 405.330.2111
Web .... www.birthchoice.org
11 Burton Pl, # C, Edmond, OK 73013
Pat Mayes, Director

Birth Choice 405.360.9555
Fax 405.348.9937
Web .... www.birthchoice.org
457 W Gray St, Norman, OK 73069-7117
Jenifer Borba, Clinic Director

Birth Choice Of Lawton 580.248.3110
Fax 580.248.3165
E-mail .... bcl@sirinet.net
5108 W Gour Blvd, Lawton, OK 73505
Rosalia Jaume, Director

Birth Choice Of Oklahoma Inc 405.495.6919
Fax 405.787.0467
5106 N Rockwell Ave, Bethany, OK 73008
Ray Merchant, Director

Birth Choice Of Stillwater Inc 405.377.5683
1309 S Husband Pl, Stillwater, OK 74074
Sandra Joneswebster, Director Volunteer

Cart House 405.422.3459
Fax 405.422.3616
E-mail .... bmcbee@cancochildadvocates.com
318 N Choctaw Ave, El Reno, OK 73036
Bonnie McBee, Executive Administrator Director

CASA 13th District 918.787.6481
Fax 918.787.6333
E-mail .... 13jdcasaok@sbcglobal.net
8 East 6th Street, Grove, OK 74345
Crystal Huff, Program Director

Catholic Charities of the Archdiocese of Oklahoma City 405.523.3000
Fax 405.523.3030
Web .... www.catholiccharitiesok.org
1501 N. Classen Boulevard, Oklahoma City, OK 73106
COA accredited organization.

Catholic Social Svcs 918.585.8167
Fax 918.582.2123
E-mail ....tsullivan@catholiccharitiestulsa.org
739 N Denver Ave, Tulsa, OK 74106-5184
Timothy Sullivan, Director

Cherokee Nation Child Care Resource Ctr 918.453.5300
Fax 918.458.7616
Web ....www.cherokeekids.org
E-mail ....ccrc@cherokee.org
22361 Bald Hill Rd, Tahlequah, OK 74464
Lori Hand, Director

Child Care Assoc Choctaw Nation 580.924.8280
Fax 580.920.4959
Web ....www.choctawnation.com
601 1/2 N. 16th, Durant, OK 74702
Marilyn Williams, Director

Child Care Resource And Referral 580.548.2318
Fax 580.548.2342
Web ....www.childcarefinder.org
E-mail ....cdsaccf@sbcglobal.net
2615 E Randolph Ave, Enid, OK 73701-4670
Dianne Junhnke, Director

Child Care Resource Ctr 918.834.2273
Fax 918.834.9339
Web ....www.ccrtulsa.org/
E-mail ....lreece@ccrctulsa.org
18 N Norwood Ave, Tulsa, OK 74115-8620
Beth Sullins, Operation Manager

Children First 405.271.7611
Fax 405.271.1011
Web ....www.health.ok.gov
E-mail ....mildredr@health.ok.gov
1000 NE 10th St, Oklahoma City, OK 73117-1207
Mildred Ramsey, Director

Childrens Advocacy Network 918.647.3814
Fax 918.647.0628
E-mail ....lccan1@windstream.net
300 Rogers Ave, Poteau, OK 74953-4228
Deanna Chancellor, Director

CommunityWorks, LLC 405.447.4499
Fax 405.447.4419
Web ....www.communityworksok.com
122 E. Eufaula Street, Norman, OK 73069
COA accredited organization.

COPE, Inc. 405.528.8686
Fax 405.528.8692
Web ....www.okcopeinc.org
2701 N Oklahoma Avenue, Oklahoma City, OK 73105
COA accredited organization.

Crossroads 405.282.0800
E-mail ....info@Crossroad.com
3077 E College Dr, Guthrie, OK 73044
Linda Stewart, Director

Ctr On Child Abuse And Neglect 405.271.8858
Fax 405.271.2931
Web www.w3.ouhsc.edu/ccan
E-mail ....barbara-bonner@ouhsc.edu
940 NE 13th Ste CHO, Oklahoma City, OK 73104-0001
Barbara L. Bonner, Director

Domestic Violence Intervention Services, Inc. 918.585.3163
Fax 918.584.1835
Web ....www.dvis.org
4300 S. Harvard Avenue, Suite 100, Tulsa, OK 74135
COA accredited organization.

Family & Children's Services, Inc. 918.587.9471
Fax 918.560.1184
Web ....www.fcsok.org
650 South Peoria Avenue, Tulsa, OK 74120-4429
COA accredited organization.

Family Ctr 918.540.1621
Fax 918.540.2205
E-mail ....familycenter@cableone.net
23 B St, Miami, OK 74354
Dan Christopher, Director

Great Plains Child Care Resource And Referral Ctr 580.726.2172
Fax 580.726.3384
Web ....www.gpccrr.org/
E-mail ....thenderson@gpccrr.org
901 S Broadway, Hobart, OK 73651-1834
Taffy Henderson, Director

Hope Outreach Parenting Ministry 580.237.2292
Fax 580.237.2293
Web ....www.hopeoutreach.org
E-mail ....lee@hopeoutreach.org
815 W Broadway Ave, Enid, OK 73701-3887
Lee Lankshaw, Director

Indian Health Care Resource Ctr Of Tulsa 918.588.1900
Fax 918.582.6405
Web ....www.ihcrc.org
E-mail ....cskeeter@ihcrc.org
550 S Peoria Ave, Tulsa, OK 74120
Carmelita Skeeter, Executive Director

Lend-A-Hand Parent-Child Center For the Prevention of Child Abuse, Inc. 405.235.9812
Fax 405.236.8383
P.O. Box 1723, Oklahoma City, OK 73101-1723
COA accredited organization.

Muscogee Creek Nation/Child Care 918.732.7680
Fax 918.758.1498
Web ....www.muscogeenation-msn.com
E-mail ....nfrank@muscogeenation-msn.com
1008 E Eufaula St, Okmulgee, OK 74447-7939
Faith Watashe, Manager

Northwest Domestic Crisis Svcs, Inc. 580.256.1215
Fax 580.256.1245
E-mail ....woodwardcrisis@sbcglobal.net
1024 22nd St, Ste 100, Woodward, OK 73801-2825
Paul Fockler, Director

Parent Child Ctr Of Tulsa 918.599.7999
Fax 918.699.0598
Web ....www.parentchildcenter.org
E-mail ....ddoherty@parentchildcenter.org
1421 S Boston Ave, Tulsa, OK 74119-3607
Desiree Doherty, Executive Director

Prevent Child Abuse OK 405.232.2500
Fax 405.232.0050
E-mail ....pcaok@sbcglobal.net
437 NW 12th St, Oklahoma City, OK 73103-3706
Billie Brown, Executive Director

Rainbow Fleet CCR&R 405.525.3111
Fax 405.525.0752
Web ....www.rainbowfleet.org/
E-mail ....ccc@rainbowfleet.org
3024 Paseo, Oklahoma City, OK 73103
Royce Junghanns, Director

The Jetty Counseling Center 405.665.4385
Fax 405.665.6396
202 South Washita, Wynnewood, OK 73098
james wallace, ex director
CARF accredited programs available.

Trinity Medical Consultants, LLC 405.317.7447
Fax 866.471.1166
Web ....trinitymedicalconsultants.org
E-mail ....kjnix@trinitymedicalconsultants.org
P.O. Box 890850, OK, OK 73170
Kelly Nix, Certified Case Manager

Tulsa Boys' Home, Inc. 918.245.0231
Fax 918.241.5031
Web ....www.tulsaboyshome.org
P.O. Box 1101, Tulsa, OK 74101-1101
COA accredited organization.

Wesleyan Youth, Inc. 405.524.4457
Fax 405.524.5762
Web ....www.wesleyanyouth.org
4500 North Classen, Suite 200, Oklahoma City, OK 73118-4823
Scott Simmons, Director: Rev
CARF accredited programs available.

Western Plains Youth And Family Svcs 580.254.5322
Fax 580.254.5335
E-mail ....kevans@wpyfs.org
1213 W Hanks Trl, Woodward, OK 73801
Kevin Evans, Executive Director

Women In Safe Home, Inc. 918.682.7879
Fax 918.682.3402
E-mail ....muskwishkl@emptychair.net
514 W Martin Luther King St, Muskogee, OK 74401
Evelyn Hibbs, Executive Director

Women's Crisis Ctr 918.647.9800
102 Austin, Poteau, OK 74953
Sissy Carden, Director

Youth Services of Tulsa, Inc. 918.582.0061
Fax 918.382.3434
Web ....www.yst.org
311 South Madison, Tulsa, OK 74120
COA accredited organization.

Youth Svc Ctr 918.287.2881
Fax 918.287.2822
E-mail ....mrwysoc@hotmail.com
1616 Mckenzie Rd, Pawhuska, OK 74056
Harold H. Huffman, Director

SPECIAL NEEDS

Autism Society of Central Oklahoma 405.370.3220
PO Box 720103, Norman, OK 73070

Congress of Parents & Teachers Inc 405.681.0750
E-mail ....director@okpta.org
2801 N Lincoln Blvd Ste 214, Oklahoma City, OK 73105
Sherry Riemer, Director

Daybreak Dynamics, Inc 918.592.1622
Fax 918.592.3442
E-mail ....don@daybreakdynamics.com
1701 S Peoria Ave, Tulsa, OK 74120

Down Syndrome Association 405.330.5025
E-mail ....president@dsaco.org
720 W Wilshire Blvd Ste 112, Central OKhlahoma, OK 74075
Mike Erhart, President

Easter Seals Oklahoma 405.239.2525
E-mail ....pporter@eastersealsoklahoma.org
701 NE 13th St, Oklahoma City, OK 73104
Paula Porter, Chief Executive Officer

Epilepsy Association of Oklahoma 405.271.3232
E-mail ....epilepsy-ok@prodigy.net
711 Stanton L Young Blvd, Ste 550, Oklahoma City, OK 73104
Ramona Hannah, Volunteer

Family Voices 405.373.3300
E-mail ....okvoices@aol.com
PO Box 32255, Oklahoma City, OK 73123

Integris Southwest Medical Center 405.644.5170
Fax 405.644.6112
E-mail ....brent.beson@integrisok.com
4221 S Western Ste 5010, Oklahoma City, OK 73109
Brent Beson Md, Director

Jim Thorpe Rehabilitation Hospital at INTEGRIS Southwest Medical Center 405.644.5200
Fax 405.644.5384
Web ....www.integrisjimthorpe.com
4219 South Western, Oklahoma City, OK 73109
CARF accredited programs available.

Oklahoma

Oklahoma

Learning Disabilities Association **918.298.1600**
E-mail ....ldao2002@sbcglobal.net
PO Box 1134, Jenks, OK 74037

McCarty Ctr f/Children w/Dev Disability **405.307.2800**
E-mail ....curt@jdmc.org
2002 E Robinson St, Norman, OK 73071
Vickey Kuesterstenn, Director

NAMI Oklahoma **405.230.1900**
E-mail ....nami-ok@swbell.net
4200 Perimeter Dr Ste 150, Oklahoma City,
OK 73111
Andi Michael, Office Manager

National Multiple Sclerosis Society **918.488.0882**
Fax 918.488.0913
E-mail ....paula.cordner@oke.nmss.org
4606 E 67th St, Bldg 7 Ste 103, Tulsa, OK 74136
Paula Cordner, Vice President

OASIS **405.271.6302**
E-mail ....oasis@ouhsc.edu
1122 NE 30th St, Oklahoma City, OK 73117
Sally Selvidge, Director

Oklahoma Autism Network **405.271.7466**
E-mail ....okautism@ouhsc.edu
1200 N Stonewall Ave, Oklahoma City, OK 73117
Rene Daman, Director

Oklahoma Handicapped Concerns **800.522.8224**
2401 NW 23rd Ste 90, Oklahoma City, OK 73107
Steve Dockes, Director

Oklahoma NeuroSpecialty **918.477.5111**
Fax 918.477.5199
Web ....www.neurorestorative.com
2408 East 81st Street, Suite 2600, Tulsa, OK 74137
CARF accredited programs available.

Oklahoma Parent Center Inc **405.379.6015**
Fax 405.379.2106
E-mail ....info@oklahomaparentscenter.org
221 NORTH BRAODWAY, Holdenville, OK 74848
Sharon House, Chief Executive Officer

Oklahoma Parents Center **877.553.4332**
E-mail ....okparentscenter@aol.com
PO Box 512, Holdenville, OK 74848

Saint Francis Rehabilitation **918.494.4200**
Web ....www.saintfrancis.com
6161 South Yale Avenue, Four South, Tulsa,
OK 74136
Nita Coffin, nursing Director
CARF accredited programs available.

Speech-Language-Hearing Association **405.271.4214**
E-mail ....oslha@hotmail.com
PO Box 53217, Oklahoma City, OK 73152

TARC **918.582.8272**
E-mail ....tarc@ddadvocacy.net
16 E 16th St Ste 405, Tulsa, OK 74119
John Gadja, Executive Director

The Children's Center Pediatric Medical Rehabilitation
Unit **405.789.6711**
Fax 405.440.6722
Web ....www.tccokc.org
6800 Northwest 39th Expressway, Bethany,
OK 73008
CARF accredited programs available.

The Rehabilitation Center at Norman Regional
Hospital **405.307.3800**
Fax 405.307.3841
Web ....www.normanregional.com
901 North Porter, Norman, OK 73071
CARF accredited programs available.

United Cerebral Palsy of Oklahoma **405.759.3562**
E-mail ....oklahoma@ucpok.org
10400 Greenbriar Pl Ste 101, Oklahoma City,
OK 73159
James Rankin, Director

SUBSTANCE ABUSE TREATMENT

ActionSteps Counseling, Inc. **918.764.9098**
Fax 319.856.8426
Web ....www.actionstepstulsa.com
5525 East 51st Street, Suite 210, Tulsa, OK 74135
Lawrence Gilbert, Director
CARF accredited programs available.

C.A.R.E. For Change, Inc. **405.524.5525**
Fax 405.524.5528
Web ....www.careforchange.org
E-mail ....info@careforchange.org
3621 North Kelley Avenue, Suite 100, Oklahoma
City, OK 73111
Dr. Kevin Mcpherson, CLINICAL DIRECTOR
CARF accredited programs available.

Eagle Ridge Family Treatment Ctr **405.282.8232**
Fax 405.282.0083
E-mail ....egriffith@eagleridgerok.org
1916 E Perkins Ave, Guthrie, OK 73044-5804
Ellen Griffith, Director

Family Recovery Counseling Center **405.606.8406**
Fax 405.606.8194
Web ....www.frcc-okc.com
E-mail ....krodgers@frcc-okc.com
3700 North Classen Boulevard, Suite 240, Oklahoma
City, OK 73118
Kathryn Rodgers, Executive Director
CARF accredited programs available.

Jack Brown Youth Regional Treatment
Center **918.453.5507**
Fax 918.458.0499
E-mail ....mmiller@cherokee.org
17091 South Muskogee, Tahlequah, OK 74464
Mike Miller, Communications Director
CARF accredited programs available.

Life Improvement Ctr **405.239.6815**
Fax 405.239.2637
Web ....www.missiontreatment.com
1214 N Hudson Ave, Oklahoma City,
OK 73103-3717
Bob Weeks, Medical Director

New Hope of Mangum **580.782.3337**
Fax 580.782.3338
Web ....newhope.com
Two Wickersham Drive, Mangum, OK 73554
CARF accredited programs available.

Roadback, Inc. **580.357.8114**
Fax 580.353.3854
E-mail ....roadback@sunnet.net
405 SW 16th St, Lawton, OK 73501-4405
Dr. Taylor, Director

Shekinah Counseling Services **580.924.6358**
Fax 580.920.1901
Web ....www.ok.gov
E-mail ....kim.cooper@dsheriff.org
4310 W University, Durant, OK 74701
Kim Cooper, Executive Director
CARF accredited programs available.

Southwest Youth And Family Svcs, Inc **405.222.5437**
Fax 405.222.5441
E-mail ....swyss1@prodigy.net
198 E Almar Dr, Chickasha, OK 73018-7327
Nick Widener, Director

The Oaks Rehabilitative Services Center **918.423.6030**
Fax 918.423.2370
Web ....www.theoaksrehab.org
628 East Creek Street, McAlester, OK 74501
CARF accredited programs available.

Turning Point Alcohol & Drug Center **918.336.4646**
Fax 918.336.8710
622 Southeast Frank Phillips Boulevard, Bartlesville,
OK 74003
BARBARA TURNER, EXECUTIVE DIRECTOR
CARF accredited programs available.

Oregon

John Kitzhaber, Governor
160 State Capitol
900 Court St. NE
Salem, OR 97301-4047
503.378.4582
503.378.6827 (Fax)
www.governor.oregon.gov

Anya Sekino, Juvenile Justice Specialist
530 Center St Ste 405
Salem, OR 97301
503.378.5115
503.378.8395 (Fax)
anya.sekino@state.or.us

Kelly Dedel, PhD, SAG Chair
1608 NW Riverscape
Portland, OR 97209
541.766.6804
541.766.6893 (Fax)
kdedel@comcast.net

CRISIS NUMBERS

Child Abuse Reporting . . .800.422.4453

STATE SERVICES

SOCIAL SERVICES

Dept of Human Svcs **503.945.5944**
Fax 503.378.2897
Web ....www.oregon.gov/dhs/index.shtml
  500 Summer St NE, #E-15, Salem, OR 97301

Oregon Child Care Div **503.947.1400**
Fax 503.947.1428
Web ....www.chilcareinoregon.org
  875 Union St NE, Salem, OR 97311-0800
  Tami Scott, Supervisor

GENERAL HEALTH SERVICES

Ctr for Child & Youth **503.494.8303**
Fax 503.494.2755
  707 SW Gaines st, Portland, OR 97239
  Marioyn Hartzell, Director

Office of Family Health OR **971.673.0233**
Fax 971.673.0231
E-mail ....katherine.bradley@state.or.us
  RSA Tower Ste 1360, Portland, OR 97232
  Katherine Bradley, Director

Oregon Dental Assoc **503.218.2010**
Fax 503.218.2009
Web ....www.oregondental.org
E-mail ....bzepp@oregondental.org
  8699 SW Sun Pl, Wilsonville, OR 97070
  William Zepp, Director

Oregon Medical Board **971.673.2700**
Fax 971.673.2670
Web ....www.oregon.gov/omb
E-mail ....omb.info@state.or.us
  1500 SW 1st Ave Ste 620, Portland, OR 97201-5847
  Kathleen Haley, Executive Director

Oregon State WIC Ofc **971.673.0040**
Fax 971.673.0071
Web ....www.oregon.gov/dhs
E-mail ....susan.woodbury@state.or.us
  800 NE Oregon St Ste 310, Portland, OR 97232
  Susan Woodbury, Manager

MENTAL HEALTH SERVICES

Addictions and Mental Health **503.945.5763**
Fax 503.378.8467
Web ....www.oregon.gov/dhs/mentalhealth
E-mail ....richard.harris@state.or.us
  500 Summer St NE Ea 6, E86, Salem, OR 97301
  Richard Harris, Administrator

Oregon Commission for the Blind **971.673.1588**
Fax 503.234.7468
E-mail ....linda.mock@state.or.us
  535 SE 12th Ave, Portland, OR 97214
  Linda Mock, Director

Vocational Rehabilitation Div **503.945.5880**
Fax 503.947.5025
  500 Summer St NE, Salem, OR 97301
  Stephanie Parrish Taylor, Administrator

JUSTICE AGENCY

Attorney General's Ofc **503.378.6002**
Fax 503.378.4017
Web ....www.state.or.us
E-mail ....cynthia.stinson@state.or.us
  1162 Court St NE, Salem, OR 97301-4095
  Synthia Stinson, Crime Victim Compensation

Correctional Education Division OR **503.934.1003**
Fax 503.378.5815
E-mail ....karen.trembley@doc.state.or.us
  1793 13th St SE, Salem, OR 97302
  Karen Trembley, Director

Dept of Corrections **503.945.0920**
Fax 503.373.1173
Web ....www.doc.state.or.us
E-mail ....max.williams@doc.state.or.us
  2575 Center St NE, Salem, OR 97301-4667
  Max Williams, Director

**Oregon CASA-Commission on Children &
Families** **503.373.1283**
Fax 503.378.8395
Web ....www.state.or.us
  530 Center St NE Ste 100, Salem, OR 97301-3754
  Iris Bell, Deputy Director

Oregon Youth Authority (OYA) **503.373.7205**
Fax 503.373.7622
Web ....www.oya.state.or.us
E-mail ....oya.info@oya.state.or.us
  530 Center St NE Ste 200, Salem, OR 97301
  Colette S Peters, Director

Victim's Advocate Program **541.473.5127**
Fax 541.473.5199
E-mail ....daoffice@malheurco.org
  251 B St W Box # 6, Vale, OR 97918
  Nancy Blodgett, Director

COURTS

Ofc of The State Court Admin **503.986.5500**
Fax 503.986.5503
  1163 State St, Supreme Court Building, Salem,
  OR 97301
  Kingsley W. Click, Administrator

POLICE AND SHERIFF

Oregon Assoc Chiefs of Police **503.315.1411**
Fax 503.315.1416
Web ....www.policechief.org
  1191 Capitol St NE, Salem, OR 97301
  Kevin Campbell, Executive Director

Oregon State Police **503.378.3720**
Fax 503.378.3720
  255 Capitol St NE 4th Fl, Salem, OR 97310
  Nancy Brown, Superintendant

Oregon State Sheriff's Assoc **503.364.4204**
Fax 503.364.2059
Web ....www.oregonsheriffs.org
E-mail ....info@oregonsheriffs.org
  330 Hood St NE, Salem, OR 97301
  Holly Russell, Executive Director

EDUCATION SERVICES

Homeless Education Program Oregon **503.947.5781**
Fax 503.378.5156
E-mail ....dona.bolt@state.or.us
  255 Capitol St NE, Salem, OR 97310
  Dona Bolt, Director

Office of Special Education OR **503.947.5782**
Fax 503.378.5156
E-mail ....robbi.perry@state.or.us
  255 Capitol St NE, Salem, OR 97310
  Robbi Perry, Education Specialist

**Oregan Vocational Rehab-Dept of Human
Svcs** **541.388.6336**
Fax 541.388.6310
Web ....www.state.or.us
E-mail ....gary.daniele@state.or.us
  1230 NE 3RD ST, STE 152, Bend, OR 97701-4376
  Gary Daniele, Branch Manager

Oregon Department of Education **503.947.5600**
Fax 503.378.5156
E-mail ....susan.castillo@state.or.us
  255 Capitol St NE, Salem, OR 97310
  Susan Castillo, Superintendent

Oregon

© 2011 Dorland Health

719

Oregon School for the Deaf 503.378.3825
Fax 503.373.7879
Web www.osd.k12.or.us

E-mail ....patti.togioka@osd.k12.or.us
999 Locust St NE, Salem, OR 97301
Patti Togioka, Director

COUNTY SERVICES

Baker County

MENTAL HEALTH SERVICES

Mountain Valley Mental Health 541.523.3646
Fax 541.523.7602
Web ....www.class.oregonvos.net
2200 4th St, Baker City, OR 97814-2615
Jen Y, Director

JUSTICE AGENCY

CASA 541.403.0405
Fax 541.523.2240
E-mail ....marycollard@bakercasa.com
2100 Main St, Baker City, OR 97814-0327
Mary Collard, Program Director

COURTS

Circuit Court 541.523.6303
Fax 541.523.9738
Web ....www.doc.state.or.us
1995 3rd St Ste 220, Baker City, OR 97814-3362
Honorable Gregory Baxter, Director

Benton County

SOCIAL SERVICES

**Community Human Svcs Child
Welfare 541.757.4121**
Fax 541.757.4214
Web ....www.state.or.us
E-mail ....sara.stankey@state.or.us
555 North West 5th St, Corvallis, OR 97330
Sara Stankey, Protective Service Supervisor

JUSTICE AGENCY

**CASA/ Voices For Children
Program 541.753.5838**
Fax 541.758.7550
Web ....www.casa-vfc.org
E-mail ....casavfc@gmail.com
442 NW 4th St, Corvallis, OR 97339
Maria Chavez Haroldson, Program Director

Juvenile Dept 541.766.6810
Fax 541.766.6071
Web ....www.co.benton.or.us
E-mail ....al.j.krug@co.benton.or.us
4185 SW Research Way Ste 100, Corvallis,
OR 97333-1783
Al Krug, Director

Clackamas County

MENTAL HEALTH SERVICES

**Mental Health Alcohol & Drug
Program 503.655.8558**
Fax 503.655.8197
Web ....www.co.clackamas.or.us
2051 Kaen Rd, Oregon City, OR 97045-1824
Cindy Becker, Director

JUSTICE AGENCY

CASA Program 503.723.0521
Fax 503.723.3836
Web ....www.casa-cc.org
E-mail ....info@casa-cc.org
1001 Malowa Ave, Ste 203, Oregon City, OR 97045
Barbara Johnson, Executive Director

COURTS

Juvenile Court 503.655.8342
Fax 503.655.8448
Web ....www.co.clackamas.or.us/juv
E-mail ....dougpo@co.clackamas.or.us
2123 Kaen Rd, Oregon City, OR 97045-4037
Doug Poppen, Juvenile Department Director

POLICE AND SHERIFF

Oregon City Police Dept 503.657.4964
Fax 503.655.0530
E-mail ....mconrad@ci.oregon-city.or.us
320 Warner Milne Rd, Oregon City, OR 97045-4046
Mike Conrad, Chief Of Police

Sheriff's Ofc 503.785.5000
Fax 503.785.5190
Web ....www.clackamas.us/sheriff
E-mail ....craigrob@co.clackamas.or.us
2223 Kaen Rd, Oregon City, OR 97045-4047
Craig Roberts, Sheriff

EDUCATION SERVICES

Clackamas ESD 503.675.4000
Fax 503.675.4202
Web www.clackesd.k12.og.us
E-mail ....bbolstad@clackesd.k12.or.us
13455 SE 97th Ave, Clackamas, OR 97015-8662
Barbara Bolstad, Special Education Director

Clatsop County

GENERAL HEALTH SERVICES

Health Dept 503.325.8500
Fax 503.325.8678
Web ....www.co.clatsop.or.us
820 Exchange St, Ste 100, Astoria, OR 97103
Margo Lalich, Director

MENTAL HEALTH SERVICES

Mental Health 503.325.5722
Fax 503.325.8483
2120 Exchange St, Ste 301, Astoria, OR 97103
Nancy Winters, Director

JUSTICE AGENCY

**North Coast Youth Correctional
Facility 503.861.7190**
Fax 503.861.9543
Web ....www.oya.state.or.us
E-mail ....dan.berger@oya.state.or.us
1250 SE 19th St, Warrenton, OR 97146-9577
Dan Berger, Superintendent

POLICE AND SHERIFF

Sheriff's Ofc 503.325.8635
Fax 503.325.8675
E-mail ....tbergen@co.clatsop.or.us
355 7th St, Astoria, OR 97103-4533
Thomas Bergen, Sheriff

EDUCATION SERVICES

**Communities In Schools Of The North
Coast 503.739.6042**
Fax 503.717.9171
E-mail ....lunchbuddies@msn.com
88732 Dawson Rd, Seaside, OR 97138-4806
Karna Cupples, Director

Columbia County

GENERAL HEALTH SERVICES

**Columbia Health District Public Health
Authority 503.397.4651**
Fax 503.397.1424
2370 Gable Rd, Saint Helens, OR 97051
Karen Ladd, Director

JUSTICE AGENCY

CASA 503.366.4133
Fax 503.397.0796
E-mail ....columbiacasa@hotmail.com
800 Port Ave, St Helens, OR 97051
Joanna, Director

Scappoose Police Department 503.543.3114
Fax 503.543.2955
E-mail ....info@scappoosepolicedepartment.com
33568 E Columbia Ave, Scappoose, OR 97056
Douglas Greisen, Chief

COURTS

Circuit Court 503.397.2327
Fax 503.397.3226
E-mail ....susan.j.hill@ojd.state.or.us
230 Strand St, Saint Helens, OR 97051
Stan Mendenhall, Juvenile Dept. Director

POLICE AND SHERIFF

Sheriff's Dept 503.366.4611
Fax 503.366.4644
E-mail ....columbiacountysherrif@co.columbia.or.us
901 Port Ave, Saint Helens, OR 97051
Jeff Dickerson, Sheriff

Coos County

SOCIAL SERVICES

DHS, Child Welfare Svcs 541.756.5500
Fax 541.756.4200
2025 Sheridan Ave, North Bend, OR 97459
Melinda Johnson, Branch Manager

MENTAL HEALTH SERVICES

Mental Health 541.756.2020
Fax 541.756.8982
Web ....www.mh.co.coos.or.us
E-mail ....ginger.swan@mh.co.coos.or.us
1975 McPherson St Ste 2, North Bend,
OR 97459-3482
Ginger Swan, Director

POLICE AND SHERIFF

Sheriff's Dept 541.396.3121
Fax 541.396.5932
Web ....www.co.coos.or.us
E-mail ....coosso@co.coos.or.us
250 N Baxter St, Coquille, OR 97423-1875
Andrew Jackson, Sheriff

Crook County

SOCIAL SERVICES

**Dept Of Human Svcs Community Human
Svcs 541.447.6207**
Fax 541.447.7213
457 Ne Ochoco Plaza Dr, Ste B, Prineville, OR 97754
Kim Bush, Supervisor For Child Welfare

GENERAL HEALTH SERVICES

Health Dept **541.447.5165**
Fax 541.447.3093
Web ....www.co.coos.or.us
375 NW Beaver St Ste 100, Prineville,
OR 97754-1802
Marion Brown, Administrator

JUSTICE AGENCY

Juvenile Dept **541.447.5161**
Fax 541.447.2527
Web ....www.co.crook.or.us
E-mail ....debra.patterson@co.crook.or.us
300 NE 3rd St, Prineville, OR 97754
Debra Patterson, Director

POLICE AND SHERIFF

Sheriff's Ofc **541.447.6398**
Fax 541.416.0353
Web ....www.crookcountysheriff.org
308 NE 2nd St, Prineville, OR 97754-1912
Jim Hinsley, Sheriff

Curry County

SOCIAL SERVICES

DHS Children, Adult & Family Svcs District 7
Ofc **541.247.7036**
Fax 541.247.6951
Web ....www.state.or.us
E-mail ....joan.earnest@dhs.or.gov
94145 5th Pl, Gold Beach, OR 97444
Joan Earnest, Supervisor

Human Resource Dept **541.247.5437**
Fax 541.247.6999
Web ....www.state.or.us
94145 5th Pl, Gold Beach, OR 97444
Meagan Riffle, Child Welfare Supervisor

GENERAL HEALTH SERVICES

Health Dept **541.247.3300**
Fax 541.247.5601
94235 Moore St, Gold Beach, OR 97444
Jan Kaplin, Administrator

MENTAL HEALTH SERVICES

Human Svcs **541.247.4082**
Fax 541.247.5058
Web ....www.co.curry.or.us
E-mail ....whited@co.curry.or.us
29821 Colvin St, Gold Beach, OR 97444
James Kaplin, Director

JUSTICE AGENCY

CASA **541.348.2505**
Fax 541.348.2505
174 Deadmond Ferry Rd, Sixes, OR 97476
Lona Kenlow, Manager

Juvenile Dept **541.247.3302**
Fax 541.247.5000
Web ....www.co.curry.or.us/juvenile
E-mail ....ken.dukek@doj.state.or.us
PO Box 746, Gold Beach, OR 97444-0746
Ken Dukek, Director

POLICE AND SHERIFF

Sheriff's Ofc **541.247.3242**
Fax 541.247.6352
Corner Of Culvin And Moore, Gold Beach, OR 97444
Josh Bishop, Sheriff

Deschutes County

SOCIAL SERVICES

Community Human Svcs Child Welfare
Program **541.388.6161**
Fax 541.388.6401
1300 NW Wall St Ste 104, Bend, OR 97701
Joni Gallinger, Child Welfare Lead Supervisor

GENERAL HEALTH SERVICES

Health Dept **541.322.7400**
Fax 541.322.7618
Web ....www.co.deschutes.or.us
E-mail ....susan_mccreedy@co.deschutes.or.us
2577 NE Courtney Dr, Bend, OR 97701-7638
Susan Mcreedy, MPH, MA, HIVCoordinator

JUSTICE AGENCY

CASA Of Central Oregon **541.389.1618**
Fax 541.383.2826
1130 NW Harryman St, Bend, OR 97701
Pam Fortier, Executive Director

Juvenile Empowerment Team
Program **541.549.2302**
Fax 541.549.1762
Web ....www.co.deschutes.or.us
E-mail ....doug_welsh@co.deschutes.or.us
6333 W Hwy 20, Bend, OR 97701
Doug Welch, Coordinator

COURTS

Circuit Court **541.388.5300**
Fax 541.388.5309
1100 NW Bond St, Bend, OR 97701
Honorable Barbara Haslinger, Judge

Juvenile Community Justice **541.388.6671**
Fax 541.383.0165
63360 NW Britta St Ste 1, Bend, OR 97701
Ken Hales, Director

Douglas County

SOCIAL SERVICES

DHS Child Welfare Programs **541.440.3373**
Fax 541.440.3448
Web ....www.oregon.gov
1937 W Harvard Ave, Roseburg, OR 97471-2720
Steve Darling, Program Manager

MENTAL HEALTH SERVICES

Mental Health **541.440.3532**
Fax 541.440.3554
Web ....www.co.douglas.or.us
E-mail ....jhollan@co.douglas.or.us
621 W Madrone St, Roseburg, OR 97470-3090
Jannet Holland, Director

JUSTICE AGENCY

CASA Program **541.672.7001**
Fax 541.440.3880
Web ....www.casaofdouglascounty.org
1000 SE Stephens St, Roseburg, OR 97470-4818
Susan Knight, Director

COURTS

Circuit Court **541.957.2409**
Fax 541.957.2461
Web ....www.doc.state.or.us
1036 SE Douglas Ave, Justice Building, Roseburg,
OR 97470-3364
Honorable Randolph Garrison, Judge

POLICE AND SHERIFF

Sheriff's Office **541.440.4450**
Fax 541.957.8140
Web ....www.co.douglas.or.us
1036 SE Douglas Ave, Roseburg, OR 97470
John Hamlin, Sheriff

EDUCATION SERVICES

Special Education **541.440.4777**
Fax 541.440.4771
Web www.douglasesd.k12.or.us
E-mail ....andy.boe@douglasesd.k12.or.us
1871 NE Stephens St, Roseburg, OR 97470-1433
Andy Boe, Director Of Special Ed

Gilliam County

SOCIAL SERVICES

DHS Children, Adult & Family Svcs **541.384.4252**
Fax 541.384.4262
Web ....www.oregon.gov
E-mail ....brian.stauff@state.or.us
103 South Main St, Condon, OR 97823
Jerry Buzzarz, District Manager

Grant County

SOCIAL SERVICES

Dept Human Svcs, Community Svcs, Child Welfare
Svcs **541.575.0728**
Fax 541.575.0656
725 W Main St Ste C, John Day, OR 97845
Jane Keil, Supervisor

DHS Children, Adult & Family Svcs **541.575.0309**
Fax 541.575.0656
E-mail ....wendy.hill@state.or.us
725 W Main St Ste A, John Day, OR 97845
Wendy Hill, District Manager

GENERAL HEALTH SERVICES

Health Dept **971.673.1222**
Fax 971.673.1299
Web ....www.oregon.gov/dhs
800 NE Oregon St Ste 225, Portland, OR 97232-2187
Bill Coulombe, Md, Deputy Public Health Director

JUSTICE AGENCY

CASA, Inc. **541.575.5574**
Fax 541.575.3601
E-mail ....casa@grantesd.k12.or.us
835 S Canyon Blvd, John Day, OR 97845-1056
Sheri Webb, Executive Director

COURTS

Circuit Court **541.575.1438**
Fax 541.575.2165
201 S Humbolt St, Canyon City, OR
Carol Page, Administrator

POLICE AND SHERIFF

Sheriff's Dept **541.575.1131**
Fax 541.575.2580
205 S Humbolt St, Criminal Justice Facility, Canyon
City, OR 97820
Glenn E. Palmer, Sheriff

Harney County

SOCIAL SERVICES

Burns Paiute Tribe Social Svcs **541.573.2088**
Fax 541.573.4217
100 Pasigo St, Burns, OR 97720
Michelle Bradach, Social Services Director

Oregon

GENERAL HEALTH SERVICES

Health Dept 541.573.2271
Fax...541.573.8388
Web...............................www.harneycounty.com
420 N Fairview Ave, Burns, OR 97720
Steve Grastey, Administrator

JUSTICE AGENCY

Eastern Oregon Youth Correctional

Facility 541.573.3133
Fax...541.573.3665
1800 W Monroe St, Burns, OR 97720
Daniel Robertson, Superintendent

COURTS

Burns School District 541.573.6811
Fax...541.573.7557
550 N Court Ave, Burns, OR 97720
Gwen Haigh, Homeless Liason Coordinator

Court Juvenile Dept 541.573.2439
Fax...541.573.8170
Web...................................www.co.harney.or.us
E-mail.....................william.cramer@co.harney.or.us
450 N Buena Vista Ave, Burns, OR 97720
Honorable William D. Cramer, Director

POLICE AND SHERIFF

Sheriff's Ofc 541.573.6156
Fax...541.573.8383
E-mail...911@co.harney.or.us
485 N Court Ave, Burns, OR 97720
Dave Glerup, Sheriff

Hood River County

SOCIAL SERVICES

Dept Of Human Svcs 541.386.2962
Fax...541.386.7066
1610 9th Ct Ste 500, Hood River, OR 97031
Bill Sheribon, Program Manager

DHS Children, Adult & Family Svcs 541.386.3199
Fax...541.386.6458
Web..www.state.or.us
E-mail...........................susan.gabay@state.or.us
1610 9th Ct, Hood River, OR 97031-1919
Susan Gabay, District Manager

GENERAL HEALTH SERVICES

Health Dept 541.386.1115
Fax...541.386.9181
Web.................................www.co.hood-river.or.us
1109 June St, Hood River, OR 97031-1595
Patricia Elliot, Rn, Nursing Supervisor

JUSTICE AGENCY

Columbia Gorge CASA Program 541.386.3468
Fax...541.386.3641
Web....................................www.nextdoorinc.org
E-mail................................casa@nextdoorinc.org
PO Box 208, Hood River, OR 97031-0007
Debbie Baskins, Program Director

COURTS

Circuit Court 541.386.3535
Fax...541.386.3465
Web......................................www.ojd.state.or.us
E-mail.......................donald.w.hull@ojd.state.or.us
309 State St, Hood River, OR 97031-2037
Honorable Donald Hull, Director

Teen Court 541.387.2367
Fax...541.386.5440
Web....................................www.nextdoorinc.org
E-mail............................teencourt@nextdoorinc.org
2149 Cascade Ave # 106A-159, Hood River,
OR 97031
Sky Vaday, Coordinator

POLICE AND SHERIFF

Sheriff's Dept 541.386.2098
Fax...541.386.3141
Web..................................www.doj.state.or.us
309 State St, Hood River, OR 97031-2037
Joe Wampoer, Sheriff

Jackson County

GENERAL HEALTH SERVICES

Health Dept 541.774.8209
Fax...541.774.7980
Web...................................www.co.jackson.or.us
1005 E Main St, Bldg A, Medford, OR 97504
Mark Orndoff, Health Director

JUSTICE AGENCY

CASA 541.734.2272
Fax...541.842.4078
Web.............................www.jacksoncountycasa.org
E-mail...................casa@jacksoncountycasa.org
613 Market St, Medford, OR 97504
Jennifer Mylenek, Executive Director

Community Juvenile Justice 541.774.4800
Fax...541.774.4868
609 W 10th St, Medford, OR 97501
Joe Ferguson, Deputy Director

COURTS

Circuit Court 541.776.7171
Fax...541.776.7057
E-mail.....................ron.grensky@ojd.state.or.us
100 S Oakdale Ave, Medford, OR 97501-3127
Honorable Ron Grensky, Judge

POLICE AND SHERIFF

Sheriff's Ofc 541.774.6800
Fax...541.776.7699
Web...................................www.co.jackson.or.us
787 W 8th St, Medford, OR 97501
Mike Winters, Sheriff

Jefferson County

SOCIAL SERVICES

Dept Of Human Svcs, Com. Human Svcs Child

Welfare 541.475.2292
Fax...541.475.6830
Web..www.state.or.us
E-mail..........................roy.jackson@state.or.us
678 NE Highway 97, Ste C, Madras, OR 97741
Roy Jackson, Child Welfare Supervisor

DHS Children, Adult & Family Svcs 541.475.6131
Fax...541.475.4697
E-mail.......................ron.parsons@dhs.oregon.gov
678 NE Highway 97, Ste A, Madras, OR 97741
Ron Parsons, Programme Manager

GENERAL HEALTH SERVICES

Health Dept 541.475.4456
Fax...541.475.0132
Web..................................www.co.jefferson.or.us
E-mail.................tom.machala@co.jefferson.or.us
715 SW 4th St Ste C, Madras, OR 97741-1022
Tom Machala, Director

JUSTICE AGENCY

Commission 541.475.2449
Fax...541.475.4454
66 SE D St Ste A, Madras, OR 97741
John Hapfield, Commissioner

Juvenile Dept 541.475.3463
Fax...541.475.1632
E-mail.............jeffrey.lichtenberg@co.jefferson.or.us
75 SE C St Ste A, Madras, OR 97741
Jeffery Lichtenberg, Director

POLICE AND SHERIFF

Sheriff's Ofc 541.475.6520
Fax...541.475.3847
Web...................................www.co.josephine.or.us
675 NW Cherry Ln, Madras, OR 97741-9409
Jim Adkins, Sheriff

Josephine County

GENERAL HEALTH SERVICES

Health Dept 541.474.5325
Fax...541.474.5353
Web...................................www.co.josephine.or.us
715 Nw Dimmick, Grants Pass, OR 97526-1802
Linda Stohlman, Director

JUSTICE AGENCY

Juvenile Dept 541.474.5186
Fax...541.474.5181
301 NW F St, Grants Pass, OR 97526
Janine Wilson, Juvenile Director

Rogue Valley Youth Correctional

Facility 541.471.2862
Fax...541.471.2861
Web....................................www.oya.state.or.us
2001 NE F St, Grants Pass, OR 97526-4813
Kim Jerin, Superintendent

COURTS

Circuit Court 541.476.2309
Fax...541.471.2079
Web......................................www.ojd.state.or.us
E-mail.......................lindi.l.baker@ojd.state.or.us
500 Nw 6Th St, Grants Pass, OR 97526-2037
Honorable Lindi L. Baker, Presiding Judge

POLICE AND SHERIFF

Sheriff's Ofc 541.474.5123
Fax...541.474.5107
E-mail...................gilljocosheriff@co.josephine.or.us
601 NW 5th St, Grants Pass, OR 97526
Gill Gibertson, Sheriff

Klamath County

SOCIAL SERVICES

Dept Of Human Svcs Child Welfare 541.883.5570
Fax...541.883.5545
Web...................................www.dhs.state.or.us
E-mail.................cyndi.kallstrom@dhs.state.or.us
700 Klamath Ave Ste 500, Klamath Falls,
OR 97601-6177
Cyndi Kallstrom, Program Manager

GENERAL HEALTH SERVICES

Health Dept 541.882.8846
Fax...541.885.3638
Web...................................www.co.klamath.or.us
E-mail...........................kdecvis@co.klamath.or.us
403 Pine St, Klamath Falls, OR 97601
Dana Finch, Aids Coordinator

MENTAL HEALTH SERVICES

Mental Health 541.882.7291
Fax...541.883.4213
3314 Vandenberg Rd, Klamath Falls, OR 97603
Ann Lynn, Ma, Director

JUSTICE AGENCY

Juvenile Dept 541.884.4167
Fax...541.885.6755
Web...................................www.co.klamath.or.us
E-mail...........................gvest@co.klamath.or.us
3331 Vandenberg Rd, Klamath Falls, OR 97603-3799
Glenn W. Vest, Director

COURTS

13th Judicial Circuit Court **541.883.5503**
Fax 541.882.6109
Web ....www.courts.oregon.gov/klamath
　316 Main St, Klamath Falls, OR 97601-6333
　Cameron Wogan, Judge

POLICE AND SHERIFF

Sheriff's Dept **541.883.5130**
Fax 541.883.4271
Web ....www.co.klamath.or.us
E-mail ....tevinger@co.klamath.or.us
　3300 Vandenberg Rd, Klamath Falls, OR 97603-3730
　Timothy Evinger, Sheriff

Lake County

SOCIAL SERVICES

Dept Of Human Svcs Child Welfare
Svcs **541.947.2273**
Fax 541.947.5076
Web ....www.state.or.us
E-mail ....charley.tracy@state.or.us
　108 N E St, Lakeview, OR 97630
　Charley Tracy, Child Welfare Supervisor

DHS Children, Adult & Family Svcs **541.947.3376**
Fax 541.947.5076
Web ....www.state.or.us
　108 N B St, Lakeview, OR 97630
　Denise Rhodes, District Manager

GENERAL HEALTH SERVICES

Public Health Dept **541.947.6045**
Fax 541.947.4563
E-mail ....lakecountypublichealth@yahoo.com
　100 N D St, Lakeview, OR 97630
　Mary Wilke, Administrator And Clinical Coordinator

COURTS

Circuit Court **541.947.6051**
Fax 541.947.3724
　513 Center St, Lakeview, OR 97630
　Bonnie Michael, Supervisor

POLICE AND SHERIFF

Sheriff's Ofc **541.947.6027**
Fax 541.947.6029
E-mail ....pamcdonald@co.lake.or.us
　513 Center St, Lakeview, OR 97630
　Phil Mcdonald, Sheriff

Lane County

SOCIAL SERVICES

Dept Of Human Svcs, Child Welfare
Program **541.686.7555**
Fax 541.485.8566
Web ....www.dhs.state.or.us
　1899 Willamette St, Eugene, OR 97401-4015
　John Radich, District Manager

Health And Human Svcs **541.682.4035**
Fax 541.682.3804
Web ....www.lanecounty.org
　151 W 7th Ave,, Eugene, OR 97401
　Robert Rockstroh, Director

Health And Human Svcs **541.682.4041**
Fax 541.682.2455
Web ....www.co.lane.or.us
E-mail ....rob.rockstroh@co.lane.or.us
　151 W 7th Ave, Ste 310, Eugene, OR 97401-2618
　Robert Rockstroh, Director

GENERAL HEALTH SERVICES

Public Health **541.682.4041**
Fax 541.682.2455
Web ....www.lanecounty.org
　151 W 7th Ste 310, Eugene, OR 97401
　Pam Stuver, Rn, Nursing Supervisor

JUSTICE AGENCY

CASA **541.984.3132**
Fax 541.984.1407
Web ....www.casa-lane.org
E-mail ....meganf@casa-lane.org
　174 Deadmond Ferry Rd, Springfield,
　OR 97477-9405
　Megan Shultz, Executive Director

Florence Work Study Camp **541.997.2076**
Fax 541.997.4217
　4859 S Jetty Rd, Florence, OR 97439
　Clint Mcclellan, Director

COURTS

Circuit Court/Youth Svcs **541.682.4726**
Fax 541.682.4773
Web ....www.ojd.state.or.us/lane
　2727 Martin Luther King Jr Blvd, Eugene, OR 97401
　Eveleen Henry, Judge

Peer Court **541.782.4232**
Fax 541.782.2285
Web ....www.efn.org
E-mail ....mikal.mcpherson@ci.oakridge.or.us
　76435 Ash St, Oakridge, OR 97463
　Mikal Mcpherson, Coordinator

Teen Court **541.682.6376**
Fax 541.682.8192
Web ....www.ci.eugene.or.us
E-mail ....bruce.h.steinmetz@ci.eugene.or.us
　870 Berntzen Rd, Eugene, OR 97402-1825
　Bruce Steinmetz, Supervisor

POLICE AND SHERIFF

Sheriff's Ofc **541.682.4150**
Fax 541.682.2366
E-mail ....thomas.turner@co.lane.or.us
　125 E 8th Ave, Eugene, OR 97401
　Thomas Turner, Sheriff

EDUCATION SERVICES

Special Education **541.461.8251**
Fax 541.461.8399
Web www.lane.k12.or.us
E-mail ....smathise@lane.k12.or.us
　1200 Highway 99 N, Eugene, OR 97402-2014
　Sue Mathisen, Director

Lincoln County

SOCIAL SERVICES

Bureau Of Indian Affairs **541.444.2679**
Fax 541.444.2243
Web ....www.bia.gov
E-mail ....lavonne.butler@bia.gov
　178 Northeast Metcalf Avenue, Siletz, OR 97380
　Lavonne Butler, Social Services Representative

Dept Of Human Svcs Comm. Human
Svcs **541.265.8557**
Fax 541.265.3237
Web ....www.dhs.state.or.us
E-mail ....debi.wright@dhs.state.or.us
　119 NE 4th St Ste 5, Newport, OR 97365-3133
　Debi Wright, Office Manager

JUSTICE AGENCY

Juvenile Dept **541.265.4158**
Fax 541.265.4156
E-mail ....alan_peterson@class.orednet.org
　753 NW Brook St, Newport, OR 97365-3812
　Alan O. Peterson, Director

COURTS

Circuit Court **541.265.4236**
Fax 541.265.7561
Web ....www.ojd.state.or.us
E-mail ....charles.p.littlehales@ojd.state.or.us
　225 W Olive St, Newport, OR 97365-3812
　Honorable Charles P. Littlehales, Director

EDUCATION SERVICES

CSC Head Start **541.336.5113**
Fax 541.336.2651
Web ....www.csc.gen.or.us
E-mail ....nperin@csc.gen.or.us
　845 NW A St, Toledo, OR 97391-1232
　Nancy Perin, Director

Linn County

SOCIAL SERVICES

Dept Of Human Resource Child
Welfare **541.967.2060**
Fax 541.967.2127
Web ....www.state.or.us
E-mail ....david.cogswell@state.or.us
　118 2nd Ave SE Ste D, Albany, OR 97321-2710
　David Cogswell, Director

Senior And Disability Svcs **541.967.8630**
Fax 541.967.6423
Web ....www.ocwcog.org
　1400 Queen Ave SE Ste 206, Albany, OR 97322
　Scott Dond, Director

GENERAL HEALTH SERVICES

Health Dept **541.967.3888**
Fax 541.926.2102
Web ....www.co.linn.or.us
E-mail ....fmoore@co.linn.or.us
　315 4th Ave SW, Albany, OR 97321-2338
　Frank Moore, Administrator

JUSTICE AGENCY

CASA **541.926.2651**
Fax 541.812.0242
E-mail ....linncountycasa@hotmail.com
　440 1st Ave, Albany, OR 97321-2232
　Lene Garrett, Executive Director

Juvenile Dept **541.967.3853**
Fax 541.967.4268
Web ....www.co.linn.or.us
E-mail ....tlynn@co.linn.or.us
　104 4th Ave SW, Albany, OR 97321-2804
　Torri Lynn, Director

Linn-Benton Juvenile Detention
Ctr **541.791.9397**
Fax 541.791.9485
　4400 Lochner Rd SE, Albany, OR 97322
　Troy Fuller, Detention Manager

COURTS

21st Judicial District Circuit Court **541.967.3841**
Fax 541.928.8725
Web ....www.ojd.state.or.us
E-mail ....daniel.murphy@ojd.state.or.us
　300 4th Ave SW, Albany, OR 97321
　Daniel Murphy, Judge

Oregon

POLICE AND SHERIFF

Sheriff's Ofc **541.967.3950**
1115 Jackson St SE, Albany, OR 97322
Tim Muller, Sheriff

Malheur County

SOCIAL SERVICES

Dept Of Human Svc Comm. Human Svcs Child
Welfare...**541.889.9194**
Fax...541.889.9588
186 East Ln Ste 3, Ontario, OR 97914
Wendy Hill, Branch Manager

GENERAL HEALTH SERVICES

Children, Adult & Family Svcs..............**541.889.9141**
Fax...541.889.2694
186 East Ln Ste 2, Ontario, OR 97914-3051
Wendy Hill, District Manager

Health Dept....................................**541.889.7279**
Fax...541.889.8468
Web..www.malheurco.org
E-mail.........................sackley@malheurco.org
1108 SW 4th St, Ontario, OR 97914-4305
Sandy Ackley, Wic Coordinator

COURTS

Circuit Court..................................**541.473.5171**
Fax...541.473.2213
251 B St W Ste 5, Vale, OR 97918-0670
Linda Cummings, Juvenile Department Director

POLICE AND SHERIFF

Sheriff's Dept................................**541.473.5126**
Fax...541.473.5504
Web..www.malheurco.org
E-mail.............................bwolfe@malheurco.org
151 B St W, Vale, OR 97918-1307
Brian E Wolfe, Sheriff

Marion County

SOCIAL SERVICES

Adoption Svcs.................................**503.947.5358**
Fax...503.945.6633
E-mail...................kathy.prouty@state.or.us
500 Summer St NE, # E-71, Salem, OR 97301
Kathryn Prouty, Program Manager

Dept Of Human Svcs Chs Marion Child
Welfare...**503.378.6800**
Fax...503.378.3061
E-mail...................mary.stovin@state.or.us
4600 25th Ave NE Ste 110, Salem, OR 97301-0100
Mary Stovin, Certification Supervisor

Dept Of Human Svcs, Self
Suficiency.....................................**503.980.6677**
Fax...503.980.6656
Web..www.oregon.gov
E-mail.................lorena.savusa@state.or.us
120 E Lincoln St, Ste 120, Woodburn, OR 97071
Lorena Savusa, Operations Manager

Oregon Emergency Management
Agency..**503.378.2911**
Fax...503.373.7833
Web..................................www.oregon.gov/omd/oem
3225 State St, Salem, OR 97301
Jay Michael Caldwel, Intrum

GENERAL HEALTH SERVICES

Health Dept....................................**503.588.5357**
Fax...503.364.6552
Web..www.zomarion.or.us
3180 Center St NE, Salem, OR 97301-4532
Ricardo Rodriguez, Health Resource Coordinator

Oregon State Hospital **503.945.2800**
Fax...503.945.2807
2600 Center St NE, Salem, OR 97301
Neena Strickland, Interim Director

Salud Medical Ctr............................**503.982.2000**
Fax...503.981.5839
E-mail...................................noram@yvfwc.org
1175 Mount Hood Ave, Woodburn, OR 97071-9060
Nora Miller, Wic Supervisor/dietitian

MENTAL HEALTH SERVICES

Developmental Disabilities Svcs..........**503.588.5288**
Fax...503.588.5290
E-mail.................sstewart@co.marion.or.us
2421 Lancaster Dr NE, Salem, OR 97305
Sandra Stewart, Team Supervisor

JUSTICE AGENCY

Hillcrest Youth Correctional
Facility..**503.986.0400**
Fax...503.986.0406
Web..................................www.corvallis.k12.or.us
E-mail.................chris.duvall@corvallis.k12.or.us
2450 Strong Rd SE Bldg 1, Salem, OR 97302-9676
Troy Greg, Superintendent

COURTS

Juvenile Court...............................**503.588.5411**
Fax...503.373.3796
Web..www.co.marion.or.us
3030 Center St NE, Salem, OR 97301-4528
Chuck Sybrandt, Assistant Director

POLICE AND SHERIFF

Sheriff's Dept................................**503.588.5094**
Fax...503.588.7931
Web..www.co.marion.or.us
100 High St NE, Salem, OR 97301-3640
Jason Myers, Sheriff

EDUCATION SERVICES

Community Action Head Start-Knight
Memorial.......................................**503.371.8571**
Fax...503.581.3012
219 19th St SE, Salem, OR 97301
Liz Salinas, TRS

Even Start Family Literacy
Program..**503.399.3130**
Fax...503.316.5321
Web..................................www.salemkaiser.org
E-mail...............whetvel_stephanie@salkeiz.k12.edu
1515 Saginaw St S, Salem, OR 97302-5130
Stephanie Whetvel, Coordinator

Morrow County

SOCIAL SERVICES

Dept Of Human Svcs.........................**541.481.9482**
Fax...541.481.2960
E-mail...................jane.gallagher@state.or.us
103 S.W. Kinkade, Boardman, OR 97818
Jyl Hobbs, Social Services Supervisor

GENERAL HEALTH SERVICES

Health Dept....................................**541.676.5421**
Fax...541.676.5652
Web..................................www.morrowcountyoregon.com
120 S Main St, Heppner, OR 97836
Sheree Smith, Rn, Public Health Director

MENTAL HEALTH SERVICES

Community Counceling Solutions...........**541.676.9161**
Fax...541.676.5662
E-mail...................kimberly.lindsay@gobhi.net
120 S Main St, Heppner, OR 97836
Kimberly Lindsay, Director Of Behavioral Health

JUSTICE AGENCY

Juvenile Dept.................................**541.676.5642**
Fax...541.676.9836
Web..................................www.class.oregonvos.net
E-mail...................carolyn.j.holt@class.oregonvos.net
120 S Main St, Heppner, OR 97836
Carolyn Holt, Juvenile Director

COURTS

Court...**541.676.5620**
Fax...541.676.5621
E-mail...................ttallman@co.morrow.or.us
100 Court St, Heppner, OR 97836-0788
Honorable Terry Tallman, Director

Multnomah County

SOCIAL SERVICES

Alberta DHA-CAF Child Welfare............**971.673.6800**
Fax...503.280.6638
Web..www.oregon.gov
E-mail...................edgar.perez@state.or.us
30 N Webster St Ste D, Portland, OR 97217-2767
Edgar Perez, Program Manager

Dept Of Human Svcs.........................**503.988.3691**
Fax...503.988.3379
Web..www.co.multnomah.or.us
E-mail...................rex.b.surface@co.multnomah.or.us
421 SW Oak St Ste 620, Portland, OR 97204-1811
Rex Surface, Developmental Disabilities Division Director

Dept Of Human Svcs.........................**503.731.4400**
Fax...503.229.5329
7825 N Lombard St, St Johns Branch, Portland,
OR 97203-3125
Edgar Perez, Regional Administrator

East DHS-CAF Child Welfare................**971.673.2100**
Fax...971.673.2020
Web..www.oregon.gov
3618 SE 122nd Ave, Portland, OR 97236-3403
Cheryl Baldomaro-Lucas, Branch Manager

Indian Social Svcs...........................**503.231.6785**
Fax...503.231.2182
Web..www.bia.gov
E-mail...................stella_charles@ios.doi.gov
911 NE 11th Ave Ste 2, Portland, OR 97232-4128
Stella Charles, Regional Social Worker

Midtown DHS-CAF Child Welfare............**971.673.1800**
Fax...971.673.1744
E-mail...................................dhs@state.or.us
1425 NE Irving St, Lloyd Plaza Building 400, Portland,
OR 97232
David Pike, Director

New Market Theater DHS-CAF Child
Welfare...**971.673.1400**
Fax...971.673.1461
E-mail...................dpike@dhs.state.or.us
50 SW 2nd Ave, Portland, OR 97204
David Pike, Program Manager

Rockwood DHS-CAF Child Welfare..........**971.673.2135**
Fax...971.673.2028
3618 SE 122nd Ave, Portland, OR 97236
Cheryl Baldomaro-lucas, Program Manager

GENERAL HEALTH SERVICES

Health Ctr.....................................**503.988.3601**
Fax...503.988.3142
12710 SE Division St, Portland, OR 97236
Deborah Cockrell, Manager

Health Ctr.....................................**503.988.5155**
Fax...503.988.5185
Web..www.multpo.us
600 NE 8th St Ste 300, Gresham, OR 97030-7318
Marsha Morrow, Manager

Health Dept 503.988.3674
Fax 503.988.3676
Web ....www.co.multnomah.or.us/health
   426 SW Stark St, Fl 8, Portland, OR 97204
   Lillian Shirley, Director

North Portland Health Ctr 503.988.5304
Fax 503.988.5305
Web ....www.co.multnomah.or.us
E-mail ....margaret.thiele@co.multnomah.or.us
   9000 N Lombard St, Portland, OR 97203-3006
   Margaret Thiele, Manager

Northeast Health Ctr 503.988.5183
Fax 503.988.5182
Web ....www.multnomahcountyoregon.com
   5329 NE M L King Blvd, Bldg 322, Portland,
   OR 97211
   Robert Saum, Manager

Portland Area Indian Health Svc 503.414.5555
Fax 503.414.5554
Web ....www.ihs.gov
   1414 NW Northrup Ste 800, Portland, OR 97209
   Bean Seyler, Director

Westside Health Ctr 503.988.5140
Fax 503.988.5180
Web ....www.multnomahcounty.gov
   426 SW Stark St, Fl 5, Portland, OR 97204
   Maroline Boss, Manager

MENTAL HEALTH SERVICES

Dept of Human Svcs 503.988.5464
Fax 503.988.3379
Web ....www.multco.us
   421 SW Oak St Ste 240, Portland, OR 97204-1811
   Dorothy Sampson, Supervisor

JUSTICE AGENCY

CASA Program 503.988.5115
Fax 503.988.5618
   1401 NE 68th Ave, Portland, OR 97213
   Mary Jaeger, Executive Director

COURTS

Juvenile Court 503.988.3460
Fax 503.988.3409
Web ....www.co.multnomah.or.us
   1401 NE 68th Ave, Portland, OR 97213-4957
   Referee Carol Herzog, Referee

POLICE AND SHERIFF

Portland Police Dept 503.823.0097
Fax 503.823.0096
Web ....www.portlandpolice.org
   1111 SW 2nd Ave, Portland, OR 97204-3262
   Mike Reese, Chief

Sheriff's Dept 503.988.4300
Fax 503.988.4316
Web ....www.mcso.us
E-mail ....sheriff@mcso.us
   501 SE Hawthorne Blvd Ste 350, Portland,
   OR 97214-3589
   Daniel Staton, Sheriff

EDUCATION SERVICES

Multnomah education Service
District 503.257.1616
Fax 503.257.1525
Web www.mesd.k12.or.us
E-mail ....bjorgens@mesd.k12.or.us
   11611 NE Ainsworth Cir, Portland, OR 97220-9017
   Kelvin Webster, Director Of Instruction

Polk County

SOCIAL SERVICES

DHS Children, Adult & Family Svcs 503.623.5526
Fax 503.623.4608
Web ....www.state.or.us
E-mail ....mike.williams@state.or.us
   177 SW Oak St, Dallas, OR 97338-1913
   Mike Williams, Program Manager

JUSTICE AGENCY

CASA 503.623.9268
Fax 503.623.7556
Web ....www.co.polk.or.us
E-mail ....casa@co.polk.or.us
   850 Main St Rm 12, Dallas, OR 97338-3129
   Chris Olsen, Case Coodinator

Juvenile Dept/ Human Svcs 503.623.2349
Fax 503.831.3013
Web ....www.co.polk.or.us
   182 SW Academy St Ste 326, Dallas, OR 97338-1900
   Trish Reding, Manager

COURTS

Circuit Court 503.623.3154
Fax 503.623.6614
   850 Main St Rm 301, Dallas, OR 97338-3176
   William Horner, Presiding Judge

POLICE AND SHERIFF

Sheriff's Dept 503.623.9251
Fax 503.623.2060
E-mail ....wolfe.robert@co.polk.or.us
   850 Main St Rm 106, Dallas, OR 97338
   Bob Wolfe, Sheriff

Sherman County

POLICE AND SHERIFF

Sheriff's Dept 541.565.3622
Fax 541.565.3312
E-mail ....scso@sherman.k12.or.us
   500 Court St, Moro, OR 97039
   Brad Lohrey, Sheriff

Tillamook County

SOCIAL SERVICES

Dept Of Human Svcs Child Welfare 503.842.5571
Fax 503.842.5028
Web ....www.state.or.us
E-mail ....dee.bristol@state.or.us
   4670 3rd St, Tillamook, OR 97141-2902
   Dee Bristol, Program Manager Of Child Welfare

DHS Children, Adult & Family Svcs 503.842.4453
Fax 503.842.3282
Web ....www.oregon.gov/dhs
E-mail ....sandy.kephart@state.or.us
   4670 3rd St, Tillamook, OR 97141-2902
   Sandy Kephart, Line Manager

GENERAL HEALTH SERVICES

Health Dept 503.842.3900
Fax 503.842.3903
Web ....www.co.tillamook.or.us
E-mail ....mrowland@co.tillamook.or.us
   801 Pacific Ave, Tillamook, OR 97141-3926
   Marty Rowland, Rn, Bsn, Home Visits/bccp/perinatal

JUSTICE AGENCY

Camp Tillamook 503.842.4243
Fax 503.842.1476
E-mail ....riguardk@tillamook.k12.or.us
   6820 Barrack Cir, Tillamook, OR 97141
   Keith Riguard, Director

COURTS

Circuit Court 503.842.2596
Fax 503.842.2597
Web ....www.ojd.state.or.us
   201 Laurel Ave, Tillamook, OR 97141-2334
   Honorable Mari Trevino, Presiding Judge

Umatilla County

SOCIAL SERVICES

Dept Of Children And Family Svcs 541.429.7300
Fax 541.429.7300
Web ....www.umatilla.nsn.us
E-mail ....theresaelisoff@ctuir.com
   46411 Timine Way, Pendleton, OR 97801
   Theresa Elisoff, Department Director

DHS And Child Welfare 541.276.9220
Fax 541.276.9349
   700 SE Emigrant Ave, Ste 200, Pendleton, OR 97801
   Linda Olson, Child Welfare Manager

GENERAL HEALTH SERVICES

Health Dept 541.278.5432
Fax 541.278.5433
Web ....www.umatilla.or.us
E-mail ....sharonw@co.umatilla.or.us
   200 SE 3rd St, Pendleton, OR 97801-2503
   Sharon Waldern, Rn, Aids Coordinator

Yellowhawk Tribal Health Ctr 541.966.9830
Fax 541.278.7579
Web ....www.yellowhawk.org
E-mail ....timgilbert@yellowhawk.org
   73265 Confederated Way, Pendleton, OR 97801
   Tim Gilbert, Chief Executive Officer

JUSTICE AGENCY

Juvenile Dept 541.278.5447
Fax 541.278.5445
   817 SE 13th St, Pendleton, OR 97801
   Kim Noisey, Administrator

COURTS

Circuit Court 541.278.0341
Fax 541.276.9030
Web ....www.ojd.state.or.us
   216 SE 4th St, Pendleton, OR 97801
   Honorable Jeffrey M. Wallace, Director

EDUCATION SERVICES

Umatilla/Morrow Head Start/WIC
Program 541.966.3354
Fax 541.966.3351
Web ....www.umchs.org
E-mail ....cwamsley@umchs.org
   1308 SW Immigrant Ave, Pendleton, OR 97801
   Cathy Wamsley, Executive Director

Union County

GENERAL HEALTH SERVICES

Center For Human Development,
Inc 541.962.8800
Fax 541.963.5272
Web ....www.chdinc.org
E-mail ....jpeasley@chdinc.org
   2301 Cove Ave, La Grande, OR 97850-2131
   Joelene Peasley, Rn, Health Nurse

JUSTICE AGENCY

Juvenile Dept 541.963.1012
Fax 541.963.1038
Web ....www.class.oregonvos.net
   1102 K Ave, La Grande, OR 97850-2131
   Jim Brougham, Director

Oregon

Oregon *(side tab)*

COURTS

Circuit Court **541.962.9500**
Fax 541.963.0444
Web .... www.unioncountycourt.org
E-mail .... russell.b.west@ojd.state.or.us
    1008 K Ave, La Grande, OR 97850-2129
    Honorable Russ West, Judge

POLICE AND SHERIFF

Sheriff's Dept **541.963.1020**
Fax 541.963.1023
Web .... www.unioncountysheriff.us
E-mail .... sheriff@union-county.org
    1109 K Ave Ste A, La Grande, OR 97850-2182
    Boyd Rasmussen, Sheriff

Wallowa County

SOCIAL SERVICES

Dept Of Human Svcs Child Welfare **541.426.4558**
Fax 541.426.3878
Web .... www.oregon.gov/dhs
E-mail .... tfisher@dhs.state.or.us
    104 Litch St, Enterprise, OR 97828
    Teresa Fisher, Supervisor

GENERAL HEALTH SERVICES

Health Dept **541.426.4848**
Fax 541.426.3627
E-mail .... lfisher@co.wallowa.or.us
    758 NW 1st St, Enterprise, OR 97828
    Laina Fisher, Rn, Administrator

MENTAL HEALTH SERVICES

Mental Health **541.426.4524**
Fax 541.426.3035
Web .... www.class.oregonvos.net
E-mail .... stephen.p.kliewer@class.oregonvos.net
    207 SW 1st St, Enterprise, OR 97828-1506
    Stephen Kliewer, Director

COURTS

Circuit Court **541.426.4991**
Fax 541.426.4992
Web .... www.co.wallowa.or.us
E-mail .... john.lawrence@co.wallowa.or.us
    101 S River St, Ste 204, Enterprise, OR 97828-1363
    John Lawrence, Juvenile Director

POLICE AND SHERIFF

Sheriff's Dept **541.426.3131**
Fax 541.426.4685
Web .... www.co.wallowa.or.us
E-mail .... wcsheriff@co.wallowa.or.us
    104 W Greenwood St Ste A, Enterprise,
    OR 97828-1384
    Fred Steen, Sheriff

Wasco County

GENERAL HEALTH SERVICES

Health Dept **541.506.2600**
Fax 541.506.2601
Web .... www.wshd.org
    419 E 7Th St, The Dalles, OR 97058-2676
    Teri Thalhoser, Director

MENTAL HEALTH SERVICES

Greater Oregon Behavioral Health **541.298.2101**
Fax 541.298.7996
E-mail .... kevin_m_campbell@class.oregonvos.net
    312 E 2nd St, The Dalles, OR 97058
    Kevin Campbell, CEO

POLICE AND SHERIFF

Sheriff's Dept **541.506.2580**
Fax 541.506.2581
    511 Washington St, Ste 102, The Dalles, OR 97058
    Rick Eiesland, Sheriff

Washington County

SOCIAL SERVICES

DHS Children, Adult & Family Svcs **503.646.9952**
Fax 503.646.4260
Web .... www.oregon.gov/dhs
    15625 SW Grey Stone Court, Beaverton, OR 97006
    Svetlana Fadden, Manager

Svcs To Children And Families **503.648.8951**
Fax 503.693.3503
    5350 NE Elam Young Pkwy, Hillsboro,
    OR 97124-6313
    Heather Kitto, Protective Services/intake/cps Supervisor

GENERAL HEALTH SERVICES

Health Dept **503.846.4402**
Fax 503.846.4490
Web .... www.co.washington.or.us
    155 N 1st Ave, # 160, Hillsboro, OR 97124
    Rod Branyan, Director, Dept. Of Health And Human Services

COURTS

**Juvenile Court, Washington City Juvenile
Dept** **503.846.8861**
Fax 503.846.8861
Web .... www.co.washington.or.us/juvenile
E-mail .... dennis_kenna@co.washington.or.us
    222 N 1st Ave, Hillsboro, OR 97124
    Dennis Kenna, Director

POLICE AND SHERIFF

Hillsboro Police Dept **503.681.6175**
Fax 503.681.6267
Web .... www.ci.hillsboro.or.us
E-mail .... careys@ci.hillsboro.or.us
    250 SE 10th Ave, Hillsboro, OR 97123-4238
    Carey Sullivan, Chief Police

Sheriff's Ofc **503.846.2700**
Fax 503.846.2719
Web .... www.co.washington.or.us
E-mail .... sheriff@co.washington.or.us
    215 SW Adams Ave, 32, Hillsboro, OR 97123
    Rob Gordon, Sheriff

EDUCATION SERVICES

Migrant Head Start/OCDC **503.570.1110**
Fax 503.682.9426
Web .... www.ocdc.net
E-mail .... donalda.dodson@ocdc.net
    9140 SW Pioneer Ct Ste E, Wilsonville,
    OR 97070-9622
    Donalda Dodson, Executive Director

Special Education **503.614.1428**
Fax 503.614.1440
Web www.nwresd.k12.or.us
E-mail .... modin@nwresd.k12.or.us
    5825 NE Ray Cir, Hillsboro, OR 97124-6436
    Mickey Odin, Deputy Superintendent Instructional Services

Wheeler County

GENERAL HEALTH SERVICES

Health Svcs Asher Clinic **541.763.2725**
Fax 541.763.2850
Web .... www.asherhealth.net
    712 Jay St, Fossil, OR 97830
    Karen Costolla, Public Health Nurse

JUSTICE AGENCY

Juvenile Dept **541.763.3200**
Fax 541.763.3299
Web .... www.class.oregonvos.net
E-mail .... cburlingame@co.wheeler.or.us
    401 4th St, Fossil, OR 97830
    Cindy Burlingame, Juvenile Department Director

POLICE AND SHERIFF

Sheriff's Dept **541.763.4101**
Fax 541.763.2006
E-mail .... sheriff@co.wheeler.or.us
    701 Adams St, Room 202, Fossil, OR 97830
    Robert Hudspeth, Sheriff

wynn County

JUSTICE AGENCY

**Corvallis House Young Womens Transition
Program** **541.757.4263**
Fax 541.757.4102
    28655 Hwy 34, Corvallis, OR 97333
    Fabian Casarez, Director

Yamhill County

SOCIAL SERVICES

**Dept. Of Human Svcs, Comm. Human Svcs And Child Welfare
Agency** **503.472.4634**
Fax 503.472.3815
    368 NE Norton Ln, McMinnville, OR 97128
    Jan Schenk, Casework Supervisor

GENERAL HEALTH SERVICES

Health Dept **503.434.7525**
Fax 503.472.9731
Web .... www.co.yamhill.or.us
    412 NE Ford St, McMinnville, OR 97128-4608
    Silas Halloran-Sceiner, Director

POLICE AND SHERIFF

Sheriff's Ofc **503.434.7506**
Fax 503.472.5330
Web .... www.co.yamhill.or.us/sheriff
    535 NE 5th St, Rm 143, McMinnville, OR 97128
    Jack Crabtree, Sheriff

SPECIAL SERVICES AGENCIES

ADOPTION AGENCIES

Adoption Agency Legal Group **541.683.1814**
Fax 541.484.7404
E-mail .... tim@tfbrewer.com
    590 W 13th Ave, Eugene, OR 97401-3461
    Tim Brewer, Director

**All God's Children Intl Families Are
Forever** **503.282.7652**
Fax 503.282.2582
Web .... www.allgodschildren.org
E-mail .... info@allgodschildren.org
    3308 NE Peerless Pl, Portland, OR 97232-2554
    Chance Paulson, Director Of Social Services

**Associated Svcs For International Adoption
(ASIA)** **503.224.1860**
Fax 503.224.1995
Web .... www.asiadopt.org
E-mail .... staff@asiadopt.org
    215 SW Hooker St, Ste 100, Portland, OR 97201
    Joy Drechsler, Director

Bethany Christian Svcs 503.200.5748
Fax 503.808.9888
Web ....www.bethany.org
E-mail ....bcsportland@bethany.org
   5319 SW West Gate Dr Ste 117, Portland, OR 97221
Edna Kuipers, Director

Bouneff & Chally 503.238.9720
Fax 503.239.3989
Web ....www.adoptionnorthwest.com
E-mail ....mail@adoptionnorthwest.com
   2722 NE 33rd Ave, Portland, OR 97212
John Chally, Attorney

Christian Family Adoptions 503.232.1211
Fax 503.232.4756
Web ....www.christianfamilyadoptions.org
E-mail ....mail@christianfamilyadoptions.org
   6040 SE Belmont St, Portland, OR 97215
Rebecca T, Director

Dexter & Moffet 503.582.9010
Fax 503.582.9940
Web ....www.oregonadopt.com
E-mail ....cdexter@oregonadopt.com
   25260 SW Parkway Ave Ste C, Wilsonville,
   OR 97070-6627
Kathy Dexter, Attorney

Holt Int'l Children's Svcs 541.687.2202
Fax 541.683.6175
Web ....www.holtintl.org
E-mail ....info@holtintl.org
   1195 City View St, Eugene, OR 97402-6700

Holt International Children's Svcs 503.244.2440
Fax 503.245.2498
Web ....www.holtintl.org
E-mail ....sharonf@holtinternational.org
   9320 SW Barbur Blvd Ste 280, Portland,
   OR 97219-5406
Sharon E. Fako, Branch Director

Journeys Of The Heart Adoption Svcs 503.681.3075
Fax 503.640.5834
Web ....www.journeysoftheheart.net
E-mail ....info@journeysoftheheart.net
   1005 NE Cornell Rd, Hillsboro, OR 97124
Susan Tompkins, Executive Director

Open Adoption & Family Svcs, Inc. 503.226.4870
Fax 503.226.4891
Web ....www.openadopt.org
E-mail ....information@openadopt.org
   5200 SW MacAdam Ave Ste 250, Portland,
   OR 97239-3888
Sherry Levine, Director

Tree Of Life Adoption Ctr 503.244.7374
Fax 503.244.7424
Web ....www.toladopt.org
E-mail ....info@toladopt.org
   5816 SE Powell Blvd Ste A, Portland, OR 97206
Bianca Marcue, Director Of International Programs

**Trillium Family Svcs/Waverly Chirldren's Home
Campus** 503.234.9591
Fax 503.205.0188
Web ....www.trillumfamily.org
   3415 SE Powell Blvd, Portland, OR 97202-1552
Keith Cheng, Md, Medical Director

ADVOCACY RESOURCES

CASA 503.338.6063
Fax 503.325.8822
E-mail ....casa@clatsopcasa.org
   10 Sixth Street, Astoria, OR 97103
Ann Lederer, Program Director

Child Advocacy Ctr 541.682.3938
Fax 541.682.8743
Web ....www.co.lane.or.us
E-mail ....tina.j.morgan@co.lane.or.us
   2675 Martin Luther King Jr Blvd, Eugene,
   OR 97401-5899
Tina Morgan, Director

Children's Advocacy Ctr 541.734.5437
Fax 541.734.2425
Web ....www.cacjc.org
E-mail ....center@cacjc.org
   816 W 10th St, Medford, OR 97201
Marlene Misch, Executive Director

Children's Advocacy Ctr 541.574.0841
Fax 541.574.0821
Web ....www.childrensadvocacycenter.net
E-mail ....lccac@acclcc.com
   122 NE 47th Street, Newport, OR 97365
Pam Salsbury, Executive Director

Children's Advocacy Ctr 541.474.5438
Fax 541.474.5181
Web ....www.co.josephine.or.us
E-mail ....tstafford@co.josephine.or.us
   304 NW D St, Grants Pass, OR 97526-2052
Tina Stafford, Child Advocate Coordinator

Kids Ctr 541.383.5958
Fax 541.383.3016
Web ....www.kidscenter.org
E-mail ....info@kidscenter.org
   1375 NW Kingston Ave, Bend, OR 97701
Shelly Smith, Director

Star Ctr 541.881.0153
Web ....www.projectdoveor.org
   415 SW 2nd Ave, Ontario, OR 97914
Cindy Ranaea, Interim Director

BEHAVIORAL HEALTH TREATMENT

Academy At Sisters 800.910.0412
Fax 541.389.2897
Web ....www.academyatsisters.org
E-mail ....cstrowd@academyatsisters.org
   63325 Silvis Road, Bend, OR 97701-9743
Stephanie Alvstad, Executive Director, J Bar J Youth Services

Armstrong Medical Practice 503.681.4166
   1809 Maple St, Forest Grove, OR 97116-1939
Scott, Armstrong, MD, Psychiatrist

**Assoc Of Oregon Community Mental Health
Programs** 503.399.7201
Fax 503.589.3101
E-mail ....gnikkel@aocweb.org
   1201 Court St NE, Ste 302, Salem, OR 97301
Gina Nikkel, Executive Director

Babe Medical Practice 503.581.7700
Fax 503.581.7799
   528 Cottage St NE Ste 320, Salem, OR 97301-3788
R Scot Babe Md, Psychiatrist

Bailey Medical Practice 541.482.9492
   208 Oak St, Ashland, OR 97520
Lisa Bailey, Psychiatrist

**Bay Area Hospital Psychiatric Outpatient
Clinic** 541.269.5333
   2085 Thompson Rd, Coos Bay, OR 97420
James Martin Md, Psychiatrist

Behel Medical Practice 503.219.9111
   2311 NW Northrup St, Portland, OR 97210
Sally Behel, Psychiatrist

Bellville Medical Practice 503.274.2661
   720 SW Washington St Ste 665, Portland,
   OR 97205-3508
Charles Bellville, Psychiatrist

Best Care Treatment Ctr 541.883.2795
Fax 541.883.8194
   2555 Main St, Klamath Falls, OR 97601
Kristie Gravet, Director

Bonner Medical Practice 503.222.0144
E-mail ....sbonnermd@comcast.net
   2250 NW Flanders St, Portland, OR 97210
Svetlana Bonner, Psychiatrist

Buckler Medical Practice 503.232.2768
Fax 503.554.3898
   414 N Meridian St, Newberg, OR 97132-2697
Robert Buckler, MD, Psychiatrist

**Catherine Freer Wilderness Therapy
Expeditions** 541.926.7252
Web ....www.cfreer.com
E-mail ....sylvia@cfreer.com
   420 Southwest Third Avenue, Albany, OR 97321
Ms. Sylvia Ebbert, Accreditation Manager
Joint Commission accredited organization.

**Catholic Community Services of the Mid-Willamette Valley
and Central Coast** 503.390.2600
Fax 503.304.1343
Web ....www.ccswv.org
   P.O. Box 20400, Keizer, OR 97307-0400
COA accredited organization.

Children's Farm Home 541.757.1852
Fax 541.750.1120
Web ....www.trilliumfamily.org
E-mail ....sboyle@trilliumfamily.org
   4455 NE Highway 20, Corvallis, OR 97330-9663
Sandy Boyle, Vice President

Christie School 503.635.3416
Fax 503.697.6932
Web ....www.christiecare.org
E-mail ....l.saxton@christiecare.org
   2507 Christie Dr, Marylhurst, OR 97036
Lynn Saxton, Executive Director

Cobblestone 541.779.8850
Fax 541.858.5441
   1237 N Riverside Ave, Ste 229, Medford, OR 97501
Peter Smith, Counselor

CODA 503.648.0753
Fax 503.648.0755
   720 SE Washington St, Hillsboro, OR 97123-4230
Jo Christensen, Supervisor

Columbia Mental Health 503.397.5211
Fax 503.397.5373
Web www.ccmh1.com
E-mail ....cindyb@ccmh1.com
   58646 Mcnulty Way, Saint Helens, OR 97051-6210
Cindy Beeks, Clinical Director

**Community Works-Lithia Springs
Programs** 541.482.8906
Fax 541.482.6462
Web ....www.community-works.org
E-mail ....sandy@community-works.org
   695 Mistletoe Rd Ste H, Ashland, OR 97520-9552
Sandra Dowling, Acting Executive Director

De Paul Treatment Centers, Inc. 503.535.1151
Fax 503.535.1190
Web ....www.depaultreatmentcenters.org
   1312 Southwest Washington Street, Portland,
   OR 97208-3007
CARF accredited programs available.

Dirkse Counseling And Consulting 503.672.9858
Fax 503.672.7668
Web ....www.dirksecc.com
E-mail ....hdirkse@dirksecc.com
   10700 SW Beaverton Hillsdale Hwy Ste 110,
   Beaverton, OR 97005-3035
Heidi Dirkse Graw, Counsellor

Oregon

Downey Medical Practice 541.758.5365
2075 NW Grant Ave, Corvallis, OR 97330-4366
Dr. Bryce Downey, Psychiatrist

Elder Medical Practice 541.754.0060
Fax 541.752.9645
E-mail ....tokdoc1@comcast.net
2045 NW Grant Ave, Corvallis, OR 97330-4366
Henry Elder, Md, Psychiatrist

Friedman Medical Practice 503.246.9337
9900 SW Wilshire St Ste 210, Portland,
OR 97225-5026
Lynn Friedman, Psychiatrist

Genesis Recovery Ctr 541.955.5569
Fax 541.789.4023
E-mail ....tjohnson@asante.org
600 S 2nd St, Central Point, OR 97502-2700
Thomas Johnson, CEO And Executive Director

Harney Behavioral Health 541.573.8376
Fax 541.573.8378
E-mail ....chris.siegner@gobhi.net
348 W Adams St, Burns, OR 97720-1710
Chris Siegner, Director

Janus Youth Programs, Inc. Kojo House 503.233.6090
Fax 503.233.6093
Web ....www.janusyouth.org
E-mail ....seedback@janusyouth.org
707 NE Couch St, Portland, OR 97232-2922
Tillie Makepeace, Program Director

Kerr Youth and Family Services 503.255.4205
Web ....www.albertinakerr.org
E-mail ....roseb@albertinakerr.org
722 Northeast 162nd Avenue, Portland, OR 97230
Ms. Rose Burke, Accreditation Manager
Joint Commission accredited organization.

Kolpia Counseling Svcs 541.482.1718
Fax 541.779.1349
Web ....www.kolpiacounseling.com
E-mail ....contact@kolpiacounseling.com
611 Siskiyou Blvd Ste 8, Ashland, OR 97520-2151
Steve Fogelman, Director

Lifeworks Northwest 503.234.3400
Fax 503.233.9424
Web ....www.lifeworksnw.org
14600 NE Corneoo Rd, Portland, OR 97229
Mary Monnat, Chief Executive Officer

Lifeworks Northwest 503.281.2804
Fax 503.281.5114
Web ....www.lifeworksnw.org
E-mail ....marym@lifeworksnw.org
5010 NE 33rd Ave, Portland, OR 97211-6946
Mary Monnat, CEO

Lifeworks Northwest 503.645.3581
Fax 503.629.8517
Web ....www.lifeworksnw.org
E-mail ....natem@lifeworksnw.org
14600 N W Cornell Rd, Portland, OR 97229-1528
Nate Mcalmond, Director Of Information Technology

Looking Glass Youth Family Svcs, Inc. 541.686.2688
Fax 541.345.7605
Web ....www.lookingglass.us
E-mail ....craig.opperman@lookingglass.us
72B Centennial Loop Ste 2, Eugene, OR 97401-2446
Chad Westphal, Operations Officer

Lutheran Community Svcs Northwest 541.883.3471
Fax 541.883.3524
E-mail ....bpickel@lcsnw.org
2545 N Eldorado Ave, Klamath Falls, OR 97601-6423
Bob Pickel, Director

New Leaf Academy of Oregon 541.318.1676
Fax 541.318.1709
Web ....www.newleafacademy.com
63050 Dickey Road, Bend, OR 97701
CARF accredited programs available.

Northwest Behavioral Healthcare Services 503.722.4470
Web ....www.northwestbhs.com
E-mail ....drghoward@gmail.com
18000 Southeast Webster Road, Gladstone,
OR 97027
Dr. George Howard, Accreditation Manager
Joint Commission accredited organization.

Northwest Human Services 503.588.5828
Web ....www.northwesthumanservices.org
E-mail ....lhackett@nwhumanservices.org
681 Center Street, NE, Salem, OR 97301
Ms. Lola Hackett, Accreditation Manager
Joint Commission accredited organization.

Providence Portland Medical Center 503.215.2349
Web ....www.providence.org
E-mail ....gina.mcgraw@providence.org
4805 Northeast Glisan Street, Portland, OR 97213
Mrs. Gina McGraw, Accreditation Manager
Joint Commission accredited organization.

Providence St. Vincent Medical Center 503.216.1234
E-mail ....michelle.haun-hood@providence.org
9205 Southwest Barnes Road, Portland, OR 97225
Ms. Michelle Haun-Hood, Accreditation Manager
Joint Commission accredited organization.

Rainrock Treatment Center 541.896.9300
Web ....www.rainrock.org
E-mail ....anthony@rainrock.org
41496 McKenzie Highway, Springfield, OR 97478
Mr. Anthony Laughlin, Accreditation Manager
Joint Commission accredited organization.

Reliane Inc 800.906.6642
Fax 877.730.5113
Web ....www.easeeap.com
1221 SW Yam Hill Ste 200, Portland, OR 97205
Donna Broock, Supervisor

Rosemont School 503.777.8090
Fax 503.788.1131
9911 SE Mount Scott Blvd, Portland, OR 97266-6302
Leslie Gurad, Director

Soastc Merlin Campus 541.476.3302
Fax 541.476.2895
E-mail ....rlieberman@soastc.org
210 Tacoma St, Grants Pass, OR 97526-7267
Bob Lieberman, Director

Soastc Ramsy Campus 541.479.5901
Fax 541.479.6329
Web ....www.soastc.org
E-mail ....knade@soastc.org
711 SW Ramsey Ave, Grants Pass, OR 97527-5500
Kierby Nade, Director

South Coast Community Resource Ctr 541.247.2412
Fax 541.247.4085
Web ....www.southcoastcrc.org
E-mail ....rbare@southcoastcrc.org
29975 Harbor Way, Gold Beach, OR 97444
Mindy Baines, CEO/Executive Director

**Southern Oregon Adolescent Study and Treatment
Center** 541.956.4943
Web ....www.soastc.org
E-mail ....mburns@soastc.org
715 SW Ramsey Avenue, Grants Pass, OR 97527
Ms. Michelle Richardson, Accreditation Manager
Joint Commission accredited organization.

St. Mary's Home 503.649.5651
Fax 503.649.7405
Web ....www.stmaryshomeforboys.org
16535 SW Tualatin Valley Highway, Beaverton,
OR 97006-5143
COA accredited organization.

Trillium Family Services 503.234.9591
Web ....www.trilliumfamily.org
E-mail ....rblum@trilliumfamily.org
3415 SE Powell Blvd, Portland, OR 97202
Mr. Richard Blum, Accreditation Manager
Joint Commission accredited organization.

**Western Psychological And Counseling Svcs
PC** 503.439.9531
Fax 503.531.3841
Web ....www.westernpsych.com
E-mail ....dquick@teleport.com
21210 NW Mauzey Rd, Hillsboro, OR 97124-9327
Daryl Quick, President

Youth Villages - ChristieCare of Oregon 503.635.3416
Web ....www.youthvillages.org
E-mail ....linda.fanning@youthvillages.org
2507 Christie Dr., Lake Oswego, OR 97034
Ms. Linda Fanning, Accreditation Manager
Joint Commission accredited organization.

CHILDREN'S HOSPITAL

Ashland Community Hospital 541.201.4000
280 Maple St, Ashland, OR 97520
Mark Marchetti, Chief Executive Officer

Bay Area Hospital 541.269.8111
1775 Thompson Rd, Coos Bay, OR 97420
Paul Janke, Chief Executive Officer

Blue Mountain Hospital 541.575.1311
170 Ford Rd, John Day, OR 97845
Sam Grant, Chief Financial Officer

Coquille Valley Hospital 541.396.3101
940 East Fifth St, Coquille, OR 97423
Denise, Administrative Assistant

Good Shepherd Healthcare System 541.667.3400
610 NW 11th St, Hermiston, OR 97838
Dennis Purke, Chief Executive Officer

Grande Ronde Hospital 541.963.8421
900 Sunset Dr, La Grande, OR 97850
James Mattes, Chief Executive Officer

Lagacy Emanuel Hospital and Health Ctr 503.413.2200
2801 North Gantenbein Ave, Portland, OR 97227
Lori Morgan, Chief Administrator

Lake District Hospital 541.947.2114
700 South J St, Lakeview, OR 97630
Gordon Ensley, Chief Executive Officer

McKenzie Willamette Medical Center 541.726.4400
1460 G St, Springfield, OR 97477
Laurine Cate, Chief Executive Officer

Mercy Medical Center 541.673.0611
2700 Stewart Pkwy, Roseburg, OR 97470
Kelly Morgan, Chief Executive Officer

Mid Columbia Medical Center 541.296.1111
1700 East 19th St, The Dalles, OR 97058

Mountian View Hospital District 541.475.3882
470 NE A Street, Madras, OR 97741
Janie Gentry, Chief Executive Officer

Oregon Health and Science Unviersity 503.494.8311
3181 SW Sam Jackson Park Rd, Portland, OR 97239
Joseph Robertson, President

Providence Seaside Hospital 503.717.7000
725 South Wahanna Rd, Seaside, OR 97138
Krista Farnham, Chief Executive Officer

Providence St Vincent Medical Center 503.216.1234
Web ....www.providence.orgAskFrmQ#6
9205 SW Barnes Rd, Portland, OR 97225
Janice Burger, Chief Executive Officer

Rogue Valley Medical Center 541.789.7000
2825 East Barnett Rd, Medford, OR 97504
Carol Towers, Administrator

Sacred Heart Medical Center 541.686.7300
   1255 Hilyard St, Eugene, OR 97401

Salem Hospital 503.561.5200
   890 Oak St, Salem, OR 97301
   Norm Gruver, Chief Executive Officer

Samaritan Albany General Hospital 541.812.4000
   1046 West Sixth Ave, Albany, OR 97321
   David Triebes, Chief Executive Officer

Samaritan Lebanon Community Hospital 541.258.2101
   525 North Santiam Hwy, Lebanon, OR 97355
   Becky Pate, Chief Executive Officer

Santiam Memorial Hospital 503.769.2175
   1401 North 10th Ave, Stayton, OR 97383
   Genny Baldwin, Nursing Director

Silverton Hospital 503.873.1500
   342 Fairview St, Silverton, OR 97381
   Richard Cagen, Vice President

St Charles Medical Center Bend 541.382.4321
   2500 NE Neff Rd, Bend, OR 97701
   Jim E, Chief Executive Officer

St Elizabeth Health Services 541.523.6461
   3325 Pocahontas Rd, Baker, OR 97814
   Ray Gibbons, Director

West Valley Hospital 503.623.8301
   525 SE Washington St, Dallas, OR 97338
   Norm Gruber, Chief Executive Officer

COUNSELING SERVICES

Choices Counseling Ctr 541.479.8847
   Fax 541.471.2679
   109 NE Manzanita Ave, Grants Pass, OR 97526-1400
   Rick Jones, Director

**Gorge Counseling And Treatment Svcs Of
Providence** 541.387.6138
   Fax 541.387.6148
   814 13th St, Hood River, OR 97031-1210
   Elke Geiger, Office Director

Grande Ronde Child Ctr 541.963.8666
   Fax 541.663.8006
   902 D Ave, La Grande, OR 97850
   Jim Sheehy, Executive Director

Klamath Youth Development Ctr 541.883.1030
   Fax 541.884.2338
   E-mail ....pcard@klamathyouth.org
   2210 N Eldorado Ave, Klamath Falls, OR 97601
   Stan Gilbert, Director

CRISIS & SHELTER CARE

Americian Domestic Violence Crisis Line 503.846.2932
   Fax 503.846.2990
   150 N 1st Ave, Hillsboro, OR 97124-3002

**Battered Persons Avocacy-Domestic
Violence** 541.957.0288
   Fax 541.672.8140
   E-mail ....vabecker@cmspan.net
   1202 SE Douglas Ave, Roseburg, OR 97470
   Vanessa Becker, Director

Brady-Angle House-Domestic Violence 503.232.1528
   Fax 503.232.6617
   Web ....www.bradleyangle.org
   E-mail ....office@bradleyangle.org
   4548 N Albina Ave #101, Portland, OR 97217
   Shiela Hale, Director

Cascade Youth And Family Ctr 541.382.0934
   Fax 541.383.3024
   E-mail ....cyfc@jbarj.org
   2125 NE Daggett Lane, Bend, OR 97701
   Pat Gundy, Program Manager

Clackamas Womens Svc 503.722.2366
   Fax 503.722.8059
   Web ....www.cwsor.org
   E-mail ....info@cwsor.org
   704 Main St Ste 200, Oregon City, OR 97045
   Melissa Earlbaum, Director

Domestic Violence 541.947.2498
   Fax 541.947.2147
   726 N 1st St, Lakeview, OR 97630
   Janine Simms, Director

**Domestic Violence Resource Ctr-Monikas
House** 503.640.5352
   Fax 503.648.6905
   3800 SW Cedar Hill Blvd # 195, Beaverton, OR 97005
   Ladonna Burgess, Executive Director

Haven-Domestic Violence Program 541.296.1662
   Fax 541.296.1904
   E-mail ....havened@gorge.net
   420 E 3rd St, The Dalles, OR 97058-0576
   Tara Koch, Executive Director

Helping Hands Against Violence Inc. 541.386.4808
   Fax 541.386.2194
   E-mail ....volunteerrh@gorge.net
   PO Box 441, Hood River, OR 97031-0015
   Lee Montavon, Director

Helpline 541.779.4357
   Fax 541.779.3317
   Web ....www.community-works.org
   900 E Main St, Medford, OR 97504-7136

Integral Youth Svcs 541.882.2053
   Fax 541.885.6809
   Web ....www.iyskfalls.org
   E-mail ....iys@iyskfalls.org
   115 N 10th St, Klamath Falls, OR 97601-5803
   Bruce Beeson, Executive Director

Janus Youth Programs/ Harry's Mother 503.233.8111
   Fax 503.233.8174
   738 NE Davis St, Portland, OR 97232-2931
   Dennis L. Morrow, Executive Director

**Klamath Crisis Ctr- Martas House- Domestic
Violence** 541.884.0390
   Fax 541.850.8435
   E-mail ....ksmav@hotmail.com
   142 Riverside Dr, Klamath Falls, OR 97601
   Wanda Powless, Director

**Listen To Kids-Domestic Violence
Program** 503.280.1388
   Fax 503.280.1392
   5135 NW St Helens Rd, Portland, OR 97210
   Jennifer Talbot, Director

Mid Valley Womens Crisis Svc 503.378.1572
   Fax 503.364.7998
   Web ....www.mvwcs.com
   E-mail ....jayne@mvwcs.com
   795 Winter St NE, Salem, OR 97301
   Jayne Downing, Director

My Sisters Place- Domestic Violence 541.574.9424
   Fax 541.574.0376
   E-mail ....info@mysistersplace.us
   934 SW 8th St, Newport, OR 97365
   Karen Shores, Director

Native American Family Healing Circle 503.288.8177
   Fax 503.288.1260
   Web ....www.nayapdx.org
   E-mail ....nicholem@nayapdx.org
   5135 NE Columbia Blvd, Portland, OR 97218-1201
   Nicole Maher, Director

**Northwest Human Svcs, Inc. Host Youth & Family
Ctr** 503.588.5825
   Fax 503.361.0383
   Web ....www.nwhumanservices.org
   1143 Liberty St NE, Salem, OR 97301-1047
   Jessica Munoz, Shelter Coordinator

Oasis Shelter Inc. Domestic Violence 541.247.7600
   Fax 541.247.0607
   Web ....www.oasisshelterhome.org
   E-mail ....lea.s@oasisshelterhome.org
   PO Box 932, Gold Beach, OR 97444-0932
   Lea Seveay, Director

Oregon J Bar J Ranch 541.389.1409
   Fax 541.389.9348
   E-mail ....salstad@jbarj.org
   62895 Hamby Rd, Bend, OR 97701-9571
   Stephanie Alstad, Director

Portland Women's Crisis Line 503.232.9751
   Fax 503.234.3749
   E-mail ....rebecca@pwcl.org
   2227 SE Division St, Portland, OR 97202
   Rebecca Peatow Nickels, Executive Director

**Project Dove-Domestice Violence
Program** 541.889.6316
   Fax 541.889.2416
   E-mail ....dove7@fmtc.com
   585 NW 1st St, Ontario, OR 97914-1701
   Cindy Renae, Interim Executive Director

Sexual Assault Support Svcs 541.484.9791
   Fax 541.342.3696
   E-mail ....monica.@sassm_lane.org
   591 W 19th Ave, Eugene, OR 97401
   Monica Galcia Montro, Co-Director

Shelter 541.474.5404
   Fax 541.474.5181
   301 NW F St, Detention Facility, Grants Pass,
   OR 97526
   Jim Goodwin, Program Manager

**Shelter From The Storm-Domestic
Violence** 541.963.7226
   Fax 541.962.7654
   E-mail ....dplshelter@eoni.com
   1111 5th St La, La Grande, OR 97850
   Darilyn Legore, Director

Siuslaw Outreach Svcs-Domestic Violence 541.997.2816
   Fax 541.997.7257
   E-mail ....sos@florencesos.org
   1576 12th St, Florence, OR 97439
   Bettie Egerton, Director

The Next Door, Inc 541.386.6665
   Fax 541.386.5440
   Web ....www.nextdoorinc.org
   E-mail ....janeth@nextdoorinc.org
   965 Tucker Rd, Hood River, OR 97031
   Janet Hamada, Executive Director

**Volunteers America Home Free-Domestic
Violence** 503.771.5503
   Fax 503.771.5347
   Web ....www.voaor.org
   E-mail ....kbillhardt@voaor.org
   3910 SE Stark St, Portland, OR 97214-2278
   Kirs Billhardt, Director

West Womens And Childrens Shelter 503.224.7718
   Fax 503.239.1257
   PO Box 2398, Portland, OR 97208-2398
   Fay Schuler, Director

Womens Crisis Ctr 503.842.9486
   Fax 503.842.6458
   Web ....www.pacifier.com
   E-mail ....rosemaryc@voaor.com
   1902 2nd St, Tillamook, OR 97141-2206
   Kathleen Marvin, Director

**Womens Crisis Support Team-Domestic
Violence** 541.479.9349
   Fax 541.472.8244
   Web ....www.wcstjoco.org
   560 NE F St Ste A PMB 430, Grants Pass,
   OR 97526-2300
   Krisanna Allbriecht, Acting Director

Womens Resource Ctr 503.397.7110
Fax 503.366.9529
E-mail ....execdir@columbia-center.org
Good Samaritan Medical Mall, Route 30, St. Helens, OR 97051
Sandra Mitchell, Director

Womens Resource Ctr-Domestic Violence 503.325.3426
Fax 503.325.7101
Web ....www.womens-resource.com
1361 Duane St, Astoria, OR 97103-4545
Pat Burness, Director

Womenspace 541.485.8232
Fax 541.686.6664
Web ....www.womenspaceinc.org
E-mail ....peggyw@womenspaceinc.org
1577 Pearl Street Suite 400 Upstairs, Eugene, OR 97401
Peggy Whalen, Executive Director

EDUCATION

Angell Job Corp 541.547.3137
Fax 541.547.5690
Web ....www.fs.fed.us
E-mail ....waynetapp@fs.fed.us
335 NE Blodgett Rd, Yachats, OR 97498-9388
Wayne Tapp, Center Director

Child Development Ctr 541.889.2393
Fax 541.889.7137
E-mail ....srobinett@mccdc.org
790 SW 7th Pl, Ontario, OR 97914
Susan Robinett, Director

Children's Learning Ctr 541.475.3628
Fax 541.475.2583
650 NE A St, Ste A, Madras, OR 97741
Kaline Rosman, Director

Community Works 541.779.2393
Fax 541.779.3317
Web ....www.community-works.org
E-mail ....info@community-works.org
201 W main st ste 2b, Medford, OR 97501

Family Nursery Volunteers Of America 503.235.8655
Fax 503.239.6233
Web ....www.voaor.org
E-mail ....vsargent@voaor.org
3910 SE Stark St, Portland, OR 97214-2278
Kay Toran, President

Kids & Company 541.451.1581
Fax 541.259.1581
Web ....www.kidcoheadstart.org
E-mail ....kidco@kidcoheadstart.org
300 Market St Ste 200, Lebanon, OR 97355-2282
Jo O'leary, Director

Lifeworks Northwest/Hilsboro 503.640.5297
Fax 503.640.5780
Web ....www.lifeworksnw.org
971 SW Walnut St, Hillsboro, OR 97123-5651
Deb Allison, Director

Open Meadow Alternative Schools 503.285.0508
Fax 503.285.0798
Web ....www.openmeadow.org
E-mail ....andrew@openmeadow.org
7654 N Crawford St, Portland, OR 97203
Andrew Moson, Executive Director

**Oregon National Guard Youth Challenge/
Program** 541.317.9623
Fax 541.318.1180
Web ....www.ngycp.org
E-mail ....joel.garibay@mil.state.or.us
23861 Dodds Rd, Bend, OR 97701-9684
Joel Jaribay, Admissions Counselor

**Salem Keizer Public School/Doug Paulus Admisitration
Ctr** 503.399.3258
Fax 503.316.3556
Web www.salkeiz.k12.or.us
E-mail ....larson_steve@salkeiz.k12.or.us
1309 Ferry St SE, Salem, OR 97301-4198
Steve Larson, Director

Springdale Job Corps Ctr 503.695.2245
Fax 503.695.2254
31224 E Historic Columbia River Hwy, Troutdale, OR 97060-9399
Naomi C, Center Director

The Academy 800.808.7515
Fax 541.572.5329
Web ....www.theacademyusa.com
E-mail ....enrollment@theacademyusa.com
51287 Hatfield Rd, Myrtle Point, OR 97458-7803
Ryan Thomas, Executive Director

Timber Lake Job Corp 503.834.2291
Fax 503.834.2333
Web ....www.fs.fed.us
59868 E Highway 224, Estacada, OR 97023-9399
Scott Olson, Center Director

Tongue Point Job Corps Ctr 503.338.5000
Fax 503.338.5099
Web ....www.tonguepoint.com
E-mail ....pyburn.nancy@jobcorps.org
37573 Highway 30 Bldg X, Astoria, OR 97103-7202
Nancy Pyburn, Center Director

**Wolf Creek Job Corps Civilian Conservation
Ctr** 541.496.3507
Fax 541.496.8515
Web ....www.wolfcreek.jopcorp.org
2010 Opportunity Ln, Glide, OR 97443
Eric Bracken, Center Director

FOSTER CARE AGENCIES

A Place Called Home 503.698.6639
Fax 503.698.4928
Web ....www.apch.org
14652 SE Sterling Ct, Clackamas, OR 97015-8292
Amy, Director

Acpo 541.957.1428
Fax 541.957.1707
E-mail ....lisascare787@cmscan.net
787 W Kenwood St, Roseburg, OR 97471-2632
Lisa Shrayder, Owner

Adoption Support Grp 541.776.6120
909 Royal Ct, Medford, OR 97504
Pam Bergreen, Program Manager

Adoptive Foster Families Supportive Adol 503.731.3147
1425 NE Irving St Bldg 400, Tigard, OR 97223

Adoptive Foster Kids In Common 971.673.5500
6443 N Lombard St, Portland, OR 97203
Dorthy A Fuller, Director

African American Families Through Adopt 503.645.6642
E-mail ....pearlysue@stanfordalumni.org
PO Box 19000, Portland, OR 97280
Sue Pearly, Organizer

Amber's Loving Care 541.966.4011
908 SW 33rd St, Pendleton, OR 97801-3623
Amber Taillon, Director

Boise Elliot School 503.916.6171
620 N Fremont, Portland, OR 97227

Caring Hearts 541.535.6308
701 1st St, Phoneix, OR 97535

Catholic Charitites 503.231.4866
E-mail ....psa@catholiccharitiesoregon.org
2740 SE Powell Blvd, Portland, OR 97202
Janice Keenan, Director

Child Welfare Srvs 971.673.2100
3618 SE 122nd Ave, Portland, OR 97236
Cheryl Baldomaro-Lucas, Branch Manager

Christian Family Adoptions 503.232.1211
Fax 503.232.4756
E-mail ....mail@christianfamilyadoptions.org
6040 Southeast Belmont St, Portland, OR 97215

Dawn House 541.474.1617
2220 Dawn Dr, Grants Pass, OR 97527-9703
Margie Webb, Owner

DHS Child Welfare 541.298.5136
700 Union St Ste 230, The Dalles, OR 97058
Bill Sheirbon, Supervisor

Dove Home Health 503.775.0469
Fax 503.771.7893
Web ....www.dovehomehealth.com
E-mail ....dove@dovehomehealth.com
3735 SE Martins St, Portland, OR 97202-7643
Orvalee Farris, Executive Director

Edgewood Home Care 541.772.0223
Fax 541.779.1636
3043 Edgewood Dr, Medford, OR 97504-9601

Foster Adopt Support Gr 541.536.1355
PO Box 559, La Pine, OR 97739

Foster Parents Assoc 541.347.4224
E-mail ....mmscott@junl.com
675 SE 10th St, Bandon, OR 97420
Marjorie Scott, President

Kinship House 503.460.2796
Fax 503.460.3750
E-mail ....officemanager@kinshiphouse.org
1823 NE 8th Ave, Portland, OR 97212
Heather Jefferis, Executive Director

Marion/Polk Foster Parents Assoc 503.364.9938
E-mail ....ischiebler@yahoo.com
3463 Hadly St NE, Salem, OR 97301
Lori Schiebler, President

Northwest Adoptive Families Inc 503.243.1356
PO Box 25355, Portland, OR 97298

Oregon Foster Parent Assoc 888.544.3402
E-mail ....ofpaoffice@aol.com
707 SE 13th ,Ste 114, Salem, OR 97301

Relatives as Parents 503.241.0799
E-mail ....orparc@nwresource.org
2950 SE Stark St Ste 130, Portland, OR 97214
Kelly Delamy, Director

Stars of David International Inc 503.226.7079
Fax 503.226.1130
E-mail ....starsdavid@aol.com
1130 SW Morrison #316, Portland, OR 97205

PEDIATRIC HOME CARE

Interim Healthcare 503.761.6050
Fax 503.761.5425
E-mail ....christinelove@ncshosting.com
9498 SW Barbur Blvd, Ste 310, Portland, OR 97219
Christine Love, Director

Interim Healthcare 541.779.0054
Fax 541.779.0880
2368 Crater Lake Ave Ste 102, Medford, OR 97504
Heather Burn, Director

Interim Healthcare 503.391.4225
Fax 503.391.2942
E-mail ....dimidy.white@ncshosting.com
960 Libert st SE, Ste 210, Salem, OR 97302
Dimidy White, Operations Manager

Interim Healthcare (Medford Staffing) 541.772.7823
Fax 541.773.7823
2368 Crater Lake Ave Ste 102, Medford, OR 97504
Heather Burns, Director

SOCIAL SERVICES

CCR&R Of Multnomah And Clackamas Mt. Hood Council Of Camp Fire 503.548.4400
Fax 503.473.8429
Web ....www.campfireusamthood.org
E-mail ....jeanne.lemieux@mhcc.edu
1006 SE Grand Ave Ste 100B, Portland,
OR 97214-2330
Jean Lemieux, Director

Central Coast Oregon Right To Life 541.444.2246
19586 Siletz Hwy, Siletz, OR 97380
Jerry Kosydar, Associate

Chehalem Youth & Family Services 503.538.4874
Fax 503.538.1271
Web ....www.cyfs.net
P.O. Box 636, Newberg, OR 97132
COA accredited organization.

Child Care Resource And Referral 971.223.6100
Fax 503.648.4175
Web ....www.caowash.org/ccr
E-mail ....ccrr@caowash.org
1001 SW Baseline St, Hillsboro, OR 97123-3822
Karen Henkemeyer, Director

Child Care Resource And Referral 503.585.2491
Fax 503.375.7580
Web ....www.mwvcaa.org/ccis
E-mail ....ccis@mwvcaa.org
2475 Center St NE, Salem, OR 97301-4520
Shannon Vandehey, Director

Child Care Resource And Referral Training And Employment Consortium 541.573.6676
Fax 541.573.5432
Web ....www.trainingemployment.org
90 W Washington St, Burns, OR 97720-1545
Tonya Fox, Supervisor

Child Care Resource Ctr 503.248.9252
Fax 503.489.2570
Web ....www.metroccrr.org
E-mail ....childcarereferrals@metroccrr.org
123 E Powell Blvd Ste 300, Gresham, OR 97030
Debbie Hoffmeister, Coordinator

Child Care Resource Network 541.776.1234
Fax 541.766.5125
Web ....www.jobcouncil.org
E-mail ....ccrnreferral@jobcouncil.org
673 Market St, Medford, OR 97504-6125
Becky Aeschbacher, Job Coach

Child Victim Assessment Ctr 541.926.2203
Fax 541.926.1378
E-mail ....abchousedoc@comcast.net
1054 29th Ave SW, Albany, OR 97321-3416
Karen Scheler, Executive Director

Ctr For Family Development 541.342.8437
Fax 541.342.1639
E-mail ....main@c-f-d.org
1258 High St, Eugene, OR 97401
Martin Waechter, Director

Douglas Cares 541.957.5646
Fax 541.957.0191
Web ....www.douglascares.net
256 SE Stephens St, Roseburg, OR 97470-3124
Evelyn Noref, Executive Director

Family Building Blocks 503.566.2132
Fax 503.566.2134
Web ....www.familybuildingblocks.org
E-mail ....smiller@familybuildingblocks.org
2425 Lancaster Dr NE, Salem, OR 97305-1220
Sue Miller, CEO/Executive Director

Family Connection 541.917.4899
Fax 541.917.4270
Web ....www.linnbenton.edu
E-mail ....connect@linnbenton.edu
6500 SW Pacific Blvd, Albany, OR 97321-3755
Pamela Dunn, Department Chairperson

Family Connections 541.672.7955
Fax 541.957.2302
Web ....www.ucancap.org
E-mail ....roy.spurgeon@ucancap.org
815 SE Oak Ave, Roseburg, OR 97470-4914
Roy Spurgeon, Director

Family Relief Nursery 541.942.4835
Fax 541.942.7359
Web ....www.oip.net
E-mail ....heathermurphy@oip.net
720 N 14th St, Cottage Grove, OR 97424-1296
Heather Murphy, CEO/Executive Director

Jasper Mountain 541.747.1235
Fax 541.747.4722
Web ....www.jaspermountain.org
37875 Jasper Lowell Road, Jasper, OR 97438
COA accredited organization.

Lane Family Connection/Lane Community College 541.463.3954
Fax 541.463.4724
Web ....www.lanecc.edu/lfc/index.htm
E-mail ....nortons@lanepc.edu
4000 E 30th Ave, Eugene, OR 97405
Sue Norton, Supervisor

Liberty House 503.540.0288
Fax 503.540.0293
E-mail ....admin@libertyhousecenter.org
2685 4th St NE, Salem, OR 97301
Gretchen Bennett, Executive Director

Looking Glass Adolescent Recovery Program 541.485.8448
Fax 541.484.7212
Web ....www.lookingglass.us
E-mail ....chris.rubin@lookingglass.us
20 E 13th Ave, Eugene, OR 97401-3535
Chris Rubin, Director

Looking Glass Youth & Family Services, Inc. 541.686.2688
Fax 541.345.7605
Web ....www.lookingglass.us
72-B Centennial Loop, Suite 2, Eugene, OR 97401
COA accredited organization.

Morrison Child and Family Services 503.258.4300
Fax 503.963.6708
Web ....www.morrisonkids.org
9911 SE Mount Scott Boulevard, Portland, OR 97266
COA accredited organization.

NARA (Native American Rehabilitation Assoc) Of The Northwest, Inc. 503.621.1069
Fax 503.621.0200
Web ....www.naranorthwest.org
E-mail ....jmercer@naranorthwest.org
17645 NW Saint Helens Rd, Portland,
OR 97231-1729
Jacqueline Mercer, Director

Newberg WIC 503.538.8779
Fax 503.538.6970
E-mail ....elizabeths@yvfwc.org
2251 E Hancock St, Newberg, OR 97132
Elizabeth Still, Wic Supervisor

Northwest Human Services 503.588.5828
Fax 503.588.5852
E-mail ....plogan@nwhumanservices.org
681 Center St. NE, Salem, OR 97301-4018
Paul Logan, Executive Director

The Boys & Girls Aid Society of Oregon 503.222.9661
Fax 503.224.5960
Web ....www.boysandgirlsaid.org
E-mail ....mbalter@boysandgirlsaid.org
018 Southwest Boundary Court, Portland, OR 97239
Michael Balter, Executive Director
CARF accredited programs available.

Umatilla Morrow Child Care Resource And Referral 541.564.6878
Fax 541.564.6879
Web ....www.umchs.org
E-mail ....shalvers@umchs.org
110 NE 4th St, Hermiston, OR 97838-1861
Starla Haverson, Director

Wemble Naalam T'at'aksni (Heal Our Children) 541.273.0711
Fax 541.273.0726
Web ....www.klm.portland.ihs.gov
E-mail ....aepool@klm.portland.ihs.gov
121 Iowa St, Klamath Falls, OR 97601-1606
Angie Pool, Director

Wics Lifeskills For Women 503.570.6609
Fax 503.570.6617
Web ....www.doc.state.or.us
E-mail ....trena.l.stewart@doc.state.or.us
24499 SW Grahams Ferry Rd, Wilsonville,
OR 97070-7523
Monica Coleman, Administrator

SPECIAL NEEDS

Autism Society of Oregon 888.288.4761
E-mail ....info@oregonautism.com
PO Box 396, Marylhurst, OR 97036

Bend Language & Learning 541.385.6002
Fax 541.385.6090
E-mail ....bendlearn@bendbroadband.com
1011 SW Emkay Dr, Ste 101, Bend, OR 97702

Bridges Academy 888.283.7362
Fax 541.383.4108
E-mail ....info@bridgesboyascademy.com
67030 Gist Rd, Bend, OR 97701
Joan Mcomber, Director

Easter Seals Oregon 503.228.5108
E-mail ....info@or.easterseals.com
5757 SW Macadam Ave, Portland, OR 97239
David ChevealLier, Chief Executive Officer

Learning Disabilities Association 503.697.6213
E-mail ....mtsoule@ix.netcom.com
PO Box 34, Marylhurst, OR 97036

Legacy Emanuel Children's Hospital Pediatric Rehabilitation Program 503.413.2444
Fax 503.413.4719
Web ....www.legacyhealth.org
2801 North Gantenbein Avenue, Portland, OR 97227
CARF accredited programs available.

Meadowood Springs Speech & Hearing Camp 541.276.2752
Fax 541.276.7227
E-mail ....info@meadowoodsprings.org
77650 Meadowood Western, Pendleton, OR 97886
Robert Hutchins, Chief Executive Officer

Mental Health Association 503.725.5953
E-mail ....beckiec@pdx.edu
1600 SW 4th Ave, Ste 900, Portland, OR 97207

NAMI Oregon 503.230.8009
E-mail ....namioregon@namior.org
4701 SE 24th Ave Ste E, Portland, OR 97202
Chris Bouneff, Director

National Multiple Sclerosis Society 503.223.9511
Fax 503.223.2912
E-mail ....info@defeatms.com
104 SW Clay St, Portland, OR 97201
Kim Southworth, Manager Of Services

Northwest Reading Clinic, Inc 503.620.2223
Fax 503.968.8486
E-mail ....nwrc@verizon.net
  7000 SW Hampton St, Ste 240, Tigard, OR 97223

Oregon Brain Injury Resource Network 541.346.0593
E-mail ....tbi@wou.edu
  345 N Monmouth Ave, Monmouth, OR 97361

Oregon Family Support Network Inc 541.342.2876
  2411 MLK Jr Blvd Ste 274, Eugene, OR 97401
  Jammie Farrish, Executive Director

Oregon FIRST (CPRC) 503.215.2268
Fax 503.215.2478
E-mail ....info@orfirst.org
  830 NE 47th Ave, Portland, OR 97213
  Pat Budo, Director

Oregon Health & Science University 503.494.5236
Fax 503.494.0966
E-mail ....Louja@ohsu.edu
  3181 SW Sam Jackson Park Rd, # L226, Portland,
  OR 97239
  Jau-Shin Lou MD, PhD Director

Oregon Parent Training & Information Ctr 503.581.8156
E-mail ....info@orpti.org
  2288 Liberty St NE, Salem, OR 97301
  Janice Robert, Director

Oregon PTA 503.234.3928
E-mail ....or_office@pta.org
  4506 SE Belmont Ste 108 B, Portland, OR 97215
  Carol Wire, Executive Director

Oregon PTI 503.581.8156
Fax 503.391.0429
E-mail ....info@orpti.org
  2288 Liberty St NE, Salem, OR 97301

**Oregon Rehabilitation Center, Sacred Heart Medical
Center** 541.686.7363
Fax 541.686.8996
Web ....www.peacehealth.org
  1255 Hilyard Street, 5NE - REHAB, Eugene, OR 97401
  CARF accredited programs available.

Portland Aspergers Network 503.284.4507
E-mail ....contact@aspergersnet.org
  3324 NE 22nd Ave, Portland, OR 97212
  Marcus Chavez, Marketing Supervisor

Prog for Low Incidence Disabilities 503.947.5760
  255 Capitol St NE, Salem, OR 97310
  Susan Castillo, Superintendent

**Special Ed Law and Advocacy in OR and
WA** 503.727.0202
Fax 503.727.0303
Web ....diane@wiscarsonlaw.com
E-mail 5037270303
  510 SW Third Ave Ste 439, Portland, OR 97204
  Aaron Hodukavich, Attorney; Diane Frost Wiscarson, Attorney/Owner

Speech-Language & Hearing Association 503.370.7019
E-mail ....john@profadminserv.com
  3415 Commercia St S, Salem, OR 97302
  John McCulley, Executive Assistant

The Arc of Oregon 503.581.2726
E-mail ....info@arcoregon.org
  1745 State St, Salem, OR 97301
  Marcie Ingoedue, Director

United Cerebral Palsy 503.777.4167
E-mail ....bthoune@ucpaorwa.org
  11731 NE Glenn Widing Dr, Portland, OR 97220

SUBSTANCE ABUSE TREATMENT

Adapt 541.672.2691
Fax 541.673.5642
  548 SE Jackson St Ste 3, Roseburg, OR 97470
  Bruce Piper, CEO

Adapt 541.474.1033
Fax 541.474.0770
Web ....www.adaptoregon.org
E-mail ....brucep@adapt-or.org
  418 NW 6th St, Grants Pass, OR 97526-2006
  Bruce Piper, Executive Director

Adapt North Bend 541.751.0357
Fax 541.751.9985
Web ....www.adaptoregon.org
  400 Virginia Ave Ste 201, North Bend, OR 97459
  Deidrie Lindsey, Director

Bridgeway Recovery Services 503.363.2021
Fax 503.363.4820
  3325 Harold Dr NE, Salem, OR 97305-1339
  Tim Murphy, Program Director

**Catherine Freer Wilderness Therapy
Expeditions** 541.926.7252
Fax 541.812.0116
Web ....www.cfreer.com
E-mail ....info@cfreer.com
  420 3rd Ave SW, Albany, OR 97321
  Robert Cooley, Phd, Owner

De Paul Treatment Centers, Inc. 503.535.1152
Fax 503.535.1190
Web ....www.depaultreatmentcenters.org
  1318 Southwest Washington Street, Portland,
  OR 97205-2327
  CARF accredited programs available.

DePaul Youth Treatment Ctrs, Inc 503.535.1181
Fax 503.528.0800
Web ....www.depaultreatmentcenters.org
E-mail ....sheilan@depaultreatmentcenters.org
  4310 NE Killingsworth St, Portland, OR 97218-1404
  Sheila North, Executive Director

Discovery Counseling 541.752.2703
Fax 541.752.8252
  260 SW Madison Office 10, Corvallis,
  OR 97330-2111
  Sherry Crew, Executive Director

Emergence 541.997.8509
Fax 541.902.0109
  1932 Pine St, Florence, OR 97439
  Michael Bean, Director

Emergence 541.393.0777
Fax 541.736.5015
Web ....www.acescounseling.org
E-mail ....mbean@acescounseling.org
  2149 Centennial Plz, Eugene, OR 97401-7909
  Michael Bean, Director

Emergence 541.767.3057
Fax 541.767.3062
Web ....www.acescounseling.org
E-mail ....mbean@acescounseling.org
  260 Gateway Blvd, Cottage Grove, OR 97424-1745
  Michael Bean, Director

Klamath Alcohol And Drug Abuse, Inc 541.882.7248
Fax 541.884.4724
E-mail ....kada@charterinternet.com
  310 S 5th St, Klamath Falls, OR 97601
  John Prosnik, CFO

**Klamath Tribes Dept Of Counseling And Family
Svc** 541.783.2219
Fax 541.783.7783
E-mail ....marvin.garcia@klamathtribes.com
  501 Chiloquin Blvd, Chiloquin, OR 97624
  Marvin Garcia, Director Of Social Services

Lifeworks Northwest 503.335.0855
Fax 503.335.8125
Web ....www.lifeworksnw.org
  2631 N Mississippi Ave, Portland, OR 97227-1616
  Sherri Lynn, Director

Looking Glass - Pathways 541.682.7979
Fax 541.682.7980
E-mail ....steve.marksfife@lookingglass.us
  2655 Martin Luther King Jr Blvd, Eugene,
  OR 97401-5899
  Steve Marks-fife, Program Director

Milestone Family Recovery Program 541.753.2230
Fax 541.758.8347
Web ....www.milestonesrecovery.com
E-mail ....tonyapritt@milestonesrecovery.com
  306 SW 8th St, Corvallis, OR 97333-4543
  Tonya Pritt, Program Director

Milestone Family Recovery/ Yes House 541.753.7801
Fax 541.753.7805
E-mail ....tanyampritt@msn.com
  404 NW 23rd St, Corvallis, OR 97330-5539
  Tanya Pritt, Program Director

Mount Bachelor Academy 541.462.3404
Fax 541.462.3430
Web ....www.mtba.com
E-mail ....www.welcomemba.com
  33051 Ne Ochoco Hwy, Prineville, OR 97754-7990
  Sharon Bitz, Executive Director

**New Directions Northwest Blue Mountain
Outpatient** 541.523.8364
Fax 541.523.8367
  2100 Main St, Baker City, OR 97814
  Beverly Dubosch, Program Manager

Northwest Behavioral Healthcare Svcs 503.722.4470
Fax 503.722.4410
Web ....www.northwestbhs.com
E-mail ....dmahler@northwestbhs.com
  18000 Webster Rd, Gladstone, OR 97027-1447
  Daniel Mahler, Executive Director

Ontrack, Inc 541.772.1777
Fax 541.734.2410
Web ....www.ontrackrecovery.org
E-mail ....info@ontrackrecovery.org
  221 W Main St, Medford, OR 97501-2728
  Rita Sullivan, Director

Ontrack, Inc. 541.864.8701
Fax 541.864.8799
E-mail ....info@ontrackrecovery.org
  3131 Avenue C, White City, OR 97503
  Rita Sullivan, Director

**Reconnections Substance Abuse
Counseling** 541.994.4198
Fax 541.574.8857
  2152 NW Mast Pl Ste B, Lincoln City,
  OR 97367-4036
  Lalorie Lager, Director

Relief Nursery 541.343.9706
Fax 541.683.3748
E-mail ....kellysu@reliesnursery.org
  1720 W 25th Ave, Eugene, OR 97405
  Kelly Suthern, CEO/Executive Director

Rimrock Trails 541.447.2631
Fax 541.447.2616
Web ....www.rimrocktrailsats.com
E-mail ....exec@rimrocktrailsats.com
  1333 NW 9th St, Prineville, OR 97754-1482
  Erica Fuller, Executive Director

Rimrock Trails 541.388.8459
Fax 541.447.2616
Web ....www.rimrocktrailsats.org
E-mail ....exec@rimrocktrailsats.com
  1010 NW 14th St, Bend, OR 97701-9475
  Erika Fuller, Director

Pennsylvania

Tom Corbett, Governor
225 Main Capitol Building
Harrisburg, PA 17120
717.787.2500
717.772.8284 (Fax)
governor@state.pa.us
www.governor.state.pa.us

Michael D. Pennington, Juvenile Justice Specialist
Juvenile Justice Program
3101 North Front St
Harrisburg, PA 17108
717.265.8461
717.772.0551 (Fax)
mpenningto@state.pa.us

Dr. Ronald Sharp, SAG Chair
Alternative Rehabilitation Communities
2743 North Front Street
Harrisburg, PA 17105
717.238.7101
717.238.6392 (Fax)
ron.sharp@arcfamily.com
www.arcfamily.com

CRISIS NUMBERS

Child Abuse Reporting . . .800.932.0313

STATE SERVICES

SOCIAL SERVICES

Dept of Public Welfare **800.692.7462**
PO Box 2675, Harrisburg, PA 17105-2675

Ofc of Children, Youth & Families **717.787.4756**
Fax 717.787.0414
Web . . . . .www.state.pa.us
17th Forster St # 131, Harrisburg, PA 17120-0001
Cathy Utz, Deputy Secretary

Pennsylvania Adoption Exchange **800.227.0225**
Fax 717.236.8510
Web . . . . .www.diakon-swan.org
E-mail .jjohnston@diakon-swan.org
471 JP Elwickdrive, Harrisburg, PA 17111
Jane Johnston, Divison Manager

GENERAL HEALTH SERVICES

**Bureau of Community Health (North Central
District)** **570.327.3400**
Fax 570.327.3748
Web . . . . .www.dsf.health.state.pa.us
1000 Commerce Park Dr Ste 109, Williamsport,
PA 17701-5475
Adrian Signor, Hiv Coordinator

Div of Child and Adult Health Svcs PA **717.772.2762**
Fax 717.772.0323
E-mail . . . . .ccass@state.pa.us
7th & Forster St, Hlth & Welfare Bldg 7th Flr E,
Harrisburg, PA 17120
C Cass, Director

Pennsylvania Dept of Health **724.773.7436**
Fax 724.773.7416
Web . . . . .www.dsf.health.state.pa.us
300 S Walnut Ln Ste 101, Beaver, PA 15009-1737
Kathrine Regiec, Community Health Nurse

State Health Ctr **724.627.3168**
Fax 724.852.4448
E-mail . . . . .mashaw@state.pa.us
432 E Oakview Dr, Waynesburg, PA 15370-9729
Marlene Shaw, Hiv Coordinator

MENTAL HEALTH SERVICES

Office of Voc Rehabilitation PA **717.787.5244**
Fax 717.783.5221
E-mail . . . . .wgannon@state.pa.us
1521 N 6th St, Harrisburg, PA 17102
W Gannon, Director

Office of Vocational Rehab PA **717.787.3201**
Fax 717.772.1629
E-mail . . . . .ddenotaris@state.pa.us
1521 N 6th st, Harrisburg, PA 17102
D Denotaris, Director

JUSTICE AGENCY

Attorney General's Ofc **717.787.3391**
Fax 717.787.8242
Strawberry Sq Fl 16, Harrisburg, PA 17120
Tom Corbett, Attorney General

**Bureau of Victim's Svcs - Victim's Compensation
Div** **717.783.5153**
Fax 717.787.4306
E-mail . . . . .bjhorn@state.pa.us
3101 N Front St, Harrisburg, PA 17110
B. J. Horn, Bureau Director

Dept of Corrections **717.975.4860**
Fax 717.703.3621
Web . . . . .www.cor.state.pa.us
2520 Lisburn Rd, Camp Hill, PA 17011
John Wetzel, Secretary

COURTS

Administrative Ofc of The Courts **215.560.6300**
Fax 215.560.6315
1515 Market St Ste 1414, Philadelphia, PA 19102
Zygmont A. Pines, Court Administrator

Juvenile Court Judge's Commission **717.787.6910**
Fax 717.783.6266
Web . . . . .www.jcjc.state.pa.us
E-mail . . . . .janderson@state.pa.us
401 Finance Building, Harrisburg, PA 17120-0018
James E. Anderson, Executive Director

POLICE AND SHERIFF

Pennsylvania Chiefs of Police Assoc **717.236.1059**
Fax 717.236.0226
Web . . . . .www.pachiefs.org
E-mail . . . . .pacops@aol.com
3905 N Front St, Harrisburg, PA 17110-1536
Amy Rosenberry, Executive Director

EDUCATION SERVICES

Bureau of Special Education PA **717.783.6913**
Fax 717.783.6139
333 Market St 7th Flr, Harrisburg, PA 17126
John Tommasini, Director

Div of Student and Safe Sch Srvs PA **717.783.6468**
Fax 717.783.6617
E-mail . . . . .swinnick@state.pa.us
333 Market St 5th Flr, Harrisburg, PA 17126

Of of Child Dev and Early Learning PA **717.346.9320**
Fax 717.787.1529
333 Market St 6th Flr, Harrisburg, PA 17126
Marci Walters, Director

Ofc of Elementary/Secondary Education **717.787.2127**
Fax 717.783.6802
Web . . . . .www.state.pa.us
E-mail .dcastelbuono@state.pa.us
333 Market St, Harrisburg, PA 17126-0001
John Tommasini, Special Ed Director

Overbrook School for the Blind **215.877.0313**
Fax 215.877.2466
Web . . . . .www.obs.org
E-mail . . . . .bmk@obs.org
6333 Malvern Ave, Philadelphia, PA 19151-2597
Gerald Kitzhoffer, Director

Pennsylvania Department of Education **717.787.5820**
Fax 717.787.7222
E-mail . . . . .00admin@state.pa.us
333 Market St, Harrisburg, PA 17126
Ronald Tomalis, Director

Pennsylvania School for the Deaf **215.951.4700**
Fax 215.951.4708
Web . . . . .www.psd.org
E-mail . . . . .info@psd.org
100 W School House Ln, Philadelphia,
PA 19144-3499
Larry Paub, Head Master

LABOR & WORKFORCE EDUCATION

Dept of Labor and Industry **717.787.5279**
Fax 717.787.8826
7th And Forrester St, Harrisburg, PA 17121
Julia Hearthway, Secretary

COUNTY SERVICES

Adams County

SOCIAL SERVICES

Assistance Ofc **717.334.6241**
Fax 717.334.4104
E-mail .... chartman@state.pa.us
225 S Franklin St, Gettysburg, PA 17325-2506
Colleen Hartman, Executive Director

Children and Youth Svcs **717.337.0110**
Fax 717.337.0616
E-mail .... info@adamscounty.us
117 Baltimore St, Room 201-B, Gettysburg,
PA 17325
Kathy Mcconaghay, Children & Youth Administrator

GENERAL HEALTH SERVICES

State Health Ctr **717.334.2112**
Fax 717.334.5011
Web .... www.health.state.pa.us
424 E Middle St, Gettysburg, PA 17325-1926
Robert E Walter, Rn, Nursing Supervisor

POLICE AND SHERIFF

Sheriff's Ofc **717.337.9828**
Fax 717.334.6521
Web .... www.adamscounty.us
E-mail .... sheriff@adamscounty.us
117 Baltimore St, Room 4, Gettysburg, PA 17325
James W. Muller, Sheriff

Allegheny County

SOCIAL SERVICES

Adoption Section **412.473.2300**
Fax 412.473.2416
400 N Lexington St, Suite 106, Pittsburgh, PA 15208
Denise Allen-brown, Director

Assistance Ofc **412.565.2151**
Fax 412.565.3660
E-mail .... pbrymn@state.pa.us
301 5th Ave Piatt Pl, Pittsburgh, PA 15222
Patricia Brymn, Executive Director

Children & Youth Svcs **412.350.5701**
One Smithfield St Ste 400, Pittsburgh, PA 15222

Children, Youth and Family Svcs **412.473.2000**
Fax 412.473.2015
E-mail .... msturdivant@dhs.county.allegheny.pa.us
400 N Lexington St Ste 104, Pittsburgh,
PA 15208-2565
Marcia Sturdivant, Deputy Director

Children, Youth and Family Svcs - Eastern Regional
Ofc **412.473.1100**
Fax 412.473.1119
E-mail .... TamaraHilko@dhs.county.allegheny.pa.us
400 N Lexington St Ste 103, Pittsburgh, PA 15208
Tamara Hilko, Director

Children, Youth and Family Svcs - Western Region
Ofc **412.565.5728**
Fax 412.565.7808
Web .... www.dpw.state.pa.us
11 Stanwix st, Rm 260, Pittsburgh, PA 15222
Elaine Bobick, Regional Children & Youth Director

Children, Youth and Family Svcs Central Regional
Ofc **412.350.3600**
Fax 412.350.6056
E-mail .... natalie.jones@alleghenycounty.us
1401 Forbes Ave Ste 101, Pittsburgh, PA 15219-5125
Natalie Jones, Director

Children, Youth and Family Svcs Mon-Valley Regional
Ofc **412.664.8900**
Fax 412.664.8914
Web .... www.dhs.county.allegheny.pa.us
E-mail .... naquino@dhs.county.allegheny.pa.us
332 5th Ave Ste 214, McKeesport, PA 15132-2616
Nancy Aquino, Director

Children, Youth and Family Svcs Northern Regional
Ofc **412.323.6100**
Fax 412.323.6108
Web .... www.county.allegheny.pa.us
1972 Clayton Ave, Pittsburgh, PA 15214-3808
John Bollie, Director

Children, Youth and Family Svcs Southern Regional
Ofc **412.488.8500**
Fax 412.488.8578
E-mail .... bbloch@county.allegheny.pa.us
2100 Water ST Ste 100, Pittsburgh, PA 15203
Bonnie Bloch, Director

Foster Care Section **412.473.2400**
Fax 412.473.2413
Web .... www.county.alleghany.pa.us/dhs
400 N Lexington St Ste 106, Pittsburgh,
PA 15208-2565

GENERAL HEALTH SERVICES

Health Dept **412.687.2243**
Fax 412.578.8325
Web .... www.achd.net
E-mail .... bdixon@achd.net
3333 Forbes Ave, Pittsburgh, PA 15213-3120
Bruce W. Dixon, Md, Director

MENTAL HEALTH SERVICES

Behavioral Health **412.350.4457**
Fax 412.350.5477
Web .... www.alleghenycounty.us/dhs
E-mail .... p.valentine@alleghenycounty.us/dhs
1 Smithfield St, Pittsburgh, PA 15222
Patricia Valentine, Dhs, Deputy Director

JUSTICE AGENCY

CASA **412.594.3606**
Fax 412.594.3607
Web .... www.pgh-casa.org
E-mail .... info@pgh-casa.org
564 Forbes Ave Ste 902, Pittsburgh, PA 15219
Melissa Protzek, Executive Director

Central Probation **412.441.9000**
Fax 412.361.6471
5231 Penn Ave Ste 100, Pittsburgh, PA 15224-1768
Kelly Fretz, Supervisor

Eastern Probation **412.241.1842**
Fax 412.242.7324
907 West St, Suite 44, Wilkinsburg, PA 15221
Tonya Muic-thail, Supervisor

Northern Probation **412.321.0365**
Fax 412.321.0181
Web .... www.alleghenycourts.pa.us
429 E Ohio St, Pittsburgh, PA 15212
Mary Tracy, Supervisor

Shuman Ctr Juvenile Detention **412.661.6806**
Fax 412.661.6471
Web .... www.county.allegheny.pa.us
7150 Highland Dr, Pittsburgh, PA 15206
William Simmons, Director

Southern Probation **412.431.5500**
Fax 412.431.6386
1700 E Carson St Ste 4, Pittsburgh, PA 15203-1759
Robert Dassal, Supervisor

POLICE AND SHERIFF

Pittsburgh Police Dept **412.323.7141**
Fax 412.323.7140
Web .... www.police.pitt.edu
E-mail .... tstangrecki@police.pitt.edu
1203 Western Ave, Office of Family Violence and
Missing Persons, Pittsburgh, PA 15233-2027
Thomas Stangrecki, Commander

Sheriff's Ofc **412.350.4700**
Fax 412.350.6388
E-mail .... pdefazio@county.allegheny.pa.us
436 Grant St Ste 111, Pittsburgh, PA 15219
William Mullen, Sheriff

EDUCATION SERVICES

Carnegie Head Start Ctr **412.276.0110**
630 Washington Ave, Carnegie, PA 15106-2837
Marilyn Rogers, Director

Special Education **412.394.5782**
Fax 412.394.5783
Web www.aiu3.net
E-mail .... donna.durno@aiu3.net
475 Waterfront Dr E, Homestead, PA 15120-1144
Donna Durno, PhD, Director

Armstrong County

SOCIAL SERVICES

Assistance Ofc **724.543.1651**
Fax 724.548.0274
E-mail .... ccox@state.pa.us
1280 N Water St, Kittanning, PA 16201
Charita Cox, Executive Director

Children and Youth Svcs **724.548.3466**
Fax 724.548.3279
Web .... www.armstrongcounty.org
E-mail .... cyf@co.armstrong.pa.us
310 S Jefferson St, Kittanning, PA 16201
Dennis Demangone, Director

GENERAL HEALTH SERVICES

State Health Ctr **724.543.2700**
Fax 724.548.1477
E-mail .... tburford@state.pa.us
245 Butler Rd Ste 1, Kittanning, PA 16201-6503
Tammy Burford, Director

MENTAL HEALTH SERVICES

Armstrong-Indiana Drug and Alcohol
Commission **724.354.2746**
Fax 724.354.3132
Web .... www.aidac.org
E-mail .... kanderson@aidac.org
10829 US Route 422, Shelocta, PA 15774-2236
Kami Anderson, Executive Director

Armstrong-Indiana MH/MR
Program **724.548.3451**
Fax 724.548.3454
Web .... www.aimhmr.org
E-mail .... mhmr@aimhmr.net
124 Armsdale Rd Ste 105, Kittanning,
PA 16201-3738
James Kuemmerle, Administrator

COURTS

Court of Common Pleas - 33rd
District **724.543.2500**
Fax 724.548.3279
Web .... www.co.armstrong.pa.us
301 S Jefferson St, Kittanning, PA 16201
Brenda C. George, Clerk Of Court

POLICE AND SHERIFF

Sheriff's Ofc......................**724.548.3265**
Fax......................................724.548.3264
Web...............................www.co.armstrong.pa.us
E-mail.........................sheriff@co.armstrong.pa.us
   500 E Market St Ste 106, Kittanning, PA 16201-1498
   Larry R. Crawford, Sheriff

Beaver County

SOCIAL SERVICES

Assistance Ofc......................**724.773.7300**
Fax......................................724.773.7859
Web.......................................www.state.pa.us
E-mail.................................braines@state.pa.us
   171 Virginia Ave, Rochester, PA 15074-1722
   Veronica Seery, Manager

Children and Youth Svcs......................**724.891.5800**
Fax......................................724.891.5801
Web...www.bccys.org
E-mail..............................webmaster@bccys.org
   1080 8th Ave, 3rd Floor, Beaver Falls, PA 15010
   Dayna Revay, Assistant Director

**Pennsylvania Dept of Public
Welfare**......................**724.891.5800**
Fax......................................724.891.5801
E-mail......................................info@bccys.org
   1080 Eighth Ave, Beaver Falls, PA 15010

GENERAL HEALTH SERVICES

Health Ctr......................**724.774.1385**
Fax......................................724.773.7416
   300 S Walnut Ln, Ste 200, Beaver, PA 15009
   Barbara Motto, Nursing Supervisor

MENTAL HEALTH SERVICES

Drug and Alcohol Program......................**724.847.6220**
Fax......................................724.847.6223
Web..www.bcbh.org
E-mail.........................kglishious@co.beaver.pa.us
   1050 8th Ave, 2nd Floor, Beaver Falls, PA 15010
   Kate Glishious, Administrator

Mental Health/Mental Retardation..........**724.847.6225**
Fax......................................724.847.6229
Web..www.bcbh.org
E-mail....................................gmike@bcbh.org
   1040 8th Ave, Beaver Falls, PA 15010-4506
   Girard Mike, Administrator

JUSTICE AGENCY

CASA Inc......................**724.728.2146**
Fax......................................724.728.0359
E-mail.............................casabc@access995.com
   250 Insurance St Ste 305, Beaver, PA 15009
   Heather Yates, Executive Director

Juvenile Svcs Div......................**724.774.8870**
Fax......................................724.728.6444
E-mail.........................rrose@beavercountypa.gov
   173 Friendship Cir, Beaver, PA 15009
   Robert R. Rose, Chief Performance Officer

POLICE AND SHERIFF

Sheriff's Ofc......................**724.728.3934**
Fax......................................724.728.2412
   810 3rd St, Beaver, PA 15009
   George David, Sheriff

Bedford County

SOCIAL SERVICES

Assistance Ofc......................**814.623.6127**
Fax......................................814.623.7310
   150 North St, Bedford, PA 15522
   Linda Brouse, Executive Director

Children and Youth Svcs......................**814.623.4804**
Fax......................................814.623.3013
Web.............................www.bedfordcountypa.org
E-mail....................ahorneff@bedfordcountypa.org
   200 S Juliana St, Bedford, PA 15522-1713
   Arthur Horneff, Director

GENERAL HEALTH SERVICES

State Health Ctr......................**814.623.2001**
   130 W Vondersmith Ave, Suite A, Bedford, PA 15522
   Vickie Gordon, Nursing Supervisor

JUSTICE AGENCY

Probation Ofc......................**814.623.4830**
Fax......................................814.623.0851
E-mail....................kbowser@bedfordcountypa.org
   200 S Juliana St, Bedford, PA 15522
   M. Keith Bowser, Chief JPO

COURTS

Court House......................**814.623.4833**
Fax......................................814.623.4831
Web.......................................www.pennswoods.net
E-mail........................dhowsare@pennswoods.net
   200 S Juliana St, Bedford, PA 15522-1713
   Honorable Daniel Lee Howsare, Senior Judge

POLICE AND SHERIFF

Sheriff's Ofc......................**814.624.2668**
Fax......................................814.624.2669
Web...www.ldelphia.net
E-mail...........................bcsheriff@ldelphia.net
   200 S Juliana St, Bedford, PA 15522-1713
   Gordon E. Diehl, Sheriff

Berks County

SOCIAL SERVICES

Assistance Ofc......................**610.736.4211**
Fax......................................610.736.4004
E-mail.......................grightmire@countyofberks.com
   625 Cherry St Ste 1, READING STATE OFFICE
   BUILDING, Reading, PA 19602
   Gary W Rightmire, Executive Director

Children and Youth Svcs......................**610.478.6700**
Fax......................................610.478.6799
Web....................................www.countyofberks.com
E-mail.......................gkovarie@countyofberks.com
   633 Court St Fl 11, Reading, PA 19601-4323
   George M. Kovarie, Executive Director

GENERAL HEALTH SERVICES

**Pennsylvania Dept of Health SE District
Ofc**......................**610.378.4352**
Fax......................................610.378.4527
E-mail...............................szurgot@state.pa.us
   625 Cherry St, Room 442, Reading, PA 19602
   Zane Szurgot, Hiv Coordinator

MENTAL HEALTH SERVICES

Council on Chemical Abuse......................**610.376.8669**
Fax......................................610.376.8423
Web.....................www.councilonchemicalabuse.org
E-mail..........gvogeljr@councilonchemicalabuse.org
   601 Penn St Ste 600, Reading, PA 19601
   George J. Vogel, Jr., Executive Director

JUSTICE AGENCY

Juvenile Probation......................**610.478.3200**
Fax......................................610.478.3251
Web....................................www.countyofberks.com
   633 Court St Fl 10, Reading, PA 19601
   Robert Williams, Chief Performance Officer

POLICE AND SHERIFF

Reading Police Dept......................**610.655.6246**
Fax......................................610.373.2169
Web..www.readingpa.org
   815 Washington St, Reading, PA 19601
   Sgt. John Solecki, Juvenile Division

EDUCATION SERVICES

Special Education......................**610.987.8510**
Fax......................................610.987.8400
Web..www.berksiu.org
E-mail......................................info@berksiu.org
   1111 Commons Blvd, Reading, PA 19605-3334
   John George, Director

Blair County

SOCIAL SERVICES

Assistance Ofc......................**814.946.7111**
Fax......................................814.941.6813
E-mail.......................................dpw@state.pa.us
   1100 Green Ave, Altoona, PA 16601-3440
   Christine Lysinger, Executive Director

**Children, Youth and Families
Services**......................**814.693.3130**
Fax......................................814.695.5640
E-mail................................mburger@blairco.org
   423 Allegheny St Ste 132, Hollidaysburg,
   PA 16648-2047
   Maryanne Burger, Director; Georgette Ayers, Assistant Administrator

COURTS

Court House......................**814.693.3080**
Fax......................................814.317.1600
   423 Allegheny St Ste 144, Hollidaysburg, PA 16648
   Honorable Hiram A.carpenter, Judge

POLICE AND SHERIFF

Sheriff's Ofc......................**814.693.3100**
Fax......................................814.695.4737
   423 Allegheny St Ste 44, Hollidaysburg, PA 16648
   Mitchell Cooper, Sheriff

Bradford County

SOCIAL SERVICES

Assistance Ofc......................**570.265.9186**
Fax......................................570.265.3061
E-mail..............................lwagner@state.pa.us
   1 Progress Plz Ste 4, Towanda, PA 18848-1656
   Leslee Wagner, Executive Director

**Children and Youth Svcs/Human
Svcs**......................**570.265.1760**
Fax......................................570.265.7066
Web...................................www.bradfordco.org
E-mail........................smithe@mail.bradfordco.org
   220 Main St Unit 1, Towanda, PA 18848-1829
   Eleanor H. Smith, Director

GENERAL HEALTH SERVICES

State Health Ctr......................**570.265.2194**
Fax......................................570.265.3274
Web....................................www.health.state.pa.us
   142 Colonial Dr, Towanda, PA 18848
   Sandie Lockwood, Hiv Coordinator

COURTS

Court House......................**570.265.1708**
Fax......................................570.265.1747
   301 Main St, Towanda, PA 18848
   Joan Shullo, Juvenile Hearing Master

Pennsylvania

POLICE AND SHERIFF

Sheriff's Dept **570.265.1701**
Fax 570.265.1734
Web ....www.bradfordco.org
E-mail ....evanss@mail.bradfordco.org
  301 Main St Rm 10, Towanda, PA 18848-1824
  Steven A. Evans, Sheriff

EDUCATION SERVICES

Bentley Creek Head Start **570.596.4334**
E-mail ....mraynor@laurelhs.org
  5252 Monkey Run Rd, Gillett, PA 16925
  Marlene Raynor, Director

Bucks County

SOCIAL SERVICES

Assistance Ofc **215.781.3334**
Fax 215.781.3438
  1214 Veterans Hwy, Bristol, PA 19007
  Everett Varain, Executive Director

Children and Youth Svcs **215.348.6900**
Fax 215.348.6989
Web ....www.buckscounty.org
E-mail ....ldrainey@co.bucks.pa.us
  4259 W Swamp Rd Ste 200, Doylestown,
  PA 18902-1033
  Lynn Rainey, Director

GENERAL HEALTH SERVICES

Health Dept **215.345.3318**
Fax 215.536.1243
Web ....www.buckscounty.org
E-mail ....sswashington@co.bucks.pa.us
  1282 Almshouse Road, Nashaminy Manor Center,
  Doylestown, PA 18901
  Sharita Washington, Hiv Educator

JUSTICE AGENCY

Detention Ctr **215.340.8300**
Fax 215.340.8355
  1750 S Easton Rd, Doylestown, PA 18901
  Ted Rice, Administrator

COURTS

Court House **215.348.6068**
Fax 215.340.8834
  55 E Court St, Doylestown, PA 18901-4318
  John Rufe, Judge

POLICE AND SHERIFF

Doylestown Borough Police **215.345.4143**
Fax 215.345.6373
Web ....www.doylestownborough.net
E-mail ....ppenecale@doylestownborough.net
  57 W Court St, Doylestown, PA 18901-4260
  Sgt. Patrick Penecale, Youth Diversion

Dublin Borough Police Dept **215.249.0272**
Fax 215.249.0857
E-mail ....pd@dublinborough.org
  119 maple ave, Dublin, PA 18917
  Brian Lehman, Police Chief

Sheriff's Ofc **215.348.6124**
Fax 215.348.6362
Web ....www.co.bucks.county.org
  55 E Court St, Bucks County Courthouse,
  Doylestown, PA 18901-4318
  Edward J. Donnelly, Sheriff

EDUCATION SERVICES

Schools Intermediate Unit 22 ....**215.348.2940**
Fax 215.340.1964
Web ....www.bucksiu.org
  705 N Shady Retreat Rd, Doylestown,
  PA 18901-2507
  Barry Galasso, Executive Director

Butler County

SOCIAL SERVICES

Assistance Ofc **724.284.8844**
Fax 724.284.8833
E-mail ....smichelott@state.pa.us
  108 Woody Dr, Butler, PA 16001-5692
  Shirley Michelotti, Executive Director

Children and Youth Svcs **724.284.5156**
Fax 724.284.1433
  124 W Diamond St, 2nd Floor, Butler, PA 16001
  Joyce Ainsworth, Director

MENTAL HEALTH SERVICES

MH/MR/Drug and Alcohol Program **724.284.5114**
Fax 724.284.5128
Web ....www.co.butler.pa.us
E-mail ....djenereski@co.butler.pa.us
  124 W Diamond St, Butler, PA 16001-5780
  Donna Jenereski, Director

POLICE AND SHERIFF

Sheriff's Dept **724.284.5245**
Fax 724.284.5248
E-mail ....mslupe@co.butler.pa.us
  300 S Main Street, Butler, PA 16001
  Michael T Slupe, Sheriff

Cambria County

SOCIAL SERVICES

Children and Youth Svcs **814.539.7454**
Fax 814.535.8210
  110 Franklin St Ste 400, Johnstown, PA 15901
  Betzi White, Administrator

GENERAL HEALTH SERVICES

State Health Ctr **814.248.3120**
Fax 814.248.3124
E-mail ....kbrugh@state.pa.us
  184 Donald Ln Ste 1, Johnstown, PA 15904
  Kirby Brugh, Hiv Coordinator

JUSTICE AGENCY

Beginnings, Inc./CASA **814.539.1919**
Fax 814.539.1308
Web ....www.beginningsinc.org
E-mail ....begcasa@ctcnet.net
  406 Main St, 2nd Floor, Johnstown, PA 15901
  Michele Diguardi, Executive Director

Juvenile Probation **814.472.4700**
Fax 814.472.8026
  401 Candlelight Dr Ste 350, Ebensburg, PA 15931
  Cynthia Wess, Chief Performance Officer

COURTS

Honerable Gerald Long's Ofc **814.472.1401**
Fax 814.472.4799
  200 S Center St, Ebensburg, PA 15931-1941
  Honorable Timothy P. Creany., President Judge

POLICE AND SHERIFF

Sheriff's Dept **814.472.1690**
Fax 814.472.8261
Web ....www.co.cambria.pa.us
E-mail ....sheriff@co.cambria.pa.us
  200 S Center St, Ebensburg, PA 15931-1941
  Bob Kolar, Sheriff

EDUCATION SERVICES

Special Education **814.940.0223**
Fax 814.949.0984
Web www.iu08.org
E-mail ....mjd@iu08.org
  4500 6th Ave, Altoona, PA 16602-1542
  Micheal Dillon, Director

Cameron County

SOCIAL SERVICES

Assistance Ofc **814.486.3757**
Fax 814.486.1379
Web ....www.dpw.state.pa.us
  411 N Chestnut St, Emporium, PA 15834-1430
  Patricia Lyle, Executive Director

Children and Youth Svcs **814.486.9351**
  20 E 5th St, Emporium, PA 15834

GENERAL HEALTH SERVICES

Health Care Ctr **814.486.1115**
E-mail ....michaelb@adelphia.net
  90 E 2nd St, Emporium, PA 15834
  Anthony Moscato, Supervisor

COURTS

Court House **814.486.2315**
Fax 814.486.3176
Web ....www.cameroncountypa.com
  20 E 5th St, Emporium, PA 15834
  Janette Burkness, Chief Performance Officer

POLICE AND SHERIFF

Sheriff's Dept **814.486.3338**
Fax 814.486.9389
E-mail ....camcosd@adelphia.net
  20 E 5th St Ste 104, Emporium, PA 15834
  Al Neyman, Sheriff

Carbon County

SOCIAL SERVICES

Assistance Ofc **610.577.9020**
Fax 610.577.9043
  101 Lehigh Dr, Lehighton, PA 18235
  Patricia Sasserath, Executive Director

Children and Youth Svcs **570.325.3644**
Fax 570.325.3647
  76 Susquehanna St, 2nd Floor, Jim Thorpe,
  PA 18229-1948
  Sally Newton, Director

GENERAL HEALTH SERVICES

State Health Ctr **570.325.6106**
Fax 570.325.6109
Web ....www.state.pa.us
E-mail ....srowe@state.pa.us
  616 North St, Jim Thorpe, PA 18229-2125
  Sue Rowe, Rn, Nursing Supervisor

JUSTICE AGENCY

Juvenile Probation Ofc **570.325.2417**
Fax 570.325.8827
Web ....www.carboncourts.com
E-mail ....jdodson@carboncourts.com
  76 Susquehanna St 1st Fl, Jim Thorpe,
  PA 18229-2039
  Jim Dodson, Chief Juvenile Officer

POLICE AND SHERIFF

Sheriff's Ofc **570.325.2821**
Fax 570.325.7860
  2 Broadway, Jim Thorpe, PA 18229
  Dwight L. Nothstein, Sheriff

Centre County

SOCIAL SERVICES

Assistance Ofc **814.863.6571**
Fax 814.689.1356
Web ....www.state.pa.us
  2580 Park Center Blvd, State College, PA 16801-3005
  Jeffrey Foreman, Executive Director

Children and Youth Svcs 814.355.6755
Fax 814.355.6939
    420 Holmes St, Willowbank Office Building,
    Bellefonte, PA 16823
    Carol Smith, Director

Youth Svc Bureau 814.237.5731
Fax 814.237.2228
Web ....www.ccysb.com
    325 W Aaron Dr, State College, PA 16803
    Andrea Boyles, Executive Director

GENERAL HEALTH SERVICES

Family Health Svcs 814.355.2762
Fax 814.355.8740
Web ....www.fhccp.org
    240 Match Factory Pl, Bellefonte, PA 16823-1366

MENTAL HEALTH SERVICES

MH MR Drug and Alcohol Admin 814.355.6744
Fax 814.355.6985
Web ....www.co.centre.pa.us
    420 Holmes St, Willowbank Bldg, Bellefonte,
    PA 16823-1401
    Kathy Arbogast, Program Specialist

JUSTICE AGENCY

Detention Home 814.355.0650
Fax 814.355.0894
E-mail ....jejj22@comcast.net
    148 Paradise Rd, Bellefonte, PA 16823-8472
    James E. Jones, Administrator

POLICE AND SHERIFF

Sheriff's Dept 814.355.6803
Fax 814.548.1111
Web ....www.co.centre.pa.us
E-mail ....sheriff@co.centre.pa.us
    213 E High St, Bellefonte, PA 16823-1982
    Denny Nau, Sheriff

Chester County

SOCIAL SERVICES

Assistance Ofc 610.466.1000
Fax 610.466.1055
E-mail ....c-chesterc@state.pa.us
    100 James Buchannan Dr, Thorndale, PA 19372
    Diane Robertson, Executive Director

Children, Youth and Families 610.344.5800
Fax 610.344.5858
E-mail ....khayes@chester.org
    601 Westtown Rd, West Chester, PA 19382
    Keith Hayes, Executive Director

GENERAL HEALTH SERVICES

Health Dept 610.344.6225
Fax 610.344.6727
Web ....www.chesco.org
    610 Westtown Rd Ste 290, West Chester, PA 19380
    Elizabeth Walls, Personal Health Services Director

MENTAL HEALTH SERVICES

Dept of Drug and Alcohol Svcs 610.344.6620
Fax 610.344.5743
E-mail ....kbowman@chesco.org
    601 Westtown Rd Ste 325, West Chester, PA 19380
    Kim P. Bowman, Executive Director

JUSTICE AGENCY

Juvenile Probation 610.344.6295
Fax 610.344.5443
E-mail ....mlmawby@chesco.org
    201 W Market St, Ste 3100, West Chester,
    PA 19380-0989
    Marietta Lamb-mawby, Chief JPO

POLICE AND SHERIFF

Sheriff's Dept 610.344.6850
Fax 610.344.6099
E-mail ....cwelsh@chesco.org
    201 W. Market Street, Suite 1201, West Chester,
    PA 19380-0989
    Carolyn B Welsh, Sheriff

Clarion County

SOCIAL SERVICES

Assistance Ofc 814.226.1700
Fax 814.226.1794
    71 Lincoln Dr, Clarion, PA 16214-3861
    Judith Gardner, Executive Director

Children & Youth Svcs 814.226.9280
    214 S 7th Ave, Ste B, Clarion, PA 16214

Children and Youth Svcs 814.226.5150
Fax 814.226.5430
    214 S 7th Ave Ste B, Clarion, PA 16214
    Kay Rupert, Director

GENERAL HEALTH SERVICES

State Health Ctr 814.226.2170
Fax 814.226.1726
Web ....www.state.pa.us
E-mail ....sgroner@state.pa.us
    162 S 2nd Ave, Applewood Center, Clarion,
    PA 16214
    Susan Groner, Community Health Nurse

JUSTICE AGENCY

Juvenile Probation Ofc 814.226.4743
Fax 814.226.1169
E-mail ....etheiss@co.clarion.pa.us
    500 Main St Ste B, Clarion, PA 16214
    Jayne Smail, Director

COURTS

Court House 814.226.9351
Fax 814.226.1097
    421 Main St, Clarion, PA 16214
    Jeffrey Himes, Clerk Of Court

POLICE AND SHERIFF

Sheriff's Dept 814.226.7611
Fax 814.226.9824
E-mail ....sheriff@co.clarion.pa.us
    421 Main St Ste 11, Clarion, PA 16214
    Rex Munsee, Sheriff

Clearfield County

SOCIAL SERVICES

Assistance Ofc 814.765.7591
Fax 814.765.0802
Web ....www.dpw.state.pa.us
E-mail ....glezanic@dpw.state.pa.us
    1121 Linden St, Clearfield, PA 16830-3317
    Gregory Lezanic, Executive Director

Children, Youth and Family Svcs 814.765.1541
Fax 814.765.2061
Web ....www.clearfieldco.org
E-mail ....fkuhn@clearfieldco.org
    650 Leonard St Ste 213, Clearfield, PA 16830-3243
    Francis Kuhn, Director

GENERAL HEALTH SERVICES

State Health Ctr 814.765.0542
Fax 814.765.0648
Web ....www.health.state.pa.us
E-mail ....vskvarka@state.pa.us
    1123 Linden St Ste 1, Clearfield, PA 16830
    Vicki Skvarka, Rn, Supervisor

MENTAL HEALTH SERVICES

Drug and Alcohol Commission 814.371.9002
Fax 814.371.9055
E-mail ....sca@cjbac.org
    104 Main St, Falls Creek, PA 15840
    Susan Ford, Executive Director

COURTS

Teen Court 814.371.0209
Fax 814.371.0209
Web ....www.clearnet.net
E-mail ....cthomas@clearnet.net
    3 S Brady St Ste 342, Du Bois, PA 15801-2160
    Christy Thomas, Master Coodinator

POLICE AND SHERIFF

Sheriff's Ofc 814.765.2641
Fax 814.765.5915
    1 N 2nd St, Suite 116, Clearfield, PA 16830
    Chester A. Hawkins, Sheriff

Clinton County

SOCIAL SERVICES

Assistance Ofc 570.748.2971
Fax 570.893.2973
Web ....www.state.pa.us
    300 Belfonte Ave, Suite 101, Lock Haven, PA 17745
    Gail, Executive Director

Children and Youth Svcs/Big Brothers & Big
Sisters 570.893.4100
After hours 570.748.2936
Phone 570.893.4101
Fax 570.893.4149
E-mail ....klinn@clintoncountypa.com
    232 E Main St, Garden Building, Lock Haven,
    PA 17745-1312
    Jennifer Sobjak, CPS Supervisor; Gerald Rosamilia, Director

GENERAL HEALTH SERVICES

State Health Ctr 570.893.2437
Fax 570.893.2733
E-mail ....creeder@state.pa.us
    215 E Church St, Lock Haven, PA 17745
    Candy Reeder, Hiv Coordinator

POLICE AND SHERIFF

Sheriff's Dept 570.893.4070
Fax 570.893.4059
Web ....www.clintoncountypa.com
E-mail ....cankney@clintoncountypa.com
    230 E Water St Ste 1, Lock Haven, PA 17745-1399
    Charles R. Ankney, Sheriff

Columbia County

SOCIAL SERVICES

Assistance Ofc 570.387.4200
Fax 570.387.4708
Web ....www.state.pa.us
E-mail ....dbelusko@state.pa.us
    27 E 7th St, Bloomsburg, PA 17815-2727
    Diane Belusko, Executive Director

Children and Youth Svcs 570.389.5700
Fax 570.389.5703
    11 W Main St, Bloomsburg, PA 17815
    Donald Pegg, Director

GENERAL HEALTH SERVICES

State Health Ctr 570.387.4257
Fax 570.387.4281
Web ....www.portal.state.pa.us
    1000 S Market St, Ste 5, Bloomsburg,
    PA 17815-2913
    Deb Antanitis, Hiv Coordinator

Pennsylvania

COURTS

Honorable Thomas A. James Ofc 570.389.5662
Fax 570.389.5621
E-mail .... jreimiller@columbiapa.org
   35 W Main St, Bloomsburg, PA 17815
Honorable Scott W. Naus, President

POLICE AND SHERIFF

Sheriff's Ofc 570.389.5622
Fax 570.389.5625
   35 W Main St, Bloomsburg, PA 17815
Tim Chamberlain, Sheriff

Crawford County

SOCIAL SERVICES

Assistance Ofc 814.333.3400
Fax 814.333.3527
E-mail .... hcouch@state.pa.us
   1084 Water St., PO Box 1187, Meadville, PA 16335
Hope F. Couch, Executive Director

Children and Youth Svcs 814.724.8380
Fax 814.337.8080
Web .... www.co.crawford.pa.us
E-mail .... mweindorf@co.crawford.pa.us
   18282 Technology Dr Ste 101, Meadville,
   PA 16335-8378
Mark Weindorf, Director

GENERAL HEALTH SERVICES

State Health Ctr 814.332.6947
Fax 814.724.6883
   847 N Main St, Park Side Commons, Meadville,
   PA 16335
Darlene Hamilton, Rn, Public Health Nurse

JUSTICE AGENCY

Probation 814.336.4061
Fax 814.333.6798
Web .... www.co.crawford.pa.us
E-mail .... sbridger@co.crawford.pa.us
   286 Chestnut St, Meadville, PA 16335-3205
Stephen Bridger, Director

COURTS

Court House 814.333.7300
Fax 814.337.0457
Web .... www.co.crawford.pa.us
E-mail .... jspataro@co.crawford.pa.us
   903 Diamond Pk, Meadville, PA 16335-2679
Honorable John Spataro, Judge

POLICE AND SHERIFF

Sheriff's Ofc 814.333.7411
Fax 814.337.5062
Web .... www.co.crawford.pa.us
   903 Diamond Park Ste 302, Meadville,
   PA 16335-2680
Walter Hoke, Sheriff

Cumberland County

SOCIAL SERVICES

Assistance Ofc 717.240.2700
Fax 717.249.8141
Web .... www.dpw.state.pa.us
E-mail .... richardl@dpw.state.pa.us
   33 Westminster Dr, Carlisle, PA 17013-4369
Richard Lytle, Executive Director

Children and Youth Svcs 717.240.6120
Fax 717.240.6433
Web .... www.ccpa.net
E-mail .... ccys@ccpa.net
   16 W High St Ste 200, Carlisle, PA 17013-2961
Ed Rouse, Intake Supervisor

GENERAL HEALTH SERVICES

State Health Ctr 717.243.5151
Fax 717.243.3171
Web .... www.health.state.pa.us
   431 E North St, Carlisle, PA 17013-2693
Stephanie Gellatly, Hiv Coordinator

MENTAL HEALTH SERVICES

Mental Health/Mental Retardation 717.240.6320
Fax 717.240.6415
Web .... www.ccpa.net
E-mail .... sherman@ccpa.net
   16 W High St Ste 301, Carlisle, PA 17013-2963
Silvia Herman, Administrator

JUSTICE AGENCY

Court House 717.240.6100
Fax 717.240.6448
   1 Court House Square, 3rd Floor, Carlisle, PA 17013
Gary Eichelberger, Commissioner

**Ctr for Juvenile Justice Training and
Research** 717.477.1414
Fax 717.477.1236
Web .... www.ship.edu
E-mail .... skvarn@ship.edu
   1871 Old Main Dr, Shippensburg University,
   Shippensburg, PA 17257-2200
Sheri Warner, Director

POLICE AND SHERIFF

Sheriff's Dept 717.240.6390
Fax 717.240.6397
Web .... www.ccpa.net
E-mail .... randerson@ccpa.net
   1 Courthouse Sq, Rm 303, Carlisle, PA 17013-3391
Ronny Anderson, Sheriff

Dauphin County

SOCIAL SERVICES

Assistance Ofc 717.787.2324
Fax 717.772.4703
Web .... www.health.state.pa.us
E-mail .... dmomy@health.state.pa.us
   2432 N 7th St, Harrisburg, PA 17110-2508
Debra Momy, Executive Director

**Bureau of Child Support
Enforcement** 717.783.9659
Fax 717.772.4936
   1303 N 7th St Frnt A, Harrisburg, PA 17102
Daniel N Richard, Director

**Central Region Ofc of Children, Youth and
Families** 717.772.7702
Fax 717.772.7071
Web .... www.state.pa.us
   Bertolino Building, 4th Floor, Harrisburg, PA 17105
Gabriel Williams, Regional Children/youth Director

Children, Youth and Families 717.787.3985
Fax 717.346.9663
Web .... www.cpw.state.pa.us
   625 Forster St, Harrisburg, PA 17120-1110
Sandra Gallagher, Director

Social Svcs for Children and Youth 717.780.7200
Fax 717.525.9921
E-mail .... scohick@dauphinc.org
   1001 N 6th St, Harrisburg, PA 17102
Sue Cohick, Director

GENERAL HEALTH SERVICES

Hamilton Health Ctr 717.232.9971
Fax 717.230.3943
   1821 Fulton St, Harrisburg, PA 17102
Regina King, Director

South Central District Ofc 717.787.8092
Fax 717.772.3151
Web .... www.health.state.pa.us
E-mail .... ptran@state.pa.us
   30 Kline Vlg, Harrisburg, PA 17104-1530
Phuoc Tran, District Executive Director

MENTAL HEALTH SERVICES

**Executive Commission on Drug and
Alcohol** 717.635.2254
Fax 717.635.2266
Web .... www.dauphenc.org
   1100 S Cameron St, Harrisburg, PA 17104
Mavis Nmoh, Executive Director

Mental Health/Mental Retardation 717.780.7050
Fax 717.780.7061
Web .... www.dauphinc.org
   100 Chestnut St Fl 1, Harrisburg, PA 17101-2518
Daniel Eisenhauer, Administrator

Ofc of Drug and Alcohol Programs 717.783.8200
Fax 717.787.6285
Web .... www.health.pa.us/bdap
E-mail .... rrothermel@state.pa.us
   2 Kline Village, Harrisburg, PA 17104
Robin Rothermel, Acting Director

COURTS

**Honorable Judge Joseph Kleinfelter
Ofc** 717.780.6650
Fax 717.255.2758
Web .... www.dauphinc.org
E-mail .... jkleinfelter@dauphinc.org
   Front & Market St, Harrisburg, PA 17101
Honorable Joseph H. Kleinfelter, Senior Judge

POLICE AND SHERIFF

Sheriff's Dept 717.780.6590
Fax 717.255.2889
   101 Market St Ste 104, Harrisburg, PA 17101
Jack R. Lotwick, Sheriff

EDUCATION SERVICES

Capital Area Head Start-Market Ctr 717.221.9848
   1300 Market St, Harrisburg, PA 17103-2231
Diane Ciucci, Administrator

**Capital Area Head Start-Marshall
Elementary** 717.541.1795
Fax 717.541.8226
Web .... www.kss.org
E-mail .... jpepper@kss.org
   301 Hale Ave, Harrisburg, PA 17104-1519
Jo Pepper, Director

**Capital Area Head Start-Martin
Luther** 717.233.4220
Fax 717.796.5374
Web www.cap4kids.org
E-mail .... karen@paheadstart.org
   1654 Walnut St, Harrisburg, PA 17103-2350
Karen Grimm-thomas, Associate Executive Director

Delaware County

SOCIAL SERVICES

Children and Youth Svcs 610.713.2000
Fax 610.713.2340
E-mail .... kleind@co.delaware.pa.us
   20 S 69th St Fl 3, Upper Darby, PA 19082
Deirdre Gordan, Director

GENERAL HEALTH SERVICES

Delaware State Health Ctr 610.447.3250
Fax 610.447.3008
Web .... www.state.pa.us
   151 W 5th St, Ste 1, Chester, PA 19013
Phyllis Britz, Administrator Nurse

MENTAL HEALTH SERVICES

Child and Adolescent and Mental Health

Svc **610.497.7700**
Fax 610.497.7711
Web .... www.crozer.org
E-mail .... colleen.healey@crozer.org
  2600 W 9th St, #3SE, Chester, PA 19013
  Colleen Healey, Ma, Mba, Director Of Clinical/special Services

Ofc of Behavioral Health **610.713.2365**
Fax 610.713.2378
Web .... www.co.delaware.pa.us
E-mail .... suleke@co.delaware.pa.us
  20 S 69th St, Upper Darby, PA 19082
  Ed Sulek, Sca Administrator

JUSTICE AGENCY

CASA/Youth Advocates Inc. **610.565.2208**
Fax 610.892.0562
Web .... www.delcocasa.org
E-mail .... casaya@verizon.net
  200 N Jackson Street, Media, PA 19063
  Ann Schenberger, Executive Director

Detention Ctr **610.891.8660**
Fax 610.891.8667
Web .... www.co.delaware.pa.us
E-mail .... murraym@co.delaware.pa.us
  370 N Middletown Rd, Media, PA 19063-5505
  Mark Murray, Director

COURTS

Court House and Governor Ctr **610.891.4000**
Fax 610.891.5498
  201 W Front St, Media, PA 19063
  Danielle Dinatteo, Msw, Juvenile Court Services Deputy Director

POLICE AND SHERIFF

City of Chester PA Police, Juvenile

Dept **610.447.7941**
Fax 610.447.7945
  160 E 7th St Fl 3, Chester, PA 19013-6041
  Sgt. Alan Davis, Supervisor

Media Police **610.565.6656**
Fax 610.892.9415
Web .... www.mediapd.org
E-mail .... mwusinich@mediapd.org
  301 N Jackson St, Media, PA 19063-2909
  Martin Wusinich, Chief Of Police

Sheriff's Dept **610.891.4296**
Fax 610.891.1765
  201 W Front St, Media, PA 19063
  Joseph F. Mcginn, Sheriff

Elk County

SOCIAL SERVICES

Assistance Ofc **814.776.1101**
Fax 814.772.7007
E-mail .... elkcao@state.pa.us
  145 Race St, Ridgway, PA 15853-1023
  Patricia Lyle, Excutive Director

Children and Youth Svcs **814.776.1553**
Fax 814.772.5158
  300 Center St, Ridgway, PA 15853
  Pamela J. Cousins, Director

GENERAL HEALTH SERVICES

State Health Ctr **814.834.5351**
Fax 814.834.5354
  778 Washington St, Saint Marys, PA 15857
  Vicki Skvarka, Rn, Nursing Supervisor

COURTS

Court House **814.776.6144**
Fax 814.772.7780
E-mail .... rmasson@ruralinc.org
  240 Main St, Ridgway, PA 15853
  Honorable Richard A. Masson, President Judge

POLICE AND SHERIFF

Sheriff's Ofc **814.776.5353**
Fax 814.776.5396
  250 Main St, Ridgway, PA 15853
  Jeffery Kriej, Sheriff

Erie County

SOCIAL SERVICES

Children and Youth Svcs **814.451.6600**
After hours 814.451.1503
Fax 814.451.6565
E-mail .... glucht@eriecountydhs.org
  154 W 9th St, Erie, PA 16501
  Cindra Vallone, CPS Admin; Mary Ann Daniels, Director

GENERAL HEALTH SERVICES

Dept. of Health **814.451.6700**
Fax 814.663.0251
E-mail .... sshampoe@ecdh.org
  43 E Washington St, Corry, PA 16407-1638
  Sonya Shampoe, Quality Assurance

Health Dept **814.451.6700**
Fax 814.451.6767
Web .... www.ecdh.org
E-mail .... dscavona@ecdh.org
  606 W 2nd St, Erie, PA 16507-1199
  Darlene Scavona, Hiv Coordinator

MENTAL HEALTH SERVICES

MH/MR Program **814.451.6800**
Fax 814.451.6868
Web .... www.eriecountygov.org
  154 W 9th St, Erie, PA 16501
  Shari Gross, Administrator

Ofc of Drug and Alcohol Abuse **814.451.6877**
Fax 814.451.6875
  155 W 8th St Ste 401, Erie, PA 16501
  John Dimattio, Executive Director

JUSTICE AGENCY

Detention Shelter **814.451.6191**
Fax 814.451.6192
  4728 Lake Pleasant Rd, Erie, PA 16504
  John Daley, Administrator

COURTS

Court House **814.451.6000**
Fax 814.451.7070
  140 W 6th St, Rm 205, Erie, PA 16501
  Dave Gianoni, Volunteers Director

POLICE AND SHERIFF

Sheriff's Dept **814.451.6254**
Fax 814.451.6323
Web .... www.eriecountysheriffs.org
  140 W 6th St, Room 18, Erie, PA 16501
  Robert Merski, Sheriff

Fayette County

SOCIAL SERVICES

Children and Youth Svcs **724.430.1283**
Fax 724.430.1240
Web .... www.fccys.org
E-mail .... dmadison@fccys.org
  130 Old New Salem Rd, Uniontown, PA 15401-8933
  Dave Madison, Director

GENERAL HEALTH SERVICES

Pensilvanya Dept Of Health **724.439.7400**
Fax 724.439.2262
Web .... www.health.state.pa.us
E-mail .... ARHALL@STATE.PA.US
  100 New Salem Rd Ste 101, Fayette County Health
  Center Bldg., Uniontown, PA 15401
  Artis Hall, Executive Director

POLICE AND SHERIFF

Sheriff's Ofc **724.430.1295**
Fax 724.430.4030
Web .... www.fayettepa.org
E-mail .... sheriff@fayettepa.org
  61 E Main St Ste 1B, Uniontown, PA 15401-3391
  Gary D. Brownfield, Sheriff

EDUCATION SERVICES

Communities In Schools Inc. **724.437.2540**
Fax 724.437.7610
Web .... www.cisofswpa.org
E-mail .... lgsmith@winbeam.com
  137 N Beeson Ave Ste 116, Uniontown,
  PA 15401-2936
  Linda Smith, Executive Director

Forest County

SOCIAL SERVICES

Assistance Ofc **814.755.3552**
Fax 814.755.3420
Web .... www.compass.state.pa.us
  171 Elm St, Tionesta, PA 16353
  Judi Gardner, Executive Director

Children & Youth Svcs **814.755.3622**
  623 Elm St PO Box 523, Tionesta, PA 16353

GENERAL HEALTH SERVICES

State Health Ctr **814.755.3564**
Fax 814.755.3542
Web .... www.health.state.pa.us
E-mail .... chscott@state.pa.us
  305 Elm St, Tionesta, PA 16353
  Cheryl Scott, Hiv Coordinator

COURTS

Forest House-Probation **814.755.3851**
Fax 814.755.7722
  526 Elm St Unit 8, Tionesta, PA 16353
  Maureen Skerda, President Judge

POLICE AND SHERIFF

Sheriff's Ofc **814.755.3541**
Fax 814.755.4404
Web .... www.co.forest.pa.us
  526 Elm St Unit 9, Tionesta, PA 16353-9724
  Robert Wolfgang, Sheriff

Franklin County

SOCIAL SERVICES

Assistance Ofc **717.264.6121**
Fax 717.264.4801
Web .... www.state.pa.us
E-mail .... mstepler@state.pa.us
  620 Norland Ave, Chambersburg, PA 17201-4205
  Michele Stepler, Executive Director

Children and Youth Svcs **717.263.1900**
Fax 717.263.1254
E-mail .... c&y@co.frankli.pa.us
  425 Franklin Farm Ln, Franklin County Human Service
  Bldg, Chambersburg, PA 17202
  Douglas Amsley, Director

Pennsylvania

GENERAL HEALTH SERVICES

State Health Ctr **717.263.4143**
Fax 717.263.5991
Web ....www.health.pa.state.us
E-mail ....lrigas@state.pa.us
518 Cleveland Ave Ste 1, Chambersburg,
PA 17201-3494
Lola Rigas, Hiv Coordinator

MENTAL HEALTH SERVICES

Mental Health/Mental Retardation **717.264.5387**
Fax 717.264.6297
E-mail ....jwadel@co.franklin.pa.us
425 Franklin Farm Ln, Chambersburg, PA 17201
Becky Greenwalt, D&A Administrator

JUSTICE AGENCY

Juvenile Probation **717.261.3122**
Fax 717.261.1157
Web ....www.co.franklin.pa.us
E-mail ....kamcgrath@co.franklin.pa.us
425 Franklin Farm Ln, Chambersburg,
PA 17202-3064
Kathleen Mcgrath, Chief Performance Officer

COURTS

Court House **717.261.3844**
Fax 717.261.3847
E-mail ....bvandrew@co.franklin.pa.us
157 Lincoln Way E, Chambersburg, PA 17201
William Vandrew, Clerk Of Court

POLICE AND SHERIFF

Sheriff's Ofc **717.261.3877**
Fax 717.261.3882
Web ....www.co.franklin.pa.us
E-mail ....danthony@co.franklin.pa.us
157 Lincoln Way E, Chambersburg, PA 17201-2233
Dane Anthony, Sheriff

Fulton County

SOCIAL SERVICES

Assistance Ofc **717.485.3151**
Fax 717.485.3713
Web ....www.state.pa.us
E-mail ....rdrover@state.pa.us
539 Fulton Dr, Mc Connellsburg, PA 17233
Michelle Stepler, Executive Director

Children & Youth Svcs **717.485.3553**
Fax 717.485.3982
Web ....www.co.fulton.pa.us
E-mail ....jsnyder@co.fulton.pa.us
219 N 2nd St Ste 201, McConnellsburg, PA 17233
Jean E. Snyder, Director

GENERAL HEALTH SERVICES

State Health Ctr **717.485.5137**
Fax 717.485.4364
E-mail ....tleese@state.pa.us
182 Buchanan Trl, Suite 160, Mc Connellsburg,
PA 17233
Theresa Leese, Hiv Coordinator

JUSTICE AGENCY

Probation Dept **717.485.3192**
Fax 717.485.6867
E-mail ....dmiller@co.fulton.pa.us
Neighbourhood Services Building, 116 W Market St
Ste 104, Mc Connellsburg, PA 17233
Daniel Miller, Chief Performance Officer

COURTS

Court House **717.485.4212**
Fax 717.485.5568
Web ....www.fultoncntypa.org
E-mail ....tco@fulton.pa.us
201 N 2nd St, Mc Connellsburg, PA 17233-1198
Patty Fix, Clerk Of Court

POLICE AND SHERIFF

Sheriff's Dept **717.485.4221**
Fax 717.485.4519
Web ....www.co.fulton.pa.us
E-mail ....kstains@co.fulton.pa.us
207 N 2nd St, Mc Connellsburg, PA 17233-1103
Keith Stains, Sheriff

Greene County

SOCIAL SERVICES

Assistance Ofc **724.627.8171**
Fax 724.627.8096
Web ....www.state.pa.us
E-mail ....ameyers@state.pa.us
100 Greene Plz, Waynesburg, PA 15370-8142
Andrea Meyers, Acting Director

Children & Youth Svcs **724.852.5217**
19 S Washington St, Waynesburg, PA 15370

MENTAL HEALTH SERVICES

MH/MR Drug and Alcohol Program **724.852.5276**
Fax 724.852.5368
Web ....www.co.greene.pa.us
E-mail ....kbennett@co.greene.pa.us
19 S Washington St Fl 3, Waynesburg,
PA 15370-2053
Karen Bennett, Administrator

JUSTICE AGENCY

Probation Dept **724.852.5250**
Fax 724.852.5344
Web ....www.co.greene.pa.us
E-mail ....cwise@co.greene.pa.us
10 E High St Ste 104, Waynesburg, PA 15370-1859
R. Craig Wise, Chief JPO

COURTS

Court House **724.852.5312**
Fax 724.627.4716
10 E High St Ste 218, Waynesburg, PA 15370
William R. Nalitz, Honorable President Judge

POLICE AND SHERIFF

Sheriff's Dept **724.627.7207**
Fax 724.852.5318
Web ....www.co.greene.pa.us
E-mail ....gcsheriff@co.greene.pa.us
10 E High St, Rm 106, Waynesburg, PA 15370
Richard C. Kethcem, Sheriff

Huntingdon County

SOCIAL SERVICES

Assistance Ofc **814.643.1170**
Fax 814.643.5441
7591 Lake Raystown Shopping Ctr, Huntingdon,
PA 16652
Vicky Wray, Executive Director

Children and Youth Svcs **814.643.3270**
Fax 814.643.7323
Web ....www.huntingdoncounty.net
E-mail ....mkough@huntingdoncounty.net
430 Penn St, Court House Annex II, Huntingdon,
PA 16652-1602
Margaret Kough, Director

POLICE AND SHERIFF

Sheriff's Ofc **814.643.0880**
Fax 814.643.8191
E-mail ....bwalters@huntingdoncounty.net
241 Mifflin St Ste 1, Huntingdon, PA 16652
William G. Walters, Sheriff

Indiana County

SOCIAL SERVICES

Assistance Ofc **724.357.2900**
Fax 724.357.2951
Web ....www.dpw.state.pa.us
2750 W Pike Rd, Indiana, PA 15701-9717
Margaret Desiderio, Executive Director

Children and Youth Svcs **724.465.3895**
Fax 724.465.3179
E-mail ....iccyspm@comcast.net
350 N 4th St, Indiana, PA 15701-2000
Paula Mcclure, Executive Director

GENERAL HEALTH SERVICES

State Health Ctr **724.357.2995**
Fax 724.357.1949
Web ....www.state.health.pa.us
75 N 2nd St, Indiana, PA 15701-2047
Anita Schilling, Hiv Coordinator

COURTS

Court House **724.465.3855**
Fax 724.465.3968
Web ....www.countyofindiana.org
E-mail ....golson@countyofindiana.org
825 Philadelphia St, Indiana, PA 15701
Honorable William Martin, Judge

POLICE AND SHERIFF

Sheriff's Dept **724.465.3930**
Fax 724.465.3937
E-mail ....icsheriff@countyofindiana.org
825 Philadelphia St, Indiana, PA 15701
Robert E. Fyock, Sheriff

EDUCATION SERVICES

Cherryhill Head Start Ctr **724.465.2022**
184 Spaulding Rd, Penn Run, PA 15765-8641
Janie Tess Gray, Director

Jefferson County

SOCIAL SERVICES

Children and Youth Svcs **814.849.3696**
Fax 814.849.4604
E-mail ....sneivell@jeffersoncountypa.com
155 Main St, Jefferson Place, Brookville, PA 15825
Susan Diane Neivell, Director

GENERAL HEALTH SERVICES

Punxsutawney Health Ctr **814.938.6630**
Fax 814.938.4278
Web ....www.health.state.pa.us
E-mail ....lfulton@health.state.pa.us
203 N Main St, Punxsutawney, PA 15767-1217
Lori Fulton, Rn, Hiv Coordinator

JUSTICE AGENCY

Probation Dept **814.849.5222**
Fax 814.849.3468
200 Main St, Brookville, PA 15825
Paul Russner, Chief JPO

COURTS

Court House **814.849.1606**
Fax 814.849.1625
Web ....www.jeffersoncopacourt.org
200 Main St Ste 104, Brookville, PA 15825
Tonya S. Geist, Clerk Of Court

POLICE AND SHERIFF

Sheriff's Dept **814.849.1616**
Fax 814.849.1614
E-mail ....cgotwald@jeffersoncountypa.com
200 Main St Ste B03, Brookville, PA 15825
Carl Gotwald, Sheriff

EDUCATION SERVICES

Brookville Head Start Ctr I **814.849.8633**
Web ....jcheadstart.com
16771 Route 322, Ste 157, Brookville, PA 15825
Amy Elkin, Director

Juniata County

SOCIAL SERVICES

Assistance Ofc **717.436.2158**
Fax 717.436.5402
E-mail ....juniatacao@state.pa.us
100 Meadow Ln, Mifflintown, PA 17059
Vicky Wray, Executive Director

Children and Youth Svcs **717.436.7707**
Fax 717.436.7708
Web ....www.acsworld.com
E-mail ....hhenry@co.juniata.pa.us
14 Industrial Cir Ste 8, Mifflintown, PA 17059-9544
Helen Henry, Director

GENERAL HEALTH SERVICES

State Health Ctr **717.527.4185**
Fax 717.527.4278
Web ....www.state.pa.us
809 Market St, Port Royal, PA 17082-9630
Linda Allen, Public Health Nurse

COURTS

Court House **717.436.7715**
Fax 717.436.7734
Bridge & Main St, Mifflintown, PA 17059
Lori Ferry, Clerk Of Court

POLICE AND SHERIFF

Sheriff's Dept **717.436.2213**
Fax 717.436.7757
Web ....www.co.juniata.pa.us
E-mail ....sheriff@co.juniata.pa.us
26 N Main St, Mifflintown, PA 17059
H. Thomas Lyter, Sheriff

Lackawanna County

SOCIAL SERVICES

Assistance Ofc **570.963.4525**
Fax 570.963.4843
Web ....www.dpw.state.pa.us
100 Lackawanna Ave Rm 200, Scranton,
PA 18503-1939
Joseph Tomascillli, Executive Director

Children & Youth Svcs **570.963.6781**
Fax 570.963.6384
Web ....www.lackawanna.org
E-mail ....browningw@lackawannacounty.org
200 Adams Ave, 4th Floor, Scranton, PA 18503
William J. Browning, Director

Northeast Region Ofc of Children, Youth &
Families **570.963.4376**
Fax 570.963.3453
Web ....www.state.pa.us
E-mail ....lpocius@state.pa.us
100 Lackawanna Ave Ofc, SCRANTON STATE OFFICE
BLDG ROOM 301, Scranton, PA 18503-1944
Jacqulyn Madeon, Acting Regional Children & Youth Director

GENERAL HEALTH SERVICES

State Health Ctr **570.963.4567**
Fax 570.963.4109
E-mail ....meernotsky@state.pa.us
100 Lackawanna Ave Frnt, SCRANTON STATE OFFICE
BLDG, Scranton, PA 02503
Michelle Eernotsky, Rn, Nurse Supervisor

MENTAL HEALTH SERVICES

Commission on Drug and Alcohol **570.963.6820**
Fax 570.963.6617
Web ....www.lackawannacounty.org
507 Linden St, 5th Fl, Scranton, PA 18503
Jeff Zerechak, Executive Director

Human Svcs Ctr **570.282.1732**
Fax 570.282.6529
Web ....www.tricountyhs.com
185 Fallbrook St, Carbondale, PA 18407-1861
Stacy Little, Executive Director

JUSTICE AGENCY

Juvenile Probation **570.963.6887**
Fax 570.963.6864
E-mail ....cliffordr@lackawannacounty.org
200 Adams Ave, 5th Fl, Scranton, PA 18503
Rick Clifford, Chief JPO

POLICE AND SHERIFF

Sheriff's Dept **570.963.6719**
Fax 570.963.6859
Web ....www.lackawannacounty.org
E-mail ....szymanskij@lackawannacounty.org
200 N Washington Ave, Scranton, PA 18503-1596
John J. Szymanski, Sheriff

Lancaster County

SOCIAL SERVICES

Children and Youth Svcs **717.299.7925**
Fax 717.299.7929
Web ....www.co.lancaster.pa.us
900 E King St, Lancaster, PA 17602-3272
Betsy Frame, Director Of Placement Services

GENERAL HEALTH SERVICES

State Health Ctr **717.299.7597**
Fax 717.396.7197
E-mail ....www.padepartmentofhealth.com
1661 Old Philadelphia Pike, Lancaster, PA 17602
Diane Miller, Supervisor

MENTAL HEALTH SERVICES

Drug & Alcohol Commission **717.299.8023**
Fax 717.293.7252
Web ....www.co.lancaster.pa.us
E-mail ....rick@co.lancaster.pa.us
150 N Queen St Ste 410, Lancaster, PA 17603-3562
Rick Kastner, Executive Director

Mental Health/Mental Retardation/Early
Intervention **717.299.8021**
Fax 717.295.3680
Web ....www.co.lancaster.pa.us
150 N Queen St Ste 610, Lancaster, PA 17603
James Laughman, Executive Director

JUSTICE AGENCY

Detention Home **717.299.7821**
Fax 717.209.3314
Web ....www.co.lancaster.pa.us
235 Circle Ave, Lancaster, PA 17602
Drew Fredericks, Director

COURTS

Juvenile Probation **717.299.8161**
Fax 717.295.5992
Web ....www.co.lancaster.pa.us
E-mail ....muellerd@co.lancaster.pa.us
50 N Duke St, Lancaster, PA 17602
Dave Mueller, Director

POLICE AND SHERIFF

East Earl Police Dept **717.354.2211**
Fax 717.355.5310
Web ....www.police.co.lancaster.pa.us
E-mail ....eastearladmin@police.co.lancaster.pa.us
128 Toddy Dr, East Earl, PA 17519-9702
Kevin Mccarthy, Police Chief

Lancaster City Police Dept **717.735.3300**
Fax 717.735.3486
39 W Chestnut St, Lancaster, PA 17603
Charles Schmidt, Administrative Captain

Sheriff's Dept **717.299.8200**
Fax 717.295.3656
Web ....www.co.lancaster.pa.us
E-mail ....sheriff@co.lancaster.pa.us
50 N Duke St, Lancaster, PA 17602-2805
Mark Reese, Sheriff

Lawrence County

SOCIAL SERVICES

Assistance Ofc **724.656.3000**
Fax 724.656.3222
Web ....www.lccap.org
108 Cascade Galleria, New Castle, PA 16101-3900
Tessa Begley, Executive Director

Children and Youth Svcs **724.658.2558**
Fax 724.658.5503
Web ....www.co.lawrence.pa.us
1001 E Washington St, New Castle, PA 16101-4429
Jane Gajda, Director

GENERAL HEALTH SERVICES

New Castle Health Ctr **724.656.3088**
Fax 724.656.3008
Web ....www.state.pa.us
E-mail ....kdecaprio@state.pa.us
106 Margaret St, New Castle, PA 16101-3913
Kathy Decaprio, Hiv Coordinator

MENTAL HEALTH SERVICES

Drug and Alcohol Commission **724.658.5580**
Fax 724.658.2427
E-mail ....lawsca@swsix.com
25 N Mill St Ste 303, New Castle, PA 16101
Judy Thompson, Executive Director

Mental Health/Mental Retardation **724.658.2538**
Fax 724.656.1503
Web ....www.lawrence.swsix.com
E-mail ....jklenotic@co.lawrence.pa.us
217 N Jefferson St Ste A, New Castle, PA 16101-2264
John Klenotic, Administrator

COURTS

Goverment Ctr **724.658.2541**
Fax 724.656.2286
Web ....www.co.lawrence.pa.us
430 Court St, New Castle, PA 16101
Honorable J. Craig Cox

POLICE AND SHERIFF

Sheriff's Ofc **724.652.5121**
Fax 724.656.2477
Web ....www.co.lawrence.pa.us
E-mail ....sheriff@co.lawrence.pa.us
430 Court St, New Castle, PA 16101-3503
Perry Quahliero, Sheriff

Pennsylvania

Lebanon County

SOCIAL SERVICES

Children and Youth Svcs **717.274.2801**
Fax 717.228.4465
E-mail .... rshowers@lebcnty.org
400 S 8th St, Municipal Bldg. Room 401, Lebanon, PA 17042
Richard Showers, Director of Social Services

Lebanon Company Assistance Ofc **717.270.3600**
Fax 717.228.2589
625 S 8th St, Lebanon, PA 17042
Jackie Zimmerman, Executive Director

GENERAL HEALTH SERVICES

Lebanon State Health Ctr **717.272.2044**
Fax 717.279.7558
E-mail .... kdrum@state.pa.us
9 N 9th St, Lebanon, PA 17046
Kimberlee Drum, District Supervisor

MENTAL HEALTH SERVICES

Commission on Drug and Alcohol **717.274.0427**
Fax 717.274.0420
Web .... www.lebcnty.org
220 E Lehman St, Lebanon, PA 17046-3930
Kevin Schrum, Acting Executive Director

Mental Health/Mental Retardation **717.274.3415**
Fax 717.274.0317
220 E Lehman St, Lebanon, PA 17046
Kevin Schrum, Administrator

JUSTICE AGENCY

Probation Ofc/Adult and Juvenile **717.273.1557**
Fax 717.273.9378
Web .... www.lebcnty.org
E-mail .... wsullivan@lebcnty.org
508 Oak St, Lebanon, PA 17042-6245
William R. Sullivan, Chief JPO/juvenile

COURTS

Court of Common Pleas - 52nd District **717.274.2801**
Fax 717.273.7490
Web .... www.lebcounty.org
400 S 8th St, Lebanon, PA 17042
Honorable Samuel A. Kline, Judge

POLICE AND SHERIFF

Sheriff's Ofc **717.228.4410**
Fax 717.279.8398
Web .... www.lebcounty.org
E-mail .... sheriff@lebcounty.org
400 S 8th St, Room 3, Lebanon, PA 17042
Michael J. Deleo, Sheriff

Lehigh County

SOCIAL SERVICES

Assistance Ofc **610.821.6509**
Fax 610.821.6705
Web .... www.lehighcounty.org
E-mail .... rmango@state.pa.us
101 S 7th St, Allentown, PA 18101-2295
Rick Mango, Director

Children and Youth Svcs **610.782.3064**
Fax 610.820.3640
17 S 7th St, Allentown, PA 18101
Pamela Buehrle, Director

GENERAL HEALTH SERVICES

Allentown Bureau of Health **610.437.7760**
Fax 610.437.8799
Web .... www.allentownpa.gov/
E-mail .... kistler@allentowncity.org
245 N 6th St Frnt, Allentown, PA 18102-4149
Vicki Kistler, Health Director

JUSTICE AGENCY

Detention Home **610.871.5960**
Fax 610.481.9347
Web .... www.lehighcounty.org
E-mail .... kevinmiller@lehighcounty.org
370 S Cedarbrook Rd, Allentown, PA 18104-5708
Kevin Miller, Assistant Administrator

COURTS

Court House **610.782.3014**
Fax 610.820.3093
Web .... www.lehighcounty.org
E-mail .... lizabethafritz@lehighcounty.org
455 W Hamilton St, Allentown, PA 18101-1602
Elizabeth A Fritz, Director Of Juvenile Probation

POLICE AND SHERIFF

Sheriff's Office **610.782.3175**
Fax 610.820.3368
Web .... www.lehighcounty.org
455 W Hamilton St, 2nd Fl, Allentown, PA 18101
Ronald W. Rossi, Sheriff

Luzerne County

SOCIAL SERVICES

Assistance Ofc **570.826.2100**
Fax 570.826.2178
Web .... www.dpw.state.pa.us
E-mail .... wschabener@state.pa.us
205 S Washington St, Wilkes Barre, PA 18711-3298
Bill Schabener, Executive Director

Children and Youth Svcs **570.826.8710**
Fax 570.821.7355
111 N Pennsylvania Ave Ste 110, Wilkes Barre, PA 18701
Frank Castano, Executive Director

GENERAL HEALTH SERVICES

Kirby Health Ctr **570.822.4278**
Fax 570.825.9926
71 N Franklin St Ofc, Wilkes Barre, PA 18701-1386
John Turner, Phd, Director

State Health Ctr **570.826.2071**
Fax 570.820.4947
665 Carey Ave Ste 2, Wilkes Barre, PA 18706
Keith Simonson, Rn, Community Health Nurse

Wilkes-Barre City Health Dept **570.208.4268**
Fax 570.208.4272
71 N Franklin St Ste 110, Wilkes Barre, PA 18711
Ted Kross, Director

MENTAL HEALTH SERVICES

Drug and Alcohol Program **570.826.8790**
Fax 570.826.3079
Web .... www.luzernecounty.org
E-mail .... michael.donahue@luzernecounty.org
20 N Pennsylvania Ave, Ste 218, Wilkes Barre, PA 18701
Michael Donahue, Administrator

Luzerne-Wyoming Mental Health **570.825.9441**
Fax 570.825.6820
Web .... www.mhmr.luzerne.pa.us
E-mail .... mhmr@mhmr.luzerne.pa.us
111 N Pennsylvania Ave Ste 200, Wilkes Barre, PA 18701-3511
Peter Rubel, Director

JUSTICE AGENCY

Juvenile Probation **570.825.1552**
Fax 570.825.1722
Web .... www.luzernecounty.org
E-mail .... jjohnson@luzcojuvprobation.com
20 N Pennsylvania Ave, Pen Place Bldg. #329, Wilkes Barre, PA 18701-3503
John E. Johnson, Deputy Chief

POLICE AND SHERIFF

Sheriff's Ofc **570.825.1651**
Fax 570.825.1849
200 N River St, Wilkes Barre, PA 18711
John Gilligan, Sheriff

Lycoming County

SOCIAL SERVICES

Assistance Ofc **570.327.3300**
Fax 570.321.6501
Web .... www.state.pa.us
E-mail .... dferrell@state.pa.us
400 Little League Blvd, Williamsport, PA 17701-4980
Donna Ferrell, Executive Director

Children & Youth Svcs **570.326.7895**
Fax 800.525.7938
E-mail .... mwestbrook@joinder.org
200 E Street Sharwell Bldg, Williamsport, PA 17701

GENERAL HEALTH SERVICES

State Health Ctr **570.327.3440**
Fax 570.327.3547
E-mail .... health@state.pa.us
1000 Commerce Park Dr Ste 106, Williamsport, PA 17701
Doug Koszalka, District Executive Director

MENTAL HEALTH SERVICES

West Branch Drug & Alcohol Abuse **570.323.8543**
Fax 570.323.8550
Web .... www.westbranchdrug-alcohol.com
E-mail .... wbcms@aol.com
213 W 4th St Unit 2, Williamsport, PA 17701-6148
Shea H. Madden, Executive Director

COURTS

Court House **570.327.2408**
Fax 570.327.2479
48 W 3rd St Unit 1, Williamsport, PA 17701-6536
Honorable Nancy Butts, Judge

POLICE AND SHERIFF

Sheriff's Ofc **570.327.2280**
Fax 570.327.2366
Web .... www.lyco.org
48 W 3rd St, Williamsport, PA 17701
R Mark Lusk, Sheriff

McKean County

SOCIAL SERVICES

Assistance Ofc **814.362.4671**
Fax 814.362.4959
Web .... www.state.pa.us
E-mail .... jkeltz@state.pa.us
68 Chestner St Ste B, Bradford, PA 16701-2011
James Keltz, Executive Director

Children and Youth Svcs **814.887.3350**
Fax 814.887.3228
E-mail .... tleerway@mckeancountyta.org
17155 Route 6, Smethport, PA 16749
Tara Erway, CPS Supervisor

MENTAL HEALTH SERVICES

Mental Health/Mental Retardation **814.772.8016**
Fax 814.772.8337
Web .... www.cemhmr.com
E-mail .... czembryki@cemhmr.com
94 Hospital St, 4th Floor, Ridgway, PA 15853
Cynthia N. Zembryki, Administrator

COURTS

Court House **814.887.3323**
Fax 814.887.2712
500 W Main St, Smethport, PA 16749
Joanne Bly, Court Administrator

Mercer County

SOCIAL SERVICES

Assistance Ofc **724.983.5000**
Fax 724.983.5706
Web ....www.state.pa.us
E-mail ....mwasser@state.pa.us
  2236 Highland Rd, Hermitage, PA 16148-2896
  Mark Wasser, Executive Director

Children and Youth Svcs **724.662.2703**
Fax 724.662.0676
  8425 Sharon Mercer Rd, Mercer, PA 16137
  Michelle Kardasz, Acting Director

GENERAL HEALTH SERVICES

North West District Health Ofc **724.662.6068**
Fax 724.662.6086
Web ....www.health.state.pa.us
  19 McQuiston Dr, Jackson Center, PA 16133-1635
  Dennis P. Fapore, District Executive Director

MENTAL HEALTH SERVICES

MH/MR Program **724.662.1550**
Fax 724.662.1724
Web ....www.mercercountybhc.org
E-mail ....catherine.main@mercercountybhc.org
  8406 Sharon Mercer Rd, Mercer, PA 16137-3138
  Catherine A. Main, Administrator

JUSTICE AGENCY

Juvenile Probation Ofc **724.662.3800**
Fax 724.662.4105
Web ....www.mcc.co.mercer.pa.us
E-mail ....mbenedetto@mcc.co.merser.pa.us
  120 Strawberry St, Mercer, PA 16137-1236
  Mark F. Benedetto, Chief JPO

POLICE AND SHERIFF

Sheriff's Ofc **724.662.6135**
Fax 724.662.1603
E-mail ....whromine@wpia.net
  205 S Erie St Ste 102, Mercer, PA 16137
  William H. Romine, Sheriff

EDUCATION SERVICES

**Special Education Midwestern
Intermediate** **724.458.6700**
Fax 724.458.5083
Web www.miu4.k12.pa.us
  453 Maple St, Grove City, PA 16127
  Cecelia Yauger, Executive Director

Mifflin County

SOCIAL SERVICES

Assistance Ofc **717.248.6746**
Fax 717.242.6099
  1125 Riverside Dr, Lewistown, PA 17044
  Vicky Wray, Executive Director

Children and Youth Svcs **717.248.3994**
Fax 717.248.6953
Web ....www.co.mifflin.pa.us
E-mail ....mseiler@co.mifflin.pa.us
  144 E Market St, Lewistown, PA 17044-2125
  Mackenzie Seiler, Director

GENERAL HEALTH SERVICES

State Health Ctr **717.242.1452**
Fax 717.242.2976
Web ....www.dsf.health.state.pa.us
  21 S Brown St, Ste 1, Lewistown, PA 17044
  Jane Shearer, Rn, Hiv Coordinator

MENTAL HEALTH SERVICES

Drug and Alcohol Abuse **717.242.1446**
Fax 717.242.1447
E-mail ....srd@tricoda.org
  68 Chestnut St, Lewistown, PA 17044
  S. Raymond Dodson, Executive Director

Mental Health/Mental Retardation **717.242.6467**
Fax 717.242.6471
Web ....www.hmjmhmr.org
  399 Green Ave Ste 200, Lewistown, PA 17044
  Christopher Wysocki, Administrator

JUSTICE AGENCY

Juvenile Probation **717.248.3953**
Fax 717.248.4425
  20 N Wayne St, Lewistown, PA 17044
  Larry Wolfe, Chief Performance Officer

COURTS

Judges Chambers **717.248.4613**
Fax 717.248.8337
  20 N Wayne St, Lewistown, PA 17044
  Melissa Fultz, Court Administrator

POLICE AND SHERIFF

Sheriff's Ofc **717.242.1105**
Fax 717.248.2907
Web ....www.co.mifflin.pa.us
  20 N Wayne St, Lewistown, PA 17044-1770
  Christopher Shade, Sheriff

Monroe County

SOCIAL SERVICES

Assistance Ofc **570.424.3030**
Fax 570.424.3915
Web ....www.compass.state.pa.us
E-mail ....cpapson@dpw.state.pa.us
  Rt 209 At Tanite Rd, Stroudsburg, PA 18360
  Christine Papson, Executive Director

Children and Youth Svcs **570.420.3590**
Fax 570.420.3598
Web ....www.co.monroe.pa.us
E-mail ....agrace@co.monroe.pa.us
  730 Phillips St, Stroudsburg, PA 18360-2246
  Adelaide Grace, Administrator

GENERAL HEALTH SERVICES

State Health Ctr **570.424.3020**
Fax 570.424.3977
Web ....www.dsf.health.state.pa.us
  Route 209 and Tanite Rd, Stroudsburg, PA 18360
  Catherine Capozzolo, Hiv Coordinator

MENTAL HEALTH SERVICES

**Carbon/Monroe/Pike Drug and Alcohol
Commission** **570.421.1960**
Fax 570.421.3548
Web ....www.cmpda.cog.pa.us
  724 Phillips St Ste A, Stroudsburg, PA 18360
  Richard L. Mroczka, Executive Director

Mental Health/Mental Retardation **570.420.1900**
Fax 570.424.7753
E-mail ....stheodorou@cmpmhmr.com
  724 Phillips St Ste 202, Stroudsburg, PA 18360
  Sheila Theodorou, Edd, Administrator

Montgomery County

SOCIAL SERVICES

Children, Youth and Human Svcs **610.278.5800**
Fax 610.278.5898
Web ....www.montcopa.org/mcocy
  1430 Dekalb St, Norristown, PA 19404
  Lori O'Connor, Director

Ofc of Child Day Care Svcs **610.278.3707**
Fax 610.278.5161
Web ....www.montcopa.org/ccis
E-mail ....cwhitson@mail.montcopa.org
  1430 Dekalb St, Norristown, PA 19401-3406
  Connie Whitson, Executive Director

GENERAL HEALTH SERVICES

Dept of Health **610.278.5117**
Fax 610.278.5167
E-mail ....publichealth@montgopa.org
  1430 Dekalb St, Norristown, PA 19404
  Shaista Ajaz, Supervisor

Health Dept Pottstown **610.970.5040**
Fax 610.970.5048
Web ....www.montcopa.org
  364 King St, Pottstown, PA 19464-5641
  Debra Chiapelli, Hiv Coordinator

MENTAL HEALTH SERVICES

Central Montgomery MH/MR Ctr **610.277.4600**
Fax 610.275.0216
Web ....www.centralmhmr.org
E-mail ....central@centralmhmr.org
  1100 Powell St, Norristown, PA 19401-3820
  Clark Bromberg, Director

**Dept Of Behavioral Health And
Disabilities** **610.278.3642**
Fax 610.278.3683
Web ....www.montcopa.org
E-mail ....jmuth@montcopa.org
  1430 Dekalb St, Norristown, PA 19401-3406
  Joanna Muth, Mr Administrator

JUSTICE AGENCY

Detention Home **610.631.1893**
Fax 610.631.5394
E-mail ....mraquet@montcopa.org
  540 Port Indian Rd, Norristown, PA 19403
  Maureen Raquet, Administrator

Juvenile Probation **610.630.2252**
Fax 610.630.1749
E-mail ....scuster@montcopa.org
  530 Port Indian Rd, Norristown, PA 19403
  Steve Custer, Chief JPO

COURTS

Court House **610.278.3993**
Fax 610.278.5192
E-mail ....margaretcarter@montgopa.org
  Swede & Airy St., Norristown, PA 19404
  Honorable S. Gerald Corso, Judge

POLICE AND SHERIFF

Sheriff's Dept **610.278.3337**
Fax 610.278.1488
  PO Box 311, Norristown, PA 19404-0311
  Eileen Behr, Sheriff

EDUCATION SERVICES

Special Education **610.539.8550**
Fax 610.539.7411
Web ....www.mciu.org
  1605 W Main St, Eagleville, PA 19403
  Dr. Lois Robinson, Special Education Director

Montour County

SOCIAL SERVICES

Assistance Ofc **570.275.7430**
Fax 570.275.7433
Web ....www.montourco.org
E-mail ....kmordan@state.pa.us
  327 Church St, Danville, PA 17821-1911
  Kathy Mordin, Executive Director

Children & Youth Svcs **570.271.3050**
  114 Woodbine Lane Ste 201, Danville, PA 17821

GENERAL HEALTH SERVICES

State Health Ctr......................................**570.275.7092**
Fax...570.275.7006
Web.............................www.dsf.health.state.pa.us
329 Church St, Danville, PA 17821-1911
Amy Reagen, Nursing Supervisor

MENTAL HEALTH SERVICES

Mental Health Mental Retardation
Program...**570.275.5422**
Fax...570.275.6610
Web...www.cmsu.org
E-mail.................................pkeating@cmsu.org
Paris Bldg, Danville, PA 17821
Phillip T. Keating, Administrator

COURTS

Court House......................................**570.271.3030**
Fax...570.271.3049
29 Mill St Ste 1, Danville, PA 17821-1999
Honorable Thomas A. James, Jr., Judge

POLICE AND SHERIFF

Sheriff's Dept....................................**570.271.3020**
Fax...570.271.3037
E-mail......................sheriffrcg@montourco.org
29 Mill St Ste 7, Danville, PA 17821
Ray C Gerringer, Sheriff

Northampton County

SOCIAL SERVICES

Assistance Ofc..................................**610.250.1700**
Fax...610.250.1839
Web.............................www.compass.state.pa.us
E-mail................lnesbitt@northamptoncounty.org
201 Larry Holmes Dr, Easton, PA 18042
Lisa Nesbitt, Executive Director

Children and Youth Svcs...................**610.559.3290**
Fax...610.559.3750
Web.......................www.northamptoncounty.org
45 N 2nd St, Easton, PA 18042-7797
Kevin Dolan, Director

GENERAL HEALTH SERVICES

Bethlehem Health Bureau..................**610.865.7087**
Fax...610.865.7326
Web.............................www.bethlehem-pa.gov
10 E Church St, City Hall, Bethlehem, PA 18018
Judith Maloney, Director

Health Ctr...**610.250.1825**
Fax...610.250.1812
Web..www.state.pa.us
1600 Northampton St, Easton, PA 18402
Susan Rowe, Nursing Supervisor

MENTAL HEALTH SERVICES

Mental Health/Ei/Dp........................**610.974.7555**
Fax...610.974.7596
520 E Broad St, Bethlehem, PA 18018
Kathleen M. Kelly, Administrator

JUSTICE AGENCY

Probation Ofc..................................**610.559.6880**
Fax...610.559.6886
650 Ferry St, Easton, PA 18042
Mike Schneider, Chief

COURTS

Court House.....................................**610.559.3000**
Fax...610.559.3106
Web................................northamptoncounty.org
669 Washington St, Easton, PA 18042-7474
Honorable William Moran, Sr.Judge

POLICE AND SHERIFF

Sheriff's Dept....................................**610.559.3084**
Fax...610.559.1785
669 Washington St, Easton, PA 18042
Randy Miller, Sheriff

EDUCATION SERVICES

Special Education..............................**610.252.5550**
Fax...610.252.5740
Web...www.ciu20.org
E-mail....................................gvogel@ciu20.org
6 Danforth Dr, Easton, PA 18045-7820
Gail Vogel, Special Education Director, Edd

Northumberland County

SOCIAL SERVICES

Assistance Ofc..................................**570.988.5900**
Fax...570.988.5918
320 Chestnut St, Sunbury, PA 17801-2714
Eugene Della-Crouse, Executive Director

Children & Youth Svcs.......................**570.988.4237**
Fax...570.988.4241
322 N 2nd St, Sunbury, PA 17801
Karen Miller, Administrator

GENERAL HEALTH SERVICES

State Health Ctr................................**570.988.5513**
Fax...570.988.5573
Web...www.state.pa.us
E-mail.............................areagan@state.pa.us
247 Pennsylvania Ave, Sunbury, PA 17801-2248
Amy Reagan, Nursing Supervisor

MENTAL HEALTH SERVICES

Drug and Alcohol.............................**570.495.2154**
Fax...570.988.4347
217 N Center St, Sunbury, PA 17801-2205
Glenda Bonetti, Director

Mental Health/Mental Retardation..........**570.495.2002**
Fax...570.988.4444
217 N Center St, Sunbury, PA 17801
Judith C. Davis, Administrator

COURTS

Court House......................................**570.988.4163**
Fax...570.988.4497
201 Market St Ste 1, Sunbury, PA 17801-3408
Kathy Strausser, Clerk of Court

Juvenile Court...................................**570.495.2174**
Fax...570.988.4574
316 N 2nd St, Bldg. 320, Sunbury, PA 17801
William Rossnock, Chief JPO

Perry County

SOCIAL SERVICES

Assistance Ofc..................................**717.582.2127**
Fax...717.582.4187
Web...............................www.dpw.state.pa.us
E-mail..........................c-perrycao@state.pa.us
100 Centre Dr, New Bloomfield, PA 17068-9675
Antonio Andradi, Executive Director

Children & Youth Svcs.......................**717.582.2076**
112 Centre Dr, New Broomfield, PA 17068

GENERAL HEALTH SERVICES

State Health Ctr................................**717.567.2011**
Fax...717.567.6920
Web...www.doh.pa.us
E-mail..............................paharris@doh.pa.us
153 Red Hill Rd, Newport, PA 17074-8603
Patricia Harris, Hiv Coordinator

POLICE AND SHERIFF

Sheriff's Ofc.....................................**717.582.5123**
Fax...717.582.5115
E-mail...............................cnace@perryco.org
2 E Main St, New Bloomfield, PA 17068
Carl E. Nace, Sheriff

Philadelphia County

SOCIAL SERVICES

Children & Youth Svcs.......................**215.683.6000**
Fax...
Web...
1515 Arch St, Philadelphia, PA 19102

Southeast Region Ofc of Children, Youth &
Families..**215.560.2249**
Fax...215.560.6893
Web...www.state.pa.us
E-mail..................rahima.shamsid@state.pa.us
801 Market St, 6th Fl Ste 6112, Philadelphia,
PA 91107-4007
Rahima Shamsid Deen-hampton, Director

GENERAL HEALTH SERVICES

Delaware Valley Community Health - Maria De Los Santos
Health Ctr...**215.291.2500**
Fax...215.291.2502
Web................www.dvch.org/maria/maria.asp
E-mail...............................crespor@dvch.org
401 W Allegheny Ave, Philadelphia, PA 19133
Rafael Crespo, HIV Counsellor

Dept of Public Health.......................**215.685.5670**
Fax...215.685.5398
Web...www.phila.gov
E-mail..........................carmen.paris@phila.gov
1101 Market St Ste 840, Philadelphia,
PA 19107-2908
Carmen Paris, District Health Care Centers Info Director

Division of Maternal Child & Family
Health...**215.685.5225**
Fax...215.685.5257
Web..............................www.philadephia.gov
1101 Market St Fl 9, Philadelphia, PA 19107-2910
Donald Schwarz, Health Commissioner

Strawberry Mansion Health Care
Ctr...**215.978.2402**
Fax...215.685.2440
Web...www.phila.gov
E-mail...............judith.samansdunn@phila.gov
2840 W Dauphin St, Philadelphia, PA 19132-4697
Jude Dunn, Director

MENTAL HEALTH SERVICES

Mental Health/Mental Retardation...........**215.238.6092**
Fax...215.238.9294
E-mail..................pschaller@philacoalition.org
1218 Chestnut St Ste 705, Philadelphia, PA 19107
Paula P. Schaller, Executive Director

Mental Health/Mental Retardation...........**215.685.5400**
E-mail..................arthur.c.evans@phila.gov
1101 Market St Fl 7, Philadelphia, PA 19107-2907
Arther C. Evans, Director

JUSTICE AGENCY

Juvenile Justice Ctr/Hope Charter
School..**215.849.2112**
Fax...215.849.0393
Web...............................www.juvenilejustice.org
100 W Coulter St, Philadelphia, PA 19144
Richard Chapman, Director

Youth Study Ctr................................**215.686.4845**
Fax...215.686.0699
3232 Henry Ave, Philadelphia, PA 19129
Mark Tiple, Executive Director

COURTS

**Juvenile Probation Dept/Family
Court** **215.686.4103**
Fax 215.686.4014
Web ....www.courts.phila.gov
E-mail ....denise.ray@courts.phila.gov
1801 Vine St, Room 214, Philadelphia, PA 19103
Dr. Denise Ray, Acting Chief Juvenile Probation Officer

POLICE AND SHERIFF

Police Dept **215.686.1776**
Fax 215.625.0612
Web ....www.phila.gov
8th Race St, Police Administration Bldg. Room 314,
Philadelphia, PA 19106
Charles Ramsey, Police Commissioner

Police Dept **215.685.3251**
Fax 215.685.3256
Web ....www.phila.gov
E-mail ....POLICE.OPER@SCU.ORG
100 E Lehigh Ave, 1st Floor, Philadelphia, PA 19125
Cpt. Darvey, Special Vicitms Unit

Sheriff's Dept **215.686.3530**
Fax 215.686.3579
100 South Broad St., 5th floor, Philadelphia,
PA 19110
John D. Green, Sheriff

EDUCATION SERVICES

A Vare Head Start Ctr **215.952.6376**
1621 E Moyamensing Ave, Philadelphia,
PA 19148-1337
Jennifer Plumber Davis, Director

AB Day Head Start **215.276.6354**
1201 E Johnson St, Philadelphia, PA 19138-1037
Jodi Jaffe, Director

Anne Frank Head Start **215.961.2005**
2000 Bowler St, Philadelphia, PA 19115-3399
Jennifer Plumber Davis, Director

Birney Head Start Ctr **215.456.3195**
900 Lindley Ave, #14, Philadelphia, PA 19141
Joe Dixon, Principal

Bregy Head Start **215.581.5680**
1700 Bigler St, Philadelphia, PA 19145-4816
Jennifer Plumber Davis, Director

Bright Beginnings Head Start **215.227.2893**
Fax 215.227.2897
2001 W Lehigh Ave, Philadelphia, PA 19132-2652
Joann Croms, Director

Broad Street Head Start **215.276.2754**
6233 N Broad St, Philadelphia, PA 19141-2007
Joanne Crooms, Director

Bryant Head Start **215.474.7466**
Web www.phila.k12.pa.us
E-mail ....vbusillo@phila.k12.pa.us
6001 Cedar Ave, Philadelphia, PA 19143-1133
Virginia Busillo, Head Teacher

Cedar Grove Head Start Ctr **215.456.0201**
401 E Tabor Rd, Philadelphia, PA 19120
Me Banes, Head Teacher

Cleveland Head Start Ctr **215.227.4415**
Fax 215.227.7197
3701 N 19th St, Philadelphia, PA 19140-3598
Christopher Byrd, Principle

De Burgos Head Start Ctr **215.291.4065**
Fax 215.291.4084
401 W Lehigh Ave, Philadelphia, PA 19133-3111
Catishi Ashlock, Head Teacher

Dick Head Start **215.236.7145**
2498 W Diamond St, Philadelphia, PA 19121-1311
Jennifer Plumer Davis, Director

Duckrey Head Start **215.978.4758**
1501 W Diamond St, Philadelphia, PA 19121-2310
Jennifer Plumer Davis, Director

Emlen Head Start **215.951.4185**
6501 Chew Ave, Philadelphia, PA 19119-2006
Richard Raisnan, Principal

Svcs for Students with Disabilities **215.400.4170**
Fax 215.400.4171
Web www.phila.k12.pa.us
E-mail ....bbtaylor@phila.k12.pa.us
440 N Broad St, Philadelphia, PA 19130-4015
Linda William, Deputy Chief

The Bright Futures-Head Start **215.875.3155**
Fax 215.875.3711
1700 Christian St, Philadelphia, PA 19146
Jennifer Plumer Davis, Director

Pike County

SOCIAL SERVICES

Assistance Ofc **570.296.6114**
Fax 570.296.4183
Web ....www.dpw.state.pa.us
E-mail ....mzegalia@dpw.state.pa.us
10 Buist Rd Ste 101, Milford, PA 18337-9311
Michael Zegalia, Executive Director

Children and Youth Svcs **570.296.3446**
Fax 570.296.3540
506 Broad St Ste 202, Milford, PA 18337
Tammy McCullough, Director

GENERAL HEALTH SERVICES

State Health Ctr **570.296.6512**
Fax 570.296.5552
E-mail ....kaengelhar@state.pa.us
10 Buist Rd Ste 401, Milford, PA 18337
Michelle Bernotsky, Supervisor

POLICE AND SHERIFF

Sheriff's Ofc **570.296.6459**
Fax 570.296.3564
500 Broad St, Milford, PA 18337
Philip Bueki, Sheriff

Potter County

SOCIAL SERVICES

Assistance Ofc **814.274.4900**
Fax 814.274.3635
269 US Hwy 6 W, Coudersport, PA 16915
James Keltz, Executive Director

Human Svcs **814.544.7315**
Fax 814.544.9062
62 North St, Roulette, PA 16746
Pauline Wolver, Drug & Alcohol Services Director

GENERAL HEALTH SERVICES

State Health Ctr **814.274.3626**
Fax 814.274.3629
E-mail ....psalek@state.pa.us
269 US Highway 6 W, Coudersport, PA 16915
Pam Salek, Rn, Community Health Nurse

COURTS

Court House **814.274.9720**
Fax 814.274.3363
1 E 2nd St Rm 30, Coudersport, PA 16915
Stephen P.b. Minor, Judge

POLICE AND SHERIFF

Sheriff's Ofc **814.274.9350**
Fax 814.274.4225
Web ....www.pottercountypa.net
E-mail ....sheriff@pottercountypa.net
1 E 2nd St Rm 24, Coudersport, PA 16915-1690
Kenneth G. Sauley, Sheriff

Schuylkill County

SOCIAL SERVICES

Assistance Ofc **570.621.3000**
Fax 570.621.3014
Web ....www.state.pa.us
2640 Woodglen Rd, Pottsville, PA 17901-1335
Mr. B Hallick, Director

Children and Youth Svcs **570.628.1050**
Fax 570.628.1012
Web ....www.co.schuylkill.pa.us
E-mail ....gcampbell@co.schuylkill.pa.us
410 N Centre St Ste 1, Pottsville, PA 17901-1737
Gerard J. Campbell, Director

GENERAL HEALTH SERVICES

State Health Ctr **570.621.3112**
Fax 570.621.3188
103 One Norwegian Plz, Pottsville, PA 17901
Greig Ditler, Supervisor

MENTAL HEALTH SERVICES

Mental Health/Mental Retardation **570.621.2700**
Fax 570.621.2797
E-mail ....dreilly@sam-inc.org
1 S 2nd St Fl 1, Pottsville, PA 17901
Debi Riley, Administrator

COURTS

Court House **570.622.5570**
Fax 570.628.1210
Web ....www.co.schuylkill.pa.us
401 N 2Nd St, Pottsville, PA 17901-1756
Ed Sheran, Schuylkill County Probation Department Cpo

Teen Court **610.326.9274**
Fax 610.326.8136
2093 E High St, Pottstown, PA 19464
Edward C. Kropp Sr., Judge

POLICE AND SHERIFF

Sheriff's Dept **570.628.1440**
Fax 570.628.1014
Web ....www.schuykill.ps.us
401 N 2nd St, Pottsville, PA 17901-1756
Joseph Groodey, Sheriff

Snyder County

SOCIAL SERVICES

Assistance Ofc **570.374.8126**
Fax 570.374.6347
E-mail ....c-snydercao@state.pa.us
570 S High St, Selinsgrove, PA 17870
James Wirth, Executive Director

Children and Youth Svcs **570.374.4570**
Fax 570.374.4351
Web ....www.snydercounty.org
E-mail ....rweir@snydercounty.org
713 Bridge St Ste 15, Selinsgrove, PA 17870-1250
Rose Weir, Director

GENERAL HEALTH SERVICES

State Health Ctr **570.837.5915**
Fax 570.837.2266
E-mail ....whoke@state.pa.us
207 W Willow Ave, Middleburg, PA 17842
Wendy Hoke, Rn, Community Health Nurse

COURTS

Court House **570.837.4202**
Fax 570.837.4275
E-mail ....tberger@snydercounty.org
9 W Market St, Middleburg, PA 17842
Teresa J. Berger, Clerk Of Court

Pennsylvania

POLICE AND SHERIFF

Sheriff's Dept.............................**570.837.3311**
Fax...570.837.0168
Web..................................www.snydercounty.org
E-mail.......................sheriff@snydercounty.org
 12 S Main St, Middleburg, PA 17842-1014
 Joseph S. Reigle Jr., Sheriff

Somerset County

SOCIAL SERVICES

Assistance Ofc.............................**814.443.3681**
Fax...814.445.4352
Web.....................................www.dpw.state.pa.us
 164 Stayrook St, Somerset, PA 15501
 Deborah Crimone, Executive Director

Children & Youth Svcs.....................**814.445.1661**
Fax...814.445.1725
Web..................................www.co.somerset.pa.us
E-mail..........................crimonec@co.somerset.pa.us
 300 N Center Ave, Ste 220, Somerset, PA 15501
 Chuck Crimone, Administrator Iii

GENERAL HEALTH SERVICES

State Health Ctr...........................**814.445.7981**
Fax...814.445.5184
Web.....................................www.health.state.pa.us
E-mail........................mbarron@state.pa.us
 651 S Center Ave, Somerset, PA 15501
 Maureen Nanna Barron, Rn, Nursing Supervisor

MENTAL HEALTH SERVICES

Drug and Alcohol Commission..............**814.445.1530**
Fax...814.445.1524
 300 N Center Ave Ste 360, Somerset, PA 15501
 Erin Howsare, Executive Director

Mental Health & Mental Retardation
Program.....................................**814.443.4891**
Fax...814.443.4898
E-mail.........................randyh@besmhmr.dst.pa.us
 245 W Race St, Somerset, PA 15501
 Randy Hay, Administrator

JUSTICE AGENCY

Juvenile Court Svcs........................**814.445.1600**
Fax...814.444.8962
Web..................................www.co.somerset.pa.us
E-mail........................saylorv@co.somerset.pa.us
 300 N Center Ave Ste 100, Somerset, PA 15501-1468
 Vicki Rascona-saylor, Chief JPO

COURTS

Court House/Admin.........................**814.445.1473**
Fax...814.445.1455
 111 E Union St, Ste 200, Somerset, PA 15501
 Honorable Eugene E. Fike, Ii, Senior Judge

POLICE AND SHERIFF

Sheriff's Ofc...............................**814.445.1502**
Fax...814.444.5851
Web..................................www.co.somerset.pa.us
E-mail.........................sheriff@co.somerset.pa.us
 111 E Union St Ste 100, Somerset, PA 15501-1416
 John Mankey, Sheriff

Sullivan County

SOCIAL SERVICES

Assistance Ofc.............................**570.946.7174**
Fax...570.946.7189
Web.....................................www.dpw.state.pa.us
E-mail.........................c-sullivan@state.pa.us
 Rt 42 Main St, Laporte, PA 18626
 Leslee Wagner, Executive Director

Children and Youth Svcs....................**570.946.4250**
Fax...570.946.4261
E-mail.....................sullicys@sullivancounty-pa.us
 245 Main St, Laporte, PA 18626
 Lisa Wilcox, Director and CPS Supervisor

POLICE AND SHERIFF

Sheriff's Dept.............................**570.946.7361**
Fax...570.946.4075
E-mail....................sheriff57@sullivancounty-pa.us
 245 muncy st, Laporte, PA 18626
 Burton R. Adams, Sheriff

Susquehanna County

SOCIAL SERVICES

Assistance Ofc.............................**570.278.3891**
Fax...570.278.9508
Web.....................................www.dpw.state.pa.us
 33 Spruce St, Montrose, PA 18801-1225

Children & Youth Svcs.....................**570.278.4600**
Fax...570.278.3273
 31 Public Ave Cnty Ofc Bldg, Montrose, PA 18801

MENTAL HEALTH SERVICES

Drug and Alcohol Commission..............**570.278.1000**
Fax...570.278.2995
 281 Chrch St 2nd Fl, Montrose, PA 18801
 Jeffrey Zerechak, Program Administrator

Tioga County

SOCIAL SERVICES

Assistance Ofc.............................**570.724.4051**
Fax...570.724.5612
Web.....................................www.dpw.state.pa.us
E-mail.........................lcannarozzi@state.pa.us
 11809 Route 6, Wellsboro, PA 16901-6793
 Louis Cannarozzi, Executive Director

Children & Youth Svcs.....................**570.724.5766**
Fax...570.724.6757
E-mail........................tchsaad@epix.net
 1873 Shumway Hill Rd, Wellsboro, PA 16901

Dept. of Human Services...................**570.724.5766**
Fax...570.724.6757
E-mail........................tchsaad@apex.net
 1873 Shumway Hill Rd, Wellsboro, PA 16901-6840
 Max Harrison, Administrator

POLICE AND SHERIFF

Sheriff's Ofc...............................**570.724.3491**
Fax...570.723.8273
Web.....................................www.tiogacountypa.us
 116 Main St, Wellsboro, PA 16901
 Tom Young, Sheriff

EDUCATION SERVICES

Elkland Head Start Ctr.....................**814.258.7490**
 117 Court St Ste H, Elkland, PA 16920-1465
 Breanne Roe, Head Teacher

Union County

SOCIAL SERVICES

Children and Youth Svcs....................**570.522.1330**
After hours..................................570.523.1113
Fax...570.522.1349
E-mail........................trishelho@unionco.org
 1610 Industrial Blvd Ste 200, Lewisburg,
 PA 17837-1292
 Toni Rishel-Ho, Director/CPS Supervisor

GENERAL HEALTH SERVICES

State Health Ctr...........................**570.523.1124**
Fax...570.523.1129
Web.....................................www.health.state.pa.us
 260 Reitz Blvd Ste 3, Lewisburg, PA 17837
 Joni Forman, Hiv Coordinator

COURTS

Court House................................**570.524.8641**
Fax...570.524.8644
 103 S 2nd St, Lewisburg, PA 17837
 Honorable Harold F. Woelfel Jr., Senior Judge

POLICE AND SHERIFF

Sheriff's Ofc...............................**570.524.8716**
Fax...570.524.8731
 103 S 2nd St, Lewisburg, PA 17837
 Ernest Ritter Iii, Sheriff

Venango County

SOCIAL SERVICES

Children and Youth Svcs....................**814.432.9743**
Fax...814.432.9728
Web.....................................www.co.venango.pa.us
E-mail.........................dschwille@co.venango.pa.us
 1 Dale Ave, Franklin, PA 16323-1333
 David Schwille, Director

MENTAL HEALTH SERVICES

Mental Health/Mental Retardation..........**814.432.9100**
Fax...814.432.9781
E-mail.........................jromero@co.venango.pa.us
 1 Dale Ave, Franklin, PA 16323
 Jayne Romero, Administrator

COURTS

Court House................................**814.432.9610**
Fax...814.432.3149
Web.....................................www.co.venango.pa.us
E-mail........................rule509admin@co.venango.pa.us
 1168 Liberty St, Franklin, PA 16323-1272
 Oliver J Lobaugh, President Judge

POLICE AND SHERIFF

Sheriff's Dept.............................**814.432.9565**
Fax...814.437.2324
 1168 Courthouse Liberty St., Franklin, PA 16323
 Eric Foy, Sheriff

Warren County

SOCIAL SERVICES

Assistance Ofc.............................**814.723.6330**
Fax...814.726.1565
Web.....................................www.dpw.state.pa.us
E-mail.........................mallen@dpw.state.pa.us
 300 Hospital Dr Ste E, Warren, PA 16365-4892
 Michelle Allen, Executive Director

Children and Youth Svcs....................**814.726.2100**
Fax...814.726.8449
E-mail........................mkushner@wc-hs.org
 27 Hospital Dr, Warren, PA 16365
 Mary Kusner, Director

GENERAL HEALTH SERVICES

State Health Ctr...........................**814.728.3566**
Fax...814.728.3570
Web.....................................www.health.state.pa.us
 2027 Pennsylvania Ave E, Warren, PA 16365
 Barbara White, Rn, Hiv Coordinator

COURTS

Court House **814.723.7550**
Fax 814.728.3452
Web ....www.warrenforestcourt.org
E-mail ....fkerdam@co.warren.pa.us
 204 4th Ave, Warren, PA 16365
 Maureen Fkerda, Judge

POLICE AND SHERIFF

Sheriff's Offc **814.723.7553**
Fax 814.726.2113
E-mail ....lkopko@warren-county.net
 407 Market St, Warren, PA 16365
 Larry E. Kopko, Sheriff

Washington County

SOCIAL SERVICES

Assistance Ofc **724.223.4300**
Fax 724.223.4675
 167 N Main St, Washington, PA 15301
 David Reese, Executive Director

Children and Youth Svcs **724.228.6884**
Fax 724.223.4713
Web ....www.co.washington.pa.us
 100 W Beau St Ste 502, Washington, PA 15301-4475
 Lori Harbert, Director

GENERAL HEALTH SERVICES

Washington State Health Ctr **724.223.4540**
Fax 724.223.4677
Web ....www.health.state.pa.us
 167 N Main St Ste 100, Washington, PA 15301
 Sandra Kniess, Community Health Supervisor

JUSTICE AGENCY

Juvenile Probation **724.228.6794**
Fax 724.250.6533
Web ....www.co.washington.pa.us
E-mail ....pendervj@co.washington.pa.us
 29 W Cherry Ave, Suite M414, Washington,
 PA 15301
 Daniel Clements, Chief

COURTS

The Honorable O'Dell-Seneca Ofc **724.228.6830**
Fax 724.250.4118
 1 S Main St Ste 2001, Washington, PA 15301
 Debbie Odell-Seneca, President Judge

POLICE AND SHERIFF

Sheriff's Ofc **724.228.6840**
Fax 724.223.4719
Web ....www.co.washington.pa.us
E-mail ....romanos@co.washington.pa.us
 100 W Beau St Ste 303, Washington, PA 15301-4432
 Samuel Romano, Sheriff

Wayne County

SOCIAL SERVICES

Children and Youth Svcs **570.253.5972**
Fax 570.253.2391
Web ....www.co.wayne.pa.us
E-mail ....lvonson@co.wayne.pa.us
 648 Park St, Suite C, Honesdale, PA 18431
 Linda Vonson, Director

GENERAL HEALTH SERVICES

Assistance Ofc **570.253.7100**
Fax 570.253.7374
Web ....www.dpw.state.pa.us
 107 8th St Ste 2, Honesdale, PA 18431
 Theresa Dux, Manager

State Health Ctr **570.253.7141**
Fax 570.253.7146
Web ....www.health.state.pa.us
 615 Erie Hts, Honesdale, PA 18431
 Michelle Bernotsky, Nursing Supervisor

COURTS

Court House **570.253.5970**
Fax 570.253.5432
Web ....www.dpw.state.pa.us
 925 Court St, Honesdale, PA 18431-1983
 Vicky Botjer, Clerk

POLICE AND SHERIFF

Sheriff's Ofc **570.253.2641**
Fax 570.253.4092
Web ....www.co.wayne.pa.us
 925 Court St Ste 1, Honesdale, PA 18431-1983
 Mark Steelman, Sheriff

Westmoreland County

SOCIAL SERVICES

Assistance Ofc **724.832.5200**
Fax 724.832.5202
Web ....www.dpw.state.pa.us
 587 Sells Ln, Greensburg, PA 15601-4458
 Linda Toy, Executive Director

Children & Youth Svcs **724.830.3300**
Fax 724.830.3364
Web ....www.co.westmoreland.pa.us
E-mail ....cmccallen@co.westmoreland.pa.us
 40 N Pennsylvania Ave Ste 310, Greensburg,
 PA 15601-2341
 Chuck McCallen, Assistant Director

GENERAL HEALTH SERVICES

Mon Valley State Health Ctr **724.684.2945**
Fax 724.684.2933
 1 Wendell Ramey Ln Ste 140, Monessen, PA 15062
 Maureen Barron, Rnc, Msn, Supervisor

State Health Ctr **724.832.5315**
Fax 724.832.5327
E-mail ....mbarron@state.pa.us
 233 W Otterman St, Greensburg, PA 15601
 Maureen Barron, Superintendent

MENTAL HEALTH SERVICES

Behavioral Health and Development
Services **724.830.3617**
Fax 724.830.3571
Web ....www.westmoreland.swsix.com
 40 N Pennsylvania Ave, 1st Floor, Greensburg,
 PA 15601
 Austin Breegle, Deputy Administrator

JUSTICE AGENCY

Juvenile Probation and Detention
Svcs **724.830.4200**
Fax 724.830.4263
Web ....http://www.co.westmoreland.pa.us/
E-mail ....pchapman@co.westmoreland.pa.us
 2771 S Grande Blvd, Greensburg, PA 15601-8922
 Peter C. Chapman, Detention Director

COURTS

Court House **724.830.3000**
Fax 724.830.3042
 2 N Main St, Rm M3, Greensburg, PA 15601
 Bryan Kline, Clerk Of Court

POLICE AND SHERIFF

Greensburg Police Dept **724.834.3800**
Fax 724.838.4304
E-mail ....wlyons@greensburgpa.org
 416 S Main St, Greensburg, PA 15601
 Walter Lyons, Chief

Sheriff's Ofc **724.830.3822**
Fax 724.830.3660
Web ....www.co.westmoreland.pa.us
E-mail ....sheriff@co.westmoreland.pa.us
 2 N Main St Bsmt 1, Greensburg, PA 15601-2436
 Chuck Moore, Deputy Chief Sheriff

EDUCATION SERVICES

Special Education **724.836.2460**
Fax 724.836.4235
Web www.wiu.k12.pa.us
E-mail ....lmatta@wiu.k12.pa.us
 102 Equity Dr, Greensburg, PA 15601-7190
 Luanne Matta, Executive Director

Wyoming County

SOCIAL SERVICES

Children and Youth Svcs **570.836.3131**
Fax 570.836.1639
E-mail ....wchs@epix.net
 819 Sr 29 S, Tunkhannock, PA 18657
 Patricia Skrynski, Director

GENERAL HEALTH SERVICES

State Health Ctr **570.836.2981**
Fax 570.836.4261
Web ....www.health.state.pa.us
 5632 SR-6, Tunkhannock, PA 18657
 Cheryl A. McGovern, Hiv Coordinator

COURTS

Court House **570.836.3200**
Fax 570.836.7244
Web ....www.wycopa.org
E-mail ....rmontross@wycopa.org
 1 Court House Sq Ofc, Tunkhannock, PA 18657-1216
 Richard D. Montross, Sheriff

York County

SOCIAL SERVICES

Assistance Ofc **717.771.1100**
Fax 717.771.1261
Web ....www.dpw.state.pa.us
E-mail ....flandau@state.pa.us
 130 N Duke St Fl 2, York, PA 17401-1113
 Frederick Landau, Executive Director

Children and Youth Svcs **717.846.8496**
Fax 717.771.9884
Web ....www.york-county.org
 100 W Market St Ste 4, York, PA 17401-1341
 James Anderson, Executive Director

GENERAL HEALTH SERVICES

York City Bureau of Health **717.849.2299**
Fax 717.843.5605
 435 W Philadephia St, York, PA 17401
 Joanne Sullivan, Director Of Nursing

MENTAL HEALTH SERVICES

MH/MR/Drug and Alcohol Program **717.771.9618**
Fax 717.771.9826
Web ....www.york-county.org
 100 W Market St, Suite 301, York, PA 17401
 Cynthia Dixon, Drug & Alcohol Program Specialist

JUSTICE AGENCY

Detention Shelter **717.840.7570**
Fax 717.840.7199
Web ....www.york-county.org
 3564 Heindel Rd, York, PA 17402
 Rondney Wagner, Director

Juvenile Probation **717.771.9567**
Fax 717.852.4925
 45 N George St, 3rd Floor, York, PA 17401
 Bryce Wickard, Deputy Chief JPO

COURTS

Senior Judges..............................717.771.9215
Fax...717.852.4931
Web.................................www.york-county.org
E-mail............................droshell@york-county.org
45 N George St, York, PA 17401-1240
Donald Shell, Clerk Of Court

POLICE AND SHERIFF

Sheriff's Ofc..............................717.771.9601
Fax...717.771.9957
Web........................www.ycex01.york-county.org
45 N George St, York, PA 17401-1240
Keuer Leber, Sheriff

SPECIAL SERVICES AGENCIES

ADOPTION AGENCIES

A Precious Gift Adoption Rsrc...............**570.842.4655**
Fax...866.254.5274
E-mail..........................apreciousgiftarc@yahoo.com
227 Bear Brook Acres Dr, Moscow, PA 18444-4104
Mary Lisa Piseczny, Director

Adagio Health..............................**412.288.2130**
Fax...412.288.9036
Web.................................www.adagiohealth.org
960 Penn Ave Ste 600, Pittsburgh, PA 15222
Richard Baird, Chief Executive Officer

Adoption by Choice..........................**814.836.9887**
Fax...814.836.9538
Web.............................www.adoptionbychoice.org
E-mail...................................abc@wccerie.org
4402 Peach St Ste 201, Erie, PA 16509
Glenna Cyphers, Director

Adoptions From The Heart...................**610.642.7200**
Fax...610.642.7938
Web.........................www.adoptionsfromtheheart.org
E-mail................adoption@adoptionsfromtheheart.org
30-31 Hampstead Circle, Wynnewood, PA 19096
Maxine G. Chalker, Msw, Lsw, Executive Director

Advantage Credit Counseling Service........**888.511.2227**
Fax...412.390.1329
Web.................................www.advantageccs.org
2403 Sidney Street, River Park Commons, Pittsburgh, PA 15203
COA accredited organization.

Best Nest...................................**215.546.8060**
Fax...215.546.8906
E-mail..............................kdesmond@bestnest.org
1709 Washington Ave, Philadelphia, PA 19146
Kathy Desmond, President/CEO

Bethany Christian Svcs.....................**724.940.2900**
Fax...724.940.2901
Web.....................................www.bethany.org
E-mail.........................bcspittsburgh@bethany.org
10521 Perry Hwy, Ste 200, Wexford, PA 15090
Sandra Mclaughlin, Director

Bethany Christian Svcs.....................**717.399.3213**
Fax...717.399.3543
Web.....................................www.bethany.org
E-mail..........................bcslancaster@bethany.org
1689 Crown Ave Ste 1, Lancaster, PA 17601-6314
Mark Unger, Director

Catholic Charities Counseling...............**814.368.8644**
Fax...814.368.6216
Web.....................................www.cccas.org
E-mail..............................lmclaughlin@cccas.org
125 Main St Rm 500, Bradford, PA 16701-2058
Lisa McLaughlin, Counsellor

Catholic Charities Counseling and Adoption Svcs...................................**814.371.4717**
90 Beaver Dr Ste 119D, Du Bois, PA 15801-2441
Joseph Haas, Executive Director

Catholic Charities, Diocese of Allentown.......**610.791.3888**
Fax...610.791.1878
Web.........................www.catholiccharityad.org
2141 Downyflake Lane, Allentown, PA 18103-4774
COA accredited organization.

Catholic Social Svcs........................**570.207.2283**
Fax...570.207.2206
E-mail..........................snocilla@cssresidential.org
516 Fig St, Scranton, PA 18505
Steven Nocilla, Executive Director

Child & Home Study Assoc..................**610.565.1544**
Fax...610.565.1567
Web.................................www.chsadoptions.org
E-mail............................info@chsadoptions.org
1029 N Providence Rd, Media, PA 19063-1404
Karen B. Burrill, Executive Director

Children's Choice Inc........................**215.551.6501**
Fax...215.551.6509
Web.................................www.childrenschoice.org
E-mail........................ssoranno@childrenschoice.org
1835 S Broad St, Philadelphia, PA 19148-2115
Steven Soranno, Supervisor

Children's Choice, Inc........................**215.831.9164**
Fax...215.831.9726
E-mail........................oxfordave@childrenschoice.org
900 E Howell St, Philadelphia, PA 19124
Carolyn Everwine, CEO

Common Sense Adoption Svcs...............**717.766.6449**
Fax...717.766.6701
Web.................................www.csas-swan.org
E-mail...........................echick@csas-swan.org
49 W Main St, Mechanicsburg, PA 17055-6262
Erin Chick, Director

Council of Three Rivers.....................**717.207.0553**
E-mail..............................kjevsevar@cotraic.org
1016 N Charlotte St, Lancaster, PA 17603
Kerry Jevsevar, Director

Craig B. Bluestein...........................**215.643.9000**
Fax...215.643.9800
Web.............................www.adoptionattorneys.com
E-mail................c.bluestein@adoptionattorneys.org
7237 Hollywood Rd, Fort Washington, PA 19034
Craig Bluestein, Director

Credit Counseling Center...................**215.396.1880**
Fax...215.396.8072
Web.................................www.ccc-credit.com
832 Second Street Pike, Richboro, PA 18954
COA accredited organization.

Elizabeth Cessna............................**412.366.4929**
Web.........................www.EverydayHypnotherapy.com
100 McKnight Park Dr, Pittsburgh, PA 15237
Elizabeth Cessna, Psychiatrist

Families United Network, Inc.................**570.546.6777**
Fax...570.546.8898
Web.................................www.families4kids.org
P.O. Box 264, Muncy, PA 17756
COA accredited organization.

Friendship House...........................**610.327.2200**
Fax...610.327.2203
Web.............................www.friendshiphousepa.org
E-mail..........................sdori@friendshiphousepa.org
152 E High St Ste 440, Pottstown, PA 19464-9543
Stacy Dori, Director

Hope For Kids, Inc...........................**814.353.0200**
Fax...814.353.1545
Web.................................www.hopeforkidsinc.org
E-mail..........................bgoldman@hopeforkidsinc.org
1400 FOX HILL RD STE 200, State College, PA 16803-1877
Brenda Goldman, President

Institute for Human Resources and Svcs.......**570.288.9386**
Fax...570.288.9112
Web.....................................www.ihrser.com
E-mail..................................hhicks@ihrser.com
250 Pierce St Ste 301, Kingston, PA 18704-5149
Robert Kotsull, Director

Int'l Assistance Group.......................**412.828.5800**
Fax...412.828.5876
Web.................................www.iagadoptions.org
E-mail............................info@iagadoptions.org
531 5th St, Oakmont, PA 15139-1626
Mary Graber, Social Worker

International Families Adoption Agency.......**215.735.7171**
Fax...215.545.3563
Web.................................www.4adoption.com
E-mail............................intlfam2003@yahoo.com
518 S 12th St, Philadelphia, PA 19147-1137
Laura Cochran, Executive Director

Jewish Family Svc...........................**717.233.1681**
Fax...717.234.8258
Web.....................................www.jssofhbg.org
E-mail..............................erabin@jssofhbg.org
3333 N Front St, Harrisburg, PA 17110
Rachel Kuhr, Director Of Adoptions

La Vida Adoption Agency....................**610.688.8008**
Fax...610.688.8028
Web.....................................www.lavida.org
E-mail..................................info@lavida.org
150 S Warner Rd Ste 144, King Of Prussia, PA 19406-2832
Lisa Johnson, Marketing Coordinator

Living Hope Adoption Agency...............**215.540.8999**
Fax...215.540.2765
Web.............................www.livinghopeadoption.org
E-mail..........................info@livinghopeadoption.org
449 Pennsylvania Ave, Fort Washington, PA 19034-3414
Samuel Fang, Director

Love The Children...........................**215.536.4181**
Web.............................www.lovethechildren.com
E-mail..........................cecelia@lovethechildren.com
221 W Broad St, Quakertown, PA 18951-1232
Cecelia Park, Executive Director

Madison Adoption Assoc....................**610.459.4970**
Fax...302.529.1976
Web.............................www.madisonadoption.com
E-mail..........................aleda.maa@comcast.net
2414 Blueball Ave, Marcus Hook, PA 19810
Aleda Madison, Executive Director

Pinebrook Family Svcs......................**610.432.3919**
Fax...610.432.5174
Web.............................www.pinebrookservices.org
402 N Fulton St, Allentown, PA 18102
Robert Jacobs, Rn, Bsn, Executive Director

Professional Family Care Svcs, Inc...........**814.255.9559**
Fax...814.255.5400
E-mail..................................jehanley@pfcs.org
937 Menoher Blvd, Johnstown, PA 15905-2838
Jim Hanley, Director

Rainbow Project............................**412.782.4457**
Fax...412.767.4808
Web.....................................www.cotraic.org
120 Charles St, Pittsburgh, PA 15238
Margaret Gold, Director

The Bair Foundation, Inc. **724.946.8711**
Fax 724.946.9612
Web ....www.bair.org
E-mail ....smiklos@bair.org
241 High St, New Wilmington, PA 16142-1116
Susan Miklos, Executive Director

Timothy Ayres LLC **814.262.2123**
Fax 814.262.2127
Web ....www.johnstownpa.com
218 College Park Plz, Johnstown, PA 15904
Timothy Ayres, Owner/attorney

Women's Christian Alliance **215.236.9911**
Fax 215.236.3559
Web ....www.wcafamily.org
1722-42 Cecil B. Moore Avenue, Philadelphia,
PA 19121-3405
COA accredited organization.

Youth Service, Inc. **215.222.3262**
Fax 215.222.2352
Web ....www.ysiphila.org
410 North 34th Street, Philadelphia, PA 19104
COA accredited organization.

ADVOCACY RESOURCES

**American Civil Liberties Union of Pennsylvania - Eastern
Ofc** **215.592.1513**
Fax 215.592.1343
Web ....www.aclupa.org
E-mail ....info@aclupa.org
125 S 9th St, Philadelphia, PA 19107
Nancy Hopkins, Executive Director

CASA **717.240.6159**
Fax 717.960.5502
Web ....www.ccpa.net/casa
E-mail ....casa@ccpa.net
16 W High St Ste 303, Carlisle, PA 17013-2919
Anita Brewster, Director

Children's Adovcacy Ctr **724.658.4688**
Fax 724.658.8810
Web ....www.jamiesonhealth.org
E-mail ....sascione@jamiesonhealth.org
1000 S Mercer St, New Castle, PA 16101
Susan Ascione, Executive Director

Juvenile Law Center **215.625.0551**
E-mail ....lrosado@jlc.org
1315 Walnut St 4th Fl, Philadelphia, PA 19107
Lourdes Rosado, Director

**Lackawanna Count Court of Common
Pleas** **570.963.6306**
E-mail ....harhutct@lackawannacounty.org
200 Adams Ave, Scranton, PA 18503
Chet Harhut, Judge

BEHAVIORAL HEALTH TREATMENT

Abel Medical Practice **215.885.2911**
Web ....www.drdavidabel.com
E-mail ....contact@drdavidabel.com
1638 Amity Rd, Jenkintown, PA 19046-1205
David Abel, MD, Psychiatrist

Abraxas Academy **610.913.8000**
Web ....www.abraxasyfs.com/
E-mail ....rmonzon@abraxasyfs.com
1000 Academy Drive, Morgantown, PA 19543
Mr. Robert Monzon, Accreditation Manager
Joint Commission accredited organization.

Abraxas I **814.927.6615**
Web ....www.abraxasyfs.com
E-mail ....cpark@abraxasyfs.com
165 Abraxas Road, Marienville, PA 16239
Mrs. Christa Park, Accreditation Manager
Joint Commission accredited organization.

Abraxas, a GEO Group Company **814.459.0618**
Web ....www.abraxasyfs.com
E-mail ....bkeep@abraxasyfs.com
429 West 6th Street, Erie, PA 16507
Ms. Bev Keep, Accreditation Manager
Joint Commission accredited organization.

Achievement Center, Inc. **814.459.2755**
Fax 814.456.4873
Web ....www.achievementctr.org
101 East Sixth Street, Erie, PA 16507
CARF accredited programs available.

Adelphoi Village, Inc. **724.520.1111**
Web ....www.adelphoivillage.org
E-mail ....jenb@adelphoivillage.org
1119 Village Way, Latrobe, PA 15650
Ms. Jennifer Beldin, Accreditation Manager
Joint Commission accredited organization.

Alan A. Axelson, MD Psychiatry **412.833.9060**
Fax 412.854.5152
180 Fort Couch Rd Ste 304, Pittsburgh,
PA 15241-1041
Alan Axelson, Psychiatrist

Albert Einstein Medical Center **215.456.7890**
Web ....www.einstein.edu
E-mail ....jordanm@einstein.edu
5501 Old York Road, Philadelphia, PA 19141
Ms. Maureen Jordan, Accreditation Manager
Joint Commission accredited organization.

Aquilo-Seara Medical Practice **610.277.5022**
Fax 610.277.5023
1717 Swede Rd, Blue Bell, PA 19422
Miguel Aquilo-Seara, MD, Psychiatrist

**Associates in Counseling & Child
Guidance** **724.983.1381**
Web ....www.accg.net
E-mail ....dmihalcin@ymail.com
272 East Connelly Boulevard, Sharon, PA 16146
Dr. Derek Mihalcin, Accreditation Manager
Joint Commission accredited organization.

Auberle **412.673.5800**
Fax 412.673.8587
Web ....www.auberle.org
1101 Hartman Street, McKeesport, PA 15132-1500
COA accredited organization.

Auerbach Medical Practice **215.567.5431**
67 Hamilton Cir, Philadelphia, PA 19130-3838
Arthur Auerbach, Md, Psychiatrist

Augusthy Medical Practice **215.483.8605**
Fax 215.643.6323
5735 Ridge Ave, Philadelphia, PA 19128
Roy Augusthy, Psychiatrist

Baker Medical Practice **215.643.1229**
956 Tennis Ave, Ambler, PA 19002-2311
Courtney Baker, MD, Psychiatrist

Bansal Medical Practice **610.327.3058**
1630 E High St, Pottstown, PA 19464
Harinder Bansal, Md, Psychiatrist

Baptist Children's Svcs **610.879.1440**
Fax 610.879.1448
Web ....www.baptistchildrensservices.org
E-mail ....lbuchholz@baptistchild.org
57 E Armat St, Philadelphia, PA 19144
Laurance Buchholz, Executive Director

Barber National Institute **215.871.0731**
Web ....www.barberinstitute.org
E-mail ....tracigardner@barberinstitute.org
1 Winding Dr Ste 150, Philadelphia, PA 19131-2994
Traci Gardner, Director

Bazelon Medical Practice **215.477.3330**
2967 W School House Ln, Philadelphia, PA 19144
Eileen Bazelon, Psychiatrist

Bazilian Medical Practice **215.782.1681**
8138 Cadwalader Ave, Elkins Park, PA 19027-2440
Stanford Bazilian, MD, Psychiatrist

Beacon Light Behavioral Health Systems **814.362.5250**
Web ....www.beacon-light.org
E-mail ....gsignor@beacon-light.org
800 East Main Street, Bradford, PA 16701
Mr. Guy Signor, Accreditation Manager
Joint Commission accredited organization.

**Belmont Center for Comprehensive
Treatment** **215.877.2000**
Web ....www.einstein.edu
E-mail ....ehlersm@einstein.edu
4200 Monument Road, Philadelphia, PA 19131
Ms. Mardi Ehlers, Accreditation Manager
Joint Commission accredited organization.

Benjamin Medical Practice **215.643.6425**
12 Mayo Pl, Dresher, PA 19025-1228
Robert Benjamin, Psychiatrist

Benson Medical Practice **610.525.2274**
1062 E Lancaster Ave Ste 7, Bryn Mawr,
PA 19010-1568
Jack Benson, MD, Psychiatrist

Berlin Medical Practice **412.682.1259**
Fax 412.276.8557
Web ....www.charlesberlin.com
E-mail ....cberlin@pitt.edu
417 S Craig St, Suite 303, Pittsburgh, PA 15213
Charles Berlin, MD, Psychiatrist

Berrettini Medical Practice **215.898.0092**
Fax 215.573.2041
E-mail ....wadeb@mail.med.upenn.edu
34 E Walnut Ln, Philadelphia, PA 19144-2003
Wade Berrettini, Md, Psychiatrist

Berschling Medical Practice **412.683.3275**
Fax 412.521.1749
E-mail ....cmbersch@sgi.net
1 Northgate Sq, Greensburg, PA 15601
Chester Berschling, MD, Psychiatrist

Bethesda Children's Home **814.724.7510**
Web ....Bethesda-Home.org
E-mail ....george.trauner@bethesda-home.org
15667 State Highway 86, Meadville, PA 16335
Mr. George Trauner, Accreditation Manager
Joint Commission accredited organization.

Boswell Medical Practice **814.861.3300**
Fax 814.861.5163
E-mail ....info@ccad-pa.com
1315 W College Ave Ste 303, State College,
PA 16801-2776
John Bosswell, Md, Psychiatrist

Boys Club and Girls Club of Lancaster **717.392.6343**
Fax 717.397.5337
Web ....www.bgclanc.org
E-mail ....kschloer@bgclanc.org
333 Dauphin Street, Lancaster, PA 17602
Karen Schloer, Chief Professional Officer Supervisor

Braun Medical Practice **610.667.3823**
109 Forrest Ave, Narberth, PA 19072
Sarah Braun, Md, Psychiatrist

Brendel Medical Practice **215.471.1576**
111 N 49th St, Philadelphia, PA 19139-2718
Erica Brendel, MD, Psychiatrist

Brenner Medical Practice **610.667.3183**
E-mail ....ibrenn@aol.com
10 Presidential Blvd, Ste 116, Bala Cynwyd,
PA 19004-1107
Ira Brenner, Psychiatrist

Burke Counseling Svcs Inc. **724.458.4330**
Fax 724.458.4550
107 Breckenridge St Ste 1, Grove City,
PA 16127-1025
Susan Burke, Director

Burkins Medical Practice 610.814.8000
Web ....www.megellanofpa.com
   3897 Adler Pl, Bethlehem, PA 18017
John Burkins, Md, Psychiatrist

Burns Medical Practice 215.496.0530
E-mail ....burns@burnsmd.com
   1601 Walnut St Ste 1109, Philadelphia,
   PA 19102-2907
David Burns, Psychiatrist

Bustleton Mental Health Institute, Inc 215.464.3838
E-mail ....bmhi@verizon.net
   1701 Grant Avenue, Philadelphia, PA 19115-3160
Ms. Elena Platonov, Accreditation Manager
Joint Commission accredited organization.

Cadieux Medical Practice 717.782.5661
   205 S Front St, Harrisburg, PA 17104-1619
Roger Cadieux, Psychiatrist

Capdeville Medical Practice 412.835.6322
   37 McMurray Rd Ste 106, Pittsburgh, PA 15241-1632
Anne Capdeville, Md, Psychiatrist

Cardamone Medical Practice 610.525.7215
   860 Old Lancaster Rd, Bryn Mawr, PA 19010
S. Joseph Cardamone, Md, Psychiatrist

Carelink 610.270.9120
Web ....www.carelink-svs.org
E-mail ....jbenedict@carelinkservices.org
   1201 Stanbridge St, Norristown, PA 19401
John Benedict, Director

Cederstrom Medical Practice 215.574.1776
Fax 215.574.1776
E-mail ....jjceder@verizon.net
   834 Chestnut St Ste T 140, Philadelphia,
   PA 19107-5113
Janice Cederstrom, Md, Psychiatrist

Centennial School Lehigh University 610.266.6500
Fax 610.266.7126
Web ....www.lehigh.edu/~insch/insc.html
E-mail ....mpg6@lehigh.edu
   2196 Ave C, Bethlehem, PA 18017
Michael George, Edd, Director

Central Montgomery Mental Health 610.270.0625
Web ....www.centralmhmr.org
E-mail ....clark@centralmhmr.org
   1217 Dekalb St, Norristown, PA 19401-3415
Clark Broomburge, Director

Central Montgomery Mental Health 610.277.4600
Web ....www.centralmhmr.org
   1109 Dekalb St, Norristown, PA 19401-3849
Emily Smith, Supervisor

Cerul Medical Practice 412.361.4144
   401 Shady Ave Ste B104, Pittsburgh, PA 15206-4458
Maurice Cerle Md, Psychiatrist

Chances 215.923.0218
   1200 Callowhill St, Philadelphia, PA 19123
Colette Green, Director

Chandragiri Medical Practice 570.963.2079
Fax 570.963.1953
   1141 Clay Ave, Scranton, PA 18510
Sanjay Chandragiri, Md, Psychiatrist

Chestnut Ridge Counseling Srvcs Inc 724.434.5437
   125 Chaffee St, Uniontown, PA 15401-4605
Mary Ann Pope, Director

Child Care Info Svcs 724.285.9431
Fax 724.285.7320
E-mail ....pw-mhartma@dpw.state.pa.us
   120 Hollywood Dr Ste 101, Butler, PA 16001-7604

Child Guidance Resource Centers 484.454.8700
Web ....cgrc.org
E-mail ....acavanaugh@cgrc.org
   2000 Old West Chester Pike, Havertown, PA 19083
Ms. Anne Cavanaugh, Accreditation Manager
Joint Commission accredited organization.

Children's Aid Home Programs 814.443.1637
Web ....www.cahprogram.org
E-mail ....lhorne@cahprogram.org
   1476 North Center Avenue, Somerset, PA 15501
Mrs. Lynne Horne, Accreditation Manager
Joint Commission accredited organization.

Children's BehavioralHealth, Inc. 814.262.0768
E-mail ....gvkelly@childrensbh.com
   203 College Park Plaza, Johnstown, PA 15904
Mr. George Kelly, Accreditation Manager
Joint Commission accredited organization.

Children's Home of Bradford 814.362.5250
Fax 814.362.2185
Web ....deacon-light.org
E-mail ....jwiseman@beacon-light.org
   800 E Main St, Bradford, PA 16701-3299
Jim Wiseman, Vice President

Children's Home of Easton 610.258.2831
Fax 610.258.3165
Web ....www.thechildrenshome.org
E-mail ....gregd@thechildrenshome.org
   2000 S 25th St, Easton, PA 18042-6096
Greg Dowty, Executive Director

Children's Service Center of Wyoming Valley,
Inc. 570.825.6425
Web ....www.cscwv.org
E-mail ....smerlina@e-csc.org
   335 South Franklin Street, Wilkes Barre, PA 18702
Mr. Steve Merlina, Accreditation Manager
Joint Commission accredited organization.

Children's Svc Ctr 570.836.2722
Fax 570.836.1068
Web ....www.cscwv.org
E-mail ....lboginski@e-csc.org
   133 W Tioga St Ste 1, Tunkhannock, PA 18657-1496
Lois Boginski, Director

Children's Svcs, Inc 215.546.3503
Fax 215.546.7977
E-mail ....dsimmons@csichild.org
   1315 Walnut St Lbby 2, Philadelphia, PA 19107-4717
Dorothy P. Simmons, Executive Director

Christopher Columbus Charter School 215.389.6000
E-mail ....roseydoc2229@aol.com
   1242 S 13th St, Philadelphia, PA 19147-4597
Ms.R Doughercy, Director

Circle C Youth and Family Svcs 412.937.1605
Fax 412.937.1236
Web ....www.circlec.net
E-mail ....rknouff@circlec.net
   2121 Noblestown Rd, Ste 100, Pittsburgh, PA 15205
Richard T. Knouff, Executive Director

Citizens Acting Together Can Help, Inc
(CATCH) 215.551.6540
Web ....www.catchinc.com
   1223 S 15th St, Philadelphia, PA 19146-3116
Dorothy Owens, Director

Cladel Medical Practice 717.469.7169
   412 S Meadow Ln, Hummelstown, PA 17036-7402
Charles Cladel, Md, Psychiatrist

Clayton Medical Practice 610.687.3033
   987 Old Eagle School Rd, Wayne, PA 19087
John Clayton, Psychiatrist

Clear Brook, Inc. 570.288.6692
E-mail ....cleabrk2@epix.net
   1100 East Northampton Street, Wilkes Barre,
   PA 18702
Mr. Thomas Housenick, Accreditation Manager
Joint Commission accredited organization.

Clovis Medical Practice 215.568.1380
   2052 Sansom St, Philadelphia, PA 19103-4417
William Clovis, Md, Psychiatrist

Cohen Medical Practice 215.355.8244
Fax 215.355.8018
   1234 Bridgetown Pike, Feasterville Trevose,
   PA 19053-2208
Rona Cohen, MD, Psychiatrist

Cohen Medical Practice 610.667.2212
Fax 314.362.7017
E-mail ....kdcohen@verizon.net
   191 Presidential Blvd Ste 116, Bala Cynwyd,
   PA 19004-1215
Kenneth Cohen, Psychiatrist

Community Behavioral Health 215.413.3100
Fax 215.413.3240
Web ....www.phila-bhs.org
   801 Market St Ste 7, Philadelphia, PA 19107
Nancy Lucas, CEO

Community Care Behavorial Health 717.731.3600
Web ....www.ccbh.com
   112 Washington Pl, Camp Hill, PA 17011
Jim Myers, Director

Community Care Behavorial Health 717.731.3649
Web ....www.ccbh.com
E-mail ....hauckk@ccbh.com
   1200 Camp Hill Byp Ste 100, Camp Hill,
   PA 17011-3700
Karen Hauck, Administrator

Community Care Behavorial Health 717.731.3645
Web ....www.ccbh.com
E-mail ....grandaj@ccbh.com
   1 Chatham Ctr, Ste 700, Pittsburgh, PA 15219-3457
Janice Granda, Administrator

Community Specialists Corporation 412.885.5200
Fax 412.885.3895
Web ....www.theacademysystem.com
   900 Agnew Road, Pittsburgh, PA 15227
CARF accredited programs available.

Concern Professional Svcs 610.384.8733
Fax 610.380.1704
E-mail ....ggirlamo@concern4kids.org
   1225 W Lincoln Hwy, Coatesville, PA 19320-1858
Greg Girolamo, Adminstrator

Confidential Counseling 570.403.5080
Fax 570.403.5079
   359 S Mountain Blvd, Mountain Top, PA 18707
Nilesh Baxi, Psychiatrist

Connellsville Counseling & Psychological Services,
LLC 724.626.8420
Fax 724.628.0898
Web ....www.connellsvillecounseling.com
   416 South Pittsburgh Street, Connellsville, PA 15425
COA accredited organization.

Cooney Medical Practice 610.645.7520
Fax 610.853.9947
Web ....www.mainlinehealth.org
E-mail ....marinac@mlhs.org
   401 Pilgrim Ln, Drexel Hill, PA 19026
Marina Cooney, Psychiatrist

Cooper Psychological 610.821.9422
Fax 610.820.6308
   1259 S Cedar Crest Blvd Rear 115, Allentown,
   PA 18103-6378
Janice Cooper, Director

Corbman Medical Practice 215.572.7212
   8302 Old York Rd Ste B14, Elkins Park,
   PA 19027-1573
Gene Corbman, Psychiatrist

Cornell Abraxas Leadership Development
Program 717.749.7440
Fax 717.749.3551
Web ....www.abraxasyfs.com
   10058 S Mountain Rd, South Mountain,
   PA 17261-0900
Craig Schmidt, Director

Cornerstone Family Health Pc **570.326.4118**
Fax 570.326.5533
E-mail ....connerstone@fpcdoctors.com
1205 Grampian Blvd Ste 3C, Williamsport,
PA 17701-1992
David Rising, Director

Council For Relationships **610.254.9238**
PO Box 209, Devon, PA 19333-0209
Ingeborg Damatra, Md, Psychiatrist

Council Rock School Dist. **215.944.2957**
1090 Eagle Rd, Newtown, PA 18940-2818
Cecilia Landsberg, School Pyschologist

Counseling & Rehabilitation Inc **610.376.3390**
1150 Berkshire Blvd Ste 245, Reading,
PA 19610-1294
Mark Gehman, Administrator

Ctr for Research on Youth and Social
Policy **215.898.2229**
Fax 215.573.2791
Web ....www.upenn.edu/crysp
E-mail ....crysp@ssw.upenn.edu
3815 Walnut St, University of Pennsylvania,
Philadelphia, PA 19104-3604
Richard J. Gelles, Phd, Dean Of Social Work/Director

Ctr For Self Realization **717.392.6003**
510 N Duke St, Lancaster, PA 17602-2208
Peter Pranckun, Psychiatrist

Curran Medical Practice **610.642.3255**
Web ....www.curranmarilynr.com
1124 Indian Creek Rd, Wynnewood, PA 19096-3409
Maryilyn Curran, MD, Psychiatrist

Curran Medical Practice **610.644.6263**
Web ....www.curranmarilynr.com
E-mail ....mcurran@curranmarilynr.com
147 W Lancaster Ave, Paoli, PA 19301-1740
Marilyn Curran, Psychiatrist

Dahle Medical Practice **717.652.0799**
12 S Mountain Rd, Harrisburg, PA 17112-2647
Ralph Dahle, Psychiatrist

Dante Medical Practice **610.667.5448**
321 Berkley Rd, Merion Station, PA 19066-1403
Lee Dante, MD, Psychiatrist

Dauler Medical Practice **814.234.1139**
212 E Mitchell Ave, State College, PA 16803-3654
Thomas Dauller, Psychiatrist

David C Norris Pc **412.578.4614**
4815 Liberty Ave ste 333, Pittsburgh, PA 15224-2156
David Norris, Psychiatrist

De La Salle Vocational **215.464.0344**
Fax 215.638.3767
Web ....www.chs-adphila.org
E-mail ....jlogan@chs-adphila.org
1265 Street Rd, Bensalem, PA 19020-4600
James Logan, Director

Della Badia Medical Practice **610.566.0886**
255 S 17th St, Lansdowne, PA 19103
Eugene Della Badia, Md, Psychiatrist

Delphia Management Corp **717.846.5139**
Fax 717.854.9494
Web ....www.yorkareahg.org
E-mail ....info@yorkareahg.org
118 N George St, York, PA 17401
Penelope Myers, Director

Denniston Medical Practice **814.456.1863**
150 E 8th St Ste A, Erie, PA 16501-1270
Baron Denniston, Md, Pyschiatrist

Desmond Medical Practice **215.362.2161**
E-mail ....robertedes@comcast.net
100 W Main St Ste 512, Lansdale, PA 19446-2020
Robert Desmond, Psychiatrist

Devereux Children's Behavioral Health
Services **484.595.6733**
Web ....www.devereux.org
E-mail ....mhetting@devereux.org
655 Sugartown Road, Malvern, PA 19355-0297
Mrs. Mary Lou Hettinger, Accreditation Manager
Joint Commission accredited organization.

Devereux Kanner Ctr **610.431.8100**
Fax 610.430.0567
Web ....www.devereux.org
390 E Boot Rd, West Chester, PA 19380-1222
Melanie Biedler, Executive Director

Devereux Pocono **570.676.3237**
Fax 570.676.4792
Web ....www.devereuxpocono.org
E-mail ....jgething@devereux.org
1547 Mill Creek Rd, Newfoundland, PA 18445-5239
Mary Seeley, Executive Director

Di Giacomo Psychiatric Assoc **610.649.6904**
121 Coulter Ave Ste 108, Ardmore, PA 19003-2418
Joseph Di Giacomo, Md, Psychiatrist

Di Ienno Medical Practice **215.885.1902**
25 Washington Ln, Wyncote, PA 19095
Joseph Dienno, Psychiatrist

Dimartini Medical Practice **412.383.3166**
Web ....www.upmc.edu
E-mail ....dimartiniaf@upmc.edu
3811 Ohara St, # 537, Pittsburgh, PA 15213-2593
Andrea Dimartini, MD, Psychiatrist

Diven Medical Practice **412.563.5777**
520 Washington Rd Ste 203, Pittsburgh,
PA 15228-2816
Judith Diven, Md, Psychiatrist

Diversified Treatment Alternatives, Inc. **570.523.3457**
E-mail ....rbabiz@ptd.net
148 Fairfield Road, Lewisburg, PA 17837
Mr. Richard Armstrong, Accreditation Manager
Joint Commission accredited organization.

Doberczak Medical Practice **215.224.3330**
Fax 215.348.9722
7900 Old York Rd, Elkins Park, PA 19027
Bohdan Doberczak, Psychiatrist

Don Guanella School **610.543.1418**
Fax 610.328.2136
E-mail ....paulholmes@servantsofcharity.org
1797 S Sproul Rd, Springfield, PA 19064-1137
Paul Holmes, Residential Coordinator

Dormont Medical Practice **215.576.8281**
1245 Highland Ave Ste 201, Abington,
PA 19001-3723
Paul Dormont, Psychiatrist

Doyle Medical Practice **215.567.4335**
Fax 215.567.4337
E-mail ....hadoylemd@comcast.net
230 S 22Nd St, Philadelphia, PA 19103-5520
Harry Doyle, Md, Psychiatrist

Dr Robin Lowey & Assoc **215.625.9655**
Fax 215.625.8524
Web ....www.drlowey.com
E-mail ....loweyassoc@aol.com
1518 walnut st ste 307, Philadelphia, PA 19102
Robin Lowey, Director

Drexel University **215.762.6922**
Fax 215.762.7889
Web ....www.drexel.edu
E-mail ....kevin.drab@drexel.edu
1016 Hunters Ln, Oreland, PA 19075-2320
Kevin Drab, Director

Drexel University Dept of Psychology **215.762.7205**
Fax 215.762.8625
Web ....www.thinkingchild.com
E-mail ....mshure@drexel.edu
245 N 15th St, # MS626, Philadelphia, PA 19102
Myrna B. Shure, Professor of Psychology

Dreyfus Medical Practice **215.545.1566**
E-mail ....rdrey001@yahoo.com
1315 Walnut St, Philadelphia, PA 19107
Robert Dreyfus, Md, Psychiatrist

Drm Inc **610.520.7775**
Web ....www.drmarbys.com
1062 E Lancaster Ave, Bryn Mawr, PA 19010-1568
Patti Mcandrews, Director

Dunbar Medical Practice **610.344.0911**
1503 Mcdaniel Dr, West Chester, PA 19380-7035
Nancy Dunbar, Md, Psychiatrist

Early Psychiatric & Counseling **570.674.3939**
PO Box 100, Mountain Top, PA 18707-0100
Shafiq Rahman, Psychiatrist

Eastern Montgomery **215.572.5400**
Fax 215.572.1555
E-mail ....msnyter@aol.com
115 E Glenside Ave, Ste 16, Glenside, PA 19038-4618
C Michael Snyter, Psychiatrist

Edward L Schacht & Assoc **215.628.2475**
PO Box 729, Blue Bell, PA 19422-0729
Edward Schacht, MD, Psychiatrist

EIHAB Human Services, Inc. **570.388.6155**
Web ....www.dioceseofscranton.org
E-mail ....catkinson@eihab.org
1200 SR 92 South, Tunkhannock, PA 18657
Ms. Christi Atkinson, Accreditation Manager
Joint Commission accredited organization.

Eisler Medical Practice **724.794.5678**
605 Kelly Blvd, Slippery Rock, PA 16057-8523
Robert Eisler, MD, Psychiatrist

Elizabethtown College **717.361.1000**
E-mail ....rankins@etown.edu
1 Alpha Dr, Elizabethtown, PA 17022-2298
Stephanie Rankin, Director

Eric W Fine Assoc **215.884.0258**
351 River Birch Cir, Elkins Park, PA 19027-1338
Eric Fine, Psychiatrist

Fairmount Behavioral Health System **215.487.4000**
Web ....www.fairmountbhs.com
E-mail ....kendall.adkins@uhsinc.com
561 Fairthorne Avenue, Philadelphia, PA 19128
Ms. Kendall Adkins, Accreditation Manager
Joint Commission accredited organization.

Family Behavioral Resources **724.438.4960**
Fax 724.438.1809
Web ....www.familybehavioralresources.com
253 S Mount Vernon Ave, Uniontown, PA 15401
Ben Paul Brinkley, Psychiatrist

Family Behavioral Resources **724.861.4700**
Fax 724.861.0444
Web ....www.familybehavioralresources.com
137 Mathews Street, Suite 1800, Greensburg,
PA 15601
CARF accredited programs available.

Family Svcs Of Western Pa **724.834.7830**
Fax 724.834.8395
Web ....www.fswp.org
E-mail ....swankw@fswp.org
104 W 4Th St, Greensburg, PA 15601-2947
Wendy Swank, Director

Feldman Medical Practice **215.546.1444**
1528 Walnut St Ste 1404, Philadelphia,
PA 19102-3610
Philp Feldman, Psychiatrist

Pennsylvania

Felins Medical Practice **570.969.1454**
426 Mulberry St Ste 412, Scranton, PA 18503-1531
Kelly Felins, MD, Psychiatrist

Fenichel Medical Practice **610.649.8940**
210 Kent Rd, Ardmore, PA 19003-3304
Gladys Fenichel, Md, Psychiatrist

Fischer Newell & Ruth **610.525.2425**
658 Black Rock Rd, Bryn Mawr, PA 19010-1802
Newell Fischer, MD, Psychiatrist

Fisher Medical Practice **215.561.0850**
2400 Chestnut St, Philadelphia, PA 19103
Fredrick Fisher, Md, Psychiatirst

Fisher Medical Practice **610.527.4930**
23 E Wynnewood Rd, Wynnewood, PA 19096
Frederick Fisher, Psychiatrist

Fishkin Medical Practice **610.667.3789**
171 Gramercy Rd, Bala Cynwyd, PA 19004-2904
Ralph Fishkin, Psychiatrist

Flaxenberg Medical Practice **610.645.0282**
E-mail ....flaxenburg@hotmail.com
385 Lancaster Ave Ste 208, Haverford,
PA 19041-1576
Gary Flaxenberg, MD, Psychiatrist

Florence Child Guidance Ctr **610.432.0521**
Fax 610.432.2692
Web ....www.pinebrookservices.org
E-mail ....dhoke@pinebrookservices.org
402 N Fulton St, Allentown, PA 18102-2002
David Hoke, Director

Foster Medical Practice **412.362.2777**
401 Shady Ave Ste C202, Pittsburgh, PA 15206-4800
Howard Foster, MD, Psychiatrist

Foundations Behavioral Health **215.345.0444**
Fax 215.345.7445
Web ....www.fbh.com
E-mail ....katherine.chapman@uhsinc.com
833 E Butler Ave, Doylestown, PA 18901-2280
Tracy Pasternak, Director Of Clinical Assessment Center

Friends Behavioral Health System, LP **215.831.4600**
Web ....www.friendshospital.com
E-mail ....davide.rawal@uhsinc.com
4641 Roosevelt Boulevard, Philadelphia,
PA 19124-2399
Mr. Davide Rawal, Accreditation Manager
Joint Commission accredited organization.

**Gateway Rehabilitation Center / Genesis
Division** **412.766.8700**
Web ....www.gatewayrehab.org
E-mail ....pamela.ramsey@gatewayrehab.org
311 Rouser Road, Moon Township, PA 15108
Ms. Pamela Ramsey, Accreditation Manager
Joint Commission accredited organization.

**Gaudenzia Chambers Hill Adolescent
Program** **717.561.0400**
Fax 717.561.0896
Web ....www.gaudenzia.org
E-mail ....vcliette@gaudenzia.org
3740 Chambers Hill Rd, Harrisburg, PA 17111-1510
Vernon Cliette, Program Director

Geisinger Medical Center **570.271.6211**
Web ....www.geisinger.org
E-mail ....kkieselhorst@geisinger.edu
100 North Academy Avenue, Danville, PA 17822
Mrs. Kessey Kieselhorst, Accreditation Manager
Joint Commission accredited organization.

Glade Run Lutheran Services **724.452.4453**
Web ....www.gladerun.org
E-mail ....bdalmagro@gladerun.org
Green Lane and Beaver Road, Zelienople, PA 16063
Mrs. Beth Dalmagro, Accreditation Manager
Joint Commission accredited organization.

Go-Group **412.208.4000**
Fax 412.227.2720
Web ....www.gogroup.com
2840 Liberty Ave, 3rd Floor, Pittsburgh, PA 15222
John Swatzberg, Vp, Youth Services

**Greater Philadelphia Health Action, Inc.
(GPHA)** **215.925.2400**
Web ....www.gphainc.org
E-mail ....jgibbs@gphainc.org
432 North 6th Street, Philadelphia, PA 19123
Ms. Jennifer Gibbs, Accreditation Manager
Joint Commission accredited organization.

Harborcreek Youth Services **814.899.7664**
Fax 814.899.3075
Web ....www.hys-erie.org
5712 Iroquois Avenue, Harborcreek, PA 16421
COA accredited organization.

Hoffman Homes, Inc. **717.359.7148**
Web ....hoffmanhomes.com
E-mail ....djohnston@hoffmanhomes.com
815 Orphanage Road, Littlestown, PA 17340
Mrs. Deborah Johnston, Accreditation Manager
Joint Commission accredited organization.

Holcomb Behavioral Health Systems **610.363.1488**
E-mail ....bdifabio@holcombbhs.org
835 Springdale Drive Suite 100, Exton, PA 19341
Mr. William DiFabio, Accreditation Manager
Joint Commission accredited organization.

Holy Family Institute **412.766.4030**
Fax 412.766.0476
Web ....www.hfi-pgh.org
8235 Ohio River Boulevard, Pittsburgh,
PA 15202-1594
COA accredited organization.

Kids Count, Incorporated **724.284.0076**
Fax 724.284.9729
Web ....www.kidscountfamilypsychological.com
403 West Jefferson Street, Butler, PA 16001
CARF accredited programs available.

**KidsPeace National Centers, Inc/KidsPeace Children's
Hosp** **610.799.8000**
Web ....www.kidspeace.org
E-mail ....espissza@kidspeace.org
4085 Independence Drive, Schnecksville, PA 18078
Mr. Edward Spisszak, Accreditation Manager
Joint Commission accredited organization.

Laughlin Children's Ctr **412.741.4087**
Fax 412.741.6808
Web ....www.laughlincenter.org
424 Frederick Ave, Sewickley, PA 15143-1572
Doug Florey, Executive Director

Lehigh Valley Hospital **610.402.8000**
Web ....www.lvh.org
E-mail ....robin.anthony@lvh.com
1200 S Cedar Crest Boulevard, Allentown, PA 18105
Mrs. Robin Anthony, Accreditation Manager
Joint Commission accredited organization.

Live Well Services, Inc. **215.968.7600**
Web ....www.livewellservicesinc.com
E-mail ....khaenle@live.com
203 Floral Vale Blvd, Yardley, PA 19067
Ms. Kim Haenle, Accreditation Manager
Joint Commission accredited organization.

Livengrin Foundation, Inc. **215.638.5200**
Web ....www.livengrin.org
E-mail ....mwoods@livengrin.org
4833 Hulmeville Road, Bensalem, PA 19020-3099
Ms. Mary Jane Woods, Accreditation Manager
Joint Commission accredited organization.

Manito Life Ctr **610.391.0689**
Web ....www.manitocenters.com
E-mail ....equus@enter.net
2160 N Cedar Crest Blvd, Allentown, PA 18104-9608
M. Lisa Schadt, Director

Mathom House **215.343.7720**
Fax 215.343.2783
Web ....www.mathomhousecare.com
E-mail ....dattryde@mathomhousecare.com
1740 S Easton Rd, Doylestown, PA 18901-2885
David Attryde, Director

Melmark School **610.353.1726**
Fax 610.353.4956
Web ....www.melmark.org
E-mail ....travismccoy@melmark.org
2600 Wayland Rd, Berwyn, PA 19312-2313
Travis Mccoy, Director Of Education

Middle Creek **724.537.4667**
Fax 724.539.7412
E-mail ....stevem@adelphoivillage.com
1116 Village Way, Latrobe, PA 15644
Steve Mortimer, Director Of Male Division

MMC Warwick House **215.491.7404**
Fax 215.491.7405
E-mail ....jfriedman@warwickfamilyservices.com
1460 Meetinghouse Rd, Warminster, PA 18974-1070
Jeffrey Friedman, Phd, Director

NorthEast Treatment Centers **215.451.7000**
Fax 215.451.7110
Web ....www.net-centers.org
499 North Fifth Street, Suite A, Philadelphia,
PA 19123
CARF accredited programs available.

Northern Tier Children's Home **814.334.5226**
Fax 814.334.8006
E-mail ....ntch_finance1@yahoo.com
4309 State Rte 49, Harrison Valley, PA 16927
Fern Burdick, Administrator

**Nulton Diagnostic and Treatment Center,
PC** **814.262.0025**
Web ....www.nulton.com
E-mail ....ljnphd@nulton.com
214 College Park Plaza, Johnstown, PA 15904
Dr. Larry Nulton, Accreditation Manager
Joint Commission accredited organization.

OMNI Health Services, Inc. **215.997.2000**
Fax 215.997.2282
Web ....www.omhsi.com
595 Bethlehem Pike, Suite 106, Heritage Executive
Campus, Montgomeryville, PA 18936-9710
CARF accredited programs available.

**Outside In School of Experiential Education,
Inc.** **724.837.1518**
Fax 724.837.0801
Web ....www.outsideinschool.com
226 Donohoe Road, Suite 111, Greensburg,
PA 15601
CARF accredited programs available.

Pamela Ralph MD PC Inc **484.472.7430**
Web ....www.spectrumbehavioralservices.com
E-mail ....pamela.ralphmd@verizon.net
1489 Baltimore Pike, Springfield, PA 19064
Ms. Pamela Ralph, Accreditation Manager
Joint Commission accredited organization.

Paoletta Counseling Services **724.662.7202**
Web ....paoletta.org
E-mail ....dawnh@svol.net
456 N Pitt St., Mercer, PA 16137
Ms. Dawn Hanaway, Accreditation Manager
Joint Commission accredited organization.

Parkside Recovery, Inc. **215.879.6116**
Fax 215.594.4304
Web ....www.nhsonline.org
　5000 Parkside Avenue, Philadelphia, PA 19131
　COA accredited organization.

PathWays PA, Inc. **610.543.5022**
Fax 610.543.1549
Web ....www.pathwayspa.org
　310 Amosland Road, Holmes, PA 19043
　COA accredited organization.

Penn Psychiatric Center **610.917.2200**
Fax 610.917.2360
　601 Gay Street, Suite 6, Phoenixville, PA 19460
　CARF accredited programs available.

Pennsylvania Clinical Schools **610.486.0778**
Fax 610.486.0751
Web ....www.uhsinc.com
　1830 Towerview Drive, Coatesville, PA 19320
　CARF accredited programs available.

Perseus House, Inc. **814.480.5900**
Web ....perseushouse.org
E-mail ....mdiplacido@perseushouse.org
　1511 Peach Street, Erie, PA 16501
　Mr. Mark DiPlacido, Accreditation Manager
　Joint Commission accredited organization.

Personal Solutions, Inc **814.623.5009**
Fax 814.623.5217
Web ....www.personalsolutionsinc.org
E-mail ....dhousel@personalsolutionsinc.org
　145 Clark Bldg. Road, Suite 5, Bedford, PA 15522
　Dawn Housel, Executive Director

Philhaven **717.273.8871**
Web ....www.philhaven.org
E-mail ....ralbert@philhaven.org
　283 South Butler Road, Mount Gretna, PA 17064
　Mr. Russ Albert, Accreditation Manager
　Joint Commission accredited organization.

Philhaven **717.735.7770**
Fax 717.735.7779
Web ....www.philhaven.org
　780 Eden Rd Ste 3, Lancaster, PA 17601
　Pam Gochenaur, Supervisor

Philhaven Harrisburg **717.230.9622**
Fax 717.230.9627
Web ....www.philhaven.org
E-mail ....emasciulli@philhaven.com
　2717 N Front St, Harrisburg, PA 17110-1221
　Emily Masciulli, Director

Philhaven Hospital **717.653.9359**
Fax 717.653.6357
Web ....www.philhaven.org
　422 Cloverleaf Rd, Elizabethtown, PA 17022-8818
　Philip Heff, CEO

Philhaven Outpatient Ctr **717.738.1125**
Fax 717.738.0606
Web ....www.philhaven.org
E-mail ....lyutzy@philhaven.com
　194 N Reading Rd, Ephrata, PA 17522
　Laverne Yutzy, CEO

Presbyterian Children's Village Services **610.525.5400**
Web ....pcv.org
E-mail ....nhouyoux@pcv.org
　452 South Roberts Road, Bryn Mawr, PA 19010
　Ms. Nancy Houyoux, Accreditation Manager
　Joint Commission accredited organization.

Pressley Ridge **412.321.6995**
Fax 412.321.5313
Web ....www.pressleyridge.org
E-mail ....scole@pressleyridge.org
　530 Marshall Ave, Pittsburgh, PA 15214-3098
　Suzanne Cole, President/CEO

Pressley Ridge **717.845.6624**
Fax 717.845.6626
Web ....www.fandcs.org
　141 E Market St, York, PA 17401-1221
　Diane Bate-Sier, Director

Pressley Ridge **717.238.8118**
Fax 717.238.8140
Web ....www.pressleyridge.org
　121 Locust St, Harrisburg, PA 17101-1411
　Adam Miller, Director

Prison **610.208.4800**
Fax 610.208.4848
　1287 County Welfare Rd, Leesport, PA 19533-9397
　Beth Miller, Director

Prison **717.245.8767**
Fax 717.245.8794
　1101 Claremont Rd, Carlisle, PA 17015-8882
　Michael Carey, Deputy Wardon

Progressions Companies, Inc. **610.941.3390**
Fax 610.941.3391
Web ....www.theprogressionscompanies.com
E-mail ....eritacco@progressionscomp.com
　521 Plymouth Road, Suite 106, Door F, Plymouth
　Meeting, PA 19462
　Ernie Ritacco, Executive Director
　CARF accredited programs available.

Psychiatric Care Systems, PC **724.941.4070**
E-mail ....jayes@pcs-pc.com
　110 Hidden Valley Road, McMurray, PA 15317
　Ms. Jaye Schweitzer, Accreditation Manager
　Joint Commission accredited organization.

Pyramid Healthcare, Inc. **814.940.0407**
Web ....www.PyramidHealthcarePA.com
E-mail ....rknab@atlanticbbn.net
　270 Lakemont Park Blvd., Altoona, PA 16602
　Mr. Rick Knab, Accreditation Manager
　Joint Commission accredited organization.

Red Rock Job Corps Ctr **570.477.2221**
Fax 570.477.3046
Web ....www.dpw.state.pa.us
　RR 487 Box 218, Lopez, PA 18628
　Kelly King, Center Director

Renfrew Ctr **877.367.3383**
Fax 215.482.7390
Web ....www.refrewcenter.com
E-mail ....foundation@renfrew.org
　475 Spring Ln, Philadelphia, PA 19128-3918
　Susan Ice, Director

Sarah A. Reed Children's Center **814.838.1954**
Web ....www.sarahreed.org
E-mail ....mdexter@sarahreed.org
　2445 West 34th Street, Erie, PA 16506
　Mrs. Marlene Dexter, Accreditation Manager
　Joint Commission accredited organization.

Sarah A. Reed Early Intervention Ctr **814.453.4309**
Fax 814.459.1191
E-mail ....dwalsh@sarahreed.org
　1020 E 10th St, Erie, PA 16503
　Dennis Walsh, Vice President

Service Access and Management, Inc. **610.236.0530**
Fax 610.236.4894
Web ....http://www.sam-inc.org
　19 North Sixth Street, Suite 300, Reading, PA 19601
　CARF accredited programs available.

Sharon Regional Health System **724.983.3911**
Web ....www.sharonregional.com
E-mail ....gcatterson@srhs-pa.org
　740 East State Street, Sharon, PA 16146
　Mrs. Virginia Catterson, Accreditation Manager
　Joint Commission accredited organization.

Shawnee Academy **570.420.8601**
Web ....www.shawneeacademy.org
E-mail ....rspangler@shawneeacademy.org
　River Road, Minisink Hills, PA 18341
　Miss Robena Spangler, Accreditation Manager
　Joint Commission accredited organization.

Silver Springs - Martin Luther School **610.825.4440**
Web ....www.silver-springs.org
E-mail ....rbartelt@silver-springs.org
　512 West Township Line Road, Plymouth Meeting,
　PA 19462-1001
　Mr. Robert Bartelt, Accreditation Manager
　Joint Commission accredited organization.

Southwood Psychiatric Hospital **412.257.2290**
E-mail ....kim.lira@yfcs.com
　2575 Boyce Plaza Road, Pittsburgh, PA 15241
　Ms. Kim Lira, Accreditation Manager
　Joint Commission accredited organization.

St. Francis - St. Joseph Homes for Children **215.638.9310**
Fax 215.244.0216
Web ....www.sfsj.org
　3400 Bristol Pike, Bensalem, PA 19020
　COA accredited organization.

St. Michael's School **570.388.6155**
Fax 570.388.6979
E-mail ....jonathan.wast@eihab.org
　Route 92 Hoban Heights, Tunkhannock, PA 18657
　Jonathan Wast, Director

St. Michael's School, Inc. **570.345.1160**
Fax 570.345.6307
E-mail ....info@stmichaelsmd.org
　25 Oak Grove Rd, Pine Grove, PA 17963
　Andy Barzaly, Director

Stairways Behavioral Health **814.453.5806**
Web ....www.stairwaysbh.org
E-mail ....rldowling@stairwaysbh.org
　2185 West 8th Street, Erie, PA 16505
　Ms. Robin Dowling, Accreditation Manager
　Joint Commission accredited organization.

Step By Step, Inc. **570.829.3477**
Fax 570.829.4090
Web ....www.stepbystepusa.com
　744 Kidder Street, Cross Valley Commons,
　Wilkes-Barre, PA 18702
　CARF accredited programs available.

The Bradley Center, Inc. **412.788.8219**
Web ....www.thebradleycenter.org
E-mail ....mgeorges@thebradleycenter.org
　5180 Campbells Run Road, Pittsburgh, PA 15205
　Ms. Megan Georges, Accreditation Manager
　Joint Commission accredited organization.

The Bradley Ctr **412.787.6140**
Fax 412.787.6147
Web ....www.thebradleycenter.org
E-mail ....lfox@thebradleycenter.org
　5180 Kimbles Run Rd., Pittsburgh, PA 15205
　Lisa Fox, CEO

The Bridge **215.342.5000**
Web ....www.phmc.org
E-mail ....mogden@phmc.org
　8400 Pine Road, Philadelphia, PA 19111
　Mr. Michael Ogden, Accreditation Manager
　Joint Commission accredited organization.

The Children's Home of Reading **610.478.8266**
Fax 610.478.8094
Web ....www.childrenshomeofrdg.org
E-mail ....vlasorsa@childrenshomeofrdg.org
　1010 Centre Ave, Reading, PA 19601-1408
　Vincent Lasorsa, President/CEO

Pennsylvania

The Children's Hospital of Philadelphia 215.590.1000
Web ....www.chop.edu
E-mail ....cassidyk@email.chop.edu
    34th Street and Civic Center Boulevard, Philadelphia, PA 19104
    Ms. Kim Cassidy, Accreditation Manager
    Joint Commission accredited organization.

The Horsham Clinic 215.643.7800
Web ....www.horshamclinic.com
E-mail ....linda.starr@uhsinc.com
    722 East Butler Pike, Ambler, PA 19002
    Ms. Linda Starr, Accreditation Manager
    Joint Commission accredited organization.

The Mars Home for Youth 724.625.3141
Fax 724.625.2226
Web ....www.marshomeforyouth.org
E-mail ....jazubryd@mhy-mars.org
    521 Route 228, Mars, PA 16046-3123
    Martin Harris, Executive Director

The Meadows Psychiatric Center 814.364.2161
Web ....www.uhsinc.com
E-mail ....cherie.lawn@uhsinc.com
    132 The Meadows Drive, Centre Hall, PA 16828
    Ms. Cherie Lawn, Accreditation Manager
    Joint Commission accredited organization.

The Reading Hospital and Medical Center 610.988.8000
Web ....readinghospital.org
E-mail ....karpovichk@readinghospital.org
    Sixth Avenue and Spruce Street, West Reading, PA 19611
    Mrs. Karen Karpovich, Accreditation Manager
    Joint Commission accredited organization.

The Renfrew Centers, Inc. 215.482.5353
Web ....www.renfrewcenter.com
E-mail ....dbuchter@renfrewcenter.com
    475 Spring Lane, Philadelphia, PA 19128
    Ms. Diane Buchter, Accreditation Manager
    Joint Commission accredited organization.

The Special Kids Network 800.986.4550
Fax 717.441.5315
Web ....www.helpinpa.state.pa.us
    1011 Mumma Rd, Ste 100, Lemoyne, PA 17043-1143

The Watson Institute Friendship Academy 412.361.2801
Fax 412.361.6775
Web ....www.thewatsoninstitute.org
    751 N. Negley Avenue, Pittsburgh, PA 15206
    COA accredited organization.

TODAY, Inc. 215.968.4713
Web ....www.todayinc.org
E-mail ....jhowell@todayinc.org
    1990 North Woodbourne Road, Newtown, PA 18940
    Dr. John Howell, Accreditation Manager
    Joint Commission accredited organization.

Tree of Life Professional Behavioral Services 215.533.5433
Web ....treeoflifeclinic.com
E-mail ....victor.m.vidal@gmail.com
    7040-7048 Castor Ave., Philadelphia, PA 19149
    Mr. Victor Vidal, Accreditation Manager
    Joint Commission accredited organization.

UHS of Doylestown, LLC 215.345.0444
Web ....www.fbh.com
E-mail ....abigail.halloran@uhsinc.com
    833 East Butler Avenue, Doylestown, PA 18901
    Mrs. Abigail Halloran, Accreditation Manager
    Joint Commission accredited organization.

Universal Community Behavioral Health 717.263.8272
Fax 717.263.8476
    144 S 8th St, Chambersburg, PA 17201
    Marci Hewitt, Head Of Partials

Universal Community Behavioral Health 814.353.3151
Fax 814.353.1876
    206 W High St, Bellefonte, PA 16823-1302
    Susan Henry, Office Manager

Universal Recovery Foundation 610.876.9000
Web ....keystonecenter.net
E-mail ....david.dorschu@uhsinc.com
    2001 Providence Avenue, Chester, PA 19013
    Mr. David Dorschu, Accreditation Manager
    Joint Commission accredited organization.

UPMC Presbyterian Shadyside 412.647.8788
E-mail ....conroylk@upmc.edu
    200 Lothrop Street, Pittsburgh, PA 15213
    Ms. Linda Conroy, Accreditation Manager
    Joint Commission accredited organization.

Warwick House, Inc. 215.491.7404
Web ....warwickfamilyservices.com/
E-mail ....jfriedman@warwickfamilyservices.com
    1460 Meetinghouse Rd., Warminster, PA 18974
    Dr. Jeffrey Friedman, Accreditation Manager
    Joint Commission accredited organization.

Western Pennsylvania PsyCare 724.728.8400
Web ....www.westernpapsychare.com
E-mail ....wppcbhrs@yahoo.com
    1607 3rd Street, Beaver, PA 15009
    Ms. Heather Morrow, Accreditation Manager
    Joint Commission accredited organization.

White Deer Run Inc. 570.538.2567
Web ....www.whitedeerrun.com
E-mail ....rmollica@crchealth.com
    360 White Deer Run Road, Allenwood, PA 17810
    Ms. Roseann Mollica, Accreditation Manager
    Joint Commission accredited organization.

Wordsworth 215.643.5400
Web ....www.wordsworth.org
E-mail ....cgratz@wordsworth.org
    3905 Ford Road, Philadelphia, PA 19131
    Ms. Caryn Gratz, Accreditation Manager
    Joint Commission accredited organization.

CHILDREN'S HOSPITAL

Abington Memorial Hospital 215.481.2000
    1200 Old York Rd, Abington, PA 19001
    Barbra O'Connell, Assistant Chief Opertor

Allegheny General Hospital 412.359.3131
    320 East North Ave, Pittsburgh, PA 15212
    Gregory Burfitt, Chief Executive Officer

Altoona Regional Hospital 814.889.2011
E-mail ....tzeek@altoonaregional.org
    620 Howard Ave, Altoona, PA 16601
    Tom Zeek, Nursing Director

Bryn Mawr Hospital 610.337.3000
Web ....www.mainlinehealth.org
    130 South Bryn Mawr Ave, Bryn Mawr, PA 19010
    Ivan Scott, Nursing Director

Chambersburg Hospital 717.267.3000
E-mail ....info@summithealth.org
    112 N Seventh St, Chambersburg, PA 17201
    Norm Nephtein, Director

Childrens Hospital of Philadelphia 215.590.1000
    34th St & Civic Center Blvd, Philadelphia, PA 19104
    Dr. Steven Altschuler, Chief Executive Officer

Community Medical Center 570.969.8000
    1800 Mulberry St, Scranton, PA 18510

Conemaugh Memorial Medical Center 814.534.9000
    1086 Franklin St, Johnstown, PA 15905
    Scott Pecker, Chief Executive Officer

Crozer Chester Medical Center 610.447.2000
    One Medical Center Blvd, Chester, PA 19013

Elk Regional Health Center 814.788.8000
    763 Johnsonburg Rd, Saint Marys, PA 15857
    Gregory Bauer, Chief Executive Officer

Ephrata Community Hospital 717.733.0311
    169 Martin Ave, Ephrata, PA 17522
    John M Corter Jr., Chief Executive Officer

Evangelical Community Hospital 570.522.2000
    One Hospital Dr, Lewisburg, PA 17837
    Michael Okeefe, President

Excela Latrobe Hospital 724.537.1000
    One Mellon Way, Latrobe, PA 15650
    Rob Rogalski, Chief Executive Officer

Excela Westmoreland Hospital 724.832.4000
    532 West Pittsburgh St, Greensburg, PA 15601
    Ronald Ott, President

Geisinger Medical Center 570.271.6211
    100 North Academy Ave, Danville, PA 17822
    Glenn Steele, Chief Executive Officer

Gnaden Huetten Memorial Hospital 610.377.1300
    211 North 12th St, Lehighton, PA 18235
    Lisa Johnson, Director

Good Samaritan Hospital 717.270.7500
    Fourth and Walnut St, Lebanon, PA 17042

Grand View Hospital 215.453.4000
    700 Lawn Ave, Sellersville, PA 18960

Grove City Medical Center 724.450.7000
    631 North Broad St Ext, Grove City, PA 16127
    Robert Jackson, Chief Executive Officer

Hamot Medical Center 814.877.6000
Web ....www.upmchamot.org
    201 State St, Erie, PA 16550
    Jim Donnelly, Chief Nursing Officer

Hanover Hospital 717.637.3711
    300 Highland Ave, Hanover, PA 17331
    George Kyriacou, President

Hazleton General Hospital 570.501.4000
    700 East Broad St, Hazleton, PA 18201
    James Edwards, Chief Executive Officer

Highlands Hospital 724.628.1500
    401 East Murphy Ave, Connellsville, PA 15425
    Michelle Cunnigham, Chief Executive Officer

Holy Redeemer Hospital and Medical Ctr 215.947.3000
    1648 Huntingdon Pike, Jenkintown, PA 19046
    Michael Laign, Chief Executive Officer

Hospital of the University of Pennsylva 215.662.4000
    3400 Spruce St, Philadelphia, PA 19104
    Ralph Muller, Chief Executive Officer

Indiana Regional Medical Center 724.357.7000
E-mail ....fwoofe@indianarmc.org
    835 Hospital Rd, Indiana, PA 15701
    Steve Woofe, Chief Executive Officer

J C Blair Memorial Hospital 814.643.2290
    1225 Warm Springs Ave, Huntingdon, PA 16652
    Joe Peluso, Chief Executive Officer

Lancaster General Hospital 717.544.5511
    555 North Duke St, Lancaster, PA 17604
    Thomas Beeman, Chief Executive Officer

Lehigh Valley Hospital 610.402.8000
    1200 South Cedar Crest Blvd, Allentown, PA 18105
    Ronald Swinfard, Chief Executive Officer

Lower Bucks Hospital 215.785.9200
    501 Bath Rd, Bristol, PA 19007
    Albert Mezzaroba, Chief Executive Officer

Marian Community Hospital 570.281.1000
    100 Lincoln Ave, Carbondale, PA 18407

Meadville Medical Center 814.333.5000
    751 Liberty ST, Meadville, PA 16335
    Phillip Pendal, Chief Executive Officer

Memorial Hospital 717.843.8623
Web ....www.mhyork.org
    325 South Belmont St, York, PA 17403
    Sally Dixon, Chief Executive Officer

Pennsylvania

Memorial Hospital.....................**610.431.5000**
701 East Marshall St, West Chester, PA 19380
Angela Coladonato, Nursing Director

Millcreek Community Hospital..............**814.864.4031**
5515 Peach St, Erie, PA 16509
Mary Eckert, Chief Executive Officer

Monongahela Valley Hospital...............**724.258.1000**
1163 Country Club Rd Rt 88, Monongahela,
PA 15063
Mary Lou Murt, Nursing Director

Moses Taylor Hospital......................**570.340.2100**
700 Quincy Ave, Scranton, PA 18510
Karen Murphy, Chief Executive Officer

Mount Nittany Medical Center.............**814.231.7000**
E-mail.........................jschachtner@nittany.org
1800 Park Ave, State College, PA 16803
Janet Schachtner, Nursing Director

Nason Hospital............................**814.224.2141**
105 Nason Dr, Roaring Spring, PA 16673
Garrett Hoover, Chief Executive Officer

Penn State Milton S Hershey Med Ctr.........**717.531.8521**
500 University Dr, Hershey, PA 17033
Donna Reck, Nursing Officer

Pinnacle Hospital..........................**717.782.3131**
E-mail.....................myoung@pinnaclehealth.org
111 South Front St, Harrisburg, PA 17101
Micheal Young, Chief Executive Officer

Pocono Medical Center....................**570.421.4000**
206 East Brown St, East Stroudsburg, PA 18301
Cathleen Cuck, Chief Executive Officer

Pottstown Memorial Medical Center.........**610.327.7000**
1600 East High St, Pottstown, PA 19464
Sharif Omar, Chief Executive Officer

Pottsville Medical Centre...................**570.621.5000**
420 South Jackson St, Pottsville, PA 17901
John Simodejka, Chief Executive Officer

Reading Hospital and Medical Center.........**610.988.8000**
Sixth Ave and Spruce St, West Reading, PA 19611
Kint Mathews, Chief Executive Officer

Regional Hospital.........................**570.348.7100**
746 Jefferson Ave, Scranton, PA 18501
Aaron Hazzard, Interim CEO

Robert Packer Hospital....................**570.888.6666**
1 Guthrie Square, Sayre, PA 18840
Bonnie Onofre, Director Of Nursing

Schuylkill Medical Center E Norwegian.......**570.621.4000**
700 East Norwegian St, Pottsville, PA 17901
John Fimodejak, Chief Executive Officer

Sharon Regional Hospital...................**724.983.3911**
740 East State St, Sharon, PA 16146
Jack Janoso, Chief Executive Officer

Somerset Hospital........................**814.443.5000**
225 South Center Ave, Somerset, PA 15501
Mike Farrell, Chief Executive Officer

St Clair Hospital..........................**412.942.4000**
1000 Bower Hill Rd, Pittsburgh, PA 15243
James Collins, President

St Joseph Medical Center...................**610.378.2000**
2500 Bernville Rd, Reading, PA 19605
John Morahan, Chief Executive Officer

St Lukes Hospital and Health Network.......**484.526.4000**
801 Ostrum ST, Bethlehem, PA 18015
Richard Anderson, Director

St Mary Medical Center....................**215.710.2000**
1201 Langhorne Newtown Rd, Langhorne, PA 19047
Greg Wozniak, Chief Executive Officer

St Vincent Health Center...................**814.452.5000**
232 West 25th St, Erie, PA 16544
Scott Whalen, Chief Executive Officer

Sunbury Community Hospital...............**570.286.3333**
Web.....................www.sunburyhospital.com
350 North Eleventh St, Sunbury, PA 17801
Jeff Hunt, Chief Executive Officer

The Childrens Home of Pittsburgh..........**412.441.4884**
5324 Penn Ave, Pittsburgh, PA 15224

Thomas Jefferson University Hospital.......**215.955.6000**
111 South 11th St, Philadelphia, PA 19107
Thomas Lewis, Chief Executive Officer

Tyler Memorial...........................**570.836.2161**
E-mail.........................denise_gieski@chs.net
5950 State Rte 6, Tunkhannock, PA 18657
Denise Gieski, Chief Executive Officer

Uniontown Hospital.......................**724.430.5000**
500 West Berkeley St, Uniontown, PA 15401
Paul Bacharach, President/CEO

UPMC Bedford Memorial...................**814.623.6161**
10455 Lincoln Hwy, Everett, PA 15537
Roger Winn, President

UPMC Mercy.............................**412.232.8111**
1400 Locust St, Pittsburgh, PA 15219
Will Cook, Director

UPMC Northwest.........................**814.676.7600**
100 Fairfield Dr, Seneca, PA 16346

Warren General Hospital...................**814.723.3300**
Two Crescent Park West, Warren, PA 16365

Washington Hospital......................**724.225.7000**
155 Wilson Ave, Washington, PA 15301
Gary Weinstein, President

Wayne Memorial Hospital..................**570.253.8100**
601 Park St, Honesdale, PA 18431
Dave Hoff, Chief Executive Officer

Western Pennsylvania Hospital.............**412.578.5000**
4800 Friendship Ave, Pittsburgh, PA 15224
Gregory Burfitt, Chief Executive Officer

Wilkes Barre General Hospital..............**570.829.8111**
575 North River St, Wilkes-Barre, PA 18764
Cor Catena, Chief Executive Officer

York Hospital............................**717.851.2345**
1001 South George ST, York, PA 17405
Vince Tasson, Manager

COUNSELING SERVICES

Agape Day Treatment.....................**724.684.4722**
Fax.....................................724.684.5802
E-mail.........................karrykool1@verizon.net
900 Summit Ave, Monessen, PA 15062-1744
Karen Orbin, Executive Director

Bethany Christian Svcs....................**215.376.6200**
Fax.....................................215.376.6191
Web.................................www.bethany.org
E-mail.............bcsftwashington@bethany.org
7827 Old York Rd, Elkins Park, PA 19027
Jennifer Chantz, Director

Catholic Charities........................**412.456.6999**
Fax.....................................412.456.6990
Web.................................www.ccpgh.org
212 9th St Ste 1000, Pittsburgh, PA 15222-3521

**Catholic Charities Counseling and Adoption
Svcs**.....................................**814.456.2091**
Fax.....................................814.456.1677
E-mail.............jheas@catholiccharitiesusa.org
329 W 10th St, Erie, PA 16502-1440
Joe Heas, Director

Catholic Social Svcs.......................**570.322.4220**
Fax.....................................570.662.7337
E-mail.............................bmakos@ptd.net
2100 Linn St, Williamsport, PA 17701-1965
Bernard Makos, Office Manager

Catholic Social Svcs.......................**215.587.3929**
Fax.....................................215.587.3676
E-mail.........................webmaster@adphila.org
222 N 17th St, Philadelphia, PA 19103-1202
Philis Adorno, Administrator

Catholic Social Svcs.......................**570.517.0892**
Fax.....................................570.476.6466
724A Phillips st, Stroudsburg, PA 18360-2545
Kris Kent, Executive Director

Catholic Social Svcs.......................**570.455.1521**
Fax.....................................570.455.2707
E-mail.........................neil@csshazleton.org
214 W Walnut St Ste 2, Hazleton, PA 18201-6280
Neil Oberto, Director

**Church of The Brethren Youth Svcs
(COBYS)**.................................**717.656.6580**
Fax.....................................717.656.3056
Web.................................www.cobys.org
E-mail.............................phil@cobys.net
1417 Oregon Rd, Leola, PA 17540-9754
Philip Hershey, Administrator

Community Alternatives, Inc................**724.652.2211**
Fax.....................................724.652.2557
Web.............................communityalt.org
700 Scotland Ln, New Castle, PA 16101-1368
Nick Riehl, Director

Family Guidance Ctr......................**610.374.4963**
Fax.....................................610.378.5403
Web......................www.familyguidancecenter.com
E-mail.............kmcconnell@familyguidancecenter.com
1235 Penn Ave Ste 205, Reading, PA 19610-2100
Ms. Mcconnell, Executive Director

Family Svc and Children's Aid Society........**814.677.4005**
Fax.....................................814.677.6159
E-mail.........................familyservices@usachoice.net
716 E 2nd St, Oil City, PA 16301-2330
Mary Kay Sarason, Executive Director

Jewish Family & Children's Svc..............**215.698.9950**
Fax.....................................215.698.2148
Web.................................www.jfcsphil.org
E-mail.........................jackd@jfcsphil.org
10125 Verree Rd Ste 200, Philadelphia,
PA 19116-3611
Jack Dembow, President

**KidsPeace National Centers-Foster Care & Community
Programs**................................**866.454.3773**
Fax.....................................570.287.1993
Web.................................www.kidspeace.org
480 Pierce St Ste 311, Kingston, PA 18704
Ray Culp, Executive Director For Foster Care & Community Programs

Methodist Svcs for Children & Families.......**215.877.1925**
Fax.....................................215.877.1942
E-mail.........................jshumate@methodistservices.org
4300 Monument Rd, Philadelphia, PA 19131-1690
Joan Shumate, Vp

New Foundations........................**215.203.8733**
Fax.....................................215.745.0329
E-mail.........................jleigh@newfoundations.com
7210 Risingsun Ave, Philadelphia, PA 19125-4375
Jen Leigh, Director

Open Door Intl, Inc.......................**610.372.2200**
Fax.....................................610.372.8660
Web.................................www.opendoorintl.com
E-mail.........................jcintron@opendoorintl.com
645 Penn St Ste 504, Reading, PA 19601-3539
Joel Cintron, Executive Director

**Presbyterian Children's Village - Preheim
Ctr**......................................**215.730.2240**
Fax.....................................215.724.4958
E-mail.........................polesky@pcv.org
6517 Chester Ave, Philadelphia, PA 19142-1718
Patrick Oleskey Msw, Lcsw, Director

RW Brown Community Ctr **215.763.0900**
Fax 215.763.8088
Web .... www.caringpeoplealliance.org
E-mail .... bhall@caringpeoplealliance.org
    1701 N 8th St, Philadelphia, PA 19122-2807
    Barbara Hall, Director

Tabor Children's Svcs **215.842.4800**
Fax 215.842.4809
    57 E Armat St, Philadelphia, PA 19144-2201
    William Haussman, Executive Director

Three Rivers Adoption Council **412.471.8722**
Fax 412.471.4861
Web www.3riversadopt.org
    307 4th Ave, Ste 310, Pittsburgh, PA 15222-2120
    Jacqueline D. Wilson, Executive Director

Try-Again Homes, Inc. **724.225.0510**
Fax 724.225.7210
Web .... www.tryagainhomes.org
E-mail .... tahed@verizon.net
    365 Jefferson Ave, Washington, PA 15301-4245
    Scott Hilliard, Director

CRISIS & SHELTER CARE

A Way Out-Domestic Violence **814.274.0368**
Fax 814.274.2230
E-mail .... awayout@zitomedia.net
    110 E 3rd St, Coudersport, PA 16915
    Freda Fultz, Director

A Womans Place-Domestic Violence **215.343.9241**
Fax 215.343.3411
Web .... www.awomansplace.org
E-mail .... info@awomansplace.org
    Almshouse Rd RR 611, Doylestown, PA 18901
    Donna J Byrne, Director

Alice Paul House-Domestic Violence **724.349.4444**
Fax 724.349.7883
E-mail .... execdirect@alicepaulhouse.org
    PO Box 417, Indiana, PA 15701-0417
    Lou Ann Williams, Director

Alle-Kiski Area Hope Ctr-Dom Violence **724.224.1100**
Fax 724.224.1123
Web .... www.akhopecenter.org
E-mail .... mbond@akhopecenter.org
    PO Box 67, Tarentum, PA 15084-0067
    Michelle Bond, Director

Allegheny Valley School **412.299.7777**
Fax 412.299.6701
Web .... www.avs.net
    1996 Ewings Mill Rd, Coraopolis, PA 15108-3380
    Cara King, Nursing Director

Anchor House **724.628.4386**
Fax 724.628.0221
    501 S Pittsburgh St, Connellsville, PA 15425-4014
    Lorin Zimmerman, Director

Child Sexual Abuse Ctr **610.891.5258**
Fax 610.891.0481
E-mail .... hardyp@co.delaware.pa.us
    100 W 6th St Ste 1, Media, PA 19063
    Pam Hardy, Program Director

Children's Aid Society **717.263.4159**
Fax 717.263.0073
E-mail .... cbrowne@cas1884.org
    255 Miller St, Chambersburg, PA 17201-1523
    Christopher Browne, CEO

Citizens Against Abuse **814.772.3838**
Fax 814.772.9270
E-mail .... elkcapsey@windstream.net
    28 Morgan Ave, Ridgway, PA 15853
    Billie Jo Weyant, Director

**Community Action Crossroads-Dom
Violence** **814.938.3580**
Fax 814.938.2575
Web .... www.jccap.org
E-mail .... Smclaughlin@Jccap.Org
    105 Grace Way, Punxsutawney, PA 15767-1209
    Susan G.f. Mclaughlin, Director

Crisis Ctr North-Domestic Violence **412.364.6728**
Fax 412.364.5787
E-mail .... info@crisiscenternorth.org
    PO Box 101093, Pittsburgh, PA 15237-8093
    Grace Coleman, Director

Dom Violence Intervention of Lebanon Co **717.273.7154**
Fax 717.273.6881
Web .... www.dviolc.org
E-mail .... Endabuse@Dviolc.Org
    PO Box 42, Lebanon, PA 17042-0042
    Lynn Snead, Director

Domestic Abuse Project **610.565.6272**
Fax 610.565.9911
Web .... www.dapdc.org
E-mail .... rconnolly@dapdc.org
    14 West 2nd St, Media, PA 19063
    Rita Buckey-connelly, Director

Domestic Violence Ctr of Chester Co **610.431.3546**
Fax 610.431.7121
E-mail .... dwideman-scott@dvccc.com
    PO Box 832, West Chester, PA 19382
    Dolly Wideman-scott, Director

Domestic Violence Svc of Lancaster **717.299.9677**
Fax 717.290.6855
E-mail .... dglover@dvslanc.org
    PO Box 359, Lancaster, PA 17608-0359
    Donna Glover, Director

**Domestic Violence Svcs - Cumberland-Perry
Co** **717.258.4806**
Fax 717.258.1677
Web .... www.Pa.Net
E-mail .... Exd@Pa.Net
    104 West Main Street, Mechanicsburg, PA 17055
    Debra Donahue, Director

Friendship House **570.342.8305**
Fax 570.341.9673
Web .... www.friendshiphousepa.org
    1509 Maple St, Scranton, PA 18505-2707
    Robert Angeloni, President

Glade Run Lutheran Svcs **724.452.4453**
Fax 724.452.6576
E-mail .... ctlockwood@gladerun.org
    70 W Beaver St., Zelienople, PA 16063
    Charles T. Lockwood, Executive Director

Helping All Victims In Need-Dom Violence **724.543.1180**
Fax 724.543.7410
E-mail .... jebhabin@winstream.net
    325 Arch St, Kittanning, PA 16201-0983
    Joellene Bowman, Director

Helpline **570.829.1341**
Fax 570.829.5055
Web .... www.helpline-nepa.info
E-mail .... helpline@fsawv.org
    31 W Market St, Wilkes Barre, PA 18701-1304
    Thomas Foley, Director

Holy Family Institute **412.766.4030**
Fax 412.766.5434
Web .... www.hfi-pgh.org
E-mail .... fanning.rita@hfi-pgh.org
    8235 Ohio River Blvd, Pittsburgh, PA 15202-1594
    Sister Rita Fanning, President

Huntingdon House-Domestic Violence **814.643.2801**
Fax 814.643.2419
E-mail .... huntingdonhouse@verizon.net
    401 7th St, Huntingdon, PA 16652
    Shanna Leonard, Director

**KidsPeace National Ctrs Diagnostic Acute Ctr/ Shelter
Care** **800.854.3123**
Fax 610.366.8480
Web .... www.kidspeace.org
E-mail .... admissions@kidspeace.org
    5300 Kidspeace Dr, Orefield, PA 18069-2098
    Jill Schaller, Program Manager

Laurel House-Domestic Violence **800.642.3150**
Fax 610.275.4018
E-mail .... bsturman@laurel-house.org
    PO Box 764, Norristown, PA 19404-0764
    Beth Sturman, Director

PA Heartland Chapter **814.849.2712**
Fax 814.371.1015
Web .... www.arcpaheartland.org
E-mail .... info@arcpaheartland.org
    109 N Brady St Ste 2, Dubois, PA 15801
    Robert Newell, Director

Protection From Abuse Coordinated Svcs **814.455.1774**
Fax 814.456.8841
    1702 French St, Erie, PA 16501
    Linda Lyons-king, Director

Sarah A. Reed Children's Ctr **814.838.1954**
Fax 814.835.2196
Web .... www.sarahreed.org
E-mail .... jmando@sarahreed.org
    2445 W 34th St, Erie, PA 16506-3599
    James Mando, President/CEO

Schuylkill Women In Crisis-Dom Violence **570.622.3991**
Fax 570.628.1836
E-mail .... swicagency@comcast.net
    PO Box 96, Pottsville, PA 17901-0096
    Sally Casey, Director

Stop Abuse For Everyone **814.226.8481**
Fax 814.226.5999
E-mail .... director1@csonline.net
    1302 E Main Street, Clarion, PA 16214
    Kimber McHenry, Director

Survivors, Inc **717.334.0589**
Fax 717.334.3576
E-mail .... terri@survivorsservices.org
    196 S Stratton St, Gettysburg, PA 17325
    Terri Hamerick, Director

Susquehanna Valley Women In Transition **570.523.1134**
Fax 570.524.9367
Web .... www.svwit.org
E-mail .... svwit@svwit.org
    PO Box 170, Lewisburg, PA 17837-0170
    Diane Baxley, Director

The Womens Ctr of Columbia Montour **570.784.6632**
Fax 570.784.6680
E-mail .... Womenctr1@Verizon.Net
    111 Market St, Bloomsburg, PA 17815
    Kathlene Russell, Director

Three Rivers Youth **412.441.5020**
Fax 412.441.5021
Web .... www.threeriversyouth.org
E-mail .... aaron.mickens@threeriversyouth.org
    6117 Broad St, Pittsburgh, PA 15206
    Aaron Mickens, V P Of Corporate Support

Today Inc **215.968.4713**
Fax 215.968.8742
Web .... www.todayinc.org
E-mail .... mildredk@todayinc.org
    1990 N Woodbourne Rd, Newtown, PA 18940
    Mildred Kenney, Intake Coordinator

Turning Point of Lehigh Valley **610.797.0530**
Fax 610.797.0585
Web .... www.turnigpointlv.org
E-mail .... dianez@turnigpointlv.org
    444 E Susquehanna St, Allentown, PA 18103-5144
    Diane Zanetti, Director

Valley Youth House Committee 610.820.0166
Fax 610.820.5907
Web .... www.valleyyouthhouse.org
E-mail .... development@valleyyouthhouse.org
531 Main St Unit 2, Bethlehem, PA 18018-5837
David Gilgoff, President/CEO

Victim Outreach Intervention Ctr 724.776.5910
Fax 724.776.6781
Web .... www.voiceforvictims.com
E-mail .... clarksmith@voiceforvictims.com
9527 Goehring Rd, Cranberry Twp, PA 16066
Elizabeth Clark-smith, Director

Victim Resource Ctr 888.822.6325
Fax 814.362.4638
24 W Corydon St, Bradford, PA 16701-2231
Nancy Chesnut, Director

Victims Intervention Program-Dom Vlnce 570.253.4401
Fax 570.253.1322
PO Box 986, Honesdale, PA 18431-0986
Michele Wolf, Director

Wasington Womens Shelter 724.437.2530
Fax 724.437.2543
Web .... www.womens-shelter.com
E-mail .... wwsadmin@earthlink.net
PO Box 995, Uniontown, PA 15401-0995
Michelle Robinson-ritter, Director

Women's Ctr 724.775.2032
Fax 724.775.2750
192 3rd St, Beaver, PA 15009
Jill Marsilio, Director

Womens Ctr-Dom Violence 570.748.9539
Fax 570.748.9549
Web .... www.kcnet.org
E-mail .... director@ccwcsafe.org
34 W Main St, Lock Haven, PA 17745-1218
Cindy Love, Director

Womens Resource Ctr-Dom Vlnce 814.238.7066
Fax 814.238.4449
Web .... www.ccwrc.org
140 W Nittany Ave, State College, PA 16801-4811
Anne Ard, Director

EDUCATION

Access Abilities, Inc. 724.832.8272
Fax 724.837.8278
Web .... http://www.accessabilities.org/
E-mail .... dforsha@accessabilities.org
2900 Seminary Dr, Greensburg, PA 15601
Debra Forsha, Childrens Services Director

Behavioral Health Assoc 610.379.1266
Fax 610.379.1288
Web .... www.bhaservices.com
325 Alum St Ste 2, Lehighton, PA 18235-2167
Colleen Giglotti, Executive Administrator

Carson Valley School 215.233.1960
Fax 215.233.2386
Web .... www.czca-pa.org
E-mail .... j.taafe@czca-pa.org
1419 Bethlehem Pike, Flourtown, PA 19031-1998
John Taaffe, Msw, Executive Director

Children's Aid Society 814.765.2686
Fax 814.765.6530
Web .... www.childaid.org
E-mail .... bonnief@childaid.org
1008 S 2nd St, Clearfield, PA 16830-3323
Bonnie Floro, Executive Director

Clelian Heights School for Exceptional Children 724.837.8120
Fax 724.837.6480
E-mail .... clelian@aol.com
135 Clelian Heights Ln, Greensburg, PA 15601
Sister Ritamary Schulz, Executive Director

Cray Youth and Family Svcs, Inc 724.654.5507
Fax 724.654.5546
E-mail .... dcopper@state.pa.us
332 Highland Ave, New Castle, PA 16101-3624
David Copper, Executive Director

Devereux Beneto Ctr 800.935.6789
Fax 610.251.2415
Web .... www.devereuxbeneto.org
655 Sugartown Rd, Malvern, PA 19355-3303
Walter J. Grono, Executive Director

Florence Crittenton Svcs 814.452.2740
Fax 814.452.3343
Web .... www.perseushouse.org
643 E 6th St, Erie, PA 16507-1796
Lisa Tamez, Executive Director

Friendship Academy 412.365.3800
Fax 412.361.6775
Web .... www.craigacademy.org
E-mail .... lKragness@craigacademy.org
255 S Negley Ave, Pittsburgh, PA 15206
Lauri Kragness, Program Director

Harborcreek Youth Svcs 814.899.7664
Fax 814.899.3075
Web .... www.hys-erie.org
E-mail .... jpetulla@hys-erie.org
5712 Iroquois Ave, Harborcreek, PA 16421-1009
John Petulla, CEO

Hoffman Homes, Inc 717.359.7148
Fax 717.359.2600
Web .... www.hoffmanhomes.com
E-mail .... cmsnider@hoffmanhomes.com
815 Orphanage Rd, Littlestown, PA 17340-9729
C Mitchell Smider, Executive Director

K.D. Tillotson School 412.881.2268
Fax 412.881.2263
Web .... www.acldonline.org
4900 Girard Rd, Pittsburgh, PA 15227
William Cohen, Md, Medical Director

Keystone Job Corps Ctr 570.788.1164
Fax 570.788.1119
Web .... www.jobcorps.org
E-mail .... fitzwater.tom@jobcorps.org
235 W Foothills Dr, Drums, PA 18222-2410
Jim McGee, Center Director

KidsPeace National Ctrs - Residential & Intensive Residential Treatment Programs 800.854.3123
Fax 610.799.8801
Web .... www.kidspeace.org
E-mail .... admissions@kidspeace.org
5300 Kidspeace Dr, Orefield, PA 18069-2098
Dr. Basen Shlewiet, Medical Director

Manito, Inc 717.375.4733
Fax 717.375.4336
Web .... www.manito-inc.com
E-mail .... rcw@manito.pa.net
7564 Browns Mill Rd, Chambersburg, PA 17202-9252
Robert C. Whitmore, Director

Martha Lloyd Community Svcs 570.297.2185
Fax 570.297.1019
Web .... www.marthalloyd.org
E-mail .... bmiller@marthalloyd.org
66 Lloyd Ln, Troy, PA 16947-1199
Bell Miller, CEO

Mayors Ofc of Community Svcs 215.685.3600
Fax 215.685.3601
Web .... www.phila.gov
E-mail .... otis.bullock@phila.gov
990 Spring Garden St, 7th Floor, Philadelphia, PA 19123-2606
Otis Bullock Jr., Executive Director

Middle Earth Academy 215.443.0280
Fax 215.443.0245
E-mail .... middleearthinc@aol.com
299 Jacksonville Rd, Warminster, PA 18974-4850
Elizabeth Quigley, President

Milton Hershey School 717.520.2100
Fax 717.520.2117
Web .... www.mhs-pa.org
1201 Homestead Ln, Hershey, PA 17033
Danny Warner, Senior Director

Nobel Learning Communities 610.719.0240
Fax 484.947.2004
Web .... www.nobellearning.com
E-mail .... george.bernstein@nlcinc.com
1190 Mcdermott Dr, West Chester, PA 19380-4022
George Bernstein, CEO

Orefield Hospital 800.854.3123
Fax 610.799.8801
Web .... www.kidspeace.org
5300 Kidpeace Dr, Orefield, PA 18069
Dr Basem Shlewiet, Medical Director

PA Cyber Charter School 724.643.1180
Fax 724.643.2845
Web .... www.pacyber.org
E-mail .... andrew.oberg@pacyber.org
1200 Midland Ave, Midland, PA 15059
Andrew Oberg, Executive Director

Pace School 412.244.1900
Fax 412.244.1902
Web .... www.paceschool.org
2432 Greensburg Pike, Pittsburgh, PA 15221
Karen Lamoureux, CEO

Perkiomen Valley Academy 610.754.7846
Fax 610.754.9077
Web .... www.pvacademy.org
E-mail .... genereralmail@pvacademy.org
2373 Hoffmansville Rd, Frederick, PA 19435
Nancy Limbeck, Executive Director

Phelps School 610.644.1754
Fax 610.644.6679
Web .... www.thephelpsschool.org
E-mail .... mreardon@thephelpsschol.org
583 Sugartown Rd, Malvern, PA 19355-2800
Michael Reardon, Principal

Philadelphia Job Corps Ctr 267.386.2888
Fax 215.334.3675
Web .... www.jobcorps.doltea.gov
E-mail .... earldene.lewis@jobcorp.org
2810 S 20th St, Philadelphia, PA 19145
Earldene Lewis, Center Director

Pittsburgh Job Corps Ctr 412.441.8700
Fax 412.441.1586
Web .... http://pittsburghjobcorp.gov
E-mail .... douglas.mark@jobcorps.org
7175 Highland Dr, Pittsburgh, PA 15206-1260
Mark Douglas, Center Director

Royer-Greaves School For Blind 610.644.1810
Fax 610.644.8164
Web .... www.royer-greazes.org
E-mail .... rgschool@aol.com
118 S Valley Rd, Paoli, PA 19301-1444
Joseph Coleman, Executive Director

Silver Springs Martin Luther School 610.825.4440
Fax 610.825.0392
Web .... www.silver-springs.org
E-mail .... nporter@silver-springs.org
512 Township Line Rd, Plymouth Meeting, PA 19462-1099
Nan Porter, Incharge

The Education Ctr at The Watson Institute 412.741.1800
Fax 412.741.2454
Web .... www.thewatsoninstitute.org
E-mail .... marilynh@thewatsoninstitute.org
301 Campmeeting Rd, Sewickley, PA 15143-8773
Michele Trettel, Med, Director

The Exchange Club Ctr for the Prevention of Child Abuse 610.429.0634
Fax 610.696.4476
Web ....www.familyservice/cc.us
E-mail ....ecfc@familyservice.us
310 N Matlack St, West Chester, PA 19380-2620
Voni Moore-mastovich, Program Director

The Quaker School at Horsham 215.674.2875
Fax 215.674.9913
Web ....www.quakerschool.org
E-mail ....rjoray@quakerschool.org
250 Meetinghouse Rd, Horsham, PA 19044-2168
Ruth Joray, Head Of School

Wesley Highland School 412.885.7017
Fax 412.885.3896
5250 Caste Dr, Pittsburgh, PA 15236
William Alexy, Director

Wesley-Spectrum Family Svcs 412.342.2300
Fax 412.342.2329
Web ....www.wesleyspectrum.org
221 Penn Ave, Pittsburgh, PA 15221-3097
Doug Muetzel, CEO

West Chester University Speech and Hearing Clinic 610.436.3402
Fax 610.436.3388
Web ....www.wcupa.edu
201 Carter Dr Ste 400, West Chester, PA 19383-0001
Jennifer W. Means, Slpd,ccc-slp, Coordinator

FOSTER CARE AGENCIES

Adoption Resources Center Inc 215.844.1082
Fax 215.842.9881
E-mail ....taralaw@aol.com
4701 Pine St, Philadelphia, PA 19143

Adoptions From the Heart 610.432.2384
Fax 610.432.8200
2212 Union Blvd, Allentown, PA 18109
Maxine Chalker, Executive Director

After Adoption and Parenting Services fo 215.879.4030
Fax 215.849.2322
E-mail ....elainefrankadopt@erols.com
3900 City Ave Bldg D ste 108, Philadelphia, PA 19131
Elaine Frank

Arrow Project 814.317.1614
Fax 814.317.1834
Web ....www.arrow.org
E-mail ....info@arrow.org
15 S Montgomery St, Hollidaysburg, PA 16648-1738
Mark A. Tennet, CEO

Association Puerto Ricans on the March 215.329.9580
Fax 215.329.4017
E-mail ....ruiz@apmphila.org
445 447 West Laray St, Philadelphia, PA 19140
Milda Ruiz, Chief Executive Officer

Bethanna Inc 215.355.6500
E-mail ....kkanyi@bethanna.org
1030 Second Street Pike, Holland, PA 18966

Catholic Charities 412.456.9999
Fax 412.456.0181
E-mail ....adoption@ccpgh.org
212 9th St, Pittsburgh, PA 15222
Susan Rauscher, Executive Director

Catholic Charities Adoption Services Spe 717.564.7115
Fax 717.564.7180
E-mail ....kbolton@hbgdiocese.org
939 E park Dr, Ste 103, Harrisburg, PA 17111
K Bolton, Manager

Catholic Charities Diocese of Allentown 610.435.1541
Fax 610.435.4367
E-mail ....rnicolella@allentowndiocese.org
530 Union Blvd, Allentown, PA 18109
Rob Nicolella, Administrator

Catholic Charities of Greensburg 724.837.1840
711 East Pittsburgh St, Greensburg, PA 15601
Monsignor Raymond Riffle, Managing Director

Catholic Social Services 215.854.7050
Fax 215.854.7056
227 North 17th St, Philadelphia, PA 19103

Catholic Social Services 800.465.0578
2100 Linn St, Williamsport, PA 17701

Community Svc Foundation 215.840.9515
Fax 215.348.1563
Web ....www.csfbuxmont.org
E-mail ....rkardon@cfsbuxmont.org
252 W Swamp Rd Ste 38, Doylestown, PA 18901-2465
Richard Kardon, Community Liaison Director

Concern 610.371.8035
Fax 610.371.8038
E-mail ....concern@concern4kids.org
1120 Hobart Ave Ste B, Reading, PA 19610
Eda Cofield, Administrator

Concern professional Family Care for Children & Youth 610.944.0445
Fax 610.944.1195
Web www.concern4kids.org
E-mail ....concern1@fast.net
1 W Main St, Fleetwood, PA 19522-1323
Glenn J. Hilgisen, Director

Concern Professional Svc 570.724.7142
Fax 570.724.6771
Web www.concern4kids.org
E-mail ....tdrake@concern4kids.org
62 Plaza Ln, Wellsboro, PA 16901-1766
Terry Drake, Director

Council Spanish Speaking Organizations 215.627.3100
Fax 215.627.7440
705 09 North Franklin St, Philadelphia, PA 19123
Joanna Otero, Director

Cove Adoptive Families 814.224.2826
E-mail ....coveadoptivefamilies@gmail.com
338 Deer Run Dr, Roaring Spring, PA 16673
Holly Keller, President

Delta Community Supports Inc 215.887.6300
Fax 215.887.6400
2210 Mount Carmel Ave, Glenside, PA 19038
Scott Eldredge, Director

Diakon Adoption and Foster Care 717.845.9113
Fax 717.852.8439
E-mail ....eshe@diakon.org
836 South George St, York, PA 17403
Shirley Cherry, Administrator

Every Child Inc 412.665.0600
Fax 412.665.0755
E-mail ....jgalbraith@everychildinc.org
6401 Penn Ave Ste 300, Pittsburgh, PA 15206

Families All Together in Their Hopes 267.391.6229
Fax 215.949.3893
14 Gamewood Rd, Levittown, PA 19057

Families United Network 570.340.1444
Fax 570.340.1440
Web www.families4kids.org
E-mail ....info@families4kids.org
1006 Pittston Ave, Scranton, PA 18505-4109
Tom Neuwhard, Administrator

Families United Network, Inc 717.766.5900
Fax 717.367.3424
E-mail ....bmarkle@families4kids.org
101 Old Schoolhouse Ln Fl 2, Mechanicsburg, PA 17052
Betty Markle, Director

Family Care for Child & Youth 724.832.0111
333 Harvey Ave Ste 1, Greensburg, PA 15601-1993
Teresa Storer, Adminstrator

Family Care Services Inc 717.263.2285
Fax 717.263.6597
E-mail ....info@familycareservices.org
4385 Edenville Rd, Chambersburg, PA 17201
Pauline Ruthrauff, Clinical Director

Family Pathways 724.284.9440
Fax 724.284.9441
E-mail ....adoptfp@zoominternet.net
100 Brugh Ave, Butler, PA 16001

Family Support Group 412.366.7113
1733 Locust Rd, Sewickley, PA 15143

Finally Families 610.358.5359
12 Hilloch Lane, Chadds Ford, PA 19317

Fireside Foster Parent Group 215.855.5128
320 Union St, Hatfield, PA 19940

Foster Parent Assoc 570.769.6896
199 Big Plum Run Rd, Lock Haven, PA 17745

Foster to Adopt Families 610.682.1504
One South Home Avenue NE, Topton, PA 19562

Friendship House Foster Care 215.438.6665
Fax 215.438.5320
Web ....www.friendshiphousepa.org
E-mail ....lbudner@friendshiphousepa.org
633 W Rittenhouse St, Suite C14, Philadelphia, PA 19144
Larry Budner, Administrator

Jewish Family Service of Greater Harrisburg, Inc. 717.233.1681
Fax 717.234.8258
Web ....www.jfsofhbg.org;www.adoptionlinkspa.org
3333 North Front Street, Harrisburg, PA 17110
COA accredited organization.

KidsPeace 570.271.0590
Fax 570.271.1147
304 Railroad St, Danville, PA 17821
George Adams, Regional Manager

National Adoption Center 215.735.9988
Fax 215.735.9410
E-mail ....nac@adopt.org
1500 Walnut St Ste 701, Philadelphia, PA 19102

NHS Human Services 717.441.9537
E-mail ....contact@nhsonline.org
4391 Sturbridge Dr, Harrisburg, PA 17110

Northern Home For Children 215.482.1423
Fax 215.508.1114
E-mail ....info@northernhome.org
5301 Ridge Ave, Philadelphia, PA 19128
Lori Kubicky, Accounts Payable

Pennsylvania Mentor, Inc. 800.765.0438
Fax 717.657.3804
E-mail ....michaella.sickes@thementornetwork.com
2090 Linglestown Road, Suite 203, Harrisburg, PA 17110-9428
Michaella Sickes, Clinical Supervisor

Pennsylvania State Resource Family Assoc 800.951.5151
471 Wick Dr, Harrisburg, PA 17111
Elaine Newkirk, President

Pennsylvania Dept of Public Welfare 724.465.3895
350 North 4th St, Indiana, PA 15701
Paula Mclure, Director

Philadelphia Family Pride 215.600.2864
PO Box 235, Spring House, PA 19477

Pittsburgh Adoption Support Group 412.767.4250
105 Church Lane, Pittsburgh, PA 15238

Presbyterian Childrens Village Services 215.878.2480
E-mail ....EBraham@pcv.org
6517 Chester Ave, Philadelphia, PA 19142
Patrick Oleskey, Director

Pressley Ridge **717.397.5241**
Fax 717.397.2530
   630 Janet Ave, Lancaster, PA 17601
   Steve Denlinger, Director

Project STAR at the Childrens Institute **724.775.0209**
Fax 724.775.1260
E-mail ....kma@the-institute.org
   1598 Virginia Ave, Monaca, PA 15061

Project STAR The Childrens Institute **412.244.3066**
Fax 412.242.7414
E-mail ....cpa@the-institute.org
   1405 Shady Ave, Pittsburgh, PA 15217
   Dr. Patricia Saunders-Madison, Manager

Rejoice Inc Foster Care Adoption Agency **717.221.0722**
Fax 717.221.0843
   1800 State St, Harrisburg, PA 17103
   Tanya William-Bell, Director

Single Adoptive Parents Delaware Valley **610.649.9045**
   1504 Knox Rd, Wynnewood, PA 19096

The Bair Foundation **717.985.6450**
   1801 Oberlin Rd, 12 Oaks Center, Middletown,
   PA 17057
   Carmen Naugle, Director

The Childrens Home Pittsburgh Lemieux
Fa **412.441.4884**
E-mail ....ncaravella@chomepgh.org
   5324 Penn Ave, Pittsburgh, PA 15224
   Pam Schanweld, Chief Executive Officer

Together as Adoptive Parents **215.256.0669**
Fax 215.513.2921
E-mail ....taplink@comcast.net
   478 Moyer Rd, Harleysville, PA 19438
   P Stevens, Chief Executive Officer

Wesley Spectrum Services Adoption
Program **412.342.2300**
Fax 412.342.2329
E-mail ....agross@wesleyspectrum.org
   221 Penn Ave, Pittsburgh, PA 15221
   Doug Muetzel, Chief Executive Officer

Womens Christian Alliance **215.236.9911**
Fax 215.236.9808
E-mail ....rwillifo@wcafamily.org
   1722 42 Cecil B Moore Ave, Philadelphia, PA 19121
   Evelyn Busby, Chief Executive Officer

World Links International Adoption Agenc **570.344.8890**
Fax 570.344.8895
   418 Jefferson Ave, Scranton, PA 18510
   Tagiana Suslin, Director

HOME MEDICAL EQUIPMENT PROVIDERS

Able Mobility Center **724.695.7882**
Fax 724.695.7883
Web ....www.ablemobility.com
   7857 Steubenville Pike, Oakdale, PA 15071
   CARF accredited programs available.

Gerber Chair Mates Inc **814.269.9531**
E-mail ....sales@gerberchairmates.com
   1171 Ringling Ave, Johnstown, PA 15902
   Dorothy Gerber, Owner

Hertz Supply Company **610.769.4900**
Fax 610.769.4908
E-mail ....volker@hertzsupply.com
   4315 Independence Dr, Schnecksville, PA 18078

Jonah & The Whale Foundation **877.495.6624**
Fax 724.772.4998
E-mail ....info@JTWF.org
   PO Box 981, Mars, PA 16046

RTA Medical Supply **610.558.6222**
Fax 610.558.6226
Web ....www.rtamedicalsupply.org
   255 Wilmington Westchester Pike, ste 2, Chatts Ford,
   PA 19317
   Cindy Deeck, Manager

WheelchairNet **412.586.6908**
Fax 412.586.6910
E-mail ....ruffing@shrs.pitt.edu
   2310 Jane St Ste 1300, Pittsburgh, PA 15203

PEDIATRIC HOME CARE

Allentown PDN **610.439.5700**
   111605 N Cedar Crest Blvd Ste 109, Allentown,
   PA 18104
   Carsa Kruppenbach, Regional Director

Bayada Nurses **215.657.7711**
Fax 215.657.5376
Web ....www.bayada.com
   607 Easton Road, Suite B3, Willow Grove, PA 19090
   Sheila Drummond, Director

Bayada Nurses **610.658.7150**
Fax 610.645.5291
Web ....www.bayada.com
   354 West Lancaster Ave, Haverford, PA 19041
   Mitzi Green, Director

Bayada Nurses **570.421.0185**
Fax 570.421.0184
Web ....www.bayadanurses.com
   128 Eagles Glenn Mall, Suite 100, Milford Road and
   Route 209, East Stroudsburg, PA 18301
   Ketty Doagla, Director

Bayada Nurses **814.835.2400**
Fax 814.836.0749
Web ....www.bayada.com
E-mail ....htirak@bayada.com
   3800 West 12th Street, Erie, PA 16505
   Heather Tirak, Director

Bayada Nurses **610.891.1636**
Fax 484.444.0132
Web ....www.bayada.com
   1023 East Baltimore Pike, Suite 303, Media,
   PA 19063
   Kathy Mcfehen, Director

Bayada Nurses **610.377.4717**
Fax 610.377.4715
Web ....www.bayada.com
   777 Blakeslee Drive East, Suite 4, Lehighton,
   PA 18235
   Beckey Boeccger, Director

Bayada Nurses **610.992.9200**
Fax 610.992.0146
Web ....www.bayada.com
   3000 Valley Forge Circle, Suite 3150, King of Prussia,
   PA 19406
   Carol McMahon, Division Director

Bayada Nurses **610.648.9200**
Fax 610.648.9446
Web ....www.bayada.com
   43 Leopard Rd Ste 300, Paoli, PA 19301
   Sylvia, Administrator

Bayada Nurses **215.293.9901**
Fax 215.293.9902
Web ....www.bayada.com
   319 West County Line Road, Hatboro, PA 19040
   Tony Messina, Director

Bayada Nurses **570.928.8032**
Fax 570.928.8468
Web ....www.bayada.com
   11026 Route 220, Dushore, PA 18614
   Melissa Soper, Director

Bayada Nurses **610.277.1100**
Fax 610.277.2566
Web ....www.bayada.com
   170 West Germantown Pike, Suite C-4, East Norriton,
   PA 19401
   Dawn King, Director

Bayada Nurses **610.406.9000**
Fax 610.406.9608
Web ....www.bayada.com
   Exeter Medical & Professional Bldg, 6 Hearthstone
   Court, Suite 104, Reading, PA 19606

Bayada Nurses **610.317.2118**
Fax 610.317.2654
Web ....www.bayada.com
   3400 Bath Pike, Suite 101, Bethlehem, PA 18017

Bayada Nurses **610.239.5955**
Fax 610.277.1085
Web ....www.bayada.com
E-mail ....msoroka@bayada.com
   266 E. Main Street, Suite 7, Norristown, PA 19401
   Marty Soroka, Director

Bayada Nurses **717.699.0880**
Fax 717.699.0885
Web ....www.bayada.com
   2045 Springwood Rd, York, PA 17403
   Karen Kunselman, Director

Bayada Nurses **717.291.9000**
Fax 717.291.9174
Web ....www.bayada.com
   1850 William Penn Way, Suite 110, Lancaster,
   PA 17601
   Cindy Fuhram, Director

Bayada Nurses **412.374.1440**
Fax 412.372.3745
Web ....www.bayada.com
   300 Oxford Drive, Suite 415, Monroeville, PA 15146
   Amy Grubb, Director

Bayada Nurses **215.721.7800**
Fax 215.721.6699
Web ....www.bayada.com
   66 South County Line Rd, Souderton, PA 18964
   Diane Granevese, Director

Bayada Nurses **215.732.5050**
Fax 215.732.9701
Web ....www.bayada.com
   1315 Walnut St., Suite 932, Philadelphia, PA 19107
   Marty Soroka, Director

Bayada Nurses **570.523.2600**
Fax 570.523.2599
Web ....www.bayada.com
   115 Farley Circle, Suite 103, Lewisburg, PA 17837
   Ruthann Kephart, Director

Bayada Nurses **610.873.8202**
Fax 610.873.8204
Web ....www.bayada.com
   361 East Lancaster Avenue, Downingtown, PA 19335
   Joan Coleman, Director

Bayada Nurses **570.883.5700**
Fax 570.883.7017
Web ....www.bayada.com
   2080 N Township Blvd, Pittston, PA 18640
   Mary Claire, Director

Bayada Nurses **215.568.6666**
Fax 215.568.8344
Web ....www.bayada.com
   1819 John F. Kennedy Boulevard, Suite 444,
   Philadelphia, PA 19103
   Bonnie Kelly, Recruiter

Bayada Nurses **215.657.3900**
Fax 215.657.9021
Web ....www.bayada.com
   607 Easton Road, Lower Level, Suite B2, Willow
   Grove, PA 19090
   Chris Bandish, Director

Pennsylvania

Bayada Nurses............................**412.374.0110**
Fax..412.372.3860
Web..............................www.bayada.com
300 Oxford Drive, Suite 410, Monroeville, PA 15146
Amy Breslin, Director

Bayada Nurses............................**570.389.1568**
Fax..570.389.9261
Web..............................www.bayada.com
1113 Old Berwick Road, Bloomsburg, PA 17815
Rick Hyneck, Director

Bayada Nurses............................**610.444.1990**
Web..............................www.bayada.com
E-mail...............................info@bayada.com
111 E Cypress St, 1st Fl, Kennett Square, PA 19348
Henry Torrie, Director

Bayada Nurses............................**610.891.9400**
Fax..610.892.9208
Web..............................www.bayada.com
100 West 6th St. Suite 201, Media, PA 19063
Henry Torrie, Director

Bayada Nurses............................**610.865.8100**
Fax..610.867.2238
Web..............................www.bayada.com
3400 Bath Pike, Suite 201, Bethlehem, PA 18017
Mark Bayada, Owner

Bayada Nurses............................**570.883.5600**
Fax..570.883.4451
Web..............................www.bayada.com
457 North Main Street, Suite 100, Pittston, PA 18640
Marian Lehman, Director

Bayada Nurses............................**215.546.9231**
Fax..215.546.8149
Web..............................www.bayada.com
1315 Walnut Street, Suite 1132, Philadelphia, PA 19107
Kevin Kuzmick, Director

Bayada Nurses............................**610.927.3900**
Fax..610.927.3948
Web..............................www.bayada.com
320 Abington Dr, Suite 330, Reading, PA 19610
Cindy Egart, Director

Bayada Nurses............................**215.752.8500**
Fax..215.752.8527
Web..............................www.bayada.com
920 Town Center Drive, Suite I-80, Langhorne, PA 19047
Lisa Soll, Director

Bayada Nurses............................**215.579.0006**
Fax..215.579.2803
Web..............................www.bayada.com
115 Pheasant Run, Suite 211, Newtown, PA 18940

Bayada Nurses............................**215.257.7091**
Fax..215.257.7093
Web..............................www.bayada.com
94 North Main Street, Sellersville, PA 18960
Greg Dean, Director

Bayada Nurses............................**610.776.7000**
Fax..610.776.7755
Web..............................www.bayada.com
317 South Cedar Crest Boulevard, Allentown, PA 18103
Heather Fotopoulos, Director

Bayada Nurses............................**717.561.8800**
Fax..717.561.5073
Web..............................www.bayada.com
750 East Park Drive, 1st Floor, Harrisburg, PA 17111
Michelle Cortez, Director

Bayada Nurses............................**215.413.0600**
Fax..215.413.0722
Web..............................www.bayada.com
190 North Independence Mall West, Suite 701, The American College of Physicians Bldg, Philadelphia, PA 19106
Jerry Shackelford, Director

Bayada Nurses............................**215.561.1200**
Fax..215.561.7450
Web..............................www.bayada.com
2 Penn Center, 1500 John F. Kennedy Boulevard, Suite 1120, Philadelphia, PA 19102
Luba Somits, Nursing Director

Bayada Nurses............................**215.988.9006**
Fax..215.988.9115
Web..............................www.bayada.com
2401 Walnut Street, 1st Floor, Suite 101, Philadelphia, PA 19103

Bayada Nurses............................**215.413.5000**
Fax..215.735.3683
Web..............................www.bayada.com
1528 Walnut Street, Suite 1210, Philadelphia, PA 19102
Megan Miller, Director

CareGivers America LLC....................**877.561.4663**
Fax..570.586.5225
Web..........................www.caregiversamerica.com
E-mail...............webinfo@caregiversamerica.com
718 S State St, Clarks Summit, PA 18411
Rebecca Jacobs, Marketing Coordinator

CIGNA Healthcare..........................**800.558.3644**
Fax..877.243.1882
E-mail.................Tammy.Smegal-Saunders@CIGNA.com
3200 Parklane, Pittsburgh, PA 15275
Tammy Smegal-Saunders, RN-Complex Case Manager

Harrisburg PDN............................**717.540.1051**
75 S Houcks Rd Ste 100, Harrisburg, PA 17109
Kelly York, Director

Interim Healthcare........................**610.434.7277**
Fax..610.434.6974
5925 Tilghman St, Ste 150, Allentown, PA 18104
Colleen K, Director

Interim Healthcare........................**570.489.6781**
Fax..570.489.1090
200 3rd St, Blakely, PA 18447

Interim Healthcare........................**814.375.9615**
Fax..814.375.1362
127 North Brady St, Ste B, DuBois, PA 15801
Bernard Kanarr, Director

Interim Healthcare........................**814.333.1293**
Fax..814.336.5666
Web..........................www.interimhealthcare.com
16269 Conneaut Lake Rd, Meadville, PA 16335
Alicia Dengler, Superintendent

Interim Healthcare........................**724.430.1460**
Fax..724.430.1465
1325 Connellsville Rd Ste 24, Lemont Furnace, PA 15456
Joyce Mertz, Branch Manager

Interim Healthcare........................**412.371.3726**
Fax..412.243.4313
1789 S Braddock Ave Ste 340, Pittsburgh, PA 15218
Roy Buchta, Executive Vice President

Interim Healthcare........................**570.546.2102**
Fax..570.546.8206
160 Chad Rd, Muncy, PA 17756
Allis Fisbhetti, President

Interim Healthcare........................**814.445.1080**
Fax..814.445.1081
512 Georgian Pl, Somerset, PA 15501
Constance Maize, Supervisor

Interim Healthcare........................**412.436.2200**
Fax..412.436.2215
1789 S Braddock Ave Ste 220, Pittsburgh, PA 15218
Roy Buchta, Vice President

Interim Healthcare........................**800.326.9543**
Fax..570.546.8206
160 Chad Rd, Muncy, PA 17756
Cathy Gurzynski, Office Manager

Interim Healthcare........................**814.254.1230**
Fax..814.254.1236
322 Warren St Ste 220, Johnstown, PA 15905
Terry Groff, Vice President

Interim Healthcare........................**610.372.4611**
Fax..610.434.6974
2001 State Hill Rd Ste 201, Wyomissing, PA 19610

Interim Healthcare........................**814.695.1242**
Fax..814.695.5613
1798 Plank Rd Ste 101, Duncansville, PA 16635
Patty Shaw, Branch Manager

Interim Healthcare........................**570.883.9773**
Fax..570.883.9779
115 New St, 115 New St, Pittston, PA 18640
Michael Zefhonfki, Administrator

Interim Healthcare........................**814.836.8836**
Fax..814.835.8175
2201 W Grandview Blvd, Erie, PA 16506
Joseph Kadlick, Vice President

Jenkintown PDN (Philadelphia)............**215.887.4009**
8080 Oldyork Rd Ste 210, elkinspark, PA 19027
Marianne Carroll, Director

Pittsburgh PDN............................**412.322.4140**
1501 Reedsdale St, Cardello Bldg Ste 4002, Pittsburgh, PA 15233
Sue Coleman, Director

Port Allegany PDN.........................**814.642.9500**
63 N Main St 2nd Fl, Port Allegany, PA 16743
Angela Barker

Reading PDN...............................**610.779.6435**
6 Hearthstone Ct Ste 204, Reading, PA 19606
Carsa Kruppenbach, Director

SOCIAL SERVICES

Adoption Ctr..............................**215.735.9988**
Fax..215.735.9410
Web..............................www.adopt.org
E-mail...............................nac@adopt.org
1500 Walnut St Ste 701, Philadelphia, PA 19102-3504
Ken Mullner, Executive Director

Allegheny Children's Initiative, Inc..........**412.431.8006**
Fax..412.431.8124
Web..............................www.pfq.org
2304 Jane Street, Pittsburgh, PA 15203
COA accredited organization.

Bethanna.................................**215.355.6500**
Fax..215.355.8617
Web..............................www.bethanna.org
1030 Second Street Pike, Southampton, PA 18966
COA accredited organization.

Blackburn Ctr Against Domestic & Sexual Violence.................................**724.837.9540**
Fax..724.837.3676
Web..............................www.blackburncenter.org
E-mail...............................anne@blackburncenter.org
1011 Old Salem Rd Ste 202, Greensburg, PA 15601
Ann Emmerling, Director

Branch...................................**570.517.0815**
Fax..570.517.0746
E-mail...............................jewishrc@verizon.net
727 Main St, Stroudsburg, PA 18360
Yehuda Salkow, Rabbi

Carson Valley Children's Aid...............**215.233.1960**
Fax..215.836.1049
Web..............................www.cvca-pa.org
1419 Bethlehem Pike, Flourtown, PA 19031
COA accredited organization.

Catholic Charities Counseling and Adoption Services, Inc.....814.456.2091
Fax....814.456.1677
Web....www.cccas.org
329 West Tenth Street, Erie, PA 16502
COA accredited organization.

Catholic Charities of the Diocese of Harrisburg, PA, Inc.....717.657.4804
Fax....717.657.8683
Web....www.hbgdiocese.org
4800 Union Deposit Road, Harrisburg, PA 17111
COA accredited organization.

Catholic Social Services, Inc.....570.822.7118
Fax....570.829.7781
Web....www.cssdioceseofscranton.org
33 East Northampton Street, Wilkes-Barre, PA 18701
COA accredited organization.

CCIS....724.836.4580
Fax....724.836.5415
Web....www.cciswestmoreland.com
4893 Rte 30, Greensburg, PA 15601
Diane Shola, Supervisor

CCIS....570.822.6500
Fax....570.822.6510
46 S Washington St, Wilkes Barre, PA 18703
John Hogan, Director

CCIS Child Care Connection....814.949.9110
Fax....814.949.1954
Web....www.hso.blarico.org
E-mail....c-mzitsch@state.pa.us
3001 Fairway Dr, Suite D, Altoona, PA 16602
Mitchelle Zitsch, Director

CCIS Northeast of Philadelphia....215.333.1560
Fax....215.333.1472
Web....www.philadelphiachildcare.org
E-mail....finkelsteinn@ccisnephila.com
1926 Grant Ave, Philadelphia, PA 19115-4307
Norma Finkelstein, Director

CCIS of Lebanon....717.274.6552
Fax....717.274.2233
E-mail....ccis@luthercare.org
730 Locust St, Lebanon, PA 17042
Ann Gunshenan, Secretary

Centchild Care Info Svcs....717.263.6549
Fax....717.263.7060
Web....www.sccap.org
E-mail....m@sccap.org
533 S Main St, Chambersburg, PA 17201-3505
Marci Place, Director

Ceridian Health & Protectivity Services....484.530.6000
Fax....484.530.5146
Web....www.ceridian.com
3043 Walton Rd Ste 110, Plymouth Meeting, PA 19462-2344
Sally, Head Of Human Resources

Child Advocacy Ctr....412.692.8664
Fax....412.692.8399
Web....www.chp.edu
E-mail....janet.squires@chp.edu
4401 Penn Ave, Pittsburgh, PA 15224
Janet Squires, Md, Program Director

Child Care Agnecy....570.325.2226
Fax....570.325.5536
E-mail....ccccis2@ptd.net
69 Broadway 3Floor, Thorpe, PA 18229
Amy Rontz, Director

Child Care Consultants, Inc....717.854.2273
Fax....717.843.4158
Web....www.childcareconsultants.org
E-mail....info@childcareconsultants.org
13 W Market St, York, PA 17401
Kathy Moir, Assistant Executive Director

Child Care Info Svc....570.988.4452
Fax....570.988.4454
Web....www.childcare.state.pa.us
E-mail....c-nrtmbrcc@state.pa.us
601 1/2 Pennsylvania Ave, Sunbury, PA 17801
Debra Jennis, Director

Child Care Info Svc....717.436.8613
Fax....717.436.2266
E-mail....jcccis@tricountyi.net
12 Weatherby Wy Rd, Mifflintown, PA 17059
Sue Dunn, Manager

Child Care Info Svc....814.337.8055
Fax....814.337.8058
E-mail....ccis1@earthlink.net
996 S Main St, Ste 102, Meadville, PA 16335
Stacey Baker, Director

Child Care Info Svc....610.344.5717
Fax....610.344.4470
E-mail....crivera@chesco.org
Gsc 601 Westtown Rd, Suite 310, West Chester, PA 19380
Caulin Chang, Director

Child Care Info Svc....215.348.1283
Fax....215.348.9397
Web....www.buckschildcare.com
E-mail....maincontact@buckschildcare.com
70 W Oakland Ave, Ste 102, Doylestown, PA 18901
Rob Feldman, Supervisor

Child Care Info Svc....570.296.3447
Fax....570.296.1959
E-mail....pw.tcasell@dpw.state.pa.us
506 Broad St, Ste B03, Milford, PA 18458
Jill Gamboni, Director

Child Care Info Svc....717.242.4346
Fax....717.242.3835
Web....www.sumcd.org
10 Bollinger Rd, Lewistown, PA 17044
Lori Artman, Coordinator

Child Care Info Svc....724.658.8874
Fax....717.242.3835
Web....www.state.pa.us
E-mail....cpilch@state.pa.us
1001 E Washington St, Suite 3, New Castle, PA 16101
Cheryl Pilch, Director

Child Care Info Svc....724.346.6171
Fax....724.346.0789
Web....www.dpw.state.pa.us
E-mail....pw-cgraham@dpw.state.pa.us
1600 Roemer Blvd, Farrell, PA 16121-1754
Richard Skody, Director

Child Care Info Svc....570.275.3996
Fax....570.275.7579
Web....www.montourchildcare.com
E-mail....pwachell@dpw.state.pa.us
398 Wall St, Danville, PA 17821-1744
Joanne Blaff, Director

Child Care Info Svc....570.836.1826
Fax....570.836.1639
Web....www.wycopa.com
E-mail....mw@wycopa.com
29 S Services Building Sr 29 S, Tunkhannock, PA 18657
Mary Foley, Director

Child Care Info Svc....724.425.1818
Fax....724.434.5865
Web....www.ccis.fayette.org
E-mail....cdecarlo@ccis.fayette.org
137 N Beeson Ave Ste 117, Uniontown, PA 15401-2936
Cheryl Decarlo, Resource and Referall Coordinator

Child Care Info Svc....724.852.5277
Fax....724.852.5297
Web....www.co.greene.pa.us
E-mail....tking@co.greene.pa.us
22 W high st, Waynesburg, PA 15370-2053
Tina King, Administrative Assistant

Child Care Info Svc of Cameron, Elk, McKean and Potter Counties....814.486.1974
Fax....814.486.0825
Web....www.state.pa.gov
E-mail....c-aschwab@state.pa.gov
135 W 4th St, Emporium, PA 15834-1123
Kenneth Straub, Executive Director

Child Care Info Svc of Clarion & Jefferson Counties....814.938.5866
Fax....814.938.5917
Web....www.jccap.org
E-mail....lbeatty@jccap.org
105 Grace Way, Punxsutawney, PA 15767-1209
Laura Beatty, Director

Child Care Info Svc of Huntingdon....814.643.4980
Fax....814.643.7298
E-mail....astreightiff@hccadc.org
52 Juniata Ave, Huntingdon, PA 16652
Amy Streightiff, Director

Child Care Info Svc of Lackawanna....570.963.6644
Fax....570.963.6319
Web....www.gpw.state.pa.us
E-mail....sallavantip@lackawannacounty.org
345 Wyoming Ave Ste 200, Scranton, PA 18503-1235
Phil Sallavanti, Director

Child Care Info Svc of Susquehanna....570.341.0811
Fax....570.558.2417
Web....www.cciswaynesusq.com
E-mail....pw-mohop@dpw.state.pa.us
1356 N Washington Ave, Scranton, PA 18509-2852
Betsy Esgro, Director

Child Care Info Svc of Warren and Forest Counties....814.726.1361
Fax....814.726.0510
Web....www.wfcaa.org
E-mail....montgomery@wfcaa.org
1209 Pennsylvania Ave W, Warren, PA 16365
Tish Montgomery, Director

Child Care Info Svcs....814.623.2002
Fax....814.623.1444
E-mail....c-wtew@state.pa.us
195 Drive In Ln, Everett, PA 15537
Ann Foore, Director

Child Care Info Svcs....610.419.4500
Fax....610.419.3888
E-mail....c-egilgoff@state.pa.us
2200 W Broad St Ste 2, Bethlehem, PA 18018
Besty Gilgoff, Director

Child Care Info Svcs....814.231.1352
Fax....814.238.2765
Web....www.cdfc.org
E-mail....awalker15@cdfc.org
2565 Park Center Blvd Ste 100, State College, PA 16801
Nicole Sheridan, Program Director

Child Care Info Svcs....814.472.6341
Fax....814.472.6460
E-mail....rkikta@cciscambria.com
300 Prave St Ste 101, Ebensburg, PA 15931-1971
Ronald Kikta, Director

Child Care Info Svcs....814.437.1906
Fax....814.432.3896
Web....www.childcare.state.pa.us
E-mail....ccis@usachoice.net
24 Front St, Franklin, PA 16323-2914
Candy Reina, Director

Child Care Info Svcs North 215.763.0100
Fax 215.763.1995
Web ....www.philadelphiachildcare.org
E-mail ....egaines@ccisnorth.org
642 N Broad St Fl 6, Philadelphia, PA 19130-3424
Jessie Cheek, Assistant Director

Child Care Info Svcs of Schuylkill 570.624.7950
Fax 570.624.7955
Web ....www.ccis-schuylkill.org
2335 W End Ave, Pottsville, PA 17901
April Wyozitch, Director

**Child Care Partnerships - YWCA of Greater
Pittsburgh** 412.261.2273
Fax 412.391.1628
Web ....www.ywcapgh.org
E-mail ....agannon@ywcapgh.org
305 Wood St, Pittsburgh, PA 15222-1914
Anthony Gannon, Director of Subsidized Child Care

**Child Care Resource Developers of Central
Region** 570.327.6949
Fax 570.322.2197
Web ....www.stepcorp.org
E-mail ....jhlarose@stepcorp.org
2138 Lincoln St, Williamsport, PA 17701-5549
John Larose, Director

Children's Crisis Treatment Ctr 215.496.0707
Fax 215.496.0742
Web ....www.cctckids.org
E-mail ....avaldes@cctckids.org
1823 Callowhill St, Philadelphia, PA 19130
Antonio Valdes, Executive Director

Children's Home of York 717.755.1033
Fax 717.755.9993
Web ....www.choyork.org
77 Shoehouse Road, York, PA 17406
COA accredited organization.

Children's Service, Incorporated 215.546.3503
Fax 215.546.4678
Web ....www.csichild.org
1315 Walnut Street, Suite 200, Philadelphia,
PA 19107-4719
COA accredited organization.

Childswork Childsplay 800.962.1141
Fax 800.262.1886
Web ....www.childswork.com
E-mail ....info@childswork.com
PO Box 1246, Wilkes-barre, PA 18703
Ken Litson, Marketing Director

Community Svcs for Children, Inc. 610.437.6000
Fax 610.437.6500
Web ....www.cscinc.org
1520 Hanover Ave, Allentown, PA 18109-2360
Paula Margarf, Executive Vp

Covenant House Pennsylvania Crisis Ctr 215.951.5411
Fax 215.951.5412
Web ....www.nineline.org
E-mail ....chill@covenanthousepa.org
31 E Armat St, Philadelphia, PA 19144-2201
Cordella Hill, Executive Director

Cradle of Hope 215.572.5937
E-mail ....cradleofhope@gmail.com
1657 The Fairway, ste #140, Jenkintown, PA 19046
Michelle Nejman, Director

Diversified Family Svcs 724.346.2123
Fax 724.346.0366
E-mail ....ntusinac@diversifiedfamily.org
5454 E State St, Hermitage, PA 16148-9441
Nancy Tusinac, Program Director

Elwyn, Inc. 610.891.2670
Fax 610.891.2413
Web ....www.elwyn.org
E-mail ....heidi_b_share@elwyn.org
111 Elwyn Rd, Media, PA 19063-4699
Heidi Becker-Share, Director of Intake/Admissions

**Episcopal Community Services of the Diocese of
Pennsylvania** 215.351.1400
Fax 215.351.1497
Web www.ecs1870.org
225 South Third Street, Philadelphia, PA 19106
COA accredited organization.

Family Resources Warm Line 412.363.1702
Fax 412.363.1724
Web ....www.familyresourcesofpa.org
E-mail ....mwarren@familyresourcesofpa.org
141 S Highland Ave, Pittsburgh, PA 15206-3932
Walter Smith, Phd, Executive Director

**Family Service Association of Wyoming
Valley** 570.823.5144
Fax 570.829.5054
Web ....www.fsawv.org
31 West Market Street, Wilkes-Barre, PA 18701
COA accredited organization.

Family Services of NW PA 814.866.4500
Fax 814.864.2677
Web ....www.fsnwpa.org
5100 Peach Street, Erie, PA 16509-2418
COA accredited organization.

Family Svcs 412.820.2050
Fax 412.820.2060
Web ....www.fswp.org
E-mail ....fswp@fswp.org
3230 William Pitt Way, Pittsburgh, PA 15238-1361
Donald Goughler, CEO

FamilyLinks, Inc. 412.343.7166
Web ....www.familylinks.org
2644 Banksville Road, Pittsburgh, PA 15216
COA accredited organization.

Glade Run Lutheran Svcs 412.661.1827
Fax 412.661.1867
Web ....www.gladerun.org
E-mail ....ostedeford@gladerun.org
5701 Centre Ave Ste L12, Pittsburgh, PA 15206-3776
Oliver Stedeford, Director

**Good Shepherd Corporation of Clarks Summit aka
Lourdesmont** 570.587.4741
Fax 570.586.0030
Web ....www.lourdesmont.com
537 Venard Road, Clarks Summit, PA 18411
COA accredited organization.

Gwen's Girls, Inc. 412.731.7670
Fax 412.731.7610
Web ....www.gwensgirls.org
7230 McPherson Blvd., Lexington Technology Park,
Pittsburgh, PA 15208
COA accredited organization.

Imperial Towers 267.256.2030
Fax 267.256.2021
3801 Conshohocken Ave # 123, Philadelphia,
PA 19131

Intercultural Family Services, Inc. 215.386.1298
Fax 215.386.9348
Web ....www.ifsinc.org
4225 Chestnut Street, Philadelphia, PA 19104
COA accredited organization.

Interface Shelter 717.236.6783
Fax 717.236.3271
E-mail ....lgrudi@hbgdiocese.org
1002 Hemlock Dr, Harrisburg, PA 17110
Hilary Hoover, Program Director

**Jewish Family & Children's Service of
Pittsburgh** 412.422.7200
Fax 412.422.9540
Web ....www.jfcspgh.org
5743 Bartlett Street, Pittsburgh, PA 15217
COA accredited organization.

Jewish Family & Childrens Service of 267.256.2100
Fax 267.256.2119
E-mail ....info@jfcsphilly.org
Greater Philadelphia, 2100 Arch St 5th Fl,
Philadelphia, PA 19103
Jack Dembow

Jewish Family and Children's Services 412.422.7200
Fax 412.422.9540
Web ....www.jfcspgh.org
E-mail ....info@jfcspgh.org
5743 Bartlett Street, Pittsburgh, PA 15217-1515
Aryeh Sherman, Executive Director

Jewish Family Service 610.921.2766
Fax 610.929.0886
E-mail ....jfrtammym@comcast.net
1100 Berkshire Blvd, Ste 125, Reading, PA 19610
Tammy Mitgang, Director

Jewish Family Service Greater Wilkes Bar 570.823.5137
Fax 570.824.4210
E-mail ....jfswb71@aol.com
71 W Northamton St, Wilkes-Barre, PA 18701
Howard Grossman, Executive Director

Jewish Family Service of the Lehigh Vally 610.821.8722
Fax 610.821.8925
E-mail ....pringelatJFS@hotmail.com
2004 Allen St, Allentown, PA 18104
Phyllis Ringel, Executive Director

Jewish Family Services of York 717.843.5011
Fax 717.846.3025
E-mail ....info@jfsyork.org
2000 Hollywood Dr, York, PA 17403
Joan Krechmer, Executive Director

**Lutheran Children and Family Service of Eastern
Pennsylvania** 215.276.5500
Fax 215.276.5533
Web ....www.lcfsinpa.org
5902 North 5th Street, Philadelphia, PA 19120
COA accredited organization.

Mandell Office 267.256.2075
Fax 267.256.2076
7607 Old York Rd Lower Level, Elkins Park, PA 19027

North East Treatment 215.739.3742
Fax 215.739.5550
Web ....www.net-centres.org
154 E Huntingdon St, Philadelphia, PA 19125-1030
Stephanie Curry, Program Director

Northeast Office 267.256.2050
Fax 267.256.2051
10125 Verree Rd, Philadelphia, PA 19116

Patient Care Advocates 610.856.1050
Fax 610.856.1050
Web ....www.patientcareadvocates.com
E-mail ....rissell@patientcareadvocates.com
409 Zion Road, Birdsboro, PA 19508
Denise Rissell Rn Ccm, President

Pennsylvania Child Care Assoc 717.657.9000
Fax 717.657.0959
Web ....www.pacca.org
E-mail ....terry@pacca.org
2300 Vartan Way Ste 103, Harrisburg,
PA 17110-9720
Terry Casey, Director

Pennsylvania Council Of Children's Svcs 717.651.1725
Fax 717.651.1729
Web ....www.pccyfs.org
E-mail ....hbgoffice@pccyfs.org
2040 Linglestown Rd Ste 109, Harrisburg,
PA 17110-9568
Bernadette Bianchi, Executive Director

Philadelphia Child Care Resources

Northwest **215.842.4820**
Fax 215.842.4826
Web ....www.philadelphiachildcare.org
E-mail ....nw@philadelphiachildcare.org
6350 Greene St Ofc 1, GROUND LEVEL SUITE,
Philadelphia, PA 19144-2519
Shirley Thomas, Executive Director

Philadelphia Children's Alliance **215.387.9500**
Fax 215.387.9513
Web ....www.philachildrensalliance.org
E-mail ....info@philachildrensalliance.org
42 S 15th St, 3 flr, Philadelphia, PA 19102-3020
Chris Kirchner, Executive Director

Pressley Ridge **412.872.9400**
Fax 412.872.9478
Web ....www.pressleyridge.org
5500 Corporate Drive, Suite 400, Pittsburgh,
PA 15237
COA accredited organization.

Pressley Ridge **717.774.3673**
Fax 717.774.3891
Web ....www.pressleyritge.org
E-mail ....abarton@pressleyritge.org
331 Bridge St Ste 200, New Cumberland,
PA 17070-2189
Amy Barton, Director

Pro-Life **610.692.4463**
Fax 610.692.4959
E-mail ....patrickcarnevale@hotmail.com
100 S High St Ste 1, West Chester, PA 19382-3261
Pat Carnevale, Director

Progress Plaza **267.256.2200**
Fax 267.256.2201
E-mail ....nfagan@jscs.com
1501 North Broad St Ste 14, Philadelphia, PA 19122
Nancy Fagan, Director

Renfrew Ctr **610.527.9360**
Fax 610.527.9361
Web ....www.renfrewcenter.com
E-mail ....hgrishkat@renfrewcenter.com
735 Old Lancaster Rd, Bryn Mawr, PA 19010-3414
Holly Grishkat, Site Director

Tabor Community Services, Inc. **717.397.5182**
Fax 717.399.4127
Web ....www.tabornet.org
P.O. Box 1676, Lancaster, PA 17608-1676
COA accredited organization.

Tabor Services Inc. **215.348.4071**
Fax 215.348.9261
Web ....www.tabor.org
601 New Britain Road, Doylestown, PA 18901
COA accredited organization.

The Bair Foundation **724.946.8711**
Fax 724.946.9612
Web ....www.bair.org
241 High Street, New Wilmington, PA 16142
COA accredited organization.

The Children's Home of Easton **610.258.2831**
Fax 610.258.3165
Web ....www.thechildrenshome.org
2000 S. 25th Street, Easton, PA 18042
COA accredited organization.

Three Rivers Youth **412.441.5020**
Fax 412.441.5021
Web ....www.threeriversyouth.org
6117 Broad Street, Pittsburgh, PA 15206
COA accredited organization.

Turning Points for Children **215.875.8200**
Fax 215.875.3411
Web ....www.turningpointsforchildren.org
415 South 15th Street, Philadelphia, PA 19146
COA accredited organization.

Wesley Spectrum Services **412.342.2300**
Fax 412.831.8868
Web ....www.wesleyspectrum.org
221 Penn Avenue, Wilkinsburg, PA 15221
COA accredited organization.

Youth Advocate Programs, Inc. **717.232.7580**
Fax 717.233.2879
Web ....www.yapinc.org
2007 North Third Street, Harrisburg, PA 17101
COA accredited organization.

SPECIAL NEEDS

Allied Services Institute of Rehabilitation

Medicine **570.348.1367**
Fax 570.341.4551
Web ....www.allied-services.org
475 Morgan Highway, Scranton, PA 18501
CARF accredited programs available.

Autism Society of Philadelphia **610.358.5256**
E-mail ....asa-info@comcast.net
1036 Nash Ave, Lansdale, PA 19446

Autism Society of Pittsburgh **412.856.7223**
4371 Northern Pike, Monroeville, PA 15146
Dan Torisky, President

AutismLink **412.364.1886**
E-mail ....info@autismlink.com
376 Wagon Wheel Trl, Wexford, PA 15090
Becca Major, Office Manager

Bryn Mawr Rehabilitation Hospital **610.251.5400**
Fax 610.889.0943
Web ....www.brynmawrrehab.org
414 Paoli Pike, Malvern, PA 19355
CARF accredited programs available.

Camphill Special School **610.469.9236**
Web ....www.camphillspecialschool.org
E-mail ....information@camphillspecialschool.org
1784 Fairview Rd, Glenmoore, PA 19343-2624
Camphill Special School is a community and school providing residential and day programs for children and youth with intellectual and developmental disabilities in kindergarten through grade twelve. The adapted Waldorf curriculum is rich in music, art, and drama. A variety of traditional and alternative therapies are offered. In addition, the Transition Program at Beaver Farm for youth ages eighteen to twenty-one provides education, therapies, and vocational experiences in Camphill's life sharing model. Financial aid is available. PA-Approved Private School. Fully accredited by MSA-CESS, NCPSA, and AWSNA.

Congress of Parents & Teachers Inc **717.564.8985**
E-mail ....info@papta.org
4804 Derry St, Harrisburg, PA 17111
Julie Lesitsky, State President

Crichton Rehabilitation Center **814.534.7900**
Fax 814.534.7930
Web ....www.conemaugh.org
320 Main Street, Fourth Floor, Patient Care Wing,
Johnstown, PA 15901
CARF accredited programs available.

Davidson School Elwyn **610.891.2000**
Fax 610.891.2903
Web ....www.elwyn.org
111 Elwyn Rd, Elwyn, PA 19063
Kyu Hwang, Director

Day School at the Children's Institute **412.420.2487**
Fax 412.420.2301
Web ....www.amazingkids.org
1405 Shady Ave, Pittsburgh, PA 15217
Cheryl Fogarey, Principal

Devereux Kanner Center **610.431.8100**
Fax 610.431.3155
Web ....www.devereuxkanner.org
390 E Boot Rd, West Chester, PA 19380
Melanie Beidler, Ex. Dir.

Dr Gertrude A Barber National Institute **814.878.5903**
Fax 814.454.2771
Web ....www.barberinstitute.org
100 Barber Pl, Erie, PA 16507
Maureen Barber-carey, Director

Drexel University College of Medicine **215.762.5035**
Fax 215.762.3899
E-mail ....office@phillyent.co
219 N Broad St, Philadelphia, PA 19104
Robert Sataloff, Chairman

Easter Seals **888.372.7280**
501 Valley View Blvd, Altoona, PA 16602
Kathy Katcher, Vice President

Easter Seals **215.879.1000**
E-mail ....cwebster@easterseals-sepa.org
3975 Conshohocken Ave, Philadelphia, PA 19131
Carl Webster, Executive Director

Easter Seals **800.587.3257**
E-mail ....tmori@westernpa.easterseals.com
2525 Railroad St, Pittsburgh, PA 15222
Annette Kasper, Manager

Epilepsy Foundation **215.629.5003**
E-mail ....efepa@efepa.org
919 Walnut St, Ste 700, Philadelphia, PA 19107
Allison McCartin, Executive Director

Epilepsy Foundation **800.361.5885**
E-mail ....pbeem@efwp.org
1501 Reedsdale St, Pittsburgh, PA 15233
Judy Painter, Executive Director

Family & Youth Support **800.688.4226**
E-mail ....pin@pinofpa.org
1211 Chestnut St 11th Fl, Philadelphia, PA 19107
William Dinwiddie, Chief Executive Officer

Getting Clear **215.230.7315**
Fax 215.230.7316
E-mail ....linda@gettingclear.com
161 Mechanics St, Doylestown, PA 18901

Good Shepherd Rehabilitation Network **610.776.3351**
Fax 610.776.3503
Web ....www.goodshepherdrehab.org
850 South Fifth Street, Allentown, PA 18103-3308
CARF accredited programs available.

Hispanos Unidos Para Ninos Excepcionale **215.425.6203**
Fax 215.425.6204
E-mail ....huneinc@aol.com
2200 N 2nd St, Philadelphia, PA 19131

HMS School for Children with Cerebral Pa **215.222.2566**
Fax 215.222.1889
Web ....www.hmsschool.org
4400 Baltimore Ave, Philadelphia, PA 19104
Diane L Gallagher, Director

Institute on Disabilities **215.204.9395**
E-mail ....dianeb@temple.edu
1601 N Broad St Rm 610, Philadelphia, PA 19122

Learning Disabilities Association **888.300.6710**
4156 Library Rd, Pittsburgh, PA 15234

Learning Disabilities Association **717.939.3731**
4751 Lindle Rd Ste 114, Harrisburg, PA 17111

LearningRx Learning Center **610.440.3600**
E-mail ....mainline.pa@learningrx.net
600 Haverford Rd, Ste 202, Haverford, PA 19041
Janet Rutzel, Director

LearningRx Learning Center **215.337.0138**
E-mail ....newtown.pa@learningrx.net
126 S State St, Newtown, PA 18940

Pennsylvania

LearningRx Learning Center 610.701.0411
E-mail ....westchester.pa@learningrx.net
704 W Nields St Unit 9, West Chester, PA 19382

Lindamood-Bell Learning Processes 610.581.7411
Fax 610.581.7898
780 W Lancaster Ave, Ste 101, Bryn Mawr, PA 19010
Nancy Bell, President/CEO

Magee Memorial Hospital for the Convalescents aka Magee Rehabilitation Hospital 215.587.3000
Fax 215.977.7218
Web ....www.mageerehab.org
1513 Race Street, Philadelphia, PA 19102-1177
Bob Coffman, Director of Community Programs
CARF accredited programs available.

Main Line Rehabilitation Associates, Inc. 610.280.0180
Fax 610.280.0192
Web ....www.mainline-rehab.com
668 Exton Commons, Exton, PA 19341
CARF accredited programs available.

MDA/ALS Ctr at Univ of Ptsbgh Med Ctr 412.647.1706
Fax 412.647.8398
E-mail ....lacomis@np.awing.upmc.edu
200 Lothrop St 7th Fl, Pittsburgh, PA 15213
David Lacomis, Director

Melmark 610.325.2939
Fax 610.325.2926
Web ....www.melmark.org
E-mail ....travismccoy@melmark.org
2600 Wayland Rd, Berwyn, PA 19312
Travis C Mccoy, Director

Mental Health/Mental Retardation 610.344.6265
Fax 610.344.5997
E-mail ....gentrekin@chesco.org
601 Westtown Rd Ste 340, West Chester,
PA 19382-4524
Lori Gallagher, Early Intervention Director

Moss Rehab 215.663.6000
Fax 215.663.8033
Web ....www.einstein.edu/facilities/mossrehab
60 E Township Line Rd, Elkins Park, PA 19027
Ruth Lefton, COO
CARF accredited programs available.

MossRehab 215.663.6100
Fax 215.663.8033
Web ....www.einstein.edu/facilities/mossrehab
60 East Township Line Road, Elkins Park, PA 19027
CARF accredited programs available.

NAMI Pennsylvania 800.223.0500
E-mail ....nami-pa@nami.org
2149 N 2nd St, Harrisburg, PA 17110
James Jorden, Executive Director

National Federation of the Blind 215.988.0888
E-mail ....nfbofpa@att.net
42 S 15th St, Ste 222, Philadelphia, PA 19102

National Multiple Sclerosis Society 215.271.1500
Fax 215.271.6122
E-mail ....PAE@nmss.org
30 S 17st Ste 800, Philadelphia, PA 19103
Tami Caesar, Chief Executive Officer

National Multiple Sclerosis Society 717.652.2108
Fax 717.652.2590
E-mail ....pac@nmss.org
2040 Linglestown Rd Ste 104, Harrisburg, PA 17110
M Adlman, Director

National Multiple Sclerosis Society 412.261.6347
Fax 412.232.1461
E-mail ....PAX@nmss.org
1501 Reedsdale St Ste 105, Pittsburgh, PA 15233
Anne Materaf, President

Neurofibromatosis Clinics Association 412.795.3029
E-mail ....info@nfpittsburgh.org
PO Box 14185, Plum, PA 15239
Jeffrey Kramer, Chief Executive Officer

Parent Education & Advocacy Leadership Ctr 412.281.4404
Fax 412.281.4408
E-mail ....lhealey@pealcenter.org
1119 Penn Ave Ste 400, Pittsburgh, PA 15222
Elisabeth Healey, Executive Director

Parent Education Network 717.600.0100
E-mail ....pen@parentednet.org
2107 Industrial Hwy, York, PA 17402
Kay Lipstiz, Director

Parent to Parent 717.540.4722
E-mail ....info@parenttoparent.org
6340 Flank Dr Ste 600, Harrisburg, PA 17112
Siona Patrick, Director

PEAL Center 866.950.1040
E-mail ....admin@pealcenter.org
1119 Penn Ave, Ste 400, Pittsburgh, PA 15222
Liz Healey, Executive Director

Pennsylvania Tourette Syndrome Assn 717.337.1134
E-mail ....sherrie@patsainc.org
132 W Middle St, Gettysburg, PA 17325
Sherrie Sponselller, Administrator

Philadelphia HUNE Inc 215.425.6203
E-mail ....huneinc@aol.com
2200 N 2nd St, Philadelphia, PA 19133

Schreiber Pediatric Rehab Center of Lancaster 717.393.0425
Fax 717.392.7107
Web ....www.schreiberpediatric.org
625 Community Way, Lancaster, PA 17603
CARF accredited programs available.

Skills of Central Pennsylvania 814.238.3245
Fax 814.238.5117
Web ....www.skillsofcentralpa.org
341 Science Park Rd Ste 6, State College, PA 16803
David M Rice, Director

Spina Bifida Association 717.786.9280
E-mail ....sbaofpa@aol.com
209 E state st, Quarryville, PA 17566
Patricia Fulcio, Executive Director

The Arc of Pennsylvania 800.692.7258
E-mail ....ssuroviec@thearcpa.org
101 S 2nd St Ste 8, Harrisburg, PA 17101

The Children's Institute 412.420.2400
Fax 412.420.2200
Web ....www.amazingkids.org
1405 Shady Avenue, Pittsburgh, PA 15217
CARF accredited programs available.

The Devereux Foundation 610.520.3000
Fax 610.542.3100
Web ....www.devereux.org
444 Devereux Dr, PO Box 638, Villanova, PA 19085
Robert Kreider, President

The Education Center at the Watson Institute 412.749.2860
Fax 412.741.1958
Web ....www.watsoninstitute.org
301 Camp Meeting Rd, Sewickley, PA 15143
Marilyn Hoyson, Chief Operating Officer

The Learning Curves 717.337.2212
Fax 717.334.2533
E-mail ....thelearningcurve@embarqmail.com
1351 Evergreen Way, Orrtanna, PA 17353

The Pathway School 610.277.0660
Fax 610.539.1493
Web ....www.pathwayschool.org
162 Egypt Rd, Norristown, PA 19403
Louise Robertson, Director Of Relations

The Power of Horses at Saddlewood Farm 610.404.1018
E-mail ....tphoffman@dejazzd.com
139 Monocacy Hill Rd, Birdsboro, PA 19508
Teri Hoffman, Executive Director

The University of Pennsylvania Cancer Ct 215.349.8895
Fax 215.349.5445
E-mail ....hampshire@uphs.upenn.edu
3400 Spruce St 2 Donner, Philadelphia, PA 19104

Thomas Jefferson University Hospitals, Inc. Comprehensive Acute Rehabilitation Unit 215.955.6565
Fax 215.955.1754
Web ....www.jeffersonhospital.org
132 South Tenth Street, Philadelphia, PA 19107
Joyce Stout, Office Manager
CARF accredited programs available.

Total Learning Centers 877.754.5511
Fax 724.940.1030
E-mail ....info@TotalLearningCenter.com
12045 Perry Hwy, Wexford, PA 15090

United Cerebral Palsy of Pennsylvania 717.441.6049
E-mail ....info@ucpofpa.org
908 N 2nd St, Harrisburg, PA 17103

Woods Services 215.750.4000
Fax 215.750.4286
Routes 413 & 213, Langhorne, PA 19047
Scott Spreat, Manager

SUBSTANCE ABUSE TREATMENT

Allentown Counseling Ctr 610.264.5521
Fax 610.264.5523
Web ....www.livinggrin.org
E-mail ....lrobinson@livengrin.org
961 Marcon Blvd Ste 304, Allentown, PA 18109-9373
Emily Roxberry, Director/program Coordinator

Caron Foundation 610.678.2332
Fax 610.678.5704
Web ....www.caron.org
E-mail ....drosenker@caronfoundation.org
17 Camp Rd., Wernersville, PA 19565
David Rosenker, Executive Vice Presiden

Community Svc Foundation 610.807.0210
Fax 610.807.0396
E-mail ....houseparents@csfbuxmont.org
544 Main St, Bethlehem, PA 18018
Susan Wachtel, Executive Director

Confront, Inc 610.433.0148
Fax 610.433.6201
E-mail ....confront@fast.net
1130 W Walnut St, Allentown, PA 18102-4797
Martin Kunda, Clinical Director

Cumberland-Perry Drug and Alcohol Commission 717.240.6300
Fax 717.240.6486
E-mail ....jcarroll@ccpa.net
16 W High St, Ste 302, Carlisle, PA 17013-2919
Jack Carroll, Executive Director

Gannondale 814.899.7659
Fax 814.898.4266
Web ....www.gannondale.org
4635 E Lake Rd, Erie, PA 16511-1499
Nancy Sabol, Executive Director

Gateway 724.876.0480
Fax 724.876.0486
Web ....www.gatewayrehab.org
E-mail ....kenramsey@gatewayrehab.org
262 Ohio River Blvd, Baden, PA 15005-1914
Ken Ramsey, CEO

Gateway 412.963.7077
Fax 412.963.7083
Web ....www.gatewayrehab.org
E-mail ....kenramsey@gatewayrehab.org
1360 Old Freeport Rd Ste 3B, Pittsburgh,
PA 15238-4102
Ken Ramsey, CEO

Pennsylvania

Gateway 724.853.7300
Fax...724.853.8018
E-mail.........................frank.salotti@ggatewayrehab.org
   1628 Roseytown Rd Ste 5, Greensburg,
   PA 15601-7584
   Frank Salotti, Director

Gateway 412.928.5940
Fax...412.928.5947
Web..................................www.gatewayrehab.org
E-mail..........................kenramsey@gatewayrehab.org
   2121 Noblestown Rd Ste 26, Pittsburgh,
   PA 15205-3917
   Ken Ramsey, CEO

Gaudenzia, Inc. 610.239.9600
Fax...610.239.9195
Web......................................www.gaudenzia.org
   106 West Main Street, Norristown, PA 19401
   sharon johnson, director
   CARF accredited programs available.

Richard J. Caron Foundation 800.678.2332
Fax...610.678.5704
Web...www.caron.org
   Galen Hall Road, Wernersville, PA 19565
   James Mulligan, medical director
   CARF accredited programs available.

The Horsham Clinic 215.643.7800
Fax...215.654.1148
Web.................................www.horshamclinic.com
E-mail.........................phyllis.weisfield@uhsinc.com
   722 E Butler Pike, Ambler, PA 19002-2310
   Tasha Hoffman, Director

Turtle Creek Valley Drug and Alcohol
Alternatives 412.381.2100
Fax...412.381.2004
Web..www.tcvmhmr.org
   70 S 22nd St, Pittsburgh, PA 15203-2143
   Mark Mariskin, Director

Pennsylvania

Rhode Island

Lincoln Chafee, Governor
Office of the Governor
State House Room 115 82 Smith St
Providence, RI 02903
401.222.2080
401.222.8096 (Fax)
www.governor.state.ri.us

Elizabeth Gilheeney, Juvenile Justice Specialist
RI Justice Commission
One Capital Hill, 4th Floor
Providence, RI 02908-5803
401.222.4494
401.222.1294 (Fax)
lizg@gw.doa.state.ri.us

Brother Brendan Gerrity, SAG Chair
Ocean Tides
635 Ocean Road
Narragansett, RI 02882
401.789.1016
401.788.0924 (Fax)
brob@oceantides.org

CRISIS NUMBERS

Child Abuse Reporting . . .800.742.4453

STATE SERVICES

SOCIAL SERVICES

Day Care Licensing Unit Rhode Island 401.528.3502
Fax 401.528.3666
   101 Friendship St, Providence, RI 02903
   Kevin Savage, Director

Dept of Children, Youth and Families 401.528.3502
Fax 401.528.3595
Web . . . . .www.dcyf.state.ri.us
E-mail . . . . .kevin.aucoin@dcyf.ri.gov
   101 Friendship St, Providence, RI 02903-3716
   Kevin Aucoin, Executive Director

Rhode Island Dept of Human Svcs 401.462.2121
Fax 401.462.3677
Web . . . . .www.dhs.ri.gov
E-mail . . . . .director@dhs.ri.gov
   600 New London Ave, Cranston, RI 02920-3041
   Sandra Powell, Director Of Human Services

**Rhode Island Emergency Management
   Agency 401.946.9996**
Fax 401.944.1891
Web . . . . .www.riema.ri.gov
E-mail . . . . .james.d.smith18@us.army.mil
   645 New London Ave, Cranston, RI 02920-3003
   J.david Smith, Executive Director

GENERAL HEALTH SERVICES

Of of Spec Healthcare Needs RI 401.222.5929
Fax 401.222.1442
E-mail . . . . .deborah.garneau@health.ri.gov
   3 Capitol Hill Rm 302, Providence, RI 02908
   Deborah Garneau, Director

Rhode Island Dept of Health 401.222.7627
Fax 401.222.4415
Web . . . . .www.health.ri.gov
E-mail . . . . .beatriz.perez@health.ri.gov
   3 Capitol Hl, Rm 409, Providence, RI 02908
   Beatriz Perez, Director

MENTAL HEALTH SERVICES

Ofc of Rehabilitation Svcs 401.421.7005
Fax 401.222.3574
Web . . . . .www.ors.ri.gov
E-mail . . . . .steveb@ors.ri.gov
   40 Fountain St Fl 4B, Providence, RI 02903-1898
   Steven Brunero, Administrator

**Rhode Island Board for the Certification of Chemical
   Dependency Professionals 401.349.3822**
Fax 401.349.3833
Web . . . . .www.ribccd.com
E-mail . . . . .ricert@msn.com
   29 Smith Ave #2, Greenville, RI 02828
   Johanna Rylands, Director

**Rhode Island Board of Mental Health
   Counselors 401.222.2827**
Fax 401.222.1272
Web . . . . .www.health.ri.gov
E-mail . . . . .charles.alexander@health.ri.gov
   3 Capitol Hl Ste 104, Providence, RI 02908-5034
   Charles Alexander, Director

Voc & Rehab Agency RI .401.421.7005
Fax 401.222.3574
E-mail . . . . .sbrunero@ors.ri.gov
   40 Fountain St, Providence, RI 02903
   Steven Brunero, Director/Administrator

JUSTICE AGENCY

Correctional Education Division RI 401.462.2507
Fax 401.462.2509
E-mail . . . . .education@doc.ri.gov
   15 Fleming Rd, Bernadette Bldg, Cranston, RI 02920
   Ralph Orleek, Chief Executive Officer

Crime Victim Compensation Program 401.222.8590
Fax 401.222.4577
   40 Fountain St Fl 1, Providence, RI 02903
   Melba Depina, Program Administrator

**Dept. of Children, Youth and Families - Div of Juvenile
   Correctional Svcs 401.462.7241**
Fax 401.462.7239
Web . . . . .www.dcyf.state.ri.us/juvcorrectns.htm
   57 Power Rd, Cranston, RI 02920-3004
   Joseph Cardin, Acting Superintendent

Rhode Island CASA 401.458.3330
Fax 401.458.3340
Web . . . . .www.familycourts.com
E-mail . . . . .ajohnson@courts.ri.gov
   1 Dorrance Plz, Rm 211, Providence, RI 02903
   Andrew Johnson, Director

Rhode Island Commission for Human Rights . . .401.222.2561
Fax 401.222.2616
E-mail . . . . .mevora@richr.state.ri.us
   180 WESTMINSTER ST STE 201, Providence,
   RI 02903-1918
   Michael D. Evora, Esq., Executive Director

Rhode Island Justice Commission 401.222.2620
Fax 401.222.1294
Web . . . . .www.rijustice.ri.gov
E-mail . . . . .tmongeau@gw.doa.state.ri.us
   1 Capitol Hill, Providence, RI 02908
   Thomas Mongeau, Executive Director

Rhode Island Legal Svcs .401.274.2652
Fax 401.453.0310
E-mail . . . . .rbarge@rils.org
   56 Pine St Ste 4, Providence, RI 02903
   Robert Barge, Executive Director

COURTS

Rhode Island Family Court 401.458.3290
Fax 401.458.3310
E-mail . . . . .jjeremiah@courts.ri.gov
   1 Dorrance Plz, Providence, RI 02903-3922
   Honorable Jeremiah S. Jeremiah Jr., Chief Family Court Judge

EDUCATION SERVICES

Of of Progressive Support and Interv RI 401.222.8477
Fax 401.222.2537
E-mail . . . . .kim.chouinard@ride.ri.gov
   255 Westminster St, Shephard Bldg Rm 524,
   Providence, RI 02903
   Kim Choinard, Educatinal Specialist

Ofc of Special Needs Svcs 401.222.3505
Fax 401.222.6030
Web . . . . .www.ride.ri.gov
E-mail .kenneth.swanson@ride.ri.gov
   255 Westminster St, Shepard Building, Providence,
   RI 02903-3414
   Kenneth Swanson, Director

Off for Diverse Learners RI 401.222.8333
Fax 401.222.6030
E-mail . . . . .karen.lovett@ride.ri.gov
   255 Westminster St, Shepard Bldg 4th Flr, Providence,
   RI 02903
   Karen Lovett, Director

**Rhode Island Commission on the Deaf & Hard of
   Hearing 401.256.5511**
Fax 401.222.5736
E-mail . . . . .cdhh@cdhh.ri.gov
   1 Capitol Hill, Providence, RI 02908
   Steven A. Florio, Executive Director

Rhode Island Dept of Elem & Secon Educat 401.222.4690
Fax 401.222.6178
E-mail . . . . .angela.teixeira@ride.ri.gov
   255 Westminster St, Providence, RI 02903
   Angela Teixeira, Director

School for the Deaf...................401.222.3525
Fax..401.243.1024
Web.....................................www.rideaf.net
　1 Corliss Park, Providence, RI 02908
　Corsino Delgado, Director

State Dept of Education....................401.222.4600
Fax..401.222.4979
Web.......................................www.ride.ri.gov
　255 Westminster St, Shepard Bldg, Providence,
　RI 02903-3400
　Anne Marie Sylvia, Hiv Ed Specialist

State Parent Resource & Info Ctr RI..........401.727.0867
Fax..401.727.4040
E-mail.............................schlesinger@ripin.org
　175 Main St, Pawtucket, RI 02860

LABOR & WORKFORCE EDUCATION

Dept of Labor and Training.................401.462.8420
Fax..401.462.8466
Web...www.elt.ri.us
　1511 Pontiac Ave, Bldg. 73-3, Cranston, RI 02920
　Charles Fogarty, Director

COUNTY SERVICES

Bristol County

SOCIAL SERVICES

Dept Of Public Welfare.....................401.253.4831
Fax..401.253.4831
Web.....................................www.bristol.ri.us
E-mail.............................ecarusi@bristolri.us
　1220 hope st, Bristol, RI 02809-2234
　Ed Carusi, Human Resource Director

MENTAL HEALTH SERVICES

East Bay Ctr..............................401.246.1195
Fax..401.246.1985
Web....................................www.eastbay.org
E-mail..........................rcrossley@eastbay.org
　2 Old County Rd, Barrington, RI 02806-1602
　Bob Crossley, CEO

Cranston County

GENERAL HEALTH SERVICES

Family Health Svcs.........................401.943.1981
Fax..401.943.2846
Web....................................www.comcap.org
　1090 Cranston St, Cranston, RI 02920
　William Hochstrasser-walsh, Director

Kent County

MENTAL HEALTH SERVICES

Kent Ctr...................................401.738.1760
Fax..401.738.7718
　2756 Post Rd, Warwick, RI 02886-3003
　David Lauterbach, Director

COURTS

District Court.............................401.822.6750
Fax..401.822.6755
Web....................................www.courts.ri.gov
E-mail............................jlafazia@courts.ri.gov
　222 Quaker Ln Ste 220, Warwick, RI 02886-0108
　Honorable Jeanie Lafazia, 1st Presiding District Court Judge

Family Court...............................401.822.6725
Fax..401.822.6730
Web....................................www.courts.ri.gov
　222 Quaker Ln Ste 200, Warwick, RI 02886-0100
　Ron Pirolli, Principal Supervisory Clerk

EDUCATION SERVICES

Special Education..........................401.734.3055
Fax..401.734.3060
Web...................................www.wpsadmin.org
　34 Warwick Lake Ave, Warwick, RI 02889-2224
　Susan Rooney, Assistant Director

Newport County

SOCIAL SERVICES

Newport Dept Of Human Svcs..............401.851.2100
Fax..401.851.2105
　110 Enterprise Ctr, Middletown, RI 02842
　Laurie Dossantos, Supervisor

JUSTICE AGENCY

Portsmouth Barracks.......................401.444.1066
Fax..401.849.4446
Web..................................www.risp.state.ri.us
E-mail...................fsullivan@risp.dps.ri.gov
　838 E Main Rd, Portsmouth, RI 02871-2128
　Frank Sullivan, Patrol Commander

COURTS

District Court.............................401.841.8350
Fax..401.841.8394
Web..................................www.courts.state.ri.us
E-mail..........................dbellamy@courts.ri.gov
　45 Washington Sq, Newport, RI 02840-2913
　Dawn Bellamy, Acting Court Clerk

Family Court...............................401.841.8340
Fax..401.848.5185
Web....................................www.courts.ri.gov
　45 Washington Sq, Newport, RI 02840-5102
　Honorable Karen Dorothy, 1st Presiding Family Court Judge

POLICE AND SHERIFF

Sheriff's Dept.............................401.841.8300
Fax..401.841.8308
E-mail..........................nptshrf@usacops.com
　45 Washington Sq, Newport, RI 02840-2913
　Joseph K. Ford, Sheriff

Providence County

SOCIAL SERVICES

**Blackstone Valley Community Action Program,
Inc...401.723.4520**
Fax..401.723.4282
Web....................................www.bvcap.org
E-mail..........................bvcap@hotmail.com
　32 Goff Ave, Pawtucket, RI 02860-2928
　Vincent Ceglie, Chief Executive Officer

Cranston District Human Svcs..............401.462.6500
Fax..401.462.6504
Web......................................www.dhs.ri.gov
E-mail...................galexander@gw.dhs.state.ri.us
　600 New London Ave, # 38, Cranston, RI 02920
　Gary Alexander, Director

**Dept Of Children, Youth And
Families....................................401.254.7000**
Fax..401.254.7068
Web......................................www.dcyf.ri.gov
E-mail...................paula.fontaine@dcyf.ri.gov
　530 Wood St, Bristol, RI 02809-2310
　Paula Fontaine, Regional Director

GENERAL HEALTH SERVICES

**Blackstone Valley Community Health
Care..401.722.0081**
Fax..401.724.2109
　964 Broad St, Central Falls, RI 02863
　Jerry Fingerut, MD, Medical Director

Visiting Nurse Svc of Greater Rhode
Island.....................................401.769.5670
Fax..401.762.2966
Web....................................www.vnsgri.org
　6 Blackstone Valley Pl, Ste 515, Lincoln, RI 02865
　Denise deHertogh, Director Nursing/Hospice Svcs.

MENTAL HEALTH SERVICES

Children's Behavioral Health...............401.528.3502
Fax..401.528.3760
　101 Friendship St, Providence, RI 02903
　Janet Anderson, Ed.d, Assistant Director

East Bay Mental Health Ctr.................401.431.9870
Fax..401.435.7486
Web....................................www.eastbay.org
E-mail..........................rcrossley@eastbay.org
　610 Wampanoag Trl, Riverside, RI 02915-1504
　Robert Crossley, CEO

JUSTICE AGENCY

Juvenile Probation.........................401.721.2600
Fax..401.721.2611
　249 Roosevelt Ave Unit 101, Pawtucket, RI 02860
　Mary Dixon, Probation Officer

Juvenile Probation Unit....................401.528.3535
Fax..401.528.3532
Web..................................www.dcyf.state.ri.us
　101 Friendship St, Fl 1, Providence, RI 02903
　Thomas Ragofta, Probation Officer

Lincoln Woods Barracks.....................401.444.1100
Fax..401.722.0490
　1575 Old Louisquisset Pike, Lincoln, RI 02865
　Lt. Glenn J. Skalubinski, Patrol Commander

COURTS

Family Court...............................401.458.3250
Fax..401.458.3120
Web....................................www.courts.ri.gov
　1 Dorrance Plz, Providence, RI 02903

POLICE AND SHERIFF

Providence Police Dept.....................401.272.3121
Fax..401.243.6432
　325 Washington St, Providence, RI 02903
　Dean Esserman, Chief Of Police

EDUCATION SERVICES

Special Education..........................401.456.9330
Fax..401.453.8699
Web.......................................www.ppsd.org
E-mail..........................andrea.soares@ppsd.org
　797 Westminster St, Providence, RI 02903-4018
　Lisa Vargas-Sinapi, Director

Washington County

JUSTICE AGENCY

Juvenile Probation..........................401.782.4160
Fax..401.782.1890
Web......................................www.dcyf.state.ri.us
E-mail.............................regina.gibb@dcyf.ri.gov
  4800 Tower Hill Rd Ste 157, Wakefield,
  RI 02879-2239
  Regina Gibb, Supervisor

POLICE AND SHERIFF

Sheriff's Ofc.................................401.782.4100
Fax..401.789.2690
Web...www.skpd.org
  4800 Tower Hill Rd Ste 239, Wakefield,
  RI 02879-2239
  Sargeant Keith Place, Sargeant

SPECIAL SERVICES AGENCIES

ADOPTION AGENCIES

Alliance For Children.........................401.725.9555
Fax..781.431.7474
Web.......................................www.allforchildren.org
E-mail..........................info@allforchildren.org
  500 Prospect St Ste 106, Pawtucket, RI 22860-6260
  Phylis Casey, Director

Jewish Family Svcs/ Adoption Options........401.331.1244
Fax..401.331.5772
Web.....................................www.adoptionoptions.org
E-mail..................................info@jfsri.org
  959 North Main St, Providence, RI 02904
  Erin Minior, Interim Director

Wide Horizons For Children.................401.421.4752
Fax..401.421.4738
Web...www.whfc.org
E-mail..............................info@whfc.org
  245 Waterman St Ste 504, Providence,
  RI 02906-5215
  Ann Rankowitz, Director

ADVOCACY RESOURCES

Mental Health Advocate....................401.462.2003
Fax..401.462.2008
Web...www.doa.ri.gov
E-mail.........................reed.cosper@doa.ri.gov
  57 Howard Ave, Louis Pasteur Bldg. 57 4th Floor,
  Cranston, RI 02920-3001
  H. Reed Cosper, Esquire, Director

Parent Support Network Of Rhode Island......401.467.6855
Fax..401.467.6903
Web..www.psnri.org
E-mail..............................c.ciano@psnri.org
  1395 Atwood Ave Ste 114, Johnston, RI 02919-4930
  Cathy Ciano, Executive Director

BEHAVIORAL HEALTH TREATMENT

Alternatives...................................401.453.4742
Web...www.nafi.com
E-mail......................ericklingaman@nafi.com
  350 Duncan Drive, Providence, RI 02906
  Mr. Eric Klingaman, Accreditation Manager
  Joint Commission accredited organization.

Blackstone Children's Home................401.729.1516
Fax..401.725.2143
  150 Walcott St, Pawtucket, RI 02860-3227
  Tracy Pearson, House Manager

Bonauto & Palmer Medical Practice.........401.351.0236
Fax..401.351.5005
Web..www.Brown.EDU
E-mail.......................barry_plummer@brown.edu
  2 Regency Plz, Ste 4, Providence, RI 02903-3153
  Dr. Palmer, Psychiatrist

Brody Medical Practice.....................401.861.4643
  295 Angell St Ste 6, Providence, RI 02906-2119
  Mark Brody, Psychiatrist

Bryant University Counseling Svcs..........401.232.6045
Fax..401.232.6948
Web..www.bryant.edu
E-mail.........................bphillips@bryant.edu
  1150 Douglas Pike Ste 1, Smithfield, RI 02917-1291
  William Phillips, MD, Psychiatrist

Butler Hospital..............................401.455.6200
Web...www.butler.org
E-mail.............................mbrinson@butler.org
  345 Blackstone Boulevard, Providence, RI 02906
  Ms. Mary Brinson, Accreditation Manager
  Joint Commission accredited organization.

Child & Family Svcs..........................401.841.8896
Fax..401.848.2336
Web..............................www.childandfamilyri.com
E-mail..........................pdibari@cfsnewport.org
  19 Valley Rd, Middletown, RI 02842-6306
  Peter Dibari, CEO

Child Development Ctr.......................401.444.5685
Fax..401.444.6115
  593 Eddy St, Rhode Island Hospital, Providence,
  RI 02903
  Pamela High, Director

CODAC, Inc..................................401.275.5039
Fax..401.942.3590
Web...www.codacinc.org
  1052 Park Avenue, Cranston, RI 02910
  CARF accredited programs available.

Community Mental Health Center, Inc........401.846.1213
Web..www.nccmhc.org
E-mail..........................mjcreely@nccmhc.org
  127 Johnnycake Hill Road, Middletown, RI 02842
  Ms. Mary Jane Creely, Accreditation Manager
  Joint Commission accredited organization.

Comprehensive Community Action, Inc........401.467.9610
Web..www.comcap.org
E-mail................whochstrasserwalsh@comcap.org
  311 Doric Avenue, Cranston, RI 02910
  Mr. William Hochstrasser-Walsh, Accreditation Manager
  Joint Commission accredited organization.

Cranston Arc.................................401.942.3445
Fax..401.943.8723
E-mail.........................rcarmody@cranstonarc.org
  60 Stamp Farm Rd, Cranston, RI 02921
  Rory Carmody, Vp Of Program Development

Cranston Arc.................................401.942.2388
Fax..401.944.7480
E-mail.......................pkrakowsky@cranstonarc.org
  665 Dyer Ave, Cranston, RI 02920-6900
  Patricia Krakowsky, Director

Di Zio Medical Practice.....................401.272.5674
  172 E Cushing St, Providence, RI 02906
  Dr. Stephen Di Zio, Psychiatrist

Drug And Alcohol Treatment Assoc Of Rhode
Island......................................401.521.5759
Fax..401.751.7850
Web...www.dataofri.org
  200 Metro Center Blvd, Providence, RI 02907-3104
  Neil Corkery, Director

East Bay Center..............................401.246.3080
Web...www.eastbay.org
E-mail..........................dcarpenter@eastbay.org
  610 Wampanoag Trail, Riverside, RI 02915
  Ms. Dorothy Carpenter, Accreditation Manager
  Joint Commission accredited organization.

Emma Pendleton Bradley Hospital...........401.432.1385
Web...www.lifespan.org
E-mail..........................mjenkins1@lifespan.org
  1011 Veterans Memorial Parkway, Riverside, RI 02915
  Ms. Mary-Ellen Jenkins, Accreditation Manager
  Joint Commission accredited organization.

Family Service of Rhode Island.............401.331.1350
Fax..401.277.3387
Web...www.familyserviceri.org
  134 Thurbers Avenue, Providence, RI 02905
  COA accredited organization.

Fellowship Health Resources................401.943.5817
Fax..401.943.1434
Web...www.fellowshiphr.org
  1257 Cranston St, Cranston, RI 02920
  Devina Neades-pope, Director

Florin Medical Practice.....................401.351.3030
  154 Waterman St, Providence, RI 02906
  Dr. Robert Florin, MD, Psychiatrist

Frank W Sullivan Ltd........................401.944.8667
Fax..212.879.8363
  960 Reservoir Ave, Cranston, RI 02910
  Dr. Craig Kaufmann, Psychiatrist

Gateway Health Care........................401.725.0450
Fax..401.722.4806
Web...www.gatewayhealth.org
E-mail......................btaylor@gatewayhealth.org
  82 Pond St, Pawtucket, RI 02860
  Belinda Taylor, Associate Director

Gateway Healthcare, Inc....................401.724.8400
Web...www.gatewayhealth.org
E-mail......................sderosa@gatewayhealth.org
  249 Roosevelt Avenue, Pawtucket, RI 02860
  Mr. Stephen DeRosa, Accreditation Manager
  Joint Commission accredited organization.

Group Medical Practice.....................401.277.0700
Fax..401.277.0744
E-mail................jennifer_friedman@brown.edu
  345 Plain St, Providence, RI 02905
  Michael Friedman MD, Psychiatrist

N R I Community Svcs Ctr...................401.235.7000
Fax..401.767.9177
Web...www.nricommunityservices.org
E-mail................cstephens@nricommunityservices.org
  55 John A Cummings Way, Woonsocket,
  RI 02895-3247
  Christian Stephens, Chief Executive Officer

NAMI Rhode Island..........................401.331.3060
Fax..401.274.3020
Web...www.namirhodeisland.org
E-mail..........................chaznami@cox.net
  154 Waderman St Ste 5B, Providence, RI 02906
  Chaz Gross, Executive Director

NRI Community Services, Inc................401.235.7000
Fax..401.769.1810
Web...www.nricommunityservices.org
  800 Clinton Street, Woonsocket, RI 08295
  CARF accredited programs available.

Phoenix House................................401.783.0782
Fax..401.783.1154
  1058 Kingstown Rd, Wakefield, RI 02879
  Kate Doktor, Director

Phoenix Houses of New England 401.331.4250
Fax 401.421.5520
Web .... www.phoenixhouse.org
99 Wayland Avenue, Suite 100, Providence, RI 02906
CARF accredited programs available.

Rhode Island Hospital 401.444.5131
Web .... www.lifespan.org
E-mail .... jehmann@lifespan.org
593 Eddy Street, Providence, RI 02903
Ms. Jeanne Ehmann, Accreditation Manager
Joint Commission accredited organization.

Tannerhill, Inc. 401.568.3650
Fax 401.568.4207
Web .... www.tannerhill.org
35 High Street, Pascoag, RI 02859
CARF accredited programs available.

The Groden Center, Inc. 401.274.6310
Fax 401.421.3280
Web .... www.grodencenter.org
E-mail .... grodencenter@grodencenter.org
86 Mount Hope Avenue, Providence, RI 02906
Patricia Levasseur, HBTS Director
CARF accredited programs available.

The Kent Center® for Human & Organizational
Development 401.732.5656
Fax 401.738.6442
Web .... www.thekentcenter.org
E-mail .... tpowell@thekentcenter.org
2756 Post Road, Suite 200, Warwick, RI 02886-0208
Thomas Powell, Director, Human Resources
CARF accredited programs available.

The Providence Center 401.528.0123
Fax 401.528.0124
Web .... www.providencecenter.org
E-mail .... wberube@provctr.org
528 North Main Street, Providence, RI 02904
Wendy Berube, Financial Director
CARF accredited programs available.

Turning Point 401.728.1030
Fax 401.724.0339
Web .... www.turningpointri.org
Five Kids Way, Pawtucket, RI 02860
Gary Stal, Assistant Director
CARF accredited programs available.

Turning The Corner 401.785.8446
Fax 401.785.8444
Web .... www.jhcdc.org
E-mail .... p.bouchard@jhcdc.org
801 Elmwood Avenue, Providence, RI 02907
Pat Bouchard, Director/Clinician
CARF accredited programs available.

Whitmarsh Corporation 401.351.7230
Fax 401.421.0198
Web .... www.whitmarshcorp.org
1055 North Main Street, Providence, RI 02904
CARF accredited programs available.

CHILDREN'S HOSPITAL

Community Hospital 401.782.8000
100 Kenyon Ave, Wakefield, RI 02879
Loius Piancola, Chief Executive Officer

Memorial Hospital 401.737.7000
455 Tollgate Rd, Warwick, RI 02886
Sandra Coletta, President

Newport Hospital 401.846.6400
11 Friendship St, Newport, RI 02840
George Vecchione, Chief Executive Officer

Rhode Island Hospital 401.444.4000
593 Eddy St, Providence, RI 02903

Westerly Hospital 401.596.6000
25 Wells St, Westerly, RI 02891
Charles Kinney, Chief Executive Officer

COUNSELING SERVICES

Bethany Christian Svcs 401.467.1395
Fax 401.467.2493
Web .... www.bethany.org
E-mail .... bcsrhodeisland@bethany.org
706 Warwick Ave, Warwick, RI 02888-2670
Pamela Wood, Director

Children's Friend And Svc 401.276.4300
Fax 401.331.3285
Web .... www.childrensfriendsri.org
E-mail .... tdeboise@cfsri.org
500 Prospect St Ste 106, Pawtucket, RI 02860-6260
Teresa Deboise, Director Program Development & Quality

Family Ministry 401.421.7833
Fax 401.453.6135
184 Broad St, Providence, RI 02903-4029
Gene Montero, Supervisor

Gateway Healthcare 401.722.3560
Fax 401.724.3120
103 Bacon St, Pawtucket, RI 02860
Dr. Steven Chabot, Director

Phoenix House 401.348.9995
Fax 401.348.2004
Web .... www.phoenixhouse.org
E-mail .... pmendoza@phoenixhouse.org
101 Franklin St, Westerly, RI 02891
Peter Mendoza, Director

Tides Family Svcs 401.822.1360
Fax 401.823.4694
Web .... www.tidesfs.org
E-mail .... michaelreis@tidesfs.org
215 Washington St, West Warwick, RI 02893
Brother Michael Reis, President

CRISIS & SHELTER CARE

Blackstone Shelter 401.723.3057
Fax 401.724.8820
Web .... www.blackstonevalleyadvocacycenter.org
E-mail .... linda@bvadvocacycenter.org
259 Central St, Central Falls, RI 28632
Linda Impagliazzo, Executive Director

Comprehensive Emergency Svcs 401.722.3560
Fax 401.365.1100
E-mail .... sbethel@gatewayhealth.org
101 Bacon St, Pawtucket, RI 02860-5402
Sandra Bethel, Supervisor

Crossroads 401.351.6500
Fax 401.421.7410
Web .... www.crossroadsri.org
E-mail .... rpartridge@crossroadsri.org
160 Broad St, Providence, RI 02903-4028
Russell Partridge, Head Of Adult Services

Sojourner House (Shelter) 401.658.4334
Fax 401.861.6157
Web .... www.sojournerri.org
E-mail .... lfisher@sojournerri.org
386 Smith St, Providence, RI 02908-3727
Lisa Fisher, Director Of Residential Services

EDUCATION

Family Resources Community Action 401.766.0900
Fax 401.766.8737
Web .... www.famresri.org
E-mail .... blessing@famresri.org
245 Main St, Woonsocket, RI 02895-3123
Ben Lessing, President/CEO

In-Sight 401.941.3322
Fax 401.941.3356
Web .... www.in-sight.org
E-mail .... cbutler@in-sight.org
43 Jefferson Blvd, Warwick, RI 02888-6400
Chris Butler, Executive Director

FOSTER CARE AGENCIES

Rhode Island Foster & Adoptive Parent 401.438.3900
E-mail .... lisa.gullette@rispa.org
55 S Brow St, East Providence, RI 02914
Lisa Gullette, Director

Stars of David International Inc 401.431.0728
E-mail .... starsdavid@aol.com
33 Edward Ave, Rumford, RI 02916

Urban League of Rhode Island Inc 401.351.5000
Fax 401.454.1946
E-mail .... langley@ulri.org
246 Prairie Ave, Providence, RI 02905
Dennis Langley, Chief Executive Officer

PEDIATRIC HOME CARE

Bayada Nurses 401.273.1112
Fax 401.273.5706
Web .... www.bayada.com
2 Charles St, Suite 1B, Providence, RI 02904
Julie Conway, Regional Director

Bayada Nurses 401.273.1112
Fax 401.273.5705
Web .... www.bayada.com
E-mail .... apacheco1@bayada.com
2 Charles Street, Suite 1A, Providence, RI 02904
Julie Conway, Regional Director

Interim Healthcare 401.272.3520
Fax 401.331.0081
245 Waterman St Ste 308, Providence, RI 02906
Julie Mark, Chief Executive Officer

SOCIAL SERVICES

Child and Family Services 401.849.2300
Fax 401.841.8841
Web .... www.childandfamilyri.com
31 John Clarke Road, Middletown, RI 02842
COA accredited organization.

Children's Friend and Service 401.276.4300
Fax 401.331.3285
Web .... www.childrensfriendri.org
153 Summer Street, Providence, RI 02903-4011
COA accredited organization.

Communities For People 401.273.7103
Fax 401.421.4608
Web .... www.communitiesforpeople.org
E-mail .... cgordon@communities-for-people.org
623 Atwells Ave Ste D103, Providence,
RI 02909-7403
Craig Gordon, Regional Director

Family Resources Community Action 401.766.0900
Fax 401.767.4075
Web .... www.famresri.org
245 Main Street, Woonsocket, RI 02895-3123
COA accredited organization.

International Institute Of Rhode Island 401.461.5940
Fax 401.467.6530
Web .... www.iiri.org
E-mail .... bshuey@iiri.org
645 Elmwood Ave, Providence, RI 02907-3313
William Shuey, Director

John Hope Settlement House 401.421.6993
Fax 401.454.5619
Web .... www.johnhope.org
7 Thomas P Whitten Way, Providence, RI 02903-4046
Peter Lee, President

Phoenix Academy 401.568.1770
Fax 401.568.3358
Web .... www.phoenixhouse.org
E-mail .... dsherlock@phoenixhouse.org
2076 Wallum Lake Rd, Pascoag, RI 02859
Dave Sherlock, Director

spurwink|ri 401.781.4380
Fax..401.781.4396
Web.......................................www.spurwink.org
  1 Spurwink Place, Cranston, RI 02910
COA accredited organization.

St. Mary's Home for Children 401.353.3900
Web...www.smhfc.org
  420 Fruit Hill Avenue, North Providence, RI 02911
COA accredited organization.

Tides Family Services, Inc....................401.822.1360
Fax..401.823.4694
Web...www.tidesfs.org
  215 Washington Street, West Warwick, RI 02893
COA accredited organization.

SPECIAL NEEDS

Autism Society of Rhode Island 401.595.0324
E-mail ....ri-rhodeisland@autismsocietyofamerica.org
  PO Box 16603, Rumford, RI 02916

Brain Injury Association 888.824.8911
E-mail ....braininjuryctr@biaofri.org
  935 Park Ave Ste 8, Cranston, RI 02910
Sharon Brinkworth, Director

Congress of Parents & Teachers 401.272.6405
E-mail ....ri_office@pta.org
  600 Mount Pleasant Ave, Providence, RI 02908

Down Syndrome Society 401.463.5751
E-mail ....coordinator@dssri.org
  99 Bald Hill Rd, Cranston, RI 02920

Harmony Hill School 401.949.0690
Fax..401.949.2060
Web...www.hhs.org
  63 Harmony Hill Rd, Chepachet, RI 02814
Janice Defrances, Principal

Mental Health Association 401.726.2285
E-mail ....mhari@mhari.org
  500 Prospect St, Pawtucket, RI 02860
Vivian Weisman, Executive Director

NAMI Rhode Island 800.749.3197
E-mail ....chaznami@cox.net
  154 Waterman St Ste 5B, Providence, RI 02906
Chaz Gross, Executive Director

National Federation of the Blind 401.433.2606
Web...www.nrbri.org
E-mail ....info@nfbri.org
  PO Box 14404, Riverside, RI 02914
Grace Pires, President

National Multiple Sclerosis Society 401.738.8383
Fax..401.738.8469
E-mail ....Catie.Dussault@rir.nmss.org
  205 Hallene Rd # 209, Warwick, RI 02886
Catie Dussault, Director Of Development

RI Parent Info Network Inc 401.270.0101
Fax..401.270.7049
E-mail ....donovan@ripin.org
  1210 Pontiac Ave, Cranston, RI 02920
Matthew Cox, Chief Executive Officer

The Autism Project 401.785.2666
E-mail ....info@theautismproject.org
  1516 Atwood Ave, Johnston, RI 02919
Joanne Quinn, Executive Director

The Spurwink School 401.781.4380
Fax..401.334.3783
Web..www.spurwinkri.org
  365 River Rd, Lincoln, RI 02865
Carleen Bellaire Med, Principal

The Wolf School 401.432.9940
Fax..401.432.9947
  215 Ferris Ave, East Providence, RI 02916
Jessica Robins Miller, Director

United Cerebral Palsy 401.728.1800
E-mail ....ucprisupport@ucpri.org
  200 Main St Ste 210, Pawtucket, RI 02860
Peter Quatcropmani, Chief Executive Officer

VSA Arts Rhode Island 401.725.0247
E-mail ....programs@vsartsri.org
  500 Prospect St, Pawtucket, RI 02860
Jeannie Chartier, Director

SUBSTANCE ABUSE TREATMENT

Codac Behavioral HealthCare 401.846.4150
Fax..401.846.9340
Web..www.codacinc.org
E-mail ....ehayes@codacinc.org
  93 Thames St, Newport, RI 02840-2536
Elizabeth Hayes, Program Director

Eastman House, Inc 401.463.8829
Fax..401.463.8879
Web...www.caritas.org
E-mail ....mdebalsi@caritasri.org
  70 E St, Cranston, RI 02920-4407
Maryanne Debalsi, Clinical Manager

Phoenix House 401.331.4200
Fax..401.453.4910
Web..www.phoenixhouse.org
E-mail ....pmendoza@phoenixhouse.org
  99 Wayland Ave, Providence, RI 02906-4314
Peter Mendoza, Director Of Out Patient Services

Project Link Women And Infants Hospital 401.453.7618
Fax..401.453.7692
Web......................................www.womenandinfants.org
E-mail ....amedeiroswihri@.org
  134 Thurbers Ave Ste 212, Providence, RI 02905
Alda Medeiros, Associate Division Manager

Star Of Rhode Island 800.747.6237
Fax..401.295.2513
  1950 Tower Hill Rd, North Kingstown, RI 02852
John Brett, Director

The Providence Ctr 401.276.4000
Fax..401.528.0124
Web......................................www.providencecenter.org
E-mail ....ajacobsen@provctr.org
  520 Hope St, Providence, RI 02906-2599
Alan Jacobsen, Director

South Carolina

sc.gov

Nikki Haley, Governor
PO Box 12267
Columbia, SC 29211
803.734.2100
803.734.5167 (Fax)
www.scgovernor.com

Bonnie Burns, Juvenile Justice Specialist
Department of Public Safety
PO Box 1993
Blythewood, SC 29016
803.896.8707
803.896.8714 (Fax)
bonnieburns@scdps.net

Nic Church, SAG Chair
140 Cedar Falls Dr
Blythewood, SC 29016
803.609.1006
sukey@netzero.com

CRISIS NUMBERS

Child Abuse Reporting . . .803.898.7318

STATE SERVICES

SOCIAL SERVICES

Dept of Social Svcs 803.898.7601
Fax 803.898.7277
Web . . . . .www.state.sc.us/dss
E-mail . . . . .kaydlette@dss.state.sc.us
  1535 Confederate Ave, Columbia, SC 29201
  Kim Aydlette, State Director

Div of Child Care Lic and Reg Srvs SC 803.898.9030
Fax 803.989.9029
  2638 Two Notch Road, Ste 200, Columbia, SC 29204
  Cynthia Lara, Director

Head Start Collaboration Office 803.898.2550
Fax 803.898.4458
Web . . . . .www.dss.state.sc.us
E-mail . . . . .mary.diggs@dss.sc.gov
  1535 Confederate Ave, 3rd Floor, Columbia,
  SC 29201
  Mary Lynne Diggs, Director Of Collaborations

South Carolina Emergency Management Div . . .803.737.8500
Fax 803.737.8570
Web . . . . .www.scemd.org
E-mail . . . . .rosborne@emd.state.sc.us
  2779 Fish Hatchery Rd, West Columbia,
  SC 29172-2096

GENERAL HEALTH SERVICES

Bureau of Public Health Svcs 803.898.0778
Web . . . . .www.scdehc.gov
  1751 Calhoun St, Columbia, SC 29201-2606
  Michael Chappell, Assistant Health Commissionr

Children with Special Health Care Needs 803.898.0784
Fax 803.898.0613
Web . . . . .www.scdhec.com
E-mail . . . . .cshcn@dhec.sc.gov
  1751 Calhoun St, Columbia, SC 29201-2606
  Cheryl Waller, Director

Div of Child w Spec Health Care Needs SC 803.898.0784
Fax 803.898.0613
E-mail . . . . .wallercj@dhec.sc.gov
  1751 Calhoun St, Columbia, SC 29211
  Cj Waller, Director

Iv of Children w Spec Health Care Needs SC 803.898.0784
Fax 803.898.0613
E-mail . . . . .wallercj@dhec.sc.gov
  1751 Calhoun St, Columbia, SC 29201
  Cj Waller, Director

South Carolina Dept of Health and Human Svcs
  Medicaid 803.898.2500
Fax 803.255.8235
Web . . . . .www.scdhhs.gov
E-mail . . . . .stone@scdhhs.gov
  1801 Main St, Columbia, SC 29201-2409
  Sylvia Stone, Director

Women, Infants & Children's Svcs 803.898.0744
Fax 803.898.0383
E-mail . . . . .walkerbw@dhec.sc.gov
  1751 Calhoun St, Columbia, SC 29201-2606
  Burnese Walker, Director

MENTAL HEALTH SERVICES

Dept of Disabilities & Special Needs 803.898.9600
Fax 803.898.9656
Web . . . . .www.ddsn.sc.gov
E-mail . . . . .sdelaney@ddsn.sc.gov
  3440 Harden St Ext, Columbia, SC 29240
  Dr. Beverly Buscemi, Director

Dept of Vocational Rehabilitation 803.896.6500
Fax 803.896.6558
Web . . . . .www.scvrd.com
E-mail . . . . .info@scvrd.state.sc.us
  1410 Boston Ave, West Columbia, SC 29170-2188
  Barbara Hollis, Commissioner

South Carolina Commission for the Blind 803.898.8700
Fax 803.898.8852
E-mail . . . . .Ljohnston@sccb.sc.gov
  1430 Confederate Ave, PO Box 2467, Columbia,
  SC 29202
  L Johnston, Director

South Carolina Professional Counselor
  Licensing 803.896.4688
Fax 803.896.4814
Web . . . . .www.llr.state.sc.us/pol/counselors
E-mail . . . . .coxk@llr.sc.gov
  110 Centerview Dr, Suite 306, Columbia, SC 29210
  Kate K. Cox, Director

South Carolina Voc Rehab Dept 803.896.6504
Fax 803.896.6529
E-mail . . . . .bhollis@scvrd.state.sc.us
  1410 Boston Ave, West Columbia, SC 29170
  B Hollis, Director

JUSTICE AGENCY

Attorney General's Ofc 803.734.3970
Fax 803.253.6283
Web . . . . .www.scattorneygeneral.org
E-mail . . . . .info@scattorneygeneral.com
  1000 Assembly St, Ste 519, Columbia, SC 29201
  Alan Wilson, Attorney General

Correctional Educational Division SC 803.896.1583
Fax 803.896.1513
E-mail . . . . .johnson.teresa@doc.state.sc.us
  4444 Broad River Rd, Columbia, SC 29210
  Teresa Johnson, Director

South Carolina Dept of Juvenile Justice 803.896.9749
Fax 803.896.9767
Web . . . . .www.state.sc.us/djj/
  4900 Broad River Rd, Columbia, SC 29212
  Margaret Barber, Director For Agency

South Carolina Law Enforcement Div 803.896.7216
Fax 803.896.7041
Web . . . . .www.sled.state.sc.gov
  4400 Broad River Rd, Columbia, SC 29221
  Reginald Lloyd, Chief

State Ofc of Victim Assistance (SOVA) 803.734.1900
Fax 803.734.1708
Web . . . . .www.sova.sc.gov
E-mail . . . . .sova@oepp.sc.gov
  1205 Pendleton St Ste 401, Columbia,
  SC 29201-3751
  Larry Barker, Program Director

COURTS

South Carolina Court Administration 803.734.1800
Fax 803.734.1355
E-mail . . . . .rfrierson@sccourts.org
  1015 Sumter St Rm 200, Columbia, SC 29201
  Rosalyn Frierson, Director

POLICE AND SHERIFF

South Carolina Law Enforcement Dept 803.737.9000
Fax 803.896.7022
  4400 Broad River Rd, Columbia, SC 29221
  Reggie Lloyd, Director

South Carolina Police Chiefs Assoc 803.790.5042
Fax 803.790.5043
Web . . . . .www.scpca.org
E-mail . . . . .mail@scpaca.org
  4701 Arcadia Rd, Columbia, SC 29260-1170
  J.c. Rowe, Executive Director

South Carolina Sheriff's Assoc 803.772.1101
Fax 803.772.1197
Web ....www.sheriffsc.com
E-mail ....sheriffsc@aol.com
   112 Westpark Blvd, Columbia, SC 29210
Jeffrey B. Moore, Executive Director

EDUCATION SERVICES

Dept of Education 803.734.8500
Fax 803.734.3389
Web ....www.ed.sc.gov
E-mail ....scsutted@ed.sc.gov
   1429 Senate St Ste 100, Columbia, SC 29201
Mick Zaif, Superintendent

Educ for Homeless Children and Youth SC 803.734.3215
Fax 803.734.3043
E-mail ....bmyers@ed.sc.gov
   1429 Senate St Ste 700 B, Columbia, SC 29201
B Myers, Director

Migrant Programs, Title 1 ....803.734.8219
Fax 803.734.3290
Web ....www.sde.state.sc.us
   1429 Senate St, Columbia, SC 29201
Betty Black, Coordinator

Office of Exceptional Children SC 803.734.8806
Fax 803.734.4824
E-mail ....mametts@ed.sc.gov
   1429 Senate St, Rm 808, Columbia, SC 29201
Marlene Metts, Director

Parent Training and Resource Ctr SC 843.266.1318
Fax 843.266.1941
E-mail ....bevmccarty@frcdsn.org
   1575 Savannah Highway Ste 6, Charleston, SC 29407
Bev Mccarty, Director

State Dept of Education/Deparment of Info 803.734.8815
Fax 803.734.3389
Web ....www.ed.sc.gov
   1429 Senate St, Ste 100, Columbia, SC 29201
Wanda Davis, Ombudsman

LABOR & WORKFORCE EDUCATION

South Carolina Dept of Commerce 803.737.0097
Fax 803.806.3533
E-mail ....ptorrey@sccommerce.com
   1201 Main St, Ste 1600, Columbia, SC 29201-3261
Margaret Torrey, Director

COUNTY SERVICES

Abbeville County

SOCIAL SERVICES

Social Svcs 864.366.5481
Fax 864.366.0045
Web ....www.state.or.us
E-mail ....richard.haynes@state.or.us
   903 W Greenwood St, Abbeville, SC 29620-5678
Richard E. Hayne, Acting County Director

GENERAL HEALTH SERVICES

Abbeville Health Dept 864.366.2131
Fax 864.366.4105
   905 W Greenwood St, Abbeville, SC 29620
Becky Campbell, Md, District Director

JUSTICE AGENCY

Dept Of Juvenile Justice 864.366.5312
Fax 864.366.9188
E-mail ....dashley@abbevillecountysc.com
   102 Court Sq, Abbeville, SC 29620
Debbie B. Ashley, County Director

POLICE AND SHERIFF

Sheriff's Ofc 864.446.6000
Fax 864.446.6050
E-mail ....chgoodwin@wctel.net
   21 Old Calhoun Falls Rd, Abbeville, SC 29620-6503
Charles H. Goodwin, Sheriff

Aiken County

SOCIAL SERVICES

Social Svcs 803.649.1111
Fax 803.643.1904
   1410 Park Ave SE, Aiken, SC 29801
Laurie Hopp, Director

MENTAL HEALTH SERVICES

South Carolina Dept Of Mental Health Hartzog
Ctr 803.278.0880
Fax 803.278.6791
   431 W Martintown Rd, North Augusta, SC 29841
Karen Gaines, Clinic Manager

JUSTICE AGENCY

Dept Of Juvenile Justice 803.641.7735
Fax 803.641.7746
   1680 Richland Ave W Ste 90, Aiken, SC 29801
Kiristy Bodie, Director Of County

Guardian Ad Litem 803.648.9919
Fax 803.641.9690
E-mail ....galaiken@oepp.sc.gov
   5170 Woodside Executive Ct, Aiken, SC 29803
Gary W. Watson, Coordinator

COURTS

Family Court 803.642.1728
Fax 803.643.0911
   109 Park Ave, Aiken, SC 29802
Honorable Vicki Snelgrove, Director

POLICE AND SHERIFF

Sheriff's Ofc 803.642.1761
Fax 803.642.7535
E-mail ....sheriff@aikencountysc.gov
   420 Hampton Ave NE, Aiken, SC 29801
Mike Hunt, Sheriff

EDUCATION SERVICES

Special Education 803.641.2624
Fax 803.641.2628
Web ....www.ed.sc.gov
E-mail ....jeanettec@aiken.k12.sc.us
   1000 Brookhaven Dr, Aiken, SC 29803-2109
Sal Minolfo, Executive Director Special Programs

Allendale County

GENERAL HEALTH SERVICES

Health Dept 803.584.3818
Fax 803.584.8107
Web ....www.dhec.net
   571 Memorial Ave, Allendale, SC 29810
Charles Long, District Health Director

JUSTICE AGENCY

Dept Of Juvenile Justice 803.584.4751
Fax 803.584.7372
   649 Railroad Ave E, Allendale, SC 29810-4729
Wayne Bennett, County Director

POLICE AND SHERIFF

Sheriff's Ofc 803.584.2361
Fax 803.584.7064
   168 Law Enforcement Rd, Fairfax, SC 29827-9012
Catherine Russell, Victim Advocate

Anderson County

GENERAL HEALTH SERVICES

Regional Health District 864.260.5541
Fax 864.260.5676
   220 Mcgee Rd, Anderson, SC 29625
Fran Human, Social Work Director

MENTAL HEALTH SERVICES

Dept Of Mental Health 864.716.2316
Fax 864.716.2321
   515 Camson Rd, Anderson, SC 29625
Kevin Hoyle, Ma, Executive Director

JUSTICE AGENCY

Guardian Ad Litem Program 864.225.2348
Fax 864.224.7335
E-mail ....galanderson@oepp.sc.gov
   2315 N Main St, Ste 214, Anderson, SC 29621
Cindy Sauer, County Coordinator

COURTS

Family Court 864.260.4038
Fax 864.260.4822
Web ....www.sccourts.org
E-mail ....bknobelj@sccourts.org
   100 S Main St, Anderson, SC 29624-1619
Honorable Edgar H. Long, Judge

POLICE AND SHERIFF

Anderson City Police Dept 864.231.2277
Fax 864.332.5717
E-mail ....mbrown@cityofandersonsc.com
   401 S Main St, Anderson, SC 29624
Martin Brown, Chief Of Police

Sheriff's Ofc 864.260.4400
Fax 864.222.3962
   305 Camson Rd, Anderson, SC 29625
John Skipper, Sheriff

EDUCATION SERVICES

Anderson District 4 ....864.646.8000
Fax 864.646.8555
Web www.anderson4.k12.sc.us
   315 E Queen St, Pendleton, SC 29670
Leedan Diea, Superintendent

Anderson School District 1 ....864.847.7344
Fax 864.847.3551
Web www.anderson1.k12.sc.us
E-mail ....keithb@anderson1.k12.sc.us
   801 N Hamilton St, Williamston, SC 29697
Dr. Brian Keith, Psychologist/special Education Coordinator

Anderson School District 2 ....864.369.7364
Fax 864.369.4006
Web www.anderson2.k12.sc.us
   10990 Belton Honea Path Hwy, Honea Path,
   SC.29650
Terry Orr, Director Of Special Services

Anderson School District 5 ....864.260.5000
Fax 864.260.5074
Web www.anderson5.net
   400 Pearman Dairy Rd, Anderson, SC 29625
Lynn Dowis, Programs For Children With Disabilities

Bamberg County

SOCIAL SERVICES

DSS And DAHS Ofc 803.245.4361
Fax 803.245.3936
　374 Log Branch Rd, Bamberg, SC 29003
　Anita Bugler, Director

GENERAL HEALTH SERVICES

Health Dept 803.245.5176
Fax 803.245.5371
　370 Log Branch Rd, Bamberg, SC 29003
　Katherin Gramling, Nursing Director

JUSTICE AGENCY

Dept Of Juvenile Justice 803.245.5184
Fax 803.245.2128
E-mail ....emgarr@scdjj.net
　1162 N st, Bamberg, SC 29003
　Edward Golden, County Director

POLICE AND SHERIFF

Sheriff's Ofc 803.245.3018
Fax 803.245.3102
E-mail ....bamcntyso@orbg.net
　456 2nd St, Bamberg, SC 29003
　J. Edward Darnell, Sheriff

Barnwell County

SOCIAL SERVICES

Social Services 803.541.1200
Fax 803.541.1209
Web ....www.state.sc.us
　10913 Ellenton St, Barnwell, SC 29812
　Carolyn Sherman, County Director

GENERAL HEALTH SERVICES

Health Dept 803.541.1061
Fax 803.541.1066
Web ....www.dhec.sc.gov
　11015 Ellenton St, Barnwell, SC 29812
　Charles Long, District Health Director

COURTS

Family Court 803.541.1033
Fax 803.541.1127
　100 Main St, #208, Barnwell, SC 29812
　Honorable Dale Moore Gable, Judge

POLICE AND SHERIFF

Sheriff's Ofc 803.541.1052
Fax 803.259.9683
Web ....www.barnwellsc.com
E-mail ....edcarroll@barnwellsc.com
　599 Joey Zorn Blvd, Barnwell, SC 29812-7345
　Ed Carroll, Sheriff

Beaufort County

SOCIAL SERVICES

Social Services 843.255.6080
Fax 843.255.6111
Web ....www.state.sc.us
E-mail ....ronald.smith@dss.sc.gov
　1905 Duke St, Beaufort, SC 29902
　Ronald Smith, Director

GENERAL HEALTH SERVICES

Health Dept 843.757.2251
Fax 843.757.2253
Web ....www.scdhec.gov
　4819 Blusston Pkwy, Bluffton, SC 29910
　Elizabeth Gebhardt, Nursing Supervisor

JUSTICE AGENCY

Dept Of Juvenile Justice 843.525.1351
Fax 843.525.9328
E-mail ....rebeat@scdjj.net
　1905 Duke St, Rm 220, Beaufort, SC 29901
　Robert Beattie, Director

Guardian Ad Litem 843.525.0779
Fax 843.522.8937
Web ....www.oepp.sc.gov
E-mail ....tgravel@oepp.sc.gov
　2201 Boundary St, Apt 308, Beaufort, SC 29902
　Tricia Gravel, Circuit Coordinator

Berkeley County

SOCIAL SERVICES

Social Svcs 843.761.8044
Fax 843.761.2779
Web ....www.state.sc.us
　2 Belt Dr, Moncks Corner, SC 29461-2801
　Charles Epps, County Director

GENERAL HEALTH SERVICES

Health Dept 843.572.3313
Fax 843.572.6812
　106 Westview Blvd, Goose Creek, SC 29445
　Cathy Wyatt, Director

JUSTICE AGENCY

Dept Of Juvenile Justice 843.761.8194
Fax 843.899.5611
E-mail ....naashe@scdjj.net
　109 W Main St, Moncks Corner, SC 29461-3748
　Nicole Ashe, County Director

COURTS

Family Court 843.719.4500
Fax 843.719.4509
E-mail ....wcreech@scjd.state.sc.us
　300 California Ave Ste B, Moncks Corner,
　SC 29461-4036
　Honorable Wayne M. Creech, Judge

POLICE AND SHERIFF

Sheriff's Ofc 843.719.4412
Fax 843.719.4427
　223 Nlive Oak Dr., Moncks Corner, SC 29461
　Wayne Dewitt, Sheriff

EDUCATION SERVICES

Special Education 843.899.8890
Fax 843.899.5297
Web www.berkley.k12.sc.us
　Berkely Education Center, Moncks Corner, SC 29461
　Susan Thomas, Director Of Programs

Calhoun County

SOCIAL SERVICES

Social Services 803.874.3384
Fax 803.874.2786
E-mail ....richard.dantzler@dsf.sc.gov
　2381 Old Bellville Rd, Saint Matthews, SC 29135
　Richard Dantzler, County Director

GENERAL HEALTH SERVICES

Health Dept 803.874.2037
Fax 803.874.4693
Web ....www.calhouncounty.org
　2837 Old Belleville Rd, Saint Matthews, SC 29135
　Toni Ocain, Nursing Supervisor/aids Coord

POLICE AND SHERIFF

Sheriff's Ofc 803.874.2741
Fax 803.874.2634
　2811 Old Eville Rd, Saint Matthews, SC 29135-1339
　Thomas S. Summers, Sheriff

Charleston County

SOCIAL SERVICES

Dept Of Social Svcs 843.953.9400
Fax 843.740.1575
Web ....www.state.sc.us/dss
E-mail ....owilliams@dss.state.sc.us
　3366 Rivers Ave, North Charleston, SC 29405-5714
　Odessa J Williams, County Director

GENERAL HEALTH SERVICES

Health Dept 843.579.4500
Fax 843.579.4623
　3 Charleston Center Dr, Charleston, SC 29401
　Ms. Mary Beth Horton, HIV Team Leader

Health Dept 843.740.1580
Fax 843.744.3671
Web ....www.scstate.gov/health
　3963 Whipper Barony Ln, North Charleston,
　SC 29405
　Carla Beckwith, Site Manager

Health Dept 843.856.1210
Fax 843.856.1189
Web ....www.dhec.sc.gov
　1189 Iron Bridge Dr Ste 100, Mt Pleasant,
　SC 29466-7413
　Jennifer Griffin, Site Manager

JUSTICE AGENCY

Dept Of Juvenile Justice 843.740.1649
Fax 843.740.1681
Web ....www.scdjj.net
E-mail ....astand@scdjj.net
　3346 Rivers Ave Ste B, North Charleston,
　SC 29405-5715
　Ashley Standafer, County Director

**Victim's Svcs/Mt Pleasant Police
Dept** 843.856.2189
Fax 843.856.2190
E-mail ....warren@mountpleasant.com
　100 Ann Edwards Ln, Mt Pleasant, SC 29464
　Stan Gragg, Captain

COURTS

Family Court 843.958.4400
Fax 843.958.4434
　100 Broad St Ste 143, Charleston, SC 29401
　Dave Mckeown, Supervisor Of Family Court

Hall 843.577.6970
Fax 843.720.3827
Web ....www.charlestoncity.org
E-mail ....publicinfo@charlestoncity.org
　80 Broad St, Charleston, SC 29401
　Joseph P Riley Jr, Mayor

POLICE AND SHERIFF

Sheriff's Ofc 843.202.1700
Fax 843.308.7344
Web ....www.charlestoncounty.org
　3505 Pinehaven Dr, North Charleston,
　SC 29405-7733
　J. Al Cannon, Jr., Sheriff

Cherokee County

SOCIAL SERVICES

Social Services 864.487.2704
Fax 864.487.2512
Web ....www.state.sc.us
E-mail ....larry.wall@dss.sc.gov
　1434 N Limestone St, Gaffney, SC 29340
　Larry Wall, County Director

GENERAL HEALTH SERVICES

Health Dept **864.487.2705**
Fax 864.487.2728
Web ....www.scdhec.net
   400 S Logan St, Gaffney, SC 29341-1609
   Matt Petrofes, Director

JUSTICE AGENCY

Dept Of Juvenile Justice **864.487.2564**
Fax 864.487.6232
   312 E Frederick St, Gaffney, SC 29340-1386
   Terry Hall, Director

COURTS

Family Court **864.487.2568**
Fax 864.487.2776
E-mail ....ubridgesj@sccourts.org
   125 E Floyd Baker Blvd, Ste 3, Gaffney, SC 29340
   Honorable Usha J. Bridges, Judge

POLICE AND SHERIFF

Sheriff's Ofc **864.489.4722**
Fax 864.487.2768
Web ....www.cherokeecountysheriff.net
E-mail ....sheriff@cherokeecountysheriff.net
   312 E Frederick St, Gaffney, SC 29340-2411
   Steve Miller, Sheriff

Chester County

SOCIAL SERVICES

Dept Of Social Svcs **803.377.8131**
Fax 803.581.8771
   115 Reedy St, Chester, SC 29706
   Robert J Smith, Jr., Director

GENERAL HEALTH SERVICES

Health Dept **803.385.6152**
Fax 803.581.3815
   129 Wylie St, Chester, SC 29706
   Richard Funderburk, District Administrator

Health Dept Clinic **803.482.6133**
Fax 803.482.7053
Web ....www.scdhec.gov
   404 Chester Ave, Great Falls, SC 29055-1206
   Liz Freeman, Supervisor

JUSTICE AGENCY

Dept Of Juvenile Justice **803.377.8104**
Fax 803.385.2891
E-mail ....rbwess@scdjj.net
   130 Wylie St, Chester, SC 29706-1792
   Rick Wessinger, County Director

Guardian Ad Litem Program **803.286.6064**
Fax 803.286.8833
Web ....www.oepp.sc.gov
E-mail ....gallancaster@oepp.sc.gov
   112 N Woodland Dr, Lancaster, SC 29720
   Paula Lance, County Coordinator

POLICE AND SHERIFF

Sheriff's Ofc **803.581.5131**
Fax 803.581.5552
   2740 Dawson Dr, Chester, SC 29706
   Richard Smith, Sheriff

EDUCATION SERVICES

Edgemoor Head Start **803.789.3601**
   1966 Westbrook Rd, Edgemoor, SC 29712
   Julie A Gaskins, Director

Chesterfield County

SOCIAL SERVICES

Social Svcs **843.623.2147**
Fax 843.623.2151
E-mail ....ralph.laney@dss.sc.gov
   201 N Page St, Chesterfield, SC 29709
   Ralph Laney, Director

GENERAL HEALTH SERVICES

Health Dept **843.623.2117**
Fax 843.623.3066
Web ....www.dhec.net
   203 N Page St, Chesterfield, SC 29709
   Susie Ingram, Aids Coordinator

JUSTICE AGENCY

Dept Of Juvenile Justice **843.623.2378**
Fax 843.623.3050
E-mail ....lbailey@scdjj.net
   101 Main St, Chesterfield, SC 29709
   Lisa Bailey, County Director

COURTS

Family Court **843.623.3080**
Fax 843.623.3402
E-mail ....rhenderson@scjd.state.sc.us
   PO Box 311, Chesterfield, SC 29709-0311
   Honorable Roger E. Henderson, Judge

Family Court **843.537.3123**
Fax 843.537.6475
E-mail ....jspruill@scjd.state.sc.us
   210 Market St, Cheraw, SC 29520-2414
   Honorable James Spruill, Judge

EDUCATION SERVICES

Cheraw Head Start Ctr **843.537.5248**
Fax 843.537.5248
   1345 Dizzy Gillespie Dr, Cheraw, SC 29520
   Cornelia Ann Smith, Director

Clarendon County

SOCIAL SERVICES

Social Svcs **803.435.4303**
Fax 803.435.2831
E-mail ....ctkirkpatrick@dss.state.sc.us
   3 S Church St, Manning, SC 29102
   Catherine Kirkpatrick, Director

JUSTICE AGENCY

Dept of Juvenile Justice **803.435.8587**
Fax 803.435.2205
   102 South Mill St, Manning, SC 29102
   Mellissa Devane, County Director

COURTS

Family Court **803.435.4210**
Fax 803.433.8008
   102 S Mill St, Manning, SC 29102
   Beulah G. Roberts, Clerk Of Court

POLICE AND SHERIFF

Sheriff's Office **803.435.4414**
Fax 803.435.0106
Web ....www.sc.rr.com
   217 Commerce St, Manning, SC 29102
   Randy Garrett, Sheriff

EDUCATION SERVICES

Fleming-Felder Head Start **803.473.2767**
Fax 803.473.2898
   1423 Hotel St, Alcolu, SC 29001
   Kathy F Wright, Director

Colleton County

SOCIAL SERVICES

Social Svcs **843.549.1894**
Fax 843.549.2942
Web ....www.dss.state.sc.us
E-mail ....csherman@dss.state.sc.us
   215 S Lemacks St, Walterboro, SC 29488-4337
   Carolyn Sherman, County Director

GENERAL HEALTH SERVICES

Health Dept **843.549.1516**
Fax 843.549.6845
   219 S. Lemacks St, Walterboro, SC 29488
   Mary Edmonds, District Director

JUSTICE AGENCY

Dept Of Juvenile Justice **843.549.1509**
Fax 843.549.1750
E-mail ....rhan@scdjj.net
   119 Lemacks St, Walterboro, SC 29488
   Wayne Bennett, Manager

Guardian Ad Litem Program **843.549.6580**
Fax 843.549.3201
E-mail ....galcolleton@oetp.sc.gov
   109 Benson St, Walterboro, SC 29488
   Linda Koehler, County Coordinator

COURTS

Family Court **843.549.5060**
Fax 843.549.1842
E-mail ....gsmoak@scjd.state.sc.us
   101 Hampton St, Walterboro, SC 29488
   Honorable Gerald C. Smoak Jr., Judge

Darlington County

SOCIAL SERVICES

Dept. of Social Svcs **843.332.2231**
Fax 843.332.2231
Web ....www.emeritus.com
E-mail ....huntersglen-ed@emeritus.com
   130 East Camden Ave, Hartsville, SC 29550
   Ron Crein, County Director

GENERAL HEALTH SERVICES

Health Dept **843.398.4400**
Fax 843.398.4418
Web ....www.dhec.sc.gov
   305 Russell St, Darlington, SC 29532-3304
   Kathy James, Rn, Nursing Supervisor

JUSTICE AGENCY

Dept Of Juvenile Justice **843.393.5641**
Fax 843.395.9648
   302 Russell St, Darlington, SC 29532-3324
   Lynn Gehrke, County Director

COURTS

Family Court **843.398.4334**
Fax 843.857.9179
   Public Square 4Th Floor, Darlington, SC 29540
   Michael S. Holt, Judge

Dillon County

SOCIAL SERVICES

Social Svcs **843.774.8284**
Fax 843.841.0253
Web ....www.wcfgroup.com
E-mail ....jrowland@wcfgroup.com
   1211 Highway 34, Dillon, SC 29536
   Jackie Rowland, County Director

GENERAL HEALTH SERVICES

Health Dept **843.774.5611**
   201 W Hampton St, Dillon, SC 29536
   Carol Hodges, Nursing Supervisor

JUSTICE AGENCY

Dept Of Juvenile Justice **843.774.4147**
Fax 843.774.5948
   200 S 5th Ave Unit C, Dillon, SC 29536
   Rhonda Dew, County Director

POLICE AND SHERIFF

Sheriff's Dept **843.841.3721**
Fax 843.841.3229
Web . . . . .www.dillonsheriff.com
E-mail . . . . .sheriffhulon@dillonsheriff.com
   305 W Hampton St, Dillon, SC 29536-3335
   Major Hulon, Sheriff

Dorchester County

SOCIAL SERVICES

Dept Of Social Svc **843.563.0103**
Fax 843.563.0137
Web . . . . .www.dorchestercounty.net
E-mail . . . . .wardj@dorchestercounty.net
   201 Johnston St, Saint George, SC 29477-2412
   Jason Ward, County Administrator

Social Svcs **843.821.0444**
Fax 843.875.2380
Web . . . . .www.scda.sc.gov
E-mail . . . . .csingleton@scda.sc.gov
   216 Orangeburg Rd, Summerville, SC 29483-8945
   Chenitta Singleton, Program Coordinator

GENERAL HEALTH SERVICES

Health Dept **843.832.0041**
Fax 843.851.9735
Web . . . . .www.dhec.sc.gov
   500 N Main St Ste 9, Summerville, SC 29483-6439
   Stephainie Friesner, Clinic Manager

JUSTICE AGENCY

Guardian Ad Litem Program **843.875.9842**
Fax 843.875.6679
   120 S Magnolia St, Ste A, Summerville, SC 29483
   Dina Dukes, County Coordinator

COURTS

Family Court **843.832.0360**
Fax 843.832.0359
   212 Deming Way Ste 4, Summerville,
   SC 29483-4707
   Lisa Bair, Scheduling Clerk

POLICE AND SHERIFF

Sheriff's Ofc **843.832.0300**
Fax 843.832.0308
Web . . . . .www.dorchestercounty.net
   212 Deming Way Ste 9, Summerville, SC 29483
   L C Knight, Sheriff

Edgefield County

SOCIAL SERVICES

Social Services **803.637.4040**
Fax 803.637.5230
   120 W.A. Reel Dr, Edgefield, SC 29824
   Mark Baker, Program Manager

EDUCATION SERVICES

Even Start **803.275.4158**
Fax 803.275.9181
Web www.edgefield.k12.sc.us
E-mail . . . . .lbaker@edgefield.k12.sc.us
   PO Box 608, Edgefield, SC 29824-0608
   Lena R. Baker, Even Start Coordinator

Learning Center **803.275.4060**
Fax 803.275.3015
Web . . . . .www.gleamshrc.org
   141 SE Diggs Rd, Trenton, SC 29847
   Phyllis Lopt, Supervisor

Fairfield County

GENERAL HEALTH SERVICES

Health Dept **803.635.6481**
Fax 803.635.1410
   1136 Kincaid Bridge Rd, Winnsboro, SC 29180-7116
   Allan Cooper, Nursing Supervisor

COURTS

Family Court **803.712.6528**
Fax 803.712.1478
   115A S Congress St, Winnsboro, SC 29180-1103
   Honorable Tommy Sprott, Judge

POLICE AND SHERIFF

Sheriff's Dept **803.635.4141**
Fax 803.635.3325
E-mail . . . . .tsmith@fairfieldsc.com
   350 Columbia Rd, Winnsboro, SC 29180
   Herman W. Young, Sheriff

Florence County

SOCIAL SERVICES

Social Svcs **843.669.3354**
Fax 843.673.9247
Web . . . . .www.dss.sc.us.gov
   2685 S Irby St Ste A, Florence, SC 29505-3439
   Nadine Livingston, Director

GENERAL HEALTH SERVICES

Lake City Health Dept **843.394.8822**
Fax 843.394.8856
Web . . . . .www.scdhec.gov
   137 N Acline St, Lake City, SC 29560-2107
   Kelly Eaddy, Nursing Director

Regional Health District **843.661.4835**
Fax 843.661.4859
   145 E Cheves St, Florence, SC 29506
   Derick Mimm, Nursing Director

JUSTICE AGENCY

Dept Of Juvenile Justice **843.665.3080**
Fax 843.679.3574
Web . . . . .www.scdjj.net
E-mail . . . . .rwcoop@scdjj.net
   180 N Irby St, Rm 702, Florence, SC 29501
   Reginald Cooper, County Director

Guardian Ad Litem Program **843.669.7940**
Fax 843.669.1062
E-mail . . . . .galflore@oepp.gov
   2110 W Jody Rd, Florence, SC 29501
   Jil Matthews, Coordinator

COURTS

Family Court **843.665.3096**
Fax 843.662.6165
   180 N Irby St, Rm 903, Florence, SC 29501
   Connie Reel-Shearin, Clerk

EDUCATION SERVICES

Even Start **843.374.8652**
Fax 843.374.2788
Web www.florence3.k12.sc.us
E-mail . . . . .doliver@florence3.k12.sc.us
   125 S. Blanding St, Lake City, SC 29560
   Dianne Oliver, Even Start Director

**Florence Darlington Technical
College-HS** **843.676.8520**
Fax 843.676.8524
   2715 W Lucas St, Florence, SC 29501
   Jennifer Reed, Director

Florence School District 2 . . . .**843.493.2502**
Fax 843.493.1912
Web www.flo2.k12.sc.us
   2121 S Pamplico Hwy, Pamplico, SC 29583
   Robert Sullivan, Superintentant

Florence School District I **843.669.4141**
Fax 843.673.1108
Web www.fsd1.net
E-mail . . . . .bdenny@FlorenceSchoolDistrict.net
   319 S Dargan St, Florence, SC 29506-2538
   Brian Denny, Director Of Student Services

School District 5 . . . .**843.386.2341**
Fax 843.386.3029
Web www.flo5.org
   156 E Marion St, Johnsonville, SC 29555
   Randy Smiley, Director Of Special Services

**Special Education/Ofc Of Exceptional
Children** **843.374.2393**
Fax 843.374.7245
Web www.florence3.org
E-mail . . . . .jwilson@florence3.k12.sc.us
   318 E Main St, Lake City, SC 29560-2116
   Juanita Wilson, Director Of The Office Of Exceptional Children

Georgetown County

SOCIAL SERVICES

Dept of Social Svcs **843.546.5134**
Fax 843.527.6465
   330 Dozier St, Georgetown, SC 29440
   Sylvia G. Mitchum, County Director

GENERAL HEALTH SERVICES

Health Dept **843.546.5593**
Fax 843.546.0456
   531 Lafayette Cir, Georgetown, SC 29440-2569

JUSTICE AGENCY

Dept Of Juvenile Justice **843.546.8723**
Fax 843.546.3896
E-mail . . . . .mybell@scdjj.net
   120 Screven St, Georgetown, SC 29442
   Melissa Bell Guenn, County Director

COURTS

Family Court **843.545.3049**
Fax 843.545.3264
   715 PRINCE ST, Georgetown, SC 29440-3631
   Elma White, Secretary

POLICE AND SHERIFF

Sheriff's Dept **843.546.5102**
Fax 843.546.2752
E-mail .acribb@georgetowncountysc.org
   430 N Fraser St, Georgetown, SC 29442
   A. Lane Cribb, Sheriff

EDUCATION SERVICES

Andrews Head Start **843.264.3419**
Fax 843.264.5511
   13072 County Line Rd, Andrews, SC 29510
   Bryan Clarke, Principal

Greenville County

SOCIAL SERVICES

Social Services **864.467.7700**
Fax 864.467.7947
   301 University Ridge, Ste 6700, Greenville, SC 29601
   Gary C. Ray, Director

GENERAL HEALTH SERVICES

Region 2 Health **864.282.4100**
Fax 864.282.4372
   200 University Ridge, Greenville, SC 29601
   Matt Petrofes, District Health Director

MENTAL HEALTH SERVICES
Commission On Alcohol And Drug
Abuse **864.467.3737**
Fax 864.467.3757
Web ....www.phonixcenter.org
  1400 Cleveland St, Greenville, SC 29607-2410
Nicholas Hogan, Clinical Director

JUSTICE AGENCY
Dept of Juvenile Justice Svcs **864.467.5875**
Fax 864.467.5899
  301 University Ridge, Ste 625, Greenville, SC 29601
Tomiko Williams, County Director

Guardian Ad Litem **864.467.5860**
Fax 864.467.5863
Web .....www.govoepp.state.sc.us-children-guardi an
E-mail ....galgreen@oepp.sc.gov
  301 University Rdg Ste 525, Greenville,
  SC 29601-3695
Patty Dellinger, Circuit Coordinator

COURTS
Family Court 13Th District **864.467.5800**
Fax 864.467.5856
Web ....www.greenvillecounty.org
  301 University Rdg, Greenville, SC 29601-3636
Robert Jenkins, Admin Judge

POLICE AND SHERIFF
Greenville Police Dept **864.271.5333**
Fax 864.467.5460
Web ....www.greenvillesc.gov
  4 McGee St Ste 1, Greenville, SC 29601
Terri Wilson, Chief Of Police

Sheriff's Ofc **864.467.5280**
Fax 864.467.5299
E-mail ....sloftis@greenvillecounty.org
  4 McGee St, Greenville, SC 29601
Steve Loftis, Sheriff

Greenwood County

SOCIAL SERVICES
Dept Of Social Svcs **864.229.5258**
Fax 864.229.4613
Web ....www.dss.sc.gov
E-mail ....thomas.turner@dss.sc.gov
  1118 Phoenix St, Greenwood, SC 29646-3918
Robin Kuler, Director

GENERAL HEALTH SERVICES
Regional Health District **864.942.3600**
Fax 864.942.3690
E-mail ....campbellb@dhec.sc.gov
  1736 Main St S, Greenwood, SC 29646-4124
Beckey Campbell, Director

JUSTICE AGENCY
Guardian Ad Litem Program **864.223.4681**
Fax 864.223.5471
E-mail ....ssmith@govoepp.state.sc.us
  702 Center St, Greenwood, SC 29646
Stacie Lee Smith, County Coordinator

COURTS
Family Court **864.942.8643**
Fax 864.229.0671
E-mail ....btunstall@scjd.state.sc.us
  528 Monument St Rm 208, Greenwood,
  SC 29646-2633
Honorable Billy A. Tunstall Jr., Judge

POLICE AND SHERIFF
Sheriff's Dept **864.942.8600**
Fax 864.942.8589
Web ....www.co.greenwood.sc.us
E-mail ....sheriff@co.greenwood.sc.us
  528 Edgefield St, Greenwood, SC 29646-2686
Dan Wideman, Sheriff

Hampton County

JUSTICE AGENCY
Dept Of Juvenile Justice **803.943.4296**
Fax 803.943.3143
  1 Court House Sq Elm St W, Hampton, SC 29924
Elaunda Williams, County Director

Guardian Ad Litem Program **803.625.2450**
Fax 803.625.2004
Web ....www.govoepp.state.sc.us
E-mail ....jbellinger@govoepp.state.sc.us
  454 2nd St, Estill, SC 29918
Jan Bellinger, Coordinator

Horry County

SOCIAL SERVICES
Social Svcs **843.915.4700**
Fax 843.915.4820
E-mail ....smitchum@dss.sc.gov
  1951 Industrial Park Rd, Conway, SC 29526
Sylvia Mitchum, Director

GENERAL HEALTH SERVICES
DHEC Loris Ofc **843.756.4027**
Fax 843.756.4039
  3811 Walnut St, Loris, SC 29569
Carolyn Howe, Rn, Clinic Supervisor

DHEC Myrtle Beach **843.448.8407**
Fax 843.448.7499
Web ....www.scdhec.gov
  700 21st Ave N, Myrtle Beach, SC 29577
Regina Miller, Head Nurse

COURTS
Family Court **843.915.5080**
Fax 843.915.6081
  1301 2nd Ave, Conway, SC 29528
Mary Catherine Britt, Family Court Supervisor

POLICE AND SHERIFF
Sheriff's Ofc **843.915.5450**
Fax 843.915.6451
Web .....www.horrycounty.org/depts/sheriff/histo ry
E-mail ....phil@roanoke.org
  1301 2nd Ave, Conway, SC 29526
Phillip E. Thompson, Sheriff

Jasper County

SOCIAL SERVICES
Social Svcs **843.726.7747**
Fax 843.726.7752
Web ....www.dss.sc.gov
E-mail ....rochelle.priester@dss.sc.gov
  10908 N Jacob Smart Blvd, Ridgeland, SC 29936
Rochelle Priester, Director

GENERAL HEALTH SERVICES
Health Dept **843.726.7788**
Fax 843.726.5320
Web ....www.scdhec.gov
  359 E Wilson St, Ridgeland, SC 29936-8523
Kathy Goen, Rn, Nursing Director

COURTS
Family Court **843.726.7710**
Fax 843.726.7782
  265 Russell St, Ridgeland, SC 29936
Honorable Gerald Smoak Jr., Director

POLICE AND SHERIFF
Sheriff's Dept **843.726.7777**
Fax 843.726.7778
Web ....www.jaspercountysc.gov
E-mail ....sheriffjenkins@jaspercountysc.gov
  12008 North Jacob Smart Blvd, Ridgeland, SC 29936
Gregory Jenkins, Sheriff

Kershaw County

SOCIAL SERVICES
Social Services **803.432.7676**
Fax 803.425.7195
E-mail ....jhannah@dss.state.sc.us
  110 E Dekalb St, Camden, SC 29020
Jeanie Hannah, Director

GENERAL HEALTH SERVICES
Health Dept **803.425.6012**
Fax 803.424.1611
  1116 Church St, Camden, SC 29020
Derrick Mims, Regional Health Director

COURTS
Family Court **803.425.1500**
Fax 803.425.1527
  1121 Broad St, Camden, SC 29020
Dana Morris, Judge

EDUCATION SERVICES
Communities In Schools **803.432.1109**
Fax 803.424.0020
Web ....www.ciskc.org
E-mail ....ciskc@yahoo.com
  905 W Dekalb St Ste A, Ste A & F, Camden,
  SC 29020-4259
Jennifer Adams, Executive Director

Head Start **803.432.2823**
Fax 803.432.9333
  1109 Campbell St, Camden, SC 29020
Georgia Mance, Director

Lancaster County

SOCIAL SERVICES
Social Services **803.286.6914**
Fax 803.285.4480
Web ....www.dss.sc.gov
E-mail ....janice.chapman@dss.sc.gov
  1837 Pageland Hwy, Human Services Complex,
  Lancaster, SC 29721
Janice Chapman, County Director

JUSTICE AGENCY
Dept Of Juvenile Justice **803.285.9447**
Fax 803.285.4375
  103 N Main St, Lancaster, SC 29720-2475
Richard Wessinger, County Director

COURTS
Cicuit Court **803.286.6990**
Fax 803.286.0696
E-mail ....bgoldsmithj@sccourts.org
  104 N Main St, Lancaster, SC 29720
Honorable Brooks P. Goldsmith, Circuit Court Judge

POLICE AND SHERIFF
Sheriff's Dept **803.283.4186**
Fax 803.286.9823
Web ....www.infoave.net
  1941 Pageland Hwy, Lancaster, SC 29720-8551
Barry Faile, Sheriff

EDUCATION SERVICES

Communities In Schools **803.285.2311**
Fax 803.285.2315
Web ....www.cisnet.org/lancaster
E-mail ....jump_cins@comporium.net
　　1240 Childrens Ave, Lancaster, SC 29720
　　Max Melton, Director

Laurens County

SOCIAL SERVICES

Social Services **864.833.0100**
Fax 864.833.1681
E-mail ....csmith@dss.state.sc.us
　　93 Human Services Rd, Clinton, SC 29325
　　Carolyn H. Smith, Director

POLICE AND SHERIFF

Sheriff's Ofc **864.984.4967**
Fax 864.984.5754
E-mail ....rchastain@laurenssheriff.com
　　216 W Main St, Laurens, SC 29360
　　Ricky W. Chastain, Sheriff

EDUCATION SERVICES

Champs Program **864.833.8377**
Fax 864.833.8435
Web ....www.presby.edu
E-mail ....nadisasa@presby.edu
　　503 S Broad St, Clinton, SC 29325-2865
　　Dr. Jerman Disasa, Director Of Champs

Lee County

SOCIAL SERVICES

Social Svcs **803.484.5376**
Fax 803.484.6435
　　820 Brown St, Bishopville, SC 29010
　　Debra Bartholoma-Pues, Director

GENERAL HEALTH SERVICES

DHEC Region 4 ....**803.484.6612**
Fax 803.484.6314
Web ....www.scdhec.gov
　　810 Brown St, Bishopville, SC 29010
　　Diana Mcdonald, Nursing Director

POLICE AND SHERIFF

Sheriff's Ofc **803.484.5353**
Fax 803.484.5794
Web ....www.sheriffone.org
E-mail ....dsimmon@leecountysc.org
　　113 Gregg St, Bishopville, SC 29010-1622
　　Daniel Simmon, Sheriff

EDUCATION SERVICES

Bishopville Head Start **803.484.5403**
Fax 803.484.6077
　　603 N Main St, Bishopville, SC 29010
　　Georgia Mance, Director

Lexington County

GENERAL HEALTH SERVICES

Health Dept **803.785.6550**
Fax 803.785.6555
　　1070 B Southlake Dr, Lexington, SC 29073
　　Barbara Charles, Supervisor

Health Dept Batesburg Ofc **803.332.6326**
Fax 803.332.2706
　　229 W Church St, Batesburg, SC 29006
　　Deborah Reynolds, Supervisor

JUSTICE AGENCY

Dept Of Juvenile Justice **803.359.5526**
Fax 803.359.5744
E-mail ....dmdors@scdjj.net
　　605 W Main St, Lexington, SC 29072
　　Max Dorsey, Regional Administrator

Guardian Ad Litem Program **803.957.6484**
Fax 803.957.6481
Web ....www.oepp.sc.gov
E-mail ....gallexington@oepp.sc.gov
　　405 E Main St, Lexington, SC 29072-3603
　　Karen Joiner, Circuit Coordinator

POLICE AND SHERIFF

Sheriff's Dept **803.785.8230**
Fax 803.785.2462
E-mail ....jmetts@lex-co.com
　　521 Gibson Rd Ste A, Lexington, SC 29072
　　James Metts, Sheriff

EDUCATION SERVICES

**Special Education/Lexington School District
2** **803.739.4024**
Fax 803.739.4066
Web www.lex2.org
E-mail ....lisa@lex2.org
　　715 9th St, West Columbia, SC 29169-7169
　　Lisa Harmon, Director Of Special Services

**Special Education/Lexington School District
3** **803.532.8005**
Fax 803.532.8000
Web www.lex3.k12.sc.us
　　338 W Columbia Ave, Batesburg, SC 29006-2028
　　Dr. Lynda Smith, Director Of Special Education

Marion County

SOCIAL SERVICES

Social Svcs **843.423.4623**
Fax 843.423.2419
Web ....www.state.sc.us
E-mail ....cdavid@dss.state.sc.us
　　137 Airport Ct Ste A, Mullins, SC 29574-6034
　　Cora David, County Director

MENTAL HEALTH SERVICES

**Commission On Alcohol And Drug
Abuse** **843.423.8292**
Fax 843.423.8294
Web ....www.pan.net
E-mail ....mccada@trinitybehadioralcare.net
　　103 Court St, Marion, SC 29571
　　William T O'Connor, Executive Director

JUSTICE AGENCY

Dept Of Juvenile Justice **843.431.1110**
Fax 843.431.1104
Web ....www.state.scus/djj
　　1305 N Main St, Marion, SC 29571-2010
　　Deborah Lakin, County Director

POLICE AND SHERIFF

Sheriff's Dept **843.423.8216**
Fax 843.423.8386
Web ....www.infoaze.net
E-mail ....mrichardson@marionsc.org
　　2715 E Highway 76 Ste C, Mullins, SC 29574-6015
　　Mark Richardson, Sheriff

Marlboro County

SOCIAL SERVICES

Social Services **843.479.7181**
Fax 843.479.6254
　　713 S Parsonage St, Bennettsville, SC 29512
　　Gerald Fogle, Director

GENERAL HEALTH SERVICES

Health Dept **843.479.6801**
Fax 843.479.9658
　　711 S Parsonage St, Bennettsville, SC 29512
　　Gloria Ridges Md, Director

MENTAL HEALTH SERVICES

Mental Health **843.454.0442**
Fax 843.454.0212
　　1035 Cheraw St, Bennettsville, SC 29512-2422
　　Janice Rozier, Msw, Executive Director

JUSTICE AGENCY

Dept Of Juvenile Justice **843.479.2961**
Fax 843.454.0569
　　205 E Market St, Bennettsville, SC 29512
　　Tracey Mcleod, County Director

POLICE AND SHERIFF

Sheriff's Ofc **843.479.5605**
Fax 843.479.2851
E-mail ....fknight@netzero.com
　　239 Troop St, Bennettsville, SC 29512-3103
　　Fred Knight, Sheriff

EDUCATION SERVICES

Blenheim Head Start Ctr **843.528.3465**
Fax 843.528.3465
　　2809 Polston Farm Rd, Blenheim, SC 29516
　　Cardylia Pearson, Director

McCormick County

SOCIAL SERVICES

Social Svcs **864.465.2140**
Fax 864.465.2125
Web ....www.state.sc.us
E-mail ....rseigler@dss.state.sc
　　215 N Mine St, McCormick, SC 29835-8363
　　Robbie Seigler, County Director

GENERAL HEALTH SERVICES

Health Dept **864.852.2511**
Fax 864.852.2827
Web ....www.scdhec.gov
　　204 Hwy 28, McCormick, SC 29835
　　Patty Gary, Nursing Supervisor

JUSTICE AGENCY

Guardian Ad Litem Program **864.333.5621**
Fax 864.333.2465
Web ....www.govoepp.state.sc.us
E-mail ....galmccor@govoepp.state.sc.us
　　PO Box 957, Mc Cormick, SC 29835-0957
　　Donna Lackey, Coordinator

POLICE AND SHERIFF

Sheriff's Dept **864.465.2520**
Fax 864.465.3181
E-mail ....mcc4sheriff@wctel.net
　　211 West Augusta St Extension, McCormick,
　　SC 29835
　　George H. Reid, Sheriff

Newberry County

SOCIAL SERVICES

Dept of Social Svcs **803.321.2155**
Fax 803.321.2168
Web ....www.dss.sc.gov
E-mail ....larry.cannon@dss.sc.gov
　　2107 Wilson Rd, Newberry, SC 29108
　　Larry Cannon, County Director

GENERAL HEALTH SERVICES

Health Dept.............................803.321.2170
Fax..803.321.2300
Web...................................www.scdhec.gov
  2111 Wilson Rd, Newberry, SC 29108-1603
Beth Bozard, Rn, Nursing Supervisor

JUSTICE AGENCY

Dept Of Juvenile Justice...................803.276.8243
Fax..803.276.3871
  1309 College St, Newberry, SC 29108
Renee Former, Director

POLICE AND SHERIFF

Sheriff's Dept.............................803.321.2211
Fax..803.321.2147
Web................................www.newberrycounty.net
E-mail..................sheriff@newberrycounty.net
  520 Wilson Rd, Newberry, SC 29108-4612
James Lee Foster, Sheriff

Oconee County

SOCIAL SERVICES

Social Svcs...............................864.638.4400
Fax..864.638.4444
E-mail.......................ebailey@dss.state.sc.us
  100 Browns Square Dr, Walhalla, SC 29691
Elaine Bailey, Director

GENERAL HEALTH SERVICES

Health Dept.............................864.882.0164
Fax..864.882.2245
E-mail.......................marchantj@dhec.sc.gov
  609 N Townville St, Seneca, SC 29678
Janet Marchant, Clinic Manager

Health Dept.............................864.638.4170
Fax..864.638.4173
Web...................................www.dhec.sc.gov
E-mail.......................campbellb@dhec.sc.gov
  200 Booker Dr, Walhalla, SC 29691-2278
Becky Campbell, Director

JUSTICE AGENCY

Dept Of Juvenile Justice...................864.638.9537
Fax..864.638.0260
  203 Booker Dr, Ste B, Walhalla, SC 29691
Kirstin Abderhalden, County Director

Guardian Ad Litem Program.................864.638.2267
Fax..864.638.9140
  80 Short St, Walhalla, SC 29691
Debra Johnson, County Coordinator

COURTS

Family Court.............................864.638.4290
Fax..864.638.4293
  205 W Main St, Walhalla, SC 29691
Beverly H Whitfield, Clerk Of Court

POLICE AND SHERIFF

Sheriff's Ofc.............................864.638.4117
Fax..864.638.4208
Web...................................www.oconeesc.com
E-mail..............................sheriff@oconeesc.com
  415 S Pine St, Walhalla, SC 29691
James E. Singleton, Sheriff

Orangeburg County

SOCIAL SERVICES

Dept of Social Svcs......................803.531.3101
Fax..803.531.2045
Web................www.state.sc.us/dss/counties.html
E-mail..........................hwilliams@sc.rr.com
  2570 Old St. Matthews Rd, Orangeburg,
  SC 29116-1087
Harold Williams, County Director

GENERAL HEALTH SERVICES

Edisto Savannah Public Health
District......................................803.536.9060
Fax..803.536.9118
Web...................................www.dhec.sc.gov
E-mail.......................greenvc@dhec.sc.gov
  1550 Carolina Ave, Orangeburg, SC 29115-4944
Vicki Green, Nursing Director

JUSTICE AGENCY

Guardian Ad Litem........................803.531.2217
Fax..803.531.5366
  1109 Doyle St, Orangeburg, SC 29116
Carol Barton, Circuit Coordinator

COURTS

Family Court.............................803.533.6260
Fax..803.534.3848
Web................................www.orangeburgcounty.org
  190 Gison St, Orangeburg, SC 29116
Honorable Anne Jones, Judge

EDUCATION SERVICES

Bowman Head Start Ctr...................803.829.3553
Fax..803.536.4657
  130 Poplar St, Orangeburg, SC 29115-3679

Pickens County

SOCIAL SERVICES

Social Svcs...............................864.898.5810
Fax..864.898.5819
  212 McDaniel Ave, Pickens, SC 29671-0158
Keith Brazier, County Director

GENERAL HEALTH SERVICES

Health Dept.............................864.898.5965
Fax..864.898.5568
Web...................................www.scdhec.gov
  200 McDaniel Ave, Pickens, SC 29671
Kathy Mcguffin, Adult Help

JUSTICE AGENCY

Dept Of Juvenile Justice...................864.878.7560
Fax..864.878.4327
  214 E Main St, # 130, Pickens, SC 29671
Brent Mcwhorter, County Director

POLICE AND SHERIFF

Sheriff's Ofc.............................864.898.5500
Fax..864.898.5531
Web................................www.pickenscosheriff.org
  216 L E C Road, Pickens, SC 29671
C. David Stone, Sheriff

Richland County

SOCIAL SERVICES

Social Svcs...............................803.714.7300
Fax..803.714.7301
E-mail.......................acarter1@dss.state.sc.us
  3220 Two Notch Rd, Columbia, SC 29204
Alan Carter, Agency Director

GENERAL HEALTH SERVICES

Regional Health District...................803.576.2900
Fax..803.576.2999
  2000 Hampton St, Columbia, SC 29204
Ernie Bell, Phd, District Health Director

JUSTICE AGENCY

Dept Of Juvenile Justice...................803.253.4050
Fax..803.253.6477
Web...................................www.scdjj.net
E-mail.......................cmartin@scdjj.net
  1701 Main St, Columbia, SC 29201-2819
Catina Martin, County Director

POLICE AND SHERIFF

Columbia Police Dept.....................803.545.3500
Fax..803.733.8252
  1 Justice Sq, Columbia, SC 29201
Randy Scott, Chief Of Police

Sheriff's Dept.............................803.576.3000
Fax..803.576.3195
Web...................................www.rcsd.net
E-mail..............................sheriff@rcsd.net
  5623 Two Notch Rd, Columbia, SC 29223
Leon Lott, Sheriff

EDUCATION SERVICES

Benedict Learning Ctr-Hs.................803.779.7156
Fax..803.779.7649
E-mail.......................lboose@gleamnshrc.org
  2007 Henry St, Columbia, SC 29204-7820
Daphne Suber, Director

Special Education........................803.738.3256
Fax..803.738.3308
E-mail.......................jhogan@richland2.org
  6831 Brookfield Rd, Columbia, SC 29206
Dr. John Hogan, Director Of Special Services

Saluda County

SOCIAL SERVICES

Social Svcs...............................864.445.2139
Fax..864.445.7088
E-mail.......................dwilson@dss.state.sc.us
  613 Newberry Hwy, Saluda, SC 29138-8903
Darron Wilson, Director

GENERAL HEALTH SERVICES

Health Dept.............................864.445.2141
Fax..864.445.7668
  613 Newberry Hwy, Saluda, SC 29138
Madora Stanfield, Supervisor

JUSTICE AGENCY

Dept Of Juvenile Justice...................864.445.8138
Fax..864.445.8139
Web...................................www.scdjj.net
E-mail.......................rbcrof@scdjj.net
  120 S Main St Ste D, Saluda, SC 29138-1754
Robbie Croft, County Director

POLICE AND SHERIFF

Sheriff's Ofc.............................864.445.2112
Fax..864.445.8829
Web...................................www.saludacounty.sc.gov
E-mail.......................salcodispatch@yahoo.com
  100 Law Enforcement Dr, Saluda, SC 29138-8791
Jason C. Booth, Sheriff

Spartanburg County

SOCIAL SERVICES

Social Svcs...............................864.596.3001
Fax..864.596.3141
  142 S Dean St Ste 104, Spartanburg, SC 29302
David Goolsby, District Health Director

GENERAL HEALTH SERVICES

Appalachia Region 2 Health...............864.596.3302
Fax..864.596.2192
Web...................................www.dhec.sc.gov
E-mail.......................vorlicda@dhec.sc.gov
  151 E Wood St, Spartanburg, SC 29303-3016
Doris Vorlick, Nursing Director

Regional Health District...................864.596.2227
Fax..864.596.3443
Web...................................www.dhec.sc.gov
E-mail.......................goolsbwd@dhec.sc.gov
  151 E Wood St, Spartanburg, SC 29305
W. David Goolsby, Md, Regional Health Director

JUSTICE AGENCY

Dept Of Juvenile Justice **864.562.4200**
Fax 864.596.2981
   180 Magnolia St, Rm 201, Spartanburg, SC 29306
Jennifer Clark, County Director

Guardian Ad Litem Program **864.573.5175**
Fax 864.583.3406
Web .... www.oepp.sc.gov
E-mail .... galspartanburg@oepp.sc.gov
   207 Magnolia St, Ste 106, Spartanburg, SC 29306
Jean Bradley, Program Coordinator

COURTS

Family Court **864.596.2588**
Fax 864.596.3898
   180 Magnolia St, Spartanburg, SC 29306
Honorable James Fraley Jr, Judge

POLICE AND SHERIFF

Sheriff's Ofc **864.503.4503**
Fax 864.503.4561
Web .... www.spartanburgcounty.org
E-mail .... admin@spartanburgcounty.org
   8045 Howard St, Spartanburg, SC 29303-1861
Chuck Wright, Sheriff

Spartanburg Police Dept **864.596.2035**
Fax 864.596.2152
   145 W Broad St, Spartanburg, SC 29306
Tony Fisher, Director Of Public Safety

EDUCATION SERVICES

Special Education **864.472.2846**
Fax 864.472.4118
Web www.spart1.org
E-mail .... trish.beason@spart1.org
   121 Wheeler St, Campobello, SC 29322
Dr. Trish Beason, Coordinator Of Students & Special Services

Special Education **864.476.3186**
Fax 864.476.8616
Web www.spart4.org
E-mail .... gcarson@spartanburg4.org
   118 Mcedco Rd, Woodruff, SC 29388
Glen Carson, Instruction Supervisor

Special Education **864.279.6000**
Fax 864.276.6061
Web www.spartanburg3.org
E-mail .... lberry@spartanburg3.org
   3535 Clifton Glendale Rd, Glendale, SC 29346
Ladson Berry, Director Of Special Education

Special Education **864.576.4212**
Fax 864.574.6265
Web www.spart6.org
E-mail .... hatcherk@spartanburg6.k12.sc.us
   1390 Cavalier Way, Roebuck, SC 29376-3367
Dr. Robert Hatchette, Assistant Superintendent Of Special Services

Special Education **864.578.0128**
Fax 864.578.8924
Web www.spartanburg2.k12.sc.us
E-mail .... turner.nancy@mail.spartanburg2.k12.sc.us
   4606 Parris Bridge Rd, Boiling Springs,
   SC 29316-5916
Nancy Turner, Director Of Special Services

**Special Education/ School District
7** **864.594.4493**
Fax 864.596.8424
Web www.spart7.org
   698 Howard St, Spartanburg, SC 29303-2964
Dr. Nettie Vaughn, Speacial Education Director

Special Education/School District 5 .... **864.949.2309**
Fax 864.439.0051
Web www.spart5.net
E-mail .... maureen.kriese@spart5.net
   100 N Danzler Rd, Duncan, SC 29334-9525
Maureen Kriese, Director Of Special Services

Sumter County

SOCIAL SERVICES

Social Services **803.773.5531**
Fax 803.778.2058
Web .... www.dss.state.sc.us
E-mail .... jwilson@dss.state.sc.us
   105 N Magnolia St, Sumter, SC 29150
Julia Wilson, CPS Supervisor

JUSTICE AGENCY

Dept Of Juvenile Justice **803.778.2368**
Fax 803.775.2377
E-mail .... mcox@scdjj.net
   38 E Calhoun St, Sumter, SC 29150-4371
Mark Cox, County Director

COURTS

Family Court **803.436.2366**
Fax 803.436.2396
Web .... www.sumtercountysc.org
E-mail .... rsmith@sumtercountysc.org
   108 N Magnolia St, Sumter, SC 29150-4900
Rogers Smith, Director

Teen Court **803.436.2723**
Fax 803.436.2084
Web .... www.sumter-sc.com
E-mail .... rfowler@sumter-sc.com
   107 E Hampton Ave, Sumter, SC 29150-4929
Ruth E. Fowler, Coordinator

POLICE AND SHERIFF

Sheriff's Dept **803.436.2790**
Fax 803.436.2081
Web .... www.sumtercountysc.org
   107 E Hampton Ave, Sumter, SC 29150-4929
Anthony Dennis, Sheriff

EDUCATION SERVICES

**Special Education/Sumter School
District** **803.469.8536**
Fax 803.469.6006
Web .... http://districtsumterschools.net
   1109 N Pike W, Sumter, SC 29153
Shawn Hagerty, Lead Psychologist

**Special Education/Sumter School District
2** **803.469.6900**
Fax 803.469.4006
   1345 Wilson Hall Rd, Sumter, SC 29150
Shawn Hagerty, Director Of Special Svcs

Union County

SOCIAL SERVICES

Social Svcs **864.429.1660**
Fax 864.429.1664
E-mail .... bishopdd@spart6.org
   200 S Mountain St, Union, SC 29379
Deborah Bishop, County Director

GENERAL HEALTH SERVICES

Health Dept **864.429.1690**
Fax 864.429.1697
Web .... www.scdhec.gov
   115 Thomas St, Union, SC 29379-2147
Paula Jennings, Rn, Nursing Director

COURTS

Family Court **864.429.1632**
Web .... www.countyofunion.com
E-mail .... bmorris@countyofunion.com
   210 W Main St, Union, SC 29379-2215
S. Bradley Morris, Clerk Of Courts

POLICE AND SHERIFF

Sheriff's Office **864.429.1612**
Fax 864.429.1628
Web .... www.unionscsheriff.com
E-mail .... info@unioncountysheriff.com
   220 West Main, Union, SC 29379
David Taylor, Sheriff

Williamsburg County

SOCIAL SERVICES

Social Services **843.355.5411**
Fax 843.355.0926
Web .... www.dss.state.sc.us
E-mail .... ctkirkpatrick@dss.state.sc.us
   831 Eastland Ave, Kingstree, SC 29556
Catherine Kirkpatrick, Director

GENERAL HEALTH SERVICES

Health Dept **843.355.6012**
Fax 843.355.9590
Web .... www.williamsburgsc.org
   520 Thurgood Marshall Hwy, Ste A, Kingstree,
   SC 29556
Leah Altman, Nursing Supervisor

POLICE AND SHERIFF

Sheriff's Ofc **843.355.6381**
Fax 843.355.7956
   126 S Jackson St, Kingstree, SC 29556-3914
Michael Johnson, Sheriff

York County

SOCIAL SERVICES

Dept of Social Svcs **803.684.2315**
Fax 803.684.8103
Web .... www.state.sc.us/dss/counties.html
E-mail .... ystewart@dss.state.sc.us
   933 Heckle Blvd, Rockhill, SC 29732
Yvonne C. Stewart, County Director

GENERAL HEALTH SERVICES

Health Dept **803.684.7004**
Fax 803.684.1103
   116 N Congress St, York, SC 29745-1531
Tina Brown, Rn, Nursing Supervisor

Health Dept **803.909.7300**
Fax 803.909.7397
Web .... www.scdhec.net/health
   1070 Heckle Blvd Ste 203, Rock Hill, SC 29732
Arelene Fincher, Supervisor

JUSTICE AGENCY

Dept Of Juvenile Justice **803.909.7500**
Fax 803.909.7440
   1070 Heckle Blvd Ste 100, Rock Hill, SC 29732-2863
Amahl Bennett, Regional Supervisor

Guardian Ad Litem Program **803.327.9997**
Fax 803.327.0335
E-mail .... galyork@oepp.sc.gov
   125 Hampton St, Ste 101, Rock Hill, SC 29730
Patti Pitzer, Circuit Coordinator

COURTS

Family Court **803.909.7100**
Fax 803.909.7140
Web .... www.yorkcountygov.com
   1070 Heckle Blvd, Bldg 2, Rock Hill, SC 29732
Barry Moss, Deputy Clerk

Juvenile Drug Treatment Court............803.909.7554
Web.................................www.yorkcountygov.com
E-mail.....................ben.motley@yorkcountygov.com
  529 S Cherry Rd, Ste 5, Rock Hill, SC 29732
Benjamin Motley, Coordinator

POLICE AND SHERIFF

Sheriff's Dept............................803.628.3059
Fax...803.628.3075
Web.................................www.yorkcountygov.com
  1675 York Hwy, Ste 2A, York, SC 29745-7496
Bruce M. Bryant, Sheriff

EDUCATION SERVICES

Avery Lake Head Start........................803.802.7587
Fax...803.802.7643
  100 Lestina Dr, Fort Mill, SC 29715
Elizabeth W. Bell, Director

Catawba Indian National Even
Start.......................................803.328.2267
  1540 Tom Steven Rd, Rock Hill, SC 29730
Melissa Harris, Headstart Program Director

Comm Dev Institute Head Start Serving
Cin..803.366.8303
Fax...803.366.1912
  1540 Tom Steven Road, Rock Hill, SC 29730
Alissa Funderburk, Director

Exceptional Students Education/Rock Hills Dept Of
Education..................................803.981.1085
Fax...803.981.1877
Web.................................www.rock-hill.k12.sc.us
E-mail.....................wbalouch@rock-hill.k12.sc.us
  1234 flint st ext, Rock Hill, SC 29730
Wendy Balouch, Director Of Exeptional Student Education

Special Education/Clover School
District...................................803.810.8400
Fax...803.222.8043
Web.................................www.clover.k12.sc.us
E-mail.....................cathy.mccarter@clover.k12.sc.us
  300 Clinton Ave, Clover, SC 29710
Cathy Mccarter, Director

SPECIAL SERVICES AGENCIES

ADOPTION AGENCIES

Adoption Resource Ctr....................704.829.7880
Fax...704.271.4247
E-mail.................................info@adoptionguides.org
  5030-A North fant st, anderson, Belmont, SC 29621
Mary Mooney, Director

Bethany Christian Svcs....................864.235.2273
Fax...864.233.6641
Web.................................www.bethany.org
E-mail.....................bcsgreenville@bethany.org
  114 Williams St Ste A, Greenville, SC 29601-3182
Jeanette E. Maxey, Lisw, Adoption Specialist

Bethany Christian Svcs....................803.779.0541
Fax...803.779.3150
Web.................................www.bethany.org/columbia_sc
E-mail.....................bcscolumbia@bethany.org
  1612 Marion St Ste 206, Columbia, SC 29201
Joann King, Director

Bowers-Rodgers Home, Inc.................864.229.1240
Fax...864.943.0612
Web.................................www.bowers-rodgers.org
  P.O. Box 1252, Greenwood, SC 29648
COA accredited organization.

Carl A Saleeby Law Ofc....................843.332.4709
Fax...843.332.2027
Web.................................www.carlsaleeby.com
E-mail.....................carl@carlsaleeby.com
  1023 W Carolina Ave, Hartsville, SC 29550-4427
Carl A Saleeby, Attorney

Carolina Hope Christian Adoption Agency,
Inc.......................................864.268.0570
Fax...864.370.0036
Web.................................www.carolinahopeadoption.org
E-mail.....................cadopt@gmail.com
  1527 Wade Hampton Blvd, Greenville, SC 29609
Laura Beauvais-godwin, Director

Catholic Charities- Diocese Of Charleston......843.402.9115
Fax...843.402.9071
Web.................................www.catholic-doc.org
E-mail.....................epeitler@catholic-doc.org
  1662 Ingram Rd, Charleston, SC 29407-4242
Deacon Edward Peitler, Director

Child Of The Heart........................843.881.2973
Fax...843.971.0600
E-mail.....................estrehale@mindspring.com
  1156 Bowman Rd Unit 200, Mt Pleasant,
  SC 29464-3858
Elena Strehle, Director

Christian Family Svcs, Inc.................803.328.2229
Fax...803.328.2240
Web.................................www.christianfamilyservices.org
E-mail.....................christianfam@comporium.net
  1069 Bayshore Dr, Rock Hill, SC 29732
Sharon Cole, Director

Dennis Wayne Catoe Law Ofc...............803.407.2500
Fax...803.612.5135
E-mail.....................dwcatoe@aol.com
  121 Executive Center Dr, Ste 218, Columbia,
  SC 29210
Dennis Wayne Catoe, Attorney

Family Service Center of South Carolina......803.733.5450
Fax...803.929.6699
Web.................................www.fsconline.org
  P.O. Box 7876, Columbia, SC 29202
COA accredited organization.

Frederick M Corley Law Ofc.................843.524.3232
Fax...843.525.4442
Web.................................www.lowcountrybankruptcy.com
  1214 King St, Beaufort, SC 29902-4934
Rick Corley, Attorney

Specialized Alternatives For Youth..........803.791.7328
Fax...803.791.4198
Web.................................www.safy.org
E-mail.....................sommersg@safy.org
  800 Dutchware Blvd, Ste 205, Columbia, SC 29210
Genice Sommers, State Director

ADVOCACY RESOURCES

Child Advocacy Ctr Of Spartanburg, Inc........864.515.9922
Fax...864.515.9919
Web.................................www.cacst.org
E-mail.....................bill@cacsp.org
  100 Washington Pl, Spartanburg, SC 29302
Bill Herrick, Executive Director

Childrens Defense Fund - S Carolina.........843.479.5310
Fax...843.479.0605
  117 Cheraw St, Bennettsville, SC 29512
Robin Sally, Director

Lowcountry Children's Ctr, Inc..............843.723.3600
Fax...843.720.7106
Web.................................www.dnlcc.org
E-mail.....................lcc@dnlcc.org
  1061 King St, Charleston, SC 29403
Dr. Elizabeth Ralston, Executive Director

BEHAVIORAL HEALTH TREATMENT

Aiken Center for Alcohol and Other Drug
Services..................................803.649.1900
Fax...803.643.2926
Web.................................www.aikencenter.org
  1105 Gregg Highway, Aiken, SC 29801
CARF accredited programs available.

Aiken-Barnwell Mental Health Center.......803.641.7700
Fax...803.641.7709
E-mail.....................kmr50@scdmh.org
  1135 Gregg Highway, Aiken, SC 29801
Katherine Roberts, Director Office of Client Affairs
CARF accredited programs available.

Alcohol and Drug Abuse Commission........843.546.6081
Fax...843.520.0341
  1423 Winyah Street, Georgetown, SC 29440
CARF accredited programs available.

Alcohol and Drug Abuse Department........843.470.4545
Fax...843.470.4557
Web.................................www.bcgov.net
  1905 Duke Street, Suite 270, Beaufort, SC 29902
CARF accredited programs available.

Alexander Medical Practice.................843.556.8177
Fax...843.571.2742
  1954 Ashley River Rd, Charleston, SC 29407
Constance Alexander Md, Psychiatrist

Alliance Human Svcs, Inc...................803.799.9025
Fax...803.931.8964
Web.................................www.thementornetwork.com
E-mail.....................lynn.morton-epps@thementornetwork.com
  3200 Devine St, Columbia, SC 29205
Lynn Morton-Epps, Director

Alston Wilkes Youth Home..................803.254.3684
Fax...803.254.3796
Web.................................www.alstonwilkessociety.org
E-mail.....................lperry@alstonwilkessociety.org
  2700 Cypress St, Columbia, SC 29205-1627
Kimberly Mcelroy, Director

AMI Kids..................................843.921.3000
Fax...843.921.0934
Web.................................www.amikids.org
  2381 Campbell Lake Rd, Patrick, SC 29584
Joshua Brown, Director

Amikids Piedmont........................864.833.4505
Fax...864.833.4507
Web.................................www.pwi-sc.org
E-mail.....................piedmont.ed@amikids.org
  20238 Highway 72 E, Clinton, SC 29325
Rickie Hardy, Director

Anderson Oconee Pickens Mental Health
Center....................................864.260.2220
Fax...864.260.2247
Web.................................www.aopmentalhealth.org
  200 McGee Road, Anderson, SC 29625
CARF accredited programs available.

Anmed Wellspring........................864.847.1050
Fax...864.847.1121
Web.................................www.anmedhealth.org
E-mail.....................joe.feleppa@anmedhealth.org
  313 Williams St, Williamston, SC 29697-1928
Joeseph Feleppa, Executive Director

Ashleigh Place............................803.284.4433
Fax...803.284.0130
Web.................................www.ashleighplace.com
E-mail.....................ashplace@bellsouth.net
  4435 Ashleigh Rd, Blackville, SC 29817-4463
Dawn Hollinsworth, Director

Axis I Center of Barnwell 803.541.1245
Fax 803.541.1247
   1644 Jackson Street, Barnwell, SC 29812
   CARF accredited programs available.

Beaufort Marine Institute 843.846.2128
Fax 843.846.4147
   60 Honeybee Island Rd, Seabrook, SC 29940
   Amy Nevells, Director

Behavioral Health Services 864.898.5800
Fax 864.898.5804
Web .... http://www.bhspickens.com
   309 East Main Street, Pickens, SC 29671
   CARF accredited programs available.

Berkeley Community Mental Health
Center 843.761.8282
Fax 843.761.7308
Web .... www.bcmhc.org
   403 Stoney Landing Road, Moncks Corner, SC 29461
   CARF accredited programs available.

Billie Hardee Home For Boys 843.393.8600
Fax 843.393.6471
Web .... www.bhhb.net
   1133 Timmonsville Hwy, ., Darlington,
   SC 29532-5077
   Wayne G. Chapman, Executive Director

Blacksburg Primary School 864.839.1106
Fax 864.839.1109
Web cherokee1.k12.sc.us
E-mail .... melinda.moore@cherokee1.k12.sc.us
   1010 E Cherokee St, Blacksburg, SC 29702-8371
   Melinda Moore, Director

Bowers-Rodgers Home, Inc. 864.229.6879
Fax 864.943.0612
Web .... www.bowers-rodgers.org
E-mail .... npierce@bowers-rodgers.org
   PO Box 1252, Greenwood, SC 29648-1252
   Nicole Pierce, Director

Boys Home of the South 864.243.3443
Fax 864.243.5743
Web .... www.boyshomeofthesouth.org
   10612 Augusta, Belton, SC 29627
   COA accredited organization.

Bullock Medical Practice 843.842.6402
Fax 415.441.1327
   19 Shelter Cove Ln, Ste 301, Hilton Head Island,
   SC 29928-3549
   Ronald Bullock, Md, Psychiatrist

Calvary Home For Children 864.296.5437
Fax 864.224.8717
Web .... www.calvaryhome.org
E-mail .... calvaryhome@bellsouth.net
   110 Calvary Home Cir, Anderson, SC 29621
   Greg Skipper, Executive Director

Camp Bennettsville I And Ii 843.479.0420
Fax 843.479.0840
E-mail .... cb1-bm@cb1.ami-fl.org
   620 Marlboro Rd, Bennettsville, SC 29512-7733
   Jerome Platt, Director

Camp White Pines 864.674.0458
Fax 864.674.0460
Web .... www.amikids.org
E-mail .... whitepines-ed@amikids.org
   742 T Bishop Rd, Jonesville, SC 29353-2342
   Zachary Thomas, Executive Director

Carolina Children's Home 803.787.2306
Fax 803.790.6554
Web .... www.carolinachildrenshome.org
   P.O. Box 4465, Columbia, SC 29240
   COA accredited organization.

Charleston Orphan House, Inc. dba Carolina Youth
Development Center 843.266.5200
Fax 843.266.5201
Web .... www.cydc.org
   5055 Lackawanna Boulevard, North Charleston,
   SC 29405
   COA accredited organization.

Cherokee Children's Home, Inc 864.487.0177
Fax 864.902.0788
E-mail .... susankharris3@hotmail.com
   215 Allison Dr, Gaffney, SC 29341-2875
   Susan Harris, Executive Director

Children's Attention Ctr 803.328.8871
Fax 803.324.0437
Web .... www.attentionhome.org
E-mail .... lsweatt-lambert@attentionhome.org
   PO Box 2912, Rock Hill, SC 29732-4912
   Libby Sweatt-lambert, Director

Circle Park Behavioral Health Services 843.665.9349
Fax 843.665.1615
Web .... www.circlepark.com
   601 Gregg Avenue, Florence, SC 29501
   CARF accredited programs available.

Clayton Medical Practice 803.252.0877
   1226 Pickens St, Columbia, SC 29201
   Brad Clayton, MD, Psychiatrist

Coastal Empire Community Mental Health
Center 843.524.8899
Fax 843.524.8179
Web .... www.state.sc.us/dmh/cmhc.htm#coast
   1050 Ribaut Road, Beaufort, SC 29902
   CARF accredited programs available.

Coastal Empire Mental Health Ctr 843.524.3378
Fax 843.524.1879
Web .... www.cecmhc.org
E-mail .... rden80@scdmh.org
   1050 Ribaut Rd, Beaufort, SC 29902-5400
   Ramon Norris, Ms, Executive Director

Columbia Area Mental Health Center 803.898.4802
Fax 803.898.4899
   2715 Colonial Drive, Columbia, SC 29203
   CARF accredited programs available.

Commission On Alcohol And Drug Abuse 803.245.4360
E-mail .... rfowler@tccada.state.sc.us
   2549 Main Hwy, Bamberg, SC 29003
   Richard S. Fowler, Executive Director

Community Mental Health Center 843.454.0841
Fax 843.454.0635
   1035 Cheraw Highway, Bennettsville, SC 29512
   CARF accredited programs available.

Community Mental Health Center 803.996.1500
Fax 803.996.1511
Web .... www.scdmh.org
E-mail .... kmr50@scdmh.org
   301 Palmetto Park Boulevard, Lexington, SC 29072
   Katherine Roberts, Medical Director
   CARF accredited programs available.

Connie Maxwell Children's Home 864.942.1400
Fax 864.942.1440
Web .... www.conniemaxwell.com
E-mail .... bendavis@conniemaxwell.com
   810 Maxwell Ave, Greenwood, SC 29646
   Dr. Ben Davis, President

Ctr For Counseling 864.457.4208
Fax 864.457.2866
   1012 S Blackstock Rd, Landrum, SC 29356
   Tara Horne, Owner and Director

Dorchester Alcohol and Drug Commission 843.871.4790
Fax 843.871.8579
Web .... www.dadc.org
   500 North Main Street, Suite 4, Summerville,
   SC 29483
   CARF accredited programs available.

Dorchester Counseling In Svcs 843.871.4793
Fax 843.832.9600
Web .... www.dadc.org
   112 W 4th N St Ste B, Summerville, SC 29483
   Bonnie Dan, Intake/secretary

Dwivedi Medical Practice 803.329.7778
E-mail .... beckymc_md@yahoo.com
   1721 Ebenezer Rd Ste 265, Rock Hill, SC 29732-5100
   Dr. Tarunendu Dwivedi, Md, Psychiatrist

Ellen Hines Smith Girls Home 864.573.9223
Fax 864.597.0815
Web .... www.spgirlshome.com
E-mail .... chamlee.lee@spgirlshome.com
   241 Cedar Springs Rd, Spartanburg, SC 29302-4639
   Chamlee Lacousti, Director

Epworth Children's Home 803.256.7394
Fax 803.212.4799
Web .... www.epworthchildrenshome.org
E-mail .... jholler@epworthsc.org
   2900 Millwood Ave, Columbia, SC 29205-1358
   John Holler, President

Excalibur Youth Services, LLC 864.679.0023
Fax 864.294.1774
Web .... www.recoveryouth.org
   5321 Old Buncombe Road, Greenville, SC 29609
   CARF accredited programs available.

Fair Play Wilderness Camp School 864.647.4311
Fax 864.647.4314
E-mail .... camp@fairplaycamp.net
   347 Wilderness Trl, Westminster, SC 29693-3404
   Judson Schrok, Director

Fairfield Behavioral Health Services 803.635.2335
Fax 803.635.9695
Web .... www.fairfieldbhs.org
   200 Calhoun Street, Winnsboro, SC 29180
   CARF accredited programs available.

Federation Of Families For Children's Mental Health Of South
Carolina 866.779.0402
Fax 803.772.5212
Web .... www.sedfansc.org
E-mail .... diane.flashnick@fedfamsc.org
   810 Dutch Sq Blvd Ste 205, Columbia, SC 29210
   Diane Revels-flashnick, Representative

Fleet & Family Support Ctr 843.764.7294
Fax 843.764.7299
Web .... www.cnic.navy.mil
E-mail .... tara.fuller@navy.mil
   1005 Jefferson Avenue Ext, Goose Creek,
   SC 29445-6049
   Tara Fuller, Director

Generations Alternative Program, Inc. 864.243.5557
Fax 864.243.5947
E-mail .... kathleen@generationsgroup.com
   821 Dunklin Bridge Road, Simpsonville, SC 29680
   Kathleen Reynolds, Director

Generations Group Homes of Greenville,
Inc. 864.243.5557
Fax 864.243.3339
Web .... www.generationsgroup.com
   P.O. Box 80009, Simpsonville, SC 29680-0009
   COA accredited organization.

Georgetown Marine Institute 843.546.5478
Fax 843.546.5652
Web .... www.amikids.org
   East Ccc Road, Hwy 17 South, Georgetown,
   SC 29442
   Steven Crist, Director

Greenhouse Runaway Shelter 803.775.3311
Fax 803.934.0691
E-mail .... info@qsbinc.com
   529 N Wise Dr, Sumter, SC 29153-8561
   Howard Mcfadden, Director

Greenville Group Home 864.233.5574
Fax 864.233.7526
  423 Vardry St, Greenville, SC 29601-3307
  Terry Hamilton, Director

**Greenville Hospital System University Medical
Center** 864.455.7000
Web ....www.ghs.org
E-mail ....mpeters@ghs.org
  701 Grove Road, Greenville, SC 29605
  Mrs. Mary Peters, Accreditation Manager
  Joint Commission accredited organization.

Greenville Mental Health Center 864.241.1040
Fax 864.241.1215
Web ....www.greenvillementalhealth.org
  124 Mallard Street, Greenville, SC 29601-4046
  CARF accredited programs available.

**Greenwood-Edgefield-McCormick-Abbeville Commission on
Alcohol and Drug Abuse dba Cornerstone** 864.227.1001
Fax 864.227.3619
Web ....www.cornerstonecares.org
  1510 Spring Street, Greenwood, SC 29646
  CARF accredited programs available.

Helping Hands of Clemson 864.654.6154
Fax 864.653.8516
E-mail ....helpinghandskids@bellsouth.net
  167 Brookbend Rd, Central, SC 29630
  Jennifer Barbour, Director

Helping Hands, Inc 803.648.3456
Fax 803.641.4161
E-mail ....clandy@helpinghandsaiken.org
  100 John Elliot Ln, Aiken, SC 29801-3612
  Carmen Landy, Director

**Jenkins Orphanage Supervised Independent Living
Program** 843.744.2429
Fax 843.529.0057
E-mail ....danieljj@bellsouth.net
  3923 Azalea Dr, North Charleston, SC 29405
  Johanna Martin-carrington, Director

John De La Howe School 864.391.2131
Fax 864.391.2135
E-mail ....marks@delahowe.k12.sc.us
  192 Gettys Rd, Mc Cormick, SC 29835-5112
  Mark William Sam, Superintendant

John K. Crosswell Home For Children 803.778.6441
Fax 803.778.6442
Web ....www.crosswellchildrenshome.org
  11 Crosswell Dr, Sumter, SC 29150
  Jerry Allred, Director

Kennedy Ctr 843.719.3000
Fax 843.719.3025
Web ....www.ekcenter.org
E-mail ....ekcenter@ekcenter.org
  306 Airport Dr, Moncks Corner, SC 29461-2629
  Jerome Tilghman, Executive Director

Lancaster Children's Home, Inc. (Boys) 803.286.5277
Fax 803.286.5459
  1335 Children Ave, Lancaster, SC 29721
  Bill Summers, Director

Lancaster Children's Home, Inc. (Girls) 803.286.6573
Fax 803.286.5459
  1287 Childrens Ave, Lancaster, SC 29720
  Annette Deese, Director

Lighthouse Care Center of Conway 843.347.8871
Web ....www.lighthousecarecenterofconway.com
E-mail ....denise.grandin@uhsinc.com
  152 Waccamaw Medical Park Drive, Conway,
  SC 29526
  Ms. Denise Grandin, Accreditation Manager
  Joint Commission accredited organization.

LRADAC 803.726.9300
Fax 803.733.1395
Web ....www.lradac.org
  2711 Colonial Drive, Columbia, SC 29203
  CARF accredited programs available.

Lutheran Family Svcs In The Carolinas Cpa 803.750.9917
Fax 803.750.9920
Web ....www.lfscarolinas.org
  1118 Union St, Columbia, SC 29201
  Ronnie Hussnan, Executive Director

Mccormick Children's Home 864.391.2931
Fax 864.391.2933
E-mail ....mcchi@wctel.net
  146 Tomb Rd, Mc Cormick, SC 29835-5116
  Laurie Franklin, Director

**Medical University of South Carolina Medical
Center** 843.792.4000
Web ....www.musc.edu
E-mail ....ellist@musc.edu
  169 Ashley Avenue, Charleston, SC 29425
  Mrs. Terri Ellis, Accreditation Manager
  Joint Commission accredited organization.

Miracle Hill Children's Home 864.878.9987
Fax 864.878.9009
Web ....www.miraclehill.org
E-mail ....jpulido@miraclehill.org
  117 Drummond Ln, Pickens, SC 29671-9500
  Jane Pulido, Director

New Foundations Home For Children, Inc. 864.225.1628
Fax 864.260.4699
Web ....http://www.newfoundationschildren.com/
  2300 Standridge Road, Anderson, SC 29625
  COA accredited organization.

New Hope Carolinas 803.328.9300
Fax 803.328.0102
Web ....www.newhopetreatment.com
  101 Sedgewood Dr, Rock Hill, SC 29732-2315
  Sam Phifer, Director

New Hope Treatment Centers, Inc. 843.572.3498
Web ....www.newhopetreatment.com
E-mail ....ericb@newhopetreatment.com
  7515 Northside Drive, Suite 200, North Charleston,
  SC 29420
  Mr. Eric Baumgartner, Accreditation Manager
  Joint Commission accredited organization.

Nurture Home 803.641.4177
Fax 803.641.4178
Web ....www.mhaacnurturehome@bellsoutn.net
E-mail ....mhaac@duesouth.net
  230 Pendelton st, Aiken, SC 29802
  Chasity Johnson, Director

Orangeburg Area Mental Health Center 803.536.1571
Fax 803.531.7798
Web ....www.state.sc.us/dmh/cmhc.htm#oburg
  2319 Saint Matthews Road, Orangeburg, SC 29118
  CARF accredited programs available.

**Orphan Aid Society, Inc. dba Joseph Jenkins Institute for
Children** 843.744.1771
Fax 843.529.0057
Web ....www.jekinsinstitute.org
  3923 Azalea Drive, N. Charleston, SC 29405
  COA accredited organization.

Palmetto Ctr 843.662.9378
Fax 843.662.0811
Web ....www.scvrd.state.sc.us
E-mail ....tlangston@scvrd.state.sc.us
  1709 Stokes Rd, Florence, SC 29501-7023
  Tom Langston, Supervisor

Palmetto Lowcountry Behavioral Health 843.747.5830
Fax 843.745.5177
Web ....www.palmettobehavioralhealth.com
  2777 Speissegger Dr, North Charleston, SC 29405
  Cherie Polley, CEO

**Palmetto Lowcountry Behavioral Health,
LLC** 843.747.5830
E-mail ....marc.turner@psysolutions.com
  2777 Speissegger Drive, Charleston, SC 29405-8299
  Mr. Marc Turner, Accreditation Manager
  Joint Commission accredited organization.

Palmetto Pee Dee Behavioral Health, LLC 843.667.0644
E-mail ....marc.turner@psysolutions.com
  601B Gregg Avenue, Florence, SC 29502
  Mr. Marc Turner, Accreditation Manager
  Joint Commission accredited organization.

Pee Dee Mental Health Center 843.317.4089
Fax 843.317.4096
Web ....http://www.state.sc.us/dmh/peedee
  125 East Cheves Street, Florence, SC 29506
  CARF accredited programs available.

**Piedmont Center for Mental Health
Services** 864.963.3421
Fax 864.967.8617
Web ....www.pcmhs.org
  20 Powderhorn Road, Simpsonville, SC 29681
  CARF accredited programs available.

Pinelands Group Homes, Inc. 843.851.0079
Fax 843.873.1002
  201 East Luke Avenue, Summerville, SC 29483
  CARF accredited programs available.

Saluda Behavioral Health System 864.445.2968
Fax 864.445.9592
  204 North Ramage Street, Saluda, SC 29138
  CARF accredited programs available.

**Santee-Wateree Community Mental Health
Center** 803.775.9364
Fax 803.773.6615
  215 North Magnolia Street, Sumter, SC 29150
  CARF accredited programs available.

Shoreline Behavioral Health Svcs 843.365.8884
Fax 843.365.6685
Web ....www.shorelinebhs.org
  2404 Wise Rd, Conway, SC 29528
  John Coffin, Director

**South Carolina Youth Advocate Program
Sil** 843.679.3189
Fax 843.678.9865
E-mail ....lcole@nyap.org
  708 Dargan St., Florence, SC 29501-4317
  Lex Cole, Executive Director

**Southeastern Childrens Home Lyman
House** 864.439.0259
Fax 864.949.0248
Web ....www.sech.org
E-mail ....info@sech.org
  115 Childrens Way, Duncan, SC 29334
  Robert C. Kimberly, Director

Spartanburg Area Mental Health Center 864.585.0366
Fax 864.585.9208
  250 Dewey Avenue, Spartanburg, SC 29303
  CARF accredited programs available.

SpringBrook Behavioral Health System 864.660.6224
Web ....www.springbrookbehavioral.com
E-mail ....lateka.sortor@springbrookbhs.com
  One Havenwood Lane, Travelers Rest,
  SC 29690-1005
  Ms. Lateka Sortor, Accreditation Manager
  Joint Commission accredited organization.

Tamassee DAR School, Inc. 864.944.1390
Fax 864.944.0097
Web ....www.tdarschool.org
  P.O. Box 8, Tamassee, SC 29686
  COA accredited organization.

Tara Hall, Inc. 843.546.3000
Fax 843.527.2156
Web ....www.tarahall.org
P.O. Box 955, Georgetown, SC 29442-0955
COA accredited organization.

The ALPHA Center: Substance Abuse and Counseling
Services 803.432.6902
Fax 803.432.6890
709 Mill Street, Camden, SC 29020
CARF accredited programs available.

The Beckman Center for Mental Health
Services 864.229.7120
Fax 864.229.5526
Web ....www.beckmancenter.com
1547 Parkway, Suite 100, Greenwood, SC 29646
CARF accredited programs available.

The Phoenix Center 864.467.3790
Fax 864.467.3779
Web ....www.phoenixcenter.org
1400 Cleveland Street, Greenville, SC 29607
CARF accredited programs available.

The Pines Residential Treatment Center-Charleston
Campus 843.851.5015
E-mail ....marc.turner@psysolutions.com
225 Midland Parkway, Summerville, SC 29485
Mr. Marc Turner, Accreditation Manager
Joint Commission accredited organization.

Three Rivers Behavioral Health, LLC 803.796.9911
Web ....www.threeriversbehavioral.org
E-mail ....shari.baker@psysolutions.com
2900 Sunset Boulevard, West Columbia, SC 29169
Ms. Shari Baker, Accreditation Manager
Joint Commission accredited organization.

Three Rivers Residential Treatment | Midlands
Campus 803.791.9918
Web ....www.psysolutions.com
E-mail ....shannon.marcus@uhsinc.com
200 Ermine Road, West Columbia, SC 29170
Mrs. Shannon Marcus, Accreditation Manager
Joint Commission accredited organization.

Trinity Behavioral Care 843.423.8292
Fax 843.423.8294
103 Court Street, Marion, SC 29571
CARF accredited programs available.

UHS of Greenville, Inc. 864.235.2335
Web ....www.thecarolinacenter.com
E-mail ....anne.palmer@uhsinc.com
2700 East Phillips Road, Greer, SC 29650
Mrs. Anne Palmer, Accreditation Manager
Joint Commission accredited organization.

Waccamaw Center for Mental Health 843.347.5060
Fax 843.347.3959
164 Waccamaw Medical Park Drive, Conway,
SC 29526
CARF accredited programs available.

Westview Behavioral Health Services 803.276.5690
Fax 803.321.2234
Web ....www.westviewbehavioral.org
800 Main Street, Newberry, SC 29108
CARF accredited programs available.

William S. Hall Psychiatric Institute 803.898.1593
Web ....www.dmh.state.sc.us
E-mail ....awb36@scdmh.org
1800 Colonial Drive, Columbia, SC 29203
Ms. Algie Bryant, Accreditation Manager
Joint Commission accredited organization.

Willowglen Academy, South Carolina, Inc. 803.473.4656
Fax 803.473.4676
Web ....www.willowglensc.com
1399 Harmony Camp Road, Greeleyville, SC 29056
CARF accredited programs available.

Windwood Farm Home for Children, Inc. 843.884.5342
Fax 843.884.1287
Web ....www.windwoodfarm.org
4857 Windwood Farm Road, Awendaw, SC 29429
COA accredited organization.

York Place, Episcopal Church Home for
Children 803.684.4011
Fax 803.628.1632
Web ....www.yorkplace.org
234 Kings Mountain Street, York, SC 29745
COA accredited organization.

CHILDREN'S HOSPITAL

Abbeville Area Medical Center 864.366.5011
420 Thomson Circle, Abbeville, SC 29620
Richard Osmus, Chief Executive Officer

Aiken Regional Medical Centers 803.641.5000
302 University Pkwy, Aiken, SC 29801
Carlos Milanes, Director

AnMed Health 864.512.1000
800 North Fant St, Anderson, SC 29621
Martha Stratton, Nursing Director

Baptist Easley Hospital 864.442.7200
200 Fleetwood Dr, Easley, SC 29640
Roddey Gettys, Chief Executive Officer

Beaufort Memorial Hospital 843.522.5200
955 Ribaut Rd, Beaufort, SC 29902
Rick Toomey, Chief Executive Officer

Bon Secours St Francis Hospital 843.402.1000
2095 Henry Tecklenburg Dr, Charleston, SC 29414
Allen Carroll, President

Carolina Pines Regional Medical Center 843.339.2100
1304 West BoBo Newsome Hwy, Hartsville, SC 29550
Steve Midkiff, Chief Executive Officer

Carolinas Hospital 843.674.5000
805 Pamplico Hwy, Florence, SC 29505

Chester Regional Medical Center 803.581.3151
1 Medical Park Dr, Chester, SC 29706
Page Vaughan, Chief Executive Officer

Chesterfield General Hospital 843.537.7881
711 Chesterfield Highway, Cheraw, SC 29520
Paul Theriot, Executive Director

Clarendon Memorial Hospital 803.435.8463
10 Hospital St, Manning, SC 29102
Edward Frye, Chief Executive Officer

Coastal Carolina Hospital 843.784.8000
1000 Medical Center Dr, Hardeeville, SC 29927
Bill Masterton, Chief Executive Officer

Colleton Medical Center 843.782.2000
501 Robertson Blvd, Walterboro, SC 29488
Mitch Mongel, Chief Executive Officer

Community Hospital 803.637.3174
300 Ridge Medical Plz, Edgefield, SC 29824
Patricia Robinson, Chief Executive Officer

Conway Medical Center 843.347.7111
300 Singleton Ridge Rd, Conway, SC 29526
Phillip Clayton, Director

Georgetown Memorial Hospital 843.527.7000
606 Black River Rd, Georgetown, SC 29440
Bruce Bailey, Director

Grand Strand Regional Medical Center 843.692.1000
809 82nd Pkwy, Myrtle Beach, SC 29572
Doug White, Chief Executive Officer

Greenville Memorial Hospital 864.455.7000
701 Grove Rd, Greenville, SC 29605
Michael Riordan, Administrator

Greer Memorial Hospital 864.848.8200
830 South Bumcombe Rd, Greer, SC 29650

Health Care System 864.833.9100
Highway 76 East, Clinton, SC 29325
Jamie Adafr, Administrator

Hilton Head Hospital 843.681.6122
25 Hospital Center, Hilton Head Island, SC 29926
Mark Oneal, Chief Executive Officer

Hospital 803.259.1000
811 Reynolds Rd, Barnwell, SC 29812

Lexington Medical Center 803.791.2000
2720 Sunset Blvd, West Columbia, SC 29169
Michael Biedger, CEO

Loris Community Hospital 843.716.7000
3655 Mitchell St, Loris, SC 29569
Arnold Greene, Director

Marlboro Park Hospital 843.479.2881
1138 Cheraw Highway, Bennettsville, SC 29512
Jeff Reece, Chief Executive Officer

Mary Black Memorial Hospital 864.573.3000
1700 Skylyn Dr, Spartanburg, SC 29307
Doug Moyer, Chief Executive Officer

McLeod Health 843.777.2000
555 East Cheves St, Florence, SC 29502
Leanne Huminski, Vice President, Nursing

McLeod Medical Center Dillon 843.774.4111
301 East Jackson St, Dillon, SC 29536
Dedoraa Locklair, Administrator

Medical Center 803.432.4311
1315 Roberts St, Camden, SC 29020

Medical Center 803.431.2000
2829 East Highway 76, Mullins, SC 29574
Don Loyd, Chief Executive Officer

Medical University of South Carolina 843.792.2300
169 Ashley Ave, Charleston, SC 29425
Ray Greenberg, President

Memorial Hospital 803.276.7570
2669 Kinard St, Newberry, SC 29108
Worn Vigus, Director

Memorial Hospital 803.245.4321
509 North St, Bamberg, SC 29003

Oconee Memorial Hospital 864.882.3351
298 Memorial Dr, Seneca, SC 29672
Jean Ward, Chief Executive Officer

Palmetto Health Baptist Columbia 803.296.5010
Taylor at Marion St, Columbia, SC 29220
Charles Beaman, Chief Executive Officer

Piedmont Medical Center 803.329.1234
222 Herlong Ave, Rock Hill, SC 29732
Charlie Miller, Chief Executive Officer

Regional Medical Center of Orangeburg 803.395.2200
3000 St Matthews Rd, Orangeburg, SC 29118
Tom Bandridge, President

Self Regional Healthcare 864.725.4111
1325 Spring St, Greenwood, SC 29646
Jim Pfeiffer, Chief Executive Officer

Shriners Hospitals for Children at Gree 864.271.3444
950 West Faris Rd, Greenville, SC 29605
Jon Davids, Chief Executive Officer

Spartanburg Regional Medical Center 864.560.6000
101 East Wood St, Spartanburg, SC 29303
Bruce Holstien, Chief Executive Officer

Springs Memorial Hospital 803.286.1214
800 West Meeting St, Lancaster, SC 29720
Doug Arbour, Chief Executive Officer

Summerville Medical Center 843.832.5000
295 Midland Pkwy, Summerville, SC 29485
Loouis Catuco, Chief Executive Officer

Trident Medical Center 843.847.4000
9330 Medical Plaza Dr, Charleston, SC 29406
Todd Tallati, Chief Executive Officer

Tuomey Regional Medical Center 803.774.9000
129 North Washington St, Sumter, SC 29150
Jill Williamson, Director

Upstate Carolina Medical Center 864.487.4271
1530 North Limestone St, Gaffney, SC 29340
Joe Havell, Chief Executive Officer

Waccamaw Community Hospital 843.652.1000
4070 Highway 17 Bypass, Murrells Inlet, SC 29576
Gayle Resetar, Chief Operating Officer

Wallace Thomson Hospital 864.427.0351
322 West South St, Union, SC 29379
Tim Merritt, Chief Executive Officer

Williamsburg Regional Hospital 843.355.8888
500 Nelson Blvd, Kingstree, SC 29556

COUNSELING SERVICES

Bethany Christian Svcs 843.629.1177
Fax 843.629.8303
Web .... www.bethany.org
E-mail .... aviele@bethany.org
1113 44 N ave, Myrgle Beach, SC 29577
Alissa Viele, Lead Staff

**Specialized Alternatives For Family And
Youth** 843.552.1220
Fax 843.552.0502
Web .... www.safy.org
3125 Ashley Phosphate Rd Ste 117, North Charleston,
SC 29418-8419
Eunice Freeman, Director

CRISIS & SHELTER CARE

Alston-Wilkes Youth Home-West 803.772.6191
Fax 803.772.5962
Web .... www.alstonwilkessociety.org
E-mail .... sbright@alstonwilkessociety.org
401 Lawand Dr, Columbia, SC 29210-7555
Samantha Bright, Director

Carolina Children's Home 803.787.2306
Fax 803.787.2642
Web .... www.carolinachildrenshome.org
E-mail .... home4kidz@caolinachildrenshome.com
3201 Trenholm Rd, Columbia, SC 29204-3371

**Carolina Youth Development Ctr/Charleston Orphan
House** 843.266.5200
Fax 843.266.5201
Web .... www.cydc.org
E-mail .... cjohnson@cydc.org
5055 Lackawanna Blvd, North Charleston,
SC 29405-4522
Barbara Kelley-duncan, Executive Director

**CASA-Family Systems Domestic Violence
Program** 803.534.2448
Fax 803.534.2594
E-mail .... gcobbhun@bellsouth.net
668 John C. Calhoun Dr, Orangeburg, SC 29115
Gilda Cobb-hunter, Director

**Citizens Against Spouse Abuse-Domestic
Violence** 843.626.7595
Fax 843.626.0168
E-mail .... citizensagains@aol.com
PO Box 912, Myrtle Beach, SC 29578-0912
Joanne Patterson, Director

Citizens Opposed To Domestic Abuse 843.770.1074
Fax 843.770.1084
Web .... www.codabft.com
E-mail .... executivedirector@codabft.com
506 Waight St, Beaufort, SC 29902-4345
Bonnie Lawrence, Director

**Compass Of Carolina-Family Violence
Intervention** 864.467.3434
Fax 864.467.3571
Web .... www.compassofcarolina.org
E-mail .... info@compassofcarolina.org
1100 Rutherford Rd, Greenville, SC 29609-3927
Hadley Mullen, Director

Crossroads At Mountain Meadows 864.246.0266
Fax 864.246.0652
Web .... www.crossroadsgrouphome.com
E-mail .... lorraine@crossroadsgrouphome.com
9522 Old White Horse Rd, Greenville,
SC 29617-6914
Lorraine Turner, Director/CEO

Cumbee Ctr To Assist Abused Persons 803.649.0480
Fax 803.641.4163
E-mail .... caap_p_ktm@bellsouth.net
135 Lancaster St SW, Aiken, SC 29802
Kay T. Mixon, Director

Family Resource Ctr-Domestic Violence 803.425.4357
Fax 803.425.5769
E-mail .... derrickfrc@bellsouth.net
1111 Broad St Ste 3A, Camden, SC 29020-3635
Christina Derrick, Executive Director

Foothills Alliance Crisis Ctr-Sexual Assault 864.231.7273
Fax 864.231.8515
Web .... www.foothillsalliance.org
216 E Calhoun St, Anderson, SC 29621

Greenville Rape Crisis-Child Abuse Ctr 864.331.0560
Fax 864.331.0565
Web .... www.grccac.org
E-mail .... sgalloway@julievalentinecenter.org
2905 White Horse Rd, Greenville, SC 29611
Shauna Galloway, Director

Hope Haven-Low Country 843.524.2256
Fax 843.524.0597
Web .... www.hophavenlc.org
E-mail .... hope2@islc.net
69 Robert Smalls Pkwy Ste 4A, Beaufort, SC 29906
Shauw Chin Capps, Director

Megs House-Domestic Violence 864.227.1421
Fax 864.229.7663
E-mail .... meghouse@embarqmail.com
112 Hampton Rd, Greenwood, SC 29648
Alice Hodges, Director

My Sister's House, Inc.-Domestic Violence 843.747.4069
Fax 843.747.6592
Web .... www.mysistershouse.org
E-mail .... eraven@mysistershouse.com
PO Box 71171, North Charleston, SC 29415
Elmire Raven, Executive Director

Palmetto Citizens Against Sexual Abuse 803.286.5232
Fax 803.286.0520
E-mail .... Cmcgriff@Comporium.Net
106 N York St, Lancaster, SC 29720-2063
Charlene Mcgriff, Director

Palmetto Place 803.786.6819
Fax 803.691.9788
E-mail .... director@palmettoplaceshelter.org
PO Box 3395, Columbia, SC 29230-3395
Marissa Merchant, Executive Director

People Against Rape-Sexual Assault 843.745.0144
Fax 843.745.0119
Web .... www.peopleagainstrape.org
E-mail .... mlocklair@peopleagainstrape.org
2154 N Center St Ste 302C, Charleston, SC 29406
Melanie Marek, Director

Safe Harbor-Domestic Violence 864.467.1177
Fax 864.467.3638
421 N Main St, Greenville, SC 29602

Safe Home 864.682.7270
Fax 864.683.3670
Web .... www.thesafehome.org
500 Academy St, Clinton, SC 29325
Dawn Ardelt, Director

Safe Home-Rape Crisis Coalition 864.583.9803
Fax 864.583.9611
Web .... www.shrcc.org
E-mail .... shrcc@aol.com
236 Union St, Spartanburg, SC 29302
Lynn Hawkins, Director

Safe Passage-Domestic Violence 803.329.3336
Fax 803.329.3515
Web .... www.safepassagesc.org
E-mail .... jalleva@safepassagesc.org
104 Oakland Ave, Rock Hill, SC 29730
Jane Alleva, Interim Executive Director

Sea Haven, Inc. 843.399.4045
Fax 843.390.1914
E-mail .... cbjack@sccoast.net
3892 Highway 9 East, LittleRiver, SC 29566
Christina B. Jackson, Executive Director

Sexual Trauma And Counseling Ctr 864.227.1623
Fax 864.227.2923
Web .... www.meta-net.net
E-mail .... stcc@meta-net.net
115 E Alexander Ave, Greenwood, SC 29646-3943
Kris Burris, Director

Sexual Trauma Svcs Of The Midlands 803.790.8208
Fax 803.790.8282
Web .... www.stsm.org
E-mail .... stsm@stsm.org
3700 Forest Dr Ste 350, Columbia, SC 29204
Ginny Waller, Director

Spartanburg Boys Home 864.583.4367
Fax 864.583.2774
Web .... www.sptbgboyshome.org
E-mail .... raneym@glennspringsacademy.org
195 Boys Home Rd, Pauline, SC 29374-2011
Michael Raney, Executive Director

Spartanburg Children's Shelter Update 864.583.7688
Fax 864.583.0398
E-mail .... vaneclark@childrenshelterupdate.org
200 Hudson L Barksdale Blvd, Spartanburg, SC 29304
Vane Clark, CEO

EDUCATION

Florence Crittenton Program Of Sc 843.722.7526
Fax 843.577.0770
Web .... www.florencecrittentonsc.org
E-mail .... info@florencecrittentonsc.org
19 Saint Margaret St, Charleston, SC 29403-3699
Lisa Belton, Director

Middle Tyger Community Ctr 864.439.7760
Fax 864.439.7034
Web .... www.middletyger.org
84 Groce Rd Ste A, Lyman, SC 29365
Wanda Fowler, Executive Director

FOSTER CARE AGENCIES

**Adoption Coalition Education and
Support** 864.322.2495
E-mail .... info@aceskids.org
PO Box 6652, Greenville, SC 29606
Denise Hopenhauer, Director

Cherished Children International Adopt 864.297.9123
Fax 864.228.7686
E-mail .... Cherishedchd2@aol.com
97 Ridgeway Rd, Greenville, SC 29607

Foster Adoptive Parents 843.565.3855
Fax 843.565.4944
411 Rick Way, Bonneau, SC 29431
Eugene Dafking, Director

Foster Parent Assoc............................864.226.0122
　1415 Hilltop Dr, Anderson, SC 29621

Foster Parents Assoc.........................803.943.9191
Fax..803.943.5365
E-mail..........................marymorris39@hotmail.com
　PO Box 1366, Hampton, SC 29924

Foster Parents Association...................843.692.1901
Fax..843.692.1900
　1806 Star Bluff Rd, Longs, SC 29568

South Carolina Foster Adoptive Parent As....803.865.2020
Fax..803.865.2020
E-mail................................cbrown39@aol.com
　PO Box 39, Elgin, SC 29045

**South Carolina Youth Advocate Program,
Inc.**..803.779.5500
Fax..803.779.8444
Web..................................www.scyap.org
　140 Stoneridge Drive, Suite 350, Columbia,
　SC 29210
　COA accredited organization.

South Caroling Dept of Social Services........843.661.2495
Fax..843.317.1599
E-mail..................sandra.kinley-delia@dss.sc.gov
　181 E Evans St Ste 112, Florence, SC 29506
　Sandra Kinley-Delia, Director

Special Link................................864.233.4872
E-mail............................speclink@infionline.net
　1201 Haywood Rd, Greenville, SC 29615

PEDIATRIC HOME CARE

Interim Healthcare..........................864.855.4421
Fax..864.855.5101
　810 Powdersville Rd Ste B, Easley, SC 29642
　Lisa Parson, Director

Interim Healthcare..........................864.487.3401
Fax..864.487.3707
　423 N Granard St, Gaffney, SC 29341
　Heather Bell, Director

Interim Healthcare..........................803.324.4166
Fax..803.324.7449
E-mail....................kellymitchum@interim-mgi.com
　154 Amendment Ave, Ste 106, Rock Hill, SC 29732
　Kelly Mitchum, Branch Manager

Interim Healthcare..........................864.627.1200
Fax..864.627.7101
　16 Hyland Rd, Greenville, SC 29615
　Connie McCamond, Executive Director

Interim Healthcare..........................864.885.0461
Fax..864.888.0918
　125 Eagles Nest Dr Ste C, Seneca, SC 29678
　Kathrine Gentry, Administrator

Interim Healthcare..........................864.587.6129
Fax..864.587.9408
　155 beacon st,, Spartanburg, SC 29334
　Ray Schroider, Chief Executive Officer

Interim Healthcare..........................864.225.2007
Fax..864.224.8843
　2001 Hwy 81 N, Anderson, SC 29621
　Cheryl Vaninter, Office Director

Interim Healthcare..........................864.587.9798
Fax..864.587.2855
　775 Spartan Blvd, Spartanburg, SC 29301
　Ray Schroder, Director

Interim Healthcare..........................864.839.1310
Fax..864.839.1312
　101 South John St Ste M, Blacksburg, SC 29702
　Ray Schroder, Chief Executive Officer

Interim Healthcare..........................803.324.4122
Fax..803.324.7449
　154 Amendment Ave Ste 106, Rock Hill, SC 29732
　Margaret Webb, Chief Operating Officer

Interim Healthcare..........................803.329.4188
Fax..803.324.7449
　154 Amendment Ave Ste 105, Rock Hill, SC 29732
　Kelly Mitchem, Branch Manager

Interim Healthcare..........................843.569.5510
Fax..843.797.5926
E-mail..................CYONCE@INTERIMHEALTHCARE.COM
　1941 Savage Rd Ste 300E, Charleston, SC 29407
　Chrissy Yonce, General Manager

Interim Healthcare Greenville Staffing.......864.627.7051
Fax..864.627.7077
　16 Hyland Rd, PO Box 12243, Greenville, SC 29612

Piedmont PDN (Greenville)..................864.295.8655
　114 Commons Blvd Ste C, Piedmont, SC 29673
　Tina Shivar

SOCIAL SERVICES

A Place For Us Ministries....................864.229.4243
Fax..864.223.7315
Web..................................www.aplaceforus.org
E-mail............................aplace@gogenesis.org
　601 Montague Ave, Greenwood, SC 29649-1437
　Tamie Price, Administrator

Alston Wilkes Society.......................803.799.2490
Fax..803.540.7223
Web..........................www.alstonwilkessociety.org
　3519 Medical Drive, Columbia, SC 29203
　COA accredited organization.

Assessment And Resource Ctr...............803.898.1693
Fax..803.898.2048
Web..........................www.dhhs.state.sc.us
　1800 Colonial Dr, Columbia, SC 29203-6827
　Angela Forand, Director

Callen-Lacey Ctr For Children...............843.761.5360
Fax..843.761.5368
Web..................................www.cydc.org
E-mail..............................tspells@cydc.org
　437 Gaillard Rd, Moncks Corner, SC 29461-7330
　Tanika Spells, Director

**Child Abuse Prevention Association
(CAPA)**......................................843.524.4350
Fax..843.525.0070
Web..........................www.capabeaufort.org
　P.O. Box 531, Beaufort, SC 29901
　COA accredited organization.

Child, Adult And Family Ctr.................803.775.7898
Fax..803.773.5246
　1175 N Guignard Dr, Sumter, SC 29151
　Hansen Brooks, Director Of Childrenæs Division

**Communities In Schools Of Charleston,
Inc.**..843.740.6793
Fax..843.740.6797
Web..................................cischarleston.org
E-mail............................jriley@cischarleston.org
　1090 E. Montague Avenue, N.Charleston, SC 29405
　Jane Riley, Executive Director

Communities In Schools Of Greenville, Inc...864.250.6737
Fax..864.250.6736
E-mail............................cissusi@mindspring.com
　506 S Pleasantburg Dr, Greenville, SC 29607
　Susi Smith, Executive Director

**Communities In Schools of the Midlands,
Inc.**..803.254.9727
Fax..803.254.0320
E-mail..............................tlinder@cism.org
　2712 Middleburg Drive, Ste 219, Columbia,
　SC 29204
　Terry Linder, Executive Director

Compass of Carolina........................864.467.3434
Fax..864.467.3571
Web..........................www.compassofcarolina.org
　1100 Rutherford Road, Greenville, SC 29609
　COA accredited organization.

Elizabeth P. Durant Children's Ctr...........843.664.4357
Fax..843.673.2006
　226 S Irby, St Florence, SC 29501
　Crystal Tuck, Program Director

Family Services, Inc.........................843.735.7806
Fax..843.735.7807
Web..................................www.fsisc.org
　4925 Lacross Road, Suite 215, North Charleston,
　SC 29406
　COA accredited organization.

**Florence Crittenton Programs of South Carolina,
Inc.**..843.722.7526
Fax..843.577.0770
Web..........................www.florencecrittentonsc.org
　19 St. Margaret Street, Charleston, SC 29403
　COA accredited organization.

Growing Home Southeast, Inc...............803.791.5513
Fax..803.739.0301
Web..........................www.growinghomese.com
　440 Knox Abbott Drive, Suite 250, Cayce,
　SC 29033-4353
　COA accredited organization.

**Interfaith Community Svcs of South
Carolina**.....................................803.252.8390
Fax..803.799.1572
Web....................www.interfaithcommunityservices.org
E-mail............lsemino@interfaithcommunityservices.org
　819 Woodrow St, Columbia, SC 29205
　Lynn Semino, Coordinator

Jewish Family Service.......................803.787.2023
Fax..803.462.1337
　306 Flora Dr, Columbia, SC 29224
　Elaine Davidson-Cohen, Director

**National Ctr For The Missing And Exploited Children,
Sc**...803.254.2326
Fax..803.254.4299
Web..................................www.missingkids.com
E-mail............................mfrierson@ncmec.org
　2008 Marion St Ste I, Columbia, SC 29201-2151
　Ernie Allen, Chief Executive Officer

Sunbelt Human Advancement Resources......864.269.0700
Fax..864.295.6151
E-mail..............................info@sharesc.org
　1200 Pendleton St, Greenville, SC 29611-4832
　Dorothy B. Mims, Director Of Community Services

Voices for South Carolina's Children.........803.256.4670
Fax..803.256.8093
Web..................................www.scchildren.org
E-mail..............................info@scchildren.org
　814 San Jacinto Blvd, Suite 307, Columbia, SC 29211
　Sue Oliver, Executive Director

SPECIAL NEEDS

Brain Injury Alliance of South Carolina........803.731.9823
E-mail........................scbraininjury@bellsouth.net
　800 Dutch Square Blvd, Ste B-225, Columbia,
　SC 29210
　Joyce Davis, Director

Congress of Parents & Teachers..............800.743.3782
　1826 Henderson St, Columbia, SC 29201

Disability Action Center Inc.................803.779.5121
Fax..803.779.0949
　136 Don Mart Ln, Columbia, SC 29201
　Kimberly Tissop, Director

Disability Resource Center...................843.225.5080
E-mail..............................info@drcilc.org
　7944 Dorchester Rd Ste 5, Charleston, SC 29418

Easter Seals South Carolina.................803.256.0735
E-mail........................deanna.lewis@eastersc.org
　3020 Farrow Rd, Columbia, SC 29203

South Carolina

Family Connection of South Carolina Inc 803.252.0914
Fax 866.420.4086
E-mail . . . . .info@familyconnectionsc.org
2712 Middleburg Dr, Ste 103-B, Columbia, SC 29204
Jackie Richard, Director

Greenville Hospital System University Medical Center - Roger
C. Peace Hospital 864.455.5993
Fax 864.455.3225
Web . . . . .www.ghs.org
E-mail . . . . .kcassas@ghs.org
701 Grove Road, Greenville, SC 29605
Kyle Cassas, Medical Director
CARF accredited programs available.

LearningRx Learning Center 843.856.0135
E-mail . . . . .charlestoneast.sc@learningrx.net
721 Long Point Rd, Ste 408, Charleston, SC 29464
Dwight Davis, Owner

Mental Health America South Carolina 803.779.5363
E-mail . . . . .jjay@mha-sc.org
1823 Gadsden St, Columbia, SC 29201
Joy Jay, Executive Director

Mohr Educational Associates, Inc 803.781.0829
Fax 803.781.0829
E-mail . . . . .Mohreduc@aol.com
15 Thames Valley Rd, PO Box 503, Irmo, SC 29063

NAMI of South Carolina .803.733.9591
E-mail . . . . .namisc@namisc.org
5000 Thurmand Mall Blvd, Columbia, SC 29201
Bill Lindsey, Executive Director

Parent Training & Resource Ctr 843.266.1318
Fax 843.266.1941
E-mail . . . . .bevmccarty@frcdsn.org
1575 Savannah Highway Ste 6, Charleston, SC 29407
Beverly McCarty, Executive Assistant

PRO-PARENTS of South Carolina 803.772.5688
Fax 803.772.5431
E-mail . . . . .proparents@proparents.or@gmail.com
652 Bush River Rd Ste 203, Columbia, SC 29210
Mary Ed, Director

QHG of South Carolina, Inc. dba Carolinas Hospital
System/Rehabilitation Services 843.661.3157
Fax 843.661.3858
Web . . . . .www.carolinashospital.com
121 East Cedar Street, Florence, SC 29501
CARF accredited programs available.

Recording for Blind & Dyslexic 802.463.1400
E-mail . . . . .lainabinet@rfbdruvc.org
4840 Forest Dr 21-164, Columbia, SC 29206

South Carolina Autism Society 803.750.6988
E-mail . . . . .scas@scautism.org
806 12th St, West Columbia, SC 29169
Craig Stoxen, Chief Executive Officer

Speech-Language-Hearing Association 888.729.3717
E-mail . . . . .scsha@scsha.com
701 Gervais St Ste 150-206, Columbia, SC 29201

The Arc of South Carolina 803.748.5020
E-mail . . . . .thearc@arcsc.org
3214 W Leapharg Rd Ste C, Columbia, SC 29201
Suzanne, Executive Director

SUBSTANCE ABUSE TREATMENT

Anderson Oconee Behavioral Health
Services 864.260.4168
Fax 864.261.7543
Web . . . . .www.aobhs.org
E-mail . . . . .karenbeck@aobhs.org
226 McGee Rd, Anderson, SC 29625
Karen Beck, Director
CARF accredited programs available.

Axis I Center of Barnwell 803.541.1245
Fax 803.541.1247
Web www.axis1.org
E-mail . . . . .prush@axis1.org
1644 Jackson St, Barnwell, SC 29812
Pam Rush, Director of Client Services
CARF accredited programs available.

Colleton Commission on Alcohol and Drug
Abuse 843.538.4343
Fax 843.538.7613
1439 Thunderbolt Drive, Walterboro, SC 29488
Ron Rickenbaker, Executive Director
CARF accredited programs available.

Commission on Alcohol and Drug Abuse 803.377.8111
Fax 803.581.5380
Web . . . . .www.hazelpittmancenter.com
130 Hudson Street, Chester, SC 29706
CARF accredited programs available.

Commission on Alcohol and Drug Abuse 803.775.6815
Fax 803.773.6232
Web . . . . .www.sumterccada.org
E-mail .gpeagler@sumterccada.org
115 N Harvin St, Third and Fourth Floors, Sumter,
SC 29150
Glenn Peagler, Director
CARF accredited programs available.

Commission on Alcohol and Drug Abuse 803.536.4900
Fax 803.531.8419
Web . . . . .www.mccordcenter.com
E-mail . . . . .rfowler@tccada.state.sc.us
910 Cook Road, Orangeburg, SC 29118
Richard Fowler, Director
CARF accredited programs available.

Commission on Alcohol and Drug Abuse 864.429.1656
Fax 864.429.1667
Web . . . . .www.uccada.org
201 South Herndon Street, Union, SC 29379
CARF accredited programs available.

Earle E Morris, Jr Alcohol And Drug Addiction Treatment
Ctr 803.935.7100
Fax 803.935.7329
Web . . . . .www.state.sc.us
610 Faison Dr, Columbia, SC 29203-3218
George Mcconnell, Director

Fresh Start 843.431.9225
Fax 843.431.9203
5452-B N. Hwy 501, Marion, SC 29571
William T O'Connor, Executive Director

GateWay Counseling Center 864.833.6500
Fax 864.833.6905
Web . . . . .www.gatewaycounseling.org
E-mail . . . . .lnelson@gatewaycounseling.org
219 Human Services Rd, Clinton, SC 29325
Leland Nelson, Executive Director
CARF accredited programs available.

Keystone Substance Abuse Services 803.324.1800
Fax 803.328.3831
Web . . . . .www.keystoneyork.org
E-mail . . . . .jmartini@keystoneyork.org
199 South Herlong Avenue, Rock Hill, SC 29732
Janet Martini, Executive Director
CARF accredited programs available.

LRADAC The Behavioral Health Center of the
Midlands 803.733.1390
Fax 803.733.1395
Web . . . . .www.lradac.org
E-mail . . . . .fsheheen@lradac.org
1800 Saint Julian Place, Suite 308, Columbia,
SC 29204
Frank Sheheen, Program Director
CARF accredited programs available.

New Life Center Commission on Alcohol and Other Drug
Abuse 803.943.2800
Fax 803.943.2267
102 Ginn Altman Ave, Ste C, Hampton, SC 29924
Ronald Rickenbaker, Director
CARF accredited programs available.

Rubicon, Inc. 843.332.4156
Fax 843.332.4159
Web . . . . .www.rubiconsc.org
510 East Carolina Avenue, Hartsville, SC 29550
CARF accredited programs available.

Spartanburg Alcohol and Drug Abuse
Commission 864.582.7588
Fax 864.582.8119
Web . . . . .www.sadac.org
E-mail . . . . .david@sadac.org
187 West Broad Street, Suites 200 and 300,
Spartanburg, SC 29306
David Forrester, Executive Director
CARF accredited programs available.

The Ernest E. Kennedy Center 843.761.8272
Fax 843.719.3025
Web . . . . .www.ekcenter.org
E-mail . . . . .jtileghman@ekcenter.org
306 Airport Drive, Moncks Corner, SC 29461
Jerome Tileghman, Executive Director
CARF accredited programs available.

Trinity Behavioral Care 843.479.5683
Fax 843.479.5685
E-mail . . . . .mdcada@trinitybehavioralcare.org
211 N Marlboro St, Bennettsville, SC 29512
William T. OConnor, Executive Director

South Dakota

www.sd.gov

Dennis Daugaard, Governor
500 East Capitol Avenue
Pierre, SD 57501
605.773.3212
605.773.4711 (Fax)
Governor@state.sd.us
www.state.sd.us

Jodi Kirschenman, Juvenile Justice Specialist
Department Of Corrections
415 North Dakota Avenue
Sioux Falls, SD 57104-2412
605.367.4653
605.367.5625 (Fax)
jodi.kirshchenman@state.sd.us

Carol Twedt, SAG Chair
Minnehaha County Commissioners
4302 South Minnesota Avenue
Sioux Falls, SD 57105
605.338.1264
605.367.8314 (Fax)
ctwedt@minnehahacounty.org

CRISIS NUMBERS

Child Abuse Reporting . . .605.773.3227

STATE SERVICES

South Dakota

SOCIAL SERVICES

Div of Child Care Srvs South Dakota 605.773.4766
Fax 605.773.7294
E-mail . . . . .ccs@state.sd.us
700 Governors Dr, Pierre, SD 57501
Pat Monson, Director

Div of Child Protection Svcs 605.773.3227
Fax 605.773.6834
E-mail . . . . .cps@state.sd.us
700 Governors Dr, Pierre, SD 57501

GENERAL HEALTH SERVICES

Child Spec Health Srvs SD 605.773.3361
Fax 605.773.5683
E-mail . . . . .barb.hemmelman@state.sd.us
600 E Capitol, Pierre, SD 57501
Barb Hemmelman, Director

Office of Family Health SD 605.773.4439
Fax 605.773.5683
E-mail . . . . .dohinfo@state.sd.us
600 E Capitol Ave, Pierre, SD 57501
Darlene Bergeleen, Director

South Dakota Dept of Health/Community Health
Services 605.394.2516
Fax 605.394.1929
909 E Saint Patrick St Ste 7, Rapid City,
SD 57701-5720
Linda Marchand, Regional Manager

MENTAL HEALTH SERVICES

Div of Mental Health 605.773.5991
Fax 605.773.7076
Web . . . . .www.dhs.sd.gov.dmh
E-mail . . . . .infomh@state.sd.us
500 E Capitol Ave, Hillsview Plaza E, Pierre, SD 57501
Shawna Fullerton, Director

Div of Srv to the Blind & Vis Imp SD 605.773.4644
Fax 605.773.5483
E-mail . . . . .eric.weiss@state.sd.us
3800 E Hwy 34 Hillsview Plz, c/o 500 E Capitol, Pierre,
SD 57501
Eric Weiss, Assistant Director

Division of Rehab Svcs South Dakota 605.773.3195
Fax 605.773.5483
500 E Capital, E Highway 34, Pierre, SD 57501
Becky Blume, Secretary

JUSTICE AGENCY

Attorney General's Ofc 605.773.3215
Fax 605.773.4106
Web . . . . .www.state.sd.us
1302 E Hwy 14 Ste 1, Pierre, SD 57501-8501
Marty Jackley, Attorney General

Correctional Educ Division SD 605.773.3478
Fax 605.773.3194
E-mail . . . . .dianna.miller@state.sd.us
3200 E Hwy 34, Pierre, SD 57501
Dianna Miller, Director

State Treatment and Rehabilitation Academy . .605.673.2521
Fax 605.673.3285
Web . . . . .www.state.sd.us
12279 Brady Dr, Custer, SD 57730-9160
Jeff Hier, Superintendent

COURTS

Court Administrator's Ofc 605.773.3474
Fax 605.773.5627
500 E Capitol Ave, Pierre, SD 57501
Nancy Allard, Judge

Court Svcs 605.394.2595
Fax 605.394.3373
E-mail . . . . .judd.thompson@ujs.state.sd.us
315 Saint Joseph St, Rapid City, SD 57701
Judd C. Thompson, Chief Court Services Officer

EDUCATION SERVICES

Dept of Education 605.773.3134
Fax 605.773.6139
Web . . . . .www.doe.sd.gov
E-mail . . . . .rick.melmer@state.sd.us
700 Governors Dr, Pierre, SD 57501
Janet Ricketts, Special Ed

Educ for Homeless Children and Youth SD 605.773.6400
Fax 605.773.3782
E-mail . . . . .laura.johnson-frame@state.sd.us
800 Governors Dr, Pierre, SD 57501
Laura Johnson Frame, Director

School for the Deaf 605.367.5200
Fax 605.367.5209
Web . . . . .www.sdsd.sbor.edu
E-mail .terry.gregersen@sdsd.sdbor.edu
2001 E 8th St, Sioux Falls, SD 57103
Terry Gregersen, Superintendent

SD Department of Education 605.773.5669
Fax 605.773.6139
E-mail . . . . .betty.leidholt@state.sd.u@sbcglobal.net
800 Governors Dr, Pierre, SD 57501
Betty Leidholt, Director

SDVA - South Dakota Vocational Assoc 605.367.7624
Fax 605.367.4372
Web . . . . .www.southeasttech.com
E-mail . . . . .jeff.holcomb@southeasttech.com
2320 N Career Ave, Southeast Technical Institute,
Sioux Falls, SD 57107-1301
Jeff Holcomb, Director

South Dakota School for the Blind and Visually
Impaired 605.626.2580
Fax 605.626.2607
Web . . . . .www.sdsbvi.northern.edu
E-mail . . . . .kaiserm@sdsbvi.northern.edu
423 17th Ave SE, Aberdeen, SD 57401-7616
Marjorie Kaiser, Superintendent

Special Education Programs SD 605.773.3678
Fax 605.773.3782
E-mail . . . . .ann.larsen@state.sd.us
800 Governors Dr Kneip Bldg, Pierre, SD 57501
Ann Larsen, Director

LABOR & WORKFORCE EDUCATION

South Dakota Dept of Labor 605.773.3101
Fax 605.773.4211
700 Governors Dr, Pierre, SD 57501
Tacy Kennison, Office Administrator

COUNTY SERVICES

South Dakota

Aurora County

SOCIAL SERVICES

Social Svcs **605.942.7150**
Fax 605.942.7751
Web .... www.state.sd.us
    401 N Main St, Plankinton, SD 57368
Deb Dickerman, Case Worker

GENERAL HEALTH SERVICES

Community Health Nursing **605.942.7163**
Fax 605.942.7163
E-mail .... julie.dykstra@state.sd.us
    401 N Main, Plankinton, SD 57368
Julie Dykstra, Public Health Nurse

Beadle County

SOCIAL SERVICES

Social Svcs **605.353.7100**
Fax 605.353.7103
Web .... www.state.sd.us
E-mail .... mickie.scheibe@state.sd.us
    110 3rd St SW Ste 200, Huron, SD 57350-2450
Mickie Scheibe, Supervisor

GENERAL HEALTH SERVICES

Community Health Nursing **605.353.7135**
Fax 605.353.6697
    495 3rd St SW, Huron, SD 57350

COURTS

3rd Circuit Court **605.353.7171**
Fax 605.353.7306
    450 3rd Street SW, Huron, SD 57350
Marie Fawcett, Court Reporter

POLICE AND SHERIFF

Sheriff's Ofc **605.353.8424**
Fax 605.353.8427
E-mail .... nancy.bcso@midconetwork.com
    455 4th St SW, Huron, SD 57350-1819
Doug Solen, Sheriff

Bennett County

SOCIAL SERVICES

Dept Of Social Svcs **605.685.6521**
Fax 605.685.6652
Web .... www.state.sd.us
    403 3rd Ave, Martin, SD 57551
Robin Sones, Supervisor

Bon Homme County

SOCIAL SERVICES

Dept Of Social Svcs **605.589.4319**
Fax 605.589.4309
Web .... www.state.sd.us
E-mail .... joe.cimpl@state.sd.us
    103 W 18th Ave, Tyndall, SD 57066
Joe Cimpl, Supervisor

GENERAL HEALTH SERVICES

Community Health Nursing **605.589.4318**
Fax 605.589.4317
E-mail .... paula.gibson@state.sd.us
    103 West 18th Ave, Tyndall, SD 57066
Paula Gibson, Rn, Community Health Nurse

Brookings County

SOCIAL SERVICES

Social Svcs **605.688.4330**
Fax 605.688.4339
    1310 Main Ave S Ste 101, Brookings, SD 57006
Dawn Johnson, CPS Supervisor

GENERAL HEALTH SERVICES

Sioux Valley Clinic Family Planning **605.697.1900**
Fax 605.697.1919
    922 22nd Ave S, Brookings, SD 57006
Dr. Jennifer Tan, CMP

MENTAL HEALTH SERVICES

East Central Mental Health Ctr **605.697.2860**
Fax 605.697.2874
    211 4th St, Brookings, SD 57006-1917
William Price, PhD, Executive Director

POLICE AND SHERIFF

Sheriff's Dept **605.696.8300**
Fax 605.696.8330
Web .... www.brookingscountysd.gov
E-mail .... sheriffmarty@brookingscountysd.gov
    315 7th Ave, Brookings, SD 57006-2000
Martin E. Stanwick, Sheriff

EDUCATION SERVICES

Brookings Head Start Ctr **605.692.7472**
E-mail .... atwick@interlakescap.com
    625 5th St, Brookings, SD 57006-2040
Kathy Natwick, Director

Brown County

SOCIAL SERVICES

Social Svcs **605.626.3160**
Fax 605.626.2610
    3401 10th Ave, Aberdeen, SD 57401-4347
Laura Wolverton, CPS Supervisor

GENERAL HEALTH SERVICES

Indian Health Svc **605.226.7531**
Fax 605.226.7321
Web .... www.home.aberdeen.ihs.gov
    115 4th Ave SE Ste 309, Aberdeen, SD 57401-4381
Donald Lee, Area Director

South Dakota Dept Of Health Aberdeen
Area **605.626.2649**
Fax 605.626.2974
E-mail .... greta.thorpe@state.sd.us
    402 S Main St, Aberdeen, SD 57401-4127
Greta Thorpe, Disease Intervention Specialist

South Dakota Urban Indian Health **605.225.1538**
Fax 605.229.2053
Web .... www.sduih.org
E-mail .... valj@sduih.org
    1315 6th Ave SE Ste 6, Aberdeen, SD 57401-4900
Val Jones, Certified Nurse Practitioner

JUSTICE AGENCY

CASA **605.225.8229**
Fax 605.225.8662
E-mail .... aberdeencasa@iw.net
    104 S Lincoln St Ste 103, Aberdeen, SD 57402
Shirley Schwab, Executive Director

Court Svcs **605.626.2275**
Fax 605.626.2441
    101 1st Ave SE, Ste 101, Aberdeen, SD 57402
Mike Burmbauch, Chief Court Officer

COURTS

5th Circuit Court **605.626.2450**
Fax 605.626.2491
E-mail .... jack.vonwald@ujs.state.sd.us
    101 1st Ave SE, Ste 101, Aberdeen, SD 57401
Honorable Jack Von-Wald, Judge

POLICE AND SHERIFF

Sheriff's Ofc **605.626.7100**
Fax 605.626.4015
Web .... www.brown.sd.us
E-mail .... bcsheriff@brown.sd.us
    22 Court St Ste 1, Aberdeen, SD 57401-4230
Mark A. Milbrandt, Sheriff

EDUCATION SERVICES

Aberdeen Head Start Ctr **605.226.3611**
Fax 605.226.0196
    305 S Main St, Ste 307, Aberdeen, SD 57401
Ms Enid Rogers, Director

Brule County

POLICE AND SHERIFF

Sheriff's Ofc **605.234.4443**
Fax 605.234.4446
E-mail .... brulecoso@brulecosheriff.org
    300 S Courtland St Ste 112, Chamberlain, SD 57325
Darrell G. Miller, Sheriff

Buffalo County

SOCIAL SERVICES

Bureau of Indian Affairs Crow Creek
Agency **605.245.2356**
Fax 605.245.2101
Web .... www.bia.gov
    134 Red Horse Rd, Fort Thompson, SD 57339
Melita Valandra, Program Manager

GENERAL HEALTH SERVICES

Bureau of Indian Affairs- Crow Creek
Agency **605.245.2311**
Fax 605.245.2343
    Samboy Dr, Fort Thompson, SD 57339
Melita Valandra, Deputy Superintendent

WIC Ofc **605.245.1539**
Fax 605.245.2722
    Highway 47, IHS Clinic, Fort Thompson, SD 57339
Madonna Long, Unit Director Of Indian Health Services

POLICE AND SHERIFF

Sheriff's Dept **605.293.3231**
Fax 605.293.3240
    112 Osman Ave, Gann Valley, SD 57341
Wayne Willman, Sheriff

Butte County

SOCIAL SERVICES

Social Svcs **605.892.2731**
Fax 605.892.3616
Web .... www.state.sd.us
E-mail .... sharon.smith@state.sd.us
    609 5th Ave, Belle Fourche, SD 57717-1405
Sharon Smith, Program Supervisor

GENERAL HEALTH SERVICES

Community Health Nursing **605.892.2523**
Fax 605.892.2524
    2398 5th Ave, Belle Fourche, SD 57717
Linda Hoxis, Community Health Nurse

COURTS

4th Circuit Court **605.892.2516**
Fax 605.892.2836
　839 5th Ave, Belle Fourche, SD 57717
　Honorable John Bastian, Judge

POLICE AND SHERIFF

Sheriff's Dept **605.892.3324**
Fax 605.723.3327
Web .... www.rushmore.com
E-mail .... fred.lamphere@buttesd.org
　839 5th Ave Ste 5, Belle Fourche, SD 57717-1719
　Fred A. Lamphere, Sheriff

Charles Mix County

SOCIAL SERVICES

Bureau Indian Affairs Yankton
Agency **605.384.3651**
Fax 605.384.3876
　29775 Main Ave, Wagner, SD 57380
　Mark Frier, Director

Dept Of Social Svcs **605.487.7607**
Fax 605.487.7429
Web .... www.state.sd.us
E-mail .... donna.paulson@state.sd.us
　3rd & Lake, Lake Andes, SD 57356
　Donna Paulson, Economic Supervisor

Yankton Sioux Tribe **605.384.3641**
Fax 605.384.5687
Web .... www.yanktonsiouxtribe.org
　100 Main St., Marty, SD 57361
　Robert Cournoyer, Chairperson

GENERAL HEALTH SERVICES

Communtiy Health Svcs **605.384.3487**
　118B Main Ave SE, Wagner, SD 57380
　Darlene Bergaline, Administrator

Dept Of Health **605.487.7094**
Fax 605.487.7380
　400 Main St, Lake Andes, SD 57356
　Barb Wiechmann, Community Health Nurse

COURTS

1st Circuit Court **605.487.7664**
Fax 605.487.7615
　400 Main St, Lake Andes, SD 57356
　Honorable Bruce V. Anderson, Judge

Clark County

POLICE AND SHERIFF

Sheriff's Dept **605.532.3822**
Fax 605.532.5953
E-mail .... clarkcosheriff@itctel.com
　200 N Commercial, Clark, SD 57225
　Robert J. Mcgraw, Sheriff

Clay County

GENERAL HEALTH SERVICES

Community Health Nursing **605.677.6767**
Fax 605.677.6760
Web .... www.claycountysd.org
E-mail .... jill.munger@state.sd.us
　211 W Main St Ste 100, Vermillion, SD 57069-2056
　Jill Munger, Rn, Community Health Nurse

COURTS

1st Circuit Court **605.677.6757**
Fax 605.677.8885
　211 W Main St, Vermillion, SD 57069
　Steven Jensen, Presiding Judge

POLICE AND SHERIFF

Sheriff's Ofc **605.677.7100**
Fax 605.677.7105
Web .... www.claysheriff.org
E-mail .... ahowe@claysheriff.org
　15 N Washington St, Vermillion, SD 57069
　Andy Howe, Sheriff

Codington County

SOCIAL SERVICES

Lutheran Social Svcs **605.882.2740**
Fax 605.882.4323
Web .... www.lsssd.org
E-mail .... cindy.hartwig@lsssd.org
　1424 9th Ave SE Ste 7, Watertown, SD 57201-5361
　Cindy Hartwig, Manager

Social Svcs **605.882.5000**
Fax 605.882.5045
E-mail .... michelle.kays@state.sd.us
　2001 9th Ave SW Ste 300, Watertown,
　SD 57201-4029
　Michelle Kays, CPS Supervisor

GENERAL HEALTH SERVICES

Community Health **605.882.5177**
Fax 605.882.5077
　14 1st Ave SE, Watertown, SD 57201
　Karla Moes, Rn, Community Health Nurse

Dept Of Health **605.882.5121**
Fax 605.882.5066
　2001 9th ave SW, Watertown, SD 57201-5134
　Lori Wagers, Disease Intervention Specialist

MENTAL HEALTH SERVICES

Human Svcs Agency **605.886.0123**
Fax 605.886.5447
Web .... www.humanservicesagency.org
　123 19th St NE, Watertown, SD 57201-2823
　Dodi Haug, Prevention Coordinator

COURTS

3rd Circuit Court **605.882.5110**
Fax 605.882.5106
Web .... www.sdjudicial.com
　14 1St Ave Se, Watertown, SD 57201-3611
　Honorable Ronald K Roehr, Judge

POLICE AND SHERIFF

Sheriff's Ofc **605.882.6280**
Fax 605.882.6283
　14 1st Ave SE, Watertown, SD 57201
　Toby Wishard, Sheriff

Corson County

SOCIAL SERVICES

Social Svcs **605.273.4513**
Fax 605.273.4322
　185 Main St, Mc Intosh, SD 57641
　Lori Ternes, Director

POLICE AND SHERIFF

Sheriff's Dept **605.273.4210**
Fax 605.273.4533
E-mail .... corsoncoso@sdplains.com
　111 2nd St E, McIntosh, SD 57641
　Keith E. Gall, Sheriff

Custer County

SOCIAL SERVICES

Social Svcs **605.673.4347**
Fax 605.673.2070
　1164 Mount Rushmore Rd Ste 3, Custer,
　SD 57730-2122
　Lori Margin, Director Of Adult Services

Davison County

SOCIAL SERVICES

Social Svcs **605.995.8000**
Fax 605.995.8929
　116 E 11Th Ave, Mitchell, SD 57301
　Bruce Wood, Superviser

GENERAL HEALTH SERVICES

Community Health **605.995.8050**
Fax 605.995.8058
Web .... www.davisoncounty.org
E-mail .... connie.fergen@state.sd.us
　115 W Twelve St, Mitchell, SD 57301-4114
　Connie Fergen, Community Health Nurse

COURTS

1st Circuit Court **605.995.8102**
Fax 605.995.8107
Web .... www.ujs.slate.sd.us
　600 N Wolfe St, Mitchell, SD 57301
　Honorable OBrian, Judge

1st Circuit Court Svcs **605.995.8100**
Fax 605.995.8649
　200 E 4th Ave, Mitchell, SD 57301
　Jon Moore, Court Services Officer

POLICE AND SHERIFF

Sheriff's Dept **605.995.8630**
Fax 605.995.8643
　1015 S Miller Ave, Mitchell, SD 57301
　David E. Miles, Sheriff

Day County

SOCIAL SERVICES

Dept of Social Svcs **605.345.3432**
Fax 605.345.4525
E-mail .... merilee.beck@state.sd.us
　711 W 1st St Ste 213, Webster, SD 57274
　Merilee Beck, Supervisior

POLICE AND SHERIFF

Sheriff's Ofc **605.345.3222**
Fax 605.345.3289
Web .... www.itctel.com
　710 W 2nd St, Webster, SD 57274-1320
　Berry Hillistael, Sheriff

Deuel County

MENTAL HEALTH SERVICES

health dept **605.874.2141**
Fax 605.874.8441
Web .... www.sanforddeuelcounty.org
　701 3rd Ave S, Clear Lake, SD 57226
　Tammy Baer, Director Community Home Health

POLICE AND SHERIFF

Sheriff's Office **605.874.8211**
Fax 605.874.2916
E-mail .... deuelco@itctel.com
　400 4th St W, Clear Lake, SD 57226
　Dave Solem, Sheriff

Dewey County

SOCIAL SERVICES

Cheyenne River Agency **605.964.6611**
Fax 605.964.4060
Web .... www.doi.gov
E-mail .... ddeane@doi.gov
　2001 Main St, Eagle Butte, SD 57625
　Dani Deane, Supervisory Social Worker

South Dakota

Social Svcs......................................605.964.4484
Fax...605.964.1200
Web...www.dsf.gov
900 Main St, Timber Lake, SD 57656
Sharon Maher, Supervisor

GENERAL HEALTH SERVICES

Dept Of Health...............................605.865.3587
Fax...605.865.3587
Web...www.state.sd.us
E-mail...........................mary.harris@state.sd.us
700 C St, Timber Lake, SD 57656
Mary Harris, Rn, Community Health Nurse

POLICE AND SHERIFF

Sheriff's Ofc...................................605.865.3330
Fax...605.865.3379
E-mail...........................ecso241@yahoo.com
702 C St, Timber Lake, SD 57656
Lesley Mayer, Sheriff

Douglas County

SOCIAL SERVICES

Social Svcs......................................605.724.2590
Fax...605.724.2204
Web...www.state.sd.us
E-mail...........................cindy.buck@state.sd.us
706 Braddock St, Armour, SD 57313
Cindy Buck, Case Worker

GENERAL HEALTH SERVICES

Public Health Svcs...........................605.724.2758
Fax...605.724.2985
708 8th St, Armour, SD 57313-2102
Heath Brouwer, Administrator

POLICE AND SHERIFF

Sheriff's Ofc...................................605.724.2238
Fax...605.724.2204
Web...www.dcssd.org
E-mail...........................dcso@unitelsd.com
706 Braddock S, Armour, SD 57313
Tim Simonsen, Sheriff

Edmunds County

SOCIAL SERVICES

Social Svcs......................................605.426.6631
Fax...605.426.6164
Web...www.state.de.us
E-mail...........................kathleen.perkinsf@state.de.us
210 2nd St, Ipswich, SD 57451
Stacy Nelson, CPS Supervisor

GENERAL HEALTH SERVICES

Public Health Svcs/Alliance Site Bowdle
Hospital...605.285.6419
Fax...605.285.6405
8001 W 5th St, Bowdle, SD 57428
Melanie Kayser, Nurse

Fall River County

POLICE AND SHERIFF

Sheriff's Ofc...................................605.745.4444
Fax...605.745.7591
Web...www.gwtc.net
E-mail...........................jtarrell@gwtc.net
906 N River St, Hot Springs, SD 57747-1309
Jeffrey D. Tarrell, Sheriff

Faulk County

POLICE AND SHERIFF

Sheriff's Ofc...................................605.598.6229
Fax...605.598.6620
Web...www.faulkcountysheriff.com
E-mail...........................fcso@venturecomm.net
924 Lafoon, Faulkton, SD 57438
Kurt Hall, Sheriff

Grant County

SOCIAL SERVICES

Social Svcs......................................605.432.9588
Fax...605.432.9563
Web...www.dfs.sd.gov
E-mail...........................june.evanson@state.sd.us
210 E 5th Ave, Milbank, SD 57252
Anzrea Fricc, Supervisor

GENERAL HEALTH SERVICES

Community Health Nursing.................605.432.4596
Fax...605.432.7516
210 E 5th Ave, Milbank, SD 57252
Joan Frerichs, Community Health Nurse

POLICE AND SHERIFF

Sheriff's Dept.................................605.432.5853
Fax...605.432.9158
Web...www.sstel.net
E-mail...........................sheriff.grantcosd@sstel.net
222 E 5th Ave, Milbank, SD 57252-2433
Kevin Owen, Sheriff

Gregory County

POLICE AND SHERIFF

Sheriff's Dept.................................605.775.2626
Fax...605.775.2499
E-mail...........................gregorycoso@gwtc.net
221 E 8th St, Burke, SD 57523
Damon R. Wolf, Sheriff

Haakon County

POLICE AND SHERIFF

Sheriff's Dept.................................605.859.2741
Fax...605.859.2730
E-mail...........................haakonso@gwec.net
140 S. Howard, Philip, SD 57567
Milvin Smith, Interim Sheriff

Hamlin County

SOCIAL SERVICES

Social Svcs......................................605.783.3641
Main St, Hayti, SD 57241
Shelley Amick, Social Services Worker

GENERAL HEALTH SERVICES

Community Health............................605.783.3681
Fax...605.783.3681
300 4th St, Hayti, SD 57241
Angela Hunter, Community Health Nurse

POLICE AND SHERIFF

Sheriff's Dept.................................605.783.3232
Fax...605.783.1330
E-mail...........................hamcoso@itctel.com
300 Fourth Street, Hayti, SD 57241
Dan T. Mack, Sheriff

Hand County

GENERAL HEALTH SERVICES

Community Health............................605.853.2147
318 W 5Th St, Miller, SD 57362
Renae Simons, Community Health Nurse

POLICE AND SHERIFF

Sheriff's Dept.................................605.853.2408
Fax...605.853.2362
Web...www.midconetwork.com
415 W 1st Ave Rm 102, Miller, SD 57362-1371
Doug Deboer, Sheriff

Hanson County

POLICE AND SHERIFF

Sheriff's Dept.................................605.239.4409
Fax...605.239.4410
E-mail...........................hcsheriff@triotel.net
720 5th St, Alexandria, SD 57311
Ranveoo Barpletg, Sheriff

Harding County

POLICE AND SHERIFF

Sheriff's Ofc...................................605.375.3414
Fax...605.375.3415
Web...www.sdplains.com
E-mail...........................hcso@sdplains.com
410 Ramsland St, Buffalo, SD 57720
William Clarkson, Sheriff

Hughes County

SOCIAL SERVICES

Dept Of Social Svcs...........................605.773.3612
Fax...605.773.5390
912 E Sioux Ave, Pierre, SD 57501
Julie Miller, Regional Manager

South Dakota Emergency Management
Agency..605.773.3231
Fax...605.773.3580
118 W Capitol Ave, Pierre, SD 57501
Kristi Turman, Director

GENERAL HEALTH SERVICES

South Dakota Dept Of Health Pierre
Area..605.773.3737
Fax...605.773.5942
Web...www.state.sd.us
E-mail...........................gail.gray@state.sd.us
615 E 4Th St, Pierre, SD 57501-1700
Gail Gray, Director

MENTAL HEALTH SERVICES

Capital Area Counseling Svcs, Inc.............605.224.5811
Fax...605.224.6921
E-mail...........................dpfrimmer@cacsnet.org
803 E Dakota Ave, Pierre, SD 57501
Dennis Pfrimmer, Executive Director

Div Of Developmental Disabilities.............605.773.3438
Fax...605.773.7562
Web...www.state.sd.us
3800 E Hwy 34, Hills View Plaza, Pierre, SD 57501
Dan Lusk, Director

JUSTICE AGENCY

Migrant Program.............................605.773.4437
Fax...605.773.3782
Web...www.state.sd.us
E-mail...........................jerry.meendering@state.sd.us
700 Governors Dr, Office of Educational Services & Support, Pierre, SD 57501
Jerry Meendering, State Director

POLICE AND SHERIFF

Pierre City Police Dept.......................605.773.7410
Fax...605.773.7417
Web...www.ci.pierre.sd.us/police
3200 E. South Dakota, Hwy. 34, Ste #13, Pierre, SD 57501
Michael Whithold, Sheriff

Hutchinson County

GENERAL HEALTH SERVICES

**Community Health Nursing Freeman Community
Hospital** **605.925.4000**
Fax 605.925.2137
Web ....www.state.sd.us
510 E 8th St, Freeman, SD 57029-2086
Polly Waltner, Community Health Nurse

**Community Health Nursing St. Benedict's
Hospital** **605.928.4411**
Fax 605.928.4406
401 W Glynn Dr, Parkston, SD 57366
Diane Baumiller, Community Health Nurse

POLICE AND SHERIFF

Sheriff's Dept **605.387.2341**
Fax 605.387.4218
E-mail ....hutchso@gwtc.net
140 Euclid St Rm 123, Olivet, SD 57052-2103
Jim Zeeb, Sheriff

Hyde County

POLICE AND SHERIFF

Sheriff's Ofc **605.852.2513**
Fax 605.852.3178
E-mail ....mike.volek@state.sd.us
412 Commercial Ave SE, Highmore, SD 57345
Mike Volek, Sheriff

Jackson County

SOCIAL SERVICES

Social Svcs **605.837.2439**
Fax 605.837.2439
Web ....www.ces.sdstate.edu
E-mail ....deckert.pat@ces.sdstate.edu
700 Main St, Kadoka, SD 57543
Pat Deckert, Supervisor

GENERAL HEALTH SERVICES

Dept Of Health **605.837.2240**
Web ....www.fns.usda.gov
720 6th Avenue, Kadoka,, SD 57543
Beverly Berry, Rn, Community Health Nurse

Jerauld County

SOCIAL SERVICES

Social Svcs **605.539.1261**
Fax 605.539.9125
Web ....www.state.sd.us
E-mail ....bruce.ward@state.sd.us
Jerauld County Courthouse, Wessington Springs,
SD 57382
Bruce Ward, Supervisor

GENERAL HEALTH SERVICES

South Dakota Dept Of Health **605.539.1271**
Fax 605.539.9546
Web ....www.horizonhealthcare.org
E-mail ....mjfeistner@horizonhealthcare.org
606 1st St NE, Wessington Springs, SD 57382
Marla Feistner, RN, Community Health Nurse

POLICE AND SHERIFF

Sheriff's Ofc **605.539.1311**
Fax 605.539.1087
E-mail ....admin@southdakotasheriffs.org
205 S. Wallace Ave, Wessington Springs, SD 57382
Jason Weber, Sheriff

Kingsbury County

SOCIAL SERVICES

Social Svcs **605.854.3501**
Fax 605.688.4339
Web ....www.state.sd.us
E-mail ....andrew.lamour@state.sd.us
1310 Main Ave S, Ste 101, Brookings,
SD 57006-3893
Andrew Lamour, Supervisor

GENERAL HEALTH SERVICES

Bell Medical Svcs **605.854.3455**
Fax 605.854.9952
Web ....www.herizonhealthcare.org
801 3rd St SW, De Smet, SD 57231-2224
John Mengenhausen, CEO

POLICE AND SHERIFF

Sheriff's Ofc **605.854.3339**
Fax 605.854.9307
Web ....www.mchsi.com
E-mail ....kingsburyso@mchsi.com
204 2nd St SE, De Smet, SD 57231
Kevin M. Scotting, Sheriff

Lake County

SOCIAL SERVICES

Dept Of Social Svcs **605.256.5683**
Fax 605.256.5043
223 S Van Eps Ave Ste 201, Madison, SD 57042
Gail Fisher, Acting Supervisor

Social Svcs **605.772.5770**
Fax 605.772.4148
Web www.k12.sd.us
E-mail ....ann.delay@k12.sd.us
223 S Van Eps Ave Ste 201, Madison, SD 57042-2888
Ann Delay, Benefit Specialist

MENTAL HEALTH SERVICES

Community Counseling Svc **605.256.9656**
Fax 605.256.2891
Web ....www.ccs-sd.org
E-mail ....info@ccs-sd.org
914 NE 3rd St, Madison, SD 57042-2435
Belinda Nelson, Chemical Dependency Director

COURTS

3rd Circuit Court **605.256.5285**
Fax 605.256.5012
200 E Center St Ste 1, Madison, SD 57042-2956
Jason Schneider, Court Services Officer

Lawrence County

GENERAL HEALTH SERVICES

Community Health Nursing **605.578.2660**
Fax 605.578.2204
9 Kirk Rd, Deadwood, SD 57732
Denise Rosenburger, Rn, Community Health Nurse

JUSTICE AGENCY

**4th Circuit Program CASA-Northern Hills
Area** **605.722.4558**
Fax 605.722.4559
Web ....www.rushmore.com
E-mail ....casadir@rushmore.com
1940 N Ave Ste 6, Spearfish, SD 57783-2938
Gypsy Petz, Executive Director

Court Svcs **605.578.2043**
Fax 605.578.1572
Web ....www.ujs.state.sd.us
E-mail ....derrick.nedved@ujs.state.sd.us
78 Sherman St, Deadwood, SD 57732
Derrick Nedved, Chief Court Services Officer

COURTS

4th Circuit Court **605.578.2044**
Fax 605.578.3613
E-mail ....michael.piscitta@ujs.state.sd.us
78 Sherman St, Deadwood, SD 57732
Honorable Randall Macy, Judge

Lincoln County

SOCIAL SERVICES

Social Svcs **605.764.5761**
Fax 605.987.3076
104 n Main St Ste 140, Canton, SD 57013
Lisa Aymar, Beneifit Specialist

COURTS

2nd Circuit Court **605.987.2801**
Fax 605.987.0046
Web ....www.lincolncountysd.org
E-mail ....ahall@lincolncountysd.org
100 E 5th St Ste 8, Canton, SD 57013-1798
Alan Hall, Court Services Officer

Marshall County

GENERAL HEALTH SERVICES

Dept Of Health **605.448.2744**
Fax 605.448.2885
909 S Main St, Britton, SD 57430
Ardi Forrester, Rn, Community Health Nurse

McCook County

SOCIAL SERVICES

Social Svcs **605.425.2271**
Fax 605.425.2064
130 W Essex Ave, Salem, SD 57058
Mariann Oyen, Case Worker

GENERAL HEALTH SERVICES

South Dakota Dept Of Health **605.425.2671**
E-mail ....kathy.deters@k12.sd.us
130 W Essex Ave, Salem, SD 57058
Kathy Deters, Rn, Community Health Nurse

POLICE AND SHERIFF

Sheriff's Dept **605.425.2761**
Fax 605.425.3144
Web ....www.mccookcosotriotel.net
E-mail ....mccookcoso@triotel.net
130 W Essex Ave, Salem, SD 57058-8901
Mark Norris, Sheriff

Meade County

SOCIAL SERVICES

Social Svcs **605.347.2588**
Fax 605.347.3767
Web ....www.state.sd.us
E-mail ....jolynn.bostrom@state.sd.us
2200 Main St, Sturgis, SD 57785-1338
Jolynn Bostrom, CPS Leadworker

GENERAL HEALTH SERVICES

Community Health Nursing **605.347.5650**
Fax 605.347.6718
Web ....www.state.sd.us
1425 Sherman St, Sturgis, SD 57785-1403
Ellen Jenter, Rn, Community Health Nurse

MENTAL HEALTH SERVICES

Northern Hills Alcohol & Drug Svcs **605.347.3003**
Fax 605.347.4944
Web ....www.abc.net
1010 Ballpark Rd Ste 1, Sturgis, SD 57785-2208
Mary Wood-fossen, Director

South Dakota

COURTS

4th Circuit Court..........................**605.347.4411**
Fax...605.347.3526
1425 Sherman St, Sturgis, SD 57785
Honorable Jerome Eckrich, Judge

POLICE AND SHERIFF

Sheriff's Dept..............................**605.347.2681**
Fax...605.347.6824
1400 Main St, Sturgis, SD 57785-1444
Ronald W. Merwin, Sheriff

Mellette County

SOCIAL SERVICES

Social Svcs..................................**605.259.3101**
Fax...605.259.3202
321 E. 4th St, White River, SD 57579
Amy Sachtjen, Supervisor

MIner County

GENERAL HEALTH SERVICES

Community Health Nursing.................**605.772.5381**
Fax...605.772.5381
400 N Main St, Howard, SD 57349
Barbara Esser, RN, Community Health Nurse

POLICE AND SHERIFF

Sheriff's Dept..............................**605.772.4501**
Fax...605.772.4148
E-mail...........................minerso@alliancecom.net
400 N Main St, Howard, SD 57349-9007
Lanny J. Klinkhammer, Sheriff

Minnehaha County

SOCIAL SERVICES

Dept Of Social Svcs........................**605.367.5444**
Fax...605.367.5473
811 E 10th St, Sioux Falls, SD 57103
Robert Zirpel, Regional Manager

GENERAL HEALTH SERVICES

**Children's Special Health Svcs Sioux Valley Children's Specialty
Clinics**.......................................**605.333.7188**
Fax...605.333.1585
Web.......................................www.usd.edu
E-mail...........................kkrabbenhoft@usd.edu
1305 W 18th St, Sioux Falls, SD 57105-0401
Kelby K. Krabbenhoft, Director

Community Health East & West.............**605.367.5228**
Fax...605.367.5596
1200 NW Ave, Sioux Falls, SD 57110
Barb Kadinger, Director

Falls Community Health.....................**605.367.8793**
Fax...605.367.8247
Web......................................www.siouxfalls.com
E-mail.........................cshafer@siouxfalls.org
521 N Main Ave Ste 100, Sioux Falls, SD 57104-5947
Charles Shafer, Medical Director

**Sanford Clinic Dowtown Womens
Health**.......................................**605.334.5099**
Fax...605.333.0245
E-mail.........................dthc@sanfordhealth.org
401 E 8th St Ste 230, Sioux Falls, SD 57103-7009
Sharon Hunt, Clinic Director

**South Dakota Ofc, Community Healthcare Assoc,
Inc**...**605.357.1515**
Fax...605.357.1510
Web.......................www.communityhealthcare.net
E-mail................................sgraff@usd.edu
1400 W 22nd St, Sioux Falls, SD 57105
Scot Graff, Executive Director

JUSTICE AGENCY

Court Svcs Dept............................**605.367.5930**
Fax...605.367.4907
425 N Dakota Ave, Sioux Falls, SD 57104-2472
Patty Vonsik, Chief Court Services Officer

COURTS

2nd Circuit Court..........................**605.367.5920**
Fax...605.367.5979
Web....................www.sdjudicial.com/2ndcircuit
425 N Dakota Ave Ste 303, Sioux Falls, SD 57104
Honorable Joseph Neiles, Judge

POLICE AND SHERIFF

Colman Police Dept........................**605.534.3611**
Fax...605.534.3611
Web.......................................www.iw.net
E-mail...............................colmanpd@iw.net
112 N Main Ave, Colman, SD 57017
Michelle Eoopman, Finance Officer

Sheriff's Dept..............................**605.367.4300**
Fax...605.367.7319
Web..........................www.minnehahacounty.org
E-mail.................mmilstead@minnehahacounty.org
320 W Fourth St, Sioux Falls, SD 57104-2495
Mike Milstead, Sheriff

Sioux Falls Police Dept....................**605.367.7212**
Fax...605.367.7228
E-mail..........................dbarthel@siouxfalls.org
320 W 4th St, Sioux Falls, SD 57104
Doug Barthel, Chief

EDUCATION SERVICES

South Dakota Achieve......................**605.336.7100**
Fax...605.338.0259
E-mail...................anne.mcfarland@achievesd.org
4100 S Western Ave, Sioux Falls, SD 57105
Anne Rieck-McFarland, CEO

Special Education..........................**605.367.7680**
Fax...605.367.6036
715 E 14th St, Sioux Falls, SD 57104
Dan Goodwin, Special Education Director

Special Education..........................**605.336.6241**
Fax...605.373.1035
Web.......................................www.sfcss.org
E-mail................................brance@sfcss.org
3100 W 41st St, Sioux Falls, SD 57105-4222
Barb Rance, Director

Special Education..........................**605.367.7956**
Fax...605.367.4638
Web.....................................www.sf.k12.sd.us
201 E 38th St, Sioux Falls, SD 57105-5815
Deb Muilenburg-wilson, Director

Moody County

GENERAL HEALTH SERVICES

Public Health...............................**605.997.3779**
Fax...605.997.3273
309 N Prairie St, Flandreau, SD 57028
Val Luze, Community Health Nurse

Pennington County

SOCIAL SERVICES

Dept of Social Svcs.........................**605.394.2525**
Fax...605.394.2568
Web......................................www.state.sd.us
510 N Cambell St Ste 101, Rapid City,
SD 57701-1701
Tom Eabe, District Manager

COURTS

7th Circuit Court..........................**605.394.2571**
Fax...605.394.6628
315 Saint Joseph St, Rapid City, SD 57701
John J. Delaney, Honorable Judge

POLICE AND SHERIFF

Sheriff's Ofc...............................**605.394.6113**
Fax...605.394.2220
E-mail.................kevin.thom@co.pennington.sd.us
300 Kansas City St Ste 100, Rapid City, SD 57701
Kevin Thom, Sheriff

EDUCATION SERVICES

Special Education..........................**605.394.4035**
Fax...605.394.5169
Web.......................................www.rcs.org
E-mail..........................troy.volesky@k12.sd.us
300 6th St, Rapid City, SD 57701
Troy Volesky, Director

Perkins County

POLICE AND SHERIFF

Sheriff's Dept..............................**605.244.5243**
Fax...605.244.5611
E-mail...................perkinscoso@sdplains.com
100 E. Main St, Bison, SD 57620
Kelly D. Serr, Sheriff

Potter County

POLICE AND SHERIFF

Sheriff's Dept..............................**605.765.9405**
Fax...605.765.2412
E-mail....................amcclain@venturecomm.net
201 S Exene St, Gettysburg, SD 57442-1521
Alan D. Mcclain, Sheriff

Roberts County

GENERAL HEALTH SERVICES

Community Health Nursing.................**605.698.4183**
Fax...605.742.1028
E-mail...........................cindy.block@state.sd.us
10 Hickory St East, Sisseton, SD 57262-1544
Cindy Block, Community Health Nurse

Indian Health services.....................**605.698.7606**
Fax...605.698.3774
Web.......................................www.ihs.gov
100 Lake Traverse Dr, Sisseton, SD 57262-1448
Lois Crawford, Clinical Director

COURTS

5th Circuit Court..........................**605.698.7528**
Fax...605.698.7559
411 2nd Ave E Ste 3, Sisseton, SD 57262-1403
Honorable Jon Flemmer, Judge

POLICE AND SHERIFF

Sheriff's Ofc...............................**605.698.7667**
Fax...605.698.7386
Web.................................www.venturecomm.net
119 24 Bia 700, Sisseton, SD 57262-1551
Jay Tasa, Sheriff

Sanborn County

GENERAL HEALTH SERVICES

Community Health Svcs....................**605.796.4510**
Fax...605.796.4510
Web......................................www.k12.sd.us
604 6th St W, Woonsocket, SD 57385
Marla Feistner, Community Health Nurse

POLICE AND SHERIFF

Sheriff's Dept 605.796.4511
Fax 605.796.4504
Web ....www.santel.net
E-mail ....sheriff@santel.net
604 W. 6Th St, Woonsocket, SD 57386
Thomas J. Fridley, Sheriff

Shannon County

SOCIAL SERVICES

Oglala Sioux Tribe 605.867.5821
Fax 605.867.6076
Web ....www.lakotamall.com
E-mail ....alex@lakotamall.com
PO Box 2070, Pine Ridge, SD 57770-2070
Alex Whiteful, President

Social Svcs 605.867.5861
Fax 605.867.1263
Web ....www.bah.state.mn.us
E-mail ....paul.anderson@bah.state.mn.us
E Highway 18, Pine Ridge, SD 57770
Paul Anderson, Program Specialist

Spink County

SOCIAL SERVICES

Social Svcs 605.472.2230
Fax 605.472.4298
210 7th Ave E, Redfield, SD 57469-1252
Amber Williams, Supervisor

GENERAL HEALTH SERVICES

Community Health Nursing 605.472.2434
Fax 605.472.2435
210 E 7th Ave, Redfield, SD 57469
Kristin Miller, Registered Nurse

POLICE AND SHERIFF

Sheriff's Dept 605.472.4595
Fax 605.472.4599
E-mail ....spinkcountyso@midconetwork.com
210 E 7th Ave Ste 1, Redfield, SD 57469
Kevin Schurch, Sheriff

Stanley County

GENERAL HEALTH SERVICES

Dept of Health 605.223.7740
8 E 2Nd Ave, Fort Pierre, SD 57532
Carmella Bourk, Rn, Community Health Nurse

COURTS

6th Circuit Court 605.773.3711
Fax 605.773.6492
104 E. Capitol Ave, Pierre, SD 57501
Honorable Lori Wilbur, Director

POLICE AND SHERIFF

Sheriff's Dept 605.223.7792
Fax 605.223.7794
Web ....www.midconetwork.com
E-mail ....scsheriff.cityftpierre@midconetwork.com
8 E. 2nd Ave, Fort Pierre, SD 57532
Bradley J. Rathbun, Sheriff

Sully County

POLICE AND SHERIFF

Sheriffs Dept 605.258.2244
Fax 605.258.2394
E-mail ....sd591@sbtc.net
700 Ash Ave, Onida, SD 57564
Bill W. Stahl, Sheriff

Todd County

SOCIAL SERVICES

**Bureau of Indian Affairs Rosebud
Agency** 605.747.2224
Fax 605.747.2805
Web ....www.bia.gov
E-mail ....cleve.hermanyhorses@bia.gov
137 Circle Dr, Rosebud, SD 57570
Cleve Her-many-horses, Superintendent

Dept Of Social Svcs 605.856.4489
Fax 605.856.2031
Web ....www.state.sd.us
E-mail ....rowles.mendoza@state.sd.us
671 N Marge Lane, Mission, SD 57555
Rowles Mendoza, Supervisor

Rosebud Sioux Tribe 605.747.2381
Fax 605.747.2905
Web ....www.rosebudsiouxtribe-nsn.org
11 Legion Ave, Rosebud, SD 57570
Shirley Big Eagle, Director Of Child And Family Services

Tripp County

GENERAL HEALTH SERVICES

Community Health 605.842.7166
Fax 605.842.7162
Web ....www.winnerregional.org
245 S Main, Winner, SD 57580
Candy Cahoy, Director

MENTAL HEALTH SERVICES

Southern Plains Mental Health Ctr 605.842.1465
Fax 605.842.2366
E-mail ....spbhs@gwtc.net
500 E 9th St, Winner, SD 57580
Donna Brown, Executive Director

COURTS

6Th Circuit Court 605.842.3551
Fax 605.842.3791
200 E 3rd St, Winner, SD 57580
Honorable Kathleen Trandahl, Director

POLICE AND SHERIFF

Sheriff's Ofc 605.842.3600
Fax 605.842.3621
Web ....www.state.sd.us
200 E 3rd St, Winner, SD 57580-1806
Clifford Schroeder, Sheriff

Turner County

GENERAL HEALTH SERVICES

Public Health Dept 605.326.5161
Fax 605.326.4057
Web ....www.pioneermemorial.org
315 N Washington St, Viborg, SD 57070-2002
Deb Hauger, Community Health Nurse

POLICE AND SHERIFF

Sheriff's Ofc 605.297.3225
Fax 605.297.3871
Web ....www.turnersheriff.com
E-mail ....byron@turnersheriff.com
400 S Main Ave, Parker, SD 57053
Byron D. Nogelmeier, Sheriff

Union County

SOCIAL SERVICES

Social Svcs 605.356.3346
Fax 605.356.3683
Web ....www.state.de.us
E-mail ....geana.austin@state.sd.us
118 W Main, Elk Point, SD 57025
Geana Austin, Supervisor

GENERAL HEALTH SERVICES

Alcester Medical Ctr 605.934.2122
Fax 605.934.1705
104 W 2Nd St, Alcester, SD 57001
Mary Carda, Executive Director

Community Health Nursing/ WIC 605.356.2644
Fax 605.356.2386
E-mail ....melissa.gregg@state.sd.us
209 E Main St Ste 240, Elk Point, SD 57025
Mellissa Greg, Clerk

Elk Point Community Health Clinic 605.356.3317
Fax 605.356.2721
Web ....www.uchf.net
204 E Main St, Elk Point, SD 57025-2334
Mary Carda, Executive Director

POLICE AND SHERIFF

Sheriff's Ofc 605.356.2679
Fax 605.356.3356
Web ....www.unioncountysd.com
E-mail ....unioncoso@iw.net
209 E Main St Ste 250, Elk Point, SD 57025
Dan Limoges, Sheriff

EDUCATION SERVICES

Elk Point Jefferson Head Start Ctr 605.356.5801
Fax 605.356.5999
E-mail ....mary.main@k12.sd.us
500 S Franklin St, Elk Point, SD 57025
Mary Main, Director

Walworth County

SOCIAL SERVICES

Dept Of Social Svcs 605.845.2922
Fax 605.845.7126
Web ....www.state.sd.us
E-mail ....lori.ternes@state.sd.us
920 6th St W, Mobridge, SD 57601-1956
Mike Kelly, Supervisor

GENERAL HEALTH SERVICES

Community Health Nursing 605.845.8127
Fax 605.845.8220
1401 10th Ave W, Mobridge, SD 57601
Shannon Friese, Director

COURTS

5th Circuit Court 605.649.7311
Fax 605.649.7624
Web ....www.ujs.state.sd.us
E-mail ....scott.myren@ujs.state.sd.us
4304 4th Ave, Selby, SD 57472
Honorable Scott Myren, Director

POLICE AND SHERIFF

Sheriff's Dept 605.649.7600
Fax 605.649.7280
E-mail ....wcs631@hotmail.com
4308 4th Ave, Selby, SD 57472
Duane E. Mohr, Sheriff

Yankton County

SOCIAL SERVICES

Dept of Social Svcs 605.668.3030
Fax 605.668.3014
Web ....www.state.sd.us
E-mail ....bryan.davis@state.sd.us
3113 Spruce St, Ste 200, Yankton, SD 57078
Bryan Davis, Supervisor

GENERAL HEALTH SERVICES

Community Health Nursing 605.260.4400
Fax 605.260.4496
321 W 3rd St, Yankton, SD 57078-4324
Jacqueline Husman, Rn, Community Health Nurse

South Dakota

Ziebach County

POLICE AND SHERIFF

Sheriff's Ofc 605.365.5177
Fax 605.365.5204
  100 Main St, Dupree, SD 57623
  Robert A. Menzel, Sheriff

SPECIAL SERVICES AGENCIES

ADOPTION AGENCIES

Aurora Plains Academy LLC 605.942.5437
Fax 605.942.5438
Web .... www.clinicarecorp.com
  1400 East 10th Street, Plankinton, SD 57368
  COA accredited organization.

Bethany Christian Svcs 605.343.7196
Fax 605.737.0978
Web .... www.bethany.org/southdakota
  2525 W Main St Ste 309, Rapid City, SD 57702
  Renee Eggebraaten, Msw/lcsw Branch Director

Black Hills Social Svcs Co-Op 605.347.4467
Fax 605.347.5223
Web .... www.bhssc.org
E-mail .... rrosenboom@bhssc.tie.net
  2885 Dixon Dr, Sturgis, SD 57785
  Ronold Rosenboom, Director

Catholic Social Svcs 605.348.6086
Fax 605.348.1050
Web .... www.catholicsocialservicesrapidcity.com
E-mail .... css@rapidnet.com
  918 5th St, Rapid City, SD 57701-3798
  James T. Kinyon, Executive Director

LDS Family Svcs 605.342.3500
Fax 763.560.1288
Web .... www.ldsfamilyservices.org
E-mail .... halesmt@ldschurch.org
  2525 W Main St Ste 310, Rapid City, SD 57702-2443
  Trifh Van De Veer, Adoption Manager

Sicangu Children And Family Svcs 605.856.4855
Fax 605.856.4830
  East Hwy 18, Mission, SD 57555
  Elizabeth Little Elk, Director

ADVOCACY RESOURCES

Volunteers Of America/Turning Point 605.334.1414
Fax 605.335.3121
Web .... www.voa-dakotas.org
E-mail .... p.bollinger@voa-dakotas.org
  1401 W 51st St, Sioux Falls, SD 57105-6657
  Pamela Bollinger, CEO

BEHAVIORAL HEALTH TREATMENT

Abbott House 605.996.2486
Fax 605.996.4585
Web .... www.abbotthouse.org
  P.O. Box 700, Mitchell, SD 57301-0700
  COA accredited organization.

Black Hills Children's Home 605.343.5422
Web .... www.chssd.org
E-mail .... vern.shafer@chssd.org
  24100 South Rockerville Road, Rapid City, SD 57701
  Mr. Vern Shafer, Accreditation Manager
  Joint Commission accredited organization.

Connections 605.430.6364
Fax 605.716.9491
  1010 Soo San Dr, Ste 201, Rapid City, SD 57702
  Dr. Jackie Gilbertson, Director

Dakota House 605.225.1013
Fax 605.225.4502
E-mail .... dkavanaugh@nemhc.org
  628 Circle Dr, Aberdeen, SD 57401-2615
  Dwane Kavanaugh, Clinical Director

Dr. O'connor & Associates LLC 605.357.8744
  111 W 39th St, Sioux Falls, SD 57105-5732
  Ellen Hohm, Director

Excel Program 605.255.4937
Fax 605.255.4838
  25292 Badger Clark Rd, Custer, SD 57730-8244
  Melody Tromburg, Program Director

Keystone Treatment Center 605.987.2751
Fax 605.558.0160
Web .... www.keystonetreatment.com
  1010 East Second Street, Canton, SD 57013
  CARF accredited programs available.

Lutheran Social Svcs 605.357.0100
Fax 605.357.0140
Web .... www.lsssd.org
E-mail .... betty.oldenkamp@lsssd.org
  705 E 41st St Ste 200, Sioux Falls, SD 57105-6048
  Betty Oldenkamp, President

McCrossan Boys Ranch 605.339.1203
Fax 605.339.3144
Web .... www.mccrossan.org
  47135 260th St, Sioux Falls, SD 57107-6428
  Brian Roegiers, Executive Director

New Beginnings Ctr 605.262.5300
Fax 605.229.1577
  1601 Milwaukee Ave NE, Aberdeen, SD 57401
  Liesl Hovel, Director

Northeastern Mental Health Ctr 605.225.1014
Fax 605.225.1017
Web .... www.anymhc.org
E-mail .... lboon@nemhc.org
  628 Circle Dr, Aberdeen, SD 57401-2615
  Laura Boon, Executive Director

Our Home, Inc. 605.352.4368
Fax 605.352.4976
Web .... www.ourhomeinc.org
  334 Third Street SW, Huron, SD 57350
  CARF accredited programs available.

Quest Program 605.255.4835
Fax 605.255.4277
  25298 Badger Clark Rd, Custer, SD 57730
  Melody Tromburg, Program Director

Sacred Heart Ctr 605.964.6062
Fax 605.964.6060
Web .... www.shconline.org
E-mail .... fmcdaniel@shconline.org
  121 Landmark Ave, EagleButte, SD 57625
  Frank Mcdaniels, Director

Sioux Falls Children's Home 605.334.6004
Web .... www.chssd.org
E-mail .... carpenter@chssd.org
  801 North Sycamore, Sioux Falls, SD 57110-5746
  Ms. Jody Carpenter, Accreditation Manager
  Joint Commission accredited organization.

Springfield Academy 605.369.2585
Fax 605.369.2829
Web .... youthservices.com
  709 Sixth Street, Springfield, SD 57062
  CARF accredited programs available.

St. Joseph's Indian School 605.234.3300
Fax 605.234.3483
Web .... www.stjo.org
  P.O. Box 89, Chamberlain, SD 57325
  COA accredited organization.

Summit Oak Ctr 605.221.2346
Fax 605.221.2404
Web .... www.lsssd.org
E-mail .... kelly.lauck@lsssd.org
  621 E Presentation St, Sioux Falls, SD 57104
  Kelly Lauck, Director

CHILDREN'S HOSPITAL

Avera Gregory Healthcare Center 605.835.8394
  400 Park Ave, Gregory, SD 57533
  Linda Engel, It Executive

Avera McKennan Hospital and Univ Hlth C 605.322.8000
  1325 S Cliff Ave, Sioux Falls, SD 57105
  Dr. David Kapaska, Regional President/CEO

Avera Queen of Peace 605.995.2000
  525 North Foster, Mitchell, SD 57301
  Tom Rafmuffen, Director

Avera Sacred Heart Hospital 605.668.8000
  501 Summit Ave, Yankton, SD 57078

Avera St Benedict Health Center 605.928.3311
  401 West Glynn Dr, Parkston, SD 57366

Avera St Lukes Hospital 605.622.5000
  305 South State St, Aberdeen, SD 574021
  Ron Jacobson, Chief Executive Officer

Freeman Regional Health Services 605.925.4000
  510 East Eighth St, Freeman, SD 57029
  Ban Gran, Chief Executive Officer

Healthcare Center 605.448.2253
  413 Ninth St, Britton, SD 57430
  Stephanie Reasy, Administrative Director

Indian Health Service Hospital 605.355.2280
  3200 Canyon Lake Dr, Rapid City, SD 57702
  Helbn Thomson, Adminstrator Officer

Lead Deadwood Regional Hospital 605.722.6101
  61 Charles St, Deadwood, SD 57732
  Sherry Smith, Chief Executive Officer

Rapid City Regional Hospital 605.719.1000
  353 Fairmont Blvd, Rapid City, SD 57701
  Tim Sughrue, Director

Sanford Mid Dakota Medical Center 605.234.5511
  300 South Byron Blvd, Chamberlain, SD 57325
  Maureen Cadwell, Director

St Marys Healthcare Center 605.224.3100
  800 East Dakota Ave, Pierre, SD 57501

St Michaels Hospital 605.589.3341
  410 West 16th Ave, Tyndall, SD 57066

U S Public Health Service Indian Hosp 605.747.2231
  Highway 18 Soldier Creek Rd, Rosebud, SD 57570

COUNSELING SERVICES

Alpha Ctr 605.361.3500
Fax 605.362.4344
Web .... www.alphacenterevents.org
E-mail .... info@officecenter.org
  801 E 41 St, Sioux Falls, SD 57105-6331
  Kim Martinez, Director

Catholic Family Svcs 605.226.1304
Fax 605.226.3274
  310 15th Ave SE, Aberdeen, SD 57401
  Jerry Klein, Director

Catholic Family Svcs 605.988.3775
Fax 605.988.3747
Web .... www.sfcatholic.org
　523 N Duluth Ave, Sioux Falls, SD 57104-2714
　Jerry Klein, Director

Lutheran Social Svcs 605.229.1500
Fax 605.229.4357
Web .... www.lutheransocialservices.com
　110 6th Ave SE Ste 200, Aberdeen, SD 57401
　Lisa Adler, Director

Lutheran Social Svcs 605.348.0477
Fax 605.348.0479
Web .... www.lsssd.org
E-mail .... alan.mccoy@lsssd.org
　2920 Sheridan Lake Rd, Rapid City, SD 57702-8191
　Alan Mccoy, Executive Director

CRISIS & SHELTER CARE

Bridges Against Domestic Violence 605.845.2110
Fax 605.845.2317
　PO Box 2, Mobridge, SD 57601-0002
　Mary Kelly, Director

Childrens Inn-Domestic Violence 605.338.0116
Fax 605.336.9511
E-mail .... children.inn@chssd.org
　409 N Western Ave, Sioux Falls, SD 57104
　Amy Carter, Director

Crisis Intervention Shelter Svc 605.347.0050
Fax 605.347.6936
E-mail .... ciss@rushmore.com
　832 Sherman St, Sturgis, SD 57785
　Pearl Gulbranson, Director

CRST- Emergency Shelter Home 605.964.6460
Fax 605.964.6463
E-mail .... diane.garraeu@state.sd.us
　1000 main st peton mall, Eagle Butte, SD 57625
　Diane Garraeu, Director

Huron YWCA Family Violence Program 605.352.4952
Fax 605.352.1648
Web .... www.midconetwork.com
E-mail .... janice.manolis@midconetwork.com
　707 Dakota Ave S, Huron, SD 57350-2725
　Janice Manolis, Director

Mitchell Area Safehouse-Domestic
Violence 605.996.6622
Fax 605.996.1603
Web .... www.santel.net
E-mail .... noabuse01@santel.net
　1809 N Wisconsin St, Mitchell, SD 57301-1067
　Wendy Figland, Executive Director

Safe Harbor-Domestic Violence 605.226.1212
Fax 605.226.2430
E-mail .... ginakarft@safeharbor.ws
　310 S Kline St, Aberdeen, SD 57402
　Gina Karft, Director

Womens Circle Crisis Ctr-Domestic
Violence 605.698.4129
Fax 205.698.3921
Web .... www.tnics.com
　392 Rehab St, Sisseton, SD 57262-3314
　Julie Watts, Director

Womens Shelter-Domestic Violence 605.665.4811
Fax 605.260.3200
　510 Broadway, Yankton, SD 57078-0675
　Jennifer Anderson, Director

EDUCATION

Boxelder Civilian Conservation Ctr 605.348.3636
Fax 605.578.1157
　22023 Job Corps Pl, Nemo, SD 57759
　Nike Devarus, Center Director

Sasd - School Administrators Of South
Dakota 605.773.2525
Fax 605.773.2520
Web .... www.sasd.org
E-mail .... john.pedersen@sasd.org
　306 E Capitol Ave Ste 150, Pierre, SD 57501-2545
　John Peterson, Executive Director

YSI Of South Dakota, Chamberlain
Academy 605.234.5525
Fax 605.234.6889
Web .... www.youthservices.com
　211 W 16th Ave, Chamberlain, SD 57325-1705
　Travis Hallock, Facility Administrator

FOSTER CARE AGENCIES

All About U Adoptions Inc 605.949.2507
E-mail .... cjgaau@gmail.com
　229 East Milbank Ave Ste 2, PO Box 408, Milbank,
　SD 57252

Childrens Home Society 605.334.3431
Fax 605.335.2776
E-mail .... crystal.wilkinson@chssd.org
　801 N Sycamore Ave, Sioux Falls, SD 57101

Sisseton Wahpeton Sioux Tribe 605.698.3992
　509 Veterans Ave, Sisseton, SD 57262
　Ken Harty, Director

PEDIATRIC HOME CARE

Interim Healthcare 605.348.5885
Fax 605.348.8262
　725 Indiana, Rapid City, SD 57701

Interim Healthcare 605.371.4253
Fax 605.371.4260
E-mail .... PAUL.IHC@MIDCOLNETWORK.COM
　3626 S Southeastern Ave, Sioux Falls, SD 57103
　Paul Millman, Owner

SOCIAL SERVICES

American Indian Svcs Inc. 605.334.4060
Fax 605.334.8415
　817 N Elmwood Ave, Sioux Falls, SD 57104
　Marilyn Meier, Executive Director

Bethany Christian Svcs 605.336.6999
Fax 605.330.0820
Web .... www.bethany.org
E-mail .... bcssiouxfalls@bethany.org
　400 S Sycamore Ave, Ste 105-2, Sioux Falls,
　SD 57110
　Judee Howard, Csw, Director

Black Hills Parent Resource Network 605.394.5120
Fax 605.394.6083
E-mail .... dglasscock@clc.tie.net
　730 E Watertown St, Rapid City, SD 57701
　Gloria Pluimer, Director

CASA 605.394.2203
Fax 605.394.3382
E-mail .... chadcatron@casaofrapidcity.com
　2650 Jackson Blvd, Rapid City, SD 57702-3474
　Chad Catron, Executive Director

Child's Voice 605.333.2226
Fax 605.333.2222
Web .... www.sanfordhealth.org
E-mail .... monica.maurer@sanfordhealth.org
　1305 W 18th St, Sioux Falls, SD 57105-0401
　Monica Maurer, Program Director

Early Childhood Connections 605.342.6464
Fax 605.394.0153
Web .... www.earlychildhoodconnections.com
E-mail .... agregory@rushmore.com
　809 South St Ste 304, Rapid City, SD 57701
　Autumn Gregory, Director

Help! Line Ctr 605.339.4357
Fax 605.332.1333
Web .... www.helplinecenter.org
E-mail .... child@helplinecenter.org
　1000 N West Ave Ste 310, Sioux Falls,
　SD 57104-1314
　Allyson Default, Clinical Director

Lutheran Social Services of South Dakota 605.357.0100
Fax 605.357.0140
Web .... www.lsssd.org
　705 East 41st Street, Suite 200, Sioux Falls,
　SD 57105-6048
　COA accredited organization.

Pierre Area Referral Svcs 605.224.8731
Fax 605.224.1278
E-mail .... pars.ece@dakota2k.net
　2520 E Franklin, Pierre, SD 57501
　Catherine Mercer, Director

Presentation College 605.225.1634
Web .... www.presentation.edu
　1500 N Main St, Aberdeen, SD 57401-1280
　Cathy Hall, Vice President

Volunteers Of America - The Dakotas 605.367.4293
Fax 605.335.5514
Web .... www.voa-dakotas.org
E-mail .... s.barnett@voa-dakotas.org
　1309 W 51st St, VOA - The Dakotas, Sioux Falls,
　SD 57105-6659
　Sheryl Barnett, Vice President

Volunteers of America, Dakotas 605.339.1199
Fax 605.335.5514
Web .... http://www.voa-dakotas.org/
　P.O. Box 89306, Sioux Falls, SD 57109-9306
　COA accredited organization.

Wellspring, Inc 605.718.4870
Fax 605.718.4878
Web .... www.wellspringrc.org
E-mail .... jay.vanhunnik@wellspringrc.org
　3402 Cottonwood St, 3402 Cottonwood St, Rapid
　City, SD 57709-1087
　Jay Vanhunnik, Executive Director

SPECIAL NEEDS

Autism Society of Central South Dakota 605.567.3394
E-mail .... sdblueangel@goldenwest.net
　19304 Robbs Flat Rd, Midland, SD 57552
　Helen Bebkwich, President

Autism Society of the Black Hills 605.415.3739
E-mail .... sheritony@rap.midco.net
　521 7th St, Rapid City, SD 57701

Avera McKennan Hospital and University Health
Center 605.322.5050
Fax 605.322.5070
Web .... www.averamckennan.org
　800 East 21st Street, Sioux Falls, SD 57117-5045
　CARF accredited programs available.

Coalition of Citizens with Disabilities 605.945.2207
E-mail .... shellyp@sd-ccd.org
　221 S Central Ave, Pierre, SD 57501
　Shelly Pass, Director

Congress of Parents & Teachers 605.224.0144
E-mail .... sd_office@pta.org
　411 E Capitol, Pierre, SD 57501

NAMI South Dakota 800.551.2531
E-mail .... namisd@midconetwork.com
　PO Box 88808, Sioux Falls, SD 57109

National Multiple Sclerosis Society 605.336.7017
Fax 605.336.8088
E-mail .... NTH@nmss.org
　2508 S Carolyn Ave, Sioux Falls, SD 57106
　Jennifer Kline, Chapter President

Parent Information & Resource Center **800.219.6247**
E-mail . . . . .llaughlin@bhssc.tie.net
  PO Box 218, Sturgis, SD 57785
  Lori Laughlin, Project Director

Regional Rehabilitation Institute **605.719.1100**
Fax 605.719.1116
Web . . . . .www.regionalrehabilitationinstitute.org
  2908 Fifth Street, Rapid City, SD 57701
  CARF accredited programs available.

Sanford USD Medical Center **605.333.1000**
Fax 605.333.4580
Web . . . . .www.sanfordhealth.org
E-mail . . . . .charles.obrian@sanfordhealth.org
  1305 West 18th Street, Sioux Falls, SD 57117
  Charles O'brien, President
  CARF accredited programs available.

South Dakota Cares **800.592.1852**
E-mail . . . . .abush@southdakotacares.org
  1351 N Harrison Ave, Pierre, SD 57501

South Dakota Parent Connection **605.361.3171**
Fax 605.361.2928
E-mail . . . . .sdpc@sdparent.org
  3701 W 49th St Ste 102, Sioux Falls, SD 57106
  Elaine Roberts, Director

Speech-Language-Hearing Association **605.274.2423**
E-mail . . . . .sdslha@yahoo.com
  PO Box 308, Sioux Falls, SD 57101

The Riggs Institute **605.693.4454**
Fax 605.693.5191
E-mail . . . . .riggs@riggsinst.org
  21106 479th Ave, White, SD 57276

SUBSTANCE ABUSE TREATMENT

Aberdeen Area Youth Regional Treatment
Center **605.845.7181**
Fax 605.845.5072
Web . . . . .www.ihs.gov/medical/programs/behavioral/
E-mail . . . . .candice.russell@ihs.gov
  12451 Hwy 1806, Mobridge, SD 57601
  Candice Russell, Executive Director
  CARF accredited programs available.

Our Home Rediscovery **605.353.1025**
Fax 605.353.1061
Web . . . . .www.ourhomeinc.org
E-mail . . . . .djones@ourhomeinc.org
  40354 210th St, Huron, SD 57350-7928
  Steve Gubbrud, Director

Youth And Family Services **605.342.4195**
Fax 605.399.0833
Web . . . . .www.youthandfamilyservices.org
E-mail . . . . .ysscc@rapidnet.com
  202 E Adams St, Rapid City, SD 57701-1261
  Holly Vanderbeek, Senior Program Director

Tennessee

Bill Haslam, Governor
Tennessee State Capital
Nashville, TN 37243-0001
615.741.2001
615.532.9711 (Fax)
phil.bredesen@state.tn.us

Debrah Stafford, Juvenile Justice Director
TN Commission on Children and Youth
Andrew Johnson Tower, 9th Floor 710 James
Robertson Parkway
Nashville, TN 37243-0800
615.532.1574
615.741.5956 (Fax)
debrah.stafford@state.tn.us

Cindy Durham, SAG Chair
Legal Aid Society of Middle Tennessee and The
Cumberlands
300 Deaderick St
Nashville, TN 37201
615.780.7125
615.244.6186 (Fax)
durhamcindy@bellsouth.net

CRISIS NUMBERS

Child Abuse Reporting . . .877.237.0004

STATE SERVICES

SOCIAL SERVICES

Child Care LIcensing Office Tennessee **615.313.4778**
Fax 615.532.9956
400 Deaderick St, Nashville, TN 37243
Lois Barrett Luke, Director

Dept of Human Svcs **615.313.4700**
Fax 615.741.4165
E-mail ....human-services.webmaster@tn.gov
400 Deaderick St, Nashville, TN 37243
David Sanchez, Child Support

Rehabilitation Services **931.380.2563**
Fax 931.380.2567
E-mail ....pattye.fort@tn.gov
6000 Trotwood Avenue, Columbia, TN 38401
Pattye Fort, Regional Supervisor

Tennessee Commission on Children & Youth ...**615.741.2633**
Fax 615.741.5956
Web ....www.state.tn.us
E-mail ....debrah.stafford@tn.gov
710 James Robertson Pkwy Fl 9, Nashville,
TN 37243-1219
Debrah Stafford, Juvenile Justice Director

GENERAL HEALTH SERVICES

Children's Special Svcs **615.741.8530**
Fax 615.741.1063
Web ....www.state.tn.us/health/mch/css.html
425 5th Ave N, 4th Floor Cordell Hull Bldg, Nashville,
TN 37243
Jacqueline Johnson, Program Director

Childrens Special Srvs TN **615.741.0361**
Fax 615.741.1063
E-mail ....tn.health@tn.gov
425 5th Ave N, Cordell Hull Bldg 4th Fl, Nashville,
TN 37243
Jacqueline Johnson, Director

Maternal and Child Health TN **615.253.3407**
Fax 615.532.2286
E-mail ....cathy.taylor@tn.gov
425 5th Ave N, Cordell Hull Bldg 4th Flr, Nashville,
TN 37243
Cathy Taylor, Director

MENTAL HEALTH SERVICES

Division of Intelectual Disabilities Services **615.532.6530**
Fax 615.532.9940
Web ....www.tn.gov/dids
500 Deaderick St Fl 15, Nashville, TN 37243
Jim Henry, Commissioner

**Ofc of Consumer Affairs - Tennessee Dept of MH and
MR** **800.560.5767**
Fax 615.253.3920
Web ....www.state.tn.us/mental
E-mail ....lisa.ragan@tn.gov
Cordell Hull Building, 3rd Floor 425 Fifth Ave N,
Nashville, TN 37243
Lisa Ragan, Director

Voc Rehab Svcs TN **615.313.4714**
Fax 615.741.4165
E-mail ....thomas.hannon@tn.gov
400 Deaderick St 15th Flr, Citizens Plz State Of Bldg,
Nashville, TN 37243
Thomas Hannon, Director

JUSTICE AGENCY

Correctional Education Division TN **615.741.1000**
Fax 615.741.1055
E-mail ....sharmila.patel@tn.gov
320 6th Ave N, Rachel Jackson Bldg 5th Flr, Nashville,
TN 37243
Sharmila Patel, Director

Dept of Children's Svcs **615.741.9725**
Fax 615.741.2559
Web ....www.state.tn.us/youth/
436 6th Ave N, 9th Floor Cordell Hull Bldg., Nashville,
TN 37243
Bonnie Hommrich, Deputy Commissioner

Dept of Safety **615.251.5166**
Fax 615.253.2091
Web ....www.state.tn.gov/safety
1150 Foster Ave, Nashville, TN 37243
Bill Gibbons, Commissioner

Dept of Treatment Facilities **615.741.8303**
Fax 615.253.8079
E-mail ....albert.dawson@tn.gov
436 6th Ave N, 7th Floor Cordell Hull Bldg., Nashville,
TN 37243
Albert Dawson, Interim Executive Director

District Atorney General Office **931.528.5015**
Fax 931.528.9359
1519 East Spring St, Ste A, Cookeville, TN 38506
Randall York, Office General

Div of Claims Admin **615.741.2734**
Fax 615.532.4979
Web ....www.state.tn.us
9th Floor, Andrew Jackson State Office Building,
Nashville, TN 37243
Amy Dunlap, Claims Supervisor

Tennessee CASA Assoc **615.242.8884**
Fax 615.242.8826
E-mail ....tncasa@bellsouth.net
501 Union St Ste 400, Nashville, TN 37219-1714
Cheryl Hultman, State Director

**Tennessee Council Of Juvenile & Family Court
Judges** **615.741.2687**
Fax 615.741.6285
E-mail ....lsykes@tscmail.state.tn.us
511 Union St Ste 600, Nashville, TN 37219
Elizabeth Sykes, Director

EDUCATION SERVICES

Division of Special Eduction TN **615.741.2851**
Fax 615.532.9412
E-mail ....joe.fisher@state.tn.us
710 James Robertson Parkway, Andrew Johnson
Tower 7th Flr, Nashville, TN 37243
Joe Fisher, Director

Educ for Homeless Children and Youth TN **615.253.5210**
Fax 615.253.5706
E-mail ....james.francis@tn.gov
710 James Robertson Pkwy, Andrew Johnson Tower
5th Flr, Nashville, TN 37243
James Francis, Director

School for the Blind **615.231.7300**
Fax 615.871.9312
Web ....www.tnscoolfortheblind.org
E-mail ....jam.oldham@tngofortheblind.org
115 Stewarts Ferry Pike, Nashville, TN 37214-2921
James Oldham, Superintendent

Support and Training for Excep Par TN **423.639.0125**
Fax 423.636.8217
E-mail ....information@tnstep.org
712 Professional Plaza, Greeneville, TN 37745
Karen Harrison, Executive Director

Tennessee School for the Deaf (TSD) **865.594.6022**
Fax 865.579.2484
Web ....www.tndeaf.org
E-mail ....tsd@tsd.k12.tn.us
2725 Island Home Blvd, Knoxville, TN 37920
Alan Mealka, Superintendent

TN State Dept of Education **615.741.2731**
Fax 615.532.4791
E-mail ....Education.Comments@tn.gov
710 James Robertson Parkway, Andrew Johnson
Tower 6th Flr, Nashville, TN 37243
Kevien Huffman, Commissioner

Tennessee

West Tennessee School for the Deaf (WTSD) **731.423.5705**
Fax 731.423.6470
Web...www.wtsd.tn.org
  100 Berryhill Dr, Jackson, TN 38301-3799
  Kristy Lindsey, Principal

LABOR & WORKFORCE EDUCATION

Tennessee Dept of Labor and Workforce
  Development **615.741.6642**
Fax 615.741.5078
  220 French Landing Dr, Nashville, TN 37243
  Karla Davis, Commissioner

COUNTY SERVICES

Anderson County

GENERAL HEALTH SERVICES

Health Dept.............................**865.425.8800**
Fax 865.457.4252
Web..www.tn.gov
  710 N Main St, Clinton, TN 37716
  Art Miller, Director

JUSTICE AGENCY

Casa of Tennessee Heartland **865.425.0888**
Fax 865.482.9977
Web..www.casatnh.org
E-mail...director@casatnh.org
  161 D Robertsville Rd, Oak Ridge, TN 37830
  Cyndy Bailes, Executive Director

Community Mediation Svcs..................**865.463.6888**
Fax 865.457.7208
  100 N Main St Rm 115, Clinton, TN 37716-3616
  John R. Selser, Executive Director

COURTS

Juvenile Court **865.259.2351**
Fax 865.463.8946
  101 S Main St ste 200, Clinton, TN 37716
  Honorable Brandon Fisher, Judge

POLICE AND SHERIFF

Sheriff's Ofc **865.457.2414**
Fax 865.457.5395
Web...www.tnacso.net
E-mail..pwhite@tnacso.net
  101 S Main St Ste 400, Clinton, TN 37716-3624
  Paul White, Sheriff

EDUCATION SERVICES

Dutch Valley Early Childhood **865.463.2833**
Fax 865.457.0152
  1044 Old Dutch Valley Rd, Clinton, TN 37716-5509
  Lisa Larson, Director

Bedford County

SOCIAL SERVICES

Dept Of Human Svcs.........................**931.685.5006**
Fax 931.685.5028
E-mail ....g.cook@co.bedford.va.us
  905 Madison St, Shelbyville, TN 37160
  Gayle Cook, Area Manager

Human Svcs/Children's Svcs................**931.454.1934**
Fax 931.461.4385
  151 Freeman St, Tullahoma, TN 37388
  Ann Aschbacher, Team Coordinator

GENERAL HEALTH SERVICES

Health Dept.................................**931.684.3426**
Fax 931.684.5860
Web...www.state.tn.gov
  140 Dover St, Shelbyville, TN 37160-2776
  Coriene Troupe, Communicable Disease Nurse

JUSTICE AGENCY

CASA- The Ctr For Family
  Development **931.684.4676**
Fax 931.684.5140
Web.................www.thecenterforfamilydevelopment.org
  100 Northside Park Dr, Shelbyville, TN 37160
  Denise Hobbs, Director

COURTS

Juvenile Court **931.684.8320**
Fax 931.684.2788
E-mail..ncashion@charter.net
  104 E Depot St, Shelbyville, TN 37160
  Nicole F. Cashion, Court Director

POLICE AND SHERIFF

Sheriff's Ofc **931.684.3232**
Fax 931.685.1322
  103 Lane Pkwy, Shelbyville, TN 37160
  Randall Boyce, Sheriff

EDUCATION SERVICES

Early Head Start **931.685.0876**
Fax 931.685.9020
  515 Tillman St, Shelbyville, TN 37160
  Barbara Davis, Director

Benton County

GENERAL HEALTH SERVICES

Health Dept.................................**731.584.4944**
Fax 731.584.8831
  225 Hospital Dr, Camden, TN 38320
  Kristie Threet, Nursing Supervisor

COURTS

Juvenile Court..............................**731.584.3050**
Fax 731.584.0475
  113 Maple Ave Ste A, Camden, TN 38320-2044
  David Johnson, Juvenile Court Judge

Bledsoe County

SOCIAL SERVICES

Dept Of Human Svcs.........................**423.447.2193**
Fax 423.447.6968
  323 Rockfort Rd, Pikeville, TN 37367
  Fred Tarsons, Director

GENERAL HEALTH SERVICES

Health Dept.................................**423.447.2149**
Fax 423.447.6777
  1185 Alvin York Hwy, Pikeville, TN 37367
  Darcy Boynton, Hiv Coordinator

POLICE AND SHERIFF

Sheriff's Ofc **423.447.2197**
Fax 423.447.7358
Web...www.bledsoe.net
E-mail.......................................bcsd1201@bledsoe.net
  130 Frazier Ave, Pikeville, TN 37367
  James Morris, Sheriff

EDUCATION SERVICES

Head Start..................................**423.447.2459**
Fax 423.447.3108
  112 College St, Pikeville, TN 37367
  Melissa Morris, Family Partnership Assistant

Blount County

GENERAL HEALTH SERVICES

Health Dept.................................**865.983.4582**
Fax 865.983.4574
  301 Mcghee St, Maryville, TN 37801
  Mickey Robert, District Director

JUSTICE AGENCY

Home Base/Helen Ross Mcnabb Ctr,
Inc...**865.637.9711**
E-mail...andy.black@mcnabb.org
  201 W Springdale Ave, Knoxville, TN 37917
  Andy Black, CEO

COURTS

Juvenile Court..............................**865.273.5935**
Fax 865.273.5941
  391 Court St, Maryville, TN 37804-5906
  Honorable William Terry Denton, Judge

POLICE AND SHERIFF

Sheriff's Ofc................................**865.273.5000**
Fax 865.273.5134
Web...www.bcso.com
  940 E Lamar Alexander Pkwy, Maryville,
  TN 37804-6201
  James L. Berrong, Sheriff

Bradley County

SOCIAL SERVICES

Dept Of Human Svcs.........................**423.478.0300**
Fax 423.559.4986
Web...www.state.tn.us
E-mail..................................allen.goldston@state.tn.us
  950 Star Vue Dr SW Ste 1, Cleveland,
  TN 37311-5700
  Allen Goldston, Area Manager

GENERAL HEALTH SERVICES

Health Dept.................................**423.728.7020**
Fax 423.479.6130
  201 Dooley St SE, Cleveland, TN 37311-6220
  Eloise Waters, County Director

COURTS

Juvenile Court..............................**423.728.7253**
Fax 423.728.7266
  1620 Johnson Blvd SE, Cleveland, TN 37311
  Terry Gallaher, Director Of Juvenile Court

POLICE AND SHERIFF

Sheriff's Ofc................................**423.728.7300**
Fax 423.473.1505
  2290 Blythe Ave SE, Cleveland, TN 37311
  J Ruth, Sheriff

Campbell County

SOCIAL SERVICES

Dept Of Human Svcs.........................**423.566.9639**
Fax 423.566.9734
E-mail.......................................dennis.prewitt@state.tn.us
  2221 Jacksboro Pike, Ste A19, La Follette, TN 37766
  Dennis Prewitt, Area Manager

GENERAL HEALTH SERVICES

Health Dept 423.562.8351
Fax 423.562.1593
162 Sharp Perkins Rd, Jacksboro, TN 37757
Kathy Nelson, Nursing Supervisor

Cannon County

SOCIAL SERVICES

Human And Children's Svcs 615.563.4051
Fax 615.563.4061
Web ....www.state.tn.us
325 Bryant Ln, Woodbury, TN 37190-1629
Melba Mooningham, CPS Supervisor

GENERAL HEALTH SERVICES

Health Dept 615.563.4243
Fax 615.563.6212
Web ....www.state.tn.us
E-mail ....janet.francis@tn.gov
301 W Main St Ste 200, Woodbury, TN 37190-1100
Janet Francis, Hiv Coordinator

COURTS

Juvenile Court 615.563.8142
Fax 615.563.6391
200 West Main St, Woodbury, TN 37190
Honorable Susan Melton, Juvenile Court Judge

Carroll County

SOCIAL SERVICES

Children's Svcs 731.986.9121
Fax 731.986.3403
20800 E Main St, Huntingdon, TN 38344-4237
Becky Hillsman, Team Leader

Dept Of Human Svcs 731.986.2554
Fax 731.986.8652
20810 E Main St, Huntingdon, TN 38344
Linda Pruitt, Field Supervisor

GENERAL HEALTH SERVICES

Health Dept 731.986.1990
Fax 731.986.1995
Web ....www.state.tn.us
E-mail ....paula.wood@state.tn.us
633 High St, Huntingdon, TN 38344-1703
Paula Wood, Nursing Supervisor

COURTS

Juvenile Court 731.986.1950
Fax 731.986.1341
E-mail ....jpearson@carroll.tn.org
99 Court Sq, Huntingdon, TN 38344
Honorable Larry J. Logan, Judge

Carter County

SOCIAL SERVICES

Human Svcs 423.543.3189
Fax 423.543.6559
E-mail ....jack.hensley@state.tn.us
206 Cherokee Park Dr Ste 1, Elizabethton, TN 37643
Jack L. Hensley, Area Manager

GENERAL HEALTH SERVICES

Carter Ounty Health Dept 423.543.2521
Fax 423.543.7348
E-mail ....caroline.hurt@tn.gov
403 E G St, Elizabethton, TN 37643
Caroline Hurt, Director

COURTS

Juvenile Court 423.542.1829
Fax 423.542.3742
900 E Elk Ave, Ste 906, Elizabethton, TN 37643
Samantha Prater, Youth Services Officer

POLICE AND SHERIFF

Sheriff's Ofc 423.542.1845
Fax 423.542.6565
E-mail ....cmathes@bristolnews.com
900 E Elk Ave Ste C, Elizabethton, TN 37643
Christ Mathes, Sheriff

Cheatham County

GENERAL HEALTH SERVICES

Health Dept 615.792.4318
Fax 615.792.6794
Web ....www.state.tn.us
162 County Services Drive, Ste 200, Ashland City, TN 37015
Vincent Pinkney, Director

COURTS

Juvenile Court 615.792.7566
Fax 615.792.2092
E-mail ....vincent.morgano@cheathamcountytn.gov
100 Public Sq Ste 231, Ashland City, TN 37015
Vincent Morgano, Youth Services Officer

POLICE AND SHERIFF

Sheriff's Ofc 615.792.2041
Fax 615.792.1040
100 Public Sq Ste 220, Ashland City, TN 37015
John H. Holder, Sheriff

Chester County

GENERAL HEALTH SERVICES

Health Dept 731.989.7108
Fax 731.989.9686
Web ....www.tn.gov
E-mail ....judy.cox@tn.gov
301 Quinco Dr, Henderson, TN 38340
Pattie Kiddy, Director

Claiborne County

SOCIAL SERVICES

Human Svcs 423.626.7285
Fax 423.626.5092
310 Court St, Tazewell, TN 37879
Richard Dalton, Area Manager

GENERAL HEALTH SERVICES

Health Dept 423.626.4291
Fax 423.626.2525
620 Davis St, Tazewell, TN 37879
Valerie, Nursing Supervisor

POLICE AND SHERIFF

Sheriff's Ofc 423.626.3385
Fax 423.626.8781
E-mail ....claibornecountysheriffoffice@netcommander.com
415 Straight Creek Rd, Tazewell, TN 37879
David Ray, Sheriff

Clay County

SOCIAL SERVICES

Dept Of Human Svcs 931.243.3183
Fax 931.243.4887
141 E Lake Ave, Celina, TN 38551
Tandy Woodard-Smith, Area Manager

GENERAL HEALTH SERVICES

Health Dept 931.243.2651
Fax 931.243.3132
115 Guffey St, Celina, TN 38551-4089
Andy Langford, Director

POLICE AND SHERIFF

Sheriff's Dept 931.243.3266
Fax 931.243.4282
E-mail ....brandon.boone@state.tn.us
400 W Lake Ave, Celina, TN 38551
Brandon Boone, Sheriff

Cocke County

SOCIAL SERVICES

Human Svcs 423.623.1291
Fax 423.625.4548
Web ....www.state.tn.us
330 Heritage Blvd Ste A, Newport, TN 37821-4257
Gail Hickman, Area Manager

COURTS

Juvenile Court 423.623.9291
Fax 423.623.9400
111 Court Ave Ste 301, Newport, TN 37821
Franky P. G. Cody, Juvenile Court Clerk

Coffee County

SOCIAL SERVICES

Human Svcs 931.723.5050
Fax 931.723.5061
Web ....www.state.tn.gov
55 Saint Bedes Dr, Manchester, TN 37355-5900
Ruthann Bryan, Area Manager

GENERAL HEALTH SERVICES

Health Dept 931.723.5134
Fax 931.723.5148
Web ....www.state.tn.us
E-mail ....susan.minger@state.tn.us
800 Parks St, Manchester, TN 37355-2482
Susan Minger, Rn, Nursing Supervisor

Tullahoma Health Ctr 931.455.9369
Fax 931.455.4827
E-mail ....tammie.geibel@tn.gov
615 Wilson Ave, Tullahoma, TN 37388-3264
Tammie Geibel, Office Supervisor

COURTS

Juvenile Court 931.723.5108
Fax 931.723.5115
Web ....www.coffeecountytn.org
E-mail ....leaton@coffeecountytn.org
300 Hillsboro Blvd, # 9, Manchester, TN 37355
Leanne Eaton, Youth Services Director

POLICE AND SHERIFF

Sheriff's Ofc 931.728.3591
Fax 931.723.5149
300 Hillsboro Blvd, Manchester, TN 37355
Stephen M. Graves, Sheriff

Crockett County

GENERAL HEALTH SERVICES

Health Dept 731.696.2505
Fax 731.696.4370
209 N Bells St, Alamo, TN 38001
Mica Rudd, Director

COURTS

Juvenile Court 731.696.5459
Fax 731.696.2514
14 S Johnson St, Alamo, TN 38001-1750
Honorable Paul Conley, Juvenile Court Judge

Tennessee

Tennessee

POLICE AND SHERIFF

Sheriff's Ofc 731.696.2104
Fax 731.696.2030
Web ....www.state.tn.us
E-mail ....sheriff@state.tn.us
884 S Cavalier Dr, Alamo, TN 38001-3839
Troy N. Klyce, Sheriff

EDUCATION SERVICES

Head Start 731.696.3217
151 Conley Rd, Alamo, TN 38001-2125
Kim Holt, Director

Cumberland County

SOCIAL SERVICES

Human Svcs 931.484.2573
Fax 931.456.2961
Web ....www.state.tn.us
E-mail ....denise.romer@state.tn.us
32 Daniel Dr, Crossville, TN 38555-4028
Denise Romer, Area Manager

GENERAL HEALTH SERVICES

Health Dept 931.484.6196
Fax 931.456.1047
Web ....www.tn.gov
131 S Webb Ave, Crossville, TN 38555
Sharon Pearson, Hiv Coordinator

COURTS

Juvenile Court 931.484.2475
Fax 931.484.5374
2 N Main St Ste 103, Crossville, TN 38555
Honorable Larry Warner, Judge

Davidson County

SOCIAL SERVICES

Children's Svcs 615.253.1400
Fax 615.532.9814
900 2nd Ave N, Nashville, TN 37243
Carla Webb, Regional Administrator

Health & Human Services 615.313.4778
Fax 615.532.9956
Web ....www.tennessee.gov
E-mail ....barbara.wall@tn.gov
400 Deaderick St, Citizens Plaza Fl 14, Nashville,
TN 37243-1403
Barbara Wall, Director

Human Svcs 615.532.4000
Fax 615.532.4341
Web ....www.state.tn.us
E-mail ....jean.brown@state.tn.us
1000 N 2nd Ave, Nashville, TN 37243-1028
Jean Brown, Area Manager

Tennessee Emergency Management
Agency 615.741.0001
Fax 615.242.9635
Web ....www.tennessee.gov
3041 Sidco Dr, Nashville, TN 37204
Jim Bassham, Director

GENERAL HEALTH SERVICES

Health Dept 615.340.5616
Fax 615.340.5665
Web ....www.health.nashville.gov
E-mail ....bo.paul@nashville.gov
311 23rd Ave N, Nashville, TN 37203
Bill Paul, Director

Middle Cumberland Regional Ofc 615.650.7000
Fax 615.262.6139
710 Hart Ln, Nashville, TN 37216-2649
Lori McDonald, Md, Medical Director

Nashville Area Indian Health Svc 615.467.1500
Fax 615.467.1580
Web ....www.ihs.gov
711 Stewarts Ferry Pike, Nashville, TN 37214-2634
Dr Harry Brown, Chief Medical Officer

Woodbine Public Health Clinic 615.862.7940
Fax 615.880.2194
224 Oriel Ave, Nashville, TN 37211
William Paul, Medical Director

MENTAL HEALTH SERVICES

Mental Health Cooperative 615.726.3340
Fax 615.743.1680
Web ....www.mhc-tn.org
E-mail ....sbuchanan@mhc-tn.org
275 Cumberland Bnd, Ste 237, Nashville, TN 37228
Susan Buchanan, Clinical Manager

JUSTICE AGENCY

CASA Program 615.425.2383
Fax 615.242.9873
Web ....www.casa-nashville.org
E-mail ....casa@casa-nashville.org
601 Woodland St, Nashville, TN 37206-4211
Jane Andrews, Executive Director

Tennessee Dept Of Children's Svcs/ Deputy
Counsel 615.741.7236
Fax 615.532.2348
Web ....www.tennessee.gov
E-mail ....douglas.e.dimond@tn.gov
436 6th Ave N, Nashville, TN 37243-9004
Doug Dimond, General Counsel

COURTS

Juvenile Court 615.862.8000
Fax 615.862.7982
100 Woodland St, Nashville, TN 37213-1215
Gaylan Smith, Intake And Crisis Intervention Division Supervisor

POLICE AND SHERIFF

Police Dept Youth Svcs 615.862.7417
Fax 615.880.3081
Web ....www.police.nashville.org
E-mail ....mpardue@police.nashville.org
200 James Robertson Pkwy, Nashville,
TN 37201-1202
M. Pardue, Captain

Sheriff's Ofc 615.862.8169
Fax 615.862.8535
Web ....www.nashville-sheriff.net
E-mail ....dhall@dcso.nashville.org
506 2nd Ave N, Nashville, TN 37201-1085
Daron Hall, Sheriff

EDUCATION SERVICES

Middle Tennessee Regional Resource Ctr
(Mtrrc) 615.532.3258
Fax 615.532.3257
Web ....www.state.tn.us
1256 Foster Ave, Nashville, TN 37210
Lewis Butler, Coordinator

Special Education 615.259.4636
Fax 615.214.8659
Web ....www.mnps.org
E-mail ....sharon.wright@mnps.org
2601 Bransford Ave, Nashville, TN 37204-2811
Sharon Wright, Executive Director

Decatur County

SOCIAL SERVICES

Human Svcs 731.852.2981
Fax 731.852.4612
E-mail ....milamm@decaturcountytn.org
425 W Highland St, Decaturville, TN 38329
Margaret D. Milam, Area Manager

GENERAL HEALTH SERVICES

Health Dept 731.852.2461
Fax 731.852.3794
155 N Pleasant St, Decaturville, TN 38329
Sheila Hensley, Nursing Supervisor

POLICE AND SHERIFF

Sheriff's Dept 731.852.3703
Fax 731.852.2871
E-mail ....dcsheriff@netease.net
138 E Main St, Decaturville, TN 38329
Roy Wyatt, Sheriff

Dekalb County

SOCIAL SERVICES

Dept Of Human Svcs 615.597.4725
Fax 615.597.8531
Web ....www.state.tn.us
E-mail ....tammy.baggenstoss@state.tn.us
715 Walker Dr, Smithville, TN 37166-2028
Tammy Baggenstoss, Area Manager

GENERAL HEALTH SERVICES

Health Dept 615.597.7599
Fax 615.597.1349
Web .....http://www.dekalbcountyhealthdepartment.org/
E-mail ....francesreece@tn.gov
254 Tiger Dr, Smithville, TN 37166
Francis Reece, Director

Dickson County

SOCIAL SERVICES

Children's Svcs 615.441.6204
Fax 615.441.6209
222 State St, Dickson, TN 37055-2082
Gail Parpy, CPS Supervisor

COURTS

Juvenile Probation/Court 615.789.0250
Fax 615.789.0295
4000 Highway 48 N, Ste 1, Charlotte, TN 37036
Honorable Andrew Jackson, Juvenile Court Judge

POLICE AND SHERIFF

Sheriff's Ofc 615.789.4130
Fax 615.789.4185
Web ....www.dicksoncounty.net
E-mail ....sheriff@dicksoncounty.net
140 County Jail Rd, Charlotte, TN 37036
Jeff Bledsoe, Sheriff

Dyer County

SOCIAL SERVICES

Children's Svcs 731.286.8304
Fax 731.286.8371
1979 Saint John Ave Ste F, Dyersburg, TN 13138
Phyllis Webb, Team Leader

Dept Of Human Svcs 731.286.8305
Fax 731.288.8008
1979 Saint John Ave Ste E, Dyersburg,
TN 38024-2156
Linda Wilkerson, Area Manager

JUSTICE AGENCY

Juvenile Probation 731.286.7827
Fax 731.286.7830
Web ....www.dyersburgtn.gov
1400 Hornbrook St, Dyersburg, TN 38024-4305
Ericka King, Youth Services Officer

COURTS

Juvenile Court 731.286.0016
Fax 731.286.1535
203 S Main Ave, Dyersburg, TN 38024-5005
Jason Hudson, Judge

Fayette County

SOCIAL SERVICES

Dept of Human Svcs............................**901.465.7334**
Fax..901.465.7376
　1818 S Hwy 64, Somerville, TN 38068-1210
　Lockett Black, Area Manager

GENERAL HEALTH SERVICES

Health Dept..**901.465.5243**
Fax..901.465.5245
Web...www.state.tn.us
E-mail...chris.morris@state.tn.us
　90 Yum Yum Rd, Somerville, TN 38068-4541
　Chris Morris, Director

POLICE AND SHERIFF

Sheriff's Ofc......................................**901.465.3456**
Fax..901.465.5299
　705 Justice Dr, Somerville, TN 38068
　James R. Bobby Riles, Sheriff

EDUCATION SERVICES

Head Start Preschool.........................**901.877.6372**
Fax..901.877.6401
　100 Thompson Dr, Moscow, TN 38057-6732
　Brandy Workerson, Director

Fentress County

SOCIAL SERVICES

Dept Of Human Svcs...........................**931.879.9976**
Fax..931.879.2955
Web...www.state.tn.us
E-mail.......................................denise.romer@state.tn.us
　240 Colonial Cir Ste B, Jamestown, TN 38556-3924
　Denise M Romer, Area Manager

GENERAL HEALTH SERVICES

Health Dept..**931.879.9936**
Fax..931.879.9938
Web..www.us.tn.gov
　240 Colonial Cir, Ste A, Jamestown, TN 38556
　Andy Langford, Director

Franklin County

SOCIAL SERVICES

Dep Of Children's Svcs.......................**931.962.1156**
Fax..931.962.1155
　2160 Cowan Hwy, Winchester, TN 37398
　Marcia Ray, Team Leader Supervisor (foster Care)

GENERAL HEALTH SERVICES

Health Dept..**931.967.3826**
Fax..931.962.1168
　338 Joyce Ln, Winchester, TN 37398
　Charlene Nunley, County Director

POLICE AND SHERIFF

Sheriff's Ofc......................................**931.962.0123**
Fax..931.967.9884
Web...www.fcsheriff.org
　420 Wilton Cir, Winchester, TN 37398
　Tim Fuller, Sheriff

Gibson County

SOCIAL SERVICES

Children's Svcs..................................**731.855.7864**
Fax..731.855.7832
E-mail...tina.williams@tn.gov
　802 Gibson Rd, Trenton, TN 38382
　Tina Williams, Team Coordinator

GENERAL HEALTH SERVICES

Health Dept Trenton Ofc...................**731.855.7601**
Fax..731.855.7603
E-mail.......................................david.nailing@tn.gov
　1250 S Manufacturers Row, Trenton, TN 38382
　David Nailing, Hiv Coordinator

COURTS

Juvenile Court...................................**731.855.7623**
Fax..731.855.7624
　ste 200, Trenton, TN 38382
　Susan Featherstone, Youth Services Director

POLICE AND SHERIFF

Sheriff's Ofc......................................**731.855.1121**
Fax..731.855.7697
　401 N College St, Trenton, TN 38382-1509
　Charles Arnold, Sheriff

Giles County

SOCIAL SERVICES

Dept of Children's Svcs......................**931.424.4004**
Fax..931.424.4005
E-mail...jamie.brown@tn.gov
　631 E Madison St, Pulaski, TN 38478
　Jamie Brown, Team Coordinator

Dept Of Human Svcs...........................**931.424.4001**
Fax..931.424.5993
E-mail.....................................shirley.williams@tn.gov
　115 S Cedar Ln, Pulaski, TN 38478-3545
　Shirley Williams, Area Manager

GENERAL HEALTH SERVICES

Health Dept..**931.363.5506**
Fax..931.424.7020
E-mail...................................dsanders@gilescounty-tn.us
　209 S Cedar Ln, Pulaski, TN 38478
　Denise Sanders, Public Health Educator

POLICE AND SHERIFF

Sheriff's Dept....................................**931.363.3505**
Fax..931.424.7039
Web...www.gilessd.com
E-mail.................................sheriff.helton@gilessd.com
　200 Thomas Gatlin Dr, Pulaski, TN 38478-9520
　Kyle Helton, Sheriff

EDUCATION SERVICES

Frances B Buchanan Head Start.........**931.565.3414**
　255 Punchins Branch Rd, Minor Hill, TN 38473
　Elizabeth Garrett, Director

Grainger County

SOCIAL SERVICES

Dept Of Human Svcs...........................**865.828.5245**
Fax..865.828.4114
　8421 Rutledge Pike, Rutledge, TN 37861
　Richard Dalton, Area Manager

GENERAL HEALTH SERVICES

Health Dept..**865.828.5247**
Fax..865.828.3594
Web...www.state.tn.us
　185 Justice Center Dr, Rutledge, TN 37861
　Susan Hodge, Nursing Supervisor

COURTS

Juvenile Court...................................**865.828.3605**
Fax..865.828.3339
　270 Justice Cr Dr, Rutledge, TN 37861
　Elizabeth Mclemore, Juvenile Court Director

POLICE AND SHERIFF

Sheriff's Ofc......................................**865.828.3613**
Fax..865.828.8802
Web..www.bcp.org
E-mail.................graingercountysheriffoffice@hotmail.com
　270 Justice Center Dr # 105, Rutledge, TN 37861
　Scott Layel, Sheriff

EDUCATION SERVICES

Bean Station Head Start....................**423.587.4500**
Fax..423.587.4509
Web...www.douglascherokee.org
E-mail.................................khale@dceaheadstart.org
　534 E First N St, Morristown, TN 37816
　Kay Hale, Director

Greene County

SOCIAL SERVICES

Dept Of Human Svcs...........................**423.639.6181**
Fax..423.787.1496
Web..www.state.tn.us/humanserv
　128 Serral Dr, Greeneville, TN 37745
　Mary Sue Brakebill, Area Manager

GENERAL HEALTH SERVICES

Health Dept..**423.798.1749**
Fax..423.798.1755
Web..www.tennessee.gov
　810 W Church St, Greeneville, TN 37744
　Rebecca A. English, Director

COURTS

Juvenile Court...................................**423.798.1736**
Fax..423.798.1733
　101 S Main St Ste 202, Greeneville, TN 37743-4932
　Rhonda Craft, Youth Services Officer

POLICE AND SHERIFF

Sheriff's Ofc......................................**423.798.1800**
Fax..423.798.1801
Web.............www.greenecountysheriffsdepartment.org
E-mail.........gcsd@greenecountysheriffsdepartment.org
　116 E Depot St, Greeneville, TN 37743-1458
　J. Steven Burns, Sheriff

Grundy County

SOCIAL SERVICES

Dept Of Human Svcs...........................**931.592.9231**
Fax..931.592.9250
E-mail...james.barry@tn.gov
　Highway 41 N, 606 Orchard Rd, Tracy City,
　TN 37387
　James Barry, Area Manager

GENERAL HEALTH SERVICES

Health Dept..**931.692.3641**
Fax..931.692.2201
Web...www.tn.gov
　1372 Main St, Altamont, TN 37301-3626
　Jalinda Bonner, Public Health Educator

POLICE AND SHERIFF

Sheriff's Ofc......................................**931.692.3860**
Fax..931.692.2400
　218 Spring St, Altamont, TN 37301
　David Brent Myers, Sheriff

Hamblen County

SOCIAL SERVICES

Dept Of Human Svcs...........................**423.585.1444**
Fax..423.587.7048
E-mail.......................................danny.meredith@tn.gov
　2416 W Andrew Johnson Hwy Ste 101, Morristown,
　TN 37814-3294
　Dearal Henard, Area Manager

Tennessee

GENERAL HEALTH SERVICES

Health Dept **423.586.6431**
Fax 423.586.6324
Web ....www.state.tn.us
  331 W Main St Ste A, Morristown, TN 37814-4622
  Michelle Weatherbie, Nursing Supervisor

COURTS

Juvenile Court **423.581.9422**
Fax 423.581.5412
  510 Allison St Ste 4, Morristown, TN 37814-4057
  Honorable Mindy Norton Seals, Juvenile Court Judge

POLICE AND SHERIFF

Sheriff's Office **423.586.3781**
Fax 423.587.1658
E-mail ....ccloer@co.hamblen.tn.us
  510 Allison St, Morristown, TN 37814
  Esco Jarnagin, Sheriff

Hamilton County

GENERAL HEALTH SERVICES

Health Dept **423.209.8000**
Fax 423.209.8001
E-mail ....tburk@mail.hamiltontn.gov
  921 E 3rd St, Chattanooga, TN 37403-2102
  Tanya Burk, Director Of Clinical Services

JUSTICE AGENCY

CASA **423.209.5232**
Fax 423.697.7876
E-mail ....deniseb@mail.hamiltontn.gov
  1600 E 3rd St, Chattanooga, TN 37404-2554
  Denise Black, Case Coordinator

COURTS

Juvenile Court **423.209.5107**
Fax 423.209.5101
  1600 E 3rd St, Chattanooga, TN 37404
  Sam Morris, Court Administrator

POLICE AND SHERIFF

Police Dept Juvenile Div **423.698.2525**
Fax 423.698.9723
Web ....www.chattanooga.gov
E-mail ....mccarary_k@mail.chattanooga.gov
  3300 Amnicola Hwy, Chattanooga, TN 37406
  Sgt. Ken Mccarary, Director

Sheriff's Dept **423.209.7000**
Fax 423.209.7001
Web ....www.hcsheriff.gov
E-mail ....jhammond@hcsheriff.gov
  600 Market St Ste G10, Chattanooga,
  TN 37402-4859
  Jim Hammond, Sheriff

EDUCATION SERVICES

Special Education **423.209.8450**
Fax 423.209.8455
  3074 Hickory Valley Rd, Chattanooga, TN 37421
  Margaret Abernathy, Director Of Special Education

Hancock County

GENERAL HEALTH SERVICES

Health Dept **423.733.2228**
Fax 423.733.2428
E-mail ....susan.venable@tn.us
  178 Willow St, Sneedville, TN 37869
  Susan Venable, Director

COURTS

Juvenile Court **423.733.2954**
Fax 423.733.2119
  1237 W Main St, Sneedville, TN 37869
  Honorable Floyd W. Rhea, Juvenile Court Judge

POLICE AND SHERIFF

Sheriff's Ofc **423.733.2250**
Fax 423.733.8868
Web ....www.state.tn.us
  265 Newtail St, Sneedville, TN 37869
  Leeman Maxey, Sheriff

Hardeman County

SOCIAL SERVICES

Human Svcs/Children's Svcs **731.658.5545**
Fax 731.658.1559
Web ....www.hancockcountytn.com.
  795 Tennessee St, Bolivar, TN 38008-2441
  Joan Johnson, Team Coordinator Children's Services

GENERAL HEALTH SERVICES

Health Dept **731.658.5291**
Fax 731.658.6536
  10825 Old Hwy 64, Bolivar, TN 38008
  Patrena Minter, Hiv Coordinator

COURTS

Juvenile Court **731.658.6382**
Fax 731.658.4584
  100 N Main St Ste 4, Bolivar, TN 38008-2300
  Ruby Cliff, Family Services Officer

POLICE AND SHERIFF

Sheriff's Ofc **731.658.3971**
Fax 731.658.3803
E-mail ....HCSD@YAHOO.COM
  505 S Main St Ste B, Bolivar, TN 38008
  John Doolen, Sheriff

Hardin County

SOCIAL SERVICES

Dept Of Human Svcs **731.925.4968**
Fax 731.925.9982
  1035 Wayne Rd Ste A, Savannah, TN 38372
  Steve Shedd, Director

GENERAL HEALTH SERVICES

Health Dept **731.925.2557**
Fax 731.925.3100
  1920 Pickwick St, Savannah, TN 38372-5309
  Pattie Kiddy, Director

POLICE AND SHERIFF

Sheriff's Ofc **731.925.3081**
Fax 731.925.5046
Web ....www.hardincountysheriff.com
E-mail ....sheriff@hardincountysheriff.com
  525 Water St, Savannah, TN 38372
  Sammy Davidson, Sheriff

Hawkins County

SOCIAL SERVICES

Dept Of Human Svcs **423.272.2606**
Fax 423.272.5349
  4017 Highway 66 S Ste 14, Rogersville, TN 37857
  Tommy Hepler, Area Manager

GENERAL HEALTH SERVICES

Health Dept **423.272.7641**
Fax 423.921.8073
E-mail ....susan.venable@state.tn.us
  201 Park Blvd, Rogersville, TN 37857
  Susan Venable, Director

Health Dept Church Hill Ofc **423.357.5341**
Fax 423.357.2231
Web ....www.hawkinscountytn.gov
E-mail ....peggy.smith@hawkinscountytn.gov
  247 Silver Lake Rd, Church Hill, TN 37642-3516
  Peggy Smith, Hiv Coordinator

COURTS

Juvenile Court **423.272.2904**
Fax 423.272.6428
Web ....www.hawkinscounty.org
  115 Justice Center Dr, Ste 1207, Rogersville,
  TN 37857-3361
  Vickie Cobb, Court Director

POLICE AND SHERIFF

Sheriff's Ofc **423.272.4848**
Fax 423.272.7019
  117 Justice Ctr Dr, Rogersville, TN 37857
  Ronnie Lawson, Sheriff

Haywood County

POLICE AND SHERIFF

Sheriff's Dept **731.772.6158**
Fax 731.772.7705
E-mail ....tnhcsd@yahoo.com
  100 Dupree Ave, Brownsville, TN 38012
  Melvin Bond, Sheriff

Henderson County

SOCIAL SERVICES

Human Svcs **731.968.3652**
Fax 731.968.4218
Web ....www.state.tn.us
E-mail ....margaret.milam@state.tn.us
  37 College Dr, Lexington, TN 38351-1938
  Margaret Milam, Area Manager

COURTS

Juvenile Court **731.968.8057**
Fax 731.967.1347
  170 Justice Center Dr, Lexington, TN 38351
  Jenny Dininger, Youth Services Officer

POLICE AND SHERIFF

Sheriff's Ofc **731.968.7541**
Fax 731.968.2620
E-mail ....bduke@hcsdtn.com
  170 C justice Ctr Dr, Lexington, TN 38351-1804
  Brian Duke, Sheriff

Henry County

SOCIAL SERVICES

Dept of Human Svcs **731.644.7350**
Fax 731.644.7400
Web ....www.state.tn.us
E-mail ....james.copeland@state.tn.us
  1023 Mineral Wells Ave Ste F, Paris, TN 38242-4938
  James Copeland, Area Manager

GENERAL HEALTH SERVICES

Health Dept **731.642.4025**
E-mail ....lori.taylor@tn.gov
  803 Joy St, Paris, TN 38242-4529
  Lori Taylor, Nursing Supervisor

COURTS

Juvenile Court **731.642.5271**
Fax 731.644.7308
  213 W Washington St Ste 202, Paris, TN 38242-4073
  Honorable Vicki Snyder, Director

Hickman County

SOCIAL SERVICES

Human Svcs/Children's Svcs **931.729.3236**
Fax 931.729.2528
Web ....www.state.tn.us
E-mail ....brenda.lane@tn.gov
  108 Progress Center Plz Ste 102, Centerville,
  TN 37033-1048
  Brenda Lane, Secretary Of Childrens Services

GENERAL HEALTH SERVICES

Health Dept **931.729.3516**
Fax 931.729.5029
Web ....www.hickmanco.com
E-mail ....health@hickmanco.com
111 Murphree Ave, Centerville, TN 37033-1418
Carla Mione, Nursing Supervisor

COURTS

Juvenile Court **931.729.4415**
Fax 931.729.6141
104 College Ave Ste 204, Centerville,
TN 37033-1453
Honorable Samuel H. Smith, Juvenile Court Judge

POLICE AND SHERIFF

Sheriff's Ofc **931.729.6143**
Fax 931.729.2491
E-mail ....randal.ward@state.tn.us
118 Church St, Centerville, TN 37033-1634
Randal Ward, Sheriff

EDUCATION SERVICES

Ctrville Head Start **931.729.5649**
Fax 931.729.5649
E-mail ....c.floyd@schra.us
104 Mary Field Ave, Centerville, TN 37033
Carmie Floyd, Director

Houston County

GENERAL HEALTH SERVICES

Health Dept **931.289.3463**
Fax 931.289.3499
60 E Court Sq, Erin, TN 37061
Ginger Lile, Nursing Supervisor

COURTS

Juvenile Court **931.289.4673**
Fax 931.289.5182
4725 E Main St, Erin, TN 37061
Donnie Sadler, Youth Services Officer

POLICE AND SHERIFF

Sheriff's Dept **931.289.4613**
Fax 931.289.5579
E-mail ....1sheriff@peoplestel.net
3330 Highway 149, Erin, TN 37061-5349
Darrell Allison, Sheriff

Humphreys County

SOCIAL SERVICES

Dept Of Human Svcs **931.296.4227**
Fax 931.296.2791
Web ....www.mdhs.state.ms.us
E-mail ....recruiter@lakesideeducation.com
1203 Highway 70 W, Waverly, TN 37185-1437
Rolisa Ethridge, Area Manager

GENERAL HEALTH SERVICES

Health Dept **931.296.2231**
Fax 931.296.4590
Web ....www.state.tn.us
E-mail ....joey.smith@state.tn.us
725 Holly Ln, Waverly, TN 37185-3284
Joey Smith, Director

COURTS

Juvenile Court **931.296.7671**
Fax 931.296.0823
102 Topson St, Rawlings Bldg, Rm 2, Waverly,
TN 37185
Betty Etheridge, County Clerk

POLICE AND SHERIFF

Sheriff's Dept **931.296.2301**
Fax 931.296.2633
E-mail ....sheriffhc@bellsouth.net
112 Thompson St, Waverly, TN 37185-2124
Chris Davis, Sheriff

Jackson County

COURTS

Juvenile Court/Probation **931.268.9314**
Fax 931.268.4555
101 E Hall Ave, Gainesboro, TN 38562-0205
Aaron Thomas, Circuit Court Clerk

Jefferson County

SOCIAL SERVICES

Human Svcs **865.397.9401**
Fax 865.397.1373
Web ....www.state.tn.us
E-mail ....danny.meredith@state.tn.us
1050 Highway 92 S, Weaver Building, Dandridge,
TN 37725-4736
Danny Meredith, Area Manager

GENERAL HEALTH SERVICES

Health Dept **865.397.3930**
Fax 865.397.1246
Web ....www.state.tn.us
E-mail ....farrah.fox@state.tn.us
931 Industrial Park Rd, Dandridge, TN 37725-4701
Farrah Fox, Public Health Educator

Johnson County

SOCIAL SERVICES

Human Svcs **423.727.7704**
Fax 423.727.8815
150 E Main St, Mountain City, TN 37683
Jack Lee Hensley, Area Manager

GENERAL HEALTH SERVICES

Health Dept **423.727.9731**
Fax 423.727.4153
715 W Main St, Mountain City, TN 37683-1217
Angie Stout, Public Health Educator

COURTS

Juvenile Court **423.727.9486**
Fax 423.727.5315
222 W Main St, Mountain City, TN 37683
Honorable William B. Hawkins, Juvenile Court Judge

Knox County

SOCIAL SERVICES

Dept Of Human Svcs **865.594.6730**
Fax 865.594.5729
Web ....www.state.tn.us
E-mail ....jerry.whaley@state.tn.us
531 Henley St Ste 210, Knoxville, TN 37902-2813
Jerry Whaley, District 1 Family Assistance Director

GENERAL HEALTH SERVICES

East Tennessee Regional Health
Dept **865.546.9221**
Fax 865.594.6008
E-mail ....janet.ridley@tn.gov
1522 Cherokee Trl, Knoxville, TN 37920-2205
Janet Ridley, Regional Director

Health Dept **865.215.5000**
Fax 865.215.5295
Web ....www.knoxcounty.org
E-mail ....marthabuchanan@knoxcounty.org
140 Dameron Ave, Knoxville, TN 37917
Martha Buchanan, Director

JUSTICE AGENCY

CASA Of East Tennessee, Inc. **865.329.3399**
Fax 865.329.3311
Web ....www.casaofeasttn.org
E-mail ....information@casaofeasttn.org
2250 Sutherland Ave, Ste C104, Knoxville, TN 37919
Ann Bowman, Executive Director

COURTS

Juvenile Court **865.215.6400**
Fax 865.215.6520
E-mail ....dale.smith@knoxcounty.org
3323 Division St, Knoxville, TN 37919-3299
Dale Smith, Court Director

EDUCATION SERVICES

East Tennessee Regional Resource Ctr
(Etrrc) **865.594.5691**
Fax 865.594.8909
2763 Island Home Blvd, Knoxville, TN 37920
Robert Winstead, Coordinator

Migrant Head Start **865.212.4011**
Fax 865.212.3631
E-mail ....jdavis@telamon.org
6424 Baum Dr, Knoxville, TN 37919
J. Davis, Director

Lake County

SOCIAL SERVICES

Human Svcs **731.253.7716**
Fax 731.253.3326
Web ....www.state.tn.gov
E-mail ....linda.wilkerson@state.tn.gov
660 Carl Perkins Pkwy, Tiptonville, TN 38079-1678
Linda Wilkerson, Area Manager

GENERAL HEALTH SERVICES

Lake Canny Health Dept **731.253.9954**
Fax 731.253.9956
Web ....www.ten.gov
400 Highway 78 South, Tiptonville, TN 38079
Tim James, Director

COURTS

Juvenile Court **731.253.7874**
Fax 731.253.8930
229 Church St Ste 8, Tiptonville, TN 38079
Roger Shirley, Youth Services Officer

POLICE AND SHERIFF

Sheriffs Ofc **731.253.7791**
Fax 731.253.6315
Web ....www.state.tn.us
E-mail ....lcsoavery48@yahoo.com
109 S Court St, Tiptonville, TN 38079-1303
Bryan Avery, Sheriff

Lauderdale County

SOCIAL SERVICES

Human Svcs **731.635.4141**
Fax 731.221.0935
Web ....www.lctn.com
417 S Washington St Lbby, Ripley, TN 38063-3437
Margaret Brewer, Area Manager

COURTS

Juvenile Court **731.635.3505**
Fax 731.635.3047
100 Court Sq Ste 3, Ripley, TN 38063-1591
Kim Coffey, Administrator

Tennessee

Tennessee

POLICE AND SHERIFF

Sheriff's Ofc **731.635.1311**
Fax 731.635.0583
E-mail ....ssanders.lcso@yahoo.com
   675 Highway 51 S, Ripley, TN 38063-4565
Steve Sanders, Sheriff

Lawrence County

GENERAL HEALTH SERVICES

Health Dept **931.762.9406**
Fax 931.766.1592
Web ....www.health.state.tn.us
   2379 Buffalo Rd, Lawrenceburg, TN 38464-4810
Jean Lewis, Hiv Coordinator

COURTS

Juvenile Court **931.766.5609**
Fax 931.766.4158
E-mail ....stphanie.wilborn@tncourts.gov
   240 W Gaines St Ste 11, Lawrenceburg,
   TN 38464-3635
Stphanie Wilborn, Youth Services Officer

Lewis County

SOCIAL SERVICES

Dept of Human Svcs **931.796.4971**
Fax 931.796.4531
E-mail ....steve.shedd@tn.gov
   47 Smith Ave, Hohenwald, TN 38462
Steve Shedd, Program Manager

GENERAL HEALTH SERVICES

Health Dept **931.796.2204**
Fax 931.796.1625
   51 Smith Ave, Hohenwald, TN 38462
David Rash, Director

COURTS

Juvenile Court **931.796.3724**
Fax 931.796.6021
   110 N Park St Rm 201, Hohenwald, TN 38462-1428
Honorable Billy W. Townsend, Juvenile Court Judge

POLICE AND SHERIFF

Sheriff's Department **931.796.5096**
Fax 931.796.3199
E-mail ....lcsd02@hotmail.com
   437 Swan Ave, Hohenwald, TN 38462-1217
Kenneth Prentice, Chief Deputy

Lincoln County

SOCIAL SERVICES

Human & Children's Svcs **931.438.1925**
Fax 931.438.1959
Web ....www.state.tn.us
   2221 Thornton Taylor Pkwy, Fayetteville,
   TN 37334-3637
Myra Monkes, Supervisor

COURTS

Juvenile Court **931.433.9989**
Fax 931.433.9318
Web ....www.lincolncountytngov.com
   112 Main Ave S Ste 207, Fayetteville, TN 37334-3075
Jeremy Ezell, Youth Services Officer

POLICE AND SHERIFF

Sheriff's Dept **931.433.9821**
Fax 931.433.9558
E-mail ....sheriff@valnet.com
   4151 Thornton Taylor Pkwy, Fayetteville, TN 37334
Murray Blackwelder, Sheriff

EDUCATION SERVICES

Amana Avenue Head Start Ctr **931.438.0397**
Fax 931.438.0397
   506 Amana Ave, Fayetteville, TN 37334-3363
Victoria Bramblett, Diirector

Loudon County

SOCIAL SERVICES

Children's Svcs **865.988.0398**
Fax 865.986.1340
   485 Pine Top St, Lenoir City, TN 37772
Sharlene Neidig, CPS Supervisor

GENERAL HEALTH SERVICES

Health Dept **865.458.2514**
Fax 865.458.8587
   600 Rayder Ave, Loudon, TN 37774
Mickey Harchis, Nursing Supervisor

COURTS

Juvenile Court **865.986.3505**
Fax 865.986.7355
   12680 Highway 11 W Ste 3, Lenoir City,
   TN 37771-8511
Rick Thomas, Juvenile Center Director

POLICE AND SHERIFF

Sheriff's Ofc **865.986.4823**
Fax 865.986.3621
   12680 Highway 11 W Ste 1, Lenoir City, TN 37771
Tim W. Guider, Sheriff

Macon County

SOCIAL SERVICES

Dept Of Human Svcs **615.666.4041**
Fax 615.666.3394
   315 Highway 52 Byp E, Lafayette, TN 37083
Debbie Bush, Area Manager

GENERAL HEALTH SERVICES

Health Dept **615.666.2142**
Fax 615.666.6153
   601 HIGHWAY 52 E, Lafayette, TN 37083
Francis Reece, Director

COURTS

Juvenile Court **615.666.2373**
Fax 615.666.5054
E-mail ....ysomacontn@nctc.com
   904 Hwy 52 Byp, Lafayette, TN 37083
Paige Waller, Youth Services Officer

POLICE AND SHERIFF

Sheriff's Ofc **615.666.3325**
Fax 615.666.6909
   902 Highway 52 Byp E, Lafayette, TN 37083-1024
Mark Gammons, Sheriff

Madison County

SOCIAL SERVICES

Administrative District Ofc And Human
Svcs **731.423.5850**
Fax 731.423.5600
   225 Martin Luther King Dr., Ste. 210, Jackson,
   TN 38301
Annette Tyler, Director

Dept Of Children Svcs **731.421.2000**
Fax 731.265.1216
   225 Dr Martin Luther King Jr Dr, Jackson,
   TN 38301-6993
Ramona Tharpe, CPS Team Leader

Dept of Human Svcs **731.426.0873**
Fax 731.427.7855
   1124 Whitehall St Ste E, Jackson, TN 38301-8742
Kimberly McDaniel, Area Manager

GENERAL HEALTH SERVICES

Regional Health Ofc **731.423.3020**
Fax 731.927.8600
E-mail ....temison@jmchd.com
   804 N Parkway, Jackson, TN 38305
Tony Emison, Md, Director

JUSTICE AGENCY

CASA **731.427.5554**
Fax 731.427.1866
Web ....www.casanet.org
E-mail ....casavolcoord@charterinternet.com
   110 Irby St, Jackson, TN 38301-6435
Amy Jones, Executive Director

Juvenile Court Svcs **731.423.6140**
Fax 731.423.6151
E-mail ....ajones@mcjuvenile.com
   224 Lexington Ave, Jackson, TN 38301
Amy Jones, Director Of Juvenile Court Services

POLICE AND SHERIFF

Sheriff's Dept **731.423.6000**
Fax 731.423.6067
E-mail ....dwoolfrk@bellsouth.net
   546 E College St, Jackson, TN 38301
David Woolfork, Sheriff

EDUCATION SERVICES

Denmark Head Start **731.427.6244**
Fax 731.427.6269
   535 Denmark Jackson Rd, Denmark, TN 38308
Bernita Perry, Director

Marion County

SOCIAL SERVICES

Dept of Human Svcs **423.942.3481**
Fax 423.942.8959
Web ....www.state.tn.us
   4926 Main St, Jasper, TN 37347-3658
Fred Parsons, Area Manager

GENERAL HEALTH SERVICES

Health Dept **423.942.2238**
Fax 423.942.9186
Web ....www.state.tn.us
E-mail ....charlene.nunley@tn.gov
   24 E 7th St, Jasper, TN 37347-2811
Charlene Nunley, County Director

COURTS

Juvenile Court **423.942.2934**
Fax 423.942.1011
   5520 Main St Hwy 41, Jasper, TN 37347
Janet Thompson, Youth Services Officer

POLICE AND SHERIFF

Sheriff's Ofc **423.942.5667**
Fax 423.942.8012
Web ....www.chatt.mindspring.com
   5 N Oak Ave, Jasper, TN 37347-3433
Ronnie Burnett, Sheriff

Marshall County

SOCIAL SERVICES

Human And Children's Svcs **931.270.2234**
Fax 931.270.2246
   1204 Nashville Hwy, Lewisburg, TN 37091-2222
Gayle Cook, Area Manager

GENERAL HEALTH SERVICES

Health Dept..............................**931.359.1551**
Fax...931.359.0542
Web.................................www.health.tn.us
    206 Legion Ave, Lewisburg, TN 37091-2898
    Wanda Moore, Nursing Supervisor

COURTS

Juvenile Court...........................**931.359.4823**
Fax...931.359.0543
Web................................www.marshalltn.com
E-mail.................e.osborne@marshalltn.com
    204 Marshall County Courthouse, Lewisburg,
    TN 37091-3372
    Elizabeth Osborne, Director

POLICE AND SHERIFF

Sheriff's Ofc............................**931.359.6122**
Fax...931.359.8539
    209 1st Ave N, Lewisburg, TN 37091-2824
    Norman Dalton, Sheriff

Maury County

GENERAL HEALTH SERVICES

Health Dept..............................**931.388.5757**
Fax...931.560.1119
Web.........................www.maurycounty-tn.gov
E-mail.............................elizabeth.cook@tn.gov
    1909 Halfspike Dr, Columbia, TN 38401-4828
    Elizabeth Cook, Health Director

JUSTICE AGENCY

Dept of Children's Svcs...............**931.380.2587**
Fax...931.380.2585
E-mail...............................lisa.banks@tn.gov
    1400 College Park Dr Ste A, Columbia, TN 38401
    Lisa Banks, Regional Manager

COURTS

Juvenile Court...........................**931.381.3690**
Fax...931.375.1119
    41 Public Sq, Columbia, TN 38401
    Kathy Kelley, Juvenile Court Clerk

POLICE AND SHERIFF

Sheriff's Ofc............................**931.380.5733**
Fax...931.380.1122
    1300 Lawson White Dr, Columbia, TN 38401
    Enoch R. George, Sheriff

EDUCATION SERVICES

Columbia Head Start Ctr..............**931.381.8762**
    1101 Bridge St # B, Columbia, TN 38401
    Sylvia Djuricin, Director

McMinn County

SOCIAL SERVICES

Dept of Human Svcs....................**423.744.2800**
Fax...423.744.2596
Web.....................................www.state.tn.us
E-mail.........................mary.jones@state.tn.us
    1008 Knight Rd Ste B, Athens, TN 37303-4634
    Mary Jones, Area Manager

GENERAL HEALTH SERVICES

Health Dept..............................**423.745.7431**
Fax...423.744.1604
    393 County Rd 554, Athens, TN 37371
    Jeannie Bentley, Director

JUSTICE AGENCY

Juvenile Services.......................**423.745.8782**
Fax...423.745.7872
E-mail.........................larryrhodes@hotmail.com
    5 S Hill St Ste D, Athens, TN 37303
    Larry Rhodes, Youth Services Officer

POLICE AND SHERIFF

Sheriff's Dept...........................**423.745.5622**
Fax...423.744.0771
E-mail...................................mcso@usit.net
    1319 S White St, Athens, TN 37303
    Joe Guy, Sheriff

McNairy County

GENERAL HEALTH SERVICES

Health Dept..............................**731.645.3474**
Fax...731.645.4530
Web...........................www.mcnairycountytn.com
    725 East Poplar, Selmer, TN 38375
    Jane Ash, Nursing Supervisor

POLICE AND SHERIFF

Sheriff's Ofc............................**731.645.1004**
Fax...731.645.3116
    300 Industrial Park Dr Ste 3, Selmer, TN 38375
    Gua Beck, Sheriff

EDUCATION SERVICES

Adamsville Head Start Ctr............**731.632.5116**
Web...........................www.swrhaheadstart.com
E-mail...................glenda.britt@swrhaheadstart.com
    305 Hughes St, Adamsville, TN 38310-2310
    Glenda Britt, Director

Meigs County

SOCIAL SERVICES

Dept Of Human Svcs....................**423.334.5787**
Fax...423.334.1250
    17619 State Highway 58 N, Decatur, TN 37322-7835
    Pat Welch, Field Supervisor

GENERAL HEALTH SERVICES

Health Dept..............................**423.334.5185**
Fax...423.334.1713
Web...............................www.health.state.tn.us
E-mail.....................anderson.hutsell@state.tn.us
    389 River Rd, Decatur, TN 37322-0157
    Anderson Hutsell, Director

COURTS

Juvenile Probation/Court...............**423.334.9673**
Fax...423.334.7201
Web...............................www.charterinternet.com
E-mail........................cpetitt@charterinternet.com
    6650 N Pone Valley Rd., Decatur, TN 37322
    Darrell Davis, Clerk

POLICE AND SHERIFF

Sheriff's Dept...........................**423.334.5268**
Fax...423.334.3165
E-mail................jmelton@meigscountysheriff.com
    410 River Rd, Decatur, TN 37322
    Jackie Melton, Sheriff

Monroe County

GENERAL HEALTH SERVICES

Health Dept..............................**423.442.3993**
Fax...423.442.9468
Web.....................................www.state.tn.us
E-mail.......................teresa.harrill@state.tn.us
    3469 New Highway 68, Madisonville, TN 37354
    Teresa Harrill, Director

COURTS

Juvenile Court...........................**423.442.5631**
Fax...423.420.9091
    310 Tellico St S Ste 1, Madisonville, TN 16415
    Martha Cook, Circuit Court Clerk

POLICE AND SHERIFF

Sheriff's Dept...........................**423.442.3911**
Fax...423.442.4306
E-mail.................shane@monroesheriff.com
    319 Hickory St, Madisonville, TN 37354
    Bill Bivens, Sheriff

Montgomery County

SOCIAL SERVICES

Dept. Of Childrens Svcs...............**931.503.3200**
Fax...931.920.7660
Web.....................................www.state.tn.us
E-mail.......................marion.biggs@state.tn.us
    350 Pageant Ln Ste 401, Clarksville, TN 37040-3813
    Marion Biggs, Pcs/juvenile Justice Coordinator

COURTS

Juvenile Court...........................**931.648.5766**
Fax...931.648.5793
    2 Millenium Plz, Rm 203, Clarksville, TN 37040
    Sandra Smith, Youth Services Officer

EDUCATION SERVICES

CMCCAA Head Start-New Providence
Ctr..**931.648.4220**
Fax...931.648.8636
Web...................................www.cmccaa.com
    207 Oak Street, Clarksville, TN 37042
    Felecia Bagwell, Director

Special Education......................**931.648.5600**
Fax...931.920.9822
Web.....................................www.cmcss.net
E-mail.......................sharon.wilson@cmcss.net
    621 Gracey Ave, Clarksville, TN 37040-4012
    Michael Harris, Director

Moore County

SOCIAL SERVICES

Human Svcs..............................**931.759.7181**
Fax...931.759.5917
E-mail................tammy.baggenstoss@state.tn.us
    251 Majors Blvd, Lynchburg, TN 37352
    Tammy Baggenstoss, Area Manager

GENERAL HEALTH SERVICES

Health Dept..............................**931.759.4251**
Fax...931.759.6380
Web.....................................www.state.tn.us
    251 Majors Blvd, Lynchburg, TN 37352-0196
    Cindy Eslick, Nursing Supervisor

COURTS

Juvenile Court...........................**931.759.7208**
Fax...931.759.7208
E-mail.................heather.smith@tencourts.gov
    196 main st, Lynchburg, TN 37352
    Honorable Terry Gregory, Judge

POLICE AND SHERIFF

Sheriff's Dept...........................**931.759.7323**
Fax...931.759.6382
E-mail...................................mcsd@cafes.net
    58 Elm St S, Lynchburg, TN 37352
    Mark Logan, Sheriff

Morgan County

GENERAL HEALTH SERVICES

Health Dept..............................**423.346.6272**
Fax...423.346.2349
    101 Hill Crest, Wartburg, TN 37887
    Donna Raines, Health Coordinator

Tennessee

COURTS

Juvenile Court **423.346.6943**
Fax 423.346.7724
E-mail ....lou.redmon@yahoo.com
    415 N. Kingston St., Wartburg, TN 37887
    Honorable Michael A. Davis, Director

POLICE AND SHERIFF

Sheriff's Ofc **423.346.6262**
Fax 423.346.3904
    414 Main St, Wartburg, TN 37887-4138
    Glen Freytag, Sheriff

EDUCATION SERVICES

Commm Action Svcs Head Start **423.346.6633**
Fax 423.346.5739
E-mail ....bvanhook@highland.net
    105 Longview Dr, Wartburg, TN 37887
    Betty Van Hook, Director

Obion County

GENERAL HEALTH SERVICES

Health Dept **731.885.8722**
Fax 731.885.4855
Web ....www.state.tn.us
    1008 Mount Zion Rd, Union City, TN 38261-7694
    Tim James, Director

West Tennessee Regional Health
Dept **731.884.2645**
Fax 731.884.2650
Web ....www.state.tn.us
    1010 Mount Zion Rd, Union City, TN 38261
    Deb White, Office Manager

COURTS

Juvenile Court **731.885.4550**
Fax 731.885.6199
    10 Bill Burnett Cir, Union City, TN 38261-3700
    Harry Johnson, Juvenile Court Clerk

POLICE AND SHERIFF

Sheriff's Ofc **731.885.5832**
Fax 731.885.6562
E-mail ....sheriff@obioncountysheriff.com
    1 Law Line, Union City, TN 38261
    Jerry Vastbinder, Sheriff

Overton County

GENERAL HEALTH SERVICES

Dept Of Human Svcs **931.823.5695**
Fax 931.823.1499
Web ....www.state.tn.us
E-mail ....tandy.woodard-smith@state.tn.us
    411 W Main St, Livingston, TN 38570-1131
    Tandy Woodard-smith, Director

Health Dept **931.823.6260**
Fax 931.823.5821
E-mail ....carl.w.brown@state.tn.us
    5880 Bradford Hicks Dr, Livingston, TN 38570
    Carla Brown, Nursing Supervisor

JUSTICE AGENCY

Bruce Myers **931.823.1297**
Fax 931.823.8243
E-mail ....brucemyerslaw@comcast.net
    213 N Church St, Livingston, TN 38570
    Shannon Fitzgerall, Youth Services Officer

Perry County

SOCIAL SERVICES

Dept Of Human Svcs **931.589.2193**
Fax 931.589.3641
E-mail ....johnson@state.tn.us
    113 Factory St, Linden, TN 37096
    Karen Johnson, Area Manager

GENERAL HEALTH SERVICES

Health Dept **931.589.2138**
Fax 931.589.5414
    31 Medical Dr, Linden, TN 37096
    Carol Minone, Nursing Supervisor

COURTS

Juvenile Court **931.589.5317**
Fax 931.589.2350
E-mail ....kris.spaid@tncourt.gov
    121 E Main St, Linden, TN 37096
    Honorable Kimberly M Hinson, Juvenile Court Judge

POLICE AND SHERIFF

Sheriff's Ofc **931.589.8803**
Fax 931.589.2006
    582 Bethel Rd, Linden, TN 37096
    Tomy Hickerson, Sheriff

Pickett County

SOCIAL SERVICES

Dept of Human Svcs **931.864.3153**
Fax 931.864.7156
Web ....www.state.tn.us
E-mail ....denise.romer@state.tn.us
    8816 Highway 111, Byrdstown, TN 38549
    Denise Romer, Area Manager

GENERAL HEALTH SERVICES

Health Dept **931.864.3178**
Fax 931.864.3376
    1013 Woodlawn Dr, Byrdstown, TN 38549
    Summer Matthews, Public Health Educator

Polk County

SOCIAL SERVICES

Human Svcs **423.338.5332**
Fax 423.338.0979
E-mail ....welch@state.tn.us
    240 Cherokee Cir, Benton, TN 37307
    Patricia Welch, Area Manager

GENERAL HEALTH SERVICES

Health Dept **423.496.3275**
Fax 423.496.4442
Web ....www.tn.gov
E-mail ....eloise.water@tn.gov
    840 Cherokee Trl, Copperhill, TN 37317
    Eloise Waters, Director

Putnam County

GENERAL HEALTH SERVICES

Health Dept **931.528.2531**
Fax 931.526.7451
    701 County Surfix Dr, Cookeville, TN 38501
    Lisa Dumbaloudh, County Director

COURTS

Juvenile Court **931.528.5541**
Fax 931.526.1833
    421 E Spring St Ste 1C07, Cookeville, TN 38501
    Honorable Nolan R. Goolsby, Juvenile Court Judge

Rhea County

SOCIAL SERVICES

Dept of Human Svcs **423.775.2681**
Fax 423.570.0534
Web ....www.state.tn.us/humanserv
E-mail ....mary.jones@state.tn.us
    224 4th Ave Ste 102, Dayton, TN 37321
    Mary Catherine Jones, Area Manager

GENERAL HEALTH SERVICES

Health Dept **423.775.7819**
Fax 423.775.8078
Web ....www.tennessee.gov
E-mail ....jeannie.bentley@tn.gov
    344 Eagle Ln, Evensville, TN 37332
    Jeannie Bentley, Director

COURTS

Juvenile Court **423.775.7839**
Fax 423.775.7893
    1475 Market St Ste 101, Dayton, TN 37321
    Honorable James W. Mckenzie, Juvenile Court Judge

Roane County

GENERAL HEALTH SERVICES

Health Dept **865.354.1220**
Fax 865.354.0112
E-mail ....donna.raines@tn.gov
    1362 N Gateway Ave, Rockwood, TN 37854-4108
    Donna Raines, Public Health Educator

COURTS

Juvenile Court **865.376.3861**
Fax 865.376.6380
    200 E Race St Ste 14, Kingston, TN 37763-2860
    Honorable Jeffrey Wicks, Juvenile Court Judge

POLICE AND SHERIFF

Sheriff's Ofc **865.376.5582**
Fax 865.717.4766
Web ....www.roanegov.org
E-mail ....jstocton@roanegov.org
    230 N 3rd St, Kingston, TN 37763-2802
    Jack Stocton, Sheriff

Robertson County

SOCIAL SERVICES

Dept Of Human Svcs **615.382.2402**
Fax 615.382.3135
    809 S Mabel St, Springfield, TN 37172
    Tony Cowan, Area Manager

GENERAL HEALTH SERVICES

Health Dept **615.384.4504**
Fax 615.384.0245
    800 S Brown St, Springfield, TN 37172
    Tanya Mitchell, Nursing Supervisor

COURTS

Juvenile Court **615.382.2324**
Fax 615.382.3113
    529 S Brown St, Springfield, TN 37172-2941
    Honorable Burton D.glover, Juvenile Court Judge

POLICE AND SHERIFF

Sheriff's Ofc **615.384.7971**
Fax 615.382.0641
E-mail ....billholt@robertsonsheriff.com
    507 S Brown St, Springfield, TN 37172
    Bill Holt, Sheriff

Rutherford County

SOCIAL SERVICES

Children's Svcs 615.217.8900
Fax 615.898.8038
    434 Jayhawk Ct, Murfreesboro, TN 37128
Deidra Lackey, Main Supervisor

Human Svcs 615.848.5153
Fax 615.848.5107
Web ....www.state.tn.us
    1711B Old Fort Pkwy, Murfreesboro, TN 37129-3338
Robert W. Priddy, Area Manager

GENERAL HEALTH SERVICES

Health Dept 615.898.7785
Fax 615.898.7829
Web ....www.rutherfordcountync.gov
E-mail ....dana.garrett@rutherfordcountync.gov
    100 W Burton St, Murfreesboro, TN 37130-3657
Dana Garrett, Director

Health Dept/ North Rutherford 615.355.6175
Fax 615.459.7996
E-mail ....andre.fresco@state.tn.us
    108 David Collins Dr, Smyrna, TN 37167-2813
Andre Fresco, Director

JUSTICE AGENCY

Juvenile Probation 615.898.7850
Fax 615.907.3148
E-mail ....tsanders@rutherfordcounty.org
    1710 S Church St, Murfreesboro, TN 37130
Teena Sanders, Director

COURTS

Juvenile Court 615.898.7972
Fax 615.217.7120
    1710 South Church, Murfreesboro, TN 37130
Honorable Donna Scott Davenport, Juvenile Court Judge

POLICE AND SHERIFF

Sheriff's Ofc 615.898.7770
Fax 615.890.5861
    940 New Salem Rd, Murfreesboro, TN 37129
Robert Arnold, Sheriff

EDUCATION SERVICES

Special Education 615.893.5812
Fax 615.904.3774
Web ....www.rcschools.net
E-mail ....gillh@rcschool.net
    2240 Southpark Dr, Rutherford County Schools,
    Murfreesboro, TN 37128-5507
Harry Gill, Phd, Director

Scott County

SOCIAL SERVICES

Human Svcs/Children's Svcs 423.663.2821
Fax 423.663.4095
    104 Fire Hall Dr, Huntsville, TN 37756
Denny Chambers, Family Supervisor

GENERAL HEALTH SERVICES

Health Dept 423.663.2445
Fax 423.663.9252
Web ....www.state.tn.us
E-mail ....art.miller@state.tn.us
    344 Court St, Huntsville, TN 37756
Art Miller, Director

Sequatchie County

SOCIAL SERVICES

Human Svcs/Children's Svcs 423.949.4621
Fax 423.949.4868
    1845 Old York Hwy E, Dunlap, TN 37327
Sam Anderson, Area Manager

GENERAL HEALTH SERVICES

Health Dept 423.949.3619
Fax 423.949.6507
Web ....www.state.tn.us
E-mail ....charlene.nunley@state.tn.us
    16939 Rankin Ave N, Dunlap, TN 37327-3710
Charlene Nunley, Director

EDUCATION SERVICES

Dunlap Head Start 423.949.5015
Fax 423.949.3754
E-mail ....dewton@svpda.org
    196 Frontage Rd, Dunlap, TN 37327
Donna Ewton, Center Team Leader

Sevier County

SOCIAL SERVICES

Children's Svcs 865.429.7012
Fax 865.908.1000
E-mail ....bobby.leverett@tn.gov
    115 Allensville Rd Ste 105, Sevierville, TN 37876
Bobby Leverett, Team Coordinator

Dept Of Human Svcs 865.429.7005
Fax 865.429.7051
E-mail ....gail.hickman@state.tn.us
    815 Dolly Parton Pkwy, Sevierville, TN 37862
Gail Hickman, Area Manager

GENERAL HEALTH SERVICES

Health Dept 865.637.6853
Fax 865.429.2689
Web ....www.seviercountytn.org
E-mail ....jchambers@seviercountytn.org
    227 Cedar St, Sevierville, TN 37862-3838
Jana Chambers, Director

Health Dept 865.453.1032
Fax 865.429.2689
E-mail ....beverly.chandler@state.tn.us
    227 Cedar St, Sevierville, TN 37862-3838
Beverly Chandler, Rn, Nursing Supervisor

COURTS

Juvenile Court 865.453.9064
Fax 865.428.2468
    125 Court Ave Ste 305W, Sevierville, TN 37862
Sandy Chambers, Director Youth Services

POLICE AND SHERIFF

Sheriff's Ofc 865.453.4668
Fax 865.774.3951
    106 W Bruce St, Sevierville, TN 37862
Ron Seals, Sheriff

Shelby County

SOCIAL SERVICES

Human Svcs 901.543.7351
Fax 901.543.6474
Web ....www.tennessee.gov\humanserv\
    170 N Main St, Memphis, TN 38103
Eva Mosby, Director

Welles-South Human Svcs 901.344.5040
Fax 901.344.3648
    3360 S 3rd St, Memphis, TN 38109-2925
Lewis Hull, Branch Manager

GENERAL HEALTH SERVICES

Health Dept 901.544.7583
Fax 901.544.7475
    814 Jefferson Ave, Memphis, TN 38105
Cynthia Tharp, Wic Deputy Director

MENTAL HEALTH SERVICES

Southeast Mental Health Ctr, Inc. 901.369.1480
Fax 901.369.1479
E-mail ....info@endeavorhouse.com
    3810 Winchester Rd, Memphis, TN 38181
Gene Lawrence, Executive Director

JUSTICE AGENCY

CASA Program 901.405.8422
Fax 901.405.8856
Web ....www.memphiscasa.org
E-mail ....memphiscasa@hotmail.com
    616 Adams Ave, Rm 123, Memphis, TN 38105
Keisha Walker, Executive Director

Juvenile Court 901.405.8581
E-mail ....tcoupe@hotmail.com
    616 Adams Ave, Memphis, TN 38105
Thomas W Coupe, Judge

COURTS

Juvenile Court 901.405.8400
Fax 901.405.8853
Web ....www.shelbyjuvenilecourt.com
    616 Adams Ave, Memphis, TN 38105-4996
Jerry W. Maness, Director Court Services

POLICE AND SHERIFF

Sex Crimes Juvenile Squad 901.545.5330
Fax 901.545.2301
    201 Poplar Ave, Rm 1123, Memphis, TN 38103
Lt Adams, Commander

EDUCATION SERVICES

Douglass Head Start 901.452.7736
Fax 901.323.1879
Web ....www.portleath.org
E-mail ....ashlee.webster@portleath.org
    1600 Ash St, Memphis, TN 38108-1927
Ashlee Webster, Director

Exceptional Children And Health
Svcs 901.416.5600
Fax 901.416.7634
E-mail ....toarminap@mcsk12.net
    2930 Airways Blvd, Memphis, TN 38116-3844
Patricia Toarmina, Executive Director

Special Education 901.321.2710
Fax 901.321.2711
Web www.scsk12.org
    5650 Woodlawn, Bartlett, TN 38134
Martha Redding, Director Of Special Education

Smith County

COURTS

Juvenile Court 615.735.0500
Fax 615.735.8261
    322 Justice Dr, Carthage, TN 37030-1561
Honorable David Bass, Juvenile Court Judge

POLICE AND SHERIFF

Sheriff's Ofc 615.735.2626
Fax 615.735.3465
    322 Justice Dr, Carthage, TN 37030-1545
Steve Hopper, Sheriff

Stewart County

SOCIAL SERVICES

Dept Of Human Svcs 931.232.5304
Fax 931.232.0085
Web ....www.state.tn.us/humanserv
E-mail ....rolisa.ethridge@tn.gov
    1011 Spring St, Dover, TN 37058-3302
Rolisa Ethridge, Area Manager

Tennessee

COURTS

Juvenile Court 931.232.6322
Fax 931.232.3124
225 Donelson Pkwy, Dover, TN 37058
Honorable Andy Brigham, Judge

POLICE AND SHERIFF

Sheriff's Ofc 931.232.5322
Fax 931.232.7948
E-mail ....stewartcosheriff@mchsi.com
117 Donelson Parkway, Dover, TN 37058
Deryk Wyatt, Sheriff

Sullivan County

GENERAL HEALTH SERVICES

Health Dept 423.279.2777
Fax 423.279.2727
Web ....www.sullivanhealth.org
15 4 Blountville Bypass, Blountville, TN 37617
Janice Urller, Administrative Assistant

COURTS

Juvenile Court, Div I 423.989.4355
Fax 423.989.5642
801 Anderson St Ste 227, Bristol, TN 37620-2298
Honorable J. Klyne Lauderback, Judge

Juvenile Court, Div II 423.224.1730
Fax 423.224.1732
200 Shelby St Ste 6, Kingsport, TN 37660
Bob Larkins, Director

POLICE AND SHERIFF

Sheriff's Ofc 423.279.7500
Fax 423.279.7613
Web ....www.scsotn.com
E-mail ....wayne@scsotn.com
140 Blountville Bypass, Blountville, TN 37617
J. Wayne Anderson, Sheriff

EDUCATION SERVICES

Bristol Tenessee City School 423.652.9451
Fax 423.652.9238
E-mail ....lillyg@btcs.org
615 Martin Luther King Jr Blvd, Bristol, TN 37620
Gary Lilly, Superintendent

Special Education 423.354.1000
Fax 423.354.1004
154 Blountville By-Pass, Blountville, TN 37617
Betty Odom, Supervisor

Sumner County

SOCIAL SERVICES

Dept of Children Services 615.451.5818
Fax 615.451.5864
393 Maple St Ste 201, Gallatin, TN 37066
Stephen Craig Raymer, Team Coordinator

GENERAL HEALTH SERVICES

Health Dept 615.206.1100
Fax 615.206.9742
Web ....www.state.tn.us
1005 Union School Rd, Gallatin, TN 37066-2084
Jan Lovell, Rn, Nursing Supervisor

Health Dept 615.824.0552
Fax 615.824.9771
Web ....www.state.tn.us
351 New Shackle Island Rd, Hendersonville,
TN 37075-2300
Hal Hendrick, Director

POLICE AND SHERIFF

Sheriff's Dept 615.452.2616
Fax 615.442.1895
Web ....www.sumnersheriff.com
117 W Smith St Rm 100, Gallatin, TN 37066-3297
Sonny Weatherford, Sheriff

EDUCATION SERVICES

Special Education 615.451.5401
Fax 615.451.6563
E-mail ....norma.dam@sumnerschools.org
695 E Main St, Gallatin, TN 37066-2472
Norma Dam, Associate Director Of Pupil Services

Tipton County

MENTAL HEALTH SERVICES

Children And Family Svcs 901.476.2364
Fax 901.476.2368
E-mail ....cfscoving@aol.com
412 Alston Ave, Covington, TN 38019
Mary Jones, Executive Director

COURTS

Juvenile Court 901.475.3315
Fax 901.475.3318
1801 S College St Ste 102, Covington, TN 38019
Honorable William A. Peeler, Juvenile Court Judge

POLICE AND SHERIFF

Sheriff's Ofc 901.475.3300
Fax 901.476.0241
Web ....www.tiptonco.com
E-mail ....sheriff@tiptonco.com
1801 S College St Ste 106, Covington,
TN 38019-3462
J. T. (pancho) Cumley, Sheriff

Trousdale County

SOCIAL SERVICES

Dept Of Human Svcs 615.374.3513
Fax 615.374.3237
Web ....www.state.tn.us/humanserv
205 E Main St, Hartsville, TN 37074
Melinda Pirolozzi, Area Manager

GENERAL HEALTH SERVICES

Health Dept 615.374.2112
Fax 615.374.1119
Web ....www.state.tn.us
541 E Main St, Hartsville, TN 37074-1220
Carla Valdez, Director

COURTS

Juvenile Court 615.374.3411
Fax 615.374.1130
200 E Main St Ste 5, Hartsville, TN 37074
Honorable Kenny Linville, Juvenile Court Judge

POLICE AND SHERIFF

Jail 615.374.2114
Fax 615.374.1101
315 E Main St, Hartsville, TN 37074
Ray A. Russell, Sheriff

Unicoi County

SOCIAL SERVICES

Human Svcs 423.743.3166
Fax 423.743.1122
E-mail ....mbrakebill@unicoicounty.org
724 Ohio Ave, Erwin, TN 37650
Mary Sue Brakebill, Area Manager

GENERAL HEALTH SERVICES

Health Dept 423.743.9103
Fax 423.743.9105
Web ....www.state.tn.us
E-mail ....steve.tipton@state.tn.us
101 Okolona Dr, Erwin, TN 37650-1387
Steve Tipton, Director

POLICE AND SHERIFF

Sheriff's Ofc 423.743.1864
Fax 423.743.3047
E-mail ....sheriff@unicoicountytn.gov
102 N Main Ave, Erwin, TN 37650
David Harris, Sheriff

Union County

SOCIAL SERVICES

Human Svcs 865.992.5802
Fax 865.992.7250
1403 Main St, Maynardville, TN 37807
Pearl Henard, Program Manager

GENERAL HEALTH SERVICES

Health Dept 865.992.3867
Fax 865.992.7238
4335 Maynardville Highway, Maynardville, TN 37807
Tammy Hamby, Public Health Educator

POLICE AND SHERIFF

Sheriff's Ofc 865.992.5212
Fax 865.992.8550
130 Veteran St, Ste B, Maynardville, TN 37807
Earl Loy Jr., Sheriff

Van Buren County

GENERAL HEALTH SERVICES

Health Dept 931.946.2643
Fax 931.946.7106
Web ....www.health.state.tn.us
907 Old McMinnville St, Spencer, TN 38585
Peggy Welch, Phn, Nursing Supervisor

POLICE AND SHERIFF

Sheriff's Ofc 931.946.2118
Fax 931.946.7446
Web ....www.state.tn.us
17 Veterans Square, Spencer, TN 38585
Barnie Evans, Sheriff

Warren County

SOCIAL SERVICES

Dept Of Human Svcs 931.473.9633
Fax 931.473.1554
Web ....www.state.tn.us/humanserv
E-mail ....tammy.baggenstoss@state.tn.us
1200 Belmont Dr, Mc Minnville, TN 37110-1341
Tammy Baggenstoss, Area Manager

GENERAL HEALTH SERVICES

Health Dept 931.473.8468
Fax 931.473.0595
Web ....www.state.tn.us
E-mail ....pat.william@state.tn.us
1401 Sparta St, Mc Minnville, TN 37110-1301
Pat William, Rn, Nursing Supervisor

COURTS

Juvenile Court 931.473.2373
Fax 931.473.3726
111 South Court Square Ste 101, McMinnville,
TN 37110
Barry Dishman, Director Of Juvenile Court

Teen Court **931.473.6043**
Fax 931.473.0614
E-mail ....bdishman@mail.state.tn.us
111 S Court Sq, Mc Minnville, TN 37110
Barry Dishman, Director

POLICE AND SHERIFF

Sheriff's Ofc **931.473.7863**
Fax 931.473.5447
108 Security Cir, Mc Minnville, TN 37110-1740
Jackie D. Matheny, Sheriff

Washington County

SOCIAL SERVICES

Human Svcs/Children's Svcs **423.434.6915**
Fax 423.434.6974
Web ....www.state.tn.us
905 Buffalo St, Johnson City, TN 37601-6847
Rita Bowman, Admin Secretary

Rehabilitation Svcs **423.434.6934**
Fax 423.434.6963
E-mail ....susan.arwood@state.tn.gov
905 Buffalo St, Johnson City, TN 37604
Susan Arwood, Regional Supervisor

GENERAL HEALTH SERVICES

Health Dept **423.975.2200**
Fax 423.975.2210
Web ....www.state.tn.us
E-mail ....wasl@mail.state.tn.us
219 Princeton Rd, Johnson City, TN 37601
James T. Carson, Director

**Northeast Tennessee Regional Health
Ofc** **423.979.3200**
Fax 423.979.3267
Web ....www.state.tn.gov
E-mail ....charlene.jessee@tn.gov
1233 Southwest Ave Ext, Johnson City,
TN 37604-6596
Charlene Jessee, Nursing Director

MENTAL HEALTH SERVICES

Comprehensive Community Svcs **423.928.6581**
Fax 423.928.6215
Web ....www.ccstreatment.com
E-mail ....ccsjc@chartertn.net
2514 1/2 Wesley St, Johnson City, TN 37601
Reve Mcdavid, President

Watauga Children And Youth Svcs **423.232.2700**
Fax 423.232.2714
Web ....www.frontierhealth.org
109 W Watauga Ave, Johnson City, TN 37604-5621
Harry Spurling, Site Director

JUSTICE AGENCY

**NE Regional Dept Of Children's
Svcs** **423.854.5311**
Fax 423.952.7016
2555 Plymouth Rd, Johnson City, TN 37601-8907
Nancy Helsabeck, Supervisor

COURTS

Johnson City Juvenile Court **423.434.6200**
Fax 423.434.9705
Web ....www.johnsoncitytn.org
E-mail ....dcupp@johnsoncitytn.org
102 W Myrtle Ave, Johnson City, TN 37601
Diane Cupp, Director Of Court Services

Juvenile Court **423.753.1728**
Fax 423.753.1814
E-mail ....adblackwell011@embarqmail.com
108 W Jackson Blvd Ste 1113, Jonesborough,
TN 37659
Angel Blackwell, Interim Director

POLICE AND SHERIFF

Sheriff's Ofc **423.788.1428**
Fax 423.788.1518
Web ....www.wcso.net
112 W Jackson Blvd, Jonesborough, TN 37659-5723
Ed Graybeal, Sheriff

EDUCATION SERVICES

Enon Head Start Ctr **423.257.8242**
106 Enon Church Rd, Jonesborough, TN 37659
Sharon Malone, Director

Head Start **423.547.8335**
Fax 423.547.8335
E-mail ....peggycampbell@k12tn.net
252 Taylortown Rd, Johnson City, TN 37601-8187
Peggy Campbell, Director

Johnson City School **423.434.5200**
Fax 423.434.5217
Web ....www.jcschools.org
100 E Maple, Johnson City, TN 37601
Richard Bales, Ed D., Director Of Schools

Special Education **423.753.1112**
Fax 423.753.1149
Web ....www.wcde.org
405 W College St, Jonesborough, TN 37659
Ronald A. Dykes, Director

Wayne County

GENERAL HEALTH SERVICES

Health Dept **931.722.3292**
Fax 931.722.7249
Web www2.state.tn.us/health
102 Jv Mangubat Dr, Waynesboro, TN 38485
Steve Hall, Director

COURTS

Juvenile Court **931.722.5519**
Fax 931.722.9949
1016 Andrew Jackson Dr, Waynesboro,
TN 38485-0367
Sheldon Fitton, Youth Services Officer

POLICE AND SHERIFF

Sheriff's Ofc **931.722.3615**
Fax 931.722.3884
Web ....www.netease.net
E-mail ....rwilson@waynetnso.com
1016 Andrew Jackson Dr Ste 101, Waynesboro,
TN 38485
Ric Wilson, Sheriff

Weakley County

SOCIAL SERVICES

Dept of Human Svcs **731.364.3128**
Fax 731.364.2348
Web ....www.state.tn.us/humanserv
E-mail ....christy.dilday@state.tn.us
8616 Highway 22, Dresden, TN 38225
Christy Dilday, Police

GENERAL HEALTH SERVICES

Health Dept **731.364.2210**
Fax 731.364.5846
9852 Highway 22, Dresden, TN 38225
Tim James, Director

COURTS

Juvenile Court **731.364.5716**
Fax 731.364.3901
E-mail ....jkeith_jones@hotmail.com
116 W Main St Rm G02, Dresden, TN 38225-1166
Keith Jones, Youth Services Officer

POLICE AND SHERIFF

Sheriff's Ofc **731.364.5454**
Fax 731.364.6840
E-mail ....mikew@titlesearcher.com
7951 Highway 22, Dresden, TN 38225
Mike A Wilson, Sheriff

White County

GENERAL HEALTH SERVICES

Health Dept **931.836.2201**
Fax 931.836.3580
135 Walker St, Sparta, TN 38583
Kendra Jared, Nursing Supervisor

POLICE AND SHERIFF

Sheriff's Ofc **931.836.3356**
Fax 931.836.1524
E-mail ....oddies@williamson-tn.org
111 Depot St, Ste 4, Sparta, TN 38583
Oddie Shoupe, Sheriff

Williamson County

GENERAL HEALTH SERVICES

Health Dept **615.794.1542**
Fax 615.790.5967
Web ....www.state.tn.us
E-mail ....becky.brumley@state.tn.us
1324 W Main St, Franklin, TN 37064-3784
Becky Brumley, Director

COURTS

Juvenile Court **615.790.5812**
Fax 615.790.5437
Web ....www.williamson-tn.org
E-mail ....badgent@bellsouth.net
408 Century Ct, Franklin, TN 37064-3986
Betsy Adgent, Director Of Juvenile Services

POLICE AND SHERIFF

Sheriff's Ofc **615.790.5560**
Fax 615.790.5627
Web ....www.williamson-tn.org
408 Century Ct, Franklin, TN 37064-3986
Jeff Long, Sheriff

Wilson County

SOCIAL SERVICES

Dept Of Chidren Svcs **615.443.2750**
Fax 615.443.2778
Web ....www.tennessee.gov
217 E High St, Ste 108, Lebanon, TN 37087
Tracy Brignac, Team Coordinator

JUSTICE AGENCY

CASA Program **615.443.2002**
Fax 615.443.2019
Web ....www.wilsoncountysasa.com
E-mail ....casa594@cs.com
102 E Main St, Lebanon, TN 37087-2725
Lora Swanson, Director

COURTS

Juvenile Court **615.444.9537**
Fax 615.444.9786
105 E High St Ste 207, Lebanon, TN 37088
Kim Nokes, Sr. Youth Services Officer

Teen Court **615.804.5464**
Fax 615.449.3282
E-mail ....blschenk@aol.com
114 Blairmont Ct, Lebanon, TN 37087-3043
Linda Schenk, Coordinator

SPECIAL SERVICES AGENCIES

ADOPTION AGENCIES

Adoption Promises **731.415.7503**
Web .... www.adoptionpromises.com
E-mail .... joanne@adoptionpromises.com
     PO Box 30204, Clarksville, TN 37040-0004
     Joanne Zambo, Director

Appalachian Family Outreach, Inc. **423.542.4245**
Fax 423.542.4369
E-mail .... lrose@appfamily.org
     2600 State Line Rd, Elizabethton, TN 37643-7204
     Larry J. Rose, Lcsw, Executive Director

Bethany Christian Svcs **901.818.9996**
Fax 901.761.9350
Web .... www.bethany.org/memphis
     1044 Brookfield Rd Ste 102, Memphis, TN 38119
     Michael Mc Donald, Director

Bethany Christian Svcs **423.622.7360**
Fax 423.622.9085
Web .... www.bethany.org
E-mail .... bcschattanooga@bethany.org
     400 S Germantown Rd, Chattanooga,
     TN 37411-5025
     Peggy Lowe, Director

Bethany Christian Svcs **615.242.0909**
Fax 615.242.9440
Web .... www.bethany.org
E-mail .... bcsnashville@bethany.org
     220 Athens Way, Ste 405, Nashville, TN 37228-1329
     Tammy Bass, Director

Byrd & Assoc Plc **615.595.2991**
Fax 615.595.2984
     317 Main St Ste 204, Franklin, TN 37064
     Rebecca Birds, Director

Catholic Charities **901.722.4700**
Fax 901.722.4791
Web .... www.ccwtn.org
E-mail .... carolyn.tisdale@acc.cdom.org
     1325 Jefferson Ave, Memphis, TN 38104-2013
     Carolyn Tisdale, Executive Director

Catholic Charities Of East TN **423.267.1297**
Fax 423.265.4923
E-mail .... Laurie@ccetn.org
     859 McCallie Ave, Ste 200, Chattanooga,
     TN 37403-2624
     Regan Schriver, Chief Executive Officer

David L Scott **615.896.7656**
Fax 615.896.7660
     722 S Church St, Murfreesboro, TN 37130-4926
     David Scott, Attorney

Harmony Adoptions **865.982.5225**
Fax 865.982.5950
Web .... www.harmony.cc
     131 Cherokee Heights Drive, Maryville, TN 37801
     COA accredited organization.

Heaven Sent Children **615.898.0803**
Fax 615.898.1990
Web .... www.heavensentchildren.com
E-mail .... angles@heavensentchildren.com
     307 N Walnut St, Murfreesboro, TN 37130-3656
     Denise Hobbs-coaer, Director

Holston United Methodist Home for Children,
Inc. **423.638.4171**
Fax 423.638.7171
Web .... www.holstonhome.org
     P.O. Box 188, Greeneville, TN 37744-9982
     COA accredited organization.

Small World Adoption Prog. **615.754.6540**
Fax 615.754.6546
Web .... www.swa.net
E-mail .... jim.savley@swa.net
     1057 Vanderbilt Rd, Mount Juliet, TN 37122-2853
     Jim Savley, Director

Youth Villages **931.525.6900**
Fax 931.525.6970
Web .... www.youthvillages.org
E-mail .... niki.sutton@youthvillages.org
     1420 Neal St Ste 202, Cookeville, TN 38501
     Niki Sutton, Office Manager

Youth Villages **931.503.0777**
Fax 931.503.0703
Web .... www.youthvillages.org
     1330 College St Ste Q, Clarksville, TN 37040
     Misty Stone, Office Manager

Youth Villages **931.589.2500**
Fax 931.589.2005
Web .... www.youthvillages.org
E-mail .... bruce.wright@youthvillages.org
     2225 Deer valley rd, Linden, TN 37096
     Bruce Wright, Director

ADVOCACY RESOURCES

CASA **615.904.6996**
Fax 615.904.1872
E-mail .... casarco@aol.com
     447 N. Front Street, Murfreesboro, TN 37130
     Susan Maguigan, Executive Director

Child Advocacy Ctr **615.384.5885**
Fax 615.384.2269
E-mail .... cacinfo@bellsouth.net
     101 5th Ave W Ste 200, Springfield, TN 37172
     Anita Cowan, Director

Child Advocacy Ctr **423.266.6918**
Fax 423.265.0620
Web .... www.cachc.org
     909 Vine St, Chattanooga, TN 37403-2320
     Shelley Mcgraw, Executive Director

Childhelp Children's Advocacy Ctrs Childhelp
USA **865.637.1753**
Fax 865.544.7150
Web .... www.childhelpusa.org
     2505 Kingston Pk, Knoxville, TN 37919-3313
     Hugh Nustrom, Executive Director

Children's Advocacy Ctr **423.279.1222**
Fax 423.323.0972
Web .... www.cacsctn.org
E-mail .... gfrye@cacsctn.org
     150 Blountville Byp, Blountville, TN 37617-4575
     Gena Frye, Executive Director

Childrens Defense Fund - Haley Farm **865.457.6466**
Fax 865.457.6464
E-mail .... cdfhaley@childrensdefence.org
     1000 Alex Haley Ln, Clinton, TN 37716
     Kenneth Liddy, Business Manager

Community Health System **615.741.0380**
Fax 615.253.2100
E-mail .... jeffgrimm@tn.gov
     425 5th Ave N, Fl 4, Nashville, TN 37247
     Jeff Grimm, Administrator

Disability Law And Advocacy Ctr Of
Tennessee **615.298.1080**
Fax 615.298.2046
Web .... www.dlactn.org
E-mail .... gethelp@dlactn.org
     2416 21st Ave S Ste 100, Nashville, TN 37212-5385
     Shirley Shea, Executive Director

Law Firm of Nancy Nelson **731.668.6687**
     245 W Sycamore, Jackson, TN 38308
     Nancy Nelson, Attorney

Law Ofc of Jere Franklin Ownby **865.633.6633**
E-mail .... jownby@ownbylawfirm.com
     3902 Glenfield Dr, Knoxville, TN 37919
     Jere Ownby, Director

Memphis Child Advocacy Ctr **901.525.2377**
Fax 901.888.4390
Web .... www.memphiscac.org
E-mail .... nwilliams@memphiscac.org
     1085 Poplar Ave, Memphis, TN 38105
     Nancy Williams, Executive Director

Pathways Of Tennessee **731.541.8200**
Fax 731.541.8327
Web .... www.wth.org
     238 Summar Dr, Jackson, TN 38301-3906
     Dr Lois King, Inpatient Program Director/medical Director

Sherry L Mahar Attorney at Law **865.691.9011**
E-mail .... smahar1450@aol.com
     300 Montvue Rd Ste F, Knoxville, TN 37919
     Sherry Lynn Mahar, Attorney

The Law Office of Mary Ward **865.671.4480**
E-mail .... maryward@tds.net
     PO Box 23382, Knoxville, TN 37933
     Mary Ward, attorney

BEHAVIORAL HEALTH TREATMENT

Acadia Village **865.970.3255**
E-mail .... jjones@acadiahealthcare.com
     2431 Jones Bend Road, Louisville, TN 37777
     Ms. Jeri Jones, Accreditation Manager
     Joint Commission accredited organization.

Advanced Horizons **901.624.3581**
E-mail .... lajunetaylor@yahoo.com
     6685 Quince Road Suite 124, Memphis, TN 38119
     Ms. June Taylor, Accreditation Manager
     Joint Commission accredited organization.

Advent Home Learning Center **423.336.5052**
Fax 423.336.8224
Web .... www.adventhome.org
     900 County Road 950, Calhoun, TN 37309
     CARF accredited programs available.

Athena Consulting & Psychlgcl **615.320.1155**
Fax 615.320.1177
Web .... www.athena-nashville.com
     1720 W End Ave, Ste 240, Nashville, TN 37203-2609
     Dr. Charles Ihrig, Psychiatrist

Baxter Medical Practice **931.858.2116**
Fax 931.858.2117
Web .... www.baxter.com
E-mail .... baxter@baxter.com
     2300 21st Ave S Ste 303, Nashville, TN 37212-4927
     Elizabeth Baxter, Pyschiatrist

Behavioral Strategies LLC **865.539.1001**
Web .... www.behavioralstrategiesllc.org
     214 S Peters Rd, Knoxville, TN 37923
     Glenda Garrison, Office Manager

Blount Memorial Hospital, Inc. **865.983.7211**
Web .... www.blountmemorial.org
E-mail .... lachapma@bmnet.com
     907 East Lamar Alexander Parkway, Maryville,
     TN 37804-5016
     Mrs. Linda Chapman, Accreditation Manager
     Joint Commission accredited organization.

Bradford Health Svcs 931.728.4442
Fax 931.723.2425
Web ....www.bradfordhealth.com
E-mail ....bbell@bradfordhealth.net
  1601 McArthur St, Manchester, TN 37355-2521
  Brad Bell, Regional Director

Bristol Regional Counseling Ctr - A Div Of Frontier Health 423.989.4500
Fax 423.989.4582
Web ....www.frontierhealth.org
E-mail ....tperry@frontierhealth.org
  26 Midway St, Bristol, TN 37620
  Tim Perry, Director

Camelot Care Ctrs Inc 865.481.3972
E-mail ....kheifner@camelotcare.com
  103 Donner Dr, Oak Ridge, TN 37830-7745
  Keith Heifner, Director

Cedar Grove 615.895.9590
Fax 615.895.9592
Web ....www.kidlinknetwork.com
  1640 Lascassas Pike, Murfreesboro, TN 37130-1609
  Robert Hoskins, Director of Admissions

Center Stone 931.461.1300
Fax 931.461.1302
E-mail ....daniel.mansfield@centerstone.org
  1803 N Jackson St, Tullahoma, TN 37388
  Dan Mansfield, Clinic Manager

Centerstone of Tennessee, Inc. 615.463.6627
Fax 615.463.6603
Web ....www.centerstone.org
  1101 Sixth Avenue North, Nashville, TN 37208
  CARF accredited programs available.

Cherokee Mental Health Ctr 865.544.0406
Fax 865.544.0480
Web ....www.cherokeehealth.com
E-mail ....dennis.freeman@cherokeehealth.com
  2018 Western Avenue, Knoxville, TN 37921
  Joel Horngerger, Mhs, Chief Operating Officer

Child & Family Tennessee 865.524.7483
Web ....www.child-family.org
E-mail ....kwright@child-family.org
  901 East Summit Hill Drive, Knoxville, TN 37915
  Ms. Kimberly Wright, Accreditation Manager
  Joint Commission accredited organization.

Child And Family TN 865.681.0552
Fax 865.681.4037
  1012 E Lamar Alexander Pkwy, Maryville, TN 37804
  Edward Steven Houston, Director

Children's Home-Chambliss Shelter 423.698.2456
Fax 423.622.6549
Web ....www.ch-cs.org
E-mail ....bgautry@ch-cs.org
  315 Gillespie Road, Chattanooga, TN 37411
  Barbara Autry, Program Director
  CARF accredited programs available.

Collierville High School 901.854.2340
Fax 901.853.3313
  1101 New Byhalia Rd, Collierville, TN 38017
  Dr Tim Setterlund, Principle

Compass Intervention Center 901.758.2002
Fax 901.758.2156
Web ....www.compassinterventioncenter.net
E-mail ....jacquelyn.burgess@uhsinc.com
  7900 Lawrance Rd, Memphis, TN 38125-2838
  Jackie Burgess, Director of Admissions

Continuum Healthcare - Memphis CMHC, LLC 901.531.1930
Fax 901.531.1940
Web ....www.continuumhealth.net
  4066 Summer Avenue, Memphis, TN 38122
  CARF accredited programs available.

Council for Alcohol and Drug Abuse Services, Inc. 423.756.7644
Web ....www.cadas.org
E-mail ....jeff.north@cadas.org
  207 Spears Avenue, Chattanooga, TN 37405
  Mr. Jeff North, Accreditation Manager
  Joint Commission accredited organization.

Counseling and Consultation Services, Inc. 423.257.6054
Web ....www.steppenstone.org
E-mail ....anitablack@candcservices.org
  110 SteppenStone Blvd., Limestone, TN 37681
  Mrs. Jacqueline Black, Accreditation Manager
  Joint Commission accredited organization.

CRC Health Tennessee, Inc. dba New Life Lodge 615.446.7034
Fax 615.446.2377
Web ....www.newlifelodge.com
  999 Girl Scout Road, Burns, TN 37029
  CARF accredited programs available.

Ctrstone 931.920.7200
Fax 931.920.7202
Web ....www.centerstone.org
E-mail ....david.guth@centerstone.org
  511 8th St, Clarksville, TN 37040-3093
  David Guth, CEO

Ctrstone Health Care Systems, Inc 615.460.4100
Fax 615.460.4104
Web ....www.centerstone.org
  1101 6th Ave N, Ella Hayes Center, Nashville, TN 37208
  David Guth, CEO

Ctrstone, Luton Mental Health Ctr, Inc 615.279.6700
Fax 615.279.6702
Web ....www.centerstone.org
E-mail ....rebecca.marshal@centerstone.org
  1921 Ransom Pl, Nashville, TN 37217-3841
  Rebecca Marshal, Clinical Director

Cumberland Heights Foundation, Inc. 615.352.1757
Web ....www.cumberlandheights.org
E-mail ....donna_fisher@cumberlandheights.org
  8283 River Road, Nashville, TN 37209
  Ms. Donna Fisher, Accreditation Manager
  Joint Commission accredited organization.

Cumberland Psychiatric Svc 931.967.6764
  155 Hospital Rd Ste D, Winchester, TN 37398-2495
  Badshah Maitra, Psychiatrist

Cumberland River Hospital 931.243.3581
Web ....www.cumberlandriverhospital.com
  100 Old Jefferson St, Celina, TN 38551
  Deborah Lambert, Director

Daybreak Treatment Center and Specialized School 901.753.4300
Web ....www.daybreaktreatment.com
E-mail ....gdelconte@daybreaktreatment.com
  2262 Germantown Road South, Germantown, TN 38138
  Dr. Garry Del Conte, Accreditation Manager
  Joint Commission accredited organization.

Debona Medical Practice 615.383.4554
Fax 615.383.4065
E-mail ....debona@comcast.net
  4301 Hillsboro Pike Ste 220, Nashville, TN 37215-3314
  Jill Debona, MD, Psychiatrist

Embry Medical Practice 865.470.2719
  7632 Gleason Dr Ste 2, Knoxville, TN 37919-6847
  Jerry Embry, Md, Psychiatrist

Foothills Care, Inc. 865.376.3464
Web ....www.foothillscare.com
E-mail ....jpedigo@foothillscare.com
  404 North Kentucky Street, Kingston, TN 37763
  Mr. James Pedigo, Accreditation Manager
  Joint Commission accredited organization.

Free Will Baptist Family Ministries, Inc. 423.639.9449
Fax 423.639.5083
Web ....www.fwbfm.com
E-mail ....adingus@fwbfm.com
  90 Stanley Lane, Greeneville, TN 37743
  Angela Dingus, Director of Best Practices
  CARF accredited programs available.

Frontier Health 423.467.3600
Fax 423.467.3710
Web ....www.frontierhealth.org
  1167 Spratlin Park Drive, Gray, TN 37615
  CARF accredited programs available.

Group Effort Foundation, Inc. 615.230.2937
Fax 615.528.3411
Web ....www.geffort.com
  PO. Box 1113, Gallatin, TN 37066
  COA accredited organization.

HCA Valley Hospital 423.894.4220
Fax 423.499.1201
Web ....www.parkridgevalley.com
  2200 Morris Hill Rd, Chattanooga, TN 37421-2842
  Nancy Toth, Director Of Childrens Division

Helen Ross McNabb Center, Inc. 865.637.9711
Fax 865.637.7180
Web ....www.mcnabbcenter.org
  201 West Springdale Avenue, Knoxville, TN 37917
  CARF accredited programs available.

Hermitage Hall 615.742.3000
Fax 615.250.2388
Web ....www.uhsinc.com
  1220 Eighth Avenue South, Nashville, TN 37203
  CARF accredited programs available.

Johnson Mental Health Ctr 423.756.2740
Fax 423.734.0813
Web ....www.vbhcs.org
E-mail ....twright@vbhcs.org
  420 Bell Ave, Chattanooga, TN 37405-3404
  Larry Thompson, Vice President

Keystone Continuum, LLC dba Mountain Youth Academy 423.727.9898
Fax 423.727.8896
  332 Hospital Road, Mountain City, TN 37683
  CARF accredited programs available.

Keystone Memphis L.L.C. 901.758.2002
Web ....www.compassinterventioncenter.net
E-mail ....mercy.estevez@uhsinc.com
  7900 Lowrance Road, Memphis, TN 38125
  Miss Mercy Estevez, Accreditation Manager
  Joint Commission accredited organization.

Lakeshore Mental Health 865.584.1561
Fax 865.450.5203
E-mail ....richard.e.thomas@state.tn.us
  5908 Lyons View Pike, Knoxville, TN 37919
  Richard Thomas, Superintendent

Lakeside Behavioral Health System, LLC 901.377.4700
Web ....www.lakesidebhs.com
E-mail ....rita.dailey@uhsinc.com
  2911 Brunswick Road, Memphis, TN 38133
  Ms. Rita Dailey, Accreditation Manager
  Joint Commission accredited organization.

Le Bonheur Ctr For Children And Parents 901.287.4700
Fax 901.287.4701
Web ....www.lebonheur.org
  5th Peabody Pl, Memphis, TN 38103
  Sandra Allen, Director

Tennessee

Lloyd C. Elam Mental Health Center **615.327.6609**
Fax 615.321.2951
Web ....www.mmc.edu
E-mail ....andrade@mmc.edu
1005 Dr. D. B. Todd Jr. Boulevard, Nashville,
TN 37208-3599
Amy Andrade, Director of Research
CARF accredited programs available.

Madison Oaks Academy **731.668.5880**
Fax 731.668.5870
Web ....www.amicarebehavioral.com
49 Old Hickory Blvd E, Jackson, TN 38305
Jessica Camarata, Human Resources Manager
CARF accredited programs available.

Mercy Ministries Of America **615.831.6987**
Fax 615.315.9749
Web ....www.mercyministries.com
E-mail ....info@mercyministries.com
15328 Old Hickory Blvd, Nashville, TN 37211-6210
Nancy Alcorn, President

Monroe Harding, Inc. **615.298.5573**
Fax 615.298.1281
Web ....www.monroeharding.org
1120 Glendale Lane, Nashville, TN 37204
COA accredited organization.

Natchez Trace Youth Academy **931.296.1183**
Fax 931.296.7576
Web ....www.natcheztraceyouthacademy.com
415 Seven Hawks Lane, Waverly, TN 37185
CARF accredited programs available.

Oak Plains Academy **931.362.4723**
Fax 931.362.2816
Web ....www.oakplainsacademy.com
1751 Oak Plains Rd, Ashland City, TN 37015
Natashia Slack, Director Of Admissions

Oakdale Home - Tennessee Baptist Children's
Home **423.369.2950**
Fax 423.369.2833
Web www.tbch4kids.org
E-mail ....oakdale@tbch4kids.org
362 Camp Howard Rd, Oakdale, TN 37829
Robert Rogers, Director

Parkridge Medical Center, Inc. **423.493.7978**
Web ....www.parkridgemedicalcenter.com
E-mail ....karen.beam@hcahealthcare.com
2333 McCallie Avenue, Chattanooga, TN 37404
Mrs. Karen Beam, Accreditation Manager
Joint Commission accredited organization.

Parkwest Medical Center **865.373.1000**
Web ....www.covenanthealth.com
E-mail ....msanford@covhlth.com
9352 Park West Boulevard, Knoxville, TN 37923
Ms. Missy Sanford, Accreditation Manager
Joint Commission accredited organization.

Pathways Of Tennessee **731.587.3854**
Fax 731.587.3850
E-mail ....kelly.yenawine@wth.org
457 Hannings Ln, Martin, TN 38237
Kelly Yenawine, Director

Pathways of Tennessee, Inc. **731.541.8200**
Web ....www.wth.net
E-mail ....pam.henson@wth.org
238 Summar Drive, Jackson, TN 38301
Mrs. Pam Henson, Accreditation Manager
Joint Commission accredited organization.

Quinco Community Mental Health Center,
Inc. **731.658.6113**
Fax 731.658.6165
Web ....www.quincomhc.org
E-mail ....darvis.gallaher@quincomhc.org
10710 Old Highway 64, Bolivar, TN 38008
Darvis Gallaher, Executive Director
CARF accredited programs available.

Ridgeview Psychiatric Hospital and Center,
Inc. **865.482.1076**
Web ....www.ridgeviewresources.com
E-mail ....whitenc@ridgevw.com
240 West Tyrone Road, Oak Ridge, TN 37830
Ms. Nancy White, Accreditation Manager
Joint Commission accredited organization.

Sequel Schools, LLC **865.376.2296**
Web ....camelotforkids.org
E-mail ....dgoldstein-higgins@sequelyouthservices.com
183 Fiddlers Lane, Kingston, TN 37763
Ms. Debbie Goldstein-Higgins, Accreditation Manager
Joint Commission accredited organization.

Tennessee Community Health Services,
Inc. **865.397.1038**
Web ....www.tncommunityhealth.com
E-mail ....trolaningle@hotmail.com
878 Hwy 92 South, Dandridge, TN 37725
Mr. T. Bruce Ingle, Accreditation Manager
Joint Commission accredited organization.

The Camelot Schools **865.376.2296**
Fax 865.376.0369
Web ....www.thecamelotschools.com
E-mail ....ryeager@thecamelotschools.com
183 Fiddlers Ln, Kingston, TN 37763-4020
Paul Hickling, C.E.O

The Oak Plains Academy **931.362.4723**
Web ....www.oakplainsacademy.com
E-mail ....karen.johnson@uhsinc.com
1751 Oak Plains Road, Ashland City, TN 37015
Ms. Karen Johnson, Accreditation Manager

The Psychiatric Hospital At Vanderbilt **615.320.7770**
Fax 615.327.7114
Web ....www.vanderbiltchildrens.com
1601 23rd Ave S, Nashville, TN 37202
Tammy Kugler, Director Of Social Services

The Renfrew of Tennessee **215.482.5353**
Web ....www.renfrewcenter.com
E-mail ....hrussock@renfrewcenter.com
1624 Westgate Circle, Ste 100, Brentwood,
TN 37027
Mr. Hayes Russock, Accreditation Manager
Joint Commission accredited organization.

The Transformation Center For Women,
LLC. **901.755.0099**
Web ....transformationmemphis.com
E-mail ....patricialduda@gmail.com
1088 Rogers Road, Cordova, TN 38018
Ms. Patricia Duda, Accreditation Manager
Joint Commission accredited organization.

Varangon Academy **901.531.1950**
E-mail ....jeunewood@varangonacademy.com
3030 Brunswick Road, Bartlett, TN 38133
Mrs. Jeune Wood, Accreditation Manager
Joint Commission accredited organization.

Wayne Halfway House, Inc. **931.722.2455**
Fax 931.722.2465
942 Andrew Jackson Drive, Waynesboro, TN 38485
COA accredited organization.

Woodridge Psychiatric Hospital **423.928.7111**
Fax 423.431.7092
Web ....www.msha.org
403 N State Of Franklin Rd, Johnson City, TN 37601
Denise Vonderxecht, CEO

Youth Town of Tennessee, Inc. **731.988.5251**
Fax 731.427.5605
Web ....www.youthtown.net
3641 Youth Town Road, Pinson, TN 38366
COA accredited organization.

Youth Villages **901.251.5000**
Web ....www.youthvillages.org
E-mail ....hughes.johnson@youthvillages.org
3320 Brother Blvd, Memphis, TN 38133
Mr. Hughes Johnson, Accreditation Manager
Joint Commission accredited organization.

CHILDREN'S HOSPITAL

Athens Regional Medical Center **423.745.1411**
1114 West Madison Ave, Athens, TN 37303
John Workman, Chief Executive Officer

Cookeville Regional Medical Center **931.528.2541**
1 Medical Center Blvd, Cookeville, TN 38501
Menachen Langer, Adminstrator Hospital

Crockett Hospital **931.762.6571**
U S Highway 43 South, Lawrenceburg, TN 38464
Jeff Noblin, Chief Executive Officer

Cumberland Medical Center **931.484.9511**
421 South Main St, Crossville, TN 38555
Barry Wagner, Chief Executive Officer

Dyersburg Regional Medical Center **731.285.2410**
400 Tickle St, Dyersburg, TN 38024
Russell Pigg, Administrator

East Tennessee Childrens Hospital **865.541.8000**
2018 Clinch Ave, Knoxville, TN 37916
Keith Goodwin, Chief Executive Officer

Erlanger Medical Center **423.778.7000**
975 East Third St, Chattanooga, TN 37403

Gateway Medical Center **931.502.1000**
651 Dunlop Lane, Clarksville, TN 37040
Tim Tutoff, Director

General Hosp **731.541.5000**
620 Skyline Dr, Jackson, TN 38301
Bob Arnald, Chief Executive Officer

Holston Valley Medical Center **423.224.4000**
130 West Ravine St, Kingsport, TN 37660

Indian Path Medical Center **423.857.7000**
2000 Brookside Dr, Kingsport, TN 37660
Monty McLaurin, President/CEO

Johnson City Medical Center **423.431.6111**
400 North State of Franklin Rd, Johnson City,
TN 37604
Dennis Vonderfecht, Chief Executive Officer

Lauderdale Community Hospital **731.221.2200**
326 Asbury Ave, Ripley, TN 38063

Laughlin Memorial Hospital **423.787.5000**
1420 Tusculum Blvd, Greeneville, TN 37745
Chuck Whitfield, Chief Executive Officer

Livingston Regional Hospital **931.823.5611**
315 Oak St, Livingston, TN 38570
Mike Meadows, Chief Executive Officer

Maury Regional Medical Hospital **931.381.1111**
1224 Trotwood Ave, Columbia, TN 38401
Robert Otwell, Chief Executive Officer

McKenzie Regional Hospital **731.352.5344**
161 Hospital Dr, McKenzie, TN 38201
Barrell Blaylock, Chief Executive Officer

McNairy Regional Hospital **731.645.3221**
705 East Poplar Ave, Selmer, TN 38375
Pamela Roberts, Chief Executive Officer

Methodist Healthcare **901.516.4000**
E-mail ....janet.hunt@mlh.org
214 Lakeview Dr, Somerville, TN 38068
Janet Hunt, Nursing Director

Northcrest Medical Center **615.384.2411**
100 North Crest Dr, Springfield, TN 37172
Scott Raynes, Chief Executive Officer

Regional Hospital of Jackson **731.661.2000**
367 Hospital Blvd, Jackson, TN 38305
Steve Grubbs, Chief Executive Officer

Riverview Regional Medical Center South 615.735.9815
130 Lebanon Hwy, Carthage, TN 37030
Jimmy Stewart, Administrator

Summit Medical Center 618.316.3000
5655 First Blvd, Hermitage, TN 37076

Sumner Regional Medical Center 615.452.4210
555 Hartsville Pike, Gallatin, TN 37066

Sycamore Shoals Hospital 423.542.1300
1501 West Elk Ave, Elizabethton, TN 37643
Dwayne Taylor, Chief Executive Officer

United Regional Medical Center 931.728.3586
1001 McArthur Dr, Manchester, TN 37355
Beverley McAvee, Director of Nursing

University Medical Center 615.444.8262
1411 Baddour Pkwy, Lebanon, TN 37087
Annley Cokrill, Marketing Director

University of Tennessee Medical Center 865.305.9000
1924 Alcoa Hwy, Knoxville, TN 37920
Joe Lanzsman, Chief Executive Officer

Vanderbilt University Medical Center 615.322.5000
1211 Medical Center Dr, Nashville, TN 37232
Nicholas Veppos, Chancelor

Wellmont Bristol Regional Medical Ctr 423.844.1121
1 Medical Park Blvd, Bristol, TN 37620
Bart Hove, Director

COUNSELING SERVICES

Assoc For Guidance, Aid, Placement And Empathy (AGAPE) 615.781.3000
Fax 615.781.8262
E-mail ....jrister@agapenashville.org
4555 Trousdale Dr, Nashville, TN 37204-4513
Terry Casey, Ph.d., Director Of Counseling Services

Carl Perkins Ctr For Prevention Of Child Abuse (West Tennessee) 731.668.4000
Fax 731.668.4093
Web ....www.carlperkinscenter.org
E-mail ....email@carlperkinscenter.org
213 Cheyenne Dr, Jackson, TN 38305-3494
Pam Nash, Executive Director

Crossroads Integrated Health Services 423.581.5342
Fax 423.581.8650
929 W 1st North St Ste A, Morristown, TN 37814
Karen E. Goins, Lcsw, Director

Exchange Club/Holland J. Stephens Ctr For The Prevention Of Child Abuse 931.823.6432
Fax 931.823.7035
E-mail ....stevencenter@twlakes.net
616 B N Church St, Livingston, TN 38570-1511
Carolyn Isbell, Executive Director

Family And Children's Svcs 615.327.0833
Fax 615.321.3906
Web ....www.fcsnashville.org
E-mail ....michael.mcsurdy@fcsnashville.org
201 23rd Ave N, Nashville, TN 37203-1571
Michael Mcsurdy, President/CEO

Greater Chattanooga Christian Svcs And Children's Home 423.499.9535
Fax 423.499.0335
Web ....www.ourgccs.org
E-mail ....gccs@ourgccs.org
6816 Ty Hi Dr, Chattanooga, TN 37421
Ernie Hedgecorth, Director

Regional Intervention Program 615.963.1177
Fax 615.963.1178
Web ....www.ripnetwork.org
E-mail ....rip@mail.state.tn.us
3411 Belmont Blvd, Nashville, TN 37215-1605
Kate Kanise, Director

Therapeutic Interventions, Inc. 615.467.7502
Fax 615.781.9408
Web ....www.tiicares.com
206 South Jefferson Street, Cookeville, TN 38501
CARF accredited programs available.

Youth Villages 423.522.2200
Fax 423.522.2180
Web ....www.youthvillages.org
E-mail ....megan.hicks@youthvillages.org
225 W 1st North St Ste 302, Morristown, TN 37814-4653
Megan Hicks, Regional Supervisor

Youth Villages 615.441.4170
Fax 615.446.7715
Web ....www.youthvillages.org
E-mail ....carla.bancroft@youthvillages.org
2043 Hwy 70 W Ste 1, Dickson, TN 37055
Carla Bancroft, Supervisor

Youth Villages 931.560.4220
Fax 931.560.4221
Web ....www.youthvillages.org
E-mail ....stephanie.grissom@youthvillages.org
115 Dyer St, Ste 1, Columbia, TN 38401-3237
Stephanie Grissom, Director

Youth Villages 423.954.8890
Fax 423.954.8880
Web ....www.youthvillages.org
E-mail ....kori.bell@youthvillages.org
5741 Cornelison Rd, Chattanooga, TN 37411-5667
Kori Bell, Director

Youth Villages 731.288.4600
Fax 731.288.4650
Web ....www.youthvillages.org
1865 US Highway 51 Byp N, Dyersburg, TN 38024-2872
Carolyn Gibson, Office Manager

CRISIS & SHELTER CARE

Avalon Ctr-Domestic Violence 931.456.0747
Fax 931.787.1057
E-mail ....cwyatt@avaloncentertn.org
100 Woodmere Mall, Ste105, Crossville, TN 38555
Carmen Wyatt, Executive Director

Bridges Of Williamson Co-Dom Violence 615.599.5777
Fax 615.599.1964
E-mail ....info@bridgesdvc.org
PO Box 1592, Franklin, TN 37065-1592
Linda Crockett-jackson, Director

Cap Inc Domestic Violence Program 901.272.2227
Fax 901.261.7555
Web ....www.caapincorporated.com
4023 Knight Arnold Rd, Memphis, TN 38118-2128
Greta Webber, Director

Cease Domestic Violence and Sexual Assault 423.581.7029
Fax 423.586.0692
E-mail ....cease@musfiber.com
135 E Louise Ave, Morristown, TN 37815
Paula Billingsley, Director

Change Is Possible-Domestic Violence 423.743.0022
Fax 423.745.0023
Web ....www.mounet.com
E-mail ....chipsfvs@embarqmail.com
217 S Main Ave, Erwin, TN 37650-1141
Carolyn Mcamis, Director

Crisis Ctr (Admin) 901.276.1111
Fax 901.726.9505
PO Box 40068, Memphis, TN 38174-0068
Mike Labonte, Director

Crisis Prevention Resource Svc-Dom VInce 423.755.2840
Fax 423.755.2897
E-mail ....rmiller@partnershipfca.org
310 East 8th St, Chattanooga, TN 37403
Rosemary Miller, Director

Ctr Against Domestic Violence 931.840.0916
Fax 931.490.3678
E-mail ....hopehouse@hopehousetn.com
2441 parkplus dr, Columbia, TN 38401
Angela Slack, Director

Damascas Road-Domestic Violence 731.336.8724
Fax 731.642.6542
E-mail ....mariannusp@yahoo.com
910 Curtis St, Paris, TN 38242-3948
Marian Paschall, Director

Families In Crisis Inc-Domestic Violence 931.473.6543
Fax 931.474.6221
PO Box 621, Mc Minnville, TN 37111-0621
Carrie Kirby, Director

Family Crisis Ctr-Domestic Violence 865.637.8000
Web ....www.child-family.org
901 E Summit Hill Dr, Knoxville, TN 37915
Elishia Jones, Director

Gracemoor Inc-Domestic Violence Program 931.738.9233
Fax 931.738.9208
E-mail ....carolyn@cheekinsurance.com
120 W Rhea St, Sparta, TN 38583
Carolyn Cheek, Director

Haven House Domestic Violence Svcs 865.983.6818
Fax 865.983.9177
Web ....www.havenhousetn.org
101 W Broadway Ste 209, Maryville, TN 37801
Jim Worneicki, Executive Director

Haven Of Hope-Domestic Violence Program 931.728.4235
Fax 931.728.0083
PO Box 1271, Manchester, TN 37349-1271
Mona Mason, Director

Homesafe In Robertson Co 615.384.8826
E-mail ....rcadvocate@bellsouth.net
PO Box 362, Springfield, TN 37172-0362
Sandra Uhles, Director

Hope Ctr-Domestic Violence Program 423.744.0599
Fax 423.744.8284
704 W Madison Ave, Athens, TN 37303
Teresa Grant, Director

House Of Hope-Domestic Violence 423.562.8325
Fax 423.562.3645
Web ....www.communityhealthoftn.com
E-mail ....rbrandenburg@chetn.org
PO Box 209, Jacksboro, TN 37757-0209
Rebecca Brandenburg, Director

Journey Ctr-Womens Support-Domestic Violence 901.466.0015
Fax 901.465.3802
PO Box 326, Somerville, TN 38068-0326
Alexandra Wardlaw, Director

Knoxville Area Rescue Ministry-Dom VInce 865.673.6551
Fax 865.673.6556
Web ....www.karm.org
E-mail ....brosen@karm.org
418 N Broadway St, Knoxville, TN 37917-7401
Burt Rosen, Director

Mary Parrish Ctr-Domestic Violence 615.256.5959
Fax 615.256.5909
E-mail ....info@maryparrish.org
131 2nd Ave. N. Ste. 500., Nashville, TN 37201
Valerie Wynn, Director

McDowell Ctr For Children 731.286.2861
Fax 731.286.2866
Web ....www.uhsinc.com
711 Highway 51 Bypass S, Dyersburg, TN 38024
Denise Lester, Clinical Director

Tennessee

Monroe Harding Children's Home 615.298.5573
Fax 615.298.1281
Web .... www.monroeharding.org
E-mail .... pattyharman@monroeharding.org
1120 Glendale Ln, Nashville, TN 37204
Mary Baker, President

Morning Star Sanctuary-Domestic Violence 615.860.0003
Fax 615.868.2241
E-mail .... angela.pearson@msdvp.org
PO Box 568, Madison, TN 37116-0568
Angela Pearson, Program Manager

Murfreesboro Domestic Violence Program 615.896.2032
Fax 615.896.1628
E-mail .... Shelter2@Bellsouth.Net
826 Memorial Blvd Ste 205, Murfeesboro, TN 37130
Deborah Johnson, Director

NW TN Economic Development Council 731.364.3228
Fax 731.364.5163
231 S Wilson St, Dresden, TN 38225
Don Ridgeway, Ex Director

Safe Passage Inc-Domestic Violence 423.232.8920
Fax 423.232.0392
Web .... www.tcadsv.org
E-mail .... jarmstrong@tcadsv.org
2203 Mckenly rd ste 210, Johnson City, TN 37604
Jondalyn Armstrong, Director

Safespace-Domestic Violence 865.453.9254
Fax 865.429.5174
E-mail .... safespace00@msn.com
636 Middle Creek Rd, Ste 3, Sevierville, TN 37862
Van Helton, Director

Salvation Army-Joy Baker Womens Shelter 865.522.4673
Fax 865.524.7748
409 N Broadway St, Knoxville, TN 37917
Marylou Hammer, Director

Tennessee Baptist Children's Home 901.386.3961
Fax 901.382.9754
Web www.tbch4kids.org
6896 Hwy 70, Memphis, TN 38133
Darren Andrus, Programme Director

The Shelter Inc-Domestic Violence 931.762.1115
Fax 931.762.8208
E-mail .... theshelter@alburd.org
PO Box 769, Lawrenceburg, TN 38464-0769
Alice Quillen, Director

Village 865.970.3255
Fax 865.970.6334
Web .... www.acadiavillage.com
2431 Jones Bend Rd, Louisville, TN 37777-5212
Mike Ham, Chief Executive Officer

Women Are Safe Inc-Domestic Violence 931.729.9885
Fax 931.729.0556
E-mail .... wastn@bellsouth.net
131 West Ave, Centerville, TN 37033
Vanessa Davis, Director

Womens Resource-Rape Assistance Prog 731.668.0411
Fax 731.668.0006
Web .... www.wraptn.org
E-mail .... mcole@wrapwesttn.org
62 Directors Row, Jackson, TN 38305-2345
Margaret Cole, Director

EDUCATION

Genesis Learning Ctrs 615.832.4222
Fax 615.832.4577
Web .... www.genesislearn.org
E-mail .... tadams@genesislearn.org
430 Allied Dr, Nashville, TN 37211-3304
Terence Adams, Director

Jacobs Creek Job Corps 423.878.4021
Fax 423.878.7034
984 Denton Valley Rd, Bristol, TN 37620
Walter West, Center Director

Link House 423.288.1828
Fax 423.288.1809
433 New Beason Well Rd, Kingsport, TN 37660
Sherri Feathers, Director

Memphis Job Corps Ctr 901.396.2800
Fax 901.396.8712
Web .... www.jobcorps.org
1555 Mcalister Dr, Memphis, TN 38116-9058
James Harris, Phd, Center Director

Siskin Childrens Home 423.648.1700
Fax 423.648.1780
Web .... www.siskin.org
E-mail .... amy.willard@siskin.org
1101 Carter St, Chattanooga, TN 37402-5017
Amy Willard, Supervisor Of Programs

Susan Gray School for Children 615.322.8200
Fax 615.322.8201
E-mail .... ruth.wolery@vanderbilt.edu
66 Peabody St, Nashville, TN 37240
Ruth Worely, Phd, Director

Tennessee Early Intervention System (Teis) 865.579.3096
Fax 865.579.5033
Web .... www.state.tn.us
E-mail .... patricia.cooper@state.tn.us
2726 Island Home Blvd, Knoxville, TN 37920-2771
Pat Cooper, Director

FOSTER CARE AGENCIES

Agape Child and Family Services 901.323.3600
111 Racine St, Memphis, TN 38111
Nichole Love, Office Manager

Catholic Charities Middle Tennessee Inc 615.352.3087
Fax 615.352.8591
E-mail .... dthomas@cctenn.org
30 White Bridge Rd, Nashville, TN 37205

Child and Family Tennessee 865.524.7483
E-mail .... dhoxworth@child-family.org
901 East Summit Hill Dr, Knoxville, TN 37915
Dan Hoxworth, Chief Executive Officer

Childhelp USA Tennessee 865.573.9943
608 Old Brookhaven Farm Rd, Seymour, TN 37865-3106
Stephanie Perdue, Director

Family and Childrens Services 615.253.3289
Fax 615.253.3326
1210 Foster Ave, Nashville, TN 37243

Foster Adoptive Care Assoc 423.727.4925
399 Mill Creek Rd, Mountain City, TN 37683
John Maze, President

Frontier Health 423.224.1067
Fax 423.224.1095
E-mail .... vbarger@frontierhealth.org
2001 Stonebrook Pl, Kingsport, TN 37660

Goodwill Homes Community Services, Inc. 901.785.6790
Fax 901.789.8351
4590 Goodwill Road, Memphis, TN 38109
CARF accredited programs available.

Heaven Sent Children Inc 615.898.0803
E-mail .... steve.heavensentchildren.com
307 North Walnut St, Murfreesboro, TN 37130
Linda Sutton, Office Manager

Magnolia Academy 931.359.3592
Fax 931.359.3599
120 Freeman Drive, Lewisburg, TN 37091
CARF accredited programs available.

Miriams Promise 615.292.3500
Fax 615.292.0368
E-mail .... info@miriamspromise.org
522 Russell St, Nashville, TN 37206
Debby Robinson, Director

Moms Alive 615.831.9208
E-mail .... momsalive@yahoo.com
PO Box 148055, Nashville, TN 37214

National Center For Children & Family 202.543.3217
E-mail .... pfrye@harmony.cc
131 Cherokee Heights Dr, Maryville, TN 37801
Shannon Catanzaro, Regional Manager

New Vision Fellowship dba Patria Center 865.588.0440
Fax 865.584.6613
Web .... www.patriafostercare.org
3343 Dewine Road, Knoxville, TN 37921
COA accredited organization.

North American Cncl Adoptable Children 615.804.5209
E-mail .... marshaboren@charter.net
2293 Clara Mathis Rd, Spring Hill, TN 37174

Tennessee Foster Care Assoc 615.355.1731
147 Jones Mill Rd, La Vergne, TN 37086
Nancy Woodall-Holmes

HOME MEDICAL EQUIPMENT PROVIDERS

Apria Healthcare Memphis 901.368.1200
E-mail .... patient_satisfaction@apria.com
4740 E Shelby Dr 104, Memphis, TN 38118

French's Medical Supplies 901.357.0932
Fax 901.357.0868
3096 Castlebay Road, Memphis, TN 38128
CARF accredited programs available.

Meridian Medical 877.909.2266
3911 Schaad Rd, Knoxville, TN 37921

National Seating & Mobility Memphis 901.362.9880
Fax 901.362.6734
E-mail .... nsm48@nsm-seating.com
3930 S Perkins Road, Memphis, TN 38118

Snells Limbs and Braces 901.725.7048
Fax 901.725.7001
7 N Bellevue Blvd, Memphis, TN 38104
Gwean Nershoen, Manager

PEDIATRIC HOME CARE

Interim Healthcare 423.928.8771
Fax 423.928.8770
2102 Forrest Dr Ste 4, Johnson City, TN 37615

Interim Healthcare 423.587.8771
Fax 423.587.8773
2482 Brights Pike, Morristown, TN 37814
Debbie Mosley, Director Of Nursing

SOCIAL SERVICES

Agape Child & Family Services, Inc. 901.323.3600
Fax 901.323.3640
Web .... www.agapemeanslove.org
P.O. Box 11411, Memphis, TN 38111
COA accredited organization.

Black Children's Institute 615.366.5530
Fax 615.360.7843
Web .... www.bcitn.org
E-mail .... bci@bcitn.org
301 Starboard Ct, Nashville, TN 37217-4249
Juanita Veasy, Director

Bridges Inc. 901.452.5600
Fax 901.320.1004
Web .... www.bridgesusa.org
E-mail .... jboyd@bridgesusa.org
477 N 5th St, Memphis, TN 38105-1869
Rev. James Boyd, President

Camelot Care Centers, Inc. **615.370.4228**
Fax 615.370.4959
Web .... www.provcorp.com
　215 Centerview Drive, Suite 300, Brentwood,
　TN 37027
　COA accredited organization.

Caring Choices **931.645.9969**
Fax 931.648.4479
Web .... www.cctenn.org
E-mail .... dthomas@cctenn.org
　1905 Madison St, Clarksville, TN 37043-5001
　Donna Thomas, Director

Chance, Cumberland Mountain School-Youth Impact & Indian Mound Residential Treatment Centers **931.528.1127**
Fax 931.372.0519
　580 south Jefferson, Suite B, Cookeville, TN 38501
　COA accredited organization.

Child Care Resource And Referral **615.277.1649**
Fax 615.277.1648
Web .... www.penstate.edu/learningsciences
E-mail .... kyoder@coe.tsuniv.edu
　3500 John A Merritt Blvd, # 9500, Nashville,
　TN 37209
　Dr Rick Vanosdall, Executive Director

Children's Bureau dba Porter-Leath **901.577.2500**
Web .... www.porterleath.org
　868 North Manassas Street, Memphis, TN 38107
　COA accredited organization.

Crisis Intervention Ctr **615.269.4357**
Fax 615.320.1273
Web .... www.crisisinterventioncenter.org
E-mail .... crisiscenterinfo@fcsnashville.org
　201 23rd Ave N, Nashville, TN 37201
　Lacrecia Dangerfield, Manager

Exchange Club Family Ctr **615.333.2644**
Fax 615.333.0822
　139 Thompson Ln, Nashville, TN 37211
　Dawn Eaton, Director

Family and Children's Service **615.320.0591**
　201 23rd Avenue North, Nashville, TN 37203
　COA accredited organization.

Florence Crittenton Agency **865.602.2021**
Fax 865.602.2039
Web .... www.fcaknox.org
E-mail .... nchristian@fcaknox.org
　1531 Dick Lonas Rd Bldg C, Knoxville,
　TN 37909-1259
　Nancy Christian, Executive Director

Jewish Community Federation Greater Chattanooga **423.493.0270**
Fax 423.493.9997
　5461 North Terrace Rd, Chattanooga, TN 37411
　Michael Dzik, Director

Jewish Family Service Nashville & Middle TN **615.354.1662**
Fax 615.301.0676
E-mail .... teri@jfsnashville.org
　801 Percy Warner Blvd, Nashville, TN 37205
　Teri Sogol

Jewish Family Services **865.690.6343**
Fax 865.694.4861
E-mail .... lberry@jewishknoxville.org
　6800 Deane Hill dr, Knoxville, TN 37919
　Laura Faye Berry, Director

Jewish Family Svcs **901.767.8511**
Fax 901.763.2348
Web .... www.jfsmemphis.org
　6560 Poplar Ave, Memphis, TN 38138
　Robert Silver, Director

Kiwanis Ctr For Child Development **731.668.9070**
Fax 731.668.6549
Web .... www.wth.org
E-mail .... ron.kwasigroh@wth.org
　32 Garland Dr, Jackson, TN 38305-3699
　Ron Kwasigroh, Mba, Director

Life Choices, Inc Admin Ofc **901.388.6262**
Fax 901.388.1225
Web .... www.pregnantwanthelp.com
E-mail .... lchoices@bellsouth.net
　5575 Raleigh Lagrange Rd, Memphis,
　TN 38134-5724
　Sue Parker, CEO

Mountain View Youth Development Ctr **865.397.0174**
Fax 865.397.0738
Web .... www.state.tn.us
　809 Peal Ln, Dandridge, TN 37725-4707
　Bill Ellis, Superintendent

My Friend's House Family and Children Services, Inc. **615.790.8553**
Fax 615.790.6377
Web .... www.myfriendshousetn.org
　626 Eastview Circle, Franklin, TN 37064
　COA accredited organization.

Oasis Ctr **615.327.4455**
Fax 615.329.1444
Web .... www.oasiscenter.org
E-mail .... hcato@oasiscenter.org
　1704 Charlotte Pike Dte 200, Nashville, TN 37203
　Hal Cato, Director

Omni Visions, Inc. **615.726.3603**
Fax 615.242.4140
Web .... www.omnivisions.com
　301 S. Perimeter Park Drive, Suite 210, Nashville,
　TN 37211
　COA accredited organization.

Porter-Leath Children's Ctr **901.577.2500**
Fax 901.577.2506
Web .... www.porter-leath.org
E-mail .... porterleath@porter-leath.org
　868 N Manassas St, Memphis, TN 38107
　Sean Lee, Executive Director

Prevent Child Abuse Of Tennessee **615.383.0994**
Fax 615.383.6089
E-mail .... carla.snodgrass@pcat.org
　4751 Trousdale Dr., Suite 201, Nashville, TN 37220
　Carla Snodgrass, Executive Director

Residential Services, Inc. **615.367.4333**
Fax 615.360.3894
Web .... www.rsifostercare.org
　1120 Glendale Lane, Nashville, TN 37204-4113
　COA accredited organization.

Smoky Mountain Children's Home **865.453.4644**
Fax 865.453.8812
　449 Mccarn Cir, Sevierville, TN 37864
　John Sweet, Director

Taft Youth Development Ctr **423.881.3201**
Fax 423.881.4617
Web .... www.state.tn.us
　900 Sr 301, Pikeville, TN 37367-7406
　Bob Bowen, Superintendent

Tennessee Children's Home, Inc. **931.486.2274**
Fax 931.486.1231
Web .... www.tennesseechildrenshome.org
　PO Box 10, Spring Hill, TN 37174
　COA accredited organization.

The Exchange Club Family Ctr **901.276.2200**
Fax 901.276.6828
Web .... www.exchangeclub.net
E-mail .... barbara.king@exchangeclub.net
　2180 Union Ave, Memphis, TN 38104-4205
　Barbara C. King, Executive Director

The Exchange Club Family Ctr **615.890.4673**
Fax 615.890.6599
Web .... www.familycentertn.org
E-mail .... jtuster@familycentertn.org
　115 Heritage Park Dr, Murfreesboro, TN 37129-0529
　Jeff Tuster, Program Director

The Florence Crittenton Agency, Inc. **865.602.2021**
Fax 865.602.2039
Web .... www.fcaknox.org
　1531 Dick Lonas Road, Knoxville, TN 37909-1218
　COA accredited organization.

The King's Daughters' School **931.388.3810**
Fax 931.388.0405
Web .... www.tkds.org
　412 W. 9th Street, Columbia, TN 38401
　COA accredited organization.

The Law Office of Mary Ward **865.671.4480**
Fax ....
Web ....
E-mail .... maryward@tds.net
　PO Box 23382, Knoxville, TN 37933
　Mary Ward, attorney

The Partnership for Families, Children and Adults **423.755.2822**
Fax 423.697.7130
Web .... www.partnershipfca.com
　1800 McCallie Avenue, Chattanooga, TN 37404
　COA accredited organization.

Waves Early Intervention Program **615.794.7955**
Fax 615.791.9179
E-mail .... moreinfo@wavesinc.com
　435 Main St Ste A, Franklin, TN 37064-2757
　Susan Vanhorn, Bs, Program Coordinator

SPECIAL NEEDS

Autism Society Middle Tennessee **615.385.2077**
　955 Woodland St, Nashville, TN 37206

Bachman Academy **423.479.4523**
Fax 423.472.2718
Web .... www.bachmanacademy.org
　414 Brymer Creek Rd, McDonald, TN 37353
　Barbara Faris, Director

Baptist Rehabilitation - Germantown **901.757.1350**
Fax 901.757.3496
Web .... www.baptistonline.org
　2100 Exeter Road, Germantown, TN 38138
　CARF accredited programs available.

Boling Center for Dvlpmntl Disabilities **901.448.6511**
Fax 901.448.7097
E-mail .... ebishop@uthsc.edu
　711 Jefferson Ave, Memphis, TN 38105
　Elizabeth Bishop, Coordinator Of Clinical Services

CARE Porject **423.622.4007**
E-mail .... lifelineministry@juno.com
　1609 McCallie Ave, Chattanooga, TN 37404
　Lisa Mattheiss, Executive Director

Congress of Parents & Teachers Inc **615.383.9740**
E-mail .... ppastateof@tnpta.org
　1905 Acklen Ave, Nashville, TN 37212
　Donald Raegon, Administrator

Easter Seals Tennessee **800.264.0078**
　2001 Woodmont Blvd, Nashville, TN 37215

Epilepsy Foundation **800.244.0768**
E-mail .... jwhitmer@epilepsytn.org
　2002 Richard Jones Rd, Ste C-202, Nashville,
　TN 37215
　Joyce Whitmer, Executive Director

Tennessee

Happy Haven Children's Home..............931.526.2052
Fax..931.372.8837
E-mail.............................happyhaven@frontiernet.net
　2311 Wakefield Dr, Cookeville, TN 38501-8084
Houston Bynum, Director

High Hopes...615.661.5437
Fax..615.309.8342
Web..www.highhopesnash.org
E-mail.............................gpowell@highhopesnash.org
　1647 Mallory Lane, Suite 103, Brentwood,
　TN 37027-2927
Gail Powell, Executive Director

**James H. and Cecile C. Quillen Rehabilitation
Hospital**..423.952.1700
Fax..423.952.1710
Web...www.msha.com
　2511 Wesley Street, Johnson City, TN 37601
CARF accredited programs available.

LearningRx Learning Center.................615.867.8717
E-mail...................murfreesboro.tn@learningrx.net
　2615 Medical Center Pkwy, Ste 1584, Murfreesboro,
　TN 37129

Lindamood-Bell Learning Processes.........901.767.2605
Fax..901.767.2608
　699 Oakleaf Office Ln, Ste 200, Memphis, TN 38117
Aisha Exford, Director

MDA/ALS Center of Memphis Mid-South......901.725.8920
Fax..901.725.9436
E-mail...tbertorini@aol.com
　8095 Club Pkwy, Cordova, TN 38016
Tulio Bertorini Md, Director

Mental Health Association...................615.269.5355
E-mail..forinfo@mhamt.org
　295 Tous Prk Blvd, Ste 201, Nashville, TN 37217
Tom Starling, Chief Executive Officer

Mercy Medical Center Rehab Care Center......865.545.6727
Fax..865.545.8133
Web...www.mercy.com
　900 East Oak Hill Avenue, Knoxville, TN 37917-4556
CARF accredited programs available.

Meritan, Inc........................................901.766.0600
Fax..901.766.0688
Web..www.meritan.org
　4700 Poplar Avenue, Memphis, TN 38117
COA accredited organization.

NAMI Tennessee.................................615.361.6608
E-mail..jstewart@namitn.org
　1101 Kermit Dr Ste 605, Nashville, TN 37217
Jack Stewart, Executive Director

National Multiple Sclerosis Society..........615.269.9055
Fax..615.269.9470
E-mail..TNS@NMSS.ORG
　4219 Hillsboro Rd Ste 306, Nashville, TN 37215

Patricia Neal Rehabilitation Center..........865.541.3600
Fax..865.541.2352
Web...www.patneal.org
　1901 Clinch Avenue, Knoxville, TN 37916
CARF accredited programs available.

Siskin Hospital for Physical Rehabilitation.....423.634.1200
Fax..423.634.1209
Web...www.siskinrehab.org
　One Siskin Plaza, Chattanooga, TN 37403
Dr Gazid Bowers, Medako Director
CARF accredited programs available.

St. Mary's Rehab Care Center..................865.545.6734
Fax..865.545.8133
Web..www.stmaryshealth.com
　900 East Oak Hill Avenue, Knoxville, TN 37917-4556
CARF accredited programs available.

Support & Traning For Excep Parents Inc.......423.639.0125
Fax..423.636.8217
E-mail.................................information@tnstep.org
　712 Professoinal Plz, Greeneville, TN 37745
Kiren Harrison, Director

Tennessee Disability Coalition..............615.383.9442
Fax..615.292.7790
E-mail................................coalition@tndisability.org
　955 Woodland St, Nashville, TN 37206

Tennessee Respite Network..................800.670.9882
E-mail..tvc@tnvoices.org
　701 Bradford Ave, Nashville, TN 37204
Charlotte Bryson, Executive Director

Tennessee Voices for Children...............615.269.7751
E-mail..tvc@tnvoices.org
　701 Bradford Ave, Nashville, TN 37204
Charlotte Bryson, Executive Director

The Arc of Tennessee.........................800.835.7077
E-mail..................................wrogers@thearctn.org
　151 Athens Way Ste 100, Nashville, TN 37228
Carrie Guiden, Executive Director

The Rehabilitation Hospital of Memphis.......901.545.6060
Fax..901.545.8926
Web...www.the-med.org
　842 Jefferson Avenue, Memphis, TN 38103
CARF accredited programs available.

The STAR Center...............................731.668.3888
Fax..731.668.1666
E-mail................................infostar@starcenter.tn.org
　1119 Old Humboldt Rd, Jackson, TN 38305
John Borden, Director

UCP of the Mid South Inc......................901.761.4277
E-mail...................................pfryer@ucpmemphis.org
　4189 Leroy Ave, Memphis, TN 38108
Peggy Fryer, President

Vanderbilt Kennedy Ctr for Excellence........615.322.8529
E-mail........................tnpathfinder@vanderbilt.edu
　1211 21se Ave S ste 539, Nashville, TN 37212
Carole Moore-Slater, Program Director

Vanderbilt University Medical Center........615.936.0060
Fax..615.936.1263
E-mail...................peter.d.donofrio@vanderbilt.edu
　1161 21nd Ave S, rm #A0118 mcn, Nashville,
　TN 37232-2551
Peter D Donofrio Md, Director

West Tennessee Rehabilitation Center........731.541.6930
Fax..731.541.6218
Web...www.wth.org
　620 Skyline Dr, Jackson, TN 38301
John Yarbrough, Director
CARF accredited programs available.

SUBSTANCE ABUSE TREATMENT

Bethlehem Ctrs Of Nashville.................615.329.3386
Fax..615.329.0261
E-mail....................mmckinney@bethlehemcentres.org
　1417 Charlotte Ave, Nashville, TN 37203-3413
Mary McKinney, CEO

Bradford Health Svcs.........................615.595.1028
Fax..615.595.8842
Web..www.bradfordhealth.org
E-mail...........................cwoods@bradfordhealth.net
　1897 General George Patton Dr Ste 116, Franklin,
　TN 37067-6319
Connie Woods, Director

**Cocaine and Alcohol Awareness Program,
Inc.**...901.360.0442
Fax..901.360.0865
Web..www.caapincorporated.com
E-mail...............................caapinc@bellsouth.net
　4023 Knight Arnold Rd, Memphis, TN 38118
CARF accredited programs available.

Cumberland Heights...........................615.352.1757
Fax..615.353.4325
Web.......................................www.cumberlandheights.org
E-mail...................jim_moore@cumberlandheights.org
　8283 River Road Pike, Nashville, TN 37209-6009
Jim Moore, Director

Texas

Rick Perry, Governor
Office of the Governor
PO Box 12428
Austin, TX 78711-2428
512.463.2000
512.463.1849 (Fax)
www.governor.state.tx.us

Ryan Clinton, Juvenile Justice Specialist
1100 San Jacinto Blvd
Austin, TX 78701-1935
512.463.1916
512.475.2440 (Fax)
ryan.clinton@governor.state.tx.us

Chief Charles Brawner, SAG Chair
901 Yorkchester Dr
Houston, TX 77079
713.365.5938
713.365.5600 (Fax)
brawnerc@springbranchisd.com

CRISIS NUMBERS

Child Abuse Reporting . . .800.252.5400

STATE SERVICES

SOCIAL SERVICES

Child Care Licensing Texas **512.438.3269**
Fax 512.339.5872
   701 W51 St, Mail Code E 550, Austin, TX 78751
Michele Adams, Acting Assistant Commisioner

Coalition of Texans With Disabilities **512.478.3366**
Fax 512.478.3370
Web . . . . .www.cotwd.org
E-mail . . . . .dborel@cotwd.org
   316 W 12th St Ste 405, Austin, TX 78701-1845
Dennis Borel, Executive Director

Texas Dept of Family & Protective Svcs **512.438.4800**
Fax 512.339.5927
Web . . . . .www.dfps.state.tx.us
E-mail . . . . .gina.gelnet@dfps.state.tx.us
   701 W 51st St, Austin, TX 78751
Gina Gelnet, Director

Texas Health and Human Svcs Commission **512.438.3011**
Fax 512.438.4220
Web . . . . .www.dads.state.tx.us
   701 W 51st St, Austin, TX 78751-2312
Chris Traylor, Commissioner

GENERAL HEALTH SERVICES

Dept of State Health Svcs **866.378.8440**
Fax 512.206.5704
Web . . . . .www.dshs.state.tx.us
E-mail . . . . .kenny.dudley@dshs.state.tx.us
   909 W 45th St, Austin, TX 78751-2803
Kenny Dudley, Director

Dept. of State Health Services **254.435.6331**
Fax 254.435.6902
E-mail . . . . .martha.payne@dshs.state.tx.us
   409 South Hill, Meridian, TX 76665-4631
Martha Payne, Public Health Nurse

Maternal and Child Health Texas **512.458.7321**
Fax 512.458.7538
E-mail . . . . .sam.cooper@dshs.state.tx.us
   11 West 49 st, Austin, TX 78756
Sam Cooper, Director

Ofc of Medicaid **512.491.1867**
Fax 512.491.1977
Web . . . . .www.hhsc.state.tx.us
E-mail . . . . .billy.millwee@hhsc.state.tx.us
   11209 Metric Blvd Ste H, Austin, TX 78758-4183
Billy Millwee, State Medicaid Director

Texas Dept of State Health Svcs- Children with Special Health Care Needs **512.458.7111**
Fax 512.458.7417
Web . . . . .www.dshs.state.tx.us/cshcn/
E-mail . . . . .lesa.walker@dshs.state.tx.us
   1100 W 49th St, Ste 442, Austin, TX 78756
Lesa Walker, Director

MENTAL HEALTH SERVICES

Dept of Asst & Rehab Svcs TX **512.424.4220**
Fax 512.424.4277
E-mail . . . . .jim.hanophy@dars.state.tx.us
   4900 N Lamar Blvd, MC 3059, Austin, TX 78751
Jim Hanophy, Director

State Board of Examiners of Psychologists **512.305.7700**
Fax 512.305.7701
Web . . . . .www.tsbep.state.tx.us
E-mail . . . . .sherry.lee@tsbep.state.tx.us
   333 Guadalupe St, Ste 2-450, Austin, TX 78701-3942
Sherry Lee, Director

JUSTICE AGENCY

Attorney General's Ofc **512.463.2100**
Fax 512.475.2994
Web . . . . .www.oag.state.tx.us
   300 W 15th St, Austin, TX 78701
Greg Abbott, Attorney General

Correctional Education Division TX **936.291.5307**
Fax 936.436.4031
E-mail . . . . .bambi.kiser@wsdtx.org
   804 Bldg B FM 2821 W, Huntsville, TX 77342
Bambi Kiser, Director

Texas CASA **512.473.2627**
Fax 512.473.8271
Web . . . . .www.texascasa.org
E-mail . . . . .jgagen@texascasa.org
   1501 W Anderson Ln, Suite B-2, Austin, TX 78757
Joe Gagen, Chief Executive Officer

Texas Juvenile Probation Commission **512.424.6700**
Fax 512.424.6717
E-mail . . . . .vicki.spriggs@tjpc.state.tx.us
   4900 N Lamar Blvd, 5th Fl, Austin, TX 78751
Vicki Spriggs, Executive Director

Texas Youth Commission **512.424.6500**
Fax 512.424.6010
Web . . . . .www.tyc.state.tx.us
E-mail . . . . .dimitria.pope@tyc.state.tx.us
   4900 N Lamar Blvd, Austin, TX 78751
Dimitria D. Pope, Acting Executive Director

COURTS

Centex Child Protection Court **254.933.5386**
Fax 254.933.5926
E-mail . . . . .judgecvo@justice.com
   104 South Main, Belton, TX 76513-3226
Rosie Craft, Court Administrator

State Ofc of Court Administration **512.463.1625**
Fax 512.463.1648
E-mail . . . . .carl.reynolds@txcourts.gov
   205 W 14th St Ste 600 Tom C. Clark Bldg, Austin, TX 78711
Carl Reynolds, Adminstrative Director

POLICE AND SHERIFF

Sheriff's Ofc **512.445.5888**
Fax 512.445.0228
Web . . . . .www.txsheriffs.org
E-mail . . . . .info@txsheriffs.org
   1601 S Interstate 35, Austin, TX 78741
Steve Westbrook, Executive Director

Sheriff's Office **903.590.2661**
Fax 903.590.2659
E-mail . . . . .jbsmith@smith-county.com
   227 N Spring Ave, Tyler, TX 75710
Tony Dana, Lieutenant / Criminal Investigations

Texas Police Chiefs Assoc **512.281.5400**
Fax 512.281.2240
Web . . . . .www.texaspolicechiefs.org
E-mail . . . . .jmclaughlin@texaspolicechiefs.org
   1312 East Hwy 290, Ste C, Elgin, TX 78621
James Mcalughin, Executive Director

EDUCATION SERVICES

Division of IDEA Coordinator TX **512.463.9414**
Fax 512.463.9560
E-mail . . . . .kathy.clayton@tea.state.tx.us
   1701 N Congress Ave, Austin, TX 78701
Kathy Clayton, Director

Texas Education Agency **512.463.8200**
Fax 512.463.6589
E-mail . . . . .teainfo@tea.state.tx.us
   1701 N Congress Ave, William B Travis Bldg, Austin, TX 78701
Harvester Pope, Director

Texas Homeless Education Office **512.475.8765**
Fax 512.471.6193
E-mail . . . . .babawawa@austin.utexas.edu
   1616 Guabalupe 3 Point 206, Austin, TX 78701
Barbara James, Project Director

Texas

Texas School for the Blind & Visually
Impaired 512.454.8631
Fax 512.206.9450
Web ....www.tsbvi.edu
E-mail ....billdaugherty@tsbl.tsbvi.edu
1100 W 45th St, Austin, TX 78756-3494

Willian Daugherty, Superintendent

Texas School for the Deaf - South Campus 512.462.5353
Fax 512.462.5313
Web ....www.tsd.state.tx.us
E-mail ....claire.bugen@tsd.state.tx.us
1102 S Congress Ave, Austin, TX 78704-1791
Diana Poeppelmeyer, Director Of Outreach

LABOR & WORKFORCE EDUCATION

Texas Workforce Commission 512.463.0735
Fax 512.463.1426
101 E 15th St Rm 608, Austin, TX 78778
Larry Temple, Executive Director

COUNTY SERVICES

Anderson County

SOCIAL SERVICES

Family and Protective Svcs 903.729.0174
Fax 817.276.3979
330 E Spring St, Palestine, TX 75801-2366
Elza Daviss, CPS Supervisor

Texas Health and Human Svcs
Commission 903.723.1905
Fax 903.723.1169
E-mail ....hhsc@state.tx.us
330 E Spring St Ste D, Palestine, TX 75801
Lisa Mass, Supervisor

GENERAL HEALTH SERVICES

Texas Dept of State Health
Services 903.729.1116
Fax 903.729.7034
Web ....www.dshs.state.tx.us
E-mail ....paul.mcgaha@dshs.state.tx.us
100 W Brazos St Ste B, Palestine, TX 75801-5095
Paul Mcgaha, Do, Regional Director

JUSTICE AGENCY

Juvenile Svcs 903.731.8201
Fax 903.729.0290
Web ....www.co.anderson.tx.us
E-mail ....acjchief@goquest.com
1120 E Crawford St, Palestine, TX 75801-3103
Emily Lane, Chief JPO

COURTS

District Court 903.723.7415
Fax 903.723.7803
Web ....www.co.anderson.tx.us
E-mail ....bwbently@hotmail.com
500 N Church St Rm 30, Palestine, TX 75801-2916
Honorable B.w. Bently, Director

POLICE AND SHERIFF

Sheriff's Ofc 903.729.6068
Fax 903.729.3022
Web ....www.co.anderson.tx.us
E-mail ....gtaylor@co.anderson.tx.us
1200 E Lacy St, Palestine, TX 75801-4851
Greg Taylor, Sheriff

Andrews County

SOCIAL SERVICES

Family and Protective Svcs 432.524.4111
Fax 432.684.2970
Web ....www.dfps.state.tx.us
E-mail ....bit.whitaker@dfps.state.tx.us
801 N Main St Ste P, Andrews, TX 79714-6318
Bit Whitaker, Director

GENERAL HEALTH SERVICES

Health Dept 432.524.1434
Fax 432.524.1461
208 NW 2nd St, Andrews, TX 79714-6308
Robert Garcia, Medical Director

COURTS

District Court 432.524.1419
Fax 432.524.2272
Web ....www.co.andrews.tx.us
E-mail ....shirleym@CO.ANDREWS.TX.US
201 Main St, Room 201, Andrews, TX 79714
Honorable Martin Nency, District

POLICE AND SHERIFF

Sheriff's Ofc 432.523.5545
Fax 432.523.5954
Web ....www.co.andrews.tx.us
E-mail ....sjones@co.andrews.tx.us
201 N Main St Rm 113, Andrews, TX 79714-6517
Sam H. Jones, Sheriff

EDUCATION SERVICES

Andrews Headstart Program 432.524.4545
Fax 432.524.9765
1303 NE 1st St, Andrews, TX 79714-3671
Brenda Rangel, Director

Angelina County

SOCIAL SERVICES

Texas Dept of Family and Protective
Svcs 936.632.7708
Fax 713.928.7679
Web ....www.hhsc.state.tx.us
1210 S Chestnut St, Lufkin, TX 75901-4850
Jennifer Claude, CPS Supervisor

GENERAL HEALTH SERVICES

Health District 936.632.1139
Fax 936.632.2640
Web ....www.memorialhealth.org
E-mail ....sshaw@memorialhealth.org
503 Hill St, Lufkin, TX 75904-2792
Sheron Shaw, Director

MENTAL HEALTH SERVICES

Lufkin State School 936.634.3353
Fax 936.853.8521
Web ....www.dads.state.tx.us
E-mail ....gale.wasson@dads.state.tx.us
6844 N US Highway 69, Pollok, TX 75969-4548
Gale Wasson, Superintendent

MR Essential Svcs / MR Svc Coor 936.639.1479
Fax 936.639.1533
Web ....www.burke-center.org
E-mail ....carolinem@burke-center.org
1915 Old Mill Rd, Lufkin, TX 75903-1835
Caroline Mcdonald, Director Of Mental Retardation

JUSTICE AGENCY

CASA Program 936.634.6725
Fax 936.634.8281
317 E. Shepherd Ave, Lufkin, TX 75902
Natalie Thornton, Executive Director

COURTS

Court 936.639.2204
Fax 936.639.2673
215 Lufkin Ave, Lufkin, TX 75901
Honorable Robert Inselmann Jr, Director

POLICE AND SHERIFF

Sheriff's Ofc 936.634.3331
Fax 936.639.4510
Web ....www.angelinacounty.net
2311 E Lufkin Ave, Lufkin, TX 75901-5129
Kent Henson, Sheriff

Aransas County

SOCIAL SERVICES

Family and Protective Svcs 361.758.6376
Web ....www.dfps.state.tx.us
524 S Commercial St, Aransas Pass, TX 78336-1810
Stephanie Diaz, Office Coordinator

Texas Health and Human Svcs
Commission 361.729.5784
Fax 361.729.8173
2718 Highway 35 N, Rockport, TX 78382
Juan Gonzalez, Program Manager

GENERAL HEALTH SERVICES

Texas Dept Of Health 361.727.1988
Fax 361.727.3530
2718 Hwy 35 N, Rockport, TX 78382
Sonya Vira, Supervisor

COURTS

Court 361.790.0100
Fax 361.727.2043
E-mail ....judge@arkansascounty.org
301 N Liveoak St, Rockport, TX 78382
Honorable C.h. Burt Mills Jr, County Judge

POLICE AND SHERIFF

Sheriff's Ofc 361.729.2222
Fax 361.790.0164
Web ....www.aransascounty.org
E-mail ....sheriff@aransascounty.org
714 E Concho St, Rockport, TX 78382-4118
William Mills, Sheriff

Armstrong County

POLICE AND SHERIFF

Sheriff's Ofc 806.226.3151
Fax 806.226.3711
E-mail ....acso@amaonline.com
110 W. 1st St, Claude, TX 79019
James R. Walker, Sheriff

Atascosa County

SOCIAL SERVICES

Texas Health and Human Svcs
Commission 830.769.3507
Fax 830.769.2572
E-mail ....arturo.loera@dhs.state.tx.us
1306 Jiffy Blvd, Jourdanton, TX 78026-1502
Arturo Loera, Texas Works Supervisor

JUSTICE AGENCY

Juvenile Probation 830.769.3222
Fax 830.769.2994
1511 Zanderson Ave, Jourdanton, TX 78026
Jill Bazan, Chief JPO

COURTS

Court 830.769.3093
Fax 830.769.2349
Web ....www.co.atascosacounty.tx.us
E-mail ....atascosacountyjudge@yahoo.com
   1 Courthouse Circle Dr Ste 101, Jourdanton,
TX 78026-3446
Honorable Dianna J. Bautista, Director

POLICE AND SHERIFF

Sheriff's Ofc **830.769.3434**
Fax 830.769.2721
Web www.2fastmail.com
E-mail ....acso3434@aol.com
   1108 Campbell Ave, Jourdanton, TX 78026-3508
Tommy W. Williams, Sheriff

EDUCATION SERVICES

Charlotte Head Start **830.277.1141**
Fax 830.277.1181
   14 Del Mar St, Charlotte, TX 78011
Rebecca Ramos, Director

Austin County

SOCIAL SERVICES

Family and Protective Svcs **979.865.9168**
Fax 713.928.7615
E-mail ....peggy.gartman@dfps.state.tx.us
   800 E Wendt St, Bellville, TX 77418
Peggy Gartman, Program Director

Texas Health And Human Svcs
Commission **979.865.9164**
Fax 979.865.5274
   800 E Wendt St, Bellville, TX 77418
Tammie Hall, Supervisor

GENERAL HEALTH SERVICES

Texas Dept of Health **979.865.5211**
Fax 979.865.9936
Web ....www.dshs.state.tx.us
E-mail ....rachel.kubala@dshs.state.tx.us
   800 E Wendt St, Bellville, TX 77418
Rachel Kubala, Clerk

COURTS

District Court **979.865.5911**
Fax 979.865.8786
   1 E Main St, Bellville, TX 77418
Sue Murphy, District Clerk

POLICE AND SHERIFF

Sheriff's Ofc **979.865.3111**
Fax 979.865.8271
E-mail ....acso100@austincountyso.org
   417 N Chesley St, Bellville, TX 77418
R. Dewayne Burger, Sheriff

EDUCATION SERVICES

Communities In Schools of Texas, Inc - Central
Texas **512.462.1771**
Fax 512.462.0825
Web ....www.cisaustin.org
E-mail ....info@cisaustin.org
   3000 S Interstate 35 Ste 200, Austin, TX 78704-6536
A Suki, Executive Director

Bailey County

SOCIAL SERVICES

Texas Health And Human Svcs
Commission **806.272.3981**
Fax 806.272.4010
   209 E Ave B, Muleshoe, TX 79347
Lesa Bermea, Unit Supervisor

COURTS

District Court **806.272.3165**
Fax 806.272.3124
Web ....www.fivearea.com
E-mail ....gordong@fivearea.com
   300 S 1st St Ste 130, Muleshoe, TX 79347-3621
Honorable Gordon Green, Director

POLICE AND SHERIFF

Sheriff's Ofc **806.272.4268**
Fax 806.272.3879
Web ....www.fivearea.com
E-mail ....baileyso@fivearea.com
   405 W 2nd St, Muleshoe, TX 79347
Richard B. Wills, Sheriff

Bandera County

GENERAL HEALTH SERVICES

Dept Of State Health Serv **830.796.7540**
Fax 830.796.8440
   702 Buck Creek Rd, Bandera, TX 78003
Martha Gromer, Rn, Public Health Nurse

COURTS

Court **830.796.3781**
Fax 830.796.4210
E-mail ....bandcojdge@indian-creek.net
   500 Main Street, Bandera, TX 78003-0877
Honorable Richard A. Evans, Director/Judge

POLICE AND SHERIFF

Sheriff's Ofc **830.796.3771**
Fax 830.796.3561
E-mail ....sheriff@indian-creek.net
   3360 Hwy 173 N, Bandera, TX 78003
Richard Smith, Acting Sheriff

Bastrop County

SOCIAL SERVICES

Texas Health And Human Svcs
Commission **512.321.3995**
Fax 512.321.8198
   3102 Loop 150 East, Bastrop, TX 78602
Nancy Flores, Supervisor

GENERAL HEALTH SERVICES

Dept of Health **512.321.3982**
Fax 512.321.4861
Web ....www.dshs.state.tx.us
E-mail ....mary.pearce@dshs.state.tx.us
   104 Loop 150 W Ste 102, Bastrop, TX 78602-4065
Mary Pearce, Rn, Nursing Supervisor

JUSTICE AGENCY

CASA **512.303.2272**
Fax 512.303.9637
   507 Water Street, Bastrop, TX 78602
Amanda Homesley, Executive Director

POLICE AND SHERIFF

Sheriff's Ofc **512.303.1080**
Fax 512.549.5195
   200 Jackson St, Bastrop, TX 78602
Terry Pickering, Sheriff

Baylor County

SOCIAL SERVICES

Texas Health And Human Svcs
Commission **940.888.3536**
Fax 940.888.3364
   115 W Morris St, Seymour, TX 76380
Carla Tartley, Supervisor

COURTS

District Court **940.889.3322**
Fax 940.889.4300
   101 S Washington St, Seymour, TX 76380-2566
Chris Jakubicek, Chief JPO

POLICE AND SHERIFF

Sheriff's Ofc **940.889.3333**
Fax 940.889.3915
E-mail ....bcsheriff@srcaccess.net
   101 S Washington St Ste 11, Seymour, TX 76380
Bob Elliott, Sheriff

Bee County

SOCIAL SERVICES

Family and Protective Svcs **361.358.4303**
Fax 361.358.9725
   1800 S Washington St, Ste 2, Beeville, TX 78102
Rita Gardner, Program Director

Texas Health And Human Svcs
Commission **361.358.9790**
Fax 361.358.2921
   1800 S Washington St, Ste 1, Beeville, TX 78102
Joe Gomez, Supervisor

GENERAL HEALTH SERVICES

Dept of State Health Svcs **361.358.2241**
Fax 361.358.0572
Web ....www.dshs.state.tx.us
E-mail ....ashley.dodds@dshs.state.tx.us
   1701 N Frontage Rd, Beeville, TX 78102-2939
Ashley Dodds, RN, Nursing Supervisor

POLICE AND SHERIFF

Sheriff's Ofc **361.362.3221**
Fax 361.362.3227
Web ....www.co.bee.tx.us
   1511 E Toledo St, Beeville, TX 78102-5308
Carlos Carrizales, Sheriff

Bell County

SOCIAL SERVICES

Family and Protective Svcs **254.939.3561**
Fax 254.939.4241
   2500 N Main St, Ste B, Belton, TX 76513
Teresa Lockett, CPS Supervisor Investigation

Family and Protective Svcs **254.526.9011**
Fax 254.501.4290
Web ....www.dfps.state.tx.us
E-mail ....martha.crappell@dfps.state.tx.us
   405 E Elms Rd, Killeen, TX 76542-6027
Martha Crappell, Office Manager

GENERAL HEALTH SERVICES

Health Deptt **254.773.4457**
Fax 254.773.7535
Web ....www.bellcountyhealth.org
E-mail ....wfarrell@bellcountyhealth.org
   201 N 8th St, Temple, TX 76501
Wayne Farrell, Director

Public Health District **254.778.4766**
Fax 254.778.2912
Web ....www.bellcountyhealth.org
E-mail ....bscurzi@bellcountyhealth.org
   509 S 9th St, Temple, TX 76504-5567
Bonnie Scurzi, Rnc, Nursing Director

MENTAL HEALTH SERVICES

Children's Mental Health Svcs **254.778.7995**
Fax 254.778.5835
   317 N 2nd St, Temple, TX 76501-3216
Jan Hensarling, Lpc

Texas (sidebar)

Mental Health/Mental Retardation 254.526.4146
Fax...254.526.9351
Web...www.cccmhmr.org
E-mail...............................chris.joslin@cccmhmr.org
  100 E Ave A, Killeen, TX 76541-4763
  Chris Joslin, Director

JUSTICE AGENCY

Dist Attorney's Ofc........................**512.854.9400**
E-mail..........................annalee.mcnelis@co.travis.tx.us
  509 W 11th St, Austin, TX 78701
  Anna Lee Mcnelis, Attorney

POLICE AND SHERIFF

Sheriff's Ofc...............................**254.933.5410**
Fax...254.933.5332
E-mail...............................dan.smith@co.bell.tx.us
  104 S Main St, Belton, TX 76513
  Dan Smith, Sheriff

EDUCATION SERVICES

**Communities In Schools of Greater Fort Hood Area,
Inc**..**254.554.2132**
Fax...254.554.2723
Web...www.hot.rr.com
E-mail...............................marycis@hot.rr.com
  4520 E Central Texas Expy Ste 106, Killeen,
  TX 76543-5276
  Mary Erwin Barr, Executive Director

Bexar County

SOCIAL SERVICES

Family and Protective Svcs................**210.333.2004**
Fax...210.337.3580
E-mail..........................deborah.north@dfps.state.tx.us
  3635 SE Military Dr, San Antonio, TX 78223-4042
  Deborah North, Foster Home Development Program Director

Housing & Human Svcs.....................**210.335.3666**
Fax...210.335.6788
E-mail...............................clientservices@bexar.org
  233 N Pecos La Trinidad Ste 590, San Antonio,
  TX 78207
  Aurora Sanchez, Executive Director

GENERAL HEALTH SERVICES

San Antonio Metro Health Dept.............**210.207.2437**
Fax...210.207.8798
  1226 NW 18th St, San Antonio, TX 78207-1300
  Linda Cook, Program Manager

**San Antonio Metropolitan Health
District**..**210.207.8730**
Fax...210.207.8999
Web...www.sanantonio.gov/health
E-mail...............................fernando.guerra@sanantonio.gov
  332 W Commerce St, Ste 307, San Antonio,
  TX 78205
  Fernando A. Guerra, Md, Mph, Director

JUSTICE AGENCY

**Texas Youth Commission - San Antonio District
Ofc**..**210.242.7800**
Fax...210.242.7845
Web...www.tyc.state.tx.us
  321 N Center Ste W200, San Antonio, TX 78202
  Ericka Barrera, Parole Supervisor

COURTS

225th District Court.........................**210.335.2233**
Fax...210.335.3950
Web...www.co.bexar.tx.us
E-mail...............................rlewis@co.bexar.tx.us
  100 Dolorosa Ste 223, San Antonio, TX 78205-3086
  Roger Lewis, Court Clerk

Teen Court...................................**210.619.1000**
Fax...210.619.1529
  1400 Schertz Pkwy, Schertz, TX 78154
  Patty Veliz, Director

POLICE AND SHERIFF

Police Dept..................................**210.207.7484**
Fax...210.207.4377
Web...www.sanantonio.gov/sapd
  214 W Nueva, San Antonio, TX 78207
  Sergeant Brian Bielefeld, Administrative Sergeant

Sheriff's Ofc...............................**210.335.6010**
Fax...210.335.6019
Web...www.bexar.org
E-mail...............................sheriffadmin@bexar.org
  200 N Comal, San Antonio, TX 78207-3505
  Ralph Lopez, Sheriff

EDUCATION SERVICES

**Communities In Schools of San Antonio,
Inc**..**210.520.8440**
Fax...210.520.1104
Web...www.cissa.org
  1616 E Commerce St, Bldg 1, San Antonio, TX 78205
  Nancy Reed, President/CEO

JJA..**210.335.8500**
Fax...210.335.8599
  1402 N Hackberry, San Antonio, TX 78208-1910
  William P. Holmes, Administrator

Special Education...........................**210.370.5200**
Fax...210.370.5753
  1314 Hines, San Antonio, TX 78208-1816
  Ronny Beard, Executive Director

Blanco County

JUSTICE AGENCY

Attorney's Office...........................**830.868.4447**
E-mail...............................coatty@moment.net
  PO Box 471, Johnson City, TX 78636
  Dean Myane, Director

POLICE AND SHERIFF

Sheriff's Ofc...............................**830.868.7104**
Fax...830.868.4577
E-mail...............................blancocountydispatch@yahoo.com
  105 North Ave G, Johnson City, TX 78636
  W.r. Bill Elsbury, Sheriff

Borden County

POLICE AND SHERIFF

Sheriff's Ofc...............................**806.756.4311**
Fax...806.756.4431
E-mail...............................billy.gannaway@co.borden.tx.us
  140 East Wilbourn Ave, Gail, TX 79738
  Billy J. Gannaway, Sheriff

Bosque County

SOCIAL SERVICES

**Texas Health and Human Svcs
Commission**...................................**254.435.2302**
Fax...254.435.2915
  401 S Hill St, Meridian, TX 76665
  Kay Watson, Supervisor

POLICE AND SHERIFF

Sheriff's Ofc...............................**254.435.2362**
Fax...254.435.2245
Web...www.bosquesheriff.com
  305 West Morgan St, Meridian, TX 76665
  Anthony Malliott, Sheriff

EDUCATION SERVICES

Clifton Head Start.........................**254.675.4076**
  303 N Ave G-13th St, Clifton, TX 76634
  Rachael Tebo, Director

Bowie County

SOCIAL SERVICES

Family and Protective Svcs................**903.791.6400**
Fax...903.791.3305
  3115 S Lake Dr, Ste 120, Texarkana, TX 75501
  Lydia Melton, Administrative Assistant

**Texas Health And Human Svcs
Commission**...................................**903.667.2504**
Fax...903.667.5215
  111 N Houston St, De Kalb, TX 75559
  Tammy Caraway, Acting Supervisor

GENERAL HEALTH SERVICES

Family Health Ctr..........................**903.798.3250**
Fax...903.793.2289
Web...www.txkusa.org/health
E-mail...............................kmoore835@aol.com
  902 W 12th St, Texarkana, TX 75501
  Kathy Moore, Director

JUSTICE AGENCY

Juvenile Justice Ctr........................**903.791.1707**
Fax...903.831.7466
E-mail...............................mary@juvenilejustice.org
  141 Plaza W, Texarkana, TX 75501-5921
  Mary Choates, Chief JPO

COURTS

District Court...............................**903.798.3004**
Fax...903.798.3301
E-mail...............................branson@txkusa.org
  100 N State Line Ave Rm 10, Texarkana,
  TX 75501-5666
  Billy Fox Branson, Court Clerk

POLICE AND SHERIFF

Sheriff's Dept..............................**903.798.3149**
Fax...903.792.0959
Web...www.txkusa.org
E-mail...............................sheriff@txkusa.org
  100 N State Line Ave Rm 18, Texarkana,
  TX 75501-5666
  James W. Prince, Sheriff

Brazoria County

SOCIAL SERVICES

Family and Protective Svcs................**979.864.1428**
Web...www.dsps.state.tx.us
E-mail...............................peggy.gartman@dsps.state.tx.us
  1504 E Mulberry St, Angleton, TX 77515-3913
  Peggy Gartman, Director

GENERAL HEALTH SERVICES

Health Dept..................................**979.864.1484**
Fax...979.864.1456
Web...www.brazoria-county.com
E-mail...............................cathys@brazoria-county.com
  432 E Mulberry St, Angleton, TX 77515-4736
  Cathy Sbrusch, Director

JUSTICE AGENCY

CASA...**979.864.1658**
Fax...979.848.8628
Web...www.yfcs.org
E-mail...............................yfcs@yfcs.org
  801 Buchta Rd, Angleton, TX 77515
  Betty Smith, Program Director

District Attorney's Office **832.835.8572**
E-mail ....Kristinc@brazoria-county.com
111 E Locust St, Ste 408-A, Angleton, TX 77515
Kristin Carr

District Attorney's Office **979.864.1230**
E-mail ....erinnb@brazoria-county.com
111 E Locust St, Ste 408-A, Angleton, TX 77515
Erinn Brown, Manager

Juvenile Probation **979.864.1210**
Fax 979.864.1215
Web ....www.brazoria-county.com
E-mail ....dcoates@brazoria-county.com
20875 Country Road 171, Angleton, TX 77515
Diana Coates, Chief JPO

COURTS

Three Rivers Cluster Court **281.756.1895**
Fax 979.864.1155
Web ....www.brazoria-county.com
E-mail ....winonaw@brazoria-county.com
111 E Locust St, Rm 317A, Angleton, TX 77515
Winona Williams, Court Reporter/Coordinator

POLICE AND SHERIFF

Sheriff's Dept **979.864.2392**
Fax 979.848.8003
E-mail ....sheriff@brazoria-county.com
3602 County Rd 45, Angleton, TX 77515
Charles S. Wagner, Sheriff

EDUCATION SERVICES

Alvin Head Start **281.331.7970**
Fax 281.585.4824
E-mail ....djohnson@headstartbc.org
1019 E House St, Alvin, TX 77511
Ms Deborah Johnson, Director

Angleton Headstart **979.849.9261**
Fax 979.849.4609
Web ....www.headstartbc.org
651 W Miller St, Angleton, TX 77515-5522
Melissa Bagwell, Director

Brazosport Headstart **979.233.5673**
Fax 979.233.4415
E-mail ....marechiga@headstartbc.org
1216 W 9th St, Freeport, TX 77541
Ms. Maria Arechiga, Director

Brazos County

SOCIAL SERVICES

Family and Protective Svcs **979.776.3637**
Fax 512.339.5944
Web ....www.dfps.state.tx.us
E-mail ....brenda.chapman@dfps.state.tx.us
2400 Osborn Ln, Bryan, TX 77803-5149
Brenda Chapman, Program Director

Texas Health and Human Svcs
Commission **979.776.1510**
Fax 979.776.7432
3000 E Villa Maria Rd, Bryan, TX 77803
Daila Yanez, Program Manager

GENERAL HEALTH SERVICES

Health Dept **979.361.4440**
Fax 979.823.2275
Web ....www.co.brazos.tx.us
E-mail ....healthdept@co.brazos.tx.us
201 N Texas Ave, Bryan, TX 77803-5317
Ken Bost, Director

JUSTICE AGENCY

Juvenile Justice Ctr **979.823.3544**
Fax 979.823.4211
1904 Hwy 21 W, Bryan, TX 77803
Doug Vance, CPO Juvenile

COURTS

District Court **979.775.7400**
Fax 979.823.6993
Web ....www.twc.state.tx.us
300 E 26th St Ste 216, Bryan, TX 77803-5360
Karen Mcqueen, County Clerk

POLICE AND SHERIFF

Sheriff's Dept **979.361.4900**
Fax 979.361.4170
1700 Hwy 21 W, Bryan, TX 77803
Christopher C. Kirk, Sheriff

Brewster County

SOCIAL SERVICES

Texas Health And Human Svcs
Commission **432.837.3338**
Fax 432.837.3591
500 W Ave H, Ste 104, Alpine, TX 79830
Margaret Santillan, Supervisor

GENERAL HEALTH SERVICES

Dept of State Health Svcs **432.837.3877**
Fax 432.837.5523
205 N Cockrell St, Alpine, TX 79830
Adriel Holt, Nursing Supervisor

JUSTICE AGENCY

Frontier CASA **432.837.7448**
Fax 432.837.0813
Web ....www.frontiercasa.org
E-mail ....frontiercasa@sbcglobal.net
108 N 6th St, Alpine, TX 79830
Ronnie Harris, Executive Director

COURTS

Court **432.837.2412**
Fax 432.837.1127
E-mail ....berta.martinez@co.brewster.tx.us
201 W Avenue E Alpine, Alpine, TX 79831
Berta Martinez, Court Clerk

POLICE AND SHERIFF

Sheriff's Ofc **432.837.3488**
Fax 432.837.5960
Web ....www.wirelessfrontier.net
E-mail ....dodson@sbcglobal.net
201 W Avenue E, Alpine, TX 79830-4626
Ronny D. Dodson, Sheriff

Briscoe County

POLICE AND SHERIFF

Sheriff's Ofc **806.823.2135**
Fax 806.823.2141
Web ....www.midplains.coop
E-mail ....tsmith@midplains.coop
415 Main St, Silverton, TX 79257
Tene Smith, Sheriff

Brooks County

SOCIAL SERVICES

Texas Health and Human Svcs
Commission **361.325.3423**
Fax 361.325.2682
Web ....www.dshs.state.tx.us
E-mail ....dalia.perez@dshs.state.tx.us
1200 E Highway 285, Falfurrias, TX 78355-5885
Dalia Perez, Rn, Supervisor

POLICE AND SHERIFF

Sheriff's Ofc **361.325.3696**
Fax 361.325.1743
Web ....www.brooks-county.com
E-mail ....reyrodriguez@brooks-county.com
801 County Road 201, Falfurrias, TX 78355
Rey Rodriguez, Sheriff

EDUCATION SERVICES

Falfurrias-Texas Migrant Council
Inc **361.325.5940**
Fax 361.325.9871
Web ....www.tmccentral.org
E-mail ....norma.moreno@mail.tmccentral.org
216 N Miller Blvd, Falfurrias, TX 78355-3534
Norma Moreno, Director

Brown County

SOCIAL SERVICES

Family And Protective Svcs **325.646.0541**
Fax 325.643.7084
E-mail ....annie.gilmore@dfps.state.tx.us
2400 crockett, Brownwood, TX 76801
Annie Gilmore, Administrative Assistant

COURTS

District Court **325.646.1987**
Fax 325.643.6396
200 S Broadway St Ste 214, Brownwood,
TX 76801-3136
Honorable Steven Ellis, Judge

POLICE AND SHERIFF

Sheriff's Dept **325.646.5518**
Fax 325.643.3826
E-mail ....bcsosheriff@browncountytx.org
1050 W Commerce St, Brownwood, TX 76801
Bobby Grubbs, Sheriff

Burleson County

SOCIAL SERVICES

Texas Health And Human Svcs
Commission **979.567.3283**
Fax 979.567.7847
500 W Highway 21, Caldwell, TX 77836-1126
Jennifer Iselt, Supervisor

COURTS

Court **979.567.2333**
Fax 979.567.2372
Web ....www.co.buleson.tx.us
E-mail ....co_judge@burlesoncounty.org
100 W Buck St Ste 306, Caldwell, TX 77836-1764
Honorable Mike Sutherland, County Court Judge

POLICE AND SHERIFF

Sheriff's Ofc **979.567.4343**
Fax 979.567.0615
E-mail ....dstroud@burlesoncounty.org
1334 State Highway 21 E, Caldwell, TX 77836
Alfred Dale Stroud, Sheriff

Burnet County

SOCIAL SERVICES

Family and Protective Svcs **512.756.6006**
Fax 512.339.5948
1104 Buchanan Dr, Ste 2, Burnet, TX 78611
Dorinda Duzan, CPS Supervisor

GENERAL HEALTH SERVICES

Texas Dept of Health Alpine Field

Ofc...**830.693.5703**
Fax..830.798.3333
Web.........................www.yourtexasbenefit.com
1016 Broadway St Ste 101, Marble Falls,
TX 78654-5502
Tammy Branham, Director

POLICE AND SHERIFF

Sheriff's Dept......................**512.756.8080**
Fax..512.756.4064
E-mail.................sheriff@burnetcountytexas.org
1601 E Polk St, Burnet, TX 78611
W T Smith, Sheriff

EDUCATION SERVICES

Burnet Early Head Start....................**512.715.0805**
Fax..512.715.0805
202 E Brier Ln, Burnet, TX 78611
Alisa Rogers, Director

Caldwell County

SOCIAL SERVICES

Texas Health And Human Svcs

Commission...............................**512.398.4541**
Fax..512.398.7436
1400 E Fm 20, Lockhart, TX 78644
Carol Nolan, Supervisor

JUSTICE AGENCY

Criminal Dist Atty.................**512.398.1811**
E-mail.............................rhicks@austin.rr.com
201 E San Antonio St, Lockhart, TX 78644
Richard Hicks Iii, District Attorney

Juvenile Probation....................**512.398.5400**
Fax..512.398.5427
Web..................................www.ccjpd.net
E-mail.............................monkerud@ccjpd.net
312 E San Antonio St, Lockhart, TX 78644-2163
Jay Monkerud, Chief JPO

COURTS

Court...**512.398.6527**
Fax..512.398.1828
Web...........................www.co.caldwell.tx.us
11104 W Airport Blvd Ste 136, Stafford,
TX 77477-3040
Honorable Edward L. Jarrett, County Court Judge

POLICE AND SHERIFF

Sheriff's Ofc.........................**512.398.6747**
Fax..512.376.4376
1204 Reed Dr, Lockhart, TX 78644-4200
Daniel C. Law, Sheriff

Calhoun County

SOCIAL SERVICES

Family and Protective Svcs.................**361.552.7222**
Fax..361.552.7789
E-mail.................diane.jones@dfps.state.tx.us
436 State Hwy 35 S, Port Lavaca, TX 77979
Diane Jones, Program Director

Health and Human Svcs

Commission...............................**361.552.9702**
Fax..361.552.1667
Web...............................www.dhs.state.tx.us
E-mail.........................patricia.scaff@dhs.state.tx.us
436 State Highway 35 S, Port Lavaca, TX 77979-2408
Patricia Scaff, Supervisor

GENERAL HEALTH SERVICES

Health Dept.............................**361.552.9721**
Fax..361.552.9722
Web...................................www.cchealth.org
117 W Ash St, Port Lavaca, TX 77979
Kathy Diepvel, Director Of Nursing

JUSTICE AGENCY

Juvenile Probation....................**361.553.4670**
Fax..361.553.4690
Web...............................www.tjpc.state.tx.us
E-mail.............................Luis.leija@calhouncotx.org
201 W Austin St Ste 9, Port Lavaca, TX 77979-4250
Luis Leija, Chief JPO

COURTS

Court...**361.553.4600**
Fax..361.553.4444
E-mail.................susan.riley@calhouncotx.org
211 S Ann St, Ste 301, Port Lavaca, TX 77979
Susan Riley, Administrative Assistant

POLICE AND SHERIFF

Sheriff's Dept......................**361.553.4646**
Fax..361.553.4668
211 S Ann St, Port Lavaca, TX 77979
B.b. Browning, Sheriff

Callahan County

SOCIAL SERVICES

Texas Health and Human Svcs

Commission...............................**325.854.1257**
Fax..325.854.2455
124 W 4th St, Baird, TX 79504
Linda Villalovos, Supervisor

POLICE AND SHERIFF

Sheriff's Ofc.........................**325.854.1444**
Fax..325.854.5998
Web...........................www.callahancounty.org
432 Market St, Baird, TX 79504-5308
John Windham, Sheriff

EDUCATION SERVICES

Central Texas Opportunities Inc - Baird Head

Start...**325.854.2626**
Fax..325.854.2626
Web...................................www.ctoinc.org
E-mail.............................sgarza@ctoinc.org
100 W 5th St, Baird, TX 79504-5321
Sharon Garza, Director

Cameron County

SOCIAL SERVICES

Family and Protective Svcs.................**956.546.5591**
Fax..956.547.7279
1060 Makinsosh Dr., Brownsville, TX 78520
Jovita Shives, Supervisor

Family and Protective Svcs.................**956.423.3690**
Fax..956.412.4622
Web...................................www.swkey.org
E-mail.............................lramirez@swkey.org
801 N 13th St Ste 23, Harlingen, TX 78550-5073
Lourdes Ramirez, Program Director

Health and Human Svcs...................**956.574.8745**
Fax..956.574.8755
Web...............................www.dshs.state.tx.us
E-mail.................alicia.infante@dshs.state.tx.us
1204 Jose Colunga Jr St, Brownsville, TX 78521-5725
Alicia Infante, Rn, Nurse

GENERAL HEALTH SERVICES

Health Dept.............................**956.943.1300**
142 Champion Ave, Port Isabel, TX 78578
Delia Sanchez, Rn, Supervisor

Health Dept.............................**956.247.3685**
Fax..956.361.8230
Web...........................www.co.cameron.tx.us
E-mail.................health@co.cameron.tx.us
1390 W Expressway 83, San Benito, TX 78586
Yvette Salinas, Health Administrator

San Benito Nursing Ofc....................**956.361.8244**
Fax..956.361.8269
E-mail.................delia.sanchez@dshs.state.tx.us
1390 W Express Way 83, San Benito, TX 78586
Delia Sanchez, Rn, Supervisor

MENTAL HEALTH SERVICES

Mentle Health.............................**956.364.8000**
Web...............................www.dshs.state.tx.us
1401 So. Rangerville Road, Harlingen, TX 78551
Sonia Keeble, Director

JUSTICE AGENCY

Amadov R. Rodriguez Juvenile Bootcamp & Education

Ctr...**956.361.3509**
Fax..956.361.4626
2330 W US Highway 77, San Benito, TX 78586-7778
Isabel Rodriguez, Director

CASA...**956.546.6545**
Fax..956.546.6612
Web...................................www.texascasa.org
E-mail.............................cwcasa@aol.com
1175 W Price Rd Ste 3, Brownsville, TX 78520-8738
Alicia Cardenas, Executive Director

Juvenile Probation Dept.....................**956.399.3075**
Fax..956.399.3705
Web...........................www.co.cameron.tx.us
E-mail.................tramirez@co.cameron.tx.us
2310 W. Highway 77, San Benito, TX 78586
Tommy Ramirez Jr., Chief JPO

Texas Youth Commission - Harlingen Parole

Ofc...**956.423.6634**
Fax..956.425.4944
E-mail.................ricardo.leal@tyc.state.tx.us
1810 W Jefferson Ave, Harlingen, TX 78550-5247
Ricardo Leal, Parole Officer

COURTS

138th District Court.......................**956.544.0877**
Fax..956.544.0881
Web...........................www.co.cameron.tx.us
974 E Harrison St, Fl 3, Brownsville, TX 78520
Eldaibo Flores, Jr, Court Reporter

POLICE AND SHERIFF

Sheriff's Dept......................**956.554.6700**
Fax..956.554.6780
Web...........................www.co.cameron.tx.us
E-mail.................sheriff@co.cameron.tx.us
7300 Old Alice Rd, Olmito, TX 78575-5132
Omar Lucio, Sheriff

EDUCATION SERVICES

Bonita Park Head Start CDC.................**956.423.0984**
Fax..956.423.0984
601 S Rangerville Rd, Apt 29-30, Harlingen,
TX 78552
Guadalupe Garcia, Director

Cameron Park Head Start Ctr.................**956.546.9686**
4176 Paredes Line Rd, Brownsville, TX 78526-1113
Harry Lincoln, Director

Casa Grande Head Start Child

Development..............................**956.423.7827**
Fax..956.412.9264
106 Troywood Cir, Harlingen, TX 78550
Ruben Tuabas, Director

Communities In Schools **956.554.7954**
Fax 956.554.9144
Web ....www.ciscameroncounty.org
   700 E Levee St, Ste 204, Brownsville, TX 78520
   Jose Luis Gonzalez, Executive Director

D J Lerma Head Start Child
Development **956.831.3267**
   5407 Austin Rd, Brownsville, TX 78521-5855
   Alma Ruiz, Director

El Ranchito Head Start Child
Development **956.399.6124**
Fax 956.399.6124
   24356 W US Highway 281, San Benito,
   TX 78586-8052
   Francis Berrout, Director

Esperanza B Garza Head Start Child
Development **956.943.2905**
   131 W Garfield St, Laguna Heights, TX 78578
   Erika Sandoval, Director

Camp County

SOCIAL SERVICES

Texas Health And Human Svcs
Commission **903.856.3678**
Fax 903.856.3998
E-mail ....deanna.pitman@hhsc.state.tx.us
   211 Mill St, Pittsburg, TX 75686
   Deanna Pitman, Case Worker

POLICE AND SHERIFF

Sheriffs Ofc **903.856.6651**
Fax 903.856.3681
   203 Tapp St, Pittsburg, TX 75686
   Alan D. Mccandless, Sheriff

Carson County

COURTS

Court House **806.537.3622**
Fax 806.537.2244
E-mail ....countyjudge@carsoncountytx.com
   500 Main Street, Panhandle, TX 79068
   Honorable Lewis W. Powers, County Court Judge

POLICE AND SHERIFF

Sheriff's Ofc **806.537.3511**
Fax 806.537.3514
E-mail ....carsonso@amaonline.com
   501 Main St, Panhandle, TX 79068
   Tam Terry, Sheriff

Cass County

SOCIAL SERVICES

Texas Health and Human Svcs and Family Protective
Svcs **903.756.5551**
Fax 903.756.7695
   213 Highway 8 N, Linden, TX 75563
   Don Farris, Supervisor

GENERAL HEALTH SERVICES

Texas Dept Of State Health Svcs **903.756.7231**
Fax 903.756.5146
E-mail ....dora.whatley@dshs.state.tx.us
   123 S Kaufman St, Linden, TX 75563
   Dora Whatley, Clinic Manager

JUSTICE AGENCY

Court **903.756.7514**
E-mail ....noemail@naccchildlaw.org
   PO Box 510, Linden, TX 75563
   Don Dowd

Juvenile Probation **903.756.7551**
Fax 903.756.5131
E-mail ....casscojuv@valornet.com
   700 W Houston St, Linden, TX 75563
   Honorable Ralph Burgess, District Judge

POLICE AND SHERIFF

Sheriff's Ofc **903.756.7511**
Fax 903.756.5434
E-mail ....sheriff.estes@casscountytx.org
   600 Highway 8 N, Linden, TX 75563
   James T. Estes, Sheriff

Castro County

SOCIAL SERVICES

Texas Health And Human Svcs
Commission **806.647.4181**
Fax 806.647.4578
   204 SE 3rd St, Dimmitt, TX 79027-2612
   Cindy Vandiver, Supervisor

GENERAL HEALTH SERVICES

Medical Ctr of Dimmitt **806.647.2194**
   300 W Halsell St, Dimmitt, TX 79027
   Gary Hardee, Md, Medical Director

COURTS

Court **806.647.4451**
Fax 806.647.4403
E-mail ....wfsccjudge@castrocounty.org
   100 E Bedford St Rm 111, Dimmitt, TX 79027-2643
   Honorable William F. Sava, Director

POLICE AND SHERIFF

Sheriff's Ofc **806.647.3311**
Fax 806.647.2189
   100 E Bedford St Rm 113, Dimmitt, TX 79027
   Sal Rivera, Sheriff

Chambers County

SOCIAL SERVICES

Texas Health And Human Svcs
Commission **409.267.3125**
Fax 409.267.3123
   204 N Texas Ave, Anahuac, TX 77514
   Jaime Pruitt, Supervisor

GENERAL HEALTH SERVICES

Health Dept **409.267.8356**
Fax 409.267.4276
E-mail ....sburgess@texashan.org
   1107 Wilcox st, Anahuac, TX 77514
   Dr. William Clay Brown Md, Pa, Director

COURTS

Court **409.267.2440**
Fax 409.267.4453
   404 Washington Ave, Anahuac, TX 77514
   Gloria Turner, Chief Juvenile Probation Officer

POLICE AND SHERIFF

Sheriff's Dept **409.267.8322**
Fax 409.267.6736
Web ....www.co.chambers.tx.us
E-mail ....jlarive@co.chambers.tx.us
   201 North Ct, Anahuac, TX 77514
   Joe Larive, Sheriff

Cherokee County

GENERAL HEALTH SERVICES

Health Dept **903.586.6191**
Fax 903.586.3572
Web ....www.cchdtexas.org
   510 E Commerce St, Jacksonville, TX 75766-4910
   Mary A. Bone, Medical Director

COURTS

Court **903.683.2324**
Fax 903.683.2393
Web ....www.co.cherokee.tx.us
   135 S Main St, Rusk, TX 75785-1355
   Honorable Chris Davis, Judge

POLICE AND SHERIFF

Sheriff's Ofc **903.683.2271**
Fax 903.683.2813
Web ....www.cox-internet.com
E-mail ....sheriff@cox-internet.com
   272 Underwood, Rusk, TX 75785-1705
   James E. Campbell, Sheriff

EDUCATION SERVICES

Alto Head Start **936.858.3548**
Fax 936.858.3548
   US N Highway 69, Alto, TX 75925
   Ms Mitchel, Director

Childress County

SOCIAL SERVICES

Texas Health and Human Svcs
Commission **940.937.6301**
Fax 940.937.6398
E-mail ....beth.miller@hhsc.state.tx.us
   801 Commerce St Unit B, Childress, TX 79201-3000
   Beth Miller, Supervisor

COURTS

Court House **940.937.2221**
Fax 940.937.0166
E-mail ....childresscojudge@childresstx.net
   100 Avenue E NW, Childress, TX 79201
   Honorable Jay Mayden, Judge

POLICE AND SHERIFF

Sheriff's Ofc **940.937.2535**
Fax 940.937.2395
E-mail ....ccso@att.net
   1005 Avenue F NE, Ste 2, Childress, TX 79201
   Michael Pigg, Sheriff

Clay County

SOCIAL SERVICES

Texas Health And Human Svcs
Commission **940.538.5201**
Fax 940.538.4376
   1101 N Bridge St, Henrietta, TX 76365
   Gary Wallace, Supervisor

POLICE AND SHERIFF

Sheriff's Ofc **940.538.5611**
Fax 940.538.5800
   215 W Gilbert St, Henrietta, TX 76365-2864
   Kenny Lemons, Sheriff

Cochran County

COURTS

Court **806.266.5508**
Fax 806.266.9027
Web ....www.co.cochran.tx.us
E-mail ....jstclair1@prodigy.net
   100 N Main St Rm 105, Morton, TX 79346-2517
   Honorable James St. Clair, County Court Judge

POLICE AND SHERIFF

Sheriff's Dept **806.266.5211**
Fax 806.266.8888
Web ....www.door.net
E-mail ....cochranso@door.net
   100 N Main St Rm B7, Morton, TX 79346-2500
   R W Stalcup, Sheriff

Coke County

POLICE AND SHERIFF

Sheriff's Dept **325.453.2717**
Fax 325.453.2597
E-mail ....cokecountyso@yahoo.com
   13 7th St, Robert Lee, TX 76945
Richard A. Styles, Sheriff

EDUCATION SERVICES

Head Start **325.453.2536**
Web ....www.cvcog.org
E-mail ....kbennett@cvcog.org
   820 Commerce St, Robert Lee, TX 76945
Cathy Bennet, Director

Coleman County

SOCIAL SERVICES

Texas Health And Human Svcs
Commission **325.625.4183**
Fax 325.625.5438
Web ....www.dshs.state.tx.us
   114 Needham St, Coleman, TX 76834-5030
Vanessa Russell, Supervisor

POLICE AND SHERIFF

Sheriff's Ofc **325.625.3506**
Fax 325.625.3509
   100 Live Oak, Coleman, TX 76834
Wade Turner, Sheriff

Collin County

SOCIAL SERVICES

Abortion Real Option for Women **972.424.0767**
Fax 972.424.5962
   700 E Park Blvd Ste 206, Plano, TX 75074
Danielle Hansen, Director

Dept of Human Svcs **972.542.0221**
Fax 972.547.5929
E-mail ....laura.vanziver@dhs.state.tx.us
   901 N McDonald St Ste 800, McKinney, TX 75069
Laura Vanziver, Unit Supervisor

GENERAL HEALTH SERVICES

Health Care Svcs **972.548.5500**
Fax 972.547.7267
Web ....www.collincountytx.gov
E-mail ....cblair@collincountytx.gov
   825 N McDonald St Ste 130, McKinney,
   TX 75069-2146
Candy Blair, Director

JUSTICE AGENCY

CASA Inc **972.529.2272**
Fax 972.529.2275
E-mail ....casa@casaofcollincounty.org
   101 E Davis St, McKinney, TX 75069
Susan Etheridge, Director

Criminal Dist Attny **972.548.4723**
Web ....www.collincountyda.gov
E-mail ....jrichardson@co.collin.tx.us
   2100 Bloomdale Rd, McKinney, TX 75071
Della Bryant, Administrator

Criminal District Attorney's Offic **972.548.4336**
E-mail ....adietrich@co.collin.tx.us
   2100 Bloomdale Rd, McKinney, TX 75071
Alyson Dietrich, Attorney

Juvenile Probation **972.548.6470**
Fax 972.548.6477
   4690 Community, McKinney, TX 75069
Joe Scott, Chief JPO

COURTS

District Court **972.548.4415**
Fax 972.548.4465
   2100 Bloomdale Rd, McKinney, TX 75071-8318
Honorable Robert T. Dry Jr., District Court 199

POLICE AND SHERIFF

Sheriff's Dept **972.547.5100**
Fax 972.547.5304
Web ....www.co.collin.tx.us/sheriff/
E-mail ....tbox@collincountytexas.gov
   4300 Community Ave, McKinney, TX 75071-2535
Terry G. Box, Sheriff

Collingsworth County

SOCIAL SERVICES

Family and Protective Svcs **806.447.2209**
Fax 432.684.2950
Web ....www.dfps.state.tx.us
E-mail ....patricia.grabber@dfps.state.tx.us
   800 W Ave, Wellington, TX 79095
Patricia Grabber, Program Director

GENERAL HEALTH SERVICES

Dept Of Health **806.447.5311**
Fax 806.447.3090
   1011 15th St, Wellington, TX 79095-3703
Jan Zlomke, Hiv Coordinator

COURTS

Court **806.447.5408**
Fax 806.447.5418
Web ....www.co.collingsworth.tx.us
E-mail ....jjohnson@co.collingsworth.tx.us
   800 West Ave, Fl 2, Rm 1, Wellington, TX 79095
Jackie Johnson, Court Clerk

POLICE AND SHERIFF

Sheriff's Ofc **806.447.2588**
Fax 806.447.5037
E-mail ....ccso810@yahoo.com
   810 Belton St, Wellington, TX 79095-2730
Joe Stewart, Sheriff

Colorado County

GENERAL HEALTH SERVICES

Texas Dept of Health - Columbus Field
Ofc **979.732.3662**
Fax 979.732.6417
E-mail ....beverly.howe@dshs.state.tx.us
   514 Washington St, Columbus, TX 78934
Beverly Howe, Nurse

COURTS

Court **979.732.2604**
Fax 979.732.9389
E-mail ....ty.prause@co.colorado.tx.us
   400 Spring St Rm 113, Columbus, TX 78934
Honorable Ty Prause, Judge

POLICE AND SHERIFF

Sheriff's Dept **979.732.2388**
Fax 979.732.6431
E-mail ....rhwied@coloradoso.net
   2215 Walnut St, Columbus, TX 78934-5008
R D Curly Wied, Sheriff

EDUCATION SERVICES

Columbus Head Start **979.733.0022**
Web ....www.ctfhs.org
E-mail ....dtorresvasquez@ctfhs.org
   4170 Highway 71, Columbus, TX 78934-4902
Dee Vasquez, Director

Comal County

SOCIAL SERVICES

Family and Protective Svcs **830.609.5033**
Fax 210.304.7734
   115 Green Valley St Ste 200, New Braunfels,
   TX 78130
Sherry Smith, CPS Supervisor

JUSTICE AGENCY

Juvenile Probation **830.221.1290**
Fax 830.608.2049
E-mail ....johnsk@co.comal.tx.us
   171 E Mill St, New Braunfels, TX 78130-5045
Byron Mueller, Assistant Chief Juvenile Probation Officer

POLICE AND SHERIFF

Sheriff's Dept **830.620.3400**
Fax 830.608.2082
Web ....www.co.comal.tx.us
   3005 W San Antonio St, New Braunfels,
   TX 78130-6963
James Bob Holder, Sheriff

EDUCATION SERVICES

Comal Head Start Ctr **830.625.1731**
Fax 830.609.5129
   2386 W San Antonio St, New Braunfels,
   TX 78130-6767
Raul Stevens, Director

Comal Head Start Ctr 4 ....**830.620.9184**
Fax 830.609.5129
   1023 W Bridge St, New Braunfels, TX 78130-5517
Raul Stevens, Director

Communities In Schools **830.620.4247**
Fax 830.620.5643
E-mail ....chrisd@cisnewbraunfels.org
   161 S Castell Ave, New Braunfels, TX 78130
Chris Douglas, Director

Comanche County

SOCIAL SERVICES

Texas Health And Human Svcs
Commission **325.356.2554**
Fax 325.356.5131
   400 Industrial Rd, Comanche, TX 76442
Vanessa Raffel, Supervisor

COURTS

District Court **325.356.2342**
Fax 325.356.2150
E-mail ....dclerkbd@htcomp.net
   101 W Central Ave Ste 301, Comanche,
   TX 76442-3264
Brenda Dickey, Court Clerk

POLICE AND SHERIFF

Sheriff's Dept **325.356.7533**
Fax 325.356.3783
   300 Industrial Blvd, Comanche, TX 76442-1700
Jeff Lambert, Sheriff

EDUCATION SERVICES

Central Texas Opportunities Inc. - Comanche Head
Start **325.356.2207**
Fax 325.356.2307
   1005 S Austin St, Comanche, TX 76442-3021
Becky Hicks, Director

DeLeon Head Start **254.893.3078**
   209 N Ball Park Loop, DeLeon, TX 76444
Baylor Plaunty, Center Supervisor

Concho County

EDUCATION SERVICES

Concho Valley Head Start **325.869.8703**
Fax 325.869.8703
Web ....www.cvcog.org
E-mail ....maryt@cvcog.org
　601 Barnett St, Eden, TX 76837
Mary Torres, Director

Cooke County

SOCIAL SERVICES

Family and Protective Svcs **940.668.7761**
Fax 817.276.3957
Web ....www.dfps.state.tx.us
E-mail ....mary.wolse@dfps.state.tx.us
　715 E California St Ste C, Gainesville, TX 76240-4168
Mary Wolse, Supervisor

Texas Health and Human Svcs
Commission **940.612.4421**
Fax 940.665.6754
Web ....www.dfps.state.tx.us
E-mail ....lisa.caraway@hhsd.state.tx.us
　326 S Commerce St, Gainesville, TX 76240-4714
Lisa Caraway, Supervisor

GENERAL HEALTH SERVICES

Dept of State Health Svcs **940.665.6397**
Fax 940.668.8823
Web ....www.dshs.state.tx.us
E-mail ....linda.williams@dshs.state.tx.us
　715 E California St Ste D, Gainesville, TX 76240-4168
Linda Williams, Rn, Supervising Nurse

JUSTICE AGENCY

Juvenile Probation **940.668.5534**
Fax 940.668.5557
Web ....www.tjpc.state.tx.us
E-mail ....jim.farquhar@tjpc.state.tx.us
　215 S Commerce St, Gainesville, TX 76240-4711
Jim Farquhar, Chief JPO

COURTS

Court **940.668.5435**
Fax 940.668.5440
Web ....www.co.cooke.tx.us
E-mail ....rebecca.lawson@co.cooke.tx.us
　100 S Dixon St, Gainesville, TX 76240-4717
Rebecca Lawson, Court Clerk

POLICE AND SHERIFF

Sheriff's Dept **940.665.3471**
Fax 940.668.3255
　300 County Road 451, Gainesville, TX 76240
Michael E. Compton, Sheriff

Coryell County

SOCIAL SERVICES

Family and Protective Svcs **254.547.4286**
Fax 512.339.5943
Web ....www.dfps.state.tx.us
　317 Casa Dr, Copperas Cove, TX 76522-3909
Kim Mansell, Program Director

Texas Health And Human Svcs
Commission **254.865.7291**
Fax 254.865.6699
E-mail ....patches.franks@hhsc.state.tx.us
　1409 E Main St Ste A, Gatesville, TX 76528-1604
Patches Franks, Case Worker

GENERAL HEALTH SERVICES

Dept of State Health Svcs (DSHS) **254.547.8383**
Fax 254.547.9463
Web ....www.dshs.state.tx.us
E-mail ....pauline.terry-culbert@dshs.state.tx.us
　312 S Main St Ste 102, Copperas Cove,
　TX 76522-2236
Pauline Terry-culbert, Rn, Nursing Supervisor

POLICE AND SHERIFF

Sheriff's Dept **254.865.7201**
Fax 254.865.7774
　510 E Leon St, Gatesville, TX 76528
Johnny Burks, Sheriff

EDUCATION SERVICES

Copperas Cove Head Start Ctr **254.547.1771**
E-mail ....pthomas@hccaa.com
　1008 North Dr, Copperas Cove, TX 76522-1942
Patricia Thomas, Director

Cottle County

SOCIAL SERVICES

Texas Health And Human Svcs
Commission **806.492.3576**
Fax 806.492.2280
　724 9th St, Paducah, TX 79248
Deaun Fields, Texas Works Advisor

Crane County

JUSTICE AGENCY

Juvenile Probation **432.558.1106**
Fax 432.558.1184
　701 S Alford St, Crane, TX 79731
Jose Martinez, Chief JPO

COURTS

Court **432.558.1100**
Fax 432.558.1188
Web ....www.co.crane.tx.us
E-mail ....john.farmer@co.crane.tx.us
　201 W 6th St, Crane, TX 79731
Honorable John Farmer, Director

POLICE AND SHERIFF

Sheriff's Dept **432.558.3571**
Fax 432.558.3743
Web ....www.co.crane.tx.us
E-mail ....sheriff@co.crane.tx.us
　201 W. 6th St, Crane, TX 79731
Robert Deleon, Sheriff

Crockett County

COURTS

District Court **325.392.5225**
Fax 325.392.3434
E-mail ....court112@verizon.net
　112th District Court, Ozona, TX 76943
Honorable Pedro Gomez, Judge

POLICE AND SHERIFF

Sheriff's Ofc **325.392.2661**
Fax 325.392.2045
Web ....www.co.crockett.tx.us
　903 Ave D, Ozana, TX 76943
Roy Glenn Sutton, Sheriff

Crosby County

SOCIAL SERVICES

Texas Health And Human Svcs
Commission **806.634.0262**
Fax 806.634.0273
　602 Harrison Ave, Lorenzo, TX 79343
Tina Morgan, Manager

JUSTICE AGENCY

Juvenile Probation **806.675.2668**
Fax 806.675.0726
　201 W Aspen St, # B-100, Crosbyton, TX 79322
Trixie Henn, JPO

COURTS

Court **806.675.2011**
Fax 806.675.2403
Web ....www.co.crosby.tx.us
E-mail ....ccjudge@windstream.net
　201 W Aspen St Ste 208, Crosbyton, TX 79322-2500
Honorable David Wigley, Judge

POLICE AND SHERIFF

Sheriff's Ofc **806.675.7301**
Fax 806.675.2804
　201 W Aspen St Ste 109, Crosbyton, TX 79322
David Barker, Sheriff

Culberson County

SOCIAL SERVICES

Texas Health And Human Svcs
Commission **432.283.9005**
Fax 432.283.9015
　700A Broadway, Van Horn, TX 79855
Margaret Santillan, Supervisor

GENERAL HEALTH SERVICES

Dept of State Health Svcs **432.283.2948**
Fax 432.283.7188
Web ....www.dshs.state.tx.us
E-mail ....phyllis.taylor@dshs.state.tx.us
　704 W Broadway, Van Horn, TX 79855
Phyllis Taylor, Rn, Nursing Supervisor

COURTS

Court **432.283.2059**
Fax 432.283.9234
Web ....www.co.culberson.tx.us
E-mail ....carlos.urias@co.culberson.tx.us
　300 La Caverna Dr, Van Horn, TX 79855
Carlos Urias, County Judge

POLICE AND SHERIFF

Sheriff's Ofc **432.283.2060**
Fax 432.283.9002
Web ....www.co.culberson.tx.us
　210 La Caverna St, Van Horn, TX 79855
Oscar E. Carrillo, Sheriff

Dallam County

GENERAL HEALTH SERVICES

Dept of State Health Svcs **806.249.6090**
Fax 806.249.5461
E-mail ....molly.pyle@dshs.state.tx.us
　407 Denver Ave, Dalhart, TX 79022
Molly Pyle, RN, Public Health Nurse

JUSTICE AGENCY

CASA 69 Inc. **806.244.2684**
Fax 806.244.7684
　414 Denver Ave Ste 103, Dalhart, TX 79022
Ann Bookout, Executive Director

COURTS

Court **806.244.2450**
Fax 806.244.2252
　414 Denver Ave Ste 301, Dalhart, TX 79022
Stephanie Fowler, Juvenile Probation Chief

Dallas County

SOCIAL SERVICES

Dallas Inter-Tribal Ctr 214.941.1050
Fax 214.941.6537
Web ....www.dfwnacc.org
209 E Jefferson Blvd, Dallas, TX 75203-2690
Rodney Stapp, Dpm, Executive Director

Family and Protective Svcs 214.951.7902
Fax 817.276.3932
8700 N Stemmons Freeway # 104, Dallas,
TX 75247-3715
Annie Flores, Administrator

GENERAL HEALTH SERVICES

Health Dept 214.819.6070
Fax 214.819.6022
Web ....www.dallascounty.org
E-mail ....klancaster@dallascounty.org
2377 N Stemmons Fwy, Ste 200, Dallas,
TX 75207-2702
Karen Lancaster, Medical Director/Health Authority

JUSTICE AGENCY

Dallas CASA, Inc 214.827.8961
Fax 214.827.8973
Web ....www.dallascasa.org
2815 Gaston Ave, Dallas, TX 75226
Beverly Levy, Executive Director

Juvenile Probation Dept 214.698.2200
Fax 214.698.5508
Web ....www.dallascounty.org
2600 Lone Star Dr Ste 5, Dallas, TX 75212-6332
Dr. Terry Smith, Director

Texas Youth Commission Dallas District
Ofc 214.678.3600
Fax 214.678.3632
Web ....www.tyc.state.tx.us
1575 W Mockingbird Ln Ste 650, Dallas, TX 75235
Diana Goodwin, Parole Supervisor

POLICE AND SHERIFF

Dallas Police Dept Youth and Family Crime
Div 214.671.4268
Fax 214.670.8245
1400 S Lamar St, Dallas, TX 75215-1801
Robert Hinton, Lieutenant

Sheriff's Dept 214.749.8641
Fax 214.653.2773
Web ....www.dallascounty.org
E-mail ....chill@dallascounty.org
133 N River Front Blvd Ste 31, Dallas,
TX 75207-4363
Lupe Valdez, Sheriff

EDUCATION SERVICES

Communities In Schools Dallas Region,
Inc. 214.827.0955
Fax 214.827.2198
Web ....www.cisdallas.org
E-mail ....sandyc@cisdallas.org
8700 N Stemmons Fwy, Suite 125, Dallas,
TX 75247-3725
Adrienne Simmons, Director of Finance

Early Head Start Lakewest
Program 214.267.0524
Fax 214.637.9034
3737 Goldman St, Dallas, TX 75212-2471
Lisa Tarrant, Director

Special Education 972.348.1700
Fax 972.231.3642
400 E Spring Valley Rd, Richardson, TX 75081
Buddy Echols, Executive Director

Dawson County

SOCIAL SERVICES

Texas Health and Human Svcs
Commission 806.872.5481
Fax 806.872.5059
E-mail ....anchesonique.pride@hhsc.state.tx.us
701 S Bryan Ave, Lamesa, TX 79331-6825
Anchesonique Pride, Supervisor

GENERAL HEALTH SERVICES

South Plains Public Health District 806.872.5863
Fax 806.872.2233
503 S 1st St, Lamesa, TX 79331
Soronya Shafer, Director Of Nursing

COURTS

Court 806.872.7544
Fax 806.872.7496
Web www.lamesa.esc17.net
E-mail ....judge@lamesa.esc17.net
501 S 1st St, Lamesa, TX 79331
Alan Wellf, Judge

POLICE AND SHERIFF

Sheriff's Ofc 806.872.7560
Fax 806.872.9396
401 S 2nd St, Lamesa, TX 79331
Kent Parchman, Sheriff

De Witt County

POLICE AND SHERIFF

Sheriff's Dept 361.275.5734
Fax 361.275.3096
E-mail ....sheriff@gvec.net
208 E Live Oak St, Cuero, TX 77954
Jode Zavesky, Sheriff

Deaf Smith County

SOCIAL SERVICES

Texas Health And Human Svcs
Commission 806.364.6841
Fax 806.363.8629
212 N 25 Mile Rd, Hereford, TX 79045
Lisa Bermea, Supervisor

GENERAL HEALTH SERVICES

Dept of Health 806.364.4579
Fax 806.364.5595
Web ....www.dshs.state.tx.us
E-mail ....elaine.taylor@dshs.state.tx.us
205 W 4th St Ste 102, Hereford, TX 79045-5357
Elaine Taylor, Rn, Public Health Nurse

MENTAL HEALTH SERVICES

Texas Panhandle Mental Health Mental
Retardation 806.364.5861
Fax 806.364.1012
Web ....www.tpmhmr.org
E-mail ....tammy.martinez@tpmhmr.org
218 N 25 Mile Ave, Hereford, TX 79045-4210
Tammy Martinez, Director

JUSTICE AGENCY

Juvenile Probation 806.363.7030
Fax 806.363.7033
Web ....www.tjpc.state.tx.us
E-mail ....pdominguez@dscjpo.net
216 E 5th St, Hereford, TX 79045-5404
Pedro Dominguez, Chief JPO

COURTS

Court 806.363.7000
Fax 806.363.7022
Web ....www.co.deaf-smith.tx.us
E-mail ....tom.simon@co.deaf-smith.tx.us
235 E 3rd St Rm 201, Hereford, TX 79045-5542
Honorable Tom Simon, Director

POLICE AND SHERIFF

Sheriff's Dept 806.364.2311
Fax 806.363.7058
Web ....www.wtrt.net
E-mail ....dscso@wtrt.net
235 E 3rd St Rm 102, Hereford, TX 79045-5542
Brent Harrison, Sheriff

Delta County

SOCIAL SERVICES

Texas Health And Human Svcs
Commission 903.395.2154
Fax 903.395.2251
E-mail ....pegi.attaways@hhsc.state.tx.us
1280 W Dallas Ave, Cooper, TX 75432-1304
Pegi Attaway, Supervisor

POLICE AND SHERIFF

Sheriff's Dept 903.395.2146
Fax 903.395.0337
E-mail ....dcso@koyote.com
200 W Bonham Ave, Cooper, TX 75432-1716
G.r. Wood, Sheriff

Denton County

SOCIAL SERVICES

Family and Protective Svcs 972.353.3640
Fax 871.276.3971
Web ....www.dfps.state.tx.us
198 Civic Cir, Lewisville, TX 75067-3424
Martin Lopez, CPS Supervisor

GENERAL HEALTH SERVICES

Health Dept 940.349.2900
Fax 940.349.2901
Web ....www.dentoncounty.com
535 S Loop 288 Ste 1003, Denton, TX 76205
Suzy Hancock, Rn, Nursing Supervisor

MENTAL HEALTH SERVICES

Mental Health and Mental Retardation
Ctr 940.381.5000
Fax 940.383.1804
Web ....www.dentonmhmr.org
2519 Scripture St, Denton, TX 76201
Bill Drybread, Executive Director

JUSTICE AGENCY

CASA Program of Denton 940.243.2272
Fax 940.243.1605
Web ....www.casadenton.org
E-mail ....info@casadenton.org
614 N Bell Ave, Denton, TX 76209
Sherri Gideon, Executive Director

Court 940.349.2120
E-mail ....robert.ramirez@dentoncounty.com
1450 E McKinney, Denton, TX 76209
Robert Ramirez, Judge

Darcy Deno Attorney at Law 817.988.9528
E-mail ....darcydeno@verizon.net
1403 McCrae Trl, Southlake, TX 76092
Darcy Deno

Juvenile Probation 940.349.2400
Fax 940.349.2402
210 S Woodrow Ln, Denton, TX 76205
Peggy Fox, Chief JPO

COURTS

Court **940.349.2520**
Fax 940.349.2521
Web ....www.dentoncounty.com
E-mail ....kimberly.mccary@dentoncounty.com
210 S Woodrow Ln, Denton, TX 76205-6304
Kimberly McCary, Judge

Justice Of The Peace **972.434.7200**
Fax 972.434.7201
Web www.dentoncounty.com/jp2
E-mail ....dianne.johnson@dentoncounty.com
6301 Main St Ste 100, The Colony, TX 75056-1634
Dianne Johnson, Court Clerk

Teen Court **940.349.7809**
Fax 940.349.8325
Web ....www.cityofdenton.com
E-mail ....rxjones@cityofdenton.com
601 E Hickory St Ste D, Denton, TX 76205-4305
Roland Jones, Juvenile Case Manager

Teen Court **817.748.8346**
Fax 817.748.8685
Web ....www.ci.southlake.tx.us
E-mail ....teencourt@ci.southlake.tx.us
600 State St Ste 1000, Southlake, TX 76092-7640
Kristin White, Coordinator

POLICE AND SHERIFF

Denton Police Dept - Family Svcs
Unit **940.349.8181**
Fax 940.349.7966
E-mail ....richard.godoy@cityofdenton.com
601 E Hickory St Ste E, Denton, TX 76205-4305
Richard Godoy, LMSW, Family Services Coordinator

Sheriff's Dept **940.898.5620**
Fax 940.349.1604
Web ....www.dentoncounty.com
E-mail ....benny.parkey@dentoncounty.com
127 N Woodrow Ln, Denton, TX 76205-6325
Benny Parkey, Sheriff

EDUCATION SERVICES

Communities In Schools **972.436.6377**
Fax 972.436.6770
Web ....www.cisnt.org
E-mail ....info@cisnt.org
1597 S Edmonds Ln, Bldg A, Lewisville, TX 75067
Dana Smith, Interim Executive Director

Dimmit County

SOCIAL SERVICES

Texas Health and Human Svcs
Commission **830.876.2456**
Fax 830.876.3355
2208 N 1st St, Carrizo Springs, TX 78834-2036
Maribel Sulaica, Office Manager

POLICE AND SHERIFF

Sheriff's Ofc **830.876.3508**
Fax 830.876.9263
E-mail ....ppd743@yahoo.com
669 Industrial Blvd, Carrizon Springs, TX 78834
Joel Gonzales, Sheriff

EDUCATION SERVICES

Carrizo Springs TMC Head Start **830.876.3551**
Fax 830.876.3556
FM Rd 186, 905 5th St S, Carrizo Springs, TX 78834
Elma Gutierrez, Director

Donley County

GENERAL HEALTH SERVICES

Texas Dept Of Health **806.874.3211**
Fax 806.874.3589
16 N Hwy 70, Clarendon, TX 79226

COURTS

Court **806.874.3625**
Fax 806.874.1181
E-mail ....domcojudge@amaonline.com
300 S. Sully, Clarendon, TX 79226
Honorable Jack Hall, County Judge

POLICE AND SHERIFF

Sheriff's Ofc **806.874.3533**
Fax 806.874.3458
300 S. Jefferson St, Clarendon, TX 79226
Charles Butch E. Blackburn Jr., Sheriff

Duval County

SOCIAL SERVICES

Texas Health And Human Svcs
Commission **361.279.3301**
Fax 361.279.2852
1102 E State Highway 44 Ste A, San Diego, TX 78384
Belinda Luna, Office Manager

JUSTICE AGENCY

Juvenile Detention Facility **361.279.2040**
Fax 361.279.3166
4998 FARM RD1329, San Diego, TX 78384
Honorable Alex Gabert, District Judge

Juvenile Probation **361.279.3322**
Fax 361.279.3166
Web ....www.tjpc.state.tx.us
E-mail ....rvcscd66@msn.com
400 E Grabis Hwy 44, San Diego, TX 78384
Noe Gonzales, CPO

Eastland County

SOCIAL SERVICES

Texas Health And Human Svcs
Commission **254.629.1713**
Fax 254.629.8402
1331 E Main St Unit B, Eastland, TX 76448-3048
Linda Villalovos, Supervisor

JUSTICE AGENCY

Juvenile Probation **254.629.8174**
Fax 254.629.8196
Web ....www.tjpc.state.tx.us
E-mail ....robin.carouth@tjpc.state.tx.us
102 N Lamar St, Eastland, TX 76448-1818
Robin Carouth, Chief JPO

COURTS

District Court **254.629.1797**
Fax 254.629.1558
Web ....www.courts.state.tx.us
E-mail ....steven.herod@courts.state.tx.us
100 W Main St Ste 302, Eastland, TX 76448-2700
Steven R. Herod, Director

POLICE AND SHERIFF

Sheriff's Ofc **254.629.1774**
Fax 254.629.2500
201 W White St, Eastland, TX 76488
Wayne Bradford, Sheriff

EDUCATION SERVICES

Central Texas Opportunites Inc -
Eastland **254.629.8503**
Fax 254.629.8503
302 N Lamar St, Eastland, TX 76448
Theresa Nelson, Lead Teacher

Central Texas Opportunites Inc - Ranger Head
Start **254.647.3998**
205 S Marston St, Ranger, TX 76470
Darla Mcdonald, Director

Central Texas Opportunities Inc - Cisco Head
Start **254.442.4401**
E-mail ....ciscohs@sbcglobal.net
308 Front St, Cisco, TX 76437-2860
Grace Sitton, Director

Ector County

SOCIAL SERVICES

Family and Protective Svcs **432.368.2400**
Fax 432.684.2979
Web ....www.dfps.state.tx.us
E-mail ....pat.trimm@dfps.state.tx.us
2525 N Grandview Ave Ste 100, Odessa,
TX 79761-1622
Pat Trimm, CPS Supervisor

Texas Health And Human Svcs
Commission **432.334.5100**
Fax 432.334.5198
3016 Kermit Hwy, Odessa, TX 79762
Sherry Beezley, Supervisor

GENERAL HEALTH SERVICES

Health Dept **432.498.4141**
Fax 432.498.4143
Web ....www.co.ector.tx.us
E-mail ....sollal@co.ector.tx.us
221 N Texas Ave, Odessa, TX 79761-5126
Gino Solla, Director

JUSTICE AGENCY

CASA **432.498.4174**
Fax 432.498.4175
Web ....www.casapba.org
E-mail ....lynn@casapba.net
300 N Grant Ave Ste 207, Odessa, TX 79761-5157
Lyn White, Executive Director

Juvenile Probation **432.362.6356**
Fax 432.362.6618
E-mail ....lou.serrano@tjpc.state.tx.us
1401 E Yukon Rd, Odessa, TX 79762
Lou Serrano, Chief JPO

POLICE AND SHERIFF

Sheriff's Ofc **432.335.3050**
Fax 432.335.3568
E-mail ....markdonaldson@ectorcountysheriff.us
2500 South Highway 385, PO Box 2066, Odessa,
TX 79760
Mark Donaldson, Sheriff

Edwards County

POLICE AND SHERIFF

Ofc of The Sheriff **830.683.5110**
Fax 830.683.2459
404 W. Austin St, Rocksprings, TX 78880
Don G. Letsinger, Sheriff

El Paso County

SOCIAL SERVICES

Family and Protective Svcs **915.542.4535**
119 N Stanton St, El Paso, TX 79999
Evatt Ramirez, Program Director-subcare

Texas Health And Human Svcs
Commission **915.834.7500**
Fax 915.834.7587
401 E Franklin Ave Ste 210, El Paso, TX 79901
Yvonne Velarde, Regional Administrator

GENERAL HEALTH SERVICES

Dept Of Public Health **915.771.5702**
Fax 915.771.5729
5115 El Paso Dr, El Paso, TX 79905
Bruce Parsons, Childrenæs Dental Program Director

JUSTICE AGENCY

CASA of El Paso **915.546.8146**
Fax 915.546.8149
Web .... www.casaofelpaso.com
E-mail .... lsaucedo@epcounty.com
    500 E San Antonio Ave Rm 312, El Paso, TX 79901
Lisa Saucedo, Executive Director

Juvenile Probation Dept **915.849.2500**
Fax 915.849.2577
    6400 Delta Dr, El Paso, TX 79905
Roger Martinez, CJPO

COURTS

District Court **915.546.2032**
Fax 915.546.2131
E-mail .... lchew@co.el-paso.tx.us
    500 E San Antonio Ave Rm 606, El Paso,
    TX 79901-2429
Honorable Linda Chew, Director

POLICE AND SHERIFF

Sheriff's Ofc **915.546.2285**
Fax 915.546.2028
Web .... www.epcounty.com
E-mail .... lsamaniego@epcounty.com
    800 E Overland Ave Fl 4, El Paso, TX 79901-2510
Leo Samaniego, Sheriff

EDUCATION SERVICES

Barcelona Head Start Ctr **915.791.4801**
    328 Barcelona Dr, El Paso, TX 79907
Bertha Quevedo, Director

Communities In Schools of El Paso,
Inc. **915.593.7317**
Fax 915.590.5451
    1401 Pendale St, El Paso, TX 79937
Robert Shaw, Executive Director

Special Education **915.780.1919**
Fax 915.780.6537
E-mail .... jvasquez@esc19.net
    6611 Boeing Dr, El Paso, TX 79925
Dr. James Vasquez, Executive Director

Ellis County

SOCIAL SERVICES

Family and Protective Svcs **972.937.0892**
Fax 817.276.3945
E-mail .... laura.ard@dfps.state.tx.us
    208 YMCA Dr, Waxahachie, TX 75165
Laura Ard, Program Director

JUSTICE AGENCY

Juvenile Probation **972.923.5160**
Fax 972.923.5165
E-mail .... darrin.ray@elliscountyjuvenileservices.com
    111 W Franklin St, Waxahachie, TX 75165
Darrin Ray, Chief CPO

COURTS

Court **972.825.5296**
Fax 972.825.5010
    101 W Main St Ste 303, Waxahachie, TX 75165-0418
Honorable Jim Barden, Director

POLICE AND SHERIFF

Sheriff's Ofc **972.825.4901**
Fax 972.825.4941
E-mail .... sheriff@ellis.org
    300 S Jackson St, Waxahachie, TX 75165
Johnny Brown, Sheriff

Erath County

SOCIAL SERVICES

Texas Health and Human Svcs
Commission **254.965.3138**
Fax 254.965.5347
    2175 W South Loop St, Stephenville, TX 76401
Jacqueline Womble, Programme Manager

COURTS

District Court **254.965.1485**
Fax 254.965.4287
Web .... www.co.erath.tx.us
    112 W College St, Stephenville, TX 76401-4214
Wanda Pringle, Dist. Clerk

POLICE AND SHERIFF

Sheriff's Dept **254.965.3338**
Fax 254.965.3598
E-mail .... erathco.sheriff@htcomp.net
    1043 Glen Rose Rd, Stephenville, TX 76401
Tommy Bryant, Sheriff

Falls County

SOCIAL SERVICES

Texas Health And Human Svcs
Commission **254.883.3555**
Fax 254.883.6921
Web .... www.dir.state.tx.us
    217 Williams St, Marlin, TX 76661-3076
Shirley Swindall, Supervisor

GENERAL HEALTH SERVICES

Texas Dept Of Health **254.883.9206**
Fax 254.883.3627
    209 Green St, Marlin, TX 76661-2313
Cheryl Davis Rn, Nurse

JUSTICE AGENCY

Juvenile Probation **254.883.1429**
Fax 254.883.3346
E-mail .... jshort@milamcounty.net
    125 Bridge St, Marlin, TX 76661
John Short, Chief JPO

COURTS

District Court **254.883.1421**
Fax 254.883.1423
    82nd District Court, Marlin, TX 76661-0075
Honorable Robert Stem, District Judge

POLICE AND SHERIFF

Sheriff's Ofc **254.883.1431**
Fax 254.883.1434
    2847 State Highway 6, Marlin, TX 76661
Ben Kirk, Sheriff

Fannin County

SOCIAL SERVICES

Texas Health and Human Svcs
Commission **903.583.5535**
Fax 903.486.9286
    1205A E Sam Rayburn Dr, Bonham, TX 75418
Donna Mcbroom, Supervisor

GENERAL HEALTH SERVICES

Community Health Svc Agency - Bonham
Clinic **903.583.6155**
Fax 903.583.3158
    920 N Center St, Bonham, TX 75418
Misty Fry, Manager

JUSTICE AGENCY

CASA Program **903.583.4339**
Fax 903.583.3074
Web .... www.fanninccc.org
    112 W 5th St, Bonham, TX 75418-4365
Sandy Barber, Executive Director

COURTS

Court **903.583.7455**
    101 E Sam Rayburn Dr Ste 101, Bonham, TX 75418
Creta L Carter Ii, County Judge

POLICE AND SHERIFF

Sheriffs Ofc **903.583.2143**
Fax 903.583.4392
E-mail .... dfoster@fanninco.net
    2375 Silo Rd, Bonham, TX 75418
Donnie Foster, Sheriff

Fayette County

SOCIAL SERVICES

Texas Health and Human Svcs
Commission **979.968.3196**
Fax 979.968.8968
    228 N Main St, La Grange, TX 78945
Connie Sneed, Texas Works Clerk

JUSTICE AGENCY

Juvenile Probation **979.968.6865**
Fax 979.968.6331
    252 N Main St, La Grange, TX 78945
Debra Byler, Chief JPO

COURTS

District Court **979.968.8500**
Fax 979.966.0799
Web .... www.cvtv.net
    151 N Washington St Ste 201, La Grange,
    TX 78945-2657
Jeff Steinhauser, District Judge

POLICE AND SHERIFF

Sheriff's Ofc **979.968.5856**
Fax 979.968.5080
Web .... www.co.fayette.tx.us
E-mail .... keith.korenek@co.fayette.tx.us
    1646 N Jefferson St, La Grange, TX 78945-5440
Keith Korenek, Sheriff

Fisher County

POLICE AND SHERIFF

Sheriff's Ofc **325.776.2273**
Fax 325.776.3269
E-mail .... fishercountydispatch@yahoo.com
    112 N Concho St, Roby, TX 79543
J.a. Robinson, Sheriff

Floyd County

JUSTICE AGENCY

Juvenile Probation **806.983.4925**
Fax 806.983.4932
E-mail .... rebamoore@amaonline.com
    111 N Wall St, Floydada, TX 79235-2840
Reba Elmoore, Chief JPO

COURTS

District Court **806.983.3384**
Fax 806.983.3796
    105 S Main St Rm 204, Floydada, TX 79235-2758
Susan Young, Coordinator

POLICE AND SHERIFF

Sheriff's Ofc **806.983.4901**
Fax 806.983.4904
    125 E California St, Floydada, TX 79235-2822
Paul Raissez, Sheriff

Foard County

POLICE AND SHERIFF

Sheriff's Ofc **940.684.1501**
Fax 940.684.1947
Web ....www.dtnspeed.net
E-mail ....sheriffbrown@live.com
　110 S 1st St, Crowell, TX 79227
　Mike Brown, Sheriff

Fort Bend County

GENERAL HEALTH SERVICES

Health Dept **281.342.6414**
Fax 281.342.7371
　4520 Reading Rd Ste A, Rosenberg, TX 77471
　Nancy Drake, Rn, Director

MENTAL HEALTH SERVICES

**Texana Mental Health Mental
Retardation** **281.239.1300**
Fax 281.232.6445
Web ....www.texanacenter.com
E-mail ....shena.timberlake@texanacenter.com
　4910 Airport Ave Ste A, Rosenberg, TX 77471-5759
　Shena Timberlake, Director Of Behavioral Health

JUSTICE AGENCY

Attorney's Office **281.341.4555**
　5403 Ave N, Rosenberg, TX 77471
　Marjorie Hancock, Director

Child Advocates of Fort Bend **281.341.9955**
Fax 281.341.0798
Web ....www.cafb.org
　5403 Avenue N, Rosenberg, TX 77471
　Ruthanne Mefford, Executive Director

**Fort Bend Country Attorney's
Office** **281.344.5212**
E-mail ....sally.brown@co.fort-bend.tx.us
　5403 Ave N, Rosenberg, TX 77471
　Sally Brown

Juvenile Probation **281.633.7400**
Fax 281.633.7344
　122 Golfview Dr, Richmond, TX 77469
　Mike Meade, Chief JPO

COURTS

Court **281.341.4460**
Fax 281.341.4440
　1422 Eugene Hyman Cir, Richmond, TX 77469-3108
　John Healey, District Attorney

POLICE AND SHERIFF

Sheriff's Ofc **281.341.4700**
Fax 281.341.4701
E-mail ....wrighmil@co.fort-bend.tx.us
　1410 Wiliams way blvd, Richmond, TX 77469
　Milton T. Wright, Sheriff

Franklin County

SOCIAL SERVICES

**Texas Health And Human Svcs
Commission** **903.537.4541**
Fax 903.537.3291
　606 Inter State 30 W, Mount Vernon, TX 75457
　Shery Mcholm, Worker

MENTAL HEALTH SERVICES

**Lakes Regional Mental Health Mental Retardation
Ctr** **972.524.4159**
Fax 972.388.2009
Web ....www.lrmhmrc.org
E-mail ....angelas@lrmhmrc.org
　400 Airport Rd, Terrell, TX 75160-4302
　Angela Spradlin, Program Director

POLICE AND SHERIFF

Sheriff's Ofc **903.537.4539**
Fax 903.537.2632
E-mail ....pfletcher@co.franklin.tx.us
　208 Texas Highway 37, Mount Vernon, TX 75457
　Paul Fletcher, Sheriff

Freestone County

SOCIAL SERVICES

**Texas Health and Human Svcs
Commission** **254.739.2572**
Fax 254.739.5104
　101 Anthony st, Teague, TX 75860-1000
　Heather Fisk, Manager

GENERAL HEALTH SERVICES

Dept Of Health **903.389.2134**
Fax 903.389.7141
Web ....www.health.state.pa.us
　920 Bateman, Fairfield, TX 75840
　Cynthia Collins, Nursing Supervisor

COURTS

District Court **903.389.2534**
Fax 903.389.8421
Web ....www.co.anderson.tx.us
　118 E Commerce, 4th Flr, Fairfield, TX 75840-0013
　Janet Chappell, District Clerk

POLICE AND SHERIFF

Sheriff's Ofc **903.389.3236**
Fax 903.389.5730
Web ....www.tpwd.state.tx.us
E-mail ....ralph.billings@tpwd.state.tx.us
　103 S Keechi St, Fairfield, TX 75840-1519
　Ralph E. Billings, Sheriff

Frio County

SOCIAL SERVICES

**Texas Health and Human Svcs
Commission** **830.334.3395**
Fax 830.334.8653
　1009 N Oak St, Pearsall, TX 78061-3408
　Thelma Siller, Office Manager

GENERAL HEALTH SERVICES

**Texas Dept of State Health Svcs - Region
8** **830.334.4104**
Fax 830.334.8251
　402 S Pecan St, Pearsall, TX 78061
　Angie Hernandez, Human Services Technician

COURTS

Court **830.334.2154**
Fax 830.334.0010
E-mail ....friojudge@hotmail.com
　500 E San Antonio St Ste 7, Pearsall, TX 78061-3145
　Honorable Carlos A. Garcia, County Judge

POLICE AND SHERIFF

Sheriff's Ofc **830.334.3311**
Fax 830.334.0053
E-mail ....friocounty3@sbcglobal.net
　502 S Cedar St, Pearsall, TX 78061-3550
　Lionel Trevino, Sheriff

Gaines County

SOCIAL SERVICES

**Texas Health And Human Svcs
Commission** **432.758.9463**
Fax 432.758.3939
　106 Nw 2Nd St, Seminole, TX 79360-3502
　Priscilla Rodriguez, Texas Works Clerk

GENERAL HEALTH SERVICES

South Plains Public Health District **432.758.4022**
Fax 432.758.6077
Web ....www.texashan.org
E-mail ....sschafer@texashan.org
　704 Hobbs Hwy, Seminole, TX 79360-3402
　Soronya Schafer, Nursing Director

Galveston County

SOCIAL SERVICES

Family and Protective Svcs **409.948.3481**
Fax 713.928.7614
　2000 Texas Ave Ste 900, Texas City, TX 77590
　Rebecca Butler, Program Specialist

**Family and Protective Svcs / Ongoing
Svcs** **409.766.5960**
Fax 713.928.7605
Web ....www.dfps.state.tx.us
E-mail ....deborah.kumar-misir@dfps.state.tx.us
　123 Rosenberg St Ste 500, Galveston,
　TX 77550-1493
　Debbie Kumar-Misir, Director

**Texas Health And Human Svcs
Commission** **409.763.0277**
Fax 409.766.5910
Web ....www.yourtexasbenefits.com
　123 Rosenberg St, Galveston, TX 77550-1493
　Mary Bacon, Supervisor

GENERAL HEALTH SERVICES

Health District **409.938.7221**
Fax 409.938.2243
Web ....www.gchd.org
E-mail ....mguidry@gchd.org
　1207 Oak St, La Marque, TX 77568-5925
　Harlan Mark Guidry, Md, Mph, Director

Health District **409.765.2528**
Fax 409.765.2510
Web ....www.gchd.org
E-mail ....jhilton@gchd.org
　4700 Broadway St Ste C113, Galveston,
　TX 77551-4224
　Jim L Hilton, Std/hiv Program Director

JUSTICE AGENCY

Attorney's Office **409.770.6040**
E-mail ....wade.greiner@co.galveston.tx.us
　600 59th St, Ste 1001, Galveston, TX 77551
　Wade Greiner, Attorney

**Texas Youth Commission Galveston District Ofc - Parole
Ofc** **409.762.3481**
Fax 409.762.5166
　6000 Broadway St Ste 107, Galveston,
　TX 77551-4386
　Elias Clark, Juvenile Parole Officer

EDUCATION SERVICES

**Communities In Schools of
Galveston** **409.765.5395**
Fax 409.762.8834
E-mail ....mtcisgalv@aol.com
　2201 Market St Ste 715, Galveston, TX 77550-1529
　Marian Thomas, Executive Director

Garza County

SOCIAL SERVICES

**Texas Health And Human Svcs
Commission** **806.495.2881**
Fax 806.495.2419
Web ....www.state.tx.us
　US Highway 84 S, Post, TX 79356
　Annie Gober, Supervisor

Texas

Texas

COURTS

Court **806.495.4405**
Fax 806.495.4482
E-mail .... lee.norman@co.garza.tx.us
300 W Main St, Post, TX 79356
Honorable Lee Norman, Judge

POLICE AND SHERIFF

Sheriff's Dept **806.495.3595**
Fax 806.990.4446
Web ....www.garzacounty.net
412 E 15 St, Post, TX 79356-3211
Cliff Laws, Sheriff

Gillespie County

SOCIAL SERVICES

Texas Health And Human Svcs

Commission **830.997.7546**
Fax 830.997.3495
1904 N Llano St, Fredericksburg, TX 78624
Barbara Peckney, Manager

COURTS

Court **830.997.7502**
Fax 830.997.9958
Web ....www.gillespiecounty.org
E-mail ....mstroeher@gillespiecounty.org
101 W Main St Rm 9, Fredericksburg,
TX 78624-3700
Honorable Mark Stroeher, Director

POLICE AND SHERIFF

Sheriff's Dept **830.997.7585**
Fax 830.997.9541
1601 E Main St, Fredericksburg, TX 78624
Buddy Mills, Sheriff

Goliad County

SOCIAL SERVICES

Texas Health And Human Svcs

Commission **361.645.3732**
Fax 361.645.3148
142 Market St, Goliad, TX 77963
Laura Freeman, Supervisor

GENERAL HEALTH SERVICES

Dept of State Health Svcs **361.645.2595**
Fax 361.645.2283
Web ....www.tdh.state.tx.us
E-mail ....mary.ashton@dshs.state.tx.us
329 W Frankin St, Goliad, TX 77963
Mary Ashton, Nurse Supervisor

JUSTICE AGENCY

Juvenile Probation **361.645.8570**
Fax 361.645.0297
Web ....www.tjpc.state.tx.us
E-mail ....alberto.garcia@tjpc.state.tx.us
127 North Courthouse Square, Goliad, TX 77963
Alberto Garcia, Chief JPO

COURTS

Court **361.645.3337**
Fax 361.645.3474
Web ....www.goliadcountytx.gov
E-mail ....hgleinser@goliadcountytx.gov
127 N Courthouse Sq, Goliad, TX 77963
Honorable Harold Gleinser, Court Judge

POLICE AND SHERIFF

Sheriff's Dept **361.645.3451**
Fax 361.645.2230
701 E End St, Goliad, TX 77963
Kirby Brumby, Sheriff

Gonzales County

SOCIAL SERVICES

Dept. of Family and Protective

Svcs **830.672.6561**
Fax 210.304.7719
Web ....www.dfps.state.tx.us
E-mail ....diane.jones@dfps.state.tx.us
1600 N Sarah Dewitt Dr Ste 222, Gonzales,
TX 78629-2714
Diane Jones, Program Director

Texas Health And Human Svcs

Commission **830.672.9247**
Fax 830.672.6545
1600 N Sarah Dewitt Dr Ste 200, Gonzales,
TX 78629-2714
Ann Andrews, Manager

GENERAL HEALTH SERVICES

Gonzales Community Health Ctr **830.672.6511**
Fax 830.672.8608
Web ....www.tachc.org
E-mail ....halla.gonzales@tachc.org
228 Saint George St, Gonzales, TX 78629
April Hall, Rn, Nursing Director

POLICE AND SHERIFF

Sheriff's Dept Visha **830.672.6524**
Fax 830.672.2517
E-mail ....gcsosheriff@stx.rr.com
1713 E Sarah Dewitt Dr, Gonzales, TX 78629
Glen A. Sachtleben, Sheriff

Gray County

SOCIAL SERVICES

Texas Health and Human Svcs

Commission **806.665.1863**
Fax 806.663.5353
1509 N Banks St, Pampa, TX 79065
Sandra Mckinney, Texas Works Supervisor

JUSTICE AGENCY

CASA **806.669.7638**
Fax 806.669.6909
E-mail ....janet@casahp.org
315 N Ballard St, Pampa, TX 79066
Janet Watts, Executive Director

COURTS

District Clerk **806.669.8010**
Fax 806.669.8053
E-mail ....sandra.burkett@graycch.com
205 N Russell St Rm 300, Pampa, TX 79065-6451
Sandra Burkett, District Clerk

Northern Panhandle Child Protection

Court **806.669.8068**
Fax 806.669.4002
E-mail ....pam.kelly@courts.state.tx.us
205 N Russell St Rm 415, Pampa, TX 79065-6458
Pam Phillips, Court Coordinator

POLICE AND SHERIFF

Sheriff's Dept **806.669.8022**
Fax 806.669.8026
E-mail ....gcsheriff@pan-tex.net
218 N Russell St, Pampa, TX 79065
Don Copeland, Sheriff

Grayson County

SOCIAL SERVICES

Family and Protective Svcs **903.892.0580**
Fax 817.276.3951
902 Cottonwood Dr, Sherman, TX 75090
John Kirk, Intake Supervisor

Texas Health And Human Svcs

Commission **903.892.0581**
Fax 903.870.5302
2001 N Loy Lake Rd Ste D, Sherman, TX 75090-0212
Bill Nicks, Office Manager

GENERAL HEALTH SERVICES

Health Dept **903.465.2878**
Fax 903.465.2978
E-mail ....bellw@co.grayson.tx.us
205 N Houston Ave, Denison, TX 75021
Wayne L. Bell, MD, Director

Health Dept **903.893.0131**
Fax 903.892.3776
Web ....www.dshs.state.tx.us
515 N Walnut St, Sherman, TX 75090-4900
Lynn Killerlain, STD/HIV Coordinator

JUSTICE AGENCY

CASA Program **903.813.5400**
Fax 903.870.0880
Web ....www.casagrayson.org
E-mail ....jgarner@casagrayson.org
100 N Travis St Ste 302, Sherman, TX 75090
Jana Garner, Executive Director

Juvenile Probation **903.786.6326**
Fax 903.786.9401
Web ....www.tjpc.state.tx.us
E-mail ....bill.bristow@tjpc.state.tx.us
86 Dyess St, Denison, TX 75020-8425
Bill C. Bristow, Chief JPO

POLICE AND SHERIFF

Sheriff's Dept **903.893.4388**
Fax 903.893.4823
Web ....www.co.grayson.tx.us
E-mail ....burkv@co.grayson.tx.us
200 S Crockett St Ste 105A, Sherman,
TX 75090-7175
J. Keith Gary, Sheriff

Gregg County

SOCIAL SERVICES

Family and Protective Svcs **903.757.0588**
Fax 903.233.5201
E-mail ....linda.cunningham@dfps.state.tx.us
2130 Alpine Rd, Longview, TX 75601-3401
Linda Cunningham, Program Director

Texas Dept Of Health And Human

Svcs **903.753.0083**
Fax 903.232.3201
E-mail ....fay.booker@dhs.state.tx.us
1750 N Eastman Rd, Longview, TX 75601-3347
Fay Booker, Director

GENERAL HEALTH SERVICES

Health Dept **903.237.2620**
Fax 903.237.2608
405 E Marshall Ave Ste 104, Longview, TX 75601
Lewis Browne, Md, Health Director

JUSTICE AGENCY

CASA Program **903.753.8093**
Fax 903.753.4841
Web ....www.etcaserves.org
E-mail ....dshelton@etcaserves.org
1230 So. High St, Bldg C, Longview, TX 75606-3839
Deena Shelton, Executive Director

Juvenile Probation **903.758.0121**
Fax 903.758.0715
E-mail ....bcanion@cablelynx.com
310 Turk St, Longview, TX 75601
Bing Canion, Chief JPO

COURTS

Court **903.758.6181**
Fax 903.237.2699
E-mail . . . . .bill.stoudt@co.gregg.tx.us
101 E Methvin St Ste 300, Longview, TX 75601
Honorable Bill Stoudt, Judge

Teen Court **903.753.9701**
Fax 903.234.2705
E-mail . . . . .teencourt@ci.longview.tx.us
302 W Cotton St, Longview, TX 75601
Lindsey Simpson, Administrator

Grimes County

SOCIAL SERVICES

Texas Health And Human Svcs
Commission **936.825.3624**
Fax 936.825.6650
E-mail .beverly.hayes@hhsc.state.tx.us
513 N La Salle St, Navasota, TX 77868-2437
Beverly Hayes, Supervisor

GENERAL HEALTH SERVICES

Dept of State Health Svcs **936.825.7476**
202 S Judson St, Navasota, TX 77868
Ann Clodfelter, Rn, Supervisor

JUSTICE AGENCY

Attorney's Office **936.873.6455**
E-mail . . . . .jon.fultz@co.grimes.tx.us
382 FM 149 W, Anderson, TX 77830
Jon Fultz

COURTS

Court **936.873.4400**
Fax 936.873.2499
Web . . . . .www.co.grimes.tx.us
E-mail . . . . .betty.shiflett@co.grimes.tx.us
100 Main St, Anderson, TX 77830
Honorable Betty Shiflett, Judge

Guadalupe County

SOCIAL SERVICES

Texas Health And Human Svcs
Commission **830.379.6525**
Fax 830.372.2167
E-mail . . . . .david.fox@hhsc.state.tx.us
314 S Saunders St, Seguin, TX 78155
David Fox, Supervisor

JUSTICE AGENCY

Juvenile Probation **830.303.1274**
Fax 830.303.5276
Web . . . . .www.co.guadalupe.tx.us
E-mail . . . . .rquiros@co.guadalupe.tx.us
2613 N Guadalupe St, Seguin, TX 78155-1499
Ron Quiros, Chief JPO

COURTS

Court **830.303.4188**
Fax 830.303.5325
Web . . . . .www.co.guadalupe.tx.us
E-mail . . . . .ljones@co.guadalupe.tx.us
101 E Court St Ste 302, Seguin, TX 78155-5742
Honorable Linda Jones, Director

POLICE AND SHERIFF

Sheriff's Ofc **830.379.1224**
Fax 830.372.5408
Web . . . . .www.co.guadalupe.tx.us
E-mail . . . . .dawnc@co.guadalupe.tx.us
2617 N Guadalupe St, Seguin, TX 78155-7356
Arnold S. Zwicke, Sheriff

Hale County

SOCIAL SERVICES

Texas Health And Human Svcs
Commission **806.293.5193**
Fax 806.296.3165
2907 W 7th St, Plainview, TX 79072-6731
Gina Billington, Supervisor

JUSTICE AGENCY

Juvenile Probation **806.291.5259**
Fax 806.291.5300
Web . . . . .www.tjpc.state.tx.us
E-mail . . . . .eryberto.subealdea@tjpc.state.tx.us
122 E 6th St, Flr 2, Plainview, TX 79072
Eryberto Subealdea, Chief JPO

COURTS

Court **806.291.5214**
Fax 806.296.7786
E-mail . . . . .ddodson@plainview.com
500 Broadway St Rm 100, Plainview, TX 79072-8050
Bill Coleman, Director

POLICE AND SHERIFF

Sheriff's Ofc **806.296.2724**
Fax 806.296.5725
Web . . . . .www.halecounty.org
E-mail . . . . .hcsheriff@halecounty.org
1900 S Columbia St, Plainview, TX 79072-9340
David B. Mull, Sheriff

EDUCATION SERVICES

Creative Zones **806.293.8014**
Fax 806.293.8018
2813 W 8th St, Plainview, TX 79072
Rachelle Martinez, Director

Hall County

SOCIAL SERVICES

Texas Health and Human Svcs
Commission **806.259.3013**
Fax 806.259.3163
E-mail . . . . .joey.salins@hhsc.state.tx.us
512 W Main St Ste 11, Memphis, TX 79245
Joey Salins, Advisor

COURTS

Court **806.259.2511**
Fax 806.259.3083
E-mail . . . . .hallcounty@dtgoftexas.com
512 W Main St Ste 4, Memphis, TX 79245-3341
Honorable Roy Powell, Director

POLICE AND SHERIFF

Sheriff's Dept **806.259.2151**
Fax 806.259.2137
E-mail . . . . .hallso.sheriff@dtgoftexas.com
512 W Main St Ste 7, Memphis, TX 79245
Tim Wiginton, Sheriff

Hamilton County

SOCIAL SERVICES

Texas Health And Human Svcs
Commission **254.386.8965**
Fax 254.386.5584
103 Park Hill Dr, Hamilton, TX 76531
Sheila Tatum, Manager

COURTS

Court **254.386.3815**
Fax 254.386.8727
E-mail . . . . .countyjudge@hamiltoncountytx.org
102 N Rice St Ste 211, Hamilton, TX 76531
Honorable Randy Mills, Director

POLICE AND SHERIFF

Sheriff's Dept **254.386.8128**
Fax 254.386.8762
Web . . . . .www.htcomp.net
E-mail . . . . .hamiltonso@htcomp.net
1108 S Rice St, Hamilton, TX 76531-9600
Gergg Bewly, Sheriff

Hansford County

COURTS

District Court **806.659.4160**
Fax 806.659.2299
Web . . . . .www.courts.state.tx.us
E-mail . . . . .william.smith@courts.state.tx.us
84th District Court, Stinnett, TX 79083-3437
Honorable William D. Smith, District Judge

POLICE AND SHERIFF

Sheriff's Ofc **806.659.4140**
Fax 806.659.2025
10 NW Court St, Spearman, TX 79081
Gary Evans, Sheriff

Hardeman County

SOCIAL SERVICES

Texas Health And Human Svcs
Commission **940.663.6307**
Fax 940.663.5392
300 S Main St, Quanah, TX 79252
Sylvia Wyriek, Office Coordinator

POLICE AND SHERIFF

Sheriff's Ofc **940.663.5374**
Fax 940.663.2597
318 Mercer St, Quanah, TX 79252-4024
Mance Nelson, Sheriff

Hardin County

JUSTICE AGENCY

Attorney's Office **409.246.5165**
E-mail . . . . .rbdutton82@yahoo.com
PO Box 516, Kountze, TX 77625
Rebecca Walton, County Attorney

Juvenile Probation **409.246.5175**
Fax 409.246.8051
Web . . . . .www.co.hardin.tx.us
E-mail . . . . .monica.kelley@co.hardin.tx.us
300 Monroe St, Flr 3, Kountze, TX 77625
Monica Kelley, Juvenile Cpo

POLICE AND SHERIFF

Sheriff's Ofc **409.246.3441**
Fax 409.246.3277
Web . . . . .www.co.hardin.tx.us
E-mail . . . . .ed.cain@co.hardin.tx.us
300 Monroe St, Kountze, TX 77625-5994
Ed J. Cain, Sheriff

Harris County

SOCIAL SERVICES

Family and Protective Svcs **713.394.4000**
Fax 713.928.7623
Web . . . . .www.co.harris.tx.us
E-mail .scott.dixon@dfps.state.tx.us
2525 Murworth Dr, Houston, TX 77054-1603
Scott Dixon, Regional Director

Texas Health And Human Svcs
Commission **713.767.2000**
Fax 713.767.2419
Web . . . . .www.hhsc.state.tx.us
5425 Polk St Ste E, Houston, TX 77023-1452
Gwen Robinson, Director

Texas

GENERAL HEALTH SERVICES

City of Houston Dept of Health - Lyons Health Ctr **713.671.3000**
Fax 713.671.3062
Web ....www.cityofhouston.gov
E-mail ....kendra.davis@houstontx.gov
5602 Lyons Ave, Houston, TX 77020-4730
Kendra Davis, Intervention Specialist

Health Clinic **281.446.4222**
Fax 281.446.9563
1730 Humble Place Dr, Humble, TX 77338-5275
Carlos Peralta, Director

Health Dept **713.439.6000**
Fax 713.439.6080
Web ....www.hcphes.org
2223 West Loop S, Houston, TX 77027
Herminia Palacio, Md, Mph, Executive Director

Health Dept - Southeast Clinic **713.740.5000**
Fax 713.740.5110
Web ....www.hcphes.org
E-mail ....narnott@hcphes.org
3737 Red Bluff Rd, Pasadena, TX 77503-3307
Nita Arnott, Assistant Manager

Health Dept Baytown Health Ctr **281.427.5195**
Fax 281.427.1785
Web ....www.hcphes.org
1000 Lee Dr, Baytown, TX 77520-6980
Fouster Fowler, Director

Ryan Wyat Grant Administration **713.439.6090**
Fax 713.439.6338
2223 West Loop S Ste 417, Houston, TX 77027
Charles Henley, Manager

JUSTICE AGENCY

CASA / Child Advocates, Inc. **713.529.1396**
Fax 713.529.1390
Web ....www.childadvocates.org
E-mail ....development@childadvocates.org
2401 Portsmouth St, Ste 210, Houston, TX 77098
Sonya Galvan, CEO

Community Youth Svcs **713.295.2500**
Fax 713.295.2541
Web ....www.hc-ts.org
6300 Chimney Rock Rd, Houston, TX 77081-4502
Ginger Harper, Program Director

Criminal District Court **713.755.7094**
E-mail ....joan_campbell@justex.net
1200 Fannin St, Houston, TX 77002
Joan Campbell, Administrator

Juvenile Probation Dept **713.222.4100**
Fax 713.222.4222
1200 Congress St Fl 1, Houston, TX 77002
Thomas Brookes, Chief JPO

Texas Youth Commission - Houston District Ofc - East Regional Ofc **713.942.4200**
Fax 713.484.5543
10165 Harwin Dr, # 180-A, Houston, TX 77036
Helen George, Quality Assurance Administrator

COURTS

Family Court Svcs **713.755.6757**
Fax 713.755.7150
1310 Prairie St Ste 620, Houston, TX 77002
Christine Covelli, Judge

Hedwig Village **713.465.6009**
Fax 713.465.6807
E-mail ....admin@thecityofhedwigvillage.com
955 Piney Point Rd, Houston, TX 77024
Beth Staton, City Administrator

POLICE AND SHERIFF

Sheriff's Ofc **713.755.6044**
Fax 713.755.6228
1200 Baker St, Houston, TX 77002
Adrian Garcia, Sheriff

EDUCATION SERVICES

Browning Head Start **713.869.1684**
Web ....www.avancehouston.org
E-mail ....rloza@avancehouston.org
607 Northwood St, Houston, TX 77009-4510
Rosalinda Loza, Director

Burnett Head Start **713.694.6300**
Fax 281.922.9197
Web ....www.hcde-texas.org
E-mail ....oreliford@hcde-texas.org
11825 Teaneck Dr, Houston, TX 77089-6120
Odessa Reliford, Director

Clayton Homes Head Start **713.228.0343**
Fax 713.227.1694
1919 Runnels St, Bldg 14, Houston, TX 77003
Ivan Hernadez, Director

Communities In Schools **713.947.3809**
Fax 713.947.0639
E-mail ....bgarcia@snowbuilding.com
3222 Burke Rd Ste 213, Pasadena, TX 77504
Robert Garcia, Executive Director

Communities In Schools Bay Area **281.486.6698**
Fax 281.486.0405
Web ....www.cisba.org
E-mail ....peterw@cisba.org
17225 El Camino Real Ste 340, Houston, TX 77058-2767
Peter Wuenschel, Edd, Executive Director

Communities In Schools of Houston, Inc. **713.654.1515**
Fax 713.655.1302
Web ....www.cishouston.org
E-mail ....ccbriggs@cis-houston.org
2150 W 18th St Ste 100, Houston, TX 77008-1283
Cynthia Briggs, Executive Director

Dogan Head Start Ctr **713.675.3002**
Fax 713.675.0920
330 Russel St, Houston, TX 77026
Ricardo Palacios, Director

Special Education **713.462.7708**
Fax 713.744.6811
E-mail ....wlmckinney@esc4.net
7145 W Tidwell Rd, Houston, TX 77092
William L. Mckinney, Phd, Executive Director

Harrison County

SOCIAL SERVICES

Family and Protective Svcs **903.938.7751**
Fax 903.927.0290
E-mail ....deirdre.phillips@dfps.state.tx.us
4105 Victory Dr, Marshall, TX 75672-4751
Deirdre Phillips, CPS Supervisor

GENERAL HEALTH SERVICES

Marshall Health Dept **903.938.8338**
Fax 903.938.8330
805 Lindsey St, Marshall, TX 75670
Ginger Garrett, Director

JUSTICE AGENCY

Juvenile Probation **903.935.4874**
Fax 903.938.7954
1401 Warren Dr, Marshall, TX 75672
Darron Forehand, Director

COURTS

Court **903.935.8406**
Fax 903.934.9668
Web ....www.co.harrison.tx.us
E-mail ....jamies@co.harrison.tx.us
200 W Houston St Ste 263, Marshall, TX 75670-4027
Honorable Jim Ammerman Ii, Judge

POLICE AND SHERIFF

Sheriff's Ofc **903.923.4000**
Fax 903.935.4884
E-mail ....tomm@co.harrison.tx.us
200 W Houston St, Court House Basement, Marshall, TX 75670
William Tom Mccool, Sheriff

EDUCATION SERVICES

Communities In Schools **903.927.1128**
Fax 903.927.1328
E-mail ....joseph.alotto@ciset.org
2400 E End Blvd S, Rm 153, Marshall, TX 75672
Joseph Alotto, Executive Director

Haskell County

SOCIAL SERVICES

Family and Protective Svcs **940.864.2694**
Fax 940.864.3707
Web ....www.dfps.state.tx.us
E-mail ....geneva.schreoder@dfps.state.tx.us
500 S 10th St, Haskell, TX 79521-7216
Geneva Schreoder, Program Director

JUSTICE AGENCY

Juvenile Probation **940.864.8910**
Fax 940.864.8166
Web ....www.wtconnect.com
E-mail ....cscddavis@wtconnect.com
1301 N 1st St, Haskell, TX 79521
Christopher Davis, Chief JPO

COURTS

District Court **940.864.2661**
Fax 940.864.6164
1 Avenue D, Haskell, TX 79521
Honorable Shane Hadaway, Judge

POLICE AND SHERIFF

Sheriff's Ofc **940.864.2345**
Fax 940.864.3370
507 S 2nd St, Haskell, TX 79521-6503
James David Halliburton, Sheriff

Hays County

SOCIAL SERVICES

Texas Health And Human Svcs Commission **512.753.2201**
Fax 512.753.2297
Web ....www.hhsc.state.tx.us
1901 Dutton Dr Ste C, San Marcos, TX 78666-7574
Donald Coleman, Supervisor

GENERAL HEALTH SERVICES

Health Dept **512.393.5520**
Fax 512.393.5530
Web ....www.co.hays.tx.us
E-mail ....priscilla_hargraves@co.hays.tx.us
401 Broadway St Ste A, San Marcos, TX 78666-7771
Priscilla Hargraves, Director

MENTAL HEALTH SERVICES

Mental Health/Mental Retardation **512.392.7151**
Fax 512.392.5444
Web ....www.hillcountry.org
1200 N Bishop St, San Marcos, TX 78666-2706
Don Bruckenhoefer, Mh Director

JUSTICE AGENCY

CASA of Central Texas **512.392.3578**
Fax 512.392.3702
Web ....www.casacentex.org
E-mail ....info@casacentex.org
　104 E Martin Luther King Dr, San Marcos, TX 78666
　Norma Blackwell, Executive Director

Juvenile Probation **512.393.7755**
Fax 512.393.7775
Web ....www.co.hays.tx.us
E-mail ....shelly.williams@co.hays.tx.us
　302 W San Antonio St, San Marcos, TX 78666-5515
　Shelly Williams, Chief JPO

COURTS

Teen Court **512.754.0500**
Fax 512.754.0726
Web ....www.gsmyc.org
E-mail ....julia@gsmyc.org
　1402 Ih 35-N, San Marcos, TX 78667
　Julia Ramsay-new, Executive Director

POLICE AND SHERIFF

Sheriff's Ofc **512.393.7800**
Fax 512.393.7879
E-mail ....sheriff@co.hays.tx.us
　1307 Uhland Rd, San Marcos, TX 78666-8217
　Gary Cutler, Sheriff

Hemphill County

COURTS

Court **806.323.6521**
Fax 806.323.5271
E-mail ....engediranch@sbcglobal.net
　400 Main St, Canadian, TX 79014-2250
　George Briant, Judge

POLICE AND SHERIFF

Sheriff's Dept **806.323.5324**
Fax 806.323.5260
Web ....www.hemphillcountysheriff.com
E-mail ....sheriff@hemphillso.com
　5th & Main St, Canadian, TX 79014
　Gary Henderson, Sheriff

Henderson County

SOCIAL SERVICES

Family and Protective Svcs **903.675.5631**
Fax 817.276.3981
Web ....www.dfps.state.tx.us
E-mail ....susan.oxford@dfps.state.tx.us
　420 Athens Brick Rd, Athens, TX 75751-2662
　Susan Oxford, CPS Supervisor

Texas Health And Human Svcs
Commission **903.675.9141**
Fax 903.677.9255
　101 W Baker St, Athens, TX 75751-4407
　Theresa Moore, Supervisor

GENERAL HEALTH SERVICES

Texas Dept of Health **903.675.7742**
Fax 903.675.3622
　708 E Corsicana St, Athens, TX 75751
　Angela Rodriguez, Nursing Supervisor

JUSTICE AGENCY

CASA **903.675.7070**
Fax 903.677.0306
E-mail ....casaleeann@embarqmail.com
　1104 E Tyler St, Athens, TX 75751
　Lee Ann Millender, Executive Director

Dist Attorney Ofc **903.675.6100**
　109 W Corsicana St Ste 103, Athens, TX 75751
　Scott McKee, Attorney

Juvenile Probation **903.677.7250**
Fax 903.677.7276
Web ....www.tjpc.state.tx.us
E-mail ....bonny.turnege@tjpc.state.tx.us
　201 E Larkin St # J, Athens, TX 75751-2020
　Bonny Turnege, Chief JPO

COURTS

District Court 173 ....**903.675.6107**
Fax 903.675.6106
Web ....www.co.henderson.tx.us
　100 E Tyler St Ste 207, Athens, TX 75751-2577
　Honorable Dan Moore, Judge

POLICE AND SHERIFF

Sheriffs Ofc **903.675.9275**
Fax 903.677.6344
　206 N Murchison St, Ste A, Athens, TX 75751
　Ray Nutt, Sheriff

Hidalgo County

SOCIAL SERVICES

Dept of Human Svcs - CPS **956.580.6563**
Fax 956.580.6581
　4015 N Conway Ave, Mission, TX 78573-1310
　Betzabell Guerra, Program Director

Family and Protective Svcs **956.682.1301**
Fax 210.304.7757
　1919 Austin Ave, McAllen, TX 78501
　Betzabel Sennet, Program Director

Family and Protective Svcs **956.381.5791**
Fax 210.304.7773
　300 E Canton Rd, Edinburg, TX 78539
　Sandra Rodriguez, Program Director

Family and Protective Svcs **956.969.9280**
Fax 210.304.7757
Web ....www.dfps.state.tx.us
　510 S Texas Blvd Ste 2, Weslaco, TX 78596-7283
　Esmeralda Castillo, CPS Supervisor

Texas Health And Human Svcs
Commission **956.383.5344**
Fax 956.316.8338
Web ....www.dfps.state.tx.us
E-mail ....raul.trevino@hhsc.state.tx.us
　2520 S Veterens Blvd, Edinburg, TX 78539-7016
　Raul Trevino, Regional Administrator

GENERAL HEALTH SERVICES

Health Dept **956.585.2461**
Fax 956.584.7144
E-mail ....vicki.carza@dshs.state.tx.us
　211 Shubach Rd, Mission, TX 78573
　Vicki Carza, Supervisor

Health Dept **956.682.6155**
Fax 956.618.5979
Web ....www.hidalgocounty.com
　300 E Hackberry Ave, McAllen, TX 78501-9200
　Norma Garza, Supervisor

Health Dept - El Tule Health Ctr **956.318.2087**
Fax 956.316.3491
　1304 S St 25 Ave, Edinburg, TX 78539-9059
　Laila Deleon, Supervisor

Health Dept - Hidalgo Health Ctr **956.843.7463**
Fax 956.843.6672
Web ....www.dshs.state.tx.us
　702 E Texano Dr, Hidalgo, TX 78557
　Cecilia Lopez, Supervisor

Health Dept Elsa **956.262.1141**
Fax 956.262.7842
　708 E Edinburg, Elsa, TX 78543
　Marisa Ayala, Nurse

Health Dept Pharr **956.787.1531**
Fax 956.783.6310
　300 W Acres Ste B, Pharr, TX 78577
　Lilia Velasco, Supervisor

Hidalgo Chealth And Human Servs **956.383.6221**
Fax 956.383.3229
Web ....www.hchd.org
E-mail ....lydia.serna@hchd.org
　1304 S 25Th St, Edinburg, TX 78542
　Lydia Serna, Director Nurses

JUSTICE AGENCY

CASA **956.381.0346**
Fax 956.381.9232
　1001 S 10th Ave, Edinburg, TX 78539
　Linda Morales, Executive Director

Evins Regional Juvenile Ctr **956.289.5500**
Fax 956.381.1425
Web ....www.tyc.state.tx.us
　3801 W Monte Cristo Rd, Edinburg, TX 78541-8169
　Jorge Ganzalez, Superintendent

Juvenile Probation **956.381.8600**
Fax 956.383.4280
Web ....www.tjpc.state.tx.us
E-mail ....isreal.sever@jpd.co.hidalgo.tx.us
　1001 N Doolittle Rd, Edinburg, TX 78542-0337
　Isreal Sever, Chief JPO

COURTS

District Court **956.318.2275**
Fax 956.318.2698
Web ....www.co.hidalgo.tx.us
E-mail ....mario.ramirez@co.hidalgo.tx.us
　100 N Closner, Edinburg, TX 78539
　Honorable Mario E. Ramirez, Director

Teen Court-Boys and Girls Club **956.383.2582**
Fax 956.381.9635
E-mail ....dmedina@edinburgkids.com
　702 S 18th Ave, c/o Boys & Girls Club, Edinburg,
　TX 78539
　Diana Medina, Teen Director

POLICE AND SHERIFF

Sheriff's Ofc **956.383.8114**
Fax 956.393.6179
Web ....www.hidalgoso.org
E-mail ....guadalupe.trevino@co.hidalgo.tx.us
　711 E El Cibolo Rd, Edinburg, TX 78542-0471
　Guadalupe Trevino, Sheriff

EDUCATION SERVICES

Communities In Schools **956.630.0016**
Fax 956.630.0019
E-mail ....cishidalgo@hotmail.com
　3700 N 10th St Ste 270, McAllen, TX 78501
　Gus Kennedy, Director

Donna Ii Head Start **956.464.2561**
Fax 956.461.6522
　1715 Miller Ave, Donna, TX 78537
　Alicia Zamora, Director

Edinburg Ii Head Start Ctr **956.380.1088**
　1200 N 1st Ave Ste A, Edinburg, TX 78539
　Maria Gutierrez, Manager

Special Education **956.984.6000**
Fax 956.984.6189
　1900 W Schunior St, Edinburg, TX 78541-2233
　Jack Damron, Executive Director

Texas

Hill County

SOCIAL SERVICES

Texas Health And Human Svcs

Commission **254.582.5321**

Fax 254.582.9019

  605 S Ivy St, Hillsboro, TX 76645-3513

Sabrina Stansberry, Supervisor

GENERAL HEALTH SERVICES

Texas Dept of State Health Svcs **254.582.7331**

Fax 254.582.1072

  214 S Bois Darc St, Hillsboro, TX 76645

Martha Payne, RN, Supervisor

COURTS

District Court **254.582.4045**

Fax 254.582.4010

E-mail ....districtjudge@co.hill.tx.us

  1 N Waco St, Hillsboro, TX 76645

Honorable F. B. (bob) Mcgregor Jr., District Judge

POLICE AND SHERIFF

Sheriff's Ofc **254.582.5313**

Fax 254.582.3848

E-mail ....sheriff@hillsboro.net

  406 Hall St, Hillsboro, TX 76645

V. Brent Button, Sheriff

Hockley County

COURTS

Court **806.894.6856**

Fax 806.894.6820

  802 Houston St, Ste 101, Levelland, TX 79336-3706

Honorable Larry D. Sprowls, Judge

POLICE AND SHERIFF

Sheriff's Dept **806.894.3126**

Fax 806.897.0750

E-mail ....kdavis@hockleycounty.org

  1310 Ave H, Levelland, TX 79336

Kevin Davis, Sheriff

Hood County

SOCIAL SERVICES

Family and Protective Svcs **817.573.8612**

Fax 817.276.3956

  1430 Southtown Dr, Granbury, TX 76048

Stephanie Williams, CPS Supervisor

Texas Health And Human Svcs

Commission **817.573.1707**

Fax 817.579.0864

  214 N Travis St, Granbury, TX 76048-2188

Kathie Robertson, Supervisor

COURTS

District Court **817.579.3233**

Fax 817.579.3243

E-mail ....rwalton@co.hood.tx.us

  1200 W Pearl St, Granbury, TX 76048

Honorable Ralph H. Walton Jr., District Judge

POLICE AND SHERIFF

Sheriff's Dept **817.579.3316**

Fax 817.573.7372

E-mail ....hoodco@co.hood.tx.us

  400 Deputy Larry Miller Dr, Granbury, TX 76048

Roger Deeds, Sheriff

Hopkins County

GENERAL HEALTH SERVICES

Texas Dept of State Health Dept **903.885.6573**

Fax 903.439.9335

E-mail ....barbara.lay@dshs.state.tx.us

  1400 College St Ste 167, Sulphur Springs,
  TX 75482-3469

Barbrah Lay, Director Of Nurses

JUSTICE AGENCY

Attorney **903.438.4017**

E-mail ....rabe@hopkinscountytx.org

  128 Jefferson Ste B, Sulphur Springs, TX 75482

Dustanna Rabe, Director

Houston County

GENERAL HEALTH SERVICES

Texas Deparment of State Health

Svcs **936.544.3559**

Fax 936.544.0280

  1034 S 4th St, Crockett, TX 75835

Bobbie Sissom, Office Manager

JUSTICE AGENCY

Juvenile Probation **936.544.3255**

Fax 936.544.5169

Web ....www.co.houston.tx.us

E-mail ....across95@hotmail.com

  401 E Houston Ave Ste C, Crockett, TX 75835-2034

Tom Streetman, Probation Officer

POLICE AND SHERIFF

Sheriff's Dept **936.544.2862**

Fax 936.544.8061

E-mail ....hcso.houstontx.us

  700 S 4 St Ste A, Crockett, TX 75835-1949

Darrell Bobbitt, Sheriff

Howard County

SOCIAL SERVICES

Dept of Family and Protective Svcs **432.263.7671**

Fax 432.263.9867

E-mail ....elaine.leonard@dfps.state.tx.us

  501 Birdwell Ln Ste 28E, Big Spring, TX 79720

Elaine Leonard, CPS Director

GENERAL HEALTH SERVICES

Texas Dept Of Health **432.263.9775**

Fax 432.263.9781

  501 Birdwell Ln Ste 28B, Big Spring, TX 79720

Dave Padilla, Manager

JUSTICE AGENCY

Juvenile Probation **432.264.2240**

Fax 432.264.2250

Web ....www.tjpc.state.tx.us

E-mail ....hcjpd@suddenlinkmail.com

  315 S Main St Ste C, Big Spring, TX 79720-2515

Gerri Randle, Chief

COURTS

Court **432.264.2213**

Fax 432.264.2215

  300 S Main St, Big Spring, TX 79720

Donna Wright, County Clerk

POLICE AND SHERIFF

Sheriff's Ofc **432.264.2244**

Fax 432.263.5355

E-mail ....walkerforsheriff@hotmail.com

  300 S Main St Ste 105, Big Spring, TX 79720-2500

Stam Parker, Sheriff

Hudspeth County

POLICE AND SHERIFF

Sheriff's Ofc **915.369.2161**

Fax 915.369.2126

E-mail ....arvinwest@direcway.com

  525 N Wilson Rd, Sierra Blanca, TX 79851

Arvin West, Sheriff

Hunt County

SOCIAL SERVICES

Family and Protective Svcs **903.455.7636**

Fax 817.276.3961

E-mail ....natalie.reynolds@dfps.state.tx.us

  2500 Stonewall St, Greenville, TX 75401

Natalie Ausby-reynolds, CPS Investigations Supervisor

Texas Health And Human Svcs

Commission **903.455.0833**

Fax 903.454.7682

  2500 Stonewall St, Ste 601, Greenville, TX 75401

Becky Ferguson, Supervisor

GENERAL HEALTH SERVICES

Health Dept **903.408.4140**

Fax 903.454.3721

E-mail ....health@huntcounty.net

  2700 Johnson St, Greenville, TX 75401

Dr. Mark Mcmahan, Director

MENTAL HEALTH SERVICES

Glen Oaks Hospital **903.454.6000**

Fax 903.455.7980

Web ....www.glenoakshospital.com

E-mail ....glenoaks@koyote.com

  301 Division St, Greenville, TX 75402-4188

Satish Narayan, Medical Director

Mental Health Mental Retardation

Ctr **903.454.0300**

Fax 903.454.8635

Web ....www.lrmhmrc.org

E-mail ....angelas@lrmhmrc.org

  4804 Wesley St, Greenville, TX 75401-5650

Angela Spradlin, Program Director

JUSTICE AGENCY

CASA **903.450.4410**

Fax 903.450.4410

Web ....www.casaforhuntcounty.org

E-mail ....casa4huntcounty@msn.com

  PO Box 1571, Greenville, TX 75403-1571

Celeste Prather, Executive Director

Juvenile Probation **903.455.8555**

Fax 903.455.3760

  2700 Johnson St, Greenville, TX 75401

Frederick Farley, Chief

POLICE AND SHERIFF

Sheriff's Ofc **903.453.6800**

Fax 903.453.6822

E-mail ....rmeeks@huntcounty.net

  2801 Stuart St, Greenville, TX 75401

Randy Meeks, Sheriff

Hutchinson County

SOCIAL SERVICES

Family and Protective Svcs **806.274.2233**

Fax 432.684.2954

Web ....www.dfps.state.tx.us

E-mail ....molly.mcguire@dfps.state.tx.us

  301 W 6th St, Borger, TX 79007-4163

Molly Mcguire, Program Director

Texas Health And Human Svcs
Commission **806.273.7517**
Fax 806.274.5028
  301 W 6th St, Ste 320, Borger, TX 79007
  Val Ferguson, Director

MENTAL HEALTH SERVICES

Borger Mental Health **806.274.2297**
Fax 806.274.2452
Web ....www.tpmhmr.org
E-mail ....libby.moore@tpmhmr.org
  412 N Main St, Borger, TX 79007-4120
  Libby Moore, Director

Mental Health/Mental Retardation **806.274.2381**
Fax 806.273.7151
Web ....www.tpmhmr.org
E-mail ....lorna.heare@tpmhmr.org
  28 Pantex St, Borger, TX 79007-7805
  Lorna Heare, Director

JUSTICE AGENCY

Juvenile Probation **806.273.0106**
Fax 806.273.0107
Web ....www.tjpc.state.tx.us
E-mail ....david.hagler@tjpc.state.tx.us
  1400 Veta St Rm 200, Borger, TX 79007-2539
  David O. Hagler, Chief JPO

COURTS

District Court **806.878.4019**
Fax 806.878.4023
  500 Main St, Stinnett, TX 79083
  Honorable John W. Lagrone, District Judge

Irion County

POLICE AND SHERIFF

Sheriff's Ofc **325.835.2551**
Fax 325.835.7024
E-mail ....jimmy.martin@co.irion.tx.us
  209 N. Parkview Ave, Mertzon, TX 76941
  Jimmy E. Martin, Sheriff

Jack County

COURTS

District Court **940.567.2141**
Fax 940.567.2696
E-mail ....districtclerk@jackcounty.org
  100 N Main St, Jacksboro, TX 76458
  Honorable John H. Fostel, Judge

POLICE AND SHERIFF

Sheriff's Dept **940.567.2161**
Fax 940.567.2144
Web ....www.jackcountylec.com
E-mail ....dannynash@jackcountylec.com
  1432 Post Oak Rd, Jacksboro, TX 76458-3119
  Danny R. Nash, Sheriff

Jackson County

SOCIAL SERVICES

Texas Health And Human Svcs
Commission **361.782.5227**
Fax 361.782.2843
  202 E Main St, Edna, TX 77957
  Irene Nieto, Supervisor

GENERAL HEALTH SERVICES

Health Dept **361.782.5221**
Fax 361.782.7312
Web ....www.dshs.state.tx.us
E-mail ....jchd@texas.han
  411 N Wells Rm 206, Edna, TX 77957-2735
  Yvonne Janssen, Nursing Supervisor

JUSTICE AGENCY

Juvenile Probation **361.782.3101**
Fax 361.782.7631
Web ....www.co.jackson.tx.us
E-mail ....jcjpd@co.jackson.tx.us
  411 N Wells St Ste 307, Edna, TX 77957-2738
  Steven Floyd Minch, Chief JPO

COURTS

Court **361.782.2352**
Fax 361.782.5253
  115 W Main St Ste 207, Edna, TX 77957
  Dennis Simons, Judge

POLICE AND SHERIFF

Sheriff's Dept **361.782.3371**
Fax 361.782.7574
Web ....www.co.jackson.tx.us
E-mail ....a.louderback@co.jackson.tx.us
  115 W Main St, Ste 104, Edna, TX 77957-2733
  Andrew Louderback, Sheriff

Jasper County

SOCIAL SERVICES

Texas Health And Human Svcs
Commission **409.384.2515**
Fax 409.383.5550
  928 Marvin Hancock Dr, Jasper, TX 75951-4752
  Steve Allison, Supervisor

GENERAL HEALTH SERVICES

Jasper & Newton Counties Health
Dept **409.384.6829**
Fax 409.384.7861
E-mail ....danny.brackin@dshs.state.tx.us
  139 W Lamar St, Jasper, TX 75951-4014
  Danny Brackin, Director

JUSTICE AGENCY

Juvenile Probation **409.384.9063**
Fax 409.381.8957
Web ....www.tjpc.state.tx.us
  121 N Austin St, Ste A001, Jasper, TX 75951-4142
  Edeska Barnes Jr., Juvenile Cpo

COURTS

District Court **409.384.3792**
Fax 409.384.9722
  121 N Austin Street # 205, Jasper, TX 75951
  Jerome Owens, Judge

POLICE AND SHERIFF

Sheriff's Dept **409.384.5417**
Fax 409.384.7016
E-mail ....jaspersheriff@ias.net
  101 Burch St, Jasper, TX 75951
  Mitchell Newman, Sheriff

Jeff Davis County

COURTS

Court **432.426.3968**
Fax 432.426.2292
E-mail ....jdcjclerk@hotmail.com
  100 Court Avenue, Fort Davis, TX 79734
  Honorable George Grubb, Director

POLICE AND SHERIFF

Sheriff's Ofc **432.426.3213**
Fax 432.426.3937
Web ....www.dot.state.tx.us
  105 Court Ave, Fort Davis, TX 79734
  Rick Mcivor, Sheriff

Jefferson County

SOCIAL SERVICES

Family and Protective Svcs **409.963.0312**
Fax 409.963.4759
  5860 9th Ave Ste B, Port Arthur, TX 77642-6010
  Mike Spell, CPS Supervisor

GENERAL HEALTH SERVICES

Beaumont Public Health Dept **409.832.4000**
Fax 409.832.4270
Web ....www.ci.beaumont.tx.us
E-mail ....thelma.johnson@kcsi.com
  950 Washington Blvd, Beaumont, TX 77705-2251
  Thelma Johnson, Aids Coordinator

Port Arthur Health Dept **409.983.8800**
Fax 409.983.8870
Web ....www.portarthur.net
  449 Austin Ave, Port Arthur, TX 77640
  Yoshi Alexander, Director

MENTAL HEALTH SERVICES

Spindletop MH Svcs **409.784.5400**
Fax 409.833.8041
E-mail ....charles.harris@stmhmr.org
  655 S 8th St, Beaumont, TX 77701
  Charles Harris, Md, Director

JUSTICE AGENCY

CASA of Southeast Texas, Inc. **409.832.2272**
Fax 409.832.8260
E-mail ....casastlm@swbell.net
  2449 Calder St, Beaumont, TX 77702
  Lanis Mcwilliams, Executive Director

COURTS

District Court **409.835.8588**
Fax 409.839.2376
Web ....www.co.jefferson.tx.us
E-mail ....jc317@co.jefferson.tx.us
  1149 Pearl St Ste 202, Beaumont, TX 77701-3681
  Honorable Larry Thorne, Director

POLICE AND SHERIFF

Sheriff's Dept **409.835.8411**
Fax 409.784.5817
Web ....www.co.jefferson.tx.us
E-mail ....sheriffs@co.jefferson.tx.us
  1001 Pearl St Ste 103, Beaumont, TX 77701-3544
  George Mitch Woods, Sheriff

EDUCATION SERVICES

Communities In Schools of Southeast Texas,
Inc. **409.832.1146**
Fax 409.832.1374
Web ....www.cisset.org
E-mail ....knewton@cisset.org
  700 N St Ste B, Beaumont, TX 77701
  Karen Newton, Executive Director

Special Education **409.923.5400**
Fax 409.923.5471
  3545 Highway 96 Byp, Silsbee, TX 77656-7164
  Cindy Fuss, Director

Jim Hogg County

COURTS

Court **361.527.3015**
Fax 361.527.5800
  102 E tilley st, Hebbronville, TX 78361-0729
  Guadalupe Canales, Director

POLICE AND SHERIFF

Sheriff's Ofc **361.527.4140**
Fax 361.527.4310
  211 E Galbraith St, Hebbronville, TX 78361
  Erasmo Alarcon Jr., Sheriff

Jim Wells County

SOCIAL SERVICES

Texas Health And Human Svcs
Commission **361.664.7490**
Fax 361.660.2280
    408 N Airport Rd, Alice, TX 78332
    Sandra Cantu, Supervisor

GENERAL HEALTH SERVICES

Dept of State Health Svcs **361.664.2019**
Fax 361.668.4000
Web ....www.dshs.state.tx.us
    408 Flournoy Rd Ste C, Alice, TX 78332-4250
    Yolanda Martinez, Supervisor

MENTAL HEALTH SERVICES

Children and Youth Mental Health
Program **361.668.6041**
Fax 361.668.0222
Web ....www.cpmhmr.org
E-mail ....lperez@cpmhmr.org
    614 W Front St, Alice, TX 78332-5046
    Linda R. Perez, Director

POLICE AND SHERIFF

Sheriff's Dept **361.668.0341**
Fax 361.668.0569
E-mail ....diana-jwso@sbcglobal.net
    300 N Cameron St, Alice, TX 78332-4796
    Oscar Lopez, Sheriff

Johnson County

SOCIAL SERVICES

Family and Protective Svcs **817.202.2200**
Fax 817.276.3963
    1501 N Robinson Rd, Cleburne, TX 76031-1829
    Stacy Reynolds, Program Director

Texas Health and Human Svcs
Commission **817.558.9990**
Fax 817.645.2216
    204 Kimberly Dr, Cleburne, TX 76031-8704
    Cyndy Finnell, Supervisor / Office Mgr

GENERAL HEALTH SERVICES

Texas Dept of State Health Svcs **817.517.2306**
Fax 817.517.2308
    108 B E Kilpatrick St, Cleburne, TX 76031
    Lori James, Nursing Supervisor

COURTS

Court at Law #1 ....**817.556.6353**
Fax 817.556.6399
    204 S Buffalo Ave, Ste 408, Cleburne, TX 76033
    Honorable Robert B. Mayfield Iii, Judge - Court 1

POLICE AND SHERIFF

Sheriffs Dept **817.556.6058**
Fax 817.556.6051
    1102 E Kilpatrick St, Cleburne, TX 76031
    Bob L. Alford, Sheriff

Jones County

SOCIAL SERVICES

Texas Health And Human Svcs
Commission **325.823.3285**
Fax 325.823.3537
    1301 So Commerial, Anson, TX 79501
    Linda Whitehorn, Coordinator

COURTS

District Court **325.823.2721**
Fax 325.823.4200
Web ....www.co.jones.tx.us
E-mail ....brooks.hagler@co.jones.tx.us
    1100 Commericial, Anson, TX 79501
    Honorable Brooks Hagler, Director

POLICE AND SHERIFF

Sheriff's Ofc **325.823.3201**
Fax 325.823.2714
E-mail ....larry.moore@co.jones.tx.us
    1100 11th St, Anson, TX 79501
    Larry A. Moore, Sheriff

Karnes County

SOCIAL SERVICES

Texas Health And Human Svcs
Commission **830.780.3961**
Fax 830.780.2512
    417 So Panna Maria, Karnes City, TX 78118
    Alice Perez, Office Manager

COURTS

Court **830.780.2562**
Fax 830.780.3227
    101 N Panna Maria Ave, Ste 2, Karnes City, TX 78118
    Barbara Shal, Judge

POLICE AND SHERIFF

Sheriff's Dept **830.780.3931**
Fax 830.780.3273
Web ....:...www.karnesec.net
E-mail ....davidjalufka@sbcglobal.net
    113 N Panna Maria Ave, Karnes City, TX 78118-2931
    David Jalufka, Sheriff

Kaufman County

JUSTICE AGENCY

Juvenile Probation **972.932.0320**
Fax ..../...972.932.0479
    300 W Mulberry St, Kaufman, TX 75142
    Laura Peace, Chief JPO

COURTS

Court **972.932.4331**
Fax 972.932.7628
    100 W Mulberry St, Kaufman, TX 75142-2049
    Honorable Arlene Norville, Director

POLICE AND SHERIFF

Sheriff's Dept **972.932.4337**
Fax 972.932.9752
E-mail ....sheriff@airmail.net
    1900 E Highway 175, Kaufman, TX 75142
    David Byrnes, Sheriff

Kendall County

SOCIAL SERVICES

Texas Health And Human Svcs
Commission **830.249.3533**
Fax 830.249.2422
    216 Market Ave Ste 100, Boerne, TX 78006
    Gloria Marene, Office Manager

GENERAL HEALTH SERVICES

Texas Dept Of Health **830.249.3511**
Fax 830.249.2691
Web ....www.dshs.state.tx.us
    216 Market Ave Ste 160, Boerne, TX 78006
    Marie Brown, Rn, Supervisor

MENTAL HEALTH SERVICES

Mental Health Svcs **830.249.9328**
Fax 830.249.9238
Web ....www.hillcountry.org
    114 E Blanco Rd, Boerne, TX 78006-2002
    Gayle Wong, Center Director

COURTS

Court **830.249.9343**
Fax 830.249.7749
Web ....www.co.kendall.tx.us
E-mail ....joanne.bradley@co.kendall.tx.us
    201 E San Antonio Dr Ste 1, Boerne, TX 78006-2027
    Joanne F. Bradley, Chief JPO

POLICE AND SHERIFF

Sheriff's Ofc **830.249.9721**
Fax 830.249.8027
Web ....www.kendallcountysheriff.com
E-mail ....roger.duncan@kendallcountysheriff.com
    6 Staudt St, Boerne, TX 78006-1820
    Roger Duncan, Sheriff

Kenedy County

POLICE AND SHERIFF

Sheriff's Dept **361.294.5205**
Fax 361.294.5260
E-mail ....kenedyso@rivnet.net
    101 La Parra Road, Sarita, TX 78385
    Ramone Salinas Iii, Sheriff

Kent County

POLICE AND SHERIFF

Sheriff's Dept **806.237.3801**
Fax 806.237.3306
Web ....www.kentcountysheriff.tx.com
    101 N Main St, Jayton, TX 79528
    Billy Skogen, Sheriff

Kerr County

SOCIAL SERVICES

Family and Protective Svcs **830.792.4303**
Fax 210.304.7720
Web ....www.dfps.state.tx.us
E-mail ....shannon.walker@dfps.state.tx.us
    819 Water St Ste 230, Kerrville, TX 78028-5324
    Shannon Walker, Local Legal Supervisor

GENERAL HEALTH SERVICES

Kerrville State Hospital **830.896.2211**
Fax 830.792.4926
    721 Thompson Dr, Kerrville, TX 78028-5199
    Jay Norwood, CEO

Texas Dept of State Health Svcs **830.896.5515**
Fax 830.257.5158
E-mail ....vicki.lebleu@dshs.state.tx.us
    819 Water St Ste 290, Kerrville, TX 78028-5324
    Vicki Lebleu, Supervisor

JUSTICE AGENCY

Hill Country CASA **830.896.2272**
Fax 830.896.2309
E-mail ....hccasa@ktc.com
    309 Earl Garrett St, Kerrville, TX 78028
    Diane L. Oehler, Executive Director

Juvenile Probation **830.896.9013**
Fax 830.896.9014
Web ....www.co.kerr.tx.us
E-mail ....jdavis@co.kerr.tx.us
    3499 Lecion Dr, Kerrville, TX 78028-5327
    Jason P. Davis, Chief JPO

POLICE AND SHERIFF

Sheriff's Dept.............................**830.896.1216**
Fax..830.896.7380
E-mail..sheriff@ktc.com
　400 Clearwater Paseo, Kerrville, TX 78028
　W.rusty R. Hierholzer, Sheriff

Kimble County

SOCIAL SERVICES

Texas Health And Human Svcs
Commission................................**325.446.2920**
Fax..325.446.4023
　1003 College St, Junction, TX 76849

POLICE AND SHERIFF

Sheriff's Dept..............................**325.446.2766**
Fax..325.446.4341
Web......................................www.co.kimble.tx.us
E-mail...............................mpc9601@yahoo.com
　415 Pecan St, Junction, TX 76849-4144
　Mike Chapman, Sheriff

King County

POLICE AND SHERIFF

Sheriff's Ofc................................**806.596.4413**
Fax..806.596.4316
Web......................................www.sheriff.co.wise.tx.us
　800 US Hwy 82 & 83 Baker, Guthrie, TX 79236
　Cotton Elliott, Sheriff

Kinney County

SOCIAL SERVICES

Texas Health and Human Svcs
Commission................................**830.563.2473**
Fax..830.563.2147
　Ellen St & Louise St, Brackettville, TX 78832
　Paula Samaniego, Social Worker

POLICE AND SHERIFF

Sheriff's Ofc................................**830.563.2788**
Fax..830.563.9114
E-mail.............................kinneyso@sbcglobal.net
　109 North St, Brackettville, TX 78832
　L.k. Burgess, Sheriff

Kleberg County

SOCIAL SERVICES

Family and Protective Svcs..................**361.516.0943**
Fax..361.592.1087
E-mail.........................maria.ramirez@dshs.state.tx.us
　1404 S 14th St, Kingsville, TX 78363-6359
　Maria Ramirez, Program Director

Texas Health And Human Svcs
Commission................................**361.592.9351**
Fax..361.592.8771
　1413 E Corral Ave, Kingsville, TX 78363-4120
　Maria Lopez, Supervisor

JUSTICE AGENCY

Juvenile Probation.......................**361.595.8551**
Fax..361.593.1315
E-mail..cvera@kcscd.com
　725 E Yoakum Ave, Kingsville, TX 78363
　Cynthia Vera, Chief JPO

COURTS

Court..**361.595.8585**
Fax..361.592.0838
　700 East Clayburg, Kingsville, TX 78363
　Honorable Juan Escobar, Judge

POLICE AND SHERIFF

Sheriff's Ofc................................**361.595.8500**
Fax..361.595.7870
Web......................................www.klebergcoso.org
　1500 E King Ave, Kingsville, TX 78363-5924
　Ed Mata, Sheriff

Knox County

SOCIAL SERVICES

Texas Health And Human Svcs
Commission................................**940.658.3524**
Fax..940.658.3430
　606 E Main St, Knox City, TX 79529
　Jo Murray Clark, Supervisor

POLICE AND SHERIFF

Sheriff's Ofc................................**940.459.2211**
Fax..940.459.2016
　104 S. Stewart St, Benjamin, TX 79505
　Dean W. Homstead, Sheriff

La Salle County

SOCIAL SERVICES

Texas Health And Human Svcs
Commission................................**830.879.3021**
Fax..830.879.3780
　202 S Stewart, Cotulla, TX 78014
　Melissa Girtman, Texas Works Advisor

GENERAL HEALTH SERVICES

South Texas Rural Health Svcs, Inc............**830.879.3047**
Fax..830.879.2940
Web..www.tachc.org
E-mail...............................ceo.strhs@tachc.org
　304 Nueces, Cotulla, TX 78014-2237
　Alfredo Zamura, CEO

COURTS

Courthouse.................................**830.879.4432**
Fax..830.879.2933
　107 Courthouse Sq, Cotulla, TX 78014
　Honorable Joel Rodriguez, County Judge

POLICE AND SHERIFF

Sheriff's Ofc................................**830.879.3044**
Fax..830.879.3623
　101 Courthouse Sq Ste 203, Cotulla, TX 78014
　Victor S. Villarreal, Sheriff

EDUCATION SERVICES

Cotulla CSA Headstart..................**830.879.3616**
Web..www.csaofsti.com
　908 Martinez, Cotulla, TX 78014-2722
　Rhonda Gonzalez, Director

Lamar County

SOCIAL SERVICES

Texas Health And Human Svcs
Commission................................**903.785.7541**
Fax..903.737.0295
Web......................................www.hhsc.state.tx.us
　1460 19th St NW, Paris, TX 75460-2304
　Davlyn Evans, Supervisor

GENERAL HEALTH SERVICES

Lamar Health Dept.........................**903.785.4561**
Fax..903.737.9924
　740 6th St SW, Paris, TX 75461
　Amanda Green, Director

MENTAL HEALTH SERVICES

Mental Health Ctr..........................**903.785.6481**
Fax..903.737.2479
Web..www.lrcs.org
E-mail...kim@lrcs.org
　395 N Main St, Paris, TX 75460
　Kim Farris, Director

JUSTICE AGENCY

CASA for Kids..............................**903.737.4346**
Fax..903.737.4308
E-mail.........................sharone@casaforkidsparis.com
　2025 NW Loop 286, Paris, TX 75460
　Sharon Eubanks, Director

Juvenile Probation.......................**903.737.2460**
Fax..903.737.2464
E-mail.............................dbruce@co.lamar.tx.us
　4315-B Bonham St, Paris, TX 75460
　Darrel Bruce, Chief Probation Officer

COURTS

District Court...............................**903.737.2427**
Fax..903.785.4905
Web......................................www.co.lamar.tx.us
　119 N Main St Ste 405, Paris, TX 75460-4288
　Marvianne Patterson, District Clerk

POLICE AND SHERIFF

Sheriff's Dept..............................**903.737.2400**
Fax..903.737.2498
E-mail........................sheriff@co.lamar.tx.us
　125 Brown Ave, Paris, TX 75460
　Billy Joe Mccoy, Sheriff

Lamb County

SOCIAL SERVICES

Texas Health And Human Svcs
Commission................................**806.385.4416**
Fax..806.385.2001
　210 E Marshall Howard Blvd, Littlefield,
　TX 79339-5632
　Lisa Bermea, Supervisor

COURTS

Court..**806.385.4222**
Fax..806.385.6485
　100 6th Dr Rm 101, Littlefield, TX 79339
　Honorable William Thompson Jr., County Judge

POLICE AND SHERIFF

Sheriff's Ofc................................**806.385.7900**
Fax..806.385.9400
Web......................................www.nts-online.net
E-mail........................gmaddox@nts-online.net
　1200 E Waylon Jennings Blvd, Littlefield,
　TX 79339-4250
　Gary Maddox, Sheriff

Lampasas County

SOCIAL SERVICES

Texas Health And Human Svcs
Commission................................**512.556.3629**
Fax..512.556.4264
　204 Riverview Dr, Lampasas, TX 76550-8003
　Deb Williamson, Office Manager

GENERAL HEALTH SERVICES

Texas Dept of State Health Svcs............**512.556.5421**
Fax..512.556.8867
Web......................................www.dshs.state.tx.us
　500 E 8th St, Lampasas, TX 76550
　Glenna Tucker Rn, Nurse

Texas

POLICE AND SHERIFF

Sheriff's Dept **512.556.8255**
Fax 512.556.5809
E-mail . . . . lcso726@yahoo.com
　　410 E 41th St, Lampasas, TX 76550
　　David Whitis, Sheriff

Lavaca County

SOCIAL SERVICES

Texas Health And Human Svcs
Commission **361.798.3244**
Fax 361.798.5047
　　1309 E Cemetery Rd, Hallettsville, TX 77964
　　John Munson, Manager

GENERAL HEALTH SERVICES

Texas Dept of State Health Svcs **361.798.4371**
Fax 361.798.4752
　　1309 E Cemetery Rd, Hallettsville, TX 77964-2975
　　Theresa Kostelnick, Supervisor

JUSTICE AGENCY

Juvenile Probation **361.798.3714**
Fax 361.798.5904
E-mail . . . . marty_maloney@yahoo.com
　　412 N Texana, Hallettsville, TX 77964-0330
　　Linda Foeh-smith, Juvenile Cpo

COURTS

District Court **361.798.2351**
Fax 361.798.5674
E-mail . . . . sherryh@lavacacounty.net
　　109 N La Grange St, Hallettsville, TX 77964
　　Sherry Henke, District Clark

POLICE AND SHERIFF

Sheriff's Ofc **361.798.2121**
Fax 361.798.1890
E-mail . . . . mharmon@co.lavaca.tx.us
　　38 Fm 318, Hallettsville, TX 77964
　　Micah C. Harmon, Sheriff

Lee County

SOCIAL SERVICES

Texas Health And Human Svcs
Commission **979.542.3621**
Fax 979.540.3649
E-mail . . . . mary.kieschnick@hhsc.state.tx.us
　　2020 N Main, Giddings, TX 78942
　　Mary Kieschnick, Case Worker

POLICE AND SHERIFF

Sheriff's Dept **979.542.2800**
Fax 979.542.1446
E-mail . . . . lcso.dispatch@co.lee.tx.us
　　2122 FM 448, Giddings, TX 78942
　　Rodney Myer, Sheriff

Leon County

SOCIAL SERVICES

Texas Health and Human Svcs
Commission **903.536.2743**
Fax 903.536.2017
　　623 W Saint Marys, Centerville, TX 75833
　　Christy Largent, Manager

GENERAL HEALTH SERVICES

Texas Dept Of Health **903.536.7155**
Fax 903.536.7155
E-mail . . . . faith.kellar@dshs.state.tx.us
　　529 Lassater St, Centerville, TX 75833
　　Faith Kellar, Rn, Supervisor

JUSTICE AGENCY

Juvenile Probation **903.536.7003**
Fax 903.536.6040
Web . . . . www.co.juvprob.tjpc.state.tx.us
E-mail . . . . leon@co.juvprob.tjpc.state.tx.us
　　113 W Main, Centerville, TX 75833
　　Karen K. Robeson, Chief JPO

COURTS

Court **903.536.2331**
Fax 903.536.7044
E-mail . . . . byron.ryder@co.leon.tx.us
　　113 E Main St, Centerville, TX 75833
　　Honorable Byron Ryder, Director

POLICE AND SHERIFF

Sheriffs Dept **903.536.2749**
Fax 903.536.4357
Web . . . . www.cji.net
E-mail . . . . leoncoso@cji.net
　　606 E St. Marys St, Centerville, TX 75833
　　Jerry Wakefield, Sheriff

Liberty County

SOCIAL SERVICES

Family and Protective Svcs **936.336.7283**
Fax 713.928.7605
Web . . . . www.dfps.state.tx.us
E-mail . . . . leisha.fisher@dfps.state.tx.us
　　1405 Monta St, Liberty, TX 77575-3561
　　Leisha Fisher, Program Director

GENERAL HEALTH SERVICES

Dept of State Health Svcs **281.592.6714**
Fax 281.593.2940
Web . . . . www.dshs.state.tx.us
　　300 Campbell St, Cleveland, TX 77327-9737
　　Hortencia Herrera, Public Health Tech.

Limestone County

GENERAL HEALTH SERVICES

Dept of State Health Svcs **254.562.3861**
Fax 254.562.4290
Web . . . . www.dshs.state.tx.us
E-mail . . . . lorraine.smith@dshs.state.tx.us
　　939 Industrial Blvd, Mexia, TX 76667-2183
　　Lorraine Smith, Manager

Texas Dept of State Health Svcs **254.562.3897**
Fax 254.562.3510
E-mail . . . . sheryl.davis@cshs.state.tx.us
　　939 Industrial Blvd, Mexia, TX 76667-2818
　　Sheryl Davis, Anp, Rnc, Nurse Incharge

JUSTICE AGENCY

Attorney's Office **254.729.3046**
E-mail . . . . roy.defriend@co.limestone.tx.us
　　200 W State St Ste 110, Groesbeck, TX 76642
　　Roy Defriend, District County Attorney

Juvenile Probation **254.729.3569**
Fax 254.729.2348
Web . . . . www.tjpc.state.tx.us
E-mail . . . . brian.swick@tjpc.state.tx.us
　　908 N Tyus St, Groesbeck, TX 76642-2011
　　Brian Swick, Chief JPO

COURTS

District Court **254.729.3206**
Fax 254.729.2960
Web . . . . www.co.limestone.tx.us
　　200 W. State St, Groesbeck, TX 76642
　　Patrick Simmons, Judge

POLICE AND SHERIFF

Sheriff's Dept **254.729.3278**
Fax 254.729.8342
Web . . . . www.co.limestone.tx.us
E-mail . . . . dwilson@co.limestone.tx.us
　　940 N Pyus St, Groesbeck, TX 76642
　　Dennis D. Wilson, Sheriff

Lipscomb County

COURTS

Court **806.862.4131**
Fax 806.862.2603
E-mail . . . . lipscombcojudge@amaonline.com
　　101 Main St, Lipscomb, TX 79056
　　Honorable Willis Smith, Judge

POLICE AND SHERIFF

Sheriff's Ofc **806.862.2611**
Fax 806.862.2214
E-mail . . . . jsrobertson@amaonline.com
　　105 E Oak, Lipscomb, TX 79056
　　James R. Robertson, Sheriff

Live Oak County

POLICE AND SHERIFF

Sheriff's Ofc **361.449.2271**
Fax 361.449.3035
Web . . . . www.co.live-oak.tx.us
E-mail . . . . county.sheriff@co.live-oak.tx.us
　　200 Larry busby dr, George West, TX 78022
　　Larry R. Busby, Sheriff

Llano County

SOCIAL SERVICES

Texas Health And Human Svcs
Commission **325.247.3270**
Fax 325.247.2302
　　1447 E State Highway 71 Unit F, Llano, TX 78643
　　Tammy Branham, Supervisor

JUSTICE AGENCY

Attorney's Office **325.247.7733**
E-mail . . . . cheryll.mabray@co.llano.tx.us
　　801 Ford St Rm 111, Llano, TX 78643
　　Beverly Gatliff, Legal-assistant

POLICE AND SHERIFF

Sheriff's Ofc **325.247.5050**
Fax 325.247.3273
E-mail . . . . lcso@moment.net
　　2001 N State Highway 16, Llano, TX 78643
　　Bill Blackburn, Sheriff

Loving County

POLICE AND SHERIFF

Sheriff's Ofc **432.377.2411**
Fax 432.377.2025
E-mail . . . . hopb37@yahoo.com
　　121 N Pegus St, Mentone, TX 79754
　　Billy B. Hopper, Sheriff

Lubbock County

SOCIAL SERVICES

Family and Protective Svcs **806.762.2680**
Fax 432.664.2956
　　7 Briercroft Office Pk, Lubbock, TX 79412
　　Michelle Behpour, Program Director

Protective Svcs Region 1 Ofc 806.762.8922
Fax 432.684.2943
Web . . . . .www.dfps.state.tx.us
E-mail . . . . .camille.gilliam@dfps.state.tx.us
    1622 10th St, Mail Code: 217-4, Lubbock,
    TX 79401-2607
    Camille Gilliam, Regional Director

GENERAL HEALTH SERVICES

Lubbock Health Dept 806.775.2933
Fax 806.775.3959
Web . . . . .www.ci.lubbock.tx.us
E-mail . . . . .tcamden@mail.ci.lubbock.tx.us
    1902 Texas Ave, Lubbock, TX 79411-2117
    Tommy Camden, Health Director

MENTAL HEALTH SERVICES

Lubbock State School 806.763.7041
Fax 806.741.3604
Web . . . . .www.mhmr.state.tx.us
    3401 N University Ave, Lubbock, TX 79415
    Libby Allen, Director

JUSTICE AGENCY

CASA 806.763.2272
Fax 806.763.2273
Web . . . . .www.casaofthesouthplains.org
    24 Briercrost Office Park, Lubbock, TX 79412
    Jennie Hill, Executive Director

Juvenile Probation 806.775.1800
Fax 806.775.1860
E-mail . . . . .les.brown@tjpc.state.tx.us
    2025 N Akron Ave, Lubbock, TX 79415
    Les Brown, Chief JPO

COURTS

District Court 806.775.1309
Fax 806.775.7996
    904 Broadway st, Lubbock, TX 79408
    Judy Parker, Judge

South Plains Foster Care Cluster
Court 806.775.1707
Fax 806.775.1718
Web . . . . .www.co.lubbock.tx.us
E-mail . . . . .khart@co.lubbock.tx.us
    904 Broadway, Room 124, Lubbock, TX 79408
    Honorable Kevin C. Hart, Associate Judge

Teen Court 806.775.2461
Fax 806.775.2468
    915 Ave J, Lubbock, TX 79413
    Robert Doty, Judge

POLICE AND SHERIFF

Sheriff's Dept 806.775.1400
Fax 806.775.1491
    811 Main St, Lubbock, TX 79401
    Kelly Rowe, Sheriff

Lynn County

SOCIAL SERVICES

Texas Health And Human Svcs
Commission 806.998.4552
Fax 806.998.5442
E-mail . . . . .amelia.gonzalez@hhsc.state.tx.us
    1521 Avenue J, Tahoka, TX 79373
    Amelia Gonzalez, Advisor

GENERAL HEALTH SERVICES

Hospital Family Wellness Clinic 806.998.4604
Fax 806.561.4047
E-mail . . . . .mrichburg@lchdhealthcare.org
    1705 Lockwood, Tahoka, TX 79373
    Melanie Richburg, Clinic Coordinator

COURTS

Court 806.561.4222
Fax 806.561.5287
E-mail . . . . .hg.franklin@co.lynn.tx.us
    Court House Square, Tahoka, TX 79373
    Honorable H. G. Franklin, Judge

POLICE AND SHERIFF

Sheriff's Dept 806.561.4505
Fax 806.561.4658
    810 Lockwood St, Tahoka, TX 79373
    Jerry D. Franklin, Sheriff

Madison County

SOCIAL SERVICES

Texas Health And Human Svcs
Commission 936.348.2727
Fax 936.348.5460
    1608 E Main St, swt 105, Madisonville, TX 77864
    Christy Fogle, Advisor

GENERAL HEALTH SERVICES

Texas Dept Of Health Madisonville
Clinic 936.348.3593
Fax 936.348.3942
Web . . . . .www.dshs.state.tx.us
    300 W School St Ste 201, Madisonville, TX 77864
    Faith Kellar, Nursing Supervisor

COURTS

Court 936.348.2670
Fax 936.348.2690
Web . . . . .www.madisoncountytx.org
E-mail .general@madisoncountytx.org
    101 W Main St Ste 110, Madisonville,
    TX 77864-1901
    Arthur Henson, County Judge

POLICE AND SHERIFF

Sheriff's Ofc 936.348.2755
Fax 936.348.3763
Web . . . . .www.madisoncountytx.org
E-mail .dan.douget@madisoncountytx.org
    2005 E Main St, Madisonville, TX 77864-2237
    Dan W. Douget, Sheriff

Marion County

POLICE AND SHERIFF

Sheriff's Ofc 903.665.7201
Fax 903.665.6491
    114 W Austin St Ste 101, Jefferson, TX 75657
    Bill Mckay, Sheriff

Martin County

SOCIAL SERVICES

Texas Health And Human Svcs
Commission 432.756.2805
Fax 432.756.3803
    310 N Saint Peter St, Stanton, TX 79782
    Jerry Flores, Regional Director

POLICE AND SHERIFF

Sheriff's Ofc 432.756.3336
Fax 432.607.2992
Web . . . . .www.crcom.net
    301 N St Peter, Stanton, TX 79782
    John Woodward, Sheriff

Mason County

JUSTICE AGENCY

Blue Bonnet CASA 325.347.6474
Fax 325.347.6439
Web . . . . .www.bluebonnetcasa.org
E-mail . . . . .lisagoehmann@bluebonnetcasa.org
    205 N Live Oak, Mason, TX 76856
    Lisa Goehmann, Executive Director

POLICE AND SHERIFF

Sheriff's Dept 325.347.5252
Fax 325.347.6194
E-mail . . . . .masoncoso@cji.net
    210 West Moreland, Mason, TX 76856
    James Nixon, Sheriff

Matagorda County

SOCIAL SERVICES

Family and Protective Svcs 979.244.4847
Fax 713.928.7165
E-mail .peggy.gartman@tdprs.state.tx.us
    2010 Ave K, Bay City, TX 77414
    Peggy Gartman, Program Director

Texas Health And Human Svcs
Commission 979.244.1662
Fax 979.245.3485
Web . . . . .www.hhsc.state.tx.us
E-mail . . . . .tammy.hall@hhsc.state.tx.us
    2010 Avenue K, Bay City, TX 77414-5110
    Tammy Hall, Supervisor

GENERAL HEALTH SERVICES

Public Health Clinic 979.245.8421
Fax 979.245.2135
    1100 Ave G, Bay City, TX 77414
    Michael G. Neret, Md, Director

JUSTICE AGENCY

Juvenile Probation 979.244.5820
Fax 979.244.3849
    2004 Kilowatt Dr, Bay City, TX 77414-3165
    Justin O'connell, Chief JPO

POLICE AND SHERIFF

Sheriff's Dept 979.245.5526
Fax 979.245.1071
E-mail . . . . .elopez@co.matagorda.tx.us
    2323 Avenue E, Bay City, TX 77414
    Gary Mathis, Sheriff

Maverick County

SOCIAL SERVICES

Family and Protective Svcs 830.757.0070
Fax 210.304.7731
Web . . . . .www.dfps.state.tx.us
E-mail .maria.ramirez@dfps.state.tx.us
    1593 S Veterans Blvd, Eagle Pass, TX 78852-6474
    Maria D. Ramirez, CPS Supervisor

Indian Social Svcs Kickapoo Traditional Tribe Of
Texas 830.757.0315
Fax 830.757.9228
    467 Lucky Eagle Drive, Eagle Pass, TX 78852
    Theresa Garza, Social Services Director

Texas Health and Human Svcs
Commission 830.773.0350
Fax 830.773.8619
    1593 S Veterans Blvd, Eagle Pass, TX 78852-6474
    J J Martinez, Supervisor

Texas

JUSTICE AGENCY

Juvenile Probation **830.773.6383**
Fax 830.757.4344
Web ....www.tjpc.state.tx.us
1200 Ferry Street, Eagle Pass, TX 78852-4485
Bruce Ballou, Chief JPO

COURTS

District Court **830.773.1151**
Fax 830.757.2720
501 E Main St, Eagle Pass, TX 78852
Honorable Amado Abascal Iii, Judge

POLICE AND SHERIFF

Sheriff's Dept **830.773.2321**
Fax 830.757.1075
Web ....www.maverickcounty.org
E-mail ....sheriffherrera@maverickcounty.org
Highway 57, Eagle Pass, TX 78852
Tomas Herrera, Sheriff

McCulloch County

SOCIAL SERVICES

Texas Health And Human Svcs
Commission **325.597.0751**
Fax 325.597.1960
Web ....www.mfrs.org
214 Lynn Gavit Road, Brady, TX 76825
Cathy Weber, Supervisor

GENERAL HEALTH SERVICES

Texas Dept Of State Health Svcs **325.597.0550**
Fax 325.597.4489
1004 S Bridge St, Brady, TX 76825-5625
Toni Keltz, Supervisor

JUSTICE AGENCY

Juvenile Probation **325.597.2753**
Fax 325.597.0723
E-mail ....c198jpd@verizon.net
208 N Church St, Brady, TX 76825
Teri Trull, Chief JPO

COURTS

Court **325.597.0733**
Fax 325.597.1731
E-mail ....judgeneal@hotmail.com
County Courthouse, Rm 103, Brady, TX 76825
Danny Neal, Judge

POLICE AND SHERIFF

Sheriff's Dept **325.597.2290**
Fax 325.597.1662
E-mail ....mccullochso@yahoo.com
300 W Main St, Brady, TX 76825
Earl Howell, Sheriff

EDUCATION SERVICES

Central Texas Opportunities Inc - Brady
Headstart **325.597.4361**
Fax 325.597.3441
601 W 10th St, Brady, TX 76825
Emily Burleson, Director

McLennan County

SOCIAL SERVICES

Texas Health And Human Svcs
Commission **254.752.4839**
Fax 254.750.7888
612 Austin Ave, Waco, TX 76706
Gloria Kirk, Program Manager

GENERAL HEALTH SERVICES

Public Health District **254.750.5450**
Fax 254.750.5673
Web ....www.ci.waco.tx.us
E-mail ....roger.barker@tdh.state.tx.us
225 W Waco Dr, Waco, TX 76707-3836
Roger Barker, Director

JUSTICE AGENCY

CASA **254.752.9330**
Fax 254.752.9655
Web ....www.advocacycntr.org
E-mail ....ddavis@advocacycntr.org
2323 Columbus Ave, Waco, TX 76701
David Davis, Executive Director

Juvenile Probation **254.757.5072**
Fax 254.799.4902
2601 Gholson Rd, Waco, TX 76704
Bobby Campos, Chief

Texas Youth Commission - Waco District Ofc - Waco
Parole **254.755.7052**
Fax 254.755.7074
Web ....www.tyc.state.tx.us
717 Franklin Ave Ste 100, Waco, TX 76701-2023
Michael Richter, Parole Officer

COURTS

District Court **254.757.5081**
Fax 254.759.5683
Web ....www.co.mclennan.tx.us
E-mail ....19th@co.mclennan.tx.us
501 Washington Ave Ste 303, Waco, TX 76701-1373
Honorable Ralph T. Strother, District Judge

EDUCATION SERVICES

Communities In Schools **254.753.6002**
Fax 254.753.4415
Web ....www.cis-hot.org
E-mail ....dmcdurham@cis-hot.org
425 Austin Ave, Flr 15, Waco, TX 76701
Doug Mcdurham, Executive Director

EOAC 25th Street Headstart Ctr **254.752.1881**
Fax 254.753.5320
E-mail north25dirhbsglobal.net
629 N 25th St, Waco, TX 76707
Marilyn Nickerson, Director

Eoac Latimer Headstart Ctr **254.412.0313**
Fax 254.867.9574
3510 Latimer St, Waco, TX 76705-2527
Monica Richmond, Director

EOAC Mart Headstart Ctr **254.876.2071**
402 S Main St, Mart, TX 76664
Lisa landfort, Director

EOAC Moody Headstart Ctr **254.853.3165**
Fax 254.853.3825
300 Ave B, Moody, TX 96556
Ms Lori Antwine, Director

EOAC Waco Headstart Ctr **254.753.5324**
Fax 254.753.5467
201 Old South Robinson Rd, Waco, TX 76711
Ms Celestina Marrujo, Director

Special Education **254.297.1212**
Fax 254.666.0823
Web www.esc12.net
2101 W Loop 340, Woodway, TX 76702-3409
Jerry Maze, Executive Director

McMullen County

POLICE AND SHERIFF

Sheriff's Dept **361.274.3311**
Fax 361.274.3736
Web ....www.grandriver.net
E-mail ....tilden@grandriver.net
401 Main, Tilden, TX 78072
Bruce E. Thomas, Sheriff

Medina County

SOCIAL SERVICES

Family and Protective Svcs **830.426.7547**
Fax 830.426.5533
E-mail ....sherry.gomez@dfps.state.tx.us
410 Carter, Hondo, TX 78861-1531
Sherry Gomez, Regional Director

Texas Health And Human Svcs
Commission **830.741.2043**
Fax 830.426.5533
410 Carter St, Hondo, TX 78861-1531
James Smith, Texas Works Supervisor

GENERAL HEALTH SERVICES

Health Dept **830.741.6191**
Fax 830.426.4202
Web ....www.dshs.state.tx.us
E-mail ....pmuennink@aol.com
3103 Ave G, Hondo, TX 78861-3532
Pam Muennink, Public Health Nurse

POLICE AND SHERIFF

Sheriff's Dept **830.741.6150**
Fax 830.741.6156
E-mail ....sheriff@medinacountytexas.org
801 Avenue Y, Hondo, TX 78861
Randy Brown, Sheriff

Menard County

POLICE AND SHERIFF

Sheriff's Dept **325.396.4705**
Fax 325.396.2458
E-mail ....menardcountyso@yahoo.com
208 Tipton St, Menard, TX 76859
Buck Miller, Sheriff

Midland County

SOCIAL SERVICES

Family and Protective Svcs **432.686.2273**
Fax 432.686.2272
901 W Wall St, Fl 2, Midland, TX 79701
Jaime Hamm, Investigation Program Director

GENERAL HEALTH SERVICES

Dept of State Health Svcs **432.683.9492**
Fax 432.684.3932
Web ....www.dshs.state.tx.us
2301 N Big Spring St, Midland, TX 79705-7649
Oscar Hernandez, STD Team Leader

Health Dept **432.681.7613**
Fax 432.681.7634
3303 W Illinois Ave Ste 22, Midland, TX 79703
Celestino Garcia, Rs, Administrator

MENTAL HEALTH SERVICES

Mental Health/Mental Retardation **432.570.3300**
Fax 432.570.3425
Web ....www.pbmhmr.com
E-mail ....lcarroll@pbmhmr.com
401 E Illinois Ave, Midland, TX 79701-4803
Larry Carroll, Executive Director

JUSTICE AGENCY

CASA **432.683.1114**
Fax 432.683.1168
Web .... www.casawtx.org
E-mail .... lilyw@casawtx.org
   201 W Wall St Ste 700, Midland, TX 79701
Lily White, Executive Director

Texas Youth Commission Midland District Parole
Ofc **432.570.7338**
Fax 432.685.6042
Web .... www.tyc.state.tx.us
E-mail .... mark.shaw@tyc.state.tx.us
   602 N Baird St Ste 101, Midland, TX 79701
Mark Shaw, Parole Officer

COURTS

Child Protection Court of The Permain
Basin **432.688.4395**
Fax 432.688.4932
E-mail .... diana_valdes@co.midland.tx.us
   500 N Loraine St Ste 500, Midland, TX 79701
Diana Valdes, Court Coordinator

Court **432.688.4401**
Fax 432.688.4926
E-mail .... mike_bradford@zomd.tx.us
   500 N Loraine 4th Fl, Midland, TX 79701
Mike Bradford, County Judge

POLICE AND SHERIFF

Sheriff's Dept **432.688.4600**
Fax 432.688.4970
Web .... www.co.midland.tx.us
   400 S. Main St, Midland, TX 79702
Gary Painter, Sheriff

EDUCATION SERVICES

Communities In Schools **432.552.2495**
Fax 432.552.3495
Web .... www.cispermianbasin.org
E-mail .... gonzalez_m@utpb.edu
   1400 N Fm 1788, Ste 1318, Midland, TX 79707
Marisela Gonzalez, Director

Special Education **432.563.2380**
Fax 432.567.3290
Web www.esc18.net
   2811 Laforce Blvd, Air Terminal, Midland, TX 79711
John Thomas, Executive Director

Milam County

SOCIAL SERVICES

Family and Protective Svcs CPS **254.697.8792**
Fax 254.697.2208
   605 W 4th St, Cameron, TX 76520-2406
Patricia Villafuna-Nves, Program Director

Texas Health And Human Svcs
Commission **254.697.2353**
Fax 254.697.6103
   605 W 4Th St, Cameron, TX 76520
Shirley Swindall, Texas Works Supervisor

GENERAL HEALTH SERVICES

Health Dept **254.697.7039**
Fax 254.697.4809
Web .... www.milamhealth.com
   209 S Houston Ave, Cameron, TX 76520
Patsy Gaines, Director

COURTS

District Court **254.697.7010**
Fax 254.697.7012
E-mail .... ed.magre@tjpc.state.tx.us
   102 S Fannin Ave Ste 4, Cameron, TX 76520-4200
Honorable Ed Magre, Director

POLICE AND SHERIFF

Sheriff's Dept **254.697.7033**
Fax 254.697.7037
E-mail .... milamsheriff@tlabwireless.net
   512 N Jefferson Ave, Ste A, Cameron, TX 76520
David Greene, Sheriff

EDUCATION SERVICES

Cameron Headstart Ctr **254.697.4240**
Fax 254.697.4240
   1402 N Austin St, Cameron, TX 76520
Ms Rebecca Rodriguez, Director

Mills County

COURTS

35th District Court **325.648.2711**
Fax 325.648.3251
Web .... www.co.mills.tx.us
E-mail .... stephen.ellis@co.mills.tx.us
   1011 Fourth St, Goldthwaite, TX 76844
Honorable Stephen Ellis, Director

POLICE AND SHERIFF

Sheriff's Dept **325.648.2245**
Fax 325.648.3797
E-mail .... sheriff@centex.net
   1007 5th St, Goldthwaite, TX 76844
Doug Storey, Sheriff

Mitchell County

SOCIAL SERVICES

Texas Health And Human Svcs
Commission **325.728.2618**
Fax 325.728.3282
   505 Chestnut St, Ste B, Colorado City, TX 79512
Jinny Rivera, Office Manager

GENERAL HEALTH SERVICES

Sheriff's Dept **325.728.5261**
Fax 325.728.8319
Web .... www.netwest.com
E-mail .... mitcoso@netwest.com
   320 Pine St, Colorado City, TX 79512-6020
Patrick B. Toombs, Sheriff

Montague County

SOCIAL SERVICES

Texas Health And Human Svcs
Commission **940.872.1196**
Fax 940.872.4448
   601 Decatur St, Bowie, TX 76230
Chriss Preda, Supervisor

JUSTICE AGENCY

Juvenile Probation **940.894.6121**
Fax 940.894.2715
Web .... www.tjpc.state.tx.us
   100 Franklin, Montague, TX 76251
Rebecca Dickson, Chief JPO

Montgomery County

SOCIAL SERVICES

Family and Protective Svcs **936.760.4701**
Fax 713.928.7614
Web .... www.dfps.state.tx.us
E-mail .... leisha.fisher@dfps.state.tx.us
   2017 N Frazier St Ste C1, Conroe, TX 77301-1242
Leisha Fisher, Program Director/CPS Supervisor

Texas Health And Human Svcs
Commission **936.539.1161**
Fax 936.760.4768
   608 N Loop 336 E, Conroe, TX 77301
Elnoar Smith, Supervisor

GENERAL HEALTH SERVICES

University Of Texas Medical Branch-
Conroe **936.525.2800**
Fax 936.539.4668
E-mail .... vicky.molan@utmb.edu
   701 E Davis St Ste A, Conroe, TX 77301
Vicky Molan, Clinic Director

JUSTICE AGENCY

CASA **936.760.4140**
Fax 936.760.4180
Web www.casaspeaks4kids.com
E-mail .... anne@casaspeaks4kids.com
   412 W Phillips St, Ste 107, Conroe, TX 77301
Anne Mcalpin, CEO

Juvenile Probation **936.760.5805**
Fax 936.760.5851
E-mail .... rleach@co.montgomery.tx.us
   200 Academy Dr, Conroe, TX 77301
Ron Leach, Chief JPO

COURTS

Court **936.539.7973**
Fax 936.760.6942
   210 W Davis St Ste 201, Conroe, TX 77301
Patrice McDonald, Judge

Teen Court **281.364.4284**
Fax 281.367.3947
E-mail .... connelly@co.montgomery.tx.us
   1520 Lakefront Cir Ste 100, The Woodlands,
   TX 77380
Edie Connelly, Judge

POLICE AND SHERIFF

Sheriff's Ofc **936.760.5872**
Fax 936.538.7797
E-mail .... tommy.gage@mctx.org
   1 Criminal Justice Dr Ste 1, Conroe, TX 77304
Tommy Gage, Sheriff

Moore County

MENTAL HEALTH SERVICES

Texas Panhandle Mental Health Mental
Retardation **806.935.5322**
Fax 806.935.6064
   310 E 1st St Rm 200, Dumas, TX 79029
Marlene Deanda, Therapist Technician

COURTS

Court **806.935.5588**
Fax 806.935.5697
Web .... www.moore.co.tx.us
E-mail .... mcjudge@moore-tx.us
   715 S Dumas Ave, Rm 202, Dumas, TX 79029-4368
Honorable Rowdy Roads, Director

POLICE AND SHERIFF

Sheriff's Dept **806.935.4145**
Fax 806.935.2699
Web .... www.moorecountytexas.com
E-mail .... sheriff@moorecountytexas.com
   700 S Bliss Ave, Dumas, TX 79029-4448
J.e. Dearmond, Sheriff

Morris County

SOCIAL SERVICES

Texas Health And Human Svcs
Commission **903.645.2283**
Fax 903.645.3806
   603 Ward St, Daingerfield, TX 75638
Vicki Stanley, Supervisor

Texas

POLICE AND SHERIFF

Sheriff's Ofc **903.645.2232**
Fax 903.645.7228
  502 Union St Ste A, Daingerfield, TX 75638-1301
  Jack Martin, Sheriff

Motley County

POLICE AND SHERIFF

Sheriff's Ofc **806.347.2234**
Fax 806.347.2220
Web ....www.co.motley.tx.us
  701 Dundee St, Matador, TX 79244
  Chris Spence, Sheriff

Nacogdoches County

SOCIAL SERVICES

Family and Protective Svcs **936.569.7931**
Fax 713.928.7684
Web ....www.dfps.state.tx.us
E-mail ....eugene.frizell@dfps.state.tx.us
  2027 N Stallings Dr, Nacogdoches, TX 75964-1255
  Eugene Frizell, Director

Texas Health And Human Svcs
Commission **936.569.6695**
Fax 936.569.6695
  2614 NW Stallings Dr, Nacogdoches, TX 75964
  Terry Miller, Supervisor

GENERAL HEALTH SERVICES

Dept of Health Svcs **936.569.7931**
Fax 713.928.7684
Web ....www.dshs.state.tx.us
  2027 N Stallings Dr, Nacogdoches, TX 75964-1255
  Dawn Johnson, Receptionist

COURTS

145th District Court **936.560.7799**
Fax 936.560.7826
Web ....www.co.nacogdoches.tx.us
E-mail ....campbell.cox@co.nacogdoches.tx.us
  101 W Main St Ste 220, Nacogdoches,
  TX 75961-4868
  Honorable Campbell Cox Ii, Director

420th District Court **936.560.7848**
Fax 936.560.7899
E-mail ....ed.klien@co.nacogdoches.tx.us
  101 W Main St Ste 210, Nacogdoches, TX 75961
  Honorable Edwin Klein, District Judge

POLICE AND SHERIFF

Sheriff's Dept **936.560.7794**
Fax 936.560.6446
E-mail ....nsoadmin@cox-internet.com
  2306 Douglass Rd, Nacogdoches, TX 75964
  Thomas C. Kerss, Sheriff

Navarro County

SOCIAL SERVICES

Family and Protective Svcs **903.872.3901**
Fax 817.276.3955
Web ....www.dfps.state.tx.us
E-mail ....laurawhipe@dfps.state.tx.us
  800 N Main St Ste B, Corsicana, TX 75110-3053
  Laura Whipe, Supervisor

Texas Health And Human Svcs
Commission **903.872.4621**
Fax 903.872.9625
Web ....www.co.navaro.tx.us
  800 N Main St Ste J, Corsicana, TX 75110-3053
  Kathy Melton, Worker Iv

JUSTICE AGENCY

CASA **903.872.3772**
Fax 903.872.3755
E-mail ....vfoggins@kidadvocates.org
  120 E 2nd Ave, Corsicana, TX 75110
  Vicki Foggins, Program Director

POLICE AND SHERIFF

Sheriff's Ofc **903.654.3001**
Fax 903.654.3044
Web ....www.co.navarro.tx.us
  312 W 2nd Ave, Corsicana, TX 75110-3004
  Leslie A. Cotton Sr., Sheriff

Newton County

SOCIAL SERVICES

Texas Health And Human Svcs
Commission **409.379.8334**
Fax 409.379.3690
  509 Main St # 100, Newton, TX 75966-3616
  Lamurl Holloway, Supervisor

POLICE AND SHERIFF

Sheriff's Dept **409.379.3636**
Fax 409.379.3071
E-mail ....joe.walker@co.newton.tx.us
  110 E Court St, Newton, TX 75966-3230
  Joe Walker, Sheriff

Nolan County

GENERAL HEALTH SERVICES

Health Dept **325.235.5463**
Fax 325.236.6856
Web ....www.nolancountyhealth.com
E-mail ....jamie.mena@dshs.state.tx.us
  301 E 12th St, Sweetwater, TX 79556-2317
  Don Waier, Director

COURTS

Court **325.235.2353**
Fax 325.236.8098
  100 E 3rd St, Ste 107A, Sweetwater, TX 79556
  Honorable David Halll, Judge

POLICE AND SHERIFF

Sheriff's Dept **325.235.5471**
Fax 325.235.5750
Web ....www.nolanso.com
  100 E 3rd St Ste 110, Sweetwater, TX 79556-4546
  David Warren, Sheriff

Nueces County

SOCIAL SERVICES

Dept of Human Svcs **361.855.2451**
Fax 361.878.3395
Web ....www.state.tn.us
E-mail ....juan.gonzalez@state.tn.us
  5155 Flynn Pkwy, Corpus Christi, TX 78411
  Juan Gonzalez, Program Director

Family and Protective Svcs **361.854.2011**
Fax 210.304.7781
E-mail ....www.dfps.state.tx.us
  4201 Greenwood Dr, Corpus Christi, TX 78416
  Clara Trainer, Program Director

GENERAL HEALTH SERVICES

Health Dept **361.826.7200**
Fax 361.826.7295
Web ....www.cctexas.com
E-mail ....doloresa@cctexas.com
  1702 Horne Rd, Corpus Christi, TX 78416-1902
  Dolores Arispe, Rn, Maternal Health Director Of Nursing

JUSTICE AGENCY

CASA Program **361.884.2272**
Fax 361.884.2279
E-mail ....nccasa@aol.com
  2602 Prescott St, Corpus Christi, TX 78404
  Page Hall, Executive Director

Juvenile Probation **361.855.7303**
Fax 361.852.5846
Web www.nueces.esc2.net
E-mail ....hflorase@co.nueces.tx.us
  2310 Gollihar Rd, Corpus Christi, TX 78415-5334
  Homer Florase, Chief JPO

POLICE AND SHERIFF

Corpus Christi Police Dept **361.886.2600**
Fax 361.888.5142
  321 John Sartain St, Corpus Christi, TX 78401-2511
  Troy Riggs, Police Chief

Sheriff's Ofc **361.887.2222**
Fax 361.887.2206
Web ....www.co.nueces.tx.us
E-mail ....jkaelin@co.nueces.tx.us
  901 Leopard St Ste 220, Corpus Christi,
  TX 78401-3602
  Jim Kaelin, Sheriff

EDUCATION SERVICES

Austin Headstart **361.882.1767**
Fax 361.887.6965
E-mail ....marismendez@nccaatx.org
  550 Guatemozin St, Corpus Christi, TX 78405-3254
  Ms Ari Semendez, Director

Curtis Place Headstart Ctr **368.837.2201**
Fax 361.387.8598
  164 Curtis Pl, Robstown, TX 78380-2845
  Olivia Rodriquez, Director

El Tejanito Head Start **361.883.0578**
Fax 361.887.8427
  4768 Old Brownsville Rd, Corpus Christi,
  TX 78405-3504
  Ms Guadalupe Gomez, Director

Ochiltree County

SOCIAL SERVICES

Texas Health And Human Svcs
Commission **806.435.4710**
Fax 806.435.9302
  101 SW 4th Ave, Perryton, TX 79070-3003
  Jackie White Head, Supervisor

COURTS

Court **806.435.8031**
Fax 806.435.2081
Web ....www.co.ochiltree.tx.us
E-mail ....ejm1@ptsi.net
  511 S Main St, Perryton, TX 79070
  Honorable Earl Mckinley, Director

District Court **806.435.8054**
Fax 806.435.8058
Web ....www.courts.state.tx.us
E-mail ....william.smith@courts.state.tx.us
  511 S Main St Rm 12, Perryton, TX 79070-3100
  Honorable William D. Smith, Judge

Teen Court **806.435.4002**
Fax 806.435.6660
  21 SE 2nd, Perryton, TX 79070
  Jamie Becerril, Coordinator

POLICE AND SHERIFF

Sheriff's Dept 806.435.8000
Fax 806.435.8011
Web ....www.ptsi.net
E-mail ....txsheriff@ptsi.net
 21 SE 6th Ave, Perryton, TX 79070-3121
 Terry Bouchard, Sheriff

Oldham County

COURTS

Court 806.267.2607
Fax 806.267.2671
E-mail ....dnallred@amaonline.com
 105 S. Main, Vega, TX 79092
 Honorable Don R. Allred, Director

POLICE AND SHERIFF

Sheriff's Dept 806.267.2162
Fax 806.267.2362
E-mail ....vegaso@amaonline.com
 105 S. Main St, Vega, TX 79092
 David T. Medlin, Sheriff

Orange County

SOCIAL SERVICES

Texas Health And Human Svcs
Commission 409.886.4475
Fax 409.883.1880
 2222 Gloria Dr, Orange, TX 77630
 Kim Ulery, Supervisor

JUSTICE AGENCY

Juvenile Probation 409.882.7885
Fax 409.882.7844
Web ....www.co.orange.tx.us
 213 Market St, Orange, TX 77630-6335
 David Moore, Chief JPO

COURTS

Court at Law 409.882.7084
Fax 409.882.7843
Web ....www.co.orange.tx.us
E-mail ....pclark@co.orange.tx.us
 801 W Division Ave, Orange, TX 77630-6353
 Honorable Pat Clark, Judge

POLICE AND SHERIFF

Sheriff's Dept 409.883.2612
Fax 409.670.4156
E-mail ....kmerritt@co.orange.tx.us
 205 S Border, Orange, TX 77631-1468
 Keith Merritt, Sheriff

Palo Pinto County

SOCIAL SERVICES

Texas Health And Human Svcs
Commission 940.325.6913
Fax 940.325.8476
E-mail ....diana.runyon@dads.state.tx.us
 4113A Highway 180 E, Mineral Wells, TX 76067
 Diana Runyon, Case Worker

GENERAL HEALTH SERVICES

Texas Dept Of State Health Svcs 940.325.7844
Fax 940.328.1499
Web ....www.dshs.state.tx.us
 413 B Hwy 180 E, Mineral Wells, TX 76067
 Myrna Uribe, Rn, Supervisor

JUSTICE AGENCY

Juvenile Probation 940.325.9232
Fax 940.325.5422
E-mail ....robert.kimbrell@co.palo-pinto.tx.us
 107 N Oak Ave, Mineral Wells, TX 76067-4944
 Robert Kimbrell, Chief Of Juvenile Probation

COURTS

Court 940.659.1253
Fax 940.659.2411
Web ....www.co.palo-pinto.tx.us
E-mail ....david.nicklas@co.palo-pinto.tx.us
 520 Oak St, Palo Pinto, TX 76484
 Honorable David Nicklas, County Judge

POLICE AND SHERIFF

Sheriff's Ofc 940.659.2085
Fax 940.659.3801
 402 Cedar St., Palo Pinto, TX 76484
 Ira Mercer, Sheriff

Panola County

SOCIAL SERVICES

Texas Health and Human Svcs
Commission 903.693.7817
Fax 903.694.2922
 1430 S Adams St, Carthage, TX 75633
 Charlene Hamilton, Director

GENERAL HEALTH SERVICES

Dept of State Health Svcs 903.693.9322
Fax 903.694.2316
 1430 S Adams St, Carthage, TX 75633
 Pat Whitaker, Rn, Supervisor

JUSTICE AGENCY

Juvenile Probation 903.693.0352
Fax 903.693.0357
E-mail ....tracyva1@juno.com
 315 W Panola St, Carthage, TX 75633-2534
 Tracy Anderson, Chief JPO

COURTS

Court 903.693.0396
Fax 903.693.3046
Web ....www.co.panola.tx.us
E-mail ....terry.bailey@co.panola.tx.us
 110 S Sycamore St, Rm 300, Carthage, TX 75633
 Honorable Terry Bailey, Director

POLICE AND SHERIFF

Sheriff's Dept 903.693.0333
Fax 903.693.9366
 314 W Wellington St, Carthage, TX 75633
 Jack Ellett, Sheriff

Parker County

SOCIAL SERVICES

Family and Protective Svcs 817.599.3084
Fax 817.276.3948
E-mail ....evla.rutherford@dfps.state.tx.us
 1501 Texas Dr Ste 200, Weatherford, TX 76086
 Evla Rutherford, Director

Texas Health And Human Svcs
Commission 817.596.7502
Fax 817.599.7417
 1950 Clear Lake Rd, Weatherford, TX 76086
 Jeri Douglas, Worker Iv

JUSTICE AGENCY

Juvenile Probation 817.594.2313
Fax 817.594.9306
Web ....www.co.parker.tx.us
E-mail ....tkidd@ci.weatherford.tx.us
 110 Throckmorton St, Weatherford, TX 76086-3330
 Tom Glenn Kidd, Chief JPO

COURTS

District Court 817.599.6591
Fax 817.598.6108
Web ....www.parkercountytx.com
 117 Fort Worth Hwy Ste 103, DISTRICT COURTS
 BLDG - BASEMENT, Weatherford, TX 76086-4440
 Honorable Don Crestman, Director

POLICE AND SHERIFF

Sheriff's Dept 817.594.8845
Fax 817.594.7809
Web ....www.itexas.net
E-mail ....larry.fowler@parkercountytx.com
 129 Hogle St, Weatherford, TX 76086-2603
 Larry Fowler, Sheriff

Pecos County

SOCIAL SERVICES

Texas Health and Human Svcs
Commission 432.336.9745
Fax 432.336.3619
 108 S Water St, Fort Stockton, TX 79735-6812
 Rey Carreon, Supervisor

JUSTICE AGENCY

Juvenile Probation 432.336.7534
Fax 432.336.5113
E-mail ....pcjp@co.pecos.tx.us
 1692 East I-10, Fort Stockton, TX 79735
 Ray Acosta, Chief JPO

COURTS

District Court 432.336.3361
Fax 432.336.3554
Web ....www.co.pecos.tx.us
E-mail ....83court@co.pecos.tx.us
 400 S Nelson St, Fort Stockton, TX 79735-7132
 Carl Pendergrass, Director

POLICE AND SHERIFF

Sheriff's Dept 432.336.3521
Fax 432.336.2519
Web ....www.co.pecos.tx.us
E-mail ....pcsheriff@co.pecos.tx.us
 1774 N. Hwy 285, Fort Stockton, TX 79735
 Cliff Harris, Sheriff

Polk County

SOCIAL SERVICES

Family and Protective Svcs 936.327.6790
Fax 936.327.6770
Web ....www.dfps.state.tx.us
E-mail ....lou.liles@dfps.state.tx.us
 1102 Martin Luther King Dr, Livingston,
 TX 77351-2644
 Lou Liles, CPS Supervisor

Texas Health And Human Svcs
Commission 936.327.5715
 1102 Martin Luther King Dr, Ste A, Livingston,
 TX 77351
 Elaine Wade, Supervisor

GENERAL HEALTH SERVICES

Texas Dept Of State Health Svcs 936.328.8242
Fax 936.328.8249
 410 E Church St Ste B, Livingston, TX 77351-2966
 Peggy Wootan, Acsw-lmsw-acp, Administrator

University Of Texas Medical Branch
(Utmb) 936.327.5003
Fax 936.327.7464
 410 E Church St Ste D, Livingston, TX 77351
 Cynthia Wimberly, Chief Clerk

JUSTICE AGENCY

Juvenile Probation **936.327.6850**
Fax 936.327.9084
   1114 Dogwood Ave, Livingston, TX 77351-2218
   Jean Leblanc, Chief JPO

POLICE AND SHERIFF

Sheriff's Ofc **936.327.6810**
Fax 936.327.6877
E-mail ....khammack@polkcountyso.com
   1733 N Washington Ave, Livingston, TX 77351
   Kenneth Hamack, Sheriff

Potter County

SOCIAL SERVICES

Dept of Family and Protective Svcs **806.358.6211**
Fax 806.354.6299
E-mail ....mollie.mcguire@dfps.state.tx.us
   3521 SW 15th Ave, Amarillo, TX 79102
   Mollie Mcguire, CPS Program Director

Texas Health and Human Svcs
Commission **806.352.5005**
Fax 806.356.3180
Web ....www.hhsc.com
   3501 SW 45th Ave Ste L, Amarillo, TX 79109-5676
   Mary Doan, Regional Director

GENERAL HEALTH SERVICES

City of Amarillo - Dept of Public
Health **806.378.6300**
Fax 806.378.6306
Web ....www.amarillopublichealth.com
   1000 Martin Rd, Amarillo, TX 79105
   Dr. Roger Smalligan, Deputy Health Director

Wyatt Community Health Ctr **806.351.7200**
Fax 806.351.7303
Web ....www.wyattclinic.com
   1411 E Amarillo Blvd, Amarillo, TX 79107
   Gena Meade, Nursing Director

MENTAL HEALTH SERVICES

Mental Health/Mental Retardation **806.354.2191**
Fax 806.354.0081
E-mail ....libby.moore@tpmhmr.org
   1500 S Taylor St, Amarillo, TX 79101-4308
   Libby Moore, Director

Texas Panhandle M.H.M.R. Svcs **806.337.1000**
Fax 806.337.1036
Web ....www.tpmhmr.org
E-mail ....michael.jenkins@tpmhmr.org
   1501 S Polk St, Amarillo, TX 79101-4228
   Bud Schertler, Executive Director

JUSTICE AGENCY

Juvenile Probation **806.349.4900**
Fax 806.349.4933
Web ....www.tjpc.state.tx.us
   900 S Polk St Ste 500, Amarillo, TX 79101-3402
   Harold Mann, Chief JPO

Texas Youth Commission **806.354.2134**
Fax 806.354.2803
   7120 W Interstate 40 Ste 140, Amarillo,
   TX 79106-2599
   Nancy Jones, Juvenile Parole Officer

COURTS

District Court **806.379.2370**
Fax 806.379.6248
E-mail ....emersond@co.potter.tx.us
   501 S Fillmore St Rm 4B, Amarillo, TX 79101-2444
   Honorable Don Emerson, Executive Director

Teen Court **806.378.9342**
Fax 806.378.9317
Web ....www.ci.amarillo.tx.us
E-mail ....jennifer.gonzalez@ci.amarillo.gov
   201 SE 4th Ave, Amarillo, TX 79101-1519
   Jennifer Gonzalez, Assistant Administrator

POLICE AND SHERIFF

Sheriff's Dept **806.379.2900**
Fax 806.379.2919
Web ....www.co.potter.tx.us
E-mail ....brianthomas@co.potter.tx.us
   608 S Pierce St, Amarillo, TX 79101-2427
   Brian Thomas, Sheriff

EDUCATION SERVICES

Special Education **806.677.5000**
Fax 806.677.5001
Web www.esc16.net
E-mail ....john.bass@esc16.net
   5800 Bell St, Amarillo, TX 79109-6230
   John Bass, Edd, Executive Director

Presidio County

SOCIAL SERVICES

Texas Health And Human Svcs
Commission **432.229.3405**
Fax 432.229.4061
   Highway 67 At Louvain, Presidio, TX 79845
   Margaret Santillan, Supervisor

Texas Health And Human Svcs
Commission **432.729.4331**
Fax 432.729.4646
E-mail ....lorindal@yahoo.com
   101 N Mesa, Marfa, TX 79843
   Lorinda Gonzalez, Worker

GENERAL HEALTH SERVICES

Dept of State Health Svcs **432.229.3481**
Fax 432.229.4802
Web ....www.dshs.state.tx.us
   701 N Bomar St, Presidio, TX 79845
   Adriel Holt, Manager

Texas Dept of State Health Svcs **432.729.4275**
Fax 432.729.4785
   101 N Mesa St, Marfa, TX 79834
   Adriel Holt, Rio Grande

COURTS

Court **432.729.4452**
Fax 432.729.4453
E-mail ....eljuez@sbcglobal.net
   301 N Highland Ave, Marfa, TX 79843
   Paul Hunt, Director

POLICE AND SHERIFF

Sheriff's Dept **432.729.4308**
Fax 432.729.3171
Web ....www.iglobal.net
E-mail ....pcso@iglobal.net
   320 N Highland St, Marfa, TX 79843
   Danny C. Dominguez, Sheriff

Rains County

SOCIAL SERVICES

Texas Health And Human Svcs
Commission **903.473.2293**
Fax 903.473.2021
   201 Doris Briggs Pkwy, Emory, TX 75440-6301
   Carla Tarpley, Worker Iv

POLICE AND SHERIFF

Sheriff's Ofc **903.473.3181**
Fax 903.473.3008
Web ....www.co.rains.tx.us
E-mail ....rso500@yahoo.com
   313 E North St, Emory, TX 75440-2411
   David Traylor, Sheriff

Randall County

SOCIAL SERVICES

Texas Health And Human Svcs
Commission **806.655.3071**
Fax 806.655.9862
Web ....www.hhsc.state.tx.us
   404 21st St, Canyon, TX 79015-4000
   Jeanne Roach, Admin Tech 1

GENERAL HEALTH SERVICES

Texas Dept Of Health **806.655.7151**
Fax 806.655.7159
Web ....www.dshs.state.tx.us
E-mail ....barry.wilson@dshs.state.tx.us
   300 Victory Dr, Canyon, TX 79016-0001
   Barry Wilson, Director

COURTS

Court in Law #1 ....**806.468.5551**
Fax 806.468.5695
Web ....www.randallcounty.org
E-mail ....ccl1@randallcounty.org
   2309 Russell Long Blvd, Ste 132, Canyon,
   TX 79015-3182
   Honorable James Anderson, Director

POLICE AND SHERIFF

Sheriff's Dept **806.468.5800**
Fax 806.468.5751
Web ....www.randallcounty.org
   9100 S Georgia St, Amarillo, TX 79118-5073
   Joel W. Richardson, Sheriff

Reagan County

POLICE AND SHERIFF

Sheriff's Dept **325.884.2929**
Fax 325.884.2252
E-mail ....reaganso@wcc.net
   320 N Plaza Ave, Big Lake, TX 76932
   Jeff Gerner, Sheriff

EDUCATION SERVICES

Big Lake Headstart **325.884.6885**
Fax 325.884.6885
E-mail ....biglakehs@cvcog.org
   1100 N Utah, Big Lake, TX 76932
   Theressa Clark, Director

Real County

SOCIAL SERVICES

Texas Health And Human Svcs
Commission **830.597.2183**
Fax 830.597.3276
Web ....www.hhsc.state.tx.us
   106 N Nueces Camp, Wood, TX 78833
   James Smith, Manager

COURTS

Court **830.232.5304**
Fax 830.232.6040
E-mail ....wsamson@co.real.tx.us
   146 Main St, Leakey, TX 78873-0446
   Honorable W.b. Samson Jr., Director

POLICE AND SHERIFF

Sheriff's Ofc **830.232.5201**
Fax 830.232.5102
  101 Main St, Leakey, TX 78873
James E. Brice, Sheriff

EDUCATION SERVICES

Campwood Headstart **830.597.6295**
Fax 830.597.6395
E-mail ....campwoodhs@yahoo.com
  301 E 2nd St, Campwood, TX 78833
Ms Sulema Martinez, Director

Red River County

SOCIAL SERVICES

Texas Health And Human Svcs
Commission **903.427.3874**
Fax 817.276.3986
  308 N Cedar St, Clarksville, TX 75426
Paula Hausler, Office Contact

COURTS

Court **903.427.2680**
Fax 903.427.5510
Web ....www.co.red-river.tx.us
E-mail ....redriver0001@yahoo.com
  200 N Walnut St, Ste 1, Clarksville, TX 75426-3022
Honorable Morris Harville, Director

POLICE AND SHERIFF

Sheriff's Ofc **903.427.3838**
Fax 903.427.5913
  500 N Cedar St, Clarksville, TX 75426
Robert Bridges, Sheriff

EDUCATION SERVICES

Clarksville Headstart **903.427.3315**
Fax 903.427.5458
  1500 W Main St, Clarksville, TX 75426
Ms. Brenda Hunt, Director

Reeves County

SOCIAL SERVICES

Texas Health And Human Svcs
Commission **432.445.5487**
Fax 432.445.9084
Web ....www.hhsc.com
E-mail ....refugio.carneon@hhsc.state.tx.us
  324 S Cypress St, Pecos, TX 79772-3104
Refugio Carneon, Supervisor

COURTS

Court **432.445.5497**
Fax 432.445.3147
E-mail ....judgeholcomve@yahoo.com
  100 E 4th St, Pecos, TX 79772
Honorable Walter M. Holcombe, Director/Judge

POLICE AND SHERIFF

Sheriff's Office **432.445.4901**
Fax 432.445.9403
E-mail ....sheriffgomez22@hotmail.com
  500 S Oak St, Pecos, TX 79772
Arnulfo Gomez, Sheriff

Refugio County

COURTS

Court **361.526.4434**
Fax 361.526.5100
  808 Commerce St, Refugio, TX 78377
Honorable Rene Mascorro, Judge

POLICE AND SHERIFF

Sheriff's Dept **361.526.2351**
Fax 361.526.1668
  808 Commerce rd, Refugio, TX 78377
Robert Bolcik, Sheriff

EDUCATION SERVICES

BCAA Headstart - Refugio **361.526.5346**
Fax 361.526.4276
  400 Booster Sta, Refugio, TX 78377-4601
Sandra May, Director

Roberts County

COURTS

Court **806.868.3721**
Fax 806.868.3381
Web ....www.co.roberts.tx.us
E-mail ....vernon.cook@co.roberts.tx.us
  Kiowa and Commercial St, Miami, TX 79059-0478
Honorable Vernon H. Cook, Judge

POLICE AND SHERIFF

Sheriff's Ofc **806.868.3121**
Fax 806.868.6521
E-mail ....rcso@pan-tx.net
  112 South Main St, Miami, TX 79059
Dana P. Miller, Sheriff

Robertson County

SOCIAL SERVICES

Texas Health and Human Svcs
Commission **979.279.3446**
Fax 979.279.5261
  101 Cedar St, Hearne, TX 77859
Anthony Rosso, Supervisor

GENERAL HEALTH SERVICES

Texas Dept Of State Health Svcs **979.279.9281**
Fax 979.279.9288
  809 West Davis #9 And 10, Hearne, TX 77859
Any Nurse, Supervisor

POLICE AND SHERIFF

Sheriff's Ofc **979.828.3299**
Fax 979.828.5845
Web ....www.tpwd.state.tx.us
E-mail ....gerald.yezak@tpwd.state.tx.us
  113 Dechard, Franklin, TX 77856
Gerald T. Yezak, Sheriff

Rockwall County

SOCIAL SERVICES

Texas Health And Human Svcs
Commission **972.771.8386**
Fax 972.771.3080
  102 S 1st St Ste A, Rockwall, TX 75032
Becky Ferguson, Supervisor

GENERAL HEALTH SERVICES

Helping Hands Community Clinic **972.722.0190**
Fax 972.772.8175
Web ....www.rockwallhelpinghands.com
  102 S 1st St Ste B, Rockwall, TX 75087
Naggie Fuller, Clinical Director

Outreach Health Svcs **972.771.9541**
Fax 972.722.5321
Web ....www.outreachhealth.com
E-mail ....shelly.parker@outreachhealth.com
  761 Justin Rd Ste C, Rockwall, TX 75087-4877
Shelly Parker, Nurse Supervisor

JUSTICE AGENCY

CASA Program **972.772.5858**
Fax 972.772.9399
E-mail ....director@lonestarcasa.org
  108 Kenway, Rockwall, TX 75087
Lucille Bell, Executive Director

COURTS

District Court **972.882.0260**
Fax 972.882.0268
Web ....www.rockwallcountytexas.com
E-mail ....kmcdaniel@rockwallcountytexas.com
  1101 Ridge Rd Ste 209, Rockwall, TX 75087-4246
Kay Mcdaniel, Court Clerk

POLICE AND SHERIFF

Sheriff's Dept **972.882.0300**
Fax 972.882.0328
Web ....www.rockwallcountytexas.com
E-mail ....heavenson@rockwallcountytexas.com
  972 T L Townsend Dr, Rockwall, TX 75087-4905
Harold W. Eavenson, Sheriff

Runnels County

SOCIAL SERVICES

Family and Protective Svcs **325.365.5733**
Fax 325.365.5811
E-mail ....vicki.hoffman@dfps.state.tx.us
  814 Hutchins Ave, Ballinger, TX 76821
Vicki Hoffman, Administrative Assistant

Texas Health and Human Svcs
Commission **325.365.2564**
Fax 325.365.2938
  2017 Hutchings, Ballinger, TX 76821
Caroline Mcnelly, Worker

GENERAL HEALTH SERVICES

Dept of State Health Svcs **325.754.4945**
Fax 325.754.4933
E-mail ....lea.angel@dshs.state.tx.us
  110 S Main St Ste 108, Winters, TX 79567
Lea Angel, Supervisor

POLICE AND SHERIFF

Sheriff's Dept **325.365.2121**
Fax 325.365.5807
Web ....www.wcc.net
E-mail ....sheriff@wcc.net
  612 Strong Ave, Ballinger, TX 76821-5719
Bill Baird, Sheriff

Rusk County

SOCIAL SERVICES

Texas Health And Human Svcs
Commission **903.657.5508**
Fax 903.655.6201
Web ....www.dfps.state.tx.us
E-mail ....danita.sampson@dfps.state.tx.us
  700 Zeid Blvd, Henderson, TX 75652-6038
Danita Sampson, Program Director

GENERAL HEALTH SERVICES

Dept of State Health Svcs **903.657.7578**
Fax 903.655.0104
Web ....www.dshs.state.tx.us
  700 Zeid Blvd, Henderson, TX 75652-6045
Any Nurse, Director

JUSTICE AGENCY

Juvenile Probation **903.657.0372**
Fax 903.657.0214
E-mail ....fay.terry@tjpc.state.tx.us
  122 N Calhoun St, Henderson, TX 75652
Fay L. Terry, Chief JPO

Texas

COURTS

Court at Law **903.657.0344**
Fax 903.657.3378
Web ....www.co.rusk.tx.us
E-mail ....chad.dean@co.rusk.tx.us
   115 N Main St Rm 201, Henderson, TX 75652-3147
   Chad Dean, Judge

POLICE AND SHERIFF

Sheriff's Ofc **903.657.3581**
Fax 903.657.8726
   210 W Charlevoix St, Henderson, TX 75652
   Danny Pirtle, Sheriff

Sabine County

SOCIAL SERVICES

Texas Health And Human Svcs
Commission **409.787.3871**
Fax 409.787.2262
Web ....www.hhsc.state.tx.us
E-mail ....cynthia.smith@hhsc.state.tx.us
   2015 Worth St, Hemphill, TX 75948
   Cynthia Smith, Worker I

POLICE AND SHERIFF

Sheriff's Dept **409.787.2266**
Fax 409.787.2150
E-mail ....scso@sabinenet.com
   310 Main Street, Hemphill, TX 75948
   Thomas N. Maddox, Sheriff

San Augustine County

POLICE AND SHERIFF

Sheriff's Ofc **936.275.2424**
Fax 936.275.5133
   219 N Harrison St, San Augustine, TX 75972
   David Smith, Sheriff

San Jacinto County

POLICE AND SHERIFF

Sheriff's Ofc **936.653.4367**
Fax 936.653.4588
   75 W Cedar Ave, Coldspring, TX 77331
   James Walters, Sheriff

San Patricio County

SOCIAL SERVICES

Texas Health And Human Svcs
Commission **361.364.1240**
Fax 361.364.1161
   1115 E Sinton St, Sinton, TX 78387-2928
   Joe Gomez, Supervisor

GENERAL HEALTH SERVICES

Dept of Public Health **361.364.6208**
Fax 361.364.6117
Web ....www.spcdph.org
E-mail ....james.mobley@dshs.state.tx.us
   313 N Rachal St, Sinton, TX 78387-2663
   James A Mobley, Medical Director

Health Dept-Ingleside **361.776.3591**
Fax 361.776.3592
Web ....www.dshs.state.tx.us
   2681 San Angelo Ave, Ingleside, TX 78362-5801
   Rebecca Garcia, Nurse

JUSTICE AGENCY

Juvenile Probation **361.364.9500**
Fax 361.364.3253
   107 W 5th St, Sinton, TX 78387
   Marla Ruvalcaba, Chief JPO

POLICE AND SHERIFF

Aransas Pass Police Dept **361.758.5224**
Fax 361.758.3402
E-mail ....djones@aransaspasstx.gov
   600 West Cleveland Boulevard., Aransas Pass,
   TX 78336
   Mr Darrell Jones, Police Chief

Sheriff's Dept **361.364.9600**
Fax 361.364.6110
E-mail ....spso600@hotmail.com
   300 N Rachal St, Sinton, TX 78387
   Charles L. Moody, Sheriff

EDUCATION SERVICES

Aransas Pass Headstart Ctr **361.758.6127**
Fax 361.758.6129
   619 N Commercial St, Aransas Pass, TX 78336-2701
   Ms Melissa Ancira, Director

San Saba County

SOCIAL SERVICES

Texas Health and Human Svcs
Commission **325.372.5188**
Fax 325.372.3297
   421 E Wallace St, San Saba, TX 76877
   Chantay Hibler, Manager

Schleicher County

POLICE AND SHERIFF

Sheriff's Dept **325.853.2737**
Fax 325.853.2713
Web ....www.wcc.net
E-mail ....drdoran@sccn2.net
   4 South Divide, Eldorado, TX 76936
   David R. Doran, Sheriff

EDUCATION SERVICES

El Dorado Headstart **325.853.3366**
Fax 325.853.3366
   826 North Divide, El Dorado, TX 76936
   Ms Suzy Ramirez, Director

Scurry County

SOCIAL SERVICES

Family and Protective Svcs **325.573.1161**
Fax 325.573.0470
Web ....www.dfps.state.tx.us
   3409 Snyder Shopping Ctr, Snyder, TX 79549-4613
   Kathy Weber, Supervisor

GENERAL HEALTH SERVICES

Health Dept **325.573.3508**
Web ....www.scurrycohealth.unit.com
E-mail ....ScurryCoHealthUnit@hotmail.com
   911 26th St, Snyder, TX 79549
   Dana Eaton, Department Head

JUSTICE AGENCY

Juvenile Probation **325.573.3703**
Fax 325.573.1221
E-mail ....sy.tabor@tjpc.state.tx.us
   2511 College Ave, Snyder, TX 79549
   Sy Tabor, Chief JPO

POLICE AND SHERIFF

Sheriff's Dept **325.573.3551**
Fax 325.573.4456
   1300 26th St, Snyder, TX 79549
   Darren Jackson, Sheriff

Shackelford County

POLICE AND SHERIFF

Sheriff's Dept **325.762.2000**
Fax 325.762.3432
E-mail ....jill@schakelfordcosheriff.com
   309 S 2nd St, Albany, TX 76430
   Ed Miller, Sheriff

Shelby County

SOCIAL SERVICES

Texas Health And Human Svcs
Commission **936.598.2451**
Fax 936.598.7259
   912 Nacogdoches St, Center, TX 75935
   Sandra Riggs, Supervisor

GENERAL HEALTH SERVICES

University Of Texas Tech Medical
Branch **936.598.7250**
Fax 936.591.0664
Web ....www.utmb.edu
E-mail ....dscott@utmb.edu
   105 Foster St, Center, TX 75935-3447
   Deborah Scott, Supervisor

COURTS

District Court **936.598.9928**
Fax 936.591.0984
Web ....www.co.panola.tx.us
E-mail ....guy.griffin@co.panola.tx.us
   200 San Augustine St Ste 3, Center, TX 75935-3959
   Honorable Guy W. Griffin, Director

POLICE AND SHERIFF

Sheriff's Dept **936.598.5600**
Fax 936.598.7893
E-mail ....shelbycoso@yahoo.com
   100 Hurst St, Center, TX 75935
   Newton Johnson, Sheriff

Sherman County

POLICE AND SHERIFF

Sheriff's Dept **806.366.5551**
Fax 806.366.3142
   701 N. 3rd St, Stratford, TX 79084
   Jack Haile, Sheriff

Smith County

SOCIAL SERVICES

Family and Protective Svcs **903.595.4841**
Fax 903.533.4133
   3303 Mineola Hwy, Tyler, TX 75702
   Colleen Mccall, Regional Director

Protective Svcs Region 4 Ofc **903.561.5359**
Fax 903.509.5154
E-mail ....judy.bowman@tdprs.state.tx.us
   302 E Rieck Rd, Mail Code: 313-5, Tyler,
   TX 75703-3824
   Judy Bowman, Regional Director For Child Protective Services

GENERAL HEALTH SERVICES

Health District **903.535.0030**
Fax 903.535.0052
E-mail ....groberts@netphd.org
   815 N Broadway Ave, Tyler, TX 75702
   George Roberts, Director

JUSTICE AGENCY

CASA For Kids of East Texas **903.597.7725**
Fax 903.597.0691
Web ....www.casaforkidsofet.org
E-mail ....patty@casaforkidsofet.org
   318 E 5th St, Tyler, TX 75701
   Patty Garner, Executive Director

Criminal Dist Attny 972.548.3607
E-mail ....mmiranda@co.collin.state.us
    2100 Bloomdale Rd, neckinney, TX 75071
Malcolm Miranda, Attorney

Juvenile Probation 903.535.0850
Fax 903.535.0866
E-mail ....bcraft@cojs.com
    2630 Morningside Dr, Tyler, TX 75708
Ross Worley, Chief Performance Officer

Texas Youth Commission 903.597.0628
Fax 903.597.7389
Web ....www.ty.state.tx.us
    1517 W Front St, Ste 277, Tyler, TX 75702
Phillip Little, Officer

COURTS

Court 903.590.4600
Fax 903.590.4615
Web ....www.smith-county.com
    100 N Broadway Ave Ste 209, Tyler, TX 75702
Joel P Baker, Judge

Somervell County

COURTS

Court 254.897.2322
Fax 254.897.7314
E-mail ....cojudge@co.somervell.tx.us
    102 NE Vine St, Glen Rose, TX 76043
Honorable Mike Ford, Judge

POLICE AND SHERIFF

Sheriff's Ofc 254.897.2242
Fax 254.897.3400
Web ....www.glenrose.org
E-mail ....greg_doyle@valornet.com
    750 E. Bo Gibbs Blvd, Glen Rose, TX 76043
Greg Doyle, Sheriff

Starr County

SOCIAL SERVICES

Social Svcs 956.487.4513
Fax 956.716.6293
Web ....www.cityofrgc.com
E-mail ....abenoit@cityofrgc.com
    400 W Eisenhower St, Rio Grande City,
    TX 78582-2528
Analisa Benoit, Program Director

GENERAL HEALTH SERVICES

Texas Dept Of State Health Svcs 956.487.5556
Fax 956.487.8865
Web ....www.dshs.state.tx.us
E-mail ....nancy.keene@dshs.state.tx.us
    606 N Garza St, Rio Grande City, TX 78582-3538
Nancy Keene, RN, Supervisor

POLICE AND SHERIFF

Sheriff's Ofc 956.487.5571
Fax 956.487.3070
Web ....www.starrcountyso.org
    100 E 6th St, Rio Grande City, TX 78582-3550
Reme Fuentes, Sheriff

Stephens County

SOCIAL SERVICES

Texas Health And Human Svcs
Commission 254.559.8291
Fax 254.559.3477
    2315 W Walker St, Breckenridge, TX 76424
Patricia Walker, Lead Worker

GENERAL HEALTH SERVICES

Texas Dept of State Health Svcs 254.559.2205
Fax 254.559.1117
    2315 W Walker St, Breckenridge, TX 76424
Dorothy Kuhmann, Manager

COURTS

District Court 254.559.6481
Fax 254.559.8127
E-mail ....sccomcrt@texasisp.com
    200 W Walker St Ste 208, Breckenridge, TX 76424
Honorable Stephen O. Crawford, District Judge

POLICE AND SHERIFF

Sheriff's Dept 254.559.2481
Fax 254.559.2882
E-mail ....scso@texasisp.com
    210 E Dyer St, Breckenridge, TX 76424-3539
Dan Young, Sheriff

Sterling County

POLICE AND SHERIFF

Sheriff's Ofc 325.378.4771
Fax 325.378.2071
    609 4th St, Sterling City, TX 76951
Tim Sanders, Sheriff

Stonewall County

POLICE AND SHERIFF

Sheriff's Dept 940.989.3333
Fax 940.989.3334
Web ....www.cji.net
E-mail ....stonewallcosd@cji.net
    432 South Jefferson St, Aspermont, TX 79502
Bill Mullen, Sheriff

Sutton County

POLICE AND SHERIFF

Sheriff's Ofc 325.387.2288
Fax 325.387.5245
E-mail ....sheriff@sonoratx.net
    309 E Oak St, Sonora, TX 76950
Joe Fincher, Sheriff

Swisher County

SOCIAL SERVICES

Texas Health And Human Svcs
Commission 806.995.2321
Fax 806.995.4514
    219 Se 2Nd St, Tulia, TX 79088
Kathy Vestal, Office Manager

COURTS

Court 806.995.3504
Fax 806.995.2214
Web ....www.co.swisher.tx.us
E-mail ....harold.keeter@swisher-tx.net
    119 S Maxwell Ave, Tulia, TX 79088-2239
Honorable Harold Keeter, Judge

POLICE AND SHERIFF

Sheriff's Dept 806.995.3326
Fax 806.995.3367
Web ....www.swisher-tx.net
    136 E Broadway Ave, Tulia, TX 79088-2306
Emmett Benavidez, Sheriff

Tarrant County

SOCIAL SERVICES

Family and Protective Svcs 817.237.9488
Fax 817.237.6371
E-mail ....belinda.morgan@dfps.state.tx.us
    3800 Adam Grubb Ste 300, Lake Worth, TX 76135
Belinda Morgan, Secretary

Family and Protective Svcs 817.989.3000
Fax 817.989.3149
E-mail ....janice.culpepper@dfps.state.tv.us
    6743 Camp Bowie Blvd, Fort Worth, TX 76116
Janice Culpepper, Program Director

Family and Protective Svcs 817.255.2300
Fax 817.276.3968
E-mail ....brenda.lund@dfps.state.tx.us
    951 W Pipeline Rd Ste 310, Hurst, TX 76053
Brenda Lund, CPS Supervisor

Family and Protective Svcs 817.548.4531
Fax 254.965.9896
E-mail ....eula.rutherford@dfps.state.tx.us
    401 W. Sanford, Arlington, TX 76011
Eula Rutherford, CPS Night Response Program Director for Region 03

Family and Protective Svcs 817.548.4500
Fax 817.548.4588
    401 W Sanford St Ste 2400, Arlington,
    TX 76011-7094
Lucy Armstrong, Program Director

Family and Protective Svcs 817.321.8600
Fax 817.276.3944
    1501 Circle Dr, Ste 360, Fort Worth, TX 76119-8736
Joyce Coleman-Alford, Director

Protective Svcs Region 3 Ofc 817.792.4400
Fax 817.276.3927
Web ....www.dfps.state.tx.us
E-mail ....lisa.black@dfps.state.tx.us
    1200 E Copeland Rd Ste 400, Arlington,
    TX 76011-4937
Lisa Black, Regional Director

Texas Dept of Family and Protective
Svcs 817.255.8700
Fax 817.255.8712
    2700 Ben Ave, Mc 128-6, Fort Worth,
    TX 76103-2947
Sandy Raef, Family Preservation Cps Supervisor

Texas Health and Human Svcs
Commission 817.625.2161
Fax 817.740.6399
    2526 Jacksboro Hwy, Fort Worth, TX 76114
Rita Sanchez, Manager

GENERAL HEALTH SERVICES

Public Health Dept 817.321.4700
Fax 817.321.5302
Web ....www.health.tarrantcounty.com
E-mail ....phcs@tarrantcounty.com
    1101 S Main St, Rm 2412, Fort Worth, TX 76104
Lou Brewer, Director

MENTAL HEALTH SERVICES

Northwest Clinic 817.569.5000
Fax 817.569.5048
Web ....www.mhmr.org
E-mail ....william.hill@mhmrtc.org
    2400 NW 24th St, Fort Worth, TX 76106-6629
Bill Hill, Director

JUSTICE AGENCY

CASA 817.877.5891
Fax 817.877.3200
Web ....www.speakupforachild.org
    101 Summit Ave Ste 505, Fort Worth,
    TX 76102-2613
Connie R Brown, Executive Director

Criminal DA's Ofc 817.884.1400
E-mail ....dwindsor@tarrantcounty.com
    401 W Belknap St, Fort Worth, TX 76196
Joe Shannon, Attorney

Criminal Dist Attny **817.255.8736**
E-mail ....perry.pack@dfps.state.tx.us
2700 Ben Ave, Fort Worth, TX 76103
Perry Pack, Attorney

Tarrent Juvenile Svcs **817.838.4600**
Fax 817.838.4633
E-mail ....srturner@tarrantcounty.com
2701 Kimbo Rd, Fort Worth, TX 76111
Randy Turner, Director

Texas Youth Commission - Fort Worth Parole
Ofc **817.378.2100**
Fax 817.626.2611
E-mail ....diana.goodwin@tyc.state.tx.us
2462 E Long Ave, Fort Worth, TX 76106
Diana Goodwin, Regional Manager

COURTS

Teen Court **817.427.6705**
Fax 817.427.6707
Web ....www.nrhtx.com
E-mail ....nettc@nrhtx.com
6720 NE Loop 820, North Richland Hills,
TX 76180-7901
Heather Hollingsworth, Coordinator

Teen Court **817.297.2201**
Fax 817.297.6178
Web ....www.ci.crowley.tx.us
201 E Main St, Crowley, TX 76036-2649
Kristi Alvaravo, Coordinator

POLICE AND SHERIFF

Sheriff's Ofc **817.884.3099**
Fax 817.212.6987
Web ....www.tarrantcounty.com
E-mail ....speel@tarrantcounty.com
200 Taylor St, Fort Worth, TX 76102-2004
Dee Anderson, Sheriff

EDUCATION SERVICES

Abram Headstart Child Div **817.459.0608**
Fax 817.459.1031
E-mail ....abram@childcareassociatescare.org
1901 E Abram St, Arlington, TX 76010
Tressa Byrd, Director

Communities In Schools **817.446.5454**
Fax 817.446.4664
Web ....www.cistarrant.org
6707 Brent Wood Fair Road, Fort Worth, TX 76112
Mike Steele, President/CEO

DCN Azle Headstart **817.237.9922**
Fax 817.237.5273
1325 SE Parkway St, Azle, TX 76020
Barbara Morris, Director

East Fort Worth Headstart **817.457.0946**
Fax 817.457.0947
5565 Truman Dr, Fort Worth, TX 76112-7652
Ms Kim Webb, Director

Forrest Hill Headstart **817.483.1227**
Fax 817.483.1340
6901 Forest Hill Dr, Fort Worth, TX 76140
Patricia Etheridge, Director

Fuller Headstart CDC **817.924.4303**
800 W Fuller Ave, Fort Worth, TX 76115
Ms Mary Finley, Director

Mansfield Child Development
Center **817.453.9315**
Fax 817.453.9328
E-mail ....mansfield@childcareassociates.org
800 E Broad St, Mansfield, TX 76063
Brenda Valenzuela, Director

Special Education Service Center **817.740.3600**
Fax 817.740.7600
3001 North Fwy, Fort Worth, TX 76106
Richard Ownby, Executive Director

Taylor County

SOCIAL SERVICES

Family and Protective Svcs **325.691.8100**
Fax 325.691.8193
E-mail ....gretchen.denny@dfps.state.tx.us
3610 Vine St, Abilene, TX 79602-6913
Gretchen Denny, Regional Director's Assistant

GENERAL HEALTH SERVICES

Health Dept **325.692.5600**
Fax 325.734.5370
Web ....www.abilenetx.com
E-mail ....kay.durilla@abilenetx.com
850 N 6th St, Abilene, TX 79601
Kay Durilla, Nursing Supervisor

MENTAL HEALTH SERVICES

Abilene State School **325.692.4053**
Fax 325.795.3854
Web ....www.dads.state.tx.us
E-mail ....linda.henshaw@dads.state.tx.us
2501 Maple St, Abilene, TX 79602-5058
Linda Hinhashaw, Superintendent

JUSTICE AGENCY

Juvenile Justice Ctr **325.691.7462**
Fax 325.691.1500
E-mail ....michael.lindsay@tjpc.state.tx.us
889 S 25th St, Abilene, TX 79602
Michael R. Lindsay, Chief JPO

COURTS

District Court **325.674.1208**
Fax 325.738.8502
300 Oak St Dept 7, Abilene, TX 79602
Honorable Sam Carroll, Judge

POLICE AND SHERIFF

Sheriff's Dept **325.674.1300**
Fax 325.672.8066
Web ....www.taylorcountytexas.org
E-mail ....brucel@taylorcountytexas.org
450 Pecan St, Abilene, TX 79602-1621
Les D Bruce, Sheriff

EDUCATION SERVICES

Communities In Schools of The Big Country
Inc **325.675.7004**
Fax 325.675.8659
Web www.esc14.net
E-mail ....cisjake.sledge@esc14.net
1850 State Highway 351, Abilene, TX 79601-4750
Jake Sledge, Director

David Crockett Early Headstart
Program **325.690.3770**
Fax 325.690.3773
3282 S 13th St, Abilene, TX 79605-4034
Ms Georgiana Reagan, Director

Early Headstart Program **325.671.4613**
Fax 325.671.4615
949 Plum St, Abilene, TX 79601
Ms Georgiana Reagan, Director

Special Education **325.675.8600**
Fax 325.675.8659
Web www.esc14.net
E-mail ....kincaid@esc14.net
1850 Highway 351, Abilene, TX 79601
Ronnie Kincaid, Executive Director

Terrell County

POLICE AND SHERIFF

Sheriff's Ofc **432.345.2525**
Fax 432.345.3056
Web ....www.co.terrell.tx.us
E-mail ....tcso222@yahoo.com
105 E Hackberry St, Sanderson, TX 79848
Clint Mcdonald, Sheriff

Terry County

SOCIAL SERVICES

Texas Health And Human Svcs
Commission **806.637.8576**
Fax 806.637.7181
101 N Avenue D, Brownfield, TX 79316
Annie Gober, Supervisor

GENERAL HEALTH SERVICES

South Plains Public Health District **806.637.2164**
Fax 806.637.4295
E-mail ....sshafer@texashan.org
919 E Main St, Brownfield, TX 79316
Soronya Shafer, Director Of Nursing

COURTS

Court **806.637.6421**
Fax 806.637.9782
Web ....www.terrycounty.org
E-mail ....jdwagner@terrycounty.org
500 W Main St Rm 102, Brownfield, TX 79316-4335
Jd Wagner, County Judge

POLICE AND SHERIFF

Sheriff's Dept **806.637.2212**
Fax 806.637.9424
1311 Tahoka Rd, Brownfield, TX 79316-4006
Larry Gilbreath, Sheriff

Throckmorton County

POLICE AND SHERIFF

Sheriff's Dept **940.849.3431**
Fax 940.849.3220
Web ....www.tgncable.com
E-mail ....throckso@tgncable.com
105 N. Minter, Throckmorton, TX 76483
John Riley, Sheriff

Titus County

SOCIAL SERVICES

Family and Protective Svcs **903.572.3483**
Fax 903.577.8804
E-mail ....melanie.cleveland@dfps.state.tx.us
303 E 11th St, Mount Pleasant, TX 75455-2531
Melanie Cleveland, Program Director

GENERAL HEALTH SERVICES

Texas Dept Of Health **903.572.9877**
Fax 903.577.8957
E-mail ....linda.thomas@dshs.state.tx.us
1014 N Jefferson Ave, Mount Pleasant,
TX 75455-3262
Linda Thomas, Nurse

JUSTICE AGENCY

Juvenile Probation Ofc **903.577.6738**
Fax 903.577.6740
Web ....www.tjpc.state.tx.us
100 W 1st St Ste 400, Mount Pleasant,
TX 75455-4453
Ronald K. Hardin, Chief JPO

COURTS

District Court.............................903.577.6736
Fax...903.577.8073
  105 W 1st St Ste 102, Mount Pleasant, TX 75455
  Honorable Danny Woodson, Director

POLICE AND SHERIFF

Sheriff's Ofc.............................903.572.6641
Fax...903.577.8038
E-mail.........................ashepard@yahoo.com
  304 S Van Buren Ave, Mount Pleasant, TX 75455
  Arvel P. Shepard, Sheriff

EDUCATION SERVICES

Communities In Schools...................903.434.8212
Fax...903.434.4416
Web..www.ntcc.edu
E-mail..............................mhenry@ntcc.edu
  2886 Farm Road 1735, Chapel Hill Road, Mount
  Pleasant, TX 75646
  Melody Henry, Director

Special Education........................903.572.8551
Fax...903.575.2712
Web...www.reg8.net
E-mail...............................rglen@reg8.net
  2230 N Edwards Ave, Mount Pleasant,
  TX 75455-2036
  Dr. Raymond Glen, Executive Director

Tom Green County

SOCIAL SERVICES

Family and Protective Svcs...................325.657.8800
Fax...432.684.2974
Web...www.twc.state.tx.us
E-mail........................myrna.baquero@dfps.state.tx.us
  622 S Oakes St Ste L, San Angelo, TX 76903-7035
  Myrna Baquero, Program Administrator

Texas Health And Human Svcs
Commission...............................325.655.0576
Fax...325.659.7653
  622 S Oakes St Ste E2, San Angelo, TX 76903
  Melody Trimbles, Supervisor

GENERAL HEALTH SERVICES

Health Dept..............................325.657.4235
Fax...325.657.4553
Web...www.sanangelotexas.us
E-mail...............sandra.villarreal@sanangelotexas.us
  106 S Chadbourne St, San Angelo, TX 76903-5808
  Sandra Villarreal, Manager

JUSTICE AGENCY

Juvenile Ctr.............................325.655.2323
Fax...325.658.6424
  1253 W 19th St, San Angelo, TX 76906
  Mark Williams, Chief JPO

COURTS

District Court.............................325.659.6569
Fax...325.658.8046
E-mail................cheryl.torres@co.tom-green.tx.us
  112 W Beauregard Ave, San Angelo, TX 76903
  Honorable Tom Gossett, Judge

POLICE AND SHERIFF

Sheriff's Dept..........................325.655.8111
Fax...325.655.5393
  222 W Harris Ave, San Angelo, TX 76903
  Truman Richey, Sheriff

EDUCATION SERVICES

Special Education........................325.658.6571
Fax...325.655.4823
Web...www.netxv.net
  612 S Irene St, San Angelo, TX 76903
  Scot Geon, Executive Director

Travis County

SOCIAL SERVICES

Family and Protective Svcs.................512.834.3195
Fax...512.339.5915
E-mail......................shirley.scott@tdprs.state.tx.us
  14000 Summit Dr Ste 100, Austin, TX 78728-7112
  Jacque Seale, Program Director Of CVS

Governor's Div of Emergency
Managers................................512.424.2138
Fax...512.424.2444
Web.....................................www.txdps.state.tx.us/dem
E-mail......................mary.lenz@txdps.state.tx.us
  5805 N Lamar Blvd, Austin, TX 78773-0001
  Mary Lenz, Public Information Officer

Health And Human Svcs Dept.............512.972.4784
Fax...512.972.5208
Web...www.ci.austin.tx.us
E-mail......................david.lurie@ci.austin.tx.us
  7201 Levander Loop, Austin, TX 78702-5168
  David Lurie, Director

Health and Human Svcs Dept, Youth
Svcs.....................................512.854.4100
Fax...512.854.4115
Web...www.co.travis.tx.us
E-mail....................sherri.fleming@co.travis.tx.us
  100 N Interstate, Austin, TX 78767
  Sherri Fleming, Executive Manager

MENTAL HEALTH SERVICES

Austin State Hospital.....................512.452.0381
Fax...512.419.2652
Web.....www.dshs.state.tx.us/mhhospitals/austin sh
E-mail......................judith.fiene@mhmr.state.tx.us
  4110 Guadalupe St, Austin, TX 78751-4223
  Carl Schock, Superintendent

Austin State School......................512.454.4731
Fax...512.374.6900
  2203 W 35th St, Austin, TX 78703-1203
  Bira Benson, Superintendent

Children and Families Svcs.................512.804.3000
Fax...512.323.9544
Web...www.atcmhmr.com
  105 W Riverside Dr Ste 120, Austin, TX 78704
  Katy Macaroy, Director

Infant Thomas Parent Program.............512.472.3142
Fax...512.804.3169
Web...www.integralcare.org
E-mail...............................laurie.ruddy@it.org
  1717 W 10th St, Austin, TX 78703-3907
  Laurie Ruddy, Program Director

Integral Care............................512.447.4141
Fax...512.440.4081
Web...www.integralcare.org
E-mail.............................david.evans@atcic.org
  1430 Collier St, Austin, TX 78704-2911
  David Evans, Executive Director

JUSTICE AGENCY

CASA......................................512.459.2272
Fax...512.459.4550
Web...www.casatravis.org
E-mail.........................casatravis@casatravis.org
  7701 N Lamar Ste 301, Austin, TX 78752
  Laura Wolf, Executive Director

Dana Mills Attorney at Law.................512.461.0593
E-mail.........................danamills2002@msn.com
  PO Box 160333, Austin, TX 78716
  Dana Mills, Attorney Officer

Juvenile Probation Dept...................512.854.7000
Fax...512.854.7065
E-mail......................estela.medina@co.travis.tx.us
  2515 S Congress Ave, Austin, TX 78704
  Estela Medina, Chief JPO

COURTS

Travis District Court.......................512.854.9000
Fax...512.708.4526
E-mail.........................john.dietz@co.travis.us
  1000 Guadalupe St, Austin, TX 78701
  John Dietz, District Judge

POLICE AND SHERIFF

Austin Police Dept.......................512.974.5750
Fax...512.974.6611
E-mail......................art.acevedo@ci.austin.tx.us
  715 E 8th St, Austin, TX 78768
  Art Acevedo, Chief

Sheriff's Ofc.............................512.854.9770
Fax...512.854.9722
E-mail......................greg.hamilton@co.travis.tx.us
  501 W 11th St, Austin, TX 78701-2103
  Greg Hamilton, Sheriff

EDUCATION SERVICES

Special Education........................512.919.5313
Fax...512.919.5215
Web...www.esc13.net
E-mail......................terri.smith@esc13.txed.net
  5701 Springdale Rd, Austin, TX 78723-3646
  Dr. Terry Smith, Executive Director

Trinity County

SOCIAL SERVICES

Texas Health and Human Svcs
Commission...............................936.642.1134
Fax...936.642.2022
E-mail......................anna.goodson@hhsc.state.tx.us
  126 W 1st st, Groveton, TX 75845
  Anna Goodson, Office Manager

POLICE AND SHERIFF

Sheriff's Ofc.............................936.642.1424
Fax...936.642.2869
Web...www.co.trinity.tx.us
E-mail.........................tcso@co.trinity.tx.us
  Hwy 287 and Main St, Groveton, TX 75845
  Ralph Montemayer, Sheriff

Tyler County

SOCIAL SERVICES

Texas Dept of Health And Human Svcs
Commission...............................903.534.9794
Fax...903.581.9210
  3613 S Broadway Ave Ste 100, Tyler, TX 75701
  Zuwena Cuba, Supervisor

JUSTICE AGENCY

Juvenile Probation........................409.283.2503
Fax...409.283.6314
  100 W Bluff St Rm 106, Woodville, TX 75979-5245
  Terry Allen, Chief JPO

POLICE AND SHERIFF

Sheriff's Ofc.............................409.283.2172
Fax...409.283.8656
Web...www.co.san-augustine.tx.us
E-mail.............................tbum911@aol.com
  702 N Magnolia St Ste 100, Woodville,
  TX 75979-4915
  David Hanning, Sheriff

Texas

Upshur County

SOCIAL SERVICES

Family and Protective Svcs **903.843.0591**
Fax 817.276.3983
   324 Yapaco St, Gilmer, TX 75644
Kieth Gailes, Program Director

Texas Health And Human Svcs
Commission **903.843.5049**
Fax 903.843.4255
E-mail ....christy.rpjas@dhs.state.tx.us
   324 Yapaco St, Gilmer, TX 75644-2360
Christy Rpjas, Medicaid Eligibility Specialist

COURTS

Court **903.843.4003**
Fax 903.843.0827
Web ....www.countyofupshur.com
E-mail ....dean.fowler@countyofupshur.com
   Courthouse Square, 100 W Tyler St Fl 3, Gilmer,
   TX 75644
Honorable Dean Fowler, Director

POLICE AND SHERIFF

Sheriff's Ofc **903.843.2541**
Fax 903.843.2368
Web ....www.countyofupshur.com
E-mail ....sheriff@countyofupshur.com
   405 Titus St Ste 6, Gilmer, TX 75644-1958
Anthony Betterton, Sheriff

Upton County

GENERAL HEALTH SERVICES

Texas Tech Rural Clinic **432.652.3677**
Fax 432.652.3678
Web ....www.ttuhsc.edu
   100 E 7th St, Mccamey, TX 79752
Nancy Johnson, Supervisor

POLICE AND SHERIFF

Sheriff's Ofc **432.693.2422**
Fax 432.693.2303
Web ....www.upton.cotx.com
E-mail ....uptons@ymail.com
   1106 N. Grand, Rankin, TX 79778
Dan W. Brown, Sheriff

Uvalde County

SOCIAL SERVICES

Texas Health And Human Svcs
Commission **830.278.7151**
Fax 830.591.4375
Web ....www.dhs.state.tx.us
E-mail ....arturo.loera@dhs.state.tx.us
   2201 E Main St, Uvalde, TX 78801-4946
Arturo Loera, Supervisor

GENERAL HEALTH SERVICES

Community Health Development **830.278.7105**
Fax 830.278.1836
Web www.chdi4health.org
   200 Evans St, Uvalde, TX 78801-5142
Rachel Hanson, CEO

Health Dept **830.278.1705**
Fax 830.278.1881
E-mail ....tbphan@uvaldecounty.com
   1021 Garner Field Rd, Uvalde, TX 78801
Terri Black, Director

COURTS

Child Protection Court of South
Texas **830.249.3343**
Fax 830.249.9335
Web ....www.uvaldecounty.com
   201 E San Antonia St Ste 224, San Antonio,
   TX 78006
Dorrah Gonzalez, Court Coordinator

POLICE AND SHERIFF

Sheriff's Dept **830.278.4101**
Fax 830.278.2986
   121 E Nopal St, Uvalde, TX 78801
Charles Mendeke, Sheriff

Val Verde County

SOCIAL SERVICES

Family and Protective Svcs **830.774.5675**
Fax 830.775.7159
Web ....www.dfps.state.tx.us
E-mail ....alma.reyes@dfps.state.tx.us
   712 E Gibbs St, Del Rio, TX 78840-4728
Alma Reyes, CPS Supervisor

Texas Health And Human Svcs
Commission **830.774.3661**
Fax 830.775.2381
   173 wild cat dr, Del Rio, TX 78840-4728
Rose Arredondo, Supervisor

GENERAL HEALTH SERVICES

Texas Dept Of Health **830.768.2800**
Fax 830.774.8683
Web ....www.dshs.state.tx.us
   1401 Las Vacas St, Del Rio, TX 78840-5239
Jose Guerra, Registered Nurse

JUSTICE AGENCY

Juvenile Probation **830.774.7557**
Fax 830.775.4854
E-mail ....jesus.soto@tjpc.state.tx.us
   200 Griner St, Del Rio, TX 78841
Jesus Rogelio Soto, Chief JPO

COURTS

District Court **830.774.7523**
Fax 830.774.1359
Web ....www.valverdecounty.org
E-mail ....info@valverdecounty.org
   100 E. Broadway 2nd Fl, Del Rio, TX 78841-1089
Honorable Enrique Fernandez, Judges

POLICE AND SHERIFF

Sheriff's Dept **830.774.7513**
Fax 830.775.9678
   295 FM 2523 (Hamilton Lane), Del Rio, TX 78841
Joe Frank Martinez, Sheriff

Van Zandt County

JUSTICE AGENCY

Juvenile Probation Ofc **903.962.6292**
Fax 903.962.6413
E-mail ....juvprobation@suddenlinkmail.com
   323 E Garland St, Grand Saline, TX 75140
Robert Colacino, Director

COURTS

Court **903.567.4071**
Fax 903.567.7216
Web ....www.vanzandtcounty.org
E-mail ....rkoches@vanzandtcounty.org
   121 E Dallas St Ste 204, Canton, TX 75103-1497
Honorable Rhita Koches, Director

District Court **903.567.4422**
Fax 903.567.5652
   121 E Dallas St Ste 301, Canton, TX 75103-1498
Honorable Teresa A. Drum, Director

POLICE AND SHERIFF

Sheriff's Dept **903.567.4133**
Fax 903.567.7835
E-mail ....sheriff@vzsheriff.com
   1220 W Dallas St, Canton, TX 75103-1016
R.p. Pat Burnett Jr., Sheriff

Victoria County

SOCIAL SERVICES

Family and Protective Svcs **361.572.8241**
Fax 361.572.3648
E-mail ....diane.jones@dfps.state.tx.us
   1502 E Airline Rd Ste 13A, Victoria, TX 77901-4116
Diane Jones, Program Director

Texas Health And Human Svcs
Commission **361.578.3523**
Fax 361.574.7467
   1502 E Airline Rd Ste 39, Victoria, TX 77901-4116
Pat Alvardo, Program Manager

GENERAL HEALTH SERVICES

University Of Texas Medical Branch-
Victoria **361.576.2110**
Fax 361.576.2375
Web ....www.utmb.edu
E-mail ....jgarcia@utmb.edu
   2603 Hospital Dr, Victoria, TX 77901-5753
Jessica Garcia, Manager

Victoria City Health Dept **361.578.6281**
Fax 361.578.7046
Web ....www.victoriacountytx.org
E-mail ....bcate@vctx.org
   2805 N Navarro St, Victoria, TX 77901-3917
Bain Cate, Md, Director

MENTAL HEALTH SERVICES

Gulf Bend Mental Health and Mental Retardation
Ctr **361.575.0611**
Fax 361.578.0506
Web ....www.gulfbend.org
E-mail ....DPOLZIN@GULFBEND.ORG
   6502 Nursery Dr Ste 100, Victoria, TX 77904
Don Polzin, Executive Director

JUSTICE AGENCY

Golden Crescent CASA **361.573.3734**
Fax 361.573.3729
Web ....www.goldencrescentcasa.org
E-mail ....gccasa@goldencrescentcasa.org
   PO Box 1627, Victoria, TX 77902-1627
Tim Hornback, Executive Director

Juvenile Probation **361.575.0399**
Fax 361.576.0134
Web ....www.co.jefferson.tx.us
E-mail ....phencerling@co.jefferson.tx.us
   97 Foster Field Dr, Victoria, TX 77904-3612
Pam S Hencerling, Chief JPO

COURTS

Court at Law **361.575.4550**
Fax 361.575.7181
E-mail ....lweiser@vctx.org
   115 N Bridge St Ste 203, Victoria, TX 77901-6544
Honorable Laura A. Weiser, County Law Judge #1

POLICE AND SHERIFF

Sheriff's Ofc **361.575.0651**
Fax 361.574.8019
Web ....www.vctx.org
E-mail ....toconnor@vctx.org
   101 N Glass St, Victoria, TX 77901-6414
T. Michael Oconner, Sheriff

EDUCATION SERVICES

Acfi Headstart/Creekstone Ranch **361.570.6690**
Fax 361.570.6690
   5609 John Stockbauer Dr, Victoria, TX 77904-1874
Ms Cynthia Johnson, Director

**Communities In Schools of The Golden
Crescent** **361.576.5872**
Fax 361.573.0225
Web ....www.gcworkforce.org
   120 S Main Pl, Ste 501, Victoria, TX 77901
Henry Guajardo, Executive Director

Special Education **361.573.0731**
Fax 361.576.4804
   1905 Leary Ln, Victoria, TX 77901
Julius D. Cano, Edd, Executive Director

Walker County

SOCIAL SERVICES

**Texas Health And Human Svcs
Commission** **936.291.2164**
Fax 936.291.0627
   306 Highway 190 E, Huntsville, TX 77340
Tamara Brown, Supervisor

GENERAL HEALTH SERVICES

Maternal And Child Health Ctr **936.295.7474**
Fax 936.295.1516
   1217 Ave M, Huntsville, TX 77340
Patty Nami, Cfnp, Clinic Director

JUSTICE AGENCY

Juvenile Probation **936.436.4994**
Fax 936.436.4997
Web ....www.co.walker.tx.us
E-mail ....jsaumell@co.walker.tx.us
   1021 University Ave, Huntsville, TX 77320-3951
Jill Saumell, Chief JPO

**Texas Youth Commission New Waverly District
Ofc** **936.344.6218**
Fax 936.344.7408
E-mail ....teresa.barnett@tyc.state.tx.us
   143 Forest Service Rd, Ste 233, New Waverly,
   TX 77358
Teresa Barnett, Quality Assurance Supervisor

COURTS

Court **936.436.4919**
Fax 936.436.4920
Web ....www.co.walker.tx.us
E-mail ....bhale@co.walker.tx.us
   1100 University Ave Ste 102, Huntsville,
   TX 77340-4640
Honorable Barbara Hale, Director

POLICE AND SHERIFF

Sheriff's Ofc **936.435.2400**
Fax 936.435.2440
E-mail ....cmcrae@co.walker.tx.us
   717 Fm 2821 Rd W Ste 500, Huntsville,
   TX 77320-3142
Clint Mcrae, Sheriff

EDUCATION SERVICES

Special Education **936.435.8400**
Fax 936.435.8484
Web www.esc6.net
E-mail ....tpoe@esc6.net
   3332 Montgomery Rd, Huntsville, TX 77340-6417
Thomas Poe, Executive Director

Waller County

JUSTICE AGENCY

Juvenile Probation **979.826.7691**
Fax 979.826.7690
E-mail ....debra.williams@tjpc.state.tx.us
   646 9th St, Hempstead, TX 77445
Debra Williams, Chief JPO

COURTS

Court **979.826.3357**
Fax 979.826.9119
   836 Austin St Ste 224, Hempstead, TX 77445
Honorable June Jackson, Director

POLICE AND SHERIFF

Sheriff's Dept **979.826.8282**
Fax 979.826.7781
E-mail ....wcsospy@aol.com
   701 Calvit St, Hempstead, TX 77445
Glenn Smith, Sheriff

Ward County

COURTS

Court **432.943.3209**
Fax 432.943.5010
E-mail ....greg.holly@co.ward.tx.us
   400 S Allen Ave, Monahans, TX 79756
Honorable Greg M. Holly, Judge

POLICE AND SHERIFF

Sheriff's Ofc **432.943.6703**
Fax 432.943.9144
E-mail ....mikel.strickland@co.ward.tx.us
   300 E 4th St, Monahans, TX 79756
Mikel Strickland, Sheriff

Washington County

SOCIAL SERVICES

**Texas Health and Human Svcs
Commission** **979.836.7951**
Fax 979.830.6155
Web ....www.hhsc.state.tx.us
   2505 Stone Hollow Dr, Brenham, TX 77833-5631

GENERAL HEALTH SERVICES

Texas Dept Of Health **979.836.1740**
Fax 979.836.3445
   100 S Chappell Hill, Brenham, TX 77833
Clara Carrias, Human Services Tech.

MENTAL HEALTH SERVICES

Brenham State School **979.836.4511**
Fax 979.277.1865
Web ....www.dads.state.tx.us
   4001 Highway 36 S, Brenham, TX 77833-9611
Robert Ham, Superintendent

COURTS

Court **979.277.6200**
Fax 979.277.6285
E-mail ....jdaniel@wacounty.com
   100 E Main St Ste 104, Brenham, TX 77833
Honorable Dorothy Morgan, Director

POLICE AND SHERIFF

Sheriff's Ofc **979.277.6251**
Fax 979.277.6258
E-mail ....sheriff@washingtoncosheriff.org
   1206 Old Independence Rd, Brenham,
   TX 77833-2400
J.w. Jankowski, Sheriff

Webb County

SOCIAL SERVICES

Family and Protective Svcs **956.728.7383**
Fax 210.304.7753
Web ....www.dfps.state.tx.us
E-mail ....adrina.ortiz@dfps.state.tx.us
   1500 N Arkansas Ave, Laredo, TX 78043-3049
Adrina Ortiz, Director

Texas Health And Human Svcs **956.722.0571**
Fax 956.718.0234
   3804 Casa Blanca Rd, Laredo, TX 78041-7627
Janie Gonzales, Supervisor/Office Coordinator

GENERAL HEALTH SERVICES

Health Dept **956.795.4900**
Fax 956.726.2632
Web ....www.ci.laredo.tx.us
   2600 Cedar Ave, Laredo, TX 78040
Hector Gonzalez, Director

COURTS

District Court **956.523.4268**
Fax 956.523.5063
Web ....www.webbcountytx.gov
E-mail ....edegollado@webbcountytx.gov
   1110 Victoria St Ste 203, Laredo, TX 78040-4421
Esther Degollado, District Clerk

POLICE AND SHERIFF

Sheriff's Dept **956.523.4503**
Fax 956.523.5059
Web ....www.webbcountytx.gov
E-mail ....rflores@webbcountytx.gov
   902 Victoria St, Laredo, TX 78040-4456
Rick Flores, Sheriff

EDUCATION SERVICES

El Cenzio Headstart Ctr **956.725.3410**
Fax 956.735.3410
   3549 Cecilia Ln, Laredo, TX 78046-7994
Rosa Jimenez, Director

Wharton County

SOCIAL SERVICES

Family and Protective Svcs **979.532.5310**
Fax 713.928.7606
   110 E Burleson St, Wharton, TX 77488
James Lebeck, Investigations Program Director

**Texas Health and Human Svcs
Commission** **979.532.5910**
Fax 979.532.3784
   404 N Alabama Rd, Wharton, TX 77488-4210
Mary Rodridudz, Supervisor

MENTAL HEALTH SERVICES

Mental Health/Mental Retardation **979.532.3098**
Fax 979.532.0312
   3007 N Richmond Rd, Wharton, TX 77488-2007
George Patterson, Md, Executive Director

**Texana Mental Health & Mental
Retardation** **281.342.6384**
Fax 281.232.3412
   4910 Airport Ave Ste A, Rosenberg, TX 77471-5759
George Patterson, CEO

Texas

JUSTICE AGENCY

Juvenile Probation **979.532.2465**
Fax 979.532.2571
Web ....www.tjpc.state.tx.us
E-mail ....holly.mccown@co.wharton.tx.us
106 E Milam, Wharton, TX 77488
Holly Mccown, Chief JPO

POLICE AND SHERIFF

Sheriff's Dept **979.532.1550**
Fax 979.282.2849
315 E Elm St, Wharton, TX 77488
Jess W. Howell Jr., Sheriff

EDUCATION SERVICES

El Campo Headstart **979.543.7056**
Fax 979.578.8708
505 Bruns St, El Campo, TX 77437
Ms Tera Smith, Director

Wheeler County

COURTS

Court **806.826.5961**
Fax 806.826.3282
Web ....www.co.wheeler.tx.us
E-mail ....cojudge@centramedia.net
401 Main St, Wheeler, TX 79096
Honorable Jerry Dan Hefley, County Judge

POLICE AND SHERIFF

Sheriff's Dept **806.826.5537**
Fax 806.826.3458
Web ....www.centramedia.net
E-mail ....wcso@centramedia.net
304 Alan L. Bean Blvd, Wheeler, TX 79096
Joel Finsterwald, Sheriff

Wichita County

SOCIAL SERVICES

Health and Human Svc
Commission **940.767.1720**
Fax 940.720.8446
1328 Oakhurst Dr, Wichita Falls, TX 76302-2722
Christy Schulte, Program Director

GENERAL HEALTH SERVICES

Health District **940.761.7800**
Fax 940.767.5242
Web ....www.health.wichitafallstx.gov
E-mail ....amy.cone@wichitafallstx.gov
1700 3rd St, Wichita Falls, TX 76302
Amy Cone, Assistant Director

MENTAL HEALTH SERVICES

North Texas State Hospital **940.692.1220**
Fax 940.689.5870
6515 Kemp Blvd, Wichita Falls, TX 76307
James E. Smith, Superintendent

JUSTICE AGENCY

Child Advocates (CASA) **940.766.0552**
Fax 940.766.0806
Web ....www.casawf.org
E-mail ....rbryant@casawf.org
808 Austin St, Wichita Falls, TX 76301-3214
Ron Bryant, Executive Director

Juvenile Probation **940.766.8225**
Fax 940.766.8183
Web ....www.co.wichita.tx.us
E-mail ....kirk.wolfe@co.wichita.tx.us
510 Lamar St, Wichita Falls, TX 76301-2511
Kirk Wolfe, Chief JPO

COURTS

District Court **940.766.8190**
Fax 940.716.8181
900 7th St Rm 303, Wichita Falls, TX 76301
Robert Brotherton, Judge

POLICE AND SHERIFF

Sheriff's Dept **940.766.8170**
Fax 940.766.8102
E-mail ....sheriff@co.wichita.tx.us
900 7th Street, Room 100, Wichita Falls, TX 76301
David Duke, Sheriff

EDUCATION SERVICES

Special Education **940.322.6928**
Fax 940.767.3836
Web www.esc9.net
301 Loop 11, Wichita Falls, TX 76306
Anne Poplin, Executive Director

Wilbarger County

SOCIAL SERVICES

Texas Health And Human Svcs
Commission **940.552.6238**
Fax 940.552.0694
1531 Cumberland St, Vernon, TX 76384
Mary Bearden, Clerk

POLICE AND SHERIFF

Sheriff's Dept **940.552.6205**
Fax 940.553.2318
Web ....www.co.wilbarger.tx.us
E-mail ....tjacobs@co.wilbarger.tx.us
1700 Wilbarger St Rm 18, Vernon, TX 76384-4748
Larry Lee, Sheriff

Willacy County

SOCIAL SERVICES

Texas Health And Human Svcs
Commission **956.689.6501**
Fax 956.689.6339
Web ....www.state.tx.us
100 N Expressway 77, Ste I, Raymondville, TX 78580

JUSTICE AGENCY

Juvenile Probation **956.689.6257**
Fax 956.689.9524
E-mail ....willacy@co.juvprob.tjpc.state.tx.us
471 W Hidalgo Ave, Raymondville, TX 78580
Raul Garza, Chief JPO

COURTS

Court **956.689.3393**
Fax 956.689.4817
Web ....www.co.willacy.tx.us
E-mail ....county.adminsitrator@co.willacy.tx.us
576 W Main St, Raymondville, TX 78580-1940
Honorable John F. Gonzales, Judge

POLICE AND SHERIFF

Sheriff's Ofc **956.689.5576**
Fax 956.689.3867
1371 Industrial Dr, Raymondville, TX 78580
Larry G. Spence, Sheriff

Williamson County

SOCIAL SERVICES

CPS Ofc **512.352.7661**
Fax 512.339.5936
301 Highland Dr, Taylor, TX 76574-1848
Lauren Blondek, CPS Supervisor

Family and Protective Svcs **512.244.6651**
Fax 512.339.5930
Web ....www.dfps.state.tx.us
E-mail ....patricia.dillasana-nunes@dfps.state.tx.us
355 Texas Ave Ste 200, Round Rock, TX 78664-2564
Patricia Dillasana-nunes, Director

GENERAL HEALTH SERVICES

Health District **512.352.4121**
Fax 512.352.4179
Web ....www.williamsoncounty.org
115 W 6Th St, Taylor, TX 76574
Rhonda Killough, Supervisor

JUSTICE AGENCY

Juvenile Svcs **512.943.3200**
Fax 512.943.3209
Web ....www.jjat.com
1821 SE Inner Loop Ste 2, Georgetown,
TX 78626-6357
Charles M. Skaggs, Chief JPO

COURTS

District Court **512.943.1277**
Fax 512.943.1276
Web ....www.co.guadalupe.tx.us
E-mail ....kanderson@co.guadalupe.tx.us
405 S Martin Luther King St Box 6, Georgetown,
TX 78626-4900
Honorable Ken Anderson, Judge

POLICE AND SHERIFF

Sheriff's Ofc **512.943.1300**
Fax 512.943.1444
508 S Rock St, Georgetown, TX 78626
James Wilson, Sheriff

EDUCATION SERVICES

Florence Head Start **254.793.3011**
Fax 254.793.3011
E-mail ....florencehs@wbco.net
203 Adams St E, Florence, TX 76527
Ms Molly Moser, Director

Wilson County

SOCIAL SERVICES

Texas Health And Human Svcs
Commission **830.393.3141**
Fax 830.393.4077
E-mail ....jlyssy@hhsc.state.tx.us
661 10Th St, Floresville, TX 78114
Janice Lyssy, Office Manager

GENERAL HEALTH SERVICES

Health Dept **830.393.6225**
Fax 830.393.0096
663 10th St, Floresville, TX 78114
Dr. Sandra Guerra Cantu, Md, Director

JUSTICE AGENCY

Hot Check Dept **830.393.7350**
Fax 830.393.7371
1420 3rd St, Floresville, TX 78114
Gloria Duron, Coordinator

POLICE AND SHERIFF

Sheriff's Dept **830.393.2535**
Fax 830.393.7402
800 10th St, Floresville, TX 78114-1860
Joe D. Tackitt Jr., Sheriff

Winkler County

SOCIAL SERVICES

Texas Health And Human Svcs

Commission **432.586.3451**
Fax 432.586.2908
    401 S Pine St, Kermit, TX 79745-4235
Sandra Trujillo, Supervisor

COURTS

Court **432.586.6658**
Fax 432.586.3223
Web ....www.co.winkler.tx.us
E-mail ....bleck@co.winkler.tx.us
    100 E winkler, Kermit, TX 79745
Honorable Bonnie Leck, County Judge

POLICE AND SHERIFF

Sheriff's Dept **432.586.3461**
Fax 432.586.3902
Web www.apex2000.net
E-mail ....wcso@apex2000.net
    1300 So. Bellaira, Kermit, TX 79745
George Keely, Sheriff

Wise County

SOCIAL SERVICES

Family and Protective Svcs **940.627.2188**
Fax 817.276.3956
    2000 W Business 380, Decatur, TX 76234
Stacy Reynolds, Program Director

Texas Health And Human Svcs

Commission **940.627.3011**
Fax 940.627.3171
    2000 W Business 380, Decatur, TX 76234
Andrea Stricland, Office Manager

JUSTICE AGENCY

CASA **940.627.7535**
Fax 940.627.7533
    114 E Main Street D, Decatur, TX 76234
Claudene Griffith, Executive Director

Juvenile Probation **940.627.7037**
Fax 940.627.5349
E-mail ....bill.austin@co.wise.tx.us
    401 Rook Ramsey Dr, Decatur, TX 76234
Bill Austin, Chief JPO

POLICE AND SHERIFF

Sheriff's Ofc **940.627.5971**
Fax 940.627.1333
Web ....www.sheriff.co.wise.tx.us
E-mail ....walkerd@sheriff.co.wise.tx.us
    200 Rook Ramsey Dr, Decatur, TX 76234-3299
David Walker, Sheriff

Wood County

SOCIAL SERVICES

Texas Health and Human Svcs

Commission **903.763.2275**
Fax 903.763.4745
    305 Goodwin, Quitman, TX 75783-2427
Joe Mccoy, Supervisor

GENERAL HEALTH SERVICES

East Texas Medical Ctr Public Health

Clinic **903.569.6124**
Fax 903.569.2467
Web ....www.etmc.org
    5875 S State Highway 37, Mineola, TX 75773
Brody Clark, Administrator

Health Dept **903.763.5406**
Fax 903.763.5407
E-mail ....wchdut@yahoo.com
    213 West Bermuda, Quitman, TX 75783
David C. Murley, Md, Medical Director

JUSTICE AGENCY

Juvenile Probation **903.763.5772**
Fax 903.763.5104
Web ....www.tjpc.state.tx.us
E-mail ....bbyers@co.wood.tx.us
    Courthouse Main, Quitman, TX 75783
Brandon Byers, Chief Performance Officer

COURTS

Court **903.763.2716**
Fax 903.763.2902
E-mail ....countyjudge@co.wood.tx.us
    100 S Main St, Quitman, TX 75783
Honorable Broyan Jeanes, Judge

POLICE AND SHERIFF

Sheriff's Ofc **903.763.2201**
Fax 903.763.5464
Web ....www.co.wood.tx.us
E-mail ....sheriff@co.wood.tx.us
    402 S Stephens St, Quitman, TX 75783
Billy Wansley, Sheriff

Yoakum County

SOCIAL SERVICES

Texas Health And Human Svcs

Commission **806.592.9111**
Fax 806.592.7542
    412 W 5th St Ste 4, Denver City, TX 79323-2755
Annie Gober, Supervisor

GENERAL HEALTH SERVICES

South Plains Public Health District **806.592.2706**
Fax 806.592.9478
E-mail ....bsalazar@crs.loc.gov
    415 Mustang Dr, Denver City, TX 79323-2749
Barbara Salazar, Lpn, Nurse

POLICE AND SHERIFF

Sheriff's Dept **806.456.2377**
Fax 806.456.5431
E-mail ....plainsso@crosswind.net
    600 9th St, Plains, TX 79355
Donald L. Corzine, Sheriff

Young County

SOCIAL SERVICES

Texas Health And Human Svcs

Commission **940.549.1371**
Fax 940.521.5090
E-mail ....nita.dye@hhsc.state.tx.us
    1202 Packing House Rd, Graham, TX 76450-3821
Mollie Ownby, Clerk

JUSTICE AGENCY

Juvenile Probation **940.549.9427**
Fax 940.549.4204
    516 4th St Ste B4, Graham, TX 76450
Donna Cook, Chief JPO

POLICE AND SHERIFF

Sheriff's Ofc **940.549.1555**
Fax 940.549.0011
E-mail ....b.walls@youngcounty.org
    315 Cliff Dr N, Graham, TX 76450
Bryan Walls, Sheriff

Zapata County

SOCIAL SERVICES

Texas Health And Human Svcs

Commission **956.765.4319**
Fax 956.765.4355
    1306 Kennedy St, Zapata, TX 78076
Olga Perez, Supervisor

GENERAL HEALTH SERVICES

Texas Dept of Health **956.765.4851**
Fax 956.765.4627
Web ....www.dshs.state.tx.us
E-mail ....belindax.garza@dshs.state.tx.us
    1306 Kennedy St, Zapata, TX 78076
Belinda Garza, Lpn, Head Nurse

JUSTICE AGENCY

Juvenile Probation **956.765.9936**
Fax 956.765.9934
Web ....www.tjpc.state.tx.us
E-mail ....sandy.pippin@tjpc.state.tx.us
    201 E 6th Ave, 347, Zapata, TX 78076
Sandy Pippin, Chief JPO

POLICE AND SHERIFF

Sheriff's Ofc **956.765.9960**
Fax 956.765.9941
E-mail ....sigigonzalez@sbcglobal.net
    2311 Stop23a, Zapata, TX 78076-2810
Sigifredo Gonzalez, Sheriff

Zavala County

SOCIAL SERVICES

Texas Health And Human Svcs

Commission **830.374.2327**
Fax 830.374.3769
Web ....www.dir.state.tx.us
    104 Juan Cornejo Dr, Crystal City, TX 78839-3544
Ramiro Hernandez, Supervisor

POLICE AND SHERIFF

Sheriff's Ofc **830.374.3615**
Fax 830.374.5933
E-mail ....eusevio.salinas@co.zavala.tx.us
    200 E Uvalde St Ste 5, Crystal City, TX 78839
Eusevio E. Salinas Jr., Sheriff

EDUCATION SERVICES

Crystal City TMC Head Start **830.374.2637**
Fax 830.374.2197
    212 Cypress Ave, Crystal City, TX 78839
Gracie Rodriguez, Director

Texas

SPECIAL SERVICES AGENCIES

ADOPTION AGENCIES

A Cradle of Hope **214.747.4500**
Fax 214.939.3001
Web ....www.calabresehuff.com
E-mail ....corla@calabreselaw.com
5944 Luther Ln Ste 875, Dallas, TX 75225-5977
Corla Calabrese, Director

A World For Children **512.218.4400**
Fax 512.218.8170
Web ....www.awfc.org
E-mail ....williss@awfc.org
1516 E Palm Valley Blvd, Bldg 3, Round Rock,
TX 78664
Sharon Willis, Executive Director

A World For Children **956.683.9917**
Fax 956.683.9915
Web ....www.awfc.org
5401 N 10th St Ste 200, McAllen, TX 78504
Arminda Garcia, Director

A World For Children **915.781.3330**
Fax 915.781.3332
Web ....www.awfc.org
1760 Airway Blvd Ste 102, El Paso, TX 79925-2054
Oscar Millan, Director

ABC Adoption Agency, Inc. **210.227.7820**
Fax 210.225.4469
417 San Pedro Ave, San Antonio, TX 78212
Michael Heim, Director

ACH Child and Family Services **817.335.4673**
Fax 682.432.1099
Web ....www.allchurchhome.org
1424 Summit Avenue, Fort Worth, TX 76102
COA accredited organization.

Adams King & Smith **903.757.3331**
Fax 903.753.8289
422 N Center St, Longview, TX 75605-4747
Chris King, Office Manager

Adoptexas **713.529.4341**
Fax 713.529.5167
Web ....www.adoptquest.com
E-mail ....dunchm3@msn.com
2020 Southwest Fwy Ste 326, Houston,
TX 77098-4807
Charolette Duncan, Director

Adoption Advisory **210.820.0000**
Fax 214.522.3502
Web ....www.adoptadvisory.com
E-mail ....texasadoption@aol.com
8546 Broadway St Ste 125, San Antonio,
TX 78217-6354
Mark Segal, Director

Adoption Advisory Inc. **214.520.0004**
Fax 214.522.3502
Web ....www.adoptadvisory.com
E-mail ....texasadoption@aol.com
3607 Fairmount St, Dallas, TX 75219
Mark Siegel, Director

Adoption Advocates, Inc. **512.477.1122**
Fax 512.477.7060
Web ....www.adoptionadvocates.net
E-mail ....info@adoptionadvocates.net
1215 Parkway, Austin, TX 78703-4132
Rory Hall, Director

Adoption Affiliates **210.824.9977**
Fax 210.824.6229
215 W Olmos, San Antonio, TX 78212
Sonya Ramiurez, Director

Adoption Affiliates **210.824.9977**
Fax 210.824.6229
Web ....www.epadoption.org
730 E Yandell Dr, El Paso, TX 79902-5314
Gerildine Lester, Director

Adoption Affiliates, Inc./Nova Health Systems **210.824.9939**
Fax 210.824.6229
Web ....www.connectinghearts.org
E-mail ....januscouve@aol.com
215 W Olmos Dr, San Antonio, TX 78212-1991
Janus Couve, Director

Adoption Alliance **210.349.3991**
Fax 210.349.8075
Web ....www.adoption-alliance.com
E-mail ....swiederin@adoption-alliance.com
7303 Blanco Rd, San Antonio, TX 78216-4934
Stacey Weederman-schmit, Director

Adoption Angels, Inc. **210.227.2229**
Fax 210.227.2241
Web ....www.adoptionangels.com
E-mail ....lore@adoptionangels.com
1511 Fredericksburg Rd, San Antonio,
TX 78201-5030
Lore Carvalho, Director

Adoption Covenant **806.741.0268**
Fax 806.741.0142
E-mail ....merinda@adoptioncovenant.com
1304 16th St, Lubbock, TX 79401
Merinda Condra, Director

Adoption Home Studies **806.778.1604**
E-mail ....johnburtran@yahoo.com
3202 Kelsey Ave, Lubbock, TX 79407-4603
John Burtran, Director

Adoptions Svcs, Inc. **817.921.0718**
Fax 817.924.4771
E-mail ....adoptsvc@charter.net
3500 Overton Park Dr W, Fort Worth,
TX 76109-2505
Eileen Anderson Stancukas, Dcsw, Lcsw, Bcd, Director

Agape Manor Home **972.840.8130**
Fax 972.840.8199
3200 Broadway St, Ste 360, Garland, TX 75043
Sabu Joseph, Lmsw, Director

Alliance Adolescent And Children Svc **512.420.8811**
Fax 512.420.0862
Web ....www.thementornetwork.com
E-mail ....lori.frasco@thementornetwork.com
1106 Clayton Ln, Ste 230, Austin, TX 78723
Lori Frasco, Director

Alternatives In Motion, Inc. **281.821.6508**
Fax 281.821.0356
Web ....www.aimadoption.org
E-mail ....dsowders@aimadoptions.org
2509 Fm 1960 Rd E, Houston, TX 77073
Denise Sowders, Maternity Services Coordinator

Arrow Project **979.848.1100**
Fax 979.848.1155
Web ....www.arrow.org
E-mail ....fhall@arrow.org
104 W Myrtle St, Angleton, TX 77515
Felecia Hall, Director

Bair Foundation **325.674.1997**
Fax 325.674.1995
E-mail ....blovell@bair.org
1500 Industrial Blvd Ste 201, Abilene, TX 79602
Bobby Lovell, Director

Bair Foundation **903.939.2247**
Fax 903.939.2599
Web ....www.bair.org
5935 Old Bullard Rd, # 100, Tyler, TX 75703
Betsy Patullo, Director Of Social Services

Bair Foundation **713.975.7699**
Fax 713.975.6950
3100 Wilcrest Dr Ste 300, Houston, TX 77042
Monte Cuba, Executive Director

Bair Foundation **915.771.9101**
Fax 915.771.0919
6070 Gateway Blvd E Ste 105, El Paso,
TX 79905-2029
Rubin Franco, Acting Director

Bair Foundation **806.355.3882**
Fax 806.355.4332
Web ....www.bair.org
E-mail ....twilliams@bair.org
7430 Golden Pond Pl, Amarillo, TX 79121
Tammy Williams, Intake Director

Bair Foundation **972.957.0030**
Fax 972.957.0039
Web ....www.bair.org
E-mail ....enelson-gammill@bair.org
4425 W Airport Fwy Ste 400, Irving, TX 75062-5831
Erika Nelson-gammill, Director

Bair Foundation **512.346.3555**
Fax 512.346.9719
Web ....www.bair.org
E-mail ....nreeves@bair.org
8840 Business Park Dr, Austin, TX 78759
Natalie Reeves, Regional Director

Bob Leonard Jr Law Ofc **817.923.4600**
Fax 817.336.8511
E-mail ....info@bobpipin.com
2800 S Hulen St Ste 210, Fort Worth, TX 76109
Beth Pipin, Director

Burke Foundation **956.723.5886**
Fax 956.723.1312
Web ....www.theburkecenter.org
E-mail ....burkfound@sbcglobal.net
6010 Mctherson Ste 110, Laredo, TX 78041-5496
Cynthia Salbedo, Case Manager

Burke Foundation **361.853.6700**
Fax 361.853.6701
Web ....www.theburkecenter.org
E-mail ....claudia@theburkecenter.org
3833 S Staples St Ste N205, Corpus Christi,
TX 78411-5215
Claudia Pichardo, Level I Agent

Cardenas Law Group **713.461.1660**
E-mail ....attycardenas@gmail.com
6750 W Loop S 720, Dlaware, TX 77401
Robert Cardenas, Manager

Caring Adoptions, Inc. **281.920.4300**
Fax 281.920.4782
Web ....www.caringadoptions.org
E-mail ....info@caringadoptions.org
11601 Katy Fwy Ste 112, Houston, TX 77079-1803
Jody Vick, LCSW,LMFT, Director of Adoptions; Patricia Jaber, BA, Post Placement Specialist; Patricia R. Bridges, MA, LCPA, Executive Director; Stephanie Warren, MSW, Birthparent Coordinator; Sue Lemmon, BA, Family Coordinator

CARING ADOPTIONS is a full service adoption agency licensed by the Texas Department of Family and Protective Services as designated by the IRS as a Section 501(c)(3) charitable organization. We have been finding families for children since 1991. Although located in Houston, Caring Adoptions works with birthmothers throughout Texas and adoptive families throughout Texas and the United States. Many of our staff have over 20 years of experience in adoption placement. "We believe in children and in creating families through adoption."

Texas

Caring Family Network Possiblities 512.719.3222
Fax 512.719.3343
Web ....www.cfntexas.com
E-mail ....rcalder@cfntexas.com
1812 Center Creek Dr, Austin, TX 78754
Renay Price, Director

CASA De Esperanza De Los Ninos 713.529.0639
Fax 713.529.9179
Web ....www.casahope.org
E-mail ....casa@casahope.org
2914 Court, Houston, TX 77054
Kathleen Foster, Director

Catholic Charities of Dallas Children and Adoption Svcs and Community Outreach 214.526.2772
Fax 214.526.2941
Web ....www.catholiccharitiesdallas.org
9461 LBJ Fwy Ste 110, Dallas, TX 75243
Barbara TenBroek, Division Director

Child Placement Ctr 254.690.5959
Fax 254.699.7057
Web ....www.childplacementcenter.org
E-mail ....s_lackmeyer@childplacementcenter.org
2212 Sunny Ln, Killeen, TX 76541-8273
Suzy Lackmeyer, Executive Director

Children and Family Institute 214.337.9979
Fax 214.337.9944
Web ....www.cfiadopt.org
5787 S Hampton Rd Ste 360, Dallas, TX 75232
Rose Jones, Director

Chosen Heritage 972.296.5111
Fax 972.298.7155
Web ....www.chosenheritage.org
E-mail ....chosenheritage1987@yahoo.com
650 Big Stone Gap Rd, Duncanville, TX 75137-2224
Stephanie Davis, Case Worker

Christian Homes & Family Svcs 800.592.4725
Fax 325.677.0332
Web ....www.christianhomes.com
E-mail ....attention@christianhomes.com
1202 Estates Dr, Abilene, TX 79602-4288
Robert D. Parkhill, Vp Of Social Services

Christian Svcs of East Texas 903.509.0558
Fax 903.509.0577
E-mail ....kbinkley@christianhomes.com
13359 State Highway 155 S, Tyler, TX 75703
Kay Binkley, Office Administrator

Circles of Care 361.852.3812
Fax 361.852.6124
Web ....www.circlesofcareinc.org
E-mail ....ledwards@circlesofcareinc.org
5333 Everhart Rd, Ste 150B, Corpus Christi, TX 78411
Lisa Edwards, President

Covenant Kids 817.516.9100
Fax 817.516.9102
Web ....www.covenantkids.org
E-mail ....klund@covenantkids.org
320 W Way Pl, Arlington, TX 76018
Karen Lund, Director

Cradle of Life Adoption Agency 409.832.3000
Fax 409.833.2817
Web ....www.cradleoflifeadoption.com
E-mail ....mwshel@ih2000.net
245 N 4th St, Beaumont, TX 77701-1920
Mel Shelander, Director

Crenshaw & Purvis Law Ofc 979.864.3200
Fax 979.848.1161
1216 N Velasco St Ste G, Angleton, TX 77515-3196
Steven Crenshaw, Attorney

DePelchin Children's Center 713.730.2335
Fax 713.802.7640
Web ....www.depelchin.org
4950 Memorial Drive, Houston, TX 77007
COA accredited organization.

Dolan Chiropractic 817.579.9444
2441 E Highway 377 Ste 101, Granbury, TX 76049

Earl S Spielman & Assoc 713.981.4200
Fax 713.513.5392
99 Detering St Ste 100, Houston, TX 77007-8225

El Paso Ctr For Children 915.565.5021
Fax 915.565.9719
2108 N Stevens St, El Paso, TX 30799
Armando Gutierrez, Programm Director

F Lakhani Law Ofcs 361.993.1313
Web ....www.flakhani.com
E-mail ....attorney@flakhani.com
1205 Airline Rd, Corpus Christi, TX 78412-3408
F Lakhani, Attorney

Family By Choice Adoption Svc 512.267.0181
Fax 512.267.0181
17811 Lafayette Park Rd, Leander, TX 78645
Susan Griffith, Program Director

Foster Care Services 210.736.1644
Fax 210.736.6570
4241 Woodcock Dr, Ste B103, San Antonio, TX 78228-1330
Katie Machuca, Director

Grace Manor 936.598.3611
Fax 936.598.5007
325 Tenaha St, Center, TX 75935-3446
Noel Wilkin, Director

Grandberry Intervention Foundation 817.561.4149
Fax 682.432.0508
Web ....www.cgifoundation.org
E-mail ....tgif_1245@yahoo.com
4109 Mansfield Hwy, Fort Worth, TX 76119
Sharon Grandberry, Director

Great Wall China Adoption 512.323.9595
Fax 512.323.9599
Web ....www.gwca.org
E-mail ....info@gwca.org
248 Addie Roy Rd Ste A102, Austin, TX 78746-4140
Snow Tan Wu, Director

Handle With Care 512.842.1163
Fax 512.847.7667
340 Barber Dr, Wimberley, TX 78676
Sharon M. Kiely, Director

Harmony Family Svcs Cpa 325.672.7200
Fax 325.672.7201
E-mail ....breedhfs@camalott.com
305 Grape St, Abilene, TX 79601
Jamie Breed, Executive Director

High Plains Children's Home 806.622.2272
Fax 806.622.2999
Web ....www.hpch.org
E-mail ....craigh@hpch.org
11461 S Western St, Amarillo, TX 79118
Craig Howard, Director

High Sky Children's Ranch 432.694.7728
Fax 432.694.9972
E-mail ....jackiec@highsky.org
8701 W County Road 60, Midland, TX 79707
Jackie Carter, Executive Director

Homes of St. Mark 713.522.2800
Fax 713.522.3769
7880 Sanfelipe Ste 11, Houston, TX 77063
Celeste Ross, CEO

Hope Cottage 214.526.8721
Fax 214.528.7168
Web ....www.hopecottage.org
E-mail ....shartwell@hopecottage.org
4209 McKinney Ave, Dallas, TX 75205
Sonya Hartwell, Executive Director

Hope For Tomorrow, Inc. 325.646.4673
Fax 325.646.4380
Web ....www.hope-for-tomorrow.com
E-mail ....jpiper@hope-for-tomorrow.com
1305 Early Blvd, Early, TX 76802-2355
Jennifer Piper, Chief Financial Officer

Hope International 214.672.9399
Fax 214.939.3001
Web ....www.hopeadoption.org
5944 Luther Ln Ste 875, Dallas, TX 75225
Dawn Ford, Executive Director

Houston Achievement Place 713.868.1943
Fax 713.869.1670
Web ....www.h-a-p.org
E-mail ....bpyykola@h-a-p.org
236 W 17th St, Houston, TX 77008-4002
Betty Pyykola, Director

Inheritance Adoptions 940.322.3678
Fax 940.322.2386
E-mail ....leaslie@inheritanceadoptions.org
1007 11th St, Wichita Falls, TX 976301
Leslie Howard, Director

Island View House 210.623.5419
Fax 210.623.1150
Web ....www.angelskeep.org
E-mail ....habhomes@angelskeep.org
9019 Old Sky Hbr, San Antonio, TX 78242-3225
Bette Eaton, Director

Jameson Ctr; The 409.765.1400
Fax 409.765.4320
E-mail ....kimberlystone@thechildrenscenterinc.org
4428 Avenue N, Galveston, TX 77553
Kimberly Stone, Director Of Foster Care

Jewish Family Svc 972.437.9950
Fax 972.437.1988
Web ....www.jfsdallas.org
E-mail ....info@jfsdallas.org
5402 Arapaho Rd, Dallas, TX 75248
Michael Fleisher, Executive Director

Kids at the Crossroads, Inc 512.346.8315
Fax 512.916.4453
Web ....www.kidsatcrossroads.com
E-mail ....kc.austin@yahoo.com
3505 Larchmont Cv, Austin, TX 78704-5914
Daniel Fry, Director

Kornerstone 817.276.9009
Fax 817.276.9084
Web ....www.safehavens.org
3221 W Pioneer Pkwy, Arlington, TX 76013
Dale Smith, Director

LDS Family Svcs 972.242.2182
Fax 972.242.2932
E-mail ....fam-tx-carrollton@ldschurch.org
1100 W Jackson Rd, Carrollton, TX 75006-1356
Eric Fernelius, Adoption Manager

Lonestar Solutions 817.265.2344
Fax 817.277.5610
E-mail ....klively@lonestarsolutions.org
1981 Stadium Oaks Court., Arlington, TX 76011
Kathleen Lively, Director

Loving Alternatives Adoptions 903.533.1288
Fax 903.533.8799
E-mail ....lovingalt@aol.com
430 South Vine Avenue, Tyler, TX 75702
Beverly Kline, Founder/director

Lutheran Social Svcs 903.939.3400
Fax 903.939.3438
E-mail ....shelley.reese@lsss.org
1800 Shiloh Rd Ste 301, Tyler, TX 75703
Shelley Reese, Director

Lutheran Social Svcs 915.598.5410
Fax 915.598.6220
6585 Montana, Ste S 100, El Paso, TX 79925
Jose Alamillo, Director

Lutheran Social Svcs **361.767.3182**
Fax 361.767.3183
  15602 Northwest Blvd Ste E, Robstown, TX 78380
Kendall Weatherford, Director

Lutheran Social Svcs **956.687.8333**
Fax 956.618.0478
Web ....www.lsss.org
E-mail ....flopez@lsss.org
  4603 N Jackson Rd Ste E, McAllen, TX 78504-6161
Frank Lopez, Director

Lutheran Social Svcs **956.791.4909**
Fax 956.791.2909
Web ....www.lsss.org
E-mail ....jmartinez@lsss.org
  102 E Calton Rd Ste 4, Laredo, TX 78041-6346
Jorge Martinez, Area Director

Lutheran Social Svcs **361.574.8331**
Fax 361.574.8334
Web ....www.lsss.org
E-mail ....tanya.pricedenson@lsss.org
  3904 John Stockbauer Dr Ste 101, Victoria,
  TX 77904-2456
Tanya Denson, Case Manager

Maria Linden PC **817.265.2948**
E-mail ....lindenlaw@sbcglobal.net
  PO Box 170444, Arlington, TX 76003
Maria Linden

Marywood Children and Family Svcs **512.472.9251**
Fax 512.949.2534
Web ....www.marywood.org
E-mail ....marywood@marrywood.org
  625 Hwy 290 E, Austin, TX 78723
Carolyn Chamberlain, Program Director

**Methodist Children's Home Foster Care
Div** **210.733.3904**
Fax 210.733.1544
Web ....www.methodistchildrenshome.org
E-mail ....mchsat@yahoo.com
  6800 Park Ten Blvd, Ste 230E, San Antonio,
  TX 78213-4220
Tim Brown, Chief Executive Officer

**Methodist Children's Home Foster Care
Div** **713.682.8911**
Fax 713.682.4229
Web ....www.methodistchildrenshome.org
E-mail ....vpeters@mchoutreach.org
  5005 Mitchelldale St Ste 119, Houston,
  TX 77092-7243
Veronica Whalon-peters, Director

Methodist Mission Home **210.696.2410**
Fax 210.699.1866
Web ....www.mmhome.org
E-mail ....helen@mmhome.org
  6487 Whitby Rd, San Antonio, TX 78240-2131
Helen Huff, Director Of Adoption Services

Money Management International, Inc. **888.845.5669**
Fax 713.394.3106
Web ....www.moneymanagement.org
  9009 West Loop South, 7th Floor, Houston,
  TX 77096-1719
COA accredited organization.

New Horizons **325.643.2264**
Fax 325.646.9013
E-mail ....mallgood@northernhs.org
  901 Ave B, Brownwood, TX 76801
Mica Allgood, Program Director

Pathways Youth and Family Svcs **830.232.6590**
Fax 830.232.6522
Web ....www.pathway.org
E-mail ....dan@pathway.org
  449 S US Highway 83, Leakey, TX 78873
Dan Johnson, Executive Director

Pathways Youth and Family Svcs **210.733.7117**
Fax 210.733.7118
E-mail ....suzette@pathways.org
  4243 Piedraf Dr E, San Antonio, TX 78228
Suzette Lamb, Director

Pathways Youth and Family Svcs **361.851.8682**
Fax 361.851.8687
Web ....www.pathway.org
E-mail ....info@pathway.org
  2820 S Padre Island Dr Ste 170, Corpus Christi,
  TX 70415
Rose Ahern, Director

Pathways Youth and Family Svcs **432.699.7763**
Fax 432.699.7959
Web ....www.pathyways.org
  1030 Andrews Hwy, Ste 200, Midland,
  TX 79701-3807
Belinda Jackson, Director

Pathways Youth Home CPA **830.232.6590**
Fax 830.232.6522
Web ....www.pathways.org
E-mail ....dan@pathway.org
  449 S US Hwy 83, Leakey, TX 78873
Dan Johnson, Executive Director

Presbyterian Children's Home **512.476.1234**
Fax 512.476.8468
Web ....www.pchas.org
  4407 Bee Caves Rd Ste 520, Austin, TX 78746
Ed Knight, President And CEO

Sherwood-Myrtie Fosters Home **254.968.2143**
Fax 254.968.8672
E-mail ....info@fostershome.org
  1779 North Graham Street, Stephenville, TX 76401
Glen Newberry, Director

South Texas Children's Home **361.375.2101**
Fax 361.375.2271
Web ....www.stchm.org
  9243 FM 2617, Pettus, TX 78146
Todd Roberson, Executive Director

Spaulding For Children **361.850.8200**
Fax 361.850.8202
Web ....www.spauldingforchildren.org
E-mail ....vfinley@spauldingforchildren.org
  500 N Waters St S Tower Ste 604, Corpus Christi,
  TX 78401
Vikki Finley, President/CEO

**Specialized Alternatives For Familiy and
Youth** **817.640.4650**
Fax 817.649.6038
Web ....www.safy.com
  201 Billings St Ste 510, Arlington, TX 76010
Fonny Wright, Director

Sunny Glen Children's Home **956.399.5356**
Fax 956.361.3668
E-mail ....jay@sunnyglen.org
  2385 W expressway 83, San Benito, TX 78586
Jay Williams, Director

Tejano Ctr **713.644.2441**
Fax 713.644.2443
Web ....www.dfps.state.tx.us
E-mail ....linda.crocker@dfps.state.tx.us
  5300 Sunrise Rd, Houston, TX 77021-3147
Linda Crocker, Director

Texas Baptist Home For Children **972.937.1321**
Fax 972.937.9510
Web ....www.tbhc.org
E-mail ....emarsh@tbhc.org
  629 Farley St, Waxahachie, TX 75165-2701
Jami Hogan, Adoption Director

Texas Mentor **817.460.1332**
Fax 817.460.1374
Web ....www.thementornetwork.com
E-mail ....holly.merritt@thementornetwork.com
  2225 E Randol Mill Rd Ste 310, Arlington, TX 76011
Holly Merritt, Director

Texas Mentor **713.432.0827**
Fax 713.432.0274
Web ....www.thementornetwork.com
E-mail ....raj.kendrick@thementornetwork.com
  6161 Savoy Dr Ste 1020, Houston, TX 77036-3343
Raj Kendrick, Director

The Arrow Project **281.210.1500**
Fax 281.847.1177
Web ....www.arrow.org
E-mail ....info@arrow.org
  2929 Fm 2920 Rd, Spring, TX 77388-3428
Andrea Pellerin, Program Director

The Bair Foundation **806.797.2247**
Fax 806.797.2225
  3501 S Loop 289, Lubbock, TX 79423
Stacey Salter, Director Of Social Services

The Bair Foundation of Texas **210.494.3415**
Fax 210.494.8741
Web ....www.bair.org
  6025 Fountainwood, San Antonio, TX 78233-4417
Taka Rowe, Executive Director

**The Children's Home of Lubbock and Family Service Agency,
Inc.** **806.762.0481**
Fax 806.762.6574
Web ....www.childrenshome.org
  P.O. Box 2824, Lubbock, TX 79408
COA accredited organization.

The Children's Shelter **210.212.2500**
Fax 210.785.9268
Web ....www.childrensshelter.org
  2939 West Woodlawn Avenue, San Antonio,
  TX 78228-5015
COA accredited organization.

Therapeutic Family Life **936.756.1800**
Fax 936.756.1808
Web ....www.tflife.org
E-mail ....hollyjones@tflife.org
  200 River Pointe Dr Ste 310, Conroe, TX 77304
Holly Jones, Director

Therapeutic Family Life **817.265.2328**
Fax 817.469.8345
E-mail ....pamelaroyao@tflife.org
  2229 Ave J,Ste 105, Arlington, TX 76006
Pamela Royao, Program Coordinator

Therapeutic Family Life **512.451.7310**
Fax 512.451.0394
Web ....www.tflife.org
  1340 Airport Commerce Dr, Ste 480, Austin,
  TX 78741
Leon J. Smith, Executive Director

Winston School; The **214.691.6950**
Fax 214.691.1509
Web ....www.winston-school.org
E-mail ....gina_shearer@winston-school.org
  5707 Royal Ln, Dallas, TX 75229-5500
Gina Shearer, Director Of External Relations

**Youth and Family Alliance, Inc. dba
LifeWorks** **512.735.2400**
Fax 512.735.2452
Web ....www.lifeworksweb.org
  8913 Collinfield Drive, Austin, TX 78758
COA accredited organization.

ADVOCACY RESOURCES

Adams King & Smith **903.757.3331**
E-mail ....ebbmob@aol.com
  422 N Center St, Longview, TX 75601
Ebb Mobley Iii, Attorney

Advocacy Ctr For Children **409.741.6000**
Fax 409.741.6004
Web ....www.galvestoncac.org
E-mail ....cccrabtree@Galvestoncac.com
　5710 Avenue S, # 1/2, Galveston, TX 77551
Carmen Crabtree, Executive Director

Advocacy Ctr For The Children Of El Paso **915.545.5400**
Fax 915.545.5414
Web ....www.advocacycenterep.org
E-mail ....oliva.susan@yahoo.com
　1100 E Cliff Dr, Bldg D, El Paso, TX 79902
Susan H. Oliva, Executive Director

Alliance For Children **817.795.9992**
Fax 817.795.9997
Web ....www.allianceforchildren.org
E-mail ....nhagan17@allianceforchildren.org
　1320 W Abram St, Ste 100, Arlington,
　TX 76013-1713
Nancy Hagan, Executive Director

Ard Law Firm **713.429.0218**
E-mail ....Sandy@ardlawfirm.com
　2876 Lost Cove Ct, Dickinson, TX 77539
Sandra Ard, Owner

Attorney & Counselor at Law **972.772.2636**
E-mail ....cmp@cathypenn.com
　1509 Summer Dr, Rockwall, TX 75032
Cathy Penn, Attorney

Attorney at Law **817.292.7702**
E-mail ....larisakeltner@me.com
　PO Box 16482, Fort Worth, TX 76162
Larisa Keltner

Auvenshine & Pratt **254.580.2443**
E-mail ....aplaw_pratt@sbcglobal.net
　PO Box 916, Hillsboro, TX 76645
Kara Pratt, Attorney

Avalos & Associates **832.242.7070**
E-mail ....cptavalos@yahoo.com
　6666 Harwin Ste 600, Houston, TX 77036
Claudia Avalos

Bain & Bain PLLC **713.629.6222**
E-mail ....atty@lawyer4u.com
　5300 Memorial Dr Ste 700, Houston, TX 77007
Bruce Bain, Attorney

Baker Law Office Atty & Counselor at Law **830.401.4565**
E-mail ....twb@baker-law.net
　6775 State Hwy 123 N, PO Box 33, Geronimo,
　TX 78115
Ty Baker

Barnes Prox Law PLLC **817.649.2700**
E-mail ....chante@barnesproxlaw.com
　1201 N Watson Rd Ste 206, Arlington, TX 76006
Chante Prox, Director

Beaty Law Office **903.342.5296**
E-mail ....beatylaw@hotmail.com
　337 N Main, PO Box 528, Winnsboro, TX 75494
Ted Beaty, Attorney

Becky Burtner Attorney at Law **903.813.0602**
E-mail ....bblaw@cableone.net
　326 W Lamar St, Sherman, TX 75090
Becky Burtner, Attorney

Bovik & Meredith PC **512.280.9096**
E-mail ....ebovik@austin.rr.com
　PO Box 150129, Austin, TX 78715
Erick Bovik

Bowen Law Group **940.566.0606**
E-mail ....chrysandra@bowen-lawgroup.com
　121 N Woodrow Suite 203, Denton, TX 76205
Chrysandra Bowen, Director

Boys and Girls Club **979.373.9668**
Fax 979.373.9665
E-mail ....pgray@bgbc.com
　202 W 1st St, Freeport, TX 77541-5702
Pamela Gray, CEO

Bridge/Children's Advocacy Ctr **806.372.2873**
Fax 806.372.2878
Web ....www.bridgecac.org
E-mail ....april@bridgecac.org
　804 Quail Creek Dr, Amarillo, TX 79124-1609
April Leming, Director

Brush Country CASA **361.595.7233**
E-mail ....brushcountrycasa@sbcglobal.net
　635 E King Ave Ste 110, Kingsville, TX 78363
Seana Towler, Executive Director

Burke Law Firm PC **832.631.6056**
E-mail ....kburke@burkelawfirm.com
　9595 Six Pines Dr, Ste 8210, The Woodlands,
　TX 77380
Kimberly Burke

Bythewood Legal Services PLLC **409.283.8800**
E-mail ....amy@bythewood.com
　102 S Charlton, Woodville, TX 75979
Amy Bythewood, Attorney

CAC **512.321.6161**
Fax 512.321.6164
Web ....www.childrensadvocacycenter.org
E-mail ....cacbastrop@austin.rr.com
　1002 Chestnut St, Bastrop, TX 78602-3304
Julie Elliott, Outreach Coordinator

CACS of Texas, Inc. **512.258.9920**
Fax 512.258.9926
Web ....www.cactx.org
E-mail ....ccrabtree@cactx.org
　1501 W Anderson Ln, Bldg B1, Austin, TX 78757
Kathy Crabtree, Executive Director

Carla B Morrison PLLC **210.391.6564**
E-mail ....carlamd6@yahoo.com
　408 Dwyer Ave, San Antonio, TX 78204
Carla Morrison, Lawyer

Carole Hurley Attorney at Law **512.345.4095**
E-mail ....churley@austin.rr.com
　8720 Silverhill Ln, Austin, TX 78759
Carole Hurley

CASA **361.573.3729**
E-mail ....deniser@goldencrescentcasa.org
　PO Box 1627
Denise Rangel, Director

CASA **979.282.9223**
Fax 979.282.9653
E-mail ....whartoncasa@sbcglobal.net
　1017 N Alabama Rd, Wharton, TX 77488-4203
Joyce Richmond, Program Director

CASA **409.457.3882**
E-mail ....mcintosh4life@aol.com
　9721 Amberjack Dr, Texas City, TX 77591
Yvette Mcintosh, Owner

CASA **817.599.6224**
E-mail ....connieplevak@casaofparkercounty.com
　200 Palo Pinto Ste 107, Weatherford, TX 76086
Connie Plevak, Director

CASA **817.877.5891**
E-mail ....randee@casatc.org
　101 Summit Ave Ste 505, Fort Worth, TX 76102
Randee Kaitcer, Supervisor

CASA In The Heart of Texas **325.643.2557**
Fax 325.643.6147
E-mail ....casa@familysc.net
　901 Avenue B, Brownwood, TX 76801
Michelle Wells, Executive Director

CASA Program **979.245.4958**
Fax 979.245.6453
E-mail ....matcocasa@sbcglobal.net
　2200 7th St Ste 2, Bay City, TX 77414-5203
Beryl Southall, Director

Castillo Law Office **512.377.1663**
E-mail ....susana.castillo@gmail.com
　504 W 7th St, Austin, TX 78701
Susana Castillo, Attorney

CDF Rio Grand Valley Office **956.687.5437**
　612 Nolana Ste 320, McAllen, TX 78504
Luisa Saenz, Director

Celeste King Attorney at Law **979.571.4776**
E-mail ....celestekinglaw@hotmail.com
　200 S Main Ste 204, Bryan, TX 77803
Celeste King

Child Advocates San Antonio **210.225.7070**
E-mail ....jtetchan@casa-satx.org
　406 San Pedro, San Antonio, TX 78212
Janet Tetchan, CEO

Child Care Svcs **512.236.9622**
Fax 512.478.8065
E-mail ....programservices@austinymca.org
　2121 E 6th St Apt 203, Austin, TX 78702
Megan Arnold, Director Of Business

Children's Advocacy Ctr **972.633.6600**
Fax 972.516.5754
Web ....www.caccollincounty.org
　2205 Los Rios Blvd, Plano, TX 75074
Lynne Mclein, CEO

Children's Advocacy Ctr **214.818.2600**
Fax 214.823.4819
Web ....www.dcac.org
E-mail ....ldavis@dcac.org
　3611 Swiss Ave, Dallas, TX 75204-6245
Lynn Davis, CEO

Children's Advocacy Ctr of The South
Plains **806.740.0251**
Fax 806.740.0252
E-mail ....caguirre@cacofsp.org
　720 Texas Ave, Lubbock, TX 79401
Carmen Aguirre, Executive Director

Children's Advocacy Network, Inc. **972.317.2818**
Fax 972.317.6989
Web ....www.cacdc.org
E-mail ....dan@cacdc.org
　1854 Cain Dr, Lewisville, TX 75077
Dan Leal, Executive Director

Children's Assessment Ctr **713.986.3300**
Fax 713.986.3553
Web ....www.cachouston.org
E-mail ....elaine.stolte@cac.hctx.net
　2500 Bolsover St, Houston, TX 77005
Elaine Stolte, Director

Children's Court **210.335.2768**
E-mail ....cmontemayor@bexar.org
　100 Dolorosa, San Antonio, TX 78205
Charles Montemayor, Executive Director

Childrens Defense Fund Texas **713.664.4080**
Fax 713.664.1975
E-mail ....CJOSEPH@CHILDRENSDEFENSE.ORG
　4500 Bissonnet Ste 260, Bellaire, TX 77401
Beth Quill, Executive Director

Childsafe **210.675.9000**
Fax 210.675.9020
Web ....www.childsafe-sa.org
　7130 W US Hwy 90, San Antonio, TX 78227
Mark Carmona, Executive Director

Christine Henry Andresen ATL **512.394.4230**
E-mail ....chrhenry@gmail.com
　3005 S Lamar Blvd, Suite D109-203, Austin,
　TX 78704
Christine Andresen

Christine R Brown-Zeto Attorney at Law **409.886.8558**
E-mail ....crbrown@exp.net
　1107 Green Ave, Orange, TX 77630
Christine Brown-zeto, Attorney

Texas

Texas

Cleaves Law Firm PLLC 817.329.8060
E-mail ....finney@cleaveslaw.com
1701 W Northwest Hwy Ste 100, Grapevine,
TX 76051
Amanda Finney, Attorney

Clemens & Spencer 210.227.7121
E-mail ....stephensk@clemens-spencer.com
112 E Pecan, Ste 1300, San Antonio, TX 78205
Kathy Stephens, Director

Clift & Associates PC 940.220.7082
E-mail ....goodtexasattorney@yahoo.com
1500 E McKinney St # 400, Denton, TX 76209
Evan Clift

Counsel to O'Neil & McConnell 281.296.9200
E-mail ....gmccon@wt.net
9001 Forest Xing Ste F, The Woodlands, TX 77381
Gail McConnell

Court Appointed Special Advocates of Deep E
Texas 936.275.8808
E-mail ....dl.casa@yahoo.com
422 E Main Box 243, Nacogdoches, TX 75961
Denise Lee

Court Appointed Special Advocates of Deep East
Texas 936.560.4711
E-mail ....casa.det@sbcglobal.net
422 E Main Box 243, Nacogdoches, TX 75961
Rebecca Carlton, Attorney

Crisp & Freeze 903.831.4004
1921 Moores Ln, Texarkana, TX 75503
Cammie Moody, Office Manager

Crista Marichalar PC 210.227.8200
E-mail ....crista@branchfamilylaw.com
501 S Main St, San Antonio, TX 78204
Crista Marichalar, Director

Ctr For Child Protection 512.472.1164
Fax 512.472.1167
Web ....www.centerforchildprotection.org
E-mail ......smartin@centerforchildprotection.org
8509 FM 969, Building 2, Austin, TX 78724
Sandra Martin, Executive Director

Curtis Alexander McCampbell & Morris PC 903.455.8113
E-mail ....lcurtis@geusnet.com
PO Box 1274, Greenville, TX 75403
Leah Curtis

David Zedler & Assoc PC 903.868.8989
E-mail ....paralegal5@verizon.net
215 1/2 N Travis, Sherman, TX 75090
David Zedler, Owner

Dennis L Smith Attorney at Law 830.257.4041
E-mail ....dlsmith@ktc.com
508 Jefferson, Kerrville, TX 78028
Dennis Smith, Attorney

DFPS 210.304.2004
3635 SE Military Dr, San Antonio, TX 78223
Ann Heiligenstein, Commissioner

DFPS 512.438.3466
E-mail ....sdenson@gmail.com
3211 Breeze Terr, Austin, TX 78722
Simi Denson

DFPS 940.612.4182
E-mail ....deanna.skiles@dfps.state.tx.us
715 E California Ste C, Gainesville, TX 76240
Deanna Skiles, Director

Donald M Crane Attorney at Law 281.392.6611
E-mail ....mmcrane56@yahoo.com
810 S Mason Rd, Ste 350, Katy, TX 77450
Donald Crane, Owner

Drucker Rutledge & Smith 281.681.3515
E-mail ....hopkins@drs-llp.com
10003 Woodloch Forest Dr, The Woodlands,
TX 77380
Kirby Hopkins, Associate

Duane L Coker & Associates PC 940.566.6649
E-mail ....ria@cokerlegal.com
1413 E McKinney St, Denton, TX 76209
Ria Sherman, Office Manager

Dunn & Dunn PC 903.567.1111
E-mail ....matt@dunnlegal.com
171 S Buffalo S, Canton, TX 75103
Matthew Dunn, Owner

Family Resource and Child Advocacy Ctr 940.549.9829
Fax 940.549.0302
E-mail ....ycfrc@brazosnet.com
729 Elm St, Graham, TX 76450
Diane Crosson, Executive Director

Garth House 409.838.9084
Fax 409.838.9106
E-mail ....mtanner@garthhouse.net
1895 McFaddin St, Beaumont, TX 77701
Marion Tanner, Executive Director

Gene Bush Law Office 936.327.7181
E-mail ....floydebush@livingston.net
Post Office Drawer 1617, Livingston, TX 77351
Gene Bush, Director

Gene Bush Law Office 936.327.1100
E-mail ....shellysitton@livingston.net
PO Drawer 1617, Livingston, TX 77351
Shelly Sitton, Attorney

General Practice 830.798.1690
E-mail ....shelllawoffice@yahoo.com
6000 N Highway 281, Marble Falls, TX 78564
Linda Bayless

Greater Waco Youth Law Project 254.715.0894
E-mail ....ann_ellis@wacoyouthlaw.com
602 James Ave, Waco, TX 76706
Ann Ellis

Greg Tate Attorney at Law 254.729.2325
E-mail ....greg@gtatelaw.com
209 W State St, Groesbeck, TX 76642
Greg Tate, Owner

Guajardo & Guajardo 512.474.9585
E-mail ....lucie@guajardo-law.com
1504 San Antonio St Ste 200, Austin, TX 78701
Lucie Jones-guajardo, Director

Haglund Law Firm PC 936.639.0007
E-mail ....aearley@haglundlaw.com
107 W Kerr Ave, Lufkin, TX 75902
April Early, Assosiate Director

Hance & Wickham PC 469.374.9600
E-mail ....shajdu@hancelaw.com
5420 LBJ Fwy Ste 626, 2 Lincoln Ctr, Dallas,
TX 75240
Jana Wickham Paul, Partner Lawyer

Harmony Home 432.333.5233
Fax 432.333.5257
Web ....www.harmonyhomecac.org
E-mail ....executivedirector@harmonyhomecac.org
910 C Grant Ave Ste C, Odessa, TX 79761-6664
Rodney Hall, Executive Director

Harvey L Cox Attorney at Law 254.562.9671
E-mail ....harvey@harveylcox.com
405 E Milam Ste 4A, Mexia, TX 76667
Harvey L Cox, Attorney

Hill Country Children's Advocacy Ctr 512.756.2607
Fax 512.756.6773
Web ....www.hccac.org
1001 N Hill St, Burnet, TX 78611
Dorris Graeter, Executive Director

Hope House Children's Advocacy Ctr 325.653.4673
Fax 325.653.5045
Web ....www.cactomgreen.org
317 Koberlin St, San Angelo, TX 76903
Heather Ward, Director

Hopkins-Laster Law Office 940.498.1222
E-mail ....karambee@aol.com
3516 Longview Dr, Denton, TX 76210
Dorothea Laster

Houston Family Law PC 713.973.5742
E-mail ....james.mahan@houstonfamilylawpc.com
11111 Katy Fwy Ste 910, Houston, TX 77079
James T Mahan, Owner

Huerta Law Firm 915.778.3700
E-mail ....jonathan915law@yahoo.com
11394 James Witt, El Paso, TX 799036
Jonathan Huerta, Attorney

James L Clark Attorney 903.897.5691
E-mail ....jamesclark27@yahoo.com
PO Box 310, Naples, TX 75568
James Clark, attorney

Janice Miles Attorney at Law 210.710.7773
E-mail ....jmileslaw@aol.com
333 W Olmos # 106, San Antonio, TX 78212
Janice Miles

John Delk Attorney at Law 903.792.2925
E-mail ....office@delklaw.com
1302 Olive St, Texarkana, TX 75501
John Delk, Attorney

Joseph Sterle Attorney at Law 903.793.4926
E-mail ....jsterle1206@wmconnect.com
1001 Texas Blvd Ste 112, Texarkana, TX 75501
Joseph Sterle

Judith Brokaw & Associates PC 713.780.1355
E-mail ....judibrokaw@aol.com
7457 Harwin St, Ste 228, Houston, TX 77036
Judith Brokaw, Attorney

Juvenile Probation Ofc 254.582.4053
Fax 254.582.4015
E-mail ....tina.lincoln@tjpc.state.tx.us
401 W Walnut St, Hillsboro, TX 76645
Tina Lincoln, Juvenile Cpo

Kernan & Clark PC 817.332.7739
E-mail ....mbfinley@swbell.net
101 Summit Ave, Fort Worth, TX 76102
Breanne Finley, Family Lawyer

Kid's Advocacy Place 830.895.4527
Fax 830.895.5140
Web ....www.kidsadvocacyplace.org
E-mail ....kap@ktc.com
313 Lesley Dr, Kerrville, TX 78028-3534
Judy Sullivan, Executive Director

Kurtis S Rudkin Attorney of Law PC 830.249.8472
E-mail ....ksrlaw@gvtc.com
910 N Main St Ste 1, Boerne, TX 78006
Kurtis Rudkin, Director

Larison Law Office 903.238.8184
E-mail ....mollylarison@yahoo.com
PO Box 232, Longview, TX 75606
Molly Larison, Director

Law Ofc of Cristina Soliz 361.668.6276
E-mail ....cristina.r.soliz@sbcglobal.net
721 E 2nd St, Alice, TX 78332
Cristina Rosales Soliz, Attorney

Law Ofc of Deborah Pritchet 214.573.7660
E-mail ....lawyer1958@yahoo.com
2201 main st ,ste 1220, Dallas, TX 75201
Deborah Pritchett, Attorney

Law Ofc of Joe B Steimel PC 940.761.5000
E-mail ....joebsteimel@sbcglobal.net
900 8th St Ste 301, Wichita Falls, TX 76307
Joe B Steimel, Attorney

Law Ofc of William J Stith PC 469.569.8248
555 Public Dr Ste 200, Plano, TX 75074
William Stith, President

Law Ofcs of Audrey E Manriquez 210.320.0641
E-mail ....amanlaw@grandecom.net
　PO Box 6315, San Antonio, TX 78209
　Audrey Manriquez

Law Ofcs of Audrey Moorehead 214.871.5085
E-mail ....audreyslaw@ymail.com
　3100 Carlisle St Ste 125, Dallas, TX 75204
　Audrey Moorehead, Attorney

Law Ofcs of Jimoh & Assoc 713.271.8484
E-mail ....jimohlawfirm@msn.com
　9894 Bissonnet Ste 340, Houston, TX 77036
　Adenrele Oladapo-jimoh, Director

Law Office of Aaryn Lamb 817.803.2620
E-mail ....aaryn@aarynlamb.com
　1135 S Main St, Grapevine, TX 76051
　Aaryn Lamb

Law Office of Aida R Rojas 210.476.8899
E-mail ....aidarojas@aidarojaslaw.com
　110 E Nueva St, San Antonio, TX 78204
　Aida Rojas

Law Office of B J Thompson 972.726.0535
E-mail ....bjt.law@ix.netcom.com
　7704 La Cosa Dr, Ste 100, Dallas, TX 75248
　B J Thompson, Attorney

Law Office of Bruce Harris 940.723.2241
E-mail ....bruceharrislaw@gmail.com
　1401 Holiday Ste 206, Wichita Falls, TX 76301
　Bruce Harris, Owner

Law Office of Candace E Hunter 512.476.9992
E-mail ....ceh@candacehunterlaw.co
　1411 West Ave Ste 200, Austin, TX 78701
　Candace Hunter, Attorney

Law Office of Chuck Smith 940.322.8100
E-mail ....chucksmith@wf.net
　901 Indiana Ave, Ste 300, Wichita Falls, TX 76301
　Chuck Smith, Attorney

Law Office of Claudia Canales 281.412.7722
E-mail ....claudia@claudiacanales.com
　2112 Grand Blvd, Pearland, TX 77581
　Claudia Canales, Attorney

Law Office Of Dana Davis Manoushagian 940.683.3712
E-mail ....danaattorney@embarqmail.com
　PO Box 127, Bridgeport, TX 76426
　Dana Manoushagian

Law Office of Dana E Fox 210.299.7627
E-mail ....fallen7998@yahoo.com
　111 Soledad Ste 300, San Antonio, TX 78205
　Dana Fox

Law Office of Debra L Parker 210.822.0620
E-mail ....debraparker@justice.com
　115 E Travis Ste 1729, San Antonio, TX 78205
　Debra Parker, Attorney

Law Office of Donald Bayne 210.930.4322
E-mail ....dsbayne@gmail.com
　3501 W Commerce, San Antonio, TX 78207
　Donald Bayne

Law Office of Donna LeLeux 281.648.2220
E-mail ....leleuxlaw@sbcglobal.net
　820 S Friendswood Dr, PO Box 1541, Friendswood,
　TX 77549
　Donna LeLeux

Law Office of Howard W Gaddis Jr 210.878.8601
E-mail ....hwgjr6780@yahoo.com
　6780 Pfeil Rd, Schertz, TX 78154
　Howard Gaddis

Law Office of Jennifer Casey 832.631.6057
E-mail ....jennifer@jcaseylawfirm.com
　9595 Six Pines Dr, Ste 408-A, The Woodlands,
　TX 77357
　Jennifer Casey

Law Office of Jennifer Perkins 214.208.2507
E-mail ....jperkins@uprlaw.com
　5930 Royal Ln Ste 378, Dallas, TX 75230
　Jennifer Perkins, Attorney

Law Office of Jenny C Parks 972.427.8888
E-mail ....lasthonestlawyer@aol.com
　1101 E Hwy 175, Crandall, TX 75114
　Jenny Parks, Attorney

Law Office of John Batchan 713.960.9563
E-mail ....jbatchat@aol.com
　11811 Pepperdine Ln, Houston, TX 77017
　John Batchan Jr

Law Office of John F DeMille 936.837.2300
E-mail ....jfd@embargmail.com
　PO Box 689, Anderson, TX 77830
　John F DeMille

Law Office of Judith Laughlin 210.572.7272
E-mail ....laughlinja@sbcglobal.net
　2600 McDullough Ave, San Antonio, TX 78212
　Judith Laughlin, Attorney

Law Office of Karina A Ramirez 713.522.6315
E-mail ....attykarinaramirez@sbcglobal.net
　110 Willard St, Houston, TX 77006
　Karina Ramirez, Attorney

Law Office of Kathy Black 281.398.5546
E-mail ....kathylawoffice@sbcglobal.net
　802 Domination Dr Ste 500, Katy, TX 77450
　Kathy Black, Attorney

Law Office of Katrina Korkus 210.834.4786
E-mail ....korkuslaw@lycos.com
　216 E Blanco Ste 101, Boerne, TX 78006
　Nina Korkus

Law Office of L Clay-Jackson 936.760.2889
　1110 N Loop 336 W Ste 500, Conroe, TX 77301
　S Martinez, Office Manager

Law Office of Lindsay Lopez 409.539.8089
E-mail ....lawofficeoflindsaylopez@yahoo.com
　2951 Marina Bay Dr Ste 130-225, Houston,
　TX 77058
　Lindsay Lopez

Law Office of Marilyn Mayse 214.475.3735
E-mail ....mmayse@swbell.net
　4306 York St, Dallas, TX 75210
　Marilyn Mayse

Law Office of Myla G Mayberry 903.758.6800
E-mail ....mylamayberry@msn.com
　211 E Tyler St Ste 200, Longview, TX 75601
　Myla Mayberry, Attorney

Law Office of Ned Wells Jr 210.826.0104
E-mail ....nedwells@grandecom.net
　PO Box 6163, San Antonio, TX 78209
　Ned Wells

Law Office of Richard Garcia Jr 210.843.8004
E-mail ....richardgarciajr@msn.com
　240 Bushnell Ave # 401, San Antonio, TX 78212
　Luis Richard Garcia, Attorney

Law Office of Rosa Ma Gonzalez 210.224.1283
E-mail ....rosamgonzalez@cs.com
　Morris K Bldg, 214 Dwyer Ste 302, San Antonio,
　TX 78204
　Rosie Gonzalez, Director

Law Office of Scott Bradney 210.299.7700
E-mail ....scott@bradneylaw.com
　111 Soledad St Ste 300, San Antonio, TX 78205
　Scott Bradney

Law Office of Sonja Sims 210.226.2227
E-mail ....sonjasimsesq@yahoo.com
　115 E Travis Ste 625, San Antonio, TX 78205
　Sonja Sims

Law Office of Steven N Harkiewicz 210.225.9000
E-mail ....snhlaw@sbcglobal.net
　2611 San Pedro, San Antonio, TX 78212
　Steven Harkiewicz

Law Office of Susan Ward 936.632.8294
E-mail ....sward@consolidated.net
　200 E Lufkin Ave, Lufkin, TX 75902
　Susan Ward, Attorney

Law Office of Theresa L Henry 281.823.9305
E-mail ....henrylaw1@comcast.net
　1100 Nasa Pkwy, Ste 310, Houston, TX 77058
　Theresa Henry

Law Office of Walden Shelton 210.696.4900
E-mail ....walden@wslaw.org
　8000 IH-10 W Ste 1500, San Antonio, TX 78230
　Walden Shelton

Law Office of Wendy Wood 979.779.9663
E-mail ....wendy@wendywoodlaw.com
　404 E 27th St Ste A, Bryan, TX 77803
　Wendy Wood, Owner

Law Office of William Gates 832.549.1868
E-mail ....gates001@net0.com
　1131 Shadeland Dr, Houston, TX 77047
　William Gates

Law Offices of AG Fortson PC 713.391.8723
E-mail ....afortson@agfortsonlaw.com
　945 McKinney St No 447, Houston, TX 77002
　Alicia Fortson

Law Offices of Beverly Smith 210.599.4722
E-mail ....justice@sbcglobal.net
　8930 Fourwinds Dr Ste 251, San Antonio, TX 78239

Law Offices of Bill Beggs 409.246.3200
E-mail ....bbeggs@beggsmac.com
　1005 S Redwood, PO Box 669, Kountze, TX 77625
　Bill Beggs

Law Offices of Jill S Williams 325.347.7623
E-mail ....jill.mcjmason@gmail.com
　PO Box 240, Mason, TX 76856
　Jill Williams

Law Offices of Lynne Corsi 214.660.9800
E-mail ....corsilaw1@tx.rr.com
　25 Highland Park Village, Ste 100-334, Dallas,
　TX 75205
　Lynne Corsi, Attorney

Law Offices of Sharon Merrick 972.235.3588
E-mail ....merrick@sharonmerrick.com
　740 E Campbell Rd, Ste 900, Richardson, TX 75081
　Sharon Merrick

Law Offices of Susan A Edwards 210.299.7641
E-mail ....edwardslegal@yahoo.com
　111 Soledad Ste 300, San Antonio, TX 78230
　Susan Edwards

Legal Aid of Northwest Texas 817.710.0013
E-mail ....williamsn@lanwt.org
　600 E Weatherford St, Fort Worth, TX 76102
　Nakiba Williams

Lori E Reeves Attorney at Law 940.627.5800
E-mail ....reeveslawyer@hotmail.com
　304 W Walnut St, Decatur, TX 76234
　Lori Reeves, Owner

Los Barrios Unidos Comm Clinic 214.878.2667
E-mail ....jmarchand@lbucc.org
　809 Singleton Blvd, Dallas, TX 75212
　John Marchand

Lovorn Law Firm PLLC 830.248.1777
E-mail ....slovorn@lovornlawfirm.com
　470 S Main St Ste 4, Boerne, TX 78006
　Shawn Lovorn, Director

Maja Scott Attorney at Law 713.320.5345
E-mail ....mscottlaw@yahoo.com
　6406 Macquarie Dr, Katy, TX 77449
　Maja Scott

Texas

Mark Barber Attorney at Law 940.761.3009
E-mail .... mbarberlaw@aol.com
 1101 Scott Ave Suite 11, Wichita Falls, TX 76301
Mark Barber, Manager

Mark Darling Attorney at Law PC 210.270.9959
E-mail .... lawdarling@yahoo.com
 434 S Main Ste 201, San Antonio, TX 78204
Mark Darling, Judge

Martin Garza and Fisher 409.765.5705
 1100 Rosenberg, Galveston, TX 77550
George Martin, Co-owner

McLaughlin Hutchison Starnes & Biard
LLP 903.785.1606
E-mail .... mhsbassistant@sbcglobal.net
 38 NW 1st St, Paris, TX 75460
Brad Hutchison, Managing Partner

Messer Potts & Messer PC 254.939.1818
E-mail .... nealepotts@sbcglobal.net
 118 S East St, Belton, TX 76513
Neale Potts, Attorney

Michael P Setty Atty Legal Assistant 903.856.6615
E-mail .... tbockman@suddenlinkmail.com
 PO Box 580, Pittsburg, TX 75686
Teresa Bockman

Michael Valverde Attorney 940.767.6330
E-mail .... mvalverde@nts-online.net
 901 Indiana Ste 500, Wichita Falls, TX 76301
Michael Valverde, Lawyer

Midland Rape Crisis & Children's Advocacy
Center 432.682.7273
Fax 432.685.0108
E-mail .... ratecrisis@aol.com
 1700 N Big Spring St, Midland, TX 79701
Jamie Poe, Executive Director

Mims & Assoc 281.931.6971
E-mail .... shermims@yahoo.com
 203 Candler Dr, Houston, TX 77037
Carnegie Mims Jr

Musick & musick LLP 832.448.1148
E-mail .... joanne@musicklawoffice.com
 397 N Sam Houston Pkwy E, Ste 325, Houston,
 TX 77060
JoAnne Musick

Natasha Hoy Attorney at Law 214.336.8591
E-mail .... natashahoy@gmail.com
 3523 McKinney Ave # 436, Dallas, TX 75204
Natasha Hoy

Norton & Wood LLP 903.823.1321
E-mail .... frontdesk@nortonandwood.com
 315 Main St, Texarkana, TX 75501
Fred Norton, Director

Ofc of Parental Representation 512.944.3788
E-mail .... cynthia.sexton@co.travis.tx.us
 209 W 9th St, Austin, TX 78704
Cynthia Sexton

Office of Child Rep 512.854.7312
E-mail .... lynn.lecropane@co.travis.tx.us
 205 w 9th st, Austin, TX 78701
Lynn Lecropane, Staff Attorney

Office of Parental Representation 512.591.7893
E-mail .... stephanie@ledesma-law.com
 401 W University Blvd, GEORGE TOWN, TX 78626
Stephanie Ledesma, Director

Ortiz-Taing Law Firm 281.486.7002
E-mail .... ortiz-tainglaw@sbcglobal.net
 2203 saint christopher st, leazue, TX 77573
Marcela Ortiz-taing, Attorney

Parental Representation 512.854.7305
E-mail .... jose.paiz@co.travis.tx.us
 209 W 9th St Ste 270, Austin, TX 78701
Jose Paiz, Administrative Associate

Patsy's House Children's Advocacy Ctr 940.322.8890
Fax 940.322.6695
E-mail .... patsyshouse@sbcglobal.net
 1411 10th St, Wichita Falls, TX 76301
Keri Goins, Executive Director

Patton Tidwell & Schroder 903.792.7080
E-mail .... canderson@texarkanlaw.com
 4605 Texas Blvd, Texarkana, TX 75503
Carly Anderson, Director

Pedley & Pedley 512.535.1481
E-mail .... pedleylaw@lawyer.com
 PO Box 201387, Austin, TX 78720
Thomas Pedley

Peltier Bosker & Griffin P C 713.461.5288
E-mail .... em_alvear@hotmail.com
 952 Echo Ln Ste 422, Houston, TX 77024

Ponce Law Firm 512.454.7700
 11900 Metric Blvd, Ste J-167, Austin, TX 78758
Griselda Ponce, Director

Printers Reynolds Attorneys 281.580.2700
E-mail .... printers@prodigy.net
 4201 Fm 1960 Rd W Ste 190, Houston, TX 77268
Vicky Reynolds, Owner

Ratekin Law Firm 903.595.1516
E-mail .... brent_ratekin@yahoo.com
 100 E Ferguson Ste 1018, Tyler, TX 75702
Brent Ratekin, Judge

Reddell Law Office 940.322.0000
E-mail .... dsreddell@yahoo.com
 900 8th St Ste 1400, Wichita Falls, TX 76301
David Reddell, Manager

Resources & Crisis Ctr 409.763.1441
E-mail .... bmartin@rccgc.org
 1802 Broadway Ste 122, Galveston, TX 77550
Bonnie Martin, Executive Director

Richard A Sacks Attorney 214.553.5566
E-mail .... sacks@wans.net
 8826 Flint Falls Dr, Dallas, TX 75243
Richard Sacks, Owner

Ritchey & Marbut LLP 512.499.8061
E-mail .... brent@rmlawoffice.net
 919 Congress Ave Ste 720, Austin, TX 78701
Brent Ritchey

Ross & Shoalmire LLP 903.223.5653
E-mail .... lisa@rossandshoalmire.com
 4112 McKnight Rd, Texarkana, TX 75503
Lisa Shoalmire, Attorney

Sabine Valley Child Protection 903.645.5695
E-mail .... terry.cowan@courts.state.tx.us
 501 Crockett Ste 3, Daingerfield, TX 75638
Gina Schnarr

Saint Legal PLLC 817.601.5345
E-mail .... james@saintlegal.com
 5751 Kroger Dr, Ste 239, Keller, TX 76244
James Saint

San Miguel Law Office PLLC 512.556.2040
E-mail .... joann@sanmiguellawoffice.comcast.net
 505 E 3rd St Ste 102, Lampasas, TX 76550
Jo Ann San Miguel, Attorney

Sarah S White Attorney at Law 903.663.4119
E-mail .... sarahswhite@msn.com
 PO Box 2521, Longview, TX 75606
Sarah White, Director

Schreier & Housewirth 817.467.5000
E-mail .... hjslaw@sbcglobal.net
 1300 S University Dr, Ste 406, Fort Worth, TX 76107
Holly Schreier

Schreier & Housewirth 817.923.9999
E-mail .... greg@fwfamilylaw.com
 1300 S University Dr, Fort Worth, TX 76107
Gregory Housewirth, Director

Shannon B Baldwin Attorney At Law 713.664.6800
E-mail .... s_baldwin_atty@msn.com
 801 Congress St, Ste 350, Houston, TX 77002
Shannon Baldwin, Attorney

Sharon Weathers Attorney 432.685.0606
E-mail .... slweathers@nts-online.net
 203 W Wall Ste 605, Midland, TX 79701
Sharon L Weathers, Attorney

Shea & Shea Attorneys at Law 903.870.7771
E-mail .... sheilashea@shealawyers.com
 105 S Travis Ste 100, Sherman, TX 75090
Sheila Shea, Director (attorneys)

Sikes & Assoc PC 817.645.6628
E-mail .... kbsikes@charter.net
 501 W Chambers St, Cleburne, TX 76033
Kimberly Sikes, Director

Sikes & Associates PC 817.646.6628
E-mail .... allena@charter.net
 501 W Chambers St, Cleburne, TX 76033
Allen Angela

Spain Law Firm 972.564.3196
E-mail .... spainlaw@gmail.com
 PO Box 756, Forney, TX 75126
Margaret Spain

Stanley Frank & Rose LLP 713.980.4381
E-mail .... pamrea@pamrealaw.com
 PO Box 431831, Houston, TX 77243
Pam Rea, Attorney

Steve P Mock & Assoc 713.660.7199
 8211-C Long Pt, Houston, TX 77055
Steve P Mock, Owner

Susan Desprez Attorney at Law 830.513.4806
E-mail .... susandlaw@gmail.com
 317 Sidney Baker S, Ste 400-237, Kerrville, TX 78028
Susan Desprez

Susan F Cobb PC 713.236.8711
E-mail .... sfcobb@msn.com
 712 Main St, Ste 1600, Houston, TX 77002
Susan Cobb

TDFPS 281.358.6556
E-mail .... brianbartko55@yahoo.com
 1942 River Falls Dr, Kingwood, TX 77339
Brian Bartko

Ted Sansom Attorney 972.771.2410
E-mail .... tedsansom@sbcglobal.net
 2305 Ridge Rd, Rockwall, TX 75087
Ted Sansom, Director

Texas Center for Judiciary 512.482.8986
E-mail .... ginnyw@yourhonor.com
 1210 San Antonio Ste 800, Austin, TX 78701
Ginny Woods, Grant Dir.

Texas Lawyers for Children 214.219.5852
E-mail .... stephanie.white@texaslawyersforchildren.org
 3131 Turtle Creek Blvd # 1018, Dallas, TX 75219
Stephanie White

Texas Rio Grande Legal Aid 956.447.4800
E-mail .... swelch@trla.org
 300 S Texas Blvd, Progreso, TX 78579
Stephanie Welch, Attorney

Texas Rio Grande Legal Aid Inc 512.374.2729
E-mail .... mcreed@trla.org
 4920 N IH-35, Austin, TX 78751
Mary Christine Reed, Director

Texas RioGrande Legal Aid 512.374.2730
E-mail .... kdietz@trla.org
 4920 N 135, Austin, TX 78751
Kevin Dietz

Texas Wesleyan Law Clinic 817.212.4123
E-mail .... krowden@law.txwes.edu
 1515 Commerce St, Fort Worth, TX 76102
Karon Rowden, Staff Attorney

The Carlson Law Firm 254.772.5653
E-mail ....tchaney@carlsonattorneys.com
1105 Wooded Acres Ste 300, Waco, TX 76710
Tomekia Chaney

The Ferguson Law Firm PC 866.878.5258
E-mail ....corey@texascriminalcounsel.com
1503 Hailey, Conroe, TX 77301
Corey Ferguson, Manager

The Griffith Law Firm PLLC 713.227.0020
E-mail ....katrinagriffith@sbcglobal.net
310 Main St, Ste 300, Houston, TX 77002
Katrina Griffith, Attorney

The Harbor 361.552.1982
Fax 361.552.4309
E-mail ....t-harbor@tisd.net
215 W Railroad St, Port Lavaca, TX 77979
Virginia Hahn, Executive Director

The Hollwarth Law Firm PLLC 903.234.0711
E-mail ....hollwarthlaw@gmail.com
208 N Green St Ste 506, Longview, TX 75606
Christina Hollwarth, Attorney

The Law Office of Lynn Davis Ward 214.739.8900
E-mail ....molly@ward-attorneys.com
8144 Walnut Hill Ln, Ste 1080, Dallas, TX 75231
Molly Gappelberg, Attorney

The Law Office of Stephen K Harmon PC 817.545.1292
E-mail ....steve.harmon@verizon.net
2516 Harwood Rd, Bedford, TX 76021
Stephen Harmon, Director

The Law Office of Zoe Meigs 817.336.2325
E-mail ....zoemeigs@msn.com
4420 W Vickery Blvd Ste 102, Fort Worth, TX 76107
Zoe Meigs, Director

The Martinez Jones Law Firm PLLC 512.452.1555
E-mail ....attorney@martinezjoneslaw.co
6010 Balcones Dr, Ste 250-A, Austin, TX 78731
Aurora Jones, Attorney

The Mathews Law Firm 512.364.6000
E-mail ....lauren@mathewsfamilylaw.com
3571 Far West Blvd Ste 32, Austin, TX 78731
Lauren Mathews, Attorney

The Parmer Law Firm PC 940.566.2500
E-mail ....libby@elizabethparmerlaw.com
121 W Hickory, Denton, TX 76201
Elizabeth Parmer, Attorney

The Romero Law Firm PC 281.220.1067
E-mail ....dmr@attorneyromero.com
17041 El Camino Real Ste 209, Houston, TX 77058
David Romero, Managing Shareholder

The Wade Office 832.681.1151
E-mail ....tlwade2004@hotmail.com
PO Box 34821, Houston, TX 77234
Tiffany Wade

The Wes Law Group PLLC 972.658.9780
E-mail ....wytaine@yahoo.com
4704 Towne Square Dr # 2622, Plano, TX 75024
Wytaine Smith

The Wise Law Firm 713.877.9473
E-mail ....mwise@wise-law.com
952 Echo Lane Ste 478, Houston, TX 77024
Mari Wise, Attorney

Thompson & Frost PC 903.796.4481
E-mail ....jwhitehorn@thompsonandfrost.co
PO Box 1046, Atlanta, TX 75551
Gary Albertson, Director

Tim Mahoney Attorney at Law PC 512.326.9944
E-mail ....tim@mahoneylawaustin.com
PO Box 1544, Austin, TX 78767
Tim Mahoney

Tucker & Calvillo 713.464.1474
E-mail ....Tuckeray@sbcglobal.net
401 St 305 Shadow Bend Dr, Houston, TX 77007
Amanda Tucker, Owner

TX DFPS 512.923.6756
E-mail ....sdenson@gmail.com
3211 Breeze Terr, Austin, TX 78722
Kelly Simi Denson

Unger & Hershkowitz 713.917.6877
E-mail ....hilary@ungerhershkowitz.com
2950 N Loop W Ste 500, Houston, TX 77092
Hilary Unger

Violet Nwokoye & Assoc 972.213.9335
E-mail ....violetnokoye@yahoo.com
3620 S Cooper St Ste 100, Arlington, TX 76015
Violet Nwokoye, Director

Wanda Brown Hiebert Attorney at Law 903.223.5291
E-mail ....wbhlaw1@aol.com
3902 Moores Ln, Texarkana, TX 75503
Wanda Hiebert, Attorney

Weismuller Law Firm 936.637.6705
E-mail ....jwj@consolidated.net
PO Box 153941, Lufkin, TX 75915
John Weismuller, Director

Winikates & Winikates 972.335.1122
E-mail ....chuckandfrances@aol.com
7700 Main St Ste E, Frisco, TX 75034
Frances Fazio

Wise & Wise 817.599.4136
E-mail ....kittywise@hotmail.com
211 N Main St, Weatherford, TX 76086
Kathleen Wise

Woodruff & Wren LLP 940.627.2162
E-mail ....jwren@woodruffwren.com
PO Box 977, Decatur, TX 76234
Jennifer Wren

Zimmerman & zimmerman 210.494.1919
E-mail ....gkzmbz@yahoo.com
PO Box 460468, San Antonio, TX 78246
Gail Zimmerman, Director

BEHAVIORAL HEALTH TREATMENT

Acadia Health Care 325.698.6600
Fax 325.698.8200
Web ....www.acadiahealthcare.org
E-mail ....rmcmurray@abilenepsychcenter.com
4225 Woods Pl, Abilene, TX 79602-7991

Aliviane No-Ad 915.775.2501
Fax 915.775.2470
Web ....www.aliviane.org
E-mail ....blenoros@aliviane.org
2007 Texas Ave, El Paso, TX 79901-1918
Blanco Lenoros, Director

Amarillo Isd 806.356.4899
Web ....www.amaisd.org
E-mail ....karen.town@amaisd.org
1250 Wallace Blvd, Amarillo, TX 79106-1741
Karen Town, Director

Amistad Therapy Ctr/ Reins Of Freedom 830.774.4447
Fax 830.774.4265
E-mail ....amistadtherapy@yahoo.com
501 W Cantu Rd Ste 400, Del Rio, TX 78840
Rebecca Slayton, Director

Angelina Mhc-Burke Ctr 936.639.2384
Fax 936.639.9888
Web ....www.burke-center.org
4103 S Medford Dr, Lufkin, TX 75901
Micela Fitzgerald, Director

Arrow Project Of Texas 512.388.2400
Fax 512.388.3237
Web ....www.arrow.org
E-mail ....infocentral@arrow.org
110 S Main St Ste 100, Round Rock, TX 78664-5272
Mark Tennant, CEO

Arrow Project Of Texas 972.360.3700
Fax 972.360.3750
Web ....www.arrow.org
E-mail ....infonorth@arrow.org
1525 N Interstate 35 E Ste 100, Carrollton,
TX 75006-5143
Sandi Harp, Program Director

Austin Child Guidance Center 512.451.2242
Web ....www.austinchildguidance.org
E-mail ....rsmith@austinchildguidance.org
810 West 45th Street, Austin, TX 78751
Mr. Russell Smith, Accreditation Manager
Joint Commission accredited organization.

Bair Foundation 254.776.5600
Fax 254.776.5618
E-mail ....wbyas@bair.org
7736 Cental Park Dr, Waco, TX 76712
Wes Byas, Director

Bannister Medical Practice 512.328.2820
1301 S Capital Of Texas Hwy Ste 240A, Austin,
TX 78746-7072
John Bannister, Psychiatrist

Bayes Achievement Center, Inc. 936.291.3391
Fax 936.291.7622
Web ....www.bayescenter.com
7517 Highway 75 South, Huntsville, TX 77340
COA accredited organization.

Baylor University 254.710.2467
Web ....www.baylor.edu
E-mail ....rod_hetzel@baylor.edu
1 Bear Pl, Waco, TX 76798-0006
Roderick Hetzel, Director

Beisel Medical Practice 512.773.0474
1015 Beecave Woods Dr, Austin, TX 78746
Lisa Beisel MD, Psychiatrist

Ben Richey's Boys Ranch 325.692.2500
Fax 325.692.2514
Web ....www.benrichey.org
501 Ben Richey Dr, Abilene, TX 79602
Pat Carriker, Director

Bennett Medical Practice 972.233.0648
Web ....www.dgapractice.com
E-mail ....rdbennett@gmail.com
6330 Lyndon B Johnson Fwy, Ste 150, Dallas,
TX 75240-6431
Robert Bennett, MD, Psychiatrist

Bennett Medical Practice 972.233.5455
E-mail ....jbennett104@sbcglobal.net
12880 Hillcrest Rd Ste 224, Dallas, TX 75230-6567
B James Bennett, Psychiatrist

Blackburn Medical Practice 713.529.2405
PO Box 667577, Houston, TX 77266-7577
Theresa Blackburn, MD, Psychiatrist

Bleiberg Medical Practice 713.665.0342
4806 Fern St, Bellaire, TX 77401-5016
Efrain Bleiberg, Psychiatrist

Boland Medical Practice 281.337.1350
914 Fm 517 Rd W Ste 201B, Dickinson,
TX 77539-3925
Howard Boland, Md, Psychiatrist

Boys Haven Of America 409.866.2400
Fax 409.866.7610
E-mail ....boyshaven@aol.com
3655 N Major Dr, Beaumont, TX 77726
Tony Castillo, Executive Director

Brandon Medical Practice **713.524.8307**
Fax 713.831.6884
   3730 Kirby Dr, Houston, TX 77098
   Thomas Brandon, MD, Psychiatrist

Bryan Federal Bureau of Prisons Camp **979.823.1879**
Fax 979.822.5014
   1100 Ursuline Ave, Bryan, TX 77805
   Clay Ork, Lieutenant

Brylowski Medical Practice **972.241.4472**
Fax 972.692.6882
   2925 Lyndon B Johnson Fwy, Dallas, TX 75234
   Andrew Brylowski, Md, Psychiatrist

Buckner Children And Family Svcs, Inc. **214.758.8023**
Fax 214.758.8152
Web .... www.buckner.org
E-mail .... ebaskin@buckner.org
   600 N Pearl St Ste 2000, Dallas, TX 75201-2874
   Evey Baskin, Manager

Burke Center **936.639.1141**
Web .... www.burke-center.org
E-mail .... donnam@burke-center.org
   2001 South Medford Drive, Lufkin, TX 75901
   Ms. Donna Moore, Accreditation Manager
   Joint Commission accredited organization.

BVCCA **979.696.5529**
Web .... www.bvcaa.org
E-mail .... abenavides@bvcaa.org
   1105 Anderson St, College Station, TX 77840
   Albert Benavides, Coordinator

Byrd's Foster Group Home, Inc. **713.699.3284**
Fax 713.699.8843
E-mail .... byrdsnestlb@prodigy.net
   5708 Hardy St, Houston, TX 77009
   Laverne Byrd, Director

Byrd's Therapeutic Group Home **281.931.7481**
Fax 281.931.0329
   882 Marcolin St, Houston, TX 77088
   Laverne M. Byrd, Director

**Canyon Lakes Residential Treatment
Center** **806.762.5782**
Web .... www.canyonlakesrtc.com
E-mail .... lenise@canyonlakesrtc.com
   2402 Canyon Lake Drive, Lubbock, TX 79415
   Mrs. Lenise Staha, Accreditation Manager
   Joint Commission accredited organization.

Cardenas Medical Practice **281.491.1370**
E-mail .... vjcmd@comcast.net
   3111 Ann Arbor Ct, Sugar Land, TX 77478-3709
   Victor Cardenas, Md, Psychiatrist

Cardona Medical Practice **713.796.9993**
Fax 713.796.9419
   7515 Main St, Houston, TX 77030
   Emilio Cardona, Md, Psychiatrist

Carl R Darnell Army Medical Ctr **254.288.8000**
   36000 Darnall Loop, Killeen, TX 76544-5095
   Commander Sargenc, Commander Of Hospital

**CEDAR CREST
HOSPITAL & RTC**
BEHAVIORAL CENTERS OF AMERICA

Cedar Crest Hospital & RTC **254.939.2100**
Fax 254.939.2334
Web .... www.cedarcresthospital.com
E-mail .... contact.CCrest@bca-corp.com
   3500 S. IH-35 , Belton, TX 76513
   *Brandy Hart, Admissions Director; David Myatt, Clinic Director; Ed
   Hernandez, D.O.N.; Ingrid Whipple, CEO; Teresa Hansen, Business
   Development Director*
   The ability for a patient to be able to move between the acute care and RTC levels
   of care if needed is a Cedar Crest advantage. Sitting on 33-acres, our Residential
   Treatment Program specializes in providing longer-term treatment for children
   and adolescents who have completed acute care inpatient programs and require
   additional treatment in a 24-hour therapeutic environment (including on-site
   school), as well as those who have failed to respond effectively in previous
   placements. Cedar Crest's Acute Care Hospital Program is a psychiatric intensive
   care program designed to stabilize a child or adolescent's immediate crisis while
   providing the patient and family with skills to help prevent or minimize future
   incidents that would require re-admission.

Central Texas Children's Home **512.243.1386**
Fax 512.243.1900
   1925 Crane Rd, Buda, TX 78610
   Tom Hagen, Director

Cherokee Home For Children **325.622.4201**
Fax 325.622.4215
Web .... www.cherokeehomeforchildren.org
E-mail .... chc@centex.net
   13355 S Hwy 16, Cherokee, TX 76832
   Delton Mcguire, Director

Child and Family Ctr **214.351.3490**
Fax 214.352.0871
Web .... www.childrenandfamilies.org
E-mail .... pyoung@childrenandfamilies.org
   8915 Harry Hines Blvd, Dallas, TX 75235-1717
   Patrick Young, Medical Director

CHRISTUS Spohn Hospital Corpus Christi **361.902.4103**
Web .... www.christusspohn.org
E-mail .... kathy.carson@christushealth.org
   2606 Hospital Boulevard, Corpus Christi,
   TX 78405-1818
   Ms. Kathy Carson, Accreditation Manager
   Joint Commission accredited organization.

Clarity Child Guidance Center **210.616.0300**
Fax 210.616.0417
Web .... www.smhc.org
E-mail .... fred.hines@claritycgc.org
   8535 Tom Slick, San Antonio, TX 78229-3367
   Fred Hines, President & CEO

Clarity Child Guidance Center **210.616.0300**
Web .... www.claritycgc.org
E-mail .... geoffrey.gentry@claritycgc.org
   8535 Tom Slick Drive, San Antonio, TX 78229
   Dr. Geoffrey Gentry, Accreditation Manager
   Joint Commission accredited organization.

Clark Psycological **936.639.4993**
Fax 936.639.6838
E-mail .... sc-ac@consolidated.net
   501 Mantooth, Luskin, TX 75904
   Frankie Clark, Director

Clayton & Pittman Group Practice **214.631.3663**
Fax 214.631.3662
   9400 N Macarthur Blvd, Irving, TX 75063-4705
   Lisa Clayton, Md, Psychiatrist

Coffey Medical Practice **512.328.2563**
Fax 512.306.8978
   7004 Bee Caves Rd Ste 105, Austin, TX 78746-5065
   Aida Coffey, Psychiatrist

Collins Medical Practice **214.361.7009**
Fax 215.232.3511
Web .... dmagazine.com
   8226 Douglas Ave, Ste 805, Dallas, TX 75225-5930
   Janet Collins, MD, Psychiatrist

Community Health Core **903.753.9744**
Fax 903.236.7970
E-mail .... star@communityhealthcore.com
   107 Woodbine Place, Longview, TX 75601
   Robert Mangham, Assistant Director

Concho Valley Home For Girls **325.655.3821**
Fax 325.653.2915
Web .... www.conchokids.org
E-mail .... cvhgces@conchokids.org
   412 Preusser St, San Angelo, TX 76903-3618
   Sammye Ruppeck, Director

CONTINUUM **713.383.0888**
Web .... www.continuum-ihs.com
E-mail .... cpeacock@continuum-ihs.com
   3003 South Loop West, Suite 475, Houston,
   TX 77054-1301
   Ms. Courtney Peacock, Accreditation Manager
   Joint Commission accredited organization.

**Continuum Baytown Community Mental Health Center,
LLC** **281.420.6900**
Fax 281.420.6990
Web .... www.continuumhealth.net
   2001 Cedar Bayou Road, Baytown, TX 77520
   CARF accredited programs available.

Continuum Hornwood, LLC **713.271.0000**
Fax 713.271.6141
Web .... www.continuumhealth.net
   6614 Hornwood Drive, Houston, TX 77074
   CARF accredited programs available.

Continuum Integrated Health Svcs, Inc **713.383.0888**
Fax 713.383.0895
Web .... continuum-ihs.com
E-mail .... bcandley@continuum-ihs.com
   3003 S Loop W Ste 475, Houston, TX 77054-1381
   Barbara Candley, Phd, Director

Cordell Medical Practice **713.669.0373**
   4545 Bissonnet St Ste 120, Bellaire, TX 77401-3115
   Linda Cordell, MD, Psychiatrist

CPC Millwood Hospital **817.261.3121**
Fax 817.261.1483
E-mail .... earnestbraumley@millwoodhospital.com
   1011 N Cooper St, Arlington, TX 76011-5517
   Dr. Earnest Braumley, Medical Director

Ctr For Emotional Wellness **281.495.9289**
Web .... www.centeroremotionalwellness.com
E-mail .... allen_counseling@sbcglobal.net
   11104 W Airport Blvd Ste 136, Stafford,
   TX 77477-3040
   Lara Allen, Director

Ctr For Life Resources **325.646.9574**
Fax 325.646.7911
E-mail .... dwhite@ctmhmr.hhscn.org
   408 Mulberry St, Brownwood, TX 76801-1639
   Dion White, Executive Director

Dallas Metrocare Svcs **214.333.7015**
Fax 214.333.4107
   1353 N Westmoreland Rd, Bldg A, Dallas, TX 75211
   Dr. James Baker, CEO

Davis Medical Practice **512.306.0050**
   202 Ashworth Dr, Austin, TX 78746-4604
   Jay Allan Davis, Psychiatrsit

**DebLin Health Concepts and Associates,
Inc.** **713.686.9194**
Web .... www.deblinhealthconcepts.com
E-mail .... djackson@deblinhealthconcepts.com
   2215 Bauer Dr., Houston, TX 77080-5528
   Ms. Debra Jackson, Accreditation Manager
   Joint Commission accredited organization.

Delaney Medical Practice 713.468.7577
　10497 Town And Country Way, Houston, TX 77024
　Catherine Delaney, Md, Psychiatrist

Depelchin Children's Ctr 713.730.2335
Fax 713.802.6307
Web ....www.depelchin.org
E-mail ....cmooney@depelchin.org
　4950 Memorial Dr, Houston, TX 77007-7440
　Curtis Mooney, Phd, CEO

Devereux Texas Treatment Network 281.335.1000
Web ....www.devereux.org
E-mail ....pgoehrin@devereux.org
　1150 Devereux Drive, League City, TX 77573
　Ms. Patricia Goehring, Accreditation Manager
　Joint Commission accredited organization.

Diaz Vogt Medical Practice 915.590.2535
　10320 Ashwood Dr, El Paso, TX 79925
　Josefina Diaz Vogt, Md, Psychiatrist

Disabilites Rights Texas 806.765.7794
Fax 806.765.0496
E-mail ....bmckinnon@advocacyinc.org
　1001 Main St Ste 300, Lubbock, TX 79401
　Billie Mckinnon, Director

Diversified Concepts / NDI 936.633.7998
Fax 936.634.4881
Web ....www.burkecenter.org
　2215 N John Redditt Dr, Lufkin, TX 75969
　Brenda Mcclendon, Manager

Dunn Medical Practice 214.987.0268
Fax 214.987.0274
Web ....www.dshs.state.tx.us
E-mail ....mitchell.dunn@dshs.state.tx.us
　5952 Royal Ln Ste 268, Dallas, TX 75230-7880
　Mitchell Dunn, MD, Psychiatrist

**Early Childhood Intervention - First Steps
Forward** 979.821.9478
Fax 979.361.9847
Web ....www.dars.state.tx.us/ecis
　302 E 24th St, Bryan, TX 77803
　Miriam Roman, Program Director

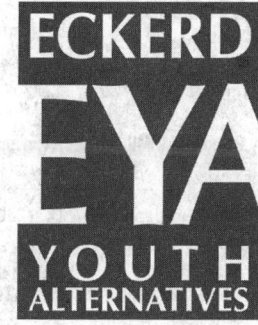

Eckerd 214.941.4435
Fax 214.941.4467
Web ....www.eckerd.org
E-mail ....admissions@eckerd.org
　400 S Zang Blvd, Ste 220, Dallas, TX 75208
　David Dennis, President & CEO; Teresa Stroud, Area Director
　Eckerd provides Diversion and Family Reunification services in the Dallas County area. Our diversion service is an outcome-driven alternative to secure detention for youth ages 10 – 17 that enables them to remain in their homes and addresses complex mental, emotional and behavioral needs while awaiting disposition. The evidence-based approach combines intensive case management and monitoring, youth life skills training, parent counseling and individualized home contact.

El Paso Child Guidance Center 915.562.1999
Fax 915.562.2008
Web ....www.elpasochildguidancecenter.org
　2701 East Yandell Drive, El Paso, TX 79903
　COA accredited organization.

El Paso Psychiatric Ctr 915.532.2202
Fax 915.534.5590
E-mail ....zulema.carrillo@dshs.state.tx.us
　4615 Alameda Ave, El Paso, TX 79905
　Zulema Carrillo, CEO

Emmite Medical Practice 713.383.0777
　7900 Fannin St, Houston, TX 77054
　Debra Emmite, MD, Psychiatrist

Eubanks Medical Practice 512.477.7676
E-mail ....veubanks@io.com
　2201 A Ln, Austin, TX 78703-3132
　Virginia Eubanks MD, Psychiatrist

Everhealth Inc 713.484.5105
Fax 713.988.9550
Web ....www.everhealth.us
　7324 Southwest Fwy, Houston, TX 77074
　Mehboob Nazarani, Psychiatrist

Family Behavior Medicine Assoc 512.335.4448
　3636 Executive Center Dr, Austin, TX 78731
　Asif Siddiqui, Psychiatrist

Family Counseling Svc 361.852.9665
Fax 361.852.2794
Web ....www.ccfamilyservices.org
　3833 S Staples St Ste S203, Corpus Christi,
　TX 78411-5228
　Christine Desrosier, Executive Director

Family Svcs of Greater Houston 713.868.4466
Fax 713.868.2619
E-mail ....nwoods@familyservices.org
　3815 Montrose Blvd Ste 200, Houston,
　TX 77006-4665
　Nyla Woods, President/CEO

Farley Medical Practice 713.521.5859
E-mail ....ajfarley@sbcglobal.net
　403 Heights Blvd, Houston, TX 77007-2519
　Arthur Farley, Md, Psychiatrist

Forgason Medical Practice 512.477.3880
　710 West Ave, Austin, TX 78701-2727
　Judy Forgason, MD, Psychiatrist

Franke Medical Practice 713.785.0101
Fax 973.299.7212
　2603 Augusta Dr Ste 805, Houston, TX 77057-5681
　Fritz Franke, Md, Psychiatrist

Frenkel Medical Practice 972.239.0811
E-mail ....rsfre@sbcglobal.net
　5310 Harvest Hill Rd, Dallas, TX 75230
　Rhoda Frenkel, Psychiatrist

Girls and Boys Town of San Antonio 210.271.1010
Fax 210.271.3333
Web ....www.girlsandboystown.org/sanantonio
　503 Urban Loop, San Antonio, TX 78204
　Wade Rascoe, Executive Director

Green Oaks Hospital 972.991.9504
Fax 972.789.1865
Web ....www.greenoakspsych.com
　7808 Clodus Fields Dr, Dallas, TX 75251-2206
　Shelly Fields, Administrator Assistant

Green Oaks Hospital Subsidiary, LP 972.770.0840
E-mail ....pam.whitley@hcahealthcare.com
　7808 Clodus Fields Drive, Dallas, TX 75251
　Ms. Pam Whitley, Accreditation Manager
　Joint Commission accredited organization.

Happy Hill Farm Academy-Home 254.897.4822
Fax 254.897.7650
　3846 N Highway 144, Granbury, TX 76048
　Chuck Shipman, Director

HappyMe.com 972.503.4803
Web ....www.happyme.com
E-mail ....bmh@happyme.com
　101 South Coit Road, Suite 212, Richardson,
　TX 75080
　Gary N. Bourland, Ma, Lmft, Lcdc, Director

Hartsell Psychological Services, Inc. 903.463.3730
Fax 903.463.3799
Web ....www.hartsellpsych.com
　2402 West Morton Street, Suite 122, Denison,
　TX 75020-3537
　CARF accredited programs available.

Heartlight Residential Teen Counseling 903.668.2173
Fax 903.668.3453
E-mail ....markgregston@heartlightministries.org
　7345 East Highway 80, Hallsville, TX 75650
　Mark Gregston, Executive Director

Hector Garza Center 210.568.8600
Web ....www.abraxasyfs.com
E-mail ....jsilva@abraxasyfs.com
　620 E. Afton Oaks, San Antonio, TX 78232
　Mr. John Silva, Accreditation Manager
　Joint Commission accredited organization.

Hendrick Home For Children 325.692.0112
Fax 325.692.6813
Web ....www.henrickhome.com
　2758 Jeanette St, Abilene, TX 79602
　David Miller, Phd, President

Hickory Trail Hospital 972.298.7323
Web ....www.hickorytrail.com
E-mail ....elicia.bunch@psysolutions.com
　2000 North Old Hickory Trail, Desoto, TX 75115
　Ms. Elicia Bunch, Accreditation Manager
　Joint Commission accredited organization.

HMIH Cedar Crest, LLC 254.939.2100
Web ....www.cedarcresthospital.com
E-mail ....ed.hernandez@bca-corp.com
　3500 South IH- 35, Belton, TX 76513
　Mr. Edmundo Hernandez, Accreditation Manager
　Joint Commission accredited organization.

Hope House, Inc. 512.515.6889
Fax 512.515.6793
Web ....www.hopehouseaustin.com
E-mail ....ginger@hopehouseaustin.com
　1705 County Rd 285, Liberty Hill, TX 78642
　Ginger Hernandez, Administrator

Independence Farm 903.874.2377
Fax 903.874.3074
Web ....www.dfps.state.tx.us
E-mail ....susan.miller@dfps.state.tx.us
　2715 Liberty Dr, Corsicana, TX 75110-9286
　Susan Miller, Director

Innovative Psychiatric Solutions, Inc. 325.829.4371
E-mail ....jnnyrmrz4@yahoo.com
　621 SW Johnson Ave. Suite C, Burleson, TX 76028
　Ms. Jennifer Ramirez, Accreditation Manager
　Joint Commission accredited organization.

IntraCare Medical Center Hospital 713.790.0949
Web ....www.intracare.org
E-mail ....jredd@intracare.org
　7601 Fannin, Houston, TX 77054
　Mr. John Redd, Accreditation Manager
　Joint Commission accredited organization.

Intracare North 281.893.7200
Fax 281.893.7646
　1120 Cypress Station Dr, Houston, TX 77090
　Javier Ruiz, Medical Director

**John Peter Smith Hospital- Behavioral
Health** 817.927.3636
Fax 817.927.3829
Web ....www.jpshealth.org
E-mail ....dsweat@jpshealth.org
　1500 S Main St, Fort Worth, TX 76104-4941
　Debbie Sweat, Director Of Nursing

Kidz Harbor, Inc 281.581.2505
Fax 281.581.9344
E-mail ....kidzharborshelter@yahoo.com
　638 Port Harbor Rd, Liverpool, TX 77577
　Angela Golbert, Administrator

Texas

La Sima Foundation, Inc 214.941.1132
Fax 214.941.1135
Web ....www.thelasimafoundation.org
E-mail ....admin@thelasimafoundation.org
777 S R L Thornton Fwy Ste 105, Dallas, TX 75203-2956
Paul Clarkson, Executive Director

Laurel Ridge Treatment Center 210.491.3551
Web ....www.laurelridgetc.com
E-mail ....sandra.browning@psysolutions.com
17720 Corporate Woods Drive, San Antonio, TX 78259
Mrs. Sandra Browning, Accreditation Manager
Joint Commission accredited organization.

Lee and Beulah Moor Children's Home 915.544.8777
Fax 915.532.1368
Web ....www.leeandbeulahmoor.org
1100 E Cliff Dr, El Paso, TX 79902-4699
Renee Tanner, Chief Executive Officer

Lena Pope Home 817.255.2500
Fax 817.731.9858
Web ....www.lenapopehome.org
3131 Sanguinet St, Fort Worth, TX 76107-5336
Todd Landry, Executive Director

Life Management Resources 972.985.7565
Web ....www.lifemanagementresources.com
E-mail ....kim@lifemanagementresources.com
3131 Custer Road, Plano, TX 75075
Ms. Kim Fred, Accreditation Manager
Joint Commission accredited organization.

Lifeworks Foster Group Home 512.458.2704
Fax 512.458.2868
Web ....www.lifeworksaustin.org
4606 Connelly St, Austin, TX 78751
Stephen M. Bewsey, Director

Medina Children's Home 830.589.2871
Fax 830.589.7129
Web ....www.armsofhope.org
21300 State Highway 16 N, Medina, TX 78055-3820
Kevin Mcdonald, CEO

Memorial Hermann Prevention and Recovery Center 713.329.7300
Web ....www.mhparc.org
E-mail ....matt.feehery@memorialhermann.org
3043 Gessner Drive, Houston, TX 77080
Mr. Matt Feehery, Accreditation Manager
Joint Commission accredited organization.

Meridell Achievement Center 512.515.2100
Web ....www.meridell.com
E-mail ....carlin.troy@uhsinc.com
12550 West Highway 29, Liberty Hill, TX 78642
Ms. Carlin Troy, Accreditation Manager
Joint Commission accredited organization.

Methodist Children's Home 972.480.8772
Fax 972.480.0467
Web ....www.methodistchildrenshome.org
13140 Coit Rd, Ste 400, Dallas, TX 75240
Mary Carpenter, Director

Methodist Home Boys Ranch 254.799.2434
Fax 254.799.0750
Web ....www.methodistchildrenshome.org
1111 Herring Ave, Waco, TX 76708-3696
Dottie Briggs, Director/Administrator

Methodist Hospital 210.575.8653
Web ....SAHealth.com
E-mail ....jan.rodriguez@mhshealth.com
7700 Floyd Curl Drive, San Antonio, TX 78229
Mrs. Jan Rodriguez, Accreditation Manager
Joint Commission accredited organization.

Metrocare Svcs 214.743.1200
Fax 214.630.3469
Web ....www.metrocareservices.org
E-mail ....jbaker@dallasmetrocare.com
1380 River Bend Dr, Dallas, TX 75247-4914
James Baker, Md, CEO

Metroplex Adventist Hospital, Inc. 254.526.7523
Web ....www.mplex.org
E-mail ....kim.henry-shahry@ahss.org
2201 South Clear Creek Road, Killeen, TX 76549
Ms. Kim Shahry, Accreditation Manager
Joint Commission accredited organization.

Mexia State School 254.562.2821
Fax 254.562.1444
E-mail ....william.lowry@dads.state.tx.us
600 North Hwy 171, Mexia, TX 76667
William H. Lowry, Superintendent

MHMR Community Center 361.886.6900
Web ....www.ncmhmr.org
E-mail ....eschlueter@ncmhmr.org
1630 South Brownlee Street, Corpus Christi, TX 78404
Mrs. Beth Schlueter, Accreditation Manager
Joint Commission accredited organization.

Millwood Hospital LP 817.261.3121
E-mail ....loring.branch@psysolutions.com
1011 North Cooper Street, Arlington, TX 76011
Mr. Loring Branch, Accreditation Manager
Joint Commission accredited organization.

Neuro Institute of Austin, L.P. 512.444.4835
Web ....www.texasneurorehab.com
E-mail ....lydia.rudy@uhsinc.com
1106 West Dittmar Road, Austin, TX 78745
Ms. Lydia Rudy, Accreditation Manager
Joint Commission accredited organization.

New Dimensions 281.333.2284
Web ....www.newdimensionsdayhospital.com
E-mail ....r.brazzel@newdimensionsdayhospital.com
1345 Space Park, Suite C, Houston, TX 77058
Mr. George Brazzel, Accreditation Manager
Joint Commission accredited organization.

New Encounters Residential Treatment 903.874.1577
4121 FM 637, Corsicana, TX 75109
Craig Tekell, Director

New Hope Youth Ctr 281.344.8050
Fax 281.342.5235
E-mail ....nhyc775@aol.com
4111 Brandt Rd, Richmond, TX 77406-8140
Cheryl Annette Miller, Director

New Life Children's Treatment Ctr 830.964.4390
Fax 830.964.4391
650 Scarbourough, Canyon Lake, TX 78133
Bob Slocun, Chief Executive Officer

Nexus Recovery Center, Inc. 214.321.0156
Web ....www.nexusrecovery.org
E-mail ....sburns@nexusrecovery.org
8733 La Prada, Dallas, TX 75228
Mrs. Stacey Burns, Accreditation Manager
Joint Commission accredited organization.

North Dallas Drug Rehabilitation Center 972.446.0972
Fax 972.245.0281
1606 South Interstate 35 East, Suite 101, Carrollton, TX 75006
COA accredited organization.

Oschner Medical Practice 210.447.7947
Fax 210.615.6966
1202 East Frontera, San Antonio, TX 78258
Audra Ochsner, Md, Psychiatrist

Our Friends' Place 214.520.6268
Fax 214.526.6219
Web ....www.ourfriendsplace.org
E-mail ....info@ourfriendsplace.org
2501 Oak Lawn Ave Ste 500, Dallas, TX 75219
Sue Thiers Hesseltine, Executive Director

Pegasus School, Inc. 512.376.2101
Fax 512.398.2760
Web ....www.pegasusschool.net
E-mail ....pegasusmdl@myway.com
896 Robin Ranch Rd, Lockhart, TX 78644-4578
Tim Brown, Placement Director

Phoenix Project, Inc 214.942.5166
Fax 214.942.6006
Web ....www.phoenixproject.org
E-mail ....ipena@dallaschallenge.org
201 S Tyler St, Dallas, TX 75208-4934
Dan Melendez, Program Director

Post Country Care 254.939.7322
Fax 254.939.8804
E-mail ....postcc@sbcglobal.net
5741 Elm Grove Rd, Belton, TX 76513
Charles Rice, Program Director

Presbyterian Children's Homes & Svcs 972.937.1319
Fax 972.937.5181
E-mail ....eknight@pchas.org
300 Brookside Rd, Waxahachie, TX 75167
Ed Knight, President/CEO

Presbyterian Children's Homes and Svcs 210.558.4770
Fax 210.558.8302
6355 Whitby Rd, San Antonio, TX 78240
Adam Crawford, Director

Presbyterian Home For Children 806.352.5771
Fax 806.352.4058
E-mail ....dfranworth@amarillochilderenhome.com
3400 Bowie St, Amarillo, TX 79109-4997
Dr Scott Sticksel, President

Red River Psychiatric Hospital 940.322.3171
Fax 940.761.5335
Web ....www.redriverhospital.com
1505 8th St, Wichita Falls, TX 76301-3106
Harvey Martin, Md, Medical Director

Refuge Svcs, Inc 806.790.6664
Fax 806.748.0972
Web ....www.refugeservices.org
E-mail ....information@refugeservices.org
PO Box 53684, Lubbock, TX 79453
Randy And Patty Mandrell, Directors

Ronald McDonald House 713.795.3500
Fax 713.795.3557
1907 Holcombe Blvd, Houston, TX 77030
Arlene Whatley, Administrator

Sabine Valley Regional MHMR Center 903.237.2323
Web ....www.sabinevalley.org
E-mail ....marlene.karger@communityhealthcore.com
107 Woodbine Place, Longview, TX 75601
Mrs. Marlene Karger, Accreditation Manager
Joint Commission accredited organization.

Salvation Army Area Command 210.352.2000
Fax 210.352.2005
Web ....www.uss.salvationarmysatx.org
515 W Elmira St, San Antonio, TX 78212-5112
Delila Marquez, Program Director

San Antonio Autistic Treatment 210.590.2107
Fax 210.590.3143
16111 Nacogdoches Rd, San Antonio, TX 78247
Ivy Zwicker, Director

SAS Healthcare, Inc 817.222.9191
E-mail ....jimmyelou.cockrell@sundancehealthcare.com
7000 US, Highway 287, Arlington, TX 76001
Ms. Jimmye Cockrell, Accreditation Manager
Joint Commission accredited organization.

Seton Home 210.533.3504
Fax 210.533.3467
Web ....www.setonhomesa.org
E-mail ....info@setonhomesa.org
1115 Mission Rd, San Antonio, TX 78210-4500
Margaret Starkey, Executive Director

Seton Shoal Creek Hospital 512.324.7142
Web ....www.seton.net
E-mail ....sbujan@seton.org
3501 Mills Avenue, Austin, TX 78731
Ms. Susan Bujan, Accreditation Manager
Joint Commission accredited organization.

Sheffield Boot Camp / A Facility of The Texas Youth Commission 432.836.4624
Fax 432.836.4472
Web ....www.tyc.state.tx.us
E-mail ....anthony.king@tyc.state.tx.us
School Rd, Sheffield, TX 79781
Mr. King, Assistant/Acting

Shiloh Treatment Center, Inc. 281.489.1290
Web ....www.shilohtreatmentcenter.com
E-mail ....kpitts@shilohtreatmentcenter.com
3926 Bahler Avenue, Manvel, TX 77578
Ms. Kellie Pitts, Accreditation Manager
Joint Commission accredited organization.

Shoreline, Inc. 361.528.3356
Web ....chemicaldependency.com
E-mail ....shorelinedr@pelicancoast.net
1220 Gregory, Taft, TX 78390
Dr. Sharel Zacharias, Accreditation Manager
Joint Commission accredited organization.

South Texas Rural Health Services, Inc. 830.879.3047
E-mail ....co.strhs@tachc.org
611 Thornton St., Cotulla, TX 78014
Ms. Lidia Rodriguez, Accreditation Manager
Joint Commission accredited organization.

Southwest Key Program 956.546.0373
Fax 956.546.0617
Web ....www.swkey.org
E-mail ....irodriguez@swkey.org
504 E Washington St, Brownsville, TX 78520-6024
Isabell Rodriguez, Director

Spindletop MHMR Services 409.839.1000
Web ....www.stmhmr.org
E-mail ....sally.walden@stmhmr.org
655 South 8th Street, Beaumont, TX 77701
Ms. Sally Walden, Accreditation Manager
Joint Commission accredited organization.

St. Peter - St. Joseph Childrens Home 210.533.1203
Fax 210.533.6199
Web ....www.stpjhome.org
E-mail ....info@stpjhome.org
919 Mission Rd, San Antonio, TX 78210-4599
James Castro, Executive Director

Stable Solutions 682.554.5104
Web ....www.stablesolutionscounseling.com
E-mail ....stablesolutions@netzero.net
4516 Boat Club Rd Ste 139, Fort Worth, TX 76135-7021
Alan Katzen, Lcsw,bcd, Director

Still Creek Boys Ranch 979.589.3206
Fax 979.589.2152
E-mail ....stillcreek@wicksonwireless.com
6055 Hearne Rd, Bryan, TX 77808
Margaret O'Quinn, Director

Summer Sky, Inc. 254.968.2907
Web ....www.summer-sky.us
E-mail ....jennifer.hmckenzie@yahoo.com
1100 McCart Street, Stephenville, TX 76401
Mrs. Jennifer Holbrook-McKenzie, Accreditation Manager
Joint Commission accredited organization.

Sundown Ranch, Inc. 903.479.3933
Web ....sundownranchinc.com
E-mail ....sundown.cathy@texascellnet.com
3120 Van Zandt County Road #2318, Canton, TX 75103
Mrs. Cathy Hanson, Accreditation Manager
Joint Commission accredited organization.

Texas Boys Ranch 806.747.3187
Fax 806.747.3193
Web ....www.texasboysranch.org
E-mail ....jsigle@texasboysranch.org
4810 N County Road 2800, Lubbock, TX 79403
John Sigle, Executive Director

Texas Cypress Creek Hospital 281.586.7600
Web ....www.cypresscreekhospital.com
E-mail ....katie.mccaslin@psysolutions.com
17750 Cali Drive, Houston, TX 77090
Mrs. Katie McCaslin, Accreditation Manager
Joint Commission accredited organization.

Texas Health Harris Methodist Hospital
HEB 817.848.4600
Web ....www.texashealth.org
E-mail ....kristinaduncan@texashealth.org
1600 Hospital Parkway, Bedford, TX 76022
Ms. Kristin Duncan, Accreditation Manager
Joint Commission accredited organization.

T E X A S
NeuroRehab
C E N T E R
Where Special Kids Get Special Care

Texas NeuroRehab Center 512.444.4835
Toll-free 800.252.5151
Web ....www.texasneurorehab.com
E-mail ....sandra.mcdaniel@uhsinc.com
1106 W Dittmar Rd, Austin, TX 78745-6328
Dr. Ed Prettyman, CEO; Sandra McDaniel, Admissions Coordinator; Terri McBryde, Business Development Director
Texas NeuroRehab Center provides specialized neurobehavioral residential treatment services for youth, ages 8-17 with IQs ranging from 40 – 90. Specialties include Neuropsychiatric, Neurobehavioral, Brain Injury, Autism, Fetal Alcohol Syndrome, Sensory Processing issues, Intermittent Explosive Disorder, Psychiatric conditions with Medical issues, Developmentally Delayed and more.

Texas Pythian Home Inc 817.594.4465
Fax 817.596.7776
Web ....www.pythianhome.org
E-mail ....lwatson@pythianhome.org
1825 Bankhead Drive, Weatherford, TX 76086
Lisa Watson, Administrator

Texas San Marcos Treatment Center, LP 512.396.8500
Web ....sanmarcostc.com
E-mail ....bwilliamson@psysolutions.com
120 Bert Brown Road, San Marcos, TX 78666
Ms. Barbara Williamson, Accreditation Manager
Joint Commission accredited organization.

The Children's Home 940.322.3141
Fax 940.322.6417
1101 30th St, Wichita Falls, TX 76302
Sheila Catron, Director

The Renfrew Center of Texas, LLC 215.482.5353
Web ....www.renfrewcenter.com
E-mail ....bsicard@renfrewcenter.com
9400 North Central Expressway, Suite 150, Dallas, TX 75231
Mr. Hayes Russock, Accreditation Manager
Joint Commission accredited organization.

Timberlawn Mental Health System 214.381.7181
Fax 214.388.6306
Web ....www.timberlawn.com
E-mail ....eric.reynolds@uhsinc.com
4600 Samuell Blvd, Dallas, TX 75228-6827
Kris Anderson-Mcgee, Admissions Director
Inpatient hospitalization, partial hospitalization, intensive outpatient and outpatient psychiatric services for individuals ages 4 and up.

Trinity Children and Family Svcs 713.957.8442
Fax 713.688.5220
Web ....www.trinityys.org
E-mail ....tjones@trinityys.org
2630 Fountain View, Houston, TX 77057-6206
Tiffani Jones, Director

Tropical Texas Behavioral Health 956.289.7000
Fax 956.289.7128
1901 South 24th Avenue, Edinburg, TX 78539
CARF accredited programs available.

TRS Behavioral Care, Inc. 713.933.1391
Web ....www.rightstep.com
E-mail ....leana.gadbois-sills@rightstep.com
902 W. Alabama Street, Houston, TX 77006
Ms. Leana Gadbois-Sills, Accreditation Manager
Joint Commission accredited organization.

Unity Children's Home 281.537.6148
Fax 281.537.2858
Web ....www.unitychildplacingagency.org
12027 Blue Mountain Dr, Houston, TX 77067-1020
Vivian Coleman Okunday, Director

University Behavioral Health of Denton 940.320.8100
Web ....ubhdenton.com
E-mail ....cindy.hunter@ubhdenton.com
2026 West University, Denton, TX 76201
Ms. Cindy Hunter, Accreditation Manager
Joint Commission accredited organization.

University Behavioral Health of El Paso LLC 915.544.4000
Web ....ubhelpaso.com
E-mail ....kim.whitelock@ubhelpaso.com
1900 Denver Ave, El Paso, TX 79902
Ms. Kim Whitelock, Accreditation Manager
Joint Commission accredited organization.

University of Texas - Psychiatric Ctr 713.741.7803
Web ....hcpc.uth.tmc.edu
E-mail ....rachel.l.mcbride@uth.tmc.edu
2800 South MacGregor Way, Houston, TX 77021
Mrs. Rachel McBride, Accreditation Manager
Joint Commission accredited organization.

West Oaks Hospital, Inc. 713.995.0909
Web ....www.westoaks.com
E-mail ....mary.goodman@psysolutions.com
6500 Hornwood Drive, Houston, TX 77074
Ms. Mary Goodman, Accreditation Manager
Joint Commission accredited organization.

West Texas Boys Ranch 325.949.1936
Fax 325.949.1930
Web ....www.wtbr.org
E-mail ....wtbradmission@wtbr.org
10223 Boys Ranch Rd, San Angelo, TX 76904-3665
Sheri Squire, Admissions Director

Whispering Hills Achievement Center 361.865.3083
Web ....www.whisperinghillstx.com
E-mail ....herb.goldsmith@gmail.com
4110 FM 609, Flatonia, TX 78941
Mr. Herb Goldsmith, Accreditation Manager
Joint Commission accredited organization.

Youth Homes 979.233.7281
Fax 979.233.0715
E-mail ....sylviacrane@thechildrenscenterinc.org
3315 Highway 523 Oyster Creek, Freeport, TX 77542
Sylvia Crane, Programe Director

CHILDREN'S HOSPITAL

Abilene Regional Medical Center 325.428.1000
6250 U S Highway 83, Abilene, TX 79606
Mike Murphy, Chief Executive Officer

Baptist St Anthonys BSA Hospital 806.212.2000
1600 Wallace Blvd, Amarillo, TX 79106
Bob Williams, Chief Executive Officer

Texas

Baylor Medical Center 214.820.0111
3500 Gaston Ave, Dallas, TX 75246
John McWhorter, President

Baylor Medical Center at Carrollton 972.492.1010
4343 North Josey Lane, Carrollton, TX 75010
Stencer Purner, Director

Baylor Medical Center at Waxahackie 972.923.7000
1405 West Jefferson St, Waxahachie, TX 75165
Jay Fox, President

Bayshore Medical Center 713.359.2000
4000 Spencer Highway, Pasadena, TX 77504
Jeff Holland, Chief Executive Officer

Bayside Community Hospital 409.267.3143
200 Hospital Dr, Anahuac, TX 77514
Ann Newton, Chief Executive Officer

Brownfield Regional Medical Center 806.637.3551
705 E Felt, Brownfield, TX 79316
Mike Click, Director

Brownsville Doctors Hospital 956.554.2000
E-mail ....youngr@bdh1.com
4750 North Expressway, Brownsville, TX 78526
Russell Young, Chief Financial Manager

Care Regional Medical Ctr 361.758.8585
1711 West Wheeler Ave, Aransas Pass, TX 78336
Jacob Uuaintana, Director

Cedar Crest Hospital & RTC 254.939.2100
Fax 254.939.2334
Web ....www.cedarcresthospital.com
E-mail ....contact.CCrest@bca-corp.com
3500 S. IH-35 , Belton, TX 76513
Brandy Hart, Admissions Director; David Myatt, Clinic Director; Ed Hernandez, D.O.N.; Ingrid Whipple, CEO; Teresa Hansen, Business Development Director
The ability for a patient to be able to move between the acute care and RTC levels of care if needed is a Cedar Crest advantage. Sitting on 33-acres, our Residential Treatment Program specializes in providing longer-term treatment for children and adolescents who have completed acute care inpatient programs and require additional treatment in a 24-hour therapeutic environment (including on-site school), as well as those who have failed to respond effectively in previous placements. Cedar Crest's Acute Care Hospital Program is a psychiatric intensive care program designed to stabilize a child or adolescent's immediate crisis while providing the patient and family with skills to help prevent or minimize future incidents that would require re-admission.

Centennial Medical Center 972.963.3333
12505 Lebanon Rd, Frisco, TX 75035
Joe Thomason, Chief Executive Officer

Central Texas Hospital 254.697.6591
806 N Crockett Ave, Cameron, TX 76520
Gill White, Director

Childrens Medical Center Dallas 214.456.7000
1935 Medical District Dr, Dallas, TX 75235
Christopher Gurovich, Chief Executive Officer

Childress Regional Medical Center 940.937.6371
Highway 83, Childress, TX 79201
John Henderson, Director

Christus Hospital St Elizabeth 409.892.7171
2830 Calder Ave, Beaumont, TX 77702

Christus Jasper Memorial Hospital 409.384.5461
1275 Marvin Hancock Dr, Jasper, TX 75951
Deborah Wiegand, Administrator

Christus Santa Rosa Childrens Hospital 210.704.2011
333 North Santa Rosa St, San Antonio, TX 78207
Michael Howard, Nurse Manager

Christus Spohn Hospital Alice 361.661.8000
2500 East Main St, Alice, TX 78332
Mark Casanova, Administrator

Christus Spohn Hospital Kleberg 361.595.1661
1311 General Cavazos Blvd, Kingsville, TX 78363
Norman McBridee, Chief Executive Officer

Christus St Catherine Hospital 281.599.5700
701 Fry Rd, Katy, TX 77450

Christus St Michael Hospital 903.614.1000
2600 St Michael Dr, Texarkana, TX 75503
Chris Karam, Chief Executive Officer

Citizens Medical Center 361.573.9181
2701 Hospital Dr, Victoria, TX 77901
David Brown, Chief Executive Officer

Clear Lake Regional Medical Center 281.332.2511
E-mail ....mary.winters@hcahealthcare.com
500 Medical Center Blvd, Webster, TX 77598
Mary Winters, Chief Nursing Officer

College Station Medical Center 979.764.5100
1604 Rock Prairie Rd, College Station, TX 77845
Tom Jackson, Chief Executive Officer

Columbus Community Hospital 979.732.2371
110 Shult Dr, Columbus, TX 78934
Rob Thomas, Chief Executive Officer

Community General Hospital 830.965.2003
230 West Miller, Dilley, TX 78017
Dr. Syed Parves, Administrator

Community Hospital 409.283.8141
1100 West Bluff St, Woodville, TX 75979
Sandra Wright, Chief Executive Officer

Community Hospital 806.592.2121
412 Mustang Ave, Denver City, TX 79323
Craig Ekrem, Chief Executive Officer

Community Hospital 806.250.2754
E-mail ....Lgatlin@ParmerMedicalCenter.com
1307 Cleveland St, Friona, TX 79035
Lance Gatlin, Chief Executive Officer

Conroe Regional Medical Center 936.539.1111
504 Medical Blvd, Conroe, TX 77304
Jerry Nash, Chief Executive Officer

Cook Childrens Medical Center 682.885.4000
801 Seventh Ave, Fort Worth, TX 76104
Ric Merrill, Chief Executive Officer

Coon Memorial Hospital and Home 806.244.4571
1411 Denver Ave, Dalhart, TX 79022
Leroy Schaffner, Chief Executive Officer

Corpus Christi Medical Center 361.761.1400
3315 South Alameda St, Corpus Christi, TX 78411
Edward Lamb, Chief Executive Officer

Covenant Childrens Hospital 806.725.1011
3610 21st St, Lubbock, TX 79410
Richard Parks, Chief Executive Officer

Covenant Hospital Levelland 806.894.4963
1900 South College Ave, Levelland, TX 79336
Gary Osborn, Administrator

Covenant Hospital Plainview 806.296.5531
2601 Dimmitt Rd, Plainview, TX 79072
Alan King, Chief Executive Officer

Cypress Fairbanks Medical Center 281.890.4285
10655 Steepletop Dr, Houston, TX 77065
Terry Wheeler, Chief Executive Officer

Del Sol Medical Center 915.595.9000
E-mail ....jacob.cincron@hca.com
10301 Gateway West, El Paso, TX 79925
Jacob Cincron, Director

Denton Regional Medical Center 940.384.3535
3535 South 1 35 East, Denton, TX 76210
Baleb Orear, Chief Executive Officer

DeTar Hospital Navarro 361.575.7441
Web ....www.detar.com
506 East San Antonio St, Victoria, TX 77901
Sammi Drehr, Nursing Director

Doctors Diagnostic Hospital 281.622.2900
1017 South Travis St, Cleveland, TX 77327
Dr. Jeff Ackerman, Administrator

Doctors Hospital at Renaissance 956.664.0036
5501 South McColl Rd, Edinburg, TX 78539

Doctors Hospital of Laredo 956.523.2000
10700 McPherson Rd, Laredo, TX 78045
Elmo Lopez, Chief Executive Officer

Driscoll Childrens Hospital 361.694.5000
3533 South Alameda St, Corpus Christi, TX 78411
Steve Woerner, Chief Executive Officer

East Texas Medical Center 903.597.0351
1000 South Beckham St, Tyler, TX 75701

East Texas Medical Center Athens 903.676.1000
2000 South Palestine St, Athens, TX 75751
Pat Wallace, Administrator

East Texas Medical Center Carthage 903.693.3841
409 Cottage Rd, Carthage, TX 75633

East Texas Medical Center Henderson 903.657.7541
300 Wilson St, Henderson, TX 75652
Mark Leitner, Director

East Texas Medical Center Pittsburg 903.856.6663
2701 US Hwy 271 N, Pittsburg, TX 75686
Elmer Ellis, President

Edinburg Regional Medical Center 956.388.6000
1102 West Trenton Rd, Edinburg, TX 78539
Linda Resendez, Chief Executive Officer

Ennis Regional Medical Center 972.875.0900
2201 West Lampasas St, Ennis, TX 75119
Dave Anderson, Chief Executive Officer

Fort Duncan Regional Medical Center 830.773.5321
3333 N Foster Maldonado Blvd, Eagle Pass, TX 78852

Golden Plains Community Hospital 806.273.1100
200 S McGee St, Borger, TX 79007
Dennis Jack, Chief Executive Officer

Good Shepherd Medical Center Marshall 903.927.6000
E-mail ....russell.colier@gsmc.org
811 South Washington Ave, Marshall, TX 75670
Russell J Collier, Chief Executive Officer

Hamilton Hospital 940.564.5521
903 West Hamilton St, Olney, TX 76374
Ray Mason, Interim

Healthbridge Childrens Hospital 281.293.7774
2929 Woodland Park Dr, Houston, TX 77082
Joseph Rasserty, Chief Executive Officer

Hendrick Medical Center 325.670.2000
1900 Pine St, Abilene, TX 79601
Tim Lancaster, Chief Executive Officer

Hereford Regional Medical Center 806.364.2141
801 E 3rd St, Hereford, TX 79045
Nathan Floyd, Chief Executive Officer

Hill Regional Hospital 254.580.8500
101 Circle Dr, Hillsboro, TX 76645
Jan Mcdlure, Chief Executive Officer

Hillcrest Baptist Medical Center 254.202.2000
3000 Herring Ave, Waco, TX 76708

Hospital 806.323.6422
1020 South Fourth St, Canadian, TX 79014
Christy Francis, Chief Executive Officer

Hospital Authority 830.278.6251
1025 Garner Field Rd, Uvalde, TX 78801

Hospital District 432.756.3345
610 N Peter St, Stanton, TX 79782
Paul McKinney, Chief Executive Officer

Hospital District 806.998.4533
2600 Lockwood, Tahoka, TX 79373
Jim Morris, Chief Executive Officer

Hospital District 979.245.6383
104 7 St, Bay City, TX 77414
Steve Smith, Chief Executive Officer

Hospital District 806.935.7171
Web ....www.mchd.com
E-mail ....a.burris@mchd.com
224 East Second St, Dumas, TX 79029
Angela Burris, Nursing Director

Houston NW Medical Center 281.440.1000
710 FM 1960 West, Houston, TX 77090
Linda Mercer, Chief Executive Officer

Huguley Memorial Medical Center 817.293.9110
11801 South Freeway, Fort Worth, TX 76115
Ken Finch, Chief Executive Officer

Huntsville Memorial Hospital 936.291.3411
110 Memorial Hospital Dr, Huntsville, TX 77340
Sally Nelson, Chief Executive Officer

JPS Health Network 817.921.3431
1500 South Main St., Fort Worth, TX 76104
Robert Early, Chief Executive Officer

Kimble Hospital 325.446.3321
2101 Main ST, Junction, TX 76849
Steve Bowen, Chief Executive Officer

Kings Daughters Hospital 254.771.8600
E-mail ....pam.pierce@swmail.sw.org
1901 SW H K Dodgen Loop, Temple, TX 76502
Pam Pierce, Nursing Supervisor

Kingwood Medical Center 281.348.8000
22999 US Highway 59, Kingwood, TX 77339

Knapp Medical Center 956.968.8567
1401 East Eighth St, Weslaco, TX 78596
Jim Summersett, Chief Executive Officer

Lake Pointe Medical Center 972.412.2273
6800 Scenic Dr, Rowlett, TX 75088
Eric Evans, Chief Executive Officer

Lake Whitney Medical Center 254.694.3165
200 North San Jacinto St, Whitney, TX 76692
Ruthaen Crow, Administrator

Lamb Healthcare Center 806.385.6411
1500 South Sunset, Littlefield, TX 79339
Jonell Wischkaemper, Chief Executive Officer

Laredo Medical Center 956.796.5000
1700 East Saunders Ave, Laredo, TX 78041
Tim Schmidt, Chief Executive Officer

Las Palmas Medical Center 915.521.1200
1801 North Oregon St, El Paso, TX 79902
Hask Hernandez, Chief Executive Officer

Lillian M Hudspeth Memorial Hospital 325.387.2521
308 Hudspeth Ave, Sonora, TX 76950
Keith Butler, Chief Executive Officer

Longview Regional Medical Center 903.758.1818
2901 N Fourth St, Longview, TX 75605
Jim Kendrick, Chief Executive Officer

McAllen Medical Center 956.632.4000
301 West Expressway 83, McAllen, TX 78503
Joe Riley, Administrator

MD Anderson Cancer 713.792.2121
1515 Holcombe Blvd, Houston, TX 77030

Medical Center Hospital 432.640.4000
500 West Fourth St, Odessa, TX 79761
Bill Webster, Chief Executive Officer

Medical Center of Arlington 817.465.3241
3301 Matlock Rd, Arlington, TX 76015
Watson Moore Borland, Chief Executive Officer

Medical Center of Lewisville 972.420.1000
500 West Main, Lewisville, TX 75057
Doug Welch, Chief Executive Officer

Medical Center of Plano 972.596.6800
E-mail ....troy.villareal@hcahealthcare.com
3901 West 15th St, Plano, TX 75075
Troy Villareal, Chief Executive Officer

Medical Center of Southeast Texas 409.724.7389
Web ....www.medicalcentersetexas.com
2555 Jimmy Johnson Blvd, Port Arthur, TX 77640
Heidi Wolf, Chief Nursing Officer

Medical City Dallas Hospital 972.566.7000
7777 Forest Lane, Dallas, TX 75230
Erol Akdamar, Chief Executive Officer

Memorial Hermann Baptist Hospital 409.212.5000
3080 College St, Beaumont, TX 77701
David Parmer, Chief Executive Officer

Memorial Hermann Baptist Orange Hosp 409.883.9361
608 Strickland Dr, Orange, TX 77630

Memorial Hermann Katy Hospital 281.644.7000
E-mail ....susan.murphy@memorialhermann.org
23900 Katy Freeway, Katy, TX 77494
Marilyn Paine, Nursing Director

Memorial Hermann Memorial City Medical 713.242.3000
921 Gessner Rd, Houston, TX 77024

Memorial Hermann Northeast 281.540.7700
18951 Memorial North, Humble, TX 77338

Memorial Hermann Texas Medical Center 713.704.4000
6411 Fannin St, Houston, TX 77030
Craig Cordella, Chief Executive Officer

Memorial Hospital 830.876.2424
704 Hospital Dr, Carrizo Springs, TX 78834
Earnest Florres, Chief Executive Officer

Memorial Hospital 956.487.5561
E-mail ....munozth@yahoo.com
2753 Hospital Court, Rio Grande City, TX 78582
Thalia Munoz, Chief Executive Officer

Memorial Hospital of East Texas 936.634.8111
1201 West Frank Ave, Lufkin, TX 75904
Melonie Amie, Human Resource Director

Memorial Medical Center 936.275.3446
511 East Hospital St, San Augustine, TX 75972
Darlene Williams, Administrator

Memorial Medical Center 936.329.8700
1717 Highway 59 Bypass, Livingston, TX 77351
David Lamonte, Chief Executive Officer

Methodist Hospital 210.575.4000
7700 Floyd Curl Dr, San Antonio, TX 78229
Sherry Schumann, Executive Assistant

Midland Memorial Hospital 732.685.1111
2200 West Illinois Ave, Midland, TX 79701

Mission Regional Medical Center 956.323.9000
900 S Bryan Rd, Mission, TX 78572
Javier, Director

Nacogdoches Memorial Hospital 936.564.4611
1204 North Mound St, Nacogdoches, TX 75961
Beth Knight, Nursing Director

Navarro Regional Hospital 903.654.6800
3201 West State Hwy 22, Corsicana, TX 75110
Xavier Villarreal, Chief Executive Officer

North Texas Hospital 940.220.0600
2801 South Mayhill Rd, Denton, TX 76208
Judith Schiros, Chief Executive Officer

Northwest Texas Hospital 806.354.1000
1501 South Coulter Ave, Amarillo, TX 79106
Kyle Sanders, Chief Executive Officer

Oak Bend Medical Center 281.341.3000
1705 Jackson St, Richmond, TX 77469
Joseph Frendenburger, Chief Executive Officer

Ochiltree General Hospital 806.435.3606
3101 Garrett Dr, Perryton, TX 79070
Jeff Barnhart, Chief Executive Officer

Odessa Regional Medical Center 432.582.8000
520 East Sixth St, Odessa, TX 79761
Michael Mets, Chief Executive Officer

Ott Kaiser Memorial Hospital 830.583.3401
3349 South Highway 181, Kenedy, TX 78119

Our Childrens House at Baylor 214.820.9838
3301 Swiss Ave, Dallas, TX 75204
Liz Youngblood, President

Palestine Regional Medical Center East 903.731.1000
2900 South Loop 256, Palestine, TX 75801

Pampa Regional Medical Center 806.665.3721
One Medical Plaza, Pampa, TX 79065
William Buck, Chief Executive Officer

Paris Regional Medical Center 903.785.4521
E-mail ....connie.murshison@parisrmc.com
820 Clarksville St, Paris, TX 75460
Connie Murshison, Nursing Supervisor

Permian Regional Medical Center 432.523.2200
720 Hospital Dr, Andrews, TX 79714
Tham Phan, Nursing Director

Physicians Surgical Hospitals of Quail 806.354.6100
6819 Plum Creek, Amarillo, TX 79124
Brad Mccall, Chief Executive Officer

Plains Memorial Hospital 806.647.2191
310 West Halsell St, Dimmitt, TX 79027
Linda Rasor, Chief Executive Officer

Presbyterian Hospital of Denton 940.898.7000
3000 I 35 North, Denton, TX 76201
Fem Morton, Chief Executive Officer

Providence Health Center 254.751.4000
6901 Medical Pkwy, Woodway, TX 76712
Ken Kayne, Chief Executive Officer

Providence Memorial Hospital 915.577.6011
2001 North Oregon St, El Paso, TX 79902
John Grah, Chief Executive Officer

Rio Grande Regional Hospital 956.632.6000
101 East Ridge Rd, McAllen, TX 78503
Kathy Dassler, Nursing Supervisor

Rolling Plains Memorial Hospital 325.235.1701
200 East Arizona St, Sweetwater, TX 79556
Donna Boatright, Administrator

San Angelo Community Medical Center 325.949.9511
3501 Knickerbocker Rd, San Angelo, TX 76904
Lisa Bibb, Human Resource Director

Scenic Mountain Medical Center 432.263.1211
1601 West 11th Pl, Big Spring, TX 79720
Larry Roger, Chief Executive Officer

Scott and White Healthcare 254.724.2111
2401 South 31st St, Temple, TX 76508
Dr. Robert Pryor, Chief Executive Officer

Shannon Medical Center 325.653.6741
120 East Harris St, San Angelo, TX 76903
Brian Horner, Director

Shriners Hospitals for Children at Houston 713.797.1616
6977 Main St, Houston, TX 77030
David Farrel, Administrator

Smithville Regional Hospital 512.237.3214
800 East Highway 71, Smithville, TX 78957
Grady Hooper, Chief Executive Officer

South Hampton Hospital 214.623.4400
2929 South Hampton Rd, Dallas, TX 75224

Southwest Surgical Hospital 817.345.4100
1612 Hurst Town Center Dr, Hurst, TX 76054

Spring Branch Medical Center 713.467.6555
8850 Long Point Rd, Houston, TX 77055
Andrew McVey, Owner

St Davids Medical Center 512.476.7111
919 East 32nd St, Austin, TX 78705
Richard Hamett, Chief Executive Officer

St Davids North Austin Medical Center 512.901.1000
12221 MoPac Expwy North, Austin, TX 78758
Tom Wilkinson, Chief Executive Officer

St Joseph Regional Health Center 979.776.3777
2801 Franciscan Dr, Bryan, TX 77802
Tony Pftzer, Chief Executive Officer

St Lukes Episcopal Hospital 832.355.1000
6720 Bertner Ave, Houston, TX 77030
Payte Fine, Chief Executive Officer

St Lukes The Woodlands Hospital 936.266.2000
17200 St Lukes Way, Conroe, TX 77384

Stamford Memorial Hospital 325.773.2725
E-mail ....rdefoore@samfordhosp.com
1601 Columbia St, Stamford, TX 79553
Mindy Flow, Director Of Nursing

Stephens Memorial Hospital 254.559.2241
200 South Geneva St, Breckenridge, TX 76424
Shane Kernell, Chief Executive Officer

Sugar Land Surgical Hospital 281.243.1000
1211 Hwy 6 Ste 70, Sugar Land, TX 77478
Marian Fohlley, Chief Executive Officer

Texas Childrens Hospital 832.824.1000
6621 Fannin St, Houston, TX 77030
Mark Wallace, Chief Executive Officer

Texas Health Arlington Memorial Hospita 817.548.6100
800 West Randol Mill Rd, Arlington, TX 76012
Kirk King, Administrator

Texas Health Harris Methodist Hosp 817.641.2551
201 Walls Dr, Cleburne, TX 76033

Texas Health Harris Methodist Hosp 254.965.1500
411 North Belknap St, Stephenville, TX 76401

Texas Health Harris Methodist Hospital 214.345.6789
8200 Walnut Hill Lane, Dallas, TX 75231
Britt Berrett, President

Texas Health Presbyterian Hospital 972.932.7200
850 Ed Hall Dr, Kaufman, TX 75142
Kathy Young, President

Texas Health Presbyterian Hospital 972.981.8000
6200 West Parker Rd, Plano, TX 75093
Jeff Canose, Chief Executive Officer

Texas Health Presbyterian WNJ 903.870.4611
500 North Highland Ave, Sherman, TX 75092
Vance Reynolds, Chief Executive Officer

Texas Scottish Rite Hospital for Child 214.559.5000
2222 Welborn St, Dallas, TX 75219
J C Montgomery, President

Texoma Medical Center 903.416.4000
Web ....www.texomamedicalcenter.net
E-mail ....contactus@thcs.org
5016 S US Hwy 75, Denison, TX 75020
Ron Coseal, Chief Executive Officer

The Physicians Centre Hospital 979.731.3100
3131 University Dr E, Bryan, TX 77802
Leeann Ford, Director Of Human Resources

Titus Regional Medical Center 903.577.6000
2001 North Jefferson Ave, Mount Pleasant, TX 75455
Ron Davis, Chief Executive Officer

Tomball Regional Hospital 281.401.7500
605 Holderrieth St, Tomball, TX 77375
Lymn Leboueff, Chief Executive Officer

TOPS Surgical Specialty Hospital 281.539.2900
17080 Red Oak Dr, Houston, TX 77090
Andrea Wappelhorst, Director of Nursing

Trinity Mother Frances Hospitals and Cl 903.593.8441
910 East Houston Ste 500, Tyler, TX 75702
Rob Rose, Vice President, Chief Nursing Officer

United Regional Hospital 760.764.7000
1600 Tenth St, Wichita Falls, TX 76301

University Hospital 210.358.4000
4502 Medical Dr, San Antonio, TX 78229
George Hernandes, Chief Executive Officer

University Medical Center 806.775.8200
602 Indiana Ave, Lubbock, TX 79415
David Allison, Executive Director

University Medical Center Brackenridge 512.324.7000
601 East 15th St, Austin, TX 78701
Greg Hartman, Chief Executive Officer

University Medical Center of El Paso 915.544.1200
4815 Alameda Ave, El Paso, TX 79905
James Valenti, Chief Executive Officer

University of Texas Medical Branch Hosp 409.772.1011
301 University Blvd, Galveston, TX 77555
David Callender, President

USMD Hospital at Arlington 817.472.3400
801 West Interstate 20, Arlington, TX 76017
Brandif Hancock, Executive Assistant

Val Verde Regional Medical Center 830.775.8566
801 Bedell Ave, Del Rio, TX 78840
Mark Strade, Chief Executive Officer

Valley Baptist Medical Center 956.389.1100
2101 Pease St, Harlingen, TX 78550
Bill Adams, President/CEO

Wadley Regional Medical Center 903.798.8000
1000 Pine St, Texarkana, TX 75501
Jeanette Akin, Director of Nursing

Wilbarger General Hospital 940.552.9351
E-mail ....kn@wghospital.com
920 Hillcrest Dr, Vernon, TX 76384
Kady Nunn, Administrator

Wise Regional Health System 940.627.5921
2000 South FM 51, Decatur, TX 76234
Todd Scrodgins, Adminstrator Director

COUNSELING SERVICES

Austin Child Guidance Ctr 512.451.2242
Fax 512.454.9204
Web ....www.austinchildguidance.org
810 W 45th St, Austin, TX 78751-2802
Russell Smith, Executive Director

Buckner Children And Family Se 903.757.9383
Fax 903.757.4714
Web ....www.buckner.org
E-mail ....dummel@buckner.org
110 E Cotton St, Longview, TX 75601-7415
David Ummel, Administrator

Casey Family Program 512.892.5890
Fax 512.892.7478
Web ....www.casey.org
E-mail ....astanley@casey.org
5201 E Riverside Dr, Austin, TX 78741-4807
Ann Stanley, Director

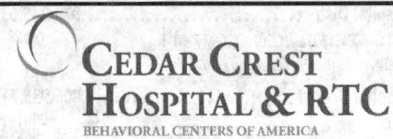

Cedar Crest Hospital & RTC 254.939.2100
Fax 254.939.2334
Web ....www.cedarcresthospital.com
E-mail ....contact.CCrest@bca-corp.com
3500 S. IH-35 , Belton, TX 76513
Brandy Hart, Admissions Director; David Myatt, Clinic Director; Ed Hernandez, D.O.N.; Ingrid Whipple, CEO; Teresa Hansen, Business Development Director

The ability for a patient to be able to move between the acute care and RTC levels of care if needed is a Cedar Crest advantage. Sitting on 33-acres, our Residential Treatment Program specializes in providing longer-term treatment for children and adolescents who have completed acute care inpatient programs and require additional treatment in a 24-hour therapeutic environment (including on-site school), as well as those who have failed to respond effectively in previous placements. Cedar Crest's Acute Care Hospital Program is a psychiatric intensive care program designed to stabilize a child or adolescent's immediate crisis while providing the patient and family with skills to help prevent or minimize future incidents that would require re-admission.

Christian Works For Children 972.960.9981
Fax 972.960.0062
Web ....www.christian-works.org
E-mail ....rpine@christian-works.org
6320 Lyndon B Johnson Fwy Ste 126, Dallas, TX 75240-6428
Rob Pine, Executive Director

Counseling and Assessment Ctr, LLP 903.581.0933
Fax 903.581.3977
E-mail ....ronroberts.ms.pc@tyler-counseling.com
1121 E Southeast Loop 323 Ste 204, Tyler, TX 75701-9660
Ron L. Roberts, Ms, Pc, Director

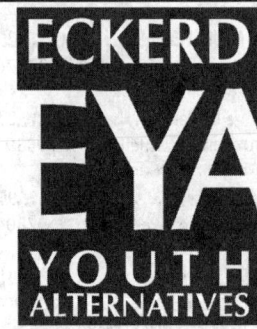

Eckerd 214.941.4435
Fax 214.941.4467
Web ....www.eckerd.org
E-mail ....admissions@eckerd.org
400 S Zang Blvd, Ste 220, Dallas, TX 75208
David Dennis, President & CEO; Teresa Stroud, Area Director
Eckerd provides Diversion and Family Reunification services in the Dallas County area. Our diversion service is an outcome-driven alternative to secure detention for youth ages 10 – 17 that enables them to remain in their homes and addresses complex mental, emotional and behavioral needs while awaiting disposition. The evidence-based approach combines intensive case management and monitoring, youth life skills training, parent counseling and individualized home contact.

Family Counseling Assoc 936.630.3799
Fax 936.639.1151
Web ....www.burke-center.org
E-mail ....jamespsmith@suddenlink.net
4101 S Medford Dr, Lufkin, TX 75901-6260
James Smith, Director

Gladney Ctr For Adoption; The 817.922.6000
Fax 817.922.5955
Web ....www.adoptionsbygladney.com
E-mail ....jl@gladney.org
6300 John Ryan Dr, Fort Worth, TX 76132-4122
Michael J. Mcmahon, President

Inner Wisdom **713.592.9292**
Fax 713.933.2269
Web ....www.innerwisdom.com
E-mail ....bgoldman@innerwisdom.com
   10777 La Concha Ln, Houston, TX 77025-1809
   Brian Goldman, Director

Lutheran Social Svc of The South **972.620.0581**
Fax 972.744.9052
Web ....www.lsss.org
   1900 Firman Dr Ste 100, Richardsom,
   TX 75081-7756
   Casey Rutan, Regional Director

Miracle Farm Inc **979.836.0901**
Fax 979.277.0939
Web ....www.miraclefarm.org
E-mail ....info@miraclefarm.org
   10802 Fm 2621, Brenham, TX 77833
   Alex Hamilton, Executive Director

CRISIS & SHELTER CARE

Aid To Victims Of Domestic Abuse **713.224.9911**
Fax 713.715.6935
Web ....www.avda-tx.org
E-mail ....jackiep@avda-tx.org
   1001 Texas St, Ste 600, Houston, TX 77002-3181
   Jackie Pontello, Director

Angel Heart Children's Shelter **512.278.1038**
Fax 512.278.1076
E-mail ....sfalco@angelheartshelter.org
   15401 Cameron Rd, Pflugerville, TX 78660
   Sheila Falco, Director

Austin Childrens Shelter **512.499.0090**
Fax 512.590.8664
Web ....www.austinchildrenshelter.org
E-mail ....info@arminsteegechildrenshelter.org
   4800 Manor Rd, Austin, TX 78703
   Armin Steege, Vice President

Avalon Ctr, Inc. **254.859.5990**
Fax 254.859.5188
E-mail ....michellesoliz@yahoo.com
   480 Highway 7, Eddy, TX 76524-2448
   Tom Burkig, Director

Azleway Boys Ranch **903.566.8444**
Fax 903.566.7696
Web ....www.azleway.org
   15892 County Rd 26, Tyler, TX 75707
   Gary Duke, Director

**Bay Area Turning Point - Domestic Violence
Program** **281.338.7600**
Fax 281.557.0290
Web ....www.bayareaturningpoint.com
E-mail ....contactus@bayareaturningpoint.com
   210 S. Walnut St, Webster, TX 77598
   Diane Savage, Director

BCFS-Foster Family Svcs **210.674.3010**
Fax 210.832.5005
   7404 W US Highway 90, San Antonio, TX 78227
   Asennet Segura, Executive Director

Bokenkamp Children's Treatment Ctr **361.994.1214**
Fax 361.994.5250
Web ....www.lsss.org
E-mail ....ssipes@lsss.org
   5517 S Alameda St, Corpus Christi, TX 78412-3202
   Sam Sipes, Vp Of Family Services

Bridge Over Troubled Water **713.472.0753**
Fax 713.472.8759
E-mail ....dmoseley@tbotw.org
   215 W. Southmore Ave, Pasadena, TX 77051
   Deborah Moseley, Director

Brookhaven Youth Ranch **254.829.1893**
Fax 254.829.1469
E-mail ....dcook@hughes.net
   5467 Rogers Hill Rd, West, TX 76691
   Dennis Cook, Director

Brown Karhan Rtc **512.894.0801**
Fax 512.858.4627
Web ....www.corehealth.com
E-mail ....cwells@corehealth.com
   3035 W Highway 290, Dripping Springs,
   TX 78620-3417
   Eric Makowski, President

Buckner Children's Village **409.866.0976**
Fax 409.866.8190
Web ....www.buckner.org
E-mail ....lmay@buckner.org
   9055 Manion Dr, Beaumont, TX 77706-3856
   Laura May, Director

Care Shelter **903.595.3553**
Fax 903.533.9837
   516 S Bonner Ave, Tyler, TX 75702
   Erick Sjer, Administrator

Catholic Family Svc **806.376.7731**
Fax 806.372.2666
   1645 NW 10th Ave, Amarillo, TX 79107-1709
   Cammie Mallard, Director

Cedar Crest Hospital & RTC **254.939.2100**
Fax 254.939.2334
Web ....www.cedarcresthospital.com
E-mail ....contact.CCrest@bca-corp.com
3500 S. IH-35 , Belton, TX 76513
Brandy Hart, Admissions Director; David Myatt, Clinic Director; Ed Hernandez, D.O.N.; Ingrid Whipple, CEO; Teresa Hansen, Business Development Director
The ability for a patient to be able to move between the acute care and RTC levels of care if needed is a Cedar Crest advantage. Sitting on 33-acres, our Residential Treatment Program specializes in providing longer-term treatment for children and adolescents who have completed acute care inpatient programs and require additional treatment in a 24-hour therapeutic environment (including on-site school), as well as those who have failed to respond effectively in previous placements. Cedar Crest's Acute Care Hospital Program is a psychiatric intensive care program designed to stabilize a child or adolescent's immediate crisis while providing the patient and family with skills to help prevent or minimize future incidents that would require re-admission.

Children's Emergency Shelter **972.932.4896**
Fax 972.962.3871
Web ....www.kaufmancounty.net
E-mail ....laretaw@kaufmancounty.net
   4090 S Houston St, Kaufman, TX 75142-3720
   Lareta Williams, Director

Children's Shelter **210.212.2500**
Fax 210.785.9268
E-mail ....arodriguez@chshel.org
   2939 W Woodlawn Ln, San Antonio, TX 78228
   Annette Rodriguez, President

Crime Victims Assistance Ctr **409.246.4300**
Fax 409.246.4377
E-mail ....judy.pace@co.hardin.tx.us
   440 W. Monroe Highway 326, Kountze, TX 77625
   Ms Judy Pace, Director

Crisis Ctr **254.629.3223**
Fax 254.629.8685
E-mail ....gstockard@eastland.net
   104 N Lamar Street, Eastland, TX 76448
   Mr Glenn Stockard, Director

Crisis Ctr **830.620.7520**
Fax 830.625.2984
E-mail ....dperez@ccccnbtx.org
   1547 E Common St, New Braunfels, TX 78131-0344
   Mr Daniel Perez, Director

Crisis Ctr **806.293.9772**
Fax 806.293.3686
Web ....www.crisisctr.com
E-mail ....kharris@crisisctr.com
   115 E 7th St, Plainview, TX 79072
   Ms Kay Harris, Director

Crisis Ctr **806.677.1701**
Fax 806.677.1702
Web www.borgerhc3.org
E-mail ....nluginbyhl@borgerhc3.org
   300 W 6th St, Borger, TX 79008
   Ms Norma Luginbyhl, Director

Crisis Ctr - Anderson/Cherokee Counties **903.586.9118**
Fax 903.589.3992
E-mail ....donaldh@mycrisiscenter.com
   700 E Cherokee St, Jacksonville, TX 75766
   Mr Donald Hammock, Director

**Cross Timbers Family Svcs - Domestic Violence
Program** **254.965.5516**
Fax 254.965.6774
Web ....www.crosstimbersfamilyservices.org
E-mail ....jodee@crosstimbersfamilyservices.org
   1794 N Graham St, Stephenville, TX 76401-0011
   Ms Jodee Lucero, Director

**Domestic Violence & Sexual Assault Survival Ctr
(Safeplace)** **512.267.7233**
Fax 512.385.0662
Web ....www.safeplace.org
E-mail ....jspamm@safeplace.org
   PO Box 19454, Austin, TX 78760-9454
   Julius Spamm, Director

Domestic Violence Prevention Program **903.796.8847**
Fax 903.799.7799
E-mail ....tschutte@dvptxk.org
   703 W Main St Ste H, Atlanta, TX 75551-3419
   Terri Schutte, Program Director

Domestic Violence Prevention Svcs **903.794.4000**
Fax 903.792.2924
E-mail ....Gayle.Martin@Dvptxk.Org
   424 Spruce St, Texarkana, TX 75504
   Ms Gayle Martin, Director

Domestic Violence Program **940.626.4585**
Fax 940.626.4117
Web ....www.wisehope.org
E-mail ....wcdvtf@embarqmail.Com
   407 S Washburn St, Decatur, TX 76234
   Pat Slayton, Director

East Texas Crisis Ctr **903.675.2137**
Fax 903.675.7874
Web ....www.etcc.org
   218 S. Palestine, Athens, TX 75751
   Donna Johnson, Director

East Texas Crisis Ctr, Inc. **903.509.2526**
Fax 903.579.2591
E-mail ....director@etcc.org
   2401 old main rd, Tyler, TX 75701-8422
   Lana Peacock, Executive Director

East Texas Open Door **903.935.2099**
Fax 903.935.2090
   410 W Grand Ave, Marshall, TX 75670
   Exa Digiozanni, Adminstrator

Everchange Male Facility **830.426.2002**
Fax 830.741.3799
   801 McHaughten, Hondo, TX 78861
   Daniel Dan Ytuarte, Director

Families In Crisis - Domestic Violence **254.634.1184**
Fax 254.526.6111
E-mail ....ficinc@earthlink.net
   PO Box 25, Killeen, TX 76540-0025
   William Hall, Director

Texas

Family Abuse Ctr 254.772.8999
Fax 254.772.4770
E-mail .... director@familyabusecenter.org
PO Box 20395, Waco, TX 76702-0395
Kathryn Reid, Director

Family Crisis Ctr - Domestic Violence 512.321.7760
Fax 512.321.7771
E-mail .... fcc@familycrisiscenter.us
431 Old Austin Highway, Bastrop, TX 78602
Ms Sherry Murphy, Director

**Family Crisis Ctr - Domestic Violence
Program** 956.423.9305
Fax 956.423.9306
Web .... www.familycrisisctr.org
E-mail .... familycrisiscenter@sbcglobal.net
616 W. Taylor, Harlingen, TX 78550
Brenda Heredia, Executive Director

**Family Crisis Ctr Domestic Violence
Program** 817.558.7171
Fax 817.641.7595
Web .... www.familycrisiscenterofjohnsoncounty.org
E-mail .... vaughnjerri@hotmail.com
1915 N Wilhite, Cleburne, TX 76033
Ms Jerri Vaughn, Director

Family Crisis Ctr of The Big Bend 432.837.7254
Fax 432.837.1303
E-mail .... lovika@sbcglobal.net
606 N 5th St, Alpine, TX 79830-3506
Lovika Dekoninck, Executive Director

**Family Life Ctr - Domestic Violence
Program** 830.426.5972
Fax 830.426.3367
E-mail .... swflc_hondo@att.net
602 Arnold, Hondo, TX 78861
Edna Cuellar, Director

**Family Time Foundation Inc - Domestic Violence
Program** 281.446.2615
Fax 281.446.3691
Web .... www.familytimecc.org
E-mail .... ftime@earthlink.net
101 E Main St, Humble, TX 77338-4512
Judy Cox, Director

Family To Family Adoption Svcs 281.342.4042
Fax 281.342.4099
E-mail .... max@fam2fam.org
1000 Austin St Ste B, Richmond, TX 77469-5275
Maxine Seiler, Director

First Step Inc 940.723.7799
Fax 940.723.1132
E-mail .... firststeprosalind@yahoo.com
624 Indiana Ave, Wichita Falls, TX 76301
Rosalind Strickland, Executive Director

Focusing Families 979.826.0000
Fax 979.826.0332
E-mail .... kmathis@focusing-families.org
910 9th St, Hempstead, TX 77445
Kim Mathis, Director

**Freedom House - Domestic Violence
Program** 817.596.7543
Fax 817.596.4369
E-mail .... Ct4fh@Sbcglobal.Net
1149 fortway Hwy, Weatherford, TX 76086
Ms Catherine Tietjen, Director

**Friends of The Family - Domestic Violence
Program** 940.665.2873
Fax 940.665.3527
Web .... www.abigailsarms.org
E-mail .... adavis@abigailsarms.org
PO Box 1221, Gainesville, TX 76241-1221
Aaron Davis, Director

Gateway Family Svcs 325.573.1822
Fax 325.573.1063
E-mail .... exedirector@gatewaysnyder.com
PO Box 1394, Snyder, TX 79550-1394
Lyndia Allen, Director

George Gervin Youth Ctr, Inc. 210.804.1786
Fax 210.804.1469
E-mail .... barbara.hawkins@gervin-school.org
6903 S Sunbelt Dr, San Antonio, TX 78214
Barbara Hawkins, Executive Director

Good Shepherd Residential Treatment 281.374.0777
Fax 281.251.8406
E-mail .... goodshepherdrtc@aol.com
23538 Coons Rd, Tomball, TX 77377
Joey Garner, Associate Clinical Director

**Grayson Crisis Ctr - Domestic Violence
Program** 903.893.3909
Fax 903.893.0892
E-mail .... crisiscentre@graysoncrisiscentre.org
4200 N Travis, Sherman, TX 75091
Rachel Morgan, Director

Hays Caldwell Womens Ctr 512.396.3404
Fax 512.353.2018
E-mail .... mjohnson@hcwc.org
PO Box 234, Hays, San Marcos, TX 78667-0234
Ms Marla Johnson, Director

Helping Hand Home For Children 512.459.3353
Fax 512.459.1658
Web .... www.helpinghandhome.org
E-mail .... hand@helpinghandhome.org
3804 Avenue B, Austin, TX 78751
Ted Keyser, Director

High Frontier 432.364.2241
Fax 432.364.2261
Web .... www.overland.net
E-mail .... highfron@overland.net
5 Mouth South Highway 118, Fort Davis, TX 79734
Barry Blevins, Director

Highland Lakes Family Crisis Ctr 830.693.3656
Fax 830.693.5624
E-mail .... hlfcc@nctv.com
PO Box 805, Marble Falls, TX 78654-0805
Alma Lahmon, Executive Director

Hill Country Crisis Council Inc 830.257.7088
Fax 830.257.7097
429 Washington, Kerrville, TX 78028
Judy Sullivan, Director

Hold My Hand-Residential Treatment Ctr 713.645.0042
Fax 713.645.8677
Web .... www.dfps.state.tx.us
E-mail .... yvonne.whitfield@dfps.state.tx.us
7722 Glenvista St, Houston, TX 77061-2118
Yvonne Whitfield, Director

Hope Allience Crisis Ctr 512.255.1212
Fax 512.255.7331
E-mail .... patty.conner@hopealliancetx.org
1011 Gattis School Rd, Ste 106, Round Rock,
TX 78664
Ms Patty Conner, Director

Houston Area Women's Ctr 713.528.6798
Fax 713.535.6363
Web .... www.hawc.org
E-mail .... rwhite@hawc.org
1010 Waugh Dr, Houston, TX 77019
Rebecca White, President/CEO

ICD- New Bridge Family Shelter 325.658.8631
Fax 325.659.2070
PO Box 5018, San Angelo, TX 76902-5018
Rebecca Harris, Director

**Kilgore Community Crisis Ctr - Domestic Violence
Program** 903.984.3019
Fax 903.983.7739
Web .... www.cablelynx.com
E-mail .... thecrisiscenter@cablelynx.com
905 Broadway Blvd, Kilgore, TX 75662-2619
Bob Casper, Director

L'amor Village 281.586.9708
Fax 281.586.9827
16540 Kuykendahl Rd, Houston, TX 77068
Julie Tezeno, Assistant Director

**Lamda Gay & Lesbian Anti Violence
Project** 206.600.4297
Fax 915.542.1901
Web .... www.lambda.org
E-mail .... avp@lambda.org
216 S Ochoa St, El Paso, TX 79901-2512
Mr Rob Knight, Director

Letot Ctr 214.357.0391
Fax 214.956.2044
E-mail .... squattrochi@dallascounty.org
10505 Denton Dr, Dallas, TX 75220-2630
Sam Quattrochi, Director

**Mission Granbury - Domestic Violence
Program** 817.579.6866
Fax 817.579.6427
Web .... www.missiongranbury.org
E-mail .... mdavis@missiongranbury.org
1310 Weatherford Hwy Ste 120, Granbury,
TX 76048-4825
Ms Mary Davis, Director

Nacogdoches Boys Ranch 936.569.0293
Fax 936.569.7207
7245 FM 1275, Nacogdoches, TX 75961
Bill Harrison, Director

**New Beginnings Ctr - Domestic Violence
Program** 972.276.0423
Fax 972.276.1344
Web .... www.newbeginningcenter.org
E-mail .... jmorrison@newbeginningcenter.org
218 N 10th St, Garland, TX 75040-6172
Ms Jennifer Morrison, Director

**New Horizon Family Ctr - Domestic Violence
Program** 281.424.3300
Fax 281.420.5773
Web .... www.newhorizonfamilycenter.org
E-mail .... ppelton-smith@newhorizonfc.org
313 S Highway 146 Ste D, Baytown, TX 77520-2206
Patrina Pelton-smith, Director

Noah Project 325.676.7107
Fax 325.676.1060
E-mail .... leighannf@noahproject.org
1802 Grape St, Abilene, TX 79601
Leighann Fry, Director

**Noah Project North - Domestic Violence
Program** 940.864.2551
E-mail .... donnasuea@noahproject.org
1 Ave D 3rd Fl, Haskell County Courthouse, Haskell,
TX 79521
Donna Sue Anders, Director

Option House ES 800.421.8336
Fax 254.634.1049
E-mail .... ctysbtx@swbell.net
601 Parmer Ave, Killeen, TX 76541-5355
Keith Wallace, Jr., Executive Director

**Panhandle Crisis Ctr & Domestic Violence
Program** 806.435.5008
Fax 806.435.5376
E-mail .... pccpcc@ptsi.net
307 S Ash St, Perryton, TX 79070
Ms Cindy Smith, Director

Pathways 830.775.9610
Fax 830.775.5364
E-mail ....ehanson@pathways.org
　309 E 14th St, Del Rio, TX 78840
　Bibi Hanson, Administrator

Pathways Youth and Family Svcs Inc. (Pathways 3-H Wilderness
Program) 830.866.3701
Fax 830.866.3705
　110 Youth Ranch Cir, Mountain Home, TX 78058
　Mark Lowman, Director

Permian Basin Community 432.580.2624
Fax 432.580.2609
　1012 W MacArthur Ave, Odessa, TX 79763
　Deborah Haiduk, Supervisor

Positive Steps 713.522.0559
Fax 713.522.0582
E-mail ....positivesteps@aol.com
　2701 Rosedale St, Houston, TX 77459
　Yvonne Hawkins, Director

Promise House, Inc. 214.941.8578
Fax 214.941.8670
Web ....www.promisehouse.org
　224 W Page Ave, Dallas, TX 75208-6631
　Harriet Boohrem, Executive Director

Rape Crisis Ctr 972.985.0951
Fax 972.612.2582
E-mail ....info@theturningpoint.org
　PO Box 866754, Plano, TX 75086-6754
　Jennifer Spugnardi, Executive Director

Renewed Stength 281.448.7550
Fax 281.448.7504
Web ....www.renewed-strength.com
E-mail ....garrett@renewed-strength.com
　110 Hambrick Rd, Houston, TX 77060-5728
　Garrett Grant, Director

Saafe House 936.291.3529
Fax 936.291.1327
Web ....www.saafehouse.org
E-mail ....jmiller@saafehouse.org
　1426 San Houston Ave, Huntsville, TX 77340
　Ms Jolene Miller, Director

Safe Place - Domestic Violence Program 432.522.7202
Fax 432.570.5315
Web ....www.safeplacenow.com
E-mail ....cwayland@safeplacenow.com
　1805 N Mariefield St, Midland, TX 79702
　Ms Carole Wayland, Director

Safe Place - Domestic Violence Program 806.935.7585
Fax 806.934.1143
Web ....www.safeplaceinc.org
E-mail ....executivedirector@safeplaceinc.org
　306 W 7th St, Dumas, TX 79029-4312
　Kelli Cummings-danford, Director

Safehaven 817.535.6462
Fax 817.259.1636
Web ....www.safehaventc.org
E-mail ....mlhafley@safehaventc.org
　6815 Manhattan Blvd, Suite 105, Fort Worth,
　TX 76120
　Stephanie Storey, Chief Programs Officer

Salvation Army Family Violence Program 214.424.7208
Fax 214.424.7210
　5302 Harry Hines Blvd, Carr P. Collins Social Service
　Center, Dallas, TX 75235-7216
　Blake Bieane, Director Operations

San Angelo Children's Emergency Shelter 325.659.0760
E-mail ....sruppecke@conchokids.org
　1919 N Chadbourne St, San Angelo, TX 76903
　Sammey Ruppecke, Director

San Marcos Treatment Ctr 512.396.8500
Fax 800.205.9739
Web ....www.sanmarcostc.com
E-mail ....sanmarcos@psysolutions.com
　120 Bert Brown St, San Marcos, TX 78666
　Cassie Schmidt, Ph.d., CEO

Scan Emergency Youth Shelter 956.725.7211
Fax 956.725.7240
Web ....www.scan-inc.org
E-mail ....carlos@scan-inc.org
　1901 La Pita Magana Rd, Laredo, TX 78046
　Carlos Briseno, Director (shelters, Street Outreach)

Shelter Agencies For Families 903.572.0973
Fax 903.572.0982
　204 Patrick St, Mt Pleasant, TX 75456
　Ms Carol Gresham, Director

Sheltering Harbour 281.379.4578
Fax 281.379.2017
Web ....www.shelteringharbour.org
E-mail ....tseals@shelteringharbour.org
　18726 Tomato St, Spring, TX 77379
　Troy Seals, Director Of Administrator

Southwest Family Life Ctr 830.278.1067
Fax 830.278.4973
E-mail ....swflc_uvalde@yahoo.com
　400 S Getty St, Uvalde, TX 78801
　Ms Edna D Quellar, Director

St. Jude's Ctr For Young Children 830.629.0659
Fax 830.629.0523
Web ....www.stjudesranch.org
E-mail ....center@stjudesranch.org
　652 Old Bear Creek Rd, New Braunfels, TX 78132
　Kimberly Chabis, Director

SW Key Program 713.635.8505
Fax 713.631.8190
　7900 Mesa Dr, Houston, TX 77028
　Estela Sanchez, Director

SW Key Program, Inc. 512.462.2181
Fax 512.462.2028
Web ....www.swkey.org
E-mail ....jsanchez@swkey.org
　3000 S Interstate 35 Ste 410, Austin, TX 78704-6536
　Juan Sanchez, Director

Teen Emergency Shelter 940.322.7671
Fax 940.322.7672
Web ....www.caswf.com
E-mail ....teenshlt@nts-online.net
　1101 30th St, Rear of Bldg, Wichita Falls,
　TX 76302-1111
　Sheila Catron, Executive Director

The Ark - Domestic Violence Program 325.643.2699
Fax 325.646.5366
Web ....www.bwoodtx.com
E-mail ....sherri.ornelas@arkshelter.org
　1004 Cordell Street, Brownwood, TX 76801
　Ms Sherri Ornelas, Executive Director

The Ark Assessment Ctr & Emergency Shelter for
Youth 361.241.6566
Fax 361.241.5279
E-mail ....theark@awesomenet.net
　12960 Leopard St, Corpus Christi, TX 78410
　Delma Trejo, Executive Director / Administrator

The Children's Ctr 409.765.5212
Fax 409.765.6094
Web ....www.thechildrenscenterinc.org
E-mail ....jamestkeel@thechildrenscenterinc.org
　2902 Broadway St, Galveston, TX 77550-4222
　James T. Keel, President/ CEO

The Nelson Ctr 940.484.8232
Fax 940.484.1385
Web ....www.lsss.org
E-mail ....marcel.lue@lsss.org
　4601 N Interstate 35, Denton, TX 76207
　Marcel Lue, Chief Executive Officer

Tralee Crisis Ctr For Women - Domestic Violence
Program 806.669.1131
Fax 806.669.1137
Web ....www.tralee.pampa.com
E-mail ....tralee@sbcglobal.net
　310 S Cuyler St, Pampa, TX 79065-7314
　Beedee Laramore, Director

Victim Svcs 432.263.3312
Fax 432.267.3626
E-mail ....shann@vservices.wtxcoxmail.com
　800 N Runnels St, Big Spring, TX 79720
　Shann Smith, Executive Director

Women & Childrens Shelter - Domestic Violence
Program 409.832.7575
Fax 409.832.6941
Web ....www.westrengthenfamilies.org
　700 North Street Suite 149., Beaumont, TX 77701
　Bonnie Nolodigi, Director

Women's Ctr 281.344.5730
Fax 281.342.9248
E-mail ....mail@fortbendwomenscenter.org
　1002 Wilson Dr, Rosenberg, TX 77471
　Vita Goodell, Executive Director

Womens Ctr - Domestic Violence Program 281.292.4155
Fax 281.292.2709
Web ....www.mcwctx.org
E-mail ....sarah@mcwctx.org
　1600 Lake Front Cir Ste 130, Spring, TX 77380-3635
　Sarah Raleigh, Executive Director

Youth Alternatives - The Bridge Emergency Shelter,
Inc. 210.340.8077
Fax 210.340.2232
E-mail ....rmya@rmya.org
　3103 West Ave, San Antonio, TX 78213-4589
　Gloria Kelly, CEO

Youth Connection/Juvenile Alternative 800.568.7776
Fax 903.868.2260
Web ....www.ntxyouthconnection.org
E-mail ....gcja@cableone.net
　1602 E Lamar Street, Sherman, TX 75090
　Bettye Finnell, Executive Director

EDUCATION

Brownson Home 361.573.7161
Fax 361.573.1523
　1616 Lone Tree Rd, Victoria, TX 77901
　Richard Gunkel, Director

Career Planning 512.448.8530
Fax 512.448.8549
Web ....www.stedwards.edu
E-mail ....barbarah@admin.stedwards.edu
　3001 S Congress Ave, Austin, TX 78704-6425
　Barbara Henderson, Program Director

Catholic Charities Community Svcs Odessa,
Inc. 432.332.1387
Fax 432.332.3240
Web ....www.catholiccharitiesodessatx.org
E-mail ....fayrod@nts-online.net
　2500 Andrews Hwy, Odessa, TX 79761
　Faye Rodriguez, Director

Catholic Family Svc, Inc. 806.765.8475
Fax 806.765.8630
Web ....www.cfslubbock.org
E-mail ....beth@cfslubbock.org
　102 Ave J, Lubbock, TX 79401
　Beth Zarate, Executive Director

Texas

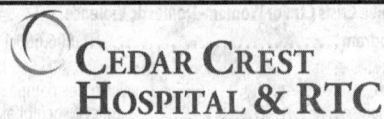

CEDAR CREST HOSPITAL & RTC
BEHAVIORAL CENTERS OF AMERICA

Cedar Crest Hospital & RTC **254.939.2100**
Fax 254.939.2334
Web .... www.cedarcresthospital.com
E-mail .... contact.CCrest@bca-corp.com
3500 S. IH-35 , Belton, TX 76513
Brandy Hart, Admissions Director; David Myatt, Clinic Director; Ed Hernandez, D.O.N.; Ingrid Whipple, CEO; Teresa Hansen, Business Development Director

The ability for a patient to be able to move between the acute care and RTC levels of care if needed is a Cedar Crest advantage. Sitting on 33-acres, our Residential Treatment Program specializes in providing longer-term treatment for children and adolescents who have completed acute care inpatient programs and require additional treatment in a 24-hour therapeutic environment (including on-site school), as well as those who have failed to respond effectively in previous placements. Cedar Crest's Acute Care Hospital Program is a psychiatric intensive care program designed to stabilize a child or adolescent's immediate crisis while providing the patient and family with skills to help prevent or minimize future incidents that would require re-admission.

City House **972.424.4626**
Fax 972.424.4934
E-mail .... tkeenan@cityhouse.org
902 E 16th St, Plano, TX 75074
Teresa Keenan, Executive Director

Covenant House Texas Crisis Ctr **713.523.2231**
Fax 713.523.6904
Web .... www.nineline.org
E-mail .... jleday-gonzaque@covenanthouse.org
1111 Lovett Blvd, Houston, TX 77006-3898
Ronda Robinson, Executive Director

Family Service Association **210.299.2400**
Fax 210.270.0545
Web .... www.family-service.org
E-mail .... dblegen@family-service.org
702 San Pedro Ave, San Antonio, TX 78212-4610
David Blegen, Manager Of Dept.

Genesis Women's Shelter Crisis Hotline **214.942.2998**
Fax 214.948.8614
E-mail .... jlangbein@genesisshelter.org
4411 Lemmon Ave Ste 201, Dallas, TX 75219-2163
Jan Langbein, Executive Director

Job Corps Region VI Ofc **972.850.4100**
Fax 214.767.2148
E-mail .... boswell.june@dol.gov
525 S Griffin St, Rm 403, Dallas, TX 75202
June Boswell, Director

River Oaks Academy Day Hospital **713.783.7200**
Fax 713.783.7286
Web .... www.riveroaksacademy.com
E-mail .... roainfo@gmail.com
10600 Richmond Ave, Houston, TX 77042
Luis Valdez Ph.D, Director

FOSTER CARE AGENCIES

A World For Children **903.581.1553**
Fax 903.581.1577
E-mail .... bakera@awfc.org
1412 Loop 323 W SW, Tyler, TX 75701
Andrea Baker, Regional Director

A World For Children **210.249.0770**
Web .... www.awfc.org
E-mail .... caquerag@awfc.org
2391 NE Loop 410 Ste 208, San Antonio, TX 78217
Guadalupa Caquera, Administrative Attendant

A World For Children **325.641.1055**
Fax 325.641.1077
Web .... www.awfc.org
E-mail .... willisp@awfc.org
504 Center Ave, Brownwood, TX 76801-2810
Paul Willis, Director

A World For Children **361.289.8887**
Fax 361.737.8433
Web .... www.awfc.org
5541 Bear Ln Ste 230, Corpus Christi, TX 78405
Gilbert Garcia, Clinical Director

A World For Children Inc **806.358.9117**
3505 Olsen Blvd Ste 103, Amarillo, TX 79109
Liegh Sexton, Director

Aarow Project **210.690.3800**
Fax 210.798.1614
Web .... www.aarow.org
8600 Wurzbach Rd Ste 801, San Antonio, TX 78240-4332
Angela Carleton, Program Director

Abrazo Adoption Associates **210.342.5683**
Fax 210.342.6547
10010 San Pedro Ste 540, San Antonio, TX 78216
Elizabeth Jurendich, Director

Adoption Access Inc **214.750.4847**
E-mail .... admin@adoptionaccess.com
8330 Meadow Rd Ste 222, Dallas, TX 75231
Debra Hug, Director

Adoption Knowledge Affiliates **512.442.8252**
E-mail .... aka@adoptionknowledge.org
PO Box 4082, Austin, TX 78765

Adoption Priorities Inc **210.494.2160**
E-mail .... info@adoptionpriorities.com
14400 Northbrook Dr Ste 200, San Antonio, TX 78232
Amanda Way, President

Adoption Services Associates **210.699.6094**
Fax 210.691.8836
E-mail .... adopt@adoptionservicesassociates.org
5370 Prue Rd, San Antonio, TX 78240

Angel Heart **817.283.2560**
Fax 817.283.7241
Web .... www.angelheartshelter.org
E-mail .... ssalco@angelheartshelter.org
610 S Industrial Blvd, Ste 220, Euless, TX 76040
Sheila Salco, Director

Bennect Chapel Support Group **936.591.1881**
Fax 936.598.5126
PO Box 1147, Shelby, Center, TX 75935
Bishop W C Morgan, Director

Buckner Adoption Maternity Services **214.319.3426**
E-mail .... adoption@buckner.org
5200 South Buckner Blvd, Dallas, TX 75227
Ade Jaquez, Administrator

Buckner Children and Family Services **806.795.7151**
Fax 806.795.9727
E-mail .... tspeed@buckner.org
129 Brentwood Ave, Lubbock, TX 79416-1601
Kathy Mcgee, Foster Care Director

CASA of Deep East Texas **936.560.4711**
Fax 936.560.4701
Web .... www.texascasa.org
E-mail .... hparsons@texascasa.org
119 North St Ste F, Nacogdoches, TX 75961-5200
Rebecca Carlton, Executive Director

Center for Children and Families **432.570.1084**
E-mail .... kbinek@centerswesttexas.org
1004 North Big Spring Ste 325, Midland, TX 79701
Ann Bradford, Director

Chosen Heritage Christian Adoption Servi **972.296.5111**
E-mail .... chosenheritage1987@yahoo.com
650 Big Stone Gap Rd, Duncanville, TX 75137
Stephanie Davies, Director

Council Adoptable Children of Austin **512.928.0702**
E-mail .... info@austin-coac.org
6600 Bradley Dr, Austin, TX 78723
Sandra Dush, Treasurer

Daybreak **254.472.0075**
Fax 254.472.0666
202 E Milam St, Mexia, TX 76667

DePelchin Children's Ctr **979.849.1919**
Fax 979.849.5846
Web .... www.depelchin.org
E-mail .... cgillespie@depelchin.org
506 N Downing Rd, Angleton, TX 77515-3945
Carol Gillespie, Director

Embrace Waiting Children Inc **214.354.9667**
E-mail .... bruce@embracetexas.org
102 Oak Glen Ct, Prosper, TX 75078
Bruce Kendrick, Director Of Outreach

Family Counseling Services **210.821.5980**
Fax 210.821.6121
E-mail .... fcounsel@msn.com
1635 NE Loop 410 #501, San Antonio, TX 78209
Erica A, Administrator

Family Services of El Paso Post Adoption **915.781.9900**
E-mail .... famserep@sbcglobal.net
6040 Surety Dr, El Paso, TX 79905
Richard Salpido, Director

Foster & Adoptive Parent Assc **903.965.4416**
207 W Main St, Bells, TX 75414
Terrance Steele, President

Great Wall China Adoption **512.323.9595**
Fax 512.323.9599
E-mail .... info@gwca.org
248 Addie Roy Rd A102, Austin, TX 78746
Snow Wu, Director

Jonathan's Place **972.303.5303**
Fax 972.303.5346
Web .... www.kidnet.org
E-mail .... lmatthews@kidnet.org
PO Box 140085, Dallas, TX 75214
Evelyn Clark, Chief Operating Officer

Lena Pope Home Inc **817.255.2628**
E-mail .... vgriffin@lenapopehome.org
3131 Sanguinet St, Fort Worth, TX 76107

Little Miracles International Inc **806.351.1100**
Fax 806.351.1533
E-mail .... info@littlemiracles.org
3418 Olsen Blvd Ste G, Amarillo, TX 79109
Lori Scott, Director

Miracle Kids Adoption Support Group **915.858.0298**
Fax 915.858.5056
8887 Buena Park, El Paso, TX 79907

Sharing Adoptive Family Exp through
Netw **817.923.4441**
E-mail .... ococfamss3@yahoo.com
2860 Evans Ave, Fort Worth, TX 76104

Smithlawn Maternity Home **806.745.2574**
E-mail .... smithlawn@windstream.net
PO Box 6451, Lubbock, TX 79493
Joe Phillips, Administrative Assistant

Spaulding for Children **713.681.6991**
Fax 713.681.9089
E-mail .... vfinley@spauldingforchildren.org
8582 Katy Freeway, Houston, TX 77024
Viki Finley, Chief Executive Officer

Tapestry **972.315.9628**
E-mail .... tapestry@irvingbible.org
2435 Kinwest Pkwy, Irving, TX 75063

Texas Foster Family Assoc **210.394.7933**
E-mail .... admin@tffa.org
18751 Castellani, San Antonio, TX 78258
Irene Clements, President

The Childrens Home of Lubbock **806.762.0481**
Fax 806.762.6574
E-mail .... sparker@childshome.org
PO Box 2824, Lubbock, TX 79408
Cindy Johnson, Director

The Childrens Shelter 210.212.2556
E-mail ....recruiter@chshel.org
2939 West Woodlawn Ave, San Antonio, TX 78228

HOME MEDICAL EQUIPMENT PROVIDERS

Alliance Tech.Medical Inc 800.848.8923
E-mail ....nsilva@alliancetechmedical
2904 Enchanted Rd, Granbury, TX 76049
Nancy Silva, Office Manager

Brazos Walking Sticks 800.880.7119
6408 Gholson Rd, Waco, TX 76705

Duramart Medical Supplies, Inc..............210.266.5277
Fax 877.744.1227
23 North Park Plaza, Brownsville, TX 78521
CARF accredited programs available.

Howell Home Medical Corporation dba Home
Medical 903.887.5533
Fax 903.887.5556
735 West Main Street, Gun Barrel City, TX 75156
CARF accredited programs available.

Judah Manufacturing Corp 800.618.9793
10440 E Northwest Hwy, Dallas, TX 75238
Lynn Trimble, Owner

Medical Mobility of Texas, LLC 214.239.2900
Fax 214.329.2905
Web ....www.medmobility.net
2422 Arbuckle Court, Dallas, TX 75229-4506
CARF accredited programs available.

Paradigm Medical 713.466.0801
Fax 713.466.0886
11875 West Little York, Suite 305, Houston,
TX 77041
CARF accredited programs available.

Rightcare Medical 972.522.1515
1106 North State Highway 360, Suite 205, Grand
Prairie, TX 75050
CARF accredited programs available.

Traner, Inc. dba Lone Star Mobility dba Lone Star Scooters of
Arlington 817.469.4777
Fax 817.795.7800
Web ....www.lonestarmobility.com
1008 North Davis Drive, Arlington, TX 76012
CARF accredited programs available.

Ultranebs 888.255.2509
502 County Road 1320, Quitman, TX 75783

PEDIATRIC HOME CARE

Austin PDN 512.248.0400
E-mail ....ahillen@psahealthcare.com
14205 N Mopac Expressway, Ste 640, Austin,
TX 78728
Amy Hillen, Director

Bellaire PDN (Houston) 832.325.1280
6575 W Loop S, Ste 500, Bellaire, TX 77401
Dawn Shelton, Director

Corpus Christi PDN 361.851.1250
4659 Everhart Ste 207, Corpus Christi, TX 78411
Dolores Garcia, Director

Dallas PDN 214.378.5009
E-mail ....kbollin@psakids.com
8200 Brookriver Dr Ste N 104, Dallas, TX 75247
Kevin Bollin, Director

Encompass 806.794.3555
Fax 806.794.9303
Web ....www.ehhi.com
E-mail ....april@ehhi.com
4709 66th Street, Lubbock, TX 79414
April Anthony, Owner

Homewatch CareGivers 817.283.4488
Fax 817.283.4499
E-mail ....lbright@homewatchcaregivers.com
1600 Airport Freeway, Suite 503, Bedford, TX 76022
Laurie Bright, Owner

Interim Healthcare 903.705.4776
Fax 903.705.4781
1021 E SE Loop 323 Ste 300, Tyler, TX 75703
Danny Malome, Administrator

Interim Healthcare 806.467.1156
Fax 806.467.1168
1901 Medi-Park Dr Ste 1058, Amarillo, TX 79106
Kathy Fufton, Director

Interim Healthcare 210.979.0208
Fax 210.340.0468
6800 Park Ten Ste 270 W, San Antonio, TX 78213
James Everitt, General Manager

Interim Healthcare 210.377.3933
Fax 210.525.1842
6800 Park Ten Ste 270 W, San Antonio, TX 78213
James Devriendt, General Manager

Interim Healthcare 806.897.1485
Fax 806.897.1487
707 College Ave Ste 106, Levelland, TX 79336
Kim Hill, Director

Interim Healthcare 325.735.2687
Fax 325.735.3718
210 W Sammy Baugh Ave, Rotan, TX 79546

Interim Healthcare 806.272.5549
Fax 806.272.5540
110 E Ave C, Muleshoe, TX 79347
Kim Hill, Director

Interim Healthcare 325.223.1957
Fax 325.223.5140
3402 Green Meadow Dr Ste B, San Angelo,
TX 76904
Shawn Owens, General Manager

Interim Healthcare 806.779.2485
Fax 806.779.2690
211 N Min St, McLean, TX 79057
Alicia Stroud, Director

Interim Healthcare 940.683.0044
Fax 940.683.0046
1903 Doctors Hospital Dr, Bridgeport, TX 76426
Sheri S., Director

Interim Healthcare 254.751.9393
Fax 254.751.7441
8004 Woodway Dr Ste 500, Woodway, TX 76712
Tammy Jordan, Supervisor

Interim Healthcare 806.675.1516
218 W Aspen, Crosbyton, TX 79322
Rita Jones, Director

Interim Healthcare 956.541.4410
Fax 956.541.4434
950 E Alton Gloor Blvd, Brownsville, TX 78521
Conrado Balli, Administrator/Owner

Interim Healthcare 817.645.9850
Fax 817.645.9869
501 N Main St Ste D, Cleburne, TX 76033
Sherry Shell, General Manager

Interim Healthcare 817.573.7474
Fax 978.777.5520
1314 Paluxy Rd, GranBury, TX 77048
Sherry Shell, General Manager

Interim Healthcare 817.847.6300
Fax 817.847.6310
6815 Manhattan Blvd, Fort Worth, TX 76120
Joe Johnson, Director

Interim Healthcare 940.627.2565
Fax 940.627.3318
1705 S FM 51 Ste 108, Decatur, TX 76234

Interim Healthcare 281.309.9001
Fax 281.309.9000
646 FM 517 Rd W Ste 201, Dickinson, TX 77539
Tracy Bozeman, President/CEO

Interim Healthcare 325.677.2047
Fax 325.677.9150
4400 Buffalo Gap Rd, Ste 2500, Abilene, TX 79606
Shawn Owen, Chief Executive Officer

Interim Healthcare 512.454.5711
Fax 512.467.9050
505 E Huntland Dr Ste 170, Austin, TX 78752
Julie Wright, Case Manager

Interim Healthcare 214.360.9090
Fax 214.987.4384
12750 Merit Dr Ste 110, Dallas, TX 75251
Jessica Mcnabb, Office Assistant

Interim Healthcare 806.288.0220
2620 Yonkers, Plainview, TX 79072
Rita Jones, Executive Director

Interim Healthcare 806.791.0042
Fax 806.797.6694
3305 100 1st St Ste 200, Lubbock, TX 79423
Jim Bullard, Chief Executive Officer

Interim Healthcare 512.868.5168
Fax 512.868.8320
503 Main St, Georgetown, TX 78626

Interim Healthcare 361.887.4850
Fax 361.887.4913
5656 Staples St, Corpus Christi, TX 78471
Linda Mitchell, Human Resource Director

Interim Healthcare 817.599.4004
Fax 817.599.4180
161 College Park, Weatherford, TX 76087
Sherry Sheall, Manager

Interim Healthcare 432.550.7593
Fax 432.618.0307
1031 ANDREWS STE 200, Midland, TX 79701
Shawn Owens, Director

Interim Healthcare 979.260.1100
Fax 979.268.4050
E-mail ....lgalloway@interimtx.com
2901 E 29th St Ste 113, Bryan, TX 77802
Linda Galloway, Director

Interim Healthcare 806.274.2800
Fax 806.274.2803
1313 W Wilson ave, Borger, TX 79007

Interim Healthcare (Lubbock Hospice) 806.791.0043
Fax 806.687.5958
3305 101St St, Lubbock, TX 79423
Janet Lusk, Administrative Assistant

Interim Healthcare (San Antonio Staffin) 210.477.1256
Fax 210.525.8715
6800 Park Ten Ste 270 W, San Antonio, TX 78213
James Dezrient, Director

McAllen PDN (Edinburg) 956.972.1920
E-mail ....marmendariz@psakids.com
5313 N McColl Rd, McAllen, TX 78504
Marivel Armendariz, Administrator

SOCIAL SERVICES

Advocacy & Pregnacy Ctr 972.436.2273
Fax 972.420.8993
E-mail ....apc.helps@sbcglobal.net
817 S Mill St Ste 112, Lewisville, TX 75067
Judy Lance, Director

Any Baby Can (ABC) 210.227.0170
Fax 210.227.0812
Web ....www.anybabycansa.org
E-mail ....ddixon@anybabycansa.org
217 Howard St, San Antonio, TX 78212-5524
Dawn Dixon, Executive Director

Texas

Armed Svcs YMCA El Paso/Ft. Bliss **915.562.8461**
Fax 915.565.0306
Web ....www.asymca.org
E-mail ....aymca1@elprr.com
   7060 Comington St, El Paso, TX 79930-4239
Jose Melendez, Executive Director

Armed Svcs YMCA Killeen **254.634.5445**
Fax 254.634.4202
E-mail ....asymca@centraltx.net
   415 N 8th St, Killeen, TX 76541-5214
Tony Mino, Executive Director

Beltway 8 South Crisis Pregnancy **281.484.0005**
Web ....www.southbeltpregnancy.org
E-mail ....lifelinecpc@att.net
   10851 Scarsdale Blvd Ste 800, Houston, TX 77089
Jean Killough, Director

Boysville, Inc. **210.659.1901**
Fax 210.659.6527
Web ....www.boysvilletexas.org
   P.O. Box 369, Converse, TX 78109-0369
COA accredited organization.

Buckner Children and Family Svcs **806.383.5488**
Fax 806.381.7094
E-mail ....tthomas@buckner.org
   2009 N Marrs St, Amarillo, TX 79107
Terry Thomas, Director

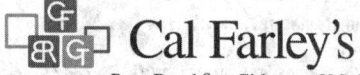

Cal Farley's
Boys Ranch® • Girlstown, U.S.A.®
& Family Resource Centers

Cal Farley's **800.687.3722**
Fax 806.372.4807
Web ....www.calfarley.org
E-mail ....info@calfarley.org
   PO Box 1890, Amarillo, TX 79174-0001
Dan Adams, President and CEO
Cal Farley's is one of America's largest privately-funded child and family service providers specializing in both residential and community-based services at no cost to the families of children in our care. We make a life-time commitment to the children served through our two campus-based programs, Cal Farley's Boys Ranch and Cal Farley's Girlstown U.S.A., where we provide professional programs and services in a Christ-centered atmosphere. The cornerstone to our success is our Model of Leadership and Service which focuses on the six core areas of human need. Cal Farley's offers a wide array of employment opportunities. For more information: (800) 687-3722, www.calfarley.org.

Camp Fire USA First Texas Council **817.831.2111**
Fax 817.831.5070
Web ....www.campfiresw.org
E-mail ....info@campfiresw.org
   2700 Meacham Blvd, Fort Worth, TX 76137
Jennifer Folzenlogen, Director Of Childcare Training

Catholic Charities **512.651.6100**
Fax 512.651.6101
Web ....www.ccctx.org
E-mail ....cynthia-colbert@austindiocese.org
   1817 E 6th St, Austin, TX 78702-2703
Cynthia Colbert, Director

Catholic Charities of Dallas, Inc. **214.520.6590**
Fax 214.520.6595
Web ....www.catholiccharitiesdallas.org
   9461 LBJ Freeway, Suite 128, Dallas, TX 75243
Joe Brogdon, Executive Director
COA accredited organization.

Catholic Charities of Southeast Texas **409.924.4400**
Fax 409.832.0145
E-mail ....catholiccharities@southeasttexas.org
   2780 Eastex Freeway, Beaumont, TX 77703
Carolyn Fernandez, President/CEO

**Catholic Charities of the Archdiocese of
Galveston-Houston** **713.526.4611**
Fax 713.874.6784
Web ....www.catholiccharities.org
   P.O. Box 66508, Houston, TX 77266
COA accredited organization.

**Catholic Charities, Diocese of Fort Worth,
Inc.** **817.534.0814**
Fax 817.535.8779
Web ....www.catholiccharitiesfortworth.org
   249 W. Thornhill Drive, Fort Worth, TX 76115
COA accredited organization.

Cedar Crest Hospital & RTC
BEHAVIORAL CENTERS OF AMERICA

Cedar Crest Hospital & RTC **254.939.2100**
Fax 254.939.2334
Web ....www.cedarcresthospital.com
E-mail ....contact.CCrest@bca-corp.com
   3500 S. IH-35 , Belton, TX 76513
Brandy Hart, Admissions Director; David Myatt, Clinic Director; Ed Hernandez, D.O.N.; Ingrid Whipple, CEO; Teresa Hansen, Business Development Director
The ability for a patient to be able to move between the acute care and RTC levels of care if needed is a Cedar Crest advantage. Sitting on 33-acres, our Residential Treatment Program specializes in providing longer-term treatment for children and adolescents who have completed acute care inpatient programs and require additional treatment in a 24-hour therapeutic environment (including on-site school), as well as those who have failed to respond effectively in previous placements. Cedar Crest's Acute Care Hospital Program is a psychiatric intensive care program designed to stabilize a child or adolescent's immediate crisis while providing the patient and family with skills to help prevent or minimize future incidents that would require re-admission.

Child Care, Inc. **940.766.4332**
Fax 940.766.2665
E-mail ....cciwftx@sbcglobal.net
   1000 Lamar St Rm 432, Wichita Falls, TX 76301
Margaret Stewart, Director

Child Guidance Ctr **210.614.7070**
Fax 210.615.0249
E-mail ....staff@cgcsanantonio.org
   2135 Babcock Rd, San Antonio, TX 78229-4410
Thomas Mathew, Director

Children's Connections Inc. **806.745.7995**
Fax 806.745.7350
Web ....www.childrensconnections.org
E-mail ....adopt@childrensconnections.org
   2514 82nd St Ste G, Lubbock, TX 79423
Deborah Phillips, CEO

**Communities In Schools of Laredo Texas
Inc** **956.791.2199**
Fax 956.725.1022
E-mail ....joecis@stx.rr.com
   101W.Hillside Rd, Suite #9, Laredo, TX 78041-5833
Jose Luis Gutierrez, Director

Compton Head Start **713.635.4142**
Fax 713.631.8598
E-mail ....gbanbolden@hcde-texas.org
   9720 Spaulding, Houston, TX 77016-4841
Gertrude Banbolden, Director

Cornerstone **936.634.4703**
Fax 936.633.7613
   2001 S Medford St, Lufkin, TX 75901
Pam Phillips, Director

**Devereux Texas Treatment Network -
Victoria** **361.575.8271**
Fax 361.575.6520
Web ....www.devereuxtx.org
   120 David Wade Drive, Victoria, TX 77902
Pam Helm, Executive Director

ECI-Infant Development Program **361.980.9652**
Fax 361.991.3419
Web ....www.ncmhmr.org
E-mail ....cmerkl@ncmhmr.org
   5110 Holly Rd, Corpus Christi, TX 78411-4737
Claire Merkle, Director

**El Paso Ctr For Children (Emergency
Shelter)** **915.562.4765**
Fax 915.850.0511
Web ....www.epccinc.org
E-mail ....privas@epccinc.org
   2116 N Stevens St, El Paso, TX 79930-5152
Patricia Rivas, Director

El Paso Ctr For Children, Inc. **915.565.8361**
Fax 915.565.0621
E-mail ....srioux@epccinc.org
   2200 N Stevens St, El Paso, TX 79930
Sandy Rioux, Executive Director

El Paso Diocese **915.872.8400**
Fax 915.872.8413
Web ....www.elpasodiocese.org
   499 Saint Matthews St, El Paso, TX 79907
Anthony C Celino, Director

El Paso Shelter For Battered Women **915.593.1000**
Fax 915.593.0012
E-mail ....skarr@cafv.org
   580 Giles, El Paso, TX 79915
Stephanie Karr, Director

Family and Protective Svcs **903.586.7626**
Fax 903.589.2227
E-mail ....suzan.ellis@dfps.state.tx.us
   502 E Pine, Jacksonville, TX 75766-4562
Suzan Ellis, CPS Supervisor

Family Counseling Service **361.852.9665**
Fax 361.852.2794
Web ....www.ccfamilyservices.org
   3833 South Staples, S203, Corpus Christi, TX 78411
COA accredited organization.

Family Outreach Ctr **956.541.5566**
Fax 956.541.7978
   455 E Levee St, Brownsville, TX 78521
Lisa Benson, President

Family Outreach of East Dallas **214.321.6292**
Fax 214.321.6426
Web ....www.prodigy.net
E-mail ....foced@prodigy.net
   9100 Diceman Dr, Dallas, TX 75218-4126
Michele Folcht, Executive Director

Family Outreach Program **361.888.6041**
Fax 361.883.1182
Web ....www.familyoutreach-cc.org
E-mail ....jody@familyoutreach-cc.org
   1444 Baldwin Blvd, Corpus Christi, TX 78404-3904
Jody Kuhl, Clinical Director

**Family Service Association of San Antonio,
Inc.** **210.299.2400**
Fax 210.299.4498
Web ....www.family-service.org
   702 San Pedro, San Antonio, TX 78212
COA accredited organization.

Family Services of Southeast Texas, Inc. **409.833.2668**
Web ....www.familyservicessetx.org
   3550 Fannin Street, Beaumont, TX 77701
COA accredited organization.

Family Support Svcs **806.342.2500**
Fax 806.372.2433
Web ....www.fss-ama.org
   1001 S Polk St, Amarillo, TX 79101-3407
Janet Byar, Interim Executive Director

Friends of The Family **940.387.5131**
Fax 940.383.1816
Web ....www.dcfof.org
E-mail ....toni@dcfof.org
    4845 S Interstate 35 E, Corinth, TX 76210
Toni Johnson-simpson, Executive Director

Gulf Coast Trades Ctr Inc **936.344.6677**
Fax 936.344.2386
Web ....www.gtctw.org
E-mail ....bgholson@gctcw.org
    143 Forest Service Rd, New Waverly, TX 77358
Bill Gholson, President

Healthy Family Initiatives **713.270.8849**
Fax 713.270.9532
Web ....www.hfihouston.org
E-mail ....hfi@hfimail.org
    7500 Beechnut St Ste 366, Houston, TX 77074-4337
Marianne L. Ehrlich, President/CEO

Jewish Family & Childrens Service **915.581.3256**
Fax 915.833.5743
E-mail ....jfcselpaso@sbcglobal.net
    401 Wallenberg Dr, El Paso, TX 79912
Emily Stuessy, Ex. Dir.

Jewish Family Service **972.437.9950**
Fax 972.437.1988
E-mail ....mfleisher@jfsdallas.org
    5402 Arapaho Rd, Dallas, TX 75248
Michael Fleisher, Director

Jewish Family Service **210.302.6920**
Fax 210.302.6952
E-mail ....jfs@jfs.sa.org
    12500 N Military Hwy Ste 250, San Antonio,
    TX 78231
Mh Livine, Ex.director

Jewish Family Service of Austin **512.250.1043**
Fax 512.257.7179
E-mail ....jfs@shalomaustin.org
    11940 Jollyville Rd Ste 110 S, Austin, TX 78759
Mitch Sudolsky, Director

Jewish Family Service of Greater Dallas **972.437.9950**
Fax 972.437.1988
Web ....www.jfsdallas.org
    5402 Arapaho Road, Dallas, TX 75248
COA accredited organization.

Jewish Family Services **713.667.9336**
E-mail ....jfs@jfshouston.org
    4131 S Brasswood, Houston, TX 77025
Linda Burger, Director

Jewish Family Services **817.569.0898**
Fax 817.569.0895
E-mail ....jfsftw@flash.net
    4049 Kingsridge Rd, Fort Worth, TX 76109
Carole Rogers, Director

K Star, Inc. **830.896.5437**
Fax 830.257.6505
Web ....www.kstar.org
E-mail ....vicki.barron@kstar.org
    1107 E. Main St, Kerrville, TX 78029-0962
Vicki Barron, Director

Laredo Job Corps Ctr **956.727.5147**
Fax 956.727.1937
    1701 Island, Laredo, TX 78044
Mike Fernandez, Center Director

Menninger Foundation; The **713.275.5000**
Fax 713.275.5107
Web ....www.menningerclinic.com
E-mail ....dyi@menninger.edu
    2801 Gessner Dr, Houston, TX 77080-2503
Donna Yi, Medical Director

Methodist Children's Home **254.753.0181**
Fax 254.755.7609
Web ....http://www.methodistchildrenshome.org
    1111 Herring Avenue, Waco, TX 76708
COA accredited organization.

Regional Crime Victim Crisis Ctr **325.677.7895**
Fax 325.670.5014
Web ....www.regionalcrime.org
E-mail ....info@regionalcrime.org
    3305 N 3rd St, Abilene, TX 79603
Diane Dotson, Director

Sacred Heart Children's Home **956.723.3343**
Fax 956.723.3409
    3310 S. Zapata Highway, Laredo, TX 78046
Sister Risidre Valdez, Administrator

South Plains Children's Shelter Inc. **806.747.4936**
Fax 806.747.4952
    1923 14th St, Lubbock, TX 79401
Phyllis Johnson, Administrator

Southwest Key Programs, Inc. **512.462.2181**
Fax 512.462.2028
Web ....www.swkey.org
    6002 Jain Lane, Austin, TX 78721
COA accredited organization.

TCAP Youth Advocate Program **817.446.9384**
Fax 817.446.9921
Web ....www.yapinc.org
    5009 Brentwood Stair Rd Ste 107, Fort Worth,
    TX 76112-2859
Kimberly Brandon, Program Director

Texas Baptist Children's Home **512.255.3682**
Fax 512.246.7089
Web ....www.tbch.org
    1101 N Mays St, Round Rock, TX 78664
Keith Dyer, Director

Texas City Action Plan To Prevent Crime
(T-CAP) **361.884.7146**
Fax 361.886.2599
    321 John Sartain St, Corpus Christi, TX 78401-2511
Commander Jesse Garcia, Director

The Pregnancy Resource Center **830.257.2166**
Fax 830.792.5644
Web ....www.thepregnancyresourcecenter.org
E-mail ....director@thepregnancyresourcecenter.org
    704 Jefferson St Ste A, Kerrville, TX 78028-4543
Laimie Johnson, Director

Therapeutic Family Life **210.348.6544**
Fax 210.348.6370
E-mail ....shawnag@tflife.org
    7704 S Loop 1604 East, Elmendorf, TX 78112
Shawna Grady, Program Coordinator

United Way **956.548.6880**
Fax 956.548.6906
Web ....www.unitedwayrgv.org
    634 E Levee St, Brownsville, TX 78520
Traci Wickett, President

YFCS Inc **512.327.1119**
Fax 512.327.4576
Web ....www.yfcs.com
E-mail ....info.yfcs@yfcs.com
    1705 S Capital of TX Hwy, Ste. 400, Austin,
    TX 78746
Kevin Sheehan, President/CEO

Youth Advocacy Program **512.444.9505**
Fax 512.326.4830
Web ....www.workersassistance.com
    4150 Freidrich Ln, Bldg SNST, Austin, TX 78744
Terry Cowan, Chief Executive Officer

SPECIAL NEEDS

A Wish With Wings **817.469.9474**
    917 West Sanford St, Arlington, TX 76012
Judy Young, Director

American Heart Association **214.373.6300**
Fax 214.373.0268
E-mail ....Review.personal.info@heart.org
    7272 Greenville Ave, Dallas, TX 75231
Nancy Brown, Chief Executive Officer

Asthma & Allergy Foundation **817.297.3132**
Web ....www.aafatexas.org
E-mail ....info@aafatexas.org
    9101 Quarter Horse Ln, Ft Worth, TX 76123
Joan Hart, Executive Director

Attention Deficit Disorders Assn **281.897.0982**
E-mail ....addaoffice@pdg.net
    12345 Jones Rd Ste 287-7, Houston, TX 77070

Autism Society of Greater Houston **713.513.7575**
    PO Box 2871, Houston, TX 77252

Brain Injury Association **512.326.1212**
E-mail ....info@biatx.org
    316 W 12th St, Ste 405, Austin, TX 78701

Centre for Neuro Skills - Texas **972.580.8500**
Fax 972.255.3162
Web ....www.neuroskills.com
    1320 West Walnut Hill Lane, Irving, TX 75038
CARF accredited programs available.

Community Parent Resource Center **915.217.2747**
E-mail ....sandra@cdicelpaso.org
    1101 E Schuster, El Paso, TX 79902
Sandra Gutierrez, Director

Connections Center **713.838.1362**
E-mail ....administrator@rdisconnect.com
    4130 Bellaire Blvd, Houston, TX 77025
Dr. Steven Gutstein, President

Disability Policy Consortium **512.371.1783**
E-mail ....info@dpctexas.org
    1016 La Posada Dr, Ste 145, Austin, TX 78752

Easter Seals Central Texas **512.478.2581**
Fax 512.476.1638
Web ....www.centraltx.easterseals.com
    1611 Headway Circle, Building 2, Austin, TX 78754
CARF accredited programs available.

Easter Seals North Texas **817.759.7900**
E-mail ....mail@easterseals-fw.org
    1555 Merrimac Cir, Ste 102, Fort Worth, TX 76107

Edinburg Regional Rehab Center **956.388.6200**
Fax 956.388.6042
Web ....www.southtexashealthsystem.com
    1102 West Trenton Road, Edinburg, TX 78539
CARF accredited programs available.

Family Support Network **979.845.4612**
E-mail ....fsn@tamu.edu
    4225 Texas A&M University, College Station,
    TX 77843

Family to Family Network **713.466.6304**
E-mail ....f2fnetwork@sbcglobal.net
    13150 FM 529 Ste 106, Houston, TX 77041

FEAT (Families For Early Autismtreatment) -
Houston **281.348.7067**
Web ....www.feathouston.org
    1120 Medical Plaza Dr Ste 100, Spring,
    TX 77380-3211
Amy Morgan Wood, Director

FirstCare Health Plans **806.784.4429**
Fax 806.784.4393
Web ....www.firstcare.com
E-mail ....jwilson@firstcare.com
    1901 W Loop 289, Suite 9, Lubbock, TX 79407
Jill Wilson Rn Ccm Cmcn, Case Manager

Gateway School **817.226.6222**
Fax 817.226.6225
Web ....www.gatewayschool.com
E-mail ....hwalber@gatewayschool.com
    2570 NW Green Oaks Blvd, Arlington,
    TX 76012-5621
Harriet R. Walber, Executive Director

Texas

Good Shepherd Medical Center 903.315.2000
Fax 903.315.2479
Web ....www.gsmc.org
 700 E Marshall Ave, Longview, TX 75601
 Ed Banos, President and CEO
 CARF accredited programs available.

Good Shepherd Medical Center 903.315.2000
Fax 903.315.2893
Web ....www.gsmc.org
 700 East Marshall Avenue, Longview, TX 75601
 CARF accredited programs available.

**Great Kids With ADHD A Texas Non-Profit
Corporation** 972.517.7498
Fax 972.517.0133
Web ....www.greatlakesacademy.us
 6000 Custer Rd Ste 7, Plano, TX 75023-5100
 Joey Wofford, Director

Hemispherectomy Foundation 817.307.9880
E-mail ....info@hemifoundation.org
 PO Box 1239, Aledo, TX 76008
 Chris Hall, Executive Director

**Highlands Regional Rehabilitation
Hospital** 915.298.7222
Fax 915.298.7298
Web ....www.highlandsrehab.com
 1395 George Dieter Drive, El Paso, TX 79936
 CARF accredited programs available.

Homeopathy Center of Houston 713.572.0343
E-mail ....center@homeopathyhouston.com
 7670 Woodway Dr, Ste 340, Houston, TX 77063
 Helen Cult, Director

Independent Living Council 512.371.7353
 5555 N Lamar Ste J103, Austin, TX 78751
 Regina Blye, Executive Director

Independent Living Research Utilization 713.520.0232
E-mail ....ilru@ilru.org
 2323 S Sheppard Ste 1000, Houston, TX 77019

Janine Sarcoidosis Outreach Foundation 832.248.6621
Fax 281.568.5775
E-mail ....sarcoidosis@jsof.org
 12600 Bissonnet A4, Houston, TX 77099

Learning Rx Center 972.432.6544
E-mail ....frisco.tx@learningrx.net
 3550 Parkwood, Ste 304, Frisco, TX 75034
 Karen Anderson, Owner

LearningRx Learning Center 903.838.0303
E-mail ....texarkana.tx@learningrx.net
 5602 Richmond Rd Crossing, Ste 104, Texarkana,
 TX 75503
 Allan Wren, Director

LearningRx Learning Center 817.562.5558
E-mail ....keller.tx@learningrx.net
 423 Keller Pkwy, Ste A, Keller, TX 76248
 Jack Reiser, Director

LearningRx Learning Center 713.839.8885
E-mail ....houstoncentral.tx@learningrx.net
 L5110 Buffalo Speedway, Ste 202, Houston,
 TX 77005
 Henry King, Executive Director

LearningRx Learning Center 832.886.5878
E-mail ....SugarLand.tx@learningrx.net
 2649 Town Center Blvd N, Sugar Land, TX 77479
 Carl Samuelson, Chief Executive Officer

LearningRx Learning Center 832.482.3082
E-mail ....thewoodlands.tx@learningrx.net
 4840 W Panther Creek Ste 205, The Woodlands,
 TX 77381
 Kimberley Bellini, Owner & Director

LearningRx Learning Center 903.295.4044
E-mail ....longview.tx@learningrx.net
 1809 NW Loop 281, Longview, TX 75604
 Margie Bell, Director

Lindamood-Bell Learning Processes 214.358.0688
Fax 214.358.0670
 4514 Travis St, Ste 302, Dallas, TX 75205

**Mabee Physical Medicine and Rehabilitation Center at Harris
Methodist Fort Worth Hospital** 817.250.2760
Fax 817.250.5596
Web ....www.harrismethodistfortworthhospital.org
 1301 Pennsylvania Avenue, Fort Worth, TX 76104
 CARF accredited programs available.

Menninger Clinic 800.351.9058
E-mail ....adminmail@menninger.edu
 2801 Gessner Dr, Houston, TX 77080
 Ian Aitken, Chief Executive Officer

Mental Health America of Texas 512.454.3706
E-mail ....lynn@mhatexas.org
 1210 San Antonio, Ste 200, Austin, TX 78701

NAMI Texas 512.693.2000
 2800 S IH-35 Ste 140, Austin, TX 78704
 Kelly Jeschke, Administrator

**National Alliance For Autism Research Texas Regional
Ofc** 972.960.6228
Fax 972.960.6228
E-mail ....cbarnold@naar.org
 6380 Lyndon B Johnson Fwy Ste 285, Dallas,
 TX 75240-6438

National Multiple Sclerosis Society 432.522.2143
Fax 432.694.7970
E-mail ....TXQ@nmss.org
 1031 Andrews Hwy Ste 201, Midland, TX 79701

National Multiple Sclerosis Society 806.468.8005
Fax 806.468.8022
E-mail ....TXP@nmss.org
 6222 Canyon Dr, Amarillo, TX 79109

National Multiple Sclerosis Society 800.344.4867
Fax 713.394.7422
 8111 N Stadium Dr, Ste 100, Houston, TX 77054

North Texas Rehabilitation Center, Inc. 940.322.0771
Fax 940.766.4943
Web ....www.ntrehab.org
 1005 Midwestern Parkway, Wichita Falls, TX 76302
 Betty Richie, Director
 CARF accredited programs available.

Pate Rehabilitation Endeavors, Inc. 972.241.9334
Fax 972.484.4739
Web ....www.paterehab.com
 2655 Villa Creek, Suite 140, Dallas, TX 75234
 CARF accredited programs available.

Path Project Partners Resource Network 409.898.4684
E-mail ....jjlambert@worldnet.att.net
 1090 Longfellow Ste B, Beaumont, TX 77706

PEN Project 806.762.1434
E-mail ....wtxpen@sbcglobal.net
 1001 Main St Ste 804, Lubbock, TX 79401

Rehab Without Walls - Texas 972.869.2415
 7801 Mesquite Bend Boulevard, Suite 108, Irving,
 TX 75063
 CARF accredited programs available.

Roy Maas' Youth Alternatives, Inc. 210.340.8077
Fax 210.340.2232
Web ....www.rmya.org
 3103 West Avenue, San Antonio, TX 78213
 COA accredited organization.

San Cristobal Ranch Academy 866.918.8383
Fax 281.313.1934
E-mail ....ageraci@ranchacademy.com
 1 Sugar Creek Ctr Blvd, Ste # 965, Sugar Land,
 TX 77478
 Scott Gilbert, Director

**Scott and White Memorial Hospital Inpatient Rehabilitation
Unit** 254.724.3240
Fax 254.724.1249
Web ....www.sw.org
 2401 South 31st Street, STC4, Temple, TX 76508
 CARF accredited programs available.

**Shannon Medical Center/Shannon Rehab
Center** 325.657.5617
Fax 325.657.5659
Web ....www.shannonhealth.com
 120 East Harris, Sixth Floor, San Angelo, TX 76903
 CARF accredited programs available.

Southwest Medical Center at Dallas 214.648.3111
Fax 214.648.7992
E-mail ....jeffrey.elliott@utsouthwestern.edu
 5323 Harry Hines Blvd, Dallas, TX 75390
 Jeffrey L Elliott MD, Director

Special Kids Inc 713.734.5355
E-mail ....speckidsinc@yahoo.com
 2600 S Loupe W, Houston, TX 77207
 Rose Ferguson, Director

Speech-Language-Hearing Association 512.494.1127
 918 Congress Ave Ste 200, Austin, TX 78701

Team Project 713.524.2147
E-mail ....prnteam@sbcglobal.net
 5005 W 34th St, Ste 207A, Houston, TX 77092
 Amy Woolsey, Project Director

**Texas Children's Hospital - Adolescent Bariatric Surgery
Program** 832.822.4868
Fax 832.825.3141
Web ....www.texaschildrens.org
E-mail ....txwalter@texaschildrens.org
 6621 Fannin, Suite 650.00, Houston, TX 77030
 Trish Walters-Salas, RN-BC, CCM, CBN

**Texas Health Presbyterian Hospital Dallas Rehabilitation
Center** 214.345.8656
Fax 214.345.2576
Web ....www.texashealth.org
 8200 Walnut Hill Lane, Dallas, TX 75231
 CARF accredited programs available.

Texas Parent to Parent 512.458.8600
E-mail ....laura@txp2p.org
 3710 Cedar St, Austin, TX 78705
 Laura Warren, Executive Director

Texas PTA 512.476.6769
E-mail ....txpta@txpta.org
 408 W 11th St, Austin, TX 78701

The Arc of Texas 512.454.6694
 8001 Centre Park Dr Ste 100, Austin, TX 78754
 Mike Bright, Executive Director

The Briarwood School 281.493.1070
Fax 281.493.1343
Web ....www.briarwoodschool.org
 12207 Whittington Dr, Houston, TX 77077
 Carole C Wills, Head Of School

**The Institute for Rehabilitation and Research (TIRR) Memorial
Hermann** 713.799.5000
Fax 713.797.7706
Web ....www.memorialhermann.org
 1333 Moursund, Houston, TX 77030
 CARF accredited programs available.

The MENTOR Network-Mentor/ABI LLC 903.877.8700
Fax 903.877.8707
Web ....www.neurorestorative.com
 11937 U.S. Highway 271, Tyler, TX 75708
 CARF accredited programs available.

The Methodist Hospital Neurological Inst 713.441.3760
E-mail ....sappel@tmhs.org
 6560 Fannin Ste 802, Houston, TX 77030
 Stanley H Appel Md, Director

The Monarch School 713.479.0800
Fax 713.464.7499
Web ....www.monarchschool.org
E-mail ....jarnold@monarchschool.org
2815 Rosefield, Houston, TX 77080
Jennifer Arnold, Business Manager

Touchstone Neurorecovery Center 936.788.7770
Fax 936.788.7785
Web ....www.nhsltd.com
9297 Wahrenberger Road, Conroe, TX 77304
Stuart Leder, medical director
CARF accredited programs available.

Tourette Syndrome Association 281.238.8096
E-mail ....tourettetexas@aol.com
3919 River Frst, Richmond, TX 77469

United Cerebral Palsy of Texas 512.472.8696
E-mail ....pfryer@ucpmemphis.org
1016 La Posada Ste 145, Austin, TX 78752

University of Texas Medicine/UTHSCSA 210.450.9700
Fax 210.450.6039
E-mail ....jacksonce@uthscsa.edu
8300 Floyd Curl Dr, San Antonio, TX 78229
Carlayne E Jackson Md, Faan Mda Clinic Director

UTSouthwestern Medical Center University
Hospitals 214.645.4890
Fax 214.645.4891
Web ....www.utsouthwestern.org
5151 Harry Hines Boulevard, Dallas, TX 75390-9295
CARF accredited programs available.

SUBSTANCE ABUSE TREATMENT

Addiction Services Division 817.569.4300
Fax 817.569.4491
Web ....www.mhmrtc.org
3840 Hulen Street, Hulen Tower North, Fort Worth,
TX 76107
Mark Dombeck, Director
CARF accredited programs available.

Alcohol And Drug Abuse Council For Concho
Valley 325.224.3481
Fax 325.224.4923
E-mail ....eas@adaccv.org
3553 W Houston Harte Expy, San Angelo,
TX 76901-2664
Eric A. Sanchez, Executive Director

Azleway Drug Treatment Program 903.636.9800
Fax 903.636.9816
Web ....www.azleway.com
E-mail ....david.trest@azleway.com
1085 Private Rd 3481, Big Sandy, TX 75755
David Trest, Director

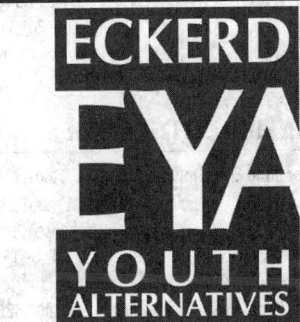

CEDAR CREST
HOSPITAL & RTC
BEHAVIORAL CENTERS OF AMERICA

Cedar Crest Hospital & RTC 254.939.2100
Fax 254.939.2334
Web ....www.cedarcresthospital.com
E-mail ....contact.CCrest@bca-corp.com
3500 S. IH-35 , Belton, TX 76513
Brandy Hart, Admissions Director; David Myatt, Clinic Director; Ed Hernandez, D.O.N.; Ingrid Whipple, CEO; Teresa Hansen, Business Development Director
The ability for a patient to be able to move between the acute care and RTC levels of care if needed is a Cedar Crest advantage. Sitting on 33-acres, our Residential Treatment Program specializes in providing longer-term treatment for children and adolescents who have completed acute care inpatient programs and require additional treatment in a 24-hour therapeutic environment (including on-site school), as well as those who have failed to respond effectively in previous placements. Cedar Crest's Acute Care Hospital Program is a psychiatric intensive care program designed to stabilize a child or adolescent's immediate crisis while providing the patient and family with skills to help prevent or minimize future incidents that would require re-admission.

Coastal Bend Council on Alcohol and Drug Abuse
(COADA) 361.854.9199
Fax 361.854.9147
E-mail ....deecaseykat@aol.com
1801 S Alameda St Ste 150, Corpus Christi,
TX 78404
Dee Ogle, Executive Director

Ctr For Success and Independence 713.426.4545
Fax 713.426.4747
Web ....www.tcsi.org
E-mail ....karl.webster@tcsi.org
3722 Pinemont Dr, Houston, TX 77018-1220
Karl Webster, Administrative Director

ECKERD
EYA
YOUTH
ALTERNATIVES

Eckerd 214.941.4435
Fax 214.941.4467
Web ....www.eckerd.org
E-mail ....admissions@eckerd.org
400 S Zang Blvd, Ste 220, Dallas, TX 75208
David Dennis, President & CEO; Teresa Stroud, Area Director
Eckerd provides Diversion and Family Reunification services in the Dallas County area. Our diversion service is an outcome-driven alternative to secure detention for youth ages 10 – 17 that enables them to remain in their homes and addresses complex mental, emotional and behavioral needs while awaiting disposition. The evidence-based approach combines intensive case management and monitoring, youth life skills training, parent counseling and individualized home contact.

Freeman Ctr 254.753.8251
Fax 254.753.5881
E-mail ....dworley@thefreemancenter.org
1401 Columbus Ave, Waco, TX 76701-1120
Dan Worley, Director

Greater Dallas Council on Alcohol and Drug Abuse
(COADA) 214.522.8600
Fax 214.521.7253
Web ....www.gdcada.org
E-mail ....dmerpolski@gdcada.org
1349 empire central dr ste 800, Dallas,
TX 75249-2138
Debbie Merpolski, CEO

Land Manor Adams House Residential Substance
Abuse 409.838.4285
Fax 409.838.4298
E-mail ....tjackson@landmanor.org
355 N 18th St, Beaumont, TX 77707
Terry Jackson, Assoc. Executive Director

Lifeworks 512.735.2100
Fax 512.735.2183
Web ....www.lifeworksaustin.org
E-mail ....susan.mcdowell@lifeworksweb.org
2001 Chicon St, Austin, TX 78722-2428
Susan Mcdowell, Executive Director

Mid-Coast Family Svcs 361.575.7842
Fax 361.575.8218
E-mail ....gstafford@midcoastfamily.org
1801 N Laurent St Ste 200, Victoria, TX 77901-5462
Jenny Stafford, Director

Nexus Recovery Ctr 214.321.0156
Fax 214.321.3096
Web ....www.nexusrecovery.org
E-mail ....bcrowell@nexusrecovery.org
8733 La Prada Dr, Dallas, TX 75228-5036
Rebecca Crowell, Director

Phoenix Academy of Dallas 214.999.1044
Fax 214.999.1058
Web ....www.phoenixhouse.org
E-mail ....mhemm@phoenixhouse.org
2345 Reagan Street, Dallas, TX 75219
Michelle Hemm, Director
CARF accredited programs available.

Shoreline, Inc. 361.528.3356
Fax 325.823.4504
Web ....www.chemicaldependency.com
E-mail ....eddie.underwood@sbcglobal.net
1220 Gregory St, Taft, TX 78390-3044
Deborah Jenkins, Executive Director

Special Health Resources of Texas 903.234.0936
Fax 903.234.9769
Web ....www.shrt.net
E-mail ....pfarmer@shrt.net
2030 S High St, Longview, TX 75602-3250
Phil Farmer, Administrator

Starlite Recovery Center 830.634.2212
Fax 830.634.2532
Web ....www.starliterecovery.com
E-mail ....info@starliterecovery.com
230 Mesa Verde Drive East, Center Point, TX 78010
Amy Swetnam, Director
CARF accredited programs available.

Summer Sky 254.968.2907
Fax 254.968.4509
Web ....www.summersky.us
E-mail ....info@summersky.us
1100 N McCart St, Stephenville, TX 76401-2430
Ty Campbell, Director

Sundown Recovery Ctr 903.479.3933
Fax 903.479.3999
Web ....www.sundownranchinc.com
E-mail ....steve@onesundown.com
3120 Vzcr 2318, Canton, TX 75103
Steve Echols, Director

Utah

Gary Herbert, Governor
State Capitol Complex E-220
PO Box 142220
Salt Lake City, UT 84114
801.538.1000
801.538.1528 (Fax)

Reg Garff, Juvenile Justice Specialist
UT State Capitol Complex
P.O Box 142330
Salt Lake City, UT 84114-2330
801.538.1372
801.538.1024 (Fax)
rgarff@utah.gov

Adam Cohen, SAG Chair
Odyssey House
344 East 100 South, Ste 301
Salt Lake City, UT 84111
801.891.2759
acohen@odysseyhouse.org

CRISIS NUMBERS

Child Abuse Reporting . . .800.678.9399

STATE SERVICES

SOCIAL SERVICES

Bureau of Child Care Licensing Utah 801.538.9084
Fax 801.538.6325
   288 North 1460 West, PO Box 142003, Salt Lake
   City, UT 84114
   S Lizotte, Director

Dept of Human Svcs 801.538.3991
   195 North 1950 West, Salt Lake City, UT 84116

Ofc of Recovery Svcs (Child Support Svcs) 801.536.8500
Fax 801.536.8636
Web . . . . .www.ors.utah.gov
E-mail . . . . .mbrasher@utah.gov
   515 E 100 S, Salt Lake City, UT 84102
   Mark Brasher, Director

Utah Division Of Emergency Management 801.538.3400
Fax 801.538.3770
Web . . . . .www.des.utah.gov
E-mail . . . . .des@utah.gov
   1110 State Office Bldg, Salt Lake City, UT 84114
   Keith Squires, Director

GENERAL HEALTH SERVICES

Bureau of Health Promotion 801.538.6141
Fax 801.538.9495
Web . . . . .health.utah.gov/bhp
E-mail . . . . .llarsen@doh.state.ut.us
   288 N 1460 W, Salt Lake City, UT 84114
   Ladene Larsen, Bureau Director

Child w Special Health Care Needs UT 801.584.8239
Fax 801.584.8488
E-mail . . . . .hollywilliams@utah.gov
   44 N Mario Capecchi Dr, Salt Lake City, UT 84114
   Holly Williams, Director

Infectious Disease Bureau/Medical Ofc Div 801.534.4600
Fax 801.534.4565
Web . . . . .www.slvhealth.org
   610 S 200 E, Room 209, Salt Lake City, UT 84111
   Debbie Dean, Np, Director

Maternal and Child Health Bureau Utah 801.538.6869
Fax 801.538.9409
E-mail . . . . .nanstreeter@utah.gov
   PO Box 142001, Salt Lake City, UT 84114
   Nan Streeter, Director

Utah AIDS Foundation 801.487.2323
Fax 801.486.3978
Web . . . . .www.utahaids.org
E-mail . . . . .mail@utahaids.org
   1408 S 1100 E, Salt Lake City, UT 84105
   Stan Penfold, Executive Director

Utah Dept of Health 801.538.6130
Fax 801.538.6479
Web . . . . .www.health.utah.gov
E-mail . . . . .dpatton@doh.state.ut.us
   288 N 1460 W, Salt Lake City, UT 84114
   David Patton, Executive Director

Utah Medicaid Info Div of Health Care
   Financing 801.538.6155
Fax 801.538.6155
Web . . . . .www.health.utah.gov/medicaid
E-mail . . . . .pmcguire@utah.gov
   288 North 1460 West, Salt Lake City, UT 84114-3101
   Paula Maguire, Director

Utah Medicaid Program Dept of Health Div of Health Care
   Financing 801.538.6406
Fax 801.538.6099
Web . . . . .www.health.utah.gov
   288 N 1460 W, Salt Lake City, UT 84116
   Michael Hales, Director

MENTAL HEALTH SERVICES

Div of Svcs for Blind & Vis Impaired UT 801.323.4343
Fax 801.323.4396
E-mail . . . . .tammiehansen@utah.gov
   250 N 1950 W, Ste B, Salt Lake City, UT 84116
   Tammie Hansen, Director

Div of Svcs for People with Disabilities 801.538.4200
Fax 801.538.4279
Web . . . . .www.dspd.utah.gov
   195 N 1950 W, Salt Lake City, UT 84116
   Paul Smith, Interim Director

Ofc of Rehabilitation 801.538.7530
Fax 801.538.7522
Web . . . . .www.usor.utah.gov
E-mail . . . . .duchida@utah.gov
   250 E 500 S, Salt Lake City, UT 84111-3204
   Donald Uchida, Executive Director

Utah DHS Div of Mental Health & Substance
   Abuse 801.538.3939
Fax 801.538.9892
Web . . . . .www.dsamh.utah.gov
E-mail . . . . .lstohl@utah.gov
   195 N 1950 W, Salt Lake City, UT 84116
   Lana Stohl, Assistant Director

Utah State Office of Rehabilitation 801.538.7530
Fax 801.538.7522
E-mail . . . . .rthelin@utah.gov
   250 E 500 S, Salt Lake City, UT 84114
   Russ Thelin, Director

JUSTICE AGENCY

Attorney Generals Ofc 801.538.9600
Fax 801.538.1121
Web . . . . .www.attorneygeneral.utah.gov
   350 N State St Ste 230, Salt Lake City, UT 84114
   Mark Shurtleff, Attorney General

Children's Justice Ctr 435.634.1134
Fax 435.673.1785
E-mail . . . . .cjc@infowest.com
   463 E 500 S, Saint George, UT 84770-3729
   Patricia Sheffield, M.s., Director

Commission on Criminal and Juvenile Justice . .801.538.1031
Fax 801.538.1024
Web . . . . .www.justice.utah.gov
E-mail . . . . .rbgordon@utah.gov
   330 State Capitol Building, Room E330, Salt Lake
   City, UT 84114
   Ron Gordon, Executive Director

Correctional Education Division UT 801.538.7989
Fax 801.538.7868
E-mail . . . . .jeff.galli@schools.utah.gov
   250 E 500 S, Salt Lake City, UT 84114
   Jeff Galli, Director

Ofc of Crime Victim Reparations 801.238.2360
Fax 801.533.4127
Web . . . . .www.crimevictim.utah.gov
   350 E 500 S Ste 200, Salt Lake City, UT 84111
   Melvin Wilson, Director

Utah Dept of Corrections 801.545.5500
Fax 801.545.5670
E-mail . . . . .tanderson@utah.gov
   14717 Minuteman Dr, Draper, UT 84020-9549
   Traci Anderson, Secretary

Youth Parole Authority 801.538.4331
Fax 801.538.4334
Web . . . . .www.jjs.utah.gov/parole/authority.com
E-mail . . . . .gwatkins@utah.com
   195 N 1950 W, Salt Lake City, UT 84116
   Garrett Watkins, Administrative Officer

COURTS

Administrative Ofc Of The Courts 801.578.3800
Fax 801.578.3843
E-mail . . . . .susanvb@email.utcourts.gov
   450 S State St, Salt Lake City, UT 84114-0241
   Susan Burke, Deputy Administrator

Utah

POLICE AND SHERIFF

Divison Of Juvenille Justice Services **801.284.0200**
Fax 801.263.9058
E-mail .... .rharrell@utah.gov
   61 W 3900 S, Salt Lake City, UT 84107-1431
   Ron Harrell, Director

Utah Assoc of Chiefs of Police **435.654.3040**
Fax 435.654.3286
Web .... .www.ciheber.ut.us
E-mail .... .erhoades@ciheber.ut.us
   301 S Main St, Heber City, UT 84032-2238
   Edward Rhodes, Chief Of Police

Utah Sheriff's Assoc **435.674.5935**
Fax 435.674.5940
Web .... .www.utahsheriffs.com
E-mail .... .gwd@infowest.com
   1169 Mesa Vista Dr, Ivins, UT 84738
   Gary W. Deland, Executive Director

EDUCATION SERVICES

Educ for Homeless Children and Youth UT **801.538.7975**
Fax 801.538.7991
E-mail .... .kreig.kelley@schools.utah.gov
   250 E 500 S, Salt Lake City, UT 84114
   Kreig Kelley, Director

Gifted & Talented **801.538.7884**
Fax 801.538.7769
Web .... .www.schools.utah.gov
E-mail .... .gerolynn.hargrove@schools.utah.gov
   250 E 500 S, Salt Lake City, UT 84111-3204
   Gerolynn Hargrove, Specialist

Migrant Head Start **801.521.4473**
Fax 801.521.6242
Web .... .www.cdlfu.org
E-mail .... .g.palza@la-familia.org
   3780 S West Temple, Salt Lake City, UT 84115-4430
   Gonzalo Palza, CEO

Special Education Services Utah **801.538.7587**
Fax 801.538.7991
E-mail .... .glenna.gallo@schools.utah.gov
   250 E 500 S, Salt Lake City, UT 84114
   Glenna Gallo, Director

State Ofc of Education **801.538.7500**
Fax 801.538.7521
Web .... .www.schools.utah.gov
   250 E 500 S, Salt Lake City, UT 84111-3284
   Verne Larsen, Director

Utah State Office of Education **801.538.7500**
Fax 801.538.7521
E-mail .... .mark.peterson@schools.utah.gov
   250 E 500 S, PO Box 144200, Salt Lake City,
   UT 84114
   Mark Peterson, Director

LABOR & WORKFORCE EDUCATION

Dept of Workforce Svcs **801.526.9210**
Fax 801.526.9211
Web .... .www.jobs.utah.gov
E-mail .... .kristencox@utah.gov
   140 E 300 S, Salt Lake City, UT 84111
   Kristen Cox, Executive Director

COUNTY SERVICES

Beaver County

GENERAL HEALTH SERVICES

Southwest Health Dept **435.438.2482**
Fax 435.438.2108
E-mail .... .dshepherd@utah.gov
   1175 N 75 W, Beaver, UT 84713
   Debbie Shepherd, Director

COURTS

Juvenile Court **435.438.5309**
Fax 435.438.5395
   2270 South 525 West, Beaver, UT 84713
   Honorable Thomas Higbee, Juvenile Court Judge

Youth Court **435.438.2301**
Fax 435.438.1519
Web www.beaver.k12.us.us
E-mail .... .shane.erickson@beaver.k12.ut.us
   195 East Center St, Beaver, UT 84713
   Shane Erickson, Director

POLICE AND SHERIFF

Sheriff's Ofc **435.438.2862**
Fax 435.438.5184
   2270 S 525 W, Beaver, UT 84173
   Cameron Noel, Sheriff

Box Elder County

COURTS

1st District Juvenile Court **435.734.4600**
Fax 435.734.4610
   43 N Main St, Brigham City, UT 84302
   Brett Folkman, Probation Supervisor

Cache County

SOCIAL SERVICES

Cache Dept Of Work Force Svcs **435.792.0300**
Fax 435.753.4933
Web .... .www.jobs.utah.gov
E-mail .... .klsloyd@utah.gov
   180 N 100 W, Logan, UT 84321-4502
   Kristen Donoviel, Director

Local And Regional Ombudsman **435.752.7242**
Fax 435.752.6962
Web .... .www.brag.utah.gov
   170 N Main St, Logan, UT 84321
   Linda Huffaker, Ombudsman/case Manager

GENERAL HEALTH SERVICES

Bear River Health Dept **435.792.6500**
Fax 435.792.6600
Web .... .www.brhd.org
E-mail .... .lbclark@utah.gov
   655 E 1300 N, Logan, UT 84341-2570
   Lapriel Clark, Rn, Np, Nursing Director

MENTAL HEALTH SERVICES

**Bear River Health Dept Substance Abuse
Program** **435.792.6420**
Fax 435.792.6437
Web .... .www.brhd.org
E-mail .... .brocka@brag.dst.ut.us
   655 E 1300 N, Logan, UT 84341-2570
   Brock Alder, Director Of Substance Abuse

JUSTICE AGENCY

Cache Valley Outreach Program **435.787.3500**
Fax 435.787.3519
Web .... .www.state.ut.us
   115 Golf Course Rd Ste E, Logan, UT 84321-5934
   Jennifer Cardis, Supervisor

Cache Valley Youth Ctr **435.713.6260**
Fax 435.713.6299
Web .... .www.cachesheriff.com
   2051 N 600 W, Logan, UT 84321-1712
   John Cizumbo, Apd

COURTS

1St District Juvenile Court **435.750.1300**
Fax 435.750.1355
E-mail .... .troyb@email.utcourts.gov
   135 N 100 W Ste 1, Logan, UT 84321-5065
   Troy Brown, Probation Officer

EDUCATION SERVICES

Bear River Head Start **435.755.0081**
Fax 435.755.0125
Web .... .www.brheadstart.org
E-mail .... .sthurgood@brheadstart.org
   852 S 100 W, Logan, UT 84321-5929
   Sarah Thurgood, Director

Carbon County

SOCIAL SERVICES

Dept Of Work Force Svcs **435.636.2300**
Fax 435.636.2376
Web .... .jobs.utah.gov
E-mail .... .setzel@utah.gov
   475 W Price River Dr, Ste 256, Price, UT 84501
   Susie Etzel, Manager

JUSTICE AGENCY

Castle Country Youth Ctr **435.636.4720**
Fax 435.636.4757
E-mail .... .biancok@carbonschools.org
   1395 S Carbon Ave, Price, UT 84501-9603
   Angela McCourt, Apd

**Family Support And Children's Justice
Ctr** **435.637.0281**
Fax 435.637.8492
Web .... .www.corbon.ut.gov
E-mail .... .shelly.wright@carob.ut.gov
   108 N 300 E, Price, UT 84501-2522
   Shelley Wright, Director

COURTS

7th District Juvenile Court **435.636.3434**
Fax 435.637.2102
Web .... .www.courtlink.utcourts.gov
   149 E 100 S, Price, UT 84501
   Connie Mower, Guardian Ad Litem Director

POLICE AND SHERIFF

Sheriff's Ofc **435.636.3251**
Fax 435.636.3212
E-mail .... .jcordova@co.carbon.ut.us
   240 W Main St, Price, UT 84501
   James Cordova, Sheriff

Utah

Daggett County

POLICE AND SHERIFF

Sheriff's Ofc **435.784.3255**
Fax 435.784.3251
Web ....www.daggett.state.ut.us
E-mail ....rellsworth@daggett.state.ut.us
    95 North 1st West, Manila, UT 84046
    Rick Ellsworth, Sheriff

Davis County

GENERAL HEALTH SERVICES

Health Dept **801.451.3340**
Fax 801.451.3144
    50 E State St, Farmington, UT 84025
    Vener Defrize, Nurse

MENTAL HEALTH SERVICES

Davis Behavioral Health **801.773.7060**
Fax 801.336.1787
Web ....www.dbhutah.net
    934 S Main St, Layton, UT 84041
    Brandon Hatch, CEO

Hill Air Force Base Substance Abuse And Mental Health Section **801.777.7909**
Fax 801.777.4490
E-mail ....ctueller@utah.gov
    7309 11th St, Bldg 545, Hill Air Force Base, UT 84056
    Lt Colonel Tueller, Director

JUSTICE AGENCY

Childrens Justice Ctr **801.451.3560**
E-mail ....doug@co.davis.ut.us
    125 South Main St, Farmington, UT 84025
    Douglas K. Miller, Director

Davis Area Youth Ctr **801.774.8767**
Fax 801.776.2954
    2465 N Main St, Ste 13A, Sunset, UT 84015
    Randy Gangwer, Apd

Davis Youth Svcs **801.447.0958**
Fax 801.447.8298
E-mail ....dnostworthy@utah.gov
    1353 N 1075 W Ste 101, Farmington, UT 84025
    Don Nostworthy, Supervisor

Farmington Bay Youth Ctr **801.451.8620**
Fax 801.451.2465
    907 W Clark Ln, Farmington, UT 84025
    Bryan Pobey, Director

Guardian Ad Litem **801.444.4340**
Fax 801.444.4345
E-mail ....karenhj@email.utcourts.gov
    427 N Wasatch Dr, Layton, UT 84041
    Patricia Fenimore, Attorney

Paramount Reflections **801.779.6521**
Fax 801.779.6530
Web ....www.cucc.us
E-mail ....bpovey@utah.gov
    523 Heritage Blvd, Ste. 2, Layton, UT 84041
    Bryan Povey, APD

COURTS

2nd District Juvenile Court **801.451.4900**
Fax 801.451.4950
Web ....www.utcourts.gov
    800 W State St, Farmington, UT 84025-4427
    Honorable Kathleen Nelson, Director

Youth Court **801.292.4486**
Fax 801.292.6355
Web ....www.westbountiful.utah.gov
    550 N 800 W, West Bountiful, UT 84087
    Beverly Haslam, Coordinator

EDUCATION SERVICES

Special Education **801.402.5261**
Fax 801.402.5189
    45 E State St, Farmington, UT 84025
    Dr Steven Hill, Director

Duchesne County

SOCIAL SERVICES

Work Force Svcs **435.722.6500**
Fax 435.722.6506
    140 W 425 S, Roosevelt, UT 84066
    Toni Ansel, Manager

JUSTICE AGENCY

Children's Justice Ctr **435.722.4843**
Fax 435.722.3918
E-mail ....cjc@ubtanet.com
    136 N Jane A. Thompson Ave (62-15), Roosevelt, UT 84066
    Cheryl Born, Director

Receiving Ctr **435.722.3226**
Fax 435.781.0840
Web ....www.hsdyc.state.ut.us
    28 W Lagoon St, Roosevelt, UT 84066-2841
    Linn Whitman, Supervisor

COURTS

District Court **435.738.2753**
Fax 435.738.2754
Web ....www.utcourts.gov
    21554 W 9000 S, Duchesne, UT 84021
    Honorable Larry Steele, Juvenile Judge

Emery County

SOCIAL SERVICES

Human Svcs - Dept Of Children And Family Svcs **435.381.4730**
Fax 435.381.4734
Web ....www.hsdcfs.utah.gov
E-mail ....cjensen@utah.gov
    1060 N Desbee Dove Road, Castle Dale, UT 84513
    Candace Jensen, Supervisor

GENERAL HEALTH SERVICES

Health Dept **435.381.2252**
Fax 435.381.5635
E-mail ....danaolsen@utah.gov
    25 W Main St, Castle Dale, UT 84513
    Dana Olsen, Public Health Nurse

POLICE AND SHERIFF

Sheriff's Ofc **435.381.2404**
Fax 435.381.2200
E-mail ....sheriff@ecso.com
    1850 N Des Bee Dove Rd, Castle Dale, UT 84513
    Greg Sunk, Sheriff

Garfield County

GENERAL HEALTH SERVICES

SW Utah Public Health Dept **435.676.8800**
Fax 435.676.8865
Web ....www.swuhealth.org
E-mail ....dblodgett@utah.gov
    609 N Main, Panguitch, UT 84759
    Dr. David Blodgett, Director

MENTAL HEALTH SERVICES

Southwest Ctr **435.676.8176**
Fax 435.676.2615
E-mail ....lmarcks@swcbh.com
    609 N Main Ste 6, Panguitch, UT 84759
    Lynda Marcks, Counsellor

POLICE AND SHERIFF

Sheriff's Ofc **435.676.2678**
Fax 435.676.1182
Web ....www.color-country.net
E-mail ....gcso@color-country.net
    375 N 700 W, Panguitch, UT 84759
    Danny Perkins, Sheriff

Grand County

GENERAL HEALTH SERVICES

Southeastern Utah District Health Dept **435.259.5602**
Fax 435.259.7369
    471 S Main St Ste 4, Moab, UT 84532-2980
    Donna Johnston, Public Health Nurse

JUSTICE AGENCY

Children's Justice Ctr **435.259.3680**
Fax 435.259.3057
Web ....www.grand.state.ut.us
E-mail ....connieh@grand.state.ut.us
    180 S 300 E Ste A, Moab, UT 84532-2620
    Connie Haycock, MSW, Director

COURTS

Juvenile Court **435.259.1353**
Fax 435.259.4081
    125 E Center St, Moab, UT 84532
    Honorable Mary Manley, Juvenile Court Judge

POLICE AND SHERIFF

Sheriff's Ofc **435.259.8115**
Fax 435.259.8651
Web ....www.grandcountysherrif.com
    125 E Center St, Moab, UT 84532
    Steven White, Sheriff

Iron County

GENERAL HEALTH SERVICES

Southwest Utah Public Health Dept **435.586.2437**
Fax 435.586.4851
Web ....www.swuhealth.org
E-mail ....speck@utah.gov
    260 DL Sargent Dr, Cedar City, UT 84721-9342
    Susan Peck, Nursing Director

JUSTICE AGENCY

Guardian Ad Litem **435.865.5330**
Fax 435.865.5334
    82 N 100 E Ste 203, Cedar City, UT 84720
    Lance Dean, Guardian Ad Litem

S.W. Utah Youth Ctr **435.867.2500**
Fax 435.867.2525
    270 E 1600 N, Cedar City, UT 84721
    Jill Mckinlay, Apd

Youth Ctr **435.586.1704**
Fax 435.586.6696
Web ....www.utah.gov
    1692 W Harding Ave, Cedar City, UT 84720-2216
    Jill Mckinley, Manager

COURTS

5th District Juvenile Court **435.867.3200**
Fax 435.867.3212
    40 N 100 E, Cedar City, UT 84720
    Joyce Barney, Chief Performance Officer

POLICE AND SHERIFF

Sheriff's Ofc **435.867.7500**
Fax 435.867.7539
Web ....www.ironcounty.net
E-mail ....mgower@ironcounty.net
    2132 N Main St, Cedar City, UT 84721-9788
    Mark Gower, Sheriff

EDUCATION SERVICES

Southwest Educational Development Ctr
(SEDC) **435.586.2865**
Fax 435.586.2868
Web www.m.sedc.k12.ut.us
E-mail ....jmckim@sped.washk12.org
520 W 800 S, Cedar City, UT 84720-6608
Randy Johnson, Director

Juab County

POLICE AND SHERIFF

Sheriff's Ofc **435.623.1349**
Fax 435.623.2899
Web ....www.juab.state.ut.us
E-mail ....aborem@juab.state.ut.us
425 W Sheep Ln, Nephi, UT 84648-2501
Alden B. Orem, Sheriff

Kane County

SOCIAL SERVICES

Div Of Child And Family Svcs **435.644.4530**
Fax 435.644.4535
Web ....www.utah.gov
E-mail ....kstapley@utah.gov
329 S 350 E Ste 3, Kanab, UT 84741
Kelly Stapley, Supervisor

GENERAL HEALTH SERVICES

South West Utah Public Health
Dept **435.644.2537**
Fax 435.644.5024
Web ....www.swuhealth.org
E-mail ....slittle@utah.gov
445 N Main, Kanab, UT 84741-3610
Susan Little, Rn, Public Health Nurse Manager

POLICE AND SHERIFF

Sheriff's Ofc **435.644.2349**
Fax 435.644.2096
Web ....www.expressweb.com
E-mail ....sheriff@expressweb.com
76 N Main St Ste 9, Kanab, UT 84741-3215
Lamont W. Smith, Sheriff

Millard County

GENERAL HEALTH SERVICES

Health Dept **435.743.5723**
55 S 400 W, Fillmore, UT 84631
Linda Stephenson, Public Health Nurse

MENTAL HEALTH SERVICES

Central Utah MH/Substance Abuse **435.743.5121**
Fax 435.743.4075
Web ....www.cucc.us
E-mail ....cindyt@cucc.us
65 W Center St, Fillmore, UT 84631
Anna Ladumas, Team Leader

COURTS

4th District Court **435.743.6223**
Fax 435.743.6923
765 S Highway 99 Ste 6, Fillmore, UT 84631-5032
Honorable James Brady, District Court Judge

4th District Juvenile Court **435.743.6608**
Fax 435.743.7905
E-mail ....peterj@email.utcourts.gov
765 S Highway 99 Ste 5, Fillmore, UT 84631
M. Peter Jacobson, Probation Officer

Youth Court/City Ofc **435.864.2759**
Fax 435.864.4313
Web ....www.delta.utah.gov
E-mail ....afinlinson@delta.utah.gov
76 N 200 W, Delta, UT 84624-9440
Ann Finlinson, Coordinator

POLICE AND SHERIFF

Sheriff's Ofc **435.743.5302**
Fax 435.743.6324
765 S Highway 99 Ste 6, Fillmore, UT 84631
Lt. Morris Burton, Teen Court Coordinator

Morgan County

POLICE AND SHERIFF

Sheriff's Ofc **801.829.0590**
Fax 801.829.0605
Web ....www.morgan.state.ut.us
48 W Young St, Morgan, UT 84050
Blaine Breshears, Sheriff

Rich County

POLICE AND SHERIFF

Sheriff's Ofc **435.793.2285**
Fax 435.793.3122
E-mail ....rcso@allwest.net
20 S Main St, Randolph, UT 84064
Dale Stacey, Sheriff

Salt Lake County

SOCIAL SERVICES

Child Protective Svcs **801.538.4100**
Fax 801.538.3993
Web ....www.utdcfsadopt.org
E-mail ....pvanwagoner@utah.gov
195 N 1950 W, Salt Lake City, UT 84116
Patti Vanwagoner, Deputy Director Of Child Division

Community Svcs Council **801.978.2452**
Fax 801.978.9565
Web ....www.csc-ut.org
E-mail ....jimp@utahfoodbank.org
3150 S 900 W, Salt Lake City, UT 84119-1504
Jim Pugh, Executive Director

Dept. Of Human Svcs Div Of Family Svcs Central
Region **801.538.4100**
Fax 801.538.3993
195 N 1950 W, Salt Lake City, UT 84116
Palmer Depaulus, Executive Director Of Human Services

GENERAL HEALTH SERVICES

Bureau Of Maternal & Child Health **801.538.6869**
Fax 801.538.9409
Web ....www.health.utah.gov
E-mail ....nanstreeter@utah.gov
288 N 1460 W, Salt Lake City, UT 84116
Nan Streeter, Director

Health Dept **801.468.2700**
Fax 801.468.2748
Web ....www.slv.org
E-mail ....gedwards@slco.org
2001 S State St # S 2500, Salt Lake City,
UT 84190-2150
Gary Edwards, Executive Director

Women, Infants And Children
(WIC) **801.534.4629**
Fax 801.534.4530
Web ....www.slvhealth.org
610 S 200 E, Ste 111, Salt Lake City, UT 84114
Brian Bennion, Division Director

JUSTICE AGENCY

Assessment And Diversion **801.957.7840**
Fax 801.957.7897
3636 Constitution Blvd, Salt Lake City, UT 84119
Sherrie Parke, Chief

Decker Lake Youth Ctr **801.954.9200**
Fax 801.954.9255
Web ....www.utah.gov
E-mail ....lmendez@utah.gov
2310 W 2770 S, Salt Lake City, UT 84119-2301
Larry Mendez, Assistant Program Director

Genesis Youth Ctr **801.576.6700**
Fax 801.576.4064
Web ....www.hsdyc.state.ut.us
14178 Pony Express Rd, Draper, UT 84020-9570
Vanessa Jarrell, Assistant Program Director

Guardian Ad Litem 3rd District Juvenile Court Salt Lake
City **801.578.3962**
Fax 801.578.3965
450 S State St Ste 22, Salt Lake City, UT 84114
Rick Smith, Case (statewide) Guardian Ad Litem Director

Icap **801.265.5961**
Fax 801.265.5969
3520 S 700 W, Salt Lake City, UT 84119-4120
Dorie Sararh, Director

Salt Lake Early Intervention
Programs **801.685.5712**
Fax 801.685.5707
3570 SW Temple, Salt Lake City, UT 84115
Donovan Bergstrom, Assistant Program Director

Salt Lake Observation And
Assessment **801.284.0230**
Fax 801.266.7591
61 W 3900 S, Salt Lake City, UT 81407
Debbie Rocha, Apd

Salt Lake Valley Detention Ctr **801.261.2060**
Fax 801.261.2732
3450 S 900 W, Salt Lake City, UT 84119
Tara Anderson, Program Director

COURTS

Peer Court **801.322.1815**
Fax 801.322.4498
Web ....www.saltlakepeercourt.org
E-mail ....slpcourt@xmission.com
645 S 200 E, Salt Lake City, UT 84111
Kathleen Zeitlin, Program Director

Wasatch Youth Court **801.265.5830**
Fax 801.265.5846
E-mail ....kgoudie@utah.gov
3534 S 700 W, Salt Lake City, UT 84119
Kyle Goudie, Apd

West Jordan Juvenile Court **801.233.9600**
Fax 801.233.9620
Web ....www.utcourts.gov
8080 Redwood Rd Ste 1700, West Jordan,
UT 84088-4648
Honorable Christine C. Decker, Juvenile Court Judge

POLICE AND SHERIFF

Sheriff's Ofc **801.468.3900**
Fax 801.468.3928
Web ....www.cjac.slco.org
E-mail ....jwinder@slco.org
2001 S State St Ste 2700, Salt Lake City,
UT 84190-0001
Jim Winder, Sheriff

Shields Orthotic Prosthetic Svcs,
Inc. **801.467.5483**
Fax 801.484.4591
Web ....www.shieldsop.com
E-mail ....info@shieldsop.com
2785 E 3300 S, Salt Lake City, UT 84109
Mike Beavers Cpo, Clinical Director

EDUCATION SERVICES

Boys And Girls Club Of South

Valley **801.284.4253**
Fax 801.288.2225
Web ....www.bgcsv.org
E-mail ....bdunn@mail.bgcsv.org
    244 E Vine St, Salt Lake City, UT 84107-4935
Bob Dunn, Executive Director

Challenger School **801.278.4797**
Fax 801.278.4798
Web ....www.challengerschool.com
E-mail ....bsalt@challengerschool.com
    4555 S 2300 E, Salt Lake City, UT 84117-4426
Brenda Salt, Director

Community Action Program Head

Start **801.359.8749**
Fax 801.596.1138
    254 E Gregson Ave, # 3020, Salt Lake City, UT 84115
Holly Collin, Off Manger

Special Education **801.578.8204**
Fax 801.578.8536
    440 E 100 S, Salt Lake City, UT 84111
Randy Shelby, Director

San Juan County

SOCIAL SERVICES

Local And Regional Ombudsmen **435.587.3225**
Fax 435.587.2447
Web ....www.sanjuancounty.org
E-mail ....tgallegos@sanjuancounty.org
    117 S Main, Monticello, UT 84535
Tammy Gallegos, Director

GENERAL HEALTH SERVICES

Southeast Utah District Health

Dept **435.637.3671**
Fax 435.637.7515
Web ....www.southeasternutahhealthdepartment.com
    28 S 100 E, Price, UT 84501
Dottie Flemett, Director Of Nursing

JUSTICE AGENCY

Canyonlands Youth Home **435.678.3140**
Fax 435.678.3079
    244 Old Run Rd, Blanding, UT 84511
Angela McCourt, Apd

POLICE AND SHERIFF

Sheriff's Ofc **435.587.2237**
Fax 435.587.2013
Web ....www.sanjuancounty.org
E-mail ....mlacy@sanjuancounty.org
    297 S Main, Monticello, UT 84535
Rick Elberedge, Sheriff

Sanpete County

SOCIAL SERVICES

Dept Of Work Force Svcs **435.835.0720**
Fax 435.835.0759
Web ....www.jobs.utah.gov
E-mail ....dwscontactus@utah.gov
    55 S Main St Ste 3, Manti, UT 84642
Todd Jorgenson, Supervisor

GENERAL HEALTH SERVICES

Manti Health Dept **435.835.2231**
Fax 435.835.2233
    40 W 200 N, Manti, UT 84642
Debra Lindsey, Nursing Supervisor

COURTS

6th District Juvenile Court **435.835.0600**
Fax 435.835.8603
    50 S Main St Ste 3, Manti, UT 84642
Sam Deleeuw, Intake Probation Officer

POLICE AND SHERIFF

Sheriff's Ofc **435.835.2191**
Fax 435.835.2143
Web ....www.sanpetesheriff.org
E-mail ....sheriff@sanpeteso.org
    1500 S 89 Hwy, Manti, UT 84642-1278
Brian Niclson, Sheriff

Sevier County

SOCIAL SERVICES

Dept Of Work Force Svcs **435.893.0000**
Fax 435.893.0002
Web ....www.jobs.utah.gov
E-mail ....lking@utah.gov
    115 E 100 S, Richfield, UT 84701-2647
Lela King, Manager

JUSTICE AGENCY

Central Utah Youth Center **435.893.2340**
Fax 435.896.8177
Web ....www.utah.gov
E-mail ....glenames@utah.gov
    449 N SR 118, Richfield, UT 84701-2378
Glen Ames, Apd

COURTS

6th District Juvenile Court **435.896.2700**
Fax 435.896.8047
Web ....www.utcourts.gov
    895 E 300 N, Richfield, UT 84701-2345
Christopher Morgan, Probation Head

POLICE AND SHERIFF

Sheriff's Ofc **435.896.2600**
Fax 435.896.6081
Web ....www.sevier.state.ut.us
E-mail ....pbarney@sevier.state.ut.us
    835 E 300 N Ste 200, Richfield, UT 84701-2344
Linda Johnson, Teen Court Coordinator

EDUCATION SERVICES

Central Utah Educational Svcs

(CUES) **435.896.4469**
Fax 435.896.4767
Web www.cues.k12.ut.us
E-mail ....glen.taylor@cues.k12.ut.us
    195 E 500 N, Richfield, UT 84701-1899
Glen Taylor, Director

Summit County

SOCIAL SERVICES

CPS **801.376.8261**
Fax 801.374.7822
E-mail ....bplatt@utah.gov
    150 E Center St Ste 5100, Provo, UT 84606-3712
Brent Platt, Regional Director

GENERAL HEALTH SERVICES

Health Dept **435.336.3234**
Fax 435.336.3067
Web ....www.summitcountyhealth.org
E-mail ....rvullough@utah.gov
    85 N 50 E, Coalville, UT 84017
Richard Vullough, Health Director

Public Health Dept **435.333.1500**
Fax 435.333.1580
Web ....www.summitcounty.org
E-mail ....mstarkuy@utah.gov
    650 Round Valley Dr, Park City, UT 84060
Myra Starkuy, Nurse Practitioner

COURTS

3rd District Juvenile Court **435.615.4324**
Fax 435.658.1067
E-mail ....korbyg@email.utcourts.gov
    6300 Silver Creek Dr Ste D, Park City, UT 84098
Korby Gines, Probation Officer

POLICE AND SHERIFF

Sheriff's Ofc **435.615.3600**
Fax 435.615.3614
Web ....www.co.summit.ut.us
E-mail ....dedmunds@co.summit.ut.us
    6300 Silver Creek Dr Ste 1, Park City, UT 84098-6209
Dave Edmunds, Sheriff

Tooele County

SOCIAL SERVICES

Dept Of Human Svcs, Dept Of Workforce

Svcs **435.833.7310**
Fax 435.833.7395
Web ....www.jobs.utah.gov
E-mail ....vchristiansen@utah.gov
    305 N Main St Ste 100, Tooele, UT 84074-1694
Jolyn Bevan, Supervisor

Human Svcs Div Of Child And Family

Svcs **435.833.7350**
Fax 435.833.7345
Web ....www.hsdcfs.state.ut.us/dcfsoffc.htm
    305 N Main St Ste 239, Tooele, UT 84074-1665
Mary Walder, Customer Service Manager

GENERAL HEALTH SERVICES

Health Dept **435.277.2300**
Fax 435.277.2304
    151 N Main St, Tooele, UT 84074
Sherrie Ahlstrom, Nursing/marketing Director

COURTS

Youth Court **435.882.4607**
Fax 435.882.7777
Web ....www.tooelecity.org
E-mail ....bbracken@tooelecity.org
    323 N Main St, Tooele, UT 84074-1652
Becky Bracken, Coordinator

Uintah County

GENERAL HEALTH SERVICES

Health Dept **435.247.1177**
Web ....www.tricountyhealth.com
    133 S 500 E, Vernal, UT 84078
Lynn Gagnon, Public Health Nurse

JUSTICE AGENCY

CASA/GAL **435.781.9370**
Fax 435.789.2759
Web ....www.casanet.org
E-mail ....carolyww@email.utcourts.gov
    920 E Highway 40, Vernal, UT 84078-2803
Carolyn White, Case Coordinator

Uintah/Dagget Children's Justice

Ctr **435.781.0105**
Fax 435.781.6573
E-mail ....jgardner@ubtanet.com
    84 N 200 W, Vernal, UT 84078-2038
Mrs. Murray, Director

COURTS

Four Direction CASA Ute Tribal Juvenile

Court **435.722.5141**
Fax 435.725.4939
E-mail ....laurai@utetribe.com
    988 E 7500 S, Fort Duchesne, UT 84026
Laura Ivie, Probation Officer

POLICE AND SHERIFF

Sheriff's Ofc **435.789.2511**
Fax 435.781.5412
Web .... www.co.uintah.ut.us
E-mail .... jmerrell@co.uintah.ut.us
   641 E 300 S Ste 250, Vernal, UT 84078-2110
Jeff Merrell, Sheriff

Utah County

SOCIAL SERVICES

Dept Of Work Forces Svcs **801.342.2600**
Fax 801.342.2727
Web .... www.jobs.utah.gov
E-mail .... mfinch@utah.gov
   1550 N Freedom Blvd, Provo, UT 84604-2573
Melissa Finch, Director

GENERAL HEALTH SERVICES

Health Dept **801.851.7000**
Fax 801.851.7009
Web .... www.utahcountyhealth.org
   151 S University Ave, Provo, UT 84601
Lynn Flinders, Family And Personal Health Director

MENTAL HEALTH SERVICES

Child And Family Svcs Youth Case
Management **801.373.4765**
Fax 801.375.4045
Web .... www.wasatch.org
   1161 E 300 N, Provo, UT 84606-3539
Catherine Johnson, Child & Family Services Director

Utah State Hospital **801.344.4400**
Fax 801.344.4291
Web .... www.utah.gov
E-mail .... rspencer@utah.gov
   1300 E Center St, Provo, UT 84606-3554
Richard Spencer, Clinical Director

Wasatch Mental Health Ctr **801.373.4760**
Fax 801.373.0639
E-mail .... jkorbanka@wasatch.org
   750 N 200 W, Provo, UT 84601
Juergen Korbanka, Director

Youth Outpatient Mental Health **801.377.1213**
Fax 801.852.3550
E-mail .... charper@wasatch.org
   1165 E 300 N, Provo, UT 84606
Colleen Harper, Program Manager

JUSTICE AGENCY

CASA/GAL **801.344.8516**
Fax 801.344.8597
E-mail .... dorothyk@email.ut.courts.gov
   32 W Center St Ste 205, Provo, UT 84601
Dee Knell, Guardian Ad Litem Coordinator

Children's Justice Ctr **801.851.8554**
Fax 801.851.8518
Web .... www.utahcountyonline.org/dept/cjc/index .asp
E-mail .... uccjc.laurab@state.ut.us
   315 S 100 E, Provo, UT 84606-4649
Laura Blanchard, Director

Lightning Peak **801.370.0503**
Fax 801.356.2380
   1955 Dakota Ln, Provo, UT 84606-6400
Sam Fherrow, Apd

Orem Case Management **801.426.7430**
Fax 801.426.7455
E-mail .... oerickson@utah.gov
   237 Mountainlands Dr, Orem, UT 84058-5114
Odell Erickson, Apd

Slate Canyon Youth Ctr **801.342.7840**
Fax 801.342.7873
   1991 S State St, Provo, UT 84060
Chris Roach, Apd

COURTS

4th District Juvenile Court **801.764.5820**
   99 E Center St, Orem, UT 84057
Mary Noonan, Juvenile Court Judge

4th District Juvenile Court **801.354.7200**
Fax 801.373.6579
E-mail .... kimbalb@email.utcourts.gov
   2021 S State St, Provo, UT 84606-6552
Kimbal Bird, Chief Performance Officer

Juvenile Court **801.763.8941**
Fax 801.763.8944
   75 E 80 N Ste 201, American Fork, UT 84003
Western Tuia, Probation Officer In Charge

Youth Court **801.756.2281**
Fax 801.763.3004
   80 East 70 North, American Fork, UT 84003
Lavon Laursen, Advisor

POLICE AND SHERIFF

Sheriff's Ofc **801.851.4000**
Fax 801.851.4009
E-mail .... ucso.jimtr@state.ut.us
   3075 N Main St, Spanish Fork, UT 84660
James O. Tracy, Sheriff

Wasatch County

SOCIAL SERVICES

Utah Dept Of Work Force Svcs **435.654.6520**
Fax 435.654.6535
Web .... www.jobs.utah.gov
E-mail .... jeknudso@utah.gov
   69 N 600 W Ste C, Heber City, UT 84032-1826
Joseph Knudson, Manager

GENERAL HEALTH SERVICES

Health Dept **435.654.2700**
Fax 435.654.2705
   55 S 500 E, Heber City, UT 84032
Gina Tuttle, Nursing Director

JUSTICE AGENCY

Children's Justice Ctr **435.657.1000**
Fax 435.654.3963
E-mail .... kjones@co.wasatch.ut.us
   1540 E 980 S, Heber City, UT 84032
Kenna Jones, Executive Director

POLICE AND SHERIFF

Sheriff's Ofc **435.654.1411**
Fax 435.657.3580
   1361 S Highway 40, Heber City, UT 84032
Todd Bonner, Sheriff

Washington County

SOCIAL SERVICES

Bureau Of Indian Affairs **435.674.9720**
Fax 435.674.9714
Web .... www.bia.gov
   180 N 200 E, Saint George, UT 84770
Kellie Youngbear, Field Rep.

Div Of Child And Family Svcs **435.652.2960**
Fax 435.652.2988
Web .... www.utah.gov
   377 E Riverside Dr Ste A, Saint George, UT 84790
Robert W. Johnson, Building Supervisor

Utah Dept Of Work Force Svcs **435.674.5627**
Fax 435.986.3595
Web .... www.jobs.utah.gov
   162 N 400 E Ste B, Saint George, UT 84770
Kristen Cox, Director

Utah Dept Of Work Force Svcs **435.674.5627**
Fax 435.986.3595
Web .... www.jobs.utah.gov
   162 N 400 E Bldg B, Saint George, UT 84770
Jan Thompson, Director

GENERAL HEALTH SERVICES

Community Health Clinic **435.986.2565**
Fax 435.986.2577
Web .... www.swuchc.com
   168 N 100 E Ste 204, Saint George, UT 84770
Nancy Neff, Executive Director

Southwest Utah Public Health
Dept **435.673.3528**
Fax 435.628.6425
E-mail .... dblodgett@utah.gov
   620 S 400 E Ste 400, Saint George, UT 84770-7063
David W Blodgett, Md, Executive Director

JUSTICE AGENCY

Dixie Area Detention **435.627.2800**
Fax 435.627.2801
Web .... www.utah.gov
E-mail .... scabana@utah.gov
   330 S 5300 W, Hurricane, UT 84737-2926
Sterling Cabana, Director

Youth Crisis Ctr **435.656.6100**
Fax 435.656.6139
   251 E 200 N, Saint George, UT 84770
Tami Fullerton, System Program Director

COURTS

5th District Juvenile Court **435.986.5730**
Fax 435.986.5739
Web .... www.courtlink.utcourts.gov
   206 W Tabernacoe, Saint George, UT 84770-2871
Honorable Hans Q. Chamberlain, Juvenile Court Judge

POLICE AND SHERIFF

Sheriff's Ofc **435.656.6500**
Fax 435.656.6666
E-mail .... washeriff@.net
   750 S 5300 W, Hurricane, UT 84737
Cory Pulsipher, Sheriff

Wayne County

POLICE AND SHERIFF

Sheriff's Ofc **435.836.2789**
Fax 435.836.2189
Web .... www.wco.state.ut.us
E-mail .... wayneso@wco.state.ut.us
   18 So. Main St, Loa, UT 84747
Kurt Taylor, Sheriff

Weber County

GENERAL HEALTH SERVICES

Health Dept **801.399.7100**
Fax 801.399.7110
Web .... www.co.weber.ut.us
E-mail .... ghouse@co.weber.ut.us
   477 23rd St, Ogden, UT 84401-1507
Gary House, Health Director

MENTAL HEALTH SERVICES

Mckay-Dee Behavioral Health
Institue **801.387.5600**
Fax 801.475.4720
Web .... www.ihc.com
   5030 Harrison Blvd, Ogden, UT 84403
Carolyn Tometich, Director Of Counseling

JUSTICE AGENCY

Mill Creek Youth Ctr **801.334.0210**
Fax 801.334.0287
   790 W 12Th St, Ogden, UT 84404
Jackie Southwick, Director

Utah

Ofc Of Community Programs 801.627.0322
Fax 801.393.7813
   145 N Monroe Blvd, Ogden, UT 84404
   Cecil Robinson, Program Director

**Ogden Observation And
Assessment** 801.627.0326
Fax 801.393.7813
   145 N Monroe Blvd, Ogden, UT 84404
   Marty Mendenhall, Adp

Project Paramount 801.621.3684
Fax 801.393.2869
   2760 Adams Ave, Ogden, UT 84403-0106
   Brian Bovey, Apd

Weber Valley Detention Ctr 801.825.2794
Fax 801.776.8976
   5470 S 2700 W, Roy, UT 84067
   Ted Grove, Apd

COURTS

2nd District Juvenile Court 801.626.3800
Fax 801.626.3827
Web ....www.utcourts.gov
   800 W State St, Farmington, UT 84025
   Honorable L. Kent Bachman, Director

POLICE AND SHERIFF

Sheriff's Ofc 801.778.6600
Fax 801.778.6668
E-mail ....tthompson@coweber.ut.us
   721 W 12Th St, Ogden, UT 84404
   Terry Thompson, Sheriff

EDUCATION SERVICES

Special Education 801.476.7800
Fax 801.476.7897
   5320 Adams Ave Parkway, Ogden, UT 84405
   Ann M. Miller, Special Ed. Director

SPECIAL SERVICES AGENCIES

ADOPTION AGENCIES

Adoption Exchange 801.265.0444
Fax 801.265.0834
Web ....www.utdcfsadopt.org
   975 E Wood Oak Ln Ste 220, Murray, UT 84117
   Kathy Searle, Utah Coordinator

Adoption Home Studies 801.671.0825
Fax 801.968.1238
Web ....www.maretadoptionstudies.homestead.com
   3717 Deann Dr, Salt Lake City, UT 84128-2528

Adoptive Family Assessments 801.943.0122
   2998 E 9690 S, Sandy, UT 84092-3542
   Elisabeth Sinlinson, Director

Adoptive Home Studies 801.592.0885
   330 E 400 S, Ste 1, Springville, UT 84663-1915
   Tammy Little, Director

Children's House Int'l 801.766.3412
Fax 801.734.3040
Web ....www.childrenshouseinternational.com
E-mail ....chilatinam@aol.com
   3053 Sage Loop Apt 2, Lehi, UT 84043-4810
   Kathy Holliday, South American Director

Dean B Ellis Attorney 801.965.8605
Fax 801.964.1344
Web ....www.adoptffc.org
E-mail ....dean@adoptffc.org
   3600 Market St, West Valley, UT 84119
   Dean B. Ellis, Attorney

Eric B Barnes 801.546.3874
Fax 801.546.4668
Web ....www.elderlaw-info.com
E-mail ....eric@elderlaw-info.com
   47 N Main St, Kaysville, UT 84037-1948
   Eric Barnes, Director

Lds Family Svcs 435.637.2991
Fax 435.637.1775
Web ....www.ldsfamilyservices.org
E-mail ....nelsonq@ldschurch.org
   630 W Price River Dr, Price, UT 84501
   Quinn Nelson, Practiioner

Lds Family Svcs 435.896.6446
Fax 435.896.8769
Web ....www.ldsfamilyservices.org
E-mail ....fam-ut-richfield@ldschurch.org
   681 N Main St, Richfield, UT 84701-1824
   Scott Henderson, Director

Lds Family Svcs 435.752.5302
Fax 435.753.9007
Web ....www.ldsfamilyservices.org
   175 W 1400 N Ste A, Logan, UT 84341-6816
   Rick Hill, Director

Utah Foster Care Foundation 801.373.3006
Fax 801.373.3004
E-mail ....moreinfo@utahfostercare.org
   252 N Orem Blvd, Orem, UT 84057-6601
   Lee Wright, Hr Manager/executive Assist.

Utah Foster Care Foundation 435.656.8065
Fax 435.656.8071
E-mail ....debbie@utahfostercare.org
   321 N Mall Dr Ste B102, Saint George,
   UT 84790-7304
   Debbie Hofhines, Area Representative

ADVOCACY RESOURCES

Utah Guardian ad Litem 435.381.5595
E-mail ....conniem@email.utcourts.gov
   PO Box 1270, Castle Dale, UT 84513
   Connie Mower

Utah Ofc of Guardian ad Litem 801.578.3848
   450 S State St # N31, Salt Lake City, UT 84106
   Rick Smith, Director

Utah Office of Guardian ad Litem 801.578.3829
E-mail ....kristinf@email.utcourts.gov
   450 S State St N31, PO Box 140241, Salt Lake City,
   UT 84122
   Kristin Fadel

Utah State Courts 801.578.3821
E-mail ....whitneyk@email.utcourts.gov
   450 S State St, Salt Lake City, UT 84114
   Whitney Kania

BEHAVIORAL HEALTH TREATMENT

Adoption Ctr Of Choice 801.224.2440
Fax 801.224.1899
Web ....www.theadoptioncenter.com
E-mail ....don@theadoptioncenter.com
   241 W 520 N, Orem, UT 84057-4696
   Don Hansen, Director

**Artec-Adolescent Residential Treatment And Education
Ctr** 801.963.4200
Fax 801.963.4299
Web ....www.vmh.com
E-mail ....randyd@vmh.com
   3809 W 6200 S, Salt Lake City, UT 84118-3725
   Randy Dow, Director

Aspen Achievement Academy 435.836.2472
Web ....www.aspenachievementacademy.com
E-mail ....ghallows@theaspenacademy.com
   98 S. Main Street, Loa, UT 84747
   Mr. Gilbert Hallows, Accreditation Manager
   Joint Commission accredited organization.

Aspen Ranch 435.836.2080
Fax 435.836.2085
Web ....www.aspenranch.com
   2000 West Dry Valley Road, Loa, UT 84747
   CARF accredited programs available.

Avalon Hills 435.753.3686
Fax 435.753.3760
Web ....www.avalonhills.org
E-mail ....doctorbenita@avalonhills.org
   7852 W 600 N, Mendon, UT 84325-9706
   Benita Quakenbush-Roberts, PhD, Executive Director

**Avalon Hills Residential Eating Disorders
Program** 435.755.0434
Web ....www.avalonhills.org
E-mail ....whitney@avalonhills.org
   196 S. 100 West, Logan, UT 84321
   Ms. Whitney Matson, Accreditation Manager
   Joint Commission accredited organization.

Benchmark Behavioral Health Systems 801.299.5300
Web ....bbhsnet.com
E-mail ....barry.woodward@psysolutions.com
   592 West 1350 South, Woods Cross, UT 84087
   Mr. Barry Woodward, Accreditation Manager
   Joint Commission accredited organization.

Canyonview 801.476.3964
   1100 Orchard Ave, Ogden, UT 84404-5058
   Mary Lamont, Director

Cardenas-Walle Medical Practice 801.274.3625
   650 Komas Dr Ste 202, Salt Lake City,
   UT 84108-1241
   Patricia Cardenas-Walle, MD, Psychiatrist

CENTER FOR CHANGE 801.224.8255
Web ....www.centerforchange.com
E-mail ....robert.clark@uhsinc.com
   1790 N STATE ST, Orem, UT 84057
   Mr. Robert Clark, Accreditation Manager
   Joint Commission accredited organization.

Cinnamon Hills Youth Crisis Center 435.674.0984
Web ....www.cinnamonhills.com
E-mail ....lisa@cinnamonhills.com
   770 East St. George Boulevard, Saint George,
   UT 84770
   Mrs. Lisa Sellers, Accreditation Manager
   Joint Commission accredited organization.

Copper Hills Youth Center 801.561.3377
Web ....www.psysolutions.com
E-mail ....phil.sheridan@uhsinc.com
   5899 West Rivendell Drive, West Jordan, UT 84081
   Mr. Phil Sheridan, Accreditation Manager
   Joint Commission accredited organization.

Cottonwood Treatment Center 801.433.2900
Fax 801.433.2999
Web ....www.cottonwoodtreatment.com
   1144 W 3300 S Ste 300, Salt Lake City,
   UT 84119-7176
   Steve Alonge, Vp Business Development

Ctr For Change 801.224.8255
Fax 801.224.8301
Web ....www.centerforchange.com
E-mail ....info@centerforchange.com
   1790 N State St, Orem, UT 84057-2025
   Michael E. Berrett, Phd, Chief Executive Officer

Discovery Academy 801.374.2121
Fax 801.373.4451
Web ....www.discoveryacademy.com
   105 N 500 W, Provo, UT 84601
   Dr. Triston Morgan, Admissions Director

EAGALA **801.754.0400**
Fax 801.754.0401
Web .... www.eagala.org
E-mail .... equine@eagala.org
270 E Main St, Santaquin, UT 84655-7076
Lynn Thomas, Lcsw, Executive Director

Heber Valley Counseling **435.654.1618**
Fax 435.654.0309
E-mail .... dhansen@co.wasatch.ut.us
55 S 500 E, Heber City, UT 84032-1918
Dennis Hansen, Director

Heritage Schools, Inc. **801.226.4600**
Web .... www.heritagertc.org
E-mail .... bnorman@heritagertc.org
5600 N Heritage School Drive, Provo, UT 84604
Mrs. Brenda Norman, Accreditation Manager
Joint Commission accredited organization.

Hightop Ranch School **435.638.7411**
Web .... www.hightopranch.com
E-mail .... justin@hightopranch.com
2860 South Highway 62, Koosharem, UT 84744
Mr. Justin Sorenson, Accreditation Manager
Joint Commission accredited organization.

Horizon House **435.586.2515**
Fax 435.865.7606
Web .... www.southwestcenter.com
54 N 200 E, Cedar City, UT 84720
Mike Deal, Executive Director

Integrity House **435.586.8336**
Web .... www.integrityhousertc.com
E-mail .... phyllischarles@integrityhousertc.com
465 W. 1600 N., Cedar City, UT 84720
Mrs. Phyllis Charles, Accreditation Manager
Joint Commission accredited organization.

Island View Residential Treatment Center **801.773.0200**
Web .... islandview-rtc.com
E-mail .... dhans@ivrtc.com
2650 West 2700 South, Syracuse, UT 84075
Dr. David Hans, Accreditation Manager
Joint Commission accredited organization.

Mountain View Hospital **801.465.9201**
Fax 801.465.7087
Web .... www.mvhpayson.com
E-mail .... jtalbert@mtnviewhospital.com
1000 E 100 N, Payson, UT 84651-1600
Jane Talbert, Nursing Director

New Haven **801.794.1218**
Fax 801.794.9558
Web .... www.newhavenrtc.com
E-mail .... lauriel@newhavenrtc.com
2096 E 7200 S, Spanish Fork, UT 84660
Laurie Laird, Education Director

Northeastern Counseling Ctr **435.725.6300**
Fax 435.725.6325
Web .... www.nccutah.org
E-mail .... roberth@nccutah.org
285 W 800 S, Roosevelt, UT 84066-3707
Robert Hall, Supervisor

Odyssey House Inc - Utah **801.322.4257**
Web .... www.odysseyhouse.org
E-mail .... elewis@odysseyhouse.org
344 East 100 South, Suite 301, Salt Lake City, UT 84111
Ms. Emily Lewis, Accreditation Manager
Joint Commission accredited organization.

Outback Theraputic Expedition **801.766.3933**
Fax 801.766.3932
Web .... www.outbacktreatment.com
E-mail .... mail@outbacktreatment.com
50 N 200 E, Lehi, UT 84043-1835
Rick Meeves, Phd, Executive Director

Primary Children's Medical Center **801.662.1000**
Web .... www.IntermountainHealthcare.org
E-mail .... rebecca.hales@imail.org
100 North Mario Capecchi Drive, Salt Lake City, UT 84113-1100
Mrs. Rebecca Hales, Accreditation Manager
Joint Commission accredited organization.

Provo Canyon School **801.491.3910**
Fax 801.491.3911
E-mail .... brent.esplin@uhsinc.com
763 N 1650 W, Springville, UT 84663
Brent Esplin, Admissions Director & Community Relations

Quest Family Services / Wilderness Quest **435.587.2801**
Web .... www.wildernessquest.com
E-mail .... jwhipple@wildernessquest.com
564 North Main, Monticello, UT 84535
Ms. Jennifer Whipple, Accreditation Manager
Joint Commission accredited organization.

Red Rock Canyon School **435.673.6111**
Web .... www.redrockcanyonschool.com
E-mail .... brian@rrrtc.com
747 E. Staint George Blvd., Saint George, UT 84770
Mr. Brian Pace, Accreditation Manager
Joint Commission accredited organization.

Salt Lake Behavioral Health **801.718.4938**
Web .... ascendhealth.net
E-mail .... lbarker@ascendhealth.net
3802 South, 7th East, Salt Lake City, UT 84106
Ms. Linda Barker, Accreditation Manager
Joint Commission accredited organization.

Second Nature Wilderness Program **435.738.2040**
Fax 435.738.2046
E-mail .... www.duchesne@snwp.com
382 W Main St, Duchesne, UT 84021
St. Joseph, Admissions Director

Solacium - New Haven **801.794.1218**
Web .... www.newhavenrtc.com
E-mail .... johns@newhavenrtc.com
2172 East 7200 South, Spanish Fork, UT 84660
Mr. John Stewart, Accreditation Manager
Joint Commission accredited organization.

Sorenson's Ranch School, Inc. **435.638.7318**
Web .... www.sorensonsranch.com
E-mail .... srs@color-country.net
410 North 100 East, Koosharem, UT 84744
Mr. Shane Sorenson, Accreditation Manager
Joint Commission accredited organization.

Southwest Ctr **435.634.5600**
Fax 435.986.8702
Web .... www.southwestcenter.com
474 W 200 North, Ste 300, Saint George, UT 84770
Michael Deal, Executive Director

Sunhawk Adolescent Recovery Center **435.656.3211**
Fax 435.656.3213
Web .... www.sunhawkrecovery.com
948 North 1300 West, Saint George, UT 84770
CARF accredited programs available.

Sunrise Residential Treatment Center **435.635.1185**
Web .... www.sunrisertc.com
E-mail .... davidp@sunrisertc.com
65 North 1150 West, Hurricane, UT 84737
Mr. Dave Prior, Accreditation Manager
Joint Commission accredited organization.

Telos Residential Treatment **801.426.8800**
Web .... www.telosrtc.com
E-mail .... latricia@telosrtc.com
870 West Center Street, Orem, UT 84057
Ms. Latricia Nell, Accreditation Manager

The Children's Ctr **801.966.4251**
Fax 801.966.4289
5242 S 4820 W, Salt Lake City, UT 84118
Douglas Goldsmith, Phd, Director

The Children's Ctr **801.582.5534**
Fax 801.582.5540
Web .... www.tccslc.org
350 S 400 E, Salt Lake City, UT 84111
Douglas Goldsmith, Phd, Director

Turn-About Ranch **435.826.4240**
Fax 435.826.4261
Web .... www.turnaboutranch.com
E-mail .... admissions@turnaboutranch.com
280 N 300 E, Escalante, UT 84726
Luke Hatch, Executive Director

Turning Point Family Care, Inc **435.674.7421**
Web .... www.turningpointfamilycare.com
E-mail .... info@turningpointfamilycare.com
115 North 300 West, B200, Washington, UT 84780
Mr. Adam Milne, Accreditation Manager
Joint Commission accredited organization.

UHS of Provo Canyon, Inc **801.227.2000**
Web .... provocanyon.com
E-mail .... jan.purkey@uhsinc.com
1350 E 750 North, Orem, UT 84097
Ms. Jan Purkey, Accreditation Manager
Joint Commission accredited organization.

UHS of Salt Lake City, LLC **801.433.2900**
Web .... cottonwoodtreatment.com
E-mail .... karen.johnson@uhsinc.com
1110 West 3300 South, South Salt Lake, UT 84119
Ms. Karen Johnson, Accreditation Manager

Uinta Academy **435.245.2600**
Fax 435.245.2605
Web .... www.uintaacademy.net
E-mail .... jsimpson@uintaacademy.net
3746 S. 4800 W, Wellsville, UT 84339
Jeff Simpson, Executive Director

University of Utah Neuropsychiatric Institute **801.583.2500**
Web .... uuhsc.utah.edu
E-mail .... rebecca.hyde@hsc.utah.edu
501 Chipeta Way, Salt Lake City, UT 84108
Ms. Rebecca Hyde, Accreditation Manager
Joint Commission accredited organization.

University Of Utah Neuropsychiatric Institute **801.583.2500**
Fax 801.582.8471
E-mail .... michael.lowry@hsc.utah.edu
501 Chipeta Way, Salt Lake City, UT 84108-1222
Michael Lowry, Medical Director

UT-TEX, Inc. **801.250.9762**
Web .... www.vistatreatmentcenters.com
E-mail .... charles@vistatreatmentcenters.com
8265 West 2700 South, Magna, UT 84044
Mr. Charles Sandy, Accreditation Manager
Joint Commission accredited organization.

Utah Medical Assoc **801.747.3500**
Fax 801.747.3501
Web .... www.utahmed.org
E-mail .... Michelle@utahmed.org
310 E 4500 S Ste 500, Salt Lake City, UT 84107-4250
Michelle Mcomber, Executive Vice President/CEO

Youth Care of Utah **801.572.6989**
Web .... www.youthcare.com
E-mail .... sastin@youthcare.com
12595 South Minuteman Drive, Draper, UT 84020
Mrs. Stacey Astin, Accreditation Manager
Joint Commission accredited organization.

Youthtrack - Utah **435.723.1799**
Web .... www.youthtrack-utah.com
E-mail .... sstringam@rescare.com
862 South Main Street # 4, Brigham City, UT 84302
Mr. Scott Stringam, Accreditation Manager
Joint Commission accredited organization.

Utah

CHILDREN'S HOSPITAL

American Fork Hospital 801.855.3300
170 N 1100 E, American Fork, UT 84003
Mike Olson, Administrator

Brigham City Community Hospital 435.734.9471
950 S Medical Dr, Brigham City, UT 84302
Richard Steeler, Chief Executive Officer

Central Valley Medical Center 435.623.3000
48 W 1500 N, Nephi, UT 84648
Mark Stoddard, Director

Davis Hospital & Medical Center 801.807.1000
1600 W Antelope Dr, Layton, UT 84041
Mike Jemsen, Chief Executive Officer

Delta Community Medical Center 435.864.5591
126 S White Sage Ave, Delta, UT 84624
James Backstrand, Chief Executive Officer

Dixie Regional Medical Center 435.251.1000
1380 E Medical Center Dr, Saint George, UT 84790
Terri Kane, Chief Executive Officer

Fillmore Community Medical Center 435.743.5591
674 S Hwy 99, Fillmore, UT 84631
Jim Beckstrand, Chief Executive Officer

**Intermountain McKay-Dee Hospital
Center** 801.387.2800
4401 Harrison Blvd, Ogden, UT 84403
Tim Pehrson, Chief Executive Officer

Logan Regional Hospital 435.716.1000
E-mail .... mike.clark@imail.org
1400 N 500 E, Logan, UT 84341
Micheal Clark, Chief Executive Officer

Moab Regional Hospital 435.719.3500
450 W Williams Way, Moab, UT 84532
Roy Varraclough, Chief Executive Officer

Ogden Regional Medical Center 801.479.2111
5475 S 500 E, Ogden, UT 84405
Mark Adams, Chief Executive Officer

Primary Children's Medical Center 801.588.2000
100 N Medical Dr, Salt Lake City, UT 84113

Sevier Valley Medical Center 435.893.4100
E-mail .... gary.beck@imail.org
1000 N Main St, Richfield, UT 84701
Gary Beck, Chief Executive Officer

Shriners Hospitals for Children at Salt 801.536.3500
Fairfax Rd & Virginia St, Salt Lake City, UT 84103
Kevin Martin, Director

Timpanogos Regional Hospital 801.714.6000
750 W 800 N, Orem, UT 84059
Keith Tintle, Chief Executive Officer

Uintah Basin Medical Center 435.722.6163
250 W 300 N 75-2, Roosevelt, UT 84066

Utah Valley Regional Medical Center 801.357.7850
1034 N 500 W, Provo, UT 84604
Steve Smoot, Chief Executive Officer

Valley View Medical Center 435.868.5000
1303 N Main St, Cedar City, UT 84721
Jason Wilson, Administrator

COUNSELING SERVICES

Lds Family Svcs 801.566.2556
Fax 801.566.2639
Web .... www.ldsfamilyservices.org
E-mail .... fam-ut-kearns@ldschurch.org
625 E 8400 S, Sandy, UT 84070-0525
Mark Glade, Director

Lds Family Svcs 435.586.4479
Fax 435.865.0023
Web .... www.ldsfamilyservices.org
E-mail .... lowk@ldschurch.org
2202 N Main St Ste 301, Cedar City, UT 84721-9791
Ken Low, Director

Lds Family Svcs 801.621.6510
Fax 801.621.7024
Web .... www.ldsfamilyservices.org
1525 Lincoln Ave Ste 2, Ogden, UT 84404-5647
Hope Manuel, Adoption Secretary

Lds Family Svcs 801.240.6500
Fax 801.240.5508
Web .... www.ldsfamilyservices.org
E-mail .... albrechtd@ldschurch.org
132 S State St Ste 100, Salt Lake City,
UT 84111-1506
David Albrecht, Director

Lds Family Svcs 435.673.6446
Fax 435.652.8020
Web .... www.ldsfamilyservices.org
E-mail .... lowek@ldschurch.org
2480 Red Cliffs Dr, Saint George, UT 84790-5457
Ken Lowe, Director

Lds Family Svcs 801.216.8000
Fax 801.216.8001
Web .... www.ldsfamilyservices.org
E-mail .... miners@ldschurch.org
433 S 500 E, American Fork, UT 84003-2527
Stephanie Miner, Director

Lds Family Svcs 801.969.4181
Fax 801.969.1291
Web .... www.ldsfamilyservices.org
E-mail .... fam-ut-westvalley@ldschurch.org
5698 W Glen Eagle Dr, West Valley, UT 84128
Jackie Webb, Director

Split Mountain Youth Ctr 435.789.2045
Fax 435.789.2245
Web .... www.uintah.net
830 E Main St, Vernal, UT 84078-2708
Lynn Whitman, Apd

CRISIS & SHELTER CARE

Alpine Academy/Ut. Youthvillage 800.244.1113
Fax 801.272.9976
Web .... www.alpineacademy.org
E-mail .... jmulitall@youthvillage.org
1280 Whistering Horse Dr, Erda, UT 84074
Janet Mulitall, Executive Director

Canyon Creek Women's Crisis Ctr 435.867.9411
Fax 435.867.9412
Web .... www.accesswest.com
PO Box 2081, Cedar City, UT 84721-2081
Cindy Baldwin, Director

Cedar Ridge Academy 435.353.4498
Fax 435.353.4898
Web .... www.cedarridge.net
E-mail .... admissions@cedarridge.net
4340 W 5625 N, Roosevelt, UT 84066
Sean Haggerty, Admissions Director

Community Abuse Prevention Svcs 435.753.2500
Fax 435.753.7054
E-mail .... jill@capsa.org
308 W 1000 N, Logan, UT 84323-3617
Jill Anderson, Director

Domestic Violence Shelter 435.843.1645
Fax 435.843.0151
305 N Main St Ste 239, Tooele, UT 84074
Janet Larsen, Director

Dove Ctr 435.628.1204
Fax 435.628.0823
E-mail .... Dove@Infowest.Com
1240 E 100 S Bldg#22, Ste 221, Saint George,
UT 84790
Katy Peterson, Director

Gateway Academy 801.463.7888
Fax 801.463.7030
Web .... www.gatewayacademy.net
E-mail .... juliebrown@gatewayacademy.net
2487 S 700 E, Salt Lake City, UT 84106-1722
Julie Brown, Executive Director

**Gentle Ironhawk Shelter- Domestic
Violence** 435.678.2445
Fax 435.678.3827
Web .... www.gentleironhawkshelter.com
E-mail .... gentleironhawkshelter@frontiernet.net
122 West 700 South, Blanding, UT 84511
Kristine Paul, Director

Life Line, Inc. 801.936.4000
Fax 801.936.8975
Web .... www.lifelineutah.com
1130 W Center St, North Salt Lake, UT 84051
Shane Peterson, Executive Director

Logan River Academy 435.755.8400
Fax 435.755.8540
Web .... www.loganriver.com
E-mail .... info@loganriver.com
1683 S Hwy 91, LOGAN, UT 84321
Larry Carter, Executive Director

New Horizons Crisis Ctr 435.896.9294
Fax 435.896.4655
Web .... www.airzip.net
145 E 100 N, Richfield, UT 84701-2615
Caron Withers, Director

Odyssey House 801.363.0203
Fax 801.359.3455
Web .... www.odysseyhouse.org
607 E 200 S, Salt Lake City, UT 84102
Christina Nielson, Director

Peace House Domestic Violence Shelter 435.647.9161
Fax 435.655.8341
Web .... www.peacehouse.org
E-mail .... colleen@peacehouse.org
1912 Sidewinder Ave 207, Park City, UT 84060
Colleen Grover, Director

Pine Creek Ranch 435.865.6849
Fax 435.586.7094
Web .... www.pinecreekranch.org
11470 E 16000 N Pinecreek Rd, Mount Pleasant,
UT 84647
Barbara Davis, Contact

South Valley Sanctuary 801.255.1095
Fax 801.255.7319
Web .... www.southvalleysanctuary.com
E-mail .... info@southvalleysanctuary.com
1853 W 7705 S, West Jordan, UT 84084
Carla Arroyo, Director

Telos Residential Treatment 801.434.8356
Fax 801.426.8825
Web .... www.telosrtc.com
E-mail .... admissions@telosrtc.com
870 W Center St, Orem, UT 84057-5202
Craig Lamont,ms,lmft, Executive Director

Turnabout/Stillwater Academy 801.484.9911
Fax 801.302.7954
Web .... www.turnabotteens.org
E-mail .... info@turnabotteens.org
11175 S Redwood Rd, South Jordan, UT 84095
Lee Caldwell, Executive Director

© 2011 Dorland Health

EDUCATION

Ability First **801.373.5044**
Fax...801.373.5094
Web...www.cucil.org
E-mail..............................sandra@cucil.org
491 N Freedom Blvd, Provo, UT 84601-2824
Sandra M. Curcio, Executive Director

Family Support Ctr **801.255.6881**
Fax...801.562.9347
Web..............................www.familysupportcenter.org
E-mail........bonnie.peters@familysupportcenter.org
777 W Center St, Midvale, UT 84047-7148
Bonnie Peters, Executive Director

Hightop Ranch School **435.638.7411**
Fax...435.638.7511
1000 S Main St, Koosharem, UT 84744-0029
Justin Sorenson, Director

Oakley School **435.783.5001**
Fax...435.783.5010
Web...................................www.oakley-school.com
E-mail..........................jmeyer@oakley-school.com
251 W Weber Canyon Rd, Oakely, UT 84055
James Meyer, Ma, Head of School/ Executive Director

Prevent Child Abuse Utah **801.393.3366**
Fax...801.805.0109
Web.............................www.preventchildabuseutah.org
E-mail..................mfloor@preventchildabuse.org
2955 Harrison Blvd Ste 104, Ogden, UT 84403
Anne Freimuth, Executive Director

Reid Learning Ctr **801.466.4214**
Fax...801.466.4214
Web.......................................www.reidschool.com
E-mail............................ereid@xmission.com
2965 Evergreen Ave, Salt Lake City, UT 84109-3161
Ethna Reid, Phd, Director

**Specialized Educational Programming
Svcs** **801.467.2122**
Fax...801.467.2148
Web...www.sepslc.com
E-mail.......................ava.eva.seps@sepslc.com
604 E Wirmington Ave, Salt Lake City,
UT 84106-2828
Ava Jane Pickering, Administrative Director

FOSTER CARE AGENCIES

A Act of Love **801.572.1696**
Fax...801.572.9303
9561 S 700 E Ste 101, Sandy, UT 84070
Kathy Kunkel, Director

A Childs Dream **360.598.6533**
E-mail.........................amadoptions@comcast.net
12111 S 4130 W, Herriman, UT 98370
Kristy Hoffman, Supervisor

All for Love Adoptions Inc **801.525.2099**
Fax...801.773.3638
E-mail...................info@allforloveadoptions.com
2916 South 2000 West, Syracuse, UT 84075

Around the World Adoptions **801.371.0968**
756 West 1150 South, Provo, UT 84601

Catholic Community Services Parent Supp **801.977.9119**
745 East 300 South St, Salt Lake City, UT 84102
Bradford Drake, Executive Director

Heart to Heart Adoptions Inc **801.563.1000**
Fax...801.563.9899
E-mail.....................bwathearttoheart@aol.com
9669 S 700 E, Sandy, UT 84070

Noahs Ark Adoptions **801.782.5344**
E-mail............................rgraser@earthlink.net
399 East 3575 North, North Ogden, UT 84414

Utah Foster Care Foundation **801.994.5205**
5296 S Commerce Dr # 400, Murray, UT 84107
Kelly Peterson, CEO

HOME MEDICAL EQUIPMENT PROVIDERS

Bulloch Drug **435.586.9651**
Fax...435.586.3473
91 North Main Street, Cedar City, UT 84720
CARF accredited programs available.

Township Professional Pharmacy **435.867.0800**
Fax...435.867.0825
108 West 1325 North, Cedar City, UT 84720
CARF accredited programs available.

SOCIAL SERVICES

**Child Care Resource And Referral Eastern
Region** **435.613.5619**
Fax...435.613.5815
Web...............www.ceu.edu/ccr%26r/default.html
E-mail..........................amackiewicz@ceu.edu
451 E 400 N, Price, UT 84501-2626

Child Care Resource And Referral Metro **801.355.4847**
Fax...801.355.7453
Web...........................www.cssutah.org/childcare
E-mail..........................encarni@cssutah.org
124 S 400 E Ste 400, Salt Lake City, UT 84111
Encarni Gallardo, Director

**Child Care Resource And Referral Northern
Region** **801.626.7837**
Fax...801.626.7668
Web...........................programs.weber.edu/ccrr
1309 University Cir, Ogden, UT 84408
Leslie Trottier, Director

**Child Care Resource And Referral Western
Region** **435.628.4843**
Fax...435.865.6902
Web.....................................www.childcarehelp.org
E-mail.........................lis@childcarehelp.org
88 E Fiddlers Canyon Rd Ste H, Cedar City, UT 84720
Lis Barker, Administrator

**Child Care Resource And Referral,
Bridgeland** **435.797.1552**
Fax...435.797.8047
Web.........................www.usuchild.usus.edu
E-mail..........................childcare@cc.usu.edu
6510 Old Main Hl, Logan, UT 84322-0001
Carrie Stott, Co-Director

Children's Svc Society **801.355.7444**
Fax...801.355.7453
Web...www.cssutah.org
E-mail............................chris@cssutah.org
124 S 400 E Ste 400, Salt Lake City, UT 84111-2133
Chris Bray, Executive Director

Family Connection Ctr **801.773.0712**
Fax...801.774.8267
Web...........................www.familyconnection4u.org
E-mail..........................valeriel@fccdavis.org
1360 E 1450 S, Clearfield, UT 84015-1611
Valerie Larkin, Office Manager

Jewish Family Service **801.746.4334**
Fax...801.746.4337
E-mail.............................ellen@jfsutah.org
1111 E Brickyard Rd Ste 109, Salt Lake City,
UT 84106
Ellen Silver, Director

Redcliff Ascent **801.491.2278**
Fax...801.491.2279
Web...................................www.redcliffascent.com
E-mail.........................steve@redcliffascent.com
757 S Main St, Springville, UT 84663-2452
Steve Nadauld, Director Of Admissions

Teens In Crisis **435.635.7333**
Fax...435.635.9203
E-mail..........................jake@2helpteens.com
171 S Main St, Hurricane, UT 84737-1953
Lezlee Shaw, Administrator

SPECIAL NEEDS

A Zen sational Gift **801.695.3635**
E-mail.........................brenwelch1@yahoo.com
4943 S 1025 E, Ogden, UT 84403

Access Utah Network **800.333.8824**
E-mail...............................accessut@utah.gov
155 S 300 W Ste 100, Salt Lake City, UT 84101

Allies with Families **801.433.2595**
E-mail.....................allies@allieswithfamilies.org
505 E 200 S # 25, Salt Lake City, UT 84102
Lori Cerar, Executive Director

Alpine Academy/Utah Youth Village **800.244.1113**
Fax...435.843.5416
Web...................................www.alpineacademy.org
1280 Whispering Horse Dr, Erda, UT 84074
Janet Mulitalo, Program Director

Art Access/VSA Arts of Utah **801.328.0703**
E-mail.............................ruth@accessart.org
230 S 500 W # 125, Salt Lake City, UT 84101

At the Crossroads **435.627.1788**
Fax...435.251.8067
E-mail.........................bryan@guidingyouth.com
1173 S 250 w, Washington, UT 84770
Bryan Dirgin, Director

Brain Injury Association **801.484.2240**
E-mail.................................biau@sisna.com
1800 SW Temple Ste 203, Salt Lake City, UT 84115
Ron Roscos, Director

Cerebral Palsy of Utah **801.266.1805**
E-mail.............................shelly@ffiutah.org
3550 S 700 W, West Valley City, UT 84119

Congress of Parents & Teachers **801.261.3100**
E-mail...............................kids@utahpta.org
5192 S Greenpine Dr, Salt Lake City, UT 84123
Gainell Rogers, President

Epilepsy Association of Utah **801.566.5949**
E-mail...............................info@epilepsyut.org
1995 W 9000 S, Level B, West Jordan, UT 84088

Family Voices of Utah **801.584.8236**
E-mail.....................utahfamilyvoices@juno.com
PO Box 144650, Salt Lake City, UT 84114

**Gentiva Rehab Without Walls/Salt Lake
City** **801.264.0213**
Fax...801.264.0219
Web...www.gentiva.com
488 East 6400 South, Suite 150, Salt Lake City,
UT 84107
CARF accredited programs available.

Intermountain Healthcare **801.285.4537**
Fax...801.285.4540
E-mail.....................clint.d.gibson@imail.org
3723 West 12600 South, Suite 450, Riverton,
UT 84065
Clint Gibson, Rn, Bsn, Ccm, Pediatric Continuum Case Manager

**Intermountain Medical Center, Neuro Specialty Rehabilitation
Unit** **801.507.1299**
Fax...801.507.1285
Web...www.ihc.com
5121 South Cottonwood Street, Murray,
UT 84157-7000
CARF accredited programs available.

MDA/ALS Ctr/Univ of Utah School of Med **801.585.7575**
Fax...801.585.2054
E-mail.................markbromberg@hsc.utah.edu
175 N Medical Dr E, Salt Lake City, UT 84132
Mark B Bromberg Md, Phd Director

Utah

Mental Health Association **801.596.3705**
E-mail...mhaut@xmission.com
  1800 SW Temple Ste 501, Salt Lake City, UT 84115

Mountain Homes Youth Ranch **866.781.2450**
Fax...435.781.2442
E-mail..admissions@mhyr.com
  247 S Vernal Ave, Vernal, UT 84078

NAMI Utah **801.323.9900**
E-mail......................................sherriwittwer@msn.com
  450 S 900 E, Salt Lake City, UT 84102
  Sherri Wittwer, Director

National Multiple Sclerosis Society **801.424.0113**
Fax...801.424.0122
E-mail.......................................utah.idaho@nmss.org
  6364 S Highland Dr Ste 101, Salt Lake City,
  UT 84121
  Annette Royle, President

Prader-Willi Syndrome Association **801.582.0998**
  2652 E Nottingham Way, Salt Lake City, UT 84108

ScenicView Academy **801.226.2550**
Fax...801.226.2550
Web..www.svacademy.org
  5455 N 250 River Run Dr, Provo, UT 84604
  Douglas Gale

Speech-Language-Hearing Association **801.402.5462**
E-mail..syspriet@ihc.com
  1379 31st St, Ogden, UT 84403

The Arc of Utah **801.364.5060**
E-mail.....................................execdirector@arcutah.org
  155 S 300 W Ste 201, Salt Lake City, UT 84101

Turn Community Services **801.486.3778**
E-mail..turn@turn.nu
  638 E Wilmington Ave, Salt Lake City, UT 84106

**University of Utah Health Care - Rehabilitation
Center** **801.585.2800**
Fax...801.585.3798
  50 North Medical Drive, 1R69 SOM, Salt Lake City,
  UT 84132
  CARF accredited programs available.

Utah Parent Center **801.272.1051**
Fax...801.272.8907
E-mail...........................upcinfo@utahparentcenter.org
  230 W 200 S Ste 1101, Saltlake City, UT 84101
  Helen Post, Executive Director

Utah Valley Rehabilitation Center **801.357.7765**
Fax...801.357.7725
Web............................www.intermountainhealthcare.org
  1034 North 500 West, Provo, UT 84604
  CARF accredited programs available.

White River Academy **866.679.8336**
Fax...435.864.3020
E-mail........................justin@whiteriveracademy.com
  275 W 100 S, Delta, UT 84624

Work Ability Utah **801.887.9500**
E-mail...cruddell@utah.gov
  1595 W 500 S, Salt Lake City, UT 84104
  Carrol Rudell, Executive Director

Utah

Vermont

Hon. Peter Shumlin, Governor
109 State Street, Pavilion
Montpelier, VT 05609-0101
802.828.3333
802.828.3339 (Fax)
www.vermont.gov/governor

Theresa Lay-Sleeper, Juvenile Justice Specialist
103 S. Main St.
Waterbury, VT 05671-2401
802.241.2953
802.241.1219 (Fax)
theresa.lay-sleeper@state.vt.us

Kreig Pinkham, SAG Chair
PO Box 627
Montpelier, VT 05601
802.229.9151
kreigpinkham@comcast.net

CRISIS NUMBERS

Child Abuse Reporting . . .800.649.5285

STATE SERVICES

SOCIAL SERVICES

Child Development Division Vermont 802.241.3110
Fax 802.241.1220
103 S Main St 3N, Waterbury, VT 05671
Reeva Murphy, Deputy Commissioner

Family Services Division 802.241.2131
Fax 802.241.2407
Web . . . . .http://www.dcf.state.vt.us
103 S Main St, Osgood 3, Waterbury, VT 05671-9800

GENERAL HEALTH SERVICES

Child w Special Health Needs VT 802.863.7338
Fax 802.863.7635
E-mail . . . . .kbean@vdh.state.vt.us
108 Cherry St, PO Box 70, Burlington, VT 05402
K Bean, Director

Maternal and Child Health VT 802.658.4179
Fax 802.863.7229
E-mail . . . . .skersch@vdh.state.vt.us
108 Cherry St, PO Box 70, Burlington, VT 05402
S Kersch, Director

MENTAL HEALTH SERVICES

**ADAP Div of Alcohol and Drug Abuse
Progams** 802.651.1550
Fax 802.651.1573
Web . . . . .www.healthvermont.gov
E-mail . . . . .barbara.cimaglio@ahs.state.vt.us
108 Cherry St Ste 207, Burlington, VT 05401-3875
Barbara Cimaglio, Deputy Commissioner

Div for the Blind & Vis Impaired VT 802.241.2210
Fax 802.241.2128
E-mail . . . . .fred.jones@ahs.state.vt.us
103 S Main St, Weeks IC Rm 109, Waterbury, VT 05671
Fred Jones, Director

VocRehab Vermont 802.241.2186
Fax 802.241.3359
E-mail . . . . .diane.dalmasse@ahs.state.vt.us
103 S Main St, Weeks Bldg, Wing 1A, Waterbury, VT 05671-2303
Diane Dalmasse, Director

JUSTICE AGENCY

Attorney General's Ofc 802.828.3171
Fax 802.828.2154
Web . . . . .www.atg.state.vt.us
E-mail . . . . .atginfo@atg.state.vt.us
109 State St, Montpelier, VT 05609-1001
Renay Putney, Administrator

Correctional Education Division VT 802.241.2273
Fax 802.241.1930
E-mail . . . . .wilhelmina.picard@ahs.state.vt.us
103 S Main St, Waterbury, VT 05671
Wilhelmina Picard, Director

Vermont Ctr for Crime Victim Svcs 802.241.1250
Fax 802.241.4337
E-mail . . . . .info@ccvs.state.vt.us
58 S Main St Ste 1, Waterbury, VT 05676
Judith Rex, Executive Director

POLICE AND SHERIFF

Vermont Assoc of Chiefs of Police 802.442.1030
Fax 802.442.1067
118 S St, Bennington, VT 05201
Paul Doucette, Chief Police

Vermont Crime Info Ctr .802.244.8727
Fax 802.241.5552
Web . . . . .www.dps.state.vt.us
103 S Main St, Waterbury, VT 05671-9800
James Baker, Manager

EDUCATION SERVICES

Dept of Education 802.828.3135
Fax 802.828.3140
Web . . . . .www.education.vermont.gov
E-mail . . . . .doe-info@state.vt.us
120 State St, Montpelier, VT 05620-2501
Gail Taylor, Standards & Assessment Director

Educ for Homeless Children and Youth VT 802.828.5148
Fax 802.828.0573
E-mail . . . . .wendy.ross@state.vt.us
120 State St, Montpelier, VT 05620
Wendy Ross, Director

Vermont Dept of Education 802.828.3135
Fax 802.828.3140
E-mail .maureengaidys@state.vt.us
120 State St, Montpelier, VT 05620
Maureen Gaidys, Commissioners Assistant

Vermont Family Network 802.876.5315
Fax 802.876.6291
E-mail . . . . .stacie.jones@vtfn.org
600 Blair Park Rd Ste 240, Williston, VT 05495
Stacie Jones, Director

Vermont Student Support Svcs Team 802.828.1622
Fax 802.828.0573
E-mail . . . . .karin.edwards@state.vt.us
120 State St, Montpelier, VT 05620
Karin Edwards, Director

LABOR & WORKFORCE EDUCATION

Dept of Labour 802.828.4000
Fax 802.828.4181
5 Green Mountain Dr, Montpelier, VT 05601
Valerei Rickert, Commissioner

COUNTY SERVICES

Addison County

COURTS

**Court Diversion And Community Justice
Projects** 802.388.3888
Fax 802.388.5754
E-mail .karen@courtdiversion.com
282 Boardman St, Middlebury, VT 05753-0881
Karen Taylor, Case Manager

Family Court 802.388.4605
Fax 802.388.4643
Web . . . . .www.state.vt.us
7 Mahady Ct Ste 3, Middlebury, VT 05753-4468
Jo Lamarche, Court Manager

Probate Court 802.388.2612
Fax 802.388.4621
Web . . . . .www.vermontjudiciary.org
7 Mahady Ct, Middlebury, VT 05753
Honorable Eleanor W. Smith, Judge

POLICE AND SHERIFF

Sheriff's Ofc 802.388.2981
Fax 802.388.2249
E-mail . . . . .jcoons@dps.state.vt.us
35 Court St, Middlebury, VT 05753-1454
James B. Coons, Sheriff

Bennington County

JUSTICE AGENCY

Ctr For Restorative Justice **802.447.1595**
Fax 802.447.6944
E-mail ....bccdp@sover.net
439 Main St Ste 2, Bennington, VT 05201
Leitha Cipriano, Director

COURTS

Bennington Probate Court **802.447.2705**
Fax 802.447.2703
Web ....www.vermontjudiciary.org
207 South St, Bennington, VT 05201
Nicole Conety, Manager

Family Court **802.447.2729**
Fax 802.447.2750
150 Veterans Memorial Dr Ste 4, Bennington,
VT 05201-1950
David Howard, Judge

POLICE AND SHERIFF

Sheriff's Ofc **802.442.4900**
Fax 802.442.7282
212 Lincoln St, Bennington, VT 05201
Chad Schmidt, Sheriff

Caledonia County

SOCIAL SERVICES

**Dept Of Prevention, Assistance, Transition & Health Access
(Path)** **802.748.5193**
Fax 802.751.3272
Web ....www.path.state.vt.us
E-mail ....lenah@path.state.vt.us
67 Eastern Ave Ste 7, Saint Johnsbury,
VT 05819-5603
Lena Hemmingway, Director

Family Svcs **802.748.8374**
Fax 802.751.3203
Web ....www.srs.state.vt.us
67 Eastern Ave Ste 4, Saint Johnsbury,
VT 05819-5603
Ruth Houtte, Director

COURTS

Family Court **802.748.6600**
Fax 802.748.6603
E-mail ....william.kennedy@state.vt.us
1126 Main St Ste 1, Saint Johnsbury, VT 05819-2764
Honorable William Kennedy, Judge

Probate Court **802.748.6605**
Fax 802.748.6603
1126 Main St, St Johnsbury, VT 05819
Honorable Ernest T. Balivet, Director

POLICE AND SHERIFF

Sheriff's Dept **802.748.6666**
Fax 802.748.1684
Web ....www.dps.state.vt.us
E-mail ....mbergero@dps.state.vt.us
1126 Main St Ste 2, Saint Johnsbury, VT 05819-2765
Michael H. Bergeron, Sheriff

Chittenden County

COURTS

Court Diversion Programs **802.864.1585**
Fax 802.864.2642
Web ....www.chit-courtdiversion.org
184 King St, Burlington, VT 05401-4534
Andy Twite, Executive Director

Criminal Court **802.651.1950**
Web ....www.vermontjudiciary.org
32 Cherry St Ste 300, Burlington, VT 05401-7305
Honorable Linda Labett, Judge

Family Court **802.651.1709**
E-mail ....thomas.crowley@state.vt.us
32 Cherry St Ste 200, Burlington, VT 05401-7305
Honorable Thomas Crowley, Director

Probate Court **802.651.1518**
Web ....www.vermontjudiciary.org
E-mail ....sfowler@vermontjudiciary.org
175 Main St, Burlington, VT 05402
Honorable Susan Fowler, Judge

Superior Court **802.863.3467**
175 Main St, Burlington, VT 05401
Carmen Cote, Operations Manager

POLICE AND SHERIFF

Police Dept **802.658.2704**
Fax 802.865.7579
Web ....www.bpdvt.org
1 North Ave, Burlington, VT 05401-5220
Michael Schirling, Chief

Sheriff's Ofc **802.863.4341**
Fax 802.863.7445
70 Ethan Allen Dr, South Burlington, VT 05402
Kevin M. Mclaughlin, Sheriff

EDUCATION SERVICES

Special Education **802.893.3220**
Fax 802.893.3213
E-mail ....tdunn@mtsd-vt.org
42 Herrick Ave, Milton, VT 05468-3037
Timothy Dunn, Administrator Of Student Services

Special Education **802.264.5999**
Fax 802.863.4774
Web ....www.csdvt.org
E-mail ....lutzc@csdvt.org
125 Laker Ln, Colchester, VT 05446
Carrie Lutz, Director

Special Education **802.655.9575**
Fax 802.861.4999
Web www.winooski.k12.vt.us
E-mail ....mmartineau@winooski.k12.vt.us
70 Normand St, Winooski, VT 05404
Mary Martineau, Administrator

Special Education **802.879.5579**
Fax 802.878.1370
Web ....www.ccsuvt.org
E-mail ....emaguire@ejhs.k12.vt.us
51 Park St, Essex Junction, VT 05452-2899
Erin Maguire, Executive Director Of Student Support Services

Special Education **802.434.2128**
Fax 802.434.2196
Web www.cesu.k12.vt.us
E-mail ....beverley.white@cesu.k12.vt.us
211 Bridge St, Richmond, VT 05477
Beverley White, Special Services Coordinator

Essex County

COURTS

Family Court **802.676.3910**
Fax 802.676.3463
Web ....www.vermontjudiciary.org
75 Courthouse Dr, Guildhall, VT 05905-0075
Judge Barbara Zander, Director

Probate Court **802.723.4770**
Fax 802.723.4770
Web ....www.dc.state.fl.us
E-mail ....ahodgdon@mail.crt.state.vt.us
49 Mill St Ext, Island Pond, VT 05846
Honorable Allen Hodgdon, Judge

Franklin County

COURTS

Family And District Court **802.524.7997**
Fax 802.524.7946
36 Lake St, Saint Albans, VT 05478-2272
Barbara Hungerford, Operations Manager

Probate Court **802.524.7948**
Web ....www.vermontjudiciary.gov
E-mail ....lbruce@mail.crt.state.vt.us
17 Church St, Saint Albans, VT 05478-1675
Honorable Laurence H. Bruce Jr., Director

POLICE AND SHERIFF

Sheriff's Ofc **802.524.2121**
Fax 802.524.7947
E-mail ....rnorris@dps.state.vt.us
30 Lake St, St Albans, VT 05478
Robert W. Norris, Sheriff

EDUCATION SERVICES

**Champlain Valley Head
Start-Highgate** **802.868.4259**
Fax 802.868.4572
219 Gore Road, Highgate Center, VT 05459
Betsy Bennett, Director

Grand Isle County

COURTS

Probate Court **802.372.8350**
Fax 802.372.3221
3677 Route 2, North Hero, VT 05474
Gaye Paquette, Court Clerk

POLICE AND SHERIFF

Sheriff's Dept **802.372.4482**
Fax 802.372.5771
3677 US Route 2, North Hero, VT 05474
Connie Allen, Sheriff

Lamoille County

SOCIAL SERVICES

Family Svcs **802.888.4576**
Fax 802.888.1343
Web ....www.srs.state.vt.us
63 Professional Dr, Morrisville, VT 05661
Barbara Constantino, District Director

COURTS

Court Diversion **802.888.5871**
Fax 802.888.5400
Web ....www.lamoillecourtdiversion.org
E-mail ....info@lamoillecourtdiversion.org
221 Main St, Hyde Park, VT 05655
Heather Hobart, Co-Director

Family And District Court **802.888.3887**
Fax 802.888.2591
Web ....www.vermontjudiciary.org
154 Main St, Hyde Park, VT 05655-0489
Honorable Dennis Pearson, Providing Judge

Probate Court **802.888.3306**
E-mail ....jmahoney@mail.crt.state.vt.us
154 E Main St, Hyde Park, VT 05655
Honorable James R. Dean Mahoney, Judge

POLICE AND SHERIFF

Sheriff's Ofc **802.888.3502**
Fax 802.888.2562
162 Commonwealth Ave, Hyde Park, VT 05655
Roger M. Marcoux Jr., Sheriff

Orange County

COURTS

Family And District Court **802.685.4610**
Fax 802.685.3246
  5 Court St, Chelsea, VT 05038-9012
Theresa Scott, Superior Court Clerk

POLICE AND SHERIFF

Sheriff's Ofc **802.685.4875**
Fax 802.685.3204
E-mail ....wbohnyak@dps.state.vt.us
  11 VT Rte 113, Chelsea, VT 05038
Bill Bohnyak, Sheriff

Orleans County

SOCIAL SERVICES

Family Svcs **802.334.6723**
Fax 802.334.3371
Web ....www.dcs.state.vt.us
E-mail ....suzanne.griesel@ahs.state.vt.us
  100 Main St Ste 230, Newport, VT 05855-4898
Suzanne Griesel, District Director

JUSTICE AGENCY

Youth Svcs/Court Diversion
Programs **802.334.7316**
Fax 802.334.8406
Web ....www.nekcavt.org
E-mail ....srbowen@nekcavt.org
  70 Main St, Newport, VT 05855-5110
Stephanie Bowen, Director Of Diversion

COURTS

District Court **802.334.3325**
Fax 802.334.2248
  217 Main St, Newport, VT 05855-4852
Honorable Robert Bent, Primary Judge

Probation Court **802.334.3366**
Fax 802.334.3385
Web ....www.vermontjudiciary.org
E-mail ....jmonette@state.vt.us
  247 Main St Ste 2, Newport, VT 05855-5565
Honorable John P. Monette, Probate Judge

Superior Court- Family & Civil
Divison **802.334.3305**
  247 Main St Ste 1, Newport, VT 05855
Honorable Robert Bent, Judge

POLICE AND SHERIFF

Sheriff's Dept **802.334.3333**
Fax 802.334.3307
E-mail ....kmartin@dps.state.vt.us
  255 Main St, Newport, VT 05855-2095
Kirt Martin, Sheriff

Rutland County

SOCIAL SERVICES

Family Svcs **802.786.5817**
Fax 802.786.8827
Web ....www.srs.state.vt.us
  88 Merchants Row, Rutland, VT 05701
John Zalenski, District Director

COURTS

Court Diversion **802.775.2479**
Fax 802.786.8890
Web ....www.rutlandcountycourtdiversion.org
  50 E Center St, Rutland, VT 05701
Rick Bjorn, Director

Fair Haven Probate Court **802.775.0114**
Web ....www.crt.state.vt.us
E-mail ....fhprobate@mail.crt.state.vt.us
  83 Central St, Rutland, VT 05701-1070
N Sheri Brown, Register

Family Court **802.786.5856**
Fax 802.786.5871
  9 Merchants Row, Rutland, VT 05701
Shelley Gartner, Magistrate

Probate Court **802.775.0114**
Fax 802.773.9682
Web ....www.dc.state.fl.us
E-mail ....kcandon@mail.crt.state.vt.us
  83 Center St, Rutland, VT 05701-4017
Honorable Kevin Candon, Director

POLICE AND SHERIFF

Sheriff's Ofc **802.775.8002**
Fax 802.775.1794
  108 Wales St, Rutland, VT 05701
Stephen Benard, Sheriff

EDUCATION SERVICES

Special Education **802.773.1917**
Fax 802.773.1927
  6 Church St, Rutland, VT 05701
Ellie Mcgarry, Director

Special Education **802.247.5757**
Fax 802.247.5548
Web ....www.rnesu.org
  49 Court Dr, Brandon, VT 05733
Marsha Bruce, Elementary And Pre-school Special Services Director

Special Education **802.287.5286**
Fax 802.287.2284
Web ....www.rswsu.org
E-mail ....bonnie.lenihan@rswsu.org
  168 York St, Poultney, VT 05764-1024
Bonnie Leniham, Director

Special Education **802.775.4342**
Fax 802.775.7319
Web ....www.rcsu.org
E-mail ....pam.reed@rcsu.org
  257 S Main St Ste 1, Rutland, VT 05701-4901
Pam Reed, Administrator

Special Education **802.775.3264**
Fax 802.775.8063
Web ....www.rssu.org
E-mail ....cgeery@rssu.org
  64 Grange Hall Rd, North Clarendon, VT 05759
Carol Geery, Director

Washington County

SOCIAL SERVICES

Agency Of Human Svcs **802.241.2220**
Fax 802.241.2979
Web ....www.ahs.state.vt.us
  103 S Main St, Waterbury, VT 05671
Peter Schmlin, Director

Family Svcs **802.479.4260**
Fax 802.476.1660
Web ....www.ahs.state.vt.us
  255 N Main St Ste 7, Barre, VT 05641-4145
Catherine Harris, Director

GENERAL HEALTH SERVICES

Dept For Children And Families/Economic Svcs
Div **802.241.2852**
Fax 802.241.2830
Web ....www.path.state.vt.us
E-mail ....steve.dale@ahs.state.vt.us
  103 S Main St, Waterbury, VT 05671-9800
Stephen Dale, Commissioner

Vermont Dept Of Health Barre District
Ofc **802.479.4200**
Fax 802.479.4230
Web ....www.healthyvermont.gov
E-mail ....jhunsber@vdh.state.vt.us
  5 Perry St Ste 250, Barre, VT 05641-4272
Jeff Hunsberger, District Director

JUSTICE AGENCY

Court Diversion Programs **802.828.0600**
Fax 802.828.0385
Web ....www.wcdiversion.org
E-mail ....wcdp@comcast.net
  73 Main St Ste 400, Montpelier, VT 05601-1026
Dennis Menard, Director

COURTS

Prevent Child Abuse Vermont **802.229.5724**
Fax 802.223.5567
Web ....www.pcavt.org
E-mail ....pcavt@pcavt.org
  94 Main St, Montpelier, VT 05601
Linda Johnson, Pca-vermont Executive Director

Probate Court **802.828.3405**
Web ....www.dc.state.fl.us
E-mail ....gbelcher@mail.crt.state.vt.us
  10 Elm St # 2, Montpelier, VT 05602-2831
Honorable George Belcher, Director

Washington Family Division **802.479.4205**
  255 N Main St Ste 3, Barre, VT 05641
Paula Trambley, Operations Manager

POLICE AND SHERIFF

Sheriff's Ofc **802.223.3001**
Fax 802.828.3611
  10 Elm St, Montpelier, VT 05601
W. Sam Hill, Sheriff

EDUCATION SERVICES

Special Education **802.223.6341**
Fax 802.223.9795
Web ....www.mpsvt.org
E-mail ....jessica@mpsvt.org
  5 High School Dr, Montpelier, VT 05602-3508
Jessica Little, Director

Special Education **802.476.6702**
Fax 802.479.5723
Web www.u61.net
E-mail ....lgossbte@u61.net
  70 Webersville Rd, Barre, VT 05641-9029
Laurie Gossens, Administrator

Windham County

COURTS

Family Court **802.257.2830**
Fax 802.257.2869
Web ....www.vermontjudiciary.org
  30 Putney Rd Ste 1, Brattleboro, VT 05301
Dawn Sanborn, Court Clerk

Westminster Probate Court **802.463.3019**
Fax 802.463.0144
E-mail ....judith.lidie@state.vt.us
  39 The Sq, Bellows Falls, VT 05101
Judith Lidie, Register

POLICE AND SHERIFF

Sheriff's Ofc **802.365.4942**
Fax 802.365.4945
E-mail ....kclark@dps.state.vt.us
  11 Jail St, Newfane, VT 05345
Keith Clark, Sheriff

EDUCATION SERVICES

Special Education.........................802.244.5186
Fax...802.882.1128
Web.....................................www.harwood.org
E-mail........................edwood@harwood.org
   458 Vt Route 100, Moretown, VT 05660-9128
Lisa Edwood, Administrator

Windsor County

GENERAL HEALTH SERVICES

Dept Of Health............................802.295.8820
Fax...802.295.8832
Web.....................................www.vdh.state.vt.us
E-mail........................rrobins@vdh.state.vt.us
   226 Holiday Dr Ste 22, White River Junction,
   VT 05001-2024
Ronnie Robinson, HIV Coordinator

Health Care & Rehabilitation Svcs............802.886.4500
Fax...802.886.4560
Web...www.hcrs.org
E-mail..............................jhayward@hcrs.org
   390 River St, Springfield, VT 05156-2226
Judith Hayward, Director

Springfield Dept Of Health..................802.885.5778
Fax...802.885.3707
   100 Mineral St Ste 104, Springfield, VT 05156
Carol Bellucci, Hiv Coordinator

COURTS

Hartford Probate Court...................802.457.1503
   62 Pleasant St, Woodstock, VT 05091
Honorable Joanne M. Ertel, Presiding Judge

Probate Court..............................802.886.2284
Fax...802.886.2285
Web....................................www.dc.state.fl.us
   Route 106, North Springfield, VT 05150

EDUCATION SERVICES

Special Education.........................802.295.8605
Fax...802.295.8603
Web................................www.hartfordschools.net
   64 Hebard St, White River Junction, VT 05001-8018
Liz Barker, Director

Special Education.........................802.885.5141
Fax...802.885.2556
Web..........................www.springfield.k12.vt.us
E-mail............................svogel@ssdvt.org
   60 Park St, Springfield, VT 05156-3023
Sarah Vogel, Director

Special Education.........................802.674.2144
Fax...802.674.6357
Web..............................www.windsor.k12.vt.us
E-mail....................mburke@windsorschools.net
   105 Main St Ste 200, Windsor, VT 05089-1317
Madelyn Burke, Special Services Director

SPECIAL SERVICES AGENCIES

ADOPTION AGENCIES

Friends In Adoption.......................802.235.2373
Fax...802.235.2311
Web.............................www.friendsinadoption.org
E-mail...................dawn@friendsinadoption.org
   44 South St, Middletown Springs, VT 05757
Dawn Smith-pliner, Executive Director

BEHAVIORAL HEALTH TREATMENT

Balaban Medical Practice..................802.860.8089
   3240 Shelburne Rd, Shelburne, VT 05482
Robert Balaban, MD, Psychiatrist

Barney Medical Practice...................802.296.8070
   2456 Christian St, Ste 202, White River Junction,
   VT 05001-9856
Christine Barney, Psychiatrist

Barss Medical Practice....................802.951.9101
   156 Battery St, Burlington, VT 05401
M Brooke Barss, MD, Psychiatrist

Bennington School, Inc....................802.447.1557
Fax...802.442.1118
Web......................www.benningtonschoolinc.org
   192 Fairview Street, Bennington, VT 05201
CARF accredited programs available.

Betts Medical Practice....................802.862.4644
   449 S Prospect St, Burlington, VT 05401-3506
Douglas Betts, MD, Psychiatrist

Brattleboro Retreat.......................802.257.7785
Web............................www.brattlebororetreat.org
E-mail..................schaput@brattlebororetreat.org
   Anna Marsh Lane, Brattleboro, VT 05302
Ms. Sharon Chaput, Accreditation Manager
Joint Commission accredited organization.

Champlain Drug And Alcohol Svcs...........802.488.7757
Fax...802.488.6431
Web......................................www.howardcenter.org
E-mail.......................bbickr@howardcenter.org
   300 Flynn Ave, Burlington, VT 05401-5301
Robert Bick, Director

CPSG Behavioral Medicine..................802.888.8320
Fax...802.888.8136
   528 Washington Hwy, Morrisville, VT 05661
Hayley Hamilton, Director

Deppe Medical Practice....................802.654.7265
E-mail.............................leigh@together.net
   PO Box 671, Colchester, VT 05446-0671
Susan Leigh Deppe, MD, Psychiatrist

Eckerd......................................800.914.3937
Fax...727.442.5911
Web..www.eckerd.org
E-mail......................admissions@eckerd.org
   876 Root Pond Rd, Fair Haven, VT 05743-9596
David Dennis, President & CEO; Francene Hazel, Director of Admissions
Eckerd provides an outdoor therapeutic services for boys and girls ages 10 – 17
with emotional and behavioral problems. The accredited and licensed program
provides educational and behavioral treatment in a year-round outdoor setting.
Youth are referred through state contracts. In addition, Eckerd is responsible for
assuring the safety, well-being, and permanency of children and youth in the
Vermont Department of Children and Families Rutland District through prevention
and protective services, and foster care and adoption.

Emmons Medical Practice...................802.865.2863
   92 Adams St, Burlington, VT 05401-4525
Robert Emmons, MD, Psychiatrist

Health Care & Rehabilitation Services of Southeastern
VT...802.886.4500
Web...www.hcrs.org
E-mail..............................abradeen@hcrs.org
   390 River Street, Springfield, VT 05156
Ms. Alice Bradeen, Accreditation Manager
Joint Commission accredited organization.

Kurn Hattin Homes.........................802.722.3336
Fax...802.722.3174
Web..www.kurnhattin.org
E-mail.............................chrisb@sover.net
   708 Kurn Hattin Rd, Westminster, VT 05158
Christopher Barry, Director

Lund Family Ctr............................802.864.7467
Fax...802.864.1619
Web...................................www.lundfamilycenter.org
E-mail.......................info@lundfamilycenter.org
   76 Glenn Rd, Burlington, VT 05401
Barbara Rachelson, Director

Northwestern Counseling and Support Services,
Inc..802.524.6554
Fax...802.527.7801
Web.......................................www.ncssinc.org
E-mail..........................info@ncssinc.org
   107 Fisher Pond Road, Saint Albans, VT 05478
Darlene Krieger, Director
CARF accredited programs available.

Spectrum Youth And Family Svcs............802.864.7423
Fax...802.660.0576
Web......................................www.spectrumvt.org
E-mail....................mredmond@spectrumvt.org
   31 Elmwood Ave, Burlington, VT 05401-4347
Mark Redmond, Executive Director

United Counseling Service..................802.442.5491
Fax...802.442.3363
Web..www.ucsvt.org
E-mail......................rprovenza@ucsvt.org
   100 Ledge Hill Drive, Bennington, VT 05201
Ralph Provenza, Executive Director
CARF accredited programs available.

Vermont Achievement Ctr...................802.775.2395
Fax...802.773.9656
E-mail.................cbucholt@vac-rutland.com
   88 Park St, Rutland, VT 05702
Kiki Mcshane, Executive Director

Vermont Medical Society...................802.223.7898
Fax...802.223.1201
Web..www.vtmd.org
E-mail......................pharrington@vtmd.org
   134 Main St, Montpelier, VT 05602-2913
Paul Harrington, Vice President

CHILDREN'S HOSPITAL

Central Vermont Medical Center............802.371.4100
   130 Fisher Rd, Barre, VT 05602
Judy Tarr, Chief Executive Officer

Fletcher Allen Health Care.................802.847.0000
   111 Colchester Ave, Burlington, VT 05401
Melinda Estes, Chief Executive Officer

Gifford Medical Center....................802.728.7000
   44 S Main St, Randolph, VT 05060

North Country Hospital & Health Center.......802.334.7331
   189 Prouty Dr, Newport, VT 05855
Claudio Fort, Chief Executive Officer

Northeastern Vermont Regional Hospital......802.748.8141
Web..www.mvrh.orh
   1315 Hospital Dr, Saint Johnsbury, VT 05819
Veronica Hychalk, Chief Nursing Officer

Rutland Regional Medical Center 802.775.7111
160 Allen St, Rutland, VT 05701
Thomas Huebner, Chief Executive Officer

Southwestern Vermont Medical Center 802.442.6361
100 Hospital Dr E, Bennington, VT 05201

Springfield Hospital 802.885.2151
25 Ridgewood Rd, Springfield, VT 05156
Glen Gordner, Chief Executive Officer

COUNSELING SERVICES

Casey Family Svcs 802.655.6688
Fax 802.655.9444
Web ....www.caseyfamilyservices.org
E-mail ....nlescher@caseyfamilyservices.org
46 Main St Ste 1A, Winooski, VT 05404-2242
Nita Lescher, Division Director

Catholic Charities 802.658.6111
Fax 802.860.0451
E-mail ....charities@vermontcatholic.org
55 Joy Dr S, Burlington, VT 05403
Lawrence Assell, Director

Children And Youth Svcs 802.476.1480
Fax 802.479.4095
Web ....www.wcmhs.org
260 Beckley Hill Rd, Barre, VT 05641
Michael Curtis, Director

Eckerd 800.914.3937
Fax 727.442.5911
Web ....www.eckerd.org
E-mail ....admissions@eckerd.org
876 Root Pond Rd, Fair Haven, VT 05743-9596
David Dennis, President & CEO; Francene Hazel, Director of Admissions
Eckerd provides an outdoor therapeutic services for boys and girls ages 10 – 17 with emotional and behavioral problems. The accredited and licensed program provides educational and behavioral treatment in a year-round outdoor setting. Youth are referred through state contracts. In addition, Eckerd is responsible for assuring the safety, well-being, and permanency of children and youth in the Vermont Department of Children and Families Rutland District through prevention and protective services, and foster care and adoption.

CRISIS & SHELTER CARE

Aware Domestic Violence Program 802.472.6463
Fax 802.472.3504
Web ....www.vtnetwork.org
E-mail ....aware@vtlink.net
88 High St, Hardwick, VT 05843
Anna Pirie, Director

Circle 802.476.6010
Fax 802.479.9310
E-mail ....bwss@sover.net
PO Box 652, Barre, VT 05641-0652
Carol Diamond, Development Coordinator

Clarina Howard Nichols Ctr-Domestic
Violence 802.888.2584
Fax 802.888.2570
Web ....www.clarina.org
E-mail ....jralph@clarina.org
PO Box 517, Morrisville, VT 05661-0517
Jane Ralph, Director

New Beginnings Inc-Domestic Violence 802.885.2368
Fax 802.885.2363
Web ....www.vermontel.net
E-mail ....newbeg@vermontel.net
12 Valley St, Springfield, VT 05156-2521

Project Against Violent Encounters 802.442.2370
Fax 802.442.6162
E-mail ....pave@pavebennington.com
PO Box 227, Bennington, VT 05201-0227
Linda Campbell, Director

Sexual Assault Crisis Team 802.476.1388
Fax 802.476.1381
E-mail ....sactwc@aol.com
4 Cottage St, Barre, VT 05641-3707
Bobbi Gagne, Director

Spruce Mountain Inn 802.454.8353
Fax 802.454.1008
Web ....www.sprucemountaininn.com
E-mail ....info@sprucemountaininn.com
155 Towne Ave, Plainfield, VT 05667
Candace Beardsley, Licsw, Executive Director

Voices Against Violence 802.524.8538
Fax 802.524.8539
Web ....www.cvoeo.org
E-mail ....klukensr@cvoeo.org
176 N Main St, Saint Albans, VT 05478-1552
Kris Lukens-rose, Director

Women Helping Battered Women 802.658.3131
Fax 802.658.3832
E-mail ....janev@whbw.org
294 N Winooski Ave Ste 213, Burlington, VT 05401
Jane Van Buren, Director

Women Safe Inc-Domestic Violence 802.388.9180
Fax 802.388.3438
E-mail ....info@womensafe.net
PO Box 67, Middlebury, VT 05753-0067
Naomi Smith, Director

Women's Crisis Ctr 802.257.7364
Fax 802.257.1683
Web ....www.womenscc.org
E-mail ....Womenscc@myfairpoint.net
PO Box 933, Brattleboro, VT 05302-0933
Vicki Sterling, Director

EDUCATION

Greenwood School 802.387.4545
Fax 802.387.5396
Web ....www.greenwood.org
E-mail ....smiller@greenwood.org
14 Greenwood Ln, Putney, VT 05346-8965
Stewart Miller, Headmaster

King George School 800.218.5122
Fax 802.467.1041
Web ....www.kinggeorgeschool.com
2684 King George Farm Rd, Sutton, VT 05867-9626
Gerard Jones, Head Of School

Northeast Kingdom Youth Svcs 802.748.8732
Fax 802.748.2383
Web ....www.nekyputhservices.org
E-mail ....nekys@nekys.org
24 Bagley St, Saint Johnsbury, VT 05819-1652
Marion Stewart, Director

Rock Point School 802.863.1104
Fax 802.863.6628
Web ....www.rockpoint.org
E-mail ....info@rockpoint.org
1 Rock Point Rd, Burlington, VT 05408-2736
Hillary Kramer, Admissions Director

Stern Ctr For Language And Learning 802.878.2332
Fax 802.878.0230
Web ....www.sterncenter.org
E-mail ....learning@sterncenter.org
135 Allen Brook Ln, Williston, VT 05495-9209
Michelle Szabo, Program Director

The Austine School And Ctr For The Deaf And Hard Of
Hearing 802.258.9500
Fax 802.254.3921
Web ....www.vcdhh.org
E-mail ....bcarter@vcdhh.org
60 Austine Dr, Brattleboro, VT 05301-2694
Bert Carter, President

The Family Place 802.649.3268
Fax 802.649.3270
Web ....www.the-family-place.org
E-mail ....elaineg@the-family-place.org
319 Us Route 5 S, Norwich, VT 05055-9431
Elaine Guenet, Director

FOSTER CARE AGENCIES

Adoption Search Support Network 802.456.8850
771 Bayne Rd, East Calais, VT 05650

Grandparents as Parents 801.864.7467
Fax 802.861.6460
76 Glen Rd PO Box 4009, Lund Family Center, Burlington, VT 05401

Vermont Childrens Aid Society 802.655.0006
Fax 802.655.0073
E-mail ....Mainadmn@vtcas.org
79 Weaver St, Winooski, VT 05404

Wide Horizons For Children 802.453.2581
E-mail ....info@whfc.org
230 College St, Burlington, VT 0Ma5401
Maryanne Ludwig, Director Of Placement Services

PEDIATRIC HOME CARE

Bayada Nurses 802.775.7272
Fax 802.773.1519
Web ....www.bayada.com
E-mail ....GSTEWART@BAYADA.COM
2 SOUTH Main Street, Suite 2, Rutland, VT 05701
Greg Stewart, Director

Bayada Nurses 802.526.2380
Fax 802.526.2518
Web ....www.bayada.com
309 Main Street, Office 1, Norwich, VT 05055
Kristin Barnum, Director

Bayada Nurses 802.254.7071
Fax 802.254.7072
Web ....www.bayada.com
23 Marlboro Road, Suite 101, Brattleboro, VT 05301
Jason Veaudry, Director

Bayada Nurses 802.655.7111
Fax 802.861.2921
Web ....www.bayada.com
110 Kimball Avenue, Suite 250, South Burlington, VT 05403
Tracey Chellis, Director

Bayada Nurses 802.442.3222
Fax 802.442.6373
Web ....www.bayada.com
194 N St, Bennington, VT 05201
Michael Nigro, Director

SOCIAL SERVICES

Boys And Girls Club 802.229.9151
Fax 802.229.2508
E-mail ....wcysb@wcysb.org
38 Elm St, Montpelier, VT 05601
Kreig Pinkham, Director

Child Care Resource 802.863.3367
Fax 802.863.4202
Web ....http://www.childcareresource.org
E-mail ....referral@childcareresource.org
181 Commerce St, Williston, VT 05495-7150
Elizabedth Meyer, Director

Child Care Support Svcs/ Vermont Achievement

Ctr **802.747.0033**
Fax 802.773.9656
Web ....www.vacvt.org
   88 Park St, Rutland, VT 05701
   Kiki Mcshane, Director

Child Care Svcs - Mary Johnson Childrens's

Ctr **802.388.4304**
Fax 802.388.3063
Web ....www.mjccvt.org
E-mail ....barbara@mjccvt.org
   81 Water St, Middlebury, VT 05753-1494
   Barbra Saunders, Co-Director

Family Ctr **802.524.6574**
Fax 802.524.1126
E-mail ....ewest@ncssinc.org
   27 Lower Newton St, Saint Albans, VT 05478-1900
   Elizabeth West, Executive Director

Lamoille Family Ctr **802.888.5229**
Fax 802.888.5392
Web ....www.lamoillefamilycenter.org
E-mail ....lfc@pshift.com
   480 Cadys Falls Rd, Morrisville, VT 05661
   Scott Johnson, Executive Director

Nekca Parent Child Ctr **802.334.4072**
Fax 802.334.4079
   32 Central St, Newport, VT 05855
   Anne Rosser, Director

O.U.R. House Of Central Vermont, Inc. **802.476.8825**
Fax 802.479.0370
   38 Summer St, Barre, VT 05641-3749
   Kerrie Grieg, Case Manager

Parent/Child Ctr **802.388.3171**
Fax 802.388.1590
Web ....www.sover.net/thepcc
E-mail ....suehardi@sover.net
   126 Monroe St, Middlebury, VT 05753
   Susan Harding, Director

Refugee Resettlement Program **802.655.1963**
Fax 802.655.4020
E-mail ....vrrp@uscrivt.org
   462 Hegeman Ave, Ste 101, Colchester, VT 05446
   Judy Scott, Deputy Director

Safer Society Foundation, Inc. **802.247.3132**
Fax 802.247.4233
Web ....www.safersociety.org
E-mail ....info@safersociety.org
   8 Conant Sq, Brandon, VT 05733
   Brenda Burchard, Executive Director

Springfield Area Parent Child Ctr **802.886.5242**
Fax 802.886.2007
Web http://www.sapcc2.com
   6 Main St, North Springfield, VT 05150-9739
   Betty Kinsman, Director

The Family Ctr **802.262.3292**
Fax 802.828.8796
Web ....www.fewcvt.org
E-mail ....dianenf@fcwcvt.org
   32 College St Ste 100, Montpelier, VT 05602-3675
   Lee Lauber, Executive Director

Twin State Women's Network **802.254.6716**
Fax 802.254.6736
Web ....www.twinstatesnetwork.org
   79 Ashworth Rd, Guildford, VT 05301
   Joe Schneiderman, Executive Director

Umbrella, Inc. **802.748.8645**
Fax 802.748.1405
Web ....www.umbrellanek.org
E-mail ....michelle@umbrellanek.org
   1222 Main St Ste 301, St Johnsbury, VT 05819
   Michelle Fay, Director

Windham Child Care Assoc **802.254.5332**
Fax 802.251.7200
Web ....http://www.windhamchildcare.org
E-mail ....info@windhamchildcare.org
   130 Birge St, Brattleboro, VT 05301-6460

SPECIAL NEEDS

AAWARE **802.229.4665**
E-mail ....info@aaware.org
   32 Main St Ste 370, Montpelier, VT 05602
   Claudia Pringles, President

Assn for Blind & Visually Impaired **800.639.5861**
E-mail ....general@vabvi.org
   60 Kimball Ave, South Burlington, VT 05403
   Steve Pouliott, Executive Director

Autism Society of Vermont **802.457.3764**
   PO Box 978, White River Junction, VT 05001
   Lisa Lawlor, Administrator

Autism Support Daily **802.985.8773**
E-mail ....info@autismsupportdaily.com
   PO Box 4556, Burlington, VT 05406
   Laurie Mumley, Director

Center for Independent Living **802.229.0501**
E-mail ....sarah.launderville@vcil.org
   11 E State St, Montpelier, VT 05602
   Sarah Launderville, Chief Executive Officer

Central Vermont Advocacy **802.223.6149**
E-mail ....cvtarc@comcast.net
   73 Main St Ste 17, Montpelier, VT 05602

Coalition for Disability Rights **802.229.0501**
E-mail ....ereil@sover.net
   11 E State St, Montpelier, VT 05602
   Ericka Reil, Director

Congress of Parents & Teachers **802.434.4078**
E-mail ....vt_office@pta.org
   PO Box 284, Richmond, VT 05477

Down Right Special **802.773.6849**
E-mail ....llombardy@aol.com
   29 Ronaldo Ct, Rutland, VT 05701

Epilepsy Foundation of Vermont **800.565.0972**
E-mail ....epilepsy@sover.net
   PO Box 6292, Rutland, VT 05702

NAMI Vermont **800.639.6480**
E-mail ....info@namivt.org
   132 S Main St, Waterbury, VT 05676

Stern Ctr for Language & Learning **800.544.4863**
Fax 802.878.0230
E-mail ....learning@sterncenter.org
   135 Allen Brook Ln, Williston, VT 05495
   John Connell, Chief Financial Officer

Vermont Family Network **802.876.5315**
E-mail ....info@vtfn.org
   600 Blair Park Rd Ste 240, Williston, VT 05495
   Pam Mccarthy, Executive Director

Vermont I-Team **802.656.7122**
Fax 802.656.1357
   Mann Hall 3rd Fl 208 Colchester Ave, Burlington,
   VT 05405
   Louise Lynch, Secretary

VSA Arts of Vermont **802.655.7772**
E-mail ....info@vsavt.org
   20 W Canal St, Winooski, VT 05404

SUBSTANCE ABUSE TREATMENT

Eckerd **800.914.3937**
Fax 727.442.5911
Web ....www.eckerd.org
E-mail ....admissions@eckerd.org
   876 Root Pond Rd, Fair Haven, VT 05743-9596
   David Dennis, President & CEO; Francene Hazel, Director of Admissions
   Eckerd provides an outdoor therapeutic services for boys and girls ages 10 – 17 with emotional and behavioral problems. The accredited and licensed program provides educational and behavioral treatment in a year-round outdoor setting. Youth are referred through state contracts. In addition, Eckerd is responsible for assuring the safety, well-being, and permanency of children and youth in the Vermont Department of Children and Families Rutland District through prevention and protective services, and foster care and adoption.

Rutland Mental Health Services, Inc. **802.775.4340**
Fax 802.747.7692
Web ....www.rmhsccn.org/services.htm
E-mail ....dquinn@rmhsccn.org
   78 South Main Street, Rutland, VT 05701
   Dan Quinn, DS Director
   CARF accredited programs available.

Valley Vista **802.222.5201**
Fax 802.222.5901
Web ....www.vvista.net
   23 Upper Plain, Bradford, VT 05033
   Shawna Hervey, Director
   CARF accredited programs available.

Virginia

myvirginia.org

Bob McDonnell, Governor
Patrick Henry Bldg, 3rd Fl
1111 E Broad St
Richmond, VA 23219
804.786.2211
804.371.6351 (Fax)
www.governor.virginia.gov

Laurel Marks, Juvenile Justice Specialist
Dept. of Criminal Justice Services
1100 Bank St
Richmond, VA 23219
804.786.3462
804.786.3414 (Fax)
Laurel.marks@dcjs.virginia.gov

Kevin Appel, SAG Chair
5600 7th St South
Arlington, VA 22204
703.380.3501
kraesq@comcast.net

CRISIS NUMBERS

Child Abuse Reporting . . .804.786.8536

STATE SERVICES

Virginia

SOCIAL SERVICES

Division of Licensing Programs VA **804.726.7156**
Fax 804.726.7132
E-mail . . . . .lynne.williams@dss.virginia.gov
  801 E Main St, Richmond, VA 23219
  Lynne Williams, Director

Virginia Dept of Social Svcs **800.552.3431**
Alternate 804.726.7000
Fax 804.726.7088
Web . . . . .www.dss.virginia.gov
E-mail . . . . .citizen.services@dss.virginia.gov
  801 E Main St, Office of Family Violence, Richmond,
  VA 23219
  Nancy Fowler, Manager

GENERAL HEALTH SERVICES

Children with Special Health Care Needs **804.864.7706**
Fax 804.864.7704
Web . . . . .www.vahealth.org/specialchildren
  109 Governor St, 8th Floor, Richmond, VA 23219
  Nancy Bullock, Director

Ofc of Comprehensive Svcs for At-Risk Youth &
** Family** **804.662.9815**
Fax 804.662.9831
Web . . . . .www.csa.virginia.gov
  1604 Santa Rosa Rd Suite 137, Richmond, VA 23229
  Alan Saunders, Chief Operating Oofice

Virginia Dept of Health **804.864.7736**
Fax 804.864.7748
Web . . . . .www.vdh.virginia.gov
E-mail . . . . .christina.benton@vdh.virginia.gov
  109 Governor St, Richmond, VA 23219-3635
  Christina Benton, Manager

Virginia Dept Of Medical Assistance Svcs **804.786.7933**
Fax 804.371.4981
Web . . . . .www.dmas.virginia.gov
  600 E Broad St Ste 1300, Richmond, VA 23219-1856
  Dr. Greig Payne, Director

Virginia Health Dept **804.864.7001**
Fax 804.864.7022
Web . . . . .www.vdh.virginia.gov
  109 Governor St, 13th Floor, Richmond, VA 23219
  Karen Remley Md Mba, State Health Commissioner

MENTAL HEALTH SERVICES

Governor's Ofc for Substance Abuse
** Prevention** **804.786.9072**
Fax 804.371.6381
E-mail . . . . .erika.fischer@governor.virginia.gov
  1111 E Broad St, Richmond, VA 23219
  Erika Fischer, Director

VA Dept of Rehab Svcs **804.662.7000**
Fax 804.662.7644
E-mail .Barbara.Tyson@drs.virginia.gov
  8004 Franklin Farms Dr, Richmond, VA 23229
  Barbara Tyson, Director

JUSTICE AGENCY

Attorney General's Ofc **804.786.2071**
Fax 804.786.1991
Web . . . . .www.vaag.com
E-mail . . . . .mailoag@oag.state.va.us
  900 E Main St, Richmond, VA 23219-3524
  Kenneth Cuccinelli, Attorney General

CASA **757.397.2799**
Fax 757.397.2994
E-mail . . . . .portsmouthcasa@fopjc.org
  600 Crawford St Ste 200, Portsmouth,
  VA 23704-3820
  Sheila Cross, Director

Crime Victims Compensation Div **800.552.4007**
Fax 804.367.1021
Web . . . . .www.cics.f.state.va.us
E-mail . . . . .cicsmail@vwc.state.va.us
  2201 West Broad Street, Suite 207, Richmond,
  VA 23220
  Mary Vail Ware, Director

Dept of Corrections **804.674.3119**
Fax 804.674.3509
Web . . . . .www.vadoc.virginia.gov
E-mail . . . . .harold.clarke@vadoc.virginia.gov
  6900 Atmore D, Richmond, VA 23225
  Harold W Clarke, Director

Dept of Juvenile Justice **804.371.0700**
Fax 804.371.0773
  700 East Franklin Street Fourth Floor., Richmond,
  VA 23218
  Helivi Holland, Director

Virginia Dept of Correctional Edu **804.225.3314**
Fax 804.786.7642
E-mail . . . . .patricia.ennis@dce.virginia.gov
  101 N 14th St, James Monroe Bldg 7th Flr,
  Richmond, VA 23219
  Patricia Ennis, Director

COURTS

Administrative Ofc Of The Courts/Supreme
** Court** **804.786.6455**
Fax 804.786.4542
Web . . . . .www.courts.state.va.us
E-mail . . . . .khade@courts.state.va.us
  100 N 9th St, Supreme Court, Richmond, VA 23219
  Karl Hade, Executive Secretary

POLICE AND SHERIFF

Virginia Assoc of Chiefs of Police **804.285.8227**
Fax 804.285.3363
Web . . . . .www.vachiefs.org
E-mail . . . . .dana@vachiefs.org
  1606 Santa Rosa Rd, Ste 134, Henrico,
  VA 23288-0001
  Dana G. Schrad, Executive Director

EDUCATION SERVICES

Dept of Education **804.225.2021**
Fax 804.786.8518
Web . . . . .www.doe.virginia.gov
E-mail . . . . .patricia.wright@doe.virginia.gov
  101 N 14th St Fl 18, Richmond, VA 23219-3684
  Dr. Patricia Wright, Superintendent Of Public Instruction

Div of Spec Educ & Student Svcs VA **804.225.3252**
Fax 804.371.8796
E-mail . . . . .cathy.pomfrey@doe.virginia.gov
  101 N 14th St, Richmond, VA 23219
  Cathy Pomfrey, Director

Educ for Homeless Children and Youth VA **757.221.4002**
Fax 757.221.5300
E-mail . . . . .homlss@wm.edu
  PO Box 8795, Williamsburg, VA 23187

Virginia School for the Deaf & Blind at
** Staunton** **540.332.9000**
Fax 540.332.9042
Web . . . . .www.vsdbs.virginia.gov
E-mail . . . . .info@vsdbs.virginia.gov
  100 New Hope Rd, Staunton, VA 24402
  Nancy Armstrong, PhD, Superintendent

LABOR & WORKFORCE EDUCATION

Virginia Employment Commission **804.786.2171**
Fax 804.225.2190
Web . . . . .www.vaemtloy.com
E-mail . . . . .jahudson@vec.state.va.us
  703 E Main St, Room 121, Richmond, VA 23219
  Jacqueline A. Hudson, Manager

COUNTY SERVICES

Accomack County

SOCIAL SERVICES

Accomack Northhampton Ctr **757.442.4438**
Fax 757.442.4438
Web ....www.nwf.org
E-mail ....spence@nwf.org
   36318 Lankford Hwy, Belle Haven, VA 23306
   Linda Spence, Director

GENERAL HEALTH SERVICES

Eastern Shore Health District **757.787.5880**
Fax 757.787.5841
   23191 Front St, Accomac, VA 23301
   Scott Chandler, Administrator

COURTS

Juvenile And Domestic Relations District
Court **757.787.0920**
Fax 757.787.4526
E-mail ....cgordon@courts.state.va.us
   23371 Front St, Accomac, VA 23301
   Honorable Croxton Gordon, Judge

Albemarle County

GENERAL HEALTH SERVICES

Thomas Jefferson Health District **434.972.6219**
Fax 434.972.4310
Web ....www.vdh.virginia.gov
E-mail ....lilian.peake@vdh.virginia.gov
   1138 Rose Hill Dr, Charlottesville, VA 22903-5128
   Lilian R Peake Md, Mph, Director

COURTS

Juvenile And Domestic Relations
Court **434.979.7165**
Fax 434.293.0211
   411 E High St, Charlottesville, VA 22902
   Jody Shelley, Clerk

POLICE AND SHERIFF

Sheriff's Ofc **434.972.4001**
Fax 434.972.4065
Web ....www.albemarle.org
   411 E High St, Charlottesville, VA 22902-5120
   J. E. Harding, Sheriff

Alleghany County

JUSTICE AGENCY

Juvenile Court Svcs Unit **540.965.1710**
Fax 540.965.1712
E-mail ....gary.conway@djj.virginia.gov
   229 Main St, Covington, VA 24426
   Gary Conway, Director

COURTS

Juvenile And Domestic Relations
Court **540.965.1720**
Fax 540.965.1722
Web ....www.courts.state.va.us
   266 W Main St, Covington, VA 24426
   Honorable Laura Dascher, Judge

Amelia County

GENERAL HEALTH SERVICES

Health Dept **804.561.2711**
Fax 804.561.2712
Web ....www.vdh.virginia.gov
   16320 Church St, Amelia Court House,
   VA 23002-4817
   Annette Wetzel, Rn, Public Health Nurse

JUSTICE AGENCY

Court Svcs **804.561.3453**
Fax 804.561.6048
Web ....www.djj.state.virginia.us
E-mail ....glamb@djj.state.va.us
   9127 Washington St, Amelia, VA 23002-0000
   Honorable George Lamb, Director

POLICE AND SHERIFF

Sheriff's Ofc **804.561.2118**
Fax 804.561.2269
E-mail ....ameliaso@tds.net
   16441 Court St, Amelia Court House, VA 23002
   Ricky Walker, Sheriff

Amherst County

SOCIAL SERVICES

Social Svcs **434.946.9330**
Fax 434.946.9319
Web ....www.dss.virginia.gov
E-mail ....glenn.sullivan@dss.virginia.gov
   224 2nd St, Amherst, VA 24521-2712
   Glenn W. Sullivan, Director

GENERAL HEALTH SERVICES

Health Dept **434.946.9408**
Fax 434.946.9409
Web ....www.vdh.state.va.us
   224 2nd St, Amherst, VA 24521-2712
   Hazel Mcsadden, Supervisor

COURTS

Juvenile And Domestic Relations
Court **434.946.9355**
Fax 434.946.9374
   113 Taylor St, Amherst, VA 24521-2705
   Barry Meeks, Probation Supervisor

POLICE AND SHERIFF

Sheriff's Ofc **434.946.9381**
Fax 434.946.9380
Web ....www.countyofamherst.com
   115 Taylor St, Amherst, VA 24521-2705
   Lemuel J. Ayers Iii, Sheriff

Appomattox County

GENERAL HEALTH SERVICES

Health Dept **434.352.2313**
Web ....www.vdh.state.va.us
   475 Court St, Appomattox, VA 24522
   Diane Pickett, Public Health Nurse

COURTS

Juvenile And Domestic Relations
Court **434.352.8225**
Fax 434.352.8635
E-mail ....mdunkum@courts.state.va.us
   297 Court St, 2nd Floor, Appomattox, VA 24522
   Honorable Marvin H. Dunkum, Jr., Judge

Arlington County

GENERAL HEALTH SERVICES

Arlington Health District **703.228.5580**
Fax 703.228.5233
Web ....www.arlingtonva.us
E-mail ....rvarghese@arlingtonva.us
   800 S Walter Reed Dr, Arlington, VA 22204-2308
   Reuben Varghese, District Director

MENTAL HEALTH SERVICES

Mental Health Svcs **703.228.5150**
Fax 703.228.5234
Web ....www.arlingtonva.us/csb
   1725 N George Mason Dr, Arlington, VA 22205
   Cindy Kemp, Executive Director

JUSTICE AGENCY

Argus House **703.228.3944**
Fax 703.522.4751
Web ....www.co.arlington.va.us/courts/jdr_court
E-mail ....wstrobach@arlingtonva.us
   1527 Clarendon Blvd, Arlington, VA 22209-2701
   Christopher Edmond, Group Home Manager

COURTS

Juvenile And Domestic Relations
Court **703.228.4600**
Fax 703.228.3741
   1425 N Courthouse Rd Ste 5100, Arlington,
   VA 22201
   Pat Romano, Court Services Director

POLICE AND SHERIFF

Sheriff's Ofc **703.228.4460**
Fax 703.228.7022
Web ....www.co.arlington.va.us
E-mail ....sheriff@co.arlington.va.us
   1425 N Courthouse Rd Ste 9100, Arlington,
   VA 22201-2629
   Beth Arthur, Sheriff

EDUCATION SERVICES

Migrant Head Start **703.243.7522**
Fax 703.243.1259
Web ....www.ecmhsp.org
   1501 leigh Hwy, Arlington, VA 22209
   Barbara Rickets, Director

Special Education **703.228.6040**
Fax 703.228.6298
Web ....www.apsva.us
E-mail ....jcrawfor@arlington.k12.va.us
   1426 N Quincy St, Arlington, VA 22207-3646
   Dr Julie Crawford, Director

Augusta County

SOCIAL SERVICES

Dept of Social Svcs **540.942.6646**
Fax 540.942.6658
Web ....www.co.augusta.va.us
E-mail ....elizabeth.middleton@dss.virginia.gov
   1200 Shenandoah Ave, Waynesboro, VA 22980-3043
   Elizabeth Middleton, Director

GENERAL HEALTH SERVICES

Central Shenandoah Health District/Staunton Augusta Health
Dept **540.332.7830**
Fax 540.885.0149
Web ....www.vdh.virginia.gov
E-mail ....cshd_sa@vdh.virginia.gov
   1414 N Augusta St, Staunton, VA 24401
   G. Douglas Larsen, Md, District Director

JUSTICE AGENCY

CASA For Childeren **540.213.2272**
Fax 540.337.9173
Web www.casa4childeren.com
E-mail ....info@casa4childeren.com
   1600 N Coalter St Ste 7, Staunton, VA 24401-2500
   Michael Nay, Executive Director

Ofc Of Youth Prevention Svcs 540.332.3806
Fax 540.332.3705
Web .... www.officeyouth.com
E-mail .... blaircl@ci.waynesboro.va.us
   900 Nelson St, Staunton, VA 24401-4725
Carol Blair, Director

Ofc On Youth Prevention Svcs
(Waynesboro) 540.942.6757
Fax 540.942.6785
Web .... www.officeonyouth
E-mail .... blaircl@ci.waynesboro.va.us
   250 S Wayne Ave Ste 101, Waynesboro,
   VA 22980-4625
Carol Blair, Director

COURTS

Juvenile And Domestic Relations

Court 540.942.6633
Fax 540.942.6793
Web .... www.courts.state.va.us
   237 Market Ave, Ste 202, Waynesboro, VA 22980
Honorable Laura Daschar, Judge

POLICE AND SHERIFF

Sheriff's Ofc 540.245.5333
Fax 540.245.5330
E-mail .... rfisher@co.augusta.va.us
   127 Lee Hwy, Verona, VA 24482
Randall D. Fisher, Sheriff

Sheriff's Ofc 540.942.6639
Fax 540.942.6794
E-mail .... harrisj@ci.waynesboro.va.us
   250 S Wayne Ave, Waynesboro, VA 22980
Joe Harris, Jr., Sheriff

Bath County

GENERAL HEALTH SERVICES

Health Dept 540.839.7246
Fax 540.839.2964
Web www.bath.k12.va.us
   51 Courthouse Hill Rd, Warm Springs, VA 24484
G. Douglas Larsen, Md, District Director

Bland County

SOCIAL SERVICES

Social Svcs 276.688.4111
Fax 276.688.4168
   612 Main St Ste 208, Bland, VA 24315
Kim Sobey, Director

GENERAL HEALTH SERVICES

Health Dept 276.688.3642
Fax 276.688.4514
E-mail .... teresa.thompson@yahoo.com
   209 Jackson St, Bland, VA 24315
Teresa Thompson, Public Health Nurse

POLICE AND SHERIFF

Sheriff's Ofc 276.688.0217
Fax 276.688.3453
   612 Main St Ste 203, Bland, VA 24315
Jerry Thompson, Sheriff

EDUCATION SERVICES

Bland Head Start Ctr 276.688.4495
Fax 276.688.4495
Web .... www.blandnews.com
E-mail .... editor@blandnews.com
   76 Cedden Street, Bland, VA 24315
Wanda Hasley, Director

Botetourt County

GENERAL HEALTH SERVICES

Health Dept 540.473.8240
Fax 540.473.8242
   21 Academy St, Fincastle, VA 24090
Stephanie Harper, District Director

JUSTICE AGENCY

Court Svcs 540.473.8244
Fax 540.473.8344
Web .... www.courts.state.va.us
E-mail .... louiskc@djj.state.va.us
   20 E Back St, Fincastle, VA 24090
Honorable Louis K. Campbell, Director

Brunswick County

GENERAL HEALTH SERVICES

Health Dept 434.848.2525
Fax 434.848.2235
E-mail .... deborah.brockwell@vdh.virginia.gov
   1632 Lawrenceville Plank Rd, Lawrenceville,
   VA 23868-3304
Deborah Brockwell, Public Health Nurse

Buchanan County

GENERAL HEALTH SERVICES

Health Dept 276.935.4592
Fax 276.935.4537
   1051 Rose Bed Road, Grundy, VA 24614
Kathy Deel, Office Supervisor

JUSTICE AGENCY

CASA Program 276.935.5808
Fax 276.935.8542
E-mail .... casa@29thjdcasa.org
   Route 460, Grundy, VA 24614
Kristy Wagnar, Director

Buckingham County

GENERAL HEALTH SERVICES

Health Dept 434.969.4244
Fax 434.969.1292
Web .... www.vdh.virginia.gov
E-mail .... rhonda.cox@vdh.virginia.gov
   13360 W James Anderson Highway, Buckingham,
   VA 23921
Rhonda Cox, Public Health Nurse

JUSTICE AGENCY

Court Svcs 434.969.4891
Fax 434.969.3138
Web .... www.djj.state.va.us
E-mail .... melissa.edward@djj.virginia.gov
   13043 W James Anderson Hwy, Buckingham,
   VA 23921
Melissa Edwards, Probation Officer

Campbell County

SOCIAL SERVICES

Social Svcs 434.332.9585
Fax 434.332.9699
Web .... www.piedmont.dss.state.va.us
E-mail .... rmv@piedmont.dss.state.va.us
   69 Kabler Ln, Rustburg, VA 24588
Richard M. Verilla, Director

GENERAL HEALTH SERVICES

Health Dept 434.332.9550
Fax 434.332.5512
Web .... www.vdh.virginia.gov
E-mail .... patricia.reed@vdh.virginia.gov
   116 Kabler Ln, Rustburg, VA 24588
Patricia Reed, Rn, Nursing Supervisor

JUSTICE AGENCY

Court Svcs 434.592.9533
Fax 434.332.9695
Web .... www.governor.virginia.gov
E-mail .... darryl.holt@governor.virginia.gov
   64 Court House Ln, Rustburg, VA 24588
Darryl Holt, Probation Supervisor

POLICE AND SHERIFF

Sheriff's Dept 434.332.9580
Fax 434.332.2710
Web .... www.co.campbell.va.us
E-mail .... sheriff@co.campbell.va.us
   87 Court House Ln, Rustburg, VA 24588-9701
Terry E. Gaddy, Sheriff

Caroline County

GENERAL HEALTH SERVICES

Health Dept 804.633.5465
Fax 804.633.5128
Web .... www.vdh.virginia.gov
   17202 Richmond Turn Pike, Milford, VA 22514
Judy Kulynth, Public Health Nurse

POLICE AND SHERIFF

Sheriff's Ofc 804.633.5400
Fax 804.633.0415
E-mail .... sheriff@carolinesheriff.org
   118 Courthouse Ln, Bowling Green, VA 22427
A.a. Lippa, Sheriff

EDUCATION SERVICES

Bowling Green Primary School 804.633.6401
Fax 804.633.2151
Web www.caroline.k12.va.us
E-mail .... jmack@caroline.k12.va.us
   17176 Richmond Tpke, Milford, VA 22514-2209
Jason Mack, Principal

Carroll County

SOCIAL SERVICES

Social Svcs 276.236.8008
Fax 276.728.9987
E-mail .... mike.jennings@dss.virginia.gov
   605 - 8 Pine St., Hillsville, VA 24343
Michael Jennings, Director

GENERAL HEALTH SERVICES

Health Dept 276.730.3180
Fax 276.730.3185
Web .... www.vdh.virginia.gov
E-mail .... kathryn.horton@vdh.virginia.gov
   605-15 Pine St, Hillsville, VA 24343-1453
Kathryn Horton, Public Health Nurse

COURTS

Juvenile And Domestic Relations

Court 276.730.3049
Fax 276.730.3104
   605 Pine St, Hillsville, VA 24343
Honorable Harriet Dorothy, Judge

POLICE AND SHERIFF

Sheriff's Ofc 276.728.4146
Fax 276.728.9992
E-mail .... ccso236@earthlink.net
   605 Pine St, Hillsville, VA 24343
H. Warren Manning, Sheriff

Virginia

Charles City

SOCIAL SERVICES

Social Svcs...................................**804.652.1708**
Fax..804.829.2430
Web...............................www.central.dss.state.va.us
E-mail.....................bma036@central.dss.state.va.us
10600 Courthouse Rd, Charles City, VA 23030
Byron M. Adkins, Director

GENERAL HEALTH SERVICES

Health Dept.................................**804.829.2490**
Fax..804.829.6702
Web..................................www.vdh.virginia.gov
E-mail.........................carol.lien@vdh.virginia.gov
7501 Adkins Rd, Charles City, VA 23030-3020
Carol Lien, Nursing Supervisor

POLICE AND SHERIFF

Sheriff's Ofc................................**804.829.9265**
Fax..804.829.2514
E-mail..........................tsbell@co.charles-city.va.us
10780 Courthouse Rd, Charles City, VA 23030
Thalia Bell, Administrator

Charlotte County

GENERAL HEALTH SERVICES

Health Dept.................................**434.542.5251**
Fax..434.542.4354
Web..................................www.vdh.virginia.gov
E-mail...............catherine.mason@vdh.virginia.gov
270 David Bruce Ave, Charlotte Court House,
VA 23923
Catherine Mason, Rn, Sr Public Health Nurse

JUSTICE AGENCY

Court Svcs...................................**434.542.5080**
Fax..434.542.5294
Web......................................www.djj.state.va.us
430 Thomas Jefferson Hwy., Charlotte Court House,
VA 23923
Tiffany H. Russell, Probation Officer

POLICE AND SHERIFF

Sheriff's Ofc................................**434.542.5141**
Fax..434.542.5100
E-mail................................tdjones@cchsheriff.com
222 Law Ln, Charlotte Court House, VA 23923
Thomas D. Jones, Sheriff

Chesterfield County

MENTAL HEALTH SERVICES

Community Svcs Board......................**804.768.7220**
Fax..804.768.9205
Web....................................www.chesterfield.gov
6801 Lucy Corr Ct Blvd, Chesterfield, VA 23832-6657
Debbie Burcham, Executive Director

JUSTICE AGENCY

CASA..**804.276.7660**
Fax..804.276.7667
E-mail......................................chcasa@comcast.net
9457 Amberdale Dr, Richmond, VA 23236-1249
Holly Abbot, Program Director

Chesterfield Detention Home...............**804.748.1460**
Fax..804.768.7735
Web................................www.chesterfield.k12.va.us
9600 Krause Rd, Chesterfield, VA 23832-6717
Joe Campbell, Director

Court Svcs...................................**804.748.1372**
Fax..804.748.7915
7000 Lucy Corr Blvd, Chesterfield, VA 23832
James Nankevis, Director

COURTS

Juvenile And Domestic Relations

Court..**804.748.1379**
Fax..804.717.6043
7000 Lucy Corr Blvd, Chesterfield, VA 23832
Bonny Davis, Judge

City of Alexandria County

JUSTICE AGENCY

Court Svcs Unit.............................**703.746.4144**
Fax..703.838.6492
Web.....................................www.alexandriava.gov
520 King St 1 Fl, Alexandria, VA 22314-3154
Lillian B. Brooks, Court Service Unit Director

Ctr Probation/Intake Dept..................**703.704.6004**
Fax..703.704.6668
E-mail............jdrdc-southcountyctr@co.fairfax.va.us
8350 Richmond Hwy Ste 119, Alexandria, VA 22309
Roxanne Tigh, Center Director

COURTS

Juvenile and Domestic Relations

Court..**703.746.4141**
Fax..703.838.4092
Web......................................www.courts.state.va.us
520 King St Ste 1, Alexandria, VA 22314-3154
Honorable Constance H. Frogale, Judge

POLICE AND SHERIFF

Criminal Investigations.....................**703.838.4711**
Fax..703.838.3844
Web....................................www.ci.alexandria.va.us
E-mail.......................peyton.jones@ci.alexandria.va.us
2034 Eisenhower Ave, 2nd Floor, Alexandria,
VA 22314
Captain Jhonson, Commander

EDUCATION SERVICES

Special Education...........................**703.824.6650**
Fax..703.931.0187
Web.......................................www.acps.k12.va.us
2000 N Beauregard St, Suite 203, Alexandria,
VA 22311
Morton Sherman, Superintendent

City of Bedford County

SOCIAL SERVICES

Social Svcs...................................**540.586.7750**
Fax..540.586.7785
Web...................................www.co.bedford.va.us
119 E Main St, Burks-Scott Bldg., Bedford,
VA 24523-2034
Kaylynn Howell, CPS Supervisor

GENERAL HEALTH SERVICES

Health District..............................**540.586.7952**
Fax..540.586.7950
Web..................................www.vdh.virginia.gov
E-mail......................kerry.gateley@vdh.virginia.gov
600 Bedford Ave, bedford, VA 24523
Kerry Gateley, Director

JUSTICE AGENCY

CASA..**540.586.4932**
Fax..540.586.9315
Web..www.cvcasa.org
E-mail................................bedford@cvcasa.org
123 E Main St Ste 203, Bedford, VA 24523
Lacey Ward, Executive Director

COURTS

Juvenile and Domestic Relations Court/Clerks

Ofc..**540.586.7641**
Fax..540.587.9395
Web......................................www.courts.state.va.us
E-mail..........................sarrington@courts.state.va.us
123 E Main St Ste 101, Bedford, VA 24523-2011
Stacey T. Arrington, Court Clerk

POLICE AND SHERIFF

Sheriff's Ofc................................**540.586.4800**
Fax..540.586.9100
Web.................................www.bedfordsherriff.org
E-mail......................mbrown@bedfordsherriff.org
1345 Falling Creek Rd, Bedford, VA 24523-3935
Michael J. Brown, Sheriff

City of Bristol County

GENERAL HEALTH SERVICES

Bristol Health Dept.........................**276.642.7335**
Fax..276.642.7347
Web...www.vdh.gov
205 Piedmont Ave, Bristol, VA 24201
Linda Price, Rn, Public Health Nurse

POLICE AND SHERIFF

Sheriff's Ofc................................**276.645.7430**
Fax..276.645.7428
Web..www.bvso.net
417 Cumberland St, Bristol, VA 24201-4303
Jack Weisenburger, Sheriff

City of Buena Vista County

POLICE AND SHERIFF

Sheriff's Ofc................................**540.261.8615**
Fax..540.261.2424
2039 Sycamore Ave, Buena Vista, VA 24416
Willie R. Hamilton Jr., Sheriff

City of Charlottesville County

POLICE AND SHERIFF

Sheriff's Dept...............................**434.970.3777**
Fax..434.970.3793
315 E High St Ste A, Charlottesville, VA 22902
James Brown, Sheriff

City of Chesapeake County

GENERAL HEALTH SERVICES

Chesapeake Health Dept.....................**757.382.8600**
Fax..757.382.8683
Web..................................www.vdh.virginia.gov
E-mail................valerie.johnson@vdh.virginia.gov
748 Battlefield Blvd N, Chesapeake, VA 23320-4941
Valerie Johnson, Nursing Supervisor

MENTAL HEALTH SERVICES

Community Svcs Board......................**757.547.9334**
Fax..757.819.6292
Web...................................www.chesapeake.va.us
224 Great Bridge Blvd, Chesapeake, VA 23327
Joseph Scislowecz, Director

POLICE AND SHERIFF

Sheriff's Dept...............................**757.382.6159**
Fax..757.382.8392
Web..................................www.cityofchesapeake.net
E-mail..........................jnewhart@cityofchesapeake.net
401 Albemarle Dr, Chesapeake, VA 23322-5503
John R. Newhart, Sheriff

City of Colonial Heights County

GENERAL HEALTH SERVICES

Colonial Heights Health Dept **804.520.9380**
Fax 804.520.9222
200 Highland Ave, Colonial Heights, VA 23834
Allison Robertson, Office Manager

POLICE AND SHERIFF

Sheriff's Dept **804.520.9352**
Fax 804.520.9248
Web ....www.colonial-hieghts.com
E-mail ....sheriff@colonial-hieghts.com
401 Temple Ave, Colonial Heights, VA 23834-2841
Todd B Wilson, Sheriff

City of Covington County

GENERAL HEALTH SERVICES

Health District **540.962.2173**
Fax 540.962.8353
Web ....www.vdh.virginia.gov
E-mail ....stephanie.harper@vdh.virginia.gov
321 E Beech St, Covington, VA 24426-2013
Stephanie Harper, District Director

City of Danville County

GENERAL HEALTH SERVICES

Danville Health Dept **434.766.9828**
Fax 434.799.5022
E-mail ....kathryn.plumb@vdh.virginia.gov
326 Taylor Dr, Danville, VA 24541
Kathryn Plumb, Bsn, Nursing Manager

POLICE AND SHERIFF

Sheriff's Dept **434.799.5135**
Fax 434.799.8719
E-mail ....sheriffsoffice@ci.danville.va.us
401 Patton St, Danville, VA 24541
Michael Mondul, Sheriff

City of Emporia County

SOCIAL SERVICES

Emporia City Dept of Social Svcs **434.634.6576**
Fax 434.634.9504
Web ....www.gedss.org
E-mail ....info@gedss.org
1748 E Atlantic St, Emporia, VA 23847-6584
Robert Henderson, Director

GENERAL HEALTH SERVICES

Emporia City Health Dept **434.348.4210**
Fax 434.348.4281
Web ....www.vdh.virginia.gov
E-mail ....bgayle@vdh.virginia.gov
140 Uriah Branch Way, Emporia, VA 23847-6315
Becky Gayle, Public Health Nurse

POLICE AND SHERIFF

Sheriff's Dept **434.634.4671**
Fax 434.634.9982
E-mail ....emporiasheriffoffice@hotmail.com
201 S Main St, Emporia, VA 23847-2025
Sam C. Brown, Sheriff

City of Fairfax County

JUSTICE AGENCY

CASA **703.273.3526**
Fax 703.273.2201
Web ....www.casafairfax.org
E-mail ....staff@casafairfax.org
4103 Chain Bridge Rd Ste 200, Fairfax,
VA 22030-4107
Lisa Banks, Executive Director

Ctr **703.383.1391**
Fax 703.324.7329
10426 Main St, Fairfax, VA 22030-3301
Bill Goodman, Director

Domestic Relations Intake **703.246.3416**
Fax 703.385.5964
E-mail ....laura.harris@fairfaxcounty.gov
4110 Chain Bridge Rd, Ste 104, Fairfax,
VA 22030-4017
Laura Harris, Director Of Domestic Relations

Juvenile Detention Ctr **703.246.2844**
Fax 703.385.1524
10650 Page Ave, Fairfax, VA 22030
George Corbin, Superintendent

COURTS

Special Svcs Unit Juvenile Court **703.246.2343**
Fax 703.273.9809
Web ....www.fairfaxcounty.gov
E-mail ....elain.lassiter@fairfaxcounty.gov
4000 Chain Bridge Rd, Fairfax, VA 22030-4017
Elain Lassiter, Director

POLICE AND SHERIFF

City Police Dept **703.385.7924**
Fax 703.359.2488
E-mail ....richard.rappoport@fairfaxva.gov
3730 Old Lee Hwy, Fairfax, VA 22030
Richard Rappoport, Police Chief

Police Dept **703.246.2195**
Fax 703.246.3876
E-mail ....chief@fairfaxcounty.gov
4100 Chambridge Rd, Fairfax, VA 22030
Col. David Rohrer, Chief

Sheriff's Ofc **703.246.3260**
Fax 703.359.4192
Web ....www.fairfaxcounty.gov
E-mail ....sbarry@fairfaxcounty.gov
4110 Chain Bridge Rd, Fairfax, VA 22030
Stan Barry, Sheriff

City of Falls Church County

SOCIAL SERVICES

Dept of Family Svcs **703.724.7500**
Fax 703.533.5525
6245 Leesburg Pike Ste 200, Falls Church,
VA 22044-2106
Margaret Showalter, Team Operations Manager

City of Franklin County

SOCIAL SERVICES

Social Svcs **757.562.8520**
Fax 757.516.6683
Web ....www.dss.virginia.gov
306 N Main St, Franklin, VA 23851-1756
Helen Reavis, Director

Social Svcs **540.483.9247**
Fax 540.483.1933
Web ....www.dss.virginia.gov
E-mail ....deborah.powell@dss.virginia.gov
11161 Virgil H Goode Hwy, Rocky Mount,
VA 24151-3367
Deborah Powell, Director

GENERAL HEALTH SERVICES

Franklin City Health Dept **757.562.6109**
Fax 757.562.2630
E-mail ....cathy.belcher@vdacs.virginia.gov
200 Fairview Dr, Franklin, VA 23851
Kathy Belcher, Public Health Nurse

Health Dept **540.484.0292**
Fax 540.484.0314
Web ....www.vdh.virginia.gov
E-mail ....nancy.timmons@vdh.virginia.gov
365 Pell Ave, Rocky Mount, VA 24151-1133
Nancy Timmons, Hiv Supervisor

JUSTICE AGENCY

Child Advocacy Program Of The Blue
Ridge **540.484.5566**
Fax 540.484.5567
E-mail ....info@southernvacac.org
300 S Main St, Rocky Mount, VA 24151
Joyce C. Moran, CEO

Court Svcs **540.483.3050**
Fax 540.483.3053
275 S Main St Ste 53, Rocky Mount, VA 24151
Fran Elgin, Court Services Unit Director

City of Fredericksburg County

GENERAL HEALTH SERVICES

Fredericksburg Health Dept **540.899.4142**
Fax 540.899.4480
Web ....www.vdh.virginia.gov
E-mail ....michelle.winters@vdh.virginia.gov
608 Jackson St, Fredericksburg, VA 22401-5719
Michelle Winters, Rn, Nursing Manager

POLICE AND SHERIFF

Sheriff's Dept **540.372.1056**
Fax 540.372.7213
513 Price Edward St, Suite 202, Fredericksburg,
VA 22404
Paul W. Higgs, Sheriff

City of Hampton County

JUSTICE AGENCY

Court Svcs **757.727.6184**
Fax 757.727.6670
E-mail ....michael.morton@djj.virginia.gov
35 Wine St, Hampton, VA 23669-4181
Michael Morton, Court Services Unit Director

COURTS

Juvenile and Domestic Relations
Court **757.727.6147**
Fax 757.727.6082
220 N King St, Hampton, VA 23669
Judy Reed, Clerk Of Court

POLICE AND SHERIFF

Police Dept **757.727.6111**
Fax 757.727.6629
Web ....www.hampton.gov
E-mail ....cjordan@hampton.gov
40 Lincoln St, Hampton, VA 23669-3597
Charles Jordan, Chief

Sheriff's Dept **757.926.2540**
Fax 757.926.2537
Web ....www.hampton.gov
E-mail ....broberts@hampton.gov
1928 W Pembroke Ave, Hampton, VA 23661-1907
Billy J. Roberts, Sheriff

EDUCATION SERVICES

Special Education **757.727.2130**
Fax 757.727.2425
E-mail ....swarren@sbo.hampton.k12.va.us
1 Franklin St, Hampton, VA 23669
Sharon Warren, Director

Virginia

City of Hopewell County

GENERAL HEALTH SERVICES

Hopewell City Health Dept **804.458.1297**
Fax 804.541.3023
   220 Appomattox St, Hopewell, VA 23860
   Gayle White, Supervisor

POLICE AND SHERIFF

Sheriff's Ofc **804.541.2300**
Fax 804.541.2326
Web ....www.hopewellsheriffoffice.us
E-mail ....ganderson@hopewellva.gov
   100 E. Broadway, Hopewell, VA 23860
   Gregory Anderson, Sheriff

City of Lynchburg County

GENERAL HEALTH SERVICES

Central Virginia Health District **434.947.6785**
Fax 434.947.2338
Web ....www.co.campbell.va.us
E-mail ....wanda.guthrie@vdh.virginia.gov
   1900 Thomson Dr, Lynchburg, VA 24501-1009
   Wanda Guthrie, Hiv Supervisor

JUSTICE AGENCY

Court Svcs **434.455.2660**
Fax 434.847.1652
   909 Court St Level B 1, Lynchburg, VA 24504
   Robert G. Wade, Court Services Unit Director

COURTS

**Juvenile and Domestic Relations Court/Clerk's
Ofc** **434.455.2670**
Fax 434.847.1442
Web ....www.courts.state.va.us
E-mail ....wlight@courts.state.va.us
   909 Court St, Lynchburg, VA 24504
   Honorable William Light, Judge

POLICE AND SHERIFF

Sheriff's Dept **434.847.1301**
Fax 434.847.1355
E-mail ....rgillispie@lynchburgva.gov
   907 Clay Street, Lynchburg, VA 24505
   Ronald L. Gillispie, Sheriff

City of Martinsville County

POLICE AND SHERIFF

Sheriff's Dept **276.403.5151**
Fax 276.403.5286
   13 Moss St S, Martinsville, VA 24114
   Stephen M. Draper, Sheriff

City of Newport News County

GENERAL HEALTH SERVICES

Peninsula Health Ctr **757.594.7300**
Fax 757.594.7714
Web ....www.vdh.state.va.us
E-mail ....lcadotte@vdh.state.va.us
   416 J Clyde Morris Blvd, Newport News,
   VA 23601-1927
   Linda Cadotte, Nursing Manager

JUSTICE AGENCY

CASA Program **757.926.3642**
Fax 757.926.6924
Web ....www.nncasa.org
   230 25th St, Newport News, VA 23607
   Patty Oneal, Director

**Dept of Juvenile Svcs Outreach and Electronic
Monitoring** **757.926.3926**
Fax 757.926.3638
Web ....www.ci.newport-news.va.us
E-mail ....dbarber@ci.newport-news.va.us
   2501 Washington Ave, Newport News,
   VA 23607-4327
   Dawn Barber, Director

COURTS

**Juvenile and Domestic Relations
Court** **757.926.3603**
Fax 757.926.3598
   2501 Huntington Ave, Newport News, VA 23607
   Ronald Bensten, Chief Judge

POLICE AND SHERIFF

Sheriff's Dept **757.926.8759**
Fax 757.926.8429
Web ....www.nngov.com
   224 26th St, Newport News, VA 23607-4406
   Gabe Morgan, Sheriff

EDUCATION SERVICES

Special Education **757.591.4597**
Fax 757.599.5605
   12465 Warwick Blvd, Newport News, VA 23606
   Michele Mitchell, Executive Director

City of Norfolk County

SOCIAL SERVICES

Dept of Human Svcs **757.664.6100**
Fax 757.664.6286
Web ....www.dss.state.va.us
E-mail ....mattie.satterfield@norfolk.gov
   741 Monticello Ave, Norfolk, VA 23510
   Mattie Satterfield, Assistant Director

GENERAL HEALTH SERVICES

Norfolk City Health District **757.683.2796**
Fax 757.683.8878
Web ....www.vdh.state.va.us
E-mail ....vstallings@vdh.state.va.us
   830 Southampton Ave Ste 200, Norfolk,
   VA 23510-1045
   Valerie Stallings, District Director

MENTAL HEALTH SERVICES

Community Svcs Board **757.823.1600**
Fax 757.823.1601
Web ....www.norfolkcsb.org
E-mail ....maureen.womack@norfolkcsb.org
   225 W Olney Rd, Norfolk, VA 23510
   Maureen Womack, Executive Director

JUSTICE AGENCY

CASA **757.664.7651**
Fax 757.683.9396
Web ....www.nationalcasa.org.
E-mail ....m.keppyle@djj.virginia.gov
   800 E City Hall Ave Fl 3, Norfolk, VA 23510-2724
   La Vern P. Savage, Director

Juvenile Court **757.664.7601**
Fax 757.683.9396
   800 E City Hall Ave Fl 3, Norfolk, VA 23510-2724
   Claudette Overton, Director

Norfolk Detention Ctr **757.441.5667**
Fax 757.441.5564
Web ....www.norfolk.gov
E-mail ....anton.ensley@norfolk.gov
   1260 Security Ln, Norfolk, VA 23502-2215
   Anton Ensley, Superintendent

POLICE AND SHERIFF

Norfolk Police Fire and Rescue **757.441.5600**
Fax 757.466.9387
   3661 E Virginia Beach Blvd, Norfolk, VA 23502
   Stanley Stein, Director

Sheriff's Dept **757.664.4951**
Fax 757.441.2531
   811 E City Hall Ave Ste 120, Norfolk, VA 23510
   Robert J. Mccabe, Sheriff

EDUCATION SERVICES

Special Education **757.628.3950**
Fax 757.628.3825
Web www.nts.k12.va.us
   800 E City Hall Ave Ste 800, Norfolk, VA 23510-2730
   Sandra Witcher, Director

City of Norton County

POLICE AND SHERIFF

Sheriffs Dept **276.679.5308**
Fax 276.679.3510
E-mail ....nortonsheriff@nortonva.gov
   681 Virginia Ave, Norton, VA 24273-0307
   Carlos J. Noaks, Sheriff

City of Petersburg County

GENERAL HEALTH SERVICES

Petersburg Health Dept **804.863.1652**
Fax 804.862.6126
Web ....www.vdh.virginia.gov
   301 Halifax St, Petersburg, VA 23803-6335
   Terry Hamner, Rn, Nursing Manager

COURTS

**Juvenile and Domestic Relations
Court** **804.733.2372**
Fax 804.733.2362
   27 E Tabb St, Petersburg, VA 23803-4518
   Beneatha Simmons, Clerk

City of Portsmouth County

GENERAL HEALTH SERVICES

Portsmouth Health Dept **757.393.8585**
Fax 757.393.8027
Web ....www.vdh.virginia.gov
   1701 High St Ste 102, Portsmouth, VA 23704-2395
   Chiquta Crew, Hiv Coordinator

JUSTICE AGENCY

Court Svcs **757.393.8571**
Fax 757.393.8478
   801 Water St Fl 5, Portsmouth, VA 23705
   David G. Lively, Court Services Unit Director

COURTS

**Juvenile and Domestic Relations
Court** **757.393.8851**
Fax 757.393.5166
Web ....www.courts.state.va.us
E-mail ....wmoore@courts.state.va.us
   603 Crawford Street, Portsmouth, VA 23705-1073
   Honorable William S. Moore, Jr., Judge

POLICE AND SHERIFF

Police Dept **757.393.8536**
Fax 757.393.5047
   311 County St Ste 100, Portsmouth, VA 23703
   Col. Ed Long, Director

Sheriff's Ofc **757.393.5461**
Fax 757.393.5042
E-mail ....watsonb@portsmouthva.gov
   701 Crawford St, Portsmouth, VA 23704-3809
   Bill Watson, Sheriff

EDUCATION SERVICES

Special Education **757.393.8658**
Fax 757.393.5289
Web www.pps.k12.va.us
E-mail ....ellen.giordano@pps.k12.va.us
   3651 Hartford St, Portsmouth, VA 23707-1205
Ellen Giordano, Coordinator

City of Radford County

POLICE AND SHERIFF

Sheriff's Ofc **540.731.5501**
Fax 540.731.5504
E-mail ....marmentrout@radford.va.us
   619 2nd St Ste 8, Radford, VA 24141
Mark Armentrout, Sheriff

City of Richmond County

SOCIAL SERVICES

Richmond City Dept Of Social Svcs **804.646.7433**
Fax 804.646.7441
Web ....www.ci.richmond.va.us
E-mail ....mcwhinpd@ci.richmond.va.us
   900 E Marshall St, Marshall Plaza Building, Richmond,
   VA 23219-1538
Paul Mc Whinney, Director

Social Svcs **804.333.4088**
Fax 804.333.0156
Web ....www.central.dss.state.va.us
E-mail ....cch159@central.dss.state.va.us
   5579 Richmond Rd, Warsaw, VA 22572
Claudette Henderson, Director

GENERAL HEALTH SERVICES

Health District **804.333.4043**
Fax 804.333.3447
Web ....www.vdh.virginia.gov
E-mail ....david.chang@vdh.virginia.gov
   5591 Richmond Rd, Warsaw, VA 22572
David Chang, District Director

Richmond City Health Dept **804.646.3153**
Fax 804.646.3111
E-mail ....donald.stern@vdh.virginia.gov
   900 E Marshall St, Fl 3, Richmond, VA 23219
Donald Stern, Public Health Director

JUSTICE AGENCY

CASA Program **804.646.0516**
Fax 804.646.0624
E-mail ....peg.ruggiero@richmondgov.com
   1600 Oliver Hill Way, Richmond, VA 23219
Peg Ruggiero, Program Director

City of Richmond Juvenile Justice
Svcs **804.646.5987**
Fax 804.646.3269
Web ....www.richmondgov.com
E-mail ....charles.kehoe@richmondgov.com
   3600 W Broad St, Ste 400, Richmond, VA 23230
Charles Kehoe, Director

Court Svcs **804.333.3380**
Fax 804.333.3181
E-mail ....george.bean@djj.virginia.gov
   5575 Richmond Rd, Warsaw, VA 22572
George H. Bean, Supervisor

Richmond Detention Outreach/Electronic
Monitoring **804.646.3372**
Fax 804.646.4795
Web www.richmond.k12.va.us
E-mail ....ladams@richmond.k12.va.us
   1700 OLIVER HILL WAY, Richmond, VA 23219-1234
Leroy Adams, Administrator Of Community Programs

COURTS

Bureau of Insurance **804.371.9741**
Fax 804.371.9873
Web ....www.scc.virginia.gov
E-mail ....bureauofinsurance@scc.virginia.gov
   1300 E Main St, Richmond, VA 23219
Jackie Cunningham, Commissioner Of Insurance

Juvenile And Domestic Relations

Court **804.333.4616**
Fax 804.333.3741
E-mail ....wbrownlee@courts.state.va.us
   201 Court Circle, Warsaw, VA 22572
Wanda F. Brownlee, Clerk Of Court

Juvenile Court **804.646.2942**
Fax 804.646.2906
   1600 Oliver Hill Way, Richmond, VA 23219-1232
Stephanie Garrison, Court Services Probation Director

POLICE AND SHERIFF

Police Dept **804.646.0400**
Fax 804.646.6400
Web ....www.ci.richmond.va.us
E-mail ....monroerd@ci.richmond.va.us
   200 W Grace St, Richmond, VA 23220-5018
Rodney Monroe, Chief

Sheriff's Ofc **804.646.0930**
Fax 804.646.0950
Web ....www.richmondgov.com
E-mail ....sheriff@richmondgov.com
   1701 Fairfield Way, Richmond, VA 23223-4221
C.p. Woody, Jr, Sheriff

State Police **804.674.2087**
Fax 804.674.2936
Web ....www.vsp.virginia.gov
E-mail ....supt@vsp.virginia.gov
   7700 Midlothian Tpke, Richmond, VA 23235
W. Steve Flaherty, Superintendent

Virginia Sheriff's Assoc **804.225.7152**
Fax 804.225.7162
Web ....www.virginiasheriffs.org
E-mail ....vsavsi@virginiasheriffs.org
   701 E Franklin St Ste 706, Richmond, VA 23219-2503
John W. Jones, Executive Director

EDUCATION SERVICES

Career & Technical Education **804.225.2051**
Fax 804.371.2456
Web ....www.doe.virginia.gov
E-mail ....lb.hall@doe.virginia.gov
   101 N 14th St 21st Fl, Richmond, VA 23219-3684
Lolita Hall, Director

Special Education **804.780.7911**
Fax 804.780.6869
Web www.richmond.k12.va.us
E-mail ....htomey@richmond.k12.va.us
   301 N 9th St, Richmond, VA 23219-1933
Harley Tomey, Director

City of Roanoke County

GENERAL HEALTH SERVICES

Health District **540.857.7800**
Fax 540.857.7529
   227 S Pollard St, Vinton, VA 24179
Susan Hoel, Manager

JUSTICE AGENCY

Court Svcs **540.387.6125**
Fax 540.387.6119
E-mail ....ddavis@roanokecountyva.gov
   400 E Main St, Salem, VA 24153-4320
David Davis, Director

Court Svcs **540.853.2565**
Fax 540.853.1589
   215 Church Ave SW, 1st Floor, Roanoke, VA 24011
Rodney C. Hubbard, Court Services Unit Director

COURTS

Juvenile and Domestic Relations District
Court **540.853.2389**
Fax 540.853.1195
Web ....www.roanokeva.gov
E-mail ....john.ferguson@roanokeva.gov
   315 Church Ave SW Ste A, Roanoke, VA 24016-5024
Honorable John Ferguson, Judge

POLICE AND SHERIFF

Police Dept **540.853.2212**
Fax 540.853.6585
   348 Campbell Ave SW, Roanoke, VA 24016
Pim Femce, Director Of Youth Bureau

Sheriff's Dept **540.853.2721**
Fax 540.853.5353
   340 Campbell Ave, Roanoke, VA 24016
Octavia Johnson, Sheriff

Sheriff's Dept **540.387.6141**
Web ....www.roanokecountyva.gov
   400 E Main St, Salem, VA 24153-4320
Mike Winston, Sheriff

City of Salem County

POLICE AND SHERIFF

Sheriff's Dept **540.389.0978**
Fax 540.375.4055
   2 E Calhoun St, Salem, VA 24153
Eric Atkins, Sheriff

EDUCATION SERVICES

Arnold Burton Child Development
Ctr **540.345.6781**
   1760 Roanoke Blvd, Salem, VA 24153-6418
Ted Hedley, Director

City of Staunton County

POLICE AND SHERIFF

Sheriff's Dept **540.332.3880**
Fax 540.332.3970
Web ....www.ci.staunton.va.us
E-mail ....caldwellal@ci.staunton.va.us
   113 E Beverley St, Ste 100, Staunton, VA 24401-4390
Alex L. Caldwell, Jr., Sheriff

City of Virginia Beach County

GENERAL HEALTH SERVICES

Community Dept. Of Human Svcs
Board **757.437.3200**
Fax 757.437.3311
Web ....www.vbgov.com
   3432 Virginia Beach Blvd, Suite 344, Virginia Beach,
   VA 23452
Robert Morin, Director

Virginia Beach Health District
Clinic **757.518.2700**
Fax 757.518.2644
   4452 Corporation Ln, Corporation Center 3, Virginia
   Beach, VA 23462
Cheryl Dunbar-manley, Hiv Case Manager

POLICE AND SHERIFF

Police Dept **757.385.4101**
Fax 757.385.4746
   2509 Princess Anne Rd, Municipal Ctr, Virginia Beach,
   VA 23456
Jim Cevera, Chief

City of Williamsburg County

SOCIAL SERVICES

Williamsburg City Dept of Human

Svcs 757.220.6161
Fax 757.220.6113
Web .... www.williamsburgva.gov
E-mail .... pwalenti@ci.williamsburg.va.us
   401 Lafayette St, Williamsburg, VA 23185-3617
   Peter P Walentisch, Director

JUSTICE AGENCY

Merrimac Ctr Detention 757.887.0225
Fax 757.887.0340
Web .... www.merrimac-center.net
E-mail .... gworkman@merrimac-center.net
   9300 Merrimac Trl, Williamsburg, VA 23185-5967
   Gina Workman, Assistant Director

COURTS

Juvenile and Domestic Relations

Court 757.564.2200
Fax 757.564.2343
   5201 Monticello Ave, Ste 3, Williamsburg, VA 23188
   Betty Miller, Clerk

Williamsburg AIDS Network 757.220.4606
Fax 757.253.0001
Web .... www.williamsburgaidsnetwork.org
E-mail .... info@williamsburgaidsnetwork.org
   479 McLaws Cir Ste 2, Williamsburg, VA 23187
   Shelly Taylor Donahue, Executive Director

POLICE AND SHERIFF

Sheriff's Dept 757.564.2220
Fax 757.564.2229
   5201 Monticello Ave Ste 5, Williamsburg,
   VA 23188-8216
   Robert J. Deeds, Sheriff

City of Winchester County

GENERAL HEALTH SERVICES

Lord Fairfax Health District 540.722.3470
Fax 540.722.3475
   150 W 10 Baker St, Winchester, VA 22601-4828
   Charles Devine, District Director

JUSTICE AGENCY

Northwestern Regional Juvenile Detention

Ctr 540.722.6174
Fax 540.722.6695
   145 Fort Collier Rd, Winchester, VA 22603
   Jim Stevenson, Superintendent

COURTS

26th Court Svc Unit (CSU) 540.667.5770
Fax 540.667.4818
Web .... www.winfredclerk.com
E-mail .... info@ci.winchester.va.us
   5 N Kent St, Winchester, VA 22601-5037
   Julie Van Winkle, Court Services Unit Director

POLICE AND SHERIFF

Sheriff's Dept 540.662.6168
Fax 540.504.6400
E-mail .... fcso@co.frederick.va.us
   1080 Coverstone Dr, Winchester, VA 22602
   Robert T. Williamson, Sheriff

Sheriff's Dept 540.667.5770
Fax 540.667.6438
Web .... www.visuallink.com
E-mail .... wpdnpba@visuallink.com
   5 N Kent St, Winchester, VA 22601-5037
   Lenny W Millholland, Sheriff

EDUCATION SERVICES

Head Start 540.869.1558
Fax 540.678.4219
Web www.wps.k12.va.us
E-mail .... judy.rodriques@wps.k12.va.us
   598 N Kent St, Winchester, VA 22601-5348
   Judy Rodriguez, Director

Clarke County

SOCIAL SERVICES

Social Svcs 540.955.3700
Fax 540.955.3958
Web .... www.dss.virginia.go
E-mail .... angie.jones@dss.virginia.gov
   311 E Main St, Berryville, VA 22611-1305
   Angie W. Jones, CPS Supervisor

GENERAL HEALTH SERVICES

Health Dept 540.955.1033
Fax 540.955.4094
Web .... www.vdh.state.va.us
   100 N Buckmarsh St, Berryville, VA 22611-1010
   Mary Border, Rn, Public Health Nurse

POLICE AND SHERIFF

Sheriff's Ofc 540.955.1234
Fax 540.955.4111
   100 N Church St, Berryville, VA 22611
   Anthony W. Roper, Sheriff

Craig County

GENERAL HEALTH SERVICES

Health Dept 540.864.5136
Fax 540.864.6454
E-mail .... pjohnston@vdh.state.va.us
   161 Main St, New Castle, VA 24127
   Pat Johnston, Public Health Nurse

COURTS

Juvenile And Domestic Relations

Court 540.864.5989
Fax 540.864.7385
E-mail .... kpritchett@courts.state.va.us
   182 Main St, Ste 5, New Castle, VA 24127
   Kelly Pritchette, Juvenile Clerk

Culpeper County

MENTAL HEALTH SERVICES

Rappahannock-Rapidan Community Svcs

Board 540.825.3100
Fax 540.825.6245
E-mail .... bduncan@rrcsb.org
   15361 Bradford Rd, Culpeper, VA 22701
   Brian D. Duncan, Executive Director

Cumberland County

GENERAL HEALTH SERVICES

Health Dpt 804.492.4661
Fax 804.492.9463
Web .... www.vdh.virginia.gov
   15 Foster Rd, Cumberland, VA 23040
   Cindy Debusk, Rn, Nurse Manager

JUSTICE AGENCY

Court Svcs 804.492.4825
Fax 804.492.3569
   1 Sheriff Ln, Cumberland, VA 23040
   Leigh Marion, Probation Chief

POLICE AND SHERIFF

Sheriff's Dept 804.492.4120
Fax 804.492.5811
   Rte 60 Cumberland Crthse Cir, Cumberland,
   VA 23040
   Darrell L. Hodges, Sheriff

Dickenson County

GENERAL HEALTH SERVICES

Health Dept 276.926.4979
Fax 276.926.4426
E-mail .... cassie.oquin@vdh.virginia.gov
   334 Brush Creek Rd, Clintwood, VA 24228
   Cassie Oquin, Administrative Office Specialist

JUSTICE AGENCY

Ofc On Youth 276.926.1670
Fax 276.926.1612
E-mail .... dcooy2000@yahoo.com
   153 Courthouse Lane, Clintwood, VA 24228
   Kim Tipton, Director

POLICE AND SHERIFF

Sheriff's Dept 276.926.1603
Fax 276.926.1606
Web www.sheriff.dc911.org
E-mail .... bobby.hammons@sheriff.dc911.org
   Court House Lane, Clintwood, VA 24228
   Bobby G. Hammons, Sheriff

Dinwiddie County

GENERAL HEALTH SERVICES

Health Dept 804.469.3771
Fax 804.469.9379
E-mail .... tracy.bishop@virginia.va.gov
   14006 Boydton Plank Rd, Dinwiddie, VA 23841
   Tracy Bishop, Nursing Supervisor

JUSTICE AGENCY

Court Svcs 804.469.4539
Fax 804.469.5381
   14008 Boydton Plank Rd, Dinwiddie, VA 23841
   Timothy L. Beard, Probation Officer

EDUCATION SERVICES

Cdi Head Start 804.469.4495
Fax 804.469.4496
   10305 Boydton Plank Rd, Dinwiddie, VA 23841-2309
   Shakee Franklin, Director

Essex County

COURTS

15Th Judicial District 804.443.3744
Fax 804.443.4122
   300 Prince St, Tappahannock, VA 22560
   Honorable R Michael Mckenney, Judge

Fairfax County

SOCIAL SERVICES

Children Child Care Assistance and

Referral 703.449.8484
Fax 703.324.3917
Web .... www.fairfaxcounty.gov/childcare/
E-mail .... carol.keil@fairfaxcounty.gov
   12011 Govt Ctr Pkwy, 8th Floor, Fairfax, VA 22035
   Carol Keil, Director

Dept of Family Svcs 703.481.4025
Fax 703.904.0671
Web .... www.fairfaxcounty.gov
   1850 Cameron Glen Dr Ste 700, Reston, VA 20190
   Lin Mcmanara, CPS Supervisor

GENERAL HEALTH SERVICES

Alexandria Health Dept **703.838.4400**
Fax 703.838.4038
Web ....www.alexandria.va.us
E-mail ....debby.dimon@vdh.virginia.gov
   4480 King St Ste 118, Alexandria, VA 22302-1300
Debby Dimon, HIV Director

Health District **703.534.8343**
Fax 703.532.1513
Web ....www.co.fairfax.va.us
   6245 Leesburg Pike Ste 500, Falls Church, VA 22044
Gloria Addo-Ayensu, District Director

JUSTICE AGENCY

**Juvenile and Domestic Relations District
Court** **703.481.4014**
Fax 703.437.8329
   1850 Cameron Glen Dr Ste 400, Reston,
   VA 20190-3310
Scott Warner, Director

Probation Svcs **703.204.1016**
Fax 703.204.2953
Web ....www.fairfaxcounty.gov
   2812 Old Lee Hwy Ste 100, Fairfax, VA 22031-4315
Johanna Palacros-Russel, Director

COURTS

Orthotic Solutions, LLC **703.849.9200**
Fax 703.849.8499
Web ....http://www.orthoticsolutions.com
E-mail ....orthotist@orthoticsolutions.com
   2802 Merrilee Dr Ste 100, Fairfax, VA 20310
Janice, Office Manager

POLICE AND SHERIFF

Sheriff's Ofc **703.248.5111**
Fax 703.248.5229
Web ....www.fallschurchva.gov
E-mail ....sbittle@fallschurchva.gov
   300 Park Ave, Falls Church, VA 22046-3301
S. Stephen Bittle, Sheriff

EDUCATION SERVICES

Special Education **703.204.3941**
Fax 703.204.3968
Web ....www.fcps.edu
E-mail ....irene.meier@fcps.edu
   2334 Gallows Rd, Dunn Loring, VA 22027-1116
Irene Meier, Special Ed Director

Fauquier County

GENERAL HEALTH SERVICES

Health Dept **540.347.6400**
Fax 540.347.6405
Web ....www.vdh.state.va.us
E-mail ....robert.bradshaw@vdh.state.va.us
   330 Hospital Dr, Ste 101, Warrenton, VA 20186
Robert Dana Bradshaw, District Director

Floyd County

GENERAL HEALTH SERVICES

Health Dept **540.745.2141**
Fax 540.745.4929
E-mail ....rkinsley@floydcova.org
   815 E Main St, Floyd, VA 24091-3750
Rebekah Kinsley, Public Health Nurse

POLICE AND SHERIFF

Sheriff's Dept **540.745.9334**
Fax 540.745.9349
Web ....www.swva.net
   100 E Main St Ste 206, Floyd, VA 24091-2101
Shannon Zeman, Sheriff

Fluvanna County

JUSTICE AGENCY

Court Svcs **434.591.1990**
Fax 434.591.1991
E-mail ....lasconoj@djj.state.va.us
   1001 Main St, Palmyra, VA 22963
Joe Lascono, Intake/Probation Officer

Giles County

GENERAL HEALTH SERVICES

Health Dept **540.921.2891**
Fax 540.921.1335
E-mail ....helen.wilson@vdh.virginia.gov
   120 N Main St Ste 2, Pearisburg, VA 24134
Helen Wilson, Public Health Nurse

JUSTICE AGENCY

29th District Court Svc Unit **540.921.3408**
Fax 540.921.3789
   507 Wenonah Ave, Ste 3, Pearisburg, VA 24134
Ronald W. Belay, Court Services Unit Director

Gloucester County

GENERAL HEALTH SERVICES

Health Dept **804.693.2445**
Fax 804.693.1398
Web ....www.vdh.virginia.gov
E-mail ....rick.hall@vdh.virginia.gov
   6882 Main St, Gloucester, VA 23061
Rick Hall, Hiv Coordinator

MENTAL HEALTH SERVICES

**Middle Peninsula/Northern Neck Counseling
Ctr** **804.693.5057**
Fax 804.693.7407
E-mail ....cwalsh@mpnn.state.va.us
   9228 George Washington Memorial Hwy, Gloucester,
   VA 23061-2468
Charles R Walsh Jr, Executive Director

COURTS

**Juvenile And Domestic Relations
Court** **804.693.4850**
Fax 804.693.7904
Web ....www.courts.state.va.us
E-mail ....tsterling@courts.state.va.us
   7400 Justice Dr, Rm 204, Gloucester, VA 23061
Tiffany R. Sterling, Court Clerk

POLICE AND SHERIFF

Sheriff's Ofc **804.693.3890**
Fax 804.693.1444
Web ....www.gloucesterva.info
   7502 Justice Dr, Gloucester, VA 23061-6101
Steve Gentry, Sheriff

Goochland County

MENTAL HEALTH SERVICES

Community Svcs Board **804.556.5400**
Fax 804.556.5403
Web ....www.co.goochland.va.us
   3058 River Rd W, Goochland, VA 23063
Susan Bergquist, Executive Director

POLICE AND SHERIFF

Sheriff's Ofc **804.556.5349**
Fax 804.556.6051
Web ....www.co.goochland.va.us
   2938 River Rd W, Goochland, VA 23063-3229
James L. Agnew, Sheriff

Grayson County

SOCIAL SERVICES

Social Svcs **276.773.2452**
Fax 276.773.2361
Web ....www.graysoncountyva.com
   129 Davis St, Independence, VA 24348
Tony Isom, Director

GENERAL HEALTH SERVICES

Health District **276.773.2961**
Fax 276.773.2240
Web ....www.vdh.virginia.gov
E-mail ....csmith@vdh.virginia.gov
   186 W Main St, Independence, VA 24348
D. Craig Smith, Md, Mph, District Director

JUSTICE AGENCY

Court Svcs **276.236.2963**
Fax 276.238.1601
E-mail ....shodgescsu@earthlink.net
   106 Calhoun St, Galax, VA 24333-3840
James Douglas Garvey, Supervisor

EDUCATION SERVICES

Fries Head Start Ctr **276.744.3345**
Web ....www.acf.hhs.gov
   76 Gilley Dr, Fries, VA 24330-4571
Vicki Myers, Director

Greene County

SOCIAL SERVICES

Dept of Social Svcs **434.985.5246**
Fax 434.985.5266
Web ....www.gcva.us
E-mail ....james.howard@dss.virginia.gov
   10009 Spotswood Trl, Stanardsville, VA 22973-2945
James E Howard, Director

GENERAL HEALTH SERVICES

Health Dept **434.985.2262**
Fax 434.985.4822
Web ....www.vdh.virginia.gov
E-mail ....lilian.peake@vdh.virginia.gov
   50 Stanard St, Stanardsville, VA 22973
Lilian R Peake Md, Mph, Health Director

Greensville County

JUSTICE AGENCY

Court Svcs **434.348.3645**
Fax 434.348.9319
E-mail ....harrisfw@comcast.net
   420 S Main St, Emporia, VA 23847
F. Woodrow Harris, Probation Supervisor

POLICE AND SHERIFF

Sheriff's Ofc **434.348.4200**
Fax 434.634.9615
E-mail ....gcso@telpage.net
   174 Uriah Branch Way, Emporia, VA 23847
James Edwards, Sheriff

Halifax County

GENERAL HEALTH SERVICES

Health Dept **434.476.4863**
Fax 434.476.4869
   1030 Cowford Rd, Halifax, VA 24558
Judy Moon, Senior Office Service Specialist

COURTS

**Juvenile And Domestic Relations
Court** **434.476.3390**
Fax 434.476.9223
   8 Court House Sq S Main St, Halifax, VA 24558
Donald W. Barker, Probation Officer

Hanover County

SOCIAL SERVICES

Social Svcs **804.365.4100**
Fax 804.365.4110
Web .... www.dss.virginia.gov
E-mail .... sheila.croffen-powell@dss.virginia.gov
    12304 Washington Hwy, Ashland, VA 23005-7646
Sheila Crossen-Powell, Director

GENERAL HEALTH SERVICES

Hanover Health District **804.365.4313**
Fax 804.365.4357
    12312 Washington Hwy, Ashland, VA 23005
Dr. Susan Davis-Fischer, District Director

JUSTICE AGENCY

Hanover CASA Program **804.365.4300**
Fax 804.365.4299
Web .... www.co.hanover.va.us
E-mail .... mdbaker@co.hanover.va.us
    12310 Washington Hwy, Ashland, VA 23005-7646
Melanie Baker, Volunteer Coordinator

COURTS

Juvenile And Domestic Relations
Court **804.537.6200**
Fax 804.537.6246
E-mail .... lynn.robbins@djj.virginia.gov
    7515 Library Drive, 2nd Floor, Hanover, VA 23069
Lynn Robbins, Supervisor Intake Unit

POLICE AND SHERIFF

Sheriff's Ofc **804.365.6110**
Fax 804.537.6390
Web .... www.co.hanover.va.us
    7522 County Complex Rd, Hanover, VA 23069
Col. David Hines, Sheriff

Henrico County

GENERAL HEALTH SERVICES

Health Dept **804.652.3190**
Fax 804.652.3188
Web .... www.vdh.virginia.gov
E-mail .... jenny.calhoun@vdh.virginia.gov
    3810 Nine Mile Rd, Henrico, VA 23223
Santmier Linda, Nurse Supervisor

Henrico Health District **804.501.4522**
Fax 804.501.4983
    8600 Dixon Powers Dr, Henrico, VA 23273
Mark Levine, District Director

JUSTICE AGENCY

CASA **804.501.1670**
Fax 804.501.2574
Web .... www.henricocasa.org
E-mail .... her11@co.henrico.va.us
    3001 Hungrey Spring Rd, Henrico, VA 23228
Barbara Herzog, Executive Director

COURTS

Dept Of Juvenile Justice **804.501.4000**
Fax 804.501.4756
Web .... www.co.henrico.va.us/jdrcourt
    4301 E Parham Rd, Henrico, VA 23273
Kay D. Frye, Court Services Director

POLICE AND SHERIFF

Henrico Police Dept **804.501.4840**
Fax 804.501.4854
Web .... www.co.henrico.va.us
E-mail .... police@co.henrico.va.us
    7721 E Parham Rd, Henrico, VA 23273-0001
Cheif D A Middleton, Chief

Sheriff's Dept **804.501.5860**
Fax 804.501.5443
E-mail .... wad52@co.henrico.va.us
    4301 E Parham Rd, Henrico, VA 23273
Michael L. Wade, Sheriff

EDUCATION SERVICES

Special Education **804.652.3866**
Fax 804.652.3400
Web www.henrico.k12.va.us
E-mail .... bgibson@henriko.k12.va.us
    3820 Nine Mile Rd, Richmond, VA 23223
Bondy Gibson, Director

Henry County

SOCIAL SERVICES

Dept Of Social Svcs **276.656.4300**
Fax 276.656.4303
Web .... www.ci.martinsville.va.us
E-mail .... atuttle@ci.martinsville.va.us
    20 Progress Dr, Martinsville, VA 24112-6208
Amy Tuttle, Director

GENERAL HEALTH SERVICES

West Piedmont Health District **276.638.2311**
Fax 276.638.3537
Web .... www.vdh.state.va.us
E-mail .... ggreen@vdh.state.va.us
    295 Commonwealth Blvd W, Martinsville,
    VA 24114-1820
Gordon Green, District Director

JUSTICE AGENCY

Focus On Youth (CASA) **276.632.7575**
Fax 276.632.3000
Web .... www.kimbanet.com
E-mail .... focus@kimbanet.com
    PO Box 1164, Martinsville, VA 24114-1164
Rhonda Brown, Executive Director

COURTS

Juvenile And Domestic Relations
Court **276.634.4830**
Fax 276.634.4836
E-mail .... robert.foster@djj.virginia.gov
    3160 Kings Mountain Rd Ste C, Martinsville,
    VA 24112-3966
Robert Foster, Court Services Unit Director

POLICE AND SHERIFF

Sheriff's Ofc **276.656.4200**
Fax 276.656.4260
    3250 Kings Mountain Rd, Martinsville, VA 24112
L.a. Perry, Acting Sheriff

Highland County

SOCIAL SERVICES

Dept of Social Svcs **540.468.2199**
Fax 540.468.3099
Web .... www.northern.dss.state.va.us
E-mail .... sharon.sponaugle@dss.virginia.gov
    158 Courthouse Ln, Monterey, VA 24465
Sharon Sponaugle, Director

GENERAL HEALTH SERVICES

Health Dept **540.468.2270**
Fax 540.468.2502
Web .... www.vdh.healthdepatment.org
E-mail .... cathy.halterman@vdh.virginia.gov
    140 Fleisher Ave, Monterey, VA 24465
Cathy Halterman, Rn, Public Health Nurse

Isle of Wight County

SOCIAL SERVICES

Dept of Social Svcs **757.365.0880**
Fax 757.365.0886
Web .... www.dss.state.va.us
    17100 Monument Cir, Ste A, Isle Of Wight, VA 23397
Pamela Barton, Director

GENERAL HEALTH SERVICES

Health Dept **757.357.4177**
Fax 757.357.2838
E-mail .... cleonard@vdh.state.va.us
    919 Fouph Church St, Smithfield, VA 23431
Carolyn Leonard, Office Supervisor

COURTS

Juvenile And Domestic Relations
Court **757.365.6237**
Fax 757.357.9086
E-mail .... rbrewbaker@courts.state.va.us
    17000 Josiah Parker Cir, Isle Of Wight, VA 23397
Robert S. Brewbaker, Jr., Judge

James City

SOCIAL SERVICES

Social Svcs **757.259.3100**
Fax 757.259.3188
Web .... www.james-city.va.us
    5249 Olde Towne Rd Ste A, Williamsburg,
    VA 23188-8111
Diana F. Hutchens, Med, Director

King and Queen County

GENERAL HEALTH SERVICES

Health Dept **804.785.6154**
Fax 804.785.2601
    167 Court House Landing Rd, King And Queen Court
    House, VA 23085
Margaret Mitchell, Nursing Supervisor

King George County

GENERAL HEALTH SERVICES

King George Health Dept **540.775.3111**
Fax 540.775.3109
    10079 Kings Hwy, King George, VA 22485
Judi Kulinych, Rn, Public Health Nurse

JUSTICE AGENCY

Juvenile Intake And Probation **540.775.9044**
Fax 540.775.2580
E-mail .... Kathleen.long@djj.virginia.gov
    9483 Kings Hwy, King George, VA 22485
Kathleen Long, Probation/Intake Officer

King William County

GENERAL HEALTH SERVICES

Health Dept **804.769.4988**
Fax 804.769.2155
E-mail .... kim.carlton@vdh.virginia.gov
    172 Courthouse Ln, King William, VA 23086
Kim Carlton, Senior Public Health Nurse

JUSTICE AGENCY

Court Svcs **804.769.4944**
Fax 804.769.0851
    41 Horse Landing Rd, King William, VA 23086
Mike Scheitle, Supervisor

POLICE AND SHERIFF

Sheriff's Dept **804.769.0999**
Fax 804.769.0334
E-mail .... kwso@kingwilliamcounty.us
    351 Court House Lane, King William, VA 23086
J.s. Walton, Sheriff

Lancaster County

GENERAL HEALTH SERVICES

Lancaster Health Dept **804.462.5197**
Fax 804.462.6211
Web ....www.vdh.virginia.gov
E-mail ....celia.collier@vdh.virginia.gov
　9049 Mary Ball Rd, Ste 100, Lancaster, VA 22503
　Celia Collier, Public Health Nurse

Lee County

GENERAL HEALTH SERVICES

Health Dept **276.346.2011**
Fax 276.346.0401
Web ....www.dgs.state.va.us
E-mail ....hmarkham@dgs.state.va.us
　134 Hill St., Jonesville, VA 24263
　Helen Markham, Rn, Public Health Nurse

JUSTICE AGENCY

Court Svcs **276.346.7723**
Fax 276.346.7707
　PO Box 352, Jonesville, VA 24263-0352
　Matt Smith, Counsellor

COURTS

Juvenile And Domestic Relations
Court **276.346.7735**
Fax 276.346.7701
Web ....www.courts.state.va.us
E-mail ....shorton@courts.state.va.us
　Courthouse Main St, Jonesville, VA 24263
　Sammie R. Horton, Clerk Of Court

POLICE AND SHERIFF

Sheriff's Ofc **276.346.1131**
Fax 276.346.2149
Web ....www.leecountysheriff.net
　Church St, Jonesville, VA 24263
　Gary B. Parsons, Sheriff

Loudoun County

JUSTICE AGENCY

Community Corrections Program **703.777.0207**
Fax 703.777.0110
Web ....www.loudoun.gov
E-mail ....district04@sov.state.va.us
　107 Loudoun St SE, Leesburg, VA 20178
　Ted Mcdaniel, Director

Juvenile Court Svc Unit **703.777.0303**
Fax 703.771.5210
Web ....www.loudoun.gov
E-mail ....jcsu@loudoun.gov
　18 E Market St, Leesburg, VA 20176-2829
　Mark V. Crowley, Director

Loudoun Detention Home **703.771.5200**
Fax 703.771.5344
Web ....www.loudoun.gov
E-mail ....michelle.smith@loudoun.gov
　42020 Loudoun Center Pl, Leesburg, VA 20175-8953
　Michelle Smith, Superintendent

Youth Svcs **703.777.0343**
Fax 703.771.5354
Web ....www.loudoun.gov/prcs
E-mail ....prcs@loudoun.gov
　215 Depot Ct SE, Leesburg, VA 20175-3017
　Dave Carver, Manager

COURTS

Juvenile And Domestic Relations
Court **703.777.0300**
Fax 703.771.5039
Web ....www.courts.state.va.us
　18 E Market St Ste 1, Leesburg, VA 20176-2829
　Eva Mari, Clerk Of Court

POLICE AND SHERIFF

Sheriff's Dept **703.777.0408**
Fax 703.771.5744
E-mail ....lcso@loudoun.org
　880 Harrison St SE, Leesburg, VA 20175
　Stephen O. Simpson, Sheriff

Louisa County

GENERAL HEALTH SERVICES

Health Dept **540.967.3703**
Fax 540.967.3706
Web ....www.vdh.state.va.us
　101 Ashley St, Louisa, VA 23093
　Donna Sheridan, Public Health Nurse

JUSTICE AGENCY

Intake **540.967.2307**
Fax 540.967.5495
E-mail ....cheryl.glavis@djj.virginia.us
　314 W Main St, Louisa, VA 23093
　James Brown, Probation Officer

COURTS

Juvenile And Domestic Relations
Court **540.967.5330**
Fax 540.967.2369
　314 W Main St, Louisa, VA 23093
　Honorable Susan Whitlock, Judge

POLICE AND SHERIFF

Sheriff's Dept **540.967.1234**
Fax 540.967.1604
Web ....www.louisa.org
　1 Woolfolk Ave, Louisa, VA 23093
　Ashland D. Fortune, Sheriff

Lunenburg County

GENERAL HEALTH SERVICES

Health Dept **434.696.2346**
Fax 434.696.1271
E-mail ....kimberly.ball@vdh.virginia.gov
　11387 Courthouse Rd, Lunenburg, VA 23952
　Kimberly Ball, Public Health Nurse

POLICE AND SHERIFF

Sheriff's Ofc **434.696.3131**
Fax 434.696.2531
E-mail ....sheriff@Lunenburgva.net
　160 Courthouse Sq, Lunenburg, VA 23952
　Arthur Townsend, Sheriff

Madison County

GENERAL HEALTH SERVICES

Health District **540.948.5481**
Fax 540.948.3841
Web ....www.vdh.va.gov
　410 N Main St, Madison, VA 22727
　Dana Bradshaw, District Director

POLICE AND SHERIFF

Sheriff's Dept **540.948.5161**
Fax 540.948.3069
E-mail ....mcsheriff@madisonco.virginia.gov
　115 Church St, Madison, VA 22727
　E.j. Weaver, Sheriff

Mathews County

SOCIAL SERVICES

Social Svcs **804.725.7192**
Fax 804.725.7086
Web ....www.vdh.virginia.gov
　536 Church St, Mathews, VA 23109-2293
　Jo Ann Wilson-harfst, Director

GENERAL HEALTH SERVICES

Health Dept **804.725.7131**
Fax 804.725.7466
Web ....www.vdh.virginia.gov
　536 Church St, Mathews, VA 23109
　Karri Murphy, Public Health Nurse

Mecklenburg County

GENERAL HEALTH SERVICES

Southside Health District **434.738.6333**
Fax 434.738.6542
Web ....www.vdh.virginia.gov
　478 Washington St, Boydton, VA 23917
　Julia Gwaltney, Supervisor

JUSTICE AGENCY

Court Svcs **434.738.6191**
Fax 434.738.6729
　911 Madison St, Boydton, VA 23917
　E. Bruce Williams, Probation Supervisor

Middlesex County

GENERAL HEALTH SERVICES

Middlesex Health Dept **804.758.2381**
Fax 804.758.4828
Web ....www.trinitylifestylesmanagement.com
E-mail ....ahatney@trinitylifestylesmanagement.com
　2780 General Puller Hwy, Saluda, VA 23149-3112
　Fredi Branch, Rn, Nursing Manager

Montgomery County

GENERAL HEALTH SERVICES

Health Dept **540.381.7100**
Fax 540.381.7104
Web ....www.vdh.virginia.gov
E-mail ....ruth.wolford@vdh.virginia.gov
　210 Pepper St S Ste A, Christiansburg,
　VA 24073-3572
　Ruth Wolford, Hiv Supervisor

Radford City Health Dept **540.831.5774**
Fax 540.831.6109
Web ....www.bdh.virginia.gov
E-mail ....info@vdh.virginia.gov
　212 3rd Ave, Radford, VA 24141-4729
　Dr. Margaret Odell, District Director

JUSTICE AGENCY

Human Serv **540.382.5776**
Fax 540.382.5780
　210 Pepper St S Ste D, Christiansburg, VA 24073
　Mary Critzer, Director

Juvenile Court Svcs **540.382.5745**
Fax 540.381.6826
E-mail ....doug.poe@djj.virginia.gov
　201 Radford St, Christiansburg, VA 24073-3344
　Doug Poe, Probation Supervisor

COURTS

Juvenile And Domestic Relations
Court **540.382.6999**
Fax 540.381.6848
E-mail ....mlong@courts.state.va.us
　1 E Main St Ste 305, Christiansburg, VA 24073-3039
　Honorable Marcus H. Long, Jr, Judge

POLICE AND SHERIFF

Sheriff's Dept **540.382.2951**
Fax 540.381.6805
Web ....www.ntelos.net
E-mail ....mcso-info@montgomerycountyva.gov
16 S Franklin St, Christiansburg, VA 24073-3514
J. Tommy Whitt, Sheriff

Nelson County

GENERAL HEALTH SERVICES

Health Dept **434.263.8315**
Fax 434.263.4304
Web ....www.nelsoncounty.org
E-mail ....pfarrar@nelsoncounty.org
63 Courthouse Sq, Lovingston, VA 22949
Dr. Lalialn Peake, District Director

JUSTICE AGENCY

Court Svcs **434.263.7035**
Fax 434.263.7033
Web ....www.djj.virginia.gov
E-mail ....nikki.germain@djj.virginia.gov
84 Courthouse Square, 2Nd Fl, Lovingston, VA 22949
Nikki St.Germain, Intake Counselor

New Kent County

POLICE AND SHERIFF

Sheriff's Dept **804.966.9500**
Fax 804.966.5050
Web ....www.co.newkent.state.va.us
12001 Courthouse Circle, New Kent, VA 23124
Farrar W. Howard Jr., Sheriff

Northampton County

SOCIAL SERVICES

Dept of Social Svcs **757.678.5153**
Fax 757.678.0475
Web ....www.co.northampton.va.us
E-mail ....richard.sterrett@dss.virginia.gov
5265 The Horns, Eastville, VA 23347
Richard B Sterrett, Director

GENERAL HEALTH SERVICES

Health District **757.442.6228**
Fax 757.442.4307
Web ....www.vdh.virginia.gov
E-mail ....benita.newby-owen@vdh.virginia.gov
7114 Lankford Hwy., Nassawadox, VA 23413
Benita Newby-Owen, Acting Director

MENTAL HEALTH SERVICES

Eastern Shore Community Svcs
Board **757.442.3636**
Fax 757.442.2319
10129 Rogers Dr, Nassawadox, VA 23413
Mark Freeze, Executive Director

COURTS

2-A Judicial District Court Svcs **757.678.0481**
Fax 757.678.0499
E-mail ....sean.miller@djj.virginia.gov
23371 Front St, Accomac, VA 23301
Sean Milner, Director

POLICE AND SHERIFF

Sheriff's Ofc **757.678.0495**
Fax 757.678.0494
Web ....www.intercom.net
E-mail ....ddoughty@northhampton.va.us
5427 Willow Oak Road, Eastville, VA 23347
David Doughty, Sheriff

EDUCATION SERVICES

Cheriton Head Start 1 ....**757.331.4897**
Fax 757.331.4380
22198 Bayside Road, Cheriton, VA 23316
Annie Collins, Director

Northumberland County

GENERAL HEALTH SERVICES

Health District **804.580.3731**
Fax 804.580.2913
Web .....www.vdh.virginia.gov/lhd/threeriv/index.htm
E-mail ....robert.strube@vdh.virginia.gov
6373 Northumberland Hwy, Ste B, Heathsville,
VA 22473
Dr. Robert Strube, Director

Nottoway County

SOCIAL SERVICES

Social Svcs **434.645.8494**
Fax 434.645.7643
Web ....www.dss.virginia.gov
E-mail ....rreitmeier@dss.virginia.gov
288 W Courthouse Rd, Nottoway, VA 23955
Robert Reitmeier, Director

GENERAL HEALTH SERVICES

Health Dept **434.645.7595**
Fax 434.645.8197
Web ....www.vdh.virginia.gov
207 W Courthouse Rd, Nottoway, VA 23955
Tammie Jackson, Rn, Public Health Nurse

JUSTICE AGENCY

Court Svcs **434.645.7929**
Fax 434.645.2144
E-mail ....kevin.jones@djj.virginia.gov
328 W Courthouse Rd, Nottoway, VA 23955
Kevin E. Jones, Jpo

POLICE AND SHERIFF

Sheriff's Dept **434.645.1630**
Fax 434.645.1915
E-mail ....ljparrish@nottowaysheriff.org
266 W. Courthouse Road, Nottoway, VA 23955
Larry J. Parrish, Sheriff

Orange County

JUSTICE AGENCY

Ofc On Youth **540.672.5484**
Fax 540.672.2311
Web ....www.orangecountyva.gov
E-mail ....avines@orangecountyva.gov
146 Madison Rd Ste 258, Orange, VA 22960-1449
Alisha Vines, Director

Page County

GENERAL HEALTH SERVICES

Health Dept **540.743.6528**
Fax 540.743.3811
75 Court Ln, Luray, VA 22835
Faye Vaughn, Office Manager

COURTS

Juvenile Court **540.743.4152**
Fax 540.743.4690
116 S Court St, Ste F, Luray, VA 22835
Susan Aleshire, Clerk Of The Court

Patrick County

JUSTICE AGENCY

Court Svcs **276.694.7209**
Fax 276.694.4007
106 Rucker St, Patrick County Administration, Stuart,
VA 24171
Robert Foster, Director

EDUCATION SERVICES

Ararat Head Start **276.251.9929**
E-mail ....gayle.clary@stepincva.com
RR 773, Ararat, VA 24053
Gayle Clary, Director

Pittsylvania County

GENERAL HEALTH SERVICES

Health Dept **434.432.7232**
Fax 434.432.7235
200 H.G. Mcgee Dr, Chatham, VA 24531
Dr. Laura Gateley, District Director

JUSTICE AGENCY

Community Policy And Management
Board **434.432.8371**
Fax 434.432.4833
18 Depot St, Chatham, VA 24531-3352
Sherry Flannagan, Chairman

COURTS

Juvenile And Domestic Relations
Court **434.432.7861**
Fax 434.432.7908
5 Bank St, Chatham, VA 24531
Cynthia Keel, Supervisor

POLICE AND SHERIFF

Sheriff's Dept **434.432.7800**
Fax 434.432.7823
E-mail ....pcso@pittgov.org
21 N Main St, Chatham, VA 24531
Mike Taylor, Sheriff

Powhatan County

SOCIAL SERVICES

Social Svcs **804.598.5630**
Fax 804.598.5614
Web ....www.powhatanva.gov
3908 Old Buckingham Rd Ste 2, Powhatan,
VA 23139-5753
Catherine Pemberton, Director

GENERAL HEALTH SERVICES

Health Dept **804.598.5680**
Fax 804.598.5688
Web ....www.vdh.virginia.gov
E-mail ....jane.emerson@vdh.virginia.gov
3908 Old Buckingham Rd Ste 3, Powhatan,
VA 23139-5753
Jane Emerson, Public Health Nurse

COURTS

Juvenile And Domestic Relations
Court **804.598.5665**
Fax 804.598.5648
E-mail ....vsouthall@courts.state.va.us
3880 Old Buckingham Rd Ste D, Powhatan,
VA 23139
Honorable Valentine W. Southall, Jr., Judge

Prince Edward County

SOCIAL SERVICES

Social Svcs.................................**434.392.3113**
Fax..434.392.8453
Web..www.dss.virginia.us
E-mail.....................roma.morris@dss.virginia.us
  111 South St, Farmville, VA 23901
  Roma Morris, Director

GENERAL HEALTH SERVICES

Piedmont Health District.................**434.392.3984**
Fax..434.392.1038
Web..www.vdh.virginia.gov
E-mail.....................alexander.samuel@vdh.virginia.gov
  111 S St, 1St Floor, Farmville, VA 23901
  Alexander Samuel, Acting District Director

JUSTICE AGENCY

Court Svcs...................................**434.392.3623**
Fax..434.315.0330
E-mail..........................har43@co.henrico.va.us
  PO Box 700, Farmville, VA 23901-0700
  Berndvine Abernathy, Probation Supervisior

Prince George County

GENERAL HEALTH SERVICES

Health Dept.................................**804.733.2630**
Fax..804.862.6127
Web.....................www.princegeorgevirginia.gov
  6450 Administration Dr, Ste 101, Prince George,
  VA 23875
  Stephanie Allen Rn, Public Health Nurse

JUSTICE AGENCY

Court Svcs Unit.............................**804.733.2786**
Fax..804.733.2787
  6610 Commons Dr, Prince George, VA 23875
  F. Woodrow Harris, Supervisor

COURTS

Juvenile And Domestic Relations

Court...**804.733.2783**
Fax..804.733.2678
Web..www.courts.state.va.us
E-mail.....................jwaymack@courts.state.va.us
  6601 Courts Dr, Prince George, VA 23875
  Honorable Jacqueline Waymack, Judge

Juvenile And Domestic Relations

Court...**804.541.2257**
Fax..804.541.2364
E-mail.....................ewinters@courts.state.va.us.
  100 E Broadway Ave, Fl 1, Hopewell, VA 23860
  John H, Weigel, Iii, Court Services Unit Director

POLICE AND SHERIFF

Sheriff's Dept...............................**804.733.2690**
Fax..804.733.2629
E-mail..........................hallin@princegeorgeva.org
  6601 Courts Drive, Prince George, VA 23875
  H.e. Allin Iii, Sheriff

Sheriff's Dept...............................**804.733.2369**
Fax..804.733.2406
Web..www.petersburg-fo.com
E-mail..........................sheriffcrawford@petersburg-fo.com
  8 Courthouse Ave, Petersburg, VA 23803-4559
  Vanessa Crawford, Sheriff

Prince William County

SOCIAL SERVICES

Social Svcs...................................**703.792.7500**
Fax..703.792.7591
Web..www.pwcgov.org
E-mail..........................jsewell@pwcgov.org
  7987 Ashton Ave, Ste 200, Manassas,
  VA 20109-8240
  Janine Sewell, Director

GENERAL HEALTH SERVICES

Prince William Health District...............**703.792.6300**
Fax..703.792.6338
Web..www.vdh.state.va.us
E-mail..........................alison.ansher@vdh.virginia.gov
  9301 Lee Ave, Manassas, VA 20110-5517
  Alison Ansher, Director

Woodbridge Health Dept...................**703.792.7300**
Fax..703.792.7311
Web..www.pwcgov.org
E-mail..........................carol.jackson@vdh.va.gov
  4001 Prince William Pkwy Ste 101, Woodbridge,
  VA 22193
  Carol Jackson, Rn, Nursing Supervisor

JUSTICE AGENCY

Juvenile Pretruss Divison Program...........**703.792.4730**
Fax..703.792.6225
E-mail..........................cwilliams@pwcgov.org
  9540 Center St Ste 303B, Manassas, VA 20110
  Carol Williams, Outreach Supervisor

COURTS

31st District Juvenile And Domestic Relations

Court...**703.792.6160**
Fax..703.792.7863
Web..www.courts.state.va.us
E-mail..........................pgluchowski@courts.state.va.us
  9311 Lee Ave Fl A, Manassas, VA 20110-5555
  Honorable Paul Gluchowski, Judge

Woodbridge East End Branch Court

Svcs..**703.792.7350**
Fax..703.792.7376
Web..........................www.courts.state.va.us/jvrdc/jvrdc.htm
  15950 Sindlinger Way, Woodbridge, VA 22191-4255
  Quattle Baun, Supervisor

POLICE AND SHERIFF

Sheriff's Dept...............................**703.792.6070**
Fax..703.792.4785
Web..www.pwcgov.org
E-mail..........................ghill@pwcgov.org
  9311 Lee Ave Fl 1A, Manassas, VA 20110-5555
  Glendell Hill, Sheriff

EDUCATION SERVICES

Special Education...........................**703.791.7287**
Fax..703.791.8803
Web..www.pwcs.edu
E-mail..........................lawsonj@pwcs.edu
  14800 Joplin Rd, Manassas, VA 20112-3909
  Jane Lawson, Phd, Director

Pulaski County

GENERAL HEALTH SERVICES

Health Dept.................................**540.994.5030**
Fax..540.994.5036
  170 4th St NW, Pulaski, VA 24301
  Molly Odell, Director

JUSTICE AGENCY

27th District Court Service Unit.............**540.980.7735**
Fax..540.980.7739
  143 3rd St NW Ste 2, Pulaski, VA 24301
  Ken Miller, Court Services Unit Director

COURTS

Juvenile And Domestic Relations

Court...**540.980.3822**
Fax..540.980.7891
Web..www.courts.state.va.us
E-mail..........................lchitwood@courts.state.va.us
  45 3rd St NW Ste 103, Pulaski, VA 24301-5041
  Honorable H. Lee Chitwood, Judge

POLICE AND SHERIFF

Sheriff's Dept...............................**540.980.7800**
Fax..540.980.7834
  86 E Main St, Pulaski, VA 24301
  James A. Davis, Sheriff

Rappahannock County

GENERAL HEALTH SERVICES

Health Dept.................................**540.675.3516**
Fax..540.675.1021
Web..www.vdh.virginia.gov
  491A Main St, Washington, VA 22747
  Currin Flynn, Rn, Public Health Nurse

JUSTICE AGENCY

Court Svcs...................................**540.675.5356**
Fax..540.675.5357
  250 Gay St, Washington, VA 22747
  Patricia Davis, Clerk

Rockbridge County

JUSTICE AGENCY

Ofc On Youth................................**540.463.4315**
Fax..540.463.5310
E-mail..........................tdunn@ci.lexington.va.us
  300 Diamond St, Lexington, VA 24450
  Tammy J. Dunn, Director

COURTS

Juvenile And Domestic Relations

Court...**540.463.5401**
Fax..540.463.4793
Web..www.djj.virginia.gov
E-mail..........................ronald.telsch@djj.virginia.gov
  150 S Main St Ste 6, Lexington, VA 24450-2364
  Ronald Telsch, Supervisor

POLICE AND SHERIFF

Sheriff's Dept...............................**540.463.7328**
Fax..540.463.5693
Web..www.rockbridge.net
E-mail..........................rcso@rockbridge.net
  258 Greenhouse Rd, Lexington, VA 24450-3717
  Robert W. Day, Sheriff

Rockingham County

GENERAL HEALTH SERVICES

Health Dept.................................**540.574.5101**
Fax..540.574.1129
  110 N Mason St, Harrisonburg, VA 22803
  G. Douglas Larson, Director

COURTS

Juvenile And Domestic Relations

Court-Probation...........................**540.564.3399**
Fax..540.564.3392
E-mail..........................mhillsman@courts.state.va.us
  53 Court Sq, Ste 212, Harrisonburg, VA 22801
  Honorable Marvin C. Hillsman, Jr., Judge

POLICE AND SHERIFF

Sheriff's Ofc................................**540.564.3800**
Fax..540.564.3865
  25 S Liberty St, Harrisonburg, VA 22801
  Donald W. Farley, Sheriff

Virginia

Russell County

SOCIAL SERVICES

Dept of Social Svcs 276.889.3031
Fax 276.889.2662
   79 Rogers St, Lebanon, VA 24266
   Carol Brunty, Director

GENERAL HEALTH SERVICES

Cumberland Plateau Health
District 276.889.7621
Fax 276.889.7695
Web ....www.vdh.state.va.us
E-mail ....jdreyzehner@vdh.state.va.us
   75 Rogers St, Lebanon, VA 24266
   John J. Dreyzehner, District Director

POLICE AND SHERIFF

Sheriff's Dept 276.889.8033
Fax 276.889.3075
Web ....www.bvunet.net
   42 Court Ave, Lebanon, VA 24266
   Steve Dye, Sheriff

EDUCATION SERVICES

Castewood Head Start Ctr 276.762.0924
Fax 804.780.8046
   Donnie Dean Dr, Castlewood, VA 24224
   Rita Bradley, Director

Scott County

GENERAL HEALTH SERVICES

Health District 276.386.1312
Fax 276.386.2116
   190 Beech St Ste 102, Gate City, VA 24251
   E Cantrell, District Director

JUSTICE AGENCY

Court Svcs 276.386.9561
Fax 276.386.2212
E-mail ....wkmcclelland@embarqmail.com
   122 Municiple Ave, Gate City, VA 24251
   Mark Thompson, Director

COURTS

Juvenile And Domestic Relations
Court 276.386.7341
Fax 276.386.2840
E-mail ....lvishnercourt.state.va.us
   202 W Jackson St, Ste 302, Gate City, VA 24251
   Jeff Hamilton, Judge

POLICE AND SHERIFF

Sheriff's Ofc 276.386.7679
Fax 276.386.2025
E-mail ....sheriff@mounet.com
   112 Water St, Gate City, VA 24251
   Jerry P. Broadwater, Sheriff

EDUCATION SERVICES

Dunggannon Head Start Ctr 276.467.2584
Fax 276.467.2584
   3308 7th Avenue, Dungannon, VA 24245
   Helen Henderson, Director

Shenandoah County

SOCIAL SERVICES

Dept Of Social Svcs 540.459.6226
Fax 540.459.6223
Web ....www.shenandoahcountyva.us
E-mail ....john.ayers@dss.virginia.gov
   494 N Main St Ste 200, Woodstock, VA 22664-1855
   John Ayers, Director

JUSTICE AGENCY

Court Svcs 540.459.6137
Fax 540.459.4161
E-mail ....donnie.grinnan@djj.virginia.gov
   215 Mill Rd Ste 209, Woodstock, VA 22664
   Donny Lee Grinnan, Probation Officer

Smyth County

GENERAL HEALTH SERVICES

Mount Rogers Health District 276.781.7450
Fax 276.781.7455
   201 Francis Marion Ln, Marion, VA 24354
   D. Craig Smith, Md, Mph, Director

COURTS

Juvenile And Domestic Relations
Court 276.782.4052
Fax 276.782.4053
   109 W Main St Ste 207, Marion, VA 24354
   Honorable Charles F. Lincoln, Judge

POLICE AND SHERIFF

Sheriff's Ofc 276.782.4056
Fax 276.782.4058
   111 W Court St, Marion, VA 24354
   R. David Bradley, Sheriff

EDUCATION SERVICES

Chilhowie Head Start Ctr 276.646.8715
Fax 276.646.8715
   809 Mason Aly, Chilhowie, VA 24319
   Wanda Halsey, Director

Southampton County

JUSTICE AGENCY

Court Svcs 757.562.8554
Fax 757.562.8557
E-mail ....morecj@djj.state.va.us
   1020 Pretlow St, Franklin, VA 23851
   Curt More, Probation Supervisor

COURTS

Juvenile And Domestic Relations
Court 757.653.2673
Fax 757.653.2656
Web ....www.courts.state.va.us
   22350 Main St, Courtland, VA 23837
   Honorable W P Council, Judge

Spotsylvania County

GENERAL HEALTH SERVICES

Health Dept 540.507.7400
Fax 540.582.2572
Web ....www.vdh.virginia.gov
   Route 208, Holbert Bldg, Spotsylvania, VA 22553
   Brooke Rossheim, District Director

JUSTICE AGENCY

CASA 540.710.6199
Fax 540.710.6162
Web ....www.rappcasa.com
E-mail ....rappcasa@verizon.net
   10401 Courthouse Rd Ste C, Spotsylvania,
   VA 22553-1719
   Jill E. Payne, Executive Director

POLICE AND SHERIFF

Sheriff's Ofc 540.582.7115
Fax 540.582.5321
E-mail ....sheriff@spotsylvania.va.us
   9101 Courthouse Rd, Spotsylvania, VA 22553
   Howard Smith, Sheriff

Stafford County

GENERAL HEALTH SERVICES

Health Dept 540.659.3101
Fax 540.659.7176
Web ....www.vdh.state.va.us
E-mail ....jjohnston@vdh.state.va.us
   1300 Courthouse Rd, Stafford, VA 22554-7232
   Jean Johnston, Nursing Supervisor

JUSTICE AGENCY

Court Svcs 540.372.1068
Fax 540.372.1155
E-mail ....vincent.butaitis@djj.virginia.gov
   601 Caroline St Ste 400, Fredericksburg,
   VA 22401-5954
   Vincent Butaitis, Deputy Director

Ofc On Youth 540.372.1149
Fax 540.372.1150
Web ....www.officeonyouth.org
E-mail ....ben@officeonyouth.org
   500 Lafayette Blvd Ste 210, Fredericksburg,
   VA 22401-6070
   Ben Nagle, Executive Director

COURTS

Juvenile And Domestic Relations
Court 540.658.8773
Fax 540.658.4640
E-mail ....jthompson@courts.state.va.us
   1300 Courthouse Rd, Stafford, VA 22555
   James B. Thompson, Clerk Of Court

POLICE AND SHERIFF

Sheriff's Dept 540.658.4450
Fax 540.658.8570
E-mail ....sheriff@co.stafford.va.us
   1225 Courthouse Rd, Stafford, VA 22555
   Charles E. Jett, Sheriff

Sussex County

SOCIAL SERVICES

Social Svcs 434.246.5511
Fax 434.246.2504
Web ....www.central.dss.state.va.us
E-mail ....chf183@central.dss.state.va.us
   20103 Princeton Rd, Newsome Bldg, Sussex,
   VA 23884
   Chequila Fields, Director

GENERAL HEALTH SERVICES

Health Dept 434.246.8611
Fax 434.246.8610
   20103 Princeton Rd, Sussex, VA 23884
   Beverly Mcgary, Public Health Nurse

Tazewell County

SOCIAL SERVICES

Social Svcs 276.988.8500
Fax 276.988.2765
Web ....www.tazewellcounty.org
   253 Chamber Dr, Tazewell, VA 24651
   Rex Texter, Director

GENERAL HEALTH SERVICES

Health Dept 276.988.5585
Fax 276.988.5471
Web ....www.vdh.virginia.gov
E-mail ....kathy.mitchell@vdh.virginia.gov
   253 Chamber Dr, Tazewell, VA 24651
   Kathy Mitchell, Public Health Nurse Supervisor

Virginia

MENTAL HEALTH SERVICES

Community Svcs Board **276.964.6702**
Fax 276.964.5669
Web ....www.cmcsb.com
E-mail ....rallison@cmcsb.com
　　113 Cumberland Rd, Cedar Bluff, VA 24609
　Ronald A. Allison, Executive Director

COURTS

Juvenile And Domestic Relations
Court **276.988.1290**
Fax 276.988.3726
Web ....www.courts.state.va.us
　　101 Main St, Tazewell, VA 24651
　Henry Barringer, Judge

Warren County

GENERAL HEALTH SERVICES

Virginia Dept Of Health **540.635.3159**
Fax 540.635.9698
Web ....http://www.vdh.state.va.us
E-mail ....charles.divine.vdh.virginia.gov
　　134 Peyton St, Front Royal, VA 22630
　Charles Divine, District Director

JUSTICE AGENCY

Juvinelle Svcs **540.636.4189**
Fax 540.636.3768
　　1 E Main St Ste 206, Front Royal, VA 22630
　James Kulp, Probation Officer

Washington County

GENERAL HEALTH SERVICES

Virginia Health Dept **276.676.5604**
Fax 276.645.1994
Web ....www.vdh.virginia.gov
E-mail ....craig.smith@vdh.virginia.gov
　　15068 Lee Hwy Ste 1000, Bristol, VA 24202-4264
　D. Craig Smith, Md, Mph, District Director

COURTS

Juvenile And Domestic Relations
Court **276.676.6284**
Fax 276.676.6268
Web ....www.djj.virginia.gov
E-mail ....randall.blevins@djj.virginia.gov
　　193 E Main St, Abingdon, VA 24210-2838
　Randall Blevins, Court Services Unit Director

POLICE AND SHERIFF

Sheriff's Dept **276.676.6000**
Fax 276.676.6248
Web ....www.washcova.com
E-mail ....fnewman@washcova.com
　　20281 Rustic Lane, Abingdon, VA 24210
　Fred P. Newman, Sheriff

EDUCATION SERVICES

Abingdon Child Development Ctr **276.628.9932**
Fax 718.325.8984
Web ....www.peopleincorp.org
　　152 Highland St SE, Abingdon, VA 24210-3718
　Ms Tomasa Gallishaw, Director

Benhams Head Start Ctr **276.466.9122**
Fax 276.628.2931
　　7741 Rich Valley Rd, Bristol, VA 24202-0439
　Robert Goldsmith, Director

Westmoreland County

GENERAL HEALTH SERVICES

Health District **804.493.1124**
Fax 804.493.9352
　　18849 Kings Hwy, A.T. Johnson Human Services Bldg,
　　Montross, VA 22520
　Chanj, Director

JUSTICE AGENCY

Westmoreland Juvenile And Domestic Relations
Court **804.493.0117**
Fax 804.493.0173
E-mail ....cviviers@courts.state.va.us
　　111 Polk St, Montross, VA 22520
　Honorable R. Michael Mckenney, Judge

Wise County

SOCIAL SERVICES

Social Svcs **276.328.8057**
Fax 276.328.8632
　　5612 N Bear Creek Rd, Wise, VA 24293
　Michael T. Mullins, Assistant Director

GENERAL HEALTH SERVICES

Lenowisco Health District **276.328.8000**
Fax 276.376.1020
Web ....www.vh.state.va.us
E-mail ....tempa.rasnick@vdh.virginia.gov
　　134 Roberts Ave SW, Wise, VA 24293
　Tempa Rasnick, Nurse Manager

COURTS

Juvenile And Domestic Relations
Court **276.328.4486**
Fax 276.328.7067
E-mail ....ewills@courts.state.va.us
　　206 E Main St # 1, Wise, VA 24293
　Honorable Elizabeth S. Wills, Judge

POLICE AND SHERIFF

Sheriff's Dept **276.328.3566**
Fax 276.328.2624
Web ....www.wiseso.net
E-mail ....sheriff@wiseso.net
　　224 Waterstreet SE, Wise, VA 24293-0916
　Ronald D. Oakes, Sheriff

EDUCATION SERVICES

Appalachia Head Start Ctr **276.565.0795**
Web ....www.kidscentralinc.com
E-mail ....dedwards@kidscentralinc.com
　　717 W Main St, Appalachia, VA 24216-1617
　Darrell Edwards, Director

Dogwood Terrace Head Start **276.523.7707**
Web ....www.dss.virginia.gov
E-mail ....darrel.edwards@dss.virginia.gov
　　181 Dogwood Terrrace, Big Stone Gap, VA 24219
　Darrel Edwards, Director

Wythe County

GENERAL HEALTH SERVICES

Health Dept **276.228.5507**
Fax 276.228.3392
Web ....www.vdh.state.va.us
　　750 W Ridge Rd, Wytheville, VA 24382-1046
　D. Craig Smith, Md, Mph, District Director

POLICE AND SHERIFF

Sheriff's Dept **276.223.6000**
Fax 276.223.6217
E-mail ....sheriff@wytheco.org
　　245 S. 4th St, Wytheville, VA 24382
　Douglas W. King, Sheriff

York County

POLICE AND SHERIFF

Sheriff's Ofc **757.890.3630**
Fax 757.890.3649
E-mail ....sheriff@yorkcounty.gov
　　301 Goodwin Neck Rd, Yorktown, VA 23692
　J.d. Diggs, Sheriff

SPECIAL SERVICES AGENCIES

ADOPTION AGENCIES

A Divorce Law Firm **757.461.9455**
Fax 757.461.9456
E-mail ....info@dmmlegal.com
　　6330 Newtown Rd Ste 200, Norfolk, VA 23502
　David Mccormick, Director

Adoption Ctr of Va **703.549.7774**
Fax 703.549.7778
Web ....www.adoptioncenter.com
E-mail ....lindaacw@aol.com
　　501 Canterbury Ln, Alexandria, VA 22314-6301
　Linda Brownlee, Director

Adoptions Together **703.689.0404**
Fax 703.689.9488
　　457 A Carlisle Dr, Herndon, VA 20170
　Janice Coldwater, Director

Beddow Marley **804.748.2277**
Fax 804.796.6775
　　9830 Lori Rd, Chesterfield, VA 23832
　Howard Marley, Owner

Bethany Christian Svc **804.360.0466**
Fax 804.726.2762
E-mail ....mbova@bethany.org
　　1510 Willow Lawn Dr Ste 203, Richmond,
　　VA 23230-3429
　Mary Beth Bova, Director

Bethany Christian Svcs **757.499.9367**
Fax 757.518.8356
Web ....www.bethany.org
　　287 Independence Blvd Ste 241, Virginia Beach,
　　VA 23462-2956
　Emily Ruppert, Director

Bethany Christian Svcs **540.373.5165**
Fax 540.373.4800
Web ....www.bethany/pregnancycenter.com
E-mail ....bcsfredricksburg@bethany.org
　　1616 Stafford Ave, Fredericksburg, VA 22401-4629
　Joan Richwine, Director

Bethany Christian Svcs **703.385.5440**
Fax 703.385.5443
Web ....www.bethany.org
E-mail ....bcsfairfax@bethany.org
　　10378 Democracy Ln Ste B, Fairfax, VA 22030-2585
　Arybeth Dova, Director

Bowen Champlin Carr Foreman **804.379.1900**
Fax 804.379.5407
Web ....www.bowenlawfirm.com
E-mail ....cbowen@bowenlawfirm.com
　　1919 Huguenot Rd Ste 300, Richmond,
　　VA 23235-4321
　Cary Bowen, Owner

Braley & Thompson **434.832.1326**
Fax 434.832.1327
E-mail ....mspaulding@rescare.com
115 Hexham Dr, Lynchburg, VA 24502-2769
Mark Spaulding, Director

Catholic Charities of the Diocese of Arlington,
Inc. **703.841.3835**
Fax 703.841.3840
Web ....www.ccda.net
200 North Glebe Road, Suite 506, Arlington,
VA 22203
COA accredited organization.

Chaplin & Gonet **804.497.7500**
Fax 804.644.5812
E-mail ....cguillory@cpglaw.com
406 W Broad St, Richmond, VA 23220-4221
Cassandra Culley, Director

Children's Home Society VA **540.226.0583**
Fax 804.353.7451
Web ....www.chsva.org
E-mail ....laura@chsva.org
2300 Fall Hill Ave Ste 238, Fredericksburg,
VA 22401-3343
Laura Ash-Brackley, Director Of Social Services

Children's Svcs of Hampton Roads/Carpe Diem of
Virginia **757.638.5500**
Fax 757.638.7740
Web ....www.childrensservicesonline.com
E-mail ....efaircloth@childrensservicesonline.com
3500 Tejo Ln Ste 100, Chesapeake, VA 23321-5258
Eliot Faircloth, Director

Commonwealth Catholic Charities **540.342.0411**
Web ....www.cccofva.org
P.O. Box 6565, Richmond, VA 23230-0565
COA accredited organization.

For Children's Sake **703.817.9890**
Fax 703.817.9860
Web ....www.fcsvirginia.com
14014 Sullyfield Cir, Ste B, Chantilly, VA 20151-1689
Deborah Evans, Founder

Forever Familys Adoption Svc **540.341.4679**
Fax 540.341.8579
Web ....www.ffasva.org
E-mail ....kwicht@ffasva.org
9 N 3rd St, Warrenton, VA 20186-3404
Kristen Wicht, Executive Director

Helping Other People's Enrichment, Inc. "H.O.P.E.",
Inc. **804.684.2555**
Fax 804.642.6722
Web ....www.hope-tfc.org
PO Box 752, Hayes, VA 23072
COA accredited organization.

Joint Council on International Children's
Svcs **703.535.8045**
Fax 703.535.8049
Web ....www.jointcouncil.org
E-mail ....intern@jointcouncil.org
117 S Saint Asaph St, Alexandria, VA 22314-3119
Tom Difilipo, Executive Director

King's Grant, A Sunnyside Community **276.634.1000**
Fax 276.634.1599
Web ....www.kingsgrant.cc
E-mail ....bsarrar@kingsgrant.cc
350 Kings Way Rd, Martinsville, VA 24112-6631
Becky Sarrar, Administrator

Rainbow Christian Svcs **703.379.1228**
Web ....www.manassaschurch.org/rainbow/
E-mail ....lynda.eubank@gmail.com
6149 Leesburg Pike, Falls Church, VA 22041
Lynda Eubank, Executive Director

Shore Adoption Svcs **757.687.8602**
Fax 757.490.6995
Web ....www.shoreadoptionservices.org
E-mail ....info@shoreadoptionservices.org
287 Independece Blvd Ste 219, Virginia Beach,
VA 23462-6541
Kimberly Vlahos, Director

UMFS **804.353.4461**
Fax 804.353.3061
Web ....www.umfs.org
3900 West Broad Street, Richmond, VA 23230
COA accredited organization.

ADVOCACY RESOURCES

Adoption Legal Svcs **703.891.2400**
E-mail ....stan@babylaw.us
1921 Gallows Rd Ste 110, Vienna, VA 22182
Stanton Phillips, Director

CASA of Central VA **434.528.2552**
Fax 434.528.2551
Web ....www.cvcasa.org
E-mail ....staff@cvcasa.org
11 Oakridge Blvd Ste 200, Lynchburg, VA 24501
Jane Francis, Executive Director

CASA of Greater Prince William **703.330.8145**
Fax 703.361.2615
E-mail ....casaofpw@earthlink.net
9384 Forestwood Ln Ste C, Manassas,
VA 20110-4748
Charlyn Hasson-brown, Executive Director

Children's Advocacy Ctr Of Bristol/Washington
Co. **276.645.5867**
Fax 276.645.0589
Web ....www.cacbwcv.org
E-mail ....kroark@cacbwcv.org
14071 Lee Hwy, Bristol, VA 24202
Kathy Roark, Executive Director

Community Psychological Resources **757.622.6794**
E-mail ....cpr@cprs.hrcoxmail.com
249 W York St, Norfolk, VA 23510
Margret McDowlen, Owner

Stop Child Abuse Now (SCAN) of Northern Virginia/Alexandria
CASA Program **703.820.9001**
Fax 703.820.9002
Web ....www.scanva.org
E-mail ....info@scanva.org
1705 Fern Street, 2nd Floor, Alexandria, VA 22302
Sonia Quinonec, Executive Director

Tidewater Youth Services Commission **757.488.9161**
Fax 757.488.9652
Web ....www.trghc.org
E-mail ....lfillipe@trghc.org
2404 Airline Blvd, Portsmouth, VA 23701-2912
Linda Fillipe, Executive Director

Youth Planning And Development **804.796.7100**
Fax 804.748.1099
E-mail ....youthservices@chesterfield.gov
9700 Krause Rd, Chesterfield, VA 23832
Jana D. Carter, Director

BEHAVIORAL HEALTH TREATMENT

Agape Counseling & Therapeutic **757.871.8734**
Fax 757.244.1103
Web ....www.agapecounselingva.com
E-mail ....the333scotts@aol.com
12 Salters Creek Rd, Suite B, Hampton, VA 23661
Sherie Mawusi, Director

Alcohol & Drug Youth Svcs **703.533.5636**
Fax 703.532.0597
107 Park Pl, Falls Church, VA 22046-4513
Chris Volz, Site Director

Alice C. Tyler Village of Childhelp East **540.399.1926**
Web ....www.childhelp.org
E-mail ....nlynn@childhelp.org
23164 Dragoon Road, Lignum, VA 22726
Mrs. Nancy Lynn, Accreditation Manager
Joint Commission accredited organization.

Alikhan Medical Practice **703.521.6004**
46 S Glebe Rd, Arlington, VA 22204
Roohi Alikhan, Psychiatrist

Anger & Stress Management Ctr Inc **703.293.9231**
Web ....www.angerawareness.com
E-mail ....lgrowe@angerawareness.com
10375 Democracy Ln Ste B, Fairfax, VA 22030-2554
Loretta Rowe, Director

Annibali Medical Practice **703.827.2247**
Fax 703.556.4093
E-mail ....joseph.annibali@verizon.net
1489 Chain Bridge Rd Ste 201, McLean,
VA 22101-5724
Joseph Annibali, MD, Psychiatrist

Arlington Psychiatric Group **703.525.5111**
Fax 703.243.9126
Web ....www.sensiblepsychiatry.com
E-mail ....lawrenceballon@gmail.com
1715 N George Mason Dr Ste 104, Arlington,
VA 22205-3639
Lawerence M. Ballon, M.D., Psychiatrist

Aurora House (Falls Church Girl's Group
Home) **703.237.6622**
Fax 703.237.6624
E-mail ....econklin@fallschurchva.gov
420 S Maple Ave, Falls Church, VA 14950
Earl Conklin, Director

Baker Medical Practice **703.759.3784**
10800 Georgetown Pike, Great Falls, VA 22066-1604
Stephen Baker, Psychiatrist

Balzarett Medical Practice **703.893.8585**
Fax 703.893.3879
8206 Leesburg Pike Ste 406, Vienna, VA 22182-2614
Josph Balzaret, Psychiatrist

Behavioral Health Services **276.926.1682**
Fax 276.926.8134
Web ....www.dcbhs.org
E-mail ....joseph.fuller@dcbhs.com
133 McClure Ave, Clintwood, VA 24228
Paulette Phillips, Clinical Services Director

Behavioral Healthcare Svcs **757.393.8618**
Fax 757.393.5226
Web ....www.portsmouthva.gov
E-mail ....wpark@portsmouthva.gov
600 Dinwiddie St, Portsmouth, VA 23704-3614
William Park, Director

Belisle Medical Practice **703.670.3772**
Fax 703.670.2611
2296 Opitz Blvd Ste 270, Woodbridge,
VA 22191-3345
Karen Belisle, Psychiatrist

Bigelow Medical Practice **703.548.7751**
109 S Fairfax St, Alexandria, VA 22314-3301
Llewellyn Bigelow, Psychiatrist

Biofeedback Clinic Of Virginia **703.370.8060**
Web ....www.burkeanimal.com
5249 Duke St Ste 210, Alexandria, VA 22307-2907
Philip Greco, MD, Psychiatrist

Blue Ridge Counseling **540.662.7555**
Fax 540.662.9105
335 Westside Station Dr, Winchester, VA 22601-2840
Glenn Claugherty, Psychiatrist

Boys Home Inc. **540.965.7700**
Fax 540.965.7702
E-mail ....dewheatley@boyshomeinc.com
306 Boys Home Rd, Covington, VA 24426-5599
Donnie Wheatley, Executive Director

Brain Injury Services of Southwest
Virginia 540.344.1200
Fax 540.344.9755
Web ....http://www.bisswva.org
302 Second Street, Third Floor, Roanoke, VA 24011
CARF accredited programs available.

Bridge House 804.333.4033
Fax 804.333.1195
Web ....www.bridgehouse.org
E-mail ....basye@rivnet.net
264 Threeway Rd, Warsaw, VA 22572-3433
Mercer V. Basye, Lpc, Director

Bridges Treatment Ctr - Centra Health Mental Health
Svcs 434.947.5700
Fax 434.947.5708
Web ....www.centrahealth.com
E-mail ....john.hendrickson@centrahealth.com
693 Leesville Rd, Lynchburg, VA 24502-2828
John Hendrickson, Md, Medical Director

Camp Medical Practice 804.285.0931
208 Overlook Rd, Henrico, VA 23229-8511
Norman Camp, Psychiatrist

Central Virginia Community Services 434.847.8050
Fax 434.455.3079
Web ....www.cvcsb.org
2241 Langhorne Rd, Lynchburg, VA 24501
Nancy Cottingham, Director
CARF accredited programs available.

Chaffee Medical Practice 703.288.9360
1317 Vincent Pl, McLean, VA 22101-3615
Melissa Chaffee, MD, Psychiatrist

Chaplin Youth Ctr 540.371.0590
Fax 540.374.5082
Web ....www.staffnet.com
E-mail ....kvantine.chaplin@verizon.net
125 Hot Top Rd, Fredericksburg, VA 22405-2676
Kristin Van Tine, Director

Cheasapeake CSB MH 757.548.7020
Fax 757.819.6292
Web ....www.chesapeakecsb.net
224 Great Bridge Blvd, Chesapeake, VA 23320-3904
Joseph Scislowicz, Director

Chesapeake Juvenile Svcs 757.382.6788
Fax 757.382.8813
Web ....www.tdh.city.chesapeake.va.us
E-mail ....staylor@tdh.city.chesapeake.va.us
420 Albemarle Dr, Chesapeake, VA 23322-5504
Sam Taylor, Superintendent

Chesterfield Community Services Board 804.768.7220
Fax 804.768.9205
Web ....www.chesterfield.gov
E-mail ....braunsteing@chesterfield.gov
6801 Lucy Corr Boulevard, Chesterfield, VA 23832
George Braunstein, Executive Director
CARF accredited programs available.

Chesterfield Youth Group Home 804.748.1612
Fax 804.748.1295
9610 Krause Rd, Chesterfield, VA 23832
Deborah S. Dugger, Director

Child and Adolescent Psychiatric Program - Virginia Baptist
Hospital 434.947.4444
Fax 434.947.4145
Web ....www.centrahealth.com
3300 Rivermont Ave, Lynchburg, VA 24503
Gregory Fisher, Medical Director

Chmiel Medical Ctr 703.281.4457
501 Church St Ne Ste #202, Vienna, VA 22180-4241
Andrew Chmiel, Psychiatrist

Christopher Newport University 757.594.7047
Fax 757.594.7639
E-mail ....atieman@cnu.edu
1 University Pl, Newport News, VA 23606
Anita Tieman, Director

Clinical Psychology Svcs 703.691.1326
Fax 703.691.3553
Web ....www.clinicalpsychologyservices.com
E-mail ....info@clinicalpsychologyservices.com
11130 Fairfax Blvd Ste 305, Fairfax, VA 22030-7173
Susan Murdock, Psycologist

Commonwealth Center for Children and
Adolescents 540.332.2100
Web ....www.ccca.dmhmrsas.virginia.gov
E-mail ....don.roe@dbhds.virginia.gov
1355 Richmond Road, Staunton, VA 24401
Dr. Don Roe, Accreditation Manager
Joint Commission accredited organization.

Community Attention Home 434.970.3343
Fax 434.970.3356
Web ....www.charlottesville.org
E-mail ....straussh@charlottesville.org
414 4th St NE, Charlottesville, VA 22902-4722
Hank Strauss, Director

Connect The Dots 757.962.9503
Fax 757.962.2700
1216 Granby St Ste 209, Norfolk, VA 23510-2622
June Wren, Director

Counseling Ctr Of Fairfax 703.385.7575
Fax 703.385.7578
Web ....www.ccf-web.com
E-mail ....cme@ccf.org
10470 Armstrong St, Fairfax, VA 22030-3648
Karen Roasller

Ctr For Clinical And Forensics 703.278.0487
10650 Main St, Fairfax, VA 22030
Sussane Oshry, Contact

Ctr For Holistic Therapy 703.370.1049
1198 Janneys Ln, Alexandria, VA 22302-3801
Luanna, Psychiatrist

Ctr for Integrative 703.255.3406
Fax 703.255.3409
307 Maple Ave W Ste k, Vienna, VA 22180-4301
Joseph Corbo, Md, Psychiatrist

Ctr for Sexual Assault Survivors 757.599.9844
Fax 757.599.9846
Web ....www.visitthecenter.org
E-mail ....sgray@visitthecenter.org
11030 Warwick Blvd, Ste A, Newport News,
VA 23601-3251
Shauna Gray, Director

Cumberland Barton House 804.228.2280
Fax 804.228.2283
2811 Moss Side Ave, Richmond, VA 23222-3536
Gay Brooks, CEO

Cumberland Hospital for Children and
Adolescents 804.966.2242
E-mail ....gay.brooks@psysolutions.com
9407 Cumberland Road, New Kent, VA 23124
Ms. Gay Brooks, Accreditation Manager
Joint Commission accredited organization.

Curcio Medical Ctr 703.790.9610
2251 Pimmit Dr Ste C3, Falls Church, VA 22043-2832
Edward Curcio, Psychiatrist

Dominion Hospital 703.538.2882
Web ....www.dominionhospital.com
E-mail ....donald.kniffen@hcahealthcare.com
2960 Sleepy Hollow Road, Falls Church, VA 22044
Mr. Donald Kniffen, Accreditation Manager
Joint Commission accredited organization.

Dunn Medical Ctr 540.428.0060
35 Horner St Ste 200, Warrenton, VA 20186-3433
Maria Dunn, Psychiatrist

Dunn Medical Practice 703.444.5700
Fax 703.404.2703
6 Pidgeon Hill Dr Ste 260, Sterling, VA 20165-6147
Cherly Dunn, Psychiatrist

Ed Murphy & Associates 540.368.3098
Web ....www.fairwindsgrouphome.com
E-mail ....ejm50@aol.com
2217 Princess Anne Street, Suite 200-1,
Fredericksburg, VA 22401
Mr. Ed Murphy, Accreditation Manager
Joint Commission accredited organization.

Elk Hill Farm 804.457.4866
Fax 804.457.2830
Web ....www.elkhill.org
E-mail ....ehfinc@aol.com
1975 Elk Hill Rd, Goochland, VA 23063
Michael Farley, Ba, Executive Director

Fairfax-Falls Church Community Services
Board 703.324.7000
Fax 703.324.7092
Web ....http://www.fairfaxcounty.gov/csb
12011 Government Center Parkway, Suite 836,
Fairfax, VA 22035-1105
CARF accredited programs available.

Family Impact, Inc 434.238.5602
Web ....www.familyimpactinc.org
E-mail ....ericmattocks@gmail.com
304 Turner Road, Ste C, Richmond, VA 23225
Mr. Eric Mattocks, Accreditation Manager
Joint Commission accredited organization.

Family Service of Roanoke Valley 540.563.5316
Fax 540.563.5254
Web ....www.fsrv.org
360 Campbell Avenue SW, Roanoke, VA 24016
COA accredited organization.

Fernando Medical Practice 757.423.3740
110 Maycox Ave Ste 2, Norfolk, VA 23505-3433
Thomas Fernando, Psychitrist

Fifteenth Judicial Circuit 540.372.1066
Fax 540.310.0637
E-mail ....smitchell@courts.state.va.us
815 Princess Anne St, Fredericksburg, VA 22401-5819
Sharron S. Mitchell, Clerk Of Court

Fisher Medical Practice 804.740.7132
9202 Waterloo Ct, Henrico, VA 23229-6024
Qwen Fisher, Psychiatrist

Flint Hill School 703.584.2300
Fax 703.242.0718
Web ....www.flinthill.org
3320 Jermantown Rd, Oakton, VA 22124
John Thomas, Headmaster

Foster Medical Practice 703.771.4186
201 S King St, Leesburg, VA 20175-2905
Douglas Foster, Psychiatrist

Grafton School, Inc. 540.542.0200
Fax 540.667.8721
Web ....www.grafton.org
E-mail ....asmith@grafton.org
120 Bellview Avenue, Winchester, VA 22601
Amy Smith, Director
CARF accredited programs available.

Graydon Manor 703.777.3485
Web ....www.graydonmanor.org
E-mail ....eroehr@graydonmanor.org
801 Children's Center Road, SW, Leesburg, VA 20175
Mrs. M. Roehr, Accreditation Manager
Joint Commission accredited organization.

Group Medical Practice 703.841.1290
Fax 703.841.1315
E-mail ....lsheehan@mind-shape.com
2501 N Glebe Rd Ste 303, Arlington, VA 22207-3558
Gary Spivack, Psychiatrist

Hallmark Youthcare - Richmond 804.784.2200
Web ....www.hallmarkyouthcare.org
E-mail ....chris.ordonia@hallmarksystems.com
12800 West Creek Parkway, Richmond, VA 23238
Ms. Christina Ordonia, Accreditation Manager
Joint Commission accredited organization.

Hanover Community Services 804.365.4289
Fax 804.365.4282
Web ....http://www.co.hanover.va.us/csb/default.
　12300 Washington Highway, Ashland, VA 23005
　CARF accredited programs available.

Henrico Area Mental Health and Retardation
Services 804.727.8581
Fax 804.727.8580
Web ....www.co.henrico.va.us/mhmr/
　10299 Woodman Road, Glen Allen, VA 23060
　CARF accredited programs available.

Inova Kellar Center 703.218.8500
Web ....www.inova.org
E-mail ....judith.lemke@inova.org
　11204 Waples Mill Road, Fairfax, VA 22030-2522
　Ms. Judith Lemke, Accreditation Manager
　Joint Commission accredited organization.

Jackson-Feild Homes 434.634.3217
Fax 434.634.7008
Web ....www.jacksonfeild.org
　546 Walnut Grove Drive, Jarratt, VA 23867
　COA accredited organization.

Jefferson Trail Treatment Center for
Children 434.977.1523
E-mail ....james.harris@psysolutions.com
　2101 Arlington Boulevard, Charlottesville, VA 22903
　Mr. James Harris, Accreditation Manager
　Joint Commission accredited organization.

Jefferson Tylors Treatment System 434.977.1523
Fax 434.977.3693
Web ....www.jeffersontaylors.com
E-mail ....taylor.davis@psysolutions.com
　2101 Arlington Blvd, Charlottesville, VA 22903-1521
　James Chrris, CEO

Jewish Family Svc of Tidewater, Inc. 757.459.4640
Fax 757.459.4643
Web ....www.jfshamptonroads.org
E-mail ....counseling@jfshamptonroads.org
　260 Grayson Rd, Virginia Beach, VA 23462-4345
　Debra F. Mayer, Lcsw, Clinical Director

Judge Patrick D. Molinari Juvenile Shelter 703.330.1660
Fax 703.330.4753
E-mail ....bjones@pwcgov.org
　8642 Wellington Rd, Manassas, VA 20109-3916
　Garderick Godgard, Supervisor

Lafayette School 434.971.8636
Fax 434.977.8529
Web ....www.lafayetteschool.net
E-mail ....lafayetteschool@netscape.net
　3020 Fontaine Ave Extended, Charlottesville,
　VA 22903
　Ron Strawley, Director

Lewis-Gale Medical Center, LLC 540.776.4000
Web ....www.lewis-gale.com
E-mail ....cami.jones@hcahealthcare.com
　1900 Electric Road, Salem, VA 24153
　Ms. Camilla Jones, Accreditation Manager
　Joint Commission accredited organization.

Liberty Point Behavioral Healthcare, LLC 540.213.0450
Web ....www.libertypointstaunton.com
E-mail ....kathryn.dickerson@uhsinc.com
　1110 Montgomery Ave., Staunton, VA 24401
　Miss Kathryn Dickerson, Accreditation Manager
　Joint Commission accredited organization.

Loudoun Youth Shelter 703.771.5300
Fax 703.771.5304
Web ....www.nafi.com
　16450 Meadowview Ct, Leesburg, VA 20175
　Barbara Wuyant, Director

Marion Youth Ctr 276.782.1990
Fax 276.782.1996
Web ....www.kidlinknetwork.com
　225 State St, Marion, VA 24354
　Susan Ferraro, Director Of Admissions

New River Valley Community Services 540.961.8300
Fax 540.557.4042
Web ....www.NRVCS.org
E-mail ....lsaltzberg@nrvcs.org
　700 University City Boulevard, Blacksburg, VA 24060
　Les Saltzberg, Director
　CARF accredited programs available.

New Vistas School 434.846.0301
Fax 434.528.1004
E-mail ....cmorgan@newvistasschool.org
　520 Eldon St, Lynchburg, VA 24501-3604
　Charlotte Morgan, Head Of School

Newport News Behavioral Health Center 757.888.0400
E-mail ....carey.chappell@uhsinc.com
　17579 Warwick Boulevard, Newport News, VA 23603
　Ms. Carey Chappell, Accreditation Manager
　Joint Commission accredited organization.

North Spring Behavioral Healthcare 703.777.0800
Web ....www.northspringleesburg.com
E-mail ....kelly.neverson@psysolutions.com
　42009 Victory Lane, Leesburg, VA 20176
　Ms. Kelly Neverson, Accreditation Manager
　Joint Commission accredited organization.

Patrick Henry Boys & Girls Plantation 434.376.2006
Fax 434.376.3003
Web ....www.patrickhenry.org
E-mail ....info@patrickhenry.org
　860 Red Hill Rd, Brookneal, VA 24528
　Robert J Day, Executive Director

Poplar Springs Hospital 804.733.6874
Web ....www.poplarsprings.com
E-mail ....christina.bargdill2@psysolutions.com
　350 Poplar Drive, Petersburg, VA 23805
　Ms. Christina Bargdill, Accreditation Manager
　Joint Commission accredited organization.

Prince William Group Home For Girls 703.791.3650
Fax 703.791.3438
Web ....www.pwcgov.org
E-mail ....tstott@pwcgov.org
　14879 Dumfries Rd, Manassas, VA 20112-3941
　Terri Stott, Director

Psychiatric Care 804.706.1282
Web ....www.chesterfield.gov
E-mail ....moehlm@chesterfield.gov
　10111 Krause Rd, Chesterfield, VA 23832-6573
　Mary Moehl, Doctor

Rappahannock Area Community Service
Board 540.373.3223
Fax 540.371.3753
Web ....www.racsb.state.va.us
　600 Jackson Street, Fredericksburg, VA 22401
　CARF accredited programs available.

Region Ten Community Services Board 434.972.1800
Fax 434.293.2015
Web ....www.regionten.org
　800 Preston Avenue, Charlottesville, VA 22903
　CARF accredited programs available.

Riverside Behavioral Health Center 757.827.1001
Web ....www.riversideonline.com
E-mail ....monika.mockatis@rivhs.com
　2244 Executive Drive, Hampton, VA 23666
　Ms. Monika Mockatis, Accreditation Manager
　Joint Commission accredited organization.

Southside Community Svcs Board 434.572.6916
Fax 434.572.4881
Web ....www.sscsb.org
　424 Hamilton Blvd, South Boston, VA 24592-5200
　Donald Burge, Executive Director

The Barry Robinson Center 757.455.6100
Web ....www.barryrobinson.org
E-mail ....nholcomb@barryrobinson.org
　443 Kempsville Road, Norfolk, VA 23502
　Ms. Nancy Holcomb, Accreditation Manager
　Joint Commission accredited organization.

The Hughes Center for Exceptional
Children 434.836.8500
Fax 434.836.8552
Web ....www.thehughescenter.com
　1601 Franklin Turnpike, Danville, VA 24540
　CARF accredited programs available.

The Pines Residential Treatment Center 757.393.0061
Web ....psysolutions.com
E-mail ....jacqueline.lipscomb@uhsinc.com
　825 Crawford Parkway, Portsmouth, VA 23704
　Ms. Jacqueline Lipscomb, Accreditation Manager
　Joint Commission accredited organization.

Vanguard Services Unlimited 703.841.0703
Fax 703.841.2316
Web ....www.vanguardservices.org
　521 North Quincy Street, Arlington, VA 22203
　CARF accredited programs available.

Virginia Beach Psychiatric Center 757.496.6000
Web ....www.vbpcweb.com
E-mail ....fran.neaves@uhsinc.com
　1100 First Colonial Road, Virginia Beach, VA 23454
　Ms. Fran Neaves, Accreditation Manager
　Joint Commission accredited organization.

Virginia Beach Psychiatric Ctr (VBPC) 757.496.6000
Fax 757.496.4550
Web ....www.absfirst.com
　1100 First Colonial Rd, Virginia Beach,
　VA 23454-2403
　Frank Gallangher, Administrator

Virginia Treatment Ctr for Children 804.828.3129
Fax 804.828.3504
Web ....www.vcuhealth.org
　515 N 10th St, Richmond, VA 23298
　Robert Cohen, Director

Visions Therapeutic Services 804.732.4281
Fax 804.862.2644
Web ....www.visionsfamilyservices.org
　408 South Sycamore Street, Petersburg, VA 23803
　CARF accredited programs available.

Woodburn Ctr for Community Mental
Health 703.573.0523
Fax 703.280.9518
Web ....www.fairfaxcounty.gov
E-mail ....charles.mauer@fairfaxcounty.gov
　3340 Woodburn Rd, Annandale, VA 22003
　Charlie Mauer, Emergency Services

Youth & Family Svcs 540.586.7652
Fax 540.587.5673
　122 E Main St, Suite G-01, Bedford, VA 24523
　Cristal Hullette, Sr. Supervisor

Youth Villages of Washington DC 703.516.6940
Web ....www.youthvillages.org
E-mail ....hughes.johnson@youthvillages.org
　2020 North 14th Street, Arlington, VA 22201
　Mr. Hughes Johnson, Accreditation Manager
　Joint Commission accredited organization.

CHILDREN'S HOSPITAL

Augusta Health 540.932.4000
　78 Medical Center Dr, Fishersville, VA 22939
　Mary Mannix, Chief Executive Officer

Bon Secours St Mary's Hospital 804.285.2011
　5801 Bremo Rd, Richmond, VA 23226
　Tony Ardavell, Chief Executive Officer

Carilion New River Valley Medical Ctr 540.731.2000
　2900 Lamb Cir, Christiansburg, VA 24073
　John Piagkowski, Chief Executive Officer

Carilion Roanoke Memorial Hospital 540.981.7000
　Belleview at Jefferson St, Roanoke, VA 24014
　Nancy Age, Chief Executive Officer

Centra Health 434.200.3000
1901 Tate Springs Rd, Lynchburg, VA 24501
George Dawson, Chief Executive Officer

Chesapeake Regional Medical Centre 757.312.8121
Web .... www.chesapeakeregional.com
736 Battlefield Blvd N, Chesapeake, VA 23320
Elaine Griffiths, Director of Nursing

Children's Hospital 757.668.7000
601 Childrens Ln, Norfolk, VA 23507
Jim Dahling, President

Clinch Valley Medical Center 276.596.6000
6801 Governor G C Perry Hwy, Richlands, VA 24641
David Darden, Chief Executive Officer

Community Hospital 276.228.0200
600 W Ridge Rd, Wytheville, VA 24382
Tim Bess, Chief Executive Officer

Community Hospital 276.782.1234
565 Radio Hill Rd, Marion, VA 24354
Lindy White, Chief Executive Officer

Culpeper Regional Hospital 540.829.4100
E-mail .... lkirk@culpeperregionalhospital.com
501 Sunset Ln, Culpeper, VA 22701
H.lee Kirk, Chief Executive Officer

Danville Regional Medical Center 434.799.2100
142 S Main St, Danville, VA 24541
Eric Deaton, Chief Executive Officer

Halifax Regional Hospital 434.517.3100
2204 Wilborn Ave, South Boston, VA 24592

Henrico Doctors' Hospital 804.289.4500
1602 Skipwith Rd, Richmond, VA 23229

Inova Alexandria Hospital 703.504.3000
4320 Seminary Rd, Alexandria, VA 22304
Christine Candio, Chief Executive Officer

Inova Fair Oaks Hospital 703.391.3600
E-mail .... john.fitzgerald@inova.org
3600 Joseph Siewick Dr, Fairfax, VA 22033
John Fitzgerald, Chief Executive Officer

Inova Fairfax Hospital 703.776.4001
3300 Gallows Rd, Falls Church, VA 22042
Reuven Pasternak, Chief Executive Officer

Inova Loudon Hospital 703.858.6000
44045 Riverside Pkwy, Leesburg, VA 20176
Randall Kelley, Administrator/CEO

Johnston-Willis Hospital 804.320.3911
7101 Jahnke Rd, Richmond, VA 23225
Peter Mararstein, Chief Executive Officer

Martha Jefferson Hospital 434.654.7000
459 Locust Ave, Charlottesville, VA 22911

Mary Washington Hospital 540.741.1100
1001 Sam Perry Blvd, Fredericksburg, VA 22401
Fred Rankin, Chief Executive Officer

Memorial Regional Medical Center 804.764.6000
8260 Atlee Rd, Mechanicsville, VA 23116
Michael Robinson, Chief Executive Officer

Montgomery Regional Hospital 540.951.1111
E-mail .... mrh@hcahealthcare.com
3700 S Main St, Blacksburg, VA 24060
Scott Hill, Chief Executive Officer

Potomac Hospital 703.670.1313
2300 Opitz Blvd, Woodbridge, VA 22191
Megan Terry, Chief Executive Officer

Prince William Hospital 703.369.8000
8700 Sudley Rd, Manassas, VA 20110
John Williams, Head Of Securities

Regional Hospital 276.236.8181
200 Hospital Dr, Galax, VA 24333
Jon Applebaum, Chief Executive Officer

Restion Hospital Center 703.689.9000
1850 Town Center Pkwy, Reston, VA 20190
Tim McManus, Chief Executive Officer

Riverside Regional Medical Center 757.594.2000
500 J Clyde Morris Blvd, Newport News, VA 23601
Dr. Partick Parcells, Chief Executive Officer

Rockingham Memorial Hospital 540.689.1000
2010 Heath Campus Dr, Harrisonburg, VA 22801
James Krauss, Chief Executive Officer

Sentara Virginia Beach General Hospital 757.395.8000
1060 First Colonial Rd, Virginia Beach, VA 23454
Dr. Raymond Troiano, President

Sentara Williamsburg Regional Center 757.984.6000
100 Sentara Circle, Williamsburg, VA 23188
David Bernd, Chief Executive Officer

Southern Virginia Regional Medical Ctr 434.348.4400
727 N Main St, Emporia, VA 23847
Brit Phelps, Chief Executive Officer

Southside Community Hospital 434.392.8811
800 Oak St, Farmville, VA 23901
EW Tibbs, President

University of Virginia Medical Center 434.924.0211
1215 Lee St, Charlottesville, VA 22908
Chris Robertson, Office Manager

**Virginia Commonwealth University Med
Ct** 804.828.9000
1250 E Marshall St, Richmond, VA 23219
John Dubal, Chief Executive Officer

Warren Memorial Hospital 540.636.0300
1000 Shenandoah Ave, Front Royal, VA 22630
Patrick Nolan, Chief Executive Officer

Wellmont Lonesome Pine Hospital 276.523.3111
1990 Holton Ave E, Big Stone Gap, VA 24219
Kellie Carter, Nursing Director

COUNSELING SERVICES

Children's Home Society 804.353.0191
Fax 804.353.7451
Web .... www.chsva.org/
E-mail .... marsh-cartern@chsva.org
4200 Fitzhugh Ave, Richmond, VA 23230-3829
Nadine Marsh-carter, President/CEO

Children's Svcs Of Virginia 703.331.0075
Fax 703.331.0078
Web .... www.childrensservicesofva.com
E-mail .... samsabbagh@csv-inc.com
7545 Presidential Ln, Manassas, VA 20109-3795
Sam Sabbagh, Executive Director

Community Solutions 757.461.5098
Fax 757.461.4088
Web .... www.community-solutions.net
E-mail .... kgreen@comsolva.com
5752 Princess Anne Rd, Virginia Beach,
VA 23462-3225
Kimberly Green, Director

KidsPeace Foster Care And Family Svcs 804.594.7214
Fax 804.594.7051
Web .... www.fostercare.com
553 Southlake Boulevard Suites A & B, Richmond,
VA 23236
Ray Culp, National Director Foster Care & Family Services

LDS Family Svcs 804.743.0727
Fax 804.743.8729
Web .... www.ldsfamilyservices.org
E-mail .... fam-va@ldsfamilyservices.org
8110 Virginia Pine Ct, Richmond, VA 23237-2203
Kurt Olsson, Counsil Manager

CRISIS & SHELTER CARE

American Redcross 804.458.6007
Fax 804.541.1988
E-mail .... andrewsr@usa.redcross.org
110 N. Main Street, Hopewell, VA 23860
Roselyn Andrews, Director

Avalon Center For Woman $ Children 757.258.5022
Fax 757.258.9523
E-mail .... cathyleen@avaloncenter.org
2968 John Tyler Hwy, Williamsburg, VA 23185
Sarah Neacham, Director

Bedford Domestic Violence Svcs 540.587.0970
Fax 540.586.1687
E-mail .... bdvs@co.bedford.va.us
PO Box 783, Bedford, VA 24523-0783
Leanne Dudley, Director

**Bethany House of Virginia Domestic
Violence** 703.658.9500
Fax 703.658.9522
6121 Lincolnia Rd Ste 303, Alexandria, VA 22312
Catherine Hassinger, Director

Cares Inc Domestic Violence Program 804.861.0849
Fax 804.722.0987
E-mail .... careshome@aol.com
244 Halifax St, Petersburg, VA 23803
Jean Grim, Social Worker

**Chesterfield Vctm Witness Asstnc
Program** 804.717.6179
Fax 804.796.6285
E-mail .... bernharde@chesterfield.gov
7000 Lucy Corr Boulevard, Chesterfield, VA 23832
Elizabeth Bernhar, Director

Counseling On Domestic Violence 540.743.4730
Fax 540.843.3251
E-mail .... debbiedart@choicesofpagecounty.org
216 W Main St, Luray, VA 22835-1235
Debbie Dart, Director

Domestic Violence Program 703.746.4911
Fax 703.746.3280
E-mail .... claire.dunn@alexandriava.gov
421 King St Ste 400, Alexandria, VA 22314-3121
Claire Dunn, Coordinator

**Doorways For Women And Family Domestic
Violence** 703.237.0881
Fax 703.237.1146
Web .... www.doorways.va.org
E-mail .... kbarnes@doorways.va.org
4600 N FAIRFAX DR, Arlington, VA 22203-4420
Kristen Barnes, Director

**Eastern Shore Coalition Against Domestic
Violence** 757.787.1329
Fax 757.787.3829
E-mail .... edrewniak@escadverizon.net
155 Market St, Onancock, VA 23417
Eleanor Drewniak, Director

Family Resource Ctr 540.483.5088
Fax 540.483.1368
E-mail .... cindytreadway@franklincountyva.org
100 S. Main St, Rocky Mount, VA 24151
Cynthia Treadway, Director

Family Resource Ctr Domestic Violence 276.625.0219
Fax 276.228.7152
E-mail .... path@frc-inc.org
2171 W Lee Hwy, Wytheville, VA 24382
Patricia Helton, Executive Director

Family Violence Prevention Program 434.348.0100
Fax 434.348.9319
E-mail .... Turnernm@Telpage.Net
420 S Main St, Emporia, VA 23847-2314
Nancy Turner, Director

First Step Response to Domestic Violence 540.434.0295
Fax 540.433.4074
E-mail .... firststepva@gmail.com
129 Franklin St, Harrisonburg, VA 22801
Candy Phillips, Director

Hampton Place 757.683.8680
Fax 757.683.2839
E-mail ....william.ford@djj.virginia.gov
   3701 Granby St, Norfolk, VA 23504-1316
Gloria Emanuel, Interem Director

Hanover Safe Place- Domestic Violence 804.752.2728
Fax 804.752.2738
   629 A N Washington Hwy, Ashland, VA 23005
Sheree Handrick, Director

Help and Emergency Responce Inc 757.485.1445
Fax 757.485.0883
Web ....www.hershelter.com
E-mail ....beth@hershelter.com
   PO Box 2187, Portsmouth, VA 23702-0187
Elizabeth Cross, Executive Director

Hope House Of Scott Domestic Violence 276.386.1373
Fax 276.386.1252
E-mail ....director@hopehousescottcounty.org
   231 W Jackson St, Gate City, VA 24251-4128
Marge Quilles, Director

Jackson-Field Homes, Inc. 434.634.3217
Fax 434.634.6467
Web ....www.jackson-fieldhomes.org
E-mail ....pdelano@jackson-fieldhomes.org
   546 Walnut Grove Dr, Jarratt, VA 23867-8611
Patricia Delano, Executive Director

Laurel Shelter Inc Domestic Violence 804.694.5552
Fax 804.694.5286
Web ....www.laurelshelterinc.org
E-mail ....cstone@ccsinc.com
   PO Box 23, Gloucester, VA 23061-0023
Cherie Stone, Director

Leesburg Victims Witness Ofc 703.777.0417
Fax 703.737.8844
Web ....www.lees-summit.mo.us
E-mail ....nick.wittmann@lees-summit.mo.us
   20 East Market Street, Leesburg, VA 22075
Nicole Wittmann, Director

Loudoun Abused Womens Shelter 703.771.3398
Fax 703.771.7865
E-mail ....susan.curtis@lcsj.org
   105 E Market St, Leesburg, VA 20176
Susan Curtis, Director

New Direction Ctr Domestic Violence 540.885.7273
Fax 540.885.0686
E-mail ....slong@newdircenter.com
   23 N New St, Staunton, VA 24401
Stacy Long, Director

Northern Virginia Family Service 703.370.3223
Fax 703.751.5197
E-mail ....cfreeman@nvfs.org
   5249 Duke St Ste 308, Alexandria, VA 22304
Carol Freeman, Program Manager

Peole Inc Domestic Violence Program 276.935.4747
Fax 276.935.4368
E-mail ....phurley@peopleinc.net
   1173 W Main St, Abingdon, VA 24210
Peggy Hurley, Director

**Rappahannock Council on Domestic
Violence** 540.373.9372
Fax 540.373.0794
E-mail ....kathy@rcdv.com
   4700 Harrison Rd, potsylvania, VA 22408
Kathy Anderson, Director

Response Inc-Domestic Violence 540.459.5599
Fax 540.459.5799
E-mail ....response@shentel.net
   PO Box 287, Woodstock, VA 22664-0287
Kristie Wilkin, Director

Richmond Detention Home 804.646.2937
Fax 804.646.2990
Web ....www.richmondgov.com
E-mail ....Diane.gadow@richmondgov.com
   1700 Oliver Hill Way, Richmond, VA 23219-1234
Dianne Gadow, Superintendent

**Safe Home System, Inc - Domestic
Violence** 540.965.3237
Fax 540.965.4490
   102 E Hawthorne St, Covington, VA 24426
Ammie Moore, Director

Safe Svcs To Abused Families 540.825.8891
Fax 540.825.2389
Web ....www.safejourneys.org
   501 E Piedmont St, Culpeper, VA 22701
George Stockes, Director

Sanctuary 540.977.3324
Fax 540.977.3376
E-mail ....jim_ohare@ci.roanoke.va.us
   108 Coyner Springs Rd, Roanoke, VA 24012-9037
Jim O'Hare, Juvenile Justice Admin.

Seton House, Inc. 757.498.4673
Fax 757.340.5768
Web ....www.setonyouthshelters.org
   642 N Lynnhaven Rd, Virginia Beach, VA 23452-5810
Angela Kellam, Interim Executive Director

**Shelter for Help in Emergency - Domestic
Violence** 434.293.6155
Fax 434.293.6156
Web ....www.shelterforhelpinemergency.org
E-mail ....mcl@shelterforhelpinemergency.org
   PO Box 3013, Charlottesville, VA 22901
Cartie Lominack, Director

**Southside Ctr Violence Prevention-Madeline's
House** 434.292.1077
Fax 434.292.1078
E-mail ....ermarshall@madelineshouse.net
   1125 W Parade Ave, Blackstone, VA 23824
Emily Marshall, Director

Southwest Legal Aid Ofc Virginia 276.783.8300
Fax 276.783.7411
E-mail ....larry@svlas.org
   227 W Cherry St, Marion, VA 24354-2535
Larry Harley, Director

The Genieve Shelter Domestic Violence 757.925.4365
Fax 757.925.2053
   1548C Holland Rd, Suffolk, VA 23434
Val Livingstone, Phd, Director

**The Haven Shelter And Svc Domestic
Violence** 804.333.1099
Fax 804.333.1150
E-mail ....haven@sylvainfo.net
   5726 Richmond Hwy, Warsaw, VA 22572
Ellen Yackell, Director

The Shelter for Abused Women 540.667.6466
Fax 540.667.0138
E-mail ....thelaurelcenter@comcast.net
   PO Box 14, Winchester, VA 22604-0014
Donna Carpenter, Director

Transitions Family Violence Svcs 757.722.2261
Fax 757.723.2717
Web ....www.transitionsfvs.org
E-mail ....mwright@transitionsfvs.org
   240 Chapel St, Hampton, VA 23669
Marcy Wright, Director

Turning Point Domestic Violence 703.221.4460
Fax 703.221.3585
Web ....www.actspwc.org
   3900 Acts Lane, Dumfries, VA 22026
Dotty Larson, Director

**Union Mission Ministries of Norfolk
Virginia** 757.427.1500
Fax 757.430.3968
Web ....www.ummnorva.org
   3000 N Landing Rd, Virginia Beach, VA 23456-2408
Linda Vaughn, Executive Director

**Virginia Rehabilitation Ctr For The Blind And Vision
Impaired** 804.371.3151
Fax 804.371.3092
Web ....www.dbvi.virginia.org
E-mail ....melody.roane@dbvi.virginia.org
   401 Azalea Ave, Richmond, VA 23227-3500
Melody Roane, Director

Westhaven Boy's Home 757.397.5371
Fax 757.397.5371
Web ....www.trghc.com
E-mail ....chooker@trghc.com
   3515 Race St, Portsmouth, VA 23707-4027
Carlos Hooker, Assistant Director

**Womens Resource New Women Domestic
Violence** 540.639.9592
Fax 540.633.2382
Web ....www.wrcnrv.org
E-mail ....director@wrcnrv.org
   1217 Grove Ave, Radford, VA 24141
Pat Brown, Director

Youth & Family Mental Health 703.704.6355
Fax 703.704.6687
   8350 Richmond Hwy, Alexandria, VA 22309
Victor Mealy, Manager

Youth Crisis Network 757.623.2627
Fax 757.623.0141
Web ....www.youthcrisisnetwork.org
E-mail ....information@youthcrisisnetwork.org
   117 W 21st St Ste 203, Norfolk, VA 23517-2246
Tracey Sanders-Mason, Executive Director

YWCA Domestic Violence Prevention Ctr 434.528.1041
Fax 434.847.2529
E-mail ....lindaawilliams@yahoo.com
   626 Church St, Lynchburg, VA 24504
Linda Alice Williams, Director

YWCA Women In Crisis 757.625.4248
Fax 757.625.1946
Web ....www.ywca-shr.com
E-mail ....reginamalveaux@ywca-shr.com
   5215 Colley Ave, Norfolk, VA 23508-2043
Regina Malveaux, Director

**YWCA-Womens Advocacy Program-Domestic
Violence** 804.643.6761
Fax 804.643.0734
E-mail ....cpond@ywcarichmond.org
   6 N 5th St, Richmond, VA 23219
Cathy Pond, Director

EDUCATION

Blue Ridge Job Corps Ctr 276.783.7221
Fax 276.783.1751
E-mail ....parsons.carol@jobcorps.org
   245 W Main St, Marion, VA 24354-2530
Carol Parsons, Center Director

Commonwealth Challenge 757.491.5932
Fax 757.491.5934
Web ....www.ngycp.org
E-mail ....laurence.apel@us.army.mil
   253 C St, Virginia Beach, VA 23451-7510
Laurence Apel, Deputy Director

Datz Foundation 703.242.8800
Fax 703.242.8804
Web ....www.datzfoundation.org
E-mail ....markeckman@hotmail.com
   311 Maple Ave W Ste E, Vienna, VA 22180-4309
Vivian Datoff, Director

Loving Families Adoption Agency 703.370.7140
Fax 703.997.2577
E-mail ....lovingfam@aol.com
12106 Mountain Rd, Lovettsville, VA 20180
Peggy Mcelligott, Ma, Lcsw, Director

Minnick Education Ctr 540.265.4281
Fax 540.265.4287
Web ....www.minnickedu.org
E-mail ....minnikc@lfsva.org
775 Dent Rd, Roanoke, VA 24019-4116
Gary Wilburn, Director Of Operations

**National Institute for Learning
Development** 757.423.8646
Fax 757.451.0970
Web ....www.nild.org
E-mail ....info@nild.org
801 Green Brier pkwy, Ste B, chasepake, VA 23320
Kathleen Hopkins, Executive Director

Northstar Academy 804.747.1003
Fax 804.747.1116
Web ....www.northstaracademy.net
E-mail ....info@northstaracademy.net
8055 Shrader Rd, Henrico, VA 23294-4217
Pat West, Director

Oakland School 434.293.9059
Fax 434.296.8930
E-mail ....information@oaklandschool.net
Boyd Tavern, Keswick, VA 22947
Carol Williams, Director

Oakwood School 703.941.5788
Fax 703.941.4186
Web ....www.oakwoodschool.com
7210 Braddock Rd, Annandale, VA 22003
Robert Mcintyre, Ba, Ma, Executive Director

**Rivermont School-Chase City Centra Health Mental Health
Svcs** 434.372.3303
Fax 434.372.3199
Web ....www.centrahealth.com
121 E 2nd St, Chase City, VA 23924
Lloyd Tannenbaum, Director

**Speech and Language Ctr of Northern
Virginia** 703.356.2833
Fax 703.356.2311
Web ....www.slcnv.org
E-mail ....info@slcnv.org
1125 Savile Ln, Mc Lean, VA 22101-1833
Karen Evans, Director Of Speech And Language Services

United Methodist Family Svcs 757.490.9791
Fax 757.490.8324
Web ....www.umfs.org
E-mail ....tidewater@umfs.org
815 Baker Rd, Suite 201, Virginia Beach, VA 23462
Adalay Wilson, Director

**VA Assoc Of Independent Specialized Education Facilities
(VAISEF)** 804.228.4513
Fax 804.228.4501
Web ....www.vaisef.org
E-mail ....kids@vaisef.org
1011 E Main St, Ste 400, Richmond, VA 23219-3537
Bill Elwood, Executive Director

**Virginia Dept For The Blind And Vision
Impaired** 804.371.3140
Fax 804.371.3390
Web ....www.vdbvi.org
E-mail ....glen.slonneger@dbvi.virginia.gov
397 Azalea Ave, Richmond, VA 23227
Glen R. Slonneger, Director

FOSTER CARE AGENCIES

**A Welcome House Adoption Program of
Pear** 804.740.7311
E-mail ....psbi@pearlsbuck.org
9412 Michelle Pl, Henrico, VA 23229

ABC Adoption Services 800.632.9312
3074 silver Maple Dr, Virginia beach, VA 23452
Susan Fox, Director

Adoption & Attachment Program 703.658.7103
E-mail ....info@adoptattach.com
8983 Hersand Dr Ste 2, Burke, VA 22015
Jeanine Harrigan, Chief Executive Officer

Adoption Resource Exchange of Virginia 804.726.7524
Fax 804.726.7499
E-mail ....sondra.draper@dss.virgina.gov
801 E Main St 11th Fl, Richmond, VA 23219
Martin Brown, Commissioner

Adoptions From the Heart 757.361.0008
E-mail ....pennyb@afth.org
1407 Stephanie Way Ste H, Chesapeake, VA 23320
Penny Bargs, Supervisor

Adoptive Families of the Fauquier Area 540.347.7279
E-mail ....laura.henson@verizon.net
7129 Auburn Mill Rd, Warrenton, VA 20187

Army Community Services 804.734.6388
1231 Mahone Ave, Fort Lee, VA 23801
Stephanie Parker, Director

Braley and Thompson 540.989.7175
Fax 540.989.9141
2965 Colonnade Dr Ste 130, Roanoke, VA 24018

Catholic Charities of the Diocese of Arl 540.371.1124
Fax 540.371.9038
305 Hanson Ave Ste 180, Fredericksburg, VA 22401
Lucy Godwin, President

**Center for Adoption Support and
Education** 301.476.8526
Fax 301.593.9203
E-mail ....caseadopt@adoptionsupport.org
8996 Burke Lake Rd Ste 201, Burke, VA 22015
Debbi Riley, Chief Executive Officer

Children's Svcs of VA 540.801.0900
Fax 540.801.0886
E-mail ....srichie@csv-inc.com
250 E Elizabeth St Ste 102, Harrisonburg, VA 22801
Faye Riephi, Director

Childrens Services of Virginia Inc 540.667.0116
Fax 540.667.0174
E-mail ....info@csv-inc.com
311 Airport Rd, Winchester, VA 22602
Sam Saddagh, Director

Commonwealth Catholic Charities Inc 804.285.5900
118 North New St, Staunton, VA 24401
Ms. Matprass, Director

Community Solutions Idl 757.962.6783
Fax 757.461.4088
520 E Little Creek Rd, Norfolk, VA 23505
Jennifer Davis, Director

Coordinators2inc 804.354.1881
Fax 804.355.1100
E-mail ....rricardo@c2adopt.org
1617 Monument Ave Ste 200, Richmond, VA 23220

Extra Special Parents 804.714.1776
Fax 804.714.1769
711 Northcost Rd, Richmond, VA 23236
Ayesha Smith, Financial Services Manager

FACES of Virginia Families 877.823.2237
701 E Franklin Ste 807, Richmond, VA 23219
Kathy B Sauter

Families for Russian and Ukrainian Adopt 703.560.6184
Fax 413.480.8257
E-mail ....info@frua.org
PO Box 2944, Merrifield, VA 22116

Family Life Services Adoption Agency 434.845.5334
Fax 434.845.3486
E-mail ....rmowens2@liberty.edu
124 Liberty Mountain Dr, PO Box 4199, Lynchburg,
VA 24502
Deanne Hamlette, Assistant Director

Fetal Alcohol Syndrome Support Group 804.520.2201
16413 Branders Bridge Rd, Chester, VA 23831
Mary Lee, Director

First Home Care 703.914.0182
Fax 703.914.3955
5515 Cherokee Ave Ste 400, Alexandria, VA 22312
Danielle Rothrock, Program Manager

Fostering Adoptive Families 434.979.9631
1510 Willow Lawn Drive, Richmond, VA 23230
Lillian Pearisher, Pregnancy Counselor

Fridays Child Adoption Services Inc 703.200.9099
Fax 540.542.0406
E-mail ....fridayschildadoption@earthlink.net
124 Amherst St, Winchester, VA 22601

**Hampton Roads Foster Adoptive Family
Fou** 757.248.6444
E-mail ....hrfaff@cox.net
1625 Tallwood Ct, Norfolk, VA 23518

People for the Adoption with Children 804.897.1223
E-mail ....mdingus2000@yahoo.com
1219 Kingcross Rd, Moon, VA 23119

Phillips Teaching Homes 703.941.3471
Fax 703.658.9056
E-mail ....Trudy.Bell@phillipsprograms.org
7010 Braddock Rd, Annandale, VA 22003

RESOLVE 703.556.7172
E-mail ....info@resolve.org
1760 Old Meadow Rd Ste 500, McLean, VA 22102
Barbara Collura, Director

**Transitions Through Adoption Parent
Supp** 804.437.0149
Fax 804.777.9035
E-mail ....cwadlington@comcast.net
11607 Arbor Highlands Terr, Chester, VA 23831

United Methodist Family Services of VA 703.941.9008
E-mail ....nova@umfs.org
5400 Shawnee Rd Ste 101, Alexandria, VA 22312
Olivia Faries, Director

United Methodist Family Services of Va 540.898.1773
E-mail ....fredericksbur@umfs.org
305 Charlotte St, Fredericksburg, VA 22401
Courtney Mills, Director

Virginia Dept of Social Services 804.365.4100
Fax 804.365.4110
12304 Washington Hwy, Ashland, VA 23005
Sheila Crossen-Powell, Director

Virginia One Church One Child 804.527.2172
Fax 804.329.3960
1214 W Graham Rd Ste 2, Richmond, VA 23220

HOME MEDICAL EQUIPMENT PROVIDERS

**Allergy & Asthma Ntwrk Mothers of
Asthm** 800.878.4403
Fax 703.288.5271
8201 Greensboro Dr Ste 300, McLean, VA 22102
Nancy Sander, President

Bristol Regional Speech & Hearing Ctr 276.669.6331
Fax 276.669.2950
E-mail ....brshc@bvu.net
2603 Osborne St, Bristol, VA 24201
Shannon Bramlette, Director

Capital Caring 703.392.6707
10520 Denlake Center St, Ste 200, Manassas,
VA 20109
Melin Davis, Chief Executive Officer

Capital Hospice Arlington **703.525.7070**
  4715 N 15th St, Halquist Memorial Inpt Center,
  Arlington, VA 22205
  Phornton Liggans, Office Manager

Capital Hospice Leesburg **703.777.7866**
  209 Gibson St NW Ste 202, Leesburg, VA 20176
  Linda Rawlett, General Manager

Cerebral Palsy of Virginia **757.497.7474**
  Fax 757.497.0868
  E-mail ....cerebralpalsey@cerebralpalsyofvirginia.org
  5825 Arrowhead Dr Ste 201, Virginia Beach,
  VA 23462
  Michelle Majority, Director

Family ALIVE ALexandrians InVolved
Ecum **703.836.2723**
  E-mail ....alivetoo@aol.com
  2723 King St, Alexandria, VA 22302
  Ken Naser, Executive Director

Home Care Alliance of Virginia Inc **804.572.6779**
  Fax 804.572.9591
  E-mail ....wstanfield@hcav.com
  5037 Halifax Rd Ste A, PO Box 888, Halifax,
  VA 24558

Home Care Delivered Inc **800.565.5644**
  Fax 888.565.4411
  4144 Innslake Dr, Glen Allen, VA 23060

Jewish Social Srv Agency **703.204.9100**
  3018 Javier Rd, Fairfax, VA 22031
  Andrew Mcgahan, Director

LC Technologies, Inc **703.385.7133**
  Fax 703.385.7137
  Web ....www.eyegaze.com
  3919 Old Lee Highway, Suite 81B, Fairfax, VA 22030
  CARF accredited programs available.

MediCorp Home Health **800.468.2219**
  Fax 540.899.3477
  2017 Plank Road Ste 101, Fredericksburg, VA 22401

Muscular Dystrophy Association **804.285.2961**
  Fax 804.282.1038
  E-mail ....richmond@mdausa.org
  8001 Franklin Farms Dr, Ste 139, Richmond,
  VA 23229
  Ashley Mauck, Health Service Coordinator

Prince William Home Med Supply Inc **703.361.4211**
  Fax 703.361.0028
  8724 Sudley Road, Manassas, VA 20110
  Sidney Cooper, Director

Rehab Hlth Care Medical Equipment **757.466.1553**
  Fax 757.455.8536
  5873 Poplar Hall Dr, Norfolk, VA 23502

Spectrum Legal **703.383.9222**
  10617 Jones St, Fairfax, VA 22031

West home Health Care Inc **804.353.7703**
  Fax 804.353.4371
  E-mail ....l.hoffman@whhci.com
  2277 Dabney Road, Richmond, VA 23230
  Linda Hoffman, Office Manager

PEDIATRIC HOME CARE

Bayada Nurses **757.565.5400**
  Fax 757.565.3560
  Web ....www.bayada.com
  7151 Richmond Road, Suite 201, Williamsburg,
  VA 23188
  Tamy Crabtree, Director

Bayada Nurses **757.229.0019**
  Fax 757.220.3917
  Web ....www.bayada.com
  263 McLaws Circle, Suite 103, Williamsburg,
  VA 23185
  Dornell Jenkins, Director

Interim Healthcare **757.873.3313**
  Fax 757.873.4598
  610 Thimble Shoals Blvd #303-B, Newport News,
  VA 23606
  Mary Sykes, Manager

Interim Healthcare **434.295.5501**
  Fax 434.295.4938
  103 S Pantops Dr Ste 205, Charlottesville, VA 22911
  Susanne Seheier, Director

Interim Healthcare **540.785.1577**
  Fax 540.785.3633
  Web ....www.interimhealthcare.com
  3920 Plank Rd Ste 210, Fredericksburg, VA 22407
  Joy Jenkins, Assistant General Manager

Interim Healthcare **434.836.4686**
  Fax 434.836.9139
  2276 Franklin Turnpike Ste 117, Danville, VA 24540

Interim Healthcare **540.381.2757**
  Fax 540.381.2769
  E-mail ....hford@interimhealthcare.com
  201 Wheatland Ct, Christiansburg, VA 24073
  Heath Ford, Office Manager

Interim Healthcare **276.236.6066**
  Fax 276.236.2599
  530 & Half E Stuart Dr, Galax, VA 24333
  Brandy Heck, Director Of Health

Interim Healthcare **757.466.1401**
  Fax 757.466.8223
  516 S Independence Blvd, Ste 106, Virginia Beach,
  VA 23452
  Peggy Butt, General Manager

Interim Healthcare **276.647.1700**
  Fax 276.647.4990
  3235 Virginia Ave, Collinsville, VA 24078
  Rebecca Thomas, Office Manager

Interim Healthcare **540.774.8686**
  Fax 540.774.0279
  4395 Electric Rd, Roanoke, VA 24018
  Mitch Davis, Owner

Interim Healthcare **540.774.8686**
  Fax 540.774.0279
  4395 Electric Rd, 4395 Electric Rd, Roanoke,
  VA 24018
  Gale Glass, Director

Interim Healthcare **276.988.6703**
  Fax 276.988.6706
  E-mail ....rsimpson@interimhealthcare.com
  557 W Main St # 4, Tazewell, VA 24651
  Rosie Simpson, Office Manager

Interim Healthcare **540.885.4413**
  Fax 540.885.7410
  16 Ivy Ridge Ln Ste 138, Fishersville, VA 22939
  Angela Babb, General Manager

Norfolk PDN **757.461.6310**
  6330 N Center Dr, Ste 142 Bldg 13, Norfolk,
  VA 23502
  Elizabeth Old, Director

Springfield PDN **703.455.4050**
  7830 Backlick Rd Ste 401, Springfield, VA 22150
  Elizabeth Adams

SOCIAL SERVICES

Abba Womens Care-Resource Ctr **540.722.4844**
  Fax 540.722.8053
  200 Weems Ln, Winchester, VA 22601-3606
  Bonnie Johsnon, Director

Adolescent and Family Growth Center,
Inc. **703.425.9200**
  Fax 703.425.9206
  Web ....www.afgcinc.com
  8000 Forbes Place, Suite 201, Springfield, VA 22151
  COA accredited organization.

Armed Svcs YMCA Hampton Roads **757.363.1884**
  Fax 757.363.1953
  Web ....www.asymcahr.org
  E-mail ....asymcahr@asymcahr.org
  1465 Lakeside Rd, Virginia Beach, VA 23455
  Bob Duetsch, Executive Director

Armed Svcs YMCA Oceana Community Ctr **757.433.2055**
  Fax 757.433.2886
  Web ....www.asymcahr.org
  E-mail ....kim.fadely@asymcahr.org
  1200 S Birdneck Rd, Virginia Beach, VA 23451-4871
  Kim Fadely, Armed Services Program Director

CASA **757.229.3306**
  Fax 757.229.3972
  E-mail ....info@colonialcasa.org
  1311 Jamestown Rd Ste 201, Williamsburg,
  VA 23185-3391
  Shawn Nason, Administrative Assistant

Catholic Charities **757.484.0703**
  Fax 757.484.1096
  Web ....www.cceva.org
  E-mail ....rwoody@cceva.org
  3804 Poplar Hill Rd Ste A, Chesapeake, VA 23321
  Rhonda Woody, Director

Catholic Charities **757.467.7707**
  Fax 757.456.2367
  Web ....www.catholiccharitiesusa.org
  E-mail ....dcalgi@cceva.org
  5361A Virginia Beach Blvd, Virginia Beach,
  VA 23462-1897
  Dominique Calgi, Executive Director

Catholic Charities of Eastern Virginia, Inc. **757.456.2366**
  Fax 757.456.2367
  Web ....www.cceva.org
  5361-A Virginia Beach Boulevard, Virginia Beach,
  VA 23462
  COA accredited organization.

CCR&R Cooperative Extension **804.633.6550**
  Fax 804.633.2429
  E-mail ....larimer@vt.edu
  111-B Ennis St, Bowling Green, VA 22427
  Debbie Larimer, Program Technician

Center for Child & Family Services, Inc. **757.838.1960**
  Fax 757.838.3280
  Web ....www.kidsandfamilies.com
  2021 Cunningham Drive, Suite 400, Hampton,
  VA 23666
  COA accredited organization.

Challenge Outreach **757.488.9610**
  Fax 757.488.9747
  Web ....www.tyscommission.org
  E-mail ....lgoodman@tyscommission.org
  2404 Airline Blvd, Portsmouth, VA 23701-2912
  Loretta A. Goodman, Director

Child and Family Connection **757.229.7940**
  Fax 757.229.8081
  Web ....http://www.childandfamilyconnection.org
  348 Mnclaws Cir Ste 3, Williamsburg,
  VA 23185-3030
  Michael Edmond, Executive Director

Child Care Link Council of Community
Svcs **540.985.0131**
  Fax 540.982.2935
  Web ....www.councilofcommunityservices.org
  E-mail ....pamkc@councilofcommunityservices.org
  502 Campbell Ave SW, Roanoke, VA 24016-3606
  Pam Kaseger, President

Child Care Resource Ctr **434.528.5437**
  Fax 434.528.1074
  Web ....www.alliancecva.org
  E-mail ....katie@alliancecva.org
  2600 Memorial Ave Ste 201, Lynchburg,
  VA 24501-2658
  Lindsey Green, Child Care Resource Specialist

Childcare Connection **804.693.9446**
Web ....www.iccc-va.org
E-mail ....ksauter@hughes.net
   3292 Rich Ln, Saluda, VA 23149
   Kathy Sauter, Director

Childcare Connection **540.433.4531**
Fax 540.564.7054
Web ....www.rhcc.com
E-mail ....mturner@rhcc.com
   411 Stone Spring Rd, Harrisonburg, VA 22801-9660
   Susan Ribelin, Administrator

Childhelp Children's Center of Virginia **703.208.1500**
Fax 703.208.1540
Web ....www.childhelp.org
E-mail ....mthorpe@childhelp.org
   11230 Waples Mill Rd., Ste. 105, Fairfax, VA 22030
   Maggie Thorpe, Center Director

Children, Youth and Family Svcs **434.296.4118**
Fax 434.295.2638
Web ....www.cyfs.org
   1000E High St, Charlottesville, VA 22902-5023
   Jaclyn Bryant, Executive Director

Choose Life Now **757.497.4070**
E-mail ....betterChoices@hrprc.org
   PO Box 66293, Virginia Beach, VA 23466
   Joan Majuire, Director

Clean, Inc **540.722.3589**
Fax 540.722.9155
Web ....www.cleaninc.org
E-mail ....info@cleaninc.org
   129 Youth Development Ct, Winchester,
   VA 22602-2430
   Michele Hutton, Office/hr Manager

Commonwealth Catholic Charities **540.344.2749**
Fax 540.344.2748
Web ....www.cccofvirginia.org
E-mail ....marge_savage@cccofva.org
   541 loake ave SW ste 118, Roanoke, VA 24016-5055
   Marge Savage, Program Manager

Community Attention System **434.970.3352**
Fax 434.970.3577
Web ....www.charlottesville.org/commattn
E-mail ....murphym@charlottesville.org
   907 E Jefferson St, Charlottesville, VA 22902-5325
   Michael Murphy, Director

Crossroads **757.258.5106**
Fax 757.258.5131
E-mail ....ronald.wallace@po.state.ct.us
   5684 Mooretown Rd, Williamsburg, VA 23188
   Ronald Wallace, Director

East Gate Ministries **540.434.4283**
Fax 540.434.3310
   1029 S High St, Harrisonburg, VA 22801-1603

Family Institute of Virginia **804.355.6876**
Fax 804.355.2597
Web ....www.familyinstituteofva.com
E-mail ....fiv1@horizon.net
   2910 Monument Ave, Richmond, VA 23221
   Grace J. Hadeed, Edd, Clinical Director

Family Lifeline **804.282.4255**
Fax 804.285.3701
Web ....www.familylifeline.org
E-mail ....gsparks@familylifeline.org
   2325 W Broad St, Richmond, VA 23220
   Grace Sparks, President/CEO

Flatwoods Job Corps Ctr **276.395.3384**
Fax 276.395.2043
Web ....www.jcdc.jobcorps.org
E-mail ....dschols@fs.fed.us
   2803 Dungannon Rd, Coeburn, VA 24230
   David Schols, Deputy Center Director

Jackson-Feild Homes, Inc. **804.355.8735**
Fax 804.353.1173
Web ....www.jacksonfeild.org
E-mail ....rchina@jacksonfeild.org
   205 N Boulevard, Richmond, VA 23220-4006
   D. Rebecca China, Executive Director

Jewish Family Service of Tidewater Inc **757.321.2223**
Fax 757.321.2260
E-mail ....ewaranch@jfshamptonroads.org
   260 Grayson Rd, Virginia Beach, VA 23462
   Ellen Waranch

Jewish Family Service of Tidewater Inc **757.321.2222**
Fax 757.321.2260
E-mail ....balevin@jfshamptonroads.org
   260 Grayson Rd, Virginia Beach, VA 23462
   Betty Ann Levin, Director

Jewish Family Svcs **757.489.3111**
Fax 757.451.1796
Web ....www.jfshamptonroads.org
   260 Grayson Rd, Virginia Beach, VA 23462
   Betty Ann Levy, Director

Jewish Family Svcs **804.282.5644**
Fax 804.285.0006
Web ....www.jfsrichmond.org
E-mail ....ljackson@jfsrichmond.org
   6718 Patterson Ave, Richmond, VA 23226-3419
   Larry Jackson, Chief Executive Officer

Lutheran Family Svcs **540.774.7100**
Fax 540.774.1084
Web ....www.lfsva.org
E-mail ....jswanson@lfsva.org
   2609 McVitty Rd, Roanoke, VA 24018-3513
   Julie Swanson, CEO

Memorial Child Guidance Clinic,
Inc.-ChildSavers **804.644.9590**
Fax 804.644.9596
Web ....www.childsavers.org
   200 North 22nd Street, Richmond, VA 23223
   COA accredited organization.

Pendleton Child Svc Ctr **757.385.4537**
Fax 757.385.4533
E-mail ....sdye@vbgov.com
   2473 N Landing Rd, Virginia Beach, VA 23456
   Susan D. Dye, Administrator

People for the Adoption with Children **804.897.1223**
Fax ....
Web ....
E-mail ....mdingus2000@yahoo.com
   1219 Kingcross Rd, Moon, VA 23119

Prevent Child Abuse Virginia **804.359.6166**
Fax 804.359.5065
E-mail ....jschuchert@pcav.org
   4901 Fitzhugh Ave Ste 200, Richmond,
   VA 23230-3531
   Johanas Schuchert, Executive Director

St. Joseph's Villa **804.553.3200**
Fax 804.553.3259
Web ....www.stjosephsvilla.net
   8000 Brook Road, Richmond, VA 23227
   COA accredited organization.

The Exchange Club Ctr For The Prevention Of Child
Abuse **540.536.1640**
Fax 540.450.1524
Web ....www.childparentcenter.org
   301 N Cameron St Ste 200, Winchester,
   VA 22601-6018
   William Germelman, Executive Director

The Planning Council **757.622.9268**
Fax 757.622.4223
Web ....www.theplanningcouncil.org
E-mail ....spurhear@theplanningcouncil.org
   5365 Robinhood Rd Ste 700, Norfolk, VA 23513
   Sizanne Purhear, President

Turning Point/Salvation Army Crisis
Hotline **540.345.0400**
Fax 540.985.5136
E-mail ....darlene.young@salvationarmy.org
   815 Salem Ave SW, Roanoke, VA 24016-3029
   Darlene Young, Director

United Methodist Family Svcs **804.353.4461**
Fax 804.353.6250
Web ....www.umfs.org
E-mail ....gpeters@umfs.org
   3900 W Broad St, Richmond, VA 23230
   Greg Peters, Chief Executive Officer

Victims Assistance Network **703.360.7273**
Fax 703.704.9185
E-mail ....fcvan@erols.com
   8350 Richmond Hwy Ste 507, Alexandria,
   VA 22309-2345
   Kathleen Kemelis, Director

Vienna Women's Ctr **703.281.2657**
Fax 703.242.1454
Web ....www.thewomenscenter.org
   133 Park St NE, Vienna, VA 22180
   Vicki Kirkbride, Executive Director

Virginia Child Care Resource and Referral
Network **804.285.0846**
Fax 804.285.0847
Web ....www.vaccrrn.org
E-mail ....sharon.veatch@vaccrrn.org
   308 Turner Rd Ste A, Richmond, VA 23225
   Sharon Veatch, Director

SPECIAL NEEDS

Academic Pediatric Association **703.556.9222**
Fax 703.556.8729
E-mail ....info@academicpeds.org
   6728 Old McLean Village Dr, McLean, VA 22101
   Sandra Titus, Office Manager

Access Minis Soaring Over Seven Sum
Adve **703.770.3832**
E-mail ....Fran.Smith@mcleanbible.o rg
   8925 Leesburg Pike, McLean, VA 22102

Acts Emergency Assistance **703.221.3186**
Fax 703.221.3189
   3900 Acts Lane, Dumfries, VA 22026
   Rebekah Mcgee, Director

Adorable Lic Home Childcare and
Preschoo **757.479.8686**
Fax 757.479.8686
E-mail ....adorablechildcare@yahoo.com
   2021 Manassas Run, Virginia Beach, VA 23464

Ashburn Psychological Services **703.723.2999**
Fax 703.723.4144
E-mail ....info@ashburnpsych.com
   44110 Ashburn Shopping Pl, Ste 251, Ashburn,
   VA 20147
   Dr. Michael Oberschneider, Director

Autism Society of Central Virginia **804.257.0192**
E-mail ....asacv@aol.com
   PO Box 29364, Richmond, VA 23242

Brain Injury Association **804.355.5748**
E-mail ....info@biav.net
   1506 Willow Lawn Dr Ste 212, Richmond, VA 23230
   Anne McDonnell, Executive Director

Children's Hospice International **800.242.4453**
Fax 703.684.0330
Web ....www.chionline.org
   1101 King St, Ste 360, Alexandria, VA 22314

Clinical Neuropsychology Services, LLC **703.231.5117**
Fax 703.875.0476
E-mail ....drpacos@clinicalneuropsychologyservices.com
   200 N Glebe Rd Ste 1050, Arlington, VA 22203
   Amy M Pacos Psyd, Licensed Psychologist

Commonwealth Autism Service **804.355.0300**
E-mail ....information@autismva.org
   2201 W Broad St, Ste 107, Richmond, VA 23220
John A Toscano, President/CEO

Discovery School Of Virginia **434.983.5616**
Fax 434.983.5617
Web ....www.discoveryschool.com
E-mail ....dsadmissions@yahoo.com
   2697 Copper Mine Road, Dillwyn, VA 23936
Don Williams, Director Of Admisions

Easter Seals Virginia **866.874.4153**
   8003 Franklin Farms Dr Ste 100, Richmond,
   VA 23229

EDAnywhere **703.433.0805**
Fax 703.433.0378
E-mail ....info@edanywhere.com
   10 Pidgeon Hill Dr, Sterling, VA 20165
Philip S Singh Ma, Chief Operating Officer

Epilepsy Foundation **800.332.1000**
E-mail ....srb3m@virginia.edu
   PO Box 800659, Charlottesville, VA 22908
Richard Dennes, Chief Executive Officer

Hajdu Cheney Support Group **757.465.8169**
E-mail ....hcsupport@cox.net
   1301 Amelia Ave, Portsmouth, VA 23707

**Inova Rehabilitation Center/Inova Mount Vernon
Hospital** **703.664.7590**
Fax 703.664.7423
Web ....www.inova.org
   2501 Parker's Lane, Alexandria, VA 22306
CARF accredited programs available.

**Kluge Children's Rehabilitation Center and Research
Institute** **434.924.8241**
Fax 434.924.2780
Web ....http://www.healthsystem.virginia.edu/int
   2270 Ivy Road, Charlottesville, VA 22903
CARF accredited programs available.

Learning Disabilities Association **804.358.5474**
E-mail ....jlokerso@vcu.edu
   3914 Monument Ave, Richmond, VA 23230

LearningRx Learning Center **757.226.0816**
E-mail ....vbtc@learningrx.net
   633 C Independence Blvd, Virginia Beach, VA 23462
Bill Mcclean, Director

LearningRx Learning Center **804.612.9959**
E-mail ....richmondw.va@learningrx.net
   9770 Gayton Rd, Richmond, VA 23238
Ed Lawrence, President

Leary School of Virginia **703.941.8150**
Fax 703.941.4237
Web ....www.learyschool.org
   6349 Lincolnia Rd, Alexandria, VA 22312
Edward Schultze, Office Manager

Little Keswick School **434.295.0457**
Fax 434.977.1892
Web ....www.littlekeswickschool.net
   PO Box 24, Keswick, VA 22947
Marc Columbus, Headmaster

Mental Health America **800.969.6642**
   2000 N Beauregard St 6 Floor, Alexandria, VA 22311
Michael King, Senior-director

Mental Health America of Virginia **866.400.6428**
E-mail ....programs@mhav.org
   3212 Cutshaw Ave Ste 315, Richmond, VA 23230
Mary Vaughan, Operations Manager

Mindwell, Clinical Psychology **703.378.7998**
Fax 703.378.6109
E-mail ....drvaria@MindWellpsychology.com
   4455 Brookfield Corporate Dr, Ste 101, Chantilly,
   VA 20151
Kristi Guadagnoli, President/CEO

NAMI Virginia **804.285.8264**
E-mail ....namiva@comcast.net
   PO Box 8260, Richmond, VA 23226

National Multiple Sclerosis Society **434.971.8010**
Fax 434.979.4475
E-mail ....VAB@nmss.org
   1 Morton Dr Ste 106, Charlottesville, VA 22903

National Multiple Sclerosis Society **800.344.4867**
Fax 804.353.5595
E-mail ....Judy.Griffin@nmss.org
   4200 Innslhae Dr Ste 301A, Glen Allen, VA 23060
Judy Griffin, Director Of Operations

National Multiple Sclerosis Society **757.490.9627**
Fax 757.490.1617
E-mail ....info@fightms.com
   760 Lynnhaven Pkwy Ste 201, Virginia Beach,
   VA 23452
Sharon Grossman, President

Online High School Education **877.433.0805**
Fax 703.433.0805
Web ....www.edanywhere.com
E-mail ....info@edanywhere.com
   10 Pidgeon Hill Dr, Ste 70, Sterling, VA 20165
Philip Singh, President & COO

**PADDA People with Attentional &
Devlpmtl** **757.591.9119**
Fax 757.591.8990
E-mail ....webmaster@padda.org
   813 Forrest Ave Ste 3, Newport News, VA 23606

Parent Educational Advocacy Trng Ctr **703.923.0010**
Fax 800.693.3514
   100 N Washington St, Ste 234, Sallscaurch,
   VA 22046
Cathy Healy, Chief Executive Officer

Parent to Parent of Virginia **804.795.1481**
E-mail ....ptpofva@aol.com
   PO Box 38341, Richmond, VA 23231

PEATC **703.923.0010**
E-mail ....partners@peatc.org
   100 N Washington St Ste 234, Falls Church,
   VA 22046

PHILLIPS School **703.941.8810**
Fax 703.658.2378
Web ....www.phillipsprograms.org
   7010 Braddock Rd, Annandale, VA 22003
Sally A Sibley, CEO

Special Education & Student Services **804.371.7421**
E-mail ....judy.hudgins@doe.virginia.gov
   PO Box 2120, Richmond, VA 23218

Speech-Language-Hearing Association **888.729.7428**
E-mail ....shavoffice@shav.org
   3126 W Cary St ste 436, Richmond, VA 23221

Spina Bifida Association **703.455.4900**
   PO Box 523415, Springfield, VA 22152

The Arc of Virginia Family **888.604.2677**
E-mail ....dholloway@arcfip.org
   2025 E Main St Ste 107, Richmond, VA 23223

The Dominion School **703.321.9091**
Fax 703.321.9017
Web ....www.thedominionschool.com
E-mail ....pelldk@aol.com
   8000 Forbes Place, Suite 102, Springfield,
   VA 22151-2315
Debbie Pell, Director

The Kellar School of Inova Kellar Ctr **703.218.8500**
Fax 703.359.0463
Web ....www.inova.org
   11204 Waples Mill Rd, Fairfax, VA 22030
Judith Lemke, Director

Timber Ridge School **540.888.3456**
Fax 540.888.4511
Web ....www.timber-ridge-school.org
   1463 New Hope Rd, Crossjunction, VA 22604 22625
John Lamanna, Director

Virginia PTA **804.264.1234**
E-mail ....info@vapta.org
   1027 Wilmer Ave, Richmond, VA 23227
Deborah Samuels, Liasone

**Winchester Rehabilitation Center/Valley
Health** **540.536.5134**
Fax 540.536.5139
Web ....www.valleyhealthlink.com
E-mail ....kcallana@valleyhealthlink.com
   333 West Cork Street, Suite 230, Winchester,
   VA 22601
Kevin Callanan, CFRE Executive Director
CARF accredited programs available.

Wiser, Inc **301.816.0432**
Fax 301.593.5177
E-mail ....wiser@wiserdc.com
   5765 F Burke Centre Pkwy, # 206, Burke, VA 22015

SUBSTANCE ABUSE TREATMENT

Al-Anon Family Group Headquarters **757.563.1600**
Fax 757.563.1655
Web ....www.al-anon.alateen.org
E-mail ....wso@al-anon.org
   1600 Corporate Landing Pkwy, Virginia Beach,
   VA 23454-5617
Ric Buchanan, Executive Director

Blackwater Outdoor Experiences **804.378.9006**
Fax 804.378.9074
Web ....www.blackwateroutdoor.com
E-mail ....admissions@blackwateroutdoor.com
   13805 Village Mill Dr Ste 203, Midlothian,
   VA 23114-4304
Dr. George Bright, Medical Director

**Community Anti-Drug Coalitions of America
(CADCA)** **800.542.2322**
Fax 703.706.0565
Web ....www.cadca.org
E-mail ....mlarson@cadca.org
   625 Slaters Ln Ste 300, Alexandria, VA 22314
Mel Larson, Vp Of Communications/memberships

Snowden of Fredericksburg **540.741.3900**
Fax 540.741.3918
   1200 Sam Perry Blvd, Fredericksburg, VA 22401-4456
Charles Scercy, Administrator

Washington

Christine Gregoire, Governor
PO Box 40002
Office of the Governor
Olympia, WA 98504-0002
360.902.4111
360.753.4110 (Fax)
www.governor.wa.gov

Ryan Pinto, Juvenile Justice Specialist
Office of Juvenile Justice
PO Box 45828
Olympia, WA 98504-5828
360.407.0202
360.407.0152 (Fax)
pintorm@dshs.wa.gov

Liz Mueller, SAG Chair
1033 Old Blyn Hwy
Sequim, WA 98382
360.681.4628
lmueller@jamestwontribe.org

CRISIS NUMBERS

Child Abuse Reporting 866.363.4276

STATE SERVICES

SOCIAL SERVICES

Child Care and Preschool Options WA 360.725.4665
Fax 360.413.3482
 PO Box 40970, Olympia, WA 98504
 Amy Blondin, Director

Child Support Enforcement Program 360.664.5000
Fax 360.664.5209
Web . . . . .www.dshs.wa.gov
 712 Pear Street Southeast, Olympia, WA 98501
 Walley McCoure, Director

Dept of Community and Human Svcs 206.263.9105
Fax 206.296.5260
Web . . . . .www.kingcounty.gov/dchs
 401 5th Ave, Suite 500, Seattle, WA 98104
 Jackie Maclean, Director

Washington Emergency Management
 Agency .253.512.7000
Fax 253.512.7200
Web . . . . .www.emd.wa.gov
E-mail . . . . .j.mullen@emd.wa.gov
 Building 20, M/S TA-20, Camp Murray,
 WA 98430-0001
 Jim Mullen, Director

GENERAL HEALTH SERVICES

Children w Spec Health Care Needs Prog 360.236.3571
Fax 360.586.7868
E-mail . . . . .cshcn.support@doh.wa.gov
 111 Israel Rd SE, Tumwater, WA 98501
 Maria Nardella, Manager

Community And Family Health 360.236.3703
Fax 360.664.4500
Web . . . . .www.doh.wa.gov
 111 Isreal Road Se Tumwater, Tumwater, WA 98502
 Aleene Mares, Assistant Secretary

Healthy Communties Office 360.236.3670
Fax 360.236.2323
E-mail . . . . .mch.support@doh.wa.gov
 111 Israel Rd SE, Tumwater, WA 98501
 Sue Grinnell, Office Director

Ofc of Community Health Systems 360.236.2800
Fax 360.664.9273
Web . . . . .www.doh.wa.gov/hsqa
 243 Israel Rd SE, Tumwater, WA 98501
 Janet Kastl, Director

Washington State Dep Of Health/ STD Serv 360.236.3460
Fax 360.236.3470
E-mail . . . . .mark.aubin@doa.wa.gov
 111 Israel Rd SE, #TC2, Tumwater, WA 98501
 Mark Aubin, Manager

Washington State Dept Of Health 360.236.4052
Fax 360.586.7424
Web . . . . .www.doh.wa.gov
E-mail . . . . .mary.selecky@doh.wa.gov
 101 Israel Rd SE, Olympia, WA 98501-5570
 Mary Selecky, Director

MENTAL HEALTH SERVICES

Div of Developmental Disabilities 360.725.3413
Fax 360.407.0955
Web www.ww1.dshs.wa.gov/ddd/index.shtml
E-mail . . . . .rolfe@dshs.wa.gov
 4450 10 Ave SE, Olympia, WA 98513
 Linda Rolfe, Phd, Director

Div of Voc Rehabilitation WA 360.725.3610
Fax 360.438.8011
E-mail . . . . .andres.aguirreruttlim@dshs.wa.gov
 PO Box 45340, Olympia, WA 98504
 Andres Aguirre, Interim Director

Div of Vocational Rehabilitation 360.725.3636
Fax 360.438.8011
Web . . . . .www.dshs.wa.gov/dvr
E-mail . . . . .krulik@dshs.wa.gov
 PO Box 45340, Olympia, WA 98504-5340
 Andres Aguirre, Director

Radar Network Agency 206.725.9696
Fax 206.760.0589
Web . . . . .www.clearinghouse.adhl.org
E-mail . . . . .clearinghouse@adhl.org
 6535 S 5th Pl, Seattle, WA 98108
 Ann Forbes, Director

JUSTICE AGENCY

Attorney General's Ofc 360.753.6200
Fax 360.664.0228
Web . . . . .www.atg.wa.gov
E-mail . . . . .rob.mckenna@atg.wa.gov
 1125 Washington St SE, Olympia, WA 98504-0001
 Rob Mckenna, Attorney General

Correctional Edu Division WA 360.725.8211
Fax 360.586.7273
E-mail .mjparis@doc1.wa.gov
 7345 Linderson Way MS 41129, Olympia, WA 98501
 MJ Paris, Director

Crime Victim Compensation Program 800.762.3716
Fax 360.902.5333
Web . . . . .www.lni.wa.gov/claimsinsurance/crimevic tims
E-mail . . . . .nnan235@lni.wa.gov
 7273 SW Linderson Way, Olympia, WA 98504-4520
 Cletus Nnanabu, Program Manager

Dept of Corrections 360.725.8213
Fax 360.664.4056
Web . . . . .www.doc.wa.gov
E-mail . . . . .doccorrespondence@doc1.wa.gov
 7345 Linderson Way SW, Olympia, WA 98501
 Eldon Vail, Secretary

Interstate Compact 360.902.8095
Fax 360.664.2808
E-mail .donjones@dsa.wa.gov
 1115 Washington St SE, Olympia, WA 98501
 Don Jones, Administrator

Washington State Assoc CASA/GAL Programs . .206.667.9716
Fax 206.667.9753
Web . . . . .www.washingtonstatecasa.org
E-mail .bjames@wacasa.org
 603 Stewart St Ste 206, Seattle, WA 98101-1249
 Barbara James, Executive Director

COURTS

Administrative Ofc Of The Courts 360.357.2129
Fax 360.956.5711
 415 12th Avenue SW, Olympia, WA 98504
 Jeff Hall, Administrator

POLICE AND SHERIFF

Sheriff's Ofc 509.962.7525
Fax 509.962.7599
E-mail . . . . .clayton.myers@co.kittitas.wa.us
 307 W. Umptanum Rd., Ellensburg, WA 98926-2887
 Clayton Myers, Undersheriff

Washington Assoc of Sheriff's and Police
 Chiefs 360.486.2380
Fax 360.486.2381
Web . . . . .www.waspc.org
E-mail . . . . .dpierce@waspc.org
 3060 Willamette Dr NE Ste 200, Olympia,
 WA 98516-6267
 Don Pierce, Executive Director

Washington State Patrol 360.753.6540
Fax 360.753.2492
Web . . . . .www.wsp.wa.gov
E-mail . . . . .jason.berry@wsp.wa.gov
 210 11th Ave SW, Olympia, WA 98504
 Captain Jason Berry, Commander Media Relations

EDUCATION SERVICES

Educ for Homeless Children and Youth WA 360.725.6050
Fax 360.664.3575
E-mail . . . . .melinda.dyer@k12.wa.us
 600 Washington St SE, Olympia, WA 98504
 Melinda Dyer, Director

Washington

Infant Toddler Early Interv Prog WA **360.725.3500**
Fax 360.413.3482
E-mail . . . . .karen.walker@del.wa.gov
   649 Woodland Square Loop SE, Lacey, WA 98503
   Karen J Walker, Director

Migrant Head Start **509.837.8909**
Fax 509.839.5803
   105 "B" So. 6th St, Sunnyside, WA 98944-2185

Parent to Parent Power WA **253.531.2022**
Fax 253.538.1126
E-mail . . . . .yvone_link@yahoo.com
   118 S 142nd St Ste B, Tacoma, WA 98444
   Yvone Link, Director

Spec Education Programs WA **360.725.6075**
Fax 360.586.0247
E-mail . . . . .doug.gill@k12.wa.us
   600 S Washington St, Olympia, WA 98504
   Doug Gill, Director

Washington PAVE **253.565.2266**
Fax 253.566.8052
E-mail . . . . .pave@wapave.org
   6316 S 12th St Ste B, Tacoma, WA 98465
   Tracy Kahoo, Executive Director

Washington State Public Instruction **360.725.6000**
Fax 360.753.6712
Web www.k12.wa.us
   600 Washington St SE, Olympia, WA 98501
   Melinda Dyer, Homeless Ed

LABOR & WORKFORCE EDUCATION

Workforce Training and Education Coordinating
   Board **360.753.5662**
Fax 360.586.5862
E-mail . . . . .epadadakis@wtb.wa.gov
   128 10th Ave SW, Olympia, WA 98504
   Eleny Padadakis, Director

COUNTY SERVICES

Adams County

SOCIAL SERVICES

Community Svcs Ofc **509.331.2100**
Fax 509.488.5068
Web . . . . .www.dshs.wa.gov
E-mail . . . . .alliskm@dshs.wa.gov
   1025 S 1St Ave, Othello, WA 99344-1845
   Karl Allison, Administrator

GENERAL HEALTH SERVICES

Health District **509.659.3315**
Fax 509.659.4109
   108 W Main Ave, Ritzville, WA 99169
   Leslie Spencer, Rn, Aids Coordinator

JUSTICE AGENCY

Juvenile Court Svcs **509.488.5646**
Fax 509.488.3425
Web . . . . .www.co.adams.wa.us
E-mail . . . . .vaughng@co.adams.wa.us
   425 E Main St, Othello, WA 99344-1146
   Vaughn Garza, Administrator

COURTS

Superior Court **509.659.3271**
Fax 509.659.0118
E-mail . . . . .sandrab@co.adams.wa.us
   210 W Broadway Ave, Ritzville, WA 99169
   Honorable Richard W. Miller, Presiding Judge

POLICE AND SHERIFF

Sheriff's Ofc **509.659.1122**
Fax 509.659.1724
E-mail . . . . .dougb@co.adams.wa.us
   210 W Broadway Ave, Ritzville, WA 99169
   Douglas Barger, Sheriff

Asotin County

SOCIAL SERVICES

Child & Family Svcs
TTY 509.751.4686
   525 5th St, Clarkston, WA 99403

Community Svcs Ofc **509.758.9842**
Fax 509.758.1294
E-mail . . . . .mervins@qwest.net
   549 5th St Ste A, Clarkston, WA 99403-1980
   Mervin Scheider, Administrator

GENERAL HEALTH SERVICES

Health Dept **509.758.3344**
Fax 509.758.8454
Web . . . . .www.ac-hd.org
E-mail . . . . .achd@ac-hd.org
   431 Elm St, Clarkston, WA 99403
   Joe Lillard, Administrator

COURTS

Superior Court **509.243.2081**
Fax 509.243.4978
Web . . . . .www.co.asotin.wa.us
E-mail . . . . .bacey@co.asotin.wa.us
   135 2nd St, Asotin, WA 99402
   Honorable William D. Acey, Judge

POLICE AND SHERIFF

Sheriff's Ofc **509.243.4717**
Fax 509.243.4719
Web . . . . .www.co.asotin.com
E-mail . . . . .kbancrost@co.asotin.wa.us
   127 2nd St, Asotin, WA 99402
   Ken Bancrost, Sheriff

Benton County

SOCIAL SERVICES

Community Svc Ofc **509.735.7119**
Fax 509.736.2857
E-mail . . . . .johno@cted.wa.gov
   1120 N Edison St, Kennewick, WA 99336-6170
   John Olivas, Administrator

Tri-Cities Children And Family Svcs **509.737.2800**
Fax 509.734.7199
   1661 Fowler St, Richland, WA 99352
   Carlos Carrillo, Area Manager

MENTAL HEALTH SERVICES

Dept Of Human Svcs **509.783.5284**
Fax 509.783.5981
   7102 W Okanogan PLte 201, Kennewick, WA 99336
   Ed Thornbrugh, Administrator

COURTS

Benton Co. Superior Court Family Court
Svcs-CASA **509.736.3071**
Fax 509.736.3057
Web . . . . .www.co.benton.wa.us
E-mail . . . . .patricia.austin@co.benton.wa.us
   7122 W Okanogan Pl Bldg A, Kennewick,
   WA 99336-2359
   Patricia Austin, Court Administrator

Superior Court/Clerks Ofc **509.735.8388**
Fax 509.736.3892
Web . . . . .www.co.benton.wa.us
   7122 W Okanogan Pl Bldg A, Kennewick,
   WA 99336-2359
   Josie Delvin, Clerk

POLICE AND SHERIFF

Sheriff's Ofc **509.735.6555**
Fax 509.783.5852
E-mail . . . . .steve.keane@co.benton.wa.us
   7122 W Okanogan Pl Bldg A, Kennewick,
   WA 99336-2359
   Steve Keane, Sheriff

Chelan County

SOCIAL SERVICES

Child & Family Svcs **509.665.5300**
   805 S Mission, Wenatchee, WA 98807

GENERAL HEALTH SERVICES

Chelan-Douglas Health District **509.886.6400**
Fax 509.886.6478
Web . . . . .www.cdhd.wa.gov
E-mail . . . . .christinabenavides@cdhd.wa.gov
   200 Valley Mall Pkwy, East Wenatchee, WA 98802
   Christina Benavides, Aids Coordinator

JUSTICE AGENCY

Chelan Douglas CASA Guardian Ad Litem
   Program **509.662.7350**
Fax 509.667.7521
Web . . . . .www.cdcasa.org
E-mail . . . . .cdcasa@nwi.net
   431 Douglas St, Wenatchee, WA 98801-2835
   Sue Baker, Program Director

Juvenile Court Svcs **509.667.6350**
Fax 509.667.6583
Web . . . . .www.co.chelan.wa.us
E-mail . . . . .phil.jans@co.chelan.wa.us
   316 Washington St, Ste 202, Wenatchee,
   WA 98801-4105
   Phil Jans, Administrator

COURTS

Superior Court **509.667.6210**
Fax 509.667.6588
E-mail . . . . .superiorcourt.judge@co.chelan.wa.us
   401 Washington St, Wenatchee, WA 98801
   Honorable John E. Bridges, Judge

POLICE AND SHERIFF

Sheriff's Ofc **509.667.6875**
Fax 509.667.6860
Web . . . . .www.co.chelan.wa.us
   401 Washington St, Level 1, Wenatchee, WA 98801
   Brian Burnett, Sheriff

EDUCATION SERVICES

Peshastin Head Start **509.548.7614**
Fax 509.548.5347
   10375 Mill Rd, Peshastin, WA 98847
   Sara Bartum, Director

Clallam County

SOCIAL SERVICES

Community Svcs Ofc **360.565.2205**
Fax 360.417.1461
   201 W 1st St, Port Angeles, WA 98362
   Karen Updike, Administrator

Forks Children And Family Svcs 360.374.3530
Fax 360.374.4076
　421 5th Ave, Forks, WA 98331
　Anita Iverson, Supervisor

GENERAL HEALTH SERVICES

Health Dept 360.417.2274
Fax 360.452.4492
Web .... www.clallam.net
E-mail .... tlocke@co.clallam.wa.us
　223 E 4th St Ste 14, Port Angeles, WA 98362-3024
　Thomas H. Locke, Md, Health Officer

Jamestown S'Kallam Tribe 360.683.1109
Fax 360.681.3405
Web .... www.jamestowntribe.org
E-mail .... info@jamestowntribe.org
　1033 Old Blyn Hwy, Sequim, WA 98382
　W. Ron Allen, Tribal Chairman/executive Director

Sophie Trevick Indian Health Ctr 360.645.2233
Fax 360.645.2723
E-mail .... tracy.lind@ihs.gov
　250 Fort St, Neah Bay, WA 98357
　Tracy Lind, Clinical Director

JUSTICE AGENCY

Juvenile And Family Svcs/CASA 360.417.2282
Fax 360.457.4875
Web .... www.clallam.net
E-mail .... ppeterson@co.clallam.wa.us
　1912 W 18Th St, Port Angeles, WA 98363
　Peter A. Peterson, Director

COURTS

Superior Court/Judges Chambers 360.417.2386
Fax 360.417.2581
E-mail .... kwilliams@co.clallam.wa.us
　223 E 4th St Ste 8, Port Angeles, WA 98362
　Honorable Kenneth Williams, Judge

Teen Court 360.417.2282
Fax 360.457.4875
Web .... www.co.clallam.net
E-mail .... drutten@co.clallam.wa.us
　1912 W 18th St, Port Angeles, WA 98363-5121
　Danetta Rutten, Juvenile Court Probation Officer

POLICE AND SHERIFF

Sheriff's Dept 360.417.2270
Fax 360.417.2498
Web .... www.clallam.net
　223 E 4th St Ste 12, Port Angeles, WA 98362
　W. L. Benedict, Sheriff

EDUCATION SERVICES

**Olympic Community Action
Program** 360.582.3872
Fax 360.582.9421
　226 N Sequim Ave, Sequim, WA 98382
　Gail Gronwall, Director

Clark County

SOCIAL SERVICES

Dept Of Community Svcs 360.397.2130
Fax 360.397.6028
Web .... www.clark.wa.gov
E-mail .... coomunity.servies@clark.wa.gov
　1601 East 4th Plane Blvd, Ste C214, Vancouver,
　WA 98661
　Connie McChhing, Administrator

GENERAL HEALTH SERVICES

Health Dept 360.397.8000
Fax 360.397.8424
Web .... www.clark.wa.gov
E-mail .... public.health@clark.wa.gov
　1601 E 4th Plain Blvd, Vancouver, WA 98663
　John Weisman, Executive Director

MENTAL HEALTH SERVICES

Columbia River Mental Health Svcs 360.993.3000
Fax 360.993.3047
Web .... www.crmhs.org
E-mail .... nancyp@crmhs.org
　6926 NE Fourth Plain Blvd, Vancouver, WA 98661
　Nancy Parker, Executive Director

Life Line Connection 360.696.1631
Fax 360.397.8450
Web .... www.lifelineconnection.org
E-mail .... info@lifelineconnection.org
　1601 E 4th Plain Blvd, Bldg 17, Vancouver,
　WA 98661
　Linn Samuels, Chief Executive Officer

JUSTICE AGENCY

Juvenile Court Svcs 360.397.2201
Fax 360.397.6109
Web .... www.clark.wa.gov
　500 W 11th St, Vancouver, WA 98660-3052
　Patrick Escamillia, Court Services Administrator

COURTS

Family Court 360.397.2326
Fax 360.397.6078
　1200 Franklin St, Vancouver, WA 98660
　Barbara Johnson, Judge

POLICE AND SHERIFF

Sheriff's Ofc 360.397.2366
Fax 360.397.2367
Web .... www.clark.wa.gov/sheriff
E-mail .... sheriff@clark.wa.gov
　707 W 13th St, Vancouver, WA 98660-2809
　Garry Lucas, Sheriff

Columbia County

GENERAL HEALTH SERVICES

Public Health Dept 509.382.2181
Fax 509.382.2942
Web .... www.columbiaco.com
E-mail .... franm@co.whitman.wa.us
　1002 S 3rd St, Num 2, Dayton, WA 99328-1606
　Timothy Moody, Md, Health Officer

POLICE AND SHERIFF

Sheriff's Dept 509.382.1100
Fax 509.382.4765
E-mail .... ccso@co.columbia.wa.us
　341 E Main St Ste 1, Dayton, WA 99328
　Walk Hessler, Sheriff

Cowlitz County

SOCIAL SERVICES

Child & Family Svcs 360.501.2601
　711 Vine, Kelso, WA 98626

GENERAL HEALTH SERVICES

Health Dept 360.414.5599
Fax 360.425.7531
Web .... www.co.cowlitz.wa.us
E-mail .... fieldsm@co.cowlitz.wa.us
　1952 9th Ave, Longview, WA 98632-4045
　Carlos Carreon, Health Officer

MENTAL HEALTH SERVICES

Peacehealth-St. John Medical Ctr 360.414.2000
Fax 360.414.2788
Web .... www.peacehealth.org
E-mail .... kron@peacehealth.org
　600 Broadway St, Longview, WA 98632-3256
　Kyle Ron, Director

JUSTICE AGENCY

CASA Program 360.414.5212
Fax 360.425.6369
Web .... www.cowlitzcountycasa.org
E-mail .... corie@cowlitzcountycasa.org
　1022 Broadway, Longview, WA 98632-3743
　Corie Dow, Executive Director

Juvenile Court Svcs 360.577.3100
Fax 360.414.9280
Web .... www.co.cowlitz.wa.us/juvenile
E-mail .... connorsc@co.cowlitz.wa.us
　1725 1st Ave, Longview, WA 98632
　Chad M. Connors, Administrator

COURTS

Superior Court/Clerk's Ofc 360.577.3016
E-mail .... clerk@co.cowlitz.wa.us
　312 SW 1st Ave Rm 233, Kelso, WA 98626
　Beverly R. Little, Clerk Of Superior Court

POLICE AND SHERIFF

Sheriff's Dept 360.577.3092
Fax 360.423.1047
Web .... www.co.cowlitz.wa.us/sheriff
E-mail .... sheriff@co.cowlitz.wa.us
　312 SW 1st Ave Rm 124, Kelso, WA 98626
　Mark S Nelson, Sheriff

Douglas County

JUSTICE AGENCY

Probation Ofc 509.884.3536
Fax 509.884.5973
Web .... www.douglas.co.wa.net
E-mail .... kstallings@co.douglas.wa.us
　110 2nd St NE Ste 100, East Wenatchee,
　WA 98802-4853
　Kim Stallings, Probation Director

COURTS

Superior Court/Clerk 509.745.8529
Fax 509.745.8027
E-mail .... jkoch@co.douglas.wa.us
　PO Box 516, Waterville, WA 98858
　Juanita Koch, County Clerk

POLICE AND SHERIFF

Sheriff's Dept 509.884.0941
Fax 509.886.1045
Web .... www.douglascountysheriff.org
E-mail .... dlaroche@co.douglas.wa.us
　110 2nd St NE, Ste 200, East Wenatchee,
　WA 98802-4800
　Harvey Gjesdal, Sheriff

Ferry County

SOCIAL SERVICES

Child & Family Svcs 509.775.2220
　89 E Delaware, Republic, WA 99166

MENTAL HEALTH SERVICES

New Alliance Counseling 509.775.3341
Fax 509.775.8906
E-mail .... rschwartz@co.stevens.wa.us
　42 Klondike Rd, Republic, WA 99166
　Dr. David Nielsen, Director

POLICE AND SHERIFF

Sheriff's Ofc 509.775.3132
Fax 509.775.1076
Web .... www.rcabletv.com
E-mail .... fcso@rcabletv.com
　175 N. Jefferson St, Republic, WA 99166
　Peter F. Warner, Sheriff

Washington

Franklin County

GENERAL HEALTH SERVICES

Benton-Franklin Health Dept **509.547.9737**
Fax 509.546.2990
Web .... www.bfhd.wa.gov
E-mail .... heatherh@bfhd.wa.gov
    412 W Clark St, Pasco, WA 99301
    Heather Hill, Communicable Disease Supervisor

POLICE AND SHERIFF

Sheriff's Dept **509.545.3501**
Fax 509.546.5802
E-mail .... rlathim@co.franklin.wa.us
    1016 N 4th Ave, Pasco, WA 99301
    Richard Lathim, Sheriff

Garfield County

GENERAL HEALTH SERVICES

Health District **509.843.3412**
Fax 509.843.1935
    121 S 10th St, Pomeroy, WA 99347
    Leta Travis, Rn, Nursing Supervisor

MENTAL HEALTH SERVICES

Mental Health Program **509.843.3791**
Fax 509.843.3548
E-mail .... gfleming@qbhs.org
    856 W Main St, Pomeroy, WA 99347
    Gayle Fleming, County Coordinator

POLICE AND SHERIFF

Sheriff's Ofc **509.843.3494**
Fax 509.843.1347
Web .... www.co.garfield.wa.us
    789 W. Main St, Pomeroy, WA 99347
    Ben Keller, Sheriff

Grant County

SOCIAL SERVICES

Child & Family Svcs **509.764.5757**
    1620 S Pioneer Way, Ste A, Moses Lake, WA 98837

GENERAL HEALTH SERVICES

Health District **509.754.6060**
Fax 509.754.0941
Web .... www.granthealth.org
E-mail .... info@granthealth.org
    35 C St NW, Ephrata, WA 98823-1685
    Jefferson Ketchel, Administrator

JUSTICE AGENCY

Youth Svcs/ Juvenile Court **509.754.5690**
Fax 509.754.5797
Web .... www.co.grant.wa.us
E-mail .... wswanson@co.grant.wa.us
    303 Abel Rd, Ephrata, WA 98823-1892
    Warren Swanson, Administrator

POLICE AND SHERIFF

Sheriff's Dept **509.754.2011**
Fax 509.754.2321
E-mail .... tjones@co.grant.wa.us
    35 C St NW, Ephrata, WA 98823
    Tom Jones, Sheriff

Grays Harbor County

SOCIAL SERVICES

Children And Family Svcs **360.537.4300**
Fax 360.533.9236
    415 W Wishkah St Ste 2B, Aberdeen,
    WA 98520-6184
    Diane Fuller, Assessment Supervisor

GENERAL HEALTH SERVICES

Health Dept **360.532.8665**
Fax 360.533.6272
Web .... www.ghphss.org
E-mail .... jbrewster@co.grays-harbor.wa.us
    2109 Sumner Ave Ste 101, Aberdeen,
    WA 98520-3600
    John Brewester, Director Of Health And Social Services

JUSTICE AGENCY

Juvenile Court Svcs **360.533.3919**
Fax 360.533.3927
Web .... www.co.grays-harbor.wa.us
    103 Hagara St, Aberdeen, WA 98520-4242
    Greg Reynvaan, Administrator

Probation Svcs **360.249.6868**
Fax 360.249.6871
    102 W Broadway Ave Rm 105, Montesano,
    WA 98563
    Mallin Shelton, Director

COURTS

Superior Court **360.249.6363**
Fax 360.249.6381
    102 W Broadway Ave Rm 203, Montesano,
    WA 98563
    Rita Zastrow, Secretary

POLICE AND SHERIFF

Sheriff's Dept **360.249.3711**
Fax 360.249.3288
Web .... www.co.grays/harber.wa.us
    100 W Broadway Ste 3, Montesano, WA 98563
    Michael J. Whelan, Sheriff

Island

SOCIAL SERVICES

Community Svcs Ofc **360.240.4700**
Fax 360.679.3524
Web .... www.islandseniorservices.org
E-mail .... lhanson@islandseniorservices.org
    656 SE Bayshore Dr Ste 1, Oak Harbor,
    WA 98277-5739
    Liz Hanson, Administrator

JUSTICE AGENCY

CASA **360.240.5560**
Fax 360.240.5521
E-mail .... carlage@co.island.wa.us
    501 N Main St, Coupeville, WA 98239
    Carla Grau-egerton, Program Coordinator

COURTS

Juvenile Court/Probation Ofc **360.679.7325**
Fax 360.678.2139
E-mail .... brookep@co.island.wa.us
    501 N Main St, Coupeville, WA 98239
    Brooke Powell, Administrator

Superior Court **360.679.7361**
Fax 360.679.7383
Web .... www.islandcounty.net
E-mail .... brookep@co.island.wa.us
    101 NE 6th St, Law And Justice Bldg., Coupeville,
    WA 98239
    Brooke Powell, Acting Admin.

POLICE AND SHERIFF

Sheriff's Ofc **360.678.4422**
Fax 360.679.7314
E-mail .... icso@co.island.wa.us
    101 NE 6th St, Coupeville, WA 98239
    Mark Brown, Sheriff

Jefferson County

SOCIAL SERVICES

Community Svcs Ofc **360.379.4300**
Fax 360.379.5017
Web .... www.co.jefferson.ny.us
E-mail .... louish@co.jefferson.ny.us
    915 Sheridan St Ste 201, Port Townsend,
    WA 98368-2931
    Louis Hundpindford, Administrator

GENERAL HEALTH SERVICES

Health Dept **360.385.9400**
Fax 360.385.9401
Web .... www.jeffersoncountypublichealth.org
    615 Sheridan St, Port Townsend, WA 98368-2476
    Jean Baldwin, Director Of Community Health

JUSTICE AGENCY

Guardian Ad Litem Program **360.385.9190**
Fax 360.385.9191
E-mail .... mbeers@co.jefferson.wa.us
    1820 Jefferson St, Port Townsend, WA 98368
    Mike Beers, Coordinator

COURTS

Superior Court & Clerk's Ofc **360.385.9125**
Fax 360.385.5672
    1820 Jefferson St, Port Townsend, WA 98368
    Honorable Craddock Verser, Judge

POLICE AND SHERIFF

Sheriff's Ofc **360.385.3831**
Fax 360.379.0513
    79 Elkins Rd, Port Hadlock, WA 98339
    Tony Hernandez, Sheriff

King County

SOCIAL SERVICES

Children And Family Svcs Region 4
Ofc **206.691.2500**
Fax 206.281.6288
    100 W Harrison St, South Tower Ste 400, Seattle,
    WA 98119-4116
    Joe Odimva, Regional Administrator

Senior Svcs **206.448.3110**
Fax 206.448.5766
Web .... www.seniorservices.org
E-mail .... denisek@seniorservices.org
    2208 2nd Ave, Seattle, WA 98121
    Denise Klein, Executive Director

GENERAL HEALTH SERVICES

Auburn Public Health Ctr **206.296.8400**
Fax 206.296.8403
Web .... www.kingcounty.gov/healthservices
    901 Auburn Way N Ste A, Auburn, WA 98002
    Karen Russell, Site Manager

Columbia Health Ctr **206.296.4650**
Fax 206.296.0580
Web .... www.kingcounty.gov/health
    4400 37th Ave S, Seattle, WA 98118
    Kathy Green, Clinical Manager

Dept Of Public Health **206.296.4600**
Web .... www.kingcounty.gov/health
    401 5Th Ave, Seattle, WA 98104
    David Fleming, Director Of Health

Downtown Public Health Ctr **206.296.4755**
Web .... www.kingcounty.gov
    2124 4th Ave, Seattle, WA 98121
    Della Lorenzen, Clinic Manager

Eastgate Public Health Ctr **206.296.4920**
Web .... www.kingcounty.gov
  14350 SE Eastgate Way, Bellevue, WA 98007
Sherman Lohn, Clinical Manager

Federal Way Health Ctr **206.296.8410**
Fax 206.296.8412
Web .... www.kingcounty.gov
  33431 13th Pl S, Federal Way, WA 98003
Karen Russell, Rn, Supervisor/site Lead

North Public Health Ctr **206.296.4765**
Fax 206.296.4886
Web .... www.metrokc.gov/health
E-mail .... david.reyes@kingcounty.gov
  10501 Meridian Ave N, Seattle, WA 98133-9509
David Reyes, Clinic Manager

Northshore Health Ofc **206.296.9787**
Fax 206.296.9826
Web .... www.kingcounty.gov
  10808 NE 145th St, Bothell, WA 98011-5200
Sally Wear, Supervisor

Renton Public Health Dept **206.296.4700**
Web .... www.kingcounty.gov/health
  3001 NE 4th St, Renton, WA 98056
Ann Metler, Site Manager

White Ctr - Public Health Ctr **206.296.4620**
Fax 206.296.4595
Web .... www.kingcounty.gov/health
E-mail .... dreyes@wcaseattle.org
  10821 8th Ave SW, Seattle, WA 98146-2225
David Reyes, Acting Site Manager

MENTAL HEALTH SERVICES

Alcohol/Drug Helpline **206.722.3700**
Web .... www.adhl.org
  6535 5th Pl S Unit MAIN, Seattle, WA 98108-3401
Ann Forbes, Director

JUSTICE AGENCY

Dependency CASA Program **206.296.1120**
Fax 206.296.1493
E-mail .... caha.group@kingcounty.gov
  1401 E Jefferson St Ste 500, Seattle, WA 98122
Racheal Dvilar, Director

Juvenile Rehabilitation Admin Region
4 .... **206.621.3400**
Fax 206.464.7812
Web .... www.dshs.wa.gov
E-mail .... patty.ondal@dshs.wa.gov
  500 Fairview Ave N, Seattle, WA 98109-5506
Patty Ondal, Regional Administrator

COURTS

Superior Court Family Court Svcs **206.205.2521**
Fax 206.205.2525
Web .... www.kingcounty.gov
  401 4th Ave N, Ste 1D, Kent, WA 98032
Jorine Moore, Director

Superior Court Family Court Svcs **206.296.9400**
Fax 206.296.9420
Web .... www.metrokc.gov/kcsc
E-mail .... dorine.moore@doh.wa.gov
  516 3rd Ave, Ste W280, Seattle, WA 98104
Dorine Moore, Program Manager

POLICE AND SHERIFF

Seattle Police Dept **206.684.4775**
Fax 206.233.0068
E-mail .... darryl.williams@ci.seattle.wa.us
  610 5th Ave, Seattle, WA 98124
Darryl Williams, Juvenile Unit Commander

EDUCATION SERVICES

Communities In Schools **206.252.8000**
Fax 206.252.8001
  1600 S Columbian Way, Seattle, WA 98108
Andhra Lutz, Principal

Kitsap County

SOCIAL SERVICES

Children And Family Svcs **360.475.3688**
Fax 360.475.3499
  3423 6th St, Ste 217, Bremerton, WA 98312
Mariann McDowell-Helmer, CPS Supervisor

Community Svcs Ofc **360.473.2200**
Fax 360.478.6960
  4710 Auto Center Blvd, Bremerton, WA 98312
Margaret Swigert, Administrator

GENERAL HEALTH SERVICES

Health District **360.337.5235**
Fax 360.337.5298
Web .... www.kitsapcountyhealth.com
  345 6th St Ste 300, Bremerton, WA 98337
Kerry Dobbelaere, Infectious Disease Program Manager

MENTAL HEALTH SERVICES

Human Svcs **360.337.7185**
Fax 360.337.7187
Web .... www.kitsapgov.com
E-mail .... aedgerton@co.kitsap.wa.us
  614 Division St, Stop MS, Port Orchard,
  WA 98366-4614
Anders Edgerton, Coordinator Of Mental Health

JUSTICE AGENCY

CASA Program **360.337.5484**
Fax 360.337.5404
E-mail .... casainfo@kitsap.wa.us
  1338 SW Old Clifton Rd, Port Orchard, WA 98367
Saeed Saber, Case Coordinator

COURTS

Superior Court **360.337.7140**
Fax 360.337.4973
Web .... www.kitsapgov.com/sc
E-mail .... rhartman@co.kitsap.wa.us
  614 Division St, Mail Stop 24, Port Orchard,
  WA 98366-4614
Honorable Russel Hartman, Presiding Judge

Youth Court **360.337.5401**
Fax 360.337.5404
  1338 SW Old Clifton Rd, Port Orchard,
  WA 98367-9113
Patty Bronson, Manager

POLICE AND SHERIFF

Port Orchard Police Dept **360.876.1700**
Fax 360.876.5546
  546 Bay St, Port Orchard, WA 98366
Alan Townsend, Chief

Sheriff's Dept **360.337.7101**
Fax 360.337.4923
Web .... www.co.kitsap.wa.us
E-mail .... sboyer@co.kitsap.wa.us
  614 Division St, # MS-37, Port Orchard, WA 98366
Steve Boyer, Sheriff

Kittitas County

SOCIAL SERVICES

Dshs - Community Svc Ofc -
Ellensburg **509.925.0400**
Fax 509.962.7736
Web .... www.dshs.wa.gov
E-mail .... oswaldd@dshs.wa.gov
  521 E Mountain View Ave, Ellensburg,
  WA 98926-3865
Don Oswald, Deputy Administrator

GENERAL HEALTH SERVICES

Public Health Dept **509.962.7515**
Fax 509.962.7581
Web .... www.co.kittitas.wa.us
E-mail .... drmark@kvch.net
  507 N Nanum St Ste 102, Ellensburg,
  WA 98926-2886
Mark Larson, Md, Health Officer

Klickitat County

SOCIAL SERVICES

Child & Family Svcs **509.773.7475**
  808 S Columbus St, Goldendale, WA 98620

GENERAL HEALTH SERVICES

Health Dept **509.773.4565**
Fax 509.773.5991
Web .... www.klickitatcounty.org
E-mail .... kevinb@co.klickitat.wa.us
  228 W Main St, # CH14, Goldendale, WA 98620
Kevin Barry, Director

Health District **509.493.1558**
Fax 509.493.4025
Web .... www.klickitatcounty.org
  501 Ne Washington St, White Salmon, WA 98672
Theresa Rundell, ARNP, Family Planning

JUSTICE AGENCY

CASA/GAL **509.773.3440**
Fax 509.773.3221
E-mail .... marlenas@co.klickitat.wa.us
  131 W Court St, Msch-16, Goldendale, WA 98620
Marlena Shupe, Program Coordinator

Child & Family Svcs **509.493.6180**
Fax ....
  221 N Main, White Salmon, WA 98672

Juvenile Court Svcs **509.773.3355**
Fax 509.773.3221
E-mail .... samc@co.klickitat.wa.us
  131 W Court St Stop 16, Goldendale, WA 98620
Sam Counts, Probation Counselor

COURTS

Superior Court **509.773.5755**
Fax 509.773.2496
Web .... www.klickitatcounty.org
  205 S Columbus Ave, # CH-29, Goldendale,
  WA 98620
Brian Altman, Judge

POLICE AND SHERIFF

Sheriff's Dept **509.773.4547**
Fax 509.773.6575
Web .... www.co.klickitat.wa.us
E-mail .... rickm@co.klickitat.wa.us
  205 S Columbus Ave Stop 7, MS-CH-7, ROOM 108,
  Goldendale, WA 98620-9052
Rick Mcomas, Sheriff

Washington

Lewis County

SOCIAL SERVICES

Washington Dept of Social Health
Service **360.807.7081**
Fax 360.330.7536
　3401 Galvin Rd PO Box 839, Centralia, WA 98531

MENTAL HEALTH SERVICES

Cascade Mental Health Care **360.748.6696**
Fax 360.748.0627
　135 W Main St, Chehalis, WA 98532
　Matt Patten, Clinical Director

JUSTICE AGENCY

Guardian Ad Litem Program **360.740.2626**
Fax 360.748.2258
Web ....www.co.lewis.wa.us
E-mail ....taniya.phillips@lewiscountyus.gov
　1255 SW Pacific Ave, Chehalis, WA 98532
　Taniya Phillips, Co-Program Coordinator

Juvenile Court Svcs **360.740.1178**
Fax 360.748.2258
　1255 SW Pacific Ave, Chehalis, WA 98532
　Holli J. Spanski, Administrator

COURTS

Superior Court Admin **360.740.1333**
Fax 360.740.2603
　345 W Main St, Fl 2, Chehalis, WA 98532
　Honorable H. John Hall, Judge

POLICE AND SHERIFF

Sheriff's Ofc **360.748.9286**
Fax 360.740.1476
E-mail ....sheriff@lewiscountywa.gov
　345 W Main St, First Floor, Chehalis, WA 98532
　Steve Mansfield, Sheriff

Lincoln County

GENERAL HEALTH SERVICES

Health Dept **509.725.2501**
Fax 509.725.1014
Web ....www.co.lincoln.wa.us
　90 Nichols St, Davenport, WA 99122
　Ed Dzedzy, Administrator And Director

COURTS

Juvenile Court **509.725.7475**
Fax 509.725.2100
E-mail ....bmanion@co.lincoln.wa.us
　450 Logan St, Davenport, WA 99122
　William Manion, Director

Mason County

SOCIAL SERVICES

Children And Family Svcs **360.432.2050**
Fax 360.432.2052
Web ....www.dshs.wa.gov
E-mail ....kat300@dshs.wa.gov
　2505 Olympic Hwy N, Ste 440, Shelton, WA 98584
　Kat Scheibner, CPS Supervisor

GENERAL HEALTH SERVICES

South Puget Intertribal Planning
Agency **360.426.3990**
Fax 360.427.8003
Web ....www.spipa.org
E-mail ....atian@spipa.org
　3104 SE Olympic Hwy, Shelton, WA 98584
　Amadeo Tian, Executive Director

JUSTICE AGENCY

Probation **360.427.9670**
Fax 360.432.5653
　615 W Alder St Ste 1, Shelton, WA 98584
　Harris H. Haertel, Probation Services Director

Okanogan County

SOCIAL SERVICES

Confederated Tribes Indian Social
Svcs **509.634.2200**
Fax 509.634.2398
Web ....www.colvilletribes.com
E-mail ....joan.grujon@colvilletribes.com
　PO Box 150, Nespelem, WA 99155-0150
　Joan Grujon, Social Services Director

GENERAL HEALTH SERVICES

Colville PHS Indian Health Ctr **509.634.2900**
Fax 509.634.2945
　29 Sand Poil, Nespelem, WA 99155
　Karol Parker, Service Unit Director

Okanogan Public Health Dept **509.422.7140**
Fax 509.422.7142
Web ....www.okanogancounty.org
　1234 2nd Ave S, Okanogan, WA 98840
　Lauri Jones, Health Director

JUSTICE AGENCY

Juvenile & Family Serv **509.422.7258**
Fax 509.422.7268
E-mail ....juvenile@co.okanogan.wa.us
　237 N 4th Ave, Okanogan, WA 98840
　Adele Hayner, Supervisor

COURTS

Superior Court **509.422.7130**
Fax 509.422.7133
E-mail ....assessor@co.okanogan.wa.us
　149 3rd North, Okanogan, WA 98840
　Honorable Jack Burchard, Judge

POLICE AND SHERIFF

Sheriff's Dept **509.422.7200**
Fax 509.422.7223
Web ....www.co.okanogan.wa.us
E-mail ....ocso@co.okanogan.wa.us
　123 5th Ave N Rm 200, Okanogan, WA 98840-9436
　Frank T. Rogers, Sheriff

Pacific County

SOCIAL SERVICES

Washington Dept of Social Health
Service **360.642.6235**
Fax 360.642.5208
　2601 Pacific Ave NE, Long Beach, WA 98631

GENERAL HEALTH SERVICES

Health Dept **360.875.9343**
Fax 360.875.9323
　1216 W Robert Bush Dr, South Bend, WA 98586
　Kathy Stoor, Director

POLICE AND SHERIFF

Sheriff's Dept **360.875.9395**
Fax 360.875.9393
E-mail ....sjohnson@co.pacific.wa.us
　300 Memorial Avenue, South Bend, WA 98586
　Scott Johnson, Sheriff

Pend Oreille County

SOCIAL SERVICES

Children And Family Svcs **509.447.6216**
Fax 509.447.5256
　1600 W 1st St, Newport, WA 99156
　Angela Newport, Supervisor

GENERAL HEALTH SERVICES

Health District **509.447.3131**
Fax 509.447.5644
Web ....www.netchd.org
E-mail ....jsteinbach@netchd.org
　605 Highway 20, Newport, WA 99156
　Jan Steinbach, Rn, Community Health Supervisor

COURTS

Superior Court/Clerk's Ofc **509.447.2435**
Fax 509.447.2734
E-mail ....townbey@pendoreille.org
　Hall Of Justice, 229 S Garden Ave, Newport,
　WA 99156
　Tammie Ownbey, County Clerk

POLICE AND SHERIFF

Sheriff's Dept **509.447.3151**
Fax 509.447:2222
　331 S. Garden Ave, Newport, WA 99156
　Alan Botzheim, Sheriff

Pierce County

SOCIAL SERVICES

Pierce Northwest Community Svcs
Ofc **253.983.6767**
Fax 253.593.2334
Web ....www.onlineapp.dshs.wa.gov
　1949 S State St, Fl 1, Tacoma, WA 98405
　Ralph Mercado, Administrator

GENERAL HEALTH SERVICES

Health Dept **253.798.6500**
Fax 253.798.6027
E-mail ....msaffold@tpchd.org
　3629 S D St, Tacoma, WA 98418-6897
　Mary Saffold, Aids Coordinator

MENTAL HEALTH SERVICES

Community Connection **253.798.4400**
Fax 253.798.4470
　1305 Tacoma Ave S Ste104, Tacoma, WA 98402
　Troy Christensen, Mental Health Manager

JUSTICE AGENCY

CASA/GAL **253.798.7349**
Fax 253.798.7649
Web ....www.wacasa.org
E-mail ....julie.lowrey@co.pierce.wa.us
　5501 6th Ave, Tacoma, WA 98406-2603
　Julie Lowery, Program Director

Probation Dept **253.798.7595**
Fax 253.798.3389
E-mail ....proadhouse@co.pierce.wa.us
　901 Tacoma Ave S Ste 200, Tacoma, WA 98402
　Patty Roadhouse, Probation Manager

COURTS

Superior Court Admin **253.798.3654**
Fax 253.798.7214
Web ....www.co.pierce.wa.us
　930 Tacoma Ave S Rm 534, Tacoma,
　WA 98402-2173
　Honorable Sergio Armijo, Director

POLICE AND SHERIFF

Sheriff's Ofc **253.798.7530**
Fax 253.798.6712
Web ....www.co.pierce.wa.us
E-mail ....ppastor@co.pierce.wa.us
　930 Tacoma Ave S, Tacoma, WA 98402-2170
　Paul Pastor, Sheriff

Tacoma Police Dept/Chief Ramsdell's
Ofc...253.591.5900
Fax..253.591.5991
  3701 S Pine St, Tacoma, WA 98409
  Donald Ramsdell, Chief

EDUCATION SERVICES

Communities In Schools.....................253.571.1114
Fax..253.571.1079
Web.................................www.cisoftacoma.org
  708 S G St, Tacoma, WA 98405
  Teresa Maxwel, Director

Communities In Schools.....................253.840.8917
Web...............................www.puyallup.piswa.org
E-mail..................maukje@puyallup.k12.wa.us
  302 Second Street SE, Puyallup, WA 98372
  Jan Mauk, Program Manager

Communities In Schools Of Lakewood,
Inc...253.589.7489
Fax..253.589.7965
E-mail...............dokeeffe@cloverpark.k12.wa.us
  6402 100th St SW, Lakewood, WA 98499-1710
  Dave O'Keeffe, Executive Director

Tacoma Public Schools Special Education
Dept..253.571.1224
Fax..253.571.1098
Web...................................www.tacoma.k12.wa.us
E-mail...................jtraufl@tacoma.k12.wa.us
  601 S 8th St, Tacoma, WA 98405
  Jennifer Traufler, Executive Director Of Student Services

San Juan County

SOCIAL SERVICES

Community Svcs Ofc.........................360.378.4196
Fax..360.378.3271
  535 Market St ste B, Friday Harbor, WA 98250
  Nancy Wolke, Administrator

GENERAL HEALTH SERVICES

Health & Community Serv...................360.378.4474
Fax..360.378.7036
Web......................................www.sanjuanco.com
  145 Rhone St, Courthouse Annex, Friday Harbor,
  WA 98250
  Susan Leff, Nursing Director

JUSTICE AGENCY

Juvenile Court Svcs.........................360.378.4620
Fax..360.378.6681
Web....................................www.co.san-juan.wa.us
E-mail.................tomk@co.san-juan.wa.us
  350 Court St Ste 4, Friday Harbor, WA 98250-7901
  Thomas Kearney, Administrator And Casa Director

POLICE AND SHERIFF

Sheriff's Ofc.................................360.378.4151
Fax..360.378.7125
E-mail..........................robn@sanjuanco.com
  96 2nd St, Friday Harbor, WA 98250
  Rob Nou, Sheriff

Skagit County

SOCIAL SERVICES

Community Svcs Ofc.........................360.416.7444
Fax..360.416.7279
  900 E College Way Ste 100, Mount Vernon,
  WA 98273
  Nancy Wolke, Administrator

GENERAL HEALTH SERVICES

Health Dept..................................360.336.9380
Fax..360.336.9401
Web......................................www.skagitcounty.net
E-mail...................sandip@co.skagit.wa.us
  700 S 2nd St Ste 301, Mount Vernon,
  WA 98273-3879
  Sandi Paciotti, Communicable Disease Supervisor

MENTAL HEALTH SERVICES

Community Svcs...............................360.336.9395
Fax..360.336.9323
E-mail............communityservices@co.skagit.wa.us
  309 S 3rd St, Mount Vernon, WA 98273-3820
  Jennifer Kingsley, Coordinator

Skagit Valley Hospital......................360.424.4111
Fax..360.428.2416
  1415 E Kincaid St, Mount Vernon, WA 98273
  Gregg Davidson, Administrator

JUSTICE AGENCY

Probation.....................................360.336.9372
Fax..360.336.9373
Web......................................www.co.skagit.wa.us
E-mail................dftcttrobatm@co.skagit.wa.us
  205 W Kincaid St, District Court, Rm. 301, Mount
  Vernon, WA 98273
  Michael Mahoney, Director

Youth And Family Svcs......................360.336.9360
Fax..360.336.9409
Web......................................www.co.skagit.wa.us
  611 S 2nd St, Mount Vernon, WA 98273-3820
  Lisa Ramsey, Administrator

COURTS

Superior Court...............................360.336.9320
Fax..360.336.9340
Web..................www.skagitcounty.net/superiorcourt
E-mail...............deliah.george@courts.wa.gov
  205 W Kincaid St, Ste 202, Mount Vernon,
  WA 98273-4225
  Deliah George, Court Administrator

Skamania County

SOCIAL SERVICES

Children And Family Svcs...................509.427.0700
Fax..509.427.2309
E-mail.......................thlo300@eshs.wa.gov
  266 SW 2nd St, Stevenson, WA 98648
  Tammy Manner, Child Protective Svcs Supervisor

COURTS

Juvenile Court Svcs.........................509.427.3715
Fax..509.427.3719
Web................www.skamaniacounty.org/juvenile
E-mail...............allinger@co.skamania.wa.us
  240 Vancouver Ave, Stevenson, WA 98648
  Jennifer Allinger, Administrator

Snohomish County

SOCIAL SERVICES

Bia Puget Sound Agency In Everett Social
Svcs..425.258.2651
Fax..425.258.1254
Web.......................................www.haskell.edu
  2707 Colby Ave Ste 1101, Everett, WA 98201-3566
  Kim Williams, Social Services Director

GENERAL HEALTH SERVICES

Snohomish Health District...................425.339.5200
Fax..425.339.5216
Web...www.snohd.org
  3020 Rucker Ave, Ste 306, Everett, WA 98201
  Gary Goldbaum, Doctor

JUSTICE AGENCY

Probation Dept...............................360.435.7720
Fax..360.435.7725
  415 E Burke Ave, Arlington, WA 98223
  Belinda Galde, Probation Officer

COURTS

Arlington Police Dept.......................360.403.3400
Fax..360.435.4677
E-mail...................edavis@ci.arlington.wa.us
  110 E 3Rd St, Arlington, WA 98223
  Emma Davis, Coordinator

Superior Court Admin.......................425.388.3421
Fax..425.388.3498
E-mail...................ronald@courts.wa.gov
  3000 Rockefeller Ave, # MS-502, Everett, WA 98201
  Honorable Ronald Castleberry, Director

POLICE AND SHERIFF

Everett Police Dept..........................425.257.8400
Fax..425.257.6501
Web......................................www.everettpolice.org
E-mail...................katwood@ci.everett.wa.us
  3002 Wetmore Ave, Everett, WA 98201-4018
  Kathy Atwood, Chief

Snohomish Co. Sheriff's Ofc/Special Investigations
Unit...425.388.6383
Fax..425.388.6300
  1509 California St, Everett, WA 98201
  John Lovick, Sheriff

Spokane County

SOCIAL SERVICES

Children And Family Svcs...................509.363.3500
Fax..509.363.4601
Web...www.dshs.wa.gov
E-mail...................abti300@dshs.wa.gov
  1313 N Atlantic St Ste 2000, Spokane,
  WA 99201-2318
  Tim Abbey, Area Administrator

Health and Human services................509.258.7502
Fax..509.258.7029
Web...................................www.spokanetribe.com
E-mail...................annd@spokanetribe.com
  6228 Old School Rd, Wellpinit, WA 99040
  Ann Dahl, Director

Washington Dept of Social Health
Service..509.363.3550
Fax..509.363.4601
  1313 N Atlantic St Ste 2000, Spokane, WA 99201

GENERAL HEALTH SERVICES

Spokane Regional Health District.............509.324.1500
Fax..509.324.1507
Web...www.srhd.org
E-mail...........................info@srhd.org
  1101 W College Ave, Spokane, WA 99201
  Joel Mccullough, Health Officer

MENTAL HEALTH SERVICES

Spokane Addictions Recovery Ctr
(SPARC).....................................509.624.3251
Fax..509.624.4505
Web.......................................www.sparcop.org
E-mail...........................markb@sparcop.org
  812 S Walnut St, Spokane, WA 99204-3326
  Mark Brownlow, Administrator

JUSTICE AGENCY

CASA/GAL....................................509.477.2468
Fax..509.477.3403
E-mail...............pdonahue@spokanecounty.org
  1208 W Mallon Ave, Spokane, WA 99201
  Pat Donahue, Program Director

Washington

Probation/Juvenile Court Svcs Detention
Ctr...**509.477.2404**
Fax..509.477.2699
Web..................................www.spokanecounty.org
E-mail......................mstudbaker@spokanecounty.org
   1208 W Mallon Ave, Spokane, WA 99201-2041
Marie Studbaker, Probation Administrator

Spokane Tribal Court...................**509.258.7717**
Fax..509.258.9223
   258 Agentcies Sq, Wellpinit, WA 99040
Gene Hughes, Administrator

POLICE AND SHERIFF

Sheriff's Ofc...............................**509.477.4739**
Fax..509.477.5641
Web..................................www.spokanesheriff.org
E-mail......................oknezovich@spokanesheriff.org
   1100 W Mallon, Spokane, WA 99260-2043
Ozzie Knezovich, Sheriff

Stevens County

SOCIAL SERVICES

Colville Tribe Children And Family
Svcs.......................................**509.634.2638**
Fax..509.634.2633
E-mail.........................daryltoulou@colvilletribes.com
   PO Box 150, Nespelem, WA 99155-0150
Daryl Toulou, Program Manager

Community Svcs Ofc.....................**509.685.5600**
Fax..509.685.5606
E-mail...............................reberfl@dshs.wa.gov
   1100 S Main St, Ste 1, Colville, WA 99114
Fritzi Reber, Administrator

GENERAL HEALTH SERVICES

David C Wynecoop Memorial Clinic...........**509.258.4517**
Fax..509.258.6757
   6203 Agency Loop Rd., Wellpinit, WA 99040
Coy Fullen, Medical Director

JUSTICE AGENCY

CASA..**509.685.0673**
Fax..509.685.0655
Web...................................www.co.stevens.wa.us
E-mail..........................pmarkel@co.stevens.wa.us
   215 S Oak St, Colville, WA 99114-2836
Patty Markel, Program Manager

Juvenile Court Svcs.....................**509.684.2549**
Fax..509.684.7569
Web...................................www.co.stevens.wa.us
E-mail.........................pholter@co.stevens.wa.us
   215 S Oak St, Rm 202, Colville, WA 99114
Paula Holter-mehren, Administrator

Rural Resources Community
Action.....................................**509.684.8421**
Fax..509.684.4740
Web.....................................www.ruralresources.org
   956 S Main St Ste A, Colville, WA 99114
Barry Lamont, Division Director

COURTS

Superior Court............................**509.684.7520**
Fax..509.685.0679
Web...................................www.co.stevens.wa.us
   215 S Oak St, Rm 209, Colville, WA 99114
Allen C Nielson, Judge

POLICE AND SHERIFF

Sheriff's Dept............................**509.684.5296**
Fax..509.684.7583
E-mail...............................tcannon@co.stevens.wa.us
   215 S Oak St, Colville, WA 99114
Kendel Alen, Sheriff

Thurston County

SOCIAL SERVICES

Children And Family Svcs Region 6
Ofc..**360.725.6800**
Fax..360.725.6766
E-mail...............................sutn300@dshs.wa.gov
   6840 Capitol Blvd SE, Bldg 3, Tumwater, WA 98501
Nancy Sutton, Regional Administrator

GENERAL HEALTH SERVICES

Health Dept...............................**360.867.2500**
Fax..360.867.2601
Web....................................www.co.thurston.wa.us
E-mail.........................swanfop@co.thurston.wa.us
   412 Lilly Rd NE, Olympia, WA 98506
Sherri Mcdonald, Director

JUSTICE AGENCY

CASA-Nisqually Tribal Court..............**360.456.5221**
Fax..360.456.5280
E-mail.....................simmons.john@nisqally-nsn.gov
   4820 She Nah Num Dr SE, Olympia, WA 98513-9105
John Simmons, Director

Juvenile Court Svcs.....................**360.709.3131**
Fax..360.709.3150
   2801 32nd Ave SW, Tumwater, WA 98512
Michael Fenton, Administrator

COURTS

Superior Court............................**360.786.5560**
Fax..360.754.4060
   2000 Lakeridge Dr SW, Bldg 2, Olympia, WA 98502
Honorable Richard Hicks, Judge

POLICE AND SHERIFF

Olympia Police Dept.....................**360.753.8300**
Fax..360.753.8143
E-mail.....................olympiapolice@ci.olympia.wa.us
   601 4th Ave E, Olympia, WA 98501
Ronnie Roberts, Chief Of Police

Sheriff's Dept............................**360.786.5500**
Fax..360.786.5275
Web...................................www.co.thurstonsheriff.org
E-mail........................edwardg@co.thurston.wa.us
   2000 Lakeridge Dr SW, Olympia, WA 98502-6001

Wahkiakum County

GENERAL HEALTH SERVICES

Health Dept...............................**360.795.6207**
Fax..360.795.6143
Web...www.doh.wa.gov
E-mail.........................brightj@co.wahkiakum.wa.us
   64 Main St, Cathlamet, WA 98612
Judy Bright, Administrator

COURTS

Superior Court............................**360.795.3558**
Fax..360.795.8813
E-mail.....................mikes@sd.co.wahkiakum.wa.us
   64 Main St, Cathlamet, WA 98612
Honorable Michael Sullivan, Judge

POLICE AND SHERIFF

Sheriff's Ofc.............................**360.795.3242**
Fax..360.795.3145
Web.......................www.sd.co.wahkiakum.wa.us
E-mail.........................dearmorej@co.wahkiakum.wa.us
   64 Main St, Cathlamet, WA 98612
Jon L Dearmore, Sheriff

Walla Walla County

SOCIAL SERVICES

Children And Family Svcs..................**509.524.4900**
Fax..509.527.4655
   206 W Poplar St, Walla Walla, WA 99362
Sonia Cole, Supervisor

Dept Of Social & Health Svcs............**509.522.4297**
Fax..509.522.4330
Web...www.dshs.wa.gov
E-mail...............................mendojs@dshs.wa.gov
   416 E Main St, Walla Walla, WA 99362-2006
Joe Mendoza, Interim Administrator

JUSTICE AGENCY

Juvenile Justice Ctr.....................**509.524.2800**
Fax..509.524.2836
Web...................................www.co.walla-walla.wa.us
E-mail.........................karow@co.walla-walla.wa.us
   455 W Rose St, Walla Walla, WA 99362-1792
Michael Bates, Director

POLICE AND SHERIFF

Sheriff's Dept............................**509.524.5400**
Fax..509.524.5480
Web...................................www.co.walla-walla.wa.us
E-mail........................sheriff@co.walla-walla.wa.us
   240 W Alder St # 101, Walla Walla, WA 99362-2807
John Turner, Sheriff

Whatcom County

SOCIAL SERVICES

Community Svcs Ofc.....................**360.714.4000**
Fax..360.714.4010
E-mail...............................johnsrs@dshs.wa.gov
   4101 Meridian St, Bellingham, WA 98226-5514
Ronnie-Sue Johnson, Administrator

MENTAL HEALTH SERVICES

Human Svcs...............................**360.676.6724**
Fax..360.676.6771
Web...................................www.co.whatcom.wa.us
   509 Girard St, Bellingham, WA 98225
Anne Deacon, Human Service Supervisor

JUSTICE AGENCY

Probation.................................**360.332.8311**
Fax..360.332.8330
E-mail...............................cityhall@ci.blaine.wa.us
   344 H St, Blaine, WA 98230-4109
Luanne Cranefield, Probation Counselor

COURTS

Teen Court...............................**360.734.9862**
Fax..360.734.4720
Web.....................................www.northwestyouthservices.org
E-mail...............................cathyb@nwys.org
   1020 N State St, Bellingham, WA 98225-5012
Cathy Beaty, Coordinator

POLICE AND SHERIFF

Sheriff's Dept............................**360.676.6650**
Fax..360.738.2494
Web...................................www.co.whatcom.wa.us
E-mail...............................belfo@co.whatcom.wa.us
   311 Grand Ave Ste B1, Bellingham, WA 98225-4038
Bill Elfo, Sheriff

Whitman County

SOCIAL SERVICES

Children And Family Svcs..................**509.397.5040**
Fax..509.397.4583
E-mail...............................shba300@dshs.wa.gov
   418 S Main St Ste 2, Colfax, WA 99111
Barb Sheffler, Supervisor

Washington

JUSTICE AGENCY

CASA/Juvenile Court Svcs **509.397.6246**
Fax 509.397.5591
Web ....www.washingtonstatecasa.org
E-mail ....casa@co.whitman.wa.us
    400 N Main St, Colfax, WA 99111-2031
    Windy Tevlin, Casa Coordinator

COURTS

Superior Court **509.397.6244**
Fax 509.397.2728
E-mail ....superiorcourt@co.whitman.wa.us
    404 N Main St, Colfax, WA 99111
    Honorable David Frazier, Director

POLICE AND SHERIFF

Sheriff's Dept **509.397.6266**
Fax 509.397.2099
Web ....www.whitmancounty.org
E-mail ....sheriff@co.whitman.wa.us
    411 N Mill St, Colfax, WA 99111-2013
    Brett J. Myers, Sheriff

Yakima County

SOCIAL SERVICES

Aeging and Long Term Care **509.965.0105**
Fax 509.965.0221
Web ....www.altcwashington.com
    7200 W Nob Hill Blvd, Yakima, WA 98908
    Lori Brown, Director

Children And Family Svcs Region 2

Ofc **509.454.6900**
Fax 509.575.2677
E-mail ....nike300@dshs.wa.gov
    315 Holton Ave, Ste 200, Yakima, WA 98902-3240
    Ken Nichols, Regional Administrator

Indian Social Svcs **509.865.2255**
Fax 509.865.2961
Web ....www.yakama.com
    401 Fort Rd, Toppenish, WA 98948
    Renee Broncheau, Social Worker

GENERAL HEALTH SERVICES

Yakima Indian Health Ctr **509.865.2102**
Fax 509.865.6237
Web ....www.yak.portland.ihs.gov
E-mail ....dhocfon@yak.portland.ihs.gov
    401 Buster Rd, Toppenish, WA 98948-9792
    Daniel Hofcon, Clinical Director

MENTAL HEALTH SERVICES

Yakima Valley Farm Workers Behavorial Health

Svcs **509.453.1344**
Fax 509.453.2209
Web ....www.yvfwc.org
E-mail ....janisl@yvfwc.org
    918 E Mead Ave, Yakima, WA 98903-3720
    Janis Luvaas, Program Director

JUSTICE AGENCY

Probation Ofc **509.574.2050**
Fax 509.574.2051
    1728 Jerome Ave, Yakima, WA 98901
    Kent Trull, Juvenile Court Manager

COURTS

Superior Court **509.574.2710**
Fax 509.574.2701
Web ....www.yakimacounty.us
E-mail ....linda.dickson@co.yakima.wa.us
    128 N 2nd St, Yakima, WA 98901
    Linda Dickson, HR Manager

POLICE AND SHERIFF

Sheriff's Dept **509.574.2500**
Fax 509.574.2501
Web ....www.co.yakima.wa.us/sheriff
    1822 S 1st St, Yakima, WA 98901-2226
    Kenneth Irwin, Sheriff

EDUCATION SERVICES

Epic Head Start **509.877.3151**
Fax 509.877.2001
    5420 Konnowac Pass Rd, Wapato, WA 98951
    Paul Daldez, Director

SPECIAL SERVICES AGENCIES

ADOPTION AGENCIES

A Ctr For Adoption Svc **206.780.1972**
Fax 206.780.1817
E-mail ....dru@drugroves.org
    602 NE Alder Ave, Bainbridge Island,
    WA 98110-3926
    Drew Martin Grosse, Office Director

A Heart's Destiny **509.218.4624**
Web ....www.aheartsdestiny.com
E-mail ....aly@aheartsdestiny.com
    10205 E 17th Ln, Spokane, WA 99206-3432
    Aly, Director

Adoption Advocates Int **360.452.4777**
Fax 360.452.1107
Web ....www.adoptionadvocates.org
E-mail ....aai@olympus.net
    709 S Peabody St, Port Angeles, WA 98362
    Merrily Ripley, Director

Adoption Legal Svc **509.462.3678**
Fax 509.462.3700
    921 W Broadway Ste 301, Spokane, WA 99201
    Mark Iverson, Director

Adoption Ministry Of YWAM **253.770.2283**
Fax 253.445.4483
E-mail ....info@adaptionministry.net
    731 W Pioneer, Puyallup, WA 98371
    Joy Casey, Executive Director

Amara Parenting And Adoption Svcs **206.260.1700**
Fax 206.260.1777
Web ....www.amaraparenting.org
E-mail ....kira@amaraparenting.org
    3300 E Union St, Seattle, WA 98122-3372
    Kira Shriber, Administrator Asst

Bethany Christian Svc **360.733.6042**
Fax 360.733.6216
Web ....www.bethany.org
E-mail ....ekuipers@bethany.org
    1031 N State St Ste 108, Bellingham, WA 98225
    Edna Kuipers, Director

Bissell Law Firm **360.705.9000**
Fax 360.705.0389
E-mail ....ginabissellslaw@comcast.net
    6510 Capital Blvd SE, Tomwater, WA 98501-6937
    Gina Bissel, Director

Brewe Layman Attorneys At Law **425.252.5167**
Fax 425.252.9055
Web ....www.brewelaw.com
E-mail ....brewe@brewelaw.com
    3525 Colby Ave Ste 333, Everett, WA 98201-4782
    Ken Brewe, Attorney

Casey Family Program **206.322.6711**
Fax 206.322.7255
Web ....www.casey.org
    1123 23rd Ave, Seattle, WA 98122
    Lyman Legters, Executive Director

Casey Family Program **509.457.8197**
Fax 509.457.6499
Web ....www.casey.org
E-mail ....lbiggs@casey.org
    404 N 3rd St, Yakima, WA 98901-2343
    Lynn Biggs, Director

Children's House International **360.380.5370**
Fax 360.383.0640
Web ....www.childrenshouseinternational.com
E-mail ....chi4adopt@aol.com
    2074 Vista Dr, Ferndale, WA 98248
    Debbie Price, Executive Director

Confidential Intermediary Svcs **509.448.3740**
Fax 509.448.0967
E-mail ....samssearch@msn.com
    625 E Paradise Rd, Spangle, WA 99031
    Diane Sams, Director

Cowan Moore Stam & Luke **509.943.2676**
Fax 509.946.4257
Web ....www.cowanmoore.com
    503 Knight St Ste A, Richland, WA 99352-4257
    Peter Attorney, Director

Elissa Kokis Law Ofc **360.943.6933**
Fax 360.943.7721
E-mail ....edholm@comcast.net
    2011 State Ave NE, Olympia, WA 98506-4760
    Ed Holmes, Director

Faith International Adoptions **253.383.1928**
Fax 253.572.6662
E-mail ....faith@faithadopt.org
    1105 Tacoma Ave S, Tacoma, WA 98402
    John Meske, Director

Fran Thoreen **360.826.3014**
Web ....www.oneglobaldirectory.com
    29517 S Skagit Hwy, Sedro Woolley, WA 98284-8601

Holman Cahill **206.547.1400**
Fax 206.547.1276
    5507 35th Ave NE, Seattle, WA 98105-5917
    David V. Anderson, Attorney

Thomas L Ledgerwood Law Ofc **509.758.1005**
    922 6th St, Clarkston, WA 99403-2079
    Thomas L. Ledgerwood, Attorney

ADVOCACY RESOURCES

CADA-Citizens Against Domestic & Sexual

Abuse **360.675.2232**
Fax 360.675.7168
Web ....www.cadacanhelp.org
E-mail ....cada@whibeey.net
    PO Box 190, Oak Harbor, WA 98277-0190
    Margie Porter, Executive Director

Children's Advocacy Ctr **360.249.0037**
Fax 360.249.0030
E-mail ....director@ghcac.org
    514 E Broadway Ave, Montesano, WA 98563-3837
    Angela Coulter, Executive Director

Columbia Legal Svcs **206.287.9665**
E-mail ....casey.trupin@columbialegal.org
    101 Yesler Way Ste 300, Seattle, WA 98104
    Casey Trupin, Attorney

Family Resource Center 509.725.4358
Fax 509.725.4360
E-mail ....lynne@frcoflincolncounty.org
620 Park Street, Davenport, WA 99122
Lynne Kuchenbuch, Executive Director

Lummi Nation Tribal Court 360.384.2301
E-mail ....jasond@lummi-nsn.gov
2616 Kwina Rd, Bellingham, WA 98226
Jason Dallmann

BEHAVIORAL HEALTH TREATMENT

Adamson Medical Practice 206.328.5135
Fax 206.328.7761
E-mail ....admin@rtadamson.com
4020 E Madison St Ste 210, Seattle, WA 98112-3150
Richard Adamson, Psychiatrist

Adler Medical Practice 206.624.3800
Fax 206.624.3801
Web ....www.forensicclinicalpsychiatry.com
E-mail ....richadler@msn.com
1700 7th Ave Ste 210, Seattle, WA 98101-1323
Richard Alder, Md, Psychiatrist

Agate Passage Psychological 206.780.0677
Fax 206.780.9419
E-mail ....bisland876@seanet.com
907 NW Lovell Ave, Bainbridge Island,
WA 98110-1722
Franklin Walker, Psychiatrist

Alliance Youth Outpatient Program 253.502.5470
Fax 253.572.1588
510 Tacoma Ave S, Tacoma, WA 98402
Terree Schmidt-Whelan, Executive Director

Archbishop Murphy High School 425.379.6363
Fax 425.385.2875
E-mail ....info@am-hs.org
12911 39th Ave SE, Everett, WA 98208
Tim Blair, Counsellor

Asian Counseling Svcs 253.697.8650
Fax 253.473.4119
Web ....www.goodsamhealth.org
E-mail ....hyunhwang@goodsamhealth.org
4301 S Pine St Ste 456, Tacoma, WA 98409-7207
Hyun Hwang, Program Manager

Aylen Jr. High School 253.841.8723
Fax 253.840.8856
E-mail ....cbuck@puyallup.k12.wa.us
101 15th St SW, Puyallup, WA 98371
Carol Buck, Administrator

Backlund Medical Practice 360.336.3892
Fax 360.336.6866
720 Main St, Mount Vernon, WA 98273
Mark Backlund, Psychiatrist

Bates Technical College 253.680.7324
111101 Yakima Ave, Tacoma, WA 98405
Lynn Phillips, Director

Baxter Medical Practice 206.682.2069
1001 4th Ave, Seattle, WA 98154
Robin Baxter, Psychiatrist

Behavioral Health Resources 360.426.1696
Fax 360.427.0357
110 W K St, Shelton, WA 98584
Lynn Hedlund, Office Manager

Bellegrove Psychiatric Group 425.453.5579
E-mail ....donaldjg@aol.com
1300 114th Ave SE, Bellevue, WA 98004
Dr. Donald Grubb, MD, Psychiatrist

Bellevue Psychiatric Group 425.455.9900
Web ....www.bellevueonline.net
1621 114th Ave SE, Bellevue, WA 98004

Bridgeways 425.513.8213
Fax 425.513.0534
Web ....www.bridgeways.org
E-mail ....dkonicki@bridgeways.org
1220 75th St SW, Everett, WA 98203
Donna Konicki, Executive Director

Broughton Medical Practice 206.526.9566
Fax 206.526.2330
4026 55th Ave NE, Seattle, WA 98105
Dr. Thomas Broughton, Psychiatrist

Carlson Medical Practice 425.454.2363
PO Box 4024, Bellevue, WA 98009-4024
Dr. Dorothy Carlson, Psychiatrist

Case Medical Practice 206.441.4116
1711 12th Ave, Seattle, WA 98122-2435
Dr. Austin Case, Psychiatrist

**Central Washington Comprehensive Mental
Health** 509.575.4084
Web ....www.cwcmh.org
E-mail ....jmaris@cwcmh.org
402 South Fourth Avenue, Yakima, WA 98902
Mr. Jack Maris, Accreditation Manager
Joint Commission accredited organization.

Child & Family 206.365.3340
1200 NE 143rd St Apt 212F, Seattle, WA 98125-3135
Mimi, Therapist

Clark Medical Practice 206.523.6798
10010 41st Ave NE, Seattle, WA 98125-8106
Dr. Owen Clark, Psychiatrist

Cohen Medical Practice 206.526.5550
Fax 843.377.1601
7817 12th Ave NE, Seattle, WA 98115-4320
Dr. Phillip Cohen, MD, Psychiatrist

Cohen Medical Practice 206.285.3960
Web ....www.seth-cohen.net
15333 Beach Dr NE, Seattle, WA 98155-7736
Dr. Seth Cohen, Psychiatrist

Community Psychiatric Clinic 206.461.3614
Fax 206.634.0094
Web ....www.cpcwa.org
11000 Lake City Way NE, Seattle, WA 98125-6748
CARF accredited programs available.

Compass Health 360.419.3500
Fax 360.419.3505
Web ....www.compasshealth.org
E-mail ....lynn.retzer@compassh.org
1100 S 2nd St, Mount Vernon, WA 98273-3210
Lynn Retzer, Director

Compass Mental Health 360.678.5555
Fax 360.678.3636
Web ....www.compasshealth.org
E-mail ....angela.tull@compassh.org
105 NW 1st St, Coupeville, WA 98239
Angela Tull, Director

Comprehensive Mental Health 509.575.4084
Fax 509.457.0759
402 S 4th Ave, Yakima, WA 98902
Rick Weaver, President/CEO

Consejo Counseling and Referral Service 206.461.4880
Fax 206.461.6989
Web ....www.consejo-wa.org
E-mail ....mario@consejo-wa.org
3808 South Angeline Street, Seattle, WA 98118
Mario Paredes, Director
CARF accredited programs available.

Conway Medical Practice 206.623.6111
Fax 206.682.4284
601 Union St Ste 1704, Seattle, WA 98101-2327
Dr. Jack Conway, Psychiatrist

Cornish College Of The Arts 206.323.1400
Fax 206.720.1011
E-mail ....info@cornish.edu
1000 Lorna St, Seattle, WA 98121
Mike Kaan, Director

Counseling Svcs Ctr 509.684.4597
Fax 509.684.5286
Web ....www.co.stevens.wa.us
E-mail ....dmnielsen@co.stevens.wa.us
165 E Hawthorne Ave, Colville, WA 99114-2629
David Nielsen, Phd, Executive Director

**Cowlitz Indian Tribe, Health and Human Services
Department** 360.575.3307
Fax 360.423.7813
Web ....www.cowlitz.org
1055 Ninth Avenue, Suite D, Longview, WA 98632
CARF accredited programs available.

Curlew Civilian Conservation Ctr 509.779.4611
Fax 509.779.0718
Web ....www.jobcorps.org
E-mail ....rhepburn@fs.fed.us
3 Campus St, Curlew, WA 99118-9601
Rodger Hepburn, Center Director

Cynthia Padden Stoddard Inc 206.782.6463
721- 1/2 Greenwood Ave N, Seattle, WA 98103
Dr.cynthia Stoddard, Md, Psychiatrist

Davis Medical Practice 206.322.0262
E-mail ....walkintochaos@msn.com
1800 NW Market St, Seattle, WA 98107
Dr. Romalee Davis, Md, Psychiatrist

Diaconu Medical Practice 425.889.5045
620 Kirkland Way, Kirkland, WA 98033
Dr. Ioana Diaconu, Psychiatrist

East Lake Counseling Group 206.284.6907
Fax 206.282.2614
200 W Mercer St Ste 207, Seattle, WA 98119-3994
Dr. Linda Luster, Psychiatrist

Edwards Medical Practice 425.637.1981
Web ....www.hbedwardsmd.com
14535 Bel Red Rd, Bellevue, WA 98007
H. Berryman Edwards, Psychiatrist

Embodied Mind & Being 206.328.3050
E-mail ....kathleen@embodiedmindandbeing.com
126 19th Ave E, Seattle, WA 98112
Kathleen Pape, Director

Evergreen Health Care 425.899.1000
Fax 425.899.2624
E-mail ....mmaeda@evergreenhealthcare.org
12040 NE 128th St, Kirkland, WA 98034-3098
Michelle Maeda, Director

Excelsior Youth Ctr 509.328.7041
Fax 509.328.7582
Web ....www.excelsioryouthcenter.com
E-mail ....bobf@4eyc.org
3754 W Indian Trail Rd, Spokane, WA 99208-4700
Robert L. Faltermeyer, Executive Director

Family Svcs 206.826.3050
Fax 877.903.0711
Web ....www.wellspring.org
E-mail ....info@wellspring.org
1900 Reinier Ave S, Seattle, WA 98144-2243
Ruthann Howell, President/CEO

First Interstate Ctr 206.624.0247
Fax 206.624.1489
601 Union St Ste 2600, Seattle, WA 98101-2302
Craig Smart, MD, Psychiatrist

Foundations Of Hope 425.343.8581
Web ....www.foundationsofhope.net
E-mail ....kathie@foundationsofhope.net
125 E Main St, Monroe, WA 98272
Kathie Reynolds, Director

Fredric Provenzaho Ph.D. **206.361.2343**
E-mail .... rkfeinberg@nwpinnacle.com
　10740 Meridian Ave N, Seattle, WA 98133
　Dr. Fredric Provenzano, Ph.d., Psychiatrist

Furedy Medical Practice **425.467.5985**
Fax 425.244.9964
　1687 114th Ave SE, Bellevue, WA 98004
　Ronald Furedy, Psychiatrist

Furst Medical Practice **206.633.1583**
　PO Box 1930, Seattle, WA 98111-1930
　Michael Furst, Psychiatrist

Grandview Medical Ctr **509.882.1855**
Fax 509.882.4998
　208 N Euclid Rd, Grandview, WA 98930-9470
　Mike Delgado, Administrator

Gray Wolf Ranch **360.385.5505**
Fax 360.385.3605
Web .... www.graywolfranch.com
　3804 Hastings Avenue West, Port Townsend,
　WA 98368
　CARF accredited programs available.

Highline West Seattle Mental Health **206.933.7299**
Fax 206.933.7025
　2600 SW Holden St, Seattle, WA 98126
　Elizabeth Warg, Administrator

Human-Equine Alliance For Learning
(Heal) **360.266.0778**
Fax 360.748.4762
Web .... www.humanequinealliance.org
E-mail .... heal@humanequinealliance.org
　184 Gish Rd, Onalaska, WA 98532
　Leigh Shambo, Msw, Director

Lakeside-Milam Recovery Centers **425.823.3116**
Fax 425.823.3132
Web .... www.lakesidemilam.com
　10322 Northeast 132nd Street, Kirkland, WA 98034
　CARF accredited programs available.

Lourdes Counseling Ctr **509.943.9104**
Fax 509.943.7241
Web .... www.lourdesonline.org
E-mail .... bmead@lourdesonline.org
　1175 Carondelet Dr, Richland, WA 99354
　Barbara Mead, Administrator

Lourdes Health Network **509.546.2278**
Web .... www.lourdeshealth.net
E-mail .... dclapp@lourdesonline.org
　520 North 4th Avenue, Pasco, WA 99302
　Ms. Denise Clapp, Accreditation Manager
　Joint Commission accredited organization.

Medical Plaza **360.582.2600**
Fax 360.582.2677
　777 N 5th Ave, Sequim, WA 98382
　John Lloyd, Md, Psychiatrist

Morning Star Boys' Ranch **509.448.1411**
Fax 509.448.1413
Web .... www.morningstarboysranch.org
　3621 S Fancher Road, 4511 s glenrose rd, Spokane,
　WA 99223
　Richard Peterson, Executive Director

Navos **206.933.7299**
Web .... www.navos.org
E-mail .... edie.herman@navos.org
　2600 Southwest Holden Street, Seattle, WA 98126
　Ms. Edie Herman, Accreditation Manager
　Joint Commission accredited organization.

Pearl Street Center / Comprehensive Mental
Health **253.396.5930**
E-mail .... rdaughtry@compmh.org
　815 South Pearl Street, Tacoma, WA 98465
　Ms. Rebecca Daughtry, Accreditation Manager
　Joint Commission accredited organization.

Providence St. Peter Hospital **360.493.7647**
Web .... www.Providence.Org
E-mail .... becky.cant@providence.org
　413 Lilly Road Northeast, Olympia, WA 98506-5166
　Ms. Becky Cant, Accreditation Manager
　Joint Commission accredited organization.

Quality Behavioral Health **509.758.3341**
Fax 509.758.8009
E-mail .... gprice@qbhs.org
　900 7th St, Clarkston, WA 99403
　Gail Price, Executive Director

Reiter Medical Practice **206.328.1366**
Fax 206.328.8150
E-mail .... jmreiter@qwest.net
　1404 E Yesler Way, Ste 201, Seattle, WA 98122-4337
　Jack Reiter, Md, Psychiatrist

Ruth Dykeman Children's Center **206.242.1698**
Fax 206.243.5321
Web .... http://www.ruthdykeman.org/
　P.O. Box 66010, Burien, WA 98166
　COA accredited organization.

Sea Mar Community Health Center **206.763.5277**
Web .... www.seamarchc.org
E-mail .... stephanietijerina@seamarchc.org
　8720 14th Av. South, Seattle, WA 98108
　Ms. Stephanie Tijerina, Accreditation Manager
　Joint Commission accredited organization.

Sea Mar Community Health Ctr **425.609.5505**
Fax 425.609.5506
Web .... www.seamar.org
　5007 Claremont Way, Everett, WA 98208-2833
　Jennifer Leonard, Clinical Director

Sea Mar Community Mental Health Ctr **360.542.8920**
Fax 360.542.8930
Web .... www.seamar.org
　1010 E College Way, Ste 100, Mount Vernon,
　WA 98273
　Cathleen Scott, Manager

Seattle Children's Home, Inc. **206.283.3300**
Web .... www.seattlechildrenshome.org
E-mail .... spoch@seattlechildrenshome.org
　2142 Tenth Avenue West, Seattle, WA 98119
　Ms. Sharon Poch, Accreditation Manager
　Joint Commission accredited organization.

Seattle Counseling Svc For Sexual
Minorities **206.323.1768**
Fax 206.323.2184
Web .... www.seattlecounseling.org
E-mail .... ann@seattlecounseling.org
　1216 Pine St Ste 300, Seattle, WA 98101-1959
　Ann Mcgettigan, Executive Director

Seattle Mental Health **425.653.4900**
Fax 425.653.4910
Web .... www.smh.org
E-mail .... robertg@smh.org
　14216 NE 21st St, Bellevue, WA 98007-3720
　Robert Gibbs, Jr., Disorders Counselor

Seattle Mental Health **253.876.7600**
Fax 253.876.7610
Web .... www.smh.org
E-mail .... sandral@smh.org
　42538 AubrumWay N, Auburn, WA 98002
　Sandra Lippencott, Counsellor

Smick Medical Practice **509.372.0407**
　3080 George Washington Way, Richland,
　WA 99354-1658
　Larry Smick, DO, Psychiatrist

Social Treatment Opportunity Programs II,
Inc. **253.471.0890**
Fax 253.471.0891
Web .... www.stopwa.com
　4301 South Pine Street, Suite 112, Tacoma,
　WA 98409
　CARF accredited programs available.

Sound Mental Health **206.302.2200**
Fax 206.302.2210
Web .... www.smh.org
　1600 East Olive Street, Seattle, WA 98122
　Lindsay Palmer, Director of Education
　CARF accredited programs available.

South Sound Mental Health Svcs **360.754.7576**
Fax 360.704.7182
Web .... www.bhr.org
E-mail .... jmasterson@bhr.org
　3857 Martin Way E, Olympia, WA 98506-5268
　John Masterson, CEO

Spring Manor **206.329.6485**
Fax 206.324.4952
E-mail .... info@adult-care.org
　1103 16th Ave, Seattle, WA 98122
　Constance Jones, Administrator

Tamarack Center **509.326.8100**
Web .... www.tamarack.org
E-mail .... tdavis@tamarack.org
　2901 W Ft. George Wright Drive, Spokane,
　WA 99224
　Mr. Tim Davis, Accreditation Manager
　Joint Commission accredited organization.

Tamarack Ctr **509.326.8100**
Fax 509.326.9358
Web .... www.tamarack.org
E-mail .... info@tamarack.org
　2901 W Fort George Wright Dr, Spokane,
　WA 99224-5253
　Tim Davis, Ms, Executive Director

The Discovery Adolescent Program **562.981.0700**
Web .... centerfordiscovery.com
E-mail .... greg.corbin@centerfordiscovery.com
　7511 176th Street SW, Edmonds, WA 98026
　Mr. Greg Corbin, Accreditation Manager
　Joint Commission accredited organization.

The Healing Lodge of the Seven Nations **509.533.6910**
Fax 509.535.2863
Web .... www.healinglodge.org
　5600 East Eighth Avenue, Spokane Valley, WA 99212
　CARF accredited programs available.

Therapeutic Health Services **206.726.4100**
Fax 206.328.3757
Web .... www.therapeutichealth.org
　1116 Summit Avenue, Seattle, WA 98101
　CARF accredited programs available.

Tyler Ranch **509.327.6900**
Fax 509.327.2859
Web .... www.tylerranch.com
E-mail .... jon@tylerranch.com
　4921 W Rosewood Ave, Spokane, WA 99208-3740
　Jon Tyler, Admissions/ Program Headmaster

University Family YMCA **206.524.1400**
Fax 206.524.8613
Web .... www.seattleymca.org
E-mail .... ushagaga@seattleymca.org
　5003 12Th Ave NE, Seattle, WA 98105-4306
　Sana Shagaga, Homeless Youth And Young Adult Services Program
　Coordinator

Valley Cities Counseling & Consultation **253.833.7444**
Web .... www.valleycities.com
E-mail .... npenman@valleycities.org
　2704 I Street NE, Auburn, WA 98002
　Ms. Nikole Penman, Accreditation Manager
　Joint Commission accredited organization.

Willapa Behavioral Health **360.642.3787**
Fax 360.642.2096
Web .... www.willapabh.org
　2204 Pacific Avenue North, Long Beach, WA 98631
　Richard Daley, Director of correspondence for Mayor
　CARF accredited programs available.

Washington

Woodinville Psychiatric **425.481.0429**
Fax 425.483.0660
Web .... www.u.washington.edu
E-mail .... drjohn@u.washington.edu
  18500 156th Ave NE Ste 201, Woodinville,
  WA 98072-4459
  Dr. John Berner, MD, Psychiatrist

Yakima Valley Farm Workers Clinic **509.865.6175**
Web .... www.yvfwc.com
E-mail .... jackp@yvfwc.org
  604 West 1st Avenue, Toppenish, WA 98948
  CDR Jack Peterson, Accreditation Manager
  Joint Commission accredited organization.

CHILDREN'S HOSPITAL

Auburn Regional Medical Center **253.833.7711**
  202 N Division Plaza One, Auburn, WA 98001
  Larry Coones, Chief Executive Officer

Central Washington Hospital **509.662.1511**
E-mail .... tracey.kasnic@cwhs.com
  1201 S Miller St, Wenatchee, WA 98801
  Tracey Kasnic, Vice President, Nursing

Harborview Medical Center **206.744.3000**
  325 Ninth Ave, Seattle, WA 98104
  Eileen Whalen, Executive Director

Harrison Medical Center **360.377.3911**
  2520 Cherry Ave, Bremerton, WA 98310
  Scott Bosh, Chief Executive Officer

Kennewick General Hospital **509.586.6111**
  900 S Auburn St, Kennewick, WA 99336
  Glen Marshel, Chief Executive Officer

Legacy Salmon Creek Hospital **360.487.1000**
  2211 NE 139th St, Vancouver, WA 98686
  Jonathan Avery, Chief Executive Officer

Lourdes Medical Center **509.547.7704**
  520 N Fourth Ave, Pasco, WA 99301
  John Ferle, Chief Executive Officer

Madigan Army Medical Center **253.968.1110**
  90408 Jackson Ave, Tacoma, WA 98431
  Commander Dallas Homas, Commander

Mary Bridge Children's Hosp & Hlth Ctr **253.403.1400**
  317 Martin Luther King Jr Way, Tacoma, WA 98405
  Diane Cecchettini, Chief Executive Officer

Newport Hospital & Health Services **509.447.2441**
  714 W Pine St, Newport, WA 99156
  Tom Wilbur, Chief Executive Officer

Ocean Beach Hospital **360.642.3181**
  174 First Ave N, Ilwaco, WA 98624
  Joe Devin, Chief Executive Officer

Olympic Medical Center **360.417.7000**
  939 Caroline St, Port Angeles, WA 98362

Prosser Memorial Hospital **509.786.2222**
  723 Memorial St, Prosser, WA 99350
  Julie Peterson, Manager

Providence Everett Medical Center **425.261.2000**
  1321 Colby Ave, Everett, WA 98206
  Dave Brooks, Chief Executive Officer

Providence Holy Family Hospital **509.482.0111**
  5633 N Lidgerwood St, Spokane, WA 99208
  Kathy Romano, Chief Executive Officer

Providence Sacred Heart Med Ctr & Child **509.474.3131**
  101 W 8th Ave, Spokane, WA 99204

Providence St Mary Medical Center **509.525.3320**
  401 W Poplar St, Walla Walla, WA 99362
  Steve Purtick, Chief Executive Officer

Providence St Peter Hospital **360.491.9480**
  413 Lilly Rd NE, Olympia, WA 98506
  Medrice Coluccio, Administrator

Pullman Regional Hospital **509.332.2541**
  835 SE Bishop Blvd, Pullman, WA 99163
  Scott Adams, Chief Executive Officer

Samaritan Healthcare **509.765.5606**
  801 E Wheeler Rd, Moses Lake, WA 98837
  Kim Garva, Human Resource Director

Skyline Hospital **509.493.1101**
  211 Skyline Dr, White Salmon, WA 98672
  Mike Madden, Chief Executive Officer

Southwest Washington Medical Center **360.256.2000**
  400 NE Mother Joseph Pl, Vancouver, WA 98664

St Joseph Hospital **360.734.5400**
  2901 Squalicum Pkwy, Bellingham, WA 98225
  Nancy Steiger, Chief Executive Officer

Sunnyside Community Hospital **509.837.1500**
  1016 Tacoma Ave, Sunnyside, WA 98944
  John Smiley, Chief Executive Officer

Swedish Medical Center First Hill **206.386.6000**
E-mail .... rod.hochman@swedish.org
  747 Broadway Ave, Seattle, WA 98122
  Rod Hochman, Chief Executive Officer

Toppenish Community Hospital **509.865.3105**
  502 W Fourth Ave, Toppenish, WA 98948
  Derrick Yu, Director

Valley Hospital & Medical Center **509.924.6650**
  12606 E Mission Ave, Spokane, WA 99216
  Dennis Barts, Chief Executive Officer

Valley Medical Center **425.228.3450**
  400 S 43rd St, Renton, WA 98055
  Richard Roodman, Chief Executive Officer

Walla Walla General Hospital **509.525.0480**
  1025 S Second Ave, Walla Walla, WA 99362
  Monty Knittel, President

Yakima Regional Medical & Cardiac Ctr **509.575.5000**
  110 S Ninth Ave, Yakima, WA 98902
  Rich Robinson, Chief Executive Officer

Yakima Valley Memorial Hospital **509.575.8000**
  2811 Tieton Dr, Yakima, WA 98902
  Rick Linneweh, Chief Executive Officer

COUNSELING SERVICES

Bethany Christian Svcs **206.367.4604**
Fax 206.367.1860
Web .... www.bethany.org/washington
E-mail .... bcsseattle@bethany.org
  12360 Lake City Way NE Ste 301, Seattle, WA 98125
  Edna Kuipers, Director

Navos **206.241.0990**
Fax 206.248.8232
E-mail .... victor.place@navos.org
  1010 S 146th St, Seattle, WA 98168-3669
  Victor Place, Director Of Child And Family Sevices

Therapeutic Health Svc Rainier Branch **206.723.1980**
Fax 206.721.3930
E-mail .... noj@therapeutichealth.org
  5802 Rainier Ave S, Seattle, WA 98118
  Norman Johnson, Executive Director

CRISIS & SHELTER CARE

Asian-Pacific Islander Family Safety Ctr **206.467.9976**
Fax 206.467.1072
Web .... www.apiwfsc.org
E-mail .... bincy@apiwfsc.org
  606 Maynard Ave S Ste 101, Seattle, WA 98104
  Bincy Jacob, Director

Aspen-Domestic Violence Program **509.925.9384**
Fax 509.925.9405
Web .... www.cwcmh.org
E-mail .... ksalvo@cwcmh.org
  707 N Pearl St, Ellensburg, WA 98926
  Katie Salvo, Program Director

Beyond Survival - Sexual Assault Resource
Center **360.533.9751**
Fax 360.538.6635
E-mail .... director@ghbeyondsurvival.com
  313 S I St, Aberdeen, WA 98520
  Dori Winningham, Executive Director

Broadview Emergency Shelter-Domestic
Violence **206.299.2500**
Fax 206.299.2514
  1501 N 45th St, Seattle, WA 98103-6708
  Deloris Hillis, Director

Community Youth Svcs **360.943.0780**
Fax 360.943.0785
Web .... www..communityyouthservices.org
E-mail .... cshelan@communityyouthservices.org
  711 State Ave NE, Fl 3, Olympia, WA 98506
  Charles Shelan, Executive Director

Comprehensive Mental Health-Sexual
Assault **509.576.4326**
Fax 509.574.5118
Web .... www.cwcmh.org
E-mail .... kfoley@cwcmh.org
  402 S 4th ave, Yakima, WA 98902
  Kim Folly, Program Manager

Connections-Domestic Violence Program **509.775.3331**
Fax 509.775.2014
E-mail .... krowemaloret@fccs1.org
  870 So Clark, Republic, WA 99166
  Kate Rowe-maloret, Director

Council On Domestic Violence-Sexual
Assault **509.427.4210**
Fax 509.427.4194
E-mail .... lbutcher@skamaniadvsa.org
  96 NW Columbia St, Stevenson, WA 98648
  Lisa Butcher, Director

Crystal Judson Family Justice Ctr **253.798.4310**
Fax 253.798.4320
Web .... www.familyjusticecenter.us
E-mail .... sadams@co.pierce.wa.us
  718 Court E, Tacoma, WA 98402-2200
  Susan Adams, Director

Domestic Abuse Womens Network **425.656.4305**
Fax 425.656.4309
Web .... www.dawnonline.org
E-mail .... dawnnetwork@dawnonline.org
  PO Box 88007, Seattle, WA 98138-2007
  Cheryl Bozarth, Director

Domestic Violence And Sexual Asault Crisis
Svcs **360.671.5714**
Fax 360.647.6015
Web .... www.dvsas.org
E-mail .... karenb@dvsas.org
  1407 Commercial St, Bellingham, WA 98225
  Karen Burke, Director

Domestic Violence Ctr Of Grays Harbor **360.538.0733**
Fax 360.537.9495
E-mail .... dvcenter@techline.com
  2306 Sumner Ave, Hoquiam, WA 98550
  Gloria Callagham, Interim Director

Domestic Violence Services **425.259.2827**
Fax 425.258.5976
Web .... www.snococbw.org
E-mail .... margaret@dvs-snoco.org
  1310 Pacific Ave Ste 5, Everett, WA 98206
  Margaret Bruland, Director

Domestic Violence Svcs-San Juans Islands **360.378.8680**
Fax 360.378.8681
Web .... www.dvsafsanjuans.org
E-mail .... Dvsasorcas@rockisland.com
  849 Spring St Ste 2, Friday Harbor, WA 98250
  Anita Castle, Director

Dove House Advocacy Services **360.385.5292**
Fax **360.379.5395**
Web ....www.dpsajeffco.org
E-mail ....director@dvsajeffco.org
   1045 10th St, Port Townsend, WA 98368-0743
Beulah Kingsolver, Director

Eastside Domestic Violence Program **425.562.8840**
Fax **425.649.0752**
   Residential St, Bellevue, WA 98007
Barbara Langdon, Director

Echo Glenn Children's Ctr **425.831.2500**
Fax **425.831.2720**
   33010 SE 99th St, Snoqualmie, WA 98065
Don Meade, Phd, Superintendent

Emergency Support Shelter-Dom Violence **360.425.1176**
Fax **360.425.3970**
Web ....www.esshelter.com
E-mail ....sherriet@cascadenetworks.net
   304 Cowlitz Way, Kelso, WA 98626-4110
Sherrie Tinoco, Director

Epic Youth Svcs- Secured Crisis Residential
Ctr **509.457.8835**
Fax **509.457.5194**
Web ....www.epicnet.org
   1106 Hathaway St, Yakima, WA 98902-1306
Amy Barlow, Program Manager

Family Renewal Shelter **253.475.9010**
Fax **253.475.0848**
E-mail ....staff@dvhelp.org
   6832 Pacific Ave, Tacoma, WA 98408
Keith Galbraith, Executive Director

Forks Abuse Programs-Domestic Violence **360.374.6411**
Fax **360.374.9885**
Web ....www.forksabuse.org
E-mail ....ann.s@forksabuseprogram.org
   81 2nd Ave, Forks, WA 98331-9118
Ann Simpson, Director

Friends Of Youth **425.869.6490**
Fax **425.869.6666**
Web ....www.friendsofyouth.org
E-mail ....info@friendsofyouth.org
   16225 NE 87th St, Ste A-6, Redmond, WA 98052
Joan Campbell, President/CEO

Gray Wolf Ranch **800.571.5505**
Fax **360.385.3605**
Web ....www.grayworlfranch.com
E-mail ....gwr@graywolfranch.com
   3804 haspings ave w, Port Townsend, WA 98368
Peter Boeschenstein, President

Human Response Network-Dom Violence **360.748.6601**
Fax **360.748.6630**
Web ....www.hrnlc.org
E-mail ....joanc@hrnlc.org
   125 NW Chehalis Ave, Chehalis, WA 98532
Joan Caywood, Director

Indochinese Cultural Svc Ctr-Domestic
Violence **253.473.5666**
Fax **253.475.8737**
Web ....www.iscs-tacoma.org,,kwacase.org
E-mail ....clee@iscs-tacoma.org
   123 E 96th st, Tacoma, WA 98445-3721
Cilde Lee, Director

Lower Valley Crisis Ctr-Domestic Violence **509.837.6689**
Fax **509.837.6918**
   600 North Ave, Sunnyside, WA 98944
Julia Heart, Interim Director

Lummi Victims Of Crime-Domestic Violence
Program **360.384.2285**
Fax **360.312.9204**
   2616 Kwina Rd, Bellingham, WA 98226
Nikki Finkbonner, Coordinator

New Beginnings-Domestic Violence
Program **206.783.4520**
Fax **206.706.0291**
Web ....www.newbegin.org
E-mail ....lloontjens@newbegin.org
   PO Box 75125, Seattle, WA 98175-0125
Lois Loontjeas, Director

New Hope Domestic Violence-Sexual Assault
Svcs **509.764.8402**
Fax **509.766.6574**
E-mail ....sfode@co.grant.wa.us
   840 E Plum St, Moses Lake, WA 98837
Suzi Fode, Director

New Horizons Ministries **206.374.0866**
Fax **206.374.0867**
E-mail ....info@nhmin.org
   2709 3rd Ave, Seattle, WA 98121-1217
Mary Steele, Executive Director

Northwest Network Btlg Survivors Abuse **206.568.7777**
Fax **206.325.2601**
Web ....www.nwnetwork.org
E-mail ....info@nwnetwork.org
   3703 S Edmunds St 99, Seattle, WA 98118
Connie Burk, Director

Orion Ctr **206.622.5555**
Fax **206.628.3227**
Web ....www.youthcare.org
E-mail ....melinda.giovengo@youthcare.org
   1828 Yale Ave, Seattle, WA 98101-1433
Melinda Giovengo, Executive Director

Pend Oreille Crime Victim Svcs **509.447.2274**
Fax **509.447.2103**
Web ....www.pofcn.org
E-mail ....jackie@pofcn.org
   730 W 1st St, Newport, WA 99156
Jackie Kiehn, Director

Phoenix Place-Dom Violence And Sexual
Asslt **509.663.7446**
Fax **509.664.0641**
Web ....www.findsafety.org
E-mail ....maryannep@nwi.net
   1207 N Wenatchee Ave., Wenatchee, WA 98801
Maryanne Preece, Director

Programs For Peaceful Living-Dom
Violence **509.493.1533**
Fax **509.493.4134**
E-mail ....Peaceful@gorge.Net
   1250 E Steuben St, Bingen, WA 98605-9087
Kirsten Poole, Director

Refugee Womens Alliance-Dom Violence **206.721.0243**
Fax **206.721.3967**
Web ....www.rewa.org
E-mail ....carlin@rewa.org
   4008 Martin Luther King Jr. Way S, Seattle,
   WA 98108
Carlin Yoophum, Program Director

Safeplace **360.754.6300**
Fax **360.786.6377**
Web ....www.safeplaceolympia.org
E-mail ....safeplace@safeplaceolympia.org
   314 Legion Way SE, Olympia, WA 98501
Mary Pontarolo, Executive Director

Salvation Army Hickman House-Domestic
Violence **206.932.5341**
Fax **206.937.6219**
   1101 Pike St, Seattle, WA 98101
Jen Plummer, Major

Skagit Domestic Violence-Sexual Assault
Svcs **360.336.9591**
Fax **360.336.9593**
Web ....www.skagitdvsas.org
   1521-B Leigh Way, Mount Vernon, WA 98273
Emily Oconnor, Director

St. James Family Ctr Charlotte House-Domestic
Violence **360.795.6401**
Fax **360.795.0806**
   25 River St, Cathlamet, WA 98612
Susan Schillios, Manager

The Support Ctr-Domesitc Violence **509.826.3221**
Fax **509.422.1742**
Web ....www.thesupportcenter.org
E-mail ....mamelong@ncidata.com
   619 2nd Ave S, Okanogan, WA 98840
Margo Amelong, Director

Turning Pointe Domestic Violence Svcs **360.426.1216**
Fax **360.426.2922**
Web ....www.turningpointe.org
   210 Pacific Ct, Shelton, WA 98584
Cheryl Cathcart, Director

Volunteers Of America, Spokane **509.624.2378**
Fax **509.624.2275**
Web ....www.voaspokane.org
E-mail ....voaspokane@voaspokane.org
   525 W 2nd Ave, Spokane, WA 99201
Marilee K. Roloff, Director

Washington Coalition Of Sexual Assault
Programs **360.754.7583**
Fax **360.786.8707**
Web ....www.wcsap.org
E-mail ....wcsap@wcsap.org
   4317 6th Ave SE Ste 102, Lacey, WA 98503-1019
Andrea Piper-Wentland, Executive Director

Womencare Shelter-Domestic Violence **360.671.8539**
Fax **360.671.0061**
Web ....www.womencareshelter.org
E-mail ....kirstenh@womencareshelter.org
   4120 Meridian St Ste 220, Bellingham,
   WA 98226-5576
Kristen Hammer, Director

EDUCATION

Brigid Collins **360.734.4616**
Fax **360.734.1763**
Web ....www.brigidcollins.org
E-mail ....bmanering@brigidcollins.org
   1231 N Garden St Ste 200, Bellingham,
   WA 98225-5162
Byron Manerine, Executive Director

Hamlin Robinson School **206.763.1167**
Fax **206.762.2419**
Web ....www.hamlinrobinson.org
E-mail ....hamlinrobinson@aol.com
   1700 E Union St, Seattle, WA 98122
John Beauregard, Director

Holly Ridge Ctr Infant-Toddler Program **360.373.2536**
Fax **360.373.4934**
Web ....www.hollyridge.org
E-mail ....hrc@hollyridge.org
   5112 NW Taylor Rd, Bremerton, WA 98312
Roxanne Bryson, Executive Director

FOSTER CARE AGENCIES

Adoption Group **360.385.5335**
E-mail ....family@little-little.com
   132 35th St, Port Townsend, WA 98368

Adoptive Friends and Families Greater Se **206.903.9664**
E-mail ....members@affgs.org
   PO Box 271, Kirkland, WA 98083

Adoptive Support Group **360.725.6773**
Fax **360.725.0744**
E-mail ....nesh300@dshs.wa.gov
   6860 Capitol Blvd, Olympia, WA 98504

Alaska Center for Rsource Families **907.279.1799**
   840 K St Ste 101, Anatone, WA 99401
Lissa Rylander

Washington

Casey Family Programs 206.282.7300
Fax 206.282.3555
Web .... www.casey.org
   2001 Eighth Avenue, Suite 2700, Seattle, WA 98121
   COA accredited organization.

Catholic Family Child Service of Yakima 509.965.7100
Fax 509.966.9750
E-mail .... pathways@cfcsyakima.org
   5301 C Tieton Dr Ste C, Yakima, WA 98908
   Daroene Darnell, Director

Childrens Home Society of Washington 206.695.3200
E-mail .... info@childrenhomesociety.org
   3300 NE 65th St, ciado, WA 98115
   Cathy Garland, Incharge Of Early Learning

Childrens House International 360.383.0623
Fax 360.383.0640
E-mail .... info@childrenadopthouse.org
   2074 vista dr, Ferndale, WA 98248
   Debbie Price, Chief Executive Officer

Cornell's Care Ctr 360.944.6211
   3302 NE 134th Ave, Vancouver, WA 98682-8062

**East Friends Family and Community
Support** 206.940.2832
Fax 360.387.7357
E-mail .... FASDSupport@aol.com
   PO Box 13182, Bothell, WA 98082

Eden Place Foster Home 360.576.3530
Fax 360.576.9932
Web .... www.adultfamilyhomereferrals.com
   206 NW 98th Cir, Vancouver, WA 98665-7573
   Debbie, President

**Families With Children Adopted from
Bulgaria** 425.823.8018
E-mail .... terrymand@aol.com
   7933 Northeast 124th St, Kirkland, WA 98034
   Terry Mandeville, President

Goldendale Adoptive Parent Group 509.773.5737
   409 Pine Street Extn, Goldendale, WA 98620
   Alice Behart, Nursing Director

Korean Focus NW 206.527.3272
   23611 SE 48th Ave, Bothell, WA 98021

Korean Identity Development Society 206.340.0937
E-mail .... Emailkids@hotmail.com
   PO Box 9272, Seattle, WA 98109

**Lifes Vision International Adoption
Children** 425.614.3938
Fax 425.749.7440
E-mail .... info@lifesvision.org
   4580 Klahanie Dr Se #514, Issaquah, WA 98029

Program for Early Parent Support 206.547.8570
   4949 Sunnyside Ave North #324, Seattle, WA 98103

Washington Adoption Resource Exchange ... 206.441.7242
E-mail .... ware@nwresource.org
   600 Stewart St Ste 1313, Seattle, WA 98101
   Kelly Belaney, Chief Executive Officer

World Association Children and Parents 206.575.4550
Fax 206.575.4148
E-mail .... wacap@wacap.org
   315 S 2nd St, Rinton, WA 98057
   Lillian Thogersen, Chief Executive Officer

HOME MEDICAL EQUIPMENT PROVIDERS

American Cancer Society Seattle 206.283.1152
Fax 800.227.2345
   2120 1st Ave N, Seattle, WA 98109

American Cancer Society Tacoma 253.272.5767
   1551 Broadway st, Ste 200, Tacoma, WA 98402

Apria Healthcare Redmond 425.881.8500
E-mail .... contactus@apria.com
   14935 NE 87th St, Redmond, WA 98052
   Derek Lafontaine, Branch Manager

Lincare Inc Auburn 253.833.6075
E-mail .... gdavis@lincare.com
   1801 W valley ste 103, Auburn, WA 98001
   Will Warren, Manager

Lincare Inc Bremerton 360.792.9414
   115 National Ave S, Bremerton, WA 98312
   Mike Dimatteo, Center Manager

Lincare Inc Everett 425.303.8797
   2808 hewitt ave 202, Everett, WA 98201
   Linda Loe, Manager

Lincare Inc Fife 253.922.3137
E-mail .... gdavis@lincare.com
   5113 Pacific Highway East, Ste 5, Tacoma, WA 98424
   Gerrele Davis, Director

Lincare Inc Mountlake Terrace 425.775.2339
   20508 56th Ave W Ste A, Linwood, WA 98036
   Mellisa Stark, Customer Service Representative

Lincare Inc Olympia 360.923.1985
E-mail .... gdavis@lincare.com
   1306 Fones Road Southeast, Olympia, WA 98501
   Gina Davis, Manager

Lincare Inc Redmond 425.486.0690
E-mail .... gdavis@lincare.com
   16120 Woodinville Redmond Rd, Redmond,
   WA 98072
   Greg Davis, Director

Lincare Inc Seattle 206.467.8069
   3220 1st Ave S Ste 102, Seattle, WA 98134
   David Aldrich, Manager

Muscular Dystrophy Assoc Seattle 206.283.2106
   701 Dexter Ave N 106, Seattle, WA 98109

Muscular Dystrophy Association WA 509.325.3747
   101 W Indiana, Spokane, WA 99205
   Jana Worthington, Director

PEDIATRIC HOME CARE

DuPont PDN (Tacoma) 253.912.4860
E-mail .... kwilbur@psakids.com
   1100 Station Dr Ste 141, DuPont, WA 98327
   Krystal Wilbur, Director

Interim Healthcare 509.456.5665
Fax 509.456.7703
   West 1625 4th Ave, Spokane, WA 99204
   Rick Morris, Owner

Interim Healthcare 206.621.8284
Fax 206.624.9107
   14900 Interurban Ave Ste 271, Burien, WA 98168

PSA Heathcare 360.423.8885
   2145 Tibbetts Dr, Longview, WA 98632
   Stephanie Yoke, Director

Vancouver PDN 360.693.7595
   2700 NE Andresen Rd Ste D-28, Vancouver,
   WA 98661
   Kaithleen Potts, Coordinator

SOCIAL SERVICES

America's Promise- Alliance For Youth 703.684.4500
Fax 703.535.3900
Web .... www.americaspromise.org
E-mail .... marguerites@americaspromise.org
   1110 Ave NW Ste 900, Vermont, WA 20005
   Margurite Konbracke, President/CEO

Camp Fire USA 206.461.8550
Fax 206.525.3351
E-mail .... jane.w@campfire-usa.org
   8511 15th Ave NE, Seattle, WA 98115
   Jane White Vulliet, CEO

Care Ctr 360.330.2229
Fax 360.330.2209
Web .... www.carecenterlifechoices.com
E-mail .... carecenter@localaccess.com
   1017 W Main St, Centralia, WA 98531
   Celeste Avy, Director

Catholic Charities Counseling 509.525.0572
Fax 509.525.0576
Web .... www.catholiccharitiesspokane.org
E-mail .... tmeliah@ccspokane.org
   408 W Poplar St, Walla Walla, WA 99362
   Tim Meliah, Director

Catholic Charities, Spokane 509.358.4250
Fax 509.358.4259
Web .... wwww.catholiccharitiesspokane.org
E-mail .... rmccann@ccspokeane.org
   12 E 5th Ave, Spokane, WA 99202-1103
   Rob Mccann, Executive Director

**Catholic Community Services of Western
Washington** 206.328.5696
Fax 206.328.5699
   100 23rd Avenue South, Seattle, WA 98144-2302
   COA accredited organization.

Catholic Family And Child Svcs 509.765.1875
Fax 509.765.1875
E-mail .... darlene@cfcsml.org
   1036 W Ivy, Moses Lake, WA 98837
   Darlene Darnele, Director

Child Care Action Council 360.754.0810
Fax 360.786.8960
Web .... www.ccacwa.org
E-mail .... annie@ccacwa.org
   3729 Griffin Ln SE, Olympia, WA 98501
   Annie Cubberly, Executive Director

Child Care Resource And Referral 253.591.2025
Fax 253.591.5764
Web http://www.cityoftacoma.org/34childcare/
E-mail .... crosenquist@cityoftacoma.org
   747 Market St, Rm 836, Tacoma, WA 98402

Child Study And Treatment Ctr 253.756.2504
Fax 253.756.3911
Web .... www.clipadministration.org
E-mail .... stevejh2@dshs.wa.gov
   8805 Steilacoom Blvd SW, Lakewood,
   WA 98498-4771
   Rick Mehlman, CEO

Children's Ctr 360.699.2244
Fax 360.699.1900
Web .... www.thechildrenscenter.org
E-mail .... management@thechildrenscenter.org
   415 W 11th St, Vancouver, WA 98660
   Pat Beckett, Executive Director

Children's Home Society 509.747.4174
Fax 509.838.3847
Web .... www.chs-wa.org
E-mail .... christier@chs-wa.org
   2323 N Discovery Pl, Spokane, WA 99216-1566
   Christy Richardson, Program Manager

Children's Home Society 360.695.1325
Fax 360.695.9803
Web .... www.chs-wa.org
   309 W 12th St, Vancouver, WA 98666-2903
   Bridget Mcleman, Regional Director

Children's Home Society Of Washington 206.695.3200
Fax 206.695.3201
Web .... www.childrenhomesociety.org
E-mail .... sharono@chs-wa.org
   3300 NE 65th Street, Seattle, WA 98115-7349
   Sharon Osborne, President

Children's Response Ctr **425.688.5130**
Fax 425.688.5672
Web ....www.childrenresponse.org
E-mail ....ddoane@u.washington.edu
　1120 112th Ave NE Ste 130, Bellevue,
　WA 98004-4505
　Deborah Doane, Director

Children's Village **509.574.3200**
Fax 509.574.3210
Web ....www.yakimamemorialhospital.org/
E-mail ....diane.patterson@yvmh.org
　3801 Kern Way, Yakima, WA 98902-6340
　Diane Patterson, Director

Columbia Basin Civilian Conservation
Corps **509.762.5581**
Fax 509.793.1758
Web ....www.jobcorps.org
　6739 24th Ave NE, Bldg 2402, Moses Lake,
　WA 98837
　Peggy Hendren, Center Director

Community Youth Services **360.943.0780**
Fax 360.943.0785
Web ....www.communityyouthservices.org
　711 State Avenue, NE, 3rd Fl., Olympia, WA 98506
　COA accredited organization.

Crossroads Resource Ctr **509.765.4425**
　102 W Broadway Ave, Moses Lake, WA 98837
　Wendy Shield, Director

EPIC - Enterprise For Progress In The
Community **509.248.3950**
Fax 509.457.0580
Web ....www.epicnet.org
E-mail ....webmaster@epicnet.org
　2902 Castlevale Rd, Ste A, Yakima, WA 98902
　Lynn Harlington, Director

Fort Simcoe Civilian Job Corps Ctr **509.874.2244**
Fax 509.874.2342
E-mail ....glibert.calac@jobcorps.org
　40 Abella Ln, White Swan, WA 98952-9748
　Glibert Calac, Center Director

Friends of Youth **425.869.6490**
Fax 425.869.6666
Web ....www.friendsofyouth.org
　16225 NE 87th Street, Suite A-6, Redmond,
　WA 98052-3536
　COA accredited organization.

Health Families **360.452.3811**
Fax 360.452.8243
Web ....www.healthyfam.org
　1210 E Front St Ste C, Port Angeles, WA 98362
　Becca Korby, Director

Hopesparks **253.565.4484**
Fax 253.565.5823
Web ....www.hopesparks.org
　6424 N 9th St, Tacoma, WA 98406-2091
　David Duae, CEO

Housing And Transitional Svcs &
Foodbank **425.259.3192**
Fax 425.303.8451
　1230 Broadway, Everett, WA 98201
　Sharon Paskewitz, Executive Director

Institute For Family Development **253.874.3630**
Fax 253.838.1670
Web ....www.institutefamily.org
E-mail ....info@institutefamily.org
　34004 16th Ave S Ste 200, Federal Way,
　WA 98003-8951
　Charlotte Booth, Msw, Executive Director

Jewish Family Service Seattle **206.461.3240**
Fax 206.461.3696
E-mail ....contactus@jfsseattle.org
　1601 16th Ave, Seattle, WA 98122
　Ken Weinberg, CEO

Kitsap Family YMCA- Bremerton **360.377.3741**
Fax 360.792.1794
Web ....www.asymca.org
　60 Magnuson Way, Bremerton, WA 98310-4537
　Jane Arlandsen, Executive Director

LDS Family Svcs **509.926.6581**
Fax 509.921.1375
E-mail ....fam-wa-spokane@ldschurch.org
　1107 E Sprague Ave, ste 202, Spokane,
　WA 99206-6848
　Patrick Cabbage, Director

Lower Columbia Community Action Child Care Resource And
Referral **360.425.3430**
Fax 360.414.8974
Web ....www.lowercolumbiacap.org
　1526 Commerce Ave, Longview, WA 98632
　Ilona Kerby, Director

Lutheran Community Services Northwest **206.901.1685**
Fax 206.244.7547
Web ....www.lcsnw.org
　4040 S. 188th Street, Suite 300, SeaTac,
　WA 98188-5070
　COA accredited organization.

Lutheran Community Svcs **206.694.5700**
Fax 206.694.5777
Web ....www.lcsnw.org
E-mail ....creed@lcsnw.org
　433 Minor Ave N, Seattle, WA 98109-5439
　Candice Reed, Personel Supervisor

Lutheran Community Svcs **509.735.6446**
Fax 509.735.6449
E-mail ....rbrunsdon@lcsnw.org
　3321 W Kennewick Ave Ste 150, Kennewick,
　WA 99336-2959
　Rochell Brunsdon, Area Director

Opportunity Council **360.734.5121**
Fax 360.734.0508
Web ....www.oppco.org
E-mail ....dave_kennet@oppco.org
　1111 Cornwall Ave Ste C, Bellingham,
　WA 98225-5039
　Dave Kennet, Executive Director

Partners With Families And Children **509.473.4810**
Fax 509.473.4840
Web ....www.inhs.org
E-mail ....partners@inhs.org
　613 S Washington St Ste B1, Spokane,
　WA 99204-2535
　Mary Ann Murphy, Executive Director

Peace For The Streets By Kids From The Streets
(PSKS) **206.726.8500**
Fax 206.726.9423
Web ....www.psks.org
E-mail ....e_simons@psks.org
　1814 Summit Ave, Seattle, WA 98122-2134
　Elene Simon, Executive Director

Ryther Child Center **206.525.5050**
Fax 206.525.9795
Web ....www.rcc.org
　2400 NE 95th Street, Seattle, WA 98115-2426
　COA accredited organization.

SCANC **509.458.7445**
Fax 509.462.7148
　707 N Ceder St, Spokane, WA 99201-1819
　Susie Seher, General Manager

Southeast Youth And Family Svcs **206.721.5542**
Fax 206.721.5917
Web ....www.scn.org/civic/seyouth
E-mail ....seyfs@uswest.net
　3722 S Hudson St, Seattle, WA 98118-1920
　Jeri White, Director

Spokane Area Jewish Family Services **509.747.7394**
Fax 509.747.7394
E-mail ....director@sajfs.org
　1322 E 30th Ave, Spokane, WA 99203
　Deborah Press

The Arthur D. Curtis Children's Justice Ctr
(CJC) **360.397.6002**
Fax 360.397.6019
E-mail ....mary.lancett@clark.wa.gov
　601 W Evergreen Blvd, Ste 101, Vancouver,
　WA 98660
　Mary Lancett, Director

The Caring Place **360.374.5010**
Fax 360.374.2174
E-mail ....thecaringplace@centurytel.net
　481 W East St, Forks, WA 98331
　Pam Cantrell, Director

The Parent Line/Lutheran Community Svcs
Northwest **360.452.5437**
Fax 360.452.5438
Web ....http://www.lcsnw.org/parentline/
E-mail ....parentline@lcsnw.org
　301 Lopez Ave, Port Angeles, WA 98362
　Nancy Martin, Director

Together! **360.493.2230**
Fax 360.413.0231
Web ....www.thurstontogether.org
E-mail ....info@thurstontogether.org
　418 Carpenter Rd SE Ste 203, Lacey, WA 98503
　Jim Cooper, Executive Director

United Indians Of All Tribes Foundation **206.285.4425**
Fax 206.282.3640
E-mail ....abradley@uiatf.com
　3801 W Govt. Way, Seattle, WA 98199
　Angie Zumsteg, Youth Services Manager

University District Youth Ctr **206.526.2992**
Fax 206.523.0330
E-mail ....richardking@cs.com
　4516 15th Ave NE, Seattle, WA 98105-4507
　Richard King, Program Manager

University St. Ministries/Teen Feed **206.522.4366**
Fax 206.522.3043
Web ....www.usministry.org
E-mail ....teenfeed@hotmail.com
　4740B University Way NE, Seattle, WA 98105
　Megan Gibaro, Director

Washington Council For Prevention Of Child Abuse &
Neglect **206.464.6151**
Fax 206.464.6642
Web ....www.wcpcan.wa.gov
E-mail ....wcpcan@dshs.wa.gov
　605 1st Ave Ste 412, Seattle, WA 98104-2224
　Joan Sharp, Director

Washington State Child Care Resource And Referral
Network **800.446.1114**
Fax 253.572.2599
Web ....www.childcarenet.org
E-mail ....childcarenet@childcarenet.org
　1551 Broadway #300, Tacoma, WA 98402
　Elizabeth Bonbright, Executive Director

Washington State Patrol Missing Children Clearinghouse
Hotline **800.543.5678**
Fax 360.704.2971
Web ....www.wsp.wa.gov
E-mail ....mtu@wsp.wa.gov
　17 Airdustrial Way, Olympia, WA 98507-2347
　Luci Stewart, Manager

SPECIAL NEEDS

Attention Deficit Disorder Resources **253.759.5085**
E-mail ....office@addresources.org
　223 Tacoma Ave Ste 100, Tacoma, WA 98402
　Kathie Dangle, Chief Executive Officer

Washington

Autism Outreach Project 360.299.4090
E-mail ....autism@esd189.org
   1601 R Ave, Anacortes, WA 98221
   Patty Yates, Administrative Assistant

Autism Today 866.928.8476
Fax 780.452.1098
Web ....www.autismtoday.com
E-mail ....karen@autismtoday.com
   1425 Broadway, Seattle, WA 98122-3854
   Karen Simmons, Director

Catholic Charities of Spokane 509.358.4250
Fax 509.358.4259
Web ....www.catholiccharitiesspokane.org
   12 East 5th Avenue, Spokane, WA 99202
   COA accredited organization.

Community Svcs for Blind 206.525.5556
E-mail ....info@sightconnection.net
   9709 NE 3rd Ave Ste 100, Seattle, WA 98115
   June Mansfield, Chief Executive Officer

Developmental Disabilities Council 360.586.3566
E-mail ....ed.hoen@cted.wa.gov
   2600 Martin Way E Ste F, Olympia, WA 98504
   Ed Hoen, Director

Easter Seals Washington 206.281.5700
   220 W Mercer Ste 120 W, Seattle, WA 98119

Epilepsy Foundation of Northwest 206.547.4551
E-mail ....mail@epilepsynw.org
   2311 N 45th St ,ste 134, Seattle, WA 98103

**Good Samaritan Hospital/Physical Medicine and
Rehabilitation** 253.697.1664
Fax 253.697.5180
Web ....www.goodsamhealth.org
E-mail ....susanmessier@goodsamhealth.org
   407 14th Ave SE, Puyallup, WA 98371
   Susan Messier, Director of Marketing
   CARF accredited programs available.

Kadlec Regional Medical Center 509.946.4611
Fax 509.942.2727
Web ....www.kadlecmed.com
   888 Swift Blvd, Richland, WA 99352
   Rand Wortman, CEO
   CARF accredited programs available.

Lindamood-Bell Learning Processes 425.827.6288
Fax 425.827.0601
   3055 112th Ave NE, Ste 108, Bellevue, WA 98004
   Meagan Norlin, Central Director

MDA/ALS Ctr-Univ of Washington Med Ctr 206.598.4590
Fax 206.598.2813
E-mail ....gtcarter@attbi.com
   1959 NE Pacific, Seattle, WA 98195
   Micheal White Weiss, Medical Officer

**National Alliance For Autism Research Pacific Northwest
Ofc** 206.464.5182
Fax 206.622.2970
Web ....www.autismspeaks.org
   159 Western Ave W Ste 484, Seattle, WA 98119-4233
   Justin Wiegimg, Director

National Multiple Sclerosis Society 206.284.4254
Fax 206.284.4972
E-mail ....msnorthwest@nmss.org
   192 Nickerson St Ste 100, Seattle, WA 98109
   Patty Shephard, President

Pacific Learning Center NW, LLC 425.672.6805
Fax 425.672.8867
E-mail ....info@plcnw.org
   21316 66th Ave W, Lynnwood, WA 98036

Parent to Parent Power (CPRC) 253.531.2022
Fax 253.538.1126
E-mail ....yvone_link@yahoo.com
   1118 S 142nd St Ste B, Tacoma, WA 98444
   Yvone Link, Director

PAVE 360.701.7012
E-mail ....weecare@olywa.net
   6316 S 12th St, Tacoma, WA 98465

PROVAIL 206.363.7303
   12550 N, Seattle, WA 98103
   Michael Hatzenbeler, Chief Executive Officer

Providence St. Peter Hospital 360.493.7640
Fax 360.493.4457
Web ....www.providence.org/swsa
   413 Lilly Road NE, Olympia, WA 98506
   CARF accredited programs available.

Rehab Without Walls-Washington 425.672.9219
   19000 33rd Avenue West, Suite 230, Lynnwood,
   WA 98036
   CARF accredited programs available.

Rural Outreach 509.335.2321
E-mail ....ftpd@familiestogether.org
   213 Smith Gym, Pullman, WA 99164
   Chris Curry, Director

Seattle Children's Hospital 206.987.1500
Fax 206.987.2651
Web ....www.seattlechildrens.org
E-mail ....laura.crooks@seattlechildrens.org
   4800 Sandpoint Way NE, Seattle, WA 98105
   Laura Crooks, Director
   CARF accredited programs available.

Special Training of Military Parents 253.565.2266
E-mail ....stop@wapave.org
   6316 S 12th St Ste B, Tacoma, WA 98465
   Heather Hebdon, Associate Director

Speech-Language-Hearing Association 206.367.8704
E-mail ....office@wslha.org
   2150 N 107th St Ste 205, Seattle, WA 98133
   Jonell Block, President

St. Christopher Academy 206.246.9751
Fax 253.639.3466
Web ....www.stchristopheracademy.com
E-mail ....jevne@stchristopheracademy.com
   4141 41st Ave SW, Seattle, WA 98116
   Darlene Jevne, Director

**St. Joseph Hospital - Center for Rehabilitation
Medicine** 360.715.6427
Fax 360.788.6613
Web ....www.peacehealth.org/Whatcom/
   809 E Chestnut St, Bellingham, WA 98225
   Robin Donaldson, Nursing Manager
   CARF accredited programs available.

St. Joseph Medical Center 253.426.6992
Fax 253.426.6002
Web ....www.fhshealth.org
   1717 South J Street, Tacoma, WA 98405
   CARF accredited programs available.

St. Luke's Rehabilitation Institute 509.838.4771
Fax 509.473.6978
Web ....www.st-lukes.org
   711 South Cowley Street, Spokane, WA 99202
   CARF accredited programs available.

STOMP 800.572.7368
E-mail ....stomp@wapave.org
   6316 S 12th St Ste B, Tacoma, WA 98465
   Heather Hebdon, Programme Coordinator

Summit Assistance Dogs 360.293.5609
E-mail ....info@summitdogs.org
   7575 Chestnut Ln, Anacortes, WA 98221

The Arc of Washington State 360.357.5596
E-mail ....info@arcwa.org
   2638 State Ave NE, Olympia, WA 98506
   Sue Elliott, Director

**University of Washington Medical Center; Harborview Medical
Center** 206.598.4803
Fax 206.744.8580
Web ....http://uwmedicine.washington.edu/Patient
   325 Ninth Avenue, Seattle, WA 98104
   CARF accredited programs available.

VSA Arts of Washington 206.443.1843
E-mail ....info@vsaaw.org
   305 Harrison St Ste 303, Seattle, WA 98109

Washington PAVE 253.565.2266
Fax 253.566.8052
E-mail ....pave@wapave.org
   6316 S 12th, Tacoma, WA 98465
   Tracy Kahlo, Director

Washington State Fathers Network 425.747.4004
E-mail ....greg.schell@kindering.org
   16120 NE 8th St, Bellevue, WA 98008
   Greg Schell, Director

**Washington State Parent to Parent
Programs** 425.641.7504
E-mail ....statep2p@earthlink.net
   2638 State Ave NE, Olympia, WA 98506
   Susan Atkins, State Coordinator

Washington State PTA 253.565.2153
E-mail ....wapta@wastatepta.org
   2003 W 65th Ave, Tacoma, WA 98466
   Denise Himes, Human Resource Accounting Mgr.

SUBSTANCE ABUSE TREATMENT

Auburn Youth Resources 253.939.2202
Fax 253.735.1894
Web www.ayr4kids.org
E-mail ....jamesbl@ayr4kids.org
   816 F St SE, Auburn, WA 98002-6121
   Jim Blanchard, Executive Director

Kent Youth And Family Svcs 253.859.0300
Fax 253.859.0745
Web ....www.kyfs.org
E-mail ....mikeh@kyfs.org
   232 2nd Ave S Ste 201, Kent, WA 98032-5862
   Mike Heinisch, Director

Sundown M Ranch 509.457.0990
Fax 509.457.5313
Web ....www.sundown.org
   2280 State Route 821, Yakima, WA 98901
   SCOTT MUNSEN, EXECUTIVE DIRECTOR
   CARF accredited programs available.

West Virginia

Early Ray Tomblin, Governor
State Capitol Complex
1900 Kanawha Blvd, East
Charleston, WV 25305
304.558.2000
304.558.5747 (Fax)
Governor@wvgov.org
www.wvgov.org

Miranda Nabors, Juvenile Justice Specialist
Division of Criminal Justice Services Beckley
1204 Kanawha Blvd, East
Charleston, WV 25301
304.558.8814 ext 213
304.558.0391 (Fax)
miranda.k.nabors@wv.gov

Vacant, SAG Chair
, WV

CRISIS NUMBERS

Child Abuse Reporting . . .800.352.6513

STATE SERVICES

SOCIAL SERVICES

Bureau for Children & Families **304.558.2400**
Fax. 304.558.4501
350 Capitol St, Charleston, WV 25301
Charles Young, Assistant Comissioner

Child Care Program West Virginia **304.558.1885**
Fax. 304.558.2059
350 Capitol St Rm B 18, Charleston, WV 25301
Judy Curry, Director

West Virginia Dept of Health & Human
Resources **304.558.0684**
Fax. 304.558.1130
Web. . . . . .www.wvdhhr.org
E-mail. . . . . .wvhhrsecretary@wv.org
1 Davis Square, Ste 100 E, Charleston, WV 25301
Dr. Michael Lewis Md, Director

GENERAL HEALTH SERVICES

DHHR Bureau for Public Health **304.558.2971**
Fax. 304.558.1035
Web. . . . . .www.wvdhhr.org
E-mail. . . . . .chriscurtis@wvdhhr.org
350 Capitol St, Room 702, Charleston, WV 25301
Chris Curtis, Commissioner

Off of Mat Child & Fam Health WV **304.558.5388**
Fax. 304.558.2183
350 Capitol St Rm 427, Charleston, WV 25301
Anne Williams, Director

MENTAL HEALTH SERVICES

DHHR Bureau for Behavioral Health & Health
Facilities **304.558.0627**
Fax. 304.558.1008
Web. . . . . .www.wvdhhr.org/bhhf
350 Capitol St, Room 350, Charleston, WV 25301
Elliott Birckhead, Director

West Virginia Div of Rehab Svcs **304.766.4601**
Fax. 304.766.4905
E-mail. . . . . .Donna.L.Ashworth@wv.gov
PO Box 50890, Charleston, WV 25305
Donna Ashworth, Director

JUSTICE AGENCY

Attorney General's Ofc **304.558.2021**
Fax. 304.558.0140
Web. . . . . .www.wvago.gov
E-mail. . . . . .consumer@wvago.gov
State Capitol, 1900 Kanawha Blvd East, Charleston,
WV 25305
Darrell V. Mcgraw Jr., Attorney General

Dept of Corrections **304.558.2036**
Fax. 304.558.5934
Web. . . . . .www.wvdoc.com
1409 Greenbriar St, Charleston, WV 25311
James Rubenstein, Commissioner

Div of Criminal Justice Svcs **304.558.8814**
Fax. 304.558.0391
Web. . . . . .www.wvcjs.com
E-mail. . . . . .nfederspiel@wvdcjs.org
1204 Kanawha Blvd E, 2nd Fl, Charleston, WV 25301
J. Norbert Federspiel, Director

Interstate Compact on Juveniles **304.558.4281**
Fax. 304.558.1212
E-mail. . . . . .mike.lacy@courtswv.gov
1900 Kanawha Blvd E, Bldg 1, Room E-100,
Charleston, WV 25305
Mike Lacy, Compact Administrator

Of of Inst Education Programs WV **304.558.8833**
Fax. 304.558.5042
E-mail. . . . . .jgreen@access.k12.wv.us
1900 Kanawha Blvd E, Bldg 6 Rm 728, Charleston,
WV 25305
J Green, Director

The Kenneth "Honey" Rubensstein Juvenile
Center **304.259.5241**
Fax. 304.259.4821
E-mail. . . . . .sbond@djs.state.wv.us
141 Forestry Camp Road, Davis, WV 26260
Stephanie Bond, Superintendent

COURTS

Administrative Ofc Of The Courts **304.558.0145**
Fax. 304.558.1212
E-mail. . . . . .steven.canterbury@courtswv.gov
1900 Kanawha Blvd E, Room E-100, Charleston,
WV 25305
Steven Canterbury, Administrative Director

POLICE AND SHERIFF

West Virginia Police Dept **304.624.1623**
Fax. 304.624.1616
Web. . . . . .www.cityofclarksburgwv.com
E-mail. . . . . .mgoff@cityofclarksburgwv.com
222 W Main St, Clarksburg, WV 26301-2908
Marshal Goff, Chief Of Police

West Virginia State Police **304.746.2177**
Fax. 304.746.2402
E-mail. . . . . .registery@wvsp.state.wv.us
725 Jefferson Rd, Charleston, WV 25309
Jeffrey Skidmore, Director

EDUCATION SERVICES

Of of Spec Prog Ext & Early Lrng WV **304.558.2696**
Fax. 304.558.3741
E-mail. . . . . .phomberg@access.k12.wv.us
1900 Kanawha Blvd E, Bldg 6 Rm 304, Charleston,
WV 25305
Pat Homberg, Director

Office Of Healthy School **304.558.8830**
Fax. 304.558.0048
Web. . . . . .www.wvde.state.us
1900 Kanawha Blvd E, Charleston, WV 25305
Linda Payne, Secratary

West Virginia Dept of Education **304.558.2681**
Fax. 304.558.0048
E-mail. . . . . .dvermill@access.k12.wv.us
1900 Kanawha Blvd E, Bldg 6 Rm 358, Charleston,
WV 25305
D Vermill, Director

West Virginia Parent Training & Info **304.624.1436**
Fax. 304.624.1438
E-mail. . . . . .wvpti@aol.com
1701 Hamill Ave, Clarksburg, WV 26301
Pat Haberbosch, Executive Director

LABOR & WORKFORCE EDUCATION

Workforce West Virginia **304.558.7024**
Fax. 304.558.9157
Web. . . . . .www.workforcewv.org
E-mail. . . . . .russell.l.fry@wv.org
112 California Ave, Room 609, Charleston, WV 25305
Russell Fry, Executive Director

West Virginia

© 2011 Dorland Health

935

Barbour County

GENERAL HEALTH SERVICES

Health Dept **304.457.1670**
Fax 304.457.1296
  23 Wabash Ave, Philippi, WV 26416
  Rochelle Sutton, Rn, Public Health Nurse

JUSTICE AGENCY

WV Industrial Home For Youth **304.782.2371**
Fax 304.782.4816
E-mail ....jmerendino@djs.state.wv.us
  7 Industrial Blvd, Salem, WV 26462
  Joe Merendino, Superintendent

COURTS

Circuit Court **304.457.3454**
Fax 304.457.2790
  8 N Main St Ste 2, Philippi, WV 26416
  Honorable Alan D. Moats, Judge

POLICE AND SHERIFF

Sheriff's Ofc **304.457.2352**
Fax 304.457.4643
E-mail ....wvdeputy801@hotmail.com
  8 N Main St Ste 1, Philippi, WV 26416-1140
  John Hawkins, Sheriff

Berkeley County

GENERAL HEALTH SERVICES

Health Dept **304.263.5131**
Fax 304.263.1067
Web ....www.bchealthdept.org
  800 Emmett Rousch Dr, Martinsburg, WV 25401
  Vickie Greenfield, Rn, Nurse Director

JUSTICE AGENCY

Probation **304.264.1969**
Fax 304.267.3710
  380 W South St Ste 1200, Martinsburg, WV 25401
  Mark Hofe, Chief Probation Officer

COURTS

Circuit Court **304.264.1918**
Fax 304.262.3139
Web ....www.softwaresystems.com
E-mail ....gsilver@softwaresystems.com
  380 W South St Ste 4400, Martinsburg,
  WV 25401-3200
  Honorable Gray Silver Iii, Judge

POLICE AND SHERIFF

Sheriff's Ofc **304.267.7000**
Fax 304.267.7118
Web ....www.berkeleycountycomm.org
  802 Emmett Rousch Dr, Martinsburg,
  WV 25401-6313
  Kenneth Lemaster, Sheriff

Boone County

GENERAL HEALTH SERVICES

Health Dept **304.369.7967**
Fax 304.369.2832
Web ....www.pandemicflu.gov
  213 Kenmore Dr, Danville, WV 25053-6890
  Julia Miller, Assistant Administrator/nurse Supervisor

COURTS

Circuit Court **304.369.7321**
Fax 304.369.7326
Web ....www.state.wv.us
  200 State St Ste 202, Madison, WV 25130-1189
  Honorable William S Thompson, Director

POLICE AND SHERIFF

Sheriff's Office **304.369.7390**
Fax 304.369.7345
  200 State St Ste 102, Madison, WV 25130
  Rodney A. Miller, Sheriff

Braxton County

GENERAL HEALTH SERVICES

Health Dept **304.765.2851**
Fax 304.765.2020
Web ....www.wvdhhr.org
  495 Old Turnpike Rd, Sutton, WV 26601-1698
  Sissy Price, Rn, Nursing Director/hiv Coordinator

COURTS

Circuit Court **304.765.2837**
Fax 304.765.2947
  300 Main St Ste 101, Sutton, WV 26601-1313
  Susan Lemon, Clerk

POLICE AND SHERIFF

Sheriff's Ofc **304.765.2838**
Fax 304.765.3241
  300 Main St, Sutton, WV 26601
  George Keener, Sheriff

Brooke County

GENERAL HEALTH SERVICES

Health Dept **304.737.3665**
Fax 304.737.3689
Web ....www.brookecountyhealthdepartment.com
  204 Courthouse Sq, Wellsburg, WV 26070
  Joseph Depetro, Md, Health Officer

JUSTICE AGENCY

A Child's Place- CASA, Ltd. **304.737.4444**
Fax 304.737.4445
Web ....www.childsplacecasa.com
E-mail ....childsplacecasa@comcast.net
  720 Charles St, Wellsburg, WV 26070-1665
  Rhonda Stubbs, Executive Director Comcast

Probation Svcs **304.737.3669**
Fax 304.737.3597
  840 Charles St, Wellsburg, WV 26070-1618
  Stacy L. Silbaugh, Probation Officer

COURTS

Circuit Court **304.737.3662**
Fax 304.737.0352
Web ....www.state.wv.us
  632 Main St, Ste 3, Wellsburg, WV 26070
  Glinda Brooks, Chief Circuit Court

POLICE AND SHERIFF

Sheriff's Ofc **304.737.3660**
Fax 304.737.3046
E-mail ....brookecounty@yahoo.com
  300 COURTHOUSE SQ, Wellsburg, WV 26070-1749
  Richard Ferguson, Sheriff

Cabell County

GENERAL HEALTH SERVICES

Health Dept **304.523.6483**
Fax 304.697.0365
Web ....www.cabellhealth.org
  703 7th Ave, Huntington, WV 25701
  Kathlene Napier, Rn, Nursing/aids Director

COURTS

Circuit Court **304.526.8622**
Fax 304.526.8699
  750 5th Ave Ste 114, Huntington, WV 25701-2019
  Honorable David M. Pancake, Chief Judge

POLICE AND SHERIFF

Sheriff's Ofc **304.526.8663**
Fax 304.526.8649
E-mail ....sheriff@cabellcounty.org
  750 5th Ave, Rm 101, Huntington, WV 25701
  Tom Mccomas, Sheriff

EDUCATION SERVICES

Special Education **304.528.5200**
Fax 304.528.5344
Web ....www.cabellcountyschools.com
E-mail ....kmccoy@access.k12.wv.us
  2850 5th Ave, Huntington, WV 25702-1436
  Kathy K. Mccoy, Special Education Services Director

Calhoun County

GENERAL HEALTH SERVICES

Mid-Ohio Valley Health Dept **304.354.6101**
Fax 304.354.6654
Web ....www.ospi.wednet.edu
E-mail ....jpriddy@wvdhhr.org
  211 6. th. Street., Parkersburg, WV 26101
  Jennifer Priddy, Nurse

EDUCATION SERVICES

Arnoldsburg Head Start **304.485.7404**
Fax 304.485.0499
  925 24th St, Arnoldsburg, WV 25234
  Ms Deborah Dennis, Director

Clay County

SOCIAL SERVICES

Health & Human Resources **304.587.4268**
Fax 304.587.2567
Web ....www.wvdhhr.org
  94 Main St, Clay, WV 25043
  Tammy Bailey, Community Services Manager

GENERAL HEALTH SERVICES

Health Dept **304.587.4269**
Fax 304.587.7415
  452 Main St, Clay, WV 25043
  Jeff Smith, Administrator

POLICE AND SHERIFF

Sheriff's Ofc **304.587.4260**
Fax 304.587.8366
  246Main St, Clay, WV 25043
  Randy Holcomb, Sheriff

EDUCATION SERVICES

Appalachian Council Head Start -
Clay **304.587.1169**
Fax 304.587.1172
Web ....www.appcouncil.com
E-mail ....shall@appcouncil.com
  136 Church St, Clay, WV 25043
  Sue Hall, Director

Fayette County

GENERAL HEALTH SERVICES

Health Dept **304.574.1617**
Fax 304.574.1370
  202 Church St, Fayetteville, WV 25840
  Linda Shieler, Administrator

New River Family Health Ctr **304.469.2905**
Fax 304.465.5486
Web ....www.pihn.org
E-mail ....linda.stein@pihn.org
　　337 Scarbro Rd, Scarbro, WV 25917
　　Linda Stein, Social Worker In Birth Center

MENTAL HEALTH SERVICES

FMRS Mental Health Council **304.574.2100**
Fax 304.574.2151
Web ....www.fmrs.org
　　209 W Maple Ave, Fayetteville, WV 25840-1400
　　Mary Redman, Chief Executive Officer

COURTS

Circuit Court **304.574.4249**
Fax 304.574.4314
E-mail ....paul@fayettecounty.com
　　100 N Court St, Fayetteville, WV 25840
　　Honorable Paul M Blake Jr, Director

POLICE AND SHERIFF

Sheriff's Ofc **304.574.4216**
Fax 304.574.2796
Web ....www.fayettesheriff.net
　　100 Church St, Fayetteville, WV 25840
　　Steve Kessler, Sheriff

Gilmer County

GENERAL HEALTH SERVICES

Health Dept **304.462.7351**
Fax 304.462.8956
E-mail ....carlnichols@wvdhr.org
　　809 Medical Dr Ste 3, Glenville, WV 26351
　　Carl Nichols, Health Officer

Grant County

GENERAL HEALTH SERVICES

Health Dept **304.257.4922**
Fax 304.257.2422
Web ....www.grantcountyhealthdepartment.com
　　Route 28 Hospital Dr, Petersburg, WV 26847
　　Sandra Glasscock, Rn, Public Health Nurse

COURTS

Circuit Court **304.257.4545**
Fax 304.257.2593
　　5 Highland Ave, Petersburg, WV 26847
　　Honorable Phil B. Jordan, Judge

Greenbrier County

GENERAL HEALTH SERVICES

Health Dept **304.645.1787**
Fax 304.645.3630
　　9207 Seneca Trl, Ronceverte, WV 24970
　　Nicki Dolan, Nurse Supervisor

JUSTICE AGENCY

Probation **304.647.6688**
Fax 304.647.6680
　　200 N. Court St, Lewisburg, WV 24901
　　Fred L Taylor, Supervisor

COURTS

Circuit Court **304.647.6626**
Fax 304.647.6666
Web ....www.state.wv.us
　　200 N Court St Ste 4, Lewisburg, WV 24901-1169
　　Honorable James J. Rowe, Judge

POLICE AND SHERIFF

Sheriff's Ofc **304.647.6634**
Fax 304.647.6636
E-mail ....gbrso@yahoo.com
　　200 N Court St Ste 3, Lewisburg, WV 24901
　　James Childers, Sheriff

EDUCATION SERVICES

Communities in Schools **304.645.5339**
Fax 304.647.3087
Web ....www.cisgreenbriercounty.org
E-mail ....ehaas@cisgc.org
　　RR 1, Box 150, Ronceverte, WV 24970
　　Emily Haas, Director

Hampshire County

SOCIAL SERVICES

Dept Of Health And Human
Resources **304.822.6900**
Fax 304.822.7609
Web ....www.wvdhhr.org
　　Route 50, Romney, WV 26757
　　Susan Radko, Community Services Manager

GENERAL HEALTH SERVICES

Health Dept **304.496.9640**
Fax 304.496.9650
Web ....www.wvdhhr.gov
E-mail ....judith.a.cox@wv.gov
　　Route 50 E, Augusta, WV 26704
　　Judy Cox, Rn, Nurse Supervisor

JUSTICE AGENCY

Probation Ofc **304.530.0241**
Fax 304.530.0242
　　204 Washington St, Moorefield, WV 26836
　　Manda Peter, Jpo

COURTS

Circuit Court **304.822.5022**
Fax 304.822.8257
　　50 S High St, Romney, WV 26757
　　Honorable Donald H. Cookman, Judge

POLICE AND SHERIFF

Sheriff's Ofc **304.822.3894**
Fax 304.822.8494
Web ....www.hampshirecountysheriffwv.com
E-mail ....nsions@hampshirecountysheriffwv.com
　　66 N High St Rm 2, Romney, WV 26757-1600
　　Nathan Sions, Sheriff

Hancock County

GENERAL HEALTH SERVICES

Health Dept **304.564.3343**
Fax 304.564.3410
Web ....www.hancockcountyhealthdept.com
　　100 N Court St, New Cumberland, WV 26047
　　Michelle Truax, Rn, Nursing Director

COURTS

Circuit Court **304.564.3311**
Fax 304.564.5014
E-mail ....bjackson@hancockcountywv.org
　　102 N Court St, New Cumberland, WV 26047
　　Brenda Jackson, Clerk

POLICE AND SHERIFF

Sheriff's Dept **304.564.3911**
Fax 304.564.4138
Web ....www.hancockcountywv.org
E-mail ....mwhite@hancockcountywv.org
　　102 N Court St, New Cumberland, WV 26047
　　Michael White, Sheriff

Hardy County

SOCIAL SERVICES

Dept Of Health And Human
Resources **304.538.2394**
Fax 304.538.2476
Web ....www.wvdhhr.org
E-mail ....stevependleton@wvdhhr.org
　　112 Beans Ln, Moorefield, WV 26836-1202
　　Steve Pendleton, Childrens Unit Supervisor

GENERAL HEALTH SERVICES

Health Dept **304.530.6355**
Fax 304.530.7684
Web ....www.hardycountyhealthdepartment.com
　　411 Spring Ave Ste 101, Moorefield, WV 26836
　　Dewey Bensenhaver, Md, Health Officer

COURTS

Circuit Court **304.530.0230**
Fax 304.530.0231
　　204 Washington St Rm 237, Moorefield, WV 26836
　　Honorable Donald H. Cookman, Chief

POLICE AND SHERIFF

Sheriff's Ofc **304.530.0222**
Fax 304.530.0223
　　204 Washington St Rm 119, Moorefield,
　　WV 26836-1155
　　Robert L. Ferrell, Sheriff

Harrison County

COURTS

Circuit Court **304.624.8640**
Fax 304.624.8710
Web ....www.harrisoncountywv.com
　　301 W Main St Ste 301, Clarksburg, WV 26301-2967
　　Tracy Keener, Jpo

Jackson County

SOCIAL SERVICES

Dept Of Health And Human
Resources **304.373.2560**
Fax 304.372.7888
Web ....www.wvdhhr.org
E-mail ....nikkiharris@wvdhhr.org
　　2139 Cedar Lakes Dr, Ripley, WV 25271-9325
　　Nikki Harris, Children Æs Unit Social Services Supervisor

GENERAL HEALTH SERVICES

Health Dept **304.372.2634**
Fax 304.372.1096
Web ....www.jacksoncountyhealthdepartment
E-mail ....susan.g.hosaflook@wv.gov
　　504 Church St S, Ripley, WV 25271
　　Susan Hosaflook, Rn, Nurse Supervisor/administrator

POLICE AND SHERIFF

Sheriff's Dept **304.373.2290**
Fax 304.372.6291
Web ....www.jacksoncountywv.org
E-mail ....jcsheriff@jacksoncountywv.org
　　100 Maple St S, Ripley, WV 25271
　　Michael Bright, Sheriff

Jefferson County

SOCIAL SERVICES

Health Dept **304.728.8415**
Fax 304.728.0529
Web ....www.dhhr.barleyco.org
　　1948 Wiltshire Rd, Charles Town, WV 25430

West Virginia

West Virginia

GENERAL HEALTH SERVICES

Health Dept **304.728.8416**
Fax 304.728.3319
   1948 Wiltshire Rd Ste 1, Kearneysville,
   WV 25430-2783
Amy Jones, Director

COURTS

Circuit Court **304.728.3231**
Fax 304.728.3398
   110 N George St, Charles Town, WV 25414-1502
Honorable David H. Sanders, Judge

POLICE AND SHERIFF

Sheriff's Ofc **304.728.3205**
Fax 304.728.3299
Web ....www.jcsdwv.netfirms.com
   102 Industrial Blvd Ste.100, kerneywayle, WV 25430
Robert Shirley, Sheriff

Kanawha County

SOCIAL SERVICES

Ofc Of Children & Families Region
II **304.746.2360**
Fax 304.558.0851
   4190 Washington St W, Charleston, WV 25313
James Kimbler, Regional Director

West Virginia Div of Homeland Security and Emergency
Mgmt **304.558.5380**
Fax 304.344.4538
E-mail ....jimmy.j.gianato@wv.gov
   1900 Kanawha Blvd E Rm 1, Charleston, WV 25305
James Gianato, Director

GENERAL HEALTH SERVICES

Community Of Rural Health Svcs **304.558.1327**
Fax 304.558.1437
Web ....www.wvochs.org
   350 Capitol St, Rm 515, Charleston, WV 25301
Joe Barker, Director

Health Dept **304.348.8080**
Fax 304.348.4756
Web ....www.kchdwv.gov
   108 Lee St E, Charleston, WV 25301
Lolita Kirk, Health Officer

JUSTICE AGENCY

Tiger Morton Juvenile Ctr **304.766.2616**
Fax 304.766.2687
E-mail ....marshall.l.berger@wv.gov
   60 Manfred Holland Way, Dunbar, WV 25064
Marshall Berger, Director

COURTS

Circuit Court **304.357.0440**
Fax 304.357.0473
   111 Court St Fl 2, Charleston, WV 25301
Steve Hanley, Court Administrator

POLICE AND SHERIFF

Sheriff's Ofc **304.357.0200**
Fax 304.357.0239
Web ....www.kanawha.us
E-mail ....michaelrutherford@kanawha.us
   301 Virginia St E, Charleston, WV 25301-2530
Michael Rutherford, Sheriff

EDUCATION SERVICES

Special Education **304.348.7740**
Fax 304.348.6671
E-mail ....sgboggs@kcs.kana.k12.wv.us
   200 Elizabeth St, Charleston, WV 25311
Sandra Boggs, Special Education Director

Lewis County

GENERAL HEALTH SERVICES

Health Dept **304.269.8218**
Fax 304.269.8220
Web ....www.wvdhhr.org
E-mail ....lchealthdept@wv.gov
   125 Court Ave, Weston, WV 26452
Dr Ben Orvick, Health Officer

Lincoln County

GENERAL HEALTH SERVICES

Health Dept **304.824.3330**
Fax 304.824.3334
Web ....www.wvdhhr.org
E-mail ....lincolnhealthdept@wvdhhr.org
   8008 Court Ave, Court House Annex, Hamlin,
   WV 25523-1418
J. Loren Smith, Do, Health Officer

Logan County

SOCIAL SERVICES

Dept Of Health And Human
Resources **304.792.7095**
Fax 304.792.7003
E-mail ....janetpoling@wvdhhr.org
   195 Dingess St, Logan, WV 25601
Darlena Ables, Community Service Manager

GENERAL HEALTH SERVICES

Health Dept **304.792.8630**
Fax 304.792.8635
Web ....www.logancountyhealthdepartment.org
   Courthouse Bldg, Room 203, Logan, WV 25601
Livia Cabauatan, Md, Health Officer

COURTS

Circuit Court **304.792.8550**
Fax 304.792.8589
   300 Stratton St Ste 311, Logan, WV 25601-3950
Honorable Eric H. Oæbriant, Director

POLICE AND SHERIFF

Sheriff's Dept **304.792.8590**
Fax 304.792.8596
Web ....www.loganbanner.com
E-mail ....sheriff@loganbanner.com
   300 Stratton St Ste 209, Logan, WV 25601-3949
W.e. Eddie Hunter, Sheriff

Marion County

GENERAL HEALTH SERVICES

Health Dept **304.366.3360**
Fax 304.363.8217
Web ....www.wvdhhr.org
E-mail ....marionchd@wvdhhr.org
   300 2nd St, Fairmont, WV 26554
Govind Patel, Md, Health Officer

JUSTICE AGENCY

Probation Dept **304.367.5464**
Fax 304.368.0274
   314 Monroe St, Bldg 2Jacobs, Fairmont, WV 26554
Thomas Carpenter, Chief

COURTS

Circuit Court **304.367.5360**
Fax 304.367.5374
   219 Adams St, Rm 211, Fairmont, WV 26554
Barbara Core, Circuit Clerk

POLICE AND SHERIFF

Sheriff's Ofc **304.367.5300**
Fax 304.367.5304
   316 Monroe, Fairmont, WV 26554
Joseph Carpenter, Sheriff

EDUCATION SERVICES

Carolina Head Start **304.287.7686**
   8th and Pine St, Carolina, WV 26563
James John Barns, Director

East Fairmont Early Head Start **304.675.4956**
Fax 304.675.4956
   817 30th St, Point Pleasant, WV 25550
Jane Hannick, Director

Edgemont Head Start **304.363.3311**
Fax 304.366.8846
Web ....www.ncwvcaa.org
E-mail ....kpetracca@ncwvcaa.org
   1000 Country Club Rd, Fairmont, WV 26554-2315
Kim Petracca, Director

Fairmont Head Start **304.363.1288**
Web ....www.acf.hhs.gov
   Center East Grafton Rd, Fairmont, WV 26554
James Barns, Director

Marshall County

GENERAL HEALTH SERVICES

Health Dept **304.845.7840**
Fax 304.843.9837
Web ....www.marshallcountyhealthdepartment.com
   513 6th St, Moundsville, WV 26041
Patti Owens, Nursing Director

COURTS

Circuit Court **304.845.2130**
Fax 304.845.3948
   600 7th St, Rm 127, Moundsville, WV 26041
Honorable Mark A. Karl, Judges

POLICE AND SHERIFF

Sheriff's Ofc **304.843.1500**
Fax 304.843.1551
E-mail ....jgruzinkas@access.k12.wv.us
   601 6th St, Moundsville, WV 26041
John Gruzinkas, Sheriff

EDUCATION SERVICES

Creative Learning Head Start **304.233.3290**
Fax 304.233.3719
E-mail ....mmidget@npheadstart.org
   1 Orchard Rd Ste 1, Wheeling, WV 26003
Marlene Midget, Director

Mason County

GENERAL HEALTH SERVICES

Health Dept **304.675.3050**
Fax 304.675.4801
Web ....www.masoncountyhealthdept.org
E-mail ....diana.l.riddle@wv.gov
   216 5th St, Point Pleasant, WV 25550-1104
Diana Riddle, Director

Pleasant Valley Hospital **304.675.4340**
Fax 304.675.5243
Web ....www.pvalley.org
E-mail ....sgartan@pvalley.org
   2520 Valley Dr, Point Pleasant, WV 25550-2092
Susan Gartan, Infection Control Nurse

COURTS

Circuit Court **304.675.4400**
Fax 304.675.7419
   200 6th St Rm 8, Point Pleasant, WV 25550
Honorable Thomas Evans, Judge

POLICE AND SHERIFF

Sheriff's Ofc **304.675.3838**
Fax 304.675.3665
Web www.access.k12.wv.us
　　200 6th St Rm 1, Point Pleasant, WV 25550-1185
　　David Anthony, Sheriff

McDowell County

GENERAL HEALTH SERVICES

Health Dept **304.448.2174**
Fax 304.448.3777
E-mail ....jesse.j.rose@wv.gov
　　Route 103, Wilcoe, WV 24895
　　Jesse J Rose, Administrator

Welch Emergency Hospital Maternity Svcs
Program **304.436.8820**
Fax 304.436.3848
　　454 McDowell St, Welch, WV 24801
　　Debbie Altizer, Nurse Manager

JUSTICE AGENCY

McDowell Probation Dept **304.436.8508**
Fax 304.436.3476
Web ....www.wvcrt.org
　　19 Wyoming St, Welch, WV 24801
　　Jerome Powell, CPO

COURTS

Circuit Court **304.436.8560**
Fax 304.436.6994
　　91 Wyoming St, Ste 201, Welch, WV 24801
　　Honorable Francine Spencer, Clerk

POLICE AND SHERIFF

Sheriff's Ofc **304.436.8541**
Fax 304.436.8578
　　90 Wyoming St Ste 117, Welch, WV 34801
　　Danny Mitchell, Sheriff

Mercer County

GENERAL HEALTH SERVICES

Health Dept **304.324.8367**
Fax 304.324.8843
　　1331 S Dr, Green Valley, Bluefield, WV 24701
　　Kathleen Wides, Md, Health Officer

JUSTICE AGENCY

Southern Regional Juvenile Detention
Ctr **304.425.9721**
Fax 304.487.5543
Web ....www.djs.state.wv.us
E-mail ....degnor@djs.state.wv.us
　　843 Shelter Rd, Princeton, WV 24740-7899
　　Dan Egnor, Director

COURTS

Circuit Court **304.487.8323**
Fax 304.425.1598
Web ....www.state.wv.us
　　1501 Main St Ste 111, Princeton, WV 24740-2600
　　Julie Ball, Clerk

POLICE AND SHERIFF

Sheriff's Ofc **304.487.8364**
Fax 304.487.8366
　　1501 Main St Ste 31, Princeton, WV 24740-2600
　　Don Meadows, Sheriff

Mineral County

GENERAL HEALTH SERVICES

Health Dept **304.788.1321**
Fax 304.788.6023
Web ....www.mineralcountyhealthdepartment.com
E-mail ....minerallhd@wv.gov
　　Harley O Staggers Sr Drive, Keyser, WV 26726
　　Carl A. Liebig, Md, Health Officer

COURTS

Circuit Court **304.788.1562**
Fax 304.788.4109
　　150 Armstrong St, Keyser, WV 26726
　　Honorable Philip B. Jordan, Judge

POLICE AND SHERIFF

Sheriff's Dept **304.788.0341**
Fax 304.788.4771
E-mail ....cafraley@mineralsheriff.com
　　150 Armstrong St, Keyser, WV 26726
　　Craig A Fraley, Sheriff

Mingo County

GENERAL HEALTH SERVICES

Health Dept **304.235.3570**
Fax 304.235.2654
Web ....www.mingocountyhealthdepartment.org
　　1st Ave And Logan St, Memorial Bldg, 2nd Floor,
　　Williamson, WV 25661
　　Nancy Johnson, Rn, Public Nurse

MENTAL HEALTH SERVICES

Logan-Mingo Area Mental Health **304.792.7130**
Fax 304.235.2929
E-mail ....micheleevans@suddenlink.net
　　2954 Buffalo Creek Rd, Chattaroy, WV 25667
　　Michelle Evans, Coordinator

COURTS

Circuit Court **304.235.0320**
Fax 304.235.0326
Web ....www.state.wv.us
　　75 E 2nd Ave Rm 232, Williamson, WV 25661-3532
　　Honorable Michael Thornsbury, Director

POLICE AND SHERIFF

Sheriff's Ofc **304.235.0300**
Fax 304.235.0436
　　2nd Ave, Williamson, WV 25661
　　Lonnie Hannah, Sheriff

EDUCATION SERVICES

Ben Creek Head Start **304.664.8927**
Fax 304.664.8927
　　HC 71, Box 101A, Wharncliffe, WV 25651-9702
　　Karen Browning, Director

Monongalia County

GENERAL HEALTH SERVICES

Health Dept **304.598.5100**
Fax 304.598.5199
Web ....www.monchd.org
　　453 Van Voorhis Rd, Morgantown, WV 26505-1200
　　Vincent Kolanko, Health Officer

JUSTICE AGENCY

CASA Program **304.599.1087**
Fax 304.599.1098
Web ....www.nationalcasa.org
E-mail ....moncasa@comcast.net
　　440 Elmer Prince Dr, Morgantown, WV 26505-3273
　　Helene Friedberg, Program Director

Probation Dept **304.291.7217**
Fax 304.291.7217
　　265 Spruce St Ste 120, Morgantown, WV 26505
　　Phyliss Stewert, Chief Probation Officer

COURTS

Teen Court **304.292.1236**
E-mail ....monteencourt@hotmail.com
　　265 Spruce St Rm 116, Morgantown, WV 26505
　　Christopher W. Mullins, Coordinator

POLICE AND SHERIFF

Sheriff's Ofc **304.291.7260**
Fax 304.291.5138
E-mail ....kkisner@monsheriff.com
　　155 Chancery Row, Morgantown, WV 26505
　　Kenneth L. Kisner, Sheriff

Monroe County

SOCIAL SERVICES

Health & Human Resources **304.772.3013**
Fax 304.772.4372
Web ....www.wvdhhr.org
　　174 Route 3 E, Union, WV 24983
　　Tina Dawdy, Operations Manager

GENERAL HEALTH SERVICES

Health Dept **304.772.3064**
Fax 304.772.5671
Web ....www.monroehealthcenter.com
　　200 Health Center Ln, Union, WV 24983
　　Roger Brady, Administrator

Morgan County

SOCIAL SERVICES

Dept Of Health And Human
Resources **304.258.1350**
Fax 304.258.3794
Web ....www.wvdhhr.org
　　64 Regal Ct, Berkeley Springs, WV 25411
　　Kathleen Bradley, Community Service Manager

COURTS

Circuit Court **304.258.8554**
Fax 304.258.7319
Web ....www.state.wv.us
E-mail ....mccircuitclerk@hotmail.com
　　77 Fairfax St Rm 302, Berkeley Springs,
　　WV 25411-1580
　　Honorable Gina M. Groh, Circuit Judge

POLICE AND SHERIFF

Sheriff's Ofc **304.258.1067**
Fax 304.258.8630
Web ....www.usacops.com
　　111 Fairfax St, Berkeley Springs, WV 25411-4800
　　Vincent Shambaugh, Sheriff

Nicholas County

GENERAL HEALTH SERVICES

Health Dept **304.872.5329**
Fax 304.872.5362
　　1 Stevens Rd, Summersville, WV 26651
　　Marsha Bailes, Nurse Director

COURTS

Circuit Court **304.872.7810**
Fax 304.872.7863
Web ....www.softwaresystems.com
　　700 Main St Ste 5, Summersville, WV 26651-1489
　　Honorable Debbie Facemire, Circuit Clerk

West Virginia

POLICE AND SHERIFF

Sheriff's Ofc 304.872.7880
Fax 304.872.7869
E-mail ....wbennett@wvncsd.com
700 Main St Ste 3, Summersville, WV 26651
Wetzel Bennett, Sheriff

Ohio County

SOCIAL SERVICES

**Dept Of Health And Human
Resources** 304.232.4411
Fax 304.232.4773
Web ....www.wvdhhr.org
407 Main St, Wheeling, WV 26003
Amanda Mccreary, Supervisor Of Childrenæs Unit

GENERAL HEALTH SERVICES

Health Dept 304.234.3682
Fax 304.234.6405
Web ....www.wvdhhr.org
E-mail ....howard.p.gamble@wv.gov
1500 Chapline St Ste 106, Wheeling,
WV 26003-3580
Howard Gamble, Administrator

JUSTICE AGENCY

Northern Regional Juvenile Ctr 304.232.3441
Fax 304.233.3371
1000 Chapline St, Wheeling, WV 26703
Linda Scott, Facility Director

YWCA 304.232.0511
Fax 304.232.0513
E-mail ....ywcawheeling@aol.com
1100 Chapline St Fl 1, Wheeling, WV 26003
Lori Jones, Business Director

COURTS

Circuit Court 304.234.3611
Fax 304.232.0550
1500 Chapline St Ste 403, Wheeling,
WV 26003-3592
Honorable Arthur M. Recht, Director

POLICE AND SHERIFF

Sheriffs Ofc 304.234.3688
Fax 304.234.3785
E-mail ....Pbutler@ohcoso.com
1500 Chapline St Ste 103, Wheeling, WV 26003
Patrick Butler, Sheriff

Pendleton County

GENERAL HEALTH SERVICES

Health Dept 304.358.7565
Fax 304.358.2471
Web ....www.pendletoncountyhealthdepartment.org
273 Mill Rd, Franklin, WV 26807
Carmen Rexroad, Md, Health Officer

POLICE AND SHERIFF

Sheriff's Ofc 304.358.2214
Fax 304.358.3293
E-mail ....pcsdlaw@pendletoncommmision.com
100 S Main St, Franklin, WV 26807
Kevin Puffenberger, Sheriff

EDUCATION SERVICES

Franklin Head Start Ctr 304.358.3036
Main St, Franklin, WV 26807
Mark Colaw, Director

Pleasants County

GENERAL HEALTH SERVICES

Pleasants Health Dept 304.684.2461
Fax 304.684.2845
Web ....www.movhd.com
605 Cherry St Ste 2, Saint Marys, WV 26170
Jennifer Mullen, Rn, Public Health Nurse

COURTS

Circuit Court 304.684.3513
Fax 304.684.3514
301 Court Ln Ste 201, Saint Marys, WV 26170-1317
Timothy Swenney, Judge

POLICE AND SHERIFF

Sheriff's Ofc 304.684.2285
Fax 304.684.2862
305 Barkwill St, Saint Marys, WV 26170-1306
Ted Maston, Sheriff

Pocahontas County

GENERAL HEALTH SERVICES

Health Dept 304.799.4154
Fax 304.799.7490
900 10th Ave Ste 9, Marlinton, WV 24954
Linda Mccoy, Rn, Nurse Supervisor

POLICE AND SHERIFF

Sheriff's Ofc 304.799.4710
Fax 304.799.2326
900 10th Ave Ste A, Marlinton, WV 24954-1333
David Jonese, Sheriff

Preston County

COURTS

Circuit Court 304.329.0047
Fax 304.329.1417
101 W Main St Rm 301, Kingwood, WV 26537
Honorable Lawrence S. Miller Jr., Judge

POLICE AND SHERIFF

Sheriff's Ofc 304.329.1611
Fax 304.329.2794
103 W Main St, Kingwood, WV 26537
Dallax Wolfe, Sheriff

Putnam County

GENERAL HEALTH SERVICES

Health Dept 304.757.2541
Fax 304.757.7287
Web ....www.wvdhhr.org/wvlocalhealth
500 Corporate Center Dr, Ste 520, Scott Depot,
WV 25560
Jacqueline Fleshman, Director

COURTS

Circuit Court 304.586.0203
Fax 304.586.0221
3389 Winfield Rd, PUTNAM COUNTY JUDICIAL
BLDG, Winfield, WV 25213-9367
Honorable O.c. Spaulding, Director

POLICE AND SHERIFF

Sheriff's Ofc 304.586.0256
Fax 304.586.0260
3389 Winfield Rd Ste 8, Winfield, WV 25213
Marr Smith, Sheriff

EDUCATION SERVICES

**Appalachian Council Head
Start-Hurricane** 304.562.6220
Fax 304.562.6220
2492 US Route 60, Hurricane, WV 25526
Barbara Reed, Director

Raleigh County

GENERAL HEALTH SERVICES

Health Dept 304.252.8531
Fax 304.252.0466
Web ....www.wvdhhr.org
E-mail ....raleighlhd@wvdhhr.org
1602 Harper Rd, Beckley, WV 25801-3310
Stan Walls, Rs Admin

MENTAL HEALTH SERVICES

FMR Mental Health Council 304.256.7100
Fax 304.256.7111
Web ....www.fmrs.org
E-mail ....karmentrout@fmrs.org
101 S Eisenhower Dr, Beckley, WV 25801-4995
Kathy Armentrout, Substance Abuse Coordinator

JUSTICE AGENCY

Probation Ofc 304.255.9133
Fax 304.255.9363
Web ....www.wvcrt.org
E-mail ....johnvoloski@wvcrt.org
117 Prince St, Beckley, WV 25801-4512
John Voloski, JPO

COURTS

Circuit Court 304.255.9135
Fax 304.255.9353
215 Main St, Beckley, WV 25801
Honorable John A. Hutchison, Judge

POLICE AND SHERIFF

Sheriff's Ofc 304.255.9300
Fax 304.255.9155
201 S Eisenhower Dr, Beckley, WV 25801
R S Tanner, Sheriff

EDUCATION SERVICES

Central Head Start 304.253.8801
Fax 304.255.9343
114 Lebanon Ln, Beckley, WV 25801
Sharon Meadows, Director

Special Education 304.256.4559
Fax 304.256.4715
Web www.access.k12.wv.us
E-mail ....cyhicks@access.k12.wv.us
301 Park Ave, Beckley, WV 25801
Cynthia Corley-hicks, Director

Randolph County

GENERAL HEALTH SERVICES

Health Dept 304.636.0396
Fax 304.637.5902
Web ....www.wvdhhr.org
E-mail ....randolphlhd@wvdhhr.org
32 Randolph Ave, Ste 101, Elkins, WV 26241-3815
Mary S. Boyd, Md, Medical Director

WIC Program 304.636.8100
Fax 304.636.8101
Web ....www.wvdhhr.org
E-mail ....sandramiller@wvdhhr.org
107 Davis St, Elkins, WV 26241-4026
Sandra Miller, Project Director

COURTS

Circuit Court 304.636.2765
Fax 304.637.3700
Web ....www.state.wv.us
2 Randolph Ave Ste 5, Elkins, WV 26241-4091
Honorable Jaymie Godwin-wilsong, Judge

© 2011 Dorland Health

Ritchie County

GENERAL HEALTH SERVICES

Mid-Ohio Valley Health Dept **304.643.2917**
Fax 304.643.4092
Web ....www.wvdhhr.org
   125 W Main St, Harrisville, WV 26362-1030
Tonia Lang, Nursing Supervisor

POLICE AND SHERIFF

Sheriff Ofc **304.643.2262**
Fax 304.643.4208
E-mail ....ritchiesheriff@hotmail.com
   109 E North St, Harrisville, WV 26362
Bryan Backus, Sheriff

Roane County

GENERAL HEALTH SERVICES

Mid-Ohio Valley Health Dept **304.927.1480**
Fax 304.927.6043
   200 E Main St, Spencer, WV 25276
Linda Carper, Office Assistant

COURTS

Circuit Court **304.927.2750**
Fax 304.927.2164
   200 Main St Ste 5, Spencer, WV 25276
Honorable David W. Nibert, Judge

POLICE AND SHERIFF

Sheriffs Ofc **304.927.3410**
Fax 304.927.4160
   200 Main St Ste 3, Spencer, WV 25276
Mikel Harper, Sheriff

Summers County

GENERAL HEALTH SERVICES

Health Dept **304.466.3388**
Fax 304.466.1230
E-mail ....sandraball@wvdhhr.org
   151 Pleasant St, Hinton, WV 25951
Sandra Ball, Rn, Nursing Director

COURTS

Circuit Court **304.466.7103**
Fax 304.466.7124
   120 Ballengee and Park Ave, Hinton, WV 25951
Honorable Robert A. Irons, Judge

POLICE AND SHERIFF

Sheriff's Ofc **304.466.7111**
Fax 304.466.7139
E-mail ....summerssheriff900@gmail.com
   123 Temple St, Hinton, WV 25951
Ed Dolphin, Sheriff

Taylor County

COURTS

Circuit Court **304.265.2480**
Fax 304.265.1404
   214 W Main St Rm 104, Grafton, WV 26354-1387
Honorable Alan D. Moats, Director

Tucker County

SOCIAL SERVICES

Health & Human Resources **304.478.3212**
Fax 304.478.4514
Web ....www.wvdhhr.org
   9346 Seneca Trl, Parsons, WV 26287
Michael Phillips, Community Services Manager

GENERAL HEALTH SERVICES

Health Dept **304.478.3572**
Fax 304.478.3864
   290 Sunnyside Ln, Parsons, WV 26287
Kimberly D Ledden, Rn, Public Health Nurse

POLICE AND SHERIFF

Sheriff's Dept **304.478.2321**
Fax 304.478.4819
   341 2nd St, Parsons, WV 26287-1242
Thomas D. Felton, Sheriff

Tyler County

POLICE AND SHERIFF

Sheriff's Ofc **304.758.4229**
Fax 304.758.0754
   121 Court St, Middlebourne, WV 26149
Earl P Kendal, Sheriff

Upshur County

GENERAL HEALTH SERVICES

Health Dept **304.472.2810**
Fax 304.472.2945
   15 N Locust St, Buckhannon, WV 26201
Josh Marsh, Administrator

COURTS

Circuit Court **304.472.2370**
Fax 304.472.2168
E-mail ....dpguadetupshurcounty.org
   38 W Main St Rm 304, Buckhannon, WV 26201
Brian Guadet, Circuit Clerk

POLICE AND SHERIFF

Sheriff's Dept **304.472.1180**
Fax 304.472.4547
   38 W Main St Rm 103, Buckhannon, WV 26201-2273
Virgil Miller, Sheriff

Wayne County

COURTS

Circuit Court **304.272.6360**
Fax 304.272.3496
   700 Hendricks St, Wayne, WV 25570
Honorable Darrell Pratt, Chief Circuit Court Judge

POLICE AND SHERIFF

Sheriff's Dept **304.272.6378**
Fax 304.272.5200
   Court House Square on Hendricks Street, Wayne,
   WV 25570
Greg Farley, Sheriff

EDUCATION SERVICES

Cabell Midland Early Head Start **304.743.7419**
Fax 304.743.7577
Web www.access.k12.wv.us
E-mail ....ktickett@access.k12.wv.us
   2300 US Rt 60 E, Owna, WV 25545
Mr. Tickett K, Director

Webster County

SOCIAL SERVICES

**Dept Of Health And Human
Resources** **304.847.2861**
Fax 304.847.7244
Web ....www.wvdhhr.org
   110 N Main St, Ste 201, Webster Springs,
   WV 26288-1058
Sharon Clayton, Intake Supervisor

GENERAL HEALTH SERVICES

Health Dept **304.847.5483**
Fax 304.847.7692
   112 Bell St, #C, Webster Springs, WV 26288
Rhonda Hayhurst, Nursing Supervisor

COURTS

Circuit Court **304.847.2421**
Fax 304.847.2062
   2 Court Sq Ste G4, Webster Springs, WV 26288-1095
Honorable Jack Alsop, Judge

POLICE AND SHERIFF

Sheriff's Ofc **304.847.2006**
Fax 304.847.2647
   2 Court Sq Ste G3, Webster Springs, WV 26288-1096
Jerry Hamrick, Sheriff

EDUCATION SERVICES

Cowen Head Start Ctr **304.226.5991**
Fax 304.226.5635
Web ....www.ncwvcaa.org
E-mail ....bmorris@ncwvcaa.org
   60 Railroad Ave, Cowen, WV 26206
Betsey Morris, Director

Wetzel County

GENERAL HEALTH SERVICES

Health Dept **304.337.2001**
Fax 304.337.2004
E-mail ....dorothylockett@wvdhhr.org
   425 S 4th Ave Ste 1, Paden City, WV 26159-1200
Dorothy Lockett, Rn, Assistant Administrator

POLICE AND SHERIFF

Sheriff's Ofc **304.455.2430**
Fax 304.455.2975
Web ....www.usfa.fema.gov
   200 Main St, New Martinsville, WV 26155
James Hoskins, Sheriff

Wirt County

GENERAL HEALTH SERVICES

Health Dept **304.275.3131**
Fax 304.275.6590
Web ....www.movhd.com
   Lower Washington St, Elizabeth, WV 26143
Gladys Mace, Public Health Nurse

POLICE AND SHERIFF

Sheriff's Ofc **304.275.4222**
Fax 304.275.3500
   1 Courthouse Square, Elizabeth, WV 26143
Keith Wilson, Sheriff

Wood County

GENERAL HEALTH SERVICES

Health Dept **304.485.7374**
Fax 304.485.7383
Web ....www.wvdhhr.org
E-mail ....janiemoore@wvdhhr.org
   211 6th St, Parkersburg, WV 26101-5191
Janie Moore, Rn, Nursing Director

JUSTICE AGENCY

Probation Svcs **304.424.1711**
Fax 304.424.1715
E-mail ....larry.johnson@courtswv.gov
   Wood County Judicial Bldg, Room 436, Parkersburg,
   WV 26101
Larry Johnson, Chief JPO

West Virginia

COURTS

Circuit Court 304.424.1700
Fax.......................................304.424.1804
  2 Government Sq Ste 133, WOOD COUNTY JUDICIAL
  BUILDING, Parkersburg, WV 26101-5393
  Honorable Robert Waters, Judge

EDUCATION SERVICES

Special Education 304.420.9655
Fax.......................................304.420.9689
Web...................................www.netassoc.net
  1210 13th St, Parkersburg, WV 26101
  Yvonne Santin, Special Education Services Director

Wyoming County

GENERAL HEALTH SERVICES

Health Dept 304.732.7941
Fax.......................................304.732.6709
  Bank & Cedar St, Pineville, WV 24874
  Gena Carter, Director Of Nursing

POLICE AND SHERIFF

Sheriff's Ofc 304.732.8000
Fax.......................................304.732.9659
Web...www.wvu.edu
E-mail ....cs.parker@mail.wvu.edu
  100 Main St, Pineville, WV 24874
  Randall Aliss, Sheriff

SPECIAL SERVICES AGENCIES

ADOPTION AGENCIES

Burlington United Methodist Family Svcs 304.720.1904
Fax.......................................304.720.1905
Web...www.bumfs.org
E-mail ....adoption@bumfs.org
  900 Washington St E, Charleston, WV 25301-1755
  Jennifer Brown, Adoption Consultant

Children's Home Society of West Virginia 304.346.0795
Fax.......................................304.346.1062
Web...www.childhswv.org
  P.O. Box 2942, Charleston, WV 25330
  COA accredited organization.

CRISS-CROSS, Inc. (CCCS of North Central
WV) 304.623.0921
Fax.......................................304.624.4089
Web......................................www.criss-crosswv.org
  209 West Pike Street, Suite B, Clarksburg, WV 26301
  COA accredited organization.

Davis-Stuart, Inc. 304.647.5577
Fax.......................................304.647.5727
Web..www.davis-stuart.org
  RR 02, Box 188A, Lewisburg, WV 24901
  COA accredited organization.

Nationaly Youth Advocate Program 304.345.6897
Fax.......................................304.343.1686
Web...www.nyap.org
  400 Allan Dr, Ste 400, Charleston, WV 25302-1702
  Patty Lewis, Director

ADVOCACY RESOURCES

Team For WV Children 304.523.9587
Fax.......................................304.523.9595
Web...www.teamwv.org
E-mail ....team@teamwv.org
  625 4th Ave, Huntington, WV 25717
  Laurie Mckeown, Executive Director

BEHAVIORAL HEALTH TREATMENT

Behavioral Health Mgmt 304.232.7232
Fax.......................................304.232.7245
  1025 Main St Ste 708, Wheeling, WV 26003-2739
  Dr. John Mcfadden, CEO

Braley & Thompson Inc 304.720.1300
Fax.......................................304.720.1378
Web...www.btkids.biz
E-mail ....kathy-baird@btkids.biz
  1 Dunbar Plz Ste A, Dunbar, WV 25064-3038
  Kathy Baird, Director

Cammack Children's Center, Inc. 304.523.3497
Fax.......................................304.529.3882
Web...www.cammack.org
  64 West 6th Avenue, Huntington, WV 25701-1751
  COA accredited organization.

Elkins Mountain Schools 304.637.8000
Web...emtns.org
E-mail ....td@emtns.org
  100 Bell Street, Elkins, WV 26241
  Ms. Christi Flynn, Accreditation Manager
  Joint Commission accredited organization.

Highland Hospital 304.926.1673
Web.....................................www.highlandhosp.com
E-mail ....qualityassurance@highlandhosp.com
  300 56th Street Southeast, Charleston, WV 25304
  Ms. Kimberly Mundy, Accreditation Manager
  Joint Commission accredited organization.

KVC Behavioral Healthcare West Virginia,
Inc. 913.334.0294
Web...www.kvc.org
E-mail ....mloehr@kvc.org
  200 Bradford Street, Charleston, WV 25301
  Mr. Matt Loehr, Accreditation Manager
  Joint Commission accredited organization.

Olympic Center Preston, Inc. 304.329.2400
E-mail ....pvgarrett3@aol.com
  Route 7 West, Manown, Kingwood, WV 26537
  Ms. Paula Garrett, Accreditation Manager
  Joint Commission accredited organization.

Prestera Center for Mental Health Services,
Inc. 304.525.1522
Fax.......................................304.525.2040
Web...www.prestera.org
  3375 U.S. Route 60 East, Huntington, WV 25705
  CARF accredited programs available.

River Park Hospital 304.526.9111
Web.....................................www.riverparkhospital.net
E-mail ....karen.yost@uhsinc.com
  1230 Sixth Avenue, Huntington, WV 25701
  Mrs. Karen Yost, Accreditation Manager
  Joint Commission accredited organization.

Shenandoah Valley Medical System, Inc. 304.263.4999
E-mail ....rjacobs@svms.net
  99 Tavern Road, Martinsburg, WV 25401
  Mr. Randy Jacobs, Accreditation Manager
  Joint Commission accredited organization.

Southern Highlands Community Mental Health
Ctr 304.425.9541
Fax.......................................304.425.1332
Web...www.shcmhc.com
  200 12th St Ext, Princeton, WV 24740-2398
  Patty Flanagan, Regional Youth Specialist

St. John's/St. Vincent's Home, Inc. 304.242.5633
Fax.......................................304.243.4911
Web.....................................www.stjohnshomeforchildren.org
  141 Key Avenue, Wheeling, WV 26003
  COA accredited organization.

United Summit Ctr 304.623.5661
Fax.......................................304.623.2989
Web...www.uscwv.org
  6 Hospital Plz, Clarksburg, WV 26301
  Diane Peasak, Case Management Director

West Virginia University Hospitals, Inc. 304.598.4200
Web...www.wvuh.com
E-mail ....briggsf@wvuh.com
  1 Medical Center Drive, Morgantown, WV 26506
  Dr. Frank Briggs, Accreditation Manager
  Joint Commission accredited organization.

CHILDREN'S HOSPITAL

Bluefield Regional Medical Center 304.327.1100
  500 Cherry St, Bluefield, WV 24701

Cabell Huntington Hospital 304.526.2000
  1340 Hal Greer Blvd, Huntington, WV 25701
  Dough Sheils, Director

Camden-Clark Memorial Hospital 304.424.2111
  800 Garfield Ave, Parkersburg, WV 26101
  Mike King, Chief Executive Officer

Charleston Area Medical Center 304.388.5432
  501 Morris St, Charleston, WV 25301
  Ron Moore, Nursing Director

City Hospital 304.264.1000
  Dry Run Rd, Martinsburg, WV 25401
  Tony Zelenka, Chief Executive Officer

Davis Memorial Hospital 304.636.3300
  Gorman Ave & Reed St, Elkins, WV 26241
  Mark Doak, Chief Executive Officer

Fairmont General Hospital 304.367.7100
  1325 Locust Ave, Fairmont, WV 26554

Grant Memorial Hospital 304.257.1026
  Route 55 W, Petersburg, WV 26847
  Marybeth Barr, Chief Executive Officer

Greenbrier Valley Medical Center 304.647.4411
  202 Maplewood Ave, Ronceverte, WV 24970

Logan Regional Medical Center 304.831.1101
  20 Hospital Dr, Logan, WV 25601
  John Walker, Chief Executive Officer

Memorial Hospital 304.847.5682
  324 Miller Mountain Dr, Webster Springs, WV 26288
  Annette Keenan, Chief Executive Officer

Monongalia General Hospital 304.598.1200
  1200 J D Anderson Dr, Morgantown, WV 26505
  Darryl Duncan, Chief Executive Officer

Ohio Valley Medical Center 304.234.0123
  2000 Eoff St, Wheeling, WV 26003
  George Couch, Executive Director

Plateau Medical Center 304.469.8600
  430 Main St, Oak Hill, WV 25901
  Chad Hatfield, Chief Executive Officer

Princeton Community Hospital 304.487.7000
  122 12th St, Princeton, WV 24740
  Wayne Griffith, Chief Executive Officer

Raleigh General Hospital 304.256.4100
  1710 Harper Rd, Beckley, WV 25801

West Virginia

Reynolds Memorial Hospital 304.845.3211
  800 Wheeling Ave, Glen Dale, WV 26038
  Jay Prager, Chief Executive Officer

St Joseph's Hospital 304.424.4111
  1824 Murdoch Ave, Parkersburg, WV 26101
  Mike King, Director

St Joseph's Hospital of Buckhannon 304.473.2000
  1 Amalia Dr, Buckhannon, WV 26201
  Sue Johnson- Phillippe, President/CEO

St Mary's Medical Center 304.526.1234
  2900 First Ave, Huntington, WV 25702

Summersville Memorial Hospital 304.872.2891
  400 Fairview Heights Rd, Summersville, WV 26651
  Debbie Hill, Chief Executive Officer

Thomas Memorial Hospital 304.766.3600
  4605 MacCorkle Ave SW, South Charleston,
  WV 25309
  Steve Dexter, President/CEO

Weirton Medical Center 304.797.6000
  601 Colliers Way, Weirton, WV 26062
  Donna Robinson, Human Resource Generalist

West Virginia University Hospitals 304.598.4000
  1 Medical Center Dr, Morgantown, WV 26506

Wheeling Hospital 304.243.3000
  1 Medical Park, Wheeling, WV 26003
  Ronald Viloi, Chief Executive Officer

COUNSELING SERVICES

Try Again Homes Inc........................304.363.5863
Fax 304.363.1345
E-mail ....tryagainhomes@bizmaa.rr.com
  1800 Locust Ave, Fairmont, WV 26554-1237
  Alison Leon, Clinical Director

CRISIS & SHELTER CARE

Branches-Domestic Violence Shelter 304.529.2382
Fax 304.529.2398
E-mail ....branchesdv@aol.com
  PO Box 403, Huntington, WV 25708-0403
  Jeniffer Borda, Director

Burlington United Methodist Family Svcs,
Inc 304.289.6010
Fax 304.289.3903
Web ....www.bumfs.org
E-mail ....mprice@bumfs.org
  1 Rainbow Ln, Burlington, WV 26710
  Michael Price, President/CEO

Children's Home Society Of West Virginia 304.346.0795
Fax 304.346.1062
Web ....www.childhsw.org
  1422 Kanawha Blvd E, Charleston, WV 25301-3002
  George L. James, Director Of Social Services

Daymark 304.340.3675
Fax 304.340.3595
Web ....www.daymark.org
E-mail ....vicki@daymark.org
  1592 Washington St E Ste 2, Charleston,
  WV 25311-2508
  Vicki Pleasant, Director Of Programs

Family Crisis Ctr-Domestic Violence 304.788.6061
Fax 304.788.6374
Web ....www.citynet.net
  207 Poplar Dr, Keyser, WV 26726
  Penny Sanders, Director

Family Refuge Ctr-Domestic Violence 304.645.6334
Fax 304.645.6586
Web ....www.familyrefugecenter.com
E-mail ....frc@wvdsl.net
  213 S Jefferson St, Lewisburg, WV 24901
  Janeal Quinnell, Director

Florence Crittenton Home and Svcs 304.242.7060
Fax 304.242.7203
Web ....www.florencecrittenton.net
E-mail ....kszafran@comcast.net
  2606 National Rd, Wheeling, WV 26003
  Kathy F. Szafran, CEO

Helinski Emergency Shelter 304.843.1577
Fax 304.843.5123
E-mail ....helinski@ysswv.com
  116 Helinski Rd, Moundsville, WV 26041-9402
  Margo Scott, Director

Rape And Domestic Violence Info Ctr 304.292.5100
Fax 304.292.0204
Web ....www.rdvic.org
E-mail ....rdvic99@earthlink.net
  160 Chancery Row, Ste 4, Morgantown, WV 26505
  Judy King Smith, Director

Samaritan House Emergency Shelter 304.233.2480
Fax 304.233.2882
Web ....www.ysswv.com
E-mail ....samaritan@ysswv.com
  1050 Eoff St, Wheeling, WV 26003-2923
  Margo Scott, Progamme Manager

Stop Abusive Family Enviroments, Inc 304.436.8117
Fax 304.436.6528
Web ....www.safewv.org
E-mail ....jthacker@yahoo.com
  Route 7, Welch, WV 24801
  Jennifer Thacker, Director

Task Force Dom Viol-Hope Inc 304.367.1100
Fax 304.367.0362
Web ....www.ma.rr.com
E-mail ....hsuttonhope@ma.rr.com
  1511 Pleasant Valley Rd, Fairmont, WV 26554
  Harriet Sutton, Director

The Lighthouse-Domestic Violence Prog 304.797.7233
Fax 304.748.0741
Web ....www.lighthousedvs.org
E-mail ....Julie_Advocate@Yahoo.Com
  PO Box 275, Weirton, WV 26062-0275
  Julie Oslewski, Director

Tug Valley Recovery Shelter-Domestic
Violence 304.235.6121
Fax 304.235.6167
E-mail ....kryan@cyberriver.net
  515 Harvey St, Williamson, WV 25661
  Kimberley Ryan, Director

West Virginia Coalition Against Domestic
Violence 304.965.3552
Fax 304.965.3572
Web ....www.wvcadv.org
E-mail ....tthomas@wvcadv.org
  5004 Elk River Rd S, Elkview, WV 25071
  Tanya Thomas, Team Coordinator

Women's Resource Ctr-Domestic Violence 304.255.2559
Fax 304.255.1585
E-mail ....health@wrc.org
  4150 Campbell St, Glen White, WV 25804
  Patricia Bailey, Director

Youth Svcs Ctr 304.599.2293
Fax 304.599.1098
  440 Elmer Prince Dr, Morgantown, WV 26505
  Christy Riggs, Executive Director

FOSTER CARE AGENCIES

Braley and Thompson Inc 304.722.6733
Fax 304.333.2323
  1 Dunbar Plz PO Box 484, Dunbar, WV 25064

Burlington United Methodist Family Servi 304.265.1338
Fax 304.265.1575
E-mail mprice2bumfs.org
  RR 3 Box 346A, Grafton, WV 26354
  Michael Price, Chief Executive Officer

Errands of Mercy Inc 304.237.6183
  305 Jasper Dr, Beckley, WV 25801

Greenbrier River Valley Foster 304.645.3248
E-mail ....kids-r-us@hotmail.com

West Virginia Foster Care Association 304.562.0723
E-mail ....drogers@missionwv.org
  168 Midland Trail Ste 1, Hurricane, WV 25526
  David Rogers, Executive Director

PEDIATRIC HOME CARE

Interim Healthcare 304.598.8900
Fax 304.598.7611
  1111 Van Voorhis Rd, 2nd Fl Ste 2, Morgantown,
  WV 26506
  Cheryl Sterner, Director

SOCIAL SERVICES

Catholic Charities Community Svcs 304.905.9860
Fax 304.233.9293
Web ....www.catholic.charities.wv.org
E-mail ....msliterhays@ccwv.org
  2000 Main St, Wheeling, WV 26003
  Mark Sliter-hays, Director

Central Child Care of West Virginia 304.382.0797
Fax 304.382.0786
E-mail ....cccwvsmidkiff@suddenlinkmail.com
  701 Virginia St W, Charleston, WV 25302
  Sharon Midkiff, Director

Child Care Resource Ctr 304.232.1603
Fax 304.232.1604
Web ....www.ccrcwv.com
E-mail ....aprilboring@wvdhhr.org
  1025 Main St, Ste 510, Wheeling, WV 26003
  Tracie Kenney, CEO

Choices CCR&R 304.485.2668
Fax 304.485.7024
Web ....www.wvdhhr.org/choices
E-mail ....karen.l.bentz@wv.gov
  4421 Emerson Ave Ste 102, Parkersburg,
  WV 26104-1200
  Karen Bentz, Director

Crittenton Services, Inc....................304.242.7060
Fax 304.242.7076
Web ....www.florencecrittenton.net
  2606 National Road, Wheeling, WV 26003
  COA accredited organization.

Daymark, Incorporated 304.340.3675
Fax 304.340.3595
Web ....www.daymark.org
  1592 Washington Street East, Suite 2, Charleston,
  WV 25311
  COA accredited organization.

Elkins Mountain School 304.637.7400
Fax 304.636.4694
Web ....www.emtns.org
  100 Bell St, Elkins, WV 26241-3700
  Pam Channel, Administrative Director

Golden Girl, Inc. 304.453.1401
Fax 304.453.6273
Web ....www.gggh.org
  P.O. Box 876, Ceredo, WV 25507
  COA accredited organization.

Goodwill Industries of KYOWVA Area, Inc.....304.525.7034
Fax 304.525.7038
Web ....www.goodwillhunting.org
  P.O. Box 7365, Huntington, WV 25776-7365
  COA accredited organization.

Link Child Care Resource & Referral 304.523.9540
Fax 304.697.4821
Web ....www.wvdhhr.org/link
  611 7th Ave Ste 200, Huntington, WV 25701-2131
  Mary Bridget, Director

West Virginia

Mountainheart Child Care Svcs **800.834.7082**
Fax 304.682.8274
Web ....www.mountain-heart.org
E-mail ....esmith@mountain-heart.org
   Rte 85, Koppeston, WV 24854
   Earl Smith, Executive Director

Youth Academy, LLC **304.363.3341**
Fax 304.363.3342
Web ....www.academyprograms.org
   Academy Programs, 7 Crosswind Drive, Fairmont,
   WV 26554
   COA accredited organization.

SPECIAL NEEDS

American Foundation for the Blind **304.523.8651**
E-mail ....techctr@afb.net
   949 3rd Ave Ste 200, Huntington, WV 25701
   Mark Uslan, Director

Autism Training Center **304.696.2332**
   1 John Marshall Dr, Huntington, WV 25755
   President Kopp, Chief Executive Officer

Brain Injury Association **304.766.4892**
   PO Box 574, Institute, WV 25112

Congress of Parents & Teachers **304.420.9576**
E-mail ....wv_office@pta.org
   PO Box 3557, Parkersburg, WV 26103

Easter Seals Rehabilitation Center, Inc. **304.242.1390**
Fax 304.243.5880
Web ....www.wv.easterseals.com
   1305 National Road, Wheeling, WV 26003
   CARF accredited programs available.

**Medical Rehabilitation Center at Charleston Area Medical
Center** **304.388.7626**
Fax 304.388.7864
Web ....www.camc.org
   501 Morris Street, Charleston, WV 25301
   CARF accredited programs available.

Mental Health Association **304.340.3512**
E-mail ....mha@wvinter.net
   1 United Way Sq, Charleston, WV 25301

Mountain State Parents-CAN **800.244.5385**
E-mail ....tisaly@mspcan.org
   1201 Garfield St, McMechen, WV 26040

Parent-Educator Resource Center **304.263.5717**
E-mail ....bcperc@yahoo.com
   509 W Martin St, Martinsburg, WV 25401

West Virginia Family Support Program **304.558.3616**
E-mail ....cassandra.l.tolliver@wv.gov
   350 Capitol St Rm 350, Charleston, WV 25301

West Virginia Health Consumers Assn **800.598.8847**
E-mail ....lorieroberts@wvmhca.org
   910 Quarrier St Ste 414, Charleston, WV 25301
   Dr. Muscari, Executive Director

Wisconsin

Scott Walker, Governor
Office of the Governor
115 E. State Capitol PO Box 7863
Madison, WI 53707
608.266.1212
608.267.8983 (Fax)
governor@wisconsin.gov
www.wisconsin.gov

Kris Moelter, Juvenile Justice Specialist
Office of Justice Assistance
1 S. Pinckney St. Suite 600
Madison, WI 53702
608.261.6626
608.266.6676 (Fax)
kristina.moelter@wisconsin.gov

Dierdre Wilson Garton, SAG Chair
1 S. Pinckney St. Suite 600
Madison, WI 53702
608.661.9106
608.661.9107 (Fax)
Dierdrewgarton@yahoo.com

CRISIS NUMBERS

Child Abuse Reporting . . .608.256.3374

STATE SERVICES

SOCIAL SERVICES

Adoption Search	608.261.8316
Fax	608.264.6750
Web	www.dhfs.state.wi.us
E-mail	mitchms@dhfs.state.wi.us

1 W Wilson St, Madison, WI 53703-3445
Mark Mitchell, Policy Coordination Section

Bureau of Early Care Regulation WI	608.266.9314
Fax	608.267.7252

201 E Washington B 200, Madison, WI 53704
Anne Carmody, Program Specialist

Wisconsin Dept of Health Family Services	608.267.3905
Fax	608.266.6836

201 E Washington Ave 2nd Fl, PO Box 8916,
Madison, WI 53706

GENERAL HEALTH SERVICES

Child & Youth w Spec Health Care Needs WI	608.266.3674
Fax	608.266.8925
E-mail	sharon.fleischfresser@dhs.wisconsin.gov

One W Wilson St, PO Box 2659, Madison, WI 53701
Sharon Fleischfresser, Director

Children With Special Health Care Needs

Program	608.267.2945
Fax	608.267.3824
Web	www.dhfs.wi.gov
E-mail	peggy.Helmquest@dhfs.wi.gov

1 W Wilson St, Madison, WI 53703-3445
Peggy Helmquest, Consultant

Dept of Health Svcs	608.266.9622
Fax	608.266.7882
Web	www.dhs.state.wi.us
E-mail	dennis.smith@wisconsin.gov

1 W Wilson St Rm 650, Madison, WI 53707
Dennis Smith, Secretary

Maternal and Child Health WI	608.266.3890
Fax	608.267.3824
E-mail	Linda.Hale@dhs.wisconsin.gov

One West Wilson St Rm 351, Madison, WI 53701
Linda Hale, Director

Wisconsin Medical Society	608.442.3800
Fax	608.442.3802
Web	www.wisconsinmedicalsociety.org

330 E Lakeside St, Madison, WI 53715
Susan Turney, Executive Vp

Wisconsin Ofc of Rural Health	608.261.1883
Fax	608.261.1893
Web	www.worh.org

310 N Midvale Blvd Ste 301, Madison, WI 53705
John Eich, Director

MENTAL HEALTH SERVICES

Div of Vocational Rehabilitation	608.261.0050
Fax	608.266.1133
Web	www.dwd.state.wi.us
E-mail	charlene.dwyer@dwd.state.wi.us

201 E Washington Ave, Rm A100, Madison,
WI 53702-0001
Charlene Dwyer, Administrator

JUSTICE AGENCY

Div Of Juvenile Corrections	608.240.5900
Fax	608.240.3370
Web	www.wi-doc.com/index_juvenile.htm

3099 E Washington Ave, Madison, WI 53708
Margart Carpenter, Administrator

Div of Law Enforcement Svcs	608.266.1221
Fax	608.266.1656
Web	www.doj.state.wi.us

17 W Main St, Madison, WI 53703
Brian O'Keefe, Administrator

Teen Court	715.736.0940
Fax	715.736.0217
Web	www.bcrjp.org
E-mail	bcrjp@chibardun.net

2850 College Dr, Rice Lake, WI 54868-2445
Ted Lewis, Executive Director

POLICE AND SHERIFF

Calumet Co. Sheriff's Dept	920.849.2335
Fax	920.849.1431
E-mail	sheriff@co.calumet.wi.us

206 Court St, Chilton, WI 53014-1127
Mark Ott, Sheriff

EDUCATION SERVICES

Homeless Education	608.261.6322
Fax	608.267.0364
Web	www.dpi.wi.gov
E-mail	mary.maronek@dpi.wi.gov

125 S Webster St, Madison, WI 53703
Mary Maronek, Coordinator

Special Education	715.261.1980
Fax	715.261.1981
Web	www.mcspecialeducation.com
E-mail	ehartwig@dwave.net

1200 Lake View Dr Ste 350, Wausau, WI 54403-6780
Eric P. Hartwig, Ph.d, Administrator Of Pupil Services

Special Education Team WI	608.266.1781
Fax	608.267.3746
E-mail	stephanie.petska@dpi.wi.gov

125 S Webster St, Madison, WI 53707
Stephanie Petska, Director

WI Dept of Public Instruction	608.266.3584
Fax	608.266.5188
E-mail	michael.thompson@dpi.wi.gov

125 S Webster St, PO Box 7841, Madison, WI 53707
Michael Thompson, Director

Wisconsin Ctr for the Blind and Visually

Impaired	608.758.6100
Fax	608.758.6161
E-mail	dan.wenzel@wcbvi.k12.wi.us

1700 W State St, Janesville, WI 53546
Dan Winzel, Director

Wisconsin School for the Deaf and Educational Svcs Ctr for

The Deaf and Hard of Hearing	262.728.7120
Fax	262.728.7160
Web	www.wsd.k12.wi.us
E-mail	alex.slappey@dpi.state.wi.us

309 W Walworth Ave, Delavan, WI 53115
Alex Slappey, Director

LABOR & WORKFORCE EDUCATION

Work Force Development	608.266.3131
Fax	608.266.1784
Web	www.dwd.state.wi.us

201 E Washington Ave, Madison, WI 53702-0001
Scott Baumbach, Director

Wisconsin

COUNTY SERVICES

Adams County

COURTS

Circuit Court..........................608.339.4215
Fax.....................................608.339.4596
Web.....................................www.wicourts.gov
E-mail.................charles.pollex@wicourts.gov
402 Main St, Friendship, WI 53934-8014
Honorable Charles A. Pollex, Judge

Ashland County

SOCIAL SERVICES

Bad River Indian Child Welfare..............715.682.7136
Fax.....................................715.682.7100
E-mail.....................................icw@badriver.com
PO Box 55, Odanah, WI 54861-0055
Catherine Pat Blanchard, ICWA Coordinator

Health & Human Svcs...................715.682.7004
Fax.....................................715.682.7924
Web.....................................www.ashborncounty.com
E-mail.................achsd@hsd.co.ashland.wi.us
630 Sanborn Ave, Ashland, WI 54806-3537
Terri Perry, Human Services Director

GENERAL HEALTH SERVICES

Bad River Clinic.........................715.682.7133
Fax.....................................715.685.7848
72718 Maple St, Odanah, WI 54861
Debra Tutor, Clinic Administrator

COURTS

Circuit Court..........................715.682.7013
Fax.....................................715.682.7919
Web.....................................www.wicourts.gov
E-mail.................robert.eaton@wicourts.gov
201 Main St W Rm 307, Ashland, WI 54806-1612
Honorable Robert E. Eaton, Circuit Judge

POLICE AND SHERIFF

Sheriff's Dept.........................715.685.7640
Fax.....................................715.682.7039
E-mail.................john.kovach@co.ashland.wi.us
220 6th St E, Ashland, WI 54806-3201
James Hnath, Chief Deputy

Barron County

COURTS

Circuit Court..........................715.537.6262
Fax.....................................715.537.6269
1420 State Highway 25 N Rm 2601, Barron, WI 54812
Honorable James C. Babler, Circuit Judge

POLICE AND SHERIFF

Sheriff's Ofc.........................715.537.5814
Fax.....................................715.537.6615
Web.....................................www.co.barron.wi.us
E-mail.................chris.fitzgerald@co.barron.wi.us
1420 State Highway 25 N, Rm 1200, Barron, WI 54812
Chris Fitzgerald, Sheriff

EDUCATION SERVICES

Cornell Cesa 11 Head Start.................715.239.3301
Fax.....................................715.239.6495
400 Woodside Dr, Cornell, WI 54732
Karen Phelps, Director

Bayfield County

SOCIAL SERVICES

Dept Of Human Svcs.....................715.373.6127
Fax.....................................715.373.6130
Web.....................................www.bayfieldcounty.org
E-mail.................eskulan@bayfieldcounty.org
117 E 5th St, Washburn, WI 54891-4522
Elizabeth Skulan, Director

Indian Social Svcs Chippewa Tribe.............715.779.3726
Fax.....................................715.779.3724
88385 Pike Rd, Highway 13, Bayfield, WI 10731
Susan Crazy, Icwa Worker

GENERAL HEALTH SERVICES

Home & Health..........................715.373.6109
Fax.....................................715.373.6307
Web.....................................www.bayfieldcounty.org
E-mail.................tkramolis@bayfieldcounty.org
117 E 6th St, Washburn, WI 54891
Terri Kramolis, Health Officer

COURTS

Circuit Court..........................715.373.6118
Fax.....................................715.373.6153
E-mail.................john.anderson@wicourts.gov
117 E 5th St, Washburn, WI 54891-4522
Honorable John Anderson, Judge

POLICE AND SHERIFF

Sheriff's Ofc.........................715.373.6300
Fax.....................................715.373.6123
E-mail.................psusienka@bayfieldcounty.org
615 2nd Ave E, Washburn, WI 54891
Paul Susienka, Sheriff

EDUCATION SERVICES

Teen Court.........................715.373.6104
Fax.....................................715.373.6304
E-mail.................ian.meeker@ces.uwex.edu
117 E 5th St, Washburn, WI 54891-4522
Ian Meeker, 4-h Youth Development Educator University Of Wisconsin Extension

Brown County

SOCIAL SERVICES

Human Svcs.........................920.448.6000
Fax.....................................920.448.6166
Web.....................................www.co.brown.wi.us
E-mail.................shoup_ba@co.brown.wi.us
111 N Jefferson St, Green Bay, WI 54305-2188
Brian Shoup, Director

Indian Social Svcs Oneida Tribe.............920.490.3700
Fax.....................................920.490.3799
2640 W Point Rd, Green Bay, WI 54304
Linda Torres, Area Manager

GENERAL HEALTH SERVICES

De Pere Health Dept.....................920.339.4054
Fax.....................................920.339.2745
Web.....................................www.ci.de/pere.wi.us
E-mail.................mdorn@mail.de-pere.org
335 S Broadway, De Pere, WI 54115-2526
Mary Dorn, Director

MENTAL HEALTH SERVICES

Community Treatment Centre.............920.391.4700
Fax.....................................920.391.4870
Web.....................................www.co.brown.wi.us
3150 Gershwin Dr, Green Bay, WI 54311
Mary Johnson, Administrator

JUSTICE AGENCY

Juvenile Court Svcs.........................920.448.6136
Fax.....................................920.448.6177
111 N Jefferson St, Green Bay, WI 54305
Scott Shackelford, Supervisor

COURTS

Circuit Court..........................920.448.4155
Fax.....................................920.448.4156
Web.....................................www.co.brown.wi.us
E-mail.................peter.naze@wicourts.gov
100 S Jefferson St, Green Bay, WI 54301-4519
Honorable Peter J. Naze, Director

POLICE AND SHERIFF

Sheriff's Dept.........................920.448.4222
Fax.....................................920.448.4206
Web.....................................www.co.brown.wi.us
300 E Walnut St, Green Bay, WI 54301-5008
Dennis N. Kocken, Sheriff

Buffalo County

SOCIAL SERVICES

Dept Of Health And Human Svcs.............608.685.4412
Fax.....................................608.685.3342
E-mail.................dhhs@buffalocounty.com
407 S 2Nd St, Alma, WI 54610
Paula Stansbury, Director

COURTS

Circuit Court..........................608.685.6212
Fax.....................................608.685.6211
Web.....................................www.wisconsincourts.gov
E-mail.................roselle.schlosser@wicourts.gov
407 S 2nd St, Alma, WI 54610-9715
Roselle Schlosser, Clerk Of Court

Burnett County

SOCIAL SERVICES

Health & Human Svcs.....................715.349.7600
Fax.....................................715.349.2140
Web.....................................www.burnettcounty.org
7410 County Rd K, Ste. 280, Siren, WI 54872
Kate Peterson, Human Services Director

GENERAL HEALTH SERVICES

Health And Human Sevices.................715.349.7600
Fax.....................................715.349.2145
Web.....................................www.burnetcounty.com
E-mail.................kmpeterson@burnettcounty.org
7410 County Rd K Ste 280, Siren, WI 54872
Kathrine Peterson, Director

COURTS

Teen Court.........................715.349.2151
Fax.....................................715.349.2102
Web.....................................www.uwex.edu/ces/cty/burnett
E-mail.................marilyn.kooiker@ces.uwex.edu
7410 County Road K Ste 107, Siren, WI 54872-9067
Marilyn Kooiker, Coordinator

POLICE AND SHERIFF

Sheriff's Dept.........................715.349.2121
Fax.....................................715.349.2176
E-mail.................droland@burnettcounty.org
7410 County Road K Ste 122, Siren, WI 54872
Dean W. Roland, Sheriff

Calumet County

SOCIAL SERVICES

Public Hlth & Human Svcs **920.849.1432**
Fax 920.849.1476
E-mail ....romenesko.todd@co.calumet.wi.us
  206 Court St, Courthouse, Chilton, WI 53014
  Todd Romenesko, Human Services Director

COURTS

Circuit Court **920.849.2361**
Fax 920.849.1483
  206 Court St, Chilton, WI 53014
  Honorable Donald A. Poppy, Judge

Chippewa County

SOCIAL SERVICES

Dept Of Human Svcs **715.726.7788**
Fax 715.726.7736
Web ....www.co.chippewa.wi.gov
E-mail ....humanservices@co.chippewa.wi.us
  711 N Bridge St Ste 306, Chippewa Falls, WI 54729
  Larry Winter, Director

GENERAL HEALTH SERVICES

Public Health Nursing **715.726.7900**
Fax 715.726.7910
Web ....www.co.chippewa.wi.us/ccdth
  711 N Bridge St, Ste 222, Chippewa Falls, WI 54729
  Jean Durch, Public Health Director

COURTS

Circuit Court **715.726.7781**
Fax 715.726.7786
Web ....www.co.chippewa.wi.us
E-mail ....karen.hepfler@wicourts.gov
  711 N Bridge St Ste 1, Chippewa Falls,
  WI 54729-1845
  Karen Hepfler, Clerk Of Court

POLICE AND SHERIFF

Sheriff's Dept **715.726.7701**
Fax 715.723.6471
Web ....www.co.chippewa.wi.us
E-mail ....sheriff@co.chippewa.wi.us
  32 E Spruce St, Chippewa Falls, WI 54729-2542
  James L. Kowalczyk, Sheriff

EDUCATION SERVICES

Chippewa Cesa 11 Head Start **715.723.1211**
Fax 715.726.3983
Web www.cesa11.k12.wi.us
E-mail ....chippewahs@sbcglobal.net
  2820 E Park Ave, Chippewa Falls, WI 54729-3598
  Sue Smalley, Director

Clark County

SOCIAL SERVICES

Dept Of Social Svcs **715.743.5233**
Fax 715.743.5242
Web ....www.co.clark.wi.uf/clarkcounty/
E-mail ....ronald.schmidt@co.clark.wi.us
  517 Court St Rm 502, Neillsville, WI 54456-1976
  Ronald Schmidt, Director

COURTS

Circuit Court **715.743.5172**
Fax 715.743.5120
Web ....www.clarkcounty.gov
  517 Court St Rm 403, Neillsville, WI 54456-1977
  Steven Walter, Judicial Assistance

POLICE AND SHERIFF

Sheriff's Dept **715.743.3157**
Fax 715.743.4350
E-mail ....gregory.herrick@co.clark.wi.us
  517 Court St Rm 308, Neillsville, WI 54456
  Gregory Herrick, Sheriff

Columbia County

SOCIAL SERVICES

Health & Human Svcs **608.742.9227**
Fax 608.742.9700
Web ....www.co.columbia.wi.us
E-mail ....susan.lorenz@co.columbia.wi.us
  2652 Murphy Rd, Portage, WI 53901-1094
  Susan Lorenz, Rn, Health Director

POLICE AND SHERIFF

Sheriff's Ofc **608.742.4166**
Fax 608.742.0598
  711 E Cook St, Portage, WI 53901
  Dennis Richards, Sheriff

EDUCATION SERVICES

Fox Lake Head Start **920.928.6100**
E-mail ....foxlakehs@renewalunlimited.net
  2900 Red Fox Run, Portage, WI 53913
  Kelly Davies, Director

Crawford County

SOCIAL SERVICES

Dept Of Human Svcs **608.326.0248**
Fax 608.326.4395
Web ....www.mhtc.net
E-mail ....humanservies@crawfordcountywi.org
  225 N Beaumont Rd Ste 326, Prairie Du Chien,
  WI 53821-1445
  Daniel McWilliams, Director

COURTS

Circuit Court **608.326.0205**
Fax 608.326.0288
  220 N Beaumont Rd, Prairie Du Chien, WI 53821
  Honorable James P Czajkowski, Judge

Dane County

SOCIAL SERVICES

Human Svcs **608.242.6200**
Fax 608.242.6293
Web ....www.countyofdane.com
  1202 Northport Dr, Madison, WI 53704-2020
  Lynn Green, Director

Sun Prairie Ofc **608.837.7380**
Fax 608.837.4399
  1460 W Main St, Sun Prairie, WI 53590-1846
  Lynn Green, Director

GENERAL HEALTH SERVICES

Madison Health Dept **608.246.4516**
Fax 608.246.5619
Web ....www.publichealthmdc.com
  2705 E Washington Ave, Madison, WI 53704-5002
  Mary Jo Hussey, Aids Coordinator

JUSTICE AGENCY

Northwestern Region **608.288.3370**
Fax 608.288.3378
Web ....www.wi-doc.gov
  2909 Landmark Pl Ste 104, Madison, WI 53713-4200
  Sue Boeke, Regional Chief

COURTS

Circuit Court **608.266.4311**
Fax 608.267.8859
  215 S Hamilton St, Rm 1000, Madison, WI 53703
  Carlo Esqueda, Director

POLICE AND SHERIFF

Madison City Police Dept **608.266.4022**
Fax 608.267.1117
Web ....www.cityofmadison.com
E-mail ....nwray@cityofmadison.com
  211 S Carroll St, Madison, WI 53703
  Noble Wray, Chief

Sheriff's Dept **608.284.6800**
Fax 608.284.6163
Web ....www.danesheriff.com
  115 W Doty St Rm 2002, Madison, WI 53703
  David Mahoney, Sheriff

EDUCATION SERVICES

Special Education **608.266.1781**
Fax 608.267.3746
Web ....www.dpi.state.wi.us
E-mail ....stephanie.petska@dpi.wi.gov
  125 S Webster St, Madison, WI 53703-3474
  Stephanie Petska, Director

Dodge County

SOCIAL SERVICES

Human Svcs **920.386.3750**
Fax 920.386.3533
Web ....www.co.dodge.wi.us
E-mail ....dtitus@co.dodge.wi.us
  143 E Center St, Juneau, WI 53039
  David Titus, Director

COURTS

Circuit Court **920.386.3570**
Fax 920.386.3587
  210 W Center St, Dodge County Justice Facility,
  Juneau, WI 53039
  Honorable Andrew Bissonnette, Judge

POLICE AND SHERIFF

Sheriff's Dept **920.386.3726**
Fax 920.386.3742
E-mail ....tnehls@co.dodge.wi.us
  124 West St, Juneau, WI 53039
  Todd Nehls, Sheriff

Door County

GENERAL HEALTH SERVICES

Public Health Dept **920.746.2234**
Fax 920.746.2320
  421 Nebraska St, Sturgeon Bay, WI 54235
  Roger Tete, Social Services Director

COURTS

Circuit Court **920.746.2482**
Fax 920.746.2470
  1209 S Duluth Ave, Door County Justice Center,
  Sturgeon Bay, WI 54235
  Honorable D. Todd Ehlers Branch 1, Judge

Douglas County

SOCIAL SERVICES

Health & Human Svcs **715.395.1304**
Fax 715.395.1370
  1316 N 14th St Ste 400, Superior, WI 54880
  Pat Schenan, Executive Director

COURTS

Circuit Court Branch 1 ....**715.395.1471**
Fax 715.395.1633
Web ....www.douglascountywi.org
  1313 Belknap St Rm 303, Superior, WI 54880-2794
  Honorable Kelly Thimm, Judge

Wisconsin

POLICE AND SHERIFF

Sheriff's Dept **715.395.1371**
Fax 715.395.1503
Web .... www.ci.superior.wi.us
E-mail .... dalbect@ci.superior.wi.us
   1316 N 14th St Ste 100, Superior, WI 54880-1774
   Thomas G. Dalbec, Sheriff

EDUCATION SERVICES

Family Forum Head Start Ctr 1 .... **715.392.6286**
Fax 715.392.6286
Web .... www.familyforum.org
E-mail .... joank@familyforum.org
   1500 N 31st St, Ste 400, Superior, WI 54880
   Joan Keeler-Pellman, Director

Family Forum Head Start Ctr 2 .... **715.392.9848**
Fax 715.392.9849
E-mail .... sfabini@familyforum.org
   518 Grand Ave, Superior, WI 54880-1217
   Sue Fabini, Director

Family Forum Head Start Ctr 5 .... **715.779.5589**
Fax 715.779.5760
Web .... www.familyforum.org
E-mail .... mappel@familyforum.org
   2231 Catlin Ave Ste 4, Superior, WI 54880-5138
   Mary Appel, Director

Dunn County

GENERAL HEALTH SERVICES

Health Dept **715.232.2388**
Fax 715.232.1132
E-mail .... wmacdougall@co.dunn.wi.us
   800 Wilson Ave Rm 20 A, Menomonie, WI 54751
   Wendy Macdougall, Public Health Director

COURTS

Circuit Court **715.232.1449**
Fax 715.232.6971
   615 Stokke Pkwy Ste 1300, Menomonie, WI 54751
   Honorable William C. Stewart Jr., Judge

Eau Claire County

SOCIAL SERVICES

Human Svcs **715.839.1200**
Fax 715.831.5658
E-mail .... eccdhs@discover-net.net
   721 Oxford Ave Ste R-1, Eau Claire, WI 54702
   Roy Sargant, Director

GENERAL HEALTH SERVICES

Health Dept **715.839.4718**
Fax 715.839.1674
   720 2nd Ave, Eau Claire, WI 54703
   Kathleen Rahl, Rn, Nursing Director

Florence County

COURTS

Circuit Court **715.528.3205**
Fax 715.528.5470
Web .... www.wicourts.gov
E-mail .... robert.kennedy@wicourts.gov
   501 Lake Ave, Fllorence, WI 54121
   Honorable Robert A. Kennedy Jr., Director

Fond du Lac County

SOCIAL SERVICES

Dept Of Social Svcs **920.929.3400**
Fax 920.929.3447
   87 Vincent St, Fond Du Lac, WI 54936
   Kim Mooney, Director

GENERAL HEALTH SERVICES

Public Health Nursing **920.929.3085**
Fax 920.929.3102
Web .... www.co.fond-du-lac.wi.us
   160 S Macy St, Fond Du Lac, WI 54935-4241
   Kathy Pauly, Hiv Coordinator

POLICE AND SHERIFF

Sheriff's Dept **920.929.3390**
Fax 920.929.3918
Web .... www.co.fond-du-lac.wi.us
   180 S Macy Street, Fond du Lac, WI 54935
   Mylan C. Fink, Jr., Sheriff

Forest County

SOCIAL SERVICES

Health & Human Svcs **715.478.3371**
Fax 715.478.5171
Web .... www.co.forest.wi.us
E-mail .... csekel@forestcountydss.com
   200 E Madison St, Crandon, WI 54520-1414
   Chuck Sekel, Social Services Director

GENERAL HEALTH SERVICES

Potawatomi Health Ctr **715.478.4300**
Fax 715.478.4499
   5415 Everbodys Rd, Crandon, WI 54502
   Linda Helmick, Health Administrator

Sokaogon Chippewa Health Clinic **715.478.5180**
Fax 715.478.5904
E-mail .... paulette_smith@hotmail.com
   3144 Vanzile Rd, Crandon, WI 54520-8880
   Paulette Smith, Acting Director

COURTS

Circuit Court **715.478.2329**
Fax 715.478.2430
Web .... www.co.forest.wi.gov
   200 E Madison St, Crandon, WI 54520-1415
   Honorable Leon Stenz, Director

Grant County

GENERAL HEALTH SERVICES

Health Dept **608.723.6416**
Fax 608.723.6501
Web .... www.co.grant.wi.gov
E-mail .... jkindrai@co.grant.wi.gov
   111 S Jefferson St Ste 141, Lancaster, WI 53813-1671
   Jeff Kindrai, Health Director

COURTS

Circuit Court **608.723.2752**
Fax 608.723.7370
   130 W Maple St, Lancaster, WI 53813
   Honorable Robert P. Van De Hey, Director

Green County

GENERAL HEALTH SERVICES

Health Dept **608.328.9390**
Fax 608.325.7575
Web .... www.greencountyhealth.org
E-mail .... rwarden@greencountywi.org
   N 3150 State Hwy 81, Government Services Building,
   Monroe, WI 53566-9397
   Roann Warden, Health Officer

Green Lake County

SOCIAL SERVICES

Dept of Health and Human Svcs **920.294.4070**
Fax 920.294.4139
E-mail .... glchhs@green-lake.wi.us
   571 County Rd A, Green Lake, WI 54941
   Leroy Dissing, Deputy Director

GENERAL HEALTH SERVICES

Public Health Dept **920.294.6771**
Fax 920.294.4139
   487 Hill St, Green Lake, WI 54941
   Sue Sleezer, CPS Supervisor

COURTS

Circuit Court **920.294.4142**
   571 County Rd A, Green Lake, WI 54941
   Mark Slate, Judge

POLICE AND SHERIFF

Sheriff's Ofc **920.294.4129**
Fax 920.294.3850
   571 County Rd A, Green Lake, WI 54941
   Mark Podoll, Sheriff

Iowa County

GENERAL HEALTH SERVICES

Health Dept **608.930.9870**
Fax 608.937.0501
Web .... www.iowacounty.org
E-mail .... june.meudt@iowacounty.org
   303 W Chapel St, Dodgeville, WI 53533-1822
   June Meudt, Rn, Director

COURTS

Circuit Court **608.935.0395**
Fax 608.935.0386
E-mail .... bill.dyke@iowacounty.org
   222 N Iowa St Ste 205, Dodgeville, WI 53533
   Honorable William D. Dyke, Judge

POLICE AND SHERIFF

Sheriff's Dept **608.935.3314**
Fax 608.935.5377
Web .... www.iowacounty.org
E-mail .... sheriff@iowacounty.org
   1205 N Bequette St, Dodgeville, WI 53533-1103
   Steven R. Michek, Sheriff

Iron County

GENERAL HEALTH SERVICES

Health Dept **715.561.2191**
Fax 715.561.2836
   502 Copper St Ste 4, Hurley, WI 54534
   Zona Wick, Director

Jackson County

SOCIAL SERVICES

**Indian Social Svcs Ho-Chunk
Nation** **715.284.9851**
Fax 715.284.9486
   720 Red Iron Rd, Black River Falls, WI 54615
   Jean Day, Division Administrator

COURTS

Circuit Court **715.284.0213**
Fax 715.284.0277
   307 Main St, Black River Falls, WI 54615
   Grant Allen, Teen Court Coordinator

POLICE AND SHERIFF

Sheriff's Ofc **715.284.9009**
Fax 715.284.0252
E-mail .... sheriff@co.jackson.wi.us
   30 N 3rd St, Black River Falls, WI 54615
   Duane M. Waldera, Sheriff

Jefferson County

GENERAL HEALTH SERVICES

Public Health Dept **920.674.7275**
Fax 920.674.7477
   1541 Annex Rd, Jefferson, WI 53549
   Gail Scott, Health Officer/director

Watertown Health Dept 920.262.8090
Fax 920.262.8096
Web .... www.ci.watertown.wi.us
　515 S 1st St, Watertown, WI 53094-4409
　Carol Quest, Rn, Health Officer

COURTS

Circuit Court 920.674.7150
Fax 920.674.7425
　320 S Main St, Jefferson, WI 53549
　Honorable William H. Hue, Judge

POLICE AND SHERIFF

Jefferson Co. Sheriff's Ofc 920.674.7310
Fax 920.674.7126
E-mail .... paulm@co.jefferson.wi.us
　411 S Center Ave, Jefferson, WI 53549
　Paul S. Milbrath, Sheriff

Juneau County

COURTS

Circuit Court 608.847.9356
Fax 608.847.9360
E-mail .... jubge.roemer@wicourts.gov
　200 Oak St, Mauston, WI 53948
　Honorable Daniel Roemer, Director

POLICE AND SHERIFF

Sheriff's Dept 608.847.5649
Fax 608.847.9401
　200 Oak St, Mauston, WI 53948-1365
　Brent H. Oleson, Sheriff

Kenosha County

SOCIAL SERVICES

Div Of Disability Svcs 262.605.6646
Fax 262.605.6649
Web .... www.co.kenosha.wi.us
　8600 Sheridan Rd Ste 500, Kenosha, WI 53143
　Laverne Jaros, Director

GENERAL HEALTH SERVICES

Health Dept 262.605.6700
Fax 262.605.6715
Web .... www.co.kenosha.wi.us
　8600 Sheridan Rd Ste 600, Kenosha, WI 53143-6515
　Frank Matto, Health Director

JUSTICE AGENCY

Juvenile Intake 262.653.2494
Fax 262.653.2533
Web .... www.co.kenosha.wi.us
E-mail .... beier.mary@mail.da.state.wi.us
　912 56th St, Rm 102, Kenosha, WI 53140
　Mary Beier, Director

POLICE AND SHERIFF

Kenosha City Police Dept 262.605.5203
Fax 262.605.5298
E-mail .... jwm309@kenoshapolice.com
　1000 55th St Ste 1, Kenosha, WI 53140
　John Morrissey, Chief

Sheriff's Dept 262.605.5101
Fax 262.605.5130
Web .... www.co.kenosha.wi.us
E-mail .... dbeth@co.kenosha.wi.us
　1000 55th St, Kenosha, WI 53140-3794
　David G. Beth, Sheriff

Kewaunee County

COURTS

Circuit Court 920.388.7113
Fax 920.388.3139
Web .... www.wicourts.gov
E-mail .... dennis.mleziva@wicourts.gov
　613 Dodge St, Kewaunee, WI 54216-1322
　Honorable Dennis Mleziva, Judge

La Crosse County

SOCIAL SERVICES

Dept Of Human Svcs 608.785.6054
Fax 608.785.6443
E-mail .... nancy.pohlman@co.la-crosse.wi.us
　300 4th St N, La Crosse, WI 54601-3228
　Jason Witt, Director

Human Svcs 608.785.5875
Fax 608.785.6443
Web .... www.co.la-crosse.wi.us
　300 N 4th St, LaCrosse, WI 54601-4002
　Cathy Hafner, Office Supervisor

La Crosse Lutheran Social Svcs 608.788.5090
Fax 608.788.6623
Web .... www.lsswis.org
E-mail .... cschroeder@lsswis.org
　2350 South Ave Ste 213, La Crosse, WI 54601-6272
　Cheryl Schroeder, Program Manager

GENERAL HEALTH SERVICES

Health Dept 608.785.9872
Fax 608.785.9846
Web .... www.co.la-crosse.wi.us
　300 4th St N, La Crosse, WI 54601
　Al Graywin, Hiv Educator

COURTS

Circuit Court 608.785.9590
Fax 608.789.7821
Web .... www.co.la-crosse.wi.us
E-mail .... ramona.gonzalez@wicourts.gov
　333 Vine St, Rm 1200, La Crosse, WI 54601
　Honorable Ramona Gonzalez, Judge

POLICE AND SHERIFF

Sheriff's Dept 608.785.9629
Fax 608.785.5640
Web .... www.co.la-crosse.wi.us/sheriff
E-mail .... helgeson.steve@co.la-crosse.wi.us
　333 Vine St, La Crosse, WI 54601
　Steve Helgeson, Sheriff

Lafayette County

GENERAL HEALTH SERVICES

Public Health Dept 608.776.4895
Fax 608.776.4885
Web .... www.lafayettecountyhealthdepartment.org
E-mail .... Debbie.Siegenthaler@lafayettecountywi.org
　729 Clay St, Darlington, WI 53530
　Debbie Siegenthaler, Rn, Health Officer

COURTS

Circuit Court 608.776.4832
Fax 608.776.4845
　626 Main St Rm 204, Darlington, WI 53530
　Catherine Mcgowan, Clerk Of Court

POLICE AND SHERIFF

Sheriff's Dept 608.776.4870
Fax 608.776.4808
Web .... www.mhtc.net
　138 W Catherine St, Darlington, WI 53530
　Scott E. Pedley, Sheriff

Langlade County

GENERAL HEALTH SERVICES

Langlade Public Health Dept 715.627.6250
Fax 715.627.6391
E-mail .... hmatucheski@co.langlade.wi.us
　1225 Langlade Rd, Antigo, WI 54409
　Holly Matucheski, Rn, Health Officer

COURTS

Circuit Court 715.627.6215
Fax 715.627.6316
　800 Clermont St, Antigo, WI 54409-1947
　Marilyn Baraniak, Clerk Of Court

Lincoln County

COURTS

Circuit Court 715.536.0319
Fax 715.536.0361
Web .... www.co.lincoln.wi.us
　1110 E Main St Ste 11, Merrill, WI 54452-2554
　Honorable Jay Tlusty, Judge

Manitowoc County

SOCIAL SERVICES

Human Svcs 920.683.4400
Fax 920.683.4908
　926 S 8th St, Manitowoc, WI 54220
　Patricia Dodge, Office Manager

GENERAL HEALTH SERVICES

Health Dept 920.683.4155
Fax 920.683.4156
Web .... www.co.manitowoc.wi.us
E-mail .... healthdepartment@co.manitowoc.wi.us
　823 Washington St, Manitowoc, WI 54220-4528
　Amy Wergin, Rn, Nursing Director

COURTS

Circuit Court 920.683.4030
Fax 920.683.2733
Web .... www.co.manitowoc.wi.us
　1010 S 8th St Ste 105, Manitowoc, WI 54220-5392
　Honorable Gerome L. Fox, Judge

POLICE AND SHERIFF

Sheriff's Dept 920.683.4200
Fax 920.683.2798
Web .... www.manitowoc-county.com
　1025 S 9th St, Manitowoc, WI 54220-5340
　Robert Herrman, Sheriff

EDUCATION SERVICES

Cesa 7 Head Start-Manitowoc 920.683.1960
Fax 920.683.3301
Web www.cesa7.k12.wi.us
　702 State St, Manitowoc, WI 54220-4034
　Jill Bodwin, Director

Marathon County

SOCIAL SERVICES

Ofc On Aging 715.261.6070
Fax 715.261.6090
Web .... www.adrc-cw.com
E-mail .... linda.weitz@adrc-cw.com
　1000 Lake View Dr, Wausau, WI 54403-6706
　Linda Weitz, Director

GENERAL HEALTH SERVICES

Health Dept 715.261.1900
Fax 715.261.1901
Web .... www.co.marathon.wi.us
　1200 Lake View Dr Ste 200, Wausau, WI 54403
　Joan Theurer, Health Officer

Wisconsin

JUSTICE AGENCY

Div Of Juvenile Corrections **715.241.8890**
Fax 715.241.8899
Web ....www.doc.state.wi.us
E-mail ....mark.frost@doc.state.wi.us
    1699 Schofield Ave Ste 120, Schofield,
    WI 54476-2332
    Mark Frost, Community Corrections Supervisor

Juvenile Facility **715.261.1770**
Fax 715.261.1774
    7015 Packer Dr, Wausau, WI 54401
    Chris Anklam, Superintendent

COURTS

Circuit Court **715.261.7500**
Fax 715.261.1319
    400 E Thomas St, Wausau, WI 54403-5554
    Honorable Greg Grau, Judge

Juvenile And Children's Court Svcs **715.261.7650**
Fax 715.261.7510
Web ....www.courts.state.va.us
E-mail ....vmtylka@mail.co.marathon.wi.us
    400 E Thomas St, Wausau, WI 54403-6435
    Vicki Tylka, Director

POLICE AND SHERIFF

Edgar Police Dept **715.352.2891**
Fax 715.352.2964
E-mail ....edgarpd@dwave.net
    224 S Third Ave, Edgar, WI 54426
    Andrew Deininger, Police Chief

Police Dept **715.261.7800**
Fax 715.261.7888
E-mail ....JEFFERY.HARDEL@CI.WAUSAU.WI.US
    515 Grand Ave, Wausau, WI 54403
    Jeff Hardel, Chief

Marinette County

COURTS

Circuit Court **715.732.7450**
Fax 715.732.7461
Web ....www.marinettecounty.com
    1926 Hall Ave, Marinette, WI 54143-1717
    Honorable Tim A. Duket, Judge

Teen Court **715.732.7510**
Fax 715.732.7513
    1926 Hall Ave, Marinette, WI 54143
    Wally Hitt, Coordinator

POLICE AND SHERIFF

Sheriff's Dept **715.732.7600**
Fax 715.732.7606
Web ....www.marinettecounty.com
E-mail ....jkanikula@marinettecounty.com
    2161 University Dr, Marinette, WI 54143-3889
    James Kanipula, Sheriff

Marquette County

SOCIAL SERVICES

Human Svcs **608.297.3124**
Fax 608.297.8718
E-mail ....mcdhs@co.marquette.wi.us
    428 Underwood Ave, Montello, WI 53949
    Jeremy Kral, Director

GENERAL HEALTH SERVICES

Health Dept **608.297.3135**
Fax 608.297.8923
E-mail ....nluedke@co.marquette.wi.us
    428 Underwood Ave, Montello, WI 53949
    Nathan Luedke, Director of Nursing

Menominee County

SOCIAL SERVICES

Health And Human Svcs **715.799.3861**
Fax 715.799.3517
Web ....www.co.menominee.wi.us
    W 3272 Wolf River Rd, Keshena, WI 54135-0280
    Rebecca Johnson, Health Director

Indian Social Svcs Menominee
Tribe **715.799.5161**
Fax 715.799.6061
Web ....www.mitw.org
E-mail ....mhusby@mitw.org
    PO Box 520, Keshena, WI 54135-0520
    Mary Husby, Director

Menominee Tribal Agency **715.799.3835**
Fax 715.799.3836
E-mail ....swilber@mitw.org
    N 2150 Kesaehkahtek, Gresham, WI 54128
    Shannon Wilber, Director

COURTS

Circuit Court **715.799.3313**
Fax 715.799.1322
    3269 Courthouse Ln, Keshena, WI 54135
    Honorable Thomas Grover, Judge

Tribal Court **715.799.3348**
Fax 715.799.4061
Web ....www.menominee.nsn.us
E-mail ....waskenette@mitw.org
    PO Box 429, Keshena, WI 54135-0429
    Honorable Windell Askenette, Judge

POLICE AND SHERIFF

Sheriff's Ofc **715.799.3357**
Fax 715.799.3595
E-mail ....meso@frontiernet.net
    W3269 Courthouse Ln, Keshena, WI 54135
    Robert Summers, Sheriff

Milwaukee County

SOCIAL SERVICES

Child Welfare Div **414.220.7000**
Fax 414.220.7062
E-mail ....arlene.happach@wisconsin.gov
    1555 N Rivercenter Dr Ste 220, Milwaukee,
    WI 53212
    Arlene Happach, Director

Human Svcs **414.289.6817**
Fax 414.289.8570
    1220 W Vliet St, Milwaukee, WI 53205
    Geri Lyday, Director

GENERAL HEALTH SERVICES

City Of Milwaukee Health Dept **414.286.3521**
Fax 414.286.5990
Web ....www.milwaukee.gov
E-mail ....lazhes@milwaukee.gov
    841 N Broadway Fl 3, Milwaukee, WI 53202-3639
    Lisa Acheson, Public Health Nurse

Cudahy Health Dept **414.769.2239**
Fax 414.769.2291
Web ....www.ci.cudahy.wi.us
E-mail ....health@ci.cudahy.wi.us
    5050 S Lake Dr, Cudahy, WI 53110-2045
    Carol Wantuch, Health Officer

Franklin Health Dept **414.425.9101**
Fax 414.427.7539
Web ....www.franklinwi.gov
E-mail ....bwucherer@franklinwi.gov
    9229 W Loomis Rd, Franklin, WI 53132
    William Wucherer, Rn, Health Officer

Greendale Health Dept **414.423.2110**
Fax 414.858.9111
Web ....www.greendale.org
E-mail ....sshepeard@greendale.org
    5650 Parking St, Greendale, WI 53129-1836
    Susan Shepeard, Health Officer

Greenfield Health Dept **414.329.5275**
Fax 414.543.5713
Web ....www.greenfieldwi.us
E-mail ....darrenr@greenfieldwi.us
    7325 W Forest Home Ave, Greenfield,
    WI 53220-3356
    Darren Rausch, Health Officer/director

Hales Corners Health Dept **414.529.6155**
Fax 414.529.6157
Web ....www.halescornerswi.org
E-mail ....dpersak@halescornerswi.org
    5635 S New Berlin Rd, Hales Corners,
    WI 53130-1775
    Debra Persak, Rn, Health Officer

North Shore Health Dept **414.371.2980**
Fax 414.371.2988
Web ....www.browndeerwi.org
E-mail ....nshd@browndeerwi.org
    4800 W Green Brook Dr, Milwaukee, WI 53223-2406
    Jamie Berg, Rn, Rs, Health Officer

Oak Creek Health Dept **414.768.6525**
Fax 414.768.5866
Web ....www.oakcreekwi.org
E-mail ....swojcinski@oakcreekwi.org
    8640 S Howell Ave, Oak Creek, WI 53154-2918
    Sue Wojcinski, Deputy Officer

Shorewood Health Dept **414.847.2710**
Fax 414.847.2714
E-mail ....jberg@villageofshorewood.org
    3930 N Murray Ave, Milwaukee, WI 53211-2385
    Jamie Berg, Health Officer

South Milwaukee Health Dept **414.768.8055**
Fax 414.768.5720
Web ....www.ci.south-milwaukee.wi.us
    2424 15th Ave, South Milwaukee, WI 53172
    Jacqueline Ove, Health Officer

STD Clinic **414.286.3631**
Fax 414.286.8173
Web ....www.milwaukee.gov
    3200 N 36th St, Milwaukee, WI 53216

Wauwatosa Health Dept **414.479.8936**
Fax 414.471.8483
Web ....www.wauwatosa.net
E-mail ....lnielsen@wauwatosa.net
    7725 W North Ave, Wauwatosa, WI 53213-1720
    Lori Nielsen, Nursing Director

West Allis Health Dept. -- Home Health
................................**414.302.8600**
Fax 414.302.8628
Web ....www.ci.west-allis.wi.us
E-mail ....snusslock@ci.west-allis.wi.us
    7120 W National Ave, West Allis, WI 53214
    Sally Nusslock, Rn, Nursing Director

MENTAL HEALTH SERVICES

Mental Health Div Child And Adolescent Treatment
Ctr **414.257.6995**
Fax 414.257.7575
E-mail ....bkamradt@milwcnty.com
    9455 W Watertown Plank Rd, Milwaukee, WI 53226
    Bruce Kamradt, Administrator/director

JUSTICE AGENCY

CASA **414.344.1220**
Fax 414.344.1230
Web .... www.kidsmatterinc.org
E-mail .... adam@kidsmatterinc.org
　1850 N Dr Martin Luther King Dr Ste 202,
　Milwaukee, WI 53212-3672
　Susan Conwell, Director

Southeastern Region/Juvenile
Corrections **414.229.0701**
Fax 414.229.0705
　4200 N Holton St Ste 120, Milwaukee, WI 53212
　Audrian Brown, Regional Chief

POLICE AND SHERIFF

Police Dept **414.933.4444**
Fax 414.935.7118
Web .... www.ci.mil.wi.us
　951 N James Lowell St, Milwaukee, WI 53233-1418
　Annie Schmidth, Communications Director

Sheriff's Dept **414.278.4766**
Fax 414.223.1386
E-mail .... dclarke@milwcnty.com
　821 W State St, Rm 107, Milwaukee, WI 53233
　David A. Clarke Jr., Sheriff

EDUCATION SERVICES

Baird Ctr Head Start-Daycare **414.645.2003**
E-mail .... mSalagado@dcscinc.com
　2210 W Becher St, Milwaukee, WI 53215
　Maria Salagado, Supervisor

Gear Up **414.227.4466**
Fax 414.227.4462
Web .... www.dpi.wi.gov
E-mail .... harriet.browne@dpi.wi.gov
　101 W Pleasant St Ste 110, Milwaukee,
　WI 53212-3963
　Harriett Brown, Education Specialist

Special Education **262.787.9500**
Fax 262.787.9501
Web www.cesa1.k12.wi.us
E-mail .... bvanharen@cesa1.k12.wi.us
　N 25 W 2331 Paul Rd, Ste 100, Pewaukee, WI 53072
　Barbara Van Haren, Edd, Director

Monroe County

SOCIAL SERVICES

Ho-Chunk Nation Dept Of Health And Social
Svcs **608.372.5202**
Fax 608.372.0889
Web www.cesa4.k12.wi.us
E-mail .... hmation@cesa4.k12.wi.us
　27374 State Highway 21, Tomah, WI 54660-4501
　Hochunk Mation, Director

Human Svcs **608.269.8600**
Fax 608.269.8935
Web .... www.co.monroe.wi.us
　14301 County Highway B Ste A-19, Sparta, WI 54656
　Gene Phillips, Director

GENERAL HEALTH SERVICES

Health Dept **608.269.8666**
Fax 608.269.8872
Web .... www.co.monroe.wi.us
E-mail .... snelson@co.monroe.wi.us
　14301 County Highway B, Sparta, WI 54656-4509
　Sharon L Nelson, Rn, Director

COURTS

Circuit Court **608.269.8741**
Fax 608.269.8781
Web .... www.wcca.wicourts.gov
E-mail .... shirley.chapiewsky@wicourts.gov
　112 S Court St RM 203, Sparta, WI 54656-1772
　Shirley Chapiewsky, Clerk Of Court

POLICE AND SHERIFF

Sheriff's Dept **608.269.2117**
Fax 608.269.8889
Web .... www.co.monroe.wi.us
E-mail .... pquirin@co.monroe.wi.us
　210 W Oak St, Sparta, WI 54656-2185
　Peter H. Quirin, Sheriff

Oconto County

SOCIAL SERVICES

Human Svcs **920.834.7000**
Fax 920.834.6889
Web .... www.co.oconto.wi.us
E-mail .... ochs@co.oconto.wi.us
　501 Park Ave, Oconto, WI 54153-1612
　Craig Johnson, Director

GENERAL HEALTH SERVICES

Public Health Dept **920.834.7033**
Fax 920.834.6889
Web .... www.co.oconto.wi.us
　501 Park Ave, Oconto, WI 54153
　Debbie Konitzer, Rn, Bsn, Health Officer

COURTS

Circuit Court **920.834.6837**
Fax 920.834.6867
Web .... www.co.oconto.wi.us
　301 Washington St, Oconto, WI 54153-1620
　Michael Judge, Judge

POLICE AND SHERIFF

Sheriff's Dept **920.834.6900**
Fax 920.834.6915
Web .... www.co.oconto.wi.us
E-mail .... mike.jansen@co.oconto.wi.us
　301 Washington St, Oconto, WI 54153-1620
　Michael R. Jansen, Sheriff

Oneida County

SOCIAL SERVICES

Human Svc Ctr **715.369.2215**
Fax 715.369.2214
Web .... www.thehumanservicecenter.org
E-mail .... ed@thehumanservicecenter.org
　705 E Timber Dr, Rhinelander, WI 54501-2859
　Davdi Bast, Director

GENERAL HEALTH SERVICES

Health Dept **715.369.6111**
Fax 715.369.6112
Web .... www.co.oneida.wi.us
E-mail .... lconlon@co.oneida.wi.us
　1 S Oneida Ave, Rhinelander, WI 54501
　Linda Conlon, Director Of Health Dept

COURTS

Clerk Of Court **715.369.6120**
Fax 715.369.6160
Web .... www.wicourts.gov
　1 Courthouse Square, Rhinelander, WI 54501
　Kenneth Gardner, Clerk Of Court

Outagamie County

SOCIAL SERVICES

Health & Human Svcs **920.832.4741**
Fax 920.832.2185
　410 S Walnut St, Appleton, WI 54911
　Rosemary Davis, Human Services Director

Human Svcs **920.832.5161**
Fax 920.832.5180
Web .... www.outagamie.wi.us
　401 S Elm St, Appleton, WI 54911-5900
　John Rathman, Deputy Director

GENERAL HEALTH SERVICES

Appleton City Health Dept **920.832.6429**
Fax 920.832.5853
Web .... www.appleton.org
　100 N Appleton St, Appleton, WI 54911
　Kathy Stromburg, Nursing Director

COURTS

Circuit Court **920.832.5131**
Fax 920.832.5115
Web .... www.co.outagamie.wi.us
E-mail .... michael.gage@wicourts.gov
　320 S Walnut St, Appleton, WI 54911-5918
　Honorable Michael Gage, Judge

POLICE AND SHERIFF

Appleton Police Dept **920.832.5500**
Fax 920.832.5553
Web .... www.appleton.org/police
E-mail .... david.walsh@appleton.org
　222 S Walnut St, Appleton, WI 54911-5899
　David Walsh, Chief

Sheriff's Dept **920.832.5646**
Fax 920.832.5263
E-mail .... gehringb@co.outagamie.wi.us
　320 S Walnut St, Appleton, WI 54911
　Brad Gehring, Sheriff

Ozaukee County

SOCIAL SERVICES

Dept Of Community Programs **262.238.8200**
Fax 262.238.8104
Web .... www.co.ozaukee.wi.us
E-mail .... rhaupt@co.ozaukee.wi.us
　121 W Main St, Port Washington, WI 53074-1813
　Robert Haupt, Director

Human Svcs **262.238.8200**
Fax 262.284.8104
Web .... www.co.ozaukee.wi.us
E-mail .... rhaupt@co.ozaukee.wi.us
　121 W Main St, Port Washington, WI 53074-1813
　Robert Haupt, Director

POLICE AND SHERIFF

Sheriff's Dept **262.377.7172**
Fax 262.284.8490
Web ....
E-mail .... mstraub@co.ozaukee.wi.us
　1201 S Spring St, Port Washington, WI 53074-2491
　Maury Straub, Sheriff

Pepin County

SOCIAL SERVICES

Health Dept **715.672.5961**
Fax 715.672.8593
Web .... www.co.wi.us
　740 7th Ave W, Durand, WI 54736
　Hyde Stewart, Health Director

POLICE AND SHERIFF

Sheriff's Ofc............................715.672.5944
Fax......................................715.672.8753
Web...........................www.co.pepin.wi.us
E-mail.................jandrews@co.pepin.wi.us
740 7Th Ave W, Durand, WI 54736-1628
John C. Andrews, Sheriff

Pierce County

COURTS

Circuit Court..........................715.273.3531
Fax......................................715.273.6855
414 W Main St, Ellsworth, WI 54011
Joseph Boles, Judge

POLICE AND SHERIFF

Sheriff's Ofc............................715.273.5051
Fax......................................715.273.6856
Web...........................www.co.pierce.wi.us
E-mail.............nancy.hove@co.pierce.wi.us
432 W. Main St, Ellsworth, WI 54011
Nancy Hove, Sheriff

EDUCATION SERVICES

Ellsworth Head Start...............715.792.2424
Fax......................................715.792.5420
Web...........................www.ellsworth.k12.wi.us
E-mail.............monak@ellsworth.k12.wi.us
N3470 US Hwy 63, Hager City, WI 54014-8232
Mona Karau, Director

Polk County

SOCIAL SERVICES

Human Svcs............................715.485.8400
Fax......................................715.485.8490
Web...........................www.co.polk.wi.us
E-mail.................sherryg@co.polk.wi.us
100 Polk County Plz Ste 50, Balsam Lake,
WI 54810-9097
Sherry G Jonnes, Director

GENERAL HEALTH SERVICES

Public Health Dept...................715.485.8500
Fax......................................715.485.8501
100 Polk County Plz Ste 180, Balsam Lake, WI 54810
Gretchen Sampson, Rn, Mph, Director

COURTS

Circuit Court..........................715.485.9293
Fax......................................715.485.9275
1005 W Main St Ste 600, Balsam Lake,
WI 54810-4406
Molly Galewyrick, Judge

Portage County

SOCIAL SERVICES

Health & Human Svcs................715.345.5350
Fax......................................715.345.5966
Web...........................www.co.portage.wi.us
E-mail.................pchhsd@co.portage.wi.us
817 Whiting Ave, Stevens Point, WI 54481
Faye Tetzloff, Health Director

COURTS

Circuit Court..........................715.346.1364
Fax......................................715.346.1236
Web...........................www.co.portage.wi.us
1516 Church St, Stevens Point, WI 54481-3501
Honorable Thomas T. Flugaur, Judge

Peer Court.............................715.341.4386
Fax......................................715.341.7481
Web...........................www.bgclubpc.org
E-mail.................info@bgclubpc.org
1007 Ellis St, Stevens Point, WI 54481
J R Wynne Kevin Quevillon, Director

POLICE AND SHERIFF

Sheriff's Ofc............................715.346.1400
Fax......................................715.346.1591
Web...........................www.co.potage.wi.us
E-mail.................charewij@co.portage.wi.us
1500 Strongs Ave, Stevens Point, WI 54481
John E. Charewicz, Sheriff

Price County

SOCIAL SERVICES

Human Svcs............................715.339.2158
Fax......................................715.339.4018
Web...........................www.co.price.wi.us
E-mail.................mary.hahn@co.price.wi.us
104 S Eyder Ave Ste 2, NORMAL BLDG, Phillips,
WI 54555-1342
Mary Hahn, Director

GENERAL HEALTH SERVICES

Health Dept...........................715.339.3054
Fax......................................715.339.3057
Web...........................www.co.price.wi.us
E-mail.............michelle.edwards@co.price.wi.us
104 S Eyder Ave Rm 203, Phillips, WI 54555
Michelle Edwards, Director

COURTS

Circuit Court..........................715.339.2353
Fax......................................715.339.5114
Web...........................www.co.price.wi.us
E-mail.................douglas.fox@wicourts.gov
126 Cherry St Rm 210, Phillips, WI 54555-1249
Honorable Douglas T. Fox, Judge

Racine County

SOCIAL SERVICES

Human Svcs............................262.638.6353
Fax......................................262.638.6369
E-mail.............jonathan.delagrave@coracine.org
1717 Taylor Ave, Racine, WI 53403
Jonathan Delagrave, Director

GENERAL HEALTH SERVICES

Caledonia/Mt Pleasant Health
Dept.....................................262.835.6429
Fax......................................262.886.5072
Web...........................www.mtpleasantwi.gov/health
10005 Northwestern Ave, Franksville, WI 53126
Margaret Guesner, Health Officer

Health Dept...........................262.763.4930
Fax......................................262.763.4928
Web...........................www.wrcht.org
E-mail.............cheryl.mazmanian@aurora.org
156 E State St, Burlington, WI 53105-1940
Cheryl Mazmanian, Health Officer

JUSTICE AGENCY

Corrective Sanctions Program.......262.884.3735
Fax......................................262.884.3733
E-mail.................Renald.nord@wi.gov
9531 Rayne Rd, Ste 3, Sturtevant, WI 53177
Agent Renald Nord, Probation Agent

COURTS

Circuit Court..........................262.636.3862
Fax......................................262.636.3341
730 Wisconsin Ave, Racine, WI 53403-1238
Honorable Dennis Barry, Judge

POLICE AND SHERIFF

Police Dept............................262.635.7700
Fax......................................262.636.9332
Web...........................www.cityofracine.org
E-mail.................david.Sametana@cityofracine.org
730 Center St, Racine, WI 53403-1186
David Sametana, Deputy Chief

Sheriff's Dept.........................262.636.3203
Fax......................................262.637.5279
Web...........................www.execpc.com
E-mail.................rsheriff@execpc.com
717 Wisconsin Ave, Racine, WI 53403-1253
Robert Carlson, Sheriff

Richland County

COURTS

Circuit Court..........................608.647.2626
Fax......................................608.647.5747
Web...........................www.wicourts.gov
E-mail.................stacy.kliest@wicourts.gov
181 W Seminary St, Richland Center, WI 53581-2356
Stacy Kliest, Clerk Of Court

Rock County

SOCIAL SERVICES

Rock Valley Community Programs
Inc.......................................608.741.4500
Fax......................................608.741.4502
Web...........................www.rvcp.org
203 W. Sunny Ln. Rd., Janesville, WI 53546
Don Tinder, Director

GENERAL HEALTH SERVICES

Health Dept...........................608.757.5440
Fax......................................608.758.8423
Web...........................www.co.rock.wi.us
3328 N US Highway 51, Janesville, WI 53545-0772
Janet Zoellner, Nursing Director

JUSTICE AGENCY

YWCA Care House.....................608.755.4750
Fax......................................608.755.4752
Web...........................www.ywca/rockcounty.org
E-mail.................carehouse@ywcarockco.com
1126 Conde St, Janesville, WI 53546-5816
Maryann Burkheimer, Coordinator

COURTS

Circuit Court..........................608.743.2200
Fax......................................608.743.2223
Web...........................www.wicourts.gov
51 S Main St, Janesville, WI 53545-3951
Honorable Richard Werner, Judge

POLICE AND SHERIFF

Sheriff's Ofc............................608.757.8000
Fax......................................608.757.8010
Web...........................www.co.rock.wi.us
E-mail.................mmeta200@hotmail.com
200 East Highway 14, Janesville, WI 53545
Robert Spoden, Sheriff

Rusk County

COURTS

Circuit Court..........................715.532.2108
Fax......................................715.532.2110
Web...........................www.wicourts.gov
311 Miner Ave E Ste L350, Ladysmith,
WI 54848-1891
Honorable Steven P. Anderson, Judge

Saint Croix County

SOCIAL SERVICES

Human Svcs............................715.246.6991
Fax......................................715.246.8225
Web...........................www.co.saint-croix.wi.us
E-mail.................fredj@co.saint-croix.wi.us
1445 N 4th St, New Richmond, WI 54017-1063
Fred Johnson, Director

COURTS

Circuit Court **715.386.4630**
Fax 715.381.4396
Web ....www.co.saint-croix.wi.us
   1101 Carmichael Rd, St Croix County Government
   Center, Hudson, WI 54016
   Lori Meyer, Clerk Of Court

POLICE AND SHERIFF

Sheriff's Dept **715.381.4320**
Fax 715.386.4606
Web ....www.co.saint-croix.wi.us
E-mail ....Johns@co.saint-croix.wi.us
   1101 Carmichael Rd, Hudson, WI 54016-7708
   John Shilts, Sheriff

Sauk County

SOCIAL SERVICES

Area Agency On Aging **608.355.3289**
Fax 608.355.4375
Web ....www.co.sauk.wi.us
   505 Broadway St, Baraboo, WI 53913
   Trish Vandre, Director

GENERAL HEALTH SERVICES

Health Dept **608.355.4300**
Fax 608.355.4329
E-mail ....bmuhlenbeck@co.sauk.wi.us
   505 Broadway St, Baraboo, WI 53913
   Beverly Muhlenbeck, Health Officer

COURTS

Circuit Court **608.355.3287**
Fax 608.355.3480
   515 Oak St, Baraboo, WI 53913
   Honorable James Evenson, Judge

POLICE AND SHERIFF

Sheriff's Dept **608.356.4895**
Fax 608.355.3598
Web ....www.co.sauk.wi.us
E-mail ....rmeister@co.sauk.wi.us
   1300 Lange Ct, Baraboo, WI 53913-3116
   Richard Meister, Sheriff

Sawyer County

SOCIAL SERVICES

Human Svcs **715.634.4806**
Fax 715.634.5387
Web ....www.sawyercounty.gov
E-mail ....ddauer@sawyerhs.hayward.wi.us
   10610 Main St, Hayward, WI 54843-6595
   Pete Sanders, Director

Indian Social Svcs Chippewa Tribel **715.634.8934**
Fax 715.634.4797
Web ....www.lco-nfn.gov
E-mail ....lcoicw@yahoo.com
   13394 W Trepania Rd, Hayward, WI 54843
   Luan Kolumbus, Director Of Indian Child Welfare

GENERAL HEALTH SERVICES

**Lac Courte Oreilles Community Health
Ctr** **715.638.5100**
Fax 715.634.6107
Web ....www.lhohc.com
   13380 W Trepania Rd, Hayward, WI 54843-2186
   Gaiashkabos, Health Administrator

Lac Courte Oreilles Health Ctr **715.638.5102**
Fax 715.634.6107
Web ....www.lhohc.com
   13380 W Trepania Rd, Hayward, WI 54843
   Gaiashkabos, Director

POLICE AND SHERIFF

Sheriff's Dept **715.634.4858**
Fax 715.634.3845
Web ....www.sawyercountygov.org
E-mail ....mschull@sawyersheriff.org
   15880 E 5th St, Hayward, WI 54843-6534
   Mark Kelsey, Sheriff

Shawano County

SOCIAL SERVICES

**Indian Social Svcs Stockbridge-Munsee
Tribes** **715.793.4111**
Fax 715.793.1307
Web ....www.mohican-nsn.gov
   N 8476 Mohheconnuck Rd, Bowler, WI 54416-9464
   Kimberly Bele, President

GENERAL HEALTH SERVICES

Health Dept **715.526.4808**
Fax 715.524.5792
E-mail ....debby.vernicke@co.shawano.wi.us
   311 N Main St, Shawano, WI 54166
   Debby Vernicke, Health Director

**Stockbridge Munsee Health And Wellness
Ctr** **715.793.4144**
Fax 715.793.5101
Web ....www.mohican.com
E-mail ....delwar.mias@mohican.com
   W 12802 County Hwy A, Bowler, WI 54416
   Delwar Mias, Assistant Director

COURTS

Clerk Of Court **715.526.9347**
Fax 715.526.4915
Web ....www.wicourts.gov
E-mail ....sue.kruger@wicourts.gov
   311 N Main St, Shawano, WI 54166-2145
   Susan Kruger, Clerk Of Court

POLICE AND SHERIFF

Sheriff's Dept **715.526.7900**
Fax 715.524.5181
E-mail ....law501@co.shawano.wi.us
   405 N Main St, Shawano, WI 54166
   Randall Wright, Sheriff

Sheboygan County

SOCIAL SERVICES

Human Svcs **920.459.3056**
Fax 920.459.6478
E-mail ....eggebtde@co.sheboygan.wi.us
   1011 N 8th St, Sheboygan, WI 53081
   Thomas Eggebrecht, Director

COURTS

Circuit Court **920.459.3068**
Fax 920.459.0541
   615 N 6th St, Sheboygan, WI 53081
   Honorable L. Edward Stengel, Judge

POLICE AND SHERIFF

Police Dept **920.459.3333**
Fax 920.459.0205
Web ....www.sheboyganpolice.com
   1315 N 23rd St, Sheboygan, WI 53081-4442
   Bomagalski Kristifer, Police Chief

Sheriff's Dept **920.459.3111**
Fax 920.459.4305
   525 N 6th St, Sheboygan, WI 53081
   Todd Priebe, Sheriff

EDUCATION SERVICES

Special Education **920.467.7894**
Fax 920.467.7885
Web www.sheboyganfalls.k12.wi.us
E-mail ....aroy@sheboyganfalls.k12.wi.us
   101 School st, Sheboygan Falls, WI 53085
   Ann Roy, Coordinator

Special Education **715.524.4616**
Fax 715.524.7016
Web www.ssd.k12.wi.us
E-mail ....cullend@ssd.k12.wi.us
   1050 S Union St, Shawano, WI 54166-3457
   Dave Cullen, Director

Taylor County

GENERAL HEALTH SERVICES

Health Dept **715.748.1410**
Fax 715.748.1417
Web ....www.co.taylor.wi.us
E-mail ....patty.krug@co.taylor.wi.us
   224 S 2nd St, Courthouse, Medford, WI 54451-1899
   Patty Krug, Rn, Director

Trempealeau County

SOCIAL SERVICES

Health & Human Svcs **715.538.2311**
Fax 715.538.4861
Web ....www.jacksoncountydhhs.org
E-mail ....c_hovell@trempealeaucounty.com
   36245 Main St, Whitehall, WI 54773-9158
   Christine Hovell, Health Director

COURTS

Teen Court **715.538.2311**
Fax 715.538.4123
Web ....www.wicourts.gov
E-mail ....jill.clark@wicourts.gov
   36245 Main St, Whitehall, WI 54773-9139
   Jill Clark, Coordinator

POLICE AND SHERIFF

Sheriff's Dept **715.538.4509**
Fax 715.538.2148
Web ....www.tremplocounty.com
E-mail ....tcsheriff@tremplocounty.com
   36245 Main St, Whitehall, WI 54773-9139
   Richard Anderson, Sheriff

EDUCATION SERVICES

**Early Learning Ctr-Strum Head
Start** **715.695.2916**
Fax 715.695.2690
E-mail ....eolson@esschools.k12.wi.us
   409 8Th Ave S, Strum, WI 54770
   Erica Olson, Director

Vernon County

GENERAL HEALTH SERVICES

Public Health Dept **608.637.5251**
Fax 608.637.5514
E-mail ....ejohnson@vernoncounty.org
   318 Sarlane Dr Cty Hwy Bb, Viroqua, WI 54665
   Elizabeth Ann Johnson, Rn, Health Officer

COURTS

Circuit Court **608.637.5340**
Fax 608.637.5554
Web ....www.vernoncounty.org
   400 Courthouse Square, Viroqua, WI 54665
   Honorable Michael Rosborough, Judge

Vilas County

GENERAL HEALTH SERVICES

Peter Christensen Health Ctr **715.588.3371**
Fax 715.588.2039
   129 Old Abe Rd, Lac Du Flambeau, WI 54538
   Adrianne Laverdure, Clinical Director

Public Health Dept **715.479.3656**
Fax 715.479.3741
Web ....www.vilaspublichealth.com
E-mail ....giegan@co.vilas.wi.us
   330 Court St, Eagle River, WI 54521-8362
   Gina Egan, Health Officer

COURTS

Circuit Court **715.479.3632**
Fax 715.479.3740
E-mail ....jerrie.vanhaverbeke@wicout.gov
   330 Court St, Eagle River, WI 54521
   Jean Numrich, Clerk Of Court

Walworth County

COURTS

Circuit Court **262.741.7012**
Fax 262.741.7050
Web ....www.co.walworth.wi.us
   1800 County Rd Nn, Fl 2, Elkhorn, WI 53121
   Honorable James L. Carlson, Judge

POLICE AND SHERIFF

Sheriff's Ofc **262.741.4400**
Fax 262.741.4645
   1770 County Trunk Nn, Elkhorn, WI 53121
   David Graves, Sheriff

Washburn County

SOCIAL SERVICES

Human Svcs **715.468.4747**
Fax 715.468.4753
Web ....www.co.washburn.wi.us
E-mail ....humanser@co.washburn.wi.us
   110 4th Ave West, Shell Lake, WI 54871
   Joan Wilson, CPS Supervisor

GENERAL HEALTH SERVICES

Health Dept **715.635.4400**
Fax 715.635.4416
Web ....www.co.washburn.wi.us/departments/health
E-mail ....health@co.washburn.wi.us
   222 Oak St, Spooner, WI 54801
   Jerri Pederson, Health Officer

COURTS

Circuit Court **715.468.4677**
Fax 715.468.4678
Web ....www.co.washburn.wi.us
E-mail ....karen.nord@wicourts.gov
   10 4Th Ave, Shell Lake, WI 54871
   Karen Nord, Clerk Of Court

Washington County

SOCIAL SERVICES

Dept Of Human Svcs **262.335.4610**
Fax 262.335.4709
E-mail ....mike.bloedom@co.washington.wi.us
   333 E Washington St Ste 3100, West Bend, WI 53095
   Michael Bloedom, Deputy Director

GENERAL HEALTH SERVICES

Home Health **262.335.4462**
Fax 262.335.4705
Web ....www.co.washington.wi.us
E-mail ....linda.walter@co.washington.wi.us
   333 E Washington St Ste 1100, West Bend, WI 53095
   Linda Walter, Health Officer and Nursing Director

POLICE AND SHERIFF

Sheriff's Dept **262.335.4378**
Fax 262.335.4429
E-mail ....info@washingtoncountysherriffwi.org
   500 N Schmidt Rd, West Bend, WI 53095
   Dale K. Schmidt, Sheriff

Waukesha County

SOCIAL SERVICES

Human Svcs **262.548.7666**
Fax 262.548.7656
Web ....www.waukeshacounty.gov
E-mail ....pschuler@waukeshacounty.gov
   500 Riverview Ave, Waukesha, WI 53188
   Peter Schuler, Director

GENERAL HEALTH SERVICES

Public Health Dept **262.896.8430**
Fax 262.970.6670
Web ....www.waukeshacounty.gov
E-mail ....pschuler@waukeshacounty.gov
   615 W Moreland Blvd, Waukesha, WI 53188
   Peter Schuler, Health Officer

JUSTICE AGENCY

The Juvenile Ctr **262.548.7731**
Fax 262.896.8031
   521 Riverview Ave, Waukesha, WI 53188
   Micheal L. Sturdevant, Manager

COURTS

Juvenile Court **262.548.7449**
Fax 262.548.7459
   521 Riverview Ave, Rm Jc103, Waukesha, WI 53188
   Kelly K. Haag, Clerk Of Juvenile Court

POLICE AND SHERIFF

Police Dept **262.524.3831**
Fax 262.524.3897
Web ....www.ci.waukesha.wi.us
   1901 Delafield St, Waukesha, WI 53188-2200
   Russell Jack, Chief

Sheriff's Dept **262.548.7126**
Fax 262.548.7887
E-mail ....dtrawicki@waukeshacounty.gov
   515 W Moreland Blvd, Waukesha, WI 53188
   Daniel J. Trawicki, Sheriff

EDUCATION SERVICES

Child And Family Ctr Headstart **262.567.7308**
   815 S Concord Rd, Oconomowoc, WI 53066-3415

Waupaca County

COURTS

Circuit Court Branch II **715.258.6425**
Fax 715.258.6440
   811 Harding St, Waupaca, WI 54981
   Honorable John P. Hoffman, Judge

POLICE AND SHERIFF

Sheriff's Dept **715.258.4466**
Fax 715.258.4471
Web ....www.co.waupaca.wi.us
   1402 Royalton St, Waupaca, WI 54981-1695
   Brad Hardell, Sheriff

Waushara County

GENERAL HEALTH SERVICES

Public Health Dept **920.787.6590**
Fax 920.787.6511
Web ....www.co.waushara.wi.us
   230 Park St, Wautoma, WI 54982-9031
   Patti Wohfiel, Health Director

COURTS

Circuit Court **920.787.0417**
Fax 920.787.0481
Web ....www.co.waushara.wi.us
E-mail ....melissa.zamzow@wicourts.gov
   209 S St Marie St, Wautoma, WI 54982-8114
   Guy Dutcher, Judge

POLICE AND SHERIFF

Sheriff's Ofc **920.787.3321**
Fax 920.787.7685
Web ....www.co.waushara.wi.us
E-mail ....sheriff@co.waushara.wi.us
   430 E Division St, Wautoma, WI 54982-6923
   David R. Peterson, Sheriff

Winnebago County

SOCIAL SERVICES

Dept Of Human Svcs **920.236.4600**
Fax 920.303.4792
Web ....www.co.winnebago.wi.us
E-mail ....dhs@co.winnebago.wi.us
   220 Washington Ave, Oshkosh, WI 54903-5030
   Bill Topel, Director

GENERAL HEALTH SERVICES

Health Dept **920.232.3000**
Fax 920.232.3370
Web ....www.co.winnebago.wi.us
E-mail ....cdraws@co.winnebago.wi.us
   112 Otter Ave, Oshkosh, WI 54903
   Cindy Draws, Hiv Coordinator

Menasha Health Dept **920.967.5119**
Fax 920.967.5247
Web ....www.cityofmenasha.wi.gov
E-mail ....mfritz@ci.menasha.wi.us
   316 Racine St, Menasha, WI 54952
   Sue Nett, Rn, Health Officer

Neenah Health Dept **920.886.6155**
Fax 920.886.6166
Web ....www.ci.neenah.wi.us
   211 Walnut St, Neenah, WI 54956
   Paul Spiegel, Interim Health Officer

Oshkosh Health Dept **920.236.5030**
Fax 920.236.5186
Web ....www.ci.oshkosh.wi.us
   215 Church Ave, Oshkosh, WI 54903
   Mark Ziemer, Interim Director

JUSTICE AGENCY

Div Of Juvenile Corrections **920.729.3900**
Fax 920.729.3903
E-mail ....john.gosar@doc.state.wi.us
   1356 American Dr, Neenah, WI 54956-1402
   John Gosar, JPPA

POLICE AND SHERIFF

Sheriff's Dept **920.236.7331**
Fax 920.236.4902
E-mail ....jamtz@co.winnebago.wi.us
   4311 Jackson St, Oshkosh, WI 54901
   John Matz, Sheriff

EDUCATION SERVICES

Special Education **920.233.2372**
Fax 920.424.3478
Web www.cesa6.k12.wi.us
E-mail ....kfuchs@cesa6.k12.wi.us
   2300 State Rd. 44, Oshkosh, WI 54903
   Keith Fuchs, Executive Director

Wood County

SOCIAL SERVICES

Human Services **715.421.8600**
Fax 715.421.8693
Web ....www.co.wood.wi.us
E-mail ....socialservices@co.wood.wi.us
　400 Market St, Wisconsin Rapids, WI 54494-4868
　Diane Cable, Director

United Way **715.421.0390**
Fax 715.421.3740
Web ....www.uwswc.org
E-mail ....bruce@uwiw.org
　351 Oak St, Wisconsin Rapids, WI 54494-4362
　Bruce Tremble, Director

GENERAL HEALTH SERVICES

Health Dept **715.387.8646**
Fax 715.389.1285
　630 S Central Ave Ste 303, Marshfield, WI 54449
　Sue Kunferman, Rn, Health Officer/director

Health Dept **715.421.8911**
Fax 715.421.8962
Web ....www.co.wood.wi.us
E-mail ....skunferman@co.wood.wi.us
　184 2Nd St N, Wisconsin Rapids, WI 54494-4162
　Susan Kunferman, Health Officer

COURTS

Circuit Court **715.421.8520**
Fax 715.421.8896
Web ....www.wicourts.com
　400 Market St, Wisconsin Rapids, WI 54494-4868
　Cindy Joosten, Clerk

POLICE AND SHERIFF

Sheriff's Dept **715.421.8715**
Fax 715.421.8754
　400 Market St, Wisconsin Rapids, WI 54495
　Thomas Reichert, Sheriff

SPECIAL SERVICES AGENCIES

ADOPTION AGENCIES

Adoption Svcs Inc **262.513.0443**
Fax 262.241.8765
Web ....www.adoptionservicesinc.com
E-mail ....info@adoptionservicesinc.com
　2727 N Grandview Blvd Ste 114, Waukesha,
　WI 53188-6100
　Donna Strayer, Director

Alliance for Children and Families **414.359.1040**
Fax 414.359.1074
Web www.alliance1.org
　11700 W. Lake Park Drive, Milwaukee, WI 53224
　COA accredited organization.

Bethany Christian Svcs **920.923.6577**
Fax 920.923.3001
Web ....www.bethany.org/wisconsin
E-mail ....bcsfonddulac@bethany.org
　101 Wisconsin American Dr Ste 400, Fond Du Lac,
　WI 54937
　Susan Hubbell, Director

Bethany Christian Svcs **262.547.6557**
Fax 262.547.3644
Web ....www.bethany.org
E-mail ....info@bethany.org
　North 14 West 23755 Stoneridge Dr, Ste 265,
　Waukesha, WI 53188
　Wendy Rhodes, Birth Parent Counselor

Community Adoption Ctr Inc **920.499.2787**
Fax 920.499.2795
E-mail ....info@CommunityAdoptionCenter.com
　926 Willard Dr, Ste 136, Green Bay, WI 54305
　Laurie Resch, Executive Director

Crossroads Adoption Svcs **715.386.5550**
Fax 715.386.5670
Web ....www.crossroadsadoption.com
E-mail ....kids@crossroadsadoption.com
　502 2nd St, Ste 205, Hudson, WI 54016
　Joan Clarkson, Director

Edward J Plagemann **414.271.3399**
Fax 414.271.9868
E-mail ....edplag@sbcglobal.net
　710 N Plankinton Ave Ste 801, Milwaukee, WI 53203
　Edward J Plagemann, Attorney

Elliott B Light-Law Ofc **715.834.6662**
　600 Scobie Ln, Eau Claire, WI 54703
　Elliot B. Light, Managing Attorney

**Family Service Association of Sheboygan,
Inc.** **920.458.3784**
Fax 920.458.3785
Web ....www.cccsonline.org
　1930 North 8th Street, Sheboygan, WI 53081
　COA accredited organization.

**Financial Information & Service Center dba CCCS of
Northeastern Wisconsin** **920.886.1000**
Fax 920.886.1005
Web ....www.fisc-cccs.org
　1800 Appleton Road, Menasha, WI 54952
　COA accredited organization.

Stowell Associates SelectStaff Inc **414.963.2600**
Fax 414.963.2605
Web ....www.elderselectstaff.com
　4485 N. Oakland Avenue, Milwaukee,
　WI 53211-1611
　COA accredited organization.

ADVOCACY RESOURCES

Frank J Remington Ctr **608.262.2030**
E-mail ....ldshear@wisc.edu
　975 Bascom Mall, Madison, WI 53706
　Leslie D Shear, Director

Legal Action of Wisconsin Inc **414.278.7722**
　230 W Wells St, Ste 800, Milwaukee, WI 53203
　John Ebbott, Executive Director

Legal Aid Society **414.225.1437**
E-mail ....pbruce@dkattorneys.com
　10201 W Watertown Plank Rd, Milwaukee, WI 53226
　Peter Bruce, Attorney

Lehto Law Office **424.778.1540**
E-mail ....dlehto@live.com
　933 N Mayfair Rd # 308, Wauwatosa, WI 53226
　Duke Lehto

**St. Agnes Hospital Domestic Violence
Program** **920.926.4207**
Fax 920.926.8875
E-mail ....willr@agnesian.com
　430 E Division St, Fond Du Lac, WI 54935-4597
　Rene Firari Will, Director

BEHAVIORAL HEALTH TREATMENT

Acacia Clinic **414.871.9111**
Fax 414.871.9121
E-mail ....help@acaciaclinic.com
　6040 W Lisbon Ave Ste 102, Milwaukee, WI 53210
　Kathy Farell, Director

Arbor Vitae Woodruff School **715.356.3282**
Fax 715.358.2933
Web www.avw.k12.wi.us
E-mail ....lcurrie@avw.k12.wi.us
　11065 Old 51 N, Woodruff, WI 54568-9721
　Lynne Currie, Director

Aurora Psychiatric Hospital **414.454.6600**
E-mail ....jamie.lewiston@aurora.org
　1220 Dewey Avenue, Wauwatosa, WI 53213
　Ms. Jamie Lewiston, Accreditation Manager
　Joint Commission accredited organization.

**Bell Therapy, Inc./Willowglen Academy,
Inc.** **414.225.4460**
Fax 414.225.4475
Web ....www.phoenixcaresystems.com
　1744 N Farwell Ave, Milwaukee, WI 53202
　La Kelvin Hill, Director of Operations
　CARF accredited programs available.

Boys & Girls Club Of The Fox Valley **920.731.0555**
Web ....bgclubfoxvalley.org
　117 S Locust St, Appleton, WI 54914-5228

Cap Svcs Inc **715.258.9575**
Web ....www.capserv.org
　101 Tower Rd, Waupaca, WI 54981-1659
　Mary Patoka, Director

Carmelite Home, Inc **414.258.4791**
Fax 414.258.8464
E-mail ....nancyssd@tds.net
　1214 Kavanaugh Pl, Milwaukee, WI 53213-2506
　James E. Lewis, Director

Community Psychological Svcs **920.324.4358**
Fax 920.324.4737
　1208 S Watertown St, Waupun, WI 53963
　Maureen Deyoung, Director

Cornerstone Counseling **262.542.3255**
　120 S Main St, Jefferson, WI 53549-1632
　Angie Gjertson, Director

Eau Claire Academy **715.834.6681**
Fax 715.834.9954
Web ....www.clinicarecorp.com
　550 N Dewey St, Eau Claire, WI 54703
　Charles Albrent, Executive Director

Family And Children's Ctr **608.785.0001**
Fax 608.785.0002
Web ....www.fcconline.org
E-mail ....jburgess@fcconline.org
　1707 Main St Fl 5TH, La Crosse, WI 54601-4286
　John Burgess, President/CEO

Family Place **608.845.2233**
E-mail ....mbk@chorus.net
　8283 N Riley Rd, Verona, WI 53593-9081
　Jack Bradt, MD, Psychiatrist

Family Service, Inc. **608.316.1127**
Fax 608.252.1333
Web ....www.fsmad.org
　128 E. Olin Avenue, Madison, WI 53713
　COA accredited organization.

Felgus Medical Practice **608.255.0669**
　660 W Washington Ave, Madison, WI 53703
　Matthew Felgus, Psychiatrist

First Step Clinic **414.578.8500**
Fax 414.578.8503
　10012 W Capitol Dr, Milwaukee, WI 53222
　Kenneth Sherry, Psychiatrist

Wisconsin

Fosdal Medical Practice 608.836.6647
Fax 608.836.5580
E-mail ....fafosdal@msn.com
  6647 Columbus Dr, Middleton, WI 53562-2814
  Frederick Fosdal, Psychiatrist

Gundersen Lutheran Medical Center, Inc. 608.782.7300
Web ....www.gundluth.org
E-mail ....crsteffe@gundluth.org
  1910 South Avenue, La Crosse, WI 54601
  Mrs. Carla Steffen, Accreditation Manager
  Joint Commission accredited organization.

Libertas Treatment Center 920.498.8600
Web ....www.libertasgb.org
E-mail ....pryan@sjcf.hshs.org
  1701 Dousman Street, Green Bay, WI 54303
  Mr. Patrick Ryan, Accreditation Manager
  Joint Commission accredited organization.

Lighthouse Clinic 414.964.9200
Fax 414.964.4816
Web ....www.thelighthouseclinic.com
  2524 E Webster Place Ste 203, Milwaukee,
  WI 53211-4253
  Margo Renner, Phd, Director

Lutheran Social Svcs 262.896.3440
Fax 262.896.3450
Web ....www.lsswis.org
E-mail ....dlawson@lsswis.org
  2000 W Bluemound Rd, Waukesha, WI 53186-2787
  David Lawson, Executive Director

Lutheran Social Svcs 715.834.2046
Fax 715.834.7563
Web ....www.lsswis.org
E-mail ....thakala@lsswis.org
  1320 W Clairemont Ave Ste 200, Eau Claire,
  WI 54701-6027
  Ted Hakala, Regional Vice President

Lutheran Social Svcs 608.277.0610
Fax 608.270.6651
Web ....www.lsswis.org
E-mail ....phill@lsswis.org
  6314 Odana Rd, Madison, WI 53719-1120
  Peggy Hill, Clinic Manager

Mendota Mental Health Institute 608.301.1046
E-mail ....labinwm@dhfs.state.wi.us
  301 Troy Drive, Madison, WI 53704
  Ms. Wendy LaBine, Accreditation Manager
  Joint Commission accredited organization.

Mental Health Assoc Of Wisconsin 262.547.0769
Fax 262.547.1609
Web ....www.mhawauk.org
E-mail ....lmclean@mhawauk.org
  South 22 West 22660 E Broadway, Ste 5S, Waukesha,
  WI 53186
  Lisa Mclean, Executive Director

Mental Health Center 608.280.2700
Fax 608.280.2707
Web ....www.mhcdc.org
  625 West Washington Avenue, Madison, WI 53703
  CARF accredited programs available.

Milwaukee Academy 414.257.3141
Fax 414.257.3151
Web ....www.clinicarecorp.com
  9501 Watertown Plank Road, Wauwatosa,
  WI 53213-0397
  COA accredited organization.

Milwaukee Psychiatric Hospital 414.454.6600
Fax 414.454.6604
  1220 Dewey Ave, Milwaukee, WI 53213-2504
  Anthony Meyers Md, Medical Director

Oconomowoc Developmental Training Ctr 262.569.5515
Fax 262.569.5513
Web ....www.odtc-wi.com
  36100 Genesee Lake Rd, Oconomowoc,
  WI 53066-9202
  Mike Purpura, Community Director

PCS - Pastoral Counseling Service 414.453.7306
Fax 414.453.7080
Web ....www.pastoralcounselingservice.org
  2825 N Mayfair Rd, Ste 101, Wauwatosa, WI 53222
  Rev. Steven Fringer, Clinic Director

Quality Addiction Management, Inc. 262.549.6600
Fax 262.549.6698
Web ....www.qam-inc.com
  2422 N. Grandview Boulevard, Waukesha, WI 53188
  COA accredited organization.

Rogers Memorial Hospital 262.646.4411
Web ....www.rogershospital.org
E-mail ....klotz@rogershospital.org
  34700 Valley Road, Oconomowoc, WI 53066
  Mrs. Kathleen Lotz, Accreditation Manager
  Joint Commission accredited organization.

Saint Rose Youth & Family Ctr 414.466.9450
Fax 414.466.0730
E-mail ....jmaro@strosecenter.org
  3801 N 88th St, Milwaukee, WI 53222-2797
  James Maro, President/CEO

Southern Oaks Girls School 262.878.6500
Fax 262.878.6520
  21425 Spring St, Union Grove, WI 53182-9727
  Sue Boeke, Superintendent

St. Aemilian-Lakeside, Inc. 414.463.1880
Fax 414.463.2770
Web ....www.st-al.org
  8901 West Capitol Drive, Milwaukee, WI 53222-2770
  COA accredited organization.

St. Joseph's Hospital 715.717.7200
Web ....www.stjoeschipfalls.com
E-mail ....dgarcia@shec.hshs.org
  2661 County Highway I, Chippewa Falls, WI 54729
  Mrs. Dawn Garcia, Accreditation Manager
  Joint Commission accredited organization.

**Wheaton Franciscan Healthcare-All Saints,
Inc.** 262.687.4011
E-mail ....kenneth.morris@wfhc.org
  3801 Spring Street, Racine, WI 53405
  Mr. Ken Morris, Accreditation Manager
  Joint Commission accredited organization.

**Wisconsin Clearinghouse For Prevention
Resources** 608.262.7507
Fax 608.262.6346
Web ....www.uhs.wisc.edu/wch/
E-mail ....nkendall@wisc.edu
  1552 University Ave, Madison, WI 53726-4084
  Nancy Kendall, Senior Librarian

Wisconsin Family Ties 608.267.6888
Fax 608.267.6801
Web ....www.wifamilyties.org
E-mail ....hugh@wifamilyties.org
  16 N Carroll St Ste 640, Madison, WI 53703-2756
  Hugh Davis, Executive Director

Wyalusing Academy 608.326.6481
Fax 608.326.6166
Web ....www.clinicarecorp.com
  601 S. Beaumont Road, Prairie du Chien, WI 53821
  COA accredited organization.

CHILDREN'S HOSPITAL

Amery Regional Medical Center 715.268.8000
  265 Griffin St E, Amery, WI 54001
  Mike Caruschak, Director

Appleton Medical Center 920.731.4101
  1818 N Meade St, Appleton, WI 54911
  Jill Case-Wirth, Nursing Director

Aspirus Wausau Hospital 715.847.2121
  333 Pine Ridge Blvd, Wausau, WI 54401
  Dwayne Ervin, Chief Executive Officer

Aurora Bay Care Medical Center 920.288.8000
  2845 Greenbrier Rd, Green Bay, WI 54311
  Daniel Meyer, Administrator

Aurora Lakeland Medical Center 262.741.2000
  W3985 County Rd NN, Elkhorn, WI 53121
  Sharon Behrens, Administrative Director Of Nursing

Aurora Medical Center 262.948.5600
E-mail ....christine.olson@aurorahelathcare.org
  10400 S 75th St, Kenosha, WI 53142
  Chris Olson, Administrator

Aurora Medical Center of Oshkosh 920.456.6000
  855 N Westhaven Dr, Oshkosh, WI 54904
  Jeff Bard, Administrator

Aurora Medical Ctr 262.673.2300
  1032 E Sumner St, Hartford, WI 53027
  Donna Wolf, Administrative Assistant

Aurora Memorial Hospital of Burlington 262.767.6000
  252 McHenry St, Burlington, WI 53105
  Vicki Wis, Administrative Assistant

Aurora Sheboygan Memorial Med Ctr 920.451.5000
  2629 N Seventh St, Sheboygan, WI 53083
  Dave Graebner, Administrator

Aurora Sinai Medical Center 414.219.2000
  945 N 12th St, Milwaukee, WI 53233
  George Hincon, President

Aurora St Luke's Medical Center 414.649.6000
  2900 W Oklahoma Ave, Milwaukee, WI 53215
  Mary O'Brien, President

Aurora West Allis Medical Center 414.328.6000
  8901 W Lincoln Ave, West Allis, WI 53227
  Rick Kellar, Administrator

Baldwin Area Medical Center 715.684.3311
  730 10th Ave, Baldwin, WI 54002
  Jean Peavey, Nursing Director

Bay Area Medical Center 715.735.6621
  3100 Shore Dr, Marinette, WI 54143
  Ed Harding, Chief Executive Officer

Beaver Dam Community Hospital 920.887.7181
E-mail ....kmiller@cdch.org
  707 S University Ave, Beaver Dam, WI 53916
  Kimberly Miller, Chief Executive Officer

Bellin Memorial Hospital 920.433.3500
  744 S Webster Ave, Green Bay, WI 54301
  Amy Stlaurent, Vice President

Beloit Memorial Hospital 608.364.5011
  1969 W Hart Rd, Beloit, WI 53511
  Gregory Britton, Chief Executive Officer

Berlin Memorial Hospital 920.361.1313
  225 Memorial Dr, Berlin, WI 54923
  John Feeney, Chief Executive Officer

Black River Memorial Hospital 715.284.5361
E-mail ....gayners@brmh.net
  711 W Adams St, Black River Falls, WI 54615
  Stan Gaynor, Chief Executive Officer

Boscobel Area Health Care 608.375.4112
  205 Parker St, Boscobel, WI 53805
  Richard Rogers, Interim Administrator

Burnett Medical Center 715.463.5353
  257 W St George Ave, Grantsburg, WI 54840
  Gordy Lewis, Chief Executive Officer

Calumet Medical Center 920.849.2386
  614 Memorial Dr, Chilton, WI 53014
  Tim Richman, Director

Children's Hospital of Wisconsin 414.266.2000
Web ....www.chw.org
E-mail ....djamieson@chw.org
  9000 W Wisconsin Ave, Wauwatosa, WI 53226
  Donna Jamieson, Nursing Director

Children's Hospital of Wisconsin-Fox Va **920.969.7900**
1300 Second Ave 3rd Fl S, Neenah, WI 54956
Tim Klunk, Director

Columbia St Mary's Hospital Milwaukee **414.291.1000**
2323 N Lake Dr, Milwaukee, WI 53211
Mark Taylor, Chief Executive Officer

Columbia St Mary's Hospital Ozaukee **262.243.7300**
13111 N Port Washington Rd, Mequon, WI 53097
Deb Friberg, Vice President

Columbus Community Hospital **920.623.2200**
1515 Park Ave, Columbus, WI 53925
John Russell, Chief Executive Officer

Community Memorial Hospital **920.846.3444**
855 S Main St, Oconto Falls, WI 54154

Community Memorial Hospital **262.251.1000**
W180 N8085 Town Hall Rd, Menomonee Falls, WI 53051
Dennis Pollard, Chief Executive Officer

Cumberland Memorial Hospital **715.822.2741**
1110 Seventh Ave, Cumberland, WI 54829
Deb Kunserman, Chief Financial Officer

Divine Savior Healthcare **608.742.4131**
E-mail ....edenman@dshealthcare.com
2817 New Pinery Rd, Portage, WI 53901
Michael Decker, Chief Executive Officer

Eagle River Memorial Hospital **715.479.7411**
201 Hospital Rd, Eagle River, WI 54521
Sheila Clough, Chief Executive Officer

Flambeau Hospital **715.762.2484**
98 Sherry Ave, Park Falls, WI 54552
Dave Grundstrom, Administrator

Fort HealthCare **920.568.5000**
611 E Sherman Ave, Fort Atkinson, WI 53538
Mike Wallace, Chief Executive Officer

Franciscan Skemp Healthcare Arcadia Cam **608.323.3341**
464 S St Joseph Ave, Arcadia, WI 54612
Barlene, Director

Franciscan Skemp Hlthcre La Crosse Camp **608.785.0940**
700 West Ave S, La Crosse, WI 54601

Good Samaritan Health Center of Merrill **715.536.5511**
601 Center Ave S, Merrill, WI 54452
Kris Mcgarigle, Director

Grant Regional Health Center **608.723.2143**
E-mail ....nclapp@grantregional.com
507 S Monroe St, Lancaster, WI 53813
Nicole Clapp, Chief Executive Officer

Holy Family Memorial Medical Center **920.320.2011**
2300 Western Ave, Manitowoc, WI 54220
Mark Herzog, Chief Executive Officer

Howard Young Medical Center **715.356.8000**
240 Maple St, Woodruff, WI 54568
Shila Clough, Chief Executive Officer

Hudson Hospital **715.531.6000**
405 Stageline Rd, Hudson, WI 54016
Marianne Furlong, Chief Executive Officer

Indianhead Medical Center **715.468.7833**
113 Fourth Ave, Shell Lake, WI 54871
Paul Naglosky, Owner

Lakeview Medical Center **715.234.1515**
1700 W Stout St, Rice Lake, WI 54868
Edward Wolf, Chief Executive Officer

Langlade Hospital **715.623.2331**
112 E Fifth Ave, Antigo, WI 54409
David Schneider, Director

Luther Hospital **715.838.3311**
1221 Whipple St, Eau Claire, WI 54702
Lynn Frank, Chief Nursing Officer

Luther Midelfort Chippewa Valley **715.568.2000**
1501 Thompson St, Bloomer, WI 54724
Ed Wittrrock, Administrator

Luther Midelfort Oakridge **715.597.3121**
13025 Eighth St, Osseo, WI 54758
Mike Ryan, Manager

Mayo Clinic Health System **608.269.2132**
310 W Main St, Sparta, WI 54656
Kim Hawthorne, Director

Mayo Clinic Health System Menomonie **715.235.5531**
2321 Stout Rd, Menomonie, WI 54751
Hank Simpson, Chief Executive Officer

Mayo Clinic Health System Northland **715.537.3186**
1222 Woodland Ave, Barron, WI 54812
Karolyn Bartell, Administrator

Medical Center **920.743.5566**
323 S 18th Ave, Sturgeon Bay, WI 54235
Jodi Hibbard, Director Of The Clinic

Memorial Health Center **715.748.8100**
135 S Gibson St, Medford, WI 54451
Gregg Olson, Chief Executive Officer

Memorial Hosp & Nursing Hom **715.532.5561**
900 College Ave W, Ladysmith, WI 54848
Michael Shaw, Chief Executive Officer

Memorial Hospital **608.776.4466**
800 Clay St, Darlington, WI 53530
Sherry Kudronowicz, Administrator

Memorial Medical Center Ashland **715.685.5500**
1615 Maple Ln, Ashland, WI 54806
Dan Hymans, Chief Executive Officer

Mercy Walworth Hospital & Medical Ctr **262.245.0535**
N2950 State Rd 67, Lake Geneva, WI 53147
Javon Vea, Chief Executive Officer

Meriter Hospital **608.417.6000**
202 S Park ST, Madison, WI 53715
Jim Woodward, Chief Executive Officer

Mile Bluff Medical Center **608.847.6161**
1050 Division St, Mauston, WI 53948
James Okese, Chief Executive Officer

Monroe Clinic **608.324.1000**
515 22nd Ave, Monroe, WI 53566
Mike Sanders, Chief Executive Officer

Moundview Memorial Hospital & Clinics **608.339.3331**
402 W Lake St, Friendship, WI 53934
Jeremy Norminton, Chief Executive Officer

New London Family Medical Center **920.531.2000**
1405 Mill St, New London, WI 54961

Oconomowoc Memorial Hospital **262.569.9400**
791 Summit Ave, Oconomowoc, WI 53066
John Robertstad, Chief Executive Officer

Osceola Medical Center **715.294.2111**
2600 65th Ave, Osceola, WI 54020
Jeff Meyer, Chief Executive Officer

Our Lady of Victory Hospital **715.644.5571**
1120 Pine St, Stanley, WI 54768
Cynthia Eichman, President

Reedsburg Area Medical Center **608.524.6487**
2000 N Dewey St, Reedsburg, WI 53959
Robert Van Meeteren, Executive Director

Richland Hospital **608.647.6321**
333 E Second St, Richland Center, WI 53581

Ripon Medical Center **920.748.3101**
933 Newbury St, Ripon, WI 54971
Kerri Heign, Director

River Falls Area Hospital **715.307.6000**
1629 E Division St, River Falls, WI 54022
David Miller, President

Riverside Medical Centre **715.258.1000**
800 Riverside Dr, Waupaca, WI 54981
Kan Poss, Chief Executive Officer

Sacred Heart Hospital **715.717.4121**
900 W Clairemont Ave, Eau Claire, WI 54701
Amy Dwyer, Chief Nursing Officer

Sacred Heart Hospital **715.453.7700**
401 W Mohawk Dr, Tomahawk, WI 54487
Monica Hilt, Chief Executive Officer

Sacred Heart St Mary's Hospitals **715.361.2000**
2251 N Shore Dr, Rhinelander, WI 54501
Monica Hilt, President/CEO

Saint Clare's Hospital **715.393.3000**
3400 Ministry Pkwy, Weston, WI 54476
Mary Krueger, Chief Executive Officer

Saint Michael's Hospital **715.346.5000**
900 Illinois Ave, Stevens Point, WI 54481
Jeff Martin, President

Sauk Prairie Memorial Hospital **608.643.3311**
80 First St, Prairie du Sac, WI 53578
Larry Schroeder, Chief Executive Officer

Southwest Health Center **608.348.2331**
1400 Eastside Rd, Platteville, WI 53818
Lisa Schweitzer, Nursing Director

Spooner Health System **715.635.2111**
819 Ash St, Spooner, WI 54801
Mike Schafer, Chief Executive Officer

St Elizabeth Hospital **920.738.2000**
1501 S Oneida St, Appleton, WI 54915
Dan Neufelder, Chief Executive Officer

St Joseph's Hospital **715.387.1713**
611 St Joseph Ave, Marshfield, WI 54449
Brian Kief, President

St Joseph's Hospital **715.723.1811**
2661 County Hwy I, Chippewa Falls, WI 54729
Joan Coffman, Chief Executive Officer

St Joseph's Hospital West Bend **262.334.5533**
3200 Pleasant Valley Rd, West Bend, WI 53095
Michael Laird, President

St Mary's Hospital **608.251.6100**
700 S Park St, Madison, WI 53715
Frank Byromb, Chief Executive Officer

St Mary's Hospital Medical Center **920.498.4200**
Web ....www.stmgb.org
1726 Shawano Ave, Green Bay, WI 54303
Therese Candle, Chief Executive Officer

Stoughton Hospital Assn **608.873.6611**
900 Ridge St, Stoughton, WI 53589
Jane Mcguire, Assistant

Tomah Memorial Hospital **608.372.2181**
321 Butts Ave, Tomah, WI 54660
Phil Stuart, Chief Executive Officer

United Hospital of Wisconsin **262.656.2261**
6308 Eighth Ave 6th Fl, Kenosha, WI 53143
Rick Schmidt, Chief Executive Officer

United Hospitals **262.656.2011**
9555 76th St, Pleasant Prairie, WI 53158
Ric Schmidt, Chief Executive Officer

University of WI Hospital & Clinics **608.263.6400**
E-mail ....dkatenbahensky@uwhealth.org
600 Highland Ave, Madison, WI 53792
Donna Katen-Bahensky, President

Upland Hills Health **608.930.8000**
800 Compassion Way, Dodgeville, WI 53533

Vernon Memorial Healthcare **608.637.2101**
E-mail ....pubrel@zmh.org
507 S Main St, Viroqua, WI 54665
Garith Steiner, Chief Executive Officer

Veterans Affairs Medical Center **608.372.3971**
500 E Veterans St, Tomah, WI 54660

Watertown Regional Medical Center 920.261.4210
125 Hospital Dr, Watertown, WI 53098

Waukesha Memorial Hospital 262.928.1000
725 American Ave, Waukesha, WI 53188
John Robertstad, President

Waupun Memorial Hospital 920.324.5581
620 W Brown St, Waupun, WI 53963
Deann Thurmer, Chief Operating Officer

Westfields Hospital 715.246.2101
535 Hospital Rd, New Richmond, WI 54017
Jean Needham, President

**Wheaton Franciscan Healthcare St
Francisco** 414.647.5000
3237 S 16th St, Milwaukee, WI 53215

**Wheaton Franciscan Hlthcre Elmbrook
Mem** 262.785.2000
19333 West North Ave, Brookfield, WI 53045
Debra Stanritge, President

Wild Rose Community Memorial Hospital 920.622.3257
601 Grove Ave, Wild Rose, WI 54984
Dawn Shouman, Administrator

COUNSELING SERVICES

Lutheran Counseling And Family Svcs 800.291.4513
Fax...414.536.8348
Web..www.lcfswi.org
E-mail..............................cmeseck@lcfswi.org
3800 North Mayfair Rd, Sheboygan, WI 53081-5018
Chuck Meseck, Director

Orion Family Svcs 608.270.2511
Fax...608.270.0467
E-mail..............................oriondir@chorus.net
6333 Odana Rd Ste 20, Madison, WI 53719-1130
Hugh Meyers, Director

**University Of Wisconsin-Madison Speech And Hearing
Clinics** 608.262.6462
Fax...608.262.6466
E-mail..............................jedward2@wisc.edu
1975 Willow Dr, Madison, WI 53706
Jan Edward, Chairman

CRISIS & SHELTER CARE

Advocates Of Ozaukee Domestic Violence 262.284.3577
Fax...262.284.4403
Web..www.advocates-oz.org
E-mail..............................execdir@advocates-oz.org
PO Box 80166, Saukville, WI 53080-0166
Barbara Fisher, Director

Asha Family Svcs Inc-Domestic Violence 414.875.1511
Fax...414.875.1217
Web..www.ashafamilyservices.org
E-mail..............................sistahasha@att.net
3719 W Center St, Milwaukee, WI 53210
Antonia Vann, Director

Assoc For The Prevention Family Violence 262.723.4653
Fax...262.723.8367
E-mail..............................apfvmail@charterinternet.com
35 S Wisconsin St, Elkhorn, WI 53121
Gen Kriahn-reed, Director

**Bad River Chippewa Tribe-Domestic
Violence** 715.682.7127
Fax...715.682.7883
Web..www.badriver.com
E-mail..............................brdap@badriver.com
72772 Elm st, Odanah, WI 54861
Heidi Burns, Director

Beloit Domestic Violence Ctr 608.364.1083
Fax...608.365.4664
Web..www.fsofswani.org
E-mail..............................Cforster@Fsofswani.Org
PO Box 476, Beloit, WI 53512-0476
Corita Forster, Director

Bethesda Lutheran Home 920.261.3050
Fax...920.261.8441
Web..www.blc.org
700 Hoffman Dr, Watertown, WI 53094
Robert Heinen, Md, Medical Director

Bolton Refuge House, Inc 715.834.0628
Fax...715.824.9634
E-mail..............................boltonrefugehouse@att.net
807 S Farwell, Eau Claire, WI 54703
Gerald Wilkie, Director

Briarpatch 608.251.6211
Fax...608.245.2551
Web..www.youthsos.org
E-mail..............................cbohrend@briarpatch.com
1955 Atwood Ave, Madison, WI 53704-5220
Casey Bohrend, Executive Director

Christine Ann Domestic Abuse Svcs 920.729.6395
Fax...920.235.2572
E-mail..............................info@christineann.net
206 Algoma Blvd, Oshkosh, WI 54901
Julie Sevola, Director

**Community Refferal Agency- Domestic
Violence** 715.825.4414
Fax...715.825.4418
403 Gandy View Ave, Milltown, WI 54858
Anne Frey, Director

Council on Domestic Violence 715.362.6841
Fax...715.362.9650
Web..www.tricountycouncil.org
3716 Country Dr Ste 1, Rhinelander, WI 54501
Shellie Holmes, Director

Ctr Against Sexual-Domestic Abuse 715.392.3136
Fax...715.392.8463
Web..www.casda.org
E-mail..............................kelly@casda.org
2231 Catlin Ave Ste 1, Superior, WI 54880
Kelly Burger, Executive Director

Daystar Inc-Domestic Violence Program 414.385.0334
Fax...414.385.0336
Web..www.astarinc.org
E-mail..............................mary.franw@astarinc.org
PO Box 2130, Milwaukee, WI 53201-2130
Mary Frances Willcoxson, Director

Domestic Abuse Intervention Svcs 608.251.1237
Fax...608.284.2134
Web..www.abuseintervention.org
E-mail..............................lauran@abuseintervention.org
PO Box 1761, Madison, WI 53701-1761
Laura Noel, Director

Domestic Abuse Project 608.374.6975
Fax...608.374.4143
E-mail..............................ceceliapoe@gmail.com
1118 W Veterans St, Tomah, WI 54656
Cecelia Poe, Assistant Director

Domestic Abuse Project 608.269.7853
Fax...608.269.7063
505 Douglas St, Sparta, WI 54656
Celia Poe, Assistant Director

Domestic Violence 715.479.2912
3716 Country Dr Ste1, Rhinelander, WI 54501
Pam Cira, Advocate

Domestic Violence Ctr 920.684.4661
Fax...920.684.6344
Web..www.dvonline.net
E-mail..............................Sue@Dvonline.Net
1127 S 22nd St, Manitowoc, WI 54220-4951
Sue Sippel, Executive Director

Family Advocates Inc-Domestic Violence 608.348.5995
Fax...608.348.3184
1101 Carmichael Rd, St Croix County Government
Center, Hudson, WI 54016-7708
Robin Wiegel, Executive Director

Family Ctr Inc 715.421.1511
Fax...715.421.3036
Web..www.familyctr.org
E-mail..............................info@familyetr.org
500 25Th St N, Wisconsin Rapids, WI 54494-5549
Arline Hillsted, Director

Family Intervention Center 608.637.7052
Fax...608.637.8500
Web..www.fccnetwork.org
E-mail..............................Sbohland@fccnetwork.Org
1321 N Main St, Viroqua, WI 54665-1156
Megan Tully, Director

Family Support Ctr-Domestic Violence 715.723.1138
Fax...715.723.8460
Web..www.chippewafallsfsc.org
E-mail..............................gerifsc@sbcglobal.net
PO Box 143, Chippewa Falls, WI 54729-0143
Geri Segal, Director

Friends Aware Of Violent Relationships 920.923.1743
Fax...920.923.9982
Web..www.solutionsfdl.com
39 N Sophia St, Fond Du Lac, WI 54935-3343
Lindy Kimble, Director

**Friends Of Abused Framilies-Domestic
Violence** 262.334.5598
Fax...262.334.7725
Web..www.fafinc.org
E-mail..............................executivedirector@fafinc.org
PO Box 117, West Bend, WI 53095-0117
Ms Lisa Krenke, Director

Golden House 920.435.0100
Fax...920.431.7286
Web..www.goldenhousegb.org
E-mail..............................karen@goldenhousegb.org
1120 University Ave, Green Bay, WI 54302-1416
Karen Faulkner, Director

Harbor House Domestic Abuse Programs 920.832.1666
Fax...920.832.1622
Web..www.harborhouseonline.org
E-mail..............................beths@harborhousedap.org
720 W 5th St, Appleton, WI 54914-5368
Beth Schnor, Director

Haven Inc-Domestic Violence 715.536.9563
Fax...715.536.3816
E-mail..............................executivedirector@haveninc.org
1106 E Edge St, Merrill, WI 54452
Judy Woller, Director

Help Of Door Co. 920.743.8785
Fax...920.743.9984
Web..www.helpofdoorcounty.org
E-mail..............................help@helpofdoorcounty.org
219 Green Bay Rd, Sturgeon Bay, WI 54235
Ursula Bunnell, Executive Director

Hmong/American Friendship Assoc. 414.344.6575
Fax...414.344.6581
Web..www.hmongamer.org
E-mail..............................loneng@hmongamer.org
3824 W Vliet St, Milwaukee, WI 53208-2848
Loneng Kiatouaakaysy, Executive Director

Homme Youth And Family Programs 715.253.2116
Fax...715.253.3586
W18105 Hemlock Rd, Wittenberg, WI 54449
Greg Robbins, Executive Director

Hope House-Domestic Violence Program 608.356.9123
Fax...608.356.9863
Web..www.hopehousescw.org
E-mail..............................ellena@hopehousescw.org
720 Ash St, Baraboo, WI 53913-1247
Ellen Allen, Director

**Lac Du Flambeau Domestic Abuse
Program** 715.588.7660
Fax...715.588.2313
Web..www.lacduflambeautribe.com
157 Cedar Ave, Lac du Flambeau, WI 54538
Sarah Careful, Director

Lutheran Social Svcs Of Wi And Upper Mi......920.458.8381
Fax....920.458.5670
Web....www.lsswis.org
E-mail....projyth@lsswis.org
706 N.9th St., Sheboygan, WI 53081
Cathy Pape, Director

New Day Shelter-Domestic Violence..........715.682.9566
Fax....715.682.6865
E-mail....shelter@centurytel.net
1900 3rd St W, Ashland, WI 54806
Kathy Roper, Director

New Horizons Shelter-Womens Ctr..........608.791.2600
Fax....608.791.2626
Web....www.centurytel.net
E-mail....akappaus@centurytel.net
1223 Main st, La Crosse, WI 54602-2031
Ann Kappaus, Director

New Horizons- Domestic Violence Program....715.538.2810
Fax....715.538.4776
36245 Main St, Whitehall, WI 54773
Deb Hansen, Director

Norris Adolescent Ctr....262.662.5900
Fax....262.662.5688
Web....www.norriscenter.org
E-mail....dharris@norriscenter.org
W247S10395 Center Dr, Mukwonago, WI 53149-9166
Don Harris, Executive Director

Oakwood Haven Domestic Violence Program....715.634.9360
Fax....715.634.9228
E-mail....Deb@Victimnomore.Org
13394 W Trepania Rd, Hayward, WI 54843
Deb Butler, Director

Outreach Against Violence....608.685.2424
Fax....608.685.2425
E-mail....buffalocountyoutreach@yahoo.com
317 S 2nd St, Alma, WI 54610
Ms Jackie Miller-oates, Director

People Against A Violent Enviornment.......920.887.3810
Fax....920.885.2270
Web....www.charterinternet.com
E-mail....pave@peopleagainstaviolentenviornment.com
PO Box 561, Beaver Dam, WI 53916-0561
Jamie Kratz-Guooickson, Director

People Against Domestic And Sexual Abuse....920.674.6748
Fax....920.674.9849
Web....www.padajc.org
E-mail....Pada@ldcnet.Com
3995 Annex Rd, Jefferson, WI 53549
Amy O'Neil, Director

Personal Development Ctr -Domestic Violence....715.384.2971
Fax....715.384.7826
E-mail....pdcinc@tznet.com
630 S Central Ave, Ste 330, Marshfield, WI 54449
Renee Schulz, Director

Personal Development Ctr Outreach Ctr.......715.743.6401
Fax....715.743.6403
E-mail....pdcclark@tznet.com
216 Sunset Pl, Neillsville, WI 54456
Tamie Englebretson, Director

Positive Alternatives....715.235.9552
Fax....715.235.1075
Web....www.positive-alternatives.org
603 Terrill Rd, Menomonie, WI 54751
Kim Edwards, Director

Rainbow House Domestic Abuse Svcs.........715.735.6656
Fax....715.735.7293
Web....www.ourrainbowhouse.com
E-mail....ourrainbowhouse@new.rr.com
1530 Main St, Marinette, WI 54143
Trish Wschbisch, Supervisor

Red Cliff Domestic Violence Program.........715.779.3826
Fax....715.779.3771
88385 Pike Rd, Bayfield, WI 54814
Barb Flynn, Director

Safe Harbor Domestic Abuse Program........920.452.8611
Fax....920.452.2687
E-mail....info@sheboygansafeharbor.org
929 Niagara Ave, Sheboygan, WI 53082
Laura Roenitz, Director

Safe Haven Of Racine, Inc....262.632.0424
Fax....262.632.8758
Web....www.safehavenofracine.org
E-mail....thandrow@safehavenofracine.org
1030 Washington Ave, Racine, WI 53403
Tamara Handrow, Director

Sojourner Family Peace Centre....414.276.1911
Fax....414.276.5001
Web....www.familypeacecenter.org
135 West Wells Street, Milwaukee, WI 53212-3866
Carmen Pitre, Director

Sojourner Truth House....414.643.1777
Fax....414.643.1790
Web....www.sojournertruthhouse.org
E-mail....kstolpman@sojournertruthhouse.org
1135 North 33 St, Milwaukee, WI 53208
Kathie Stolpman, Director

Support Connections, Inc....262.548.9187
Fax....262.548.0789
Web....www.upwi.org
434 Madison St, Waukesha, WI 53188-3519
Nancy, Executive Director

The Bridge To Hope....715.235.9074
Fax....715.235.9073
Web....www.thebridgetohope.com
E-mail....manager@thebridgetohope.com
PO Box 700, Menomonie, WI 54751-0700
Naomi Cummings, Director

The Womens Ctr Inc.-Domestic Violence.......262.547.4600
Fax....262.522.3882
Web....www.twcwaukesha.org
E-mail....Mfkingsbury@twcwaukesha.Org
505 N East Ave, Waukesha, WI 53186
Marie Kingsbury, Director

Time Out Domestic Violence Program........715.635.5245
Fax....715.635.5245
Web....www.timeoutabuseshelter.org
E-mail....timeoutwashburn@yahoo.com
103 Oak St, Spooner, WI 54801-1439
Wendy Brown, Interim Director

Time-Out Family Abuse Shelter....715.532.6976
Fax....715.532.0972
619 Lake Ave W, Ladysmith, WI 54848
Wendy Brown, Executive Assistant

Turning Point Victims Domestic And Sexual Violence....715.425.6751
Fax....715.425.6908
Web....www.turningpoint-wi.org
E-mail....Info@Turningpoint-Wi.Org
445 W Johnson St, River Falls, WI 54022-0304
Kim Wojicik, Executive Director

Violence Intervention Project Inc....920.487.2111
Fax....920.487.2110
E-mail....vitaddv@vitadb.net
1405 Division St, Algoma, WI 54201-1431
Laura Giddley, Agency Advocate

Walkers Point Youth And Family Ctr..........414.647.8200
Fax....414.672.5340
Web....www.walkerspoint.org
E-mail....walkersp@sbcglobal.net
2030 W National Ave, Milwaukee, WI 53204-1157
Andre Olton, Executive Director

Weave....608.258.0077
PO Box 46037, Madison, WI 53744-6037

Wisconsin Associaton For Runaway Svcs......608.241.2649
E-mail....pbalke@sbcglobal.net
2318 E Dayton St, Madison, WI 53704-4949
Patricia Balke, Executive Director

Women And Children's Horizons....262.656.3500
Fax....262.656.3402
Web....www.wchkenosha.org
E-mail....kcomstock@wchkenosha.org
2525 63rd St, Kenosha, WI 53143-4333
Kathryn Comstock, Director

EDUCATION

Lutheran Counseling And Family Svcs........888.867.4840
Fax....414.536.8648
Web....www.lcfswi.org
E-mail....stevel@campluther.com
260 Vincent St, Fond Du Lac, WI 54935-5331
Steve Lande, Therapist

Marquette University Speech And Hearing Clinic....414.288.7426
Fax....414.288.3980
Web....www.marquette.edu/chs/sppa
E-mail....jacqueline.podewils@marquette.edu
604 N 16th St, Milwaukee, WI 53233-2117
Jacqueline Podewils, Coordinator

Path....877.842.7284
Fax....608.663.1271
Web....www.pathinc.org
E-mail....pgrimmer@pathinc.org
6000 Gisholt Dr Ste 109, Madison, WI 53713-4816
Peggy Grimmer, E. Regional Director

Picada-Prevention And Intervention Ctr For Alcohol And Drug Abuse....608.316.1118
Fax....608.252.1333
E-mail....dougm@fsmad.org
128 E Olin Ave Ste 100, Madison, WI 53713-1467
Doug Mcclain, Program Coordinator

Saint Coletta Of Wisconsin....920.674.4330
Fax....920.674.4603
Web....www.stcolettawi.org
E-mail....tloduca@stcolettawi.org
4637 County Trunk, Jefferson, WI 53549-9799
Toni Loduca, President, CEO

Vip Svcs, Inc....262.723.4043
Fax....262.723.4984
811 E Geneva St, Elkhorn, WI 53121-2008
Cindy Simonsen, Executive Director

Wisconsin Challenge Academy....608.269.9000
Fax....608.269.9001
E-mail....challange@wisconsin.gov
656 S O St, Fort Mccoy, WI 54656
M.g. Maclaren, Director

Wisconsin Council On Children And Families....608.284.0580
Fax....608.284.0583
Web....www.wccf.org
555 W Washington Ave Ste 200, Madison, WI 53703
Kenneth Taylor, Executive Director

FOSTER CARE AGENCIES

Adoptive Foster Families Support Group......920.623.3551
North 348 Hwy 89, Columbus, WI 53925

Anu Family Services Inc.....................**715.386.1547**
Fax...715.386.2541
   516 2nd St Ste 209, Hudson, WI 54016
   Amelia Franck Meyer, Chief Executive Officer

Catholic Charities Madison..................**608.833.4800**
E-mail..jrobinson@ccmadison.org
   426 South Yellowstone Dr, Ste 100, Madison,
   WI 53719
   J Robinson, Director

Families from Columbia.....................**920.845.2075**
   718 Marcks Lane, Luxemburg, WI 54217

Family Service of NE Wisconsin Inc.........**920.436.4360**
Fax...920.432.5966
E-mail........................postadoption@familyservicesnew.org
   300 Crooks St, Green Bay, WI 54301
   Tom Martin, President

Friends of Adoption.........................**715.832.6644**
E-mail..creppe@cclse.org
   448 S Dewey St, Eau Claire, WI 54703

Lutheran Counseling Family Services........**414.536.8333**
E-mail..adoption@lcfswi.org
   3800 North Mayfair Rd, Milwaukee, WI 53222
   Lisa Huebner, Administrative Assistant

Lutheran Social Services of Wisconsin.......**715.833.0992**
Fax...715.833.9466
   1320 West Clairemont Ave, Ste 200, Eau Claire,
   WI 54701
   Ted Hakala, Vice President

NAMASTE...................................**262.968.4564**
E-mail...nreinbold@wi.rr.com
   546 Black Earth Ct, Lancaster, WI 53813

Ours Through Adoption of NE Wisconsin.......**920.435.2626**
E-mail........................OursThroughAdoption@yahoo.com
   807 Linden Dr, Green Bay, WI 54311

SideKicks...................................**608.654.7607**
Fax...608.269.1850
   11672 Mascot Ave, Cashton, WI 54619

Special Needs Adoption Parent Support.......**262.376.0259**
   357 Juniper Ct, Grafton, WI 53024

Transracial Families of Milwaukee...........**414.486.7553**
E-mail....................transracialfamiliesmilw@hotmail.com
   PO Box 370961, Milwaukee, WI 53237

United Foster Parent Assoc of Greater Mi......**414.525.1163**
   12828 Woods Rd, Muskego, WI 53150

Voices United Inc............................**414.327.7717**
E-mail...voicesunitedmilw@aol.com
   8727 West Harrison Ave, West Allis, WI 53227
   Kia Rudolph, Director

Wisconsin Foster Adoptive Parent Assoc.......**920.725.4450**
   901 7th St, Menasha, WI 54952

HOME MEDICAL EQUIPMENT PROVIDERS

PEDDLER, LLC...............................**920.965.0040**
Fax...920.965.0041
Web..WWW.THE-PEDDLER.COM
E-mail..MSOLE15030@AOL.COM
   3225 FINGER ROAD STE"C", GREEN BAY, WI 54311
   MICHAEL M. SOLETSKI, MEMBER OWNER

Phoenix Pharmacy, Inc.......................**414.225.4478**
Fax...414.225.4476
Web..www.phoenixcaresystems.com
   1845 North Farwell Avenue, Suite 200, Milwaukee,
   WI 53202
   CARF accredited programs available.

PEDIATRIC HOME CARE

Interim Healthcare..........................**715.834.1313**
Fax...715.834.1323
   4257 Southtowne Dr Ste 3, Eau Claire, WI 54701
   Chad Shaw, Office Manager

Interim Healthcare..........................**715.377.9617**
Fax...715.377.9623
   594 Outpost Cir Ste G, Hudson, WI 54016

Interim Healthcare..........................**920.494.9444**
Fax...920.494.5668
   2555 Continental Ct Ste 4, Green Bay, WI 54311
   Kathy, Chief Executive Officer

Interim Healthcare..........................**715.842.7707**
Fax...715.842.9890
   2402 Grand Ave, Wausau, WI 54403
   Jan Kocha, Owner

Interim Healthcare..........................**608.238.0268**
Fax...608.238.7308
E-mail..interimhealthcare@tm.net
   702 N Blackhawk Ave Ste 215, Madison, WI 53705
   Don Utter, Director

SOCIAL SERVICES

Aurora Family Service........................**414.342.4560**
Fax...414.345.4934
   P.O. Box 080440, Milwaukee, WI 53208
   COA accredited organization.

Catholic Charities...........................**414.771.2881**
Fax...414.771.6095
Web..www.archmil.org
E-mail..sxiong@ccmke.org
   2021 N 60th St, Milwaukee, WI 53208-1641
   Steven Xiong, Director Of Refugee Resettlement Services

Catholic Charities Inc........................**608.782.0710**
Fax...608.782.0702
Web..www.cclse.org
E-mail..info@cclse.org
   3710 East Ave S, La Crosse, WI 54601-7215
   Karen Becker, Assistant Executive Director

**Catholic Charities of the Diocese of Green Bay,
Inc.**...**920.272.8234**
Fax...920.437.4067
Web...www.gbdioc.org
   P.O. Box 23825, Green Bay, WI 54305-3825
   COA accredited organization.

**Catholic Charities, Inc. - Diocese of
Madison**......................................**608.821.3100**
Fax...608.821.3125
Web..www.ccmadison.org
   P.O. Box 46550, Madison, WI 53744-6550
   COA accredited organization.

**Child Care Partnership Resource And Referral
Ctr**..**715.831.1700**
Fax...715.836.7580
Web...www.childcarereferral.org
E-mail.......................ccpart@westerndairyland.org
   418 Wisconsin St, Eau Claire, WI 54703-3566
   Dotty Lillo, Director

Children's Service Society of Wisconsin.......**414.453.1400**
Fax...414.453.3389
Web..www.cssw.org
   620 S. 76th Street, Suite 120, Milwaukee, WI 53214
   COA accredited organization.

Children's Svc Society........................**414.453.1400**
Fax...414.453.3389
Web..www.cssw.org
   620 S 76th St Ste 120, Milwaukee, WI 53214-1549
   Amy Herbst, President

Children's Svc Society Of Wisconsin..........**262.633.3591**
Fax...262.633.2619
Web..www.cssw.org
E-mail..amy.hurps@cssw.org
   2505 N Ste 205, Racine, WI 53406-3350
   Amy Hurps, Director

Children's Svcs Society.......................**262.544.5333**
Fax...262.544.5393
Web..www.cssw.org
E-mail.............................lorrie.kessler@cssw.org
   1570 E Morland blvd, Waukesha, WI 53186-4968
   Lorrie Kessler, Office Manager

Children's Trust Fund.........................**608.266.3737**
Fax...608.266.3792
E-mail.......................maryanne.snyder@wisconsin.gov
   110 E Main St Ste 614, Madison, WI 53703-5144
   Mary Anne Snyder, Director

Community Coordinated Child Care, Inc.........**608.271.9181**
Fax...608.271.5380
Web...www.4-c.org
E-mail..info@4-c.org
   5 Odana Court, Madison, WI 53719-1120
   Jody Bartnick, Executive Director

**Family And Childcare Resources Of NE WI
Inc**..**920.432.8899**
Fax...920.432.6677
Web..www.fcrnew.org
E-mail...plaulla@fcrnew.org
   201 W walnut St, Green Bay, WI 54303
   Plaulla Brese, Director

Family Connections, Inc.......................**920.457.1999**
Fax...920.451.0043
Web..............................www.familyconnectionscc.org
E-mail......................kateh@familyconnectionscc.org
   2508 S 8Th St, Sheboygan, WI 53081-6332
   Kate Hilterberant, Executive Director

**Family Services of Northeast Wisconsin,
Inc.**...**920.436.6800**
Fax...920.437.3540
Web...www.familyservicesnew.org
   300 Crooks Street, Green Bay, WI 54301
   COA accredited organization.

**Family Services of Southern Wisconsin & Northern Illinois,
Inc.**...**608.365.1244**
Fax...608.365.4097
Web...www.fsofswani.org
   423 Bluff Street, Beloit, WI 53511
   COA accredited organization.

Forward Svc Corp.............................**715.479.5175**
Fax...715.479.1947
Web..www.fsc-corp.org
E-mail...kholtorp@fsc-corp.org
   102 N Main St, Eagle River, WI 54521
   Pamela Nowak, Team Leader

Foward Svcs Corp.............................**715.478.5490**
Fax...715.478.5498
Web..www.fsc-corp.org
E-mail...ktupper@fsc-corp.org
   108 S Lake Ave Apt 5, Crandon, WI 54520-1488
   Kathy, Policy Coordinator

Jewish Family Services........................**414.390.5800**
Fax...414.225.1340
   1300 N Jackson St, Milwaukee, WI 53202
   Sylvan Leabman, Chief Executive Officer

Jewish Social Services of Madison............**608.278.1808**
Fax...608.278.7814
E-mail...office@jssmadison.org
   6434 Enterprise Ln, Madison, WI 53719
   Terrie Goren, Executive Director

Job Ctr.....................................**920.208.5800**
Fax...920.208.5900
   3620 Wilgus Ave, Sheboygan, WI 53081
   Liz Mehloch, Director

Job Ctr.....................................**920.929.3912**
Fax...920.929.3924
Web..www.fdlco.wi.gov
E-mail...patti.sabel@fdlco.wi.gov
   349 N Peters Ave, Fond Du Lac, WI 54935-2021
   Patty Sabel, Policy Coordinator

Lutheran Social Services of Wisconsin & Upper Michigan, Inc. **414.281.4400**
Fax 414.325.3124
Web ....www.lsswis.org
647 W. Virginia St., #300, Milwaukee, WI 53204
COA accredited organization.

Maximus **414.760.6060**
Fax 414.760.5190
6550 N 76th St, Milwaukee, WI 53233
Mario Zuniga, Director

Maximus **414.607.0477**
Fax 414.607.0466
Web ....www.maximus.com
1304 S 70th St, Mezzanine Level, Milwaukee, WI 53214-3153
Gabriella Borda-rossell, Policy Coordinator

Milwaukee Care Connection **414.553.8775**
Web ....http://milwaukeecareconnection.com
E-mail ....Director@milwaukeecareconnection.com
P.O. Box 64537, Milwaukee, WI 53204
Cari Garcia, BS, CPNCC, CSAC, Perinatal Health Educator/Case Manager/Director

Oneida Ctr For Self-Sufficiency **920.490.6800**
Fax 920.490.6803
2640 W Point Rd, Green Bay, WI 54313
Priscilla Leverance, Director

Oshkosh Area Workforce **920.232.6200**
Fax 920.303.3161
Web ....www.co.winnebago.wi.us
E-mail ....akriegel@co.winnebago.wi.us
315 Algoma Blvd Ste 107, Oshkosh, WI 54901-4787
Ann Kriegel, Policy Coordinator

Ozaukee Works **262.376.4120**
Fax 262.376.4125
Web ....www.co.ozaukee.wi.us
E-mail ....bbink@co.ozaukee.wi.us
885 Badger Cir, Grafton, WI 53024-9436
Bernadette Bink, Lead Worker

Parenting Network **414.671.5575**
Fax 414.671.1750
Web ....www.theparentingnetwork.org
E-mail ....info@theparentingnetwork.org
7516 W Burleigh St, Milwaukee, WI 53210-1030
Jan Buchler, Director

Parenting Place, Inc **608.784.4519**
Fax 608.796.0098
Web ....www.centurytel.net
E-mail ....frclax@parentingplace.net
1500 Green Bay St, La Crosse, WI 54601
Jodi Weduch, Director

Pauquette Children's Svcs **608.742.8004**
Fax 608.742.7937
Web ....www.pauquetteadoptions.org
E-mail ....info@pauquetteadoptions.org
315 W Conant St, Portage, WI 53901-2101
Brian Tool, Director

Project Bridges Child Care Resource And Referral **715.479.0337**
Fax 715.479.0338
Web ....www.hyhc.com
E-mail ....bridges@hyhc.com
201 Hospital Rd, Eagle River, WI 54521-8835
Robin Mainhardt, Director

Rawhide Boys Ranch **920.982.6100**
Fax 920.982.5040
Web ....www.rawhide.org
E-mail ....info@rawhide.org
E7475 Rawhide Rd, New London, WI 54961-9052
John Solberg, Executive Director

Reality Works, Inc. **715.830.2040**
Fax 715.830.2050
Web ....www.realityworksinc.com
E-mail ....information@realityworksinc.com
2709 Mondovi Rd Ste 1, Eau Claire, WI 54701-6181
Scott Allison, Marketing Manager

St. Charles Youth and Family Services, Inc. **414.476.3710**
Fax 414.778.5985
151 S. 84th Street, Milwaukee, WI 53214
COA accredited organization.

The Hope Ctr For The Prevention Of Child Abuse **920.233.3360**
Fax 920.232.0109
E-mail ....wschwalde@familyservicesnew.org
36 Broad Ste 150, Oshkosh, WI 54901
Wendy Schwalde, Program Coordinator

University Of Wisconsin River Falls Speech And Hearing Clinic **715.425.3801**
Fax 715.425.3181
Web ....www.uwrf.edu
410 S 3rd St, B31 Wyman Education Bldg., River Falls, WI 54022
Dr. Michael Harris, Chairperson

Wisconsin Assoc Of Family And Children's Agencies **608.257.5939**
Fax 608.257.6067
Web ....www.wafca.org
E-mail ....lhall@wafca.org
131 W Wilson St Ste 901, Madison, WI 53703-3259
Linda Hall, Executive Director

SPECIAL NEEDS

Alianza Latina Aplicando Soluciones **414.643.0022**
Fax 414.643.0023
E-mail ....alianza.latino07@yahoo.com
1615 S 22nd ST Ste 109, Milwaukee, WI 53204
Ivelis Perez, Director

Autism Society of Wisconsin **920.558.4602**
E-mail ....asw@asw4autism.org
1477 Kenwood Dr, Menasha, WI 54952
Kelly Brodhagen, Office Manager

Cardiac Arrhythmias Research and Education **920.833.7000**
Fax 920.833.7005
E-mail ....care@careforhearts.org
427 Fulton St, Seymour, WI 54165
M J Gordon, Executive Director

Center for Deaf & Hard of Hearing **414.604.2200**
E-mail ....cchd@wi.com
10243 W National Ave, West Allis, WI 53227
Dorothy Kerr, Executive Director

Cerebral Palsy of Mideast Wisconsin **920.424.4071**
E-mail ....cp@cpmideastwis.com
PO Box 1241, Oshkosh, WI 54903
Judy Britton, Director

Down Syndrome Association **414.327.3729**
E-mail ....info@dsaw.org
3211 S Lake Dr, Ste 113, Saint Francis, WI 53235
Ron Malloy, Executive Director

Easter Seals Wisconsin **608.277.8288**
101 Nob Hill Rd Ste 301, Madison, WI 53713

Family Voices **608.233.3726**
E-mail ....barb@fvofwi.org
PO Box 55029, Madison, WI 53705

Froedtert Memorial Lutheran Hospital - Inpatient Rehabilitation Programs **414.805.3000**
Fax 414.259.7927
Web ....www.froedtert.com
9200 West Wisconsin Avenue, Milwaukee, WI 53226
CARF accredited programs available.

Kids With Heart National Assoc for Child **920.498.0058**
Fax 920.498.0058
E-mail ....michelle@kidswithheart.org
1578 Careful Dr, Greenbay, WI 54304
Michelle Rintamaki, Executive Director

Learning Disabilities Association **866.532.9472**
E-mail ....info@ldawisconsin.com
PO Box 14690

LearningRx Learning Center **920.884.3040**
E-mail ....greenbay.wi@learningrx.net
2201 S Oneida St, Green Bay, WI 54304
Dena Martin, Chief Executive Officer

LearningRx Learning Center **920.882.2006**
E-mail ....appleton.wi@learningrx.com
3169 W Van Roy Rd, Ste 11, Appleton, WI 54195
Edward Jedlieka, President

Madison Area Down Syndrome Society **608.692.7653**
E-mail ....info@madss.org
301 N Broom St Unit 101, Madison, WI 53703
Sterling Lynk, Executive Manager

MDA/ALS Clinical Research Center **608.263.6616**
Fax 608.265.0172
E-mail ....lotz@neurology.wisc.edu
600 Highland Ave # H4-622, Madison, WI 53792
Barend P Lotz Md, Director

Mental Health America of Wisconsin **414.276.3122**
E-mail ....info@mhawisconsin.org
600 W Virginia St Ste 502, Milwaukee, WI 53204
Christina Finnel, Chief Executive Officer

Meriter Hospital - Physical Medicine and Rehabilitation **608.267.6177**
Fax 608.267.6687
Web ....www.meriter.com
E-mail ....scasali@meriter.com
202 South Park Street, Madison, WI 53715
Sherry Casali, Director of Emergency Services
CARF accredited programs available.

MUMS **920.336.5333**
E-mail ....mums@netnet.net
150 Custer CT, Green Bay, WI 54301

NAMI Wisconsin **800.236.2988**
E-mail ....nami@namiwisconsin.org
4223 W Beltline Hwy, Madison, WI 53711
Andrea Clark, Secretary

National Multiple Sclerosis Society **262.369.4400**
Fax 262.369.4410
E-mail ....info@wisms.org
1120 James Dr Ste A, Hartland, WI 53029
Judy Meyer, Administrator

Parent to Parent of Wisconsin **888.266.0028**
E-mail ....get-connected@p2pwi.org
1020 Kabel Ave, Rhinelander, WI 54501

Prader-Willi Syndrome Association **920.882.6371**
E-mail ....wisconsin@pwsaofwi.org
2701 N Alexander St, Appleton, WI 54911

Sacred Heart Rehabilitation Institute **414.298.6700**
Fax 414.298.6737
Web ....www.columbia-stmarys.org
2025 East Newport Avenue, Milwaukee, WI 53211
Deb Frieberg, CEO
CARF accredited programs available.

Shepherds College **262.878.6351**
Fax 262.878.3402
Web ....www.shephardscollege.org
E-mail ....info@shephardscollege.org
1805 15th Ave, Union Grove, WI 53182
Chris Wright, Director

Speech-Language-Pathology & Audiology **800.545.0640**
E-mail ....wsha@wisha.org
1360 Regent St # 154, Madison, WI 53713

St. Vincent Hospital Regional Rehabilitation
Program 920.433.0111
Fax 920.431.3291
Web ....www.stvincenthospital.org
 835 South Van Buren Street, Green Bay, WI 54301
 CARF accredited programs available.

The Arc 877.272.8400
E-mail ....arcw@att.net
 2800 Royal Ave # 209, Madison, WI 53713

Theda Clark Medical Center/Inpatient Rehabilitation
Unit 920.720.7248
Fax 920.729.3062
Web ....www.thedacare.org
 130 Second Street, Neenah, WI 54956
 CARF accredited programs available.

United Cerebral Palsy Of Southeastern
Wisconsin 414.329.4500
E-mail ....info@ucp-sew.org
 7519 W Oklahoma Ave, Milwaukee, WI 53219
 Mary Schkowitch, Human Resource Director

University of Wisconsin Hospital and Clinics Rehabilitation
Unit 608.263.8388
Fax 608.265.8883
Web ....www.uwhealth.org
E-mail ....jpowers@uwhealth.org
 600 Highland Ave, Madison, WI 53792-2424
 Jane Powers, Director, Orthopedics and Reha, Rehab-General Services
 CARF accredited programs available.

VSA Arts of Wisconsin Inc 608.241.2131
E-mail ....vsawis@vsawis.org
 4785 Hayes Rd Ste 201, Madison, WI 53704
 Kathy Wagner, President

Waisman Center for Excellence in 608.263.7148
E-mail ....hecht@waisman.wisc.edu
 1500 Highland Ave, Madison, WI 53705
 Ann Harris, Director

Wisconsin FACETS 414.374.4645
Fax 414.374.4655
E-mail ....wifacets@wifacets.org
 2714 N Dr Martin L King Dr, Milwaukee, WI 53212
 Janice Serak, Director

Wisconsin Family Ties 608.267.6888
E-mail ....info@wifamilyties.org
 16 N Carroll St Ste 230, Madison, WI 53703
 Hugh Davis, Executive Director

Wisconsin First Step 800.642.7837
E-mail ....wispubhealth@mch-hotlines.org
 1900 South Ave, La Crosse, WI 54601
 Mary Mundt Reckase, Director

Wisconsin PTA 608.244.1455
E-mail ....wi_office@pta.org
 4797 Hayes Rd Ste 102, Madison, WI 53704
 Kim Henvers, Director

SUBSTANCE ABUSE TREATMENT

Libertas Treatment Ctr 920.498.8600
Fax 920.496.2027
Web ....www.libertas.org/greenbay
E-mail ....pryan@sjcf.hshs.org
 1701 Dousman St, Green Bay, WI 54303-3211
 Patrick Ryan, Program Director

Social Development Commission 414.906.2700
Fax 414.906.2719
Web ....www.cr-sdc.org
E-mail ....gporath@cr-sdc.org
 4041 N Richards St, Milwaukee, WI 53212
 Gale Porath, Head Start Director

St. Agnes Hospital Addiction Svcs Toll
Free 800.922.3400
Fax 920.926.8962
Web ....www.agnesian.com
 430 E Division St, Fond Du Lac, WI 54935
 Jim Salasek, Addiction Services Director

Wisconsin Regional Teen Institute 715.836.3636
Fax 715.836.5263
E-mail ....kroenigj@uwec.edu
 210 Water St, Eau Claire, WI 54702-4004
 George Kroninger, Interim State Director

Wyoming

Matt Mead, Governor
124 State Capital Building
Cheyenne, WY 82002
307.777.7434
307.632.3909 (Fax)
governor@state.wy.us
www.wyoming.gov/governor

Lindee Renneisen, Juvenile Justice Specialist
Department of Family Services
2300 Capital Ave, 3rd Fl
Cheyenne, WY 82002
307.777.5536
307.777.3659 (Fax)
lrenne1@state.wy.us

Beth Evans, SAG Chair
PO Box 86
Cheyenne, WY 82003
307.632.5409
307.632.6533 (Fax)
bethevans3@bresnan.net

CRISIS NUMBERS

Child Abuse Reporting . . .307.777.3663

STATE SERVICES

SOCIAL SERVICES

Dept of Family Svcs **307.777.7564**
Fax...307.777.7747
Web......................................www.dfsweb.state.wy.us
E-mail.....................................steve.corsi@wyo.gov
  2300 Capitol Ave, 3rd Floor Hathaway Bldg.,
  Cheyenne, WY 82002-0001
  Steve Corsi, Director

Div of Victims Svcs.......................**307.777.7200**
Fax...307.777.6683
E-mail.....................................jtenna@state.wy.us
  122 W 25th St, Herschler Bldg., 1W, Cheyenne,
  WY 82002-0001
  Julie L. Tennant-caine, Director

Division of Early Childhood Wyoming **307.777.5491**
Fax...307.777.3659
  2300 Capitol Ave, Hathway Bldg Third Flr, Cheyenne,
  WY 82002
  M Weber, Director

Head Start Assoc...........................**307.766.2454**
Fax...307.766.2549
Web..www.uwyo.edu
E-mail..................................rhusnage@uwyo.edu
  1000 E University Ave, Department 4298, Laramie,
  WY 82071-2000
  Rick Hufnagel, Collaboration Director

GENERAL HEALTH SERVICES

Childrens Spec Health Program WY **307.777.7942**
Fax...307.777.7215
E-mail.............................lynne.moore@wyo.go
  6101 Yellowstone Rd Ste 420, Cheyenne, WY 82002
  Lynne Moore, Director

Dept Of Health.............................**307.777.7656**
Fax...307.777.7439
Web.................................wdh.state.wy.us/wdh
E-mail................................bshera@state.wy.us
  2300 Capitol Ave Ste 401, Cheyenne,
  WY 82002-0001
  Brent D. Sherard, Director

Maternal and Family Health Section WY **307.777.6921**
Fax...307.777.8687
E-mail..............................wdh@health.wyo.gov
  6101 Yellowstone Rd Ste 420, Cheyenne, WY 82002

WDH Preventive Health & Safety Div (PHSD) ...**307.777.7172**
Fax...307.777.5402
Web...www.state.wy.us
E-mail.........................lindachasson@wyo.gov
  6101 Yellowstone Rd, Cheyenne, WY 82002-0001
  Linda Chasson, Administrator

Wyoming Hospital Assoc.....................**307.632.9344**
Fax...307.632.9347
Web....................................www.wyohospitals.com
E-mail...........................dan@wyohospitals.com
  2005 Warren Ave, Cheyenne, WY 82001-3725
  Daniel Perdue, President

MENTAL HEALTH SERVICES

Div of Vocational Rehab WY **307.777.7389**
Fax...307.777.5939
E-mail...................................jmcint@state.wy.us
  122 W 25th St, Herschler Bldg 1E, Cheyenne,
  WY 82002
  Jim McIntosh, Administrator

Mental Health and Substance Abuse **307.777.6494**
Fax...307.777.5580
Web...................................www.health.wyo.gov
  6101 Yellowstone Rd Ste 220, Cheyenne, WY 82002
  Chris Newman, Administrator

Wyoming State Hospital.....................**307.789.3464**
Fax...307.789.7373
  831 S Highway 150, Evanston, WY 82931
  Robert Stahl, Administrator

JUSTICE AGENCY

Attorney General's Ofc.....................**307.777.7841**
Fax...307.777.6869
E-mail.......................agwebmaster@state.wy.us
  123 State Capitol Bldg, 200 West 24th St, Cheyenne,
  WY 82002
  Bruce Salzburg, Attorney General

Correctional Education Division WY **307.777.6104**
Fax...307.777.7846
E-mail.........................babbot@wdoc.state.wy.us
  1934 Wyott Dr Ste 100, Cheyenne, WY 82002

Dept of Corrections........................**307.777.7208**
Fax...307.777.7479
E-mail.........................blampe@wdoc.state.wy.us
  1934 Wyott Dr Ste 100, Cheyenne, WY 82002-0001
  Robert Lampert, Director

Dept of Family Svcs Div of Juvenile Svcs **307.777.6285**
Fax...307.777.3659
Web..........................www.dfsweb.state.wy.us/
  2300 Capitol Ave, 3rd Floor Hathaway Bldg.,
  Cheyenne, WY 82002
  Debra Dugan-doty, Administrator For Juvenile Services

COURTS

Administrative Ofc Of The Courts **307.777.7678**
Fax...307.777.3447
E-mail....................jodendahl@courts.state.wy.us
  2301 Capitol Ave, Cheyenne, WY 82001
  Joann Odendahl, State Court Administrator

POLICE AND SHERIFF

Wyoming Div Of Criminal Investigation **307.777.7181**
Fax...307.777.7252
  208 S college, Cheyenne, WY 82002
  Forrest C. Bright, Director

EDUCATION SERVICES

Dept of Education...........................**307.777.7673**
Fax...307.777.6234
Web..www.k12.wy.us
  2300 Capitol Ave Fl 2, Cheyenne, WY 82002-0001
  Christine Steele, Fedral Programms

Educ for Homeless Children and Youth WY ...**307.777.5315**
Fax...307.777.7633
E-mail............................csteel@educ.state.wy.us
  23000 Capitol Ave, Hathaway Bldg 1st Flr, Cheyenne,
  WY 82002
  C Steel, Director

Special Programs Unit WY **307.777.2553**
Fax...307.777.2556
E-mail..........................byates1@educ.state.wy.us
  320 W Main, Riverton, WY 82501
  B Yates, Director

Wyoming Dept of Education **307.777.7690**
Fax...307.777.6234
  2300 Capitol Ave, Hathaway Bldg 2nd Flr, Cheyenne,
  WY 82002
  Cindy Hill, Superintendent

Wyoming Parent Information Center **307.684.2277**
Fax...307.684.5314
E-mail...................................tdawson@wpic.org
  500 W Lott St Ste A, Buffalo, WY 82834
  Terri Dawson, Director

LABOR & WORKFORCE EDUCATION

Dept of Workforce Svcs.....................**307.777.8716**
Fax...307.777.7106
E-mail...................................dgriff2@state.wy.us
  122 W 25th St, Cheyenne, WY 82002-0001
  Cynthia Sandez, Director

Wyoming

COUNTY SERVICES

Albany County

SOCIAL SERVICES

Region 4 Family Svcs **307.745.7324**
Fax 307.742.8848
   2020 E Grand Ave, Ste 400, Laramie, WY 82070
Carolyn Yeaman, District Manager

MENTAL HEALTH SERVICES

Mental Health Ctr **307.745.8915**
Fax 307.745.8761
   1263 N 15th St, Laramie, WY 82072
Carol Sprabery, Ms, Md, Clinic Director

JUSTICE AGENCY

Dept Of Corrections Div Of Field
Svcs **307.742.2451**
Fax 307.742.7901
Web ....www.dc.state.fl.us
   2020 E Grand Ave Ste 390, Laramie, WY 82070-4388
Mike Schluck, Southern District Deputy Administrator

COURTS

2Nd District Court **307.745.3337**
E-mail ....jad@courts.state.wy.us
   525 E Grand Ave, Rm 303, Laramie, WY 82070
Honorable Jeffrey A. Donnell, Judge

POLICE AND SHERIFF

Sheriff's Ofc **307.721.5322**
Fax 307.721.2500
E-mail ....domalley@co.albany.wy.us
   525 E Grand Ave Rm 101, Laramie, WY 82070
David O'Malley, Sheriff

Big Horn County

GENERAL HEALTH SERVICES

Public Health Nursing **307.548.6591**
Fax 307.548.6517
E-mail ....phnlovell@wyo.gov
   757 Great Western Ave, Lovell, WY 82431
Susan Wiley, Rn, Office Manager

Public Health Nursing **307.765.2371**
Fax 307.765.2381
Web ....www.health.wyo.gov
E-mail ....susan.wiley@wyo.gov
   417 South 2nd, Greybull, WY 82426
Susan Wiley, Rn, Bsn, Nursing Director

POLICE AND SHERIFF

Basin Police Dept **307.568.2341**
Fax 307.568.2274
E-mail ....townofbasin@tctwest.net
   209 S 4th St, Basin, WY 82410
Christopher Kampbell, Police Chief

EDUCATION SERVICES

Absaroka Basin/Greybull/Hdst **307.568.2032**
Fax 307.568.2032
   609 Rue Ave, Basin, WY 82410
Elaine Laird, Director

Campbell County

GENERAL HEALTH SERVICES

Public Health Nursing **307.682.7275**
Fax 307.682.0374
Web ....www.ccgov.net
E-mail ....dga50@ccgov.net
   2301 South 4J, Gillette, WY 82718-5341
Della Amend, Rn, Nursing Director

JUSTICE AGENCY

CASA **307.687.9440**
Fax 307.682.1175
E-mail ....casa@collinscom.net
   300 S Carey Ave, Gillette, WY 82716
Rhea Parsons, Executive Director

Dept Of Corrections Div Of Field
Svcs **307.682.2440**
Fax 307.682.6454
   1301 W 3rd St, Gillette, WY 82716
Kelly Peters, District Supervisor

COURTS

6Th District Court **307.686.8517**
Fax 307.687.6426
E-mail ....jd6@courts.state.wy.us
   500 S Gillette Ave Ste 2400, Gillette, WY 82716
Honorable John R. Perry, Judge

POLICE AND SHERIFF

Sheriff's Ofc **307.687.6160**
Fax 307.682.0307
Web ....www.ccgov.net/departments/sheriff
   600 W Boxelder Rd, Gillette, WY 82718-5219
William H. Pownall, Sheriff

EDUCATION SERVICES

Even Start Program **307.682.1314**
Fax 307.682.5171
Web www.ccsd.k12.wy.us
E-mail ....hmathes@ccsd.k12.wy.us
   1000 W 8th St, Gillette, WY 82716
Helen Mathes, Even Start Director

Carbon County

SOCIAL SERVICES

Rawlins Family Svcs **307.328.0612**
Fax 307.328.2801
Web ....www.dfsweb.state.wy.us
E-mail ....kmccla@state.wy.us
   215 W Buffalo St Rm 359, Rawlins, WY 82301-5660
Karla Mcclaren, Manager

GENERAL HEALTH SERVICES

Public Health Nursing **307.328.2607**
Fax 307.328.2602
Web ....www.health.wyo.gov
E-mail ....bridget.hettgar@health.wyo.gov
   215 W Buffalo St # 136, Rawlins, WY 82301
Bridget Hettgar, Rn, Bsn, Nursing Director

Saratoga Ofc Of Public Health Nursing
Svcs **307.326.5371**
Fax 307.326.5735
Web ....www.wyo.giv
   201 S River St, Saratoga, WY 82331
Susan Bartlett, Rn, Bsn, Public Health Nurse

Wic **307.328.2606**
Fax 307.328.2609
Web ....www.wdh.state.wy.us
   215 W Buffalo Street # 384, Rawlins, WY 82301
Sharon Pribyl, Regional Nutritionist

JUSTICE AGENCY

Dept Of Corrections Div Of Field
Svcs **307.324.2545**
Fax 307.324.2916
E-mail ....rob.doty@wyo.gov
   214 4th St, Rm 8, Rawlins, WY 82301
Rob Doty, Southern District Deputy Administrator

COURTS

2Nd District Court Ofc Of The Clerk **307.328.2683**
   415 W Pine St Rm 201, Rawlins, WY 82301-5566
Honorable Wade E. Waldrip, Court Judge

POLICE AND SHERIFF

Sheriff's Ofc **307.324.2776**
Fax 307.328.2782
   415 W Pine St, Rawlins, WY 82301
Jerald R. Colson, Sheriff

Converse County

SOCIAL SERVICES

Family Svcs **307.358.3138**
Fax 307.358.4238
E-mail ....rlinso@state.wy.us
   219 N Russell Ave, Douglas, WY 82633
Richard Linson, District Manager

GENERAL HEALTH SERVICES

Public Health Dept **307.358.2536**
Fax 307.358.3941
Web ....www.coffey.com
   442 E Center St, Douglas, WY 82633-2422
Sharon Kilmer, Rn, Nursing Manager

JUSTICE AGENCY

Dept Of Corrections Div Of Field
Svcs **307.777.7208**
Fax 307.777.7846
Web ....www.wdoc.state.wy.us
   1934 wyatt dr ste 100, Cheynne, WY 80002
Robert Lambert, Director Of Dept. Of Corrections

COURTS

8th District Court **307.358.5693**
Fax 307.358.6343
   107 N 5th St, Douglas, WY 82633
Honorable John Brooks, District Judge

POLICE AND SHERIFF

Sheriff's Dept **307.358.4700**
Fax 307.358.6703
Web ....www.sheriff.conversecounty.org
E-mail ....clintbecker@sheriff.conversecounty.org
   107 N 5th St Rm 239, Douglas, WY 82633-2449
Clint Becker, Sheriff

Crook County

GENERAL HEALTH SERVICES

Dept Of Family Svcs **307.283.2014**
Fax 307.283.1606
Web ....www.state.wy.us
   102 N 5th St, Sundance, WY 82729
Kathy Deiss, Manager

Public Health **307.283.1142**
Fax 307.283.1143
Web ....www.health.wyo.gov
E-mail ....barbara.coy@wyo.gov
   420 1/2 E Main St, Sundance, WY 82729
Barbara Coy, Nursing Director

MENTAL HEALTH SERVICES

Northern Wyoming Mental Health
Ctr **307.283.3636**
Fax 307.283.2898
E-mail ....gerrys@rtconnect.net
   420 1/2 Main St, Sundance, WY 82729
Gerry Solyst, Msw, County Manager

POLICE AND SHERIFF

Sheriff's Dept **307.283.1225**
Fax 307.283.2990
Web ....www.collinscom.net
E-mail ....sstahla@collinscom.net
　309 Cleveland St, Sundance, WY 82729
Steve J. Stahla, Sheriff

Fremont County

SOCIAL SERVICES

Abba's House **307.856.0999**
E-mail ....abbashouse@wyoming.com
　108 S 7th St E, Riverton, WY 82501
Darlene Soule, Director

Eastern Shoshone Dept Social Svcs **307.332.6591**
Fax 307.332.6593
　104 Fort Washakie St, Fort Washakie, WY 82514
Larry Mcadams, Director

Family Svcs **307.856.6521**
Fax 307.856.7937
Web ....www.state.wy.us
E-mail ....eheime@state.wy.us
　120 N 6th St E, Riverton, WY 82501-4405
Ed Heimer, District Manager

GENERAL HEALTH SERVICES

**Eastern Shoshone Tribe Wic
Program** **307.332.6733**
Fax 307.332.4196
　106 Black Coal Dr Fort, Washakie, WY 82514
Sherry Ferris, Coordinator

Public Health Nursing **307.332.1074**
Fax 307.332.1064
E-mail ....phnfre@state.wy.us
　450 N 2nd St Rm 350, Lander, WY 82520
Julie Twist Rn, Mph, Nursing Manager

Public Health Nursing **307.856.6979**
Fax 307.856.6850
Web ....www.state.wy.us
E-mail ....phnriverton@help.wy.gov
　322 N 8th St W, Fl 2, Riverton, WY 82501
Julie Twist, Rn, Phn, Supervisor

WIC **307.332.1034**
Fax 307.332.1031
　450 N 2nd St, Rm 160E, Lander, WY 82520
Nancy Sersen, Director

JUSTICE AGENCY

**Dept Of Corrections Div Of Field
Svcs** **307.856.0720**
Fax 307.857.3765
　609 E Madison Ave Ste 2, Riverton, WY 82501
Jeremy Vukich, District Supervisor

**Dept Of Corrections Div Of Field
Svcs** **307.332.4363**
Fax 307.332.8593
　331 Main St Ste 2, Lander, WY 82520
William Payne, Northern District Deputy Administrator

COURTS

9th District Court **307.332.4592**
Fax 307.332.4059
E-mail ....nyoung@courts.state.wy.us
　450 N 2nd St Rm 260, Lander, WY 82520
Honorable Norman E. Young, Judge

Goshen County

SOCIAL SERVICES

Family Svcs **307.532.2191**
Fax 307.532.4666
Web ....www.state.wy.us
　1618 E M St, Torrington, WY 82240-3508
Richard R. Linson, Manager

GENERAL HEALTH SERVICES

Public Health Nursing **307.532.4069**
Fax 307.532.4060
　2025 Campbell Dr Ste 1, Torrington, WY 82240
Cathy Grace, Rn, Bsn, Nursing Director

WIC **307.532.5881**
Fax 307.532.3210
Web ....www.state.wy.us
E-mail ....bfeagl@state.wy.us
　2025 Campbell Dr Ste 2, Torrington,
　WY 82240-1549
Bobbi Feagler, RN, Supervisor

MENTAL HEALTH SERVICES

Peak Wellness Ctr **307.532.4091**
Fax 307.532.8409
E-mail ....jburian@peakwellnesscenter.org
　501 Albany Ave, Torrington, WY 82240
Joel Burian, Clinical Director

JUSTICE AGENCY

**Dept Of Corrections Div Of Field
Svcs** **307.532.7244**
Fax 307.532.4263
E-mail ....lswartwood@doc.state.wy.us
　1610 East M St, Torrington, WY 82240
Linda Swartwood, Southern District Deputy Administrator

COURTS

8th District Court **307.532.3004**
Fax 307.532.2563
E-mail ....kgk@courts.state.wy.us
　2125 East Ave, Torrington, WY 82240-1055
Honorable Keith G. Kautz, Judge

POLICE AND SHERIFF

Sheriff's Dept **307.532.4026**
Fax 307.532.7590
　2120 E B St, Torrington, WY 82240
Donald J. Murphy, Sheriff

Hot Springs County

POLICE AND SHERIFF

Sheriff's Dept **307.864.2622**
Fax 307.864.5116
Web ....www.hscounty.com
E-mail ....sheriff@hscounty.com
　417 Arapahoe St Rm 1, Thermopolis,
　WY 82443-2746
Lou A. Falgoust, Sheriff

Johnson County

SOCIAL SERVICES

Dept Of Family Svcs **307.684.7281**
Fax 307.684.7966
　381 N Main St, Buffalo, WY 82834
Kathy Deiss, Manager

GENERAL HEALTH SERVICES

Public Health Nursing **307.684.2564**
Web ....www.johnsoncountywyoming.org
　85 Klondike Dr, Buffalo, WY 82834
Ann Romano-jarvis, Bsn, Nursing Manager

JUSTICE AGENCY

**Dept Of Corrections Div Of Field
Svcs** **307.684.7601**
Fax 307.684.1450
Web ....www.wdoc.state.wy.us
E-mail ....mwake@wdoc.state.wy.us
　600 Veterans Ln, Rm 4, Buffalo, WY 82834
Marv Wake, Northern District Deputy Administrator

Victim And Witness Assistance **307.684.2233**
Fax 307.684.0878
Web ....www.jcfcc.vcn.com
E-mail ....jcfcc@jcfcc.org
　255 E Fetterman St, Buffalo, WY 82834
Mary Kay Stafford, Director

POLICE AND SHERIFF

Sheriff's Dept **307.684.5581**
Fax 307.684.5585
E-mail ....jcsheriff@vcn.com
　639 Fort St, Buffalo, WY 82834-2317
Stephen F. Kozisek, Sheriff

EDUCATION SERVICES

Absaroka Head Start **307.684.9062**
Fax 307.684.9062
E-mail ....swright@uwyo.edu
　201 Aspen Dr, Buffalo, WY 82834
Sallie Wright, Director

Laramie County

SOCIAL SERVICES

Child Support Enforcement Div **307.777.6948**
Fax 307.777.5588
Web ....www.dfsweb.state.wy.us/
E-mail ....blyttle@state.wy.us
　122 W 25th St Fl 1, Cheyenne, WY 82002-0001
Brenda Lyttle, Iv-d Director

**Protective Svcs Div (Child And
Adult)** **307.777.6073**
Fax 307.777.3693
Web ....www.dfswyo.gov
　2300 Capital Ave, 3rd floor, Cheyenne, WY 82002
Eydie Trautwein, Administrator

GENERAL HEALTH SERVICES

Mental Health Div **307.777.2432**
　6101 N Yellowstone St, Cheyenne, WY 82002-0001
Chuck Hayes, Administrator

Public Health Dept **307.633.4000**
Fax 307.633.4005
Web ....www.laramiecounty.com
　100 Central Ave, Ste 261, Cheyenne, WY 82007
Katheryn McKee, Rn, Nursing Manager

Public Health Nursing **307.633.4000**
Fax 307.633.4005
　100 Central Ave, Cheyenne, WY 82007
Gus Lopez, Director

WIC Program **307.777.7494**
Fax 307.777.5643
Web ....www.state.wy.us
　6101 Yellowstone Rd Ste 510, Cheyenne,
　WY 82002-0001
Janet Moran Rd, Msd, Wic Director

JUSTICE AGENCY

CASA **307.638.1151**
Fax 307.638.1154
Web ....www.casalc.org
　211 W 18th St., Cheyenne, WY 82001
Betsy Putnam, Director

Dept Of Corrections Div Of Field
Svcs.............................307.777.7208
Fax..............................307.777.8537
   1934 Wyott Dr Ste 100, Cheyenne, WY 82002
   Bob Lambert, Director

COURTS

1st District Court.................307.633.4291
Fax..............................307.633.4465
E-mail................tcampbell@courts.state.wy.us
   309 W 20th St, Ste 3300, Cheyenne, WY 82001
   Tom Campbell, Judge

Municipal Court..................307.633.4422
Fax..............................307.633.4471
Web.........................www.cheyennecity.org
   309 W 20th St, Rm 2100, Cheyenne, WY 82001
   Honorable Paul Galeotos, Judge

POLICE AND SHERIFF

Police Dept.....................307.637.6524
Fax..............................307.637.6599
Web...............................www.sisna.com
E-mail.........................cpddet@sisna.com
   2020 Capitol Ave, Cheyenne, WY 82001-3699
   Brian Kozak, Chief

Sheriff's Ofc....................307.633.4700
Fax..............................307.633.4723
   1910 Pioneer Ave, Cheyenne, WY 82001
   Daniel Glick, Sheriff

EDUCATION SERVICES

Special Education................307.771.2174
Fax..............................307.771.2180
Web...........................www.laramie1.k12.wy.us
E-mail..................ahunter@laramie1.k12.wy.us
   2810 House Ave, Cheyenne, WY 82001-2860
   Alice Hunter, Director Of Special Services

Wyoming Family Literacy - Cheyenne
Center..........................307.433.0393
E-mail....................eskarenl@questoffice.net
   5113 Ridge Rd Ste 9, Cheyenne, WY 82009
   Karen Loken, Director

Lincoln County

SOCIAL SERVICES

Dept Of Family Svcs..............307.877.6670
Fax..............................307.877.5794
Web...............................www.state.wy.us
E-mail........................kcarter@state.wy.us
   1100 Pine Ave, Kemmerer, WY 83101
   Keith Carter, Manager

GENERAL HEALTH SERVICES

Public Health Nursing............307.877.3780
Fax..............................307.828.3114
Web.........................www.lincolncounty.org
E-mail........................csweeney@lcwy.org
   925 Sage Ave Ste 106, Kemmerer, WY 83101-3129
   Constance E. Sweeney, County Nurse Manager

JUSTICE AGENCY

Dept Of Corrections
Probation/Parole.................307.877.6322
Fax..............................307.877.6322
   1100 Pine Ave Suite C, Kemmerer, WY 83101
   Barb Janicek, District Supervisor

POLICE AND SHERIFF

Sheriff's Dept...................307.877.3971
Fax..............................307.877.3622
Web...............................www.co.lincoln.wy.us
E-mail....................tsmith@co.lincoln.wy.us
   1032 Beech Ave, Kemmerer, WY 83101-3110
   Shane Johnson, Sheriff

Natrona County

GENERAL HEALTH SERVICES

Casper Natrona Home & Health -- Country
Dept............................307.235.9340
Fax..............................307.237.2036
   475 S Spruce St, Casper, WY 82601
   Mary Heim, Fnp, Disease Prevention Director

Hemry Home......................307.265.1007
Fax..............................307.265.1008
   523 S Beach, Casper, WY 82601
   Dick Dresang, Director

JUSTICE AGENCY

CASA............................307.237.0889
Fax..............................307.234.2779
Web.........................wwww.mcmurry.net
E-mail..................chandra.casa@mcmurry.net
   1701 E E St, Casper, WY 82601-2171
   Chandra Burgess, Program Director

Dept Of Corrections Div Of Field
Svcs.............................307.234.2261
Fax..............................307.234.2811
   305 SW Wyoming Blvd, Mills, WY 82644
   Bill Payne, Deputy Administrator

Juvenile Detention Ctr...........307.234.0057
Fax..............................307.234.0067
Web.........................www.cornerstoneprograms.com
   201 N David St Fl 3, Casper, WY 82601-1827
   Jason Strohbehn, Executive Director

COURTS

7th District Court...............307.235.9253
Fax..............................307.235.9505
   115 N Center St Ste 200, Rm 214, Casper, WY 82601
   Honorable W. Thomas Sullins, Judge

POLICE AND SHERIFF

Police Dept.....................307.235.8278
Fax..............................307.235.7512
   201 N David St Fl 1, Casper, WY 82601
   Chris Walsh, Police Chief

Sheriff's Dept...................307.235.9282
Fax..............................307.235.9252
   201 N David St Fl 2, Casper, WY 82601
   Mark Benton, Sheriff

EDUCATION SERVICES

Early Headstart.................307.265.9562
Fax..............................307.265.9563
   4981 W Buick St, Mills, WY 82644
   Jeana Olsen, Director

Niobrara County

GENERAL HEALTH SERVICES

Public Health Dept...............307.334.2609
Fax..............................307.334.2619
E-mail.........................lmellott@state.wy.us
   611 E 6th St, Lusk, WY 82225
   Lisa Mellott, Public Health Nurse

POLICE AND SHERIFF

Sheriff's Ofc....................307.334.2240
Fax..............................307.334.3453
Web.........................www.netcommander.com
E-mail....................rzerbe@netcommander.com
   416 S Elm St, Lusk, WY 82225
   Rick Zerbe, Sheriff

Park County

SOCIAL SERVICES

Family Svcs.....................307.587.6246
Fax..............................307.527.7183
Web...............................www.state.wy.us
   1301 Rumsey Ave, Cody, WY 82414-3798
   Ed Heimer, District Manager

COURTS

5Th District Court...............307.527.8670
Fax..............................307.527.8676
Web.........................www.courts.state.wy.us
E-mail........................sc@courts.state.wy.us
   1002 Sheridan Ave, Cody, WY 82414
   Honorable Steven Cranfill, Judge

EDUCATION SERVICES

Cody Head Start.................307.527.6454
Fax..............................307.527.6454
Web.........................www.hyperformer.com
E-mail...................stephanie@hyperformer.com
   308 16th St, Cody, WY 82414
   Ms Stephanie Moller, Director

Platte County

JUSTICE AGENCY

Dept Of Corrections Probation And
Parole...........................307.322.4653
Fax..............................307.322.3566
Web.........................www.wdoc.state.wy.us
E-mail........................jsmith@wdoc.state.wy.us
   1560 Johnston Street, Wheatland, WY 82201
   Jeri Smith, Administrative Assistant

POLICE AND SHERIFF

Sheriff's Dept...................307.322.2331
Fax..............................307.322.1343
E-mail.......................swkeigley@yahoo.com
   850 Maple St, Wheatland, WY 82201
   Steve W. Keigley, Sheriff

Sheridan County

JUSTICE AGENCY

Dept Of Corrections Div Of Field
Svcs.............................307.672.5411
Fax..............................307.674.9879
   65 Coffeen Ave, Sheridan, WY 82801
   Tony Garber, District Supervisor

COURTS

4Th Judicial District............307.674.4478
Fax..............................307.674.4470
   224 S Main St, Ste B11j, Sheridan, WY 82801
   Honorable John G Fenn, Judge

POLICE AND SHERIFF

Sheriff's Dept...................307.672.3455
Fax..............................307.672.7293
E-mail...............dhofmeier@sheridancountysheriff.com
   54 W 13th St, Sheridan, WY 82801
   Dave W. Hofmeier, Sheriff

Sublette County

POLICE AND SHERIFF

Sheriff's Dept...................307.367.4378
Fax..............................307.367.4360
E-mail.........................scso@coffey.com
   35 1/2 South Tyler St, Pinedale, WY 82941
   Dave Lankford, Sheriff

Sweetwater County

SOCIAL SERVICES

Dept of Family Svcs **307.352.2500**
Fax 307.352.2560
Web ....www.state.wy.us
E-mail ....kcarte@state.wy.us
　2451 Foothill Blvd Ste 103, Rock Springs,
　WY 82901-5696
　Keith Carter, District Manager

GENERAL HEALTH SERVICES

Green River Public Health Nursing

Svc **307.872.3944**
Fax 307.872.3983
　550 Uinta Dr Ste E, Green River, WY 80935
　Janet Gerken, Nursing Manager

Sweetwater Community Nursing

Svcs **307.922.5390**
Fax 307.922.5496
E-mail ....gerkenj@sweet.wy.us
　731 C St Ste 315, Rock Springs, WY 82901
　Janet Gerken, Director

JUSTICE AGENCY

Dept Of Corrections Div Of Field

Svcs **307.875.2030**
Fax 307.875.3579
　140 Commerce Dr Ste A, Green River, WY 82935
　Kimberly Bramwell, District Supervisor

POLICE AND SHERIFF

Sheriff's Offc **307.872.6350**
Fax 307.872.6379
E-mail ....scso@swcmail.co.sweet.wy.us
　50 W Flaming Gorge Way, Green River, WY 82935
　Rich Haskell, Sheriff

Teton County

GENERAL HEALTH SERVICES

Public Health Nursing **307.733.6401**
Fax 307.733.8747
Web ....www.tetoncounty.org
　460 E Pearl, Jackson, WY 83001
　Terri Gregory, Nursing Director

WIC **307.734.1060**
Fax 307.734.8620
Web ....health.wyo.gov
E-mail ....connie.burk@health.wyo.gov
　460 E Pearl Ste 3, Jackson, WY 83001
　Constance Burk, Chief Performance Officer

JUSTICE AGENCY

Dept Of Corrections Div Of Field

Svcs **307.733.5453**
Fax 307.734.5707
　125 E Pearl Ste 20, Jackson, WY 83001
　Linda Swartwood, Southern District Deputy Administrator

COURTS

9Th District Court **307.733.1461**
Fax 307.734.8954
Web ....www.courts.state.wy.us
　180 S King St, Jackson, WY 83001
　Timothy Day, District Court Judge

POLICE AND SHERIFF

Sheriff's Dept **307.733.4052**
Fax 307.732.7131
Web ....www.tetonsheriff.org
E-mail ....jwhalan@tetonsheriff.org
　180 South King St, Jackson, WY 83001
　Jim Whalan, Sheriff

Uinta County

GENERAL HEALTH SERVICES

Dept Of Public Health Nursing **307.789.9203**
Fax 307.789.6635
Web ....www.uintacounty.com
　350 City View Dr Ste 101, Evanston, WY 82930-5305
　Patricia Arnold, Nursing Manager

JUSTICE AGENCY

Dept Of Corrections Div Of Field

Svcs **307.789.9653**
Fax 307.789.2558
Web ....www.doc.state.wy.us
　1575 South Highway 150 #L, Evanston, WY 82931
　Linda Swartwood, Southern District Deputy Administrator

COURTS

3rd District Court **307.789.7002**
Fax 307.783.0357
Web ....www.courts.state.wy.us
　225 9th St, Evanston, WY 82930-3415
　Honorable Dennis L. Sanderson, Director

POLICE AND SHERIFF

Sheriff's Ofc **307.783.1000**
Fax 307.783.1028
Web ....www.uintacounty.com
E-mail ....lonapoli@unitacounty.com
　77 County Road 109, Evanston, WY 82930-9797
　Lou Napoli, Sheriff

Washakie County

GENERAL HEALTH SERVICES

Public Health Nursing Svc **307.347.3278**
Fax 307.347.3270
E-mail ....phnworland@health.wyo.gov
　1007 Robertson Ave, Worland, WY 82401
　Lori Schaal, Rn, Nursing Manager

WIC **307.347.9249**
Fax 307.347.3027
　2010 Robertson Ave, Worland, WY 82401-2902
　Kathleen Nichols, Director

JUSTICE AGENCY

Dept Of Corrections Div Of Field

Svcs **307.347.4368**
Fax 307.347.8710
　1702 Robertson Ave, Worland, WY 82401
　Bill Payne, Northern District Deputy Administrator

POLICE AND SHERIFF

Sheriff's Ofc **307.347.2242**
Fax 307.347.6110
E-mail ....wcso201@rtconnect.com
　100 N 10th St, Worland, WY 82401
　Steve Rakness, Sheriff

EDUCATION SERVICES

Absaroka Head Start **307.347.4192**
Fax 307.347.4777
Web ....www.ashs.org
E-mail ....abshs@ashs.org
　1121 Big Horn Ave, Worland, WY 82401
　Jamie Stockwell, Director

Weston County

SOCIAL SERVICES

Dept Of Family Svcs **307.746.4657**
Fax 307.746.2588
Web ....www.state.wy.us
E-mail ....kathy.deiss@wy.gov
　2013 W Main St Ste 101, Newcastle, WY 82701-2411
　Kathy Diess, Manager

POLICE AND SHERIFF

Sheriff's Dept **307.746.4441**
Fax 307.746.3404
E-mail ....wcso@rtconnect.net
　25 N Sumner Ave, Newcastle, WY 82701-2137
　Bryan Coldard, Sheriff

SPECIAL SERVICES AGENCIES

ADOPTION AGENCIES

Casey Family Programs **307.638.2564**
Fax 307.632.5251
Web ....www.casey.org
E-mail ....bmckinney@casey.org
　130 Hobbs Ave, Cheyenne, WY 82009-4723
　Brenden Mckinney, Director

BEHAVIORAL HEALTH TREATMENT

Attention Homes, Inc. **307.778.7832**
Fax 307.778.2576
Web ....www.attentionhomes.com
　714 West Fox Farm Road, Cheyenne, WY 82007
　CARF accredited programs available.

Big Horn Basin Counseling Services **307.568.2020**
Fax 307.568.2053
　116 South Third Street, Basin, WY 82410
　CARF accredited programs available.

Cathedral Home for Children **307.745.8997**
Web ....www.cathedralhome.org
E-mail ....pthobro@cathedralhome.org
　4989 North 3rd Street, Laramie, WY 82073
　Ms. Patricia Thobro, Accreditation Manager
　Joint Commission accredited organization.

Cathedral Home For Children **307.745.8997**
Fax 307.742.6146
Web ....www.cathedralhome.org
E-mail ....rhaas@cathedralhome.org
　4989 N 3rd St, Laramie, WY 82073
　Robin J. Haas, Executive Director

Central Wyoming Counseling Center **307.237.9583**
Fax 307.265.7277
Web ....www.cwcc.us
　1430 Wilkins Circle, Casper, WY 82601
　CARF accredited programs available.

Climb Wyoming **307.778.0094**
Web ....www.climbwyoming.org
E-mail ....molly@climbwyoming.org
　123 E 17th ST, Cheyenne, WY 82001-2442
　Molly Kruger, Director

Cloud Peak Counseling Center **307.347.6165**
Fax 307.347.6166
Web ....www.cloudpeakcc.org
　206 South Seventh Street, Worland, WY 82401
　CARF accredited programs available.

Counseling Center **307.324.7156**
Fax 307.328.1651
Web ....www.cccounselingcenter.org
　721 West Maple Street, Rawlins, WY 82301
　CARF accredited programs available.

Counseling Services, Inc. **307.864.3138**
Fax 307.864.3139
　121 South Fourth Street, Thermopolis, WY 82443
　CARF accredited programs available.

Wyoming

Fremont Counseling Svc 307.332.2231
Fax 307.332.9338
  748 Main St, Lander, WY 82520
Jerry Mcadams, Executive Director

High Country Behavioral Health 307.885.9883
Fax 307.885.5206
Web ....www.HighCountryCounseling.com
E-mail ....degrendele@highcountrycounseling.com
  389 Adams Street, Afton, WY 83110
Christee Degrendele, director of YWCA
CARF accredited programs available.

Jackson Hole Community Counseling
Center 307.733.2046
Fax 307.733.6289
Web ....www.jhccc.org
  640 East Broadway, Jackson, WY 83001
CARF accredited programs available.

Jeffrey C. Wartol Academy 307.633.8040
Fax 307.634.9936
E-mail ....jharrison@fcs-inc.net
  3304 I80 Service Rd, Cheyenne, WY 82009-8781
Miguel Herrera, Executive Director

Mountain Regional Services, Inc. 307.789.3710
Fax 307.789.0823
Web ....www.mrsi.org
  50 Allegiance Circle, Evanston, WY 82930
CARF accredited programs available.

New Directions 307.237.6033
Fax 307.265.7277
  1514 E 12th St Ste 101, Casper, WY 82601-7123
Carol King, Supervisor

Normative Services, Inc. 307.674.6878
Web ....www.normativeservices.com
E-mail ....bpatterson@normativeservices.com
  5 Lane Lane, Sheridan, WY 82801
Mr. Bud Patterson, Accreditation Manager
Joint Commission accredited organization.

Northern Wyoming Mental Health Center,
Inc. 307.672.8958
Fax 307.672.8950
Web ....www.wyomentalhealth.org
E-mail ....lynnewhittington@nwymhc.org
  909 Long Drive, Suite C, Sheridan, WY 82801
Lynne Whittington, Director
CARF accredited programs available.

Peak Wellness Center 307.632.9362
Fax 307.638.8256
Web ....www.peakwellnesscenter.org
  510 West 29th Street, Cheyenne, WY 82001
CARF accredited programs available.

Pine Ridge 307.332.5700
Fax 307.335.6465
  1320 Bishop Randall Dr, Lander, WY 82520
Robin Walker, Rn, Director Of Nursing

Pioneer Counseling Services 307.789.7915
Fax 307.789.6009
Web ....pioneermhc.org
  350 City View Drive, Suite 302, Evanston, WY 82930
CARF accredited programs available.

Solutions For Life 307.358.2846
Fax 307.358.5329
Web ....www.wysfl.com
  1841 Madora Avenue, Douglas, WY 82633
CARF accredited programs available.

St. Joseph's Children's Home 307.532.4197
Web ....stjoseph-wy.org
E-mail ....slower@stjoseph-wy.org
  1419 Main Street, Torrington, WY 82240
Ms. Stormy Lower, Accreditation Manager
Joint Commission accredited organization.

Trinity Teen Solutions, Inc. 307.645.3384
Fax 307.645.3385
Web ....www.trinityteensolutions.com
E-mail ....admissions@trinityteensolutions.com
  89 Road 8 RA, Powell, WY 82435
Angie Woodward, RN, Director; Jerry Woodward, Director; Justin McColl, MA, LPC, Clinical Director
Trinity Teen Solutions, Inc. is a Christian Residential Treatment Facility located on a 4,000 acre ranch that helps troubled teen girls ages 12-17 and young women ages 18-25, find the beauty within, heal past wounds, grow inner strength, instill a conscience and learn to manage themselves in today's difficult society. We utilize multiple therapeutic approaches that are effective for each unique individual in individual therapy, group therapy and family therapy sessions helping the entire family to heal.

Wyoming Behavioral Institute 307.237.7444
Web ....wbihelp.com
E-mail ....nadine.dexter@uhsinc.com
  2521 East 15th Street, Casper, WY 82609
Mrs. Nadine Dexter, Accreditation Manager
Joint Commission accredited organization.

Wyoming State Hospital 307.789.3464
Fax 307.789.5277
Web ....www.mentalhealth.state.wy.us/hospital
  831 Highway 150 South, Evanston, WY 82931
Brent Sherard, Director and State Health Officer
CARF accredited programs available.

Yellowstone Behavioral Health Center 307.587.2197
Fax 307.527.6218
  2538 Big Horn Avenue, Cody, WY 82414
CARF accredited programs available.

YES House 307.686.0669
Fax 307.686.2121
Web ....www.youthemergencyservices.org
  700 Longmont Street, Gillette, WY 82716
Sherilyn England, Executive Director
CARF accredited programs available.

Youth Crisis Center, Inc. 307.577.5718
Fax 307.577.5716
  915 South McKinley Street, Casper, WY 82601
CARF accredited programs available.

CHILDREN'S HOSPITAL

Cheyenne Regional Medical Center 307.634.2273
E-mail ....dalen.frantz@crmcwy.org
  214 E 23rd St, Cheyenne, WY 82001
Dr. John Lucas, Chief Executive Officer

Evanston Regional Hospital 307.789.3636
  190 Arrowhead Dr, Evanston, WY 82930
George Winn, Chief Executive Officer

Healthcare Center 307.684.5521
  497 W Lott St, Buffalo, WY 82834
Sandy Ward, Chief Executive Officer

Ivinson Memorial Hospital 307.742.2141
  255 N 30th St, Laramie, WY 82072
Aaron Alcercer, Director

Memorial Hospital 307.362.3711
  1200 College Dr, Rock Springs, WY 82901
Jerry Klein, Chief Executive Officer

Memorial Hospital 307.864.3121
  150 E Arapahoe St, Thermopolis, WY 82443
Charles Mayer, Chief Executive Officer

Memorial Hospital 307.322.3636
  201 14th St, Wheatland, WY 82201
John Dean Bangelo, Chief Executive Officer

Sheridan Memorial Hospital 307.672.1000
E-mail ....mikemccafferty@sheridanhospital.org
  1401 W Fifth St, Sheridan, WY 82801
Mike Mccafferty, Chief Executive Officer

South Lincoln Medical Center 307.877.4401
  711 Onyx St, Kemmerer, WY 83101
Eric Doley, Chief Executive Officer

Wyoming Medical Center 307.577.7201
  1233 E Second St, Casper, WY 82601
Vicki Diamon, Administrator

COUNSELING SERVICES

Trinity Teen Solutions, Inc. 307.645.3384
Fax 307.645.3385
Web ....www.trinityteensolutions.com
E-mail ....admissions@trinityteensolutions.com
  89 Road 8 RA, Powell, WY 82435
Angie Woodward, RN, Director; Jerry Woodward, Director; Justin McColl, MA, LPC, Clinical Director
Trinity Teen Solutions, Inc. is a Christian Residential Treatment Facility located on a 4,000 acre ranch that helps troubled teen girls ages 12-17 and young women ages 18-25, find the beauty within, heal past wounds, grow inner strength, instill a conscience and learn to manage themselves in today's difficult society. We utilize multiple therapeutic approaches that are effective for each unique individual in individual therapy, group therapy and family therapy sessions helping the entire family to heal.

Wyoming Children's Society 307.632.7619
Fax 307.632.3056
Web ....www.wyomingcs.org
E-mail ....wyomingcs@wyomingcs.org
  314 E 21st St, Cheyenne, WY 82001
Carol Lindly, Director

CRISIS & SHELTER CARE

Advocacy And Resource Ctr-Dom Vlnce 307.672.7471
Fax 307.672.5259
Web ....www.arcsheridan.org
E-mail ....arc@sheridan.org
  136 Coffeen Ave, Sheridan, WY 82801
Bonnie Young, Director

Cares Domestic Violence Program 307.568.3377
Fax 307.568.2503
E-mail ....hoffman@tctwest.net
  420 State Highway 30, Basin, WY 82410
Ms Leslie Hoffman, Director

Coalition Agnst Fmly Vlnce 307.358.6148
Fax 307.358.2706
Web ....www.communicomm.com
  126 N 5th St, Douglas, WY 82633-2406
Cathy Freezer-Jones, Director

Crisis Intervention Svcs-Dom Vlnce 307.587.3545
Fax 307.527.7801
  1220 13th St, Cody, WY 82414-3618
Ms Lisa Velker, Director

Crisis Prevention And Responce 307.347.4992
Fax 307.347.6194
E-mail ....cprc@rtconnect.net
  101 N 19th St, Worland, WY 82401
Jeanne Core, Director

Domestic Violence Program 307.324.7071
Fax 307.324.7075
E-mail ....Cove711@Yahoo.Com
  711 W Pine St, Rawlins, WY 82301
Rhonda Jacobs, Director

Family Violence-Sexual Assault Svcs **307.283.2415**
E-mail ....ccfv@collinscom.net
123 Edna, Sundance, WY 82729
Sandra Stevens, Director

Focus-Domestic Violence Program **307.746.2748**
Fax 307.746.4940
Web ....www.rtconnect.net
E-mail ....anatchke@yahoo.com
719 Washington Blvd Unit C, Newcastle,
WY 82701-2987
Amy Natchke, Director

Helpmate Crisis Ctr-Domestic Violence **307.334.3416**
Fax 307.334.5516
E-mail ....luhelpmt@luskhelpmate.org
330 S Main St, Lusk, WY 82225-0089
Marcia Bruegger, Director

Lander Girls Group Home **307.332.5490**
Fax 307.332.5491
2228 N 2nd St, Lander, WY 82520
Stacey Doerr, Executive Director

Mt. Carmel Youth Ranch Bunkhouse **307.645.3380**
Fax 307.645.3054
E-mail ....admissions@mtcarmelyouthranch.com
428 Road 1Af, Powell, WY 82435
Gerald Schneider, Director

Project Safe-Domestic Violence Program **307.322.4794**
Fax 307.322.4797
Web ....www.qwestoffice.net
E-mail ....beaton@Qwestoffice.Net
1207 9th St, Wheatland, WY 82201
Becky Eaton, Director

Riverton Boys Group Home **307.856.2643**
Fax 307.856.2646
Web ....www.bresnan.net
E-mail ....sdoerr@bresnan.net
11 Minter Ln, Riverton, WY 82501-8959
Stacey Doerr, Executive Director

Volunteers Of America **307.672.0475**
Fax 307.672.0476
E-mail ....Jholsinger@voanr.org
1876 S Sheridan Ave, Sheridan, WY 82801
Jeff Holsinger, CEO

EDUCATION

Normative Svcs, Inc **307.674.6878**
Fax 307.674.7781
E-mail ....cwillandt@normativeservices.com
5 Lane Ln, Sheridan, WY 82801-8630
Carolyn Willandt, Director

**Northwest Wyoming Board Of Cooperative Educational
Svcs** **307.864.2171**
Fax 307.864.9463
Web ....www.nwboces.com
E-mail ....carolync@rtconnect.net
250 E Arapahoe St, Thermopolis, WY 82443
Carolyn Conor, Administrative Director

Self-Help Ctr **307.235.2814**
Fax 307.472.4307
E-mail ....shc300@hotmail.com
441 S Center St Ste 300, Casper, WY 82601-2859
Liz Baron, Executive Director

TRINITY TEEN SOLUTIONS, INC.
A journey that enriches her mind, body, and soul

Trinity Teen Solutions, Inc. **307.645.3384**
Fax 307.645.3385
Web ....www.trinityteensolutions.com
E-mail ....admissions@trinityteensolutions.com
89 Road 8 RA, Powell, WY 82435
Angie Woodward, RN, Director; Jerry Woodward, Director; Justin McColl, MA, LPC, Clinical Director
Trinity Teen Solutions, Inc. is a Christian Residential Treatment Facility located on a 4,000 acre ranch that helps troubled teen girls ages 12-17 and young women ages 18-25, find the beauty within, heal past wounds, grow inner strength, instill a conscience and learn to manage themselves in today's difficult society. We utilize multiple therapeutic approaches that are effective for each unique individual in individual therapy, group therapy and family therapy sessions helping the entire family to heal.

Vernon C. Condie Home For Girls and Boys **307.754.8400**
E-mail ....youth@tritel.net
468 Hamilton Way, Powell, WY 82435-3112
Ty Barrus, Director

Wyoming Boys School **307.347.6144**
Fax 307.347.4869
1550 US Highway 20 S, Worland, WY 82401
Steve Wake, Education Director

Wyoming Girls' School **307.674.7476**
Fax 307.674.4909
Web ....www.state.wy.us
3500 Big Horn Ave, Sheridan, WY 82801-9351
Jim Lyon Jr., Clinical Director/Substance Abuse Supervisor

PEDIATRIC HOME CARE

Interim Healthcare **307.266.1152**
Fax 307.577.8041
1010 E First St Ste A, Casper, WY 82601
Kary Pickett, Administrator

SOCIAL SERVICES

Catholic Charities **307.637.0554**
Fax 307.632.2346
E-mail ....bmayor@charitieswyoming.org
2315 Bent Ave, Cheyenne, WY 82003-0907
Robert Mayor, Director

**Child Care Finder Northeastern Wyoming
Ofc** **307.266.1236**
Fax 307.266.4410
Web ....http://www.cnswyoming.org
E-mail ....info@cnswyoming.org
800 Werner Ct Ste 210, Casper, WY 82601
Heidi Dickers, Director

**Child Care Finder Northwestern Wyoming
Ofc** **307.754.8457**
Fax 307.266.4410
Web ....http://www.childrens-nutrition.com
E-mail ....ckolesien@cmswyoming.org
375 N Cheyenne St, Powell, WY 82435
Heidi Dickerson, Director

**Child Care Finder Southeastern Wyoming
Ofc** **307.638.2091**
Fax 307.266.4410
Web ....www.childrens-nutrition.com
E-mail ....cheyenneccf@wyoming.com
1651 Carey Ave Ste 1C, Cheyenne, WY 82001
Kim Lamb, Manager Of Child Finder

Curran Seeley Foundation **307.367.3433**
Fax 307.367.3858
Web ....www.curranseeley.com
E-mail ....ed@curranseeley.com
21 Franklin, Pinedale, WY 82941
Ed Wigg, Director

Vernon C. Condie Home For Boys **307.754.9255**
Web ....www.bresnan.net
E-mail ....nwtc@bresnan.net
483 Hamilton Way, Powell, WY 82435-3111
Spencer Condie, On-site Director

Wyoming Children's Society **307.632.7619**
Fax 307.632.3056
Web ....www.wyomingcs.org
314 East 21st Street, Cheyenne, WY 82001
COA accredited organization.

SPECIAL NEEDS

ARC **307.577.4913**
E-mail ....arc_nc@tribcsp.com
PO Box 393, Casper, WY 82602

Autism Society Gateway Chapter **314.749.7225**
E-mail ....jinman279@aol.com
1311 Wells Ave, Fairview, WY 83119

Brain Injury Association **800.473.1767**
E-mail ....biaw@tribcsp.com
111 W 2nd St Ste 106, Casper, WY 82601
Dawn Racko, Chief Executive Officer

Easter Seals Wyoming **307.672.2816**
E-mail ....anitab@esgw.org
991 Joe St, Sheridan, WY 82801
Anita B, Director

Independent Living Rehabilitation Inc **307.266.6956**
E-mail ....khoff@wilr.org
305 W 1st St, Casper, WY 82601
Ken Hoff, Executive Director

NAMI Wyoming **888.882.4968**
E-mail ....aedwards@nami.org
133 W 6th, Casper, WY 82601
Anna Edwards, Director

National Multiple Sclerosis Society **307.433.9590**
Fax 307.433.8657
E-mail ....WYY@nmss.org
525 Randall Ave Ste 105, Cheyenne, WY 82001

Parent Information Center **307.684.2277**
Fax 307.684.5314
E-mail ....tdawson@wpic.org
500 W Lott St Ste A, Buffalo, WY 82834
T Dawson, Director

Renew **307.672.7481**
E-mail ....ceo@renew-wyo.com
1969 S Sheridan Ave, Sheridan, WY 82801
Larry Samson, Chief Executive Officer

Services for Independent Living **800.266.3061**
E-mail ....wsil@wyoming.com
1156 S 2nd St, Lander, WY 82520
Susan S, Operations Manager

Uplift **888.875.4383**
E-mail ....pnikkel@upliftwy.org
4007 Greenway St Ste 201, Cheyenne, WY 82001
Kim Conner, Director

Wyoming Epilepsy Association **866.634.5329**
E-mail ....admin@wyomingepilepsy.org
1603 capital ave, ste 301, Cheyenne, WY 82001

Wyoming Paintbrush **307.237.8618**
239 W 1st St, Casper, WY 82601
Maryann Smith, Assistant Director

Wyoming PTA **307.265.4674**
E-mail ....president@wyominpta.org
3031 E 12th St, Casper, WY 82609

Wyoming

SUBSTANCE ABUSE TREATMENT

Big Horn Basin Adolescent Programs Girls's
Home **307.568.2222**
Fax 307.568.2982
E-mail ....bghrn@tctwest.net
   967 Hwy 20 S, Basin, WY 82410-0858
Lynne Davies, Director

Solutions For Life **307.358.2846**
Fax 307.358.5329
Web ....www.wysfl.com
   1841 Madora Ave, Douglas, WY 82633
Peggy Hays, Executive Director
CARF accredited programs available.

Southwest Counseling Service **307.352.6677**
Fax 307.352.6614
Web ....www.swcounseling.org
E-mail ....mlove@swcounseling.org
   2300 Foothill Boulevard, Rock Springs, WY 82901
Michal Zanett-love, Program Director
CARF accredited programs available.

Trinity Teen Solutions, Inc. **307.645.3384**
Fax 307.645.3385
Web ....www.trinityteensolutions.com
E-mail ....admissions@trinityteensolutions.com
   89 Road 8 RA, Powell, WY 82435
Angie Woodward, RN, Director; Jerry Woodward, Director; Justin
McColl, MA, LPC, Clinical Director

Trinity Teen Solutions, Inc. is a Christian Residential Treatment Facility located on a 4,000 acre ranch that helps troubled teen girls ages 12-17 and young women ages 18-25, find the beauty within, heal past wounds, grow inner strength, instill a conscience and learn to manage themselves in today's difficult society. We utilize multiple therapeutic approaches that are effective for each unique individual in individual therapy, group therapy and family therapy sessions helping the entire family to heal.

The National Directory of

Children, Youth & Families Services

THE PROFESSIONALS' REFERENCE 2012

PART II

WHO'S WHO IN CHILDREN, YOUTH & FAMILIES PROGRAMS

Federal Government

National Organizations and Associations

Federal Government Agencies

EXECUTIVE BRANCH

Ofc of Domestic Policy **202.456.5594**
Fax 202.456.5557
Web ....www.whitehouse.gov
1600 Pennsylvania Ave, Washington, DC 20500
Melody Barnes, Assistant to President for Domestic Policy

**Ofc of Management and
Budget** **202.395.3080**
Fax 202.395.3888
Web ....www.whitehouse.gov
E-mail ....porszag@omb.eop.gov
725 17th St NW, Washington, DC 20503-0004
Peter Orszag, Director

**Ofc of National Drug Control
Policy** **202.395.6700**
Fax 202.395.6680
Web ....www.whitehousedrugpolicy.gov
E-mail ....executive_secretariat@ondcp.elp.gov
750 17th St NW, Washington, DC 20503
Richard Gil Kerlikowski, Director

Ofc of The Public Liason **202.456.2380**
Fax 202.456.6218
Web ....www.whitehouse.gov
1600 Pennsylvania Ave NW Rm 144, Washington,
DC 20502-0001
Kal Penn, Associate Director

The White House **202.456.1414**
Fax 202.456.2461
Web ....www.whitehouse.gov
E-mail ....president@whitehouse.gov
1600 Pennsylvania Ave NW, Washington,
DC 20500-0004
Barack Obama, President

HOUSE COMMITTEE

Committee on Appropriations **202.225.2771**
Fax 202.225.2112
Web ....www.house.gov
The Capitol, H-218, Washington, DC 20510-0001
David Obey, Chairman

**Committee on Education and
Workforce** **202.225.4527**
Fax 202.225.9571
Web ....www.house.gov
2101 Rayburn House Ofc Bldg, Room 2181,
Washington, DC 20515
John Kline, Ranking

**Committee on Government
Reform** **202.225.5074**
Fax 202.225.3974
B350 A Rayburn House Of C Building, Washington,
DC 20515-0001
Donna Harkins, Office Manager

Committee on the Judiciary **202.225.3951**
Fax 202.225.7682
Web ....www.judiciary.house.gov
E-mail ....john.coyers@mail.house.gov
Rayburn House Ofc Bldg, Rm 2138, Washington,
DC 20515
Perry Applebaum, Chief Counsel

**Committee on Ways and
Means** **202.225.3625**
Fax 202.225.2610
Web ....waysandmeans.house.gov
1102 Longworth House Ofc Bldg, Washington,
DC 20515-0001
Charles B. Rangel, Chairman

SENATE COMMITTEE

Committee on Appropriations **202.224.7363**
Fax 202.224.2100
Web ....www.appropriations.senate.gov
The Capitol Rm S128, Washington, DC 20510
Daniel Inouye, Chairman

Committee on Finance **202.224.4515**
Fax 202.228.0554
Dirksen Senate Rm SD-428, Washington, DC 20510
Scott Mulhauser, Senior Advisor and Councel

**Committee on Health, Education, Labor &
Pensions** **202.224.5375**
Fax 202.228.5044
Dirksen Senate Ofc Bldg, Rm SD-428, Washington,
DC 20510-0001
Lory Yudin, Director

Committee on Indian Affairs **202.224.2251**
Fax 202.224.5429
Web ....www.senate.gov
Hart Senate Ofc Bldg, Room 838, Washington,
DC 20510
Byron L. Dorgan, Chairman

Committee on the Judiciary **202.224.5225**
Fax 202.224.9102
Web ....www.judiciary.senate.gov
Dirksen Senate Ofc Bldg, Washington,
DC 20510-0001
Senator Patrick Leahy, Chairman

DEPARTMENT OF HEALTH AND HUMAN SERVICES

**ACF Admin For Native Americans
(ANA)** **202.690.7776**
Fax 202.690.7441
Web ....www.acf.dhhs.gov
E-mail ....anacomments@acf.hhs.gov
901 D St SW Ste E, Aerospace Bldg, Washington,
DC 20024-2198
Caroline Gary, Deputy Commissioner

**ACF Admin on Children, Youth &
Families** **202.205.8347**
Fax 202.205.9721
Web ....www.acf.dhhs.gov
E-mail ....ionya.taylor@acfd.hhs.gov
1250 Maryland Ave Sw, Washington,
DC 20024-2141
Dr. Maiso Bryant, Acting Commissioner

**Admin for Children & Families
(ACF)** **202.401.9200**
Fax 202.401.5770
Web ....www.acf.hhs.gov
Aerospace Bldg Fl 6, Washington, DC 20447
David Hansill, Assistant Secretary

**Administration on Developmental
Disabilities** **202.690.6590**
Fax 202.205.8037
Web ....www.acf.hhs.gov/programs/add
E-mail ....faith.mccormick@acf.hhs.gov
200 Independence Ave SW, Hubert H Humphrey Bldg
Room 405D, Washington, DC 20201
Faith McCormick, Director

**Agency For Healthcare Research & Quality
(AHRQ)** **301.427.1364**
Fax 301.427.2168
Web ....www.ahrq.hhs.gov
E-mail ....cclancy@ahrq.gov
540 Gaither Rd, Suite 200, Rockville, MD 20850
Dr Carolyn Clancy, Director

**Agency For Toxic Substances And Disease
Registry** **404.498.0070**
Fax 404.498.0094
Web ....www.cdc.gov
E-mail ....haf6@cdc.gov
1600 Clifton Rd NE, MS-E29, Atlanta,
GA 30329-4018
Howard Frumkin MD, PhD, Administrator

**BHPR National AIDS Education & Training Ctrs
(AETC)** **301.443.6364**
Fax 301.443.9887
Web ....www.hrsa.gov
E-mail ....lwegamn@hrsa.gov
5600 Fishers Ln # 7-05, Rockville, MD 20857-0002
Lynn Wagman, Chief of HIV Education

**BPHC Div of Programs for Special Populations
(DPSP)** **301.594.4420**
Fax 301.594.2470
Web ....www.hrsa.gov
5600 Fishers Ln, Room 1761, Rockville,
MD 20852-1750
John Cafazza, Director

Bureau of Indian Affairs **202.208.5116**
Fax 202.208.5320
Web ....www.doi.gov/bureau-indian-affairs.html
E-mail ....jeroldgidner@bia.gov
1849 C St NW, Interior Bldg, Washington, DC 20240
Jerry Gidner, Director

**CDC National Ctr For Infectious Diseases
(NCID)** **404.639.3401**
Fax 404.639.3039
Web ....www.cdc.gov/ncidod
1600 Clifton Rd Ne, Mailstop C-12, Atlanta,
GA 30329-4027
Thomas Hearn, Acting Director

**CDC NCHS Div of Health Examination
Statistics** **301.458.4500**
Fax 301.458.4028
Web ....www.cdc.gov/nchs
E-mail ....cjohnson@cdc.gov
3311 Toledo Rd, MS P08, Hyattsville,
MD 20782-2064
Clifford L Johnson, Director

Children's Bureau **202.205.8618**
Fax 202.205.9721
Web ....www.acf.hhs.gov\programs\cb
1250 Maryland Ave SW, 8th Floor, Washington,
DC 20024
Joe Bock, Acting Associate Commissioner

**Ctr For Substance Abuse
Treatment** **240.276.2420**
Fax 240.276.2430
Web ....prevention.samhsa.gov/
E-mail ....dennis-romero@samhsa.hhs.gov
1 Choke Cherry Rd, Rockville, MD 20857-0001
Francis Hoffman, Director

Ctrs for Disease Control and Prevention
...........................**770.488.4696**
Fax 770.488.4422
Web ....www.cdc.gov
E-mail ....lgalaska@cdc.gov
4770 Buford Hwy, MS K-02, Atlanta, GA 30341-3717
Louise Galaska, Director

**Ctrs for Disease Control and Prevention National Ctr on
Health Statistics** **301.458.4000**
TTY 866.458.NCHS
Fax 866.441.Nchs
Web ....www.cdc.gov/nchs
E-mail ....cnh2uy@cdc.gov
3311 Toledo Rd, Hyattsville, MD 20782-2064
Edward Sondik, MD, Director

Federal Agencies

Ctrs for Disease Control and Prevention National Institute for Occupational Safety and Health **202.245.0600**
Phone 202.245.0625
Fax 202.245.0664
　395 E St SW Ste 9100, Washington, DC 20201-0004
　Christine Branche, Acting Director

Ctrs for Medicare & Medicaid Svcs (CMS) **410.786.3000**
Fax 202.690.6262
Web ....www.cms.gov
E-mail ....leslie.norwalk@cms.hhs.gov
　7500 Security Blvd, Windsor Mill, MD 21244-1849
　Michael O'Donnell, Administrator

Ctrs For Medicare and Medicaid Svcs (CMS), Ctr For Beneficiary Choices **215.861.4240**
Web ....www.medicare.gov
　7500 Security Blvd, Windsor Mill, MD 21244-1849
　Jim McCaslin, Head of Beneficiary Operations

DHS Ofc on Women's Health **202.690.7650**
Fax 202.690.7172
Web www.4woman.gov
E-mail ....frances-goins@hhs.gov
　200 Independence Ave SW Rm 718E, Washington, DC 20201-0004
　Frances Ashe-Goins, Director

Family & Youth Svcs Bureau **202.205.8102**
Fax 202.205.9721
E-mail ....karen.morison@acf.hhs.gov
　1250 Maryland Ave SW, 8th Floor, Washington, DC 20024
　Karen Burke Morison, Associate Commissioner

Food and Drug Admin **301.443.1544**
Fax 301.443.3100
Web ....www.fda.gov
E-mail ....margaret.hamburg@fda.hhs.gov
　5600 Fishers Ln # HF-1, Rockville, MD 20857-0002
　Margaret Hamburg, Commissioner

Food and Drug Admin, Ctr For Drug Evaluation and Research **301.827.4573**
Fax 301.827.7748
Web ....www.fda.gov/cder
E-mail ....woodcockj@cder.fda.gov
　5600 Fishers Ln Ste 1, Rockville, MD 20852-1712
　Lee Woodcock, Director

Health Care Financing Admin **202.690.6726**
Fax 202.690.6262
Web ....www.cms.gov
　H Hubert Humphrey Bldg 314 G, Washington, DC 20201
　Donald Bewick, Administrator

Health Care Systems Bureau **301.443.3300**
Fax 301.443.1221
Web ....www.hrsa.gov/osp
　5600 Fishers Ln 12 105, Bethesda, MD 20857
　Joyce Somsak, Associate Administrator

Health Resources and Svcs Admin **301.443.3376**
Fax 301.443.1989
Web ....www.hrsa.gov
E-mail ....mwakefield@hrsa.gov
　Parklawn, 5600 Fishers Lane, Rockville, MD 20857-0001
　Mary Wakefield, Administrator

Health Resources and Svcs Admin Migrant Health Ctrs - Eastern **919.469.5701**
Fax 919.469.1263
　2500 Gateway Centre Blvd Ste 100, Morrisville, NC 27560-6206
　Benjamin Money, CEO

HHS Ofc of Inspector General **202.619.3148**
Fax 202.401.3196
Web ....www.oig.hhs.gov
E-mail ....daniel.levinson@oig.hhs.gov
　330 Independence Ave SW Rm 5250, Washington, DC 20201-0003
　Dan Levinson, Inspector General

HRSA Ofc Of Minority Health **301.443.2964**
Fax 301.443.7853
Web ....www.hrsa.gov
　5600 Fishers Ln Rm 12-70, Rockville, MD 20857-0002
　Deborah Willis-Fillinger, Director

HRSA/Bureau of Health Professions (BHPR) **301.443.5794**
Fax 301.443.2111
Web ....www.bhpr.hrsa.gov
E-mail ....despinosa@hrsa.gov
　5600 Fishers Ln # 905, Rockville, MD 20857-0002
　Diana Espinosa, Deputy Director

HRSAA/Maternal and Child Health Bureau (MCHB) **301.443.2170**
Fax 301.443.1797
Web ....www.hrsa.gov
E-mail ....pvandyck@hrsa.gov
　5600 Fishers Ln # 18-05, Rockville, MD 20857-0002
　Peter Vandyck, MS, MD, MPH, Associate Administrator

IHS Maternal & Child Health **301.443.5070**
Fax 301.443.1522
Web ....www.ihs.gov
E-mail ....judith.thierry@ihs.gov
　12300 Twinbrook Pkwy Ste 450, Rockville, MD 20852-1646
　Judith Thierry, MD, Coordinator

Medicare Payment Advisory Commission **202.220.3700**
Fax 202.220.3759
Web ....www.medpac.gov
E-mail ....mmiller@medpac.gov
　601 New Jersey Ave NW Ste 9000, Washington, DC 20001-2044
　Mark Miller, Executive Director

National Ctr for HIV, STD, and TB Prevention (NCHSTP) **404.639.8000**
Fax 404.639.8600
Web ....www.cdc.gov/nchstp
E-mail ....pkl8@cdc.gov
　1600 Clifton Road NE, Atlanta, GA 30333
　Kevin Fenton, Director

National Heart Lung and Blood Institute **301.592.8573**
Fax 301.251.1223
E-mail ....nhlbiinfo@rover.nhlbi.nih.gov
　PO Box 30105, Bethesda, MD 20824

National Heart, Lung, and Blood Institute Health Info Ctr **301.592.8573**
Fax 301.592.8563
Web ....www.nhlbi.nih.gov/nhlbi/
E-mail ....NHLBLinfo@rover.nhlbi.nih.gov
　PO Box 30105, Bethesda, MD 20824-0105
　Susan Shurin, Deputy Director

National Immunization Program **404.639.8200**
Fax 404.639.8626
　12 Corporate Square Mall NE, Bldg. 12, Atlanta, GA 30329
　Anne Schucht, MD, MPH, Acting Director

National Institute of Mental Health **301.443.3675**
Fax 301.443.2578
Web ....www.nimh.nih.gov
E-mail ....gweiblin@nih.gov
　6001 Executive Blvd Rm 8235, Bethesda, MD 20892-0001
　Thomas Insel, Director

National Institute of Mental Health **301.443.4525**
Fax 301.443.4045
Web ....www.nimh.nih.gov/ormhr/index.cfm
E-mail ....nimhpress@nih.gov
　6001 Executive Blvd, MSC 6931 Room 7-130, Bethesda, MD 20892-0001
　Dr. Thomas Insel, Director

National Institute of Mental Health - The Child Psychiatry Branch **301.496.6080**
Fax 301.402.0296
E-mail ....rapoporj@mail.nih.gov
　10 Center Dr, Bldg 10 Room 3N202, Bethesda, MD 20892
　Judith Rapoport, Branch Chief

National Institute of Mental Health- Ofc of Rural Mental Health Research (ORMHR) **301.443.1193**
Fax 301.443.8552
Web ....www.nimh.nih.gov/ormhr/index.cfm
E-mail ....marquez1@mail.nih.gov
　6001 Executive Blvd Rm 8125, Bethesda, MD 20892
　Ernest Marquez, Director

National Institute On Deafness and Other Communication Disorders **301.496.7243**
Web ....www.nidcd.nih.gov/index.asp
E-mail ....nidcdinfo@nidcd.nih.gov
　31 Center Dr Ste 2320, National Institute of Health, Bethesda, MD 20892
　Patricia Blessing, Chief, OHCPL

National Institute on Drug Abuse **301.443.6480**
Fax 301.443.9127
Web ....www.nida.nih.gov
　6001 Executive Blvd Rm 5274, Bethesda, MD 20892
　Nora D. Volkow, Director

National Institutes Of Health National Ctr On Sleep Disorders Research **301.435.0199**
Fax 301.480.3451
Web ....www.nhlbi.nih.gov/sleep
E-mail ....twerym@nhlbi.nih.gov
　670 Rockledge Dr, One Rockledge Centre Ste 6022, Bethesda, MD 20892-0001
　Michael Twery, Director

National Institutes of Mental Health **301.443.3673**
Fax 301.443.2578
Web ....www.nimh.nih.gov
E-mail ....tinsel@mail.nih.gov
　6001 Executive Blvd, MSC 9669 Rm 8235, Bethesda, MD 20892-0001
　Thomas Insel, Director

NIH National Cancer Institute (NCI) **301.496.4000**
Web ....www.nci.nih.gov
　900 Rockville Height, Bethesda, MD 20892
　John Niederhuber, Director

NIH National Institute of Child Health & Human Development (NICHD) **301.496.3454**
Fax 301.402.1104
Web ....www.nichd.nih.gov
E-mail ....guttmach@mail.nih.gov
　31 Center Dr, MSC 2425 Bldg. 31, Rm 2A03, Bethesda, MD 20892-0001
　Alan Guttmacher, Director

NIH National Institute on Alcohol Abuse and Alcoholism (NIAAA) **301.443.3860**
Fax 301.480.1726
Web ....www.niaaa.nih.gov
E-mail ....kwarren@willco.niaaa.nih.gov
　5635 Fishers Ln, Mailstop Code 9304, Bethesda, MD 20892-0001
　Kenneth R. Warren, MD, Director

North West Regional Primary Care Assoc **206.783.3004**
Fax 206.783.4311
Web ....www.nwrpca.org
　6512 23rd Ave NW, Suite 305, Seattle, WA 98117
　Bruce Gray, CEO

Ofc of Assistant Secretary for Planning and Evaluation **202.690.7858**
Fax 202.690.7383
　H Hubert Humphrey Bldg Rm 415-F, Washington, DC 20201
　Donald B. Moulds, Principal Deputy Assistant Secretary For Planning And Evaluation

Ofc of Commissioned Corps Operations **240.453.6000**
Fax 240.453.6120
Web .... www.dcp.psc.gov
E-mail .... lawrence.furman@hhs.gov
1101 Wootton Pkwy, Plaza Level Suite 100, Rockville, MD 20852-1060
Lawrence J. Furman, Director

Ofc of Community Svcs **202.401.9333**
Fax 202.401.4694
Web .... www.acf.hhs.gov/programs/ocs/
901 SW D St Fl 5, Washington, DC 20447
Yolanda Butler, Director

Ofc of General Counsel **202.690.7741**
Fax 202.690.7998
E-mail .... geraldine.adair@hhs.gov
200 Independence Ave SW Ste 713F, Washington, DC 20201
Mark Childress, Acting General Counsel

Ofc of Population Affairs Clearinghouse **866.640.7827**
Fax 866.592.3299
Web .... www.opaclearinghouse.org
E-mail .... info@opaclearinghouse.org
7910 Woodmont Ave Ste 600, Bethesda, MD 20814-3064
Mary Nalaschi, Manager

Ofc of Public Health and Science **202.690.7000**
Fax 202.690.7203
Web .... www.hhs.gov
E-mail .... howard.koh@hhs.gov
200 Independence Ave SW, Hubert H. Humphrey Bldg Room 716-G, Washington, DC 20201-0004
Howard Koh, MD, MPH, Assistant Secretary

Ofc of The Assistant Secretary for Legislation **202.690.7627**
Fax 202.690.7380
Web .... www.hhs.gov
200 Independence Ave SW Ste 416, Washington, DC 20201-0004
Jim Esquea, Assistant Secretary

OGC Food & Drug Div **301.827.1137**
Fax 301.827.3054
Web .... www.fda.gov
Parklawn Building 5600 Fishers Ln Rm 605 Mail Code Gcf 1, Rockville, MD 20857
Michael Landa, Acting Chief Counsel

PHS Ofc of Population Affairs **240.453.2800**
Fax 240.453.2889
Web .... www.hhs.gov\opa
E-mail .... marilyn.keefe@hhs.gov
1101 Wootton Pkwy Ste 700, Rockville, MD 20852-1074
Marilyn Keefe, Director

Presidents Committee for People with Intellectual Disabilities **202.619.0634**
Fax 202.205.9519
Web .... www.acf.gov
E-mail .... lroach@acf.hhs.gov
701 Aerospace, Washington, DC 20447-0001
Laverdia Roach, Acting Executive Director

Public Health Div **301.443.2644**
Fax 301.443.2639
5600 Fishers Ln Rm 4A-53, Rockville, MD 20857
David Benor, Associate General Counsel

Substance Abuse and Mental Health Svcs Admin (SAMHSA) **240.276.2000**
Fax 240.276.2010
Web .... www.samshsa.gov
1 Choke Cherry Rd, Rockville, MD 20857
Joe Faha, Legislative Consultant

Substance Abuse and Mental Health Svcs Admin Ctr **240.276.1310**
Fax 240.276.1320
1 Choke Cherry Rd Rm 6-1051, Rockville, MD 20857
Anna Marsh, Deputy Director

The National Ctr For Farm Worker Health **512.312.2700**
Fax 512.312.2600
Web .... www.ncfh.org
E-mail .... info@ncfh.org
1770 Fm 967, Buda, TX 78610
Bobby Ryder, CEO

DEPARTMENT OF HOUSING AND URBAN DEVELOPMENT

Community Planning and Development **202.708.2690**
Fax 202.708.3336
Web .... www.hud.gov
451 7th St SW, Washington, DC 20410
Pam Williams, Special Assistant

Dept of Housing and Urban Development (HUD) **202.275.9200**
Fax 202.275.6691
Web .... www.hud.gov
E-mail .... helpdesk@huduser.org
451 7th St SW Rm 5204, Washington, DC 20410
John E. Hall, Field Office Director

Federal Housing Commissioner **202.708.2601**
Fax 202.708.2580
Web .... www.hud.gov
451 7th St SW, Washington, DC 20410
David Stevens, Assistant Secretary

Inspector General **202.708.0430**
Fax 202.708.4829
Web .... www.hud.gov
E-mail .... hotline@hugoig.gov
451 7th St SW, Washington, DC 20410
Kenneth Donohue, Inspector General

Public and Indian Housing **202.708.0950**
Fax 202.619.8478
451 7th St SW, Washington, DC 20410
Sandra Henriquez, Assistant Secretary

DEPARTMENT OF JUSTICE

Americans With Disabilities Act (ADA) Info Line Civil Rights Div **800.514.0301**
Fax 202.307.1198
Web .... www.ada.gov
950 Pennsylvania Ave NW, Washington, DC 20530
John L. Wodatch, Chief

Child Exploitation and Obscenity Section **202.514.5780**
Fax 202.514.1793
Web .... http://www.usdoj.gov/criminal/ceos/
E-mail .... andrew.oosterbaan@usdoj.gov
1400 New York Ave NW, Bond Building Rm 600, Washington, DC 20005-2107
Andrew Oosterbaan, Chief

Civil Rights Div **202.376.7700**
Fax 202.376.7672
Web .... www.usccr.gov
624 9th St NW, Washington, DC 20425-0002
Martin Dannenfelser, Staff Director

Dept of Justice **202.514.2000**
Fax 202.307.6777
Web .... www.usdoj.gov
E-mail .... eric.holder@usdoj.gov
950 Pennsylvania Ave, Washington, DC 20530-0009
Eric Holder, Attorney General

Drug Enforcement Admin **202.305.8500**
Fax 202.307.7965
Web .... www.dea.gov
801 I St, Washington, DC 20001
Ava Cooper Davis, Director

Drug Enforcement Admin **202.307.1000**
Fax 203.307.4715
Web .... www.dea.gov
E-mail .... michele.m.leonhart@usdoj.gov
2401 Jefferson Davis Hwy, Mailstop Aes, Alexandria, VA 22301-1055
Michelle Leonhart, Acting Director

Drug Enforcement Admin Detroit Div **313.234.4000**
Fax 313.234.4149
Web .... www.dea.gov
431 Howard St, Detroit, MI 48226-2507
Robert L. Corso, Special Agent in Charge

Drug Enforcement Admin San Francisco Div **415.436.7900**
Fax 415.436.7877
Web .... www.dea.gov
450 Golden Gate Ave Ste 36035, San Francisco, CA 94102
Anthony Williams, Director

Drug Enforcement Admin, New York Div **212.337.3900**
Fax 212.337.1536
Web .... www.dea.gov
E-mail .... john.p.gilbride@usdoj.gov
99 10th Ave, New York, NY 10011-4713
John Gilbride, Special Agent in Charge

Drug Enforcement Admin, Philadelphia Div **215.861.3474**
Fax 215.861.3281
Web .... www.dea.gov
E-mail .... michele.m.leonhart@usdoj.gov
600 Arch St Ste 10224, William Green Building Suite 10224, Philadelphia, PA 19106-1650
Michele M. Leonhart, Administrator

Drug Enforcement Admin, Seattle Div **206.553.5443**
Fax 206.553.5302
Web .... www.dea.gov
400 2nd Ave W, Seattle, WA 98119-4013
Arnold Moorin, Special Agent in Charge

Drug Policy Info Clearinghouse **800.666.3332**
Fax 301.519.5212
Web .... www.whitehousedrugpolicy.gov
E-mail .... ondcp@ncjrs.gov
PO Box 6000, Rockville, MD 20849-6000-6000
Gil Kerlikowske, Director

Federal Bureau of Investigation **202.324.3000**
935 Pennsylvania Ave NW, Washington, DC 20535
Robert Mueller, Director

Federal Bureau of Alcohol, Tobacco, Firearms and Explosives **202.648.8700**
Fax 202.648.9622
Web .... www.atf.gov
E-mail .... michelle.beck@atf.gov
99 New York Ave NE, Washington, DC 20226
Kenneth E. Melson, Deputy Director

Justice Programs Ofc **202.307.5933**
Fax 202.514.7805
810 7th St NW, Washington, DC 20531
Laurie Robinson, Director

Ofc of Juvenile Justice and Delinquency **202.307.5911**
Fax 202.307.2093
Web .... www.ojjdp.ncjrs.gov
810 7th St NW, Washington, DC 20531
Jeff Slowkowski, Administrator

Ofc of The Attorney General **202.514.2001**
Fax 202.307.6777
Web .... www.usdoj.gov
950 Pennsylvania Ave NW, Washington, DC 20530-0001
Eric H. Holder, Jr., Attorney General

Ofc of The Inspector General **202.514.3435**
Fax 202.514.4001
Web .... www.doj/oig.gov
950 Pennsylvania Ave NW Ste 4706, Washington, DC 20530
Glenn A Fine, Inspector General

Ofc of Tribal Justice **202.514.8812**
Fax 202.514.9078
Web .... www.usdoj.gov/otj

E-mail .... lawrence.baca@usdoj.gov
950 Pennsylvania Ave NW, Washington,
DC 20530-0001
Lawerence Baca, Deputy Director

**Ofc on Violence Against
Women 202.307.6026**
Fax 202.307.3911
Web .... www.ojp.usdoj.gov
E-mail .... ovw@usdoj.gov
800 K St NW Ste 920, Washington, DC 20530-0001
Susan Carbon, Director

**US Commission On Civil Rights- Midwestern Regional
Ofc 312.353.8311**
Fax 312.353.8324
Web .... www.usccr.gov
55 W Monroe St Ste 410, Chicago, IL 60603
David Mussat, Director

**US Commission On Civil Rights- Southern Regional
Ofc 404.562.7000**
Fax 404.562.7005
61 Forsyth St SW, Suite16t126, Atlanta, GA 30303
Peter Minarik, Director

**US Commission On Civil Rights-Western Regional
Ofc 213.894.3437**
Fax 213.894.0508
300 N Los Angeles St Ste 2010, Los Angeles,
CA 90012-3322
Peter Minarik, PhD, Acting Director

US Probation Ofc 702.388.6428
Fax 702.388.6731
Web .... www.ustreas.gov
300 Las Vegas Blvd S Ste 1200, Las Vegas,
NV 89101-5813
Christopher Hansen, CPO

DEPARTMENT OF DEFENSE

Dept of Defense 703.545.6700
1000 Defense Pentagon, Washington,
DC 20301-1000
Robert M. Gates, Secretary, 703.607.4693

Tri-Care Management Activity 303.676.3713
Fax 303.676.3775
16401 E Centretech Pkwy, Aurora, CO 80011-9066
Reta Michak, Director

DEPARTMENT OF LABOR

**Employment and Training Admin Ofc of Adult
Svcs 202.693.3527**
Fax 877.889.5627
Web .... www.dol.gov/dol/aboudol/visit.html

E-mail .... contact.oasam@dol.gov
200 Constitution Ave NW Rm S-2235, Washington,
DC 20210-0001
Greg Weltz, Director

**Ofc of Departmental Equal Employment
Opportunity 202.708.3362**
Fax 202.401.2843
Web .... www.hud.gov
E-mail .... linda_b_washington@hud.gov
451 7th St SW, Washington, DC 20410-0001
Linda Bradford, Director

**Ofc of Disability Employment
Policy 202.693.7880**
Fax 202.693.7888
Web .... áwww.dol.gov/odep
200 Constitution Ave NW Rm S-1303, Washington,
DC 20210-0001
Kathy Martinez, Director

**Ofc of Small Business
Programs 202.693.6460**
Fax 202.693.6485
Web .... www.dol.gov
E-mail .... contact-osbp@dol.gov
200 Constitution Ave NW Rm C-2318, Washington,
DC 20210-0001
Jose (Joe) A. Lira, Director

DEPARTMENT OF EDUCATION

**BPHC Health Ctr &
Development 301.594.4300**
Fax 301.594.4997
5600 Fishers Ln Ste 1, Mail Stop 17C26, Rockville,
MD 20852-1712
Stella Eziashi, RN, MPH, Deputy Director for Program Mgmt.

**Ctr for Faith-Based and Community
Initiatives 202.401.0003**
Phone 202.219.3045
Fax 202.260.8969
E-mail .... faith.cbo@edgov
400 Maryland Ave SW, Washington, DC 20202-0001
John Porter, Director

Dept of Education 202.401.3000
Fax 202.401.0596
Web .... www.ed.gov
E-mail .... info@ed.gov
400 Maryland Ave SW Ste 7W301, Washington,
DC 20202-0001
Arne Duncan, Secretary

**Institute of Educational
Sciences 202.219.1385**
Fax 202.219.1466

Web .... www.ies.gov
E-mail .... john.easton@ed.gov
555 New Jersey Ave Rm 600, Washington,
DC 20208-0002
John Easton, Director

DEPARTMENT OF VETERANS' AFFAIRS

Dept of Veterans Affairs (VA) 202.273.5400
Phone 202.273.5700
Fax 202.273.8782
Web .... www.va.gov
810 Vermont Ave NW, Washington, DC 20420-0001
Eric K. Shinseki, Secretary

**Vet Ctr/Dept Of Veterans
Affairs 401.739.0167**
Fax 401.739.7705
Web .... www.vetcenter.va.gov
E-mail .... berne.greene@med.va.gov
2038 Warwick Ave, Warwick, RI 02889-2433
Berne Greene, Team Leader

DEPARTMENT OF THE INTERIOR

Dept of The Interior 202.208.7351
Fax 202.208.6956
Web .... www.interior.gov
E-mail .... dirk_kempthorne@ios.doi.gov
Department of the Interior, 1849 C St NW,
Washington, DC 20240
Ken Salazar, Secretary

NATIONAL COUNCIL ON DISABILITY

National Council on Disability 202.272.2004
Fax 202.272.2022
Web .... www.ncd.gov
1331 F St NW Ste 850, Washington, DC 20004
Jonathan Young, Chair

ENVIRONMENTAL PROTECTION AGENCY

Ofc of the Administrator 202.564.4700
Fax 202.501.1450
Web .... www.epa.gov
1200 Pennsylvania Ave NW, Ariel Rios Bldg,
Washington, DC 20460-0001
Lisa Jackson, Administrator

EQUAL OPPORTUNITY COMMISSION

**Equal Opportunity
Commission 202.663.4900**
Fax 703.997.4890
Web .... www.eeoc.gov
E-mail .... info@ask.eeoc.gov
1801 L St NW, Washington, DC 20507-0001
Stewart Ishimaru, Chair

National Organizations

Private non-profit organizations continue to serve a number of important roles across America. They provide a multitude of direct services with volunteers and paid employees, act as advocates and protectors of legal rights, medical services, and seek to raise the level of knowledge among caring professions. Many of these organizations have clearinghouse and resource center services available.

The following guide contains information about major national agencies; both service organizations and professional associations. The list includes only organizations whose membership is national in scope or whose operations are conducted in a sufficient number of states to be considered of national impact.

ORGANIZATION

Action for Child Protection 704.845.2121
Fax 704.845.8577
Web .... www.actionchildprotection.org
2101 Sardis Rd N Ste 204, Charlotte, NC 28227
Kay Thomas, Business Manager

ADVOCAP Head Start 920.922.7760
Fax 920.922.7214
E-mail .... bettyc@advocap.org
19 W 1st St, Fond du Lac, WI 54935-4122
Betty Clausen, Director

Alliance For Families And Children 414.359.1040
Fax 414.359.1074
Web www.alliance1.org
E-mail .... bes9039@nyp.org
11700 W Lake Park Dr, Milwaukee, WI 53224-3021
Peter Goldberg, President/CEO

Alliance For Justice 202.822.6070
Fax 202.822.6068
Web .... www.afj.org
E-mail .... alliance@afj.org
11 Dupont Cir NW, Fl 2, Washington, DC 20036
Nan Aron, Executive Director/president

American Academy of Addiction Psychiatry 401.524.3076
Fax 401.272.0922
Web .... www.aaap.org
E-mail .... information@aaap.org
400 Massasoit Ave, Ste 307, East Providence, RI 02914
Kathryn Kates-wessel, Executive Director

American Academy Of Adoption Attorneys 202.832.2222
Fax 202.293.2309
Web .... www.adoptionattorneys.org
E-mail .... m.bower@adoptionattorneys.org
1300 19th St NW, Washington, DC 20036
Martin Bower, President

American Assoc Of Family And Consumer Sciences (AAFCS) 703.706.4600
Fax 703.706.4663
Web .... www.aafcs.org
400 N Columbus St Ste 202, Alexandria, VA 22314
Carolyn Jackson, Executive Director

American Bar Association Center On Children and The Law 202.662.1720
Fax 202.662.1755
Web .... www.abanet.org/child
E-mail .... davidsonha@staff.abanet.org
740 15th St., NW, Washington, DC 20005-1022
Eva Klain, Director, Child Law Health Projects

American Counseling Assoc 703.823.9800
Fax 800.473.2329
Web .... www.counseling.org
E-mail .... mevans@counseling.org
5999 Stevenson Ave Ste 200, Alexandria, VA 22304
Marcheta Evans, President

American Humane Association 303.792.9900
Fax 303.792.5333
Web .... www.americanhumane.org
E-mail .... info@americanhumane.org
63 Inverness Dr E, Englewood, CO 80112-5117
Robin Ganzert, Chief Executive Officer

American Nurses Assoc (ANA) 301.628.5000
Fax 301.628.5001
Web .... www.nursingworld.org
E-mail .... bblakeney@partners.org
8515 Georgia Ave Ste 400, Silver Spring, MD 20910-3492
Barbara Blakeney, RN, President

American Pharmaceutical Assoc (APHA) 800.237.2742
Fax 202.783.2351
Web .... www.aphanet.org
E-mail .... webmaster@mail.aphanet.org
2215 Constitution Ave NW, Washington, DC 20037-2985
Linda Gainey, Chief Executive Officer

American Public Health Assoc 202.777.2742
Fax 202.777.2534
Web .... www.apha.org
E-mail .... comments@apha.org
800 I St NW, Washington, DC 20001-3710
Georges Benjamin, M.d., Facp Executive Director

American Public Human Svcs Assoc 202.682.0100
Fax 202.289.6555
Web .... www.aphsa.org
E-mail .... jerry.friedman@aphsa.org
810 1st St NE Ste 500, Washington, DC 20002-4207
Jerry Friedman, Executive Director

American Red Cross - National Headquarters 202.303.4498
2025 E St NW, Washington, DC 20006

American School Health Assoc 330.678.1601
Fax 330.678.4526
Web .... www.ashaweb.org
E-mail .... asha@ashaweb.org
7263 State, Route 43, Kent, OH 44240-5960
Susan F. Wooley, Phd, Ches, Fasha, Director

American Social Health Assoc 919.361.8400
Fax 919.361.8425
Web .... www.ashastd.org
E-mail .... lynnbarclay@ashastd.org
1005 Slater Rd Ste 330, Durham, NC 27703
Lynn Baclay, President/CEO

American Speech-Language-Hearing Assoc (ASHA) 800.638.8255
Fax 301.296.5777
Web .... www.asha.org
E-mail .... actioncenter@asha.org
2200 Research Blvd, Rockville, MD 20850
Arlene Pietranton, Executive Director

American Youth Work Ctr 202.785.0764
Fax 202.728.0657
Web .... www.youthtoday.org
E-mail .... info@youthtoday.org
1023 15th St NW, Ste 350, Washington, DC 20005
Sara Fritz, Executive Director

Arch National Respite Network 919.490.5577
Fax 919.490.4905
Web .... www.respite.org
E-mail .... mmathers@chtop.org
800 Eastowne Dr Ste 105, Chapel Hill, NC 27514-2215
Mike Mathers, Executive Director

Armed Svcs YMCA of the USA 703.313.9600
Fax 703.313.9668
Web .... www.asymca.org
E-mail .... ssimms@asymca.org
6359 Walker Ln, Ste 200, Alexandria, VA 22310-3230
Susan Simms, Program Director

Asian and Pacific Islander Institute on Domestic Violence 415.954.9988
Fax 415.954.9999
Web .... www.apiahf.org
450 Sutter St Rm 600, San Francisco, CA 94108-3908
Christella Huang, Policy Director

Assoc For Childhood Education International 301.570.2111
Fax 301.570.2212
Web .... www.acei.org
E-mail .... aceihq@aol.com
17904 Georgia Ave Ste 215, Olney, MD 20832
Diane Whitehead, Executive Director

Assoc of Maternal and Child Health Programs 202.775.0436
Fax 202.775.0061
Web .... www.amchp.org
E-mail .... mfraser@amchp.org
2030 M St Ste 350, Washington, DC 20036
Michael Fraser, Director

Assoc Of Women's Health, Obstetric And Neonatal Nurses (AWHONN) 202.261.2400
Fax 202.728.0575
Web .... www.awhonn.org
2000 L St NW Ste 740, Washington, DC 20036
Joe Isaacs, Executive Director

Bill And Melinda Gates Foundation 206.709.3140
Fax 206.709.3280
Web .... www.gatesfoundation.org
E-mail .... info@gatesfoundation.org
1551 Eastlake Ave E, Seattle, WA 98102
Bill Gates, President

Boy Scouts of America 972.580.2000
Fax 972.580.2502
Web .... www.bsascouting.org
1325 W Walnut Hill Ln, Irving, TX 75038-3096
Bob Mazzuca, Chief Of Scouting

Boys Town National Research Hospital 402.498.6540
Fax 402.498.6638
Web .... www.girlsandboystown.org
E-mail .... peb@boystown.org
555 N 30th St, Omaha, NE 68131-2198
Patrick Brookhouser, Medical Director

Bureau Of Indian Affairs, Law Enforcement, Child Abuse 505.346.2868
Fax 505.346.2866
Web .... www.bia.gov
E-mail .... jbreuninger@f2laser.com
4505 Columbine Ave NE, Albuquerque, NM 87113-2238
Marcelino Goerbines, Acting Director

Bureau of Justice Assistance Clearinghouse 202.616.6500
Fax 202.305.1367
Web .... www.ncjrs.org
E-mail .... askbja@usdoj.gov
810 7th St. NW, 4th Floor, Washington, DC 20531
Gale Farquahar, State Policy Advisor

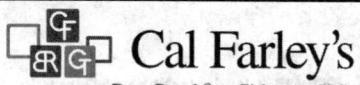

Cal Farley's

Boys Ranch® • Girlstown, U.S.A.®
& Family Resource Centers

Cal Farley's **800.687.3722**
Fax 806.372.4807
Web ....www.calfarley.org
E-mail ....info@calfarley.org
PO Box 1890, Amarillo, TX 79174-0001
Dan Adams, President and CEO

Cal Farley's is one of America's largest privately-funded child and family service providers specializing in both residential and community-based services at no cost to the families of children in our care. We make a life-time commitment to the children served through our two campus-based programs, Cal Farley's Boys Ranch and Cal Farley's Girlstown U.S.A., where we provide professional programs and services in a Christ-centered atmosphere. The cornerstone to our success is our Model of Leadership and Service which focuses on the six core areas of human need. Cal Farley's offers a wide array of employment opportunities. For more information: (800) 687-3722, www.calfarley.org.

Camp Fire USA **816.285.2010**
Fax 816.285.9444
Web ....www.campfireusa.org
E-mail ....jill.pasewalk@campfireusa.org
1100 Walnut St Ste 1900, Kansas City, MO 64106
Jill Pasewalk, President

Cancer Care Inc. **212.712.8080**
Fax 212.719.8495
Web ....www.cancercare.org
E-mail ....info@cancercare.org
275 7th Ave Fl 22, New York, NY 10001-6754
Diane Blum, Executive Director

**Cancer Treatment Ctrs of
America** **800.615.3055**
Fax 847.342.7400
Web ....www.cancercenter.com
E-mail ....cgulley@brmc.com
1336 Basswood Rd, Schaumburg, IL 60173-4544
Cheryl Gulley, Director Of Health

**Candlelighters Childhood Cancer
Foundation** **301.962.3520**
Fax 301.962.3521
Web ....www.candlelighters.org
E-mail ....staff@candlelighters.org
3910 Warner St, Kensington, MD 20895
Ruth Hoffman, Executive Director

**Caring For Every Child's Mental Health
Campaign** **202.331.9816**
Fax 202.331.9420
Web ....www.vancomm.com
E-mail ....mrodriguez@vancomm.com
2121 K St NW Ste 650, Washington, DC 20037
Maria Rodriguez, President

Catholic Charities USA **703.549.1390**
Fax 703.549.1656
Web ....www.catholiccharitiesusa.org
E-mail ....lsnyder@catholiccharitiesusa.org
66 Canal Center Plz Ste 600, Alexandria, VA 22314
Larry Snyder, President

**CDC National Prevention Info
Network** **800.458.5231**
Fax 888.282.7681
Web ....www.cdcnpin.org
E-mail ....info@cdcnpin.org
PO Box 6003, Rockville, MD 20849-6003
Melissa Beaupierre, Director

Charles Stewart Mott Fdtn **810.238.5651**
Fax 810.766.1753
Web ....www.mott.org
E-mail ....info@mott.org
503 S Saginaw St Ste 1200, Flint, MI 48502
William S White, President/CEO

Child Find of America Inc. **800.716.3468**
Phone 845.883.6060
Fax 845.883.6614
Web ....www.childfindofamerica.org

E-mail ....dlinder351@aol.com
PO Box 277, New Paltz, NY 12561
Donna Linder, Executive Director

Child Health Foundation **410.992.5512**
Fax 410.992.5641
Web ....www.childhealthfoundation.org
10630 Little Patuxent Parkway, Suite 126, columbia,
MD 21044
Maureen Black, Chairman

**Children's Institute International
incope** **213.385.5100**
Fax 213.260.7791
Web ....www.childrensinstitute.org
2121 W Temple St, Los Angeles, CA 90026
Mary Emmons, President/CEO

**Children's National Medical
Ctr** **202.476.5000**
Fax 202.476.4492
Web ....www.childrensnational.org
E-mail ....tbear@childrensnational.org
111 Michigan Ave NW, Washington, DC 20010
Edwin Zechman, Chief Executive Officer

Children's Research Triangle **312.726.4152**
Fax 312.726.4021
Web ....www.childstudy.org
180 N Michigan Ave Ste 700, Chicago, IL 60601
Ira Chasnoff, Md, Director

**Children's Voices, Family Choices, Community
Solutions** **817.871.6648**
Fax 817.871.7372
Web ....www.fortworthgov.org
E-mail ....sherwin.daryani@fortworthgov.org
1800 University Dr, Fort Worth, TX 76107-3405
Sherwin Daryani, Human Service Manager

Coalition for Juvenile Justice **202.467.0864**
Fax 202.887.0738
Web ....www.juvjustice.org
E-mail ....info@juvjustice.org
1710 Rd Island Ave NW, 10th Fl, Washington,
DC 20036
Nancy Gannon Hornberger, Acting Executive Director

Coleman Foundation **312.902.7120**
Fax 312.902.7124
Web ....www.colemanfoundation.org
E-mail ....mhennessy@colemanfoundation.org
651 W Washington Blvd, Ste 306, Chicago, IL 60661
Micheal W. Hennessy, President/CEO

**Commission on Accreditation of Rehabilitation Facilities
(CARF) International** **888.281.6531**
Fax 520.318.1129
Web ....www.carf.org
4891 E Grant Rd, Tucson, AZ 85712-2704

**Commission on Mental and Physical Disability Law -
American Bar Assoc** **202.662.1570**
Fax 202.662.1032
Web ....www.abanet.org/disability
740 15th St NW, 9th Fl, Washington, DC 20005
John Parry, Director

**Community Memorial
Foundation** **630.654.4729**
Fax 630.654.3402
Web ....www.cmfdn.org
E-mail ....info@cmfdn.org
15 Spinning Wheel Rd Ste 326, Hinsdale,
IL 60521-7675
Jim Durkan, President

Cord Blood Donor Foundation **650.635.1452**
Fax 650.635.1428
Web ....www.cordblooddonor.org
1200 Bayhill Dr, Ste 301, San Bruno, CA 94066

**Corporation For National And Community Svc Learn
And Serve America** **202.606.5000**
Fax 202.606.3475
Web ....www.learnandserve.gov
1201 New York Ave NW, Washington,
DC 20525-0001
Robert Delasco, CEO

**Council for Exceptional
Children** **703.620.3660**
Fax 703.264.9494
Web ....www.cec.sped.org
2900 Crystal Dr Ste 1000, Arlington, VA 22202-5704
Bruce Ramirez, Executive Director

COA

COUNCIL ON
ACCREDITATION

FOUNDED
1977

Council On Accreditation **866.262.8088**
Fax 212.797.1428
Web ....www.coanet.org
E-mail ....jseoane@coanet.org
45 Broadway, 29th Floor, New York, NY 10006
Joseph Seoane, Director Of Client Relations

Founded in 1977, the Council on Accreditation (COA) is a not-for-profit independent accreditor of the full continuum of community-based human service organizations in the United States and Canada. Today, more than 1,800 organizations serving more than 7 million vulnerable individuals, children and families are members of COA's "Community of Excellence." COA accreditation is supported by twenty-five (25) national and international organizations, a cadre of over 1,000 volunteers and an international board of trustees. Please visit us at www.coanet.org.

**Covenant House International
Headquarters** **212.727.4000**
Fax 212.727.4992
Web ....www.covenanthouse.org
5 Penn Plz Fl 3, New York, NY 10001
Kevin Ryan, President

Covenant House Nineline **800.999.9999**
Fax 212.989.9098
Web ....www.nineline.org
E-mail ....gortiz@covenanthouse.org
5 Penn Plz Fl 2, New York, NY 10001-1841
Gilbert Ortiz, Director

Ctr For Lifelong Learning **202.939.9475**
Fax 202.775.8578
Web ....www.acenet.edu
E-mail ....silvia_robinson@ace.nche.edu
1 Dupont Cir NW Ste 250, Washington,
DC 20036-1141
Silvia Robinson, Executive Director Of Ged Testing Service

**Ctr for the Advancing of
Health** **202.387.2829**
Fax 202.387.2857
Web ....www.cfah.org
E-mail ....info@cfah.org
2000 Florida Ave NW Ste 210, Washington,
DC 20009-1231
Jessie C Gruman, President

**Ctr for the Study of Social
Policy** **202.371.1565**
Fax 202.371.1472
Web ....www.cssp.org
E-mail ....frank.farrow@cssp.org
1575 I St NW Ste 500, Washington, DC 20005
Frank Farrow, Director

Dana-Farber Cancer Institute **617.632.3000**
Web ....www.dfci.harvard.edu
E-mail ....edward_benz@dfci.harvard.edu
44 Binney St, Boston, MA 02115-6084
Edward Benz, Chief Executive Officer

**Education Commission Of The
States** **303.299.3600**
Fax 303.296.8332

National Organizations

Web ....www.ecs.org
E-mail ....ecs@ecs.org
700 Broadway Ste 810, Denver, CO 80203
Roger Sampson, Director

Education Development Ctr 617.969.7100
Fax 617.969.5979
Web ....www.edc.org
E-mail ....lluedtke@edc.org
55 Chapel St, Ste 1, Newton, MA 02458-1042
Luther Luedtke, President

**Edyth Bush Charitable
Foundation 407.647.4322**
Fax 407.647.7716
Web ....www.edythbush.org
E-mail ....dodahowski@edythbush.org
199 E Welbourne Ave Ste 100, Winter Park,
FL 32789-4365
David A. Odahowski, President/CEO

El Pomar Foundation 719.633.7733
Fax 719.577.5702
Web ....www.elpomar.org
E-mail ....grants@elpomar.org
10 Lake Cir, Executive Office, Colorado Springs,
CO 80906-4201
Bill Hybl, CEO/Chairman

Families Anonymous, Inc..............310.815.8010
Fax 310.815.9682
Web ....www.familiesanonymous.org
11048 Washington Blvd, Culver City, CA 90232
Mark M, Chairperson

**Family Development Resources,
Inc. 435.649.5822**
Fax 435.649.9599
Web ....www.nurturingparenting.com
E-mail ....fdr@nurturingparenting.com
3070 Rasmussen Rd Ste 190, Park City,
UT 84098-5543
Steven J. Bavolek, President

Faye McBeth Foundation 414.272.2626
Fax 414.272.6235
Web ....www.fayemcbeath.org
E-mail ....info@fayemcbeath.org
101 W Pleasant St. Ste 210, Milwaukee,
WI 53212-3157
Scott E. Gelzer, Executive Director

Focus On The Family 800.232.6459
Fax 719.531.3424
Web ....www.focusonthefamily.com
E-mail ....jackie.kent@fotf.org
8605 Explorer Dr, Focus On The Family, Colorado
Springs, CO 80920-1051
Jackie Kent, Director

**Foster Family-Based Treatment Assoc
(FFTA) 201.343.2246**
Fax 201.489.6719
Web ....www.ffta.org
E-mail ....mcole@ffta.org
294 Union St, Hackensack, NJ 07601-4303
Melissa Cole, Administrator

Girl Scouts of the USA 212.852.8000
Fax 212.852.6517
Web ....www.girlscouts.org
E-mail ....kcloninger@girlscouts.org
420 5th Ave Fl 9, New York, NY 10018-2798
Kathy Cloninger, CEO

**Girls and Boys Town National Resource and Training
Ctr 800.545.5771**
Fax 402.498.1280
Web ....www.girlsandboystown.org/nrtc
E-mail ....nrtcmarketing@girlsandboystown.org
14100 Crawford St, Boys Town, NE 68010-7520
Jose Bolton, Sr., Associate Executive Director

Girls and Boys Town USA 402.498.1920
Fax 402.498.3378
Web ....www.girlsandboystown.org
E-mail ....davisj@boystown.org
13603 Flanagan Blvd, Boys Town, NE 68010-7501
Jerry Davis, Associate Executive Director

**Grace Contrino Abrams Peace Education
Foundation 305.576.5075**
Fax 305.576.3106
Web ....www.peaceeducation.org
E-mail ....lvb@peace-ed.org
1900 Biscayne Blvd, Miami, FL 33132-1025
Lloyd Van Bylevelt, President

**Great Program (Gang Resistance Education And
Training) 800.726.7070**
Fax 850.386.5356
Web ....www.iir.com/great
E-mail ....information@great-online.org
2050 Centre Pointe Blvd., Tallahassee, FL 32308
Ron Doyle, Director

**Guttmacher Institute
Headquarters 212.248.1111**
Fax 212.248.1951
Web ....www.guttmacher.org
E-mail ....info@guttmacher.org
125 Maiden Ln Frnt 7, New York, NY 10038
Sharon Camp, CEO

**Hazelden Ctr For Youth &
Families 763.509.3800**
Fax 763.559.0149
Web ....www.hazelden.org
E-mail ....jerry.schulz@hazelden.org
11505 36th Ave N, Minneapolis, MN 55441
Jerry Schulz, Medical Director

**Helen Keller National Ctr For Deaf-Blind Youth And
Adults (HKNC) 516.944.8900**
Fax 516.944.7302
Web ....www.hknc.org
E-mail ....hkncinfo@rnc.com
141 Middle Neck Rd, Sands Point, NY 11050
Joseph Mcnulty, Director

Hemophilia Health Svcs 973.276.0254
Fax 973.276.0998
Web ....www.hrahemo.com
E-mail ....mmccullough@hemophiliafed.org
45 Route 46 E, Ste 609, Pine Brook, NJ 07058
Maureen Mccullough, Branch Manager

Honeywell International 973.455.2000
Fax 973.455.4807
Web ....www.honeywell.com
E-mail ....myhoneywell@honeywell.com
101 Columbia Rd, Morristown, NJ 07962
David Cote, Chief Executive Officer

**Hospice Foundation of
America 800.854.3402**
Fax 202.638.5312
Web ....www.hospicefoundation.org
E-mail ....atucci@hospicefoundation.org
1621 Connecticut Ave NW, Ste 300, Washington,
DC 20009
Amy Tucci, CEO

**Institute for Educational
Leadership 202.822.8405**
Fax 202.872.4050
Web ....www.iel.org
E-mail ....iel@iel.org
4455 Connecticut Ave NW Ste 310, Washington,
DC 20008-2328
Martin Blank, President

**Institute for the Study of Child, Family &
Communities 734.487.0372**
Fax 734.487.0284
Web ....www.iscfc.emich.edu
E-mail ....iscfc@emich.edu
203 Boone Hall, Eastern Michigan University,
Ypsilanti, MI 48197-2212
David Clifford, Phd, Administrative Director

**International Assoc of Chiefs of
Police 703.836.6767**
Fax 703.836.5375
Web ....www.theiacp.org
515 N Washington St, Alexandria, VA 22314
John Firman, Director

**International Child Resource Institute -
Icri 510.644.1000**
Fax 510.525.4106

Web ....www.icrichild.org
E-mail ....kjaffe@igc.org
1581 Le Roy Ave, Berkeley, CA 94708
Kenneth Jaffe, Executive Director

**International Social Svc United States of America
Branch 443.451.1200**
Fax 443.451.1220
Web ....www.iss-usa.org
E-mail ....iss-usa@iss-usa.org
200 E Lexington St Ste 1700, Baltimore,
MD 21202-3533
Julie Gilbert Rosicky, Executive Director

Jewish Fund For Justice 212.213.2113
Fax 212.213.2233
Web ....www.jewishjustice.org
E-mail ....jfjustice@jfjustice.org
330 7th Ave Ste 1902, New York, NY 10001
Simon Greer, President/CEO

**John S. & James L. Knight
Foundation 305.908.2600**
Fax 305.908.2698
Web ....www.knightfdn.org
200 South Biscayne Blvd., Wachovia Financial Center
Suite 3300, Miami, FL 33131
Alberto Ibarguen, President/CEO

June & Julian Foss Foundation 877.244.3677
Web ....www.fossfoundation.org
E-mail ....administrator@fossfoundation.org
5510 Orchard St W, Suite B2-501, Tacoma,
WA 98467

Kempe Children's Center 888.828.6222
Fax 303.864.5351
Web ....www.naccchildlaw.org
E-mail ....advocate@naccchildlaw.org
13123 E 16th Ave B390, Aurora, CO 80045
Maureen Farrell-Stevenson, President

KidsPeace Children's Hospital 610.799.8800
Fax 610.799.8801
Web ....www.kidspeace.org
5300 Kidspeace Dr, Orefield, PA 18069
Barbara Hacker, Executive Director

**KidsPeace National Ctrs For Kids In
Crisis 610.799.8819**
Fax 610.799.8801
Web ....www.teencentral.net
E-mail ....ctod@kidspeace.org
5300 Kidspeace Dr, Orefield, PA 18069-2098
C.T ODonnell, II, President/CEO

Laurel Ridge Treatment Ctr 210.491.9400
Fax 210.491.3550
Web ....www.laurelridgetc.com
17720 Corporate Woods Dr, San Antonio,
TX 78259-3509
Dan Thomas, CEO

**Learning Disabilities Assoc of
America 412.341.1515**
Fax 412.344.0224
Web ....www.ldaamerica.org
E-mail ....info@ldaamerica.org
4156 Library Rd, Pittsburgh, PA 15234
Maryclare Reynolds, Executive Director

Levi Strauss & Co 415.501.6000
Fax 415.501.3939
Web ....www.levistrauss.com
E-mail ....tfay-bustillios@levi.com
1155 Battery St, San Francisco, CA 94111
Theresa Fay-Bustillios, VP Of Community Affairs

Lilly Endowment, Inc..................317.924.5471
Fax 317.926.4431
Web ....www.lillyendowment.org
2801 N Meridian St, Indianapolis, IN 46208
Clay Robbins, Assistant In Finance

**Lumina Foundation For
Education 317.951.5300**
Fax 317.951.5063
Web ....www.luminafoundation.org
E-mail ....mmanta@luminafoundation.org
30 S. Meridian St., Ste. 700, Arlington, VA 22201
Martha Manta, Executive Director

Make-A-Wish Foundation of
America **602.279.9474**
Fax 602.279.0855
Web ....www.wish.org
E-mail ....jmyers@good-sam.com
  4742 N 24th St, Ste 400, Phoenix, AZ 85016
  David Williams, CEO

Mary Reynolds Babcock
Foundation **336.748.9222**
Fax 336.777.0095
Web ....www.mrbf.org
E-mail ....info@mrbf.org
  2920 Reynolda Rd, Winston Salem, NC 27106-3016
  Gayle Williams, Executive Director

Maternal and Child Health Info Resource
Ctr **202.842.2000**
Fax 202.728.9469
Web ....www.mchbhrsa.gov/mchirc
E-mail ....mchirc@hsrnet.com
  1200 NW 18th St Ste 700, Washington,
  DC 20036-2531
  Renee Schwalberg, Director

MedicAlert Foundation **800.432.5378**
Fax 209.669.2495
Web ....www.medicalert.org
E-mail ....customerservice@medicalert.org
  2323 Colorado Ave, Turlock, CA 95382

Mental Health America **703.684.7722**
Fax 703.684.5968
E-mail ....dshern@mentalhealthamerica.net
  2000 N Beauregard St, 6th Floor, Alexandria,
  VA 22311
  David Shern, Executive Director

MGC Publications **414.352.3219**
Web ....www.bmtresources.org
E-mail ....mytransplant@sbcglobal.net
  1208 E Hermitage Rd, Bayside, WI 53217

Mops International **303.733.5353**
Fax 303.733.5770
Web ....www.mops.org
E-mail ....info@mops.org
  2370 S Trenton Way Unit E, Denver, CO 80231-3844
  Kim Garrett, Office Manager

Muscular Dystrophy Assoc **503.223.3177**
Fax 503.223.3026
E-mail ....portlandorsouth@mdausa.org
  4800 SW Macadam Ave Ste 205, Portland,
  OR 97239-3928
  Dana Voelker, Executive Director

Naccra National Assoc for Childcare Resource and
Referral Agencies **703.341.4100**
Fax 703.341.4101
Web ....www.naccrra.org
E-mail ....linda.smith@naccrra.org
  1515 North Court House, road 11th Foor Arlington,
  Lanham, MD 22201
  Linda Smith, Executive Director

National 4-H Council **301.961.2820**
Fax 301.961.2894
Web ....www.fourhcouncil.edu
E-mail ....dfloyd@fourhcouncil.edu
  7100 Connecticut Ave, Chevy Chase,
  MD 20815-4999
  Donald T. Floyd Jr., President/CEO

National Alliance For Hispanic
Health **202.387.5000**
Fax 202.265.8027
Web ....www.hispanichealth.org
E-mail ....alliance@hispanichealth.org
  1501 16th St NW, Washington, DC 20036
  Jane L. Delgado, President/CEO

National Assembly on School Based Health
Care **202.638.5872**
Fax 202.638.5879
Web ....www.nasbhc.org
E-mail ....info@nasbhc.org
  1010 Vermont Ave NW Ste 600, Washington,
  DC 20005
  Linda Juszczak, Executive Director

National Assoc for Children's Behavioral
Health **202.857.9735**
Fax 202.362.5145
Web ....www.nacbh.org
E-mail ....nacbh@verizon.net
  1025 Connecticut Ave NW Ste 1012, Washington,
  DC 20036-5417
  Joy Midman, Director

National Assoc For The Education Of Young
Children **202.232.8777**
Fax 202.328.1846
Web ....www.naeyc.org
E-mail ....jdaniel@naeyc.org
  1313 L St NW, Ste 500, Washington, DC 20005
  Jerlean Daniel, Executive Director

National Assoc Of Anorexia Nervosa And Associated
Disorders (ANAD) **630.577.1330**
Fax 630.577.1323
Web ....www.anad.org
E-mail ....anadhelp@anad.org
  PO Box 640, Naperville, IL 60566
  Patricia Santucci, President

National Assoc Of Black Social
Workers **202.678.4570**
Fax 202.678.4572
Web ....www.nabsw.org
E-mail ....harambee@nabsw.org
  2305 Martin Luther King Jr Ave SE, Washington,
  DC 20020-5813
  Zelma S. Smith, Co-Chairperson

National Assoc of Children's Hospitals and Related
Institutions **703.684.1355**
Fax 703.684.1589
Web ....www.childrenshospital.net
E-mail ....lmcandrews@nachri.org
  401 Wythe St, Alexandria, VA 22314-1915
  Lawrence A. Mcandrews, President/CEO

National Assoc Of Counsel For
Children **303.864.5320**
Fax 303.864.5351
Web ....www.naccchildlaw.org
E-mail ....ventrell.marvin@tchden.org
  1825 Marion St, Ste 242, Denver, CO 80218
  Marvin Ventrell, Esq., President/CEO

National Assoc of Elementary School
Principals **703.684.3345**
Fax 800.396.2377
Web ....www.naesp.org
E-mail ....naesp@naesp.org
  1615 Duke St, Alexandria, VA 22314-3406
  Gail Connelly, Executive Director

National Assoc Of Psychiatric Health
Systems **202.393.6700**
Fax 202.783.6041
Web ....www.naphs.org
E-mail ....naphs@naphs.org
  701 N 13Th St, Ste 950, Milwaukee, WI 53233
  Kathleen Mccaan, Director

NASW
National Association of Social Workers

National Association of Social Workers
(NASW) **202.408.8600**
Fax 202.336.8234
Web ....www.socialworkers.org
E-mail ....membership@naswdc.org
  750 First Street, NE, Ste 700, Washington, DC 20002
  Elizabeth J. Clark, PhD, ACSW, MPH, NASW Executive Director; Tracy Whitaker, DSW, ACSW, NASW Center for Research Studies Director; Stephanie Chambers, ACSW, NASW Credentialing Center Manager; Joan Levy Zlotnik, PhD, ACSW, NASW Social Work Policy Institute Director
  NASW is the largest membership organization of professional social workers. It promotes, develops, and protects the practice of social work and social workers. NASW also seeks to enhance the well-being of individuals, families, and communities through its advocacy.

National Attention Deficit Disorder
Assoc **856.439.0500**
Fax 856.439.0525
Web ....www.add.org
E-mail ....velliott@ahint.com
  15000 Commerce Pkwy Ste C, Mount Laurel,
  NJ 08054-2212
  Vicky Elliott, Director

National Black Child Development Institute -
NBCDI **202.833.2220**
Fax 202.833.8222
Web ....www.nbcdi.org/
E-mail ....moreinfo@nbcdi.org
  1313 L St NW, Ste 110, Washington, DC 20005-4139
  Carol Brunsonday, Director

National Bone Marrow Transplant
Link **248.358.1886**
Fax 248.358.1889
Web ....www.nbmtlink.org
E-mail ....info@nbmtlink.org
  20411 W Twelve Mile Rd #108, Southfield, MI 48076
  Myra Jacobs, Executive Director

National Center for Learning
Disabilities **888.575.7373**
Fax 212.545.9665
Web ....www.ld.org
  381 S Park Ave, Ste 1401, New York, NY 10016-8829
  James Wendorf, Executive Director

National Child Labor
Committee **212.840.1801**
Fax 212.768.0963
Web ....www.kapow.org
E-mail ....nclckapow@aol.com
  1501 Broadway, Ste 1908, New York, NY 10036
  Susan Ladner, Vice President

National Child Safety Council **517.764.6070**
Fax 517.764.3068
Web ....www.nationalchildfsafetycouncil.com
  4065 Page Ave, Michigan Center, MI 49204
  Timothy Bagwell, Executive Director

National Child Welfare Resource Ctr for Organizational
Improvement **207.780.5810**
Fax 207.780.5817
Web ....www.muskie.usm.main.edu/helpkids
E-mail ....helpkids@usm.maine.edu
  400 Congress St Ste 500, Portland, ME 04101-3547
  Peter Watson, Director

National Children's Advocacy
Ctr **256.533.5437**
Fax 256.534.6883
Web ....www.nationalcac.org
  210 Pratt Ave Ne, Huntsville, AL 35801
  Chris Newlin, Executive Director

National Children's Alliance **202.548.0090**
Fax 202.548.0099
Web ....www.nca-online.org
E-mail ....nchandler@nca-online.org
  516 C St NE Ste 100, Washington, DC 20002-5807
  Nancy Chandler, Executive Director

National Children's Ctr **202.722.2300**
Fax 202.722.2383
Web ....www.sjcs.org
E-mail ....aginsberg@sjcs.org
  6200 2nd St NW, Washington, DC 20011-1493
  Arthur Ginsberg, Mha, Executive Director

National Clearinghouse On Alcohol and Drug
Info **800.729.6686**
Fax 240.221.4292
Web ....www.ncadi.samhsa.gov
  PO Box 2345, Rockville, MD 20847-2345
  Denise Crute, Deputy Director

National Clearinghouse on Families and
Youth **301.608.8098**
Fax 301.608.8721
E-mail ....ncfy@acf.hhs.gov
  5515 Security Ln, North Bethesda, MD 20852
  Jennifer Rich, Director

National Coalition Against Domestic
Violence **303.839.1852**
Fax 303.831.9251

Web ....www.ncadv.org
1120 Lincoln St Ste 1603, Denver, CO 80203
Rita Smith, Executive Director

National Coalition for the
Homeless **202.462.4822**
Fax 202.462.4823
Web ....www.nationalhomeless.org
E-mail ....info@nationalhomeless.org
2201 P St NW, Washington, DC 20037
Michael Stoops, Director

National Collaboration for Youth (National
Assembly) **202.347.2080**
Fax 202.393.4517
Web ....www.nassembly.org
E-mail ....irv@nassembly.org
1319 F St NW, Ste 402, Washington, DC 20004-1112
Irv Katz, President/CEO

National Consortium On
Deaf-Blindness **800.438.9376**
Fax 503.838.8150
Web ....www.nationaldb.org
E-mail ....info@nationaldb.org
345 Monmouth Ave N, Monmouth, OR 97361-1329
D. Jay Gense, Ed.S., Director

National Council for Community Behavioral
Healthcare **301.984.6200**
Fax 301.881.7159
Web ....www.nccbh.org
E-mail ....lindar@nccbh.org
12300 Twinbrook Pkwy Ste 320, Rockville,
MD 20852
Linda Rosenberg, President/CEO

National Council Of Aging **202.479.1200**
Fax 202.479.0735
Web ....www.ncoa.org
E-mail ....james.firman@ncoa.org
1901 L St NW, Washington, DC 20036
James Firman, President

National Council Of Jewish
Women **212.645.4048**
Fax 212.645.7466
Web ....www.ncjw.org
E-mail ....action@ncjw.org
53 W 23rd St Fl 6, New York, NY 10010-4237
Marsha Atkind, President

National Council of Juvenile and Family Court Judges
(NCJFCJ) **775.784.6012**
Fax 775.784.6628
Web ....www.ncjfcj.org
E-mail ....staff@ncjfcj.org
1041 S Virginia St, 3rd Floor, Reno, NV 89557
Mary Kay Bickett, Executive Director

National Council Of YMCA's of The
USA **312.977.0031**
Fax 312.977.0059
Web ....www.ymca.net
E-mail ....fulsillment@ymca.net
101 N Wacker Dr Fl 14, Chicago, IL 60606
Neil Mccol, CEO

National Council On Child Abuse And Family
Violence **202.429.6695**
Fax 202.521.3479
Web ....www.nccafv.org
E-mail ....info@nccafv.org
1025 Connecticut Ave NW Ste 1000, Washington,
DC 20036-5417
Linda Baker, Arch Director

National Council on Crime and
Delinquency **510.208.0500**
Fax 510.208.0511
Web ....www.sf.nccd-crc.org
E-mail ....info@sf.nccd-crc.org
1970 Broadway St Ste 500, Oakland, CA 94612
Alex Busansky, President

National Court Appointed Special Advocate (CASA)
Assoc **206.270.0072**
Fax 206.270.0078
Web ....www.nationalcasa.org

E-mail ....nationalcasa@nationalcasa.org
100 W Harrison St, Ste 500, Seattle, WA 98119
Michael Piraino, CEO

National Criminal Justice Reference Svc
(NCJRS) **301.519.5000**
Fax 301.519.5212
Web ....www.ncjrs.gov
E-mail ....dkozloski@aspensys.com
2277 Research Blvd, Rockville, MD 20850
Dolores Kozloski, Director

National Ctr For Children In
Poverty **646.284.9600**
Fax 646.284.9623
Web ....www.nccp.org
E-mail ....kreader@nccp.org
215 W 125th St Fl 3, New York, NY 10027-4426
Dr. Lee Kreader, Director

National Ctr for Juvenile
Justice **412.227.6950**
Fax 412.227.6955
Web ....www.ncjj.org
E-mail ....ncjj@ncjj.org
3700 S Water St Ste 200, Pittsburgh, PA 15203-2368
Patricia Camtie, Director

National Ctr for Lesbian Rights
(NCLR) **415.392.6257**
Fax 415.392.8442
Web ....www.nclrights.org
E-mail ....kkendell@nclrights.org
870 Market St Ste 370, San Francisco,
CA 94102-3091
Kate Kendell, Director

National Ctr for Prosecution of Child
Abuse **703.549.9222**
Fax 703.836.3195
Web ....www.ndaa.org
44 Canal Center Plaza, Suite 110, Alexandria,
VA 22314
Suzanna Tiapula, Deputy Director

National Ctr for State Courts **757.253.2000**
Fax 757.259.1520
Web ....www.ncsconline.org
300 Newport Ave, Williamsburg, VA 23185-4147
Mary McQueen, President

National Ctr on Institutions and Alternatives/Augustus
Institute **703.684.0373**
Fax 703.684.6037
Web ....www.ncianet.org
E-mail ....jmiller@ncianet.org
3125 Mount Vernon Ave, Alexandria, VA 22305-2640
Jerome Miller, President

National Diabetes Info
Clearinghouse **800.860.8747**
Fax 703.738.4929
Web ....www.diabetes.niddk.nih.gov
E-mail ....ndic@info.niddk.nih.gov
1 Information Way, Bethesda, MD 20892-0001
Griffin P. Rogers, Director

National Dissemination Ctr for Children With Disabilities
(NICHCY) **800.695.0285**
Fax 202.884.8441
Web ....www.nichcy.org
E-mail ....nichcy@aed.org
1825 Connecticut Ave NW Ste 625, Washington,
DC 20009-5733
Elaine Mulligan, Director

National District Attorney's
Assoc **703.549.9222**
Fax 703.836.3195
Web ....www.ndaa.org
44 Canal Center Plz Ste 110, Alexandria, VA 22314
Scott Burns, Executive Director

National Down Syndrome
Society **212.460.9330**
Fax 212.979.2873
Web ....www.ndss.org
E-mail ....info@ndss.org
666 Broadway, New York, NY 10012
Jon Colman, President

National Eating Disorders
Assoc **800.931.2237**
Fax 206.829.8501
Web ....www.nationaleatingdisorders.org
E-mail ....info@nationaleatingdisorders.org
603 Stewart St Ste 803, Seattle, WA 98101-1264
Lynn Grese, Chief Operating Officer

National Education Assoc
(NEA) **202.833.4000**
Fax 202.822.7974
Web ....www.nea.org
E-mail ....jwilson@nea.org
1201 16th St NW, Washington, DC 20002
John Wilson, Director

National Exchange Club Foundation For The Prevention
Of Child Abuse **419.535.3232**
Fax 419.535.1989
Web ....www.nationalexchangeclub.org
3050 W Central Ave, Toledo, OH 43606-1700
Jim Hartley, Executive Vice President

National Family Caregivers
Assoc **301.942.6430**
Fax 301.942.2302
Web ....www.thefamilycaregiver.org
E-mail ....info@thefamilycaregiver.org
10400 Connecticut Ave Ste 500, Kensington,
MD 20895-3944
Suzanne Mince, Chief Executive Officer

National Foster Parent Assoc **800.557.5238**
Fax 800.938.5777
Web ....www.nfpaonline.org
E-mail ....info@nfpaonline.org
1102 Praire Ridge Trl, Pflugerville, TX 78660
Irene Clements, President

National Foundation For Cancer
Research **301.654.1250**
Fax 301.654.5824
Web ....www.nfcr.org
E-mail ....info@nfcr.org
4600 East West Hwy, Ste 525, Bethesda, MD 20814
Michael Wang, Chief Science Officer

National Gardening Assoc Youth Garden Grants
Program **800.538.7476**
Fax 802.864.6889
Web ....www.kidsgardening.org
1100 Dorset St, South Burlington, VT 05403
Michael Metallo, President

National Head Start Assoc **703.739.0875**
Fax 703.739.0878
Web ....www.nhsa.org
1651 Prince St, Alexandria, VA 22314
Carolyn Stennett, Deputy Director

National Health Info Ctr **301.565.4167**
Fax 301.984.4256
Web ....www.healthfinder.gov
E-mail ....info@nhic.org
PO Box 1133, Washington, DC 20013-1133
Eric Davis, CEO/Executive Director

National Hemophilia
Foundation **212.328.3700**
Fax 212.328.3777
Web ....www.hemophilia.org
E-mail ....handi@hemophilia.org
116 W 32nd St Fl 11, New York, NY 10001-3212
Val Bias, CEO

National Hispanic Medical Assoc -
NHMA **202.628.5895**
Fax 202.628.5898
Web ....www.nhmamd.org
E-mail ....nhma@nhmamd.org
1411 K St NW Ste 1100, Washington, DC 20005
Elaina Rios, Director

National Indian Child Welfare
Assoc **503.222.4044**
Fax 503.222.4007
Web ....www.nicwa.org
E-mail ....info@nicwa.org
5100 SW MacAdam Ave Ste 300, Portland,
OR 97239-3878
Terry Cross, Executive Director

National Institute On Out Of School Time 781.283.2547
Fax 781.283.3657
Web ....www.niost.org
E-mail ....niost@wellesley.edu
106 Central St, Wellesley Hills, MA 02481
Ellen Gannett, President/CEO

National Lead Info Ctr 800.424.5323
Fax 585.232.3111
Web ....www.epa.gov/lead/nlic
E-mail ....hotline.lead@epamail.epa.gov
422 Clinton Ave S, Rochester, NY 14620-1103
Patty Albert, Nursing Director

National League For Nursing 212.363.5555
Fax 212.812.0393
Web ....www.nln.org
61 Broadway Fl 33, New York, NY 10006-2833
Dr. Beverly Malone, CEO

National League of Cities/Children & Families In Cities 202.626.3000
Fax 202.626.3043
Web ....www.nlc.org
E-mail ....info@nlc.org
1301 Pennsylvania Ave NW Ste 550, Washington, DC 20004
Donald Borut, Director

National Library Svc for the Blind and Physically Handicapped 202.707.5100
Fax 202.707.0712
Web ....www.loc.gov/nls
E-mail ....nls@loc.gov
1291 Taylor St NW, Washington, DC 20542-0001
Ruth Scovill, Director

National Marrow Donor Program 800.627.7692
Fax 612.627.5877
Web ....www.marrow.org
3001 Broadway St NE, Ste 500, Minneapolis, MN 55413

National Network to End Domestic Violence, Inc. 202.543.5566
Fax 202.543.5626
Web ....www.nnedv.org
E-mail ....nnedv@nnedv.org
2001 S St NW Ste 400, Washington, DC 20009
Cindy Southworth, Director Of Technology

National Organization for Victim Assistance 800.879.6682
Fax 703.535.5500
Web ....www.trynova.org
510 King St, Ste 424, Alexandria, VA 22314
Will Marling, Executive Director

National Patient Travel Ctr 800.296.1217
Fax 800.550.1767
Web ....www.patienttravel.org
4620 Haygood Rd Ste 1, Virginia Beach, VA 23455

National Rehabilitation Info Ctr (NARIC) 301.459.5900
Fax 301.459.4263
Web ....www.naric.com
E-mail ....naricinfo@heitechservices.com
8201 Corporate Dr Ste 600, Hyattsville, MD 20785-2245
Mark Odum, Project Director

National Resource Ctr For Youth Svcs 918.660.3700
Fax 918.660.3737
Web ....www.nrcys.ou.edu
E-mail ....pcorreia@ou.edu
4502 E.41St St, Bldg.4 West, Pulsa, OK 74135
Peter R. Correia Iii, Executive Director

National Resource Ctr On Native American Aging (NRCNAA) 701.777.6780
Fax 701.777.6779
Web ....www.medicine.nodak.edu/crh/nrcnaa
E-mail ....alan.allery@mail.und.nodak.edu
501 N Columbia Rd, Ste 4909, Grand Forks, ND 58203
Dr. Alan Allery, Director

National Runaway Switchboard 773.880.9860
Fax 773.929.5150
Web www.1800runaway.org
E-mail ....sspiegler@1800runaway.org
3080 N Lincoln Ave, Chicago, IL 60657
Maureen Blaha, Executive Director
NRS provides Crisis Intervention for youth, up to age 21, who are thinking of leaving home or who have already left home. Information referral from our online database. Conference calls can be made between families through our toll free hotline. Message d

National School Safety Ctr 805.373.9977
Web ....www.schoolsafety.us
E-mail ....ronaldstephens@schoolsafety.us
141 Duesenberg Dr Ste 7 B, Thousand Oaks, CA 91362-3480
Ronald D. Stephens, Executive Director

National Sexual Violence Resource Ctr 877.739.3895
Fax 717.909.0714
Web ....www.nsvrc.org
E-mail ....kbaker@nsvrc.org
123 N Enola Dr, Enola, PA 17025-2521
Karen Baker, Project Director

National Sheriff's Assoc 703.836.7827
Fax 703.683.6541
Web ....www.sheriffs.org
E-mail ....jthompson@sheriffs.org
1450 Duke St, Alexandria, VA 22314-3490
John Thompson, Deputy Director

National SIDS/Infant Death Resource Ctr 703.821.8955
Fax 703.821.2098
Web ....www.sidcenter.org
E-mail ....kaykerns@crestviewmanor.com
8280 Greensboro Dr Ste 300, Mc Lean, VA 22102-3807
Nandini Ganesh, Manager

National Women's Health Network (NWHN) 202.682.2640
Fax 202.347.1168
Web ....www.nwhn.org
E-mail ....cpearson@womenshealthnetwork.org
1413 K St NW Fl 4, Washington, DC 20005
Cynthia Pearson, Executive Director

National Youth Employment Coalition 202.659.1064
Fax 202.659.0399
Web ....www.nyec.org
E-mail ....nyec@nyec.org
1836 Jefferson Pl NW, Washington, DC 20036-2505
Marla Thakor, CEO

National Youth Gang Info Ctr 850.385.0600
Fax 850.386.5356
Web ....www.iir.com/nygc
E-mail ....jmoore@iir.com
2050 Centre Pointe Blvd, Tallahassee, FL 32308
John Moore, Director

National Youth Violence Prevention Resource Ctr 866.723.3968
Fax 301.562.1001
Web ....www.safeyouth.org
E-mail ....nyvprc@safeyouth.org
8401 Colesville Road #200, Silver Spring, MD 20910
Winonna Gause, Program Manager

Omega Institute for Holistic Studies 845.266.4444
Fax 845.266.4828
Web ....www.eomega.org
E-mail ....registration@eomega.org
150 Lake Dr, Rhinebeck, NY 12572-3252
Michael Craft, Programs Director

Operation Comfort 818.762.5007
Fax 818.509.3507
Web ....www.operationcomfort.com
E-mail ....dr.josedavidcohen@sbcglobal.net
10653 Riverside Dr, National Office, North Hollywood, CA 91602-2341
Dr. Steven Sherman, Co-Director

Orphan Foundation of America 571.203.0270
Fax 571.203.0273
Web ....www.orphan.org
E-mail ....office@fc2success.org
21351 Gentry Dr Ste 130, Sterling, VA 20166
Eileen Mccaffrey, Director

Otto Bremer Foundation 651.227.8036
Fax 651.312.3665
Web ....www.fdncenter.org/grantmaker/bremer
E-mail ....john-kostishack@bremer.com
445 Minnesota St Ste 2250, Saint Paul, MN 55101
John Kostishack, Executive Director

Outward Bound Intercept 888.837.5205
Web ....www.outwardbound.org
E-mail ....info@outwardbound.org
910 Jackson Street, Golden, CO 80401
Julie Hignell, Executive Director

Parents as Teachers National Ctr, Inc. 314.432.4330
Fax 314.432.8963
Web ....www.parentsasteachers.org
2228 Ball Dr, Saint Louis, MO 63146-8602
Cheryle Dyle-palmer, M.a., Chief Operating Officer

Parents, Families & Friends of Lesbians & Gays (PFLAG) 202.467.8180
Fax 202.467.8194
Web ....www.pflag.org
E-mail ....info@pflag.org
1828 L St NW Ste 660, Washington, DC 20036
Jody Huckaby, Deputy Executive Director

Patient Advocate Foundation 800.532.5274
Fax 757.873.8999
Web ....www.patientadvocate.org
E-mail ....Erinm@Patientadvocate.Org
700 Thimble Shoals Blvd Ste 200, Newport News, VA 23606
Erin Marshall, Director Of Information Technology

Pew Charitable Trusts 215.575.9050
Fax 215.575.4939
Web ....www.pewtrusts.org
E-mail ....info@pewtrusts.org
2005 Market St Ste 1700, Philadelphia, PA 19103-7077
Rebecca W. Rimel, President

Police Foundation 202.833.1460
Fax 202.659.9149
Web ....www.policefoundation.org
E-mail ....info@policefoundation.org
1201 Connecticut Ave NW Ste 200, Washington, DC 20036
Hubert Williams, President

Polly Klaas Foundation 707.769.1334
Fax 707.769.4019
Web ....www.pollyklaas.org
E-mail ....info@pollyklaas.org
312 Western Ave, Petaluma, CA 94952-2919
Robert De Leo, Executive Director
Operates a nationwide 24-hour toll-free missing child hotline, disseminates child safety information, supports legislation benefiting children and helps build safer communities.

Public Welfare Foundation 202.965.1800
Fax 202.265.8851
Web ....www.publicwelfare.org
E-mail ....reviewcommittee@publicwelfare.org
1200 U St Nw, Washington, DC 20009-4443
Mary McCoymonc, President

Reading Is Fundamental 202.536.3400
Fax 202.536.3516
Web ....www.rif.org
E-mail ....cmackall@rif.org
1255 23 St Ste 300, Washington, DC 20037
Chandra Mackall, Office Manager

Richard King Mellon Foundation 412.392.2800
Fax 412.392.2837
Web ....www.fdncenter.org/grantmaker/rkmellon

E-mail ....rkm@foundationcenter.org
500 Grant St Ste 4106, One Mellon Center,
Pittsburgh, PA 15219
Seward Prosser Mellon, President

Robert F. Kennedy Memorial **202.463.7575**
Fax 202.463.6606
Web ....www.rfkmemorial.org
1367 Connecticut Ave NW Ste 200, Washington,
DC 20036-1859
Robert Q. Kreider, President/CEO

Robert Sterling Clark
Foundation **212.288.8900**
Fax 212.288.1033
Web ....www.rsclark.org
E-mail ....rscf@rsclark.org
135 E 64th St, New York, NY 10065-7045
Margaret Ayers, President/CEO

Robert Wood Johnson
Foundation **609.452.8701**
Fax 609.987.8845
Web ....www.rwjf.org
E-mail ....rwjfmail@rwjf.org
Route 1 College Road, Princeton, NJ 08543
Risa Lavisso-mourey, President/CEO

Save The Children **203.221.4000**
Fax 203.227.5667
Web ....www.savethechildren.org
54 Wilton Rd, Westport, CT 06880-3131
Mark K. Shriver, VP/Managing Director of Programs

Search Institute **612.376.8955**
Fax 612.376.8956
Web ....www.search-institute.org
E-mail ....si@search-institute.org
615 1st Ave NE Ste 125, Minneapolis,
MN 55413-2677
Peter Benson, President

Sexuality Information & Education Council of The United
States (SIECUS) **202.265.2405**
Fax 202.462.2340
Web ....www.siecus.org
E-mail ....siecus@siecus.org
1706 NW R St, Washington, DC 20009
Jen Heitel-Yakush, Public Policy Director

Skillman Foundation **313.393.1185**
Fax 313.393.1187
Web ....www.skillman.org
E-mail ....mailbox@skillman.org
100 Talon Centre Dr Ste 100, Detroit,
MI 48207-4266
Tonya Allen, Program Director

Spaulding for Children **248.443.7080**
Fax 248.443.2845
Web ....www.spaulding.org
E-mail ....awilliams@spaulding.org
16250 Northland Drive, Suite 100, McLean,
VA 22102
Addie Williams, President/CEO
COA accredited organization.

Staples Foundation for
Learning **508.253.5000**
Fax 508.253.8989
Web ....www.staplesfoundation.org
E-mail ....investor@staples.com
500 Staples Dr, #4, Framingham, MA 01702
Ronald Sargent, President/CEO

Street Law, Inc. **301.589.1130**
Fax 301.589.1131
Web ....www.streetlaw.org
E-mail ....eobrien@streetlaw.org
1010 Wayne Ave Ste 870, Silver Spring,
MD 20910-5663
Edward L. OBrien, Executive Director

Surdana Foundation **212.557.0010**
Fax 212.557.0003
Web ....www.surdna.org
E-mail ....questions@surdna.org
330 Madison Ave Fl 30, New York, NY 10017-5016
Edwin Skloot, President

T E X A S
NeuroRehab
C E N T E R
Where Special Kids Get Special Care

Texas NeuroRehab Center **512.444.4835**
Toll-free 800.252.5151
Web ....www.texasneurorehab.com
E-mail ....sandra.mcdaniel@uhsinc.com
1106 W Dittmar Rd, Austin, TX 78745-6328
Terri McBryde, Business Development Director; Dr. Ed Prettyman, CEO;
Sandra McDaniel, Admissions Coordinator

Texas NeuroRehab Center provides specialized neurobehavioral residential
treatment services for youth, ages 8-17 with IQs ranging from 40 – 90. Specialties
include Neuropsychiatric, Neurobehavioral, Brain Injury, Autism, Fetal Alcohol
Syndrome, Sensory Processing issues, Intermittent Explosive Disorder, Psychiatric
conditions with Medical issues, Developmentally Delayed and more.

The After-School Corporation **646.943.8700**
Fax 646.943.8800
Web ....www.tascorp.org
E-mail ....info@tascorp.org
1440 Broadway Fl 16, New York, NY 10018-2320
Lucy Friedman, President

The Allstate Foundation **847.402.5502**
Fax 847.326.7517
Web ....www.allstate.com/foundation
2775 Sanders Rd, Suite F4, Northbrook, IL 60062

The American Academy of Child and Adolescent
Psychiatry **202.966.7300**
Fax 202.966.2891
Web ....www.aacap.org
E-mail ....vqanthony@aacap.org
3615 Wisconsin Ave NW, Washington,
DC 20016-3007
Virginia Anthony, Executive Director

The American Legion Child Welfare Foundation,
Inc. **317.630.1202**
Fax 317.630.1369
Web ....www.cwf-inc.org
E-mail ....admin@cwf-inc.org
700 N Pennsylvania St, Indianapolis, IN 46206
Jill Druskis, Executive Director

The Annenburg Foundation **610.341.9066**
Fax 610.964.8688
Web ....www.annenburgfoundation.org
150 N. Radnor-Chester Road Radnor Financial Center,
Ste. A-200, Campbell, CA 95008
Gillian Norris- Szanto, Program Director

The Annie E. Casey
Foundation **410.547.6600**
Fax 410.547.6624
Web ....www.aecf.org
E-mail ....webmail@aecf.org
701 Saint Paul St, Baltimore, MD 21202
Patrick Mccarthy, President

The Arc of The United States **202.783.2229**
Fax 202.783.8250
Web ....www.thearc.org
E-mail ....berns@thearc.org
1660 L Street, NW, Suite 301, Washington,
DC 20036
Peter Berns, Director

The Bureau For At-Risk Youth **800.999.6884**
Fax 516.349.5521
Web ....www.at-risk.com
E-mail ....info@at-risk.com
45 Executive Dr Ste 201, Plainview, NY 11803-1738
Edward W. Werz, CEO

The Commonwealth Fund **212.606.3800**
Fax 212.606.3500
Web ....www.commonwealthfund.org
E-mail ....info@cmwf.org
1 E 75th St, New York, NY 10021-2677
Karen Davis, President

The Compassionate Friends **877.969.0010**
Fax 630.990.0246
Web ....www.compassionatefriends.org
E-mail ....pat@compassionatefriends.org
900 Jorie Blvd. Suite 78, Oak Brook, IL 60523
Patricia Loder, Director

The Corps Network. **202.737.6272**
Fax 202.737.6277
Web ....www.corpsnetworks.org
1100 Gee st NW ste 1000, Washington, DC 20005
Sally Prouty, President/CEO

The Duke Endowment **704.376.0291**
Fax 704.376.9336
Web ....www.dukeendowment.org
100 N Tryon St Ste 3500, Charlotte, NC 28202-4001
Eugene W. Cochrane, Jr., President

The Edna McConnell Clark
Foundation **212.551.9100**
Fax 212.421.9325
Web ....www.emcf.org
E-mail ....info@emcf.org
415 Madison Ave Fl 10, New York, NY 10017
Nancy Roob, President

The Fine Gold Center for
Children **781.466.9555**
Fax 781.890.4900
Web ....www.thegenesisfund.org/nbdc.php
E-mail ....nbdc@thegenesisfund.org
52 2nd Ave Ste 520, Waltham, MA 02451
Caroline Hobbs, Executive Director

The Ford Foundation **212.573.5000**
Fax 212.351.3677
Web ....www.fordfound.org
E-mail ....secretary@fordfound.org
320 E 43rd St, New York, NY 10017
Luis Ubinas, President

The Foundation Ctr **212.620.4230**
Fax 212.807.3677
Web ....www.foundationcenter.org
E-mail ....communications@foundationcenter.org
79 5th Ave, 2nd Fl, New York, NY 10003
Brad Smith, President

The George Gund Foundation **216.241.3114**
Fax 216.241.6560
Web ....www.gundfoundation.org
E-mail ....info@gundfdn.org
45 W Prospect Ave Ste 1845, 1845 GUILDHALL BLDG,
Cleveland, OH 44115
David T. Abbot, Executive Director

The Harm Reduction Coalition **212.213.6376**
Fax 212.213.6582
Web ....www.harmreduction.org
E-mail ....hrc@harmreduction.org
22 W 27th St Fl 5, New York, NY 10001-6905
Allan Clear, Executive Director

The James Irvine Foundation **415.777.2244**
Fax 415.777.0869
Web ....www.irvine.org
575 Market St Ste 3400, San Francisco, CA 94105
James Canales, President/CEO

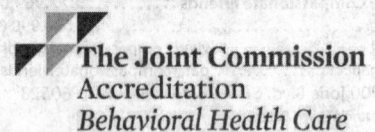

The Joyce Foundation 312.782.2464
Fax 312.782.4160
Web ....www.joycefdn.org
E-mail ....info@joycefdn.org
70 W Madison Street, Suite 2750, Chicago,
IL 60602-4317
Ellen S. Alberding, Director

The Kresge Foundation 248.643.9630
Fax 248.643.0588
Web ....www.kresge.org
E-mail ....info@kresge.org
3215 W Big Beaver Rd, Suite 150, Troy, MI 48084
Elizabeth C. Sullivan, Senior Vp

**The National Alliance On Mental
Illness** 603.225.5359
Fax 603.228.8848
Web ....www.naminh.org
E-mail ....info@naminh.org
15 Green St, Concord, NH 03301-4020
Ken Norton, Executive Director

**The Nurturing Father's
Program** 941.953.9556
Fax 941.953.9552
Web ....www.nuturingfathers.com
3277 Fruitville Rd # 1D, Sarasota, FL 34237
Mark Perlman, Publisher

The Pittsburgh Foundation 412.391.5122
Fax 412.391.7259
Web ....www.pittsburghfoundation.org
E-mail ....brelsfordj@pghfdn.org
5 Ppg Place, Ste 250, Pittsburg, PA 15222
Jonathan Brelsford, Director Of It

United Cerebral Palsy Assoc 202.776.0406
Fax 202.776.0414
Web ....www.ucp.org
E-mail ....national@ucp.org
1660 L St NW Ste 700, Washington, DC 20036
Steve Bennett, President/CEO

United Seamen's Svcs 718.369.3818
Fax 718.369.3024
Web ....www.uss/ammla.com

E-mail ....ussammla@ix.netcom.com
635 4th Ave, Brooklyn, NY 11232
Roger T. Korner, Executive Director

**United States Conference Of Catholic Bishops/Migrant
And Refugee Svcs.** 202.541.3000
Fax 202.722.8747
Web ....www.usccb.org
E-mail ....mrs@usccb.org
3211 4th St NE, Washington, DC 20017-1104
Johnny Young, Executive Director

United Way Of America 703.836.7112
Fax 703.683.7840
Web ....www.unitedway.org
E-mail ....brian.gallagher@uwa.unitedway.org
701 N. Fairfax St., Alexandra, VA 22079
Bryan Gallagher, Executive Director

**US Bancorp Piper Jaffray
Foundation** 612.303.6000
Fax 612.303.8199
Web ....www.piperjaffray.com
E-mail ....info@pjc.com
US Bancorp Center, 800 Nicollet Mall, Minneapolis,
MN 55402
Andew Duff, CEO

**US Psychiatric Rehabilitation
Assoc** 410.789.7054
Fax 410.789.7675
Web ....www.uspra.org
E-mail ....mgranahan@uspra.org
601 Global Way Ste 106, Linthicum Heights,
MD 21090-2265
Marcie Granhan, Director

**VFW National Home For
Children** 517.663.1521
Fax 517.663.3727
Web ....www.vfwnationalhome.org
E-mail ....mail@vfwnationalhome.org
3573 S Waverly Rd, Eaton Rapids, MI 48827-9799
Patrice Green, Director

**Visiting Angels Living Assistance
Services** 813.752.0008
Fax 813.634.7105
Web ....www.visitingangels.com/hillsborough
E-mail ....vangels@verizon.net
3830 Sun City Center Blvd. #102, Sun City Center,
FL 33573
Debbie Waldecker, Csa, President

**Volunteers Of America National Headquarters
Ofc** 800.899.0089
Fax 703.341.7000
Web ....www.volunteersofamerica.org
E-mail ....info@voa.org
1660 Duke St, Alexandria, VA 22314
Mike King, President/CEO

W.K. Kellogg Foundation 269.968.1611
Fax 269.968.0413
Web ....www.wkkf.org
1 Michigan Ave. E, Battle Creek, VA 49017
Sterling Speirn, President

Wallace Foundation 212.251.9700
Fax 212.679.6990
Web ....www.wallacefoundation.org
E-mail ....cdevita@wallacefoundation.org
510 Penn Plaza, 7th Floor, New York, NY 10001
M. Christine Devita, President

William Penn Foundation 215.988.1830
Fax 215.988.1823
Web ....www.williampennfoundation.org
E-mail ....moreinfo@williampennfoundation.org
100 N 18th St. 2 Logan Sq, 11Th Fl, Philadelphia,
PA 19103
Seather Houston, President And Chief Executive Officer

**William Randolph Hearst
Foundation** 212.586.5404
Fax 212.586.1917
Web ....www.hearstfdn.org
300 W 57th St, Fl 26, New York, NY 10019
Mason Granger, Grants Program Director

William T. Grant Foundation 212.752.0071
Fax 212.752.1398
Web ....www.wtgrantfoundation.org
E-mail ....info@wtgrantfdn.org
570 Lexington Ave 18th Fl, New York, NY 10022
Robert C. Granger, President

Woods Fund of Chicago 312.782.2698
Fax 312.782.4155
Web ....www.woodsfund.org
E-mail ....application@woodsfund.org
360 N Michigan Ave, Ste 1600, Flint, MI 48503
Laura Washington, Chief Admin

YMCA of the USA 202.835.9043
Fax 202.835.9030
Web ....www.ymca.net
E-mail ....audrey.haynes@ymca.net
1129 20th St Ste 301, Washington, DC 20036
Audrey Haynes, Director of Goverment Relations

**Youth Crime Watch Of
America** 305.670.2409
Fax 305.670.3805
Web ....www.ignitusworldwide.org
E-mail ....cdicarlo@ignitusworldwide.org
9200 S Dadeland Blvd Ste 417, Miami, FL 33156
Christopher Dicarlo, Director

Youth Law Ctr 415.543.3379
Fax 415.956.9022
Web ....www.ylc.org
E-mail ....info@ylc.org
200 Pine St Ste 300, San Francisco, CA 94104
Carol Shauffer, Director

Youth Svc America 202.296.2992
Fax 202.296.4030
Web ....www.ysa.org
E-mail ....info@ysa.org
1101 15th St NW Ste 200, Washington,
DC 20005-5007
Steven A. Culbertson, President/CEO

YWCA-Washington Ofc 202.467.0801
Fax 202.467.0802
Web ....www.ywca.org
E-mail ....ygrac@ywca.org
202518th St NW, Ste 1100, Washington,
DC 20036-5226
Lorraine Cole, CEO

**Zero To Three, National Ctr for Infants, Toddlers and
Families** 202.638.1144
Fax 202.638.0851
Web ....www.zerothree.org
1255 M 23 St NW Ste 200, Washington, DC 20037
Melmeb Mathew, Director